The College Blue Book®

47th Edition

Narrative Descriptions

The College Blue Book®

47th Edition

Narrative Descriptions

MACMILLAN REFERENCE USA
A part of Gale, a Cengage Company

GALE
A Cengage Company

The College Blue Book, 47th Edition Volume 1

Project Editor: Anthony Boussie

Editorial Support Services: Wayne Fong

Composition and Electronic Prepress: Amy Darga

Manufacturing: Rita Wimberley

For product information and technology assistance, contact us at
Gale Customer Support, 1-800-877-4253.
For permission to use material from this text or product,
submit all requests online at **www.cengage.com/permissions.**
Further permissions questions can be emailed to
permissionrequest@cengage.com

Gale
27500 Drake Rd.
Farmington Hills, MI, 48331-3535

ISBN-13: 978-0-02-866505-4 (6 vol. set)
ISBN-13: 978-0-02-866506-1 (vol. 1)

ISSN 1082-7064

This title is also available as an e-book.
ISBN-13: 978-0-02-866512-2 (set)
Contact your Gale sales representative for ordering information.

Printed in Mexico
1 2 3 4 5 6 7 23 22 21 20 19

Contents

The College Blue Book® has been a standard, professional reference on higher education since it was first published in 1923. New features have been added during the intervening years to keep pace with the changing needs for information about our educational facilities. The information, especially in the areas of tuition, room and board, enrollment figures, library holdings, is constantly changing. It is difficult to maintain up-to-date figures in these areas, as many schools change tuition and related costs on an ongoing basis. We therefore urge our readers to check directly with the schools for the most current cost information.

CONTENTS OF EACH VOLUME

Volume 1: Narrative Descriptions

Nearly 4,100 colleges in the United States and Canada are fully described. Entrance requirements are detailed and campus facilities and costs are described. A map of each U.S. state and Canadian province is included and each college has a grid index for easy location. Web sites are also listed.

Volume 2: Tabular Data

Colleges are listed alphabetically by state or province. Information about costs, accreditation, enrollment figures, faculty, and names of the chief administrative officers are given for each school.

Volume 3: Degrees Offered by College and Subject

In Part I, the name of each college is listed alphabetically by state or province, with a list of the subject areas for which degrees are offered. Part II includes an alphabetical listing of subject areas for which degrees are granted by one or more institutions of higher education.

Volume 4: Occupational Education

Over 5,700 schools in the United States and Canada that provide occupational or technical training are fully described, offering such information as tuition costs, enrollment figures, and entrance requirements. Two indexes are provided: an alphabetical listing of schools in the "Index of Occupational Education Schools," in addition to the "Curricula and Areas of Instruction" index.

Volume 5: Scholarships, Fellowships, Grants, and Loans

This volume provides a listing of more than 6,000 sources of financial aid for students wishing to further their education. Split alphabetically into eight broad subject areas (each containing several more specialized concentrations of study), as well as a general section, each listing provides basic information about a specific award, including eligibility requirements, amount of award, and application deadlines.

Volume 6: Distance Learning Programs

Responding to this rapidly growing trend in postsecondary education, this volume features comprehensive profiles of nearly 1,000 institutions offering distance learning programs within the United States and Canada.

FOR MORE INFORMATION

We are always open to suggestions and recommendations for improvement of The College Blue Book® from our readers and from the educational professions. Please contact: Editor, The College Blue Book

Macmillan Reference USA

27500 Drake Rd.

Farmington Hills, MI 48331-3535

Phone: (248)699-4253

Toll-free: 800-877-4253

Fax: (248)699-8075

Email: anthony.boussie@cengage.com

Web site: www.gale.com

The decision to continue education beyond high school years, the selection of a collegiate institution, and the area of study to be pursued are some of the essential experiences necessary for students to determine their futures. Alternatives of choice institutions, work selection, job opportunities, professional training, or even discontinuing any further education are all selective decisions open to the students.

Nearly all students today have opportunities to continue education beyond high school. There are more schools accepting wider ranges of student ability and interest than ever before. This means more effort, more planning, and more personal study in making the college choice.

Self Appraisal

The best place to begin is with oneself. An appraisal with objective, honest answers is necessary. What are the personal potentials as a student? Where has the best performance been? What are the probabilities for improvement? What are the reasons for really wanting to go to college; is it for intellectual development, vocational preparation, or simply to satisfy a desire for status? What are the personal ideas of college? What is expected from the college experience? Have career plans been made? Where are the academic abilities? What subjects are preferred? What is the quality of performance in the preferred areas of study? What is the overall grade average? What is the class rank in high school? In what subject areas is there the greatest interest? What is the quality of work in these areas? Are interests and performance generally consistent? Are the expressed and recorded interests truly and accurately reflecting the inward wishes? What was liked best about the high school experience? Has the college preparatory program been followed in high school? What were the social and cultural experiences during high school years that were most meaningful? What was considered, if anything, to be lacking?

Well-thought-out answers to these and similar questions are helpful. Discussions of such topics with counselors, parents, and teachers increases the probability of success in college selection, attendance, and completion.

The counselor today is an extremely valued resource person available to assist the student. When an effective working team of counselor-student-parent actually exists, the probabilities for the student making selective choices that prove to be the "right" ones are unquestionably the greatest. The better the student and the counselor know one another, the more effective the guidance and counseling program will be. For this to occur, the opportunity for face-to-face student-counselor discussion needs to start in the latter elementary school years and continue through high school and college.

College Appraisals

Research is continuing in the areas of college admissions and student success. The identification and understanding of causes of success and failure need professional study. However, one thing is apparent: the more careful the preparations and planning by the student, the better the chances of college admission and success.

Systemized planning should begin early. The more self-understanding and knowledge about available colleges one has, the better one can plan with corresponding success. Certainly, early in the high school career, students should be reviewing detailed information on colleges and universities with the counselor, noting academic requirements such as scholastic performance, course requirements, costs and other particular qualities of individual collegiate institutions. There is no single one-and-only college for the student. Colleges have personalities just as the students do. There are always several colleges with academic and social climates compatible and acceptable to each student.

Entrance requirements, courses available, costs, size of student body, academic pressure, special programs, geographical location, and specialty schools are some of the considerations of every student in appraising available colleges.

The College Blue Book® is dedicated to providing detailed information regarding collegiate institutions throughout the United States and Canada. Students and counselors should browse through The College Blue Book® and become familiar with the colleges of our country and neighboring Canada. As interest sharpens and narrows, a more selective and in-depth study of institutions should be made.

Where feasible, students should plan visits to college campuses. Campus visiting may begin during the summer between the sophomore and junior years of high school. The best time to be on a college campus, however, is during the regular term with a carefully planned visit in the spring semester of the junior year. Preparatory plans should be made with the high school counselor, reviewing discussions of earlier personal conferences. Advance arrangements should be made with admission officers of the colleges the student expects to visit. The admission officer's name and telephone number will be found in most instances in *The College Blue Book*® volume entitled *Tabular Data*. The admissions officer in many cases will want to know whether the student has actually applied for admission and probably the areas the student may plan to major in or other special interests the student has in the particular institution. The student should have prepared a summary of personal data. If possible, high school students should also talk to students of the colleges they wish to attend.

The growth of community colleges has opened up another avenue for students, especially those of limited finances or those who have not decided on their ultimate educational goals. Students will find many of these community colleges offer an excellent opportunity to gain a solid college background. Then one can choose a four-year institution to complete an undergraduate degree.

Any regular high school graduate can find a school that will accept him or her. Many students need to be encouraged to consider the smaller, private and public colleges of good standing.

Students entering professional training such as engineering or law might consider small schools that have cooperative programs with major universities. A knowledgeable student, through planning and guidance, can avoid unnecessary disappointment. A college career can be quite beneficial to the student who spends three to four years on a small campus and one, two, or three additional years of graduate work on another, larger campus.

Costs

Costs are continuing to rise. Tuition charges as listed herein should only be used as a guide. It would be wise to check with the institution of interest to be sure of having the most up-to-date information available.

Should the need for financial aid be a factor in selecting a college, a college-bound student should be aware that the best single source of financial assistance and information is the financial aid officer or admission director at the college. It is most important for the student to contact the finance office as early as possible during the student's senior year in high school. A principal source of financial assistance is the major federal undergraduate aid programs. Applications can be obtained from the college. Most colleges and universities also offer financial assistance in several forms including academic and general scholarships, grants-in-aid, student loans, and part-time work. For more information, see volume 5 of *The College Blue Book*®: *Scholarships, Fellowships, Grants, and Loans*.

Two-year Colleges

Two-year colleges, referred to as junior colleges or community colleges, both public and private, offer programs that prepare students for technical and semiprofessional careers in business and technology fields, and for transfer to senior colleges. There are hundreds of two-year colleges providing comprehensive programs meeting the lower division requirements of virtually all four-year colleges and universities.

There are decided advantages for some students to enroll in a two-year college. Some of these are: less cost, home residence, availability of highly specialized programs, opportunity for the student to mature, a smaller student body, and generally a closer relationship to the faculty. The development of two-year colleges across the nation is one of the most vital forces in education today. The two-year college is neither an extension of high school, nor a little senior college. It has its own identity, sphere of service, and contribution to make to American education. The comprehensive community college is considered one of the best means of accommodating the demands of higher education, embracing the increasing variety of abilities of students graduating from high schools, preparing students in the technological and semiprofessional occupations, and all in an economical manner.

One very important caution needs to be heeded by students enrolling in two-year colleges who are planning to continue their work through a bachelor's program. Students expecting to transfer should very carefully study the requirements of the institution they ultimately plan to attend. In conference with the junior college counselor, a careful review of the planned program should be made to be sure the contemplated courses at the junior college will satisfy the requirements of the senior institution. Students who depart from prescribed courses stated by the senior institution or fail in any of these courses may experience difficulty with admission or normal progress toward the bachelor degree.

Liberal Arts Colleges

The liberal arts colleges offer four years of college and award the Bachelor of Arts and the Bachelor of Science degrees. The curriculum for the first two years is usually broad with an emphasis in the humanities, natural sciences, and cultural history of our society. The last two years may provide a concentration of specific programs such as pre-medicine or pre-law leading to graduate professional training.

Students considering professional training at the graduate level should keep this in mind as they plan their work at the liberal arts college. Graduate schools in some cases have strict preparatory requirements. Familiarity with these requirements can greatly assist in making the transfer to graduate level without loss of credit or time.

Specialized Institutions

Four-year institutions of technology are examples of the more specialized schools where concentration in a specialty is intensively pursued throughout the college career. Most of these institutions are quite selective in admission practice and may require more high school mathematics and science than most other schools for entrance. These programs lead to engineering degrees in many fields emphasizing technology and science. Recently there has been a broadening of the program of the first two years, but, in general, such a program is not nearly as comprehensive and varied as the liberal arts college. The demand for engineers and scientists with specially developed skills creates great competition for entrance into schools of technology.

There are other specialized institutions such as conservatories of music, seminaries, medical and law schools, institutions specializing in teacher training, or schools of the fine arts, most of which require specialized preparation for entrance.

Universities

The university is generally composed of a number of degree-granting colleges and schools where both bachelor and graduate degrees are grouped under one administrative head. Bachelor degrees at the university may be earned in liberal arts or one of the professions such as engineering or the physical sciences. The university, to some extent, combines what is available at the liberal arts college with the specialized institution. Complete professional training in such areas as law, medicine, and science is available on the university campus.

As a rule, universities have much larger student bodies than colleges. In order to meet the demand, most state universities have established several campuses. Many state universities are very selective in admitting students. This is particularly true for a student who is applying for admission from out-of-state.

Entrance Examinations

There are more applicants than there is room for students on many campuses. As this demand increases, colleges and universities attempt to identify those applicants who are most likely to succeed on their campuses. A quality scholastic record has more influence on acceptance and admission than any other single factor. High school grades predict with better accuracy than any other single measurement what college grades and success will be. The more selective colleges and universities may choose students who come out highest on quantitative criteria, that is, high school scholastic averages combined with test scores. Some institutions have far more applicants (whose scholastic records and test scores are of a maximum quality) than they can accept. In such cases, applicants are sometimes screened and accepted on the basis of categories according to residence in the state or region, special talents, minority groups, or relationship to alumni. Such procedures are used in an attempt to influence the makeup of the enrollment.

When investigating several schools, one of the most accurate ways for evaluation of an institution is to consider test scores and the high school rank order of the students actually on campus. In many instances this is more informative than the announced admission policies.

College testing is required by many colleges and universities for entering students; some have developed their own tests and over the years have established norms for such tests. Most institutions requiring tests for entrance, however, now use either the test of the American College Testing Program (ACT) or the examinations of the College Entrance Examination Board. The College Entrance Examination Board offers the Preliminary Scholastic Assessment Test/National Merit Scholarship Qualifying Test (PSAT/ NMSQT), the Scholastic Assessment Test I: Reasoning Test (Verbal and Math), and the SAT II: Subject Tests.

Coaching, tutoring, drill, and memorization of facts can do little to improve the scores of the standardized examinations. It is recommended that students not invest time and money in cramming in hopes of improving test scores. Students can do their best preparation in general reading, completing their school assignments, and arriving on the proper day of the test rested and refreshed.

American College Testing Assessment (ACT)

The ACT Assessment provided by the American College Testing Program covers four subject areas: English, mathematics, reading, and science reasoning. The ACT test is scored on a range of 1 to 36. The ACT is administered at various test sites in the United States and other countries on specified dates throughout the year. Many colleges and universities recommend that prospective students take the examination early in the senior year.

The tests provide estimates of the students' current level of educational development in knowledge skill areas often required in college work. The ACT college testing program was founded in 1959. It is a nonprofit educational service offering programs in testing and financial need analysis.

Scholastic Assessment Tests (SAT)

The SAT I: Reasoning Test is an examination to measure the verbal and mathematics abilities students have developed both in and out of school. The SAT II: Subject Tests, which some colleges require for admission or placement purposes, consist of 22 separate tests that cover subjects such as literature, history, math, languages, chemistry, biology, and physics. Unlike the SAT I, which measures more general abilities, the SAT II tests measure the students' knowledge of a particular subject and their ability to apply that knowledge. Because of this, students should try to take a SAT II Test as soon as possible after completion of their last course in that subject.

The SAT I and II tests are given on certain dates throughout the year at various test centers in the United States and foreign countries. The combination of the student's academic record and the SAT scores, along with other pertinent secondary information enables admissions officers to estimate how well the student will perform on a particular college campus. The SAT is scored on a scale of 200 minimum to 800 maximum.

Admission Policies

One of the most important considerations in planning is to note when colleges and universities request applications, and to be sure that the applications are complete and forwarded during the appropriate periods. Failure in any way in this procedure will usually automatically disqualify a student from acceptance.

Counselors can provide students with freshman profiles on many of the institutions. Studying *The College Blue Book®*, particularly the volume *Tabular Data,* provides a great amount of information on the kind of student bodies found on the campuses of American institutions. There are four general classifications of admission policies. An understanding of these provides valuable guidelines in identifying colleges for consideration.

Most Selective: Many more students apply who meet the announced admission requirements than the college could possibly accept. In addition to requiring outstanding academic records, personal recommendations are required from the high school, and identification of any special qualities of the student should be made known. In this regard, the high school recommendation made to the collegiate institution requires special attention.

Many times, particularly at selective institutions, the high school recommendation actually provides the necessary edge for admission. The recommendation should be on time, carefully providing all information called for, and finally, be precise and detailed in citing personal qualities of the applicant.

All these qualities, however, do not guarantee acceptance. It is strongly recommended that qualified students apply to more than one institution of this type, and that not all applications should be made to the same type of institution.

Very Selective: Colleges having a very selective procedure in accepting students require ACT scores of 23 or over, or an SAT I score of 600 or more. Students should rank in the top 10 to 12 percent of their high school graduating classes. In addition, strong recommendations stressing particular talents and achievements are necessary. Applications should be made to several institutions of this type.

Selective: An ACT of 20 or over, or an SAT I score of 550 or more is generally necessary. Applications for admission to selective colleges and universities are usually called for in the spring prior to fall entry. In many situations, applications may be submitted in the fall of the senior year with final confirmation to be made after all grades are recorded and confirmed upon graduation from high school.

Least Selective: The fourth classification represents those institutions that will accept students with a C average on their high school work. In certain unusual instances, and under special situations, even the selective institutions may accept students who are in this category, particularly if the scores on the ACT are in the mid-20's or are in excess of 500 on the SAT I. Generally, for acceptance in the less selective schools, students should have an ACT composite score of 17 or a SAT I score of 450.

Entrance examinations may or may not be required. Occasionally, if examinations are required, the results are used for student placement rather than admission. Most high school graduates can meet the requirements for entry and will be accepted. It should be pointed out, however, that in some cases an institution may be liberal in acceptance but carefully screens candidates for graduation. In such an institution, a high attrition rate may occur.

Open Enrollment Policy: This is becoming more common, particularly with the public community colleges. Many students will find this privilege most helpful in continuing their formal education beyond high school. Such a policy enables those students to have a second chance who have failed to perform up to their ability during their high school years. Enrollment and attendance may enable the student to complete a most rewarding vocational program or to later transfer and complete the Bachelor degree, which otherwise might not have been possible because of the deficiency in the high school scholastic record.

A number of colleges and universities, particularly the publicly supported ones, have adopted the open enrollment policy. In response to a feeling of community responsibility, they accept any student who has a diploma (or G.E.D. equivalency certificate) from an accredited high school. This procedure allows students from disadvantaged and minority backgrounds, who might otherwise be denied such an opportunity, to acquire a college education and prepare for a meaningful occupation. These institutions have not lowered their graduation requirements; they have, instead, created opportunities for more students to satisfy these requirements.

Do not assume the erroneous generality that the tougher it is to get into an institution, the better the quality; or the easier to enter, the poorer the school. In fact, there is research evidence available indicating that it may be wise to re-examine some of our traditional notions and attitudes regarding admissions. Not all degree programs on any particular campus are equally outstanding. Every institution has its particular strengths in programs available. Certain institutions are excellent places for some kinds of students in some kinds of programs, but no institution is the one most suited for everyone.

Nearly 4,100 institutions of higher education, in the United States and Canada, are described in this volume of *The College Blue Book*® including universities, senior colleges, two-year colleges, and specialized institutions. The data has been gathered by direct contact with all institutions as well as by inspection of the most current college catalogues available. The arrangement of information is alphabetical by state and by college within each state.

No judgments or evaluations have been made in these entries, but many applicable facts have been presented to assist the reader in making his or her own.

To assist the user of this volume in making a valid evaluation and comparison of schools, information on each school has been standardized as follows: privately or publicly supported or church-related; level: university, college, graduate school; for whom: men, women, co-educational; type: liberal arts, technological, theological, teacher education, professional; names of degrees granted; fields of specialization, schools, or departments; term system: semester, quarter, trimester; enrollment; size of faculty and faculty-student ratio; regional accreditation; number of volumes in library; cooperative education (work-study) program availability; existence of a ROTC program; entrance requirements; costs per year; collegiate environment; community environment.

There are six regional accrediting commissions covering the United States that evaluate colleges and schools. Gener-

ally, these regional agencies grant accreditation to an entire institution of higher learning. They are as follows: Middle States Association of Colleges and Schools, New England Association of Schools and Colleges, North Central Association of Colleges and Schools, Northwest Association of Schools and Colleges, Southern Association of Colleges and Schools, and Western Association of Schools and Colleges.

An important consideration should be mentioned again, one which *The College Blue Book*® stresses at several points; the "right" college for Student A may not be the "right" college for Student B. A large enrollment, a small teacher-student ratio, an enormous library and exacting entrance requirements do not necessarily mean that this is the best school. Consider all the factors available: is it in a small, rural college town or a huge, vibrating metropolis; does the student need readily available transportation; does this school have specific programs the student is interested in; if seeking a profession, does the school have professional accreditation; does it have on-campus dormitories, or must the student seek other housing arrangements; do expenses fall within the student's budget; can the entrance requirements be met; if accepted, what are the chances of graduating; if the student is not sure just exactly what is wanted in the way of a career, will this school provide opportunities to find out? This revised edition of *The College Blue Book*® has been designed to assist in answering these questions and others that the college bound student may have.

■ ALABAMA AGRICULTURAL AND MECHANICAL UNIVERSITY

4900 Meridian St.
Huntsville, AL 35811
Tel: (256)372-5000; Free: 800-553-0816
Fax: (256)372-5881
Web Site: www.aamu.edu
Description: State-supported, university, coed. Awards bachelor's, master's, and doctoral degrees and post-master's certificates. Founded 1875. Setting: 2,001-acre suburban campus. Endowment: $29.3 million. Research spending for the previous fiscal year: $10.7 million. Educational spending for the previous fiscal year: $3630 per student. Total enrollment: 5,814. Faculty: 290 (289 full-time, 1 part-time). Student-undergrad faculty ratio is 20:1. 5,363 applied, 51% were admitted. Full-time: 4,592 students, 52% women, 48% men. Part-time: 348 students, 54% women, 46% men. 31% from out-of-state. 0.1% American Indian or Alaska Native, non-Hispanic/Latino; 0.3% Hispanic/Latino; 96% Black or African American, non-Hispanic/Latino; 0.2% Asian, non-Hispanic/Latino; 0.9% international. 13% 25 or older, 4% transferred in. Retention: 75% of full-time freshmen returned the following year. Academic areas with the most degrees conferred: business/marketing; education; biological/life sciences; engineering. Core. Calendar: semesters. Academic remediation for entering students, services for LD students, advanced placement, honors program, independent study, distance learning, double major, summer session for credit, part-time degree program, adult/continuing education programs, co-op programs and internships, graduate courses open to undergrads. Off campus study at Georgia Institute of Technology, Oakwood College, University of Alabama in Huntsville, Calhoun Community College, Athens State College. Study abroad program. ROTC: Army.
Entrance Requirements: Options: electronic application, deferred admission. Required: high school transcript, minimum 2 high school GPA, ACT. Recommended: 1 recommendation. Entrance: minimally difficult. Application deadline: 6/15. Notification: continuous.
Collegiate Environment: Orientation program. Drama-theater group, choral group, marching band, student-run newspaper, radio station. Social organizations: 85 open to all; national fraternities, national sororities, local fraternities, local sororities; 50% of eligible men and 50% of eligible women are members. Most popular organizations: University Voices Gospel Choir, University Choir and Band, Elementary/Early Childhood Club, National Alliance of Business Students. Major annual events: Homecoming, Annual All-Campus Convocation, Women's Week and Men's Week. Student services: health clinic, personal-psychological counseling. Campus security: 24-hour patrols, late night transport-escort service, controlled dormitory access. J. F. Drake Learning Resources Center. Operations spending for the previous fiscal year: $2.6 million. 1,000 computers available on campus for general student use. A campuswide network can be accessed from student residence rooms and from off campus. Staffed computer lab on campus.
Community Environment: Population 166,000. Located in the northern part of the state, within the city limits of Huntsville, on U.S. Highways 231 and 431, which pass through the business section of the city. Huntsville may be reached by bus, and Northwest, American, and Delta airlines Taxi service is available to the community from all transportation centers. (See also University of Alabama Huntsville).

■ ALABAMA STATE UNIVERSITY

915 S Jackson St.
Montgomery, AL 36101-0271
Tel: (334)229-4100; Free: 800-253-5037
Fax: (334)229-4984
E-mail: fwilliams@alasu.edu
Web Site: www.alasu.edu
Description: State-supported, university, coed. Part of Alabama Commission on Higher Education. Awards bachelor's, master's, and doctoral degrees and post-master's certificates. Founded 1867. Setting: 172-acre urban campus. Endowment: $89.3 million. Research spending for the previous fiscal year: $29.1 million. Educational spending for the previous fiscal year: $6464 per student. Total enrollment: 4,413. Faculty: 409 (227 full-time, 182 part-time). Student-undergrad faculty ratio is 17:1. 7,588 applied, 98% were admitted. 16% from top quarter of their high school class, 60% from top half. Full-time: 3,643 students, 63% women, 37% men. Part-time: 260 students, 55% women, 45% men. Students come from 41 states and territories, 24 other countries, 34% from out-of-state. 0.1% American Indian or Alaska Native, non-Hispanic/Latino; 0.9% Hispanic/Latino; 94% Black or African American, non-Hispanic/Latino; 0.4% Asian, non-Hispanic/Latino; 0.1% Native Hawaiian or other Pacific Islander, non-Hispanic/Latino; 1% international. 37% 25 or older, 34% live on campus, 4% transferred in. Retention: 59% of full-time freshmen returned the following year. Academic areas with the most degrees conferred: health professions and related sciences; education; business/marketing. Core. Calendar: semesters. Academic remediation for entering students, advanced placement, self-designed majors, freshman honors college, honors program, independent study, distance learning, double major, summer session for credit, part-time degree program, co-op programs and internships, graduate courses open to undergrads. ROTC: Army (c), Air Force.
Entrance Requirements: Options: electronic application, early admission, deferred admission. Required: high school transcript, minimum 2 high school GPA, SAT or ACT. Recommended: essay, interview. Entrance: minimally difficult. Notification: continuous. SAT Reasoning Test deadline: 7/31. SAT Subject Test deadline: 7/31. Transfer credits accepted: Yes.
Costs Per Year: Application fee: $25. One-time mandatory fee: $150. State resident tuition: $8328 full-time, $347 per credit hour part-time. Nonresident tuition: $16,656 full-time, $694 per credit hour part-time. Mandatory fees: $2740 full-time, $446 per term part-time. Full-time tuition and fees vary according to class time, course level, course load, degree level, program, and student level. Part-time tuition and fees vary according to class time, course level, course load, degree level, program, and student level. College room and board: $6050. Room and board charges vary according to board plan and housing facility.
Collegiate Environment: Orientation program. Drama-theater group, choral group, marching band, student-run newspaper, radio station. Social organizations: 64 open to all; national fraternities, national sororities, local fraternities, local sororities; 13% of eligible men and 27% of eligible women are members. Most popular organizations: Alabama State University Marching Band, Alpha Kappa Alpha Sorority Inc, Empower Ministry, Nu Alpha Nu Service Fraternity Inc, Delta Sigma Theta Sorority Inc. Major annual events: Founder's Day Convocation, Fall Convocation, Homecoming Week Activities. Student services: health clinic, personal-psychological counseling. Campus security: 24-hour emergency response devices and patrols, late night transport-escort service. 2,479 college housing spaces available; 2,341 were occupied in 2018-19. No special consideration for freshman housing applicants. Options: men-only, women-only housing available. Levi Watkins Learning Center plus 1 other. Books: 437,312 (physical), 69,796 (digital/electronic); Serial titles: 1,607 (physical), 6,084 (digital/electronic); Databases: 192. Weekly public service hours: 78; study areas open 24

hours, 5-7 days a week; students can reserve study rooms. Operations spending for the previous fiscal year: $1.6 million. 805 computers available on campus for general student use. A campuswide network can be accessed from student residence rooms and from off campus. Students can access the following: online class registration. Staffed computer lab on campus (open 24 hours a day) provides training in use of computers, software, and the Internet.

Community Environment: Population approximately 200,000. Capital of Alabama. A city known for its stately homes, many of which belong to the antebellum days. The city is also known for its magnolia trees, its southern traditions and culture, and its southern hospitality. Excellent air and highway connections. Montgomery is the home of the Alabama State Capitol Building, the first capital of the Confederacy, the Department of Archives and History, the Montgomery Public Library, Maxwell Air Force Base and Gunter Field, the Air University, and the very large Garrett Coliseum. The South Alabama State Fair, Southern Horse Show, an annual rodeo, an annual indoor track tournament, and other similar functions are held in the Garrett Coliseum. Located here is the First White House of the Confederacy, the home of the Jefferson Davis when Montgomery was the Confederate Capital.

■ **AMRIDGE UNIVERSITY**
1200 Taylor Rd.
Montgomery, AL 36117
Tel: (334)387-3877; Free: 888-790-8080
Fax: (334)387-3878
Web Site: www.amridgeuniversity.edu
Description: Independent, university, coed, affiliated with Church of Christ. Awards associate, bachelor's, master's, and doctoral degrees. Founded 1967. Setting: 10-acre urban campus. Endowment: $8 million. Educational spending for the previous fiscal year: $2600 per student. Total enrollment: 758. Faculty: 56 (36 full-time, 20 part-time). Student-undergrad faculty ratio is 12:1. Full-time: 176 students, 72% women, 28% men. Part-time: 180 students, 64% women, 36% men. Students come from 46 states and territories, 48% from out-of-state. 0.6% American Indian or Alaska Native, non-Hispanic/Latino; 2% Hispanic/Latino; 79% Black or African American, non-Hispanic/Latino; 0.6% Asian, non-Hispanic/Latino. 91% 25 or older. Core. Calendar: semesters. Academic remediation for entering students, services for LD students, advanced placement, accelerated degree program, independent study, distance learning, double major, summer session for credit, part-time degree program, external degree program, adult/continuing education programs, internships, graduate courses open to undergrads.
Entrance Requirements: Options: electronic application, early admission, international baccalaureate accepted. Required: high school transcript, minimum 2 high school GPA, ACT. Required for some: SAT or ACT. Entrance: minimally difficult. Application deadline: rolling. Transfer credits accepted: Yes.
Collegiate Environment: Orientation program. Most popular organization: Amridge University Student Advisory Committee. Campus security: 24-hour emergency response devices, security guards. College housing not available. Southern Christian University Library. Books: 90,000 (physical); Databases: 12. Weekly public service hours: 50. Operations spending for the previous fiscal year: $105,000. 5 computers available on campus for general student use. A computer is required for all students. A campuswide network can be accessed from off-campus. Students can access the following: online class registration. Staffed computer lab on campus provides training in use of computers, software, and the Internet.
Community Environment: Southern Christian University is a 9-acre campus located in Montgomery, the capital city of Alabama adjacent to Interstate 85. This city is strategically located in the central part of the state. Montgomery is the fourth largest city in the state in terms of population, offering residential areas, parks and playgrounds, school and universities, museums, a zoo, and the capitol facilities. Montgomery has two major U.S. Air Force installations, as well as a number of historical sites. The city has an abundance of good housing and a variety of employment opportunities.

■ **ATHENS STATE UNIVERSITY**
300 N Beaty St.
Athens, AL 35611
Tel: (256)233-8100; Free: 800-522-0272
Fax: (256)233-8164
Web Site: www.athens.edu
Description: State-supported, upper-level, coed. Awards bachelor's and master's degrees. Founded 1822. Setting: 45-acre small town campus. Total enrollment: 3,001. Faculty: 196 (81 full-time, 115 part-time). Student-

undergrad faculty ratio is 17:1. Full-time: 1,210 students, 69% women, 31% men. Part-time: 1,759 students, 66% women, 34% men. Students come from 18 states and territories, 2 other countries, 4% from out-of-state. 2% American Indian or Alaska Native, non-Hispanic/Latino; 3% Hispanic/Latino; 13% Black or African American, non-Hispanic/Latino; 0.9% Asian, non-Hispanic/Latino; 0.1% Native Hawaiian or other Pacific Islander, non-Hispanic/Latino. 64% 25 or older, 21% transferred in. Academic areas with the most degrees conferred: business/marketing; education; liberal arts/general studies. Core. Calendar: semesters. Advanced placement, independent study, distance learning, double major, summer session for credit, part-time degree program, adult/continuing education programs, co-op programs and internships. Off campus study at Oakwood College, Alabama Agricultural and Mechanical University, University of Alabama in Huntsville. Study abroad program.
Entrance Requirements: Transfer credits accepted: Yes.
Costs Per Year: Application fee: $30. State resident tuition: $6060 full-time. Nonresident tuition: $12,120 full-time. Mandatory fees: $750 full-time.
Collegiate Environment: Drama-theater group, student-run newspaper. Most popular organizations: SGA, Accounting, Art, PE. Major annual events: Homecoming, Welcome Back Cookouts, Halloween Carnival. Student services: personal-psychological counseling. Campus security: 24-hour emergency response devices and patrols. Athens State University Library. Books: 83,092 (physical), 255,950 (digital/electronic); Serial titles: 289 (physical), 296,023 (digital/electronic); Databases: 23,955. Students can reserve study rooms. 210 computers available on campus for general student use. A campuswide network can be accessed. Students can access the following: online class registration, transcripts, e-mail. Staffed computer lab on campus.
Community Environment: Located in the Tennessee Valley, Athens (population 20,972) is in Limestone County which has an overall population of 72,446. The town is noted for its fine antebellum homes, including the large Founders Hall, built in 1843. With an average temperature of 60 degrees and convenient to air (Huntsville), rail, and within two hours of Nashville and Birmingham, this is a rich, rapidly growing area for farming and industry. State Parks at Wheeler, Wilson Lakes, and Guntersville Reservoir provide for swimming, boating, fishing, and camping.

■ **AUBURN UNIVERSITY**
Auburn University, AL 36849
Tel: (334)844-4000; Free: 800-AUBURN9
E-mail: admissions@auburn.edu
Web Site: www.auburn.edu
Description: State-supported, university, coed. Awards bachelor's, master's, and doctoral degrees and post-master's certificates. Founded 1856. Setting: 1,875-acre small town campus with easy access to Atlanta, Birmingham. Endowment: $768.1 million. Research spending for the previous fiscal year: $145.6 million. Educational spending for the previous fiscal year: $10,975 per student. Total enrollment: 30,440. Faculty: 1,606 (1,375 full-time, 231 part-time). Student-undergrad faculty ratio is 19:1. 20,742 applied, 75% were admitted. 32% from top 10% of their high school class, 62% from top quarter, 89% from top half. 50 National Merit Scholars. Full-time: 22,460 students, 50% women, 50% men. Part-time: 2,168 students, 37% women, 63% men. Students come from 52 states and territories, 67 other countries, 36% from out-of-state. 0.4% American Indian or Alaska Native, non-Hispanic/Latino; 3% Hispanic/Latino; 5% Black or African American, non-Hispanic/Latino; 2% Asian, non-Hispanic/Latino; 0.1% Native Hawaiian or other Pacific Islander, non-Hispanic/Latino; 7% international. 4% 25 or older, 19% live on campus, 5% transferred in. Retention: 90% of full-time freshmen returned the following year. Academic areas with the most degrees conferred: business/marketing; engineering; biological/life sciences. Core. Calendar: semesters. ESL program, services for LD students, advanced placement, accelerated degree program, freshman honors college, honors program, independent study, distance learning, double major, summer session for credit, part-time degree program, adult/continuing education programs, co-op programs and internships, graduate courses open to undergrads. Off campus study. Study abroad program. ROTC: Army, Naval, Air Force.
Entrance Requirements: Options: electronic application, early admission, early action, international baccalaureate accepted. Required: essay, high school transcript, minimum 2 high school GPA, SAT or ACT. Recommended: minimum 3 high school GPA. Required for some: minimum 3 high school GPA. Entrance: moderately difficult. Application deadlines: 1/15, 11/1 for early action. Notification: 2/1. SAT Reasoning Test deadline: 1/15. Transfer credits accepted: Yes.
Costs Per Year: Application fee: $50. State resident tuition: $9624 full-time,

$401 per semester hour part-time. Nonresident tuition: $28,872 full-time, $1203 per semester hour part-time. Mandatory fees: $1652 full-time, $826 per term part-time. Full-time tuition and fees vary according to program and reciprocity agreements. Part-time tuition and fees vary according to course load, program, and reciprocity agreements. College room and board: $13,332. College room only: $7860. Room and board charges vary according to board plan and housing facility.

Collegiate Environment: Orientation program. Drama-theater group, choral group, marching band, student-run newspaper, radio station. Social organizations: 512 open to all; national fraternities, national sororities; 21% of eligible men and 43% of eligible women are members. Most popular organizations: Student Government Association, University Program Council, IMPACT (volunteer opportunities), International Student Organization, student media (AU Plainsman newspaper, WEGL radio, Glomerata yearbook, Eagle Eye television, AU Circle literary journal). Major annual events: Hey Day, UPC Concert, BIG Event. Student services: health clinic, personal-psychological counseling. Campus security: 24-hour emergency response devices and patrols, late night transport-escort service, controlled dormitory access. 4,737 college housing spaces available; 4,679 were occupied in 2018-19. No special consideration for freshman housing applicants. Options: coed, men-only, women-only housing available. R. B. Draughon Library plus 3 others. Books: 4.6 million (physical), 1 million (digital/electronic); Serial titles: 76,345 (physical), 94,890 (digital/electronic); Databases: 245. Study areas open 24 hours, 5-7 days a week. Operations spending for the previous fiscal year: $17.5 million. 1,722 computers available on campus for general student use. Computer purchase/lease plans available. A campuswide network can be accessed. Students can access the following: online class registration, bursar payments, course materials. Staffed computer lab on campus provides training in use of computers, software, and the Internet.

Community Environment: Auburn (population 50,000) is located on U.S. 29 and Interstate 85, 55 miles east of Montgomery, 120 miles southeast of Birmingham, and 120 miles southwest of Atlanta, Georgia. Auburn University is the pride of the city. With the many churches in the area there is a cultural atmosphere which makes for pleasant living. Chewacla State Park is nearby for swimming and picnicking. The city has two well-equipped parks, a country club and 2 public courses for golf, a stadium for athletic games and many facilities for intramural sports including fields, swimming pools, racquetball and tennis courts, and a student activities building. Azaleas and camellias may be seen on the grounds of the university and many of the beautiful homes.

■ **AUBURN UNIVERSITY AT MONTGOMERY**
PO Box 244023
Montgomery, AL 36124-4023
Tel: (334)244-3000; Free: 800-227-2649
Fax: (334)244-3795
Web Site: www.aum.edu
Description: State-supported, comprehensive, coed. Part of Auburn University. Awards bachelor's, master's, and doctoral degrees and post-master's certificates. Founded 1967. Setting: 500-acre urban campus. System endowment: $50.1 million. Research spending for the previous fiscal year: $421,157. Educational spending for the previous fiscal year: $7487 per student. Total enrollment: 5,211. Faculty: 330 (212 full-time, 118 part-time). Student-undergrad faculty ratio is 15:1. 5,941 applied, 93% were admitted. 14% from top 10% of their high school class, 38% from top quarter, 78% from top half. Full-time: 3,554 students, 66% women, 34% men. Part-time: 1,078 students, 64% women, 36% men. 6% from out-of-state. 0.4% American Indian or Alaska Native, non-Hispanic/Latino; 1% Hispanic/Latino; 41% Black or African American, non-Hispanic/Latino; 2% Asian, non-Hispanic/Latino; 0.1% Native Hawaiian or other Pacific Islander, non-Hispanic/Latino; 5% international. 21% 25 or older, 25% live on campus, 11% transferred in. Retention: 67% of full-time freshmen returned the following year. Academic areas with the most degrees conferred: health professions and related sciences; business/marketing; computer and information sciences. Core. Calendar: semesters. Academic remediation for entering students, ESL program, services for LD students, advanced placement, honors program, independent study, distance learning, double major, summer session for credit, part-time degree program, co-op programs and internships, graduate courses open to undergrads. Off campus study at Huntingdon College, Alabama State University, Faulkner University. Study abroad program. ROTC: Army, Air Force (c).
Entrance Requirements: Open admission. Options: electronic application, early admission. Required: high school transcript, minimum 2.3 high school

GPA, SAT or ACT. Entrance: moderately difficult. Notification: continuous. SAT Reasoning Test deadline: 8/1. Transfer credits accepted: Yes.
Costs Per Year: Application fee: $0. One-time mandatory fee: $125. State resident tuition: $7752 full-time, $323 per credit part-time. Nonresident tuition: $17,424 full-time, $726 per credit part-time. Mandatory fees: $868 full-time. College room and board: $7090. College room only: $4690.
Collegiate Environment: Orientation program. Drama-theater group, choral group, student-run newspaper. Social organizations: 52 open to all; national fraternities, national sororities, local fraternities; 2% of eligible men and 5% of eligible women are members. Most popular organizations: Student Government Association, Campus Activities Board, Panhellenic Association, Accounting Club. Major annual events: AUMFest, Shriek Week, Week of Welcome. Student services: health clinic, personal-psychological counseling. Campus security: 24-hour emergency response devices and patrols, student patrols, late night transport-escort service, controlled dormitory access. 996 college housing spaces available; all were occupied in 2018-19. No special consideration for freshman housing applicants. Option: coed housing available. Auburn University at Montgomery Library. Books: 340,819 (physical), 1.2 million (digital/electronic). Weekly public service hours: 84; students can reserve study rooms. 500 computers available on campus for general student use. A campuswide network can be accessed from student residence rooms. Students can access the following: online class registration. Staffed computer lab on campus.
Community Environment: See Alabama State University.

■ **BEVILL STATE COMMUNITY COLLEGE**
1411 Indiana Ave.
Jasper, AL 35501
Tel: (205)387-0511
E-mail: melissa.stowe@bscc.edu
Web Site: www.bscc.edu
Description: State-supported, 2-year, coed. Part of Alabama Community College System. Awards certificates, transfer associate, and terminal associate degrees. Founded 1969. Setting: 245-acre rural campus with easy access to Birmingham. Educational spending for the previous fiscal year: $3138 per student. Total enrollment: 3,872. Faculty: 283 (114 full-time, 169 part-time). Student-undergrad faculty ratio is 17:1. Full-time: 1,583 students, 56% women, 44% men. Part-time: 2,289 students, 61% women, 39% men. Students come from 10 states and territories, 2% from out-of-state. 0.1% American Indian or Alaska Native, non-Hispanic/Latino; 2% Hispanic/Latino; 15% Black or African American, non-Hispanic/Latino; 0.3% Asian, non-Hispanic/Latino. 25% 25 or older, 7% transferred in. Retention: 59% of full-time freshmen returned the following year. Core. Calendar: semesters. Academic remediation for entering students, services for LD students, advanced placement, honors program, distance learning, summer session for credit, part-time degree program, adult/continuing education programs, co-op programs. Off campus study.
Entrance Requirements: Open admission. Options: electronic application, early admission. Required: high school transcript. Entrance: noncompetitive. Application deadline: rolling. Notification: continuous. Transfer credits accepted: Yes.
Costs Per Year: State resident tuition: $3870 full-time, $129 per credit hour part-time. Nonresident tuition: $7740 full-time, $258 per credit hour part-time. Mandatory fees: $900 full-time, $29 per credit hour part-time. Full-time tuition and fees vary according to course load and program. Part-time tuition and fees vary according to course load and program. College room only: $1300. Room charges vary according to location.
Collegiate Environment: Drama-theater group, choral group. Social organizations: 6 open to all. Most popular organizations: Student Government Association, Campus Ministries, Circle K, Outdoorsmen Club, Sigma Kappa Delta. Major annual events: Spring Fling, National Alcohol Awareness Week. Main library plus 5 others. Books: 113,246 (physical); Serial titles: 3,563 (physical); Databases: 15. Weekly public service hours: 56. Operations spending for the previous fiscal year: $709,307. 1,200 computers available on campus for general student use. A campuswide network can be accessed from student residence rooms and from off campus. Students can access the following: online class registration, Business Office payments. Staffed computer lab on campus provides training in use of computers, software, and the Internet.
Community Environment: The Sumiton and Jasper Campuses are in urban areas. The Fayette and Hamilton Campuses are in small towns.

■ **BIRMINGHAM-SOUTHERN COLLEGE**
900 Arkadelphia Rd.
Birmingham, AL 35254

Tel: (205)226-4600; Free: 800-523-5793
Fax: (205)226-3074
Web Site: www.bsc.edu
Description: Independent Methodist, 4-year, coed. Awards bachelor's degrees. Founded 1856. Setting: 196-acre urban campus with easy access to Birmingham. Endowment: $51.7 million. Educational spending for the previous fiscal year: $8624 per student. Total enrollment: 1,231. Faculty: 114 (86 full-time, 28 part-time). Student-undergrad faculty ratio is 13:1. 1,846 applied, 65% were admitted. 29% from top 10% of their high school class, 61% from top quarter, 82% from top half. 1 National Merit Scholar. Full-time: 1,208 students, 47% women, 53% men. Part-time: 23 students, 52% women, 48% men. Students come from 33 states and territories, 18 other countries, 41% from out-of-state. 0.9% American Indian or Alaska Native, non-Hispanic/Latino; 3% Hispanic/Latino; 8% Black or African American, non-Hispanic/Latino; 4% Asian, non-Hispanic/Latino. 2% 25 or older, 85% live on campus, 2% transferred in. Retention: 85% of full-time freshmen returned the following year. Academic areas with the most degrees conferred: business/marketing; visual and performing arts; psychology. Core. Calendar: 4-1-4. Advanced placement, self-designed majors, honors program, independent study, double major, summer session for credit, part-time degree program, co-op programs and internships. Off campus study at University of Alabama at Birmingham, Samford University, Miles College, Montevallo. Study abroad program. ROTC: Army (c), Air Force (c).
Entrance Requirements: Options: electronic application, early admission, early decision, early action, deferred admission, international baccalaureate accepted. Required: high school transcript, minimum 2.5 high school GPA, 1 recommendation. Recommended: essay, interview, SAT or ACT. Required for some: interview. Entrance: moderately difficult. Application deadlines: 11/1 for early decision, 11/15 for early action. Notification: 3/1, 12/1 for early decision, 12/15 for early action. SAT Reasoning Test deadline: 3/1. SAT Subject Test deadline: 3/1. Transfer credits accepted: Yes.
Costs Per Year: Application fee: $50. One-time mandatory fee: $300. Comprehensive fee: $29,950 includes full-time tuition ($16,353), mandatory fees ($1297), and college room and board ($12,300). College room only: $6950. Room and board charges vary according to board plan, housing facility, and location.
Collegiate Environment: Orientation program. Drama-theater group, choral group, marching band, student-run newspaper. Social organizations: 84 open to all; national fraternities, national sororities; 35% of eligible men and 53% of eligible women are members. Most popular organizations: Student Government Association, Quest II Event Programming, Black Student Union, Multi- Cultural Awareness Organization, Reformed University Fellowship. Major annual events: SOCO Spring Concert, Halloween on the Hilltop Community Event, Homecoming. Student services: health clinic, personal-psychological counseling. Campus security: 24-hour emergency response devices and patrols, late night transport-escort service, controlled dormitory access, vehicle safety inspections for students, emergency phone stations throughout campus. Charles Andrew Rush Learning Center/N. E. Miles Library. Students can reserve study rooms. Operations spending for the previous fiscal year: $1 million. 306 computers available on campus for general student use. Computer purchase/lease plans available. A computer is required for all students. A campuswide network can be accessed. Students can access the following: online class registration. Staffed computer lab on campus provides training in use of computers and software.
Community Environment: See Birmingham Southern College.

■ **BISHOP STATE COMMUNITY COLLEGE**
351 N Broad St.
Mobile, AL 36603-5898
Tel: (251)405-7000
Fax: (251)438-5403
Web Site: www.bishop.edu
Description: State-supported, 2-year, coed. Part of Alabama Community College System. Awards certificates, transfer associate, and terminal associate degrees. Founded 1965. Setting: 9-acre urban campus. Total enrollment: 3,896. Faculty: 187 (118 full-time, 69 part-time). Student-undergrad faculty ratio is 23:1. Full-time: 2,171 students, 56% women, 44% men. Part-time: 1,725 students, 65% women, 35% men. Students come from 8 states and territories, 32 other countries, 3% from out-of-state. 0.7% American Indian or Alaska Native, non-Hispanic/Latino; 1% Hispanic/Latino; 62% Black or African American, non-Hispanic/Latino; 2% Asian, non-Hispanic/Latino; 0.2% Native Hawaiian or other Pacific Islander, non-Hispanic/Latino; 2% international. 60% 25 or older, 10% transferred in. Retention: 41% of full-time freshmen returned the following year. Core. Calendar: semesters.

Academic remediation for entering students, services for LD students, advanced placement, accelerated degree program, independent study, distance learning, summer session for credit, part-time degree program, adult/continuing education programs, co-op programs and internships.
Entrance Requirements: Open admission. Options: electronic application, early admission, deferred admission. Required: high school transcript. Entrance: noncompetitive. Application deadline: rolling. Notification: continuous until 9/17. Transfer credits accepted: Yes.
Collegiate Environment: Orientation program. Drama-theater group, choral group. Campus security: 24-hour emergency response devices and patrols, 24-hour electronic alert system. Minnie Slade Bishop Library plus 3 others. 600 computers available on campus for general student use. A campuswide network can be accessed from off-campus. Students can access the following: online class registration. Staffed computer lab on campus provides training in use of computers, software, and the Internet.
Community Environment: See University of South Alabama.

■ **CALHOUN COMMUNITY COLLEGE**
PO Box 2216
Decatur, AL 35609-2216
Tel: (256)306-2500
Fax: (256)306-2877
E-mail: admissions@calhoun.edu
Web Site: www.calhoun.edu
Description: State-supported, 2-year, coed. Part of Alabama College System. Awards certificates, transfer associate, and terminal associate degrees. Founded 1965. Setting: suburban campus. Total enrollment: 11,212. Student-undergrad faculty ratio is 26:1. 2% from out-of-state. 39% 25 or older. Core. Calendar: semesters. Academic remediation for entering students, ESL program, services for LD students, advanced placement, accelerated degree program, independent study, distance learning, summer session for credit, part-time degree program, adult/continuing education programs, co-op programs.
Entrance Requirements: Open admission except for nursing, dental services programs. Required for some: high school transcript, SAT or ACT. Entrance: noncompetitive. Application deadline: rolling. Notification: continuous.
Collegiate Environment: Drama-theater group, choral group, student-run newspaper. Student services: personal-psychological counseling. Campus security: 24-hour patrols. Brewer Library plus 2 others.

■ **CENTRAL ALABAMA COMMUNITY COLLEGE**
1675 Cherokee Rd.
Alexander City, AL 35011-0699
Tel: (256)234-6346
Fax: (256)234-0384
Web Site: www.cacc.edu
Description: State-supported, 2-year, coed. Part of Alabama College System. Awards certificates, transfer associate, and terminal associate degrees. Founded 1965. Setting: 100-acre small town campus. Research spending for the previous fiscal year: $34,245. Total enrollment: 2,177. Faculty: 193 (52 full-time, 141 part-time). Student-undergrad faculty ratio is 15:1. Full-time: 1,304 students, 63% women, 37% men. Part-time: 873 students, 73% women, 27% men. Students come from 6 states and territories. 16% 25 or older. Core. Calendar: semesters. Academic remediation for entering students, services for LD students, advanced placement, distance learning, summer session for credit, part-time degree program, adult/continuing education programs, co-op programs and internships.
Entrance Requirements: Open admission. Option: early admission. Required: high school transcript. Required for some: interview, SAT or ACT. Entrance: noncompetitive. Application deadline: 9/9.
Collegiate Environment: Orientation program. Drama-theater group, choral group, student-run radio station. Social organizations: 6 open to all. Most popular organizations: Cultural Unity, Baptist Campus Ministry, Student Government Association, Phi Theta Kappa. Major annual events: Fall Fest, Spring Fest. Student services: personal-psychological counseling. Campus security: evening security. Thomas D. Russell Library. Operations spending for the previous fiscal year: $235,461. 70 computers available on campus for general student use. A campuswide network can be accessed from off-campus. Students can access the following: online class registration. Staffed computer lab on campus.
Community Environment: Alexander City (population 14,957) is recognized as a city with great civic pride and a sound business climate. It is a pivotal point of transportation: 78 miles southeast of Birmingham, 55 miles

northeast of Montgomery, 123 miles southwest of Atlanta, and 70 miles northwest of Columbus, GA. Childersburg is strategically located on Highway 280, 35 miles southeast of Birmingham, 76 miles north of Montgomery, and 42 miles southwest of Anniston. Both campuses are located in one of the South's principal industrial areas. Industries are diversified yet bolstered by the large payrolls of two leading textile corporations and a leading paper products company. Electrical energy, various foundries, emerging high tech companies, and many small businesses comprise the economic base of the College's service area. Both cities are favored with a mild climate year round, with outstanding recreational and sports facilities. In Alexander City, Lake Martin is the focus of boating, swimming, fishing, and camping. In Childersburg, Logan Martin Lake and Lay Lake allow for sports and recreational activities.

■ **CHATTAHOOCHEE VALLEY COMMUNITY COLLEGE**
2602 College Dr.
Phenix City, AL 36869-7928
Tel: (334)291-4900
Fax: (334)291-4994
Web Site: www.cv.edu
Description: State-supported, 2-year, coed. Part of Alabama College System. Awards certificates, transfer associate, and terminal associate degrees. Founded 1974. Setting: 103-acre small town campus. Total enrollment: 1,697. Faculty: 124 (35 full-time, 89 part-time). Student-undergrad faculty ratio is 20:1. 405 applied, 100% were admitted. Full-time: 944 students, 63% women, 37% men. Part-time: 753 students, 65% women, 35% men. 0.5% American Indian or Alaska Native, non-Hispanic/Latino; 4% Hispanic/Latino; 42% Black or African American, non-Hispanic/Latino; 1% Asian, non-Hispanic/Latino; 0.2% Native Hawaiian or other Pacific Islander, non-Hispanic/Latino. 38% 25 or older, 16% transferred in. Retention: 54% of full-time freshmen returned the following year. Core. Calendar: semesters. Academic remediation for entering students, services for LD students, advanced placement, self-designed majors, honors program, distance learning, summer session for credit, part-time degree program, adult/continuing education programs. Off campus study at Troy State University.
Entrance Requirements: Open admission. Option: early admission. Required: high school transcript. Entrance: noncompetitive. Application deadline: rolling. Notification: continuous. Preference given to state residents. Transfer credits accepted: Yes.
Collegiate Environment: Orientation program. Drama-theater group, choral group. Student services: personal-psychological counseling. Campus security: 24-hour emergency response devices and patrols. Estelle Bain Owens Learning Resource Center and Library.

■ **COASTAL ALABAMA COMMUNITY COLLEGE**
1900 Hwy. 31 S
Bay Minette, AL 36507
Tel: (251)580-2100; Free: 800-381-3722
Fax: (251)580-2285
E-mail: cmikkelsen@faulknerstate.edu
Web Site: www.coastalalabama.edu
Description: State-supported, 2-year, coed. Part of Alabama Community College System. Awards certificates, transfer associate, and terminal associate degrees. Founded 1965. Setting: 105-acre small town campus. Total enrollment: 3,323. Faculty: 227 (86 full-time, 141 part-time). Student-undergrad faculty ratio is 15:1. Full-time: 2,139 students, 61% women, 39% men. Part-time: 1,184 students, 67% women, 33% men. 3% from out-of-state. 39% 25 or older, 9% live on campus. Calendar: semesters. Academic remediation for entering students, services for LD students, advanced placement, honors program, part-time degree program, adult/continuing education programs, co-op programs and internships.
Entrance Requirements: Open admission. Options: early admission, deferred admission. Required: high school transcript. Entrance: noncompetitive. Application deadline: rolling. Notification: continuous until 8/18.
Costs Per Year: Application fee: $0. State resident tuition: $3870 full-time, $129 per credit hour part-time. Nonresident tuition: $7740 full-time, $258 per credit hour part-time. Mandatory fees: $870 full-time, $29 per credit hour part-time. Full-time tuition and fees vary according to class time, course level, course load, program, and student level. Part-time tuition and fees vary according to class time, course level, course load, program, and student level. College room and board: $5900. Room and board charges vary according to board plan and housing facility.
Collegiate Environment: Orientation program. Drama-theater group, choral group, student-run newspaper. Social organizations: national fraternities.

Most popular organizations: Student Government Association, Pow-Wow Leadership Society, Phi Theta Kappa, Association of Computational Machinery, Phi Beta Lambda. Major annual events: Back-to-School Luau and Dance, Spring Fling, Homecoming Week Activities. Student services: personal-psychological counseling. Campus security: 24-hour emergency response devices and patrols, controlled dormitory access. Austin R. Meadows Library plus 3 others. Books: 66,811 (physical); Serial titles: 2,924 (physical); Databases: 67. Weekly public service hours: 40. 225 computers available on campus for general student use. A campuswide network can be accessed. Students can access the following: online class registration. Staffed computer lab on campus.

■ **COLUMBIA SOUTHERN UNIVERSITY**
21982 University Ln.
Orange Beach, AL 36561
Tel: (251)981-3771; Free: 800-977-8449
Fax: (251)981-3815
Web Site: www.columbiasouthern.edu
Description: Proprietary, comprehensive, coed. Awards associate, bachelor's, master's, and doctoral degrees and post-master's certificates (offers only distance learning degree programs). Founded 1993. Setting: small town campus. Total enrollment: 21,104. Faculty: 477 (163 full-time, 314 part-time). Student-undergrad faculty ratio is 70:1. Full-time: 8,397 students, 43% women, 57% men. Part-time: 6,848 students, 29% women, 71% men. Students come from 58 states and territories. 1% American Indian or Alaska Native, non-Hispanic/Latino; 5% Hispanic/Latino; 17% Black or African American, non-Hispanic/Latino; 2% Asian, non-Hispanic/Latino; 0.1% Native Hawaiian or other Pacific Islander, non-Hispanic/Latino; 0.1% international. 93% 25 or older, 12% transferred in. Core. Calendar: Non-standard Term: 9-weeks of instruction, LifePace Learning: 10-week courses that are self-paced. Academic remediation for entering students, services for LD students, distance learning, part-time degree program, adult/continuing education programs. Off campus study.
Entrance Requirements: Open admission. Option: electronic application. Entrance: noncompetitive. Application deadline: rolling. Transfer credits accepted: Yes.
Costs Per Year: Application fee: $0. One-time mandatory fee: $135. Tuition: $5520 full-time, $235 per credit hour part-time.
Collegiate Environment: Social organizations: 3 open to all. Most popular organizations: Student Veteran Association, American Criminal Justice Association, Delta Epsilon Tou (DET) - Alumni Honor Society. Campus security: 24-hour emergency response devices, On-line Institutions. College housing not available. CSU Online Library.

■ **COMMUNITY COLLEGE OF THE AIR FORCE**
CCAF/DESS
100 S Turner Blvd.
Montgomery, AL 36114-3011
Tel: (334)649-5000
E-mail: gwendolyn.ford@us.af.mil
Web Site: www.airuniversity.af.mil/Barnes/CCAF
Description: Federally supported, 2-year, coed. Part of Air University. Awards certificates and terminal associate degrees (courses conducted at 125 branch locations worldwide for members of the U.S. Air Force). Founded 1972. Setting: suburban campus. Total enrollment: 268,763. Faculty: 6,144 (all full-time). 31,231 applied, 100% were admitted. Full-time: 268,763 students, 19% women, 81% men. 34% 25 or older. Core. Calendar: continuous. Academic remediation for entering students, advanced placement, independent study, distance learning, adult/continuing education programs, internships. Off campus study.
Entrance Requirements: Open admission. Option: electronic application. Required: high school transcript, interview, military physical, good character, criminal background check, Armed Services Vocational Aptitude Battery (ASVAB). Entrance: noncompetitive. Application deadline: rolling. Notification: continuous. Transfer credits accepted: Yes.
Costs Per Year: Application fee: $0. Comprehensive fee: $0. Air Force Tuition Assistance (TA) provides 100% tuition and fees for courses taken by active duty personnel.
Collegiate Environment: Major annual events: Armed Forces Day activities, Memorial Day Activities, Veteran's Day activities. Student services: legal services, health clinic, personal-psychological counseling. Campus security: 24-hour emergency response devices and patrols. Air Force Library Service.

■ **ENTERPRISE STATE COMMUNITY COLLEGE**
600 Plz. Dr.
Enterprise, AL 36330

Tel: (334)347-2623
Web Site: www.escc.edu
Description: State-supported, 2-year, coed. Part of Alabama College System. Awards certificates, diplomas, transfer associate, and terminal associate degrees. Founded 1965. Setting: 100-acre small town campus. Total enrollment: 3,410. Faculty: 105 (53 full-time, 52 part-time). Student-undergrad faculty ratio is 18:1. Full-time: 906 students, 47% women, 53% men. Part-time: 622 students, 50% women, 50% men. 5% from out-of-state. 29% 25 or older, 7% transferred in. Core. Calendar: semesters. Academic remediation for entering students, ESL program, services for LD students, advanced placement, accelerated degree program, honors program, independent study, distance learning, summer session for credit, part-time degree program, adult/continuing education programs, internships.
Entrance Requirements: Open admission. Required: high school transcript. Entrance: noncompetitive. Application deadline: rolling. Notification: continuous. SAT Reasoning Test deadline: 7/15. SAT Subject Test deadline: 7/15.
Collegiate Environment: Orientation program. Drama-theater group, choral group, student-run newspaper. Student services: personal-psychological counseling, women's center. Campus security: security personnel. Snuggs Hall.
Community Environment: Population 23,000, Enterprise has a cosmopolitan atmosphere. Due to its proximity to Fort Rucker, approximately 35% of its populace hail from all states in the union and many foreign countries. It enjoys a mild climate. Bus, railroad and a local airport serve the area. There is excellent shopping downtown, plus three shopping centers in the area. The college has a summer work program arranged with the city and local firms; part-time jobs are also available at Fort Rucker, six miles from Enterprise. The community contains many churches, a community center, and most major social, civic, and service groups as well as many city-sponsored programs for recreation.

■ **FAULKNER UNIVERSITY**
5345 Atlanta Hwy.
Montgomery, AL 36109-3398
Tel: (334)386-7324; Free: 800-879-9816
Fax: (334)386-7268
E-mail: nscott@faulkner.edu
Web Site: www.faulkner.edu
Description: Independent, university, coed, affiliated with Church of Christ. Awards associate, bachelor's, master's, and doctoral degrees. Founded 1942. Setting: 75-acre urban campus with easy access to Montgomery. Endowment: $20.4 million. Total enrollment: 3,350. Faculty: 280 (124 full-time, 156 part-time). Student-undergrad faculty ratio is 12:1. 2,446 applied, 45% were admitted. Full-time: 1,744 students, 60% women, 40% men. Part-time: 928 students, 61% women, 39% men. Students come from 42 states and territories, 29 other countries, 13% from out-of-state. 0.2% American Indian or Alaska Native, non-Hispanic/Latino; 2% Hispanic/Latino; 43% Black or African American, non-Hispanic/Latino; 0.5% Asian, non-Hispanic/Latino; 0.4% Native Hawaiian or other Pacific Islander, non-Hispanic/Latino; 2% international. 42% 25 or older, 25% live on campus, 21% transferred in. Retention: 58% of full-time freshmen returned the following year. Academic areas with the most degrees conferred: business/marketing; homeland security, law enforcement, firefighting, and protective services; education. Core. Calendar: semesters. Academic remediation for entering students, ESL program, services for LD students, advanced placement, accelerated degree program, freshman honors college, honors program, independent study, distance learning, double major, summer session for credit, part-time degree program, adult/continuing education programs, internships. Off campus study at Huntingdon College and Auburn University Montgomery, cooperative agreement for ROTC students with Auburn University Montgomery and Alabama State University. Study abroad program. ROTC: Army (c), Air Force (c).
Entrance Requirements: Options: electronic application, early admission, deferred admission, international baccalaureate accepted. Required: high school transcript, minimum 2 high school GPA. Recommended: essay, 2 recommendations, interview. Required for some: SAT or ACT. Entrance: minimally difficult. Application deadline: rolling. Notification: continuous. SAT Reasoning Test deadline: 7/31. SAT Subject Test deadline: 7/31. Transfer credits accepted: Yes.
Costs Per Year: Application fee: $0. Comprehensive fee: $29,240 includes full-time tuition ($19,880), mandatory fees ($1810), and college room and board ($7550). College room only: $3600. Full-time tuition and fees vary according to class time, course load, location, and program. Room and board charges vary according to board plan and housing facility. Part-time tuition:

$675 per semester hour. Part-time mandatory fees: $375 per term. Part-time tuition and fees vary according to class time, course load, location, and program.
Collegiate Environment: Orientation program. Drama-theater group, choral group, marching band, student-run newspaper. Social organizations: 26 open to all; local sororities; 21% of eligible men and 32% of eligible women are members. Most popular organizations: Student Government, Marching Band, Dinner Theatre, Acappella Chorus, Phi Lambda/Kappa Social Clubs. Major annual events: Homecoming, Jamboree, Lectureships. Student services: health clinic, personal-psychological counseling. Campus security: 24-hour emergency response devices and patrols, late night transport-escort service, controlled dormitory access. Gus Nichols Library System plus 4 others. Books: 121,708 (physical), 159,003 (digital/electronic); Serial titles: 2,098 (physical), 142,578 (digital/electronic); Databases: 134. Weekly public service hours: 74. Operations spending for the previous fiscal year: $1.7 million. 496 computers available on campus for general student use. A campuswide network can be accessed. Students can access the following: online class registration, student account access. Staffed computer lab on campus.
Community Environment: See Alabama State University.

■ **FORTIS COLLEGE (MOBILE)**
7033 Airport Blvd.
Mobile, AL 36608
Tel: (251)344-1203; Free: 855-4-FORTIS
Fax: (334)344-1299
Web Site: www.fortis.edu
Description: Proprietary, 2-year, coed. Awards certificates, diplomas, transfer associate, and terminal associate degrees. Founded 1984.

■ **FORTIS COLLEGE (MONTGOMERY)**
3470 Eastdale Cir.
Montgomery, AL 36117
Tel: (334)244-1827; Free: 855-4-FORTIS
Web Site: www.fortis.edu
Description: Proprietary, 2-year, coed. Awards certificates, diplomas, transfer associate, and terminal associate degrees.

■ **FORTIS COLLEGE (MONTGOMERY)**
3736 Atlanta Hwy.
Montgomery, AL 36109
Tel: (334)272-3857; Free: 855-4-FORTIS
Web Site: www.fortis.edu
Description: Proprietary, 2-year, coed. Awards certificates, diplomas, and transfer associate degrees.

■ **FORTIS INSTITUTE**
100 London Pky.
Ste. 150
Birmingham, AL 35211
Tel: (205)940-7800; Free: 855-4-FORTIS
Web Site: www.fortis.edu
Description: Proprietary, 2-year, coed. Awards certificates, diplomas, transfer associate, and terminal associate degrees.

■ **GADSDEN STATE COMMUNITY COLLEGE**
PO Box 227
Gadsden, AL 35902-0227
Tel: (256)549-8200; Free: 800-226-5563
Fax: (256)549-8444
E-mail: info@gadsdenstate.edu
Web Site: www.gadsdenstate.edu
Description: State-supported, 2-year, coed. Part of Alabama Community College System. Awards certificates, transfer associate, and terminal associate degrees. Founded 1965. Setting: 275-acre small town campus with easy access to Birmingham. Total enrollment: 5,018. Faculty: 303 (149 full-time, 154 part-time). Student-undergrad faculty ratio is 17:1. Full-time: 2,576 students, 55% women, 45% men. Part-time: 2,442 students, 65% women, 35% men. Students come from 8 states and territories, 45 other countries. 1% American Indian or Alaska Native, non-Hispanic/Latino; 3% Hispanic/Latino; 19% Black or African American, non-Hispanic/Latino; 0.5% Asian, non-Hispanic/Latino; 0.1% Native Hawaiian or other Pacific Islander, non-Hispanic/Latino; 2% international. 33% 25 or older, 2% live on campus, 6% transferred in. Core. Calendar: semesters. Academic remediation for enter-

ing students, ESL program, services for LD students, advanced placement, honors program, distance learning, summer session for credit, part-time degree program, external degree program, adult/continuing education programs, co-op programs and internships. Study abroad program. ROTC: Army.

Entrance Requirements: Open admission. Options: electronic application, early admission, deferred admission. Required: high school transcript. Entrance: noncompetitive. Application deadline: rolling.

Costs Per Year: Application fee: $0. State resident tuition: $3840 full-time, $160 per credit hour part-time. Nonresident tuition: $6936 full-time, $289 per credit hour part-time. Full-time tuition varies according to reciprocity agreements. Part-time tuition varies according to reciprocity agreements.

Collegiate Environment: Orientation program. Drama-theater group, choral group. Social organizations: 13 open to all; Service/civic, faith-based, spirit, academic; 10% of eligible men and 10% of eligible women are members. Most popular organizations: National Society of Leadership and Success, Student Government Association, Circle K, International Club, Cardinal Spirit Club. Major annual events: Get on Board Day, G-Day, Constitution Week. Student services: personal-psychological counseling. Campus security: 24-hour patrols. Meadows Library plus 2 others. Books: 79,933 (physical), 62,846 (digital/electronic); Databases: 75. 2,240 computers available on campus for general student use. Computer purchase/lease plans available. A campuswide network can be accessed. Students can access the following: online class registration. Staffed computer lab on campus provides training in use of computers, software, and the Internet.

Community Environment: Gadsden (population 37,405) is the county seat, and is the 6th largest in Alabama. Buses and railroads serve the area. Noccalula Falls is located in the City. Industry includes steel, rubber, farm machinery, and cotton mills.

■ **GEORGE C. WALLACE COMMUNITY COLLEGE**
1141 Wallace Dr.
Dothan, AL 36303-9234
Tel: (334)983-3521; Free: 800-543-2426
Fax: (334)983-3600
E-mail: ksaulsberry@wallace.edu
Web Site: www.wallace.edu
Description: State-supported, 2-year, coed. Part of The Alabama Community College System. Awards certificates, diplomas, transfer associate, and terminal associate degrees. Founded 1949. Setting: 258-acre rural campus. Total enrollment: 4,645. Faculty: 226 (131 full-time, 95 part-time). Student-undergrad faculty ratio is 17:1. Full-time: 1,929 students, 62% women, 38% men. Part-time: 2,716 students, 67% women, 33% men. Students come from 7 states and territories, 1% from out-of-state. 0.4% American Indian or Alaska Native, non-Hispanic/Latino; 3% Hispanic/Latino; 28% Black or African American, non-Hispanic/Latino; 0.8% Asian, non-Hispanic/Latino; 0.1% Native Hawaiian or other Pacific Islander, non-Hispanic/Latino. 31% 25 or older, 7% transferred in. Core. Calendar: semesters. Academic remediation for entering students, ESL program, advanced placement, independent study, distance learning, part-time degree program, adult/continuing education programs, co-op programs. Off campus study.

Entrance Requirements: Open admission. Options: electronic application, early admission. Required: high school transcript. Recommended: SAT or ACT. Entrance: noncompetitive. Application deadline: rolling. Transfer credits accepted: Yes.

Costs Per Year: Application fee: $0. State resident tuition: $3870 full-time, $129 per credit hour part-time. Nonresident tuition: $7740 full-time, $258 per credit hour part-time. Mandatory fees: $810 full-time, $27 per credit hour part-time. Full-time tuition and fees vary according to reciprocity agreements. Part-time tuition and fees vary according to reciprocity agreements.

Collegiate Environment: Orientation program. Drama-theater group, student-run newspaper. Social organizations: 28 open to all. Student services: personal-psychological counseling. Campus security: 24-hour patrols. Learning Resources Centers. Books: 35,060 (physical), 659 (digital/electronic); Serial titles: 50 (physical), 8 (digital/electronic); Databases: 9. 240 computers available on campus for general student use. A campuswide network can be accessed from off-campus. Students can access the following: online class registration. Staffed computer lab on campus provides training in use of computers, software, and the Internet.

■ **GEORGE CORLEY WALLACE STATE COMMUNITY COLLEGE**
PO Box 2530
Selma, AL 36702

Tel: (334)876-9227
Fax: (334)876-9250
Web Site: www.wccs.edu
Description: State-supported, 2-year, coed. Part of Alabama College System. Awards certificates, diplomas, transfer associate, and terminal associate degrees. Founded 1966. Setting: small town campus. Total enrollment: 1,781. 31% 25 or older. Core. Calendar: semesters. Academic remediation for entering students, services for LD students, advanced placement, independent study, summer session for credit, part-time degree program, adult/continuing education programs.

Entrance Requirements: Open admission. Options: early admission, deferred admission. Entrance: noncompetitive. Application deadline: rolling.

Collegiate Environment: Orientation program. Choral group. Campus security: 24-hour patrols. George Corley Wallace Library.

Community Environment: Selma, population 19,400 enjoys a temperate climate. Railroad, bus and air service is available for the area. There are many churches in the city, as well as hospitals, a library, and theaters. Gulf beaches are only 180 miles away. Part-time employment is available. Major civic, fraternal and veteran's organizations are represented. A traditional Market Day is held in October.

■ **H. COUNCILL TRENHOLM STATE COMMUNITY COLLEGE**
1225 Air Base Blvd.
Montgomery, AL 36108
Tel: (334)420-4200; Free: 866-753-4544
Fax: (334)420-4201
E-mail: tmcbryde@trenholmstate.edu
Web Site: www.trenholmstate.edu
Description: State-supported, 2-year, coed. Part of Alabama Community College System. Awards certificates, diplomas, and transfer associate degrees. Founded 1966. Setting: 83-acre urban campus with easy access to Montgomery. Total enrollment: 1,845. Faculty: 142 (55 full-time, 87 part-time). Student-undergrad faculty ratio is 15:1. 2,619 applied, 31% were admitted. Students come from 2 states and territories. 0.1% American Indian or Alaska Native, non-Hispanic/Latino; 2% Hispanic/Latino; 68% Black or African American, non-Hispanic/Latino; 1% Asian, non-Hispanic/Latino; 0.1% international. 30% 25 or older. Retention: 60% of full-time freshmen returned the following year. Core. Calendar: semesters. Academic remediation for entering students, ESL program, services for LD students, advanced placement, independent study, distance learning, summer session for credit, part-time degree program, external degree program, adult/continuing education programs, co-op programs and internships.

Entrance Requirements: Open admission. Options: electronic application, early admission, international baccalaureate accepted. Required: high school transcript. Required for some: SAT or ACT. Application deadline: rolling. Transfer credits accepted: Yes.

Costs Per Year: Application fee: $0. State resident tuition: $3720 full-time, $129 per credit hour part-time. Nonresident tuition: $7440 full-time, $258 per credit hour part-time. Mandatory fees: $624 full-time, $26 per credit hour part-time.

Collegiate Environment: Orientation program. Social organizations: 8% of men are members. Most popular organizations: Student Government Association, Future Business Leaders of America, National Society of Leadership and Science, Phi Theta Kappa, Council of Peer Educators. Major annual events: Student Appreciation Day, Annual Black History Month Program, Career Fair. Student services: personal-psychological counseling. Campus security: 24-hour patrols. Trenholm State Learning Resources plus 2 others. Books: 10,315 (physical), 36,943 (digital/electronic); Serial titles: 91 (physical), 59 (digital/electronic); Databases: 18. Weekly public service hours: 108. Operations spending for the previous fiscal year: $989,137. 659 computers available on campus for general student use. A campuswide network can be accessed from off-campus. Students can access the following: online class registration, electronic emergency notification system. Staffed computer lab on campus provides training in use of computers, software, and the Internet.

■ **HERITAGE CHRISTIAN UNIVERSITY**
PO Box HCU
Florence, AL 35630
Tel: (256)766-6610; Free: 800-367-3565
Fax: (256)760-0981
E-mail: bmckinnon@hcu.edu
Web Site: www.hcu.edu
Description: Independent, comprehensive, coed, affiliated with Church of

Christ. Awards associate, bachelor's, and master's degrees. Founded 1971. Setting: 43-acre small town campus. Endowment: $6 million. Research spending for the previous fiscal year: $8142. Educational spending for the previous fiscal year: $6552 per student. Total enrollment: 88. Faculty: 20 (5 full-time, 15 part-time). Student-undergrad faculty ratio is 5:1. 8 applied, 100% were admitted. Full-time: 27 students, 19% women, 81% men. Part-time: 36 students, 14% women, 86% men. Students come from 14 states and territories, 1 other country, 48% from out-of-state. 3% Hispanic/Latino; 8% Black or African American, non-Hispanic/Latino; 3% international. 66% 25 or older, 60% live on campus, 19% transferred in. Retention: 33% of full-time freshmen returned the following year. Core. Calendar: semesters. Academic remediation for entering students, accelerated degree program, independent study, distance learning, summer session for credit, part-time degree program, external degree program, adult/continuing education programs, co-op programs and internships, graduate courses open to undergrads.

Entrance Requirements: Open admission. Options: electronic application, early admission, deferred admission, international baccalaureate accepted. Required: high school transcript, minimum 2 high school GPA, 3 recommendations. Recommended: interview. Required for some: TOEFL for international students. Entrance: noncompetitive. Application deadline: rolling. Notification: 7/1. Preference given to applicants interested in preaching in Churches of Christ. Transfer credits accepted: Yes.

Collegiate Environment: Most popular organizations: Missions Club, Preachers Club, Student Government Association, Christian Ladies Organization, HCU Skit Team. Major annual events: Evangelism Seminar, Area-Wide Singing, Annual Theatre Event. Student services: personal-psychological counseling. Overton Memorial Library. Operations spending for the previous fiscal year: $121,227. 12 computers available on campus for general student use. Computer purchase/lease plans available. A campuswide network can be accessed from student residence rooms. Students can access the following: online class registration. Staffed computer lab on campus provides training in use of computers, software, and the Internet.

■ **HERZING UNIVERSITY**
280 W Valley Ave.
Birmingham, AL 35209
Tel: (205)916-2800; Free: 800-596-0724
Fax: (205)916-2807
Web Site: www.herzing.edu/birmingham
Description: Independent, 4-year, coed. Part of Herzing Institutes, Inc. Awards associate and bachelor's degrees. Founded 1965. Setting: 4-acre urban campus. Calendar: semesters. Summer session for credit.

■ **HUNTINGDON COLLEGE**
1500 E Fairview Ave.
Montgomery, AL 36106-2148
Tel: (334)833-4497; Free: 800-763-0313
Fax: (334)833-4347
E-mail: admiss@hawks.huntingdon.edu
Web Site: www.huntingdon.edu
Description: Independent United Methodist, 4-year, coed. Awards bachelor's degrees. Founded 1854. Setting: 70-acre suburban campus with easy access to Birmingham. Endowment: $48.2 million. Educational spending for the previous fiscal year: $7073 per student. Total enrollment: 1,102. Faculty: 101 (47 full-time, 54 part-time). Student-undergrad faculty ratio is 15:1. 2,074 applied, 56% were admitted. 13% from top 10% of their high school class, 27% from top quarter, 69% from top half. Full-time: 878 students, 47% women, 53% men. Part-time: 224 students, 68% women, 32% men. Students come from 22 states and territories, 4 other countries, 30% from out-of-state. 0.5% American Indian or Alaska Native, non-Hispanic/Latino; 6% Hispanic/Latino; 21% Black or African American, non-Hispanic/Latino; 0.5% Asian, non-Hispanic/Latino; 0.3% Native Hawaiian or other Pacific Islander, non-Hispanic/Latino; 0.1% international. 15% 25 or older, 68% live on campus, 9% transferred in. Retention: 65% of full-time freshmen returned the following year. Academic areas with the most degrees conferred: business/marketing; parks and recreation; biological/life sciences. Core. Calendar: semesters. Services for LD students, advanced placement, self-designed majors, freshman honors college, honors program, independent study, distance learning, double major, summer session for credit, part-time degree program, adult/continuing education programs, internships. Off campus study at Students may participate in the Marine Environmental Sciences Consortium located in Dauphin Island, AL. Study abroad program. ROTC: Army (c), Air Force (c).

Entrance Requirements: Open admission. Options: electronic application, deferred admission, international baccalaureate accepted. Required: high school transcript, SAT or ACT. Required for some: essay, 3 recommendations, interview, audition required for music majors; portfolio recommended for art majors. Entrance: moderately difficult. Application deadlines: rolling, rolling for nonresidents. Notification: continuous, continuous for nonresidents. Transfer credits accepted: Yes.

Costs Per Year: Comprehensive fee: $36,900 includes full-time tuition ($25,900), mandatory fees ($1500), and college room and board ($9500). Full-time tuition and fees vary according to course load and program. Room and board charges vary according to housing facility. Part-time tuition: $1080 per credit hour. Part-time tuition varies according to course load and program.

Collegiate Environment: Orientation program. Drama-theater group, choral group, marching band, student-run newspaper. Social organizations: 40 open to all; national fraternities, national sororities; 18% of eligible men and 42% of eligible women are members. Most popular organizations: Student Government Association, Campus Activities Board, Voice of Justice, Freshman Forum, Exchange Club. Major annual events: Countess of Huntingdon Ball, Welcome Back Week Events, Miss Huntingdon Pageant. Student services: health clinic, personal-psychological counseling. Campus security: 24-hour emergency response devices and patrols, late night transport-escort service, controlled dormitory access, electronic video surveillance, weather alert broadcasts. Houghton Memorial Library. Books: 91,034 (physical), 103,891 (digital/electronic); Serial titles: 187 (physical), 41,336 (digital/electronic); Databases: 114. Students can reserve study rooms. Operations spending for the previous fiscal year: $550,987. 9 computers available on campus for general student use. A campuswide network can be accessed from student residence rooms and from off campus. Students can access the following: online class registration.

Community Environment: Huntingdon's location in Montgomery gives students easy access to Gulf beaches (3 hours south), mountains (2 hours north), and major metropolitan areas (Birmingham, 90 miles; Atlanta, 180 miles; New Orleans 300 miles). Montgomery, Alabama's capital city, is an historic area rich in tradition and culture.

■ **HUNTSVILLE BIBLE COLLEGE**
904 Oakwood Ave.
Huntsville, AL 35811-1632
Tel: (256)539-0834
Web Site: www.huntsvillebiblecollege.org
Description: Independent, comprehensive, coed. Awards associate, bachelor's, and master's degrees.

■ **J. F. DRAKE STATE COMMUNITY AND TECHNICAL COLLEGE**
3421 Meridian St. N
Huntsville, AL 35811-1584
Tel: (256)539-8161; Free: 888-413-7253
E-mail: kristin.treadway@drakestate.edu
Web Site: www.drakestate.edu
Description: State-supported, 2-year, coed. Part of Alabama Community College System. Awards certificates, transfer associate, and terminal associate degrees. Founded 1961. Setting: 6-acre urban campus. Total enrollment: 996. Faculty: 79 (31 full-time, 48 part-time). Student-undergrad faculty ratio is 15:1. Full-time: 484 students, 58% women, 42% men. Part-time: 512 students, 56% women, 44% men. Students come from 2 states and territories. 48% 25 or older, 11% transferred in. Retention: 41% of full-time freshmen returned the following year. Core. Calendar: semesters. Academic remediation for entering students, ESL program, services for LD students, distance learning, part-time degree program, co-op programs and internships.

Entrance Requirements: Open admission. Options: electronic application, deferred admission. Required: high school transcript. Entrance: noncompetitive. Application deadline: rolling. Notification: continuous. Transfer credits accepted: Yes.

Collegiate Environment: Orientation program. Social organizations: 4 open to all. Most popular organizations: Phi Beta Lambda, SkillsUSA, Phi Theta Kappa, National Technical Honor Society. Major annual events: Student Government Election, Miss Drake Pageant, Spring Fling. Campus security: 24-hour patrols. S.C. O'Neal Library and Technology Center.

■ **J F INGRAM STATE TECHNICAL COLLEGE**
5375 Ingram Rd.
Deatsville, AL 36022

Web Site: www.istc.edu

Description: State-supported, 2-year, coed. Awards certificates, transfer associate, and terminal associate degrees.

■ **JACKSONVILLE STATE UNIVERSITY**

700 Pelham Rd., N

Jacksonville, AL 36265-1602

Tel: (256)782-5781; Free: 800-231-5291

Fax: (256)782-5291

E-mail: info@jsu.edu

Web Site: www.jsu.edu

Description: State-supported, comprehensive, coed. Awards bachelor's, master's, and doctoral degrees and post-master's certificates. Founded 1883. Setting: 459-acre small town campus with easy access to Birmingham. Research spending for the previous fiscal year: $3.3 million. Total enrollment: 8,514. Faculty: 473 (315 full-time, 158 part-time). Student-undergrad faculty ratio is 18:1. 4,979 applied, 53% were admitted. 17% from top 10% of their high school class, 41% from top quarter, 73% from top half. Full-time: 5,480 students, 56% women, 44% men. Part-time: 2,081 students, 60% women, 40% men. 16% from out-of-state. 0.7% American Indian or Alaska Native, non-Hispanic/Latino; 1% Hispanic/Latino; 18% Black or African American, non-Hispanic/Latino; 0.7% Asian, non-Hispanic/Latino; 0.1% Native Hawaiian or other Pacific Islander, non-Hispanic/Latino; 2% international. 23% 25 or older, 16% live on campus, 8% transferred in. Retention: 78% of full-time freshmen returned the following year. Academic areas with the most degrees conferred: health professions and related sciences; business/marketing; education. Core. Calendar: semesters. Academic remediation for entering students, ESL program, services for LD students, advanced placement, accelerated degree program, freshman honors college, honors program, independent study, distance learning, double major, summer session for credit, part-time degree program, adult/continuing education programs, co-op programs and internships, graduate courses open to undergrads. Study abroad program. ROTC: Army.

Entrance Requirements: Options: electronic application, early admission, deferred admission. Required: high school transcript, SAT or ACT. Required for some: minimum X high school GPA. Entrance: moderately difficult. Application deadline: rolling. Notification: continuous. Transfer credits accepted: Yes.

Costs Per Year: Application fee: $35. State resident tuition: $9720 full-time, $324 per credit hour part-time. Nonresident tuition: $19,554 full-time, $648 per credit hour part-time. Mandatory fees: $1210 full-time, $6 per credit hour part-time, $515 per term part-time.

Collegiate Environment: Orientation program. Drama-theater group, choral group, marching band, student-run newspaper, radio station. Social organizations: 100 open to all; national fraternities, national sororities, local fraternities, local sororities; 15% of eligible men and 19% of eligible women are members. Most popular organizations: Student Government Association, Archaeology Club, Campus Fellowship Clubs, Computer Science Club, Biology Club. Major annual events: Homecoming, Founder's Day. Student services: health clinic, personal-psychological counseling. Campus security: 24-hour emergency response devices and patrols, student patrols, late night transport-escort service, controlled dormitory access, night security officer in female residence halls. Houston Cole Library. Books: 711,815 (physical), 32,128 (digital/electronic); Databases: 307. Weekly public service hours: 87. Operations spending for the previous fiscal year: $133,745. 350 computers available on campus for general student use. A campuswide network can be accessed from student residence rooms and from off campus. Students can access the following: online class registration. Staffed computer lab on campus.

Community Environment: Population 8,800, Jacksonville is relatively small and free from the many distractions of a large city. The community is easily accessible by good roads and is 6 miles from Fort McClellan (a military installation), 12 miles from Anniston, 22 miles from Gadsden, 75 miles from Birmingham, and 100 miles from Atlanta, GA. The climate is pleasant.

■ **JEFFERSON STATE COMMUNITY COLLEGE**

2601 Carson Rd.

Birmingham, AL 35215-3098

Tel: (205)853-1200; Free: 800-239-5900

Fax: (205)856-8547

E-mail: lowens@jeffstateonline.com

Web Site: www.jeffersonstate.edu

Description: State-supported, 2-year, coed. Part of Alabama Community College System. Awards certificates, transfer associate, and terminal associate degrees. Founded 1965. Setting: 351-acre suburban campus with easy access to Birmingham. Endowment: $1.3 million. Educational spending for the previous fiscal year: $2101 per student. Total enrollment: 8,840. Faculty: 440 (144 full-time, 296 part-time). Student-undergrad faculty ratio is 19:1. 4,989 applied, 57% were admitted. Full-time: 2,647 students, 56% women, 44% men. Part-time: 6,193 students, 63% women, 37% men. Students come from 30 states and territories, 52 other countries, 2% from out-of-state. 0.3% American Indian or Alaska Native, non-Hispanic/Latino; 5% Hispanic/Latino; 25% Black or African American, non-Hispanic/Latino; 2% Asian, non-Hispanic/Latino; 0.1% Native Hawaiian or other Pacific Islander, non-Hispanic/Latino; 3% international. 35% 25 or older, 10% transferred in. Retention: 53% of full-time freshmen returned the following year. Core. Calendar: semesters. Academic remediation for entering students, ESL program, services for LD students, advanced placement, honors program, independent study, distance learning, summer session for credit, part-time degree program, adult/continuing education programs, internships. ROTC: Army (c), Air Force (c).

Entrance Requirements: Open admission Jeff State has an open admissions policy for all programs except Allied Health Programs. Options: electronic application, early admission, deferred admission. Required for some: high school transcript. Entrance: noncompetitive. Application deadline: rolling. Notification: continuous. Transfer credits accepted: Yes.

Costs Per Year: Application fee: $0. State resident tuition: $160 per credit hour part-time. Nonresident tuition: $289 per credit hour part-time. Part-time tuition varies according to course load.

Collegiate Environment: Orientation program. Choral group. Social organizations: 6 open to all. Most popular organizations: Student Government Association, Phi Theta Kappa, Sigma Kappa Delta, Jefferson State Ambassadors, Enactus. Major annual events: Black History Month Program, Spring Fling, Jeff Fest. Campus security: 24-hour patrols. Jefferson State Libraries plus 4 others. Books: 63,660 (physical), 193,910 (digital/electronic); Serial titles: 234 (physical), 296,861 (digital/electronic); Databases: 52. Weekly public service hours: 62. Operations spending for the previous fiscal year: $817,670. 302 computers available on campus for general student use. A campuswide network can be accessed from off-campus. Students can access the following: online class registration. Staffed computer lab on campus provides training in use of computers, software, and the Internet.

Community Environment: See University of Alabama Birmingham.

■ **JUDSON COLLEGE**

302 Bibb St.

Marion, AL 36756

Tel: (334)683-5100; Free: 800-447-9472

Fax: (334)683-5158

E-mail: admissions@judson.edu

Web Site: www.judson.edu

Description: Independent Baptist, 4-year, coed. Awards associate and bachelor's degrees. Founded 1838. Setting: 118-acre rural campus with easy access to Birmingham. Endowment: $15.4 million. Educational spending for the previous fiscal year: $11,912 per student. Total enrollment: 374. Faculty: 45 (30 full-time, 15 part-time). Student-undergrad faculty ratio is 8:1. 329 applied, 63% were admitted. 25% from top 10% of their high school class, 49% from top quarter, 78% from top half. 2 valedictorians. Full-time: 249 students, 99% women, 1% men. Part-time: 125 students, 90% women, 10% men. Students come from 22 states and territories, 3 other countries, 19% from out-of-state. 0.5% American Indian or Alaska Native, non-Hispanic/Latino; 0.8% Hispanic/Latino; 15% Black or African American, non-Hispanic/Latino; 0.5% Asian, non-Hispanic/Latino; 0.3% Native Hawaiian or other Pacific Islander, non-Hispanic/Latino; 2% international. 34% 25 or older, 51% live on campus, 7% transferred in. Retention: 70% of full-time freshmen returned the following year. Core. Calendar: semesters plus 2-month term in May and June. Academic remediation for entering students, services for LD students, advanced placement, accelerated degree program, self-designed majors, honors program, independent study, distance learning, double major, summer session for credit, part-time degree program, external degree program, adult/continuing education programs, internships. Off campus study at Judson College students enroll and participate in the ROTC classes at Marion Military Institute, a cross-town institution. Study abroad program. ROTC: Army (c).

Entrance Requirements: Options: electronic application, early admission, deferred admission, international baccalaureate accepted. Required: high school transcript, minimum 2 high school GPA, SAT or ACT. Entrance: moderately difficult. Application deadline: rolling. Notification: continuous. SAT Reasoning Test deadline: 8/1. Transfer credits accepted: Yes.

Costs Per Year: Application fee: $42. Comprehensive fee: $29,100 includes full-time tuition ($17,240), mandatory fees ($1270), and college room and board ($10,590). College room only: $5960. Full-time tuition and fees vary according to course load, degree level, and program. Room and board charges vary according to board plan. Part-time tuition: $585 per credit hour. Part-time mandatory fees: $645 per term. Part-time tuition and fees vary according to course load, degree level, and program.

Collegiate Environment: Orientation program. Drama-theater group, choral group, student-run newspaper. Social organizations: 26 open to all. Most popular organizations: Student Government Association, Campus Ministries, Faith-Based Service Learning Activities, Ambassadors, Science Club. Major annual events: Marion Matters, Pageant, Rose Sunday. Student services: personal-psychological counseling. Campus security: 24-hour emergency response devices and patrols, late night transport-escort service, controlled dormitory access. Bowling Library. Books: 62,633 (physical), 145,000 (digital/electronic); Serial titles: 60 (physical), 44,447 (digital/electronic); Databases: 93. Weekly public service hours: 63; students can reserve study rooms. Operations spending for the previous fiscal year: $22,524. 56 computers available on campus for general student use. A campuswide network can be accessed. Students can access the following: online class registration.

■ **LAWSON STATE COMMUNITY COLLEGE**
3060 Wilson Rd., SW
Birmingham, AL 35221-1798
Tel: (205)925-2515
Fax: (205)929-6316
E-mail: jshelley@lawsonstate.edu
Web Site: www.lawsonstate.edu

Description: State-supported, 2-year, coed. Part of Alabama Community College System. Awards certificates, transfer associate, and terminal associate degrees. Founded 1949. Setting: 30-acre urban campus. Total enrollment: 3,031. Faculty: 209 (82 full-time, 127 part-time). Student-undergrad faculty ratio is 17:1. 1,596 applied, 82% were admitted. 1 class president. Full-time: 1,791 students, 58% women, 42% men. Part-time: 1,240 students, 62% women, 38% men. Students come from 14 states and territories, 1 other country, 1% from out-of-state. 0.1% American Indian or Alaska Native, non-Hispanic/Latino; 1% Hispanic/Latino; 75% Black or African American, non-Hispanic/Latino; 0.4% Asian, non-Hispanic/Latino; 0.2% Native Hawaiian or other Pacific Islander, non-Hispanic/Latino; 0.1% international. 35% 25 or older, 1% live on campus, 7% transferred in. Retention: 52% of full-time freshmen returned the following year. Core. Calendar: semesters. Academic remediation for entering students, services for LD students, advanced placement, honors program, distance learning, summer session for credit, part-time degree program, adult/continuing education programs, co-op programs and internships.

Entrance Requirements: Open admission except for nursing, medical technology programs. Options: electronic application, international baccalaureate accepted. Required: high school transcript. Entrance: noncompetitive. Application deadline: rolling. Notification: continuous. Transfer credits accepted: Yes.

Costs Per Year: Application fee: $0. State resident tuition: $3900 full-time, $130 per credit hour part-time. Nonresident tuition: $7800 full-time, $260 per credit hour part-time. Mandatory fees: $860 full-time, $28 per credit hour part-time, $10 per term part-time. College room and board: $4760.

Collegiate Environment: Choral group. Social organizations: 8 open to all. Most popular organizations: Student Government Association, Phi Theta Kappa, Kappa Beta Delta Honor Society, Phi Beta Lambda, Social Work Club. Major annual events: Homecoming, Miss Lawson State, L Week Activities. Student services: personal-psychological counseling. Campus security: 24-hour emergency response devices and patrols, controlled dormitory access. Lawson State Library. Operations spending for the previous fiscal year: $159,803. 484 computers available on campus for general student use. Computer purchase/lease plans available. A campuswide network can be accessed from student residence rooms. Students can access the following: online class registration. Staffed computer lab on campus provides training in use of computers, software, and the Internet.

Community Environment: See University of Alabama - Birmingham.

■ **LURLEEN B. WALLACE COMMUNITY COLLEGE**
PO Box 1418
Andalusia, AL 36420-1418
Tel: (334)222-6591
Web Site: www.lbwcc.edu

Description: State-supported, 2-year, coed. Part of Alabama Community College System. Awards certificates, transfer associate, and terminal associate degrees. Founded 2003. Setting: 200-acre small town campus. Total enrollment: 1,784. Faculty: 105 (56 full-time, 49 part-time). Student-undergrad faculty ratio is 17:1. Full-time: 880 students, 61% women, 39% men. Part-time: 904 students, 53% women, 47% men. Students come from 9 states and territories, 8 other countries, 4% from out-of-state. 0.6% American Indian or Alaska Native, non-Hispanic/Latino; 1% Hispanic/Latino; 25% Black or African American, non-Hispanic/Latino; 0.6% Asian, non-Hispanic/Latino; 0.3% international. 23% 25 or older, 6% transferred in. Calendar: semesters. Academic remediation for entering students, honors program, independent study, distance learning, summer session for credit, part-time degree program, co-op programs.

Entrance Requirements: Open admission. Option: electronic application. Required: high school transcript. Entrance: noncompetitive. Application deadlines: rolling, rolling for nonresidents. Transfer credits accepted: Yes.

Costs Per Year: Application fee: $0. State resident tuition: $3870 full-time, $129 per credit hour part-time. Nonresident tuition: $7740 full-time, $258 per credit hour part-time. Mandatory fees: $870 full-time, $29 per credit hour part-time. Full-time tuition and fees vary according to course load. Part-time tuition and fees vary according to course load.

Collegiate Environment: Orientation program. Drama-theater group, choral group. Social organizations: 11 open to all. Most popular organizations: Student Government Association, Student Ambassadors, Campus Civitan, Christian Student Ministries, Saints Angels. Major annual events: Saints' Day, Blue/White Day. Student services: personal-psychological counseling. College housing not available. Lurleen B. Wallace Library plus 3 others. Students can reserve study rooms. Operations spending for the previous fiscal year: $307,430. 350 computers available on campus for general student use. A campuswide network can be accessed. Students can access the following: online class registration. Staffed computer lab on campus.

■ **MARION MILITARY INSTITUTE**
1101 Washington St.
Marion, AL 36756
Tel: (334)683-2300; Free: 800-664-1842
Fax: (334)683-2380
E-mail: bcrawford@marionmilitary.edu
Web Site: www.marionmilitary.edu

Description: State-supported, 2-year, coed. Part of Alabama Community College System. Awards transfer associate degrees. Founded 1842. Setting: 130-acre rural campus with easy access to Birmingham. Total enrollment: 446. Faculty: 28 (20 full-time, 8 part-time). Student-undergrad faculty ratio is 16:1. 1,065 applied, 56% were admitted. Full-time: 442 students, 23% women, 77% men. Part-time: 4 students, 100% women. Students come from 45 states and territories, 51% from out-of-state. 1% American Indian or Alaska Native, non-Hispanic/Latino; 6% Hispanic/Latino; 17% Black or African American, non-Hispanic/Latino; 3% Asian, non-Hispanic/Latino; 0.7% Native Hawaiian or other Pacific Islander, non-Hispanic/Latino. 1% 25 or older, 100% live on campus, 4% transferred in. Retention: 40% of full-time freshmen returned the following year. Core. Calendar: semesters. Academic remediation for entering students, ESL program, services for LD students, honors program. Study abroad program. ROTC: Army, Air Force (c).

Entrance Requirements: Options: electronic application, deferred admission. Required: high school transcript, minimum 2 high school GPA, SAT or ACT. Entrance: moderately difficult. Application deadline: rolling. Notification: continuous. SAT Reasoning Test deadline: 8/1. SAT Subject Test deadline: 8/1. Transfer credits accepted: Yes.

Costs Per Year: Application fee: $30. One-time mandatory fee: $2470. State resident tuition: $6000 full-time, $200 per credit hour part-time. Nonresident tuition: $12,000 full-time, $400 per credit hour part-time. Mandatory fees: $948 full-time, $19 per credit hour part-time. Full-time tuition and fees vary according to course load. College room and board: $4950.

Collegiate Environment: Orientation program. Drama-theater group, choral group, marching band. Social organizations: 12 open to all. Most popular organizations: Honor Guard, White Knights Precision Drill Team, Swamp Fox, Marching Band, Scabbard and Blade. Major annual events: Military Ball, Gymkhana, Intramurals. Student services: health clinic, personal-psychological counseling. Campus security: 24-hour patrols. Baer Memorial Library. Weekly public service hours: 65; study areas open 24 hours, 5-7 days a week. 101 computers available on campus for general student use. A campuswide network can be accessed from student residence rooms. Students can access the following: online class registration. Staffed computer lab on campus provides training in use of software.

Community Environment: See Judson College.

■ **MILES COLLEGE**
5500 Myron Massey Blvd.
Fairfield, AL 35064
Tel: (205)929-1000; Free: 800-445-0708
E-mail: admissions@miles.edu
Web Site: www.miles.edu
Description: Independent Christian Methodist Episcopal, 4-year, coed. Awards bachelor's degrees. Founded 1905. Setting: 76-acre suburban campus. Endowment: $13.1 million. Research spending for the previous fiscal year: $1.2 million. Educational spending for the previous fiscal year: $4196 per student. Total enrollment: 1,738. Faculty: 147 (105 full-time, 42 part-time). Student-undergrad faculty ratio is 14:1. 2,905 applied, 26% were admitted. Full-time: 1,589 students, 53% women, 47% men. Part-time: 149 students, 66% women, 34% men. Students come from 23 states and territories, 21% from out-of-state. 20% 25 or older, 40% live on campus, 23% transferred in. Retention: 60% of full-time freshmen returned the following year. Academic areas with the most degrees conferred: business/marketing; foreign languages and literature; public administration and social services. Core. Calendar: semesters. Academic remediation for entering students, services for LD students, accelerated degree program, honors program, double major, summer session for credit, part-time degree program, adult/continuing education programs, co-op programs and internships. Off campus study at BACHE: UAB, Samford, Birmingham Southern. ROTC: Army (c), Air Force (c).
Entrance Requirements: Open admission. Recommended: ACT. Required for some: essay, high school transcript. Entrance: noncompetitive. Application deadline: 8/23. Notification: continuous.
Collegiate Environment: Orientation program. Drama-theater group, choral group, marching band, student-run newspaper. Social organizations: 20 open to all; national fraternities, national sororities, local fraternities, local sororities; 18% of eligible men and 22% of eligible women are members. Most popular organizations: choir, Education Club, Student Government Association, Phi Beta Lambda Business Club, Communications Club. Major annual events: Founders' Day, Homecoming, M-Day. Student services: health clinic, personal-psychological counseling. Campus security: 24-hour emergency response devices and patrols. C.A. Kirkeedoll Learning Resources Center. Operations spending for the previous fiscal year: $262,000. 50 computers available on campus for general student use. Staffed computer lab on campus.
Community Environment: See University of Alabama - Birmingham.

■ **NORTHEAST ALABAMA COMMUNITY COLLEGE**
PO Box 159
Rainsville, AL 35986-0159
Tel: (256)228-6001
Web Site: www.nacc.edu
Description: State-supported, 2-year, coed. Part of Alabama Community College System. Awards certificates, transfer associate, and terminal associate degrees. Founded 1963. Setting: 117-acre rural campus. Total enrollment: 2,704. Faculty: 148 (42 full-time, 106 part-time). Student-undergrad faculty ratio is 22:1. Full-time: 1,193 students, 61% women, 39% men. Part-time: 1,511 students, 62% women, 38% men. Students come from 3 states and territories. 3% American Indian or Alaska Native, non-Hispanic/Latino; 8% Hispanic/Latino; 2% Black or African American, non-Hispanic/Latino; 0.8% Asian, non-Hispanic/Latino. 24% 25 or older, 13% transferred in. Core. Calendar: semesters. Academic remediation for entering students, ESL program, services for LD students, advanced placement, accelerated degree program, honors program, independent study, distance learning, double major, summer session for credit, part-time degree program, adult/continuing education programs, co-op programs and internships.
Entrance Requirements: Open admission. Required: high school transcript. Entrance: noncompetitive. Application deadline: rolling. Notification: continuous. Transfer credits accepted: Yes.
Costs Per Year: Application fee: $0. State resident tuition: $3870 full-time, $129 per credit hour part-time. Nonresident tuition: $7740 full-time, $258 per credit hour part-time. Mandatory fees: $870 full-time, $29 per credit hour part-time.
Collegiate Environment: Orientation program. Drama-theater group, choral group. Student services: personal-psychological counseling. Campus security: 24-hour emergency response devices. Cecil B. Word Learning Resources Center. Books: 62,979 (physical), 47,085 (digital/electronic); Serial titles: 95 (physical); Databases: 49. Weekly public service hours: 58;

students can reserve study rooms. 529 computers available on campus for general student use. A campuswide network can be accessed. Students can access the following: online class registration. Staffed computer lab on campus provides training in use of computers, software, and the Internet.
Community Environment: Rainsville, population 5,000, is in a mountainous area with a very pleasant temperate climate. The town is 58 miles from commercial airline service, six miles from Interstate 59, and eight miles from rail service. Protestant churches, and hospitals in Fort Payne and Scottsboro service the community. Recreational activities include good fishing, boating, camping, and hiking at nearby state parks.

■ **NORTHWEST-SHOALS COMMUNITY COLLEGE**
PO Box 2545
Muscle Shoals, AL 35662
Tel: (256)331-5200
Fax: (256)331-5366
E-mail: tom.carter@nwscc.edu
Web Site: www.nwscc.edu
Description: State-supported, 2-year, coed. Part of Alabama Community College System. Awards certificates and transfer associate degrees. Founded 1963. Setting: 210-acre small town campus. Endowment: $733,034. Total enrollment: 3,440. Faculty: 157 (73 full-time, 84 part-time). Student-undergrad faculty ratio is 20:1. 1,833 applied, 100% were admitted. Full-time: 1,436 students, 56% women, 44% men. Part-time: 2,004 students, 60% women, 40% men. Students come from 3 states and territories, 2 other countries. 0.9% American Indian or Alaska Native, non-Hispanic/Latino; 6% Hispanic/Latino; 8% Black or African American, non-Hispanic/Latino; 0.5% Asian, non-Hispanic/Latino; 1% international. 20% 25 or older, 3% transferred in. Core. Calendar: semesters. Academic remediation for entering students, services for LD students, advanced placement, accelerated degree program, honors program, independent study, distance learning, double major, summer session for credit, part-time degree program, adult/continuing education programs, co-op programs and internships. Off campus study.
Entrance Requirements: Open admission except for nursing, practical nursing, emergency medical services, medical assisting technology programs. Option: electronic application. Required: high school transcript. Entrance: noncompetitive. Application deadline: rolling. Transfer credits accepted: Yes.
Costs Per Year: Application fee: $0. State resident tuition: $3870 full-time, $129 per credit hour part-time. Nonresident tuition: $7740 full-time, $258 per credit hour part-time. Mandatory fees: $841 full-time, $27 per credit hour part-time. Full-time tuition and fees vary according to course load. Part-time tuition and fees vary according to course load.
Collegiate Environment: Choral group. Social organizations: 22 open to all. Most popular organizations: Student Government Association, Science Club, Phi Theta Kappa, Baptist Campus Ministry, Northwest-Shoals Singers. Major annual events: Back-to-School Cookout, Spring Fling, Blood Drive. Campus security: 24-hour emergency response devices. Larry W. McCoy Learning Resource Center. Books: 65,800 (physical), 27,000 (digital/electronic); Databases: 2. Weekly public service hours: 62. Operations spending for the previous fiscal year: $325,003. 900 computers available on campus for general student use. A campuswide network can be accessed from off-campus. Students can access the following: online class registration. Staffed computer lab on campus.

■ **OAKWOOD UNIVERSITY**
7000 Adventist Blvd.
Huntsville, AL 35896
Tel: (256)726-7000; Free: 800-824-5312
Fax: (256)726-7404
E-mail: admission@oakwood.edu
Web Site: www.oakwood.edu
Description: Independent Seventh-day Adventist, comprehensive, coed. Awards associate, bachelor's, and master's degrees. Founded 1896. Setting: 1,200-acre campus. Total enrollment: 1,824. Faculty: 171 (103 full-time, 68 part-time). Student-undergrad faculty ratio is 14:1. 1,492 applied, 57% were admitted. 12% from top 10% of their high school class, 26% from top quarter, 50% from top half. Full-time: 1,712 students, 58% women, 42% men. Part-time: 112 students, 65% women, 35% men. Students come from 43 states and territories, 21 other countries, 81% from out-of-state. 13% 25 or older, 64% live on campus, 6% transferred in. Retention: 69% of full-time freshmen returned the following year. Academic areas with the most degrees conferred: business/marketing; biological/life sciences; psychology. Core.

Calendar: semesters. Academic remediation for entering students, advanced placement, honors program, double major, part-time degree program, internships. Off campus study at members of the Alabama Center for Higher Education, The University of Alabama in Huntsville. Study abroad program.
Entrance Requirements: Options: early action, deferred admission. Required: high school transcript, minimum 2 high school GPA, SAT or ACT. Required for some: essay. Entrance: minimally difficult. Application deadlines: rolling, 3/30 for early action. Notification: 4/15 for early action.
Collegiate Environment: Orientation program. Choral group, student-run newspaper, radio station. Most popular organization: United Student Movement. Major annual events: Homecoming, Graduation, Youth Motivational Task Force Week. Student services: health clinic, personal-psychological counseling. Campus security: 24-hour patrols, student patrols, late night transport-escort service. Eva B. Dykes Library. 350 computers available on campus for general student use. A campuswide network can be accessed from student residence rooms and from off campus. Students can access the following: online class registration. Staffed computer lab on campus.
Community Environment: See University of Alabama - Huntsville.

■ **REID STATE TECHNICAL COLLEGE**
100 Hwy. 83
Evergreen, AL 36401-0588
Tel: (251)578-1313
Fax: (251)578-5355
E-mail: mwilson@rstc.edu
Web Site: www.rstc.edu
Description: State-supported, 2-year, coed. Part of Alabama Community College System. Awards certificates and terminal associate degrees. Founded 1966. Setting: 26-acre rural campus. Total enrollment: 392. Faculty: 31 (19 full-time, 12 part-time). Student-undergrad faculty ratio is 12:1. 59 applied, 100% were admitted. Full-time: 181 students, 59% women, 41% men. Part-time: 211 students, 53% women, 47% men. Students come from 3 states and territories, 1% from out-of-state. 0.3% American Indian or Alaska Native, non-Hispanic/Latino; 0.8% Hispanic/Latino; 49% Black or African American, non-Hispanic/Latino; 0.3% Native Hawaiian or other Pacific Islander, non-Hispanic/Latino. 32% 25 or older. Calendar: semesters. Academic remediation for entering students, services for LD students, independent study, double major, summer session for credit, part-time degree program, adult/continuing education programs, internships.
Entrance Requirements: Open admission. Options: electronic application, early admission. Required: high school transcript. Entrance: noncompetitive. Application deadline: rolling. Transfer credits accepted: Yes.
Costs Per Year: Application fee: $0. State resident tuition: $4356 full-time, $129 per credit hour part-time. Nonresident tuition: $8712 full-time, $258 per credit hour part-time. Mandatory fees: $1080 full-time, $30 per credit hour part-time. Full-time tuition and fees vary according to course load and program. Part-time tuition and fees vary according to course load and program.
Collegiate Environment: Orientation program. Social organizations: 2 open to all. Most popular organizations: Student Government Association, National Vocational-Technical Society, Who's Who. Major annual events: Talent Show, Hair Show. Student services: personal-psychological counseling. Campus security: 24-hour emergency response devices, day and evening security guard. Edith A. Gray Library. Books: 6,392 (physical), 150,480 (digital/electronic); Databases: 2. 80 computers available on campus for general student use. A campuswide network can be accessed from off-campus. Staffed computer lab on campus (open 24 hours a day).

■ **REMINGTON COLLEGE-MOBILE CAMPUS**
828 Downtowner Loop W
Mobile, AL 36609
Tel: (251)343-8200; Free: 800-323-8122
Fax: (251)343-0577
Web Site: www.remingtoncollege.edu
Description: Independent, primarily 2-year, coed. Awards diplomas, transfer associate, terminal associate, and bachelor's degrees. Setting: 5-acre suburban campus. Calendar: quarters. Services for LD students, adult/continuing education programs, co-op programs.
Entrance Requirements: Entrance: noncompetitive.
Collegiate Environment: Main library plus 1 other.

■ **SAMFORD UNIVERSITY**
800 Lakeshore Dr.
Birmingham, AL 35229

Tel: (205)726-2011; Free: 800-888-7218
Fax: (205)726-2171
E-mail: blkenned@samford.edu
Web Site: www.samford.edu
Description: Independent Baptist, university, coed. Awards bachelor's, master's, and doctoral degrees and post-master's certificates. Founded 1841. Setting: 212-acre suburban campus. Endowment: $297.5 million. Educational spending for the previous fiscal year: $15,252 per student. Total enrollment: 5,589. Faculty: 549 (361 full-time, 188 part-time). Student-undergrad faculty ratio is 12:1. 3,884 applied, 82% were admitted. 33% from top 10% of their high school class, 59% from top quarter, 86% from top half. 2 National Merit Scholars, 56 class presidents, 219 student government officers. Full-time: 3,453 students, 67% women, 33% men. Part-time: 82 students, 63% women, 37% men. Students come from 40 states and territories, 24 other countries, 68% from out-of-state. 0.1% American Indian or Alaska Native, non-Hispanic/Latino; 3% Hispanic/Latino; 6% Black or African American, non-Hispanic/Latino; 1% Asian, non-Hispanic/Latino; 1% international. 3% 25 or older, 67% live on campus, 4% transferred in. Retention: 91% of full-time freshmen returned the following year. Academic areas with the most degrees conferred: health professions and related sciences; business/marketing; family and consumer sciences; communication/journalism; visual and performing arts. Core. Calendar: 4-1-4. Services for LD students, accelerated degree program, honors program, independent study, distance learning, double major, summer session for credit, part-time degree program, adult/continuing education programs, internships, graduate courses open to undergrads. Off campus study at University of Alabama at Birmingham, Birmingham-Southern College, Miles College, and University of Montevallo. Study abroad program. ROTC: Army (c), Air Force.
Entrance Requirements: Options: electronic application, early admission, deferred admission, international baccalaureate accepted. Required: essay, high school transcript, 1 recommendation, SAT or ACT. Required for some: interview. Entrance: moderately difficult. Application deadlines: 4/30, 4/30 for nonresidents. Notification: continuous until 11/1, continuous until 11/1 for nonresidents. SAT Reasoning Test deadline: 5/1. Transfer credits accepted: Yes. Applicants placed on waiting list: 174. Wait-listed applicants offered admission: 24.
Costs Per Year: Application fee: $40. Comprehensive fee: $43,830 includes full-time tuition ($32,000), mandatory fees ($850), and college room and board ($10,980). College room only: $5970. Part-time tuition: $1070 per credit. Part-time mandatory fees: $355 per term.
Collegiate Environment: Orientation program. Drama-theater group, choral group, marching band, student-run newspaper, radio station. Social organizations: 100 open to all; national fraternities, national sororities; 33% of eligible men and 55% of eligible women are members. Most popular organizations: Student Government Association, Greek Chapters and councils, Campus Ministries. Major annual events: Homecoming, Family Weekend, Hanging of the Green and Lighting of the Way. Student services: health clinic, personal-psychological counseling. Campus security: 24-hour emergency response devices and patrols, late night transport-escort service. College housing designed to accommodate 2,375 students; 2,397 undergraduates lived in college housing during 2018-19. Freshmen guaranteed college housing. On-campus residence required through sophomore year. Options: men-only, women-only housing available. University Library plus 2 others. Books: 574,434 (physical), 299,458 (digital/electronic); Serial titles: 6,045 (physical), 117,199 (digital/electronic); Databases: 296. Weekly public service hours: 99; students can reserve study rooms. Operations spending for the previous fiscal year: $7.2 million. 330 computers available on campus for general student use. A campuswide network can be accessed from student residence rooms and from off campus. Students can access the following: online class registration, free online storage and tech support. Staffed computer lab on campus provides training in use of computers, software, and the Internet.
Community Environment: See University of Alabama - Birmingham.

■ **SELMA UNIVERSITY**
1501 Lapsley St.
Selma, AL 36701-5299
Tel: (334)872-2533
Web Site: www.selmauniversity.edu
Description: Independent Baptist, comprehensive, coed. Awards bachelor's and master's degrees. Founded 1878. Setting: 50-acre small town campus. Endowment: $2.5 million. Educational spending for the previous fiscal year: $2500 per student. Total enrollment: 420. Faculty: 36 (15 full-time, 21 part-time). Student-undergrad faculty ratio is 12:1. 1% from top 10% of their high

school class, 4% from top quarter, 37% from top half. Full-time: 333 students, 73% women, 27% men. Part-time: 65 students, 42% women, 58% men. Students come from 7 states and territories, 4% from out-of-state. 0.5% Hispanic/Latino; 96% Black or African American, non-Hispanic/Latino. 57% 25 or older, 85% live on campus, 39% transferred in. Retention: 37% of full-time freshmen returned the following year. Core. Calendar: semesters. Academic remediation for entering students, independent study, double major, summer session for credit. Off campus study.

Entrance Requirements: Required: essay, high school transcript, 3 recommendations. Recommended: SAT or ACT. Required for some: SAT or ACT.

Collegiate Environment: Orientation program. Choral group. Most popular organizations: Ministers Union, Student Government. Campus security: 24-hour patrols. Stone Douglas. Operations spending for the previous fiscal year: $125,000.

■ **SHELTON STATE COMMUNITY COLLEGE**
9500 Old Greensboro Rd.
Tuscaloosa, AL 35405
Tel: (205)391-2211
Fax: (205)391-2426
E-mail: schastine@sheltonstate.edu
Web Site: www.sheltonstate.edu
Description: State-supported, 2-year, coed. Part of Alabama Community College System. Awards certificates, diplomas, transfer associate, and terminal associate degrees. Founded 1979. Setting: 202-acre small town campus with easy access to Birmingham. Total enrollment: 5,068. Faculty: 222 (91 full-time, 131 part-time). Student-undergrad faculty ratio is 25:1. Full-time: 2,468 students, 51% women, 49% men. Part-time: 2,600 students, 62% women, 38% men. 5% from out-of-state. 0.3% American Indian or Alaska Native, non-Hispanic/Latino; 0.5% Hispanic/Latino; 34% Black or African American, non-Hispanic/Latino; 1% Asian, non-Hispanic/Latino; 0.4% international. 23% 25 or older, 9% transferred in. Retention: 58% of full-time freshmen returned the following year. Core. Calendar: semesters. Academic remediation for entering students, services for LD students, advanced placement, accelerated degree program, distance learning, double major, summer session for credit, part-time degree program, adult/continuing education programs, co-op programs. ROTC: Army (c), Air Force (c).
Entrance Requirements: Open admission except for practical nursing, registered nursing, and respiratory technician programs. Option: electronic application. Required: high school transcript. Entrance: noncompetitive. Application deadline: rolling. Transfer credits accepted: Yes.
Collegiate Environment: Orientation program. Drama-theater group, choral group. Social organizations: 9 open to all. Most popular organizations: Phi Theta Kappa, Student Government Association, African American Cultural Association, Red Cross Club. Campus security: 24-hour emergency response devices and patrols. Brooks-Cork Library plus 1 other. 800 computers available on campus for general student use. A campuswide network can be accessed from off-campus. Students can access the following: online class registration. Staffed computer lab on campus.

■ **SNEAD STATE COMMUNITY COLLEGE**
220 N Walnut St.
Boaz, AL 35957-0734
Tel: (256)593-5120
Fax: (256)593-7180
E-mail: jcannon@snead.edu
Web Site: www.snead.edu
Description: State-supported, 2-year, coed. Part of Alabama College System. Awards certificates, transfer associate, and terminal associate degrees. Founded 1898. Setting: 42-acre small town campus with easy access to Birmingham. Endowment: $2.6 million. Educational spending for the previous fiscal year: $2121 per student. Total enrollment: 2,161. Student-undergrad faculty ratio is 23:1. Full-time: 1,538 students, 58% women, 42% men. Part-time: 623 students, 68% women, 32% men. Students come from 11 states and territories, 1% from out-of-state. 3% American Indian or Alaska Native, non-Hispanic/Latino; 11% Hispanic/Latino; 6% Black or African American, non-Hispanic/Latino; 0.8% Asian, non-Hispanic/Latino; 0.2% Native Hawaiian or other Pacific Islander, non-Hispanic/Latino. 35% transferred in. Retention: 61% of full-time freshmen returned the following year. Core. Calendar: semesters. Academic remediation for entering students, services for LD students, advanced placement, accelerated degree program, self-designed majors, independent study, distance learning, summer session for credit, part-time degree program, adult/continuing education programs, internships.

Entrance Requirements: Open admission. Options: electronic application, early admission, deferred admission. Required: high school transcript. Required for some: interview. Entrance: noncompetitive. Transfer credits accepted: Yes.
Collegiate Environment: Drama-theater group, choral group. Social organizations: 13 open to all. Most popular organizations: Phi Theta Kappa, Ambassadors, Student Government Association. Major annual events: Ham and Biscuit Day, Club Week, Homecoming. Campus security: 24-hour patrols. Learning Resource Center. Books: 6,430 (physical), 99,766 (digital/electronic); Serial titles: 15 (physical); Databases: 57.
Community Environment: Boaz (population 7,893) is located 60 miles north of Birmingham, and has an average temperature of 65 degrees. Employment is available in industry and business. Churches, civic and social organizations are located in the city. Guntersville Lake is ten miles from Boaz. The town is a shopping outlet center, one of the largest in the U.S.

■ **SOUTH UNIVERSITY**
5355 Vaughn Rd.
Montgomery, AL 36116-1120
Tel: (334)395-8800; Free: 866-629-2962
Fax: (334)395-8859
Web Site: www.southuniversity.edu/montgomery
Description: Independent, comprehensive, coed. Part of Education Management Corporation. Awards associate, bachelor's, and master's degrees and post-master's certificates. Founded 1887. Calendar: quarters.

■ **SOUTHERN UNION STATE COMMUNITY COLLEGE**
PO Box 1000, Roberts St.
Wadley, AL 36276
Tel: (256)395-2211
Fax: (256)395-2215
E-mail: info@suscc.edu
Web Site: www.suscc.edu
Description: State-supported, 2-year, coed. Part of Alabama College System. Awards certificates, diplomas, transfer associate, and terminal associate degrees. Founded 1922. Setting: rural campus. Total enrollment: 4,971. Student-undergrad faculty ratio is 25:1. 12% from out-of-state. 23% 25 or older. Retention: 58% of full-time freshmen returned the following year. Calendar: semesters. Academic remediation for entering students, advanced placement, distance learning, summer session for credit, part-time degree program, adult/continuing education programs. ROTC: Air Force (c).
Entrance Requirements: Open admission. Options: early admission, deferred admission. Required: high school transcript. Entrance: noncompetitive. Application deadline: rolling. Notification: continuous.
Collegiate Environment: Campus security: 24-hour patrols, controlled dormitory access. McClintock-Ensminger Library.
Community Environment: Population 648. Located in East Central Alabama approximately 90 miles southwest of Atlanta, and the same distance southeast of Birmingham. Wadley is on Alabama State Highways 22 and 77. Gently rolling farm and woodland, healthful country atmosphere. Easy access to neighboring cities for shopping and recreation. Hospital in Roanoke.

■ **SPRING HILL COLLEGE**
4000 Dauphin St.
Mobile, AL 36608-1791
Tel: (251)380-4000; Free: 800-SHC-6704
Fax: (251)460-2186
E-mail: bfinley@shc.edu
Web Site: www.shc.edu
Description: Independent Roman Catholic (Jesuit), comprehensive, coed. Awards bachelor's and master's degrees and post-master's certificates. Founded 1830. Setting: 450-acre suburban campus. Total enrollment: 1,395. Faculty: 137 (88 full-time, 49 part-time). Student-undergrad faculty ratio is 14:1. 8,587 applied, 66% were admitted. 19% from top 10% of their high school class, 51% from top quarter, 81% from top half. Full-time: 1,257 students, 62% women, 38% men. Part-time: 13 students, 46% women, 54% men. 58% from out-of-state. 0.6% American Indian or Alaska Native, non-Hispanic/Latino; 3% Hispanic/Latino; 16% Black or African American, non-Hispanic/Latino; 1% Asian, non-Hispanic/Latino; 0.2% Native Hawaiian or other Pacific Islander, non-Hispanic/Latino; 5% international. 2% 25 or older, 71% live on campus, 2% transferred in. Retention: 72% of full-time freshmen returned the following year. Academic areas with the most degrees conferred: business/marketing; health professions and related sciences;

psychology. Core. Calendar: semesters. Academic remediation for entering students, services for LD students, advanced placement, accelerated degree program, self-designed majors, honors program, independent study, distance learning, double major, summer session for credit, part-time degree program, adult/continuing education programs, internships. Off campus study at Marine Environmental Sciences Consortium. Study abroad program. ROTC: Army (c), Air Force (c).

Entrance Requirements: Options: electronic application, early admission, deferred admission, international baccalaureate accepted. Required: essay, high school transcript, 1 recommendation, SAT or ACT. Recommended: minimum 2.5 high school GPA, interview. Entrance: moderately difficult. Notification: continuous, continuous for nonresidents. SAT Reasoning Test deadline: 7/15. Transfer credits accepted: Yes.

Costs Per Year: Application fee: $25. Comprehensive fee: $52,926 includes full-time tuition ($37,078), mandatory fees ($2386), and college room and board ($13,462). College room only: $7108. Full-time tuition and fees vary according to course load. Room and board charges vary according to board plan and housing facility. Part-time tuition: $1104 per credit hour. Part-time mandatory fees: $57 per credit hour. Part-time tuition and fees vary according to course load.

Collegiate Environment: Orientation program. Drama-theater group, choral group, student-run newspaper. Social organizations: 49 open to all; national fraternities, national sororities; 26% of eligible men and 28% of eligible women are members. Most popular organizations: Fraternities and sororities, SHAPe, National Society of Leadership and Success, Peer One Project, Chemistry Club. Major annual events: CajunFest, Christmas on the Hill, Campus Mardi Gras. Student services: health clinic, personal-psychological counseling. Campus security: 24-hour emergency response devices and patrols, late night transport-escort service, controlled dormitory access. 1,157 college housing spaces available. Freshmen guaranteed college housing. On-campus residence required through senior year. Option: coed housing available. Marnie and John Burke Memorial Library plus 1 other.

Community Environment: See University of South Alabama.

■ STILLMAN COLLEGE
PO Drawer 1430, 3600 Stillman Blvd.
Tuscaloosa, AL 35403-9990
Tel: (205)349-4240; Free: 800-841-5722
Fax: (205)366-8996
Web Site: www.stillman.edu
Description: Independent, 4-year, coed, affiliated with Presbyterian Church (U.S.A.). Awards bachelor's degrees. Founded 1876. Setting: 100-acre urban campus with easy access to Birmingham. Endowment: $18.2 million. Educational spending for the previous fiscal year: $3897 per student. Total enrollment: 1,072. Faculty: 61 (54 full-time, 7 part-time). Student-undergrad faculty ratio is 18:1. 3,491 applied, 44% were admitted. 12% from top 10% of their high school class, 38% from top quarter, 69% from top half. 4 valedictorians. Full-time: 1,032 students, 53% women, 47% men. Part-time: 40 students, 60% women, 40% men. Students come from 25 states and territories, 10 other countries, 35% from out-of-state. 0.1% American Indian or Alaska Native, non-Hispanic/Latino; 0.8% Hispanic/Latino; 93% Black or African American, non-Hispanic/Latino. 5% 25 or older, 63% live on campus, 13% transferred in. Retention: 61% of full-time freshmen returned the following year. Academic areas with the most degrees conferred: health professions and related sciences; biological/life sciences; business/marketing. Core. Calendar: semesters. Academic remediation for entering students, advanced placement, honors program, independent study, distance learning, double major, summer session for credit, co-op programs and internships. ROTC: Army (c).

Entrance Requirements: Options: electronic application, early admission, early decision, deferred admission, international baccalaureate accepted. Required: high school transcript, minimum 2.5 high school GPA, SAT and SAT Subject Tests or ACT. Recommended: essay, interview, SAT, ACT, SAT Subject Tests. Entrance: minimally difficult. Application deadlines: rolling, 7/1 for early decision. Notification: 7/15 for early decision. Transfer credits accepted: Yes.

Collegiate Environment: Orientation program. Drama-theater group, choral group, marching band, student-run newspaper. Social organizations: 15 open to all; national fraternities, national sororities; 3% of eligible men and 5% of eligible women are members. Most popular organizations: Stillman Blue Pride Marching Band, Sophisticated Unlimited Modeling Troupe, Christian Student Association, Student Government Association, Students in Free Enterprise (SIFE). Major annual events: Homecoming, Founders' Day,

Christmas Concert. Student services: health clinic, personal-psychological counseling. Campus security: 24-hour patrols. Sheppard Library. Operations spending for the previous fiscal year: $238,840. 150 computers available on campus for general student use. A campuswide network can be accessed from student residence rooms. Students can access the following: online class registration. Staffed computer lab on campus.

Community Environment: See University of Alabama.

■ STRAYER UNIVERSITY-BIRMINGHAM CAMPUS
3570 Grandview Pky.
Ste. 200
Birmingham, AL 35243
Tel: (205)453-6300; Free: 888-311-0355
Web Site: www.strayer.edu
Description: Proprietary, comprehensive, coed. Awards associate, bachelor's, and master's degrees.

■ STRAYER UNIVERSITY-HUNTSVILLE CAMPUS
4955 Corporate Dr.
Huntsville, AL 35805
Tel: (256)665-9800; Free: 888-311-0355
Web Site: www.strayer.edu
Description: Proprietary, comprehensive, coed. Awards associate, bachelor's, and master's degrees.

■ TALLADEGA COLLEGE
627 W Battle St.
Talladega, AL 35160-2354
Tel: (256)362-0206; Free: 866-540-3956
Fax: (256)362-2268
Web Site: www.talladega.edu
Description: Independent, 4-year, coed. Awards associate and bachelor's degrees. Founded 1867. Setting: 130-acre small town campus with easy access to Birmingham. Endowment: $3.3 million. Total enrollment: 780. Faculty: 64 (39 full-time, 25 part-time). Student-undergrad faculty ratio is 20:1. 2,047 applied, 15% were admitted. Full-time: 760 students, 47% women, 53% men. Part-time: 20 students, 65% women, 35% men. Students come from 30 states and territories, 3 other countries, 39% from out-of-state. 0.1% American Indian or Alaska Native, non-Hispanic/Latino; 5% Hispanic/Latino; 87% Black or African American, non-Hispanic/Latino; 2% international. 7% 25 or older, 65% live on campus, 9% transferred in. Retention: 59% of full-time freshmen returned the following year. Academic areas with the most degrees conferred: business/marketing; public administration and social services; psychology. Core. Calendar: semesters. ESL program, services for LD students, accelerated degree program, independent study, distance learning, double major, summer session for credit, part-time degree program, adult/continuing education programs, internships. Off campus study at 7 members of the Alabama Center for Higher Education. Study abroad program.

Entrance Requirements: Options: electronic application, early admission, international baccalaureate accepted. Required: high school transcript, minimum 2 high school GPA, SAT or ACT. Entrance: moderately difficult. Application deadlines: rolling, rolling for early action. Notification: continuous.

Collegiate Environment: Orientation program. Choral group, marching band. Social organizations: 35 open to all; national fraternities, national sororities; 15% of eligible men and 25% of eligible women are members. Most popular organizations: Student Government Association, Crimson Ambassadors, Students in Free Enterprise (SIFE), Talladega College Choir, Social Work Club. Major annual events: Dega Day, Founder's Weekend/Homecoming, Alumni Weekend. Student services: health clinic, personal-psychological counseling. Campus security: 24-hour patrols, late night transport-escort service, campus police. Savery Library. Books: 100,000 (physical); Serial titles: 1,922 (digital/electronic); Databases: 244. Weekly public service hours: 77; students can reserve study rooms. Operations spending for the previous fiscal year: $268,605. 186 computers available on campus for general student use. A campuswide network can be accessed from student residence rooms and from off campus. Students can access the following: online class registration. Staffed computer lab on campus provides training in use of software and the Internet.

Community Environment: Population 17,149, Talladega is at the heart of a fertile valley in the foothills of the Blue Ridge Mountains, 55 miles to Birmingham. Bus service is available and the closest airline is in Anniston, 20 miles away. Its elevation gives it a healthy climate with an average temperature of 63.3 degrees, and annual rainfall of 54.3 inches. The highest point in Alabama, Cheaha Mountain, is 17 miles north in Talladega National Forest. Home of the Alabama School for Blind, and Alabama School for Deaf, the community has theatres, supervised playgrounds, and parks, with hunting, fishing, and hiking facilities.

■ **TROY UNIVERSITY**
University Ave.
Troy, AL 36082
Tel: (334)670-3000; Free: 800-551-9716
Fax: (334)670-3815
E-mail: bstar@troy.edu
Web Site: www.troy.edu
Description: State-supported, comprehensive, coed. Part of Troy University System. Awards associate, bachelor's, master's, and doctoral degrees and post-master's certificates. Founded 1887. Setting: 906-acre small town campus. Endowment: $104.4 million. Research spending for the previous fiscal year: $257,335. Educational spending for the previous fiscal year: $4072 per student. Total enrollment: 17,521. Faculty: 1,079 (531 full-time, 548 part-time). Student-undergrad faculty ratio is 15:1. 6,565 applied, 90% were admitted. Full-time: 9,491 students, 60% women, 40% men. Part-time: 4,509 students, 60% women, 40% men. Students come from 48 states and territories, 61 other countries, 31% from out-of-state. 0.5% American Indian or Alaska Native, non-Hispanic/Latino; 4% Hispanic/Latino; 30% Black or African American, non-Hispanic/Latino; 0.9% Asian, non-Hispanic/Latino; 0.1% Native Hawaiian or other Pacific Islander, non-Hispanic/Latino; 5% international. 37% 25 or older, 16% live on campus, 11% transferred in. Retention: 70% of full-time freshmen returned the following year. Academic areas with the most degrees conferred: business/marketing; psychology; homeland security, law enforcement, firefighting, and protective services. Core. Calendar: semesters. Academic remediation for entering students, ESL program, services for LD students, advanced placement, accelerated degree program, honors program, independent study, distance learning, double major, summer session for credit, part-time degree program, internships, graduate courses open to undergrads. Study abroad program. ROTC: Army, Air Force.
Entrance Requirements: Options: electronic application, deferred admission, international baccalaureate accepted. Required: high school transcript, minimum x high school GPA, rigor of secondary school record, SAT or ACT. Application deadline: rolling. Transfer credits accepted: Yes.
Costs Per Year: Application fee: $30. State resident tuition: $10,415 full-time, $325 per credit hour part-time. Nonresident tuition: $20,830 full-time, $650 per credit hour part-time. Mandatory fees: $2045 full-time, $43 per credit hour part-time, $50 per term part-time. Full-time tuition and fees vary according to location and program. Part-time tuition and fees vary according to location and program. College room and board: $8185. College room only: $4592. Room and board charges vary according to board plan and housing facility.
Collegiate Environment: Orientation program. Drama-theater group, choral group, marching band, student-run newspaper. Social organizations: 193 open to all; national fraternities, national sororities; 9% of eligible men and 13% of eligible women are members. Most popular organizations: T-Day/ Athletic Events (Homecoming), Activities Council, Pep Rallies. Major annual events: Homecoming, Honors Convocation, Commencement. Student services: health clinic, personal-psychological counseling. Campus security: 24-hour emergency response devices and patrols, student patrols, late night transport-escort service, controlled dormitory access. Lurleen B. Wallace Library (Troy Campus) plus 2 others. Books: 603,904 (physical), 277,690 (digital/electronic); Serial titles: 213 (physical), 134,396 (digital/electronic); Databases: 261. Operations spending for the previous fiscal year: $3.4 million. 1,935 computers available on campus for general student use. A campuswide network can be accessed from student residence rooms and from off campus. Students can access the following: online class registration. Staffed computer lab on campus.
Community Environment: Population 13,935, Troy is located at the junction of U.S. Highways 231 and 29 and is 50 miles from Montgomery, the state capital. There is regular bus service. The citizens take great interest in the University, and extend a cordial welcome to students. There are numerous social, church, civic and school organizations which provide cultural enrichment for the citizens and for the students of the University. Recreational facilities include parks for swimming, tennis courts, a lake for fishing, and two golf courses.

■ **TUSKEGEE UNIVERSITY**
1200 W Montgomery Rd.
Tuskegee Institute, AL 36088

Tel: (334)727-8011; Free: 800-622-6531
E-mail: cgriffin@mytu.tuskegee.edu
Web Site: www.tuskegee.edu
Description: Independent, comprehensive, coed. Awards bachelor's, master's, and doctoral degrees. Founded 1881. Setting: 5,000-acre small town campus. Endowment: $113.7 million. Research spending for the previous fiscal year: $19 million. Total enrollment: 2,995. Faculty: 207 (194 full-time, 13 part-time). Student-undergrad faculty ratio is 14:1. 7,529 applied, 53% were admitted. 20% from top 10% of their high school class, 60% from top quarter, 100% from top half. Full-time: 2,430 students, 62% women, 38% men. Part-time: 55 students, 58% women, 42% men. Students come from 39 states and territories, 5 other countries, 60% from out-of-state. 0.1% American Indian or Alaska Native, non-Hispanic/Latino; 0.3% Hispanic/ Latino; 78% Black or African American, non-Hispanic/Latino; 0.2% Asian, non-Hispanic/Latino; 0.3% international. 4% 25 or older, 63% live on campus, 2% transferred in. Retention: 70% of full-time freshmen returned the following year. Academic areas with the most degrees conferred: engineering; psychology; agriculture. Core. Calendar: semesters. Academic remediation for entering students, ESL program, honors program, summer session for credit, part-time degree program, co-op programs and internships, graduate courses open to undergrads. Off campus study at Alabama Center for Higher Education. ROTC: Army, Naval, Air Force.
Entrance Requirements: Options: electronic application, early admission. Required: high school transcript, minimum 3 high school GPA, SAT or ACT. Recommended: SAT. Entrance: moderately difficult. Application deadline: 4/15. Transfer credits accepted: Yes.
Collegiate Environment: Orientation program. Drama-theater group, choral group, marching band, student-run newspaper. Social organizations: 6 open to all; national fraternities, national sororities; 7% of eligible men and 8% of eligible women are members. Most popular organizations: Student Government, Marching Band, State Clubs, Fraternities, Sororities. Major annual events: Homecoming, Choir Christmas Concert, Scholarship Night. Student services: health clinic, personal-psychological counseling. Campus security: 24-hour emergency response devices and patrols, late night transport-escort service. Hollis B. Frissell Library plus 3 others. Books: 370,430 (physical), 2,330 (digital/electronic); Serial titles: 1,810 (physical), 836 (digital/ electronic); Databases: 175. Students can reserve study rooms. Operations spending for the previous fiscal year: $1.1 million. 1,000 computers available on campus for general student use. Computer purchase/lease plans available. A campuswide network can be accessed from student residence rooms and from off campus. Students can access the following: online class registration. Staffed computer lab on campus provides training in use of computers, software, and the Internet.
Community Environment: Tuskegee, population 11,590, is approximately 40 miles east of Montgomery, AL, the state capital, and 120 miles south of Atlanta, GA. Travelers may fly to Montgomery's Dannelly Field and drive to Tuskegee via Interstate 85 north or fly to Atlanta and drive to Tuskegee via Interstate 85 south. Dannelly field is served by American, Delta, Northwest Airlink, and USA Express airlines. Commercial bus transportation is available to Tuskegee from Montgomery, Atlanta, and other nearby cities. Churches of all major denominations, a library and a museum contribute to the cultural atmosphere of the town. Motels and hotels are located in the area. The town also has various fraternal, civic, and veteran's organizations.

■ **UNITED STATES SPORTS ACADEMY**
One Academy Dr.
Daphne, AL 36526-7055
Tel: (251)626-3303; Free: 800-223-2668
Fax: (251)621-2527
Web Site: www.ussa.edu
Description: Independent, upper-level, coed. Awards bachelor's, master's, and doctoral degrees. Founded 1972. Setting: 10-acre suburban campus. Total enrollment: 291. Faculty: 24 (6 full-time, 18 part-time). Student-undergrad faculty ratio is 41:1. 96% from out-of-state. 0.8% American Indian or Alaska Native, non-Hispanic/Latino; 10% Hispanic/Latino; 11% Black or African American, non-Hispanic/Latino; 2% Asian, non-Hispanic/Latino. 64% 25 or older. Academic areas with the most degrees conferred: education; parks and recreation. Core. Calendar: continuous. Distance learning, part-time degree program, graduate courses open to undergrads.
Entrance Requirements: Transfer credits accepted: Yes.
Costs Per Year: Tuition: $14,652 full-time, $407 per credit hour part-time. Mandatory fees: $1320 full-time.
Collegiate Environment: Orientation program. Most popular organization:

Alumni Association. Campus security: Electronically operated building entrances. United States Sports Academy Library plus 1 other. Weekly public service hours: 5.

■ THE UNIVERSITY OF ALABAMA
Tuscaloosa, AL 35487
Tel: (205)348-6010; Free: 800-933-BAMA
Fax: (205)348-9046
E-mail: admissions@ua.edu
Web Site: www.ua.edu
Description: State-supported, university, coed. Part of University of Alabama System. Awards bachelor's, master's, and doctoral degrees and post-master's certificates. Founded 1831. Setting: 1,026-acre suburban campus with easy access to Birmingham. Endowment: $683.2 million. Research spending for the previous fiscal year: $67.4 million. Educational spending for the previous fiscal year: $10,894 per student. Total enrollment: 38,563. Faculty: 1,898 (1,382 full-time, 516 part-time). Student-undergrad faculty ratio is 23:1. 38,129 applied, 53% were admitted. 39% from top 10% of their high school class, 60% from top quarter, 83% from top half. 152 National Merit Scholars. Full-time: 29,923 students, 55% women, 45% men. Part-time: 3,382 students, 62% women, 38% men. Students come from 51 states and territories, 60 other countries, 60% from out-of-state. 0.3% American Indian or Alaska Native, non-Hispanic/Latino; 5% Hispanic/Latino; 10% Black or African American, non-Hispanic/Latino; 1% Asian, non-Hispanic/Latino; 0.1% Native Hawaiian or other Pacific Islander, non-Hispanic/Latino; 2% international. 7% 25 or older, 24% live on campus, 5% transferred in. Retention: 87% of full-time freshmen returned the following year. Academic areas with the most degrees conferred: business/marketing; engineering; communication/journalism. Core. Calendar: semesters. Academic remediation for entering students, ESL program, services for LD students, advanced placement, accelerated degree program, self-designed majors, freshman honors college, honors program, independent study, distance learning, double major, summer session for credit, part-time degree program, external degree program, adult/continuing education programs, co-op programs and internships, graduate courses open to undergrads. Off campus study at UA is a member of the Academic Common Market of the Southern Regional Education Board which allows students of member institutions to pursue specified degrees outside their state of residence. The UA System Cooperative Exchange Program permits a student on one UA system campus to enroll in a course on another UA system campus. Through the National Student Exchange (NSE) program qualified students have the opportunity to study for a semester or an academic year at other participating universities. Study abroad program. ROTC: Army, Air Force.
Entrance Requirements: Options: electronic application, early admission, international baccalaureate accepted. Required: high school transcript, minimum 3 high school GPA, SAT or ACT. Required for some: essay, 2 recommendations, interview. Entrance: moderately difficult. Application deadline: 5/1. Notification: continuous. SAT Reasoning Test deadline: 4/1. Transfer credits accepted: Yes.
Costs Per Year: Application fee: $40. State resident tuition: $10,780 full-time. Nonresident tuition: $29,230 full-time. Full-time tuition varies according to course load. College room and board: $10,102. College room only: $6300. Room and board charges vary according to board plan, housing facility, and location.
Collegiate Environment: Orientation program. Drama-theater group, choral group, marching band, student-run newspaper, radio station. Social organizations: 535 open to all; national fraternities, national sororities, local fraternities, local sororities, co-educational, religious, professional; 24% of eligible men and 36% of eligible women are members. Most popular organizations: ABXY Gaming Network, Residence Hall Association, International Student Association, Student Government Association, Black Student Union. Major annual events: Homecoming/Football, Get On Board Day/Week of Welcome, Honors Week. Student services: legal services, health clinic, personal-psychological counseling, women's center. Campus security: 24-hour emergency response devices and patrols, late night transport-escort service, controlled dormitory access, 24-hour patrols by University of Alabama Police (UAPD), certified law enforcement personnel. Amelia Gayle Gorgas Library plus 8 others. Books: 3.3 million (physical), 1.5 million (digital/electronic); Serial titles: 419 (physical), 199,096 (digital/electronic); Databases: 589. Weekly public service hours: 146; study areas open 24 hours, 5-7 days a week; students can reserve study rooms. Operations spending for the previous fiscal year: $21.7 million. 2,500 computers available on campus for general student use. A campuswide network can be accessed from student residence rooms and from off campus. Students can

access the following: online class registration. Staffed computer lab on campus (open 24 hours a day) provides training in use of computers and software.
Community Environment: Tuscaloosa, with a population of approximately 81,000, is the fifth largest city in Alabama. The city is located 50 miles southwest of Birmingham, 100 miles northwest of Montgomery, the state capital, and 220 miles east of Atlanta, GA. The community is served by major bus, rail, and air services. Modern shopping and service facilities are accessible in the immediate area.

■ THE UNIVERSITY OF ALABAMA AT BIRMINGHAM
1720 2nd Ave. S
Birmingham, AL 35294
Tel: (205)934-4011; Free: 800-421-8743
Fax: (205)975-7114
Web Site: www.uab.edu
Description: State-supported, university, coed. Part of University of Alabama System. Awards bachelor's, master's, and doctoral degrees and post-master's certificates. Founded 1969. Setting: 323-acre urban campus with easy access to Birmingham. Endowment: $424.5 million. Research spending for the previous fiscal year: $263.5 million. Educational spending for the previous fiscal year: $17,548 per student. Total enrollment: 20,902. Faculty: 975 (880 full-time, 95 part-time). 7,555 applied, 92% were admitted. Full-time: 9,677 students, 59% women, 41% men. Part-time: 3,457 students, 60% women, 40% men. Students come from 45 states and territories, 50 other countries, 13% from out-of-state. 0.3% American Indian or Alaska Native, non-Hispanic/Latino; 3% Hispanic/Latino; 26% Black or African American, non-Hispanic/Latino; 6% Asian, non-Hispanic/Latino; 2% international. 23% 25 or older, 22% live on campus, 12% transferred in. Retention: 84% of full-time freshmen returned the following year. Academic areas with the most degrees conferred: health professions and related sciences; business/marketing; education. Core. Calendar: semesters. Academic remediation for entering students, ESL program, services for LD students, advanced placement, accelerated degree program, self-designed majors, freshman honors college, honors program, independent study, distance learning, double major, summer session for credit, part-time degree program, adult/continuing education programs, co-op programs and internships, graduate courses open to undergrads. Off campus study at University of Alabama in Huntsville, University of Alabama, Birmingham Area Consortium for Higher Education. Study abroad program. ROTC: Army, Air Force (c).
Entrance Requirements: Options: electronic application, early admission, deferred admission, international baccalaureate accepted. Required: high school transcript, SAT or ACT. Entrance: moderately difficult. Application deadline: 6/1. Notification: continuous. SAT Reasoning Test deadline: 6/1. Transfer credits accepted: Yes.
Costs Per Year: Application fee: $30. State resident tuition: $10,710 full-time, $357 per credit hour part-time. Nonresident tuition: $24,630 full-time, $821 per credit hour part-time. Full-time tuition varies according to course load, degree level, program, and reciprocity agreements. Part-time tuition varies according to course load, degree level, program, and reciprocity agreements. College room and board: $11,682. College room only: $7532. Room and board charges vary according to board plan and housing facility.
Collegiate Environment: Orientation program. Drama-theater group, choral group, marching band, student-run newspaper, radio station. Social organizations: 150 open to all; national fraternities, national sororities, local fraternities; 8% of eligible men and 10% of eligible women are members. Most popular organizations: campus ministries, service-oriented groups, sports-affiliated groups. Major annual events: Spring Fest, Welcome Week, Talent Search. Student services: health clinic, personal-psychological counseling, women's center. Campus security: 24-hour emergency response devices and patrols, late night transport-escort service, controlled dormitory access. Mervyn Sterne Library plus 2 others. Books: 1.3 million (physical). Students can reserve study rooms. Operations spending for the previous fiscal year: $10.7 million.

■ THE UNIVERSITY OF ALABAMA IN HUNTSVILLE
301 Sparkman Dr.
Huntsville, AL 35899
Tel: (256)824-1000; Free: 800-UAH-CALL
Fax: (256)824-6073
E-mail: uahadmissions@uah.edu
Web Site: www.uah.edu
Description: State-supported, university, coed. Part of University of

Alabama System. Awards bachelor's, master's, and doctoral degrees and post-master's certificates. Founded 1950. Setting: 400-acre suburban campus. Endowment: $66.9 million. Research spending for the previous fiscal year: $64.7 million. Educational spending for the previous fiscal year: $8825 per student. Total enrollment: 8,468. Faculty: 542 (326 full-time, 216 part-time). Student-undergrad faculty ratio is 17:1. 4,545 applied, 76% were admitted. 29% from top 10% of their high school class, 56% from top quarter, 85% from top half. Full-time: 5,257 students, 42% women, 58% men. Part-time: 1,250 students, 40% women, 60% men. 16% from out-of-state. 1% American Indian or Alaska Native, non-Hispanic/Latino; 4% Hispanic/Latino; 11% Black or African American, non-Hispanic/Latino; 4% Asian, non-Hispanic/Latino; 3% international. 20% 25 or older, 21% live on campus, 12% transferred in. Retention: 83% of full-time freshmen returned the following year. Academic areas with the most degrees conferred: engineering; business/marketing; health professions and related sciences. Core. Calendar: semesters. Academic remediation for entering students, ESL program, services for LD students, advanced placement, self-designed majors, freshman honors college, honors program, independent study, distance learning, double major, summer session for credit, part-time degree program, co-op programs and internships, graduate courses open to undergrads. Off campus study at Academic Common Market, Alabama Agricultural and Mechanical University, Oakwood College, Athens State College, John C. Calhoun State Community College. Study abroad program. ROTC: Army (c).

Entrance Requirements: Options: electronic application, deferred admission, international baccalaureate accepted. Required: high school transcript, SAT or ACT. Entrance: moderately difficult. Application deadline: 8/17. Notification: continuous, continuous for nonresidents. SAT Reasoning Test deadline: 8/17. Transfer credits accepted: Yes.

Costs Per Year: Application fee: $30. State resident tuition: $9730 full-time, $427 per credit hour part-time. Nonresident tuition: $21,378 full-time, $944 per credit hour part-time. Mandatory fees: $984 full-time. Full-time tuition and fees vary according to course load and program. Part-time tuition varies according to course load and program. College room and board: $10,094. Room and board charges vary according to board plan and housing facility.

Collegiate Environment: Orientation program. Drama-theater group, choral group, student-run newspaper. Social organizations: 129 open to all; national fraternities, national sororities; 5% of eligible men and 5% of eligible women are members. Most popular organizations: Student Government Association, Student Run Sports, International Student Association, CRU, Blue Crew. Major annual events: Week of Welcome, Spring Fling, Homecoming. Student services: health clinic, personal-psychological counseling. Campus security: 24-hour emergency response devices and patrols, late night transport-escort service, controlled dormitory access, 24/7 dispatch center, community policing efforts. Louis Salmon Library. Books: 239,503 (physical), 387,481 (digital/electronic); Serial titles: 3,441 (physical), 42,868 (digital/electronic); Databases: 133. Operations spending for the previous fiscal year: $3 million. 1,227 computers available on campus for general student use. A campuswide network can be accessed from student residence rooms and from off campus. Students can access the following: online class registration. Staffed computer lab on campus provides training in use of computers, software, and the Internet.

■ UNIVERSITY OF MOBILE

5735 College Pky.
Mobile, AL 36613
Tel: (251)675-5990; Free: 800-946-7267
E-mail: hgivens@umobile.edu
Web Site: www.umobile.edu

Description: Independent Southern Baptist, comprehensive, coed. Awards associate, bachelor's, and master's degrees. Founded 1961. Setting: 880-acre suburban campus. Endowment: $23.2 million. Educational spending for the previous fiscal year: $7176 per student. Total enrollment: 1,604. Faculty: 172 (73 full-time, 99 part-time). Student-undergrad faculty ratio is 14:1. 935 applied, 62% were admitted. 38% from top 10% of their high school class, 62% from top quarter, 81% from top half. Full-time: 1,152 students, 63% women, 37% men. Part-time: 291 students, 71% women, 29% men. Students come from 30 states and territories, 21 other countries, 18% from out-of-state. 1% American Indian or Alaska Native, non-Hispanic/Latino; 2% Hispanic/Latino; 19% Black or African American, non-Hispanic/Latino; 1% Asian, non-Hispanic/Latino; 0.1% Native Hawaiian or other Pacific Islander, non-Hispanic/Latino; 3% international. 22% 25 or older, 45% live on campus, 7% transferred in. Retention: 69% of full-time freshmen returned the following year. Academic areas with the most degrees conferred: business/

marketing; health professions and related sciences; interdisciplinary studies. Core. Calendar: semesters. Academic remediation for entering students, services for LD students, advanced placement, accelerated degree program, honors program, independent study, distance learning, double major, summer session for credit, part-time degree program, adult/continuing education programs, internships, graduate courses open to undergrads. ROTC: Army (c), Air Force (c).

Entrance Requirements: Options: electronic application, deferred admission, international baccalaureate accepted. Required: high school transcript, minimum 2.75 high school GPA, SAT or ACT. Entrance: moderately difficult. Application deadline: rolling. Notification: continuous. SAT Reasoning Test deadline: 8/1. SAT Subject Test deadline: 8/1. Transfer credits accepted: Yes.

Costs Per Year: Application fee: $25. Comprehensive fee: $32,730 includes full-time tuition ($21,620), mandatory fees ($1410), and college room and board ($9700). Full-time tuition and fees vary according to course load and program. Room and board charges vary according to board plan and housing facility. Part-time tuition: $772 per credit hour. Part-time tuition varies according to course load and program.

Collegiate Environment: Orientation program. Drama-theater group, choral group. Social organizations: 27 open to all. Most popular organizations: Campus Activity Board, Campus Ministry, Student Government Association, Student Nurse Organization. Major annual events: Ram Rush, Christmas Spectacular, Covers. Student services: personal-psychological counseling. Campus security: 24-hour emergency response devices and patrols, controlled dormitory access, text alerts. J. L. Bedsole Library. Books: 66,089 (physical), 157,420 (digital/electronic); Serial titles: 153 (physical), 151,115 (digital/electronic); Databases: 80. Operations spending for the previous fiscal year: $463,299. 100 computers available on campus for general student use. A campuswide network can be accessed. Students can access the following: online class registration. Staffed computer lab on campus provides training in use of computers, software, and the Internet.

Community Environment: See University of South Alabama.

■ UNIVERSITY OF MONTEVALLO

Station 6001
Montevallo, AL 35115
Tel: (205)665-6000; Free: 800-292-4349
E-mail: admissions@montevallo.edu
Web Site: www.montevallo.edu

Description: State-supported, comprehensive, coed. Awards bachelor's and master's degrees and post-master's certificates. Founded 1896. Setting: 160-acre small town campus with easy access to Birmingham. Endowment: $20.6 million. Research spending for the previous fiscal year: $12,813. Educational spending for the previous fiscal year: $10,875 per student. Total enrollment: 2,616. Faculty: 230 (152 full-time, 78 part-time). Student-undergrad faculty ratio is 14:1. 3,882 applied, 48% were admitted. Full-time: 2,063 students, 67% women, 33% men. Part-time: 222 students, 67% women, 33% men. Students come from 36 states and territories, 26 other countries, 13% from out-of-state. 0.4% American Indian or Alaska Native, non-Hispanic/Latino; 5% Hispanic/Latino; 17% Black or African American, non-Hispanic/Latino; 1% Asian, non-Hispanic/Latino; 0.2% Native Hawaiian or other Pacific Islander, non-Hispanic/Latino; 3% international. 1% 25 or older, 48% live on campus, 8% transferred in. Retention: 76% of full-time freshmen returned the following year. Academic areas with the most degrees conferred: visual and performing arts; education; business/marketing. Core. Calendar: semesters. Academic remediation for entering students, services for LD students, advanced placement, accelerated degree program, honors program, independent study, distance learning, double major, summer session for credit, part-time degree program, internships, graduate courses open to undergrads. Study abroad program. ROTC: Army (c), Air Force (c).

Entrance Requirements: Options: electronic application, early admission, deferred admission, international baccalaureate accepted. Required: high school transcript, minimum 2 high school GPA, SAT or ACT. Recommended: interview. Entrance: moderately difficult. Application deadline: 8/15. Notification: 9/1. SAT Reasoning Test deadline: 8/15. SAT Subject Test deadline: 8/15. Transfer credits accepted: Yes.

Costs Per Year: Application fee: $30. State resident tuition: $12,090 full-time, $403 per credit hour part-time. Nonresident tuition: $25,110 full-time, $837 per credit hour part-time. Mandatory fees: $670 full-time. College room and board: $7836. College room only: $4906. Room and board charges vary according to housing facility.

Collegiate Environment: Orientation program. Drama-theater group, choral group, student-run newspaper. Social organizations: 97 open to all; national fraternities, national sororities; 18% of eligible men and 21% of eligible women are members. Most popular organizations: Student Government Association, University Programming Council, Campus Ministries, Greek Life, Environmental Club. Major annual events: College Night, Spring Fest, Back to School Bash. Student services: health clinic, personal-psychological counseling. Campus security: 24-hour emergency response devices and patrols, late night transport-escort service, controlled dormitory access. 1,340 college housing spaces available; 1,145 were occupied in 2018-19. Freshmen guaranteed college housing. On-campus residence required in freshman year. Options: coed, men-only, women-only housing available. Carmichael Library. Students can reserve study rooms. Operations spending for the previous fiscal year: $1.3 million. 340 computers available on campus for general student use. A campuswide network can be accessed from student residence rooms and from off campus. Students can access the following: online class registration. Staffed computer lab on campus.

Community Environment: Montevallo (population 5,092) is near the center of the state, and is accessible by automobile. Montevallo is 32 miles south of Birmingham and 68 miles north of Montgomery, and has a mild year-round climate. There are a library, golf course, municipal park, and many churches in the city. Recreational activities include hunting, lake and stream fishing, boating and water skiing on nearby lakes. Students belonging to church denominations that are not represented in Montevallo hold services in the Religious Association Room of the Student Union Building.

■ **UNIVERSITY OF NORTH ALABAMA**
One Harrison Plz.
Florence, AL 35632-0001
Tel: (256)765-4100; Free: 800-TALK-UNA
Fax: (256)765-4329
E-mail: admissions@una.edu
Web Site: www.una.edu
Description: State-supported, comprehensive, coed. Awards bachelor's and master's degrees and post-master's certificates. Founded 1830. Setting: 200-acre urban campus with easy access to Huntsville. Endowment: $32.6 million. Research spending for the previous fiscal year: $104,620. Educational spending for the previous fiscal year: $5896 per student. Total enrollment: 7,457. Faculty: 429 (266 full-time, 163 part-time). Student-undergrad faculty ratio is 19:1. 3,969 applied, 70% were admitted. Full-time: 5,150 students, 60% women, 40% men. Part-time: 1,071 students, 58% women, 42% men. Students come from 42 states and territories, 38 other countries, 17% from out-of-state. 0.9% American Indian or Alaska Native, non-Hispanic/Latino; 3% Hispanic/Latino; 15% Black or African American, non-Hispanic/Latino; 0.6% Asian, non-Hispanic/Latino; 0.1% Native Hawaiian or other Pacific Islander, non-Hispanic/Latino; 3% international. 11% 25 or older, 29% live on campus, 10% transferred in. Retention: 76% of full-time freshmen returned the following year. Academic areas with the most degrees conferred: business/marketing; health professions and related sciences; education. Core. Calendar: semesters. Academic remediation for entering students, ESL program, services for LD students, advanced placement, accelerated degree program, self-designed majors, honors program, independent study, distance learning, double major, summer session for credit, part-time degree program, external degree program, co-op programs and internships, graduate courses open to undergrads. Off campus study. Study abroad program. ROTC: Army.
Entrance Requirements: Options: electronic application, early admission, deferred admission, international baccalaureate accepted. Required: high school transcript, minimum 2 high school GPA, 13 approved units from high school academic core, SAT or ACT. Entrance: minimally difficult. Application deadline: rolling. Notification: continuous. Transfer credits accepted: Yes.
Costs Per Year: Application fee: $35. State resident tuition: $8310 full-time, $277 per credit hour part-time. Nonresident tuition: $16,620 full-time, $554 per credit hour part-time. Mandatory fees: $2060 full-time, $238 per credit hour part-time. Full-time tuition and fees vary according to course load and program. Part-time tuition and fees vary according to course load and program. College room and board: $7700. Room and board charges vary according to board plan, housing facility, and student level.
Collegiate Environment: Orientation program. Drama-theater group, choral group, marching band, student-run newspaper. Social organizations: 124 open to all; national fraternities, national sororities, local fraternities, local sororities; 11% of eligible men and 18% of eligible women are members. Most popular organizations: Phi Mu, Alpha Gamma Delta, Zeta Tau Alpha, Alpha Delta Pi, Student Government Association. Major annual events: The Big Deal, Step Sing, Spring Concert. Student services: health clinic, personal-psychological counseling, women's center. Campus security: 24-

hour emergency response devices and patrols, student patrols, late night transport-escort service, controlled dormitory access. Collier Library plus 3 others. Books: 225,076 (physical), 469,260 (digital/electronic); Serial titles: 4,070 (physical), 55,929 (digital/electronic); Databases: 182. Weekly public service hours: 98; students can reserve study rooms. Operations spending for the previous fiscal year: $165,104. 925 computers available on campus for general student use. A campuswide network can be accessed. Students can access the following: online class registration. Staffed computer lab on campus provides training in use of computers, software, and the Internet.
Community Environment: Population 36,480. Florence is contiguous to the towns of Sheffield, Tuscumbia, and Muscle Shoals City; it is part of an urban center with a population of 142,000. Area lakes and camping sites attract vacationists and sportsmen from all over the nation. Florence is served by buses and airlines; has excellent public schools, churches, libraries, recreation facilities, cultural centers; several radio stations and a television station.

■ **UNIVERSITY OF SOUTH ALABAMA**
307 University Blvd.
Mobile, AL 36688-0002
Tel: (251)460-6101; Free: 800-872-5247
Fax: (251)460-7025
E-mail: recruitment@southalabama.edu
Web Site: www.southalabama.edu
Description: State-supported, university, coed. Awards bachelor's, master's, and doctoral degrees and post-master's certificates. Founded 1963. Setting: 1,225-acre suburban campus. Endowment: $152.6 million. Research spending for the previous fiscal year: $32.6 million. Educational spending for the previous fiscal year: $9082 per student. Total enrollment: 14,834. Faculty: 1,038 (590 full-time, 448 part-time). Student-undergrad faculty ratio is 18:1. 6,688 applied, 79% were admitted. Full-time: 8,637 students, 59% women, 41% men. Part-time: 1,656 students, 57% women, 43% men. Students come from 41 states and territories, 67 other countries, 18% from out-of-state. 0.6% American Indian or Alaska Native, non-Hispanic/Latino; 4% Hispanic/Latino; 23% Black or African American, non-Hispanic/Latino; 3% Asian, non-Hispanic/Latino; 0.2% Native Hawaiian or other Pacific Islander, non-Hispanic/Latino; 3% international. 21% 25 or older, 22% live on campus, 7% transferred in. Retention: 74% of full-time freshmen returned the following year. Academic areas with the most degrees conferred: health professions and related sciences; business/marketing; education; engineering. Core. Calendar: semesters. Academic remediation for entering students, ESL program, services for LD students, advanced placement, accelerated degree program, self-designed majors, freshman honors college, honors program, independent study, distance learning, double major, summer session for credit, part-time degree program, adult/continuing education programs, co-op programs and internships, graduate courses open to undergrads. Study abroad program. ROTC: Army, Air Force.
Entrance Requirements: Options: electronic application, early admission, deferred admission, international baccalaureate accepted. Required: high school transcript. Recommended: minimum 2.5 high school GPA. Required for some: essay, minimum 3.5 high school GPA, 1 recommendation, minimum high school GPA of 3.0 for Accelerated College Enrollment Program, minimum high school GPA of 3.5 for Early Admission, SAT or ACT. Entrance: moderately difficult. Application deadlines: 7/15, 7/15 for nonresidents. Notification: continuous, continuous for nonresidents. SAT Reasoning Test deadline: 7/15. SAT Subject Test deadline: 7/15. Transfer credits accepted: Yes.
Collegiate Environment: Orientation program. Drama-theater group, choral group, marching band, student-run newspaper, radio station. Social organizations: 207 open to all; national fraternities, national sororities. Most popular organizations: Student Government Association, African American Student Association, Council of International Student Organizations, Alpha Epsilon Delta Pre-Health Professions, Panhellenic Council. Major annual events: Homecoming, Get on Board Day, Greek Week. Student services: legal services, health clinic, personal-psychological counseling, women's center. Campus security: 24-hour emergency response devices and patrols, late night transport-escort service, controlled dormitory access. 3,431 college housing spaces available; 2,263 were occupied in 2018-19. No special consideration for freshman housing applicants. Option: coed housing available. Marx Library plus 5 others. Operations spending for the previous fiscal year: $7.2 million.
Community Environment: Mobile, with a population 564,000 in the greater metropolitan area, has a temperate climate. In July and August the average high temperature is 91 degrees, and the average low temperature is 73.

Airlines, buses and railroads serve the area. The city has libraries, churches of all major denominations, theaters, and museums. Excellent facilities for boating, fishing, and swimming are available. Mobile hosts the annual Senior Bowl, Alabama Deep Sea Fishing Rodeo, Azalea Trail Run, and the oldest Mardi Gras celebration in the country. Part-time work is available.

■ **THE UNIVERSITY OF WEST ALABAMA**
Livingston, AL 35470
Tel: (205)652-3400; Free: 888-636-8800
E-mail: belliott@uwa.edu
Web Site: www.uwa.edu
Description: State-supported, comprehensive, coed. Awards associate, bachelor's, and master's degrees and post-master's certificates. Founded 1835. Setting: 514-acre small town campus. Endowment: $38,085. Research spending for the previous fiscal year: $684,673. Total enrollment: 5,206. Faculty: 302 (118 full-time, 184 part-time). Student-undergrad faculty ratio is 13:1. 8,870 applied, 40% were admitted. Full-time: 1,836 students, 59% women, 41% men. Part-time: 323 students, 52% women, 48% men. Students come from 30 states and territories, 24 other countries, 19% from out-of-state. 0.4% American Indian or Alaska Native, non-Hispanic/Latino; 2% Hispanic/Latino; 43% Black or African American, non-Hispanic/Latino; 0.3% Asian, non-Hispanic/Latino; 5% international. 20% 25 or older, 41% live on campus, 16% transferred in. Retention: 62% of full-time freshmen returned the following year. Academic areas with the most degrees conferred: interdisciplinary studies; business/marketing; education. Core. Calendar: semesters. Academic remediation for entering students, ESL program, services for LD students, advanced placement, accelerated degree program, self-designed majors, freshman honors college, honors program, independent study, distance learning, double major, summer session for credit, part-time degree program, co-op programs and internships. Study abroad program. ROTC: Air Force (c).
Entrance Requirements: Options: electronic application, deferred admission. Required: high school transcript, minimum 2 high school GPA, SAT or ACT. Entrance: minimally difficult. Application deadline: rolling. Notification: continuous. SAT Reasoning Test deadline: 8/18. SAT Subject Test deadline: 8/18. Transfer credits accepted: Yes.
Costs Per Year: Application fee: $40. State resident tuition: $8450 full-time, $325 per hour part-time. Nonresident tuition: $16,900 full-time, $650 per hour part-time. Mandatory fees: $1590 full-time. Full-time tuition and fees vary according to course load. Part-time tuition varies according to course load. College room and board: $7316. College room only: $4620. Room and board charges vary according to board plan, housing facility, and student level.
Collegiate Environment: Orientation program. Drama-theater group, choral group, marching band, student-run newspaper. Social organizations: 64 open to all; national fraternities, national sororities, local fraternities; 10% of eligible men and 10% of eligible women are members. Most popular organizations: Student Government Association, RHA, Phi Mu, Alpha Sigma Alpha, Blue Key. Major annual events: Serendipity Talent Show, Springfest, Bingo for Bucks. Student services: health clinic, personal-psychological counseling. Campus security: 24-hour emergency response devices and patrols, student patrols, late night transport-escort service, controlled dormitory access. 1,019 college housing spaces available; 902 were occupied in 2018-19. Freshmen guaranteed college housing. On-campus residence required in freshman year. Option: coed housing available. Julia Tutwiler Library plus 1 other. Books: 176,910 (physical), 1,789 (digital/electronic); Serial titles: 11 (physical); Databases: 39. Weekly public service hours: 96; students can reserve study rooms. Operations spending for the previous fiscal year: $699,202. 600 computers available on campus for general student use. A campuswide network can be accessed from student residence rooms. Students can access the following: online class registration. Staffed computer lab on campus.
Community Environment: Livingston (population 3,000) is the Sumter County Seat, and is located on Interstate 59/20 and Alabama Highway 28. It is 116 miles southwest of Birmingham, 130 miles west of Montgomery, and 37 miles east of Meridian, Mississippi. The climate is mild. Fishing and hunting are excellent.

■ **WALLACE STATE COMMUNITY COLLEGE**
801 Main St.
Hanceville, AL 35077-2000
Tel: (256)352-8000; Free: 866-350-9722
Fax: (256)352-8228
Web Site: www.wallacestate.edu
Description: State-supported, 2-year, coed. Awards diplomas, transfer associate, and terminal associate degrees. Founded 1966. Setting: 216-acre rural campus with easy access to Birmingham. Total enrollment: 6,311. Student-undergrad faculty ratio is 23:1. 2% from out-of-state. 35% 25 or older. Retention: 49% of full-time freshmen returned the following year. Calendar: semesters. Academic remediation for entering students, advanced placement, summer session for credit, part-time degree program, co-op programs.
Entrance Requirements: Open admission for technical, liberal arts programs. Options: early admission, deferred admission. Required: high school transcript. Entrance: noncompetitive. Application deadline: rolling. Notification: continuous.
Collegiate Environment: Orientation program. Choral group. Student services: personal-psychological counseling. Wallace State College Library.
Community Environment: Hanceville is a rural community with a population of approximately 3,100, situated midway between Birmingham and Decatur. It is located on state highway 31 with easy access to I-65, both of which connect Decatur and Birmingham.

■ ALASKA BIBLE COLLEGE
248 E Elmwood Ave.
Palmer, AK 99645
Tel: (907)745-3201; Free: 800-478-7884
Fax: (907)745-3210
E-mail: admissions@akbible.edu
Web Site: www.akbible.edu
Description: Independent nondenominational, 4-year, coed. Awards associate and bachelor's degrees. Founded 1966. Setting: 2-acre small town campus with easy access to Anchorage, AK. Total enrollment: 50. Faculty: 12 (3 full-time, 9 part-time). Student-undergrad faculty ratio is 4:1. Full-time: 29 students, 21% women, 79% men. Part-time: 21 students, 48% women, 52% men. Students come from 7 states and territories, 2 other countries, 10% from out-of-state. 4% American Indian or Alaska Native, non-Hispanic/Latino; 4% Hispanic/Latino; 2% Black or African American, non-Hispanic/Latino. 15% 25 or older, 25% live on campus, 40% transferred in. Retention: 20% of full-time freshmen returned the following year. Academic area with the most degrees conferred: theology and religious vocations. Core. Calendar: semesters. Academic remediation for entering students, advanced placement, independent study, distance learning, double major, part-time degree program, internships. Off campus study.
Entrance Requirements: Open admission. Options: electronic application, deferred admission. Required: essay, high school transcript, minimum 2 high school GPA, 3 recommendations, SAT or ACT. Entrance: minimally difficult. Application deadline: 7/1. Notification: continuous until 7/15. SAT Subject Test deadline: 8/15. Transfer credits accepted: Yes.
Costs Per Year: Application fee: $35. Comprehensive fee: $15,300 includes full-time tuition ($9000), mandatory fees ($600), and college room and board ($5700). Part-time tuition: $375 per credit hour. Part-time mandatory fees: $50 per term.
Collegiate Environment: Orientation program. Alaska Bible College Ball Memorial Library. Books: 32,000 (physical); Serial titles: 46 (physical); Databases: 1. Weekly public service hours: 40. 2 computers available on campus for general student use. A computer is required for all students. A campuswide network can be accessed from student residence rooms. Students can access the following: online class registration.
Community Environment: Glennallen is a rural community that has developed on the crossroads between Anchorage, Fairbanks, and Valdez. The original impetus for the community's growth was the construction of the Alcan Highway for communication during the war years. The climate of Glennallen area runs to extremes with the temperature falling to 50 degrees or more below zero for short periods in midwinter, and rising to 70 degrees or more above zero by the close of the school year in May. Sports such as hunting, fishing, hiking, rafting, and cross country skiing are common recreational activities.

■ ALASKA CAREER COLLEGE
1415 E Tudor Rd.
Anchorage, AK 99507
Tel: (907)563-7575
Web Site: www.alaskacareercollege.edu
Description: Proprietary, 2-year, coed. Awards certificates, diplomas, and terminal associate degrees. Setting: 20-acre urban campus. Calendar: continuous.
Entrance Requirements: Notification: continuous, rolling for early decision plan 1, rolling for early decision plan 2, rolling for early action.

■ ALASKA CHRISTIAN COLLEGE
35109 Royal Pl.
Soldotna, AK 99669
Tel: (907)260-7422
Web Site: www.alaskacc.edu
Description: Independent, 2-year, coed. Awards certificates, transfer associate, and terminal associate degrees.

■ ALASKA PACIFIC UNIVERSITY
4101 University Dr.
Anchorage, AK 99508-4672
Tel: (907)561-1266; Free: 800-252-7528
Fax: (907)564-8317
E-mail: admissions@alaskapacific.edu
Web Site: www.alaskapacific.edu
Description: Independent, comprehensive, coed. Awards associate, bachelor's, master's, and doctoral degrees. Founded 1959. Setting: 170-acre urban campus. Total enrollment: 547. Faculty: 82 (28 full-time, 54 part-time). Student-undergrad faculty ratio is 10:1. 474 applied, 55% were admitted. Full-time: 209 students, 61% women, 39% men. Part-time: 85 students, 67% women, 33% men. Students come from 2 other countries. 14% American Indian or Alaska Native, non-Hispanic/Latino; 1% Hispanic/Latino; 4% Black or African American, non-Hispanic/Latino; 3% Asian, non-Hispanic/Latino; 0.7% Native Hawaiian or other Pacific Islander, non-Hispanic/Latino. 26% live on campus, 19% transferred in. Retention: 46% of full-time freshmen returned the following year. Academic areas with the most degrees conferred: business/marketing; biological/life sciences; psychology. Core. Calendar: semesters. Academic remediation for entering students, services for LD students, advanced placement, accelerated degree program, self-designed majors, independent study, distance learning, double major, summer session for credit, part-time degree program, adult/continuing education programs, internships, graduate courses open to undergrads. Study abroad program. ROTC: Air Force (c).
Entrance Requirements: Options: electronic application, deferred admission, international baccalaureate accepted. Required: high school transcript, minimum 2.5 high school GPA. Entrance: minimally difficult. Application deadline: 8/1. Notification: continuous, continuous for nonresidents. Transfer credits accepted: Yes.
Costs Per Year: Application fee: $25. Comprehensive fee: $29,060 includes full-time tuition ($20,350), mandatory fees ($480), and college room and board ($8230). Full-time tuition and fees vary according to course load, degree level, program, and reciprocity agreements. Room and board charges vary according to board plan and housing facility.
Collegiate Environment: Orientation program. Drama-theater group, choral group, student-run newspaper. Social organizations: 13 open to all. Most popular organizations: ASAPU (Associated Students of Alaska Pacific University), Photography Club, Dive Club, Basketball club, Spectrum Club. Major annual events: Octoberfest, Winter Ball, Spring Dance. Student services: personal-psychological counseling. Campus security: 24-hour emergency response devices, student patrols, late night transport-escort service, controlled dormitory access. Consortium Library. Students can reserve study rooms. 105 computers available on campus for general student use. A campuswide network can be accessed from student residence rooms and from off campus. Students can access the following: online class registration. Staffed computer lab on campus provides training in use of computers, software, and the Internet.

Community Environment: Alaska Pacific University is located in Anchorage, a modern, dynamic city with half the population of Alaska. To the west is Cook Inlet, named for the famous English explorer, while mountains rise to the south, east, and north, creating a mild climate. The drive south leads to the ski resort at Alyeska, the glacier at Portage and the famous fishing of the Kenai. To the north lie the Alaska Range and Mount McKinley. Anchorage is a young city on the move. Anchorage's per capita income is twice the national average. Anchorage is lively. Dog teams race down Fourth Avenue during the winter Fur Rendezvous while opera, symphony, theater and a steady stream of rock stars, dance troupes, and artists provide cultural events for every taste. Winters are moderated by the warm Japanese current while summers are blessed with a sun that never sets. Daily intercontinental flights link Anchorage to Hawaii, Tokyo, Beijing, Moscow, Stockholm, London, and New York.

■ **CHARTER COLLEGE**
2221 E Northern Lights Blvd.
Ste. 120
Anchorage, AK 99508
Tel: (907)277-1000; Free: 888-200-9942
Fax: (907)274-3342
Web Site: www.chartercollege.edu
Description: Proprietary, primarily 2-year, coed. Awards certificates, transfer associate, terminal associate, and bachelor's degrees. Founded 1985. Setting: urban campus. Total enrollment: 516. Faculty: 43 (10 full-time, 33 part-time). Student-undergrad faculty ratio is 15:1. 69% 25 or older. Calendar: quarters. Summer session for credit, part-time degree program, adult/continuing education programs, internships.
Entrance Requirements: Open admission. Required: high school transcript, interview. Entrance: noncompetitive. Application deadline: rolling. Notification: continuous.
Collegiate Environment: Orientation program. Campus security: 24-hour emergency response devices. Charter College Library.

■ **ILISAGVIK COLLEGE**
UIC/Narl
Barrow, AK 99723
Tel: (907)852-3333
Fax: (907)852-2729
E-mail: tennessee.judkins@ilisagvik.edu
Web Site: www.ilisagvik.edu
Description: State-supported, 2-year, coed. Awards certificates, diplomas, and transfer associate degrees. Founded 1995. Setting: 7-acre rural campus. Endowment: $4.7 million. Educational spending for the previous fiscal year: $128,066 per student. Total enrollment: 271. Faculty: 35 (11 full-time, 24 part-time). Student-undergrad faculty ratio is 7:1. 17 applied, 100% were admitted. 1% from out-of-state. 63% American Indian or Alaska Native, non-Hispanic/Latino; 2% Hispanic/Latino; 2% Black or African American, non-Hispanic/Latino; 7% Asian, non-Hispanic/Latino; 4% Native Hawaiian or other Pacific Islander, non-Hispanic/Latino; 3% international. 56% 25 or older, 10% live on campus. Core. Calendar: semesters. Academic remediation for entering students, ESL program, services for LD students, independent study, distance learning, double major, summer session for credit, part-time degree program, co-op programs and internships. Off campus study.
Entrance Requirements: Open admission. Option: deferred admission. Required: high school transcript, minimum 2 high school GPA. Recommended: ACCUPLACER. Required for some: copy of Alaska Native Shareholder/Native American Tribal Affiliation card for Natives. Entrance: noncompetitive. Application deadline: 8/14. Notification: continuous. Transfer credits accepted: Yes.
Collegiate Environment: Orientation program. Most popular organizations: Student Government, Barrow Camera Club, Ilisagvik Green Team, Aglaun Literary Journal. Major annual events: Welcome Back Bonfire/Barbeque, Student Orientation, Annual Haunted House. Student services: personal-psychological counseling. Campus security: 24-hour emergency response devices and patrols, controlled dormitory access. Tuzzy Consortium Library. Books: 43,561 (physical), 56,345 (digital/electronic); Serial titles: 150 (physical). Weekly public service hours: 60; students can reserve study rooms.

■ **UNIVERSITY OF ALASKA ANCHORAGE**
3211 Providence Dr.
Anchorage, AK 99508
Tel: (907)786-1800

Fax: (907)786-4888
E-mail: enroll@uaa.alaska.edu
Web Site: www.uaa.alaska.edu
Description: State-supported, comprehensive, coed. Part of University of Alaska System. Awards associate, bachelor's, master's, and doctoral degrees and post-master's certificates. Founded 1954. Setting: 428-acre urban campus. Total enrollment: 17,321. Faculty: 1,406 (678 full-time, 728 part-time). Student-undergrad faculty ratio is 12:1. 3,533 applied, 80% were admitted. 13% from top 10% of their high school class, 33% from top quarter, 62% from top half. Full-time: 7,485 students, 47% women, 53% men. Part-time: 8,978 students, 38% women, 62% men. 9% from out-of-state. 7% American Indian or Alaska Native, non-Hispanic/Latino; 7% Hispanic/Latino; 4% Black or African American, non-Hispanic/Latino; 8% Asian, non-Hispanic/Latino; 0.9% Native Hawaiian or other Pacific Islander, non-Hispanic/Latino; 2% international. 48% 25 or older, 5% transferred in. Retention: 72% of full-time freshmen returned the following year. Core. Calendar: semesters. Academic remediation for entering students, ESL program, services for LD students, advanced placement, self-designed majors, honors program, independent study, distance learning, double major, summer session for credit, part-time degree program, adult/continuing education programs, co-op programs and internships, graduate courses open to undergrads. Off campus study at members of the National Student Exchange, Western Interstate Commission for Higher Education, Western Undergraduate Exchange. Study abroad program. ROTC: Army, Air Force.
Entrance Requirements: Open admission selective admission to some programs. Options: electronic application, deferred admission. Required: minimum 2 high school GPA. Required for some: high school transcript. Entrance: noncompetitive. Application deadline: 6/15. Notification: continuous.
Costs Per Year: Application fee: $50. State resident tuition: $6360 full-time, $212 per credit part-time. Nonresident tuition: $22,530 full-time, $751 per credit part-time. Mandatory fees: $1328 full-time. College room and board: $12,200.
Collegiate Environment: Orientation program. Drama-theater group, choral group, student-run newspaper, radio station. Social organizations: national fraternities, national sororities. Most popular organizations: Accounting Club, African-American Students Association, Association of Latin-American Spanish Students, Inter-Varsity Christian Fellowship, Student Nurses Association. Major annual events: UAA orientation programs, Great Alaska Shootout Basketball Tournament. Student services: health clinic, personal-psychological counseling, women's center. Campus security: 24-hour emergency response devices and patrols, student patrols, late night transport-escort service, controlled dormitory access. Consortium Library.
Community Environment: Anchorage, population 275,000, is a friendly, modern progressive city and the largest in Alaska. Summertime temperatures range between 60 and 70 degrees. The winters are less severe in Anchorage than in many U.S. cities. Anchorage is the major stopover point for most international transpolar flights. Living costs are higher than in the continental U.S., with an average living cost (plus tuition) of approximately $11,000 to $14,000 per year. The city bustles with growth and activity; cultural interests are wide range and include a symphony orchestra, museums, a theater group and a dance company. Recreation facilities include theaters, golf courses, bowling alleys, swimming pools, public beaches, skating rinks, ball parks, and several excellent ski areas. Hunting and fishing are easily accessible. There are several hospitals within the city which is near Ft. Richardson Army Post and Elmendorf AFB.

■ **UNIVERSITY OF ALASKA ANCHORAGE, KENAI PENINSULA COLLEGE**
156 College Rd.
Soldotna, AK 99669-9798
Tel: (907)262-0300; Free: 877-262-0330
Fax: (907)262-0322
E-mail: jmcotterell@kpc.alaska.edu
Web Site: www.kpc.alaska.edu
Description: State-supported, primarily 2-year, coed. Part of University of Alaska System. Awards certificates, transfer associate, terminal associate, and bachelor's degrees. Founded 1964. Setting: 360-acre rural campus. Total enrollment: 2,733. Core. Calendar: semesters. Academic remediation for entering students, ESL program, services for LD students, advanced placement, distance learning, double major, part-time degree program, adult/continuing education programs, co-op programs.
Entrance Requirements: Open admission. Option: electronic application. Required: high school transcript, ACT, SAT or ACCUPLACER. Entrance: noncompetitive. Application deadline: rolling. Transfer credits accepted: Yes.

Collegiate Environment: Orientation program. Student services: health clinic. Campus security: 24-hour emergency response devices. Kenai Peninsula College Library.

Community Environment: Soldotna, population 4,000, is located on the coast and enjoys a cool climate during the spring and summer months. Public transportation in and out of Kenai is mainly by air and highway with some bus service available. The city has a library, museum, many churches, and a full-service hospital. Recreation includes hunting, fishing, boating, water sports, and clam digging. Annual Kenai days around the middle of July is a traditional event. Part-time employment is available.

■ UNIVERSITY OF ALASKA ANCHORAGE, KODIAK COLLEGE

117 Benny Benson Dr.
Kodiak, AK 99615-6643
Tel: (907)486-4161; Free: 800-486-7660
Fax: (907)486-1252
Web Site: www.koc.alaska.edu

Description: State-supported, 2-year, coed. Part of University of Alaska System. Awards certificates, transfer associate, and terminal associate degrees. Founded 1968. Setting: 68-acre rural campus. Total enrollment: 479. Faculty: (11 full-time). Student-undergrad faculty ratio is 13:1. 56 applied, 77% were admitted. Students come from 18 states and territories, 3 other countries. 12% American Indian or Alaska Native, non-Hispanic/Latino; 8% Hispanic/Latino; 2% Black or African American, non-Hispanic/Latino; 6% Asian, non-Hispanic/Latino; 0.8% Native Hawaiian or other Pacific Islander, non-Hispanic/Latino; 2% international. Core. Calendar: semesters. Academic remediation for entering students, advanced placement, distance learning, double major, summer session for credit, part-time degree program, adult/continuing education programs. Study abroad program.

Entrance Requirements: Open admission. Option: electronic application. Required: ACCUPLACER. Required for some: high school transcript. Entrance: noncompetitive. Application deadline: rolling. Transfer credits accepted: Yes.

Collegiate Environment: Orientation program. Social organizations: 2 open to all. Most popular organizations: PHI THETA KAPPA, student government. Carolyn Floyd Library. 40 computers available on campus for general student use. Computer purchase/lease plans available. A campuswide network can be accessed. Students can access the following: online class registration. Staffed computer lab on campus provides training in use of computers, software, and the Internet.

Community Environment: Population 6,200. Kodiak, located in the Gulf of Alaska on Kodiak Island, was once a Russian settlement. It has always looked to the sea for its livelihood and in 1968 became the largest fishing port in dollar volume in the United States. Transportation to Kodiak is an interesting trip by automobile. The Alaska Marine Highway ferry, Tustumena, serves Kodiak regularly. There is direct flight service from Anchorage. The city of Kodiak is the largest town in the Kodiak Island group and is the oldest permanent settlement in Alaska. The city is situated on the northeastern corner of Kodiak Island nestled at the foot of the 1,400 foot Pillar Mountain, overlooking the island-studded harbor of St. Paul. This northerly section of the City of Kodiak was rebuilt following the Good Friday earthquake and tidal wave of 1964. The average temperature in January is 30 degrees and in August, 55 degrees. The annual rainfall is 60 inches spread throughout the year. A number of churches, and service organizations are found in the city.

■ UNIVERSITY OF ALASKA ANCHORAGE, MATANUSKA-SUSITNA COLLEGE

PO Box 2889
Palmer, AK 99645-2889
Tel: (907)745-9774
Fax: (907)745-9747
E-mail: info@matsu.alaska.edu
Web Site: www.matsu.alaska.edu

Description: State-supported, 2-year, coed. Part of University of Alaska System. Awards certificates, transfer associate, and terminal associate degrees. Founded 1958. Setting: 950-acre small town campus with easy access to Anchorage. Total enrollment: 1,782. Faculty: 116 (26 full-time, 90 part-time). Student-undergrad faculty ratio is 16:1. 45% 25 or older. Retention: 55% of full-time freshmen returned the following year. Core. Calendar: semesters. Academic remediation for entering students, advanced placement, independent study, distance learning, double major, summer session for credit, part-time degree program, adult/continuing education programs, co-op programs and internships. Off campus study at Alaska Pacific University, University of Alaska Anchorage.

Entrance Requirements: Open admission. Option: electronic application. Required: high school transcript. Entrance: noncompetitive. Application deadline: 9/15. Notification: 9/30. Transfer credits accepted: Yes.

Collegiate Environment: Orientation program. Choral group, student-run newspaper. Most popular organizations: Student Government, Math Club, Phi Theta Kappa, Basketball, Students for Christ. Major annual events: Fall BBQ and resource fair, Spring BBQ. Campus security: 24-hour patrols. Al Okeson Library. 207 computers available on campus for general student use. A campuswide network can be accessed. Students can access the following: online class registration. Staffed computer lab on campus provides training in use of computers.

Community Environment: Population 6,920, Palmer is a rural town with subarctic climate. A branch of the Alaska Railroad and bus service to Anchorage serve this area. There are churches, a library, museum, hospital, and a health center in the town. Recreational activities include fishing, boating, ice skating and some swimming. There are good shopping facilities available. Palmer has the usual civic organizations found in most U.S. cities. The Alaska State Fair is the fourth weekend of August through Labor Day weekend each year.

■ UNIVERSITY OF ALASKA FAIRBANKS

PO Box 757500
Fairbanks, AK 99775-7520
Tel: (907)474-7211; Free: 800-478-1823
Fax: (907)474-5379
Web Site: www.uaf.edu

Description: State-supported, university, coed. Part of University of Alaska System. Awards associate, bachelor's, master's, and doctoral degrees. Founded 1917. Setting: 2,250-acre small town campus. Endowment: $98.9 million. Research spending for the previous fiscal year: $141.4 million. Educational spending for the previous fiscal year: $15,349 per student. Total enrollment: 7,744. Faculty: 831 (481 full-time, 350 part-time). Student-undergrad faculty ratio is 8:1. 1,631 applied, 77% were admitted. 21% from top 10% of their high school class, 49% from top quarter, 73% from top half. Full-time: 3,022 students, 51% women, 49% men. Part-time: 3,696 students, 63% women, 37% men. Students come from 51 states and territories, 32 other countries, 14% from out-of-state. 14% American Indian or Alaska Native, non-Hispanic/Latino; 7% Hispanic/Latino; 3% Black or African American, non-Hispanic/Latino; 2% Asian, non-Hispanic/Latino; 0.5% Native Hawaiian or other Pacific Islander, non-Hispanic/Latino; 1% international. 40% 25 or older, 36% live on campus, 5% transferred in. Retention: 77% of full-time freshmen returned the following year. Academic areas with the most degrees conferred: engineering; business/marketing; homeland security, law enforcement, firefighting, and protective services. Core. Calendar: semesters. Academic remediation for entering students, ESL program, services for LD students, advanced placement, accelerated degree program, self-designed majors, honors program, independent study, distance learning, double major, summer session for credit, part-time degree program, external degree program, co-op programs and internships, graduate courses open to undergrads. Off campus study at National Student Exchange. Study abroad program. ROTC: Army.

Entrance Requirements: Options: electronic application, deferred admission, international baccalaureate accepted. Required: high school transcript, minimum 2.5 high school GPA, SAT or ACT. Entrance: minimally difficult. Application deadline: 6/15. Notification: continuous, continuous for nonresidents. SAT Reasoning Test deadline: 6/15. Transfer credits accepted: Yes.

Costs Per Year: Application fee: $50. State resident tuition: $7020 full-time, $212 per credit hour part-time. Nonresident tuition: $23,190 full-time, $751 per credit hour part-time. Mandatory fees: $1780 full-time. Full-time tuition and fees vary according to course level, course load, location, program, and reciprocity agreements. Part-time tuition varies according to course level, course load, location, program, and reciprocity agreements. College room and board: $8930. College room only: $4200. Room and board charges vary according to board plan, housing facility, and location.

Collegiate Environment: Orientation program. Drama-theater group, choral group, student-run newspaper, radio station. Social organizations: 80 open to all. Most popular organizations: Chi Alpha, Yoga Club, Aurora Aerial Arts, Festival of Native Arts, Gender and Sexuality Alliance. Major annual events: Starvation Gulch, Melt Down, Winter Carnival. Student services: legal services, health clinic, personal-psychological counseling. Campus security: 24-hour emergency response devices and patrols, student patrols, late night transport-escort service, controlled dormitory access, ID check at door of residence halls, crime prevention and safety workshops. Rasmuson Library plus 1 other. Books: 533,679 (physical), 324,260 (digital/electronic); Serial titles: 222,847 (physical), 30,490 (digital/electronic); Databases: 175. Weekly public service hours: 87; students can reserve study rooms. Operations spending for the previous fiscal year: $6.8 million. 125 computers available on campus for general student use. A campuswide network can be accessed from student residence rooms and from off campus. Students can access the following: online class registration, university portal. Staffed computer lab on campus provides training in use of computers, software, and the Internet.

Community Environment: The campus overlooks the Tanana Valley and the city of Fairbanks. Offering the amenities of larger communities, Fairbanks maintains the atmosphere of smaller, more personal towns. One hundred miles south is Denali National Park, home to North America's tallest mountain—Mt. McKinley. Closer lay the vast wilderness that makes up the Great Interior of Alaska. Adventure is unlimited here—hiking, biking, climbing, canoeing, skiing, dog mushing, and other recreational activities abound. Winters are cold, with an annual snowfall of 70 inches. Summers bring temperatures in the 80s and 24 hours of daylight, perfect weather for the activities Alaska has to offer.

■ **UNIVERSITY OF ALASKA, PRINCE WILLIAM SOUND COLLEGE**
PO Box 97
Valdez, AK 99686-0097
Tel: (907)834-1600; Free: 800-478-8800
Fax: (907)834-1627
E-mail: drunge@pwscc.edu
Web Site: www.pwsc.alaska.edu

Description: State-supported, 2-year, coed. Part of University of Alaska System. Awards certificates, diplomas, transfer associate, and terminal associate degrees. Founded 1978. Setting: small town campus. Endowment: $62,630. Research spending for the previous fiscal year: $5000. Educational spending for the previous fiscal year: $283 per student. Student-undergrad faculty ratio is 5:1. 120 applied, 78% were admitted. Students come from 2 other countries, 13% from out-of-state. 74% 25 or older, 2% live on campus. Core. Calendar: semesters. Academic remediation for entering students, ESL program, services for LD students, advanced placement, independent study, distance learning, double major, summer session for credit, adult/continuing education programs, co-op programs and internships.

Entrance Requirements: Open admission. Options: electronic application, early admission. Required: high school transcript. Recommended: SAT or ACT, ACCUPLACER. Entrance: noncompetitive. Application deadline: rolling. Transfer credits accepted: Yes.

Collegiate Environment: Drama-theater group. Social organizations: 4 open to all. Most popular organizations: Student Association, Phi Theta Kappa Honor Society, Archery Team/Club. Major annual events: Sponsored Halloween Event, New School-Year Glacier and Wildlife Cruise. Student services: personal-psychological counseling. Campus security: student patrols, controlled dormitory access, housing manager supervision. Valdez Consortium Library. Operations spending for the previous fiscal year: $40,000. 16 computers available on campus for general student use. A campuswide network can be accessed from student residence rooms. Students can access the following: online class registration. Staffed computer lab on campus provides training in use of computers, software, and the Internet.

■ **UNIVERSITY OF ALASKA SOUTHEAST**
11120 Glacier Hwy.
Juneau, AK 99801
Tel: (907)796-6457; Free: 877-465-4827
Fax: (907)796-6365
E-mail: admissions@uas.alaska.edu
Web Site: www.uas.alaska.edu

Description: State-supported, comprehensive, coed. Part of University of Alaska System. Awards associate, bachelor's, and master's degrees and post-master's certificates. Founded 1972. Setting: 198-acre small town campus. Research spending for the previous fiscal year: $1.1 million. Educational spending for the previous fiscal year: $11,035 per student. Total enrollment: 3,458. Faculty: 229 (102 full-time, 127 part-time). Student-undergrad faculty ratio is 9:1. 655 applied. 8% from top 10% of their high school class, 28% from top quarter, 52% from top half. Full-time: 860 students, 57% women, 43% men. Part-time: 2,213 students, 68% women, 32% men. Students come from 42 states and territories, 7 other countries, 11% from out-of-state. 46% 25 or older, 17% live on campus, 8% transferred in. Retention: 61% of full-time freshmen returned the following year. Academic areas with the most degrees conferred: business/marketing; liberal arts/general studies; social sciences. Core. Calendar: semesters.

Academic remediation for entering students, services for LD students, advanced placement, self-designed majors, independent study, distance learning, double major, summer session for credit, part-time degree program, adult/continuing education programs, co-op programs and internships, graduate courses open to undergrads. Off campus study at National Student Exchange. Study abroad program.

Entrance Requirements: Open admission. Options: electronic application, deferred admission. Required: high school transcript, minimum 2 high school GPA. Recommended: SAT or ACT. Required for some: essay. Entrance: noncompetitive. Application deadline: 9/9. Notification: continuous, continuous for nonresidents. Transfer credits accepted: Yes.

Collegiate Environment: Orientation program. Student-run newspaper, radio station. Most popular organizations: Wooch.een, Native Student Club, Sustainability Club, Alpha Phi Omega, The Beatniks, UAS Improv Club. Major annual events: Orientation Week, Banff Mountain Film Festival, Bonfire. Student services: health clinic, personal-psychological counseling. Campus security: 24-hour emergency response devices and patrols, late night transport-escort service, controlled dormitory access. Egan Memorial Library. Operations spending for the previous fiscal year: $1.9 million.

Community Environment: Situated on the shores of scenic Auke Lake, with the famous Mendenhall Glacier in clear sight, the main campus is only a few miles from the heart of downtown Juneau, the capital of Alaska. Nestled between 4,000-foot snow-capped peaks on one side and the sparkling water of Gastineau Channel on the other, Juneau was the first Alaskan city founded after the American purchase of Alaska in 1867. The city is centrally located in the Tongass National Forest, the nation's largest. The combined city and borough encompass 3,108 square miles of land, ranging from tundra, to moss-draped forests, to wind-blown mountain peaks. Juneau's population is approximately 30,900 and provides numerous cultural, academic, and professional opportunities.

■ **UNIVERSITY OF ALASKA SOUTHEAST, KETCHIKAN CAMPUS**
2600 7th Ave.
Ketchikan, AK 99901-5798
Tel: (907)225-6177
Fax: (907)225-3624
E-mail: ketch.info@uas.alaska.edu
Web Site: www.ketch.alaska.edu

Description: State and locally supported, 2-year, coed. Part of University of Alaska System. Awards transfer associate and terminal associate degrees. Founded 1954. Setting: 51-acre small town campus. Calendar: semesters. Part-time degree program, adult/continuing education programs. Off campus study at University of Alaska Southeast, Sheldon Jackson College.

Entrance Requirements: Required: high school transcript. Required for some: essay. Entrance: noncompetitive. Application deadline: rolling.

Collegiate Environment: Orientation program. Campus security: 24-hour emergency response devices. Ketchikan Campus Library.

Community Environment: Population 7,400. Located on the Revillagigedo Island 600 miles northwest of Seattle; climate is very wet - 13 feet of rain per year. Airlines and water transportation serves the area. Extensive access to the Tongass National Forest and intercoastal waterways.

■ **UNIVERSITY OF ALASKA SOUTHEAST, SITKA CAMPUS**
1332 Seward Ave.
Sitka, AK 99835-9418
Tel: (907)747-6653; Free: 800-478-6653
Fax: (907)747-7747
E-mail: ktgordon@uas.alaska.edu
Web Site: www.uas.alaska.edu/sitka

Description: State-supported, primarily 2-year, coed. Part of University of Alaska System. Administratively affiliated with University of Alaska Southeast. Awards certificates, diplomas, transfer associate, terminal associate, bachelor's, and master's degrees. Founded 1962. Setting: small town campus. Total enrollment: 1,552. Faculty: 59 (19 full-time, 40 part-time). Student-undergrad faculty ratio is 13:1. Students come from 10 states and territories, 2 other countries. 65% 25 or older. Calendar: semesters. Academic remediation for entering students, ESL program, services for LD students, advanced placement, independent study, distance learning, double major, summer session for credit, part-time degree program, adult/continuing education programs, co-op programs and internships. Off campus study at University of Alaska system, all branches. Study abroad program.

Entrance Requirements: Open admission. Options: electronic application, early admission, deferred admission. Required: high school transcript, minimum 2 high school GPA. Required for some: essay. Entrance: noncompetitive. Application deadline: rolling. Notification: continuous. Transfer credits accepted: Yes.

Collegiate Environment: Orientation program. Social organizations: 2 open to all. Most popular organizations: Student Government Association, Phi Theta Kappa Honor Society. Major annual events: Campus-Wide Picnic, Halloween (campus trick-or-treating and haunted house for community children), Bi-Annual Stress Fair. Student services: personal-psychological counseling. Campus security: 24-hour emergency response devices. Egan Library. 13 computers available on campus for general student use. A campuswide network can be accessed from student residence rooms and from off campus. Students can access the following: online class registration, online student financial accounts and payment capability. Staffed computer lab on campus provides training in use of computers, software, and the Internet.

Community Environment: Population 8,980. Sitka is the original capital of Russian-America and was the site of the transfer of Alaska from Russia to the United States in 1867. Many historic sites and museums convey these historic origins, as well as the strong Northwest Coast Native heritage of the region. The rainy climate is mild and comparable to that of Seattle or Portland. Located on Baranof Island, adjacent to the mainland coast of the Southeast Alaskan panhandle, Sitka is surrounded by the heavily forested mountains of the Tongass National Forest. It is served by daily jet service, as well as small regional air carriers. The Alaska Marine Highway System provides weekly passenger and vehicle transportation from the southern terminal of Bellingham, Washington, and the northern terminal of Haines, Alaska. A regional center for health services, business, and education, Sitka has two hospitals, several small but important museums, two colleges, and a State-operated boarding high school.

■ **ARGOSY UNIVERSITY, PHOENIX**
2233 W Dunlap Ave.
Phoenix, AZ 85021
Tel: (602)216-2600; Free: 866-216-2777
Fax: (602)216-2601
Web Site: www.argosy.edu/phoenix-arizona/default.aspx
Description: Proprietary, university, coed. Awards associate, bachelor's, master's, and doctoral degrees. Founded 1997. Setting: urban campus. Calendar: semesters.

■ **ARIZONA CHRISTIAN UNIVERSITY**
2625 E Cactus Rd.
Phoenix, AZ 85032-7042
Tel: (602)489-5300; Free: 800-247-2697
E-mail: lambert.cruz@arizonachristian.edu
Web Site: arizonachristian.edu
Description: Independent Conservative Baptist, 4-year, coed. Awards associate and bachelor's degrees. Founded 1960. Setting: 19-acre urban campus with easy access to Phoenix. Total enrollment: 700. Faculty: 88 (17 full-time, 71 part-time). Student-undergrad faculty ratio is 16:1. 246 applied, 99% were admitted. Full-time: 643 students, 35% women, 65% men. Part-time: 57 students, 44% women, 56% men. 29% from out-of-state. 1% American Indian or Alaska Native, non-Hispanic/Latino; 22% Hispanic/Latino; 15% Black or African American, non-Hispanic/Latino; 0.7% Asian, non-Hispanic/Latino; 0.3% Native Hawaiian or other Pacific Islander, non-Hispanic/Latino; 4% international. 15% 25 or older, 32% live on campus. Academic areas with the most degrees conferred: business/marketing; theology and religious vocations; education. Core. Calendar: semesters. Academic remediation for entering students, services for LD students, advanced placement, independent study, distance learning, double major, summer session for credit, part-time degree program, adult/continuing education programs, internships. Study abroad program. ROTC: Air Force (c).
Entrance Requirements: Required: essay, high school transcript, minimum 2 high school GPA, 1 recommendation, SAT or ACT. SAT Reasoning Test deadline: 8/15.
Costs Per Year: Application fee: $30. Comprehensive fee: $36,150 includes full-time tuition ($25,476) and college room and board ($10,674). College room only: $5400. Full-time tuition varies according to class time, course load, and program. Room and board charges vary according to board plan. Part-time tuition: $1062 per credit hour. Part-time tuition varies according to class time, course load, and program.
Collegiate Environment: Orientation program. Choral group. Social organizations: 10 open to all; 18% of eligible men and 21% of eligible women are members. Most popular organizations: Joseph Story Pre-Law Society, International Student Association, Pre-Medicine Club, Flock Council and Flock Leaders, Reason and Religion. Major annual events: Homecoming, Welcome Week, Fall Festival. Student services: personal-psychological counseling. Campus security: 24-hour emergency response devices, student patrols, late night transport-escort service, controlled dormitory access, 20-hour patrol with a guard on call on weekdays, 24-hour patrol by trained security personnel on weekends. R. S. Beal Library. Books: 28,496 (physical), 19,581 (digital/electronic); Serial titles: 471 (physical), 32 (digital/electronic); Databases: 18. Weekly public service hours: 76. 37 computers available on campus for general student use. Students can access the following: online class registration.

■ **ARIZONA COLLEGE**
4425 W Olive Ave.
Ste. 300
Glendale, AZ 85302-3843
Tel: (602)222-9300
Fax: (602)200-8726
E-mail: lhicks@arizonacollege.edu
Web Site: www.arizonacollege.edu
Description: Proprietary, 2-year, coed. Awards terminal associate degrees. Founded 1992. Total enrollment: 740. Student-undergrad faculty ratio is 16:1. 62% 25 or older. Calendar: quarters.
Entrance Requirements: Required: interview. Entrance: noncompetitive.

■ **ARIZONA COLLEGE-MESA**
163 N Dobson Rd.
Mesa, AZ 85201
Web Site: www.arizonacollege.edu
Description: Proprietary, 4-year, coed. Awards associate and bachelor's degrees.

■ **ARIZONA STATE UNIVERSITY AT THE DOWNTOWN PHOENIX CAMPUS**
411 N Central Ave.
Phoenix, AZ 85004
Tel: (602)496-4636
E-mail: admissions@asu.edu
Web Site: campus.asu.edu/downtown
Description: State-supported, university, coed. Administratively affiliated with Arizona State University. Awards bachelor's, master's, and doctoral degrees and post-master's certificates. Founded 2006. Setting: 18-acre urban campus with easy access to Phoenix. Total enrollment: 11,465. Faculty: 635 (554 full-time, 81 part-time). Student-undergrad faculty ratio is 19:1. 5,340 applied, 77% were admitted. 35% from top 10% of their high school class, 72% from top quarter, 95% from top half. 2 National Merit Scholars. Full-time: 7,956 students, 68% women, 32% men. Part-time: 946 students, 62% women, 38% men. Students come from 36 other countries, 27% from out-of-state. 2% American Indian or Alaska Native, non-Hispanic/Latino; 31% Hispanic/Latino; 6% Black or African American, non-Hispanic/Latino; 5% Asian, non-Hispanic/Latino; 0.2% Native Hawaiian or other Pacific Islander, non-Hispanic/Latino; 2% international. 16% 25 or older, 17% live on campus, 10% transferred in. Retention: 86% of full-time freshmen returned the following year. Academic areas with the most degrees conferred: health professions and related sciences; parks and recreation; homeland security, law enforcement, firefighting, and protective services. Core. Calendar: semesters. Services for LD students, advanced placement, accelerated degree program, self-designed majors, freshman honors college, honors program, independent study, distance learning, double major, summer session for credit, part-time degree program, co-op programs and internships, graduate courses open to undergrads. Off campus study at ASU / Draper University Entrepreneurship Incubator Program: ASU has partnered with Draper University to create an immersive program where innovation thrives, through a unique in-residence experience featuring ASU faculty and curriculum at Draper University in San Mateo, California. In just four months, students will gain the tools and knowledge to launch and grow their own

startup, and turn powerful ideas into reality. Visit: https://entrepreneurship. asu.edu/learn/Svsemester. Study abroad program. ROTC: Army (c), Naval (c), Air Force (c).

Entrance Requirements: Options: electronic application, deferred admission, international baccalaureate accepted. Required: high school transcript, minimum 3 high school GPA. Recommended: SAT or ACT. Required for some: essay, recommendations, additional requirements for Honors College and certain majors, SAT or ACT, SAT Subject Tests. Entrance: moderately difficult. Application deadline: rolling. Notification: continuous until 9/1. Transfer credits accepted: Yes.

Costs Per Year: Application fee: $50. State resident tuition: $10,104 full-time, $702 per credit hour part-time. Nonresident tuition: $27,618 full-time, $1151 per credit hour part-time. Mandatory fees: $718 full-time. College room and board: $14,584. College room only: $9536. Room and board charges vary according to board plan.

Collegiate Environment: Orientation program. Drama-theater group, student-run newspaper, radio station. Social organizations: 113 open to all. Most popular organizations: Student Nurses Association, American Medical Student Association, Exercise and Wellness Organization, Student Nutrition Council, Physical Therapy Club. Major annual events: Sparky's Carnival, Welcome Back BBQ, Taylor Fest. Student services: health clinic, personal-psychological counseling. Campus security: 24-hour emergency response devices and patrols, late night transport-escort service, controlled dormitory access, LiveSafe smart phone application, surveillance camera in some residence halls. Downtown Phoenix campus Library. Books: 3.9 million (physical), 963,136 (digital/electronic); Serial titles: 72,649 (physical), 73,043 (digital/electronic); Databases: 650. Weekly public service hours: 149; study areas open 24 hours, 5-7 days a week; students can reserve study rooms. 486 computers available on campus for general student use. Computer purchase/lease plans available. A campuswide network can be accessed from student residence rooms and from off campus. Students can access the following: online class registration. Staffed computer lab on campus provides training in use of computers, software, and the Internet.

■ **ARIZONA STATE UNIVERSITY AT THE POLYTECHNIC CAMPUS**
7001 E Williams Field Rd.
Mesa, AZ 85212
Tel: (480)727-1585
Fax: (480)727-1008
E-mail: admissions@asu.edu
Web Site: campus.asu.edu/polytechnic
Description: State-supported, university, coed. Administratively affiliated with Arizona State University. Awards bachelor's, master's, and doctoral degrees. Founded 1996. Setting: 575-acre suburban campus with easy access to Phoenix. Total enrollment: 4,809. Faculty: 219 (204 full-time, 15 part-time). Student-undergrad faculty ratio is 21:1. 2,483 applied, 76% were admitted. 20% from top 10% of their high school class, 50% from top quarter, 88% from top half. 1 National Merit Scholar. Full-time: 3,683 students, 31% women, 69% men. Part-time: 556 students, 30% women, 70% men. Students come from 52 other countries, 22% from out-of-state. 1% American Indian or Alaska Native, non-Hispanic/Latino; 21% Hispanic/Latino; 5% Black or African American, non-Hispanic/Latino; 6% Asian, non-Hispanic/Latino; 0.6% Native Hawaiian or other Pacific Islander, non-Hispanic/Latino; 8% international. 23% 25 or older, 23% live on campus, 12% transferred in. Retention: 85% of full-time freshmen returned the following year. Academic areas with the most degrees conferred: engineering; biological/life sciences; business/marketing. Core. Calendar: semesters. Services for LD students, advanced placement, accelerated degree program, self-designed majors, freshman honors college, honors program, independent study, distance learning, double major, summer session for credit, part-time degree program, co-op programs and internships, graduate courses open to undergrads. Off campus study at ASU / Draper University Entrepreneurship Incubator Program: ASU has partnered with Draper University to create an immersive program where innovation thrives, through a unique in-residence experience featuring ASU faculty and curriculum at Draper University in San Mateo, California. In just four months, students will gain the tools and knowledge to launch and grow their own startup, and turn powerful ideas into reality. Visit: https://entrepreneurship.asu.edu/learn/Svsemester. Study abroad program. ROTC: Army (c), Naval (c), Air Force (c).
Entrance Requirements: Options: electronic application, deferred admission, international baccalaureate accepted. Required: high school transcript, minimum 3 high school GPA. Recommended: SAT or ACT. Required for some: essay, recommendations, additional requirements for Honors College

and certain majors, SAT or ACT, SAT Subject Tests. Entrance: moderately difficult. Application deadline: rolling. Notification: continuous until 9/1. Transfer credits accepted: Yes.
Costs Per Year: Application fee: $50. State resident tuition: $9613 full-time, $667 per credit hour part-time. Nonresident tuition: $26,238 full-time, $1094 per credit hour part-time. Mandatory fees: $718 full-time. College room and board: $11,683. College room only: $6635. Room and board charges vary according to board plan and housing facility.
Collegiate Environment: Orientation program. Drama-theater group, student-run newspaper. Social organizations: 81 open to all. Most popular organizations: Pre-Health Club, AIGA Polytechnic, Environmental Resource Management Club, Computer Science, Disc Golf Club. Major annual events: Devils Royale, Fall Welcome, Innovation Showcase. Student services: health clinic, personal-psychological counseling. Campus security: 24-hour emergency response devices and patrols, late night transport-escort service, controlled dormitory access, LiveSafe smart phone application, surveillance camera in some residence halls. Polytechnic campus Library. Books: 3.9 million (physical), 963,136 (digital/electronic); Serial titles: 72,649 (physical), 73,043 (digital/electronic); Databases: 650. Weekly public service hours: 149; study areas open 24 hours, 5-7 days a week; students can reserve study rooms. 535 computers available on campus for general student use. Computer purchase/lease plans available. A campuswide network can be accessed from student residence rooms and from off campus. Students can access the following: online class registration. Staffed computer lab on campus provides training in use of computers, software, and the Internet.

■ **ARIZONA STATE UNIVERSITY AT THE TEMPE CAMPUS**
Tempe, AZ 85287
Tel: (480)965-2100
Fax: (482)965-1608
E-mail: admissions@asu.edu
Web Site: www.asu.edu
Description: State-supported, university, coed. Administratively affiliated with Arizona State University. Awards bachelor's, master's, and doctoral degrees and post-master's certificates (profile includes data for the West, Polytechnic and Downtown Phoenix campuses). Founded 1885. Setting: 661-acre urban campus with easy access to Phoenix. Total enrollment: 51,164. Faculty: 2,283 (2,135 full-time, 148 part-time). Student-undergrad faculty ratio is 22:1. 24,127 applied, 84% were admitted. 34% from top 10% of their high school class, 64% from top quarter, 90% from top half. 119 National Merit Scholars. Full-time: 38,814 students, 44% women, 56% men. Part-time: 3,613 students, 39% women, 61% men. Students come from 116 other countries, 25% from out-of-state. 1% American Indian or Alaska Native, non-Hispanic/Latino; 21% Hispanic/Latino; 4% Black or African American, non-Hispanic/Latino; 7% Asian, non-Hispanic/Latino; 0.2% Native Hawaiian or other Pacific Islander, non-Hispanic/Latino; 13% international. 11% 25 or older, 22% live on campus, 7% transferred in. Retention: 87% of full-time freshmen returned the following year. Academic areas with the most degrees conferred: business/marketing; engineering; social sciences. Core. Calendar: semesters. ESL program, services for LD students, advanced placement, accelerated degree program, self-designed majors, freshman honors college, honors program, independent study, distance learning, double major, summer session for credit, part-time degree program, co-op programs and internships, graduate courses open to undergrads. Off campus study at ASU / Draper University Entrepreneurship Incubator Program: ASU has partnered with Draper University to create an immersive program where innovation thrives, through a unique in-residence experience featuring ASU faculty and curriculum at Draper University in San Mateo, California. In just four months, students will gain the tools and knowledge to launch and grow their own startup, and turn powerful ideas into reality. Visit: https://entrepreneurship.asu.edu/learn/Svsemester. Study abroad program. ROTC: Army, Naval, Air Force.
Entrance Requirements: Options: electronic application, deferred admission, international baccalaureate accepted. Required: high school transcript, minimum 3 high school GPA. Recommended: SAT or ACT. Required for some: essay, recommendations, additional requirements for Honors College and certain majors, SAT or ACT, SAT Subject Tests. Entrance: moderately difficult. Application deadline: rolling. Notification: continuous until 9/1. Transfer credits accepted: Yes.
Costs Per Year: Application fee: $50. State resident tuition: $10,104 full-time, $702 per credit hour part-time. Nonresident tuition: $27,618 full-time, $1151 per credit hour part-time. Mandatory fees: $718 full-time. College room and board: $12,648. College room only: $7600. Room and board charges vary according to board plan and housing facility.

Collegiate Environment: Orientation program. Drama-theater group, choral group, marching band, student-run newspaper. Social organizations: 852 open to all; national fraternities, national sororities, local fraternities, local sororities; 10% of eligible men and 17% of eligible women are members. Most popular organizations: Sun Devil Ski Club, Residence Hall Association, Alpha Epsilon Delta, American Medical Student Association, Software Developers Association. Major annual events: Devils on Mill, Passport to ASU, Homecoming. Student services: health clinic, personal-psychological counseling. Campus security: 24-hour emergency response devices and patrols, late night transport-escort service, controlled dormitory access, LiveSafe smart phone application, surveillance cameras in some residence halls. Hayden Library plus 3 others. Books: 3.9 million (physical), 963,136 (digital/electronic); Serial titles: 72,649 (physical), 73,043 (digital/electronic); Databases: 650. Weekly public service hours: 149; study areas open 24 hours, 5-7 days a week; students can reserve study rooms. 2,421 computers available on campus for general student use. Computer purchase/lease plans available. A campuswide network can be accessed from student residence rooms and from off campus. Students can access the following: online class registration. Staffed computer lab on campus (open 24 hours a day) provides training in use of computers, software, and the Internet.

■ **ARIZONA STATE UNIVERSITY AT THE WEST CAMPUS**
4701 W Thunderbird Rd.
Glendale, AZ 85306
Tel: (602)543-5500
E-mail: admissions@asu.edu
Web Site: campus.asu.edu/west
Description: State-supported, university, coed. Administratively affiliated with Arizona State University. Awards bachelor's, master's, and doctoral degrees. Founded 1984. Setting: 278-acre urban campus with easy access to Phoenix. Total enrollment: 4,063. Faculty: 292 (273 full-time, 19 part-time). Student-undergrad faculty ratio is 14:1. 2,231 applied, 80% were admitted. 32% from top 10% of their high school class, 66% from top quarter, 94% from top half. 1 National Merit Scholar. Full-time: 3,078 students, 60% women, 40% men. Part-time: 552 students, 53% women, 47% men. Students come from 30 other countries, 14% from out-of-state. 1% American Indian or Alaska Native, non-Hispanic/Latino; 32% Hispanic/Latino; 5% Black or African American, non-Hispanic/Latino; 5% Asian, non-Hispanic/Latino; 0.3% Native Hawaiian or other Pacific Islander, non-Hispanic/Latino; 6% international. 24% 25 or older, 14% live on campus, 17% transferred in. Retention: 88% of full-time freshmen returned the following year. Academic areas with the most degrees conferred: business/marketing; psychology; education. Core. Calendar: semesters. ESL program, services for LD students, advanced placement, accelerated degree program, self-designed majors, freshman honors college, honors program, independent study, distance learning, double major, summer session for credit, part-time degree program, co-op programs and internships, graduate courses open to undergrads. Off campus study at ASU / Draper University Entrepreneurship Incubator Program: ASU has partnered with Draper University to create an immersive program where innovation thrives, through a unique in-residence experience featuring ASU faculty and curriculum at Draper University in San Mateo, California. In just four months, students will gain the tools and knowledge to launch and grow their own startup, and turn powerful ideas into reality. Visit: https://entrepreneurship.asu.edu/learn/Svsemester. Study abroad program. ROTC: Army (c), Naval (c), Air Force (c).
Entrance Requirements: Options: electronic application, deferred admission, international baccalaureate accepted. Required: high school transcript, minimum 3 high school GPA. Recommended: SAT or ACT. Required for some: essay, recommendations, additional requirements for Honors College and certain majors, SAT or ACT, SAT Subject Tests. Entrance: moderately difficult. Application deadline: rolling. Notification: continuous until 9/1. Transfer credits accepted: Yes.
Costs Per Year: Application fee: $50. State resident tuition: $9613 full-time, $667 per credit hour part-time. Nonresident tuition: $26,238 full-time, $1094 per credit hour part-time. Mandatory fees: $718 full-time. College room and board: $11,588. College room only: $6540. Room and board charges vary according to board plan.
Collegiate Environment: Orientation program. Drama-theater group, choral group, student-run newspaper. Social organizations: 76 open to all. Most popular organizations: Hispanic Honor Society, Teachers of the Future, Business to Business, W. P. Carey MBA Association, American Medical Student Association. Major annual events: Sparky's Carnival and Fun Run, Finals Breakfast, West Fest. Student services: health clinic, personal-psychological counseling. Campus security: 24-hour emergency response devices and

patrols, late night transport-escort service, controlled dormitory access, LiveSafe smart phone application, surveillance camera in some residence halls. Fletcher Library at the West campus. Books: 3.9 million (physical), 963,136 (digital/electronic); Serial titles: 72,649 (physical), 73,043 (digital/electronic); Databases: 650. Weekly public service hours: 149; study areas open 24 hours, 5-7 days a week; students can reserve study rooms. 612 computers available on campus for general student use. Computer purchase/lease plans available. A campuswide network can be accessed from student residence rooms and from off campus. Students can access the following: online class registration. Staffed computer lab on campus provides training in use of computers, software, and the Internet.

■ **ARIZONA WESTERN COLLEGE**
2020 S Ave. 8E
Yuma, AZ 85365
Tel: (928)317-6000; Free: 888-293-0392
Fax: (928)344-7730
E-mail: nicole.harral@azwestern.edu
Web Site: www.azwestern.edu
Description: State and locally supported, 2-year, coed. Part of Arizona State Community College System. Awards certificates, transfer associate, and terminal associate degrees. Founded 1962. Setting: 640-acre rural campus. Total enrollment: 7,557. Faculty: 378 (123 full-time, 255 part-time). Student-undergrad faculty ratio is 19:1. Full-time: 2,221 students, 54% women, 46% men. Part-time: 5,336 students, 60% women, 40% men. Students come from 32 states and territories, 29 other countries, 3% from out-of-state. 1% American Indian or Alaska Native, non-Hispanic/Latino; 72% Hispanic/Latino; 2% Black or African American, non-Hispanic/Latino; 0.9% Asian, non-Hispanic/Latino; 0.4% Native Hawaiian or other Pacific Islander, non-Hispanic/Latino; 2% international. 62% 25 or older, 6% live on campus. Core. Calendar: semesters. Academic remediation for entering students, ESL program, services for LD students, advanced placement, honors program, independent study, distance learning, summer session for credit, part-time degree program, adult/continuing education programs, co-op programs.
Entrance Requirements: Open admission except for the nursing program, massage therapy program, and radiologic technology program. Options: electronic application, early admission, deferred admission, international baccalaureate accepted. Required for some: SAT or ACT. Entrance: noncompetitive. Application deadline: rolling. Transfer credits accepted: Yes.
Costs Per Year: Application fee: $0. State resident tuition: $2520 full-time, $84 per credit part-time. Nonresident tuition: $9510 full-time, $317 per credit part-time. Full-time tuition varies according to course load, program, and reciprocity agreements. Part-time tuition varies according to course load, program, and reciprocity agreements. College room and board: $6678. College room only: $2240. Room and board charges vary according to board plan and housing facility.
Collegiate Environment: Orientation program. Drama-theater group, choral group, student-run newspaper, radio station. Social organizations: 47 open to all. Most popular organizations: Student Government Association, Spirit Squad, Dance Team, Matador Ambassadors, Presidential Leadership Society. Major annual events: Job Fair, Transfer Fair, Family Night. Student services: health clinic, personal-psychological counseling. Campus security: 24-hour emergency response devices and patrols, student patrols, late night transport-escort service, controlled dormitory access. Arizona Western College and NAU-Yuma Library. Books: 58,607 (physical), 207,815 (digital/electronic); Serial titles: 406 (physical), 13,815 (digital/electronic); Databases: 49. Weekly public service hours: 68; students can reserve study rooms. 1,796 computers available on campus for general student use. A campuswide network can be accessed from student residence rooms and from off campus. Students can access the following: online class registration. Staffed computer lab on campus provides training in use of computers, software, and the Internet.
Community Environment: Yuma, population 84,700, is on the bank of the Colorado River, midway between Phoenix and San Diego. This is a metropolitan area with a warm, dry climate. Rail, air, and all other modes of transportation are available. There are over 50 churches of major denominations, a public library, historic Yuma Territorial Prison and Museum, Yuma Fine Arts Association, Community Concert Association, the St. Thomas Mission, and many civic, fraternal, and veteran's organizations. Recreational activities include boating, fishing, water skiing, and hunting. The Silver Spur Rodeo is in February; the County Fair is in April. Part-time employment is available.

■ **BROOKLINE COLLEGE (PHOENIX)**
2445 W Dunlap Ave.
Ste. 100
Phoenix, AZ 85021
Tel: (602)242-6265; Free: 800-793-2428
Fax: (602)973-2572
E-mail: tdean@brooklinecollege.edu
Web Site: brooklinecollege.edu
Description: Proprietary, comprehensive, coed. Awards associate, bachelor's, and master's degrees. Founded 1979. Setting: urban campus with easy access to Phoenix. Total enrollment: 1,468. Faculty: 43 (22 full-time, 21 part-time). Student-undergrad faculty ratio is 25:1. 66% 25 or older. Academic area with the most degrees conferred: business/marketing. Core. Calendar: continuous. Accelerated degree program, distance learning, part-time degree program.
Entrance Requirements: Open admission. Option: electronic application. Required: interview. Entrance: noncompetitive. Application deadline: rolling. Notification: continuous. Transfer credits accepted: Yes.
Collegiate Environment: Orientation program. Major annual events: Job Fairs, Holiday-Themed Student Gatherings. Campus security: 24-hour emergency response devices. Learning Resource Center. 25 computers available on campus for general student use. A campuswide network can be accessed from off-campus. Staffed computer lab on campus provides training in use of computers, software, and the Internet.

■ **BROOKLINE COLLEGE (TEMPE)**
1140 S Priest Dr.
Tempe, AZ 85281
Tel: (480)545-8755; Free: 888-886-2428
Fax: (480)926-1371
E-mail: ckindred@brooklinecollege.edu
Web Site: brooklinecollege.edu
Description: Proprietary, 4-year, coed. Awards associate and bachelor's degrees. Founded 1982. Setting: urban campus with easy access to Phoenix. Total enrollment: 415. Faculty: 37 (15 full-time, 22 part-time). Student-undergrad faculty ratio is 11:1. 62% 25 or older. Core. Calendar: continuous. Accelerated degree program, part-time degree program.
Entrance Requirements: Open admission. Option: electronic application. Required: interview. Entrance: noncompetitive. Application deadline: rolling. Notification: continuous. Transfer credits accepted: Yes.
Collegiate Environment: Orientation program. Campus security: 24-hour emergency response devices. Learning Resource Center. 20 computers available on campus for general student use. A campuswide network can be accessed from off-campus. Staffed computer lab on campus provides training in use of computers, software, and the Internet.

■ **BROOKLINE COLLEGE (TUCSON)**
5441 E 22nd St.
Ste. 125
Tucson, AZ 85711
Tel: (520)748-9799; Free: 888-292-2428
Fax: (520)748-9355
E-mail: lpechota@brooklinecollege.edu
Web Site: brooklinecollege.edu
Description: Proprietary, 4-year, coed. Awards associate and bachelor's degrees. Founded 1979. Setting: urban campus with easy access to Tucson. Total enrollment: 507. Faculty: 34. Student-undergrad faculty ratio is 16:1. 48% 25 or older. Core. Calendar: continuous. Accelerated degree program, part-time degree program.
Entrance Requirements: Open admission. Option: electronic application. Required: interview. Entrance: noncompetitive. Application deadline: rolling. Notification: continuous. Transfer credits accepted: Yes.
Collegiate Environment: Orientation program. Campus security: 24-hour emergency response devices. Learning Resource Center. 25 computers available on campus for general student use. A campuswide network can be accessed from off-campus. Staffed computer lab on campus provides training in use of computers, software, and the Internet.

■ **CARRINGTON COLLEGE-MESA**
1001 W Southern Ave.
Ste. 130
Mesa, AZ 85210
Tel: (480)212-1600
Web Site: www.carrington.edu

Description: Proprietary, 2-year, coed. Part of Carrington Colleges Group, Inc. Awards certificates and terminal associate degrees. Founded 1977. Setting: suburban campus. Total enrollment: 599. Faculty: 30 (6 full-time, 24 part-time). Student-undergrad faculty ratio is 41:1. Full-time: 565 students, 84% women, 16% men. Part-time: 34 students, 82% women, 18% men. 2% from out-of-state. 39% 25 or older, 14% transferred in.
Entrance Requirements: Required: essay, high school transcript, interview. Entrance: noncompetitive. Notification: continuous.

■ **CARRINGTON COLLEGE-PHOENIX EAST**
2149 W Dunlap Ave.
Ste. 100
Phoenix, AZ 85021
Tel: (602)216-7700
Web Site: www.carrington.edu
Description: Proprietary, 2-year, coed. Part of Carrington Colleges Group, Inc. Awards certificates and terminal associate degrees. Setting: urban campus. Total enrollment: 261. Faculty: 47 (13 full-time, 34 part-time). Student-undergrad faculty ratio is 8:1. Full-time: 178 students, 65% women, 35% men. Part-time: 83 students, 77% women, 23% men. 1% from out-of-state. 3% American Indian or Alaska Native, non-Hispanic/Latino; 37% Hispanic/Latino; 8% Black or African American, non-Hispanic/Latino; 6% Asian, non-Hispanic/Latino; 0.4% Native Hawaiian or other Pacific Islander, non-Hispanic/Latino. 66% 25 or older, 19% transferred in.
Entrance Requirements: Open admission. Required: essay, high school transcript, interview. Entrance: noncompetitive. Notification: continuous.

■ **CARRINGTON COLLEGE-PHOENIX NORTH**
8503 N 27th Ave.
Phoenix, AZ 85051
Tel: (602)393-5900
Web Site: www.carrington.edu
Description: Proprietary, 2-year, coed. Part of Carrington Colleges Group, Inc. Awards certificates and terminal associate degrees. Founded 1976. Setting: urban campus. Total enrollment: 653. Faculty: 15 (14 full-time, 1 part-time). Student-undergrad faculty ratio is 35:1. Full-time: 653 students, 87% women, 13% men. 3% from out-of-state. 7% American Indian or Alaska Native, non-Hispanic/Latino; 57% Hispanic/Latino; 7% Black or African American, non-Hispanic/Latino; 0.9% Asian, non-Hispanic/Latino; 0.6% Native Hawaiian or other Pacific Islander, non-Hispanic/Latino. 29% 25 or older, 15% transferred in.
Entrance Requirements: Required: essay, high school transcript, interview. Entrance: noncompetitive. Notification: continuous.

■ **CENTRAL ARIZONA COLLEGE**
8470 N Overfield Rd.
Coolidge, AZ 85128
Tel: (520)494-5444; Free: 800-237-9814
Fax: (520)426-4234
E-mail: james.moore@centralaz.edu
Web Site: www.centralaz.edu
Description: Public, 2-year, coed. Awards certificates, transfer associate, and terminal associate degrees. Founded 1961. Setting: 850-acre rural campus with easy access to Phoenix. Total enrollment: 7,913. Faculty: 210 (94 full-time, 116 part-time). Student-undergrad faculty ratio is 14:1. Full-time: 2,976 students, 63% women, 37% men. Part-time: 4,937 students, 59% women, 41% men. Students come from 4 other countries. 13% 25 or older, 17% live on campus. Core. Calendar: semesters. Academic remediation for entering students, services for LD students, self-designed majors, honors program, independent study, distance learning, summer session for credit, part-time degree program, adult/continuing education programs, internships. Study abroad program.
Entrance Requirements: Open admission except for nursing program. Options: electronic application, early admission, deferred admission. Entrance: noncompetitive. Application deadline: rolling. Notification: continuous. Transfer credits accepted: Yes.
Collegiate Environment: Orientation program. Drama-theater group, choral group, student-run newspaper. Major annual events: Track and Field Events, Basketball Games, Baseball Games. Student services: personal-psychological counseling. Campus security: 24-hour emergency response devices and patrols, late night transport-escort service. Learning Resource Center. 1,500 computers available on campus for general student use. A campuswide network can be accessed from student residence rooms.

Students can access the following: online class registration. Staffed computer lab on campus provides training in use of computers, software, and the Internet.

Community Environment: Population 8,000. Coolidge is located in Pinal County near the intersection of two major interstate freeways that serve the areas of Southern California and Arizona's two principal cities, Phoenix and Tucson. One can be in the heart of either city within an hour. There are four Native American Reservations in the county. The area is rich in history of mining, cattle and agriculture. Few places on earth have more hours of sunshine a year than south-central Pinal County, which averages approximately 4,000 hours per year according to U.S. Weather Bureau records.

■ **CHAMBERLAIN COLLEGE OF NURSING**
2149 W Dunlap Ave.
Phoenix, AZ 85021
Tel: (602)331-2720; Free: 877-751-5783
Fax: (602)749-4653
Web Site: www.chamberlain.edu

Description: Proprietary, 4-year, coed. Awards bachelor's degrees. Total enrollment: 633. Faculty: 83 (13 full-time, 70 part-time). Student-undergrad faculty ratio is 12:1. Full-time: 338 students, 83% women, 17% men. Part-time: 295 students, 86% women, 14% men. 7% from out-of-state. 0.8% American Indian or Alaska Native, non-Hispanic/Latino; 20% Hispanic/Latino; 4% Black or African American, non-Hispanic/Latino; 7% Asian, non-Hispanic/Latino; 0.2% Native Hawaiian or other Pacific Islander, non-Hispanic/Latino; 0.2% international. 64% 25 or older, 28% transferred in. Academic area with the most degrees conferred: health professions and related sciences. Calendar: semesters. Accelerated degree program, distance learning.

Entrance Requirements: Option: deferred admission. Required: SAT or ACT.

■ **CHANDLER-GILBERT COMMUNITY COLLEGE**
2626 E Pecos Rd.
Chandler, AZ 85225-2479
Tel: (480)732-7000
E-mail: alexander.gadberry@cgc.edu
Web Site: www.cgc.maricopa.edu

Description: State and locally supported, 2-year, coed. Part of Maricopa County Community College District System. Awards certificates, diplomas, transfer associate, and terminal associate degrees. Founded 1985. Setting: 188-acre suburban campus with easy access to Phoenix. Total enrollment: 14,906. Faculty: 568 (140 full-time, 428 part-time). Student-undergrad faculty ratio is 27:1. Full-time: 4,178 students, 47% women, 53% men. Part-time: 10,728 students, 56% women, 44% men. Students come from 20 states and territories, 2% from out-of-state. 2% American Indian or Alaska Native, non-Hispanic/Latino; 24% Hispanic/Latino; 4% Black or African American, non-Hispanic/Latino; 6% Asian, non-Hispanic/Latino; 0.3% Native Hawaiian or other Pacific Islander, non-Hispanic/Latino. 19% 25 or older. Core. Calendar: semesters. Academic remediation for entering students, ESL program, services for LD students, advanced placement, freshman honors college, honors program, independent study, summer session for credit, part-time degree program. Study abroad program.

Entrance Requirements: Open admission except for nursing and aviation programs. Option: electronic application. Entrance: noncompetitive.

Costs Per Year: Application fee: $0. Area resident tuition: $2040 full-time, $85 per credit hour part-time. State resident tuition: $9624 full-time, $401 per credit hour part-time. Nonresident tuition: $7824 full-time, $326 per credit hour part-time. Mandatory fees: $30 full-time, $15 per term part-time. Full-time tuition and fees vary according to reciprocity agreements. Part-time tuition and fees vary according to reciprocity agreements.

Collegiate Environment: Orientation program. Choral group, student-run radio station. Student services: personal-psychological counseling. Campus security: 24-hour emergency response devices and patrols, late night transport-escort service. Chandler-Gilbert Community College Library.

■ **COCHISE COUNTY COMMUNITY COLLEGE DISTRICT**
901 N Colombo Ave.
Sierra Vista, AZ 85635-2317
Tel: (520)364-7943; Free: 800-593-9567
Fax: (520)364-0236
E-mail: quickd@cochise.edu
Web Site: www.cochise.edu

Description: State and locally supported, 2-year, coed. Awards certificates, transfer associate, and terminal associate degrees (profile includes campuses in Douglas and Sierra Vista, AZ). Founded 1962. Setting: 732-acre rural campus with easy access to Tucson. Educational spending for the previous fiscal year: $2660 per student. Total enrollment: 3,918. Faculty: 296 (98 full-time, 198 part-time). Student-undergrad faculty ratio is 16:1. 1,412 applied, 100% were admitted. Full-time: 1,519 students, 57% women, 43% men. Part-time: 2,399 students, 55% women, 45% men. Students come from 17 states and territories, 2 other countries, 8% from out-of-state. 0.7% American Indian or Alaska Native, non-Hispanic/Latino; 46% Hispanic/Latino; 5% Black or African American, non-Hispanic/Latino; 2% Asian, non-Hispanic/Latino; 0.3% Native Hawaiian or other Pacific Islander, non-Hispanic/Latino; 1% international. 13% 25 or older, 2% live on campus, 3% transferred in. Retention: 63% of full-time freshmen returned the following year. Core. Calendar: semesters. Academic remediation for entering students, ESL program, services for LD students, advanced placement, honors program, independent study, distance learning, summer session for credit, part-time degree program, adult/continuing education programs, co-op programs and internships.

Entrance Requirements: Open admission except for nursing and aviation programs. Options: electronic application, deferred admission, international baccalaureate accepted. Recommended: high school transcript. Required for some: high school transcript. Entrance: noncompetitive. Application deadline: rolling. Notification: continuous. Transfer credits accepted: Yes.

Costs Per Year: Application fee: $0. State resident tuition: $2550 full-time, $85 per credit hour part-time. Nonresident tuition: $7800 full-time, $260 per credit hour part-time. Full-time tuition varies according to course load, program, and reciprocity agreements. Part-time tuition varies according to course load, program, and reciprocity agreements. College room and board: $7272. College room only: $2310. Room and board charges vary according to housing facility.

Collegiate Environment: Orientation program. Drama-theater group, choral group. Social organizations: 37 open to all. Most popular organizations: Phi Theta Kappa, Student Nurses Association, Respiratory Therapy Student Association, Verses: Slam Poetry Club, Dance Club. Major annual events: Haunted Union, Back to School BBQ & Club Fair, Pit Fire. Student services: personal-psychological counseling. Campus security: 24-hour emergency response devices and patrols, late night transport-escort service. Andrea Cracchiolo plus 1 other. Books: 55,145 (physical), 40,945 (digital/electronic); Serial titles: 22 (physical), 7,401 (digital/electronic); Databases: 16. Weekly public service hours: 45. Operations spending for the previous fiscal year: $420,865. 797 computers available on campus for general student use. A campuswide network can be accessed from student residence rooms and from off campus. Students can access the following: online class registration, online catalog. Staffed computer lab on campus provides training in use of computers, software, and the Internet.

■ **COCONINO COMMUNITY COLLEGE**
2800 S Lonetree Rd.
Flagstaff, AZ 86001
Tel: (928)527-1222; Free: 800-350-7122
Fax: (928)526-1821
E-mail: veronica.hipolito@coconino.edu
Web Site: www.coconino.edu

Description: State-supported, 2-year, coed. Awards certificates, transfer associate, and terminal associate degrees. Founded 1991. Setting: 5-acre small town campus. Endowment: $322,526. Educational spending for the previous fiscal year: $3319 per student. Total enrollment: 3,608. Faculty: 154 (34 full-time, 120 part-time). Student-undergrad faculty ratio is 25:1. 2,629 applied. Full-time: 1,134 students, 47% women, 53% men. Part-time: 2,474 students, 53% women, 47% men. 18% American Indian or Alaska Native, non-Hispanic/Latino; 18% Hispanic/Latino; 1% Black or African American, non-Hispanic/Latino; 1% Asian, non-Hispanic/Latino; 0.2% Native Hawaiian or other Pacific Islander, non-Hispanic/Latino. 9% 25 or older, 22% transferred in. Retention: 58% of full-time freshmen returned the following year. Core. Calendar: semesters. Academic remediation for entering students, honors program, independent study, distance learning, summer session for credit, part-time degree program, adult/continuing education programs, internships. Study abroad program. ROTC: Air Force.

Entrance Requirements: Open admission. Option: electronic application. Entrance: noncompetitive. Application deadline: rolling. Notification: continuous.

Costs Per Year: State resident tuition: $2616 full-time, $109 per credit hour part-time. Nonresident tuition: $9156 full-time, $381.50 per credit hour part-time. Mandatory fees: $168 full-time, $7 per credit hour part-time. Full-time tuition and fees vary according to course level and program. Part-time tuition and fees vary according to course level and program.

Collegiate Environment: Orientation program. Most popular organizations: Art Club, Clay Club, Dance Club, Native American Club, Video Gaming Club. Major annual events: Registration Celebration, student, staff, and visiting artists exhibits, Student Cultural, Music and Dance Performances. Campus security: 24-hour emergency response devices, student patrols, late night transport-escort service, security patrols during hours of operation, electronic access throughout the campuses with security cards. Information Resources and Library Services. Operations spending for the previous fiscal year: $68,270.

■ **COLLEGEAMERICA-FLAGSTAFF**
399 S Malpais Ln.
Flagstaff, AZ 86001
Tel: (928)774-1934; Free: 800-622-2894
Fax: (928)526-3468
Web Site: www.collegeamerica.edu

Description: Independent, primarily 2-year, coed. Awards transfer associate, terminal associate, and bachelor's degrees. Setting: small town campus. Total enrollment: 205. Faculty: 14 (9 full-time, 5 part-time). Student-undergrad faculty ratio is 15:1. Full-time: 205 students, 75% women, 25% men. 60% American Indian or Alaska Native, non-Hispanic/Latino; 11% Hispanic/Latino; 1% Black or African American, non-Hispanic/Latino. Core. Calendar: quarters modules. Academic remediation for entering students, internships.

Entrance Requirements: Open admission. Required: essay, high school transcript, interview, references. Entrance: noncompetitive.

Collegiate Environment: Orientation program. Main library plus 1 other.

■ **COLLEGEAMERICA-PHOENIX**
9801 N Metro Pky. E
Phoenix, AZ 85051
Tel: (602)257-7522; Free: 800-622-2894
Fax: (602)246-3063
Web Site: www.collegeamerica.edu

Description: Independent, primarily 2-year, coed. Awards terminal associate and bachelor's degrees.

■ **DEVRY UNIVERSITY-PHOENIX CAMPUS**
2149 W Dunlap Ave.
Phoenix, AZ 85021
Tel: (602)749-4500; Free: 866-338-7934
Web Site: www.devry.edu

Description: Proprietary, comprehensive, coed. Part of DeVry University. Awards associate, bachelor's, and master's degrees. Founded 1967. Setting: urban campus. Total enrollment: 616. Faculty: 79 (13 full-time, 66 part-time). Student-undergrad faculty ratio is 11:1. Full-time: 263 students, 30% women, 70% men. Part-time: 252 students, 30% women, 70% men. 11% from out-of-state. 3% American Indian or Alaska Native, non-Hispanic/Latino; 27% Hispanic/Latino; 6% Black or African American, non-Hispanic/Latino; 6% Asian, non-Hispanic/Latino. 67% 25 or older, 26% transferred in. Calendar: semesters. Part-time degree program, adult/continuing education programs.

Entrance Requirements: Option: deferred admission. Required: high school transcript, interview. Entrance: minimally difficult. Application deadline: rolling. Notification: continuous.

Collegiate Environment: Orientation program. Learning Resource Center.

■ **DINÉ COLLEGE**
PO Box 98
Tsaile, AZ 86556
Tel: (520)724-6600; Free: 877-988-DINE
Fax: (520)724-3349
E-mail: louise@dinecollege.edu
Web Site: www.dinecollege.edu

Description: Federally supported, 2-year, coed. Awards certificates, transfer associate, and terminal associate degrees. Founded 1968. Setting: 1,200-acre rural campus. Total enrollment: 1,657. Full-time: 815 students, 69% women, 31% men. Part-time: 842 students, 79% women, 21% men. 46% 25 or older. Core. Calendar: semesters. Academic remediation for entering students, services for LD students, summer session for credit, part-time

degree program, adult/continuing education programs. Off campus study at members of the American Indian Higher Education Consortium, Arizona State University.

Entrance Requirements: Open admission. Option: early admission. Required: high school transcript, Certificate of Indian Blood form for Native American Students. Entrance: noncompetitive. Application deadline: rolling. Notification: continuous. Preference given to Native Americans.

Collegiate Environment: Orientation program. Social organizations: 7 open to all. Most popular organizations: Associate Students of Navajo Community College, Bar-N-Rodeo Club, Red Dawn Indian Club, Native American Church. Major annual events: Fall Bash, Spring Fling, Farewell Dance. Student services: health clinic, personal-psychological counseling. Campus security: 24-hour emergency response devices and patrols, student patrols, late night transport-escort service. Tsaile-Navajo Community College Library plus 1 other. 418 computers available on campus for general student use. A campuswide network can be accessed from student residence rooms and from off campus. Staffed computer lab on campus provides training in use of computers.

■ **DUNLAP-STONE UNIVERSITY**
19820 N 7th St.
Ste. No.100
Phoenix, AZ 85024
Tel: (602)648-5750; Free: 800-474-8013
Fax: (602)648-5755
Web Site: www.dunlap-stone.edu

Description: Proprietary, comprehensive, coed. Awards associate, bachelor's, and master's degrees. Founded 1995. Setting: urban campus with easy access to Phoenix. Total enrollment: 500. Faculty: 100 (all part-time). Student-undergrad faculty ratio is 15:1. Students come from 25 states and territories. 75% 25 or older. Core. Calendar: semesters 3 semesters per year (fall, spring, summer). Academic remediation for entering students, advanced placement, accelerated degree program, independent study, distance learning, internships.

Entrance Requirements: Open admission. Options: electronic application, deferred admission, international baccalaureate accepted. Application deadline: rolling. Notification: continuous. Transfer credits accepted: Yes.

■ **EASTERN ARIZONA COLLEGE**
615 N Stadium Ave.
Thatcher, AZ 85552-0769
Tel: (928)428-8472; Free: 800-678-3808
Fax: (928)428-8462
E-mail: admissions@eac.edu
Web Site: www.eac.edu

Description: State and locally supported, 2-year, coed. Part of Arizona State Community College System. Awards certificates, transfer associate, and terminal associate degrees. Founded 1888. Setting: small town campus. Endowment: $5.3 million. Research spending for the previous fiscal year: $248,230. Educational spending for the previous fiscal year: $4550 per student. Total enrollment: 6,365. Faculty: 340 (97 full-time, 243 part-time). Student-undergrad faculty ratio is 19:1. 818 applied, 100% were admitted. Full-time: 1,957 students, 45% women, 55% men. Part-time: 4,408 students, 60% women, 40% men. Students come from 25 states and territories, 24 other countries, 3% from out-of-state. 6% American Indian or Alaska Native, non-Hispanic/Latino; 20% Hispanic/Latino; 3% Black or African American, non-Hispanic/Latino; 0.9% Asian, non-Hispanic/Latino; 0.8% Native Hawaiian or other Pacific Islander, non-Hispanic/Latino; 1% international. 30% 25 or older, 3% live on campus, 1% transferred in. Core. Calendar: semesters. Academic remediation for entering students, services for LD students, advanced placement, independent study, distance learning, double major, summer session for credit, part-time degree program, adult/continuing education programs, co-op programs and internships. Study abroad program.

Entrance Requirements: Open admission except for nursing program, some emergency medical technology programs. Options: electronic application, early admission, deferred admission. Recommended: high school transcript. Entrance: noncompetitive. Application deadline: rolling. Notification: continuous. Transfer credits accepted: Yes.

Costs Per Year: Application fee: $0. State resident tuition: $2040 full-time, $85 per credit hour part-time. Nonresident tuition: $9000 full-time, $375 per credit hour part-time. Full-time tuition varies according to program. Part-time tuition varies according to program. College room and board: $6595. Room and board charges vary according to board plan.

Collegiate Environment: Orientation program. Drama-theater group, choral group, marching band. Social organizations: 20 open to all. Most popular organizations: Latter-Day Saints Student Association, Criminal Justice Student Association, Multicultural Council, Phi Theta Kappa, Mark Allen Dorm Club. Major annual events: Fall Homecoming, Fall Campus Picnic, Yearbook Party. Student services: personal-psychological counseling. Campus security: 24-hour emergency response devices, late night transport-escort service, controlled dormitory access, 20-hour patrols by trained security personnel. Alumni Library plus 1 other. Books: 37,902 (physical), 968 (digital/electronic); Serial titles: 637 (physical); Databases: 41. Weekly public service hours: 80; students can reserve study rooms. Operations spending for the previous fiscal year: $606,835. 686 computers available on campus for general student use. A campuswide network can be accessed. Students can access the following: online class registration. Staffed computer lab on campus provides training in use of computers, software, and the Internet.

Community Environment: Population over 4,000. Thatcher is located in the broad valley of the Gila River. It is on Highway 70 about 75 miles east of the junction of Highways 60 and 70 at Globe, about 165 miles east of Phoenix, and 250 miles west of El Paso. Nearby Safford, with a population of over 8,900, is the county seat of government for Graham County. In addition, it serves as the hotel and shopping center for the upper Gila Valley. The area enjoys an invigorating climate with sunshine 90% of the year; rainfall is approximately nine inches during the year. The valley is flanked by the 10,000-foot Graham Mountains, Gila Mountain Range, Indian Hot Springs, Red Knolls Desert Theatre, Coolidge Dam, and the Great Surface copper mines. All are within easy driving distance. Elevation: 3,000.

■ **EMBRY-RIDDLE AERONAUTICAL UNIVERSITY-PRESCOTT**
3700 Willow Creek Rd.
Prescott, AZ 86301-3720
Tel: (928)777-3728; Free: 800-888-3728
Fax: (928)777-3740
Web Site: www.prescott.erau.edu
Description: Independent, comprehensive, coed. Awards bachelor's and master's degrees. Founded 1978. Setting: 547-acre small town campus with easy access to Phoenix. Endowment: $40.6 million. Research spending for the previous fiscal year: $1.7 million. Educational spending for the previous fiscal year: $12,962 per student. Total enrollment: 2,776. Faculty: 185 (124 full-time, 61 part-time). Student-undergrad faculty ratio is 17:1. 2,859 applied, 67% were admitted. 32% from top 10% of their high school class, 26% from top quarter, 28% from top half. Full-time: 2,592 students, 25% women, 75% men. Part-time: 134 students, 19% women, 81% men. Students come from 51 states and territories, 39 other countries, 76% from out-of-state. 0.4% American Indian or Alaska Native, non-Hispanic/Latino; 13% Hispanic/Latino; 2% Black or African American, non-Hispanic/Latino; 6% Asian, non-Hispanic/Latino; 0.6% Native Hawaiian or other Pacific Islander, non-Hispanic/Latino; 6% international. 8% 25 or older, 44% live on campus, 4% transferred in. Retention: 81% of full-time freshmen returned the following year. Academic areas with the most degrees conferred: transportation and materials moving; engineering; social sciences. Core. Calendar: semesters. ESL program, services for LD students, advanced placement, accelerated degree program, freshman honors college, honors program, distance learning, double major, summer session for credit, part-time degree program, co-op programs and internships, graduate courses open to undergrads. Study abroad program. ROTC: Army, Air Force.
Entrance Requirements: Options: electronic application, deferred admission, international baccalaureate accepted. Required: high school transcript, minimum 2 high school GPA, medical examination for flight students. Recommended: essay, minimum 3 high school GPA, 2 recommendations, interview, SAT or ACT. Entrance: moderately difficult. Application deadlines: rolling, rolling for nonresidents. Notification: continuous, continuous for nonresidents. Transfer credits accepted: Yes.
Costs Per Year: Application fee: $50. One-time mandatory fee: $150. Comprehensive fee: $48,426 includes full-time tuition ($35,424), mandatory fees ($1284), and college room and board ($11,718). College room only: $6882. Part-time tuition: $1476 per credit hour. Part-time mandatory fees: $642 per term.
Collegiate Environment: Orientation program. Choral group, student-run newspaper. Social organizations: 120 open to all; national fraternities, national sororities. Most popular organizations: Hawaii Club, Strike Eagles, Theta XI, American Institute of Aeronautics (AIAA), Arnold Air Society. Major annual events: October West/Homecoming, Spring Fling, Hawaii Club Luau. Student services: health clinic, personal-psychological

counseling, women's center. Campus security: 24-hour emergency response devices and patrols, student patrols, late night transport-escort service, controlled dormitory access. 1,199 undergraduates lived in college housing during 2018-19. Freshmen guaranteed college housing. On-campus residence required in freshman year. Option: coed housing available. Christine & Steven F. Udvar-Hazy Library & Learning Center. Books: 26,008 (physical), 249,693 (digital/electronic); Serial titles: 137 (physical), 54,540 (digital/electronic); Databases: 90. Students can reserve study rooms. Operations spending for the previous fiscal year: $1.2 million.
Community Environment: The Prescott area is one of the most colorful areas of the Bradshaw Mountains and has an approximate population of 40,400. The campus is surrounded by a national forest, rolling ranchlands, hiking trails, and wilderness areas. The city of Phoenix is approximately 90 miles away.

■ **ESTRELLA MOUNTAIN COMMUNITY COLLEGE**
3000 N Dysart Rd.
Avondale, AZ 85392
Tel: (623)935-8000
Web Site: www.estrellamountain.edu
Description: State and locally supported, 2-year, coed. Part of Maricopa County Community College District System. Awards certificates, transfer associate, and terminal associate degrees. Founded 1992. Setting: urban campus with easy access to Phoenix. Total enrollment: 9,344. Student-undergrad faculty ratio is 22:1. Full-time: 3,124 students, 56% women, 44% men. Part-time: 6,220 students, 62% women, 38% men. 2% American Indian or Alaska Native, non-Hispanic/Latino; 51% Hispanic/Latino; 8% Black or African American, non-Hispanic/Latino; 4% Asian, non-Hispanic/Latino; 0.4% Native Hawaiian or other Pacific Islander, non-Hispanic/Latino; 0.3% international. 28% 25 or older, 7% transferred in. Core. Calendar: semesters. Academic remediation for entering students, ESL program, services for LD students, advanced placement, honors program, independent study, distance learning, summer session for credit, part-time degree program, adult/continuing education programs, co-op programs. ROTC: Air Force (c).
Entrance Requirements: Open admission. Option: electronic application. Entrance: noncompetitive. Transfer credits accepted: Yes.
Collegiate Environment: Orientation program. Social organizations: 18 open to all. Most popular organizations: Phi Theta Kappa, Men Of Color Association (MOCA), Movimiento Estudiantil Chicano de Aztlan (MEChA), Savings and Investment Club. Major annual events: Spring Fling, Hispanic Heritage Month, Welcome Week. Student services: personal-psychological counseling. Campus security: 24-hour emergency response devices and patrols, late night transport-escort service. Estrella Mountain Library. 500 computers available on campus for general student use. A campuswide network can be accessed. Students can access the following: online class registration. Staffed computer lab on campus provides training in use of computers and the Internet.

■ **FORTIS COLLEGE**
555 N 18th St., Ste. 110
Phoenix, AZ 85006
Tel: (602)254-3099; Free: 855-4-FORTIS
Web Site: www.fortis.edu
Description: Proprietary, 2-year, coed. Awards certificates, diplomas, transfer associate, and terminal associate degrees.

■ **GATEWAY COMMUNITY COLLEGE**
108 N 40th St.
Phoenix, AZ 85034-1795
Tel: (602)286-8000
Fax: (602)286-8003
E-mail: enroll@gatewaycc.edu
Web Site: www.gatewaycc.edu
Description: State and locally supported, 2-year, coed. Part of Maricopa County Community College District System. Administratively affiliated with GateWay Community College. Awards certificates, diplomas, transfer associate, and terminal associate degrees. Founded 1968. Setting: 20-acre urban campus. Total enrollment: 6,801. Faculty: 490 (99 full-time, 391 part-time). Student-undergrad faculty ratio is 18:1. 716 applied, 100% were admitted. Full-time: 191 students, 52% women, 48% men. Part-time: 525 students, 43% women, 57% men. 4% American Indian or Alaska Native, non-Hispanic/Latino; 26% Hispanic/Latino; 11% Black or African American, non-Hispanic/Latino; 4% Asian, non-Hispanic/Latino; 0.2% Native Hawaiian or other Pacific Islander, non-Hispanic/Latino; 1% international. Core.

Calendar: semesters. Academic remediation for entering students, ESL program, services for LD students, advanced placement, accelerated degree program, freshman honors college, honors program, independent study, distance learning, double major, summer session for credit, part-time degree program, adult/continuing education programs, co-op programs and internships. Off campus study. Study abroad program. ROTC: Army (c), Air Force (c).

Entrance Requirements: Open admission except for health science, nursing programs. Options: electronic application, early admission, deferred admission. Required for some: high school transcript, interview. Entrance: noncompetitive. Application deadline: rolling. Notification: continuous. Transfer credits accepted: Yes.

Collegiate Environment: Orientation program. Student services: personal-psychological counseling, women's center. Campus security: 24-hour emergency response devices and patrols, student patrols, late night transport-escort service. GateWay Library.

■ **GLENDALE COMMUNITY COLLEGE**
6000 W Olive Ave.
Glendale, AZ 85302-3090
Tel: (623)845-3000
Fax: (623)845-3329
E-mail: admissions.recruitment@gccaz.edu
Web Site: www.gccaz.edu
Description: State and locally supported, 2-year, coed. Part of Maricopa County Community College District System. Awards certificates, transfer associate, and terminal associate degrees. Founded 1965. Setting: 222-acre suburban campus with easy access to Phoenix. Total enrollment: 21,361. Faculty: 923 (277 full-time, 646 part-time). Full-time: 7,335 students, 49% women, 51% men. Part-time: 14,026 students, 56% women, 44% men. Retention: 58% of full-time freshmen returned the following year. Core. Calendar: semesters. Academic remediation for entering students, ESL program, services for LD students, advanced placement, freshman honors college, honors program, distance learning, double major, summer session for credit, part-time degree program, adult/continuing education programs, co-op programs and internships. Off campus study. Study abroad program. ROTC: Army (c), Air Force (c).
Entrance Requirements: Open admission. Options: electronic application, international baccalaureate accepted. Required for some: high school transcript. Entrance: noncompetitive. Application deadline: 8/20. Notification: continuous until 8/20. Transfer credits accepted: Yes.
Collegiate Environment: Orientation program. Drama-theater group, choral group, marching band, student-run newspaper. Most popular organizations: Phi Theta Kappa, M.E.Ch.A. (Movimiento Estudiantil Chicano de Aztlan), Associated Student Government, Biotechnology Club, Compass. Student services: legal services, personal-psychological counseling. Campus security: 24-hour patrols, student patrols, late night transport-escort service. Library/Media Center plus 1 other. 2,500 computers available on campus for general student use. A campuswide network can be accessed from off-campus. Students can access the following: online class registration. Staffed computer lab on campus provides training in use of computers, software, and the Internet.

■ **GRAND CANYON UNIVERSITY**
3300 W Camelback Rd.
Phoenix, AZ 85017-1097
Tel: (602)249-3300; Free: 800-800-9776
Fax: (602)589-2580
E-mail: admissionsonline@gcu.edu
Web Site: www.gcu.edu
Description: Independent Southern Baptist, comprehensive, coed. Awards bachelor's, master's, and doctoral degrees and post-master's certificates. Founded 1949. Setting: 100-acre urban campus with easy access to Phoenix. 0.7% American Indian or Alaska Native, non-Hispanic/Latino; 6% Hispanic/Latino; 22% Black or African American, non-Hispanic/Latino; 2% Asian, non-Hispanic/Latino; 0.2% Native Hawaiian or other Pacific Islander, non-Hispanic/Latino; 0.1% international. 40% live on campus. Academic areas with the most degrees conferred: education; health professions and related sciences; business/marketing. Core. Calendar: semesters. Academic remediation for entering students, ESL program, advanced placement, accelerated degree program, freshman honors college, honors program, independent study, distance learning, double major, summer session for credit, part-time degree program, adult/continuing education programs, co-op programs and internships, graduate courses open to undergrads. Off

campus study at Coalition for Christian Colleges and Universities. Study abroad program. ROTC: Army, Air Force (c).
Entrance Requirements: Options: electronic application, early admission, deferred admission, international baccalaureate accepted. Required: high school transcript, minimum 2.75 high school GPA. Recommended: SAT or ACT. Entrance: moderately difficult. Application deadline: rolling. Notification: continuous. Transfer credits accepted: Yes.
Collegiate Environment: Orientation program. Drama-theater group, choral group. Social organizations: 24 open to all. Most popular organizations: International Student Association, Fellowship of Christian Athletes, Student Nurses Association, Canyon Crazies, AZ Hosa. Major annual events: Welcome Week, ASGCU Events, Home Basketball Games. Student services: health clinic, personal-psychological counseling. Campus security: 24-hour emergency response devices and patrols, late night transport-escort service, controlled dormitory access, staffed gates to enter campus after non-business hours. Fleming Library. 65 computers available on campus for general student use. A campuswide network can be accessed from student residence rooms and from off campus. Students can access the following: online class registration. Staffed computer lab on campus.
Community Environment: See Phoenix College.

■ **INTERNATIONAL BAPTIST COLLEGE AND SEMINARY**
2211 W Germann Rd.
Chandler, AZ 85286
Tel: (480)245-7903; Free: 800-422-4858
E-mail: admissions@ibconline.edu
Web Site: www.ibcs.edu
Description: Independent Baptist, comprehensive, coed. Awards associate, bachelor's, and master's degrees. Founded 1980. Setting: 12-acre suburban campus with easy access to Phoenix. Total enrollment: 91. Student-undergrad faculty ratio is 7:1. 33% from out-of-state. 22% 25 or older. Core. Calendar: 4-1-4. Part-time degree program, graduate courses open to undergrads.
Entrance Requirements: Open admission. Option: early admission. Required: essay, high school transcript, 3 recommendations. Application deadline: 8/20.
Collegiate Environment: Choral group. Social organizations: local fraternities, local sororities.

■ **MESA COMMUNITY COLLEGE**
1833 W Southern Ave.
Mesa, AZ 85202-4866
Tel: (480)461-7000; Free: 866-532-4983
Fax: (480)461-7805
E-mail: admissionsandrecords@mesacc.edu
Web Site: www.mesacc.edu
Description: State and locally supported, 2-year, coed. Part of Maricopa County Community College District System. Awards certificates and transfer associate degrees. Founded 1965. Setting: 160-acre urban campus with easy access to Phoenix. Total enrollment: 20,424. Faculty: 973 (300 full-time, 673 part-time). Student-undergrad faculty ratio is 21:1. 4% American Indian or Alaska Native, non-Hispanic/Latino; 28% Hispanic/Latino; 6% Black or African American, non-Hispanic/Latino; 4% Asian, non-Hispanic/Latino; 0.4% Native Hawaiian or other Pacific Islander, non-Hispanic/Latino; 2% international. Core. Calendar: semesters. Academic remediation for entering students, ESL program, services for LD students, advanced placement, self-designed majors, freshman honors college, honors program, independent study, distance learning, summer session for credit, part-time degree program, adult/continuing education programs, co-op programs. Off campus study at Servicemembers Opportunity Colleges. Study abroad program. ROTC: Army (c), Air Force (c).
Entrance Requirements: Open admission. Options: electronic application, early admission, deferred admission. Entrance: noncompetitive. Application deadline: 9/1. Notification: continuous. Transfer credits accepted: Yes.
Costs Per Year: Application fee: $0. State resident tuition: $2550 full-time, $85 per credit hour part-time. Nonresident tuition: $9780 full-time, $326 per credit hour part-time. Mandatory fees: $30 full-time, $15 per term part-time. Full-time tuition and fees vary according to course load and reciprocity agreements. Part-time tuition and fees vary according to course load and reciprocity agreements.
Collegiate Environment: Orientation program. Drama-theater group, choral group, student-run newspaper. Social organizations: 42 open to all. Most popular organizations: MECHA, International Student Association, American Indian Association, Asian/Pacific Islander Club. Major annual events: Bash,

Homecoming. Student services: legal services, personal-psychological counseling. Campus security: 24-hour emergency response devices and patrols, student patrols. Information Commons. Students can reserve study rooms. 600 computers available on campus for general student use. A campuswide network can be accessed from off-campus. Students can access the following: online class registration.

Community Environment: Population 442,780, Arizona's third largest city, located 16 miles east of Phoenix, adjacent to Tempe, and near the Superstition Mountains. The average yearly temperature is 68.3 degrees, low humidity and 86 percent of the daylight hours are sunny. Mesa is a beautiful and friendly city; there are part-time jobs available for the college students. Most kinds of sports and recreation facilities available, plus many cultural activities.

■ **MOHAVE COMMUNITY COLLEGE**
1971 Jagerson Ave.
Kingman, AZ 86409
Tel: (928)757-4331; Free: 888-664-2832
Fax: (928)757-0808
E-mail: amasterson@mohave.edu
Web Site: www.mohave.edu
Description: State-supported, 2-year, coed. Awards certificates, diplomas, and transfer associate degrees. Founded 1971. Setting: 160-acre small town campus. Total enrollment: 4,071. Faculty: 282 (75 full-time, 207 part-time). Student-undergrad faculty ratio is 13:1. Full-time: 809 students, 56% women, 44% men. Part-time: 3,262 students, 69% women, 31% men. Students come from 19 states and territories, 5% from out-of-state. 2% American Indian or Alaska Native, non-Hispanic/Latino; 25% Hispanic/Latino; 1% Black or African American, non-Hispanic/Latino; 2% Asian, non-Hispanic/Latino; 0.4% Native Hawaiian or other Pacific Islander, non-Hispanic/Latino; 0.7% international. 47% 25 or older. Core. Calendar: semesters. Academic remediation for entering students, ESL program, independent study, distance learning, summer session for credit, part-time degree program, adult/continuing education programs, co-op programs.
Entrance Requirements: Open admission except for nursing, dental hygiene, surgical technology. Options: electronic application, early admission, deferred admission. Entrance: noncompetitive. Application deadline: rolling. Notification: continuous.
Costs Per Year: State resident tuition: $2430 full-time, $81 per credit hour part-time. Nonresident tuition: $8505 full-time, $283.50 per credit hour part-time. Mandatory fees: $210 full-time, $7 per credit hour part-time. Full-time tuition and fees vary according to program. Part-time tuition and fees vary according to program.
Collegiate Environment: Orientation program. Social organizations: 27 open to all. Most popular organizations: Art Club, Phi Theta Kappa, Computer Club (MC4), Science Club, Student Government. Major annual events: Spirit Day, Student Recognition, Welcome Back Bash. Campus security: late night transport-escort service. College housing not available. Mohave Community College Library. 120 computers available on campus for general student use. A campuswide network can be accessed. Students can access the following: online class registration. Staffed computer lab on campus provides training in use of computers, software, and the Internet.
Community Environment: The College campuses are accessible by all forms of transportation: bus, rail and air. The area is a rapidly expanding one, offering a variety of year-round activities due to its arid climate. Lake Havasu City boasts the famous London Bridge and English Village. The areas provide opportunities for hunting, fishing, camping and water sports.

■ **NATIONAL PARALEGAL COLLEGE**
717 E Maryland Ave.
Phoenix, AZ 85014
Tel: (845)371-9101; Free: 800-371-6105
Web Site: nationalparalegal.edu
Description: Proprietary, comprehensive, coed. Awards associate, bachelor's, and master's degrees. Founded 2003. Educational spending for the previous fiscal year: $2116 per student. Total enrollment: 891. Faculty: 33 (5 full-time, 28 part-time). Student-undergrad faculty ratio is 28:1. 2,331 applied, 85% were admitted. Full-time: 752 students, 89% women, 11% men. Part-time: 24 students, 79% women, 21% men. Students come from 51 states and territories, 4 other countries, 96% from out-of-state. 0.4% American Indian or Alaska Native, non-Hispanic/Latino; 5% Hispanic/Latino; 7% Black or African American, non-Hispanic/Latino; 1% Asian, non-Hispanic/Latino; 0.6% Native Hawaiian or other Pacific Islander, non-Hispanic/Latino. 87% 25 or older, 15% transferred in. Retention: 58% of full-time freshmen

returned the following year. Academic area with the most degrees conferred: law/legal studies. Core. Calendar: continuous new session each month. Academic remediation for entering students, accelerated degree program, distance learning, summer session for credit, part-time degree program, graduate courses open to undergrads.
Entrance Requirements: Options: electronic application, international baccalaureate accepted. Recommended: essay, interview. Required for some: high school transcript. Application deadline: rolling. Notification: continuous. Transfer credits accepted: Yes.
Costs Per Year: Application fee: $0. One-time mandatory fee: $195. Tuition: $7800 full-time, $325 per credit part-time. Full-time tuition varies according to course load. Part-time tuition varies according to course load. Tuition guaranteed not to increase for student's term of enrollment.
Collegiate Environment: Orientation program. Jones eGlobal Library. Books: 27,803 (digital/electronic); Databases: 56. Weekly public service hours: 168. Operations spending for the previous fiscal year: $722,862.

■ **NORTHERN ARIZONA UNIVERSITY**
S San Francisco St.
Flagstaff, AZ 86011
Tel: (928)523-9011; Free: 888-628-2968
Fax: (928)523-0226
E-mail: admissions@nau.edu
Web Site: www.nau.edu
Description: State-supported, university, coed. Part of Arizona University System. Awards bachelor's, master's, and doctoral degrees and post-master's certificates. Founded 1899. Setting: 683-acre small town campus. Endowment: $30.5 million. Research spending for the previous fiscal year: $36.1 million. Educational spending for the previous fiscal year: $6142 per student. Total enrollment: 31,057. Faculty: 1,725 (1,132 full-time, 593 part-time). Student-undergrad faculty ratio is 19:1. 36,875 applied, 81% were admitted. 21% from top 10% of their high school class, 51% from top quarter, 82% from top half. Full-time: 21,990 students, 59% women, 41% men. Part-time: 5,096 students, 63% women, 37% men. Students come from 50 states and territories, 70 other countries, 28% from out-of-state. 3% American Indian or Alaska Native, non-Hispanic/Latino; 24% Hispanic/Latino; 3% Black or African American, non-Hispanic/Latino; 2% Asian, non-Hispanic/Latino; 0.3% Native Hawaiian or other Pacific Islander, non-Hispanic/Latino; 4% international. 19% 25 or older, 35% live on campus, 10% transferred in. Retention: 76% of full-time freshmen returned the following year. Academic areas with the most degrees conferred: business/marketing; health professions and related sciences; liberal arts/general studies. Core. Calendar: semesters. ESL program, services for LD students, advanced placement, accelerated degree program, freshman honors college, honors program, independent study, distance learning, double major, summer session for credit, part-time degree program, co-op programs and internships, graduate courses open to undergrads. Off campus study at National Student Exchange. Study abroad program. ROTC: Army, Air Force.
Entrance Requirements: Options: electronic application, deferred admission, international baccalaureate accepted. Required: high school transcript, minimum 2.5 high school GPA, 16 college preparatory courses with minimum 2.0 in each subject. Recommended: SAT, SAT Subject Tests. Entrance: moderately difficult. Application deadline: rolling. Notification: continuous. SAT Reasoning Test deadline: 9/1. SAT Subject Test deadline: 9/1. Transfer credits accepted: Yes.
Costs Per Year: Application fee: $25. State resident tuition: $10,390 full-time, $742 per credit hour part-time. Nonresident tuition: $24,654 full-time, $1027 per credit hour part-time. Mandatory fees: $1174 full-time, $14 per credit hour part-time, $343 per term part-time. Full-time tuition and fees vary according to course load, location, and reciprocity agreements. Part-time tuition and fees vary according to course load, location, and reciprocity agreements. College room and board: $10,334. College room only: $7100. Room and board charges vary according to board plan and housing facility. Tuition guaranteed not to increase for student's term of enrollment.
Collegiate Environment: Orientation program. Drama-theater group, choral group, marching band, student-run newspaper, radio station. Social organizations: 393 open to all; national fraternities, national sororities; 3% of eligible men and 4% of eligible women are members. Most popular organizations: Louie's Cupboard, Feral Cat Alliance, American Medical Student Association, National Alliance on Mental Illness local chapter, National Society of Collegiate Scholars. Major annual events: Welcome Week, Family Weekend, Homecoming Week. Student services: legal services, health clinic, personal-psychological counseling. Campus security: 24-hour emergency response devices and patrols, late night transport-escort service,

controlled dormitory access. Cline Library plus 1 other. Books: 574,711 (physical), 237,606 (digital/electronic); Serial titles: 6,264 (physical), 93,756 (digital/electronic); Databases: 146. Weekly public service hours: 117; students can reserve study rooms. Operations spending for the previous fiscal year: $7.8 million. 294 computers available on campus for general student use. Computer purchase/lease plans available. A campuswide network can be accessed from student residence rooms and from off campus. Students can access the following: online class registration, computer repair service available on campus. Staffed computer lab on campus provides training in use of computers, software, and the Internet.

Community Environment: Flagstaff, population 57,300, is a city of Seven Wonders in the heart of the Coconino National Forest located at the foot of the San Francisco Peaks. Mountain slopes, canyons, buttes, Indian ruins, forests, and deserts mingle in a setting forever challenging in its appeal. The elevation, the protection provided by the forest, and the Arizona sunshine give Flagstaff unsurpassed year round climate. Recreational activities include hiking, bicycling, boating, fishing, and hunting. Skiing is nearby as are the Grand Canyon, the Petrified forest, numerous Indian villages, and national monuments.

■ NORTHLAND PIONEER COLLEGE
PO Box 610
Holbrook, AZ 86025
Tel: (928)524-7311; Free: 800-266-7845
Fax: (928)524-7612
Web Site: www.npc.edu

Description: State and locally supported, 2-year, coed. Part of Arizona State Community College System. Awards certificates, transfer associate, and terminal associate degrees. Founded 1974. Setting: 50-acre rural campus. Educational spending for the previous fiscal year: $5000 per student. Total enrollment: 4,636. Faculty: 226 (73 full-time, 153 part-time). Student-undergrad faculty ratio is 17:1. Full-time: 946 students, 63% women, 37% men. Part-time: 3,690 students, 67% women, 33% men. Students come from 17 states and territories, 3 other countries, 0.01% from out-of-state. 67% 25 or older, 1% transferred in. Core. Calendar: semesters. ESL program, services for LD students, advanced placement, freshman honors college, honors program, independent study, distance learning, double major, summer session for credit, part-time degree program, co-op programs and internships.

Entrance Requirements: Open admission. Option: early admission. Entrance: noncompetitive. Application deadline: rolling. Transfer credits accepted: Yes.

Collegiate Environment: Drama-theater group, choral group. Campus security: evening security. Northland Pioneer College Library. Operations spending for the previous fiscal year: $506,078. 200 computers available on campus for general student use. A campuswide network can be accessed from off-campus. Students can access the following: online class registration. Staffed computer lab on campus provides training in use of computers, software, and the Internet.

Community Environment: The service area of 21,000 square miles has a population of approximately 154,000 people. The service area includes parts of three Indian reservations. The economy is based primarily on agriculture, tourism, and the lumber industry.

■ PARADISE VALLEY COMMUNITY COLLEGE
18401 N 32nd St.
Phoenix, AZ 85032-1200
Tel: (602)787-6500
Fax: (602)787-6625
Web Site: www.pvc.maricopa.edu

Description: State and locally supported, 2-year, coed. Part of Maricopa County Community College District System. Awards certificates, transfer associate, and terminal associate degrees. Founded 1985. Setting: urban campus. Total enrollment: 9,951. Faculty: 542 (98 full-time, 444 part-time). 4% from out-of-state. Core. Calendar: semesters. Academic remediation for entering students, ESL program, services for LD students, advanced placement, accelerated degree program, honors program, independent study, distance learning, summer session for credit, part-time degree program, adult/continuing education programs, co-op programs and internships. Off campus study. Study abroad program. ROTC: Army (c).

Entrance Requirements: Open admission. Option: early admission. Entrance: noncompetitive. Application deadline: rolling. Transfer credits accepted: Yes.

Collegiate Environment: Orientation program. Drama-theater group, choral

group, student-run newspaper. Social organizations: 16 open to all; national fraternities, Phi Theta Kappa. Most popular organizations: Phi Theta Kappa, International Student Club, Recreational Outing Club, AWARE, Student Christian Association. Major annual events: International Education Week, Black American Month/Hispanic Week/Women's Week. Student services: personal-psychological counseling. Campus security: 24-hour emergency response devices and patrols, late night transport-escort service. Paradise Valley Community College Library plus 1 other. 500 computers available on campus for general student use. A campuswide network can be accessed from off-campus. Students can access the following: online class registration. Staffed computer lab on campus provides training in use of computers, software, and the Internet.

■ THE PARALEGAL INSTITUTE AT BRIGHTON COLLEGE
8777 E Via de Ventura, Ste. 300
Scottsdale, AZ 85258
Tel: (602)212-0501; Free: 800-354-1254
E-mail: paralegalinst@mindspring.com
Web Site: www.theparalegalinstitute.edu

Description: Proprietary, 2-year, coed. Awards diplomas and terminal associate degrees. Founded 1974. Faculty: 4 (1 full-time, 3 part-time). 500 applied, 25% were admitted.

■ PENN FOSTER COLLEGE
14300 N Northsight Blvd.
Ste. 120
Scottsdale, AZ 85260
Tel: (480)947-6644; Free: 800-471-3232
Web Site: www.pennfostercollege.edu

Description: Proprietary, primarily 2-year, coed. Awards certificates, transfer associate, terminal associate, and bachelor's degrees. Total enrollment: 24,527. Faculty: 203 (40 full-time, 163 part-time). Students come from 50 states and territories, 5 other countries. Academic areas with the most degrees conferred: business/marketing; law/legal studies. Core. Calendar: continuous. Academic remediation for entering students, services for LD students, accelerated degree program, independent study, distance learning, part-time degree program, external degree program. Off campus study.

Entrance Requirements: Open admission. Option: electronic application. Required: high school transcript. Application deadlines: rolling, rolling for nonresidents. Transfer credits accepted: Yes.

Collegiate Environment: Orientation program. Most popular organization: Online Community-Hosted Academic Interest Groups. Penn Foster College Online Library.

■ PHOENIX COLLEGE
1202 W Thomas Rd.
Phoenix, AZ 85013-4234
Tel: (602)285-7800
Fax: (602)285-7700
E-mail: kathy.french@pcmail.maricopa.edu
Web Site: www.pc.maricopa.edu

Description: County-supported, 2-year, coed. Part of Maricopa County Community College District System. Awards certificates, diplomas, transfer associate, and terminal associate degrees. Founded 1920. Setting: 58-acre urban campus. Total enrollment: 12,676. Faculty: 766 (161 full-time, 605 part-time). Student-undergrad faculty ratio is 17:1. Retention: 60% of full-time freshmen returned the following year. Core. Calendar: semesters. Academic remediation for entering students, ESL program, services for LD students, advanced placement, freshman honors college, honors program, independent study, distance learning, summer session for credit, part-time degree program, adult/continuing education programs, co-op programs and internships. Off campus study. Study abroad program. ROTC: Army (c), Naval (c), Air Force (c).

Entrance Requirements: Open admission. Options: electronic application, early admission, deferred admission. Entrance: noncompetitive. Application deadline: rolling. Notification: continuous. Transfer credits accepted: Yes.

Costs Per Year: Application fee: $0. Area resident tuition: $2040 full-time, $85 per credit hour part-time. State resident tuition: $9624 full-time, $401 per credit hour part-time. Nonresident tuition: $7824 full-time, $326 per credit hour part-time. Mandatory fees: $30 full-time, $15 per term part-time. Full-time tuition and fees vary according to reciprocity agreements. Part-time tuition and fees vary according to course load and reciprocity agreements.

Collegiate Environment: Orientation program. Drama-theater group, choral group. Social organizations: 27 open to all. Most popular organizations:

Student Leadership Council (SLC), MEChA Movimiento Estudiantil Chicanos de Aztlan, ALE Asociacion Latina Estudiantil, Rainbow Spectrum - Gay, Straight, Whatever alliance, International Club. Major annual events: Homecoming Week, Bear Day, Hispanic Heritage Month. Student services: personal-psychological counseling. Campus security: 24-hour emergency response devices and patrols, student patrols, late night transport-escort service. Fannin Library. 1,816 computers available on campus for general student use. A campuswide network can be accessed from off-campus. Students can access the following: online class registration. Staffed computer lab on campus provides training in use of computers.

Community Environment: Phoenix, population over one million, is a thriving industrial and agricultural city. Easily accessible, served by railroads, buses and airlines, the city has many churches, libraries, museums, and theatres, as well as numerous fine restaurants, hotels, and motels. It is located in proximity to many scenic and historical places of interest including the Grand Canyon, the Petrified Forest, Montezuma Castle, and Oak Creek Canyon. It is one of the outstanding winter resorts of America with The Valley of the Sun nearby.

■ PIMA COMMUNITY COLLEGE
4905 E Broadway Blvd.
Tucson, AZ 85709-1010
Tel: (520)206-4666
Fax: (520)884-6728
E-mail: tbenson@pima.edu
Web Site: www.pima.edu
Description: State and locally supported, 2-year, coed. Awards certificates, diplomas, transfer associate, and terminal associate degrees. Founded 1966. Setting: 486-acre urban campus with easy access to Tucson. Total enrollment: 26,613. 2% American Indian or Alaska Native, non-Hispanic/Latino; 41% Hispanic/Latino; 5% Black or African American, non-Hispanic/Latino; 3% Asian, non-Hispanic/Latino; 0.3% Native Hawaiian or other Pacific Islander, non-Hispanic/Latino. Core. Calendar: semesters. Academic remediation for entering students, ESL program, services for LD students, advanced placement, self-designed majors, honors program, independent study, distance learning, summer session for credit, part-time degree program, adult/continuing education programs, co-op programs and internships. Off campus study. ROTC: Army (c), Naval (c), Air Force (c).
Entrance Requirements: Open admission. Options: electronic application, international baccalaureate accepted. Entrance: noncompetitive. Transfer credits accepted: Yes.
Collegiate Environment: Orientation program. Drama-theater group, choral group, student-run newspaper. Student services: health clinic. Pima Community College Library.
Community Environment: See University of Arizona.

■ PIMA MEDICAL INSTITUTE (MESA)
2160 S Power Rd.
Mesa, AZ 85209
Tel: (480)898-9898; Free: 800-477-PIMA
Web Site: www.pmi.edu
Description: Proprietary, 2-year, coed. Awards certificates, transfer associate, and terminal associate degrees. Setting: urban campus. Core. Distance learning, co-op programs and internships.
Entrance Requirements: Required: high school transcript, interview, Wonderlic Scholastic Level Exam (SLE).
Collegiate Environment: Orientation program.

■ PIMA MEDICAL INSTITUTE (MESA)
957 S Dobson Rd.
Mesa, AZ 85202
Tel: (480)644-0267; Free: 800-477-PIMA
Fax: (480)649-5249
Web Site: www.pmi.edu
Description: Proprietary, primarily 2-year, coed. Part of Vocational Training Institutes, Inc. Awards certificates, terminal associate, and bachelor's degrees. Founded 1985. Setting: urban campus. Total enrollment: 958. 58% 25 or older. Calendar: modular. Distance learning.
Entrance Requirements: Required: interview, Wonderlic aptitude test. Required for some: high school transcript. Entrance: minimally difficult.
Collegiate Environment: E-Global.

■ PIMA MEDICAL INSTITUTE (PHOENIX)
13610 N Black Canyon Hwy.
Phoenix, AZ 85029

Web Site: www.pmi.edu
Description: Proprietary, 2-year, coed.

■ PIMA MEDICAL INSTITUTE (TUCSON)
3350 E Grant Rd.
Tucson, AZ 85716
Tel: (520)326-1600; Free: 800-477-PIMA
Fax: (520)326-4125
Web Site: www.pmi.edu
Description: Proprietary, primarily 2-year, coed. Part of Vocational Training Institutes, Inc. Awards certificates, terminal associate, and bachelor's degrees. Founded 1972. Setting: urban campus. Total enrollment: 900. 45% 25 or older. Calendar: modular. Academic remediation for entering students, accelerated degree program, distance learning, adult/continuing education programs, co-op programs and internships.
Entrance Requirements: Option: early admission. Required: interview, Wonderlic Scholastic Level Exam (SLE). Required for some: high school transcript. Entrance: minimally difficult.
Collegiate Environment: Orientation program. E-Global.

■ PRESCOTT COLLEGE
220 Grove Ave.
Prescott, AZ 86301
Tel: (928)350-2100; Free: 877-350-2100
Fax: (928)776-5157
E-mail: admissions@prescott.edu
Web Site: www.prescott.edu
Description: Independent, comprehensive, coed. Awards bachelor's, master's, and doctoral degrees and post-master's certificates. Founded 1966. Setting: 13-acre small town campus. Endowment: $1.5 million. Research spending for the previous fiscal year: $295,942. Educational spending for the previous fiscal year: $3631 per student. Total enrollment: 703. Faculty: 115 (66 full-time, 49 part-time). Student-undergrad faculty ratio is 9:1. 167 applied, 80% were admitted. Full-time: 267 students, 57% women, 43% men. Part-time: 89 students, 69% women, 31% men. Students come from 47 states and territories, 10 other countries, 90% from out-of-state. 4% American Indian or Alaska Native, non-Hispanic/Latino; 7% Hispanic/Latino; 1% Black or African American, non-Hispanic/Latino; 1% Asian, non-Hispanic/Latino; 0.8% international. 7% 25 or older, 16% live on campus, 29% transferred in. Retention: 79% of full-time freshmen returned the following year. Academic areas with the most degrees conferred: education; natural resources/environmental science; parks and recreation. Core. Calendar: semesters (4-week blocks followed by 10-week terms for each quarter). Services for LD students, advanced placement, self-designed majors, independent study, distance learning, double major, summer session for credit, external degree program, adult/continuing education programs, internships, graduate courses open to undergrads. Off campus study at Eco League, a five-college consortium of schools that includes Alaska Pacific University, Green Mountain College, Northland College, and College of the Atlantic. Consortium for Innovative Environments in Learning (CIEL), is an eleven-college consortium consisting of: Alverno College, Berea College, Daemen College, The Evergreen State College, Fairhaven College at Western Washington University, Gallatin School of Individualized Study, Hampshire College, Johnson C. Smith University, New College of Florida, Pitzer College. Study abroad program.
Entrance Requirements: Options: electronic application, early decision, deferred admission, international baccalaureate accepted. Required: essay, high school transcript, 1 recommendation, SAT or ACT. Required for some: interview. Entrance: moderately difficult. Application deadlines: 8/15, 12/1 for early decision. Notification: continuous, continuous for nonresidents, 12/15 for early decision. SAT Reasoning Test deadline: 8/15. Transfer credits accepted: Yes. Early decision applicants: 12. Early decision applicants admitted: 7.
Costs Per Year: Application fee: $0. One-time mandatory fee: $1075. Comprehensive fee: $38,170 includes full-time tuition ($29,880), mandatory fees ($590), and college room and board ($7700). College room only: $6900. Full-time tuition and fees vary according to course load. Room and board charges vary according to board plan and housing facility.
Collegiate Environment: Orientation program. Drama-theater group, choral group. Social organizations: 16 open to all; 45% of eligible men and 55% of eligible women are members. Most popular organizations: Student Union, Catalyst, WEB (Women's Empowerment Breakthrough), HUB (Helping Understand Bikes), Aztlan Center. Major annual events: Drag Show, Earth Day Week, Student Awards Ceremony. Student services: personal-

psychological counseling. Campus security: 24-hour emergency response devices, late night transport-escort service, controlled dormitory access. Prescott College Library. Operations spending for the previous fiscal year: $602,409. 100 computers available on campus for general student use. A campuswide network can be accessed from student residence rooms. Students can access the following: learning management system, free e-portfolios. Staffed computer lab on campus provides training in use of computers, software, and the Internet.

Community Environment: Located a mile high in the forested mountains of central Arizona, Prescott has a moderate climate and four seasons. Described by"Arizona Highways" magazine as"Everybody's Hometown," the community is known for its friendly atmosphere and small town charm. It was the capital of the Territory of Arizona back in the 1800s and the old governor's mansion still stands today. The town is rich in local history including gold-mining lore, cowboys, and the historic Roughriders. Classic Victorian homes line the streets. With clean air, abundant sunshine, and natural beauty in every direction, the Prescott area is truly an enjoyable place to live.

■ **THE REFRIGERATION SCHOOL**
4210 E Washington St.
Phoenix, AZ 85034-1816
Tel: (602)275-7133; Free: 888-943-4822
E-mail: info@rsiaz.edu
Web Site: www.refrigerationschool.com

Description: Proprietary, 2-year, coed. Administratively affiliated with Tulsa Welding School, Inc. Awards certificates, diplomas, and terminal associate degrees. Founded 1965. Setting: urban campus. Total enrollment: 688. Student-undergrad faculty ratio is 34:1. 6% from out-of-state. 6% American Indian or Alaska Native, non-Hispanic/Latino; 20% Hispanic/Latino; 8% Black or African American, non-Hispanic/Latino; 0.7% Asian, non-Hispanic/Latino; 0.6% Native Hawaiian or other Pacific Islander, non-Hispanic/Latino. 72% 25 or older. Retention: 72% of full-time freshmen returned the following year. Calendar: continuous.

Costs Per Year: Tuition: $19,699 full-time. Mandatory fees: $1879 full-time. Full-time tuition and fees vary according to program.

■ **RIO SALADO COLLEGE**
2323 W 14th St.
Tempe, AZ 85281-6950
Tel: (480)517-8000; Free: 800-729-1197
Fax: (480)517-8199
Web Site: www.riosalado.edu

Description: State and locally supported, 2-year, coed. Part of Maricopa County Community College District System. Awards certificates, transfer associate, and terminal associate degrees. Founded 1978. Setting: urban campus. Educational spending for the previous fiscal year: $1807 per student. Total enrollment: 20,865. Faculty: 1,170. Student-undergrad faculty ratio is 13:1. 13,332 applied, 100% were admitted. Students come from 38 other countries, 4% from out-of-state. 43% 25 or older. Core. Calendar: semesters. Academic remediation for entering students, ESL program, services for LD students, advanced placement, accelerated degree program, honors program, independent study, distance learning, double major, summer session for credit, part-time degree program, external degree program, adult/continuing education programs, co-op programs and internships.

Entrance Requirements: Open admission except for dental hygiene program. Options: electronic application, early admission, deferred admission. Entrance: noncompetitive. Application deadline: rolling. Transfer credits accepted: Yes.

Costs Per Year: Application fee: $0. State resident tuition: $2040 full-time, $85 per credit hour part-time. Nonresident tuition: $5900 full-time, $215 per credit hour part-time. Mandatory fees: $30 full-time, $15 per term part-time. Full-time tuition and fees vary according to course load and reciprocity agreements. Part-time tuition and fees vary according to course load and reciprocity agreements.

Collegiate Environment: Orientation program. Social organizations: Phi Theta Kappa honors society; 1% of eligible men and 1% of eligible women are members. Student services: personal-psychological counseling. Campus security: 24-hour emergency response devices, late night transport-escort service. Rio Salado Library and Information Center. Operations spending for the previous fiscal year: $197,853. 500 computers available on campus for general student use. A campuswide network can be accessed from off-campus. Students can access the following: online class registration. Staffed computer lab on campus provides training in use of computers, software, and the Internet.

■ **SCOTTSDALE COMMUNITY COLLEGE**
9000 E Chaparral Rd.
Scottsdale, AZ 85256-2626
Tel: (480)423-6000
Fax: (480)423-6200
E-mail: laura.krueger@scottsdalecc.edu
Web Site: www.scottsdalecc.edu

Description: State and locally supported, 2-year, coed. Part of Maricopa County Community College District System. Awards certificates, diplomas, transfer associate, and terminal associate degrees. Founded 1969. Setting: 160-acre urban campus with easy access to Phoenix. Total enrollment: 9,458. Faculty: 489 (159 full-time, 330 part-time). Student-undergrad faculty ratio is 18:1. Students come from 50 states and territories, 1% from out-of-state. 5% American Indian or Alaska Native, non-Hispanic/Latino; 19% Hispanic/Latino; 4% Black or African American, non-Hispanic/Latino; 3% Asian, non-Hispanic/Latino; 0.4% Native Hawaiian or other Pacific Islander, non-Hispanic/Latino; 1% international. 36% 25 or older. Core. Calendar: semesters. Academic remediation for entering students, ESL program, services for LD students, advanced placement, honors program, summer session for credit, part-time degree program, adult/continuing education programs, co-op programs and internships. Off campus study at Service-members Opportunity Colleges. Study abroad program.

Entrance Requirements: Open admission. Options: electronic application, early admission. Entrance: noncompetitive. Application deadline: rolling. Notification: continuous. Transfer credits accepted: Yes.

Collegiate Environment: Orientation program. Drama-theater group, choral group, student-run newspaper, radio station. Social organizations: 20 open to all. Most popular organizations: Student Leadership Forum, International Community Club, Phi Theta Kappa, Music Industry Club, SCC ASID-Interior Design group. Major annual events: Commencement, Excellence Under the Stars, College to the Community. Student services: personal-psychological counseling. Campus security: 24-hour emergency response devices and patrols, student patrols, late night transport-escort service, 24-hour automatic surveillance cameras. Scottsdale Community College Library. Books: 44,599 (physical), 163,245 (digital/electronic); Serial titles: 608 (physical), 14 (digital/electronic); Databases: 66. Weekly public service hours: 62; students can reserve study rooms. 202 computers available on campus for general student use. A campuswide network can be accessed from off-campus. Students can access the following: online class registration. Staffed computer lab on campus provides training in use of software and the Internet.

Community Environment: See Phoenix College.

■ **SESSIONS COLLEGE FOR PROFESSIONAL DESIGN**
51 W Third St.
Ste. E-301
Tempe, AZ 85281
Tel: (480)212-1704; Free: 800-258-4115
Fax: (480)212-1705
E-mail: admissions@sessions.edu
Web Site: www.sessions.edu

Description: Proprietary, 2-year, coed. Awards certificates and terminal associate degrees. Part-time degree program, adult/continuing education programs.

Entrance Requirements: Option: early admission. Required: essay, high school transcript, portfolio. Application deadline: 7/15. Notification: continuous.

■ **SOUTH MOUNTAIN COMMUNITY COLLEGE**
7050 S Twenty-fourth St.
Phoenix, AZ 85040
Tel: (602)243-8000
Fax: (602)243-8329
Web Site: www.southmountaincc.edu

Description: State and locally supported, 2-year, coed. Part of Maricopa County Community College District System. Awards certificates, transfer associate, and terminal associate degrees. Founded 1979. Setting: 108-acre suburban campus. Total enrollment: 5,138. Student-undergrad faculty ratio is 20:1. 6% from out-of-state. 44% 25 or older. Retention: 55% of full-time freshmen returned the following year. Calendar: semesters. Academic remediation for entering students, advanced placement, summer session for credit, part-time degree program, adult/continuing education programs. ROTC: Air Force (c).

Entrance Requirements: Open admission. Entrance: noncompetitive. Application deadline: 8/22. Notification: continuous until 8/22.
Collegiate Environment: Campus security: late night transport-escort service, 18-hour patrols, campus lockdown. Learning Resource Center.
Community Environment: Located near both downtown Phoenix and Tempe, the college is just minutes from I-10 and Superstition freeways and Arizona State University. Ample parking is available. The college is served by the Phoenix Transit Bus System. Affordable housing, shopping, and services are within easy commuting distance. The campus is located in the shadow of South Mountain Park, the largest municipal park in the United States.

■ **SOUTHWEST INSTITUTE OF HEALING ARTS**
1100 E Apache Blvd.
Tempe, AZ 85281
Tel: (480)994-9244; Free: 888-504-9106
Fax: (480)994-3228
Web Site: www.swiha.org
Description: Proprietary, 2-year, coed. Awards terminal associate degrees. Founded 1992. Total enrollment: 1,752. Calendar: quarters.
Entrance Requirements: Entrance: noncompetitive.

■ **SOUTHWEST UNIVERSITY OF VISUAL ARTS**
2525 N Country Club Rd.
Tucson, AZ 85716-2505
Tel: (520)325-0123; Free: 800-825-8753
Fax: (520)325-5535
Web Site: www.suva.edu
Description: Proprietary, comprehensive, coed. Awards bachelor's and master's degrees. Founded 1983. Setting: suburban campus with easy access to Tucson. Total enrollment: 188. Faculty: 28 (11 full-time, 17 part-time). 15% from top 10% of their high school class, 25% from top quarter, 35% from top half. 1 class president, 1 valedictorian. Full-time: 133 students, 50% women, 50% men. Part-time: 44 students, 45% women, 55% men. Students come from 12 states and territories, 7% from out-of-state. 2% American Indian or Alaska Native, non-Hispanic/Latino; 41% Hispanic/Latino; 5% Black or African American, non-Hispanic/Latino; 0.6% Asian, non-Hispanic/Latino. 87% 25 or older, 2% transferred in. Retention: 78% of full-time freshmen returned the following year. Academic areas with the most degrees conferred: visual and performing arts; architecture. Core. Calendar: semester with a full summer program. Services for LD students, double major, summer session for credit, part-time degree program, co-op programs and internships. Study abroad program. ROTC: Army (c).
Entrance Requirements: Required: essay, high school transcript, interview. Required for some: ACT ASSET.
Collegiate Environment: Orientation program. Major annual events: Haunted House/October Festival, Gallery (fall and spring). Southwest University of Visual Arts Library plus 1 other. Books: 6,013 (physical); Serial titles: 85 (physical), 28 (digital/electronic); Databases: 62. Weekly public service hours: 65. Operations spending for the previous fiscal year: $50,000. 40 computers available on campus for general student use. A campuswide network can be accessed. Students can access the following: online class registration. Staffed computer lab on campus (open 24 hours a day) provides training in use of computers, software, and the Internet.

■ **TOHONO O'ODHAM COMMUNITY COLLEGE**
PO Box 3129
Sells, AZ 85634
Tel: (520)383-8401
Fax: (520)383-8403
E-mail: gbenevidez@tocc.edu
Web Site: www.tocc.edu
Description: Public, 2-year, coed. Awards certificates, diplomas, transfer associate, and terminal associate degrees. Founded 1998. Setting: 42-acre rural campus. Endowment: $362,851. Research spending for the previous fiscal year: $199,934. Educational spending for the previous fiscal year: $5597 per student. Total enrollment: 462. Faculty: 47 (15 full-time, 32 part-time). Student-undergrad faculty ratio is 10:1. Full-time: 144 students, 68% women, 32% men. Part-time: 318 students, 60% women, 40% men. Students come from 11 states and territories, 5% from out-of-state. 90% American Indian or Alaska Native, non-Hispanic/Latino; 1% Hispanic/Latino; 3% Black or African American, non-Hispanic/Latino. 58% 25 or older, 10% live on campus, 21% transferred in. Retention: 27% of full-time freshmen returned the following year. Core. Calendar: semesters. Academic remediation for entering students, services for LD students, double major, summer session for credit, part-time degree program, adult/continuing education programs, co-op programs.
Entrance Requirements: Open admission. Option: electronic application.

Required: high school transcript. Entrance: noncompetitive. Application deadline: rolling. Notification: continuous, rolling for early decision. Transfer credits accepted: Yes.
Costs Per Year: Application fee: $0.
Collegiate Environment: Orientation program. Social organizations: 4 open to all. Most popular organizations: Student Senate, AISES, Archery Club. Major annual events: O'odham Tas, Blessing Ceremony. Student services: personal-psychological counseling. Campus security: 24-hour patrols. 39 college housing spaces available; all were occupied in 2018-19. No special consideration for freshman housing applicants. Options: coed, men-only, women-only housing available. Tohono O'odham Community College Library plus 1 other. Books: 13,355 (physical); Serial titles: 210 (physical); Databases: 210. Weekly public service hours: 44. Operations spending for the previous fiscal year: $205,605. 73 computers available on campus for general student use. A campuswide network can be accessed from student residence rooms and from off campus. Students can access the following: online class registration, tablets used in some courses. Staffed computer lab on campus provides training in use of computers, software, and the Internet.

■ **UNIVERSAL TECHNICAL INSTITUTE**
10695 W Pierce St.
Avondale, AZ 85323
Tel: (602)264-4164; Free: 800-510-5072
Fax: (602)264-6412
Web Site: www.uti.edu
Description: Proprietary, 2-year, coed. Awards terminal associate degrees. Founded 1965. Total enrollment: 1,730. Student-undergrad faculty ratio is 23:1. 49% from out-of-state. 14% 25 or older. Retention: 78% of full-time freshmen returned the following year.
Entrance Requirements: Open admission. Required: interview. Entrance: minimally difficult.

■ **UNIVERSITY OF ADVANCING TECHNOLOGY**
2625 W Baseline Rd.
Tempe, AZ 85283-1042
Tel: (602)383-8228; Free: 800-658-5744
Fax: (602)383-8222
E-mail: admissions@uat.edu
Web Site: www.uat.edu
Description: Proprietary, comprehensive, coed. Awards associate, bachelor's, and master's degrees. Founded 1983. Setting: urban campus with easy access to Phoenix, AZ. Total enrollment: 1,073. Faculty: 60 (31 full-time, 29 part-time). Student-undergrad faculty ratio is 13:1. Full-time: 1,013 students, 8% women, 92% men. 0.7% American Indian or Alaska Native, non-Hispanic/Latino; 7% Hispanic/Latino; 7% Black or African American, non-Hispanic/Latino; 3% Asian, non-Hispanic/Latino; 0.3% Native Hawaiian or other Pacific Islander, non-Hispanic/Latino; 2% international. 22% live on campus. Calendar: semesters. Independent study, distance learning, double major, summer session for credit, co-op programs and internships, graduate courses open to undergrads.
Entrance Requirements: Option: electronic application. Required: essay, high school transcript. Required for some: minimum 2.5 high school GPA, SAT or ACT. Application deadline: rolling. Transfer credits accepted: Yes.
Collegiate Environment: Orientation program. Student-run newspaper. Most popular organizations: Web Club, Gaming Club, Animation Club, Video Club, Student Government. Major annual events: Technology Forums, LAN parties, luncheons. Campus security: 24-hour patrols. University of Advancing Computer Technology Library. 400 computers available on campus for general student use. Computer purchase/lease plans available. A campuswide network can be accessed from student residence rooms and from off campus. Students can access the following: online class registration. Staffed computer lab on campus provides training in use of computers, software, and the Internet.

■ **THE UNIVERSITY OF ARIZONA**
Tucson, AZ 85721
Tel: (520)621-2211
Fax: (520)621-9799
Web Site: www.arizona.edu
Description: State-supported, university, coed. Part of Arizona Board of Regents. Awards bachelor's, master's, and doctoral degrees and postmaster's certificates. Founded 1885. Setting: 392-acre urban campus. Endowment: $754.4 million. Research spending for the previous fiscal year: $391,122. Total enrollment: 44,831. Faculty: 2,347 (1,985 full-time, 362 part-time). Student-undergrad faculty ratio is 15:1. 33,608 applied, 84% were admitted. 34% from top 10% of their high school class, 61% from top quarter, 85% from top half. 32 National Merit Scholars. Full-time: 29,783 students, 53% women, 47% men. Part-time: 5,340 students, 45% women, 55% men.

Students come from 53 states and territories, 112 other countries, 31% from out-of-state. 1% American Indian or Alaska Native, non-Hispanic/Latino; 27% Hispanic/Latino; 4% Black or African American, non-Hispanic/Latino; 5% Asian, non-Hispanic/Latino; 0.3% Native Hawaiian or other Pacific Islander, non-Hispanic/Latino; 8% international. 10% 25 or older, 20% live on campus, 7% transferred in. Retention: 83% of full-time freshmen returned the following year. Academic areas with the most degrees conferred: business/marketing; biological/life sciences; health professions and related sciences. Core. Calendar: semesters. ESL program, services for LD students, advanced placement, accelerated degree program, self-designed majors, freshman honors college, honors program, independent study, distance learning, double major, summer session for credit, part-time degree program, external degree program, adult/continuing education programs, co-op programs and internships, graduate courses open to undergrads. Off campus study. Study abroad program. ROTC: Army, Naval, Air Force.

Entrance Requirements: Options: electronic application, deferred admission, international baccalaureate accepted. Required: high school transcript. Recommended: essay, interview, SAT or ACT. Required for some: minimum 3 high school GPA. Entrance: moderately difficult. Application deadline: 5/1. Notification: continuous. Preference given to Arizona residents. SAT Reasoning Test deadline: 5/1. SAT Subject Test deadline: 5/1. Transfer credits accepted: Yes.

Collegiate Environment: Orientation program. Drama-theater group, choral group, marching band, student-run newspaper, radio station. Social organizations: 400 open to all; national fraternities, national sororities, local fraternities, local sororities. Most popular organizations: Alpha Epsilon Delta, Wildcats Committed to Animal Rescue and Education, Physiology, Psi Chi Chapter, Investments Club. Major annual events: Spring Fling Carnival, Cultural Programs, Family Weekend. Student services: legal services, health clinic, personal-psychological counseling, women's center. Campus security: 24-hour patrols, student patrols, late night transport-escort service, controlled dormitory access, emergency telephones. University of Arizona Main Library plus 4 others. Books: 3.1 million (physical), 1.8 million (digital/electronic); Serial titles: 6.3 million (physical), 101,171 (digital/electronic); Databases: 835. Weekly public service hours: 94; study areas open 24 hours, 5-7 days a week; students can reserve study rooms. Operations spending for the previous fiscal year: $31.7 million. 514 computers available on campus for general student use. Computer purchase/lease plans available. A campuswide network can be accessed from student residence rooms and from off campus. Students can access the following: online class registration. Staffed computer lab on campus (open 24 hours a day) provides training in use of computers, software, and the Internet.

Community Environment: Tucson is in a'valley of the Sonoran Desert, and is surrounded by mountain ranges. Approximately 700,000 reside in the metropolitan area. Just north of the city are ski slopes and ponderosa pines as well as canyons and grassy meadows, which are popular with hikers and climbers. Yet Tucson has mild winters (average yearly temperature of 85 degrees) and attracts golf, tennis, and other sports enthusiasts year-round. The city has a professional symphony orchestra, opera company, theater company, and ballet, in addition to outstanding medical facilities. Located sixty miles north of Mexico, the community reflects the cultures of its Native American, Spanish, Mexican, and pioneer forefathers.

■ **UNIVERSITY OF ARIZONA SOUTH**
1140 N Colombo Ave.
Sierra Vista, AZ 85635
Description: State-supported, upper-level, coed.

■ **UNIVERSITY OF PHOENIX-ONLINE CAMPUS**
3157 E Elwood St.
Phoenix, AZ 85034-7209
Tel: (602)387-7000; Free: 866-766-0766
Web Site: www.phoenix.edu
Description: Proprietary, comprehensive, coed. Awards associate, bachelor's, master's, and doctoral degrees and post-master's certificates. Founded 1989. Total enrollment: 292,797. Faculty: 11,477 (158 full-time, 11,319 part-time). Full-time: 236,109 students, 69% women, 31% men. 80% 25 or older. Academic areas with the most degrees conferred: business/marketing; computer and information sciences; health professions and related sciences. Core. Calendar: continuous. Services for LD students, advanced placement, accelerated degree program, independent study, distance learning, external degree program, adult/continuing education programs, graduate courses open to undergrads.
Entrance Requirements: Open admission. Options: electronic application, deferred admission, international baccalaureate accepted. Required: 1

recommendation. Required for some: high school transcript. Entrance: noncompetitive. Application deadline: rolling.
Collegiate Environment: University Library. Operations spending for the previous fiscal year: $6.8 million.

■ **UNIVERSITY OF PHOENIX-PHOENIX CAMPUS**
1625 W Fountainhead Pky.
Tempe, AZ 85282-2371
Tel: (602)557-2000; Free: 866-766-0766
Web Site: www.phoenix.edu
Description: Proprietary, comprehensive, coed. Awards bachelor's and master's degrees and post-master's certificates. Founded 1976. Setting: urban campus. Total enrollment: 5,379. Faculty: 985 (76 full-time, 909 part-time). Full-time: 3,718 students, 59% women, 41% men. 82% 25 or older. Academic areas with the most degrees conferred: business/marketing; computer and information sciences; health professions and related sciences. Core. Calendar: continuous. Services for LD students, advanced placement, accelerated degree program, independent study, distance learning, external degree program, adult/continuing education programs, graduate courses open to undergrads.
Entrance Requirements: Open admission. Options: electronic application, deferred admission. Required: 1 recommendation. Required for some: high school transcript. Entrance: noncompetitive. Application deadline: rolling.
Collegiate Environment: Campus security: 24-hour patrols, late night transport-escort service. University Library. Operations spending for the previous fiscal year: $6.8 million.

■ **YAVAPAI COLLEGE**
1100 E Sheldon St.
Prescott, AZ 86301-3297
Tel: (928)445-7300; Free: 800-922-6787
Fax: (928)776-2151
E-mail: registration@yc.edu
Web Site: www.yc.edu
Description: State and locally supported, 2-year, coed. Part of Arizona State Community College System. Awards certificates, transfer associate, and terminal associate degrees. Founded 1966. Setting: 100-acre small town campus. Educational spending for the previous fiscal year: $4772 per student. Total enrollment: 8,276. Faculty: 404 (112 full-time, 292 part-time). Student-undergrad faculty ratio is 15:1. Full-time: 1,917 students, 55% women, 45% men. Part-time: 6,359 students, 61% women, 39% men. 18% from out-of-state. 70% 25 or older, 5% live on campus. Core. Calendar: semesters. Academic remediation for entering students, ESL program, services for LD students, advanced placement, honors program, independent study, distance learning, summer session for credit, part-time degree program, adult/continuing education programs, co-op programs and internships. Off campus study at Northern Arizona University, Old Dominion University. ROTC: Army (c), Air Force (c).
Entrance Requirements: Open admission except for nursing, gunsmithing and independent filmmaking. Options: early admission, deferred admission. Required: high school transcript. Required for some: essay. Entrance: noncompetitive. Application deadline: rolling.
Collegiate Environment: Orientation program. Drama-theater group, choral group, student-run newspaper. Social organizations: 20 open to all. Most popular organizations: Re-Entry Club, Student Nurses Association, Native American Club, International Club, VICA (Vocational Industrial Clubs of America). Major annual events: Welcome Week, Homecoming/Parents' Weekend, Earth Day. Student services: health clinic, personal-psychological counseling, women's center. Campus security: 24-hour emergency response devices and patrols, student patrols, late night transport-escort service, controlled dormitory access. Yavapai College Library. Operations spending for the previous fiscal year: $1 million. 651 computers available on campus for general student use. A campuswide network can be accessed from student residence rooms and from off campus. Staffed computer lab on campus.
Community Environment: Population 40,360. The city of Prescott is imbued with thoroughly Western informality. The city is easily reached from all parts of the United States by regularly scheduled airlines and bus service. Climate is ideal, embracing four seasons, but without the extremes of heat, cold, dryness, or dampness. Employment opportunities are average for a community of this size. Prescott has a community concert program, and an active interest in the arts provides cultural atmosphere. Prescott Frontier Days are held during the July Fourth weekend; this is the original cowboy rodeo of America. The Yavapai County Fair is held during September. There is horse racing at Prescott Downs on weekends from Memorial Day through Labor Day.

■ ARKANSAS BAPTIST COLLEGE

1621 Dr. Martin Luther King, Jr. Dr.
Little Rock, AR 72202-6067
Tel: (501)374-7856
Web Site: www.arkansasbaptist.edu
Description: Independent Baptist, 4-year, coed. Awards associate and bachelor's degrees. Founded 1884. Setting: urban campus. Total enrollment: 626. Faculty: 38 (18 full-time, 20 part-time). Student-undergrad faculty ratio is 22:1. 3% from top 10% of their high school class, 25% from top quarter, 30% from top half. Students come from 29 states and territories, 1 other country, 17% from out-of-state. 32% 25 or older, 13% live on campus. Retention: 34% of full-time freshmen returned the following year. Core. Calendar: semesters. Academic remediation for entering students, independent study, summer session for credit, part-time degree program, co-op programs and internships.
Entrance Requirements: Open admission. Options: electronic application, deferred admission. Required: high school transcript. Recommended: ACT. Required for some: ACT Compass. Entrance: minimally difficult. Application deadline: rolling.
Collegiate Environment: Orientation program. Choral group, marching band. Social organizations: national fraternities, national sororities; 25% of eligible men and 75% of eligible women are members. Most popular organizations: Phi Beta Lambda, International Club, Student Government Association, Choral/Band Organization. Major annual events: Arkansas Baptist College Health Fair, Arkansas Baptist College Honors Convocation, Arts/Beats and Cuisines. J. C. Oliver Library. 35 computers available on campus for general student use. A campuswide network can be accessed from student residence rooms and from off campus. Staffed computer lab on campus.

■ ARKANSAS NORTHEASTERN COLLEGE

PO Box 1109
Blytheville, AR 72316-1109
Tel: (870)762-1020
Fax: (870)763-3704
Web Site: www.anc.edu
Description: State-supported, 2-year, coed. Awards certificates, transfer associate, and terminal associate degrees. Founded 1975. Setting: 80-acre small town campus with easy access to Memphis. Endowment: $187,500. Educational spending for the previous fiscal year: $5048 per student. Total enrollment: 1,416. 501 applied, 100% were admitted. 17% from top 10% of their high school class. 3 valedictorians. Full-time: 610 students, 60% women, 40% men. Part-time: 806 students, 68% women, 32% men. Students come from 5 states and territories, 18% from out-of-state. 0.2% American Indian or Alaska Native, non-Hispanic/Latino; 3% Hispanic/Latino; 27% Black or African American, non-Hispanic/Latino; 0.5% Asian, non-Hispanic/Latino; 0.1% Native Hawaiian or other Pacific Islander, non-Hispanic/Latino. 45% 25 or older, 5% transferred in. Retention: 83% of full-time freshmen returned the following year. Core. Calendar: semesters. Academic remediation for entering students, advanced placement, distance learning, double major, summer session for credit, part-time degree program, adult/continuing education programs.
Entrance Requirements: Open admission except for nursing program. Option: deferred admission. Recommended: high school transcript. Entrance: noncompetitive. Application deadline: rolling. Notification: continuous.
Costs Per Year: Application fee: $0. Area resident tuition: $1960 full-time,

$70 per credit hour part-time. State resident tuition: $2240 full-time, $80 per credit hour part-time. Nonresident tuition: $3640 full-time, $130 per credit hour part-time. Mandatory fees: $358 full-time, $11 per credit hour part-time, $25 per term part-time. Full-time tuition and fees vary according to course load. Part-time tuition and fees vary according to course load.
Collegiate Environment: Orientation program. Drama-theater group, choral group. Social organizations: 10 open to all. Most popular organizations: Gamma Beta Phi, Association of Childhood Education International, Nursing Club, Cultural Diversity, Adult Student Association. Major annual events: Fall Funfest, Spring Funfest, Evening Student Appreciation Night. Campus security: 24-hour patrols. Adams/Vines Library. Operations spending for the previous fiscal year: $326,910. 280 computers available on campus for general student use. A campuswide network can be accessed from off-campus. Students can access the following: online class registration. Staffed computer lab on campus provides training in use of computers and the Internet.
Community Environment: In a rural area with a population of 16,600.

■ ARKANSAS STATE UNIVERSITY

PO Box 600
State University, AR 72467
Tel: (870)972-2100; Free: 800-382-3030
Fax: (870)972-2090
E-mail: admissions@astate.edu
Web Site: www.astate.edu
Description: State-supported, comprehensive, coed. Part of Arkansas State University System. Awards associate, bachelor's, master's, and doctoral degrees and post-master's certificates. Founded 1909. Setting: 1,376-acre small town campus with easy access to Memphis. Endowment: $54.9 million. Research spending for the previous fiscal year: $9 million. Educational spending for the previous fiscal year: $4005 per student. Total enrollment: 13,410. Faculty: 711 (505 full-time, 206 part-time). Student-undergrad faculty ratio is 17:1. 5,346 applied, 70% were admitted. 27% from top 10% of their high school class, 49% from top quarter, 74% from top half. Full-time: 7,295 students, 56% women, 44% men. Part-time: 2,297 students, 60% women, 40% men. Students come from 41 states and territories, 50 other countries, 11% from out-of-state. 0.4% American Indian or Alaska Native, non-Hispanic/Latino; 3% Hispanic/Latino; 13% Black or African American, non-Hispanic/Latino; 0.8% Asian, non-Hispanic/Latino; 0.1% Native Hawaiian or other Pacific Islander, non-Hispanic/Latino; 5% international. 19% 25 or older, 30% live on campus, 9% transferred in. Retention: 76% of full-time freshmen returned the following year. Academic areas with the most degrees conferred: education; health professions and related sciences; business/marketing. Core. Calendar: semesters. Academic remediation for entering students, ESL program, services for LD students, advanced placement, accelerated degree program, honors program, independent study, distance learning, double major, summer session for credit, part-time degree program, internships, graduate courses open to undergrads. Off campus study at Arkansas State University-Beebe, Arkansas State University-Mountain Home, Arkansas State University-Newport, Arkansas State University Mid-South, Arkansas State University-Paragould, Arkansas Northeastern College, East Arkansas Community College. Study abroad program. ROTC: Army.
Entrance Requirements: Options: electronic application, early admission, international baccalaureate accepted. Required: high school transcript, minimum 2.75 high school GPA, minimum ACT composite score of 21, im-

munization, Selective Service, SAT or ACT. Recommended: ACT. Required for some: ACT ASSET; ACT Compass; TOEFL, IELTS, PTE, iTEP, or Proof of English Proficiency for international students. Entrance: moderately difficult. Application deadline: rolling. Notification: continuous. SAT Reasoning Test deadline: 8/22. SAT Subject Test deadline: 8/22. Transfer credits accepted: Yes.

Collegiate Environment: Orientation program. Drama-theater group, choral group, marching band, student-run newspaper, radio station. Social organizations: 175 open to all; national fraternities, national sororities; 16% of eligible men and 13% of eligible women are members. Most popular organizations: Honors College, Volunteer A-State, Baptist Collegiate Ministry, Black Student Association, Student Activities Board. Major annual events: Welcome Week, Order of the Pack, Homecoming. Student services: health clinic, personal-psychological counseling. Campus security: 24-hour emergency response devices and patrols, student patrols, late night transport-escort service, controlled dormitory access, check-in desk, video surveillance cameras. Dean B. Ellis Library. Books: 386,049 (physical), 452,194 (digital/electronic); Serial titles: 353 (physical), 40,469 (digital/electronic); Databases: 163. Weekly public service hours: 103; students can reserve study rooms. Operations spending for the previous fiscal year: $4.7 million. 800 computers available on campus for general student use. Computer purchase/lease plans available. A campuswide network can be accessed from student residence rooms and from off campus. Students can access the following: online class registration. Staffed computer lab on campus (open 24 hours a day) provides training in use of computers, software, and the Internet.

Community Environment: Jonesboro is located on Crowley's Ridge, bordering the rich Mississippi Delta Agricultural and Industrial Center. Buses, railroads and airlines service the area. Jonesboro is 65 miles from Memphis, 133 miles from Little Rock, and 261 miles from St. Louis. The mean temperature is 60 degrees, and the average annual rainfall is 50 inches. There are more than 102 active clubs, and organizations, theaters, a Community Center, and several city parks in the city. Lake Frierson State Park and Craighead Forest Park and lake are nearby.

■ **ARKANSAS STATE UNIVERSITY-BEEBE**
PO Box 1000
Beebe, AR 72012-1000
Tel: (501)882-3600; Free: 800-632-9985
Fax: (501)882-8370
E-mail: rdhudson@asub.edu
Web Site: www.asub.edu
Description: State-supported, 2-year, coed. Part of Arkansas State University System. Awards certificates, transfer associate, and terminal associate degrees. Founded 1927. Setting: 320-acre small town campus with easy access to Memphis. Total enrollment: 4,491. Faculty: 97 (63 full-time, 34 part-time). Student-undergrad faculty ratio is 30:1. 3,451 applied, 54% were admitted. 2 class presidents, 1 valedictorian, 20 student government officers. Full-time: 2,601 students, 60% women, 40% men. Part-time: 1,890 students, 59% women, 41% men. Students come from 20 states and territories, 1% from out-of-state. 32% 25 or older, 12% live on campus, 6% transferred in. Retention: 64% of full-time freshmen returned the following year. Core. Calendar: semesters. Academic remediation for entering students, advanced placement, honors program, distance learning, summer session for credit, part-time degree program, adult/continuing education programs. ROTC: Army.
Entrance Requirements: Open admission. Options: electronic application, deferred admission. Required: high school transcript. Entrance: noncompetitive. Application deadline: rolling. Notification: continuous.
Collegiate Environment: Orientation program. Drama-theater group, choral group. Social organizations: 19 open to all. Most popular organizations: Student Arkansas Education Association, Art Club, Agri Club, Social Science Club, Leadership Council. Major annual events: Organizational Fair, Harvestfest/Spring Dance, Leadership Council activities. Student services: personal-psychological counseling. Campus security: 24-hour emergency response devices and patrols. Abington Library. 375 computers available on campus for general student use. A campuswide network can be accessed from student residence rooms and from off campus. Students can access the following: online class registration. Staffed computer lab on campus.

■ **ARKANSAS STATE UNIVERSITY MID-SOUTH**
2000 W Broadway
West Memphis, AR 72301
Tel: (870)733-6722; Free: 866-733-6722

Fax: (870)733-6719
E-mail: landerson@asumidsouth.edu
Web Site: www.asumidsouth.edu
Description: State-supported, 2-year, coed. Part of Arkansas State University System. Awards certificates, transfer associate, and terminal associate degrees. Founded 1993. Setting: 80-acre suburban campus with easy access to Memphis. Endowment: $967,261. Educational spending for the previous fiscal year: $3581 per student. Total enrollment: 1,423. Faculty: 104 (35 full-time, 69 part-time). Student-undergrad faculty ratio is 14:1. 492 applied, 100% were admitted. Full-time: 356 students, 69% women, 31% men. Part-time: 957 students, 68% women, 32% men. Students come from 5 states and territories, 2 other countries, 1% from out-of-state. 0.6% American Indian or Alaska Native, non-Hispanic/Latino; 4% Hispanic/Latino; 56% Black or African American, non-Hispanic/Latino; 0.7% Asian, non-Hispanic/Latino; 0.1% Native Hawaiian or other Pacific Islander, non-Hispanic/Latino; 0.7% international. 22% 25 or older, 3% transferred in. Retention: 40% of full-time freshmen returned the following year. Core. Calendar: semesters. Academic remediation for entering students, services for LD students, advanced placement, independent study, distance learning, summer session for credit, part-time degree program, adult/continuing education programs, internships.
Entrance Requirements: Open admission. Option: early admission. Required: SAT, ACT or ACT Compass. Entrance: noncompetitive. Application deadline: rolling. Notification: continuous. Transfer credits accepted: Yes.
Costs Per Year: Application fee: $0. Area resident tuition: $92 full-time, $92 per credit hour part-time. State resident tuition: $112 full-time, $112 per credit hour part-time. Nonresident tuition: $152 full-time, $152 per credit hour part-time. Mandatory fees: $514 full-time, $22 per credit hour part-time, $5 per term part-time.
Collegiate Environment: Orientation program. Most popular organizations: Phi Theta Kappa, Baptist Collegiate Ministry, SkillsUSA-VICA. Major annual events: Student Appreciation Day, Stress Free Zone, Job Fair. Student services: health clinic, personal-psychological counseling. Campus security: 24-hour emergency response devices, security during class hours. College housing not available. Sandra C. Goldsby Library. Operations spending for the previous fiscal year: $146,944. 60 computers available on campus for general student use. A campuswide network can be accessed. Students can access the following: online class registration. Staffed computer lab on campus provides training in use of computers.

■ **ARKANSAS STATE UNIVERSITY-MOUNTAIN HOME**
1600 S College St.
Mountain Home, AR 72653
Tel: (870)508-6100
E-mail: dparrish@asumh.edu
Web Site: www.asumh.edu
Description: State-supported, 2-year, coed. Part of Arkansas State University System. Awards certificates and terminal associate degrees. Founded 2000. Setting: 136-acre small town campus. Core. Calendar: semesters. Academic remediation for entering students, ESL program, services for LD students, advanced placement, honors program, independent study, distance learning, summer session for credit, part-time degree program, co-op programs and internships. ROTC: Army.
Entrance Requirements: Open admission. Option: electronic application. Required: high school transcript. Recommended: SAT or ACT, ACT Compass, ACT ASSET. Entrance: noncompetitive. Notification: continuous. Transfer credits accepted: Yes.
Collegiate Environment: Orientation program. Social organizations: 13 open to all; Phi Theta Kappa Honor Society. Most popular organizations: Phi Theta Kappa, Circle K, Criminal Justice Club, Mortuary Science Club, Student Ambassadors. Major annual events: Gaston Lecture Club events, Jingle-on-the-Green, Arvest Concert Series. Campus security: security during hours of operation. Norma Wood Library.

■ **ARKANSAS STATE UNIVERSITY-NEWPORT**
7648 Victory Blvd.
Newport, AR 72112
Tel: (870)512-7800; Free: 800-976-1676
Web Site: www.asun.edu
Description: State-supported, 2-year, coed. Part of Arkansas State University System. Awards certificates, diplomas, transfer associate, and terminal associate degrees. Founded 1989. Setting: 189-acre rural campus. Endowment: $2 million. Total enrollment: 2,270. Faculty: 157 (71 full-time, 86 part-time). Student-undergrad faculty ratio is 17:1. 354 applied, 100% were

admitted. Full-time: 1,039 students, 62% women, 38% men. Part-time: 1,231 students, 59% women, 41% men. Students come from 8 states and territories, 1 other country, 5% from out-of-state. 0.5% American Indian or Alaska Native, non-Hispanic/Latino; 3% Hispanic/Latino; 14% Black or African American, non-Hispanic/Latino; 0.6% Asian, non-Hispanic/Latino; 0.2% international. 46% 25 or older, 4% transferred in. Core. Calendar: semesters. Academic remediation for entering students, services for LD students, advanced placement, independent study, distance learning, double major, summer session for credit, part-time degree program, external degree program, adult/continuing education programs, co-op programs and internships. Off campus study.

Entrance Requirements: Open admission. Option: electronic application. Required: high school transcript, SAT or ACT or ACT Compass. Recommended: SAT or ACT, SAT and SAT Subject Tests or ACT, SAT Subject Tests. Entrance: noncompetitive. Application deadlines: rolling, rolling for early decision plan 1, rolling for early decision plan 2, rolling for early action. Notification: continuous, rolling for early decision plan 1, rolling for early decision plan 2, rolling for early action. Transfer credits accepted: Yes.

Costs Per Year: Application fee: $0. State resident tuition: $2880 full-time, $96 per credit hour part-time. Nonresident tuition: $4710 full-time, $157 per credit hour part-time. Mandatory fees: $600 full-time, $20 per credit hour part-time. Full-time tuition and fees vary according to course load and program. Part-time tuition and fees vary according to course load and program.

Collegiate Environment: Orientation program. Most popular organizations: Phi Theta Kappa, Phi Beta Lambda, Service Veterans Organization. Major annual events: Welcome Week, Spring Fling, Fall Fling. Campus security: text-based alert system; campus police 8-5 on-site. College housing not available. Harryette M. Hodges and Kaneaster Hodges, Sr. Library plus 2 others. Books: 11,653 (physical), 27 (digital/electronic); Databases: 6. Weekly public service hours: 40. Operations spending for the previous fiscal year: $148,167. 430 computers available on campus for general student use. A campuswide network can be accessed. Students can access the following: online class registration. Staffed computer lab on campus provides training in use of computers, software, and the Internet.

■ ARKANSAS TECH UNIVERSITY
215 W O St.
Russellville, AR 72801
Tel: (479)968-0389; Free: 800-582-6953
Fax: (479)964-0522
E-mail: tech.enroll@atu.edu
Web Site: www.atu.edu

Description: State-supported, comprehensive, coed. Awards associate, bachelor's, master's, and doctoral degrees and post-master's certificates. Founded 1909. Setting: 559-acre small town campus. Endowment: $37.4 million. Research spending for the previous fiscal year: $5.3 million. Educational spending for the previous fiscal year: $4856 per student. Total enrollment: 12,101. Faculty: 605 (371 full-time, 234 part-time). Student-undergrad faculty ratio is 19:1. 5,122 applied, 90% were admitted. 15% from top 10% of their high school class, 36% from top quarter, 66% from top half. Full-time: 5,696 students, 59% women, 41% men. Part-time: 4,755 students, 57% women, 43% men. 4% from out-of-state. 0.6% American Indian or Alaska Native, non-Hispanic/Latino; 7% Hispanic/Latino; 7% Black or African American, non-Hispanic/Latino; 1% Asian, non-Hispanic/Latino; 0.1% Native Hawaiian or other Pacific Islander, non-Hispanic/Latino; 4% international. 21% 25 or older, 28% live on campus, 4% transferred in. Retention: 70% of full-time freshmen returned the following year. Academic areas with the most degrees conferred: interdisciplinary studies; health professions and related sciences; business/marketing. Core. Calendar: semesters. Academic remediation for entering students, ESL program, services for LD students, advanced placement, accelerated degree program, honors program, independent study, distance learning, double major, summer session for credit, part-time degree program, adult/continuing education programs, internships, graduate courses open to undergrads. Off campus study. Study abroad program. ROTC: Army (c).

Entrance Requirements: Options: electronic application, early action, deferred admission, international baccalaureate accepted. Required: high school transcript, minimum 2 high school GPA, SAT or ACT. Entrance: moderately difficult. Notification: continuous. SAT Reasoning Test deadline: 8/15. SAT Subject Test deadline: 8/15. Transfer credits accepted: Yes.

Costs Per Year: Application fee: $0. State resident tuition: $6780 full-time, $226 per credit hour part-time. Nonresident tuition: $13,560 full-time, $452 per credit hour part-time. Mandatory fees: $2288 full-time, $76.25 per credit

hour part-time. Full-time tuition and fees vary according to course load and location. Part-time tuition and fees vary according to course load and location. College room and board: $7870. College room only: $4542. Room and board charges vary according to board plan, housing facility, and location.

Collegiate Environment: Orientation program. Drama-theater group, choral group, marching band, student-run newspaper, radio station. Social organizations: 227 open to all; national fraternities, national sororities, local fraternities, local sororities; 4% of eligible men and 4% of eligible women are members. Student services: health clinic, personal-psychological counseling. Campus security: 24-hour emergency response devices and patrols, student patrols, late night transport-escort service, controlled dormitory access. Freshmen guaranteed college housing. On-campus residence required through sophomore year. Options: coed, men-only, women-only housing available. Ross Pendergraft Library and Technology Center. Books: 154,336 (physical), 386,793 (digital/electronic); Serial titles: 5,478 (physical), 73,489 (digital/electronic); Databases: 279. Students can reserve study rooms. Operations spending for the previous fiscal year: $2.3 million. 1,190 computers available on campus for general student use. Computer purchase/lease plans available. A campuswide network can be accessed from student residence rooms and from off campus. Students can access the following: online class registration. Staffed computer lab on campus provides training in use of computers, software, and the Internet.

Community Environment: Russellville, the crossroads for State Highways 7, 22, 124, and 64, is located equidistant from Little Rock, Hot Springs, Harrison, and Fort Smith. Interstate 40 passes just north of Russellville, a city of 25,000. A 36,600 acre lake, formed by a lock and dam on the navigable Arkansas River, lies southwest of the city. The area, served by airplane, rail, and bus lines, is experiencing vigorous industrial development, which includes the construction of the first nuclear power plant in the Southwest. Recreational facilities in the area include lakes, picnic areas, city parks, swimming pools, tennis courts, and private country clubs. There are the usual civic organizations of a city. Part-time employment is available in stores and on campus.

■ BAPTIST HEALTH COLLEGE LITTLE ROCK
11900 Colonel Glenn Rd.
Ste. 100
Little Rock, AR 72210-2820
Tel: (501)202-7415
Fax: (501)202-7406
Web Site: www.bhclr.edu

Description: Independent, 2-year, coed, affiliated with Baptist Church. Awards certificates, transfer associate, and terminal associate degrees. Founded 1921.

■ BLACK RIVER TECHNICAL COLLEGE
1410 Hwy. 304 E
Pocahontas, AR 72455
Tel: (870)248-4000
Fax: (870)248-4100
Web Site: www.blackrivertech.edu

Description: State-supported, 2-year, coed. Awards transfer associate and terminal associate degrees. Founded 1972. Setting: 55-acre small town campus. Total enrollment: 1,933. 50% 25 or older. Calendar: semesters. Academic remediation for entering students, services for LD students, self-designed majors, honors program, summer session for credit, part-time degree program, co-op programs and internships.

Entrance Requirements: Open admission except for nursing program. Required for some: high school transcript, interview, ACT, ACT ASSET, or SAT. Entrance: noncompetitive. Application deadline: rolling.

Collegiate Environment: Orientation program. Campus security: night patrol. Black River Technical College Library.

■ BRYAN UNIVERSITY
3704 W Walnut St.
Rogers, AR 72756
Tel: (479)899-6644
Web Site: www.bryanu.edu

Description: Proprietary, 2-year, coed. Awards diplomas and terminal associate degrees.

■ CENTRAL BAPTIST COLLEGE
1501 College Ave.
Conway, AR 72032

Tel: (501)329-6872; Free: 800-205-6872
Web Site: www.cbc.edu

Description: Independent Baptist, 4-year, coed. Awards associate and bachelor's degrees. Founded 1952. Setting: 11-acre small town campus. Total enrollment: 832. Faculty: 87 (30 full-time, 57 part-time). Student-undergrad faculty ratio is 12:1. 318 applied, 62% were admitted. Full-time: 658 students, 45% women, 55% men. Part-time: 174 students, 53% women, 47% men. Students come from 19 states and territories, 12 other countries, 26% from out-of-state. 1% American Indian or Alaska Native, non-Hispanic/Latino; 3% Hispanic/Latino; 19% Black or African American, non-Hispanic/Latino; 0.1% Asian, non-Hispanic/Latino; 2% Native Hawaiian or other Pacific Islander, non-Hispanic/Latino; 2% international. 70% 25 or older, 9% transferred in. Retention: 73% of full-time freshmen returned the following year. Core. Calendar: semesters. Academic remediation for entering students, services for LD students, advanced placement, independent study, distance learning, summer session for credit, part-time degree program, adult/continuing education programs, internships. ROTC: Army (c).

Entrance Requirements: Options: electronic application, early admission. Required: high school transcript, SAT or ACT. Entrance: minimally difficult. Application deadline: 8/15. Transfer credits accepted: Yes.

Costs Per Year: Application fee: $0. Comprehensive fee: $23,700 includes full-time tuition ($14,700), mandatory fees ($1500), and college room and board ($7500). Full-time tuition and fees vary according to course load. Room and board charges vary according to board plan and housing facility. Part-time tuition: $490 per credit hour. Part-time mandatory fees: $750 per term. Part-time tuition and fees vary according to course load.

Collegiate Environment: Orientation program. Drama-theater group, choral group, student-run newspaper, radio station. Social organizations: 11 open to all. Major annual events: Hall Wars, Homecoming, Harvest Party. Student services: personal-psychological counseling. Campus security: controlled dormitory access. Story Library. Students can reserve study rooms. 70 computers available on campus for general student use. A campuswide network can be accessed from student residence rooms. Students can access the following: online class registration. Staffed computer lab on campus provides training in use of computers, software, and the Internet.

Community Environment: See University of Central Arkansas.

■ **COLLEGE OF THE OUACHITAS**
One College Cir.
Malvern, AR 72104
Tel: (501)337-5000
Fax: (501)337-9382
E-mail: jhunt@coto.edu
Web Site: www.coto.edu

Description: State-supported, 2-year, coed. Awards certificates, transfer associate, and terminal associate degrees. Founded 1972. Setting: 11-acre small town campus with easy access to Little Rock. Educational spending for the previous fiscal year: $5687 per student. Total enrollment: 1,272. Faculty: 98 (39 full-time, 59 part-time). Full-time: 384 students, 71% women, 29% men. Part-time: 888 students, 49% women, 51% men. Students come from 3 states and territories, 1% from out-of-state. 0.6% American Indian or Alaska Native, non-Hispanic/Latino; 5% Hispanic/Latino; 14% Black or African American, non-Hispanic/Latino; 0.5% Asian, non-Hispanic/Latino; 0.2% Native Hawaiian or other Pacific Islander, non-Hispanic/Latino; 0.1% international. 50% 25 or older, 22% transferred in. Core. Calendar: semesters. Academic remediation for entering students, services for LD students, advanced placement, accelerated degree program, freshman honors college, honors program, independent study, distance learning, double major, summer session for credit, part-time degree program, co-op programs and internships.

Entrance Requirements: Open admission except for nursing and cosmetology programs. Options: electronic application, early admission, deferred admission. Required: high school transcript, immunizations. Entrance: noncompetitive. Application deadline: rolling. Notification: continuous. Transfer credits accepted: Yes.

Costs Per Year: State resident tuition: $2850 full-time, $95 per credit hour part-time. Nonresident tuition: $5700 full-time, $190 per credit hour part-time. Mandatory fees: $830 full-time, $28 per credit hour part-time. Full-time tuition and fees vary according to course load and program. Part-time tuition and fees vary according to course load and program. Tuition guaranteed not to increase for student's term of enrollment.

Collegiate Environment: Orientation program. Major annual event: Awards Ceremony. Student services: personal-psychological counseling. Campus security: 24-hour emergency response devices and patrols. College of the Ouachitas Library/Learning Resource Center. Students can reserve study rooms. Operations spending for the previous fiscal year: $125,184. 225 computers available on campus for general student use. A campuswide network can be accessed from off-campus. Students can access the following: online class registration. Staffed computer lab on campus provides training in use of computers, software, and the Internet.

■ **COSSATOT COMMUNITY COLLEGE OF THE UNIVERSITY OF ARKANSAS**
183 College Dr.
De Queen, AR 71832
Tel: (870)584-4471; Free: 800-844-4471
E-mail: tcobb@cccua.edu
Web Site: www.cccua.edu

Description: State-supported, 2-year, coed. Part of University of Arkansas System. Awards certificates, transfer associate, and terminal associate degrees. Founded 1991. Setting: 30-acre rural campus. Endowment: $76,785. Total enrollment: 1,575. Faculty: 84 (36 full-time, 48 part-time). Student-undergrad faculty ratio is 15:1. Students come from 8 states and territories, 1 other country, 2% from out-of-state. 3% American Indian or Alaska Native, non-Hispanic/Latino; 18% Hispanic/Latino; 11% Black or African American, non-Hispanic/Latino; 0.9% Asian, non-Hispanic/Latino; 0.3% Native Hawaiian or other Pacific Islander, non-Hispanic/Latino. 30% 25 or older. Calendar: semesters. Academic remediation for entering students, services for LD students, advanced placement, accelerated degree program, honors program, independent study, distance learning, double major, summer session for credit, part-time degree program, co-op programs and internships. Off campus study.

Entrance Requirements: Open admission. Option: electronic application. Recommended: high school transcript. Entrance: noncompetitive. Transfer credits accepted: Yes.

Collegiate Environment: Orientation program. Student-run radio station. Social organizations: 6 open to all. Most popular organizations: Student Ambassadors, Phi Theta Kappa, ALPNA, VICA (Vocational Industrial Clubs of America), Multi Diversity. Major annual events: Thanksgiving Dinner, Spring Fling, Ice Cream Social, Movie night. Student services: health clinic, personal-psychological counseling. Campus security: daytime campus police force, evening patrol by city police force. The Educational Resource Center. Operations spending for the previous fiscal year: $112,829. 208 computers available on campus for general student use. A campuswide network can be accessed from off-campus. Students can access the following: online class registration. Staffed computer lab on campus provides training in use of computers, software, and the Internet.

■ **CROWLEY'S RIDGE COLLEGE**
100 College Dr.
Paragould, AR 72450-9731
Tel: (870)236-6901; Free: 800-264-1096
Fax: (870)236-7748
Web Site: www.crc.edu

Description: Independent, 4-year, coed, affiliated with Church of Christ. Awards associate and bachelor's degrees. Founded 1964. Setting: 150-acre small town campus. Total enrollment: 214. Calendar: semesters. Academic remediation for entering students, honors program, independent study, distance learning, summer session for credit, part-time degree program.

Entrance Requirements: Open admission. Option: electronic application. Required: high school transcript, recommendation form filled out by high school. Required for some: interview. Entrance: noncompetitive. Application deadline: rolling.

Costs Per Year: Application fee: $0. Comprehensive fee: $19,250 includes full-time tuition ($11,250), mandatory fees ($1650), and college room and board ($6350). College room only: $2800. Room and board charges vary according to board plan and housing facility. Part-time tuition: $375 per hour. Part-time mandatory fees: $42 per hour. Part-time tuition and fees vary according to course load.

Collegiate Environment: Orientation program. Drama-theater group, choral group. Learning Center.

■ **EAST ARKANSAS COMMUNITY COLLEGE**
1700 Newcastle Rd.
Forrest City, AR 72335-2204
Tel: (870)633-4480; Free: 877-797-3222
Fax: (870)633-7222
E-mail: dadams@eacc.edu

Web Site: www.eacc.edu

Description: State-supported, 2-year, coed. Awards certificates, transfer associate, and terminal associate degrees. Founded 1974. Setting: 40-acre small town campus with easy access to Memphis. Total enrollment: 1,547. Faculty: 95 (39 full-time, 56 part-time). Student-undergrad faculty ratio is 18:1. Full-time: 779 students, 73% women, 27% men. Part-time: 768 students, 69% women, 31% men. 45% 25 or older. Core. Calendar: semesters. Academic remediation for entering students, services for LD students, advanced placement, honors program, summer session for credit, part-time degree program, adult/continuing education programs.

Entrance Requirements: Open admission. Options: early admission, deferred admission. Required: high school transcript. Entrance: minimally difficult. Application deadline: rolling. Notification: continuous.

Collegiate Environment: Drama-theater group, choral group. Social organizations: 4 open to all. Most popular organizations: Gamma Beta Phi, Baptist Student Union, Student Activities Committee, Lambda Alpha Epsilon. Major annual events: Spring Barbecue, Homecoming. Student services: personal-psychological counseling. Campus security: 24-hour emergency response devices, 16-hour patrols by trained security personnel. Learning Resource Center plus 1 other. 35 computers available on campus for general student use. A campuswide network can be accessed. Students can access the following: online class registration. Staffed computer lab on campus provides training in use of computers, software, and the Internet.

Community Environment: Forrest City, with a population of 14,078, is the county seat of St. Francis County.

■ **ECCLESIA COLLEGE**
9653 Nations Dr.
Springdale, AR 72762
Tel: (479)248-7236
Web Site: www.ecollege.edu

Description: Independent Christian, comprehensive, coed. Awards associate, bachelor's, and master's degrees. Founded 1995. Setting: 200-acre small town campus with easy access to Northwest Arkansas. Total enrollment: 247. Faculty: 75 (18 full-time, 57 part-time). Student-undergrad faculty ratio is 10:1. 211 applied, 31% were admitted. Full-time: 191 students, 40% women, 60% men. Part-time: 55 students, 45% women, 55% men. 75% live on campus. Retention: 57% of full-time freshmen returned the following year. Core. Calendar: semesters. ESL program, independent study, distance learning, double major, internships, graduate courses open to undergrads.

Entrance Requirements: Option: electronic application. Required: essay, high school transcript, minimum 2 high school GPA, 1 recommendation, interview, SAT or ACT. Entrance: noncompetitive. Application deadline: rolling. Notification: continuous. SAT Reasoning Test deadline: 8/15. SAT Subject Test deadline: 8/15. Transfer credits accepted: Yes.

Collegiate Environment: Orientation program. Drama-theater group, choral group. Social organizations: 4 open to all. Most popular organizations: Service Learning, Student Council, Worship Team, Missions. Major annual events: Spirit Week, Fall Festival/Homecoming, Talent/No Talent Annual Show. Student services: personal-psychological counseling. Campus security: student patrols. Ecclesia College Library.

■ **HARDING UNIVERSITY**
915 E Market Ave.
Searcy, AR 72149-0001
Tel: (501)279-4000; Free: 800-477-4407
Fax: (501)279-4865
E-mail: admissions@harding.edu
Web Site: www.harding.edu

Description: Independent, university, coed, affiliated with Church of Christ. Awards bachelor's, master's, and doctoral degrees and post-master's certificates. Founded 1924. Setting: 350-acre small town campus with easy access to Little Rock. Endowment: $128.7 million. Research spending for the previous fiscal year: $224,102. Educational spending for the previous fiscal year: $12,416 per student. Total enrollment: 5,121. Faculty: 403 (305 full-time, 98 part-time). Student-undergrad faculty ratio is 14:1. 1,927 applied, 68% were admitted. 23% from top 10% of their high school class, 50% from top quarter, 77% from top half. 11 National Merit Scholars. Full-time: 3,742 students, 54% women, 46% men. Part-time: 232 students, 50% women, 50% men. Students come from 54 states and territories, 49 other countries, 72% from out-of-state. 0.3% American Indian or Alaska Native, non-Hispanic/Latino; 4% Hispanic/Latino; 4% Black or African American, non-Hispanic/Latino; 0.8% Asian, non-Hispanic/Latino; 6% international. 5% 25 or older, 91% live on campus, 3% transferred in. Retention: 85% of full-

time freshmen returned the following year. Academic areas with the most degrees conferred: business/marketing; health professions and related sciences; education. Core. Calendar: semesters. Academic remediation for entering students, ESL program, services for LD students, advanced placement, accelerated degree program, self-designed majors, freshman honors college, honors program, independent study, distance learning, double major, summer session for credit, part-time degree program, adult/continuing education programs, co-op programs and internships, graduate courses open to undergrads. Study abroad program. ROTC: Army (c).

Entrance Requirements: Options: electronic application, early admission, early action, deferred admission, international baccalaureate accepted. Required: essay, high school transcript, 3 recommendations, SAT or ACT. Entrance: moderately difficult. Application deadline: rolling. Notification: continuous. SAT Reasoning Test deadline: 7/1. Transfer credits accepted: Yes.

Costs Per Year: Application fee: $50. Comprehensive fee: $26,644 includes full-time tuition ($19,140), mandatory fees ($500), and college room and board ($7004). College room only: $3658. Full-time tuition and fees vary according to course load. Room and board charges vary according to board plan and housing facility. Part-time tuition: $638 per credit hour. Part-time mandatory fees: $25 per credit hour. Part-time tuition and fees vary according to course load.

Collegiate Environment: Orientation program. Drama-theater group, choral group, marching band, student-run newspaper, radio station. Social organizations: 120 open to all. Most popular organizations: Bisons for Christ, Harding in Action, Spring Break Campaigns, HUmanity. Major annual events: Spring Sing Festival, Homecoming, Bisons for Christ. Student services: health clinic, personal-psychological counseling. Campus security: 24-hour emergency response devices and patrols, student patrols, late night transport-escort service, controlled dormitory access. 3,245 college housing spaces available; 2,795 were occupied in 2018-19. Freshmen guaranteed college housing. On-campus residence required through senior year. Options: men-only, women-only housing available. Brackett Library plus 1 other. Books: 187,838 (physical), 382,577 (digital/electronic); Serial titles: 925 (physical), 82,048 (digital/electronic); Databases: 185. Students can reserve study rooms. Operations spending for the previous fiscal year: $1.4 million. 512 computers available on campus for general student use. A campuswide network can be accessed from student residence rooms and from off campus. Students can access the following: online class registration. Staffed computer lab on campus provides training in use of computers, software, and the Internet.

Community Environment: Searcy is a small town located approximately 50 miles from Little Rock. The climate is temperate. A public library, two large hospitals, many churches, and a variety of shops serve the city of 20,000. Greer's Ferry Lake, with approximately 400 miles of shoreline, is located within 30 miles of campus. The Little Red River, which is famous for its rainbow trout, runs through the edge of Searcy. About 45 minutes from Harding, the University owns a 1,200 acre camp consisting of many log buildings, bluffs, and horse stables.

■ **HENDERSON STATE UNIVERSITY**
1100 Henderson St.
Arkadelphia, AR 71999-0001
Tel: (870)230-5000; Free: 800-228-7333
Fax: (870)230-5144
E-mail: bentonb@hsu.edu
Web Site: www.hsu.edu

Description: State-supported, comprehensive, coed. Awards bachelor's and master's degrees and post-master's certificates. Founded 1890. Setting: 151-acre small town campus with easy access to Little Rock. Total enrollment: 3,565. Faculty: 257 (177 full-time, 80 part-time). Student-undergrad faculty ratio is 15:1. 4,072 applied, 66% were admitted. 15% from top 10% of their high school class, 36% from top quarter, 69% from top half. Full-time: 2,791 students, 57% women, 43% men. Part-time: 275 students, 59% women, 41% men. Students come from 27 states and territories, 26 other countries, 14% from out-of-state. 0.4% American Indian or Alaska Native, non-Hispanic/Latino; 4% Hispanic/Latino; 23% Black or African American, non-Hispanic/Latino; 0.8% Asian, non-Hispanic/Latino; 0.1% Native Hawaiian or other Pacific Islander, non-Hispanic/Latino; 1% international. 13% 25 or older, 43% live on campus, 7% transferred in. Retention: 60% of full-time freshmen returned the following year. Core. Calendar: semesters. Academic remediation for entering students, services for LD students, advanced placement, freshman honors college, honors program, distance learning, double major, summer session for credit, part-time degree program, internships, graduate courses open to undergrads. Off campus study at Ouachita Baptist University. Study abroad program. ROTC: Army (c).

Entrance Requirements: Options: electronic application, deferred admission. Required: high school transcript, SAT or ACT. Recommended: minimum 2.5 high school GPA, ACT. Required for some: essay, 3 recommendations. Entrance: moderately difficult. Application deadline: 7/15. Notification: continuous. Transfer credits accepted: Yes.

Collegiate Environment: Orientation program. Drama-theater group, choral group, marching band, student-run newspaper, radio station. Social organizations: 85 open to all; national fraternities, national sororities, local fraternities, local sororities. Most popular organizations: Heart and Key, Student Government Association, Residence Hall Association. Major annual events: Homecoming, Spring Fling, Parent's Weekend. Student services: health clinic, personal-psychological counseling. Campus security: 24-hour emergency response devices and patrols, late night transport-escort service, controlled dormitory access, Reddie Rides offered at night. Huie Library plus 1 other. Books: 225,859 (physical), 142,000 (digital/electronic); Databases: 223. Weekly public service hours: 80; students can reserve study rooms. 125 computers available on campus for general student use. A campuswide network can be accessed from student residence rooms and from off campus. Students can access the following: online class registration. Staffed computer lab on campus.

Community Environment: Arkadelphia is 55 miles southwest of Little Rock, and 35 miles south of Hot Springs, America's oldest national park. Arkadelphia is a modern, progressive city, and a well-known educational center. The Missouri Pacific Railroad, U.S. Interstate 30, U.S. Highway 67, and state highways make this city easily accessible from all parts of the state.

■ **HENDRIX COLLEGE**
1600 Washington Ave.
Conway, AR 72032
Tel: (501)329-6811; Free: 800-277-9017
Fax: (501)450-3843
E-mail: adm@hendrix.edu
Web Site: www.hendrix.edu
Description: Independent United Methodist, comprehensive, coed. Awards bachelor's and master's degrees. Founded 1876. Setting: 180-acre suburban campus with easy access to Little Rock. Endowment: $185.5 million. Total enrollment: 1,249. Faculty: 136 (104 full-time, 32 part-time). Student-undergrad faculty ratio is 11:1. 1,465 applied, 80% were admitted. 60% from top 10% of their high school class, 81% from top quarter, 96% from top half. Full-time: 1,228 students, 52% women, 48% men. Part-time: 10 students, 40% women, 60% men. 0.8% American Indian or Alaska Native, non-Hispanic/Latino; 6% Hispanic/Latino; 7% Black or African American, non-Hispanic/Latino; 5% Asian, non-Hispanic/Latino; 2% international. 1% transferred in. Retention: 83% of full-time freshmen returned the following year. Academic areas with the most degrees conferred: social sciences; biological/life sciences; psychology. Core. Calendar: semesters. ESL program, services for LD students, advanced placement, self-designed majors, independent study, double major, co-op programs and internships, graduate courses open to undergrads. Off campus study at American University, Associated Colleges of the South. Study abroad program. ROTC: Army (c).

Entrance Requirements: Options: electronic application, early action, international baccalaureate accepted. Required: essay, high school transcript, SAT or ACT. Recommended: 1 recommendation. Required for some: interview. Entrance: very difficult. Application deadlines: 6/1, 11/15 for early action. Notification: continuous, 12/15 for early action. SAT Reasoning Test deadline: 6/1. SAT Subject Test deadline: 6/1. Transfer credits accepted: Yes.

Costs Per Year: Application fee: $40. Comprehensive fee: $58,074 includes full-time tuition ($45,440), mandatory fees ($350), and college room and board ($12,284). College room only: $6324. Full-time tuition and fees vary according to course load. Room and board charges vary according to board plan and housing facility. Part-time tuition: $5680 per course. Part-time tuition varies according to course load.

Collegiate Environment: Orientation program. Drama-theater group, choral group, student-run newspaper, radio station. Social organizations: 70 open to all. Student services: health clinic, personal-psychological counseling. Campus security: 24-hour emergency response devices and patrols, late night transport-escort service, controlled dormitory access. Olin C. and Marjorie H. Bailey Library plus 1 other. Weekly public service hours: 83; study areas open 24 hours, 5-7 days a week.

Community Environment: See University of Central Arkansas.

■ **JEFFERSON REGIONAL MEDICAL CENTER SCHOOL OF NURSING**
1600 W 40th Ave.
Pine Bluff, AR 71603
Tel: (870)541-7850
Web Site: www.jrmc.org/school-of-nursing
Description: Independent, 2-year, coed. Awards certificates, transfer associate, and terminal associate degrees. Founded 1981.

■ **JOHN BROWN UNIVERSITY**
2000 W University St.
Siloam Springs, AR 72761-2121
Tel: (479)524-9500; Free: 877-JBU-INFO
Fax: (479)524-9548
E-mail: jburgess@jbu.edu
Web Site: www.jbu.edu
Description: Independent interdenominational, comprehensive, coed. Awards associate, bachelor's, and master's degrees and post-master's certificates. Founded 1919. Setting: 200-acre small town campus. Endowment: $113.3 million. Research spending for the previous fiscal year: $209,735. Educational spending for the previous fiscal year: $8559 per student. Total enrollment: 2,613. Faculty: 239 (87 full-time, 152 part-time). Student-undergrad faculty ratio is 14:1. 1,198 applied, 76% were admitted. 29% from top 10% of their high school class, 58% from top quarter, 83% from top half. Full-time: 1,490 students, 59% women, 41% men. Part-time: 482 students, 50% women, 50% men. Students come from 41 states and territories, 50 other countries, 49% from out-of-state. 2% American Indian or Alaska Native, non-Hispanic/Latino; 6% Hispanic/Latino; 2% Black or African American, non-Hispanic/Latino; 2% Asian, non-Hispanic/Latino; 0.1% Native Hawaiian or other Pacific Islander, non-Hispanic/Latino; 5% international. 16% 25 or older, 58% live on campus, 7% transferred in. Retention: 82% of full-time freshmen returned the following year. Academic areas with the most degrees conferred: business/marketing; visual and performing arts; engineering. Core. Calendar: semesters. Academic remediation for entering students, ESL program, services for LD students, accelerated degree program, self-designed majors, honors program, independent study, distance learning, double major, part-time degree program, external degree program, adult/continuing education programs, co-op programs and internships, graduate courses open to undergrads. Study abroad program. ROTC: Army (c), Air Force (c).

Entrance Requirements: Options: electronic application, deferred admission. Required: essay, high school transcript, minimum 2.5 high school GPA, 2 recommendations. Recommended: interview. Required for some: SAT or ACT. Entrance: moderately difficult. Application deadline: rolling. Notification: continuous. Transfer credits accepted: Yes.

Costs Per Year: Application fee: $25. Comprehensive fee: $36,152 includes full-time tuition ($25,750), mandatory fees ($1178), and college room and board ($9224). College room only: $4424. Full-time tuition and fees vary according to course load and degree level. Room and board charges vary according to board plan and housing facility. Part-time tuition: $858 per credit hour. Part-time mandatory fees: $295 per term. Part-time tuition and fees vary according to course load and degree level.

Collegiate Environment: Orientation program. Drama-theater group, choral group, student-run newspaper, radio station. Social organizations: 31 open to all. Most popular organizations: Student Government Association, Student Ministries Organization, Student Activities Club, Student Missionary Fellowship, Enactus. Major annual events: Homecoming, Christmas Candlelight Service, Parent's Weekend. Student services: health clinic, personal-psychological counseling. Campus security: 24-hour emergency response devices and patrols, late night transport-escort service, controlled dormitory access. Arutunoff Learning Resource Center plus 4 others. Books: 105,116 (physical), 329,913 (digital/electronic); Serial titles: 1,032 (physical), 67,078 (digital/electronic); Databases: 144. Weekly public service hours: 110; students can reserve study rooms. Operations spending for the previous fiscal year: $656,929. 250 computers available on campus for general student use. A campuswide network can be accessed from student residence rooms and from off campus. Students can access the following: online class registration. Staffed computer lab on campus provides training in use of computers, software, and the Internet.

Community Environment: Located in the Benton County foothills of the beautiful Ozarks. The town is easily accessible from all parts of the state. The seasons are delightfully mild. Siloam Springs is far enough south to insure mild winters, and the summer nights are pleasantly cool. Northwest Arkansas is considered a very healthful location, and is noted as a summer retreat for many tourists from all sections of the United States.

■ LYON COLLEGE

PO Box 2317
Batesville, AR 72503-2317
Tel: (870)793-9813; Free: 800-423-2542
Fax: (870)698-4622
E-mail: admissions@lyon.edu
Web Site: www.lyon.edu

Description: Independent Presbyterian, 4-year, coed. Awards bachelor's degrees. Founded 1872. Setting: 136-acre small town campus. Total enrollment: 672. Faculty: 57 (43 full-time, 14 part-time). Student-undergrad faculty ratio is 14:1. 1,652 applied, 64% were admitted. 27% from top 10% of their high school class, 49% from top quarter, 82% from top half. Full-time: 652 students, 44% women, 56% men. Part-time: 20 students, 65% women, 35% men. 32% from out-of-state. 2% American Indian or Alaska Native, non-Hispanic/Latino; 8% Hispanic/Latino; 7% Black or African American, non-Hispanic/Latino; 3% Asian, non-Hispanic/Latino; 4% international. 2% 25 or older, 70% live on campus, 7% transferred in. Retention: 62% of full-time freshmen returned the following year. Academic areas with the most degrees conferred: psychology; biological/life sciences; business/marketing. Core. Calendar: semesters. Advanced placement, accelerated degree program, self-designed majors, independent study, double major, summer session for credit, part-time degree program, internships. Off campus study at University of Arkansas Community College at Batesville (UACCB). Study abroad program.

Entrance Requirements: Options: electronic application, early admission, early action, deferred admission, international baccalaureate accepted. Required: high school transcript, minimum 2.5 high school GPA, SAT or ACT. Required for some: essay, 2 recommendations. Entrance: moderately difficult. Application deadline: rolling. Notification: continuous. SAT Reasoning Test deadline: 8/7. SAT Subject Test deadline: 8/20. Transfer credits accepted: Yes.

Costs Per Year: Application fee: $0. Comprehensive fee: $37,900 includes full-time tuition ($28,200), mandatory fees ($590), and college room and board ($9110). Full-time tuition and fees vary according to course load. Room and board charges vary according to board plan and housing facility. Part-time tuition: $930 per credit hour. Part-time mandatory fees: $590 per year. Part-time tuition and fees vary according to course load.

Collegiate Environment: Orientation program. Drama-theater group, choral group, student-run newspaper. Social organizations: national fraternities, national sororities, local fraternities, local sororities. Most popular organizations: Wesley Fellowship, Gay-Straight Alliance, Alpha Xi Delta Sorority, Fellowship of Christian Athletes, Young Democrats/Japanese Culture Club. Major annual events: Service Day, Arkansas Scottish Festival, Homecoming Weekend. Student services: health clinic, personal-psychological counseling. Campus security: 24-hour patrols, late night transport-escort service, controlled dormitory access. Mabee-Simpson Library.

Community Environment: Batesville is located on the banks of the White River, in the foothills of the Ozarks 90 miles north of Little Rock, and 120 miles northwest of Memphis. The climate is mild, summer mean is 78 degrees and the winter mean is 40 degrees. Average annual rainfall is 48 inches. There are many churches in the area, a fine city library, hospitals, and 4 radio stations and cable TV.

■ NATIONAL PARK COLLEGE

101 College Dr.
Hot Springs, AR 71913
Tel: (501)760-4222
Fax: (501)760-4100
Web Site: www.np.edu

Description: State and locally supported, 2-year, coed. Part of Arkansas Department of Higher Education. Awards certificates, diplomas, transfer associate, and terminal associate degrees. Founded 1973. Setting: 50-acre suburban campus with easy access to Little Rock. Endowment: $11.3 million. Total enrollment: 2,996. Faculty: 160 (100 full-time, 60 part-time). Student-undergrad faculty ratio is 18:1. 4,969 applied, 100% were admitted. Full-time: 1,237 students, 59% women, 41% men. Part-time: 1,759 students, 61% women, 39% men. 2% from out-of-state. 63% 25 or older, 17% transferred in. Retention: 100% of full-time freshmen returned the following year. Core. Calendar: semesters. Academic remediation for entering students, services for LD students, advanced placement, self-designed

majors, honors program, independent study, distance learning, double major, summer session for credit, part-time degree program, external degree program, adult/continuing education programs, co-op programs and internships. Study abroad program.

Entrance Requirements: Open admission except for nursing, allied health programs. Options: early admission, deferred admission. Required: high school transcript, ACT, SAT and SAT Subject Tests or ACT, ACCUPLACER. Entrance: noncompetitive. Application deadline: rolling.

Collegiate Environment: Orientation program. Choral group. Social organizations: 15 open to all; 15% of eligible men and 15% of eligible women are members. Most popular organizations: Student Government Association, Nighthawk Singers, Intramurals, Phi Theta Kappa, Anime Club. Major annual events: Turkey Bowl, Spring Fling, Job Fair. Student services: personal-psychological counseling. Campus security: 24-hour emergency response devices, Campus Resource Officer. NATIONAL PARK COLLEGE LIBRARY. Operations spending for the previous fiscal year: $280,000. 270 computers available on campus for general student use. A campuswide network can be accessed from off-campus. Staffed computer lab on campus.

■ NORTH ARKANSAS COLLEGE

1515 Pioneer Dr.
Harrison, AR 72601
Tel: (870)743-3000; Free: 800-679-6622
Fax: (870)391-3339
E-mail: charlam@northark.edu
Web Site: www.northark.edu

Description: State and locally supported, 2-year, coed. Awards certificates, transfer associate, and terminal associate degrees. Founded 1974. Setting: 40-acre small town campus. Total enrollment: 2,429. Faculty: 139. Student-undergrad faculty ratio is 19:1. 927 applied, 100% were admitted. Full-time: 1,491 students, 59% women, 41% men. Part-time: 938 students, 61% women, 39% men. Students come from 1 other country, 2% from out-of-state. 44% 25 or older, 10% transferred in. Retention: 50% of full-time freshmen returned the following year. Core. Calendar: semesters. Academic remediation for entering students, services for LD students, advanced placement, freshman honors college, honors program, independent study, distance learning, summer session for credit, part-time degree program, adult/continuing education programs, internships.

Entrance Requirements: Open admission. Option: deferred admission. Required for some: high school transcript. Application deadline: rolling. Notification: continuous. Transfer credits accepted: Yes.

Costs Per Year: Application fee: $0. Area resident tuition: $1988 full-time, $71 per credit hour part-time. State resident tuition: $2688 full-time, $96 per credit hour part-time. Nonresident tuition: $4732 full-time, $169 per credit hour part-time. Mandatory fees: $672 full-time, $24 per credit hour part-time. Full-time tuition and fees vary according to course load and program. Part-time tuition and fees vary according to course load and program.

Collegiate Environment: Orientation program. Drama-theater group. Social organizations: 8 open to all. Most popular organizations: Phi Beta Lambda, Phi Theta Kappa, Student Nurses Association, VICA (Vocational Industrial Clubs of America), Baptist Student Union. Major annual events: Cookouts, Homecoming, plays. Student services: personal-psychological counseling. Campus security: 24-hour emergency response devices. North Arkansas College Library plus 1 other. 270 computers available on campus for general student use. A campuswide network can be accessed from off-campus. Students can access the following: online class registration, Portal. Staffed computer lab on campus provides training in use of computers, software, and the Internet.

■ NORTHWEST ARKANSAS COMMUNITY COLLEGE

One College Dr.
Bentonville, AR 72712
Tel: (479)986-4000; Free: 800-995-6922
E-mail: admissions@nwacc.edu
Web Site: www.nwacc.edu

Description: State-supported, 2-year, coed. Awards certificates, transfer associate, and terminal associate degrees. Founded 1989. Setting: 77-acre suburban campus. Educational spending for the previous fiscal year: $4400 per student. Total enrollment: 7,715. Faculty: 475 (154 full-time, 321 part-time). Student-undergrad faculty ratio is 18:1. 2% American Indian or Alaska Native, non-Hispanic/Latino; 16% Hispanic/Latino; 2% Black or African American, non-Hispanic/Latino; 3% Asian, non-Hispanic/Latino; 0.3% Native Hawaiian or other Pacific Islander, non-Hispanic/Latino; 2% international. Retention: 59% of full-time freshmen returned the following year. Core.

Calendar: semesters. Academic remediation for entering students, ESL program, services for LD students, advanced placement, accelerated degree program, self-designed majors, honors program, independent study, distance learning, double major, summer session for credit, part-time degree program, adult/continuing education programs, co-op programs and internships. Study abroad program. ROTC: Army (c), Air Force (c).

Entrance Requirements: Open admission. Option: electronic application. Required: high school transcript. Application deadline: rolling. Notification: continuous. Transfer credits accepted: Yes.

Costs Per Year: Area resident tuition: $2250 full-time, $75 per credit hour part-time. State resident tuition: $3675 full-time, $122.50 per credit hour part-time. Nonresident tuition: $3750 full-time, $125 per credit hour part-time. Mandatory fees: $988 full-time, $29.25 per credit hour part-time, $55 per term part-time. Full-time tuition and fees vary according to program. Part-time tuition and fees vary according to program.

Collegiate Environment: Orientation program. Drama-theater group, choral group, student-run newspaper. Social organizations: 18 open to all. Most popular organizations: Student Advisory Activity Council, Gamma Beta Phi, Phi Beta Lambda, Student Nurses Association, Enactus. Major annual events: Pizza with the President, Student Organization Fair, Fall Festival. Student services: personal-psychological counseling. Campus security: 24-hour emergency response devices and patrols. Pauline Whitaker Library plus 1 other. 300 computers available on campus for general student use. A campuswide network can be accessed. Students can access the following: online class registration. Staffed computer lab on campus provides training in use of computers, software, and the Internet.

■ **OUACHITA BAPTIST UNIVERSITY**
410 Ouachita St.
Arkadelphia, AR 71998-0001
Tel: (870)245-5000; Free: 800-342-5628
Fax: (870)245-5500
E-mail: motll@obu.edu
Web Site: www.obu.edu
Description: Independent Baptist, 4-year, coed. Awards associate and bachelor's degrees. Founded 1886. Setting: 200-acre small town campus with easy access to Little Rock. Endowment: $118,705. Research spending for the previous fiscal year: $204,898. Educational spending for the previous fiscal year: $8851 per student. Total enrollment: 1,660. Faculty: 170 (109 full-time, 61 part-time). Student-undergrad faculty ratio is 12:1. 2,162 applied, 64% were admitted. 33% from top 10% of their high school class, 55% from top quarter, 84% from top half. 2 National Merit Scholars, 16 valedictorians. Full-time: 1,529 students, 55% women, 45% men. Part-time: 101 students, 70% women, 30% men. Students come from 28 states and territories, 22 other countries, 32% from out-of-state. 0.6% American Indian or Alaska Native, non-Hispanic/Latino; 5% Hispanic/Latino; 8% Black or African American, non-Hispanic/Latino; 0.4% Asian, non-Hispanic/Latino; 0.1% Native Hawaiian or other Pacific Islander, non-Hispanic/Latino; 2% international. 4% 25 or older, 97% live on campus, 3% transferred in. Retention: 83% of full-time freshmen returned the following year. Academic areas with the most degrees conferred: business/marketing; biological/life sciences; communication/journalism; visual and performing arts. Core. Calendar: semesters. Academic remediation for entering students, ESL program, advanced placement, accelerated degree program, honors program, independent study, distance learning, double major, summer session for credit, part-time degree program, adult/continuing education programs, co-op programs and internships. Off campus study at Henderson State University. Study abroad program. ROTC: Army.
Entrance Requirements: Options: deferred admission, international baccalaureate accepted. Required: high school transcript, minimum 2.75 high school GPA, SAT or ACT. Recommended: interview. Entrance: moderately difficult. Notification: continuous. SAT Reasoning Test deadline: 8/15. SAT Subject Test deadline: 8/15. Transfer credits accepted: Yes.
Costs Per Year: Application fee: $0. Comprehensive fee: $35,900 includes full-time tuition ($27,280), mandatory fees ($620), and college room and board ($8000). College room only: $6280. Part-time tuition: $725 per credit hour.
Collegiate Environment: Orientation program. Drama-theater group, choral group, marching band, student-run newspaper. Social organizations: 60 open to all; local fraternities, local sororities; 23% of eligible men and 33% of eligible women are members. Most popular organizations: Phi Beta Lambda, Student Foundation, Student Education Association, Campus Activities Board, International Club. Major annual events: Tiger Tunes, Tiger Traks, Homecoming. Student services: health clinic, personal-psychological

counseling. Campus security: 24-hour emergency response devices and patrols, controlled dormitory access. 1,559 college housing spaces available; 1,415 were occupied in 2018-19. Freshmen guaranteed college housing. On-campus residence required through senior year. Options: men-only, women-only housing available. Riley-Hickingbotham Library plus 2 others. Books: 160,398 (physical), 12,821 (digital/electronic); Serial titles: 1,723 (physical), 41,230 (digital/electronic); Databases: 150. Weekly public service hours: 80; students can reserve study rooms. Operations spending for the previous fiscal year: $850,582. 275 computers available on campus for general student use. Computer purchase/lease plans available. A campuswide network can be accessed from student residence rooms and from off campus. Students can access the following: student Web portal. Staffed computer lab on campus (open 24 hours a day) provides training in use of computers, software, and the Internet.

Community Environment: Ouachita Baptist University is located in Arkadelphia, Arkansas, about 70 miles southwest of Little Rock on I-30 and 35 miles south of Hot Springs. There is frequent Amtrak service to and from the city. Facilities for air transportation are available both in Hot Springs and Little Rock. Arkadelphia has a population of more than 10,000, including the students of Ouachita and Henderson State University.

■ **OZARKA COLLEGE**
PO Box 10
Melbourne, AR 72556
Tel: (870)368-7371; Free: 800-821-4335
Fax: (870)368-4733
E-mail: dmmowery@ozarka.edu
Web Site: www.ozarka.edu
Description: State-supported, 2-year, coed. Awards certificates, transfer associate, and terminal associate degrees. Founded 1973. Setting: 40-acre rural campus. Total enrollment: 1,600. Faculty: 71 (31 full-time, 40 part-time). Student-undergrad faculty ratio is 20:1. 1% from out-of-state. 43% 25 or older. Core. Calendar: semesters. Academic remediation for entering students, services for LD students, advanced placement, distance learning, summer session for credit, external degree program, internships.
Entrance Requirements: Open admission except for nursing and information science technology programs. Options: electronic application, deferred admission. Required: high school transcript. Recommended: minimum 2 high school GPA. Required for some: essay, interview. Entrance: noncompetitive. Application deadline: 8/19.
Collegiate Environment: Orientation program. Drama-theater group. Social organizations: 7 open to all. Most popular organizations: VICA (Vocational Industrial Clubs of America), Phi Beta Lambda, Drama Club, HOSA, Phi Theta Kappa. Major annual events: Community Service Day, Career Day. Student services: personal-psychological counseling. Campus security: security patrols after business hours. Ozarka College Library. Operations spending for the previous fiscal year: $171,858. 114 computers available on campus for general student use. A campuswide network can be accessed from off-campus. Students can access the following: online class registration. Staffed computer lab on campus.

■ **PHILANDER SMITH COLLEGE**
900 W Daisy Bates Dr.
Little Rock, AR 72202-3799
Tel: (501)375-9845; Free: 800-446-6772
Fax: (501)370-5225
Web Site: www.philander.edu
Description: Independent United Methodist, 4-year, coed. Awards bachelor's degrees. Founded 1877. Setting: 25-acre urban campus. Total enrollment: 765. Faculty: 66 (36 full-time, 30 part-time). Student-undergrad faculty ratio is 16:1. 3,330 applied, 52% were admitted. 15% from top 10% of their high school class, 32% from top quarter, 59% from top half. Full-time: 725 students, 61% women, 39% men. Part-time: 40 students, 65% women, 35% men. Students come from 24 states and territories, 8 other countries, 49% from out-of-state. 1% Hispanic/Latino; 92% Black or African American, non-Hispanic/Latino; 0.4% Asian, non-Hispanic/Latino; 0.1% Native Hawaiian or other Pacific Islander, non-Hispanic/Latino; 3% international. 14% 25 or older, 63% live on campus, 9% transferred in. Retention: 63% of full-time freshmen returned the following year. Academic areas with the most degrees conferred: business/marketing; social sciences; public administration and social services; biological/life sciences. Core. Calendar: semesters. Academic remediation for entering students, services for LD students, advanced placement, accelerated degree program, independent study, distance learning, double major, summer session for credit, part-time degree

program, adult/continuing education programs, co-op programs and internships. Study abroad program. ROTC: Army (c).

Entrance Requirements: Open admission. Options: electronic application, deferred admission, international baccalaureate accepted. Required: high school transcript, SAT or ACT. Entrance: minimally difficult. Application deadlines: rolling, rolling for nonresidents. Notification: continuous, continuous for nonresidents. SAT Reasoning Test deadline: 7/15. SAT Subject Test deadline: 7/15. Transfer credits accepted: Yes.

Collegiate Environment: Orientation program. Drama-theater group, choral group. Social organizations: 20 open to all; national fraternities, national sororities; 80% of eligible men and 75% of eligible women are members. Most popular organizations: Student Government Association, Panther Programming Council, Panther Dolls, Panther Newscast, Religious Life Council. Major annual events: Bless the Mic, Renaissance Awards, Health & Wellness Fair. Student services: health clinic, personal-psychological counseling. Campus security: 24-hour emergency response devices and patrols, student patrols, controlled dormitory access. D. W. Reynolds Library & Technology Center. Books: 74,152 (physical), 20,575 (digital/electronic); Serial titles: 190 (physical), 166 (digital/electronic); Databases: 47. Weekly public service hours: 81; students can reserve study rooms. 225 computers available on campus for general student use. A campuswide network can be accessed from student residence rooms and from off campus. Students can access the following: online class registration. Staffed computer lab on campus provides training in use of computers, software, and the Internet.

Community Environment: See University of Arkansas - Little Rock.

■ PHILLIPS COMMUNITY COLLEGE OF THE UNIVERSITY OF ARKANSAS

PO Box 785
Helena, AR 72342-0785
Tel: (870)338-6474
Fax: (870)338-7542
Web Site: www.pccua.edu

Description: State and locally supported, 2-year, coed. Part of University of Arkansas System. Awards certificates, transfer associate, and terminal associate degrees. Founded 1965. Setting: 80-acre small town campus with easy access to Memphis. Total enrollment: 2,337. 32% 25 or older. Core. Calendar: semesters. Academic remediation for entering students, services for LD students, advanced placement, summer session for credit, part-time degree program, adult/continuing education programs.

Entrance Requirements: Open admission except for nursing, medical laboratory technician programs. Option: early admission. Entrance: noncompetitive. Application deadline: 8/25. Notification: continuous until 8/25.

Collegiate Environment: Drama-theater group, choral group, student-run newspaper. Student services: personal-psychological counseling. Campus security: 24-hour patrols.

Community Environment: Helena is in a suburban area, and blessed with a mild, warm climate. There are churches of major denominations, libraries, a museum, an accredited general hospital, and major civic and service organizations.

■ REMINGTON COLLEGE-LITTLE ROCK CAMPUS

10600 Colonel Glenn Rd.
Ste. 100
Little Rock, AR 72204
Tel: (501)303-4385; Free: 800-323-8122
Fax: (501)225-3819
Web Site: www.remingtoncollege.edu

Description: Independent, 2-year, coed. Awards terminal associate degrees.

■ SHORTER COLLEGE

604 Locust St.
North Little Rock, AR 72114-4885
Tel: (501)374-6305
Fax: (501)374-9333
Web Site: www.shortercollege.edu

Description: Independent African Methodist Episcopal, 2-year, coed. Awards transfer associate and terminal associate degrees. Founded 1886. Setting: urban campus. Total enrollment: 106. Faculty: 24 (9 full-time, 15 part-time). 2% from top half of their high school class. Students come from 5 states and territories. 50% 25 or older. Core. Calendar: semesters.

Academic remediation for entering students, summer session for credit, part-time degree program, external degree program, adult/continuing education programs, co-op programs.

Entrance Requirements: Open admission. Options: early admission, deferred admission. Required: high school transcript, ACT. Entrance: noncompetitive. Application deadline: rolling.

Collegiate Environment: Orientation program. Most popular organizations: Business Club, Natural Science Club, Social Science Club, Campus Ministry, Student Government Association. Major annual events: Founder's Day, Homecoming. Student services: legal services, health clinic, personal-psychological counseling. A. W. Young Library. 10 computers available on campus for general student use. Staffed computer lab on campus.

■ SOUTH ARKANSAS COMMUNITY COLLEGE

PO Box 7010
El Dorado, AR 71731-7010
Tel: (870)862-8131; Free: 800-955-2289
Fax: (870)864-7122
E-mail: dinman@southark.edu
Web Site: www.southark.edu

Description: State-supported, 2-year, coed. Part of Arkansas Department of Higher Education. Awards certificates, transfer associate, and terminal associate degrees. Founded 1975. Setting: 4-acre small town campus. Endowment: $1 million. Educational spending for the previous fiscal year: $2511 per student. Total enrollment: 1,368. Full-time: 612 students, 75% women, 25% men. Part-time: 756 students, 67% women, 33% men. Students come from 2 states and territories, 40% from out-of-state. 43% 25 or older. Retention: 46% of full-time freshmen returned the following year. Core. Calendar: semesters. Academic remediation for entering students, services for LD students, advanced placement, summer session for credit, part-time degree program, adult/continuing education programs, internships.

Entrance Requirements: Open admission. Options: early admission, deferred admission. Required: high school transcript. Recommended: SAT or ACT. Entrance: noncompetitive. Application deadline: 8/25.

Collegiate Environment: Orientation program. Choral group. Student services: personal-psychological counseling. Campus security: security guard. South Arkansas Community College Library. 75 computers available on campus for general student use. A campuswide network can be accessed from off-campus. Students can access the following: online class registration. Staffed computer lab on campus provides training in use of computers, software, and the Internet.

Community Environment: El Dorado is the seat of Union County, lying 117 miles south of Little Rock. Important industries are timber, poultry, oil, and chemicals. Bus and air service is available. Community services include a public library, two hospitals, several churches, an arts center, and good shopping facilities. There is good hunting and fishing in the general area, and water sports on nearby lakes and rivers.

■ SOUTHEAST ARKANSAS COLLEGE

1900 Hazel St.
Pine Bluff, AR 71603
Tel: (870)543-5900; Free: 888-SEARC TC
Web Site: www.seark.edu

Description: State-supported, 2-year, coed. Awards certificates, transfer associate, and terminal associate degrees. Founded 1991. Setting: 42-acre urban campus with easy access to Little Rock. Endowment: $559,963. Total enrollment: 1,304. Faculty: 102 (55 full-time, 47 part-time). Student-undergrad faculty ratio is 13:1. Full-time: 582 students, 69% women, 31% men. Part-time: 722 students, 70% women, 30% men. Students come from 3 states and territories, 1 other country. 0.1% American Indian or Alaska Native, non-Hispanic/Latino; 2% Hispanic/Latino; 57% Black or African American, non-Hispanic/Latino; 0.9% Asian, non-Hispanic/Latino; 0.1% Native Hawaiian or other Pacific Islander, non-Hispanic/Latino; 0.1% international. 46% 25 or older, 5% transferred in. Retention: 63% of full-time freshmen returned the following year. Calendar: semesters. Academic remediation for entering students, services for LD students, advanced placement, accelerated degree program, honors program, independent study, distance learning, double major, summer session for credit, part-time degree program, co-op programs and internships.

Entrance Requirements: Open admission. Options: electronic application, early admission. Required: high school transcript. Recommended: SAT and SAT Subject Tests or ACT. Required for some: ACCUPLACER (if no other test scores are available, or test scores are older than 3 years). Entrance: noncompetitive. Notification: continuous. Transfer credits accepted: Yes.

Costs Per Year: Application fee: $0. State resident tuition: $2820 full-time, $94 per credit hour part-time. Nonresident tuition: $5640 full-time, $188 per credit hour part-time. Mandatory fees: $640 full-time, $21 per credit hour part-time, $5 per term part-time. Full-time tuition and fees vary according to location and program. Part-time tuition and fees vary according to location and program.

Collegiate Environment: Orientation program. Choral group. Social organizations: Phi Theta Kappa honor society. Most popular organizations: Phi Beta Lambda, HOSA, Phi Theta Kappa, Student Senate. Major annual events: Spring Fling, Back to School Bash, Honors and Awards Program. Student services: personal-psychological counseling. Campus security: 24-hour patrols. Southeast Arkansas College Library. Books: 11,605 (physical), 94 (digital/electronic); Serial titles: 164 (physical), 8 (digital/electronic); Databases: 6. 62 computers available on campus for general student use. A campuswide network can be accessed. Students can access the following: online class registration. Staffed computer lab on campus provides training in use of computers, software, and the Internet.

■ SOUTHERN ARKANSAS UNIVERSITY-MAGNOLIA

100 E University
Magnolia, AR 71753
Tel: (870)235-4000; Free: 800-332-7286
Fax: (870)235-5005
Web Site: www.saumag.edu

Description: State-supported, comprehensive, coed. Part of Southern Arkansas University System. Awards associate, bachelor's, and master's degrees. Founded 1909. Setting: 1,390-acre small town campus. Endowment: $38.5 million. Research spending for the previous fiscal year: $418,131. Educational spending for the previous fiscal year: $4709 per student. Total enrollment: 4,468. Faculty: 296 (166 full-time, 130 part-time). Student-undergrad faculty ratio is 18:1. 3,552 applied, 69% were admitted. 16% from top 10% of their high school class, 37% from top quarter, 71% from top half. Full-time: 3,018 students, 55% women, 45% men. Part-time: 524 students, 60% women, 40% men. Students come from 38 states and territories, 7 other countries, 23% from out-of-state. 0.7% American Indian or Alaska Native, non-Hispanic/Latino; 4% Hispanic/Latino; 26% Black or African American, non-Hispanic/Latino; 1% Asian, non-Hispanic/Latino; 0.2% Native Hawaiian or other Pacific Islander, non-Hispanic/Latino; 2% international. 11% 25 or older, 54% live on campus, 5% transferred in. Retention: 65% of full-time freshmen returned the following year. Academic areas with the most degrees conferred: business/marketing; psychology; education. Core. Calendar: semesters. Academic remediation for entering students, ESL program, services for LD students, advanced placement, accelerated degree program, freshman honors college, honors program, independent study, distance learning, double major, summer session for credit, part-time degree program, adult/continuing education programs, internships, graduate courses open to undergrads. Study abroad program.

Entrance Requirements: Options: electronic application, early admission, deferred admission, international baccalaureate accepted. Required: high school transcript, SAT or ACT. Recommended: ACT. Required for some: interview. Entrance: moderately difficult. Application deadline: 8/27. Transfer credits accepted: Yes.

Costs Per Year: Application fee: $0. State resident tuition: $6840 full-time, $228 per credit hour part-time. Nonresident tuition: $10,950 full-time, $365 per credit hour part-time. Mandatory fees: $1836 full-time. Full-time tuition and fees vary according to course load. Part-time tuition varies according to course load. College room and board: $6240. College room only: $3110. Room and board charges vary according to board plan and housing facility.

Collegiate Environment: Orientation program. Drama-theater group, choral group, marching band, student-run newspaper, radio station. Social organizations: 120 open to all; national fraternities, national sororities; 1% of eligible men and 1% of eligible women are members. Most popular organizations: Student Government Association, Student Activities Board, Resident Hall Association, Residential College, International Student Association. Major annual events: Homecoming, Parents' Day, Spring Fling. Student services: health clinic, personal-psychological counseling. Campus security: 24-hour emergency response devices, student patrols, late night transport-escort service, controlled dormitory access. 1,992 college housing spaces available; 1,950 were occupied in 2018-19. Freshmen guaranteed college housing. On-campus residence required through sophomore year. Options: coed, men-only, women-only housing available. Magale Library. Books: 138,050 (physical), 10,973 (digital/electronic); Serial titles: 130 (physical), 86 (digital/electronic); Databases: 187. Weekly public service hours: 87. Operations spending for the previous fiscal year: $1.2 million. 199 computers avail-

able on campus for general student use. A campuswide network can be accessed from student residence rooms and from off campus. Students can access the following: online class registration. Staffed computer lab on campus provides training in use of computers, software, and the Internet.

■ SOUTHERN ARKANSAS UNIVERSITY TECH

6415 Spellman Rd.
Camden, AR 71701
Tel: (870)574-4500
Fax: (870)574-4520
E-mail: lsmith@sautech.edu
Web Site: www.sautech.edu

Description: State-supported, 2-year, coed. Part of Southern Arkansas University System. Awards certificates, transfer associate, and terminal associate degrees. Founded 1967. Setting: 96-acre rural campus. System endowment: $1.7 million. Educational spending for the previous fiscal year: $7323 per student. Total enrollment: 1,650. Faculty: 93 (32 full-time, 61 part-time). Student-undergrad faculty ratio is 17:1. 954 applied, 100% were admitted. 4% from top 10% of their high school class, 50% from top quarter, 84% from top half. Full-time: 501 students, 43% women, 57% men. Part-time: 1,149 students, 54% women, 46% men. Students come from 12 states and territories, 2 other countries, 10% from out-of-state. 0.4% American Indian or Alaska Native, non-Hispanic/Latino; 3% Hispanic/Latino; 36% Black or African American, non-Hispanic/Latino; 0.5% Asian, non-Hispanic/Latino; 0.1% Native Hawaiian or other Pacific Islander, non-Hispanic/Latino; 0.1% international. 47% 25 or older, 2% live on campus, 1% transferred in. Core. Calendar: semesters. Academic remediation for entering students, services for LD students, advanced placement, accelerated degree program, freshman honors college, honors program, independent study, distance learning, double major, summer session for credit, part-time degree program, external degree program, adult/continuing education programs, co-op programs and internships. Off campus study at Arkansas Fire Training Academy-Fire and Emergency Response;Arkansas Environmental Training Academy-Wastewater, Solid Waste, Water Treatment; Arkansas Law Enforcement Training Academy-Law Enforcement; Arkansas Game and Fish Academy-Wildlife and Fisheries Enforcement; SAU Tech Welding Academy, Magnolia-Welding; Texarkana Airport-Aviation Maintenance.

Entrance Requirements: Open admission except for practical nursing program. Options: electronic application, deferred admission. Required: high school transcript. Application deadline: 8/15. Notification: continuous. Transfer credits accepted: Yes.

Collegiate Environment: Orientation program. Drama-theater group, student-run radio station. Social organizations: 11 open to all. Most popular organizations: Phi Beta Lambda, TEC@Tech, Allied Health Student Club, Aviation Club, Multimedia Club. Major annual events: Student Appreciation Day, Ed-U-Fest, Fall Preview Day. Student services: personal-psychological counseling, women's center. Campus security: 24-hour emergency response devices and patrols, late night transport-escort service. Southern Arkansas University Tech Learning Resource Center. Books: 17,910 (physical), 17,020 (digital/electronic); Serial titles: 964 (physical), 176 (digital/electronic); Databases: 9. Weekly public service hours: 45; students can reserve study rooms. Operations spending for the previous fiscal year: $183,175. 350 computers available on campus for general student use. A campuswide network can be accessed from student residence rooms and from off campus. Students can access the following: online class registration. Staffed computer lab on campus provides training in use of computers, software, and the Internet.

■ STRAYER UNIVERSITY-LITTLE ROCK CAMPUS

10825 Financial Centre Pky.
Ste. 400
Little Rock, AR 72211
Tel: (501)708-0600; Free: 888-311-0355
Web Site: www.strayer.edu

Description: Proprietary, comprehensive, coed. Awards bachelor's and master's degrees.

■ UNIVERSITY OF ARKANSAS

1 University of Arkansas
Fayetteville, AR 72701
Tel: (479)575-2000; Free: 800-377-8632
Fax: (479)575-7515
E-mail: uofa@uark.edu
Web Site: www.uark.edu

Description: State-supported, university, coed. Part of University of Arkansas System. Awards bachelor's, master's, and doctoral degrees and post-master's certificates. Founded 1871. Setting: 718-acre urban campus. Total enrollment: 27,778. Faculty: 1,401 (1,192 full-time, 209 part-time). Student-undergrad faculty ratio is 19:1. 18,732 applied, 77% were admitted. 25% from top 10% of their high school class, 52% from top quarter, 84% from top half. 42 National Merit Scholars. Full-time: 21,005 students, 54% women, 46% men. Part-time: 2,381 students, 52% women, 48% men. Students come from 47 states and territories, 85 other countries, 46% from out-of-state. 0.9% American Indian or Alaska Native, non-Hispanic/Latino; 9% Hispanic/Latino; 4% Black or African American, non-Hispanic/Latino; 2% Asian, non-Hispanic/Latino; 0.1% Native Hawaiian or other Pacific Islander, non-Hispanic/Latino; 3% international. 7% 25 or older, 25% live on campus, 6% transferred in. Retention: 84% of full-time freshmen returned the following year. Academic areas with the most degrees conferred: business/marketing; engineering; health professions and related sciences. Core. Calendar: semesters. Academic remediation for entering students, ESL program, services for LD students, advanced placement, accelerated degree program, self-designed majors, freshman honors college, honors program, independent study, distance learning, double major, summer session for credit, part-time degree program, co-op programs and internships, graduate courses open to undergrads. Off campus study at Northwest Arkansas Community College, Great Plains IDEA Consortium. Study abroad program. ROTC: Army, Air Force.

Entrance Requirements: Options: electronic application, early action, international baccalaureate accepted. Required: high school transcript, minimum 3 high school GPA, minimum ACT Composite score of 20 or SAT total (math and EBRW only) of 1030, completion of 16 core academic units, SAT or ACT. Required for some: essay. Entrance: moderately difficult. Application deadlines: 8/1, 8/1 for nonresidents, 11/1 for early action. Notification: continuous until 9/1, continuous until 9/1 for nonresidents, 12/15 for early action. SAT Reasoning Test deadline: 8/1. SAT Subject Test deadline: 8/1. Transfer credits accepted: Yes. Applicants placed on waiting list: 399. Wait-listed applicants offered admission: 134. Early action applicants: 14,236. Early action applicants admitted: 12,522.

Costs Per Year: Application fee: $40. State resident tuition: $7384 full-time, $246.12 per credit hour part-time. Nonresident tuition: $23,422 full-time, $780.71 per credit hour part-time. Mandatory fees: $1746 full-time, $58.18 per credit hour part-time. Full-time tuition and fees vary according to course load, location, and program. Part-time tuition and fees vary according to course load, location, and program. College room and board: $11,020. College room only: $7090. Room and board charges vary according to board plan, housing facility, and location.

Collegiate Environment: Orientation program. Drama-theater group, choral group, marching band, student-run newspaper, radio station. Social organizations: 430 open to all; national fraternities, national sororities, local fraternities, local sororities; 23% of eligible men and 39% of eligible women are members. Most popular organizations: Associated Student Government, Catholic Campus Ministry, Chinese Students and Scholars, Alpha Lambda Delta, Student Alumni Association. Major annual events: Razorbash/Welcome Weeks, Homecoming Week, Headliner Concerts/Distinguished Lectures. Student services: legal services, health clinic, personal-psychological counseling, women's center. Campus security: 24-hour emergency response devices and patrols, student patrols, late night transport-escort service, controlled dormitory access. 6,130 college housing spaces available; 5,932 were occupied in 2018-19. Freshmen guaranteed college housing. On-campus residence required in freshman year. Options: coed, women-only housing available. David W. Mullins Library plus 4 others. Books: 2 million (physical), 593,016 (digital/electronic); Serial titles: 60,187 (physical), 147,231 (digital/electronic); Databases: 331. Weekly public service hours: 109; students can reserve study rooms. 675 computers available on campus for general student use. Computer purchase/lease plans available. A campuswide network can be accessed from student residence rooms and from off campus. Students can access the following: online class registration. Staffed computer lab on campus provides training in use of computers, software, and the Internet.

■ **UNIVERSITY OF ARKANSAS COMMUNITY COLLEGE AT BATESVILLE**
PO Box 3350
Batesville, AR 72503
Tel: (870)612-2000; Free: 800-508-7878
Fax: (870)793-4988
E-mail: amy.foree@uaccb.edu

Web Site: www.uaccb.edu

Description: State-supported, 2-year, coed. Part of University of Arkansas System. Awards certificates, transfer associate, and terminal associate degrees. Setting: small town campus. Total enrollment: 1,315. Student-undergrad faculty ratio is 19:1. Full-time: 750 students, 65% women, 35% men. Part-time: 565 students, 69% women, 31% men. Students come from 2 states and territories. 0.9% American Indian or Alaska Native, non-Hispanic/Latino; 5% Hispanic/Latino; 3% Black or African American, non-Hispanic/Latino; 0.9% Asian, non-Hispanic/Latino; 0.2% Native Hawaiian or other Pacific Islander, non-Hispanic/Latino; 0.2% international. 40% 25 or older, 4% transferred in. Retention: 60% of full-time freshmen returned the following year. Core. Calendar: semesters. Academic remediation for entering students, ESL program, services for LD students, advanced placement, self-designed majors, independent study, distance learning, double major, summer session for credit, part-time degree program, external degree program, adult/continuing education programs, co-op programs and internships. Off campus study.

Entrance Requirements: Open admission. Option: electronic application. Required: high school transcript, minimum ACT composite score of 15 or minimum COMPASS reading score of 63. Recommended: ACT, ACT ASSET, ACT Compass, or SAT. Entrance: noncompetitive. Application deadline: rolling. Notification: continuous.

Collegiate Environment: Orientation program. Choral group. Most popular organizations: Student Government Association, Phi Kappa Theta, Circle K International, Non-Traditional Students Organization, Renaissance Club. Major annual events: Welcome Back Cookout, Annual Birthday Party, Student Success Symposium. Campus security: trained security officers during hours of operation, security cameras, emergency alerts systems. University of Arkansas Community College at Batesville Library.

■ **UNIVERSITY OF ARKANSAS COMMUNITY COLLEGE AT HOPE**
PO Box 140
Hope, AR 71802
Tel: (870)777-5722
Fax: (870)722-5957
Web Site: www.uacch.edu

Description: State-supported, 2-year, coed. Part of University of Arkansas System. Awards certificates, diplomas, transfer associate, and terminal associate degrees. Founded 1966. Setting: 60-acre rural campus. Total enrollment: 1,360. Faculty: 91 (40 full-time, 51 part-time). Student-undergrad faculty ratio is 15:1. 540 applied, 100% were admitted. Full-time: 666 students, 68% women, 32% men. Part-time: 694 students, 67% women, 33% men. Students come from 5 states and territories, 7% from out-of-state. 0.8% American Indian or Alaska Native, non-Hispanic/Latino; 7% Hispanic/Latino; 37% Black or African American, non-Hispanic/Latino; 0.4% Asian, non-Hispanic/Latino; 0.1% Native Hawaiian or other Pacific Islander, non-Hispanic/Latino. 37% 25 or older, 6% transferred in. Retention: 42% of full-time freshmen returned the following year. Core. Calendar: semesters. Academic remediation for entering students, services for LD students, advanced placement, accelerated degree program, independent study, distance learning, double major, summer session for credit, part-time degree program, internships. Off campus study.

Entrance Requirements: Open admission. Option: early admission. Required: high school transcript. Recommended: SAT or ACT, ACT Compass. Entrance: noncompetitive. Application deadline: rolling. Notification: continuous. Transfer credits accepted: Yes.

Collegiate Environment: Orientation program. Social organizations: 11 open to all. Most popular organizations: Phi Theta Kappa, Arkansas Licensed Practical Nursing Association, Campus Crusaders for Christ, Technical and Industrial Club, Fine Arts Club. Major annual event: Annual Fish Fry. Campus security: 24-hour emergency response devices, on-campus security during class hours. University of Arkansas Community College at Hope Library. Operations spending for the previous fiscal year: $187,710. 50 computers available on campus for general student use. A campuswide network can be accessed. Students can access the following: online class registration. Staffed computer lab on campus provides training in use of computers, software, and the Internet.

■ **UNIVERSITY OF ARKANSAS COMMUNITY COLLEGE AT MORRILTON**
1537 University Blvd.
Morrilton, AR 72110
Tel: (501)977-2000; Free: 800-264-1094
Fax: (501)354-9948

E-mail: grierlindsey@uaccm.edu
Web Site: www.uaccm.edu
Description: State-supported, 2-year, coed. Part of University of Arkansas System. Awards certificates, transfer associate, and terminal associate degrees. Founded 1961. Setting: 89-acre rural campus. Educational spending for the previous fiscal year: $2568 per student. Total enrollment: 1,902. Faculty: 73 (53 full-time, 20 part-time). Student-undergrad faculty ratio is 22:1. 1,234 applied, 74% were admitted. Full-time: 1,033 students, 57% women, 43% men. Part-time: 869 students, 70% women, 30% men. Students come from 4 states and territories, 3 other countries. 0.3% American Indian or Alaska Native, non-Hispanic/Latino; 8% Hispanic/Latino; 8% Black or African American, non-Hispanic/Latino; 0.7% Asian, non-Hispanic/Latino; 0.1% Native Hawaiian or other Pacific Islander, non-Hispanic/Latino; 2% international. 33% 25 or older, 9% transferred in. Calendar: semesters. Academic remediation for entering students, services for LD students, advanced placement, independent study, distance learning, double major, summer session for credit, part-time degree program, co-op programs and internships.
Entrance Requirements: Options: electronic application, early admission, deferred admission. Required: high school transcript. Recommended: SAT or ACT, ACT Compass, ACCUPLACER. Required for some: immunization records, prior college transcript(s). Entrance: noncompetitive. Application deadline: rolling. Notification: continuous. Transfer credits accepted: Yes.
Costs Per Year: Application fee: $0. Area resident tuition: $2730 full-time, $91 per credit hour part-time. State resident tuition: $3030 full-time, $101 per credit hour part-time. Nonresident tuition: $3900 full-time, $130 per credit hour part-time. Mandatory fees: $1160 full-time, $39 per credit hour part-time, $10 per term part-time. Full-time tuition and fees vary according to course load and program. Part-time tuition and fees vary according to course load and program.
Collegiate Environment: Orientation program. Social organizations: 13 open to all; Phi Theta Kappa and Phi Beta Lambda Academic Honor. Most popular organizations: Phi Theta Kappa, Student Activities Board, National Technical Honors Society, Thrive Student Ministries, Computer Information Systems Club. Major annual events: Spring Fling, Fall Fest, Halloween Bash. Student services: personal-psychological counseling. Campus security: 24-hour emergency response devices, late night transport-escort service. College housing not available. E. Allen Gordon Library. Books: 27,196 (physical), 177,896 (digital/electronic); Serial titles: 81 (physical); Databases: 35. Weekly public service hours: 66; students can reserve study rooms. Operations spending for the previous fiscal year: $238,807. 520 computers available on campus for general student use. A campuswide network can be accessed from off-campus. Students can access the following: online class registration. Staffed computer lab on campus provides training in use of computers, software, and the Internet.

■ **UNIVERSITY OF ARKANSAS-FORT SMITH**
PO Box 3649
Fort Smith, AR 72913-3649
Tel: (479)788-7000; Free: 888-512-5466
Fax: (479)788-7003
E-mail: kelly.westeen@uafortsmith.edu
Web Site: uafs.edu
Description: State and locally supported, comprehensive, coed. Part of University of Arkansas System. Awards associate, bachelor's, and master's degrees. Founded 1928. Setting: 170-acre suburban campus. Endowment: $79.4 million. Educational spending for the previous fiscal year: $5534 per student. Total enrollment: 6,823. Faculty: 412 (236 full-time, 176 part-time). Student-undergrad faculty ratio is 18:1. 4,001 applied, 56% were admitted. Full-time: 4,581 students, 57% women, 43% men. Part-time: 2,242 students, 54% women, 46% men. Students come from 33 states and territories, 23 other countries, 14% from out-of-state. 3% American Indian or Alaska Native, non-Hispanic/Latino; 9% Hispanic/Latino; 5% Black or African American, non-Hispanic/Latino; 5% Asian, non-Hispanic/Latino; 0.1% Native Hawaiian or other Pacific Islander, non-Hispanic/Latino; 2% international. 28% 25 or older, 13% live on campus, 6% transferred in. Retention: 66% of full-time freshmen returned the following year. Academic areas with the most degrees conferred: business/marketing; education; interdisciplinary studies. Core. Calendar: semesters. Academic remediation for entering students, ESL program, services for LD students, advanced placement, accelerated degree program, honors program, independent study, distance learning, double major, summer session for credit, part-time degree program, external degree program, adult/continuing education programs, co-op programs and internships. Off campus study. Study abroad program. ROTC: Army, Air Force (c).

Entrance Requirements: Options: electronic application, deferred admission, international baccalaureate accepted. Required: high school transcript, minimum 2 high school GPA, SAT, ACT or ACT Compass. Entrance: minimally difficult. Application deadline: rolling. SAT Reasoning Test deadline: 8/7. Transfer credits accepted: Yes.
Costs Per Year: Application fee: $0. State resident tuition: $4989 full-time, $166.30 per credit hour part-time. Nonresident tuition: $13,830 full-time, $461 per credit hour part-time. Mandatory fees: $2,138 full-time, $66.75 per credit hour part-time, $68 per term part-time. Full-time tuition and fees vary according to course load and program. Part-time tuition and fees vary according to course load and program. College room and board: $8226. Room and board charges vary according to board plan and housing facility.
Collegiate Environment: Orientation program. Drama-theater group, choral group, student-run newspaper. Social organizations: 82 open to all; national fraternities, national sororities; 5% of eligible men and 5% of eligible women are members. Most popular organizations: Campus Activities Board, Phi Beta Lambda, Student Alumni Association, Non-Traditional Students, Grand Avenue Baptist College Ministry (Reach). Major annual events: Campus Picnic and Block Party, Haunted Union, Homecoming. Student services: health clinic, personal-psychological counseling. Campus security: 24-hour emergency response devices and patrols, student patrols, late night transport-escort service, controlled dormitory access. Boreham Library. Operations spending for the previous fiscal year: $1.1 million. 1,553 computers available on campus for general student use. A campuswide network can be accessed from student residence rooms and from off campus. Students can access the following: online class registration, online subscription databases, information portal, online course management system and online courses.

■ **UNIVERSITY OF ARKANSAS AT LITTLE ROCK**
2801 S University Ave.
Little Rock, AR 72204-1099
Tel: (501)569-3000; Free: 800-482-8892
Fax: (501)569-8915
E-mail: twharrison@ualr.edu
Web Site: www.ualr.edu
Description: State-supported, university, coed. Part of University of Arkansas System. Awards associate, bachelor's, master's, and doctoral degrees and post-master's certificates. Founded 1927. Setting: 229-acre urban campus. Total enrollment: 11,645. Faculty: 740 (453 full-time, 287 part-time). Student-undergrad faculty ratio is 13:1. 1,751 applied, 59% were admitted. 15% from top 10% of their high school class, 41% from top quarter, 73% from top half. Full-time: 4,921 students, 56% women, 44% men. Part-time: 4,463 students, 63% women, 37% men. 2% from out-of-state. 0.3% American Indian or Alaska Native, non-Hispanic/Latino; 7% Hispanic/Latino; 27% Black or African American, non-Hispanic/Latino; 2% Asian, non-Hispanic/Latino; 3% international. 36% 25 or older, 2% live on campus, 12% transferred in. Retention: 71% of full-time freshmen returned the following year. Core. Calendar: semesters. Academic remediation for entering students, ESL program, advanced placement, accelerated degree program, self-designed majors, freshman honors college, honors program, independent study, distance learning, double major, summer session for credit, part-time degree program, adult/continuing education programs, co-op programs and internships, graduate courses open to undergrads. Study abroad program. ROTC: Army.
Entrance Requirements: Options: electronic application, early admission, deferred admission. Required: high school transcript, minimum 2.5 high school GPA, proof of immunization, SAT or ACT. Entrance: minimally difficult. Transfer credits accepted: Yes.
Collegiate Environment: Orientation program. Drama-theater group, student-run newspaper, radio station. Social organizations: national fraternities, national sororities, local fraternities, local sororities. Most popular organizations: Student Government, University Program Council, Housing Activities Council, International Student Organization, Panhellenic Council. Major annual events: Homecoming Week, Greek Week, Black History Month. Student services: health clinic. Campus security: 24-hour emergency response devices and patrols, student patrols, late night transport-escort service, controlled dormitory access. Ottenheimer Library.

■ **UNIVERSITY OF ARKANSAS FOR MEDICAL SCIENCES**
4301 W Markham
Little Rock, AR 72205-7199
Tel: (501)686-5000
Web Site: www.uams.edu

Description: State-supported, university, coed. Part of University of Arkansas System. Awards associate, bachelor's, master's, and doctoral degrees (bachelor's degree is upper-level). Founded 1879. Setting: 10-acre urban campus with easy access to Little Rock. Endowment: $317.3 million. Research spending for the previous fiscal year: $118.5 million. Educational spending for the previous fiscal year: $49,649 per student. Total enrollment: 2,869. Faculty: 521 (449 full-time, 72 part-time). Student-undergrad faculty ratio is 7:1. Full-time: 503 students, 83% women, 17% men. Part-time: 171 students, 76% women, 24% men. Students come from 14 states and territories, 4 other countries, 5% from out-of-state. 0.3% American Indian or Alaska Native, non-Hispanic/Latino; 5% Hispanic/Latino; 12% Black or African American, non-Hispanic/Latino; 3% Asian, non-Hispanic/Latino; 0.6% international. 45% 25 or older, 44% transferred in. Academic area with the most degrees conferred: health professions and related sciences. Core. Calendar: semesters. Services for LD students, independent study, distance learning, double major, summer session for credit, part-time degree program, adult/continuing education programs, internships, graduate courses open to undergrads. Off campus study. Study abroad program.
Entrance Requirements: Option: electronic application. Required: high school transcript, minimum x high school GPA. Required for some: essay, interview, national entrance exam scores. Transfer credits accepted: Yes.
Collegiate Environment: Orientation program. Student services: health clinic, personal-psychological counseling. Campus security: 24-hour emergency response devices and patrols, late night transport-escort service, controlled dormitory access. Medical Sciences Library. Books: 27,764 (physical), 2,356 (digital/electronic); Serial titles: 96,524 (physical), 62,819 (digital/electronic); Databases: 120. Weekly public service hours: 87; study areas open 24 hours, 5-7 days a week. Operations spending for the previous fiscal year: $3.8 million.

■ **UNIVERSITY OF ARKANSAS AT MONTICELLO**
346 University Dr.
Monticello, AR 71656
Tel: (870)367-6811; Free: 800-844-1826
Fax: (870)460-1321
E-mail: admissions@uamont.edu
Web Site: www.uamont.edu
Description: State-supported, comprehensive, coed. Part of University of Arkansas System. Awards associate, bachelor's, and master's degrees. Founded 1909. Setting: 1,600-acre small town campus. Endowment: $2.5 million. Research spending for the previous fiscal year: $120,040. Educational spending for the previous fiscal year: $2456 per student. Total enrollment: 3,920. Faculty: 240 (172 full-time, 68 part-time). Student-undergrad faculty ratio is 16:1. 2,761 applied, 46% were admitted. Full-time: 2,676 students, 57% women, 43% men. Part-time: 1,126 students, 69% women, 31% men. 12% from out-of-state. 0.4% American Indian or Alaska Native, non-Hispanic/Latino; 2% Hispanic/Latino; 33% Black or African American, non-Hispanic/Latino; 0.3% Asian, non-Hispanic/Latino; 0.4% international. 31% 25 or older, 25% live on campus. Retention: 40% of full-time freshmen returned the following year. Academic areas with the most degrees conferred: business/marketing; health professions and related sciences; parks and recreation. Core. Calendar: semesters. Academic remediation for entering students, services for LD students, advanced placement, accelerated degree program, independent study, distance learning, double major, summer session for credit, part-time degree program, graduate courses open to undergrads. Off campus study. ROTC: Army.
Entrance Requirements: Open admission except for nursing program. Options: early admission, deferred admission. Required: high school transcript, proof of immunization. Entrance: noncompetitive. Application deadline: 8/1. Transfer credits accepted: Yes.
Collegiate Environment: Orientation program. Drama-theater group, choral group, marching band, student-run newspaper. Social organizations: 84 open to all; national fraternities, national sororities; 10% of eligible men and 10% of eligible women are members. Major annual events: Homecoming Events, Greek Week. Student services: health clinic, personal-psychological counseling. Campus security: 24-hour emergency response devices and patrols. Fred J. Taylor Library and Technology Center. Operations spending for the previous fiscal year: $883,554. 400 computers available on campus for general student use. A campuswide network can be accessed from student residence rooms and from off campus. Students can access the following: online class registration. Staffed computer lab on campus.

■ **UNIVERSITY OF ARKANSAS AT PINE BLUFF**
1200 N University Dr.
Pine Bluff, AR 71601-2799

Tel: (870)575-8000; Free: 800-264-6585
Fax: (870)543-2021
Web Site: www.uapb.edu
Description: State-supported, comprehensive, coed. Part of University of Arkansas System. Awards associate, bachelor's, master's, and doctoral degrees. Founded 1873. Setting: 327-acre urban campus. Endowment: $3.5 million. Research spending for the previous fiscal year: $7.5 million. Educational spending for the previous fiscal year: $7727 per student. Total enrollment: 2,658. Faculty: 199 (161 full-time, 38 part-time). Student-undergrad faculty ratio is 15:1. 4,452 applied, 46% were admitted. Full-time: 2,312 students, 56% women, 44% men. Part-time: 233 students, 60% women, 40% men. Students come from 37 states and territories, 14 other countries, 38% from out-of-state. 0.2% American Indian or Alaska Native, non-Hispanic/Latino; 1% Hispanic/Latino; 92% Black or African American, non-Hispanic/Latino; 0.4% Asian, non-Hispanic/Latino; 1% international. 14% 25 or older, 41% live on campus, 6% transferred in. Retention: 71% of full-time freshmen returned the following year. Academic areas with the most degrees conferred: business/marketing; homeland security, law enforcement, firefighting, and protective services; biological/life sciences. Core. Calendar: semesters. Academic remediation for entering students, ESL program, services for LD students, advanced placement, accelerated degree program, honors program, independent study, distance learning, double major, summer session for credit, part-time degree program, external degree program, adult/continuing education programs, co-op programs and internships, graduate courses open to undergrads. Off campus study at University of Arkansas, University of Arkansas at Little Rock, University of Arkansas at Monticello, University of Arkansas Community College at Hope. ROTC: Army.
Entrance Requirements: Open admission. Options: electronic application, early admission, deferred admission, international baccalaureate accepted. Required: high school transcript, minimum 2 high school GPA, SAT or ACT. Application deadline: rolling. Notification: continuous.
Collegiate Environment: Orientation program. Drama-theater group, choral group, marching band, student-run newspaper. Social organizations: 45 open to all; national fraternities, national sororities, local fraternities, local sororities; 25% of eligible men and 25% of eligible women are members. Most popular organizations: Union Programming Board, Student Government Association, Pan Hellenic Council, Lion Year Book, Arkansawyer Newspaper. Major annual events: Homecoming, Unity Fest, Founders' Week Activities. Student services: health clinic, personal-psychological counseling. Campus security: 24-hour emergency response devices and patrols. John Brown Watson Memorial Library plus 4 others. Operations spending for the previous fiscal year: $1.2 million. 175 computers available on campus for general student use. A campuswide network can be accessed from student residence rooms and from off campus. Students can access the following: online class registration. Staffed computer lab on campus provides training in use of computers, software, and the Internet.

■ **UNIVERSITY OF ARKANSAS-PULASKI TECHNICAL COLLEGE**
3000 W Scenic Dr.
North Little Rock, AR 72118
Tel: (501)812-2200
Fax: (501)812-2316
E-mail: catkins@pulaskitech.edu
Web Site: www.pulaskitech.edu
Description: State-supported, 2-year, coed. Awards certificates, transfer associate, and terminal associate degrees. Founded 1945. Setting: 40-acre urban campus with easy access to Little Rock. Educational spending for the previous fiscal year: $1145 per student. Total enrollment: 10,255. Faculty: 473 (153 full-time, 320 part-time). Student-undergrad faculty ratio is 25:1. 3,193 applied, 100% were admitted. Full-time: 4,856 students, 62% women, 38% men. Part-time: 5,399 students, 70% women, 30% men. Students come from 5 states and territories, 1% from out-of-state. 60% 25 or older, 6% transferred in. Core. Calendar: semesters. Academic remediation for entering students, services for LD students, advanced placement, distance learning, summer session for credit, part-time degree program.
Entrance Requirements: Open admission except for allied health programs. Option: electronic application. Required: high school transcript. Entrance: noncompetitive. Application deadline: rolling. Transfer credits accepted: Yes.
Collegiate Environment: Orientation program. Drama-theater group, choral group. Major annual events: Spanish Language Department's Fiesta, Spring Fling, Fall Carnival. Campus security: certified law enforcement personnel 7 am to 11 pm. Ottenheimer Library. Operations spending for the previous fis-

cal year: $706,478. 233 computers available on campus for general student use. A campuswide network can be accessed from off-campus. Students can access the following: online registration for continuing students only. Staffed computer lab on campus provides training in use of computers, software, and the Internet.

■ UNIVERSITY OF ARKANSAS RICH MOUNTAIN

1100 College Dr.
Mena, AR 71953
Tel: (479)394-7622
Fax: (479)394-2628
E-mail: wmcdaniel@uarichmountain.edu
Web Site: www.uarichmountain.edu

Description: State and locally supported, 2-year, coed. Part of University of Arkansas System. Awards certificates, transfer associate, and terminal associate degrees. Founded 1983. Setting: 40-acre small town campus. Total enrollment: 938. 155 applied, 100% were admitted. Full-time: 456 students, 73% women, 27% men. Part-time: 482 students, 90% women, 10% men. 2% American Indian or Alaska Native, non-Hispanic/Latino; 4% Hispanic/Latino; 0.3% Black or African American, non-Hispanic/Latino; 1% Asian, non-Hispanic/Latino; 0.2% Native Hawaiian or other Pacific Islander, non-Hispanic/Latino; 1% international. 60% 25 or older. Retention: 61% of full-time freshmen returned the following year. Core. Calendar: semesters. Academic remediation for entering students, ESL program, services for LD students, advanced placement, distance learning, double major, summer session for credit, part-time degree program, adult/continuing education programs.

Entrance Requirements: Open admission. Options: electronic application, early admission. Required: high school transcript. Application deadlines: rolling, rolling for nonresidents. Notification: continuous, continuous for nonresidents. Transfer credits accepted: Yes.

Costs Per Year: Application fee: $0. Area resident tuition: $1944 full-time, $81 per credit hour part-time. State resident tuition: $2280 full-time, $95 per credit hour part-time. Nonresident tuition: $3000 full-time, $125 per credit hour part-time. Mandatory fees: $936 full-time, $39 per credit hour part-time. Full-time tuition and fees vary according to course load and program. Part-time tuition and fees vary according to course load and program.

Collegiate Environment: Drama-theater group. Campus security: campus security on duty during college hours. St. John Library. Books: 14,668 (physical), 13,747 (digital/electronic); Databases: 27. Students can reserve study rooms.

■ UNIVERSITY OF CENTRAL ARKANSAS

201 Donaghey Ave.
Conway, AR 72035-0001
Tel: (501)450-5000; Free: 800-243-8245
Fax: (501)450-5228
Web Site: www.uca.edu

Description: State-supported, university, coed. Awards bachelor's, master's, and doctoral degrees and post-master's certificates. Founded 1907. Setting: 356-acre small town campus. Total enrollment: 11,177. Faculty: 723 (558 full-time, 165 part-time). Student-undergrad faculty ratio is 16:1. 5,541 applied, 91% were admitted. 21% from top 10% of their high school class, 49% from top quarter, 81% from top half. Full-time: 7,863 students, 61% women, 39% men. Part-time: 1,562 students, 53% women, 47% men. Students come from 45 states and territories, 72 other countries, 10% from out-of-state. 0.5% American Indian or Alaska Native, non-Hispanic/Latino; 5% Hispanic/Latino; 16% Black or African American, non-Hispanic/Latino; 2% Asian, non-Hispanic/Latino; 0.1% Native Hawaiian or other Pacific Islander, non-Hispanic/Latino; 5% international. 9% 25 or older, 40% live on campus, 7% transferred in. Retention: 74% of full-time freshmen returned the following year. Academic areas with the most degrees conferred: business/marketing; health professions and related sciences; education. Core. Calendar: semesters. Academic remediation for entering students, ESL program, services for LD students, advanced placement, accelerated degree program, freshman honors college, honors program, independent study, distance learning, double major, summer session for credit, part-time degree program, co-op programs and internships, graduate courses open to undergrads. Study abroad program. ROTC: Army.

Entrance Requirements: Options: electronic application, early admission, deferred admission, international baccalaureate accepted. Required: high school transcript, SAT or ACT. Required for some: minimum 2.75 GPA, minimum ACT score of 21 or SAT score of 1450. Entrance: moderately difficult. Application deadline: rolling. Notification: continuous. Transfer credits accepted: Yes.

Costs Per Year: Application fee: $25. State resident tuition: $6,523 full-time, $217.43 per credit hour part-time. Nonresident tuition: $13,046 full-time, $434.86 per credit hour part-time. Mandatory fees: $2,228 full-time. Full-time tuition and fees vary according to course load. Part-time tuition varies according to course load. College room and board: $6854. Room and board charges vary according to board plan and housing facility.

Collegiate Environment: Orientation program. Drama-theater group, choral group, marching band, student-run newspaper, radio station. Social organizations: 199 open to all; national fraternities, national sororities; 4% of eligible men and 9% of eligible women are members. Most popular organizations: Bears Den, Greek Organizations. Major annual events: Homecoming, Miss UCA Pageant, Family Day. Student services: health clinic, personal-psychological counseling, women's center. Campus security: 24-hour emergency response devices and patrols, student patrols, late night transport-escort service, controlled dormitory access. 3,658 college housing spaces available; 3,333 were occupied in 2018-19. Freshmen guaranteed college housing. On-campus residence required in freshman year. Options: coed, men-only, women-only housing available. Torreyson Library plus 1 other. Books: 326,160 (physical), 16,245 (digital/electronic); Serial titles: 2,955 (physical), 368,249 (digital/electronic); Databases: 143. Study areas open 24 hours, 5-7 days a week; students can reserve study rooms. 610 computers available on campus for general student use. A campuswide network can be accessed from student residence rooms and from off campus. Students can access the following: online class registration. Staffed computer lab on campus (open 24 hours a day).

Community Environment: Conway, population 52,000, is a growing center served by major highways, the Union Pacific Railway, and Little Rock National Airport which is 35 miles away. It is within a few miles of the geographic center of the state. Lake Conway, which covers approximately 6,500 acres, between Conway and Little Rock, is one of the principal resorts of the state. The Arkansas River, the largest to cross the state, is less than ten miles from Conway. Conway is a city with three colleges and is the government seat of Faulkner County. It has a diverse economic background, which includes manufacturers, education, government and service industries. Several major manufacturing firms including Kimberly Clark, Nucor Steel, Touksen and AmTran have facilities here. Axiom, a data processing center, has its corporation headquarters located in Conway and employs approximately 2,000 people. The city has many beautiful residences, churches, businesses, and public buildings.

■ UNIVERSITY OF THE OZARKS

415 N College Ave.
Clarksville, AR 72830-2880
Tel: (479)979-1000; Free: 800-264-8636
Fax: (479)979-1355
E-mail: admiss@ozarks.edu
Web Site: www.ozarks.edu

Description: Independent Presbyterian, 4-year, coed. Awards bachelor's degrees. Founded 1834. Setting: small town campus. Total enrollment: 651. Faculty: 56. Student-undergrad faculty ratio is 13:1. 744 applied, 97% were admitted. 43% from out-of-state. 0.9% American Indian or Alaska Native, non-Hispanic/Latino; 10% Hispanic/Latino; 6% Black or African American, non-Hispanic/Latino; 0.3% Asian, non-Hispanic/Latino; 0.2% Native Hawaiian or other Pacific Islander, non-Hispanic/Latino; 12% international. 5% 25 or older, 76% live on campus. Calendar: semesters. Part-time degree program.

Entrance Requirements: Options: deferred admission, international baccalaureate accepted. Required: minimum 2 high school GPA, SAT or ACT. Required for some: essay, high school transcript, interview. Entrance: moderately difficult. SAT Reasoning Test deadline: 8/15. Transfer credits accepted: Yes.

Collegiate Environment: Orientation program. Drama-theater group, choral group, student-run radio station. Student services: health clinic, personal-psychological counseling. Campus security: 24-hour emergency response devices and patrols, late night transport-escort service, electronically operated building entrances. Robson Library.

Community Environment: Clarksville is the county seat of Johnson County. The town lies 105 miles northwest of Little Rock on Interstate 40, & is 65 miles east of Fort Smith. The Continental bus line serves this area. Primarily an agricultural community, it also has some manufacturing. There are motel accommodations, and a hospital. A swimming pool, athletic fields, baseball park, football field, tennis courts, and all the outdoor sports are available. Annual events include the Peach Festival.

■ WILLIAMS BAPTIST COLLEGE

60 W Fulbright Ave.
Walnut Ridge, AR 72476
Tel: (870)886-6741; Free: 800-722-4434
E-mail: awatson@wbcoll.edu
Web Site: www.wbcoll.edu

Description: Independent Southern Baptist, comprehensive, coed. Awards associate, bachelor's, and master's degrees. Founded 1941. Setting: 180-acre rural campus. Total enrollment: 469. Faculty: 50 (26 full-time, 24 part-time). Student-undergrad faculty ratio is 14:1. 665 applied, 60% were admitted. Full-time: 423 students, 48% women, 52% men. Part-time: 46 students, 70% women, 30% men. Students come from 23 states and territories, 7 other countries, 29% from out-of-state. 0.2% American Indian or Alaska Native, non-Hispanic/Latino; 3% Hispanic/Latino; 9% Black or African American, non-Hispanic/Latino; 6% international. 65% live on campus, 7% transferred in. Academic areas with the most degrees conferred: psychology; liberal arts/general studies; education. Core. Calendar: semesters. Services for LD students, advanced placement, self-designed majors, independent study, double major, summer session for credit, part-time degree program, adult/continuing education programs, internships. Off campus study at Coalition for Christian Colleges and Universities. Study abroad program. ROTC: Army (c).

Entrance Requirements: Options: electronic application, early admission. Required: high school transcript, minimum 2.6 high school GPA, SAT or ACT. Required for some: essay, 2 recommendations, interview. Entrance: minimally difficult. Application deadline: rolling. SAT Reasoning Test deadline: 8/15. SAT Subject Test deadline: 8/15. Transfer credits accepted: Yes.

Collegiate Environment: Orientation program. Drama-theater group, choral group. Most popular organizations: Student Government, Student Activities Board, Bancroft Society, Cultural Awareness, International Student Society. Major annual events: Williams Idol, Freshman Follies, Harvest Fest. Student services: health clinic, personal-psychological counseling. Campus security: 24-hour emergency response devices and patrols, student patrols, late night transport-escort service, controlled dormitory access. Felix Goodson Library plus 1 other. Books: 60,000 (physical), 100,000 (digital/electronic); Serial titles: 17 (physical), 5 (digital/electronic); Databases: 102. Weekly public service hours: 87; students can reserve study rooms. 70 computers available on campus for general student use. A campuswide network can be accessed from student residence rooms. Students can access the following: online class registration. Staffed computer lab on campus provides training in use of computers, software, and the Internet.

Community Environment: Walnut Ridge is a rural area with a temperate climate. Railroads serve the area as well as a city airport. There are churches of major denominations, a public library, and a hospital. Recreational activities include boating and water sports. The city has Lions and Kiwanis organizations. An annual county fair is held. Part-time employment opportunities are limited.

■ **ABRAHAM LINCOLN UNIVERSITY**
3530 Wilshire Blvd.
Ste. 1430
Los Angeles, CA 90010
Tel: (213)252-5100
Fax: (213)252-5113
Description: Proprietary, comprehensive, coed.

■ **ACADEMY OF ART UNIVERSITY**
79 New Montgomery St.
San Francisco, CA 94105-3410
Tel: (415)274-2200; Free: 800-544-ARTS
Fax: (415)263-4130
Web Site: www.academyart.edu
Description: Proprietary, comprehensive, coed. Awards associate, bachelor's, and master's degrees. Founded 1929. Setting: 3-acre urban campus. Total enrollment: 10,616. Faculty: 1,138 (243 full-time, 895 part-time). Student-undergrad faculty ratio is 14:1. 2,363 applied, 100% were admitted. Full-time: 4,090 students, 54% women, 46% men. Part-time: 3,316 students, 64% women, 36% men. Students come from 50 states and territories, 99 other countries, 44% from out-of-state. 0.5% American Indian or Alaska Native, non-Hispanic/Latino; 11% Hispanic/Latino; 6% Black or African American, non-Hispanic/Latino; 6% Asian, non-Hispanic/Latino; 0.7% Native Hawaiian or other Pacific Islander, non-Hispanic/Latino; 28% international. 41% 25 or older, 14% live on campus, 14% transferred in. Retention: 78% of full-time freshmen returned the following year. Academic areas with the most degrees conferred: visual and performing arts; computer and information sciences; communication technologies; engineering technologies. Core. Calendar: semesters. Academic remediation for entering students, ESL program, services for LD students, independent study, distance learning, summer session for credit, part-time degree program, adult/continuing education programs, internships. Study abroad program. ROTC: Army (c).
Entrance Requirements: Open admission. Options: electronic application, early admission, deferred admission, international baccalaureate accepted. Required: high school transcript. Recommended: interview. Entrance: noncompetitive. Application deadline: rolling. Notification: continuous. Transfer credits accepted: Yes.
Costs Per Year: Application fee: $50. Comprehensive fee: $46,700 includes full-time tuition ($28,890), mandatory fees ($300), and college room and board ($17,510). College room only: $11,740. Part-time tuition: $963 per credit. Part-time mandatory fees: $963 per credit.
Collegiate Environment: Orientation program. Drama-theater group, choral group, student-run newspaper, radio station. Social organizations: 20 open to all; national fraternities, national sororities. Most popular organizations: Tea Time Animation, Beyond the Front Row, Drawaholics Anonymous Crew, Comics and Concept Art Club, Chinese Student Association. Major annual events: Spring Show, Industry on Campus Series, Halloweek, Club Mixer. Campus security: 24-hour emergency response devices and patrols, late night transport-escort service, controlled dormitory access. 1,649 college housing spaces available; 1,305 were occupied in 2018-19. Freshmen guaranteed college housing. Options: coed, men-only, women-only housing available. Academy of Art University Library. Books: 38,441 (physical), 9,675 (digital/electronic); Serial titles: 185 (physical), 400,000 (digital/electronic); Databases: 22. Weekly public service hours: 83; students can reserve study rooms. 900 computers available on campus for general student use. A campuswide network can be accessed. Students can access the following: online class registration, support for students taking online courses. Staffed computer lab on campus provides training in use of computers, software, and the Internet.
Community Environment: Lining the street between the Powell and Sutter buildings are several of San Francisco's finest art galleries. The area provides an ideal environment for studying and developing as an artist.

■ **ADVANCED COLLEGE (SOUTH GATE)**
13180 Paramount Blvd.
South Gate, CA 90280
Tel: (562)408-6969
Web Site: www.advancedcollege.edu
Description: Proprietary, 2-year, coed. Awards certificates, transfer associate, and terminal associate degrees.

■ **ADVANCED COLLEGE (STOCKTON)**
8838 NW Ln.
Stockton, CA 95210
Web Site: www.advancedcollege.edu
Description: Proprietary, 2-year, coed. Founded 2017.

■ **ADVANCED COMPUTING INSTITUTE**
3470 Wilshire Blvd. 11th Fl.
Los Angeles, CA 90010-3911
Web Site: www.advancedcomputinginstitute.edu
Description: Proprietary, 2-year, coed. Awards certificates, diplomas, transfer associate, and terminal associate degrees.

■ **ADVANCED TRAINING ASSOCIATES**
1810 Gillespie Way
Ste. 104
El Cajon, CA 92020
Tel: (619)596-2766; Free: 800-720-2125
Fax: (619)596-4526
Web Site: www.advancedtraining.edu
Description: Proprietary, 2-year, coed. Awards certificates, diplomas, transfer associate, and terminal associate degrees.

■ **ALLAN HANCOCK COLLEGE**
800 S College Dr.
Santa Maria, CA 93454-6399
Tel: (805)922-6966; Free: 866-342-5242
Fax: (805)922-3477
Web Site: www.hancockcollege.edu
Description: District-supported, 2-year, coed. Awards certificates, transfer associate, and terminal associate degrees. Founded 1920. Setting: 120-acre small town campus. Endowment: $1.1 million. Research spending for the previous fiscal year: $78,392. Educational spending for the previous fiscal year: $1690 per student. Total enrollment: 10,387. Faculty: 594 (152 full-time, 442 part-time). Student-undergrad faculty ratio is 17:1. Full-time: 2,996 students, 54% women, 46% men. Part-time: 7,391 students, 56% women, 44% men. Students come from 27 states and territories, 12 other countries. Core. Calendar: semesters. ESL program, services for LD students,

advanced placement, distance learning, summer session for credit, part-time degree program, adult/continuing education programs, co-op programs. Study abroad program.

Entrance Requirements: Open admission except for nursing, drama, fire technology programs. Option: electronic application. Entrance: noncompetitive. Application deadline: rolling. Notification: continuous. Transfer credits accepted: Yes.

Collegiate Environment: Orientation program. Drama-theater group, choral group, student-run newspaper. Social organizations: 10 open to all. Most popular organizations: MECHA, AHC Student Club, Club Med (medical), Hancock Christian Fellowship, VICA (Vocational Industrial Clubs of America). Major annual events: Chili Cook-Off, Blood Drive, Spring Fest. Student services: legal services, health clinic, personal-psychological counseling. Campus security: 24-hour emergency response devices and patrols, student patrols, late night transport-escort service. Learning Resources Center. Operations spending for the previous fiscal year: $252,771. 200 computers available on campus for general student use. Staffed computer lab on campus.

Community Environment: Santa Maria is located in the Central Coast region on United States Highway 101, 175 miles north of Los Angeles and 262 miles south of San Francisco. Average temperature ranges from 45 degrees minimum to 68.2 degrees maximum. Greyhound Bus and United Airlines serve the area. Santa Maria has a hospital, churches, a library, and a number of manufacturing firms. A municipal swimming pool, golf courses, parks and playgrounds provide facilities for sports. Hunting and fishing opportunities are good.

■ **ALLIANT INTERNATIONAL UNIVERSITY-SAN DIEGO**
10455 Pomerado Rd.
San Diego, CA 92131
Tel: (858)271-4300; Free: 866-825-5426
Fax: (858)635-4739
E-mail: admissions@alliant.edu
Web Site: www.alliant.edu

Description: Independent, university, coed. Part of Alliant International University. Awards bachelor's, master's, and doctoral degrees. Founded 1952. Setting: 60-acre suburban campus with easy access to San Diego. Total enrollment: 3,046. Faculty: 520. Student-undergrad faculty ratio is 15:1. Students come from 7 states and territories, 12 other countries, 10% from out-of-state. 50% 25 or older. Core. Calendar: semesters. Academic remediation for entering students, ESL program, services for LD students, advanced placement, distance learning, summer session for credit, part-time degree program, internships, graduate courses open to undergrads.

Entrance Requirements: Options: electronic application, deferred admission, international baccalaureate accepted. Required: high school transcript, minimum 2 high school GPA. Entrance: minimally difficult. Transfer credits accepted: Yes.

Collegiate Environment: Orientation program. Social organizations: 12 open to all. Most popular organizations: Residence Hall Association, Latino Students Association, Finance Club, Student Government, Sigma Iota Epsilon. Student services: health clinic, personal-psychological counseling. Campus security: 24-hour patrols. Walter Library. 100 computers available on campus for general student use. A campuswide network can be accessed. Students can access the following: online class registration, degree completion status. Staffed computer lab on campus provides training in use of computers, software, and the Internet.

■ **AMDA COLLEGE AND CONSERVATORY OF THE PERFORMING ARTS, LOS ANGELES CAMPUS**
6305 Yucca St.
Los Angeles, CA 90028
Tel: (323)469-3300; Free: 888-474-9444
Fax: (323)469-3350
E-mail: admissionsteam@amda.edu
Web Site: www.amda.edu

Description: Proprietary, 4-year, coed. Awards bachelor's degrees. Setting: urban campus. Total enrollment: 1,495.

Entrance Requirements: Required: essay, high school transcript, 2 recommendations, in-person or video audition. Entrance: moderately difficult. Application deadline: rolling.

■ **AMERICA EVANGELICAL UNIVERSITY**
1818 S Western Ave.
Los Angeles, CA 90006

Description: Independent religious, comprehensive, coed.

■ **AMERICAN ACADEMY OF DRAMATIC ARTS-LOS ANGELES**
1336 N La Brea Ave.
Hollywood, CA 90028
Tel: (323)464-2777; Free: 800-222-2867
Fax: (323)464-1250
E-mail: shong@aada.edu
Web Site: www.aada.edu

Description: Independent, 2-year, coed. Awards certificates, diplomas, and transfer associate degrees. Founded 1974. Setting: 4-acre urban campus with easy access to Los Angeles. Endowment: $1.7 million. Total enrollment: 303. Faculty: 50 (9 full-time, 41 part-time). Student-undergrad faculty ratio is 12:1. 481 applied, 79% were admitted. Full-time: 303 students, 60% women, 40% men. Students come from 27 states and territories, 37 other countries, 53% from out-of-state. 0.3% American Indian or Alaska Native, non-Hispanic/Latino; 8% Hispanic/Latino; 10% Black or African American, non-Hispanic/Latino; 1% Asian, non-Hispanic/Latino; 0.3% Native Hawaiian or other Pacific Islander, non-Hispanic/Latino; 33% international. 11% 25 or older, 1% transferred in. Core. Calendar: semesters. Services for LD students, internships.

Entrance Requirements: Options: electronic application, deferred admission. Required: essay, high school transcript, 2 recommendations, interview, audition. Recommended: minimum 2 high school GPA. Entrance: moderately difficult. Application deadline: rolling. Notification: continuous. Transfer credits accepted: Yes.

Costs Per Year: Application fee: $50. Comprehensive fee: $46,815 includes full-time tuition ($34,410), mandatory fees ($750), and college room and board ($11,655).

Collegiate Environment: Choral group. Major annual events: Student Cabaret, Holiday Events, Industry Insight Series. Student services: personal-psychological counseling. Campus security: 24-hour emergency response devices and patrols, controlled dormitory access. Bryn Morgan Library. Books: 15,000 (physical); Serial titles: 1,000 (physical). Weekly public service hours: 53. Operations spending for the previous fiscal year: $141,973. 8 computers available on campus for general student use. A campuswide network can be accessed from off-campus. Staffed computer lab on campus provides training in use of computers, software, and the Internet.

■ **AMERICAN CAREER COLLEGE (ANAHEIM)**
1200 N Magnolia Ave.
Anaheim, CA 92801
Tel: (714)763-9066; Free: 877-832-0790
Web Site: americancareercollege.edu

Description: Proprietary, 2-year, coed. Awards certificates, diplomas, and terminal associate degrees. Total enrollment: 1,808. Student-undergrad faculty ratio is 16:1. 685 applied, 77% were admitted. 48% 25 or older.

Entrance Requirements: Required: high school transcript.

Costs Per Year: One-time mandatory fee: $25. Tuition: $18,200 full-time. Full-time tuition varies according to course load and program.

■ **AMERICAN CAREER COLLEGE (LOS ANGELES)**
4021 Rosewood Ave.
Los Angeles, CA 90004
Tel: (323)668-7555; Free: 877-832-0790
Web Site: americancareercollege.edu

Description: Proprietary, 2-year, coed. Awards certificates, diplomas, and terminal associate degrees. Founded 1978. Total enrollment: 1,764. Student-undergrad faculty ratio is 15:1. 676 applied, 86% were admitted. 39% 25 or older.

Entrance Requirements: Required: high school transcript.

Costs Per Year: Tuition: $17,050 full-time. Mandatory fees: $1150 full-time. Full-time tuition and fees vary according to class time, course level, and program.

■ **AMERICAN CAREER COLLEGE (ONTARIO)**
3130 E Sedona Ct.
Ontario, CA 91764
Tel: (909)218-3253; Free: 877-832-0790
Web Site: americancareercollege.edu

Description: Proprietary, 2-year, coed. Awards certificates, diplomas, and terminal associate degrees. Total enrollment: 1,115. Student-undergrad faculty ratio is 31:1. 352 applied, 76% were admitted. 42% 25 or older.

Entrance Requirements: Required: high school transcript.
Costs Per Year: One-time mandatory fee: $25. Tuition: $17,050 full-time. Mandatory fees: $1150 full-time. Full-time tuition and fees vary according to course load and program.

■ AMERICAN MEDICAL SCIENCES CENTER

225 W Broadway, Ste. 115
Glendale, CA 91204-5108
Web Site: www.amsc.edu
Description: Proprietary, 2-year, coed. Awards diplomas, transfer associate, and terminal associate degrees.

■ AMERICAN RIVER COLLEGE

4700 College Oak Dr.
Sacramento, CA 95841-4286
Tel: (916)484-8011
Web Site: www.arc.losrios.edu
Description: District-supported, 2-year, coed. Part of Los Rios Community College District System. Awards certificates, transfer associate, and terminal associate degrees. Founded 1955. Setting: 153-acre suburban campus. Total enrollment: 33,821. 55% 25 or older. Core. Calendar: semesters. Academic remediation for entering students, ESL program, services for LD students, advanced placement, summer session for credit, part-time degree program, adult/continuing education programs, co-op programs.
Entrance Requirements: Open admission except for nursing, respiratory therapy programs. Options: early admission, deferred admission. Entrance: noncompetitive. Application deadline: rolling.
Collegiate Environment: Drama-theater group, student-run newspaper. Student services: health clinic, personal-psychological counseling, women's center. Campus security: 24-hour emergency response devices and patrols, student patrols, late night transport-escort service.
Community Environment: See California State University - Sacramento.

■ AMERICAN UNIVERSITY OF HEALTH SCIENCES

1600 E Hill St.
Bldg. No.1
Signal Hill, CA 90755
Tel: (562)988-2278
Fax: (562)988-1791
Web Site: www.auhs.edu
Description: Proprietary, comprehensive, coed. Awards bachelor's and master's degrees. Total enrollment: 249. Full-time: 249 students, 80% women, 20% men. Students come from 1 other country. 0.8% American Indian or Alaska Native, non-Hispanic/Latino; 17% Hispanic/Latino; 10% Black or African American, non-Hispanic/Latino; 60% Asian, non-Hispanic/Latino; 0.4% international. 65% 25 or older, 20% transferred in. Retention: 83% of full-time freshmen returned the following year. Core. Academic remediation for entering students.
Entrance Requirements: Options: early admission, deferred admission, international baccalaureate accepted. Required: essay, high school transcript, interview. Entrance: moderately difficult. Transfer credits accepted: Yes.
Collegiate Environment: Orientation program. Student-run newspaper. Student services: personal-psychological counseling. AUHS Library. 20 computers available on campus for general student use. A computer is required for all students. A campuswide network can be accessed. Staffed computer lab on campus provides training in use of computers, software, and the Internet.

■ ANGELES COLLEGE

3440 Wilshire Blvd., Ste. 310
Los Angeles, CA 90010
Tel: (213)487-2211
Web Site: www.angelescollege.edu
Description: Proprietary, 4-year, coed. Awards associate and bachelor's degrees.

■ ANTELOPE VALLEY COLLEGE

3041 W Ave. K
Lancaster, CA 93536-5426
Tel: (661)722-6300
Fax: (661)943-5573
Web Site: www.avc.edu
Description: District-supported, primarily 2-year, coed. Part of California Community College System. Awards certificates, transfer associate, terminal associate, and bachelor's degrees. Founded 1929. Setting: 135-acre suburban campus with easy access to Los Angeles. Endowment: $4.6 million. Research spending for the previous fiscal year: $457,245. Educational spending for the previous fiscal year: $3039 per student. Total enrollment: 14,125. Faculty: 622 (174 full-time, 448 part-time). Student-undergrad faculty ratio is 24:1. 2,105 applied, 100% were admitted. Full-time: 4,031 students, 54% women, 46% men. Part-time: 10,094 students, 60% women, 40% men. Students come from 10 states and territories, 1 other country. 0.3% American Indian or Alaska Native, non-Hispanic/Latino; 53% Hispanic/Latino; 16% Black or African American, non-Hispanic/Latino; 4% Asian, non-Hispanic/Latino; 0.2% Native Hawaiian or other Pacific Islander, non-Hispanic/Latino; 0.1% international. 37% 25 or older. Core. Calendar: semesters. Academic remediation for entering students, ESL program, services for LD students, advanced placement, honors program, independent study, distance learning, summer session for credit, part-time degree program, external degree program, co-op programs. Study abroad program. ROTC: Army (c), Naval (c), Air Force (c).
Entrance Requirements: Open admission. Options: electronic application, early admission. Entrance: noncompetitive. Application deadline: rolling. Notification: continuous. Transfer credits accepted: Yes.
Collegiate Environment: Orientation program. Drama-theater group. Social organizations: 24 open to all. Major annual events: Cinco de Mayo, Transfer Colleges Day, Community Day. Student services: health clinic, personal-psychological counseling. Campus security: 24-hour emergency response devices and patrols, late night transport-escort service. Antelope Valley College Library. Books: 54,721 (physical), 8,152 (digital/electronic); Serial titles: 10 (physical); Databases: 65. Weekly public service hours: 58; students can reserve study rooms. Operations spending for the previous fiscal year: $1.3 million. 160 computers available on campus for general student use. A campuswide network can be accessed from off-campus. Students can access the following: online class registration. Staffed computer lab on campus provides training in use of computers, software, and the Internet.
Community Environment: Population 134,000. Lancaster is located in the center of the Antelope Valley in a semidesert region. Lancaster has over 350 days of sunshine a year and the climate is the reason that the United States Air Force and almost every manufacturer of aircraft build and maintain establishments in this area. There has been a great increase in population and excellent employment opportunities have developed in proportion to the growth.

■ ANTIOCH UNIVERSITY LOS ANGELES

400 Corporate Pointe
Culver City, CA 90230
Tel: (310)578-1080; Free: 800-726-8462
Fax: (310)827-4742
E-mail: admissions@antiochla.edu
Web Site: www.antioch.edu/los-angeles
Description: Independent, upper-level, coed. Part of Antioch University. Awards bachelor's, master's, and doctoral degrees and post-master's certificates. Founded 1972. Setting: 1-acre urban campus with easy access to Los Angeles. Total enrollment: 628. Full-time: 83 students, 37% women, 63% men. Part-time: 167 students, 66% women, 34% men. Students come from 13 states and territories, 3 other countries, 1% from out-of-state. 0.4% American Indian or Alaska Native, non-Hispanic/Latino; 29% Hispanic/Latino; 20% Black or African American, non-Hispanic/Latino; 5% Asian, non-Hispanic/Latino; 0.4% Native Hawaiian or other Pacific Islander, non-Hispanic/Latino; 0.4% international. 5% 25 or older. Academic area with the most degrees conferred: liberal arts/general studies. Core. Calendar: quarters. Academic remediation for entering students, services for LD students, advanced placement, accelerated degree program, self-designed majors, independent study, distance learning, double major, summer session for credit, part-time degree program, adult/continuing education programs, co-op programs and internships, graduate courses open to undergrads.
Costs Per Year: Application fee: $60. Tuition: $27,160 full-time, $679 per credit hour part-time. Mandatory fees: $400 full-time. Full-time tuition and fees vary according to course load and program. Part-time tuition varies according to course load and program.
Collegiate Environment: Orientation program. Student-run newspaper, radio station. Student services: personal-psychological counseling. Campus security: 24-hour emergency response devices, late night transport-escort service. Operations spending for the previous fiscal year: $20,000.

■ **ANTIOCH UNIVERSITY SANTA BARBARA**
602 Anacapa St.
Santa Barbara, CA 93101-1581
Tel: (805)962-8179; Free: 866-526-8462
Fax: (805)962-4786
E-mail: jgrater@antioch.edu
Web Site: www.antioch.edu/santa-barbara
Description: Independent, upper-level, coed. Part of Antioch University. Awards bachelor's, master's, and doctoral degrees. Founded 1977. Setting: urban campus. Total enrollment: 528. Faculty: 78 (9 full-time, 69 part-time). Students come from 10 states and territories, 3 other countries, 1% from out-of-state. 24% Hispanic/Latino; 4% Black or African American, non-Hispanic/Latino; 3% Asian, non-Hispanic/Latino; 9% international. 22% 25 or older. Academic area with the most degrees conferred: liberal arts/general studies. Core. Calendar: quarters. Academic remediation for entering students, services for LD students, accelerated degree program, self-designed majors, independent study, distance learning, summer session for credit, part-time degree program, external degree program, co-op programs and internships, graduate courses open to undergrads. Off campus study.
Entrance Requirements: Transfer credits accepted: Yes.
Costs Per Year: Application fee: $60. Tuition: $17,820 full-time, $495 per credit hour part-time. Mandatory fees: $400 full-time. Full-time tuition and fees vary according to course load, degree level, and program. Part-time tuition varies according to course load, degree level, and program.
Collegiate Environment: Orientation program. Student-run newspaper. Campus security: late night transport-escort service. Sage Library. 16 computers available on campus for general student use. A campuswide network can be accessed from off-campus. Students can access the following: online class registration. Staffed computer lab on campus provides training in use of computers, software, and the Internet.

■ **APT COLLEGE**
1939 Palomar Oaks Way
Ste. A
Carlsbad, CA 92011
Free: 800-431-8488
Fax: (888)431-8588
Web Site: www.aptc.edu
Description: Proprietary, 2-year, coed. Awards certificates and terminal associate degrees. Founded 1993.

■ **ARGOSY UNIVERSITY, LOS ANGELES**
5230 Pacific Concourse, Ste. 200
Los Angeles, CA 90045
Tel: (310)531-9700; Free: 866-505-0332
Web Site: www.argosy.edu/locations/los-angeles
Description: Proprietary, university, coed. Awards associate, bachelor's, master's, and doctoral degrees.

■ **ARGOSY UNIVERSITY, ORANGE COUNTY**
601 S Lewis St.
Orange, CA 92868
Tel: (714)620-3700; Free: 800-716-9598
Web Site: www.argosy.edu/locations/los-angeles-orange-county
Description: Proprietary, university, coed. Awards associate, bachelor's, master's, and doctoral degrees. Setting: urban campus. Calendar: semesters.

■ **THE ART INSTITUTE OF CALIFORNIA-HOLLYWOOD, A CAMPUS OF ARGOSY UNIVERSITY**
5250 Lankershim Blvd.
North Hollywood, CA 91601
Tel: (818)299-5100; Free: 877-468-6232
Web Site: www.artinstitutes.edu/hollywood
Description: Proprietary, 4-year, coed. Part of Education Management Corporation. Awards associate and bachelor's degrees. Founded 1992. Setting: urban campus. Calendar: quarters.

■ **THE ART INSTITUTE OF CALIFORNIA-SAN DIEGO, A CAMPUS OF ARGOSY UNIVERSITY**
7650 Mission Valley Rd.
San Diego, CA 92108
Tel: (858)598-1200; Free: 866-275-2422
Web Site: www.artinstitutes.edu/sandiego

Description: Proprietary, 4-year, coed. Part of Education Management Corporation. Awards associate and bachelor's degrees. Founded 1981. Setting: urban campus. Calendar: quarters.

■ **ARTCENTER COLLEGE OF DESIGN**
1700 Lida St.
Pasadena, CA 91103
Tel: (626)396-2200
Fax: (626)795-0578
E-mail: kit.baron@artcenter.edu
Web Site: www.artcenter.edu
Description: Independent, comprehensive, coed. Awards bachelor's and master's degrees. Founded 1930. Setting: 163-acre suburban campus with easy access to Los Angeles. Total enrollment: 2,251. Student-undergrad faculty ratio is 9:1. Full-time: 1,717 students, 55% women, 45% men. Part-time: 288 students, 48% women, 52% men. Students come from 51 other countries, 32% from out-of-state. 0.2% American Indian or Alaska Native, non-Hispanic/Latino; 12% Hispanic/Latino; 1% Black or African American, non-Hispanic/Latino; 33% Asian, non-Hispanic/Latino; 0.3% Native Hawaiian or other Pacific Islander, non-Hispanic/Latino; 32% international. 29% 25 or older, 9% transferred in. Retention: 80% of full-time freshmen returned the following year. Academic areas with the most degrees conferred: visual and performing arts; engineering technologies; communication technologies. Core. Calendar: semesters. Services for LD students, advanced placement, independent study, summer session for credit, internships, graduate courses open to undergrads. Off campus study at Occidental College, California Institute of Technology, Drucker School of Management. Study abroad program.
Entrance Requirements: Options: electronic application, deferred admission, international baccalaureate accepted. Required: essay, portfolio. Required for some: high school transcript, SAT or ACT. Entrance: very difficult. Transfer credits accepted: Yes.
Costs Per Year: Application fee: $50. Tuition: $42,816 full-time, $1785 per credit part-time. Mandatory fees: $600 full-time.
Collegiate Environment: Orientation program. Social organizations: 61 open to all. Most popular organizations: ACSG, Christian Fellowship, Stop Motion Club, Art Center Business Club, Fine Art Society. Major annual events: Late Night Breakfast, All Campus BBQ, The Annual. Student services: personal-psychological counseling. Campus security: 24-hour emergency response devices and patrols, late night transport-escort service. James Lemont Fogg Memorial Library plus 1 other. Books: 101,955 (physical), 1 million (digital/electronic); Serial titles: 592 (physical), 36,738 (digital/electronic); Databases: 46. Weekly public service hours: 63. 470 computers available on campus for general student use. Computer purchase/lease plans available. A campuswide network can be accessed from off-campus. Students can access the following: online class registration. Staffed computer lab on campus (open 24 hours a day) provides training in use of computers, software, and the Internet.
Community Environment: See California Institute of Technology.

■ **ASHFORD UNIVERSITY**
8620 Spectrum Ctr. Blvd.
San Diego, CA 92123
Free: 866-711-1700
Web Site: www.ashford.edu
Description: Proprietary, comprehensive, coed. Awards associate, bachelor's, and master's degrees. Founded 1918. Setting: 24-acre small town campus with easy access to Chicago. Endowment: $1.4 million. Research spending for the previous fiscal year: $26,474. Educational spending for the previous fiscal year: $3227 per student. Total enrollment: 10,568. Faculty: 748 (45 full-time, 703 part-time). Student-undergrad faculty ratio is 37:1. Full-time: 9,761 students, 77% women, 23% men. Part-time: 105 students, 70% women, 30% men. Students come from 9 states and territories. Retention: 45% of full-time freshmen returned the following year. Core. Calendar: semesters. Academic remediation for entering students, advanced placement, freshman honors college, honors program, independent study, distance learning, double major, summer session for credit, part-time degree program, external degree program, internships.
Entrance Requirements: Options: electronic application, early admission, deferred admission. Required: high school transcript. Recommended: minimum 2.0 high school GPA, interview. Required for some: interview, SAT or ACT. Entrance: minimally difficult. Application deadline: rolling. Notification: continuous.
Collegiate Environment: Orientation program. Drama-theater group, choral

group, student-run newspaper. Social organizations: 21 open to all. Most popular organizations: Student Senate, Student Ambassadors, Hall Council, Black Student Union, Student Iowa State Education Association. Major annual events: Brother/Sister Weekend, Matriculation Ceremony, Pep Rally and Homecoming. Student services: health clinic, personal-psychological counseling. Campus security: 24-hour emergency response devices and patrols, student patrols, late night transport-escort service, controlled dormitory access, self-defense education, lighted pathways. The Franciscan University of the Prairies Library. Operations spending for the previous fiscal year: $159,661. 109 computers available on campus for general student use. Computer purchase/lease plans available. Students can access the following: online class registration. Staffed computer lab on campus.

Community Environment: Clinton, Iowa (population 27,000), situated midway between Chicago and Des Moines, is home to a minor league baseball team, a symphony orchestra, a pre-professional ballet company, summer stock theater, art shows, and other cultural events. Clinton is 45 minutes from the Quad Cities, three hours from Chicago, and five hours from Minneapolis. The quality of life in the city and on campus is typical of the wholesome lifestyle the Midwest is known for throughout the country.

■ **AZUSA PACIFIC UNIVERSITY**
901 E Alosta Ave.
Azusa, CA 91702-7000
Tel: (626)969-3434; Free: 800-TALK-APU
E-mail: admissions@apu.edu
Web Site: www.apu.edu
Description: Independent nondenominational, university, coed. Awards bachelor's, master's, and doctoral degrees and post-master's certificates. Founded 1899. Setting: 60-acre suburban campus with easy access to Los Angeles. Total enrollment: 9,926. Faculty: 1,511 (485 full-time, 1,026 part-time). Student-undergrad faculty ratio is 10:1. 8,939 applied, 60% were admitted. Full-time: 5,075 students, 66% women, 34% men. Part-time: 596 students, 69% women, 31% men. 20% from out-of-state. 0.2% American Indian or Alaska Native, non-Hispanic/Latino; 32% Hispanic/Latino; 5% Black or African American, non-Hispanic/Latino; 10% Asian, non-Hispanic/Latino; 1% Native Hawaiian or other Pacific Islander, non-Hispanic/Latino; 3% international. 6% 25 or older, 6% transferred in. Retention: 83% of full-time freshmen returned the following year. Academic areas with the most degrees conferred: health professions and related sciences; business/marketing; psychology. Core. Calendar: semesters. Academic remediation for entering students, ESL program, services for LD students, advanced placement, accelerated degree program, freshman honors college, honors program, independent study, distance learning, double major, summer session for credit, part-time degree program, adult/continuing education programs, co-op programs and internships, graduate courses open to undergrads. Off campus study. Study abroad program. ROTC: Army, Air Force (c).
Entrance Requirements: Options: electronic application, early action. Required: essay, high school transcript, minimum 3 high school GPA, 1 recommendation, SAT composite of 990 (writing excluded) or ACT composite 19, SAT or ACT. Required for some: interview. Entrance: moderately difficult. Application deadlines: 6/1, 11/15 for early action. Notification: continuous until 10/1, 1/15 for early action. SAT Reasoning Test deadline: 7/1. SAT Subject Test deadline: 7/1. Transfer credits accepted: Yes.
Costs Per Year: Tuition: $36,926 full-time, $1596 per unit part-time. Mandatory fees: $580 full-time. Full-time tuition and fees vary according to course load and degree level. Part-time tuition varies according to course load and degree level. College room only: $5770. Room charges vary according to housing facility.
Collegiate Environment: Orientation program. Drama-theater group, choral group, marching band, student-run newspaper, radio station. Student services: health clinic, personal-psychological counseling, women's center. Campus security: 24-hour emergency response devices and patrols, student patrols, late night transport-escort service, controlled dormitory access. Marshburn Memorial Library plus 3 others. Study areas open 24 hours, 5-7 days a week; students can reserve study rooms.
Community Environment: Azusa is in a suburban area 26 miles east of Los Angeles with a temperate climate. Bus, air, and rail services are nearby. The city has a public library, churches of major denominations, hospitals, and clinics within a 10-mile radius. Mountains and beaches are within easy driving distance and Azusa is close to the cultural and recreational advantages of Los Angeles County.

■ **BAKERSFIELD COLLEGE**
1801 Panorama Dr.
Bakersfield, CA 93305-1299
Tel: (661)395-4011
Fax: (661)395-4230
Web Site: www.bakersfieldcollege.edu
Description: District-supported, 2-year, coed. Part of California Community College System. Awards transfer associate and terminal associate degrees. Founded 1913. Setting: 175-acre urban campus. Total enrollment: 15,001. 50% 25 or older. Core. Calendar: semesters. Academic remediation for entering students, ESL program, services for LD students, advanced placement, accelerated degree program, summer session for credit, part-time degree program, adult/continuing education programs, co-op programs and internships.
Entrance Requirements: Open admission except for registered nursing, radiologic technology programs. Entrance: noncompetitive. Application deadline: rolling. Preference given to district residents for nursing, radiologic technology programs.
Collegiate Environment: Orientation program. Drama-theater group, choral group, student-run newspaper, radio station. Student services: health clinic, women's center. Campus security: 24-hour patrols, late night transport-escort service. Grace Van Dyke Bird Library. 650 computers available on campus for general student use. A campuswide network can be accessed. Staffed computer lab on campus.
Community Environment: See California State University Bakersfield.

■ **BARSTOW COMMUNITY COLLEGE**
2700 Barstow Rd.
Barstow, CA 92311-6699
Tel: (760)252-2411
Fax: (760)252-1875
Web Site: www.barstow.edu
Description: District-supported, 2-year, coed. Part of California Community College System. Awards certificates, transfer associate, and terminal associate degrees. Founded 1959. Setting: 50-acre small town campus. Total enrollment: 4,791. Student-undergrad faculty ratio is 35:1. 56% 25 or older. Core. Calendar: semesters. Academic remediation for entering students, ESL program, services for LD students, self-designed majors, summer session for credit, part-time degree program, external degree program, adult/continuing education programs, co-op programs.
Entrance Requirements: Open admission except for allied health programs. Options: early admission, deferred admission. Recommended: high school transcript. Entrance: noncompetitive. Application deadline: rolling.
Collegiate Environment: Drama-theater group, student-run newspaper. Student services: personal-psychological counseling. Campus security: evening security personnel. Thomas Kimball Library.
Community Environment: This is a desert community with a dry, warm climate. The Santa Fe and Union Pacific Railroads meet here. Greyhound and Orange Belt bus service is also available. The city has a county library, hospital, many churches, including numerous Protestant Churches, an Episcopal Church, a Roman Catholic Church, a Jewish Synagogue. There is a Community Players Association, which presents locally produced programs. Lectures and concerts are presented throughout the year. Part-time employment is available. Barstow has 4 parks and swimming pools for recreation. There are 82 civic, fraternal, and veterans organizations.

■ **BERGIN UNIVERSITY OF CANINE STUDIES**
5860 Labath Ave.
Rohnert Park, CA 94928
Tel: (707)545-3647
Web Site: www.berginu.edu
Description: Independent, comprehensive, coed. Awards associate, bachelor's, and master's degrees. Founded 1991. Calendar: semesters.

■ **BERKELEY CITY COLLEGE**
2050 Ctr. St.
Berkeley, CA 94704-5102
Tel: (510)981-2800
Fax: (510)841-7333
E-mail: mrivas@peralta.edu
Web Site: www.berkeleycitycollege.edu
Description: District-supported, 2-year, coed. Part of California Community College System. Administratively affiliated with Peralta Community College

District. Awards certificates, transfer associate, and terminal associate degrees. Founded 1974. Setting: urban campus with easy access to San Francisco, Oakland. Educational spending for the previous fiscal year: $5609 per student. Total enrollment: 7,645. Faculty: 312 (62 full-time, 250 part-time). Student-undergrad faculty ratio is 35:1. 1% from out-of-state. 0.5% American Indian or Alaska Native, non-Hispanic/Latino; 12% Hispanic/Latino; 18% Black or African American, non-Hispanic/Latino; 16% Asian, non-Hispanic/Latino; 0.5% Native Hawaiian or other Pacific Islander, non-Hispanic/Latino. 65% 25 or older. Calendar: semesters. Academic remediation for entering students, ESL program, services for LD students, advanced placement, self-designed majors, independent study, distance learning, double major, summer session for credit, part-time degree program, adult/continuing education programs, co-op programs and internships. Off campus study at University of California, Berkeley; California State University, East Bay; and Mills College, Oakland. Study abroad program.

Entrance Requirements: Recommended: high school transcript.

Collegiate Environment: Orientation program. Choral group, student-run newspaper. Social organizations: 20 open to all; Phi Theta Kappa, Community College Honor Students. Most popular organizations: Civic Engagement Club, Global Studies Club, Indigenous Student Alliance, The National Society of Leadership and Success, The Digital Arts Club (DAC). Major annual events: Club Rush, Global Awareness Day, Earth Day. Student services: health clinic, personal-psychological counseling. Campus security: 24-hour patrols. Susan A. Duncan Library plus 1 other. 300 computers available on campus for general student use. Computer purchase/lease plans available. A campuswide network can be accessed from off-campus. Students can access the following: online class registration. Staffed computer lab on campus provides training in use of computers, software, and the Internet.

■ **BETHESDA UNIVERSITY**
730 N Euclid St.
Anaheim, CA 92801
Tel: (714)517-1945
Fax: (714)517-1948
Web Site: www.buc.edu
Description: Independent, comprehensive, coed, affiliated with Full Gospel World Mission. Awards bachelor's, master's, and doctoral degrees. Founded 1978. Setting: suburban campus with easy access to Los Angeles. Total enrollment: 345. 19 applied, 95% were admitted. 35% 25 or older. Core. Calendar: semesters. ESL program, accelerated degree program, independent study, double major, summer session for credit, part-time degree program, adult/continuing education programs, internships. Study abroad program.

Entrance Requirements: Open admission. Options: early admission, international baccalaureate accepted. Required: essay, high school transcript, minimum 2.0 high school GPA, 2 recommendations, interview, 2 photographs. Entrance: minimally difficult. Application deadline: 8/11. Notification: continuous until 8/25.

Collegiate Environment: Orientation program. Student services: personal-psychological counseling. Campus security: student patrols, late night transport-escort service, 24-hour security monitor. Library plus 1 other.

■ **BEVERLY HILLS DESIGN INSTITUTE**
8484 Wilshire Blvd., Ste. 730
Beverly Hills, CA 90211
Tel: (310)360-8888
Fax: (310)857-6974
Web Site: www.bhdi.edu
Description: Proprietary, primarily 2-year, coed. Awards transfer associate, terminal associate, and bachelor's degrees. Setting: urban campus with easy access to Los Angeles. Faculty: 4 (3 full-time, 1 part-time). Retention: 75% of full-time freshmen returned the following year. Core. ESL program, double major.

Entrance Requirements: Open admission. Options: electronic application, early admission, international baccalaureate accepted. Required: essay, interview. Recommended: SAT or ACT. Required for some: high school transcript. Entrance: noncompetitive. Transfer credits accepted: Yes.

Collegiate Environment: Orientation program. Campus security: 24-hour emergency response devices and patrols. Main library plus 1 other.

■ **BIOLA UNIVERSITY**
13800 Biola Ave.
La Mirada, CA 90639-0001

Tel: (562)903-6000; Free: 800-652-4652
Fax: (562)903-4709
E-mail: admissions@biola.edu
Web Site: www.biola.edu
Description: Independent interdenominational, university, coed. Awards bachelor's, master's, and doctoral degrees and post-master's certificates. Founded 1908. Setting: 95-acre suburban campus with easy access to Los Angeles. Total enrollment: 6,095. Faculty: 536 (274 full-time, 262 part-time). Student-undergrad faculty ratio is 15:1. 3,926 applied, 69% were admitted. 30% from top 10% of their high school class, 59% from top quarter, 88% from top half. Full-time: 3,947 students, 64% women, 36% men. Part-time: 144 students, 60% women, 40% men. 26% from out-of-state. 0.2% American Indian or Alaska Native, non-Hispanic/Latino; 20% Hispanic/Latino; 2% Black or African American, non-Hispanic/Latino; 17% Asian, non-Hispanic/Latino; 0.3% Native Hawaiian or other Pacific Islander, non-Hispanic/Latino; 3% international. 5% 25 or older, 65% live on campus, 6% transferred in. Retention: 84% of full-time freshmen returned the following year. Core. Calendar: 4-1-4. ESL program, services for LD students, advanced placement, honors program, independent study, distance learning, double major, summer session for credit, part-time degree program, adult/continuing education programs, co-op programs and internships. Off campus study at the Biola Department of Physical Science, in cooperation with the University of Southern California's School of Engineering and Boston University's School of Engineering, offers a program allowing students interested in engineering, biblical studies and liberal arts to receive two degrees in five years. Students can earn credit at USC and work toward their degrees while also enrolled and taking classes here at Biola. Study abroad program. ROTC: Army (c), Air Force (c).

Entrance Requirements: Options: electronic application, early decision, early action, deferred admission, international baccalaureate accepted. Required: essay, high school transcript, SAT or ACT. Recommended: minimum 3 high school GPA. Required for some: interview. Entrance: moderately difficult. Application deadlines: 3/1, 11/15 for early action. Notification: 4/1, 4/1 for nonresidents, 1/15 for early action. SAT Reasoning Test deadline: 5/1. Transfer credits accepted: Yes.

Costs Per Year: Application fee: $45. Comprehensive fee: $51,800 includes full-time tuition ($40,488) and college room and board ($11,312). College room only: $6200. Full-time tuition varies according to course load and degree level. Room and board charges vary according to board plan and housing facility. Part-time tuition: $1687 per credit hour. Part-time tuition varies according to course load and degree level.

Collegiate Environment: Orientation program. Drama-theater group, choral group, student-run newspaper, radio station. Social organizations: 60 open to all; 50% of eligible men and 55% of eligible women are members. Most popular organizations: Adventure Club, Guerilla Film Society, Biola Cross-Fit, Xopoc Dance Team, Lacrosse Club. Major annual events: Mock Rock, Nation Ball, Midnight Madness. Student services: health clinic, personal-psychological counseling. Campus security: 24-hour emergency response devices and patrols, late night transport-escort service, controlled dormitory access. Biola University Library plus 1 other. Books: 550,000 (physical); Databases: 259. Weekly public service hours: 100; students can reserve study rooms.

Community Environment: Population 50,000. La Mirada is a suburban area less than one hour from the Los Angeles International Airport. The Santa Fe Railroad and buses serve the area as does the Santa Ana Freeway. There are libraries, churches, and a hospital. Part-time employment is available. The beaches are 20 miles away and the mountains are an hour and half drive with Knott's Berry Farm and Disneyland a few minutes from campus.

■ **BRANDMAN UNIVERSITY**
16355 Laguna Canyon Rd.
Irvine, CA 92618
Tel: (949)753-4774; Free: 800-746-0082
Fax: (949)753-7875
E-mail: lecompte@brandman.edu
Web Site: www.brandman.edu
Description: Independent, comprehensive, coed. Part of Chapman University System. Awards associate, bachelor's, master's, and doctoral degrees and post-master's certificates. Founded 1958. Setting: 7-acre suburban campus with easy access to Greater Los Angeles Area. Student-undergrad faculty ratio is 15:1. 96 applied, 79% were admitted. Academic areas with the most degrees conferred: business/marketing; psychology; social sciences. Core. Calendar: trimesters. Academic remediation for enter-

ing students, services for LD students, advanced placement, accelerated degree program, independent study, distance learning, double major, summer session for credit, part-time degree program, adult/continuing education programs, co-op programs and internships, graduate courses open to undergrads. Off campus study.

Entrance Requirements: Options: electronic application, deferred admission, international baccalaureate accepted. Required: high school transcript, minimum 2 high school GPA. Required for some: essay, 3 recommendations, 3 letters of recommendation, CPR certification, immunizations, professional liability insurance, RN licensure, and prerequisite coursework for RN-BSN program. Application deadlines: rolling, rolling for nonresidents. Notification: continuous for nonresidents, rolling for early decision. Transfer credits accepted: Yes.

Costs Per Year: Tuition: $15,000 full-time, $500 per credit hour part-time. Mandatory fees: $380 full-time, $95 per term part-time.

Collegiate Environment: Orientation program. Social organizations: 5 open to all. Most popular organizations: Social Work Student Association, Society for Human Resource Management, Nursing Honor Society, Early Childhood Education Leadership, Pi Alpha Honor Society for Social Workers. Major annual events: Orientation, Career services events/alumni events, Commencement workshops. Student services: personal-psychological counseling. Campus security: late night transport-escort service. College housing not available. Leatherby Library plus 1 other. Books: 300,000 (physical), 17,000 (digital/electronic); Serial titles: 265 (physical), 71,000 (digital/electronic); Databases: 300. Weekly public service hours: 65; study areas open 24 hours, 5-7 days a week; students can reserve study rooms. 769 computers available on campus for general student use. A campuswide network can be accessed. Students can access the following: online class registration.

■ **BRYAN COLLEGE**
2065 N Marshall Ave.
El Cajon, CA 92020
Tel: (916)649-2400; Free: 866-649-2400
Description: Proprietary, 2-year, coed. Awards terminal associate degrees. Founded 1995. Total enrollment: 436. Student-undergrad faculty ratio is 11:1. 374 applied, 63% were admitted. 3% from out-of-state. 60% 25 or older.
Entrance Requirements: Required: interview.

■ **BRYAN UNIVERSITY**
3580 Wilshire Blvd.
Los Angeles, CA 90010
Tel: (213)484-8850
Fax: (213)483-3936
Web Site: losangeles.bryanuniversity.edu
Description: Proprietary, 2-year, coed. Awards terminal associate degrees. Founded 1940.

■ **BUTTE COLLEGE**
3536 Butte Campus Dr.
Oroville, CA 95965-8399
Tel: (530)895-2511
Fax: (530)895-2345
Web Site: www.butte.edu
Description: District-supported, 2-year, coed. Part of California Community College System. Awards certificates, transfer associate, and terminal associate degrees. Founded 1966. Setting: 928-acre rural campus with easy access to Sacramento. Total enrollment: 12,290. Student-undergrad faculty ratio is 25:1. 6,239 applied, 100% were admitted. Full-time: 5,330 students, 50% women, 50% men. Part-time: 6,960 students, 54% women, 46% men. 2% American Indian or Alaska Native, non-Hispanic/Latino; 15% Hispanic/Latino; 3% Black or African American, non-Hispanic/Latino; 6% Asian, non-Hispanic/Latino; 0.4% Native Hawaiian or other Pacific Islander, non-Hispanic/Latino; 1% international. Core. Calendar: semesters. Academic remediation for entering students, ESL program, services for LD students, advanced placement, accelerated degree program, honors program, independent study, distance learning, double major, summer session for credit, part-time degree program, adult/continuing education programs, co-op programs and internships. Study abroad program.

Entrance Requirements: Open admission except for allied health, criminal justice, fire science programs. Options: electronic application, early admission, deferred admission. Required for some: high school transcript. Entrance: noncompetitive. Application deadline: rolling.

Collegiate Environment: Orientation program. Drama-theater group, student-run newspaper. Social organizations: 36 open to all. Most popular

organizations: Phi Theta Kappa - International Honor society for Community College Students, Ag Ambassadors, Horticulture Club, International Club, Sigma Alpha Pi (National society of Leadership). Major annual events: Spring Carnival, Diversity Days, Earth Day. Student services: health clinic, personal-psychological counseling. Campus security: 24-hour emergency response devices and patrols, student patrols. Frederick S. Montgomery Library.

Community Environment: Butte College is located in the geographical center of Butte County, population 215,881, at the edge of the Sierra Foothills. The county's amenities include a clean environment, moderate climate, ready access to necessities and luxuries and proximity to recreational areas, including the huge Lake Oroville.

■ **CABRILLO COLLEGE**
6500 Soquel Dr.
Aptos, CA 95003-3194
Tel: (831)479-6100
Fax: (831)479-6425
E-mail: tabolton@cabrillo.edu
Web Site: www.cabrillo.edu
Description: District-supported, 2-year, coed. Part of California Community College System. Awards certificates, transfer associate, and terminal associate degrees. Founded 1959. Setting: 120-acre small town campus with easy access to San Jose. Total enrollment: 15,974. Student-undergrad faculty ratio is 26:1. 46% 25 or older. Core. Calendar: semesters. Academic remediation for entering students, ESL program, services for LD students, advanced placement, honors program, independent study, distance learning, double major, summer session for credit, part-time degree program, adult/continuing education programs, co-op programs and internships. Study abroad program.

Entrance Requirements: Open admission except for international applicants. Option: early admission. Required for some: high school transcript. Entrance: noncompetitive. Application deadline: rolling.

Collegiate Environment: Drama-theater group, student-run newspaper. Student services: health clinic, personal-psychological counseling, women's center. Campus security: 24-hour emergency response devices and patrols, late night transport-escort service. Cabrillo College Library.

Community Environment: Aptos is a suburban area nine miles from Santa Cruz, with a temperate climate. There is a municipal library, churches of major denominations within a ten mile area, and 2 hospitals in the county. Excellent water sports area for swimming, surfing and deep sea fishing. Fine shopping facilities are available. The University of California at Santa Cruz is nearby.

■ **CALIFORNIA BAPTIST UNIVERSITY**
8432 Magnolia Ave.
Riverside, CA 92504-3206
Tel: (951)689-5771; Free: 877-228-8866
E-mail: admissions@calbaptist.edu
Web Site: www.calbaptist.edu
Description: Independent Southern Baptist, comprehensive, coed. Awards associate, bachelor's, master's, and doctoral degrees. Founded 1950. Setting: 160-acre suburban campus with easy access to Los Angeles. Endowment: $41.8 million. Educational spending for the previous fiscal year: $8625 per student. Total enrollment: 9,941. Faculty: 872 (336 full-time, 536 part-time). Student-undergrad faculty ratio is 17:1. 5,039 applied, 77% were admitted. 18% from top 10% of their high school class, 46% from top quarter, 79% from top half. 8 valedictorians. Full-time: 6,367 students, 62% women, 38% men. Part-time: 1,047 students, 65% women, 35% men. Students come from 47 states and territories, 31 other countries, 8% from out-of-state. 0.6% American Indian or Alaska Native, non-Hispanic/Latino; 36% Hispanic/Latino; 7% Black or African American, non-Hispanic/Latino; 5% Asian, non-Hispanic/Latino; 1% Native Hawaiian or other Pacific Islander, non-Hispanic/Latino; 2% international. 24% 25 or older, 40% live on campus, 11% transferred in. Retention: 77% of full-time freshmen returned the following year. Academic areas with the most degrees conferred: health professions and related sciences; psychology; business/marketing. Core. Calendar: 2-4-4-2. Academic remediation for entering students, ESL program, services for LD students, advanced placement, accelerated degree program, honors program, distance learning, double major, summer session for credit, part-time degree program, adult/continuing education programs, internships, graduate courses open to undergrads. Off campus study at Council for Christian Colleges and Universities, Los Angeles Film Institute, The Washington Semester. Study abroad program. ROTC: Army, Air Force (c).

Entrance Requirements: Options: electronic application, early action, deferred admission, international baccalaureate accepted. Required: essay, minimum 2 high school GPA, SAT or ACT. Recommended: SAT and SAT Subject Tests or ACT. Required for some: high school transcript. Entrance: moderately difficult. Application deadline: rolling. Notification: continuous. SAT Reasoning Test deadline: 8/1. SAT Subject Test deadline: 8/1. Transfer credits accepted: Yes.

Costs Per Year: Application fee: $45. One-time mandatory fee: $310. Comprehensive fee: $45,638 includes full-time tuition ($31,668), mandatory fees ($1810), and college room and board ($12,160). College room only: $5860. Full-time tuition and fees vary according to course load, location, and program. Room and board charges vary according to board plan and housing facility. Part-time tuition: $1218 per unit. Part-time mandatory fees: $175 per term. Part-time tuition and fees vary according to course load, location, and program.

Collegiate Environment: Orientation program. Drama-theater group, choral group, student-run newspaper. Social organizations: 81 open to all. Most popular organizations: International Service Projects, United States Service Projects, CBU Crazies (Campus Spirit), Summer of Service, Associated Students of California Baptist University (government and leadership). Major annual events: Fortuna Bowl/Homecoming, Midnight Madness (basketball season kick-off), Yule Festival. Student services: health clinic, personal-psychological counseling. Campus security: 24-hour emergency response devices and patrols, late night transport-escort service, controlled dormitory access. Annie Gabriel Library. Books: 130,837 (physical), 190,918 (digital/electronic); Serial titles: 59,915 (physical), 21,548 (digital/electronic); Databases: 83. Weekly public service hours: 101; students can reserve study rooms. Operations spending for the previous fiscal year: $1.5 million. 279 computers available on campus for general student use. Computer purchase/lease plans available. A campuswide network can be accessed from student residence rooms and from off campus. Students can access the following: online class registration, online course evaluations. Staffed computer lab on campus provides training in use of computers, software, and the Internet.

Community Environment: See University of California Riverside.

■ CALIFORNIA CHRISTIAN COLLEGE

5364 E Belmont Ave.
Fresno, CA 93727
Tel: (559)251-4215
E-mail: admissions@calchristiancollege.edu
Web Site: www.calchristiancollege.edu

Description: Independent Free Will Baptist, 4-year, coed. Awards associate and bachelor's degrees. Setting: urban campus. Endowment: $166,018. Educational spending for the previous fiscal year: $2427 per student. Total enrollment: 16. Faculty: 7 (1 full-time, 6 part-time). 3 applied, 100% were admitted. Full-time: 7 students, 14% women, 86% men. Part-time: 9 students, 33% women, 67% men. Students come from 2 states and territories, 0.2% from out-of-state. 6% American Indian or Alaska Native, non-Hispanic/Latino; 44% Hispanic/Latino; 19% Black or African American, non-Hispanic/Latino. 2% 25 or older, 19% live on campus, 13% transferred in. Core. Calendar: semesters. Academic remediation for entering students, independent study, distance learning, part-time degree program, co-op programs.

Entrance Requirements: Open admission. Options: electronic application, international baccalaureate accepted. Required: essay, high school transcript, minimum 2 high school GPA, 2 recommendations, statement of faith, moral/ethical statement, math and English exams. Recommended: interview, SAT or ACT. Entrance: noncompetitive. Application deadline: rolling. Notification: continuous. Transfer credits accepted: Yes.

Costs Per Year: Application fee: $40. Tuition: $8880 full-time, $370 per unit part-time. Mandatory fees: $610 full-time, $305 per term part-time.

Collegiate Environment: Orientation program. Major annual events: Fall Hike, Banquet. Student services: personal-psychological counseling. Cortese Library. Books: 17,572 (physical); Serial titles: 12 (physical). Weekly public service hours: 15. Operations spending for the previous fiscal year: $30,944. 12 computers available on campus for general student use. A campuswide network can be accessed from student residence rooms. Staffed computer lab on campus provides training in use of computers, software, and the Internet.

■ CALIFORNIA COAST UNIVERSITY

925 N Spurgeon St.
Santa Ana, CA 92701

Tel: (714)547-9625; Free: 888-CCU-UNIV
Web Site: www.calcoast.edu

Description: Proprietary, comprehensive, coed. Awards associate, bachelor's, master's, and doctoral degrees (distance learning only). Founded 1973.

Entrance Requirements: Required: high school transcript, resume.

■ CALIFORNIA COLLEGE OF THE ARTS

1111 Eighth St.
San Francisco, CA 94107
Tel: (415)703-9500; Free: 800-447-1ART
Fax: (415)703-9539
E-mail: enroll@cca.edu
Web Site: www.cca.edu

Description: Independent, comprehensive, coed. Awards bachelor's and master's degrees. Founded 1907. Setting: 4-acre urban campus with easy access to San Francisco, Oakland. Endowment: $30.3 million. Total enrollment: 1,983. Faculty: 485 (100 full-time, 385 part-time). Student-undergrad faculty ratio is 9:1. 3,077 applied, 70% were admitted. Full-time: 1,442 students, 64% women, 36% men. Part-time: 86 students, 66% women, 34% men. Students come from 49 states and territories, 53 other countries, 32% from out-of-state. 0.2% American Indian or Alaska Native, non-Hispanic/Latino; 12% Hispanic/Latino; 6% Black or African American, non-Hispanic/Latino; 18% Asian, non-Hispanic/Latino; 0.8% Native Hawaiian or other Pacific Islander, non-Hispanic/Latino; 35% international. 16% 25 or older, 22% live on campus, 9% transferred in. Retention: 82% of full-time freshmen returned the following year. Academic areas with the most degrees conferred: visual and performing arts; architecture; communication technologies. Core. Calendar: semesters. Academic remediation for entering students, ESL program, services for LD students, advanced placement, self-designed majors, independent study, double major, summer session for credit, part-time degree program, external degree program, internships, graduate courses open to undergrads. Off campus study at AICAD Mobility Program. Study abroad program.

Entrance Requirements: Option: electronic application. Required: essay, minimum 2 high school GPA, 1 recommendation, portfolio of creative work. Required for some: high school transcript, interview. Application deadline: rolling. Notification: continuous. Transfer credits accepted: Yes.

Costs Per Year: Application fee: $70. Tuition: $48,648 full-time, $2027 per unit part-time. Mandatory fees: $500 full-time, $170 per term part-time. College room only: $10,136. Room charges vary according to housing facility.

Collegiate Environment: Orientation program. Student-run radio station. Social organizations: 27 open to all; national fraternities, national sororities, Alpha Rho Chi (coed); 1% of eligible men and 1% of eligible women are members. Most popular organizations: Student of Color Coalition, International Student Alliance, Chimera Council, Animation Resource Center, MyChina. Major annual events: Chimerapalooza, Holiday Lunch, Holiday Fair. Student services: personal-psychological counseling. Campus security: 24-hour emergency response devices and patrols, late night transport-escort service, controlled dormitory access. Meyer Library plus 1 other. Operations spending for the previous fiscal year: $773,000. 400 computers available on campus for general student use. Computer purchase/lease plans available. A computer is required for all students. A campuswide network can be accessed from student residence rooms and from off campus. Students can access the following: online class registration, online course evaluations, learning management system, media applications, software training, print payments. Staffed computer lab on campus (open 24 hours a day) provides training in use of computers, software, and the Internet.

Community Environment: See Laney College.

■ CALIFORNIA COLLEGE SAN DIEGO (NATIONAL CITY)

700 Bay Marina Dr.
Ste. 100
National City, CA 91950
Tel: (619)680-4421; Free: 800-622-3188
Web Site: www.cc-sd.edu

Description: Independent, 4-year, coed. Awards associate and bachelor's degrees.

■ CALIFORNIA COLLEGE SAN DIEGO (SAN DIEGO)

6602 Convoy Ct.
Ste. 100
San Diego, CA 92111
Tel: (619)293-0190; Free: 800-622-3188

Web Site: www.cc-sd.edu

Description: Proprietary, 4-year, coed. Awards associate and bachelor's degrees. Total enrollment: 1,299. Student-undergrad faculty ratio is 19:1. 62% 25 or older. Retention: 89% of full-time freshmen returned the following year.

Entrance Requirements: Open admission.

■ **CALIFORNIA COLLEGE SAN DIEGO (SAN MARCOS)**
277 Rancheros Dr.
Ste. 200
San Marcos, CA 92069
Tel: (760)621-4333; Free: 800-622-3188
Web Site: www.cc-sd.edu

Description: Independent, 4-year, coed. Awards associate and bachelor's degrees.

■ **CALIFORNIA INSTITUTE OF THE ARTS**
24700 McBean Pky.
Valencia, CA 91355-2340
Tel: (661)255-1050; Free: 800-545-2787
E-mail: admiss@calarts.edu
Web Site: www.calarts.edu

Description: Independent, comprehensive, coed. Awards bachelor's, master's, and doctoral degrees. Founded 1961. Setting: 60-acre suburban campus with easy access to Los Angeles. Endowment: $101.6 million. Educational spending for the previous fiscal year: $20,789 per student. Total enrollment: 1,448. Faculty: 340 (160 full-time, 180 part-time). Student-undergrad faculty ratio is 7:1. 2,145 applied, 25% were admitted. Full-time: 943 students, 60% women, 40% men. Part-time: 6 students, 17% women, 83% men. Students come from 20 states and territories, 25 other countries, 34% from out-of-state. 0.5% American Indian or Alaska Native, non-Hispanic/Latino; 15% Hispanic/Latino; 7% Black or African American, non-Hispanic/Latino; 11% Asian, non-Hispanic/Latino; 0.6% Native Hawaiian or other Pacific Islander, non-Hispanic/Latino; 15% international. 12% 25 or older, 40% live on campus, 9% transferred in. Retention: 86% of full-time freshmen returned the following year. Academic area with the most degrees conferred: visual and performing arts. Core. Calendar: semesters. Services for LD students, advanced placement, self-designed majors, independent study, summer session for credit, co-op programs and internships, graduate courses open to undergrads. Study abroad program.

Entrance Requirements: Options: electronic application, international baccalaureate accepted. Required: essay, high school transcript, 2 recommendations, portfolio or audition. Required for some: 3 recommendations, interview. Entrance: very difficult. Application deadlines: 1/5, rolling for nonresidents. Notification: continuous until 4/1. Transfer credits accepted: Yes.

Costs Per Year: Application fee: $70. Tuition: $48,660 full-time. Mandatory fees: $616 full-time.

Collegiate Environment: Orientation program. Drama-theater group, choral group, student-run radio station. Most popular organizations: Student Council, FISK - Graphic Arts Club, Soccer Club, Korean Bible Study, Black Student Union. Major annual events: Spring Event, Town Hall Meetings, Tea & Sympathy. Student services: health clinic, personal-psychological counseling. Campus security: 24-hour emergency response devices and patrols, late night transport-escort service, controlled dormitory access. Division of Library and Information Resources. Operations spending for the previous fiscal year: $1.4 million. 42 computers available on campus for general student use. A campuswide network can be accessed from student residence rooms and from off campus. Students can access the following: online class registration. Staffed computer lab on campus provides training in use of computers, software, and the Internet.

Community Environment: Valencia is located on the Golden State Freeway (Interstate 5) 35 miles north of Los Angeles, and historically has been devoted to agriculture and cattle ranching. The area, encompassing the towns of Newhall, Saugus, Valencia and Castaic, is surrounded by the Tehachapi Mountains to the North, the San Gabriel to the east and the Santa Susana to the west. In the last 10 years light industry and numerous housing developments have contributed to the city's growth.

■ **CALIFORNIA INSTITUTE OF ARTS & TECHNOLOGY**
2820 Camino Del Rio S
Ste. 100
San Diego, CA 92108
Description: Proprietary, 2-year, coed.

■ **CALIFORNIA INSTITUTE OF INTEGRAL STUDIES**
1453 Mission St.
San Francisco, CA 94103
Tel: (415)575-6100
Fax: (415)575-1264
E-mail: admissions@ciis.edu
Web Site: www.ciis.edu

Description: Independent, upper-level, coed. Awards bachelor's, master's, and doctoral degrees. Founded 1968. Setting: urban campus with easy access to San Francisco. Endowment: $1.9 million. Educational spending for the previous fiscal year: $12,599 per student. Total enrollment: 1,417. Faculty: 199 (64 full-time, 135 part-time). Student-undergrad faculty ratio is 11:1. Full-time: 47 students, 81% women, 19% men. Part-time: 3 students, 100% women. Students come from 4 states and territories, 4 other countries, 1% from out-of-state. 14% Hispanic/Latino; 14% Black or African American, non-Hispanic/Latino; 2% Asian, non-Hispanic/Latino; 8% international. 99% 25 or older, 62% transferred in. Academic area with the most degrees conferred: interdisciplinary studies. Core. Calendar: semesters. Accelerated degree program, independent study, distance learning, summer session for credit, external degree program, adult/continuing education programs, graduate courses open to undergrads.

Entrance Requirements: Transfer credits accepted: Yes. Applicants placed on waiting list: 0.

Costs Per Year: Application fee: $65. Tuition: $19,792 full-time, $825 per unit part-time. Mandatory fees: $430 full-time, $215 per term part-time.

Collegiate Environment: Orientation program. Drama-theater group. Most popular organizations: Student Alliance, People of Color, Queer@CIIS, International Students and Friends, AWARE - Awaking to Whiteness and Racism Everywhere. Student services: personal-psychological counseling. The Laurance S. Rockefeller Library plus 1 other. Operations spending for the previous fiscal year: $927,108. 25 computers available on campus for general student use. A campuswide network can be accessed from off-campus. Students can access the following: online class registration. Staffed computer lab on campus.

Community Environment: See San Francisco State University.

■ **CALIFORNIA INSTITUTE OF TECHNOLOGY**
1200 E California Blvd.
Pasadena, CA 91125-0001
Tel: (626)395-6811
Fax: (626)683-3026
Web Site: www.caltech.edu

Description: Independent, university, coed. Awards bachelor's, master's, and doctoral degrees and post-master's certificates. Founded 1891. Setting: 124-acre suburban campus with easy access to Los Angeles. Endowment: $2.9 billion. Research spending for the previous fiscal year: $256.5 million. Educational spending for the previous fiscal year: $104,953 per student. Total enrollment: 2,233. Faculty: 374 (332 full-time, 42 part-time). Student-undergrad faculty ratio is 3:1. 8,208 applied, 7% were admitted. 96% from top 10% of their high school class, 100% from top quarter, 100% from top half. Full-time: 948 students, 45% women, 55% men. Students come from 46 states and territories, 23 other countries, 63% from out-of-state. 14% Hispanic/Latino; 1% Black or African American, non-Hispanic/Latino; 40% Asian, non-Hispanic/Latino; 9% international. 1% 25 or older, 86% live on campus, 1% transferred in. Retention: 98% of full-time freshmen returned the following year. Academic areas with the most degrees conferred: engineering; physical sciences; computer and information sciences. Core. Calendar: quarters. ESL program, services for LD students, self-designed majors, independent study, double major, co-op programs, graduate courses open to undergrads. Off campus study at Occidental College, Art Center College of Design. Study abroad program. ROTC: Army (c), Air Force (c).

Entrance Requirements: Options: electronic application, early admission, early action, deferred admission. Required: essay, high school transcript, 2 recommendations, SAT or ACT, SAT and SAT Subject Tests or ACT, SAT Subject Tests. Entrance: most difficult. Application deadlines: 1/3, 11/1 for early action. Notification: 4/1, 12/15 for early action. SAT Reasoning Test deadline: 12/31. SAT Subject Test deadline: 12/31. Transfer credits accepted: Yes. Applicants placed on waiting list: 634. Wait-listed applicants offered admission: 6.

Costs Per Year: Application fee: $75. One-time mandatory fee: $500. Comprehensive fee: $71,244 includes full-time tuition ($52,506), mandatory fees ($2094), and college room and board ($16,644). College room only: $9615.

Collegiate Environment: Orientation program. Drama-theater group, choral

group, student-run newspaper. Social organizations: 100 open to all. Most popular organizations: Instrumental music groups, Entrepreneur's Club, Glee Club, Theater Arts, Ultimate Disc Club. Major annual events: Ditch Day, International Day, Pre-Frosh Weekend. Student services: health clinic, personal-psychological counseling, women's center. Campus security: 24-hour emergency response devices and patrols, late night transport-escort service, controlled dormitory access. 876 college housing spaces available; 820 were occupied in 2018-19. Freshmen guaranteed college housing. On-campus residence required in freshman year. Option: coed housing available. Sherman Fairchild Library plus 5 others. Books: 276,995 (physical), 74,744 (digital/electronic); Serial titles: 6,183 (physical), 5,495 (digital/electronic); Databases: 197. Weekly public service hours: 168; study areas open 24 hours, 5-7 days a week; students can reserve study rooms. Operations spending for the previous fiscal year: $1.3 million. 75 computers available on campus for general student use. Computer purchase/lease plans available. A campuswide network can be accessed from student residence rooms and from off campus. Students can access the following: online class registration. Staffed computer lab on campus provides training in use of computers, software, and the Internet.

Community Environment: Population 143,700, Pasadena is located at the foot of the San Gabriel Mountains, the center of a large metropolitan area with ideal climate throughout the year. The famous Huntington Library, located in nearby San Marino, is open to the public and makes available its rich resources for scholarly research work in numerous fields. Pasadena has many cultural activities in the fields of art, music, and literature. The finest talent in America can be seen and heard in Pasadena and Los Angeles. Exhibits of famous artists and art instruction are provided by the community. The annual New Year's Day Tournament of Roses is held in the winter, and nearby is the Rose Bowl that seats 104,000 people.

■ **CALIFORNIA INTERCONTINENTAL UNIVERSITY**

17310 Red Hill Ave., No.200
Irvine, CA 92614
Tel: (909)396-6090; Free: 866-687-2258
Fax: (909)804-5151
Web Site: caluniversity.edu
Description: Proprietary, comprehensive, coed. Awards bachelor's and master's degrees.
Entrance Requirements: Required: high school transcript.

■ **CALIFORNIA JAZZ CONSERVATORY**

2087 Addison St.
Berkeley, CA 94704
Description: Independent, 4-year, coed.

■ **CALIFORNIA LUTHERAN UNIVERSITY**

60 W Olsen Rd.
Thousand Oaks, CA 91360-2787
Tel: (805)492-2411; Free: 877-258-3678
Fax: (805)493-3114
E-mail: cluadm@clunet.edu
Web Site: www.callutheran.edu
Description: Independent Lutheran, comprehensive, coed. Awards bachelor's, master's, and doctoral degrees and post-master's certificates. Founded 1959. Setting: 290-acre suburban campus with easy access to Los Angeles. Endowment: $109.1 million. Educational spending for the previous fiscal year: $11,651 per student. Total enrollment: 4,383. Faculty: 458 (195 full-time, 263 part-time). Student-undergrad faculty ratio is 16:1. 5,752 applied, 71% were admitted. 24% from top 10% of their high school class, 63% from top quarter, 92% from top half. Full-time: 2,942 students, 57% women, 43% men. Part-time: 117 students, 56% women, 44% men. Students come from 39 states and territories, 32 other countries, 11% from out-of-state. 0.3% American Indian or Alaska Native, non-Hispanic/Latino; 33% Hispanic/Latino; 4% Black or African American, non-Hispanic/Latino; 5% Asian, non-Hispanic/Latino; 0.5% Native Hawaiian or other Pacific Islander, non-Hispanic/Latino; 3% international. 4% 25 or older, 52% live on campus, 8% transferred in. Retention: 83% of full-time freshmen returned the following year. Academic areas with the most degrees conferred: business/marketing; communication/journalism; psychology. Core. Calendar: semesters. Services for LD students, advanced placement, accelerated degree program, self-designed majors, honors program, independent study, double major, summer session for credit, part-time degree program, adult/continuing education programs, co-op programs and internships, graduate courses

open to undergrads. Off campus study at Wagner College, American University (Washington Semester). Study abroad program. ROTC: Army (c), Air Force (c).

Entrance Requirements: Options: electronic application, early action, deferred admission, international baccalaureate accepted. Required: essay, high school transcript, minimum 2.8 high school GPA, 1 recommendation, SAT or ACT. Recommended: minimum 3 high school GPA, interview. Entrance: moderately difficult. Application deadline: 1/1. Notification: 4/1, 1/15 for early action. SAT Reasoning Test deadline: 5/1. Transfer credits accepted: Yes. Applicants placed on waiting list: 358. Wait-listed applicants offered admission: 3. Early action applicants: 2,905. Early action applicants admitted: 2,337.

Costs Per Year: Application fee: $25. Comprehensive fee: $58,483 includes full-time tuition ($43,900), mandatory fees ($483), and college room and board ($14,100). College room only: $7590.

Collegiate Environment: Orientation program. Drama-theater group, choral group, student-run newspaper, radio station. Social organizations: 119 open to all. Most popular organizations: Student Government, recreation, sports fan, or club sports related, service organizations, campus ministry or other religiously affiliated organization, multicultural organizations. Major annual events: Club Lu, Midnight Madness, Involvement Fair. Student services: health clinic, personal-psychological counseling, women's center. Campus security: 24-hour emergency response devices and patrols, late night transport-escort service, controlled dormitory access, escort service, shuttle service. College housing designed to accommodate 1,380 students; 1,448 undergraduates lived in college housing during 2018-19. Freshmen guaranteed college housing. On-campus residence required through junior year. Option: coed housing available. Pearson Library. Books: 93,605 (physical), 250,900 (digital/electronic); Serial titles: 13 (physical), 75,211 (digital/electronic); Databases: 155. Weekly public service hours: 105; students can reserve study rooms. Operations spending for the previous fiscal year: $1.6 million. 543 computers available on campus for general student use. A campuswide network can be accessed from student residence rooms and from off campus. Students can access the following: online class registration. Staffed computer lab on campus (open 24 hours a day) provides training in use of computers, software, and the Internet.

Community Environment: Located in the Conejo Valley, Thousand Oaks has a mild pleasant climate with temperatures ranging from a mean low of 57 degrees in winter to a mean high of 77 degrees in summer. Average rainfall is 14 inches, the rainy season being between October and April. Buses, trains and airlines serve the area. Principal industries are electronics, aerospace, research, insurance and manufacturing. There are numerous shopping areas in Thousand Oaks. Recreational facilities include the community center, theatres, championship golf courses, Lake Sherwood, and the marinas in Oxnard and Ventura. Pacific Ocean Beaches are thirty minutes from The Campus.

■ **CALIFORNIA MIRAMAR UNIVERSITY**

3550 Camino Del Rio N
Ste. 208
San Diego, CA 92108
Tel: (858)653-3000; Free: 877-570-5678
Fax: (858)653-6786
Web Site: www.calmu.edu
Description: Proprietary, comprehensive, coed. Awards associate, bachelor's, and master's degrees.
Entrance Requirements: Required: high school transcript, resume.

■ **CALIFORNIA POLYTECHNIC STATE UNIVERSITY, SAN LUIS OBISPO**

1 Grand Ave.
San Luis Obispo, CA 93407
Tel: (805)756-1111
E-mail: admissions@calpoly.edu
Web Site: www.calpoly.edu
Description: State-supported, comprehensive, coed. Part of California State University System. Awards bachelor's and master's degrees. Founded 1901. Setting: 6,000-acre suburban campus. Total enrollment: 21,812. Faculty: 1,486 (958 full-time, 528 part-time). Student-undergrad faculty ratio is 19:1. 54,663 applied, 30% were admitted. 59% from top 10% of their high school class, 89% from top quarter, 99% from top half. 20 National Merit Scholars. Full-time: 20,272 students, 49% women, 51% men. Part-time: 765 students, 40% women, 60% men. 14% from out-of-state. 0.1% American Indian or Alaska Native, non-Hispanic/Latino; 17% Hispanic/Latino; 0.8% Black or

African American, non-Hispanic/Latino; 13% Asian, non-Hispanic/Latino; 0.2% Native Hawaiian or other Pacific Islander, non-Hispanic/Latino; 2% international. 3% 25 or older, 32% live on campus, 4% transferred in. Retention: 94% of full-time freshmen returned the following year. Academic areas with the most degrees conferred: engineering; business/marketing; agriculture. Core. Calendar: quarters. Academic remediation for entering students, ESL program, services for LD students, advanced placement, honors program, distance learning, double major, summer session for credit, part-time degree program, co-op programs and internships, graduate courses open to undergrads. Off campus study at Other units of the California State University system. Study abroad program. ROTC: Army.

Entrance Requirements: Option: electronic application. Required: high school transcript, SAT or ACT. Entrance: moderately difficult. Application deadline: 11/30. Notification: 4/1. SAT Reasoning Test deadline: 12/1. Transfer credits accepted: Yes. Applicants placed on waiting list: 6,643. Waitlisted applicants offered admission: 2,436.

Costs Per Year: Application fee: $55. State resident tuition: $5742 full-time, $3330 per year part-time. Nonresident tuition: $17,622 full-time, $8082 per year part-time. Mandatory fees: $4074 full-time, $3307 per year part-time. Full-time tuition and fees vary according to course load, degree level, and program. Part-time tuition and fees vary according to course load, degree level, and program. College room and board: $13,796. College room only: $8259. Room and board charges vary according to housing facility.

Collegiate Environment: Orientation program. Drama-theater group, choral group, marching band, student-run newspaper, radio station. Social organizations: national fraternities, national sororities, local fraternities, local sororities; 7% of eligible men and 11% of eligible women are members. Student services: legal services, health clinic, personal-psychological counseling, women's center. Campus security: 24-hour emergency response devices and patrols, student patrols, late night transport-escort service. No special consideration for freshman housing applicants. On-campus residence required in freshman year. Option: coed housing available. Robert E. Kennedy Library.

Community Environment: San Luis Obispo, located midway between San Francisco and Los Angeles, is 12 miles from the Pacific Ocean. The average high winter temperature is in the 60s, and the summer high average is in the 70s. Buses, trains and airlines serve the area. There are 3 hospitals and a student health center. Student housing is available in campus dormitories and college approved housing in the city. Part time work is available in the community. Recreation includes surfing, fishing, clamming, golfing, hunting, boating and swimming. The Mission San Luis Obispo de Tolosa was founded in 1772, named for the Bishop of Toulouse, an Italian saint of the 13th century.

■ **CALIFORNIA STATE POLYTECHNIC UNIVERSITY, POMONA**
3801 W Temple Ave.
Pomona, CA 91768-2557
Tel: (909)869-7659
Fax: (909)869-4529
E-mail: dlbrandon@cpp.edu
Web Site: www.cpp.edu

Description: State-supported, comprehensive, coed. Part of California State University System. Awards bachelor's, master's, and doctoral degrees. Founded 1938. Setting: 1,400-acre urban campus with easy access to Los Angeles. Endowment: $96.1 million. Research spending for the previous fiscal year: $1.8 million. Educational spending for the previous fiscal year: $6615 per student. Total enrollment: 25,894. Faculty: 1,244 (607 full-time, 637 part-time). Student-undergrad faculty ratio is 25:1. 36,574 applied, 55% were admitted. Full-time: 21,668 students, 47% women, 53% men. Part-time: 2,651 students, 40% women, 60% men. Students come from 34 states and territories, 107 other countries, 1% from out-of-state. 0.2% American Indian or Alaska Native, non-Hispanic/Latino; 43% Hispanic/Latino; 3% Black or African American, non-Hispanic/Latino; 22% Asian, non-Hispanic/Latino; 0.2% Native Hawaiian or other Pacific Islander, non-Hispanic/Latino; 7% international. 17% 25 or older, 10% live on campus, 13% transferred in. Retention: 87% of full-time freshmen returned the following year. Academic areas with the most degrees conferred: business/marketing; engineering; social sciences; biological/life sciences. Core. Calendar: quarters. Academic remediation for entering students, ESL program, services for LD students, advanced placement, freshman honors college, honors program, distance learning, double major, summer session for credit, part-time degree program, adult/continuing education programs, co-op programs and internships, graduate courses open to undergrads. Off campus study at other units

of the California State University System, Desert Studies Consortium, Southern California Ocean Studies Consortium. Study abroad program. ROTC: Army.

Entrance Requirements: Option: electronic application. Required: high school transcript, minimum 2 high school GPA, SAT or ACT. Entrance: moderately difficult. Application deadline: 11/30. Notification: continuous. SAT Reasoning Test deadline: 1/31. Transfer credits accepted: Yes.

Costs Per Year: Application fee: $55. State resident tuition: $5742 full-time. Nonresident tuition: $17,622 full-time, $396 per credit hour part-time. Mandatory fees: $1611 full-time. Full-time tuition and fees vary according to course load, degree level, and program. Part-time tuition varies according to course load, degree level, and program. College room and board: $17,358. College room only: $9766. Room and board charges vary according to board plan and housing facility.

Collegiate Environment: Orientation program. Drama-theater group, choral group, student-run newspaper. Social organizations: 400 open to all; national fraternities, national sororities, local fraternities, local sororities; 2% of eligible men and 1% of eligible women are members. Most popular organizations: Rose Float Club, Mexican American Student Association (MASA), Barkada - Filipino American Student Association, American Marketing Association, Cal Poly Society of Accountants. Major annual events: Homecoming, BroncoFusion, Hot Dog Caper. Student services: health clinic, personal-psychological counseling, women's center. Campus security: 24-hour emergency response devices and patrols, student patrols, late night transport-escort service, controlled dormitory access, video camera surveillance. University Library. Books: 576,734 (physical), 246,874 (digital/electronic); Serial titles: 278,011 (physical), 13,335 (digital/electronic); Databases: 143. Weekly public service hours: 92; study areas open 24 hours, 5-7 days a week; students can reserve study rooms. Operations spending for the previous fiscal year: $5.4 million. 2,117 computers available on campus for general student use. Computer purchase/lease plans available. A campuswide network can be accessed from student residence rooms and from off campus. Staffed computer lab on campus provides training in use of computers, software, and the Internet.

Community Environment: Cal Poly Pomona is located just 35 miles southeast of downtown Los Angeles in the heart of Southern California. Near business and industry, the university's location is ideal for internships and/or employment. Cal Poly Pomona is also suitable for recreation: the beach, the desert, ski slopes, museums, Disneyland, and much more are just a short drive away.

■ **CALIFORNIA STATE UNIVERSITY, BAKERSFIELD**
9001 Stockdale Hwy.
Bakersfield, CA 93311
Tel: (661)664-2011; Free: 800-788-2782
Fax: (661)664-3188
E-mail: admissions@csub.edu
Web Site: www.csub.edu

Description: State-supported, comprehensive, coed. Part of California State University System. Awards bachelor's, master's, and doctoral degrees. Founded 1970. Setting: 575-acre urban campus. Total enrollment: 10,493. Faculty: 678 (338 full-time, 340 part-time). Student-undergrad faculty ratio is 26:1. 5,429 applied, 100% were admitted. Full-time: 7,906 students, 62% women, 38% men. Part-time: 1,290 students, 60% women, 40% men. 1% from out-of-state. 0.5% American Indian or Alaska Native, non-Hispanic/Latino; 61% Hispanic/Latino; 5% Black or African American, non-Hispanic/Latino; 6% Asian, non-Hispanic/Latino; 0.2% Native Hawaiian or other Pacific Islander, non-Hispanic/Latino; 5% international. 72% 25 or older, 4% live on campus, 13% transferred in. Retention: 77% of full-time freshmen returned the following year. Academic areas with the most degrees conferred: liberal arts/general studies; education; business/marketing. Calendar: semesters. Part-time degree program, external degree program, adult/continuing education programs.

Entrance Requirements: Options: electronic application, deferred admission. Required: high school transcript. Required for some: SAT or ACT. Preference given to state residents. SAT Subject Test deadline: December.

Collegiate Environment: Orientation program. Campus security: 24-hour emergency response devices and patrols, late night transport-escort service. Option: coed housing available. Walter W. Stiern Library.

Community Environment: Bakersfield is the county seat of Kern County which is noted for its rich agriculture, petroleum, and light industries. The city is located 112 miles north of Los Angeles and 295 miles south of San Francisco. Airline, bus, transcontinental railroad, and Amtrak services are available in the area. Bakersfield is considered the trading center of the

Southern San Joaquin Valley. Central California beaches are located approximately 100 miles west of the campus. Shirley Meadow ski area is 51 miles northeast of Bakersfield, 20 minutes from Lake Isebella. The county is home to world-famous Edwards Air Force Base. Part-time employment is available.

■ CALIFORNIA STATE UNIVERSITY CHANNEL ISLANDS

One University Dr.
Camarillo, CA 93012
Tel: (805)437-8400
Fax: (805)437-8951
E-mail: prospective.student@csuci.edu
Web Site: www.csuci.edu

Description: State-supported, comprehensive, coed. Part of California State University System. Awards bachelor's, master's, and doctoral degrees. Founded 2002. Setting: suburban campus. Total enrollment: 3,599. Faculty: 294 (89 full-time, 205 part-time). Student-undergrad faculty ratio is 15:1. 5,562 applied, 53% were admitted. 3% from out-of-state. 25% 25 or older, 23% live on campus. Retention: 76% of full-time freshmen returned the following year. Academic areas with the most degrees conferred: liberal arts/general studies; psychology; business/marketing. Academic remediation for entering students, services for LD students, advanced placement, double major. Study abroad program.

Entrance Requirements: Required: high school transcript, minimum 2.0 high school GPA, SAT or ACT. Recommended: minimum 3.0 high school GPA. Entrance: noncompetitive.

Collegiate Environment: Student-run newspaper. Social organizations: local fraternities, local sororities. Student services: health clinic, personal-psychological counseling, women's center. Campus security: 24-hour emergency response devices and patrols, late night transport-escort service, controlled dormitory access. John Spoor Broome Library at Channel Islands.

■ CALIFORNIA STATE UNIVERSITY, CHICO

400 W First St.
Chico, CA 95929-0722
Tel: (530)898-4636; Free: 800-542-4426
Fax: (530)898-6456
Web Site: www.csuchico.edu

Description: State-supported, comprehensive, coed. Part of California State University System. Awards bachelor's and master's degrees and post-master's certificates. Founded 1887. Setting: 119-acre small town campus. Endowment: $64.7 million. Research spending for the previous fiscal year: $3.9 million. Educational spending for the previous fiscal year: $9052 per student. Total enrollment: 18,073. Faculty: 987 (503 full-time, 484 part-time). Student-undergrad faculty ratio is 24:1. 23,964 applied, 65% were admitted. 35% from top 10% of their high school class, 76% from top quarter, 100% from top half. Full-time: 15,237 students, 53% women, 47% men. Part-time: 1,183 students, 51% women, 49% men. 1% from out-of-state. 0.5% American Indian or Alaska Native, non-Hispanic/Latino; 34% Hispanic/Latino; 3% Black or African American, non-Hispanic/Latino; 5% Asian, non-Hispanic/Latino; 0.2% Native Hawaiian or other Pacific Islander, non-Hispanic/Latino; 3% international. 11% 25 or older, 2% live on campus, 9% transferred in. Retention: 85% of full-time freshmen returned the following year. Academic areas with the most degrees conferred: business/marketing; health professions and related sciences; social sciences. Core. Calendar: semesters. Academic remediation for entering students, ESL program, services for LD students, advanced placement, self-designed majors, honors program, independent study, distance learning, double major, summer session for credit, part-time degree program, external degree program, adult/continuing education programs, co-op programs and internships, graduate courses open to undergrads. Off campus study at other units of the California State University System, National Student Exchange. Study abroad program.

Entrance Requirements: Options: electronic application, deferred admission, international baccalaureate accepted. Required: high school transcript, GPA from 10th/11th grade college preparatory courses, SAT or ACT. Entrance: moderately difficult. Notification: 3/1. SAT Reasoning Test deadline: 12/31. SAT Subject Test deadline: 12/31. Transfer credits accepted: Yes.

Collegiate Environment: Orientation program. Drama-theater group, choral group, student-run newspaper, radio station. Social organizations: 174 open to all; national fraternities, national sororities, local fraternities, local sororities; 1% of eligible men and 1% of eligible women are members. Most popular organizations: Chico Snow Club, Chico State Nursing Club, Pre-

Medical Association, Health Professionals Association, Exercise Physiology Majors Club. Major annual events: Choose Chico, Cats in the Community, Wildcat Welcome. Student services: legal services, health clinic, personal-psychological counseling, women's center. Campus security: 24-hour emergency response devices and patrols, student patrols, late night transport-escort service, controlled dormitory access. 2,239 college housing spaces available; all were occupied in 2018-19. Freshmen given priority for college housing. Options: coed, women-only housing available. Meriam Library plus 1 other. Books: 544,345 (physical), 306,440 (digital/electronic); Serial titles: 72,555 (physical). Study areas open 24 hours, 5-7 days a week; students can reserve study rooms. Operations spending for the previous fiscal year: $4.3 million. 1,328 computers available on campus for general student use. Computer purchase/lease plans available. A campuswide network can be accessed from student residence rooms and from off campus. Students can access the following: online class registration, student account information, calendar, transcripts. Staffed computer lab on campus (open 24 hours a day) provides training in use of computers, software, and the Internet.

Community Environment: Chico is located close to the northern end of the Sacramento Valley and is one of the oldest communities in the state. Today Chico has a population of 71,427 (105,000 in the Greater Chico area) and Butte county has a population of 215,800. It is considered the business center for a large agricultural area, which produces an abundance of rice, grains, nuts, and fruits. Winters are mild and summers are hot, averaging 95-105 degrees. Regional airlines connect Chico with adjacent cities, including San Francisco and Sacramento. Greyhound Bus service is available. Chico is the home of Bidwell Park, one of the largest and most beautiful municipal parks in the nation. Lower Bidwell Park starts near the campus and extends 10 miles east along the Big Chico creek. The park offers swimming, hiking, a municipal golf course, horseback riding, a children's park, picnic areas, and softball fields among its recreational facilities. Biking is a favorite (and practical) means of transportation. Local Public Bus transportation is free to university students and personnel. Skiing facilities are only two hours away. Bidwell Mansion, located on campus, is now a historical site maintained by the Department of Parks and Recreation. Part-time employment is available but scarce.

■ CALIFORNIA STATE UNIVERSITY, DOMINGUEZ HILLS

1000 E Victoria St.
Carson, CA 90747-0001
Tel: (310)243-3300
E-mail: info@csudh.edu
Web Site: www.csudh.edu

Description: State-supported, comprehensive, coed. Part of California State University System. Awards bachelor's and master's degrees and post-master's certificates. Founded 1960. Setting: 350-acre urban campus with easy access to Los Angeles. Endowment: $11 million. Research spending for the previous fiscal year: $335,054. Educational spending for the previous fiscal year: $7288 per student. Total enrollment: 15,179. Faculty: 842 (277 full-time, 565 part-time). Student-undergrad faculty ratio is 21:1. 12,094 applied, 77% were admitted. Full-time: 10,043 students, 62% women, 38% men. Part-time: 3,073 students, 64% women, 36% men. Students come from 15 states and territories, 37 other countries. 0.1% American Indian or Alaska Native, non-Hispanic/Latino; 62% Hispanic/Latino; 12% Black or African American, non-Hispanic/Latino; 9% Asian, non-Hispanic/Latino; 0.3% Native Hawaiian or other Pacific Islander, non-Hispanic/Latino; 5% international. 35% 25 or older, 5% live on campus, 21% transferred in. Retention: 77% of full-time freshmen returned the following year. Academic areas with the most degrees conferred: business/marketing; health professions and related sciences; psychology. Core. Calendar: semesters. Academic remediation for entering students, services for LD students, advanced placement, accelerated degree program, self-designed majors, honors program, independent study, distance learning, double major, summer session for credit, part-time degree program, external degree program, co-op programs, graduate courses open to undergrads. Off campus study at other institutions of the California State University System, National Student Exchange. Study abroad program. ROTC: Army, Air Force (c).

Entrance Requirements: Options: electronic application, international baccalaureate accepted. Required: high school transcript. Required for some: SAT or ACT. Entrance: moderately difficult. Application deadline: rolling. Notification: continuous. Preference given to state residents. SAT Reasoning Test deadline: 2/15. Transfer credits accepted: Yes.

Costs Per Year: Application fee: $55. State resident tuition: $6937 full-time, $3330 per year part-time. Nonresident tuition: $16,441 full-time, $396 per

unit part-time. Mandatory fees: $1195 full-time, $1195 per year part-time. Full-time tuition and fees vary according to course load, program, and reciprocity agreements. Part-time tuition and fees vary according to course load, program, and reciprocity agreements. College room and board: $12,540. Room and board charges vary according to housing facility.

Collegiate Environment: Orientation program. Drama-theater group, choral group, student-run newspaper, radio station. Social organizations: 115 open to all; national fraternities, national sororities. Most popular organizations: American Marketing Association, Phi Sigma Sigma, Organization of African Studies, Latino Student Business Association, Circle K. Major annual events: Welcome Week, Toro Days, Unity Fest. Student services: health clinic, personal-psychological counseling, women's center. Campus security: 24-hour emergency response devices and patrols, student patrols, late night transport-escort service. Leo F. Cain Educational Resource Center. Books: 457,885 (physical), 300,523 (digital/electronic); Serial titles: 6,542 (physical), 75,366 (digital/electronic); Databases: 94. Weekly public service hours: 81; students can reserve study rooms. Operations spending for the previous fiscal year: $4.4 million. 1,100 computers available on campus for general student use. A campuswide network can be accessed. Students can access the following: online class registration. Staffed computer lab on campus provides training in use of computers and the Internet.

Community Environment: This is a metropolitan area in Los Angeles County with a Mediterranean climate. Trains, buses and airlines serve the area. Carson is surrounded by freeways, which makes the larger nearby cities easy to reach. The city has churches, hospitals, a YMCA building and library. The State Department of Employment, which is located in Torrance, has established a program designed to aid students in finding employment.

■ CALIFORNIA STATE UNIVERSITY, EAST BAY

25800 Carlos Bee Blvd.
Hayward, CA 94542-3000
Tel: (510)885-3000
Fax: (510)885-3816
E-mail: dave.vasquez@csueastbay.edu
Web Site: www.csueastbay.edu

Description: State-supported, comprehensive, coed. Part of California State University System. Awards bachelor's, master's, and doctoral degrees. Founded 1957. Setting: 343-acre suburban campus with easy access to San Francisco Bay Area. Total enrollment: 15,435. Faculty: 882 (388 full-time, 494 part-time). Student-undergrad faculty ratio is 22:1. 15,963 applied, 74% were admitted. Full-time: 11,306 students, 62% women, 38% men. Part-time: 1,692 students, 60% women, 40% men. Students come from 21 states and territories, 54 other countries, 1% from out-of-state. 0.2% American Indian or Alaska Native, non-Hispanic/Latino; 34% Hispanic/Latino; 10% Black or African American, non-Hispanic/Latino; 24% Asian, non-Hispanic/Latino; 0.9% Native Hawaiian or other Pacific Islander, non-Hispanic/Latino; 6% international. 67% 25 or older, 18% transferred in. Retention: 75% of full-time freshmen returned the following year. Academic areas with the most degrees conferred: business/marketing; health professions and related sciences; social sciences. Core. Calendar: quarters. Academic remediation for entering students, ESL program, services for LD students, advanced placement, accelerated degree program, self-designed majors, honors program, independent study, distance learning, double major, summer session for credit, part-time degree program, adult/continuing education programs, co-op programs and internships, graduate courses open to undergrads. Off campus study at Regional Association of East Bay Colleges and Universities, National Student Exchange. Study abroad program.

Entrance Requirements: Options: electronic application, international baccalaureate accepted. Required: high school transcript, minimum 2 high school GPA, California State University eligibility index. Required for some: SAT or ACT. Entrance: minimally difficult. Application deadline: 11/30. Notification: continuous. SAT Reasoning Test deadline: 2/1. Transfer credits accepted: Yes.

Costs Per Year: Application fee: $55. State resident tuition: $5742 full-time, $3330 per term part-time. Nonresident tuition: $18,714 full-time, $7290 per term part-time. Mandatory fees: $1197 full-time, $364 per term part-time. Full-time tuition and fees vary according to program and reciprocity agreements. Part-time tuition and fees vary according to course load, program, and reciprocity agreements. College room and board: $13,980. Room and board charges vary according to board plan, housing facility, and student level.

Collegiate Environment: Orientation program. Drama-theater group, choral group, marching band, student-run newspaper. Social organizations: 109 open to all; national fraternities, national sororities, local fraternities, local

sororities, Cultural Fraternities and Sororities. Most popular organizations: Tau Sigma Hour Society, East Bay Student Nursing Association, Golden Key Honor Society, Black Student Union, Sigma Sigma Sigma Society. Major annual events: Al Fresco Fall Welcome Festival, Homecoming Week, Spring Mayhem Concert/Festival. Student services: health clinic, personal-psychological counseling. Campus security: 24-hour emergency response devices and patrols, student patrols, late night transport-escort service, controlled dormitory access. Hayward Campus Library. Books: 630,855 (physical), 233,485 (digital/electronic); Serial titles: 10,905 (physical), 107,791 (digital/electronic); Databases: 133. Weekly public service hours: 101; students can reserve study rooms. 700 computers available on campus for general student use. Computer purchase/lease plans available. A campuswide network can be accessed from student residence rooms and from off campus. Students can access the following: online class registration. Staffed computer lab on campus (open 24 hours a day) provides training in use of computers, software, and the Internet.

Community Environment: Population 140,000 in a metropolitan area of 5 1/2 million. Hayward is a suburban area near Oakland, Berkeley, San Francisco and San Jose. The climate is mild. All modes of transportation serve the area. The university's proximity to all major Bay Area cities provides access to museums, art galleries, plays, concerts, and libraries as well as to the recreational opportunities of the bay. The climate makes outdoor recreation a year-round activity. Its nearness to ocean and mountain areas offer recreational diversity.

■ CALIFORNIA STATE UNIVERSITY, FRESNO

5241 N Maple Ave.
Fresno, CA 93740-8027
Tel: (559)278-4240
Fax: (559)278-4715
E-mail: andyhe@csufresno.edu
Web Site: www.csufresno.edu

Description: State-supported, comprehensive, coed. Part of California State University System. Awards bachelor's, master's, and doctoral degrees and post-master's certificates. Founded 1911. Setting: 1,399-acre urban campus. Total enrollment: 24,403. Faculty: 1,360 (686 full-time, 674 part-time). Student-undergrad faculty ratio is 21:1. 18,731 applied, 54% were admitted. 15% from top 10% of their high school class, 80% from top quarter, 100% from top half. Full-time: 18,194 students, 58% women, 42% men. Part-time: 3,334 students, 57% women, 43% men. 1% from out-of-state. 0.3% American Indian or Alaska Native, non-Hispanic/Latino; 50% Hispanic/Latino; 3% Black or African American, non-Hispanic/Latino; 14% Asian, non-Hispanic/Latino; 0.2% Native Hawaiian or other Pacific Islander, non-Hispanic/Latino; 6% international. 4% live on campus, 10% transferred in. Retention: 79% of full-time freshmen returned the following year. Academic areas with the most degrees conferred: business/marketing; health professions and related sciences; psychology; agriculture. Core. Calendar: semesters. Academic remediation for entering students, ESL program, services for LD students, advanced placement, accelerated degree program, self-designed majors, freshman honors college, honors program, independent study, distance learning, double major, summer session for credit, part-time degree program, adult/continuing education programs, co-op programs and internships, graduate courses open to undergrads. Off campus study at other units of the California State University System. Study abroad program. ROTC: Army, Air Force.

Entrance Requirements: Options: electronic application, international baccalaureate accepted. Required: high school transcript, minimum 2 high school GPA, SAT or ACT. Entrance: minimally difficult. Preference given to state residents. SAT Reasoning Test deadline: 1/16. SAT Subject Test deadline: 1/16. Transfer credits accepted: Yes.

Collegiate Environment: Orientation program. Drama-theater group, choral group, marching band, student-run newspaper, radio station. Social organizations: national fraternities, national sororities, local fraternities, local sororities. Major annual events: Vintage Days, Welcome Week, Commencement. Student services: health clinic, personal-psychological counseling, women's center. Campus security: 24-hour emergency response devices and patrols, late night transport-escort service, controlled dormitory access. Henry Madden Library.

Community Environment: Fresno (population 461,000) is located in the heart of the San Joaquin Valley, at the center of the state. The climate is mild all year. All modes of transportation serve the area. Fresno is in an agricultural area producing figs, grapes and cotton. Roma Winery and several other wineries are located here; other industries include processing and packing of fruit, the manufacture of cottonseed oil, livestock and poultry feed, agricultural equipment and aircraft parts. There are facilities in the area for swimming, fishing, sailing, water skiing, horseback riding, hiking, rock climbing and all the winter sports. Three national parks and two national forests are nearby.

■ **CALIFORNIA STATE UNIVERSITY, FULLERTON**
800 N State College Blvd.
Fullerton, CA 92831-3599
Tel: (657)278-2011
E-mail: admissions@fullerton.edu
Web Site: www.fullerton.edu
Description: State-supported, comprehensive, coed. Part of California State University System. Awards bachelor's, master's, and doctoral degrees and post-master's certificates. Founded 1957. Setting: 236-acre suburban campus with easy access to Los Angeles. Endowment: $52.6 million. Research spending for the previous fiscal year: $1.2 million. Educational spending for the previous fiscal year: $7636 per student. Total enrollment: 40,280. Faculty: 2,146 (993 full-time, 1,153 part-time). Student-undergrad faculty ratio is 30:1. 51,415 applied, 43% were admitted. 21% from top 10% of their high school class, 68% from top quarter, 96% from top half. Full-time: 27,907 students, 57% women, 43% men. Part-time: 6,844 students, 54% women, 46% men. 1% from out-of-state. 0.1% American Indian or Alaska Native, non-Hispanic/Latino; 44% Hispanic/Latino; 2% Black or African American, non-Hispanic/Latino; 22% Asian, non-Hispanic/Latino; 0.2% Native Hawaiian or other Pacific Islander, non-Hispanic/Latino; 6% international. 22% 25 or older, 6% live on campus, 11% transferred in. Retention: 88% of full-time freshmen returned the following year. Academic areas with the most degrees conferred: business/marketing; communication/journalism; health professions and related sciences. Core. Calendar: semesters. Academic remediation for entering students, services for LD students, advanced placement, self-designed majors, honors program, independent study, distance learning, double major, summer session for credit, part-time degree program, adult/continuing education programs, co-op programs and internships. Off campus study at other institutions of the California State University System. Study abroad program. ROTC: Army.
Entrance Requirements: Options: electronic application, international baccalaureate accepted. Required: high school transcript, minimum 2 high school GPA, SAT or ACT. Entrance: moderately difficult. Application deadline: 12/15. Notification: continuous. Preference given to state residents. Transfer credits accepted: Yes.
Costs Per Year: Application fee: $55. Area resident tuition: $6895 full-time. State resident tuition: $6895 full-time. Nonresident tuition: $16,399 full-time. Mandatory fees: $1149 full-time.
Collegiate Environment: Orientation program. Drama-theater group, choral group, student-run newspaper, radio station. Social organizations: 325 open to all; national fraternities, national sororities, local fraternities, local sororities. Most popular organizations: Pan-Hellenic Council, American Marketing Association, Lacrosse Club, Samaritans (volunteer service club), Human Services Student Association. Major annual events: Block Party, Spring Concert, Snow Day. Student services: legal services, health clinic, personal-psychological counseling, women's center. Campus security: 24-hour emergency response devices and patrols, student patrols, late night transport-escort service, controlled dormitory access. Freshmen given priority for college housing. Options: coed, men-only, women-only housing available. Pollak Library. Operations spending for the previous fiscal year: $6.8 million. 2,000 computers available on campus for general student use. A campuswide network can be accessed from student residence rooms and from off campus. Students can access the following: online class registration. Staffed computer lab on campus provides training in use of computers, software, and the Internet.
Community Environment: Fullerton is in a metropolitan area with a temperate climate. Airlines, buses and trains serve the area. Freeways make all neighboring cities easily accessible. Fullerton is an area of many cultural interests, in art, music and theatre. The city is near Disneyland and the California Angel Stadium; 35 miles from Hollywood and Los Angeles. Recreational facilities include the beaches and the mountains which are both within easy driving distance. Part-time work is available. The major service clubs are represented in the city.

■ **CALIFORNIA STATE UNIVERSITY, LONG BEACH**
1250 Bellflower Blvd.
Long Beach, CA 90840
Tel: (562)985-4111
E-mail: janice.miller@csulb.edu

Web Site: www.csulb.edu
Description: State-supported, comprehensive, coed. Part of California State University System. Awards bachelor's, master's, and doctoral degrees. Founded 1949. Setting: 320-acre suburban campus with easy access to Los Angeles. Endowment: $77.2 million. Research spending for the previous fiscal year: $2.6 million. Educational spending for the previous fiscal year: $8608 per student. Total enrollment: 36,846. Faculty: 2,322 (1,035 full-time, 1,287 part-time). Student-undergrad faculty ratio is 24:1. 69,578 applied, 31% were admitted. Full-time: 27,462 students, 57% women, 43% men. Part-time: 3,985 students, 53% women, 47% men. 1% from out-of-state. 0.1% American Indian or Alaska Native, non-Hispanic/Latino; 43% Hispanic/Latino; 4% Black or African American, non-Hispanic/Latino; 22% Asian, non-Hispanic/Latino; 0.3% Native Hawaiian or other Pacific Islander, non-Hispanic/Latino; 6% international. 16% 25 or older, 4% live on campus, 13% transferred in. Retention: 87% of full-time freshmen returned the following year. Academic areas with the most degrees conferred: business/marketing; visual and performing arts; health professions and related sciences. Core. Calendar: semesters. ESL program, accelerated degree program, self-designed majors, honors program, independent study, double major, part-time degree program, adult/continuing education programs, internships, graduate courses open to undergrads. Study abroad program. ROTC: Army, Air Force (c).
Entrance Requirements: Option: electronic application. Required: high school transcript, SAT or ACT. Recommended: ACT. Required for some: minimum 3 high school GPA. Entrance: moderately difficult. Notification: continuous. Preference given to local residents. Transfer credits accepted: Yes.
Costs Per Year: Application fee: $55. State resident tuition: $5742 full-time, $3330 per year part-time. Nonresident tuition: $16,038 full-time, $4752 per year part-time. Mandatory fees: $1056 full-time, $1060 per year part-time. Full-time tuition and fees vary according to course level, course load, degree level, and program. Part-time tuition and fees vary according to course level, course load, degree level, and program. College room and board: $12,750. College room only: $8200. Room and board charges vary according to board plan.
Collegiate Environment: Orientation program. Drama-theater group, choral group, student-run newspaper, radio station. Social organizations: 300 open to all; national fraternities, national sororities, local fraternities, local sororities; 0.02% of eligible men and 0.02% of eligible women are members. Major annual events: Kaleidoscope Spring Festival, Odyssey Theme Year. Student services: legal services, health clinic, personal-psychological counseling, women's center. Campus security: 24-hour emergency response devices and patrols, student patrols, late night transport-escort service, controlled dormitory access. 2,700 college housing spaces available; 2,583 were occupied in 2018-19. Option: coed housing available. CSULB University Library. Books: 681,649 (physical), 1 million (digital/electronic); Serial titles: 16,851 (physical), 105,038 (digital/electronic); Databases: 227. Weekly public service hours: 97. Operations spending for the previous fiscal year: $1.2 million. 2,000 computers available on campus for general student use. A campuswide network can be accessed from student residence rooms and from off campus. Students can access the following: online class registration. Staffed computer lab on campus provides training in use of computers, software, and the Internet.
Community Environment: Long Beach is approximately 20 miles south of Los Angeles and has a Mediterranean climate. The eight mile beach area provides the finest and safest public bathing on the Pacific Coast, having the largest protected harbor in North America. All modes of transportation serve the area. There are 25 city parks which provide facilities for golf, tennis, baseball, swimming, shuffleboard, and lawn bowling, as well as a sports arena and a municipal auditorium.

■ **CALIFORNIA STATE UNIVERSITY, LOS ANGELES**
5151 State University Dr.
Los Angeles, CA 90032-8530
Tel: (323)343-3000
Fax: (323)343-2670
E-mail: admission@calstatela.edu
Web Site: www.calstatela.edu
Description: State-supported, comprehensive, coed. Part of California State University System. Awards bachelor's, master's, and doctoral degrees and post-master's certificates. Founded 1947. Setting: 175-acre urban campus with easy access to Los Angeles. Endowment: $32.9 million. Research spending for the previous fiscal year: $2.8 million. Educational spending for the previous fiscal year: $6641 per student. Total enrollment: 27,685.

Faculty: 1,712 (644 full-time, 1,068 part-time). Student-undergrad faculty ratio is 24:1. 39,854 applied, 42% were admitted. Full-time: 20,600 students, 58% women, 42% men. Part-time: 3,404 students, 55% women, 45% men. 0.3% from out-of-state. 0.1% American Indian or Alaska Native, non-Hispanic/Latino; 68% Hispanic/Latino; 3% Black or African American, non-Hispanic/Latino; 13% Asian, non-Hispanic/Latino; 0.1% Native Hawaiian or other Pacific Islander, non-Hispanic/Latino; 7% international. 23% 25 or older, 10% live on campus, 12% transferred in. Retention: 82% of full-time freshmen returned the following year. Academic areas with the most degrees conferred: business/marketing; social sciences; health professions and related sciences. Core. Calendar: quarters. Academic remediation for entering students, ESL program, services for LD students, advanced placement, accelerated degree program, self-designed majors, freshman honors college, honors program, independent study, distance learning, double major, summer session for credit, part-time degree program, adult/continuing education programs, co-op programs and internships, graduate courses open to undergrads. Off campus study at other units of the California State University System. Study abroad program. ROTC: Army (c), Air Force (c).
Entrance Requirements: Options: electronic application, early admission. Required: high school transcript, SAT or ACT. Entrance: moderately difficult. Application deadlines: 11/30, 11/30 for nonresidents, 11/30 for early decision plan 1, 11/30 for early decision plan 2. Notification: 8/30, 4/1 for nonresidents. SAT Reasoning Test deadline: 7/15. SAT Subject Test deadline: 7/15. Transfer credits accepted: Yes.
Costs Per Year: Application fee: $55. Area resident tuition: $5742 full-time. State resident tuition: $5742 full-time. Nonresident tuition: $17,622 full-time, $396 per unit part-time. Mandatory fees: $1,020 full-time. College room and board: $12,918. College room only: $8785.
Collegiate Environment: Orientation program. Drama-theater group, choral group, student-run newspaper, radio station. Social organizations: 146 open to all; national fraternities, national sororities, local fraternities; 1% of eligible men and 1% of eligible women are members. Most popular organizations: Phi Alpha Theta History Honor Society, National Student Speech Language, Student Dietetic Association, Film Productions, Child Development Association. Major annual events: Golden Eagle 3K, Homecoming, Welcome Week. Student services: legal services, health clinic, personal-psychological counseling, women's center. Campus security: 24-hour emergency response devices and patrols, student patrols, late night transport-escort service, controlled dormitory access. 1,061 college housing spaces available; 553 were occupied in 2018-19. No special consideration for freshman housing applicants. John F. Kennedy Memorial Library. Books: 537,271 (physical), 86,220 (digital/electronic); Serial titles: 7,843 (physical), 83,822 (digital/electronic); Databases: 230. Weekly public service hours: 99. Operations spending for the previous fiscal year: $5.6 million. 1,500 computers available on campus for general student use. A campuswide network can be accessed from student residence rooms and from off campus. Students can access the following: online class registration. Staffed computer lab on campus provides training in use of computers, software, and the Internet.
Community Environment: See University of California - Los Angeles.

■ **CALIFORNIA STATE UNIVERSITY MARITIME ACADEMY**
200 Maritime Academy Dr.
Vallejo, CA 94590
Tel: (707)654-1000; Free: 800-561-1945
Fax: (707)648-4204
Web Site: www.csum.edu
Description: State-supported, comprehensive, coed. Part of California State University System. Awards bachelor's and master's degrees. Founded 1929. Setting: 64-acre suburban campus with easy access to San Francisco. Total enrollment: 1,090. Faculty: 106 (71 full-time, 35 part-time). Student-undergrad faculty ratio is 16:1. 1,156 applied, 67% were admitted. Full-time: 1,007 students, 18% women, 82% men. Part-time: 43 students, 16% women, 84% men. 13% from out-of-state. 0.3% American Indian or Alaska Native, non-Hispanic/Latino; 20% Hispanic/Latino; 2% Black or African American, non-Hispanic/Latino; 9% Asian, non-Hispanic/Latino; 0.6% Native Hawaiian or other Pacific Islander, non-Hispanic/Latino; 0.8% international. 12% 25 or older, 66% live on campus, 6% transferred in. Retention: 75% of full-time freshmen returned the following year. Academic areas with the most degrees conferred: transportation and materials moving; engineering technologies; business/marketing. Core. Calendar: semesters. Academic remediation for entering students, advanced placement, summer session for credit, internships. Study abroad program. ROTC: Naval (c), Air Force (c).
Entrance Requirements: Options: electronic application, early action. Required: high school transcript, minimum 2 high school GPA, health form,

SAT or ACT. Entrance: moderately difficult. Application deadlines: 11/30, 10/31 for early action. Notification: continuous, 12/15 for early action. Preference given to California residents who meet the admissions resident index. SAT Reasoning Test deadline: 1/10. Applicants placed on waiting list: 122. Wait-listed applicants offered admission: 0.
Collegiate Environment: Orientation program. Choral group, student-run newspaper. Most popular organizations: Sailing Club, Dive Club, drill team. Major annual events: Changeover Dance, Homecoming, open house. Student services: health clinic, personal-psychological counseling. Campus security: 24-hour patrols, student patrols.
Community Environment: Vallejo has a population of 117,500 and is located on the north shore of the Carquinez Strait, adjacent to San Pablo Bay.

■ **CALIFORNIA STATE UNIVERSITY, MONTEREY BAY**
100 Campus Ctr.
Seaside, CA 93955-8001
Tel: (831)582-3000
Fax: (831)582-3540
Web Site: www.csumb.edu
Description: State-supported, comprehensive, coed. Part of California State University System. Awards bachelor's and master's degrees. Founded 1994. Setting: 1,387-acre small town campus with easy access to San Jose. Total enrollment: 7,545. Faculty: 476 (167 full-time, 309 part-time). Student-undergrad faculty ratio is 26:1. 12,423 applied, 59% were admitted. 14% from top 10% of their high school class, 46% from top quarter, 84% from top half. Full-time: 6,051 students, 64% women, 36% men. Part-time: 665 students, 51% women, 49% men. 2% from out-of-state. 0.7% American Indian or Alaska Native, non-Hispanic/Latino; 41% Hispanic/Latino; 5% Black or African American, non-Hispanic/Latino; 6% Asian, non-Hispanic/Latino; 1% Native Hawaiian or other Pacific Islander, non-Hispanic/Latino; 6% international. 21% 25 or older, 14% transferred in. Retention: 83% of full-time freshmen returned the following year. Academic areas with the most degrees conferred: business/marketing; psychology; liberal arts/general studies. Core. Calendar: semesters. Academic remediation for entering students, services for LD students, advanced placement, accelerated degree program, self-designed majors, independent study, distance learning, double major, summer session for credit, part-time degree program, co-op programs and internships, graduate courses open to undergrads. Off campus study at Monterey Institute of International Studies (MIIS). Study abroad program. ROTC: Air Force (c).
Entrance Requirements: Options: electronic application, deferred admission, international baccalaureate accepted. Required: high school transcript, minimum 2 high school GPA, SAT or ACT. Entrance: moderately difficult. SAT Reasoning Test deadline: 1/31. SAT Subject Test deadline: 1/31. Transfer credits accepted: Yes.
Collegiate Environment: Orientation program. Drama-theater group, choral group, student-run newspaper, radio station. Social organizations: national fraternities, national sororities, local sororities. Student services: health clinic, personal-psychological counseling, women's center. Campus security: 24-hour emergency response devices and patrols, student patrols, late night transport-escort service, controlled dormitory access. Freshmen given priority for college housing. On-campus residence required through sophomore year. Option: coed housing available. The Tanimura & Antle Family Memorial Library.

■ **CALIFORNIA STATE UNIVERSITY, NORTHRIDGE**
18111 Nordhoff St.
Northridge, CA 91330
Tel: (818)677-1200
Fax: (818)677-3766
Web Site: www.csun.edu
Description: State-supported, comprehensive, coed. Part of California State University System. Awards bachelor's, master's, and doctoral degrees. Founded 1958. Setting: 356-acre urban campus with easy access to Los Angeles. Total enrollment: 38,716. Faculty: 2,093 (906 full-time, 1,187 part-time). Student-undergrad faculty ratio is 27:1. 34,856 applied, 51% were admitted. Full-time: 29,279 students, 55% women, 45% men. Part-time: 5,621 students, 49% women, 51% men. 0.1% American Indian or Alaska Native, non-Hispanic/Latino; 49% Hispanic/Latino; 5% Black or African American, non-Hispanic/Latino; 10% Asian, non-Hispanic/Latino; 0.1% Native Hawaiian or other Pacific Islander, non-Hispanic/Latino; 8% international. Retention: 80% of full-time freshmen returned the following year. Core. Calendar: semesters. Academic remediation for entering students, ESL

program, services for LD students, advanced placement, self-designed majors, independent study, distance learning, double major, summer session for credit, part-time degree program, adult/continuing education programs, internships, graduate courses open to undergrads. Off campus study. Study abroad program. ROTC: Army (c), Air Force (c).

Entrance Requirements: Option: electronic application. Required: high school transcript, SAT or ACT. Entrance: moderately difficult. Notification: continuous. Preference given to state residents for business administration, engineering, computer science, economics programs. SAT Reasoning Test deadline: 1/15.

Costs Per Year: Application fee: $55. State resident tuition: $6888 full-time. Nonresident tuition: $396 per unit part-time. College room and board: $11,122. Room and board charges vary according to board plan and housing facility.

Collegiate Environment: Orientation program. Drama-theater group, choral group, student-run newspaper, radio station. Social organizations: national fraternities, national sororities. Student services: health clinic, personal-psychological counseling, women's center. Campus security: 24-hour emergency response devices, late night transport-escort service. Oviatt Library plus 1 other. Students can reserve study rooms.

Community Environment: Located north of Los Angeles and part of the Los Angeles metropolitan area. Climate is mild; all modes of transportation available in the Los Angeles area. The community facilities include churches, library, hospitals and all the service organizations are represented. Part-time employment available in this center for electronic and space research and development; about three-quarters of the students work. Northridge enjoys the cultural and recreational advantages of Los Angeles and is 20 miles from the Pacific Ocean and near the mountain areas for winter sports.

■ **CALIFORNIA STATE UNIVERSITY, SACRAMENTO**
6000 J St.
Sacramento, CA 95819
Tel: (916)278-6011
E-mail: admissions@csus.edu
Web Site: www.csus.edu
Description: State-supported, comprehensive, coed. Part of California State University System. Awards bachelor's, master's, and doctoral degrees. Founded 1947. Setting: 300-acre urban campus. Total enrollment: 30,670. Faculty: 1,648 (690 full-time, 958 part-time). Student-undergrad faculty ratio is 25:1. 24,137 applied, 68% were admitted. 100% from top half of their high school class. Full-time: 22,829 students, 57% women, 43% men. Part-time: 5,235 students, 52% women, 48% men. 1% from out-of-state. 0.3% American Indian or Alaska Native, non-Hispanic/Latino; 31% Hispanic/Latino; 6% Black or African American, non-Hispanic/Latino; 21% Asian, non-Hispanic/Latino; 0.7% Native Hawaiian or other Pacific Islander, non-Hispanic/Latino; 3% international. 23% 25 or older, 7% live on campus, 13% transferred in. Retention: 83% of full-time freshmen returned the following year. Academic areas with the most degrees conferred: business/marketing; education; social sciences. Core. Calendar: semesters. ESL program, services for LD students, advanced placement, accelerated degree program, self-designed majors, honors program, independent study, distance learning, double major, summer session for credit, part-time degree program, adult/continuing education programs, co-op programs and internships. Off campus study at Other units of the California State University System. Study abroad program. ROTC: Army (c), Air Force.

Entrance Requirements: Options: electronic application, early action, international baccalaureate accepted. Required: minimum 2 high school GPA, SAT or ACT. Required for some: high school transcript. Entrance: moderately difficult. Application deadline: 11/30. Notification: continuous until 3/1, 12/1 for early action. Applicants placed on waiting list: 1,905. Wait-listed applicants offered admission: 206.

Costs Per Year: Application fee: $55. State resident tuition: $5742 full-time, $1665 per term part-time. Nonresident tuition: $17,622 full-time, $396 per credit hour part-time. Mandatory fees: $1192 full-time, $731 per term part-time. College room and board: $14,396. College room only: $9774. Room and board charges vary according to board plan and housing facility.

Collegiate Environment: Orientation program. Drama-theater group, choral group, marching band, student-run newspaper, radio station. Social organizations: national fraternities, national sororities. Student services: legal services, health clinic, personal-psychological counseling, women's center. Campus security: 24-hour emergency response devices and patrols, student patrols, late night transport-escort service, controlled dormitory access. California State University, Sacramento Library. Students can reserve study rooms.

Community Environment: Sacramento, the capital of California, is the gateway to historic Gold Rush country and the High Sierra vacation regions. All modes of transportation serve the area; San Francisco is a two-hour drive on the freeway. The cultural center of Northern California, Sacramento has the historic Crocker Art Gallery, symphony orchestra, summer theater series, state library, a state museum, a state railroad museum and the Sacramento History Center. Numerous part time jobs on campus and in the city are available through the Student Placement Office and the California Department of Employment. There are many post-college vocational opportunities with defense industries, two air bases, state and local government and other growing industrial and high-tech firms. Off campus housing is available to students. There are many points of interest and a great number of recreational facilities in the Sacramento area; parks, zoo, golf courses, boating and fishing on the American and Sacramento Rivers. Squaw Valley, 100 miles away, was the home of the 1960 Olympics for winter sports. There are good health facilities and a wide range of fraternal and civic organizations.

■ **CALIFORNIA STATE UNIVERSITY, SAN BERNARDINO**
5500 University Pky.
San Bernardino, CA 92407
Tel: (909)537-5000
E-mail: moreinfo@mail.csusb.edu
Web Site: www.csusb.edu
Description: State-supported, comprehensive, coed. Part of California State University System. Awards bachelor's, master's, and doctoral degrees. Founded 1965. Setting: 430-acre suburban campus with easy access to Los Angeles. Total enrollment: 19,973. Faculty: 1,022 (467 full-time, 555 part-time). Student-undergrad faculty ratio is 28:1. 16,042 applied, 55% were admitted. Full-time: 16,110 students, 61% women, 39% men. Part-time: 1,744 students, 57% women, 43% men. 0.2% American Indian or Alaska Native, non-Hispanic/Latino; 65% Hispanic/Latino; 5% Black or African American, non-Hispanic/Latino; 5% Asian, non-Hispanic/Latino; 0.2% Native Hawaiian or other Pacific Islander, non-Hispanic/Latino; 7% international. 19% 25 or older, 6% live on campus, 14% transferred in. Retention: 86% of full-time freshmen returned the following year. Academic areas with the most degrees conferred: business/marketing; psychology; social sciences. Core. Calendar: quarters. Academic remediation for entering students, services for LD students, advanced placement, accelerated degree program, self-designed majors, honors program, independent study, distance learning, double major, summer session for credit, part-time degree program, co-op programs and internships. Off campus study at WICHE/WUE - Western Undergraduate Exchange. Study abroad program. ROTC: Army, Air Force.

Entrance Requirements: Options: electronic application, early admission, early action. Required: high school transcript, minimum 2 high school GPA. Recommended: SAT or ACT. Entrance: moderately difficult. Application deadline: rolling. Notification: continuous. SAT Reasoning Test deadline: 6/30. SAT Subject Test deadline: 9/1. Transfer credits accepted: Yes.

Costs Per Year: Application fee: $55. State resident tuition: $5472 full-time. Nonresident tuition: $11,880 full-time, $264 per credit hour part-time. Mandatory fees: $1184 full-time. College room and board: $12,711. Room and board charges vary according to board plan and housing facility.

Collegiate Environment: Orientation program. Drama-theater group, choral group, student-run newspaper, radio station. Social organizations: national fraternities, national sororities, local fraternities, local sororities; 4% of eligible men and 4% of eligible women are members. Student services: legal services, health clinic, personal-psychological counseling, women's center. Campus security: 24-hour emergency response devices and patrols, student patrols, late night transport-escort service. 1,837 college housing spaces available; 1,118 were occupied in 2018-19. Freshmen given priority for college housing. Options: coed, women-only housing available. Pfau Library.

Community Environment: Population 198,550. San Bernardino is located 58 miles east of Los Angeles at the foot of the San Bernardino Mountains. Climate is ideal with 312 days of sunshine a year. Citrus groves surround the city. Greyhound and Trailways bus lines and Santa Fe Railroad serve the area. The nearest airport is Ontario International. San Bernardino has art galleries, Swing Auditorium, theaters, many churches, and a library. Pacific Ocean beaches provide water sports. Resort areas of Lake Arrowhead and Big Bear Lake in the mountains have facilities for water sports and winter sports. Cajon Pass offers a scenic drive through the mountains into the Mojave Desert; City Creek Highway connects with the Rim of the World Drive at Running Springs.

■ **CALIFORNIA STATE UNIVERSITY, SAN MARCOS**
333 S Twin Oaks Valley Rd.
San Marcos, CA 92096-0001

Tel: (760)750-4000
Fax: (760)750-4030
E-mail: apply@csusm.edu
Web Site: www.csusm.edu
Description: State-supported, comprehensive, coed. Part of California State University System. Awards bachelor's and master's degrees. Founded 1990. Setting: 304-acre suburban campus with easy access to San Diego. Total enrollment: 14,504. Faculty: 907 (290 full-time, 617 part-time). Student-undergrad faculty ratio is 26:1. 17,648 applied, 58% were admitted. Full-time: 11,400 students, 62% women, 38% men. Part-time: 2,562 students, 57% women, 43% men. 4% from out-of-state. 0.3% American Indian or Alaska Native, non-Hispanic/Latino; 47% Hispanic/Latino; 3% Black or African American, non-Hispanic/Latino; 9% Asian, non-Hispanic/Latino; 0.2% Native Hawaiian or other Pacific Islander, non-Hispanic/Latino; 5% international. 2% 25 or older, 80% live on campus, 15% transferred in. Retention: 77% of full-time freshmen returned the following year. Academic areas with the most degrees conferred: health professions and related sciences; social sciences; business/marketing. Core. Calendar: semesters. Academic remediation for entering students, ESL program, services for LD students, advanced placement, self-designed majors, independent study, distance learning, double major, summer session for credit, part-time degree program, adult/continuing education programs, internships. Off campus study. Study abroad program. ROTC: Army (c), Naval (c), Air Force (c).
Entrance Requirements: Options: electronic application, international baccalaureate accepted. Required: high school transcript, SAT or ACT. Entrance: moderately difficult. Notification: continuous. SAT Reasoning Test deadline: 2/15.
Costs Per Year: Application fee: $55. State resident tuition: $5742 full-time. Nonresident tuition: $15,246 full-time. College room and board: $13,227.
Collegiate Environment: Orientation program. Drama-theater group, choral group, student-run newspaper. Social organizations: national fraternities, national sororities. Student services: health clinic, personal-psychological counseling, women's center. Campus security: 24-hour emergency response devices and patrols, student patrols, late night transport-escort service. Kellogg Library. Books: 215,402 (physical), 268,189 (digital/electronic); Serial titles: 3,130 (physical), 81,643 (digital/electronic); Databases: 100. Weekly public service hours: 100; students can reserve study rooms.

■ **CALIFORNIA STATE UNIVERSITY, STANISLAUS**
One University Cir.
Turlock, CA 95382
Tel: (209)667-3122; Free: 800-300-7420
Fax: (209)667-3333
E-mail: outreach_help_desk@csustan.edu
Web Site: www.csustan.edu
Description: State-supported, comprehensive, coed. Part of California State University System. Awards bachelor's, master's, and doctoral degrees. Founded 1957. Setting: 228-acre suburban campus. Endowment: $11.6 million. Research spending for the previous fiscal year: $1.6 million. Educational spending for the previous fiscal year: $8938 per student. Total enrollment: 10,003. Faculty: 651 (341 full-time, 310 part-time). Student-undergrad faculty ratio is 23:1. 8,069 applied, 77% were admitted. Full-time: 7,460 students, 66% women, 34% men. Part-time: 1,431 students, 63% women, 37% men. Students come from 17 states and territories, 18 other countries, 1% from out-of-state. 0.3% American Indian or Alaska Native, non-Hispanic/Latino; 53% Hispanic/Latino; 2% Black or African American, non-Hispanic/Latino; 10% Asian, non-Hispanic/Latino; 0.5% Native Hawaiian or other Pacific Islander, non-Hispanic/Latino; 4% international. 20% 25 or older, 8% live on campus, 11% transferred in. Retention: 81% of full-time freshmen returned the following year. Academic areas with the most degrees conferred: business/marketing; psychology; social sciences. Core. Calendar: semesters. Academic remediation for entering students, ESL program, services for LD students, advanced placement, self-designed majors, honors program, independent study, distance learning, double major, summer session for credit, part-time degree program, co-op programs and internships, graduate courses open to undergrads. Off campus study at other units of the California State University System. Study abroad program.
Entrance Requirements: Options: electronic application, international baccalaureate accepted. Recommended: minimum 3 high school GPA. Required for some: high school transcript, SAT or ACT. Entrance: moderately difficult. Application deadline: 11/30. Notification: continuous. SAT Reasoning Test deadline: 12/1. Transfer credits accepted: Yes.
Costs Per Year: Application fee: $55. State resident tuition: $5742 full-time. Nonresident tuition: $18,956 full-time. Mandatory fees: $1334 full-time. Full-time tuition and fees vary according to reciprocity agreements. College room and board: $10,542. College room only: $6827. Room and board charges vary according to board plan and housing facility.
Collegiate Environment: Orientation program. Drama-theater group, choral group, student-run newspaper, radio station. Social organizations: 121 open to all; national fraternities, national sororities, local fraternities, local sororities; 5% of eligible men and 6% of eligible women are members. Most popular organizations: Alpha Xi Delta, Phi Sigma Sigma, Kappa Sigma, Tau Kappa Epsilon, Theta Chi. Major annual events: Warrior Day, Welcome Back Concert, Warriors Up All Night. Student services: health clinic, personal-psychological counseling, women's center. Campus security: 24-hour emergency response devices and patrols, student patrols, late night transport-escort service, controlled dormitory access. Vasche Library. Books: 514,045 (physical), 8,002 (digital/electronic); Serial titles: 634 (physical), 60,803 (digital/electronic); Databases: 187. Weekly public service hours: 90; students can reserve study rooms. Operations spending for the previous fiscal year: $2.5 million. 200 computers available on campus for general student use. A campuswide network can be accessed from student residence rooms and from off campus. Students can access the following: online class registration. Staffed computer lab on campus.
Community Environment: Population 67,700. This is a growing and prosperous residential community in a rural area of central California. Dairying is of major importance; turkeys, melons, grapes and peaches are the chief products. The area is served by bus and railroad. One general hospital, one clinic, many churches, three libraries and most all of the major fraternal and civic organizations are represented in Turlock. Part-time employment opportunities are average. Special events are the Stanislaus County Fair and the Annual Chamber of Commerce Roundup Week in the fall. A summer concert series is held at the university.

■ **CALIFORNIA UNIVERSITY OF MANAGEMENT AND SCIENCES**
721 N Euclid St.
Anaheim, CA 92801
Tel: (714)533-3946
Web Site: www.calums.edu
Description: Independent, comprehensive, coed. Awards associate, bachelor's, and master's degrees. Founded 1998. Calendar: quarters.

■ **CAMBRIDGE JUNIOR COLLEGE**
990-A Klamath Ln.
Yuba City, CA 95993
Tel: (530)674-9199
Web Site: www.cambridge.edu
Description: Proprietary, 2-year, coed. Awards certificates and terminal associate degrees. Setting: suburban campus with easy access to Sacramento. Total enrollment: 162. 147 applied. Full-time: 162 students, 91% women, 9% men. 49% 25 or older. Retention: 89% of full-time freshmen returned the following year.
Entrance Requirements: Required: high school transcript, interview.
Collegiate Environment: 80 computers available on campus for general student use.

■ **CAÑADA COLLEGE**
4200 Farm Hill Blvd.
Redwood City, CA 94061-1099
Tel: (650)306-3100
Fax: (650)306-3457
Web Site: www.canadacollege.edu
Description: District-supported, 2-year, coed. Part of San Mateo County Community College District System. Awards certificates, transfer associate, and terminal associate degrees. Founded 1968. Setting: 131-acre suburban campus with easy access to San Francisco, San Jose. Endowment: $150,000. Research spending for the previous fiscal year: $439,510. Educational spending for the previous fiscal year: $2935 per student. Total enrollment: 5,433. Faculty: 241 (81 full-time, 160 part-time). Student-undergrad faculty ratio is 16:1. 394 applied. Full-time: 406 students, 57% women, 43% men. Part-time: 5,027 students, 64% women, 36% men. 2% from out-of-state. 0.2% American Indian or Alaska Native, non-Hispanic/Latino; 36% Hispanic/Latino; 3% Black or African American, non-Hispanic/Latino; 10% Asian, non-Hispanic/Latino; 2% Native Hawaiian or other Pacific Islander, non-Hispanic/Latino; 5% international. Core. Calendar: semesters. Academic remediation for entering students, ESL program, services for LD students, advanced placement, accelerated degree program, honors program, independent study, distance learning, double major, summer ses-

sion for credit, part-time degree program, adult/continuing education programs, co-op programs and internships. Study abroad program. ROTC: Army (c), Naval (c), Air Force (c).

Entrance Requirements: Open admission except for radiologic technology programs. Option: electronic application. Recommended: high school transcript. Entrance: noncompetitive. Application deadline: rolling. Transfer credits accepted: Yes.

Collegiate Environment: Orientation program. Drama-theater group, choral group. Social organizations: 28 open to all. Most popular organizations: Phi Theta Kappa, DREAMers Club, Community First, Glee Club, Civil Liberties Club. Major annual events: Club Rush, Holi Fest, Spirit Week. Student services: health clinic, personal-psychological counseling. Campus security: 24-hour emergency response devices and patrols, late night transport-escort service, 12-hour patrols by trained security personnel. Books: 25,000 (physical), 230,000 (digital/electronic); Serial titles: 40 (physical), 20,000 (digital/electronic); Databases: 45. Weekly public service hours: 64; students can reserve study rooms. Operations spending for the previous fiscal year: $669,610. 756 computers available on campus for general student use. Computer purchase/lease plans available. A campuswide network can be accessed from off-campus. Students can access the following: online class registration. Staffed computer lab on campus provides training in use of computers, software, and the Internet.

■ **CARRINGTON COLLEGE-CITRUS HEIGHTS**
7301 Greenback Ln.
Ste. A
Citrus Heights, CA 95621
Tel: (916)722-8200
Web Site: www.carrington.edu

Description: Proprietary, 2-year, coed. Part of Carrington Colleges Group, Inc. Awards certificates and terminal associate degrees. Total enrollment: 448. Faculty: 28 (13 full-time, 15 part-time). Student-undergrad faculty ratio is 24:1. Full-time: 432 students, 86% women, 14% men. Part-time: 16 students, 81% women, 19% men. 1% American Indian or Alaska Native, non-Hispanic/Latino; 22% Hispanic/Latino; 5% Black or African American, non-Hispanic/Latino; 4% Asian, non-Hispanic/Latino; 0.9% Native Hawaiian or other Pacific Islander, non-Hispanic/Latino; 0.2% international. 39% 25 or older, 17% transferred in.

Entrance Requirements: Required: essay, high school transcript, interview. Notification: continuous.

■ **CARRINGTON COLLEGE-PLEASANT HILL**
380 Civic Dr.
Ste. 300
Pleasant Hill, CA 94523
Tel: (925)609-6650
Web Site: www.carrington.edu

Description: Proprietary, 2-year, coed. Part of Carrington Colleges Group, Inc. Awards certificates and terminal associate degrees. Founded 1997. Total enrollment: 437. Faculty: 36 (19 full-time, 17 part-time). Student-undergrad faculty ratio is 26:1. Full-time: 357 students, 81% women, 19% men. Part-time: 80 students, 83% women, 17% men. 1% from out-of-state. 0.5% American Indian or Alaska Native, non-Hispanic/Latino; 32% Hispanic/Latino; 11% Black or African American, non-Hispanic/Latino; 16% Asian, non-Hispanic/Latino; 3% Native Hawaiian or other Pacific Islander, non-Hispanic/Latino; 0.7% international. 48% 25 or older, 24% transferred in.

Entrance Requirements: Required: essay, high school transcript, interview. Notification: continuous.

■ **CARRINGTON COLLEGE-POMONA**
901 Corporate Ctr. Dr.
Ste. 300
Pomona, CA 91768
Tel: (909)868-5800; Free: 877-206-2106
Web Site: www.carrington.edu

Description: Proprietary, 2-year, coed. Awards terminal associate degrees. Total enrollment: 356. Faculty: 17 (15 full-time, 2 part-time). Student-undergrad faculty ratio is 21:1. Full-time: 273 students, 88% women, 12% men. Part-time: 83 students, 87% women, 13% men. 0.3% American Indian or Alaska Native, non-Hispanic/Latino; 63% Hispanic/Latino; 3% Black or African American, non-Hispanic/Latino; 4% Asian, non-Hispanic/Latino; 0.8% Native Hawaiian or other Pacific Islander, non-Hispanic/Latino. 32% 25 or older, 16% transferred in.

Entrance Requirements: Notification: continuous.

■ **CARRINGTON COLLEGE-SACRAMENTO**
8909 Folsom Blvd.
Sacramento, CA 95826
Tel: (916)361-1660
Web Site: www.carrington.edu

Description: Proprietary, 2-year, coed. Part of Carrington Colleges Group, Inc. Awards certificates and terminal associate degrees. Founded 1967. Total enrollment: 1,186. Faculty: 80 (36 full-time, 44 part-time). Student-undergrad faculty ratio is 14:1. Full-time: 935 students, 91% women, 9% men. Part-time: 251 students, 89% women, 11% men. 11% from out-of-state. 1% American Indian or Alaska Native, non-Hispanic/Latino; 31% Hispanic/Latino; 9% Black or African American, non-Hispanic/Latino; 12% Asian, non-Hispanic/Latino; 2% Native Hawaiian or other Pacific Islander, non-Hispanic/Latino; 0.3% international. 50% 25 or older, 11% transferred in.

Entrance Requirements: Required: essay, high school transcript, interview. Notification: continuous.

■ **CARRINGTON COLLEGE-SAN JOSE**
5883 Rue Ferrari
Ste. 125
San Jose, CA 95138
Tel: (408)960-0161
Web Site: www.carrington.edu

Description: Proprietary, 2-year, coed. Part of Carrington Colleges Group, Inc. Awards certificates and terminal associate degrees. Founded 1999. Total enrollment: 715. Faculty: 50 (18 full-time, 32 part-time). Student-undergrad faculty ratio is 24:1. Full-time: 654 students, 85% women, 15% men. Part-time: 61 students, 84% women, 16% men. 54% Hispanic/Latino; 2% Black or African American, non-Hispanic/Latino; 16% Asian, non-Hispanic/Latino; 3% Native Hawaiian or other Pacific Islander, non-Hispanic/Latino; 0.8% international. 47% 25 or older, 13% transferred in.

Entrance Requirements: Required: essay, high school transcript, interview. Notification: continuous.

■ **CARRINGTON COLLEGE-SAN LEANDRO**
15555 E 14th St.
Ste. 500
San Leandro, CA 94578
Tel: (510)276-3888
Web Site: www.carrington.edu

Description: Proprietary, 2-year, coed. Part of Carrington Colleges Group, Inc. Awards certificates and terminal associate degrees. Founded 1986. Total enrollment: 416. Faculty: 17 (11 full-time, 6 part-time). Student-undergrad faculty ratio is 31:1. Full-time: 398 students, 90% women, 10% men. Part-time: 18 students, 72% women, 28% men. 26% from out-of-state. 0.5% American Indian or Alaska Native, non-Hispanic/Latino; 51% Hispanic/Latino; 19% Black or African American, non-Hispanic/Latino; 9% Asian, non-Hispanic/Latino; 2% Native Hawaiian or other Pacific Islander, non-Hispanic/Latino; 0.5% international. 53% 25 or older, 16% transferred in.

Entrance Requirements: Required: essay, high school transcript, interview. Notification: continuous.

■ **CARRINGTON COLLEGE-STOCKTON**
1313 W Robinhood Dr.
Ste. B
Stockton, CA 95207
Tel: (209)956-1240
Web Site: www.carrington.edu

Description: Proprietary, 2-year, coed. Awards certificates and terminal associate degrees. Total enrollment: 545. Faculty: 22 (8 full-time, 14 part-time). Student-undergrad faculty ratio is 42:1. Full-time: 533 students, 86% women, 14% men. Part-time: 12 students, 83% women, 17% men. 0.4% American Indian or Alaska Native, non-Hispanic/Latino; 53% Hispanic/Latino; 9% Black or African American, non-Hispanic/Latino; 10% Asian, non-Hispanic/Latino; 2% Native Hawaiian or other Pacific Islander, non-Hispanic/Latino; 0.4% international. 24% 25 or older, 16% transferred in.

Entrance Requirements: Notification: continuous.

■ **CASA LOMA COLLEGE-VAN NUYS**
6725 Kester Ave.
Van Nuys, CA 91405
Tel: (818)785-2726
Web Site: www.casalomacollege.edu

Description: Independent, 2-year, coed. Awards transfer associate and terminal associate degrees.

■ **CBD COLLEGE**
3699 Wilshire Blvd., 4th Fl.
Los Angeles, CA 90010
Tel: (213)427-2200
Description: Independent, 2-year, coed.

■ **CERRITOS COLLEGE**
11110 Alondra Blvd.
Norwalk, CA 90650-6298
Tel: (562)860-2451
Web Site: www.cerritos.edu
Description: District-supported, 2-year, coed. Part of California Community College System. Awards certificates, transfer associate, and terminal associate degrees. Founded 1956. Setting: 140-acre suburban campus with easy access to Los Angeles. Research spending for the previous fiscal year: $561,915. Educational spending for the previous fiscal year: $3345 per student. Total enrollment: 22,043. Faculty: 845 (269 full-time, 576 part-time). 38,002 applied, 65% were admitted. Full-time: 7,209 students, 54% women, 46% men. Part-time: 14,834 students, 55% women, 45% men. Students come from 32 other countries, 1% from out-of-state. 5% American Indian or Alaska Native, non-Hispanic/Latino; 70% Hispanic/Latino; 3% Black or African American, non-Hispanic/Latino; 8% Asian, non-Hispanic/Latino; 0.6% Native Hawaiian or other Pacific Islander, non-Hispanic/Latino; 0.7% international. 35% 25 or older, 2% transferred in. Core. Calendar: semesters. Academic remediation for entering students, ESL program, services for LD students, advanced placement, honors program, independent study, distance learning, double major, summer session for credit, part-time degree program. Study abroad program.
Entrance Requirements: Open admission. Options: electronic application, early admission, deferred admission. Entrance: noncompetitive. Application deadline: rolling.
Collegiate Environment: Orientation program. Drama-theater group, choral group, student-run newspaper, radio station. Social organizations: 55 open to all. Most popular organizations: WPMD Student Radio, Anxiety Gaming Club, Commercial Radio Club, Abilities Empowered, Student Athlete Captain's Club. Major annual events: Welcome Day, Falcon Games, Zombie Fest. Student services: health clinic, personal-psychological counseling. Campus security: 24-hour emergency response devices and patrols, student patrols, late night transport-escort service. Wilford Michael Library. Books: 117,647 (physical), 13,466 (digital/electronic); Databases: 66. Weekly public service hours: 71; students can reserve study rooms. Operations spending for the previous fiscal year: $1.9 million. 400 computers available on campus for general student use. A campuswide network can be accessed from off-campus. Students can access the following: online class registration. Staffed computer lab on campus.
Community Environment: Norwalk is an urban area 17 miles from Los Angeles. The climate is subtropical. There is bus and rail service to Los Angeles, where other major transportation facilities are located. The city has many community facilities, industrial firms and retail outlets. Part-time work is available.

■ **CERRO COSO COMMUNITY COLLEGE**
3000 College Heights Blvd.
Ridgecrest, CA 93555-9571
Tel: (760)384-6100
Fax: (760)375-4776
E-mail: hostash@cerrocoso.edu
Web Site: www.cerrocoso.edu
Description: District-supported, 2-year, coed. Part of Kern Community College District System. Awards certificates, transfer associate, and terminal associate degrees. Founded 1973. Setting: 320-acre small town campus. Total enrollment: 4,577. 61% 25 or older. Core. Calendar: semesters. Academic remediation for entering students, ESL program, services for LD students, honors program, distance learning, summer session for credit, part-time degree program, adult/continuing education programs, co-op programs.
Entrance Requirements: Open admission except for nursing program. Option: early admission. Recommended: high school transcript. Entrance: noncompetitive. Application deadline: rolling.
Collegiate Environment: Orientation program. Student services: personal-psychological counseling. Campus security: patrols by trained security personnel. Walter Stiern Memorial Library.

■ **CHABOT COLLEGE**
25555 Hesperian Blvd.
Hayward, CA 94545-5001
Tel: (510)723-6600
Web Site: www.chabotcollege.edu
Description: District-supported, 2-year, coed. Part of California Community College System. Awards certificates, transfer associate, and terminal associate degrees. Founded 1961. Setting: 245-acre suburban campus with easy access to San Francisco. Total enrollment: 13,229. 43% 25 or older. Core. Calendar: semesters. Academic remediation for entering students, ESL program, services for LD students, advanced placement, self-designed majors, distance learning, double major, summer session for credit, part-time degree program, adult/continuing education programs, internships. Off campus study at Mills College; California State University, Hayward. Study abroad program. ROTC: Army (c), Air Force (c).
Entrance Requirements: Open admission except for dental hygiene, nursing, emergency medical technician programs. Option: electronic application. Required: high school transcript. Entrance: noncompetitive. Notification: continuous. Preference given to state residents.
Collegiate Environment: Orientation program. Drama-theater group, choral group, student-run newspaper, radio station. Student services: legal services, personal-psychological counseling. Campus security: 24-hour emergency response devices, late night transport-escort service. Chabot Library.
Community Environment: See California State University - Hayward.

■ **CHAFFEY COLLEGE**
5885 Haven Ave.
Rancho Cucamonga, CA 91737-3002
Tel: (909)652-6000
E-mail: erlinda.martinez@chaffey.edu
Web Site: www.chaffey.edu
Description: District-supported, 2-year, coed. Part of California Community College System. Awards certificates, transfer associate, and terminal associate degrees. Founded 1883. Setting: 200-acre suburban campus with easy access to Los Angeles. Total enrollment: 21,399. Student-undergrad faculty ratio is 24:1. 34% 25 or older. Core. Calendar: semesters. Academic remediation for entering students, ESL program, services for LD students, advanced placement, honors program, summer session for credit, part-time degree program, adult/continuing education programs, co-op programs and internships. Study abroad program. ROTC: Army (c).
Entrance Requirements: Open admission. Option: early admission. Entrance: noncompetitive. Application deadline: rolling. Notification: continuous.
Collegiate Environment: Drama-theater group, choral group, student-run newspaper, radio station. Student services: health clinic, personal-psychological counseling. Campus security: 24-hour emergency response devices, late night transport-escort service. Chaffey College Library.
Community Environment: Rancho Cucamonga is a suburban community 44 miles east of Los Angeles. With the west end of San Bernardino County the area has a population of 1,999,300. It has dry climate conditions, with temperatures ranging from 25 to 112 degrees during the year. Farming, namely citrus and grapes, is the main economy. Rail, bus, and air (Ontario International Airport) serve the area. There are four hospitals nearby.

■ **CHAMBERLAIN COLLEGE OF NURSING**
10971 Sun Ctr. Dr.
Rancho Cordova, CA 95670
Web Site: www.chamberlain.edu
Description: Proprietary, 4-year, coed.

■ **CHAPMAN UNIVERSITY**
One University Dr.
Orange, CA 92866
Tel: (714)997-6815; Free: 888-CUAPPLY
Fax: (714)997-6713
E-mail: admit@chapman.edu
Web Site: www.chapman.edu
Description: Independent, comprehensive, coed, affiliated with Christian Church (Disciples of Christ). Administratively affiliated with Brandman University. Awards bachelor's, master's, and doctoral degrees. Founded 1861. Setting: 78-acre suburban campus with easy access to Los Angeles. Endowment: $352.6 million. Research spending for the previous fiscal year: $8.1 million. Educational spending for the previous fiscal year: $15,359 per

student. Total enrollment: 9,392. Faculty: 1,089 (489 full-time, 600 part-time). Student-undergrad faculty ratio is 14:1. 13,170 applied, 57% were admitted. 37% from top 10% of their high school class, 78% from top quarter, 95% from top half. Full-time: 6,515 students, 61% women, 39% men. Part-time: 505 students, 52% women, 48% men. Students come from 50 states and territories, 57 other countries, 31% from out-of-state. 0.1% American Indian or Alaska Native, non-Hispanic/Latino; 15% Hispanic/Latino; 2% Black or African American, non-Hispanic/Latino; 12% Asian, non-Hispanic/Latino; 0.3% Native Hawaiian or other Pacific Islander, non-Hispanic/Latino; 4% international. 2% 25 or older, 33% live on campus, 6% transferred in. Retention: 91% of full-time freshmen returned the following year. Academic areas with the most degrees conferred: business/marketing; visual and performing arts; communication/journalism. Core. Calendar: 4-1-4. Academic remediation for entering students, services for LD students, advanced placement, self-designed majors, honors program, independent study, distance learning, double major, summer session for credit, part-time degree program, adult/continuing education programs, internships, graduate courses open to undergrads. Off campus study. Study abroad program. ROTC: Army (c), Air Force (c).

Entrance Requirements: Options: electronic application, early decision, early action, international baccalaureate accepted. Required: essay, high school transcript, 1 recommendation, SAT or ACT. Recommended: SAT Subject Tests. Required for some: audition for music, dance, and theatre majors; portfolio for art and film majors; supplemental application for all talent-based majors. Entrance: very difficult. Application deadlines: 1/15, 11/1 for early decision, 11/1 for early action. Notification: 3/15, 1/10 for early action. SAT Reasoning Test deadline: 1/31. SAT Subject Test deadline: 6/1. Transfer credits accepted: Yes.

Costs Per Year: Application fee: $70. Comprehensive fee: $68,552 includes full-time tuition ($52,340), mandatory fees ($384), and college room and board ($15,828). College room only: $10,900. Room and board charges vary according to board plan and housing facility. Part-time tuition: $1625 per credit hour. Part-time tuition varies according to course load.

Collegiate Environment: Orientation program. Drama-theater group, choral group, student-run newspaper, radio station. Social organizations: 150 open to all; national fraternities, national sororities; 25% of eligible men and 48% of eligible women are members. Major annual events: Homecoming, Spring Sizzle, Midnight Breakfast. Student services: health clinic, personal-psychological counseling. Campus security: 24-hour emergency response devices and patrols, late night transport-escort service, controlled dormitory access, full safety education program. Leatherby Libraries plus 1 other. Books: 339,051 (physical), 17,371 (digital/electronic); Serial titles: 267 (physical), 69,372 (digital/electronic); Databases: 287. Weekly public service hours: 127; students can reserve study rooms. Operations spending for the previous fiscal year: $6.7 million.

Community Environment: Orange is located 32 miles southeast of Los Angeles and 94 miles north of San Diego. Its climate is mild with a very low rainfall. It is accessible by car, bus or train and plane. Orange County Airport is a short distance away, and Los Angeles International Airport is a 45-minute drive away. As the name implies, Orange lies in a vast citrus belt; avocados are also grown here. All the necessary facilities of a city are available as well as many recreational facilities for swimming, golf, surfing, skiing, fishing, hunting, and boating. Beaches and mountain resorts are nearby.

■ **CHARLES R. DREW UNIVERSITY OF MEDICINE AND SCIENCE**
1731 E 120th St.
Los Angeles, CA 90059
Tel: (323)563-4800
Web Site: www.cdrewu.edu
Description: Independent, comprehensive, coed. Awards associate, bachelor's, master's, and doctoral degrees and post-master's certificates. Founded 1966. Setting: 11-acre urban campus with easy access to Los Angeles. Endowment: $90 million. Research spending for the previous fiscal year: $15 million. Educational spending for the previous fiscal year: $15,576 per student. Total enrollment: 543. Faculty: 201 (46 full-time, 155 part-time). Student-undergrad faculty ratio is 10:1. 61 applied, 90% were admitted. Full-time: 114 students, 60% women, 40% men. Part-time: 25 students, 52% women, 48% men. Students come from 3 states and territories, 5 other countries, 2% from out-of-state. 45% Hispanic/Latino; 25% Black or African American, non-Hispanic/Latino; 15% Asian, non-Hispanic/Latino; 4% international. 66% 25 or older, 37% transferred in. Academic area with the most degrees conferred: health professions and related sciences. Core. Calendar: semesters. Academic remediation for entering students, services

for LD students, advanced placement, independent study, summer session for credit, part-time degree program, adult/continuing education programs, internships. Study abroad program.

Entrance Requirements: Options: electronic application, early admission, early decision, early action, deferred admission. Required: essay, high school transcript, minimum 2 high school GPA. Required for some: pre-admission assessment exams, SAT or ACT. Entrance: moderately difficult. Application deadline: 7/30. Notification: continuous. Transfer credits accepted: Yes.

Costs Per Year: Application fee: $35. One-time mandatory fee: $100. Comprehensive fee: $27,166 includes full-time tuition ($13,872) and college room and board ($13,294). Full-time tuition varies according to course load, degree level, and program. Part-time tuition: $578 per unit. Part-time tuition varies according to course load, degree level, and program.

Collegiate Environment: Orientation program. Social organizations: 18 open to all. Most popular organizations: Student Government, Critical Exploration of Academic Literature (CEAL), Charles R. Drew University Alumni Association, Pre-Health Society, Pre-Dental Society. Major annual events: Black History Month, Hispanic Heritage Month, Project Santa Claus. Student services: personal-psychological counseling. Campus security: 24-hour emergency response devices, late night transport-escort service. Health Sciences Library. Books: 6,436 (physical), 3,500 (digital/electronic); Serial titles: 596 (physical), 11,765 (digital/electronic); Databases: 38. Weekly public service hours: 91; students can reserve study rooms. Operations spending for the previous fiscal year: $1.1 million. 90 computers available on campus for general student use. A campuswide network can be accessed. Students can access the following: online class registration, Campus wide wireless network. Staffed computer lab on campus provides training in use of computers, software, and the Internet.

■ **CITRUS COLLEGE**
1000 W Foothill Blvd.
Glendora, CA 91741-1899
Tel: (626)963-0323
E-mail: admissions@citruscollege.edu
Web Site: www.citruscollege.edu
Description: District-supported, 2-year, coed. Part of California Community College System. Awards certificates, diplomas, and transfer associate degrees. Founded 1915. Setting: 104-acre small town campus with easy access to Los Angeles. Total enrollment: 12,780. Faculty: 509 (155 full-time, 354 part-time). Student-undergrad faculty ratio is 30:1. 11,388 applied, 100% were admitted. Full-time: 4,921 students, 52% women, 48% men. Part-time: 7,859 students, 54% women, 46% men. 0.2% American Indian or Alaska Native, non-Hispanic/Latino; 61% Hispanic/Latino; 4% Black or African American, non-Hispanic/Latino; 8% Asian, non-Hispanic/Latino; 0.1% Native Hawaiian or other Pacific Islander, non-Hispanic/Latino; 4% international. Core. Calendar: semesters. Academic remediation for entering students, ESL program, services for LD students, advanced placement, honors program, distance learning, double major, summer session for credit, part-time degree program, co-op programs. Study abroad program.

Entrance Requirements: Open admission. Options: electronic application, early decision. Required: high school transcript. Entrance: noncompetitive. Application deadline: rolling. Transfer credits accepted: Yes. Early decision applicants: 663. Early decision applicants admitted: 663.

Collegiate Environment: Orientation program. Drama-theater group, choral group, student-run newspaper. Social organizations: 29 open to all. Most popular organizations: Student Government, Alpha Gamma Sigma (AGS), Veterans Network, International Friendship Club, Citrus Business Association (CBA). Major annual events: Fall Fest, Spring Fest, Club Rush. Student services: legal services, health clinic, personal-psychological counseling. Campus security: 24-hour patrols, student patrols, late night transport-escort service. Hayden Library. Students can reserve study rooms. 1,100 computers available on campus for general student use. A campuswide network can be accessed. Students can access the following: online class registration. Staffed computer lab on campus provides training in use of computers, software, and the Internet.

Community Environment: See Azusa Pacific University.

■ **CITY COLLEGE OF SAN FRANCISCO**
50 Phelan Ave.
San Francisco, CA 94112-1821
Tel: (415)239-3000
Fax: (415)239-3936
E-mail: mleyba@ccsf.edu

Web Site: www.ccsf.edu

Description: District-supported, 2-year, coed. Part of California Community College System. Awards certificates, diplomas, transfer associate, and terminal associate degrees. Founded 1935. Setting: 56-acre urban campus. Total enrollment: 32,950. Student-undergrad faculty ratio is 23:1. 53% 25 or older. Core. Calendar: semesters. Academic remediation for entering students, ESL program, services for LD students, advanced placement, summer session for credit, part-time degree program, adult/continuing education programs, internships. Off campus study at members of The San Francisco Consortium. Study abroad program.

Entrance Requirements: Open admission. Option: early admission. Entrance: noncompetitive. Application deadline: 8/9. Notification: continuous.

Collegiate Environment: Orientation program. Drama-theater group, student-run newspaper. Student services: health clinic, personal-psychological counseling, women's center. Campus security: 24-hour emergency response devices and patrols, late night transport-escort service. Louise and Claude Rosenberg, Jr. Library plus 2 others.

Community Environment: See San Francisco State University.

■ CLAREMONT MCKENNA COLLEGE

500 E 9th St.
Claremont, CA 91711
Tel: (909)621-8000
E-mail: jennifer.sandoval@cmc.edu
Web Site: www.cmc.edu

Description: Independent, comprehensive, coed. Awards bachelor's and master's degrees. Founded 1946. Setting: 69-acre suburban campus with easy access to Los Angeles. Endowment: $835.3 million. Total enrollment: 1,327. Faculty: 179 (157 full-time, 22 part-time). Student-undergrad faculty ratio is 8:1. 6,272 applied, 9% were admitted. 78% from top 10% of their high school class, 93% from top quarter, 100% from top half. Full-time: 1,321 students, 48% women, 52% men. Part-time: 3 students, 33% women, 67% men. Students come from 49 states and territories, 43 other countries, 54% from out-of-state. 15% Hispanic/Latino; 4% Black or African American, non-Hispanic/Latino; 11% Asian, non-Hispanic/Latino; 0.1% Native Hawaiian or other Pacific Islander, non-Hispanic/Latino; 16% international. 0.4% 25 or older, 96% live on campus, 1% transferred in. Retention: 96% of full-time freshmen returned the following year. Academic areas with the most degrees conferred: social sciences; interdisciplinary studies; psychology. Core. Calendar: semesters. Services for LD students, advanced placement, self-designed majors, honors program, independent study, double major, internships, graduate courses open to undergrads. Off campus study at The Claremont Colleges. Study abroad program. ROTC: Army, Air Force (c).

Entrance Requirements: Options: electronic application, early decision, deferred admission, international baccalaureate accepted. Required: essay, high school transcript, 3 recommendations, SAT or ACT. Recommended: interview. Required for some: SAT Subject Tests, TOEFL or IELTS for students for whom English is not their first language and the primary language of instruction in high school was not English. Entrance: most difficult. Application deadlines: 1/5, 11/1 for early decision plan 1, 1/5 for early decision plan 2. Notification: 4/1, 12/15 for early decision plan 1, 2/15 for early decision plan 2. SAT Reasoning Test deadline: 1/15. Transfer credits accepted: Yes. Applicants placed on waiting list: 1,037. Wait-listed applicants offered admission: 25. Early decision applicants: 771. Early decision applicants admitted: 193.

Costs Per Year: Application fee: $70. Comprehensive fee: $73,775 includes full-time tuition ($56,190), mandatory fees ($285), and college room and board ($17,300). College room only: $9300. Part-time tuition: $9365 per course.

Collegiate Environment: Orientation program. Drama-theater group, choral group, student-run newspaper, radio station. Social organizations: 70 open to all. Most popular organizations: Associated Students of Claremont McKenna College, College Programming Board, Asian Pacific American Mentoring Program (APAM). Major annual events: Monte Carlo, McKenna-palooza, Pirate Party. Student services: health clinic, personal-psychological counseling. Campus security: 24-hour emergency response devices and patrols, student patrols, late night transport-escort service, controlled dormitory access. 1,236 college housing spaces available; 1,172 were occupied in 2018-19. Freshmen guaranteed college housing. On-campus residence required in freshman year. Option: coed housing available. Claremont Colleges Library plus 2 others. Books: 1 million (physical), 2.2 million (digital/electronic); Serial titles: 28,182 (physical), 81,005 (digital/electronic); Databases: 490. Weekly public service hours: 111; students can reserve study rooms. 220 computers available on campus for general student use. A

campuswide network can be accessed. Students can access the following: online class registration. Staffed computer lab on campus (open 24 hours a day) provides training in use of computers, software, and the Internet.

■ CLOVIS COMMUNITY COLLEGE

10309 N Willow Ave.
Fresno, CA 93730
Web Site: www.cloviscollege.edu
Description: Public, 2-year, coed.

■ COASTLINE COMMUNITY COLLEGE

11460 Warner Ave.
Fountain Valley, CA 92708-2597
Tel: (714)546-7600
Fax: (714)241-6288
Web Site: www.coastline.edu

Description: District-supported, 2-year, coed. Part of Coast Community College District System. Awards certificates and transfer associate degrees. Founded 1976. Setting: urban campus with easy access to Orange County. Total enrollment: 11,431. Faculty: 296 (55 full-time, 241 part-time). Student-undergrad faculty ratio is 32:1. Full-time: 2,488 students, 51% women, 49% men. Part-time: 8,943 students, 38% women, 62% men. 0.8% American Indian or Alaska Native, non-Hispanic/Latino; 28% Hispanic/Latino; 12% Black or African American, non-Hispanic/Latino; 22% Asian, non-Hispanic/Latino; 0.5% Native Hawaiian or other Pacific Islander, non-Hispanic/Latino. 72% 25 or older. Core. Calendar: semesters. Academic remediation for entering students, ESL program, services for LD students, advanced placement, accelerated degree program, honors program, independent study, distance learning, double major, summer session for credit, part-time degree program, external degree program, adult/continuing education programs, co-op programs and internships. Off campus study. Study abroad program.

Entrance Requirements: Open admission. Options: electronic application, early admission. Recommended: high school transcript. Entrance: noncompetitive. Application deadline: rolling. Transfer credits accepted: Yes.

Costs Per Year: Application fee: $0. State resident tuition: $1104 full-time, $46 per unit part-time. Nonresident tuition: $6648 full-time, $231 per unit part-time. Mandatory fees: $32 full-time. Full-time tuition and fees vary according to course load. Part-time tuition varies according to course load.

Collegiate Environment: Student services: health clinic, personal-psychological counseling. Campus security: 24-hour emergency response devices. College housing not available. Coastline Virtual Library plus 1 other.

■ COGSWELL POLYTECHNICAL COLLEGE

191 Baypointe Pky.
San Jose, CA 95134
Tel: (408)541-0100; Free: 800-264-7955
Fax: (408)747-0764
E-mail: rhenson@cogswell.edu
Web Site: www.cogswell.edu

Description: Proprietary, comprehensive, coed. Awards bachelor's and master's degrees. Founded 1887. Setting: 2-acre suburban campus with easy access to San Francisco, San Jose. Educational spending for the previous fiscal year: $8220 per student. Total enrollment: 608. Faculty: 89 (16 full-time, 73 part-time). Student-undergrad faculty ratio is 13:1. 231 applied, 65% were admitted. Full-time: 436 students, 30% women, 70% men. Part-time: 172 students, 28% women, 72% men. Students come from 13 states and territories, 3 other countries, 7% from out-of-state. 0.8% American Indian or Alaska Native, non-Hispanic/Latino; 20% Hispanic/Latino; 5% Black or African American, non-Hispanic/Latino; 22% Asian, non-Hispanic/Latino; 1% Native Hawaiian or other Pacific Islander, non-Hispanic/Latino; 2% international. 18% 25 or older, 8% transferred in. Retention: 78% of full-time freshmen returned the following year. Academic areas with the most degrees conferred: communication technologies; visual and performing arts; computer and information sciences. Core. Calendar: semesters. Academic remediation for entering students, advanced placement, distance learning, double major, summer session for credit, part-time degree program, adult/continuing education programs, co-op programs and internships.

Entrance Requirements: Options: electronic application, deferred admission. Required: essay, high school transcript, minimum 2 high school GPA. Recommended: minimum 2.7 high school GPA, interview, SAT or ACT. Required for some: recommendations, portfolio for Digital Art and Animation, Digital Audio Technology and Game Design Art majors. Entrance: moderately difficult. Application deadline: rolling. Notification: continuous. Transfer credits accepted: Yes.

Costs Per Year: Application fee: $0. Tuition: $19,056 full-time, $794 per credit part-time. Mandatory fees: $1000 full-time, $500 per term part-time. Full-time tuition and fees vary according to course load. Part-time tuition and fees vary according to course load. College room only: $11,000. Room charges vary according to housing facility.

Collegiate Environment: Orientation program. Choral group. Most popular organizations: ASB, Game Development club, Audio Production and Engineering club, Comic Club, E-Sports. Major annual events: Founders' Day, Cogswell Excellence Awards, Game Nights. Student services: personal-psychological counseling. Campus security: 24-hour emergency response devices. Cogswell College Library. Books: 5,007 (physical); Serial titles: 920 (physical); Databases: 14. Operations spending for the previous fiscal year: $59,175. 224 computers available on campus for general student use. A campuswide network can be accessed from off-campus. Students can access the following: online class registration. Staffed computer lab on campus provides training in use of computers, software, and the Internet.

■ **THE COLBURN SCHOOL CONSERVATORY OF MUSIC**
200 S Grand Ave.
Los Angeles, CA 90012
Tel: (213)621-2200
Fax: (213)621-2110
E-mail: admissions@colburnschool.edu
Web Site: www.colburnschool.edu
Description: Independent, comprehensive, coed. Awards bachelor's and master's degrees. Founded 1980. Setting: urban campus with easy access to Los Angeles. Total enrollment: 115. Faculty: 46. Student-undergrad faculty ratio is 3:1. 701 applied, 10% were admitted. Full-time: 55 students, 47% women, 53% men. 100% live on campus. Academic area with the most degrees conferred: visual and performing arts. Core. Calendar: semesters. Academic remediation for entering students, ESL program, advanced placement, double major.
Entrance Requirements: Options: electronic application, deferred admission, international baccalaureate accepted. Required: essay, high school transcript, 2 recommendations, interview, pre-screening DVD, in-person audition by invitation. Recommended: SAT or ACT. Entrance: most difficult. Application deadline: 12/1. Notification: 4/1. Transfer credits accepted: Yes.
Costs Per Year: Application fee: $120. Comprehensive fee: $3000 includes full-time tuition ($0), mandatory fees ($3000), and college room and board ($0). Full scholarships covering tuition, room and board are awarded to all students enrolled in the Conservatory (to the extent that this amount is not underwritten by outside scholarships).
Collegiate Environment: Orientation program. Student services: personal-psychological counseling. Campus security: 24-hour emergency response devices and patrols, controlled dormitory access. Colburn School Library. 12 computers available on campus for general student use. A campuswide network can be accessed from student residence rooms.

■ **COLLEGE OF ALAMEDA**
555 Ralph Appezzato Memorial Pky.
Alameda, CA 94501-2109
Tel: (510)522-7221
Web Site: alameda.peralta.edu
Description: District-supported, 2-year, coed. Part of Peralta Community College District System. Awards certificates, transfer associate, and terminal associate degrees. Founded 1970. Setting: 62-acre urban campus with easy access to San Francisco. Total enrollment: 7,302. Student-undergrad faculty ratio is 32:1. 44% 25 or older. Calendar: semesters. Academic remediation for entering students, services for LD students, summer session for credit, part-time degree program, adult/continuing education programs, co-op programs. Off campus study at other units of the Peralta Community College District System.
Entrance Requirements: Open admission. Entrance: noncompetitive. Application deadline: rolling.
Collegiate Environment: Student-run newspaper. Student services: women's center. Learning Resources Center.
Community Environment: See Laney College.

■ **COLLEGE OF THE CANYONS**
26455 Rockwell Canyon Rd.
Santa Clarita, CA 91355
Tel: (661)259-7800
Fax: (661)362-3979
E-mail: jasmine.ruys@canyons.edu

Web Site: www.canyons.edu
Description: District-supported, 2-year, coed. Part of California Community College System. Awards certificates, transfer associate, and terminal associate degrees. Founded 1969. Setting: 224-acre suburban campus with easy access to Los Angeles. Educational spending for the previous fiscal year: $4685 per student. Total enrollment: 20,489. Faculty: 737 (186 full-time, 551 part-time). Student-undergrad faculty ratio is 17:1. Full-time: 6,445 students, 50% women, 50% men. Part-time: 13,420 students, 44% women, 56% men. Students come from 49 other countries, 3% from out-of-state. 0.2% American Indian or Alaska Native, non-Hispanic/Latino; 47% Hispanic/Latino; 5% Black or African American, non-Hispanic/Latino; 10% Asian, non-Hispanic/Latino; 0.3% Native Hawaiian or other Pacific Islander, non-Hispanic/Latino; 0.9% international. 24% 25 or older, 41% transferred in. Core. Calendar: semesters. Academic remediation for entering students, ESL program, services for LD students, advanced placement, accelerated degree program, honors program, distance learning, double major, summer session for credit, part-time degree program, adult/continuing education programs, co-op programs and internships. Study abroad program.
Entrance Requirements: Open admission Selected admissions for nursing program. Option: electronic application. Recommended: high school transcript. Application deadlines: rolling, rolling for nonresidents. Notification: continuous. Transfer credits accepted: Yes.
Costs Per Year: Application fee: $0. Area resident tuition: $46 per credit part-time. State resident tuition: $1104 full-time, $46 per credit part-time. Nonresident tuition: $7752 full-time, $323 per credit part-time. Mandatory fees: $52 full-time.
Collegiate Environment: Orientation program. Drama-theater group, choral group, student-run newspaper. Major annual events: Job Fair, MajorQuest, Welcome Week. Student services: health clinic, personal-psychological counseling, women's center. Campus security: 24-hour emergency response devices, late night transport-escort service. College housing not available. College of the Canyons Library. Books: 59,059 (physical), 138,941 (digital/electronic); Serial titles: 58 (physical), 2 (digital/electronic); Databases: 53. Weekly public service hours: 116; students can reserve study rooms. Operations spending for the previous fiscal year: $878,276. 2,075 computers available on campus for general student use. A campuswide network can be accessed. Students can access the following: online class registration. Staffed computer lab on campus provides training in use of computers, software, and the Internet.
Community Environment: The Valencia-Newhall-Saugus-Canyon Country communities comprise the city of Santa Clarita located 32 miles northwest of Los Angeles near the San Fernando Valley. The average mean temperature is 65 degrees. Community facilities include hospitals, churches, a library, newspapers and banks. Recreational facilities include theaters, parks, a riding stable and golf courses. Desert area and many secluded canyons are nearby. The Castaic Reservoir water recreation area opened in 1970.

■ **COLLEGE OF THE DESERT**
43-500 Monterey Ave.
Palm Desert, CA 92260-9305
Tel: (760)346-8041
Web Site: www.collegeofthedesert.edu
Description: District-supported, 2-year, coed. Part of California Community College System. Awards certificates, diplomas, transfer associate, and terminal associate degrees. Founded 1958. Setting: 160-acre small town campus. Total enrollment: 11,146. Faculty: 554 (154 full-time, 400 part-time). Student-undergrad faculty ratio is 23:1. 2,599 applied, 100% were admitted. Full-time: 4,434 students, 53% women, 47% men. Part-time: 6,712 students, 57% women, 43% men. Students come from 20 states and territories, 1% from out-of-state. 0.4% American Indian or Alaska Native, non-Hispanic/Latino; 72% Hispanic/Latino; 3% Black or African American, non-Hispanic/Latino; 3% Asian, non-Hispanic/Latino; 0.1% Native Hawaiian or other Pacific Islander, non-Hispanic/Latino; 1% international. 35% 25 or older, 3% transferred in. Retention: 71% of full-time freshmen returned the following year. Core. Calendar: semesters. Academic remediation for entering students, ESL program, services for LD students, distance learning, double major, summer session for credit, part-time degree program, adult/continuing education programs, co-op programs. Study abroad program.
Entrance Requirements: Open admission. Option: electronic application. Recommended: high school transcript. Entrance: noncompetitive. Application deadline: rolling. Notification: continuous. Transfer credits accepted: Yes.
Costs Per Year: Application fee: $0. State resident tuition: $1297 full-time, $46 per credit hour part-time. Nonresident tuition: $7625 full-time, $252 per credit hour part-time. Mandatory fees: $38 full-time, $38 per term part-time.

Collegiate Environment: Orientation program. Drama-theater group, student-run newspaper, radio station. Social organizations: 44 open to all; Phi Theta Kappa. Student services: health clinic, personal-psychological counseling. Campus security: 24-hour emergency response devices and patrols. College of the Desert Library. Weekly public service hours: 56; students can reserve study rooms. 54 computers available on campus for general student use. A campuswide network can be accessed. Students can access the following: online class registration, online catalogs. Staffed computer lab on campus provides training in use of computers, software, and the Internet.

Community Environment: Palm Desert is a resort area with a population of 47,000, where the climate is temperate. Buses and planes serve the area; Highway 111 goes through town. There are churches of major denominations, civic and service groups, and hospitals are nearby. Indio and Palm Springs have such recreational activities as boating, fishing, water skiing, and hiking. There are nearby mountains for winter sports. The area is a major center for golf and tennis tournaments.

■ **COLLEGE OF MARIN**
835 College Ave.
Kentfield, CA 94904
Tel: (415)457-8811
Fax: (415)883-2632
Web Site: www.marin.edu
Description: District-supported, 2-year, coed. Part of California Community College System. Awards certificates, transfer associate, and terminal associate degrees. Founded 1926. Setting: 410-acre suburban campus with easy access to San Francisco. Total enrollment: 5,026. Faculty: 312 (114 full-time, 198 part-time). 0.2% American Indian or Alaska Native, non-Hispanic/Latino; 31% Hispanic/Latino; 3% Black or African American, non-Hispanic/Latino; 8% Asian, non-Hispanic/Latino; 0.3% Native Hawaiian or other Pacific Islander, non-Hispanic/Latino; 1% international. Core. Calendar: semesters. Academic remediation for entering students, ESL program, services for LD students, advanced placement, distance learning, double major, summer session for credit, part-time degree program, co-op programs.
Entrance Requirements: Open admission. Option: electronic application. Entrance: noncompetitive. Application deadline: rolling. Transfer credits accepted: Yes.
Costs Per Year: State resident tuition: $1380 full-time, $46 per credit part-time. Nonresident tuition: $9210 full-time, $307 per credit part-time. Mandatory fees: $110 full-time.
Collegiate Environment: Orientation program. Drama-theater group, choral group, student-run newspaper. Student services: health clinic, personal-psychological counseling. Campus security: 24-hour emergency response devices and patrols, security cameras. College housing not available. Main library plus 1 other.
Community Environment: Kentfield is suburban community in a beautiful countryside across the Golden Gate from San Francisco. Located on a peninsula with the Pacific Ocean on one side and San Francisco Bay on the other. A mild climate averaging 70 degrees; average rainfall 36 inches per year. The Golden Gate bus line serves the area. Entertainment and recreational facilities are close by and shopping facilities are good. Good opportunities for part-time employment.

■ **COLLEGE OF THE REDWOODS**
7351 Tompkins Hill Rd.
Eureka, CA 95501-9300
Tel: (707)476-4100; Free: 800-641-0400
Web Site: www.redwoods.edu
Description: District-supported, 2-year, coed. Part of California Community College System. Awards certificates, transfer associate, and terminal associate degrees. Founded 1964. Setting: 322-acre small town campus. Total enrollment: 7,634. Student-undergrad faculty ratio is 23:1. 47% 25 or older. Core. Calendar: semesters. Academic remediation for entering students, ESL program, services for LD students, advanced placement, honors program, distance learning, summer session for credit, part-time degree program, adult/continuing education programs, co-op programs. Off campus study at Oregon Institute of Technology, Rogue Community College, Southern Oregon University.
Entrance Requirements: Open admission except for nursing program or international students. Option: early admission. Entrance: noncompetitive. Application deadline: rolling.
Collegiate Environment: Student services: health clinic, personal-

psychological counseling. Campus security: 24-hour emergency response devices and patrols, late night transport-escort service. College of the Redwoods Library.
Community Environment: Eureka is located on the north coast of Humboldt Bay, 283 miles north of San Francisco; the climate is cool and humid. Buses and railroads serve the area, airlines to connecting flights in San Francisco, Oakland, Sacramento and Portland are available. Community facilities include two hospitals, a medical center, churches, libraries, and a good downtown shopping area. The city provides a park, a community recreation building and a 18 hole golf course. Fishing and hunting are excellent; mountain area very near. In Summer, salmon fishing is good in Humboldt and Trinidad Bay north of the city; in early fall, steelhead and salmon are caught in the Eel Mud, and Trinity Rivers nearby. Eureka sponsors an annual Rhododendron Festival and two fairs each year.

■ **COLLEGE OF SAN MATEO**
1700 W Hillsdale Blvd.
San Mateo, CA 94402-3784
Tel: (650)574-6161
Web Site: www.collegeofsanmateo.edu
Description: District-supported, 2-year, coed. Part of California Community College System. Awards certificates, transfer associate, and terminal associate degrees. Founded 1922. Setting: 150-acre suburban campus. Total enrollment: 11,310. Student-undergrad faculty ratio is 26:1. 45% 25 or older. Core. Calendar: semesters. Academic remediation for entering students, ESL program, services for LD students, advanced placement, accelerated degree program, honors program, summer session for credit, part-time degree program, adult/continuing education programs, co-op programs and internships. Study abroad program. ROTC: Army (c), Naval (c), Air Force (c).
Entrance Requirements: Open admission except for nursing program. Option: early admission. Entrance: noncompetitive. Application deadline: rolling.
Collegiate Environment: Orientation program. Student-run newspaper. Student services: health clinic, personal-psychological counseling. Campus security: 24-hour emergency response devices and patrols. College of San Mateo Library.
Community Environment: San Mateo, located on picturesque El Camino Real, is an attractive residential suburb, 19 miles south of San Francisco. Climate is moderate and the city claims to have an average of 258 days of sunshine each year. San Mateo has access to all major forms of transportation and has a municipal transit system. There are many churches, hospitals, and libraries. An outstanding retail shopping center is found on the Peninsula. Recreational facilities include golf courses, yacht harbor, public beach, public parks and the Bay Meadows Race Track.

■ **COLLEGE OF THE SEQUOIAS**
915 S Mooney Blvd.
Visalia, CA 93277-2234
Tel: (559)730-3700
Web Site: www.cos.edu
Description: District-supported, 2-year, coed. Part of California Community College System. Awards certificates, transfer associate, and terminal associate degrees. Founded 1925. Setting: 215-acre small town campus with easy access to Fresno. Endowment: $3 million. Educational spending for the previous fiscal year: $2900 per student. Total enrollment: 13,449. Faculty: 510 (185 full-time, 325 part-time). Student-undergrad faculty ratio is 27:1. Full-time: 5,147 students, 54% women, 46% men. Part-time: 8,302 students, 57% women, 43% men. Students come from 15 states and territories, 6 other countries, 0.1% from out-of-state. 41% 25 or older, 53% transferred in. Core. Calendar: semesters. Academic remediation for entering students, ESL program, services for LD students, advanced placement, accelerated degree program, freshman honors college, honors program, distance learning, double major, summer session for credit, part-time degree program, adult/continuing education programs, co-op programs and internships. Off campus study. Study abroad program. ROTC: Air Force (c).
Entrance Requirements: Open admission except for nursing, engineering, chemistry, math, English programs. Required: high school transcript. Entrance: noncompetitive. Application deadline: 8/15. Notification: continuous.
Collegiate Environment: Orientation program. Drama-theater group, choral group, student-run newspaper. Social organizations: 35 open to all. Most popular organizations: MECHA, Ag Club, Alpha Gamma Sigma, Paralegal Association, Sports Medicine Club. Major annual events: Homecoming, Multicultural Fair, Tech Prep Expo. Student services: health clinic, personal-psychological counseling, women's center. Campus security: 24-hour

emergency response devices and patrols, student patrols, late night transport-escort service, 18-hour patrols by trained security personnel. College of the Sequoias Library. Operations spending for the previous fiscal year: $620,000. 250 computers available on campus for general student use. A campuswide network can be accessed from off-campus. Students can access the following: online class registration. Staffed computer lab on campus provides training in use of computers, software, and the Internet.

Community Environment: Visalia is 42 miles southeast of Fresno. It is the Tulare County seat and is situated in the fertile San Joaquin Valley. It ranks highest in the world in agricultural production of citrus fruits, dairy products, olives, cotton, and walnuts. A number of manufacturers and industrial plants are located here. Bus, rail, and air lines serve the area. The community has churches, hospitals, a symphony orchestra, ballet, theatres, 20 city parks, and 5 golf courses. Tulare County Park provides recreational facilities for picnicking and water sports. Nearby is the High Sierra mountain wonderland in the Sierra National Forest.

■ **COLLEGE OF THE SISKIYOUS**
800 College Ave.
Weed, CA 96094-2899
Tel: (530)938-5555; Free: 888-397-4339
Fax: (530)938-5227
E-mail: admissions-weed@siskyous.edu
Web Site: www.siskiyous.edu
Description: District-supported, 2-year, coed. Part of California Community College System. Awards certificates, transfer associate, and terminal associate degrees. Founded 1957. Setting: 260-acre rural campus. Total enrollment: 3,045. Student-undergrad faculty ratio is 20:1. 54% 25 or older. Core. Calendar: semesters. Academic remediation for entering students, ESL program, services for LD students, advanced placement, self-designed majors, honors program, independent study, distance learning, double major, summer session for credit, part-time degree program, adult/continuing education programs, co-op programs and internships.
Entrance Requirements: Open admission. Options: early admission, deferred admission. Entrance: noncompetitive. Application deadline: rolling. Notification: continuous.
Collegiate Environment: Orientation program. Drama-theater group, choral group, student-run newspaper. Student services: legal services, health clinic, personal-psychological counseling, women's center. Campus security: 24-hour emergency response devices, controlled dormitory access. College of the Siskiyous Library.
Community Environment: Centrally located in Siskiyou County, just off Interstate 5, the historic lumber town of Weed lies nestled at the base of majestic 14,162-foot Mt. Shasta. At the midpoint between two major population centers - Medford, Oregon, to the north and Redding to the south - Weed is easily accessible by airline, train and bus services. The climate features four distinct seasons with an average snowfall of 24 inches. Outdoor enthusiasts will delight in the spectacular alpine environment of this rural northern California region, which provides for a wide variety of recreational activities including downhill and cross-country skiing, snowboarding, hunting, fishing, hiking, rock climbing, wind surfing, and more.

■ **COLUMBIA COLLEGE**
11600 Columbia College Dr.
Sonora, CA 95370
Tel: (209)588-5100
E-mail: ccadmissions@yosemite.edu
Web Site: www.gocolumbia.edu
Description: District-supported, 2-year, coed. Part of Yosemite Community College District System. Awards certificates, diplomas, transfer associate, and terminal associate degrees. Founded 1968. Setting: 200-acre rural campus. Endowment: $312,432. Educational spending for the previous fiscal year: $2781 per student. Total enrollment: 2,424. Faculty: 51 (44 full-time, 7 part-time). Student-undergrad faculty ratio is 19:1. Full-time: 717 students, 50% women, 50% men. Part-time: 1,707 students, 60% women, 40% men. Students come from 2 states and territories, 1% from out-of-state. 2% American Indian or Alaska Native, non-Hispanic/Latino; 16% Hispanic/Latino; 2% Black or African American, non-Hispanic/Latino; 2% Asian, non-Hispanic/Latino; 0.4% Native Hawaiian or other Pacific Islander, non-Hispanic/Latino. 38% 25 or older, 12% transferred in. Core. Calendar: semesters. Academic remediation for entering students, ESL program, services for LD students, independent study, distance learning, summer session for credit, part-time degree program, co-op programs. Off campus study.

Entrance Requirements: Open admission. Options: electronic application, early admission. Recommended: high school transcript. Entrance: noncompetitive. Application deadline: rolling. Notification: continuous. Preference given to EOPS and students with disabilities, students who have earned consecutive units and terms. Transfer credits accepted: Yes.
Collegiate Environment: Orientation program. Drama-theater group, choral group, student-run newspaper. Most popular organizations: Associated Students (leadership and governance), Veterans Club, Debate Club. Major annual events: Welcome Week, Student Elections and Transfer Day, Cram Night. Student services: health clinic, personal-psychological counseling. Campus security: 24-hour emergency response devices and patrols, late night transport-escort service. Columbia College Library plus 1 other. Books: 40,828 (physical), 19,501 (digital/electronic); Serial titles: 4,151 (physical); Databases: 75. Weekly public service hours: 50; students can reserve study rooms. Operations spending for the previous fiscal year: $397,928. 50 computers available on campus for general student use. Computer purchase/lease plans available. A campuswide network can be accessed. Students can access the following: online class registration, online orientation, tutoring, library and multimedia classrooms. Staffed computer lab on campus provides training in use of computers and the Internet.

■ **COLUMBIA COLLEGE HOLLYWOOD**
18618 Oxnard St.
Tarzana, CA 91356
Tel: (818)345-8414; Free: 800-785-0585
Fax: (818)345-9053
E-mail: admissions@columbiacollege.edu
Web Site: www.columbiacollege.edu
Description: Independent, 4-year, coed. Awards associate and bachelor's degrees. Founded 1952. Setting: 1-acre urban campus with easy access to Los Angeles. Total enrollment: 359. Faculty: (52 full-time). Student-undergrad faculty ratio is 33:1. 196 applied, 57% were admitted. 8% from top 10% of their high school class, 23% from top quarter, 44% from top half. 1 class president. Students come from 5 other countries, 42% from out-of-state. 17% Hispanic/Latino; 16% Black or African American, non-Hispanic/Latino; 7% Asian, non-Hispanic/Latino. 10% 25 or older. Retention: 81% of full-time freshmen returned the following year. Core. Calendar: quarters. Accelerated degree program, summer session for credit, part-time degree program, adult/continuing education programs.
Entrance Requirements: Options: electronic application, deferred admission. Required: essay, high school transcript, minimum 2 high school GPA, 2 recommendations, interview. Recommended: portfolio. Entrance: minimally difficult. Application deadline: rolling. Notification: continuous. Transfer credits accepted: Yes.
Collegiate Environment: Orientation program. Drama-theater group. Major annual event: Alumni Weekend. Student services: personal-psychological counseling. Campus security: 24-hour emergency response devices and patrols, late night transport-escort service. Columbia College Hollywood Library plus 1 other. 12 computers available on campus for general student use. A computer is required for all students. Students can access the following: online class registration. Staffed computer lab on campus.
Community Environment: The college is located close to freeways, public transportation, housing, and major recreational areas in Southern California.

■ **COMMUNITY CHRISTIAN COLLEGE**
251 Tennessee St.
Redlands, CA 92373
Tel: (909)335-8863
Fax: (909)335-9101
E-mail: emelendez@cccollege.edu
Web Site: www.cccollege.edu
Description: Independent Christian, 2-year, coed. Awards transfer associate and terminal associate degrees. Founded 1994. Total enrollment: 74. Student-undergrad faculty ratio is 5:1. 35% 25 or older. Retention: 41% of full-time freshmen returned the following year.
Entrance Requirements: Open admission.

■ **COMPTON COLLEGE**
1111 E Artesia Blvd.
Compton, CA 90221-5393
Tel: (310)900-1600
Fax: (310)900-1692
Web Site: www.compton.edu
Description: District-supported, 2-year, coed. Part of California Community

College System. Awards transfer associate and terminal associate degrees. Founded 1927. Setting: 83-acre urban campus with easy access to Los Angeles. Total enrollment: 7,900. Faculty: 347 (100 full-time, 247 part-time). 1,650 applied, 100% were admitted. Students come from 4 states and territories, 25 other countries. 69% 25 or older. Core. Calendar: semesters. Academic remediation for entering students, ESL program, services for LD students, advanced placement, honors program, summer session for credit, part-time degree program, adult/continuing education programs.
Entrance Requirements: Open admission. Option: early admission. Entrance: noncompetitive. Application deadline: rolling. Notification: continuous.
Collegiate Environment: Drama-theater group. Student services: personal-psychological counseling. Campus security: 24-hour patrols. Compton Community College Library. 30 computers available on campus for general student use.
Community Environment: Located between the cities of Los Angeles and Long Beach in the center of a large residential area. The population of the city is now about 95,600. The city offers a mild climate and many days of sun. Mountains and the beaches are both nearby which provide a wealth of recreational activities. Work for room and board in private homes may be secured, part-time employment is also available.

■ **CONCORDE CAREER COLLEGE (GARDEN GROVE)**
12951 S Euclid St.
Ste. 101
Garden Grove, CA 92840
Tel: (714)703-1900
Fax: (714)530-4737
E-mail: cbecker@concorde.edu
Web Site: www.concorde.edu
Description: Proprietary, 2-year, coed. Awards certificates and terminal associate degrees. Total enrollment: 698. Student-undergrad faculty ratio is 22:1. 216 applied, 100% were admitted. 56% 25 or older.
Entrance Requirements: Required: high school transcript.

■ **CONCORDE CAREER COLLEGE (NORTH HOLLYWOOD)**
12412 Victory Blvd.
North Hollywood, CA 91606
Tel: (818)766-8151
Fax: (818)766-1587
E-mail: mvolker@concorde.edu
Web Site: www.concorde.edu
Description: Proprietary, 2-year, coed. Awards certificates and terminal associate degrees. Founded 1955. Total enrollment: 650. Student-undergrad faculty ratio is 20:1. 253 applied, 100% were admitted. 45% 25 or older.
Entrance Requirements: Required: high school transcript.

■ **CONCORDE CAREER COLLEGE (SAN BERNARDINO)**
201 E Airport Dr.
San Bernardino, CA 92408
Tel: (909)884-8891
Web Site: www.concorde.edu
Description: Proprietary, 2-year, coed. Awards certificates and terminal associate degrees. Founded 1967.

■ **CONCORDE CAREER COLLEGE (SAN DIEGO)**
4393 Imperial Ave.
Ste. 100
San Diego, CA 92113
Tel: (619)688-0800
Web Site: www.concorde.edu
Description: Proprietary, 2-year, coed. Awards certificates and terminal associate degrees.

■ **CONCORDIA UNIVERSITY IRVINE**
1530 Concordia W
Irvine, CA 92612-3299
Tel: (949)854-8002; Free: 800-229-1200
Fax: (949)854-6894
E-mail: admission@cui.edu
Web Site: www.cui.edu
Description: Independent, comprehensive, coed, affiliated with Lutheran Church-Missouri Synod. Part of The Concordia University System. Awards associate, bachelor's, master's, and doctoral degrees (associate's degree for international students only). Founded 1972. Setting: 70-acre suburban campus with easy access to Los Angeles. System endowment: $35.1 million. Educational spending for the previous fiscal year: $7167 per student. Total enrollment: 4,182. Faculty: 458 (111 full-time, 347 part-time). Student-undergrad faculty ratio is 17:1. 3,995 applied, 62% were admitted. 20% from top 10% of their high school class, 48% from top quarter, 83% from top half. Full-time: 1,673 students, 63% women, 37% men. Part-time: 128 students, 55% women, 45% men. Students come from 40 states and territories, 32 other countries, 18% from out-of-state. 0.4% American Indian or Alaska Native, non-Hispanic/Latino; 24% Hispanic/Latino; 5% Black or African American, non-Hispanic/Latino; 8% Asian, non-Hispanic/Latino; 0.4% Native Hawaiian or other Pacific Islander, non-Hispanic/Latino; 5% international. 14% 25 or older, 47% live on campus, 8% transferred in. Retention: 78% of full-time freshmen returned the following year. Academic areas with the most degrees conferred: health professions and related sciences; business/marketing; psychology. Core. Calendar: semesters. Academic remediation for entering students, services for LD students, advanced placement, accelerated degree program, honors program, independent study, distance learning, double major, summer session for credit, part-time degree program, adult/continuing education programs, internships. Off campus study at all other universities in the Concordia University System. Study abroad program. ROTC: Army (c).
Entrance Requirements: Options: electronic application, early action, deferred admission, international baccalaureate accepted. Required: high school transcript, SAT or ACT. Recommended: essay, minimum 2.8 high school GPA, 1 recommendation, interview. Entrance: moderately difficult. Application deadlines: 7/27, 7/27 for nonresidents, 2/15 for early action. Notification: continuous, continuous for nonresidents, 3/1 for early action. SAT Reasoning Test deadline: 6/1. Transfer credits accepted: Yes.
Costs Per Year: Application fee: $50. Comprehensive fee: $48,610 includes full-time tuition ($35,990), mandatory fees ($750), and college room and board ($11,870). College room only: $6840. Part-time tuition: $1056 per credit.
Collegiate Environment: Orientation program. Drama-theater group, choral group, student-run newspaper. Social organizations: 15 open to all; 40% of eligible men and 60% of eligible women are members. Most popular organizations: intramurals, Screaming Eagles, Lacrosse, Abbey West, LEAD Student Activities. Major annual events: Midnight Madness (fall), CultureFest, Homecoming. Student services: health clinic, personal-psychological counseling. Campus security: 24-hour emergency response devices and patrols, student patrols, late night transport-escort service. 1,024 college housing spaces available; 832 were occupied in 2018-19. Freshmen guaranteed college housing. On-campus residence required in freshman year. Options: coed, women-only housing available. Concordia University Library. Books: 72,408 (physical), 196,626 (digital/electronic); Serial titles: 42 (physical), 22,390 (digital/electronic); Databases: 40. Weekly public service hours: 89. Operations spending for the previous fiscal year: $593,489. 64 computers available on campus for general student use. A campuswide network can be accessed from student residence rooms. Students can access the following: online class registration.

■ **CONTRA COSTA COLLEGE**
2600 Mission Bell Dr.
San Pablo, CA 94806-3195
Tel: (510)235-7800
E-mail: ar@contracosta.edu
Web Site: www.contracosta.edu
Description: District-supported, 2-year, coed. Part of Contra Costa Community College District and California Community College System. Awards certificates, transfer associate, and terminal associate degrees. Founded 1948. Setting: 83-acre small town campus with easy access to San Francisco. Total enrollment: 8,316. Student-undergrad faculty ratio is 26:1. 44% 25 or older. Core. Calendar: semesters. Academic remediation for entering students, ESL program, services for LD students, accelerated degree program, self-designed majors, honors program, independent study, distance learning, summer session for credit, part-time degree program, adult/continuing education programs, co-op programs and internships. Off campus study at University of California, Berkeley; members of the Regional Association of East Bay Colleges and Universities. Study abroad program.
Entrance Requirements: Open admission. Option: early admission. Entrance: noncompetitive. Application deadline: rolling.
Collegiate Environment: Drama-theater group, student-run newspaper. Student services: personal-psychological counseling, women's center. Campus security: 24-hour emergency response devices and patrols, student patrols, late night transport-escort service. Contra Costa College Library.

Community Environment: San Pablo is located on San Francisco Bay north of Richmond and Oakland on Highway 40. Buses and railroads serve the area. The city has 70 major industries; skilled and unskilled labor opportunities are available. San Pablo community facilities include churches, library and hospitals. Recreational facilities are provided by the beaches nearby and the mountain resort area for winter sports, which are approximately a three hour drive.

■ COPPER MOUNTAIN COLLEGE

6162 Rotary Way
Joshua Tree, CA 92252
Tel: (760)366-3791; Free: 866-366-3791
E-mail: gbrown@cmccd.edu
Web Site: www.cmccd.edu

Description: District-supported, 2-year, coed. Awards certificates, transfer associate, and terminal associate degrees. Founded 1966. Setting: 26-acre rural campus. Endowment: $102,297. Total enrollment: 2,500. Faculty: 112 (21 full-time, 91 part-time). 720 applied, 90% were admitted. 2% American Indian or Alaska Native, non-Hispanic/Latino; 13% Hispanic/Latino; 7% Black or African American, non-Hispanic/Latino; 4% Asian, non-Hispanic/Latino. 52% 25 or older. Core. Calendar: semesters. Academic remediation for entering students, ESL program, services for LD students, advanced placement, honors program, independent study, distance learning, summer session for credit, internships. Off campus study.

Entrance Requirements: Open admission. Option: electronic application. Application deadline: rolling. Notification: continuous. Preference given to Registered Nursing program. Transfer credits accepted: Yes.

Collegiate Environment: Orientation program. Drama-theater group. Social organizations: 6 open to all. Most popular organizations: Student Government, Literary Magazine, Christian Club, Service Club, Culture Club. Major annual events: University Day, Spring Fling, Community Services Fair. Campus security: 24-hour emergency response devices. Greenleaf Library. 175 computers available on campus for general student use. A campuswide network can be accessed. Students can access the following: online class registration. Staffed computer lab on campus.

■ COSUMNES RIVER COLLEGE

8401 Ctr. Pky.
Sacramento, CA 95823-5799
Tel: (916)691-7344
Fax: (916)691-7375
Web Site: www.crc.losrios.edu

Description: District-supported, 2-year, coed. Part of Los Rios Community College District System. Awards certificates, transfer associate, and terminal associate degrees. Founded 1970. Setting: 180-acre suburban campus with easy access to Sacramento. Total enrollment: 14,545. Student-undergrad faculty ratio is 34:1. 41% 25 or older. Core. Calendar: semesters. Academic remediation for entering students, ESL program, services for LD students, advanced placement, accelerated degree program, freshman honors college, honors program, independent study, distance learning, double major, summer session for credit, part-time degree program, adult/continuing education programs, co-op programs and internships. Off campus study. Study abroad program.

Entrance Requirements: Open admission except for international applicants. Options: electronic application, early admission. Entrance: noncompetitive. Application deadline: 8/1. Notification: continuous until 8/15.

Collegiate Environment: Orientation program. Drama-theater group, choral group, student-run newspaper, radio station. Student services: health clinic, personal-psychological counseling. Campus security: 24-hour emergency response devices and patrols, student patrols, late night transport-escort service. Cosumnes River College Library plus 1 other.

Community Environment: See California State University - Sacramento.

■ CRAFTON HILLS COLLEGE

11711 Sand Canyon Rd.
Yucaipa, CA 92399-1799
Tel: (909)794-2161
Fax: (909)389-9141
Web Site: www.craftonhills.edu

Description: District-supported, 2-year, coed. Part of California Community College System. Awards certificates, transfer associate, and terminal associate degrees. Founded 1972. Setting: 526-acre small town campus with easy access to Los Angeles. Total enrollment: 6,380. Student-undergrad faculty ratio is 33:1. 32% 25 or older. Core. Calendar: semesters. Academic

remediation for entering students, services for LD students, advanced placement, self-designed majors, distance learning, summer session for credit, part-time degree program, adult/continuing education programs, co-op programs.

Entrance Requirements: Open admission. Options: early admission, deferred admission. Required for some: high school transcript. Entrance: noncompetitive. Application deadline: rolling. Notification: continuous. Preference given to district residents.

Collegiate Environment: Drama-theater group. Student services: health clinic, personal-psychological counseling, women's center. Campus security: 24-hour patrols, late night transport-escort service. Crafton Hills College Library.

Community Environment: See California State University - San Bernardino.

■ CUESTA COLLEGE

PO Box 8106
San Luis Obispo, CA 93403-8106
Tel: (805)546-3100
Web Site: www.cuesta.edu

Description: District-supported, 2-year, coed. Administratively affiliated with San Luis Obispo County Community College District. Awards certificates, transfer associate, and terminal associate degrees. Founded 1964. Setting: 129-acre rural campus. Total enrollment: 12,025. Student-undergrad faculty ratio is 27:1. 31% 25 or older. Core. Calendar: semesters. Academic remediation for entering students, ESL program, services for LD students, advanced placement, honors program, independent study, distance learning, double major, summer session for credit, part-time degree program, adult/continuing education programs, co-op programs and internships. Off campus study. Study abroad program. ROTC: Army (c).

Entrance Requirements: Open admission. Options: electronic application, early admission, deferred admission. Required: high school transcript. Recommended: essay. Entrance: noncompetitive. Application deadline: rolling. Notification: continuous. Preference given to district residents.

Collegiate Environment: Orientation program. Drama-theater group, choral group, student-run newspaper, radio station. Student services: legal services, health clinic, personal-psychological counseling. Campus security: 24-hour emergency response devices and patrols, late night transport-escort service. Cuesta College Library.

Community Environment: See California Polytechnic State University - San Luis Obispo.

■ CUYAMACA COLLEGE

900 Rancho San Diego Pky.
El Cajon, CA 92019-4304
Tel: (619)660-4000
E-mail: susan.topham@gcccd.edu
Web Site: www.cuyamaca.edu

Description: District-supported, 2-year, coed. Part of Grossmont-Cuyamaca Community College District. Awards certificates, diplomas, transfer associate, and terminal associate degrees. Founded 1978. Setting: 165-acre suburban campus with easy access to San Diego. Educational spending for the previous fiscal year: $2692 per student. Total enrollment: 7,706. Faculty: 645 (84 full-time, 561 part-time). Full-time: 1,636 students, 56% women, 44% men. Part-time: 6,070 students, 56% women, 44% men. Students come from 8 other countries. Core. Calendar: semesters. Academic remediation for entering students, ESL program, services for LD students, advanced placement, self-designed majors, honors program, distance learning, double major, summer session for credit, part-time degree program, adult/continuing education programs, co-op programs and internships. Off campus study. Study abroad program. ROTC: Army (c), Air Force (c).

Entrance Requirements: Open admission. Options: electronic application, early admission. Entrance: noncompetitive. Application deadline: rolling. Transfer credits accepted: Yes.

Collegiate Environment: Orientation program. Drama-theater group, student-run newspaper. Student services: health clinic, personal-psychological counseling. Campus security: 24-hour emergency response devices and patrols, late night transport-escort service. Library plus 1 other. Operations spending for the previous fiscal year: $1.9 million. 396 computers available on campus for general student use. A campuswide network can be accessed from off-campus. Students can access the following: online class registration. Staffed computer lab on campus provides training in use of computers, software, and the Internet.

■ **CYPRESS COLLEGE**
9200 Valley View
Cypress, CA 90630-5897
Tel: (714)484-7000
Fax: (714)761-3934
E-mail: admissions@cypresscollege.edu
Web Site: www.cypresscollege.edu
Description: District-supported, 2-year, coed. Part of California Community College System. Awards certificates, transfer associate, and terminal associate degrees. Founded 1966. Setting: 108-acre suburban campus with easy access to Los Angeles. Total enrollment: 15,439. Student-undergrad faculty ratio is 26:1. 33% 25 or older. Core. Calendar: semesters. Academic remediation for entering students, ESL program, services for LD students, advanced placement, freshman honors college, honors program, independent study, distance learning, double major, summer session for credit, part-time degree program, adult/continuing education programs, co-op programs and internships. Off campus study. Study abroad program.
Entrance Requirements: Open admission. Recommended: high school transcript. Entrance: noncompetitive. Application deadline: 8/25.
Collegiate Environment: Orientation program. Drama-theater group, choral group, student-run newspaper. Student services: legal services, health clinic, personal-psychological counseling, women's center. Campus security: 24-hour emergency response devices. Cypress College Library plus 1 other.
Community Environment: Cypress is a rapidly growing suburban city, 20 miles east of Los Angeles. The climate is dry and mild. Buses, trains, freeway system and the Los Angeles International Airport 20 miles away all serve the area. The city has three private hospitals, twelve churches, a library, and an amphitheater. There are city parks, a golf course, swimming pool and a gymnasium for those interested in sports. Anaheim Stadium is seven miles away, Disneyland five and one-half miles, Knotts Berry Farm and Movieland Wax Museum two and one-half miles. Beaches and mountain areas provide additional recreational facilities and are within easy driving distance. Many universities and colleges are nearby.

■ **DE ANZA COLLEGE**
21250 Stevens Creek Blvd.
Cupertino, CA 95014-5793
Tel: (408)864-5678
Fax: (408)864-8329
Web Site: www.deanza.fhda.edu
Description: District-supported, 2-year, coed. Part of California Community College System. Awards certificates, diplomas, transfer associate, and terminal associate degrees. Founded 1967. Setting: 112-acre suburban campus with easy access to San Francisco, San Jose. Total enrollment: 20,808. Faculty: 845 (290 full-time, 555 part-time). Student-undergrad faculty ratio is 25:1. Full-time: 9,940 students, 46% women, 54% men. Part-time: 10,868 students, 53% women, 47% men. 0.5% American Indian or Alaska Native, non-Hispanic/Latino; 28% Hispanic/Latino; 4% Black or African American, non-Hispanic/Latino; 46% Asian, non-Hispanic/Latino; 0.8% Native Hawaiian or other Pacific Islander, non-Hispanic/Latino. Core. Calendar: quarters. Academic remediation for entering students, ESL program, services for LD students, self-designed majors, honors program, independent study, distance learning, summer session for credit, part-time degree program, adult/continuing education programs, internships. Study abroad program. ROTC: Army (c), Air Force (c).
Entrance Requirements: Application deadlines: rolling, rolling for nonresidents. Notification: continuous, continuous for nonresidents.
Costs Per Year: State resident tuition: $0 full-time. Nonresident tuition: $5760 full-time, $163 per unit part-time. Mandatory fees: $1116 full-time, $31 per unit part-time, $55.08 per term part-time.
Collegiate Environment: Orientation program. Drama-theater group, choral group, student-run newspaper. Most popular organizations: Student Nurses Association, Phi Theta Kappa, Automotive Club, Vietnamese Club, Filipino Club. Major annual events: Graduation, Orientation, Club Day. Student services: legal services, health clinic, personal-psychological counseling. Campus security: 24-hour emergency response devices, student patrols, late night transport-escort service. A. Robert DeHart Learning Center. Study areas open 24 hours, 5-7 days a week; students can reserve study rooms. 800 computers available on campus for general student use. Computer purchase/lease plans available. A campuswide network can be accessed. Students can access the following: online class registration. Staffed computer lab on campus provides training in use of computers, software, and the Internet.
Community Environment: Cupertino, population 52,171, is within an hour's

drive from San Francisco. Buses and trains serve the area and the San Jose International Airport is nearby for air transportation. There are parks, playgrounds and nearby beaches for recreational activities as well as the cultural advantages of the San Francisco Bay Area.

■ **DESIGN INSTITUTE OF SAN DIEGO**
8555 Commerce Ave.
San Diego, CA 92121
Tel: (858)566-1200; Free: 800-619-4337
Fax: (858)566-2711
E-mail: admissions@disd.edu
Web Site: www.disd.edu
Description: Proprietary, 4-year, coed. Awards bachelor's degrees. Founded 1977. Setting: urban campus with easy access to San Diego. Total enrollment: 126. Faculty: 26 (5 full-time, 21 part-time). Student-undergrad faculty ratio is 9:1. 14 applied, 50% were admitted. Full-time: 80 students, 94% women, 6% men. Part-time: 46 students, 80% women, 20% men. Students come from 28 states and territories, 5 other countries. 2% American Indian or Alaska Native, non-Hispanic/Latino; 17% Hispanic/Latino; 7% Black or African American, non-Hispanic/Latino; 10% Asian, non-Hispanic/Latino; 0.8% Native Hawaiian or other Pacific Islander, non-Hispanic/Latino; 6% international. 44% 25 or older, 10% transferred in. Retention: 75% of full-time freshmen returned the following year. Academic area with the most degrees conferred: visual and performing arts. Core. Calendar: semesters. Services for LD students, self-designed majors, summer session for credit, part-time degree program, adult/continuing education programs, internships. Study abroad program.
Entrance Requirements: Options: electronic application, early decision. Required: essay, high school transcript, 2 recommendations. Recommended: minimum 2 high school GPA, interview. Required for some: official transcripts from all colleges attended. Transfer credits accepted: Yes.
Costs Per Year: One-time mandatory fee: $139. Tuition: $23,850 full-time, $993.75 per unit part-time. Mandatory fees: $10 full-time, $10 per year part-time. Full-time tuition and fees vary according to class time, course load, and program. Part-time tuition and fees vary according to class time, course load, and program.
Collegiate Environment: Orientation program. Social organizations: 4 open to all; student chapters of ASID and IIDA. Most popular organizations: ASID Student Chapter, IIDA Student Chapter, Student Mentor Program, Student Ambassador. Major annual events: American Institute of Architects Career Fair, IIDA San Diego Haute Couture Fashion Show, ASID Kitchen and Bath Tour. Campus security: security guard patrols during the semester from 5:30 - 10:30 pm Monday through Thursday, no classes on Friday past 5:00 pm. DISD Library. Books: 6,179 (physical); Serial titles: 84 (physical); Databases: 1. Weekly public service hours: 56. 64 computers available on campus for general student use. A campuswide network can be accessed from off-campus. Students can access the following: computer lab tutors and support from the IT Department. Staffed computer lab on campus provides training in use of computers, software, and the Internet.

■ **DEVRY UNIVERSITY-FOLSOM CAMPUS**
950 Iron Point Rd.
Folsom, CA 95630
Tel: (916)351-3700; Free: 866-338-7934
Web Site: www.devry.edu
Description: Proprietary, comprehensive, coed. Awards bachelor's and master's degrees.

■ **DEVRY UNIVERSITY-FREMONT CAMPUS**
6600 Dumbarton Cir.
Fremont, CA 94555
Tel: (510)574-1200; Free: 866-338-7934
Web Site: www.devry.edu
Description: Proprietary, comprehensive, coed. Awards associate, bachelor's, and master's degrees. Founded 1998. Setting: suburban campus with easy access to San Francisco. Calendar: semesters.
Entrance Requirements: Application deadline: rolling. Notification: continuous.

■ **DEVRY UNIVERSITY-FRESNO CAMPUS**
7575 N Fresno St.
Fresno, CA 93720
Tel: (559)439-8595; Free: 866-338-7934
Fax: (559)439-8598

Web Site: www.devry.edu

Description: Proprietary, 4-year, coed.

■ **DEVRY UNIVERSITY-LONG BEACH CAMPUS**

3880 Kilroy Airport Way
Long Beach, CA 90806
Tel: (562)427-0861; Free: 866-338-7934
Web Site: www.devry.edu

Description: Proprietary, comprehensive, coed. Part of DeVry University. Awards associate, bachelor's, and master's degrees. Founded 1984. Setting: urban campus. Calendar: semesters.

Entrance Requirements: Application deadline: rolling. Notification: continuous.

■ **DEVRY UNIVERSITY-POMONA CAMPUS**

901 Corporate Ctr. Dr.
Pomona, CA 91768
Tel: (909)622-8866; Free: 866-338-7934
Fax: (909)623-5666
Web Site: www.devry.edu

Description: Proprietary, comprehensive, coed. Part of DeVry University. Awards associate, bachelor's, and master's degrees. Founded 1983. Setting: urban campus. Total enrollment: 964. Faculty: 61 (11 full-time, 50 part-time). Student-undergrad faculty ratio is 19:1. Full-time: 281 students, 34% women, 66% men. Part-time: 503 students, 41% women, 59% men. 6% from out-of-state. 0.1% American Indian or Alaska Native, non-Hispanic/Latino; 42% Hispanic/Latino; 9% Black or African American, non-Hispanic/Latino; 11% Asian, non-Hispanic/Latino; 2% Native Hawaiian or other Pacific Islander, non-Hispanic/Latino; 2% international. 77% 25 or older, 21% transferred in. Calendar: semesters. Part-time degree program, adult/continuing education programs.

Entrance Requirements: Option: deferred admission. Required: high school transcript, interview. Entrance: minimally difficult. Application deadline: rolling. Notification: continuous.

■ **DEVRY UNIVERSITY-SAN DIEGO CAMPUS**

2655 Camino Del Rio N, Ste. 360
San Diego, CA 92108
Tel: (619)683-2446; Free: 866-338-7934
Fax: (619)683-2448
Web Site: www.devry.edu

Description: Proprietary, comprehensive, coed. Awards associate, bachelor's, and master's degrees. Calendar: semesters.

Entrance Requirements: Application deadline: rolling. Notification: continuous.

■ **DEVRY UNIVERSITY-SHERMAN OAKS CAMPUS**

15301 Ventura Blvd., Bldg. D-100
Sherman Oaks, CA 91403
Tel: (818)713-8111; Free: 866-338-7934
Web Site: www.devry.edu

Description: Proprietary, comprehensive, coed. Awards associate, bachelor's, and master's degrees.

Entrance Requirements: Application deadline: rolling. Notification: continuous.

■ **DIABLO VALLEY COLLEGE**

321 Golf Club Rd.
Pleasant Hill, CA 94523
Tel: (925)685-1230
Fax: (925)685-1551
E-mail: idorn@dvc.edu
Web Site: www.dvc.edu

Description: District-supported, 2-year, coed. Part of Contra Costa Community College District. Awards certificates, transfer associate, and terminal associate degrees. Founded 1949. Setting: 100-acre suburban campus with easy access to San Francisco. Total enrollment: 22,567. Faculty: 805 (255 full-time, 550 part-time). Student-undergrad faculty ratio is 17:1. Students come from 16 states and territories, 68 other countries, 0.2% from out-of-state. 38% 25 or older. Retention: 61% of full-time freshmen returned the following year. Core. Calendar: semesters. Academic remediation for entering students, services for LD students, advanced placement, self-designed

majors, summer session for credit, part-time degree program, adult/continuing education programs, co-op programs. Study abroad program. ROTC: Air Force (c).

Entrance Requirements: Open admission. Option: early admission. Recommended: high school transcript. Entrance: noncompetitive. Application deadline: 8/15.

Collegiate Environment: Drama-theater group, choral group, student-run newspaper. Student services: women's center. Campus security: 24-hour emergency response devices and patrols, student patrols. Diablo Valley College Library. 450 computers available on campus for general student use. A campuswide network can be accessed from off-campus. Students can access the following: online class registration. Staffed computer lab on campus.

Community Environment: Population 33,000. Pleasant Hill is a suburban residential community that has an average winter temperature of 46.4 degrees and summer temperature of 71.8 degrees. It is located 22 miles from San Francisco. All transportation facilities are available nearby. Churches representing 14 denominations, a hospital and excellent shopping facilities comprise the town. Employment opportunities are available. Pleasant Hill enjoys the cultural atmosphere of the San Francisco Bay Area. A nearby beach area provides recreational facilities; the mountain area for winter sports is accessible for a weekend trip.

■ **DOMINICAN UNIVERSITY OF CALIFORNIA**

50 Acacia Ave.
San Rafael, CA 94901-2298
Tel: (415)457-4440; Free: 888-323-6763
Fax: (415)485-3214
E-mail: rich.toledo@dominican.edu
Web Site: www.dominican.edu

Description: Independent, comprehensive, coed, affiliated with Roman Catholic Church. Awards bachelor's and master's degrees. Founded 1890. Setting: 85-acre suburban campus with easy access to San Francisco. Endowment: $28.3 million. Research spending for the previous fiscal year: $707,811. Educational spending for the previous fiscal year: $6779 per student. Total enrollment: 1,750. Faculty: 328 (106 full-time, 222 part-time). Student-undergrad faculty ratio is 9:1. 1,867 applied, 76% were admitted. 20% from top 10% of their high school class, 57% from top quarter, 89% from top half. Full-time: 1,135 students, 73% women, 27% men. Part-time: 167 students, 75% women, 25% men. Students come from 27 states and territories, 13 other countries, 9% from out-of-state. 0.7% American Indian or Alaska Native, non-Hispanic/Latino; 20% Hispanic/Latino; 5% Black or African American, non-Hispanic/Latino; 26% Asian, non-Hispanic/Latino; 1% Native Hawaiian or other Pacific Islander, non-Hispanic/Latino; 1% international. 18% 25 or older, 35% live on campus, 4% transferred in. Retention: 86% of full-time freshmen returned the following year. Academic areas with the most degrees conferred: health professions and related sciences; business/marketing; biological/life sciences. Core. Calendar: semesters. Accelerated degree program, self-designed majors, honors program, independent study, distance learning, double major, part-time degree program, external degree program, adult/continuing education programs, internships, graduate courses open to undergrads. Off campus study at University of California, Berkeley, Aquinas College, St. Thomas Aquinas College, Barry University. Study abroad program.

Entrance Requirements: Options: electronic application, deferred admission, international baccalaureate accepted. Required: essay, high school transcript, minimum 2 high school GPA, 1 recommendation, SAT or ACT. Recommended: interview. Entrance: moderately difficult. Application deadline: 2/1. Notification: continuous until 10/15. SAT Reasoning Test deadline: 8/1. SAT Subject Test deadline: 1/3. Transfer credits accepted: Yes.

Costs Per Year: Application fee: $0. Comprehensive fee: $59,340 includes full-time tuition ($44,240), mandatory fees ($450), and college room and board ($14,650). College room only: $8280. Full-time tuition and fees vary according to course load. Room and board charges vary according to board plan. Part-time tuition: $1850 per credit hour. Part-time mandatory fees: $150 per term. Part-time tuition and fees vary according to course load.

Collegiate Environment: Orientation program. Drama-theater group, choral group, student-run newspaper, radio station. Social organizations: 25 open to all. Most popular organizations: Filipino Cultural Club, BSU, Perceptions, Global Ambassadors, Intramural Club/Programming. Major annual events: Shield Day, Penguin Ball, Ecumenical Thanksgiving Dinner. Student services: health clinic, personal-psychological counseling. Campus security: 24-hour patrols, late night transport-escort service, controlled dormitory access. Archbishop Alemany Library. Books: 110,523 (physical); Databases: 84. Operations spending for the previous fiscal year: $1.5 million. 195 computers available on campus for general student use. A campuswide network can be accessed from student residence rooms. Students can access the following: online class registration, office software. Staffed computer lab on campus provides training in use of computers, software, and the Internet.

Community Environment: Located in the hills of Marin County 25 minutes from San Francisco across the Golden Gate Bridge, Dominican is close enough to permit easy access to the city's diverse cultural attractions - the opera, symphony, theaters and playhouses. The campus adjoins San Rafael (pop. 55,700), with a climate rated as one of the six most ideal in the world, in addition to a wide variety of libraries, museums and churches. The nearby cities of Mill Valley, Bolinas, and Sausalito harbor a large community of writers, painters and other artists, and a diverse collection of shops, restaurants and galleries. Five state parks and beaches lie within easy reach, including Muir Woods, the Golden Gate National Recreational Area, and the Point Reyes National Seashore.

■ EAST LOS ANGELES COLLEGE

1301 Avenida Cesar Chavez
Monterey Park, CA 91754
Tel: (323)265-8650
Fax: (323)265-8763
E-mail: allredjp@elac.edu
Web Site: www.elac.edu

Description: District-supported, 2-year, coed. Part of Los Angeles Community College District System. Awards certificates, transfer associate, and terminal associate degrees. Founded 1945. Setting: 84-acre urban campus with easy access to Los Angeles. Total enrollment: 31,749. Faculty: 829 (231 full-time, 598 part-time). Full-time: 8,063 students, 56% women, 44% men. Part-time: 23,686 students, 56% women, 44% men. Students come from 17 states and territories, 0.1% from out-of-state. 33% 25 or older, 11% transferred in. Core. Calendar: semesters. Academic remediation for entering students, ESL program, services for LD students, advanced placement, accelerated degree program, self-designed majors, freshman honors college, honors program, independent study, distance learning, double major, summer session for credit, part-time degree program, adult/continuing education programs, co-op programs and internships. Off campus study at Respiratory Therapy at Santa Monica City College. Study abroad program.

Entrance Requirements: Open admission. Options: electronic application, early admission. Required: international students require TOEFL score of 450, CBT score 133, iBT score 45 or higher. Recommended: high school transcript. Entrance: noncompetitive. Application deadline: rolling. Notification: continuous until 9/2. Transfer credits accepted: Yes.

Collegiate Environment: Orientation program. Drama-theater group, choral group, marching band, student-run newspaper. Social organizations: 22 open to all. Most popular organizations: Administration of Justice, American Society of Engineers and Architects, Society of Hispanic Professional Engineers, MENTE, Asian Student Intercultural Association (A.S.I.A) and the International Student Club, Chicano/Community for Creative Medicine, Science Associations, Advocates and Educators for Young Children, Child Development Club. Major annual events: Cinco de Mayo, Scholarship Awards Banquet, Vincent Price Art Museum exhibits. Student services: health clinic, personal-psychological counseling. Campus security: 24-hour emergency response devices and patrols, late night transport-escort service, Los Angeles County Sheriff Sub-station. ELAC Helen Miller Bailey Library plus 2 others. 1,000 computers available on campus for general student use. A campuswide network can be accessed from off-campus. Students can access the following: online class registration, subject specific computer labs and specialized computer/software. Staffed computer lab on campus provides training in use of computers, software, and the Internet.

■ EAST SAN GABRIEL VALLEY REGIONAL OCCUPATIONAL PROGRAM & TECHNICAL CENTER

1501 W Del Norte Ave.
West Covina, CA 91790
Tel: (626)472-5195
Web Site: www.esgvrop.org

Description: District-supported, 2-year, coed. Awards certificates, transfer associate, and terminal associate degrees.

■ EL CAMINO COLLEGE

16007 Crenshaw Blvd.
Torrance, CA 90506-0001

Tel: (310)532-3670; Free: 866-ELCAMINO
Fax: (310)660-3818
Web Site: www.elcamino.edu

Description: District-supported, 2-year, coed. Part of California Community College System. Awards certificates, diplomas, and transfer associate degrees. Founded 1947. Setting: 15-acre urban campus with easy access to Los Angeles. Total enrollment: 24,895. Faculty: 983 (333 full-time, 650 part-time). Student-undergrad faculty ratio is 15:1. Full-time: 7,729 students, 51% women, 49% men. Part-time: 17,166 students, 56% women, 44% men. Students come from 17 states and territories, 30 other countries, 10% from out-of-state. 42% 25 or older, 22% transferred in. Retention: 78% of full-time freshmen returned the following year. Core. Calendar: semesters. Academic remediation for entering students, ESL program, services for LD students, advanced placement, freshman honors college, honors program, independent study, distance learning, summer session for credit, part-time degree program, co-op programs and internships. Study abroad program.

Entrance Requirements: Open admission. Options: electronic application, early admission. Required: high school transcript. Entrance: noncompetitive. Application deadline: rolling. Notification: continuous.

Collegiate Environment: Orientation program. Drama-theater group, choral group, marching band, student-run newspaper. Social organizations: 20 open to all. Most popular organizations: Hispanic Club, Kiwanis International, North American Indian Club, Math Club, Cinema Club. Major annual events: Homecoming, Student Elections, College Transfer Fairs. Student services: health clinic, personal-psychological counseling, women's center. Campus security: 24-hour emergency response devices and patrols, late night transport-escort service. El Camino College Schauerman Library. 151 computers available on campus for general student use. A campuswide network can be accessed. Students can access the following: online class registration. Staffed computer lab on campus.

Community Environment: Torrance, situated in southwest Los Angeles County, is a suburb of Los Angeles and does enjoy the advantages of the city's cultural and recreational facilities. All forms of commercial transportation are convenient. Outstanding shopping centers are in the city as well as all the other usual community facilities. Climate is normally sunny and mild. Beaches and mountains are within easy driving distance for recreation.

■ EMPIRE COLLEGE

3035 Cleveland Ave.
Santa Rosa, CA 95403
Tel: (707)546-4000; Free: 877-395-8535
Fax: (707)546-4058
Web Site: www.empcol.edu

Description: Proprietary, 2-year, coed. Awards certificates, diplomas, and terminal associate degrees. Founded 1961. Setting: suburban campus with easy access to San Francisco. Total enrollment: 900. 72% 25 or older. Calendar: continuous. Double major.

Entrance Requirements: Option: international baccalaureate accepted. Required: high school transcript, interview, Wonderlic aptitude test. Required for some: essay. Entrance: minimally difficult. Application deadline: rolling.

Collegiate Environment: Orientation program. Campus security: 24-hour emergency response devices.

■ EPIC BIBLE COLLEGE

4330 Auburn Blvd.
Sacramento, CA 95841
Tel: (916)348-4689
Fax: (916)334-2315
Web Site: epic.edu

Description: Independent nondenominational, comprehensive, coed. Awards associate, bachelor's, master's, and doctoral degrees. Founded 1974. Total enrollment: 242. 216 applied. 61% 25 or older. Calendar: quarters.

Entrance Requirements: Required: high school transcript.

■ EVERGREEN VALLEY COLLEGE

3095 Yerba Buena Rd.
San Jose, CA 95135-1598
Tel: (408)274-7900
Fax: (408)223-9351
Web Site: www.evc.edu

Description: District-supported, 2-year, coed. Part of California Community College System. Awards certificates, transfer associate, and terminal associate degrees. Founded 1975. Setting: 175-acre urban campus. Total enrollment: 11,186. Student-undergrad faculty ratio is 32:1. 44% 25 or older. Core. Calendar: semesters. Academic remediation for entering students, ESL program, services for LD students, advanced placement, accelerated degree program, freshman honors college, honors program, independent study, distance learning, summer session for credit, part-time degree program, adult/continuing education programs, co-op programs. Off campus study at other community colleges in the area. ROTC: Army (c).

Entrance Requirements: Open admission except for nursing program. Option: early admission. Entrance: noncompetitive. Application deadline: rolling. Notification: continuous.

Collegiate Environment: Drama-theater group, choral group. Student services: health clinic, personal-psychological counseling. Campus security: 24-hour emergency response devices, late night transport-escort service, patrols by trained security personnel. Evergreen Valley College Library.

Community Environment: See San Jose State University.

■ FEATHER RIVER COLLEGE

570 Golden Eagle Ave.
Quincy, CA 95971-9124
Tel: (530)283-0202; Free: 800-442-9799
Fax: (530)283-3757
E-mail: info@frc.edu
Web Site: www.frc.edu
Description: District-supported, primarily 2-year, coed. Part of California Community College System. Awards certificates, diplomas, transfer associate, terminal associate, and bachelor's degrees. Founded 1968. Setting: 420-acre rural campus. Endowment: $48,167. Educational spending for the previous fiscal year: $7884 per student. Total enrollment: 2,079. Faculty: 98 (26 full-time, 72 part-time). Student-undergrad faculty ratio is 21:1. Students come from 30 states and territories, 7 other countries, 8% from out-of-state. 2% American Indian or Alaska Native, non-Hispanic/Latino; 30% Hispanic/Latino; 11% Black or African American, non-Hispanic/Latino; 6% Asian, non-Hispanic/Latino; 1% Native Hawaiian or other Pacific Islander, non-Hispanic/Latino; 0.9% international. 54% 25 or older. Core. Calendar: semesters plus summer and winter terms. Academic remediation for entering students, ESL program, services for LD students, advanced placement, independent study, distance learning, double major, summer session for credit, part-time degree program, adult/continuing education programs, co-op programs.

Entrance Requirements: Open admission The rule is open admission, except for the Licensed Vocational Nursing and BS in Equine and Ranch Management programs. Options: electronic application, international baccalaureate accepted. Recommended: ACCUPLACER. Entrance: noncompetitive. Transfer credits accepted: Yes.

Costs Per Year: Application fee: $0. State resident tuition: $1380 full-time, $46 per credit part-time. Nonresident tuition: $8430 full-time, $281 per credit part-time. Mandatory fees: $81 full-time, $1.50 per credit part-time, $18 per term part-time. Full-time tuition and fees vary according to course load. Part-time tuition and fees vary according to course load. College room only: $5350. Room charges vary according to housing facility.

Collegiate Environment: Orientation program. Drama-theater group, choral group. Social organizations: 8 open to all. Most popular organizations: Phi Theta Kappa Honor Society, International and Cultural Club, Horse Show Team, Student Environmental Association, Student Alliance for Equity. Major annual events: New Student Orientation, Cultural Fair, Chili Cook-off. Student services: health clinic, personal-psychological counseling. Campus security: student patrols, part-time private security company patrols. Feather River College Library. Books: 24,291 (physical), 350,000 (digital/electronic); Serial titles: 98 (physical), 28,376 (digital/electronic); Databases: 35. Weekly public service hours: 61; students can reserve study rooms. Operations spending for the previous fiscal year: $74,221. 116 computers available on campus for general student use. A campuswide network can be accessed from student residence rooms. Students can access the following: online class registration. Staffed computer lab on campus provides training in use of computers, software, and the Internet.

■ FIDM/FASHION INSTITUTE OF DESIGN & MERCHANDISING, LOS ANGELES CAMPUS

919 S Grand Ave.
Los Angeles, CA 90015-1421
Tel: (213)624-1200; Free: 800-624-1200
Fax: (213)624-4799
E-mail: saronson@fidm.edu
Web Site: www.fidm.edu
Description: Proprietary, 4-year, coed. Part of FIDM/Fashion Institute of

Design & Merchandising. Awards associate and bachelor's degrees (also includes Orange County Campus). Founded 1969. Setting: urban campus with easy access to Los Angeles. Total enrollment: 2,159. Student-undergrad faculty ratio is 13:1. 1,728 applied, 53% were admitted. Full-time: 2,140 students, 90% women, 10% men. Part-time: 14 students, 86% women, 14% men. 50% from out-of-state. Academic areas with the most degrees conferred: business/marketing; visual and performing arts; family and consumer sciences. Core. Calendar: quarters. Academic remediation for entering students, ESL program, services for LD students, advanced placement, accelerated degree program, independent study, distance learning, summer session for credit, part-time degree program, adult/continuing education programs, co-op programs and internships. Off campus study. Study abroad program.

Entrance Requirements: Options: electronic application, deferred admission, international baccalaureate accepted. Required: essay, high school transcript, minimum 2.5 high school GPA, 3 recommendations, interview, major-determined project. Recommended: SAT and SAT Subject Tests or ACT. Entrance: moderately difficult. Application deadlines: rolling, rolling for nonresidents. Notification: continuous, continuous for nonresidents. Transfer credits accepted: Yes.

Costs Per Year: Application fee: $25. Tuition: $31,015 full-time. Mandatory fees: $1295 full-time.

Collegiate Environment: Orientation program. Social organizations: Phi Theta Kappa Honor Society. Most popular organizations: Cross-Cultural Student Alliance, Fashion Industry Club, Phi Theta Kappa Honor Society, Student Council, FIDM MODE Magazine. Major annual events: Debut Fashion Show, Toys for Tots Toy Drive, MODE Launch Party. Student services: personal-psychological counseling. Campus security: 24-hour emergency response devices and patrols, late night transport-escort service. College housing not available. FIDM Los Angeles Campus Library. Books: 48,534 (physical), 2,778 (digital/electronic); Serial titles: 548 (physical); Databases: 39. Students can reserve study rooms. 433 computers available on campus for general student use. A campuswide network can be accessed from student residence rooms and from off campus. Students can access the following: online class registration. Staffed computer lab on campus provides training in use of computers, software, and the Internet.

■ FIDM/FASHION INSTITUTE OF DESIGN & MERCHANDISING, ORANGE COUNTY CAMPUS

17590 Gillette Ave.
Irvine, CA 92614
Tel: (949)851-6200; Free: 888-974-3436
Fax: (949)851-6808
Web Site: www.fidm.edu
Description: Proprietary, 2-year, coed. Part of FIDM/Fashion Institute of Design & Merchandising. Awards transfer associate and terminal associate degrees. Founded 1981. Setting: urban campus with easy access to Los Angeles. Total enrollment: 71. Faculty: 11 (all part-time). Student-undergrad faculty ratio is 7:1. 127 applied, 57% were admitted. Full-time: 67 students, 88% women, 12% men. Part-time: 4 students, 75% women, 25% men. Students come from 11 states and territories, 5 other countries, 12% from out-of-state. 5% 25 or older, 24% transferred in. Core. Calendar: quarters. Academic remediation for entering students, ESL program, services for LD students, advanced placement, accelerated degree program, independent study, distance learning, summer session for credit, part-time degree program, adult/continuing education programs, co-op programs and internships. Study abroad program.

Entrance Requirements: Options: electronic application, deferred admission, international baccalaureate accepted. Required: essay, high school transcript, minimum 2.5 high school GPA, 3 recommendations, interview, entrance project. Recommended: SAT or ACT. Entrance: moderately difficult. Application deadline: rolling. Transfer credits accepted: Yes.

Costs Per Year: Application fee: $225. Tuition: $32,075 full-time, $685 per credit hour part-time. Mandatory fees: $1152 full-time. Full-time tuition and fees vary according to degree level and program. Part-time tuition varies according to degree level and program.

Collegiate Environment: Orientation program. Social organizations: Phi Theta Kappa Honor Society. Most popular organizations: Cross-Cultural Student Alliance, Fashion Industry Club, Phi Theta Kappa (national honor society), Student Council, FIDM MODE Magazine. Major annual events: Debut, Toys for Tots Toy Drive, MODE Launch Party. Student services: personal-psychological counseling. Campus security: 24-hour emergency response devices, late night transport-escort service, security guard escort. FIDM Orange County Campus Library. Students can reserve study rooms.

48 computers available on campus for general student use. A campuswide network can be accessed from off-campus. Students can access the following: online class registration. Staffed computer lab on campus provides training in use of computers, software, and the Internet.

■ **FIDM/FASHION INSTITUTE OF DESIGN & MERCHANDISING, SAN DIEGO CAMPUS**

350 Tenth Ave.
3rd Fl.
San Diego, CA 92101
Tel: (619)235-2049; Free: 800-243-3436
Fax: (619)232-4322
E-mail: dbaca@fidm.edu
Web Site: www.fidm.edu

Description: Proprietary, 2-year, coed. Part of FIDM/Fashion Institute of Design & Merchandising. Awards transfer associate and terminal associate degrees. Founded 1985. Setting: urban campus with easy access to San Diego. Total enrollment: 66. Faculty: 12 (1 full-time, 11 part-time). Student-undergrad faculty ratio is 5:1. 110 applied, 45% were admitted. Full-time: 61 students, 92% women, 8% men. Part-time: 5 students, 80% women, 20% men. Students come from 17 states and territories, 4 other countries, 23% from out-of-state. 9% 25 or older, 50% transferred in. Retention: 82% of full-time freshmen returned the following year. Core. Calendar: quarters. Academic remediation for entering students, ESL program, services for LD students, advanced placement, accelerated degree program, independent study, distance learning, summer session for credit, part-time degree program, adult/continuing education programs, co-op programs and internships. Study abroad program.

Entrance Requirements: Options: electronic application, deferred admission, international baccalaureate accepted. Required: essay, high school transcript, minimum 2.5 high school GPA, 3 recommendations, interview, major-determined project. Recommended: SAT or ACT. Entrance: moderately difficult. Application deadline: rolling. Transfer credits accepted: Yes.

Costs Per Year: Application fee: $225. Tuition: $32,075 full-time. Mandatory fees: $1152 full-time. Full-time tuition and fees vary according to degree level and program.

Collegiate Environment: Orientation program. Social organizations: Phi Theta Kappa Honor Society. Most popular organizations: Cross-Cultural Student Alliance, Fashion Industry Club, Phi Theta Kappa (national honor society), Student Council, FIDM MODE Magazine. Major annual events: Debut Fashion Show, Toys for Tots Toy Drive, MODE Launch Party. Student services: personal-psychological counseling. Campus security: 24-hour emergency response devices and patrols. FIDM San Diego Campus Library. Students can reserve study rooms. 36 computers available on campus for general student use. A campuswide network can be accessed from off-campus. Students can access the following: online class registration. Staffed computer lab on campus provides training in use of computers, software, and the Internet.

■ **FIDM/FASHION INSTITUTE OF DESIGN & MERCHANDISING, SAN FRANCISCO CAMPUS**

55 Stockton St.
San Francisco, CA 94108-5829
Tel: (415)675-5200; Free: 800-422-3436
Fax: (415)296-7299
E-mail: sbadalamenti@fidm.edu
Web Site: www.fidm.edu

Description: Proprietary, 4-year, coed. Part of FIDM/Fashion Institute of Design & Merchandising. Awards associate and bachelor's degrees. Founded 1973. Setting: urban campus with easy access to San Francisco. Total enrollment: 279. Faculty: 40 (all part-time). Student-undergrad faculty ratio is 7:1. 198 applied, 37% were admitted. Full-time: 229 students, 88% women, 12% men. Part-time: 50 students, 90% women, 10% men. Students come from 15 states and territories, 13 other countries, 6% from out-of-state. 19% 25 or older, 21% transferred in. Retention: 96% of full-time freshmen returned the following year. Academic area with the most degrees conferred: business/marketing. Core. Calendar: quarters. Academic remediation for entering students, ESL program, services for LD students, advanced placement, accelerated degree program, honors program, independent study, distance learning, summer session for credit, part-time degree program, adult/continuing education programs, co-op programs and internships. Off campus study at Fashion Institute of Design and Merchandising, Los Angeles Campus. Study abroad program.

Entrance Requirements: Options: electronic application, deferred admis-

sion, international baccalaureate accepted. Required: essay, high school transcript, minimum 2.5 high school GPA, 3 recommendations, interview, major-determined project. Recommended: SAT or ACT. Entrance: moderately difficult. Application deadline: rolling. Transfer credits accepted: Yes.

Costs Per Year: Application fee: $225. Tuition: $32,075 full-time, $685 per credit hour part-time. Mandatory fees: $1152 full-time. Full-time tuition and fees vary according to degree level and program. Part-time tuition varies according to degree level and program.

Collegiate Environment: Orientation program. Social organizations: Phi Theta Kappa Honor Society. Most popular organizations: Cross-Cultural Student Alliance, Fashion Industry Club, Phi Theta Kappa- National Honor Society, Student Council, FIDM MODE Magazine. Major annual events: Debut Fashion Show, Toys for Tots Toy Drive, MODE Launch Party. Student services: personal-psychological counseling. Campus security: 24-hour emergency response devices and patrols, security escorts. FIDM San Francisco Library. Students can reserve study rooms. 135 computers available on campus for general student use. A campuswide network can be accessed from off-campus. Students can access the following: online class registration. Staffed computer lab on campus provides training in use of computers, software, and the Internet.

■ **FOLSOM LAKE COLLEGE**

10 College Pky.
Folsom, CA 95630
Tel: (916)608-6500
Web Site: www.flc.losrios.edu

Description: District-supported, 2-year, coed. Part of Los Rios Community College District System. Awards certificates, diplomas, transfer associate, and terminal associate degrees. Founded 2004. Setting: suburban campus with easy access to Sacramento. Total enrollment: 9,352. Faculty: 295 (109 full-time, 186 part-time). Student-undergrad faculty ratio is 32:1. Core. Academic remediation for entering students, ESL program, services for LD students, advanced placement, independent study, distance learning, summer session for credit, co-op programs and internships. Study abroad program.

Entrance Requirements: Option: electronic application. Recommended: high school transcript. Application deadline: rolling. Transfer credits accepted: Yes.

Collegiate Environment: Orientation program. Drama-theater group, choral group. Social organizations: Phi Theta Kappa. Student services: health clinic, personal-psychological counseling. Campus security: 24-hour emergency response devices and patrols, late night transport-escort service. Library. 131 computers available on campus for general student use. Computer purchase/lease plans available. A campuswide network can be accessed from off-campus. Students can access the following: online class registration. Staffed computer lab on campus provides training in use of computers, software, and the Internet.

■ **FOOTHILL COLLEGE**

12345 El Monte Rd.
Los Altos Hills, CA 94022-4599
Tel: (650)949-7777
E-mail: acedshawna@hda.edu
Web Site: www.foothill.edu

Description: District-supported, 2-year, coed. Part of Foothill-DeAnza Community College District. Awards certificates, transfer associate, and terminal associate degrees. Founded 1958. Setting: 122-acre suburban campus with easy access to San Jose. System endowment: $15 million. Educational spending for the previous fiscal year: $908 per student. Total enrollment: 15,765. Faculty: 538 (184 full-time, 354 part-time). 5,697 applied, 100% were admitted. 10% from top 10% of their high school class, 35% from top quarter, 50% from top half. Students come from 16 states and territories, 109 other countries, 1% from out-of-state. 0.3% American Indian or Alaska Native, non-Hispanic/Latino; 19% Hispanic/Latino; 4% Black or African American, non-Hispanic/Latino; 22% Asian, non-Hispanic/Latino; 1% Native Hawaiian or other Pacific Islander, non-Hispanic/Latino; 6% international. Core. Calendar: quarters. Academic remediation for entering students, ESL program, services for LD students, advanced placement, accelerated degree program, self-designed majors, honors program, independent study, distance learning, summer session for credit, part-time degree program, adult/continuing education programs, co-op programs and internships. Off campus study at DeAnza College. Study abroad program. ROTC: Army (c), Air Force (c).

Entrance Requirements: Open admission except for allied health

programs. Option: electronic application. Recommended: high school transcript. Entrance: noncompetitive. Application deadline: rolling. Notification: continuous. Transfer credits accepted: Yes.

Collegiate Environment: Orientation program. Drama-theater group, choral group, student-run newspaper, radio station. Social organizations: 45 open to all. Major annual events: Career Day, Club Day, Transfer Day. Student services: legal services, health clinic, personal-psychological counseling. Campus security: 24-hour emergency response devices and patrols, late night transport-escort service. Hubert H. Semans Library. Operations spending for the previous fiscal year: $238,000. 400 computers available on campus for general student use. A campuswide network can be accessed from off-campus. Students can access the following: online class registration. Staffed computer lab on campus.

Community Environment: This is a suburban area with temperate climate averaging 50 to 80 degrees. Los Altos Hills is strictly residential but all recreational and commercial facilities and services may be found in the neighboring cities of Palo Alto, Los Altos, Mountain View and Sunnyvale.

■ **FREMONT COLLEGE**
18000 Studebaker Rd.
Ste. 900A
Cerritos, CA 90703
Tel: (562)809-5100; Free: 800-373-6668
Fax: (562)809-7100
E-mail: info@fremont.edu
Web Site: www.fremont.edu
Description: Proprietary, primarily 2-year, coed. Awards diplomas, terminal associate, and bachelor's degrees.

■ **FRESNO CITY COLLEGE**
1101 E University Ave.
Fresno, CA 93741-0002
Tel: (559)442-4600
E-mail: fcc.admissions@fresnocitycollege.edu
Web Site: www.fresnocitycollege.edu
Description: District-supported, 2-year, coed. Part of California Community College System. Awards certificates, transfer associate, and terminal associate degrees. Founded 1910. Setting: 103-acre urban campus. Total enrollment: 25,511. Student-undergrad faculty ratio is 28:1. 40% 25 or older. Core. Calendar: semesters. Academic remediation for entering students, ESL program, services for LD students, advanced placement, freshman honors college, honors program, summer session for credit, part-time degree program, co-op programs. Off campus study at Reedley College; California State University, Fresno. Study abroad program. ROTC: Army (c), Air Force (c).
Entrance Requirements: Open admission. Options: early admission, deferred admission. Required: high school transcript. Entrance: noncompetitive. Application deadline: rolling. Notification: continuous.
Collegiate Environment: Orientation program. Drama-theater group, choral group, marching band, student-run newspaper. Student services: health clinic, personal-psychological counseling. Campus security: 24-hour emergency response devices and patrols, late night transport-escort service. Fresno City College Library.
Community Environment: See California State University - Fresno.

■ **FRESNO PACIFIC UNIVERSITY**
1717 S Chestnut Ave.
Fresno, CA 93702-4709
Tel: (559)453-2000; Free: 800-660-6089
Fax: (559)453-2007
E-mail: andy.johnson@fresno.edu
Web Site: www.fresno.edu
Description: Independent, comprehensive, coed, affiliated with Mennonite Brethren Church. Awards associate, bachelor's, and master's degrees. Founded 1944. Setting: 50-acre suburban campus with easy access to Fresno. Total enrollment: 3,596. Faculty: 479 (83 full-time, 396 part-time). Student-undergrad faculty ratio is 13:1. 644 applied, 68% were admitted. 25% from top 10% of their high school class, 56% from top quarter, 89% from top half. Full-time: 2,077 students, 71% women, 29% men. Part-time: 362 students, 74% women, 26% men. 3% from out-of-state. 2% American Indian or Alaska Native, non-Hispanic/Latino; 28% Hispanic/Latino; 8% Black or African American, non-Hispanic/Latino; 7% Asian, non-Hispanic/Latino; 0.9% Native Hawaiian or other Pacific Islander, non-Hispanic/Latino; 0.8% international. 10% 25 or older, 45% live on campus, 21% transferred

in. Retention: 83% of full-time freshmen returned the following year. Academic areas with the most degrees conferred: education; business/marketing; liberal arts/general studies. Core. Calendar: semesters. ESL program, services for LD students, advanced placement, accelerated degree program, self-designed majors, honors program, independent study, distance learning, double major, summer session for credit, part-time degree program, adult/continuing education programs, co-op programs and internships, graduate courses open to undergrads. Off campus study at California State University, Fresno; Mennonite Brethren Biblical Seminary; San Joaquin College of Law. Study abroad program.
Entrance Requirements: Options: electronic application, early admission, deferred admission. Required: essay, high school transcript, 1 recommendation, SAT or ACT. Recommended: minimum 3.1 high school GPA. Required for some: interview. Entrance: moderately difficult. SAT Reasoning Test deadline: 7/8. Transfer credits accepted: Yes.
Costs Per Year: Application fee: $40. Comprehensive fee: $41,408 includes full-time tuition ($31,966), mandatory fees ($492), and college room and board ($8950). Full-time tuition and fees vary according to course level, degree level, program, and student level. Room and board charges vary according to board plan and housing facility. Part-time tuition: $1106 per credit. Part-time mandatory fees: $238 per term. Part-time tuition and fees vary according to course level, degree level, program, and student level.
Collegiate Environment: Orientation program. Drama-theater group, choral group, student-run newspaper. Major annual events: Homecoming, M.C.C. Sale. Student services: health clinic, personal-psychological counseling. Campus security: 24-hour emergency response devices and patrols, student patrols, late night transport-escort service, controlled dormitory access, 24-hour monitored closed-circuit security cameras. Hiebert Library.
Community Environment: See California State University Fresno.

■ **FULLERTON COLLEGE**
321 E Chapman Ave.
Fullerton, CA 92832-2095
Tel: (714)992-7000
Web Site: www.fullcoll.edu
Description: District-supported, 2-year, coed. Part of California Community College System. Awards certificates, transfer associate, and terminal associate degrees. Founded 1913. Setting: 79-acre suburban campus with easy access to Los Angeles. Total enrollment: 24,588. Faculty: 939 (352 full-time, 587 part-time). Student-undergrad faculty ratio is 26:1. Students come from 28 states and territories, 1% from out-of-state. 0.6% American Indian or Alaska Native, non-Hispanic/Latino; 57% Hispanic/Latino; 4% Black or African American, non-Hispanic/Latino; 17% Asian, non-Hispanic/Latino. 28% 25 or older. Retention: 61% of full-time freshmen returned the following year. Core. Calendar: semesters. Academic remediation for entering students, ESL program, services for LD students, advanced placement, honors program, summer session for credit, part-time degree program, adult/continuing education programs, co-op programs. Study abroad program. ROTC: Army (c), Naval (c), Air Force (c).
Entrance Requirements: Open admission. Options: electronic application, early admission. Entrance: noncompetitive. Application deadline: rolling.
Costs Per Year: State resident tuition: $1148 full-time, $46 per credit hour part-time. Nonresident tuition: $6010 full-time, $140 per credit hour part-time. Mandatory fees: $24 full-time, $34 per year part-time. Full-time tuition and fees vary according to course load. Part-time tuition and fees vary according to course load.
Collegiate Environment: Drama-theater group, student-run newspaper, radio station. Student services: legal services, health clinic, personal-psychological counseling, women's center. William T. Boyce Library.
Community Environment: See California State University - Fullerton.

■ **GAVILAN COLLEGE**
5055 Santa Teresa Blvd.
Gilroy, CA 95020-9599
Tel: (408)847-1400
Fax: (408)848-4801
Web Site: www.gavilan.edu
Description: District-supported, 2-year, coed. Part of California Community College System. Awards certificates, diplomas, transfer associate, and terminal associate degrees. Founded 1919. Setting: 150-acre rural campus with easy access to San Jose. Total enrollment: 5,267. Faculty: 324 (74 full-time, 250 part-time). Student-undergrad faculty ratio is 30:1. Full-time: 1,767 students, 51% women, 49% men. Part-time: 3,500 students, 52% women, 48% men. Students come from 5 states and territories, 0.1% from out-of-

state. 0.6% American Indian or Alaska Native, non-Hispanic/Latino; 51% Hispanic/Latino; 3% Black or African American, non-Hispanic/Latino; 6% Asian, non-Hispanic/Latino; 0.4% Native Hawaiian or other Pacific Islander, non-Hispanic/Latino. 46% 25 or older, 100% transferred in. Retention: 69% of full-time freshmen returned the following year. Core. Calendar: semesters. Academic remediation for entering students, ESL program, services for LD students, advanced placement, honors program, independent study, distance learning, summer session for credit, part-time degree program, adult/continuing education programs, co-op programs and internships. Study abroad program.

Entrance Requirements: Open admission. Option: international baccalaureate accepted. Entrance: noncompetitive. Application deadline: rolling. Notification: continuous. Transfer credits accepted: Yes.

Collegiate Environment: Orientation program. Drama-theater group, choral group, student-run newspaper. Social organizations: 23 open to all. Most popular organizations: EOPS, Rho Alpha Mu (Honor Society), Science Alliance, TADAA Drama Club, Vets Club. Major annual events: Back to School Week, Science Alive, Career Fair. Student services: health clinic, personal-psychological counseling. Campus security: 24-hour emergency response devices. Gavilan Library. 50 computers available on campus for general student use. A campuswide network can be accessed. Students can access the following: online class registration. Staffed computer lab on campus provides training in use of computers, software, and the Internet.

Community Environment: Gilroy has a population of 45,700 and is located 77 miles south of San Francisco; served by buses and railroads. There are churches, a hospital, a library, and radio station. Gilroy has theatres, parks, civic organizations, and a public swimming pool for recreational activities; nearby are beaches and five state parks.

■ **GLENDALE CAREER COLLEGE**
240 N Brand Blvd., Lower Level
Glendale, CA 91203
Tel: (818)243-1131
Fax: (818)243-7650
Web Site: www.glendalecareer.com
Description: Proprietary, 2-year, coed. Awards certificates, diplomas, transfer associate, and terminal associate degrees.

■ **GLENDALE COMMUNITY COLLEGE**
1500 N Verdugo Rd.
Glendale, CA 91208-2894
Tel: (818)240-1000
Fax: (818)549-9436
E-mail: scombs@glendale.edu
Web Site: www.glendale.edu
Description: District-supported, 2-year, coed. Part of California Community College System. Awards certificates, transfer associate, and terminal associate degrees. Founded 1927. Setting: 119-acre urban campus with easy access to Los Angeles. Total enrollment: 16,781. Student-undergrad faculty ratio is 28:1. 40% 25 or older. Core. Calendar: semesters. Academic remediation for entering students, ESL program, services for LD students, advanced placement, honors program, independent study, distance learning, summer session for credit, part-time degree program, adult/continuing education programs, co-op programs and internships. Study abroad program.

Entrance Requirements: Open admission. Options: electronic application, early admission, deferred admission. Recommended: high school transcript. Entrance: noncompetitive. Application deadline: rolling.

Collegiate Environment: Orientation program. Drama-theater group, choral group, student-run newspaper. Student services: health clinic, personal-psychological counseling. Campus security: student patrols, late night transport-escort service. Glendale Community College Library.

■ **GNOMON SCHOOL OF VISUAL EFFECTS**
1015 N Cahuenga Blvd.
Ste. 54301
Hollywood, CA 90038
Tel: (323)466-6663
Description: Proprietary, 4-year, coed.

■ **GOLDEN GATE UNIVERSITY**
536 Mission St.
San Francisco, CA 94105-2968
Tel: (415)442-7000; Free: 800-448-3381

Fax: (415)442-7807
E-mail: info@ggu.edu
Web Site: www.ggu.edu
Description: Independent, university, coed. Awards associate, bachelor's, master's, and doctoral degrees. Founded 1901. Setting: urban campus with easy access to San Francisco Bay Area. Endowment: $29.8 million. Educational spending for the previous fiscal year: $7600 per student. Total enrollment: 2,685. Faculty: 489 (30 full-time, 459 part-time). Student-undergrad faculty ratio is 16:1. Full-time: 231 students, 29% women, 71% men. Part-time: 244 students, 57% women, 43% men. Students come from 14 states and territories, 6% from out-of-state. 12% American Indian or Alaska Native, non-Hispanic/Latino; 16% Hispanic/Latino; 0.6% Black or African American, non-Hispanic/Latino; 2% Asian, non-Hispanic/Latino; 26% Native Hawaiian or other Pacific Islander, non-Hispanic/Latino; 2% international. 90% 25 or older, 96% transferred in. Retention: 50% of full-time freshmen returned the following year. Academic areas with the most degrees conferred: business/marketing; computer and information sciences. Core. Calendar: trimesters. Academic remediation for entering students, ESL program, advanced placement, accelerated degree program, distance learning, summer session for credit, part-time degree program, adult/continuing education programs, internships, graduate courses open to undergrads. Off campus study at The San Francisco Consortium.

Entrance Requirements: Options: electronic application, deferred admission, international baccalaureate accepted. Required: high school transcript, minimum 2 high school GPA. Recommended: essay, minimum 3 high school GPA. Required for some: minimum 3.2 high school GPA, interview. Entrance: moderately difficult. Application deadline: rolling. Notification: continuous. Transfer credits accepted: Yes.

Collegiate Environment: Student-run newspaper. Social organizations: 16 open to all. Most popular organizations: American Marketing Association, Korean Student Association, Japanese Student Association, Thai Student Association, Computing Society. Major annual events: International Cultural Celebration Day, Welcome Party, Farewell party. Student services: personal-psychological counseling. Campus security: late night transport-escort service. Golden Gate University Library plus 1 other. Books: 43,127 (physical), 15,700 (digital/electronic); Serial titles: 55,000 (digital/electronic); Databases: 116. Weekly public service hours: 90; students can reserve study rooms. Operations spending for the previous fiscal year: $599,634. 40 computers available on campus for general student use. Computer purchase/lease plans available. A campuswide network can be accessed. Students can access the following: online class registration. Staffed computer lab on campus provides training in use of computers, software, and the Internet.

Community Environment: See San Francisco State University.

■ **GOLDEN WEST COLLEGE**
PO Box 2748, 15744 Golden W St.
Huntington Beach, CA 92647-2748
Tel: (714)892-7711
Web Site: www.goldenwestcollege.edu
Description: District-supported, 2-year, coed. Part of Coast Community College District System. Awards certificates, transfer associate, and terminal associate degrees. Founded 1966. Setting: 122-acre suburban campus with easy access to Los Angeles. Endowment: $7.6 million. Educational spending for the previous fiscal year: $2458 per student. Total enrollment: 12,394. Faculty: 534 (128 full-time, 406 part-time). Student-undergrad faculty ratio is 33:1. 11,210 applied, 100% were admitted. Full-time: 4,394 students, 48% women, 52% men. Part-time: 8,000 students, 55% women, 45% men. 1% from out-of-state. 0.3% American Indian or Alaska Native, non-Hispanic/Latino; 32% Hispanic/Latino; 2% Black or African American, non-Hispanic/Latino; 28% Asian, non-Hispanic/Latino; 0.5% Native Hawaiian or other Pacific Islander, non-Hispanic/Latino; 2% international. 29% 25 or older. Retention: 71% of full-time freshmen returned the following year. Core. Calendar: semesters plus summer session. Academic remediation for entering students, ESL program, services for LD students, advanced placement, self-designed majors, honors program, independent study, distance learning, summer session for credit, part-time degree program, external degree program, adult/continuing education programs, co-op programs and internships. Study abroad program. ROTC: Air Force (c).

Entrance Requirements: Open admission except for nursing program. Options: electronic application, early admission. Recommended: high school transcript. Required for some: essay. Entrance: noncompetitive. Application deadline: rolling. Notification: continuous.

Collegiate Environment: Orientation program. Drama-theater group, choral

group, student-run newspaper. Major annual events: College Transfer Day, Gold Rush Days. Student services: legal services, health clinic, personal-psychological counseling. Campus security: 24-hour emergency response devices and patrols, late night transport-escort service. Golden West College Library plus 1 other. Weekly public service hours: 48; students can reserve study rooms. Operations spending for the previous fiscal year: $1.2 million. 1,546 computers available on campus for general student use. Computer purchase/lease plans available. A campuswide network can be accessed. Students can access the following: online class registration. Staffed computer lab on campus provides training in use of computers, software, and the Internet.

Community Environment: Huntington Beach is located in the northern coastal region of Orange County, which is 35 miles southeast of Los Angeles. The climate is moderate with a mean yearly temperature of 70 degrees. All major transportation facilities available. Eight miles of the finest, safest beach in California is located here. The city has three public golf courses and parks for recreational activities. This is one of the fastest growing cities in the west.

■ **GRACE MISSION UNIVERSITY**
1645 W Valencia Dr.
Fullerton, CA 92833
Tel: (714)525-0088
Web Site: www.gm.edu
Description: Independent, comprehensive, coed. Awards bachelor's and master's degrees.

■ **GROSSMONT COLLEGE**
8800 Grossmont College Dr.
El Cajon, CA 92020-1799
Tel: (619)644-7000
Fax: (619)644-7922
Web Site: www.grossmont.edu
Description: District-supported, 2-year, coed. Part of California Community College System. Awards certificates, transfer associate, and terminal associate degrees. Founded 1961. Setting: 135-acre suburban campus with easy access to San Diego. Total enrollment: 20,335. Student-undergrad faculty ratio is 29:1. 35% 25 or older. Core. Calendar: semesters. Academic remediation for entering students, ESL program, services for LD students, advanced placement, self-designed majors, honors program, summer session for credit, part-time degree program, adult/continuing education programs, co-op programs and internships. ROTC: Army (c), Air Force (c).
Entrance Requirements: Open admission. Option: early admission. Entrance: noncompetitive. Application deadline: 8/12. Notification: continuous until 8/12.
Collegiate Environment: Drama-theater group, choral group, student-run newspaper, radio station. Student services: legal services, health clinic, personal-psychological counseling. Campus security: 24-hour emergency response devices, student patrols, late night transport-escort service. Lewis F. Smith Learning Resource Center.
Community Environment: El Cajon is situated east of San Diego in a suburban community with a Mediterranean climate. Gillespie Airport and buses serve the area. The County Branch Library is located here; there are churches of all denominations. Employment is available through the California Department of Employment which is located on the Grossmont college campus. There are recreational facilities at both the beaches and in the nearby mountain area. Annual festivities include the "Mother Goose Parade.".

■ **GURNICK ACADEMY OF MEDICAL ARTS**
2121 S El Camino Real, Bldg. C 2000
San Mateo, CA 94403
Tel: (650)685-6616
Web Site: www.gurnick.edu
Description: Proprietary, primarily 2-year, coed. Awards certificates, diplomas, transfer associate, terminal associate, and bachelor's degrees.

■ **HARTNELL COLLEGE**
411 Central Ave.
Salinas, CA 93901
Tel: (831)755-6700
Web Site: www.hartnell.edu
Description: District-supported, 2-year, coed. Part of California Community College System. Awards certificates, transfer associate, and terminal associ-

ate degrees. Founded 1920. Setting: 50-acre small town campus with easy access to San Jose. Total enrollment: 10,451. Student-undergrad faculty ratio is 35:1. 46% 25 or older. Core. Calendar: semesters. Academic remediation for entering students, ESL program, services for LD students, self-designed majors, honors program, summer session for credit, part-time degree program, adult/continuing education programs, co-op programs. Study abroad program.
Entrance Requirements: Open admission except for allied health programs. Options: early admission, deferred admission. Required for some: high school transcript. Entrance: noncompetitive. Application deadline: rolling. Notification: continuous.
Collegiate Environment: Drama-theater group, choral group, student-run newspaper. Student services: women's center. Campus security: 24-hour emergency response devices, student patrols, late night transport-escort service. Hartnell College Library plus 1 other.
Community Environment: Population 146,400. Salinas is the county seat of Monterey County, 106 miles south of San Francisco on Highway 101. Southern Pacific Railroad, Greyhound bus and United Airlines serve the area. The Santa Lucia Mountains are to the west of Salinas and the Gabilan foothills to the east. Agriculture is the chief factor of economy in Salinas with new industries designed to take advantage of the abundant harvest. The climate is comfortable, the average temperature being 57 degrees. Salinas has a great number of churches, YMCA, theatres, community concert association, Monterey County symphony, a variety of civic, fraternal and veteran's organizations. John Steinbeck was born here. Part-time employment opportunities for students available in nearby recreational areas, agriculture, industrial and commercial firms. The recreational facilities include nine municipal recreation centers, a municipal golf course, private country clubs, the Monterey Peninsula playland area, the famous white sandy beaches of Carmel, a 20-minute drive away, flying clubs, a ski club, and many hobby clubs. This is the location of the oldest and largest four-day California Rodeo.

■ **HARVEY MUDD COLLEGE**
301 Platt Blvd.
Claremont, CA 91711-5994
Tel: (909)621-8000
Fax: (909)621-8360
Web Site: www.hmc.edu
Description: Independent, 4-year, coed. Part of The Claremont Colleges. Awards bachelor's degrees. Founded 1955. Setting: 33-acre suburban campus with easy access to Los Angeles. Endowment: $298.9 million. Research spending for the previous fiscal year: $3.3 million. Educational spending for the previous fiscal year: $33,772 per student. Total enrollment: 844. Faculty: 115 (106 full-time, 9 part-time). Student-undergrad faculty ratio is 8:1. 4,078 applied, 15% were admitted. 90% from top 10% of their high school class, 100% from top quarter, 100% from top half. Full-time: 844 students, 48% women, 52% men. 57% from out-of-state. 0.5% American Indian or Alaska Native, non-Hispanic/Latino; 18% Hispanic/Latino; 4% Black or African American, non-Hispanic/Latino; 17% Asian, non-Hispanic/Latino; 0.5% Native Hawaiian or other Pacific Islander, non-Hispanic/Latino; 10% international. 1% 25 or older, 1% transferred in. Retention: 98% of full-time freshmen returned the following year. Academic areas with the most degrees conferred: engineering; physical sciences; interdisciplinary studies. Core. Calendar: semesters. Services for LD students, self-designed majors, double major, internships. Off campus study at The Claremont Colleges. Study abroad program. ROTC: Army (c), Air Force (c).
Entrance Requirements: Options: electronic application, early admission, early decision, deferred admission. Required: essay, high school transcript, 3 recommendations, SAT or ACT, SAT Subject Tests. Recommended: interview. Entrance: most difficult. Application deadlines: 1/5, 11/15 for early decision plan 1, 1/5 for early decision plan 2. Notification: 4/1, 12/15 for early decision plan 1, 2/15 for early decision plan 2. SAT Reasoning Test deadline: 2/15. SAT Subject Test deadline: 2/15. Transfer credits accepted: Yes. Applicants placed on waiting list: 510. Wait-listed applicants offered admission: 63. Early decision applicants: 504. Early decision applicants admitted: 81.
Costs Per Year: Application fee: $70. One-time mandatory fee: $250. Comprehensive fee: $74,753 includes full-time tuition ($56,331), mandatory fees ($295), and college room and board ($18,127). College room only: $9888. Room and board charges vary according to board plan. Part-time tuition: $1760 per unit. Part-time tuition varies according to course load.
Collegiate Environment: Orientation program. Drama-theater group, choral group, student-run newspaper, radio station. Most popular organizations: Claremont Colleges Ballroom Dance Company, Science Bus, Society of

Women Engineers (SWE), Intervarsity Christian Fellowship, Gonzo Unicycle Madness (Unicycle Club). Major annual events: 5-Class Competition, Noisy Minutes, Claremont Colleges Humans vs. Zombies. Student services: health clinic, personal-psychological counseling, women's center. Campus security: 24-hour emergency response devices and patrols, late night transport-escort service, controlled dormitory access. Claremont Colleges Library plus 1 other.

■ HEALTHCARE CAREER COLLEGE

8527 Alondra Blvd., No.174
Paramount, CA 90723
Tel: (562)804-1239
Description: Proprietary, 2-year, coed.

■ HOLY NAMES UNIVERSITY

3500 Mountain Blvd.
Oakland, CA 94619-1699
Tel: (510)436-1000; Free: 800-430-1321
Fax: (510)436-1325
E-mail: admissions@hnu.edu
Web Site: www.hnu.edu
Description: Independent Roman Catholic, comprehensive, coed. Awards bachelor's and master's degrees and post-master's certificates. Founded 1868. Setting: 60-acre urban campus with easy access to San Francisco. Educational spending for the previous fiscal year: $8992 per student. Total enrollment: 884. Faculty: 169 (51 full-time, 118 part-time). Student-undergrad faculty ratio is 8:1. 2,713 applied, 53% were admitted. Full-time: 543 students, 62% women, 38% men. Part-time: 48 students, 83% women, 17% men. 7% from out-of-state. 0.2% American Indian or Alaska Native, non-Hispanic/Latino; 43% Hispanic/Latino; 18% Black or African American, non-Hispanic/Latino; 9% Asian, non-Hispanic/Latino; 2% Native Hawaiian or other Pacific Islander, non-Hispanic/Latino; 3% international. 19% 25 or older, 51% live on campus. Retention: 82% of full-time freshmen returned the following year. Academic areas with the most degrees conferred: health professions and related sciences; business/marketing; psychology. Core. Calendar: semesters. Academic remediation for entering students, ESL program, services for LD students, advanced placement, accelerated degree program, self-designed majors, honors program, independent study, distance learning, double major, summer session for credit, part-time degree program, adult/continuing education programs, internships, graduate courses open to undergrads. Study abroad program. ROTC: Army (c), Air Force (c).
Entrance Requirements: Options: electronic application, deferred admission, international baccalaureate accepted. Required: essay, high school transcript, 1 recommendation, minimum 1 recommendation, SAT or ACT. Required for some: interview. Entrance: moderately difficult. Application deadline: rolling. Notification: continuous.
Costs Per Year: Application fee: $20. Comprehensive fee: $52,506 includes full-time tuition ($38,800), mandatory fees ($516), and college room and board ($13,190). College room only: $6812. Full-time tuition and fees vary according to course level, course load, degree level, program, and reciprocity agreements. Room and board charges vary according to board plan and housing facility. Part-time tuition: $1331 per unit. Part-time mandatory fees: $258 per term. Part-time tuition and fees vary according to course level, course load, degree level, program, and reciprocity agreements.
Collegiate Environment: Orientation program. Drama-theater group, choral group. Social organizations: 10 open to all. Most popular organizations: Drama Club, Latinos Unidos, Black Student Union, Biology Club, Hiking Club. Major annual events: CORE Festival, Founder' Day, Convocation. Student services: personal-psychological counseling. Campus security: 24-hour emergency response devices, late night transport-escort service, controlled dormitory access, 24-hour security main gate. Cushing Library. Books: 41,811 (physical), 137,046 (digital/electronic); Databases: 49. Students can reserve study rooms. Operations spending for the previous fiscal year: $520,278. 92 computers available on campus for general student use. A campuswide network can be accessed from student residence rooms. Students can access the following: online class registration. Staffed computer lab on campus (open 24 hours a day) provides training in use of computers, software, and the Internet.
Community Environment: The College is located in the Oakland hills, overlooking San Francisco Bay and San Francisco itself. The campus is within 15-45 minutes of all the rich cultural, recreational, and sports activities of San Francisco, Berkeley and Oakland. Easy day trips can be made to the wine country, beaches, ski areas and National Parks.

■ HOMESTEAD SCHOOLS

23844 Hawthorne Blvd., Ste. 200
Torrance, CA 90505
Tel: (310)791-9975
Description: Independent, upper-level, coed.

■ HOPE INTERNATIONAL UNIVERSITY

2500 E Nutwood Ave.
Fullerton, CA 92831-3138
Tel: (714)879-3901; Free: 866-722-HOPE
Fax: (714)526-0231
Web Site: www.hiu.edu
Description: Independent, comprehensive, coed, affiliated with Christian Churches and Churches of Christ. Awards associate, bachelor's, and master's degrees. Founded 1928. Setting: 16-acre suburban campus with easy access to Los Angeles. Total enrollment: 1,162. Faculty: 234 (40 full-time, 194 part-time). Student-undergrad faculty ratio is 9:1. 786 applied, 28% were admitted. 10% from top 10% of their high school class, 35% from top quarter, 61% from top half. Full-time: 582 students, 57% women, 43% men. Part-time: 144 students, 56% women, 44% men. 7% from out-of-state. 1% American Indian or Alaska Native, non-Hispanic/Latino; 29% Hispanic/Latino; 8% Black or African American, non-Hispanic/Latino; 4% Asian, non-Hispanic/Latino; 0.6% Native Hawaiian or other Pacific Islander, non-Hispanic/Latino; 2% international. 8% 25 or older, 48% live on campus, 17% transferred in. Retention: 72% of full-time freshmen returned the following year. Academic areas with the most degrees conferred: liberal arts/general studies; family and consumer sciences; theology and religious vocations; business/marketing. Core. Calendar: 4-1-4. Academic remediation for entering students, ESL program, services for LD students, advanced placement, independent study, distance learning, double major, part-time degree program, adult/continuing education programs, internships, graduate courses open to undergrads. Off campus study. Study abroad program. ROTC: Army (c).
Entrance Requirements: Options: electronic application, international baccalaureate accepted. Required: essay, high school transcript, minimum 2.5 high school GPA, 2 recommendations, rank in upper 50% of high school class, SAT or ACT. Required for some: interview. Entrance: moderately difficult. Application deadlines: rolling, rolling for nonresidents. Notification: continuous, continuous for nonresidents. SAT Reasoning Test deadline: 8/1. SAT Subject Test deadline: 8/1. Transfer credits accepted: Yes.
Costs Per Year: Application fee: $40. Comprehensive fee: $43,890 includes full-time tuition ($32,250), mandatory fees ($1150), and college room and board ($10,490). College room only: $5000. Full-time tuition and fees vary according to course level, course load, degree level, location, program, and reciprocity agreements. Room and board charges vary according to board plan. Part-time tuition: $1465 per credit hour. Part-time tuition varies according to course level, course load, degree level, location, program, and reciprocity agreements.
Collegiate Environment: Orientation program. Drama-theater group, choral group, student-run newspaper. Most popular organizations: Campus Ministries, International Student Organization, Musical Theater, Student Government, Student Publications. Major annual events: Happy House (Halloween event for neighborhood children and families), Spring Fever. Student services: personal-psychological counseling. Campus security: 24-hour emergency response devices and patrols, late night transport-escort service, controlled dormitory access. Darling Library.
Community Environment: See California State University - Fullerton.

■ HUMBOLDT STATE UNIVERSITY

1 Harpst St.
Arcata, CA 95521-8299
Tel: (707)826-3011; Free: 866-850-9556
Fax: (707)826-6194
E-mail: hsuinfo@humboldt.edu
Web Site: www.humboldt.edu
Description: State-supported, comprehensive, coed. Part of California State University System. Awards bachelor's and master's degrees and post-master's certificates. Founded 1913. Setting: 161-acre rural campus. Total enrollment: 7,774. Faculty: 548 (239 full-time, 309 part-time). Student-undergrad faculty ratio is 22:1. 10,957 applied, 75% were admitted. 5% from top 10% of their high school class, 31% from top quarter, 71% from top half. Full-time: 6,700 students, 57% women, 43% men. Part-time: 495 students, 49% women, 51% men. Students come from 51 states and territories, 33 other countries, 6% from out-of-state. 1% American Indian or Alaska Native,

non-Hispanic/Latino; 35% Hispanic/Latino; 4% Black or African American, non-Hispanic/Latino; 3% Asian, non-Hispanic/Latino; 0.3% Native Hawaiian or other Pacific Islander, non-Hispanic/Latino; 1% international. 25% 25 or older, 26% live on campus, 14% transferred in. Retention: 71% of full-time freshmen returned the following year. Academic areas with the most degrees conferred: natural resources/environmental science; biological/life sciences; social sciences. Core. Calendar: semesters. Academic remediation for entering students, ESL program, services for LD students, advanced placement, self-designed majors, honors program, independent study, distance learning, double major, summer session for credit, part-time degree program, adult/continuing education programs, co-op programs and internships, graduate courses open to undergrads. Off campus study at members of the National Student Exchange, California State University System. Study abroad program.

Entrance Requirements: Options: electronic application, deferred admission, international baccalaureate accepted. Required: high school transcript, minimum 2 high school GPA. Required for some: SAT or ACT. Entrance: minimally difficult. Notification: continuous. Preference given to state residents. SAT Reasoning Test deadline: 1/15. SAT Subject Test deadline: 1/15. Transfer credits accepted: Yes.

Costs Per Year: Application fee: $55. State resident tuition: $5742 full-time, $3330 per term part-time. Nonresident tuition: $17,622 full-time, $396 per credit part-time. Mandatory fees: $1934 full-time, $1492 part-time. College room and board: $13,562. College room only: $6216.

Collegiate Environment: Orientation program. Drama-theater group, choral group, marching band, student-run newspaper, radio station. Social organizations: 187 open to all; national fraternities, national sororities, local sororities; 1% of eligible men and 1% of eligible women are members. Most popular organizations: Bicycle Learning Center, Campus Center for Appropriate Technology (CCAT), Youth Educational Services, HOLA, MECHA. Major annual events: Homecoming, Dialogue on Race (seminars and guest speakers), Film Festival. Student services: health clinic, personal-psychological counseling, women's center. Campus security: 24-hour emergency response devices and patrols, late night transport-escort service, controlled dormitory access. 2,025 college housing spaces available; 2,005 were occupied in 2018-19. Freshmen guaranteed college housing. Option: coed housing available. Humbolot State University Library. Books: 487,338 (physical), 165,816 (digital/electronic); Serial titles: 34,235 (physical), 190 (digital/electronic); Databases: 89. Weekly public service hours: 100; students can reserve study rooms. 1,098 computers available on campus for general student use. Computer purchase/lease plans available. A campuswide network can be accessed from student residence rooms and from off campus. Students can access the following: online class registration. Staffed computer lab on campus.

Community Environment: Arcata, population 16,900, is located on the north shore of Humboldt Bay in northwestern California with an unrestricted panorama of mountains, bay, dairy and farm lands, sand dunes, and the Pacific Ocean. It is eight miles north of Eureka, and 275 miles north of San Francisco. Industry includes lumbering, manufacturing of wood products, tourism and dairy products. Humboldt Bay region climate is moist, but stimulating, with no extremes of heat or cold. Summer and fall are considered particularly delightful seasons. Buses and airlines serve the area. The city has a library, churches and the usual service clubs. Recreational opportunities include river rafting, kayaking, backpacking, hunting, trout fishing in mountain streams, salmon fishing in Humboldt and Trinidad Bays, and deep sea fishing. There is an Azalea Reserve, three miles north.

■ **HUMPHREYS UNIVERSITY**
6650 Inglewood Ave.
Stockton, CA 95207-3896
Tel: (209)478-0800
Fax: (209)478-8721
Web Site: www.humphreys.edu

Description: Independent, comprehensive, coed. Awards associate, bachelor's, master's, and doctoral degrees. Founded 1896. Setting: 10-acre suburban campus with easy access to San Francisco. Total enrollment: 756. 71% 25 or older. Core. Calendar: quarters. Academic remediation for entering students, advanced placement, accelerated degree program, self-designed majors, summer session for credit, part-time degree program, adult/continuing education programs, co-op programs and internships.

Entrance Requirements: Open admission. Options: early admission, deferred admission. Required: high school transcript, minimum 2 high school GPA. Recommended: interview. Entrance: noncompetitive. Application deadline: rolling.

Costs Per Year: Application fee: $35. Tuition: $14,292 full-time, $397 per credit hour part-time. Full-time tuition varies according to course load. Part-time tuition varies according to course load.

Collegiate Environment: Most popular organizations: Business Club, Paralegal Club, Student Council, Collegiate Secretaries International. Major annual events: Hot Dog Day (quarterly BBQ), Annual Christmas Dinner, Students Versus Staff Softball. Campus security: 24-hour patrols, late night transport-escort service. Humphreys College Library plus 1 other. 40 computers available on campus for general student use. Staffed computer lab on campus.

Community Environment: See University of the Pacific.

■ **IMPERIAL VALLEY COLLEGE**
380 E Aten Rd.
Imperial, CA 92251-0158
Tel: (760)352-8320
Web Site: www.imperial.edu

Description: District-supported, 2-year, coed. Part of California Community College System. Awards certificates, transfer associate, and terminal associate degrees. Founded 1922. Setting: 160-acre rural campus. Research spending for the previous fiscal year: $154,660. Total enrollment: 7,828. Faculty: 283. Student-undergrad faculty ratio is 28:1. 1,724 applied, 100% were admitted. 0.1% American Indian or Alaska Native, non-Hispanic/Latino; 91% Hispanic/Latino; 1% Black or African American, non-Hispanic/Latino; 0.6% Asian, non-Hispanic/Latino. 31% 25 or older. Calendar: semesters. Academic remediation for entering students, ESL program, services for LD students, advanced placement, accelerated degree program, self-designed majors, distance learning, double major, summer session for credit, part-time degree program, adult/continuing education programs.

Entrance Requirements: Open admission. Option: electronic application. Recommended: high school transcript. Required for some: high school transcript. Application deadline: rolling. Notification: continuous.

Collegiate Environment: Orientation program. Drama-theater group, choral group, student-run newspaper. Social organizations: 29 open to all. Most popular organizations: Student Support Services Club, Pre-School Mothers, Care Club, Christian Club, Nursing Club. Major annual events: Welcome Back BBQ, Career Fair, Health Fair. Student services: health clinic, personal-psychological counseling. Campus security: student patrols, emergency phone poles on campus. Spencer Library. Databases: 45. Weekly public service hours: 57; students can reserve study rooms. Operations spending for the previous fiscal year: $692,180. 235 computers available on campus for general student use. A campuswide network can be accessed from student residence rooms and from off campus. Students can access the following: online class registration. Staffed computer lab on campus provides training in use of computers and the Internet.

Community Environment: Imperial is in the southern desert area of California known as the Imperial Valley. It has a very dry climate. The Chocolate Mountains are separated from Imperial by a ribbon of sand dunes. Buses and airlines serve the area. The surrounding Imperial Valley is a large and abundant agricultural area. There are six small cities in surrounding area that provide additional employment opportunities. The annual midwinter fair and the Christmas Parade are here at Imperial.

■ **INSTITUTE OF TECHNOLOGY**
564 W Herndon Ave.
Clovis, CA 93612
Tel: (559)297-4500
Web Site: www.iot.edu

Description: Proprietary, 2-year, coed. Awards certificates, transfer associate, and terminal associate degrees.

■ **INTERIOR DESIGNERS INSTITUTE**
1061 Camelback Rd.
Newport Beach, CA 92660
Tel: (949)675-4451
Fax: (949)759-0667
Web Site: www.idi.edu

Description: Proprietary, comprehensive, coed. Awards associate, bachelor's, and master's degrees. Founded 1984. Setting: 1-acre suburban campus with easy access to Los Angeles, San Diego. Total enrollment: 468. 67% 25 or older. Part-time degree program.

Entrance Requirements: Required: high school transcript.

Collegiate Environment: Social organizations: ASID, IIDA student chapters. Main library plus 1 other.

■ **INTERNATIONAL SPORTS SCIENCES ASSOCIATION**
1015 Mark Ave.
Carpinteria, CA 93013
Description: Proprietary, 2-year, coed.

■ **IRVINE VALLEY COLLEGE**
5500 Irvine Ctr. Dr.
Irvine, CA 92618
Tel: (949)451-5100
Fax: (949)559-3443
Web Site: www.ivc.edu
Description: District-supported, 2-year, coed. Part of Saddleback Community College District. Awards certificates, transfer associate, and terminal associate degrees. Founded 1979. Setting: 20-acre suburban campus with easy access to Los Angeles. Total enrollment: 10,511. Faculty: 344 (94 full-time, 250 part-time). 55% 25 or older. Core. Calendar: semesters. Academic remediation for entering students, ESL program, services for LD students, advanced placement, summer session for credit, part-time degree program, adult/continuing education programs, co-op programs.
Entrance Requirements: Open admission. Option: early admission. Entrance: noncompetitive. Application deadline: rolling. Notification: continuous.
Collegiate Environment: Drama-theater group, student-run newspaper. Student services: health clinic, personal-psychological counseling, women's center. Campus security: late night transport-escort service. Irvine Valley College Library. 125 computers available on campus for general student use. Staffed computer lab on campus.

■ **JOHN F. KENNEDY UNIVERSITY**
100 Ellinwood Way
Pleasant Hill, CA 94523-4817
Tel: (925)969-3300; Free: 800-696-JFKU
Fax: (925)254-6964
Web Site: www.jfku.edu
Description: Independent, upper-level, coed. Administratively affiliated with National University System. Awards bachelor's, master's, and doctoral degrees. Founded 1964. Setting: 5-acre suburban campus with easy access to San Francisco. Endowment: $1.5 million. Educational spending for the previous fiscal year: $5881 per student. Total enrollment: 1,580. Faculty: 237. Student-undergrad faculty ratio is 8:1. Full-time: 54 students, 57% women, 43% men. Part-time: 233 students, 78% women, 22% men. 89% 25 or older, 7% transferred in. Academic areas with the most degrees conferred: psychology; law/legal studies; business/marketing. Core. Calendar: quarters semesters for law school. Services for LD students, advanced placement, self-designed majors, independent study, summer session for credit, part-time degree program, adult/continuing education programs, graduate courses open to undergrads. Off campus study at University of California, Berkeley, California State University, Hayward, Contra Costa College, Laney College.
Collegiate Environment: Student services: personal-psychological counseling. Campus security: late night transport-escort service. Robert M. Fisher Library plus 1 other. Operations spending for the previous fiscal year: $1.4 million. 50 computers available on campus for general student use. Students can access the following: online class registration. Staffed computer lab on campus.
Community Environment: Orinda, population 18,259, is located just east of the Oakland-Berkeley Hills. Oakland, 10 miles away, and San Francisco, 20 miles, are easily accessed. Climate is mild the year round, with the average temperature 65-70 degrees.

■ **JOHN PAUL THE GREAT CATHOLIC UNIVERSITY**
155 W Grand Ave.
Escondido, CA 92025
Tel: (858)653-6740
E-mail: mharold@jpcatholic.com
Web Site: www.jpcatholic.edu
Description: Independent, comprehensive, coed, affiliated with Roman Catholic Church. Awards bachelor's and master's degrees. Founded 2006. Setting: 3-acre urban campus with easy access to San Diego. Total enrollment: 308. Faculty: 41 (8 full-time, 33 part-time). Student-undergrad faculty ratio is 15:1. 220 applied, 90% were admitted. 15% from top 10% of their high school class, 27% from top quarter, 67% from top half. Full-time: 268 students, 44% women, 56% men. Part-time: 18 students, 28% women, 72% men. Students come from 35 states and territories, 4 other countries, 48% from out-of-state. 26% Hispanic/Latino; 2% Black or African American, non-Hispanic/Latino; 3% Asian, non-Hispanic/Latino; 0.7% Native Hawaiian or other Pacific Islander, non-Hispanic/Latino; 3% international. 9% 25 or older, 77% live on campus, 9% transferred in. Retention: 80% of full-time freshmen returned the following year. Academic areas with the most degrees conferred: visual and performing arts; business/marketing. Core. Calendar: quarters. Advanced placement, independent study, distance learning, double major, summer session for credit, part-time degree program, internships, graduate courses open to undergrads. Study abroad program.
Entrance Requirements: Options: electronic application, deferred admission. Required: essay, high school transcript, minimum 2.6 high school GPA. Recommended: interview. Required for some: SAT or ACT. Entrance: moderately difficult. Application deadline: rolling. Notification: continuous. Transfer credits accepted: Yes.
Costs Per Year: Application fee: $50. Tuition: $26,100 full-time, $700 per credit part-time. Mandatory fees: $900 full-time. College room only: $7710. Tuition guaranteed not to increase for student's term of enrollment.
Collegiate Environment: Orientation program. Drama-theater group, choral group, student-run newspaper. Social organizations: 7 open to all; Residential Households; 30% of eligible men and 30% of eligible women are members. Most popular organizations: Student government, Knights of Columbus, Flag football, Swing dance club, Gaming club. Major annual events: Coffee House, Film Festivals, Winter Formal. Student services: personal-psychological counseling. Campus security: student patrols. 229 college housing spaces available; 219 were occupied in 2018-19. Freshmen guaranteed college housing. On-campus residence required through senior year. Options: men-only, women-only housing available. John Paul the Great Catholic University Library. Books: 21,325 (physical); Serial titles: 1 (physical), 1 (digital/electronic); Databases: 1. 35 computers available on campus for general student use. A computer is required for all students. A campuswide network can be accessed.

■ **LA SIERRA UNIVERSITY**
4500 Riverwalk Pky.
Riverside, CA 92505
Tel: (951)785-2000; Free: 800-874-5587
Fax: (951)785-2901
E-mail: iteheda@lasierra.edu
Web Site: www.lasierra.edu
Description: Independent Seventh-day Adventist, comprehensive, coed. Part of Seventh-Day Adventist Education System. Awards bachelor's, master's, and doctoral degrees and post-master's certificates. Founded 1922. Setting: 150-acre suburban campus with easy access to Los Angeles. System endowment: $17.2 million. Research spending for the previous fiscal year: $91,214. Educational spending for the previous fiscal year: $8751 per student. Total enrollment: 2,356. Faculty: 118 (94 full-time, 24 part-time). Student-undergrad faculty ratio is 15:1. 4,688 applied, 49% were admitted. 13% from top 10% of their high school class, 42% from top quarter, 81% from top half. Full-time: 1,647 students, 60% women, 40% men. Part-time: 195 students, 56% women, 44% men. Students come from 48 states and territories, 138 other countries, 11% from out-of-state. 0.3% American Indian or Alaska Native, non-Hispanic/Latino; 47% Hispanic/Latino; 7% Black or African American, non-Hispanic/Latino; 17% Asian, non-Hispanic/Latino; 1% Native Hawaiian or other Pacific Islander, non-Hispanic/Latino; 11% international. 9% 25 or older, 25% live on campus, 8% transferred in. Retention: 89% of full-time freshmen returned the following year. Academic areas with the most degrees conferred: homeland security, law enforcement, firefighting, and protective services; business/marketing; biological/life sciences. Core. Calendar: quarters. Academic remediation for entering students, ESL program, services for LD students, advanced placement, accelerated degree program, self-designed majors, honors program, independent study, distance learning, double major, summer session for credit, part-time degree program, adult/continuing education programs, internships, graduate courses open to undergrads. Off campus study at Loma Linda University. Study abroad program.
Entrance Requirements: Options: electronic application, deferred admission, international baccalaureate accepted. Required: high school transcript, minimum 2 high school GPA, Eligibility Index Table (combination of GPA and test scores), SAT or ACT. Required for some: essay, 1 recommendation, interview. Entrance: minimally difficult. Application deadline: 2/1. Notification: continuous. Preference given to Seventh-day Adventists. Transfer credits accepted: Yes.
Costs Per Year: Application fee: $0. Comprehensive fee: $41,985 includes

full-time tuition ($32,580), mandatory fees ($990), and college room and board ($8415). College room only: $4628. Part-time tuition: $905 per quarter hour.

Collegiate Environment: Orientation program. Drama-theater group, choral group, student-run newspaper. Social organizations: 29 open to all. Most popular organizations: Pre Dentistry, Pre Med, Enactus (SIFE), International Club, Black Student Association. Major annual events: Christmas Candlelight Concert, Festival of Nations, Annual Convocation. Student services: health clinic, personal-psychological counseling, women's center. Campus security: 24-hour emergency response devices and patrols, student patrols, late night transport-escort service, controlled dormitory access. 850 college housing spaces available; 589 were occupied in 2018-19. Freshmen guaranteed college housing. Options: coed, men-only, women-only housing available. University Library plus 1 other. Books: 246,563 (physical), 155,250 (digital/electronic); Serial titles: 610 (physical); Databases: 121. Weekly public service hours: 76; students can reserve study rooms. Operations spending for the previous fiscal year: $1.3 million. 300 computers available on campus for general student use. Computer purchase/lease plans available. A computer is required for all students. A campuswide network can be accessed from student residence rooms and from off campus. Students can access the following: online class registration, student portals. Staffed computer lab on campus provides training in use of computers, software, and the Internet.

Community Environment: See University of California Riverside.

■ **LAGUNA COLLEGE OF ART & DESIGN**

2222 Laguna Canyon Rd.
Laguna Beach, CA 92651-1136
Tel: (949)376-6000; Free: 800-255-0762
Fax: (949)376-6009
E-mail: mkeyes@lcad.edu
Web Site: www.lcad.edu

Description: Independent, comprehensive, coed. Awards bachelor's and master's degrees. Founded 1962. Setting: 9-acre small town campus with easy access to Los Angeles. Endowment: $1.7 million. Educational spending for the previous fiscal year: $6512 per student. Total enrollment: 612. Faculty: 146 (18 full-time, 128 part-time). Student-undergrad faculty ratio is 12:1. 472 applied, 39% were admitted. 15 National Merit Scholars, 5 class presidents, 12 valedictorians, 31 student government officers. Students come from 32 states and territories, 13 other countries, 42% from out-of-state. 0.5% American Indian or Alaska Native, non-Hispanic/Latino; 19% Hispanic/Latino; 2% Black or African American, non-Hispanic/Latino; 18% Asian, non-Hispanic/Latino; 0.7% Native Hawaiian or other Pacific Islander, non-Hispanic/Latino; 2% international. 22% 25 or older, 11% live on campus. Retention: 97% of full-time freshmen returned the following year. Academic area with the most degrees conferred: visual and performing arts. Core. Calendar: semesters. Services for LD students, independent study, double major, part-time degree program, internships. Off campus study at Art College Exchange, Association of Independent Colleges of Art and Design.

Entrance Requirements: Options: early admission, deferred admission, international baccalaureate accepted. Required: essay, high school transcript, minimum 2.5 high school GPA, portfolio. Recommended: SAT or ACT. Required for some: 2 recommendations, interview. Entrance: very difficult. Application deadline: rolling. Notification: continuous. Transfer credits accepted: Yes.

Costs Per Year: Application fee: $45. Tuition: $30,700 full-time, $1267 per unit part-time. Full-time tuition varies according to course load and degree level. Part-time tuition varies according to course load and degree level. College room only: $10,000.

Collegiate Environment: Orientation program. Social organizations: 20% of eligible men and 20% of eligible women are members. Major annual event: Student Juried Art Exhibition. Student services: personal-psychological counseling. Campus security: 24-hour patrols, late night transport-escort service. Dennis and Leslie Power Library plus 1 other. Weekly public service hours: 54. Operations spending for the previous fiscal year: $170,179. 85 computers available on campus for general student use. A computer is required for all students. A campuswide network can be accessed from student residence rooms. Students can access the following: online class registration. Staffed computer lab on campus provides training in use of software and the Internet.

■ **LAKE TAHOE COMMUNITY COLLEGE**

One College Dr.
South Lake Tahoe, CA 96150-4524

Tel: (530)541-4660
Fax: (530)541-7852
E-mail: admissions@ltcc.edu
Web Site: www.ltcc.edu

Description: District-supported, 2-year, coed. Part of California Community College System. Awards certificates, transfer associate, and terminal associate degrees. Founded 1975. Setting: 164-acre small town campus. Total enrollment: 5,700. Faculty: 200 (41 full-time, 159 part-time). 450 applied, 100% were admitted. Core. Calendar: quarters. Academic remediation for entering students, ESL program, services for LD students, advanced placement, independent study, distance learning, double major, summer session for credit, part-time degree program, co-op programs and internships. Study abroad program.

Entrance Requirements: Open admission. Options: electronic application, early admission. Recommended: high school transcript. Entrance: noncompetitive. Application deadline: rolling. Notification: continuous.

Collegiate Environment: Orientation program. Drama-theater group, choral group. Social organizations: 8 open to all. Most popular organizations: Associated Student Council, Alpha Gamma Sigma, Foreign Language Club, Art Club, Performing Arts League. Major annual events: Welcome Back BBQ, Club Day. Student services: personal-psychological counseling. Campus security: 24-hour emergency response devices, late night transport-escort service. Lake Tahoe Community College Library. Operations spending for the previous fiscal year: $307,421. 135 computers available on campus for general student use. A campuswide network can be accessed. Students can access the following: online class registration. Staffed computer lab on campus.

■ **LANEY COLLEGE**

900 Fallon St.
Oakland, CA 94607-4893
Tel: (510)834-5740
Web Site: www.laney.edu

Description: District-supported, 2-year, coed. Part of Peralta Community College District System. Awards certificates, transfer associate, and terminal associate degrees. Founded 1953. Setting: urban campus with easy access to San Francisco. Research spending for the previous fiscal year: $68,724. Total enrollment: 13,463. Faculty: 451 (118 full-time, 333 part-time). Full-time: 2,424 students, 57% women, 43% men. Part-time: 11,039 students, 58% women, 42% men. 57% 25 or older. Core. Calendar: semesters. Academic remediation for entering students, services for LD students, summer session for credit, part-time degree program, adult/continuing education programs.

Entrance Requirements: Open admission. Option: early admission. Entrance: noncompetitive. Application deadline: rolling.

Collegiate Environment: Drama-theater group, student-run newspaper. Most popular organizations: La Raza Club, African Student Union, Vision Christian Society, Asian/Pacific Islander Club, Vietnamese Student Club. Major annual events: Cinco de Mayo, Black History Month, Multicultural Day. Laney Library. 30 computers available on campus for general student use.

Community Environment: Oakland is the fourth largest city in the state. Located on the mainland side of San Francisco Bay; adjoined on the north by Berkeley; on the south by Alameda and San Leandro. Climate is mild and the average temperature is 65.9 degrees. All modes of transportation are available; the Oakland Airport is a 12-minute drive. Oakland has all the advantages of a large metropolitan area, being a part of the San Francisco Bay Area. Numerous churches, museums, libraries, hospitals, service groups, and organizations are in the city. Oakland has many tourist attractions and recreational facilities. Lake Merritt, a 160-acre body of salt water, is the only tidal lake in the heart of any American city. There are parks, golf courses, swimming pools within a short distance.

■ **LAS POSITAS COLLEGE**

3000 Campus Hill Dr.
Livermore, CA 94551
Tel: (925)424-1000
Fax: (925)443-0742
Web Site: www.laspositascollege.edu

Description: District-supported, 2-year, coed. Part of California Community College System. Awards certificates, diplomas, transfer associate, and terminal associate degrees. Founded 1988. Setting: 150-acre suburban campus with easy access to Oakland, San Francisco. Total enrollment: 8,044. 50% 25 or older. Core. Calendar: semesters. Academic remediation

for entering students, ESL program, services for LD students, advanced placement, self-designed majors, summer session for credit, part-time degree program, internships.
Entrance Requirements: Open admission. Recommended: high school transcript. Entrance: noncompetitive.
Collegiate Environment: Drama-theater group, choral group, student-run newspaper. Social organizations: 23 open to all. Student services: health clinic, personal-psychological counseling. Campus security: 24-hour emergency response devices, late night transport-escort service. Learning Resource Center.

■ **LASSEN COMMUNITY COLLEGE**
Hwy. 139
Susanville, CA 96130
Tel: (530)257-6181
Fax: (530)257-8964
Web Site: www.lassencollege.edu
Description: District-supported, 2-year, coed. Part of California Community College System. Awards certificates, transfer associate, and terminal associate degrees. Founded 1925. Setting: 100-acre rural campus. Total enrollment: 2,161. Faculty: 204 (44 full-time, 160 part-time). Students come from 12 states and territories, 3 other countries. 58% 25 or older. Core. Calendar: semesters. Academic remediation for entering students, ESL program, services for LD students, advanced placement, summer session for credit, part-time degree program, adult/continuing education programs, co-op programs and internships. Off campus study at members of the Northeastern California Higher Education Council.
Entrance Requirements: Open admission. Option: early admission. Recommended: high school transcript. Entrance: noncompetitive. Application deadline: rolling. Notification: continuous.
Collegiate Environment: Drama-theater group, student-run newspaper. Most popular organization: Lassen Student Union. Major annual events: Career Day, Vocational Olympics, Skunk Days. Student services: legal services, health clinic. Lassen College Library. 30 computers available on campus for general student use. Staffed computer lab on campus.

■ **LAURUS COLLEGE**
81 Higuera St., Ste. 110
San Luis Obispo, CA 93401
Tel: (805)267-1690
Web Site: www.lauruscollege.edu
Description: Proprietary, 2-year, coed. Awards certificates, transfer associate, and terminal associate degrees.

■ **LEARNET ACADEMY**
3251 W 6th St., 2nd Fl.
Los Angeles, CA 90020
Tel: (213)387-4242
Web Site: www.learnet.edu
Description: Proprietary, 2-year, coed. Awards certificates, transfer associate, and terminal associate degrees.

■ **LIFE PACIFIC COLLEGE**
1100 Covina Blvd.
San Dimas, CA 91773-3298
Tel: (909)599-5433; Free: 877-886-5433
Fax: (909)599-6690
E-mail: adm@lifepacific.edu
Web Site: www.lifepacific.edu
Description: Independent, 4-year, coed, affiliated with International Church of the Foursquare Gospel. Awards associate and bachelor's degrees. Founded 1923. Setting: 9-acre suburban campus with easy access to Los Angeles. Endowment: $2.6 million. Educational spending for the previous fiscal year: $4570 per student. Total enrollment: 514. Faculty: 38 (16 full-time, 22 part-time). Student-undergrad faculty ratio is 16:1. 75 applied, 100% were admitted. 8% from top 10% of their high school class, 21% from top quarter, 42% from top half. Students come from 39 states and territories, 3 other countries, 44% from out-of-state. 27% 25 or older, 50% live on campus. Retention: 77% of full-time freshmen returned the following year. Academic area with the most degrees conferred: theology and religious vocations. Core. Calendar: semesters. Services for LD students, advanced placement, accelerated degree program, independent study, distance learning, summer

session for credit, part-time degree program, external degree program, adult/continuing education programs, co-op programs and internships. Study abroad program.
Entrance Requirements: Options: electronic application, deferred admission, international baccalaureate accepted. Required: essay, high school transcript, minimum 2.0 high school GPA, 1 recommendation, Christian testimony, SAT or ACT. Entrance: minimally difficult. Application deadline: 5/1. Notification: continuous.
Collegiate Environment: Orientation program. Drama-theater group, choral group. Major annual events: Spring/Fall Retreats, Winter Social, Spring Social. Student services: personal-psychological counseling. Campus security: 24-hour emergency response devices, student patrols, part-time security personnel. Life Pacific College Alumni Library. Operations spending for the previous fiscal year: $223,812. 46 computers available on campus for general student use. A campuswide network can be accessed from student residence rooms. Students can access the following: online class registration. Staffed computer lab on campus provides training in use of computers, software, and the Internet.
Community Environment: San Dimas is a suburban community approximately 45 minutes from Los Angeles, located at the foothills of the San Gabriel Mountains.

■ **LINCOLN UNIVERSITY**
401 15th St.
Oakland, CA 94612
Tel: (510)628-8010; Free: 888-810-9998
Fax: (510)628-8026
E-mail: admissions@lincolnuca.edu
Web Site: www.lincolnuca.edu
Description: Independent, comprehensive, coed. Awards bachelor's, master's, and doctoral degrees. Founded 1919. Setting: urban campus. Total enrollment: 1,048. Faculty: 34 (14 full-time, 20 part-time). Student-undergrad faculty ratio is 17:1. 111 applied, 57% were admitted. Students come from 20 other countries. 6% Hispanic/Latino; 6% Black or African American, non-Hispanic/Latino; 18% Asian, non-Hispanic/Latino; 2% Native Hawaiian or other Pacific Islander, non-Hispanic/Latino; 52% international. 50% 25 or older. Academic areas with the most degrees conferred: health professions and related sciences; business/marketing. Core. Calendar: semesters. Double major, summer session for credit.
Entrance Requirements: Options: electronic application, deferred admission. Required: essay, high school transcript, minimum 2 high school GPA. Required for some: recommendations, interview. Entrance: minimally difficult. Application deadline: 7/13. Transfer credits accepted: Yes.
Collegiate Environment: Orientation program. Major annual events: Annual Ski Trip, Welcome Barbeque, Welcome Free Lunch. Student services: personal-psychological counseling. Campus security: 24-hour emergency response devices. Lincoln University Library. Books: 14,400 (physical), 128,000 (digital/electronic); Serial titles: 350 (physical), 5,050 (digital/electronic); Databases: 19. 39 computers available on campus for general student use. A campuswide network can be accessed. Staffed computer lab on campus provides training in use of computers, software, and the Internet.

■ **LOMA LINDA UNIVERSITY**
11139 Anderson St.
Loma Linda, CA 92350
Tel: (909)558-1000; Free: 800-422-4558
Fax: (909)558-4577
Web Site: www.llu.edu
Description: Independent Seventh-day Adventist, university, coed. Awards associate, bachelor's, master's, and doctoral degrees and post-master's certificates (associate degree and nursing students may enter at the sophomore level). Founded 1905. Setting: small town campus with easy access to Los Angeles. Endowment: $135.9 million. Research spending for the previous fiscal year: $31.6 million. Educational spending for the previous fiscal year: $27,730 per student. Total enrollment: 4,270. Faculty: 840 (557 full-time, 283 part-time). Student-undergrad faculty ratio is 8:1. Full-time: 885 students, 70% women, 30% men. Part-time: 347 students, 76% women, 24% men. Students come from 29 states and territories, 30 other countries, 12% from out-of-state. 50% 25 or older, 27% live on campus, 18% transferred in. Academic area with the most degrees conferred: health professions and related sciences. Calendar: quarters. ESL program, independent study, distance learning, internships. Off campus study.
Entrance Requirements: Option: deferred admission.
Collegiate Environment: Most popular organizations: Students for

International Mission Services, Black Health Professional Association, Association of Latin American Students. Major annual events: Annual Convocation, Welcome Back Bash. Student services: health clinic, personal-psychological counseling. Campus security: 24-hour emergency response devices and patrols, late night transport-escort service. Del E. Webb Memorial Library. Operations spending for the previous fiscal year: $3.6 million. 160 computers available on campus for general student use. A campuswide network can be accessed from student residence rooms and from off campus. Students can access the following: online class registration, online courses. Staffed computer lab on campus provides training in use of computers, software, and the Internet.

Community Environment: Loma Linda is located 56 miles east of Los Angeles, between Redlands, San Bernardino, and Riverside. The climate is pleasant and mild. Loma Linda is a medical center that has three hospitals, including the 515-bed University Medical Center and the 500-bed Jerry L. Pettis Memorial Veterans Hospital. Pacific ocean beaches, ski slopes, and lakes for boating and water skiing are all within a one-hour drive. Part-time and full-time work is available.

■ **LONG BEACH CITY COLLEGE**
4901 E Carson St.
Long Beach, CA 90808-1780
Tel: (562)938-4353
Web Site: www.lbcc.edu
Description: District-supported, 2-year, coed. Part of California Community College System. Awards certificates, transfer associate, and terminal associate degrees. Founded 1927. Setting: 40-acre urban campus with easy access to Los Angeles. Total enrollment: 27,894. Student-undergrad faculty ratio is 30:1. 45% 25 or older. Core. Calendar: semesters. Academic remediation for entering students, ESL program, services for LD students, advanced placement, honors program, distance learning, summer session for credit, part-time degree program, adult/continuing education programs, internships.
Entrance Requirements: Open admission except for nursing program. Option: early admission. Recommended: high school transcript. Entrance: noncompetitive. Application deadline: rolling.
Collegiate Environment: Drama-theater group, choral group, student-run newspaper, radio station. Social organizations: local fraternities, local sororities. Student services: legal services, health clinic, personal-psychological counseling, women's center. Campus security: 24-hour emergency response devices and patrols, student patrols, late night transport-escort service. Long Beach City College Library plus 1 other.

■ **LOS ANGELES ACADEMY OF FIGURATIVE ART**
16926 Saticoy St.
Van Nuys, CA 91406
Description: Proprietary, 4-year, coed.

■ **LOS ANGELES CITY COLLEGE**
855 N Vermont Ave.
Los Angeles, CA 90029-3590
Tel: (323)953-4000
Fax: (323)953-4536
E-mail: anderst@lacitycollege.edu
Web Site: www.lacitycollege.edu
Description: District-supported, 2-year, coed. Part of Los Angeles Community College District (LACCD). Awards certificates, diplomas, transfer associate, and terminal associate degrees. Founded 1929. Setting: 42-acre urban campus. Educational spending for the previous fiscal year: $4688 per student. Total enrollment: 16,556. Faculty: 450 (185 full-time, 265 part-time). 33,147 applied, 76% were admitted. Full-time: 4,671 students, 55% women, 45% men. Part-time: 11,885 students, 56% women, 44% men. 2% American Indian or Alaska Native, non-Hispanic/Latino; 50% Hispanic/Latino; 9% Black or African American, non-Hispanic/Latino; 15% Asian, non-Hispanic/Latino; 4% international. 62% 25 or older, 6% transferred in. Core. Calendar: semesters. Academic remediation for entering students, ESL program, services for LD students, advanced placement, accelerated degree program, freshman honors college, honors program, distance learning, double major, summer session for credit, part-time degree program, adult/continuing education programs, co-op programs and internships. Study abroad program. ROTC: Army (c), Naval (c), Air Force (c).
Entrance Requirements: Open admission except for international students, radiological technology, dental technology, nursing programs; Theater Academy. Option: electronic application. Recommended: high school

transcript. Entrance: noncompetitive. Application deadline: 9/5. Notification: continuous until 9/5. Transfer credits accepted: Yes.
Costs Per Year: Application fee: $0. State resident tuition: $1220 full-time, $46 per unit part-time. Nonresident tuition: $7128 full-time, $297 per unit part-time. Mandatory fees: $24 full-time, $12 per term part-time.
Collegiate Environment: Orientation program. Drama-theater group, choral group, student-run newspaper. Major annual events: Graduation, Deans Tea. Student services: health clinic, personal-psychological counseling. Campus security: 24-hour emergency response devices and patrols, student patrols, late night transport-escort service. Martin Luther King Jr. Library. Books: 155,954 (physical), 195,000 (digital/electronic); Serial titles: 87 (physical); Databases: 60. Weekly public service hours: 77; students can reserve study rooms. Operations spending for the previous fiscal year: $2 million. 200 computers available on campus for general student use. A campuswide network can be accessed from off-campus. Students can access the following: online class registration. Staffed computer lab on campus provides training in use of computers, software, and the Internet.
Community Environment: See University of California - Los Angeles.

■ **LOS ANGELES COUNTY COLLEGE OF NURSING AND ALLIED HEALTH**
1237 N Mission Rd.
Los Angeles, CA 90033
Tel: (323)226-4911
Fax: (323)226-6427
Web Site: www.dhs.lacounty.gov/wps/portal/dhs/conah
Description: District-supported, 2-year, coed. Awards terminal associate degrees. Founded 1895. Total enrollment: 333. Student-undergrad faculty ratio is 4:1. 82% 25 or older. Calendar: semesters.
Entrance Requirements: Required: TEAS, version V.

■ **LOS ANGELES FILM SCHOOL**
6363 Sunset Blvd.
Hollywood, CA 90028
Tel: (323)860-0789; Free: 877-952-3456
Web Site: www.lafilm.edu
Description: Proprietary, 4-year, coed. Administratively affiliated with Full Sail University. Awards associate and bachelor's degrees. Founded 1999. Setting: urban campus with easy access to Hollywood. Total enrollment: 1,358. Faculty: 116 (103 full-time, 13 part-time). 1,505 applied, 85% were admitted. Students come from 48 states and territories, 16 other countries, 32% from out-of-state. 47% 25 or older. Core. Calendar: continuous. Services for LD students, advanced placement, accelerated degree program, distance learning, adult/continuing education programs, co-op programs.
Entrance Requirements: Open admission. Option: electronic application. Required: essay, high school transcript, interview. Entrance: noncompetitive. Transfer credits accepted: Yes.
Collegiate Environment: Orientation program. Campus security: 24-hour patrols. Main library plus 1 other. 8 computers available on campus for general student use. Computer purchase/lease plans available. A computer is required for all students. A campuswide network can be accessed from off-campus. Staffed computer lab on campus provides training in use of software.

■ **LOS ANGELES HARBOR COLLEGE**
1111 Figueroa Pl.
Wilmington, CA 90744-2397
Tel: (310)233-4000
Fax: (310)233-4223
Web Site: www.lahc.edu
Description: District-supported, 2-year, coed. Part of Los Angeles Community College District System. Awards certificates, transfer associate, and terminal associate degrees. Founded 1949. Setting: 80-acre suburban campus with easy access to Los Angeles. Research spending for the previous fiscal year: $206,778. Educational spending for the previous fiscal year: $2057 per student. Total enrollment: 10,181. Faculty: 422 (113 full-time, 309 part-time). Student-undergrad faculty ratio is 47:1. Full-time: 2,812 students, 57% women, 43% men. Part-time: 7,369 students, 62% women, 38% men. Students come from 14 states and territories, 15 other countries. 35% 25 or older. Core. Calendar: semesters. Academic remediation for entering students, ESL program, services for LD students, advanced placement, accelerated degree program, freshman honors college, honors program, independent study, distance learning, double major, summer session for

credit, part-time degree program, adult/continuing education programs, co-op programs. Off campus study at California State University, Dominguez Hills. Study abroad program.

Entrance Requirements: Open admission except for nursing program. Options: electronic application, early admission, deferred admission. Entrance: noncompetitive. Application deadline: 9/3. Transfer credits accepted: Yes.

Collegiate Environment: Orientation program. Drama-theater group, choral group, student-run newspaper. Social organizations: 13 open to all. Most popular organizations: Alpha Gamma Sigma, EOP&S, Creando Un Nuevo Futuro, Psychology Club, Honors Transfer Program. Major annual events: ASO Elections, Blood Drives, Club Rush Day. Student services: legal services, health clinic, personal-psychological counseling. Campus security: 24-hour emergency response devices and patrols, late night transport-escort service. Harbor College Library. Operations spending for the previous fiscal year: $738,905. 725 computers available on campus for general student use. A campuswide network can be accessed from off-campus. Students can access the following: online class registration. Staffed computer lab on campus provides training in use of computers and software.

Community Environment: The Harbor College service area encompasses a multicultural population of 369,907 persons who live in the communities of San Pedro, Wilmington, Carson, Gardena, Lomita, Harbor City, and on the Palos Verdes Peninsula and parts of South Los Angeles. A business, industrial, shipping and civic center of the Port of Los Angeles, Wilmington is located in the heart of the Southern California oil refining district. Points of interest are Marineland, the Queen Mary, Ports O' Call Village, and a Korean Liberty Bell, all within easy driving distance.

■ **LOS ANGELES MISSION COLLEGE**
13356 Eldridge Ave.
Sylmar, CA 91342-3245
Tel: (818)364-7600
Web Site: www.lamission.edu

Description: District-supported, 2-year, coed. Part of Los Angeles Community College District System, California Community Colleges. Awards certificates, transfer associate, and terminal associate degrees. Founded 1974. Setting: 33-acre urban campus with easy access to Los Angeles. Total enrollment: 10,191. Faculty: 354 (80 full-time, 274 part-time). Full-time: 2,338 students, 58% women, 42% men. Part-time: 7,853 students, 61% women, 39% men. 2% from out-of-state. 0.2% American Indian or Alaska Native, non-Hispanic/Latino; 76% Hispanic/Latino; 3% Black or African American, non-Hispanic/Latino; 5% Asian, non-Hispanic/Latino; 0.1% Native Hawaiian or other Pacific Islander, non-Hispanic/Latino; 1% international. 35% 25 or older, 9% transferred in. Retention: 71% of full-time freshmen returned the following year. Core. Calendar: semesters. Academic remediation for entering students, ESL program, services for LD students, advanced placement, honors program, independent study, distance learning, double major, summer session for credit, part-time degree program, adult/continuing education programs, internships. Off campus study. Study abroad program.

Entrance Requirements: Open admission. Option: early admission. Entrance: noncompetitive. Application deadline: rolling. Notification: continuous.

Costs Per Year: State resident tuition: $1196 full-time, $46 per unit part-time. Nonresident tuition: $7514 full-time, $297 per unit part-time. Mandatory fees: $24 full-time, $12 per term part-time. Part-time tuition and fees vary according to course load.

Collegiate Environment: Orientation program. Drama-theater group, choral group. Student services: health clinic, personal-psychological counseling. Campus security: 24-hour emergency response devices and patrols, late night transport-escort service. Los Angeles Mission College Library.

■ **LOS ANGELES ORT COLLEGE-LOS ANGELES**
6435 Wilshire Blvd.
Los Angeles, CA 90048
Tel: (213)966-5444
Fax: (213)966-5455

Description: Independent, 2-year, coed, affiliated with Jewish faith. Founded 1985.

■ **LOS ANGELES PIERCE COLLEGE**
6201 Winnetka Ave.
Woodland Hills, CA 91371-0001
Tel: (818)710-4123
Fax: (818)710-9844

Web Site: www.piercecollege.edu

Description: District-supported, 2-year, coed. Part of Los Angeles Community College District System. Awards certificates, transfer associate, and terminal associate degrees. Founded 1947. Setting: 425-acre suburban campus with easy access to Los Angeles. Total enrollment: 16,255. Faculty: 558. 26,070 applied, 100% were admitted. Students come from 2 states and territories, 48 other countries. 48% 25 or older. Core. Calendar: semesters. Academic remediation for entering students, ESL program, services for LD students, advanced placement, honors program, independent study, distance learning, summer session for credit, part-time degree program, adult/continuing education programs, co-op programs and internships. Study abroad program.

Entrance Requirements: Open admission except for nursing, honors programs. Options: electronic application, early admission. Entrance: noncompetitive. Application deadline: 8/20.

Collegiate Environment: Orientation program. Drama-theater group, choral group, student-run newspaper. Social organizations: 28 open to all. Most popular organizations: Alpha Gamma Sigma, Club Latino United for Education, United African-American Student Association, Hillel, Filipino Club. Major annual events: Club Day, Job Fair, University Day. Student services: health clinic, personal-psychological counseling, women's center. Campus security: 24-hour patrols, late night transport-escort service. Pierce College Library plus 1 other. 60 computers available on campus for general student use. A campuswide network can be accessed. Staffed computer lab on campus.

Community Environment: Woodland Hills is a suburban area of Los Angeles with a subtropical climate, and known as a beautiful residential area. Buses serve the area. The community has a library, hospital, churches, and civic and service organizations. Nearby are shopping centers, theatres, and a public park with a swimming pool. The Pacific Ocean is within easy driving distance. Part-time employment is available.

■ **LOS ANGELES SOUTHWEST COLLEGE**
1600 W Imperial Hwy.
Los Angeles, CA 90047-4810
Tel: (323)241-5225
Web Site: www.lasc.edu

Description: District-supported, 2-year, coed. Part of Los Angeles Community College District System. Awards certificates, diplomas, transfer associate, and terminal associate degrees. Founded 1967. Setting: 69-acre urban campus. Research spending for the previous fiscal year: $321,616. Total enrollment: 6,000. Faculty: 223 (75 full-time, 148 part-time). Students come from 20 states and territories, 4 other countries. 63% 25 or older. Core. Calendar: semesters. Academic remediation for entering students, ESL program, services for LD students, accelerated degree program, freshman honors college, honors program, summer session for credit, part-time degree program, adult/continuing education programs, co-op programs and internships.

Entrance Requirements: Open admission except for nursing program. Option: early admission. Recommended: essay, minimum 2.0 high school GPA. Required for some: high school transcript. Entrance: noncompetitive. Application deadline: 9/9. Notification: continuous until 9/9.

Collegiate Environment: Choral group, student-run newspaper. Social organizations: 8 open to all. Campus security: 24-hour emergency response devices and patrols, student patrols, late night transport-escort service. Main library plus 1 other. Operations spending for the previous fiscal year: $329,727. 40 computers available on campus for general student use. A campuswide network can be accessed from off-campus. Staffed computer lab on campus.

Community Environment: See University of California - Los Angeles.

■ **LOS ANGELES TRADE-TECHNICAL COLLEGE**
400 W Washington Blvd.
Los Angeles, CA 90015-4108
Tel: (213)763-7000
Fax: (213)748-7334
Web Site: www.lattc.edu

Description: District-supported, 2-year, coed. Part of Los Angeles Community College District System. Awards certificates, diplomas, transfer associate, and terminal associate degrees. Founded 1925. Setting: 25-acre urban campus. Total enrollment: 13,194. Faculty: 443 (200 full-time, 243 part-time). Full-time: 4,160 students, 56% women, 44% men. Part-time: 9,034 students, 49% women, 51% men. 47% 25 or older. Core. Calendar: semesters. Academic remediation for entering students, ESL program, services for LD students, advanced placement, summer session for credit, part-time degree program, adult/continuing education programs, co-op programs.

Entrance Requirements: Option: electronic application. Recommended: high school transcript. Entrance: noncompetitive. Application deadline: 9/7.

Collegiate Environment: Orientation program. Student services: health clinic, personal-psychological counseling, women's center. Campus security: 24-hour patrols, student patrols, late night transport-escort service. Los Angeles Trade-Technical College Library. Books: 2,640 (physical), 6,799 (digital/electronic); Serial titles: 93 (physical), 41 (digital/electronic); Databases: 48. Weekly public service hours: 52. 200 computers available on campus for general student use. A campuswide network can be accessed. Students can access the following: online class registration. Staffed computer lab on campus provides training in use of software and the Internet.

Community Environment: See University of California - Los Angeles.

■ LOS ANGELES VALLEY COLLEGE

5800 Fulton Ave.
Valley Glen, CA 91401
Tel: (818)947-2600
Fax: (818)947-2610
Web Site: www.lavc.edu

Description: District-supported, 2-year, coed. Part of Los Angeles Community College District System. Awards certificates, transfer associate, and terminal associate degrees. Founded 1949. Setting: 105-acre suburban campus with easy access to Los Angeles. Research spending for the previous fiscal year: $296,912. Educational spending for the previous fiscal year: $4101 per student. Total enrollment: 17,957. Students come from 20 states and territories, 21 other countries. 50% Hispanic/Latino; 5% Black or African American, non-Hispanic/Latino; 8% Asian, non-Hispanic/Latino; 0.2% Native Hawaiian or other Pacific Islander, non-Hispanic/Latino; 0.7% international. 41% 25 or older. Retention: 84% of full-time freshmen returned the following year. Academic areas with the most degrees conferred: liberal arts/general studies; social sciences; health professions and related sciences. Core. Calendar: semesters. Academic remediation for entering students, ESL program, services for LD students, self-designed majors, honors program, independent study, distance learning, double major, summer session for credit, part-time degree program, adult/continuing education programs, co-op programs and internships.

Entrance Requirements: Open admission except for allied health programs. Options: electronic application, early admission. Recommended: high school transcript. Entrance: noncompetitive. Application deadline: rolling.

Collegiate Environment: Orientation program. Drama-theater group, choral group, student-run newspaper, radio station. Student services: legal services, health clinic, personal-psychological counseling, women's center. Campus security: 24-hour emergency response devices and patrols, student patrols, late night transport-escort service. Los Angeles Valley Library. Operations spending for the previous fiscal year: $1.1 million.

■ LOS MEDANOS COLLEGE

2700 E Leland Rd.
Pittsburg, CA 94565-5197
Tel: (925)439-2181
Fax: (925)439-8797
Web Site: www.losmedanos.net

Description: District-supported, 2-year, coed. Part of California Community College System. Awards certificates, transfer associate, and terminal associate degrees. Founded 1974. Setting: 120-acre suburban campus with easy access to San Francisco. Research spending for the previous fiscal year: $70,348. Educational spending for the previous fiscal year: $1873 per student. Total enrollment: 7,152. Faculty: 244 (104 full-time, 140 part-time). Students come from 3 states and territories, 15 other countries, 0.2% from out-of-state. 56% 25 or older. Core. Calendar: semesters. Academic remediation for entering students, ESL program, services for LD students, advanced placement, honors program, independent study, double major, summer session for credit, part-time degree program, co-op programs. Study abroad program.

Entrance Requirements: Open admission. Required for some: high school transcript. Entrance: noncompetitive. Application deadline: 8/29. Notification: continuous until 8/29.

Collegiate Environment: Orientation program. Choral group, student-run newspaper. Social organizations: 16 open to all. Most popular organizations:

Alpha Gamma Sigma, Christian Fellowship Club, Student Nurses Association, La Raza Club. Student services: women's center. Campus security: 24-hour patrols, student patrols, late night transport-escort service. Learning Resource Center. Operations spending for the previous fiscal year: $926,689. 200 computers available on campus for general student use. Students can access the following: online class registration. Staffed computer lab on campus.

■ LOYOLA MARYMOUNT UNIVERSITY

1 LMU Dr.
Los Angeles, CA 90045
Tel: (310)338-2700; Free: 800-LMU-INFO
Fax: (310)338-2797
Web Site: www.lmu.edu

Description: Independent Roman Catholic, comprehensive, coed. Awards bachelor's, master's, and doctoral degrees and post-master's certificates. Founded 1911. Setting: 142-acre suburban campus with easy access to Los Angeles. Endowment: $477.6 million. Total enrollment: 9,838. Student-undergrad faculty ratio is 10:1. 17,846 applied, 47% were admitted. 44% from top 10% of their high school class, 73% from top quarter, 96% from top half. Full-time: 6,466 students, 56% women, 44% men. Part-time: 234 students, 46% women, 54% men. Students come from 93 other countries, 32% from out-of-state. 22% Hispanic/Latino; 7% Black or African American, non-Hispanic/Latino; 10% Asian, non-Hispanic/Latino; 0.2% Native Hawaiian or other Pacific Islander, non-Hispanic/Latino; 10% international. 3% 25 or older, 50% live on campus, 7% transferred in. Retention: 90% of full-time freshmen returned the following year. Academic areas with the most degrees conferred: business/marketing; visual and performing arts; social sciences. Core. Calendar: semesters. ESL program, advanced placement, accelerated degree program, self-designed majors, honors program, independent study, distance learning, double major, part-time degree program, internships, graduate courses open to undergrads. Study abroad program. ROTC: Army (c), Air Force.

Entrance Requirements: Options: electronic application, early admission, early decision, early action, deferred admission, international baccalaureate accepted. Required: essay, high school transcript, 1 recommendation, SAT or ACT. Recommended: portfolio or audition required for animation, dance, music, and theatre arts programs, portfolio optional for production (film and television) and studio arts programs. Required for some: portfolio or audition required for animation, dance, music, and theatre arts programs, portfolio optional for production (film and television) and studio arts programs. Application deadlines: 1/15, 11/1 for early decision, 11/1 for early action. Notification: continuous, 12/1 for early decision, 12/20 for early action. SAT Reasoning Test deadline: 2/1. Transfer credits accepted: Yes. Applicants placed on waiting list: 3,765. Wait-listed applicants offered admission: 6. Early decision applicants: 234. Early decision applicants admitted: 117. Early action applicants: 6,168. Early action applicants admitted: 3,786.

Costs Per Year: Application fee: $60. One-time mandatory fee: $350. Comprehensive fee: $63,357 includes full-time tuition ($47,470), mandatory fees ($702), and college room and board ($15,185). College room only: $10,785. Full-time tuition and fees vary according to reciprocity agreements. Room and board charges vary according to board plan and housing facility. Part-time tuition: $1981 per credit hour. Part-time mandatory fees: $8 per credit hour, $65 per term. Part-time tuition and fees vary according to course load.

Collegiate Environment: Orientation program. Drama-theater group, choral group, student-run newspaper, radio station. Social organizations: 201 open to all; national fraternities, national sororities; 19% of eligible men and 25% of eligible women are members. Student services: health clinic, personal-psychological counseling. Campus security: 24-hour emergency response devices and patrols, late night transport-escort service. 3,215 college housing spaces available; all were occupied in 2018-19. Freshmen given priority for college housing. Options: coed, men-only, women-only housing available. William H. Hannon Library. Study areas open 24 hours, 5-7 days a week; students can reserve study rooms. 820 computers available on campus for general student use. Computer purchase/lease plans available. A campuswide network can be accessed from student residence rooms and from off campus. Students can access the following: online class registration. Staffed computer lab on campus (open 24 hours a day).

Community Environment: See University of California - Los Angeles.

■ MARYMOUNT CALIFORNIA UNIVERSITY

30800 Palos Verdes Dr. E
Rancho Palos Verdes, CA 90275-6299

Tel: (310)377-5501
Fax: (310)377-6223
E-mail: mpuerto@marymountcalifornia.edu
Web Site: www.marymountcalifornia.edu
Description: Independent Roman Catholic, comprehensive, coed. Awards associate, bachelor's, and master's degrees. Founded 1932. Setting: 26-acre suburban campus with easy access to Los Angeles. Endowment: $10.7 million. Educational spending for the previous fiscal year: $7515 per student. Total enrollment: 761. Faculty: 61 (34 full-time, 27 part-time). Student-undergrad faculty ratio is 16:1. 1,621 applied, 85% were admitted. Full-time: 721 students, 49% women, 51% men. Part-time: 14 students, 43% women, 57% men. 11% from out-of-state. 0.3% American Indian or Alaska Native, non-Hispanic/Latino; 40% Hispanic/Latino; 7% Black or African American, non-Hispanic/Latino; 5% Asian, non-Hispanic/Latino; 0.4% Native Hawaiian or other Pacific Islander, non-Hispanic/Latino; 18% international. 7% 25 or older, 34% live on campus, 11% transferred in. Retention: 53% of full-time freshmen returned the following year. Academic areas with the most degrees conferred: business/marketing; psychology; liberal arts/general studies. Core. Calendar: semesters. Academic remediation for entering students, ESL program, services for LD students, advanced placement, accelerated degree program, honors program, independent study, distance learning, summer session for credit, part-time degree program, adult/continuing education programs, co-op programs and internships, graduate courses open to undergrads. Off campus study. Study abroad program.
Entrance Requirements: Options: electronic application, early admission, deferred admission, international baccalaureate accepted. Required: high school transcript. Recommended: minimum 2 high school GPA, SAT or ACT. Required for some: essay, interview. Entrance: minimally difficult. Notification: continuous until 9/1. SAT Reasoning Test deadline: 8/31. SAT Subject Test deadline: 8/31. Transfer credits accepted: Yes.
Costs Per Year: Application fee: $50. One-time mandatory fee: $300. Comprehensive fee: $50,800 includes full-time tuition ($34,134), mandatory fees ($2000), and college room and board ($14,666). College room only: $9250. Room and board charges vary according to board plan and housing facility. Part-time tuition: $1475 per credit hour. Part-time mandatory fees: $700 per year.
Collegiate Environment: Orientation program. Drama-theater group, choral group. Social organizations: 17 open to all; Phi Theta Kappa; 55% of eligible men and 55% of eligible women are members. Most popular organizations: Latinos Unidos, Student Veterans Organization, Marymount Pride, Black Student Union, Society for Advancement of Management (SAM). Major annual events: Service Days, Club Days, Spring Formal. Student services: health clinic, personal-psychological counseling. Campus security: 24-hour emergency response devices and patrols, late night transport-escort service, controlled dormitory access. Freshmen given priority for college housing. Option: coed housing available. College Library plus 1 other. Books: 23,246 (physical), 135,971 (digital/electronic); Serial titles: 255 (physical), 30,329 (digital/electronic); Databases: 51. Weekly public service hours: 60; students can reserve study rooms. Operations spending for the previous fiscal year: $305,406. 210 computers available on campus for general student use. Computer purchase/lease plans available. A campuswide network can be accessed from student residence rooms and from off campus. Students can access the following: online class registration. Staffed computer lab on campus provides training in use of computers, software, and the Internet.

■ **THE MASTER'S UNIVERSITY**
21726 Placerita Canyon Rd.
Santa Clarita, CA 91321-1200
Tel: (661)259-3540; Free: 800-568-6248
E-mail: admissions@masters.edu
Web Site: www.masters.edu
Description: Independent nondenominational, comprehensive, coed. Awards bachelor's, master's, and doctoral degrees. Founded 1927. Setting: 110-acre suburban campus with easy access to Los Angeles. Endowment: $15.4 million. Educational spending for the previous fiscal year: $8034 per student. Total enrollment: 1,908. Faculty: 212 (51 full-time, 161 part-time). Student-undergrad faculty ratio is 12:1. 617 applied, 66% were admitted. 31% from top 10% of their high school class, 69% from top quarter, 90% from top half. Full-time: 975 students, 48% women, 52% men. Part-time: 365 students, 41% women, 59% men. Students come from 40 states and territories, 25 other countries, 36% from out-of-state. 0.1% American Indian or Alaska Native, non-Hispanic/Latino; 10% Hispanic/Latino; 2% Black or African American, non-Hispanic/Latino; 5% Asian, non-Hispanic/Latino; 0.1% Native Hawaiian or other Pacific Islander, non-Hispanic/Latino; 4%

international. 4% 25 or older, 74% live on campus, 7% transferred in. Retention: 85% of full-time freshmen returned the following year. Academic areas with the most degrees conferred: business/marketing; theology and religious vocations; liberal arts/general studies. Core. Calendar: semesters. Academic remediation for entering students, services for LD students, advanced placement, accelerated degree program, independent study, distance learning, double major, summer session for credit, part-time degree program, external degree program, adult/continuing education programs, co-op programs and internships. Study abroad program. ROTC: Army (c), Air Force (c).
Entrance Requirements: Options: electronic application, early admission, early action, deferred admission, international baccalaureate accepted. Required: essay, high school transcript, minimum 2.75 high school GPA, 2 recommendations, SAT or ACT. Recommended: interview. Entrance: moderately difficult. Application deadlines: 9/1, 11/15 for early action. Notification: continuous until 11/1, 12/1 for early action. SAT Reasoning Test deadline: 8/1. Transfer credits accepted: Yes.
Costs Per Year: Application fee: $40. Comprehensive fee: $36,590 includes full-time tuition ($24,950), mandatory fees ($440), and college room and board ($11,200). Full-time tuition and fees vary according to class time, course load, location, and program. Room and board charges vary according to board plan. Part-time tuition: $1050 per credit hour. Part-time tuition varies according to class time, course load, location, and program.
Collegiate Environment: Orientation program. Drama-theater group, choral group. Social organizations: 15 open to all. Most popular organizations: University Singers Choir, Summer Missions, Intramural Sports, Church Ministries, Theatre Arts Group. Major annual events: Truth and Life Conference, Monty's, Disney Day. Student services: health clinic, personal-psychological counseling. Campus security: 24-hour patrols. Robert L. Powell Library plus 1 other. Books: 98,047 (physical), 210,005 (digital/electronic); Serial titles: 657 (physical), 18,615 (digital/electronic); Databases: 33. Weekly public service hours: 74. Operations spending for the previous fiscal year: $207,441. 57 computers available on campus for general student use. A computer is required for all students. A campuswide network can be accessed from student residence rooms and from off campus. Students can access the following: online class registration. Staffed computer lab on campus provides training in use of computers and the Internet.

■ **MENDOCINO COLLEGE**
1000 Hensley Creek Rd.
Ukiah, CA 95482-0300
Tel: (707)468-3000
Fax: (707)468-3430
Web Site: www.mendocino.edu
Description: District-supported, 2-year, coed. Part of California Community College System. Awards certificates, transfer associate, and terminal associate degrees. Founded 1973. Setting: 127-acre rural campus. Endowment: $6.4 million. Educational spending for the previous fiscal year: $4088 per student. Total enrollment: 3,614. Faculty: 294 (51 full-time, 243 part-time). Student-undergrad faculty ratio is 16:1. 660 applied, 100% were admitted. Full-time: 1,296 students, 55% women, 45% men. Part-time: 2,318 students, 63% women, 37% men. Students come from 16 states and territories, 2 other countries. 5% American Indian or Alaska Native, non-Hispanic/Latino; 23% Hispanic/Latino; 3% Black or African American, non-Hispanic/Latino; 3% Asian, non-Hispanic/Latino; 0.6% Native Hawaiian or other Pacific Islander, non-Hispanic/Latino. 40% 25 or older, 4% transferred in. Core. Calendar: semesters. Academic remediation for entering students, ESL program, services for LD students, advanced placement, honors program, independent study, distance learning, summer session for credit, part-time degree program, adult/continuing education programs, co-op programs and internships.
Entrance Requirements: Open admission. Options: electronic application, early admission, deferred admission. Required: high school transcript. Entrance: noncompetitive. Application deadline: rolling. Notification: continuous. Preference given to state residents. Transfer credits accepted: Yes.
Collegiate Environment: Orientation program. Drama-theater group, choral group, student-run radio station. Social organizations: 14 open to all. Campus security: late night transport-escort service, security patrols 6 pm to 10 pm. Lowery Library. Operations spending for the previous fiscal year: $404,311. 90 computers available on campus for general student use. A campuswide network can be accessed from off-campus. Students can access the following: online class registration. Staffed computer lab on campus provides training in use of computers, software, and the Internet.

MENLO COLLEGE

1000 El Camino Real
Atherton, CA 94027-4301
Free: 800-556-3656
E-mail: admissions@menlo.edu
Web Site: www.menlo.edu

Description: Independent, 4-year, coed. Awards bachelor's degrees. Founded 1927. Setting: 45-acre small town campus with easy access to San Francisco. Endowment: $25.6 million. Educational spending for the previous fiscal year: $7850 per student. Total enrollment: 777. Faculty: 101 (30 full-time, 71 part-time). Student-undergrad faculty ratio is 14:1. 2,195 applied, 41% were admitted. 2 valedictorians. Full-time: 758 students, 46% women, 54% men. Part-time: 19 students, 21% women, 79% men. Students come from 26 states and territories, 35 other countries, 19% from out-of-state. 0.5% American Indian or Alaska Native, non-Hispanic/Latino; 23% Hispanic/Latino; 6% Black or African American, non-Hispanic/Latino; 10% Asian, non-Hispanic/Latino; 2% Native Hawaiian or other Pacific Islander, non-Hispanic/Latino; 14% international. 9% 25 or older, 60% live on campus, 12% transferred in. Retention: 77% of full-time freshmen returned the following year. Academic areas with the most degrees conferred: business/marketing; psychology. Core. Calendar: semesters. Academic remediation for entering students, ESL program, services for LD students, advanced placement, accelerated degree program, self-designed majors, independent study, double major, summer session for credit, part-time degree program, adult/continuing education programs, internships. Study abroad program. ROTC: Air Force (c).

Entrance Requirements: Options: electronic application, early admission, early action, deferred admission, international baccalaureate accepted. Required: essay, high school transcript, 1 recommendation, SAT or ACT. Recommended: minimum 2.5 high school GPA, interview. Entrance: moderately difficult. Application deadlines: 4/1, 11/15 for early action. Notification: 1/15 for early action. Transfer credits accepted: Yes.

Costs Per Year: Application fee: $40. Comprehensive fee: $57,025 includes full-time tuition ($42,050), mandatory fees ($750), and college room and board ($14,225). Room and board charges vary according to housing facility. Part-time tuition: $1753 per unit.

Collegiate Environment: Orientation program. Student-run newspaper. Social organizations: 38 open to all. Most popular organizations: International Club, Student Government, SERV, Finance Club, Hawaiian Club. Major annual events: OAKtober Fest, Luau, Apollo night (talent show). Student services: personal-psychological counseling, women's center. Campus security: 24-hour emergency response devices and patrols, controlled dormitory access. Bowman Library. Books: 47,340 (physical), 17,379 (digital/electronic); Serial titles: 76 (physical); Databases: 42. Weekly public service hours: 95; students can reserve study rooms. Operations spending for the previous fiscal year: $500,000. 220 computers available on campus for general student use. A campuswide network can be accessed from student residence rooms and from off campus. Students can access the following: online class registration. Staffed computer lab on campus provides training in use of computers, software, and the Internet.

Community Environment: This is a residential community 30 miles south of San Francisco and 20 miles north of San Jose. The climate is moderate. The Southern Pacific Railroad, and Pacific Greyhound Bus serve the area with San Francisco International Airport 16 miles north. Activities are planned for all ages at the recreation center and many parks and playgrounds.

MERCED COLLEGE

3600 M St.
Merced, CA 95348-2898
Tel: (209)384-6000
Fax: (209)384-6339
Web Site: www.mccd.edu

Description: District-supported, 2-year, coed. Part of California Community College System. Awards certificates, transfer associate, and terminal associate degrees. Founded 1962. Setting: 653-acre small town campus. System endowment: $3.2 million. Total enrollment: 11,552. Faculty: 516 (182 full-time, 334 part-time). Student-undergrad faculty ratio is 26:1. 2,593 applied, 100% were admitted. 2% from out-of-state. 51% 25 or older. Core. Calendar: semesters. Academic remediation for entering students, ESL program, services for LD students, advanced placement, accelerated degree program, self-designed majors, honors program, independent study, distance learning, double major, summer session for credit, part-time degree program, adult/continuing education programs, co-op programs. Off campus study at several local community colleges.

Entrance Requirements: Open admission except for allied health programs or international students. Options: electronic application, early admission. Recommended: high school transcript. Entrance: noncompetitive. Application deadline: rolling. Notification: continuous. Transfer credits accepted: Yes.

Collegiate Environment: Orientation program. Drama-theater group, choral group, student-run newspaper. Social organizations: 32 open to all. Student services: personal-psychological counseling. Campus security: 24-hour patrols. Lesher Library plus 1 other. Databases: 76. Weekly public service hours: 56; students can reserve study rooms. 400 computers available on campus for general student use. A campuswide network can be accessed. Students can access the following: online class registration.

Community Environment: Merced is a rural, suburban area with a dry temperate climate. All forms of transportation serve the area. The community has a library, churches, theatres, a symphony, two general hospitals and all national service clubs. Merced is located at the foot of the Sierra Nevada Mountains and near Yosemite National Park, which provides recreational facilities for camping, hiking, fishing, and skiing, the major winter sport. Job opportunities are good during the summer.

MERRITT COLLEGE

12500 Campus Dr.
Oakland, CA 94619-3196
Tel: (510)531-4911
E-mail: hperdue@peralta.cc.ca.us
Web Site: www.merritt.edu

Description: District-supported, 2-year, coed. Part of Peralta Community College District System. Awards certificates, transfer associate, and terminal associate degrees. Founded 1953. Setting: 130-acre urban campus with easy access to San Francisco. Total enrollment: 6,944. 65% 25 or older. Core. Calendar: semesters. Academic remediation for entering students, ESL program, services for LD students, summer session for credit, part-time degree program, adult/continuing education programs, co-op programs. Off campus study at Holy Names College; Mills College; University of California, Berkeley.

Entrance Requirements: Open admission. Options: early admission, deferred admission. Entrance: noncompetitive. Application deadline: 8/28. Notification: continuous.

Collegiate Environment: Student-run newspaper. Student services: women's center. Merritt College Library.

Community Environment: See Laney College.

MILLS COLLEGE

5000 MacArthur Blvd.
Oakland, CA 94613-1000
Tel: (510)430-2255; Free: 800-87-MILLS
Fax: (510)430-3314
E-mail: admission@mills.edu
Web Site: www.mills.edu

Description: Independent, comprehensive. Awards bachelor's, master's, and doctoral degrees. Founded 1852. Setting: 135-acre urban campus with easy access to San Francisco. Endowment: $184.9 million. Research spending for the previous fiscal year: $3.5 million. Educational spending for the previous fiscal year: $18,707 per student. Total enrollment: 1,309. Faculty: 174 (82 full-time, 92 part-time). Student-undergrad faculty ratio is 10:1. 965 applied, 87% were admitted. 25% from top 10% of their high school class, 55% from top quarter, 90% from top half. 2 National Merit Scholars, 76 student government officers. Full-time: 739 students, 100% women. Part-time: 22 students, 100% women. Students come from 37 states and territories, 4 other countries, 19% from out-of-state. 0.4% American Indian or Alaska Native, non-Hispanic/Latino; 28% Hispanic/Latino; 9% Black or African American, non-Hispanic/Latino; 10% Asian, non-Hispanic/Latino; 0.1% Native Hawaiian or other Pacific Islander, non-Hispanic/Latino; 0.9% international. 15% 25 or older, 64% live on campus, 11% transferred in. Retention: 77% of full-time freshmen returned the following year. Academic areas with the most degrees conferred: social sciences; psychology; English. Core. Calendar: semesters. Services for LD students, advanced placement, accelerated degree program, self-designed majors, independent study, double major, summer session for credit, part-time degree program, adult/continuing education programs, co-op programs and internships, graduate courses open to undergrads. Off campus study at University of California, Berkeley, California State University, Hayward, Sonoma State University, 9 other California colleges, American University, Agnes Scott College, Barnard College, Fisk University, Hollins College,

Howard University, Manhattanville College, Mount Holyoke College, Simmons College, Spelman College, Swarthmore College, Wellesley College, Wheaton College. Study abroad program. ROTC: Army (c).

Entrance Requirements: Options: electronic application, early admission, early action, deferred admission, international baccalaureate accepted. Required: essay, high school transcript, 1 recommendation, college transcripts. Recommended: interview. Entrance: moderately difficult. Application deadlines: 1/15, 11/15 for early action. Notification: 3/30. Transfer credits accepted: Yes. Early action applicants: 264. Early action applicants admitted: 223.

Costs Per Year: Application fee: $50. Comprehensive fee: $43,705 includes full-time tuition ($28,765), mandatory fees ($1492), and college room and board ($13,448). College room only: $7064. Full-time tuition and fees vary according to course load. Room and board charges vary according to board plan and housing facility. Part-time tuition: $1199 per semester hour. Part-time mandatory fees: $1492 per year. Part-time tuition and fees vary according to course load.

Collegiate Environment: Orientation program. Drama-theater group, choral group, student-run newspaper. Social organizations: 63 open to all; 100% of women are members. Most popular organizations: Associated Students of Mills College, The Campanil, The Mills Choir, Mujeres Unidas, Asian Pacific Islander Student Association. Major annual events: Black and White Ball, Midnight Breakfast, Spring Fling. Student services: health clinic, personal-psychological counseling, women's center. Campus security: 24-hour emergency response devices and patrols, late night transport-escort service, controlled dormitory access. 795 college housing spaces available; 487 were occupied in 2018-19. Freshmen guaranteed college housing. Options: coed, women-only housing available. F. W. Olin Library. Books: 190,417 (physical), 156,636 (digital/electronic); Serial titles: 153 (physical), 51,607 (digital/electronic); Databases: 39. Weekly public service hours: 89; students can reserve study rooms. Operations spending for the previous fiscal year: $1.1 million. 335 computers available on campus for general student use. Computer purchase/lease plans available. A campuswide network can be accessed from student residence rooms and from off campus. Students can access the following: online class registration, online degree audit. Staffed computer lab on campus provides training in use of computers, software, and the Internet.

Community Environment: See Laney College.

■ **MIRACOSTA COLLEGE**
One Barnard Dr.
Oceanside, CA 92056
Tel: (760)757-2121; Free: 888-201-8480
Fax: (760)795-6609
E-mail: admissions@miracosta.edu
Web Site: www.miracosta.edu

Description: District-supported, 2-year, coed. Part of California Community College System. Awards certificates, diplomas, transfer associate, and terminal associate degrees. Founded 1934. Setting: 131-acre suburban campus with easy access to San Diego. Endowment: $5 million. Educational spending for the previous fiscal year: $3776 per student. Total enrollment: 14,687. Faculty: 634 (148 full-time, 486 part-time). Student-undergrad faculty ratio is 23:1. Full-time: 5,024 students, 52% women, 48% men. Part-time: 9,663 students, 59% women, 41% men. 2% from out-of-state. 0.3% American Indian or Alaska Native, non-Hispanic/Latino; 33% Hispanic/Latino; 3% Black or African American, non-Hispanic/Latino; 6% Asian, non-Hispanic/Latino; 0.5% Native Hawaiian or other Pacific Islander, non-Hispanic/Latino; 1% international. 32% 25 or older. Core. Calendar: semesters. Academic remediation for entering students, ESL program, services for LD students, advanced placement, accelerated degree program, self-designed majors, honors program, independent study, distance learning, double major, summer session for credit, part-time degree program, adult/continuing education programs, co-op programs and internships. Study abroad program.

Entrance Requirements: Open admission except for nursing program. Options: electronic application, early admission, deferred admission, international baccalaureate accepted. Entrance: noncompetitive. Application deadline: rolling. Transfer credits accepted: Yes.

Collegiate Environment: Orientation program. Drama-theater group, choral group, student-run newspaper. Social organizations: 43 open to all. Most popular organizations: Inter Varsity Christian Fellowship, Accounting and Business Club, Backstage Players (Drama), Gay Straight Alliance, Puente Diversity Network. Major annual events: Graduation, College Recruitment Day, Welcome Back College Hour. Student services: health clinic, personal-psychological counseling. Campus security: 24-hour emergency response devices, student patrols, late night transport-escort service, trained security personnel during class hours. MiraCosta College Library. Operations spending for the previous fiscal year: $138,890. 1,000 computers available on campus for general student use. A campuswide network can be accessed from off-campus. Students can access the following: online class registration. Staffed computer lab on campus.

■ **MISSION COLLEGE**
3000 Mission College Blvd.
Santa Clara, CA 95054-1897
Tel: (408)855-5083
Web Site: www.missioncollege.edu

Description: District-supported, 2-year, coed. Part of California Community College System. Awards certificates, diplomas, transfer associate, and terminal associate degrees. Founded 1977. Setting: 167-acre urban campus with easy access to San Francisco, San Jose. Endowment: $6.8 million. Educational spending for the previous fiscal year: $4269 per student. Total enrollment: 7,868. Faculty: 324 (138 full-time, 186 part-time). Student-undergrad faculty ratio is 22:1. Students come from 18 other countries, 0.3% from out-of-state. 60% 25 or older. Retention: 77% of full-time freshmen returned the following year. Core. Calendar: semesters. Academic remediation for entering students, ESL program, services for LD students, advanced placement, honors program, independent study, distance learning, double major, summer session for credit, part-time degree program, adult/continuing education programs, co-op programs and internships. ROTC: Army (c), Air Force (c).

Entrance Requirements: Open admission except for nursing program. Option: electronic application. Entrance: noncompetitive. Application deadline: rolling. Notification: continuous. Transfer credits accepted: Yes.

Costs Per Year: Application fee: $0. State resident tuition: $46 per unit part-time. Nonresident tuition: $234 per unit part-time. Mandatory fees: $60.50 per year part-time.

Collegiate Environment: Orientation program. Choral group. Social organizations: 12 open to all; 1% of eligible men and 1% of eligible women are members. Most popular organizations: Puente, Associated Student Government. Student services: legal services, health clinic, personal-psychological counseling. Campus security: 24-hour emergency response devices, late night transport-escort service, district police department, evening administrators. Mission College Library. Books: 65,071 (physical); Serial titles: 19,025 (digital/electronic); Databases: 59. Weekly public service hours: 55; students can reserve study rooms. Operations spending for the previous fiscal year: $900,000. 120 computers available on campus for general student use. A campuswide network can be accessed from off-campus. Students can access the following: online class registration. Staffed computer lab on campus provides training in use of computers, software, and the Internet.

■ **MODESTO JUNIOR COLLEGE**
435 College Ave.
Modesto, CA 95350-5800
Tel: (209)575-6498
E-mail: mjcadmissions@mail.yosemite.cc.ca.us
Web Site: www.mjc.edu

Description: District-supported, 2-year, coed. Part of Yosemite Community College District System. Awards certificates, transfer associate, and terminal associate degrees. Founded 1921. Setting: 229-acre urban campus. Educational spending for the previous fiscal year: $4217 per student. Total enrollment: 19,307. Faculty: 612 (267 full-time, 345 part-time). Student-undergrad faculty ratio is 29:1. Full-time: 6,874 students, 55% women, 45% men. Part-time: 12,433 students, 61% women, 39% men. 36% 25 or older, 4% transferred in. Retention: 73% of full-time freshmen returned the following year. Core. Calendar: semesters. Academic remediation for entering students, ESL program, services for LD students, advanced placement, honors program, independent study, distance learning, summer session for credit, part-time degree program, adult/continuing education programs, co-op programs. Study abroad program.

Entrance Requirements: Open admission. Option: electronic application. Recommended: high school transcript. Entrance: noncompetitive. Application deadline: rolling. Notification: continuous.

Collegiate Environment: Orientation program. Drama-theater group, choral group, student-run newspaper, radio station. Social organizations: 24 open to all. Most popular organizations: Young Farmers, Red Nations, Psychology Club, Alpha Gamma Sigma, MECHA. Major annual events: Transfer Day/

College Night, Job Fair, Club Fair. Student services: health clinic, personal-psychological counseling. Campus security: 24-hour emergency response devices and patrols, late night transport-escort service. Modesto Junior College Library. 137 computers available on campus for general student use. A campuswide network can be accessed from off-campus. Students can access the following: online class registration. Staffed computer lab on campus provides training in use of computers, software, and the Internet.

Community Environment: Modesto is located in the heart of the San Joaquin Valley and is the access point for the Sonora Pass vacationland in the Stanislaus National Forest, Mother Lode Country and the Big Oak Flat route to Yosemite. Modesto is the county seat of Stanislaus County. Churches of all denominations, a library, hospitals, plus the usual businesses make up the City of Modesto. There are 20 parks, playgrounds, golf courses, tennis courts, swimming pools for recreational facilities plus areas where there is boating, fishing, hunting and skiing. Part-time employment is available.

■ **MONTEREY PENINSULA COLLEGE**
980 Fremont St.
Monterey, CA 93940-4799
Tel: (831)646-4000
Fax: (831)655-2627
Web Site: www.mpc.edu

Description: District-supported, 2-year, coed. Part of California Community College System. Awards certificates, transfer associate, and terminal associate degrees. Founded 1947. Setting: 87-acre small town campus. Total enrollment: 14,074. Faculty: 317 (136 full-time, 181 part-time). Students come from 29 states and territories, 47 other countries. Core. Calendar: semesters. Academic remediation for entering students, ESL program, services for LD students, advanced placement, summer session for credit, part-time degree program, adult/continuing education programs, co-op programs.

Entrance Requirements: Open admission except for nonresident aliens. Option: early admission. Entrance: noncompetitive. Application deadline: rolling. Notification: continuous.

Collegiate Environment: Drama-theater group, choral group, student-run newspaper. Student services: health clinic, personal-psychological counseling, women's center. Campus security: 24-hour emergency response devices, late night transport-escort service. Monterey Peninsula College Library. 120 computers available on campus for general student use. A campuswide network can be accessed from off-campus. Staffed computer lab on campus.

Community Environment: Monterey Peninsula's population is approximately 150,000 including the cities of Carmel, Carmel Valley, Marina, Monterey, Pacific Grove, Pebble Beach, and Seaside. Monterey is a good two hour drive south of San Francisco on Highway 1. Airlines and buses serve the area. The climate is pleasing: average summer temperature is 60 and winter average is 51 degrees. This is the home of the Bach Festival, Golf Tournaments, Sports Car Races, the Monterey Jazz and Blues Festivals, and the County Fair. Artists, photographers, and writers enjoy Monterey for its beautiful scenery and good weather. Little theatre groups, music groups, art council and symphony guilds make up the cultural atmosphere of the city. Monterey Peninsula is a popular playground with several golf courses, facilities for fishing, boating, hunting and tennis. There are twelve championship golf courses in the area.

■ **MOORPARK COLLEGE**
7075 Campus Rd.
Moorpark, CA 93021-1695
Tel: (805)378-1400
Web Site: www.moorparkcollege.edu

Description: District-supported, 2-year, coed. Part of Ventura County Community College District System. Awards certificates, transfer associate, and terminal associate degrees. Founded 1967. Setting: 121-acre small town campus with easy access to Los Angeles. Total enrollment: 13,750. Faculty: 577 (176 full-time, 401 part-time). Student-undergrad faculty ratio is 30:1. Students come from 50 other countries. 28% 25 or older. Core. Calendar: semesters. Academic remediation for entering students, ESL program, services for LD students, advanced placement, honors program, independent study, distance learning, summer session for credit, part-time degree program, adult/continuing education programs, co-op programs and internships.

Entrance Requirements: Open admission except for nursing, exotic animal training programs. Options: electronic application, early admission, deferred

admission. Recommended: high school transcript. Required for some: high school transcript. Entrance: noncompetitive. Application deadline: rolling. Notification: continuous.

Collegiate Environment: Student-run newspaper. Major annual event: Multicultural Day. Student services: health clinic, personal-psychological counseling, women's center. Campus security: 24-hour patrols. 80 computers available on campus for general student use. Students can access the following: online class registration. Staffed computer lab on campus.

Community Environment: See California Lutheran University.

■ **MORENO VALLEY COLLEGE**
16130 Lasselle St.
Moreno Valley, CA 92551
Tel: (951)571-6100
E-mail: admissions@mvc.edu
Web Site: www.mvc.edu

Description: District-supported, 2-year, coed. Awards transfer associate and terminal associate degrees. Founded 2010. Setting: suburban campus. Total enrollment: 10,413. Faculty: 437 (75 full-time, 362 part-time). Academic remediation for entering students, ESL program, honors program, distance learning.

Entrance Requirements: Open admission. Option: electronic application. Application deadline: rolling. Notification: continuous.

Collegiate Environment: Campus security: late night transport-escort service.

■ **MOUNT SAINT MARY'S UNIVERSITY**
12001 Chalon Rd.
Los Angeles, CA 90049
Tel: (310)954-4000; Free: 800-999-9893
E-mail: admissions@msmu.edu
Web Site: www.msmu.edu

Description: Independent Roman Catholic, comprehensive, coed. Administratively affiliated with Sisters of St. Joseph of Carondelet. Awards associate, bachelor's, master's, and doctoral degrees and post-master's certificates. Founded 1925. Setting: 56-acre urban campus with easy access to Los Angeles. Endowment: $138.5 million. Research spending for the previous fiscal year: $149,392. Educational spending for the previous fiscal year: $9653 per student. Total enrollment: 3,280. Faculty: 453 (106 full-time, 347 part-time). Student-undergrad faculty ratio is 11:1. 2,352 applied, 81% were admitted. 9% from top 10% of their high school class, 43% from top quarter, 78% from top half. Full-time: 2,054 students, 96% women, 4% men. Part-time: 547 students, 87% women, 13% men. Students come from 12 states and territories, 16 other countries, 3% from out-of-state. 0.2% American Indian or Alaska Native, non-Hispanic/Latino; 64% Hispanic/Latino; 7% Black or African American, non-Hispanic/Latino; 15% Asian, non-Hispanic/Latino; 0.5% Native Hawaiian or other Pacific Islander, non-Hispanic/Latino; 0.1% international. 29% 25 or older, 24% live on campus, 2% transferred in. Retention: 76% of full-time freshmen returned the following year. Academic areas with the most degrees conferred: health professions and related sciences; social sciences; business/marketing. Core. Calendar: semesters. Academic remediation for entering students, ESL program, services for LD students, advanced placement, accelerated degree program, self-designed majors, honors program, independent study, distance learning, double major, summer session for credit, part-time degree program, co-op programs and internships, graduate courses open to undergrads. Off campus study at University of Southern California, University of California, Los Angeles, Sisters of Saint Joseph College Consortium, University of Judaism. Study abroad program.

Entrance Requirements: Options: electronic application, early admission, early action, international baccalaureate accepted. Required: essay, high school transcript, minimum 2.45 high school GPA, 1 recommendation. Recommended: 2 recommendations, interview. Required for some: SAT or ACT. Application deadlines: 8/1, 12/1 for early action. Notification: continuous, 1/30 for early action. SAT Reasoning Test deadline: 8/1. Transfer credits accepted: Yes. Early action applicants: 885. Early action applicants admitted: 771.

Costs Per Year: Comprehensive fee: $53,405 includes full-time tuition ($40,018), mandatory fees ($1152), and college room and board ($12,235). Full-time tuition and fees vary according to course load, degree level, and program. Room and board charges vary according to board plan and housing facility.

Collegiate Environment: Orientation program. Drama-theater group, choral group, student-run newspaper. Social organizations: 31 open to all; national sororities, local sororities; 1% of women are members. Most popular organizations: Sakura Society, Pangkat Pilipino, MSMU Women in Film, Athenian Print, Na Pua O Ka'Aina (NPOKA). Major annual events: Lighting of the Circle, Student Involvement Fair, Spring Carnival. Student services: health clinic, personal-psychological counseling, women's center. Campus security: 24-hour emergency response devices and patrols, late night transport-escort service, controlled dormitory access. Charles Willard Coe Library plus 1 other. Books: 88,758 (physical), 396,855 (digital/electronic); Serial titles: 168 (physical), 39,316 (digital/electronic); Databases: 215. Weekly public service hours: 91; study areas open 24 hours, 5-7 days a week. Operations spending for the previous fiscal year: $2.2 million. 170 computers available on campus for general student use. A campuswide network can be accessed from student residence rooms and from off campus. Students can access the following: online class registration. Staffed computer lab on campus provides training in use of computers, software, and the Internet.

■ MT. SAN ANTONIO COLLEGE

1100 N Grand Ave.
Walnut, CA 91789-1399
Tel: (909)594-5611
Web Site: www.mtsac.edu

Description: District-supported, 2-year, coed. Part of California Community College System. Awards certificates, diplomas, transfer associate, and terminal associate degrees. Founded 1946. Setting: 421-acre suburban campus with easy access to Los Angeles. Total enrollment: 29,960. Faculty: 1,328 (420 full-time, 908 part-time). Student-undergrad faculty ratio is 24:1. Full-time: 2,581 students, 48% women, 52% men. Part-time: 1,987 students, 49% women, 51% men. 0.1% American Indian or Alaska Native, non-Hispanic/Latino; 63% Hispanic/Latino; 4% Black or African American, non-Hispanic/Latino; 17% Asian, non-Hispanic/Latino; 0.3% Native Hawaiian or other Pacific Islander, non-Hispanic/Latino; 2% international. Retention: 79% of full-time freshmen returned the following year. Core. Calendar: semesters. Academic remediation for entering students, ESL program, services for LD students, advanced placement, honors program, independent study, distance learning, double major, summer session for credit, part-time degree program, adult/continuing education programs, co-op programs. Study abroad program. ROTC: Army, Air Force.

Entrance Requirements: Open admission. Options: electronic application, early admission, deferred admission. Required for some: high school transcript. Notification: continuous.

Costs Per Year: State resident tuition: $1288 full-time, $46 per unit part-time. Nonresident tuition: $9352 full-time, $334 per unit part-time. Mandatory fees: $62 full-time, $62 per term part-time. Full-time tuition and fees vary according to course load and program. Part-time tuition and fees vary according to course load and program.

Collegiate Environment: Orientation program. Drama-theater group, choral group, student-run radio station. Social organizations: 40 open to all. Most popular organizations: Alpha Gamma Sigma, Muslim Student Association, Student Government, Asian Student Association, Kasama-Filipino Student Organization. Major annual events: Cinco de Mayo, Asian Awareness Week, Join-a-Club. Student services: health clinic, personal-psychological counseling, women's center. Campus security: 24-hour emergency response devices and patrols, late night transport-escort service. Learning Resources Center. Books: 75,587 (physical), 82,336 (digital/electronic); Databases: 113. Students can reserve study rooms. 3,000 computers available on campus for general student use. A campuswide network can be accessed from off-campus. Students can access the following: online class registration. Staffed computer lab on campus provides training in use of computers, software, and the Internet.

■ MT. SAN JACINTO COLLEGE

1499 N State St.
San Jacinto, CA 92583-2399
Tel: (909)487-6752
Fax: (909)654-6738
Web Site: www.msjc.edu

Description: District-supported, 2-year, coed. Part of California Community College System. Awards certificates, diplomas, transfer associate, and terminal associate degrees. Founded 1963. Setting: 180-acre suburban campus with easy access to San Diego. Endowment: $1.6 million. Research spending for the previous fiscal year: $427,967. Educational spending for the previous fiscal year: $10,052 per student. Total enrollment: 14,170. Faculty: 671 (131 full-time, 540 part-time). Student-undergrad faculty ratio is 27:1.

15,299 applied, 100% were admitted. Full-time: 5,105 students, 56% women, 44% men. Part-time: 9,065 students, 58% women, 42% men. Students come from 4 states and territories. 0.5% American Indian or Alaska Native, non-Hispanic/Latino; 43% Hispanic/Latino; 8% Black or African American, non-Hispanic/Latino; 6% Asian, non-Hispanic/Latino; 0.5% Native Hawaiian or other Pacific Islander, non-Hispanic/Latino. 36% 25 or older, 7% transferred in. Retention: 70% of full-time freshmen returned the following year. Core. Calendar: semesters. Academic remediation for entering students, ESL program, services for LD students, advanced placement, honors program, distance learning, double major, summer session for credit, part-time degree program, adult/continuing education programs. Off campus study at Citrus College. Study abroad program.

Entrance Requirements: Open admission except for nursing program. Option: early admission. Recommended: high school transcript. Entrance: noncompetitive. Application deadline: rolling. Transfer credits accepted: Yes.

Collegiate Environment: Drama-theater group. Student services: personal-psychological counseling. Campus security: part-time trained security personnel. Milo P. Johnson Library plus 1 other. Operations spending for the previous fiscal year: $1.2 million.

■ MT. SIERRA COLLEGE

800 Royal Oaks Dr.
Ste. 101
Monrovia, CA 91016
Tel: (626)873-2100; Free: 888-828-8800
Fax: (626)359-5528
Web Site: www.mtsierra.edu

Description: Proprietary, 4-year, coed. Awards bachelor's degrees. Founded 1990. Setting: 5-acre suburban campus. Total enrollment: 131. Full-time: 113 students, 26% women, 74% men. Part-time: 18 students, 39% women, 61% men. 0.8% American Indian or Alaska Native, non-Hispanic/Latino; 35% Hispanic/Latino; 3% Black or African American, non-Hispanic/Latino; 29% Asian, non-Hispanic/Latino; 2% Native Hawaiian or other Pacific Islander, non-Hispanic/Latino. Core. Calendar: quarters. Summer session for credit, adult/continuing education programs.

Entrance Requirements: Options: electronic application, international baccalaureate accepted. Required: essay, high school transcript, interview. Entrance: moderately difficult.

Collegiate Environment: Orientation program. Campus security: 24-hour emergency response devices, student patrols, late night transport-escort service. Mt. Sierra College Learning Resource Center.

■ MTI COLLEGE

5221 Madison Ave.
Sacramento, CA 95841
Tel: (916)339-1500
Fax: (916)339-0305
Web Site: www.mticollege.edu

Description: Proprietary, 2-year, coed. Awards diplomas, transfer associate, and terminal associate degrees. Founded 1965. Setting: 5-acre suburban campus with easy access to Sacramento. Total enrollment: 900. Student-undergrad faculty ratio is 15:1. 629 applied, 62% were admitted. 62% 25 or older. Calendar: continuous.

Entrance Requirements: Required: essay, high school transcript, interview, MTI Assessment. Transfer credits accepted: Yes.

■ MUSICIANS INSTITUTE

1655 N McCadden Pl.
Hollywood, CA 90028
Tel: (323)462-1384; Free: 800-255-PLAY
Fax: (323)462-6978
Web Site: www.mi.edu

Description: Proprietary, 4-year, coed. Awards associate and bachelor's degrees. Founded 1976. Setting: urban campus. Total enrollment: 1,337. Faculty: 204 (108 full-time, 96 part-time). Student-undergrad faculty ratio is 10:1. 1,201 applied, 98% were admitted. Students come from 54 other countries. 1% American Indian or Alaska Native, non-Hispanic/Latino; 13% Hispanic/Latino; 7% Black or African American, non-Hispanic/Latino; 4% Asian, non-Hispanic/Latino; 0.5% Native Hawaiian or other Pacific Islander, non-Hispanic/Latino; 25% international. 32% 25 or older. Calendar: quarters. Services for LD students, summer session for credit, part-time degree program, internships.

Entrance Requirements: Options: electronic application, deferred admission, international baccalaureate accepted. Required: high school transcript,

1 recommendation. Required for some: essay, 2 recommendations, SAT or ACT. Entrance: minimally difficult. Application deadline: rolling. Notification: continuous. SAT Reasoning Test deadline: 7/31. SAT Subject Test deadline: 7/31. Transfer credits accepted: Yes.

Collegiate Environment: Orientation program. Student services: personal-psychological counseling. Campus security: 24-hour emergency response devices and patrols. Musicians Institute Library.

■ **NAPA VALLEY COLLEGE**
2277 Napa-Vallejo Hwy.
Napa, CA 94558-6236
Tel: (707)253-3000; Free: 800-826-1077
Fax: (707)253-3064
Web Site: www.napavalley.edu
Description: District-supported, 2-year, coed. Part of California Community College System. Awards certificates, transfer associate, and terminal associate degrees. Founded 1942. Setting: 188-acre suburban campus with easy access to San Francisco. Total enrollment: 6,908. Faculty: 311 (99 full-time, 212 part-time). Student-undergrad faculty ratio is 22:1. 2,000 applied, 100% were admitted. Full-time: 1,909 students, 57% women, 43% men. Part-time: 4,999 students, 62% women, 38% men. Retention: 66% of full-time freshmen returned the following year. Core. Calendar: semesters. Academic remediation for entering students, ESL program, services for LD students, advanced placement, distance learning, summer session for credit, part-time degree program, co-op programs. Study abroad program.
Entrance Requirements: Open admission except for allied health programs. Required for some: high school transcript. Entrance: noncompetitive. Application deadline: rolling.
Collegiate Environment: Drama-theater group, choral group, student-run newspaper. Most popular organizations: Hispano-Americano Club, African-American Club, Environmental Action Coalition, International Student Club, Phi Theta Kappa. Major annual events: Black History Month, Cinco de Mayo, Native American Pow Wow. Student services: personal-psychological counseling, women's center. Campus security: late night transport-escort service. Napa Valley College Library plus 1 other. 90 computers available on campus for general student use. Staffed computer lab on campus.
Community Environment: Population 74,700. The town of Napa, in the southern wine district, is the center of a fruit and nut raising region as well as the southeastern entrance to the Redwood Empire. Located in the Napa Valley area, there are numerous wineries, most of which are open to the public for tours. The climate is delightful. Buses and trains serve the area. Napa has churches of all denominations, hospitals, clinics, and libraries. Recreation includes parks, picnic grounds, swimming pools, and golf courses.

■ **NATIONAL CAREER COLLEGE**
14355 Roscoe Blvd.
Panorama City, CA 91402
Tel: (818)988-2300
Web Site: www.nccusa.edu
Description: Proprietary, 2-year, coed. Awards transfer associate and terminal associate degrees.

■ **NATIONAL POLYTECHNIC COLLEGE**
6630 Telegraph Rd.
Commerce, CA 90040
Tel: (323)728-9636
Web Site: www.npcollege.edu
Description: Proprietary, 2-year, coed. Awards certificates, transfer associate, and terminal associate degrees.

■ **NATIONAL UNIVERSITY**
11255 N Torrey Pines Rd.
La Jolla, CA 92037-1011
Tel: (619)563-7100; Free: 800-628-8648
Fax: (619)563-7299
Web Site: www.nu.edu
Description: Independent, comprehensive, coed. Part of National University System. Awards associate, bachelor's, master's, and doctoral degrees and post-master's certificates. Founded 1971. Setting: urban campus with easy access to San Diego. Total enrollment: 16,930. Faculty: 1,390 (265 full-time, 1,125 part-time). Student-undergrad faculty ratio is 17:1. Full-time: 2,884 students, 56% women, 44% men. Part-time: 4,851 students, 58% women, 42% men. Students come from 52 states and territories, 75 other countries,

11% from out-of-state. 0.5% American Indian or Alaska Native, non-Hispanic/Latino; 26% Hispanic/Latino; 10% Black or African American, non-Hispanic/Latino; 9% Asian, non-Hispanic/Latino; 1% Native Hawaiian or other Pacific Islander, non-Hispanic/Latino; 2% international. 82% 25 or older, 43% transferred in. Retention: 50% of full-time freshmen returned the following year. Academic areas with the most degrees conferred: health professions and related sciences; business/marketing; education. Core. Calendar: continuous. Academic remediation for entering students, ESL program, services for LD students, advanced placement, accelerated degree program, independent study, distance learning, double major, summer session for credit, part-time degree program, adult/continuing education programs, co-op programs and internships, graduate courses open to undergrads. Off campus study. Study abroad program. ROTC: Army (c), Air Force (c).
Entrance Requirements: Open admission. Options: electronic application, deferred admission, international baccalaureate accepted. Required: high school transcript, minimum 2 high school GPA. Required for some: essay. Entrance: noncompetitive. Application deadline: rolling. Notification: continuous. Transfer credits accepted: Yes.
Costs Per Year: Tuition: $13,320 full-time, $370 per unit part-time.
Collegiate Environment: Orientation program. Campus security: 24-hour emergency response devices and patrols, late night transport-escort service. College housing not available. National University Library. Books: 201,123 (physical), 368,486 (digital/electronic); Serial titles: 3,050 (physical), 95,256 (digital/electronic); Databases: 190. Weekly public service hours: 72; students can reserve study rooms. 2,800 computers available on campus for general student use. A campuswide network can be accessed from off-campus. Students can access the following: online class registration. Staffed computer lab on campus provides training in use of computers, software, and the Internet.

■ **NEW YORK FILM ACADEMY**
3300 Riverside Dr.
Burbank, CA 91505
Tel: (818)333-3558
Fax: (818)333-3557
E-mail: studios@nyfa.edu
Web Site: www.nyfa.edu
Description: Independent, comprehensive, coed. Awards associate, bachelor's, and master's degrees. Founded 1992. Setting: suburban campus with easy access to Los Angeles, New York, Miami.
Entrance Requirements: Required: essay, high school transcript, 2 recommendations, portfolio, SAT or ACT.

■ **NEWSCHOOL OF ARCHITECTURE AND DESIGN**
1249 F St.
San Diego, CA 92101-6634
Tel: (619)235-4100; Free: 800-490-7081
E-mail: knielson@newschoolarch.edu
Web Site: www.newschoolarch.edu
Description: Proprietary, comprehensive, coed. Awards bachelor's and master's degrees. Founded 1980. Setting: 1-acre urban campus. Total enrollment: 515. Student-undergrad faculty ratio is 9:1. 39 applied, 79% were admitted. Full-time: 368 students, 31% women, 69% men. Part-time: 40 students, 33% women, 67% men. 0.2% American Indian or Alaska Native, non-Hispanic/Latino; 36% Hispanic/Latino; 3% Black or African American, non-Hispanic/Latino; 8% Asian, non-Hispanic/Latino; 0.2% Native Hawaiian or other Pacific Islander, non-Hispanic/Latino; 22% international. Retention: 62% of full-time freshmen returned the following year. Core. Calendar: quarters. Academic remediation for entering students, ESL program, advanced placement, accelerated degree program, summer session for credit, part-time degree program, adult/continuing education programs, co-op programs and internships, graduate courses open to undergrads. Off campus study. Study abroad program.
Entrance Requirements: Options: electronic application, early decision, international baccalaureate accepted. Required: essay, minimum 2.5 high school GPA. Recommended: recommendations, SAT or ACT. Required for some: high school transcript, portfolio. Entrance: moderately difficult. Application deadlines: rolling, 8/30 for nonresidents, 7/1 for early decision. Notification: continuous, continuous for nonresidents. SAT Reasoning Test deadline: 8/18. SAT Subject Test deadline: 8/15. Transfer credits accepted: Yes.
Collegiate Environment: Orientation program. Student-run newspaper. Social organizations: 7 open to all. Most popular organizations: American

Institute of Architects student chapter, Student Council, Night Owls, Alpha Rho Chi - Numisius Chapter, CMSA. Major annual events: Convocation, Day of Service, Welcome Week. Student services: personal-psychological counseling. Campus security: 24-hour emergency response devices. Richard Welsh Library at NewSchool of Architecture and Design. Books: 15,502 (physical), 123 (digital/electronic); Serial titles: 52 (physical), 1 (digital/electronic); Databases: 8. Weekly public service hours: 68.

■ **NORCO COLLEGE**
2001 Third St.
Norco, CA 92860
Tel: (951)372-7000
E-mail: admissionsnorco@norcocollege.edu
Web Site: www.norcocollege.edu
Description: District-supported, 2-year, coed. Awards certificates, transfer associate, and terminal associate degrees. Founded 2010. Setting: 141-acre urban campus with easy access to Los Angeles. Total enrollment: 9,399. Faculty: 271 (68 full-time, 203 part-time). 0.3% American Indian or Alaska Native, non-Hispanic/Latino; 57% Hispanic/Latino; 6% Black or African American, non-Hispanic/Latino; 6% Asian, non-Hispanic/Latino; 3% Native Hawaiian or other Pacific Islander, non-Hispanic/Latino. Academic remediation for entering students, ESL program, services for LD students, honors program, distance learning, summer session for credit.
Entrance Requirements: Open admission. Option: electronic application. Application deadline: rolling. Notification: continuous.
Collegiate Environment: Orientation program.

■ **NORTH-WEST COLLEGE**
2121 W Garvey Ave.
West Covina, CA 91790
Tel: (626)960-5046; Free: 888-408-4211
Fax: (626)960-7985
Web Site: www.nw.edu
Description: Proprietary, 2-year, coed. Awards certificates, transfer associate, and terminal associate degrees. Founded 1966.

■ **NORTHCENTRAL UNIVERSITY**
2488 Historic Decatur Rd.
Ste. 100
San Diego, CA 92106
Free: 866-776-0331
Web Site: www.ncu.edu
Description: Proprietary, upper-level, coed. Awards bachelor's, master's, and doctoral degrees and post-master's certificates (offers only distance learning programs). Total enrollment: 10,698. Faculty: 478 (93 full-time, 385 part-time). Full-time: 14 students, 57% women, 43% men. Part-time: 75 students, 75% women, 25% men. Students come from 29 states and territories, 1 other country. 1% American Indian or Alaska Native, non-Hispanic/Latino; 9% Hispanic/Latino; 21% Black or African American, non-Hispanic/Latino; 2% Asian, non-Hispanic/Latino. 94% 25 or older, 15% transferred in. Academic areas with the most degrees conferred: psychology; business/marketing; education. Core. Calendar: continuous. Services for LD students, accelerated degree program, distance learning, part-time degree program.
Entrance Requirements: Transfer credits accepted: Yes.
Collegiate Environment: Northcentral University Library (Virtual). Databases: 123. Weekly public service hours: 79. Operations spending for the previous fiscal year: $853,855.

■ **NORTHWESTERN POLYTECHNIC UNIVERSITY**
47671 Westinghouse Dr.
Fremont, CA 94539-7482
Tel: (510)592-9688
Fax: (510)657-8975
E-mail: admission@npu.edu
Web Site: www.npu.edu
Description: Independent, comprehensive, coed. Awards bachelor's, master's, and doctoral degrees. Founded 1984. Setting: 3-acre urban campus with easy access to San Francisco, San Jose. Total enrollment: 927. Faculty: 87 (31 full-time, 56 part-time). Student-undergrad faculty ratio is 16:1. 249 applied, 99% were admitted. Students come from 7 states and territories, 11 other countries, 7% from out-of-state. 45% 25 or older, 12% live on campus. Retention: 89% of full-time freshmen returned the following year. Core. Calendar: trimesters. ESL program, advanced placement,

distance learning, summer session for credit, part-time degree program, adult/continuing education programs, graduate courses open to undergrads.
Entrance Requirements: Options: electronic application, deferred admission, international baccalaureate accepted. Required: high school transcript, minimum 2 high school GPA. Recommended: SAT. Required for some: essay, interview. Application deadline: 8/2. Notification: continuous.
Collegiate Environment: Orientation program. Most popular organizations: NPU Student Association, Table Tennis Club, IEEE Student Chapter, softball club. Major annual events: Halloween Party, Dance Party, Picnic. Campus security: late night transport-escort service. Northwest Polytechnic University Library. Operations spending for the previous fiscal year: $750,000. 200 computers available on campus for general student use. A campuswide network can be accessed from student residence rooms and from off campus. Students can access the following: online class registration, online learning resource services. Staffed computer lab on campus.

■ **NOTRE DAME DE NAMUR UNIVERSITY**
1500 Ralston Ave.
Belmont, CA 94002-1908
Tel: (650)508-3500; Free: 800-263-0545
Fax: (650)508-3660
Web Site: www.ndnu.edu
Description: Independent Roman Catholic, comprehensive, coed. Awards bachelor's, master's, and doctoral degrees. Founded 1851. Setting: 50-acre suburban campus with easy access to San Francisco. Endowment: $22.5 million. Educational spending for the previous fiscal year: $12,046 per student. Total enrollment: 1,625. Faculty: 230 (54 full-time, 176 part-time). Student-undergrad faculty ratio is 11:1. 2,056 applied, 80% were admitted. 8% from top 10% of their high school class, 28% from top quarter, 61% from top half. Full-time: 722 students, 66% women, 34% men. Part-time: 215 students, 69% women, 31% men. Students come from 24 states and territories, 27 other countries, 10% from out-of-state. 0.2% American Indian or Alaska Native, non-Hispanic/Latino; 43% Hispanic/Latino; 6% Black or African American, non-Hispanic/Latino; 11% Asian, non-Hispanic/Latino; 2% Native Hawaiian or other Pacific Islander, non-Hispanic/Latino; 6% international. 28% 25 or older, 46% live on campus, 10% transferred in. Retention: 68% of full-time freshmen returned the following year. Academic areas with the most degrees conferred: business/marketing; psychology; public administration and social services. Core. Calendar: semesters. Academic remediation for entering students, ESL program, services for LD students, advanced placement, accelerated degree program, self-designed majors, independent study, double major, summer session for credit, part-time degree program, adult/continuing education programs, co-op programs and internships, graduate courses open to undergrads. Off campus study at Trinity College (DC), Emmanuel College (MA). Study abroad program. ROTC: Air Force (c).
Entrance Requirements: Options: electronic application, early admission, early action, deferred admission, international baccalaureate accepted. Required: essay, high school transcript, SAT or ACT. Required for some: interview, audition for music programs. Entrance: moderately difficult. Application deadline: rolling. Notification: continuous. SAT Reasoning Test deadline: 8/1. Transfer credits accepted: Yes.
Costs Per Year: Application fee: $50. Comprehensive fee: $49,844 includes full-time tuition ($34,910), mandatory fees ($440), and college room and board ($14,494). College room only: $9312. Room and board charges vary according to board plan and housing facility. Part-time tuition: $1126 per credit hour. Part-time mandatory fees: $50 per term. Part-time tuition and fees vary according to course load and program.
Collegiate Environment: Orientation program. Drama-theater group, choral group, student-run newspaper. Social organizations: 23 open to all. Student services: health clinic, personal-psychological counseling. Campus security: 24-hour emergency response devices and patrols, late night transport-escort service, controlled dormitory access. The Carl Gellert and Celia Berta Gellert Library plus 1 other. Books: 88,990 (physical), 194,534 (digital/electronic); Databases: 50. 100 computers available on campus for general student use. A campuswide network can be accessed from student residence rooms and from off campus. Students can access the following: online class registration. Staffed computer lab on campus provides training in use of computers, software, and the Internet.
Community Environment: Population 24,500, Belmont is located 25 miles south of San Francisco, and has the advantages of a suburban location. The climate is ideal. The average high is 69.5 degrees, the low 47 degrees and the average rainfall is 19.8 inches. It is on the main line of Southern Pacific Railroad and San Francisco International Airport is 12 miles away. Students

attending Notre Dame are close enough to San Francisco to enjoy all the cultural and recreational benefits such as major drama, music, and opera productions, films, rock group performances, and professional and collegiate sports. The beaches of the Pacific Ocean are 12 miles away. Two hours to the north is the wine country, and a few hours' drive east are the historic gold country, Lake Tahoe, and the Sierra Nevada Range with famous facilities for skiing and other winter sports.

■ **OCCIDENTAL COLLEGE**
1600 Campus Rd.
Los Angeles, CA 90041-3314
Tel: (323)259-2500; Free: 800-825-5262
Fax: (323)341-4875
E-mail: admission@oxy.edu
Web Site: www.oxy.edu
Description: Independent, comprehensive, coed. Awards bachelor's and master's degrees. Founded 1887. Setting: 120-acre urban campus with easy access to Los Angeles. Endowment: $413.4 million. Research spending for the previous fiscal year: $3.1 million. Educational spending for the previous fiscal year: $20,429 per student. Total enrollment: 2,055. Faculty: 277 (188 full-time, 89 part-time). Student-undergrad faculty ratio is 9:1. 6,775 applied, 42% were admitted. 62% from top 10% of their high school class, 86% from top quarter, 99% from top half. Full-time: 2,035 students, 58% women, 42% men. Part-time: 20 students, 55% women, 45% men. Students come from 47 states and territories, 58 other countries, 51% from out-of-state. 14% Hispanic/Latino; 5% Black or African American, non-Hispanic/Latino; 13% Asian, non-Hispanic/Latino; 0.2% Native Hawaiian or other Pacific Islander, non-Hispanic/Latino; 7% international. 81% live on campus, 2% transferred in. Retention: 91% of full-time freshmen returned the following year. Academic areas with the most degrees conferred: social sciences; biological/life sciences; visual and performing arts. Core. Calendar: semesters. Services for LD students, advanced placement, self-designed majors, honors program, independent study, double major, internships. Off campus study at Exchange programs with Caltech and Art Center College of Design. Study abroad program. ROTC: Army (c), Air Force (c).
Entrance Requirements: Options: electronic application, early admission, early decision, deferred admission, international baccalaureate accepted. Required: essay, high school transcript, 2 recommendations, SAT or ACT. Recommended: interview, SAT Subject Tests. Entrance: very difficult. Application deadlines: 1/15, 11/15 for early decision plan 1, 1/1 for early decision plan 2. Notification: 3/25, 12/15 for early decision plan 1. SAT Reasoning Test deadline: 2/1. SAT Subject Test deadline: 2/1. Transfer credits accepted: Yes. Applicants placed on waiting list: 1,088. Wait-listed applicants offered admission: 0. Early decision applicants: 307. Early decision applicants admitted: 150.
Costs Per Year: Application fee: $65. Comprehensive fee: $72,610 includes full-time tuition ($55,980), mandatory fees ($596), and college room and board ($16,034). College room only: $9124. Part-time tuition: $2333 per unit.
Collegiate Environment: Orientation program. Drama-theater group, choral group, student-run newspaper, radio station. Social organizations: 101 open to all; national fraternities, national sororities, local sororities; 16% of eligible men and 22% of eligible women are members. Most popular organizations: Dance Production, Outdoor Club, Hawai'i Club, Ski & Snowboard Club, Pulse. Major annual events: Dance Production, Fall Fest/Spring Fest, Apollo Night. Student services: health clinic, personal-psychological counseling, women's center. Campus security: 24-hour emergency response devices and patrols, late night transport-escort service, controlled dormitory access, Surveillance cameras; emergency notification system; blue light phones. 1,624 college housing spaces available; all were occupied in 2018-19. Freshmen guaranteed college housing. On-campus residence required through junior year. Options: coed, women-only housing available. Mary Norton Clapp Library and Academic Commons plus 2 others. Study areas open 24 hours, 5-7 days a week; students can reserve study rooms. Operations spending for the previous fiscal year: $2.6 million. 200 computers available on campus for general student use. Computer purchase/lease plans available. A campuswide network can be accessed. Students can access the following: online class registration. Staffed computer lab on campus (open 24 hours a day) provides training in use of computers, software, and the Internet.
Community Environment: See University of California - Los Angeles.

■ **OHLONE COLLEGE**
43600 Mission Blvd.
Fremont, CA 94539-5884

Tel: (510)659-6000
Web Site: www.ohlone.edu
Description: District-supported, 2-year, coed. Part of California Community College System. Awards certificates, transfer associate, and terminal associate degrees (profile includes campuses in Fremont and Newark CA). Founded 1967. Setting: 530-acre suburban campus with easy access to San Jose. Total enrollment: 11,318. Faculty: 451 (115 full-time, 336 part-time). Student-undergrad faculty ratio is 27:1. Students come from 11 states and territories, 40 other countries, 0.2% from out-of-state. 0.2% American Indian or Alaska Native, non-Hispanic/Latino; 18% Hispanic/Latino; 4% Black or African American, non-Hispanic/Latino; 30% Asian, non-Hispanic/Latino; 0.7% Native Hawaiian or other Pacific Islander, non-Hispanic/Latino; 3% international. 45% 25 or older. Retention: 55% of full-time freshmen returned the following year. Core. Calendar: semesters. Academic remediation for entering students, ESL program, services for LD students, advanced placement, self-designed majors, honors program, distance learning, double major, summer session for credit, part-time degree program, external degree program, adult/continuing education programs, co-op programs and internships. Off campus study at California Community College system and California State University system. Study abroad program. ROTC: Army (c), Air Force (c).
Entrance Requirements: Open admission except for nursing, respiratory therapy, physical therapy assistant, interpreter preparation programs. Option: early admission. Required for some: high school transcript. Entrance: noncompetitive. Application deadline: rolling. Notification: continuous. Transfer credits accepted: Yes.
Collegiate Environment: Orientation program. Drama-theater group, choral group, student-run newspaper, radio station. Most popular organizations: Associated Students of Ohlone (ASOC), American Sign Language Club (ASL Club), Asian Pacific American Student Association, M.E.Ch.A. Club (Spanish: Movimiento Estudiantil Chican@ de Aztlan), Science and Math Seminar Series (Science, Math, and Engineering). Major annual events: Spring and Fall Career Expo, Transfer Days, Freshman Days. Student services: health clinic, personal-psychological counseling. Campus security: 24-hour emergency response devices and patrols, late night transport-escort service. Ohlone College Library plus 1 other. 250 computers available on campus for general student use. A campuswide network can be accessed. Students can access the following: online class registration. Staffed computer lab on campus provides training in use of computers, software, and the Internet.
Community Environment: The Fremont area is one of the faster growing areas of California. Mild climate is enjoyed in this city located on the San Francisco Bay. Fremont is within easy driving distance of San Francisco, Berkeley, Oakland and Palo Alto, and enjoys the cultural advantages of those cities. Beaches are nearby for swimming, boating and fishing. There are numerous golf courses and parks for recreational facilities. Shopping facilities are good.

■ **ORANGE COAST COLLEGE**
2701 Fairview Rd.
Costa Mesa, CA 92626
Tel: (714)432-5072
Web Site: www.orangecoastcollege.edu
Description: District-supported, 2-year, coed. Part of Coast Community College District System. Awards certificates, transfer associate, and terminal associate degrees. Founded 1947. Setting: 164-acre suburban campus with easy access to Los Angeles. Endowment: $18.2 million. Research spending for the previous fiscal year: $598,626. Educational spending for the previous fiscal year: $2761 per student. Total enrollment: 21,731. Faculty: 691 (261 full-time, 430 part-time). Student-undergrad faculty ratio is 32:1. Full-time: 8,561 students, 46% women, 54% men. Part-time: 13,170 students, 50% women, 50% men. Students come from 75 other countries, 2% from out-of-state. 0.2% American Indian or Alaska Native, non-Hispanic/Latino; 34% Hispanic/Latino; 2% Black or African American, non-Hispanic/Latino; 20% Asian, non-Hispanic/Latino; 5% international. 28% 25 or older, 10% transferred in. Core. Calendar: semesters plus summer session. Academic remediation for entering students, ESL program, services for LD students, advanced placement, self-designed majors, freshman honors college, honors program, distance learning, double major, summer session for credit, part-time degree program, external degree program, adult/continuing education programs, co-op programs and internships. Off campus study at Golden West College, Coastline Community College. Study abroad program. ROTC: Army (c), Air Force (c).
Entrance Requirements: Open admission. Option: electronic application. Entrance: noncompetitive. Application deadline: rolling. Notification: continuous. Transfer credits accepted: Yes.

Costs Per Year: Application fee: $0. State resident tuition: $1288 full-time, $46 per unit part-time. Nonresident tuition: $8876 full-time, $256 per unit part-time. Mandatory fees: $900 full-time, $140 per term part-time.

Collegiate Environment: Orientation program. Drama-theater group, choral group, student-run newspaper. Social organizations: 68 open to all. Most popular organizations: Architecture Club, Circle K, Doctors of Tomorrow, Speech, Theater, and Debate, Vietnamese Student Association. Major annual events: Club Rush, ASOCC Angel Tree Gift Drive, Coast Days. Student services: legal services, health clinic, personal-psychological counseling. Campus security: 24-hour emergency response devices and patrols, student patrols, late night transport-escort service. Main library plus 1 other. Books: 108,078 (physical), 24,666 (digital/electronic); Serial titles: 91 (physical), 4 (digital/electronic); Databases: 59. Weekly public service hours: 64; students can reserve study rooms. Operations spending for the previous fiscal year: $1.8 million. 1,515 computers available on campus for general student use. Computer purchase/lease plans available. A campuswide network can be accessed from off-campus. Students can access the following: online class registration. Staffed computer lab on campus.

Community Environment: Costa Mesa, three miles inland from the Pacific Ocean and Highway 101-A, is at the edge of Newport Beach. The city has a moderate climate - mild winters, and cool summer breezes from the ocean. Orange County's economy is derived from defense manufacture, electronics, light industry, housing, business, agriculture, and tourism. The campus is located within 15 minutes of the Orange County Performing Arts Center; Irvine Industrial Center (home of many high-tech industries); South Coast Plaza (one of the nation's largest shopping malls); and the University of California at Irvine (a major educational and research institution). The Los Angeles Museum, Pasadena Art Gallery, and the Griffith Park Observatory and planetarium are 50 miles away. The mountains and the desert are an easy two-hour drive. Recreational activities locally are boating, fishing, and all forms of water sports to be found on its beaches, canals, and waterways. Part-time employment is available.

■ **OTIS COLLEGE OF ART AND DESIGN**
9045 Lincoln Blvd.
Los Angeles, CA 90045-9785
Tel: (310)665-6800; Free: 800-527-OTIS
Fax: (310)665-6805
Web Site: www.otis.edu
Description: Independent, comprehensive, coed. Awards bachelor's and master's degrees. Founded 1918. Setting: 5-acre urban campus. Educational spending for the previous fiscal year: $36,350 per student. Total enrollment: 1,086. Faculty: 272 (55 full-time, 217 part-time). Student-undergrad faculty ratio is 4:1. 1,584 applied, 46% were admitted. Full-time: 1,018 students, 65% women, 35% men. Part-time: 14 students, 50% women, 50% men. Students come from 26 states and territories, 15 other countries, 13% from out-of-state. 0.6% American Indian or Alaska Native, non-Hispanic/Latino; 13% Hispanic/Latino; 3% Black or African American, non-Hispanic/Latino; 32% Asian, non-Hispanic/Latino; 0.3% Native Hawaiian or other Pacific Islander, non-Hispanic/Latino; 19% international. 9% live on campus, 11% transferred in. Retention: 81% of full-time freshmen returned the following year. Academic areas with the most degrees conferred: visual and performing arts; architecture. Core. Calendar: semesters. Academic remediation for entering students, services for LD students, advanced placement, self-designed majors, freshman honors college, honors program, independent study, double major, summer session for credit, adult/continuing education programs, co-op programs and internships. Off campus study at the Consortium of East Coast Art Schools. Study abroad program.
Entrance Requirements: Options: electronic application, early admission. Required: essay, high school transcript, minimum 2.5 high school GPA, portfolio, SAT or ACT. Recommended: interview. Entrance: moderately difficult. Application deadline: rolling. Notification: continuous.
Collegiate Environment: Orientation program. Social organizations: 15 open to all. Most popular organizations: Student Government Association, international students organization, Otis Students in Service (OASIS), Literary Magazine Club, Campus Crusade. Major annual events: Otis Scholarship Benefit Fashion Show, Senior Exhibitions, Orientation. Student services: personal-psychological counseling. Campus security: 24-hour patrols. Milliard Sheets Library plus 1 other. 400 computers available on campus for general student use. A campuswide network can be accessed. Students can access the following: online class registration. Staffed computer lab on campus provides training in use of computers, software, and the Internet.

■ **OXNARD COLLEGE**
4000 S Rose Ave.
Oxnard, CA 93033-6699
Tel: (805)986-5800
Fax: (805)986-5806
E-mail: jdiaz@vcccd.edu
Web Site: www.oxnardcollege.edu
Description: District-supported, 2-year, coed. Part of Ventura County Community College District System. Awards certificates, diplomas, and transfer associate degrees. Founded 1975. Setting: 119-acre urban campus. Endowment: $5.8 million. Educational spending for the previous fiscal year: $4068 per student. Total enrollment: 7,006. Faculty: 230 (88 full-time, 142 part-time). Student-undergrad faculty ratio is 30:1. Full-time: 1,958 students, 53% women, 47% men. Part-time: 5,048 students, 55% women, 45% men. Students come from 3 states and territories. 34% 25 or older, 13% transferred in. Retention: 73% of full-time freshmen returned the following year. Core. Calendar: semesters. Academic remediation for entering students, ESL program, services for LD students, advanced placement, accelerated degree program, honors program, independent study, distance learning, double major, summer session for credit, part-time degree program.
Entrance Requirements: Open admission. Options: electronic application, early admission. Recommended: high school transcript. Entrance: noncompetitive. Application deadline: rolling. Notification: continuous. Transfer credits accepted: Yes.
Collegiate Environment: Orientation program. Drama-theater group. Student services: health clinic, personal-psychological counseling, women's center. Campus security: 24-hour patrols, late night transport-escort service. Oxnard College Library. Books: 47,874 (physical), 141,577 (digital/electronic); Serial titles: 422 (physical), 9 (digital/electronic); Databases: 12. Students can reserve study rooms. Operations spending for the previous fiscal year: $59,875. 116 computers available on campus for general student use. A campuswide network can be accessed. Students can access the following: online class registration. Staffed computer lab on campus provides training in use of computers, software, and the Internet.
Community Environment: The city of Oxnard has a population of approximately 183,600 people, and is located on the Gold Coast of California, situated about 45 miles south of Santa Barbara and 60 miles north of Los Angeles. The climate has been described as Mediterranean. Oxnard has seven miles of shoreline with wide, uncrowded beaches. It is a paradise for people who love to boat, surf and sport-fish. There are many museums and points of historical interest. Some of the major annual events include the California Strawberry Festival in May, Fiestas Patrias Celebration in September, and the Parade of Lights in December.

■ **PACIFIC COLLEGE**
3160 Red Hill Ave.
Costa Mesa, CA 92626
Tel: (714)662-4402
Web Site: www.pacific-college.edu
Description: Proprietary, 4-year, coed. Awards associate and bachelor's degrees.

■ **PACIFIC OAKS COLLEGE**
55 W Eureka St.
Pasadena, CA 91103
Tel: (626)397-1300; Free: 877-314-2380
Fax: (626)397-1317
E-mail: admissions@pacificoaks.edu
Web Site: www.pacificoaks.edu
Description: Independent, upper-level, coed. Part of The Chicago School Education System. Awards bachelor's and master's degrees and post-master's certificates. Founded 1945. Setting: 2-acre small town campus with easy access to Los Angeles, San Gabriel Valley. Endowment: $7.3 million. Research spending for the previous fiscal year: $236,517. Educational spending for the previous fiscal year: $9523 per student. Total enrollment: 1,028. Faculty: 125 (27 full-time, 98 part-time). Student-undergrad faculty ratio is 22:1. 339 applied, 77% were admitted. Full-time: 17 students, 88% women, 12% men. Part-time: 240 students, 96% women, 4% men. 91% 25 or older, 21% transferred in. Core. Calendar: semesters summer sessions and 2 intensive sessions. Independent study, distance learning, summer session for credit, part-time degree program, adult/continuing education programs, internships, graduate courses open to undergrads. Off campus study at Four College Consortium.

Entrance Requirements: Transfer credits accepted: Yes.

Collegiate Environment: Orientation program. Social organizations: 4 open to all. Most popular organizations: Latina/o Support Group, Student Empowerment Group, Teacher Education Student Association, Marriage, Family Therapy Student Association. Andrew Norman Library plus 1 other. Operations spending for the previous fiscal year: $188,124. 25 computers available on campus for general student use. A campuswide network can be accessed from off-campus. Students can access the following: online class listings. Staffed computer lab on campus.

Community Environment: See California Institute of Technology.

■ **PACIFIC STATES UNIVERSITY**
3424 Wilshire Blvd.
12th Fl.
Los Angeles, CA 90010
Tel: (323)731-2383; Free: 888-200-0383
Fax: (323)731-7276
E-mail: admissions@psuca.edu
Web Site: www.psuca.edu

Description: Independent, comprehensive, coed. Awards bachelor's, master's, and doctoral degrees. Founded 1928. Setting: 1-acre urban campus. Total enrollment: 175. Faculty: 34 (7 full-time, 27 part-time). Student-undergrad faculty ratio is 5:1. Full-time: 19 students, 37% women, 63% men. Students come from 6 other countries. 16% Asian, non-Hispanic/Latino; 79% international. 50% 25 or older, 21% transferred in. Retention: 90% of full-time freshmen returned the following year. Academic area with the most degrees conferred: business/marketing. Core. Calendar: quarters. Academic remediation for entering students, ESL program, accelerated degree program, independent study, distance learning, double major, adult/continuing education programs.

Entrance Requirements: Open admission. Options: electronic application, deferred admission, international baccalaureate accepted. Required: high school transcript, minimum 2.5 high school GPA. Recommended: essay, SAT or ACT. Required for some: TOEFL or IELTS. Entrance: noncompetitive. Application deadline: rolling. Notification: continuous. Transfer credits accepted: Yes.

Collegiate Environment: Orientation program. Campus security: patrols by trained security personnel during campus hours. University Library plus 1 other. Students can reserve study rooms. 50 computers available on campus for general student use. A campuswide network can be accessed. Staffed computer lab on campus provides training in use of the Internet.

■ **PACIFIC UNION COLLEGE**
One Angwin Ave.
Angwin, CA 94508-9707
Tel: (707)965-6311; Free: 800-862-7080
Fax: (707)965-6390
E-mail: enroll@puc.edu
Web Site: www.puc.edu

Description: Independent Seventh-day Adventist, comprehensive, coed. Awards associate, bachelor's, and master's degrees. Founded 1882. Setting: 200-acre rural campus with easy access to San Francisco Bay Area. Total enrollment: 1,555. Faculty: 143 (97 full-time, 46 part-time). Student-undergrad faculty ratio is 13:1. 2,041 applied, 45% were admitted. Full-time: 1,358 students, 56% women, 44% men. Part-time: 192 students, 73% women, 27% men. 16% from out-of-state. 0.3% American Indian or Alaska Native, non-Hispanic/Latino; 28% Hispanic/Latino; 9% Black or African American, non-Hispanic/Latino; 20% Asian, non-Hispanic/Latino; 2% Native Hawaiian or other Pacific Islander, non-Hispanic/Latino; 3% international. 14% 25 or older, 71% live on campus, 8% transferred in. Retention: 76% of full-time freshmen returned the following year. Academic areas with the most degrees conferred: health professions and related sciences; business/marketing; biological/life sciences. Core. Calendar: quarters. Academic remediation for entering students, services for LD students, advanced placement, honors program, independent study, double major, summer session for credit, part-time degree program, adult/continuing education programs, co-op programs and internships, graduate courses open to undergrads. Off campus study. Study abroad program.

Entrance Requirements: Options: electronic application, deferred admission, international baccalaureate accepted. Required: high school transcript, minimum 2.3 high school GPA, 3 recommendations, SAT or ACT. Entrance: moderately difficult. SAT Reasoning Test deadline: 9/15. SAT Subject Test deadline: 9/15. Transfer credits accepted: Yes.

Costs Per Year: Application fee: $30. Comprehensive fee: $29,370 includes

full-time tuition ($20,415), mandatory fees ($645), and college room and board ($8310). College room only: $4860. Part-time tuition: $850 per unit. Part-time mandatory fees: $215 per term.

Collegiate Environment: Orientation program. Drama-theater group, choral group, student-run newspaper. Most popular organizations: Student Association, Business Club, Asian Student Association, Korean Adventist Student Association, Student Organization of Latinos. Major annual events: Fall Festival, All College Get Acquainted Party, Talent show. Student services: health clinic, personal-psychological counseling, women's center. Campus security: 24-hour emergency response devices and patrols, late night transport-escort service. W.E. Nelson Memorial Library.

Community Environment: This is a rural un-incorporated area on Howell Mountain, an extinct volcano, 80 miles from San Francisco. The climate is not extreme, although it is not unusual to have as much as 60 inches of rain in the winter. Bus service is available in St. Helena; railroads and airlines serve the San Francisco Bay area. Freeways are nearby. A hospital is located five miles from Angwin. Employment is available for students.

■ **PALO ALTO UNIVERSITY**
1791 Arastradero Rd.
Palo Alto, CA 94304
Tel: (650)433-3800; Free: 800-818-6136
Fax: (650)493-6147
E-mail: undergrad@paloaltou.edu
Web Site: www.paloaltou.edu

Description: Independent, upper-level, coed. Awards bachelor's, master's, and doctoral degrees. Setting: rural campus with easy access to San Francisco Bay Area/Silicon Valley. Endowment: $2.4 million. Research spending for the previous fiscal year: $1.5 million. Educational spending for the previous fiscal year: $16,046 per student. Total enrollment: 1,070. Faculty: 25 (2 full-time, 23 part-time). Student-undergrad faculty ratio is 12:1. Full-time: 113 students, 65% women, 35% men. Part-time: 8 students, 50% women, 50% men. Students come from 4 other countries. 0.8% American Indian or Alaska Native, non-Hispanic/Latino; 7% Hispanic/Latino; 0.8% Black or African American, non-Hispanic/Latino; 9% Native Hawaiian or other Pacific Islander, non-Hispanic/Latino; 7% international. 59% 25 or older, 49% transferred in. Academic area with the most degrees conferred: psychology. Core. Calendar: quarters. Academic remediation for entering students, services for LD students, distance learning, summer session for credit, internships.

Entrance Requirements: Transfer credits accepted: Yes.

Costs Per Year: Tuition: $17,451 full-time. Mandatory fees: $5301 full-time. Full-time tuition and fees vary according to class time. Tuition guaranteed not to increase for student's term of enrollment.

Collegiate Environment: Orientation program. Student services: personal-psychological counseling. Omar Seddiqui Research Library. Books: 1,771 (physical), 257,269 (digital/electronic); Serial titles: 2 (physical), 221,448 (digital/electronic); Databases: 53. Weekly public service hours: 71; students can reserve study rooms. Operations spending for the previous fiscal year: $752,562. 14 computers available on campus for general student use. A campuswide network can be accessed. Students can access the following: online class registration.

■ **PALO VERDE COLLEGE**
One College Dr.
Blythe, CA 92225
Tel: (760)921-5500
Fax: (760)921-5590
E-mail: diana.rodriguez@paloverde.edu
Web Site: www.paloverde.edu

Description: District-supported, 2-year, coed. Part of California Community College System. Awards transfer associate and terminal associate degrees. Founded 1947. Setting: 10-acre small town campus. Total enrollment: 3,516. Student-undergrad faculty ratio is 23:1. 74% 25 or older. Core. Calendar: semesters. Academic remediation for entering students, ESL program, services for LD students, advanced placement, summer session for credit, part-time degree program, adult/continuing education programs, internships.

Entrance Requirements: Open admission. Option: early admission. Recommended: high school transcript. Entrance: noncompetitive. Application deadline: rolling. Notification: continuous.

Collegiate Environment: Drama-theater group, student-run newspaper. Student services: personal-psychological counseling. Campus security: student patrols, security personnel during hours of operation. Palo Verde College Library.

Community Environment: Blythe, in the Palo Verde Valley, is on Interstate 10, 225 miles east of Los Angeles and 165 miles west of Phoenix. The climate is dry and temperate. It is an agricultural region with year-round farming. Greyhound Bus serves the area. There is a public library, 30 churches, a hospital, 2 clinics and the usual civic organizations. Recreation includes hunting, boating, and fishing on the Colorado River. There are good part-time employment opportunities.

■ **PALOMAR COLLEGE**
1140 W Mission Rd.
San Marcos, CA 92069-1487
Tel: (760)744-1150
Fax: (760)744-2932
E-mail: kmagnuson@palomar.edu
Web Site: www.palomar.edu
Description: District-supported, 2-year, coed. Part of California Community College System. Awards certificates and transfer associate degrees. Founded 1946. Setting: 156-acre suburban campus with easy access to San Diego. Total enrollment: 25,244. Faculty: 1,380 (300 full-time, 1,080 part-time). Student-undergrad faculty ratio is 21:1. 37% 25 or older. Core. Calendar: semesters. Academic remediation for entering students, ESL program, services for LD students, advanced placement, distance learning, summer session for credit, part-time degree program, co-op programs and internships. ROTC: Air Force (c).
Entrance Requirements: Open admission. Option: electronic application. Entrance: noncompetitive. Application deadline: rolling. Notification: continuous. Transfer credits accepted: Yes.
Costs Per Year: Application fee: $0. State resident tuition: $1338 full-time, $46 per unit part-time. Nonresident tuition: $8030 full-time, $285 per unit part-time. Mandatory fees: $60 full-time, $1 per unit part-time, $19 per term part-time.
Collegiate Environment: Orientation program. Drama-theater group, choral group, student-run newspaper, radio station. Social organizations: 40 open to all. Most popular organizations: SNAP (Student Nursing Association of Palomar College), Alpha Omega Rho Chapter of Phi Theta Kappa (international honor society), Active Minds, Student Veterans Organization, MEChA (Chicano organization). Major annual events: Discover Palomar, Comet Celebration, Springfest. Student services: health clinic, personal-psychological counseling. Campus security: 24-hour emergency response devices and patrols, late night transport-escort service. Palomar College Library plus 1 other. Books: 100,000 (physical); Serial titles: 689 (physical). Weekly public service hours: 64. 2,000 computers available on campus for general student use. A campuswide network can be accessed. Students can access the following: online class registration. Staffed computer lab on campus.

■ **PASADENA CITY COLLEGE**
1570 E Colorado Blvd.
Pasadena, CA 91106-2041
Tel: (626)585-7123
Fax: (626)585-7915
Web Site: www.pasadena.edu
Description: District-supported, 2-year, coed. Part of California Community College System. Awards certificates, diplomas, transfer associate, and terminal associate degrees. Founded 1924. Setting: 55-acre urban campus with easy access to Los Angeles. Educational spending for the previous fiscal year: $4672 per student. Total enrollment: 27,324. Faculty: 1,077 (416 full-time, 661 part-time). Student-undergrad faculty ratio is 25:1. Full-time: 10,422 students, 50% women, 50% men. Part-time: 16,902 students, 54% women, 46% men. Students come from 28 states and territories, 20 other countries, 2% from out-of-state. 0.1% American Indian or Alaska Native, non-Hispanic/Latino; 51% Hispanic/Latino; 4% Black or African American, non-Hispanic/Latino; 23% Asian, non-Hispanic/Latino; 0.1% Native Hawaiian or other Pacific Islander, non-Hispanic/Latino; 3% international. 27% 25 or older, 92% transferred in. Retention: 74% of full-time freshmen returned the following year. Core. Calendar: semesters. Academic remediation for entering students, ESL program, services for LD students, advanced placement, honors program, independent study, distance learning, double major, summer session for credit, part-time degree program, adult/continuing education programs, internships. Study abroad program.
Entrance Requirements: Open admission except for international students. Option: electronic application. Entrance: noncompetitive. Application deadline: rolling. Notification: continuous. Transfer credits accepted: Yes.
Costs Per Year: State resident tuition: $1348 full-time, $46 per unit part-

time. Nonresident tuition: $6272 full-time, $280 per unit part-time. Mandatory fees: $60 full-time, $24 per term part-time. Full-time tuition and fees vary according to course load. Part-time tuition and fees vary according to course load.
Collegiate Environment: Orientation program. Drama-theater group, choral group, marching band, student-run newspaper. Social organizations: 68 open to all. Most popular organizations: AGS Honor Society, TROPA, Candela Salsa, International Students, Ujima. Major annual events: Commencement Ceremony, Convocation. Student services: legal services, health clinic, personal-psychological counseling. Campus security: 24-hour emergency response devices and patrols, late night transport-escort service, cadet patrols. Pasadena City College Library plus 1 other. Books: 133,975 (physical), 35,619 (digital/electronic); Databases: 56. Weekly public service hours: 54; students can reserve study rooms. Operations spending for the previous fiscal year: $2.3 million. 4,000 computers available on campus for general student use. A campuswide network can be accessed from off-campus. Students can access the following: online class registration. Staffed computer lab on campus provides training in use of computers, software, and the Internet.
Community Environment: See California Institute of Technology.

■ **PCI COLLEGE**
17215 Studebaker Rd. No.310
Cerritos, CA 90703
Tel: (562)916-5055
Description: Proprietary, 2-year, coed. Calendar: continuous.

■ **PEPPERDINE UNIVERSITY**
24255 Pacific Coast Hwy.
Malibu, CA 90263
Tel: (310)506-4000
Fax: (310)506-4861
E-mail: falone.serna@pepperdine.edu
Web Site: www.pepperdine.edu
Description: Independent, university, coed, affiliated with Church of Christ. Awards bachelor's, master's, and doctoral degrees. Founded 1937. Setting: 830-acre suburban campus with easy access to Los Angeles. Endowment: $861.6 million. Research spending for the previous fiscal year: $3.1 million. Educational spending for the previous fiscal year: $14,558 per student. Total enrollment: 7,961. Faculty: 694 (393 full-time, 301 part-time). Student-undergrad faculty ratio is 13:1. 11,704 applied, 40% were admitted. 57% from top 10% of their high school class, 85% from top quarter, 96% from top half. Full-time: 3,336 students, 60% women, 40% men. Part-time: 291 students, 46% women, 54% men. Students come from 54 states and territories, 71 other countries, 45% from out-of-state. 0.4% American Indian or Alaska Native, non-Hispanic/Latino; 14% Hispanic/Latino; 5% Black or African American, non-Hispanic/Latino; 10% Asian, non-Hispanic/Latino; 0.2% Native Hawaiian or other Pacific Islander, non-Hispanic/Latino; 13% international. 6% 25 or older, 57% live on campus, 2% transferred in. Retention: 91% of full-time freshmen returned the following year. Academic areas with the most degrees conferred: business/marketing; communication/journalism; social sciences. Core. Calendar: semesters. Services for LD students, advanced placement, self-designed majors, honors program, independent study, distance learning, double major, summer session for credit, part-time degree program, adult/continuing education programs, internships, graduate courses open to undergrads. Study abroad program. ROTC: Army (c), Air Force (c).
Entrance Requirements: Options: electronic application, international baccalaureate accepted. Required: essay, high school transcript, 2 recommendations, SAT or ACT. Entrance: very difficult. Application deadline: 1/5. Notification: 4/1. SAT Reasoning Test deadline: 1/5. Transfer credits accepted: Yes. Applicants placed on waiting list: 1,386. Wait-listed applicants offered admission: 2.
Costs Per Year: Application fee: $65. Comprehensive fee: $69,252 includes full-time tuition ($53,680), mandatory fees ($252), and college room and board ($15,320). Room and board charges vary according to board plan and housing facility. Part-time tuition: $1685 per credit hour.
Collegiate Environment: Orientation program. Drama-theater group, choral group, student-run newspaper, radio station. Social organizations: 110 open to all; national fraternities, national sororities; 19% of eligible men and 28% of eligible women are members. Most popular organizations: Latino Student Association, Black Student Union, Interfraternity Council, International Justice Mission. Major annual events: Homecoming, Songfest, Family Weekend. Student services: health clinic, personal-psychological counsel-

ing. Campus security: 24-hour emergency response devices and patrols, student patrols, late night transport-escort service, controlled dormitory access, front gate security, 24-hour security in residence halls, controlled access, crime prevention programs. 2,211 undergraduates lived in college housing during 2018-19. Freshmen guaranteed college housing. On-campus residence required through sophomore year. Options: men-only, women-only housing available. Payson Library plus 5 others. Books: 311,392 (physical), 356,075 (digital/electronic); Serial titles: 312 (physical), 66,464 (digital/electronic); Databases: 128. Weekly public service hours: 112; students can reserve study rooms. Operations spending for the previous fiscal year: $6.6 million. 240 computers available on campus for general student use. Computer purchase/lease plans available. A campuswide network can be accessed from student residence rooms and from off campus. Students can access the following: online class registration. Staffed computer lab on campus provides training in use of computers, software, and the Internet.
Community Environment: See University of California - Los Angeles.

■ **PIMA MEDICAL INSTITUTE**
780 Bay Blvd.
Chula Vista, CA 91910
Tel: (619)425-3200; Free: 800-477-PIMA
Fax: (619)425-3450
Web Site: www.pmi.edu
Description: Proprietary, primarily 2-year, coed. Administratively affiliated with Vocational Training Institutes, Inc. Awards certificates, terminal associate, and bachelor's degrees. Founded 1998. Setting: urban campus. Total enrollment: 813. 42% 25 or older. Core. Calendar: modular. Distance learning, co-op programs and internships.
Entrance Requirements: Required: high school transcript, interview, Wonderlic Scholastic Level Exam (SLE). Entrance: minimally difficult.
Collegiate Environment: Orientation program. E-Global.

■ **PITZER COLLEGE**
1050 N Mills Ave.
Claremont, CA 91711-6101
Tel: (909)621-8000; Free: 800-748-9371
Fax: (909)621-8770
E-mail: admission@pitzer.edu
Web Site: www.pitzer.edu
Description: Independent, 4-year, coed. Part of The Claremont Colleges. Awards bachelor's degrees. Founded 1963. Setting: 35-acre suburban campus with easy access to Los Angeles. Endowment: $141.5 million. Research spending for the previous fiscal year: $732,006. Educational spending for the previous fiscal year: $23,050 per student. Total enrollment: 1,106. Faculty: 108 (82 full-time, 26 part-time). Student-undergrad faculty ratio is 11:1. 4,358 applied, 13% were admitted. 62% from top 10% of their high school class, 83% from top quarter, 98% from top half. Full-time: 1,083 students, 56% women, 44% men. Part-time: 23 students, 61% women, 39% men. Students come from 46 states and territories, 33 other countries, 56% from out-of-state. 0.3% American Indian or Alaska Native, non-Hispanic/Latino; 14% Hispanic/Latino; 6% Black or African American, non-Hispanic/Latino; 10% Asian, non-Hispanic/Latino; 0.3% Native Hawaiian or other Pacific Islander, non-Hispanic/Latino; 12% international. 2% 25 or older, 73% live on campus, 2% transferred in. Retention: 91% of full-time freshmen returned the following year. Academic areas with the most degrees conferred: social sciences; interdisciplinary studies; natural resources/environmental science. Core. Calendar: semesters. ESL program, services for LD students, advanced placement, self-designed majors, honors program, independent study, double major, summer session for credit, part-time degree program, adult/continuing education programs, co-op programs and internships. Off campus study at The Claremont Colleges (Claremont McKenna College, Scripps College, Harvey Mudd College, and Pomona College), Claremont McKenna College Silicon Valley Program, Northern Arizona University School of Indigenous Studies, Spelman College, Colby College, Bard College Globalization and International Affairs Program, Haverford College, Sarah Lawrence College. Study abroad program. ROTC: Army (c), Air Force (c).
Entrance Requirements: Options: electronic application, early decision, deferred admission, international baccalaureate accepted. Required: essay, high school transcript, minimum 2 high school GPA, 3 recommendations. Recommended: interview. Required for some: SAT or ACT. Entrance: very difficult. Application deadlines: 1/1, 1/1 for nonresidents, 11/15 for early decision plan 1, 1/1 for early decision plan 2. Notification: 4/1, 4/1 for nonresidents, 12/18 for early decision plan 1, 2/15 for early decision plan 2.

SAT Reasoning Test deadline: 1/1. Transfer credits accepted: Yes. Applicants placed on waiting list: 707. Wait-listed applicants offered admission: 4. Early decision applicants: 456. Early decision applicants admitted: 135.
Costs Per Year: Application fee: $70. Comprehensive fee: $70,900 includes full-time tuition ($53,776), mandatory fees ($280), and college room and board ($16,844). College room only: $9720. Room and board charges vary according to board plan and housing facility. Part-time tuition: $6722 per course. Part-time mandatory fees: $280 per year. Part-time tuition and fees vary according to course load.
Collegiate Environment: Orientation program. Drama-theater group, choral group, student-run newspaper, radio station. Social organizations: 60 open to all. Most popular organizations: Pitzer Outdoor Adventure, Live Your Best Life Records, Latino Student Union, Pitzer International Student Association, Asian Pacific American Coalition. Major annual events: Kohoutek Festival, Rockabilly Festival, One Night Only (ONO) Festival. Student services: health clinic, personal-psychological counseling, women's center. Campus security: 24-hour emergency response devices and patrols, late night transport-escort service, controlled dormitory access. 840 college housing spaces available; 825 were occupied in 2018-19. Freshmen guaranteed college housing. On-campus residence required in freshman year. Option: coed housing available. Honnold Library plus 3 others. Books: 1 million (physical), 2.2 million (digital/electronic); Serial titles: 28,182 (physical), 81,005 (digital/electronic); Databases: 490. Weekly public service hours: 107; students can reserve study rooms. Operations spending for the previous fiscal year: $1.6 million.

■ **PLATT COLLEGE (ALHAMBRA)**
1000 S Fremont A9W
Alhambra, CA 91803
Tel: (636)300-5444; Free: 888-80-PLATT
Fax: (323)258-8532
Web Site: www.plattcollege.edu
Description: Proprietary, primarily 2-year, coed. Awards certificates, diplomas, transfer associate, terminal associate, and bachelor's degrees. Founded 1987. Setting: suburban campus. Total enrollment: 116. 43% 25 or older. Core. Calendar: continuous. Academic remediation for entering students, accelerated degree program, summer session for credit, internships.
Entrance Requirements: Required: interview, CPAt. Required for some: essay. Entrance: minimally difficult. Application deadline: rolling. Notification: continuous.
Collegiate Environment: Orientation program. Campus security: parking lot security. Platt College Library.

■ **PLATT COLLEGE (ANAHEIM)**
1551 S Douglass Rd.
Anaheim, CA 92806
Description: Proprietary, 2-year, coed.

■ **PLATT COLLEGE (ONTARIO)**
3700 Inland Empire Blvd.
Ontario, CA 91764
Tel: (909)941-9410; Free: 888-80-PLATT
Fax: (909)989-8974
Web Site: www.plattcollege.edu
Description: Proprietary, primarily 2-year, coed. Awards certificates, diplomas, transfer associate, and bachelor's degrees. Total enrollment: 604. 39% 25 or older. Calendar: continuous. Academic remediation for entering students, accelerated degree program, honors program, independent study, summer session for credit, internships.
Entrance Requirements: Required: essay, interview, CPAt. Entrance: minimally difficult. Application deadline: rolling. Notification: continuous.
Collegiate Environment: Orientation program. Main Library-Platt College.

■ **PLATT COLLEGE (RIVERSIDE)**
6465 Sycamore Canyon Blvd.
Ste. 100
Riverside, CA 92507
Tel: (951)572-4300; Free: 888-807-5288
Web Site: www.plattcollege.edu
Description: Proprietary, 4-year, coed. Awards associate and bachelor's degrees.

■ **PLATT COLLEGE SAN DIEGO**
6250 El Cajon Blvd.
San Diego, CA 92115-3919

Tel: (619)265-0107; Free: 866-752-8826
Fax: (619)265-8655
E-mail: sgallup@platt.edu
Web Site: www.platt.edu
Description: Proprietary, 4-year, coed. Awards bachelor's degrees. Founded 1879. Setting: 1-acre suburban campus. Educational spending for the previous fiscal year: $18,220 per student. Total enrollment: 369. Faculty: 27 (11 full-time, 16 part-time). Student-undergrad faculty ratio is 21:1. Full-time: 369 students, 27% women, 73% men. Students come from 4 states and territories, 5% from out-of-state. 1% American Indian or Alaska Native, non-Hispanic/Latino; 25% Hispanic/Latino; 11% Black or African American, non-Hispanic/Latino; 9% Asian, non-Hispanic/Latino; 1% international. 61% 25 or older. Core. Calendar: continuous. Academic remediation for entering students, accelerated degree program, adult/continuing education programs, co-op programs. Study abroad program.
Entrance Requirements: Open admission. Options: early admission, deferred admission, international baccalaureate accepted. Required: essay, high school transcript, interview, Wonderlic aptitude test. Recommended: SAT and SAT Subject Tests or ACT. Application deadline: rolling. Notification: continuous.
Collegiate Environment: Major annual events: Art Show on Campus, Graduation Ceremonies. Student services: personal-psychological counseling. Campus security: 24-hour emergency response devices, surveillance cameras, security guard for evening session. Platt College San Diego Library. Operations spending for the previous fiscal year: $60,200.

■ POINT LOMA NAZARENE UNIVERSITY
3900 Lomaland Dr.
San Diego, CA 92106-2899
Tel: (619)849-2200; Free: 800-733-7770
Fax: (619)849-2579
E-mail: admissions@pointloma.edu
Web Site: www.pointloma.edu
Description: Independent Nazarene, comprehensive, coed. Awards bachelor's, master's, and doctoral degrees and post-master's certificates. Founded 1902. Setting: 93-acre suburban campus with easy access to San Diego. Total enrollment: 4,653. Faculty: 490 (148 full-time, 342 part-time). Student-undergrad faculty ratio is 14:1. 3,473 applied, 69% were admitted. 39% from top 10% of their high school class, 70% from top quarter, 91% from top half. Full-time: 2,656 students, 64% women, 36% men. Part-time: 540 students, 70% women, 30% men. Students come from 42 states and territories, 19 other countries, 17% from out-of-state. 0.4% American Indian or Alaska Native, non-Hispanic/Latino; 27% Hispanic/Latino; 2% Black or African American, non-Hispanic/Latino; 7% Asian, non-Hispanic/Latino; 0.9% Native Hawaiian or other Pacific Islander, non-Hispanic/Latino; 1% international. 15% 25 or older, 56% live on campus, 12% transferred in. Retention: 85% of full-time freshmen returned the following year. Academic areas with the most degrees conferred: health professions and related sciences; business/marketing; social sciences. Core. Calendar: semesters. Academic remediation for entering students, services for LD students, advanced placement, accelerated degree program, honors program, independent study, distance learning, double major, summer session for credit, part-time degree program, external degree program, adult/continuing education programs, internships, graduate courses open to undergrads. Off campus study at American University, Coalition for Christian Colleges and Universities. Study abroad program. ROTC: Army (c), Naval (c), Air Force (c).
Entrance Requirements: Options: electronic application, early action, international baccalaureate accepted. Required: essay, high school transcript, minimum 2.8 high school GPA, 2 recommendations, SAT or ACT. Recommended: SAT, ACT. Entrance: moderately difficult. Application deadlines: 2/15, 11/15 for early action. Notification: 4/1. SAT Reasoning Test deadline: 3/1. Transfer credits accepted: Yes.
Costs Per Year: Application fee: $55. Comprehensive fee: $46,150 includes full-time tuition ($35,100), mandatory fees ($600), and college room and board ($10,450). Full-time tuition and fees vary according to course load and program. Room and board charges vary according to board plan. Part-time tuition: $1465 per credit hour. Part-time tuition varies according to course load and program.
Collegiate Environment: Orientation program. Drama-theater group, choral group, student-run newspaper, radio station. Major annual event: Homecoming. Student services: health clinic, personal-psychological counseling, women's center. Campus security: 24-hour patrols, student patrols, late night transport-escort service. 1,762 college housing spaces available. Freshmen

guaranteed college housing. On-campus residence required through sophomore year. Options: men-only, women-only housing available. Ryan Library. 346 computers available on campus for general student use. A campuswide network can be accessed from student residence rooms and from off campus. Students can access the following: online class registration. Staffed computer lab on campus provides training in use of computers, software, and the Internet.
Community Environment: San Diego is an area of matchless climate and spectacular scenery. Resident institutions provide ample resources in research, culture, entertainment, and recreation. They involve the University of California, San Diego; San Diego State University; University of San Diego; San Diego Symphony; San Diego Opera; Scripps Institute of Oceanography; Palomar Observatory; and Balboa Park with its world famous Zoo, Natural History Museum, Fine Arts Gallery, Old Globe Theatre, Museum of Man, Photographic Arts Museum, Aerospace Museum, Starlight Opera, and Reuben H. Fleet Space Theatre and Museum. Los Angeles is two and one-half hours driving time to the north and Mexico thirty minutes to the south. The Laguna Mountains are to the east.

■ POMONA COLLEGE
333 N College Way
Claremont, CA 91711
Tel: (909)621-8000
Fax: (909)621-8403
Web Site: www.pomona.edu
Description: Independent, 4-year, coed. Awards bachelor's degrees. Founded 1887. Setting: 140-acre suburban campus with easy access to Los Angeles. Endowment: $2.2 billion. Total enrollment: 1,704. Faculty: 240 (186 full-time, 54 part-time). Student-undergrad faculty ratio is 8:1. 9,045 applied, 8% were admitted. 94% from top 10% of their high school class, 100% from top quarter, 100% from top half. Full-time: 1,683 students, 50% women, 50% men. Part-time: 21 students, 24% women, 76% men. Students come from 53 states and territories, 63 other countries, 70% from out-of-state. 0.5% American Indian or Alaska Native, non-Hispanic/Latino; 16% Hispanic/Latino; 9% Black or African American, non-Hispanic/Latino; 14% Asian, non-Hispanic/Latino; 0.3% Native Hawaiian or other Pacific Islander, non-Hispanic/Latino; 12% international. 98% live on campus, 1% transferred in. Retention: 98% of full-time freshmen returned the following year. Academic areas with the most degrees conferred: social sciences; biological/life sciences; computer and information sciences. Core. Calendar: semesters. Services for LD students, advanced placement, self-designed majors, independent study, double major, internships. Off campus study at Claremont Colleges Consortium (Harvey Mudd College, Scripps College, Claremont McKenna College, Pitzer College), plus Swarthmore College, Colby College, Smith College, and Spelman College. Study abroad program. ROTC: Army (c), Air Force (c).
Entrance Requirements: Options: electronic application, early admission, early decision, deferred admission, international baccalaureate accepted. Required: essay, high school transcript, 2 recommendations, SAT or ACT. Recommended: supplemental forms for visual and performing arts and science research. Entrance: most difficult. Application deadlines: 1/1, 11/1 for early decision plan 1, 1/1 for early decision plan 2. Notification: 4/1, 12/15 for early decision plan 1, 2/15 for early decision plan 2. SAT Reasoning Test deadline: 1/1. SAT Subject Test deadline: 1/1. Transfer credits accepted: Yes. Applicants placed on waiting list: 934. Wait-listed applicants offered admission: 16. Early decision applicants: 1,080. Early decision applicants admitted: 208.
Costs Per Year: Application fee: $70. Comprehensive fee: $69,496 includes full-time tuition ($52,412), mandatory fees ($368), and college room and board ($16,716). Room and board charges vary according to board plan.
Collegiate Environment: Orientation program. Drama-theater group, choral group, student-run newspaper, radio station. Social organizations: 220 open to all; local fraternities, 1 co-ed fraternity. Most popular organizations: Student Government, music/choral organizations, service organizations, intramural sports, outdoor activities club. Major annual events: Harwood Halloween Costume Party, Ski/Beach Day, Smiley Dorm '80s-themed Party. Student services: health clinic, personal-psychological counseling, women's center. Campus security: 24-hour emergency response devices and patrols, late night transport-escort service, controlled dormitory access. Honnold/Mudd Library plus 4 others. 180 computers available on campus for general student use. A campuswide network can be accessed. Students can access the following: online class registration. Staffed computer lab on campus (open 24 hours a day) provides training in use of computers, software, and the Internet.

■ PORTERVILLE COLLEGE
100 E College Ave.
Porterville, CA 93257-6058
Tel: (559)791-2200
Fax: (559)791-2349
Web Site: www.portervillecollege.edu
Description: District-supported, 2-year, coed. Part of Kern Community College District System. Awards certificates, transfer associate, and terminal associate degrees. Founded 1927. Setting: 60-acre rural campus. Endowment: $1.3 million. Total enrollment: 5,024. Faculty: 140 (60 full-time, 80 part-time). 3,586 applied, 100% were admitted. Students come from 4 other countries. 48% 25 or older. Core. Calendar: semesters. Academic remediation for entering students, services for LD students, advanced placement, distance learning, summer session for credit, part-time degree program, adult/continuing education programs.
Entrance Requirements: Open admission. Options: electronic application, early admission. Required: high school transcript. Entrance: noncompetitive. Application deadline: rolling.
Collegiate Environment: Orientation program. Drama-theater group, choral group. Student services: health clinic, personal-psychological counseling. Campus security: 24-hour emergency response devices, student patrols. Porterville College Library/Media Center. Operations spending for the previous fiscal year: $404,219. 350 computers available on campus for general student use. A campuswide network can be accessed. Students can access the following: online class registration. Staffed computer lab on campus.
Community Environment: Population 45,000, Porterville is located in southeastern Tulare County and is in a vast olive, grape, peach, walnut, cotton, and citrus growing area. The annual rainfall is 11.47 inches with an annual mean temperature of 62.8 degrees. Bus transportation is available to the airports and rail stations. The community has many churches, a library, auditorium, a community concert and theatre series each year, and an excellent shopping center with several new shopping centers in outlying areas. Recreational activities include fishing, camping, hunting in season, golf, boating, tennis, and skiing. Porterville is a 1 1/2 hour drive from Sequoia National Park; 2 1/2 hours from Kings Canyon National Park; and 3 hours from Yosemite National Park. Employment opportunities are good.

■ PROFESSIONAL GOLFERS CAREER COLLEGE
26109 Ynez Rd.
Temecula, CA 92591
Tel: (909)693-2963; Free: 800-877-4380
Fax: (909)693-2863
E-mail: garygilleon@golfcollege.edu
Web Site: www.golfcollege.edu
Description: Independent, 2-year, coed. Awards terminal associate degrees. Setting: rural campus. Total enrollment: 282. Faculty: 23 (5 full-time, 18 part-time). Student-undergrad faculty ratio is 15:1. 40 applied, 100% were admitted. Full-time: 282 students, 4% women, 96% men. Students come from 50 states and territories, 13 other countries, 75% from out-of-state. 1% American Indian or Alaska Native, non-Hispanic/Latino; 4% Hispanic/Latino; 1% Black or African American, non-Hispanic/Latino; 2% Asian, non-Hispanic/Latino; 0.7% Native Hawaiian or other Pacific Islander, non-Hispanic/Latino; 12% international. 50% 25 or older, 26% live on campus. Retention: 69% of full-time freshmen returned the following year. Core. Calendar: semesters. ESL program.
Entrance Requirements: Open admission. Options: early admission, deferred admission. Required: high school transcript, 3 recommendations. Application deadline: rolling. Transfer credits accepted: Yes.
Collegiate Environment: Orientation program. Major annual events: Semester Golf Tournament, International Cup, President's Cup. Student services: personal-psychological counseling. Professional Golfers Career College. Operations spending for the previous fiscal year: $24,325. 20 computers available on campus for general student use. Staffed computer lab on campus (open 24 hours a day).

■ PROVIDENCE CHRISTIAN COLLEGE
1539 E Howard St.
Pasadena, CA 91124
Tel: (626)696-4000
Fax: (626)696-4040
Web Site: www.providencecc.edu
Description: Independent Christian, 4-year, coed. Awards associate and bachelor's degrees.

■ REEDLEY COLLEGE
995 N Reed Ave.
Reedley, CA 93654-2099
Tel: (559)638-3641
Web Site: www.reedleycollege.edu
Description: District-supported, 2-year, coed. Part of State Center Community College District System. Awards certificates, diplomas, transfer associate, and terminal associate degrees. Founded 1926. Setting: 350-acre rural campus. Total enrollment: 14,573. Faculty: 844 (194 full-time, 650 part-time). Students come from 15 states and territories. 0.1% American Indian or Alaska Native, non-Hispanic/Latino; 41% Hispanic/Latino; 2% Black or African American, non-Hispanic/Latino; 5% Asian, non-Hispanic/Latino. Core. Calendar: semesters. Academic remediation for entering students, ESL program, services for LD students, advanced placement, freshman honors college, honors program, independent study, distance learning, summer session for credit, part-time degree program, adult/continuing education programs, co-op programs. Study abroad program. ROTC: Air Force (c).
Entrance Requirements: Open admission. Option: international baccalaureate accepted. Required: high school transcript. Entrance: noncompetitive. Application deadline: rolling. Notification: continuous until 8/1.
Collegiate Environment: Orientation program. Drama-theater group, choral group, student-run newspaper. Student services: personal-psychological counseling. Campus security: 24-hour emergency response devices, late night transport-escort service, 24-hour on-campus police dispatcher. Reedley College Library. 303 computers available on campus for general student use. A campuswide network can be accessed from student residence rooms and from off campus. Students can access the following: online class registration. Staffed computer lab on campus.
Community Environment: Population 22,300. Reedley is in a rural area southeast of Fresno with a temperate climate. The rich farmlands around Reedley produce a diversity of crops, including citrus fruits, plums, peaches, grapes, tomatoes, celery and walnuts. The community has 19 packing houses, two wineries, and a sawmill. There are a number of churches, a public library and a hospital. Part-time employment is available. Reedley is near Kings Canyon and Sequoia National Parks which provide recreational activities. Major civic, fraternal and veteran's organizations are part of the town.

■ RIO HONDO COLLEGE
3600 Workman Mill Rd.
Whittier, CA 90601-1699
Tel: (562)692-0921
Fax: (562)692-9318
Web Site: www.riohondo.edu
Description: District-supported, 2-year, coed. Part of California Community College System. Awards certificates, transfer associate, and terminal associate degrees. Founded 1960. Setting: 128-acre suburban campus with easy access to Los Angeles. Faculty: 560 (190 full-time, 370 part-time). Student-undergrad faculty ratio is 34:1. Students come from 5 states and territories, 0.2% from out-of-state. 0.2% American Indian or Alaska Native, non-Hispanic/Latino; 77% Hispanic/Latino; 2% Black or African American, non-Hispanic/Latino; 6% Asian, non-Hispanic/Latino; 0.1% Native Hawaiian or other Pacific Islander, non-Hispanic/Latino; 0.3% international. Core. Calendar: semesters. Academic remediation for entering students, ESL program, services for LD students, advanced placement, honors program, distance learning, summer session for credit, part-time degree program, adult/continuing education programs. Study abroad program. ROTC: Army (c), Naval (c), Air Force (c).
Entrance Requirements: Open admission. Entrance: noncompetitive. Application deadline: rolling. Notification: continuous. Transfer credits accepted: Yes.
Collegiate Environment: Drama-theater group, choral group, student-run newspaper, radio station. Social organizations: 29 open to all. Student services: legal services, health clinic, personal-psychological counseling, women's center. Campus security: 24-hour patrols, late night transport-escort service. Library and Learning Resource Center plus 1 other. Books: 88,245 (physical); Serial titles: 104 (physical); Databases: 12. Weekly public service hours: 68; students can reserve study rooms. 150 computers available on campus for general student use. A campuswide network can be accessed. Students can access the following: online class registration. Staffed computer lab on campus provides training in use of computers, software, and the Internet.
Community Environment: Small ex-urban community, 23 miles from downtown Los Angeles. Population of approximately 84,400. Small business and manufacturing predominate.

■ **RIVERSIDE CITY COLLEGE**
4800 Magnolia Ave.
Riverside, CA 92506-1299
Tel: (909)222-8000
Fax: (909)222-8037
E-mail: admissionsriverside@rcc.edu
Web Site: www.rcc.edu
Description: District-supported, 2-year, coed. Part of California Community College System. Awards certificates and terminal associate degrees. Founded 1916. Setting: 108-acre suburban campus with easy access to Los Angeles. Total enrollment: 18,586. Faculty: 665 (222 full-time, 443 part-time). 33% 25 or older. Calendar: semesters. Academic remediation for entering students, ESL program, honors program, distance learning. Study abroad program.
Entrance Requirements: Open admission except for nursing program. Option: electronic application. Application deadline: rolling. Notification: continuous.
Collegiate Environment: Campus security: late night transport-escort service.
Community Environment: See University of California Riverside.

■ **SACRAMENTO CITY COLLEGE**
3835 Freeport Blvd.
Sacramento, CA 95822-1386
Tel: (916)558-2111
Fax: (916)558-2190
Web Site: www.scc.losrios.edu
Description: District-supported, 2-year, coed. Part of California Community College System. Awards certificates, diplomas, transfer associate, and terminal associate degrees. Founded 1916. Setting: 60-acre urban campus. Total enrollment: 21,890. Faculty: 554. Student-undergrad faculty ratio is 30:1. 5% from top 10% of their high school class, 10% from top quarter, 25% from top half. 50% 25 or older. Core. Calendar: semesters. Academic remediation for entering students, ESL program, services for LD students, advanced placement, self-designed majors, honors program, summer session for credit, part-time degree program, adult/continuing education programs, co-op programs. Off campus study at University of California, Davis; California State University, Sacramento. Study abroad program.
Entrance Requirements: Open admission. Entrance: noncompetitive. Application deadline: rolling. Notification: continuous.
Collegiate Environment: Orientation program. Drama-theater group, choral group, student-run newspaper. Most popular organizations: BOSS, African Student Alliance, Asian Pacific Club, MECHA, SMEC. Major annual events: Welcome Back Day, Peoples' Day. Student services: personal-psychological counseling, women's center. Campus security: 24-hour emergency response devices and patrols, student patrols, late night transport-escort service. Sacramento City College Library. Operations spending for the previous fiscal year: $995,408. 450 computers available on campus for general student use. A campuswide network can be accessed from off-campus. Staffed computer lab on campus.

■ **SADDLEBACK COLLEGE**
28000 Marguerite Pky.
Mission Viejo, CA 92692
Tel: (949)582-4500
Fax: (949)347-8315
E-mail: earaiza@saddleback.edu
Web Site: www.saddleback.edu
Description: District-supported, 2-year, coed. Awards certificates and transfer associate degrees. Founded 1967. Setting: 200-acre suburban campus with easy access to Los Angeles, San Diego. Total enrollment: 18,371. Faculty: 754 (215 full-time, 539 part-time). Full-time: 6,621 students, 50% women, 50% men. Part-time: 11,750 students, 58% women, 42% men. Students come from 23 other countries. 61% 25 or older. Core. Calendar: semesters. Academic remediation for entering students, ESL program, services for LD students, advanced placement, honors program, distance learning, summer session for credit, part-time degree program, adult/continuing education programs, co-op programs. Off campus study at Irvine Valley College. Study abroad program.
Entrance Requirements: Open admission. Option: early admission. Entrance: noncompetitive. Application deadline: rolling.
Collegiate Environment: Drama-theater group, choral group, student-run newspaper, radio station. Social organizations: 19 open to all. Student services: legal services, health clinic, personal-psychological counseling,

women's center. Campus security: 24-hour emergency response devices and patrols, late night transport-escort service. James B. Utt Memorial Library. 200 computers available on campus for general student use. A campuswide network can be accessed. Staffed computer lab on campus.
Community Environment: Mission Viejo is largely a residential community located in the rolling hills midway between Los Angeles and San Diego. This is one of Orange County's fast growing areas, with a dry temperate climate. Good shopping facilities are available with most major department stores represented. Buses serve the area and Orange County Airport is only a short drive away. Beach resorts are located nearby for all water sports. The mountains are approximately a two-hour drive and ski slopes abound in the Big Bear area.

■ **SAE EXPRESSION COLLEGE**
6601 Shellmound St.
Emeryville, CA 94608
Tel: (510)654-2934; Free: 877-833-8800
Web Site: www.sae.edu
Description: Proprietary, 4-year, coed. Awards bachelor's degrees.

■ **SAINT MARY'S COLLEGE OF CALIFORNIA**
1928 Saint Mary's Rd.
Moraga, CA 94575
Tel: (925)631-4000; Free: 800-800-4SMC
Fax: (925)376-7193
E-mail: smcadmit@stmarys-ca.edu
Web Site: www.stmarys-ca.edu
Description: Independent Roman Catholic, upper-level, coed. Awards bachelor's, master's, and doctoral degrees. Founded 1863. Setting: 420-acre suburban campus with easy access to San Francisco. Endowment: $178.6 million. Educational spending for the previous fiscal year: $14,560 per student. Total enrollment: 3,913. Faculty: 500 (226 full-time, 274 part-time). Student-undergrad faculty ratio is 11:1. 4,676 applied, 82% were admitted. Full-time: 2,614 students, 59% women, 41% men. Part-time: 163 students, 61% women, 39% men. Students come from 43 states and territories, 30 other countries, 12% from out-of-state. 0.4% American Indian or Alaska Native, non-Hispanic/Latino; 26% Hispanic/Latino; 4% Black or African American, non-Hispanic/Latino; 11% Asian, non-Hispanic/Latino; 1% Native Hawaiian or other Pacific Islander, non-Hispanic/Latino; 3% international. 3% 25 or older, 60% live on campus, 6% transferred in. Retention: 86% of full-time entering class returned the following year. Academic areas with the most degrees conferred: business/marketing; social sciences; liberal arts/general studies; psychology. Core. Calendar: 4-1-4. Services for LD students, advanced placement, self-designed majors, honors program, independent study, double major, summer session for credit, part-time degree program, adult/continuing education programs, internships, graduate courses open to undergrads. Off campus study. Study abroad program. ROTC: Army (c).
Entrance Requirements: SAT Reasoning Test deadline: 3/15. Transfer credits accepted: Yes. Applicants placed on waiting list: 214. Wait-listed applicants offered admission: 34. Early action applicants: 1,756. Early action applicants admitted: 1,577.
Costs Per Year: Application fee: $60. Comprehensive fee: $62,650 includes full-time tuition ($47,130), mandatory fees ($150), and college room and board ($15,370). Room and board charges vary according to board plan and housing facility. Part-time tuition: $5906 per course. Part-time mandatory fees: $75 per term.
Collegiate Environment: Orientation program. Drama-theater group, choral group, student-run newspaper, radio station. Social organizations: 57 open to all; Gael Sisterhood, Gael Brotherhood, Phi Kappa Phi. Most popular organizations: Gael Force, Campus Activities Board, LASA-Latin American Student Association-Black Student Union, La Hermandad, Asian Pacific American Student Association. Major annual events: Dances, Cultural Nights. Student services: health clinic, personal-psychological counseling, women's center. Campus security: 24-hour emergency response devices and patrols, late night transport-escort service. St. Albert Hall Library. Books: 179,912 (physical), 179,777 (digital/electronic); Serial titles: 926 (physical), 150,000 (digital/electronic); Databases: 219. Weekly public service hours: 102; study areas open 24 hours, 5-7 days a week; students can reserve study rooms. Operations spending for the previous fiscal year: $3.6 million. 244 computers available on campus for general student use. A campuswide network can be accessed from student residence rooms and from off campus. Students can access the following: online class registration, student

accounts. Staffed computer lab on campus provides training in use of computers, software, and the Internet.

■ THE SALVATION ARMY COLLEGE FOR OFFICER TRAINING AT CRESTMONT

30840 Hawthorne Blvd.
Rancho Palos Verdes, CA 90275
Tel: (310)377-0481
Fax: (310)265-6565
Web Site: www.crestmont.edu

Description: Independent Salvation Army, 2-year, coed. Administratively affiliated with The Salvation Army. Awards transfer associate and terminal associate degrees. Founded 1921. Setting: 44-acre suburban campus with easy access to Los Angeles. Total enrollment: 59. Faculty: 27 (21 full-time, 6 part-time). Student-undergrad faculty ratio is 3:1. Full-time: 59 students, 63% women, 37% men. Students come from 14 states and territories, 67% from out-of-state. 20% Hispanic/Latino; 7% Black or African American, non-Hispanic/Latino; 5% Asian, non-Hispanic/Latino; 2% Native Hawaiian or other Pacific Islander, non-Hispanic/Latino. 88% 25 or older, 100% live on campus. Retention: 98% of full-time freshmen returned the following year. Academic area with the most degrees conferred: theology and religious vocations. Core. Calendar: quarters. Academic remediation for entering students, ESL program, accelerated degree program, self-designed majors, independent study, distance learning, external degree program, co-op programs and internships. Off campus study.

Entrance Requirements: Required: essay, high school transcript, 2 recommendations, interview. Entrance: noncompetitive. Application deadline: 6/1. Notification: 8/20. Preference given to members of the Salvation Army.

Collegiate Environment: Orientation program. Drama-theater group, choral group. Major annual event: Performing Arts Production. Student services: health clinic, personal-psychological counseling. Campus security: 24-hour emergency response devices and patrols. The Salvation Army Elfman Memorial Library plus 1 other. Books: 45,000 (physical).

■ SAMUEL MERRITT UNIVERSITY

3100 Telegraph Ave.
Oakland, CA 94609-3108
Tel: (510)869-6511; Free: 800-607-6377
Fax: (510)869-6525
Web Site: www.samuelmerritt.edu

Description: Independent, upper-level, coed. Awards bachelor's, master's, and doctoral degrees and post-master's certificates (bachelor's degree offered jointly with Saint Mary's College of California). Founded 1909. Setting: 1-acre urban campus with easy access to San Francisco. Endowment: $47.1 million. Research spending for the previous fiscal year: $72,035. Educational spending for the previous fiscal year: $8024 per student. Total enrollment: 2,141. Faculty: 392 (166 full-time, 226 part-time). Student-undergrad faculty ratio is 10:1. Full-time: 564 students, 77% women, 23% men. Part-time: 355 students, 90% women, 10% men. Students come from 3 states and territories, 0.2% from out-of-state. 0.1% American Indian or Alaska Native, non-Hispanic/Latino; 22% Hispanic/Latino; 6% Black or African American, non-Hispanic/Latino; 23% Asian, non-Hispanic/Latino; 1% Native Hawaiian or other Pacific Islander, non-Hispanic/Latino. 74% 25 or older, 24% transferred in. Academic area with the most degrees conferred: health professions and related sciences. Core. Calendar: trimesters. Academic remediation for entering students, services for LD students, advanced placement, accelerated degree program, independent study, distance learning, part-time degree program, co-op programs and internships, graduate courses open to undergrads. Off campus study at Holy Names University, Mills College, St. Mary's College, Notre Dame de Namur University.

Entrance Requirements: Transfer credits accepted: Yes.

Collegiate Environment: Orientation program. Social organizations: 15 open to all. Most popular organizations: Student Body Association, California Podiatric Medical Students'; Association (CPMSA), International Healthcare Club, Community Service Honor Society, Scholars in Service. Major annual events: Fall Welcome BBQ, Zombie Health Symposium, Spring BBQ. Student services: health clinic, personal-psychological counseling. Campus security: 24-hour emergency response devices and patrols, late night transport-escort service, 24-hour controlled access. John A. Graziano Memorial Library. Books: 8,453 (physical), 337 (digital/electronic); Serial titles: 714 (physical), 19,832 (digital/electronic); Databases: 22. Weekly public service hours: 86; students can reserve study rooms. Operations spending for the previous fiscal year: $986,278. 160 computers available on

campus for general student use. A campuswide network can be accessed. Students can access the following: online class registration. Staffed computer lab on campus.

■ SAN BERNARDINO VALLEY COLLEGE

701 S Mount Vernon Ave.
San Bernardino, CA 92410-2748
Tel: (909)384-4400
Web Site: www.valleycollege.edu

Description: District-supported, 2-year, coed. Part of San Bernardino Community College District System. Awards certificates, diplomas, transfer associate, and terminal associate degrees. Founded 1926. Setting: 82-acre campus with easy access to Los Angeles. Total enrollment: 1,540. Faculty: 375 (175 full-time, 200 part-time). Students come from 2 states and territories. 55% 25 or older. Core. Calendar: semesters. Academic remediation for entering students, services for LD students, summer session for credit, part-time degree program, co-op programs.

Entrance Requirements: Open admission. Entrance: noncompetitive. Application deadline: 8/29.

Collegiate Environment: Drama-theater group, student-run newspaper, radio station. Student services: health clinic, personal-psychological counseling, women's center. 180 computers available on campus for general student use. Staffed computer lab on campus.

Community Environment: See California State University - San Bernardino.

■ SAN DIEGO CHRISTIAN COLLEGE

200 Riverview Pky.
Santee, CA 92071
Tel: (619)201-8700; Free: 800-676-2242
Fax: (619)440-0209
E-mail: christine.roberts@sdcc.edu
Web Site: www.sdcc.edu

Description: Independent nondenominational, comprehensive, coed. Awards associate, bachelor's, and master's degrees. Founded 1970. Setting: 10-acre suburban campus with easy access to San Diego. Endowment: $656,599. Educational spending for the previous fiscal year: $6694 per student. Total enrollment: 916. Faculty: 97 (21 full-time, 76 part-time). Student-undergrad faculty ratio is 17:1. 433 applied, 52% were admitted. 14% from top 10% of their high school class, 43% from top quarter, 74% from top half. Full-time: 713 students, 51% women, 49% men. Part-time: 167 students, 65% women, 35% men. Students come from 46 states and territories, 12 other countries, 19% from out-of-state. 0.7% American Indian or Alaska Native, non-Hispanic/Latino; 21% Hispanic/Latino; 12% Black or African American, non-Hispanic/Latino; 3% Asian, non-Hispanic/Latino; 1% Native Hawaiian or other Pacific Islander, non-Hispanic/Latino; 1% international. 36% 25 or older, 28% live on campus, 15% transferred in. Retention: 66% of full-time freshmen returned the following year. Academic areas with the most degrees conferred: theology and religious vocations; business/marketing; interdisciplinary studies. Core. Calendar: semesters. Academic remediation for entering students, services for LD students, advanced placement, accelerated degree program, self-designed majors, freshman honors college, independent study, distance learning, double major, summer session for credit, part-time degree program, external degree program, adult/continuing education programs, internships. Off campus study at Consortium of Christian Colleges and Universities (CCCU). Study abroad program. ROTC: Army (c), Air Force (c).

Entrance Requirements: Options: electronic application, deferred admission. Required: essay, high school transcript, 1 recommendation. Recommended: minimum 2.75 high school GPA. Required for some: interview, SAT or ACT. Entrance: minimally difficult. Application deadline: rolling. Notification: continuous. SAT Reasoning Test deadline: 8/15. Transfer credits accepted: Yes.

Collegiate Environment: Orientation program. Drama-theater group, choral group. Social organizations: 15 open to all. Most popular organizations: ASB - Student Government, Service and Community Engagement, Ministry Teams, Flight team, Intramurals. Major annual events: Fall Community Impact Event, Truth and Purpose Conference, Heritage Days. Student services: health clinic, personal-psychological counseling. Campus security: 24-hour emergency response devices, late night transport-escort service.

San Diego Christian College. Books: 64,247 (physical), 338,731 (digital/electronic); Serial titles: 257 (physical), 24,477 (digital/electronic); Databases: 106. Weekly public service hours: 75; students can reserve study rooms. Operations spending for the previous fiscal year: $355,474. 35 computers available on campus for general student use. A campuswide network can be accessed from student residence rooms and from off campus. Students can access the following: online storage, Web-based programs. Staffed computer lab on campus provides training in use of computers and the Internet.

Community Environment: The campus is two miles from the center of El Cajon, a suburb of San Diego. The location of the college affords short travel distances to nearby mountain, desert and beach resorts.

■ SAN DIEGO CITY COLLEGE

1313 Park Blvd.
San Diego, CA 92101-4787
Tel: (619)388-3400
Fax: (619)388-3063
E-mail: lhumphri@sdccd.edu
Web Site: www.sdcity.edu

Description: District-supported, 2-year, coed. Part of San Diego Community College District System. Awards certificates and transfer associate degrees. Founded 1914. Setting: 60-acre urban campus with easy access to San Diego, Tijuana. Endowment: $166,270. Educational spending for the previous fiscal year: $11,466 per student. Total enrollment: 16,930. Faculty: 803 (167 full-time, 636 part-time). Student-undergrad faculty ratio is 35:1. 0.3% American Indian or Alaska Native, non-Hispanic/Latino; 47% Hispanic/Latino; 13% Black or African American, non-Hispanic/Latino; 9% Asian, non-Hispanic/Latino; 0.5% Native Hawaiian or other Pacific Islander, non-Hispanic/Latino. Core. Calendar: semesters. Academic remediation for entering students, ESL program, services for LD students, self-designed majors, honors program, independent study, distance learning, summer session for credit, part-time degree program, external degree program, adult/continuing education programs, co-op programs. Off campus study at San Diego State University. ROTC: Air Force (c).

Entrance Requirements: Open admission. Option: electronic application. Required for some: high school transcript. Entrance: noncompetitive. Application deadline: rolling. Transfer credits accepted: Yes.

Collegiate Environment: Orientation program. Drama-theater group, choral group, student-run newspaper, radio station. Social organizations: 34 open to all. Most popular organizations: Alpha Gamma Sigma, Association of United Latin American Students, MECHA, Afrikan Student Union, Student Nurses Association. Major annual events: World Cultures Day I, World Cultures Day II, Entrepreneurs' Day. Student services: health clinic, personal-psychological counseling. Campus security: 24-hour emergency response devices and patrols, late night transport-escort service. San Diego City College Library. Operations spending for the previous fiscal year: $1.2 million. 150 computers available on campus for general student use. A campuswide network can be accessed from off-campus. Students can access the following: online class registration. Staffed computer lab on campus provides training in use of computers, software, and the Internet.

Community Environment: See San Diego State University.

■ SAN DIEGO MESA COLLEGE

7250 Mesa College Dr.
San Diego, CA 92111-4998
Tel: (619)388-2600
Fax: (619)388-2968
E-mail: csawyer@sdccd.edu
Web Site: www.sdmesa.edu

Description: District-supported, 2-year, coed. Part of San Diego Community College District System. Awards certificates, diplomas, and transfer associate degrees. Founded 1964. Setting: 104-acre suburban campus. Total enrollment: 25,464. Faculty: 723 (199 full-time, 524 part-time). 0.4% American Indian or Alaska Native, non-Hispanic/Latino; 31% Hispanic/Latino; 7% Black or African American, non-Hispanic/Latino; 16% Asian, non-Hispanic/Latino; 0.7% Native Hawaiian or other Pacific Islander, non-Hispanic/Latino. 38% 25 or older. Core. Calendar: semesters. Academic remediation for entering students, ESL program, services for LD students, honors program, independent study, summer session for credit, part-time degree program, external degree program, adult/continuing education programs.

Collegiate Environment: Drama-theater group, choral group, student-run newspaper. Social organizations: 30 open to all. Most popular organizations:

Alpha Gamma Sigma, Black Student Union, MECHA, Associated Student Government, Vietnamese Student Association. Major annual events: Festival of Colors, Job Fair, Club Rush/Back to School Reception. Student services: health clinic, personal-psychological counseling. Campus security: 24-hour emergency response devices and patrols, late night transport-escort service. Learning Resource Center- Library. 350 computers available on campus for general student use. Students can access the following: online class registration. Staffed computer lab on campus provides training in use of computers.

Community Environment: See San Diego State University.

■ SAN DIEGO MIRAMAR COLLEGE

10440 Black Mountain Rd.
San Diego, CA 92126-2999
Tel: (619)388-7800
Fax: (619)388-7801
E-mail: dstack@sdccd.edu
Web Site: www.sdmiramar.edu

Description: District-supported, 2-year, coed. Part of San Diego Community College District System. Awards certificates and transfer associate degrees. Founded 1969. Setting: 120-acre suburban campus. Total enrollment: 10,650. 48% 25 or older. Calendar: semesters. Academic remediation for entering students, ESL program, services for LD students, advanced placement, accelerated degree program, self-designed majors, honors program, independent study, distance learning, double major, summer session for credit, part-time degree program, adult/continuing education programs, co-op programs. Study abroad program.

Entrance Requirements: Open admission. Option: electronic application. Entrance: noncompetitive.

Collegiate Environment: Student-run newspaper. Student services: health clinic, personal-psychological counseling. Campus security: 24-hour emergency response devices and patrols. Miramar College Library.

■ SAN DIEGO STATE UNIVERSITY

5500 Campanile Dr.
San Diego, CA 92182
Tel: (619)594-5200; Free: 855-594-3983
Web Site: www.sdsu.edu

Description: State-supported, university, coed. Part of California State University System. Awards bachelor's, master's, and doctoral degrees. Founded 1897. Setting: 288-acre urban campus with easy access to San Diego. Endowment: $305.8 million. Research spending for the previous fiscal year: $50.8 million. Educational spending for the previous fiscal year: $11,238 per student. Total enrollment: 34,881. Faculty: 1,888 (933 full-time, 955 part-time). Student-undergrad faculty ratio is 27:1. 69,043 applied, 34% were admitted. 29% from top 10% of their high school class, 68% from top quarter, 93% from top half. Full-time: 27,398 students, 55% women, 45% men. Part-time: 2,995 students, 50% women, 50% men. Students come from 54 states and territories, 114 other countries, 11% from out-of-state. 0.3% American Indian or Alaska Native, non-Hispanic/Latino; 31% Hispanic/Latino; 4% Black or African American, non-Hispanic/Latino; 13% Asian, non-Hispanic/Latino; 0.2% Native Hawaiian or other Pacific Islander, non-Hispanic/Latino; 7% international. 13% 25 or older, 19% live on campus, 11% transferred in. Retention: 89% of full-time freshmen returned the following year. Academic areas with the most degrees conferred: business/marketing; social sciences; engineering; health professions and related sciences. Core. Calendar: semesters. ESL program, services for LD students, advanced placement, self-designed majors, freshman honors college, honors program, independent study, distance learning, double major, summer session for credit, part-time degree program, external degree program, internships, graduate courses open to undergrads. Off campus study at other units of the California State University System. Study abroad program. ROTC: Army, Naval (c), Air Force.

Entrance Requirements: Options: electronic application, international baccalaureate accepted. Required: high school transcript, SAT or ACT. Entrance: very difficult. Application deadline: 11/30. SAT Reasoning Test deadline: November. SAT Subject Test deadline: November. Transfer credits accepted: Yes. Applicants placed on waiting list: 2,853. Wait-listed applicants offered admission: 46.

Costs Per Year: Application fee: $55. Area resident tuition: $5742 full-time. State resident tuition: $5742 full-time. Nonresident tuition: $17,622 full-time. Mandatory fees: $1768 full-time. College room and board: $17,752.

Collegiate Environment: Orientation program. Drama-theater group, choral group, marching band, student-run newspaper, radio station. Social

organizations: 310 open to all; national fraternities, national sororities. Most popular organizations: AB Samahan, Asian Pacific Student Alliance, Enviro-Business Society, M.E.Ch.A de SDSU, Social fraternities and sororities, including both general and culturally based organizations. Major annual events: Student Involvement Expo (showcasing student organizations, community service, involvement activities), Welcome Week, Aztec Nights. Student services: health clinic, personal-psychological counseling, women's center. Campus security: 24-hour emergency response devices and patrols, student patrols, late night transport-escort service, controlled dormitory access. Freshmen given priority for college housing. On-campus residence required through sophomore year. Option: coed housing available. Malcolm A. Love Library. Books: 1.3 million (physical), 1 million (digital/electronic); Serial titles: 45,107 (physical), 92,142 (digital/electronic); Databases: 317. Weekly public service hours: 168; study areas open 24 hours, 5-7 days a week; students can reserve study rooms. Operations spending for the previous fiscal year: $14.4 million. 2,000 computers available on campus for general student use. A campuswide network can be accessed from student residence rooms and from off campus. Students can access the following: online class registration, learning management system. Staffed computer lab on campus (open 24 hours a day) provides training in use of computers, software, and the Internet.

Community Environment: San Diego lies along and around one of the world's ten most beautiful protected natural harbors. It has 19 miles of beautiful beaces and a very special "sea-washed, air-conditioned climate." The maximum average temperature of 70.8 degrees and a minimum of 55.4 degrees make the climate very special. The population of San Diego is 1,255,540 with a greater metropolitan area population of 2,166,200. The Santa Fe Railroad, buses, and a number of major airlines serve the area. The city is a manufacturing and shipping center, with its main industries being tourism, agriculture, and defense. The county is the country's largest producer of avocados. It has a public library with 30 branches, nine general hospitals, numerous museums, galleries, and churches. Residents and visitors will find many golf courses, all aquatic sports, hiking, mountain climbing, horseback riding, fishing and hunting, and skiing and other snow sports nearby. This area is home of the San Diego Chargers professional football team, and the San Diego Padres professional baseball team. Known as a winter playground, it has 19 miles of Pacific Ocean shores with beautiful beaches.

■ **SAN DIEGO STATE UNIVERSITY-IMPERIAL VALLEY CAMPUS**
720 Heber Ave.
Calexico, CA 92231
Tel: (760)768-5500
E-mail: transfer@mail.sdsu.edu
Web Site: www.ivcampus.sdsu.edu
Description: State-supported, comprehensive, coed. Awards bachelor's and master's degrees. Total enrollment: 1,003. 50,100 applied. 38% 25 or older. Distance learning. Study abroad program.

■ **SAN FRANCISCO ART INSTITUTE**
800 Chestnut St.
San Francisco, CA 94133
Tel: (415)771-7020; Free: 800-345-SFAI
E-mail: admissions@sfai.edu
Web Site: www.sfai.edu
Description: Independent, comprehensive, coed. Awards bachelor's and master's degrees. Founded 1871. Setting: 4-acre urban campus with easy access to San Francisco. Endowment: $10.3 million. Educational spending for the previous fiscal year: $10,399 per student. Total enrollment: 433. Faculty: 92 (22 full-time, 70 part-time). Student-undergrad faculty ratio is 9:1. 451 applied, 75% were admitted. Full-time: 279 students, 62% women, 38% men. Part-time: 20 students, 75% women, 25% men. Students come from 37 states and territories, 20 other countries, 64% from out-of-state. 15% Hispanic/Latino; 2% Black or African American, non-Hispanic/Latino; 8% Asian, non-Hispanic/Latino; 21% international. 20% 25 or older, 36% live on campus, 14% transferred in. Retention: 51% of full-time freshmen returned the following year. Academic areas with the most degrees conferred: visual and performing arts; social sciences. Core. Calendar: semesters. Academic remediation for entering students, ESL program, services for LD students, honors program, independent study, distance learning, summer session for credit, internships. Off campus study at Association of Independent Colleges of Art and Design (AICAD). Study abroad program.
Entrance Requirements: Options: electronic application, early action, deferred admission, international baccalaureate accepted. Required: essay,

high school transcript, 1 recommendation, portfolio and artist statement for BFA applicants, critical essay for BA applicants. Recommended: minimum 2.5 high school GPA, interview, SAT or ACT. Entrance: moderately difficult. Application deadlines: rolling, 11/15 for early action. Notification: continuous. Transfer credits accepted: Yes.
Costs Per Year: Application fee: $75. One-time mandatory fee: $200. Comprehensive fee: $62,243 includes full-time tuition ($45,664), mandatory fees ($870), and college room and board ($15,709). College room only: $11,650. Full-time tuition and fees vary according to degree level. Room and board charges vary according to housing facility. Part-time tuition: $2000 per credit. Part-time tuition varies according to degree level.
Collegiate Environment: Orientation program. Student-run newspaper, radio station. Social organizations: 8 open to all. Most popular organizations: Student Union, LOGS (Legion of Graduate Students), Film Club, Photo Club, SFAeye. Major annual events: MFA—A Exhibition, Walter & McBean Galleries Openings, SFAI Alumni Weekend + Exhibition. Student services: personal-psychological counseling. Campus security: 24-hour patrols, security cameras. Anne Bremer Memorial Library plus 1 other. Books: 32,775 (physical); Serial titles: 126 (physical), 791 (digital/electronic); Databases: 6. Weekly public service hours: 59. Operations spending for the previous fiscal year: $341,106. 150 computers available on campus for general student use. A campuswide network can be accessed. Students can access the following: online class registration. Staffed computer lab on campus provides training in use of computers, software, and the Internet.
Community Environment: See San Francisco State University.

■ **SAN FRANCISCO CONSERVATORY OF MUSIC**
50 Oak St.
San Francisco, CA 94102
Tel: (415)864-7326
Fax: (415)503-6299
E-mail: admit@sfcm.edu
Web Site: www.sfcm.edu
Description: Independent, comprehensive, coed. Awards bachelor's and master's degrees and post-master's certificates. Founded 1917. Setting: 2-acre urban campus with easy access to San Francisco Bay Area. Endowment: $41.3 million. Educational spending for the previous fiscal year: $29,294 per student. Total enrollment: 414. Faculty: 134 (29 full-time, 105 part-time). Student-undergrad faculty ratio is 7:1. 429 applied, 42% were admitted. Full-time: 204 students, 43% women, 57% men. Part-time: 1 student, 100% women. Students come from 25 states and territories, 15 other countries, 55% from out-of-state. 1% American Indian or Alaska Native, non-Hispanic/Latino; 6% Hispanic/Latino; 6% Black or African American, non-Hispanic/Latino; 8% Asian, non-Hispanic/Latino; 30% international. 9% 25 or older, 64% live on campus, 3% transferred in. Retention: 76% of full-time freshmen returned the following year. Academic area with the most degrees conferred: visual and performing arts. Core. Calendar: semesters. Academic remediation for entering students, ESL program, services for LD students, advanced placement, independent study, co-op programs and internships.
Entrance Requirements: Options: electronic application, deferred admission. Required: essay, high school transcript, minimum 2.5 high school GPA, 2 recommendations, audition, pre-screen recording in select areas. Required for some: interview. Entrance: very difficult. Application deadline: 12/1. Notification: 4/1. Transfer credits accepted: Yes. Applicants placed on waiting list: 42. Wait-listed applicants offered admission: 14.
Costs Per Year: Application fee: $110. Comprehensive fee: $62,625 includes full-time tuition ($45,000), mandatory fees ($1110), and college room and board ($16,515). College room only: $12,710. Part-time tuition: $1980 per credit. Part-time mandatory fees: $1110 per year.
Collegiate Environment: Orientation program. Drama-theater group, choral group. Social organizations: 2 open to all. Most popular organizations: Yoga Group, Student Counsel. Major annual events: Halloween Party, SF Giants Baseball Game, End of Year Carnival. Student services: personal-psychological counseling. Campus security: 24-hour emergency response devices and patrols, controlled dormitory access, resident assistant on-call for residential hall residents, after hours on-call mental health counseling. San Francisco Conservatory of Music Library. Books: 24,129 (physical), 31,094 (digital/electronic); Serial titles: 64 (physical), 448 (digital/electronic); Databases: 11. Weekly public service hours: 72. Operations spending for the previous fiscal year: $312,204. 12 computers available on campus for general student use. A campuswide network can be accessed from student residence rooms. Students can access the following: online class registration. Staffed computer lab on campus provides training in use of computers, software, and the Internet.

Community Environment: See San Francisco State University.

■ **SAN FRANCISCO STATE UNIVERSITY**
1600 Holloway Ave.
San Francisco, CA 94132-1722
Tel: (415)338-1100
Web Site: www.sfsu.edu
Description: State-supported, university, coed. Part of California State University System. Awards bachelor's, master's, and doctoral degrees and post-master's certificates. Founded 1899. Setting: 142-acre urban campus. Endowment: $83.7 million. Total enrollment: 29,586. Faculty: 1,764 (765 full-time, 999 part-time). 35,606 applied, 72% were admitted. Full-time: 22,159 students, 57% women, 43% men. Part-time: 4,339 students, 50% women, 50% men. 1% from out-of-state. 0.1% American Indian or Alaska Native, non-Hispanic/Latino; 34% Hispanic/Latino; 6% Black or African American, non-Hispanic/Latino; 26% Asian, non-Hispanic/Latino; 0.4% Native Hawaiian or other Pacific Islander, non-Hispanic/Latino; 7% international. 19% 25 or older, 15% live on campus, 13% transferred in. Retention: 79% of full-time freshmen returned the following year. Academic areas with the most degrees conferred: business/marketing; communication/journalism; social sciences. Core. Calendar: semesters. Academic remediation for entering students, ESL program, services for LD students, advanced placement, accelerated degree program, self-designed majors, honors program, independent study, distance learning, double major, summer session for credit, part-time degree program, adult/continuing education programs, co-op programs and internships, graduate courses open to undergrads. Off campus study at The San Francisco Consortium, 22 other institutions of the California State University System. Study abroad program. ROTC: Army (c), Air Force (c).
Entrance Requirements: Options: electronic application, international baccalaureate accepted. Required: high school transcript, SAT or ACT. Entrance: moderately difficult. Notification: 12/1. SAT Reasoning Test deadline: 1/26.
Costs Per Year: Application fee: $55. Area resident tuition: $5742 full-time. State resident tuition: $5742 full-time. Nonresident tuition: $17,622 full-time. Mandatory fees: $1518 full-time. College room and board: $13,462.
Collegiate Environment: Orientation program. Drama-theater group, choral group, student-run newspaper, radio station. Social organizations: 87 open to all; national fraternities, national sororities, local fraternities, local sororities. Major annual events: Cultural/Activities Fair, Associated Students Craft Fair, Campus Health Fairs. Student services: legal services, health clinic, personal-psychological counseling, women's center. Campus security: 24-hour emergency response devices and patrols, student patrols, late night transport-escort service, controlled dormitory access. Freshmen given priority for college housing. Options: coed, women-only housing available. J. Paul Leonard Library. Study areas open 24 hours, 5-7 days a week; students can reserve study rooms. 2,000 computers available on campus for general student use. Computer purchase/lease plans available. A campuswide network can be accessed from student residence rooms and from off campus. Students can access the following: online class registration. Staffed computer lab on campus (open 24 hours a day) provides training in use of computers, software, and the Internet.
Community Environment: San Francisco is one of the most cosmopolitan cities in the United States. It is the financial center of the west, and an important industrial city. A great port, it serves as the terminus for Trans-Pacific and coastwise steamship lines and airlines. The city is located on hills at the end of a narrow peninsula with the Pacific Ocean on one side and the San Francisco Bay on the other. The annual temperature averages 57 degrees. San Francisco Bay is the largest landlocked harbor in the world, and is the home of the beautiful Golden Gate Bridge. All modes of transportation serve the area. A large civic center includes the city hall, public library, civic auditorium, state building, federal office building, health center, opera house and war memorial building. The opera house is the only municipally owned opera house in America. Job opportunities vary considerably but are available. San Francisco has 438 churches, 52 public parks, and 100 theaters. Recreational facilities are numerous for all water sports, hiking, and fishing. Mountain resort areas are approximately a three hour drive. Famous Chinatown is located here, as is the picturesque Fisherman's Wharf.

■ **SAN JOAQUIN DELTA COLLEGE**
5151 Pacific Ave.
Stockton, CA 95207-6370
Tel: (209)954-5151
Fax: (209)954-5600

E-mail: ksea@deltacollege.edu
Web Site: www.deltacollege.edu
Description: District-supported, 2-year, coed. Part of California Community College System. Awards certificates, transfer associate, and terminal associate degrees. Founded 1935. Setting: 165-acre urban campus with easy access to Sacramento. Educational spending for the previous fiscal year: $3500 per student. Total enrollment: 18,102. Faculty: 544 (222 full-time, 322 part-time). Student-undergrad faculty ratio is 27:1. Students come from 20 states and territories, 0.2% from out-of-state. 0.3% American Indian or Alaska Native, non-Hispanic/Latino; 44% Hispanic/Latino; 13% Black or African American, non-Hispanic/Latino; 17% Asian, non-Hispanic/Latino; 0.5% Native Hawaiian or other Pacific Islander, non-Hispanic/Latino; 0.3% international. 31% 25 or older. Retention: 77% of full-time freshmen returned the following year. Core. Calendar: semesters. Academic remediation for entering students, ESL program, services for LD students, advanced placement, honors program, independent study, distance learning, summer session for credit, part-time degree program, adult/continuing education programs, co-op programs.
Entrance Requirements: Open admission except for nursing. Options: electronic application, early admission, international baccalaureate accepted. Entrance: noncompetitive. Application deadline: rolling. Notification: continuous.
Collegiate Environment: Orientation program. Drama-theater group, choral group, student-run newspaper, radio station. Student services: legal services, personal-psychological counseling. Campus security: 24-hour emergency response devices and patrols, late night transport-escort service. Goleman Library plus 1 other. Operations spending for the previous fiscal year: $1.4 million. 400 computers available on campus for general student use. A campuswide network can be accessed from off-campus. Students can access the following: online class registration. Staffed computer lab on campus.
Community Environment: See University of the Pacific.

■ **SAN JOAQUIN VALLEY COLLEGE (BAKERSFIELD)**
201 New Stine Rd.
Bakersfield, CA 93309
Tel: (661)834-0126; Free: 866-544-7898
E-mail: admissions@sjvc.edu
Web Site: www.sjvc.edu/campuses/central-california/bakersfield
Description: Proprietary, 2-year, coed. Part of San Joaquin Valley College. Awards certificates and terminal associate degrees. Founded 1977. Setting: suburban campus with easy access to Bakersfield. Total enrollment: 864. Faculty: 57 (23 full-time, 34 part-time). Student-undergrad faculty ratio is 25:1. 1% American Indian or Alaska Native, non-Hispanic/Latino; 57% Hispanic/Latino; 5% Black or African American, non-Hispanic/Latino; 3% Asian, non-Hispanic/Latino; 0.2% Native Hawaiian or other Pacific Islander, non-Hispanic/Latino; 3% international. 47% 25 or older. Core. Calendar: continuous.
Entrance Requirements: Required for some: essay, high school transcript, interview. Entrance: noncompetitive. Application deadline: rolling. Notification: continuous.
Collegiate Environment: Orientation program. Social organizations: 6 open to all. Most popular organizations: CAMA Club, RACT Club, Business Club, Student Council, National Technical Honor Society. Major annual events: Thanksgiving Turkey Feed, All-School Luau, student celebrations.

■ **SAN JOAQUIN VALLEY COLLEGE (FRESNO)**
295 E Sierra Ave.
Fresno, CA 93710
Tel: (559)448-8282; Free: 866-544-7898
E-mail: admissions@sjvc.edu
Web Site: www.sjvc.edu/campuses/central-california/fresno
Description: Proprietary, 2-year, coed. Part of San Joaquin Valley College. Awards certificates and terminal associate degrees. Setting: urban campus with easy access to Fresno. Total enrollment: 1,019. Faculty: 55 (19 full-time, 36 part-time). Student-undergrad faculty ratio is 33:1. 1% American Indian or Alaska Native, non-Hispanic/Latino; 57% Hispanic/Latino; 4% Black or African American, non-Hispanic/Latino; 5% Asian, non-Hispanic/Latino; 0.7% Native Hawaiian or other Pacific Islander, non-Hispanic/Latino; 2% international. 41% 25 or older. Core. Calendar: continuous.
Entrance Requirements: Required for some: essay, 1 recommendation, interview. Entrance: noncompetitive. Application deadline: rolling. Notification: continuous.
Collegiate Environment: Orientation program. Social organizations: 4 open

to all. Most popular organizations: Associated Student Body, American Medical Technologists, State and County Dental Assistants Association, Arts and Entertainment. Major annual events: March of Dimes Fundraiser, Christmas Toy Drive, Thanksgiving Food Drive.

■ **SAN JOAQUIN VALLEY COLLEGE (HANFORD)**
215 W 7th St.
Hanford, CA 93230
Tel: (559)584-8840; Free: 866-544-7898
Web Site: www.sjvc.edu/campuses/central-california/hanford
Description: Proprietary, 2-year, coed. Awards certificates and terminal associate degrees. Setting: small town campus with easy access to Fresno. Total enrollment: 275. Faculty: 6 (4 full-time, 2 part-time). Student-undergrad faculty ratio is 59:1. 1% American Indian or Alaska Native, non-Hispanic/Latino; 62% Hispanic/Latino; 4% Black or African American, non-Hispanic/Latino; 1% Asian, non-Hispanic/Latino; 4% international. 45% 25 or older. Calendar: continuous.

■ **SAN JOAQUIN VALLEY COLLEGE (HESPERIA)**
9331 Mariposa Rd.
Hesperia, CA 92344
Tel: (760)948-1947; Free: 866-544-7898
Web Site: www.sjvc.edu/campuses/southern-california/victor-valley
Description: Proprietary, 2-year, coed. Part of San Joaquin Valley College. Awards certificates and terminal associate degrees. Setting: suburban campus with easy access to San Bernadino. Total enrollment: 679. Faculty: 40 (10 full-time, 30 part-time). Student-undergrad faculty ratio is 34:1. 1% American Indian or Alaska Native, non-Hispanic/Latino; 53% Hispanic/Latino; 12% Black or African American, non-Hispanic/Latino; 1% Asian, non-Hispanic/Latino; 0.7% Native Hawaiian or other Pacific Islander, non-Hispanic/Latino; 1% international. 41% 25 or older. Calendar: continuous.

■ **SAN JOAQUIN VALLEY COLLEGE (LANCASTER)**
42135 10th St. W
Ste. 147
Lancaster, CA 93534
Tel: (661)974-8282; Free: 866-544-7898
Web Site: www.sjvc.edu/campuses/southern-california/antelope-valley
Description: Proprietary, 2-year, coed. Part of San Joaquin Valley College. Awards certificates and terminal associate degrees. Founded 2012. Setting: suburban campus. Total enrollment: 328. Faculty: 18 (2 full-time, 16 part-time). Student-undergrad faculty ratio is 45:1. 0.6% American Indian or Alaska Native, non-Hispanic/Latino; 52% Hispanic/Latino; 21% Black or African American, non-Hispanic/Latino; 1% Asian, non-Hispanic/Latino; 2% Native Hawaiian or other Pacific Islander, non-Hispanic/Latino; 2% international. 43% 25 or older. Calendar: continuous.

■ **SAN JOAQUIN VALLEY COLLEGE (ONTARIO)**
4580 Ontario Mills Pky.
Ontario, CA 91764
Tel: (909)948-7582; Free: 866-544-7898
E-mail: admissions@sjvc.edu
Web Site: www.sjvc.edu/campuses/southern-california/ontario
Description: Proprietary, 2-year, coed. Part of San Joaquin Valley College. Awards certificates and terminal associate degrees. Setting: urban campus with easy access to Los Angeles. Total enrollment: 994. Faculty: 97 (34 full-time, 63 part-time). Student-undergrad faculty ratio is 18:1. 0.3% American Indian or Alaska Native, non-Hispanic/Latino; 61% Hispanic/Latino; 6% Black or African American, non-Hispanic/Latino; 6% Asian, non-Hispanic/Latino; 2% Native Hawaiian or other Pacific Islander, non-Hispanic/Latino; 2% international. 49% 25 or older. Core. Calendar: continuous.
Entrance Requirements: Required for some: essay, interview. Entrance: noncompetitive. Application deadline: rolling. Notification: continuous.
Collegiate Environment: Orientation program. Most popular organizations: Students in Free Enterprise (SIFE), Associated Student Body, Fitness Club, Ambassador Club, Diversity Club. Major annual events: Career Expo (job fair), Awards Ceremony, Spring Fling.

■ **SAN JOAQUIN VALLEY COLLEGE (RANCHO CORDOVA)**
11050 Olson Dr.
Ste. 210
Rancho Cordova, CA 95670
Tel: (916)638-7582; Free: 866-544-7898
E-mail: admissions@sjvc.edu

Web Site: www.sjvc.edu/campuses/northern-california/rancho-cordova
Description: Proprietary, 2-year, coed. Part of San Joaquin Valley College. Awards certificates and terminal associate degrees. Setting: suburban campus with easy access to Sacramento. Total enrollment: 158. Faculty: 12 (5 full-time, 7 part-time). Student-undergrad faculty ratio is 22:1. 10% Hispanic/Latino; 2% Black or African American, non-Hispanic/Latino; 18% Asian, non-Hispanic/Latino; 4% Native Hawaiian or other Pacific Islander, non-Hispanic/Latino; 4% international. 80% 25 or older. Core. Calendar: continuous.
Entrance Requirements: Required for some: essay, interview. Entrance: noncompetitive. Application deadline: rolling. Notification: continuous.
Collegiate Environment: Most popular organizations: Associated Student Body, Diversity Committee. Major annual events: Constitution Day Activities, Campus Dress Down Day, Christmas Toy Drive.

■ **SAN JOAQUIN VALLEY COLLEGE (SALIDA)**
5380 Pirrone Rd.
Salida, CA 95368
Tel: (209)543-8800; Free: 866-544-7898
E-mail: admissions@sjvc.edu
Web Site: www.sjvc.edu/campuses/northern-california/modesto
Description: Proprietary, 2-year, coed. Part of San Joaquin Valley College. Awards certificates and terminal associate degrees. Setting: suburban campus. Total enrollment: 465. Faculty: 29 (8 full-time, 21 part-time). Student-undergrad faculty ratio is 31:1. 0.2% American Indian or Alaska Native, non-Hispanic/Latino; 47% Hispanic/Latino; 3% Black or African American, non-Hispanic/Latino; 6% Asian, non-Hispanic/Latino; 2% Native Hawaiian or other Pacific Islander, non-Hispanic/Latino; 3% international. 46% 25 or older. Core. Calendar: continuous.
Entrance Requirements: Required for some: essay, interview. Entrance: noncompetitive. Application deadline: rolling. Notification: continuous.
Collegiate Environment: Orientation program. Social organizations: 2 open to all. Most popular organizations: Associated Student Body, Book Club. Major annual events: Student Appreciation Day, March of Dimes, Cancer Relay.

■ **SAN JOAQUIN VALLEY COLLEGE (TEMECULA)**
27270 Madison Ave.
Ste. 103
Temecula, CA 92590
Tel: (951)296-6015; Free: 866-544-7898
E-mail: admissions@sjvc.edu
Web Site: www.sjvc.edu/campuses/southern-california/temecula
Description: Proprietary, 2-year, coed. Part of San Joaquin Valley College. Awards certificates and terminal associate degrees. Setting: urban campus with easy access to Los Angeles. Total enrollment: 728. Faculty: 43 (13 full-time, 30 part-time). Student-undergrad faculty ratio is 32:1. 1% American Indian or Alaska Native, non-Hispanic/Latino; 40% Hispanic/Latino; 7% Black or African American, non-Hispanic/Latino; 6% Asian, non-Hispanic/Latino; 2% Native Hawaiian or other Pacific Islander, non-Hispanic/Latino; 5% international. 52% 25 or older. Calendar: continuous.

■ **SAN JOAQUIN VALLEY COLLEGE (VISALIA)**
8344 W Mineral King Ave.
Visalia, CA 93291
Tel: (559)651-2500; Free: 866-544-7898
E-mail: admissions@sjvc.edu
Web Site: www.sjvc.edu/campuses/central-california/visalia
Description: Proprietary, 2-year, coed. Part of San Joaquin Valley College. Awards certificates and terminal associate degrees. Founded 1977. Setting: suburban campus with easy access to Fresno. Total enrollment: 1,294. Faculty: 101 (42 full-time, 59 part-time). Student-undergrad faculty ratio is 21:1. 0.9% American Indian or Alaska Native, non-Hispanic/Latino; 54% Hispanic/Latino; 2% Black or African American, non-Hispanic/Latino; 6% Asian, non-Hispanic/Latino; 0.5% Native Hawaiian or other Pacific Islander, non-Hispanic/Latino; 3% international. 56% 25 or older. Core. Calendar: continuous. Academic remediation for entering students.
Entrance Requirements: Required for some: essay, high school transcript, interview. Entrance: noncompetitive. Application deadline: rolling. Notification: continuous.
Collegiate Environment: Orientation program. Social organizations: 4 open to all. Most popular organizations: Associated Student Body, Students in Free Enterprise (SIFE), American Medical Technologists, National and Technical Honor Society. Major annual events: Student Appreciation Day,

March of Dimes Fundraiser, Constitution Day. Campus security: late night transport-escort service, full-time security personnel. SJVC Visalia Campus Library.

■ **SAN JOAQUIN VALLEY COLLEGE-FRESNO AVIATION CAMPUS**
4985 E Anderson Ave.
Fresno, CA 93727
Tel: (559)453-0123; Free: 866-544-7898
E-mail: admissions@sjvc.edu
Web Site: www.sjvc.edu/campuses/central-california/fresno-aviation
Description: Proprietary, 2-year, coed. Part of San Joaquin Valley College. Awards terminal associate degrees. Setting: urban campus with easy access to Fresno. Total enrollment: 130. Faculty: 8 (3 full-time, 5 part-time). Student-undergrad faculty ratio is 26:1. 0.8% American Indian or Alaska Native, non-Hispanic/Latino; 34% Hispanic/Latino; 2% Black or African American, non-Hispanic/Latino; 11% Asian, non-Hispanic/Latino; 0.8% Native Hawaiian or other Pacific Islander, non-Hispanic/Latino; 4% international. 62% 25 or older. Core. Calendar: semesters.
Entrance Requirements: Required for some: essay, high school transcript, interview. Entrance: noncompetitive. Application deadline: rolling. Notification: continuous.
Collegiate Environment: Orientation program. Most popular organization: RC Club (radio controlled airplane). Major annual events: AMT Day, Student Appreciation Day, Veteran's Day.

■ **SAN JOAQUIN VALLEY COLLEGE-ONLINE**
8344 W Mineral King Ave.
Visalia, CA 93291
Tel: (559)734-7582; Free: 866-544-7898
E-mail: admissions@sjvc.edu
Web Site: www.sjvc.edu/online-programs
Description: Proprietary, 2-year, coed. Part of San Joaquin Valley College. Awards certificates and terminal associate degrees. Setting: suburban campus. Total enrollment: 1,005. Faculty: 50 (11 full-time, 39 part-time). Student-undergrad faculty ratio is 42:1. 0.9% American Indian or Alaska Native, non-Hispanic/Latino; 17% Hispanic/Latino; 32% Black or African American, non-Hispanic/Latino; 2% Asian, non-Hispanic/Latino; 0.1% Native Hawaiian or other Pacific Islander, non-Hispanic/Latino; 0.6% international. 75% 25 or older. Core. Calendar: continuous.
Entrance Requirements: Option: electronic application. Required for some: essay, interview. Application deadline: rolling. Notification: continuous.
Collegiate Environment: Orientation program.

■ **SAN JOSE CITY COLLEGE**
2100 Moorpark Ave.
San Jose, CA 95128-2799
Tel: (408)298-2181
Web Site: www.sjcc.edu
Description: District-supported, 2-year, coed. Part of San Jose/Evergreen Community College District System. Awards transfer associate and terminal associate degrees. Founded 1921. Setting: 58-acre urban campus. Total enrollment: 9,805. 50% 25 or older. Core. Calendar: semesters. Academic remediation for entering students, ESL program, services for LD students, advanced placement, self-designed majors, summer session for credit, part-time degree program, adult/continuing education programs, co-op programs. ROTC: Army (c), Air Force (c).
Entrance Requirements: Open admission. Options: early admission, deferred admission. Entrance: noncompetitive. Application deadline: rolling. Preference given to district residents.
Collegiate Environment: Drama-theater group, student-run newspaper, radio station. Student services: health clinic. San Jose City College Library.
Community Environment: See San Jose State University.

■ **SAN JOSE STATE UNIVERSITY**
One Washington Sq.
San Jose, CA 95192-0001
Tel: (408)924-1000
Fax: (408)924-2050
Web Site: www.sjsu.edu
Description: State-supported, comprehensive, coed. Part of California State University System. Awards bachelor's, master's, and doctoral degrees. Founded 1857. Setting: 152-acre urban campus. Total enrollment: 32,423. Faculty: 1,858 (720 full-time, 1,138 part-time). Student-undergrad faculty ratio is 28:1. 36,243 applied, 55% were admitted. Full-time: 23,099 students,

50% women, 50% men. Part-time: 4,228 students, 46% women, 54% men. Students come from 42 states and territories, 122 other countries, 1% from out-of-state. 0.1% American Indian or Alaska Native, non-Hispanic/Latino; 28% Hispanic/Latino; 3% Black or African American, non-Hispanic/Latino; 36% Asian, non-Hispanic/Latino; 0.5% Native Hawaiian or other Pacific Islander, non-Hispanic/Latino; 8% international. 19% 25 or older, 14% live on campus, 14% transferred in. Retention: 83% of full-time freshmen returned the following year. Academic areas with the most degrees conferred: business/marketing; engineering; visual and performing arts. Core. Calendar: semesters. Academic remediation for entering students, services for LD students, advanced placement, self-designed majors, honors program, independent study, distance learning, double major, summer session for credit, part-time degree program, adult/continuing education programs, internships, graduate courses open to undergrads. Off campus study at other institutions of the California State University System. Study abroad program. ROTC: Army (c), Air Force.
Entrance Requirements: Option: electronic application. Required: high school transcript, SAT or ACT. Entrance: very difficult. Application deadline: 12/15. Notification: continuous until 12/15. Preference given to state residents. SAT Reasoning Test deadline: 1/3. Transfer credits accepted: Yes.
Costs Per Year: Application fee: $55. State resident tuition: $5742 full-time, $1665 per term part-time. Nonresident tuition: $15,246 full-time, $4041 per term part-time. Mandatory fees: $1946 full-time, $1946 per year part-time. College room and board: $16,442. College room only: $11,642. Room and board charges vary according to board plan, housing facility, and location.
Collegiate Environment: Orientation program. Drama-theater group, choral group, marching band, student-run newspaper, radio station. Social organizations: national fraternities, national sororities, local fraternities, local sororities. Major annual events: Weeks of Welcome, Spartan Speaker Series, Homecoming. Student services: health clinic, personal-psychological counseling, women's center. Campus security: 24-hour emergency response devices and patrols, student patrols, late night transport-escort service. Freshmen given priority for college housing. On-campus residence required in freshman year. Options: coed, men-only, women-only housing available. Dr. Martin Luther King Jr. Library plus 1 other. Books: 1.2 million (physical), 801,700 (digital/electronic); Serial titles: 1.3 million (physical), 1.3 million (digital/electronic); Databases: 408. Weekly public service hours: 139.
Community Environment: Population 912,332. 15th largest city in U.S. Located in the Santa Clara Valley, known worldwide as"Silicon Valley". 50 miles south of San Francisco, and 30 miles from the Pacific Ocean. The Mount Hamilton Range rises to 4,209 feet on the east, and the Santa Cruz Range provides the western view. San Jose was the first capital of California. Recreational facilities are numerous, including Alum Rock Park, six miles away which includes a museum, picnic grounds, active mineral springs, a large swimming pool, mineral baths, and several miles of marked trails. Mountain resort areas are within easy driving distance for the major winter sports. Points of interest are Lick Observatory on the summit of Mount Hamilton, Rosicrucian Egyptian Temple, Oriental Museum, Winchester Mystery House.

■ **SANTA ANA COLLEGE**
1530 W 17th St.
Santa Ana, CA 92706-3398
Tel: (714)564-6000
Web Site: www.sac.edu
Description: District-supported, 2-year, coed. Part of California Community College System. Awards certificates, transfer associate, and terminal associate degrees. Founded 1915. Setting: 58-acre urban campus with easy access to Los Angeles. Total enrollment: 22,189. Faculty: 1,296 (249 full-time, 1,047 part-time). Student-undergrad faculty ratio is 20:1. 4% from out-of-state. 63% 25 or older. Core. Calendar: semesters. Academic remediation for entering students, ESL program, services for LD students, advanced placement, accelerated degree program, freshman honors college, honors program, distance learning, summer session for credit, part-time degree program, external degree program, adult/continuing education programs, co-op programs. Study abroad program. ROTC: Air Force (c).
Entrance Requirements: Open admission. Option: early admission. Entrance: noncompetitive. Application deadline: 8/21.
Collegiate Environment: Drama-theater group, choral group, student-run newspaper. Social organizations: 23 open to all. Most popular organizations: Students of Diverse Cultures, Students United for Better Education, Phi Beta Kappa, Alpha Gamma Sigma, Puente. Major annual events: International Festival, Club Rush, Cinco de Mayo. Student services: legal services, health clinic, personal-psychological counseling, women's center. Campus security:

late night transport-escort service. McNeally Library. 100 computers available on campus for general student use. A campuswide network can be accessed. Staffed computer lab on campus.

■ SANTA BARBARA BUSINESS COLLEGE (BAKERSFIELD)

5300 California Ave.
Bakersfield, CA 93309
Tel: (661)835-1100
Web Site: www.sbbcollege.edu
Description: Proprietary, primarily 2-year, coed. Awards transfer associate, terminal associate, and bachelor's degrees.

■ SANTA BARBARA BUSINESS COLLEGE (SANTA MARIA)

303 E Plz. Dr.
Santa Maria, CA 93454
Tel: (805)922-8256
Web Site: www.sbbcollege.edu
Description: Proprietary, primarily 2-year, coed. Awards transfer associate, terminal associate, and bachelor's degrees.

■ SANTA BARBARA BUSINESS COLLEGE (VENTURA)

4839 Market St.
Ventura, CA 93003
Tel: (805)339-2999
Web Site: www.sbbcollege.edu
Description: Proprietary, 4-year, coed. Awards associate and bachelor's degrees.

■ SANTA BARBARA CITY COLLEGE

721 Cliff Dr.
Santa Barbara, CA 93109-2394
Tel: (805)965-0581
E-mail: admissions@sbcc.edu
Web Site: www.sbcc.edu
Description: District-supported, 2-year, coed. Part of California Community College System. Awards certificates and terminal associate degrees. Founded 1908. Setting: 65-acre small town campus. Endowment: $21.1 million. Educational spending for the previous fiscal year: $2587 per student. Total enrollment: 18,092. Faculty: 806 (266 full-time, 540 part-time). Student-undergrad faculty ratio is 27:1. 4,448 applied, 100% were admitted. Full-time: 7,952 students, 50% women, 50% men. Part-time: 10,140 students, 56% women, 44% men. Students come from 66 other countries, 6% from out-of-state. 0.7% American Indian or Alaska Native, non-Hispanic/Latino; 29% Hispanic/Latino; 3% Black or African American, non-Hispanic/Latino; 3% Asian, non-Hispanic/Latino; 1% Native Hawaiian or other Pacific Islander, non-Hispanic/Latino; 10% international. 29% 25 or older, 5% transferred in. Core. Calendar: semesters. Academic remediation for entering students, ESL program, services for LD students, advanced placement, honors program, independent study, distance learning, double major, summer session for credit, part-time degree program, adult/continuing education programs, co-op programs and internships. Study abroad program. ROTC: Army (c).
Entrance Requirements: Open admission. Options: electronic application, early admission. Recommended: high school transcript. Entrance: noncompetitive. Application deadline: 8/19. Notification: continuous. Transfer credits accepted: Yes.
Collegiate Environment: Orientation program. Choral group. Social organizations: 50 open to all. Most popular organizations: IDEAS, Video Game Club, Glee Club, Marketing Club, Project H.O.P.E. Major annual events: Commencement, Dorantes Lecture, President's Honor Roll Reception. Student services: health clinic, personal-psychological counseling. Campus security: 24-hour emergency response devices and patrols, late night transport-escort service. Eli Luria Library. Operations spending for the previous fiscal year: $1.1 million. 1,340 computers available on campus for general student use. A campuswide network can be accessed from off-campus. Students can access the following: online class registration, online application process. Staffed computer lab on campus provides training in use of computers, software, and the Internet.
Community Environment: See University of California Santa Barbara.

■ SANTA CLARA UNIVERSITY

500 El Camino Real
Santa Clara, CA 95053
Tel: (408)554-4000

Fax: (408)554-5255
E-mail: admission@scu.edu
Web Site: www.scu.edu
Description: Independent Roman Catholic (Jesuit), university, coed. Awards bachelor's, master's, and doctoral degrees. Founded 1851. Setting: 106-acre suburban campus with easy access to San Francisco, San Jose. Endowment: $905.9 million. Research spending for the previous fiscal year: $5.4 million. Educational spending for the previous fiscal year: $16,782 per student. Total enrollment: 8,629. Faculty: 906 (542 full-time, 364 part-time). Student-undergrad faculty ratio is 11:1. 15,061 applied, 54% were admitted. 57% from top 10% of their high school class, 87% from top quarter, 99% from top half. Full-time: 5,411 students, 50% women, 50% men. Part-time: 88 students, 44% women, 56% men. Students come from 53 states and territories, 36 other countries, 29% from out-of-state. 0.1% American Indian or Alaska Native, non-Hispanic/Latino; 18% Hispanic/Latino; 3% Black or African American, non-Hispanic/Latino; 16% Asian, non-Hispanic/Latino; 0.2% Native Hawaiian or other Pacific Islander, non-Hispanic/Latino; 4% international. 1% 25 or older, 56% live on campus, 3% transferred in. Retention: 94% of full-time freshmen returned the following year. Academic areas with the most degrees conferred: business/marketing; engineering; social sciences. Core. Calendar: quarters. Services for LD students, advanced placement, self-designed majors, honors program, independent study, double major, summer session for credit, co-op programs and internships, graduate courses open to undergrads. Off campus study at American University. Study abroad program. ROTC: Army, Air Force (c).
Entrance Requirements: Options: electronic application, early admission, early decision, early action, deferred admission, international baccalaureate accepted. Required: essay, high school transcript, 1 recommendation, SAT or ACT. Entrance: very difficult. Application deadlines: 1/7, 11/1 for early decision, 11/1 for early action. Notification: 4/1, 12/23 for early decision, 12/23 for early action. SAT Reasoning Test deadline: 1/7. Transfer credits accepted: Yes. Applicants placed on waiting list: 2,397. Wait-listed applicants offered admission: 39. Early decision applicants: 305. Early decision applicants admitted: 226. Early action applicants: 5,841. Early action applicants admitted: 4,095.
Costs Per Year: Application fee: $60. Comprehensive fee: $66,621 includes full-time tuition ($51,081), mandatory fees ($630), and college room and board ($14,910). Room and board charges vary according to board plan and housing facility. Part-time tuition: $1419 per unit. Part-time tuition varies according to course load.
Collegiate Environment: Orientation program. Drama-theater group, choral group, marching band, student-run newspaper, radio station. Social organizations: 139 open to all. Major annual events: Fall Concert, Global Village (multicultural event), Relay for Life. Student services: health clinic, personal-psychological counseling. Campus security: 24-hour emergency response devices and patrols, late night transport-escort service, controlled dormitory access. University Library plus 1 other. Books: 606,483 (physical), 658,072 (digital/electronic); Serial titles: 14,096 (physical), 84,245 (digital/electronic); Databases: 356. Weekly public service hours: 121; students can reserve study rooms. Operations spending for the previous fiscal year: $10.3 million.
Community Environment: Santa Clara is known as the"Mission City." It has an ideal climate, with a mean temperature of 71 degrees. Buses, trains and airlines serve the area. Community facilities include churches, a community symphony orchestra and an art gallery. Santa Clara is in the heart of"Silicon Valley," a dynamic center of high technology and progressive businesses. There are numerous part-time work opportunities. Recreational facilities include miles of beaches within a 30-minute drive of the university. San Francisco is 50 miles to the north.

■ SANTA MONICA COLLEGE

1900 Pico Blvd.
Santa Monica, CA 90405-1628
Tel: (310)434-4000
Web Site: www.smc.edu
Description: District-supported, 2-year, coed. Part of California Community College System. Awards certificates, transfer associate, and terminal associate degrees. Founded 1929. Setting: 40-acre urban campus with easy access to Los Angeles. Total enrollment: 30,830. Full-time: 2,860 students, 48% women, 52% men. Part-time: 15,176 students, 53% women, 47% men. 8% from out-of-state. 0.1% American Indian or Alaska Native, non-Hispanic/Latino; 46% Hispanic/Latino; 10% Black or African American, non-Hispanic/Latino; 7% Asian, non-Hispanic/Latino; 0.2% Native Hawaiian or other Pacific Islander, non-Hispanic/Latino; 11% international. 22% 25 or older,

96% transferred in. Core. Calendar: semester plus optional winter and summer terms. Academic remediation for entering students, ESL program, services for LD students, advanced placement, honors program, independent study, distance learning, summer session for credit, part-time degree program, adult/continuing education programs, co-op programs and internships. Study abroad program. ROTC: Army (c).

Entrance Requirements: Open admission. Option: early admission. Required: high school transcript. Entrance: noncompetitive. Application deadline: 8/30. Notification: continuous until 8/30.

Collegiate Environment: Orientation program. Drama-theater group, choral group, student-run newspaper. Student services: legal services, health clinic, personal-psychological counseling, women's center. Campus security: 24-hour emergency response devices and patrols, student patrols, late night transport-escort service. Santa Monica College Library.

Community Environment: A residential city and beach resort, Santa Monica is part of the Los Angeles metropolitan area. The temperature averages 64.2 degrees. All forms of major transportation serve the area. Excellent shopping facilities are in the city. Part-time employment is available. Beach area includes Ocean Park, Malibu Beach, and Will Rogers State Beach, providing recreational activities in addition to the city facilities for outdoor sports.

■ **SANTA ROSA JUNIOR COLLEGE**
1501 Mendocino Ave.
Santa Rosa, CA 95401-4395
Tel: (707)527-4011
Web Site: www.santarosa.edu
Description: District-supported, 2-year, coed. Part of California Community College System. Awards certificates, transfer associate, and terminal associate degrees. Founded 1918. Setting: 100-acre urban campus with easy access to San Francisco. Endowment: $41.3 million. Research spending for the previous fiscal year: $332,990. Educational spending for the previous fiscal year: $3268 per student. Total enrollment: 26,800. 5,889 applied, 100% were admitted. Students come from 36 other countries, 3% from out-of-state. 0.7% American Indian or Alaska Native, non-Hispanic/Latino; 34% Hispanic/Latino; 2% Black or African American, non-Hispanic/Latino; 5% Asian, non-Hispanic/Latino; 0.3% Native Hawaiian or other Pacific Islander, non-Hispanic/Latino. 46% 25 or older. Core. Calendar: semesters. Academic remediation for entering students, ESL program, services for LD students, advanced placement, independent study, distance learning, summer session for credit, part-time degree program, adult/continuing education programs, co-op programs and internships. Off campus study. Study abroad program.
Entrance Requirements: Open admission except for allied health programs. Options: electronic application, early admission, international baccalaureate accepted. Entrance: noncompetitive. Application deadline: rolling. Notification: continuous. Transfer credits accepted: Yes.
Collegiate Environment: Orientation program. Drama-theater group, choral group, student-run newspaper. Social organizations: 32 open to all. Most popular organizations: AG Ambassadors, MECHA, Alpha Gamma Sigma, Phi Theta Kappa, Puente. Major annual events: Day Under the Oaks (college open house), Club Days. Student services: health clinic, personal-psychological counseling. Campus security: 24-hour emergency response devices and patrols, student patrols. Doyle Library plus 1 other. Students can reserve study rooms. Operations spending for the previous fiscal year: $2.5 million. 1,700 computers available on campus for general student use. A campuswide network can be accessed from off-campus. Students can access the following: online class registration. Staffed computer lab on campus provides training in use of computers, software, and the Internet.
Community Environment: Sonama County, located 50 miles north of San Francisco, is well known for its rolling hills, grassy valleys, vineyards and spectacular coast. The county's moderate climate is characterized by average afternoon temperatures in the lower 80's during the summer and mid-50's in the winter. Average annual rainfall is approximately 30 inches. Santa Rosa is the county seat and commercial center for the north coast's Redwood Empire. The city enjoys an abundance of urban amenities including schools and colleges, business centers, three general hospitals and a family residency program as well as local theatres, the Santa Rosa Symphony, and the Luther Burbank Center for the Performing Arts. Nearby parks offer miles of hiking and riding trails as well as facilities for sailing, swimming, fishing, picnicking and camping.

■ **SANTIAGO CANYON COLLEGE**
8045 E Chapman Ave.
Orange, CA 92869

Tel: (714)628-4900
Fax: (714)564-4379
Web Site: www.sccollege.edu
Description: District-supported, 2-year, coed. Part of California Community College System. Awards certificates, transfer associate, and terminal associate degrees. Founded 2000. Setting: suburban campus with easy access to Los Angeles. Total enrollment: 8,371. Faculty: 417 (92 full-time, 325 part-time). Student-undergrad faculty ratio is 23:1. Full-time: 7,987 students, 44% women, 56% men. Part-time: 6,096 students, 47% women, 53% men. Students come from 6 other countries, 6% from out-of-state. 50% 25 or older, 1% transferred in. Core. Calendar: semesters. Academic remediation for entering students, ESL program, services for LD students, advanced placement, freshman honors college, honors program, distance learning, summer session for credit, part-time degree program, external degree program, adult/continuing education programs, co-op programs.
Collegiate Environment: Orientation program. Campus security: 24-hour emergency response devices, late night transport-escort service. Santiago Canyon College Library. 45 computers available on campus for general student use.

■ **SCRIPPS COLLEGE**
1030 Columbia Ave.
Claremont, CA 91711-3948
Tel: (909)621-8000; Free: 800-770-1333
Fax: (909)621-8323
E-mail: admission@scrippscollege.edu
Web Site: www.scrippscollege.edu
Description: Independent, 4-year, women only. Awards bachelor's degrees. Founded 1926. Setting: 35-acre suburban campus with easy access to Los Angeles. Total enrollment: 1,067. Faculty: 126 (97 full-time, 29 part-time). Student-undergrad faculty ratio is 10:1. 3,160 applied, 24% were admitted. 69% from top 10% of their high school class, 98% from top quarter, 100% from top half. Full-time: 1,042 students. Part-time: 6 students. 55% from out-of-state. 14% Hispanic/Latino; 4% Black or African American, non-Hispanic/Latino; 17% Asian, non-Hispanic/Latino; 0.2% Native Hawaiian or other Pacific Islander, non-Hispanic/Latino; 5% international. 0.1% 25 or older, 94% live on campus, 1% transferred in. Retention: 92% of full-time freshmen returned the following year. Academic areas with the most degrees conferred: biological/life sciences; social sciences; psychology. Core. Calendar: semesters. Services for LD students, advanced placement, accelerated degree program, self-designed majors, independent study, double major, co-op programs and internships. Off campus study at 5 members of The Claremont Colleges, Colby College, Spelman College, American University (Washington Semester), George Washington University. Study abroad program. ROTC: Army (c), Air Force (c).
Entrance Requirements: Options: electronic application, early admission, early decision, deferred admission, international baccalaureate accepted. Required: essay, high school transcript, 2 recommendations, school report completed by the student's secondary school counselor, SAT or ACT. Recommended: minimum 3 high school GPA. Entrance: very difficult. Application deadlines: 1/4, 11/15 for early decision plan 1, 1/4 for early decision plan 2. Notification: 4/1, 12/15 for early decision plan 1, 2/15 for early decision plan 2. SAT Reasoning Test deadline: 2/15. Transfer credits accepted: Yes. Applicants placed on waiting list: 780. Wait-listed applicants offered admission: 4. Early decision applicants: 281. Early decision applicants admitted: 90.
Costs Per Year: Application fee: $60. Comprehensive fee: $71,956 includes full-time tuition ($54,806), mandatory fees ($218), and college room and board ($16,932). College room only: $9220. Full-time tuition and fees vary according to course load and degree level. Room and board charges vary according to board plan. Part-time tuition: $6851 per course. Part-time tuition varies according to course load and degree level.
Collegiate Environment: Orientation program. Drama-theater group, choral group, student-run newspaper, radio station. Social organizations: 350 open to all. Most popular organization: Scripps Associated Students. Major annual events: 5-College Carnival, Week of Welcome, Spring Fling. Student services: health clinic, personal-psychological counseling, women's center. Campus security: 24-hour emergency response devices and patrols, late night transport-escort service, controlled dormitory access. 945 college housing spaces available. Freshmen guaranteed college housing. On-campus residence required in freshman year. Option: women-only housing available. Honnold/Mudd Library plus 2 others. Students can reserve study rooms.
Community Environment: The Claremont consortium consists of five

undergraduate institutions and the Claremont Graduate University — all located in an area approximately one square mile in size.

■ SHASTA BIBLE COLLEGE

2951 Goodwater Ave.
Redding, CA 96002
Tel: (530)221-4275; Free: 800-800-4SBC
E-mail: registrar@shasta.edu
Web Site: www.shasta.edu

Description: Independent nondenominational, comprehensive, coed. Awards associate, bachelor's, and master's degrees. Founded 1971. Setting: 55-acre small town campus. Educational spending for the previous fiscal year: $2502 per student. Total enrollment: 50. Faculty: 37 (9 full-time, 28 part-time). Student-undergrad faculty ratio is 3:1. 18 applied, 83% were admitted. Full-time: 29 students, 31% women, 69% men. Part-time: 15 students, 47% women, 53% men. Students come from 6 states and territories, 3 other countries, 25% from out-of-state. 10% Hispanic/Latino; 4% Black or African American, non-Hispanic/Latino; 8% Asian, non-Hispanic/Latino; 2% Native Hawaiian or other Pacific Islander, non-Hispanic/Latino. 53% 25 or older, 77% live on campus, 30% transferred in. Retention: 63% of full-time freshmen returned the following year. Core. Calendar: semesters. Academic remediation for entering students, accelerated degree program, independent study, distance learning, double major, summer session for credit, part-time degree program, adult/continuing education programs, co-op programs.

Entrance Requirements: Open admission. Options: electronic application, early admission, international baccalaureate accepted. Required: essay, high school transcript, 4 recommendations. Required for some: interview. Entrance: noncompetitive. Application deadline: rolling. Notification: continuous. Transfer credits accepted: Yes.

Collegiate Environment: Orientation program. Choral group, student-run newspaper. Social organizations: 1 open to all. Most popular organization: Associated Student Body. Major annual events: Weekend Retreat, Associated Student Body Monthly Activities. Student services: personal-psychological counseling. Campus security: 24-hour emergency response devices, student patrols. Faye Messler Library. Operations spending for the previous fiscal year: $37,953. 7 computers available on campus for general student use. A campuswide network can be accessed. Staffed computer lab on campus.

■ SHASTA COLLEGE

11555 Old Oregon Trl.
Redding, CA 96049-6006
Tel: (530)242-7500
Web Site: www.shastacollege.edu

Description: District-supported, 2-year, coed. Part of California Community College System. Awards certificates, transfer associate, and terminal associate degrees. Founded 1948. Setting: 336-acre rural campus. Endowment: $1.3 million. Research spending for the previous fiscal year: $175,040. Educational spending for the previous fiscal year: $1944 per student. Total enrollment: 10,240. Faculty: 491 (146 full-time, 345 part-time). 3,586 applied, 100% were admitted. Full-time: 4,336 students, 59% women, 41% men. Part-time: 5,904 students, 62% women, 38% men. 2% from out-of-state. 56% 25 or older. Core. Calendar: semesters. Academic remediation for entering students, ESL program, services for LD students, advanced placement, honors program, distance learning, double major, summer session for credit, part-time degree program, adult/continuing education programs, co-op programs and internships.

Entrance Requirements: Open admission. Option: early admission. Required: high school transcript. Entrance: noncompetitive. Application deadline: rolling. Notification: continuous.

Collegiate Environment: Orientation program. Drama-theater group, choral group, student-run newspaper. Social organizations: 8 open to all. Most popular organizations: Associated Student Body, Environmental Resource Leadership Club, Intercultural Club, Inter-Varsity Christian Fellowship, Music Education National Conference. Major annual events: Cinco De Mayo, 'Tis The Season, Halloween Festivities. Student services: health clinic, personal-psychological counseling. Campus security: 24-hour emergency response devices, student patrols, late night transport-escort service, 16-hour patrols by trained security personnel. Shasta College Learning Resource Center. Operations spending for the previous fiscal year: $885,790. 154 computers available on campus for general student use. A campuswide network can be accessed from off-campus. Staffed computer lab on campus.

Community Environment: Redding is located at the northern end of the Sacramento Valley and is served by buses, railroads and airlines. The city provides unlimited recreational opportunities; Shasta National Forest, Sacramento Canyon, Mount Shasta, Shasta Dam which is the second largest concrete dam in the world and Shasta Lake which encompasses 30,000 acres. Excellent fishing, camping, picnicking and swimming in the area. Redding is a trade center with good shopping facilities.

■ SIERRA COLLEGE

5100 Sierra College Blvd.
Rocklin, CA 95677
Tel: (916)624-3333
Web Site: www.sierracollege.edu

Description: District-supported, 2-year, coed. Part of California Community College System. Awards certificates, transfer associate, and terminal associate degrees. Founded 1936. Setting: 327-acre suburban campus with easy access to Sacramento. Total enrollment: 19,165. Faculty: 870 (158 full-time, 712 part-time). Student-undergrad faculty ratio is 25:1. 24,000 applied, 100% were admitted. Full-time: 6,477 students, 53% women, 47% men. Part-time: 9,991 students, 57% women, 43% men. Students come from 22 states and territories, 8 other countries, 1% from out-of-state. 1% American Indian or Alaska Native, non-Hispanic/Latino; 8% Hispanic/Latino; 4% Black or African American, non-Hispanic/Latino; 9% Asian, non-Hispanic/Latino; 0.8% Native Hawaiian or other Pacific Islander, non-Hispanic/Latino; 0.5% international. 35% 25 or older, 1% live on campus. Retention: 68% of full-time freshmen returned the following year. Core. Calendar: semesters. Academic remediation for entering students, ESL program, services for LD students, advanced placement, accelerated degree program, honors program, independent study, distance learning, double major, summer session for credit, part-time degree program, internships. Off campus study. Study abroad program.

Entrance Requirements: Open admission. Options: electronic application, early admission. Entrance: noncompetitive. Application deadline: rolling. Notification: continuous. Transfer credits accepted: Yes.

Collegiate Environment: Orientation program. Drama-theater group, choral group, student-run newspaper. Social organizations: 32 open to all. Most popular organizations: Drama Club, Student Government, Art Club, Band, Aggie Club. Major annual events: Scholarship Awards Banquet, Kids' Day, Sierra Daze. Student services: health clinic, personal-psychological counseling. Campus security: 24-hour emergency response devices and patrols, late night transport-escort service. 148 college housing spaces available; 135 were occupied in 2018-19. No special consideration for freshman housing applicants. Option: coed housing available. Leary Resource Center plus 1 other. Operations spending for the previous fiscal year: $865,210. 430 computers available on campus for general student use. A campuswide network can be accessed from off-campus. Students can access the following: online class registration. Staffed computer lab on campus provides training in use of computers, software, and the Internet.

Community Environment: Population 49,626. Rocklin is located on Interstate 80 in the Loomis Basin, 23 miles northeast of Sacramento; the center of a large deciduous fruit-raising area. All forms of transportation available at nearby cities of Auburn and Roseville. Rocklin has libraries, hospitals, clinics, a health department, churches, and civic, fraternal, and veteran's organizations. Industry includes three lumber mills and a granite quarry. Recreational activities include swimming, picnicking, skiing, fishing and hunting. Seasonal and part-time employment is available.

■ SIMPSON UNIVERSITY

2211 College View Dr.
Redding, CA 96003-8606
Tel: (530)224-5600; Free: 888-9-SIMPSON
Fax: (530)226-4861
E-mail: admissions@simpsonu.edu
Web Site: www.simpsonu.edu

Description: Independent, comprehensive, coed, affiliated with The Christian and Missionary Alliance. Awards associate, bachelor's, and master's degrees and post-master's certificates. Founded 1921. Setting: 100-acre suburban campus. Endowment: $5.9 million. Educational spending for the previous fiscal year: $7276 per student. Total enrollment: 1,012. Faculty: 139 (43 full-time, 96 part-time). Student-undergrad faculty ratio is 11:1. 627 applied, 52% were admitted. 19% from top 10% of their high school class, 51% from top quarter, 78% from top half. Full-time: 741 students, 66% women, 34% men. Part-time: 49 students, 65% women, 35% men. Students come from 23 states and territories, 9 other countries, 12% from out-of-state. 3% American Indian or Alaska Native, non-Hispanic/Latino;

16% Hispanic/Latino; 4% Black or African American, non-Hispanic/Latino; 4% Asian, non-Hispanic/Latino; 0.5% Native Hawaiian or other Pacific Islander, non-Hispanic/Latino; 1% international. 28% 25 or older, 41% live on campus, 9% transferred in. Retention: 82% of full-time freshmen returned the following year. Academic areas with the most degrees conferred: business/marketing; psychology; health professions and related sciences. Core. Calendar: semesters. Academic remediation for entering students, services for LD students, advanced placement, accelerated degree program, self-designed majors, honors program, independent study, distance learning, double major, summer session for credit, part-time degree program, adult/continuing education programs, internships, graduate courses open to undergrads. Off campus study at Council for Christian Colleges and Universities. Study abroad program.

Entrance Requirements: Options: electronic application, early action, deferred admission. Required: essay, high school transcript, minimum 3 high school GPA, 1 recommendation, Christian commitment, SAT or ACT. Recommended: SAT and SAT Subject Tests or ACT. Required for some: interview. Entrance: moderately difficult. Application deadlines: 8/1, 12/1 for early action. Notification: continuous. Transfer credits accepted: Yes.

Costs Per Year: Application fee: $35. Comprehensive fee: $38,924 includes full-time tuition ($29,750), mandatory fees ($450), and college room and board ($8724). College room only: $4900. Full-time tuition and fees vary according to course load. Room and board charges vary according to board plan and housing facility. Part-time tuition: $1240 per credit hour. Part-time tuition varies according to course load.

Collegiate Environment: Orientation program. Drama-theater group, choral group, student-run newspaper. Social organizations: 16 open to all. Most popular organizations: Summer Missions Trips, Biology Club, Boxing Club. Major annual events: Homecoming Weekend, Exposure Film Festival, Nite Life. Student services: health clinic, personal-psychological counseling. Campus security: 24-hour emergency response devices and patrols, student patrols, late night transport-escort service, controlled dormitory access, emergency whistle program and monthly campus safety meetings. Start-Kilgour Memorial Library. Books: 103,721 (physical), 369,714 (digital/electronic); Serial titles: 340 (physical), 28,286 (digital/electronic); Databases: 54. Weekly public service hours: 93; students can reserve study rooms. Operations spending for the previous fiscal year: $339,030. 50 computers available on campus for general student use. A campuswide network can be accessed from student residence rooms. Students can access the following: online class registration.

■ **SKYLINE COLLEGE**
3300 College Dr.
San Bruno, CA 94066-1698
Tel: (650)738-4100
E-mail: stats@smccd.net
Web Site: skylinecollege.edu
Description: District-supported, 2-year, coed. Part of San Mateo County Community College District System. Awards certificates, transfer associate, and terminal associate degrees. Founded 1969. Setting: 125-acre suburban campus with easy access to San Francisco. Total enrollment: 8,359. Faculty: 333 (119 full-time, 214 part-time). Student-undergrad faculty ratio is 25:1. Full-time: 2,486 students, 47% women, 53% men. Part-time: 5,873 students, 56% women, 44% men. Students come from 9 other countries, 2% from out-of-state. 9% 25 or older. Core. Calendar: semesters. Academic remediation for entering students, ESL program, services for LD students, advanced placement, honors program, distance learning, summer session for credit, part-time degree program, adult/continuing education programs, co-op programs. Study abroad program.

Entrance Requirements: Open admission except for international students or auto technology, respiratory therapy, cosmetology, concurrent high school, emergency medical, surgical technician programs. Required for some: high school transcript. Entrance: noncompetitive. Application deadline: rolling.

Collegiate Environment: Choral group, student-run newspaper. Social organizations: 15 open to all. Student services: health clinic, personal-psychological counseling. Campus security: security guards during hours of operation. Skyline College Library. 220 computers available on campus for general student use. Computer purchase/lease plans available. A campuswide network can be accessed from off-campus. Students can access the following: online class registration, student account information. Staffed computer lab on campus provides training in use of computers, software, and the Internet.

Community Environment: Population 39,750. San Bruno, located 12 miles south of San Francisco, is known as "The Airport City." The climate is temperate all year long, with cool, often foggy summers. All modes of transportation serve the area. This is a residential community with regional shopping centers, churches, library, and hospitals in nearby cities. Cultural advantages of San Francisco are appreciated by the people in San Bruno since it is so near.

■ **SOKA UNIVERSITY OF AMERICA**
1 University Dr.
Aliso Viejo, CA 92656
Tel: (949)480-4000; Free: 888-600-SOKA
Fax: (949)480-4001
E-mail: eespejo@soka.edu
Web Site: www.soka.edu
Description: Independent, comprehensive, coed. Awards bachelor's and master's degrees. Founded 1987. Setting: 103-acre suburban campus with easy access to Los Angeles, San Diego. Endowment: $1.2 billion. Total enrollment: 442. Faculty: 73 (46 full-time, 27 part-time). Student-undergrad faculty ratio is 8:1. 462 applied, 39% were admitted. 33% from top 10% of their high school class, 48% from top quarter, 19% from top half. Full-time: 428 students, 66% women, 34% men. Students come from 30 states and territories, 31 other countries, 57% from out-of-state. 12% Hispanic/Latino; 4% Black or African American, non-Hispanic/Latino; 13% Asian, non-Hispanic/Latino; 0.5% Native Hawaiian or other Pacific Islander, non-Hispanic/Latino; 44% international. 99% live on campus. Retention: 92% of full-time freshmen returned the following year. Academic area with the most degrees conferred: liberal arts/general studies. Core. Calendar: semesters. Services for LD students, independent study, co-op programs and internships. Off campus study. Study abroad program.

Entrance Requirements: Options: electronic application, early admission, early action, deferred admission, international baccalaureate accepted. Required: essay, high school transcript, 2 recommendations, IERF evaluation for course work completed abroad, SAT or ACT. Recommended: interview. Entrance: most difficult. Application deadlines: 1/15, 11/1 for early action. Notification: 3/1, 12/1 for early action. SAT Reasoning Test deadline: 1/15. Transfer credits accepted: No. Applicants placed on waiting list: 59. Wait-listed applicants offered admission: 0. Early action applicants: 124. Early action applicants admitted: 32.

Costs Per Year: Application fee: $45. Comprehensive fee: $47,014 includes full-time tuition ($32,250), mandatory fees ($1732), and college room and board ($13,032). Part-time tuition: $1344 per credit hour.

Collegiate Environment: Orientation program. Choral group. Social organizations: 31 open to all; 70% of eligible men and 70% of eligible women are members. Most popular organizations: Josho Daiko (Japanese Drum Club), Rhythmission (Hip Hop Dance Club), Sualseros (Salsa Dance Club), Ka Pilina Ho'olokahi (Hawaiian Dance Club), Soul Wings (Choir). Major annual events: The Festivals (celebration of art), The ASB (student volunteers in community service projects), Winter Formal. Student services: health clinic, personal-psychological counseling. Campus security: 24-hour emergency response devices and patrols, student patrols, late night transport-escort service, controlled dormitory access. 500 college housing spaces available; 411 were occupied in 2018-19. Freshmen guaranteed college housing. On-campus residence required through senior year. Options: coed, men-only, women-only housing available. Daisaku and Kaneko Ikeda Library. Books: 95,080 (physical), 261,022 (digital/electronic); Serial titles: 96 (physical), 7,563 (digital/electronic); Databases: 170. Study areas open 24 hours, 5-7 days a week; students can reserve study rooms. 100 computers available on campus for general student use. Computer purchase/lease plans available. A computer is required for all students. A campuswide network can be accessed from student residence rooms and from off campus. Students can access the following: online class registration, course and administrative applications. Staffed computer lab on campus (open 24 hours a day) provides training in use of computers, software, and the Internet.

■ **SOLANO COMMUNITY COLLEGE**
4000 Suisun Valley Rd.
Fairfield, CA 94534
Tel: (707)864-7000
Fax: (707)864-7175
Web Site: www.solano.edu
Description: District-supported, 2-year, coed. Part of California Community College System. Awards certificates, diplomas, transfer associate, and terminal associate degrees. Founded 1945. Setting: 192-acre suburban campus with easy access to Sacramento, San Francisco. Total enrollment:

10,927. Faculty: 374 (147 full-time, 227 part-time). Student-undergrad faculty ratio is 27:1. 10,927 applied. Students come from 6 other countries, 1% from out-of-state. 46% 25 or older. Core. Calendar: semesters. Academic remediation for entering students, ESL program, services for LD students, advanced placement, honors program, independent study, distance learning, double major, summer session for credit, part-time degree program, adult/continuing education programs, co-op programs. Off campus study at California State University, Hayward; University of California, Davis; University of California, Berkeley. Study abroad program.

Entrance Requirements: Open admission. Options: electronic application, early admission, deferred admission. Entrance: noncompetitive. Application deadline: rolling. Transfer credits accepted: Yes.

Collegiate Environment: Orientation program. Drama-theater group, choral group, student-run newspaper. Social organizations: national fraternities. Student services: health clinic, personal-psychological counseling. Campus security: 24-hour patrols, student patrols, late night transport-escort service. Solano Community College Library. 300 computers available on campus for general student use. A campuswide network can be accessed from off-campus. Students can access the following: online class registration. Staffed computer lab on campus.

■ **SONOMA STATE UNIVERSITY**
1801 E Cotati Ave.
Rohnert Park, CA 94928-3609
Tel: (707)664-2880
E-mail: natalie.kalogiannis@sonoma.edu
Web Site: www.sonoma.edu

Description: State-supported, comprehensive, coed. Part of California State University System. Awards bachelor's and master's degrees. Founded 1960. Setting: 280-acre small town campus with easy access to San Francisco. Endowment: $47.1 million. Research spending for the previous fiscal year: $1 million. Educational spending for the previous fiscal year: $6635 per student. Total enrollment: 9,201. Faculty: 597 (251 full-time, 346 part-time). Student-undergrad faculty ratio is 23:1. 14,129 applied, 92% were admitted. Full-time: 7,855 students, 62% women, 38% men. Part-time: 710 students, 53% women, 47% men. 0.4% American Indian or Alaska Native, non-Hispanic/Latino; 34% Hispanic/Latino; 2% Black or African American, non-Hispanic/Latino; 5% Asian, non-Hispanic/Latino; 0.3% Native Hawaiian or other Pacific Islander, non-Hispanic/Latino; 3% international. 9% 25 or older, 32% live on campus, 9% transferred in. Retention: 80% of full-time freshmen returned the following year. Academic areas with the most degrees conferred: business/marketing; social sciences; psychology. Core. Calendar: semesters. Academic remediation for entering students, ESL program, services for LD students, advanced placement, accelerated degree program, self-designed majors, honors program, independent study, distance learning, double major, summer session for credit, part-time degree program, adult/continuing education programs, co-op programs and internships, graduate courses open to undergrads. Off campus study at other units of the California State University System, National Student Exchange, Mills College. Study abroad program. ROTC: Army (c), Air Force (c).

Entrance Requirements: Options: electronic application, early admission. Required: high school transcript, SAT or ACT. Entrance: moderately difficult. Application deadline: rolling. Notification: continuous. SAT Reasoning Test deadline: 12/30.

Collegiate Environment: Orientation program. Drama-theater group, choral group, student-run newspaper, radio station. Social organizations: national fraternities, national sororities, local fraternities, local sororities. Major annual events: Welcome Week, Student Orientation, Big Nite. Student services: legal services, health clinic, personal-psychological counseling, women's center. Campus security: 24-hour emergency response devices and patrols, student patrols, late night transport-escort service, controlled dormitory access. Freshmen given priority for college housing. Option: coed housing available. Jean and Charles Schultz Information Center plus 1 other. Students can reserve study rooms. Operations spending for the previous fiscal year: $3.1 million.

Community Environment: Population 41,100. Rohnert Park is a rapidly growing suburban community with temperate climate. Located near Santa Rosa (pop. 153,000) in Sonoma County. Buses and airlines serve the area. Community facilities include many shopping centers, civic and sports clubs. Recreational facilities include swimming pools, baseball parks, a community park, golf courses and others within a 20 mile radius. Rohnert Park has the annual Founders Day Parade. There are five hospitals within a 10 mile radius. The Valley of the Moon, San Francisco, the Russian River recreation areas, Redwood National Park and Lake Tahoe are all within driving distance

from an hour to a half day. Sonoma county produces premium wine and is the location of many famous wineries.

■ **SOUTH COAST COLLEGE**
2011 W Chapman Ave.
Orange, CA 92868
Tel: (714)867-5009; Free: 877-568-6130
Fax: (714)867-5026
Web Site: www.southcoastcollege.edu

Description: Proprietary, 2-year, coed. Awards terminal associate degrees. Founded 1961. Total enrollment: 368.

Entrance Requirements: Entrance: noncompetitive.

■ **SOUTHERN CALIFORNIA INSTITUTE OF ARCHITECTURE**
960 E Third St.
Los Angeles, CA 90013
Tel: (213)613-2200
Fax: (213)613-0524
E-mail: admissions@sciarc.edu
Web Site: www.sciarc.edu

Description: Independent, comprehensive, coed. Awards bachelor's and master's degrees. Founded 1972. Setting: urban campus with easy access to Los Angeles. Total enrollment: 502. Faculty: 68 (29 full-time, 39 part-time). Student-undergrad faculty ratio is 12:1. 214 applied, 73% were admitted. Full-time: 254 students, 38% women, 62% men. Part-time: 1 student, 100% men. 14% Hispanic/Latino; 0.8% Black or African American, non-Hispanic/Latino; 18% Asian, non-Hispanic/Latino; 0.4% Native Hawaiian or other Pacific Islander, non-Hispanic/Latino; 51% international. 21% 25 or older, 11% transferred in. Retention: 94% of full-time freshmen returned the following year. Academic area with the most degrees conferred: architecture. Core. Calendar: semesters. Academic remediation for entering students, ESL program, advanced placement, summer session for credit, co-op programs and internships, graduate courses open to undergrads. Study abroad program.

Entrance Requirements: Options: electronic application, deferred admission, international baccalaureate accepted. Required: essay, high school transcript, 3 recommendations, portfolio of creative visual work, resume, statement of purpose, SAT or ACT. Recommended: minimum 3 high school GPA. Required for some: interview. Entrance: moderately difficult. Application deadline: 1/15. Notification: continuous until 4/1. SAT Reasoning Test deadline: 1/15. Transfer credits accepted: Yes. Applicants placed on waiting list: 28. Wait-listed applicants offered admission: 15.

Costs Per Year: Application fee: $85. Tuition: $43,760 full-time. Mandatory fees: $1100 full-time. Full-time tuition and fees vary according to course load.

Collegiate Environment: Orientation program. Social organizations: 1 open to all. Most popular organization: Student Union. Major annual events: Commencement, End-of-Year Exhibition, Thesis Presentations. Student services: personal-psychological counseling. Campus security: 24-hour emergency response devices and patrols, electronically operated school entrances 24/7. Kappe Library plus 1 other. Books: 30,177 (physical), 127,353 (digital/electronic); Serial titles: 76 (physical), 8 (digital/electronic); Databases: 19. 85 computers available on campus for general student use. A campuswide network can be accessed from off-campus. Students can access the following: online class registration. Staffed computer lab on campus provides training in use of computers, software, and the Internet.

■ **SOUTHERN CALIFORNIA INSTITUTE OF TECHNOLOGY**
525 N Muller St.
Anaheim, CA 92801
Tel: (714)520-5552
E-mail: admissions@scitech.edu
Web Site: www.scitech.edu

Description: Proprietary, 4-year, coed. Awards associate and bachelor's degrees. Founded 1987. Setting: urban campus with easy access to Anaheim, Los Angeles, San Diego. Research spending for the previous fiscal year: $300,000. Educational spending for the previous fiscal year: $1200 per student. Total enrollment: 538. Student-undergrad faculty ratio is 21:1. Full-time: 538 students, 7% women, 93% men. 0.2% American Indian or Alaska Native, non-Hispanic/Latino; 46% Hispanic/Latino; 8% Black or African American, non-Hispanic/Latino; 15% Asian, non-Hispanic/Latino; 1% Native Hawaiian or other Pacific Islander, non-Hispanic/Latino. 69% 25 or older. Retention: 86% of full-time freshmen returned the following year. Core. ESL program, accelerated degree program, double major, adult/continuing education programs.

Entrance Requirements: Required: interview, entrance exam. Required for some: high school transcript.

Collegiate Environment: Orientation program. Campus security: late night transport-escort service. SCIT Library plus 1 other. 300 computers available on campus for general student use. A campuswide network can be accessed. Staffed computer lab on campus (open 24 hours a day) provides training in use of computers, software, and the Internet.

■ **SOUTHERN CALIFORNIA SEMINARY**
2075 E Madison Ave.
El Cajon, CA 92019
Tel: (619)201-8999; Free: 888-389-7244
Fax: (619)201-8975
Web Site: www.socalsem.edu
Description: Independent interdenominational, comprehensive, coed. Awards associate, bachelor's, master's, and doctoral degrees. Founded 1946. Setting: 15-acre suburban campus with easy access to San Diego, CA. Endowment: $115,260. Total enrollment: 235. Faculty: 42 (11 full-time, 31 part-time). 20 applied, 45% were admitted. Full-time: 17 students, 29% women, 71% men. Part-time: 43 students, 37% women, 63% men. Students come from 10 states and territories, 21% from out-of-state. 2% American Indian or Alaska Native, non-Hispanic/Latino; 13% Hispanic/Latino; 22% Black or African American, non-Hispanic/Latino; 17% Asian, non-Hispanic/Latino; 2% international. 88% 25 or older, 7% live on campus, 23% transferred in. Retention: 29% of full-time freshmen returned the following year. Academic area with the most degrees conferred: theology and religious vocations. Core. Calendar: trimesters. Services for LD students, advanced placement, independent study, distance learning, double major, summer session for credit, part-time degree program, adult/continuing education programs, co-op programs and internships, graduate courses open to undergrads. Off campus study.
Entrance Requirements: Options: electronic application, early admission, deferred admission, international baccalaureate accepted. Required: essay, high school transcript, minimum 2 high school GPA, 2 recommendations, interview. Entrance: moderately difficult. Application deadlines: rolling, rolling for early decision plan 1, rolling for early decision plan 2, rolling for early action. Notification: continuous, rolling for early decision plan 1, rolling for early decision plan 2, rolling for early action. Transfer credits accepted: Yes.
Collegiate Environment: Orientation program. Campus security: 24-hour emergency response devices and patrols. SCS Library. Books: 22,304 (physical), 338,731 (digital/electronic); Serial titles: 74 (physical), 24 (digital/electronic); Databases: 106. Weekly public service hours: 60. Operations spending for the previous fiscal year: $114,581. 8 computers available on campus for general student use. A campuswide network can be accessed from student residence rooms and from off campus. Students can access the following: online class registration. Staffed computer lab on campus provides training in use of computers, software, and the Internet.

■ **SOUTHERN STATES UNIVERSITY**
1094 Cudahy Pl.
Ste. 120
San Diego, CA 92110
Description: Proprietary, comprehensive, coed.

■ **SOUTHWESTERN COLLEGE**
900 Otay Lakes Rd.
Chula Vista, CA 91910-7299
Tel: (619)421-6700
Web Site: www.swccd.edu
Description: District-supported, 2-year, coed. Part of California Community College system. Awards certificates, transfer associate, and terminal associate degrees. Founded 1961. Setting: 158-acre suburban campus with easy access to City of San Diego. Endowment: $1.2 million. Research spending for the previous fiscal year: $42,830. Educational spending for the previous fiscal year: $15,521 per student. Total enrollment: 18,413. Faculty: 919 (214 full-time, 705 part-time). Student-undergrad faculty ratio is 22:1. Full-time: 7,405 students, 53% women, 47% men. Part-time: 11,008 students, 53% women, 47% men. 31% 25 or older, 5% transferred in. Retention: 74% of full-time freshmen returned the following year. Calendar: semesters. Academic remediation for entering students, ESL program, services for LD students, advanced placement, honors program, independent study, distance learning, summer session for credit, part-time degree program, external degree program, adult/continuing education programs, co-op programs and internships. Study abroad program.

Entrance Requirements: Open admission. Options: electronic application, early admission. Required for some: high school transcript. Entrance: noncompetitive. Application deadlines: rolling, rolling for nonresidents. Notification: continuous, continuous for nonresidents. Transfer credits accepted: Yes.
Costs Per Year: State resident tuition: $1288 full-time. Nonresident tuition: $6552 full-time. Mandatory fees: $100 full-time, $46 per unit part-time, $100 per year part-time. Full-time tuition and fees vary according to course load. Part-time fees vary according to course load.
Collegiate Environment: Orientation program. Drama-theater group, choral group, student-run newspaper. Student services: health clinic, personal-psychological counseling. Campus security: 24-hour emergency response devices and patrols, late night transport-escort service. Southwestern College Library/Learning Resource Center plus 3 others. Books: 104,784 (physical), 26,161 (digital/electronic); Serial titles: 191 (physical), 18 (digital/electronic); Databases: 58. Weekly public service hours: 126; students can reserve study rooms. Operations spending for the previous fiscal year: $1.1 million. 300 computers available on campus for general student use. A campuswide network can be accessed. Students can access the following: online class registration. Staffed computer lab on campus provides training in use of computers, software, and the Internet.

■ **SPARTAN COLLEGE OF AERONAUTICS AND TECHNOLOGY**
8911 Aviation Blvd.
Inglewood, CA 90301
Tel: (310)337-4444; Free: 800-879-0554
Fax: (866)451-0818
Web Site: www.spartan.edu
Description: Proprietary, 2-year, coed. Awards terminal associate degrees. Founded 1942. Total enrollment: 411. Student-undergrad faculty ratio is 19:1. 28% 25 or older. Retention: 98% of full-time freshmen returned the following year. Calendar: quarters.
Entrance Requirements: Open admission.

■ **STANBRIDGE UNIVERSITY**
2041 Business Ctr. Dr.
Irvine, CA 92612
Tel: (949)794-9090
Fax: (949)794-9094
Web Site: www.stanbridge.edu
Description: Proprietary, comprehensive, coed. Awards associate, bachelor's, and master's degrees.

■ **STANFORD UNIVERSITY**
450 Serra Mall
Stanford, CA 94305-2004
Tel: (650)723-2300
Fax: (650)725-2846
Web Site: www.stanford.edu
Description: Independent, university, coed. Awards bachelor's, master's, and doctoral degrees. Founded 1891. Setting: 8,180-acre suburban campus with easy access to San Francisco, San Jose. Research spending for the previous fiscal year: $1.1 billion. Educational spending for the previous fiscal year: $104,781 per student. Total enrollment: 16,914. Faculty: 1,637 (1,613 full-time, 24 part-time). Student-undergrad faculty ratio is 4:1. 43,997 applied, 5% were admitted. 95% from top 10% of their high school class, 99% from top quarter, 100% from top half. Full-time: 7,034 students, 49% women, 51% men. Students come from 52 states and territories, 76 other countries, 58% from out-of-state. 1% American Indian or Alaska Native, non-Hispanic/Latino; 16% Hispanic/Latino; 6% Black or African American, non-Hispanic/Latino; 21% Asian, non-Hispanic/Latino; 0.3% Native Hawaiian or other Pacific Islander, non-Hispanic/Latino; 9% international. 1% 25 or older, 93% live on campus, 1% transferred in. Retention: 98% of full-time freshmen returned the following year. Academic areas with the most degrees conferred: engineering; interdisciplinary studies; computer and information sciences. Core. Calendar: quarters. ESL program, services for LD students, advanced placement, self-designed majors, honors program, independent study, distance learning, double major, summer session for credit, internships, graduate courses open to undergrads. Off campus study at Howard University; Spelman College; Morehouse College. Study abroad program. ROTC: Army (c), Naval (c), Air Force (c).
Entrance Requirements: Options: electronic application, early action, deferred admission, international baccalaureate accepted. Required: essay, high school transcript, 2 recommendations, SAT or ACT. Recommended:

SAT Subject Tests. Entrance: most difficult. Application deadlines: 1/3, 11/1 for early action. Notification: 4/1, 12/15 for early action. SAT Reasoning Test deadline: 1/15. SAT Subject Test deadline: 1/15. Transfer credits accepted: Yes. Applicants placed on waiting list: 1,569. Wait-listed applicants offered admission: 55.

Costs Per Year: Application fee: $90. Comprehensive fee: $67,117 includes full-time tuition ($50,703), mandatory fees ($651), and college room and board ($15,763). Room and board charges vary according to board plan.

Collegiate Environment: Orientation program. Drama-theater group, choral group, marching band, student-run newspaper, radio station. Social organizations: 625 open to all; national fraternities, national sororities, local fraternities, 29 social Greek letter organizations; 19% of eligible men and 25% of eligible women are members. Most popular organizations: Ram's Head (theatre club), Axe Committee (athletic support), Business Association of Stanford Entrepreneurial Students, Asian-American Student Association, Stanford Daily. Major annual events: Big Game, Gaities, Fountain Hopping. Student services: legal services, health clinic, personal-psychological counseling, women's center. Campus security: 24-hour emergency response devices and patrols, late night transport-escort service, controlled dormitory access. Green Library plus 20 others. Books: 9.5 million (physical), 1.5 million (digital/electronic); Serial titles: 77,000 (physical). Study areas open 24 hours, 5-7 days a week; students can reserve study rooms. Operations spending for the previous fiscal year: $161.7 million. 1,000 computers available on campus for general student use. Computer purchase/lease plans available. A campuswide network can be accessed from student residence rooms and from off campus. Students can access the following: online class registration. Staffed computer lab on campus (open 24 hours a day) provides training in use of computers, software, and the Internet.

Community Environment: Stanford is an unincorporated campus adjacent to Palo Alto. Palo Alto with a population of 56,900 is located 30 miles south of San Francisco with an ideal climate, the summer average being 70 degrees and the winter average 55 degrees. The average rainfall is 15.5 inches. The city is served by all modes of transportation, the San Francisco Airport being 18 miles north. Palo Alto has three libraries, a museum, art gallery, hotels, hospitals, and churches. The Silicon Valley, in large part an offspring of Stanford, begins at campus edge. The cultural and recreation opportunities of San Francisco and San Jose are added to the many of the Stanford campus and the surrounding area. The Pacific Ocean is 32 miles to the west; the Monterey peninsula is 75 miles to the south. The Sierra Nevada, 160 miles away and the site of several national parks, are a popular resort area for camping, hiking, and skiing.

■ STUDIO SCHOOL
1201 W 5th St.
Los Angeles, CA 90017
Web Site: www.studioschool.org
Description: Proprietary, 4-year, coed.

■ SUM BIBLE COLLEGE & THEOLOGICAL SEMINARY
735 105th Ave.
Oakland, CA 94603
Tel: (510)567-6174; Free: 888-567-6174
Web Site: www.sum.edu
Description: Independent interdenominational, comprehensive, coed. Awards associate, bachelor's, and master's degrees. Founded 1991. Total enrollment: 139. Faculty: 22 (4 full-time, 18 part-time). Student-undergrad faculty ratio is 11:1. 111 applied, 59% were admitted. Full-time: 133 students, 44% women, 56% men. Part-time: 6 students, 17% women, 83% men. 45% transferred in. Calendar: trimesters. Distance learning.

Entrance Requirements: Option: deferred admission. Required: essay, 2 recommendations, interview, pastoral recommendation. Application deadline: rolling. Notification: continuous.

■ TAFT COLLEGE
29 Cougar Ct.
Taft, CA 93268
Tel: (661)763-7700
Fax: (661)763-7705
E-mail: ncook@taftcollege.edu
Web Site: www.taftcollege.edu
Description: District-supported, 2-year, coed. Part of California Community College System. Awards certificates, transfer associate, and terminal associate degrees. Founded 1922. Setting: 15-acre small town campus. Endowment: $14,405. Total enrollment: 9,500. Faculty: 91 (37 full-time, 54 part-

time). 812 applied, 100% were admitted. Full-time: 505 students, 60% women, 40% men. Part-time: 8,995 students, 18% women, 82% men. Students come from 1 other country, 5% from out-of-state. 6% live on campus, 3% transferred in. Core. Calendar: semesters. Academic remediation for entering students, ESL program, services for LD students, advanced placement, honors program, independent study, distance learning, summer session for credit, part-time degree program, adult/continuing education programs.

Entrance Requirements: Open admission. Option: electronic application. Required for some: high school transcript. Entrance: noncompetitive. Application deadline: rolling. Transfer credits accepted: Yes.

Collegiate Environment: Orientation program. Student-run newspaper. Social organizations: 4 open to all; Phi Theta Kappa. Most popular organizations: International Club, Alpha Gamma Sigma, Rotaract, ASB Club. Major annual events: International Day, Spring Fling. Student services: personal-psychological counseling. Campus security: 24-hour emergency response devices, controlled dormitory access, parking lot security. Taft College Library. Operations spending for the previous fiscal year: $263,133. 91 computers available on campus for general student use. A campuswide network can be accessed. Students can access the following: online class registration. Staffed computer lab on campus provides training in use of computers.

Community Environment: The population of Taft is 9,100. Centrally located two and one-half hours north of Los Angeles, Taft has a mild climate with hot summers. The city, surrounded by oilfields, is an important supply point for field equipment. Churches of all denominations, hospital, library, and shopping facilities make up the town. Part-time employment is available. Recreational facilities include a theatre, golf course, and more. Apartments are available.

■ THEATRE OF ARTS
1536 N Highland Ave.
Hollywood, CA 90028
Description: Proprietary, 2-year, coed.

■ THOMAS AQUINAS COLLEGE
10000 Ojai Rd.
Santa Paula, CA 93060
Tel: (805)525-4417; Free: 800-634-9797
Fax: (805)525-9342
E-mail: admissions@thomasaquinas.edu
Web Site: www.thomasaquinas.edu
Description: Independent Roman Catholic, 4-year, coed. Awards bachelor's degrees. Founded 1971. Setting: 131-acre rural campus with easy access to Los Angeles. System endowment: $22.5 million. Educational spending for the previous fiscal year: $14,538 per student. Total enrollment: 370. Faculty: 39 (31 full-time, 8 part-time). Student-undergrad faculty ratio is 11:1. 192 applied, 72% were admitted. 54% from top 10% of their high school class, 72% from top quarter, 91% from top half. Full-time: 370 students, 52% women, 48% men. Students come from 43 states and territories, 7 other countries, 60% from out-of-state. 0.5% American Indian or Alaska Native, non-Hispanic/Latino; 16% Hispanic/Latino; 0.8% Black or African American, non-Hispanic/Latino; 2% Asian, non-Hispanic/Latino; 0.3% Native Hawaiian or other Pacific Islander, non-Hispanic/Latino; 2% international. 2% 25 or older, 99% live on campus. Retention: 90% of full-time freshmen returned the following year. Academic area with the most degrees conferred: liberal arts/general studies. Core. Calendar: semesters. Co-op programs.

Entrance Requirements: Options: electronic application, international baccalaureate accepted. Required: essay, high school transcript, 3 recommendations, SAT or ACT. Recommended: minimum 3 high school GPA. Required for some: interview. Entrance: very difficult. Application deadline: rolling. Notification: continuous. Transfer credits accepted: No. Applicants placed on waiting list: 28. Wait-listed applicants offered admission: 14.

Costs Per Year: Application fee: $0. Comprehensive fee: $33,400 includes full-time tuition ($25,000) and college room and board ($8400).

Collegiate Environment: Orientation program. Drama-theater group, choral group. Social organizations: 5 open to all. Most popular organizations: Musical Groups (Choir, Chamber Orchestra), Theatre Groups, Language Clubs, Pro-Life Ministry, Religious groups. Major annual events: St. Thomas Aquinas Day, Presidents Day Formal Dinner, St. Patrick's Day Celebration. Student services: personal-psychological counseling. Campus security: daily security patrol. St. Bernardine Library. Books: 62,852 (physical); Serial titles: 78 (physical); Databases: 1. Students can reserve study rooms. Operations spending for the previous fiscal year: $193,669. 20 computers available on campus for general student use. A campuswide network can be accessed from student residence rooms. Staffed computer lab on campus provides training in use of computers, software, and the Internet.

Community Environment: The college is located in a rural setting 60 miles from Los Angeles and 45 miles from Santa Barbara. It is bordered on three sides by Los Padres National Forest.

■ **TOURO COLLEGE LOS ANGELES**
1317 N Crescent Heights Blvd.
West Hollywood, CA 90046
Tel: (323)822-9700
Web Site: www.touro.edu/losangeles
Description: Independent, 4-year, coed. Awards bachelor's degrees. Founded 2005. Calendar: semesters.
Costs Per Year: Tuition: $16,940 full-time, $710 per credit hour part-time. Mandatory fees: $300 full-time, $150 per term part-time. Full-time tuition and fees vary according to program. Part-time tuition and fees vary according to program. Tuition guaranteed not to increase for student's term of enrollment.

■ **TOURO UNIVERSITY WORLDWIDE**
10601 Calle Lee, Ste. 179
Los Alamitos, CA 90720
Tel: (818)575-6800
Web Site: www.tuw.edu
Description: Independent, comprehensive, coed. Awards associate, bachelor's, master's, and doctoral degrees. Total enrollment: 1,304. Faculty: 119 (13 full-time, 106 part-time). Student-undergrad faculty ratio is 22:1. Full-time: 244 students, 76% women, 24% men. Part-time: 240 students, 64% women, 36% men. Students come from 39 states and territories, 2 other countries. 9% Hispanic/Latino; 21% Black or African American, non-Hispanic/Latino; 3% Asian, non-Hispanic/Latino; 0.6% Native Hawaiian or other Pacific Islander, non-Hispanic/Latino. 74% 25 or older, 19% transferred in. Retention: 50% of full-time freshmen returned the following year. Academic areas with the most degrees conferred: business/marketing; psychology; health professions and related sciences. Core. Services for LD students, honors program, distance learning, part-time degree program, internships.
Entrance Requirements: Open admission. Option: electronic application. Transfer credits accepted: Yes.
Costs Per Year: Application fee: $0. Tuition: $10,800 full-time, $400 per credit hour part-time. Full-time tuition varies according to program. Part-time tuition varies according to program. Tuition guaranteed not to increase for student's term of enrollment.

■ **TRIDENT UNIVERSITY INTERNATIONAL**
5757 Plz. Dr., Ste. 100
Cypress, CA 90630
Tel: (714)816-0366
Fax: (714)816-0367
Web Site: www.trident.edu
Description: Independent, university, coed. Awards bachelor's, master's, and doctoral degrees and post-master's certificates (offers only online degree programs). Setting: urban campus. Student-undergrad faculty ratio is 25:1. Core. Calendar: 4 12-week sessions per year. Academic remediation for entering students, services for LD students, accelerated degree program, distance learning, double major, summer session for credit, part-time degree program.
Entrance Requirements: Open admission. Options: electronic application, international baccalaureate accepted. Required: high school transcript. Recommended: interview. Required for some: essay. Entrance: minimally difficult. Application deadline: rolling. Notification: continuous. Transfer credits accepted: Yes.
Collegiate Environment: Orientation program. Trident University International Library.

■ **UNITED STATES UNIVERSITY**
7675 Mission Valley Rd.
San Diego, CA 92108
Tel: (619)477-6310; Free: 888-422-3381
Fax: (619)477-7340
Web Site: www.usuniversity.edu
Description: Proprietary, comprehensive, coed. Awards bachelor's and master's degrees.
Entrance Requirements: Required: high school transcript, interview.

Collegiate Environment: Orientation program.

■ **UNITEK COLLEGE**
4670 Auto Mall Pky.
Fremont, CA 94538
Tel: (510)249-1060
Fax: (510)249-9125
Web Site: www.unitekcollege.edu
Description: Proprietary, 2-year, coed. Awards certificates and terminal associate degrees.

■ **UNIVERSITY OF ANTELOPE VALLEY**
44055 N Sierra Hwy.
Lancaster, CA 93534
Tel: (661)726-1911
Web Site: www.uav.edu
Description: Proprietary, comprehensive, coed. Awards associate, bachelor's, and master's degrees.

■ **UNIVERSITY OF CALIFORNIA, BERKELEY**
Berkeley, CA 94720
Tel: (510)642-6000
Fax: (510)642-7333
Web Site: www.berkeley.edu
Description: State-supported, university, coed. Part of University of California System. Awards bachelor's, master's, and doctoral degrees. Founded 1868. Setting: 1,232-acre urban campus with easy access to San Francisco. Total enrollment: 41,910. Faculty: 2,340 (1,608 full-time, 732 part-time). Student-undergrad faculty ratio is 18:1. 85,057 applied, 17% were admitted. 98% from top 10% of their high school class, 100% from top quarter, 100% from top half. Full-time: 29,105 students, 53% women, 47% men. Part-time: 1,219 students, 52% women, 48% men. 16% from out-of-state. 0.1% American Indian or Alaska Native, non-Hispanic/Latino; 15% Hispanic/Latino; 2% Black or African American, non-Hispanic/Latino; 35% Asian, non-Hispanic/Latino; 0.1% Native Hawaiian or other Pacific Islander, non-Hispanic/Latino; 12% international. 6% 25 or older, 25% live on campus, 7% transferred in. Retention: 97% of full-time freshmen returned the following year. Academic areas with the most degrees conferred: social sciences; engineering; biological/life sciences. Core. Calendar: semesters. ESL program, services for LD students, advanced placement, accelerated degree program, self-designed majors, honors program, independent study, double major, summer session for credit, adult/continuing education programs, internships, graduate courses open to undergrads. Off campus study at Holy Names College, Mills College, Dominican College, John F. Kennedy University, San Francisco State University, Sonoma State University, California State University, Hayward. Study abroad program. ROTC: Army, Naval, Air Force.
Entrance Requirements: Options: electronic application, international baccalaureate accepted. Required: essay, SAT or ACT. Recommended: SAT Subject Tests. Application deadline: 11/30. Notification: 3/31. Preference given to state residents. SAT Reasoning Test deadline: 12/31. SAT Subject Test deadline: 12/31. Applicants placed on waiting list: 7,459. Wait-listed applicants offered admission: 2,045.
Costs Per Year: Application fee: $70. State resident tuition: $11,442 full-time. Nonresident tuition: $40,434 full-time. Mandatory fees: $2742 full-time. College room and board: $16,160. Room and board charges vary according to board plan and housing facility.
Collegiate Environment: Orientation program. Drama-theater group, choral group, marching band, student-run newspaper, radio station. Social organizations: national fraternities, national sororities, local fraternities, local sororities. Student services: legal services, health clinic, personal-psychological counseling, women's center. Campus security: 24-hour emergency response devices and patrols, late night transport-escort service, controlled dormitory access, Office of Emergency Preparedness. Doe Library.
Community Environment: The City of Berkeley (population 100,744) has a long history as one of America's most lively, culturally diverse, and politically adventurous cities. The surrounding San Francisco Bay Area offers culture, entertainment, and natural beauty without rival, much of it within easy reach by BART (Bay Area Rapid Transit).

■ **UNIVERSITY OF CALIFORNIA, DAVIS**
One Shields Ave.
Davis, CA 95616

Tel: (530)752-1011
Fax: (530)752-6363
Web Site: www.ucdavis.edu
Description: State-supported, university, coed. Part of University of California System. Awards bachelor's, master's, and doctoral degrees and post-master's certificates. Founded 1908. Setting: 5,300-acre suburban campus with easy access to San Francisco. Total enrollment: 38,035. Faculty: 2,133 (1,568 full-time, 565 part-time). 76,377 applied, 41% were admitted. Full-time: 30,058 students, 61% women, 39% men. Part-time: 752 students, 51% women, 49% men. 5% from out-of-state. 0.2% American Indian or Alaska Native, non-Hispanic/Latino; 22% Hispanic/Latino; 2% Black or African American, non-Hispanic/Latino; 27% Asian, non-Hispanic/Latino; 0.4% Native Hawaiian or other Pacific Islander, non-Hispanic/Latino; 17% international. 6% 25 or older, 25% live on campus, 10% transferred in. Retention: 92% of full-time freshmen returned the following year. Academic areas with the most degrees conferred: social sciences; biological/life sciences; psychology. Core. Calendar: quarters. Academic remediation for entering students, ESL program, services for LD students, advanced placement, self-designed majors, freshman honors college, honors program, independent study, double major, summer session for credit, part-time degree program, adult/continuing education programs, internships, graduate courses open to undergrads. Study abroad program. ROTC: Army, Naval (c), Air Force (c).
Entrance Requirements: Option: electronic application. Required: essay, high school transcript, high school subject requirements, SAT or ACT. Entrance: very difficult. Notification: 3/15. SAT Reasoning Test deadline: 1/31. SAT Subject Test deadline: 1/31. Applicants placed on waiting list: 9,213. Wait-listed applicants offered admission: 24.
Costs Per Year: Application fee: $70. State resident tuition: $11,502 full-time. Nonresident tuition: $40,497 full-time. Mandatory fees: $2961 full-time. College room and board: $15,765. Room and board charges vary according to board plan.
Collegiate Environment: Orientation program. Drama-theater group, choral group, marching band, student-run newspaper, radio station. Social organizations: national fraternities, national sororities, local fraternities, local sororities, state fraternities and sororities. Major annual events: Picnic Day, Whole Earth Festival, Cultural Days. Student services: legal services, health clinic, personal-psychological counseling, women's center. Campus security: 24-hour emergency response devices and patrols, student patrols, late night transport-escort service, controlled dormitory access, Campus Violence Prevention Program (CVPP). Freshmen guaranteed college housing. Options: coed, women-only housing available. Peter J. Shields Library plus 6 others. Books: 4.9 million (physical), 1.3 million (digital/electronic); Serial titles: 106,593 (physical).
Community Environment: Population 60,700. Located in the center of the Sacramento Valley, the climate is typical of the Great Central Valley of California - cool in the winter and warm in the long dry summer season. January average temperatures range from a low of 37 to a high of 54 degrees; July average temperatures range 57 to 97 degrees. The average annual rainfall is 17 inches. The agricultural region surrounding Davis produces numerous crops including tomatoes, alfalfa, wheat and corn. Berkeley and San Francisco are within one hour by train, bus or car. Part-time employment is available either on or off campus. Davis is only 2-3 hours from the Lake Tahoe vacation area in the Sierra Nevada Mountains.

■ UNIVERSITY OF CALIFORNIA, IRVINE

Irvine, CA 92697
Tel: (949)824-5011
Web Site: www.uci.edu
Description: State-supported, university, coed. Part of University of California System. Awards bachelor's, master's, and doctoral degrees. Founded 1965. Setting: 1,477-acre suburban campus with easy access to Los Angeles. Research spending for the previous fiscal year: $282.9 million. Educational spending for the previous fiscal year: $20,075 per student. Total enrollment: 35,982. Faculty: 1,702 (1,364 full-time, 338 part-time). Student-undergrad faculty ratio is 18:1. 95,065 applied, 29% were admitted. 98% from top 10% of their high school class, 100% from top quarter, 100% from top half. Full-time: 29,250 students, 52% women, 48% men. Part-time: 486 students, 44% women, 56% men. Students come from 46 states and territories, 78 other countries, 3% from out-of-state. 0.1% American Indian or Alaska Native, non-Hispanic/Latino; 26% Hispanic/Latino; 2% Black or African American, non-Hispanic/Latino; 36% Asian, non-Hispanic/Latino; 0.3% Native Hawaiian or other Pacific Islander, non-Hispanic/Latino; 17% international. 5% 25 or older, 38% live on campus, 9% transferred in. Reten-

tion: 93% of full-time freshmen returned the following year. Academic areas with the most degrees conferred: social sciences; engineering; psychology. Core. Calendar: quarters. ESL program, services for LD students, advanced placement, accelerated degree program, honors program, independent study, distance learning, double major, summer session for credit, internships, graduate courses open to undergrads. Off campus study at other campuses of University of California System. Study abroad program. ROTC: Army, Air Force (c).
Entrance Requirements: Options: electronic application, international baccalaureate accepted. Required: essay, high school transcript, SAT or ACT. Entrance: very difficult. Application deadline: 11/30. Notification: 3/31. SAT Reasoning Test deadline: 12/31. SAT Subject Test deadline: 12/31. Transfer credits accepted: Yes. Applicants placed on waiting list: 12,522. Wait-listed applicants offered admission: 136.
Costs Per Year: Application fee: $70. State resident tuition: $11,442 full-time. Nonresident tuition: $40,434 full-time. Mandatory fees: $4172 full-time. College room and board: $15,263. Room and board charges vary according to board plan and housing facility.
Collegiate Environment: Orientation program. Drama-theater group, choral group, marching band, student-run newspaper, radio station. Social organizations: 650 open to all; national fraternities, national sororities, local fraternities, local sororities; 9% of eligible men and 9% of eligible women are members. Major annual events: Celebrate UCI (open house), Homecoming, Shocktoberfest. Student services: health clinic, personal-psychological counseling. Campus security: 24-hour emergency response devices and patrols, student patrols, late night transport-escort service, controlled dormitory access. 11,532 college housing spaces available; 11,471 were occupied in 2018-19. Freshmen guaranteed college housing. Options: coed, men-only, women-only housing available. Langson Library plus 4 others. Books: 2 million (physical), 1.3 million (digital/electronic); Serial titles: 4,309 (physical), 177,370 (digital/electronic); Databases: 1,652. Study areas open 24 hours, 5-7 days a week; students can reserve study rooms. Operations spending for the previous fiscal year: $26.8 million. 1,500 computers available on campus for general student use. A campuswide network can be accessed from student residence rooms and from off campus. Students can access the following: online class registration. Staffed computer lab on campus (open 24 hours a day) provides training in use of computers, software, and the Internet.
Community Environment: UCI's location combines the cultural and economic resources of an urban area along with access to the scenic, recreational areas of Southern California. Located 50 miles south of Los Angeles, five miles from the Pacific Ocean, and nestled in 1,477 acres of coastal foothills near Newport Beach, UCI lies amid rapidly growing residential communities and a dynamic international business environment of Orange County and the surrounding region. The sailing and surfing beaches of Newport, Laguna, and Huntington are a 10-minute bike ride from campus, while hiking trails, desert camping, or mountain resorts for snow boarding and skiing are within two-hour's travel distance from Irvine. The campus itself is a natural arboretum of native species, as well as trees and shrubs from all over the world. Adjacent to the campus, the San Joaquin Freshwater Marsh serves as a natural classroom or peaceful refuge, with trails for viewing the rich diversity of wildlife. Within walking distance of the University are shops and restaurants, bookstores, markets, a post office, and a theatre. Complementing UCI cultural events throughout the academic year is the Orange County arts and entertainment environment. It offers everything from small venues for bands and performers to galleries, museums, the Irvine Barclay Theater, the Orange County Performing Arts Center, and the Pacific Symphony. Within a one- to two-hour drive are the metropolitan attractions of Los Angeles and San Diego, as well as desert and mountain recreational opportunities.

■ UNIVERSITY OF CALIFORNIA, LOS ANGELES

405 Hilgard Ave.
Los Angeles, CA 90095
Tel: (310)825-4321
Web Site: www.ucla.edu
Description: State-supported, university, coed. Part of University of California System. Awards bachelor's, master's, and doctoral degrees. Founded 1919. Setting: 419-acre urban campus with easy access to Los Angeles. Endowment: $3.6 billion. Research spending for the previous fiscal year: $805.8 million. Total enrollment: 45,930. Faculty: 3,180 (2,266 full-time, 914 part-time). Student-undergrad faculty ratio is 17:1. 113,761 applied, 14% were admitted. 97% from top 10% of their high school class, 100% from top quarter, 100% from top half. Full-time: 31,009 students, 58% women, 42%

men. Part-time: 568 students, 45% women, 55% men. 13% from out-of-state. 0.2% American Indian or Alaska Native, non-Hispanic/Latino; 22% Hispanic/Latino; 3% Black or African American, non-Hispanic/Latino; 28% Asian, non-Hispanic/Latino; 0.3% Native Hawaiian or other Pacific Islander, non-Hispanic/Latino; 12% international. 5% 25 or older, 48% live on campus, 11% transferred in. Retention: 97% of full-time freshmen returned the following year. Academic areas with the most degrees conferred: social sciences; biological/life sciences; psychology. Core. Calendar: quarters. Services for LD students, advanced placement, accelerated degree program, self-designed majors, freshman honors college, independent study, double major, summer session for credit, internships, graduate courses open to undergrads. Off campus study. Study abroad program. ROTC: Army, Naval, Air Force.

Entrance Requirements: Options: electronic application, international baccalaureate accepted. Required: essay, high school transcript, SAT or ACT. Entrance: very difficult. Application deadline: 11/30. Notification: 3/31. SAT Reasoning Test deadline: 1/15. SAT Subject Test deadline: 1/15. Transfer credits accepted: Yes.

Costs Per Year: Application fee: $70. One-time mandatory fee: $165. State resident tuition: $11,442 full-time. Nonresident tuition: $40,434 full-time. Mandatory fees: $2108 full-time. College room and board: $15,816. Room and board charges vary according to board plan and housing facility.

Collegiate Environment: Orientation program. Drama-theater group, choral group, marching band, student-run newspaper, radio station. Social organizations: 1,000 open to all; national fraternities, national sororities, local fraternities, local sororities. Major annual events: Bruin Bash, Blue and Gold Week, Spring Sing. Student services: legal services, health clinic, personal-psychological counseling, women's center. Campus security: 24-hour emergency response devices and patrols, student patrols, late night transport-escort service, controlled dormitory access. Freshmen guaranteed college housing. Option: coed housing available. Charles E. Young Research Library plus 13 others. Books: 13.8 million (physical), 2.1 million (digital/electronic); Serial titles: 9,543 (physical), 99,598 (digital/electronic); Databases: 1,794. Weekly public service hours: 104; study areas open 24 hours, 5-7 days a week; students can reserve study rooms. Operations spending for the previous fiscal year: $58.2 million. 4,000 computers available on campus for general student use. A campuswide network can be accessed from student residence rooms and from off campus. Students can access the following: online class registration, 24/7 Chat with a Librarian. Staffed computer lab on campus (open 24 hours a day) provides training in use of computers, software, and the Internet.

Community Environment: Los Angeles is a major metropolitan center with a semiarid climate. There are very fine museums and libraries in the city, and a music center, which contribute to the cultural atmosphere of the city. Los Angeles has many points of interest, and is near enough to the beaches and to the mountains for all sports. There are excellent metropolitan shopping centers.

■ **UNIVERSITY OF CALIFORNIA, MERCED**
5200 N Lake Rd.
Merced, CA 95343
Tel: (209)228-4400
E-mail: admissions@ucmerced.edu
Web Site: www.ucmerced.edu
Description: State-supported, university, coed. Part of University of California System. Awards bachelor's, master's, and doctoral degrees. Setting: 815-acre small town campus with easy access to Fresno. Endowment: $38,592. Research spending for the previous fiscal year: $21.8 million. Educational spending for the previous fiscal year: $7635 per student. Total enrollment: 8,540. Faculty: 407 (371 full-time, 36 part-time). Student-undergrad faculty ratio is 18:1. 25,121 applied, 66% were admitted. Full-time: 211,185 students, 2% women, 98% men. Part-time: 68 students, 46% women, 54% men. Students come from 13 states and territories, 13 other countries. 0.1% American Indian or Alaska Native, non-Hispanic/Latino; 55% Hispanic/Latino; 5% Black or African American, non-Hispanic/Latino; 19% Asian, non-Hispanic/Latino; 0.6% Native Hawaiian or other Pacific Islander, non-Hispanic/Latino; 7% international. 8% 25 or older, 38% live on campus, 1% transferred in. Retention: 86% of full-time freshmen returned the following year. Academic areas with the most degrees conferred: biological/life sciences; engineering; psychology. Core. Academic remediation for entering students, services for LD students, advanced placement, independent study, double major, summer session for credit, part-time degree program, internships. Off campus study at Merced College. Study abroad program.
Entrance Requirements: Options: electronic application, international bac-

calaureate accepted. Required: essay, high school transcript, minimum 3.0 high school GPA for California residents, SAT or ACT. Entrance: moderately difficult. Notification: 3/1. SAT Reasoning Test deadline: 1/15. SAT Subject Test deadline: 1/15. Transfer credits accepted: Yes.
Costs Per Year: Application fee: $70. State resident tuition: $11,502 full-time, $2875 per term part-time. Nonresident tuition: $39,516 full-time, $9879 per term part-time. Mandatory fees: $2125 full-time, $2125 per year part-time. Full-time tuition and fees vary according to course load. Part-time tuition and fees vary according to course load. College room and board: $16,454. Room and board charges vary according to board plan.
Collegiate Environment: Orientation program. Drama-theater group, choral group, marching band, student-run newspaper, radio station. Social organizations: 140 open to all; national fraternities, national sororities, local fraternities; 8% of eligible men and 11% of eligible women are members. Most popular organizations: Philipino American Alliance, Vietnamese Student Association, Intervarsity Christian Fellowship, Latino Associated Students, Hip Hop Movement. Major annual events: Asian Fest, Bobcat Day, Dance Off. Student services: legal services, health clinic, personal-psychological counseling, women's center. Campus security: 24-hour emergency response devices and patrols, student patrols, late night transport-escort service, controlled dormitory access. College housing designed to accommodate 2,774 students; 2,957 undergraduates lived in college housing during 2018-19. Freshmen guaranteed college housing. Option: coed housing available. Kolligian Library. Books: 140,278 (physical), 1.7 million (digital/electronic); Serial titles: 100,836 (physical). Weekly public service hours: 97; students can reserve study rooms. Operations spending for the previous fiscal year: $4.5 million. 220 computers available on campus for general student use. A campuswide network can be accessed from student residence rooms and from off campus. Students can access the following: online class registration, student calendar, 10Gb online cloud storage, free office software. Staffed computer lab on campus provides training in use of computers, software, and the Internet.

■ **UNIVERSITY OF CALIFORNIA, RIVERSIDE**
900 University Ave.
Riverside, CA 92521-0102
Tel: (951)827-1012
Fax: (951)827-6344
E-mail: discover@ucr.edu
Web Site: www.ucr.edu
Description: State-supported, university, coed. Part of University of California System. Awards bachelor's, master's, and doctoral degrees. Founded 1954. Setting: 1,200-acre suburban campus with easy access to Los Angeles. Endowment: $252.5 million. Research spending for the previous fiscal year: $144.8 million. Educational spending for the previous fiscal year: $40,371 per student. Total enrollment: 23,922. Faculty: 1,173 (878 full-time, 295 part-time). Student-undergrad faculty ratio is 22:1. 49,082 applied, 51% were admitted. 94% from top 10% of their high school class, 100% from top quarter, 100% from top half. Full-time: 20,210 students, 55% women, 45% men. Part-time: 371 students, 38% women, 62% men. Students come from 23 states and territories, 95 other countries, 1% from out-of-state. 0.1% American Indian or Alaska Native, non-Hispanic/Latino; 42% Hispanic/Latino; 3% Black or African American, non-Hispanic/Latino; 34% Asian, non-Hispanic/Latino; 0.2% Native Hawaiian or other Pacific Islander, non-Hispanic/Latino; 3% international. 5% 25 or older, 30% live on campus, 9% transferred in. Retention: 89% of full-time freshmen returned the following year. Academic areas with the most degrees conferred: social sciences; biological/life sciences; business/marketing. Core. Calendar: quarters. Services for LD students, advanced placement, accelerated degree program, honors program, independent study, distance learning, double major, summer session for credit, part-time degree program, adult/continuing education programs, internships, graduate courses open to undergrads. Off campus study at University of California, Santa Barbara, University of California, Davis, University of California, Los Angeles, Cal State San Bernardino. Study abroad program. ROTC: Army (c), Air Force (c).
Entrance Requirements: Options: electronic application, international baccalaureate accepted. Required: essay, high school transcript, minimum 3 high school GPA, SAT or ACT. Entrance: very difficult. Application deadlines: 11/30, 11/30 for nonresidents. Notification: continuous until 3/1, continuous until 3/1 for nonresidents. SAT Reasoning Test deadline: 12/1. SAT Subject Test deadline: 12/1. Transfer credits accepted: Yes. Applicants placed on waiting list: 11,058. Wait-listed applicants offered admission: 1,143.
Costs Per Year: Application fee: $70. State resident tuition: $11,442 full-time, $5721 per year part-time. Nonresident tuition: $40,434 full-time,

$20,217 per year part-time. Mandatory fees: $4191 full-time, $1397 per term part-time. Full-time tuition and fees vary according to course load. Part-time tuition and fees vary according to course load. College room and board: $17,475. Room and board charges vary according to board plan and housing facility.

Collegiate Environment: Orientation program. Drama-theater group, choral group, student-run newspaper, radio station. Social organizations: 452 open to all; national fraternities, national sororities, local fraternities, local sororities, coed fraternities; 6% of eligible men and 10% of eligible women are members. Most popular organizations: American Red Cross at University of California Riverside, American Medical Student Association, Running Club At UCR, Katipunan Pilipino Student Organization, Circle K International. Major annual events: Block Party Fall Concert, Spring Splash Concert, Homecoming. Student services: legal services, health clinic, personal-psychological counseling, women's center. Campus security: 24-hour emergency response devices and patrols, student patrols, late night transport-escort service, controlled dormitory access. 7,000 college housing spaces available; 6,202 were occupied in 2018-19. Freshmen guaranteed college housing. Option: coed housing available. Tomas Rivera Library plus 4 others. Books: 3 million (physical), 938,175 (digital/electronic); Serial titles: 71,249 (physical); Databases: 1,713. Weekly public service hours: 96; study areas open 24 hours, 5-7 days a week; students can reserve study rooms. 556 computers available on campus for general student use. Computer purchase/lease plans available. A campuswide network can be accessed from student residence rooms and from off campus. Students can access the following: online class registration, online viewing of financial information. Staffed computer lab on campus provides training in use of computers, software, and the Internet.

Community Environment: Population 290,000. A suburban area 60 miles east of Los Angeles with a temperate climate, Riverside is an important residential and commercial center in Riverside County. This city launched the navel orange industry in southern California. Major transportation facilities are available. Riverside has churches of the major denominations, a library, hospitals and all public health services. Recreational activities include all water sports. Beaches, desert and mountain/ski resort areas are nearby.

■ **UNIVERSITY OF CALIFORNIA, SAN DIEGO**
9500 Gilman Dr.
La Jolla, CA 92093
Tel: (858)534-2230
E-mail: admissionsreply@ucsd.edu
Web Site: www.ucsd.edu

Description: State-supported, university, coed. Part of University of California System. Awards bachelor's, master's, and doctoral degrees. Founded 1959. Setting: 1,976-acre suburban campus with easy access to San Diego. Total enrollment: 35,772. Faculty: 1,348 (1,123 full-time, 225 part-time). Student-undergrad faculty ratio is 19:1. 88,428 applied, 34% were admitted. 100% from top 10% of their high school class, 100% from top quarter, 100% from top half. 49 National Merit Scholars. Full-time: 28,067 students, 49% women, 51% men. Part-time: 425 students, 44% women, 56% men. Students come from 52 states and territories, 92 other countries, 6% from out-of-state. 0.4% American Indian or Alaska Native, non-Hispanic/Latino; 18% Hispanic/Latino; 2% Black or African American, non-Hispanic/Latino; 38% Asian, non-Hispanic/Latino; 0.2% Native Hawaiian or other Pacific Islander, non-Hispanic/Latino; 20% international. 4% 25 or older, 39% live on campus, 10% transferred in. Retention: 94% of full-time freshmen returned the following year. Academic areas with the most degrees conferred: social sciences; biological/life sciences; engineering. Core. Calendar: quarters. ESL program, services for LD students, advanced placement, accelerated degree program, self-designed majors, freshman honors college, honors program, independent study, double major, summer session for credit, co-op programs and internships, graduate courses open to undergrads. Off campus study at Dartmouth College, Spelman College, Morehouse College. Study abroad program. ROTC: Army (c), Naval (c), Air Force (c).

Entrance Requirements: Options: electronic application, international baccalaureate accepted. Required: essay, high school transcript, minimum 2.8 high school GPA, SAT and SAT Subject Tests or ACT, ACT Assessment with Writing or SAT Reasoning Test, plus two SAT Subject Tests. Required for some: minimum 3.4 high school GPA. Entrance: very difficult. Application deadline: 11/30. Notification: 3/31. Preference given to state residents. SAT Reasoning Test deadline: 1/15. SAT Subject Test deadline: 1/15. Transfer credits accepted: Yes.

Collegiate Environment: Orientation program. Drama-theater group, choral group, marching band, student-run newspaper, radio station. Social organizations: 501 open to all; national fraternities, national sororities; 12% of eligible men and 14% of eligible women are members. Major annual events: SunGod Festival, On Campus Concerts, Sporting Events. Student services: legal services, health clinic, personal-psychological counseling, women's center. Campus security: 24-hour emergency response devices and patrols, student patrols, late night transport-escort service, crime prevention programs. Geisel Library plus 1 other. Books: 3.5 million (physical), 958,000 (digital/electronic). Study areas open 24 hours, 5-7 days a week; students can reserve study rooms.

Community Environment: La Jolla is within the corporate limits of San Diego and is a popular resort with a rocky coast and fine beaches. San Diego lies along and around one of the world's ten most beautiful protected natural harbors, and has a very special seawashed, air-conditioned climate. The maximum average temperature of 70.8 degrees and a minimum of 55.4 degrees makes the climate very special. Amtrak, buses, a trolley system, and major airlines all serve the area. The city is a major center for biomedical, high technology electronics and wireless communication industries. Other industries include shipbuilding, shipping, and fishing. San Diego County is the country's largest producer of avocados. San Diego has a large public library system, hospitals, museums, galleries, and churches. Within San Diego County are numerous golf courses, all aquatic sports, hiking, camping, mountain climbing, horseback riding, snow sports, fishing and hunting. Sea World, the world-famous San Diego Zoo and Wild Animal Park, Balboa Park, and the Anza Borrego Desert State Park also provide recreational opportunities. This is the home of the 1994 AFC Champion San Diego Chargers, the professional football team, and the 1998 National League Champion San Diego Padres professional baseball team. Known as a winter playground, it has 70 miles of beautiful beaches. Population of San Diego is 1,255,500, with a greater metropolitan area population of 2,853,00.

■ **UNIVERSITY OF CALIFORNIA, SANTA BARBARA**
1210 Cheadle Hall
Santa Barbara, CA 93106-2014
Tel: (805)893-8000
E-mail: admissions@sa.ucsb.edu
Web Site: www.ucsb.edu

Description: State-supported, university, coed. Part of University of California System. Awards bachelor's, master's, and doctoral degrees and post-master's certificates. Founded 1909. Setting: 989-acre suburban campus. Endowment: $155 million. Total enrollment: 25,057. Faculty: 1,163 (994 full-time, 169 part-time). Student-undergrad faculty ratio is 17:1. 80,319 applied, 33% were admitted. 100% from top 10% of their high school class, 100% from top quarter, 100% from top half. Full-time: 21,776 students, 54% women, 46% men. Part-time: 410 students, 47% women, 53% men. Students come from 51 states and territories, 81 other countries, 4% from out-of-state. 3% 25 or older, 38% live on campus, 10% transferred in. Retention: 92% of full-time freshmen returned the following year. Core. Calendar: quarters plus 6-week summer term. ESL program, services for LD students, advanced placement, accelerated degree program, self-designed majors, honors program, independent study, double major, summer session for credit, co-op programs and internships, graduate courses open to undergrads. Off campus study at other campuses of the University of California System. Study abroad program. ROTC: Army, Air Force (c).

Entrance Requirements: Options: electronic application, international baccalaureate accepted. Required: essay, high school transcript, SAT or ACT. Recommended: SAT Subject Tests. Required for some: interview. Entrance: very difficult. Application deadline: 11/30. Notification: 3/31. SAT Reasoning Test deadline: 12/30. SAT Subject Test deadline: 12/30. Transfer credits accepted: Yes. Applicants placed on waiting list: 6,650. Wait-listed applicants offered admission: 960.

Costs Per Year: Application fee: $70. State resident tuition: $12,570 full-time. Nonresident tuition: $41,562 full-time. Mandatory fees: $1854 full-time. College room and board: $15,273. Room and board charges vary according to board plan and housing facility.

Collegiate Environment: Orientation program. Drama-theater group, choral group, student-run newspaper, radio station. Social organizations: national fraternities, national sororities, local fraternities, local sororities. Major annual event: Extravaganza (spring concert with national acts). Student services: legal services, health clinic, personal-psychological counseling, women's center. Campus security: 24-hour emergency response devices and patrols, student patrols, late night transport-escort service, controlled dormitory access. Davidson Library plus 1 other. Weekly public service hours: 96; study areas open 24 hours, 5-7 days a week; students can reserve study rooms.

Community Environment: The University is located in Goleta, a suburb of Santa Barbara. Santa Barbara is a county seat, the largest city between Los Angeles and San Francisco, and is known as the "Riviera of the Pacific." The city lies at the foot of the Santa Ynez Mountains, facing the Pacific Ocean. The climate is moderate, and the temperature varies only 7 degrees in summer and winter. All modes of transportation serve the area, and hotel and motel accommodations are numerous. Santa Barbara has all the community facilities plus many points of interest, a planetarium, botanic garden, natural history, art, historical museums, and more. The annual horse show, Old Spanish Days, August Fiesta, Semana Nautica (Marine sports week), and flower shows are the highlights of the year. Active music organizations and the Symphony Orchestra are an important part of the cultural life of the city. Recreational facilities include golf courses, tennis courts, water sports at the beach, and many other activities.

■ UNIVERSITY OF CALIFORNIA, SANTA CRUZ

1156 High St.
Santa Cruz, CA 95064
Tel: (831)459-0111
Fax: (831)459-4452
E-mail: admissions@ucsc.edu
Web Site: www.ucsc.edu

Description: State-supported, university, coed. Part of University of California System. Awards bachelor's, master's, and doctoral degrees. Founded 1965. Setting: 2,000-acre small town campus with easy access to San Francisco, San Jose. Endowment: $207.1 million. Research spending for the previous fiscal year: $93.9 million. Educational spending for the previous fiscal year: $9781 per student. Total enrollment: 19,700. Faculty: 839 (611 full-time, 228 part-time). Student-undergrad faculty ratio is 19:1. 55,355 applied, 47% were admitted. 96% from top 10% of their high school class, 100% from top quarter, 100% from top half. Full-time: 17,255 students, 49% women, 51% men. Part-time: 537 students, 44% women, 56% men. Students come from 47 states and territories, 50 other countries, 4% from out-of-state. 0.1% American Indian or Alaska Native, non-Hispanic/Latino; 28% Hispanic/Latino; 2% Black or African American, non-Hispanic/Latino; 22% Asian, non-Hispanic/Latino; 0.2% Native Hawaiian or other Pacific Islander, non-Hispanic/Latino; 8% international. 5% 25 or older, 51% live on campus, 10% transferred in. Retention: 88% of full-time freshmen returned the following year. Academic areas with the most degrees conferred: biological/life sciences; social sciences; psychology. Core. Calendar: quarters. Services for LD students, advanced placement, accelerated degree program, self-designed majors, freshman honors college, honors program, independent study, double major, summer session for credit, co-op programs and internships, graduate courses open to undergrads. Off campus study at other campuses of the University of California System, University of New Hampshire, University of New Mexico. Study abroad program. ROTC: Army (c), Naval (c), Air Force (c).

Entrance Requirements: Options: electronic application, international baccalaureate accepted. Required: essay, high school transcript, minimum 3 high school GPA, minimum high school GPA of 3.0 for California residents, 3.4 for non-residents, SAT or ACT. Required for some: minimum 3.4 high school GPA. Entrance: very difficult. Application deadline: 11/30. Notification: 3/31. Preference given to Qualified state residents. SAT Reasoning Test deadline: 7/15. Transfer credits accepted: Yes. Applicants placed on waiting list: 12,504. Wait-listed applicants offered admission: 149.

Costs Per Year: Application fee: $70. State resident tuition: $11,502 full-time. Nonresident tuition: $39,516 full-time. Mandatory fees: $2507 full-time. College room and board: $16,407. Room and board charges vary according to board plan and housing facility.

Collegiate Environment: Orientation program. Drama-theater group, choral group, marching band, student-run newspaper, radio station. Social organizations: 184 open to all; national fraternities, national sororities, local fraternities, local sororities; 7% of eligible men and 8% of eligible women are members. Most popular organizations: Bayanihan, +Chinese Student Association, +City on a Hill Press, +College Panhellenic & Inter-Greek Council, +Indian Student Association. Major annual events: Martin Luther King Jr. Convocation, Multicultural Festival, UCSC Slug Run. Student services: health clinic, personal-psychological counseling, women's center. Campus security: 24-hour emergency response devices and patrols, late night transport-escort service, controlled dormitory access. Freshmen guaranteed college housing. Options: coed, men-only, women-only housing available. UCSC Library. Books: 1.1 million (physical), 1.1 million (digital/electronic); Serial titles: 44,167 (physical), 72,348 (digital/electronic); Databases: 538. Weekly public service hours: 94; students can reserve study rooms. Operations spending for the previous fiscal year: $14.1 million.

Community Environment: The City of Santa Cruz, population 54,760, and other nearby communities are easily accessible via the local bus system. The area has long been a popular resort because of its recreational offerings, which include 10 miles of beaches, a widely varied coastal zone, and the densely wooded Santa Cruz Mountains. The temperate climate is characterized by sunny summer days with foggy mornings and rain in the winter. Many of the city's Victorian houses have been restored in recent years, and its main shopping street has been revitalized. For its size, Santa Cruz has a remarkable variety of outstanding restaurants in all price ranges. Numerous cultural activities are sponsored by the University, the local junior college, and community organizations.

■ UNIVERSITY OF LA VERNE

1950 Third St.
La Verne, CA 91750-4443
Tel: (909)593-3511; Free: 800-876-4858
Fax: (909)593-0965
E-mail: admissions@ulv.edu
Web Site: www.laverne.edu

Description: Independent, university, coed. Awards bachelor's, master's, and doctoral degrees (also offers continuing education program with significant enrollment not reflected in profile). Founded 1891. Setting: 66-acre suburban campus with easy access to Los Angeles. Total enrollment: 4,752. Faculty: 534 (236 full-time, 298 part-time). Student-undergrad faculty ratio is 12:1. 7,276 applied, 51% were admitted. 20% from top 10% of their high school class, 48% from top quarter, 84% from top half. Full-time: 2,721 students, 58% women, 42% men. Part-time: 77 students, 62% women, 38% men. Students come from 22 states and territories, 36 other countries, 4% from out-of-state. 0.1% American Indian or Alaska Native, non-Hispanic/Latino; 57% Hispanic/Latino; 5% Black or African American, non-Hispanic/Latino; 5% Asian, non-Hispanic/Latino; 0.5% Native Hawaiian or other Pacific Islander, non-Hispanic/Latino; 7% international. 3% 25 or older, 30% live on campus, 7% transferred in. Retention: 83% of full-time freshmen returned the following year. Academic areas with the most degrees conferred: business/marketing; education; social sciences. Core. Calendar: 4-1-4. Academic remediation for entering students, ESL program, services for LD students, advanced placement, self-designed majors, freshman honors college, honors program, independent study, distance learning, double major, summer session for credit, part-time degree program, adult/continuing education programs, internships, graduate courses open to undergrads. Off campus study. Study abroad program. ROTC: Army (c).

Entrance Requirements: Options: electronic application, deferred admission, international baccalaureate accepted. Required: essay, high school transcript, 2 recommendations, SAT or ACT. Entrance: moderately difficult. Application deadline: 2/1. Notification: continuous. SAT Reasoning Test deadline: 8/31. SAT Subject Test deadline: 8/31. Transfer credits accepted: Yes.

Costs Per Year: Application fee: $50. Comprehensive fee: $57,690 includes full-time tuition ($43,004), mandatory fees ($1496), and college room and board ($13,190). Part-time tuition: $1260 per semester hour.

Collegiate Environment: Orientation program. Drama-theater group, choral group, student-run newspaper, radio station. Social organizations: 72 open to all; national fraternities, national sororities, local sororities. Most popular organizations: Associated Students of La Verne, Latino Student Forum, Black Student Union, Psi Chi, Voices in Action. Major annual events: Homecoming, International Fair, Spring Formal. Student services: health clinic, personal-psychological counseling. Campus security: 24-hour emergency response devices and patrols, late night transport-escort service, controlled dormitory access. No special consideration for freshman housing applicants. Options: coed, men-only, women-only housing available. Wilson Library. Students can reserve study rooms.

Community Environment: La Verne is a suburban area approximately 35 miles east of Los Angeles, Pasadena, Beverly Hills and Hollywood. MetroLink railroad system and the Metropolitan Bus Lines provide access in and out of Los Angeles. La Verne is overshadowed on the north by the snowcapped San Gabriel Mountains, which rise to a height of 10,000 feet. La Verne is within easy driving distance of the beaches and mountains which provide both summer and winter recreational activities.

■ UNIVERSITY OF THE PACIFIC

3601 Pacific Ave.
Stockton, CA 95211-0197
Tel: (209)946-2344
Fax: (209)946-2413

E-mail: admissions@pacific.edu
Web Site: www.pacific.edu

Description: Independent, university, coed. Awards bachelor's, master's, and doctoral degrees. Founded 1851. Setting: 175-acre suburban campus with easy access to Sacramento. Total enrollment: 6,255. Faculty: 823 (442 full-time, 381 part-time). Student-undergrad faculty ratio is 13:1. 13,064 applied, 65% were admitted. 34% from top 10% of their high school class, 68% from top quarter, 94% from top half. Full-time: 3,452 students, 55% women, 45% men. Part-time: 96 students, 45% women, 55% men. 7% from out-of-state. 0.4% American Indian or Alaska Native, non-Hispanic/Latino; 20% Hispanic/Latino; 3% Black or African American, non-Hispanic/Latino; 36% Asian, non-Hispanic/Latino; 0.5% Native Hawaiian or other Pacific Islander, non-Hispanic/Latino; 6% international. 6% 25 or older, 44% live on campus, 6% transferred in. Retention: 85% of full-time freshmen returned the following year. Academic areas with the most degrees conferred: business/marketing; engineering; biological/life sciences. Core. Calendar: semesters. Academic remediation for entering students, ESL program, services for LD students, advanced placement, accelerated degree program, self-designed majors, honors program, independent study, double major, summer session for credit, part-time degree program, co-op programs and internships. ROTC: Air Force (c).

Entrance Requirements: Options: electronic application, early action, international baccalaureate accepted. Required: essay, high school transcript, SAT or ACT. Recommended: SAT and SAT Subject Tests or ACT. Entrance: moderately difficult. Application deadlines: 8/15, 11/15 for early action. Notification: continuous, 1/15 for early action. SAT Reasoning Test deadline: 8/20. SAT Subject Test deadline: 8/20. Applicants placed on waiting list: 185. Wait-listed applicants offered admission: 36.

Costs Per Year: Application fee: $35. Comprehensive fee: $61,690 includes full-time tuition ($47,480), mandatory fees ($560), and college room and board ($13,650). Room and board charges vary according to board plan and housing facility. Part-time tuition: $1638 per credit hour. Part-time tuition varies according to course load.

Collegiate Environment: Orientation program. Drama-theater group, choral group, student-run newspaper, radio station. Social organizations: national fraternities, national sororities, local fraternities. Student services: legal services, health clinic, personal-psychological counseling. Campus security: 24-hour emergency response devices and patrols, late night transport-escort service, controlled dormitory access. University of the Pacific Library plus 1 other.

Community Environment: Stockton, population 286,900, is located 80 miles east of San Francisco and 40 miles south of Sacramento. The city is located in a rich agricultural region. All major forms of transportation serve the area. Stockton has 110 churches, general hospitals, a library, museum, and fine shopping facilities. Recreational facilities include theaters, parks, playgrounds, stadiums, a large events center, and a baseball stadium. The city is only a short drive away from facilities for water skiing, sailing, and golf, and the Sierra Nevada mountain range is also nearby.

■ **UNIVERSITY OF THE PEOPLE**
225 S Lake Ave.
Ste. 300
Pasadena, CA 91101
Web Site: www.uopeople.edu

Description: Private, comprehensive, coed.

■ **UNIVERSITY OF PHOENIX-BAY AREA CAMPUS**
3590 N First St.
San Jose, CA 95134-1805
Tel: (925)416-4100; Free: 866-766-0766
Web Site: www.phoenix.edu

Description: Proprietary, comprehensive, coed. Awards bachelor's and master's degrees. Setting: urban campus. Total enrollment: 2,240. Faculty: 318 (29 full-time, 289 part-time). Full-time: 1,676 students, 64% women, 36% men. 82% 25 or older. Core. Calendar: continuous. Services for LD students, advanced placement, accelerated degree program, independent study, distance learning, external degree program, adult/continuing education programs, graduate courses open to undergrads.

Entrance Requirements: Open admission. Options: electronic application, deferred admission. Required: 1 recommendation. Required for some: high school transcript. Entrance: noncompetitive. Application deadline: rolling.

Collegiate Environment: Campus security: late night transport-escort service. University Library. Operations spending for the previous fiscal year: $6.8 million.

■ **UNIVERSITY OF PHOENIX-CENTRAL VALLEY CAMPUS**
45 River Park Pl. W
Ste. 101
Fresno, CA 93720-1552
Free: 866-766-0766
Web Site: www.phoenix.edu

Description: Proprietary, comprehensive, coed. Awards bachelor's and master's degrees. Founded 2004. Setting: urban campus. Total enrollment: 2,235. Faculty: 272 (31 full-time, 241 part-time). Full-time: 1,928 students, 71% women, 29% men. 3% from out-of-state. 73% 25 or older. Academic areas with the most degrees conferred: business/marketing; public administration and social services; homeland security, law enforcement, firefighting, and protective services. Core. Services for LD students, advanced placement, accelerated degree program, independent study, distance learning, graduate courses open to undergrads.

Entrance Requirements: Open admission. Options: electronic application, deferred admission. Required: 1 recommendation. Required for some: high school transcript. Entrance: noncompetitive. Application deadline: rolling.

Collegiate Environment: Campus security: late night transport-escort service. Operations spending for the previous fiscal year: $6.8 million.

■ **UNIVERSITY OF PHOENIX-SACRAMENTO VALLEY CAMPUS**
2860 Gateway Oaks Dr.
Ste. 200
Sacramento, CA 95833-4334
Tel: (916)923-2107; Free: 866-766-0766
Fax: (916)923-3914
Web Site: www.phoenix.edu

Description: Proprietary, comprehensive, coed. Awards bachelor's and master's degrees. Founded 1993. Setting: urban campus. Total enrollment: 3,842. Faculty: 518 (49 full-time, 469 part-time). Full-time: 3,162 students, 69% women, 31% men. 81% 25 or older. Core. Calendar: continuous. Services for LD students, advanced placement, accelerated degree program, independent study, distance learning, external degree program, adult/continuing education programs, graduate courses open to undergrads.

Entrance Requirements: Open admission. Options: electronic application, deferred admission. Required: 1 recommendation. Required for some: high school transcript. Entrance: noncompetitive. Application deadline: rolling.

Collegiate Environment: Campus security: late night transport-escort service. University Library. Operations spending for the previous fiscal year: $6.8 million.

■ **UNIVERSITY OF PHOENIX-SAN DIEGO CAMPUS**
9645 Granite Ridge Dr.
San Diego, CA 92123
Tel: (800)473-4346; Free: 866-766-0766
Fax: (858)576-0032
Web Site: www.phoenix.edu

Description: Proprietary, comprehensive, coed. Awards bachelor's and master's degrees. Founded 1988. Setting: urban campus. Total enrollment: 3,212. Faculty: 399 (30 full-time, 369 part-time). Full-time: 2,500 students, 59% women, 41% men. 79% 25 or older. Core. Calendar: continuous. Services for LD students, advanced placement, accelerated degree program, independent study, distance learning, external degree program, adult/continuing education programs, graduate courses open to undergrads.

Entrance Requirements: Open admission. Options: electronic application, deferred admission. Required: 1 recommendation. Required for some: high school transcript. Entrance: noncompetitive. Application deadline: rolling.

Collegiate Environment: Campus security: late night transport-escort service. University Library. Operations spending for the previous fiscal year: $6.8 million.

■ **UNIVERSITY OF REDLANDS**
1200 E Colton Ave.
Redlands, CA 92373-0999
Tel: (909)793-2121; Free: 800-455-5064
Fax: (909)335-4089
E-mail: belinda_sandoval@redlands.edu
Web Site: www.redlands.edu

Description: Independent, comprehensive, coed. Awards bachelor's, master's, and doctoral degrees and post-master's certificates. Founded 1907. Setting: 160-acre small town campus with easy access to Los Angeles. Endowment: $110.8 million. Educational spending for the previous fiscal year: $10,533 per student. Total enrollment: 5,215. 4,790 applied, 68%

were admitted. 38% from top 10% of their high school class, 68% from top quarter, 90% from top half. Full-time: 2,709 students, 58% women, 42% men. Part-time: 784 students, 49% women, 51% men. Students come from 43 states and territories, 14 other countries. 0.8% American Indian or Alaska Native, non-Hispanic/Latino; 27% Hispanic/Latino; 5% Black or African American, non-Hispanic/Latino; 6% Asian, non-Hispanic/Latino; 0.6% Native Hawaiian or other Pacific Islander, non-Hispanic/Latino; 1% international. 3% transferred in. Retention: 85% of full-time freshmen returned the following year. Core. Calendar: 4-4-1. Academic remediation for entering students, services for LD students, advanced placement, self-designed majors, honors program, independent study, double major, part-time degree program, adult/continuing education programs, internships, graduate courses open to undergrads. Off campus study at members of the Association for Innovation in Higher Education, American University. Study abroad program. ROTC: Army (c), Air Force (c).

Entrance Requirements: Options: electronic application, early admission, early decision, early action, deferred admission, international baccalaureate accepted. Required: essay, high school transcript, 2 recommendations, SAT or ACT. Recommended: interview. Entrance: moderately difficult. Application deadlines: 1/15, 11/15 for early decision, 11/15 for early action. Notification: continuous until 3/1, 1/15 for early decision, 1/15 for early action. SAT Reasoning Test deadline: 4/1. Transfer credits accepted: Yes. Applicants placed on waiting list: 131. Wait-listed applicants offered admission: 47.

Costs Per Year: Application fee: $50. One-time mandatory fee: $150. Comprehensive fee: $63,782 includes full-time tuition ($49,154), mandatory fees ($350), and college room and board ($14,278). Room and board charges vary according to board plan and housing facility. Part-time tuition: $1537 per credit hour. Part-time mandatory fees: $116 per year. Part-time tuition and fees vary according to course load.

Collegiate Environment: Orientation program. Drama-theater group, choral group, student-run newspaper, radio station. Social organizations: 120 open to all; local fraternities, local sororities; 10% of eligible men and 13% of eligible women are members. Most popular organizations: Associated Students, service organizations, cultural organizations, social awareness groups. Major annual events: Homecoming, Living on Common Ground Multicultural Festival, Convocation Lecture Series. Student services: health clinic, personal-psychological counseling, women's center. Campus security: 24-hour emergency response devices and patrols, student patrols, late night transport-escort service, controlled dormitory access. Armacost Library. Operations spending for the previous fiscal year: $1.9 million. 804 computers available on campus for general student use. A campuswide network can be accessed from student residence rooms and from off campus. Students can access the following: online class registration. Staffed computer lab on campus provides training in use of computers, software, and the Internet.

Community Environment: Redlands is located halfway between Los Angeles and Palm Springs. It has a mild climate. The average yearly temperature is 65 degrees, and the average rainfall 14.45 inches. Once a principal center for navel oranges, the city has developed a more diversified economy in recent years. There are 60 churches, a community hospital and satellite clinics, a city library, fraternal and social service organizations, and museums. Buses serve the area, and the Ontario International Airport is 30 minutes from the campus. Through the Office of Community Service Learning and other organizations, students at the university have many opportunities to interact with community members.

■ UNIVERSITY OF SAINT KATHERINE

1637 Capalina Rd.
San Marcos, CA 92069
Tel: (760)471-1316
Fax: (760)471-1314
E-mail: admissions@stkath.org
Web Site: www.usk.edu

Description: Independent Christian, 4-year, coed. Awards bachelor's degrees. Setting: 2-acre suburban campus with easy access to San Diego, CA. Endowment: $32,123. Educational spending for the previous fiscal year: $8638 per student. Total enrollment: 44. Faculty: 14 (2 full-time, 12 part-time). Student-undergrad faculty ratio is 9:1. 21 applied, 62% were admitted. Full-time: 44 students, 39% women, 61% men. Students come from 12 states and territories, 30% from out-of-state. 2% American Indian or Alaska Native, non-Hispanic/Latino; 20% Hispanic/Latino; 5% Black or African American, non-Hispanic/Latino. 5% 25 or older, 25% live on campus, 11% transferred in. Retention: 46% of full-time freshmen returned the following year. Academic areas with the most degrees conferred: biological/life sciences; interdisciplinary studies; English. Core. Calendar: semesters.

Academic remediation for entering students, services for LD students, advanced placement, self-designed majors, independent study, double major, part-time degree program, adult/continuing education programs, co-op programs and internships. Study abroad program.

Entrance Requirements: Option: electronic application. Required: essay, high school transcript, minimum 2.5 high school GPA, 2 recommendations, interview, SAT or ACT. Application deadlines: 7/15, rolling for nonresidents. SAT Reasoning Test deadline: 8/15. SAT Subject Test deadline: 8/15. Transfer credits accepted: Yes.

Costs Per Year: Application fee: $0. Comprehensive fee: $35,398 includes full-time tuition ($23,500), mandatory fees ($1800), and college room and board ($10,098). Part-time tuition: $783 per unit. Part-time mandatory fees: $900 per term.

Collegiate Environment: Orientation program. Student-run newspaper. Social organizations: 2 open to all; FCA, OCF; 10% of eligible men and 10% of eligible women are members. Most popular organizations: Fellowship of Christian Athletes, Orthodox Christian Fellowship. Major annual events: Orientation, Forum Lectures, Softball Game. Student services: personal-psychological counseling. Saint Katherine College Library plus 1 other. Books: 12,500 (physical); Serial titles: 10 (physical); Databases: 5. Operations spending for the previous fiscal year: $1600. 25 computers available on campus for general student use. A computer is required for all students. A campuswide network can be accessed from student residence rooms and from off campus. Students can access the following: online class registration. Staffed computer lab on campus provides training in use of computers, software, and the Internet.

■ UNIVERSITY OF SAN DIEGO

5998 Alcala Park
San Diego, CA 92110-2492
Tel: (619)260-4600; Free: 800-248-4873
E-mail: admissions@sandiego.edu
Web Site: www.sandiego.edu

Description: Independent Roman Catholic, university, coed. Awards bachelor's, master's, and doctoral degrees. Founded 1949. Setting: 180-acre urban campus with easy access to San Diego. Endowment: $530 million. Research spending for the previous fiscal year: $5.1 million. Total enrollment: 9,073. Faculty: 998 (476 full-time, 522 part-time). Student-undergrad faculty ratio is 14:1. 13,287 applied, 53% were admitted. 33% from top 10% of their high school class, 69% from top quarter, 97% from top half. 19 valedictorians. Full-time: 5,678 students, 55% women, 45% men. Part-time: 177 students, 45% women, 55% men. Students come from 48 states and territories, 64 other countries, 56% from out-of-state. 0.3% American Indian or Alaska Native, non-Hispanic/Latino; 20% Hispanic/Latino; 4% Black or African American, non-Hispanic/Latino; 7% Asian, non-Hispanic/Latino; 0.3% Native Hawaiian or other Pacific Islander, non-Hispanic/Latino; 10% international. 5% 25 or older, 46% live on campus, 5% transferred in. Retention: 90% of full-time freshmen returned the following year. Academic areas with the most degrees conferred: business/marketing; biological/life sciences; engineering. Core. Calendar: 4-1-4. ESL program, services for LD students, advanced placement, honors program, independent study, double major, summer session for credit, part-time degree program, internships, graduate courses open to undergrads. Study abroad program. ROTC: Army (c), Naval, Air Force (c).

Entrance Requirements: Options: electronic application, deferred admission, international baccalaureate accepted. Required: essay, high school transcript, 1 recommendation, SAT or ACT. Entrance: very difficult. Application deadlines: 12/15, 12/15 for nonresidents. Notification: 2/20, continuous until 2/20 for nonresidents. SAT Reasoning Test deadline: 1/15. Transfer credits accepted: Yes. Applicants placed on waiting list: 2,205. Wait-listed applicants offered admission: 2.

Costs Per Year: Application fee: $55. Comprehensive fee: $65,312 includes full-time tuition ($50,450), mandatory fees ($736), and college room and board ($14,126). Part-time tuition: $1740 per credit. Part-time mandatory fees: $376 per year.

Collegiate Environment: Orientation program. Drama-theater group, choral group, marching band, student-run newspaper, radio station. Social organizations: 170 open to all; national fraternities, national sororities; 18% of eligible men and 29% of eligible women are members. Most popular organizations: American Marketing Association - USD Chapter, Student Vegans United, Be Blue - Go Green, Asian Student Organization, International Student Organization. Major annual events: Alcala Bazaar (clubs and organizations fair), Big Blue Bash/Homecoming Concert, Spring Ole Music Festival. Student services: legal services, health clinic, personal-psychological counseling, women's center. Campus security: 24-hour emergency response devices and patrols, late night transport-escort service, controlled dormitory access. College housing designed to accommodate 2,500 students; 2,675 undergraduates lived in college housing during 2018-19. Freshmen guaranteed college housing. On-campus residence required through sophomore year. Options: coed, men-only, women-only housing available. Helen K. and James S. Copley Library plus 1 other. Books: 455,753 (physical), 870,474 (digital/electronic); Serial titles: 10,446 (physical), 146,831 (digital/electronic); Databases: 391. Weekly public service hours: 116; students can reserve study rooms. Operations spending for the previous fiscal year: $8.2 million. 1,066 computers available on campus for general student use. Computer purchase/lease plans available. A campuswide network can be accessed from student residence rooms and from off campus. Students can access the following: online class registration. Staffed computer lab on campus provides training in use of computers, software, and the Internet.

Community Environment: Known for many reasons as"America's Finest City," San Diego has an almost perfect climate with warm, sunny days and cool evenings. Throughout the year, students can take advantage of San Diego's many outdoor recreational and cultural opportunities. The museums of Balboa Park, the Old Globe Theatre, the Zoo, Sea World, the beaches, the opera, and downtown San Diego and La Jolla are only minutes away. The rapidly developing economy of Greater San Diego provides varied employment opportunities for the USD graduate.

■ UNIVERSITY OF SAN FRANCISCO

2130 Fulton St.
San Francisco, CA 94117
Tel: (415)422-5555; Free: 800-CALL-USF
Fax: (415)422-2217
E-mail: admissions@usfca.edu
Web Site: www.usfca.edu

Description: Independent Roman Catholic (Jesuit), university, coed. Awards bachelor's, master's, and doctoral degrees and post-master's certificates. Founded 1855. Setting: 55-acre urban campus with easy access to San Francisco Bay Area. Endowment: $345.5 million. Research spending for the previous fiscal year: $2.7 million. Educational spending for the previous fiscal year: $16,898 per student. Total enrollment: 10,714. Faculty: 1,179 (488 full-time, 691 part-time). Student-undergrad faculty ratio is 14:1. 18,411 applied, 65% were admitted. 40% from top 10% of their high school class, 73% from top quarter, 95% from top half. Full-time: 6,435 students, 63% women, 37% men. Part-time: 269 students, 60% women, 40% men. Students come from 54 states and territories, 83 other countries, 17% from out-of-state. 0.2% American Indian or Alaska Native, non-Hispanic/Latino; 21% Hispanic/Latino; 4% Black or African American, non-Hispanic/Latino; 24% Asian, non-Hispanic/Latino; 0.6% Native Hawaiian or other Pacific Islander, non-Hispanic/Latino; 14% international. 7% 25 or older, 36% live on campus, 6% transferred in. Retention: 83% of full-time freshmen returned the following year. Academic areas with the most degrees conferred: business/marketing; health professions and related sciences; social sciences. Core. Calendar: 4-1-4. ESL program, services for LD students, advanced placement, accelerated degree program, self-designed majors, freshman honors college, honors program, independent study, distance learning, double major, summer session for credit, part-time degree program, external degree program, adult/continuing education programs, co-op programs and internships, graduate courses open to undergrads. Off campus study at American University. Study abroad program. ROTC: Army, Air Force (c).

Entrance Requirements: Options: electronic application, early admission, early decision, early action, deferred admission, international baccalaureate accepted. Required: essay, high school transcript, 1 recommendation, SAT or ACT. Recommended: minimum 2.5 high school GPA. Required for some: TOEFL, IELTS or PTE Academic if English is not the student's native language. Entrance: moderately difficult. Application deadlines: 1/15, 11/1 for early decision, 11/1 for early action. Notification: continuous until 3/15, 12/1 for early decision, 12/14 for early action. SAT Reasoning Test deadline: 1/15. Transfer credits accepted: Yes. Applicants placed on waiting list: 1,474. Waitlisted applicants offered admission: 2. Early decision applicants: 97. Early decision applicants admitted: 46. Early action applicants: 4,503. Early action applicants admitted: 3,215.

Costs Per Year: Application fee: $70. Comprehensive fee: $65,692 includes full-time tuition ($49,740), mandatory fees ($542), and college room and board ($15,410). College room only: $10,470. Part-time tuition: $1770 per credit hour. Part-time mandatory fees: $271 per term.

Collegiate Environment: Orientation program. Drama-theater group, choral group, marching band, student-run newspaper, radio station. Social organizations: 134 open to all; national fraternities, national sororities; 4% of eligible men and 9% of eligible women are members. Student services: health clinic, personal-psychological counseling, women's center. Campus security: 24-hour emergency response devices and patrols, student patrols, late night transport-escort service, controlled dormitory access. 2,600 college housing spaces available; 2,500 were occupied in 2018-19. Freshmen guaranteed college housing. On-campus residence required in freshman year. Options: coed, women-only housing available. Gleeson Libraryschke Center plus 1 other. Books: 580,130 (physical), 664,362 (digital/electronic); Serial titles: 7,960 (physical), 135,406 (digital/electronic); Databases: 348. Weekly public service hours: 136; study areas open 24 hours, 5-7 days a week; students can reserve study rooms. Operations spending for the previous fiscal year: $11 million. 257 computers available on campus for general student use. Computer purchase/lease plans available. A campuswide network can be accessed. Students can access the following: online class registration. Staffed computer lab on campus (open 24 hours a day) provides training in use of computers, software, and the Internet.

Community Environment: The University of San Francisco is located in the heart of one the world's most dynamic cities. San Francisco's diversity and geographical compactness afford opportunities for community involvement and employment experiences that few other cities can match.

■ UNIVERSITY OF SOUTHERN CALIFORNIA

University Park Campus
Los Angeles, CA 90089
Tel: (213)740-2311
Fax: (213)740-6364
E-mail: admitusc@usc.edu
Web Site: www.usc.edu

Description: Independent, university, coed. Awards bachelor's, master's, and doctoral degrees and post-master's certificates. Founded 1880. Setting: 229-acre urban campus with easy access to Los Angeles. Endowment: $4.6 billion. Total enrollment: 45,687. Faculty: 3,523 (2,133 full-time, 1,390 part-time). Student-undergrad faculty ratio is 8:1. 56,676 applied, 16% were admitted. 88% from top 10% of their high school class, 96% from top quarter, 100% from top half. 230 National Merit Scholars. Full-time: 18,631 students, 52% women, 48% men. Part-time: 539 students, 43% women, 57% men. Students come from 8 states and territories, 6 other countries, 35% from out-of-state. 0.1% American Indian or Alaska Native, non-Hispanic/Latino; 14% Hispanic/Latino; 5% Black or African American, non-Hispanic/Latino; 20% Asian, non-Hispanic/Latino; 0.2% Native Hawaiian or other Pacific Islander, non-Hispanic/Latino; 14% international. 4% 25 or older, 30% live on campus, 7% transferred in. Academic areas with the most degrees conferred: business/marketing; visual and performing arts; social sciences. Core. Calendar: semesters. ESL program, self-designed majors, honors program, independent study, distance learning, double major, summer session for credit, part-time degree program, external degree program, co-op programs and internships, graduate courses open to undergrads. Study abroad program. ROTC: Army, Naval, Air Force.

Entrance Requirements: Options: electronic application, deferred admission, international baccalaureate accepted. Required: essay, high school transcript, SAT or ACT. Entrance: most difficult. Application deadline: 1/15. Notification: 4/1, 4/1 for nonresidents. SAT Reasoning Test deadline: 2/20. SAT Subject Test deadline: 2/20. Transfer credits accepted: Yes.

Costs Per Year: Application fee: $85. One-time mandatory fee: $350. Comprehensive fee: $69,208 includes full-time tuition ($53,448), mandatory fees ($875), and college room and board ($14,885). College room only: $8985. Full-time tuition and fees vary according to program. Room and board charges vary according to board plan and housing facility. Part-time tuition: $1800 per credit hour. Part-time tuition varies according to course load and program.

Collegiate Environment: Orientation program. Drama-theater group, choral group, marching band, student-run newspaper, radio station. Social organizations: 850 open to all; national fraternities, national sororities, local fraternities, local sororities; 26% of eligible men and 27% of eligible women are members. Major annual events: CONQUEST, Springfest, Songfest. Student services: legal services, health clinic, personal-psychological counseling, women's center. Campus security: 24-hour emergency response devices and patrols, student patrols, late night transport-escort service, controlled dormitory access. Doheny Memorial Library plus 23 others.

Community Environment: Located in the heart of Los Angeles, USC exposes undergraduates to one of the world's great cosmopolitan centers. Students take advantage of this setting through internships with major corporations, new technology ventures, the entertainment industry, museums and galleries, non-profit organizations, and government agencies. Across the street from the campus in Exposition Park are museums, gardens, and the Memorial Coliseum. The nearby Figueroa Boulevard "Sports and Entertainment Corridor" includes the Shrine Auditorium, frequent host to the Grammy and Oscar events; the enormous Los Angeles Convention Center; the Staples Arena, which hosts the Lakers, Kings, and Clippers, and the 2000 Democratic Convention; and the Los Angeles Music Center, which offers world-class theatre, concerts, and opera. The campus is minutes away from the beaches of Santa Monica and Venice and also offers easy access to the hiking and bike trails of the Santa Monica Mountains. Local ski resorts are about a 90-minute drive from the campus.

■ **UNIVERSITY OF THE WEST**
1409 Walnut Grove Ave.
Rosemead, CA 91770
Tel: (626)571-8811
Fax: (626)571-1413
Web Site: www.uwest.edu
Description: Independent, comprehensive, coed. Awards bachelor's, master's, and doctoral degrees and post-master's certificates. Founded 1991. Setting: 10-acre suburban campus with easy access to Los Angeles, Pasadena, Long Beach. Research spending for the previous fiscal year: $13,307. Educational spending for the previous fiscal year: $6877 per student. Total enrollment: 358. Faculty: 55 (14 full-time, 41 part-time). Student-undergrad faculty ratio is 10:1. 235 applied, 85% were admitted. Full-time: 99 students, 56% women, 44% men. Part-time: 7 students, 43% women, 57% men. Students come from 5 states and territories, 10 other countries, 4% from out-of-state. 2% American Indian or Alaska Native, non-Hispanic/Latino; 45% Hispanic/Latino; 0.9% Black or African American, non-Hispanic/Latino; 8% Asian, non-Hispanic/Latino; 37% international. 1% 25 or older, 36% live on campus, 15% transferred in. Retention: 83% of full-time freshmen returned the following year. Core. Calendar: semesters. Academic remediation for entering students, ESL program, accelerated degree program, independent study, double major, summer session for credit, part-time degree program, adult/continuing education programs, co-op programs and internships, graduate courses open to undergrads.
Entrance Requirements: Options: electronic application, deferred admission, international baccalaureate accepted. Required: essay, high school transcript, minimum 2 high school GPA, 3 recommendations. Required for some: interview. Entrance: minimally difficult. Application deadline: 6/15. Notification: 7/15, 7/15 for nonresidents. Transfer credits accepted: Yes.
Costs Per Year: Application fee: $50. Comprehensive fee: $22,524 includes full-time tuition ($14,490), mandatory fees ($950), and college room and board ($7084). College room only: $4364. Full-time tuition and fees vary according to course load, degree level, and program. Room and board charges vary according to board plan. Part-time tuition: $483 per credit hour. Part-time mandatory fees: $390 per term. Part-time tuition and fees vary according to course load, degree level, and program.
Collegiate Environment: Orientation program. Social organizations: 10 open to all. Most popular organizations: Buddhawest Club, Music Club, Explorer Club, Badminton Club, Chaplaincy Club. Major annual events: Opening BBQ, Christmas Holiday Celebration. Student services: personal-psychological counseling. Campus security: 24-hour emergency response devices and patrols, controlled dormitory access. University of the West Library plus 1 other. Students can reserve study rooms. Operations spending for the previous fiscal year: $221,667. 501 computers available on campus for general student use. A campuswide network can be accessed from student residence rooms. Students can access the following: online class registration. Staffed computer lab on campus (open 24 hours a day) provides training in use of software.

■ **VALLEY COLLEGE OF MEDICAL CAREERS**
8399 Topanga Canyon Blvd.
Ste. 200
West Hills, CA 91304
Tel: (818)883-9002
Web Site: www.vcmc.edu
Description: Proprietary, 2-year, coed. Awards certificates, transfer associate, and terminal associate degrees.

■ **VANGUARD UNIVERSITY OF SOUTHERN CALIFORNIA**
55 Fair Dr.
Costa Mesa, CA 92626

Tel: (714)556-3610; Free: 800-722-6279
Fax: (714)966-5460
E-mail: admissions@vanguard.edu
Web Site: www.vanguard.edu
Description: Independent, comprehensive, coed, affiliated with Assemblies of God. Awards associate, bachelor's, and master's degrees. Founded 1920. Setting: 38-acre suburban campus with easy access to Los Angeles. Total enrollment: 2,169. Faculty: 240 (69 full-time, 171 part-time). Student-undergrad faculty ratio is 14:1. 4,414 applied, 40% were admitted. 13% from top 10% of their high school class, 41% from top quarter, 78% from top half. Full-time: 1,588 students, 68% women, 32% men. Part-time: 260 students, 63% women, 37% men. 10% from out-of-state. 0.3% American Indian or Alaska Native, non-Hispanic/Latino; 42% Hispanic/Latino; 5% Black or African American, non-Hispanic/Latino; 4% Asian, non-Hispanic/Latino; 1% Native Hawaiian or other Pacific Islander, non-Hispanic/Latino; 2% international. 16% 25 or older, 50% live on campus, 5% transferred in. Retention: 75% of full-time freshmen returned the following year. Academic areas with the most degrees conferred: business/marketing; psychology; health professions and related sciences; parks and recreation. Core. Calendar: semesters. Services for LD students, advanced placement, accelerated degree program, independent study, distance learning, double major, summer session for credit, part-time degree program, adult/continuing education programs, internships, graduate courses open to undergrads. Off campus study at Council for Christian Colleges and Universities: Los Angeles Film Studies Center (LAFSC), American Studies Program (ASP), Washington Journalism Center (WJC). Study abroad program. ROTC: Army (c), Air Force (c).
Entrance Requirements: Options: electronic application, early admission, early action, deferred admission, international baccalaureate accepted. Required: essay, high school transcript, minimum 2.8 high school GPA, 2 recommendations, SAT or ACT. Required for some: interview. Entrance: moderately difficult. Notification: 5/1. Preference given to Christians. SAT Reasoning Test deadline: 8/1.
Costs Per Year: Application fee: $45. Comprehensive fee: $45,050 includes full-time tuition ($34,500), mandatory fees ($600), and college room and board ($9950). College room only: $6000.
Collegiate Environment: Orientation program. Drama-theater group, choral group, student-run newspaper. Most popular organizations: local outreach, Global Missions, student organizations/clubs, choral groups. Major annual events: Harvest Party, All-School Party, Mr. VU. Student services: health clinic, personal-psychological counseling, women's center. Campus security: 24-hour emergency response devices and patrols, student patrols, late night transport-escort service, controlled dormitory access. Freshmen guaranteed college housing. Options: coed, men-only, women-only housing available. O. Cope Budge Library. Students can reserve study rooms. 100 computers available on campus for general student use. A campuswide network can be accessed. Students can access the following: online class registration. Staffed computer lab on campus.
Community Environment: The college is adjacent to Newport Beach, the pleasure boat harbor of the West. See Orange Coast College.

■ **VENTURA COLLEGE**
4667 Telegraph Rd.
Ventura, CA 93003-3899
Tel: (805)654-6400
Fax: (805)654-6466
E-mail: sbricker@vcccd.net
Web Site: www.venturacollege.edu
Description: District-supported, 2-year, coed. Part of California Community College System. Awards certificates, diplomas, transfer associate, and terminal associate degrees. Founded 1925. Setting: 103-acre suburban campus with easy access to Los Angeles. Total enrollment: 13,551. Faculty: 522 (136 full-time, 386 part-time). Student-undergrad faculty ratio is 26:1. 2,652 applied. 11% from out-of-state. Core. Calendar: semesters. Academic remediation for entering students, ESL program, services for LD students, advanced placement, independent study, summer session for credit, part-time degree program, adult/continuing education programs, internships.
Entrance Requirements: Open admission. Required: high school transcript. Entrance: noncompetitive. Application deadline: rolling. Notification: continuous.
Collegiate Environment: Orientation program. Drama-theater group, choral group, student-run newspaper. Most popular organizations: Pan American Student Union, MECHA, Automotive Technology Club, Campus Christian Fellowship, Asian-American Club. Major annual events: ASB Welcome

Barbecue, Cinco de Mayo, Native American International Pow Wow. Student services: health clinic, personal-psychological counseling, women's center. Campus security: 24-hour emergency response devices and patrols, student patrols. Ventura College Library. 500 computers available on campus for general student use. Students can access the following: online class registration. Staffed computer lab on campus.

Community Environment: Ventura is the county seat of Ventura County as well as one of the oldest settlements on the coast. The climate is pleasant and smog-free all year with rain during a few months in the winter and spring. The city is located in the South Central Coast Region, 63 miles northwest of Los Angeles and is served by the Southern Pacific Railroad, Greyhound Bus Lines, and various airlines. Community facilities include hospitals, libraries, churches, and many civic and service organizations. Other facilities include recreation centers, a golf course, and the county fair grounds. An extensive ocean coastline, forest reserves, and mountains all combine to make the area ideal for outdoor recreation.

■ **VICTOR VALLEY COLLEGE**
18422 Bear Valley Rd.
Victorville, CA 92395
Tel: (760)245-4271
Fax: (760)245-9745
E-mail: moong@vvc.edu
Web Site: www.vvc.edu
Description: District-supported, 2-year, coed. Part of California Community College System. Awards certificates, diplomas, transfer associate, and terminal associate degrees. Founded 1961. Setting: 253-acre small town campus with easy access to Los Angeles. Student-undergrad faculty ratio is 26:1. 3% from out-of-state. 31% 25 or older. Retention: 61% of full-time freshmen returned the following year. Academic areas with the most degrees conferred: homeland security, law enforcement, firefighting, and protective services; liberal arts/general studies; health professions and related sciences. Core. Calendar: semesters. Academic remediation for entering students, ESL program, services for LD students, advanced placement, accelerated degree program, honors program, independent study, distance learning, double major, summer session for credit, part-time degree program, co-op programs and internships. Off campus study. Study abroad program.
Entrance Requirements: Open admission except for allied health programs. Entrance: noncompetitive. Application deadline: rolling. Notification: continuous.
Collegiate Environment: Orientation program. Drama-theater group, choral group, student-run newspaper. Most popular organizations: Black Student Union, Drama Club, Rugby, Phi Theta Kappa. Major annual events: Back to School BBQ, MLK Day, Cinco de Mayo. Student services: health clinic, personal-psychological counseling. Campus security: 24-hour emergency response devices and patrols, late night transport-escort service, part-time trained security personnel. Learning Resource Center.
Community Environment: Victorville is a suburban area with a dry temperate climate. Amtrak, Santa Fe and Union Pacific Railroads, and Greyhound bus lines serve the area. The town has a library, churches of major denominations, hospitals, major civic organizations, and shopping facilities. Part-time employment opportunities are good. Victorville is the distributing point for an irrigated agricultural area. The San Bernardino County Fair is held here each year around Labor Day.

■ **WEST COAST ULTRASOUND INSTITUTE**
291 S La Cienega Blvd.
Ste. 500
Beverly Hills, CA 90211
Tel: (310)289-5123
Web Site: wcui.edu
Description: Proprietary, primarily 2-year, coed. Awards diplomas, transfer associate, terminal associate, and bachelor's degrees. Calendar: quarters.

■ **WEST COAST UNIVERSITY (ANAHEIM)**
1477 S Manchester Ave.
Anaheim, CA 92802
Tel: (714)782-1700
Web Site: westcoastuniversity.edu
Description: Proprietary, 4-year, coed. Awards bachelor's degrees. Calendar: semesters.

■ **WEST COAST UNIVERSITY (NORTH HOLLYWOOD)**
12215 Victory Blvd.
North Hollywood, CA 91606

Tel: (323)315-5207; Free: 866-508-2684
Web Site: www.westcoastuniversity.edu
Description: Proprietary, comprehensive, coed. Awards bachelor's and master's degrees. Founded 1909. Total enrollment: 1,792. 24 applied, 83% were admitted. 69% 25 or older.

■ **WEST COAST UNIVERSITY (ONTARIO)**
2855 E Guasti Rd.
Ontario, CA 91761
Tel: (909)467-6100
Web Site: westcoastuniversity.edu
Description: Proprietary, 4-year, coed. Awards bachelor's degrees. Calendar: semesters.

■ **WEST HILLS COLLEGE COALINGA**
300 Cherry Ln.
Coalinga, CA 93210-1399
Tel: (559)934-2000; Free: 800-266-1114
Fax: (559)934-1511
E-mail: sandradagnino@westhillscollege.com
Web Site: www.westhillscollege.com
Description: District-supported, 2-year, coed. Part of California Community College System. Awards certificates, diplomas, transfer associate, and terminal associate degrees. Founded 1932. Setting: 193-acre small town campus. Total enrollment: 2,965. Student-undergrad faculty ratio is 24:1. 35% 25 or older. Core. Calendar: semesters. Academic remediation for entering students, ESL program, services for LD students, advanced placement, independent study, distance learning, summer session for credit, part-time degree program, adult/continuing education programs, co-op programs. Off campus study at Central California Consortium. Study abroad program.
Entrance Requirements: Open admission. Option: early admission. Recommended: high school transcript. Entrance: noncompetitive. Application deadline: rolling. Notification: continuous. Preference given to district residents.
Collegiate Environment: Orientation program. Drama-theater group. Student services: personal-psychological counseling. West Hills Community College Library.

■ **WEST HILLS COLLEGE LEMOORE**
555 College Ave.
Lemoore, CA 93245
Tel: (559)925-3000
Web Site: www.westhillscollege.com
Description: District-supported, 2-year, coed. Awards certificates, transfer associate, and terminal associate degrees.

■ **WEST LOS ANGELES COLLEGE**
9000 Overland Ave.
Culver City, CA 90230-3519
Tel: (310)287-4200
Fax: (310)841-0396
Web Site: www.lacolleges.net
Description: District-supported, 2-year, coed. Part of Los Angeles Community College District System. Awards transfer associate and terminal associate degrees. Founded 1969. Setting: 69-acre urban campus with easy access to Los Angeles. Total enrollment: 11,866. 50% 25 or older. Retention: 61% of full-time freshmen returned the following year. Core. Calendar: semesters. Academic remediation for entering students, ESL program, services for LD students, advanced placement, honors program, summer session for credit, part-time degree program, adult/continuing education programs, co-op programs. ROTC: Army (c), Air Force (c).
Entrance Requirements: Open admission. Option: early admission. Recommended: high school transcript. Entrance: noncompetitive. Application deadline: 8/16.
Collegiate Environment: Choral group. Student services: health clinic, personal-psychological counseling. Campus security: 24-hour patrols.
Community Environment: Culver City is an industrial and residential city located near Los Angeles. The world's largest motion picture studio, Metro-Goldwyn-Mayer, was located here, as well as the Desilu Studios. All forms of transportation serve the area; Los Angeles International Airport is near. Churches of all major denominations are in the area; there are excellent shopping facilities available.

■ **WEST VALLEY COLLEGE**
14000 Fruitvale Ave.
Saratoga, CA 95070-5698
Tel: (408)867-2200
Fax: (408)867-5033
E-mail: barbara_ogilvie@westvalley.edu
Web Site: www.westvalley.edu
Description: District-supported, 2-year, coed. Part of California Community College System. Awards certificates, transfer associate, and terminal associate degrees. Founded 1963. Setting: 143-acre small town campus with easy access to San Francisco, San Jose. Total enrollment: 12,893. Student-undergrad faculty ratio is 28:1. 46% 25 or older. Retention: 75% of full-time freshmen returned the following year. Core. Calendar: semesters. Academic remediation for entering students, ESL program, services for LD students, honors program, summer session for credit, part-time degree program, adult/continuing education programs, co-op programs and internships. ROTC: Army (c), Air Force (c).
Entrance Requirements: Open admission. Option: early admission. Entrance: noncompetitive. Application deadline: rolling. Notification: continuous. Preference given to district residents.
Collegiate Environment: Orientation program. Drama-theater group, student-run newspaper. Student services: health clinic, personal-psychological counseling. West Valley College Library.
Community Environment: See San Jose State University.

■ **WESTCLIFF UNIVERSITY**
16715 Von Karman Ave.
Irvine, CA 92606
Description: Proprietary, comprehensive, coed.

■ **WESTMONT COLLEGE**
955 La Paz Rd.
Santa Barbara, CA 93108-1099
Tel: (805)565-6000; Free: 800-777-9011
Fax: (805)565-6234
Web Site: www.westmont.edu
Description: Independent nondenominational, 4-year, coed. Awards bachelor's degrees. Founded 1937. Setting: 111-acre suburban campus with easy access to Los Angeles. Endowment: $84 million. Research spending for the previous fiscal year: $238,446. Educational spending for the previous fiscal year: $16,973 per student. Total enrollment: 1,277. Faculty: 154 (96 full-time, 58 part-time). Student-undergrad faculty ratio is 11:1. 2,937 applied, 62% were admitted. 28% from top 10% of their high school class, 63% from top quarter, 89% from top half. Full-time: 1,266 students, 61% women, 39% men. Part-time: 11 students, 73% women, 27% men. Students come from 41 states and territories, 20 other countries, 27% from out-of-state. 0.2% American Indian or Alaska Native, non-Hispanic/Latino; 18% Hispanic/Latino; 2% Black or African American, non-Hispanic/Latino; 8% Asian, non-Hispanic/Latino; 0.6% Native Hawaiian or other Pacific Islander, non-Hispanic/Latino; 2% international. 2% 25 or older, 95% live on campus, 4% transferred in. Retention: 82% of full-time freshmen returned the following year. Academic areas with the most degrees conferred: business/marketing; parks and recreation; biological/life sciences. Core. Calendar: semesters. Academic remediation for entering students, services for LD students, advanced placement, accelerated degree program, self-designed majors, honors program, double major, summer session for credit, internships. Off campus study at Christian College Consortium (12 other liberal arts institutions), Council of Christian Colleges & Universities (made up of 180 worldwide institutions—with 10 semester study abroad programs—'bestsemseter.com') American University, Trinity Christian College, Calvin College, Eastern University, IAU, CIEE Paris, IES Vienna, USAC, Organization for Tropical Studies, Brethren Colleges Abroad, NYU, Christians for Environmental Stewardship. Study abroad program. ROTC: Army (c), Air Force (c).
Entrance Requirements: Options: electronic application, early action, international baccalaureate accepted. Required: essay, high school transcript, 1 recommendation, SAT or ACT. Recommended: interview. Required for some: interview. Entrance: moderately difficult. Application deadlines: rolling, 11/15 for early action. Notification: continuous, 12/1 for early action. Transfer credits accepted: Yes. Applicants placed on waiting list: 0. Wait-listed applicants offered admission: 0. Early action applicants: 1,641. Early action applicants admitted: 1,120.
Costs Per Year: Application fee: $0. Comprehensive fee: $61,240 includes

full-time tuition ($45,410), mandatory fees ($1184), and college room and board ($14,646). College room only: $8996. Part-time tuition: $2120 per unit.
Collegiate Environment: Orientation program. Drama-theater group, choral group, student-run newspaper. Social organizations: 62 open to all. Most popular organizations: Student Ministries, Student Government, Competitive Athletics, Music, Art and Theater ensembles, Intramural Sports. Major annual events: Potter's Clay (service project to Mexico), Spring Sing (campus-wide talent competition), Fall/Spring Formal Dances. Student services: health clinic, personal-psychological counseling, women's center. Campus security: 24-hour emergency response devices and patrols, late night transport-escort service, controlled dormitory access. 1,137 college housing spaces available; 1,075 were occupied in 2018-19. Freshmen guaranteed college housing. On-campus residence required through senior year. Option: coed housing available. Roger John Voskuyl Library. Books: 129,978 (physical), 186,115 (digital/electronic); Serial titles: 418 (physical), 70,790 (digital/electronic); Databases: 68. Weekly public service hours: 102; study areas open 24 hours, 5-7 days a week; students can reserve study rooms. Operations spending for the previous fiscal year: $1 million. 100 computers available on campus for general student use. A campuswide network can be accessed. Students can access the following: online class registration. Staffed computer lab on campus provides training in use of computers, software, and the Internet.
Community Environment: See University of California - Santa Barbara.

■ **WHITTIER COLLEGE**
13406 E Philadelphia St.
Whittier, CA 90608-0634
Tel: (562)907-4200
Fax: (562)907-4870
E-mail: admission@whittier.edu
Web Site: www.whittier.edu
Description: Independent, comprehensive, coed. Awards bachelor's, master's, and doctoral degrees. Founded 1887. Setting: 95-acre suburban campus with easy access to Los Angeles. Endowment: $117 million. Research spending for the previous fiscal year: $1.5 million. Educational spending for the previous fiscal year: $14,732 per student. Total enrollment: 1,784. Faculty: 162 (117 full-time, 45 part-time). Student-undergrad faculty ratio is 12:1. 6,220 applied, 76% were admitted. 18% from top 10% of their high school class, 34% from top quarter, 93% from top half. Full-time: 1,699 students, 58% women, 42% men. Part-time: 33 students, 64% women, 36% men. Students come from 33 states and territories, 27 other countries, 23% from out-of-state. 0.5% American Indian or Alaska Native, non-Hispanic/Latino; 51% Hispanic/Latino; 5% Black or African American, non-Hispanic/Latino; 7% Asian, non-Hispanic/Latino; 0.3% Native Hawaiian or other Pacific Islander, non-Hispanic/Latino; 3% international. 0.5% 25 or older, 45% live on campus, 5% transferred in. Retention: 76% of full-time freshmen returned the following year. Academic areas with the most degrees conferred: social sciences; business/marketing; parks and recreation. Core. Calendar: 4-1-4. Academic remediation for entering students, services for LD students, advanced placement, accelerated degree program, self-designed majors, independent study, distance learning, double major, summer session for credit, adult/continuing education programs, internships, graduate courses open to undergrads. Off campus study. Study abroad program. ROTC: Army (c).
Entrance Requirements: Options: electronic application, early action, deferred admission, international baccalaureate accepted. Required: essay, high school transcript, minimum 2.5 high school GPA, 2 recommendations. Recommended: minimum 2.5 high school GPA, interview, SAT Subject Tests. Required for some: minimum 3 high school GPA, SAT or ACT. Entrance: moderately difficult. Application deadlines: rolling, rolling for nonresidents, 11/15 for early action. Notification: continuous, continuous for nonresidents. Transfer credits accepted: Yes. Early action applicants: 1,296. Early action applicants admitted: 972.
Costs Per Year: Application fee: $50. Comprehensive fee: $61,856 includes full-time tuition ($47,496), mandatory fees ($390), and college room and board ($13,970). College room only: $7666. Full-time tuition and fees vary according to course load. Room and board charges vary according to board plan. Part-time tuition: $1979 per semester hour. Part-time tuition varies according to course load.
Collegiate Environment: Orientation program. Drama-theater group, choral group, student-run newspaper, radio station. Social organizations: 70 open to all; Societies (gender-specific and coed); 9% of eligible men and 14% of eligible women are members. Most popular organizations: Hispanic Students Association, Hawaiian Islander Club, Black Student Union, Asian Students

Association, Environment & Sustainability - Raising Awareness for the Environment / Urban Agriculture / Food Recovery Network. Major annual events: Spring Sing, Sportsfest, Homecoming. Student services: health clinic, personal-psychological counseling. Campus security: 24-hour emergency response devices and patrols, late night transport-escort service, controlled dormitory access. 831 college housing spaces available Free: 800 were occupied in 2018-19. Freshmen guaranteed college housing. On-campus residence required through junior year. Option: coed housing available. Bonnie Bell Wardman Library plus 1 other. Books: 180,054 (physical), 178,258 (digital/electronic); Serial titles: 2,730 (physical), 222,633 (digital/electronic); Databases: 67. Study areas open 24 hours, 5-7 days a week; students can reserve study rooms. 175 computers available on campus for general student use. Computer purchase/lease plans available. A campuswide network can be accessed from student residence rooms and from off campus. Students can access the following: online class registration. Staffed computer lab on campus.

Community Environment: Whittier enjoys a beautiful setting at the foot of the Puente Hills, in a suburban area in southeast Los Angeles County. The climate is pleasant with a minimum temperature of 53 degrees, a maximum temperature of 73 degrees, and an average rainfall of 15 inches. Buses and railroads serve the area with connection to the Los Angeles International Airport via helicopter, and to the metropolitan area via the freeway system. Modern shopping facilities are available in addition to many manufacturing plants. Recreational facilities include parks, theaters, nearby Disneyland, beaches, and mountains less than one hour away. The Whittier College School of Law is the only ABA accredited Law School in Orange County, California.

■ WILLIAM JESSUP UNIVERSITY

2121 University Ave.
Rocklin, CA 95765
Tel: (916)577-2200
Fax: (916)577-1813
E-mail: admissions@jessup.edu
Web Site: www.jessup.edu

Description: Independent nondenominational, comprehensive, coed. Awards associate, bachelor's, and master's degrees. Founded 1939. Setting: 126-acre suburban campus with easy access to Sacramento. Research spending for the previous fiscal year: $100,000. Educational spending for the previous fiscal year: $22,626 per student. Total enrollment: 1,161. Faculty: 200 (38 full-time, 162 part-time). Student-undergrad faculty ratio is 11:1. 522 applied, 76% were admitted. 19% from top 10% of their high school class, 43% from top quarter, 76% from top half. Full-time: 906 students, 58% women, 42% men. Part-time: 191 students, 58% women, 42% men. Students come from 15 states and territories, 3 other countries, 5% from out-of-state. 0.8% American Indian or Alaska Native, non-Hispanic/Latino; 19% Hispanic/Latino; 5% Black or African American, non-Hispanic/Latino; 4% Asian, non-Hispanic/Latino; 0.5% Native Hawaiian or other Pacific Islander, non-Hispanic/Latino; 0.3% international. 9% 25 or older, 46% live on campus, 12% transferred in. Retention: 79% of full-time freshmen returned the following year. Academic areas with the most degrees conferred: psychology; theology and religious vocations; business/marketing. Core. Calendar: semesters. Services for LD students, advanced placement, accelerated degree program, independent study, distance learning, double major, summer session for credit, part-time degree program, adult/continuing education programs, internships. Off campus study at Council for Christian Colleges and Universities. Study abroad program. ROTC: Air Force (c).

Entrance Requirements: Options: electronic application, international baccalaureate accepted. Required: essay, high school transcript, minimum 2 high school GPA, SAT or ACT. Recommended: 1 recommendation, interview. Required for some: 1 recommendation, interview. Entrance: moderately difficult. Application deadline: 8/15. Notification: continuous. SAT Reasoning Test deadline: 8/15. Transfer credits accepted: Yes.

Costs Per Year: Application fee: $45. One-time mandatory fee: $75. Comprehensive fee: $44,870 includes full-time tuition ($32,950), mandatory fees ($600), and college room and board ($11,320). College room only: $5800. Full-time tuition and fees vary according to course load. Room and board charges vary according to board plan and housing facility. Part-time tuition: $1390 per unit. Part-time tuition varies according to course load.

Collegiate Environment: Orientation program. Drama-theater group, choral group. Major annual events: Humans vs. Zombies, Fall Week of Welcome, Air Band Competition. Student services: personal-psychological counseling.

Campus security: 24-hour patrols, student patrols, late night transport-escort service, controlled dormitory access, day and evening patrols by trained security personnel. Paul Nystrom Library plus 1 other. Operations spending for the previous fiscal year: $754,000. 55 computers available on campus for general student use. A campuswide network can be accessed from student residence rooms and from off campus. Students can access the following: online class registration. Staffed computer lab on campus provides training in use of computers, software, and the Internet.

Community Environment: See San Jose State University.

■ WOODBURY UNIVERSITY

7500 N Glenoaks Blvd.
Burbank, CA 91504-1052
Tel: (818)767-0888; Free: 800-784-WOOD
Fax: (818)504-9320
Web Site: www.woodbury.edu

Description: Independent, comprehensive, coed. Awards bachelor's and master's degrees. Founded 1884. Setting: 22-acre suburban campus with easy access to Los Angeles. Total enrollment: 1,173. Faculty: 217 (64 full-time, 153 part-time). Student-undergrad faculty ratio is 9:1. 2,120 applied, 66% were admitted. Full-time: 993 students, 52% women, 48% men. Part-time: 66 students, 47% women, 53% men. 15% from out-of-state. 0.1% American Indian or Alaska Native, non-Hispanic/Latino; 35% Hispanic/Latino; 3% Black or African American, non-Hispanic/Latino; 9% Asian, non-Hispanic/Latino; 0.4% Native Hawaiian or other Pacific Islander, non-Hispanic/Latino; 15% international. 25% 25 or older, 21% live on campus, 15% transferred in. Retention: 77% of full-time freshmen returned the following year. Academic areas with the most degrees conferred: business/marketing; architecture; visual and performing arts. Core. Calendar: semesters. Academic remediation for entering students, services for LD students, advanced placement, self-designed majors, independent study, double major, summer session for credit, part-time degree program, internships. Study abroad program.

Entrance Requirements: Options: electronic application, deferred admission, international baccalaureate accepted. Required: high school transcript, minimum 2.5 high school GPA. Recommended: essay, 1 recommendation. Entrance: moderately difficult. Application deadline: rolling. Notification: continuous. SAT Reasoning Test deadline: 3/1. Transfer credits accepted: Yes.

Costs Per Year: Application fee: $75. Comprehensive fee: $53,250 includes full-time tuition ($39,712), mandatory fees ($1470), and college room and board ($12,068). College room only: $7508. Part-time tuition: $1293 per credit hour. Part-time mandatory fees: $1293 per credit, $735 per term.

Collegiate Environment: Orientation program. Social organizations: national fraternities, national sororities, local fraternities. Student services: health clinic, personal-psychological counseling. Campus security: 24-hour patrols, late night transport-escort service, controlled dormitory access. 224 college housing spaces available. Freshmen given priority for college housing. Option: coed housing available. Los Angeles Times Library. Books: 57,193 (physical), 80,142 (digital/electronic); Serial titles: 322 (physical), 53,689 (digital/electronic); Databases: 44.

Community Environment: Southern California is famous for the variety of terrain it offers and the array of activities available to its residents. Valleys, mountains, beaches, and deserts enable Woodbury students to escape to practically any climate they wish. Woodbury is surrounded by a residential neighborhood in a city known as the heart of the entertainment industry. Students are just minutes away from the many benefits of southern California: historical and cultural events and museums, world-class entertainment, professional sporting events, and vast beaches, deserts, mountains, and valleys for recreational leisure.

■ WOODLAND COMMUNITY COLLEGE

2300 E Gibson Rd.
Woodland, CA 95776
Tel: (530)661-5700
Web Site: wcc.yccd.edu

Description: District-supported, 2-year, coed. Awards transfer associate degrees. Total enrollment: 3,188. 39% 25 or older.

■ WORLD MISSION UNIVERSITY

500 Shatto Pl.
Ste. 600
Los Angeles, CA 90020
Tel: (213)385-2322

Web Site: www.wmu.edu

Description: Independent, comprehensive, coed, affiliated with Evangelical Christian Church. Awards bachelor's and master's degrees.

■ **YESHIVA OHR ELCHONON CHABAD/WEST COAST TALMUDICAL SEMINARY**
7215 Waring Ave.
Los Angeles, CA 90046-7660
Tel: (213)937-3763
Web Site: www.yoec.edu

Description: Independent Jewish, 4-year, men only. Awards bachelor's degrees. Founded 1953. Setting: 4-acre urban campus. Total enrollment: 135. 68 applied, 100% were admitted. Core. Calendar: semesters. Academic remediation for entering students, honors program, summer session for credit, adult/continuing education programs, internships. Off campus study at Central Yeshiva Tomchei Tmimim-Lubavitch, Rabbinical College of America, Talmudical Seminary Oholei Torah.

Entrance Requirements: Options: early admission, deferred admission. Required: high school transcript, minimum 2.0 high school GPA, interview, oral examination. Entrance: moderately difficult. Application deadline: rolling. Notification: continuous. Preference given to applicants with religious commitment.

Collegiate Environment: Student services: personal-psychological counseling. Campus security: 24-hour emergency response devices, student patrols. Yeshiva Ohr Elchonon Chabad Library plus 3 others.

■ **YUBA COLLEGE**
2088 N Beale Rd.
Marysville, CA 95901-7699
Tel: (530)741-6700
Fax: (530)741-3541

Web Site: yc.yccd.edu

Description: District-supported, 2-year, coed. Part of California Community College System. Awards certificates and transfer associate degrees. Founded 1927. Setting: 160-acre rural campus with easy access to Sacramento. Total enrollment: 8,564. Student-undergrad faculty ratio is 29:1. 45% 25 or older. Retention: 63% of full-time freshmen returned the following year. Core. Calendar: semesters. Academic remediation for entering students, ESL program, services for LD students, advanced placement, distance learning, double major, summer session for credit, part-time degree program.

Entrance Requirements: Open admission. Option: electronic application. Required: high school transcript. Entrance: noncompetitive. Application deadline: rolling.

Collegiate Environment: Orientation program. Drama-theater group, choral group. Student services: health clinic, personal-psychological counseling, women's center. Campus security: 24-hour patrols, student patrols. Learning Resource Center and Library.

Community Environment: Marysville is 50 miles north of Sacramento, has a moderate climate, and is the center of a rich agricultural area. Amtrak serves the area. The city has a hospital, churches, shopping center, and civic organizations. Excellent boating, hunting and fishing facilities are available.

■ **ZAYTUNA COLLEGE**
2401 Le Conte Ave.
Berkeley, CA 94709
Tel: (510)356-4760
Fax: (510)327-2688
E-mail: admissions@zaytuna.org
Web Site: www.zaytuna.edu

Description: Independent, 4-year, coed, affiliated with Muslim faith. Awards bachelor's degrees.

ADAMS STATE UNIVERSITY

208 Edgemont Blvd.
Alamosa, CO 81101
Tel: (719)587-7011; Free: 800-824-6494
Fax: (719)587-7522
Web Site: www.adams.edu
Description: State-supported, comprehensive, coed. Awards associate, bachelor's, master's, and doctoral degrees. Founded 1921. Setting: 90-acre small town campus with easy access to Pueblo. Endowment: $64,882. Research spending for the previous fiscal year: $76. Educational spending for the previous fiscal year: $5189 per student. Total enrollment: 3,086. Faculty: 221 (98 full-time, 123 part-time). Student-undergrad faculty ratio is 15:1. 1,698 applied, 99% were admitted. 7% from top 10% of their high school class, 26% from top quarter, 56% from top half. Full-time: 1,481 students, 47% women, 53% men. Part-time: 510 students, 36% women, 64% men. 39% from out-of-state. 1% American Indian or Alaska Native, non-Hispanic/Latino; 35% Hispanic/Latino; 8% Black or African American, non-Hispanic/Latino; 0.7% Asian, non-Hispanic/Latino; 0.5% Native Hawaiian or other Pacific Islander, non-Hispanic/Latino; 0.6% international. 27% 25 or older, 45% live on campus, 12% transferred in. Retention: 54% of full-time freshmen returned the following year. Academic areas with the most degrees conferred: business/marketing; liberal arts/general studies; parks and recreation; social sciences. Core. Calendar: semesters. Academic remediation for entering students, services for LD students, advanced placement, accelerated degree program, self-designed majors, independent study, distance learning, double major, summer session for credit, part-time degree program, external degree program, adult/continuing education programs, co-op programs and internships, graduate courses open to undergrads. Off campus study at members of the Consortium of State Colleges in Colorado, National Student Exchange. Study abroad program.
Entrance Requirements: Options: electronic application, early admission, deferred admission, international baccalaureate accepted. Required: high school transcript, minimum 2 high school GPA, SAT. Recommended: ACT, SAT or ACT. Required for some: essay, audition for music majors, portfolio for art majors. Entrance: moderately difficult. Application deadline: rolling. Notification: continuous. SAT Reasoning Test deadline: 8/1. Transfer credits accepted: Yes.
Costs Per Year: Application fee: $30. State resident tuition: $5736 full-time, $239 per credit hour part-time. Nonresident tuition: $16,752 full-time, $698 per credit hour part-time. Mandatory fees: $3,704 full-time, $151.19 per credit hour part-time. Full-time tuition and fees vary according to course load and location. Part-time tuition and fees vary according to course load and location. College room and board: $8782. College room only: $4222. Room and board charges vary according to board plan and housing facility. Tuition guaranteed not to increase for student's term of enrollment.
Collegiate Environment: Orientation program. Drama-theater group, choral group, marching band, student-run newspaper, radio station. Social organizations: 40 open to all. Most popular organizations: Student Programming Board, Student government, Semillas de la Tierra, Newman Club, Fellowship of Christian Athletes. Major annual events: Homecoming, Martin Luther King Week, ASU Cares Days. Student services: personal-psychological counseling. Campus security: 24-hour emergency response devices and patrols, student patrols, late night transport-escort service, controlled dormitory access. Freshmen guaranteed college housing. On-campus residence required through sophomore year. Options: coed, men-only, women-only housing available. Nielsen Library. Books: 252 (physical),

891 (digital/electronic); Serial titles: 102 (physical), 372 (digital/electronic); Databases: 60. Weekly public service hours: 84. Operations spending for the previous fiscal year: $788,184. 322 computers available on campus for general student use. A campuswide network can be accessed from student residence rooms and from off campus. Students can access the following: online class registration. Staffed computer lab on campus (open 24 hours a day) provides training in use of computers, software, and the Internet.
Community Environment: Located in the center of San Luis Valley, an extensive grazing and farming area larger than the state of Connecticut, Alamosa is completely surrounded by mountain ranges. It has an ideal climate, with an average yearly temperature of 65 degrees. A commuter airline and a bus line serve the area. Alamosa has churches, radio stations, libraries, hotels and motels, a hospital and a number of civic, social, cultural, fraternal and veterans organizations.

AIMS COMMUNITY COLLEGE

Box 69
5401 W 20th St.
Greeley, CO 80632-0069
Tel: (970)330-8008
E-mail: wgreen@chiron.aims.edu
Web Site: www.aims.edu
Description: District-supported, 2-year, coed. Awards certificates, diplomas, transfer associate, and terminal associate degrees. Founded 1967. Setting: 185-acre urban campus with easy access to Denver. Total enrollment: 4,588. Faculty: 273 (91 full-time, 182 part-time). Student-undergrad faculty ratio is 18:1. Full-time: 1,701 students, 50% women, 50% men. Part-time: 2,887 students, 61% women, 39% men. 48% 25 or older. Retention: 80% of full-time freshmen returned the following year. Core. Calendar: semesters. Academic remediation for entering students, ESL program, advanced placement, self-designed majors, freshman honors college, honors program, summer session for credit, part-time degree program, external degree program, adult/continuing education programs, co-op programs. ROTC: Air Force (c).
Entrance Requirements: Open admission. Options: early admission, deferred admission. Entrance: noncompetitive. Application deadline: rolling.
Collegiate Environment: Drama-theater group, choral group, student-run newspaper, radio station. Major annual events: Fall-In Activity, Winter Fest, Spring-Fest/Blowout Activity. Student services: personal-psychological counseling, women's center. Campus security: 24-hour emergency response devices, day and evening patrols by trained security personnel. Aims Community College Library. 1,000 computers available on campus for general student use. Computer purchase/lease plans available. A campuswide network can be accessed from off-campus. Students can access the following: online class registration. Staffed computer lab on campus provides training in use of computers, software, and the Internet.
Community Environment: See University of Northern Colorado.

AMERICAN SENTINEL UNIVERSITY

2260 S Xanadu Way, Ste. 310
Aurora, CO 80014
Free: 800-729-2427
Web Site: www.americansentinel.edu
Description: Proprietary, comprehensive, coed. Awards associate, bachelor's, and master's degrees. Founded 1988.
Entrance Requirements: Required: high school transcript, resume.

■ ARAPAHOE COMMUNITY COLLEGE

5900 S Santa Fe Dr.
Littleton, CO 80160-9002
Tel: (303)797-4222
Fax: (303)797-5970
Web Site: www.arapahoe.edu
Description: State-supported, primarily 2-year, coed. Part of Colorado Community College and Occupational Education System. Awards certificates, diplomas, transfer associate, terminal associate, and bachelor's degrees. Founded 1965. Setting: 52-acre suburban campus with easy access to Denver. Total enrollment: 9,962. Faculty: 489 (102 full-time, 387 part-time). Student-undergrad faculty ratio is 23:1. 3,851 applied, 100% were admitted. Full-time: 1,860 students, 53% women, 47% men. Part-time: 8,837 students, 60% women, 40% men. Students come from 47 states and territories, 2 other countries, 15% from out-of-state. 0.4% American Indian or Alaska Native, non-Hispanic/Latino; 14% Hispanic/Latino; 2% Black or African American, non-Hispanic/Latino; 4% Asian, non-Hispanic/Latino; 0.3% Native Hawaiian or other Pacific Islander, non-Hispanic/Latino; 1% international. 43% 25 or older, 5% transferred in. Core. Calendar: semesters. Academic remediation for entering students, ESL program, services for LD students, advanced placement, accelerated degree program, independent study, distance learning, double major, summer session for credit, part-time degree program, external degree program, adult/continuing education programs, co-op programs and internships. Off campus study. Study abroad program. ROTC: Army (c), Air Force (c).
Entrance Requirements: Open admission. Options: electronic application, early admission, deferred admission, international baccalaureate accepted. Entrance: noncompetitive. Application deadlines: rolling, rolling for nonresidents. Notification: continuous, continuous for nonresidents. Transfer credits accepted: Yes.
Costs Per Year: Application fee: $0. State resident tuition: $4467 full-time, $148.90 per credit hour part-time. Nonresident tuition: $18,327 full-time, $610.90 per credit hour part-time. Mandatory fees: $344 full-time. Full-time tuition and fees vary according to program and reciprocity agreements. Part-time tuition varies according to program and reciprocity agreements.
Collegiate Environment: Orientation program. Drama-theater group, choral group, student-run newspaper. Most popular organizations: American Society of Interior Designers, National Society of Leadership and Success, Phi Theta Kappa, Student Veterans of America, Transfer Club. Major annual events: Welcome Week, End of Semester BBQ, Stress Free Finals Week. Student services: personal-psychological counseling. Campus security: 24-hour emergency response devices and patrols, late night transport-escort service. College housing not available. Weber Center for Learning Resources plus 1 other. Books: 28,076 (physical), 442 (digital/electronic).
Community Environment: Littleton is a suburban area 10 miles from Denver with seasonal variations in temperature. There are churches of all denominations, shopping centers, and medical clinics, with all forms of transportation available. Community facilities include parks with playground equipment, public swimming pools, indoor tennis courts, fairgrounds, golf courses and an ice rink. Skiing in the nearby mountains is excellent. Part-time employment is available.

■ ASPEN UNIVERSITY

720 S Colorado Blvd., Ste. 1150N
Denver, CO 80246-1930
Tel: (303)333-4224; Free: 800-441-4746
Fax: (303)336-1144
Web Site: www.aspen.edu
Description: Independent, comprehensive, coed. Awards bachelor's, master's, and doctoral degrees. Founded 1987. Total enrollment: 2,000. Calendar: 5 terms per year.
Entrance Requirements: Option: electronic application. Entrance: moderately difficult. Transfer credits accepted: Yes.

■ BEL-REA INSTITUTE OF ANIMAL TECHNOLOGY

1681 S Dayton St.
Denver, CO 80247
Tel: (303)751-8700; Free: 800-950-8001
Fax: (303)751-9969
Web Site: www.belrea.edu
Description: Proprietary, 2-year, coed. Awards terminal associate degrees. Founded 1971. Setting: 6-acre suburban campus with easy access to Denver. Total enrollment: 400. 414 applied. Students come from 20 states and territories, 40% from out-of-state. 39% 25 or older. Core. Calendar:

quarters. Academic remediation for entering students, services for LD students, summer session for credit, part-time degree program, internships. Off campus study.
Entrance Requirements: Open admission. Options: electronic application, early admission, deferred admission. Required: essay, high school transcript, minimum 2.5 high school GPA, interview. Entrance: moderately difficult. Application deadline: rolling. Transfer credits accepted: Yes.
Collegiate Environment: Orientation program. Social organizations: 3 open to all. Bel-Rea Institute Library. Weekly public service hours: 38.

■ COLLEGEAMERICA-COLORADO SPRINGS

2020 N Academy Blvd.
Colorado Springs, CO 80909
Tel: (719)227-0170; Free: 800-622-2894
Fax: (719)637-0806
Web Site: www.collegeamerica.edu
Description: Independent, primarily 2-year, coed. Awards terminal associate and bachelor's degrees. Total enrollment: 675. Student-undergrad faculty ratio is 22:1. 61% 25 or older.

■ COLLEGEAMERICA-DENVER

1385 S Colorado Blvd.
Denver, CO 80222
Tel: (303)534-0226; Free: 800-622-2894
Web Site: www.collegeamerica.edu
Description: Independent, 2-year, coed. Awards terminal associate degrees. Founded 1962. Setting: urban campus. Total enrollment: 110. Student-undergrad faculty ratio is 10:1. Calendar: continuous. Academic remediation for entering students, accelerated degree program, distance learning, co-op programs.
Entrance Requirements: Entrance: noncompetitive.
Collegiate Environment: Orientation program.

■ COLLEGEAMERICA-FORT COLLINS

4601 S Mason St.
Fort Collins, CO 80525
Tel: (970)221-2769; Free: 800-622-2894
Fax: (970)223-6060
Web Site: www.collegeamerica.edu
Description: Independent, primarily 2-year, coed. Awards terminal associate and bachelor's degrees. Founded 1962. Setting: suburban campus. Total enrollment: 120. 57% 25 or older. Core. Calendar: continuous. Honors program, independent study, distance learning, co-op programs and internships.
Entrance Requirements: Open admission. Option: international baccalaureate accepted. Required: essay, high school transcript, interview. Recommended: minimum 2 high school GPA. Entrance: minimally difficult. Notification: continuous. Transfer credits accepted: Yes.
Collegiate Environment: Orientation program.

■ COLORADO ACADEMY OF VETERINARY TECHNOLOGY

2766 Janitell Rd.
Colorado Springs, CO 80906
Tel: (719)219-9636
Fax: (719)302-5577
Web Site: www.cavt.edu
Description: Proprietary, 2-year, coed. Awards certificates, transfer associate, and terminal associate degrees.

■ COLORADO CHRISTIAN UNIVERSITY

8787 W Alameda
Lakewood, CO 80226
Tel: (303)963-3000; Free: 800-44-FAITH
E-mail: jomartin@ccu.edu
Web Site: www.ccu.edu
Description: Independent interdenominational, comprehensive, coed. Awards associate, bachelor's, and master's degrees. Founded 1914. Setting: 26-acre suburban campus with easy access to Denver. Total enrollment: 1,343. Student-undergrad faculty ratio is 15:1. 1,925 applied, 62% were admitted. Students come from 50 states and territories, 17 other countries, 50% from out-of-state. 55% live on campus. Retention: 78% of full-time freshmen returned the following year. Core. Calendar: semesters. Academic remediation for entering students, services for LD students, advanced placement, accelerated degree program, self-designed majors,

honors program, independent study, distance learning, double major, summer session for credit, part-time degree program, adult/continuing education programs, co-op programs and internships, graduate courses open to undergrads. Off campus study at Colorado Institute of Art, Metropolitan State College, University of Colorado at Denver, Red Rocks Community College. Study abroad program. ROTC: Army (c).

Entrance Requirements: Options: electronic application, early admission, deferred admission, international baccalaureate accepted. Required: essay, high school transcript, 2 recommendations, interview, Spiritual Recommendation, SAT or ACT. Required for some: minimum 2.8 high school GPA, 3 recommendations, interview. Entrance: moderately difficult. Application deadline: 8/1.

Costs Per Year: Application fee: $30. Comprehensive fee: $40,886 includes full-time tuition ($29,870), mandatory fees ($500), and college room and board ($10,516). College room only: $2915. Full-time tuition and fees vary according to course load. Room and board charges vary according to board plan and housing facility.

Collegiate Environment: Orientation program. Drama-theater group, choral group. Social organizations: Omicron Delta Kappa, In His Service. Student services: health clinic, personal-psychological counseling, women's center. Campus security: 24-hour emergency response devices and patrols, student patrols. Clifton Fowler Library.

Community Environment: See University of Denver.

■ THE COLORADO COLLEGE

14 E Cache La Poudre St.
Colorado Springs, CO 80903-3294
Tel: (719)389-6000; Free: 800-542-7214
Fax: (719)389-6282
E-mail: admission@coloradocollege.edu
Web Site: www.coloradocollege.edu

Description: Independent, comprehensive, coed. Awards bachelor's and master's degrees (master's degree in education only). Founded 1874. Setting: 90-acre urban campus with easy access to Denver. Endowment: $765.2 million. Research spending for the previous fiscal year: $1.9 million. Educational spending for the previous fiscal year: $28,244 per student. Total enrollment: 2,144. Faculty: 235 (201 full-time, 34 part-time). Student-undergrad faculty ratio is 10:1. 8,546 applied, 15% were admitted. 75% from top 10% of their high school class, 97% from top quarter, 99% from top half. 21 valedictorians. Full-time: 2,098 students, 55% women, 45% men. Part-time: 16 students, 63% women, 37% men. Students come from 49 states and territories, 46 other countries, 83% from out-of-state. 0.6% American Indian or Alaska Native, non-Hispanic/Latino; 9% Hispanic/Latino; 2% Black or African American, non-Hispanic/Latino; 5% Asian, non-Hispanic/Latino; 0.1% Native Hawaiian or other Pacific Islander, non-Hispanic/Latino; 9% international. 80% live on campus, 2% transferred in. Retention: 96% of full-time freshmen returned the following year. Academic areas with the most degrees conferred: social sciences; biological/life sciences; physical sciences. Core. Calendar: 8 blocks of 3 1/2 week courses. ESL program, services for LD students, advanced placement, self-designed majors, independent study, double major, summer session for credit, internships. Off campus study at American University, Woods Hole Marine Biological Laboratory Ecosystems Center, Associated Colleges of the Midwest Programs. Study abroad program. ROTC: Army (c).

Entrance Requirements: Options: electronic application, early decision, early action, deferred admission, international baccalaureate accepted. Required: essay, high school transcript, 2 recommendations. Recommended: interview. Required for some: SAT or ACT. Entrance: very difficult. Application deadlines: 1/15, 11/10 for early decision plan 1, 1/15 for early decision plan 2, 11/10 for early action. Notification: 4/1, 12/15 for early decision plan 1, 12/19 for early action. SAT Reasoning Test deadline: 1/15. SAT Subject Test deadline: 1/15. Transfer credits accepted: Yes. Applicants placed on waiting list: 851. Wait-listed applicants offered admission: 60. Early decision applicants: 1,119. Early decision applicants admitted: 307. Early action applicants: 3,485. Early action applicants admitted: 639.

Costs Per Year: Application fee: $60. One-time mandatory fee: $250. Comprehensive fee: $71,042 includes full-time tuition ($57,612), mandatory fees ($474), and college room and board ($12,956). College room only: $7756. Part-time tuition: $9681 per course.

Collegiate Environment: Orientation program. Drama-theater group, choral group, student-run newspaper. Social organizations: 140 open to all; national fraternities, national sororities. Major annual events: Homecoming, Winter Ball, Annual Arts and Crafts. Student services: health clinic, personal-psychological counseling. Campus security: 24-hour emergency response

devices and patrols, late night transport-escort service, controlled dormitory access. 1,692 college housing spaces available. Freshmen guaranteed college housing. On-campus residence required through junior year. Options: coed, men-only, women-only housing available. Tutt Library plus 1 other. Books: 392,705 (physical), 319,616 (digital/electronic); Serial titles: 4,239 (physical), 80,330 (digital/electronic); Databases: 324. Weekly public service hours: 114; students can reserve study rooms. Operations spending for the previous fiscal year: $3.5 million. 400 computers available on campus for general student use. A campuswide network can be accessed from student residence rooms and from off campus. Students can access the following: online class registration. Staffed computer lab on campus provides training in use of computers, software, and the Internet.

Community Environment: Colorado Springs, metropolitan population of 587,500, is located 70 miles south of Denver at the foot of Pikes Peak. It is known for its healthful climate and spectacular scenery. the area averages more than 310 days of sunshine each year, has clean air, low humidity, cool summer nights, and mild winters. Bus, air, and good highways serve the area. The city has a fine arts center, opera, symphony, theatre, museums, art galleries, and numerous fine hotels, and motels. Areas for skiing, hunting, fishing, backpacking, and camping are nearby.

■ COLORADO MESA UNIVERSITY

1100 N Ave.
Grand Junction, CO 81501-3122
Tel: (970)248-1020; Free: 800-982-MESA
Fax: (970)248-1973
E-mail: admissions@coloradomeas.edu
Web Site: www.coloradomesa.edu

Description: State-supported, comprehensive, coed. Awards associate, bachelor's, master's, and doctoral degrees. Founded 1925. Setting: 90-acre suburban campus. Endowment: $27.7 million. Research spending for the previous fiscal year: $344,013. Educational spending for the previous fiscal year: $5297 per student. Total enrollment: 9,735. Faculty: 572 (295 full-time, 277 part-time). Student-undergrad faculty ratio is 21:1. 6,982 applied, 82% were admitted. 11% from top 10% of their high school class, 29% from top quarter, 59% from top half. Full-time: 7,277 students, 52% women, 48% men. Part-time: 2,318 students, 58% women, 42% men. Students come from 47 states and territories, 14 other countries, 14% from out-of-state. 0.7% American Indian or Alaska Native, non-Hispanic/Latino; 18% Hispanic/Latino; 2% Black or African American, non-Hispanic/Latino; 2% Asian, non-Hispanic/Latino; 0.5% Native Hawaiian or other Pacific Islander, non-Hispanic/Latino; 1% international. 20% 25 or older, 23% live on campus, 7% transferred in. Retention: 74% of full-time freshmen returned the following year. Academic areas with the most degrees conferred: business/marketing; parks and recreation; health professions and related sciences. Core. Calendar: semesters. Academic remediation for entering students, services for LD students, advanced placement, accelerated degree program, honors program, distance learning, double major, summer session for credit, part-time degree program, internships, graduate courses open to undergrads. Off campus study at National Student Exchange Program. Study abroad program.

Entrance Requirements: Options: electronic application, deferred admission, international baccalaureate accepted. Required: high school transcript, SAT or ACT. Recommended: 2 recommendations. Entrance: minimally difficult. Application deadline: rolling. Notification: continuous. SAT Reasoning Test deadline: 8/15. SAT Subject Test deadline: 8/15. Transfer credits accepted: Yes.

Costs Per Year: Application fee: $30. State resident tuition: $8343 full-time, $278.10 per credit hour part-time. Nonresident tuition: $21,540 full-time, $718 per credit hour part-time. Mandatory fees: $900 full-time, $30 per credit hour part-time. Full-time tuition and fees vary according to course load. Part-time tuition and fees vary according to course load. College room and board: $10,925. College room only: $6000. Room and board charges vary according to board plan and housing facility.

Collegiate Environment: Orientation program. Drama-theater group, choral group, marching band, student-run newspaper, radio station. Social organizations: 189 open to all; national fraternities, national sororities. Most popular organizations: Environmental Club, Student Body Association, KMSA radio station, Rodeo Club, Campus Residents Association. Major annual events: Homecoming, Spring Fling, Unityfest. Student services: legal services, health clinic, personal-psychological counseling. Campus security: 24-hour emergency response devices and patrols, late night transport-escort service, controlled dormitory access. John U. Tomlinson Library. Books: 202,919 (physical), 162,000 (digital/electronic); Databases: 116. Weekly public service hours: 94; study areas open 24 hours, 5-7 days a week; students can reserve study rooms. Operations spending for the previous fiscal year: $2.1 million. 525 computers available on campus for general student use. A campuswide network can be accessed from student residence rooms and from off campus. Students can access the following: online class registration. Staffed computer lab on campus provides training in use of computers, software, and the Internet.

Community Environment: Grand Junction is located in an irrigated valley in the heart of a vast vacationland that is also rich in energy-related natural resources. The climate is invigorating, sunny, and mild. The community has churches of many denominations, excellent public schools, library facilities, cultural programs, city parks, golf courses, tennis courts, 4 hospitals, and good transportation services including three major airlines. Recreational activities in the nearby mountains and deserts include hiking, camping, boating, river rafting, fishing, hunting, cross-country and downhill skiing, and more.

■ **COLORADO MOUNTAIN COLLEGE (GLENWOOD SPRINGS)**
3000 County Rd. 114
Glenwood Springs, CO 81601
Tel: (970)945-7481; Free: 800-621-8559
E-mail: vvalentine@coloradomtn.edu
Web Site: www.coloradomtn.edu

Description: District-supported, 4-year, coed. Part of Colorado Mountain College District System. Awards associate and bachelor's degrees. Founded 1965. Setting: 680-acre rural campus. Total enrollment: 5,847. Faculty: 544 (109 full-time, 435 part-time). Student-undergrad faculty ratio is 13:1. 686 applied, 100% were admitted. Full-time: 1,875 students, 46% women, 54% men. Part-time: 3,972 students, 59% women, 41% men. 0.9% American Indian or Alaska Native, non-Hispanic/Latino; 15% Hispanic/Latino; 1% Black or African American, non-Hispanic/Latino; 0.8% Asian, non-Hispanic/Latino; 0.1% Native Hawaiian or other Pacific Islander, non-Hispanic/Latino; 0.2% international. 70% 25 or older, 44% live on campus. Core. Calendar: semesters. Academic remediation for entering students, ESL program, services for LD students, advanced placement, honors program, independent study, distance learning, double major, summer session for credit, part-time degree program, adult/continuing education programs, co-op programs and internships. Study abroad program.

Entrance Requirements: Open admission except for nursing, photography, and veterinary technology programs, Law Enforcement Training Academy. Options: electronic application, early admission, deferred admission, international baccalaureate accepted. Required: high school transcript. Recommended: SAT or ACT. Entrance: noncompetitive. Application deadline: rolling. Transfer credits accepted: Yes.

Costs Per Year: Application fee: $0. Area resident tuition: $2400 full-time, $80 per credit hour part-time. State resident tuition: $5400 full-time, $180 per credit hour part-time. Nonresident tuition: $13,590 full-time, $453 per credit hour part-time. College room and board: $10,322. College room only: $6000.

Collegiate Environment: Orientation program. Drama-theater group, student-run newspaper. Most popular organizations: Student Government, Outdoor activities, World Awareness Society, Peer Mentors, Student Activities Board. Major annual events: Spring Fest, Outdoor Activities, X Games. Student services: health clinic, personal-psychological counseling. Campus security: 24-hour emergency response devices, student patrols, controlled dormitory access. Quigley Library. 65 computers available on campus for general student use. A campuswide network can be accessed from student residence rooms. Students can access the following: online class registration. Staffed computer lab on campus provides training in use of computers, software, and the Internet.

Community Environment: Glenwood Springs is an urban area with a moderate climate; a beautiful place to live. Railroads and buses serve the area and charter air service is available. Glenwood Springs is the county seat of Garfield County, and has the best shopping facilities in the county. The city has churches of all major denominations, library, museum, theatres, hospital and many of the civic clubs. Hot mineral springs have made Glenwood Springs a popular resort. Seven miles above the town is the Shoshone Hydroelectric Plant. The Colorado employment office is located here; several businesses hire part-time workers. Over 1,000 miles of fishing streams and more than 100 lakes are accessible from Glenwood Springs. The Sunlight Ski area is located nine miles south of the town; it has a 7,000 foot double chair lift. Aspen and Snowmass are 45 miles away. Other recreational activities include fishing, hiking, hunting and tennis. Strawberry day is an annual event in June.

■ **COLORADO MOUNTAIN COLLEGE (LEADVILLE)**
901 S Hwy. 24
Leadville, CO 80461
Tel: (719)486-2015; Free: 800-621-8559
E-mail: joinus@coloradomtn.edu
Web Site: www.coloradomtn.edu

Description: District-supported, 4-year, coed. Part of Colorado Mountain College District System. Awards associate and bachelor's degrees. Founded 1965. Setting: 200-acre rural campus. Total enrollment: 1,209. Faculty: (16 full-time). Student-undergrad faculty ratio is 12:1. 55% 25 or older, 30% live on campus. Core. Calendar: semesters. Academic remediation for entering students, ESL program, services for LD students, advanced placement, self-designed majors, honors program, independent study, distance learning, double major, summer session for credit, part-time degree program, adult/continuing education programs, co-op programs and internships. Off campus study. Study abroad program.

Entrance Requirements: Open admission. Options: electronic application, early admission, deferred admission, international baccalaureate accepted. Required: high school transcript. Recommended: SAT or ACT. Entrance: noncompetitive. Application deadline: rolling. Transfer credits accepted: Yes.

Collegiate Environment: Orientation program. Most popular organizations: Environmental Club, Outdoor Club, Student Activities Board. Major annual events: Rail Jam, Winter Skjol, Leadville 100. Student services: health clinic, personal-psychological counseling. Campus security: 24-hour emergency response devices, student patrols, controlled dormitory access. Leadville Campus Library plus 1 other. 30 computers available on campus for general student use. A campuswide network can be accessed from student residence rooms. Students can access the following: online class registration. Staffed computer lab on campus provides training in use of computers, software, and the Internet.

Community Environment: Leadville, situated at an altitude of 10,000 feet, is a rural community with a dry climate. Leadville has been the center of a famous mining district since the Placer Mines were opened in 1860. It became the silver capital and one of Colorado's greatest mining camps. Mining and tourism are major industries at the present. The city has a library, branch museum of the Colorado State Historical Society, churches, medical clinic and a hospital. Part-time work opportunities are available nearby. Recreation activities are numerous and include ice skating, golfing, tennis, fishing, soccer, bowling, swimming. There is skiing at Ski Cooper on the top of Tennessee Pass 12 miles north of Leadville and at nearby Copper Mountain, Vail, Keystone, Breckenridge and A-Basin. The World's Championship Pack Burro Race is an annual event the first weekend in August.

■ **COLORADO MOUNTAIN COLLEGE (STEAMBOAT SPRINGS)**
1275 Crawford Ave.
Steamboat Springs, CO 80487
Tel: (970)870-4444; Free: 800-621-8559
E-mail: jbrazill@coloradomtn.edu
Web Site: www.coloradomtn.edu

Description: District-supported, 4-year, coed. Part of Colorado Mountain College District System. Awards associate and bachelor's degrees. Founded 1965. Setting: 10-acre small town campus. Total enrollment: 2,606. Faculty: (25 full-time). Student-undergrad faculty ratio is 12:1. 30% 25 or older, 44% live on campus. Core. Calendar: semesters. Academic remediation for entering students, ESL program, services for LD students, advanced placement, honors program, independent study, distance learning, double major, summer session for credit, part-time degree program, adult/continuing education programs, co-op programs and internships. Off campus study. Study abroad program.

Entrance Requirements: Open admission. Options: electronic application, early admission, deferred admission, international baccalaureate accepted. Required: high school transcript. Recommended: SAT or ACT. Entrance: noncompetitive. Application deadline: rolling. Transfer credits accepted: Yes.

Costs Per Year: Application fee: $0. Area resident tuition: $2400 full-time, $80 per credit part-time. State resident tuition: $5400 full-time, $180 per credit part-time. Nonresident tuition: $13,590 full-time, $453 per credit part-time. College room and board: $10,322. College room only: $6000.

Collegiate Environment: Orientation program. Student-run newspaper. Social organizations: 8 open to all. Most popular organizations: Student Government, Sky Club, Ski Club, International Club, Phi Theta Kappa. Major annual events: Spring Fling, Winter Carnival, Rail Jam. Student services: health clinic, personal-psychological counseling. Campus security: 24-hour emergency response devices, student patrols, controlled dormitory access.

Main library plus 1 other. 60 computers available on campus for general student use. A campuswide network can be accessed from student residence rooms and from off campus. Students can access the following: online class registration. Staffed computer lab on campus provides training in use of computers, software, and the Internet.

Community Environment: Steamboat Springs is 175 miles northwest of Denver. A permanent population of 9,000 swells to over 25,000 on Christmas Eve, largely due to the attraction of the town's famous champagne powder. The town flourishes with the contrasting influences of working cattle ranches and a world-class ski resort. The surrounding area offers unlimited opportunities for downhill and cross-country skiing, and hunting. Students learn additional outdoor skills through college-sponsored activities such as winter survival, desert camping, and orienteering.

■ COLORADO NORTHWESTERN COMMUNITY COLLEGE

500 Kennedy Dr.
Rangely, CO 81648-3598
Tel: (970)675-2261; Free: 800-562-1105
Fax: (970)675-3343
Web Site: www.cncc.edu

Description: State-supported, 2-year, coed. Part of Colorado Community College and Occupational Education System. Awards certificates, transfer associate, and terminal associate degrees. Founded 1962. Setting: 150-acre rural campus. Total enrollment: 1,154. Faculty: 93 (38 full-time, 55 part-time). Student-undergrad faculty ratio is 13:1. 863 applied, 100% were admitted. Full-time: 484 students, 62% women, 38% men. Part-time: 670 students, 59% women, 41% men. 21% from out-of-state. 0.4% American Indian or Alaska Native, non-Hispanic/Latino; 13% Hispanic/Latino; 3% Black or African American, non-Hispanic/Latino; 1% Asian, non-Hispanic/Latino; 0.3% Native Hawaiian or other Pacific Islander, non-Hispanic/Latino; 2% international. 33% 25 or older, 45% live on campus, 10% transferred in. Retention: 46% of full-time freshmen returned the following year. Calendar: semesters. Academic remediation for entering students, services for LD students, advanced placement, self-designed majors, independent study, distance learning, double major, summer session for credit, part-time degree program, adult/continuing education programs, internships.

Entrance Requirements: Open admission Dental hygiene and nursing programs are competitive entry. Options: electronic application, early admission, deferred admission, international baccalaureate accepted. Required: high school transcript. Required for some: 3 recommendations. Entrance: noncompetitive. Application deadlines: rolling, rolling for nonresidents. Notification: continuous, continuous for nonresidents. Transfer credits accepted: Yes.

Costs Per Year: Application fee: $0. State resident tuition: $4467 full-time, $148.90 per credit hour part-time. Nonresident tuition: $7446 full-time, $248.20 per credit hour part-time. Mandatory fees: $467 full-time, $14.65 per credit hour part-time, $13.75 per term part-time. Full-time tuition and fees vary according to course load, location, and program. Part-time tuition and fees vary according to course load, location, and program. College room and board: $7370. College room only: $2687. Room and board charges vary according to board plan, housing facility, and location.

Collegiate Environment: Orientation program. Student services: health clinic, personal-psychological counseling. Campus security: student patrols, late night transport-escort service, controlled dormitory access. 300 college housing spaces available. Freshmen guaranteed college housing. On-campus residence required in freshman year. Option: coed housing available. Colorado Northwestern Community College Library plus 1 other. Books: 19,000 (physical), 10,524 (digital/electronic); Serial titles: 137 (physical); Databases: 47. Students can reserve study rooms. 400 computers available on campus for general student use. A campuswide network can be accessed. Students can access the following: online class registration. Staffed computer lab on campus provides training in use of computers, software, and the Internet.

Community Environment: Rangely is a rural community (population 2,000) located on the western slope of Colorado, 300 miles northwest of Denver and 130 miles west of Steamboat Springs. It is a friendly community that offers a sharp change of pace from the urban areas. Excellent area for cross-country skiing, backpacking, river rafting, fishing and hunting. Close to Dinosaur National Monument and Flaming Gorge Dam and Reservoir. The area is two hours from downhill skiing at Steamboat Springs, Powder Horn and Sunlight Mountain. Community recreation facilities include: The Taylor Draw Dam Reservoir, a nine-hole golf course, tennis courts, a fitness trail, an ice skating rink, an indoor Olympic-size swimming pool, racquetball courts, and a dance and aerobics room. Bus and airport facilities are nearby.

■ COLORADO SCHOOL OF MINES

1500 Illinois St.
Golden, CO 80401-1887
Tel: (303)273-3000; Free: 800-446-9488
Fax: (303)273-3509
E-mail: admissions@mines.edu
Web Site: www.mines.edu

Description: State-supported, university, coed. Awards bachelor's, master's, and doctoral degrees and post-master's certificates. Founded 1874. Setting: 499-acre small town campus with easy access to Denver. Endowment: $246.1 million. Research spending for the previous fiscal year: $60.3 million. Educational spending for the previous fiscal year: $16,040 per student. Total enrollment: 6,268. Faculty: 572 (304 full-time, 268 part-time). Student-undergrad faculty ratio is 15:1. 12,661 applied, 49% were admitted. 59% from top 10% of their high school class, 85% from top quarter, 100% from top half. Full-time: 4,707 students, 30% women, 70% men. Part-time: 247 students, 29% women, 71% men. Students come from 51 states and territories, 43 other countries, 41% from out-of-state. 0.4% American Indian or Alaska Native, non-Hispanic/Latino; 9% Hispanic/Latino; 1% Black or African American, non-Hispanic/Latino; 4% Asian, non-Hispanic/Latino; 0.1% Native Hawaiian or other Pacific Islander, non-Hispanic/Latino; 6% international. 5% 25 or older, 30% live on campus, 3% transferred in. Retention: 92% of full-time freshmen returned the following year. Academic areas with the most degrees conferred: engineering; computer and information sciences; mathematics and statistics. Core. Calendar: semesters. Services for LD students, advanced placement, accelerated degree program, honors program, independent study, double major, summer session for credit, co-op programs and internships, graduate courses open to undergrads. Off campus study at Red Rocks Community College, Front Range Community College, Community College of Aurora, Community College of Denver, Arapahoe Community College. Study abroad program. ROTC: Army, Air Force.

Entrance Requirements: Options: electronic application, deferred admission. Required: high school transcript, SAT or ACT. Recommended: minimum 3.8 high school GPA, rank in upper quartile of high school class. Required for some: essay, interview. Entrance: very difficult. Notification: continuous until 10/1. SAT Reasoning Test deadline: 2/1. Transfer credits accepted: Yes. Applicants placed on waiting list: 1,280. Wait-listed applicants offered admission: 16.

Costs Per Year: Application fee: $45. State resident tuition: $16,650 full-time. Nonresident tuition: $36,270 full-time.

Collegiate Environment: Orientation program. Drama-theater group, choral group, marching band, student-run newspaper, radio station. Social organizations: 255 open to all; national fraternities, national sororities; 14% of eligible men and 21% of eligible women are members. Most popular organizations: Society of Women Engineers, Residence Hall Association, Associated Students of Colorado School of Mines, Student Professional Societies/ and/ Religious Organizations, Multicultural Engineering Program. Major annual events: Engineers' Days (E-Days), Celebration of Mines, Career Day. Student services: health clinic, personal-psychological counseling, women's center. Campus security: 24-hour emergency response devices and patrols, late night transport-escort service, controlled dormitory access, campus policy department. 1,882 college housing spaces available; 1,560 were occupied in 2018-19. Freshmen guaranteed college housing. On-campus residence required in freshman year. Option: coed housing available. Arthur Lakes Library. Books: 369,304 (physical), 732,071 (digital/electronic); Serial titles: 527 (physical), 197,641 (digital/electronic); Databases: 162. Weekly public service hours: 107; students can reserve study rooms. Operations spending for the previous fiscal year: $3.4 million. 1,000 computers available on campus for general student use. Computer purchase/lease plans available. A campuswide network can be accessed from student residence rooms and from off campus. Students can access the following: online class registration. Staffed computer lab on campus provides training in use of computers, software, and the Internet.

Community Environment: CSM is located in Golden, only 15 miles west of Denver's downtown business district. Golden is a community of 15,000 people nestled in the foothills of the Rocky Mountains. Maintaining a distinct identity from the other Denver suburbs, Golden is also home to the National Earthquake Center and the National Renewable Energy Laboratory. Many CSM students enjoy the outdoors, and favorite summer activities include hiking, jogging, camping, and bicycling. During the winter months, skiing is the major activity with some of the world's best slopes virtually in CSM's backyard. With a population of over two million people, nearby Denver offers all the attractions of a major metropolitan area. As a commercial, transportation, and financial center for the Rocky Mountain region, Denver is home to many government agencies, colleges and universities, and business involved in natural resources, computers, and biotechnology.

■ COLORADO SCHOOL OF TRADES
1575 Hoyt St.
Lakewood, CO 80215-2996
Tel: (303)233-4697; Free: 800-234-4594
Fax: (303)233-4723
Web Site: www.schooloftrades.edu
Description: Proprietary, 2-year, coed. Awards terminal associate degrees. Founded 1947. Setting: suburban campus. Total enrollment: 134. Faculty: (10 full-time). Student-undergrad faculty ratio is 12:1. 174 applied, 87% were admitted. Full-time: 134 students, 1% women, 99% men. 88% from out-of-state.
Entrance Requirements: Required: essay, high school transcript, interview.
Costs Per Year: Application fee: $25. Tuition: $21,350 full-time. Mandatory fees: $150 full-time. Tuition guaranteed not to increase for student's term of enrollment.
Collegiate Environment: 6 computers available on campus for general student use.

■ COLORADO STATE UNIVERSITY
Fort Collins, CO 80523
Tel: (970)491-1101
Fax: (970)491-7799
E-mail: admissions@colostate.edu
Web Site: www.colostate.edu
Description: State-supported, university, coed. Part of Colorado State University System. Awards bachelor's, master's, and doctoral degrees. Founded 1870. Setting: 4,773-acre urban campus with easy access to Denver. Endowment: $356 million. Research spending for the previous fiscal year: $374.9 million. Educational spending for the previous fiscal year: $11,449 per student. Total enrollment: 33,694. Faculty: 1,692 (1,049 full-time, 643 part-time). Student-undergrad faculty ratio is 18:1. 24,496 applied, 84% were admitted. 20% from top 10% of their high school class, 46% from top quarter, 81% from top half. 2 National Merit Scholars, 60 valedictorians. Full-time: 22,310 students, 51% women, 49% men. Part-time: 4,090 students, 55% women, 45% men. Students come from 55 states and territories, 76 other countries, 26% from out-of-state. 0.4% American Indian or Alaska Native, non-Hispanic/Latino; 14% Hispanic/Latino; 2% Black or African American, non-Hispanic/Latino; 3% Asian, non-Hispanic/Latino; 0.2% Native Hawaiian or other Pacific Islander, non-Hispanic/Latino; 4% international. 10% 25 or older, 30% live on campus, 7% transferred in. Retention: 84% of full-time freshmen returned the following year. Academic areas with the most degrees conferred: business/marketing; biological/life sciences; engineering. Core. Calendar: semesters. ESL program, services for LD students, advanced placement, accelerated degree program, honors program, independent study, distance learning, double major, summer session for credit, part-time degree program, adult/continuing education programs, co-op programs and internships, graduate courses open to undergrads. Off campus study at Aims Community College, Northern Colorado Graduate Exchange Agreement. Study abroad program. ROTC: Army, Air Force.
Entrance Requirements: Options: electronic application, early action, deferred admission, international baccalaureate accepted. Required: essay, high school transcript, 1 recommendation, SAT or ACT. Entrance: moderately difficult. Application deadline: 7/1. Notification: continuous until 9/15, rolling for early action. Transfer credits accepted: Yes. Early action applicants: 15,787. Early action applicants admitted: 14,172.
Costs Per Year: Application fee: $50. State resident tuition: $9426 full-time, $428.20 per credit hour part-time. Nonresident tuition: $27,327 full-time, $1366 per credit hour part-time. Mandatory fees: $2405 full-time, $59.29 per credit hour part-time, $296.45 per term part-time. College room and board: $11,964. College room only: $5746.
Collegiate Environment: Orientation program. Drama-theater group, choral group, marching band, student-run newspaper, radio station. Social organizations: 440 open to all; national fraternities, national sororities, local fraternities, local sororities; 5% of eligible men and 7% of eligible women are members. Most popular organizations: Photography at Colorado State University, Outdoor Club at CSU, Biomedical Student Association, Criminal Justice Organization, Colorado State University Zoology Club. Major annual events: Homecoming Weekend, Monfort Lecture Series, President's Fall Address and University Picnic. Student services: legal services, health clinic,

personal-psychological counseling, women's center. Campus security: 24-hour emergency response devices and patrols, student patrols, late night transport-escort service, controlled dormitory access. 8,102 college housing spaces available; 4,574 were occupied in 2018-19. Freshmen guaranteed college housing. On-campus residence required in freshman year. Option: coed housing available. William E. Morgan Library plus 1 other. Books: 1.2 million (physical), 1.1 million (digital/electronic); Serial titles: 45,581 (physical), 104,097 (digital/electronic); Databases: 345. Weekly public service hours: 108; study areas open 24 hours, 5-7 days a week; students can reserve study rooms. Operations spending for the previous fiscal year: $19.7 million. 1,700 computers available on campus for general student use. Computer purchase/lease plans available. A campuswide network can be accessed from student residence rooms and from off campus. Students can access the following: online class registration, personalized portal services including transcripts and financials (billing, financial aid). Staffed computer lab on campus (open 24 hours a day) provides training in use of computers, software, and the Internet.
Community Environment: Fort Collins, a community of 110,000 is situated at the foot of the Rocky Mountains. The excellent climate and beautiful mountains create an ideal college setting about 65 miles north of Denver. The city has many churches, a local airport, hospital, hotels, motels, and is the shopping center of Northern Colorado. Part-time employment is available for students and some full-time employment is available for graduates.

■ COLORADO STATE UNIVERSITY-GLOBAL CAMPUS
8000 E Maplewood Ave.
Greenwood Village, CO 80111
Tel: (720)279-0159; Free: 800-920-6723
Web Site: csuglobal.edu
Description: State-supported, comprehensive, coed. Awards bachelor's and master's degrees.

■ COLORADO STATE UNIVERSITY-PUEBLO
2200 Bonforte Blvd.
Pueblo, CO 81001-4901
Tel: (719)549-2100
Fax: (719)549-2419
E-mail: info@csupueblo.edu
Web Site: www.csupueblo.edu
Description: State-supported, comprehensive, coed. Part of Colorado State University System. Awards bachelor's, master's, and doctoral degrees. Founded 1933. Setting: 279-acre small town campus with easy access to Colorado Springs. Endowment: $18.2 million. Research spending for the previous fiscal year: $2.8 million. Educational spending for the previous fiscal year: $3615 per student. Total enrollment: 6,736. Faculty: 349 (176 full-time, 173 part-time). Student-undergrad faculty ratio is 14:1. 2,435 applied, 95% were admitted. 13% from top 10% of their high school class, 35% from top quarter, 67% from top half. Full-time: 3,134 students, 51% women, 49% men. Part-time: 1,251 students, 54% women, 46% men. Students come from 40 states and territories, 37 other countries, 14% from out-of-state. 0.6% American Indian or Alaska Native, non-Hispanic/Latino; 33% Hispanic/Latino; 6% Black or African American, non-Hispanic/Latino; 1% Asian, non-Hispanic/Latino; 0.3% Native Hawaiian or other Pacific Islander, non-Hispanic/Latino; 2% international. 24% 25 or older, 16% live on campus, 9% transferred in. Retention: 68% of full-time freshmen returned the following year. Academic areas with the most degrees conferred: business/marketing; health professions and related sciences; social sciences. Core. Calendar: semesters. Academic remediation for entering students, ESL program, services for LD students, advanced placement, accelerated degree program, honors program, independent study, distance learning, double major, summer session for credit, part-time degree program, external degree program, co-op programs and internships, graduate courses open to undergrads. Off campus study at CSU-Pueblo Tower, CSU-Pueblo Fort Carson. Study abroad program. ROTC: Army.
Entrance Requirements: Options: electronic application, deferred admission, international baccalaureate accepted. Required: minimum 2 high school GPA, SAT or ACT. Required for some: essay, interview. Entrance: minimally difficult. Application deadlines: 8/1, 8/1 for nonresidents. Notification: continuous until 9/15, continuous until 9/15 for nonresidents. SAT Reasoning Test deadline: 8/1. SAT Subject Test deadline: 8/1. Transfer credits accepted: Yes.
Costs Per Year: Application fee: $25. Area resident tuition: $8174 full-time, $272 per credit hour part-time. State resident tuition: $8174 full-time, $272 per credit hour part-time. Nonresident tuition: $24,573 full-time, $819 per

credit hour part-time. Mandatory fees: $2472 full-time, $82.40 per credit hour part-time, $1236 per term part-time. College room and board: $10,784. College room only: $6140.

Collegiate Environment: Orientation program. Choral group, marching band, student-run newspaper, radio station. Social organizations: 72 open to all; national fraternities, national sororities; 1% of eligible men and 1% of eligible women are members. Most popular organizations: Fellowship of Christian Athletes, Black Student Union, Latinx Student Union, National Society of Leadership and Success, Southern Colorado Assoc. of Nursing Students (SCANS). Major annual events: Student Involvement and Employment Fair, Annual Spring Concert, Homecoming/PackFest. Student services: health clinic, personal-psychological counseling. Campus security: 24-hour emergency response devices and patrols, student patrols, late night transport-escort service, controlled dormitory access. 924 college housing spaces available; 693 were occupied in 2018-19. Freshmen guaranteed college housing. On-campus residence required through sophomore year. Option: coed housing available. CSU-Pueblo University Library. Books: 183,220 (physical), 227,551 (digital/electronic); Serial titles: 2,882 (physical), 157,848 (digital/electronic); Databases: 426. Weekly public service hours: 93; students can reserve study rooms. Operations spending for the previous fiscal year: $115,657. 870 computers available on campus for general student use. Computer purchase/lease plans available. A campuswide network can be accessed. Students can access the following: online class registration. Staffed computer lab on campus provides training in use of computers, software, and the Internet.

Community Environment: Pueblo is a city of approximately 100,000 people located on the Arkansas River on the eastern slope of the Rocky Mountains. The city is a manufacturing and retail center for southeastern Colorado with a mild and semiarid climate. Recreational activities including skiing, hiking, camping, boating, fishing, and swimming are available in Pueblo and its immediate vicinity. The city and the university cooperate to provide cultural activities including a symphony orchestra and theatrical productions.

■ COLORADO TECHNICAL UNIVERSITY AURORA

3151 S Vaughn Way
Aurora, CO 80014
Tel: (303)632-2300; Free: 888-309-6555
Web Site: www.coloradotech.edu

Description: Proprietary, comprehensive, coed. Administratively affiliated with Colorado Technical University. Awards associate, bachelor's, and master's degrees. Founded 1965. Setting: 1-acre urban campus with easy access to Denver. Total enrollment: 733. Faculty: 163. Full-time: 229 students, 45% women, 55% men. Part-time: 344 students, 49% women, 51% men. 6% from out-of-state. 68% 25 or older, 13% transferred in. Academic areas with the most degrees conferred: computer and information sciences; business/marketing; homeland security, law enforcement, firefighting, and protective services. Core. Calendar: quarters. Academic remediation for entering students, services for LD students, advanced placement, accelerated degree program, independent study, distance learning, double major, summer session for credit, part-time degree program, adult/continuing education programs, co-op programs and internships, graduate courses open to undergrads.

Entrance Requirements: Options: electronic application, deferred admission, international baccalaureate accepted. Required: interview. Application deadline: rolling. Notification: continuous.

Collegiate Environment: Orientation program. Campus security: 24-hour emergency response devices and patrols, late night transport-escort service. 230 computers available on campus for general student use. A campuswide network can be accessed. Staffed computer lab on campus.

■ COLORADO TECHNICAL UNIVERSITY COLORADO SPRINGS

4435 N Chestnut St.
Colorado Springs, CO 80907
Tel: (719)598-0200; Free: 866-942-6555
Web Site: www.coloradotech.edu

Description: Proprietary, university, coed. Administratively affiliated with Colorado Technical University. Awards associate, bachelor's, master's, and doctoral degrees. Founded 1965. Setting: 14-acre suburban campus with easy access to Denver. Total enrollment: 2,359. Faculty: 343. 5% from out-of-state. 80% 25 or older. Academic areas with the most degrees conferred: computer and information sciences; business/marketing; homeland security, law enforcement, firefighting, and protective services. Core. Calendar: quarters. Academic remediation for entering students, services for LD

students, advanced placement, accelerated degree program, independent study, distance learning, double major, summer session for credit, part-time degree program, adult/continuing education programs, co-op programs and internships, graduate courses open to undergrads. ROTC: Army (c).

Entrance Requirements: Options: electronic application, deferred admission, international baccalaureate accepted. Required: interview. Entrance: minimally difficult. Application deadline: rolling. Notification: continuous.

Collegiate Environment: Orientation program. Campus security: 24-hour emergency response devices, late night transport-escort service. 400 computers available on campus for general student use. A campuswide network can be accessed. Staffed computer lab on campus.

Community Environment: Colorado Tech is located at the foot of beautiful Pikes Peak. This ideal location provides convenient access to Colorado's magnificent outdoor recreational facilities: skiing, camping, hunting, fishing, and backpacking. Beautiful Colorado Springs and its environs constitute a progressive, growing city of approximately 400,000.

■ COLORADO TECHNICAL UNIVERSITY ONLINE

4435 N Chestnut St.
Colorado Springs, CO 80907
Free: 866-813-1836
Web Site: www.coloradotech.edu

Description: Proprietary, comprehensive, coed. Administratively affiliated with Colorado Technical University. Awards associate, bachelor's, and master's degrees. Total enrollment: 25,797. Faculty: 613. Full-time: 23,094 students, 65% women, 35% men. 83% 25 or older, 22% transferred in. Academic areas with the most degrees conferred: business/marketing; homeland security, law enforcement, firefighting, and protective services; computer and information sciences. Core. Calendar: quarters. Academic remediation for entering students, services for LD students, advanced placement, accelerated degree program, distance learning, double major, part-time degree program, adult/continuing education programs, graduate courses open to undergrads.

Entrance Requirements: Options: electronic application, deferred admission, international baccalaureate accepted. Required: interview. Entrance: minimally difficult. Application deadline: rolling. Notification: continuous.

Collegiate Environment: Orientation program.

■ COMMUNITY COLLEGE OF AURORA

16000 E CentreTech Pky.
Aurora, CO 80011-9036
Tel: (303)360-4700
Web Site: www.ccaurora.edu

Description: State-supported, 2-year, coed. Part of Colorado Community College System. Awards certificates, transfer associate, and terminal associate degrees. Founded 1983. Setting: suburban campus with easy access to Denver. Total enrollment: 7,982. Faculty: 371 (69 full-time, 292 part-time). Student-undergrad faculty ratio is 20:1. Full-time: 1,867 students, 55% women, 45% men. Part-time: 6,115 students, 59% women, 41% men. Students come from 60 other countries, 2% from out-of-state. 0.5% American Indian or Alaska Native, non-Hispanic/Latino; 30% Hispanic/Latino; 18% Black or African American, non-Hispanic/Latino; 6% Asian, non-Hispanic/Latino; 0.4% Native Hawaiian or other Pacific Islander, non-Hispanic/Latino; 4% international. 27% 25 or older, 5% transferred in. Retention: 54% of full-time freshmen returned the following year. Academic areas with the most degrees conferred: liberal arts/general studies; visual and performing arts; computer and information sciences. Core. Calendar: semesters. Academic remediation for entering students, ESL program, services for LD students, independent study, distance learning, summer session for credit, part-time degree program, external degree program, adult/continuing education programs, co-op programs and internships. Off campus study at T. H. Pickens Technical Vocational Center.

Entrance Requirements: Required for some: high school transcript.

Costs Per Year: Area resident tuition: $3825 full-time. State resident tuition: $3825 full-time, $148.90 per credit hour part-time. Nonresident tuition: $14,913 full-time, $610.90 per credit hour part-time. Mandatory fees: $251 full-time, $66.40 per credit hour part-time, $66.40.

Collegiate Environment: Orientation program. Drama-theater group. Student services: women's center. Campus security: late night transport-escort service. College housing not available. Community College of Aurora Learning Resource Center. Books: 3,374 (physical), 252,009 (digital/electronic); Serial titles: 11 (physical), 22,725 (digital/electronic); Databases: 84. Weekly public service hours: 63.

■ **COMMUNITY COLLEGE OF DENVER**
PO Box 173363
Denver, CO 80217-3363
Tel: (303)556-2600
E-mail: andrew.garcia@ccd.edu
Web Site: www.ccd.edu
Description: State-supported, 2-year, coed. Part of Colorado Community College System. Awards certificates, transfer associate, and terminal associate degrees. Founded 1970. Setting: 124-acre urban campus. Total enrollment: 8,556. Faculty: 393 (108 full-time, 285 part-time). Student-undergrad faculty ratio is 25:1. 3,829 applied, 100% were admitted. Full-time: 2,441 students, 55% women, 45% men. Part-time: 6,115 students, 59% women, 41% men. 2% from out-of-state. 0.8% American Indian or Alaska Native, non-Hispanic/Latino; 33% Hispanic/Latino; 11% Black or African American, non-Hispanic/Latino; 5% Asian, non-Hispanic/Latino; 0.2% Native Hawaiian or other Pacific Islander, non-Hispanic/Latino; 7% international. 35% 25 or older. Academic areas with the most degrees conferred: liberal arts/general studies; health professions and related sciences; business/marketing. Core. Calendar: semesters. Academic remediation for entering students, ESL program, services for LD students, advanced placement, accelerated degree program, freshman honors college, honors program, independent study, distance learning, double major, summer session for credit, part-time degree program, external degree program, adult/continuing education programs, co-op programs and internships. Off campus study at Metropolitan State College, University of Colorado at Denver. Study abroad program. ROTC: Army.
Entrance Requirements: Open admission except for health occupation, essential skills programs, and computer information systems programs. Options: electronic application, early admission, deferred admission. Entrance: noncompetitive.
Costs Per Year: Application fee: $0. Comprehensive fee: $439. Area resident tuition: $145 per credit hour part-time. State resident tuition: $145 per credit hour part-time. Nonresident tuition: $593 per credit hour part-time.
Collegiate Environment: Orientation program. Choral group, student-run newspaper. Most popular organizations: Phi Theta Kappa, Black Student Alliance, La Mision, SAFI, Chinese Culture Club. Major annual events: Haunted Harvest, Cinco de Mayo, Welcome Back Picnic. Student services: health clinic, personal-psychological counseling. Campus security: 24-hour emergency response devices and patrols, late night transport-escort service. College housing not available. Auraria Library.
Community Environment: See University of Denver.

■ **CONCORDE CAREER COLLEGE**
111 N Havana St.
Aurora, CO 80010
Tel: (303)861-1151
Web Site: www.concorde.edu
Description: Proprietary, 2-year, coed. Awards certificates and terminal associate degrees. Founded 1966.

■ **DENVER COLLEGE OF NURSING**
1401 19th St.
Denver, CO 80202
Tel: (303)292-0015; Free: 888-479-5550
Fax: (720)974-0290
Web Site: www.denvercollegeofnursing.edu
Description: Proprietary, 4-year, coed. Awards bachelor's degrees.

■ **DEVRY UNIVERSITY-WESTMINSTER CAMPUS**
1870 W 122nd Ave.
Westminster, CO 80234
Tel: (303)280-7400; Free: 866-338-7934
Web Site: www.devry.edu
Description: Proprietary, comprehensive, coed. Awards associate, bachelor's, and master's degrees. Founded 1945. Setting: urban campus. Total enrollment: 276. Faculty: 30 (all part-time). Student-undergrad faculty ratio is 14:1. Full-time: 75 students, 43% women, 57% men. Part-time: 164 students, 51% women, 49% men. 7% from out-of-state. 0.4% American Indian or Alaska Native, non-Hispanic/Latino; 18% Hispanic/Latino; 7% Black or African American, non-Hispanic/Latino; 3% Asian, non-Hispanic/Latino; 0.4% international. 81% 25 or older, 19% transferred in. Calendar: semesters. Accelerated degree program, honors program, distance learning. Study abroad program.
Entrance Requirements: Option: deferred admission. Application deadline: rolling. Notification: continuous.

■ **FORT LEWIS COLLEGE**
1000 Rim Dr.
Durango, CO 81301-3999
Tel: (970)247-7010; Free: 877-FLC-COLO
Fax: (970)247-7179
E-mail: admission@fortlewis.edu
Web Site: www.fortlewis.edu
Description: State-supported, comprehensive, coed. Awards bachelor's and master's degrees. Founded 1911. Setting: 350-acre small town campus. Endowment: $9 million. Research spending for the previous fiscal year: $968,078. Educational spending for the previous fiscal year: $7750 per student. Total enrollment: 3,316. Faculty: 241 (170 full-time, 71 part-time). Student-undergrad faculty ratio is 15:1. 4,198 applied, 91% were admitted. 11% from top 10% of their high school class, 22% from top quarter, 68% from top half. Full-time: 2,879 students, 52% women, 48% men. Part-time: 388 students, 47% women, 53% men. 55% from out-of-state. 27% American Indian or Alaska Native, non-Hispanic/Latino; 11% Hispanic/Latino; 1% Black or African American, non-Hispanic/Latino; 0.6% Asian, non-Hispanic/Latino; 0.2% Native Hawaiian or other Pacific Islander, non-Hispanic/Latino; 0.8% international. 100% 25 or older, 42% live on campus, 10% transferred in. Retention: 62% of full-time freshmen returned the following year. Academic areas with the most degrees conferred: business/marketing; parks and recreation; social sciences. Core. Calendar: semesters modified trimesters. Academic remediation for entering students, services for LD students, advanced placement, self-designed majors, honors program, independent study, double major, summer session for credit, internships. Study abroad program.
Entrance Requirements: Options: electronic application, deferred admission, international baccalaureate accepted. Required: high school transcript, SAT or ACT. Recommended: essay, 2 recommendations. Required for some: interview. Entrance: moderately difficult. Application deadlines: 8/1 for nonresidents, 11/15 for early action. Notification: continuous for nonresidents, 12/31 for early action. SAT Reasoning Test deadline: 8/1. SAT Subject Test deadline: 8/1. Transfer credits accepted: Yes.
Costs Per Year: Application fee: $40. State resident tuition: $7056 full-time, $294 per credit hour part-time. Nonresident tuition: $17,712 full-time, $738 per credit hour part-time. Mandatory fees: $1984 full-time, $66.70 per credit hour part-time. Full-time tuition and fees vary according to course load and reciprocity agreements. Part-time tuition and fees vary according to course load and reciprocity agreements. College room and board: $9878. College room only: $4796. Room and board charges vary according to board plan and housing facility.
Collegiate Environment: Orientation program. Drama-theater group, student-run newspaper, radio station. Social organizations: 63 open to all. Most popular organizations: KDUR - Campus/community radio, Environmental Center, Student Union Productions, Dance Co-Motion, Master Plan Ministries. Major annual events: SkyFest, Homecoming, Hozhoni Days. Student services: legal services, health clinic, personal-psychological counseling. Campus security: 24-hour emergency response devices and patrols, late night transport-escort service, controlled dormitory access. Freshmen given priority for college housing. On-campus residence required in freshman year. Option: coed housing available. John F. Reed Library plus 1 other. Books: 138,839 (physical), 213,585 (digital/electronic); Serial titles: 4 (physical), 170,201 (digital/electronic); Databases: 74. Weekly public service hours: 80; study areas open 24 hours, 5-7 days a week; students can reserve study rooms. Operations spending for the previous fiscal year: $506,901. 825 computers available on campus for general student use. A campuswide network can be accessed from student residence rooms and from off campus. Students can access the following: online class registration. Staffed computer lab on campus (open 24 hours a day) provides training in use of computers, software, and the Internet.
Community Environment: Durango is located in the Four-Corners region where the states of Colorado, Utah, Arizona, and New Mexico come to a common point. Durango has magnificent mountain landscapes and glistening sunshine at an elevation of 6,700 feet. A modern jet port serves the area. Near Durango nestled in the spruce of the high country gleam thousands of mountain lakes, including two of the larger, Lemon and Vallecito. A few miles south is Navajo Lake, which extends into New Mexico. Agriculture and tourism are an integral part of the economy, as is retailing education, medicine, and law. La Plata County is home to over 47,000 people, and Durango has a population of over 15,500. Purgatory ski area offers complete ski resort facilities.

■ FRONT RANGE COMMUNITY COLLEGE

3645 W 112th Ave.
Westminster, CO 80031
Tel: (303)466-8811
E-mail: miori.gidley@frontrange.edu
Web Site: www.frontrange.edu

Description: State-supported, 2-year, coed. Part of Community Colleges of Colorado System. Awards certificates, transfer associate, and terminal associate degrees. Founded 1968. Setting: 90-acre suburban campus with easy access to Denver. Endowment: $550,411. Educational spending for the previous fiscal year: $4331 per student. Total enrollment: 18,880. Faculty: 970 (245 full-time, 725 part-time). Student-undergrad faculty ratio is 19:1. 5,106 applied, 100% were admitted. Full-time: 4,999 students, 52% women, 48% men. Part-time: 13,881 students, 58% women, 42% men. Students come from 43 states and territories, 85 other countries, 2% from out-of-state. 0.7% American Indian or Alaska Native, non-Hispanic/Latino; 19% Hispanic/Latino; 2% Black or African American, non-Hispanic/Latino; 3% Asian, non-Hispanic/Latino; 0.2% Native Hawaiian or other Pacific Islander, non-Hispanic/Latino; 3% international. 34% 25 or older, 10% transferred in. Retention: 59% of full-time freshmen returned the following year. Core. Calendar: semesters. Academic remediation for entering students, ESL program, services for LD students, advanced placement, self-designed majors, freshman honors college, honors program, independent study, distance learning, double major, summer session for credit, part-time degree program, co-op programs and internships. Off campus study at Metropolitan State College, University of Colorado at Denver, Colorado State University. Study abroad program. ROTC: Army (c), Air Force (c).

Entrance Requirements: Open admission. Options: electronic application, early admission, deferred admission, international baccalaureate accepted. Entrance: noncompetitive. Transfer credits accepted: Yes.

Costs Per Year: Application fee: $0. State resident tuition: $3574 full-time, $148.92 per credit hour part-time. Nonresident tuition: $14,662 full-time, $610.92 per credit hour part-time. Mandatory fees: $412 full-time, $206 per term part-time. Full-time tuition and fees vary according to program. Part-time tuition and fees vary according to program.

Collegiate Environment: Orientation program. Drama-theater group, student-run newspaper. Most popular organizations: Student Government Association, Student Colorado Registry of Interpreters for the Deaf, Students in Free Enterprise (SIFE), Gay-Straight Alliance, Recycling Club. Major annual events: Spring Fling, Chili Cook-Off, Culture Days. Student services: personal-psychological counseling. Campus security: 24-hour emergency response devices and patrols, late night transport-escort service. College housing not available. College Hill Library plus 2 others. Books: 32,801 (physical), 546 (digital/electronic); Databases: 12. Weekly public service hours: 54; students can reserve study rooms. Operations spending for the previous fiscal year: $1.5 million.

Community Environment: See University of Denver.

■ IBMC COLLEGE

3842 S Mason St.
Fort Collins, CO 80525
Tel: (970)223-2669; Free: 800-495-2669
E-mail: jshoup@ibmc.edu
Web Site: www.ibmc.edu

Description: Proprietary, 2-year, coed. Awards certificates, diplomas, and terminal associate degrees. Founded 1987. Setting: suburban campus with easy access to Denver. Educational spending for the previous fiscal year: $4531 per student. Total enrollment: 1,020. Faculty: 115 (46 full-time, 69 part-time). Student-undergrad faculty ratio is 8:1. 1,064 applied, 92% were admitted. Full-time: 1,020 students, 85% women, 15% men. 3% from out-of-state. 0.6% American Indian or Alaska Native, non-Hispanic/Latino; 20% Hispanic/Latino; 1% Black or African American, non-Hispanic/Latino; 0.5% Asian, non-Hispanic/Latino; 0.2% Native Hawaiian or other Pacific Islander, non-Hispanic/Latino. 63% 25 or older. Retention: 69% of full-time freshmen returned the following year. Core. Calendar: continuous. Accelerated degree program, honors program, summer session for credit, adult/continuing education programs, co-op programs and internships.

Entrance Requirements: Open admission. Option: electronic application. Required: high school transcript, interview. Application deadline: rolling. Transfer credits accepted: Yes.

Collegiate Environment: Orientation program. Most popular organizations: Alpha Beta Kappa, Circle of Hope, Relay for Life, Peer Mentoring, Peer Tutor. Major annual events: Nine News Health Fair, Student Assembly, Student Appreciation BBQ. IBMC College plus 8 others. Books: 834 (physical),

124,000 (digital/electronic); Databases: 1. Operations spending for the previous fiscal year: $62,784. 118 computers available on campus for general student use. Computer purchase/lease plans available. A campuswide network can be accessed from off-campus. Staffed computer lab on campus provides training in use of computers, software, and the Internet.

■ INTELLITEC COLLEGE (COLORADO SPRINGS)

2315 E Pikes Peak Ave.
Colorado Springs, CO 80909
Tel: (719)632-7626; Free: 800-748-2282
Fax: (719)632-7451
Web Site: www.intelliteccollege.edu

Description: Proprietary, 2-year, coed. Part of Technical Trades Institute, Inc. Awards certificates, diplomas, and terminal associate degrees. Founded 1965. Setting: 2-acre urban campus with easy access to Denver. Total enrollment: 587. 57% 25 or older. Core. Calendar: 6-week terms. Advanced placement, double major.

Entrance Requirements: Open admission. Required: high school transcript, interview. Entrance: noncompetitive. Application deadline: rolling.

Collegiate Environment: Orientation program. Campus security: 24-hour emergency response devices.

■ INTELLITEC COLLEGE (GRAND JUNCTION)

772 Horizon Dr.
Grand Junction, CO 81506
Tel: (970)245-8101; Free: 800-748-2282
Fax: (970)243-8074
Web Site: www.intelliteccollege.edu

Description: Proprietary, 2-year, coed. Awards certificates, diplomas, and transfer associate degrees. Setting: small town campus. Student-undergrad faculty ratio is 22:1. Calendar: continuous.

Entrance Requirements: Open admission. Required: high school transcript, interview. Entrance: noncompetitive. Transfer credits accepted: Yes.

Collegiate Environment: Orientation program.

■ JOHNSON & WALES UNIVERSITY

7150 Montview Blvd.
Denver, CO 80220
Tel: (303)256-9300; Free: 877-598-3368
Fax: (303)256-9333
E-mail: den@admissions.jwu.edu
Web Site: www.jwu.edu/denver

Description: Independent, comprehensive, coed. Awards associate, bachelor's, and master's degrees. Founded 1993. Setting: small town campus. Total enrollment: 1,388. Faculty: 127 (52 full-time, 75 part-time). Student-undergrad faculty ratio is 16:1. 2,319 applied, 81% were admitted. Full-time: 1,227 students, 60% women, 40% men. Part-time: 129 students, 57% women, 43% men. 63% from out-of-state. 0.4% American Indian or Alaska Native, non-Hispanic/Latino; 19% Hispanic/Latino; 9% Black or African American, non-Hispanic/Latino; 2% Asian, non-Hispanic/Latino; 0.1% Native Hawaiian or other Pacific Islander, non-Hispanic/Latino; 1% international. 17% 25 or older, 47% live on campus, 7% transferred in. Retention: 75% of full-time freshmen returned the following year. Academic areas with the most degrees conferred: family and consumer sciences; business/marketing; personal and culinary services. Core. Calendar: quarters. Academic remediation for entering students, ESL program, services for LD students, advanced placement, accelerated degree program, honors program, independent study, summer session for credit, part-time degree program, adult/continuing education programs, co-op programs and internships. Study abroad program. ROTC: Army.

Entrance Requirements: Options: electronic application, early admission, deferred admission, international baccalaureate accepted. Required: high school transcript. Recommended: minimum 2 high school GPA. Required for some: essay, minimum 2.75 high school GPA, interview, SAT or ACT. Entrance: moderately difficult.

Collegiate Environment: Orientation program. Drama-theater group, student-run newspaper. Campus security: 24-hour emergency response devices and patrols, student patrols, late night transport-escort service. Johnson & Wales University Library.

■ LAMAR COMMUNITY COLLEGE

2401 S Main St.
Lamar, CO 81052-3999
Tel: (719)336-2248; Free: 800-968-6920

Fax: (719)336-2448
E-mail: admissions@lamarcc.edu
Web Site: www.lamarcc.edu
Description: State-supported, 2-year, coed. Part of Colorado Community College and Occupational Education System. Awards certificates, diplomas, transfer associate, and terminal associate degrees. Founded 1937. Setting: 125-acre small town campus. Educational spending for the previous fiscal year: $4906 per student. Total enrollment: 791. Faculty: 46 (16 full-time, 30 part-time). Student-undergrad faculty ratio is 21:1. 455 applied, 100% were admitted. Full-time: 404 students, 48% women, 52% men. Part-time: 387 students, 59% women, 41% men. Students come from 29 states and territories, 9 other countries, 10% from out-of-state. 0.9% American Indian or Alaska Native, non-Hispanic/Latino; 23% Hispanic/Latino; 5% Black or African American, non-Hispanic/Latino; 0.1% Asian, non-Hispanic/Latino; 0.1% Native Hawaiian or other Pacific Islander, non-Hispanic/Latino; 6% international. 18% 25 or older, 20% live on campus, 5% transferred in. Retention: 49% of full-time freshmen returned the following year. Core. Calendar: semesters. Academic remediation for entering students, ESL program, services for LD students, advanced placement, self-designed majors, independent study, distance learning, double major, summer session for credit, part-time degree program, adult/continuing education programs, co-op programs and internships.
Entrance Requirements: Open admission. Options: electronic application, early admission, international baccalaureate accepted. Entrance: noncompetitive. Application deadline: 9/16. Preference given to state residents. Transfer credits accepted: Yes.
Costs Per Year: Application fee: $0. State resident tuition: $3574 full-time, $148.92 per credit hour part-time. Nonresident tuition: $5956 full-time, $248.17 per credit hour part-time. Mandatory fees: $376 full-time, $376 per year part-time. Full-time tuition and fees vary according to course load, program, and reciprocity agreements. Part-time tuition and fees vary according to course load, program, and reciprocity agreements. College room and board: $6588. College room only: $2214. Room and board charges vary according to housing facility.
Collegiate Environment: Orientation program. Major annual events: Antelope Night, Graduation, Nursing Pinning. Student services: health clinic, personal-psychological counseling. Campus security: 24-hour emergency response devices and patrols, student patrols, late night transport-escort service, controlled dormitory access. Learning Resources Center. Books: 10,825 (physical), 1 (digital/electronic); Serial titles: 23 (physical); Databases: 1. Weekly public service hours: 53. Operations spending for the previous fiscal year: $6710. 60 computers available on campus for general student use. A campuswide network can be accessed. Students can access the following: online class registration. Staffed computer lab on campus provides training in use of computers.
Community Environment: Lamar is an All-America City located at the junction of U.S. Highways 50, 287, and 385 with a dry climate and a population of 8,400. Livestock and poultry are primary concerns in this extensively irrigated area for which Lamar is a trading center. Airlines, railroads and buses serve the area. The community facilities include churches, a hospital and clinics, a library and various civic clubs. Part-time employment is available. The recreational activities include hunting, fishing, boating, golfing, swimming, and baseball.

■ **LINCOLN COLLEGE OF TECHNOLOGY**
11194 E 45th Ave.
Denver, CO 80239
Tel: (303)722-5724; Free: 844-215-1513
Fax: (303)778-8264
Web Site: www.lincolntech.edu
Description: Proprietary, 2-year, coed. Awards certificates, diplomas, and terminal associate degrees. Founded 1963. Setting: urban campus. Total enrollment: 952. 400 applied, 100% were admitted. 25% 25 or older. Core. Calendar: 8 6-week terms. Services for LD students, summer session for credit, co-op programs.
Entrance Requirements: Entrance: moderately difficult. Application deadline: rolling.
Collegiate Environment: Orientation program. Student services: personal-psychological counseling. Campus security: 24-hour emergency response devices and patrols. Denver Automotive and Diesel College Library plus 1 other.

■ **METROPOLITAN STATE UNIVERSITY OF DENVER**
890 Auraria Pky.
Denver, CO 80204

Tel: (303)556-5740
Web Site: www.msudenver.edu
Description: State-supported, comprehensive, coed. Awards bachelor's and master's degrees. Founded 1963. Setting: 175-acre urban campus with easy access to Denver. Endowment: $7.1 million. Research spending for the previous fiscal year: $22,827. Educational spending for the previous fiscal year: $5867 per student. Total enrollment: 20,304. Faculty: 1,449 (562 full-time, 887 part-time). Student-undergrad faculty ratio is 17:1. 11,435 applied, 64% were admitted. 2% from top 10% of their high school class, 14% from top quarter, 49% from top half. Full-time: 12,759 students, 52% women, 48% men. Part-time: 6,907 students, 56% women, 44% men. 4% from out-of-state. 0.5% American Indian or Alaska Native, non-Hispanic/Latino; 27% Hispanic/Latino; 6% Black or African American, non-Hispanic/Latino; 4% Asian, non-Hispanic/Latino; 0.3% Native Hawaiian or other Pacific Islander, non-Hispanic/Latino; 0.6% international. 40% 25 or older, 11% transferred in. Retention: 62% of full-time freshmen returned the following year. Academic areas with the most degrees conferred: business/marketing; psychology; interdisciplinary studies; health professions and related sciences. Core. Calendar: semesters. Services for LD students, advanced placement, accelerated degree program, self-designed majors, honors program, independent study, distance learning, double major, summer session for credit, part-time degree program, external degree program, adult/continuing education programs, co-op programs and internships. Off campus study at 3 members of the Consortium of State Colleges in Colorado, University of Colorado at Denver, Community College of Denver. Study abroad program. ROTC: Army, Air Force (c).
Entrance Requirements: Open admission for applicants 20 years or older who are high school graduates, have GED, or have 30 transferable credits from another college. Options: electronic application, deferred admission, international baccalaureate accepted. Required: high school transcript, SAT or ACT. Recommended: minimum 2 high school GPA. Required for some: SAT, ACT. Entrance: minimally difficult. Application deadline: 7/1. Notification: continuous. SAT Reasoning Test deadline: 8/1. Transfer credits accepted: Yes.
Costs Per Year: Application fee: $25. State resident tuition: $6,245 full-time, $345.20 per credit hour part-time. Nonresident tuition: $19,426 full-time, $809.40 per credit hour part-time. Mandatory fees: $1,421 full-time, $23.30 per credit hour part-time, $360.70 per term part-time. Full-time tuition and fees vary according to course load and location. Part-time tuition and fees vary according to course load and location.
Collegiate Environment: Orientation program. Drama-theater group, choral group, student-run newspaper, radio station. Social organizations: national fraternities, national sororities. Student services: legal services, health clinic, personal-psychological counseling, women's center. Campus security: 24-hour emergency response devices and patrols, late night transport-escort service. Auraria Library. 808 computers available on campus for general student use. A campuswide network can be accessed from off-campus. Students can access the following: online class registration. Staffed computer lab on campus provides training in use of computers, software, and the Internet.
Community Environment: See University of Denver.

■ **MORGAN COMMUNITY COLLEGE**
920 Barlow Rd.
Fort Morgan, CO 80701-4399
Tel: (970)542-3100; Free: 800-622-0216
E-mail: kim.maxwell@morgancc.edu
Web Site: www.morgancc.edu
Description: State-supported, 2-year, coed. Part of Colorado Community College and Occupational Education System. Awards certificates, transfer associate, and terminal associate degrees. Founded 1967. Setting: 20-acre small town campus with easy access to Denver. Endowment: $2.7 million. Educational spending for the previous fiscal year: $6375 per student. Total enrollment: 1,474. Faculty: 93 (31 full-time, 62 part-time). Student-undergrad faculty ratio is 14:1. Full-time: 327 students, 68% women, 32% men. Part-time: 1,147 students, 65% women, 35% men. Students come from 8 states and territories, 1% from out-of-state. 0.7% American Indian or Alaska Native, non-Hispanic/Latino; 23% Hispanic/Latino; 3% Black or African American, non-Hispanic/Latino; 0.5% Asian, non-Hispanic/Latino; 0.1% Native Hawaiian or other Pacific Islander, non-Hispanic/Latino; 2% international. 25% 25 or older, 2% transferred in. Retention: 62% of full-time freshmen returned the following year. Core. Calendar: semesters. Academic remediation for entering students, services for LD students, advanced placement, honors

program, independent study, distance learning, double major, summer session for credit, part-time degree program, adult/continuing education programs, internships.

Entrance Requirements: Open admission. Options: electronic application, early admission, deferred admission. Recommended: high school transcript. Entrance: noncompetitive. Application deadlines: rolling, rolling for nonresidents. Notification: continuous, continuous for nonresidents. Transfer credits accepted: Yes.

Collegiate Environment: Orientation program. Student-run newspaper. Campus security: security cameras, local police patrols, free public phones. Learning Resource Center. Books: 6,205 (physical), 205,240 (digital/electronic); Serial titles: 15 (physical), 18,964 (digital/electronic); Databases: 23. Operations spending for the previous fiscal year: $194,227. 60 computers available on campus for general student use. A campuswide network can be accessed from off-campus. Students can access the following: online class registration. Staffed computer lab on campus provides training in use of computers, software, and the Internet.

Community Environment: Morgan County has an abundant supply of facilities for recreational enjoyment. In addition to the athletic activities close at hand, the students have access to the metropolitan offerings in Denver, one hour away, and the beautiful Rocky Mountains, a two hour drive on Interstate highways.

■ **NAROPA UNIVERSITY**
2130 Arapahoe Ave.
Boulder, CO 80302-6697
Tel: (303)444-0202; Free: 800-772-6951
Fax: (303)444-0410
E-mail: kwills@naropa.edu
Web Site: www.naropa.edu

Description: Independent, comprehensive, coed. Awards bachelor's and master's degrees. Founded 1974. Setting: 12-acre urban campus with easy access to Denver. Endowment: $7.6 million. Educational spending for the previous fiscal year: $12,790 per student. Total enrollment: 966. Faculty: 153 (50 full-time, 103 part-time). Student-undergrad faculty ratio is 9:1. 105 applied, 100% were admitted. Full-time: 367 students, 65% women, 35% men. Part-time: 30 students, 63% women, 37% men. Students come from 41 states and territories, 12 other countries, 63% from out-of-state. 0.3% American Indian or Alaska Native, non-Hispanic/Latino; 11% Hispanic/Latino; 1% Black or African American, non-Hispanic/Latino; 1% Asian, non-Hispanic/Latino; 0.3% Native Hawaiian or other Pacific Islander, non-Hispanic/Latino; 3% international. 37% 25 or older, 18% live on campus, 22% transferred. Retention: 58% of full-time freshmen returned the following year. Academic areas with the most degrees conferred: psychology; interdisciplinary studies; natural resources/environmental science; parks and recreation. Core. Calendar: semesters. Services for LD students, advanced placement, self-designed majors, independent study, double major, summer session for credit, part-time degree program, co-op programs and internships, graduate courses open to undergrads. Off campus study at University of Colorado-Boulder Extended Studies Consortium. Study abroad program.

Entrance Requirements: Options: electronic application, deferred admission, international baccalaureate accepted. Required: high school transcript. Required for some: essay, 1 recommendation, interview. Entrance: moderately difficult. Application deadline: rolling. Notification: continuous. Transfer credits accepted: Yes.

Costs Per Year: Application fee: $50. Comprehensive fee: $45,139 includes full-time tuition ($31,620), mandatory fees ($670), and college room and board ($12,849). Room and board charges vary according to housing facility. Part-time tuition: $995 per credit. Part-time mandatory fees: $310 per term. Part-time tuition and fees vary according to course load.

Collegiate Environment: Orientation program. Drama-theater group, choral group. Social organizations: 34 open to all. Most popular organizations: Student Union of Naropa, ROOT: Reconnecting on Outdoor Terrain, Team Tapas (yoga club), Community of Color and Allies, Naropa Zazen. Major annual events: Halloween Dance, Practice Day, Leadership and Activism Dinner. Student services: personal-psychological counseling. Campus security: late night transport-escort service, controlled dormitory access, foot and vehicle patrol 4:30 pm to midnight, 24 hour on-call Safety and Security Manager. Allen Ginsberg Library plus 2 others. Books: 36,333 (physical), 177,800 (digital/electronic); Serial titles: 335 (physical), 33,467 (digital/electronic); Databases: 47. Weekly public service hours: 69. Operations spending for the previous fiscal year: $483,464. 48 computers available on campus for general student use. A campuswide network can be accessed from student residence rooms and from off campus. Students can access

the following: online class registration. Staffed computer lab on campus provides training in use of computers, software, and the Internet.

■ **NATIONAL AMERICAN UNIVERSITY (CENTENNIAL)**
8242 S University Blvd.
Ste. 100
Centennial, CO 80122
Tel: (303)542-7000; Free: 877-628-5211
Web Site: www.national.edu

Description: Proprietary, 4-year, coed. Awards associate and bachelor's degrees.

■ **NATIONAL AMERICAN UNIVERSITY (COLORADO SPRINGS)**
1915 Jamboree Dr.
Ste. 185
Colorado Springs, CO 80920
Tel: (719)590-8300; Free: 855-369-9397
Fax: (719)277-0589
Web Site: www.national.edu

Description: Proprietary, 4-year, coed. Awards associate and bachelor's degrees. Founded 1941. Setting: 1-acre suburban campus with easy access to Denver. Total enrollment: 285. 88% 25 or older. Core. Calendar: quarters. Academic remediation for entering students, ESL program, accelerated degree program, independent study, distance learning, double major, summer session for credit, part-time degree program, external degree program, adult/continuing education programs, internships. Off campus study.

Entrance Requirements: Open admission. Option: deferred admission. Required: high school transcript, interview. Entrance: noncompetitive. Application deadline: rolling.

Collegiate Environment: Orientation program. Campus security: late night transport-escort service. National American University Library.

■ **NATIONAL AMERICAN UNIVERSITY (COLORADO SPRINGS SOUTH)**
1079 Space Ctr. Dr.
Ste. 140
Colorado Springs, CO 80915
Tel: (719)208-3800; Free: 855-369-9397
Web Site: www.national.edu

Description: Proprietary, 4-year, coed. Awards associate and bachelor's degrees.

■ **NAZARENE BIBLE COLLEGE**
1111 Academy Loop Park
Colorado Springs, CO 80910
Tel: (719)884-5000; Free: 800-873-3873
Fax: (719)884-5199
E-mail: semcconnaughey@nbc.edu
Web Site: www.nbc.edu

Description: Independent, 4-year, coed, affiliated with Church of the Nazarene. Awards associate and bachelor's degrees. Founded 1967. Setting: 64-acre urban campus with easy access to Colorado Springs. Total enrollment: 769. Faculty: 148 (9 full-time, 139 part-time). Student-undergrad faculty ratio is 6:1. 129 applied, 14% were admitted. Full-time: 89 students, 45% women, 55% men. Part-time: 680 students, 39% women, 61% men. Students come from 48 states and territories, 14 other countries, 89% from out-of-state. 0.9% American Indian or Alaska Native, non-Hispanic/Latino; 9% Hispanic/Latino; 7% Black or African American, non-Hispanic/Latino; 2% Asian, non-Hispanic/Latino; 0.5% Native Hawaiian or other Pacific Islander, non-Hispanic/Latino. 92% 25 or older, 12% transferred in. Academic areas with the most degrees conferred: theology and religious vocations; education. Core. Calendar: trimesters. Academic remediation for entering students, advanced placement, accelerated degree program, independent study, distance learning, double major, summer session for credit, part-time degree program, internships.

Entrance Requirements: Open admission. Options: electronic application, deferred admission, international baccalaureate accepted. Required: official transcripts from all prior colleges. Required for some: high school transcript. Entrance: noncompetitive. Application deadline: rolling. Notification: continuous. Transfer credits accepted: Yes.

Costs Per Year: Application fee: $0. Tuition: $10,800 full-time, $450 per credit hour part-time. Mandatory fees: $960 full-time, $40 per credit hour part-time. Full-time tuition and fees vary according to program and reciprocity agreements. Part-time tuition and fees vary according to program and reciprocity agreements.

Collegiate Environment: Orientation program. Student services: personal-psychological counseling. Campus security: 24-hour security personnel on campus. Trimble Library. Books: 47,287 (physical), 1,502 (digital/electronic); Serial titles: 285 (physical), 3,145 (digital/electronic); Databases: 14. Weekly public service hours: 51. 10 computers available on campus for general student use. A campuswide network can be accessed. Staffed computer lab on campus.

Community Environment: See The Colorado College.

■ **NORTHEASTERN JUNIOR COLLEGE**
100 College Ave.
Sterling, CO 80751-2399
Tel: (970)521-6600; Free: 800-626-4637
Fax: (970)522-4945
E-mail: adam.kunkel@njc.edu
Web Site: www.njc.edu
Description: State-supported, 2-year, coed. Part of Colorado Community College and Occupational Education System. Awards certificates, transfer associate, and terminal associate degrees. Founded 1941. Setting: 65-acre small town campus. Total enrollment: 1,547. Faculty: 95 (49 full-time, 46 part-time). Student-undergrad faculty ratio is 16:1. 894 applied, 100% were admitted. Full-time: 896 students, 46% women, 54% men. Part-time: 651 students, 66% women, 34% men. Students come from 29 states and territories, 11 other countries, 7% from out-of-state. 1% American Indian or Alaska Native, non-Hispanic/Latino; 14% Hispanic/Latino; 4% Black or African American, non-Hispanic/Latino; 1% Asian, non-Hispanic/Latino; 0.1% Native Hawaiian or other Pacific Islander, non-Hispanic/Latino; 5% international. 18% 25 or older, 40% live on campus, 5% transferred in. Core. Calendar: semesters. Academic remediation for entering students, ESL program, services for LD students, advanced placement, accelerated degree program, honors program, distance learning, double major, summer session for credit, part-time degree program, adult/continuing education programs, co-op programs and internships.
Entrance Requirements: Open admission. Option: electronic application. Recommended: high school transcript. Entrance: noncompetitive. Application deadline: rolling. Notification: continuous. Transfer credits accepted: Yes.
Costs Per Year: Application fee: $0. State resident tuition: $4467 full-time, $148.90 per credit hour part-time. Nonresident tuition: $6701 full-time, $223.35 per credit hour part-time. Mandatory fees: $605 full-time, $23.79 per credit hour part-time, $14 per term part-time. Full-time tuition and fees vary according to course load and reciprocity agreements. Part-time tuition and fees vary according to course load and reciprocity agreements. College room and board: $7080. College room only: $3058. Room and board charges vary according to board plan and housing facility.
Collegiate Environment: Orientation program. Drama-theater group, choral group. Social organizations: 25 open to all. Most popular organizations: Associated Student Government, Post Secondary Agriculture (PAS), Crossroads, NJC Ambassadors, Business Club. Major annual events: Region Nine Basketball and Volleyball Games, Frederick Winters (hypnotist), $2 movie nights on Thursdays. Student services: health clinic, personal-psychological counseling. Campus security: 24-hour emergency response devices, late night transport-escort service, controlled dormitory access. Monahan Library. Books: 24,184 (physical), 105,876 (digital/electronic); Serial titles: 104 (physical), 86 (digital/electronic); Databases: 8. Weekly public service hours: 71. 170 computers available on campus for general student use. Computer purchase/lease plans available. A computer is required for all students. A campuswide network can be accessed from student residence rooms. Students can access the following: online class registration. Staffed computer lab on campus provides training in use of computers, software, and the Internet.
Community Environment: Sterling, population 12,500, in northeastern Colorado on the South Platte River, has a mild climate. Trains and buses serve the area. Community facilities include churches, hospitals, libraries, a health center, and museum. Recreational activities include golf, tennis, swimming, bowling, roller skating, and boating. Rooming houses and private homes are available for student housing. The County Fair and Overland Trail Roundup are annual events. Part-time work is available.

■ **OTERO JUNIOR COLLEGE**
1802 Colorado Ave.
La Junta, CO 81050-3415
Tel: (719)384-6831
Fax: (719)384-6880

E-mail: lauren.berg@ojc.edu
Web Site: www.ojc.edu
Description: State-supported, 2-year, coed. Part of Colorado Community College System. Awards certificates, transfer associate, and terminal associate degrees. Founded 1941. Setting: 40-acre rural campus. Endowment: $1.5 million. Total enrollment: 1,449. Faculty: 75. Student-undergrad faculty ratio is 19:1. Students come from 20 states and territories, 15 other countries, 10% from out-of-state. 1% American Indian or Alaska Native, non-Hispanic/Latino; 32% Hispanic/Latino; 3% Black or African American, non-Hispanic/Latino; 0.8% Asian, non-Hispanic/Latino; 0.5% Native Hawaiian or other Pacific Islander, non-Hispanic/Latino; 3% international. 32% 25 or older. Retention: 53% of full-time freshmen returned the following year. Core. Calendar: semesters. Academic remediation for entering students, advanced placement, honors program, distance learning, summer session for credit, part-time degree program, external degree program, adult/continuing education programs, internships.
Entrance Requirements: Open admission except for nursing program. Options: electronic application, early admission. Recommended: high school transcript. Entrance: noncompetitive. Application deadline: 8/15. Notification: continuous. Transfer credits accepted: Yes.
Costs Per Year: Application fee: $0. State resident tuition: $3574 full-time, $148.90 per credit hour part-time. Nonresident tuition: $5956 full-time, $248.20 per credit hour part-time. Mandatory fees: $400 full-time, $13.46 per credit hour part-time. Full-time tuition and fees vary according to course load. Part-time tuition and fees vary according to course load. College room and board: $6864. Room and board charges vary according to board plan and housing facility.
Collegiate Environment: Orientation program. Drama-theater group, choral group. Campus security: 24-hour patrols, late night transport-escort service, controlled dormitory access. Wheeler Library. 100 computers available on campus for general student use. A campuswide network can be accessed from student residence rooms and from off campus. Students can access the following: online class registration. Staffed computer lab on campus provides training in use of computers, software, and the Internet.
Community Environment: La Junta is located in the rich agricultural and stock-raising territory of the Arkansas River Valley with a mild year-round climate; the average mean temperature being 54.1 degrees, and the average yearly precipitation, 13.61 inches. The community facilities include a library, churches, many shopping facilities, hotels, motels, hospital and a community sponsored concert association. La Junta has many civic and service organizations. Industries include canning, manufacture of copper tubings and the renovation of railroad cars. The Kid's Rodeo is held here each year in August.

■ **PIKES PEAK COMMUNITY COLLEGE**
5675 S Academy Blvd.
Colorado Springs, CO 80906-5498
Tel: (719)576-7711; Free: 866-411-7722
Fax: (719)540-7614
Web Site: www.ppcc.edu
Description: State-supported, 2-year, coed. Part of Colorado Community College and Occupational Education System. Awards certificates, transfer associate, and terminal associate degrees. Founded 1968. Setting: 287-acre urban campus with easy access to Denver. Total enrollment: 13,572. 45% 25 or older. Core. Calendar: semesters. Academic remediation for entering students, ESL program, services for LD students, advanced placement, independent study, distance learning, double major, summer session for credit, part-time degree program, adult/continuing education programs, co-op programs and internships. ROTC: Army (c).
Entrance Requirements: Open admission. Option: international baccalaureate accepted. Required for some: high school transcript. Entrance: noncompetitive. Application deadline: rolling.
Collegiate Environment: Orientation program. Drama-theater group, student-run newspaper. Student services: women's center. Campus security: 24-hour emergency response devices and patrols, late night transport-escort service. PPCC Library plus 1 other.
Community Environment: Colorado Springs, a community of approximately 278,000 people, is situated 70 miles south of Denver. The dry, temperate climate and 310 days of sunshine annually make it a highly desirable place to live year-round. Many high technology industries are located in Colorado Springs. Housing is readily available and buses serve all parts of the city. Skiing, hiking, fishing, hunting, backpacking, and camping can be enjoyed within a one-half hour to one hour drive from Colorado Springs.

■ PIMA MEDICAL INSTITUTE (AURORA)

13750 E Mississippi Ave.

Aurora, CO 80012

Tel: (303)368-7462; Free: 800-477-PIMA

Web Site: www.pmi.edu

Description: Proprietary, 2-year, coed. Awards certificates, transfer associate, and terminal associate degrees.

■ PIMA MEDICAL INSTITUTE (COLORADO SPRINGS)

5725 Mark Dabling Blvd.

Colorado Springs, CO 80919

Tel: (719)482-7462; Free: 800-477-PIMA

Web Site: www.pmi.edu

Description: Proprietary, 2-year, coed. Awards certificates, transfer associate, and terminal associate degrees. Setting: urban campus. Core. Distance learning, co-op programs and internships.

Entrance Requirements: Required: high school transcript, interview, Wonderlic Scholastic Level Exam (SLE).

Collegiate Environment: Orientation program.

■ PIMA MEDICAL INSTITUTE (DENVER)

7475 Dakin St.

Denver, CO 80221

Tel: (303)426-1800; Free: 800-477-PIMA

Fax: (303)412-8752

Web Site: www.pmi.edu

Description: Proprietary, primarily 2-year, coed. Part of Vocational Training Institutes, Inc. Awards certificates, terminal associate, and bachelor's degrees. Founded 1988. Setting: urban campus. Total enrollment: 922. 59% 25 or older. Calendar: modular. Academic remediation for entering students, distance learning, co-op programs and internships.

Entrance Requirements: Required: interview, Wonderlic Scholastic Level Exam (SLE). Required for some: high school transcript. Entrance: minimally difficult.

Collegiate Environment: E-Global.

■ PLATT COLLEGE

3100 S Parker Rd., Ste. 200

Aurora, CO 80014-3141

Tel: (303)369-5151

Web Site: www.plattcolorado.edu

Description: Proprietary, 4-year, coed. Awards associate and bachelor's degrees. Founded 1986. Setting: suburban campus. Total enrollment: 134. 15 applied. 64% 25 or older. Calendar: continuous. Academic remediation for entering students, advanced placement.

Entrance Requirements: Required: high school transcript, interview. Entrance: noncompetitive. Application deadline: rolling.

Collegiate Environment: Orientation program.

■ PUEBLO COMMUNITY COLLEGE

900 W Orman Ave.

Pueblo, CO 81004-1499

Tel: (719)549-3200; Free: 888-642-6017

Fax: (719)549-3012

E-mail: barbara.benedict@pueblocc.edu

Web Site: www.pueblocc.edu

Description: State-supported, primarily 2-year, coed. Part of Colorado Community College System. Awards certificates, transfer associate, terminal associate, and bachelor's degrees. Founded 1933. Setting: 35-acre urban campus. Endowment: $1.1 million. Educational spending for the previous fiscal year: $9792 per student. Total enrollment: 5,617. Faculty: 349 (97 full-time, 252 part-time). Student-undergrad faculty ratio is 16:1. 1,186 applied, 100% were admitted. Full-time: 1,770 students, 49% women, 51% men. Part-time: 3,880 students, 57% women, 43% men. Students come from 23 states and territories, 1% from out-of-state. 2% American Indian or Alaska Native, non-Hispanic/Latino; 32% Hispanic/Latino; 5% Black or African American, non-Hispanic/Latino; 5% Asian, non-Hispanic/Latino; 0.2% Native Hawaiian or other Pacific Islander, non-Hispanic/Latino; 0.6% international. 49% 25 or older, 9% transferred in. Retention: 10% of full-time freshmen returned the following year. Academic area with the most degrees conferred: health professions and related sciences. Core. Calendar: semesters. Academic remediation for entering students, ESL program, services for LD students, advanced placement, accelerated degree program, honors

program, independent study, distance learning, double major, summer session for credit, part-time degree program, co-op programs and internships.

Entrance Requirements: Open admission. Options: electronic application, early admission, deferred admission. Entrance: noncompetitive. Application deadline: rolling. Notification: continuous until 9/1. Transfer credits accepted: Yes.

Costs Per Year: Application fee: $0. State resident tuition: $4300 full-time, $179.95 per credit hour part-time. Nonresident tuition: $15,060 full-time, $627.50 per credit hour part-time. Mandatory fees: $750 full-time, $20.60 per credit hour part-time, $57.59 per term part-time.

Collegiate Environment: Orientation program. Drama-theater group, choral group. Social organizations: 20 open to all. Most popular organizations: Phi Theta Kappa, Welding Club, Culinary Arts Club, Performing Arts Club, Art Club. Major annual events: Welcome Back Week, Fall Festival, Spring Fling. Student services: health clinic, personal-psychological counseling. Campus security: 24-hour emergency response devices and patrols, late night transport-escort service. College housing not available. PCC Library. Books: 19,162 (physical), 33,004 (digital/electronic); Serial titles: 695 (physical), 7,707 (digital/electronic); Databases: 12. Weekly public service hours: 60. Operations spending for the previous fiscal year: $81,722. 1,180 computers available on campus for general student use. Computer purchase/lease plans available. A campuswide network can be accessed from off-campus. Students can access the following: online class registration. Staffed computer lab on campus provides training in use of computers, software, and the Internet.

Community Environment: Pueblo, population 103,500, is 42 miles south of Colorado Springs and 112 miles south of Denver on I-25. The original site of Pueblo was a crossroad for Indians, Spanish troops, friars, fur trappers, and explorers. A trading post was built in 1842 and served travelers on their way to California. Pueblo's location as the focal point for travel to the Rocky Mountain Empire continues to serve business and industry in the area. Puebloans enjoy clean air, uncrowded highways, and nearby water and mountain recreation set in the warm pleasant atmosphere of the Southwest. Pueblo boasts a fine community college, a university, symphony orchestra, chorale, ballet, theatrical groups, and a beautiful arts center.

■ RED ROCKS COMMUNITY COLLEGE

13300 W 6th Ave.

Lakewood, CO 80228-1255

Tel: (303)914-6600

Fax: (303)914-6666

E-mail: admissions@rrcc.edu

Web Site: www.rrcc.edu

Description: State-supported, 2-year, coed. Part of Colorado Community College and Occupational Education System. Awards certificates, transfer associate, and terminal associate degrees. Founded 1969. Setting: 141-acre urban campus with easy access to Denver. Educational spending for the previous fiscal year: $2770 per student. Total enrollment: 9,028. Faculty: 511 (93 full-time, 418 part-time). Student-undergrad faculty ratio is 23:1. 3,258 applied, 100% were admitted. Full-time: 2,854 students, 45% women, 55% men. Part-time: 6,174 students, 52% women, 48% men. Students come from 27 other countries, 6% from out-of-state. 1% American Indian or Alaska Native, non-Hispanic/Latino; 13% Hispanic/Latino; 2% Black or African American, non-Hispanic/Latino; 2% Asian, non-Hispanic/Latino; 0.3% Native Hawaiian or other Pacific Islander, non-Hispanic/Latino; 1% international. 53% 25 or older, 22% transferred in. Calendar: semesters. Academic remediation for entering students, ESL program, services for LD students, honors program, distance learning, summer session for credit, part-time degree program, adult/continuing education programs, co-op programs. Off campus study at Metropolitan State College, University of Colorado at Denver, Colorado School of Mines. Study abroad program. ROTC: Army (c), Air Force (c).

Entrance Requirements: Open admission. Options: electronic application, early admission, international baccalaureate accepted. Entrance: noncompetitive. Application deadline: rolling. Notification: continuous. Transfer credits accepted: Yes.

Collegiate Environment: Orientation program. Drama-theater group. Student services: health clinic, personal-psychological counseling. Campus security: 24-hour emergency response devices and patrols. Marvin Buckels Library. Operations spending for the previous fiscal year: $140,278. 128 computers available on campus for general student use. A campuswide network can be accessed. Students can access the following: online class registration. Staffed computer lab on campus provides training in use of computers, software, and the Internet.

Community Environment: See Colorado School of Mines.

■ **REGIS UNIVERSITY**
3333 Regis Blvd.
Denver, CO 80221-1099
Tel: (303)458-4100; Free: 800-388-2366
Fax: (303)964-5534
E-mail: sengel@regis.edu
Web Site: www.regis.edu
Description: Independent Roman Catholic (Jesuit), comprehensive, coed. Awards bachelor's, master's, and doctoral degrees and post-master's certificates. Founded 1877. Setting: 90-acre urban campus with easy access to Denver, Colorado. Endowment: $65.1 million. Educational spending for the previous fiscal year: $7498 per student. Total enrollment: 7,907. Faculty: 704 (311 full-time, 393 part-time). Student-undergrad faculty ratio is 13:1. 7,282 applied, 60% were admitted. 25% from top 10% of their high school class, 56% from top quarter, 86% from top half. Full-time: 2,373 students, 65% women, 35% men. Part-time: 1,588 students, 53% women, 47% men. Students come from 53 states and territories, 11 other countries, 40% from out-of-state. 0.4% American Indian or Alaska Native, non-Hispanic/Latino; 19% Hispanic/Latino; 4% Black or African American, non-Hispanic/Latino; 4% Asian, non-Hispanic/Latino; 0.3% Native Hawaiian or other Pacific Islander, non-Hispanic/Latino; 6% international. 40% 25 or older, 22% live on campus, 7% transferred in. Retention: 79% of full-time freshmen returned the following year. Academic areas with the most degrees conferred: health professions and related sciences; business/marketing; computer and information sciences. Core. Calendar: semesters. Academic remediation for entering students, services for LD students, advanced placement, accelerated degree program, self-designed majors, freshman honors college, honors program, independent study, distance learning, double major, summer session for credit, part-time degree program, adult/continuing education programs, co-op programs and internships, graduate courses open to undergrads. Off campus study. Study abroad program. ROTC: Army (c), Naval (c), Air Force (c).
Entrance Requirements: Options: electronic application, deferred admission, international baccalaureate accepted. Required: essay, high school transcript, SAT or ACT. Required for some: 1 recommendation, interview. Entrance: moderately difficult. SAT Reasoning Test deadline: 8/1. SAT Subject Test deadline: 8/1. Transfer credits accepted: Yes.
Costs Per Year: Application fee: $0. Comprehensive fee: $48,370 includes full-time tuition ($36,460), mandatory fees ($350), and college room and board ($11,560). College room only: $6600. Full-time tuition and fees vary according to class time, course level, course load, degree level, location, program, reciprocity agreements, and student level. Room and board charges vary according to board plan and housing facility. Part-time tuition: $1139 per semester hour. Part-time tuition varies according to class time, course level, course load, degree level, location, program, reciprocity agreements, and student level.
Collegiate Environment: Orientation program. Drama-theater group, choral group, student-run newspaper, radio station. Social organizations: 32 open to all. Major annual event: Ranger Week. Student services: health clinic, personal-psychological counseling. Campus security: 24-hour emergency response devices and patrols, student patrols, late night transport-escort service, controlled dormitory access. 929 college housing spaces available; 862 were occupied in 2018-19. Freshmen given priority for college housing. On-campus residence required in freshman year. Option: coed housing available. Dayton Memorial Library. Books: 247,545 (physical), 182,210 (digital/electronic); Serial titles: 1,558 (physical), 112,666 (digital/electronic); Databases: 260. Students can reserve study rooms. Operations spending for the previous fiscal year: $3.7 million. 600 computers available on campus for general student use. Computer purchase/lease plans available. A campuswide network can be accessed from student residence rooms and from off campus. Students can access the following: online class registration. Staffed computer lab on campus (open 24 hours a day) provides training in use of computers, software, and the Internet.
Community Environment: See University of Denver.

■ **ROCKY MOUNTAIN COLLEGE OF ART + DESIGN**
1600 Pierce St.
Lakewood, CO 80214
Tel: (303)753-6046; Free: 800-888-ARTS
Fax: (303)759-4970
E-mail: mabraham@rmcad.edu
Web Site: www.rmcad.edu

Description: Proprietary, comprehensive, coed. Awards bachelor's and master's degrees. Founded 1963. Setting: 23-acre urban campus with easy access to Denver. Total enrollment: 1,096. Faculty: 205 (38 full-time, 167 part-time). Student-undergrad faculty ratio is 9:1. Full-time: 688 students, 64% women, 36% men. Part-time: 391 students, 64% women, 36% men. Students come from 52 states and territories, 5 other countries, 53% from out-of-state. 3% American Indian or Alaska Native, non-Hispanic/Latino; 11% Hispanic/Latino; 6% Black or African American, non-Hispanic/Latino; 3% Asian, non-Hispanic/Latino; 1% international. 49% 25 or older, 45% transferred in. Retention: 52% of full-time freshmen returned the following year. Academic areas with the most degrees conferred: visual and performing arts; computer and information sciences; communication technologies. Core. Calendar: semesters. Academic remediation for entering students, services for LD students, advanced placement, accelerated degree program, independent study, distance learning, summer session for credit, part-time degree program, co-op programs and internships. Off campus study. Study abroad program.
Entrance Requirements: Open admission. Options: electronic application, international baccalaureate accepted. Required: essay, high school transcript, minimum 2 high school GPA, interview, portfolio. Entrance: moderately difficult. Application deadline: rolling. Notification: continuous. Transfer credits accepted: Yes.
Collegiate Environment: Orientation program. Social organizations: 9 open to all. Most popular organizations: The American Institute of Graphic Arts (AIGA), The American Society of Interior Designers (ASID), Gay-Straight Alliance, Game Art + Design Club, Animation Club. Major annual events: Annual Student Exhibition, Welcome Back Week, Art and Music Festival. Student services: personal-psychological counseling. Campus security: 24-hour emergency response devices, late night transport-escort service, patrols by trained security personnel during campus hours. Rocky Mountain College of Art and Design Library plus 1 other. Books: 15,325 (physical), 189,000 (digital/electronic); Serial titles: 1,842 (physical), 3,293 (digital/electronic); Databases: 36. Weekly public service hours: 76; students can reserve study rooms. Operations spending for the previous fiscal year: $120,000. 320 computers available on campus for general student use. Computer purchase/lease plans available. A computer is required for all students. A campuswide network can be accessed. Students can access the following: online class registration, discounted software/hardware, RTD/public transit, printers, scanners, equipment check-out (i.e. cameras, laptops). Staffed computer lab on campus provides training in use of computers, software, and the Internet.

■ **SPARTAN COLLEGE OF AERONAUTICS AND TECHNOLOGY**
10851 W 120th Ave.
Broomfield, CO 80021
Tel: (303)466-1714; Free: 800-510-3216
Fax: (303)469-3797
Web Site: www.spartan.edu
Description: Proprietary, 2-year, coed. Awards certificates, diplomas, and terminal associate degrees. Founded 1965. Total enrollment: 590. Faculty: 48. Calendar: continuous.

■ **TRINIDAD STATE JUNIOR COLLEGE**
600 Prospect St.
Trinidad, CO 81082-2396
Tel: (719)846-5011; Free: 800-621-8752
Fax: (719)846-5667
E-mail: bernadine.degarbo@trinidadstate.edu
Web Site: www.trinidadstate.edu
Description: State-supported, 2-year, coed. Part of Colorado Community College and Occupational Education System. Awards certificates, diplomas, transfer associate, and terminal associate degrees. Founded 1925. Setting: 17-acre small town campus. Total enrollment: 1,783. Faculty: 161 (50 full-time, 111 part-time). Student-undergrad faculty ratio is 13:1. Full-time: 882 students, 53% women, 47% men. Part-time: 901 students, 63% women, 37% men. Students come from 33 states and territories, 8 other countries, 13% from out-of-state. 1% American Indian or Alaska Native, non-Hispanic/Latino; 41% Hispanic/Latino; 2% Black or African American, non-Hispanic/Latino; 0.7% Asian, non-Hispanic/Latino; 0.1% Native Hawaiian or other Pacific Islander, non-Hispanic/Latino; 1% international. 43% 25 or older, 12% live on campus, 8% transferred in. Retention: 60% of full-time freshmen returned the following year. Calendar: semesters. Academic remediation for entering students, ESL program, services for LD students, advanced placement, accelerated degree program, self-designed majors, independent

study, distance learning, double major, summer session for credit, part-time degree program, adult/continuing education programs, co-op programs and internships.

Entrance Requirements: Open admission except for nursing, gunsmith, and electric line technician programs. Option: deferred admission. Required: high school transcript. Entrance: noncompetitive. Application deadline: rolling. Notification: continuous. Transfer credits accepted: Yes.

Costs Per Year: Application fee: $0. State resident tuition: $4972 full-time, $174.98 per credit hour part-time. Nonresident tuition: $7951 full-time, $274.28 per credit hour part-time. Full-time tuition varies according to course load, location, program, and reciprocity agreements. Part-time tuition varies according to course load, location, program, and reciprocity agreements. College room and board: $6898. Room and board charges vary according to board plan.

Collegiate Environment: Orientation program. Drama-theater group. Campus security: 24-hour emergency response devices, trained security personnel patrol after campus hours. Freudenthal Memorial Library. 125 computers available on campus for general student use. A campuswide network can be accessed from student residence rooms and from off campus. Students can access the following: online class registration.

Community Environment: Located in South Central Colorado, Trinidad is the County Seat of Las Animas County and was a trading post on the Old Santa Fe Trail. Good highways, busses, and the railroad serve the area. Leading industries are coal production, farming, and ranching. The area offers Monument Lake, a 1,200-acre city owned park with fishing, boating and camping; Trinidad Lake, located 36 miles west of Trinidad in scenic Stonewall Valley, with water skiing, fishing, boating, camping, hiking and a recreation area; Cuchara Ski Area, located 50 miles west of Trinidad in scenic Cuchara valley.

■ **UNITED STATES AIR FORCE ACADEMY**
HQ USAFA/A9A
2304 Cadet Dr., Ste. 3800
USAF Academy, CO 80840-5025
Tel: (719)333-1818; Free: 800-443-9266
Fax: (719)333-3012
Web Site: www.usafa.edu

Description: Federally supported, 4-year, coed. Awards bachelor's degrees. Founded 1954. Setting: 18,000-acre suburban campus with easy access to Colorado Springs, Denver. Endowment: $106.7 million. Research spending for the previous fiscal year: $55.4 million. Educational spending for the previous fiscal year: $63,472 per student. Total enrollment: 4,237. Faculty: 502 (501 full-time, 1 part-time). Student-undergrad faculty ratio is 9:1. 9,894 applied, 15% were admitted. 52% from top 10% of their high school class, 81% from top quarter, 97% from top half. 94 National Merit Scholars, 122 class presidents, 97 valedictorians, 386 student government officers. Full-time: 4,237 students, 25% women, 75% men. Students come from 54 states and territories, 23 other countries, 88% from out-of-state. 0.3% American Indian or Alaska Native, non-Hispanic/Latino; 11% Hispanic/Latino; 6% Black or African American, non-Hispanic/Latino; 5% Asian, non-Hispanic/Latino; 0.7% Native Hawaiian or other Pacific Islander, non-Hispanic/Latino; 1% international. 2% 25 or older, 100% live on campus. Retention: 88% of full-time freshmen returned the following year. Academic areas with the most degrees conferred: engineering; social sciences; business/marketing. Core. Calendar: semesters. Academic remediation for entering students, ESL program, advanced placement, honors program, independent study, summer session for credit, internships. Off campus study at U.S. Military Academy (West Point), U.S. Naval Academy (Annapolis), U. S. Coast Guard Academy. Study abroad program.

Entrance Requirements: Options: electronic application, international baccalaureate accepted. Required: essay, high school transcript, 1 recommendation, interview, authorized nomination, Candidate Fitness Assessment, medical examination, SAT or ACT. Entrance: most difficult. Application deadline: 12/31. Notification: continuous until 10/15. SAT Reasoning Test deadline: 1/31. Transfer credits accepted: Yes.

Costs Per Year: Application fee: $0. Comprehensive fee: $0. Tuition, room and board, and medical and dental care are provided by the US government. Each cadet receives a salary from which to pay for uniforms, supplies, and personal expenses.

Collegiate Environment: Drama-theater group, choral group, marching band, student-run radio station. Social organizations: 97 open to all. Most popular organizations: Recreational Ski Club, Men's and Women's Rugby Club, Cycling Club, Aviation Club, Drum and Bugle Corps. Major annual events: National Character and Leadership Symposium, Football Games,

Graduation. Student services: legal services, health clinic, personal-psychological counseling, women's center. Campus security: 24-hour emergency response devices and patrols, late night transport-escort service, controlled dormitory access, self-defense education, well-lit campus, Charge of Quarters. McDermott Library plus 1 other. Books: 463,745 (physical), 74,225 (digital/electronic); Serial titles: 229 (physical), 325 (digital/electronic); Databases: 36. Weekly public service hours: 83. Operations spending for the previous fiscal year: $4.7 million.

■ **UNIVERSITY OF COLORADO BOULDER**
Boulder, CO 80309
Tel: (303)492-1411
Fax: (303)492-7115
E-mail: apply@colorado.edu
Web Site: www.colorado.edu

Description: State-supported, university, coed. Part of University of Colorado System. Awards bachelor's, master's, and doctoral degrees and post-master's certificates. Founded 1876. Setting: 600-acre suburban campus with easy access to Denver. Endowment: $596 million. Research spending for the previous fiscal year: $463.6 million. Educational spending for the previous fiscal year: $16,192 per student. Total enrollment: 35,230. 36,149 applied, 80% were admitted. 29% from top 10% of their high school class, 59% from top quarter, 90% from top half. 6 National Merit Scholars, 204 valedictorians. Full-time: 26,917 students, 44% women, 56% men. Part-time: 2,174 students, 41% women, 59% men. Students come from 52 states and territories, 82 other countries, 42% from out-of-state. 0.2% American Indian or Alaska Native, non-Hispanic/Latino; 12% Hispanic/Latino; 2% Black or African American, non-Hispanic/Latino; 6% Asian, non-Hispanic/Latino; 0.1% Native Hawaiian or other Pacific Islander, non-Hispanic/Latino; 7% international. 5% 25 or older, 28% live on campus, 5% transferred in. Retention: 88% of full-time freshmen returned the following year. Academic areas with the most degrees conferred: biological/life sciences; engineering; business/marketing. Core. Calendar: semesters. ESL program, services for LD students, advanced placement, accelerated degree program, self-designed majors, freshman honors college, honors program, independent study, distance learning, double major, summer session for credit, part-time degree program, adult/continuing education programs, co-op programs and internships, graduate courses open to undergrads. Off campus study at other units of the University of Colorado System. Study abroad program. ROTC: Army, Naval, Air Force.

Entrance Requirements: Options: electronic application, early action, deferred admission, international baccalaureate accepted. Required: essay, high school transcript, 1 recommendation, SAT or ACT. Recommended: minimum 3 high school GPA. Required for some: audition for music program. Entrance: moderately difficult. Application deadlines: 1/15, 11/15 for early action. Notification: 4/1, 2/1 for early action. SAT Reasoning Test deadline: 1/15. Transfer credits accepted: Yes. Applicants placed on waiting list: 1,159.

Costs Per Year: Application fee: $50. One-time mandatory fee: $232. State resident tuition: $10,728 full-time. Nonresident tuition: $35,482 full-time. Mandatory fees: $1804 full-time. Full-time tuition and fees vary according to program. College room and board: $14,418. Room and board charges vary according to board plan, housing facility, and location. Tuition guaranteed not to increase for student's term of enrollment.

Collegiate Environment: Orientation program. Drama-theater group, choral group, marching band, student-run newspaper, radio station. Social organizations: 400 open to all; national fraternities, national sororities, local fraternities, local sororities; 12% of eligible men and 20% of eligible women are members. Most popular organizations: Student Government, CU Gaming, Boulder Freeride, Neuroscience Club, Association of Holistic Wellness. Major annual events: Conference on World Affairs, Parents' Weekend, Global Jam. Student services: legal services, health clinic, personal-psychological counseling, women's center. Campus security: 24-hour patrols, student patrols, late night transport-escort service, controlled dormitory access, University police department, LifeLine Response app connecting to police dispatch center. Norlin Library plus 5 others. Books: 664,601 (physical), 984,952 (digital/electronic); Databases: 594. Students can reserve study rooms. Operations spending for the previous fiscal year: $23.9 million. 1,689 computers available on campus for general student use. Computer purchase/lease plans available. A campuswide network can be accessed from student residence rooms and from off campus. Students can access the following: online class registration, training, tutorials, workshops, seminars, standard and academic software, student government voting. Staffed computer lab on campus provides training in use of computers, software, and the Internet.

■ UNIVERSITY OF COLORADO COLORADO SPRINGS

1420 Austin Bluffs Pky.
Colorado Springs, CO 80918
Tel: (719)255-8227; Free: 800-990-8227
E-mail: cbeiswan@uccs.edu
Web Site: www.uccs.edu

Description: State-supported, university, coed. Part of University of Colorado System. Awards bachelor's, master's, and doctoral degrees and post-master's certificates. Founded 1965. Setting: 532-acre urban campus with easy access to Colorado Springs. Total enrollment: 12,932. Faculty: 774 (444 full-time, 330 part-time). Student-undergrad faculty ratio is 19:1. 9,909 applied, 93% were admitted. 14% from top 10% of their high school class, 38% from top quarter, 74% from top half. Full-time: 8,171 students, 51% women, 49% men. Part-time: 2,637 students, 56% women, 44% men. Students come from 44 states and territories, 71 other countries, 12% from out-of-state. 0.2% American Indian or Alaska Native, non-Hispanic/Latino; 18% Hispanic/Latino; 4% Black or African American, non-Hispanic/Latino; 3% Asian, non-Hispanic/Latino; 0.3% Native Hawaiian or other Pacific Islander, non-Hispanic/Latino; 0.9% international. 25% 25 or older, 16% live on campus, 12% transferred in. Retention: 66% of full-time freshmen returned the following year. Academic areas with the most degrees conferred: business/marketing; health professions and related sciences; biological/life sciences. Core. Calendar: semesters. ESL program, services for LD students, advanced placement, accelerated degree program, self-designed majors, honors program, independent study, distance learning, double major, summer session for credit, part-time degree program, co-op programs and internships, graduate courses open to undergrads. Off campus study at (1) Medical Lab Science with the University of Nebraska-Omaha, (2) RN to BSN with several Colorado community colleges, (3) concurrent enrollment with University of Colorado Denver and University of Colorado Boulder (4) concurrent enrollment with Pikes Peak Community College, (5) National Student Exchange. Study abroad program. ROTC: Army.

Entrance Requirements: Options: electronic application, deferred admission, international baccalaureate accepted. Required: high school transcript, SAT or ACT. Entrance: moderately difficult. Application deadline: rolling. Notification: continuous. Transfer credits accepted: Yes.

Costs Per Year: Application fee: $50. One-time mandatory fee: $140. State resident tuition: $8850 full-time, $295 per credit hour part-time. Nonresident tuition: $23,280 full-time, $776 per credit hour part-time. Mandatory fees: $1613 full-time. Full-time tuition and fees vary according to course load, degree level, location, program, reciprocity agreements, and student level. Part-time tuition varies according to course load, degree level, location, program, reciprocity agreements, and student level. College room and board: $10,500. Room and board charges vary according to board plan, housing facility, and student level.

Collegiate Environment: Orientation program. Drama-theater group, choral group, student-run newspaper, radio station. Social organizations: 200 open to all; national fraternities, national sororities; 2% of eligible men and 2% of eligible women are members. Most popular organizations: Fans Initiating Growth Honor and Tradition (spirit club), Pi Beta Phi, Sustainability Club, Gamers (computing), El Circulo. Major annual events: Black-Out Night (basketball), Disorientation Week, Back to the Bluffs Homecoming. Student services: health clinic, personal-psychological counseling. Campus security: 24-hour emergency response devices and patrols, late night transport-escort service, controlled dormitory access, emergency text messaging, state-authorized campus police and public safety department. Kraemer Family Library. Books: 337,790 (physical), 168,770 (digital/electronic); Serial titles: 3,020 (physical); Databases: 154. Students can reserve study rooms.

■ UNIVERSITY OF COLORADO DENVER

PO Box 173364
Denver, CO 80217-3364
Tel: (303)556-2400
Fax: (303)556-2398
E-mail: admissions@ucdenver.edu
Web Site: www.ucdenver.edu

Description: State-supported, university, coed. Part of University of Colorado System. Awards bachelor's, master's, and doctoral degrees and post-master's certificates. Founded 1912. Setting: 171-acre urban campus with easy access to Denver, CO. Endowment: $564.7 million. Total enrollment: 25,645. Faculty: 4,825 (3,989 full-time, 836 part-time). Student-undergrad faculty ratio is 15:1. 11,315 applied, 64% were admitted. 22% from top 10% of their high school class, 48% from top quarter, 81% from top

half. Full-time: 8,980 students, 54% women, 46% men. Part-time: 7,463 students, 57% women, 43% men. 9% from out-of-state. 0.3% American Indian or Alaska Native, non-Hispanic/Latino; 24% Hispanic/Latino; 5% Black or African American, non-Hispanic/Latino; 10% Asian, non-Hispanic/Latino; 0.1% Native Hawaiian or other Pacific Islander, non-Hispanic/Latino; 8% international. 27% 25 or older, 9% transferred in. Retention: 72% of full-time freshmen returned the following year. Academic areas with the most degrees conferred: business/marketing; health professions and related sciences; social sciences. Core. Calendar: semesters. ESL program, services for LD students, advanced placement, accelerated degree program, self-designed majors, honors program, independent study, distance learning, double major, summer session for credit, part-time degree program, co-op programs and internships, graduate courses open to undergrads. Off campus study at Metropolitan State College, Community College of Denver, University of Northern Colorado, Colorado State University, University of Colorado Colorado Springs, University of Colorado Boulder. Study abroad program. ROTC: Army (c), Air Force (c).

Entrance Requirements: Options: electronic application, deferred admission, international baccalaureate accepted. Required: minimum 2.5 high school GPA, SAT or ACT. Required for some: minimum 3 high school GPA, audition, portfolio, entrance exam. Entrance: moderately difficult. Application deadline: rolling for nonresidents. Notification: continuous, continuous for nonresidents. SAT Reasoning Test deadline: 8/1. SAT Subject Test deadline: 8/1. Transfer credits accepted: Yes.

Costs Per Year: Application fee: $50. State resident tuition: $9900 full-time, $330 per credit hour part-time. Nonresident tuition: $30,510 full-time, $1017 per credit hour part-time. Mandatory fees: $1495 full-time, $1098 per year part-time. Full-time tuition and fees vary according to course level, course load, degree level, location, program, reciprocity agreements, and student level. Part-time tuition and fees vary according to course level, course load, degree level, location, program, reciprocity agreements, and student level. College room and board: $12,620. College room only: $8800. Room and board charges vary according to board plan.

Collegiate Environment: Orientation program. Drama-theater group, choral group, student-run newspaper. Social organizations: 250 open to all. Most popular organizations: Veterans Student Organization (Service), Golden Key Honor Society (Academic), Minority Association for Pre-Health Students (Health), Future Doctors of Denver, Intercultural Club Beijing (Cultural and Social). Major annual events: Distinguished Lecture Series, Spring Fling, CU Denver Block Party. Student services: health clinic, personal-psychological counseling, women's center. Campus security: 24-hour emergency response devices and patrols, student patrols, late night transport-escort service. College housing not available. Auraria Library plus 1 other. Books: 573,818 (physical), 325,936 (digital/electronic); Serial titles: 5,780 (physical), 92,591 (digital/electronic); Databases: 308. Weekly public service hours: 85; students can reserve study rooms. 750 computers available on campus for general student use. A campuswide network can be accessed from student residence rooms and from off campus. Students can access the following: online class registration. Staffed computer lab on campus provides training in use of computers, software, and the Internet.

■ UNIVERSITY OF DENVER

2199 S University Blvd.
Denver, CO 80208
Tel: (303)871-2000; Free: 800-525-9495
Fax: (303)871-3301
E-mail: admission@du.edu
Web Site: www.du.edu

Description: Independent, university, coed. Awards bachelor's, master's, and doctoral degrees and post-master's certificates. Founded 1864. Setting: 125-acre urban campus with easy access to Denver. Endowment: $711.3 million. Research spending for the previous fiscal year: $15.6 million. Total enrollment: 11,434. Faculty: 1,290 (733 full-time, 557 part-time). Student-undergrad faculty ratio is 11:1. 19,904 applied, 58% were admitted. 38% from top 10% of their high school class, 73% from top quarter, 95% from top half. Full-time: 5,494 students, 54% women, 46% men. Part-time: 271 students, 47% women, 53% men. Students come from 57 states and territories, 52 other countries, 62% from out-of-state. 0.2% American Indian or Alaska Native, non-Hispanic/Latino; 11% Hispanic/Latino; 2% Black or African American, non-Hispanic/Latino; 4% Asian, non-Hispanic/Latino; 0.1% Native Hawaiian or other Pacific Islander, non-Hispanic/Latino; 7% international. 2% 25 or older, 50% live on campus, 3% transferred in. Retention: 87% of full-time freshmen returned the following year. Academic areas with the most degrees conferred: business/marketing; social sciences;

psychology. Core. Calendar: quarters semesters for law school. ESL program, services for LD students, advanced placement, accelerated degree program, self-designed majors, freshman honors college, honors program, independent study, distance learning, double major, summer session for credit, part-time degree program, adult/continuing education programs, co-op programs and internships, graduate courses open to undergrads. Off campus study. Study abroad program. ROTC: Army (c), Air Force (c).

Entrance Requirements: Options: electronic application, early admission, early decision, early action, deferred admission, international baccalaureate accepted. Required: essay, high school transcript, 1 recommendation, SAT or ACT. Recommended: 2 recommendations. Required for some: minimum X high school GPA. Entrance: moderately difficult. Application deadlines: 1/15, 11/1 for early decision plan 1, 1/15 for early decision plan 2, 11/1 for early action. Notification: 3/15, 12/15 for early decision plan 1, 2/20 for early decision plan 2, 1/15 for early action. SAT Reasoning Test deadline: 2/1. Transfer credits accepted: Yes. Applicants placed on waiting list: 500. Waitlisted applicants offered admission: 1. Early decision applicants: 363. Early decision applicants admitted: 168. Early action applicants: 6,286. Early action applicants admitted: 6,252.

Costs Per Year: Application fee: $65. Comprehensive fee: $63,561 includes full-time tuition ($49,392), mandatory fees ($1164), and college room and board ($13,005). College room only: $8100. Full-time tuition and fees vary according to course load and program. Room and board charges vary according to board plan and housing facility. Part-time tuition: $1372 per credit hour. Part-time tuition varies according to course load and program.

Collegiate Environment: Orientation program. Drama-theater group, choral group, student-run newspaper, radio station. Social organizations: 90 open to all; national fraternities, national sororities, local fraternities; 25% of eligible men and 30% of eligible women are members. Most popular organizations: Club Sports Council, Alpine Club, DU Programs Board, Greek Life Council, Residence Hall Association. Major annual events: Homecoming, Winter Carnival, May Days. Student services: health clinic, personal-psychological counseling, women's center. Campus security: 24-hour emergency response devices and patrols, late night transport-escort service, controlled dormitory access, 24-hour locked residence hall entrances. Anderson Academic Commons plus 1 other. Books: 1.7 million (physical), 2.3 million (digital/electronic); Serial titles: 594,063 (physical), 218,954 (digital/electronic); Databases: 1,306. Weekly public service hours: 145; study areas open 24 hours, 5-7 days a week; students can reserve study rooms. Operations spending for the previous fiscal year: $14.4 million. 150 computers available on campus for general student use. Computer purchase/lease plans available. A computer is required for all students. A campuswide network can be accessed from student residence rooms and from off campus. Students can access the following: online class registration. Staffed computer lab on campus provides training in use of computers, software, and the Internet.

Community Environment: Denver is a metropolitan area, capital of Colorado, situated at the foot of the Rocky Mountains. The climate is temperate and considered healthful. The State Museum, Art Museum, Museum of Natural History, many public and private hospitals, churches, and the fine shopping areas make up the city. Part-time employment opportunities are good. Denver is the gateway to the playgrounds of the mountains; the city's mountain parks of 20,000 acres include the Genesee Mountain with its game preserve. There are lakes in the area for water sports and fishing. Denver has become a great center for snow sports activities, with several of the best known ski areas located 55 to 85 miles from Denver in the Arapaho National Forest. The annual National Western Stock Show is in January.

■ **UNIVERSITY OF NORTHERN COLORADO**
Greeley, CO 80639
Tel: (970)351-1890; Free: 888-700-4UNC
E-mail: admissions@unco.edu
Web Site: www.unco.edu
Description: State-supported, university, coed. Awards bachelor's, master's, and doctoral degrees. Founded 1890. Setting: 237-acre suburban campus with easy access to Denver. Endowment: $87.6 million. Research spending for the previous fiscal year: $5.5 million. Educational spending for the previous fiscal year: $10,643 per student. Total enrollment: 12,862. Faculty: 872 (514 full-time, 358 part-time). Student-undergrad faculty ratio is 18:1. 8,294 applied, 91% were admitted. 12% from top 10% of their high school class, 36% from top quarter, 72% from top half. 22 valedictorians. Full-time: 8,047 students, 64% women, 36% men. Part-time: 1,829 students, 68% women, 32% men. Students come from 49 states and territories, 39 other countries, 14% from out-of-state. 0.4% American Indian or Alaska Native, non-

Hispanic/Latino; 22% Hispanic/Latino; 4% Black or African American, non-Hispanic/Latino; 2% Asian, non-Hispanic/Latino; 0.2% Native Hawaiian or other Pacific Islander, non-Hispanic/Latino; 1% international. 11% 25 or older, 34% live on campus, 7% transferred in. Retention: 72% of full-time freshmen returned the following year. Academic areas with the most degrees conferred: health professions and related sciences; education; business/marketing. Core. Calendar: semesters. ESL program, services for LD students, advanced placement, accelerated degree program, self-designed majors, honors program, independent study, distance learning, double major, summer session for credit, part-time degree program, external degree program, adult/continuing education programs, co-op programs and internships, graduate courses open to undergrads. Off campus study at National Student Exchange. Study abroad program. ROTC: Army, Air Force.

Entrance Requirements: Options: electronic application, deferred admission, international baccalaureate accepted. Required: high school transcript, SAT or ACT. Required for some: essay. Entrance: moderately difficult. Application deadlines: 8/1, 8/1 for nonresidents. Notification: continuous, 9/1 for nonresidents. SAT Reasoning Test deadline: 8/1. Transfer credits accepted: Yes.

Costs Per Year: Application fee: $50. One-time mandatory fee: $250. Area resident tuition: $7830 full-time, $294.75 per credit hour part-time. State resident tuition: $7830 full-time, $294.75 per credit hour part-time. Nonresident tuition: $19,518 full-time, $755 per credit hour part-time. Mandatory fees: $2358 full-time, $111.35 per credit hour part-time. College room and board: $11,204. College room only: $5304.

Collegiate Environment: Orientation program. Drama-theater group, choral group, marching band, student-run newspaper. Social organizations: 130 open to all; national fraternities, national sororities, local fraternities; 6% of eligible men and 5% of eligible women are members. Most popular organizations: Fraternities and Sororities, Club Sports, Campus Religious/Spiritual Organizations, Academic Clubs, Services Clubs. Major annual events: Homecoming, Spring Concert, Welcome Week. Student services: legal services, health clinic, personal-psychological counseling, women's center. Campus security: 24-hour emergency response devices and patrols, student patrols, late night transport-escort service, controlled dormitory access. 3,435 college housing spaces available; 3,077 were occupied in 2018-19. Freshmen guaranteed college housing. On-campus residence required in freshman year. Options: coed, women-only housing available. James A. Michener Library plus 2 others. Books: 1.3 million (physical), 473,007 (digital/electronic); Serial titles: 19,480 (physical), 85,939 (digital/electronic); Databases: 210. Weekly public service hours: 97; students can reserve study rooms. Operations spending for the previous fiscal year: $7.4 million. 1,723 computers available on campus for general student use. Computer purchase/lease plans available. A campuswide network can be accessed from student residence rooms and from off campus. Students can access the following: online class registration. Staffed computer lab on campus provides training in use of computers, software, and the Internet.

Community Environment: Located one hour north of Denver and one hour east of Rocky Mountain National Park, the city of Greeley has a population of more than 87,500. It has a symphony, rock and jazz concerts, community theatre, and the largest 4th of July rodeo in the country. The dry, desert climate produces sunny days and cool nights. There is some snow and very little rain.

■ **WESTERN STATE COLORADO UNIVERSITY**
600 N Adams St.
Gunnison, CO 81231
Tel: (970)943-0120; Free: 800-876-5309
Fax: (970)943-7069
Web Site: www.western.edu
Description: State-supported, comprehensive, coed. Awards bachelor's and master's degrees. Founded 1901. Setting: 381-acre rural campus. Total enrollment: 3,039. Faculty: 166 (120 full-time, 46 part-time). Student-undergrad faculty ratio is 18:1. 1,972 applied, 89% were admitted. 7% from top 10% of their high school class, 21% from top quarter, 46% from top half. Full-time: 1,883 students, 41% women, 59% men. Part-time: 729 students, 53% women, 47% men. 29% from out-of-state. 0.6% American Indian or Alaska Native, non-Hispanic/Latino; 11% Hispanic/Latino; 3% Black or African American, non-Hispanic/Latino; 0.8% Asian, non-Hispanic/Latino; 0.2% Native Hawaiian or other Pacific Islander, non-Hispanic/Latino; 0.5% international. 1% 25 or older, 47% live on campus, 5% transferred in. Retention: 69% of full-time freshmen returned the following year. Academic areas with the most degrees conferred: business/marketing; parks and recreation; biological/life sciences; social sciences. Core. Calendar: semesters.

Academic remediation for entering students, services for LD students, advanced placement, honors program, independent study, double major, summer session for credit, part-time degree program, adult/continuing education programs, internships, graduate courses open to undergrads. Off campus study at State Colleges of Colorado, National Student Exchange. Study abroad program.

Entrance Requirements: Options: electronic application, deferred admission, international baccalaureate accepted. Required: essay, high school transcript, SAT or ACT. Recommended: minimum 2.5 high school GPA. Entrance: moderately difficult. Application deadline: rolling. Notification: continuous until 10/1. Transfer credits accepted: Yes.

Costs Per Year: Application fee: $30. State resident tuition: $6624 full-time, $276 per credit hour part-time. Nonresident tuition: $18,096 full-time, $754 per credit hour part-time. Mandatory fees: $3812 full-time. College room and board: $9704. College room only: $5030.

Collegiate Environment: Orientation program. Drama-theater group, choral group, student-run newspaper, radio station. Most popular organizations: Mountain Search and Rescue Team, Student Government Association, Rodeo Club, wilderness pursuits, Peak Productions. Major annual events: Earth Day, Homecoming, Family Weekend. Student services: health clinic,

personal-psychological counseling. Campus security: 24-hour emergency response devices and patrols, student patrols, late night transport-escort service, controlled dormitory access. 1,241 college housing spaces available; 1,231 were occupied in 2018-19. Freshmen guaranteed college housing. On-campus residence required through sophomore year. Option: coed housing available. Leslie J. Savage Library plus 1 other. Weekly public service hours: 101; students can reserve study rooms. 215 computers available on campus for general student use. A campuswide network can be accessed from campus residence rooms and from off campus. Students can access the following: online class registration. Staffed computer lab on campus provides training in use of computers, software, and the Internet.

Community Environment: Gunnison is a community with a population of about 5,200. Western State students are welcome to participate in all kinds of cultural, political, recreational, and religious activities offered by the community. The summer climate and the natural beauties of the region annually attract millions of tourists. Winter sports enthusiasts enjoy excellent skiing at Crested Butte Mountain Resort and Monarch Ski Area and ice fishing on Colorado's Blue Mesa Reservoir, which is located just 9 miles from the campus.

■ ALBERTUS MAGNUS COLLEGE
700 Prospect St.
New Haven, CT 06511-1189
Tel: (203)773-8550; Free: 800-578-9160
Fax: (203)785-8652
E-mail: admissions@albertus.edu
Web Site: www.albertus.edu
Description: Independent Roman Catholic, comprehensive, coed. Awards associate, bachelor's, and master's degrees and post-master's certificates. Founded 1925. Setting: 50-acre suburban campus. Total enrollment: 1,555. Faculty: 134 (52 full-time, 82 part-time). Student-undergrad faculty ratio is 14:1. 780 applied, 67% were admitted. 5% from top 10% of their high school class, 37% from top quarter, 58% from top half. 16 student government officers. Full-time: 1,034 students, 65% women, 35% men. Part-time: 186 students, 77% women, 23% men. Students come from 10 states and territories, 3 other countries, 5% from out-of-state. 0.2% American Indian or Alaska Native, non-Hispanic/Latino; 18% Hispanic/Latino; 34% Black or African American, non-Hispanic/Latino; 0.5% Asian, non-Hispanic/Latino; 2% international. 53% 25 or older, 40% live on campus, 9% transferred in. Retention: 84% of full-time freshmen returned the following year. Core. Calendar: semesters. Academic remediation for entering students, ESL program, services for LD students, advanced placement, accelerated degree program, self-designed majors, freshman honors college, honors program, independent study, distance learning, double major, summer session for credit, part-time degree program, adult/continuing education programs, internships, graduate courses open to undergrads. Study abroad program.
Entrance Requirements: Options: electronic application, deferred admission. Required: high school transcript, minimum 2 high school GPA, 1 recommendation, SAT or ACT. Recommended: SAT Subject Tests. Required for some: essay, interview. Entrance: moderately difficult. Application deadline: rolling. Notification: continuous. SAT Reasoning Test deadline: 8/30. Transfer credits accepted: Yes.
Costs Per Year: Application fee: $35. Comprehensive fee: $45,260 includes full-time tuition ($31,570), mandatory fees ($490), and college room and board ($13,200). Full-time tuition and fees vary according to program. Room and board charges vary according to board plan. Part-time tuition: $1315 per credit. Part-time tuition varies according to program.
Collegiate Environment: Orientation program. Drama-theater group, choral group. Social organizations: 10 open to all. Most popular organizations: Student Alumni Association, Student Government Association, M.A.L.E.S Club, Service Club, Honors Club. Major annual events: Candlelight Ceremony, Fall Festival, Spring Semi-Formal/Winter Wonderland. Student services: health clinic, personal-psychological counseling. Campus security: 24-hour emergency response devices and patrols, late night transport-escort service, controlled dormitory access. Rosary Hall. Books: 38,339 (physical), 148,500 (digital/electronic); Databases: 88. 117 computers available on campus for general student use. A campuswide network can be accessed from student residence rooms and from off campus. Students can access the following: online class registration, online class sessions. Staffed computer lab on campus provides training in use of computers, software, and the Internet.
Community Environment: See Yale University.

■ ASNUNTUCK COMMUNITY COLLEGE
170 Elm St.
Enfield, CT 06082-3800

Tel: (860)253-3000
Fax: (860)253-9310
E-mail: janilowski@asnuntuck.edu
Web Site: www.asnuntuck.edu
Description: State-supported, 2-year, coed. Part of Connecticut State Colleges & Universities (CSCU). Awards certificates, transfer associate, and terminal associate degrees. Founded 1972. Setting: 36-acre suburban campus. Endowment: $137,046. Educational spending for the previous fiscal year: $9632 per student. Total enrollment: 1,945. Faculty: 141 (31 full-time, 110 part-time). Student-undergrad faculty ratio is 17:1. 398 applied, 99.9% were admitted. Full-time: 652 students, 42% women, 58% men. Part-time: 1,293 students, 43% women, 57% men. 8% from out-of-state. 0.3% American Indian or Alaska Native, non-Hispanic/Latino; 13% Hispanic/Latino; 16% Black or African American, non-Hispanic/Latino; 3% Asian, non-Hispanic/Latino. 49% 25 or older, 16% transferred in. Retention: 68% of full-time freshmen returned the following year. Core. Calendar: semesters. Academic remediation for entering students, ESL program, services for LD students, advanced placement, self-designed majors, independent study, distance learning, double major, summer session for credit, part-time degree program, adult/continuing education programs, co-op programs and internships.
Entrance Requirements: Open admission. Option: deferred admission. Required: high school transcript, interview. Entrance: noncompetitive. Application deadline: rolling. Notification: continuous. Transfer credits accepted: Yes.
Costs Per Year: Application fee: $20. State resident tuition: $4464 full-time. Nonresident tuition: $13,232 full-time.
Collegiate Environment: Orientation program. Student-run radio station. Campus security: 24-hour emergency response devices, late night transport-escort service. ACC Library plus 1 other.

■ BAIS BINYOMIN ACADEMY
132 Prospect St.
Stamford, CT 06901-1202
Tel: (203)325-4351
Description: Independent Jewish, 4-year, men only. Awards bachelor's degrees. Founded 1976. Total enrollment: 63. Student-undergrad faculty ratio is 9:1. 26 applied, 100% were admitted. 96% from out-of-state. Retention: 77% of full-time freshmen returned the following year. Calendar: trimesters.

■ CAPITAL COMMUNITY COLLEGE
950 Main St.
Hartford, CT 06103
Tel: (860)906-5000
E-mail: jphillips@ccc.commnet.edu
Web Site: www.ccc.commnet.edu
Description: State-supported, 2-year, coed. Part of Connecticut State Colleges & Universities (CSCU). Awards certificates, transfer associate, and terminal associate degrees. Founded 1946. Setting: 10-acre urban campus. Total enrollment: 4,280. 54% 25 or older. Calendar: semesters. Academic remediation for entering students, ESL program, services for LD students, advanced placement, accelerated degree program, independent study, distance learning, double major, summer session for credit, part-time degree program, adult/continuing education programs, internships.

Entrance Requirements: Open admission except for nursing, emergency medical technology, radiological technology programs. Recommended: high school transcript. Entrance: noncompetitive. Application deadline: rolling. Notification: continuous until 9/1.

Collegiate Environment: Drama-theater group, choral group. Student services: personal-psychological counseling. Campus security: late night transport-escort service, security staff during hours of operation, emergency telephones 7 am - 11 pm. Arthur C. Banks, Jr. Library plus 1 other.

■ **CENTRAL CONNECTICUT STATE UNIVERSITY**
1615 Stanley St.
New Britain, CT 06050-4010
Tel: (860)832-3200
Fax: (860)832-2522
E-mail: admissions@ccsu.edu
Web Site: www.ccsu.edu

Description: State-supported, comprehensive, coed. Part of Connecticut State Colleges & Universities (CSCU). Awards bachelor's, master's, and doctoral degrees and post-master's certificates. Founded 1849. Setting: 314-acre suburban campus. Endowment: $72.7 million. Research spending for the previous fiscal year: $2.1 million. Educational spending for the previous fiscal year: $11,962 per student. Total enrollment: 11,822. Faculty: 977 (448 full-time, 529 part-time). Student-undergrad faculty ratio is 16:1. 7,903 applied, 67% were admitted. 10% from top 10% of their high school class, 27% from top quarter, 61% from top half. Full-time: 7,576 students, 47% women, 53% men. Part-time: 1,970 students, 44% women, 56% men. Students come from 30 states and territories, 25 other countries, 4% from out-of-state. 0.1% American Indian or Alaska Native, non-Hispanic/Latino; 16% Hispanic/Latino; 12% Black or African American, non-Hispanic/Latino; 5% Asian, non-Hispanic/Latino; 0.1% Native Hawaiian or other Pacific Islander, non-Hispanic/Latino; 1% international. 15% 25 or older, 25% live on campus, 11% transferred in. Retention: 74% of full-time freshmen returned the following year. Academic areas with the most degrees conferred: business/marketing; social sciences; psychology. Core. Calendar: semesters. Academic remediation for entering students, ESL program, services for LD students, advanced placement, self-designed majors, honors program, independent study, distance learning, double major, summer session for credit, part-time degree program, adult/continuing education programs, co-op programs and internships, graduate courses open to undergrads. Off campus study at members of the Inter-Institutional Student Exchange Program. Study abroad program. ROTC: Army (c), Air Force (c).

Entrance Requirements: Option: electronic application. Required: high school transcript, minimum 2 high school GPA, 2 recommendations, SAT or ACT. Required for some: essay, interview, high school class rank. Entrance: moderately difficult. Notification: continuous until 10/15. SAT Reasoning Test deadline: 6/1. SAT Subject Test deadline: 6/1. Transfer credits accepted: Yes. Applicants placed on waiting list: 188. Wait-listed applicants offered admission: 178.

Costs Per Year: Application fee: $50. Comprehensive fee: $0. College room only: $7130. Part-time mandatory fees: $298 per credit, $78 per term. Area resident tuition: $5924 full-time, $247 per credit part-time. State resident tuition: $5924 full-time, $247 per credit part-time. Nonresident tuition: $17,726 full-time, $247 per credit part-time. Mandatory fees: $5144 full-time, $298 per credit part-time, $78 per term part-time. College room and board: $12,528. College room only: $7130.

Collegiate Environment: Orientation program. Drama-theater group, choral group, student-run newspaper, radio station. Social organizations: 140 open to all; national fraternities, national sororities; 1% of eligible men and 1% of eligible women are members. Most popular organizations: Inter-Residence Council, student radio station, Program Board (C.A.N.), Student Government Association, A Cappella Society. Major annual events: Homecoming/Family Day, Spring Concert, Spring Week. Student services: health clinic, personal-psychological counseling, women's center. Campus security: 24-hour emergency response devices and patrols, student patrols, late night transport-escort service, controlled dormitory access. 2,512 college housing spaces available; 2,327 were occupied in 2018-19. No special consideration for freshman housing applicants. Options: coed, women-only housing available. Elihu Burritt Library plus 1 other. Books: 449,293 (physical), 199,200 (digital/electronic); Serial titles: 6,833 (physical), 89,498 (digital/electronic); Databases: 151. Weekly public service hours: 84. Operations spending for the previous fiscal year: $5.2 million. 450 computers available on campus for general student use. A campuswide network can be accessed from student residence rooms and from off campus. Students can access the following: online class registration. Staffed computer lab on campus provides training in use of computers, software, and the Internet.

Community Environment: Population 71,250. Known as the"Hardware City of the World," New Britain is located nine miles southwest of Hartford. Sleigh bells were the first items manufactured here. Now there are 250 manufacturing establishments and over 600 retail outlets. Access to New York City is by train, and there is commercial air service nearby. New Britain has 44 churches of major denominations, outstanding hospital facilities and is now undertaking urban renewal projects. Points of interest are the New Britain Institute and Art Museum, memorial monuments, municipal golf course and the parks.

■ **CHARTER OAK STATE COLLEGE**
55 Paul Manafort Dr.
New Britain, CT 06053-2142
Tel: (860)515-3800
Web Site: www.charteroak.edu

Description: State-supported, comprehensive, coed. Part of Connecticut State Colleges & Universities (CSCU). Awards associate, bachelor's, and master's degrees (offers only external degree programs). Founded 1973. Setting: suburban campus with easy access to Hartford, CT. Total enrollment: 1,500. Faculty: 186 (all part-time). Student-undergrad faculty ratio is 12:1. Students come from 43 states and territories, 20% from out-of-state. 0.4% American Indian or Alaska Native, non-Hispanic/Latino; 16% Hispanic/Latino; 17% Black or African American, non-Hispanic/Latino; 2% Asian, non-Hispanic/Latino; 0.7% international. 91% 25 or older. Academic areas with the most degrees conferred: liberal arts/general studies; business/marketing; health professions and related sciences. Core. Calendar: semesters. Services for LD students, advanced placement, accelerated degree program, self-designed majors, independent study, distance learning, double major, summer session for credit, part-time degree program, external degree program, adult/continuing education programs. Off campus study.

Entrance Requirements: Open admission. Options: electronic application, deferred admission. Required: 9 college-level credits, minimum 16 years of age. Entrance: noncompetitive. Transfer credits accepted: Yes.

Costs Per Year: Application fee: $75. State resident tuition: $9300 full-time, $310 per credit part-time. Nonresident tuition: $12,240 full-time, $408 per credit part-time. Mandatory fees: $861 full-time, $287 per term part-time. Full-time tuition and fees vary according to course load. Part-time tuition and fees vary according to course load.

Collegiate Environment: Orientation program.

■ **CONNECTICUT COLLEGE**
270 Mohegan Ave.
New London, CT 06320
Tel: (860)447-1911
Fax: (860)439-4301
E-mail: admission@conncoll.edu
Web Site: www.conncoll.edu

Description: Independent, 4-year, coed. Awards bachelor's degrees. Founded 1911. Setting: 750-acre small town campus with easy access to Providence, RI. Endowment: $318.3 million. Research spending for the previous fiscal year: $1.3 million. Educational spending for the previous fiscal year: $20,414 per student. Total enrollment: 1,844. Faculty: 233 (172 full-time, 61 part-time). Student-undergrad faculty ratio is 9:1. 6,433 applied, 38% were admitted. 49% from top 10% of their high school class, 80% from top quarter, 98% from top half. Full-time: 1,798 students, 62% women, 38% men. Part-time: 46 students, 43% women, 57% men. Students come from 40 states and territories, 41 other countries, 83% from out-of-state. 0.1% American Indian or Alaska Native, non-Hispanic/Latino; 9% Hispanic/Latino; 4% Black or African American, non-Hispanic/Latino; 5% Asian, non-Hispanic/Latino; 0.1% Native Hawaiian or other Pacific Islander, non-Hispanic/Latino; 7% international. 99% live on campus, 2% transferred in. Retention: 91% of full-time freshmen returned the following year. Academic areas with the most degrees conferred: social sciences; biological/life sciences; visual and performing arts. Core. Calendar: semesters. Services for LD students, advanced placement, accelerated degree program, self-designed majors, independent study, double major, part-time degree program, adult/continuing education programs, internships. Off campus study. Study abroad program.

Entrance Requirements: Options: electronic application, early decision, deferred admission, international baccalaureate accepted. Required: essay, high school transcript, 2 recommendations. Recommended: interview. Entrance: very difficult. Application deadlines: 1/1, 11/15 for early decision. Notification: 3/31, 12/15 for early decision. SAT Reasoning Test deadline: 2/15. SAT Subject Test deadline: 2/15. Transfer credits accepted: Yes. Applicants placed on waiting list: 1,385. Wait-listed applicants offered admission: 22. Early decision applicants: 362. Early decision applicants admitted: 226.

Costs Per Year: Application fee: $0. Comprehensive fee: $69,970 includes full-time tuition ($54,500), mandatory fees ($320), and college room and board ($15,150). College room only: $8750. Part-time tuition: $1622 per credit hour.

Collegiate Environment: Orientation program. Drama-theater group, choral group, student-run newspaper, radio station. Social organizations: 80 open to all. Major annual events: Floralia, Social dances, Cultural and athletic events. Student services: health clinic, personal-psychological counseling, women's center. Campus security: 24-hour emergency response devices and patrols, late night transport-escort service, controlled dormitory access. 1,748 college housing spaces available; 1,655 were occupied in 2018-19. Freshmen guaranteed college housing. On-campus residence required through junior year. Option: coed housing available. Charles Shain Library plus 1 other. Weekly public service hours: 115.

Community Environment: On the west bank of the Thames River, three miles from Long Island Sound, known historically as "The Whaling City." New London is a maritime center located midway between Boston and New York. It is a popular summer resort. Ocean Beach Park, a fifty-acre tract, borders a half-mile-long beach and provides recreational facilities. New London is the location of the annual Yale-Harvard Crew Races held each June.

■ **EASTERN CONNECTICUT STATE UNIVERSITY**
83 Windham St.
Willimantic, CT 06226-2295
Tel: (860)465-5000
Web Site: www.easternct.edu

Description: State-supported, comprehensive, coed. Part of Connecticut State Colleges & Universities (CSCU). Awards associate, bachelor's, and master's degrees. Founded 1889. Setting: 182-acre small town campus with easy access to Hartford. Endowment: $13.3 million. Research spending for the previous fiscal year: $1.9 million. Educational spending for the previous fiscal year: $9736 per student. Total enrollment: 5,261. Faculty: 499 (198 full-time, 301 part-time). Student-undergrad faculty ratio is 16:1. 5,370 applied, 64% were admitted. 11% from top 10% of their high school class, 32% from top quarter, 73% from top half. Full-time: 4,267 students, 54% women, 46% men. Part-time: 830 students, 56% women, 44% men. Students come from 20 states and territories, 63 other countries, 5% from out-of-state. 0.1% American Indian or Alaska Native, non-Hispanic/Latino; 10% Hispanic/Latino; 7% Black or African American, non-Hispanic/Latino; 3% Asian, non-Hispanic/Latino; 0.2% Native Hawaiian or other Pacific Islander, non-Hispanic/Latino; 1% international. 11% 25 or older, 53% live on campus, 9% transferred in. Retention: 73% of full-time freshmen returned the following year. Academic areas with the most degrees conferred: business/marketing; liberal arts/general studies; communication/journalism. Core. Calendar: semesters. Services for LD students, advanced placement, accelerated degree program, self-designed majors, honors program, independent study, distance learning, double major, summer session for credit, part-time degree program, external degree program, co-op programs and internships, graduate courses open to undergrads. Off campus study at Eastern has domestic exchange programs (the National Student Exchange), but also partnerships with 10 Canadian Universities, Chiang Mai Rajabhat (Thailand), Universite Catholique de Lyon (France), 9 German Universities, The American University of Athens (Greece), and Queen Margaret University (Scotland). Study abroad program. ROTC: Army (c), Air Force (c).

Entrance Requirements: Options: electronic application, deferred admission. Required: high school transcript. Recommended: essay, rank in upper 50% of high school class. Required for some: interview. Entrance: moderately difficult. Application deadline: rolling. Notification: continuous. Transfer credits accepted: Yes. Applicants placed on waiting list: 122. Wait-listed applicants offered admission: 27.

Costs Per Year: Application fee: $50. State resident tuition: $5678 full-time, $529 per credit hour part-time. Nonresident tuition: $11,932 full-time, $529 per credit hour part-time. Part-time tuition varies according to course load. College room and board: $13,520. College room only: $7758. Room and board charges vary according to board plan and housing facility.

Collegiate Environment: Orientation program. Drama-theater group, choral group, student-run newspaper, radio station. Social organizations: 77 open to all. Most popular organizations: Repertory Dance Troupe, Rugby Club, Biology Club, Education Club, Psychology Club. Major annual events: Arts and Lecture, University Hour, Springfest. Student services: health clinic, personal-psychological counseling, women's center. Campus security: 24-

hour emergency response devices and patrols, student patrols, late night transport-escort service, controlled dormitory access. J. Eugene Smith Library. Operations spending for the previous fiscal year: $127,699. 2,500 computers available on campus for general student use. Computer purchase/lease plans available. A campuswide network can be accessed from student residence rooms and from off campus. Students can access the following: online class registration. Staffed computer lab on campus provides training in use of computers, software, and the Internet.

Community Environment: Located 28 miles from Hartford and New London and halfway between Boston and New York, Willimantic, with a population of approximately 16,000, is primarily a retail and service center for eastern Connecticut. Bus service connects the city with major transportation facilities in Hartford, Providence, and New York. Willimantic has excellent health and hospital services and recreational facilities include the Willimantic Golf Course and nearby lakes and state parks.

■ **FAIRFIELD UNIVERSITY**
1073 N Benson Rd.
Fairfield, CT 06824
Tel: (203)254-4000
Fax: (203)254-4199
E-mail: admis@fairfield.edu
Web Site: www.fairfield.edu

Description: Independent Roman Catholic (Jesuit), comprehensive, coed. Awards bachelor's, master's, and doctoral degrees and post-master's certificates. Founded 1942. Setting: 200-acre suburban campus with easy access to New York City. Endowment: $361.5 million. Research spending for the previous fiscal year: $1.3 million. Educational spending for the previous fiscal year: $14,880 per student. Total enrollment: 5,273. Faculty: 622 (282 full-time, 340 part-time). Student-undergrad faculty ratio is 12:1. 11,361 applied, 60% were admitted. 37% from top 10% of their high school class, 77% from top quarter, 96% from top half. 26 National Merit Scholars, 158 class presidents, 3 valedictorians, 171 student government officers. Full-time: 3,989 students, 60% women, 40% men. Part-time: 188 students, 55% women, 45% men. Students come from 35 states and territories, 49 other countries, 72% from out-of-state. 0.1% American Indian or Alaska Native, non-Hispanic/Latino; 7% Hispanic/Latino; 2% Black or African American, non-Hispanic/Latino; 3% Asian, non-Hispanic/Latino; 4% international. 3% 25 or older, 73% live on campus, 1% transferred in. Retention: 90% of full-time freshmen returned the following year. Academic areas with the most degrees conferred: business/marketing; health professions and related sciences; communication/journalism. Core. Calendar: semesters. Services for LD students, advanced placement, accelerated degree program, self-designed majors, honors program, independent study, distance learning, double major, summer session for credit, part-time degree program, adult/continuing education programs, internships, graduate courses open to undergrads. Off campus study. Study abroad program. ROTC: Army (c), Air Force (c).

Entrance Requirements: Options: electronic application, early admission, early decision, early action, deferred admission, international baccalaureate accepted. Required: essay, high school transcript, 1 recommendation. Recommended: interview. Entrance: very difficult. Application deadlines: 1/15, 11/15 for early decision plan 1, 1/15 for early decision plan 2, 11/1 for early action. Notification: 4/1, 12/15 for early decision plan 1, 2/15 for early decision plan 2, 12/20 for early action. SAT Reasoning Test deadline: 1/15. Transfer credits accepted: Yes. Applicants placed on waiting list: 3,287. Wait-listed applicants offered admission: 11. Early decision applicants: 161. Early decision applicants admitted: 142. Early action applicants: 6,555. Early action applicants admitted: 4,007.

Costs Per Year: Application fee: $60. One-time mandatory fee: $300. Comprehensive fee: $63,060 includes full-time tuition ($47,650), mandatory fees ($700), and college room and board ($14,710). Full-time tuition and fees vary according to class time, course level, course load, degree level, and program. Room and board charges vary according to board plan and housing facility. Part-time tuition: $725 per credit hour. Part-time mandatory fees: $60 per term. Part-time tuition and fees vary according to class time, course level, course load, degree level, and program.

Collegiate Environment: Orientation program. Drama-theater group, choral group, student-run newspaper, radio station. Social organizations: 123 open to all. Most popular organizations: Fairfield University Student Association (FUSA), Inter-Residential Housing Associations (IRHA), Commuter Student Association (CSA), Play Like a Girl (PLAG), Intramural/Club Sports. Major annual events: Presidential Ball, Red Sea Madness/FUSA Concert, Fall Activities Fair. Student services: health clinic, personal-psychological counseling. Campus security: 24-hour emergency response devices and patrols, late night transport-escort service, controlled dormitory access. 3,157 college housing spaces available; 3,015 were occupied in 2018-19. Freshmen guaranteed college housing. Option: coed housing available. DiMenna-Nyselius Library. Books: 373,440 (physical), 924,527 (digital/electronic); Serial titles: 1,843 (physical), 52,268 (digital/electronic); Databases: 209. Weekly public service hours: 104; study areas open 24 hours, 5-7 days a week; students can reserve study rooms. Operations spending for the previous fiscal year: $2.8 million. 150 computers available on campus for general student use. Computer purchase/lease plans available. A campuswide network can be accessed from student residence rooms and from off campus. Students can access the following: online class registration. Staffed computer lab on campus provides training in use of computers, software, and the Internet.

Community Environment: Population 58,000. Fairfield is a suburban area one hour north of New York City on the Long Island Sound. The climate is temperate. The Metro-North New Haven branch railroad serves the area, as well as the Connecticut Turnpike and Merritt Parkway. Community facilities include libraries, churches and shopping areas. Part-time employment opportunities are available. Beaches are nearby for water sports; other sports include golf and tennis. A special annual event is the Dogwood Festival.

■ GATEWAY COMMUNITY COLLEGE

20 Church St.
New Haven, CT 06510
Tel: (203)285-2000; Free: 800-390-7723
Fax: (203)285-2018
E-mail: jcarberry@gatewayct.edu
Web Site: www.gwcc.commnet.edu

Description: State-supported, 2-year, coed. Part of Connecticut Community -Technical College System. Awards certificates, transfer associate, and terminal associate degrees. Founded 1992. Setting: 5-acre urban campus with easy access to New York City. Total enrollment: 8,201. Faculty: 581 (107 full-time, 474 part-time). Student-undergrad faculty ratio is 17:1. 3,522 applied, 97% were admitted. Full-time: 2,590 students, 51% women, 49% men. Part-time: 5,611 students, 62% women, 38% men. 0.2% American Indian or Alaska Native, non-Hispanic/Latino; 22% Hispanic/Latino; 26% Black or African American, non-Hispanic/Latino; 4% Asian, non-Hispanic/Latino; 0.5% international. 42% 25 or older, 9% transferred in. Core. Calendar: semesters. Academic remediation for entering students, ESL program, services for LD students, advanced placement, independent study, distance learning, summer session for credit, part-time degree program, external degree program, adult/continuing education programs, internships. Off campus study at Southern Connecticut State University.

Entrance Requirements: Open admission except for radiological technology, pharmacy technology, engineering technologies programs. Options: early admission, deferred admission. Required: high school transcript. Required for some: essay, interview. Entrance: noncompetitive. Application deadline: 9/1. Notification: continuous until 9/1. Transfer credits accepted: Yes.

Collegiate Environment: Drama-theater group, student-run newspaper. Student services: personal-psychological counseling, women's center. Campus security: late night transport-escort service. Gateway Community College Library plus 2 others. 556 computers available on campus for general student use. A campuswide network can be accessed from off-campus. Students can access the following: online class registration. Staffed computer lab on campus provides training in use of computers, software, and the Internet.

■ GOODWIN COLLEGE

One Riverside Dr.
East Hartford, CT 06118
Tel: (860)528-4111; Free: 800-889-3282
Fax: (860)291-9550
E-mail: nlentino@goodwin.edu
Web Site: www.goodwin.edu

Description: Independent, primarily 2-year, coed. Awards certificates, transfer associate, terminal associate, and bachelor's degrees. Founded 1999. Setting: 660-acre suburban campus with easy access to Hartford. Total enrollment: 3,440. Faculty: 312 (90 full-time, 222 part-time). Student-undergrad faculty ratio is 10:1. 480 applied. Full-time: 612 students, 74% women, 26% men. Part-time: 2,828 students, 83% women, 17% men. 3% from out-of-state. 0.3% American Indian or Alaska Native, non-Hispanic/Latino; 17% Hispanic/Latino; 22% Black or African American, non-Hispanic/

Latino; 2% Asian, non-Hispanic/Latino; 0.1% Native Hawaiian or other Pacific Islander, non-Hispanic/Latino; 0.1% international. 14% transferred in. Retention: 62% of full-time freshmen returned the following year. Core. Calendar: semesters. Academic remediation for entering students, ESL program, services for LD students, advanced placement, distance learning, double major, summer session for credit, part-time degree program, adult/continuing education programs, internships. Off campus study.

Entrance Requirements: Open admission selective admission to some programs. Options: electronic application, early admission, deferred admission, international baccalaureate accepted. Required: essay, high school transcript, minimum 2 high school GPA, medical exam. Recommended: 2 recommendations, interview. Entrance: minimally difficult. Transfer credits accepted: Yes.

Costs Per Year: Application fee: $50. Tuition: $19,988 full-time, $707 per credit hour part-time. Mandatory fees: $900 full-time.

Collegiate Environment: Orientation program. Choral group. Student services: personal-psychological counseling. Campus security: 24-hour emergency response devices, late night transport-escort service, evening security patrolman. Hoffman Family Library.

■ HOLY APOSTLES COLLEGE AND SEMINARY

33 Prospect Hill Rd.
Cromwell, CT 06416-2005
Tel: (860)632-3010
Fax: (860)632-3030
E-mail: pkucer@holyapostles.edu
Web Site: www.holyapostles.edu

Description: Independent Roman Catholic, comprehensive, coed. Awards associate, bachelor's, and master's degrees and post-master's certificates. Founded 1956. Setting: 17-acre suburban campus with easy access to Hartford, New Haven. Total enrollment: 546. Faculty: 83 (16 full-time, 67 part-time). Student-undergrad faculty ratio is 2:1. 10 applied, 100% were admitted. Full-time: 60 students, 52% women, 48% men. Part-time: 106 students, 51% women, 49% men. Students come from 33 states and territories, 4 other countries, 48% from out-of-state. 14% Hispanic/Latino; 0.7% Black or African American, non-Hispanic/Latino; 6% Asian, non-Hispanic/Latino; 29% international. 66% 25 or older, 7% transferred in. Academic areas with the most degrees conferred: theology and religious vocations; English; social sciences. Core. Calendar: semesters. Academic remediation for entering students, ESL program, services for LD students, independent study, summer session for credit, part-time degree program, external degree program, adult/continuing education programs, graduate courses open to undergrads.

Entrance Requirements: Open admission. Options: deferred admission, international baccalaureate accepted. Required: high school transcript, 2 recommendations, SAT or ACT. Recommended: SAT, ACT. Required for some: interview. Entrance: noncompetitive. Application deadlines: rolling, rolling for nonresidents. Transfer credits accepted: Yes.

Collegiate Environment: Orientation program. Social organizations: 1 open to all. Most popular organization: Pro-Life Organization. Major annual events: Christmas Party, Graduation. College housing not available. Holy Apostles College and Seminary Library. Books: 60,000 (physical); Serial titles: 145 (physical), 32 (digital/electronic); Databases: 5. Weekly public service hours: 70. Operations spending for the previous fiscal year: $37,300. 10 computers available on campus for general student use. A campuswide network can be accessed from student residence rooms. Students can access the following: online class registration. Staffed computer lab on campus provides training in use of computers, software, and the Internet.

■ HOUSATONIC COMMUNITY COLLEGE

900 Lafayette Blvd.
Bridgeport, CT 06604-4704
Tel: (203)332-5000
Web Site: www.housatonic.edu

Description: State-supported, 2-year, coed. Part of Connecticut State Colleges & Universities (CSCU). Awards certificates, transfer associate, and terminal associate degrees. Founded 1967. Setting: 4-acre urban campus with easy access to New York City. Total enrollment: 5,138. Faculty: 378 (80 full-time, 298 part-time). Student-undergrad faculty ratio is 16:1. 3,606 applied, 100% were admitted. Full-time: 1,729 students, 54% women, 46% men. Part-time: 3,409 students, 65% women, 35% men. 0.2% American Indian or Alaska Native, non-Hispanic/Latino; 33% Hispanic/Latino; 31% Black or African American, non-Hispanic/Latino; 3% Asian, non-Hispanic/Latino; 0.1% Native Hawaiian or other Pacific Islander, non-Hispanic/Latino;

0.7% international. 41% 25 or older, 7% transferred in. Retention: 57% of full-time freshmen returned the following year. Core. Calendar: semesters. Academic remediation for entering students, ESL program, services for LD students, advanced placement, honors program, independent study, distance learning, double major, summer session for credit, part-time degree program, adult/continuing education programs, co-op programs and internships. Off campus study.

Entrance Requirements: Open admission except for medical laboratory technician, allied health, physical therapy programs. Options: electronic application, deferred admission. Required: high school transcript. Entrance: noncompetitive. Application deadline: rolling. Notification: continuous. Transfer credits accepted: Yes.

Collegiate Environment: Orientation program. Drama-theater group, student-run newspaper. Social organizations: 16 open to all; honor societies, clubs. Most popular organizations: Student Senate, Association of Latin American Students, Community Action Network, Drama Club, Phi Theta Kappa. Major annual events: Spring Outing, Courtyard Festivals, Jazz Concerts. Student services: personal-psychological counseling, women's center. Campus security: 24-hour emergency response devices, late night transport-escort service. Housatonic Community College Library. Books: 55,000 (physical), 45,290 (digital/electronic); Serial titles: 104 (physical); Databases: 99. Students can reserve study rooms. 700 computers available on campus for general student use. A campuswide network can be accessed. Students can access the following: online class registration, online catalog, online refresher option in math/English, computer labs. Staffed computer lab on campus provides training in use of computers, software, and the Internet.

Community Environment: See University of Bridgeport.

■ MANCHESTER COMMUNITY COLLEGE
PO Box 1046
Manchester, CT 06045-1046
Tel: (860)512-3000
Fax: (860)647-6238
Web Site: www.manchestercc.edu

Description: State-supported, 2-year, coed. Part of Connecticut State Colleges & Universities (CSCU). Awards certificates, transfer associate, and terminal associate degrees. Founded 1963. Setting: small town campus. Total enrollment: 6,003. Faculty: 421 (93 full-time, 328 part-time). Student-undergrad faculty ratio is 16:1. 2,367 applied, 100% were admitted. Full-time: 2,004 students, 53% women, 47% men. Part-time: 3,999 students, 56% women, 44% men. 0.2% American Indian or Alaska Native, non-Hispanic/Latino; 23% Hispanic/Latino; 19% Black or African American, non-Hispanic/Latino; 6% Asian, non-Hispanic/Latino; 0.1% Native Hawaiian or other Pacific Islander, non-Hispanic/Latino. 31% 25 or older, 14% transferred in. Retention: 60% of full-time freshmen returned the following year. Calendar: semesters. Part-time degree program, adult/continuing education programs.

Entrance Requirements: Open admission Open admission policy as described above for all students, and selective admission to some programs. Option: electronic application. Required: high school transcript. Entrance: noncompetitive.

Costs Per Year: Application fee: $20. Area resident tuition: $3912 full-time, $163 per credit hour part-time. State resident tuition: $3912 full-time, $163 per credit hour part-time. Nonresident tuition: $11,736 full-time, $489 per credit hour part-time. Mandatory fees: $552 full-time.

Collegiate Environment: Orientation program. College housing not available.

■ MIDDLESEX COMMUNITY COLLEGE
100 Training Hill Rd.
Middletown, CT 06457-4889
Tel: (860)343-5800
Fax: (860)344-7488
E-mail: mshabazz@mxcc.commnet.edu
Web Site: www.mxcc.commnet.edu

Description: State-supported, 2-year, coed. Part of Connecticut State Colleges & Universities (CSCU). Awards certificates, transfer associate, and terminal associate degrees. Founded 1966. Setting: 38-acre suburban campus with easy access to Hartford. Endowment: $287,691. Educational spending for the previous fiscal year: $2500 per student. Total enrollment: 2,952. Faculty: 147 (44 full-time, 103 part-time). Student-undergrad faculty ratio is 22:1. 993 applied. Full-time: 1,186 students, 50% women, 50% men. Part-time: 1,766 students, 63% women, 37% men. Students come from 6

states and territories, 10 other countries, 1% from out-of-state. 37% 25 or older, 9% transferred in. Retention: 54% of full-time freshmen returned the following year. Academic remediation for entering students, ESL program, services for LD students, advanced placement, honors program, independent study, distance learning, double major, summer session for credit, part-time degree program, adult/continuing education programs, co-op programs and internships. Off campus study at other units of the Connecticut Community College System.

Entrance Requirements: Open admission except for radiological technology, human services, drug and alcohol counseling, broadcast journalism, ophthalmic design and dispensing programs. Options: electronic application, early admission, deferred admission. Required: high school transcript, CPT. Entrance: noncompetitive. Application deadline: rolling. Transfer credits accepted: Yes.

Collegiate Environment: Orientation program. Drama-theater group, student-run newspaper. Social organizations: 10 open to all. Most popular organizations: Phi Theta Kappa, Human Services Association, Peace and Justice Club, Poetry Club, International Student Club. Major annual events: International Day, Spring Festival, Senior Art Exhibit. Campus security: 24-hour emergency response devices and patrols. Jean Burr Smith Library. 80 computers available on campus for general student use. Computer purchase/lease plans available. A campuswide network can be accessed from off-campus. Students can access the following: online class registration. Staffed computer lab on campus provides training in use of computers, software, and the Internet.

■ MITCHELL COLLEGE
437 Pequot Ave.
New London, CT 06320-4498
Tel: (860)701-5000; Free: 800-443-2811
Fax: (860)444-1209
E-mail: admissions@mitchell.edu
Web Site: www.mitchell.edu

Description: Independent, 4-year, coed. Awards associate and bachelor's degrees. Founded 1938. Setting: 67-acre suburban campus with easy access to Hartford, CT and Providence RI. Endowment: $8.8 million. Educational spending for the previous fiscal year: $5311 per student. Total enrollment: 723. Faculty: 91 (23 full-time, 68 part-time). Student-undergrad faculty ratio is 14:1. 787 applied, 74% were admitted. Full-time: 615 students, 43% women, 57% men. Part-time: 108 students, 49% women, 51% men. Students come from 28 states and territories, 10 other countries, 37% from out-of-state. 2% American Indian or Alaska Native, non-Hispanic/Latino; 11% Hispanic/Latino; 14% Black or African American, non-Hispanic/Latino; 2% Asian, non-Hispanic/Latino; 2% international. 9% 25 or older, 59% live on campus, 5% transferred in. Retention: 81% of full-time freshmen returned the following year. Academic areas with the most degrees conferred: business/marketing; homeland security, law enforcement, firefighting, and protective services; parks and recreation. Core. Calendar: semesters. Services for LD students, advanced placement, self-designed majors, independent study, double major, summer session for credit, part-time degree program, co-op programs and internships.

Entrance Requirements: Options: electronic application, early admission, early decision, deferred admission. Required: essay, high school transcript, minimum 2 high school GPA, 1 recommendation. Recommended: interview. Entrance: minimally difficult. Application deadlines: rolling, 11/15 for early decision. Notification: continuous, 12/1 for early decision.

Collegiate Environment: Orientation program. Drama-theater group, choral group, student-run radio station. Social organizations: 29 open to all. Most popular organizations: Mitchell College Drama Society, Sigma Alpha Pi Leadership Society, Behavioral Science, Early Childhood, Gaming Club. Major annual events: Founder's Day/Picnic/Activities Fair, Leadership Speakers Series, Awards Ceremony/Strawberry Festival. Student services: health clinic, personal-psychological counseling. Campus security: 24-hour emergency response devices and patrols, student patrols, late night transport-escort service, controlled dormitory access. Mitchell College Library. Books: 33,182 (physical), 8,168 (digital/electronic); Databases: 46. Weekly public service hours: 81. Operations spending for the previous fiscal year: $412,798. 176 computers available on campus for general student use. Computer purchase/lease plans available. A campuswide network can be accessed from student residence rooms and from off campus. Students can access the following: online student portfolios, online course requests. Staffed computer lab on campus provides training in use of computers, software, and the Internet.

Community Environment: Small city of 30,000. Southern Connecticut is one of the country's fastest-growing tourist attractions. Campus is located at the confluence of the Thames River and Long Island Sound. The college maintains its own beach and 26-acre wooded park.

■ NAUGATUCK VALLEY COMMUNITY COLLEGE
750 Chase Pky.
Waterbury, CT 06708-3000
Tel: (203)575-8040
Fax: (203)596-8766
E-mail: nrosamilio@nv.edu
Web Site: www.nvcc.commnet.edu

Description: State-supported, 2-year, coed. Part of Connecticut State Colleges & Universities (CSCU). Awards certificates, transfer associate, and terminal associate degrees. Founded 1992. Setting: 110-acre urban campus. Total enrollment: 6,378. Faculty: 431 (96 full-time, 335 part-time). Student-undergrad faculty ratio is 17:1. 2,359 applied, 92% were admitted. Full-time: 2,173 students, 50% women, 50% men. Part-time: 4,205 students, 60% women, 40% men. Students come from 7 states and territories, 2 other countries, 0.3% from out-of-state. 0.2% American Indian or Alaska Native, non-Hispanic/Latino; 30% Hispanic/Latino; 11% Black or African American, non-Hispanic/Latino; 3% Asian, non-Hispanic/Latino; 0.2% Native Hawaiian or other Pacific Islander, non-Hispanic/Latino; 0.3% international. 35% 25 or older, 10% transferred in. Retention: 59% of full-time freshmen returned the following year. Core. Calendar: semesters. Academic remediation for entering students, ESL program, services for LD students, advanced placement, accelerated degree program, honors program, independent study, distance learning, summer session for credit, part-time degree program, external degree program, adult/continuing education programs, co-op programs and internships. Off campus study at other institutions in the CSCU system.

Entrance Requirements: Open admission selective admission in nursing, allied health, technician programs. Options: electronic application, deferred admission. Required: high school transcript, ACCUPLACER. Required for some: interview. Entrance: noncompetitive. Application deadline: rolling. Notification: continuous. Transfer credits accepted: Yes.

Costs Per Year: Application fee: $20. State resident tuition: $4424 full-time, $163 per credit hour part-time. Nonresident tuition: $13,192 full-time, $489 per credit hour part-time. Mandatory fees: $15 per term part-time. Part-time tuition and fees vary according to course load.

Collegiate Environment: Orientation program. Drama-theater group, choral group, student-run newspaper. Social organizations: 35 open to all. Most popular organizations: Student Senate, Choral Society, Automotive Technician Club, Human Service Club, Legal Assistant Club. Major annual events: Awards Ceremony, Spring Picnic, Club Expo. Student services: personal-psychological counseling, women's center. Campus security: 24-hour emergency response devices and patrols, late night transport-escort service, security escort service. Max R. Traurig Learning Resource Center. Books: 38,400 (physical); Serial titles: 108 (physical); Databases: 12. Weekly public service hours: 65; students can reserve study rooms. 450 computers available on campus for general student use. A campuswide network can be accessed. Students can access the following: online class registration. Staffed computer lab on campus.

Community Environment: See Teikyo Post University.

■ NORTHWESTERN CONNECTICUT COMMUNITY COLLEGE
Park Pl. E
Winsted, CT 06098-1798
Tel: (860)738-6300
Fax: (860)379-4465
E-mail: admissions@nwcc.commnet.edu
Web Site: www.nwcc.commnet.edu

Description: State-supported, 2-year, coed. Part of Connecticut State Colleges & Universities (CSCU). Awards certificates, transfer associate, and terminal associate degrees. Founded 1965. Setting: 5-acre small town campus with easy access to Hartford. Total enrollment: 1,549. Full-time: 457 students, 60% women, 40% men. Part-time: 1,092 students, 68% women, 32% men. Students come from 3 states and territories, 1% from out-of-state. 8% Hispanic/Latino; 2% Black or African American, non-Hispanic/Latino; 1% Asian, non-Hispanic/Latino; 0.1% Native Hawaiian or other Pacific Islander, non-Hispanic/Latino; 0.1% international. 43% 25 or older, 9% transferred in. Retention: 55% of full-time freshmen returned the following year. Core. Calendar: semesters. Academic remediation for entering students, ESL program, services for LD students, independent study, distance learning, summer session for credit, part-time degree program, internships.

Entrance Requirements: Open admission except for physical therapy as-

sistant, drug and alcohol counseling programs. Option: deferred admission. Entrance: noncompetitive. Application deadline: rolling. Notification: continuous.

Collegiate Environment: Orientation program. Student-run newspaper. Campus security: evening security patrols. Northwestern Connecticut Community-Technical College Learning Center.

Community Environment: Population 7,321. Winsted is a suburban community with a temperate climate. It has shopping areas, library, churches, and a YMCA. Airport facilities are 30 miles away, but easy to reach. Recreational facilities are good, including excellent fishing in surrounding areas, boating on Highland Lake, and winter sports at Sundown ski area about three miles southeast.

■ NORWALK COMMUNITY COLLEGE
188 Richards Ave.
Norwalk, CT 06854-1655
Tel: (203)857-7000
Fax: (203)857-3335
E-mail: admissions@ncc.commnet.edu
Web Site: www.ncc.commnet.edu

Description: State-supported, 2-year, coed. Part of Connecticut State Colleges & Universities (CSCU). Awards certificates, transfer associate, and terminal associate degrees. Founded 1961. Setting: 30-acre suburban campus with easy access to New York City. Total enrollment: 5,800. Faculty: 397 (104 full-time, 293 part-time). Student-undergrad faculty ratio is 18:1. Full-time: 2,047 students, 54% women, 46% men. Part-time: 3,822 students, 62% women, 38% men. 1% from out-of-state. 0.2% American Indian or Alaska Native, non-Hispanic/Latino; 37% Hispanic/Latino; 17% Black or African American, non-Hispanic/Latino; 5% Asian, non-Hispanic/Latino; 0.2% Native Hawaiian or other Pacific Islander, non-Hispanic/Latino; 2% international. 37% 25 or older, 7% transferred in. Retention: 61% of full-time freshmen returned the following year. Core. Calendar: semesters. Academic remediation for entering students, ESL program, services for LD students, advanced placement, independent study, distance learning, summer session for credit, part-time degree program, co-op programs and internships.

Entrance Requirements: Open admission. Options: electronic application, deferred admission. Required: high school transcript, 4 math courses, 3 science courses, 2 labs, immunization form. Entrance: noncompetitive. Transfer credits accepted: Yes.

Collegiate Environment: Orientation program. Drama-theater group, choral group, student-run newspaper. Social organizations: Phi Theta Kappa Honor Society. Most popular organizations: Student World Assembly, Accounting Club, Literature Club, Art Club, Phi Theta Kappa. Major annual events: Welcome Back Club Fair, Day of Thanks, Spring Fling. Student services: personal-psychological counseling, women's center. Campus security: late night transport-escort service, all buildings secured each evening, foot patrols and vehicle patrols by security from 7 am-11 pm. Everett I. L. Baker Library.

Community Environment: Norwalk is a urban community located on Long Island Sound and is 50 minutes by rail from Grand Central Station in New York City. Community facilities include major shopping areas, libraries, churches, a symphony orchestra, and the Silvermine Guild Artists.

■ PAIER COLLEGE OF ART, INC.
20 Gorham Ave.
Hamden, CT 06514-3902
Tel: (203)287-3031
E-mail: paier.admission@snet.net
Web Site: www.paiercollegeofart.edu

Description: Proprietary, 4-year, coed. Awards bachelor's degrees. Founded 1946. Setting: 3-acre suburban campus with easy access to New York City. Total enrollment: 79. Faculty: 25 (9 full-time, 16 part-time). Student-undergrad faculty ratio is 3:1. 20 applied, 75% were admitted. 25% from top half of their high school class. Full-time: 48 students, 79% women, 21% men. Part-time: 31 students, 55% women, 45% men. Students come from 2 states and territories, 1 other country. 11% Hispanic/Latino; 11% Black or African American, non-Hispanic/Latino; 5% Asian, non-Hispanic/Latino. 9% 25 or older, 10% transferred in. Retention: 92% of full-time freshmen returned the following year. Academic area with the most degrees conferred: visual and performing arts. Core. Calendar: semesters plus 1 summer session. Academic remediation for entering students, services for LD students, advanced placement, independent study, part-time degree program, internships. Study abroad program.

Entrance Requirements: Option: early admission. Required: high school transcript, minimum 2 high school GPA, 2 recommendations, interview, portfolio, interview, SAT or ACT. Recommended: essay. Transfer credits accepted: Yes.

Costs Per Year: Application fee: $25. Tuition: $17,100 full-time, $570 per credit hour part-time. Mandatory fees: $470 full-time, $190 per term part-time. Part-time tuition and fees vary according to course load.

Collegiate Environment: Orientation program. Student-run newspaper. Social organizations: 2 open to all. Most popular organizations: Student Council, School Newspaper. Major annual events: Winter Art Show and Sale, Spring Art Show and Sale, Fall Paier Picnic. Adele K. Paier Memorial Library. Books: 14,300 (physical), 167 (digital/electronic); Serial titles: 80 (physical). 50 computers available on campus for general student use. Computer purchase/lease plans available. Staffed computer lab on campus provides training in use of computers, software, and the Internet.

■ POST UNIVERSITY

800 Country Club Rd.
Waterbury, CT 06723-2540
Tel: (203)596-4500; Free: 800-345-2562
Fax: (203)756-5810
Web Site: www.post.edu

Description: Independent, comprehensive, coed. Awards associate, bachelor's, and master's degrees and post-master's certificates. Founded 1890. Setting: 70-acre suburban campus with easy access to Hartford. Educational spending for the previous fiscal year: $2470 per student. Total enrollment: 8,540. Student-undergrad faculty ratio is 20:1. 4,078 applied, 63% were admitted. Full-time: 2,617 students, 61% women, 39% men. Part-time: 5,227 students, 67% women, 33% men. Students come from 29 states and territories, 24 other countries, 71% from out-of-state. 0.8% American Indian or Alaska Native, non-Hispanic/Latino; 7% Hispanic/Latino; 25% Black or African American, non-Hispanic/Latino; 1% Asian, non-Hispanic/Latino; 0.5% Native Hawaiian or other Pacific Islander, non-Hispanic/Latino; 1% international. 65% 25 or older, 51% live on campus, 31% transferred in. Retention: 39% of full-time freshmen returned the following year. Academic areas with the most degrees conferred: business/marketing; homeland security, law enforcement, firefighting, and protective services; public administration and social services. Core. Calendar: semesters. ESL program, services for LD students, advanced placement, accelerated degree program, freshman honors college, honors program, independent study, distance learning, double major, summer session for credit, part-time degree program, co-op programs and internships. Off campus study.

Entrance Requirements: Options: electronic application, deferred admission, international baccalaureate accepted. Required: high school transcript, minimum 2 high school GPA, 1 recommendation, SAT or ACT. Recommended: essay, interview. Entrance: moderately difficult. Application deadline: rolling. Notification: continuous. SAT Reasoning Test deadline: 8/15. Transfer credits accepted: Yes.

Costs Per Year: Application fee: $0. Comprehensive fee: $40,150 includes full-time tuition ($28,250), mandatory fees ($1300), and college room and board ($10,600). Full-time tuition and fees vary according to class time, course level, course load, degree level, location, program, and student level. Room and board charges vary according to housing facility. Part-time tuition: $945 per credit hour. Part-time tuition varies according to class time, course level, course load, degree level, location, program, and student level.

Collegiate Environment: Orientation program. Drama-theater group, choral group. Social organizations: 25 open to all; 60% of eligible men and 60% of eligible women are members. Most popular organizations: Equine Club, Newman Club, GSA, Accounting Club, Choir. Major annual events: Fall Weekend, Winter Weekend, Spring Weekend. Student services: health clinic, personal-psychological counseling. Campus security: 24-hour emergency response devices and patrols, late night transport-escort service, controlled dormitory access, annual and semi-annual emergency preparedness training for students and staff. Trauriq Library and Resource Center. Books: 10,320 (physical), 160,000 (digital/electronic); Serial titles: 250 (physical), 36,199 (digital/electronic); Databases: 43. Weekly public service hours: 75; students can reserve study rooms. Operations spending for the previous fiscal year: $468,607. 150 computers available on campus for general student use. Computer purchase/lease plans available. A campuswide network can be accessed. Students can access the following: online class registration, software applications. Staffed computer lab on campus provides training in use of computers, software, and the Internet.

Community Environment: Waterbury is a city of approximately 110,000, located in the northwest part of the state. There are three other colleges in

the area and 15 other institutions of higher learning within a 30-minute drive. The Greater Waterbury area offers ample opportunities for cultural, athletic, and recreational activities.

■ QUINEBAUG VALLEY COMMUNITY COLLEGE

742 Upper Maple St.
Danielson, CT 06239-1440
Tel: (860)774-1130
Fax: (860)774-7768
E-mail: qu_isd@commnet.edu
Web Site: www.qvcc.edu

Description: State-supported, 2-year, coed. Part of Connecticut State Colleges & Universities (CSCU). Awards certificates, transfer associate, and terminal associate degrees. Founded 1971. Setting: 60-acre rural campus. Total enrollment: 1,779. Faculty: 126 (29 full-time, 97 part-time). Student-undergrad faculty ratio is 18:1. 586 applied, 98% were admitted. Full-time: 669 students, 60% women, 40% men. Part-time: 1,110 students, 73% women, 27% men. Students come from 3 states and territories, 1% from out-of-state. 41% 25 or older, 9% transferred in. Core. Calendar: semesters. Academic remediation for entering students, ESL program, advanced placement, independent study, distance learning, summer session for credit, part-time degree program, external degree program, adult/continuing education programs, internships. Study abroad program.

Entrance Requirements: Open admission. Options: electronic application, early admission, deferred admission. Recommended: high school transcript. Required for some: high school transcript. Entrance: noncompetitive. Application deadline: 9/1. Notification: continuous until 9/1.

Collegiate Environment: Orientation program. Campus security: evening security guard. Audrey Beck Library. 80 computers available on campus for general student use. A campuswide network can be accessed. Staffed computer lab on campus.

Community Environment: Population, 4,285. Located in Northeastern Connecticut, Danielson is in the midst of a semi-rural area which is supported by poultry and dairy industries. Outdoor recreational possibilities abound. The Connecticut turnpike provides easy access to New London, Old Mystic, Massachusetts and Rhode Island.

■ QUINNIPIAC UNIVERSITY

275 Mount Carmel Ave.
Hamden, CT 06518-1940
Tel: (203)582-8200; Free: 800-462-1944
Fax: (203)582-6347
E-mail: admissions@qu.edu
Web Site: www.qu.edu

Description: Independent, comprehensive, coed. Awards bachelor's, master's, and doctoral degrees and post-master's certificates. Founded 1929. Setting: 600-acre suburban campus with easy access to New Haven, Hartford. Endowment: $481.6 million. Research spending for the previous fiscal year: $3.1 million. Educational spending for the previous fiscal year: $19,455 per student. Total enrollment: 10,200. Faculty: 1,084 (378 full-time, 706 part-time). Student-undergrad faculty ratio is 16:1. 22,071 applied, 74% were admitted. 22% from top 10% of their high school class, 51% from top quarter, 91% from top half. 19 valedictorians. Students come from 45 states and territories, 51 other countries, 71% from out-of-state. 0.1% American Indian or Alaska Native, non-Hispanic/Latino; 9% Hispanic/Latino; 4% Black or African American, non-Hispanic/Latino; 3% Asian, non-Hispanic/Latino; 2% international. 2% 25 or older, 75% live on campus. Retention: 86% of full-time freshmen returned the following year. Academic areas with the most degrees conferred: health professions and related sciences; business/marketing; communication/journalism. Core. Calendar: semesters. Services for LD students, advanced placement, accelerated degree program, honors program, independent study, distance learning, double major, summer session for credit, part-time degree program, internships, graduate courses open to undergrads. Study abroad program. ROTC: Army (c), Air Force (c).

Entrance Requirements: Options: electronic application, early decision, deferred admission, international baccalaureate accepted. Required: essay, high school transcript, 1 recommendation. Recommended: minimum 3 high school GPA, interview. Required for some: minimum 3 high school GPA, SAT or ACT. Entrance: moderately difficult. Application deadlines: 2/1, 11/1 for early decision. Notification: continuous, continuous for nonresidents. SAT Reasoning Test deadline: 2/1. Transfer credits accepted: Yes. Applicants placed on waiting list: 177. Wait-listed applicants offered admission: 6. Early decision applicants: 426. Early decision applicants admitted: 145.

Costs Per Year: Application fee: $65. Comprehensive fee: $62,950 includes

full-time tuition ($45,540), mandatory fees ($2420), and college room and board ($14,990). Room and board charges vary according to board plan and housing facility. Part-time tuition: $1045 per credit hour. Part-time mandatory fees: $45 per credit hour. Part-time tuition and fees vary according to class time and course load.

Collegiate Environment: Orientation program. Drama-theater group, choral group, student-run newspaper, radio station. Social organizations: 145 open to all; national fraternities, national sororities, local fraternities; 24% of eligible men and 30% of eligible women are members. Most popular organizations: Student Government, Social Programming Board, Drama Club, Chronicle (student newspaper), dance company. Major annual events: Campus Concerts, Student/Faculty Holiday Dinner, Midnight Madness (athletics). Student services: health clinic, personal-psychological counseling, women's center. Campus security: 24-hour emergency response devices and patrols, late night transport-escort service, controlled dormitory access, text message emergency notification system. Arnold Bernhard Library plus 3 others. Books: 135,000 (physical), 500,000 (digital/electronic); Databases: 190. Weekly public service hours: 93; study areas open 24 hours, 5-7 days a week; students can reserve study rooms. Operations spending for the previous fiscal year: $4.7 million. 600 computers available on campus for general student use. Computer purchase/lease plans available. A computer is required for all students. A campuswide network can be accessed from student residence rooms and from off campus. Students can access the following: online class registration, e-commerce and Q card for local merchants, food service, dorm card access. Staffed computer lab on campus provides training in use of computers, software, and the Internet.

Community Environment: Hamden, population 58,180. Sleeping Giant Mountain State Park is adjacent to the campus and has 1700 acres for walking and hiking.

■ SACRED HEART UNIVERSITY

5151 Park Ave.
Fairfield, CT 06825
Tel: (203)371-7999
Fax: (203)371-7889
E-mail: osullivank6@sacredheart.edu
Web Site: www.sacredheart.edu

Description: Independent Roman Catholic, comprehensive, coed. Awards bachelor's, master's, and doctoral degrees and post-master's certificates (also offers part-time program with significant enrollment not reflected in profile). Founded 1963. Setting: 350-acre suburban campus with easy access to New York City. Endowment: $167.6 million. Educational spending for the previous fiscal year: $9631 per student. Total enrollment: 8,958. Faculty: 954 (317 full-time, 637 part-time). Student-undergrad faculty ratio is 14:1. 10,740 applied, 60% were admitted. 10% from top 10% of their high school class, 35% from top quarter, 72% from top half. Full-time: 5,130 students, 64% women, 36% men. Part-time: 844 students, 74% women, 26% men. Students come from 39 states and territories, 30 other countries, 62% from out-of-state. 0.2% American Indian or Alaska Native, non-Hispanic/Latino; 12% Hispanic/Latino; 5% Black or African American, non-Hispanic/Latino; 2% Asian, non-Hispanic/Latino; 0.1% Native Hawaiian or other Pacific Islander, non-Hispanic/Latino; 1% international. 10% 25 or older, 52% live on campus, 4% transferred in. Retention: 83% of full-time freshmen returned the following year. Academic areas with the most degrees conferred: health professions and related sciences; business/marketing; psychology. Core. Calendar: semesters. Academic remediation for entering students, ESL program, services for LD students, advanced placement, accelerated degree program, self-designed majors, honors program, independent study, distance learning, double major, summer session for credit, part-time degree program, adult/continuing education programs, co-op programs and internships, graduate courses open to undergrads. Study abroad program. ROTC: Air Force (c).

Entrance Requirements: Options: electronic application, early admission, early decision, early action, deferred admission, international baccalaureate accepted. Required: high school transcript, 1 recommendation. Recommended: essay. Required for some: interview, interview for Early Decision candidates. Entrance: moderately difficult. Application deadlines: rolling, 12/1 for early decision. Notification: continuous, 12/15 for early decision. Transfer credits accepted: Yes. Early decision applicants: 199. Early decision applicants admitted: 170. Early action applicants: 7,103. Early action applicants admitted: 1,061.

Costs Per Year: Application fee: $50. Comprehensive fee: $56,730 includes full-time tuition ($41,150), mandatory fees ($270), and college room and board ($15,310). College room only: $10,500. Room and board charges vary

according to board plan and housing facility. Part-time tuition: $625 per credit hour. Part-time mandatory fees: $115 per term. Part-time tuition and fees vary according to course load.

Collegiate Environment: Orientation program. Drama-theater group, choral group, marching band, student-run newspaper, radio station. Social organizations: 193 open to all; national fraternities, national sororities, local fraternities; 27% of eligible men and 47% of eligible women are members. Most popular organizations: Alpha Sigma Lambda Honor Society, Inter Resident Council, Student Nursing Association, Habitat for Humanity, Pre-PT Club. Major annual events: Campus Spring Concert, President's Gala, Pack the Pitt. Student services: health clinic, personal-psychological counseling. Campus security: 24-hour emergency response devices and patrols, late night transport-escort service, controlled dormitory access, Bystander Intervention, Personal Safety Escort Program, Silent Witness Program, crime prevention announcements, SHU Safe App. 2,929 college housing spaces available; 2,835 were occupied in 2018-19. Freshmen guaranteed college housing. On-campus residence required through sophomore year. Option: coed housing available. Ryan Matura Library plus 1 other. Books: 89,846 (physical), 228,647 (digital/electronic); Serial titles: 412 (physical), 62,191 (digital/electronic); Databases: 140. Weekly public service hours: 119; students can reserve study rooms. Operations spending for the previous fiscal year: $2 million. 499 computers available on campus for general student use. A computer is required for all students. A campuswide network can be accessed from student residence rooms and from off campus. Students can access the following: online class registration. Staffed computer lab on campus provides training in use of computers, software, and the Internet.

Community Environment: Sacred Heart University is located in coastal Fairfield, Connecticut, one hour northeast of New York City. Numerous Fortune 500 companies are headquartered in Fairfield County providing students with unique opportunities for outside learning and hands-on experience. Transportation, restaurants, shopping malls, movies, theaters, and beaches are all easily accessible.

■ SOUTHERN CONNECTICUT STATE UNIVERSITY

501 Crescent St.
New Haven, CT 06515-1355
Tel: (203)392-5200
Fax: (203)392-5727
E-mail: haakonsena1@southernct.edu
Web Site: www.southernct.edu

Description: State-supported, comprehensive, coed. Part of Connecticut State Colleges & Universities (CSCU). Awards bachelor's, master's, and doctoral degrees and post-master's certificates. Founded 1893. Setting: 168-acre suburban campus with easy access to New York City. Total enrollment: 10,320. Faculty: 964 (423 full-time, 541 part-time). Student-undergrad faculty ratio is 14:1. 8,625 applied, 64% were admitted. 1% from top 10% of their high school class, 8% from top quarter, 39% from top half. Full-time: 6,830 students, 63% women, 37% men. Part-time: 1,133 students, 56% women, 44% men. Students come from 29 states and territories, 9 other countries, 4% from out-of-state. 0.3% American Indian or Alaska Native, non-Hispanic/Latino; 14% Hispanic/Latino; 17% Black or African American, non-Hispanic/Latino; 4% Asian, non-Hispanic/Latino; 0.1% Native Hawaiian or other Pacific Islander, non-Hispanic/Latino; 0.6% international. 14% 25 or older, 33% live on campus, 9% transferred in. Retention: 77% of full-time freshmen returned the following year. Academic areas with the most degrees conferred: health professions and related sciences; business/marketing; liberal arts/general studies. Core. Calendar: semesters. Academic remediation for entering students, services for LD students, advanced placement, accelerated degree program, self-designed majors, freshman honors college, honors program, independent study, distance learning, double major, summer session for credit, part-time degree program, co-op programs and internships, graduate courses open to undergrads. Off campus study at New England Board of Higher Education. Study abroad program. ROTC: Army (c), Air Force (c).

Entrance Requirements: Options: electronic application, deferred admission, international baccalaureate accepted. Required: essay, high school transcript, SAT or ACT. Entrance: moderately difficult. Application deadline: rolling. Notification: continuous. Transfer credits accepted: Yes.

Costs Per Year: Application fee: $50. State resident tuition: $5642 full-time, $238 per credit hour part-time. Nonresident tuition: $16,882 full-time, $238 per credit hour part-time. Mandatory fees: $5312 full-time, $322 per credit hour part-time, $85 per term part-time. Full-time tuition and fees vary according to course load and reciprocity agreements. Part-time tuition and fees vary according to course load. College room and board: $12,860. College room only: $7046. Room and board charges vary according to board plan and housing facility.

Collegiate Environment: Orientation program. Drama-theater group, choral group, marching band, student-run newspaper, radio station. Social organizations: 161 open to all; national fraternities, national sororities, local sororities; 1% of eligible men and 1% of eligible women are members. Most popular organizations: Student Government Association, Psychology Club, Habitat for Humanity, Crescent Players, Black Student Union. Major annual events: Spring Week, Homecoming Week, Convocation. Student services: health clinic, personal-psychological counseling, women's center. Campus security: 24-hour emergency response devices and patrols, late night transport-escort service, controlled dormitory access. Hilton C. Buley Library. Books: 478,191 (physical), 135,134 (digital/electronic); Serial titles: 14,528 (physical), 158 (digital/electronic); Databases: 203. Students can reserve study rooms. 1,000 computers available on campus for general student use. A campuswide network can be accessed from student residence rooms and from off campus. Students can access the following: online class registration. Staffed computer lab on campus provides training in use of computers, software, and the Internet.

Community Environment: Metropolitan.

■ **THREE RIVERS COMMUNITY COLLEGE**
574 New London Tpke.
Norwich, CT 06360
Tel: (860)215-9000
Fax: (860)886-0691
E-mail: admissions@trcc.commnet.edu
Web Site: www.threerivers.edu
Description: State-supported, 2-year, coed. Part of Connecticut State Colleges & Universities (CSCU). Awards certificates, transfer associate, and terminal associate degrees (engineering technology programs are offered on the Thames Valley Campus; liberal arts, transfer and career programs are offered on the Mohegan Campus). Founded 1963. Setting: 40-acre suburban campus with easy access to Hartford. Educational spending for the previous fiscal year: $6740 per student. Total enrollment: 4,187. Faculty: 302 (68 full-time, 234 part-time). Student-undergrad faculty ratio is 16:1. Full-time: 1,340 students, 51% women, 49% men. Part-time: 2,847 students, 63% women, 37% men. Students come from 5 states and territories, 1% from out-of-state. 0.7% American Indian or Alaska Native, non-Hispanic/Latino; 17% Hispanic/Latino; 8% Black or African American, non-Hispanic/Latino; 4% Asian, non-Hispanic/Latino; 0.3% Native Hawaiian or other Pacific Islander, non-Hispanic/Latino; 0.2% international. 40% 25 or older, 9% transferred in. Retention: 63% of full-time freshmen returned the following year. Calendar: semesters. Part-time degree program, adult/continuing education programs.
Entrance Requirements: Open admission except for nursing, drug and alcohol rehabilitation counseling, paramedic programs. Options: electronic application, early admission, deferred admission. Recommended: high school transcript. Entrance: noncompetitive. Application deadline: rolling. Notification: continuous. Transfer credits accepted: Yes.
Costs Per Year: One-time mandatory fee: $80. State resident tuition: $4464 full-time, $163 per credit hour part-time. Nonresident tuition: $13,232 full-time, $489 per credit hour part-time. Mandatory fees: $472 full-time. Full-time tuition and fees vary according to course load and reciprocity agreements. Part-time tuition varies according to course load and reciprocity agreements.
Collegiate Environment: Orientation program. Student-run newspaper. Campus security: 24-hour emergency response devices, late night transport-escort service, 14-hour patrols by trained security personnel. Three Rivers Community College Learning Resource Center plus 1 other. Operations spending for the previous fiscal year: $620,855.

■ **TRINITY COLLEGE**
300 Summit St.
Hartford, CT 06106-3100
Tel: (860)297-2000
Fax: (860)297-2287
Web Site: www.trincoll.edu
Description: Independent, comprehensive, coed. Awards bachelor's and master's degrees. Founded 1823. Setting: 100-acre urban campus. Endowment: $551.8 million. Research spending for the previous fiscal year: $1.9 million. Educational spending for the previous fiscal year: $61,087 per student. Total enrollment: 2,397. Faculty: 295 (193 full-time, 102 part-time).

Student-undergrad faculty ratio is 10:1. 7,569 applied, 33% were admitted. 43% from top 10% of their high school class, 80% from top quarter, 97% from top half. Full-time: 2,165 students, 48% women, 52% men. Part-time: 124 students, 46% women, 54% men. Students come from 44 states and territories, 63 other countries, 84% from out-of-state. 0.1% American Indian or Alaska Native, non-Hispanic/Latino; 7% Hispanic/Latino; 6% Black or African American, non-Hispanic/Latino; 4% Asian, non-Hispanic/Latino; 9% international. 90% live on campus, 1% transferred in. Retention: 88% of full-time freshmen returned the following year. Academic areas with the most degrees conferred: social sciences; area and ethnic studies; biological/life sciences; psychology. Core. Calendar: semesters. Advanced placement, accelerated degree program, self-designed majors, honors program, independent study, double major, summer session for credit, part-time degree program, adult/continuing education programs, internships, graduate courses open to undergrads. Off campus study at members of the Twelve College Exchange Program, Hartford Consortium for Higher Education. Study abroad program. ROTC: Army (c).
Entrance Requirements: Options: electronic application, early admission, early decision, deferred admission, international baccalaureate accepted. Required: essay, high school transcript, 3 recommendations. Recommended: interview. Entrance: most difficult. Application deadlines: 1/1, 11/15 for early decision plan 1, 1/1 for early decision plan 2. Notification: 4/1, 12/15 for early decision plan 1, 2/15 for early decision plan 2. SAT Reasoning Test deadline: 1/15. SAT Subject Test deadline: 1/15. Applicants placed on waiting list: 1,796. Wait-listed applicants offered admission: 83. Early decision applicants: 506. Early decision applicants admitted: 300.
Costs Per Year: Application fee: $60. Comprehensive fee: $71,660 includes full-time tuition ($54,340), mandatory fees ($2570), and college room and board ($14,750). College room only: $9600. Full-time tuition and fees vary according to course load and program. Room and board charges vary according to board plan.
Collegiate Environment: Orientation program. Drama-theater group, choral group, student-run newspaper, radio station. Social organizations: 104 open to all; national fraternities, national sororities, local fraternities, local sororities, coed fraternities; 20% of eligible men and 16% of eligible women are members. Most popular organizations: Friends Active in Community Engagement and Service (FACES), The Mill, Student Government Association, Relay for Life, Multi-Cultural Affairs Council. Major annual events: Spring Weekend, Homecoming. Student services: health clinic, personal-psychological counseling, women's center. Campus security: 24-hour emergency response devices and patrols, late night transport-escort service, controlled dormitory access. Trinity College Library plus 1 other. Operations spending for the previous fiscal year: $4 million. 249 computers available on campus for general student use. A campuswide network can be accessed from student residence rooms and from off campus. Students can access the following: online class registration, Web pages. Staffed computer lab on campus provides training in use of computers, software, and the Internet.

■ **TUNXIS COMMUNITY COLLEGE**
271 Scott Swamp Rd.
Farmington, CT 06032-3026
Tel: (860)773-1300
E-mail: pmccluskey@tunxis.edu
Web Site: www.tunxis.edu
Description: State-supported, 2-year, coed. Part of Connecticut State Colleges & Universities (CSCU). Awards certificates, transfer associate, and terminal associate degrees. Founded 1969. Setting: 12-acre suburban campus with easy access to Hartford. Total enrollment: 4,079. Faculty: 239 (67 full-time, 172 part-time). Student-undergrad faculty ratio is 17:1. Full-time: 1,594 students, 51% women, 49% men. Part-time: 2,485 students, 59% women, 41% men. Students come from 6 states and territories, 2% from out-of-state. 0.2% American Indian or Alaska Native, non-Hispanic/Latino; 19% Hispanic/Latino; 7% Black or African American, non-Hispanic/Latino; 4% Asian, non-Hispanic/Latino; 0.1% international. 38% 25 or older. Retention: 61% of full-time freshmen returned the following year. Core. Calendar: semesters. Academic remediation for entering students, ESL program, services for LD students, honors program, independent study, distance learning, double major, summer session for credit, part-time degree program, adult/continuing education programs, co-op programs and internships.
Entrance Requirements: Open admission except for dental hygiene. Option: deferred admission. Required: high school transcript. Entrance: noncompetitive. Application deadline: rolling. Notification: continuous. Transfer credits accepted: Yes.

Costs Per Year: Application fee: $20. State resident tuition: $3912 full-time, $163 per semester hour part-time. Nonresident tuition: $11,736 full-time, $489 per semester hour part-time. Mandatory fees: $552 full-time, $8 per semester hour part-time, $111 per term part-time.

Collegiate Environment: Orientation program. Drama-theater group, student-run newspaper. Social organizations: 14 open to all. Most popular organizations: Phi Theta Kappa, Student American Dental Hygiene Association (SADHA), Human Services Club, Student Newspaper, Criminal Justice Club. Major annual events: Writer's Festival, Campus Barbecue, International Students' Day. Campus security: 24-hour emergency response devices. Tunxis Community College Library. Students can reserve study rooms. Operations spending for the previous fiscal year: $166,377. 354 computers available on campus for general student use. A campuswide network can be accessed from off-campus. Students can access the following: online class registration. Staffed computer lab on campus provides training in use of computers, software, and the Internet.

Community Environment: Farmington was settled in 1640 and incorporated in 1645. It is a suburban, residential town with a population of 25,000.

■ UNITED STATES COAST GUARD ACADEMY

15 Mohegan Ave.
New London, CT 06320-8100
Tel: (860)444-8444; Free: 800-883-8724
Fax: (860)444-8289
E-mail: daniel.v.pinch@uscga.edu
Web Site: www.uscga.edu

Description: Federally supported, 4-year, coed. Awards bachelor's degrees. Founded 1876. Setting: 103-acre suburban campus with easy access to Providence, Hartford. Educational spending for the previous fiscal year: $52,293 per student. Total enrollment: 1,045. Faculty: 161 (138 full-time, 23 part-time). Student-undergrad faculty ratio is 7:1. 2,021 applied, 15% were admitted. 41% from top 10% of their high school class, 79% from top quarter, 97% from top half. Full-time: 1,045 students, 35% women, 65% men. Students come from 52 states and territories, 12 other countries, 95% from out-of-state. 0.3% American Indian or Alaska Native, non-Hispanic/Latino; 9% Hispanic/Latino; 6% Black or African American, non-Hispanic/Latino; 7% Asian, non-Hispanic/Latino; 0.2% Native Hawaiian or other Pacific Islander, non-Hispanic/Latino; 3% international. 100% live on campus. Retention: 95% of full-time freshmen returned the following year. Academic areas with the most degrees conferred: engineering; business/marketing; social sciences. Core. Calendar: semesters. Academic remediation for entering students, advanced placement, honors program, independent study, double major, summer session for credit, internships. Off campus study at Connecticut College, U.S. Military Academy (West Point), U.S. Naval Academy and the U.S. Air Force Academy.

Entrance Requirements: Options: electronic application, early action, deferred admission. Required: essay, high school transcript, 3 recommendations, medical examination, physical fitness examination, SAT or ACT. Recommended: interview. Entrance: very difficult. Application deadlines: 2/1, rolling for nonresidents, 11/15 for early action. Notification: continuous until 4/15, continuous until 4/15 for nonresidents, 2/1 for early action. SAT Reasoning Test deadline: 3/1. SAT Subject Test deadline: 3/1. Transfer credits accepted: No. Applicants placed on waiting list: 33. Wait-listed applicants offered admission: 28. Early action applicants: 686. Early action applicants admitted: 98.

Costs Per Year: Application fee: $0. Comprehensive fee: $0. Tuition, room and board, and medical and dental care are provided by the US government. Each cadet receives a salary from which to pay for uniforms, supplies, and personal expenses.

Collegiate Environment: Orientation program. Drama-theater group, choral group, marching band. Social organizations: 70 open to all. Most popular organizations: Club Sports, Musical activities, Multicultural Club, Officers Christian Fellowship, International Dance Club. Major annual events: Homecoming, Parents' Weekend, Community Service Day. Student services: legal services, health clinic, personal-psychological counseling. Campus security: 24-hour patrols, late night transport-escort service, controlled dormitory access, cadets staff a 24-hour Watch Office. USCG Academy Library. Students can reserve study rooms. Operations spending for the previous fiscal year: $647,992. 280 computers available on campus for general student use. A computer is required for all students. A campuswide network can be accessed from student residence rooms and from off campus. Staffed computer lab on campus provides training in use of computers, software, and the Internet.

■ UNIVERSITY OF BRIDGEPORT

126 Park Ave.
Bridgeport, CT 06604
Tel: (203)576-4000; Free: 800-EXCEL-UB
Fax: (203)576-4941
E-mail: admit@bridgeport.edu
Web Site: www.bridgeport.edu

Description: Independent, comprehensive, coed. Awards associate, bachelor's, master's, and doctoral degrees and post-master's certificates. Founded 1927. Setting: 86-acre urban campus with easy access to New York City. Endowment: $38 million. Research spending for the previous fiscal year: $122,000. Educational spending for the previous fiscal year: $21,793 per student. Total enrollment: 5,434. Faculty: 559 (147 full-time, 412 part-time). Student-undergrad faculty ratio is 16:1. 7,947 applied, 54% were admitted. 8% from top 10% of their high school class, 31% from top quarter, 64% from top half. Full-time: 2,300 students, 62% women, 38% men. Part-time: 829 students, 71% women, 29% men. Students come from 40 states and territories, 48 other countries, 32% from out-of-state. 0.8% American Indian or Alaska Native, non-Hispanic/Latino; 22% Hispanic/Latino; 34% Black or African American, non-Hispanic/Latino; 4% Asian, non-Hispanic/Latino; 0.2% Native Hawaiian or other Pacific Islander, non-Hispanic/Latino; 13% international. 30% 25 or older, 37% live on campus, 10% transferred in. Retention: 71% of full-time freshmen returned the following year. Academic areas with the most degrees conferred: business/marketing; health professions and related sciences; psychology. Core. Calendar: semesters. Academic remediation for entering students, ESL program, services for LD students, advanced placement, accelerated degree program, self-designed majors, honors program, independent study, distance learning, double major, summer session for credit, part-time degree program, adult/continuing education programs, co-op programs and internships, graduate courses open to undergrads. Off campus study at Fairfield University, Sacred Heart University. Study abroad program.

Entrance Requirements: Options: electronic application, early admission, deferred admission. Required: essay, high school transcript, minimum 2 high school GPA, SAT or ACT. Recommended: 1 recommendation, interview. Required for some: 2 recommendations, interview, portfolio, audition. Entrance: moderately difficult. Application deadline: rolling. Notification: continuous. Transfer credits accepted: Yes.

Costs Per Year: Application fee: $25. Tuition: $30,750 full-time, $1025 per credit hour part-time. Mandatory fees: $2110 full-time, $220 per term part-time. Full-time tuition and fees vary according to course load and program. Part-time tuition and fees vary according to course load and program.

Collegiate Environment: Orientation program. Choral group, student-run newspaper. Social organizations: 60 open to all; national fraternities, national sororities, local fraternities, local sororities; 1% of eligible men and 2% of eligible women are members. Most popular organizations: Student Congress, International Relations Club, Black Students Alliance, Latin America Club, Martial Arts Club. Major annual events: International Festival, Spring Week Events, Halloween Bash. Student services: health clinic, personal-psychological counseling. Campus security: 24-hour emergency response devices and patrols, student patrols, late night transport-escort service, controlled dormitory access. Wahlstrom Library. Books: 144,829 (physical), 210,775 (digital/electronic); Serial titles: 957 (physical), 68,477 (digital/electronic); Databases: 81. Weekly public service hours: 90. Operations spending for the previous fiscal year: $1.3 million. 300 computers available on campus for general student use. A campuswide network can be accessed. Students can access the following: online class registration. Staffed computer lab on campus provides training in use of computers, software, and the Internet.

Community Environment: Bridgeport is named for the first drawbridge erected over the Pequonock River and is easily accessible by auto, bus and train, automobiles using the Merrit Parkway and the Connecticut Thruway. Bridgeport is the home of P.T. Barnum. Barnum Institute of Science and History and the Museum of Art, Science and Industry is located in Bridgeport. Seaside Park, a 225-acre park stretching two and one half miles along Long Island Sound, offers opportunities for swimming and field sports. Beardsley Park has woodland walks and drives, a large lake and a zoo. Sixty-five percent of Connecticut's largest corporations are located in Fairfield County. These companies provide students with excellent opportunities for employment, before and after graduation.

■ UNIVERSITY OF CONNECTICUT

Storrs, CT 06269
Tel: (860)486-2000

Fax: (860)486-1476

E-mail: beahusky@uconn.edu

Web Site: www.uconn.edu

Description: State-supported, university, coed. Awards associate, bachelor's, master's, and doctoral degrees and post-master's certificates. Founded 1881. Setting: 4,099-acre rural campus. Endowment: $367 million. Research spending for the previous fiscal year: $177.3 million. Total enrollment: 26,541. Faculty: 1,589 (1,223 full-time, 366 part-time). Student-undergrad faculty ratio is 16:1. 31,280 applied, 50% were admitted. 50% from top 10% of their high school class, 85% from top quarter, 98% from top half. 77 valedictorians. Full-time: 17,677 students, 50% women, 50% men. Part-time: 718 students, 40% women, 60% men. Students come from 43 states and territories, 79 other countries, 22% from out-of-state. 0.1% American Indian or Alaska Native, non-Hispanic/Latino; 8% Hispanic/Latino; 5% Black or African American, non-Hispanic/Latino; 10% Asian, non-Hispanic/Latino; 4% international. 3% 25 or older, 71% live on campus, 4% transferred in. Retention: 93% of full-time freshmen returned the following year. Core. Calendar: semesters. ESL program, services for LD students, advanced placement, accelerated degree program, self-designed majors, honors program, independent study, distance learning, double major, summer session for credit, part-time degree program, adult/continuing education programs, co-op programs and internships, graduate courses open to undergrads. Off campus study at other public institutions in Connecticut. Study abroad program. ROTC: Army, Air Force.

Entrance Requirements: Options: electronic application, deferred admission. Required: essay, high school transcript, SAT or ACT. Recommended: 2 recommendations. Entrance: moderately difficult. Application deadline: 1/15. Notification: 3/1. SAT Reasoning Test deadline: 1/15. Transfer credits accepted: Yes. Applicants placed on waiting list: 4,107. Wait-listed applicants offered admission: 1,409.

Costs Per Year: Application fee: $70. State resident tuition: $12,848 full-time, $536 per credit part-time. Nonresident tuition: $35,216 full-time, $1468 per credit part-time. Mandatory fees: $2882 full-time. Part-time tuition varies according to course load. College room and board: $12,874. College room only: $7028. Room and board charges vary according to board plan, housing facility, and location.

Collegiate Environment: Orientation program. Drama-theater group, choral group, marching band, student-run newspaper, radio station. Social organizations: 582 open to all; national fraternities, national sororities, local fraternities, local sororities; 10% of eligible men and 13% of eligible women are members. Major annual events: Husky WOW (Week of Welcome), Homecoming, Winter Weekend/One Ton Sundae. Student services: health clinic, personal-psychological counseling, women's center. Campus security: 24-hour emergency response devices, late night transport-escort service. Homer Babbidge Library plus 3 others. Operations spending for the previous fiscal year: $23.1 million. 2,220 computers available on campus for general student use. Computer purchase/lease plans available. A campuswide network can be accessed from student residence rooms and from off campus. Students can access the following: online class registration. Staffed computer lab on campus provides training in use of computers, software, and the Internet.

Community Environment: Storrs, population 11,000, is in a rural area 25 miles east of Hartford and 70 miles south of Boston. The climate is temperate. Buses serve the area with other modes of transportation available in Hartford. Community facilities include various houses of worship and a small shopping area. Willimantic, nine miles away, has a hospital and additional shopping facilities. There are recreational activities at nearby lakes and State Parks. Part-time employment opportunities are limited.

■ **UNIVERSITY OF HARTFORD**

200 Bloomfield Ave.

West Hartford, CT 06117-1599

Tel: (860)768-4100; Free: 800-947-4303

Fax: (860)768-4961

E-mail: admissions@hartford.edu

Web Site: www.hartford.edu

Description: Independent, comprehensive, coed. Awards associate, bachelor's, master's, and doctoral degrees and post-master's certificates. Founded 1877. Setting: 320-acre suburban campus with easy access to Hartford. Endowment: $164.5 million. Research spending for the previous fiscal year: $2.9 million. Educational spending for the previous fiscal year: $15,295 per student. Total enrollment: 6,561. Faculty: 875 (355 full-time, 520 part-time). Student-undergrad faculty ratio is 9:1. 14,043 applied, 81% were admitted. Full-time: 4,460 students, 51% women, 49% men. Part-time: 609

students, 55% women, 45% men. Students come from 47 states and territories, 45 other countries, 45% from out-of-state. 0.3% American Indian or Alaska Native, non-Hispanic/Latino; 13% Hispanic/Latino; 15% Black or African American, non-Hispanic/Latino; 4% Asian, non-Hispanic/Latino; 0.1% Native Hawaiian or other Pacific Islander, non-Hispanic/Latino; 6% international. 8% 25 or older, 61% live on campus, 5% transferred in. Retention: 73% of full-time freshmen returned the following year. Academic areas with the most degrees conferred: visual and performing arts; business/marketing; health professions and related sciences. Core. Calendar: semesters. Academic remediation for entering students, ESL program, services for LD students, advanced placement, self-designed majors, honors program, independent study, distance learning, double major, summer session for credit, part-time degree program, adult/continuing education programs, co-op programs and internships, graduate courses open to undergrads. Off campus study at members of the Hartford Consortium for Higher Education. Study abroad program. ROTC: Army (c), Air Force (c).

Entrance Requirements: Options: electronic application, early admission, early action, deferred admission. Required: high school transcript, SAT or ACT. Recommended: essay, 2 recommendations, interview. Entrance: moderately difficult. Application deadline: rolling. Notification: continuous. Transfer credits accepted: Yes.

Costs Per Year: Application fee: $35. Comprehensive fee: $53,170 includes full-time tuition ($37,802), mandatory fees ($2892), and college room and board ($12,476). College room only: $8008. Full-time tuition and fees vary according to program. Room and board charges vary according to board plan and housing facility. Part-time tuition: $550 per credit hour. Part-time tuition varies according to course load and program.

Collegiate Environment: Orientation program. Drama-theater group, choral group, student-run newspaper, radio station. Social organizations: 45 open to all; national fraternities, national sororities; 17% of eligible men and 21% of eligible women are members. Most popular organizations: Program Council, Brothers and Sisters United, Hillel, Student Government Association, Residence Hall Association. Major annual events: Hawks Fest, Lacrosse Under the Light, Midnight Mania. Student services: legal services, health clinic, personal-psychological counseling, women's center. Campus security: 24-hour emergency response devices and patrols, late night transport-escort service, controlled dormitory access, bicycle patrols. Mortensen Library plus 1 other. Books: 287,556 (physical), 2,540 (digital/electronic); Serial titles: 1,479 (physical), 56,360 (digital/electronic); Databases: 229. Weekly public service hours: 104. Operations spending for the previous fiscal year: $3.4 million. 400 computers available on campus for general student use. A campuswide network can be accessed from student residence rooms and from off campus. Students can access the following: online class registration, student Web pages. Staffed computer lab on campus.

Community Environment: The University is located in a suburban area of West Hartford, four miles from the center of Hartford. In addition to the many activities available on campus, the proximity to a metropolitan area affords a multitude of cultural, educational and recreational opportunities.

■ **UNIVERSITY OF NEW HAVEN**

300 Boston Post Rd.

West Haven, CT 06516

Tel: (203)932-7000; Free: 800-342-5864

Fax: (203)937-0756

E-mail: jriendeau@newhaven.edu

Web Site: www.newhaven.edu

Description: Independent, comprehensive, coed. Awards associate, bachelor's, master's, and doctoral degrees and post-master's certificates. Founded 1920. Setting: 82-acre suburban campus with easy access to New Haven. Total enrollment: 6,867. Faculty: 662 (258 full-time, 404 part-time). Student-undergrad faculty ratio is 16:1. 10,426 applied, 84% were admitted. 13% from top 10% of their high school class, 42% from top quarter, 78% from top half. Full-time: 4,768 students, 54% women, 46% men. Part-time: 324 students, 45% women, 55% men. Students come from 44 states and territories, 32 other countries, 55% from out-of-state. 0.4% American Indian or Alaska Native, non-Hispanic/Latino; 12% Hispanic/Latino; 12% Black or African American, non-Hispanic/Latino; 3% Asian, non-Hispanic/Latino; 0.1% Native Hawaiian or other Pacific Islander, non-Hispanic/Latino; 4% international. 7% 25 or older, 53% live on campus, 4% transferred in. Retention: 76% of full-time freshmen returned the following year. Academic areas with the most degrees conferred: homeland security, law enforcement, firefighting, and protective services; business/marketing; engineering. Core. Calendar: 4-1-4. Academic remediation for entering students, ESL program, services for LD students, advanced placement, accelerated degree program, honors program, independent study, distance learning, double major, summer session for credit, part-time degree program, adult/continuing education programs, co-op programs and internships, graduate courses open to undergrads. Off campus study. Study abroad program. ROTC: Army, Air Force (c).

Entrance Requirements: Options: electronic application, early decision, early action. Required: essay, high school transcript, SAT or ACT. Recommended: interview. Entrance: moderately difficult. Application deadlines: rolling, rolling for nonresidents, 12/1 for early decision, 12/15 for early action. Notification: continuous, continuous for nonresidents, 12/15 for early decision, 1/15 for early action. Transfer credits accepted: Yes. Applicants placed on waiting list: 499. Wait-listed applicants offered admission: 35. Early decision applicants: 82. Early decision applicants admitted: 60.

Costs Per Year: Application fee: $50. Comprehensive fee: $55,170 includes full-time tuition ($37,870), mandatory fees ($1400), and college room and board ($15,900). College room only: $10,150. Full-time tuition and fees vary according to course load and program. Room and board charges vary according to board plan and housing facility. Part-time tuition: $1260 per credit hour. Part-time mandatory fees: $105 per term. Part-time tuition and fees vary according to class time, course load, and program.

Collegiate Environment: Orientation program. Drama-theater group, marching band, student-run newspaper, radio station. Social organizations: 140 open to all; national fraternities, national sororities, local fraternities, local sororities. Student services: health clinic, personal-psychological counseling. Campus security: 24-hour emergency response devices and patrols, student patrols, late night transport-escort service, controlled dormitory access. 2,923 college housing spaces available; 2,648 were occupied in 2018-19. Freshmen guaranteed college housing. Option: coed housing available. Marvin K. Peterson Library.

Community Environment: Located in West Haven, a town with a population of 52,900; ten minutes from downtown New Haven. Cultural attractions include the Shubert Theater, The Palace, Long Wharf Theater, Yale Repertory Theater. The university is accessible to many shopping malls and the beaches of Long Island Sound.

■ **UNIVERSITY OF SAINT JOSEPH**
1678 Asylum Ave.
West Hartford, CT 06117-2700
Tel: (860)232-4571; Free: 866-442-8752
Fax: (860)233-5695
Web Site: www.usj.edu
Description: Independent Roman Catholic, comprehensive, coed. Awards bachelor's, master's, and doctoral degrees and post-master's certificates. Founded 1932. Setting: 90-acre suburban campus with easy access to Hartford. Total enrollment: 2,405. Faculty: 301 (134 full-time, 167 part-time). Student-undergrad faculty ratio is 9:1. 649 applied, 90% were admitted. 31% from top 10% of their high school class, 54% from top quarter, 84% from top half. Full-time: 654 students, 99% women, 1% men. Part-time: 156 students, 92% women, 8% men. Students come from 15 states and territories, 5% from out-of-state. 0.2% American Indian or Alaska Native, non-Hispanic/Latino; 15% Hispanic/Latino; 14% Black or African American, non-Hispanic/Latino; 5% Asian, non-Hispanic/Latino; 0.9% international. 1% 25 or older, 51% live on campus, 7% transferred in. Retention: 75% of full-time freshmen returned the following year. Academic areas with the most degrees conferred: health professions and related sciences; public administration and social services; family and consumer sciences. Core. Calendar: semesters. Services for LD students, advanced placement, accelerated degree program, self-designed majors, honors program, independent study, distance learning, double major, summer session for credit, part-time degree program, adult/continuing education programs, internships, graduate courses open to undergrads. Off campus study. Study abroad program.

Entrance Requirements: Options: electronic application, deferred admission. Required: high school transcript, 1 recommendation. Recommended: essay, interview. Required for some: SAT or ACT. Entrance: moderately difficult. Application deadline: rolling. Notification: continuous. SAT Reasoning Test deadline: 8/15. SAT Subject Test deadline: 8/15. Transfer credits accepted: Yes.

Costs Per Year: Application fee: $50. Comprehensive fee: $50,601 includes full-time tuition ($37,361), mandatory fees ($1812), and college room and board ($11,428). College room only: $6438. Full-time tuition and fees vary according to course load, degree level, location, program, and student level. Room and board charges vary according to board plan and housing facility. Part-time tuition: $843 per credit hour. Part-time mandatory fees: $60 per

credit hour. Part-time tuition and fees vary according to course load, degree level, location, program, and student level.

Collegiate Environment: Orientation program. Drama-theater group, choral group. Student services: health clinic, personal-psychological counseling. Campus security: 24-hour emergency response devices and patrols, late night transport-escort service, controlled dormitory access. Pope Pius XII Library. 72 computers available on campus for general student use. A campuswide network can be accessed from student residence rooms and from off campus. Students can access the following: online class registration. Staffed computer lab on campus.

Community Environment: The campus is located in a suburban community within 5 miles of Hartford, the capital of Connecticut. Known as the Insurance City, Hartford offers multiple internship and employment possibilities and diverse attractions such as ballet, opera, theater, symphony, museums, historic landmarks, sporting events, shopping, churches, and hospitals. Many volunteer opportunities are also available.

■ **WESLEYAN UNIVERSITY**
45 Wyllys Ave.
Middletown, CT 06459
Tel: (860)685-2000
Fax: (860)685-3001
E-mail: admission@wesleyan.edu
Web Site: www.wesleyan.edu
Description: Independent, university, coed. Awards bachelor's, master's, and doctoral degrees and post-master's certificates. Founded 1831. Setting: 316-acre suburban campus with easy access to Hartford, CT; New Haven, CT; Springfield, MA. Endowment: $1.1 billion. Total enrollment: 3,217. Faculty: 438 (367 full-time, 71 part-time). Student-undergrad faculty ratio is 8:1. 12,706 applied, 17% were admitted. 57% from top 10% of their high school class, 85% from top quarter, 98% from top half. Full-time: 2,928 students, 55% women, 45% men. Part-time: 81 students, 48% women, 52% men. Students come from 50 states and territories, 54 other countries, 93% from out-of-state. 12% Hispanic/Latino; 6% Black or African American, non-Hispanic/Latino; 7% Asian, non-Hispanic/Latino; 12% international. 7% 25 or older, 99% live on campus, 1% transferred in. Retention: 96% of full-time freshmen returned the following year. Academic areas with the most degrees conferred: social sciences; psychology; area and ethnic studies. Calendar: semesters. Services for LD students, advanced placement, accelerated degree program, self-designed majors, honors program, independent study, double major, summer session for credit, internships, graduate courses open to undergrads. Off campus study at Woods Hole Oceanographic Institution, Twelve College Exchange Programs, Williams College/Mystic Seaport Program, Connecticut College/National Theater Institute. Study abroad program. ROTC: Air Force (c).

Entrance Requirements: Options: electronic application, early admission, early decision, deferred admission, international baccalaureate accepted. Required: essay, high school transcript, 2 recommendations. Recommended: interview. Required for some: SAT and SAT Subject Tests or ACT. Entrance: most difficult. Application deadlines: 1/1, 11/15 for early decision. Notification: 4/1, 12/15 for early decision. SAT Reasoning Test deadline: 2/15. SAT Subject Test deadline: 2/15. Transfer credits accepted: Yes. Applicants placed on waiting list: 1,965. Wait-listed applicants offered admission: 0. Early decision applicants: 1,080. Early decision applicants admitted: 406.

Costs Per Year: Application fee: $55. Comprehensive fee: $72,728 includes full-time tuition ($56,704), mandatory fees ($300), and college room and board ($15,724).

Collegiate Environment: Orientation program. Drama-theater group, choral group, student-run newspaper, radio station. Social organizations: 263 open to all; national fraternities, national sororities, local fraternities, local sororities; 4% of eligible men and 1% of eligible women are members. Most popular organizations: Mock Trial, Athletic Clubs, Spectrum, Burlesque, Espwesso. Major annual events: WesFest (annual festival for admitted students), Fall Student Groups Fair, Spring Fling Concert. Student services: health clinic, personal-psychological counseling. Campus security: 24-hour emergency response devices and patrols, late night transport-escort service, controlled dormitory access, Self-defense classes offered by certified instructors. 2,937 college housing spaces available. Freshmen guaranteed college housing. On-campus residence required through senior year. Options: coed, men-only, women-only housing available. Olin Memorial Library plus 1 other. Books: 1.2 million (physical), 502,915 (digital/electronic); Serial titles: 7,507 (physical), 86,968 (digital/electronic); Databases: 332. Weekly public service hours: 113. 118 computers available on campus for general student use. Computer purchase/lease plans available. A campuswide network can be accessed from student residence rooms and from off campus. Students can access the following: online class registration, electronic portfolio, course drop/add, learning management system, software training. Staffed computer lab on campus (open 24 hours a day) provides training in use of computers and software.

Community Environment: Population 47,400. In central Connecticut, 15 miles south of Hartford and 20 miles north of New Haven, Middletown is an important research and manufacturing center. Buses and railroads serve the area with an airline service nearby. Middletown has 21 churches of all denominations, hospital, three libraries with branches, several inns, motels, theatres and a shopping area. The various civic, fraternal and veterans organizations are active within the city. Parks, tennis courts, basketball courts, ball fields, picnic grounds and swimming pool provide facilities for recreation.

■ WESTERN CONNECTICUT STATE UNIVERSITY
181 White St.
Danbury, CT 06810-6885
Tel: (203)837-8200; Free: 877-837-WCSU
Fax: (203)837-8320
Web Site: www.wcsu.edu

Description: State-supported, comprehensive, coed. Part of Connecticut State Colleges & Universities (CSCU). Awards associate, bachelor's, master's, and doctoral degrees and post-master's certificates. Founded 1903. Setting: 340-acre urban campus with easy access to New York City. Endowment: $19.1 million. Research spending for the previous fiscal year: $1.1 million. Educational spending for the previous fiscal year: $12,987 per student. Total enrollment: 5,642. Faculty: 614 (223 full-time, 391 part-time). Student-undergrad faculty ratio is 13:1. 5,375 applied, 79% were admitted. 7% from top 10% of their high school class, 23% from top quarter, 59% from top half. Full-time: 4,128 students, 52% women, 48% men. Part-time: 900 students, 53% women, 47% men. Students come from 13 states and territories, 2 other countries, 15% from out-of-state. 0.2% American Indian or Alaska Native, non-Hispanic/Latino; 19% Hispanic/Latino; 10% Black or African American, non-Hispanic/Latino; 4% Asian, non-Hispanic/Latino; 0.1% Native Hawaiian or other Pacific Islander, non-Hispanic/Latino. 17% 25 or older, 30% live on campus, 10% transferred in. Retention: 74% of full-time freshmen returned the following year. Academic areas with the most degrees conferred: business/marketing; health professions and related sciences; homeland security, law enforcement, firefighting, and protective services. Core. Calendar: semesters. Services for LD students, advanced placement, self-designed majors, honors program, independent study, distance learning, summer session for credit, part-time degree program, co-op programs and internships, graduate courses open to undergrads. Study abroad program. ROTC: Army (c), Air Force (c).

Entrance Requirements: Options: electronic application, deferred admission, international baccalaureate accepted. Required: high school transcript. Recommended: SAT, SAT or ACT. Required for some: essay, interview. Entrance: moderately difficult. Application deadline: rolling. Notification: continuous. Preference given to state residents. Transfer credits accepted: Yes.

Costs Per Year: Application fee: $50. State resident tuition: $5924 full-time, $247 per credit hour part-time. Nonresident tuition: $17,726 full-time, $247 per credit hour part-time. Mandatory fees: $5420 full-time, $291 per credit part-time, $60 per term part-time. College room and board: $13,452. College room only: $7794.

Collegiate Environment: Orientation program. Drama-theater group, choral group, student-run newspaper, radio station. Social organizations: 83 open to all; national fraternities, national sororities, local sororities; 3% of eligible men and 5% of eligible women are members. Most popular organizations: National Society of Collegiate Scholars, Criminology Club, Jazz Club, American Marketing Club, Meteorology. Major annual events: WCSU Theatre Arts Department Productions, WCSU Annual 'Roots & Shoots' hosting of Dr. Jane Goodall, The President's Lecture Series. Student services: health clinic, personal-psychological counseling, women's center. Campus security: 24-hour emergency response devices and patrols, student patrols, late night transport-escort service, controlled dormitory access. 1,601 college housing spaces available; 1,461 were occupied in 2018-19. No special consideration for freshman housing applicants. Option: coed housing available. Ruth Haas Library plus 2 others. Books: 204,701 (physical), 240,140 (digital/electronic); Serial titles: 302 (physical), 67,162 (digital/electronic); Databases: 188. Weekly public service hours: 144; students can reserve study rooms. Operations spending for the previous fiscal year: $3.5 million. 1,034 computers available on campus for general student use. A campuswide network can be accessed from student residence rooms and from off

campus. Students can access the following: online class registration, online payment. Staffed computer lab on campus provides training in use of computers, software, and the Internet.

Community Environment: Population 78,700, Danbury is within easy commuting distance of Stamford, Waterbury, Bridgeport, New Haven, and Torrington. Cultural centers in Danbury and in the surrounding cities are within easy reach. Trains and buses serve the area. Recreational facilities include nearby Candlewood Lake for swimming, boating, and fishing. Part time work is available in the community.

■ YALE UNIVERSITY
New Haven, CT 06520
Tel: (203)432-4771
Fax: (203)432-9392
E-mail: student.questions@yale.edu
Web Site: www.yale.edu

Description: Independent, university, coed. Awards bachelor's, master's, and doctoral degrees and post-master's certificates. Founded 1701. Setting: 342-acre urban campus with easy access to New York City. Endowment: $25.6 billion. Research spending for the previous fiscal year: $550.9 million. Total enrollment: 12,974. Faculty: 1,716 (1,215 full-time, 501 part-time). Student-undergrad faculty ratio is 6:1. 32,914 applied, 7% were admitted. 94% from top 10% of their high school class, 99% from top quarter, 100% from top half. Full-time: 5,743 students, 50% women, 50% men. Part-time: 3 students, 100% men. Students come from 50 states and territories, 89 other countries, 93% from out-of-state. 0.6% American Indian or Alaska Native, non-Hispanic/Latino; 13% Hispanic/Latino; 7% Black or African American, non-Hispanic/Latino; 18% Asian, non-Hispanic/Latino; 0.1% Native Hawaiian or other Pacific Islander, non-Hispanic/Latino; 11% international. 0.6% 25 or older, 84% live on campus, 1% transferred in. Retention: 99% of full-time freshmen returned the following year. Academic areas with the most degrees conferred: social sciences; biological/life sciences; history. Core. Calendar: semesters. ESL program, services for LD students, advanced placement, accelerated degree program, self-designed majors, honors program, independent study, double major, summer session for credit, part-time degree program, internships, graduate courses open to undergrads. Study abroad program. ROTC: Army (c), Naval, Air Force.

Entrance Requirements: Options: electronic application, early action, deferred admission, international baccalaureate accepted. Required: essay, high school transcript, 3 recommendations, SAT or ACT. Recommended: interview, SAT Subject Tests. Entrance: most difficult. Application deadlines: 1/1, 11/1 for early action. Notification: 4/1, 12/15 for early action. SAT Reasoning Test deadline: 3/1. SAT Subject Test deadline: 3/1. Transfer credits accepted: Yes. Applicants placed on waiting list: 1,098. Wait-listed applicants offered admission: 73. Early action applicants: 4,653. Early action applicants admitted: 753.

Costs Per Year: Application fee: $80. Comprehensive fee: $69,430 includes full-time tuition ($53,430) and college room and board ($16,000). College room only: $9000. Room and board charges vary according to board plan.

Collegiate Environment: Orientation program. Drama-theater group, choral group, marching band, student-run newspaper, radio station. Social organizations: 400 open to all; national fraternities, national sororities, local fraternities. Major annual events: Spring Fling Concert, Fall Show, Yale Symphony Orchestra Halloween Show. Student services: health clinic, personal-psychological counseling, women's center. Campus security: 24-hour emergency response devices and patrols, late night transport-escort service, controlled dormitory access. Sterling Memorial Library plus 15 others. Books: 13.8 million (physical), 1.8 million (digital/electronic). Weekly public service hours: 93; students can reserve study rooms. Operations spending for the previous fiscal year: $33.1 million. 450 computers available on campus for general student use. Computer purchase/lease plans available. A campuswide network can be accessed from student residence rooms and from off campus. Students can access the following: online class registration. Staffed computer lab on campus (open 24 hours a day) provides training in use of computers, software, and the Internet.

Community Environment: Southern Connecticut's major city, New Haven is in many respects a college town. The average temperature is 50.7 degrees. Buses, railroads, and airlines serve the area. New Haven is engaged in one of the most successful urban renewal projects in the country, restoring and rebuilding housing, community facilities and commercial redevelopment. Points of interest are the museums and libraries. New Haven also has the usual civic organizations, hospitals, shopping centers, hotels and motels. Employment is available. The recreational facilities include theaters, swimming areas, tennis courts, archery ranges, indoor swimming pool, bowling alleys, riding stables, roller skating rinks, municipal golf course and many parks. Important manufacturing establishments are located here.

■ **DELAWARE COLLEGE OF ART AND DESIGN**
600 N Market St.
Wilmington, DE 19801
Tel: (302)622-8000
Fax: (302)622-8870
E-mail: agullo@dcad.edu
Web Site: www.dcad.edu
Description: Independent, 2-year, coed. Administratively affiliated with Corcoran College of Art and Design. Awards transfer associate degrees. Founded 1997. Setting: 1-acre urban campus. Endowment: $65,295. Educational spending for the previous fiscal year: $4884 per student. Total enrollment: 210. Faculty: 27 (7 full-time, 20 part-time). Student-undergrad faculty ratio is 8:1. 322 applied, 58% were admitted. Full-time: 192 students, 52% women, 48% men. Part-time: 18 students, 78% women, 22% men. Students come from 9 states and territories, 45% from out-of-state. 19% 25 or older, 50% live on campus, 10% transferred in. Retention: 54% of full-time freshmen returned the following year. Core. Calendar: semesters. Academic remediation for entering students, services for LD students, advanced placement, double major, summer session for credit, part-time degree program, adult/continuing education programs. Off campus study at regional galleries and museums. Study abroad program.
Entrance Requirements: Options: electronic application, deferred admission. Required: essay, high school transcript, minimum 2.0 high school GPA, interview, portfolio. Entrance: moderately difficult. Application deadline: rolling. Notification: continuous until 8/15.
Collegiate Environment: Orientation program. Information Resource Center plus 1 other. Operations spending for the previous fiscal year: $33,247. 68 computers available on campus for general student use. A campuswide network can be accessed from student residence rooms and from off campus. Students can access the following: student Web space. Staffed computer lab on campus.

■ **DELAWARE STATE UNIVERSITY**
1200 N DuPont Hwy.
Dover, DE 19901-2277
Tel: (302)857-6290; Free: 800-845-2544
Fax: (302)857-6352
E-mail: ehill@desu.edu
Web Site: www.desu.edu
Description: State-supported, university, coed. Part of Delaware Higher Education Commission. Awards bachelor's, master's, and doctoral degrees. Founded 1891. Setting: 400-acre small town campus. Total enrollment: 4,353. 7,636 applied, 45% were admitted. 7% from top 10% of their high school class, 25% from top quarter, 62% from top half. Full-time: 3,571 students, 66% women, 34% men. Part-time: 480 students, 64% women, 36% men. 51% from out-of-state. 0.3% American Indian or Alaska Native, non-Hispanic/Latino; 7% Hispanic/Latino; 75% Black or African American, non-Hispanic/Latino; 0.6% Asian, non-Hispanic/Latino; 0.1% Native Hawaiian or other Pacific Islander, non-Hispanic/Latino; 2% international. 6% 25 or older, 58% live on campus, 5% transferred in. Retention: 71% of full-time freshmen returned the following year. Academic areas with the most degrees conferred: social sciences; communication/journalism; parks and recreation. Core. Calendar: semesters. Academic remediation for entering students, ESL program, services for LD students, advanced placement, accelerated degree program, honors program, independent study, distance learning, double major, summer session for credit, part-time degree program, adult/

continuing education programs, co-op programs and internships, graduate courses open to undergrads. Off campus study at University of Delaware. Study abroad program. ROTC: Army, Air Force.
Entrance Requirements: Options: electronic application, early admission. Required: high school transcript, minimum 2 high school GPA. Entrance: moderately difficult. Preference given to state residents. Transfer credits accepted: Yes. Applicants placed on waiting list: 368.
Collegiate Environment: Orientation program. Drama-theater group, choral group, marching band, student-run newspaper, radio station. Social organizations: national fraternities, national sororities. Most popular organizations: SGA, NPHC, Women's Senate, RHA, Men's Council. Major annual events: Welcome Week, Commencement, Homecoming Week. Student services: health clinic, personal-psychological counseling, women's center. Campus security: 24-hour emergency response devices and patrols, student patrols, late night transport-escort service, controlled dormitory access. William C. Jason Library.
Community Environment: Dover, the capital of Delaware, is 75 miles from Philadelphia, 85 miles from Baltimore, 90 miles from Washington, DC, and 160 miles from New York City. Railway and bus are available in the area. Dover is an agricultural section noted for fruit, produce, grains and poultry. Many fine old colonial homes steeped in the traditions of the activity of the old town are found in the area."The Green" is the center of activity of the old town and still the hub from which radiate many of the political and government activities of both the city and the state. Located 10 miles south of "The Green" is Barratt's Chapel, often called the "Cradle of Methodism in America." Each year on Dover Days, the first Saturday and Sunday in May, many historic homes are open to the public for a small fee. Dover is the home of the largest air freight terminal in the world. General Food's multimillion-dollar Jell-O plant and Playtex Corporation are also located here.

■ **DELAWARE TECHNICAL & COMMUNITY COLLEGE, JACK F. OWENS CAMPUS**
PO Box 610
Georgetown, DE 19947
Tel: (302)856-5400
Fax: (302)856-9461
Web Site: www.dtcc.edu
Description: State-supported, 2-year, coed. Part of Delaware Technical and Community College System. Awards certificates, diplomas, transfer associate, and terminal associate degrees. Founded 1967. Setting: small town campus. Total enrollment: 4,429. 1,717 applied, 100% were admitted. Full-time: 1,981 students, 56% women, 44% men. Part-time: 2,448 students, 67% women, 33% men. 0.6% American Indian or Alaska Native, non-Hispanic/Latino; 7% Hispanic/Latino; 19% Black or African American, non-Hispanic/Latino; 2% Asian, non-Hispanic/Latino; 0.1% Native Hawaiian or other Pacific Islander, non-Hispanic/Latino; 3% international. Retention: 55% of full-time freshmen returned the following year. Calendar: semesters. Part-time degree program.
Entrance Requirements: Open admission except for nursing, allied health, and energy programs. Options: electronic application, early admission, deferred admission. Required for some: high school transcript. Entrance: noncompetitive. Preference given to state residents.
Collegiate Environment: Orientation program. Campus security: 24-hour emergency response devices, late night transport-escort service. Stephen J. Betze Library.

■ DELAWARE TECHNICAL & COMMUNITY COLLEGE, STANTON/ GEORGE CAMPUS

300 N Orange St.
Wilmington, DE 19801
Tel: (302)571-5300
Web Site: www.dtcc.edu

Description: State-supported, 2-year, coed. Part of Delaware Technical and Community College System. Awards certificates, diplomas, transfer associate, and terminal associate degrees. Founded 1968. Setting: urban campus. Total enrollment: 7,035. 3,826 applied, 100% were admitted. Full-time: 2,616 students, 52% women, 48% men. Part-time: 4,419 students, 62% women, 38% men. 0.4% American Indian or Alaska Native, non-Hispanic/Latino; 10% Hispanic/Latino; 28% Black or African American, non-Hispanic/Latino; 4% Asian, non-Hispanic/Latino; 0.2% Native Hawaiian or other Pacific Islander, non-Hispanic/Latino; 2% international. Retention: 52% of full-time freshmen returned the following year. Calendar: semesters. Part-time degree program.

Entrance Requirements: Open admission except for allied health, nursing and energy programs. Options: electronic application, early admission, deferred admission. Required for some: high school transcript. Entrance: noncompetitive. Application deadline: rolling. Notification: continuous. Transfer credits accepted: Yes.

Collegiate Environment: Orientation program. Campus security: 24-hour emergency response devices, late night transport-escort service. Stanton Campus Library and John Eugene Derrickson Memorial Library.

■ DELAWARE TECHNICAL & COMMUNITY COLLEGE, TERRY CAMPUS

100 Campus Dr.
Dover, DE 19901
Tel: (302)857-1000
Fax: (302)857-1296
E-mail: terry-info@dtcc.edu
Web Site: www.dtcc.edu

Description: State-supported, 2-year, coed. Part of Delaware Technical and Community College System. Awards certificates, diplomas, transfer associate, and terminal associate degrees. Founded 1972. Setting: small town campus. Total enrollment: 2,955. 1,351 applied, 100% were admitted. Full-time: 1,285 students, 59% women, 41% men. Part-time: 1,670 students, 69% women, 31% men. 0.4% American Indian or Alaska Native, non-Hispanic/Latino; 6% Hispanic/Latino; 29% Black or African American, non-Hispanic/Latino; 2% Asian, non-Hispanic/Latino; 0.1% Native Hawaiian or other Pacific Islander, non-Hispanic/Latino; 0.8% international. Retention: 52% of full-time freshmen returned the following year. Calendar: semesters. Part-time degree program.

Entrance Requirements: Open admission except for allied health, nursing, and energy. Options: electronic application, early admission, deferred admission. Required for some: high school transcript. Entrance: noncompetitive. Preference given to state residents.

Collegiate Environment: Orientation program. Campus security: 24-hour emergency response devices, late night transport-escort service.

Community Environment: See Delaware State University.

■ GOLDEY-BEACOM COLLEGE

4701 Limestone Rd.
Wilmington, DE 19808-1999
Tel: (302)998-8814; Free: 800-833-4877
Fax: (302)996-5408
E-mail: admissions@gbc.edu
Web Site: www.gbc.edu

Description: Independent, comprehensive, coed. Awards associate, bachelor's, and master's degrees. Founded 1886. Setting: 24-acre suburban campus with easy access to Philadelphia. Endowment: $47.4 million. Total enrollment: 1,352. Faculty: 56 (18 full-time, 38 part-time). Student-undergrad faculty ratio is 26:1. Full-time: 462 students, 55% women, 45% men. Part-time: 163 students, 57% women, 43% men. Students come from 12 states and territories, 24 other countries, 33% from out-of-state. 0.2% American Indian or Alaska Native, non-Hispanic/Latino; 8% Hispanic/Latino; 24% Black or African American, non-Hispanic/Latino; 5% Asian, non-Hispanic/Latino; 9% international; 9% 25 or older, 32% live on campus, 9% transferred in. Retention: 85% of full-time freshmen returned the following year. Academic areas with the most degrees conferred: business/marketing; social sciences; psychology. Core. Calendar: semesters. Academic remediation for entering students, advanced placement, accelerated degree

program, honors program, double major, summer session for credit, part-time degree program, co-op programs and internships, graduate courses open to undergrads.

Entrance Requirements: Required: high school transcript, minimum 2 high school GPA, SAT or ACT. Required for some: 1 recommendation, interview.

Collegiate Environment: Orientation program. Student-run newspaper. Social organizations: 14 open to all. Most popular organizations: Student Athletic Advisory Committee, Alpha Chi, Resident Student Association, Student Ambassadors, International Student Association. Major annual events: Drive In Movie Night, Homecoming, New York City Trip. Campus security: 24-hour emergency response devices and patrols, student patrols, late night transport-escort service. J. Wilbur Hirons Library. Operations spending for the previous fiscal year: $282,032. 159 computers available on campus for general student use. A campuswide network can be accessed from student residence rooms and from off campus. Students can access the following: campus Web. Staffed computer lab on campus provides training in use of computers, software, and the Internet.

Community Environment: Known as the"Chemical Capital of the World," Wilmington (pop. 72,786) lies on the west bank of the Delaware River in northern Delaware. Railroads and airlines serve the area. Almost 300 industries are located in the area. A great variety of items are shipped from Wilmington, including such products as automobiles, airplanes, steel, clothing, hosiery, machinery, paper and paper products. Points of interest include Holy Trinity Church (Old Swedes), Wilmington Institute, Free Library, Brandywine Park, Fort Christian State Park, Delaware Art Center, Hagley Museum, Old Town Hall, and the Henry Francis du Pont Winterthur Museum. Nearby are Longwood Gardens and the Brandywine Museum.

■ UNIVERSITY OF DELAWARE

210 S College Ave.
Newark, DE 19716
Tel: (302)831-2000
Fax: (302)831-6905
E-mail: admissions@udel.edu
Web Site: www.udel.edu

Description: State-related, university, coed. Awards associate, bachelor's, master's, and doctoral degrees. Founded 1743. Setting: 1,000-acre small town campus with easy access to Philadelphia, Baltimore. Total enrollment: 22,965. Faculty: 1,776 (1,247 full-time, 529 part-time). Student-undergrad faculty ratio is 13:1. 27,803 applied, 60% were admitted. 32% from top 10% of their high school class, 66% from top quarter, 92% from top half. Full-time: 17,432 students, 58% women, 42% men. Part-time: 1,514 students, 53% women, 47% men. 62% from out-of-state. 0.1% American Indian or Alaska Native, non-Hispanic/Latino; 8% Hispanic/Latino; 5% Black or African American, non-Hispanic/Latino; 5% Asian, non-Hispanic/Latino; 0.1% Native Hawaiian or other Pacific Islander, non-Hispanic/Latino; 5% international. 3% 25 or older, 40% live on campus, 2% transferred in. Retention: 91% of full-time freshmen returned the following year. Academic areas with the most degrees conferred: business/marketing; health professions and related sciences; social sciences. Core. Calendar: 4-1-4. Academic remediation for entering students, ESL program, services for LD students, advanced placement, accelerated degree program, self-designed majors, honors program, independent study, distance learning, double major, summer session for credit, part-time degree program, adult/continuing education programs, co-op programs and internships, graduate courses open to undergrads. Off campus study. Study abroad program. ROTC: Army, Air Force.

Entrance Requirements: Options: electronic application, early admission, deferred admission, international baccalaureate accepted. Required: essay, high school transcript, 1 recommendation, SAT or ACT. Recommended: SAT Subject Tests. Required for some: SAT Subject Tests. Entrance: moderately difficult. Application deadline: 1/15. Notification: 11/1. Preference given to state residents. SAT Reasoning Test deadline: 1/15. SAT Subject Test deadline: 1/15. Applicants placed on waiting list: 5,006. Wait-listed applicants offered admission: 136.

Costs Per Year: Application fee: $75. State resident tuition: $12,250 full-time, $510 per credit hour part-time. Nonresident tuition: $32,880 full-time, $1370 per credit hour part-time. Mandatory fees: $1430 full-time. College room and board: $12,862. College room only: $7798. Room and board charges vary according to board plan and housing facility.

Collegiate Environment: Orientation program. Drama-theater group, choral group, marching band, student-run newspaper, radio station. Social organizations: national fraternities, national sororities, local fraternities. Student services: health clinic, personal-psychological counseling, women's center. Campus security: 24-hour emergency response devices and patrols, student patrols, late night transport-escort service, controlled dormitory access. Hugh Morris Library.

Community Environment: The campus is located in Newark, Delaware, a city of 24,000, which is situated halfway between Philadelphia and Baltimore on I-95. The location is ideal for students who want the advantages of a small community and easy access to the educational, cultural, and social opportunities offered in nearby metropolitan area.

■ WESLEY COLLEGE

120 N State St.
Dover, DE 19901-3875
Tel: (302)736-2300; Free: 800-937-5398
Fax: (302)736-2301
E-mail: christopher.jester@wesley.edu
Web Site: www.wesley.edu

Description: Independent United Methodist, comprehensive, coed. Awards associate, bachelor's, and master's degrees and post-master's certificates. Founded 1873. Setting: 40-acre small town campus. Total enrollment: 1,770. Faculty: 170 (70 full-time, 100 part-time). 2,933 applied, 63% were admitted. Full-time: 1,345 students, 51% women, 49% men. Part-time: 316 students, 44% women, 56% men. Students come from 28 states and territories, 4 other countries, 57% from out-of-state. 1% American Indian or Alaska Native, non-Hispanic/Latino; 6% Hispanic/Latino; 37% Black or African American, non-Hispanic/Latino; 1% Asian, non-Hispanic/Latino. 13% 25 or older, 66% live on campus, 2% transferred in. Retention: 54% of full-time freshmen returned the following year. Academic areas with the most degrees conferred: business/marketing; health professions and related sciences; education. Core. Calendar: semesters. Academic remediation for entering students, ESL program, services for LD students, advanced placement, freshman honors college, independent study, summer session for credit, part-time degree program, external degree program, adult/continuing education programs, co-op programs and internships, graduate courses open to undergrads. Off campus study. Study abroad program. ROTC: Army (c).

Entrance Requirements: Option: electronic application. Required: essay, high school transcript, minimum 2.2 high school GPA, 1 recommendation, SAT. Recommended: interview. Required for some: exam for nursing. Entrance: moderately difficult. Application deadline: rolling.

Collegiate Environment: Orientation program. Drama-theater group, choral group, student-run newspaper. Social organizations: 20 open to all; national fraternities, national sororities, local fraternities, local sororities; 3% of eligible men and 3% of eligible women are members. Most popular organizations: Student Activity Board, Student Government Association, National Coeducation Community Service Organization. Major annual events: Homecoming, Families' Day, reunion. Student services: health clinic, personal-psychological counseling. Campus security: 24-hour patrols, controlled dormitory access. Robert H. Parker Library. 225 computers available on campus for general student use. Computer purchase/lease plans available. A campuswide network can be accessed from student residence

rooms and from off campus. Students can access the following: online class registration. Staffed computer lab on campus provides training in use of computers, software, and the Internet.

■ WILMINGTON UNIVERSITY

320 N DuPont Hwy.
New Castle, DE 19720-6491
Tel: (302)328-9401; Free: 877-967-5464
Fax: (302)328-5902
E-mail: undergradadmissions@wilmu.edu
Web Site: www.wilmu.edu

Description: Independent, university, coed. Awards associate, bachelor's, master's, and doctoral degrees and post-master's certificates. Founded 1967. Setting: 17-acre suburban campus with easy access to Philadelphia. Endowment: $73.9 million. Total enrollment: 14,118. Faculty: 2,466 (125 full-time, 2,341 part-time). Student-undergrad faculty ratio is 17:1. 1,662 applied, 99% were admitted. Full-time: 3,037 students, 57% women, 43% men. Part-time: 5,403 students, 69% women, 31% men. Students come from 45 states and territories, 74 other countries, 33% from out-of-state. 1% American Indian or Alaska Native, non-Hispanic/Latino; 2% Hispanic/Latino; 21% Black or African American, non-Hispanic/Latino; 2% Asian, non-Hispanic/Latino; 0.2% Native Hawaiian or other Pacific Islander, non-Hispanic/Latino; 2% international. 66% 25 or older, 12% transferred in. Retention: 64% of full-time freshmen returned the following year. Academic areas with the most degrees conferred: business/marketing; health professions and related sciences; interdisciplinary studies. Core. Calendar: semesters. Academic remediation for entering students, ESL program, accelerated degree program, independent study, distance learning, double major, summer session for credit, part-time degree program, external degree program, adult/continuing education programs, co-op programs and internships. Study abroad program. ROTC: Army (c), Air Force (c).

Entrance Requirements: Open admission. Options: electronic application, early admission, deferred admission. Required: high school transcript. Recommended: interview. Entrance: noncompetitive. Application deadline: rolling. Notification: continuous. Transfer credits accepted: Yes.

Costs Per Year: Application fee: $25. Tuition: $8928 full-time, $372 per credit part-time. Mandatory fees: $50 full-time, $25 per term part-time. Full-time tuition and fees vary according to degree level and location. Part-time tuition and fees vary according to degree level and location.

Collegiate Environment: Orientation program. Most popular organizations: Student Government Association, Green Team, Photography Club, WU Student United Way, Wildcat Cheerleaders. Major annual events: Commencement, Homecoming. Campus security: 24-hour emergency response devices and patrols, late night transport-escort service. Robert C. and Dorothy M. Peoples Library plus 1 other. Books: 104,530 (physical), 179,000 (digital/electronic); Serial titles: 50 (physical), 98,000 (digital/electronic). 600 computers available on campus for general student use. A campuswide network can be accessed. Students can access the following: online class registration. Staffed computer lab on campus.

■ AMERICAN UNIVERSITY

4400 Massachusetts Ave., NW
Washington, DC 20016-8001
Tel: (202)885-1000
Fax: (202)885-6014
E-mail: admissions@american.edu
Web Site: www.american.edu

Description: Independent Methodist, university, coed. Awards associate, bachelor's, master's, and doctoral degrees. Founded 1893. Setting: 84-acre suburban campus with easy access to Washington, DC. Endowment: $676.4 million. Research spending for the previous fiscal year: $56 million. Educational spending for the previous fiscal year: $15,365 per student. Total enrollment: 14,311. Faculty: 1,517 (818 full-time, 699 part-time). Student-undergrad faculty ratio is 11:1. 18,984 applied, 32% were admitted. Full-time: 7,952 students, 62% women, 38% men. Part-time: 335 students, 57% women, 43% men. Students come from 55 states and territories, 123 other countries, 83% from out-of-district. 0.1% American Indian or Alaska Native, non-Hispanic/Latino; 12% Hispanic/Latino; 7% Black or African American, non-Hispanic/Latino; 7% Asian, non-Hispanic/Latino; 0.1% Native Hawaiian or other Pacific Islander, non-Hispanic/Latino; 13% international. 2% 25 or older, 4% transferred in. Retention: 88% of full-time freshmen returned the following year. Academic areas with the most degrees conferred: social sciences; business/marketing; communication/journalism. Core. Calendar: semesters. ESL program, services for LD students, advanced placement, accelerated degree program, self-designed majors, honors program, independent study, distance learning, double major, summer session for credit, part-time degree program, co-op programs and internships, graduate courses open to undergrads. Off campus study at Consortium of Universities of the Washington Metropolitan Area: American University (DC), Catholic University of America (DC), Gallaudet University (DC), George Mason University (VA), The George Washington University (DC), Corcoran College of Art + Design (DC), Georgetown University (DC), Howard University (DC), Marymount University (VA), Trinity Washington University (DC), the University of the District of Columbia (DC), and the University of Maryland (MD). Study abroad program. ROTC: Army (c), Air Force (c).

Entrance Requirements: Options: electronic application, early admission, early decision, deferred admission, international baccalaureate accepted. Required: essay, high school transcript. Recommended: 2 recommendations. Entrance: very difficult. Application deadlines: 11/15, 11/15 for early decision. Notification: 4/1, 12/31 for early decision. SAT Reasoning Test deadline: 1/1. Transfer credits accepted: Yes. Applicants placed on waiting list: 4,598. Wait-listed applicants offered admission: 188. Early decision applicants: 974. Early decision applicants admitted: 791.

Costs Per Year: Application fee: $70. Comprehensive fee: $64,769 includes full-time tuition ($49,070), mandatory fees ($819), and college room and board ($14,880). College room only: $9996. Part-time tuition: $1635 per credit hour.

Collegiate Environment: Orientation program. Drama-theater group, choral group, student-run newspaper, radio station. Social organizations: 200 open to all; national fraternities, national sororities, local fraternities, local sororities; 9% of eligible men and 11% of eligible women are members. Most popular organizations: Kennedy Political Union, Habitat for Humanity, Student government, Amnesty International, Multiple Ethnic and religious organizations. Major annual events: Kennedy Political Union Award-Winning Speaker Series, Founder' Day, Campus Beautification Day. Student services: health clinic, personal-psychological counseling, women's center.

Campus security: 24-hour emergency response devices and patrols, late night transport-escort service, controlled dormitory access. 4,600 college housing spaces available. Freshmen guaranteed college housing. Option: coed housing available. Bender Library plus 1 other. Books: 700,000 (physical), 800,000 (digital/electronic); Serial titles: 650 (physical), 145,000 (digital/electronic); Databases: 500. Study areas open 24 hours, 5-7 days a week; students can reserve study rooms. 700 computers available on campus for general student use. A campuswide network can be accessed from student residence rooms and from off campus. Students can access the following: online class registration, online e-support through learning management system. Staffed computer lab on campus (open 24 hours a day) provides training in use of computers, software, and the Internet.

Community Environment: Washington, D.C., is located on the Potomac River between Maryland and Virginia. It is a beautiful and historic city of impressive buildings and residential neighborhoods, with a vibrant, diverse international character. All major forms of transportation are available: the Metro bus and subway system, historic Union Railroad Station, and three major airports serve Washington. The National Zoo, Rock Creek Park, and the C&O Canal are some of the city's finest recreation areas. Shopping facilities are excellent. Points of interest for students include government sites such as the U.S. Capitol, Senate and House office buildings, U.S. Treasury, Supreme Court, Federal Bureau of Investigation, and the White House; cultural institutions such as the Folger Shakespeare Library, Library of Congress, Smithsonian Institute, U.S. Holocaust Memorial Museum, Frederick Douglass Museum, National Gallery of Art, National Archives, Islamic Center, Washington Cathedral, and John F. Kennedy Center for the Performing Arts; scientific institutions such as the National Bureau of Standards, Naval Observatory, and the nearby National Institutes of Health; and international organizations such as the World Bank, Pan American Union, and the embassies and legations of many nations.

■ THE CATHOLIC UNIVERSITY OF AMERICA

Cardinal Station
Washington, DC 20064
Tel: (202)319-5000; Free: 800-673-2772
Fax: (202)319-6533
E-mail: cua-admissions@cua.edu
Web Site: www.catholic.edu

Description: Independent, university, coed, affiliated with Roman Catholic Church. Awards bachelor's, master's, and doctoral degrees and post-master's certificates. Founded 1887. Setting: 176-acre urban campus with easy access to Washington DC. Total enrollment: 5,956. Faculty: 793 (377 full-time, 416 part-time). Student-undergrad faculty ratio is 7:1. 6,096 applied, 84% were admitted. Full-time: 3,198 students, 53% women, 47% men. Part-time: 134 students, 55% women, 45% men. Students come from 49 states and territories, 31 other countries, 96% from out-of-district. 0.2% American Indian or Alaska Native, non-Hispanic/Latino; 14% Hispanic/Latino; 4% Black or African American, non-Hispanic/Latino; 4% Asian, non-Hispanic/Latino; 0.1% Native Hawaiian or other Pacific Islander, non-Hispanic/Latino; 6% international. 4% 25 or older, 58% live on campus, 3% transferred in. Retention: 87% of full-time freshmen returned the following year. Academic areas with the most degrees conferred: business/marketing; engineering; social sciences. Core. Calendar: semesters. ESL program, services for LD students, advanced placement, accelerated degree program, honors program, independent study, distance learning, double major, summer session for credit, part-time degree program, external degree program, adult/continuing education programs, co-op programs and internships, graduate courses open to undergrads. Off campus study at members of the Consortium of Universities of the Washington Metropolitan Area. Study abroad program. ROTC: Army (c), Naval (c), Air Force (c).

Entrance Requirements: Options: electronic application, early decision, early action, deferred admission, international baccalaureate accepted. Required: essay, high school transcript, 1 recommendation. Recommended: minimum 3 high school GPA, interview. Entrance: moderately difficult. Application deadlines: 1/15, 11/15 for early decision plan 1, 1/15 for early decision plan 2, 11/1 for early action. Notification: 3/15, 12/20 for early decision plan 1, 2/15 for early decision plan 2, 12/20 for early action. SAT Reasoning Test deadline: 2/15. Transfer credits accepted: Yes. Applicants placed on waiting list: 323. Wait-listed applicants offered admission: 17. Early decision applicants: 131. Early decision applicants admitted: 112. Early action applicants: 3,387. Early action applicants admitted: 2,928.

Costs Per Year: Application fee: $55. Comprehensive fee: $63,006 includes full-time tuition ($46,950), mandatory fees ($796), and college room and board ($15,260). Part-time mandatory fees: $1860 per credit hour.

Collegiate Environment: Orientation program. Drama-theater group, choral group, student-run newspaper, radio station. Social organizations: 109 open to all; national fraternities, national sororities; 1% of eligible men and 1% of eligible women are members. Most popular organizations: College Republicans, Habitat for Humanity, Student Nurse's Association, Cardinals for Life, College Democrats. Major annual events: Luaupalooza, Fall Fiesta, Late Night Breakfast. Student services: legal services, health clinic, personal-psychological counseling. Campus security: 24-hour emergency response devices and patrols, late night transport-escort service, controlled dormitory access, controlled access of academic buildings. 2,050 college housing spaces available; 1,913 were occupied in 2018-19. Freshmen guaranteed college housing. On-campus residence required through sophomore year. Options: men-only, women-only housing available. Mullen Library plus 1 other. Books: 734,247 (physical), 390,119 (digital/electronic); Serial titles: 342,482 (physical), 135,001 (digital/electronic); Databases: 482. Weekly public service hours: 102. 542 computers available on campus for general student use. A campuswide network can be accessed from student residence rooms and from off campus. Students can access the following: online class registration. Staffed computer lab on campus (open 24 hours a day) provides training in use of computers, software, and the Internet.

Community Environment: See American University.

■ GALLAUDET UNIVERSITY

800 Florida Ave., NE
Washington, DC 20002-3625
Tel: (202)651-5000; Free: 800-995-0550
Fax: (202)651-5774
Web Site: www.gallaudet.edu

Description: Independent, university, coed. Awards bachelor's, master's, and doctoral degrees and post-master's certificates (Undergraduate programs are open primarily to the students with hearing-impairments). Founded 1864. Setting: 99-acre urban campus. Total enrollment: 1,566. Faculty: 269 (181 full-time, 88 part-time). Student-undergrad faculty ratio is 7:1. 507 applied, 67% were admitted. Full-time: 1,082 students, 52% women, 48% men. Part-time: 39 students, 56% women, 44% men. Students come from 50 states and territories, 21 other countries, 97% from out-of-district. 0.6% American Indian or Alaska Native, non-Hispanic/Latino; 10% Hispanic/Latino; 16% Black or African American, non-Hispanic/Latino; 4% Asian, non-Hispanic/Latino; 0.5% Native Hawaiian or other Pacific Islander, non-Hispanic/Latino; 7% international. 24% 25 or older, 82% live on campus, 10% transferred in. Retention: 80% of full-time freshmen returned the following year. Academic areas with the most degrees conferred: business/marketing; communication/journalism; foreign languages and literature. Core. Calendar: semesters. Academic remediation for entering students, ESL program, services for LD students, advanced placement, self-designed majors, honors program, independent study, distance learning, double major, summer session for credit, part-time degree program, adult/continuing education programs, internships, graduate courses open to undergrads. Off campus study at Consortium of Universities of the Washington Metropolitan Area. Study abroad program.

Entrance Requirements: Options: electronic application, deferred admission. Required: essay, high school transcript, 2 recommendations, audiogram, SAT or ACT. Recommended: ACT. Required for some: interview. Entrance: moderately difficult. Application deadline: rolling. Notification: continuous. Transfer credits accepted: Yes.

Costs Per Year: Application fee: $50. Comprehensive fee: $30,780 includes

full-time tuition ($16,512), mandatory fees ($526), and college room and board ($13,742). College room only: $7512. Full-time tuition and fees vary according to course load. Room and board charges vary according to board plan and housing facility. Part-time tuition: $688 per credit hour. Part-time tuition varies according to course load.

Collegiate Environment: Orientation program. Drama-theater group, student-run newspaper. Social organizations: 16 open to all; national fraternities, national sororities, local fraternities, local sororities; 11% of eligible men and 6% of eligible women are members. Most popular organizations: Student Body Government, The Buff and Blue, Rainbow Society, Green Grow. Major annual events: Homecoming, RIT/Gallaudet Weekend. Student services: health clinic, personal-psychological counseling. Campus security: 24-hour emergency response devices and patrols, late night transport-escort service, controlled dormitory access. Merrill Learning Center. Books: 121,359 (physical), 547,506 (digital/electronic); Serial titles: 4,142 (physical), 71,930 (digital/electronic); Databases: 79. Weekly public service hours: 90; students can reserve study rooms. 400 computers available on campus for general student use. A campuswide network can be accessed from student residence rooms and from off campus. Students can access the following: online class registration. Staffed computer lab on campus provides training in use of computers, software, and the Internet.

Community Environment: See American University.

■ THE GEORGE WASHINGTON UNIVERSITY

2121 I St., NW
Washington, DC 20052
Tel: (202)994-1000
Web Site: www.gwu.edu

Description: Independent, university, coed. Awards associate, bachelor's, master's, and doctoral degrees and post-master's certificates. Founded 1821. Setting: 36-acre urban campus. Total enrollment: 27,973. 26,987 applied, 41% were admitted. Full-time: 10,893 students, 61% women, 39% men. Part-time: 1,106 students, 50% women, 50% men. Students come from 57 states and territories, 97 other countries, 97% from out-of-district. 0.1% American Indian or Alaska Native, non-Hispanic/Latino; 10% Hispanic/Latino; 7% Black or African American, non-Hispanic/Latino; 10% Asian, non-Hispanic/Latino; 0.1% Native Hawaiian or other Pacific Islander, non-Hispanic/Latino; 11% international. 10% 25 or older, 61% live on campus, 6% transferred in. Retention: 91% of full-time freshmen returned the following year. Academic areas with the most degrees conferred: social sciences; business/marketing; health professions and related sciences. Core. Calendar: semesters. Services for LD students, advanced placement, accelerated degree program, self-designed majors, honors program, independent study, distance learning, double major, summer session for credit, part-time degree program, adult/continuing education programs, co-op programs and internships, graduate courses open to undergrads. Off campus study at members of the Consortium of Universities of the Washington Metropolitan Area. Study abroad program. ROTC: Army (c), Naval, Air Force (c).

Entrance Requirements: Options: electronic application, early admission, early decision, deferred admission. Required: essay, high school transcript, 2 recommendations. Required for some: SAT and SAT Subject Tests or ACT. Entrance: most difficult. Application deadlines: 1/1, 11/1 for early decision. Notification: 4/1, 4/1 for early decision. SAT Reasoning Test deadline: 1/1. SAT Subject Test deadline: 1/1. Transfer credits accepted: Yes. Applicants placed on waiting list: 5,629. Wait-listed applicants offered admission: 16. Early decision applicants: 1,471. Early decision applicants admitted: 802.

Collegiate Environment: Orientation program. Drama-theater-group, choral group, marching band, student-run newspaper, radio station. Social organizations: national fraternities, national sororities. Most popular organizations: Program Board, Student Association, Residence Hall Association, College Democrats, College Republicans. Major annual events: Homecoming, Welcome Week, Colonial Inauguration. Student services: legal services, health clinic, personal-psychological counseling. Campus security: 24-hour emergency response devices and patrols, late night transport-escort service, controlled dormitory access. Gelman Library.

Community Environment: See American University.

■ GEORGETOWN UNIVERSITY

37th and O Sts., NW
Washington, DC 20057
Tel: (202)687-0100
Fax: (202)687-6660
Web Site: www.georgetown.edu

Description: Independent Roman Catholic (Jesuit), university, coed. Awards bachelor's, master's, and doctoral degrees and post-master's certificates. Founded 1789. Setting: 104-acre urban campus with easy access to Washington, DC. Total enrollment: 19,005. Faculty: 2,166 (1,044 full-time, 1,122 part-time). Student-undergrad faculty ratio is 11:1. 21,462 applied, 16% were admitted. 90% from top 10% of their high school class, 97% from top quarter, 100% from top half. Full-time: 6,987 students, 56% women, 44% men. Part-time: 476 students, 54% women, 46% men. Students come from 52 states and territories, 105 other countries, 98% from out-of-district. 10% Hispanic/Latino; 6% Black or African American, non-Hispanic/Latino; 9% Asian, non-Hispanic/Latino; 0.1% Native Hawaiian or other Pacific Islander, non-Hispanic/Latino; 14% international. 3% 25 or older, 78% live on campus, 3% transferred in. Retention: 96% of full-time freshmen returned the following year. Academic areas with the most degrees conferred: social sciences; business/marketing; interdisciplinary studies. Core. Calendar: semesters. Academic remediation for entering students, ESL program, services for LD students, advanced placement, self-designed majors, honors program, independent study, distance learning, double major, summer session for credit, part-time degree program, adult/continuing education programs, internships, graduate courses open to undergrads. Off campus study at Members of the Consortium of Universities of the Washington Metropolitan Area. Study abroad program. ROTC: Army, Naval (c), Air Force (c).

Entrance Requirements: Options: electronic application, early action, deferred admission, international baccalaureate accepted. Required: essay, high school transcript, 2 recommendations, interview, SAT or ACT. Recommended: SAT Subject Tests. Entrance: most difficult. Application deadlines: 1/10, 11/1 for early action. Notification: 4/1, 12/15 for early action. SAT Reasoning Test deadline: 1/10. SAT Subject Test deadline: 1/10. Applicants placed on waiting list: 2,473. Wait-listed applicants offered admission: 50.

Costs Per Year: Application fee: $75. Comprehensive fee: $71,181 includes full-time tuition ($53,520), mandatory fees ($584), and college room and board ($17,077). College room only: $11,180. Full-time tuition and fees vary according to course load and program. Room and board charges vary according to board plan and housing facility. Part-time tuition: $2230 per credit hour. Part-time tuition varies according to course load and program.

Collegiate Environment: Orientation program. Drama-theater group, choral group, student-run newspaper, radio station. Social organizations: 268 open to all. Most popular organizations: Georgetown University Student Association (Student Government), International Relations Club, College Democrats, Georgetown University Grilling Society, Black Student Alliance. Major annual events: Homecoming Block Party, GU Day, Student Activities Fair. Student services: health clinic, personal-psychological counseling, women's center. Campus security: 24-hour emergency response devices and patrols, late night transport-escort service, controlled dormitory access, student guards at residence halls and academic facilities. Joseph Mark Lauinger Memorial Library plus 6 others. Books: 2.4 million (physical), 1.9 million (digital/electronic); Serial titles: 52,479 (physical), 275,836 (digital/electronic); Databases: 1,556. Weekly public service hours: 100; study areas open 24 hours, 5-7 days a week; students can reserve study rooms. 430 computers available on campus for general student use. A campuswide network can be accessed from student residence rooms and from off campus. Students can access the following: online class registration. Staffed computer lab on campus (open 24 hours a day) provides training in use of computers, software, and the Internet.

Community Environment: See American University.

■ **HOWARD UNIVERSITY**
2400 Sixth St., NW
Washington, DC 20059-0002
Tel: (202)806-6100; Free: 800-822-6363
E-mail: admission@howard.edu
Web Site: www.howard.edu

Description: Independent, university, coed. Awards bachelor's, master's, and doctoral degrees and post-master's certificates. Founded 1867. Setting: 256-acre urban campus with easy access to Washington. Endowment: $590.7 million. Research spending for the previous fiscal year: $42.4 million. Educational spending for the previous fiscal year: $23,014 per student. Total enrollment: 10,002. Faculty: 1,520 (1,149 full-time, 371 part-time). Student-undergrad faculty ratio is 10:1. 15,163 applied, 49% were admitted. 24% from top 10% of their high school class, 52% from top quarter, 83% from top half. Full-time: 6,412 students, 68% women, 32% men. Part-time: 471 students, 64% women, 36% men. Students come from 48 states and territories, 41 other countries, 96% from out-of-district. 0.7% American Indian or Alaska Native, non-Hispanic/Latino; 0.5% Hispanic/Latino; 90% Black or African American, non-Hispanic/Latino; 1% Asian, non-Hispanic/Latino; 0.1% Native Hawaiian or other Pacific Islander, non-Hispanic/Latino; 5% international. 7% 25 or older, 56% live on campus, 4% transferred in. Retention: 89% of full-time freshmen returned the following year. Academic areas with the most degrees conferred: business/marketing; communication/journalism; physical sciences. Core. Calendar: semesters. Academic remediation for entering students, services for LD students, advanced placement, accelerated degree program, honors program, independent study, distance learning, double major, summer session for credit, part-time degree program, co-op programs and internships, graduate courses open to undergrads. Off campus study at 9 members of the Consortium of Universities of the Washington Metropolitan Area; over 21 colleges and universities including Duke University University of California, Berkeley; Smith College; Vassar College; Williams College. Study abroad program. ROTC: Army, Air Force.

Entrance Requirements: Options: electronic application, early admission, early action, deferred admission, international baccalaureate accepted. Required: essay, high school transcript, SAT or ACT. Required for some: 2 recommendations. Entrance: moderately difficult. Application deadlines: 2/15, 11/1 for early action. Notification: continuous until 4/1, 12/20 for early action. Transfer credits accepted: Yes.

Costs Per Year: Application fee: $45. Comprehensive fee: $40,651 includes full-time tuition ($24,966), mandatory fees ($1790), and college room and board ($13,895). Part-time tuition: $1045 per credit hour.

Collegiate Environment: Orientation program. Drama-theater group, choral group, marching band, student-run newspaper, radio station. Social organizations: 155 open to all; national fraternities, national sororities, local fraternities; 3% of eligible men and 5% of eligible women are members. Most popular organizations: Howard University Student Association, Undergraduate Student Assembly, Campus Pals, International Student Organization, Entrepreneurial Society, Howard University. Major annual events: Homecoming, Spring Black Arts Festival, Residence Hall Week. Student services: health clinic, personal-psychological counseling. Campus security: 24-hour emergency response devices and patrols, student patrols, late night transport-escort service, controlled dormitory access, security lighting. Howard University Libraries plus 7 others. Study areas open 24 hours, 5-7 days a week; students can reserve study rooms. Operations spending for the previous fiscal year: $9.3 million. 6,343 computers available on campus for general student use. A campuswide network can be accessed from student residence rooms and from off campus. Students can access the following: online class registration, student residential network. Staffed computer lab on campus (open 24 hours a day) provides training in use of computers, software, and the Internet.

Community Environment: See American University.

■ **NATIONAL INTELLIGENCE UNIVERSITY**
Washington, DC 20340-5100
Tel: (202)231-5642
Fax: (202)373-2171
Web Site: www.ni-u.edu

Description: Federally supported, upper-level, coed. Founded 1963. Calendar: quarters.

■ **STRAYER UNIVERSITY-TAKOMA PARK CAMPUS**
6830 Laurel St., NW
Washington, DC 20012
Tel: (202)722-8100; Free: 888-311-0355
Web Site: www.strayer.edu

Description: Proprietary, comprehensive, coed. Awards associate, bachelor's, and master's degrees.

■ **STRAYER UNIVERSITY-WASHINGTON CAMPUS**
1133 15th St., NW
Washington, DC 20005
Tel: (202)408-2400; Free: 888-311-0355
Web Site: www.strayer.edu

Description: Proprietary, comprehensive, coed. Awards associate, bachelor's, and master's degrees.

■ **TRINITY WASHINGTON UNIVERSITY**
125 Michigan Ave., NE
Washington, DC 20017-1094
Tel: (202)884-9000; Free: 800-IWANTTC
Fax: (202)884-9229

Web Site: www.trinitydc.edu

Description: Independent Roman Catholic, comprehensive, women only. Awards bachelor's and master's degrees. Founded 1897. Setting: 26-acre urban campus. Total enrollment: 1,630. 800 applied. 38% 25 or older. Core. Calendar: semesters. Academic remediation for entering students, ESL program, services for LD students, advanced placement, accelerated degree program, self-designed majors, honors program, independent study, double major, summer session for credit, part-time degree program, external degree program, adult/continuing education programs, co-op programs and internships, graduate courses open to undergrads. Off campus study at Georgetown University; George Washington University; American University; Catholic University of America; University of Maryland, College Park; University of the District of Columbia; Marymount University. Study abroad program. ROTC: Army (c).

Entrance Requirements: Options: electronic application, early action, deferred admission, international baccalaureate accepted. Required: essay, high school transcript, minimum 2.0 high school GPA, 1 recommendation. Recommended: interview, SAT or ACT. Entrance: moderately difficult. Application deadlines: 3/1, 12/1 for early action. Notification: 1/1 for early action.

Collegiate Environment: Orientation program. Drama-theater group, choral group, student-run newspaper. Student services: health clinic, personal-psychological counseling. Campus security: 24-hour emergency response devices and patrols, late night transport-escort service, controlled dormitory access. Sister Helen Sheehan Library plus 1 other.

■ **UNIVERSITY OF THE DISTRICT OF COLUMBIA**

4200 Connecticut Ave., NW
Washington, DC 20008-1175
Tel: (202)274-5000
E-mail: nicole.daniels@udc.edu
Web Site: www.udc.edu

Description: District-supported, comprehensive, coed. Awards associate, bachelor's, master's, and doctoral degrees. Founded 1976. Setting: 28-acre urban campus. Endowment: $41.5 million. Research spending for the previous fiscal year: $4.8 million. Educational spending for the previous fiscal year: $10,436 per student. Total enrollment: 4,803. Faculty: 576 (260 full-time, 316 part-time). Student-undergrad faculty ratio is 11:1. Full-time: 1,902 students, 56% women, 44% men. Part-time: 2,589 students, 68% women, 32% men. 0.2% American Indian or Alaska Native, non-Hispanic/Latino; 9% Hispanic/Latino; 62% Black or African American, non-Hispanic/Latino; 3% Asian, non-Hispanic/Latino; 0.1% Native Hawaiian or other Pacific Islander, non-Hispanic/Latino; 3% international. Retention: 52% of full-time freshmen returned the following year. Academic areas with the most degrees conferred: business/marketing; law/legal studies; social sciences. Core. Calendar: semesters. Academic remediation for entering students, ESL program, services for LD students, accelerated degree program, honors program, summer session for credit, part-time degree program, external degree program, adult/continuing education programs, co-op programs and internships, graduate courses open to undergrads. Off campus study at members of the Consortium of Universities of the Washington Metropolitan Area. ROTC: Army (c), Air Force (c).

Entrance Requirements: Open admission students in the Community College. Options: electronic application, deferred admission. Required: high school transcript. Required for some: SAT. Entrance: minimally difficult. Application deadline: 8/1. Notification: continuous until 8/15. Preference given to district residents. Transfer credits accepted: Yes.

Costs Per Year: Application fee: $35. District resident tuition: $7392 full-time, $308 per credit hour part-time. Nonresident tuition: $15,528 full-time, $647 per credit hour part-time. Mandatory fees: $860 full-time, $430 per term part-time. Full-time tuition and fees vary according to course load and location. Part-time tuition and fees vary according to course load.

Collegiate Environment: Drama-theater group, choral group, marching band, student-run newspaper. Social organizations: 61 open to all; national fraternities, national sororities, local fraternities, local sororities; 4% of eligible men and 6% of eligible women are members. Most popular organizations: Caribbean Student Association, Theater Arts Ensemble, National Association for the Advancement of Colored People. Major annual events: Homecoming, Basketball Games, Miss UDC Pageant. Student services: health clinic, personal-psychological counseling. Campus security: 24-hour emergency response devices and patrols. Learning Resources Division Library plus 1 other. Operations spending for the previous fiscal year: $4.1 million. 1,586 computers available on campus for general student use. A campuswide network can be accessed. Students can access the following: online class registration. Staffed computer lab on campus.

Community Environment: See American University.

■ **UNIVERSITY OF THE POTOMAC**

1401 H St., NW
Washington, DC 20005
Tel: (202)686-0876; Free: 888-686-0876
Fax: (202)686-0818
E-mail: gina.riceholland@potomac.edu
Web Site: www.potomac.edu

Description: Proprietary, comprehensive, coed. Administratively affiliated with Linden Education. Awards associate, bachelor's, and master's degrees. Founded 1991. Setting: urban campus with easy access to Washington DC; Tysons, VA. Total enrollment: 276. Faculty: 52 (3 full-time, 49 part-time). Student-undergrad faculty ratio is 5:1. 114 applied, 96% were admitted. Full-time: 109 students, 37% women, 63% men. Students come from 12 states and territories, 10 other countries, 60% from out-of-district. 0.9% American Indian or Alaska Native, non-Hispanic/Latino; 3% Hispanic/Latino; 43% Black or African American, non-Hispanic/Latino; 35% international. 64% 25 or older, 11% transferred in. Retention: 67% of full-time freshmen returned the following year. Academic areas with the most degrees conferred: business/marketing; computer and information sciences. Core. Calendar: 6 8-week terms. Services for LD students, honors program, distance learning, part-time degree program, external degree program, adult/continuing education programs.

Entrance Requirements: Open admission. Options: electronic application, international baccalaureate accepted. Required: interview. Entrance: noncompetitive. Application deadline: rolling. Notification: continuous. Transfer credits accepted: Yes.

Collegiate Environment: Orientation program. Major annual events: Student Government Association Elections, Annual SGA and alumni cookout and Career Fair, Rock the Vote. Campus security: late night transport-escort service. Learning Resource Center - Washington Campus plus 1 other. Books: 4,500 (physical); Serial titles: 20 (physical), 5 (digital/electronic); Databases: 5. Weekly public service hours: 35. 28 computers available on campus for general student use. A campuswide network can be accessed. Students can access the following: student portal, access to learning management system.

■ ACADEMY FOR NURSING AND HEALTH OCCUPATIONS
5154 Okeechobee Blvd.
Ste. 201
West Palm Beach, FL 33417
Tel: (561)683-1400
Web Site: www.anho.edu
Description: Proprietary, 2-year, coed. Awards certificates, transfer associate, and terminal associate degrees.

■ ADVANCE SCIENCE COLLEGE
3750 W 12 Ave.
Hialeah, FL 33012
Tel: (305)827-5452
Web Site: www.asicollege.edu
Description: Proprietary, 2-year, coed. Awards certificates, transfer associate, and terminal associate degrees.

■ ADVENTHEALTH UNIVERSITY
671 Winyah Dr.
Orlando, FL 32803
Tel: (407)303-7747; Free: 800-500-7747
Web Site: www.adu.edu
Description: Independent, comprehensive, coed. Awards associate, bachelor's, master's, and doctoral degrees. Founded 1992. Setting: 9-acre urban campus with easy access to Orlando. Endowment: $8 million. Research spending for the previous fiscal year: $21,781. Total enrollment: 1,705. Faculty: 256 (91 full-time, 165 part-time). Student-undergrad faculty ratio is 8:1. 267 applied, 87% were admitted. Full-time: 528 students, 81% women, 19% men. Part-time: 813 students, 79% women, 21% men. Students come from 40 states and territories, 11 other countries, 23% from out-of-state. 0.2% American Indian or Alaska Native, non-Hispanic/Latino; 32% Hispanic/Latino; 19% Black or African American, non-Hispanic/Latino; 5% Asian, non-Hispanic/Latino; 0.6% Native Hawaiian or other Pacific Islander, non-Hispanic/Latino; 2% international. 48% 25 or older, 11% live on campus, 11% transferred in. Retention: 66% of full-time freshmen returned the following year. Academic areas with the most degrees conferred: health professions and related sciences; biological/life sciences. Core. Calendar: trimesters. Academic remediation for entering students, services for LD students, freshman honors college, independent study, distance learning, double major, summer session for credit, internships.
Entrance Requirements: Options: electronic application, early admission, early action, deferred admission, international baccalaureate accepted. Required: high school transcript, minimum 2.5 high school GPA. Required for some: SAT or ACT, TOEFL for non-native English Speakers. Entrance: minimally difficult. Application deadlines: 7/1, 7/1 for nonresidents, 5/1 for early action. Notification: 7/15, 7/15 for nonresidents. SAT Reasoning Test deadline: 7/1. SAT Subject Test deadline: 7/1. Transfer credits accepted: Yes. Early action applicants: 266. Early action applicants admitted: 211.
Costs Per Year: Application fee: $20. Tuition: $15,300 full-time, $510 per credit hour part-time. Mandatory fees: $600 full-time, $300 per term part-time. College room only: $4200.
Collegiate Environment: Orientation program. Drama-theater group, choral group. Social organizations: 10 open to all. Most popular organizations: Student Nursing Association, Student Occupational Therapy Association, Pre Physician Assistant, Pre PT/OT, Campus Ministries. Major annual events: Convocation, International Food Festival, Spring Picnic. Student services: personal-psychological counseling. Campus security: 24-hour emergency response devices and patrols, controlled dormitory access. 184 college housing spaces available; 113 were occupied in 2018-19. No special consideration for freshman housing applicants. Option: coed housing available. R. A. Williams Library. Books: 11,979 (physical), 19,173 (digital/electronic); Serial titles: 25 (physical), 28,121 (digital/electronic); Databases: 120. Weekly public service hours: 65; students can reserve study rooms. Operations spending for the previous fiscal year: $1.1 million. 51 computers available on campus for general student use. A computer is required for all students. A campuswide network can be accessed. Students can access the following: online class registration, Online Registration.

■ ALBIZU UNIVERSITY, MIAMI CAMPUS
2173 NW 99th Ave.
Miami, FL 33172-2209
Tel: (305)593-1223; Free: 800-GO-TO-CAU
Fax: (305)592-7930
E-mail: matorres@albizu.edu
Web Site: www.albizu.edu
Description: Independent, comprehensive, coed. Part of Carlos Albizu University. Awards bachelor's, master's, and doctoral degrees. Founded 1980. Setting: 18-acre urban campus. Research spending for the previous fiscal year: $25,550. Educational spending for the previous fiscal year: $5397 per student. Total enrollment: 1,046. Faculty: 56 (8 full-time, 48 part-time). Student-undergrad faculty ratio is 11:1. 25 applied, 72% were admitted. Full-time: 234 students, 66% women, 34% men. Part-time: 122 students, 81% women, 19% men. 0.3% American Indian or Alaska Native, non-Hispanic/Latino; 58% Hispanic/Latino; 0.6% Black or African American, non-Hispanic/Latino; 0.3% Asian, non-Hispanic/Latino; 35% international. 78% 25 or older, 8% transferred in. Retention: 42% of full-time freshmen returned the following year. Core. Calendar: trimesters. Academic remediation for entering students, ESL program, services for LD students, accelerated degree program, independent study, distance learning, double major, summer session for credit, part-time degree program, adult/continuing education programs, co-op programs and internships.
Entrance Requirements: Options: electronic application, international baccalaureate accepted. Required: high school transcript, minimum 2 high school GPA, 2 recommendations, interview. Entrance: moderately difficult. Application deadline: rolling. Notification: continuous. Transfer credits accepted: Yes.
Collegiate Environment: Orientation program. Student-run newspaper. Social organizations: 9 open to all. Most popular organizations: Student Council, Psi Chi, Kappa Delta Pi, Military Psychology Chapter, Neuropsychology Club. Major annual events: Student Council Elections, Town Hall Meetings, Career Fairs. Campus security: 24-hour emergency response devices and patrols, late night transport-escort service. Albizu Library. Books: 27,760 (physical), 22,900 (digital/electronic); Serial titles: 295 (physical), 17,034 (digital/electronic); Databases: 73. Weekly public service hours: 66. Operations spending for the previous fiscal year: $232,950. 268 computers available on campus for general student use. A campuswide network can be accessed from off-campus. Students can access the following: online class registration, campus portal, virtual library, 24/7 support, Cloud computing, learning center. Staffed computer lab on campus provides training in use of computers, software, and the Internet.

■ **ALTIERUS CAREER COLLEGE**
3319 W Hillsborough Ave.
Tampa, FL 33614
Tel: (813)879-6000
Fax: (813)871-2483
Web Site: www.altierus.edu
Description: Independent, primarily 2-year, coed. Part of Zenith Education Group. Awards diplomas, terminal associate, bachelor's, and master's degrees. Founded 1890. Setting: 4-acre urban campus. Total enrollment: 3,430. Faculty: 61 (13 full-time, 48 part-time). Student-undergrad faculty ratio is 20:1. 2,225 applied, 74% were admitted. Full-time: 2,750 students, 63% women, 37% men. Part-time: 636 students, 69% women, 31% men. Students come from 15 states and territories, 3 other countries. 51% 25 or older, 1% transferred in. Core. Calendar: quarters. ESL program, advanced placement, accelerated degree program, self-designed majors, independent study, distance learning, double major, summer session for credit, part-time degree program, external degree program, adult/continuing education programs, co-op programs and internships.
Entrance Requirements: Options: deferred admission, international baccalaureate accepted. Required: high school transcript, CPAt. Required for some: SAT, ACT. Entrance: minimally difficult. Application deadline: rolling. Notification: continuous.
Collegiate Environment: Social organizations: 6 open to all; coed fraternity; 7% of eligible men and 13% of eligible women are members. Most popular organizations: Legal Network, Phi Beta Lambda, Ambassadors Club. Major annual events: Clean City Day, Health Fair. Campus security: 24-hour emergency response devices, evening and Saturday afternoon patrols by trained security personnel. Tampa College Library. Operations spending for the previous fiscal year: $90,000. 113 computers available on campus for general student use. Staffed computer lab on campus.

■ **AMERICAN COLLEGE FOR MEDICAL CAREERS**
5959 Lake Ellenor Dr.
Orlando, FL 32809
Tel: (407)738-4488; Free: 888-599-7887
Fax: (407)386-7522
Web Site: www.acmc.edu
Description: Proprietary, 4-year, coed. Awards associate and bachelor's degrees.

■ **AMERICAN MEDICAL ACADEMY**
12215 SW 112 St.
Miami, FL 33186-4830
Web Site: www.ama.edu
Description: Proprietary, 2-year, coed. Awards diplomas, transfer associate, and terminal associate degrees.

■ **ARGOSY UNIVERSITY, TAMPA**
1403 N Howard Ave.
Tampa, FL 33607
Tel: (813)393-5290; Free: 800-850-6488
Fax: (813)246-4045
Web Site: www.argosy.edu/locations/tampa
Description: Proprietary, university, coed. Part of Education Management Corporation. Awards associate, bachelor's, master's, and doctoral degrees. Setting: urban campus. Calendar: semesters.

■ **THE ART INSTITUTE OF TAMPA, A BRANCH OF MIAMI INTERNATIONAL UNIVERSITY OF ART & DESIGN**
Parkside at Tampa Bay Park
4401 N Himes Ave., Ste. 150
Tampa, FL 33614
Tel: (813)873-2112; Free: 866-703-3277
Fax: (813)873-2171
Web Site: www.artinstitutes.edu/tampa
Description: Proprietary, 4-year, coed. Part of Education Management Corporation. Awards associate and bachelor's degrees. Setting: suburban campus. Calendar: quarters.

■ **ATA CAREER EDUCATION**
7351 Spring Hill Dr.
Ste. 11
Spring Hill, FL 34606
Tel: (352)684-3007

Web Site: www.atafl.edu
Description: Proprietary, 2-year, coed. Awards diplomas, transfer associate, and terminal associate degrees.

■ **ATLANTIS UNIVERSITY**
1442 Biscayne Blvd.
Miami, FL 33132
Web Site: www.atlantisuniversity.edu
Description: Proprietary, comprehensive, coed.

■ **AVE MARIA UNIVERSITY**
5050 Ave. Maria Blvd.
Ave Maria, FL 34142
Tel: (239)280-2556; Free: 877-283-8648
Fax: (239)352-2392
Web Site: www.avemaria.edu
Description: Independent Roman Catholic, comprehensive, coed. Awards bachelor's, master's, and doctoral degrees. Founded 2002. Setting: 790-acre small town campus. Endowment: $2.5 million. Educational spending for the previous fiscal year: $9458 per student. Total enrollment: 1,108. Faculty: 93 (67 full-time, 26 part-time). Student-undergrad faculty ratio is 14:1. 2,703 applied, 43% were admitted. Full-time: 1,046 students, 51% women, 49% men. Part-time: 22 students, 45% women, 55% men. Students come from 48 states and territories, 15 other countries, 55% from out-of-state. 0.6% American Indian or Alaska Native, non-Hispanic/Latino; 15% Hispanic/Latino; 5% Black or African American, non-Hispanic/Latino; 3% Asian, non-Hispanic/Latino; 2% international. 1% 25 or older, 90% live on campus, 7% transferred in. Retention: 72% of full-time freshmen returned the following year. Core. Calendar: semesters. Services for LD students, accelerated degree program, honors program, independent study, double major, summer session for credit, internships, graduate courses open to undergrads. Study abroad program.
Entrance Requirements: Options: electronic application, deferred admission, international baccalaureate accepted. Required: high school transcript, minimum 2.8 high school GPA, activities list, SAT or ACT. Required for some: essay, 2 recommendations, interview. Entrance: moderately difficult. Application deadline: rolling. Notification: continuous. SAT Reasoning Test deadline: 8/20.
Collegiate Environment: Orientation program. Drama-theater group, choral group, student-run newspaper. Social organizations: 55 open to all; 50% of eligible men and 50% of eligible women are members. Most popular organizations: Students for Life, Drama Club, Student Government Association, Intercollegiate Studies Institute, Faith in Action Ministry. Major annual events: Annunciation Feast, Battle of the Bands, Octoberfest. Student services: health clinic, personal-psychological counseling. Campus security: 24-hour patrols, controlled dormitory access, County Sheriff workstation on campus with deputy patrols. Canizaro Library. Operations spending for the previous fiscal year: $387,975.

■ **AVIATOR COLLEGE OF AERONAUTICAL SCIENCE & TECHNOLOGY**
3800 St. Lucie Blvd.
Fort Pierce, FL 34946
Tel: (772)466-4822
Web Site: aviator.edu/FlightSchool
Description: Proprietary, 2-year, coed. Awards certificates, transfer associate, and terminal associate degrees.

■ **THE BAPTIST COLLEGE OF FLORIDA**
5400 College Dr.
Graceville, FL 32440
Tel: (850)263-3261; Free: 800-328-2660
Fax: (850)263-7506
Web Site: www.baptistcollege.edu
Description: Independent Southern Baptist, comprehensive, coed. Awards associate, bachelor's, and master's degrees. Founded 1943. Setting: 250-acre small town campus. Endowment: $7.8 million. Total enrollment: 448. Faculty: 67 (26 full-time, 41 part-time). Student-undergrad faculty ratio is 9:1. 113 applied, 62% were admitted. Full-time: 280 students, 47% women, 53% men. Part-time: 147 students, 32% women, 68% men. Students come from 16 states and territories, 1 other country, 25% from out-of-state. 0.5% American Indian or Alaska Native, non-Hispanic/Latino; 4% Hispanic/Latino; 7% Black or African American, non-Hispanic/Latino; 0.2% Asian, non-Hispanic/Latino; 0.7% Native Hawaiian or other Pacific Islander, non-

Hispanic/Latino; 0.2% international. 44% 25 or older, 39% live on campus, 9% transferred in. Retention: 74% of full-time freshmen returned the following year. Academic areas with the most degrees conferred: theology and religious vocations; visual and performing arts; psychology. Core. Calendar: semesters. Academic remediation for entering students, services for LD students, advanced placement, independent study, distance learning, double major, summer session for credit, part-time degree program, internships.

Entrance Requirements: Open admission. Options: electronic application, deferred admission, international baccalaureate accepted. Required: essay, high school transcript, minimum 2.5 high school GPA, 2 recommendations, Christian/church member for 1 year minimum, SAT or ACT. Recommended: interview. Entrance: noncompetitive. Application deadline: 8/11. Notification: continuous. Preference given to professing Christians who are members of an Evangelical church. Transfer credits accepted: Yes.

Costs Per Year: Application fee: $25. Comprehensive fee: $16,012 includes full-time tuition ($10,500), mandatory fees ($900), and college room and board ($4612). Room and board charges vary according to board plan and housing facility. Part-time tuition: $350 per credit hour. Part-time mandatory fees: $30 per credit hour.

Collegiate Environment: Orientation program. Drama-theater group, choral group. Social organizations: 3 open to all. Most popular organizations: Baptist Collegiate Ministry, College Choir, AACC. Major annual events: Lakeside Echo, Halloween Carnival, BCF Olympics. Student services: personal-psychological counseling. Campus security: student patrols, patrols by police officers 11 pm to 7 am. Ida J. MacMillan Library plus 1 other. Books: 90,006 (physical), 88,931 (digital/electronic); Serial titles: 5,602 (physical), 5,602 (digital/electronic); Databases: 16. Weekly public service hours: 66. Operations spending for the previous fiscal year: $324,842. 25 computers available on campus for general student use. A campuswide network can be accessed from student residence rooms. Students can access the following: online class registration. Staffed computer lab on campus provides training in use of computers, software, and the Internet.

Community Environment: Graceville is in northwest Florida near the borders of Alabama, Florida and Georgia. 23 miles north is Dothan, Alabama, and 20 miles southeast is Marianna, Florida. Railroads and buses serve the area. One excellent shopping center is available.

■ **BARRY UNIVERSITY**
11300 NE Second Ave.
Miami Shores, FL 33161-6695
Tel: (305)899-3000; Free: 800-695-2279
Fax: (305)899-2971
Web Site: www.barry.edu
Description: Independent Roman Catholic, university, coed. Awards bachelor's, master's, and doctoral degrees and post-master's certificates. Founded 1940. Setting: 122-acre suburban campus with easy access to Miami. Total enrollment: 7,358. Faculty: 735 (325 full-time, 410 part-time). Student-undergrad faculty ratio is 13:1. 5,110 applied, 85% were admitted. 100% from top quarter of their high school class. Full-time: 2,991 students, 62% women, 38% men. Part-time: 514 students, 49% women, 51% men. 20% from out-of-state. 0.5% American Indian or Alaska Native, non-Hispanic/Latino; 34% Hispanic/Latino; 34% Black or African American, non-Hispanic/Latino; 1% Asian, non-Hispanic/Latino; 0.2% Native Hawaiian or other Pacific Islander, non-Hispanic/Latino; 8% international. 43% 25 or older, 30% live on campus, 16% transferred in. Retention: 61% of full-time freshmen returned the following year. Academic areas with the most degrees conferred: business/marketing; health professions and related sciences; public administration and social services. Core. Calendar: semesters. Academic remediation for entering students, ESL program, services for LD students, advanced placement, accelerated degree program, honors program, independent study, distance learning, double major, summer session for credit, part-time degree program, adult/continuing education programs, internships, graduate courses open to undergrads. Off campus study at St. Thomas Aquinas College, Dominican College of San Rafael. Study abroad program. ROTC: Army (c), Air Force (c).

Entrance Requirements: Options: electronic application, early admission, deferred admission. Required: high school transcript, minimum 2 high school GPA, SAT or ACT. Recommended: interview. Required for some: essay. Entrance: moderately difficult. Application deadline: rolling. Notification: continuous.

Costs Per Year: Application fee: $30. Comprehensive fee: $40,800 includes full-time tuition ($29,700) and college room and board ($11,100). Room and board charges vary according to housing facility. Part-time tuition: $925 per credit hour. Part-time tuition varies according to course load.

Collegiate Environment: Orientation program. Drama-theater group, choral group, student-run newspaper, radio station. Social organizations: 27 open to all; national fraternities, national sororities. Most popular organizations: Student Government Association, Campus Activities Board, SCUBA Society, Caribbean Students Association, Jamaican Association. Major annual events: Founder's Day, Spring and Fall Formals, Festival of Nations. Student services: health clinic, personal-psychological counseling. Campus security: 24-hour emergency response devices and patrols, late night transport-escort service. Monsignor William Barry Memorial Library plus 1 other. 368 computers available on campus for general student use. A campuswide network can be accessed from student residence rooms and from off campus. Students can access the following: online class registration, learning management system. Staffed computer lab on campus.

Community Environment: Located only minutes from the cities of Miami and Ft. Lauderdale, Barry University offers easy access to the recreational facilities and cultural opportunities of Florida's Gold Coast area. Golf, tennis, swimming, skin and scuba diving, sailing and waterskiing are available all year long. Professional football, basketball, soccer, and hockey teams play in South Florida. The Miami Beach Theater of the Performing Arts, Coconut Grove Playhouse and the New World Symphony provide a full season of highly acclaimed performances. Well known personalities entertain regularly in the area. The Miami/Ft. Lauderdale area provides ready access to beaches, recreational, and ecological features including the Florida Keys, the Everglades, and National, State and Marine parks.

■ **BEACON COLLEGE**
105 E Main St.
Leesburg, FL 34748
Tel: (352)787-7660
Fax: (352)787-0721
E-mail: dherold@beaconcollege.edu
Web Site: www.beaconcollege.edu
Description: Independent, 4-year, coed. Awards bachelor's degrees. Founded 1989. Setting: 19-acre small town campus with easy access to Orlando. Endowment: $83,990. Educational spending for the previous fiscal year: $13,459 per student. Total enrollment: 348. Faculty: 37 (28 full-time, 9 part-time). Student-undergrad faculty ratio is 11:1. 261 applied, 53% were admitted. Full-time: 344 students, 41% women, 59% men. Part-time: 4 students, 100% women. Students come from 37 states and territories, 3 other countries, 71% from out-of-state. 0.6% American Indian or Alaska Native, non-Hispanic/Latino; 6% Hispanic/Latino; 15% Black or African American, non-Hispanic/Latino; 3% Asian, non-Hispanic/Latino; 0.3% Native Hawaiian or other Pacific Islander, non-Hispanic/Latino; 1% international. 4% 25 or older, 85% live on campus, 10% transferred in. Retention: 68% of full-time freshmen returned the following year. Academic areas with the most degrees conferred: business/marketing; computer and information sciences; public administration and social services. Core. Calendar: semesters. Academic remediation for entering students, services for LD students, advanced placement, honors program, independent study, double major, summer session for credit, adult/continuing education programs, co-op programs and internships. Study abroad program.

Entrance Requirements: Options: electronic application, early admission, deferred admission, international baccalaureate accepted. Required: high school transcript, 3 recommendations, psycho-educational evaluation showing diagnosed learning disability or ADHD. Recommended: minimum 2 high school GPA, interview. Entrance: moderately difficult. Application deadline: rolling. Notification: 8/1. Transfer credits accepted: Yes. Applicants placed on waiting list: 0. Wait-listed applicants offered admission: 0.

Costs Per Year: Application fee: $50. Comprehensive fee: $50,406 includes full-time tuition ($39,016) and college room and board ($11,390). College room only: $7216. Full-time tuition varies according to course load. Room and board charges vary according to housing facility. Part-time tuition: $1300 per credit hour. Part-time tuition varies according to course load.

Collegiate Environment: Orientation program. Drama-theater group, student-run radio station. Social organizations: 28 open to all; national fraternities, national sororities, local fraternities, local sororities, Gamma Beta Phi; 35% of eligible men and 10% of eligible women are members. Most popular organizations: Gamma Beta Phi, Performance Club, Psychology & Human Services Club, Nerd Culture Club, Equine Club. Major annual events: Parents' Weekend, Club Fair, Spring and Halloween Dance Nights. Student services: health clinic, personal-psychological counseling. Campus security: 24-hour emergency response devices and patrols, student patrols, late night transport-escort service. Beacon College Library. Books: 11,113 (physical), 346,154 (digital/electronic); Serial titles: 40 (physical); Databases:

15. Weekly public service hours: 76; students can reserve study rooms. Operations spending for the previous fiscal year: $182,526. 150 computers available on campus for general student use. A campuswide network can be accessed from student residence rooms and from off campus. Staffed computer lab on campus provides training in use of computers, software, and the Internet.

■ **BELHAVEN UNIVERSITY**
5200 Vineland Rd.
Ste. 100
Orlando, FL 32811
Tel: (407)804-1424; Free: 877-804-1424
Fax: (407)661-1732
Web Site: orlando.belhaven.edu
Description: Independent Presbyterian, comprehensive, coed. Awards associate, bachelor's, and master's degrees. Founded 1999. Calendar: semesters.
Entrance Requirements: Required: high school transcript. Required for some: essay, resume.

■ **BETHUNE-COOKMAN UNIVERSITY**
640 Dr. Mary McLeod Bethune Blvd.
Daytona Beach, FL 32114-3099
Tel: (386)481-2000; Free: 800-448-0228
Fax: (386)481-2010
E-mail: portert@cookman.edu
Web Site: www.cookman.edu
Description: Independent Methodist, comprehensive, coed. Awards bachelor's and master's degrees. Founded 1904. Setting: 60-acre urban campus with easy access to Orlando. System endowment: $47.9 million. Research spending for the previous fiscal year: $636,269. Educational spending for the previous fiscal year: $6704 per student. Total enrollment: 4,143. Faculty: 278 (194 full-time, 84 part-time). Student-undergrad faculty ratio is 16:1. 11,652 applied, 54% were admitted. 2% from top 10% of their high school class, 9% from top quarter, 40% from top half. 6 student government officers. Full-time: 3,755 students, 62% women, 38% men. Part-time: 237 students, 60% women, 40% men. Students come from 40 states and territories, 20 other countries, 27% from out-of-state. 0.1% American Indian or Alaska Native, non-Hispanic/Latino; 3% Hispanic/Latino; 78% Black or African American, non-Hispanic/Latino; 0.1% Asian, non-Hispanic/Latino; 2% international. 5% 25 or older, 66% live on campus, 3% transferred in. Retention: 67% of full-time freshmen returned the following year. Academic areas with the most degrees conferred: liberal arts/general studies; business/marketing; homeland security, law enforcement, firefighting, and protective services. Core. Calendar: semesters. Academic remediation for entering students, advanced placement, accelerated degree program, honors program, independent study, distance learning, double major, summer session for credit, part-time degree program, adult/continuing education programs, co-op programs and internships, graduate courses open to undergrads. Study abroad program. ROTC: Army (c), Air Force (c).
Entrance Requirements: Options: electronic application, early admission, deferred admission, international baccalaureate accepted. Required: high school transcript, minimum 2.25 high school GPA, 1 recommendation, medical history, SAT or ACT. Recommended: essay. Required for some: interview. Entrance: minimally difficult. Application deadline: 6/30. Notification: continuous. Transfer credits accepted: Yes.
Costs Per Year: Application fee: $25. One-time mandatory fee: $300. Comprehensive fee: $24,226 includes full-time tuition ($13,844), mandatory fees ($970), and college room and board ($9412). Full-time tuition and fees vary according to degree level. Room and board charges vary according to housing facility. Part-time tuition: $576.80 per credit hour. Part-time mandatory fees: $50 per credit hour. Part-time tuition and fees vary according to course load and degree level.
Collegiate Environment: Orientation program. Drama-theater group, choral group, marching band, student-run newspaper, radio station. Social organizations: 77 open to all; national fraternities, national sororities, local fraternities, local sororities; 6% of eligible men and 13% of eligible women are members. Most popular organizations: National Council of Negro Women, Gamma Sigma Sigma Sorority, Phenomenal Woman Think Tank, What's Next Dance Company, NAACP. Major annual events: Homecoming, Commencement, Career Fair. Student services: health clinic, personal-psychological counseling. Campus security: 24-hour emergency response devices and patrols, student patrols, late night transport-escort service. Carl S. Swisher Library plus 1 other. Books: 83,794 (physical), 269,009 (digital/

electronic); Serial titles: 20 (physical), 36,000 (digital/electronic); Databases: 34. Weekly public service hours: 92; study areas open 24 hours, 5-7 days a week; students can reserve study rooms. 846 computers available on campus for general student use. A campuswide network can be accessed from student residence rooms and from off campus. Students can access the following: online class registration. Staffed computer lab on campus (open 24 hours a day) provides training in use of computers, software, and the Internet.
Community Environment: Daytona Beach is a resort area located on the Atlantic Ocean with a subtropical climate. All modes of transportation serve the area. The community facilities include two libraries, two museums, many churches, a hospital and major civic organizations. Part-time employment opportunities are available. Recreational activities include water sports, stock car racing, motor bike racing, and archery. Beach drivers almost outnumber swimmers. Spring vacation brings an influx of college students. Special events include the Antique Car Meet and car racing known as the Speed Week.

■ **BROWARD COLLEGE**
111 E Las Olas Blvd.
Fort Lauderdale, FL 33301-2298
Tel: (954)201-7350
E-mail: walexand@broward.edu
Web Site: www.broward.edu
Description: State-supported, primarily 2-year, coed. Part of Florida College System. Awards certificates, diplomas, transfer associate, terminal associate, and bachelor's degrees. Founded 1960. Setting: urban campus with easy access to Miami. Total enrollment: 43,715. Student-undergrad faculty ratio is 30:1. Full-time: 13,327 students, 55% women, 45% men. Part-time: 30,388 students, 61% women, 39% men. Students come from 143 other countries. 0.2% American Indian or Alaska Native, non-Hispanic/Latino; 34% Hispanic/Latino; 35% Black or African American, non-Hispanic/Latino; 3% Asian, non-Hispanic/Latino; 0.2% Native Hawaiian or other Pacific Islander, non-Hispanic/Latino; 3% international. 37% 25 or older, 3% transferred in. Academic areas with the most degrees conferred: business/marketing; education; computer and information sciences. Core. Calendar: trimesters. Academic remediation for entering students, ESL program, services for LD students, advanced placement, accelerated degree program, self-designed majors, honors program, distance learning, summer session for credit, part-time degree program, adult/continuing education programs, co-op programs. Study abroad program. ROTC: Army.
Entrance Requirements: Open admission. Options: electronic application, early admission, deferred admission. Required for some: high school transcript. Entrance: noncompetitive. Preference given to state residents. Transfer credits accepted: Yes.
Collegiate Environment: Orientation program. Drama-theater group, choral group, student-run newspaper. Social organizations: local fraternities, local sororities. Student services: personal-psychological counseling, women's center. Campus security: 24-hour emergency response devices and patrols, late night transport-escort service. South Regional/Broward Community College Library.
Community Environment: Fort Lauderdale, population 167,000, is located on the Atlantic Ocean coastline, 25 miles north of Miami. The climate is subtropical and the average year-round temperature is 75 degrees.

■ **CAMBRIDGE COLLEGE OF HEALTHCARE & TECHNOLOGY**
5150 Linton Blvd.
Ste. 340
Delray Beach, FL 33484
Tel: (561)381-4990
Web Site: www.cambridgehealth.edu
Description: Proprietary, 2-year, coed. Awards transfer associate degrees.

■ **CHAMBERLAIN COLLEGE OF NURSING (JACKSONVILLE)**
5200 Belfort Rd.
Jacksonville, FL 32256
Tel: (904)251-8110; Free: 877-751-5783
Fax: (904)251-8390
Web Site: www.chamberlain.edu
Description: Proprietary, 4-year, coed. Awards bachelor's degrees. Total enrollment: 485. Faculty: 38 (13 full-time, 25 part-time). Student-undergrad faculty ratio is 11:1. Full-time: 120 students, 84% women, 16% men. Part-time: 365 students, 89% women, 11% men. 8% from out-of-state. 10% Hispanic/Latino; 30% Black or African American, non-Hispanic/Latino; 8%

Asian, non-Hispanic/Latino; 0.8% Native Hawaiian or other Pacific Islander, non-Hispanic/Latino. 74% 25 or older, 35% transferred in. Academic area with the most degrees conferred: health professions and related sciences. Calendar: semesters. Accelerated degree program, distance learning.

Entrance Requirements: Option: deferred admission. Required: SAT or ACT.

■ **CHAMBERLAIN COLLEGE OF NURSING (MIRAMAR)**
2300 SW 145th Ave.
Miramar, FL 33027
Tel: (954)885-3510; Free: 877-751-5783
Fax: (954)885-3601
Web Site: www.chamberlain.edu
Description: Proprietary, 4-year, coed. Awards bachelor's degrees. Total enrollment: 567. Faculty: 73 (13 full-time, 60 part-time). Student-undergrad faculty ratio is 9:1. Full-time: 147 students, 88% women, 12% men. Part-time: 420 students, 84% women, 16% men. 2% from out-of-state. 0.2% American Indian or Alaska Native, non-Hispanic/Latino; 41% Hispanic/Latino; 29% Black or African American, non-Hispanic/Latino; 5% Asian, non-Hispanic/Latino; 0.2% international. 70% 25 or older, 29% transferred in. Academic area with the most degrees conferred: health professions and related sciences. Accelerated degree program, distance learning.
Entrance Requirements: Option: deferred admission. Required: SAT or ACT. Entrance: moderately difficult. Application deadline: rolling. Notification: continuous.

■ **CHIPOLA COLLEGE**
3094 Indian Cir.
Marianna, FL 32446-3065
Tel: (850)526-2761
Fax: (850)718-2388
E-mail: rehbergk@chipola.edu
Web Site: www.chipola.edu
Description: State-supported, primarily 2-year, coed. Awards certificates, transfer associate, terminal associate, and bachelor's degrees. Founded 1947. Setting: 105-acre rural campus. Total enrollment: 2,104. Faculty: 127 (39 full-time, 88 part-time). Student-undergrad faculty ratio is 24:1. Full-time: 859 students, 59% women, 41% men. Part-time: 1,245 students, 62% women, 38% men. Students come from 7 states and territories, 6 other countries, 8% from out-of-state. 1% American Indian or Alaska Native, non-Hispanic/Latino; 5% Hispanic/Latino; 15% Black or African American, non-Hispanic/Latino; 0.7% Asian, non-Hispanic/Latino; 0.1% Native Hawaiian or other Pacific Islander, non-Hispanic/Latino; 0.5% international. 37% 25 or older, 7% transferred in. Core. Calendar: semesters. Academic remediation for entering students, services for LD students, advanced placement, honors program, independent study, distance learning, summer session for credit, part-time degree program, adult/continuing education programs.
Entrance Requirements: Open admission. Option: early admission. Required: high school transcript. Entrance: noncompetitive. Application deadline: rolling. Notification: continuous. Transfer credits accepted: Yes.
Costs Per Year: Application fee: $0. State resident tuition: $104 per credit hour part-time. Nonresident tuition: $298.33 per credit hour part-time. Part-time tuition varies according to degree level.
Collegiate Environment: Drama-theater group, choral group, student-run newspaper. Major annual events: Fall Festival, Homecoming, Spring Frolics. Campus security: night security personnel. Chipola Library. Books: 30,000 (physical), 67,000 (digital/electronic); Serial titles: 150 (physical); Databases: 100. Weekly public service hours: 60; students can reserve study rooms. 80 computers available on campus for general student use. A campuswide network can be accessed from off-campus. Students can access the following: online class registration. Staffed computer lab on campus (open 24 hours a day) provides training in use of computers, software, and the Internet.
Community Environment: Marianna, located in northwest Florida, has an annual average temperature of 68.1 degrees and an average rainfall of 54.51 inches. Buses serve the area along the U.S. Highway 90. Community facilities include a hospital, several motels, a library, churches, and two radio stations. The Florida Caverns State Park, three miles north, has extensive limestone caverns with guided trips available. Picnic areas, campsites, rock gardens, a museum, and golf course are located here. There are fine beaches for all water sports, and excellent hunting in the area.

■ **CITY COLLEGE (ALTAMONTE SPRINGS)**
177 Montgomery Rd.
Altamonte Springs, FL 32714

Tel: (407)831-9816
Fax: (407)831-1147
Web Site: www.citycollege.edu
Description: Independent, primarily 2-year, coed. Awards diplomas, terminal associate, and bachelor's degrees. Total enrollment: 217. Faculty: 37 (2 full-time, 35 part-time). Student-undergrad faculty ratio is 17:1. Full-time: 217 students, 84% women, 16% men. 62% 25 or older. Retention: 47% of full-time freshmen returned the following year. Calendar: semesters.
Entrance Requirements: Required: high school transcript, interview, TABE. Entrance: noncompetitive.
Collegiate Environment: Orientation program. 50 computers available on campus for general student use. A campuswide network can be accessed. Staffed computer lab on campus provides training in use of computers, software, and the Internet.

■ **CITY COLLEGE (FORT LAUDERDALE)**
2000 W Commercial Blvd.
Ste. 200
Fort Lauderdale, FL 33309
Tel: (954)492-5353; Free: 866-314-5681
Fax: (954)491-1965
Web Site: www.citycollege.edu
Description: Independent, primarily 2-year, coed. Awards certificates, terminal associate, and bachelor's degrees. Founded 1984. Total enrollment: 677. Student-undergrad faculty ratio is 20:1. 129 applied, 91% were admitted. 64% 25 or older. Calendar: semesters.
Entrance Requirements: Required: high school transcript, interview, TABE.

■ **CITY COLLEGE (GAINESVILLE)**
7001 NW 4th Blvd.
Gainesville, FL 32607
Tel: (352)335-4000
Fax: (352)335-4303
Web Site: www.citycollege.edu
Description: Independent, primarily 2-year, coed. Awards certificates, terminal associate, and bachelor's degrees. Founded 1986. Total enrollment: 426. Student-undergrad faculty ratio is 15:1. 43 applied, 98% were admitted. 67% 25 or older. Calendar: semesters.
Entrance Requirements: Required: high school transcript, interview, TABE.

■ **CITY COLLEGE (HOLLYWOOD)**
6565 Taft St.
Hollywood, FL 33024
Tel: (954)744-1777; Free: 866-314-5681
Fax: (954)983-0118
Web Site: www.citycollege.edu
Description: Independent, primarily 2-year, coed. Awards transfer associate, terminal associate, and bachelor's degrees.

■ **CITY COLLEGE (MIAMI)**
9300 S Dadeland Blvd.
Ste. 200
Miami, FL 33156
Tel: (305)666-9242
Fax: (305)666-9243
Web Site: www.citycollege.edu
Description: Independent, primarily 2-year, coed. Awards certificates, terminal associate, and bachelor's degrees. Founded 1997. Total enrollment: 416. Student-undergrad faculty ratio is 22:1. 107 applied, 62% were admitted. 54% 25 or older. Calendar: semesters.
Entrance Requirements: Required: high school transcript, interview, TABE.

■ **COLLEGE OF BUSINESS AND TECHNOLOGY-CUTLER BAY CAMPUS**
19151 S Dixie Hwy.
Cutler Bay, FL 33157
Tel: (305)273-4499
Web Site: www.cbt.edu
Description: Proprietary, 2-year, coed. Administratively affiliated with College of Business and Technology-Miami. Awards certificates, diplomas, and transfer associate degrees. Founded 2009. Setting: urban campus with easy access to Miami. Total enrollment: 137. Faculty: 23 (5 full-time, 18 part-time). Student-undergrad faculty ratio is 13:1. Full-time: 137 students, 38% women, 62% men. 79% Hispanic/Latino; 14% Black or African American, non-

Hispanic/Latino; 3% Asian, non-Hispanic/Latino. 73% 25 or older. Core. Calendar: semesters. Academic remediation for entering students, services for LD students, independent study, adult/continuing education programs, co-op programs.

Entrance Requirements: Open admission. Required: high school transcript, interview. Entrance: minimally difficult. Transfer credits accepted: Yes.

Costs Per Year: Application fee: $25. Tuition: $11,952 full-time. Mandatory fees: $1500 full-time.

Collegiate Environment: Orientation program. Campus security: security guard patrol, local police department patrol. CBT College-Cutler Bay Library. Books: 2,140 (physical); Serial titles: 20 (physical); Databases: 50. Operations spending for the previous fiscal year: $36,162. 50 computers available on campus for general student use. A campuswide network can be accessed from off-campus. Staffed computer lab on campus provides training in use of computers and the Internet.

■ **COLLEGE OF BUSINESS AND TECHNOLOGY-FLAGLER CAMPUS**
8230 W Flagler St.
Miami, FL 33144
Tel: (305)273-4499
Web Site: www.cbt.edu

Description: Proprietary, 2-year, coed. Administratively affiliated with College of Business and Technology-Miami. Awards certificates, diplomas, and transfer associate degrees. Founded 1988. Setting: urban campus. Total enrollment: 256. Faculty: 33 (6 full-time, 27 part-time). Student-undergrad faculty ratio is 17:1. Full-time: 256 students, 1% women, 99% men. 99% Hispanic/Latino; 0.4% Black or African American, non-Hispanic/Latino. 83% 25 or older. Core. Calendar: semesters. Academic remediation for entering students, ESL program, services for LD students, independent study, adult/continuing education programs, co-op programs.

Entrance Requirements: Open admission. Required: high school transcript, interview. Entrance: minimally difficult. Transfer credits accepted: Yes.

Costs Per Year: Application fee: $25. Tuition: $11,952 full-time. Mandatory fees: $1500 full-time.

Collegiate Environment: Orientation program. Campus security: security guard patrol, local police department patrol. CBT College-Flagler Library. Books: 1,516 (physical); Serial titles: 6 (physical); Databases: 50. Operations spending for the previous fiscal year: $40,545. 50 computers available on campus for general student use. A campuswide network can be accessed from off-campus. Staffed computer lab on campus provides training in use of computers and the Internet.

■ **COLLEGE OF BUSINESS AND TECHNOLOGY-HIALEAH CAMPUS**
935 W 49 St.
Hialeah, FL 33012
Tel: (305)273-4499
Web Site: www.cbt.edu

Description: Proprietary, 2-year, coed. Administratively affiliated with College of Business - Miami. Awards certificates, diplomas, and transfer associate degrees. Founded 1988. Setting: urban campus with easy access to Miami. Total enrollment: 200. Faculty: 32 (7 full-time, 25 part-time). Student-undergrad faculty ratio is 14:1. Full-time: 200 students, 3% women, 97% men. 100% Hispanic/Latino; 0.5% Black or African American, non-Hispanic/Latino. 84% 25 or older. Core. Calendar: semesters. Academic remediation for entering students, ESL program, services for LD students, independent study, adult/continuing education programs, co-op programs.

Entrance Requirements: Open admission. Required: high school transcript, interview. Entrance: minimally difficult. Transfer credits accepted: Yes.

Costs Per Year: Application fee: $25. Tuition: $11,952 full-time. Mandatory fees: $1500 full-time.

Collegiate Environment: Orientation program. Campus security: local police department patrols. CBT College-Hialeah Library. Books: 897 (physical); Serial titles: 7 (physical); Databases: 50. Operations spending for the previous fiscal year: $32,386. 50 computers available on campus for general student use. A campuswide network can be accessed from off-campus. Staffed computer lab on campus provides training in use of computers and the Internet.

■ **COLLEGE OF BUSINESS AND TECHNOLOGY-MAIN CAMPUS**
8700 W Flagler St., Ste. 420
Miami, FL 33174
Tel: (305)273-4499
Fax: (305)273-5216
Web Site: www.cbt.edu

Description: Proprietary, primarily 2-year, coed. Administratively affiliated with College of Business and Technology. Awards certificates, diplomas, transfer associate, and bachelor's degrees. Founded 1988. Setting: urban campus. Total enrollment: 10. Faculty: 1 (all full-time). Student-undergrad faculty ratio is 10:1. Full-time: 10 students, 80% women, 20% men. 100% Hispanic/Latino. 70% 25 or older. Academic area with the most degrees conferred: business/marketing. Core. Calendar: semesters. Academic remediation for entering students, ESL program, independent study, adult/continuing education programs, co-op programs.

Entrance Requirements: Open admission. Required: high school transcript, interview. Entrance: minimally difficult. Transfer credits accepted: Yes.

Costs Per Year: Application fee: $25. Tuition: $11,952 full-time. Mandatory fees: $1500 full-time.

Collegiate Environment: Orientation program. Campus security: security guard posted at main entrance, local police department. CBT College-Miami Branch Library (Use Flagler). Books: 590 (physical); Serial titles: 8 (physical); Databases: 50. Operations spending for the previous fiscal year: $5500. 15 computers available on campus for general student use. A campuswide network can be accessed from off-campus. Staffed computer lab on campus provides training in use of computers and the Internet.

■ **COLLEGE OF BUSINESS AND TECHNOLOGY-MIAMI GARDENS**
5190 NW 167 St.
Miami Gardens, FL 33014
Tel: (305)273-4499
Web Site: www.cbt.edu

Description: Proprietary, primarily 2-year, coed. Administratively affiliated with College of Business and Technology-Miami. Awards certificates, diplomas, transfer associate, and bachelor's degrees. Founded 2012. Setting: urban campus with easy access to Miami. Total enrollment: 91. Faculty: 15 (3 full-time, 12 part-time). Student-undergrad faculty ratio is 15:1. Full-time: 91 students, 33% women, 67% men. 81% Hispanic/Latino; 18% Black or African American, non-Hispanic/Latino. 81% 25 or older. Academic area with the most degrees conferred: business/marketing. Core. Calendar: semesters. Academic remediation for entering students, services for LD students, independent study, adult/continuing education programs, co-op programs.

Entrance Requirements: Open admission. Required: high school transcript, interview. Entrance: minimally difficult. Transfer credits accepted: Yes.

Costs Per Year: Application fee: $25. Tuition: $11,952 full-time. Mandatory fees: $1500 full-time.

Collegiate Environment: Orientation program. Campus security: local police department. CBT College-Miami Gardens Library. Books: 1,085 (physical); Serial titles: 18 (physical); Databases: 50. Operations spending for the previous fiscal year: $42,725. 50 computers available on campus for general student use. A campuswide network can be accessed from off-campus. Staffed computer lab on campus provides training in use of computers and the Internet.

■ **COLLEGE OF CENTRAL FLORIDA**
3001 SW College Rd.
Ocala, FL 34474
Tel: (352)854-2322
Fax: (352)237-3747
E-mail: austina@cf.edu
Web Site: www.cf.edu

Description: State and locally supported, primarily 2-year, coed. Part of Florida College System. Awards certificates, diplomas, transfer associate, terminal associate, and bachelor's degrees. Founded 1957. Setting: 139-acre small town campus. Endowment: $65.4 million. Total enrollment: 6,820. 4,090 applied, 39% were admitted. Full-time: 3,016 students, 59% women, 41% men. Part-time: 3,804 students, 66% women, 34% men. 3% from out-of-state. 0.4% American Indian or Alaska Native, non-Hispanic/Latino; 15% Hispanic/Latino; 14% Black or African American, non-Hispanic/Latino; 2% Asian, non-Hispanic/Latino; 0.5% Native Hawaiian or other Pacific Islander, non-Hispanic/Latino; 2% international. 20% 25 or older, 6% transferred in. Academic areas with the most degrees conferred: business/marketing; education. Core. Calendar: semesters. Academic remediation for entering students, ESL program, services for LD students, advanced placement, freshman honors college, honors program, independent study, distance learning, summer session for credit, part-time degree program, adult/continuing education programs, co-op programs and internships.

Entrance Requirements: Open admission. Options: electronic application, early admission. Required: high school transcript. Entrance: noncompetitive. Application deadline: rolling. Notification: continuous. Transfer credits accepted: Yes.

Costs Per Year: Application fee: $30. Area resident tuition: $107.10 per credit hour part-time. State resident tuition: $107.10 per credit part-time. Nonresident tuition: $421.88 per credit hour part-time.

Collegiate Environment: Orientation program. Drama-theater group, choral group, student-run newspaper. Social organizations: 45 open to all. Most popular organizations: Inspirational Choir, Model United Nations, Performing Arts, Phi Theta Kappa (PTK), Student Nurses Association. Major annual events: Welcome Back, Club Rush, International Food Festival. Student services: personal-psychological counseling. Campus security: 24-hour emergency response devices and patrols, student patrols, late night transport-escort service. College housing not available. Clifford B. Stearns Learning Resources Center. Books: 75,935 (physical), 43,910 (digital/electronic); Databases: 152. Students can reserve study rooms. Operations spending for the previous fiscal year: $706,783. 2,500 computers available on campus for general student use. A campuswide network can be accessed. Students can access the following: online class registration. Staffed computer lab on campus provides training in use of computers, software, and the Internet.

Community Environment: Ocala, the county seat, is the largest city in Marion County, and the hub of local economic and cultural activity. Service and light manufacturing industries provide the majority of employment opportunities, although agriculture is also important to the area. The 450 horse farms in the Ocala area rival Kentucky as the home of the best American thoroughbreds. Ocala boasts a mild climate, beautiful countryside, and is in close proximity to major tourist and recreational facilities. Numerous lakes provide fishing and other water sports. Ocala has 16 parks and playgrounds, two municipal swimming pools, and an 18-hole public golf course. The Sunshine Christmas Parade is an annual event.

■ **CONCORDE CAREER INSTITUTE (JACKSONVILLE)**
7259 Salisbury Rd.
Jacksonville, FL 32256
Tel: (904)725-0525
Fax: (904)721-9944
Web Site: www.concorde.edu
Description: Proprietary, 2-year, coed. Awards certificates and terminal associate degrees. Founded 1968.

■ **CONCORDE CAREER INSTITUTE (MIRAMAR)**
10933 Marks Way
Miramar, FL 33025
Tel: (954)731-8880
Web Site: www.concorde.edu
Description: Proprietary, 2-year, coed. Awards certificates and terminal associate degrees.

■ **CONCORDE CAREER INSTITUTE (ORLANDO)**
3444 McCrory Pl.
Orlando, FL 32803
Tel: (407)812-3060
Web Site: www.concorde.edu
Description: Proprietary, 2-year, coed. Awards certificates and terminal associate degrees.

■ **CONCORDE CAREER INSTITUTE (TAMPA)**
4202 W Spruce St.
Tampa, FL 33607
Tel: (813)874-0094
Fax: (813)872-6884
Web Site: www.concorde.edu
Description: Proprietary, 2-year, coed. Awards certificates and terminal associate degrees. Founded 1978.

■ **DAYTONA COLLEGE**
469 S Nova Rd.
Ormond Beach, FL 32174-8445
Tel: (386)267-0565
Web Site: www.daytonacollege.edu
Description: Proprietary, 2-year, coed. Awards certificates, diplomas, transfer associate, and terminal associate degrees.

■ **DAYTONA STATE COLLEGE**
1200 W International Speedway Blvd.
Daytona Beach, FL 32114
Tel: (386)506-3000
E-mail: karen.sanders@daytonastate.edu
Web Site: www.daytonastate.edu
Description: State-supported, primarily 2-year, coed. Part of Florida College System. Awards certificates, diplomas, transfer associate, and bachelor's degrees. Founded 1957. Setting: 100-acre suburban campus with easy access to Orlando. Endowment: $13.4 million. Educational spending for the previous fiscal year: $3612 per student. Total enrollment: 13,737. Faculty: 913 (266 full-time, 647 part-time). Student-undergrad faculty ratio is 16:1. Full-time: 7,848 students, 58% women, 42% men. Part-time: 11,682 students, 65% women, 35% men. Students come from 26 other countries, 2% from out-of-state. 0.2% American Indian or Alaska Native, non-Hispanic/Latino; 17% Hispanic/Latino; 13% Black or African American, non-Hispanic/Latino; 2% Asian, non-Hispanic/Latino; 0.1% Native Hawaiian or other Pacific Islander, non-Hispanic/Latino; 0.2% international. 40% 25 or older. Academic areas with the most degrees conferred: business/marketing; health professions and related sciences; education. Core. Calendar: semesters. Academic remediation for entering students, ESL program, services for LD students, advanced placement, freshman honors college, honors program, independent study, distance learning, summer session for credit, part-time degree program, external degree program, adult/continuing education programs, co-op programs and internships. Off campus study. Study abroad program. ROTC: Army (c), Air Force (c).

Entrance Requirements: Open admission Open admission to majority except nursing, allied health, public services programs, limited access and bachelor's programs. Options: electronic application, early admission, deferred admission, international baccalaureate accepted. Required: high school transcript. Entrance: noncompetitive. Application deadline: rolling. Notification: continuous. Transfer credits accepted: Yes.

Costs Per Year: State resident tuition: $3,071 full-time, $102.38 per credit hour part-time. Nonresident tuition: $11,960 full-time, $398.65 per credit hour part-time. Mandatory fees: $33 full-time, $1.10 per credit hour part-time. Full-time tuition and fees vary according to course level and course load. Part-time tuition and fees vary according to course level and course load.

Collegiate Environment: Orientation program. Drama-theater group, choral group, student-run newspaper. Social organizations: 48 open to all; national fraternities, national sororities; 6% of eligible men and 8% of eligible women are members. Most popular organizations: Phi Theta Kappa International Honors Society, Student Government Association, Student Respiratory Therapy Club, Business Club, Student Paralegal Club. Major annual events: International Cultural Festival, Outstanding Student Awards Convocation, Welcome Back Student Days. Student services: personal-psychological counseling, women's center. Campus security: 24-hour emergency response devices and patrols, late night transport-escort service, emergency alert system capable of delivering text messages, voice calls, and email messages to college email accounts. College housing not available. Mary Karl Memorial Learning Resources Center plus 1 other. Books: 36,000 (physical), 175,000 (digital/electronic); Serial titles: 164 (physical); Databases: 100. Weekly public service hours: 68; students can reserve study rooms. Operations spending for the previous fiscal year: $985,801. 3,200 computers available on campus for general student use. A campuswide network can be accessed. Students can access the following: online class registration. Staffed computer lab on campus provides training in use of computers and software.
Community Environment: See Bethune-Cookman College.

■ **DEVRY UNIVERSITY-JACKSONVILLE CAMPUS**
5200 Belfort Rd., Ste. 175
Jacksonville, FL 32256
Tel: (904)367-4942; Free: 866-338-7934
Web Site: www.devry.edu
Description: Proprietary, comprehensive, coed. Awards associate, bachelor's, and master's degrees.
Entrance Requirements: Application deadline: rolling. Notification: continuous.

■ **DEVRY UNIVERSITY-MIRAMAR CAMPUS**
2300 SW 145th Ave.
Miramar, FL 33027
Tel: (954)499-9775; Free: 866-338-7934
Web Site: www.devry.edu
Description: Proprietary, comprehensive, coed. Part of DeVry University.

Awards associate, bachelor's, and master's degrees. Founded 2002. Total enrollment: 406. Faculty: 33 (3 full-time, 30 part-time). Student-undergrad faculty ratio is 18:1. Full-time: 103 students, 44% women, 56% men. Part-time: 143 students, 48% women, 52% men. 7% from out-of-state. 56% Hispanic/Latino; 23% Black or African American, non-Hispanic/Latino; 0.8% Asian, non-Hispanic/Latino; 3% international. 87% 25 or older, 20% transferred in. Calendar: semesters. Part-time degree program.

Entrance Requirements: Option: deferred admission. Required: high school transcript, interview. Entrance: minimally difficult. Application deadline: rolling. Notification: continuous.

■ DEVRY UNIVERSITY-ORLANDO CAMPUS

7352 Greenbriar Pky.
Orlando, FL 32819
Tel: (407)345-2800; Free: 866-338-7934
Web Site: www.devry.edu

Description: Proprietary, comprehensive, coed. Part of DeVry University. Awards associate, bachelor's, and master's degrees. Founded 2000. Setting: urban campus. Total enrollment: 764. Faculty: 29 (6 full-time, 23 part-time). Student-undergrad faculty ratio is 31:1. Full-time: 213 students, 44% women, 56% men. Part-time: 321 students, 45% women, 55% men. 7% from out-of-state. 26% Hispanic/Latino; 22% Black or African American, non-Hispanic/Latino; 2% Asian, non-Hispanic/Latino; 0.4% Native Hawaiian or other Pacific Islander, non-Hispanic/Latino; 2% international. 79% 25 or older, 23% transferred in. Calendar: semesters. Part-time degree program, adult/continuing education programs.

Entrance Requirements: Option: deferred admission. Required: high school transcript, interview. Entrance: minimally difficult. Application deadline: rolling. Notification: continuous.

Collegiate Environment: Orientation program. Learning Resource Center.

■ EASTERN FLORIDA STATE COLLEGE

1519 Clearlake Rd.
Cocoa, FL 32922-6597
Tel: (321)632-1111
Fax: (321)633-4565
E-mail: cocoaadmissions@brevardcc.edu
Web Site: www.easternflorida.edu

Description: State-supported, primarily 2-year, coed. Part of Florida Community College System. Awards certificates, transfer associate, terminal associate, and bachelor's degrees. Founded 1960. Setting: 100-acre suburban campus with easy access to Orlando. Total enrollment: 16,711. Faculty: 1,008 (239 full-time, 769 part-time). Student-undergrad faculty ratio is 23:1. 6,438 applied, 100% were admitted. Full-time: 5,929 students, 52% women, 48% men. Part-time: 10,782 students, 61% women, 39% men. Students come from 67 other countries. 0.6% American Indian or Alaska Native, non-Hispanic/Latino; 10% Hispanic/Latino; 11% Black or African American, non-Hispanic/Latino; 2% Asian, non-Hispanic/Latino; 0.3% Native Hawaiian or other Pacific Islander, non-Hispanic/Latino; 0.7% international. 33% 25 or older. Core. Calendar: semesters. Academic remediation for entering students, ESL program, services for LD students, advanced placement, accelerated degree program, honors program, independent study, distance learning, double major, summer session for credit, part-time degree program, external degree program, adult/continuing education programs, co-op programs and internships. Study abroad program. ROTC: Army, Air Force.

Entrance Requirements: Open admission. Options: electronic application, early admission, international baccalaureate accepted. Required: high school transcript. Entrance: noncompetitive. Application deadline: rolling. Notification: continuous.

Collegiate Environment: Orientation program. Drama-theater group, choral group, student-run newspaper. Most popular organizations: Phi Theta Kappa, The Green Team, African-American Student Union, Student Government Association, Cosmetology in Action. Major annual events: Spring Festival, Black History month, Student Welcome Back Days. Student services: women's center. Campus security: 24-hour emergency response devices and patrols. UCF Library. Operations spending for the previous fiscal year: $1.8 million. 2,051 computers available on campus for general student use. A campuswide network can be accessed from off-campus. Students can access the following: online class registration. Staffed computer lab on campus.

Community Environment: Cocoa, a suburban area with a subtropical climate, is the leading shipping point for the famous Indian River citrus fruits, and a resort town. Airline and bus service provide transportation for the area.

Community facilities include four hospitals, two clinics and many churches. Recreational activities are water sports, golf, bowling and fishing. Part-time employment is limited.

■ ECKERD COLLEGE

4200 54th Ave. S
Saint Petersburg, FL 33711
Tel: (727)867-1166; Free: 800-456-9009
Fax: (727)866-2304
E-mail: admissions@eckerd.edu
Web Site: www.eckerd.edu

Description: Independent Presbyterian, 4-year, coed. Awards bachelor's degrees. Founded 1958. Setting: 188-acre suburban campus with easy access to Tampa. Endowment: $58.3 million. Total enrollment: 1,999. Faculty: 180 (151 full-time, 29 part-time). Student-undergrad faculty ratio is 12:1. 4,830 applied, 68% were admitted. Full-time: 1,940 students, 67% women, 33% men. Part-time: 60 students, 60% women, 40% men. Students come from 46 states and territories, 42 other countries, 79% from out-of-state. 0.4% American Indian or Alaska Native, non-Hispanic/Latino; 8% Hispanic/Latino; 3% Black or African American, non-Hispanic/Latino; 3% Asian, non-Hispanic/Latino; 0.2% Native Hawaiian or other Pacific Islander, non-Hispanic/Latino; 4% international. 88% live on campus, 2% transferred in. Retention: 81% of full-time freshmen returned the following year. Academic areas with the most degrees conferred: biological/life sciences; natural resources/environmental science; psychology. Core. Calendar: 4-1-4. Services for LD students, advanced placement, accelerated degree program, self-designed majors, honors program, independent study, double major, summer session for credit, part-time degree program, external degree program, adult/continuing education programs, internships. Off campus study. Study abroad program. ROTC: Army (c), Air Force (c).

Entrance Requirements: Options: electronic application, early action, deferred admission, international baccalaureate accepted. Required: essay, high school transcript, SAT or ACT. Recommended: interview, SAT Subject Tests. Entrance: moderately difficult. Application deadlines: rolling, 11/15 for early action. Notification: continuous. SAT Reasoning Test deadline: 3/15. SAT Subject Test deadline: 3/15. Transfer credits accepted: Yes. Applicants placed on waiting list: 79. Wait-listed applicants offered admission: 0. Early action applicants: 2,387. Early action applicants admitted: 1,911.

Costs Per Year: Application fee: $40. Comprehensive fee: $55,206 includes full-time tuition ($42,428), mandatory fees ($616), and college room and board ($12,162). College room only: $6362. Room and board charges vary according to board plan and housing facility.

Collegiate Environment: Orientation program. Drama-theater group, choral group, student-run newspaper, radio station. Social organizations: 105 open to all. Most popular organizations: Marine Science Club, Water Search and Rescue Team, The Current (student newspaper), A cappella Vocal Group, Organization of Students. Major annual events: Festival of Hope, Kappa Carnival, Springtopia. Student services: health clinic, personal-psychological counseling, women's center. Campus security: 24-hour emergency response devices and patrols, student patrols, late night transport-escort service, controlled dormitory access. 1,786 college housing spaces available; 1,733 were occupied in 2018-19. Freshmen guaranteed college housing. On-campus residence required in freshman year. Options: coed, women-only housing available. Peter Armacost Library. Books: 156,516 (physical), 168,633 (digital/electronic); Serial titles: 773 (physical), 182,151 (digital/electronic); Databases: 201. 300 computers available on campus for general student use. A campuswide network can be accessed from student residence rooms and from off campus. Students can access the following: online class registration, free computer repair shop. Staffed computer lab on campus (open 24 hours a day) provides training in use of computers, software, and the Internet.

Community Environment: St. Petersburg, known as the"Sunshine City," has a wonderful semitropical climate. The city is the state's fourth largest, and is the most important tourist center on the west coast of Florida. The city has 33 miles of shoreline on the Gulf of Mexico and several fresh water lakes: an excellent location for all water sports. Other sports are baseball, basketball, soccer, cross country, volleyball, softball, golf, and tennis. This is the spring training area for several major league baseball teams. The Tampa Bay area also is home to football's Buccaneers, baseball's Devil Rays, hockey's Lightning, and the international headquarters of the Women's Tennis Association. Numerous points of interest include the Florida International Museum, Fort DeSoto Park, Sunshine Skyway, the St. Petersburg Museum of Fine Arts, the Dali Museum, and Tropicana Field.

■ **EDWARD WATERS COLLEGE**
1658 Kings Rd.
Jacksonville, FL 32209-6199
Tel: (904)470-8000; Free: 888-898-3191
Fax: (904)470-8039
Web Site: www.ewc.edu
Description: Independent African Methodist Episcopal, 4-year, coed. Awards bachelor's degrees. Founded 1866. Setting: 50-acre urban campus. Total enrollment: 751. Faculty: 81 (36 full-time, 45 part-time). Student-undergrad faculty ratio is 9:1. 1,611 applied, 23% were admitted. Students come from 21 states and territories, 4 other countries, 19% from out-of-state. 0.3% American Indian or Alaska Native, non-Hispanic/Latino; 1% Hispanic/Latino; 94% Black or African American, non-Hispanic/Latino; 0.1% Native Hawaiian or other Pacific Islander, non-Hispanic/Latino. Retention: 53% of full-time freshmen returned the following year. Academic areas with the most degrees conferred: business/marketing; homeland security, law enforcement, firefighting, and protective services; biological/life sciences. Core. Calendar: semesters. Academic remediation for entering students, services for LD students, self-designed majors, honors program, summer session for credit, part-time degree program, adult/continuing education programs, co-op programs and internships. Off campus study at University of North Florida. ROTC: Army (c).
Entrance Requirements: Open admission. Option: electronic application. Required: high school transcript, 2 recommendations, medical forms, SAT or ACT. Entrance: noncompetitive. Application deadline: rolling. Notification: continuous. Transfer credits accepted: Yes.
Collegiate Environment: Drama-theater group, choral group, marching band. Social organizations: national fraternities, national sororities. Student services: health clinic, personal-psychological counseling. Campus security: 24-hour emergency response devices and patrols, student patrols, late night transport-escort service, controlled dormitory access. Centennial Library. 200 computers available on campus for general student use. A campuswide network can be accessed. Students can access the following: online class registration. Staffed computer lab on campus (open 24 hours a day) provides training in use of computers, software, and the Internet.
Community Environment: See Jacksonville University.

■ **EMBRY-RIDDLE AERONAUTICAL UNIVERSITY-DAYTONA**
600 S Clyde Morris Blvd.
Daytona Beach, FL 32114-3900
Tel: (386)226-6000; Free: 800-862-2416
Fax: (386)226-7070
Web Site: www.daytonabeach.erau.edu
Description: Independent, university, coed. Awards associate, bachelor's, master's, and doctoral degrees. Founded 1926. Setting: 289-acre suburban campus with easy access to Orlando. Endowment: $90.4 million. Research spending for the previous fiscal year: $16.4 million. Educational spending for the previous fiscal year: $15,184 per student. Total enrollment: 6,610. 6,017 applied, 65% were admitted. 20% from top 10% of their high school class, 49% from top quarter, 82% from top half. Full-time: 5,601 students, 23% women, 77% men. Part-time: 383 students, 23% women, 77% men. Students come from 52 states and territories, 97 other countries, 63% from out-of-state. 0.2% American Indian or Alaska Native, non-Hispanic/Latino; 14% Hispanic/Latino; 5% Black or African American, non-Hispanic/Latino; 5% Asian, non-Hispanic/Latino; 0.2% Native Hawaiian or other Pacific Islander, non-Hispanic/Latino; 13% international. 9% 25 or older, 39% live on campus, 3% transferred in. Retention: 82% of full-time freshmen returned the following year. Academic areas with the most degrees conferred: transportation and materials moving; engineering; business/marketing. Core. Calendar: semesters. Academic remediation for entering students, ESL program, services for LD students, advanced placement, accelerated degree program, honors program, double major, summer session for credit, part-time degree program, co-op programs and internships, graduate courses open to undergrads. Study abroad program. ROTC: Army, Naval, Air Force.
Entrance Requirements: Options: electronic application, deferred admission, international baccalaureate accepted. Required: high school transcript, minimum 2 high school GPA. Recommended: essay, 2 recommendations, SAT or ACT. Required for some: medical examination for flight students. Entrance: moderately difficult. Application deadline: rolling. Notification: continuous. Transfer credits accepted: Yes.
Costs Per Year: Application fee: $50. One-time mandatory fee: $150. Comprehensive fee: $48,614 includes full-time tuition ($35,424), mandatory fees ($1444), and college room and board ($11,746). College room only: $7080. Part-time tuition: $1476 per credit hour. Part-time mandatory fees: $722 per term.

Collegiate Environment: Orientation program. Drama-theater group, choral group, student-run newspaper, radio station. Social organizations: 150 open to all; national fraternities, national sororities. Most popular organizations: Eagle Wing, Future Professional Pilots Association, African Student Association, Caribbean Student Association, Sigma Gamma Tau. Major annual events: Homecoming, spring concert, hypnotist performance. Student services: health clinic, personal-psychological counseling, women's center. Campus security: 24-hour emergency response devices and patrols, student patrols, late night transport-escort service, controlled dormitory access. 2,290 undergraduates lived in college housing during 2018-19. Freshmen guaranteed college housing. On-campus residence required in freshman year. Option: coed housing available. Jack R. Hunt Memorial Library. Books: 53,116 (physical), 122,788 (digital/electronic); Serial titles: 456 (physical), 78,964 (digital/electronic); Databases: 172. Students can reserve study rooms. Operations spending for the previous fiscal year: $4.6 million. 355 computers available on campus for general student use. A campuswide network can be accessed from student residence rooms and from off campus. Students can access the following: online class registration. Staffed computer lab on campus (open 24 hours a day) provides training in use of software.
Community Environment: Daytona Beach has a population of approximately 500,000 in the immediate vicinity, and the campus itself has approximately 4,500 students. Boasting one of the finest recreational beaches in the world, it is also home to the Daytona International Speedway. Other major attractions include Walt Disney World and Sea World near Orlando (approximately 80 miles away). The area provides ample housing and excellent opportunities for part-time employment for ERAU students.

■ **EMBRY-RIDDLE AERONAUTICAL UNIVERSITY-WORLDWIDE**
600 S Clyde Morris Blvd.
Daytona Beach, FL 32114-3900
Tel: (386)226-6910; Free: 800-522-6787
Fax: (386)226-6984
Web Site: www.worldwide.erau.edu
Description: Independent, comprehensive, coed. Awards associate, bachelor's, master's, and doctoral degrees (programs offered at 100 military bases worldwide). Founded 1970. System endowment: $3.6 million. Research spending for the previous fiscal year: $364,000. Educational spending for the previous fiscal year: $5526 per student. Total enrollment: 15,549. 1,264 applied, 59% were admitted. Full-time: 2,872 students, 15% women, 85% men. Part-time: 8,799 students, 13% women, 87% men. 0.5% American Indian or Alaska Native, non-Hispanic/Latino; 15% Hispanic/Latino; 8% Black or African American, non-Hispanic/Latino; 5% Asian, non-Hispanic/Latino; 0.9% Native Hawaiian or other Pacific Islander, non-Hispanic/Latino; 3% international. 12% transferred in. Academic areas with the most degrees conferred: transportation and materials moving; business/marketing; mechanic and repair technologies. Core. Calendar: 5 9-week terms with monthly starts. Services for LD students, advanced placement, accelerated degree program, independent study, distance learning, double major, summer session for credit, part-time degree program, external degree program, co-op programs, graduate courses open to undergrads. Off campus study at Servicemembers Opportunity Colleges. Study abroad program. ROTC: Army, Naval, Air Force.
Entrance Requirements: Options: electronic application, deferred admission, international baccalaureate accepted. Required: minimum 2 high school GPA. Required for some: high school transcript, 2 recommendations, SAT or ACT. Entrance: minimally difficult. Application deadline: rolling. Notification: continuous. Transfer credits accepted: Yes.
Costs Per Year: Application fee: $50. Tuition: $413 per credit hour part-time.
Collegiate Environment: Orientation program. Jack R. Hunt Memorial Library located in Daytona Beach. Books: 53,116 (physical), 122,788 (digital/electronic); Serial titles: 456 (physical), 78,964 (digital/electronic); Databases: 172. Operations spending for the previous fiscal year: $1.5 million.

■ **EVERGLADES UNIVERSITY (BOCA RATON)**
5002 T-Rex Ave., Ste. 100
Boca Raton, FL 33431
Tel: (561)912-1211; Free: 888-772-6077
Fax: (561)912-1191
Web Site: www.evergladesuniversity.edu
Description: Independent, comprehensive, coed. Awards bachelor's and master's degrees. Founded 1989. Setting: suburban campus with easy access to Fort Lauderdale. Educational spending for the previous fiscal year:

$3726 per student. Total enrollment: 1,451. Faculty: 229 (91 full-time, 138 part-time). Student-undergrad faculty ratio is 10:1. 354 applied, 84% were admitted. Full-time: 1,284 students, 53% women, 47% men. Part-time: 29 students, 45% women, 55% men. Students come from 20 states and territories, 1 other country, 37% from out-of-state. 0.7% American Indian or Alaska Native, non-Hispanic/Latino; 15% Hispanic/Latino; 17% Black or African American, non-Hispanic/Latino; 2% Asian, non-Hispanic/Latino; 0.3% Native Hawaiian or other Pacific Islander, non-Hispanic/Latino; 0.1% international. 81% 25 or older, 1% transferred in. Retention: 43% of full-time freshmen returned the following year. Academic areas with the most degrees conferred: health professions and related sciences; business/marketing; transportation and materials moving. Core. Calendar: semesters. Academic remediation for entering students, services for LD students, advanced placement, distance learning, summer session for credit, co-op programs. Off campus study.

Entrance Requirements: Open admission. Option: electronic application. Required: high school transcript, University entrance examination (minimum score of 15) or ACT/SAT scores (minimum composite score of 17 ACT or a combined score of 1200 on SAT). Required for some: SAT or ACT. Entrance: noncompetitive. Application deadline: rolling. Notification: continuous. Transfer credits accepted: Yes.

Collegiate Environment: Orientation program. Campus security: 24-hour emergency response devices and patrols, late night transport-escort service. Everglades University Library. Books: 19,974 (physical), 122,000 (digital/electronic); Serial titles: 48 (physical), 5,180 (digital/electronic); Databases: 55. Weekly public service hours: 6. Operations spending for the previous fiscal year: $205,026. 19 computers available on campus for general student use. Staffed computer lab on campus provides training in use of computers, software, and the Internet.

■ EVERGLADES UNIVERSITY (MAITLAND)

850 Trafalgar Ct., Ste. 100
Maitland, FL 32751
Tel: (407)277-0311; Free: 866-289-1078
Fax: (407)482-9801
Web Site: www.evergladesuniversity.edu

Description: Independent, comprehensive, coed. Awards bachelor's and master's degrees. Setting: suburban campus with easy access to Orlando. Educational spending for the previous fiscal year: $3726 per student. Total enrollment: 1,451. Faculty: 229 (91 full-time, 138 part-time). Student-undergrad faculty ratio is 10:1. 354 applied, 84% were admitted. Full-time: 1,284 students, 53% women, 47% men. Part-time: 29 students, 45% women, 55% men. Students come from 20 states and territories, 1 other country, 37% from out-of-state. 0.7% American Indian or Alaska Native, non-Hispanic/Latino; 15% Hispanic/Latino; 17% Black or African American, non-Hispanic/Latino; 2% Asian, non-Hispanic/Latino; 0.3% Native Hawaiian or other Pacific Islander, non-Hispanic/Latino; 0.1% international. 81% 25 or older, 1% transferred in. Retention: 43% of full-time freshmen returned the following year. Academic areas with the most degrees conferred: health professions and related sciences; business/marketing; transportation and materials moving. Core. Calendar: semesters. Academic remediation for entering students, services for LD students, advanced placement, distance learning, summer session for credit, co-op programs. Off campus study.

Entrance Requirements: Open admission. Option: electronic application. Required: high school transcript, University entrance examination (minimum score of 15) or ACT/SAT scores (minimum composite score of 17 ACT or a combined score of 1200 on SAT). Entrance: noncompetitive. Application deadline: rolling. Notification: continuous. Transfer credits accepted: Yes.

Collegiate Environment: Orientation program. Campus security: 24-hour emergency response devices and patrols, late night transport-escort service. Everglades University Library. Books: 19,974 (physical), 122,000 (digital/electronic); Serial titles: 48 (physical), 5,180 (digital/electronic); Databases: 55. Weekly public service hours: 6. Operations spending for the previous fiscal year: $205,026. 25 computers available on campus for general student use. Staffed computer lab on campus provides training in use of computers, software, and the Internet.

■ EVERGLADES UNIVERSITY (SARASOTA)

6001 Lake Osprey Dr. No.110
Sarasota, FL 34240
Tel: (561)912-1211; Free: 888-854-8308
Fax: (941)907-6634
Web Site: www.evergladesuniversity.edu

Description: Independent, comprehensive, coed. Awards bachelor's and master's degrees. Founded 2003. Setting: urban campus with easy access to Sarasota. Educational spending for the previous fiscal year: $3726 per student. Total enrollment: 1,451. Faculty: 229 (91 full-time, 138 part-time). Student-undergrad faculty ratio is 10:1. 354 applied, 84% were admitted. Full-time: 1,284 students, 53% women, 47% men. Part-time: 29 students, 45% women, 55% men. Students come from 20 states and territories, 1 other country, 37% from out-of-state. 0.7% American Indian or Alaska Native, non-Hispanic/Latino; 15% Hispanic/Latino; 17% Black or African American, non-Hispanic/Latino; 2% Asian, non-Hispanic/Latino; 0.3% Native Hawaiian or other Pacific Islander, non-Hispanic/Latino; 0.1% international. 81% 25 or older, 1% transferred in. Retention: 43% of full-time freshmen returned the following year. Academic areas with the most degrees conferred: health professions and related sciences; business/marketing; transportation and materials moving. Core. Calendar: semesters. Academic remediation for entering students, services for LD students, advanced placement, distance learning, summer session for credit, co-op programs. Off campus study.

Entrance Requirements: Open admission. Option: electronic application. Required: high school transcript, University entrance examination (minimum score of 15) or ACT/SAT scores (minimum composite score of 17 ACT or a combined score of 1200 on SAT). Entrance: noncompetitive. Application deadline: rolling. Notification: continuous. Transfer credits accepted: Yes.

Collegiate Environment: Orientation program. Campus security: 24-hour emergency response devices and patrols, late night transport-escort service. Everglades University Library. Books: 19,974 (physical), 122,000 (digital/electronic); Serial titles: 48 (physical), 5,180 (digital/electronic); Databases: 55. Weekly public service hours: 6. Operations spending for the previous fiscal year: $205,026. 25 computers available on campus for general student use. Staffed computer lab on campus provides training in use of computers, software, and the Internet.

■ FLAGLER COLLEGE

74 King St.
Saint Augustine, FL 32085-1027
Tel: (904)829-6481; Free: 800-304-4208
Fax: (904)826-0094
E-mail: rbranch@flagler.edu
Web Site: www.flagler.edu

Description: Independent, comprehensive, coed. Awards bachelor's and master's degrees. Founded 1968. Setting: 49-acre small town campus with easy access to Jacksonville. Endowment: $49 million. Educational spending for the previous fiscal year: $6579 per student. Total enrollment: 2,689. Faculty: 249 (121 full-time, 128 part-time). Student-undergrad faculty ratio is 16:1. 4,921 applied, 57% were admitted. Full-time: 1,392 students, 36% women, 64% men. Part-time: 1,284 students, 97% women, 3% men. Students come from 46 states and territories, 51 other countries, 43% from out-of-state. 0.3% American Indian or Alaska Native, non-Hispanic/Latino; 6% Hispanic/Latino; 4% Black or African American, non-Hispanic/Latino; 0.9% Asian, non-Hispanic/Latino; 0.1% Native Hawaiian or other Pacific Islander, non-Hispanic/Latino; 4% international. 6% 25 or older, 44% live on campus, 7% transferred in. Retention: 72% of full-time freshmen returned the following year. Academic areas with the most degrees conferred: business/marketing; visual and performing arts; communication/journalism. Core. Calendar: semesters. Academic remediation for entering students, services for LD students, advanced placement, honors program, independent study, distance learning, double major, summer session for credit, part-time degree program, adult/continuing education programs, co-op programs and internships, graduate courses open to undergrads. Study abroad program.

Entrance Requirements: Options: electronic application, early admission, early decision, deferred admission, international baccalaureate accepted. Required: essay, high school transcript, recommendations, SAT or ACT. Required for some: interview, interview for early admission. Application deadlines: 3/1, 11/1 for early decision. Notification: 3/31, 12/15 for early decision. SAT Reasoning Test deadline: 3/1. Transfer credits accepted: Yes. Applicants placed on waiting list: 0. Wait-listed applicants offered admission: 0. Early decision applicants: 462. Early decision applicants admitted: 281.

Costs Per Year: Application fee: $50. Comprehensive fee: $30,290 includes full-time tuition ($18,850), mandatory fees ($100), and college room and board ($11,340). College room only: $5800. Full-time tuition and fees vary according to location. Room and board charges vary according to board plan and housing facility. Part-time tuition: $645 per credit hour. Part-time tuition varies according to location.

Collegiate Environment: Orientation program. Drama-theater group, choral

group, student-run newspaper, radio station. Social organizations: 45 open to all. Most popular organizations: Student Government Association, Inter-Varsity, International Student Club, Flagler College Volunteers, Phi Alpha Omega (women's service club). Major annual events: Midnight Breakfast, Bachelor Bid, Harry Potter Great Hall Experience. Student services: health clinic, personal-psychological counseling. Campus security: 24-hour emergency response devices and patrols, student patrols, late night transport-escort service, controlled dormitory access, transport/escort service is provided from 6:00 pm until 6:00 am daily. Proctor Library. Books: 102,047 (physical), 212,689 (digital/electronic); Serial titles: 630 (physical), 44,000 (digital/electronic); Databases: 60. Weekly public service hours: 100; students can reserve study rooms. Operations spending for the previous fiscal year: $854,255. 343 computers available on campus for general student use. A campuswide network can be accessed from student residence rooms and from off campus. Students can access the following: online class registration, local and remote printing to campus printers, remote access to intranet files. Staffed computer lab on campus provides training in use of computers, software, and the Internet.

Community Environment: St. Augustine, the nation's oldest city, has a very mild climate; average high temperature is 79.9 degrees and the average low is 58.3 degrees. The city is located approximately 40 miles south of Jacksonville, near the Atlantic coast. St. Augustine is undergoing a restoration program to extend over a twenty-year period that will return the entire area to an authentic likeness of its colonial days. The leading industries are tourist trade, airplane rebuilding, aluminum extrusion, boat-building, food processing, and shrimp fishing. Recreation facilities include championship golf courses, beaches, tennis courts, and the ocean for deep sea fishing. The Matanzas River affords miles of protected waters for boating and fishing. The city has churches of all denominations, numerous hotels and motels, 2 hospitals, and a library. All major civic and fraternal organizations are represented. Sightseeing tours are available by trains and horse-drawn carriages. There are many points of interest, some of which are the Cathedral of St. Augustine, Lightner Museum, Marineland, Alligator Farm, Casa Del Hidalgo, the World Golf Village, Fountain of Youth, Mission of Nombre De Dios, Oldest Schoolhouse, the Zimenes House, Memorial Presbyterian Church, and the Castillo de San Marcos.

■ **FLAGLER COLLEGE-TALLAHASSEE**
444 Appleyard Dr.
Tallahassee, FL 32304
Tel: (850)201-8070
Web Site: www.flagler.edu
Description: Independent, 4-year, coed. Awards bachelor's degrees. Founded 2000.

■ **FLORIDA AGRICULTURAL AND MECHANICAL UNIVERSITY**
Tallahassee, FL 32307-3200
Tel: (850)599-3000; Free: 866-642-1198
Fax: (850)561-2428
E-mail: ugrdadmissions@famu.edu
Web Site: www.famu.edu
Description: State-supported, university, coed. Part of State University System of Florida. Awards associate, bachelor's, master's, and doctoral degrees and post-master's certificates. Founded 1887. Setting: 419-acre urban campus with easy access to Jacksonville. Endowment: $96.4 million. Research spending for the previous fiscal year: $24.5 million. Educational spending for the previous fiscal year: $10,844 per student. Total enrollment: 10,021. Faculty: 682 (539 full-time, 143 part-time). Student-undergrad faculty ratio is 16:1. 8,976 applied, 39% were admitted. 11% from top 10% of their high school class, 25% from top quarter, 73% from top half. Full-time: 6,958 students, 65% women, 35% men. Part-time: 1,179 students, 60% women, 40% men. Students come from 42 states and territories, 43 other countries, 14% from out-of-state. 4% Hispanic/Latino; 85% Black or African American, non-Hispanic/Latino; 0.6% Asian, non-Hispanic/Latino; 0.5% international. 8% 25 or older, 30% live on campus, 6% transferred in. Retention: 81% of full-time freshmen returned the following year. Academic areas with the most degrees conferred: health professions and related sciences; interdisciplinary studies; business/marketing. Core. Calendar: semesters. Academic remediation for entering students, services for LD students, advanced placement, accelerated degree program, honors program, independent study, distance learning, double major, summer session for credit, part-time degree program, adult/continuing education programs, co-op programs and internships, graduate courses open to undergrads. Off campus study at Florida State University. Study abroad program. ROTC: Army, Naval, Air Force (c).

Entrance Requirements: Options: electronic application, early admission, international baccalaureate accepted. Required: essay, high school transcript, minimum 2.5 high school GPA, 3 recommendations, SAT or ACT. Recommended: minimum 3 high school GPA. Required for some: interview, audition for music major applicants. Entrance: moderately difficult. Notification: continuous. Preference given to state residents, extracurricular activities, volunteer work, work experience, and alumni/ae relations. SAT Reasoning Test deadline: 5/15. Transfer credits accepted: Yes.

Costs Per Year: Application fee: $30. State resident tuition: $5645 full-time, $188 per credit hour part-time. Nonresident tuition: $17,585 full-time. Mandatory fees: $140 full-time. College room and board: $10,838. College room only: $6012.

Collegiate Environment: Orientation program. Drama-theater group, choral group, marching band, student-run newspaper, radio station. Social organizations: 126 open to all; national fraternities, national sororities; 2% of eligible men and 3% of eligible women are members. Most popular organizations: National Council of Negro Women, FAMU Chapter, American Society of Mechanical Engineers, Psi Chi International Honor Society, Caribbean Student Association, Academy of Student Pharmacists/Student National Pharmaceutical Association. Major annual events: Homecoming Convocation, Career Expo, Welcome Week. Student services: health clinic, personal-psychological counseling. Campus security: 24-hour emergency response devices and patrols, late night transport-escort service, controlled dormitory access. 2,547 college housing spaces available; 2,494 were occupied in 2018-19. Freshmen given priority for college housing. On-campus residence required in freshman year. Options: coed, men-only, women-only housing available. Samuel H. Coleman Memorial Library plus 4 others. Books: 1.1 million (physical), 468,561 (digital/electronic); Serial titles: 17,167 (physical), 240,002 (digital/electronic); Databases: 314. Weekly public service hours: 135; study areas open 24 hours, 5-7 days a week; students can reserve study rooms. Operations spending for the previous fiscal year: $5.9 million. 4,000 computers available on campus for general student use. A campuswide network can be accessed from student residence rooms and from off campus. Students can access the following: online class registration. Staffed computer lab on campus provides training in use of computers, software, and the Internet.

Community Environment: Tallahassee, a community of varied interests, provides an ideal setting for a thriving comprehensive university. The community abounds in a broad range of programs and activities, including three institutions of higher education; city, county, and state government; civic and community organizations; art galleries; theater and music archives, libraries and museums; state parks and recreational facilities; tree-shaded streets and highways; and a 13,500-seat Civic Center.

■ **FLORIDA ATLANTIC UNIVERSITY**
777 Glades Rd.
Boca Raton, FL 33431-0991
Tel: (561)297-3000
Web Site: www.fau.edu
Description: State-supported, university, coed. Part of State University System of Florida. Awards associate, bachelor's, master's, and doctoral degrees and post-master's certificates. Founded 1961. Setting: 850-acre suburban campus with easy access to Miami, Fort Lauderdale, West Palm Beach. Endowment: $299.3 million. Research spending for the previous fiscal year: $47.9 million. Total enrollment: 29,772. Faculty: 1,473 (906 full-time, 567 part-time). Student-undergrad faculty ratio is 24:1. 17,120 applied, 59% were admitted. 12% from top 10% of their high school class, 41% from top quarter, 81% from top half. Full-time: 16,443 students, 56% women, 44% men. Part-time: 8,126 students, 56% women, 44% men. Students come from 47 states and territories, 119 other countries, 6% from out-of-state. 0.2% American Indian or Alaska Native, non-Hispanic/Latino; 28% Hispanic/Latino; 20% Black or African American, non-Hispanic/Latino; 4% Asian, non-Hispanic/Latino; 0.1% Native Hawaiian or other Pacific Islander, non-Hispanic/Latino; 3% international. 22% 25 or older, 19% live on campus, 9% transferred in. Retention: 82% of full-time freshmen returned the following year. Academic areas with the most degrees conferred: business/marketing; interdisciplinary studies; psychology; health professions and related sciences. Core. Calendar: semesters. ESL program, services for LD students, advanced placement, accelerated degree program, freshman honors college, honors program, independent study, distance learning, double major, summer session for credit, part-time degree program, adult/continuing education programs, co-op programs and internships, graduate courses open to undergrads. Off campus study at other members of the State University System of Florida. Study abroad program. ROTC: Army, Air Force (c).

Entrance Requirements: Options: electronic application, early admission, deferred admission, international baccalaureate accepted. Required: high school transcript, SAT or ACT. Entrance: moderately difficult. Notification: continuous. SAT Reasoning Test deadline: 5/1. Transfer credits accepted: Yes.

Costs Per Year: Application fee: $30. State resident tuition: $6039 full-time, $105.07 per credit hour part-time. Nonresident tuition: $21,595 full-time, $598.93 per credit hour part-time. Mandatory fees: $96.22 part-time. College room and board: $11,950. College room only: $8238.

Collegiate Environment: Orientation program. Drama-theater group, choral group, marching band, student-run newspaper, radio station. Social organizations: 230 open to all; national fraternities, national sororities, local fraternities, local sororities; 4% of eligible men and 6% of eligible women are members. Most popular organizations: American Society of Civil Engineers, Dive Club, Pre-Law Society, Submarine Club, American Criminal Justice Society. Major annual events: Homecoming, Fall Festival, Festival of Nations. Student services: health clinic, personal-psychological counseling, women's center. Campus security: 24-hour emergency response devices and patrols, student patrols, late night transport-escort service, controlled dormitory access. 4,452 college housing spaces available; 4,371 were occupied in 2018-19. Freshmen guaranteed college housing. On-campus residence required in freshman year. Option: coed housing available. S. E. Wimberly Library plus 2 others. Books: 907,932 (physical), 1.3 million (digital/electronic); Serial titles: 31,489 (physical), 194,584 (digital/electronic); Databases: 628. Study areas open 24 hours, 5-7 days a week. 1,350 computers available on campus for general student use. A campus-wide network can be accessed from student residence rooms and from off campus. Students can access the following: online class registration. Staffed computer lab on campus (open 24 hours a day) provides training in use of computers, software, and the Internet.

Community Environment: A resort and suburban area located on Florida's east coast, Boca Raton is 40 miles north of Miami and 25 miles from Ft. Lauderdale and Palm Beach airports. The area enjoys a subtropical climate. Local industry includes large regional centers for Sensormatic, Siemens, Motorola and other high tech multinational corporations. Several shopping centers, a library, many houses of worship, and two hospitals are some of the community facilities. Cultural activities are many. Recreational activities include swimming, tennis, golf, surf casting, and deep-sea fishing. There are three public beaches and numerous superior golf courses nearby. Everglades National Park lies to the west and south.

■ **FLORIDA CAREER COLLEGE (BOYNTON BEACH)**
1749 N Congress Ave.
Boynton Beach, FL 33426
Web Site: www.floridacareercollege.edu
Description: Proprietary, 2-year, coed.

■ **FLORIDA CAREER COLLEGE (HIALEAH)**
3750 W 18th Ave.
Hialeah, FL 33012
Free: 888-852-7272
Web Site: www.floridacareercollege.edu
Description: Proprietary, 2-year, coed.

■ **FLORIDA CAREER COLLEGE (JACKSONVILLE)**
6600 Youngerman Cir.
Jacksonville, FL 32244
Web Site: www.floridacareercollege.edu
Description: Proprietary, 2-year, coed.

■ **FLORIDA CAREER COLLEGE (LAUDERDALE LAKES)**
3383 N State Rd. 7
Lauderdale Lakes, FL 33319
Web Site: www.floridacareercollege.edu
Description: Proprietary, 2-year, coed.

■ **FLORIDA CAREER COLLEGE (MARGATE)**
3271 N State Rd. 7
Margate, FL 33063
Web Site: www.floridacareercollege.edu
Description: Proprietary, 2-year, coed.

■ **FLORIDA CAREER COLLEGE (MIAMI)**
1321 SW 107th Ave.
Ste. 201B

Miami, FL 33174
Tel: (305)553-6065; Free: 888-852-7272
Fax: (305)225-0128
Web Site: www.floridacareercollege.edu
Description: Proprietary, 2-year, coed. Awards certificates, diplomas, and terminal associate degrees. Founded 1982. Setting: urban campus. Total enrollment: 3,952. 45% 25 or older. Core. Calendar: quarters. Academic remediation for entering students, independent study, summer session for credit, part-time degree program.
Entrance Requirements: Open admission. Option: deferred admission. Required: high school transcript, interview. Entrance: noncompetitive. Application deadline: rolling. Notification: continuous.
Collegiate Environment: Orientation program. Campus security: 24-hour emergency response devices. Resource Center plus 1 other.

■ **FLORIDA CAREER COLLEGE (ORLANDO)**
989 N Semoran Blvd.
Orlando, FL 32807
Web Site: www.floridacareercollege.edu
Description: Proprietary, 2-year, coed.

■ **FLORIDA CAREER COLLEGE (PEMBROKE PINES)**
7891 Pines Blvd.
Pembroke Pines, FL 33024
Free: 888-852-7272
Web Site: www.floridacareercollege.edu
Description: Proprietary, 2-year, coed.

■ **FLORIDA CAREER COLLEGE (TAMPA)**
9950 Princess Palm Ave.
Tampa, FL 33619
Web Site: www.floridacareercollege.edu
Description: Proprietary, 2-year, coed.

■ **FLORIDA CAREER COLLEGE (WEST PALM BEACH)**
6058 Okeechobee Blvd.
West Palm Beach, FL 33417
Free: 888-852-7272
Web Site: www.floridacareercollege.edu
Description: Proprietary, 2-year, coed.

■ **FLORIDA COLLEGE**
119 N Glen Arven Ave.
Temple Terrace, FL 33617
Tel: (813)988-5131
Fax: (813)899-6772
E-mail: admissions@floridacollege.edu
Web Site: www.floridacollege.edu
Description: Independent, 4-year, coed. Awards associate and bachelor's degrees. Founded 1944. Setting: 95-acre suburban campus with easy access to Tampa. Endowment: $16.5 million. Research spending for the previous fiscal year: $10,000. Educational spending for the previous fiscal year: $3157 per student. Total enrollment: 508. Faculty: 52 (34 full-time, 18 part-time). Student-undergrad faculty ratio is 13:1. 331 applied, 74% were admitted. Full-time: 494 students, 52% women, 48% men. Part-time: 22 students, 73% women, 27% men. Students come from 34 states and territories, 6 other countries. 0.8% American Indian or Alaska Native, non-Hispanic/Latino; 7% Hispanic/Latino; 7% Black or African American, non-Hispanic/Latino; 1% Asian, non-Hispanic/Latino; 2% international. 81% live on campus. Academic areas with the most degrees conferred: liberal arts/general studies; business/marketing; education. Core. Calendar: semesters. Academic remediation for entering students, advanced placement, independent study, summer session for credit. ROTC: Army (c), Air Force (c).
Entrance Requirements: Options: electronic application, international baccalaureate accepted. Required: high school transcript, minimum 2 high school GPA, 2 recommendations, SAT or ACT. Required for some: essay for international students. Entrance: moderately difficult. Notification: continuous. SAT Reasoning Test deadline: 8/1. Transfer credits accepted: Yes.
Collegiate Environment: Orientation program. Drama-theater group, choral group. Social organizations: 16 open to all; coed societies; 75% of eligible men and 75% of eligible women are members. Most popular organizations: Co-ed Societies, ROTARACT CLUB, NAFME, SBGA, Footlighters. Major annual events: Beach Devotionals, Spring Banquet, MOSI Singings. Student

services: health clinic, personal-psychological counseling. Campus security: controlled dormitory access. 669 college housing spaces available; 446 were occupied in 2018-19. Freshmen guaranteed college housing. On-campus residence required through sophomore year. Options: men-only, women-only housing available. Chatlos Library. Operations spending for the previous fiscal year: $241,549. 85 computers available on campus for general student use. A campuswide network can be accessed from student residence rooms and from off campus. Staffed computer lab on campus provides training in use of computers, software, and the Internet.

Community Environment: Located near Tampa, Temple Terrace has a subtropical climate. Buses serve the area. Community facilities include a library, churches, and one community college and two universities. Part-time employment is limited. Sport activities include boating, fishing, golf, professional baseball, football and soccer. Cultural and recreational facilities, broad and varied, are also available in Tampa.

■ FLORIDA GATEWAY COLLEGE

149 SE College Pl.
Lake City, FL 32025
Tel: (386)752-1822
Fax: (386)755-1521
E-mail: admissions@fgc.edu
Web Site: www.fgc.edu

Description: State-supported, primarily 2-year, coed. Part of Florida Community College System. Awards certificates, diplomas, transfer associate, terminal associate, and bachelor's degrees. Founded 1962. Setting: 132-acre small town campus with easy access to Jacksonville. Total enrollment: 2,912. Faculty: 188 (65 full-time, 123 part-time). Student-undergrad faculty ratio is 14:1. Full-time: 831 students, 60% women, 40% men. Part-time: 2,081 students, 66% women, 34% men. Students come from 2 states and territories. 0.4% American Indian or Alaska Native, non-Hispanic/Latino; 5% Hispanic/Latino; 11% Black or African American, non-Hispanic/Latino; 1% Asian, non-Hispanic/Latino; 0.1% international. 33% 25 or older, 3% transferred in. Academic area with the most degrees conferred: health professions and related sciences. Core. Calendar: semesters. Academic remediation for entering students, ESL program, services for LD students, advanced placement, accelerated degree program, honors program, independent study, distance learning, summer session for credit, part-time degree program, adult/continuing education programs, co-op programs. Off campus study.

Entrance Requirements: Open admission except for nursing, EMS, physical therapist assistant, practical nursing, paramedic, phlebotomy, and patient care assistant programs. Option: electronic application. Required for some: high school transcript. Entrance: noncompetitive. Application deadline: 8/6. Notification: continuous. Transfer credits accepted: Yes.

Costs Per Year: Application fee: $0. State resident tuition: $2,368 full-time, $103.32 per credit hour part-time. Nonresident tuition: $11,747 full-time, $391.57 per credit hour part-time. Full-time tuition varies according to course level, course load, degree level, program, reciprocity agreements, and student level. Part-time tuition varies according to course level, course load, degree level, program, reciprocity agreements, and student level.

Collegiate Environment: Orientation program. Drama-theater group, choral group. Social organizations: 5 open to all. Most popular organizations: Anime Club, Art Club, FGC Board Game Club, Gay Straight Alliance, Rotaract. Major annual events: Fall Fest, Multicultural Day, Spring Fling. Student services: personal-psychological counseling. Campus security: 24-hour emergency response devices and patrols. Wilson S. Rivers Library and Media Center. 150 computers available on campus for general student use. A campuswide network can be accessed. Students can access the following: online class registration. Staffed computer lab on campus provides training in use of computers, software, and the Internet.

Community Environment: Lake City is the county seat of Columbia County, located midway between Atlanta and Miami. It has a temperate climate. Community facilities include excellent hospital and health facilities and fine motel accommodations. Annual deer and bear hunting is staged in nearby Osceola National Forest. Numerous lakes and streams are well stocked with bass, bream, and speckled perch. Tubing on the nearby Ichetucknee River is popular with students.

■ FLORIDA GULF COAST UNIVERSITY

10501 FGCU Blvd. S
Fort Myers, FL 33965-6565
Tel: (239)590-1000; Free: 888-889-1095
Fax: (239)590-7894

Web Site: www.fgcu.edu

Description: State-supported, comprehensive, coed. Part of State University System of Florida. Awards associate, bachelor's, master's, and doctoral degrees and post-master's certificates. Founded 1991. Setting: 760-acre suburban campus. Endowment: $72.9 million. Research spending for the previous fiscal year: $10 million. Educational spending for the previous fiscal year: $5699 per student. Total enrollment: 14,983. Faculty: 760 (465 full-time, 295 part-time). Student-undergrad faculty ratio is 22:1. 13,832 applied, 64% were admitted. 13% from top 10% of their high school class, 36% from top quarter, 75% from top half. Full-time: 10,947 students, 56% women, 44% men. Part-time: 2,873 students, 53% women, 47% men. Students come from 45 states and territories, 84 other countries, 7% from out-of-state. 0.2% American Indian or Alaska Native, non-Hispanic/Latino; 21% Hispanic/Latino; 7% Black or African American, non-Hispanic/Latino; 2% Asian, non-Hispanic/Latino; 0.2% Native Hawaiian or other Pacific Islander, non-Hispanic/Latino; 2% international. 11% 25 or older, 22% live on campus, 7% transferred in. Retention: 80% of full-time freshmen returned the following year. Academic areas with the most degrees conferred: business/marketing; communication/journalism; health professions and related sciences. Core. Calendar: semesters. Academic remediation for entering students, services for LD students, advanced placement, accelerated degree program, honors program, independent study, distance learning, double major, summer session for credit, part-time degree program, co-op programs and internships, graduate courses open to undergrads. Off campus study. Study abroad program.

Entrance Requirements: Options: electronic application, deferred admission, international baccalaureate accepted. Required: high school transcript, minimum 2.5 high school GPA, SAT or ACT. Entrance: moderately difficult. Application deadline: 5/1. Notification: continuous. Transfer credits accepted: Yes.

Costs Per Year: Application fee: $30. State resident tuition: $4191 full-time. Nonresident tuition: $22,328 full-time. Mandatory fees: $1927 full-time. Full-time tuition and fees vary according to course load. College room and board: $8620. College room only: $4820. Room and board charges vary according to board plan.

Collegiate Environment: Orientation program. Drama-theater group, student-run newspaper. Social organizations: 146 open to all; national fraternities, national sororities; 6% of eligible men and 10% of eligible women are members. Most popular organizations: Student Government, Ignite (Religious Organization), International Club, Martial Arts Club, Physical Therapy Association. Major annual events: Nest Fest (annual concert), Fright Night (Halloween party), Eaglepalooza (campus recreation festival). Student services: health clinic, personal-psychological counseling. Campus security: 24-hour emergency response devices and patrols, late night transport-escort service. Library Services plus 1 other. Books: 242,131 (physical), 73,000 (digital/electronic); Serial titles: 128,865 (digital/electronic); Databases: 389. Students can reserve study rooms. Operations spending for the previous fiscal year: $5.3 million. 1,029 computers available on campus for general student use. Computer purchase/lease plans available. A campuswide network can be accessed from student residence rooms and from off campus. Students can access the following: online class registration, online admissions and advising. Staffed computer lab on campus.

■ FLORIDA INSTITUTE OF TECHNOLOGY

150 W University Blvd.
Melbourne, FL 32901-6975
Tel: (321)674-8000; Free: 800-888-4348
Fax: (321)723-9468
Web Site: www.fit.edu

Description: Independent, university, coed. Awards bachelor's, master's, and doctoral degrees and post-master's certificates. Founded 1958. Setting: 130-acre suburban campus with easy access to Orlando. Total enrollment: 6,402. Faculty: 526 (306 full-time, 220 part-time). Student-undergrad faculty ratio is 15:1. 8,898 applied, 63% were admitted. 28% from top 10% of their high school class, 60% from top quarter, 88% from top half. Full-time: 3,269 students, 29% women, 71% men. Part-time: 366 students, 30% women, 70% men. Students come from 52 states and territories, 110 other countries, 50% from out-of-state. 0.2% American Indian or Alaska Native, non-Hispanic/Latino; 9% Hispanic/Latino; 6% Black or African American, non-Hispanic/Latino; 3% Asian, non-Hispanic/Latino; 0.4% Native Hawaiian or other Pacific Islander, non-Hispanic/Latino; 32% international. 1% 25 or older, 45% live on campus, 6% transferred in. Retention: 80% of full-time freshmen returned the following year. Academic areas with the most degrees conferred: engineering; business/marketing; transportation and materials moving. Core. Calendar: semesters. Academic remediation for entering students, ESL program, services for LD students, advanced placement, accelerated degree program, self-designed majors, independent study, distance learning, double major, summer session for credit, part-time degree program, adult/continuing education programs, co-op programs and internships, graduate courses open to undergrads. Study abroad program. ROTC: Army.

Entrance Requirements: Options: electronic application, deferred admission, international baccalaureate accepted. Required: essay, high school transcript, minimum 2.6 high school GPA, 1 recommendation, SAT or ACT. Recommended: minimum 3.3 high school GPA, interview. Entrance: moderately difficult. Application deadline: rolling. Notification: continuous. SAT Reasoning Test deadline: 7/1. Transfer credits accepted: Yes.

Costs Per Year: Comprehensive fee: $54,730 includes full-time tuition ($41,100), mandatory fees ($750), and college room and board ($12,880). College room only: $7000. Full-time tuition and fees vary according to course load and program. Room and board charges vary according to board plan and housing facility. Part-time tuition: $1170 per credit hour.

Collegiate Environment: Orientation program. Drama-theater group, choral group, student-run newspaper, radio station. Social organizations: 123 open to all; national fraternities, national sororities; 8% of eligible men and 3% of eligible women are members. Most popular organizations: Florida Institute of Technology Society for Science Fiction and Fantasy (FITSSFF), International Student Services Organization (ISSO), Student Government Association (SGA), Surf Club, Campus Activities Board. Major annual events: Homecoming, International Fest, President's Picnic. Student services: health clinic, personal-psychological counseling, women's center. Campus security: 24-hour emergency response devices and patrols, late night transport-escort service, controlled dormitory access. Evans Library. Books: 131,564 (physical), 728,454 (digital/electronic); Serial titles: 1,605 (physical), 56,994 (digital/electronic); Databases: 161. Weekly public service hours: 96; students can reserve study rooms. 254 computers available on campus for general student use. A campuswide network can be accessed from student residence rooms and from off campus. Students can access the following: online class registration. Staffed computer lab on campus provides training in use of computers, software, and the Internet.

Community Environment: Florida Tech is located in the city of Melbourne, Brevard County, on Florida's space coast, approximately 30 miles south of Spaceport, 60 miles east of Orlando and 170 miles north of Miami. It is 5 minutes from the Melbourne International Airport, which is host to 2 major airlines. Recreation includes public swimming pools, golf courses, a tourist club with facilities for a number of sports, a harbor, and a yacht basin. Fresh and salt water fishing are available.

■ **FLORIDA INTERNATIONAL UNIVERSITY**
11200 SW 8th St.
Miami, FL 33199
Tel: (305)348-2000
Fax: (305)348-3648
E-mail: admiss@fiu.edu
Web Site: www.fiu.edu

Description: State-supported, university, coed. Part of State University System of Florida. Awards bachelor's, master's, and doctoral degrees. Founded 1965. Setting: 576-acre urban campus with easy access to Miami. Endowment: $196.3 million. Research spending for the previous fiscal year: $110.1 million. Educational spending for the previous fiscal year: $6714 per student. Total enrollment: 56,851. Faculty: 2,440 (1,275 full-time, 1,165 part-time). Student-undergrad faculty ratio is 25:1. 14,861 applied, 51% were admitted. 25% from top 10% of their high school class, 58% from top quarter, 90% from top half. Full-time: 26,697 students, 57% women, 43% men. Part-time: 20,889 students, 57% women, 43% men. Students come from 47 states and territories, 140 other countries, 4% from out-of-state. 0.1% American Indian or Alaska Native, non-Hispanic/Latino; 67% Hispanic/Latino; 13% Black or African American, non-Hispanic/Latino; 2% Asian, non-Hispanic/Latino; 0.1% Native Hawaiian or other Pacific Islander, non-Hispanic/Latino; 6% international. 23% 25 or older, 7% live on campus, 11% transferred in. Retention: 89% of full-time freshmen returned the following year. Academic areas with the most degrees conferred: business/marketing; psychology; social sciences; communication/journalism; health professions and related sciences. Core. Calendar: semesters. Services for LD students, advanced placement, accelerated degree program, freshman honors college, honors program, independent study, distance learning, double major, summer session for credit, part-time degree program, adult/continuing

education programs, co-op programs and internships, graduate courses open to undergrads. Off campus study at National Student Exchange Program. Study abroad program. ROTC: Army, Air Force.

Entrance Requirements: Options: electronic application, international baccalaureate accepted. Required: high school transcript, SAT or ACT. Required for some: portfolio or audition, TOEFL for applicants whose native language is not English. Entrance: moderately difficult. Application deadline: 11/1. Notification: continuous. SAT Reasoning Test deadline: 7/1. SAT Subject Test deadline: 7/1. Transfer credits accepted: Yes.

Costs Per Year: Application fee: $30. State resident tuition: $6168 full-time, $205.47 per credit hour part-time. Nonresident tuition: $18,566 full-time, $618.87 per credit hour part-time. Mandatory fees: $390 full-time. College room and board: $10,882. College room only: $6984. Room and board charges vary according to board plan and housing facility.

Collegiate Environment: Orientation program. Drama-theater group, choral group, marching band, student-run newspaper, radio station. Social organizations: 558 open to all; national fraternities, national sororities. Most popular organizations: Students for Community Service, Black Student Leadership Council, Hospitality Management Student Club, Hispanic Students Association, Haitian Students Organization. Major annual events: Relay for Life (fund-raising event), Dance Marathon (fund-raising event), Welcome Week. Student services: health clinic, personal-psychological counseling, women's center. Campus security: 24-hour emergency response devices and patrols, late night transport-escort service, controlled dormitory access. Steven and Dorothea Green Library plus 4 others. Books: 1.5 million (physical), 443,863 (digital/electronic); Serial titles: 63,945 (physical), 111,662 (digital/electronic); Databases: 808. Weekly public service hours: 112; students can reserve study rooms. Operations spending for the previous fiscal year: $19.3 million.

Community Environment: The Greater Miami area offers cultural diversity and a dynamic economic and aesthetic climate. South Florida is a major center of higher education and stands at the forefront of international trading, finance and banking, as well as tourism and a developing high technology industry. Miami International Airport is served by more airlines than any other airport in the country. One of the most culturally diverse cities in America, Miami has many distinctive neighborhoods. Both visual and performing arts thrive in Miami. The Metro-Dade Cultural Complex in downtown Miami houses the Metropolitan Library, the Museum of South Florida, and the Center for the Fine Arts. The city also maintains both an opera and three ballet companies. A wealth of galleries, libraries, and theaters are valuable resources. The greater Miami area also hosts many professional sports events and offers year round recreation activities such as fishing, boating, scuba diving, wind surfing, snorkeling, swimming, and deep-sea fishing.

■ **FLORIDA KEYS COMMUNITY COLLEGE**
5901 College Rd.
Key West, FL 33040-4397
Tel: (305)296-9081
Web Site: www.fkcc.edu

Description: State-supported, primarily 2-year, coed. Part of Florida College System. Awards certificates, transfer associate, terminal associate, and bachelor's degrees. Founded 1965. Setting: 20-acre small town campus. Total enrollment: 1,030. Faculty: (28 full-time). Student-undergrad faculty ratio is 12:1. Full-time: 363 students, 49% women, 51% men. Part-time: 667 students, 64% women, 36% men. 0.3% American Indian or Alaska Native, non-Hispanic/Latino; 27% Hispanic/Latino; 9% Black or African American, non-Hispanic/Latino; 2% Asian, non-Hispanic/Latino; 0.4% Native Hawaiian or other Pacific Islander, non-Hispanic/Latino; 0.9% international. 37% 25 or older, 10% transferred in. Core. Calendar: semesters. Academic remediation for entering students, ESL program, services for LD students, advanced placement, self-designed majors, independent study, distance learning, double major, summer session for credit, part-time degree program, adult/continuing education programs, co-op programs and internships.

Entrance Requirements: Open admission except for nursing program, criminal justice programs, and BAS degree. Options: electronic application, early admission, deferred admission. Required for some: essay, high school transcript, recommendations. Entrance: noncompetitive. Application deadline: rolling. Notification: continuous.

Costs Per Year: Application fee: $30. State resident tuition: $2483 full-time, $109 per credit hour part-time. Nonresident tuition: $9933 full-time, $439 per credit hour part-time. Mandatory fees: $793 full-time. Full-time tuition and fees vary according to degree level. Part-time tuition varies according to degree level. College room only: $10,508.

Collegiate Environment: Orientation program. Choral group. Student services: personal-psychological counseling. Campus security: 24-hour patrols. Florida Keys Community College Library. Students can reserve study rooms.

Community Environment: Key West is the southernmost city in the continental United States. It is a tropical island 157 miles southwest of Miami with an Old-World atmosphere. The setting is a blend of Cuban, West Indian, and Bahamian. The climate is warm and the air is almost pollen free. A rich and colorful history is retained in a thriving modern city. All forms of transportation serve the area. Searstown and four shopping centers are among the nation's most unique, all having a tropical flair. Year-round outdoor recreation includes a coral reef several miles offshore and provides some of the world's finest fishing and diving. Numerous points of interest are the Audubon house, Ernest Hemingway Home and Museum, Martello Gallery and Museum, the Lighthouse and the Military Museum.

■ **FLORIDA MEMORIAL UNIVERSITY**
15800 NW 42nd Ave.
Miami Gardens, FL 33054
Tel: (305)626-3600; Free: 800-822-1362
Web Site: www.fmuniv.edu
Description: Independent, comprehensive, coed, affiliated with Baptist Church. Awards bachelor's and master's degrees. Founded 1879. Setting: 77-acre suburban campus. Endowment: $6.7 million. Total enrollment: 1,750. Faculty: 173 (105 full-time, 68 part-time). Student-undergrad faculty ratio is 12:1. 5,286 applied, 39% were admitted. Full-time: 1,516 students, 63% women, 37% men. Part-time: 153 students, 56% women, 44% men. Students come from 37 states and territories, 15 other countries, 12% from out-of-state. 30% 25 or older, 8% transferred in. Retention: 70% of full-time freshmen returned the following year. Academic areas with the most degrees conferred: education; business/marketing; law/legal studies. Core. Calendar: semesters. Academic remediation for entering students, ESL program, freshman honors college, honors program, summer session for credit, part-time degree program, external degree program, co-op programs and internships. Off campus study. ROTC: Army, Air Force (c).
Entrance Requirements: Open admission. Options: electronic application, international baccalaureate accepted. Required: essay, high school transcript, minimum 2.2 high school GPA, 2 recommendations. Recommended: SAT or ACT. Entrance: noncompetitive. Application deadline: 7/1. Notification: continuous.
Collegiate Environment: Orientation program. Drama-theater group, student-run newspaper. Social organizations: national fraternities, national sororities. Student services: health clinic. Florida Memorial College Library. 200 computers available on campus for general student use. A campuswide network can be accessed from student residence rooms and from off campus. Students can access the following: online class registration. Staffed computer lab on campus provides training in use of computers and software.

■ **FLORIDA NATIONAL UNIVERSITY**
4425 W 20th Ave.
Hialeah, FL 33012
Tel: (305)821-3333
Fax: (305)362-0595
E-mail: rlopez@fnu.edu
Web Site: www.fnu.edu
Description: Proprietary, comprehensive, coed. Awards associate, bachelor's, and master's degrees and post-master's certificates. Founded 1982. Setting: 4-acre urban campus with easy access to Miami. Educational spending for the previous fiscal year: $7517 per student. Total enrollment: 4,169. Faculty: 150 (79 full-time, 71 part-time). Student-undergrad faculty ratio is 31:1. 1,785 applied, 95% were admitted. 7 student government officers. Full-time: 2,899 students, 70% women, 30% men. Part-time: 1,124 students, 75% women, 25% men. Students come from 22 states and territories, 31 other countries, 1% from out-of-state. 0.1% American Indian or Alaska Native, non-Hispanic/Latino; 82% Hispanic/Latino; 3% Black or African American, non-Hispanic/Latino; 0.3% Asian, non-Hispanic/Latino; 0.1% Native Hawaiian or other Pacific Islander, non-Hispanic/Latino; 13% international. 64% 25 or older, 7% transferred in. Retention: 98% of full-time freshmen returned the following year. Academic areas with the most degrees conferred: health professions and related sciences; business/marketing; homeland security, law enforcement, firefighting, and protective services. Core. Calendar: semesters. Academic remediation for entering students, ESL program, services for LD students, advanced placement, accelerated degree program, independent study, distance learning, summer session for credit, part-time degree program, adult/continuing education programs, co-op programs and internships.

Entrance Requirements: Open admission. Options: electronic application, deferred admission, international baccalaureate accepted. Required: high school transcript, interview, SAT or ACT. Entrance: moderately difficult. Application deadline: rolling. Notification: continuous. Transfer credits accepted: Yes.
Costs Per Year: Application fee: $0. Tuition: $13,200 full-time, $550 per credit hour part-time. Mandatory fees: $488 full-time. Tuition guaranteed not to increase for student's term of enrollment.
Collegiate Environment: Orientation program. Student-run newspaper. Social organizations: 5 open to all; national fraternities, Honor Society; 2% of eligible men and 3% of eligible women are members. Most popular organizations: Student Government Association, Bible Club, Salsa Club, W.I.C.S (Women Community Service), Criminal Justice Society. Major annual events: Founders' Week, Celebration Of the 4th of July, Thanksgiving Day. Campus security: 24-hour emergency response devices. Hialeah Campus Library plus 1 other. Books: 21,521 (physical), 144,218 (digital/electronic); Serial titles: 55 (physical), 196,357 (digital/electronic); Databases: 32. Weekly public service hours: 69; students can reserve study rooms. Operations spending for the previous fiscal year: $481,342. 300 computers available on campus for general student use. A campuswide network can be accessed from off-campus. Students can access the following: online class registration. Staffed computer lab on campus provides training in use of computers, software, and the Internet.

■ **FLORIDA POLYTECHNIC UNIVERSITY**
4700 Research Way
Lakeland, FL 33805
Tel: (863)583-9050
Description: State-supported, comprehensive, coed. Awards bachelor's and master's degrees. Total enrollment: 1,456. Faculty: 92 (64 full-time, 28 part-time). Student-undergrad faculty ratio is 18:1. 1,207 applied, 56% were admitted. 22% from top 10% of their high school class, 57% from top quarter, 92% from top half. Full-time: 1,329 students, 13% women, 87% men. Part-time: 110 students, 17% women, 83% men. 2% from out-of-state. 0.5% American Indian or Alaska Native, non-Hispanic/Latino; 18% Hispanic/Latino; 5% Black or African American, non-Hispanic/Latino; 4% Asian, non-Hispanic/Latino; 0.2% Native Hawaiian or other Pacific Islander, non-Hispanic/Latino; 2% international. 7% 25 or older, 44% live on campus. Retention: 72% of full-time freshmen returned the following year. Academic areas with the most degrees conferred: engineering; computer and information sciences; business/marketing. Calendar: semesters. Accelerated degree program, independent study, internships. Study abroad program.
Entrance Requirements: Options: early admission, deferred admission. Application deadline: 5/1. Notification: continuous until 9/1. SAT Reasoning Test deadline: 5/1.
Costs Per Year: Application fee: $30. State resident tuition: $3,167 full-time, $105.07 per credit part-time. Nonresident tuition: $19,217 full-time, $105.07 per credit part-time. Mandatory fees: $1,787 full-time. College room and board: $11,430. College room only: $7286.
Collegiate Environment: Student-run newspaper.

■ **THE FLORIDA SCHOOL OF TRADITIONAL MIDWIFERY**
810 E University Ave., 2nd Fl.
Gainesville, FL 32601
Tel: (352)338-0766
Fax: (352)338-2013
E-mail: info@midwiferyschool.org
Web Site: www.midwiferyschool.org
Description: Independent, 2-year, women only. Awards terminal associate degrees. Founded 1993. Calendar: quarters.

■ **FLORIDA SOUTHERN COLLEGE**
111 Lake Hollingsworth Dr.
Lakeland, FL 33801-5698
Tel: (863)680-4111; Free: 800-274-4131
Fax: (863)680-4120
Web Site: www.flsouthern.edu
Description: Independent, comprehensive, coed, affiliated with United Methodist Church. Awards bachelor's, master's, and doctoral degrees and post-master's certificates. Founded 1885. Setting: 113-acre suburban campus with easy access to Tampa, Orlando. Endowment: $91.4 million. Educational spending for the previous fiscal year: $7959 per student. Total enrollment: 3,190. Faculty: 317 (149 full-time, 168 part-time). Student-undergrad faculty ratio is 15:1. 7,254 applied, 50% were admitted. 30% from

top 10% of their high school class, 61% from top quarter, 87% from top half. 10 class presidents, 12 valedictorians, 6 student government officers. Full-time: 2,502 students, 64% women, 36% men. Part-time: 221 students, 72% women, 28% men. Students come from 48 states and territories, 46 other countries, 35% from out-of-state. 1% American Indian or Alaska Native, non-Hispanic/Latino; 12% Hispanic/Latino; 6% Black or African American, non-Hispanic/Latino; 3% Asian, non-Hispanic/Latino; 0.1% Native Hawaiian or other Pacific Islander, non-Hispanic/Latino; 3% international. 1% 25 or older, 79% live on campus, 3% transferred in. Retention: 82% of full-time freshmen returned the following year. Academic areas with the most degrees conferred: business/marketing; health professions and related sciences; biological/life sciences. Core. Calendar: semesters. Advanced placement, accelerated degree program, self-designed majors, honors program, independent study, distance learning, double major, summer session for credit, part-time degree program, external degree program, adult/continuing education programs, internships, graduate courses open to undergrads. Off campus study at United Nations Semester, American University, Drew University, Washington Center, Duke University, Lake Erie College. Study abroad program. ROTC: Army, Air Force (c).

Entrance Requirements: Options: electronic application, early admission, early decision, deferred admission, international baccalaureate accepted. Required: high school transcript, minimum 2 high school GPA, 1 recommendation, SAT or ACT. Recommended: essay, interview. Entrance: moderately difficult. Application deadlines: 5/1, 5/1 for nonresidents, 11/1 for early decision. Notification: continuous, continuous for nonresidents, 12/1 for early decision. SAT Reasoning Test deadline: 8/20. Transfer credits accepted: Yes. Early decision applicants: 114. Early decision applicants admitted: 67.

Costs Per Year: Application fee: $0. One-time mandatory fee: $100. Comprehensive fee: $48,018 includes full-time tuition ($35,600), mandatory fees ($748), and college room and board ($11,670). College room only: $7070. Room and board charges vary according to board plan and housing facility. Part-time tuition: $998 per credit hour. Part-time tuition varies according to class time and course load.

Collegiate Environment: Orientation program. Drama-theater group, choral group, student-run newspaper. Social organizations: 126 open to all; national fraternities, national sororities; 29% of eligible men and 35% of eligible women are members. Most popular organizations: Astronomy Club, FLoSoCo, Beyond (Campus Ministry), ACE, Garden Club. Major annual events: Blast-off, Winter Wonderland, Fairwell Festival. Student services: health clinic, personal-psychological counseling. Campus security: 24-hour emergency response devices and patrols, student patrols, late night transport-escort service, controlled dormitory access. 2,157 college housing spaces available; 2,054 were occupied in 2018-19. Freshmen guaranteed college housing. On-campus residence required through senior year. Options: coed, men-only, women-only housing available. Roux Library plus 1 other. Books: 160,667 (physical), 167,731 (digital/electronic); Serial titles: 22 (physical), 97,772 (digital/electronic); Databases: 118. Weekly public service hours: 104; students can reserve study rooms. 490 computers available on campus for general student use. Computer purchase/lease plans available. A campuswide network can be accessed from student residence rooms. Students can access the following: online class registration, campus portal. Staffed computer lab on campus provides training in use of computers, software, and the Internet.

Community Environment: Lakeland is located in the geographical center of Florida, 35 miles East of Tampa, 50 miles west of Orlando, 100 miles from the Atlantic Ocean, 35 miles from Disney World and 60 miles from the Gulf of Mexico. The Seaboard Coast Line Railroad serves the area. The "World's Citrus Center" is the permanent spring training headquarters of the Detroit Tigers. Excellent shopping facilities in the city; a civic center, concert association, and community theatre are part of the lively community. Recreational facilities include 12 lakes within the city for excellent fishing, golf courses, boating, hiking, and waterskiing. The annual Orange Cup Regatta Hydroplane Race is held the weekend closest to February 1st.

■ **FLORIDA SOUTHWESTERN STATE COLLEGE**
8099 College Pky.
Fort Myers, FL 33919
Tel: (239)489-9300
Fax: (239)489-9399
E-mail: admissions@fsw.edu
Web Site: www.fsw.edu
Description: State and locally supported, primarily 2-year, coed. Part of Florida College System. Awards certificates, transfer associate, terminal as-

sociate, and bachelor's degrees. Founded 1962. Setting: 413-acre urban campus. Endowment: $731,365. Educational spending for the previous fiscal year: $3030 per student. Total enrollment: 16,616. Faculty: 536 (186 full-time, 350 part-time). Student-undergrad faculty ratio is 31:1. 5,769 applied, 81% were admitted. Full-time: 5,708 students, 59% women, 41% men. Part-time: 10,908 students, 63% women, 37% men. Students come from 46 states and territories, 27 other countries, 4% from out-of-state. 0.4% American Indian or Alaska Native, non-Hispanic/Latino; 28% Hispanic/Latino; 10% Black or African American, non-Hispanic/Latino; 2% Asian, non-Hispanic/Latino; 0.2% Native Hawaiian or other Pacific Islander, non-Hispanic/Latino; 2% international. 26% 25 or older, 2% live on campus, 4% transferred in. Retention: 66% of full-time freshmen returned the following year. Academic areas with the most degrees conferred: health professions and related sciences; business/marketing; education. Core. Calendar: semesters. Academic remediation for entering students, ESL program, services for LD students, advanced placement, accelerated degree program, honors program, independent study, distance learning, double major, summer session for credit, part-time degree program, co-op programs and internships. Off campus study. Study abroad program.

Entrance Requirements: Open admission. Options: electronic application, early admission, deferred admission, international baccalaureate accepted. Required: high school transcript. Entrance: noncompetitive. Application deadline: 8/17. Notification: continuous. Transfer credits accepted: Yes.

Costs Per Year: Application fee: $30. State resident tuition: $2436 full-time, $81.21 per credit hour part-time. Nonresident tuition: $9750 full-time, $325 per credit hour part-time. Mandatory fees: $964 full-time, $32.15 per credit hour part-time. Full-time tuition and fees vary according to degree level. Part-time tuition and fees vary according to degree level. College room and board: $8000. College room only: $6000. Room and board charges vary according to board plan.

Collegiate Environment: Orientation program. Drama-theater group, choral group. Social organizations: 30 open to all. Campus security: 24-hour emergency response devices and patrols, late night transport-escort service, controlled dormitory access, Rave Guardian app for students, faculty, and staff. Richard H. Rush Library. Books: 45,355 (physical), 28,410 (digital/electronic); Databases: 128. Weekly public service hours: 79. Operations spending for the previous fiscal year: $1.5 million. 2,700 computers available on campus for general student use. A campuswide network can be accessed from student residence rooms and from off campus. Students can access the following: online class registration. Staffed computer lab on campus.

Community Environment: Edison Community College campuses are located on the sunny coast of southwest Florida, between Naples and Tampa. The climate is semitropical. The offshore islands have many attractive beaches, and majestic Royal Palms line the streets. All modes of transportation serve the area. Tourism, commercial fishing, shrimping and livestock production are important industries. The community facilities include churches of all denominations, hospitals, little theater groups, dances, and lecture halls. The saltwater bays and freshwater lakes nearby are among the finest fishing grounds anywhere. Other sports include boating, hunting, horseback riding, golf, bowling, tennis, shuffleboard and greyhound racing in Bonita Springs. TECO Arena is home to minor league hockey and basketball teams. A minor league baseball team also plays in Fort Myers. The Boston Red Sox and Minnesota Twins have their spring training camps in Fort Myers.

■ **FLORIDA STATE COLLEGE AT JACKSONVILLE**
501 W State St.
Jacksonville, FL 32202-4030
Tel: (904)632-3000; Free: 888-873-1145
Fax: (904)632-3393
E-mail: pbiegel@fscj.edu
Web Site: www.fscj.edu
Description: State-supported, primarily 2-year, coed. Part of Florida College System. Awards certificates, diplomas, transfer associate, terminal associate, and bachelor's degrees. Founded 1963. Setting: 844-acre urban campus. Endowment: $44.6 million. Educational spending for the previous fiscal year: $6266 per student. Total enrollment: 25,514. Faculty: 1,180 (401 full-time, 779 part-time). Student-undergrad faculty ratio is 21:1. Full-time: 7,819 students, 57% women, 43% men. Part-time: 17,695 students, 61% women, 39% men. 0.3% American Indian or Alaska Native, non-Hispanic/Latino; 7% Hispanic/Latino; 25% Black or African American, non-Hispanic/Latino; 4% Asian, non-Hispanic/Latino; 0.5% Native Hawaiian or other Pacific Islander, non-Hispanic/Latino; 0.8% international. 45% 25 or older, 6% transferred in. Academic areas with the most degrees conferred:

business/marketing; computer and information sciences; education. Core. Calendar: semesters. Academic remediation for entering students, ESL program, services for LD students, advanced placement, accelerated degree program, honors program, independent study, distance learning, double major, summer session for credit, part-time degree program, adult/continuing education programs, co-op programs and internships. Off campus study at Jacksonville Naval Station, Jacksonville, FL; Mayport Naval Air Station, Jacksonville, FL; Cecil Field Naval Air Station, Jacksonville, FL; Naval Aviation Technical Training Center, Pensacola, FL. Study abroad program. ROTC: Naval (c).

Entrance Requirements: Open admission for lower level programs. Options: electronic application, early admission, deferred admission, international baccalaureate accepted. Required for some: high school transcript. Entrance: noncompetitive. Application deadline: rolling. Transfer credits accepted: Yes.

Collegiate Environment: Orientation program. Drama-theater group, choral group, student-run newspaper, radio station. Most popular organizations: Phi Theta Kappa, Forensic Team, Brain Bowl Team, International Student Association, DramaWorks. Major annual event: FSCJ Talent/Variety Show. Student services: personal-psychological counseling, women's center. Campus security: 24-hour emergency response devices and patrols, late night transport-escort service. Florida State College at Jacksonville Library and Learning Commons plus 7 others. Operations spending for the previous fiscal year: $2.2 million. 4,800 computers available on campus for general student use. A campuswide network can be accessed. Students can access the following: online class registration, 1 TB Online file storage, free office software. Staffed computer lab on campus provides training in use of computers, software, and the Internet.

■ FLORIDA STATE UNIVERSITY
600 W College Ave.
Tallahassee, FL 32306
Tel: (850)644-2525
Fax: (850)644-0197
Web Site: www.fsu.edu

Description: State-supported, university, coed. Part of State University System of Florida. Awards associate, bachelor's, master's, and doctoral degrees and post-master's certificates. Founded 1851. Setting: 477-acre suburban campus. Endowment: $639.4 million. Total enrollment: 41,447. Faculty: 1,774 (1,448 full-time, 326 part-time). Student-undergrad faculty ratio is 22:1. 35,334 applied, 49% were admitted. 41% from top 10% of their high school class, 83% from top quarter, 99% from top half. Full-time: 29,370 students, 57% women, 43% men. Part-time: 3,723 students, 48% women, 52% men. Students come from 51 states and territories, 102 other countries, 11% from out-of-state. 0.2% American Indian or Alaska Native, non-Hispanic/Latino; 20% Hispanic/Latino; 8% Black or African American, non-Hispanic/Latino; 2% Asian, non-Hispanic/Latino; 0.1% Native Hawaiian or other Pacific Islander, non-Hispanic/Latino; 2% international. 5% 25 or older, 20% live on campus, 6% transferred in. Retention: 94% of full-time freshmen returned the following year. Academic areas with the most degrees conferred: business/marketing; social sciences; biological/life sciences. Core. Calendar: semesters. ESL program, services for LD students, advanced placement, accelerated degree program, honors program, independent study, distance learning, double major, summer session for credit, part-time degree program, co-op programs and internships, graduate courses open to undergrads. Off campus study at Florida Agricultural and Mechanical University, Tallahassee Community College. Study abroad program. ROTC: Army, Naval (c), Air Force.

Entrance Requirements: Options: electronic application, early admission, deferred admission, international baccalaureate accepted. Required: high school transcript, SAT or ACT. Recommended: essay. Entrance: very difficult. Application deadline: 2/7. Notification: 3/28. SAT Reasoning Test deadline: 2/7. Transfer credits accepted: Yes.

Costs Per Year: Application fee: $30. State resident tuition: $4,640 full-time, $215.55 per credit hour part-time. Nonresident tuition: $19,806 full-time, $721.10 per credit hour part-time. Mandatory fees: $1,867 full-time. Full-time tuition and fees vary according to course load, degree level, and location. Part-time tuition varies according to course load, degree level, and location. College room and board: $10,458. College room only: $6380. Room and board charges vary according to board plan and housing facility.

Collegiate Environment: Orientation program. Drama-theater group, choral group, marching band, student-run newspaper, radio station. Social organizations: 650 open to all; national fraternities, national sororities, local fraternities, local sororities; 19% of eligible men and 25% of eligible women

are members. Most popular organizations: Student Government, Honors Program, Golden Key Honor Society, Marching Chiefs, Intramural Sports. Major annual events: Family Weekend, Homecoming, Dance Marathon. Student services: legal services, health clinic, personal-psychological counseling, women's center. Campus security: 24-hour emergency response devices and patrols, late night transport-escort service, controlled dormitory access. Robert Manning Strozier Library plus 8 others. Books: 2.3 million (physical), 1.6 million (digital/electronic); Serial titles: 125,007 (digital/electronic); Databases: 1,144. Weekly public service hours: 134; study areas open 24 hours, 5-7 days a week; students can reserve study rooms. Operations spending for the previous fiscal year: $20.6 million. 1,100 computers available on campus for general student use. A computer is required for all students. A campuswide network can be accessed from student residence rooms and from off campus. Students can access the following: online class registration, course home pages, course search, online fee payment. Staffed computer lab on campus (open 24 hours a day) provides training in use of computers, software, and the Internet.

Community Environment: Situated in north Florida, FSU is nestled in the heart of Tallahassee, the state's capital city. A classic college town, Tallahassee is not only one of Florida's oldest and fastest growing cities, it is also part of the"other Florida" with its rolling hills, canopy roads, mild climate, and southern hospitality. More than 100 state and federal agencies furnish students with opportunities for internships, research, and work-study programs that match all areas of academic interest. Part-time jobs are plentiful. In addition, Tallahassee affords a rich offering of social, cultural, and recreational activities, making it an excellent place to live, study, and grow.

■ FLORIDA TECHNICAL COLLEGE
12900 Challenger Pky.
Orlando, FL 32826
Tel: (407)447-7300; Free: 888-574-2082
Web Site: www.ftccollege.edu

Description: Proprietary, 2-year, coed. Part of Fore Front Education, Inc. Awards certificates, diplomas, and terminal associate degrees. Founded 1982. Setting: 1-acre urban campus. Total enrollment: 1,355. 379 applied. 56% 25 or older. Core. Calendar: quarters. Advanced placement, accelerated degree program, independent study, distance learning, double major, external degree program.

Entrance Requirements: Option: international baccalaureate accepted. Required: high school transcript, interview. Recommended: essay. Entrance: minimally difficult.

Collegiate Environment: Orientation program. Student-run newspaper. Florida Technical College Learning Resource Center.

■ FORTIS COLLEGE (CUTLER BAY)
19600 S Dixie Hwy.
Ste. B
Cutler Bay, FL 33157
Tel: (786)345-5300; Free: 855-4-FORTIS
Web Site: www.fortis.edu

Description: Proprietary, primarily 2-year, coed. Awards certificates, diplomas, transfer associate, terminal associate, and bachelor's degrees.

■ FORTIS COLLEGE (ORANGE PARK)
700 Blanding Blvd.
Ste. 16
Orange Park, FL 32065
Tel: (904)269-7086; Free: 855-4-FORTIS
Fax: (904)269-6664
Web Site: www.fortis.edu

Description: Proprietary, 2-year, coed. Awards certificates, diplomas, transfer associate, and terminal associate degrees. Total enrollment: 349.
Entrance Requirements: Entrance: noncompetitive.

■ FORTIS INSTITUTE (PENSACOLA)
4081 E Olive Rd.
Ste. B
Pensacola, FL 32514
Tel: (850)476-7607; Free: 855-4-FORTIS
Web Site: www.fortis.edu

Description: Proprietary, 2-year, coed. Awards certificates, diplomas, transfer associate, and terminal associate degrees.

■ **FORTIS INSTITUTE (PORT SAINT LUCIE)**
9022 S US Hwy. 1
Port Saint Lucie, FL 34952
Tel: (772)221-9799; Free: 855-4-FORTIS
Web Site: www.fortis.edu
Description: Proprietary, 2-year, coed. Awards certificates, diplomas, transfer associate, and terminal associate degrees.

■ **FULL SAIL UNIVERSITY**
3300 University Blvd.
Winter Park, FL 32792-7437
Tel: (407)679-6333; Free: 800-226-7625
Fax: (407)678-0070
E-mail: admissions@fullsail.com
Web Site: www.fullsail.edu
Description: Proprietary, comprehensive, coed. Awards associate, bachelor's, and master's degrees. Founded 1979. Setting: 190-acre suburban campus with easy access to Orlando. Total enrollment: 8,921. Faculty: 702. Student-undergrad faculty ratio is 8:1. Students come from 50 states and territories, 40 other countries, 70% from out-of-state. Retention: 84% of full-time freshmen returned the following year. Core. Calendar: modular. Academic remediation for entering students, services for LD students, summer session for credit, co-op programs and internships.
Entrance Requirements: Open admission. Option: electronic application. Required: high school transcript. Required for some: minimum 'A' average in Algebra II. Application deadline: rolling.
Collegiate Environment: Orientation program. Most popular organizations: Student Chapter of Audio Engineering Society, Digital Art and Design Association, International Film Society, Student Art League, Student Association of Real-World Advancement. Major annual events: Annual Speech Tournament, Success Seminar, Entertainment Business. Student services: personal-psychological counseling. Campus security: 24-hour patrols. Full Sail Library plus 1 other.

■ **GALEN COLLEGE OF NURSING**
11101 Roosevelt Blvd. N
Saint Petersburg, FL 33716
Tel: (727)577-1497; Free: 877-223-7040
Web Site: www.galencollege.edu
Description: Proprietary, 2-year, coed. Awards transfer associate degrees.

■ **GULF COAST STATE COLLEGE**
5230 W Hwy. 98
Panama City, FL 32401-1058
Tel: (850)769-1551
Fax: (850)913-3308
E-mail: swagner1@gulfcoast.edu
Web Site: www.gulfcoast.edu
Description: State-supported, primarily 2-year, coed. Part of Florida College System. Awards certificates, transfer associate, terminal associate, and bachelor's degrees. Founded 1957. Setting: 80-acre urban campus. Endowment: $30.5 million. Educational spending for the previous fiscal year: $6211 per student. Total enrollment: 5,379. Faculty: 329 (141 full-time, 188 part-time). Student-undergrad faculty ratio is 19:1. Full-time: 1,840 students, 58% women, 42% men. Part-time: 3,539 students, 61% women, 39% men. Students come from 13 states and territories, 3% from out-of-state. 0.9% American Indian or Alaska Native, non-Hispanic/Latino; 7% Hispanic/Latino; 12% Black or African American, non-Hispanic/Latino; 3% Asian, non-Hispanic/Latino; 0.6% international. 37% 25 or older, 3% transferred in. Academic areas with the most degrees conferred: health professions and related sciences; business/marketing; communication technologies. Core. Calendar: semesters. Academic remediation for entering students, ESL program, services for LD students, advanced placement, accelerated degree program, honors program, independent study, distance learning, double major, summer session for credit, part-time degree program, external degree program, adult/continuing education programs, co-op programs. Off campus study. Study abroad program.
Entrance Requirements: Open admission. Options: electronic application, early admission, deferred admission, international baccalaureate accepted. Required: high school transcript. Entrance: noncompetitive. Application deadline: rolling. Notification: continuous. Transfer credits accepted: Yes.
Costs Per Year: Application fee: $20. State resident tuition: $2370 full-time, $98.75 per credit hour part-time. Nonresident tuition: $8633 full-time, $359.71 per credit hour part-time. Mandatory fees: $620 full-time, $25.83 per

credit hour part-time. Full-time tuition and fees vary according to degree level. Part-time tuition and fees vary according to degree level.
Collegiate Environment: Orientation program. Drama-theater group, choral group, student-run newspaper, radio station. Social organizations: 25 open to all; Phi Theta Kappa Honor Society. Most popular organization: Student Government Association. Major annual events: Welcome Back Week, Drive in Movies, Leadership Conference. Student services: personal-psychological counseling. Campus security: 24-hour patrols, late night transport-escort service, patrols by trained security personnel during campus hours. Gulf Coast State College Library. Books: 32,529 (physical), 57,578 (digital/electronic); Serial titles: 43 (physical), 55,302 (digital/electronic); Databases: 176. Operations spending for the previous fiscal year: $530,414. 1,000 computers available on campus for general student use. A campuswide network can be accessed. Students can access the following: online class registration. Staffed computer lab on campus provides training in use of computers, software, and the Internet.
Community Environment: Panama City is an urban area with a temperate climate and is recognized as one of the most progressive industrial and resort cities in the state. A municipal marina includes a city hall, an auditorium, a library, and berths for about 400 boats. Community facilities include libraries, churches of major denominations, two hospitals and several clinics; shopping facilities are excellent. Some part-time employment is available. The city's industries include tourism, oil companies, wholesale fisheries, chemical production, boat manufacturing. Outdoor sports include golfing, yachting, sailing, water skiing and swimming. Panama City is a noted sport fishing center for both fresh and salt water fish.

■ **GWINNETT INSTITUTE**
1900 N Alafaya Trl.
Orlando, FL 32826
Tel: (407)434-8700
Web Site: www.gwinnettcollege.edu/locations/orlando
Description: Proprietary, 2-year, coed. Awards diplomas, transfer associate, and terminal associate degrees.

■ **HEALTH CAREER INSTITUTE**
1764 N Congress Ave.
West Palm Beach, FL 33409
Description: Proprietary, 2-year, coed.

■ **HERZING UNIVERSITY**
1865 SR 436
Winter Park, FL 32792
Tel: (407)641-5227; Free: 800-596-0724
Fax: (407)478-0501
Web Site: www.herzing.edu/orlando
Description: Independent, 4-year, coed. Awards associate and bachelor's degrees. Founded 1989. Calendar: semesters.

■ **HILLSBOROUGH COMMUNITY COLLEGE**
PO Box 31127
Tampa, FL 33631-3127
Tel: (813)253-7000
Fax: (813)253-7196
E-mail: jyoung92@hccfl.edu
Web Site: www.hccfl.edu
Description: State-supported, 2-year, coed. Part of Florida College System. Awards certificates, transfer associate, and terminal associate degrees. Founded 1968. Setting: urban campus with easy access to Tampa, Clearwater, St. Petersburg. Total enrollment: 27,061. Faculty: 1,410 (312 full-time, 1,098 part-time). Student-undergrad faculty ratio is 24:1. Full-time: 10,924 students, 51% women, 49% men. Part-time: 16,137 students, 61% women, 39% men. Students come from 42 states and territories, 128 other countries, 1% from out-of-state. 0.4% American Indian or Alaska Native, non-Hispanic/Latino; 29% Hispanic/Latino; 18% Black or African American, non-Hispanic/Latino; 3% Asian, non-Hispanic/Latino; 0.2% Native Hawaiian or other Pacific Islander, non-Hispanic/Latino; 3% international. 35% 25 or older, 26% transferred in. Core. Calendar: semesters. Academic remediation for entering students, ESL program, services for LD students, advanced placement, honors program, independent study, distance learning, summer session for credit, part-time degree program, co-op programs and internships. Off campus study. Study abroad program. ROTC: Army (c), Air Force (c).
Entrance Requirements: Open admission except for limited capacity allied

health programs. Options: electronic application, early admission, international baccalaureate accepted. Required: high school transcript. Entrance: noncompetitive. Application deadline: rolling. Transfer credits accepted: Yes.

Costs Per Year: Application fee: $0. State resident tuition: $2505 full-time, $104.39 per credit hour part-time. Nonresident tuition: $9111 full-time, $379.61 per credit hour part-time.

Collegiate Environment: Orientation program. Drama-theater group, choral group, student-run newspaper, radio station. Student services: personal-psychological counseling. Campus security: 24-hour emergency response devices and patrols, late night transport-escort service. Dale Mabry Library plus 4 others. Books: 109,428 (physical), 44,898 (digital/electronic); Serial titles: 578 (physical), 47,889 (digital/electronic); Databases: 124.

Community Environment: See University of South Florida.

■ **HOBE SOUND BIBLE COLLEGE**
PO Box 1065
Hobe Sound, FL 33475-1065
Tel: (772)546-5534
Fax: (561)545-1422
E-mail: elizabethmcmillan@hsbc.edu
Web Site: www.hsbc.edu

Description: Independent nondenominational, 4-year, coed. Awards associate and bachelor's degrees. Founded 1960. Setting: 84-acre small town campus. Endowment: $755,758. Educational spending for the previous fiscal year: $2892 per student. Faculty: 22 (8 full-time, 14 part-time). Student-undergrad faculty ratio is 13:1. 29 applied, 100% were admitted. Core. Calendar: semesters. Academic remediation for entering students, ESL program, advanced placement, independent study, distance learning, double major, summer session for credit, external degree program, internships.

Entrance Requirements: Open admission. Option: early admission. Required: essay, high school transcript, 3 recommendations, photograph, medical report, SAT or ACT. Entrance: noncompetitive. Application deadline: rolling. Notification: continuous until 8/30. Preference given to applicants committed to Wesleyan-Armenian theological position. Transfer credits accepted: Yes.

Costs Per Year: Application fee: $25. Comprehensive fee: $12,710 includes full-time tuition ($5600), mandatory fees ($940), and college room and board ($6170). College room only: $2370. Part-time tuition: $325 per credit hour. Part-time mandatory fees: $940 per year. Part-time tuition and fees vary according to course load.

Collegiate Environment: Orientation program. Choral group. Campus security: student patrols, late night transport-escort service, controlled dormitory access. College Library. Operations spending for the previous fiscal year: $62,439. 13 computers available on campus for general student use. A campuswide network can be accessed. Staffed computer lab on campus provides training in use of the Internet.

■ **HODGES UNIVERSITY**
2655 Northbrooke Dr.
Naples, FL 34119
Tel: (239)513-1122; Free: 800-466-8017
Fax: (239)513-9071
Web Site: www.hodges.edu

Description: Independent, comprehensive, coed. Awards associate, bachelor's, and master's degrees. Founded 1990. Setting: 31-acre suburban campus with easy access to Miami. Endowment: $2.8 million. Educational spending for the previous fiscal year: $17,053 per student. Total enrollment: 1,724. Faculty: 119 (59 full-time, 60 part-time). Student-undergrad faculty ratio is 5:1. Full-time: 991 students, 57% women, 43% men. Part-time: 496 students, 70% women, 30% men. Students come from 32 states and territories, 4% from out-of-state. 61% 25 or older, 16% transferred in. Academic areas with the most degrees conferred: business/marketing; interdisciplinary studies; health professions and related sciences. Core. Calendar: trimesters. Academic remediation for entering students, ESL program, services for LD students, advanced placement, accelerated degree program, independent study, distance learning, double major, summer session for credit, part-time degree program, external degree program, adult/continuing education programs, co-op programs and internships.

Entrance Requirements: Options: electronic application, deferred admission, international baccalaureate accepted. Required: essay, high school transcript, interview. Required for some: 2 recommendations, CPAt. Entrance: minimally difficult. Application deadline: rolling. Notification: continuous. Transfer credits accepted: Yes.

Costs Per Year: Application fee: $20. Tuition: $13,680 full-time, $570 per credit hour part-time. Mandatory fees: $500 full-time, $250 per term part-time.

Collegiate Environment: Orientation program. Most popular organizations: Ambassadors, Paralegal Club, Institute of Managerial Accountants, Sports club, Entrepreneurial Club. Major annual events: Student Recognition Banquet, Salvation Army Food Drive, Seasonal Socials. Student services: personal-psychological counseling. Campus security: late night transport-escort service, building security. Terry P. McMahan Libraries plus 1 other. Operations spending for the previous fiscal year: $713,295. 1,500 computers available on campus for general student use. A campuswide network can be accessed. Students can access the following: online class registration, student portal providing single sign-on access, learning management system, online storage, student calendar.

■ **HOPE COLLEGE OF ARTS AND SCIENCES**
1200 SW 3rd St.
Pompano Beach, FL 33069
Web Site: www.hcas.edu

Description: Proprietary, 2-year, coed.

■ **INDIAN RIVER STATE COLLEGE**
3209 Virginia Ave.
Fort Pierce, FL 34981-5596
Tel: (772)462-4700; Free: 866-792-4772
Fax: (772)462-4796
E-mail: estrock@irsc.edu
Web Site: www.irsc.edu

Description: State-supported, 4-year, coed. Part of Florida Community College System. Awards associate and bachelor's degrees. Founded 1960. Setting: 713-acre small town campus. Total enrollment: 17,665. Faculty: 859 (239 full-time, 620 part-time). Student-undergrad faculty ratio is 22:1. 1,877 applied, 100% were admitted. Full-time: 5,950 students, 53% women, 47% men. Part-time: 11,715 students, 64% women, 36% men. Students come from 19 states and territories, 110 other countries, 10% from out-of-state. 0.3% American Indian or Alaska Native, non-Hispanic/Latino; 18% Hispanic/Latino; 18% Black or African American, non-Hispanic/Latino; 2% Asian, non-Hispanic/Latino; 0.2% Native Hawaiian or other Pacific Islander, non-Hispanic/Latino; 1% international. 29% 25 or older, 14% transferred in. Core. Calendar: semesters. Academic remediation for entering students, ESL program, services for LD students, advanced placement, independent study, distance learning, summer session for credit, part-time degree program, adult/continuing education programs.

Entrance Requirements: Open admission. Options: early admission, deferred admission. Required: high school transcript. Entrance: noncompetitive. Application deadline: rolling. Notification: continuous. Transfer credits accepted: Yes.

Collegiate Environment: Orientation program. Drama-theater group, choral group. Social organizations: local fraternities, local sororities. Student services: health clinic, personal-psychological counseling, women's center. Campus security: 24-hour emergency response devices and patrols. Charles S. Miley Learning Resource Center. 3,400 computers available on campus for general student use. A campuswide network can be accessed. Students can access the following: online class registration. Staffed computer lab on campus.

Community Environment: A midsize city on the east coast of Florida with a subtropical climate, the area is known for citrus fruits and winter vegetables. Florida's Turnpike, I-95, the Florida East Coast Railroad and the Greyhound bus line serve the area. Community facilities include public libraries, YMCA, churches, hospitals, mental health centers, beaches and recreational activities. Part-time employment opportunities are moderate. Swimming from two ocean beaches, golf and sports fishing are the principal outdoor sports.

■ **JACKSONVILLE UNIVERSITY**
2800 University Blvd. N
Jacksonville, FL 32211
Tel: (904)256-8000; Free: 800-225-2027
Fax: (904)256-7086
Web Site: www.ju.edu

Description: Independent, comprehensive, coed. Awards bachelor's, master's, and doctoral degrees and post-master's certificates. Founded 1934. Setting: 260-acre suburban campus with easy access to Jacksonville, Saint Augustine. Endowment: $44.7 million. Research spending for the previous fiscal year: $2 million. Educational spending for the previous fiscal year: $26,111 per student. Total enrollment: 4,213. Faculty: 429 (240 full-time, 189 part-time). Student-undergrad faculty ratio is 11:1. 4,298 applied, 90% were admitted. Full-time: 2,292 students, 56% women, 44% men. Part-time: 628 students, 77% women, 23% men. Students come from 52 states and territories, 49 other countries, 35% from out-of-state. 0.3% American Indian or Alaska Native, non-Hispanic/Latino; 12% Hispanic/Latino; 21% Black or African American, non-Hispanic/Latino; 3% Asian, non-Hispanic/Latino; 0.4% Native Hawaiian or other Pacific Islander, non-Hispanic/Latino; 7% international. 29% 25 or older, 47% live on campus, 8% transferred in. Retention: 77% of full-time freshmen returned the following year. Academic areas with the most degrees conferred: health professions and related sciences; business/marketing; social sciences. Core. Calendar: semesters. Academic remediation for entering students, ESL program, services for LD students, advanced placement, accelerated degree program, self-designed majors, freshman honors college, honors program, independent study, distance learning, double major, summer session for credit, part-time degree program, adult/continuing education programs, co-op programs and internships, graduate courses open to undergrads. Off campus study at Florida Coastal School of Law; Dual-degree engineering programs also are offered in cooperation with Columbia University, Georgia Institute of Technology, University of Florida, University of Miami, Washington University in St. Louis, Mercer University, and Stevens Institute of Technology; Aviation Program is offered in cooperation with Delta Connection Academy, owned and operated by Delta Air Lines and Aerosim Flight Academy. Study abroad program. ROTC: Army, Naval.

Entrance Requirements: Options: electronic application, early admission, deferred admission, international baccalaureate accepted. Required: high school transcript, minimum 2 high school GPA. Recommended: interview. Required for some: essay, 2 recommendations, audition for music, dance, and theater majors; portfolio for art, computer art, and design majors; interview for the Honors Program. Entrance: moderately difficult. Application deadline: rolling. Notification: continuous. SAT Reasoning Test deadline: 6/1. SAT Subject Test deadline: 6/1. Transfer credits accepted: Yes.

Costs Per Year: Application fee: $30. Comprehensive fee: $52,470 includes full-time tuition ($38,140) and college room and board ($14,330). College room only: $9200. Part-time tuition: $1275 per credit hour. Part-time mandatory fees: $625 per credit hour.

Collegiate Environment: Orientation program. Drama-theater group, choral group, marching band, student-run newspaper, radio station. Social organizations: 106 open to all; national fraternities, national sororities, local fraternities, local sororities; 13% of eligible men and 19% of eligible women are members. Most popular organizations: Honor Student Association - Academic, Campus Connection 838 - Religious - Social, International Students Association - Social, Alpha Delta Pi - Sorority, Student Veterans of America - Special Interest. Major annual events: Homecoming, Win the Fin Spirit Competition, Amphitheater Concerts. Student services: health clinic, personal-psychological counseling. Campus security: 24-hour emergency response devices and patrols, student patrols, late night transport-escort service, controlled dormitory access, trained security patrols during evening hours. 1,344 college housing spaces available; 1,336 were occupied in 2018-19. Freshmen guaranteed college housing. On-campus residence required through junior year. Options: coed, men-only, women-only housing available. Carl S. Swisher Library. Books: 187,294 (physical), 268,187 (digital/electronic); Serial titles: 7,434 (physical), 55,516 (digital/electronic); Databases: 69. Weekly public service hours: 88; students can reserve study rooms. 400 computers available on campus for general student use. Computer purchase/lease plans available. A campuswide network can be accessed from student residence rooms and from off campus. Students can access the following: online class registration, learning management systems. Staffed computer lab on campus provides training in use of computers.

Community Environment: Jacksonville is located on the St. John's River near the Atlantic Ocean and has a temperate climate characterized by short mild winters and long relatively warm summers with the average temperature being 67.8 degrees. The city functions as the financial, industrial, transportation, and commercial center of Florida. Along with the usual community facilities, there are seven hospitals, churches of almost all denominations, excellent shopping facilities, a civic performing arts center which features the finest of concerts, plays, and ballet, and many little theatre groups. Jacksonville and the surrounding area provide ample beaches and facilities for yachting, swimming, fishing, and golfing. The Friendship Park on the south side of the St. Johns River contains the spectacular Friendship Fountain and marina. A sports complex consists of the Coliseum, Alltell,

Stadium, home of the NFL Jacksonville Jaguars; and Wolfson Park, home of the minor league baseball Jacksonville Suns. Part-time employment is available.

■ **JOHNSON UNIVERSITY FLORIDA**
1011 Bill Beck Blvd.
Kissimmee, FL 34744-5301
Tel: (407)847-8966; Free: 888-468-6322
Fax: (321)206-2007
E-mail: djohnson@johnsonu.edu
Web Site: www.johnsonu.edu

Description: Independent, comprehensive, coed, affiliated with Christian Churches and Churches of Christ. Administratively affiliated with Johnson University. Awards associate, bachelor's, and master's degrees. Founded 1976. Setting: 40-acre small town campus with easy access to Orlando. Total enrollment: 206. Faculty: 33 (10 full-time, 23 part-time). Student-undergrad faculty ratio is 10:1. 133 applied, 65% were admitted. Full-time: 187 students, 41% women, 59% men. Part-time: 14 students, 21% women, 79% men. Students come from 16 states and territories, 3 other countries, 15% from out-of-state. 20% Hispanic/Latino; 16% Black or African American, non-Hispanic/Latino; 0.5% Asian, non-Hispanic/Latino; 0.5% Native Hawaiian or other Pacific Islander, non-Hispanic/Latino; 4% international. 15% 25 or older, 74% live on campus, 29% transferred in. Retention: 67% of full-time freshmen returned the following year. Academic areas with the most degrees conferred: theology and religious vocations; health professions and related sciences; education. Core. Calendar: semesters. Advanced placement, independent study, distance learning, double major, summer session for credit, part-time degree program, adult/continuing education programs, internships. Study abroad program.

Entrance Requirements: Options: electronic application, early admission, deferred admission. Required: essay, high school transcript, minimum 2.5 high school GPA, 3 recommendations, SAT or ACT. Required for some: interview. Entrance: minimally difficult. Application deadlines: 7/15, 7/15 for nonresidents. Notification: continuous until 8/15. Transfer credits accepted: Yes.

Costs Per Year: Application fee: $35. Comprehensive fee: $24,378 includes full-time tuition ($15,480), mandatory fees ($1440), and college room and board ($7458). Part-time tuition: $500 per credit hour.

Collegiate Environment: Orientation program. Choral group. Social organizations: 4 open to all. Most popular organizations: Student Government Association, Harvesters (Missions), Timothy club (preachers), Ultimate Frisbee. Major annual events: Fall Fling, Christmas Banquet, Missions Banquet. Student services: personal-psychological counseling. Campus security: controlled dormitory access. 221 college housing spaces available; 146 were occupied in 2018-19. No special consideration for freshman housing applicants. Options: men-only, women-only housing available. Library. Books: 35,023 (physical), 345,536 (digital/electronic); Serial titles: 120 (physical), 44,275 (digital/electronic); Databases: 2,145. 16 computers available on campus for general student use. A campuswide network can be accessed. Students can access the following: online class registration.

■ **JOHNSON & WALES UNIVERSITY**
1701 NE 127th St.
North Miami, FL 33181
Tel: (305)892-7000; Free: 866-598-3567
Fax: (305)892-7030
E-mail: mia@admissions.jwu.edu
Web Site: www.jwu.edu/northmiami

Description: Independent, 4-year, coed. Awards associate and bachelor's degrees. Founded 1992. Setting: 8-acre suburban campus with easy access to Miami. Total enrollment: 1,752. Faculty: 79 (57 full-time, 22 part-time). Student-undergrad faculty ratio is 25:1. 4,049 applied, 76% were admitted. Full-time: 1,576 students, 63% women, 37% men. Part-time: 176 students, 60% women, 40% men. 53% from out-of-state. 0.2% American Indian or Alaska Native, non-Hispanic/Latino; 23% Hispanic/Latino; 31% Black or African American, non-Hispanic/Latino; 0.4% Asian, non-Hispanic/Latino; 0.1% Native Hawaiian or other Pacific Islander, non-Hispanic/Latino; 10% international. 28% 25 or older, 55% live on campus, 6% transferred in. Retention: 69% of full-time freshmen returned the following year. Academic areas with the most degrees conferred: English; family and consumer sciences; law/legal studies. Core. Calendar: quarters. Academic remediation for entering students, ESL program, services for LD students, advanced placement, accelerated degree program, honors program, independent study, summer session for credit, part-time degree program, co-op programs and internships. Study abroad program.

Entrance Requirements: Options: early admission, deferred admission, international baccalaureate accepted. Required: high school transcript. Recommended: minimum 2 high school GPA. Required for some: essay, interview, SAT or ACT. Entrance: moderately difficult. Application deadline: rolling. Notification: continuous.

Collegiate Environment: Orientation program. Social organizations: national fraternities, national sororities, local fraternities, local sororities. Student services: personal-psychological counseling. Campus security: 24-hour emergency response devices and patrols, video camera surveillance throughout campus. Florida Campus Library.

■ **JONES TECHNICAL INSTITUTE**
8813 Western Way
Jacksonville, FL 32256
Web Site: www.jtech.org
Description: Proprietary, 2-year, coed.

■ **JOSE MARIA VARGAS UNIVERSITY**
10131 Pines Blvd.
Pembroke Pines, FL 33026
Tel: (954)322-4446
Web Site: www.jmvu.edu
Description: Proprietary, comprehensive, coed. Awards associate, bachelor's, and master's degrees.

■ **KEISER UNIVERSITY**
1500 NW 49th St.
Fort Lauderdale, FL 33309
Tel: (954)776-4456; Free: 888-534-7379
Web Site: www.keiseruniversity.edu
Description: Independent, university, coed. Awards associate, bachelor's, master's, and doctoral degrees and post-master's certificates (profile includes data from campuses located in Daytona Beach, Fort Lauderdale, Fort Myers, Jacksonville, Lakeland, Melbourne, Miami, Orlando, Pembroke Pines, Port St. Lucie, Sarasota, Tallahassee, Tampa, and West Palm Beach; not all programs offered at all locations, but many classes offered 100% online). Founded 1977. Setting: urban campus. Total enrollment: 17,129. Faculty: 1,440 (1,023 full-time, 417 part-time). Student-undergrad faculty ratio is 12:1. Full-time: 12,007 students, 67% women, 33% men. Part-time: 4,032 students, 72% women, 28% men. Students come from 54 states and territories, 11% from out-of-state. 0.3% American Indian or Alaska Native, non-Hispanic/Latino; 31% Hispanic/Latino; 20% Black or African American, non-Hispanic/Latino; 2% Asian, non-Hispanic/Latino; 0.3% international. 63% 25 or older, 4% transferred in. Retention: 90% of full-time freshmen returned the following year. Academic areas with the most degrees conferred: business/marketing; health professions and related sciences; homeland security, law enforcement, firefighting, and protective services. Core. Calendar: 3 semesters per year. ESL program, advanced placement, distance learning, summer session for credit, part-time degree program, internships.

Entrance Requirements: Options: electronic application, international baccalaureate accepted. Required: high school transcript, SAT or ACT or Wonderlic aptitude test. Application deadline: rolling. Notification: continuous. Transfer credits accepted: Yes.

Costs Per Year: Application fee: $55. Tuition: $28,320 full-time, $1180 per credit hour part-time. Mandatory fees: $1760 full-time. College room only: $6224.

Collegiate Environment: Orientation program. Most popular organizations: Student Government Association, Phi Theta Kappa, Sigma Beta Delta International Honor Society, Alpha Phi Sigma National Honor Society, Student Nurses Association. Campus security: 24-hour patrols, late night transport-escort service, AlertNow Rapid Communications Service, Campus Response Teams. Keiser University Library. Books: 150,394 (physical), 145,000 (digital/electronic); Serial titles: 188 (physical), 29 (digital/electronic); Databases: 257.

■ **LAKE-SUMTER STATE COLLEGE**
9501 US Hwy. 441
Leesburg, FL 34788-8751
Tel: (352)787-3747
E-mail: admissinquiry@lscc.edu
Web Site: www.lssc.edu
Description: State and locally supported, 2-year, coed. Part of Florida College System. Awards certificates, diplomas, and transfer associate degrees.

Founded 1962. Setting: 112-acre suburban campus with easy access to Orlando. Endowment: $3.9 million. Total enrollment: 4,929. Faculty: 428 (84 full-time, 344 part-time). Student-undergrad faculty ratio is 17:1. 1,353 applied, 100% were admitted. Full-time: 1,641 students, 59% women, 41% men. Part-time: 3,288 students, 64% women, 36% men. 1% from out-of-state. 29% 25 or older, 5% transferred in. Core. Calendar: semesters. Academic remediation for entering students, services for LD students, advanced placement, independent study, distance learning, double major, summer session for credit, part-time degree program, adult/continuing education programs, co-op programs and internships. Off campus study.

Entrance Requirements: Open admission except for nursing program. Option: electronic application. Required: high school transcript. Entrance: noncompetitive. Application deadline: rolling. Notification: continuous. Transfer credits accepted: Yes.

Collegiate Environment: Orientation program. Drama-theater group, choral group, student-run newspaper. Social organizations: 19 open to all. Most popular organizations: Phi Theta Kappa, Student Government Association, Theatre Arts Society, Nursing Student's Association, Safire. Student services: women's center. Campus security: 24-hour emergency response devices. Lake-Sumter Community College Library. Operations spending for the previous fiscal year: $699,594. 825 computers available on campus for general student use. A campuswide network can be accessed from off-campus. Students can access the following: online class registration. Staffed computer lab on campus provides training in use of computers, software, and the Internet.

Community Environment: Leesburg is a rapidly growing rural area with a temperate climate, located in central Florida near the shores of Lakes Griffin and Harris, within easy driving distance of metropolitan areas. Community facilities include numerous libraries, churches, general hospitals, active major civic and service groups. Part-time and full-time employment are available. Many forms of recreation are found, including fishing, swimming, golf, tennis, shuffleboard, water skiing and hunting. Lake Griffin State Park nearby provides additional recreational facilities.

■ **LYNN UNIVERSITY**
3601 N Military Trl.
Boca Raton, FL 33431-5598
Tel: (561)237-7000; Free: 800-888-5966
Fax: (561)241-3552
E-mail: spapaleo@lynn.edu
Web Site: www.lynn.edu
Description: Independent, comprehensive, coed. Awards associate, bachelor's, master's, and doctoral degrees and post-master's certificates. Founded 1962. Setting: 123-acre suburban campus with easy access to Fort Lauderdale. Total enrollment: 3,010. Faculty: 183 (127 full-time, 56 part-time). Student-undergrad faculty ratio is 17:1. 3,003 applied, 85% were admitted. Full-time: 1,826 students, 50% women, 50% men. Part-time: 378 students, 40% women, 60% men. Students come from 44 states and territories, 81 other countries, 41% from out-of-state. 0.3% American Indian or Alaska Native, non-Hispanic/Latino; 15% Hispanic/Latino; 11% Black or African American, non-Hispanic/Latino; 1% Asian, non-Hispanic/Latino; 17% international. 11% 25 or older, 46% live on campus, 17% transferred in. Retention: 69% of full-time freshmen returned the following year. Academic areas with the most degrees conferred: business/marketing; communication/journalism; homeland security, law enforcement, firefighting, and protective services. Core. Calendar: semesters plus 3 summer sessions. Academic remediation for entering students, ESL program, services for LD students, advanced placement, accelerated degree program, self-designed majors, independent study, distance learning, double major, summer session for credit, part-time degree program, co-op programs and internships, graduate courses open to undergrads. Study abroad program. ROTC: Air Force (c).

Entrance Requirements: Options: electronic application, early admission, early action, deferred admission, international baccalaureate accepted. Required: essay, high school transcript. Recommended: interview, SAT or ACT. Required for some: audition for Conservatory of Music. Entrance: moderately difficult. Application deadlines: 3/1, 11/15 for early action. Notification: continuous until 12/15, 12/15 for early action. SAT Reasoning Test deadline: 8/1. Transfer credits accepted: Yes. Applicants placed on waiting list: 9. Wait-listed applicants offered admission: 7. Early action applicants: 1,004. Early action applicants admitted: 762.

Costs Per Year: Application fee: $45. One-time mandatory fee: $1000. Comprehensive fee: $50,380 includes full-time tuition ($35,960), mandatory fees ($2250), and college room and board ($12,170). Full-time tuition and fees vary according to program. Room and board charges vary according to board plan and housing facility. Part-time tuition: $1040 per credit hour. Part-time tuition varies according to course load and program.

Collegiate Environment: Orientation program. Drama-theater group, student-run newspaper, radio station. Social organizations: 32 open to all; national fraternities, national sororities; 5% of eligible men and 4% of eligible women are members. Most popular organizations: Knights of the Round Table, intramural groups, student newspaper, Student Activities Board, Greek Life. Major annual events: Founder's Day, Holiday Gala, Spring Carnival. Student services: health clinic, personal-psychological counseling, women's center. Campus security: 24-hour emergency response devices and patrols, late night transport-escort service, controlled dormitory access, video monitor at residence entrances. Eugene M. and Christine E. Lynn Library. Books: 58,952 (physical), 239,257 (digital/electronic); Serial titles: 401 (physical), 43,029 (digital/electronic); Databases: 118. Weekly public service hours: 96. Operations spending for the previous fiscal year: $977,646. 150 computers available on campus for general student use. Computer purchase/lease plans available. A campuswide network can be accessed from student residence rooms and from off campus. Students can access the following: online registration with advisor approval for juniors, seniors and MBA students. Staffed computer lab on campus.

Community Environment: See Florida Atlantic University.

■ MARCONI INTERNATIONAL UNIVERSITY
111 NE 1st St., 6th Fl.
Miami, FL 33132
Tel: (305)266-7678
E-mail: info@marconiinternational.org
Web Site: www.miuniversity.edu
Description: Proprietary, comprehensive, coed. Awards bachelor's and master's degrees.

■ MED-LIFE INSTITUTE (KISSIMMEE)
4727 W Irlo Bronson Memorial Hwy.
Kissimmee, FL 34746
Web Site: www.medlifeinstitute.com
Description: Proprietary, 2-year, coed.

■ MED-LIFE INSTITUTE (LAUDERDALE LAKES)
4000 N State Rd. 7
Lauderdale Lakes, FL 33319
Web Site: www.medlifeinstitute.com
Description: Proprietary, 2-year, coed.

■ MED-LIFE INSTITUTE (NAPLES)
4995 E Tamiami Trl.
Naples, FL 34112
Web Site: www.medlifeinstitute.com
Description: Proprietary, 2-year, coed.

■ MEDICAL PREP INSTITUTE OF TAMPA BAY
2304 E Busch Blvd.
Tampa, FL 33612
Description: Proprietary, 2-year, coed.

■ MERIDIAN COLLEGE
7020 Professional Pky. E
Sarasota, FL 34240
Tel: (941)377-4880
Web Site: www.meridian.edu
Description: Proprietary, 2-year, coed. Awards diplomas, transfer associate, and terminal associate degrees. Founded 1982.

■ MIAMI DADE COLLEGE
300 NE Second Ave.
Miami, FL 33132
Tel: (305)237-8888
Fax: (305)237-3761
E-mail: evizoso@mdc.edu
Web Site: www.mdc.edu
Description: State and locally supported, primarily 2-year, coed. Part of Florida College System. Awards certificates, transfer associate, terminal associate, and bachelor's degrees. Founded 1960. Setting: urban campus. Endowment: $137.1 million. Educational spending for the previous fiscal year: $2845 per student. Total enrollment: 56,001. Faculty: 2,355 (704 full-

time, 1,651 part-time). Student-undergrad faculty ratio is 26:1. 44,910 applied, 100% were admitted. Full-time: 23,589 students, 57% women, 43% men. Part-time: 32,412 students, 58% women, 42% men. Students come from 37 states and territories, 165 other countries, 0.4% from out-of-state. 0.1% American Indian or Alaska Native, non-Hispanic/Latino; 70% Hispanic/Latino; 14% Black or African American, non-Hispanic/Latino; 1% Asian, non-Hispanic/Latino; 0.1% Native Hawaiian or other Pacific Islander, non-Hispanic/Latino; 6% international. 28% 25 or older, 1% transferred in. Academic areas with the most degrees conferred: business/marketing; health professions and related sciences; homeland security, law enforcement, firefighting, and protective services. Core. Calendar: 16-16-6-6. Academic remediation for entering students, ESL program, services for LD students, advanced placement, accelerated degree program, freshman honors college, honors program, independent study, distance learning, summer session for credit, part-time degree program, adult/continuing education programs, co-op programs and internships. Off campus study. Study abroad program. ROTC: Army, Air Force (c).

Entrance Requirements: Open admission. Options: electronic application, early admission, international baccalaureate accepted. Required: high school transcript. Entrance: noncompetitive. Application deadline: rolling. Notification: continuous. Transfer credits accepted: Yes.

Costs Per Year: Application fee: $30. One-time mandatory fee: $30. State resident tuition: $1,987 full-time, $82.78 per credit hour part-time. Nonresident tuition: $7,947 full-time, $331.11 per credit hour part-time. Mandatory fees: $851 full-time, $35.44 per credit hour part-time. Full-time tuition and fees vary according to course load, degree level, and program. Part-time tuition and fees vary according to course load, degree level, and program.

Collegiate Environment: Orientation program. Drama-theater group, choral group, student-run newspaper, radio station. Social organizations: 40 open to all; 40% of eligible men and 60% of eligible women are members. Most popular organizations: Student Government Association, Phi Theta Kappa, Phi Beta Lambda (business), Future Educators of America Professional, Kappa Delta Pi Honor Society (education). Major annual events: Miami International Film Festival, Miami Book Fair International, Graduation Commencement Ceremony. Student services: health clinic, personal-psychological counseling. Campus security: 24-hour emergency response devices and patrols, student patrols, late night transport-escort service, Emergency Mass Notification System (EMNS), campus public address systems, LiveSafe mobile safety App for students/employees. Miami Dade College Learning Resources plus 9 others. Books: 185,820 (physical), 60,221 (digital/electronic); Serial titles: 708 (physical), 46,482 (digital/electronic); Databases: 126. Weekly public service hours: 69; students can reserve study rooms. Operations spending for the previous fiscal year: $363,797. 9,655 computers available on campus for general student use. A campuswide network can be accessed. Students can access the following: online class registration, admissions, student feedback of faculty, financial aid. Staffed computer lab on campus provides training in use of computers, software, and the Internet.

Community Environment: See Florida International University.

■ MIAMI INTERNATIONAL UNIVERSITY OF ART & DESIGN
1501 Biscayne Blvd., Ste. 100
Miami, FL 33132-1418
Tel: (305)428-5700; Free: 800-225-9023
Fax: (305)374-7946
Web Site: www.artinstitutes.edu/miami
Description: Proprietary, comprehensive, coed. Part of Education Management Corporation. Awards associate, bachelor's, and master's degrees. Founded 1965. Setting: urban campus. Calendar: quarters.
Community Environment: See Barry University.

■ MIAMI REGIONAL UNIVERSITY
700 S Royal Poinciana Blvd.
Miami Springs, FL 33166
Tel: (305)442-9223
Web Site: www.mru.edu
Description: Proprietary, comprehensive, coed. Awards associate, bachelor's, and master's degrees.

■ MILLENNIA ATLANTIC UNIVERSITY
3801 NW 97th Ave.
Doral, FL 33178
Tel: (786)331-1000

Web Site: www.maufl.edu

Description: Proprietary, comprehensive, coed. Awards associate, bachelor's, and master's degrees. Calendar: semesters.

■ NEW COLLEGE OF FLORIDA

5800 Bay Shore Rd.
Sarasota, FL 34243
Tel: (941)487-5000
Web Site: www.ncf.edu

Description: State-supported, comprehensive, coed. Part of State University System of Florida. Awards bachelor's and master's degrees. Founded 1960. Setting: 110-acre suburban campus with easy access to Tampa-St. Petersburg. Endowment: $41.5 million. Research spending for the previous fiscal year: $784,844. Educational spending for the previous fiscal year: $13,319 per student. Total enrollment: 837. Faculty: 122 (88 full-time, 34 part-time). Student-undergrad faculty ratio is 10:1. 1,340 applied, 77% were admitted. 37% from top 10% of their high school class, 66% from top quarter, 93% from top half. 5 National Merit Scholars. Full-time: 808 students, 62% women, 38% men. Students come from 40 states and territories, 20 other countries, 17% from out-of-state. 17% Hispanic/Latino; 3% Black or African American, non-Hispanic/Latino; 3% Asian, non-Hispanic/Latino; 2% international. 3% 25 or older, 79% live on campus, 4% transferred in. Retention: 76% of full-time freshmen returned the following year. Academic areas with the most degrees conferred: liberal arts/general studies; interdisciplinary studies; natural resources/environmental science. Core. Calendar: 4-1-4. Services for LD students, accelerated degree program, self-designed majors, freshman honors college, honors program, independent study, double major, summer session for credit, internships, graduate courses open to undergrads. Off campus study at National Student Exchange and the Consortium for Innovative Environments in Learning. Study abroad program.

Entrance Requirements: Options: electronic application, early admission, early decision, deferred admission, international baccalaureate accepted. Required: essay, high school transcript, 1 recommendation, SAT or ACT. Recommended: minimum 3 high school GPA. Entrance: very difficult. Application deadline: 4/15. Notification: 4/25. SAT Reasoning Test deadline: 4/15. Transfer credits accepted: Yes. Applicants placed on waiting list: 72. Wait-listed applicants offered admission: 9. Early decision applicants: 0. Early decision applicants admitted: 0.

Costs Per Year: Application fee: $30. State resident tuition: $6916 full-time. Nonresident tuition: $29,944 full-time.

Collegiate Environment: Orientation program. Drama-theater group, choral group, student-run newspaper, radio station. Social organizations: 63 open to all; 45% of eligible men and 65% of eligible women are members. Most popular organizations: Dance Collective, Queery, New College Student Alliance, Generation Action, Bullsharks Dive Club. Major annual events: Late Night Breakfast, Dance Collective Performances, New Prom. Student services: health clinic, personal-psychological counseling. Campus security: 24-hour emergency response devices and patrols, student patrols, late night transport-escort service, controlled dormitory access, campus police are state certified police officers and available 24/7. College housing designed to accommodate 629 students; 632 undergraduates lived in college housing during 2018-19. Freshmen guaranteed college housing. On-campus residence required through senior year. Option: coed housing available. Jane Bancroft Cook Library. Books: 226,520 (physical), 26,632 (digital/electronic); Serial titles: 1,411 (physical), 1,899 (digital/electronic); Databases: 210. Weekly public service hours: 96. Operations spending for the previous fiscal year: $1.1 million. 105 computers available on campus for general student use. A campuswide network can be accessed from student residence rooms and from off campus. Students can access the following: online class registration. Staffed computer lab on campus provides training in use of computers, software, and the Internet.

■ NEW WORLD SCHOOL OF THE ARTS

300 NE 2nd Ave.
Miami, FL 33132
Tel: (305)237-3135
Fax: (305)237-3794
E-mail: eferrer2@mdc.edu
Web Site: www.mdc.edu/nwsa

Description: State-supported, 4-year, coed. Administratively affiliated with Miami Dade County Public Schools, Miami Dade College, and the University of Florida. Awards associate and bachelor's degrees. Founded 1984. Setting: 5-acre urban campus with easy access to Miami-Dade, Broward, Palm

Beach Counties. Endowment: $8.3 million. Total enrollment: 335. Faculty: 77 (22 full-time, 55 part-time). Student-undergrad faculty ratio is 5:1. 384 applied, 52% were admitted. Full-time: 335 students, 57% women, 43% men. Students come from 12 states and territories, 9 other countries, 4% from out-of-state. 62% Hispanic/Latino; 13% Black or African American, non-Hispanic/Latino; 4% Asian, non-Hispanic/Latino. 12% 25 or older, 6% transferred in. Retention: 70% of full-time freshmen returned the following year. Academic area with the most degrees conferred: visual and performing arts. Core. Calendar: semesters. Academic remediation for entering students, ESL program, services for LD students, advanced placement, freshman honors college, independent study, distance learning, summer session for credit, co-op programs and internships. Study abroad program.

Entrance Requirements: Options: electronic application, early decision. Required: essay, high school transcript, 2 recommendations, interview, audition or portfolio submission. Recommended: SAT or ACT. Entrance: noncompetitive. Application deadline: rolling. Notification: continuous, rolling for early decision. Transfer credits accepted: Yes.

Collegiate Environment: Orientation program. Social organizations: Student Government Association; 15% of eligible men and 25% of eligible women are members. Most popular organization: Student Government. Major annual event: Rising Stars. Student services: personal-psychological counseling. Campus security: 24-hour emergency response devices and patrols. Miami Dade Community College Library (Wolfson Campus) plus 1 other. Students can reserve study rooms. 100 computers available on campus for general student use. Computer purchase/lease plans available. A campuswide network can be accessed from off-campus. Students can access the following: online class registration. Staffed computer lab on campus provides training in use of computers, software, and the Internet.

■ NORTH FLORIDA COMMUNITY COLLEGE

325 NW Turner Davis Dr.
Madison, FL 32340
Tel: (850)973-2288; Free: 866-937-6322
Fax: (850)973-1696
Web Site: www.nfcc.edu

Description: State-supported, 2-year, coed. Awards certificates, transfer associate, and terminal associate degrees. Founded 1958. Setting: 109-acre small town campus. Total enrollment: 1,297. Faculty: 44 (25 full-time, 19 part-time). Student-undergrad faculty ratio is 18:1. Full-time: 593 students, 64% women, 36% men. Part-time: 704 students, 65% women, 35% men. 31% 25 or older. Core. Calendar: semesters. Academic remediation for entering students, services for LD students, advanced placement, accelerated degree program, honors program, distance learning, summer session for credit, part-time degree program, adult/continuing education programs.

Entrance Requirements: Open admission. Option: early admission. Required: high school transcript, minimum 2.0 high school GPA. Entrance: noncompetitive. Application deadline: rolling.

Collegiate Environment: Drama-theater group, choral group, student-run newspaper. Social organizations: 7 open to all; local sororities. Most popular organizations: Student Government Association, Sentinel Ambassadors, Phi Theta Kappa, African-American Student Union, Fellowship of Christian Athletes. Major annual event: Octoberfest. Student services: women's center. Campus security: 24-hour emergency response devices. Dr. Marshall Hamilton Library. 275 computers available on campus for general student use. A campuswide network can be accessed. Students can access the following: online class registration. Staffed computer lab on campus.

Community Environment: Madison is located in a rural area with a temperate climate. Railroads and buses serve the area along with three highways. Community facilities include a public library, hospital, ten churches, and major civic and fraternal organizations. Within easy reach are large shopping and cultural centers. Recreational facilities include a golf course, recreation center, and many facilities for all water sports. Part-time employment opportunities are limited.

■ NORTHWEST FLORIDA STATE COLLEGE

100 College Blvd.
Niceville, FL 32578-1295
Tel: (850)678-5111
E-mail: cooperk@nwfsc.edu
Web Site: www.nwfsc.edu

Description: State and locally supported, primarily 2-year, coed. Part of Florida College System. Awards certificates, transfer associate, terminal associate, and bachelor's degrees. Founded 1963. Setting: 264-acre small town campus. Endowment: $28.6 million. Educational spending for the previous fiscal year: $5136 per student. Total enrollment: 6,938. Faculty: 266 (102 full-time, 164 part-time). Student-undergrad faculty ratio is 26:1. Full-time: 2,758 students, 59% women, 41% men. Part-time: 4,180 students, 59% women, 41% men. Students come from 12 states and territories, 4% from out-of-state. 0.5% American Indian or Alaska Native, non-Hispanic/Latino; 7% Hispanic/Latino; 9% Black or African American, non-Hispanic/Latino; 3% Asian, non-Hispanic/Latino; 0.4% Native Hawaiian or other Pacific Islander, non-Hispanic/Latino; 0.5% international. 45% 25 or older, 7% transferred in. Academic areas with the most degrees conferred: business/marketing; education; health professions and related sciences. Core. Calendar: semesters plus summer sessions. Academic remediation for entering students, ESL program, services for LD students, advanced placement, accelerated degree program, independent study, distance learning, summer session for credit, part-time degree program, adult/continuing education programs, internships. Study abroad program. ROTC: Army.

Entrance Requirements: Open admission. Option: electronic application. Required: high school transcript. Entrance: noncompetitive. Application deadline: rolling. Notification: continuous. Preference given to state residents. Transfer credits accepted: Yes.

Collegiate Environment: Orientation program. Drama-theater group, choral group. Social organizations: 18 open to all. Most popular organizations: Student Nurses Association, Ambassadors, Pre-Professional Educators Association, Campus Christian Fellowship, Film Club. Major annual events: College Night, Student Government Association Picnic, Student Government Association Picnic. Student services: women's center. Northwest Florida State College Learning Resources Center. Operations spending for the previous fiscal year: $908,962. 643 computers available on campus for general student use. A campuswide network can be accessed from off-campus. Students can access the following: online class registration, course/instructor evaluations. Staffed computer lab on campus provides training in use of computers, software, and the Internet.

Community Environment: Twin cities with temperate climate, largely residential in nature. Many residents are military retirees or civil service personnel. Airlines and Greyhound and AmTrak buses serve the area. Large shopping centers are within easy driving distance. Part-time job opportunities for students are limited.

■ NOVA SOUTHEASTERN UNIVERSITY

3301 College Ave.
Fort Lauderdale, FL 33314-7796
Tel: (954)262-7300; Free: 800-541-NOVA
Fax: (954)262-3967
Web Site: www.nova.edu

Description: Independent, university, coed. Awards associate, bachelor's, master's, and doctoral degrees and post-master's certificates. Founded 1964. Setting: 314-acre suburban campus. Endowment: $117.8 million. Research spending for the previous fiscal year: $20.1 million. Educational spending for the previous fiscal year: $16,823 per student. Total enrollment: 20,793. Faculty: 1,602 (805 full-time, 797 part-time). Student-undergrad faculty ratio is 17:1. 7,779 applied, 58% were admitted. 39% from top 10% of their high school class, 55% from top quarter, 88% from top half. Full-time: 3,154 students, 67% women, 33% men. Part-time: 1,343 students, 80% women, 20% men. Students come from 47 states and territories, 66 other countries, 22% from out-of-state. 0.2% American Indian or Alaska Native, non-Hispanic/Latino; 27% Hispanic/Latino; 15% Black or African American, non-Hispanic/Latino; 10% Asian, non-Hispanic/Latino; 0.1% Native Hawaiian or other Pacific Islander, non-Hispanic/Latino; 6% international. 23% 25 or older, 25% live on campus, 13% transferred in. Retention: 79% of full-time freshmen returned the following year. Academic areas with the most degrees conferred: health professions and related sciences; biological/life sciences; business/marketing. Core. Calendar: trimesters. Academic remediation for entering students, services for LD students, advanced placement, freshman honors college, honors program, independent study, distance learning, double major, summer session for credit, part-time degree program, adult/continuing education programs, internships. Off campus study. Study abroad program.

Entrance Requirements: Options: electronic application, early admission, early decision, early action, deferred admission, international baccalaureate accepted. Required: minimum 3 high school GPA, SAT or ACT. Required for some: essay, high school transcript. Entrance: moderately difficult. Application deadlines: 2/1, 11/1 for early decision, 11/1 for early action. Notification: continuous, 10/16 for early decision, rolling for early action. SAT Reasoning Test deadline: 2/1. Transfer credits accepted: Yes. Early decision applicants: 285. Early decision applicants admitted: 115. Early action applicants: 2,600. Early action applicants admitted: 1,965.

Costs Per Year: Application fee: $50. Tuition: $29,940 full-time, $998 per credit hour part-time. Mandatory fees: $960 full-time. Full-time tuition and fees vary according to program. Part-time tuition varies according to course load and program. College room only: $9938. Room charges vary according to housing facility.

Collegiate Environment: Orientation program. Drama-theater group, choral group, student-run newspaper, radio station. Social organizations: 100 open to all; national fraternities, national sororities; 25% of eligible men and 24% of eligible women are members. Most popular organizations: HOSA: Future Health Professionals, Make-a Meal Service Organization, Student Government Association, Delta Epsilon Iota, Pre-Med. Major annual events: CommunityFest, Sharkapalooza, Homecoming. Student services: health clinic, personal-psychological counseling. Campus security: 24-hour emergency response devices and patrols, late night transport-escort service, controlled dormitory access, shuttle bus service. Alvin Sherman Library, Research, and Information Technology Center plus 4 others. Books: 498,823 (physical), 379,928 (digital/electronic); Serial titles: 6,035 (physical), 20,738 (digital/electronic); Databases: 577. Study areas open 24 hours, 5-7 days a week; students can reserve study rooms. Operations spending for the previous fiscal year: $13,276. 3,000 computers available on campus for general student use. A campuswide network can be accessed from student residence rooms and from off campus. Students can access the following: online class registration. Staffed computer lab on campus (open 24 hours a day) provides training in use of computers, software, and the Internet.

Community Environment: Nova Southeastern University is located on a 227-acre site west of Fort Lauderdale in the town of Davie, 10 miles inland from the Atlantic Ocean and easily accessible from major U.S. and state highways including the Sunshine State Parkway. The climate is subtropical and the average year-round temperature is 75 degrees. Nova Southeastern University is situated in close proximity to Broward Community College and to the Nova complex of elementary, middle and high schools.

■ NRI INSTITUTE OF HEALTH SCIENCES

500 Royal Palm Beach Blvd.
Royal Palm Beach, FL 33411
Description: Proprietary, 2-year, coed.

■ PALM BEACH ATLANTIC UNIVERSITY

901 S Flagler Dr.
West Palm Beach, FL 33416-4708
Tel: (561)803-2000; Free: 888-GO-TO-PBA
E-mail: joseph_bryan@pba.edu
Web Site: www.pba.edu

Description: Independent nondenominational, comprehensive, coed. Awards bachelor's, master's, and doctoral degrees. Founded 1968. Setting: 100-acre urban campus with easy access to Miami-Dade County. Endowment: $81.2 million. Research spending for the previous fiscal year: $36,353. Educational spending for the previous fiscal year: $8865 per student. Total enrollment: 3,705. Faculty: 373 (180 full-time, 193 part-time). Student-undergrad faculty ratio is 12:1. 1,444 applied, 95% were admitted. Full-time: 2,269 students, 65% women, 35% men. Part-time: 586 students, 56% women, 44% men. 36% from out-of-state. 0.2% American Indian or Alaska Native, non-Hispanic/Latino; 16% Hispanic/Latino; 9% Black or African American, non-Hispanic/Latino; 2% Asian, non-Hispanic/Latino; 0.3% Native Hawaiian or other Pacific Islander, non-Hispanic/Latino; 5% international. 12% 25 or older, 48% live on campus, 8% transferred in. Retention: 75% of full-time freshmen returned the following year. Academic areas with the most degrees conferred: business/marketing; psychology; health professions and related sciences. Core. Calendar: semesters. Academic remediation for entering students, services for LD students, advanced placement, accelerated degree program, self-designed majors, honors program, independent study, distance learning, double major, summer session for credit, part-time degree program, adult/continuing education programs, internships, graduate courses open to undergrads. Off campus study at Council of Christian Colleges and Universities, Center for Experiential Learning, Center for Integrated Science Learning, Center for franchising. Study abroad program. ROTC: Army (c).

Entrance Requirements: Options: electronic application, early admission, early action, deferred admission, international baccalaureate accepted. Required: essay, high school transcript, SAT or ACT. Required for some: interview. Entrance: moderately difficult. Application deadline: rolling. Notification: continuous. SAT Reasoning Test deadline: 8/1. Transfer credits accepted: Yes.

Costs Per Year: Application fee: $50. Tuition: $31,920 full-time, $767 per credit hour part-time. Mandatory fees: $580 full-time. College room only: $5530.

Collegiate Environment: Orientation program. Drama-theater group, choral group, student-run newspaper. Social organizations: 50 open to all; Impact Leadership Team. Most popular organizations: Impact Leadership Team, Nursing Student Association, Nurses Christian Fellowship, Student Government, Sigma Alpha Omega. Major annual events: Christival, Paradise Weekend, Sailfish Cup. Student services: health clinic, personal-psychological counseling. Campus security: 24-hour emergency response devices and patrols, late night transport-escort service, controlled dormitory access. Freshmen guaranteed college housing. On-campus residence required through senior year. Options: coed, men-only, women-only housing available. Warren Library plus 1 other. Books: 143,334 (physical), 126,921 (digital/electronic); Serial titles: 114 (physical), 121,795 (digital/electronic); Databases: 143. Weekly public service hours: 100; students can reserve study rooms. Operations spending for the previous fiscal year: $1 million. 350 computers available on campus for general student use. A campuswide network can be accessed. Students can access the following: online class registration. Staffed computer lab on campus (open 24 hours a day) provides training in use of computers, software, and the Internet.

Community Environment: West Palm Beach is the county seat of Palm Beach County, one of the fastest-growing areas in Florida. The campus is minutes away from the Atlantic Ocean and just across the Intracoastal Waterway from Palm Beach. Cultural, athletic and recreational events abound, and a railway system offers easy access to Fort Lauderdale and Miami.

■ **PALM BEACH STATE COLLEGE**
4200 Congress Ave.
Lake Worth, FL 33461-4796
Tel: (561)967-7222
Web Site: www.palmbeachstate.edu
Description: State-supported, 4-year, coed. Part of Florida College System. Awards associate and bachelor's degrees. Founded 1933. Setting: 114-acre urban campus with easy access to West Palm Beach. Endowment: $18.3 million. Educational spending for the previous fiscal year: $3866 per student. Total enrollment: 30,052. Faculty: 1,170 (323 full-time, 847 part-time). Student-undergrad faculty ratio is 23:1. 5,653 applied, 100% were admitted. Full-time: 8,303 students, 51% women, 49% men. Part-time: 21,749 students, 60% women, 40% men. Students come from 23 states and territories. 0.2% American Indian or Alaska Native, non-Hispanic/Latino; 31% Hispanic/Latino; 26% Black or African American, non-Hispanic/Latino; 3% Asian, non-Hispanic/Latino; 0.2% Native Hawaiian or other Pacific Islander, non-Hispanic/Latino; 2% international. 30% 25 or older, 4% transferred in. Core. Calendar: semesters. Academic remediation for entering students, ESL program, services for LD students, advanced placement, self-designed majors, freshman honors college, honors program, independent study, distance learning, double major, summer session for credit, part-time degree program, adult/continuing education programs, co-op programs and internships. Off campus study. Study abroad program.

Entrance Requirements: Open admission except for nursing, dental hygiene, radiography, respiratory therapy, firefighter, police and corrections programs. Options: electronic application, early admission, deferred admission. Required: high school transcript. Recommended: SAT and SAT Subject Tests or ACT. Entrance: noncompetitive. Application deadline: 8/20. Notification: continuous until 8/20. Preference given to state residents. Transfer credits accepted: Yes.

Costs Per Year: Application fee: $40. One-time mandatory fee: $40. State resident tuition: $3050 full-time, $101 per credit hour part-time. Nonresident tuition: $11,740 full-time, $363 per credit hour part-time. Mandatory fees: $20 full-time. Full-time tuition and fees vary according to degree level. Part-time tuition varies according to degree level.

Collegiate Environment: Orientation program. Drama-theater group, choral group, student-run newspaper. Social organizations: national fraternities. Most popular organizations: Student Government, Phi Theta Kappa, Students for International Understanding, Black Student Union, Drama Club. Major annual event: Graduation. Student services: health clinic, personal-psychological counseling, women's center. Campus security: 24-hour emergency response devices and patrols. Harold C. Manor Library plus 5 others. Weekly public service hours: 72; students can reserve study rooms. Operations spending for the previous fiscal year: $1.2 million.

Community Environment: Located south of West Palm Beach, Lake Worth has an annual average temperature of 75 degrees and an average rainfall of 61.72 inches. All modes of transportation serve the area. Recreational activities are golfing, shuffleboard, polo, tennis, swimming, water skiing, jai alai, deep sea and fresh water fishing. Deep sea fishing for sailfish, surf fishing for pompano and blue fish are excellent; fresh water fishing at Lake Osborne. Points of interest are the Palm Beach Speedway, Kennel Club Race Track, and art galleries.

■ **PASCO-HERNANDO STATE COLLEGE**
10230 Ridge Rd.
New Port Richey, FL 34654-5199
Tel: (727)847-2727; Free: 877-TRY-PHSC
Fax: (727)816-3450
E-mail: carrioe@phsc.edu
Web Site: www.phsc.edu
Description: State-supported, primarily 2-year, coed. Part of Florida College System. Awards certificates, diplomas, transfer associate, terminal associate, and bachelor's degrees. Founded 1972. Setting: 142-acre suburban campus with easy access to Tampa. Total enrollment: 10,206. Faculty: 377 (125 full-time, 252 part-time). Student-undergrad faculty ratio is 26:1. Full-time: 4,004 students, 56% women, 44% men. Part-time: 6,202 students, 64% women, 36% men. Students come from 50 states and territories, 7 other countries, 2% from out-of-state. 0.4% American Indian or Alaska Native, non-Hispanic/Latino; 14% Hispanic/Latino; 4% Black or African American, non-Hispanic/Latino; 2% Asian, non-Hispanic/Latino; 0.2% Native Hawaiian or other Pacific Islander, non-Hispanic/Latino; 0.2% international. 62% 25 or older. Retention: 53% of full-time freshmen returned the following year. Core. Calendar: semesters. Academic remediation for entering students, services for LD students, advanced placement, accelerated degree program, honors program, independent study, distance learning, double major, summer session for credit, part-time degree program, adult/continuing education programs, co-op programs and internships. Off campus study at other members of the Florida College System and the State University System of Florida. ROTC: Army (c).

Entrance Requirements: Open admission. Option: electronic application. Required: high school transcript. Recommended: SAT and SAT Subject Tests or ACT, PERT. Entrance: noncompetitive. Application deadline: rolling. Notification: continuous. Transfer credits accepted: Yes.

Collegiate Environment: Orientation program. Drama-theater group, choral group. Social organizations: 38 open to all. Most popular organizations: Student Government Association, Phi Theta Kappa, Phi Beta Lambda, Human Services, Legal Eagles. Major annual events: Peace Week, Arts & Culture Week, Get Acquainted Day. Student services: personal-psychological counseling. Campus security: security personnel while college classes are being held. Alric Pottberg Library plus 1 other.

Community Environment: See Saint Leo University.

■ **PENSACOLA CHRISTIAN COLLEGE**
250 Brent Ln.
Pensacola, FL 32503-2267
Tel: (850)478-8496; Free: 800-722-4636
Web Site: www.pcci.edu
Description: Independent Christian, comprehensive, coed. Awards associate, bachelor's, master's, and doctoral degrees. Founded 1974.

■ **PENSACOLA STATE COLLEGE**
1000 College Blvd.
Pensacola, FL 32504-8998
Tel: (850)484-1000
Fax: (850)484-1826
E-mail: kdutremble@pensacolastate.edu
Web Site: www.pensacolastate.edu
Description: State-supported, primarily 2-year, coed. Part of Florida College System. Awards certificates, diplomas, transfer associate, and bachelor's degrees. Founded 1948. Setting: 130-acre urban campus with easy access to Mobile, Alabama. Endowment: $11.3 million. Educational spending for the previous fiscal year: $3206 per student. Total enrollment: 9,655. Faculty: 599 (180 full-time, 419 part-time). Student-undergrad faculty ratio is 19:1. 2,892 applied, 100% were admitted. Full-time: 3,583 students, 58% women, 42% men. Part-time: 6,072 students, 62% women, 38% men. Students come from 37 states and territories, 5% from out-of-state. 0.8% American Indian or Alaska Native, non-Hispanic/Latino; 7% Hispanic/Latino; 15% Black or African American, non-Hispanic/Latino; 3% Asian, non-Hispanic/Latino; 0.4% Native Hawaiian or other Pacific Islander, non-Hispanic/Latino; 0.4% international. 62% 25 or older, 7% transferred in. Retention: 72% of full-time

freshmen returned the following year. Academic areas with the most degrees conferred: business/marketing; health professions and related sciences. Core. Calendar: semesters. Academic remediation for entering students, ESL program, services for LD students, advanced placement, honors program, independent study, distance learning, double major, summer session for credit, part-time degree program, external degree program, adult/continuing education programs, co-op programs and internships. ROTC: Army.

Entrance Requirements: Open admission Open admissions policy applies to all programs except for some health related fields. Options: electronic application, early admission, international baccalaureate accepted. Required: high school transcript. Entrance: noncompetitive. Application deadline: 8/30. Notification: continuous until 8/30. Transfer credits accepted: Yes.

Costs Per Year: Application fee: $30. One-time mandatory fee: $30. State resident tuition: $2510 full-time, $104.58 per credit hour part-time. Nonresident tuition: $10,074 full-time, $419.76 per credit hour part-time. Full-time tuition varies according to course level and degree level. Part-time tuition varies according to course level and degree level.

Collegiate Environment: Orientation program. Drama-theater group, choral group, student-run newspaper. Social organizations: 54 open to all. Most popular organizations: Student Government Association, Health Occupations Students of America (HOSA), SkillsUSA, African-American Student Association, Forestry Club. Major annual events: Stressless Fest, Lumberjack Festival, Campus Safety Month. Student services: personal-psychological counseling. Campus security: 24-hour emergency response devices and patrols, late night transport-escort service. Edward M. Chadbourne Library plus 3 others. Students can reserve study rooms. Operations spending for the previous fiscal year: $1.4 million. 1,700 computers available on campus for general student use. Computer purchase/lease plans available. A campuswide network can be accessed. Students can access the following: online class registration. Staffed computer lab on campus provides training in use of computers, software, and the Internet.

Community Environment: Pensacola Junior College offers courses at five locations in Escambia and Santa Rosa counties in northwest Florida. Famous for the white sand beaches of the Emerald Coast, Pensacola is the center of a growing metropolitan area of a third of a million residents. Pensacola is the "Cradle of Naval Aviation" and several Navy bases are located in the area, including the Pensacola Naval Air Station, Whiting Field, Corry Field, and Saufley Field. The white beaches of the Gulf of Mexico are a mecca for tourists. The area is served by the University of West Florida as well as Pensacola Junior College. In addition, the city has numerous museums, galleries, and historical areas, including Seville Quarter, a part of Pensacola dating back to the mid 1700s. Florida's First Place City continues to grow and expand.

■ **POLK STATE COLLEGE**
999 Ave. H, NE
Winter Haven, FL 33881-4299
Tel: (863)297-1000
Fax: (863)297-1060
Web Site: www.polk.edu
Description: State-supported, 4-year, coed. Part of Florida College System. Awards associate and bachelor's degrees. Founded 1964. Setting: 98-acre suburban campus with easy access to Orlando, Tampa. Educational spending for the previous fiscal year: $3141 per student. Total enrollment: 10,659. Faculty: 392 (161 full-time, 231 part-time). Student-undergrad faculty ratio is 25:1. Full-time: 3,627 students, 61% women, 39% men. Part-time: 7,032 students, 64% women, 36% men. Students come from 6 states and territories, 5 other countries, 1% from out-of-state. 0.2% American Indian or Alaska Native, non-Hispanic/Latino; 22% Hispanic/Latino; 16% Black or African American, non-Hispanic/Latino; 2% Asian, non-Hispanic/Latino; 0.1% Native Hawaiian or other Pacific Islander, non-Hispanic/Latino; 0.9% international. 31% 25 or older, 5% transferred in. Academic areas with the most degrees conferred: liberal arts/general studies; health professions and related sciences; homeland security, law enforcement, firefighting, and protective services; business/marketing. Core. Calendar: semesters 16-16-6-6. Academic remediation for entering students, ESL program, services for LD students, advanced placement, accelerated degree program, honors program, independent study, distance learning, double major, summer session for credit, part-time degree program, adult/continuing education programs, co-op programs and internships. Off campus study. Study abroad program. ROTC: Army (c), Air Force (c).

Entrance Requirements: Open admission. Options: electronic application, early admission, deferred admission, international baccalaureate accepted.

Required: high school transcript. Entrance: noncompetitive. Application deadline: rolling. Notification: continuous. Transfer credits accepted: Yes.

Costs Per Year: Application fee: $0. State resident tuition: $3367 full-time, $112.22 per credit hour part-time. Nonresident tuition: $12,272 full-time, $409.06 per credit hour part-time. Full-time tuition varies according to course level, course load, and degree level. Part-time tuition varies according to course level, course load, and degree level.

Collegiate Environment: Orientation program. Drama-theater group, choral group. Social organizations: 37 open to all. Most popular organizations: Florida Student Nursing Association, Honors Program Student Council, Phi Theta Kappa (PTK), Student Government Association, SALO (Student Activities and Leadership Office). Major annual events: Welcome Week, Hispanic Heritage Month, Intramural Sports. Student services: legal services, personal-psychological counseling. Campus security: 24-hour emergency response devices and patrols. Polk State College Libraries plus 1 other. Books: 82,640 (physical), 110,114 (digital/electronic). Operations spending for the previous fiscal year: $1.3 million. 800 computers available on campus for general student use. A campuswide network can be accessed. Students can access the following: online class registration. Staffed computer lab on campus provides training in use of computers, software, and the Internet.

■ **POLYTECHNIC UNIVERSITY OF PUERTO RICO, MIAMI CAMPUS**
8180 NW 36th St.
Ste. 401
Miami, FL 33166
Tel: (305)592-7659; Free: 888-729-7659
Web Site: www.pupr.edu/miami
Description: Independent, comprehensive, coed. Awards bachelor's and master's degrees. Setting: urban campus with easy access to Miami-Dade. Student-undergrad faculty ratio is 10:1.
Entrance Requirements: Option: electronic application. Transfer credits accepted: Yes.

■ **POLYTECHNIC UNIVERSITY OF PUERTO RICO, ORLANDO CAMPUS**
550 N Econlockhatchee Trl.
Orlando, FL 32825
Tel: (407)677-7000; Free: 888-577-POLY
Fax: (407)677-5082
Web Site: www.pupr.edu/orlando
Description: Independent, comprehensive, coed. Awards bachelor's and master's degrees. Total enrollment: 192. Student-undergrad faculty ratio is 8:1. 75 applied, 89% were admitted. 68% 25 or older.

■ **PRAXIS INSTITUTE**
1850 SW 8th St.
4th Fl.
Miami, FL 33135
Tel: (305)642-4104
Web Site: www.praxis.edu
Description: Proprietary, 2-year, coed. Awards diplomas, transfer associate, and terminal associate degrees.

■ **PROFESSIONAL HANDS INSTITUTE**
10 NW 42 Ave., Ste. 200
Miami, FL 33126
Tel: (305)442-6011
Web Site: prohands.edu
Description: Proprietary, 2-year, coed. Awards diplomas, transfer associate, and terminal associate degrees.

■ **RASMUSSEN COLLEGE FORT MYERS**
9160 Forum Corporate Pky.
Ste. 100
Fort Myers, FL 33905
Tel: (239)477-2100; Free: 888-549-6755
Fax: (239)477-2101
E-mail: susan.hammerstrom@rasmussen.edu
Web Site: www.rasmussen.edu
Description: Proprietary, 4-year, coed. Part of Rasmussen College System. Awards associate and bachelor's degrees. Setting: suburban campus. Total enrollment: 423. Faculty: 59 (10 full-time, 49 part-time). Student-undergrad faculty ratio is 22:1. 45 applied, 96% were admitted. Full-time: 260 students, 77% women, 23% men. Part-time: 163 students, 71% women, 29% men.

67% 25 or older. Core. Calendar: quarters. Academic remediation for entering students, accelerated degree program, distance learning, double major, summer session for credit, part-time degree program, adult/continuing education programs, internships.

Entrance Requirements: Options: electronic application, early admission, deferred admission. Required: high school transcript, minimum 2 high school GPA, institutional exam. Required for some: interview. Entrance: minimally difficult. Application deadline: rolling. Transfer credits accepted: Yes.

Collegiate Environment: Orientation program. Rasmussen College Library - Fort Myers. 129 computers available on campus for general student use. A campuswide network can be accessed from off-campus.

■ **RASMUSSEN COLLEGE LAND O' LAKES**
18600 Fernview St.
Land O' Lakes, FL 34638
Tel: (813)435-3601; Free: 888-549-6755
E-mail: susan.hammerstrom@rasmussen.edu
Web Site: www.rasmussen.edu
Description: Proprietary, 4-year, coed. Part of Rasmussen College System. Awards associate and bachelor's degrees. Setting: suburban campus. Total enrollment: 207. Faculty: 33 (4 full-time, 29 part-time). Student-undergrad faculty ratio is 22:1. 8 applied, 100% were admitted. Full-time: 80 students, 68% women, 32% men. Part-time: 127 students, 60% women, 40% men. 77% 25 or older. Core. Calendar: quarters. Academic remediation for entering students, accelerated degree program, distance learning, double major, summer session for credit, part-time degree program, adult/continuing education programs, internships.
Entrance Requirements: Options: electronic application, early admission, deferred admission. Required: high school transcript, minimum 2 high school GPA, institutional exam. Required for some: interview. Entrance: minimally difficult. Application deadline: rolling. Transfer credits accepted: Yes.
Collegiate Environment: Orientation program. Rasmussen College Library - Land O' Lakes. 61 computers available on campus for general student use. A campuswide network can be accessed from off-campus.

■ **RASMUSSEN COLLEGE NEW PORT RICHEY**
8661 Citizens Dr.
New Port Richey, FL 34654
Tel: (727)942-0069; Free: 888-549-6755
Fax: (727)938-5709
E-mail: dwayne.bertotto@rasmussen.edu
Web Site: www.rasmussen.edu
Description: Proprietary, 4-year, coed. Part of Rasmussen College System. Awards associate and bachelor's degrees. Setting: suburban campus. Total enrollment: 680. Faculty: 36 (17 full-time, 19 part-time). Student-undergrad faculty ratio is 22:1. 29 applied, 93% were admitted. Full-time: 573 students, 84% women, 16% men. Part-time: 107 students, 84% women, 16% men. 72% 25 or older. Core. Calendar: quarters. Academic remediation for entering students, accelerated degree program, distance learning, double major, summer session for credit, part-time degree program, adult/continuing education programs, internships.
Entrance Requirements: Options: electronic application, early admission, deferred admission. Required: high school transcript, minimum 2 high school GPA, institutional exam. Required for some: interview. Entrance: minimally difficult. Application deadline: rolling. Transfer credits accepted: Yes.
Collegiate Environment: Orientation program. Rasmussen College Library - New Port Richey. 118 computers available on campus for general student use. A campuswide network can be accessed from off-campus.

■ **RASMUSSEN COLLEGE OCALA**
4755 SW 46th Ct.
Ocala, FL 34474
Tel: (352)629-1941; Free: 888-549-6755
Fax: (352)629-0926
E-mail: dwayne.bertotto@rasmussen.edu
Web Site: www.rasmussen.edu
Description: Proprietary, 4-year, coed. Part of Rasmussen College System. Awards associate and bachelor's degrees. Founded 1984. Setting: suburban campus with easy access to Orlando. Total enrollment: 1,447. Faculty: 44 (10 full-time, 34 part-time). Student-undergrad faculty ratio is 22:1. 92 applied, 92% were admitted. Full-time: 1,182 students, 84% women, 16% men. Part-time: 265 students, 88% women, 12% men. Core. Calendar: quarters. Academic remediation for entering students, accelerated degree program,

distance learning, double major, summer session for credit, part-time degree program, adult/continuing education programs, internships.
Entrance Requirements: Open admission. Options: electronic application, early admission, deferred admission. Required: high school transcript, minimum 2 high school GPA, institutional exam. Required for some: interview. Entrance: minimally difficult. Application deadline: rolling. Transfer credits accepted: Yes.
Collegiate Environment: Orientation program. Rasmussen College Library - Ocala. 124 computers available on campus for general student use. A campuswide network can be accessed from off-campus.

■ **RASMUSSEN COLLEGE OCALA SCHOOL OF NURSING**
2100 SW 22nd Pl.
Ocala, FL 34471
Tel: (352)291-8560; Free: 888-549-6755
E-mail: susan.hammerstrom@rasmussen.edu
Web Site: www.rasmussen.edu
Description: Proprietary, 4-year, coed. Part of Rasmussen College System. Awards associate and bachelor's degrees. Setting: suburban campus. Total enrollment: 4,326. Faculty: 43 (17 full-time, 26 part-time). Student-undergrad faculty ratio is 22:1. 107 applied, 92% were admitted. Full-time: 2,058 students, 85% women, 15% men. Part-time: 2,268 students, 86% women, 14% men. Core. Calendar: quarters. Academic remediation for entering students, accelerated degree program, distance learning, double major, summer session for credit, part-time degree program, adult/continuing education programs, internships.
Entrance Requirements: Options: electronic application, early admission, deferred admission. Required: high school transcript, minimum 2 high school GPA, institutional exam. Required for some: interview. Entrance: minimally difficult. Application deadline: rolling. Transfer credits accepted: Yes.
Collegiate Environment: Orientation program. Rasmussen College Library - Ocala.

■ **RASMUSSEN COLLEGE TAMPA/BRANDON**
4042 Park Oaks Blvd.
Ste. 100
Tampa, FL 33610
Tel: (813)246-7600; Free: 888-549-6755
E-mail: susan.hammerstrom@rasmussen.edu
Web Site: www.rasmussen.edu
Description: Proprietary, 4-year, coed. Part of Rasmussen College System. Awards associate and bachelor's degrees. Setting: suburban campus. Total enrollment: 358. Faculty: 62 (9 full-time, 53 part-time). Student-undergrad faculty ratio is 22:1. 33 applied, 97% were admitted. Full-time: 143 students, 71% women, 29% men. Part-time: 215 students, 73% women, 27% men. 74% 25 or older. Core. Calendar: quarters. Academic remediation for entering students, accelerated degree program, distance learning, double major, summer session for credit, part-time degree program, adult/continuing education programs, internships.
Entrance Requirements: Options: electronic application, early admission, deferred admission. Required: high school transcript, minimum 2 high school GPA, institutional exam. Required for some: interview. Entrance: minimally difficult. Application deadline: rolling. Transfer credits accepted: Yes.
Collegiate Environment: Orientation program. Rasmussen College Library - Tampa. 47 computers available on campus for general student use. A campuswide network can be accessed from off-campus.

■ **REMINGTON COLLEGE-HEATHROW CAMPUS**
7131 Business Park Ln.
Lake Mary, FL 32746
Tel: (407)562-5500; Free: 800-323-8122
Web Site: www.remingtoncollege.edu
Description: Independent, 2-year, coed. Awards transfer associate and terminal associate degrees.

■ **RINGLING COLLEGE OF ART AND DESIGN**
2700 N Tamiami Trl.
Sarasota, FL 34234-5895
Tel: (941)351-5100; Free: 800-255-7695
Fax: (941)359-7517
E-mail: admissions@ringling.edu
Web Site: www.ringling.edu
Description: Independent, 4-year, coed. Awards bachelor's degrees. Founded 1931. Setting: 49-acre urban campus with easy access to Tampa-

St. Petersburg. Endowment: $47.5 million. Educational spending for the previous fiscal year: $20,110 per student. Total enrollment: 1,456. Faculty: 173 (112 full-time, 61 part-time). Student-undergrad faculty ratio is 11:1. 1,995 applied, 64% were admitted. Full-time: 1,395 students, 68% women, 32% men. Part-time: 61 students, 56% women, 44% men. Students come from 48 states and territories, 56 other countries, 54% from out-of-state. 0.3% American Indian or Alaska Native, non-Hispanic/Latino; 17% Hispanic/Latino; 4% Black or African American, non-Hispanic/Latino; 9% Asian, non-Hispanic/Latino; 0.1% Native Hawaiian or other Pacific Islander, non-Hispanic/Latino; 16% international. 7% 25 or older, 71% live on campus, 6% transferred in. Retention: 84% of full-time freshmen returned the following year. Academic areas with the most degrees conferred: visual and performing arts; communication technologies; communication/journalism. Core. Calendar: semesters. Academic remediation for entering students, ESL program, services for LD students, advanced placement, independent study, summer session for credit, part-time degree program, internships. Off campus study at Association of Independent Colleges of Art and Design Mobility Program, New York Studio Program, Consortium of Colleges on the Creative Coast, International Center for Photography. Study abroad program.

Entrance Requirements: Options: electronic application, early action, deferred admission, international baccalaureate accepted. Required: essay, high school transcript, minimum 2 high school GPA, 2 recommendations, portfolio, resume. Recommended: interview. Entrance: moderately difficult. Application deadlines: rolling, 11/1 for early action. Notification: continuous, 12/15 for early action. Transfer credits accepted: Yes. Applicants placed on waiting list: 5. Early action applicants: 161. Early action applicants admitted: 30.

Costs Per Year: Application fee: $70. Comprehensive fee: $61,090 includes full-time tuition ($42,330), mandatory fees ($4090), and college room and board ($14,670). Full-time tuition and fees vary according to course load, program, and student level. Room and board charges vary according to board plan and housing facility. Part-time tuition: $1972 per credit hour. Part-time tuition varies according to program and student level.

Collegiate Environment: Orientation program. Drama-theater group, choral group. Social organizations: 29 open to all. Most popular organizations: Student Government Association, Digital Painting Sketch Club, Resident Student Association, MOSAIC, Quidditch Team. Major annual events: Illest of Illustrators, Best of Ringling Opening, International Harvest Fest. Student services: legal services, health clinic, personal-psychological counseling. Campus security: 24-hour emergency response devices and patrols, late night transport-escort service, controlled dormitory access, lighted campus. Alfred R. Goldstein Library. Books: 51,891 (physical), 133,879 (digital/electronic); Serial titles: 12,169 (physical); Databases: 28. Weekly public service hours: 84; study areas open 24 hours, 5-7 days a week; students can reserve study rooms. Operations spending for the previous fiscal year: $265,614. 1,000 computers available on campus for general student use. A computer is required for all students. A campuswide network can be accessed. Students can access the following: online class registration, central file storage, high performance computing labs. Staffed computer lab on campus (open 24 hours a day) provides training in use of computers, software, and the Internet.

■ ROLLINS COLLEGE

1000 Holt Ave.
Winter Park, FL 32789-4499
Tel: (407)646-2000
Fax: (407)646-2600
E-mail: admissions@rollins.edu
Web Site: www.rollins.edu

Description: Independent, comprehensive, coed. Awards bachelor's, master's, and doctoral degrees. Founded 1885. Setting: 80-acre suburban campus with easy access to Orlando. Endowment: $354.8 million. Educational spending for the previous fiscal year: $14,243 per student. Total enrollment: 2,590. Faculty: 231 (all full-time). Student-undergrad faculty ratio is 10:1. 5,055 applied, 72% were admitted. 29% from top 10% of their high school class, 62% from top quarter, 90% from top half. Full-time: 2,027 students, 60% women, 40% men. Part-time: 7 students, 29% women, 71% men. Students come from 41 states and territories, 57 other countries, 45% from out-of-state. 0.1% American Indian or Alaska Native, non-Hispanic/Latino; 18% Hispanic/Latino; 4% Black or African American, non-Hispanic/Latino; 3% Asian, non-Hispanic/Latino; 9% international. 2% 25 or older, 62% live on campus, 4% transferred in. Retention: 86% of full-time freshmen returned the following year. Academic areas with the most degrees

conferred: business/marketing; communication/journalism; social sciences. Core. Calendar: semesters. Academic remediation for entering students, services for LD students, advanced placement, accelerated degree program, self-designed majors, honors program, independent study, double major, summer session for credit, part-time degree program, adult/continuing education programs, internships. Off campus study at Domestic universities offering domestic study are: American University-Washington DC Internship, Duke University-Beaufort Marine Lab (NC); Domestic universities offering international study are: Hollins University-Paris, Trinity College-Rome, Intercollegiate Center for Classical Studies (Duke)-Rome; Domestic institutions offering international study are: ISA-Buenos Aires, Argentina, Rome, and Italy, SIT-Various locations throughout the world, CAPA-London, England. Study abroad program.

Entrance Requirements: Options: electronic application, early admission, early decision, deferred admission, international baccalaureate accepted. Required: essay, high school transcript, 1 recommendation, Selection of Test Score Waived Option (TSWO) or official SAT/ACT scores. Recommended: minimum 2 high school GPA, interview. Entrance: moderately difficult. Application deadlines: 2/1, 11/15 for early decision. Notification: 4/1. SAT Reasoning Test deadline: 2/15. SAT Subject Test deadline: 2/15. Transfer credits accepted: Yes. Applicants placed on waiting list: 171. Wait-listed applicants offered admission: 16. Early decision applicants: 338. Early decision applicants admitted: 197.

Costs Per Year: Application fee: $50. Comprehensive fee: $64,230 includes full-time tuition ($49,760) and college room and board ($14,470). College room only: $8720. Room and board charges vary according to housing facility.

Collegiate Environment: Orientation program. Drama-theater group, choral group, student-run newspaper, radio station. Social organizations: 115 open to all; national fraternities, national sororities, local fraternities, local sororities; 36% of eligible men and 35% of eligible women are members. Most popular organizations: Black Student Union, Student Government Association, Eco-Rollins, Spectrum, WPRK 91.5. Major annual events: LipSync, Fox Day BBQ, R Community Fair. Student services: health clinic, personal-psychological counseling, women's center. Campus security: 24-hour emergency response devices and patrols, late night transport-escort service, controlled dormitory access. 1,300 college housing spaces available; 1,224 were occupied in 2018-19. Freshmen guaranteed college housing. On-campus residence required through sophomore year. Options: coed, men-only, women-only housing available. Olin Library. Books: 204,677 (physical), 236,421 (digital/electronic); Serial titles: 117 (physical), 104,688 (digital/electronic); Databases: 107. Weekly public service hours: 96; study areas open 24 hours, 5-7 days a week; students can reserve study rooms. Operations spending for the previous fiscal year: $2.5 million. 254 computers available on campus for general student use. A campuswide network can be accessed from student residence rooms and from off campus. Students can access the following: online class registration. Staffed computer lab on campus (open 24 hours a day) provides training in use of computers, software, and the Internet.

Community Environment: Within the metropolitan area of which Orlando is the center, Winter Park is a residential area of great beauty. This area of Florida is popularly known as"The Lake Region." Orange groves, subtropical forest, flowering shrubs and trees are the dominant features of the landscape. Scenic boat trips may be taken through a chain of four lakes. Annual events are the Sidewalk Arts Festival and a Bach festival held on the campus of Rollins College.

■ SABER COLLEGE

3990 W Flagler St.
Ste. 103
Miami, FL 33134
Tel: (305)443-9170
Web Site: www.sabercollege.edu

Description: Independent, 2-year, coed. Awards transfer associate and terminal associate degrees.

■ ST. JOHN VIANNEY COLLEGE SEMINARY

2900 SW 87th Ave.
Miami, FL 33165-3244
Tel: (305)223-4561
Web Site: www.sjvcs.edu

Description: Independent Roman Catholic, 4-year, coed. Awards bachelor's degrees. Founded 1959. Setting: 33-acre urban campus. 10 applied, 100%

were admitted. 24% 25 or older. Core. Calendar: semesters. Academic remediation for entering students, ESL program, advanced placement, internships.

Entrance Requirements: Required: high school transcript, minimum 2.0 high school GPA, 1 recommendation, psychological examination. Recommended: interview, SAT or ACT. Entrance: moderately difficult. Application deadline: rolling. Preference given to candidates for the priesthood.

Collegiate Environment: Orientation program. Choral group. Student services: legal services, personal-psychological counseling. Campus security: 24-hour emergency response devices, student patrols. Maytag Memorial Library.

■ ST. JOHNS RIVER STATE COLLEGE
5001 Saint Johns Ave.
Palatka, FL 32177-3897
Tel: (386)312-4200
Fax: (386)312-4292
Web Site: www.sjrstate.edu

Description: State-supported, 2-year, coed. Awards certificates, diplomas, transfer associate, and terminal associate degrees. Founded 1958. Setting: 105-acre small town campus with easy access to Jacksonville. Total enrollment: 6,086. Faculty: 265 (111 full-time, 154 part-time). Student-undergrad faculty ratio is 24:1. Core. Calendar: semesters. Academic remediation for entering students, services for LD students, advanced placement, accelerated degree program, distance learning, summer session for credit, part-time degree program, adult/continuing education programs.

Entrance Requirements: Open admission. Option: early admission. Required: high school transcript. Entrance: noncompetitive. Application deadline: rolling. Notification: continuous.

Collegiate Environment: Orientation program. Choral group, student-run newspaper. Campus security: 24-hour patrols. 450 computers available on campus for general student use. A campuswide network can be accessed. Students can access the following: online class registration. Staffed computer lab on campus.

■ SAINT LEO UNIVERSITY
PO Box 6665
Saint Leo, FL 33574-6665
Tel: (352)588-8200; Free: 800-334-5532
Fax: (352)588-8257
E-mail: admissions@saintleo.edu
Web Site: www.saintleo.edu

Description: Independent Roman Catholic, comprehensive, coed. Awards associate, bachelor's, master's, and doctoral degrees. Founded 1889. Setting: 280-acre rural campus with easy access to Tampa, Orlando. Endowment: $67.6 million. Total enrollment: 5,232. Faculty: 194 (119 full-time, 75 part-time). Student-undergrad faculty ratio is 14:1. 3,507 applied, 84% were admitted. 15% from top 10% of their high school class, 30% from top quarter, 69% from top half. 1 valedictorian. Full-time: 2,022 students, 56% women, 44% men. Part-time: 64 students, 56% women, 44% men. Students come from 46 states and territories, 66 other countries, 26% from out-of-state. 0.5% American Indian or Alaska Native, non-Hispanic/Latino; 21% Hispanic/Latino; 14% Black or African American, non-Hispanic/Latino; 2% Asian, non-Hispanic/Latino; 12% international. 6% 25 or older, 67% live on campus, 6% transferred in. Retention: 72% of full-time freshmen returned the following year. Academic areas with the most degrees conferred: business/marketing; homeland security, law enforcement, firefighting, and protective services; computer and information sciences. Core. Calendar: semesters. Academic remediation for entering students, ESL program, services for LD students, advanced placement, accelerated degree program, honors program, independent study, distance learning, double major, summer session for credit, part-time degree program, adult/continuing education programs, internships. Study abroad program. ROTC: Army, Air Force.

Entrance Requirements: Options: electronic application, early admission, deferred admission, international baccalaureate accepted. Required: high school transcript, 1 recommendation. Recommended: interview. Entrance: moderately difficult. Application deadline: rolling. Notification: continuous. Transfer credits accepted: Yes.

Costs Per Year: Comprehensive fee: $35,000 includes full-time tuition ($23,100), mandatory fees ($650), and college room and board ($11,250). College room only: $6000.

Collegiate Environment: Orientation program. Drama-theater group, choral group, student-run newspaper. Social organizations: 60 open to all; national fraternities, national sororities, local fraternities, local sororities; 9% of

eligible men and 16% of eligible women are members. Most popular organizations: Caribbean Student Association, Alpha Phi Omega, Intercultural Student Association, Opus Fides, Pacioli Accounting Club. Major annual events: Spring Fling, Family Fall Festival, Campus Activities Board Bingo Night. Student services: health clinic, personal-psychological counseling. Campus security: 24-hour emergency response devices and patrols, late night transport-escort service, controlled dormitory access. 1,544 college housing spaces available; 1,395 were occupied in 2018-19. Freshmen given priority for college housing. On-campus residence required through junior year. Options: coed, men-only, women-only housing available. Cannon Memorial Library plus 1 other. Books: 86,985 (physical), 363,788 (digital/electronic); Serial titles: 1,430 (physical), 100,630 (digital/electronic); Databases: 121. Weekly public service hours: 112. Operations spending for the previous fiscal year: $2.2 million. 150 computers available on campus for general student use. Computer purchase/lease plans available. A campuswide network can be accessed from student residence rooms and from off campus. Students can access the following: online class registration. Staffed computer lab on campus provides training in use of computers, software, and the Internet.

Community Environment: Saint Leo is located 25 miles north of Tampa, and 38 miles from Tampa International Airport. Semitropical climate. Orlando and Disney World are 65 miles to the east.

■ ST. PETERSBURG COLLEGE
PO Box 13489
Saint Petersburg, FL 33733-3489
Tel: (727)341-3600
Fax: (727)341-3150
E-mail: information@spcollege.edu
Web Site: www.spcollege.edu

Description: State and locally supported, 4-year, coed. Awards associate and bachelor's degrees. Founded 1927. Setting: 410-acre suburban campus with easy access to Tampa. Total enrollment: 29,835. Faculty: 1,585 (377 full-time, 1,208 part-time). 5,852 applied, 34% were admitted. Full-time: 8,466 students, 55% women, 45% men. Part-time: 21,369 students, 62% women, 38% men. 0.3% American Indian or Alaska Native, non-Hispanic/Latino; 13% Hispanic/Latino; 14% Black or African American, non-Hispanic/Latino; 4% Asian, non-Hispanic/Latino; 0.2% Native Hawaiian or other Pacific Islander, non-Hispanic/Latino; 0.8% international. Academic areas with the most degrees conferred: health professions and related sciences; business/marketing; education. Core. Calendar: semesters. Academic remediation for entering students, ESL program, services for LD students, advanced placement, accelerated degree program, freshman honors college, honors program, distance learning, summer session for credit, part-time degree program, external degree program, adult/continuing education programs, co-op programs and internships. Off campus study. Study abroad program. ROTC: Army (c).

Entrance Requirements: Open admission. Options: electronic application, early admission, international baccalaureate accepted. Required: high school transcript. Entrance: noncompetitive. Application deadline: rolling. Notification: continuous. Transfer credits accepted: Yes.

Collegiate Environment: Orientation program. Drama-theater group, choral group, student-run newspaper. Student services: women's center. Campus security: late night transport-escort service. M. M. Bennett Library.

■ ST. THOMAS UNIVERSITY
16401 NW 37th Ave.
Miami Gardens, FL 33054-6459
Tel: (305)625-6000; Free: 800-367-9010
Fax: (305)628-6591
E-mail: ajnoriega@stu.edu
Web Site: www.stu.edu

Description: Independent Roman Catholic, university, coed. Awards bachelor's, master's, and doctoral degrees and post-master's certificates. Founded 1961. Setting: 140-acre suburban campus with easy access to Miami, FL. Endowment: $25.6 million. Total enrollment: 4,549. Faculty: 497 (95 full-time, 402 part-time). Student-undergrad faculty ratio is 11:1. 2,538 applied, 41% were admitted. Full-time: 932 students, 52% women, 48% men. Part-time: 1,980 students, 60% women, 40% men. Students come from 28 states and territories, 23 other countries, 11% from out-of-state. 44% Hispanic/Latino; 26% Black or African American, non-Hispanic/Latino; 0.3% Asian, non-Hispanic/Latino; 15% international. 22% 25 or older, 40% live on campus, 10% transferred in. Retention: 68% of full-time freshmen returned the following year. Academic areas with the most degrees conferred:

business/marketing; homeland security, law enforcement, firefighting, and protective services; psychology. Core. Calendar: semesters. Academic remediation for entering students, ESL program, services for LD students, advanced placement, accelerated degree program, honors program, independent study, distance learning, double major, summer session for credit, part-time degree program, external degree program, adult/continuing education programs, internships, graduate courses open to undergrads. Study abroad program. ROTC: Air Force (c).

Entrance Requirements: Options: electronic application, international baccalaureate accepted. Required: high school transcript, minimum 2.5 high school GPA. Recommended: essay, 1 recommendation, SAT or ACT. Required for some: interview. Entrance: moderately difficult. Transfer credits accepted: Yes.

Costs Per Year: Application fee: $40. Comprehensive fee: $42,780 includes full-time tuition ($30,900), mandatory fees ($180), and college room and board ($11,700). College room only: $7200. Full-time tuition and fees vary according to course load and program. Room and board charges vary according to board plan and housing facility. Part-time tuition: $1030 per credit hour. Part-time mandatory fees: $75 per course, $120 per term. Part-time tuition and fees vary according to course load and program.

Collegiate Environment: Orientation program. Choral group, marching band. Social organizations: 10 open to all; 8% of eligible men and 10% of eligible women are members. Most popular organizations: Psychology Club, Nursing Students Association, Criminal Justice, Caribbean Students Association, Future Teachers of America. Major annual events: Freshman Convocation, Spring Homecoming, Battle of the Halls. Student services: health clinic, personal-psychological counseling. Campus security: 24-hour emergency response devices and patrols, late night transport-escort service, controlled dormitory access. St. Thomas University Library plus 1 other. Books: 555,242 (physical), 479,232 (digital/electronic); Serial titles: 146,423 (physical), 146,423 (digital/electronic); Databases: 410. Weekly public service hours: 101; students can reserve study rooms. 100 computers available on campus for general student use. A campuswide network can be accessed from student residence rooms. Students can access the following: online class registration. Staffed computer lab on campus.

■ **SAN IGNACIO UNIVERSITY**
10395 NW 41st St.
Ste. 125
Doral, FL 33178
Web Site: www.sanignaciouniversity.edu
Description: Proprietary, comprehensive, coed.

■ **SANTA FE COLLEGE**
3000 NW 83rd St.
Gainesville, FL 32606
Tel: (352)395-5000
Fax: (352)395-5581
Web Site: www.sfcollege.edu
Description: State and locally supported, 4-year, coed. Part of Florida College System. Awards associate and bachelor's degrees (offers bachelor's degrees in conjunction with Saint Leo College). Founded 1966. Setting: 187-acre suburban campus with easy access to Jacksonville. Total enrollment: 15,745. Faculty: 829 (245 full-time, 584 part-time). Student-undergrad faculty ratio is 25:1. Full-time: 6,777 students, 53% women, 47% men. Part-time: 8,968 students, 57% women, 43% men. Students come from 28 states and territories, 61 other countries, 2% from out-of-state. 0.5% American Indian or Alaska Native, non-Hispanic/Latino; 12% Hispanic/Latino; 16% Black or African American, non-Hispanic/Latino; 2% Asian, non-Hispanic/Latino; 0.4% Native Hawaiian or other Pacific Islander, non-Hispanic/Latino; 1% international. 30% 25 or older, 11% transferred in. Core. Calendar: semesters. Academic remediation for entering students, ESL program, services for LD students, advanced placement, honors program, independent study, distance learning, summer session for credit, part-time degree program, adult/continuing education programs, co-op programs and internships. Study abroad program. ROTC: Army (c), Air Force (c).
Entrance Requirements: Open admission. Options: electronic application, early admission, international baccalaureate accepted. Required: high school transcript. Required for some: essay, interview. Entrance: noncompetitive. Application deadline: rolling. Notification: continuous. Transfer credits accepted: Yes.
Collegiate Environment: Orientation program. Drama-theater group, choral group, student-run newspaper. Student services: legal services, health clinic, personal-psychological counseling, women's center. Campus security: 24-hour emergency response devices and patrols. Lawrence W. Tyree Library.

Community Environment: See University of Florida.

■ **SCHILLER INTERNATIONAL UNIVERSITY**
8560 Ulmerton Rd.
Largo, FL 33771
Tel: (727)736-5082; Free: 800-261-9751
Fax: (727)734-0359
E-mail: admissions@schiller.edu
Web Site: www.schiller.edu
Description: Independent, comprehensive, coed. Part of Schiller International University. Awards associate, bachelor's, and master's degrees. Founded 1991. Setting: 4-acre suburban campus with easy access to Tampa. Total enrollment: 673. Faculty: 66 (2 full-time, 64 part-time). Student-undergrad faculty ratio is 16:1. Full-time: 153 students, 37% women, 63% men. Part-time: 38 students, 50% women, 50% men. Students come from 11 states and territories, 50 other countries. 85% live on campus. Academic areas with the most degrees conferred: business/marketing; interdisciplinary studies; psychology. Core. Calendar: semesters. ESL program, advanced placement, accelerated degree program, self-designed majors, honors program, independent study, distance learning, double major, summer session for credit, part-time degree program, adult/continuing education programs, co-op programs and internships, graduate courses open to undergrads. Off campus study. Study abroad program.
Entrance Requirements: Options: electronic application, deferred admission, international baccalaureate accepted. Required: essay, high school transcript. Recommended: minimum 2 high school GPA, interview. Entrance: minimally difficult. Application deadline: rolling. Notification: continuous. Transfer credits accepted: Yes.
Collegiate Environment: Orientation program. Most popular organizations: Student Government, Model United Nations. Major annual events: International Food Festivals, Picnic in the Park, Horse Back Riding. Student services: personal-psychological counseling. Campus security: night patrols. SIU Library. 42 computers available on campus for general student use. A campuswide network can be accessed. Staffed computer lab on campus provides training in use of computers, software, and the Internet.

■ **SEMINOLE STATE COLLEGE OF FLORIDA**
100 Weldon Blvd.
Sanford, FL 32773-6199
Tel: (407)708-4722
Fax: (407)328-2395
Web Site: www.seminolestate.edu
Description: State and locally supported, primarily 2-year, coed. Part of Florida College System. Awards certificates, diplomas, transfer associate, terminal associate, and bachelor's degrees. Founded 1966. Setting: 200-acre small town campus with easy access to Orlando. Endowment: $24.6 million. Educational spending for the previous fiscal year: $2641 per student. Total enrollment: 17,706. Faculty: 798 (209 full-time, 589 part-time). Student-undergrad faculty ratio is 26:1. 4,587 applied, 64% were admitted. Full-time: 6,137 students, 48% women, 52% men. Part-time: 11,569 students, 59% women, 41% men. Students come from 21 states and territories, 68 other countries, 3% from out-of-state. 0.3% American Indian or Alaska Native, non-Hispanic/Latino; 24% Hispanic/Latino; 16% Black or African American, non-Hispanic/Latino; 3% Asian, non-Hispanic/Latino; 0.3% Native Hawaiian or other Pacific Islander, non-Hispanic/Latino; 2% international. 43% 25 or older, 7% transferred in. Retention: 52% of full-time freshmen returned the following year. Academic areas with the most degrees conferred: business/marketing; computer and information sciences; engineering technologies. Core. Calendar: semesters. Academic remediation for entering students, ESL program, services for LD students, advanced placement, accelerated degree program, honors program, independent study, distance learning, double major, summer session for credit, part-time degree program, external degree program, adult/continuing education programs, co-op programs and internships. Study abroad program. ROTC: Army.
Entrance Requirements: Open admission except for physical therapy, respiratory therapy, nursing programs. Options: electronic application, early admission, deferred admission, international baccalaureate accepted. Required: high school transcript, minimum 2 high school GPA. Entrance: noncompetitive. Application deadline: rolling. Notification: continuous. Transfer credits accepted: Yes.
Costs Per Year: Application fee: $0. State resident tuition: $3131 full-time, $104.38 per credit hour part-time. Nonresident tuition: $12,739 full-time, $381.87 per credit hour part-time. Full-time tuition varies according to degree level. Part-time tuition varies according to degree level.

Collegiate Environment: Orientation program. Drama-theater group, choral group, student-run newspaper. Social organizations: 50 open to all. Most popular organizations: Phi Beta Lambda, Phi Theta Kappa, Student Government Association, Sigma Phi Gamma, Hispanic Student Association. Major annual events: Welcome Back, Career Fair, Club Fair. Student services: personal-psychological counseling. Campus security: 24-hour emergency response devices and patrols, late night transport-escort service. Seminole State Library at Sanford Lake Mary plus 3 others. Books: 67,023 (physical), 145,374 (digital/electronic); Serial titles: 520 (physical), 18,003 (digital/electronic); Databases: 130. Weekly public service hours: 60; students can reserve study rooms. Operations spending for the previous fiscal year: $622,773. 300 computers available on campus for general student use. A campuswide network can be accessed from off-campus. Students can access the following: online class registration, online syllabi. Staffed computer lab on campus provides training in use of computers, software, and the Internet.

Community Environment: A residential city with subtropical climate. Sanford is located 20 miles northeast of Orlando. Air service is available through Orlando International Airport, and Amtrak serves the area. Part-time employment for students is available in the metropolitan Orlando Area. Lake Monroe is a recreation area nearby with a municipal zoo, picnic facilities and playground. Other sports include boating, fishing, tennis, and more. The close proximity to Orlando offers many convenient cultural and recreational activities.

■ **SOUTH FLORIDA BIBLE COLLEGE AND THEOLOGICAL SEMINARY**
2200 SW 10th St.
Deerfield Beach, FL 33442
Tel: (954)428-8980
Web Site: www.sfbc.edu
Description: Proprietary, comprehensive, coed. Awards associate, bachelor's, and master's degrees.

■ **SOUTH FLORIDA STATE COLLEGE**
600 W College Dr.
Avon Park, FL 33825-9356
Tel: (863)453-6661
Fax: (863)453-0165
Web Site: www.southflorida.edu
Description: State-supported, primarily 2-year, coed. Part of Florida State College System. Awards certificates, diplomas, transfer associate, terminal associate, and bachelor's degrees. Founded 1965. Setting: 228-acre rural campus with easy access to Tampa, St. Petersburg, Orlando. Endowment: $6.2 million. Educational spending for the previous fiscal year: $6593 per student. Total enrollment: 2,885. Faculty: 156 (60 full-time, 96 part-time). Student-undergrad faculty ratio is 16:1. 673 applied. 5% from top 10% of their high school class, 10% from top quarter, 34% from top half. Full-time: 975 students, 57% women, 43% men. Part-time: 1,910 students, 67% women, 33% men. 3% from out-of-state. 0.2% American Indian or Alaska Native, non-Hispanic/Latino; 37% Hispanic/Latino; 11% Black or African American, non-Hispanic/Latino; 2% Asian, non-Hispanic/Latino; 0.3% Native Hawaiian or other Pacific Islander, non-Hispanic/Latino; 1% international. 44% 25 or older, 4% transferred in. Core. Calendar: semesters. Academic remediation for entering students, ESL program, services for LD students, advanced placement, independent study, distance learning, summer session for credit, part-time degree program, adult/continuing education programs, co-op programs and internships.
Entrance Requirements: Open admission. Options: electronic application, early admission, deferred admission, international baccalaureate accepted. Required: high school transcript. Entrance: noncompetitive. Application deadline: rolling. Notification: continuous. Transfer credits accepted: Yes.
Costs Per Year: Application fee: $15. One-time mandatory fee: $15. State resident tuition: $2593 full-time, $104.52 per credit hour part-time. Nonresident tuition: $9722 full-time, $394.31 per credit hour part-time. Full-time tuition varies according to course level, course load, degree level, and program. Part-time tuition varies according to course level, course load, degree level, and program. College room and board: $6040. College room only: $2040.
Collegiate Environment: Orientation program. Social organizations: 25 open to all; 40% of eligible men and 60% of eligible women are members. Most popular organizations: Phi Theta Kappa, Phi Beta Lambda, Art Club, Anime and Gaming Club, Basketball Club. Major annual events: Fall Fest, Club Rush, College Week. Student services: personal-psychological

counseling. Campus security: 24-hour emergency response devices and patrols, late night transport-escort service. Library Services. Operations spending for the previous fiscal year: $718,778. 85 computers available on campus for general student use. Computer purchase/lease plans available. A campuswide network can be accessed. Students can access the following: online class registration. Staffed computer lab on campus provides training in use of computers, software, and the Internet.

Community Environment: An urban area in south central Florida; semitropical climate and a tourist center. Trains and buses serve the area. Citrus production is the main source of income. Part time employment is limited to eating establishments and grocery stores. Recreational activities are numerous; they include golfing, bowling, tennis, shuffleboard, water sports, hunting, fishing and camping. Avon Park has many active civic organizations. The annual International Jamboree and Cultural Series is a special event.

■ **SOUTH UNIVERSITY (ROYAL PALM BEACH)**
University Centre
9801 Belvedere Rd.
Royal Palm Beach, FL 33411
Tel: (561)273-6500; Free: 866-629-2902
Fax: (561)697-9944
Web Site: www.southuniversity.edu/west-palm-beach
Description: Independent, comprehensive, coed. Part of Education Management Corporation. Awards associate, bachelor's, and master's degrees. Founded 1899. Calendar: quarters.

■ **SOUTH UNIVERSITY (TAMPA)**
4401 N Himes Ave.
Ste. 175
Tampa, FL 33614
Tel: (813)393-3800; Free: 800-846-1472
Web Site: www.southuniversity.edu/tampa
Description: Independent, comprehensive, coed. Part of Education Management Corporation. Awards associate, bachelor's, master's, and doctoral degrees and post-master's certificates.

■ **SOUTHEASTERN COLLEGE-WEST PALM BEACH**
1756 N Congress Ave.
West Palm Beach, FL 33409
Tel: (561)433-2330
Web Site: www.sec.edu
Description: Proprietary, 2-year, coed. Awards certificates, diplomas, and terminal associate degrees. Founded 1988. Setting: urban campus. Total enrollment: 558. Full-time: 269 students, 84% women, 16% men. Part-time: 289 students, 82% women, 18% men. Students come from 6 states and territories, 2% from out-of-state. 0.2% American Indian or Alaska Native, non-Hispanic/Latino; 36% Hispanic/Latino; 36% Black or African American, non-Hispanic/Latino; 2% Asian, non-Hispanic/Latino. 70% 25 or older. ESL program, services for LD students, advanced placement, accelerated degree program, distance learning, summer session for credit, part-time degree program, adult/continuing education programs, co-op programs and internships. Off campus study.
Entrance Requirements: Open admission. Option: international baccalaureate accepted. Required: high school transcript, interview, Wonderlic Assessment, TEAS. Required for some: essay, minimum X high school GPA, recommendations. Application deadlines: rolling, rolling for early decision plan 1, rolling for early decision plan 2, rolling for early action. Notification: continuous, rolling for early decision plan 1, rolling for early decision plan 2, rolling for early action. Transfer credits accepted: Yes.
Costs Per Year: Application fee: $55. Tuition: $18,944 full-time, $789 per credit hour part-time. Full-time tuition varies according to course load and program. Part-time tuition varies according to course load and program.
Collegiate Environment: Orientation program. Campus security: 24-hour patrols, late night transport-escort service. Southeastern College Library. Books: 1,728 (physical); Serial titles: 26 (physical); Databases: 5. Weekly public service hours: 50.

■ **SOUTHEASTERN UNIVERSITY**
1000 Longfellow Blvd.
Lakeland, FL 33801-6099
Tel: (863)667-5000; Free: 800-500-8760
Fax: (863)667-5200
E-mail: admission@seu.edu

Web Site: www.seu.edu

Description: Independent, comprehensive, coed, affiliated with Assemblies of God. Awards associate, bachelor's, master's, and doctoral degrees and post-master's certificates. Founded 1935. Setting: 87-acre suburban campus with easy access to Tampa, Orlando. Endowment: $9.3 million. Educational spending for the previous fiscal year: $4366 per student. Total enrollment: 8,759. Faculty: 613 (162 full-time, 451 part-time). Student-undergrad faculty ratio is 20:1. 4,996 applied, 48% were admitted. 9% from top 10% of their high school class, 26% from top quarter, 58% from top half. Full-time: 4,909 students, 58% women, 42% men. Part-time: 2,799 students, 57% women, 43% men. 49% from out-of-state. 0.5% American Indian or Alaska Native, non-Hispanic/Latino; 21% Hispanic/Latino; 14% Black or African American, non-Hispanic/Latino; 1% Asian, non-Hispanic/Latino; 0.5% Native Hawaiian or other Pacific Islander, non-Hispanic/Latino; 1% international. 19% 25 or older, 31% live on campus, 12% transferred in. Retention: 68% of full-time freshmen returned the following year. Academic areas with the most degrees conferred: theology and religious vocations; business/marketing; education. Core. Calendar: semesters. Academic remediation for entering students, services for LD students, advanced placement, honors program, independent study, distance learning, double major, summer session for credit, part-time degree program, adult/continuing education programs, co-op programs and internships, graduate courses open to undergrads. Off campus study. Study abroad program. ROTC: Army (c).

Entrance Requirements: Open admission. Options: electronic application, early admission, deferred admission, international baccalaureate accepted. Required: essay, high school transcript, 1 recommendation, SAT or ACT. Required for some: interview. Entrance: minimally difficult. Notification: 6/1. Transfer credits accepted: Yes.

Costs Per Year: Application fee: $40. Comprehensive fee: $35,702 includes full-time tuition ($24,870), mandatory fees ($1000), and college room and board ($9832). Part-time tuition: $1036 per credit hour.

Collegiate Environment: Orientation program. Drama-theater group, choral group, student-run newspaper, radio station. Social organizations: 26 open to all. Major annual events: SEU Conference, Battle of the Dorms, Club Rush. Student services: health clinic, personal-psychological counseling. Campus security: 24-hour emergency response devices and patrols, late night transport-escort service, controlled dormitory access. Freshmen guaranteed college housing. On-campus residence required through sophomore year. Options: men-only, women-only housing available. Steelman Library. Books: 79,844 (physical), 215,769 (digital/electronic). 220 computers available on campus for general student use. A campuswide network can be accessed from student residence rooms and from off campus. Students can access the following: online class registration, network programs.

■ **SOUTHERN TECHNICAL COLLEGE (FORT MYERS)**

1685 Medical Ln.
Fort Myers, FL 33907
Tel: (239)939-4766; Free: 877-347-5492
Fax: (239)936-4040
E-mail: tquinlan@southerntech.edu
Web Site: www.southerntech.edu/locations/ft-myers

Description: Proprietary, 4-year, coed. Awards associate and bachelor's degrees. Founded 1940. Setting: 1-acre urban campus. Educational spending for the previous fiscal year: $25,607 per student. Total enrollment: 1,259. Faculty: 160 (16 full-time, 144 part-time). Student-undergrad faculty ratio is 16:1. Full-time: 883 students, 75% women, 25% men. Part-time: 376 students, 84% women, 16% men. 1% American Indian or Alaska Native, non-Hispanic/Latino; 22% Hispanic/Latino; 15% Black or African American, non-Hispanic/Latino; 1% Asian, non-Hispanic/Latino; 0.2% Native Hawaiian or other Pacific Islander, non-Hispanic/Latino; 1% international. 66% 25 or older, 20% transferred in. Retention: 33% of full-time freshmen returned the following year. Core. Calendar: quarters. Academic remediation for entering students, advanced placement, independent study, distance learning, summer session for credit, part-time degree program, co-op programs.

Entrance Requirements: Open admission. Options: electronic application, international baccalaureate accepted. Required: high school transcript. Entrance: noncompetitive. Application deadline: rolling. Notification: continuous. Transfer credits accepted: Yes.

Collegiate Environment: Orientation program. Social organizations: 1 open to all. Most popular organization: Alpha Beta Kappa Honors Society. Campus security: evening security guard. Learning Resource Center. Operations spending for the previous fiscal year: $190,517.

■ **SOUTHERN TECHNICAL COLLEGE (ORLANDO)**

1485 Florida Mall Ave.
Orlando, FL 32809
Tel: (407)438-6000; Free: 877-347-5492
E-mail: relie@southerntech.edu
Web Site: www.southerntech.edu

Description: Proprietary, 2-year, coed. Awards diplomas and transfer associate degrees. Setting: 1-acre urban campus with easy access to Greater Orlando. Educational spending for the previous fiscal year: $9306 per student. Total enrollment: 1,445. Faculty: 57 (all full-time). Student-undergrad faculty ratio is 25:1. Full-time: 1,445 students, 57% women, 43% men. 0.6% American Indian or Alaska Native, non-Hispanic/Latino; 27% Hispanic/Latino; 40% Black or African American, non-Hispanic/Latino; 0.6% Asian, non-Hispanic/Latino; 0.4% Native Hawaiian or other Pacific Islander, non-Hispanic/Latino; 0.1% international. Core. Calendar: quarters. Academic remediation for entering students, advanced placement, independent study, distance learning, summer session for credit.

Entrance Requirements: Open admission. Entrance: noncompetitive. Application deadline: rolling. Notification: continuous. Transfer credits accepted: Yes.

Collegiate Environment: Orientation program. Social organizations: 1 open to all. Most popular organization: Alpha Beta Kappa Honors Sociiety. Major annual event: Quarterly Award Ceremony. Campus security: evening security guard. STC Library. Operations spending for the previous fiscal year: $155,614. 30 computers available on campus for general student use. Staffed computer lab on campus provides training in use of computers, software, and the Internet.

■ **SOUTHERN TECHNICAL COLLEGE (TAMPA)**

3910 Riga Blvd.
Tampa, FL 33619
Tel: (813)630-4401; Free: 877-347-5492
Web Site: www.southerntech.edu/locations/tampa

Description: Proprietary, primarily 2-year, coed. Awards diplomas, terminal associate, and bachelor's degrees. Founded 1974. Calendar: quarters.

■ **STATE COLLEGE OF FLORIDA MANATEE-SARASOTA**

5840 26th St. W
Bradenton, FL 34206-7046
Tel: (941)752-5000
Fax: (941)727-6177
E-mail: lewym@scf.edu
Web Site: www.scf.edu

Description: State-supported, 4-year, coed. Part of Florida Community College System. Awards associate and bachelor's degrees. Founded 1957. Setting: 100-acre suburban campus with easy access to Tampa-St. Petersburg. Total enrollment: 9,073. Faculty: 444 (160 full-time, 284 part-time). 2,935 applied, 100% were admitted. Full-time: 3,659 students, 56% women, 44% men. Part-time: 5,414 students, 65% women, 35% men. Students come from 30 states and territories, 39 other countries, 4% from out-of-state. 34% 25 or older, 7% transferred in. Core. Calendar: semesters. Academic remediation for entering students, ESL program, services for LD students, advanced placement, honors program, independent study, distance learning, double major, summer session for credit, part-time degree program, external degree program, co-op programs.

Entrance Requirements: Open admission except for allied health programs. Options: electronic application, early admission. Required: high school transcript. Entrance: noncompetitive. Application deadline: 8/20. Notification: continuous. Transfer credits accepted: Yes.

Collegiate Environment: Orientation program. Drama-theater group, choral group, student-run newspaper. Social organizations: 36 open to all. Most popular organizations: Student Government Association, Phi Theta Kappa, American Chemical Society Student Affiliate, Campus Ministry, Medical Community Club. Major annual events: Fall Frolic, Spring Fling, Great Safe Holiday Break Campaign. Campus security: 24-hour emergency response devices and patrols, late night transport-escort service. Sara Harlee Library. Books: 129,690 (physical), 731,905 (digital/electronic); Databases: 140. 1,000 computers available on campus for general student use. A campuswide network can be accessed from off-campus. Students can access the following: online class registration. Staffed computer lab on campus provides training in use of computers, software, and the Internet.

Community Environment: A suburban area with a subtropical climate, Bradenton is located on the west coast and is known as"The Friendly City;" the hub of activities are in Manatee County. Air service at the Bradenton-

Sarasota airport are available. Shopping centers, hospital, city parks, theaters and a modern municipal auditorium are part of the community facilities. The city is a rich agricultural area, producing, processing and shipping citrus fruits, winter vegetables and gladiola. Recreational facilities include beaches, a municipal pier, yacht basin, boat launching, and fishing. Points of interest are the South Florida Museum and Planetarium, and the De Soto National Memorial. The Pittsburgh Pirates baseball team trains here. A De Soto celebration is an annual event in March. Venice, Florida, is located approximately 42 miles south of the Bradenton campus. Some part-time employment is available.

■ STETSON UNIVERSITY

421 N Woodland Blvd.
Deland, FL 32723
Tel: (386)822-7000; Free: 800-688-0101
Fax: (386)822-8832
E-mail: admissions@stetson.edu
Web Site: www.stetson.edu

Description: Independent, comprehensive, coed. Awards bachelor's, master's, and doctoral degrees and post-master's certificates. Founded 1883. Setting: 159-acre small town campus with easy access to Orlando. Endowment: $242.9 million. Research spending for the previous fiscal year: $570,986. Total enrollment: 4,341. Faculty: 432 (266 full-time, 166 part-time). Student-undergrad faculty ratio is 13:1. 13,330 applied, 68% were admitted. 22% from top 10% of their high school class, 54% from top quarter, 86% from top half. 8 valedictorians. Full-time: 3,111 students, 56% women, 44% men. Part-time: 39 students, 62% women, 38% men. Students come from 43 states and territories, 64 other countries, 26% from out-of-state. 0.1% American Indian or Alaska Native, non-Hispanic/Latino; 17% Hispanic/Latino; 8% Black or African American, non-Hispanic/Latino; 2% Asian, non-Hispanic/Latino; 0.1% Native Hawaiian or other Pacific Islander, non-Hispanic/Latino; 6% international. 2% 25 or older, 64% live on campus, 4% transferred in. Retention: 76% of full-time freshmen returned the following year. Academic areas with the most degrees conferred: business/marketing; social sciences; visual and performing arts; psychology. Core. Calendar: semesters. Services for LD students, advanced placement, accelerated degree program, self-designed majors, honors program, independent study, distance learning, double major, summer session for credit, part-time degree program, internships, graduate courses open to undergrads. Off campus study at American University. Study abroad program. ROTC: Army (c), Air Force (c).

Entrance Requirements: Options: electronic application, early action, deferred admission, international baccalaureate accepted. Required: essay, high school transcript, 1 recommendation. Recommended: interview. Required for some: SAT or ACT. Entrance: moderately difficult. Application deadline: rolling. Notification: continuous. SAT Reasoning Test deadline: 7/15. Transfer credits accepted: Yes. Applicants placed on waiting list: 977. Wait-listed applicants offered admission: 436.

Costs Per Year: Application fee: $50. Comprehensive fee: $61,498 includes full-time tuition ($47,270), mandatory fees ($360), and college room and board ($13,868). College room only: $8142. Part-time tuition: $1190 per credit hour.

Collegiate Environment: Orientation program. Drama-theater group, choral group, student-run newspaper, radio station. Social organizations: 125 open to all; national fraternities, national sororities; 29% of eligible men and 32% of eligible women are members. Most popular organizations: Caribbean Student Association, Fellowship of Christian Athletes, Kaleidoscope (promotes inclusivity), Black Student Association, Hatter Productions. Major annual events: Homecoming/Greenfeather, HatterPalooza (spring concert), Winter Wonderland (snow in Florida). Student services: health clinic, personal-psychological counseling. Campus security: 24-hour emergency response devices and patrols, student patrols, late night transport-escort service, controlled dormitory access. 2,051 college housing spaces available; 2,028 were occupied in 2018-19. Freshmen guaranteed college housing. On-campus residence required through junior year. Options: coed, men-only, women-only housing available. duPont-Ball Library plus 1 other. Books: 230,712 (physical), 194,199 (digital/electronic); Serial titles: 227 (physical), 159,553 (digital/electronic); Databases: 134. Weekly public service hours: 104; students can reserve study rooms. Operations spending for the previous fiscal year: $1.7 million. 600 computers available on campus for general student use. A campuswide network can be accessed from student residence rooms and from off campus. Students can access the following: online class registration. Staffed computer lab on campus (open 24 hours a day) provides training in use of computers, software, and the Internet.

■ STRAYER UNIVERSITY-BAYMEADOWS CAMPUS

8375 Dix Ellis Trl.
Ste. 200
Jacksonville, FL 32256
Tel: (904)538-1000; Free: 888-311-0355
Web Site: www.strayer.edu
Description: Proprietary, comprehensive, coed. Awards associate, bachelor's, and master's degrees.

■ STRAYER UNIVERSITY-FORT LAUDERDALE CAMPUS

2307 W Broward Blvd.
Ste. 100
Fort Lauderdale, FL 33312
Tel: (954)745-6960; Free: 888-311-0355
Web Site: www.strayer.edu
Description: Proprietary, comprehensive, coed. Awards associate, bachelor's, and master's degrees.

■ STRAYER UNIVERSITY-MAITLAND CAMPUS

901 N Lake Destiny Rd.
Ste. 370
Maitland, FL 32751
Tel: (407)618-5900; Free: 888-311-0355
Web Site: www.strayer.edu
Description: Proprietary, comprehensive, coed. Awards associate, bachelor's, and master's degrees.

■ STRAYER UNIVERSITY-MIRAMAR CAMPUS

15620 SW 29th St.
Hollywood, FL 33027
Tel: (954)378-2400; Free: 888-311-0355
Web Site: www.strayer.edu
Description: Proprietary, comprehensive, coed. Awards associate, bachelor's, and master's degrees.

■ STRAYER UNIVERSITY-ORLANDO EAST CAMPUS

2200 N Alafaya Trl.
Ste. 500
Orlando, FL 32826
Tel: (407)926-2000; Free: 888-311-0355
Web Site: www.strayer.edu
Description: Proprietary, comprehensive, coed. Awards associate, bachelor's, and master's degrees.

■ STRAYER UNIVERSITY-PALM BEACH GARDENS CAMPUS

11025 RCA Ctr. Dr.
Ste. 200
West Palm Beach, FL 33410
Tel: (561)904-3000; Free: 888-311-0355
Web Site: www.strayer.edu
Description: Proprietary, comprehensive, coed. Awards associate, bachelor's, and master's degrees.

■ STRAYER UNIVERSITY-SAND LAKE CAMPUS

8529 S Park Cir.
Orlando, FL 32819
Tel: (407)264-9400; Free: 888-311-0355
Web Site: www.strayer.edu
Description: Proprietary, comprehensive, coed. Awards associate, bachelor's, and master's degrees.

■ STRAYER UNIVERSITY-TAMPA EAST CAMPUS

5650 Breckenridge Park Dr.
Ste. 300
Tampa, FL 33610
Tel: (813)663-0100; Free: 888-311-0355
Web Site: www.strayer.edu
Description: Proprietary, comprehensive, coed. Awards associate, bachelor's, and master's degrees.

■ TALLAHASSEE COMMUNITY COLLEGE

444 Appleyard Dr.
Tallahassee, FL 32304-2895
Tel: (850)201-6200

E-mail: admissions@tcc.fl.edu

Web Site: www.tcc.fl.edu

Description: State and locally supported, primarily 2-year, coed. Part of Florida College System. Awards certificates, transfer associate, terminal associate, and bachelor's degrees. Founded 1966. Setting: 214-acre suburban campus. Endowment: $9.3 million. Educational spending for the previous fiscal year: $3410 per student. Total enrollment: 11,782. Faculty: 724 (173 full-time, 551 part-time). Student-undergrad faculty ratio is 22:1. Full-time: 5,830 students, 50% women, 50% men. Part-time: 5,952 students, 58% women, 42% men. Students come from 15 states and territories, 78 other countries, 6% from out-of-state. 0.3% American Indian or Alaska Native, non-Hispanic/Latino; 13% Hispanic/Latino; 30% Black or African American, non-Hispanic/Latino; 2% Asian, non-Hispanic/Latino; 0.1% Native Hawaiian or other Pacific Islander, non-Hispanic/Latino; 1% international. 19% 25 or older, 6% transferred in. Retention: 56% of full-time freshmen returned the following year. Core. Calendar: semesters. Academic remediation for entering students, ESL program, services for LD students, advanced placement, accelerated degree program, honors program, independent study, distance learning, summer session for credit, part-time degree program, external degree program, adult/continuing education programs. Off campus study at Florida Agricultural and Mechanical University, Florida State University. Study abroad program. ROTC: Army (c), Naval (c), Air Force (c).

Entrance Requirements: Open admission All but allied health programs. Options: electronic application, early admission, deferred admission. Required: high school transcript. Entrance: noncompetitive. Application deadline: 8/1. Transfer credits accepted: Yes.

Costs Per Year: Application fee: $0. State resident tuition: $2002 full-time, $100.83 per credit hour part-time. Nonresident tuition: $7982 full-time, $387.27 per credit hour part-time. Mandatory fees: $24 full-time.

Collegiate Environment: Orientation program. Drama-theater group, choral group, student-run newspaper. Social organizations: 22 open to all. Most popular organizations: Student Government Association, International Student Organization, Phi Theta Kappa, Model United Nations, Honors Council. Major annual events: Student/Faculty days, Volunteer Fair, Career Expo. Student services: personal-psychological counseling. Campus security: 24-hour emergency response devices and patrols, late night transport-escort service. Tallahassee Community College Library. Books: 82,774 (physical), 53,129 (digital/electronic); Serial titles: 59 (physical), 42,687 (digital/electronic); Databases: 105. Weekly public service hours: 68; students can reserve study rooms. Operations spending for the previous fiscal year: $1.2 million. 1,733 computers available on campus for general student use. A campuswide network can be accessed from off-campus. Students can access the following: online class registration. Staffed computer lab on campus provides training in use of computers, software, and the Internet.

Community Environment: See Florida State University.

■ **TALMUDIC UNIVERSITY**

4000 Alton Rd.

Miami Beach, FL 33140

Tel: (305)534-7050

Fax: (305)534-8444

E-mail: yandtg@gmail.com

Web Site: www.talmudicu.edu

Description: Independent Jewish, comprehensive, men only. Awards bachelor's and master's degrees. Founded 1974. Setting: urban campus with easy access to Miami. Educational spending for the previous fiscal year: $10,000 per student. Total enrollment: 35. Faculty: 6 (all full-time). Student-undergrad faculty ratio is 5:1. 10 applied, 80% were admitted. Full-time: 30 students. Students come from 5 states and territories, 5 other countries, 95% from out-of-state. 0.5% 25 or older, 99% live on campus, 83% transferred in. Retention: 50% of full-time freshmen returned the following year. Core. Calendar: semesters. Academic remediation for entering students, ESL program, honors program, independent study, summer session for credit, part-time degree program, adult/continuing education programs, graduate courses open to undergrads. Study abroad program.

Entrance Requirements: Options: early admission, deferred admission, international baccalaureate accepted. Required: high school transcript, interview. Recommended: essay. Entrance: moderately difficult. Application deadline: rolling. Notification: continuous.

Collegiate Environment: Student services: personal-psychological counseling. Beis Medrash plus 1 other.

■ **TRINITY BAPTIST COLLEGE**

800 Hammond Blvd.

Jacksonville, FL 32221

Tel: (904)596-2400; Free: 800-786-2206

Fax: (904)596-2531

E-mail: mgibson@tbc.edu

Web Site: www.tbc.edu

Description: Independent Baptist, comprehensive, coed. Awards associate, bachelor's, and master's degrees. Founded 1974. Setting: 148-acre urban campus with easy access to Jacksonville. Total enrollment: 280. 350 applied, 51% were admitted. Students come from 21 states and territories, 4 other countries, 23% from out-of-state. 18% 25 or older. Core. Calendar: semesters. Academic remediation for entering students, services for LD students, advanced placement, accelerated degree program, independent study, distance learning, double major, summer session for credit, part-time degree program, adult/continuing education programs, internships, graduate courses open to undergrads.

Entrance Requirements: Options: electronic application, early admission. Required: essay, high school transcript, 2 recommendations. Required for some: interview, SAT or ACT. Entrance: moderately difficult. Application deadline: rolling. Notification: continuous until 8/15. Transfer credits accepted: Yes.

Costs Per Year: Application fee: $35. Comprehensive fee: $19,180 includes full-time tuition ($10,990), mandatory fees ($1150), and college room and board ($7040). Full-time tuition and fees vary according to course load. Part-time tuition: $458 per credit hour. Part-time mandatory fees: $575 per term. Part-time tuition and fees vary according to course load.

Collegiate Environment: Orientation program. Drama-theater group, choral group, student-run newspaper. Student services: health clinic, personal-psychological counseling. Campus security: 24-hour emergency response devices and patrols, controlled dormitory access. 21 computers available on campus for general student use. A campuswide network can be accessed from student residence rooms. Students can access the following: online class registration. Staffed computer lab on campus.

■ **TRINITY COLLEGE OF FLORIDA**

2430 Welbilt Blvd.

Trinity, FL 34655

Tel: (727)376-6911; Free: 800-388-0869

Fax: (727)376-0781

E-mail: ashady@trinitycollege.edu

Web Site: www.trinitycollege.edu

Description: Independent nondenominational, 4-year, coed. Awards associate and bachelor's degrees. Founded 1932. Setting: 40-acre small town campus with easy access to Tampa. Endowment: $726,911. Educational spending for the previous fiscal year: $4510 per student. Total enrollment: 189. Faculty: 22 (8 full-time, 14 part-time). Student-undergrad faculty ratio is 9:1. 61 applied, 92% were admitted. Full-time: 163 students, 45% women, 55% men. Part-time: 26 students, 54% women, 46% men. Students come from 15 states and territories, 3 other countries, 10% from out-of-state. 1% American Indian or Alaska Native, non-Hispanic/Latino; 18% Hispanic/Latino; 26% Black or African American, non-Hispanic/Latino; 2% Asian, non-Hispanic/Latino; 2% international. 40% 25 or older, 49% live on campus, 25% transferred in. Retention: 54% of full-time freshmen returned the following year. Academic areas with the most degrees conferred: theology and religious vocations; business/marketing; psychology. Core. Calendar: semesters. Academic remediation for entering students, services for LD students, advanced placement, accelerated degree program, honors program, independent study, distance learning, double major, summer session for credit, part-time degree program, adult/continuing education programs, co-op programs. Off campus study.

Entrance Requirements: Options: electronic application, deferred admission, international baccalaureate accepted. Required: essay, high school transcript, 2 recommendations, SAT or ACT. Recommended: minimum 2.2 high school GPA. Required for some: interview. Entrance: noncompetitive. Application deadline: 7/31. Notification: continuous, continuous for nonresidents. SAT Reasoning Test deadline: 7/31. SAT Subject Test deadline: 7/31. Transfer credits accepted: Yes.

Costs Per Year: Application fee: $35. Comprehensive fee: $23,315 includes full-time tuition ($15,300), mandatory fees ($1040), and college room and board ($6975). Full-time tuition and fees vary according to course load and program. Part-time tuition: $510 per credit hour. Part-time mandatory fees: $520 per term. Part-time tuition and fees vary according to course load and program.

Collegiate Environment: Choral group. Social organizations: 4 open to all. Most popular organizations: Student Government Association, Great Commission Missionary Fellowship, Prayer Group, Trinity Against Trafficking. Major annual events: Commencement, Missions Conference, Campus Preview. Student services: personal-psychological counseling. Campus security: student patrols, security cameras. Raymond H. Center, M.D. Library. Books: 33,116 (physical), 165,300 (digital/electronic); Serial titles: 38 (physical); Databases: 9. Weekly public service hours: 60. Operations spending for the previous fiscal year: $86,943. 17 computers available on campus for general student use. A campuswide network can be accessed from student residence rooms. Students can access the following: online class registration. Staffed computer lab on campus provides training in use of computers, software, and the Internet.

Community Environment: See Clearwater Christian College.

■ ULTIMATE MEDICAL ACADEMY CLEARWATER
1255 Cleveland St.
Clearwater, FL 33755
Tel: (727)298-8685; Free: 888-205-2510
Web Site: www.ultimatemedical.edu

Description: Independent, 2-year, coed. Awards diplomas and terminal associate degrees. Founded 1994. Setting: urban campus with easy access to Tampa. Total enrollment: 274. Full-time: 247 students, 92% women, 8% men. 1% American Indian or Alaska Native, non-Hispanic/Latino; 11% Hispanic/Latino; 44% Black or African American, non-Hispanic/Latino; 0.7% Asian, non-Hispanic/Latino. 80% 25 or older. Core. Calendar: continuous. Services for LD students, distance learning, part-time degree program.

Entrance Requirements: Open admission. Required: high school transcript. Transfer credits accepted: Yes.

■ ULTIMATE MEDICAL ACADEMY ONLINE
3101 W Dr. Martin Luther King Jr. Blvd.
Tampa, FL 33607
Tel: (727)298-8685; Free: 888-205-2510
E-mail: onlineadmissions@ultimatemedical.edu
Web Site: www.ultimatemedical.edu

Description: Independent, 2-year, coed. Awards diplomas and terminal associate degrees. Setting: urban campus. Total enrollment: 16,411. Full-time: 13,017 students, 94% women, 6% men. Part-time: 3,394 students, 94% women, 6% men. Students come from 50 states and territories. 1% American Indian or Alaska Native, non-Hispanic/Latino; 8% Hispanic/Latino; 54% Black or African American, non-Hispanic/Latino; 0.5% Asian, non-Hispanic/Latino; 0.4% Native Hawaiian or other Pacific Islander, non-Hispanic/Latino. 80% 25 or older. Retention: 80% of full-time freshmen returned the following year. Core. Calendar: continuous. Services for LD students, distance learning, part-time degree program.

Entrance Requirements: Open admission. Option: electronic application. Required: high school transcript. Transfer credits accepted: Yes.

■ UNILATINA INTERNATIONAL COLLEGE
3130 Commerce Pky.
Miramar, FL 33025
Web Site: www.unilatina.edu

Description: Proprietary, 4-year, coed.

■ UNIVERSAL CAREER SCHOOL
10720 W Flagler St.
Ste. 21
Sweetwater, FL 33174
Tel: (305)485-7700
Web Site: www.ucs.edu

Description: Proprietary, 2-year, coed. Awards diplomas, transfer associate, and terminal associate degrees.

■ UNIVERSITY OF CENTRAL FLORIDA
4000 Central Florida Blvd.
Orlando, FL 32816
Tel: (407)823-2000
Fax: (407)823-3419
E-mail: admission@ucf.edu
Web Site: www.ucf.edu

Description: State-supported, university, coed. Part of State University System of Florida. Awards associate, bachelor's, master's, and doctoral degrees and post-master's certificates. Founded 1963. Setting: 1,415-acre

suburban campus with easy access to Orlando. Endowment: $161.6 million. Research spending for the previous fiscal year: $143.7 million. Total enrollment: 68,571. Faculty: 2,123 (1,619 full-time, 504 part-time). Student-undergrad faculty ratio is 30:1. 41,816 applied, 43% were admitted. 34% from top 10% of their high school class, 73% from top quarter, 97% from top half. 82 National Merit Scholars, 56 valedictorians. Full-time: 41,852 students, 54% women, 46% men. Part-time: 17,061 students, 55% women, 45% men. Students come from 50 states and territories, 132 other countries, 7% from out-of-state. 0.2% American Indian or Alaska Native, non-Hispanic/Latino; 28% Hispanic/Latino; 11% Black or African American, non-Hispanic/Latino; 6% Asian, non-Hispanic/Latino; 0.2% Native Hawaiian or other Pacific Islander, non-Hispanic/Latino; 2% international. 17% 25 or older, 17% live on campus, 12% transferred in. Retention: 90% of full-time freshmen returned the following year. Academic areas with the most degrees conferred: business/marketing; health professions and related sciences; psychology. Core. Calendar: semesters. ESL program, services for LD students, advanced placement, accelerated degree program, freshman honors college, honors program, independent study, distance learning, double major, summer session for credit, part-time degree program, adult/continuing education programs, co-op programs and internships, graduate courses open to undergrads. Off campus study. Study abroad program. ROTC: Army, Air Force.

Entrance Requirements: Options: electronic application, early admission, international baccalaureate accepted. Required: minimum 2.5 high school GPA, SAT or ACT. Recommended: essay. Required for some: high school transcript. Entrance: moderately difficult. Application deadline: 5/1. Notification: continuous. Preference given to state residents who are designated as Talented 20. SAT Reasoning Test deadline: 5/1. Transfer credits accepted: Yes. Applicants placed on waiting list: 6,327. Wait-listed applicants offered admission: 54.

Costs Per Year: Application fee: $30. State resident tuition: $6368 full-time, $212.28 per credit hour part-time. Nonresident tuition: $22,467 full-time, $748.89 per credit hour part-time. Full-time tuition varies according to course load. Part-time tuition varies according to course load. College room and board: $9617. College room only: $5400. Room and board charges vary according to board plan and housing facility.

Collegiate Environment: Orientation program. Drama-theater group, choral group, marching band, student-run radio station. Social organizations: 672 open to all; national fraternities, national sororities, local fraternities, local sororities; 5% of eligible men and 7% of eligible women are members. Most popular organizations: Volunteer UCF, RWC Intramural Sports, Fraternity and Sorority Life, Multicultural Student Center and Organizations, Knight-thon Dance Marathon. Major annual events: Homecoming Week, Pegasus Palooza (Welcome Week), Universal Knights. Student services: legal services, health clinic, personal-psychological counseling, women's center. Campus security: 24-hour emergency response devices and patrols, late night transport-escort service, controlled dormitory access. 11,608 college housing spaces available; 10,355 were occupied in 2018-19. Freshmen given priority for college housing. Option: coed housing available. University Libraries plus 3 others. Books: 1.6 million (physical), 181,480 (digital/electronic); Serial titles: 737 (physical), 68,194 (digital/electronic); Databases: 481. Weekly public service hours: 105; students can reserve study rooms. Operations spending for the previous fiscal year: $16 million. 4,113 computers available on campus for general student use. A campus-wide network can be accessed from student residence rooms and from off campus. Students can access the following: online class registration. Staffed computer lab on campus provides training in use of computers, software, and the Internet.

Community Environment: Orlando has become a focal point for business and major industry, easily accessible by major forms of public transportation, and serves as a regional retail market for eight counties and over a million people. The area's reputation as a tourism mecca has brought a resultant surge in the hospitality industry as well. It also is an important agricultural center, noted for citrus and truck gardening. The temperate climate year-round provides ideal conditions for numerous recreational opportunities: fishing, boating, dog and horse racing, Jai-Alai, golf, tennis, and other outdoor activities. Points of interest include Walt Disney World, Epcot Center, MGM Studios, Universal Studios, Sea World, plus such seasonal attractions as the Church Street Station, Citrus Open Golf Tournament, Walt Disney World Golf Classic, Orlando Horse Show, Central Florida Fair, Orlando Magic Pro-Basketball, and Citrus Bowl. Cultural activities are widespread in the Orlando-Winter Park area, and include annual Sidewalk Art Festivals, Orlando Shakespeare Festival, the Florida Symphony Orchestra, Central

Florida Civic Theatre, and the John Young Museum and Planetarium, located adjacent to the Loch Haven Art Center.

■ UNIVERSITY OF FLORIDA
Gainesville, FL 32611
Tel: (352)392-3261
Web Site: www.ufl.edu

Description: State-supported, university, coed. Part of Board of Trustees. Awards associate, bachelor's, master's, and doctoral degrees and post-master's certificates. Founded 1853. Setting: 2,000-acre suburban campus with easy access to Jacksonville. Endowment: $1.7 million. Research spending for the previous fiscal year: $865.1 million. Educational spending for the previous fiscal year: $15,961 per student. Total enrollment: 52,218. 38,905 applied, 39% were admitted. 77% from top 10% of their high school class, 97% from top quarter, 100% from top half. 197 National Merit Scholars. Full-time: 32,209 students, 57% women, 43% men. Part-time: 3,282 students, 48% women, 52% men. Students come from 51 states and territories, 140 other countries, 7% from out-of-state. 0.2% American Indian or Alaska Native, non-Hispanic/Latino; 22% Hispanic/Latino; 6% Black or African American, non-Hispanic/Latino; 9% Asian, non-Hispanic/Latino; 0.4% Native Hawaiian or other Pacific Islander, non-Hispanic/Latino; 3% international. 3% 25 or older, 22% live on campus, 6% transferred in. Academic areas with the most degrees conferred: engineering; business/marketing; social sciences; biological/life sciences. Core. Calendar: semesters. ESL program, services for LD students, advanced placement, accelerated degree program, self-designed majors, honors program, independent study, distance learning, double major, summer session for credit, part-time degree program, external degree program, adult/continuing education programs, co-op programs and internships, graduate courses open to undergrads. Off campus study at Miami New World School of the Arts, Miami-Dade Community College (http://nwsa.mdc.edu/); Gator Engineering at State College of Florida (https://www.eng.ufl.edu/students/students/state-college-partnerships/gescf/); Gator Engineering at Santa Fe College (https://www.eng.ufl.edu/students/students/state-college-partnerships/gator-engineering-santa-fe/); Abraham Baldwin Agricultural College (https://www.abac.edu/); Tuskegee University (https://www.tuskegee.edu/about_us.aspx. Study abroad program. ROTC: Army, Naval, Air Force.

Entrance Requirements: Option: electronic application. Required: essay, SAT or ACT. Required for some: high school transcript, SAT Subject Tests. Entrance: very difficult. Application deadline: 3/1. Notification: 2/9. SAT Reasoning Test deadline: 12/31. SAT Subject Test deadline: 12/31. Transfer credits accepted: Yes.

Collegiate Environment: Orientation program. Drama-theater group, choral group, marching band, student-run newspaper, radio station. Social organizations: 941 open to all; national fraternities, national sororities; 17% of eligible men and 22% of eligible women are members. Most popular organizations: Student Government, Hispanic Student Association, Black Student Union, Inter-Residence Hall Association, Asian American Student Union. Major annual events: Gator Growl/Homecoming, New Student Convocation, Welcome Assemblies. Student services: legal services, health clinic, personal-psychological counseling, women's center. Campus security: 24-hour emergency response devices and patrols, student patrols, late night transport-escort service, controlled dormitory access, crime and rape prevention programs. 8,001 college housing spaces available; 7,962 were occupied in 2018-19. No special consideration for freshman housing applicants. Option: coed housing available. George A. Smathers Libraries plus 7 others. Books: 5.8 million (physical), 1.5 million (digital/electronic); Serial titles: 2,716 (physical), 125,667 (digital/electronic); Databases: 1,092. Weekly public service hours: 168; study areas open 24 hours, 5-7 days a week; students can reserve study rooms. Operations spending for the previous fiscal year: $34.4 million. 1,327 computers available on campus for general student use. A campuswide network can be accessed from student residence rooms and from off campus. Students can access the following: online class registration, course management system; virtual labs/applications. Staffed computer lab on campus (open 24 hours a day) provides training in use of computers, software, and the Internet.

Community Environment: Gainesville is the county seat of Alachua County located on the rolling highlands of north-central Florida midway between the Gulf of Mexico and the Atlantic Ocean. The climate is subtropical with an average mean temperature of 70 degrees. Railroads, buses and airlines serve the area. Gainesville is the focal point of diversified industrial and agricultural activities. The city facilities include churches of many denominations, center for science, education and medicine, medical center with hospital, museum and numerous civic organizations. Recreational facilities include golf courses, swimming at nearby springs, boating and freshwater

fishing in surrounding lakes and rivers. Both the Atlantic Ocean and the Gulf of Mexico are within a two-hour drive. Off-campus housing is available for over 20,000 students in addition to university housing.

■ UNIVERSITY OF FORT LAUDERDALE
4093 NW 16th St.
Lauderhill, FL 33313
Tel: (954)486-7728
Web Site: uftl.edu

Description: Independent Christian, comprehensive, coed. Awards associate, bachelor's, and master's degrees. Founded 1995. Calendar: semesters.

■ UNIVERSITY OF MIAMI
PO Box 248025
Coral Gables, FL 33124
Tel: (305)284-2211
Fax: (305)284-2507
E-mail: mreid@miami.edu
Web Site: www.miami.edu

Description: Independent, university, coed. Awards bachelor's, master's, and doctoral degrees and post-master's certificates. Founded 1925. Setting: 239-acre suburban campus with easy access to Miami. Endowment: $948.6 million. Research spending for the previous fiscal year: $240 million. Educational spending for the previous fiscal year: $31,225 per student. Total enrollment: 17,003. Faculty: 1,614 (1,115 full-time, 499 part-time). Student-undergrad faculty ratio is 12:1. 30,634 applied, 36% were admitted. 46% from top 10% of their high school class, 77% from top quarter, 94% from top half. 13 valedictorians. Full-time: 10,216 students, 52% women, 48% men. Part-time: 616 students, 57% women, 43% men. Students come from 53 states and territories, 102 other countries, 55% from out-of-state. 0.1% American Indian or Alaska Native, non-Hispanic/Latino; 23% Hispanic/Latino; 8% Black or African American, non-Hispanic/Latino; 5% Asian, non-Hispanic/Latino; 15% international. 5% 25 or older, 39% live on campus, 6% transferred in. Retention: 91% of full-time freshmen returned the following year. Academic areas with the most degrees conferred: business/marketing; biological/life sciences; social sciences. Core. Calendar: semesters. Academic remediation for entering students, ESL program, services for LD students, advanced placement, accelerated degree program, self-designed majors, honors program, independent study, distance learning, double major, summer session for credit, part-time degree program, co-op programs and internships, graduate courses open to undergrads. Off campus study at Washington Semester Program, American University. Study abroad program. ROTC: Army, Air Force.

Entrance Requirements: Options: electronic application, early admission, early decision, early action, deferred admission, international baccalaureate accepted. Required: essay, high school transcript, 1 recommendation, SAT or ACT. Required for some: college transcript(s) and statement of good standing from prior institution(s), auditions for selected academic programs, SAT and SAT Subject Tests or ACT. Entrance: very difficult. Application deadlines: 1/1, 11/1 for early decision plan 1, 1/1 for early decision plan 2, 11/1 for early action. Notification: 4/1, 1/1 for early decision plan 1, 3/1 for early decision plan 2, 2/1 for early action. SAT Reasoning Test deadline: 1/1. SAT Subject Test deadline: 11/1. Transfer credits accepted: Yes. Applicants placed on waiting list: 8,286. Wait-listed applicants offered admission: 71. Early decision applicants: 954. Early decision applicants admitted: 609. Early action applicants: 11,852. Early action applicants admitted: 5,977.

Costs Per Year: Application fee: $70. Comprehensive fee: $64,334 includes full-time tuition ($48,720), mandatory fees ($1506), and college room and board ($14,108). College room only: $8120. Full-time tuition and fees vary according to course load. Room and board charges vary according to board plan and housing facility. Part-time tuition: $2030 per credit hour. Part-time mandatory fees: $260 per term. Part-time tuition and fees vary according to course load and program.

Collegiate Environment: Orientation program. Drama-theater group, choral group, marching band, student-run newspaper, radio station. Social organizations: 286 open to all; national fraternities, national sororities; 21% of eligible men and 18% of eligible women are members. Most popular organizations: Hurricane Productions, Federation of Club Sports, Association of Greek Letter Organizations, Panhellenic Council, Scuba Club. Major annual events: Homecoming, SportsFest, Hug the Lake OR HP Canes Carnival. Student services: health clinic, personal-psychological counseling. Campus security: 24-hour emergency response devices and patrols, student patrols, late night transport-escort service, controlled dormitory access, programs, seminars, activities, classes and publications are available to students, faculty, staff, parents and friends. Otto G. Richter Library plus 6 others. Books: 2.8 million (physical), 1 million (digital/electronic); Serial titles: 1,216 (physical), 113,585 (digital/electronic); Databases: 677. Weekly public service hours: 118; students can reserve study rooms. Operations spending for the previous fiscal year: $23.7 million. 400 computers available on campus for general student use. Computer purchase/lease plans available. A campuswide network can be accessed from student residence rooms and from off campus. Students can access the following: online class registration, online bill payment, online housing registration. Staffed computer lab on campus provides training in use of computers, software, and the Internet.

Community Environment: A part of the metropolitan Miami area, Coral Gables is known as"City Beautiful" with the mildest climate in the United States. The Miami International Airport is nearby. The city offers a distinguished retail shopping district, the opera, theatre, ballet, concerts, the Vizcaya Museum, and Lowe Art Gallery. Recreational activities are numerous including swimming, golf, tennis, boating, sport fishing, and snorkeling and scuba diving among the only coral reefs in the continental United States, in the Florida Keys. The Everglades National Park is 1 hour away.

■ **UNIVERSITY OF NORTH FLORIDA**
1 UNF Dr.
Jacksonville, FL 32224
Tel: (904)620-1000
Fax: (904)620-1040
E-mail: admissions@unf.edu
Web Site: www.unf.edu

Description: State-supported, comprehensive, coed. Part of State University System of Florida. Awards associate, bachelor's, master's, and doctoral degrees and post-master's certificates (doctoral degree in education only). Founded 1965. Setting: 1,300-acre urban campus with easy access to Jacksonville, FL. Endowment: $107.1 million. Research spending for the previous fiscal year: $7 million. Educational spending for the previous fiscal year: $8424 per student. Total enrollment: 16,775. Faculty: 977 (570 full-time, 406 part-time). Student-undergrad faculty ratio is 18:1. 14,330 applied, 61% were admitted. 16% from top 10% of their high school class, 41% from top quarter, 76% from top half. Full-time: 10,457 students, 56% women, 44% men. Part-time: 4,037 students, 55% women, 45% men. Students come from 48 states and territories, 65 other countries, 4% from out-of-state. 0.2% American Indian or Alaska Native, non-Hispanic/Latino; 13% Hispanic/Latino; 9% Black or African American, non-Hispanic/Latino; 5% Asian, non-Hispanic/Latino; 0.1% Native Hawaiian or other Pacific Islander, non-Hispanic/Latino; 2% international. 18% 25 or older, 22% live on campus, 10% transferred in. Retention: 81% of full-time freshmen returned the following year. Academic areas with the most degrees conferred: health professions and related sciences; business/marketing; psychology. Core. Calendar: semesters. ESL program, services for LD students, advanced placement, accelerated degree program, honors program, independent study, distance learning, double major, summer session for credit, part-time degree program, adult/continuing education programs, co-op programs and internships, graduate courses open to undergrads. Off campus study at State University System of Florida. Study abroad program. ROTC: Army, Naval (c).

Entrance Requirements: Options: electronic application, deferred admission, international baccalaureate accepted. Required: high school transcript, minimum 2.5 high school GPA, SAT or ACT. Recommended: minimum 3 high school GPA. Required for some: essay. Entrance: moderately difficult. Application deadline: rolling. Notification: continuous. SAT Reasoning Test deadline: 8/10. Transfer credits accepted: Yes.

Costs Per Year: Application fee: $30. State resident tuition: $4281 full-time, $142.70 per credit hour part-time. Nonresident tuition: $17,999 full-time, $599.97 per credit hour part-time. Mandatory fees: $2113 full-time, $70.43 per credit hour part-time. Full-time tuition and fees vary according to course load. Part-time tuition and fees vary according to course load. College room and board: $9846. College room only: $5772. Room and board charges vary according to board plan and housing facility.

Collegiate Environment: Orientation program. Drama-theater group, choral group, student-run newspaper, radio station. Social organizations: 246 open to all; national fraternities, national sororities, local fraternities, local sororities. Most popular organizations: Student Government Association, African American Student Association, International Student Association, Filipino Student Association, National Education Association. Major annual events: Homecoming, Earth Music Fest, Toga Party. Student services: health clinic, personal-psychological counseling, women's center. Campus security: 24-hour emergency response devices and patrols, late night transport-escort

service, controlled dormitory access, electronic parking lot security. 3,500 college housing spaces available; 3,383 were occupied in 2018-19. Freshmen guaranteed college housing. Option: coed housing available. Thomas G. Carpenter Library. Books: 568,299 (physical), 543,121 (digital/electronic); Serial titles: 12,479 (physical), 211,959 (digital/electronic); Databases: 284. Students can reserve study rooms. Operations spending for the previous fiscal year: $4.6 million. 700 computers available on campus for general student use. Computer purchase/lease plans available. A campuswide network can be accessed from student residence rooms and from off campus. Students can access the following: online class registration, reduced prices for students on certain business and design software. Staffed computer lab on campus provides training in use of computers.

Community Environment: See Jacksonville University.

■ **UNIVERSITY OF SOUTH FLORIDA**
4202 E Fowler Ave.
Tampa, FL 33620-9951
Tel: (813)974-2011
Fax: (813)974-9689
Web Site: www.usf.edu

Description: State-supported, university, coed. Part of State University System of Florida. Awards associate, bachelor's, master's, and doctoral degrees. Founded 1956. Setting: 1,562-acre urban campus. System endowment: $480.4 million. Total enrollment: 43,838. Faculty: 2,028 (1,299 full-time, 729 part-time). Student-undergrad faculty ratio is 24:1. 28,623 applied, 47% were admitted. 34% from top 10% of their high school class, 71% from top quarter, 94% from top half. Full-time: 24,833 students, 55% women, 45% men. Part-time: 7,405 students, 52% women, 48% men. Students come from 145 other countries, 6% from out-of-state. 0.2% American Indian or Alaska Native, non-Hispanic/Latino; 21% Hispanic/Latino; 10% Black or African American, non-Hispanic/Latino; 7% Asian, non-Hispanic/Latino; 0.2% Native Hawaiian or other Pacific Islander, non-Hispanic/Latino; 7% international. 15% 25 or older, 18% live on campus, 12% transferred in. Retention: 91% of full-time freshmen returned the following year. Academic areas with the most degrees conferred: health professions and related sciences; business/marketing; biological/life sciences; social sciences. Core. Calendar: semesters. Academic remediation for entering students, services for LD students, advanced placement, accelerated degree program, freshman honors college, honors program, distance learning, double major, summer session for credit, part-time degree program, adult/continuing education programs, co-op programs and internships, graduate courses open to undergrads. Off campus study at members of the National Student Exchange, State University System of Florida. Study abroad program. ROTC: Army, Naval, Air Force.

Entrance Requirements: Options: electronic application, early admission, deferred admission, international baccalaureate accepted. Required: SAT or ACT. Recommended: high school transcript. Notification: continuous. SAT Reasoning Test deadline: 5/1. Transfer credits accepted: Yes.

Costs Per Year: Application fee: $30. Area resident tuition: $4559 full-time, $151.95 per credit hour part-time. Nonresident tuition: $15,473 full-time, $515.77 per credit hour part-time. Mandatory fees: $1851 full-time. College room and board: $11,610. College room only: $7752.

Collegiate Environment: Orientation program. Drama-theater group, choral group, marching band, student-run newspaper, radio station. Social organizations: national fraternities, national sororities. Most popular organizations: Student Government, Campus Activities Board, USF Ambassadors, Student Admissions Representatives. Major annual events: Homecoming, Welcome Week, University lecture series. Student services: legal services, health clinic, personal-psychological counseling, women's center. Campus security: 24-hour emergency response devices and patrols, student patrols, late night transport-escort service, controlled dormitory access. Option: coed housing available. Tampa Campus Library plus 5 others. Books: 1.8 million (physical), 652,513 (digital/electronic); Serial titles: 537 (physical), 58,975 (digital/electronic); Databases: 939. Weekly public service hours: 116; study areas open 24 hours, 5-7 days a week; students can reserve study rooms. 825 computers available on campus for general student use. A campuswide network can be accessed from student residence rooms and from off campus. Students can access the following: online class registration. Staffed computer lab on campus (open 24 hours a day) provides training in use of computers and the Internet.

Community Environment: Tampa, located on the west coast of Florida, is the seventh largest port in the nation. It is a significant industrial and commercial center; the second largest city in the state. A fine harbor with a 34 foot channel to the Gulf of Mexico is located here. It is important in trade and travel to and from Central and South America. Annual mean temperature is 72.3 degrees, the average rainfall is 49 inches. All modes of travel serve the area. Industries include cigar manufacturing, phosphate, beer, cement, cans, wire and cable, and canned citrus fruits and vegetables. Tampa is a tourist city with many recreational facilities; yacht basin, golf courses, tennis clubs, saddle clubs, swimming pools, bowling alleys, baseball diamonds, and basketball courts. Salt water fishing is excellent. Swimming is excellent all year in Tampa Bay, and at the municipal beach on Courtney Campell Causeway. The Tampa Bay Buccaneers is the local NFL team and the Cincinnati Reds make Tampa their spring training quarters. Points of interest are the Busch Gardens, Lowry Park, Tampa Art Institute, and the Tampa Museum.

■ **UNIVERSITY OF SOUTH FLORIDA, ST. PETERSBURG**
140 Seventh Ave. S
Saint Petersburg, FL 33701
Tel: (727)873-7748
E-mail: admissions@usfsp.edu
Web Site: www.usfsp.edu
Description: State-supported, comprehensive, coed. Part of University of South Florida System. Awards bachelor's and master's degrees. Founded 1965. Setting: 48-acre urban campus with easy access to Tampa. Endowment: $19.1 million. Research spending for the previous fiscal year: $4.2 million. Educational spending for the previous fiscal year: $15,196 per student. Total enrollment: 4,980. Faculty: 301 (158 full-time, 143 part-time). Student-undergrad faculty ratio is 16:1. 5,575 applied, 40% were admitted. 17% from top 10% of their high school class, 46% from top quarter, 84% from top half. Full-time: 2,837 students, 63% women, 37% men. Part-time: 1,497 students, 62% women, 38% men. 4% from out-of-state. 0.3% American Indian or Alaska Native, non-Hispanic/Latino; 17% Hispanic/Latino; 8% Black or African American, non-Hispanic/Latino; 3% Asian, non-Hispanic/Latino; 0.1% Native Hawaiian or other Pacific Islander, non-Hispanic/Latino; 0.7% international. 26% 25 or older, 17% live on campus, 13% transferred in. Academic areas with the most degrees conferred: business/marketing; social sciences; biological/life sciences. Core. Calendar: semesters. Services for LD students, freshman honors college, honors program, independent study, distance learning, double major, summer session for credit, internships, graduate courses open to undergrads. Study abroad program. ROTC: Army.
Entrance Requirements: Open admission. Options: early admission, early action, international baccalaureate accepted. Required: high school transcript, minimum 2.5 high school GPA, SAT or ACT. Application deadline: 5/1. SAT Reasoning Test deadline: 4/15.
Costs Per Year: Application fee: $30. State resident tuition: $4206 full-time, $140.21 per credit hour part-time. Nonresident tuition: $15,120 full-time, $504.03 per credit hour part-time. Mandatory fees: $1615 full-time, $54.03 per credit hour part-time. College room and board: $11,160. Room and board charges vary according to board plan and housing facility.
Collegiate Environment: Orientation program. Drama-theater group, student-run newspaper, radio station. Social organizations: 100 open to all. Most popular organizations: Student Government, Harborside Activities Board, Delta Sigma Pi, Multicultural Activities Council, HERD Step Team. Major annual events: Welcome Week, Spring Fling, Leadership Retreats. Student services: health clinic, personal-psychological counseling. Campus security: 24-hour emergency response devices and patrols, late night transport-escort service, controlled dormitory access. Nelson Poynter Memorial Library. Books: 212,904 (physical), 693,313 (digital/electronic); Serial titles: 7,817 (physical), 64,928 (digital/electronic); Databases: 939. Weekly public service hours: 79; students can reserve study rooms. Operations spending for the previous fiscal year: $1.3 million. 125 computers available on campus for general student use. Computer purchase/lease plans available. A campuswide network can be accessed from student residence rooms and from off campus. Students can access the following: online class registration. Staffed computer lab on campus provides training in use of computers, software, and the Internet.

■ **UNIVERSITY OF SOUTH FLORIDA SARASOTA-MANATEE**
8350 N Tamiami Trl.
Sarasota, FL 34243
Tel: (941)359-4200
E-mail: bavery@sar.usf.edu
Web Site: www.usfsm.edu
Description: State-supported, comprehensive, coed. Part of University of South Florida System. Awards associate, bachelor's, and master's degrees

and post-master's certificates. Founded 1956. Setting: 31-acre urban campus with easy access to Tampa. Endowment: $10.8 million. Research spending for the previous fiscal year: $133,660. Educational spending for the previous fiscal year: $6344 per student. Total enrollment: 2,069. Faculty: 160 (91 full-time, 69 part-time). Student-undergrad faculty ratio is 14:1. 771 applied, 32% were admitted. 20% from top 10% of their high school class, 54% from top quarter, 84% from top half. 1 valedictorian, 5 student government officers. Full-time: 1,008 students, 60% women, 40% men. Part-time: 908 students, 62% women, 38% men. 3% from out-of-state. 0.4% American Indian or Alaska Native, non-Hispanic/Latino; 16% Hispanic/Latino; 5% Black or African American, non-Hispanic/Latino; 2% Asian, non-Hispanic/Latino; 3% international. 44% 25 or older, 18% transferred in. Retention: 89% of full-time freshmen returned the following year. Academic areas with the most degrees conferred: business/marketing; social sciences; psychology; education. Core. Calendar: semesters. Services for LD students, advanced placement, honors program, independent study, distance learning, double major, summer session for credit, part-time degree program, internships. Study abroad program. ROTC: Army (c), Naval (c), Air Force (c).
Entrance Requirements: Options: electronic application, deferred admission, international baccalaureate accepted. Required: high school transcript, minimum 3.3 high school GPA, SAT or ACT. Recommended: essay, minimum 3.3 high school GPA, 2 recommendations, SAT Subject Tests. Required for some: minimum 3.3 high school GPA, interview. Entrance: moderately difficult. Application deadline: 3/1 for nonresidents. Notification: continuous, continuous for nonresidents. SAT Reasoning Test deadline: 5/1. SAT Subject Test deadline: 5/1. Transfer credits accepted: Yes.
Costs Per Year: Application fee: $30. State resident tuition: $4206 full-time, $140.21 per credit hour part-time. Nonresident tuition: $15,120 full-time, $504.03 per credit hour part-time. Mandatory fees: $1381 full-time, $45.71 per credit hour part-time, $10 per term part-time. Full-time tuition and fees vary according to course load and program. Part-time tuition and fees vary according to course load and program.
Collegiate Environment: Orientation program. Social organizations: 32 open to all. Most popular organizations: Box Office Bulls, The Adventure Club, Gamers' Club, Student Veteran Society, The Criminology Club. Major annual events: The Bullpen, USFSM Week Carnival, Week of Welcome. Student services: health clinic, personal-psychological counseling. Campus security: 24-hour emergency response devices and patrols, late night transport-escort service. College housing not available. USF Libraries. Books: 1,231 (physical), 721,020 (digital/electronic); Serial titles: 65,050 (digital/electronic); Databases: 941. Weekly public service hours: 96; students can reserve study rooms. Operations spending for the previous fiscal year: $666,117. 61 computers available on campus for general student use. Computer purchase/lease plans available. A computer is required for all students. A campuswide network can be accessed from off-campus. Students can access the following: online class registration. Staffed computer lab on campus provides training in use of computers, software, and the Internet.

■ **THE UNIVERSITY OF TAMPA**
401 W Kennedy Blvd.
Tampa, FL 33606-1490
Tel: (813)253-3333; Free: 888-MINARET
Fax: (813)254-4955
E-mail: admissions@ut.edu
Web Site: www.ut.edu
Description: Independent, comprehensive, coed. Awards bachelor's and master's degrees and post-master's certificates. Founded 1931. Setting: 110-acre urban campus with easy access to Tampa-St. Petersburg, Clearwater. Total enrollment: 9,335. Faculty: 795 (372 full-time, 423 part-time). Student-undergrad faculty ratio is 17:1. 22,310 applied, 49% were admitted. 17% from top 10% of their high school class, 48% from top quarter, 82% from top half. Full-time: 8,146 students, 59% women, 41% men. Part-time: 297 students, 52% women, 48% men. Students come from 50 states and territories, 140 other countries, 71% from out-of-state. 0.1% American Indian or Alaska Native, non-Hispanic/Latino; 13% Hispanic/Latino; 5% Black or African American, non-Hispanic/Latino; 2% Asian, non-Hispanic/Latino; 0.2% Native Hawaiian or other Pacific Islander, non-Hispanic/Latino; 9% international. 4% 25 or older, 51% live on campus, 6% transferred in. Retention: 76% of full-time freshmen returned the following year. Academic areas with the most degrees conferred: business/marketing; social sciences; communication/journalism. Core. Calendar: semesters. Academic remediation for entering students, ESL program, services for LD students, advanced placement, honors program, independent study, double major, summer ses-

sion for credit, part-time degree program, adult/continuing education programs, co-op programs and internships. Study abroad program. ROTC: Army, Naval (c), Air Force (c).

Entrance Requirements: Options: electronic application, early admission, early action, deferred admission, international baccalaureate accepted. Required: essay, high school transcript, minimum 2 high school GPA, SAT or ACT. Recommended: interview. Required for some: 1 recommendation. Entrance: moderately difficult. Application deadlines: rolling, 11/15 for early action. Notification: continuous until 10/1. SAT Reasoning Test deadline: 8/1. SAT Subject Test deadline: 8/1. Transfer credits accepted: Yes. Applicants placed on waiting list: 2,872. Wait-listed applicants offered admission: 279. Early action applicants: 15,465. Early action applicants admitted: 8,901.

Costs Per Year: Application fee: $40. Comprehensive fee: $40,018 includes full-time tuition ($27,206), mandatory fees ($2002), and college room and board ($10,810). Full-time tuition and fees vary according to class time, course load, and program. Room and board charges vary according to board plan and housing facility. Part-time tuition: $579 per credit hour. Part-time mandatory fees: $40 per term. Part-time tuition and fees vary according to class time, course load, and program.

Collegiate Environment: Orientation program. Drama-theater group, choral group, student-run newspaper, radio station. Social organizations: 200 open to all; national fraternities, national sororities; 6% of eligible men and 11% of eligible women are members. Most popular organizations: Greek Life, student government, PEACE (volunteer organization), Student Productions, Minaret. Major annual events: Student Productions Major Concert, Homecoming Game, Leadership Awards Night. Student services: health clinic, personal-psychological counseling, women's center. Campus security: 24-hour emergency response devices and patrols, student patrols, late night transport-escort service, controlled dormitory access. 4,509 college housing spaces available; 4,318 were occupied in 2018-19. Freshmen given priority for college housing. Option: coed housing available. Macdonald Kelce Library. Books: 195,067 (physical), 145,016 (digital/electronic); Serial titles: 1,214 (physical), 190,560 (digital/electronic); Databases: 214. Weekly public service hours: 100; students can reserve study rooms. 791 computers available on campus for general student use. Computer purchase/lease plans available. A campuswide network can be accessed from student residence rooms and from off campus. Students can access the following: online class registration. Staffed computer lab on campus provides training in use of computers, software, and the Internet.

Community Environment: The university is situated along the Hillsborough River adjacent to the downtown area of Tampa, Florida. The city of Tampa (population 326,000) is part of the Tampa Bay metropolitan area of over 2 million. This rapidly growing area is a business and resort center featuring year-round sunshine with school year temperatures averaging 60-80 degrees Fahrenheit and excellent job prospects. Tampa's ultramodern international airport is just 15 minutes from campus. The city is easily accessible by interstate highway, bus or rail. Tampa is 30 minutes from the beaches of the Gulf of Mexico and 60 minutes from Central Florida's parks and amusement areas such as Walt Disney World.

■ UNIVERSITY OF WEST FLORIDA
11000 University Pky.
Pensacola, FL 32514-5750
Tel: (850)474-2000; Free: 800-263-1074
Fax: (850)474-2096
E-mail: admissions@uwf.edu
Web Site: www.uwf.edu

Description: State-supported, comprehensive, coed. Part of State University System of Florida. Awards associate, bachelor's, master's, and doctoral degrees and post-master's certificates. Founded 1963. Setting: 1,600-acre suburban campus. Endowment: $62.8 million. Research spending for the previous fiscal year: $8.8 million. Educational spending for the previous fiscal year: $5238 per student. Total enrollment: 12,798. Faculty: 606 (338 full-time, 268 part-time). Student-undergrad faculty ratio is 21:1. 7,104 applied, 42% were admitted. 14% from top 10% of their high school class, 38% from top quarter, 74% from top half. Full-time: 7,164 students, 56% women, 44% men. Part-time: 3,036 students, 58% women, 42% men. Students come from 50 states and territories, 79 other countries, 9% from out-of-state. 0.5% American Indian or Alaska Native, non-Hispanic/Latino; 9% Hispanic/Latino; 13% Black or African American, non-Hispanic/Latino; 3% Asian, non-Hispanic/Latino; 0.3% Native Hawaiian or other Pacific Islander, non-Hispanic/Latino; 3% international. 29% 25 or older, 18% live on campus, 12% transferred in. Retention: 72% of full-time freshmen returned the following year. Academic areas with the most degrees conferred: health

professions and related sciences; business/marketing; social sciences. Core. Calendar: semesters. ESL program, services for LD students, advanced placement, honors program, independent study, distance learning, summer session for credit, part-time degree program, co-op programs and internships, graduate courses open to undergrads. Off campus study at other members of the State University System of Florida. Study abroad program. ROTC: Army, Air Force.

Entrance Requirements: Options: electronic application, early admission, deferred admission, international baccalaureate accepted. Required: high school transcript, minimum 2.5 high school GPA, SAT and SAT Subject Tests or ACT. Entrance: moderately difficult. Application deadline: 6/1. Notification: continuous. Preference given to applicants with associate degrees from Florida public junior colleges. SAT Reasoning Test deadline: 6/1. SAT Subject Test deadline: 6/1.

Collegiate Environment: Orientation program. Drama-theater group, choral group, student-run newspaper. Social organizations: 154 open to all; national fraternities, national sororities, local sororities; 18% of eligible men and 18% of eligible women are members. Most popular organizations: National Society of Leadership and Service, Baptist Collegiate Ministries, Alpha Chi Omega, Alpha Delta Pi, Student Alumni Association. Major annual events: Argo Arrival, Homecoming, CAB After Dark. Student services: health clinic, personal-psychological counseling. Campus security: 24-hour emergency response devices and patrols, student patrols, late night transport-escort service, controlled dormitory access. John C. Pace Library plus 2 others. Books: 834,298 (physical), 163,625 (digital/electronic); Serial titles: 288 (physical), 80,370 (digital/electronic); Databases: 167. Weekly public service hours: 107. Operations spending for the previous fiscal year: $3.7 million. 1,228 computers available on campus for general student use. Computer purchase/lease plans available. A campuswide network can be accessed from student residence rooms and from off campus. Students can access the following: online class registration. Staffed computer lab on campus provides training in use of computers, software, and the Internet.

Community Environment: Pensacola is Florida's westernmost metropolitan area, situated approximately 50 miles east of Mobile, Alabama. A mild climate and more than 200 miles of Gulf and bay shoreline combine to produce an environment perfect for outdoor recreation. Pensacola is the home of the largest naval air training facility in the United States and of Florida's largest industrial plant. Boating, skin diving, swimming, surfing, and sailing are among the numerous water-related sports enjoyed practically year-round. More than 20 miles of Pensacola Beach are within the confines of the National Seashore, including historic Fort Pickens. Numerous museums and related facilities provide amateur historians with a wealth of exploring. The U.S. Naval Air Training museum provides a historical compendium of naval aviation in the United States. Such annual events as the Fiesta of Five Flags, the Gulf Coast Fine Arts Festival and the West Florida Music Festival draw thousands of people annually.

■ VALENCIA COLLEGE
PO Box 3028
Orlando, FL 32802-3028
Tel: (407)299-5000
E-mail: lherlocker@valenciacollege.edu
Web Site: valenciacollege.edu

Description: State-supported, 4-year, coed. Part of Florida College System. Awards associate and bachelor's degrees. Founded 1967. Setting: 654-acre urban campus with easy access to Orlando. Endowment: $70.3 million. Educational spending for the previous fiscal year: $2952 per student. Total enrollment: 44,833. Faculty: 1,956 (585 full-time, 1,371 part-time). Student-undergrad faculty ratio is 23:1. 11,352 applied, 98% were admitted. Full-time: 16,165 students, 55% women, 45% men. Part-time: 28,668 students, 58% women, 42% men. Students come from 20 states and territories, 182 other countries, 4% from out-of-state. 0.3% American Indian or Alaska Native, non-Hispanic/Latino; 35% Hispanic/Latino; 16% Black or African American, non-Hispanic/Latino; 4% Asian, non-Hispanic/Latino; 0.3% Native Hawaiian or other Pacific Islander, non-Hispanic/Latino; 4% international. 25% 25 or older, 7% transferred in. Academic areas with the most degrees conferred: health professions and related sciences; engineering technologies. Core. Calendar: semesters. Academic remediation for entering students, ESL program, services for LD students, advanced placement, accelerated degree program, freshman honors college, honors program, independent study, distance learning, double major, summer session for credit, part-time degree program, external degree program, adult/continuing education programs, co-op programs and internships. Study abroad program. ROTC: Army (c), Naval (c).

Entrance Requirements: Open admission except for high school dual enrollment, the Criminal Justice Institute, dance performance, film production, allied health sciences programs, fire science, and bachelor's programs. Options: electronic application, early admission, deferred admission, international baccalaureate accepted. Recommended: high school transcript. Required for some: high school transcript, professional license for some allied health bachelors programs. Application deadlines: rolling, rolling for nonresidents. Transfer credits accepted: Yes.

Costs Per Year: Application fee: $35. State resident tuition: $2473 full-time. Nonresident tuition: $9383 full-time. Full-time tuition varies according to degree level.

Collegiate Environment: Orientation program. Drama-theater group, choral group, student-run newspaper. Social organizations: 60 open to all; Honors Society, Phi Theta Kappa, Phi Beta Lambda; 10% of eligible men and 10% of eligible women are members. Most popular organizations: National Society for Leadership and Success, PTK, Honors, Gay-Straight Alliance, Valencia Hospitality. Major annual events: Week Of Welcome, Spirit Day, International Education Week. Student services: personal-psychological counseling. Campus security: 24-hour emergency response devices and patrols, late night transport-escort service, video monitoring for certain areas. Library plus 4 others. Books: 153,869 (physical), 180,848 (digital/electronic); Serial titles: 261 (physical), 52,262 (digital/electronic); Databases: 188. Weekly public service hours: 87; students can reserve study rooms. Operations spending for the previous fiscal year: $3 million.

Community Environment: See University of Central Florida.

■ **WARNER UNIVERSITY**

13895 US Hwy. 27
Lake Wales, FL 33859
Tel: (863)638-1426; Free: 800-309-9563
E-mail: admissions@warner.edu
Web Site: www.warner.edu

Description: Independent, comprehensive, coed, affiliated with Church of God. Awards associate, bachelor's, and master's degrees. Founded 1968. Setting: 320-acre rural campus with easy access to Tampa, Orlando. Endowment: $3 million. Educational spending for the previous fiscal year: $3468 per student. Total enrollment: 970. Faculty: 99 (35 full-time, 64 part-time). Student-undergrad faculty ratio is 16:1. 391 applied, 58% were admitted. 10% from top 10% of their high school class, 30% from top quarter, 66% from top half. 1 National Merit Scholar. Full-time: 778 students, 57% women, 43% men. Part-time: 143 students, 62% women, 38% men. Students come from 27 states and territories, 17 other countries, 13% from out-of-state. 46% 25 or older, 41% live on campus, 8% transferred in. Retention: 57% of full-time freshmen returned the following year. Academic areas with the most degrees conferred: business/marketing; education; theology and religious vocations. Core. Calendar: semesters. Academic remediation for entering students, ESL program, advanced placement, accelerated degree program, independent study, distance learning, double major, summer session for credit, part-time degree program, adult/continuing education programs, internships. Study abroad program.

Entrance Requirements: Options: electronic application, deferred admission. Required: high school transcript, minimum 2.25 high school GPA, 1 recommendation, SAT or ACT. Recommended: essay. Required for some: interview, portfolio of standardized tests for home-schooled students. Entrance: minimally difficult. Application deadline: rolling. Notification: continuous.

Collegiate Environment: Orientation program. Choral group, student-run newspaper. Social organizations: 4 open to all. Most popular organizations: concert choir, Fellowship of Christian Athletes, Young Americans, Student Government Association. Major annual events: Spring Banquet, Warner Weekend. Student services: health clinic, personal-psychological counseling. Campus security: 24-hour emergency response devices and patrols, late night transport-escort service, controlled dormitory access. Pontious Learning Resource Center. Operations spending for the previous fiscal year: $336,106. 75 computers available on campus for general student use. A campuswide network can be accessed. Staffed computer lab on campus.

Community Environment: See Webber College.

■ **WEBBER INTERNATIONAL UNIVERSITY**

1201 N Scenic Hwy.
Babson Park, FL 33827-0096
Tel: (863)638-1431; Free: 800-741-1844
Fax: (863)638-2823
E-mail: admissions@webber.edu
Web Site: www.webber.edu

Description: Independent, comprehensive, coed. Awards associate, bachelor's, and master's degrees. Founded 1927. Setting: 110-acre small town campus with easy access to Orlando. Total enrollment: 683. Faculty: 41 (21 full-time, 20 part-time). Student-undergrad faculty ratio is 21:1. 912 applied, 49% were admitted. 4% from top 10% of their high school class, 19% from top quarter, 63% from top half. Full-time: 585 students, 29% women, 71% men. Part-time: 42 students, 33% women, 67% men. Students come from 24 states and territories, 20 other countries, 20% from out-of-state. 0.2% American Indian or Alaska Native, non-Hispanic/Latino; 12% Hispanic/Latino; 33% Black or African American, non-Hispanic/Latino; 0.5% Asian, non-Hispanic/Latino; 1% Native Hawaiian or other Pacific Islander, non-Hispanic/Latino; 19% international. 6% 25 or older, 53% live on campus, 12% transferred in. Retention: 52% of full-time freshmen returned the following year. Academic areas with the most degrees conferred: business/marketing; parks and recreation; homeland security, law enforcement, firefighting, and protective services. Core. Calendar: semesters. Academic remediation for entering students, services for LD students, advanced placement, accelerated degree program, freshman honors college, honors program, distance learning, double major, summer session for credit, part-time degree program, adult/continuing education programs, co-op programs and internships. Study abroad program.

Entrance Requirements: Options: electronic application, international baccalaureate accepted. Required: high school transcript, minimum 2 high school GPA. Recommended: essay. Required for some: recommendations, interview, SAT or ACT. Entrance: moderately difficult. Application deadline: 8/1. Notification: continuous. SAT Reasoning Test deadline: 8/1. Transfer credits accepted: Yes.

Costs Per Year: Application fee: $0. Comprehensive fee: $35,410 includes full-time tuition ($23,380), mandatory fees ($2736), and college room and board ($9294). Full-time tuition and fees vary according to class time, course load, and program. Room and board charges vary according to board plan, gender, and housing facility. Part-time tuition: $366 per credit hour. Part-time tuition varies according to class time, course load, and program.

Collegiate Environment: Orientation program. Student-run newspaper. Most popular organizations: Student Leadership Association, Phi Beta Lambda, Society of International Students, Fellowship of Christian Athletes, Rotaract. Major annual events: Homecoming, Halloween Party, Beach Party. Student services: health clinic, personal-psychological counseling. Campus security: 24-hour emergency response devices and patrols, late night transport-escort service. Grace and Roger Babson Library. Books: 1,041 (physical); Databases: 127. Weekly public service hours: 70; students can reserve study rooms. 92 computers available on campus for general student use. A campuswide network can be accessed from off-campus. Students can access the following: online class registration. Staffed computer lab on campus provides training in use of computers, software, and the Internet.

■ **WEST COAST UNIVERSITY**

9250 NW 36th St.
Doral, FL 33178
Tel: (786)501-7070
Web Site: westcoastuniversity.edu

Description: Proprietary, 4-year, coed. Awards bachelor's degrees.

■ **YESHIVA GEDOLAH RABBINICAL COLLEGE**

1140 Alton Rd.
Miami Beach, FL 33139
Tel: (305)673-5664
Fax: (305)532-9820

Description: Independent Jewish, 5-year, men only. Awards bachelor's and master's degrees. Total enrollment: 47.

Entrance Requirements: Open admission.

■ ABRAHAM BALDWIN AGRICULTURAL COLLEGE
2802 Moore Hwy.
Tifton, GA 31793
Tel: (229)391-5001; Free: 800-733-3653
Fax: (229)386-7006
E-mail: dwebb@abac.edu
Web Site: www.abac.edu

Description: State-supported, 4-year, coed. Part of University System of Georgia. Awards associate and bachelor's degrees. Founded 1933. Setting: 421-acre small town campus. Total enrollment: 3,327. Faculty: 162 (94 full-time, 68 part-time). Student-undergrad faculty ratio is 24:1. 2,927 applied, 79% were admitted. 8% from top 10% of their high school class, 23% from top quarter, 43% from top half. Full-time: 2,475 students, 50% women, 50% men. Part-time: 852 students, 67% women, 33% men. Students come from 17 states and territories, 11 other countries, 2% from out-of-state. 18% 25 or older, 32% live on campus, 18% transferred in. Retention: 67% of full-time freshmen returned the following year. Academic area with the most degrees conferred: agriculture. Core. Calendar: semesters. Academic remediation for entering students, services for LD students, advanced placement, honors program, double major, summer session for credit, part-time degree program, internships. Off campus study at East Central Technical College (ECTC), Moultrie Technical College (MTC). Study abroad program.

Entrance Requirements: Options: electronic application, early admission, deferred admission, international baccalaureate accepted. Required: high school transcript, SAT or ACT. Required for some: minimum high school GPA of 2.0 for College Prep Diploma and 2.2 for Tech Prep Diploma. Entrance: minimally difficult.

Costs Per Year: Application fee: $20. State resident tuition: $3126 full-time, $104.20 per semester hour part-time. Nonresident tuition: $11,548 full-time, $398.94 per semester hour part-time. Mandatory fees: $1002 full-time, $374 per term part-time.

Collegiate Environment: Orientation program. Drama-theater group, choral group, student-run newspaper, radio station. Social organizations: 40 open to all; national fraternities, national sororities. Most popular organizations: Campus Activities Board, Baptist Collegiate Ministry, Forestry/Wildlife Club, Agriculture Engineering Technology, Residence Hall Association. Major annual events: Welcome Week, George Scott Day. Student services: health clinic, personal-psychological counseling. Campus security: 24-hour emergency response devices and patrols, controlled dormitory access. Baldwin Library.

Community Environment: A rural area between Macon and Valdosta having a temperate climate. All modes of transportation serve the area. Scheduled airlines are nearby at Moultrie and Albany. Tifton is an agricultural area; plants are grown here and then sent north for transplanting. Other products are tobacco, cotton, peanuts, melons, commercial grasses and livestock. Part and full-time employment is good. Recreational activities include hunting, tennis, golf, swimming and other water sports.

■ AGNES SCOTT COLLEGE
141 E College Ave.
Decatur, GA 30030-3797
Tel: (404)471-6000; Free: 800-868-8602
Fax: (404)471-6414
Web Site: www.agnesscott.edu

Description: Independent, comprehensive, women only, affiliated with Presbyterian Church (U.S.A.). Awards bachelor's and master's degrees. Founded 1889. Setting: 100-acre urban campus with easy access to Atlanta. Endowment: $229.4 million. Total enrollment: 1,030. Faculty: 133 (81 full-time, 52 part-time). Student-undergrad faculty ratio is 10:1. 1,625 applied, 70% were admitted. 28% from top 10% of their high school class, 60% from top quarter, 85% from top half. Full-time: 985 students. Part-time: 11 students. Students come from 41 states and territories, 28 other countries, 42% from out-of-state. 0.2% American Indian or Alaska Native, non-Hispanic/Latino; 13% Hispanic/Latino; 31% Black or African American, non-Hispanic/Latino; 8% Asian, non-Hispanic/Latino; 0.1% Native Hawaiian or other Pacific Islander, non-Hispanic/Latino; 7% international. 1% 25 or older, 84% live on campus, 1% transferred in. Retention: 79% of full-time freshmen returned the following year. Academic areas with the most degrees conferred: biological/life sciences; social sciences; psychology. Core. Calendar: semesters. Services for LD students, advanced placement, accelerated degree program, self-designed majors, independent study, distance learning, double major, summer session for credit, part-time degree program, adult/continuing education programs, internships. Off campus study at Washington Semester at American University, members of Atlanta Regional Consortium for Higher Education, Georgia Tech, Emory University. Study abroad program. ROTC: Army (c), Air Force (c).

Entrance Requirements: Options: electronic application, early admission, early decision, early action, deferred admission, international baccalaureate accepted. Required: essay, high school transcript. Recommended: interview. Required for some: SAT and SAT Subject Tests or ACT. Entrance: moderately difficult. Application deadlines: 11/1 for early decision, 11/15 for early action. Notification: 4/15, 12/1 for early decision, 1/15 for early action. Transfer credits accepted: Yes. Early decision applicants: 24. Early decision applicants admitted: 22.

Costs Per Year: Comprehensive fee: $55,360 includes full-time tuition ($42,360), mandatory fees ($330), and college room and board ($12,670). Part-time tuition: $1765 per credit hour.

Collegiate Environment: Orientation program. Drama-theater group, choral group, marching band, student-run newspaper, radio station. Social organizations: 79 open to all. Major annual events: Black Cat, Agnes Scott Writers' Festival, Spring Annual Research Conference (SpARC). Student services: health clinic, personal-psychological counseling. Campus security: 24-hour emergency response devices and patrols, late night transport-escort service, controlled dormitory access. 916 college housing spaces available; 818 were occupied in 2018-19. Freshmen guaranteed college housing. On-campus residence required through senior year. Option: women-only housing available. McCain Library. Books: 240,240 (physical), 57,182 (digital/electronic); Databases: 474. Study areas open 24 hours, 5-7 days a week. 450 computers available on campus for general student use. A campuswide network can be accessed from student residence rooms and from off campus. Students can access the following: online class registration. Staffed computer lab on campus (open 24 hours a day) provides training in use of software.

Community Environment: See Clark Atlanta University.

■ ALBANY STATE UNIVERSITY
504 College Dr.
Albany, GA 31705-2717
Tel: (229)430-4600; Free: 800-822-7267
Fax: (229)430-3936
E-mail: enrollmentservices@asurams.edu
Web Site: www.asurams.edu

Description: State-supported, comprehensive, coed. Part of University System of Georgia. Awards bachelor's and master's degrees and post-master's certificates. Founded 1903. Setting: 232-acre urban campus. Endowment: $1.8 million. Total enrollment: 3,041. Faculty: 155 (125 full-time, 30 part-time). Student-undergrad faculty ratio is 19:1. 2,915 applied, 50% were admitted. 11% from top 10% of their high school class, 32% from top quarter, 70% from top half. Full-time: 2,194 students, 66% women, 34% men. Part-time: 400 students, 65% women, 35% men. 0.3% American Indian or Alaska Native, non-Hispanic/Latino; 2% Hispanic/Latino; 90% Black or African American, non-Hispanic/Latino; 0.1% Asian, non-Hispanic/Latino; 0.4% international. 21% 25 or older, 39% live on campus, 6% transferred in. Retention: 67% of full-time freshmen returned the following year. Academic areas with the most degrees conferred: business/marketing; education; homeland security, law enforcement, firefighting, and protective services. Core. Calendar: semesters. Academic remediation for entering students, services for LD students, advanced placement, honors program, independent study, distance learning, double major, summer session for credit, part-time degree program, adult/continuing education programs, co-op programs and internships, graduate courses open to undergrads. Off campus study at Abraham Baldwin Agricultural College, Bainbridge College, Waycross College. Study abroad program. ROTC: Army.

Entrance Requirements: Options: electronic application, early admission, deferred admission, international baccalaureate accepted. Required: high school transcript, minimum 2.22 high school GPA, SAT or ACT. Required for some: SAT and SAT Subject Tests or ACT. Entrance: minimally difficult. Notification: continuous, continuous for nonresidents. SAT Reasoning Test deadline: 6/1. Transfer credits accepted: Yes.

Costs Per Year: Application fee: $25. State resident tuition: $4956 full-time, $165.20 per credit hour part-time. Nonresident tuition: $18,032 full-time, $601.07 per credit hour part-time. Mandatory fees: $1770 full-time. Full-time tuition and fees vary according to course load and degree level. Part-time tuition varies according to course load and degree level. College room and board: $8476. College room only: $5266. Room and board charges vary according to board plan and housing facility.

Collegiate Environment: Orientation program. Drama-theater group, choral group, marching band, student-run newspaper, radio station. Social organizations: 50 open to all; national fraternities, national sororities. Most popular organizations: ASU Anointed Gospel Choir, ASU Pan-Hellenic Council (Greeks), Peer Educators, SIFE (Students In Free Enterprise), Student Government Association. Major annual events: Homecoming Week/Convocation, SGA Leadership Conference, Founder's Day/Collegiate Relay for Life. Student services: health clinic, personal-psychological counseling. Campus security: 24-hour emergency response devices and patrols, late night transport-escort service, controlled dormitory access, ConnectED Emergency E-mail, Emergency sirens, Active Shooter Team, Certified Police Officers. James Pendergrast Memorial Library.

Community Environment: The campus is situated in a progressive community that affords a variety of advantages. Albany is located on the Flint River. Air transportation is accessible at the Southwest Georgia Regional Airport. The Marine Corps Supply Center is located here. Albany's economy is broadly based on agriculture, manufacturing, and business from the nearby military bases. The most notable industry is the production of papershell pecans; more than 700,000 pecan trees cover 60,000 acres in the vicinity. The Spanish peanut industry and other diversified businesses and farming contribute to the city's high rating in retail sales. Part-time employment is available. Radium Springs, four miles south, has the largest natural spring in the state.

■ **ALBANY TECHNICAL COLLEGE**
1704 S Slappey Blvd.
Albany, GA 31701
Tel: (229)430-3500; Free: 877-261-3113
Fax: (229)430-5155
Web Site: www.albanytech.edu
Description: State-supported, 2-year, coed. Part of Technical College System of Georgia. Awards certificates, diplomas, and terminal associate degrees. Founded 1961. Total enrollment: 3,251. Full-time: 1,401 students, 62% women, 38% men. Part-time: 1,850 students, 63% women, 37% men. 1% from out-of-state. 0.1% American Indian or Alaska Native, non-Hispanic/Latino; 1% Hispanic/Latino; 79% Black or African American, non-Hispanic/Latino; 0.4% Asian, non-Hispanic/Latino. Retention: 52% of full-time freshmen returned the following year. Calendar: quarters. Distance learning.
Entrance Requirements: Open admission selective admission to some programs. Option: early admission. Required: high school transcript. Entrance: noncompetitive.

Collegiate Environment: Albany Technical College Library and Media Center.

■ **ALTIERUS CAREER COLLEGE**
1750 Beaver Ruin Rd.
Ste. 500
Norcross, GA 30093
Tel: (770)921-1085
Description: Independent, 2-year, coed. Part of Zenith Education Group.

■ **AMERICAN INTERCONTINENTAL UNIVERSITY ATLANTA**
6600 Peachtree-Dunwoody Rd.
500 Embassy Row
Atlanta, GA 30328
Tel: (404)965-6500; Free: 800-353-1744
Fax: (404)965-6501
Web Site: www.aiuniv.edu
Description: Proprietary, comprehensive, coed. Administratively affiliated with American InterContinental University. Awards associate, bachelor's, and master's degrees. Founded 1970. Setting: 2-acre urban campus. Total enrollment: 585. Faculty: 55. Full-time: 315 students, 56% women, 44% men. Part-time: 119 students, 69% women, 31% men. 47% 25 or older, 10% transferred in. Academic areas with the most degrees conferred: business/marketing; homeland security, law enforcement, firefighting, and protective services; computer and information sciences. Core. Calendar: quarters. Academic remediation for entering students, accelerated degree program, distance learning, part-time degree program, adult/continuing education programs, co-op programs.
Entrance Requirements: Options: electronic application, deferred admission, international baccalaureate accepted. Required: essay, high school transcript, interview. Application deadline: rolling. Notification: continuous.
Collegiate Environment: Orientation program.

■ **ANDREW COLLEGE**
501 College St.
Cuthbert, GA 39840
Tel: (229)732-2171; Free: 800-664-9250
Fax: (229)732-2176
E-mail: admissions@andrewcollege.edu
Web Site: www.andrewcollege.edu
Description: Independent United Methodist, 2-year, coed. Awards certificates and transfer associate degrees. Founded 1854. Setting: 40-acre rural campus. Faculty: 22 (17 full-time, 5 part-time). Student-undergrad faculty ratio is 12:1. Students come from 13 other countries. 1% 25 or older. Core. Calendar: semesters. Academic remediation for entering students, ESL program, services for LD students, advanced placement, honors program, summer session for credit, part-time degree program.
Entrance Requirements: Options: electronic application, early admission, deferred admission. Required: high school transcript, SAT or ACT. Recommended: minimum 2 high school GPA. Required for some: essay, 1 recommendation, interview. Entrance: moderately difficult. Application deadline: 8/15.
Collegiate Environment: Orientation program. Drama-theater group, choral group. Campus security: 24-hour patrols, controlled dormitory access, campus police. Pitts Library. 50 computers available on campus for general student use. A campuswide network can be accessed from student residence rooms and from off campus. Staffed computer lab on campus provides training in use of computers.
Community Environment: Cuthbert is a rural community 40 miles from Albany, and 55 miles from Columbus. Its climate is ideal. Airline services are available one hour away. Part-time employment exists for students. Community facilities include a library, churches, and good shopping. A public recreation center, two swimming pools, golf course and nearby lakes provide facilities for fishing, boating and water skiing.

■ **ARGOSY UNIVERSITY, ATLANTA**
980 Hammond Dr.
Ste. 100
Atlanta, GA 30328
Tel: (770)671-1200; Free: 888-671-4777
Fax: (770)671-0476
Web Site: www.argosy.edu/locations/atlanta
Description: Proprietary, university, coed. Part of Education Management

Corporation. Awards associate, bachelor's, master's, and doctoral degrees. Founded 1990. Setting: suburban campus. Calendar: semesters.

■ THE ART INSTITUTE OF ATLANTA

6600 Peachtree Dunwoody Rd., NE
100 Embassy Row
Atlanta, GA 30328
Tel: (770)394-8300; Free: 800-275-4242
Fax: (770)394-0008
Web Site: www.artinstitutes.edu/atlanta
Description: Proprietary, 4-year, coed. Part of Education Management Corporation. Awards associate and bachelor's degrees. Founded 1949. Setting: 7-acre suburban campus. Calendar: quarters.
Community Environment: Just north of Atlanta's city limits, the campus is located in one of Atlanta's fastest growing business and residential districts and provides easy access to public transportation, shopping, housing, restaurants, and jobs for students.

■ ASHWORTH COLLEGE

6625 The Corners Pky.
Ste. 500
Norcross, GA 30092
Tel: (770)729-8400; Free: 800-957-5412
Fax: (770)729-9296
Web Site: www.ashworthcollege.edu
Description: Proprietary, comprehensive, coed. Administratively affiliated with Professional Career Development, LLC. Awards associate, bachelor's, and master's degrees and post-master's certificates. Setting: suburban campus with easy access to Atlanta. Total enrollment: 57,650. Students come from 50 states and territories, 32 other countries, 90% from out-of-state. Core. Calendar: semesters. Advanced placement, accelerated degree program, independent study, distance learning, summer session for credit, part-time degree program, external degree program, adult/continuing education programs. Off campus study.
Entrance Requirements: Open admission. Option: electronic application. Required: high school transcript. Entrance: noncompetitive. Notification: continuous. Transfer credits accepted: Yes.
Collegiate Environment: Orientation program. Social organizations: honor society.

■ ATHENS TECHNICAL COLLEGE

800 US Hwy. 29 N
Athens, GA 30601-1500
Tel: (706)355-5000
Fax: (706)369-5753
Web Site: www.athenstech.edu
Description: State-supported, 2-year, coed. Part of Technical College System of Georgia. Awards certificates, diplomas, and terminal associate degrees. Founded 1958. Setting: suburban campus. Total enrollment: 4,210. Full-time: 1,036 students, 54% women, 46% men. Part-time: 3,174 students, 66% women, 34% men. 0.4% from out-of-state. 0.1% American Indian or Alaska Native, non-Hispanic/Latino; 7% Hispanic/Latino; 20% Black or African American, non-Hispanic/Latino; 3% Asian, non-Hispanic/Latino; 0.1% Native Hawaiian or other Pacific Islander, non-Hispanic/Latino. Retention: 63% of full-time freshmen returned the following year. Calendar: quarters. Distance learning.
Entrance Requirements: Open admission selective admission to some programs. Option: early admission. Required: high school transcript. Entrance: noncompetitive.
Costs Per Year: Application fee: $25. State resident tuition: $89 per credit hour part-time. Nonresident tuition: $178 per credit hour part-time. Mandatory fees: $361 per term part-time.

■ ATLANTA METROPOLITAN STATE COLLEGE

1630 Metropolitan Pky., SW
Atlanta, GA 30310-4498
Tel: (404)756-4000
E-mail: admissions@atlm.edu
Web Site: www.atlm.edu
Description: State-supported, 2-year, coed. Part of University System of Georgia. Awards transfer associate and terminal associate degrees. Founded 1974. Setting: 68-acre urban campus. Total enrollment: 2,241. Student-undergrad faculty ratio is 23:1. 22% from out-of-state. 40% 25 or older. Retention: 56% of full-time freshmen returned the following year. Core.

Calendar: semesters. Academic remediation for entering students, services for LD students, independent study, distance learning, summer session for credit, part-time degree program, adult/continuing education programs, co-op programs. Study abroad program.
Entrance Requirements: Option: electronic application. Required: high school transcript, certificate of immunization. Entrance: minimally difficult. Application deadline: 7/15. Notification: continuous until 8/12.
Costs Per Year: Application fee: $20. State resident tuition: $2366 full-time, $98.60 per credit hour part-time. Nonresident tuition: $8830 full-time, $367.94 per credit hour part-time. Mandatory fees: $1780 full-time, $435 per term part-time.
Collegiate Environment: Orientation program. Drama-theater group, choral group, student-run newspaper. Student services: personal-psychological counseling. Campus security: 24-hour emergency response devices and patrols. Atlanta Metropolitan College Library.
Community Environment: The College, though within view of the city, is situated on a 83-acre wooded tract. It is located next to Atlanta Technical College, and is convenient to major bus lines and Hartsfield International Airport, and is adjacent to Interstate 75-85 South.

■ ATLANTA TECHNICAL COLLEGE

1560 Metropolitan Pky., SW
Atlanta, GA 30310
Tel: (404)225-4400
Fax: (404)752-0809
Web Site: www.atlantatech.edu
Description: State-supported, 2-year, coed. Part of Technical College System of Georgia. Awards certificates, diplomas, and terminal associate degrees. Founded 1945. Total enrollment: 3,775. Full-time: 1,406 students, 60% women, 40% men. Part-time: 2,369 students, 72% women, 28% men. 0.2% from out-of-state. 0.1% American Indian or Alaska Native, non-Hispanic/Latino; 3% Hispanic/Latino; 91% Black or African American, non-Hispanic/Latino; 1% Asian, non-Hispanic/Latino; 0.1% Native Hawaiian or other Pacific Islander, non-Hispanic/Latino. Retention: 55% of full-time freshmen returned the following year. Calendar: quarters. Distance learning. Study abroad program.
Entrance Requirements: Open admission selective admission to some programs. Option: early admission. Required: high school transcript. Entrance: noncompetitive.

■ AUGUSTA TECHNICAL COLLEGE

3200 Augusta Tech Dr.
Augusta, GA 30906
Tel: (706)771-4000
Fax: (706)771-4016
Web Site: www.augustatech.edu
Description: State-supported, 2-year, coed. Part of Technical College System of Georgia. Awards certificates, diplomas, and terminal associate degrees. Founded 1961. Setting: urban campus. Total enrollment: 4,370. Full-time: 1,721 students, 53% women, 47% men. Part-time: 2,649 students, 58% women, 42% men. 5% from out-of-state. 0.4% American Indian or Alaska Native, non-Hispanic/Latino; 4% Hispanic/Latino; 48% Black or African American, non-Hispanic/Latino; 1% Asian, non-Hispanic/Latino; 0.1% Native Hawaiian or other Pacific Islander, non-Hispanic/Latino. Retention: 57% of full-time freshmen returned the following year. Calendar: quarters. Distance learning.
Entrance Requirements: Open admission selective admission to some programs. Option: early admission. Required: high school transcript. Entrance: noncompetitive.
Collegiate Environment: Information Technology Center.

■ AUGUSTA UNIVERSITY

1120 15th St.
Augusta, GA 30912
Tel: (706)721-0211; Free: 800-519-3388
Fax: (706)721-3461
Web Site: www.augusta.edu
Description: State-supported, university, coed. Part of University System of Georgia. Awards associate, bachelor's, master's, and doctoral degrees and post-master's certificates. Founded 1828. Setting: 670-acre urban campus. Endowment: $9.4 million. Research spending for the previous fiscal year: $47.3 million. Educational spending for the previous fiscal year: $8222 per student. Total enrollment: 7,938. Faculty: 1,482 (960 full-time, 522 part-time). 2,151 applied, 59% were admitted. Full-time: 4,133 students, 64% women,

36% men. Part-time: 1,000 students, 65% women, 35% men. Students come from 45 states and territories, 13 other countries, 13% from out-of-state. 0.3% American Indian or Alaska Native, non-Hispanic/Latino; 6% Hispanic/Latino; 24% Black or African American, non-Hispanic/Latino; 2% Asian, non-Hispanic/Latino; 0.4% Native Hawaiian or other Pacific Islander, non-Hispanic/Latino; 1% international. 21% 25 or older, 10% transferred in. Retention: 75% of full-time freshmen returned the following year. Academic areas with the most degrees conferred: health professions and related sciences; business/marketing; psychology. Core. Calendar: semesters. ESL program, services for LD students, advanced placement, honors program, independent study, distance learning, double major, summer session for credit, adult/continuing education programs, internships, graduate courses open to undergrads. Off campus study. Study abroad program. ROTC: Army. **Entrance Requirements:** Options: electronic application, early action. Required: Freshman Index (FI), SAT or ACT. Required for some: high school transcript. Application deadlines: 7/1, 11/15 for early action. Transfer credits accepted: Yes.

Costs Per Year: Application fee: $50. State resident tuition: $6724 full-time, $224.14 per credit hour part-time. Nonresident tuition: $21,726 full-time, $724.20 per credit hour part-time. Mandatory fees: $1920 full-time. Full-time tuition and fees vary according to course load, location, and program. Part-time tuition varies according to course load, location, and program. College room only: $5800. Room charges vary according to housing facility.

Collegiate Environment: Orientation program. Drama-theater group, choral group, student-run newspaper. Social organizations: 160 open to all; national fraternities, national sororities. Major annual events: Homecoming, Pig Out (student appreciation day), Lyceum Series. Student services: health clinic, personal-psychological counseling. Campus security: 24-hour emergency response devices and patrols, late night transport-escort service. Main library plus 2 others. Operations spending for the previous fiscal year: $4.4 million.

Community Environment: Augusta is the second largest city in Georgia with a metropolitan-area population of around 500,000. The city offers a wide array of cultural and recreational activities, including a world-class Riverwalk, the site of many activities including the Augusta Invitation Regatta (a national collegiate rowing event) and the Augusta Southern Nationals, dubbed the World's Richest Drag Boat Race. The city also is a short drive from the huge Lake Thurmond Reservoir. Outdoor activities such as water-skiing, swimming, boating, and camping abound. Kid-friendly sites include the Funsville Amusement Park, Krystal River Water Park, and Augusta Iceforum, an ice-skating rink. Attractions that promise both fun and enlightenment include the National Science Center's Fort Discovery, the Morris Museum of Art, the Georgia Golf Hall of Fame, the Lucy Craft Laney Museum of Black History, the Augusta Cotton Exchange Welcome Center and Museum, and the Augusta Museum of History. Augusta has many association dedicated to the performing and visual arts, including the Fort Gordon Dinner Theater, Augusta Opera Association, the Augusta Ballet, the Augusta Players, the Augusta Symphony, and the Augusta Art Association. The Medical College of Georgia, Augusta State University, and Paine College often bring prestigious films, speakers, and special events to the city. Augusta is within an easy three-hour drive of Atlanta, the University of Georgia, the Atlantic Ocean, and the mountains. The sporting life is ubiquitous throughout Augusta, whether you consider yourself an athlete or spectator. The city is home to professional baseball and ice hockey teams. The city annually hosts the Augusta Futurity, the largest cutting-horse futurity in the eastern United States. And of course, Augusta is world-renowned as the home of the Masters Golf Tournament. Augusta is a leading health care center of the Southeast and has a rapidly developing and diversified industrial base. The area's nine hospitals serve the Southeast and beyond.

■ **BERRY COLLEGE**
2277 Martha Berry Hwy. NW
Mount Berry, GA 30149
Tel: (706)232-5374; Free: 800-237-7942
Fax: (706)236-2248
E-mail: admissions@berry.edu
Web Site: www.berry.edu
Description: Independent interdenominational, comprehensive, coed. Awards bachelor's and master's degrees. Founded 1902. Setting: 27,000-acre suburban campus with easy access to Atlanta. Endowment: $968.5 million. Research spending for the previous fiscal year: $380,132. Educational spending for the previous fiscal year: $13,945 per student. Total enrollment: 2,110. Faculty: 230 (165 full-time, 65 part-time). Student-undergrad faculty ratio is 11:1. 3,883 applied, 62% were admitted. 34% from top 10% of their

high school class, 66% from top quarter, 92% from top half. 8 valedictorians. Full-time: 1,945 students, 61% women, 39% men. Part-time: 33 students, 48% women, 52% men. Students come from 37 states and territories, 9 other countries, 32% from out-of-state. 0.3% American Indian or Alaska Native, non-Hispanic/Latino; 7% Hispanic/Latino; 5% Black or African American, non-Hispanic/Latino; 2% Asian, non-Hispanic/Latino; 0.1% Native Hawaiian or other Pacific Islander, non-Hispanic/Latino; 0.6% international. 1% 25 or older, 89% live on campus, 2% transferred in. Retention: 78% of full-time freshmen returned the following year. Academic areas with the most degrees conferred: biological/life sciences; business/marketing; psychology. Core. Calendar: semesters. Services for LD students, advanced placement, self-designed majors, honors program, independent study, double major, summer session for credit, part-time degree program, adult/continuing education programs, internships, graduate courses open to undergrads. Study abroad program.

Entrance Requirements: Options: electronic application, early admission, early decision, early action, international baccalaureate accepted. Required: essay, high school transcript, 1 recommendation, SAT or ACT. Recommended: interview. Required for some: 2 recommendations. Entrance: moderately difficult. Application deadline: 7/20. Notification: continuous. SAT Reasoning Test deadline: 7/20. Transfer credits accepted: Yes. Applicants placed on waiting list: 27. Wait-listed applicants offered admission: 0. Early decision applicants: 87. Early decision applicants admitted: 48. Early action applicants: 1,558. Early action applicants admitted: 1,296.

Costs Per Year: Application fee: $0. Comprehensive fee: $49,326 includes full-time tuition ($36,330), mandatory fees ($226), and college room and board ($12,770). College room only: $7220. Room and board charges vary according to board plan and housing facility. Part-time tuition: $1211 per credit hour.

Collegiate Environment: Orientation program. Drama-theater group, choral group, student-run newspaper. Social organizations: 75 open to all. Most popular organizations: Student Government Association, Campus Outreach, Block-n-Bridle, Allied Health, Athletes Bettering the Community. Major annual events: Mountain Day, Conson Wilson Lecture Series, BCTC Theatre Season. Student services: health clinic, personal-psychological counseling. Campus security: 24-hour emergency response devices and patrols, controlled dormitory access, lighted pathways, gated campus, mobile police patrols, identification of valuables, limited access to campus, on-campus police officers. Memorial Library plus 1 other. Books: 246,222 (physical), 664,520 (digital/electronic); Serial titles: 7,978 (physical), 44,764 (digital/electronic); Databases: 224. Weekly public service hours: 106; students can reserve study rooms. Operations spending for the previous fiscal year: $1.9 million. 200 computers available on campus for general student use. A campuswide network can be accessed from student residence rooms and from off campus. Students can access the following: online class registration. Staffed computer lab on campus provides training in use of computers, software, and the Internet.

Community Environment: Located on Highway 27 between Chattanooga and Atlanta, Mount Berry is in the mountains of North Georgia in Floyd County, adjoining Rome. Recreation, cultural facilities and transportation are found in Rome.

■ **BEULAH HEIGHTS UNIVERSITY**
892 Berne St., SE
Atlanta, GA 30316
Tel: (404)627-2681; Free: 888-777-BHBC
Fax: (404)627-0702
E-mail: bianca.phillips@beulah.edu
Web Site: www.beulah.edu
Description: Independent Pentecostal, comprehensive, coed. Awards associate, bachelor's, master's, and doctoral degrees. Founded 1918. Setting: 10-acre urban campus with easy access to Atlanta. Educational spending for the previous fiscal year: $7298 per student. Total enrollment: 356. Faculty: 97 (12 full-time, 85 part-time). Student-undergrad faculty ratio is 5:1. 16 applied, 100% were admitted. Full-time: 181 students, 49% women, 51% men. Part-time: 168 students, 49% women, 51% men. Students come from 22 states and territories, 12 other countries, 30% from out-of-state. 4% Hispanic/Latino; 73% Black or African American, non-Hispanic/Latino; 7% Asian, non-Hispanic/Latino; 0.5% international. 98% 25 or older, 14% live on campus, 15% transferred in. Retention: 57% of full-time freshmen returned the following year. Academic areas with the most degrees conferred: theology and religious vocations; business/marketing. Core. Calendar: semesters. Academic remediation for entering students, ESL program, services for LD students, advanced placement, accelerated degree program, independent

study, distance learning, double major, summer session for credit, part-time degree program, adult/continuing education programs, co-op programs and internships. Off campus study.

Entrance Requirements: Open admission. Options: electronic application, early admission, international baccalaureate accepted. Required: essay, high school transcript, minimum 2 high school GPA, 2 recommendations, Statement of Faith. Recommended: interview, SAT or ACT. Required for some: TOEFL for international students. Entrance: noncompetitive. Application deadline: rolling. Notification: continuous. Transfer credits accepted: Yes.

Costs Per Year: Application fee: $50. Tuition: $10,440 full-time, $318 per credit hour part-time. Mandatory fees: $610 full-time, $310 per term part-time. Full-time tuition and fees vary according to course load. College room only: $6750. Room charges vary according to housing facility.

Collegiate Environment: Orientation program. Choral group, student-run newspaper. Social organizations: 3 open to all; Beta Eta Kappa Honor Society; 5% of eligible men and 10% of eligible women are members. Most popular organizations: Chapel Choir, Student Government Association, Club Give. Major annual events: Discovery Days, Annual College Banquet, International Day. Student services: personal-psychological counseling. Campus security: 24-hour emergency response devices and patrols. Barth Memorial Library. Books: 51,672 (physical). Weekly public service hours: 57. Operations spending for the previous fiscal year: $119,719. 28 computers available on campus for general student use. A campuswide network can be accessed from student residence rooms and from off campus. Students can access the following: online class registration. Staffed computer lab on campus provides training in use of computers and the Internet.

Community Environment: See Clark Atlanta University.

■ **BRENAU UNIVERSITY**
500 Washington St., SE
Gainesville, GA 30501
Tel: (770)534-6299; Free: 800-252-5119
Fax: (770)534-6114
E-mail: rlian@brenau.edu
Web Site: www.brenau.edu

Description: Independent, comprehensive, coed. Awards associate, bachelor's, master's, and doctoral degrees and post-master's certificates (also offers coed evening and weekend programs with significant enrollment not reflected in profile). Founded 1878. Setting: 57-acre suburban campus with easy access to Atlanta. Endowment: $47.9 million. Educational spending for the previous fiscal year: $8513 per student. Total enrollment: 2,842. Faculty: 97 (66 full-time, 31 part-time). Student-undergrad faculty ratio is 11:1. 1,902 applied, 65% were admitted. 10% from top 10% of their high school class, 32% from top quarter, 67% from top half. Full-time: 1,090 students, 91% women, 9% men. Part-time: 664 students, 89% women, 11% men. Students come from 27 states and territories, 15 other countries, 7% from out-of-state. 0.4% American Indian or Alaska Native, non-Hispanic/Latino; 10% Hispanic/Latino; 29% Black or African American, non-Hispanic/Latino; 2% Asian, non-Hispanic/Latino; 0.1% Native Hawaiian or other Pacific Islander, non-Hispanic/Latino; 5% international. 50% 25 or older, 23% live on campus, 16% transferred in. Retention: 50% of full-time freshmen returned the following year. Academic areas with the most degrees conferred: health professions and related sciences; business/marketing; education. Core. Calendar: semesters. Academic remediation for entering students, services for LD students, advanced placement, accelerated degree program, honors program, independent study, distance learning, double major, summer session for credit, part-time degree program, internships. Study abroad program.

Entrance Requirements: Options: electronic application, deferred admission, international baccalaureate accepted. Required for some: essay, high school transcript, minimum 2 high school GPA, interview. Entrance: moderately difficult. Application deadlines: rolling, rolling for nonresidents. Notification: continuous, continuous for nonresidents. Transfer credits accepted: Yes.

Costs Per Year: Application fee: $0. Comprehensive fee: $43,290 includes full-time tuition ($29,370), mandatory fees ($1420), and college room and board ($12,500). Part-time tuition: $979 per semester hour.

Collegiate Environment: Orientation program. Drama-theater group, choral group, student-run newspaper, radio station. Social organizations: 46 open to all; national sororities; 9% of women are members. Most popular organizations: Student Activities Board, Student Government Association, Black Student Association, International Student Association, Her Campus. Major annual events: Midnight Breakfast, Convocation, Winter Weekend.

Student services: health clinic, personal-psychological counseling, women's center. Campus security: 24-hour emergency response devices and patrols, late night transport-escort service. 536 college housing spaces available; 443 were occupied in 2018-19. Freshmen guaranteed college housing. On-campus residence required through junior year. Options: men-only, women-only housing available. Brenau Trustee Library. Books: 83,560 (physical), 431,102 (digital/electronic); Serial titles: 190 (physical), 64,642 (digital/electronic); Databases: 155. Weekly public service hours: 76; students can reserve study rooms. Operations spending for the previous fiscal year: $598,475. 157 computers available on campus for general student use. A campuswide network can be accessed from student residence rooms and from off campus. Students can access the following: online class registration. Staffed computer lab on campus provides training in use of computers, software, and the Internet.

■ **BREWTON-PARKER COLLEGE**
201 David-Eliza Fountain Cir.
Mount Vernon, GA 30445
Tel: (912)583-2241; Free: 800-342-1087
Fax: (912)583-4498
E-mail: admissions@bpc.edu
Web Site: www.bpc.edu

Description: Independent Southern Baptist, 4-year, coed. Awards associate and bachelor's degrees. Founded 1904. Setting: 280-acre rural campus. Total enrollment: 783. Faculty: 75 (29 full-time, 46 part-time). Student-undergrad faculty ratio is 13:1. 589 applied, 54% were admitted. 24% from top 10% of their high school class, 40% from top quarter, 66% from top half. Full-time: 438 students, 43% women, 57% men. Part-time: 345 students, 41% women, 59% men. Students come from 18 states and territories, 6 other countries, 11% from out-of-state. 0.1% American Indian or Alaska Native, non-Hispanic/Latino; 4% Hispanic/Latino; 18% Black or African American, non-Hispanic/Latino; 0.4% Asian, non-Hispanic/Latino; 0.5% Native Hawaiian or other Pacific Islander, non-Hispanic/Latino; 0.6% international. 9% 25 or older, 67% live on campus, 7% transferred in. Retention: 49% of full-time freshmen returned the following year. Academic areas with the most degrees conferred: business/marketing; education; parks and recreation. Core. Calendar: semesters. Academic remediation for entering students, services for LD students, advanced placement, accelerated degree program, honors program, independent study, distance learning, double major, summer session for credit, part-time degree program, co-op programs and internships.

Entrance Requirements: Options: electronic application, international baccalaureate accepted. Required: high school transcript, minimum 2 high school GPA, SAT or ACT. Entrance: minimally difficult. Application deadline: 8/1. Notification: continuous. Transfer credits accepted: Yes.

Costs Per Year: Application fee: $35. One-time mandatory fee: $200. Comprehensive fee: $26,620 includes full-time tuition ($16,940), mandatory fees ($1300), and college room and board ($8380). College room only: $3300. Full-time tuition and fees vary according to course load, location, and program. Room and board charges vary according to board plan and housing facility. Part-time tuition: $500 per credit hour. Part-time mandatory fees: $700 per year. Part-time tuition and fees vary according to course load, location, and program.

Collegiate Environment: Orientation program. Drama-theater group, choral group, student-run newspaper. Social organizations: 26 open to all; local fraternities, local sororities. Most popular organizations: Council of Intramural Activities, Student Activities Council, Student Government Association, Circle K, Baptist Student Union. Major annual events: Homecoming Weekend, Fall Festival, Black History Month. Student services: personal-psychological counseling. Campus security: 24-hour emergency response devices, controlled dormitory access, campus security is provided from 6 pm to 6 am. Fountain-New Library. Books: 88,734 (physical); Serial titles: 6,729 (physical); Databases: 290. Weekly public service hours: 78; students can reserve study rooms. 99 computers available on campus for general student use. A campuswide network can be accessed from student residence rooms. Students can access the following: online class registration, Printers. Staffed computer lab on campus provides training in use of computers, software, and the Internet.

■ **BROWN COLLEGE OF COURT REPORTING**
1900 Emery St. NW
Ste. 200
Atlanta, GA 30318
Tel: (404)876-1227

Fax: (404)876-4415
Web Site: www.bccr.edu
Description: Proprietary, 2-year, coed. Awards certificates, transfer associate, and terminal associate degrees. Founded 1972.

■ CARVER COLLEGE
3870 Cascade Rd. SW
Atlanta, GA 30331
Tel: (404)527-4520
Fax: (404)527-4526
E-mail: info@carver.edu
Web Site: www.carver.edu
Description: Independent nondenominational, 4-year, coed. Awards associate and bachelor's degrees. Founded 1943. Setting: 16-acre urban campus with easy access to Atlanta. Total enrollment: 104. Faculty: 19 (2 full-time, 17 part-time). Student-undergrad faculty ratio is 6:1. 49 applied, 100% were admitted. Full-time: 62 students, 26% women, 74% men. Part-time: 42 students, 43% women, 57% men. Students come from 4 states and territories, 4 other countries, 1% from out-of-state. 65% Black or African American, non-Hispanic/Latino; 1% Asian, non-Hispanic/Latino; 34% international. 72% 25 or older, 36% live on campus. Retention: 56% of full-time freshmen returned the following year. Academic area with the most degrees conferred: theology and religious vocations. Core. Calendar: semesters. Academic remediation for entering students, double major, summer session for credit, part-time degree program, adult/continuing education programs, co-op programs. Off campus study.
Entrance Requirements: Open admission. Option: international baccalaureate accepted. Required: essay, high school transcript, minimum 2 high school GPA, 2 recommendations. Recommended: interview. Required for some: interview. Entrance: noncompetitive. Application deadline: 8/1. Transfer credits accepted: Yes.
Collegiate Environment: Orientation program. Drama-theater group, choral group. Social organizations: 4 open to all; 14% of eligible men and 10% of eligible women are members. Most popular organizations: Student Government Association, Student Missions Organization, Carver Praise Team, Thespian Club. Major annual events: Carver Homecoming, W.D. Hungerpiller Bible Conference, Herman Conley Missions Conference. Student services: personal-psychological counseling. Campus security: 24-hour patrols, late night transport-escort service. Carver Bible College Library plus 1 other. Study areas open 24 hours, 5-7 days a week; students can reserve study rooms. Operations spending for the previous fiscal year: $8935. 7 computers available on campus for general student use. A campuswide network can be accessed. Staffed computer lab on campus (open 24 hours a day) provides training in use of computers, software, and the Internet.

■ CENTRAL GEORGIA TECHNICAL COLLEGE
80 Cohen Walker Dr.
Warner Robins, GA 31088
Tel: (478)988-6800; Free: 866-430-0135
Web Site: www.centralgatech.edu
Description: State-supported, 2-year, coed. Part of Technical College System of Georgia. Awards certificates, diplomas, and terminal associate degrees. Founded 1966. Setting: suburban campus. Total enrollment: 7,762. Full-time: 2,380 students, 63% women, 37% men. Part-time: 5,382 students, 65% women, 35% men. 1% from out-of-state. 0.3% American Indian or Alaska Native, non-Hispanic/Latino; 3% Hispanic/Latino; 52% Black or African American, non-Hispanic/Latino; 1% Asian, non-Hispanic/Latino; 0.1% Native Hawaiian or other Pacific Islander, non-Hispanic/Latino. Retention: 51% of full-time freshmen returned the following year. Calendar: quarters. Distance learning.
Entrance Requirements: Open admission selective admission to some programs. Option: early admission. Required: high school transcript. Entrance: noncompetitive.

■ CHAMBERLAIN COLLEGE OF NURSING
5775 Peachtree Dunwoody Rd. NE
Ste. A-100
Atlanta, GA 30342
Tel: (404)250-8500; Free: 877-751-5783
Fax: (404)250-8599
Web Site: www.chamberlain.edu
Description: Proprietary, 4-year, coed. Awards bachelor's degrees. Total enrollment: 996. Faculty: 128 (37 full-time, 91 part-time). Student-undergrad faculty ratio is 8:1. Full-time: 285 students, 91% women, 9% men. Part-time:

711 students, 91% women, 9% men. 1% from out-of-state. 0.3% American Indian or Alaska Native, non-Hispanic/Latino; 7% Hispanic/Latino; 43% Black or African American, non-Hispanic/Latino; 7% Asian, non-Hispanic/Latino; 0.2% Native Hawaiian or other Pacific Islander, non-Hispanic/Latino; 0.6% international. 74% 25 or older, 29% transferred in. Academic area with the most degrees conferred: health professions and related sciences.
Entrance Requirements: Option: deferred admission. Required: SAT or ACT. Application deadline: rolling. Notification: continuous.

■ CHATTAHOOCHEE TECHNICAL COLLEGE
980 S Cobb Dr., SE
Marietta, GA 30060
Tel: (770)528-4545
Fax: (770)528-4578
Web Site: www.chattahoocheetech.edu
Description: State-supported, 2-year, coed. Part of Technical College System of Georgia. Awards certificates, diplomas, and terminal associate degrees. Founded 1961. Setting: suburban campus. Total enrollment: 9,999. Full-time: 2,813 students, 51% women, 49% men. Part-time: 7,186 students, 58% women, 42% men. 0.2% from out-of-state. 0.5% American Indian or Alaska Native, non-Hispanic/Latino; 12% Hispanic/Latino; 30% Black or African American, non-Hispanic/Latino; 3% Asian, non-Hispanic/Latino; 0.1% Native Hawaiian or other Pacific Islander, non-Hispanic/Latino. Retention: 52% of full-time freshmen returned the following year. Calendar: quarters. Distance learning.
Entrance Requirements: Open admission selective admission to some programs. Option: early admission. Required: high school transcript. Entrance: noncompetitive.

■ CLARK ATLANTA UNIVERSITY
223 James P. Brawley Dr., SW
Atlanta, GA 30314
Tel: (404)880-8000; Free: 800-688-3228
Fax: (404)880-6174
E-mail: cauadmissions@cau.edu
Web Site: www.cau.edu
Description: Independent United Methodist, university, coed. Awards bachelor's, master's, and doctoral degrees and post-master's certificates. Founded 1865. Setting: 126-acre urban campus. Endowment: $68.5 million. Research spending for the previous fiscal year: $7.3 million. Educational spending for the previous fiscal year: $7347 per student. Total enrollment: 3,992. Faculty: 281 (179 full-time, 102 part-time). Student-undergrad faculty ratio is 20:1. 13,940 applied, 58% were admitted. 12% from top 10% of their high school class, 28% from top quarter, 70% from top half. Full-time: 3,187 students, 73% women, 27% men. Part-time: 115 students, 62% women, 38% men. Students come from 43 states and territories, 10 other countries, 64% from out-of-state. 0.1% American Indian or Alaska Native, non-Hispanic/Latino; 0.1% Hispanic/Latino; 85% Black or African American, non-Hispanic/Latino; 0.1% Asian, non-Hispanic/Latino; 6% international. 5% 25 or older, 64% live on campus, 6% transferred in. Retention: 70% of full-time freshmen returned the following year. Academic areas with the most degrees conferred: business/marketing; communication/journalism; psychology. Core. Calendar: semesters. Academic remediation for entering students, services for LD students, advanced placement, accelerated degree program, honors program, independent study, double major, summer session for credit, part-time degree program, adult/continuing education programs, co-op programs and internships. Off campus study at University Center in Georgia, Atlanta University Center. Study abroad program. ROTC: Army (c), Naval (c).
Entrance Requirements: Options: electronic application, early admission, deferred admission, international baccalaureate accepted. Required: essay, high school transcript, minimum 2.5 high school GPA, 2 recommendations, SAT or ACT. Required for some: interview. Entrance: moderately difficult. Application deadline: 6/1. Notification: continuous. SAT Reasoning Test deadline: 5/1. Transfer credits accepted: Yes.
Costs Per Year: Application fee: $35. Comprehensive fee: $31,710 includes full-time tuition ($20,680), mandatory fees ($1506), and college room and board ($9524). Room and board charges vary according to board plan and housing facility. Part-time tuition: $862 per credit hour.
Collegiate Environment: Orientation program. Drama-theater group, choral group, marching band, student-run newspaper, radio station. Social organizations: 80 open to all; national fraternities, national sororities; 3% of eligible men and 12% of eligible women are members. Most popular organizations: Spirit Boosters, Pre-Alumni Council, Campus Activities Board,

Orientation Guides, National Association for the Advancement of Colored People. Major annual events: Homecoming, Greek Symposium, Miss Clark Atlanta University Pageants. Student services: health clinic, personal-psychological counseling. Campus security: 24-hour emergency response devices and patrols, late night transport-escort service, controlled dormitory access. Robert W. Woodruff Library. Operations spending for the previous fiscal year: $4.6 million. 741 computers available on campus for general student use. A campuswide network can be accessed from student residence rooms. Students can access the following: online class registration. Staffed computer lab on campus provides training in use of computers, software, and the Internet.

Community Environment: One mile east of the campus lie the mirrored skyscrapers and modern expressways of Atlanta. The World Congress Center, the Civic Center, the Arts Alliance Center (home of the Atlanta Symphony Orchestra and the Atlantic Ballet Company), the Martin Luther King, Jr. Center for Nonviolent Social Change, the Dome (home of the Atlanta Falcons football team), the Jimmy Carter Presidential Library, and outstanding entertainment features, such as Underground Atlanta, Stone Mountain Park, and Six Flags Over Georgia amusement park, mark Atlanta as the capital of the Sun Belt.

■ CLAYTON STATE UNIVERSITY

2000 Clayton State Blvd.
Morrow, GA 30260-0285
Tel: (678)466-4000
E-mail: csc-info@clayton.edu
Web Site: www.clayton.edu

Description: State-supported, comprehensive, coed. Part of University System of Georgia. Awards associate, bachelor's, and master's degrees. Founded 1969. Setting: 163-acre suburban campus with easy access to Atlanta. Total enrollment: 7,003. Faculty: 346 (231 full-time, 115 part-time). Student-undergrad faculty ratio is 17:1. 2,117 applied, 48% were admitted. Full-time: 3,742 students, 68% women, 32% men. Part-time: 2,813 students, 70% women, 30% men. 4% from out-of-state. 0.2% American Indian or Alaska Native, non-Hispanic/Latino; 6% Hispanic/Latino; 61% Black or African American, non-Hispanic/Latino; 6% Asian, non-Hispanic/Latino; 0.1% Native Hawaiian or other Pacific Islander, non-Hispanic/Latino; 1% international. 43% 25 or older, 18% live on campus, 12% transferred in. Retention: 68% of full-time freshmen returned the following year. Academic areas with the most degrees conferred: health professions and related sciences; business/marketing; liberal arts/general studies. Core. Calendar: semesters. Academic remediation for entering students, ESL program, services for LD students, advanced placement, self-designed majors, freshman honors college, honors program, independent study, distance learning, double major, summer session for credit, part-time degree program, adult/continuing education programs, co-op programs and internships. Off campus study. Study abroad program. ROTC: Army (c), Naval (c), Air Force (c).

Entrance Requirements: Options: electronic application, early admission, deferred admission. Required: high school transcript, proof of immunization, SAT or ACT. Entrance: minimally difficult. Application deadline: 7/17. Notification: continuous. SAT Reasoning Test deadline: 7/1.

Costs Per Year: Application fee: $40. State resident tuition: $4956 full-time, $165.20 per credit hour part-time. Nonresident tuition: $18,032 full-time, $601.07 per credit hour part-time. Mandatory fees: $1454 full-time. Full-time tuition and fees vary according to course load. Part-time tuition varies according to course load. College room and board: $10,180. College room only: $6400. Room and board charges vary according to board plan and housing facility.

Collegiate Environment: Orientation program. Drama-theater group, choral group, student-run newspaper, radio station. Social organizations: national fraternities, national sororities. Major annual events: Homecoming, Spring Fling. Student services: health clinic, personal-psychological counseling. Campus security: 24-hour emergency response devices and patrols, late night transport-escort service, controlled dormitory access, lighted pathways. Clayton State University Library. 3,500 computers available on campus for general student use. A computer is required for all students. A campuswide network can be accessed from student residence rooms and from off campus. Students can access the following: online class registration.

Community Environment: See Clark Atlanta University.

■ COASTAL PINES TECHNICAL COLLEGE

1701 Carswell Ave.
Waycross, GA 31503
Tel: (912)287-6584; Free: 877-ED-AT-OTC

Fax: (912)287-4865
Web Site: www.coastalpines.edu

Description: State-supported, 2-year, coed. Part of Technical College System of Georgia. Awards certificates, diplomas, and terminal associate degrees. Setting: small town campus. Total enrollment: 2,775. Full-time: 615 students, 69% women, 31% men. Part-time: 2,160 students, 57% women, 43% men. 0.3% from out-of-state. 0.3% American Indian or Alaska Native, non-Hispanic/Latino; 4% Hispanic/Latino; 27% Black or African American, non-Hispanic/Latino; 1% Asian, non-Hispanic/Latino; 0.1% Native Hawaiian or other Pacific Islander, non-Hispanic/Latino. Retention: 68% of full-time freshmen returned the following year. Calendar: quarters. Distance learning.

Entrance Requirements: Open admission selective admission to some programs. Option: early admission. Required: high school transcript. Entrance: noncompetitive.

■ COLLEGE OF COASTAL GEORGIA

One College Dr.
Brunswick, GA 31520
Tel: (912)279-5700; Free: 800-675-7235
Fax: (912)262-3072
E-mail: admiss@ccga.edu
Web Site: www.ccga.edu

Description: State-supported, 4-year, coed. Part of University System of Georgia. Awards associate and bachelor's degrees. Founded 1961. Setting: 193-acre small town campus with easy access to Jacksonville. Endowment: $8.8 million. Educational spending for the previous fiscal year: $6553 per student. Total enrollment: 3,546. Faculty: 190 (107 full-time, 83 part-time). Student-undergrad faculty ratio is 19:1. 1,611 applied, 93% were admitted. Full-time: 2,078 students, 67% women, 33% men. Part-time: 1,468 students, 70% women, 30% men. Students come from 27 states and territories, 44 other countries, 5% from out-of-state. 0.3% American Indian or Alaska Native, non-Hispanic/Latino; 6% Hispanic/Latino; 19% Black or African American, non-Hispanic/Latino; 2% Asian, non-Hispanic/Latino; 0.1% Native Hawaiian or other Pacific Islander, non-Hispanic/Latino; 1% international. 23% 25 or older, 18% live on campus, 6% transferred in. Retention: 59% of full-time freshmen returned the following year. Academic areas with the most degrees conferred: business/marketing; health professions and related sciences; psychology. Core. Calendar: semesters. Academic remediation for entering students, services for LD students, advanced placement, honors program, distance learning, double major, summer session for credit, part-time degree program, internships. Study abroad program.

Entrance Requirements: Options: electronic application, early admission, deferred admission, international baccalaureate accepted. Required: high school transcript, minimum 2 high school GPA, immunization records, proof of residency, SAT or ACT. Entrance: minimally difficult. Application deadlines: 8/5, 8/5 for nonresidents. Notification: continuous. SAT Reasoning Test deadline: 8/1. SAT Subject Test deadline: 8/1. Transfer credits accepted: Yes.

Costs Per Year: Application fee: $25. One-time mandatory fee: $25. State resident tuition: $3126 full-time, $104.20 per credit hour part-time. Nonresident tuition: $11,548 full-time, $384.94 per credit hour part-time. Mandatory fees: $1570 full-time, $455 per term part-time. Full-time tuition and fees vary according to course load. Part-time tuition and fees vary according to course load. College room and board: $10,036. College room only: $6416. Room and board charges vary according to board plan, housing facility, and location.

Collegiate Environment: Orientation program. Student-run newspaper. Social organizations: 42 open to all. Most popular organizations: International Association, Coastal Georgia Association of Nursing Students, Urban Gaming Club, Association of Coastal Educators, CCGA Biology Club. Major annual events: Halloween Dance, Homecoming Dance, Coastal's Got Talent. Student services: health clinic, personal-psychological counseling. Campus security: 24-hour emergency response devices and patrols, late night transport-escort service, controlled dormitory access. 642 college housing spaces available; all were occupied in 2018-19. Freshmen guaranteed college housing. On-campus residence required in freshman year. Option: coed housing available. Clara Wood Gould Memorial Library. Books: 54,662 (physical), 150,476 (digital/electronic); Serial titles: 109 (physical), 168,333 (digital/electronic); Databases: 338. Weekly public service hours: 77; students can reserve study rooms. Operations spending for the previous fiscal year: $797,162. 395 computers available on campus for general student use. A campuswide network can be accessed from student residence rooms. Students can access the following: online class registration. Staffed computer lab on campus provides training in use of computers, software, and the Internet.

Community Environment: Brunswick is the county seat of Glynn County, which includes the historic resort islands of St. Simons, Sea Island, and Jekyll Island. The climate is mild with a mean temperature of 68 degrees. Bus and rail serve the area. Besides being a tourist center, it is an industrial city. Recreational activities are unlimited including golf, bowling, fresh, salt water, and deep sea fishing, tennis, picnicking, surfing, and water skiing at excellent beaches. Numerous points of historical interest are in or near Brunswick. Kings Bay Naval Submarine Base and the Federal Law Enforcement Training Center are nearby.

■ **COLUMBUS STATE UNIVERSITY**

4225 University Ave.

Columbus, GA 31907-5645

Tel: (706)568-2001; Free: 866-264-2035

Fax: (706)568-2123

Web Site: www.columbusstate.edu

Description: State-supported, comprehensive, coed. Part of University System of Georgia. Awards associate, bachelor's, master's, and doctoral degrees and post-master's certificates. Founded 1958. Setting: 132-acre suburban campus with easy access to Atlanta. Total enrollment: 8,452. Faculty: 564 (292 full-time, 272 part-time). Student-undergrad faculty ratio is 17:1. 3,483 applied, 53% were admitted. 13% from top 10% of their high school class, 37% from top quarter, 67% from top half. Full-time: 4,693 students, 60% women, 40% men. Part-time: 2,105 students, 59% women, 41% men. Students come from 31 states and territories, 35 other countries, 15% from out-of-state. 0.4% American Indian or Alaska Native, non-Hispanic/Latino; 6% Hispanic/Latino; 38% Black or African American, non-Hispanic/Latino; 2% Asian, non-Hispanic/Latino; 0.1% Native Hawaiian or other Pacific Islander, non-Hispanic/Latino; 1% international. 25% 25 or older, 20% live on campus, 10% transferred in. Retention: 76% of full-time freshmen returned the following year. Academic areas with the most degrees conferred: health professions and related sciences; business/marketing; homeland security, law enforcement, firefighting, and protective services. Core. Calendar: semesters. Academic remediation for entering students, ESL program, services for LD students, advanced placement, accelerated degree program, freshman honors college, honors program, independent study, distance learning, double major, summer session for credit, part-time degree program, adult/continuing education programs, co-op programs and internships, graduate courses open to undergrads. Off campus study. Study abroad program. ROTC: Army.

Entrance Requirements: Options: electronic application, early admission, deferred admission, international baccalaureate accepted. Required: high school transcript, minimum 2.5 high school GPA, proof of immunization, SAT or ACT. Entrance: minimally difficult. Application deadline: 6/30. Notification: continuous. SAT Reasoning Test deadline: 6/30. Transfer credits accepted: Yes.

Costs Per Year: Application fee: $40. State resident tuition: $5330 full-time, $177.67 per credit hour part-time. Nonresident tuition: $18,812 full-time, $627.07 per credit hour part-time. Mandatory fees: $1870 full-time, $935 per term part-time. Full-time tuition and fees vary according to course load, degree level, and program. Part-time tuition and fees vary according to course load, degree level, and program. College room and board: $10,762. College room only: $6712. Room and board charges vary according to board plan and housing facility.

Collegiate Environment: Orientation program. Drama-theater group, choral group, student-run newspaper. Social organizations: 90 open to all; national fraternities, national sororities, local sororities; 5% of eligible men and 5% of eligible women are members. Most popular organizations: Student Government Association, Student Activities Council, Campus Ministry Association, African Students Association, SABER Student Newspaper. Major annual events: Homecoming, Greek Week, Black History Month. Student services: health clinic, personal-psychological counseling. Campus security: 24-hour emergency response devices and patrols, late night transport-escort service, controlled dormitory access. Simon Schwob Memorial Library plus 1 other. Books: 379,660 (physical); Serial titles: 1,103 (physical). 3,053 computers available on campus for general student use. A campuswide network can be accessed from student residence rooms and from off campus. Students can access the following: online class registration. Staffed computer lab on campus (open 24 hours a day) provides training in use of computers, software, and the Internet.

Community Environment: Columbus, Georgia's second largest city, is located in the Chattahoochee Valley, 100 miles south of Atlanta on the Georgia-Alabama border, having an annual mean temperature of 65 degrees and annual rainfall of 37 inches. All forms of transportation serve the area.

Columbus is one of the South's largest textile centers, a regional retail center, and manufacturers high-tech industrial products, iron and metal goods, hosiery, processed foods, soft drinks, candy and peanut products. Cultural facilities are the churches, libraries, symphony orchestra, Museum of Arts and Sciences, Fort Benning Little Theatre, and Springer Opera House which is the State Theatre. With the completion of the dam projects on the Chattahoochee River and the Apalachicola River in Florida, Columbus became a port city. A navigable waterway extends to the Gulf of Mexico and the Intracoastal Canal. Oliver Dam provides facilities for all water sports. There are recreational facilities at community centers, golf courses, bowling alleys, and swimming pools.

■ **COLUMBUS TECHNICAL COLLEGE**

928 Manchester Expy.

Columbus, GA 31904-6572

Tel: (706)649-1800

Fax: (706)649-1937

Web Site: www.columbustech.edu

Description: State-supported, 2-year, coed. Part of Technical College System of Georgia. Awards certificates, diplomas, and terminal associate degrees. Founded 1961. Setting: urban campus. Total enrollment: 3,228. Full-time: 910 students, 63% women, 37% men. Part-time: 2,318 students, 66% women, 34% men. 13% from out-of-state. 0.3% American Indian or Alaska Native, non-Hispanic/Latino; 6% Hispanic/Latino; 44% Black or African American, non-Hispanic/Latino; 2% Asian, non-Hispanic/Latino; 0.3% Native Hawaiian or other Pacific Islander, non-Hispanic/Latino. Retention: 53% of full-time freshmen returned the following year. Calendar: quarters. Distance learning.

Entrance Requirements: Open admission selective admission to some programs. Option: early admission. Required: high school transcript. Entrance: noncompetitive.

Collegiate Environment: Columbus Technical College Library.

■ **COVENANT COLLEGE**

14049 Scenic Hwy.

Lookout Mountain, GA 30750

Tel: (706)820-1560; Free: 888-451-2683

E-mail: admissions@covenant.edu

Web Site: www.covenant.edu

Description: Independent, comprehensive, coed, affiliated with Presbyterian Church in America. Awards bachelor's and master's degrees (master's degree in education only). Founded 1955. Setting: 350-acre suburban campus. Total enrollment: 1,046. Faculty: 102 (62 full-time, 40 part-time). Student-undergrad faculty ratio is 13:1. 672 applied, 97% were admitted. 28% from top 10% of their high school class, 57% from top quarter, 85% from top half. Full-time: 969 students, 52% women, 48% men. Part-time: 33 students, 61% women, 39% men. 70% from out-of-state. 0.3% American Indian or Alaska Native, non-Hispanic/Latino; 2% Hispanic/Latino; 3% Black or African American, non-Hispanic/Latino; 1% Asian, non-Hispanic/Latino; 4% international. 1% 25 or older, 83% live on campus, 3% transferred in. Retention: 86% of full-time freshmen returned the following year. Academic areas with the most degrees conferred: social sciences; visual and performing arts; English. Core. Calendar: semesters. Academic remediation for entering students, ESL program, services for LD students, advanced placement, self-designed majors, independent study, double major, summer session for credit, part-time degree program, adult/continuing education programs, internships. Off campus study. Study abroad program. ROTC: Army (c).

Entrance Requirements: Options: electronic application, early admission, early action, deferred admission, international baccalaureate accepted. Required: essay, high school transcript, minimum 2.5 high school GPA, 2 recommendations, interview, SAT or ACT. Entrance: moderately difficult. SAT Reasoning Test deadline: 2/1.

Costs Per Year: Application fee: $35. Comprehensive fee: $46,300 includes full-time tuition ($34,660), mandatory fees ($980), and college room and board ($10,660). Part-time tuition: $1490 per credit hour.

Collegiate Environment: Orientation program. Drama-theater group, choral group, student-run newspaper, radio station. Student services: health clinic, personal-psychological counseling, women's center. Campus security: controlled dormitory access, night security guards. Freshmen guaranteed college housing. On-campus residence required through junior year. Option: coed housing available. Kresge Memorial Library.

Community Environment: Located 5 miles from Chattanooga, TN, and 120 miles from Atlanta, GA, Lookout Mountain is a suburban community that enjoys the cultural, recreational and social facilities of Chattanooga. The community has churches of all denominations, a library, various cultural opportunities, an aquarium, several hospitals, and health center at nearby Chattanooga. Part-time jobs are available.

■ DALTON STATE COLLEGE
650 College Dr.
Dalton, GA 30720
Tel: (706)272-4436; Free: 800-829-4436
Fax: (706)272-2530
E-mail: klogan@daltonstate.edu
Web Site: www.daltonstate.edu

Description: State-supported, 4-year, coed. Part of University System of Georgia. Awards associate and bachelor's degrees. Founded 1963. Setting: 144-acre small town campus. Endowment: $33.6 million. Educational spending for the previous fiscal year: $7595 per student. Total enrollment: 5,188. Faculty: 271 (173 full-time, 98 part-time). Student-undergrad faculty ratio is 19:1. 1,414 applied. Full-time: 3,334 students, 58% women, 42% men. Part-time: 1,854 students, 62% women, 38% men. Students come from 13 states and territories, 53 other countries, 3% from out-of-state. 0.3% American Indian or Alaska Native, non-Hispanic/Latino; 23% Hispanic/Latino; 4% Black or African American, non-Hispanic/Latino; 1% Asian, non-Hispanic/Latino; 0.1% Native Hawaiian or other Pacific Islander, non-Hispanic/Latino; 3% international. 19% 25 or older, 4% live on campus. Retention: 73% of full-time freshmen returned the following year. Academic areas with the most degrees conferred: business/marketing; health professions and related sciences; education. Core. Calendar: semesters. Academic remediation for entering students, ESL program, services for LD students, advanced placement, self-designed majors, independent study, distance learning, double major, summer session for credit, part-time degree program, adult/continuing education programs, co-op programs and internships. Off campus study. Study abroad program.

Entrance Requirements: Open admission. Options: electronic application, deferred admission. Required: high school transcript, SAT or ACT. Entrance: noncompetitive. Application deadline: 7/1. Notification: continuous. SAT Reasoning Test deadline: 8/1. SAT Subject Test deadline: 8/1. Transfer credits accepted: Yes.

Costs Per Year: Application fee: $30. State resident tuition: $3126 full-time, $104.20 per credit hour part-time. Nonresident tuition: $11,548 full-time, $384.94 per credit hour part-time. Mandatory fees: $1120 full-time, $460 per term part-time. Full-time tuition and fees vary according to course load and program. Part-time tuition and fees vary according to course load and program.

Collegiate Environment: Orientation program. Social organizations: 43 open to all; national fraternities, national sororities. Most popular organizations: Lambda Alpha Eplison (Criminal Justice), Rotaract, College Republicans, Beta Chi Nu (Biology), LASO (Latin American Student Organization). Major annual events: Fall Family Festival, Week of Welcome, Homecoming. Campus security: 24-hour emergency response devices and patrols. Derrell C. Roberts Library. Books: 143,415 (physical), 99,973 (digital/electronic); Databases: 72. Students can reserve study rooms. 730 computers available on campus for general student use. A campuswide network can be accessed from student residence rooms. Students can access the following: online class registration. Staffed computer lab on campus provides training in use of computers, software, and the Internet.

Community Environment: Dalton is an urban area 20 miles south of the Tennessee line. The climate is mild year-round. This is known as the"Carpet Capital of the World." Railroads and buses serve the area. Commercial air transportation is available at Chattanooga, 31 miles distant. Fishing is excellent in the many surrounding lakes. Nearby mountains offer opportunities for hunting, fishing, hiking, and other sports. Recreation within the city includes a supervised recreation program at the center with swimming, football, baseball, softball, tennis, and an indoor picnic area.

■ DEVRY UNIVERSITY-ALPHARETTA CAMPUS
2555 Northwinds Pky.
Alpharetta, GA 30009
Tel: (770)619-3600; Free: 866-338-7934
Web Site: www.devry.edu

Description: Proprietary, comprehensive, coed. Part of DeVry University. Awards associate, bachelor's, and master's degrees. Founded 1997. Setting: suburban campus with easy access to Atlanta. Calendar: semesters.

Entrance Requirements: Application deadline: rolling. Notification: continuous.

■ DEVRY UNIVERSITY-DECATUR CAMPUS
1 W Ct. Sq., Ste. 100
Decatur, GA 30030
Tel: (404)270-2700; Free: 866-338-7934
Web Site: www.devry.edu

Description: Proprietary, comprehensive, coed. Part of DeVry University. Awards associate, bachelor's, and master's degrees. Founded 1969. Setting: suburban campus. Total enrollment: 1,087. Faculty: 76 (9 full-time, 67 part-time). Student-undergrad faculty ratio is 21:1. Full-time: 395 students, 56% women, 44% men. Part-time: 508 students, 55% women, 45% men. 6% from out-of-state. 0.2% American Indian or Alaska Native, non-Hispanic/Latino; 4% Hispanic/Latino; 51% Black or African American, non-Hispanic/Latino; 1% Asian, non-Hispanic/Latino; 0.2% Native Hawaiian or other Pacific Islander, non-Hispanic/Latino; 1% international. 83% 25 or older, 26% transferred in. Calendar: semesters. Part-time degree program, adult/continuing education programs.

Entrance Requirements: Option: deferred admission. Required: high school transcript, interview. Entrance: minimally difficult. Application deadline: rolling. Notification: continuous.

Collegiate Environment: Orientation program. Learning Resource Center.

■ EAST GEORGIA STATE COLLEGE
131 College Cir.
Swainsboro, GA 30401-2699
Tel: (478)289-2000
Fax: (478)289-2038
Web Site: www.ega.edu

Description: State-supported, primarily 2-year, coed. Part of University System of Georgia. Awards certificates, transfer associate, terminal associate, and bachelor's degrees. Founded 1973. Setting: 207-acre rural campus. Total enrollment: 3,001. Student-undergrad faculty ratio is 26:1. Full-time: 2,308 students, 58% women, 42% men. Part-time: 693 students, 60% women, 40% men. Students come from 5 states and territories, 1 other country, 0.2% from out-of-state. 0.2% American Indian or Alaska Native, non-Hispanic/Latino; 4% Hispanic/Latino; 44% Black or African American, non-Hispanic/Latino; 0.9% Asian, non-Hispanic/Latino; 0.1% Native Hawaiian or other Pacific Islander, non-Hispanic/Latino; 0.3% international. 10% 25 or older, 12% live on campus, 9% transferred in. Retention: 1% of full-time freshmen returned the following year. Academic area with the most degrees conferred: biological/life sciences. Core. Calendar: semesters. Academic remediation for entering students, services for LD students, advanced placement, honors program, independent study, distance learning, summer session for credit, part-time degree program, adult/continuing education programs. Off campus study. Study abroad program.

Entrance Requirements: Options: early admission, deferred admission. Required: high school transcript. Entrance: minimally difficult. Application deadline: rolling. Notification: continuous. Transfer credits accepted: Yes.

Costs Per Year: Application fee: $20. State resident tuition: $2780 full-time, $92.67 per credit hour part-time. Nonresident tuition: $10,526 full-time, $350.87 per credit hour part-time. Mandatory fees: $1196 full-time, $340 per term part-time. Full-time tuition and fees vary according to class time, course load, location, and student level. Part-time tuition and fees vary according to class time, course load, location, and student level. College room and board: $8784. College room only: $6240. Room and board charges vary according to location.

Collegiate Environment: Orientation program. Drama-theater group, choral group, student-run newspaper. Student services: health clinic, personal-psychological counseling. Campus security: 24-hour patrols, late night transport-escort service, controlled dormitory access. East Georgia College Library. Students can reserve study rooms.

Community Environment: Swainsboro, the county seat of Emanuel County, is located in the southeast section of Georgia near the Center of the vast southern pine forest. The climate is mild with an annual mean temperature of 66 degrees; the average rainfall is 42 inches. Transportation is provided by the Georgia and Florida Railroad and Greyhound. Community facilities include one hospital, 24 churches, restaurants, hotels, motels, and shopping areas. Industry, agriculture, and forestry are important to the economy of the area. Agricultural products include cotton, tobacco, peanuts, soybeans, corn, and potatoes. Some of the industries manufacture sprinkler system valves, furniture, dressed lumber, seed processing, playground equipment, knitwear, molded plastics, screws, rivets, and component parts. A well-staffed and budgeted recreation department offers many recreational opportunities to youth. Fish ponds are in abundance in Emanuel County. Many fresh water streams are filled with trout and bream. Quail and wild turkeys abound and there are excellent reserves for hunting. The first week in May is set aside for the annual Emanuel County Pine Tree Festival.

■ EMMANUEL COLLEGE
181 Springs St.
Franklin Springs, GA 30639
Tel: (706)245-7226; Free: 800-860-8800
E-mail: admissions@ec.edu
Web Site: www.ec.edu
Description: Independent, 4-year, coed, affiliated with Pentecostal Holiness Church. Awards associate and bachelor's degrees. Founded 1919. Setting: 90-acre rural campus with easy access to Atlanta, GA. Endowment: $5.2 million. Educational spending for the previous fiscal year: $4500 per student. Total enrollment: 920. Faculty: 88 (48 full-time, 40 part-time). Student-undergrad faculty ratio is 15:1. 1,089 applied, 42% were admitted. Full-time: 811 students, 47% women, 53% men. Part-time: 109 students, 66% women, 34% men. Students come from 30 states and territories, 20 other countries, 31% from out-of-state. 0.3% American Indian or Alaska Native, non-Hispanic/Latino; 6% Hispanic/Latino; 14% Black or African American, non-Hispanic/Latino; 0.8% Asian, non-Hispanic/Latino; 0.8% Native Hawaiian or other Pacific Islander, non-Hispanic/Latino; 8% international. 5% 25 or older, 60% live on campus, 6% transferred in. Retention: 58% of full-time freshmen returned the following year. Academic areas with the most degrees conferred: business/marketing; parks and recreation; education. Core. Calendar: semesters. Services for LD students, advanced placement, honors program, independent study, distance learning, summer session for credit, part-time degree program, internships. Study abroad program.
Entrance Requirements: Options: electronic application, early admission, deferred admission, international baccalaureate accepted. Required: essay, high school transcript, SAT or ACT. Required for some: interview. Entrance: minimally difficult. Notification: continuous until 8/1. SAT Reasoning Test deadline: 8/1. Transfer credits accepted: Yes.
Costs Per Year: Application fee: $25. Comprehensive fee: $28,612 includes full-time tuition ($20,352), mandatory fees ($360), and college room and board ($7900). Part-time tuition: $856 per credit hour.
Collegiate Environment: Orientation program. Drama-theater group, choral group. Social organizations: 15 open to all. Most popular organizations: Students in Free Enterprise (SIFE), Fellowship of Christian Athletes, SOS, BSU, International Students Club. Major annual events: Feast of Ingathering, Homecoming Weekend, Spring Musical. Student services: personal-psychological counseling. Campus security: 24-hour patrols. 590 college housing spaces available; 553 were occupied in 2018-19. Freshmen guaranteed college housing. On-campus residence required through sophomore year. Options: men-only, women-only housing available. Shaw-Leslie Library plus 1 other. Books: 41,206 (physical), 50,364 (digital/electronic); Serial titles: 99 (physical); Databases: 124. Weekly public service hours: 84; students can reserve study rooms. Operations spending for the previous fiscal year: $169,820. 80 computers available on campus for general student use. A campuswide network can be accessed from student residence rooms and from off campus. Students can access the following: online class registration. Staffed computer lab on campus.

■ EMORY UNIVERSITY
201 Dowman Dr.
Atlanta, GA 30322-1100
Tel: (404)727-6123; Free: 800-727-6036
E-mail: admiss@emory.edu
Web Site: www.emory.edu
Description: Independent Methodist, university, coed. Awards bachelor's, master's, and doctoral degrees and post-master's certificates (enrollment figures include Emory University, Oxford College; application data for main campus only). Founded 1836. Setting: 631-acre suburban campus with easy access to Atlanta. Endowment: $6.9 billion. Research spending for the previous fiscal year: $447.8 million. Educational spending for the previous fiscal year: $44,906 per student. Total enrollment: 14,273. Faculty: 1,222 (1,066 full-time, 156 part-time). Student-undergrad faculty ratio is 9:1. 23,747 applied, 22% were admitted. 83% from top 10% of their high school class, 97% from top quarter, 100% from top half. Full-time: 6,794 students, 59% women, 41% men. Part-time: 143 students, 67% women, 33% men. Students come from 55 states and territories, 84 other countries, 78% from out-of-state. 0.1% American Indian or Alaska Native, non-Hispanic/Latino; 9% Hispanic/Latino; 8% Black or African American, non-Hispanic/Latino; 20% Asian, non-Hispanic/Latino; 16% international. 1% 25 or older, 65% live on campus, 1% transferred in. Retention: 93% of full-time freshmen returned the following

year. Academic areas with the most degrees conferred: social sciences; business/marketing; biological/life sciences. Core. Calendar: semesters. ESL program, services for LD students, advanced placement, honors program, independent study, double major, summer session for credit, co-op programs and internships, graduate courses open to undergrads. Off campus study at Atlanta Regional Council for Higher Education (ARCHE); Washington Semester, American University. Study abroad program. ROTC: Army (c), Naval (c), Air Force (c).
Entrance Requirements: Options: electronic application, early admission, early decision, deferred admission, international baccalaureate accepted. Required: essay, high school transcript, 2 recommendations, SAT or ACT. Entrance: most difficult. Application deadlines: 1/1, 11/1 for early decision plan 1, 1/1 for early decision plan 2. Notification: 4/1, 12/15 for early decision plan 1, 2/15 for early decision plan 2. SAT Reasoning Test deadline: 1/1. SAT Subject Test deadline: 1/1. Transfer credits accepted: Yes. Applicants placed on waiting list: 4,277. Wait-listed applicants offered admission: 41. Early decision applicants: 2,475. Early decision applicants admitted: 678.
Costs Per Year: Application fee: $75. Comprehensive fee: $65,762 includes full-time tuition ($50,590), mandatory fees ($716), and college room and board ($14,456). College room only: $8306. Room and board charges vary according to board plan and housing facility. Part-time tuition: $2108 per credit hour.
Collegiate Environment: Orientation program. Drama-theater group, choral group, student-run newspaper, radio station. Social organizations: 252 open to all; national fraternities, national sororities, local fraternities; 26% of eligible men and 29% of eligible women are members. Most popular organizations: Volunteer Emory, music/theater, Student Government, Outdoor Emory, Hillel. Major annual events: Heritage/Homecoming Week, Wonderful Wednesdays, Dooley's Ball and Spring Festival. Student services: legal services, health clinic, personal-psychological counseling, women's center. Campus security: 24-hour emergency response devices and patrols, student patrols, late night transport-escort service, controlled dormitory access. Robert W. Woodruff Library plus 8 others. Books: 2.3 million (physical), 943,697 (digital/electronic); Serial titles: 78,038 (physical), 156,766 (digital/electronic); Databases: 892. Operations spending for the previous fiscal year: $49.7 million.
Community Environment: Emory is located in a residential area of Atlanta, 6 miles from downtown. Atlanta, capital of Georgia, is the commercial, industrial and financial giant of the southeast. It is located in the foothills of the Blue Ridge Mountains. Atlanta was host to the 1996 Olympic Games. Atlanta's moderate climate permits year-round golf, fishing and outdoor living. All major forms of public transportation are available. Peachtree Street is experiencing one of the biggest building booms in the country. Peachtree Center includes the Atlanta Merchandise Mart, and the 22-story regency Hyatt Hotel. Bridges 22 stories above the street connect buildings on the Peachtree Center. The city is the cultural center of the South with a symphony, art center, and theaters. Atlanta is a major business and manufacturing center that produces more that 3,500 different commodities. Excellent part-time employment opportunities are available. Recreational activities include all major sports, swimming, golfing, boating, horseback riding, tennis, and fishing. Many spectator sports events take place in the Atlanta Stadium.

■ FORT VALLEY STATE UNIVERSITY
1005 State University Dr.
Fort Valley, GA 31030
Tel: (478)825-6211; Free: 877-462-3878
Fax: (478)825-6394
E-mail: admissap@fvsu.edu
Web Site: www.fvsu.edu
Description: State-supported, comprehensive, coed. Part of University System of Georgia. Awards bachelor's and master's degrees and post-master's certificates. Founded 1895. Setting: 1,365-acre small town campus. Total enrollment: 2,594. Faculty: 142 (129 full-time, 13 part-time). Student-undergrad faculty ratio is 16:1. 2,228 applied, 24% were admitted. Full-time: 1,947 students, 58% women, 42% men. Part-time: 282 students, 69% women, 31% men. 4% from out-of-state. 0.3% Hispanic/Latino; 96% Black or African American, non-Hispanic/Latino; 0.1% Asian, non-Hispanic/Latino. 19% 25 or older, 40% live on campus, 4% transferred in. Retention: 57% of full-time freshmen returned the following year. Academic areas with the most degrees conferred: homeland security, law enforcement, firefighting, and protective services; business/marketing; psychology; education. Core. Calendar: semesters. Academic remediation for entering students, services for LD students, advanced placement, freshman honors college, honors

program, independent study, distance learning, double major, summer session for credit, part-time degree program, adult/continuing education programs, internships, graduate courses open to undergrads. Off campus study. ROTC: Army.

Entrance Requirements: Options: electronic application, early admission, deferred admission. Required: high school transcript, SAT or ACT. Entrance: moderately difficult. SAT Reasoning Test deadline: June.

Costs Per Year: Application fee: $20. State resident tuition: $4956 full-time, $165.20 per credit hour part-time. Nonresident tuition: $18,032 full-time, $601.07 per credit hour part-time. Mandatory fees: $1708 full-time, $565 per term part-time. Full-time tuition and fees vary according to course load, degree level, and student level. Part-time tuition and fees vary according to course load, degree level, and student level. College room and board: $8084. College room only: $4540. Room and board charges vary according to board plan, housing facility, and student level.

Collegiate Environment: Orientation program. Drama-theater group, choral group, marching band, student-run newspaper, radio station. Social organizations: national fraternities, national sororities. Most popular organizations: Drama Group, Christian Student Organization, Habitat for Humanity, Debate Club. Major annual events: Founders' Day, Black History Observance, Annual Fall Convocation. Student services: health clinic, personal-psychological counseling. Campus security: 24-hour emergency response devices and patrols, student patrols, late night transport-escort service. Henry A. Hunt Memorial Library.

Community Environment: Fort Valley is a small town with a temperate climate. It is the main peach-growing section of the state. Miles of blooming peach orchards adorn the roadways in the spring. Community facilities include churches of major denominations, a library, and hospital. The Blue Bird Body Company, manufacturers of school bus bodies, is also located here. Part-time employment opportunities are available in Peach and surrounding counties. The Massee Lane Farms located five miles southwest of the City has one of the finest collections of camellias in the country.

■ **FORTIS COLLEGE**
2140 S Cobb Dr.
Smyrna, GA 30080
Tel: (770)980-0002; Free: 855-4-FORTIS
Fax: (770)980-0811
Web Site: www.fortis.edu
Description: Proprietary, 2-year, coed. Awards certificates, diplomas, transfer associate, and terminal associate degrees. Founded 1968.

■ **GEORGIA COLLEGE & STATE UNIVERSITY**
231 W Hancock St.
Milledgeville, GA 31061
Tel: (478)445-5004; Free: 800-342-0471
Fax: (478)445-6795
E-mail: admissions@gcsu.edu
Web Site: www.gcsu.edu
Description: State-supported, comprehensive, coed. Part of University System of Georgia. Awards bachelor's, master's, and doctoral degrees and post-master's certificates. Founded 1889. Setting: 680-acre small town campus. Endowment: $44 million. Research spending for the previous fiscal year: $570,476. Educational spending for the previous fiscal year: $6735 per student. Total enrollment: 6,989. Faculty: 416 (331 full-time, 85 part-time). Student-undergrad faculty ratio is 17:1. 4,329 applied, 78% were admitted. Full-time: 5,410 students, 63% women, 37% men. Part-time: 548 students, 58% women, 42% men. Students come from 20 states and territories, 27 other countries, 1% from out-of-state. 0.1% American Indian or Alaska Native, non-Hispanic/Latino; 6% Hispanic/Latino; 5% Black or African American, non-Hispanic/Latino; 1% Asian, non-Hispanic/Latino; 0.5% international. 1% 25 or older, 36% live on campus, 4% transferred in. Retention: 85% of full-time freshmen returned the following year. Academic areas with the most degrees conferred: business/marketing; health professions and related sciences; parks and recreation. Core. Calendar: semesters. ESL program, services for LD students, advanced placement, accelerated degree program, self-designed majors, freshman honors college, honors program, independent study, distance learning, double major, summer session for credit, part-time degree program, external degree program, internships, graduate courses open to undergrads. Study abroad program. ROTC: Army (c).

Entrance Requirements: Options: electronic application, early admission, early action, deferred admission, international baccalaureate accepted. Required: proof of immunization, SAT or ACT. Required for some: essay,

high school transcript, SAT Subject Tests. Entrance: moderately difficult. Application deadline: rolling for nonresidents. Notification: continuous, continuous for nonresidents. SAT Reasoning Test deadline: 4/1. Transfer credits accepted: Yes. Applicants placed on waiting list: 94. Wait-listed applicants offered admission: 8. Early action applicants: 2,424. Early action applicants admitted: 1,888.

Costs Per Year: Application fee: $40. State resident tuition: $7324 full-time. Nonresident tuition: $26,038 full-time. Mandatory fees: $2022 full-time. Full-time tuition and fees vary according to course load, location, and program. College room and board: $12,964. College room only: $7208. Room and board charges vary according to board plan, housing facility, and location.

Collegiate Environment: Orientation program. Drama-theater group, choral group, student-run newspaper, radio station. Social organizations: 172 open to all; national fraternities, national sororities; 23% of eligible men and 40% of eligible women are members. Most popular organizations: Alpha Lambda Delta, Circle K, Gamma Beta Phi, Swipe out Hunger, Wesley Foundation of Campus Ministries. Major annual events: Homecoming Week, Midnight Breakfast, Greek Weekend. Student services: health clinic, personal-psychological counseling, women's center. Campus security: 24-hour emergency response devices and patrols, student patrols, late night transport-escort service, controlled dormitory access. 2,237 college housing spaces available; 2,111 were occupied in 2018-19. Freshmen guaranteed college housing. On-campus residence required in freshman year. Option: coed housing available. Ina Dillard Russell Library plus 1 other. Books: 168,202 (physical), 490,414 (digital/electronic); Serial titles: 4,160 (physical), 159,746 (digital/electronic); Databases: 374. Weekly public service hours: 102; students can reserve study rooms. Operations spending for the previous fiscal year: $2.4 million. 900 computers available on campus for general student use. A campuswide network can be accessed from student residence rooms and from off campus. Students can access the following: online class registration. Staffed computer lab on campus provides training in use of computers, software, and the Internet.

■ **GEORGIA GWINNETT COLLEGE**
1000 University Ctr. Ln.
Lawrenceville, GA 30043
Tel: (678)407-5000; Free: 877-704-4422
E-mail: ggcadmissions@ggc.edu
Web Site: www.ggc.edu
Description: State-supported, 4-year, coed. Part of University System of Georgia. Awards associate and bachelor's degrees. Setting: 260-acre suburban campus with easy access to Atlanta. Research spending for the previous fiscal year: $48,282. Educational spending for the previous fiscal year: $14,035 per student. Total enrollment: 12,287. Faculty: 674 (450 full-time, 224 part-time). Student-undergrad faculty ratio is 18:1. 4,073 applied, 88% were admitted. 3% from top 10% of their high school class, 12% from top quarter, 43% from top half. Full-time: 8,289 students, 56% women, 44% men. Part-time: 3,998 students, 56% women, 44% men. Students come from 36 states and territories, 122 other countries, 1% from out-of-state. 0.1% American Indian or Alaska Native, non-Hispanic/Latino; 19% Hispanic/Latino; 32% Black or African American, non-Hispanic/Latino; 11% Asian, non-Hispanic/Latino; 0.2% Native Hawaiian or other Pacific Islander, non-Hispanic/Latino; 2% international. 20% 25 or older, 5% live on campus, 6% transferred in. Retention: 67% of full-time freshmen returned the following year. Academic areas with the most degrees conferred: business/marketing; computer and information sciences; psychology. Core. Calendar: semesters. Academic remediation for entering students, ESL program, services for LD students, advanced placement, honors program, double major, summer session for credit, part-time degree program, internships. Study abroad program. ROTC: Army.

Entrance Requirements: Open admission. Options: electronic application, deferred admission, international baccalaureate accepted. Required: high school transcript, minimum 2 high school GPA, SAT or ACT. Entrance: noncompetitive. Application deadline: 6/1. SAT Reasoning Test deadline: 5/9. SAT Subject Test deadline: 5/9. Transfer credits accepted: Yes.

Costs Per Year: Application fee: $20. State resident tuition: $3920 full-time, $131 per credit hour part-time. Nonresident tuition: $14,634 full-time, $488 per credit hour part-time. Mandatory fees: $1714 full-time, $480 per term part-time. Full-time tuition and fees vary according to course load. Part-time tuition and fees vary according to course load. College room and board: $13,086. College room only: $9838. Room and board charges vary according to board plan and housing facility.

Collegiate Environment: Orientation program. Major annual events: March through the Arch, Common Reading Initiative, GGC Idol. Student services:

health clinic, personal-psychological counseling. Campus security: 24-hour emergency response devices and patrols, student patrols, late night transport-escort service, controlled dormitory access. Daniel J. Kaufman Library and Learning Center. Books: 76,355 (physical), 118,119 (digital/electronic); Serial titles: 141 (physical), 5,119 (digital/electronic); Databases: 112. Weekly public service hours: 79; students can reserve study rooms. 243 computers available on campus for general student use. A campuswide network can be accessed from student residence rooms and from off campus. Students can access the following: online class registration. Staffed computer lab on campus provides training in use of computers, software, and the Internet.

■ GEORGIA HIGHLANDS COLLEGE
3175 Cedartown Hwy.
Rome, GA 30161
Tel: (706)802-5000; Free: 800-332-2406
Fax: (706)295-6610
E-mail: cgraham@highlands.edu
Web Site: www.highlands.edu
Description: State-supported, primarily 2-year, coed. Part of University System of Georgia. Awards transfer associate, terminal associate, and bachelor's degrees. Founded 1970. Setting: 226-acre suburban campus with easy access to Atlanta. Endowment: $40,227. Total enrollment: 6,184. Faculty: 277 (129 full-time, 148 part-time). Student-undergrad faculty ratio is 21:1. Full-time: 2,885 students, 59% women, 41% men. Part-time: 3,299 students, 64% women, 36% men. Students come from 23 states and territories, 1% from out-of-state. 0.2% American Indian or Alaska Native, non-Hispanic/Latino; 15% Hispanic/Latino; 16% Black or African American, non-Hispanic/Latino; 2% Asian, non-Hispanic/Latino; 0.1% Native Hawaiian or other Pacific Islander, non-Hispanic/Latino. 21% 25 or older, 6% transferred in. Retention: 67% of full-time freshmen returned the following year. Academic area with the most degrees conferred: health professions and related sciences. Core. Calendar: semesters. Academic remediation for entering students, services for LD students, advanced placement, honors program, independent study, distance learning, double major, summer session for credit, part-time degree program, co-op programs. Study abroad program.
Entrance Requirements: Options: electronic application, deferred admission, international baccalaureate accepted. Required: high school transcript, minimum 2 high school GPA. Recommended: SAT or ACT. Required for some: COMPASS. Entrance: noncompetitive. Notification: continuous. Transfer credits accepted: Yes.
Costs Per Year: Application fee: $30. One-time mandatory fee: $30. State resident tuition: $2,224 full-time, $92.67 per credit hour part-time. Nonresident tuition: $8,421 full-time, $350.87 per credit hour part-time. Mandatory fees: $1064 full-time, $412 per term part-time. Full-time tuition and fees vary according to course load and location. Part-time tuition and fees vary according to course load and location.
Collegiate Environment: Orientation program. Student-run newspaper. Social organizations: 45 open to all. Most popular organizations: Association of Nursing Students, Green Highlands, Brother 2 Brother, Student Government Association, Phi Theta Kappa. Major annual events: Fall Frenzy, Spring Fling, Week of Welcome. Student services: personal-psychological counseling. Campus security: 24-hour emergency response devices and patrols, emergency phone/email alert system. College housing not available. Georgia Highlands College Library-Floyd Campus plus 4 others. Books: 79,592 (physical), 178,561 (digital/electronic); Serial titles: 48 (physical), 4,380 (digital/electronic); Databases: 382. Weekly public service hours: 58; students can reserve study rooms. Operations spending for the previous fiscal year: $252,063. 867 computers available on campus for general student use. A campuswide network can be accessed from off-campus. Students can access the following: online class registration. Staffed computer lab on campus provides training in use of software.
Community Environment: See Shorter College.

■ GEORGIA INSTITUTE OF TECHNOLOGY
225 N Ave., NW
Atlanta, GA 30332-0001
Tel: (404)894-2000
Fax: (404)853-9163
E-mail: admission@gatech.edu
Web Site: www.gatech.edu
Description: State-supported, university, coed. Part of University System of Georgia. Awards bachelor's, master's, and doctoral degrees. Founded 1885.

Setting: 400-acre urban campus. Endowment: $2 billion. Educational spending for the previous fiscal year: $11,778 per student. Total enrollment: 29,370. Faculty: 1,285 (1,115 full-time, 170 part-time). Student-undergrad faculty ratio is 22:1. 31,497 applied, 23% were admitted. 88% from top 10% of their high school class, 98% from top quarter, 99% from top half. Full-time: 14,898 students, 38% women, 62% men. Part-time: 674 students, 35% women, 65% men. Students come from 54 states and territories, 127 other countries, 35% from out-of-state. 7% Hispanic/Latino; 7% Black or African American, non-Hispanic/Latino; 21% Asian, non-Hispanic/Latino; 9% international. 4% 25 or older, 43% live on campus, 4% transferred in. Retention: 97% of full-time freshmen returned the following year. Academic areas with the most degrees conferred: engineering; computer and information sciences; business/marketing. Core. Calendar: semesters. Academic remediation for entering students, ESL program, services for LD students, advanced placement, accelerated degree program, self-designed majors, honors program, independent study, distance learning, summer session for credit, part-time degree program, co-op programs and internships, graduate courses open to undergrads. Off campus study at Dual Degree Programs are in many of the schools in the University System of Georgia, including Morehouse College, Spelman College, Clark Atlanta University, and other historically black colleges and universities (HBCU); and predominantly women's colleges in the southeast; and member institutions of ARCHE-Atlanta Regional Council for Higher Education. Study abroad program. ROTC: Army, Naval, Air Force.
Entrance Requirements: Options: electronic application, early admission, early action, deferred admission, international baccalaureate accepted. Required: essay, high school transcript, SAT or ACT. Application deadlines: 1/1, 10/15 for early action. Notification: 3/15, 1/13 for early action. Preference given to qualified state residents and non-residents who are legacies of the Institute. SAT Reasoning Test deadline: 12/2. Transfer credits accepted: Yes. Applicants placed on waiting list: 4,241. Wait-listed applicants offered admission: 21. Early action applicants: 15,893. Early action applicants admitted: 5,290.
Costs Per Year: Application fee: $75. State resident tuition: $10,008 full-time, $2974 per term part-time. Nonresident tuition: $30,604 full-time, $9081 per term part-time. Mandatory fees: $2410 full-time, $1205 per term part-time. Part-time tuition and fees vary according to course load. College room and board: $14,126. College room only: $9286. Room and board charges vary according to board plan, housing facility, and student level.
Collegiate Environment: Orientation program. Drama-theater group, choral group, marching band, student-run newspaper, radio station. Social organizations: 573 open to all; national fraternities, national sororities; 23% of eligible men and 31% of eligible women are members. Major annual events: GT Night at Six Flags, Homecoming, Sting Break. Student services: legal services, health clinic, personal-psychological counseling, women's center. Campus security: 24-hour emergency response devices and patrols, late night transport-escort service, controlled dormitory access, lighted pathways/sidewalks, emergency notification system, self-defense education, emergency telephones, shuttle buses, video cameras. Georgia Institute of Technology Library plus 1 other. Books: 909,730 (physical), 1 million (digital/electronic); Serial titles: 12,999 (physical), 29,621 (digital/electronic); Databases: 336. Weekly public service hours: 168; study areas open 24 hours, 5-7 days a week; students can reserve study rooms. Operations spending for the previous fiscal year: $17.2 million. 2,500 computers available on campus for general student use. A computer is required for all students. A campuswide network can be accessed from student residence rooms and from off campus. Students can access the following: online class registration, access to a virtual lab environment from a personal device or GT computer. Staffed computer lab on campus provides training in use of computers, software, and the Internet.
Community Environment: See Clark Atlanta University.

■ GEORGIA MILITARY COLLEGE
201 E Greene St.
Old Capitol Bldg.
Milledgeville, GA 31061-3398
Tel: (478)387-4900; Free: 800-342-0413
Fax: (478)445-2688
Web Site: www.gmc.edu
Description: Public, primarily 2-year, coed. Awards transfer associate and bachelor's degrees. Founded 1879. Setting: small town campus. System endowment: $1.5 million. Educational spending for the previous fiscal year: $2396 per student. Total enrollment: 8,595. Faculty: 890 (125 full-time, 765 part-time). Student-undergrad faculty ratio is 15:1. 3,475 applied, 78% were

admitted. Full-time: 4,270 students, 58% women, 42% men. Part-time: 4,325 students, 63% women, 37% men. Students come from 36 states and territories, 12 other countries, 4% from out-of-state. 3% American Indian or Alaska Native, non-Hispanic/Latino; 7% Hispanic/Latino; 42% Black or African American, non-Hispanic/Latino; 2% Asian, non-Hispanic/Latino; 0.4% Native Hawaiian or other Pacific Islander, non-Hispanic/Latino; 0.2% international. 31% 25 or older, 3% live on campus, 29% transferred in. Retention: 46% of full-time freshmen returned the following year. Core. Calendar: quarters. Academic remediation for entering students, services for LD students, advanced placement, self-designed majors, independent study, distance learning, double major, summer session for credit, part-time degree program, co-op programs. Off campus study. Study abroad program. ROTC: Army.

Entrance Requirements: Open admission except for the Early Commissioning Program. Options: electronic application, early admission, deferred admission, international baccalaureate accepted. Required for some: high school transcript, interview. Entrance: noncompetitive. Application deadline: rolling. Transfer credits accepted: Yes.

Costs Per Year: Application fee: $35. State resident tuition: $5445 full-time, $121 per credit hour part-time. Nonresident tuition: $5445 full-time, $121 per credit hour part-time. Mandatory fees: $679 full-time, $15.08 per credit hour part-time. Full-time tuition and fees vary according to location. Part-time tuition and fees vary according to location. College room and board: $7500. College room only: $3150. Room and board charges vary according to location.

Collegiate Environment: Orientation program. Drama-theater group, choral group, student-run newspaper. Social organizations: 20 open to all; Phi Theta Kappa Honor Society, Alpha Phi Omega; 1% of eligible men and 1% of eligible women are members. Most popular organizations: Student Government Association, Alpha Phi Omega National Service Fraternity, Phi Theta Kappa, Drama Club, Biology Club. Major annual events: Military parades, Convocation, Musical and Theater Performances. Student services: health clinic. Campus security: 24-hour emergency response devices and patrols, controlled dormitory access. Sibley Cone Library plus 1 other. Books: 38,125 (physical), 57,769 (digital/electronic); Serial titles: 52 (physical); Databases: 331. Weekly public service hours: 68. Operations spending for the previous fiscal year: $235,570. 835 computers available on campus for general student use. A campuswide network can be accessed from student residence rooms and from off campus. Students can access the following: online class registration. Staffed computer lab on campus provides training in use of computers, software, and the Internet.

Community Environment: Milledgeville, an educational center, was the state capital from 1807 to 1867. Georgia Military College occupies the old state house. Railroads and buses serve the area. Some of the industries are spinning, canning, manufacture of clay products, and mobile homes. Job opportunities are numerous in textile plants. Nearby Lake Sinclair provides boating, fishing and water skiing. The early nineteenth-century homes add atmosphere and beauty to community life.

■ GEORGIA NORTHWESTERN TECHNICAL COLLEGE

One Maurice Culberson Dr.
Rome, GA 30161
Tel: (706)295-6963; Free: 866-983-GNTC
Fax: (706)295-6944
Web Site: www.gntc.edu

Description: State-supported, 2-year, coed. Part of Technical College System of Georgia. Awards certificates, diplomas, and terminal associate degrees. Founded 1962. Setting: small town campus with easy access to Atlanta. Total enrollment: 6,016. Full-time: 1,809 students, 58% women, 42% men. Part-time: 4,207 students, 63% women, 37% men. 1% from out-of-state. 0.2% American Indian or Alaska Native, non-Hispanic/Latino; 13% Hispanic/Latino; 10% Black or African American, non-Hispanic/Latino; 0.6% Asian, non-Hispanic/Latino. Retention: 64% of full-time freshmen returned the following year. Calendar: quarters. Distance learning.

Entrance Requirements: Open admission selective admission to some programs. Option: early admission. Required: high school transcript. Entrance: noncompetitive.

Costs Per Year: Application fee: $25. State resident tuition: $2670 full-time, $89 per credit hour part-time. Nonresident tuition: $5340 full-time, $178 per credit hour part-time.

■ GEORGIA PIEDMONT TECHNICAL COLLEGE

495 N Indian Creek Dr.
Clarkston, GA 30021-2397

Tel: (404)297-9522
Fax: (404)294-4234
Web Site: www.gptc.edu

Description: State-supported, 2-year, coed. Part of Technical College System of Georgia. Awards certificates, diplomas, and terminal associate degrees. Founded 1961. Setting: suburban campus. Total enrollment: 4,103. Full-time: 897 students, 57% women, 43% men. Part-time: 3,206 students, 67% women, 33% men. 0.1% from out-of-state. 0.1% American Indian or Alaska Native, non-Hispanic/Latino; 3% Hispanic/Latino; 82% Black or African American, non-Hispanic/Latino; 2% Asian, non-Hispanic/Latino; 0.1% Native Hawaiian or other Pacific Islander, non-Hispanic/Latino. Retention: 59% of full-time freshmen returned the following year. Calendar: quarters. Distance learning.

Entrance Requirements: Open admission selective admission to some programs. Option: early admission. Required: high school transcript. Entrance: noncompetitive.

■ GEORGIA SOUTHERN UNIVERSITY

1332 Southern Dr.
Statesboro, GA 30458
Tel: (912)478-4636
Fax: (912)681-5635
E-mail: admissions@georgiasouthern.edu
Web Site: www.georgiasouthern.edu

Description: State-supported, university, coed. Part of University System of Georgia. Awards bachelor's, master's, and doctoral degrees and post-master's certificates. Founded 1906. Setting: 900-acre small town campus. Endowment: $47.7 million. Research spending for the previous fiscal year: $15.4 million. Educational spending for the previous fiscal year: $6025 per student. Total enrollment: 26,408. Faculty: 1,387 (1,111 full-time, 276 part-time). Student-undergrad faculty ratio is 22:1. 11,522 applied, 68% were admitted. 18% from top 10% of their high school class, 44% from top quarter, 77% from top half. Full-time: 19,483 students, 54% women, 46% men. Part-time: 3,651 students, 56% women, 44% men. Students come from 50 states and territories, 86 other countries, 6% from out-of-state. 0.4% American Indian or Alaska Native, non-Hispanic/Latino; 7% Hispanic/Latino; 25% Black or African American, non-Hispanic/Latino; 2% Asian, non-Hispanic/Latino; 0.1% Native Hawaiian or other Pacific Islander, non-Hispanic/Latino; 1% international. 14% 25 or older, 26% live on campus, 6% transferred in. Retention: 78% of full-time freshmen returned the following year. Academic areas with the most degrees conferred: business/marketing; health professions and related sciences; parks and recreation. Core. Calendar: semesters. Academic remediation for entering students, ESL program, services for LD students, advanced placement, accelerated degree program, self-designed majors, honors program, independent study, distance learning, double major, summer session for credit, part-time degree program, adult/continuing education programs, co-op programs and internships, graduate courses open to undergrads. Off campus study at A consortium of institutions including Georgia Southern University, Clayton State University, Columbus State University, and Georgia Southwestern State University. Study abroad program. ROTC: Army.

Entrance Requirements: Options: electronic application, early admission, deferred admission, international baccalaureate accepted. Required: minimum 2.5 high school GPA, SAT or ACT. Required for some: high school transcript. Entrance: moderately difficult. Application deadlines: 5/1, 5/1 for nonresidents. Notification: continuous, continuous for nonresidents. SAT Reasoning Test deadline: 5/1. SAT Subject Test deadline: 5/1. Transfer credits accepted: Yes.

Costs Per Year: Application fee: $30. State resident tuition: $5330 full-time, $177.67 per credit hour part-time. Nonresident tuition: $18,812 full-time, $627.07 per credit hour part-time. Mandatory fees: $2092 full-time, $1046 per term part-time. Full-time tuition and fees vary according to course load, degree level, location, and program. Part-time tuition and fees vary according to course load, degree level, location, and program. College room and board: $10,070. College room only: $6320. Room and board charges vary according to board plan, housing facility, and location.

Collegiate Environment: Orientation program. Drama-theater group, choral group, marching band, student-run newspaper, radio station. Social organizations: 280 open to all; national fraternities, national sororities, https://students.georgiasouthern.edu/greeklife/; 9% of eligible men and 10% of eligible women are members. Most popular organizations: Residence Hall Association, Campus Religious Ministries, Student Government Association, Club Sports and Recreation, Greek Life. Major annual events: Welcome Week, Homecoming Week, Finals Feast. Student services: legal services, health clinic, personal-psychological counseling, women's center. Campus security: 24-hour emergency response devices and patrols, student patrols, late night transport-escort service, controlled dormitory access. 6,376 college housing spaces available; 5,794 were occupied in 2018-19. Freshmen given priority for college housing. On-campus residence required in freshman year. Option: coed housing available. Henderson Library. Books: 649,104 (physical), 656,518 (digital/electronic); Serial titles: 15,006 (physical), 104,711 (digital/electronic); Databases: 325. Weekly public service hours: 143; study areas open 24 hours, 5-7 days a week; students can reserve study rooms. Operations spending for the previous fiscal year: $9.7 million. 3,743 computers available on campus for general student use. Computer purchase/lease plans available. A campuswide network can be accessed from student residence rooms and from off campus. Students can access the following: online class registration, online degree audit, online career services, and online healthcare. Staffed computer lab on campus (open 24 hours a day) provides training in use of computers, software, and the Internet.

Community Environment: Georgia Southern ranks among the safest college communities in the country. Its hometown of Statesboro is a neighborly college town and the seat of Bulloch County (50,000 residents). Because the campus and community have grown up together over the past century, shopping, services, and housing are tuned to student's needs. Just an hour down the road are the historic seaside city of Savannah and the beaches of Tybee Island.

■ GEORGIA SOUTHERN UNIVERSITY-ARMSTRONG CAMPUS

11935 Abercorn St.
Savannah, GA 31419-1997
Tel: (912)344-2576; Free: 800-633-2349
Fax: (912)921-5462
E-mail: amysmith@georgiasouthern.com
Web Site: www.georgiasouthern.edu

Description: State-supported, comprehensive, coed. Part of University System of Georgia. Awards associate, bachelor's, master's, and doctoral degrees and post-master's certificates. Founded 1935. Setting: 267-acre suburban campus. Endowment: $12.2 million. Total enrollment: 7,041. Faculty: 478 (290 full-time, 188 part-time). Student-undergrad faculty ratio is 16:1. 2,047 applied, 78% were admitted. Full-time: 4,513 students, 66% women, 34% men. Part-time: 1,768 students, 67% women, 33% men. Students come from 43 states and territories, 67 other countries, 13% from out-of-state. 0.4% American Indian or Alaska Native, non-Hispanic/Latino; 8% Hispanic/Latino; 26% Black or African American, non-Hispanic/Latino; 3% Asian, non-Hispanic/Latino; 0.3% Native Hawaiian or other Pacific Islander, non-Hispanic/Latino; 2% international. 29% 25 or older, 19% live on campus, 9% transferred in. Retention: 65% of full-time freshmen returned the following year. Academic areas with the most degrees conferred: health professions and related sciences; education; biological/life sciences. Core. Calendar: semesters. Academic remediation for entering students, services for LD students, advanced placement, honors program, independent study, distance learning, double major, summer session for credit, part-time degree program, adult/continuing education programs, co-op programs and internships, graduate courses open to undergrads. Off campus study. Study abroad program. ROTC: Army, Naval (c).

Entrance Requirements: Option: electronic application. Required: high school transcript, minimum 2.5 high school GPA, SAT or ACT. Required for some: SAT Subject Tests. Transfer credits accepted: Yes.

Costs Per Year: Application fee: $30. State resident tuition: $5330 full-time, $177.67 per credit hour part-time. Nonresident tuition: $18,812 full-time, $627.07 per credit hour part-time. Mandatory fees: $1054 full-time, $527 per term part-time. Full-time tuition and fees vary according to course load, location, and program. Part-time tuition and fees vary according to course load, location, and program. College room and board: $10,630. Room and board charges vary according to board plan and housing facility.

Collegiate Environment: Orientation program. Drama-theater group, choral group, student-run newspaper. Social organizations: 83 open to all; national fraternities, national sororities, local fraternities, local sororities. Most popular organizations: Hispanic Outreach and Leadership at Armstrong (HOLA), Student Government Association, Campus Union Board, Gay Straight Alliance, Collegiate 100. Major annual events: Beach Bash, Celebrate, Spring Fling. Student services: health clinic, personal-psychological counseling. Campus security: 24-hour emergency response devices and patrols, student patrols, late night transport-escort service, controlled dormitory access, personal safety app. Lane Library plus 1 other. Books: 207,421 (physical), 215,400 (digital/electronic); Serial titles: 500 (physical), 2,000 (digital/

electronic); Databases: 300. Weekly public service hours: 108; students can reserve study rooms. 300 computers available on campus for general student use. A campuswide network can be accessed from student residence rooms. Students can access the following: online class registration.

Community Environment: The college is located on the southside of Savannah, 30 miles from the Atlantic Ocean. All modes of transportation are available. Savannah is a highly industrialized metropolitan area with only minor agricultural activities. Industrial plants number over 350. This city is considered to be one of the first planned cities in North America. The charm of the city comes from the cobblestoned riverfront, and the many squares shaded by majestic oak trees. Points of interest include Factor's Walk, Savannah riverfront shopping, Johnson Square, Pink House, Owens-Thomas House, Cathedral of St. John the Baptist, Independent Presbyterian Church, Colonial Park, and many others.

■ GEORGIA SOUTHWESTERN STATE UNIVERSITY

800 Georgia Southwestern State University Dr.
Americus, GA 31709-4693
Tel: (229)928-1273; Free: 800-338-0082
Fax: (229)931-2983
E-mail: admissions@gsw.edu
Web Site: www.gsw.edu

Description: State-supported, comprehensive, coed. Part of University System of Georgia. Awards bachelor's and master's degrees and post-master's certificates. Founded 1906. Setting: 250-acre small town campus. Endowment: $35.6 million. Research spending for the previous fiscal year: $81,678. Educational spending for the previous fiscal year: $5345 per student. Total enrollment: 3,052. Faculty: 166 (119 full-time, 47 part-time). Student-undergrad faculty ratio is 18:1. 1,279 applied, 67% were admitted. 12% from top 10% of their high school class, 36% from top quarter, 72% from top half. Full-time: 1,779 students, 62% women, 38% men. Part-time: 827 students, 65% women, 35% men. Students come from 25 states and territories, 33 other countries, 4% from out-of-state. 0.2% American Indian or Alaska Native, non-Hispanic/Latino; 6% Hispanic/Latino; 26% Black or African American, non-Hispanic/Latino; 1% Asian, non-Hispanic/Latino; 0.2% Native Hawaiian or other Pacific Islander, non-Hispanic/Latino; 2% international. 22% 25 or older, 32% live on campus, 10% transferred in. Retention: 65% of full-time freshmen returned the following year. Academic areas with the most degrees conferred: business/marketing; education; health professions and related sciences. Core. Calendar: semesters. Academic remediation for entering students, ESL program, services for LD students, advanced placement, accelerated degree program, honors program, distance learning, double major, summer session for credit, part-time degree program, internships, graduate courses open to undergrads. Study abroad program.

Entrance Requirements: Options: electronic application, early admission, deferred admission, international baccalaureate accepted. Required: high school transcript, minimum 2 high school GPA, college preparatory curriculum, SAT or ACT. Recommended: interview. Entrance: moderately difficult. Application deadline: 7/21. Notification: continuous. SAT Reasoning Test deadline: 7/21. SAT Subject Test deadline: 7/21. Transfer credits accepted: Yes.

Costs Per Year: Application fee: $25. State resident tuition: $4956 full-time, $165.20 per credit hour part-time. Nonresident tuition: $18,032 full-time, $601.07 per credit hour part-time. Mandatory fees: $1380 full-time, $448 per term part-time. Full-time tuition and fees vary according to course load, location, and program. Part-time tuition and fees vary according to course load, location, and program. College room and board: $8120. College room only: $4070. Room and board charges vary according to board plan and housing facility.

Collegiate Environment: Orientation program. Drama-theater group, choral group, student-run newspaper. Social organizations: 25 open to all; national fraternities, national sororities; 9% of eligible men and 8% of eligible women are members. Most popular organizations: National sororities and fraternities, African Student Association, Enactus, Outdoor Club, International Student Association. Major annual events: Homecoming, Student Appreciation Day, Taste of the World. Student services: health clinic, personal-psychological counseling. Campus security: 24-hour emergency response devices and patrols, late night transport-escort service, controlled dormitory access. James Earl Carter Library. Books: 207,635 (physical), 68,397 (digital/electronic); Serial titles: 76 (physical), 81 (digital/electronic); Databases: 277. Weekly public service hours: 72; students can reserve study rooms. Operations spending for the previous fiscal year: $637,900.

260 computers available on campus for general student use. A campuswide network can be accessed from student residence rooms and from off campus. Students can access the following: online class registration. Staffed computer lab on campus provides training in use of computers, software, and the Internet.

Community Environment: Americus is located 135 miles south of Atlanta, the climate is mild with a yearly mean temperature of 65.7 degrees, and an annual rainfall of 49 inches. Airlines serve the area. The usual community facilities include a hospital, library, the newly restored Rylander Theatre, daily newspaper, radio stations, clinics, and shopping centers. Manufactured products include shirts, lumber, nails, auto parts, and paper products. Kaolin and Bauxite mines are nearby. Outdoor sports include tennis, baseball, golf and basketball. Historic sites in Americus include Plains, home of President Jimmy Carter, Andersonville National Cemetery and Civil War prison site, and Souther field where Charles Lindbergh made his first solo flight. Americus is also home to International Habitat for Humanity.

■ **GEORGIA STATE UNIVERSITY**

33 Gilmer St.
Atlanta, GA 30302-3083
Tel: (404)651-2000
E-mail: onestopshop@gsu.edu
Web Site: www.gsu.edu

Description: State-supported, university, coed. Part of University System of Georgia. Awards associate, bachelor's, master's, and doctoral degrees and post-master's certificates. Founded 1913. Setting: 109-acre urban campus with easy access to Atlanta. Endowment: $167.1 million. Research spending for the previous fiscal year: $176 million. Educational spending for the previous fiscal year: $6682 per student. Total enrollment: 34,274. Faculty: 1,581 (1,160 full-time, 421 part-time). Student-undergrad faculty ratio is 23:1. 19,838 applied, 57% were admitted. 43% from top 10% of their high school class, 100% from top quarter, 100% from top half. Full-time: 21,041 students, 59% women, 41% men. Part-time: 6,149 students, 58% women, 42% men. Students come from 53 states and territories, 129 other countries, 4% from out-of-state. 0.1% American Indian or Alaska Native, non-Hispanic/Latino; 12% Hispanic/Latino; 41% Black or African American, non-Hispanic/Latino; 14% Asian, non-Hispanic/Latino; 3% international. 17% 25 or older, 21% live on campus, 6% transferred in. Retention: 83% of full-time freshmen returned the following year. Academic areas with the most degrees conferred: business/marketing; social sciences; psychology. Core. Calendar: semesters. ESL program, services for LD students, advanced placement, honors program, independent study, distance learning, double major, summer session for credit, part-time degree program, co-op programs and internships. Study abroad program. ROTC: Army, Naval (c), Air Force (c).

Entrance Requirements: Options: electronic application, early admission, early action, deferred admission, international baccalaureate accepted. Required: high school transcript, minimum 2.8 high school GPA, college preparatory curriculum as specified by the University System of Georgia Board of Regents, combined SAT of 830, minimum Freshman Index of 2500, SAT or ACT. Recommended: essay, 1 recommendation. Entrance: moderately difficult. Application deadlines: 3/1, 3/1 for nonresidents, 11/15 for early action. Notification: 4/15, 4/15 for nonresidents, 12/15 for early action. SAT Reasoning Test deadline: 3/1. Transfer credits accepted: Yes.

Costs Per Year: Application fee: $60. State resident tuition: $8730 full-time, $291 per credit hour part-time. Nonresident tuition: $27,304 full-time, $910.14 per credit hour part-time. Mandatory fees: $2128 full-time, $1064 per term part-time. Part-time tuition and fees vary according to course load. College room and board: $14,692. College room only: $10,824. Room and board charges vary according to board plan and housing facility.

Collegiate Environment: Orientation program. Drama-theater group, choral group, marching band, student-run newspaper, radio station. Social organizations: 456 open to all; national fraternities, national sororities, local fraternities; 4% of eligible men and 4% of eligible women are members. Most popular organizations: Spotlight Programs Board, Fraternities/Sororities, Service Organizations, Academic Organizations, Sports Clubs. Major annual events: Welcome Week, Panther Prowl, Homecoming. Student services: health clinic, personal-psychological counseling. Campus security: 24-hour emergency response devices and patrols, late night transport-escort service, controlled dormitory access. 5,490 college housing spaces available; all were occupied in 2018-19. Freshmen given priority for college housing. Option: coed housing available. University Library plus 6 others. Books: 1.9 million (physical), 686,132 (digital/electronic); Serial titles: 21,654 (digital/electronic). Students can reserve study rooms. Operations spending for the previous fiscal year: $18.3 million. 2,040 computers available on campus for

general student use. A campuswide network can be accessed from student residence rooms and from off campus. Students can access the following: online class registration. Staffed computer lab on campus provides training in use of computers, software, and the Internet.

Community Environment: See Clark Atlanta University.

■ **GORDON STATE COLLEGE**

419 College Dr.
Barnesville, GA 30204-1762
Tel: (678)359-5555; Free: 800-282-6504
Web Site: www.gordonstate.edu

Description: State-supported, primarily 2-year, coed. Part of University System of Georgia. Awards transfer associate, terminal associate, and bachelor's degrees. Founded 1852. Setting: 235-acre small town campus with easy access to Atlanta. Total enrollment: 3,986. Faculty: 197 (122 full-time, 75 part-time). Student-undergrad faculty ratio is 21:1. 2,982 applied, 83% were admitted. 1% from out-of-state. 0.1% American Indian or Alaska Native, non-Hispanic/Latino; 4% Hispanic/Latino; 38% Black or African American, non-Hispanic/Latino; 1% Asian, non-Hispanic/Latino. 15% 25 or older. Academic areas with the most degrees conferred: public administration and social services; health professions and related sciences; biological/life sciences. Core. Calendar: semesters. Academic remediation for entering students, services for LD students, advanced placement, accelerated degree program, honors program, distance learning, double major, summer session for credit, part-time degree program, adult/continuing education programs, co-op programs and internships. Off campus study. Study abroad program.

Entrance Requirements: Options: electronic application, early admission. Required: high school transcript, SAT or ACT. Application deadline: rolling. Transfer credits accepted: Yes.

Costs Per Year: Application fee: $30. State resident tuition: $3126 full-time, $104 per credit hour part-time. Nonresident tuition: $11,548 full-time, $385 per credit hour part-time. Mandatory fees: $1166 full-time, $550 per term part-time. College room and board: $8408. Room and board charges vary according to board plan and housing facility.

Collegiate Environment: Orientation program. Drama-theater group, choral group, student-run newspaper. Social organizations: 35 open to all. Most popular organizations: Campus Activity Board, Student Government Association, Earth Wind Fire (science club), Student African American Brotherhood (SAAB), Swazi Step Team. Major annual events: Spring Fling, October Fest, Turkey Trot. Student services: health clinic, personal-psychological counseling. Campus security: 24-hour emergency response devices and patrols, student patrols, controlled dormitory access, Resident Assistants and Resident Directors in housing, parking patrol. Dorothy W. Hightower Collaborative Learning Center and Library. Books: 103,423 (physical), 35,999 (digital/electronic); Serial titles: 401 (physical), 87,985 (digital/electronic); Databases: 325. Weekly public service hours: 73. 466 computers available on campus for general student use. A campuswide network can be accessed from student residence rooms. Students can access the following: online class registration. Staffed computer lab on campus provides training in use of computers, software, and the Internet.

■ **GUPTON-JONES COLLEGE OF FUNERAL SERVICE**

5141 Snapfinger Woods Dr.
Decatur, GA 30035-4022
Tel: (770)593-2257; Free: 800-848-5352
Fax: (770)593-1891
Web Site: www.gupton-jones.edu

Description: Independent, 2-year, coed. Part of Pierce Mortuary Colleges, Inc. Awards terminal associate degrees. Founded 1920. Setting: 3-acre suburban campus with easy access to Atlanta. Total enrollment: 232. Faculty: 9 (7 full-time, 2 part-time). Student-undergrad faculty ratio is 28:1. Full-time: 232 students, 59% women, 41% men. Students come from 15 states and territories, 2 other countries, 86% from out-of-state. 70% Black or African American, non-Hispanic/Latino. 77% 25 or older, 13% transferred in. Retention: 84% of full-time freshmen returned the following year. Core. Calendar: quarters. Services for LD students, advanced placement, accelerated degree program.

Entrance Requirements: Open admission. Option: electronic application. Required: high school transcript, health questionnaire. Entrance: noncompetitive. Application deadline: rolling. Transfer credits accepted: Yes.

Collegiate Environment: Social organizations: 2 open to all; national fraternities; 15% of eligible men and 30% of eligible women are members. Most popular organization: Student Council. Major annual events: Freshman Picnic, Local Blood Drive, Freshman Orientation. Campus security: 24-hour emergency response devices. Russell Millison Library. Books: 4,000 (physical). 24 computers available on campus for general student use. A campuswide network can be accessed from off-campus. Students can access the following: online class registration. Staffed computer lab on campus provides training in use of computers, software, and the Internet.

■ **GWINNETT COLLEGE (LILBURN)**
4230 Lawrenceville Hwy.
Ste. 11
Lilburn, GA 30047
Tel: (770)381-7200
Web Site: www.gwinnettcollege.edu
Description: Proprietary, 2-year, coed. Awards diplomas, transfer associate, and terminal associate degrees. Founded 1976.

■ **GWINNETT COLLEGE (MARIETTA)**
1130 Northchase Pky.
Ste. 100
Marietta, GA 30067
Tel: (770)859-9779
Web Site: www.gwinnettcollege.edu/locations/marietta
Description: Proprietary, 2-year, coed. Awards diplomas, transfer associate, and terminal associate degrees.

■ **GWINNETT COLLEGE (SANDY SPRINGS)**
6690 Roswell Rd. NE
Ste. 2200
Sandy Springs, GA 30328
Tel: (770)457-2021
Web Site: www.gwinnettcollege.edu/locations/sandy-springs
Description: Proprietary, 2-year, coed.

■ **GWINNETT TECHNICAL COLLEGE**
5150 Sugarloaf Pky.
Lawrenceville, GA 30043-5702
Tel: (770)962-7580
Web Site: www.gwinnetttech.edu
Description: State-supported, 2-year, coed. Part of Technical College System of Georgia. Awards certificates, diplomas, and terminal associate degrees. Founded 1984. Setting: 88-acre suburban campus. Total enrollment: 7,479. Full-time: 1,636 students, 51% women, 49% men. Part-time: 5,843 students, 61% women, 39% men. 0.2% from out-of-state. 0.2% American Indian or Alaska Native, non-Hispanic/Latino; 15% Hispanic/Latino; 33% Black or African American, non-Hispanic/Latino; 8% Asian, non-Hispanic/Latino; 0.2% Native Hawaiian or other Pacific Islander, non-Hispanic/Latino. Retention: 56% of full-time freshmen returned the following year. Calendar: semesters. ESL program, services for LD students, distance learning, summer session for credit, part-time degree program.
Entrance Requirements: Open admission selective admission to some programs. Options: electronic application, early admission. Required: high school transcript. Entrance: noncompetitive. Transfer credits accepted: Yes.
Collegiate Environment: Orientation program. Student services: personal-psychological counseling. Campus security: 24-hour emergency response devices and patrols. Gwinnett Technical College Library plus 1 other.

■ **HERZING UNIVERSITY**
3393 Peachtree Rd.
Ste. 1003
Atlanta, GA 30326
Tel: (404)816-4533; Free: 800-596-0724
Fax: (404)816-5576
Web Site: www.herzing.edu/atlanta
Description: Independent, 4-year, coed. Awards associate and bachelor's degrees. Founded 1949. Setting: urban campus with easy access to Atlanta. Calendar: semesters.
Entrance Requirements: Transfer credits accepted: Yes.

■ **INTERACTIVE COLLEGE OF TECHNOLOGY (CHAMBLEE)**
5303 New Peachtree Rd.
Chamblee, GA 30341
Tel: (770)216-2960; Free: 800-447-2011
Fax: (770)216-2989
Web Site: ict.edu
Description: Proprietary, 2-year, coed. Part of Interactive Learning Systems.

Awards certificates, diplomas, and terminal associate degrees. Setting: 14-acre suburban campus. Total enrollment: 312. Student-undergrad faculty ratio is 25:1. 80% 25 or older. Core. Calendar: semesters. Academic remediation for entering students, ESL program, advanced placement, accelerated degree program, independent study, double major, part-time degree program, adult/continuing education programs, internships.
Entrance Requirements: Open admission. Option: international baccalaureate accepted. Required: high school transcript, interview. Application deadline: rolling.
Collegiate Environment: Orientation program.

■ **INTERACTIVE COLLEGE OF TECHNOLOGY (GAINESVILLE)**
2323 Browns Bridge Rd.
Gainesville, GA 30504
Tel: (678)450-0550
Web Site: ict.edu
Description: Proprietary, 2-year, coed. Awards certificates, diplomas, and terminal associate degrees. Setting: small town campus. Calendar: semesters. Academic remediation for entering students, ESL program, distance learning, co-op programs and internships.
Entrance Requirements: Required: high school transcript, interview.

■ **INTERACTIVE COLLEGE OF TECHNOLOGY (MORROW)**
1580 Southlake Pky.
Ste. C
Morrow, GA 30260
Tel: (770)960-1298
Web Site: ict.edu
Description: Proprietary, 2-year, coed. Awards diplomas, transfer associate, and terminal associate degrees. Calendar: semesters.

■ **KENNESAW STATE UNIVERSITY**
1000 Chastain Rd.
Kennesaw, GA 30144
Tel: (470)578-6000
Fax: (770)423-6541
Web Site: www.kennesaw.edu
Description: State-supported, comprehensive, coed. Part of University System of Georgia. Awards bachelor's, master's, and doctoral degrees and post-master's certificates. Founded 1963. Setting: 602-acre suburban campus with easy access to Atlanta. Endowment: $40.3 million. Research spending for the previous fiscal year: $1.5 million. Educational spending for the previous fiscal year: $5581 per student. Total enrollment: 35,420. Faculty: 1,941 (1,182 full-time, 759 part-time). Student-undergrad faculty ratio is 20:1. 13,427 applied, 58% were admitted. 16% from top 10% of their high school class, 45% from top quarter, 80% from top half. Full-time: 24,150 students, 49% women, 51% men. Part-time: 8,124 students, 44% women, 56% men. Students come from 54 states and territories, 129 other countries, 13% from out-of-state. 0.2% American Indian or Alaska Native, non-Hispanic/Latino; 10% Hispanic/Latino; 21% Black or African American, non-Hispanic/Latino; 5% Asian, non-Hispanic/Latino; 0.1% Native Hawaiian or other Pacific Islander, non-Hispanic/Latino; 2% international. 19% 25 or older, 16% live on campus, 7% transferred in. Retention: 79% of full-time freshmen returned the following year. Academic areas with the most degrees conferred: business/marketing; computer and information sciences; engineering. Core. Calendar: semesters. ESL program, services for LD students, advanced placement, freshman honors college, honors program, distance learning, double major, summer session for credit, part-time degree program, adult/continuing education programs, co-op programs and internships, graduate courses open to undergrads. Off campus study at University System of Georgia - Comprised of 26 Institutions. Study abroad program. ROTC: Army (c), Naval (c), Air Force (c).
Entrance Requirements: Options: electronic application, early admission, early action. Required: high school transcript, minimum 2.5 high school GPA. Entrance: moderately difficult. Application deadlines: 5/3, 5/3 for nonresidents, 11/1 for early action. Notification: continuous until 12/1, 12/1 for nonresidents, 12/8 for early action. SAT Reasoning Test deadline: 5/3. SAT Subject Test deadline: 5/3. Transfer credits accepted: Yes.
Costs Per Year: Application fee: $40. State resident tuition: $5426 full-time, $181 per credit hour part-time. Nonresident tuition: $19,152 full-time, $638 per credit hour part-time. Mandatory fees: $2006 full-time, $1003 per term part-time. Full-time tuition and fees vary according to course load, degree level, location, program, and student level. Part-time tuition and fees vary according to course load, degree level, location, program, and student level.

College room and board: $11,467. Room and board charges vary according to board plan, housing facility, and student level.

Collegiate Environment: Orientation program. Drama-theater group, choral group, marching band, student-run newspaper, radio station. Social organizations: 275 open to all; national fraternities, national sororities; 17% of eligible men and 21% of eligible women are members. Most popular organizations: Kennesaw Activities Board, African American Student Alliance, International Student Association, KSU eSports Organization, IEEE Computer Society. Major annual events: KSU Live: Homecoming concert, Pumpkin Launch, Dance Marathon hosted by Miracle at KSU. Student services: health clinic, personal-psychological counseling. Campus security: 24-hour emergency response devices and patrols, student patrols, late night transport-escort service, controlled dormitory access. 5,200 college housing spaces available; all were occupied in 2018-19. Freshmen given priority for college housing. Option: coed housing available. Kennesaw State University Library System plus 2 others. Books: 378,276 (physical), 656,005 (digital/electronic); Serial titles: 1,273 (physical), 115,672 (digital/electronic); Databases: 476. Students can reserve study rooms. Operations spending for the previous fiscal year: $6.2 million. 4,500 computers available on campus for general student use. Computer purchase/lease plans available. A campuswide network can be accessed from student residence rooms and from off campus. Students can access the following: online class registration. Staffed computer lab on campus provides training in use of computers, software, and the Internet.

Community Environment: A suburban area of Marietta, the average winter temperature is 45 degrees, the average summer temperature is 80 degrees, with an average rainfall of 50 inches. Community facilities include churches, and civic organizations with hospitals and shopping areas in Marietta. In view is Kennesaw Mountain, site of Civil War battles and the"The Great Locomotive Chase.".

■ LAGRANGE COLLEGE

601 Broad St.
Lagrange, GA 30240-2999
Tel: (706)880-8000; Free: 800-593-2885
Fax: (706)880-8040
E-mail: hphillips@lagrange.edu
Web Site: www.lagrange.edu

Description: Independent United Methodist, comprehensive, coed. Awards bachelor's and master's degrees. Founded 1831. Setting: 120-acre small town campus with easy access to Atlanta. Endowment: $56.4 million. Educational spending for the previous fiscal year: $12,297 per student. Total enrollment: 1,029. Faculty: 113 (76 full-time, 37 part-time). Student-undergrad faculty ratio is 11:1. 1,511 applied, 48% were admitted. 8% from top 10% of their high school class, 38% from top quarter, 78% from top half. 3 class presidents, 18 valedictorians, 21 student government officers. Full-time: 631 students, 68% women, 32% men. Part-time: 46 students, 74% women, 26% men. Students come from 19 states and territories, 7 other countries, 16% from out-of-state. 0.6% American Indian or Alaska Native, non-Hispanic/Latino; 1% Hispanic/Latino; 19% Black or African American, non-Hispanic/Latino; 1% Asian, non-Hispanic/Latino; 1% international. 9% 25 or older, 58% live on campus, 13% transferred in. Retention: 60% of full-time freshmen returned the following year. Academic areas with the most degrees conferred: health professions and related sciences; business/marketing; parks and recreation. Core. Calendar: 4-1-4. Services for LD students, advanced placement, accelerated degree program, self-designed majors, independent study, distance learning, double major, summer session for credit, part-time degree program, adult/continuing education programs, internships, graduate courses open to undergrads. Study abroad program.

Entrance Requirements: Options: electronic application, deferred admission, international baccalaureate accepted. Required: essay, high school transcript, SAT or ACT. Required for some: minimum 2.5 high school GPA, 3 recommendations, interview, SAT, ACT. Entrance: moderately difficult. Application deadline: rolling. Notification: continuous. SAT Reasoning Test deadline: 8/15. Transfer credits accepted: Yes.

Costs Per Year: Application fee: $0. One-time mandatory fee: $150. Comprehensive fee: $42,130 includes full-time tuition ($30,170), mandatory fees ($330), and college room and board ($11,630). College room only: $6430. Full-time tuition and fees vary according to class time, course load, degree level, and program. Room and board charges vary according to board plan and housing facility. Part-time tuition: $1240 per semester hour. Part-time tuition varies according to class time, course load, degree level, and program.

Collegiate Environment: Orientation program. Drama-theater group, choral

group, marching band, student-run newspaper. Social organizations: 27 open to all; national fraternities, national sororities, local fraternities; 22% of eligible men and 33% of eligible women are members. Most popular organizations: Campus Circle, LC Miracle, Panhellenic (Sorority Leadership), Black Student Union, Student Government. Major annual events: Spirit and Traditions Kickoff, May Days/Step Sing, Vegas on the Hill. Student services: health clinic, personal-psychological counseling. Campus security: 24-hour patrols, controlled dormitory access, mass notification system (e2Campus) to send emergency messages to students and employees. 662 college housing spaces available; 499 were occupied in 2018-19. Freshmen guaranteed college housing. On-campus residence required through senior year. Options: coed, men-only, women-only housing available. Frank and Laura Lewis Library. Books: 83,082 (physical), 351,244 (digital/electronic); Serial titles: 23 (physical), 21 (digital/electronic); Databases: 192. Weekly public service hours: 84; study areas open 24 hours, 5-7 days a week; students can reserve study rooms. Operations spending for the previous fiscal year: $739,540. 116 computers available on campus for general student use. A campuswide network can be accessed from student residence rooms and from off campus. Students can access the following: online class registration. Staffed computer lab on campus provides training in use of computers, software, and the Internet.

■ LANIER TECHNICAL COLLEGE

2990 Landrum Education Dr.
Oakwood, GA 30566
Tel: (770)531-6300
Fax: (770)531-6328
Web Site: www.laniertech.edu

Description: State-supported, 2-year, coed. Part of Technical College System of Georgia. Awards certificates, diplomas, and terminal associate degrees. Founded 1964. Total enrollment: 3,626. Full-time: 1,034 students, 57% women, 43% men. Part-time: 2,602 students, 58% women, 42% men. 0.1% from out-of-state. 0.5% American Indian or Alaska Native, non-Hispanic/Latino; 16% Hispanic/Latino; 9% Black or African American, non-Hispanic/Latino; 3% Asian, non-Hispanic/Latino; 0.3% Native Hawaiian or other Pacific Islander, non-Hispanic/Latino. Retention: 60% of full-time freshmen returned the following year. Calendar: quarters. Distance learning.

Entrance Requirements: Open admission selective admission to some programs. Option: early admission. Required: high school transcript. Entrance: noncompetitive.

■ LIFE UNIVERSITY

1269 Barclay Cir.
Marietta, GA 30060-2903
Tel: (770)426-2600; Free: 800-543-3202
Web Site: www.life.edu

Description: Independent, comprehensive, coed. Awards associate, bachelor's, master's, and doctoral degrees. Founded 1974. Setting: 96-acre suburban campus with easy access to Atlanta Metro. Research spending for the previous fiscal year: $560,847. Educational spending for the previous fiscal year: $11,076 per student. Total enrollment: 2,746. Faculty: 183 (128 full-time, 55 part-time). Student-undergrad faculty ratio is 12:1. 701 applied, 37% were admitted. Full-time: 727 students, 51% women, 49% men. Part-time: 166 students, 72% women, 28% men. Students come from 54 states and territories, 46 other countries, 43% from out-of-state. 1% American Indian or Alaska Native, non-Hispanic/Latino; 24% Hispanic/Latino; 25% Black or African American, non-Hispanic/Latino; 3% Asian, non-Hispanic/Latino; 2% international. 22% 25 or older, 10% live on campus, 13% transferred in. Retention: 62% of full-time freshmen returned the following year. Academic areas with the most degrees conferred: biological/life sciences; business/marketing; health professions and related sciences. Core. Calendar: quarters. Academic remediation for entering students, ESL program, services for LD students, advanced placement, accelerated degree program, self-designed majors, independent study, distance learning, double major, summer session for credit, part-time degree program, co-op programs and internships, graduate courses open to undergrads. Off campus study. Study abroad program.

Entrance Requirements: Option: electronic application. Required: high school transcript, minimum 2 high school GPA, SAT or ACT. Entrance: minimally difficult. Notification: continuous. Transfer credits accepted: Yes.

Costs Per Year: Application fee: $50. Tuition: $11,703 full-time, $249 per credit hour part-time. Mandatory fees: $1491 full-time. Full-time tuition and fees vary according to course load.

Collegiate Environment: Orientation program. Student-run newspaper.

Social organizations: 73 open to all. Most popular organizations: Student Ambassadors, Campus Activities Board, League of Chiropractic Women, Functional Neurology Club, Hispanic Club. Major annual events: The Spring Summer and Fall Life Fest, Quarterly Chillax Event, Welcome Back Party. Student services: health clinic, personal-psychological counseling. Campus security: 24-hour emergency response devices and patrols, controlled dormitory access. 412 college housing spaces available. No special consideration for freshman housing applicants. Option: coed housing available. Library & Learning Services. Books: 33,771 (physical), 39,225 (digital/electronic); Serial titles: 66 (physical), 31,104 (digital/electronic); Databases: 25. Weekly public service hours: 98; students can reserve study rooms. Operations spending for the previous fiscal year: $1.1 million.

■ **LINCOLN COLLEGE OF TECHNOLOGY**
2359 Windy Hill Rd.
Marietta, GA 30067
Tel: (770)226-0056; Free: 844-215-1513
Web Site: www.lincolntech.edu
Description: Proprietary, 2-year, coed. Awards certificates, transfer associate, and terminal associate degrees.

■ **LUTHER RICE COLLEGE & SEMINARY**
3038 Evans Mill Rd.
Lithonia, GA 30038-2454
Tel: (770)484-1204; Free: 800-442-1577
E-mail: admissions@lutherrice.edu
Web Site: www.lutherrice.edu
Description: Independent Baptist, comprehensive, coed. Awards bachelor's, master's, and doctoral degrees. Founded 1962. Setting: 5-acre suburban campus with easy access to Atlanta. Endowment: $556,351. Educational spending for the previous fiscal year: $2573 per student. Total enrollment: 1,079. Faculty: 35 (15 full-time, 20 part-time). Student-undergrad faculty ratio is 24:1. 31 applied. Full-time: 58 students, 21% women, 79% men. Part-time: 293 students, 32% women, 68% men. Students come from 29 states and territories, 2 other countries, 42% from out-of-state. 0.3% American Indian or Alaska Native, non-Hispanic/Latino; 1% Hispanic/Latino; 43% Black or African American, non-Hispanic/Latino; 0.6% Asian, non-Hispanic/Latino. 88% 25 or older, 48% transferred in. Retention: 50% of full-time freshmen returned the following year. Calendar: semesters. Independent study, distance learning, summer session for credit, part-time degree program, adult/continuing education programs, co-op programs.
Entrance Requirements: Open admission. Options: electronic application, international baccalaureate accepted. Required: essay, high school transcript, recommendations, Bible exam. Entrance: noncompetitive. Application deadline: rolling. Transfer credits accepted: Yes.
Costs Per Year: Application fee: $50. One-time mandatory fee: $175. Tuition: $8520 full-time, $274 per credit hour part-time. Mandatory fees: $1000 full-time, $100 per course part-time. Full-time tuition and fees vary according to degree level and location. College room only: $13,496. Room charges vary according to location.
Collegiate Environment: Orientation program. Social organizations: 1 open to all. Most popular organization: SGA - Student Government Association. Major annual events: Chapel, New Student Orientation. Student services: personal-psychological counseling. Campus security: 24-hour emergency response devices. Smith Library. Weekly public service hours: 41. Operations spending for the previous fiscal year: $196,816. 13 computers available on campus for general student use. A campuswide network can be accessed from off-campus. Students can access the following: online class registration, Online tutoring.

■ **MERCER UNIVERSITY**
1501 Mercer University Dr.
Macon, GA 31207
Tel: (478)301-2700; Free: 800-MERCER-U
Fax: (478)301-2828
E-mail: karafa_sp@mercer.edu
Web Site: www.mercer.edu
Description: Independent Baptist, university, coed. Awards bachelor's, master's, and doctoral degrees and post-master's certificates. Founded 1833. Setting: 150-acre urban campus. Total enrollment: 7,315. Faculty: 755 (392 full-time, 363 part-time). Student-undergrad faculty ratio is 13:1. 4,749 applied, 73% were admitted. 37% from top 10% of their high school class, 68% from top quarter, 92% from top half. Full-time: 3,310 students, 54% women, 46% men. Part-time: 62 students, 48% women, 52% men. Students come from 39 states and territories, 39 other countries, 16% from out-of-state. 0.2% American Indian or Alaska Native, non-Hispanic/Latino; 6% Hispanic/Latino; 19% Black or African American, non-Hispanic/Latino; 9% Asian, non-Hispanic/Latino; 0.1% Native Hawaiian or other Pacific Islander, non-Hispanic/Latino; 3% international. 2% 25 or older, 76% live on campus, 2% transferred in. Retention: 89% of full-time freshmen returned the following year. Academic areas with the most degrees conferred: engineering; business/marketing; biological/life sciences. Core. Calendar: semesters. ESL program, services for LD students, advanced placement, accelerated degree program, self-designed majors, honors program, independent study, distance learning, double major, summer session for credit, part-time degree program, adult/continuing education programs, co-op programs and internships. Off campus study. Study abroad program. ROTC: Army.
Entrance Requirements: Options: electronic application, early action, deferred admission, international baccalaureate accepted. Required: essay, high school transcript, minimum 3.25 high school GPA, 1 recommendation, SAT or ACT. Recommended: interview. Entrance: moderately difficult. Application deadlines: 7/1, 3/1 for early action. Notification: continuous, rolling for early action. SAT Reasoning Test deadline: 7/1. Transfer credits accepted: Yes.
Costs Per Year: Application fee: $50. Comprehensive fee: $49,416 includes full-time tuition ($36,594), mandatory fees ($300), and college room and board ($12,522). College room only: $6364. Full-time tuition and fees vary according to location. Room and board charges vary according to board plan, housing facility, location, and student level. Part-time tuition: $1220 per credit hour. Part-time mandatory fees: $10 per credit hour. Part-time tuition and fees vary according to course load and location.
Collegiate Environment: Orientation program. Drama-theater group, choral group, marching band, student-run newspaper, radio station. Social organizations: 125 open to all; national fraternities, national sororities, local fraternities, local sororities; 27% of eligible men and 29% of eligible women are members. Major annual events: Mercer Madness, Homecoming, Bearstock (bands). Student services: health clinic, personal-psychological counseling. Campus security: 24-hour emergency response devices and patrols, student patrols, late night transport-escort service, controlled dormitory access. 2,566 college housing spaces available; 2,533 were occupied in 2018-19. Freshmen guaranteed college housing. On-campus residence required through junior year. Options: coed, men-only, women-only housing available. Jack Tarver Library plus 3 others. Study areas open 24 hours, 5-7 days a week; students can reserve study rooms.

■ **MIDDLE GEORGIA STATE UNIVERSITY**
100 University Pky.
Macon, GA 31206
Tel: (478)471-2700; Free: 877-238-8664
Fax: (478)471-2846
Web Site: www.mga.edu
Description: State-supported, comprehensive, coed. Part of University System of Georgia. Awards associate, bachelor's, and master's degrees. Founded 2015. Setting: 419-acre urban campus with easy access to Atlanta. Endowment: $874,853. Research spending for the previous fiscal year: $361,612. Educational spending for the previous fiscal year: $6462 per student. Total enrollment: 7,341. Faculty: 387 (256 full-time, 131 part-time). Student-undergrad faculty ratio is 19:1. 4,841 applied, 94% were admitted. Full-time: 4,507 students, 55% women, 45% men. Part-time: 2,714 students, 62% women, 38% men. Students come from 32 states and territories, 6 other countries, 2% from out-of-state. 0.1% American Indian or Alaska Native, non-Hispanic/Latino; 5% Hispanic/Latino; 33% Black or African American, non-Hispanic/Latino; 3% Asian, non-Hispanic/Latino; 0.1% Native Hawaiian or other Pacific Islander, non-Hispanic/Latino; 0.2% international. 29% 25 or older, 19% live on campus, 9% transferred in. Retention: 65% of full-time freshmen returned the following year. Academic areas with the most degrees conferred: health professions and related sciences; business/marketing; computer and information sciences. Core. Calendar: semesters. Academic remediation for entering students, services for LD students, advanced placement, honors program, independent study, distance learning, double major, summer session for credit, part-time degree program, co-op programs and internships. Study abroad program.
Entrance Requirements: Options: electronic application, early admission, international baccalaureate accepted. Required: high school transcript, minimum 2 high school GPA, SAT or ACT. Entrance: minimally difficult. Application deadline: rolling. Notification: continuous. SAT Reasoning Test deadline: 7/15. SAT Subject Test deadline: 7/15. Transfer credits accepted: Yes.

Costs Per Year: Application fee: $30. State resident tuition: $3326 full-time, $110.87 per credit hour part-time. Nonresident tuition: $12,286 full-time, $409.54 per credit hour part-time. Mandatory fees: $1282 full-time. Full-time tuition and fees vary according to program. Part-time tuition varies according to program. College room and board: $7614. College room only: $5390. Room and board charges vary according to board plan, housing facility, and location.

Collegiate Environment: Orientation program. Drama-theater group, choral group, marching band, student-run newspaper. Social organizations: 59 open to all; national fraternities, national sororities. Most popular organizations: Brothers of Leadership and Distinction (BOLD), Middle Georgia State Association of Nursing Students (MGSANS), Black Student Unification (BSU), Student Government Association (SGA), International Students and Studies Association (ISSA). Major annual events: Spring Fling, Homecoming, Student Leadership Awards. Student services: health clinic, personal-psychological counseling. Campus security: 24-hour emergency response devices and patrols, late night transport-escort service. Macon State University Library. Books: 125,996 (physical), 246,646 (digital/electronic); Serial titles: 85 (physical), 51,575 (digital/electronic); Databases: 138. Weekly public service hours: 23; students can reserve study rooms. 500 computers available on campus for general student use. A campuswide network can be accessed from student residence rooms and from off campus. Students can access the following: online class registration. Staffed computer lab on campus provides training in use of software and the Internet.

Community Environment: See Mercer University - Macon.

■ **MILLER-MOTTE TECHNICAL COLLEGE (AUGUSTA)**
621 Frontage Rd. NW
Augusta, GA 30907
Tel: (706)396-8000; Free: 800-705-9182
Web Site: www.miller-motte.edu
Description: Proprietary, 2-year, coed. Awards certificates, transfer associate, and terminal associate degrees.

■ **MILLER-MOTTE TECHNICAL COLLEGE (COLUMBUS)**
1800 Box Rd.
Columbus, GA 31907
Tel: (706)225-5002; Free: 800-705-9182
Web Site: www.miller-motte.edu
Description: Proprietary, 2-year, coed. Awards certificates, transfer associate, and terminal associate degrees.

■ **MILLER-MOTTE TECHNICAL COLLEGE (MACON)**
175 Tom Hill Sr. Blvd.
Macon, GA 31210
Tel: (478)803-4800; Free: 800-705-9182
Web Site: www.miller-motte.edu
Description: Proprietary, 2-year, coed. Awards certificates, transfer associate, and terminal associate degrees.

■ **MOREHOUSE COLLEGE**
830 Westview Dr., SW
Atlanta, GA 30314
Tel: (404)681-2800; Free: 800-851-1254
Fax: (404)659-6536
Web Site: www.morehouse.edu
Description: Independent, 4-year, men only. Awards bachelor's degrees. Founded 1867. Setting: 66-acre urban campus with easy access to Atlanta, Georgia. Total enrollment: 2,202. Faculty: 217 (169 full-time, 48 part-time). Student-undergrad faculty ratio is 12:1. 2,349 applied, 74% were admitted. 12% from top 10% of their high school class, 36% from top quarter, 66% from top half. Full-time: 2,090 students. Part-time: 112 students. Students come from 41 states and territories, 13 other countries, 72% from out-of-state. 0.2% American Indian or Alaska Native, non-Hispanic/Latino; 0.6% Hispanic/Latino; 94% Black or African American, non-Hispanic/Latino; 0.1% Asian, non-Hispanic/Latino; 1% international. 3% 25 or older, 61% live on campus, 3% transferred in. Retention: 84% of full-time freshmen returned the following year. Academic areas with the most degrees conferred: social sciences; business/marketing; biological/life sciences. Core. Calendar: semesters. Academic remediation for entering students, services for LD students, advanced placement, honors program, independent study, double major, summer session for credit, part-time degree program, co-op programs

and internships. Off campus study at Atlanta University Center (AUC); Clark Atlanta University, Spelman College. Study abroad program. ROTC: Army, Naval, Air Force (c).

Entrance Requirements: Options: electronic application, early admission, early decision, early action, deferred admission. Required: essay, high school transcript, interview, SAT or ACT. Recommended: minimum 3 high school GPA, SAT and SAT Subject Tests or ACT. Entrance: moderately difficult. Application deadlines: 2/1, 11/1 for early action. Notification: 3/15, 12/15 for early action. SAT Reasoning Test deadline: 2/15. SAT Subject Test deadline: 2/15. Transfer credits accepted: Yes. Applicants placed on waiting list: 112. Wait-listed applicants offered admission: 57. Early decision applicants: 61. Early decision applicants admitted: 61. Early action applicants: 616.

Costs Per Year: Application fee: $50. Comprehensive fee: $41,012 includes full-time tuition ($25,368), mandatory fees ($2206), and college room and board ($13,438). College room only: $7510. Full-time tuition and fees vary according to course load. Room and board charges vary according to board plan and housing facility. Part-time tuition: $1046 per credit hour. Part-time tuition varies according to course load.

Collegiate Environment: Orientation program. Drama-theater group, choral group, marching band, student-run newspaper. Social organizations: national fraternities; 3% of eligible undergrads are members. Most popular organizations: Morehouse College Glee Club, Morehouse Business Association, SGA, Morehouse Public Health Association, Pre-Law Society. Major annual events: Homecoming, Founders' Week, Commencement/Reunion. Student services: health clinic, personal-psychological counseling. Campus security: 24-hour patrols, late night transport-escort service, controlled dormitory access, emergency call boxes, safety tips and awareness training. Atlanta University Center Robert R. Woodruff Library. Students can reserve study rooms. 1,158 computers available on campus for general student use. A campuswide network can be accessed from student residence rooms and from off campus. Students can access the following: online class registration, on-campus computer repair service, computer helpline. Staffed computer lab on campus (open 24 hours a day) provides training in use of computers, software, and the Internet.

Community Environment: See Clark Atlanta University.

■ **NORTH GEORGIA TECHNICAL COLLEGE**
1500 Georgia Hwy. 197, N
Clarkesville, GA 30523
Tel: (706)754-7700
Fax: (706)754-7777
Web Site: www.northgatech.edu
Description: State-supported, 2-year, coed. Part of Technical College System of Georgia. Awards certificates, diplomas, and terminal associate degrees. Founded 1943. Total enrollment: 2,838. Full-time: 918 students, 52% women, 48% men. Part-time: 1,920 students, 64% women, 36% men. 1% from out-of-state. 0.5% American Indian or Alaska Native, non-Hispanic/Latino; 5% Hispanic/Latino; 8% Black or African American, non-Hispanic/Latino; 1% Asian, non-Hispanic/Latino; 0.1% Native Hawaiian or other Pacific Islander, non-Hispanic/Latino. Retention: 61% of full-time freshmen returned the following year. Calendar: quarters. Distance learning.

Entrance Requirements: Open admission selective admission to some programs. Option: early admission. Required: high school transcript. Entrance: noncompetitive.

■ **OCONEE FALL LINE TECHNICAL COLLEGE**
1189 Deepstep Rd.
Sandersville, GA 31082
Tel: (478)553-2050; Free: 877-399-8324
Fax: (478)553-2118
Web Site: www.oftc.edu
Description: State-supported, 2-year, coed. Part of Technical College System of Georgia. Awards certificates, diplomas, and terminal associate degrees. Total enrollment: 1,404. Full-time: 362 students, 65% women, 35% men. Part-time: 1,042 students, 62% women, 38% men. 0.1% American Indian or Alaska Native, non-Hispanic/Latino; 2% Hispanic/Latino; 45% Black or African American, non-Hispanic/Latino; 0.5% Asian, non-Hispanic/Latino. Retention: 52% of full-time freshmen returned the following year. Calendar: quarters. Distance learning.

Entrance Requirements: Open admission selective admission to some programs. Option: early admission. Required: high school transcript. Entrance: noncompetitive.

■ OGEECHEE TECHNICAL COLLEGE

One Joe Kennedy Blvd.
Statesboro, GA 30458
Tel: (912)681-5500; Free: 800-646-1316
Web Site: www.ogeecheetech.edu
Description: State-supported, 2-year, coed. Part of Technical College System of Georgia. Awards certificates, diplomas, and terminal associate degrees. Founded 1989. Setting: small town campus. Total enrollment: 1,904. Full-time: 732 students, 67% women, 33% men. Part-time: 1,172 students, 69% women, 31% men. 1% from out-of-state. 0.2% American Indian or Alaska Native, non-Hispanic/Latino; 4% Hispanic/Latino; 33% Black or African American, non-Hispanic/Latino; 0.5% Asian, non-Hispanic/Latino; 0.2% Native Hawaiian or other Pacific Islander, non-Hispanic/Latino. Retention: 58% of full-time freshmen returned the following year. Calendar: quarters. Distance learning.
Entrance Requirements: Open admission selective admission to some programs. Option: early admission. Required: high school transcript. Entrance: noncompetitive.

■ OGLETHORPE UNIVERSITY

4484 Peachtree Rd., NE
Atlanta, GA 30319-2797
Tel: (404)261-1441; Free: 800-428-4484
Fax: (404)364-8500
E-mail: lleusch@oglethorpe.edu
Web Site: www.oglethorpe.edu
Description: Independent, 4-year, coed. Awards bachelor's degrees. Founded 1835. Setting: 102-acre suburban campus with easy access to Atlanta. Endowment: $33.9 million. Educational spending for the previous fiscal year: $7304 per student. Total enrollment: 1,264. Faculty: 115 (65 full-time, 50 part-time). 2,203 applied, 62% were admitted. 23% from top 10% of their high school class, 47% from top quarter, 85% from top half. Full-time: 1,212 students, 58% women, 42% men. Part-time: 52 students, 44% women, 56% men. Students come from 34 states and territories, 28 other countries, 21% from out-of-state. 0.8% American Indian or Alaska Native, non-Hispanic/Latino; 11% Hispanic/Latino; 24% Black or African American, non-Hispanic/Latino; 5% Asian, non-Hispanic/Latino; 0.1% Native Hawaiian or other Pacific Islander, non-Hispanic/Latino; 9% international. 8% 25 or older, 53% live on campus. Retention: 80% of full-time freshmen returned the following year. Academic areas with the most degrees conferred: business/marketing; social sciences; English. Core. Calendar: semesters. Services for LD students, advanced placement, accelerated degree program, self-designed majors, honors program, independent study, double major, summer session for credit, part-time degree program, adult/continuing education programs, co-op programs and internships. Off campus study at Atlanta Regional Consortium for Higher Education, 19 colleges and universities in the Atlanta area. Study abroad program. ROTC: Army (c), Naval (c), Air Force (c).
Entrance Requirements: Options: electronic application, early admission, early action, deferred admission, international baccalaureate accepted. Required: essay, high school transcript, 1 recommendation, SAT or ACT. Recommended: minimum 2.5 high school GPA, interview. Entrance: very difficult. Application deadlines: rolling, rolling for nonresidents. Notification: continuous. Transfer credits accepted: Yes.
Costs Per Year: Application fee: $50. Comprehensive fee: $53,510 includes full-time tuition ($39,580), mandatory fees ($530), and college room and board ($13,400). Part-time tuition: $1647 per credit hour.
Collegiate Environment: Orientation program. Drama-theater group, choral group, student-run newspaper. Social organizations: 43 open to all; national fraternities, national sororities, local sororities; 22% of eligible men and 18% of eligible women are members. Most popular organizations: SGA, Oglethorpe South Asian Club (OSAC), Historical Martial Arts (HMA), Oglethorpe Latinx Organization ((H)OLA), mOUthing Off Improv. Major annual events: Boar's Head, Dead Day's Eve, Quadfest. Student services: health clinic, personal-psychological counseling. Campus security: 24-hour emergency response devices and patrols, late night transport-escort service, controlled dormitory access. 764 college housing spaces available; 671 were occupied in 2018-19. Freshmen guaranteed college housing. On-campus residence required through sophomore year. Option: coed housing available. Philip Weltner Library. Books: 129,876 (physical), 936,821 (digital/electronic); Serial titles: 278 (physical), 27,589 (digital/electronic); Databases: 308. Weekly public service hours: 81; study areas open 24 hours, 5-7 days a week. Operations spending for the previous fiscal year: $399,534. 65 computers available on campus for general student use.

Computer purchase/lease plans available. A campuswide network can be accessed. Students can access the following: online class registration. Staffed computer lab on campus (open 24 hours a day) provides training in use of computers, software, and the Internet.
Community Environment: Oglethorpe students enjoy the scenic setting of a suburban campus combined with the opportunities of a great international city. Atlanta offers professional and amateur art and entertainment, professional and amateur sports, renowned intellectual and research activities, and world-class dining and enjoyment opportunities. It also offers small town values of friendliness, courtesy, and respect. Students can find part-time employment, internships, cultural activities, and an active job placement program, all of which are enhanced by the Atlanta location.

■ PAINE COLLEGE

1235 15th St.
Augusta, GA 30901-3182
Tel: (706)821-8200; Free: 800-476-7703
Fax: (706)821-8293
E-mail: rwoodson@paine.edu
Web Site: www.paine.edu
Description: Independent Methodist, 4-year, coed. Awards bachelor's degrees. Founded 1882. Setting: 65-acre urban campus with easy access to Columbia, SC. Endowment: $8.4 million. Educational spending for the previous fiscal year: $5991 per student. Total enrollment: 502. Faculty: 47 (31 full-time, 16 part-time). Student-undergrad faculty ratio is 10:1. 3,964 applied, 25% were admitted. Students come from 18 states and territories, 7 other countries, 17% from out-of-state. 0.6% American Indian or Alaska Native, non-Hispanic/Latino; 2% Hispanic/Latino; 77% Black or African American, non-Hispanic/Latino; 0.2% Asian, non-Hispanic/Latino; 2% international. 5% 25 or older, 42% live on campus. Retention: 35% of full-time freshmen returned the following year. Academic areas with the most degrees conferred: social sciences; business/marketing; communication/journalism. Core. Calendar: semesters. Academic remediation for entering students, services for LD students, advanced placement, accelerated degree program, honors program, independent study, distance learning, double major, summer session for credit, part-time degree program, adult/continuing education programs, internships. Off campus study. Study abroad program. ROTC: Army (c).
Entrance Requirements: Options: electronic application, early admission, deferred admission. Required: high school transcript, minimum 2 high school GPA, 2 recommendations, SAT or ACT. Required for some: score of 500 on each Georgia high school exit exam. Entrance: minimally difficult. Application deadline: 7/1. Notification: continuous, continuous for nonresidents. SAT Reasoning Test deadline: 7/1. SAT Subject Test deadline: 7/1. Transfer credits accepted: Yes.
Costs Per Year: Application fee: $25. Comprehensive fee: $22,757 includes full-time tuition ($14,205), mandatory fees ($1890), and college room and board ($6662). College room only: $3526. Full-time tuition and fees vary according to class time and course load. Room and board charges vary according to housing facility. Part-time tuition: $527 per credit hour. Part-time tuition varies according to class time and course load.
Collegiate Environment: Orientation program. Drama-theater group, choral group, student-run newspaper. Social organizations: 10 open to all; national fraternities, national sororities; 5% of eligible men and 3% of eligible women are members. Most popular organizations: Wesley Fellowship, Alpha Kappa Mu National Honor Society, International Student Association, National Association for the Advancement of Colored People, Creme de la Creme Models. Major annual events: Homecoming, Conference on the Black Experience, Harlem Renaissance. Student services: personal-psychological counseling. Campus security: 24-hour emergency response devices and patrols, late night transport-escort service. Collins-Callaway Library. Books: 70,791 (physical), 137,762 (digital/electronic); Serial titles: 205 (physical). Weekly public service hours: 83; students can reserve study rooms. Operations spending for the previous fiscal year: $209,485. 130 computers available on campus for general student use. A campuswide network can be accessed from student residence rooms and from off campus. Students can access the following: online class registration. Staffed computer lab on campus provides training in use of computers, software, and the Internet.
Community Environment: Augusta, located on the Savannah River in east central Georgia, is a river port and industrial center, and is the third leading producer of clay products in the southeast. All forms of transportation are available. Recreational facilities include lakes for fishing, boating and hunting, golf courses, horseback riding, and polo. The famous Augusta National Golf Club course, home of the Masters Golf Tournament, is located here.

Some of the points of interest are the Mackay Trading Post, Meadow Garden, Fort Augusta, Confederate Monument, New Savannah Bluff Lock and Dam System, churches of historic interest, and two large enclosed shopping malls, one of which is the largest in Georgia.

■ PIEDMONT COLLEGE
1021 Central Ave.
Demorest, GA 30535
Tel: (706)778-3000; Free: 800-277-7020
Fax: (706)776-6635
E-mail: bboonstra@piedmont.edu
Web Site: www.piedmont.edu

Description: Independent, comprehensive, coed, affiliated with United Church of Christ. Awards bachelor's, master's, and doctoral degrees and post-master's certificates. Founded 1897. Setting: 186-acre rural campus with easy access to Atlanta. Endowment: $53 million. Educational spending for the previous fiscal year: $8227 per student. Total enrollment: 2,490. Faculty: 293 (134 full-time, 159 part-time). Student-undergrad faculty ratio is 10:1. 1,379 applied, 60% were admitted. 6% from top 10% of their high school class, 28% from top quarter, 67% from top half. Full-time: 1,153 students, 65% women, 35% men. Part-time: 109 students, 70% women, 30% men. Students come from 24 states and territories, 8 other countries, 7% from out-of-state. 0.4% American Indian or Alaska Native, non-Hispanic/Latino; 6% Hispanic/Latino; 11% Black or African American, non-Hispanic/Latino; 1% Asian, non-Hispanic/Latino; 0.1% Native Hawaiian or other Pacific Islander, non-Hispanic/Latino; 0.8% international. 18% 25 or older, 74% live on campus, 9% transferred in. Retention: 61% of full-time freshmen returned the following year. Academic areas with the most degrees conferred: health professions and related sciences; education; business/marketing. Core. Calendar: semesters. Services for LD students, advanced placement, accelerated degree program, self-designed majors, honors program, independent study, distance learning, double major, summer session for credit, part-time degree program, adult/continuing education programs, co-op programs and internships, graduate courses open to undergrads. Off campus study at Piedmont College, Athens, GA. Study abroad program.

Entrance Requirements: Options: electronic application, early admission, deferred admission, international baccalaureate accepted. Required: high school transcript, SAT or ACT. Recommended: essay. Required for some: interview. Entrance: moderately difficult. SAT Reasoning Test deadline: 7/15. Transfer credits accepted: Yes.

Costs Per Year: Application fee: $0. Comprehensive fee: $37,216 includes full-time tuition ($26,492), mandatory fees ($200), and college room and board ($10,524). Part-time tuition: $1011 per credit hour. Part-time mandatory fees: $100 per term.

Collegiate Environment: Orientation program. Drama-theater group, choral group, student-run newspaper, radio station. Social organizations: 42 open to all; 2% of eligible men and 7% of eligible women are members. Most popular organizations: Campus Activity Board, Student Government Association, Team Piedmont, National Society of Leadership and Success, American Marketing Association-Piedmont Chapter. Major annual events: Welcome Week, Spring Formal, Stress Less Week/Late Night Breakfast. Student services: personal-psychological counseling. Campus security: 24-hour emergency response devices and patrols, late night transport-escort service. 769 college housing spaces available; 703 were occupied in 2018-19. Freshmen guaranteed college housing. On-campus residence required through sophomore year. Options: coed, men-only, women-only housing available. Arrendale Library plus 2 others. Books: 85,631 (physical), 766,654 (digital/electronic); Serial titles: 76 (physical); Databases: 197. Students can reserve study rooms. Operations spending for the previous fiscal year: $607,770. 225 computers available on campus for general student use. A campuswide network can be accessed from student residence rooms and from off campus. Students can access the following: online class registration. Staffed computer lab on campus.

Community Environment: Demorest, located in Habersham County in the northeastern corner of Georgia, is in the foothills of the southern Blue Ridge Mountains. The climate is considered unusually healthful. Buses serve the area with rail service in Toccoa, eighteen miles away and Hartfield International Airport in Atlanta, 75 miles southwest by major highway.

■ POINT UNIVERSITY
507 W 10th St.
West Point, GA 31833
Tel: (706)385-1000; Free: 855-37-POINT

E-mail: admissions@point.edu
Web Site: point.edu

Description: Independent Christian, comprehensive, coed. Awards associate, bachelor's, and master's degrees. Founded 1937. Setting: small town campus with easy access to Atlanta, GA and Montgomery, AL. Total enrollment: 2,248. Faculty: 183 (45 full-time, 138 part-time). Student-undergrad faculty ratio is 15:1. 1,228 applied, 53% were admitted. 9% from top 10% of their high school class, 22% from top quarter, 63% from top half. Full-time: 1,108 students, 53% women, 47% men. Part-time: 1,105 students, 57% women, 43% men. Students come from 29 states and territories, 19 other countries, 28% from out-of-state. 0.5% American Indian or Alaska Native, non-Hispanic/Latino; 5% Hispanic/Latino; 26% Black or African American, non-Hispanic/Latino; 2% Asian, non-Hispanic/Latino; 0.2% Native Hawaiian or other Pacific Islander, non-Hispanic/Latino; 2% international. 25% 25 or older, 56% live on campus, 6% transferred in. Retention: 50% of full-time freshmen returned the following year. Academic areas with the most degrees conferred: theology and religious vocations; business/marketing; psychology. Core. Calendar: semesters. Services for LD students, advanced placement, accelerated degree program, independent study, distance learning, double major, summer session for credit, part-time degree program, adult/continuing education programs, graduate courses open to undergrads.

Entrance Requirements: Options: electronic application, deferred admission, international baccalaureate accepted. Required: high school transcript, minimum 2 high school GPA, 1 recommendation. Required for some: essay, college transcript if applicable. Entrance: moderately difficult. Notification: continuous. SAT Reasoning Test deadline: 8/1. SAT Subject Test deadline: 8/1. Transfer credits accepted: Yes.

Costs Per Year: Application fee: $0. Comprehensive fee: $29,285 includes full-time tuition ($20,085), mandatory fees ($1200), and college room and board ($8000). College room only: $4000. Part-time tuition: $650 per credit hour.

Collegiate Environment: Orientation program. Choral group, marching band. Social organizations: 11 open to all. Most popular organizations: Student Government Association, Community Concert Band, Campus Life Ministers, Campus Activities Board, Fellowship of Christian Athletes (FCA). Major annual events: Homecoming, Men's & Women's Weeks, Honors Chapel. Student services: personal-psychological counseling. Campus security: 24-hour patrols. 500 college housing spaces available; 369 were occupied in 2018-19. Freshmen guaranteed college housing. On-campus residence required through sophomore year. Options: men-only, women-only housing available. Point University Library plus 1 other. 115 computers available on campus for general student use. A campuswide network can be accessed from student residence rooms. Students can access the following: online class registration. Staffed computer lab on campus provides training in use of computers, software, and the Internet.

Community Environment: A suburban area with temperate climate, East Point is served by all major forms of transportation. Along with the usual community facilities, the opportunities are excellent for part-time employment.

■ REFORMED UNIVERSITY
1724 Atkinson Rd.
Lawrenceville, GA 30043
Description: Independent religious, comprehensive, coed.

■ REINHARDT UNIVERSITY
7300 Reinhardt Cir.
Waleska, GA 30183-2981
Tel: (770)720-5600
Fax: (770)720-5602
E-mail: lls@reinhardt.edu
Web Site: www.reinhardt.edu

Description: Independent, comprehensive, coed, affiliated with United Methodist Church. Awards associate, bachelor's, and master's degrees. Founded 1883. Setting: 600-acre rural campus with easy access to Atlanta. Total enrollment: 1,566. Faculty: (83 full-time). Student-undergrad faculty ratio is 12:1. 1,172 applied, 90% were admitted. Full-time: 1,307 students, 49% women, 51% men. Part-time: 166 students, 47% women, 53% men. 7% from out-of-state. 0.4% American Indian or Alaska Native, non-Hispanic/Latino; 8% Hispanic/Latino; 18% Black or African American, non-Hispanic/Latino; 1% Asian, non-Hispanic/Latino; 0.1% Native Hawaiian or other Pacific Islander, non-Hispanic/Latino; 0.1% international. 21% 25 or older, 47% live on campus, 7% transferred in. Retention: 60% of full-time freshmen returned the following year. Academic areas with the most degrees conferred: business/marketing; health professions and related sciences; homeland security, law enforcement, firefighting, and protective services. Core. Calendar: semesters. Academic remediation for entering students, services for LD students, advanced placement, self-designed majors, freshman honors college, honors program, independent study, distance learning, double major, summer session for credit, part-time degree program, adult/continuing education programs, co-op programs and internships. Off campus study. Study abroad program.

Entrance Requirements: Options: electronic application, early admission, deferred admission. Required: high school transcript, minimum 2 high school GPA, SAT or ACT. Entrance: moderately difficult. Transfer credits accepted: Yes.

Costs Per Year: Comprehensive fee: $34,800 includes full-time tuition ($23,300), mandatory fees ($1000), and college room and board ($10,500). Part-time tuition: $792 per credit hour.

Collegiate Environment: Orientation program. Drama-theater group, choral group, student-run newspaper. Student services: health clinic, personal-psychological counseling. Campus security: 24-hour emergency response devices and patrols, late night transport-escort service, controlled dormitory access. Freshmen guaranteed college housing. On-campus residence required in freshman year. Options: men-only, women-only housing available. Hill Freeman Library/Spruill Learning Center plus 1 other. Books: 61,496 (physical), 183,453 (digital/electronic); Serial titles: 52 (physical), 27,855 (digital/electronic); Databases: 167.

Community Environment: Waleska is located on the summit of a ridge, an hour's drive from metropolitan Atlanta. The high altitude assures a crisp, dry atmosphere and a year-round climate never excelled in its healthful and invigorating qualities. The picturesque southern foothills of the Blue Ridge Mountains surround Waleska.

■ **SAE INSTITUTE ATLANTA**
215 Peachtree St. NE
Atlanta, GA 30303
Tel: (404)526-9366
Fax: (404)526-9367
Web Site: www.sae.edu

Description: Proprietary, 2-year, coed. Awards diplomas, transfer associate, and terminal associate degrees.

■ **SAVANNAH COLLEGE OF ART AND DESIGN**
342 Bull St.
Savannah, GA 31402-3146
Tel: (912)525-5000; Free: 800-869-7223
Fax: (912)238-2436
E-mail: admission@scad.edu
Web Site: www.scad.edu

Description: Independent, comprehensive, coed. Awards bachelor's and master's degrees. Founded 1978. Setting: urban campus. Total enrollment: 14,832. Faculty: 726 (578 full-time, 148 part-time). Student-undergrad faculty ratio is 20:1. 14,797 applied, 72% were admitted. Full-time: 10,305 students, 69% women, 31% men. Part-time: 1,912 students, 64% women, 36% men. Students come from 53 states and territories, 111 other countries, 80% from out-of-state. 0.6% American Indian or Alaska Native, non-Hispanic/Latino; 7% Hispanic/Latino; 10% Black or African American, non-Hispanic/Latino; 5% Asian, non-Hispanic/Latino; 0.5% Native Hawaiian or other Pacific Islander, non-Hispanic/Latino; 22% international. 8% 25 or older, 44% live on campus, 5% transferred in. Retention: 85% of full-time freshmen returned the following year. Academic areas with the most degrees conferred: visual and performing arts; communication technologies; communication/journalism. Core. Calendar: quarters. ESL program, services for LD students, advanced placement, accelerated degree program, independent study, distance learning, double major, summer session for credit, part-time degree program, co-op programs and internships. Off campus study. Study abroad program.

Entrance Requirements: Options: electronic application, early admission, deferred admission, international baccalaureate accepted. Required: SAT or ACT, TOEFL scores are required for International students. Recommended: essay, interview. Required for some: essay, high school transcript, interview, portfolio/audition for performing arts, riding, writing, or visual arts. Entrance: moderately difficult. Application deadline: rolling. Notification: continuous. Transfer credits accepted: Yes.

Costs Per Year: Application fee: $40. One-time mandatory fee: $500. Comprehensive fee: $52,737 includes full-time tuition ($37,575) and college room and board ($15,162). College room only: $10,224. Part-time tuition: $4175 per course.

Collegiate Environment: Orientation program. Drama-theater group, choral group, student-run newspaper, radio station. Social organizations: 121 open to all. Major annual events: Sidewalk Arts Festival, Savannah Film Festival, Sand Arts Festival. Student services: health clinic, personal-psychological counseling. Campus security: 24-hour emergency response devices and patrols, late night transport-escort service, controlled dormitory access. 4,564 college housing spaces available; all were occupied in 2018-19. Freshmen given priority for college housing. Option: coed housing available. Jen Library plus 4 others. Books: 264,695 (physical), 215,544 (digital/electronic); Serial titles: 901 (physical), 50,630 (digital/electronic); Databases: 81. Weekly public service hours: 106; students can reserve study rooms. 3,464 computers available on campus for general student use. A campuswide network can be accessed from student residence rooms and from off campus. Students can access the following: online class registration. Staffed computer lab on campus (open 24 hours a day) provides training in use of computers, software, and the Internet.

Community Environment: The college is located in the downtown historic district of Savannah, Georgia, only minutes from Georgia's golden coast. The metropolitan area population is 313,000. Savannah is a popular tourist area, creating activities available to students throughout the year. Students enjoy new-age technology in an old-world evironment. A free campus bus service transports students to and from classes.

■ **SAVANNAH STATE UNIVERSITY**
3219 College St.
Savannah, GA 31404
Tel: (912)358-4778; Free: 800-788-0478
E-mail: potierd@savannahstate.edu
Web Site: www.savannahstate.edu

Description: State-supported, comprehensive, coed. Part of University System of Georgia. Awards associate, bachelor's, and master's degrees. Founded 1890. Setting: 173-acre suburban campus. Endowment: $5.4 million. Research spending for the previous fiscal year: $1.4 million. Educational spending for the previous fiscal year: $5390 per student. Total enrollment: 4,800. Faculty: 220 (191 full-time, 29 part-time). Student-undergrad faculty ratio is 21:1. 2,950 applied, 83% were admitted. Full-time: 4,062 students, 58% women, 42% men. Part-time: 583 students, 56% women, 44% men. Students come from 44 states and territories, 46 other countries, 7% from out-of-state. 0.3% American Indian or Alaska Native, non-Hispanic/Latino; 8% Hispanic/Latino; 82% Black or African American, non-Hispanic/Latino; 0.1% Asian, non-Hispanic/Latino; 0.1% Native Hawaiian or other Pacific Islander, non-Hispanic/Latino; 1% international. 9% 25 or older, 6% transferred in. Retention: 62% of full-time freshmen returned the following year. Academic areas with the most degrees conferred: business/marketing; biological/life sciences; homeland security, law enforcement, firefighting, and protective services. Core. Calendar: semesters. Academic remediation for entering students, ESL program, services for LD students, advanced placement, accelerated degree program, honors program, independent study, distance learning, double major, summer session for credit, part-time degree program, adult/continuing education programs, co-op programs and internships. Off campus study at Armstrong State University. Study abroad program. ROTC: Army, Naval.

Entrance Requirements: Options: electronic application, early admission, deferred admission, international baccalaureate accepted. Required: high school transcript, minimum 2.3 high school GPA, SAT or ACT. Recommended: SAT. Required for some: essay, interview, SAT Subject Tests. Entrance: minimally difficult. Application deadline: 7/15. Notification: continuous. SAT Reasoning Test deadline: 7/15. Transfer credits accepted: Yes.

Collegiate Environment: Orientation program. Drama-theater group, choral group, marching band, student-run newspaper, radio station. Social organizations: 62 open to all; national fraternities, national sororities, local fraternities, local sororities; 35% of eligible men and 38% of eligible women are members. Most popular organizations: Marching band, Wesleyan Gospel Choir, Residence Hall Association, Student Government Association, Tiger Ambassadors. Major annual events: Homecoming, Spring Fling Activities, Martin Luther King Observance Day. Student services: health clinic, personal-psychological counseling, women's center. Campus security: 24-hour emergency response devices and patrols, late night transport-escort service, controlled dormitory access. Asa H. Gordon Library. Books: 108,766 (physical), 185,056 (digital/electronic); Serial titles: 217 (physical), 2,000 (digital/electronic); Databases: 298. Weekly public service hours: 84. 200 computers available on campus for general student use. A campuswide network can be accessed from student residence rooms. Students can access the following: online class registration, free office software download, virtual computer lab, loaner laptops during semester. Staffed computer lab on campus provides training in use of computers, software, and the Internet. **Community Environment:** See Armstrong Atlantic State University.

■ SAVANNAH TECHNICAL COLLEGE

5717 White Bluff Rd.
Savannah, GA 31405
Tel: (912)443-5700; Free: 800-769-6362
Fax: (912)352-4362
Web Site: www.savannahtech.edu

Description: State-supported, 2-year, coed. Part of Technical College System of Georgia. Awards certificates, diplomas, and terminal associate degrees. Founded 1929. Setting: urban campus. Total enrollment: 3,938. Full-time: 1,393 students, 52% women, 48% men. Part-time: 2,545 students, 65% women, 35% men. 2% from out-of-state. 0.5% American Indian or Alaska Native, non-Hispanic/Latino; 7% Hispanic/Latino; 45% Black or African American, non-Hispanic/Latino; 3% Asian, non-Hispanic/Latino; 0.2% Native Hawaiian or other Pacific Islander, non-Hispanic/Latino. Retention: 60% of full-time freshmen returned the following year. Calendar: quarters. Distance learning.

Entrance Requirements: Open admission selective admission to some programs. Option: early admission. Required: high school transcript. Entrance: noncompetitive.

■ SHORTER UNIVERSITY

315 Shorter Ave.
Rome, GA 30165
Tel: (706)291-2121; Free: 800-868-6980
Fax: (706)236-1515
Web Site: www.shorter.edu

Description: Independent Baptist, comprehensive, coed. Awards associate, bachelor's, and master's degrees. Founded 1873. Setting: 155-acre small town campus with easy access to Atlanta. Endowment: $14.8 million. Educational spending for the previous fiscal year: $6323 per student. 1,820 applied, 61% were admitted. 12% from top 10% of their high school class, 34% from top quarter, 69% from top half. 54% live on campus. Retention: 53% of full-time freshmen returned the following year. Academic areas with the most degrees conferred: business/marketing; homeland security, law enforcement, firefighting, and protective services; parks and recreation. Core. Calendar: semesters. Academic remediation for entering students, services for LD students, advanced placement, self-designed majors, honors program, independent study, double major, summer session for credit, part-time degree program, adult/continuing education programs, internships. Off campus study at Berry College. Study abroad program.

Entrance Requirements: Options: electronic application, early admission, deferred admission. Required: essay, high school transcript, SAT or ACT. Recommended: minimum 2 high school GPA, 1 recommendation, interview. Required for some: interview, audition for music and theater programs. Entrance: moderately difficult. Application deadline: 8/25. Notification: continuous. SAT Reasoning Test deadline: 8/11. Transfer credits accepted: Yes.

Costs Per Year: Application fee: $25. Comprehensive fee: $31,770 includes full-time tuition ($21,940), mandatory fees ($430), and college room and board ($9400). College room only: $5000. Full-time tuition and fees vary according to course load, location, and program. Room and board charges vary according to board plan and housing facility. Part-time tuition: $550 per credit hour. Part-time mandatory fees: $8 per credit hour. Part-time tuition and fees vary according to location and program.

Collegiate Environment: Orientation program. Drama-theater group, choral group, marching band, student-run newspaper, radio station. Social organizations: 15 open to all; national fraternities, national sororities, local sororities; 9% of eligible men and 23% of eligible women are members. Most popular organizations: Baptist Collegiate Ministries, Student Government Association, Fellowship of Christian Athletes, Habitat for Humanity, SAVE (Students Advocating Volunteer Efforts). Major annual events: Celebrate Shorter, Midnight Breakfast and Welcome Week, Convocation. Student services: health clinic, personal-psychological counseling. Campus security: 24-hour emergency response devices and patrols. Livingston Library. Books: 118,322 (physical), 575,620 (digital/electronic); Serial titles: 1,183 (physical), 117,578 (digital/electronic); Databases: 233. Students can reserve study rooms. Operations spending for the previous fiscal year: $551,719. 100 computers available on campus for general student use. A campuswide network can be accessed from student residence rooms. Students can ac-

cess the following: online class registration. Staffed computer lab on campus (open 24 hours a day) provides training in use of computers, software, and the Internet.

■ SOUTH GEORGIA STATE COLLEGE

100 W College Park Dr.
Douglas, GA 31533-5098
Tel: (912)260-4200; Free: 800-342-6364
Fax: (912)389-4392
Web Site: www.sgc.edu

Description: State-supported, primarily 2-year, coed. Part of University System of Georgia. Awards transfer associate and bachelor's degrees. Founded 1906. Setting: 340-acre small town campus. Endowment: $286,240. Educational spending for the previous fiscal year: $2507 per student. Total enrollment: 2,579. Faculty: 115 (61 full-time, 54 part-time). Student-undergrad faculty ratio is 27:1. Full-time: 1,877 students, 59% women, 41% men. Part-time: 702 students, 68% women, 32% men. Students come from 17 states and territories, 2 other countries, 5% from out-of-state. 0.4% American Indian or Alaska Native, non-Hispanic/Latino; 4% Hispanic/Latino; 32% Black or African American, non-Hispanic/Latino; 0.8% Asian, non-Hispanic/Latino; 0.1% Native Hawaiian or other Pacific Islander, non-Hispanic/Latino; 0.2% international. 19% 25 or older, 13% live on campus, 5% transferred in. Core. Calendar: semesters. Academic remediation for entering students, services for LD students, advanced placement, distance learning, double major, summer session for credit, part-time degree program, adult/continuing education programs. Study abroad program.

Entrance Requirements: Options: electronic application, early admission, deferred admission. Required: high school transcript. Entrance: minimally difficult. Application deadline: rolling. Notification: continuous. Transfer credits accepted: Yes.

Collegiate Environment: Orientation program. Drama-theater group, choral group, student-run newspaper. Social organizations: 28 open to all. Most popular organizations: Intramural Sports, Cultural Exchange Club, Georgia Association of Nursing Students, Student Government Association, Phi Theta Kappa Honors Society. Major annual events: Week of Welcome, Hawk Fest, Spring Fling. Student services: personal-psychological counseling. Campus security: 24-hour emergency response devices and patrols, controlled dormitory access. William S. Smith Library plus 1 other.

Community Environment: Douglas is situated in the southern part of Georgia; having a delightful climate, winters are mild, and the summers pleasant. This community is one of the largest tobacco markets in the South. Livestock, poultry, naval stores, light industry, and the manufacture of mobile homes. Part-time employment is available for students. The community facilities include churches of all denominations, regional library, hospital, community concert association. Recreational facilities are the golf course, recreation center, tennis courts, pools, etc.

■ SOUTH GEORGIA TECHNICAL COLLEGE

900 S Georgia Tech Pky.
Americus, GA 31709
Tel: (229)931-2394
Fax: (229)931-2459
Web Site: www.southgatech.edu

Description: State-supported, 2-year, coed. Part of Technical College System of Georgia. Awards certificates, diplomas, and terminal associate degrees. Founded 1948. Total enrollment: 1,829. Full-time: 917 students, 48% women, 52% men. Part-time: 912 students, 57% women, 43% men. 4% from out-of-state. 0.1% American Indian or Alaska Native, non-Hispanic/Latino; 3% Hispanic/Latino; 54% Black or African American, non-Hispanic/Latino; 0.5% Asian, non-Hispanic/Latino. Retention: 64% of full-time freshmen returned the following year. Calendar: quarters. Distance learning.

Entrance Requirements: Open admission selective admission to some programs. Option: early admission. Required: high school transcript. Entrance: noncompetitive.

■ SOUTH UNIVERSITY

709 Mall Blvd.
Savannah, GA 31406
Tel: (912)201-8000; Free: 866-629-2901
Fax: (912)201-8070
Web Site: www.southuniversity.edu/savannah

Description: Independent, comprehensive, coed. Part of Education

Management Corporation. Awards associate, bachelor's, master's, and doctoral degrees and post-master's certificates. Founded 1899. Calendar: quarters.

■ **SOUTHEASTERN TECHNICAL COLLEGE**
3001 E First St.
Vidalia, GA 30474
Tel: (912)538-3100
Fax: (912)538-3156
Web Site: www.southeasterntech.edu
Description: State-supported, 2-year, coed. Part of Technical College System of Georgia. Awards certificates, diplomas, and terminal associate degrees. Founded 1989. Total enrollment: 1,563. Full-time: 435 students, 70% women, 30% men. Part-time: 1,128 students, 73% women, 27% men. 0.1% from out-of-state. 8% Hispanic/Latino; 27% Black or African American, non-Hispanic/Latino; 0.2% Asian, non-Hispanic/Latino. Retention: 53% of full-time freshmen returned the following year. Calendar: quarters. Distance learning.
Entrance Requirements: Open admission selective admission to some programs. Option: early admission. Required: high school transcript. Entrance: noncompetitive.

■ **SOUTHERN CRESCENT TECHNICAL COLLEGE**
501 Varsity Rd.
Griffin, GA 30223
Tel: (770)228-7348
Fax: (770)229-3227
Web Site: www.sctech.edu
Description: State-supported, 2-year, coed. Part of Technical College System of Georgia. Awards certificates, diplomas, and terminal associate degrees. Founded 1965. Setting: small town campus. Total enrollment: 4,703. Full-time: 1,601 students, 60% women, 40% men. Part-time: 3,102 students, 69% women, 31% men. 0.1% from out-of-state. 0.2% American Indian or Alaska Native, non-Hispanic/Latino; 5% Hispanic/Latino; 44% Black or African American, non-Hispanic/Latino; 1% Asian, non-Hispanic/Latino. Retention: 58% of full-time freshmen returned the following year. Calendar: quarters. Distance learning.
Entrance Requirements: Open admission selective admission to some programs. Option: early admission. Required: high school transcript. Entrance: noncompetitive.
Collegiate Environment: Griffin Technical College Library.

■ **SOUTHERN REGIONAL TECHNICAL COLLEGE**
15689 US 19 N
Thomasville, GA 31792
Tel: (229)225-4096
Fax: (229)225-4330
Web Site: www.southwestgatech.edu
Description: State-supported, 2-year, coed. Part of Technical College System of Georgia. Awards certificates, diplomas, and terminal associate degrees. Founded 1963. Total enrollment: 3,521. Full-time: 1,164 students, 71% women, 29% men. Part-time: 2,357 students, 62% women, 38% men. 1% from out-of-state. 0.3% American Indian or Alaska Native, non-Hispanic/Latino; 6% Hispanic/Latino; 33% Black or African American, non-Hispanic/Latino; 0.4% Asian, non-Hispanic/Latino. Retention: 61% of full-time freshmen returned the following year. Calendar: quarters. Distance learning.
Entrance Requirements: Open admission selective admission to some programs. Options: electronic application, early admission. Required: high school transcript. Entrance: noncompetitive.

■ **SPELMAN COLLEGE**
350 Spelman Ln., SW
Atlanta, GA 30314-4399
Tel: (404)681-3643; Free: 800-982-2411
Fax: (404)215-7788
E-mail: admiss@spelman.edu
Web Site: www.spelman.edu
Description: Independent, 4-year, women only. Awards bachelor's degrees. Founded 1881. Setting: 39-acre urban campus with easy access to Atlanta. Endowment: $367.9 million. Research spending for the previous fiscal year: $5.7 million. Educational spending for the previous fiscal year: $14,456 per student. Total enrollment: 2,137. Faculty: 241 (173 full-time, 68 part-time). Student-undergrad faculty ratio is 11:1. 8,344 applied, 40% were admitted. 26% from top 10% of their high school class, 53% from top quarter, 89%

from top half. Full-time: 2,086 students. Part-time: 51 students. Students come from 42 states and territories, 9 other countries, 72% from out-of-state. 2% American Indian or Alaska Native, non-Hispanic/Latino; 0.1% Hispanic/Latino; 97% Black or African American, non-Hispanic/Latino; 0.8% international. 1% 25 or older, 67% live on campus, 2% transferred in. Retention: 89% of full-time freshmen returned the following year. Academic areas with the most degrees conferred: social sciences; psychology; biological/life sciences. Core. Calendar: semesters. Services for LD students, advanced placement, self-designed majors, honors program, independent study, double major, part-time degree program, adult/continuing education programs, co-op programs and internships. Off campus study at Atlanta University Center Consortium, Council on International Educational Exchange, Institute for the International Education Studies, Atlanta Regional Consortia for Higher Education (ARCHE), Associated Colleges of the South (ACS), Georgia Independent College Association, Pitzer College International and Domestic Exchange. Study abroad program. ROTC: Army (c), Naval (c), Air Force (c).
Entrance Requirements: Options: electronic application, early admission, early decision, early action, deferred admission, international baccalaureate accepted. Required: essay, high school transcript, minimum 2 high school GPA, 2 recommendations, SAT or ACT. Required for some: SAT and SAT Subject Tests or ACT. Entrance: very difficult. Application deadlines: 2/1, 11/1 for early decision, 11/15 for early action. Notification: 4/1, 12/15 for early decision, 12/31 for early action. SAT Reasoning Test deadline: 2/1. Transfer credits accepted: Yes. Applicants placed on waiting list: 546. Wait-listed applicants offered admission: 20. Early decision applicants: 292. Early decision applicants admitted: 105. Early action applicants: 2,832. Early action applicants admitted: 1,647.
Costs Per Year: Application fee: $40. One-time mandatory fee: $250. Comprehensive fee: $42,929 includes full-time tuition ($25,151), mandatory fees ($3913), and college room and board ($13,865). College room only: $8128. Part-time tuition: $1040 per credit hour. Part-time mandatory fees: $1,457 per term.
Collegiate Environment: Orientation program. Drama-theater group, choral group, student-run newspaper. Social organizations: 86 open to all; national sororities; 6% of eligible undergrads are members. Most popular organizations: Glee Club, Theater Program, Student Government, Honors Program, Religious Groups. Major annual events: Founder's Day, Spelman-Morehouse Homecoming, Research Day. Student services: health clinic, personal-psychological counseling, women's center. Campus security: 24-hour emergency response devices and patrols, late night transport-escort service, controlled dormitory access, lighted pathways/sidewalks. Robert Woodruff Library plus 1 other. Books: 489,081 (physical), 139,636 (digital/electronic); Serial titles: 987 (physical), 122,146 (digital/electronic); Databases: 317. Weekly public service hours: 95; students can reserve study rooms. Operations spending for the previous fiscal year: $2.6 million. 700 computers available on campus for general student use. A campuswide network can be accessed from student residence rooms and from off campus. Students can access the following: online class registration. Staffed computer lab on campus (open 24 hours a day) provides training in use of computers, software, and the Internet.
Community Environment: See Clark Atlanta University.

■ **STRAYER UNIVERSITY-AUGUSTA CAMPUS**
1330 Augusta W Pky.
Augusta, GA 30909
Tel: (706)855-8233; Free: 888-311-0355
Web Site: www.strayer.edu
Description: Proprietary, comprehensive, coed. Awards associate, bachelor's, and master's degrees.

■ **STRAYER UNIVERSITY-CHAMBLEE CAMPUS**
3355 NE Expy.
Ste. 100
Atlanta, GA 30341
Tel: (770)454-9270; Free: 888-311-0355
Web Site: www.strayer.edu
Description: Proprietary, comprehensive, coed. Awards associate, bachelor's, and master's degrees.

■ **STRAYER UNIVERSITY-COBB COUNTY CAMPUS**
3101 Towercreek Pky., SE
Ste. 700
Atlanta, GA 30339

Tel: (770)612-2170; Free: 888-311-0355
Web Site: www.strayer.edu
Description: Proprietary, comprehensive, coed. Awards associate, bachelor's, and master's degrees.

■ **STRAYER UNIVERSITY-COLUMBUS CAMPUS**
408 12th St.
Ste. 102
Columbus, GA 31901
Tel: (706)225-5300; Free: 888-311-0355
Web Site: www.strayer.edu
Description: Proprietary, comprehensive, coed. Awards associate, bachelor's, and master's degrees.

■ **STRAYER UNIVERSITY-DOUGLASVILLE CAMPUS**
4655 Timber Ridge Dr.
Douglasville, GA 30135
Tel: (678)715-2200; Free: 888-311-0355
Web Site: www.strayer.edu
Description: Proprietary, comprehensive, coed. Awards associate, bachelor's, and master's degrees.

■ **STRAYER UNIVERSITY-LITHONIA CAMPUS**
3120 Stonecrest Blvd.
Ste. 200
Lithonia, GA 30038
Tel: (678)323-7700; Free: 888-311-0355
Web Site: www.strayer.edu
Description: Proprietary, comprehensive, coed. Awards associate, bachelor's, and master's degrees.

■ **STRAYER UNIVERSITY-MORROW CAMPUS**
3000 Corporate Ctr. Dr.
Ste. 100
Morrow, GA 30260
Tel: (678)422-4100; Free: 888-311-0355
Web Site: www.strayer.edu
Description: Proprietary, comprehensive, coed. Awards associate, bachelor's, and master's degrees.

■ **STRAYER UNIVERSITY-SAVANNAH CAMPUS**
8001 Chatham Ctr. Dr.
Ste. 300
Savannah, GA 31405
Tel: (912)921-2900; Free: 888-311-0355
Web Site: www.strayer.edu
Description: Proprietary, comprehensive, coed. Awards associate, bachelor's, and master's degrees.

■ **THOMAS UNIVERSITY**
1501 Millpond Rd.
Thomasville, GA 31792-7499
Tel: (229)226-1621; Free: 800-538-9784
E-mail: rgagliano@thomasu.edu
Web Site: www.thomasu.edu
Description: Independent, comprehensive, coed. Awards associate, bachelor's, and master's degrees and post-master's certificates. Founded 1950. Setting: 24-acre small town campus. Endowment: $4.2 million. Educational spending for the previous fiscal year: $13,286 per student. Total enrollment: 1,596. Faculty: 53 (51 full-time, 2 part-time). Student-undergrad faculty ratio is 6:1. 359 applied, 23% were admitted. Full-time: 438 students, 49% women, 51% men. Part-time: 676 students, 73% women, 27% men. Students come from 14 states and territories, 11 other countries, 35% from out-of-state. 9% live on campus, 34% transferred in. Core. Calendar: semesters. Academic remediation for entering students, services for LD students, advanced placement, accelerated degree program, independent study, distance learning, double major, summer session for credit, part-time degree program, adult/continuing education programs, co-op programs and internships. Study abroad program.
Entrance Requirements: Open admission. Options: electronic application, early admission, deferred admission, international baccalaureate accepted. Required: high school transcript. Entrance: minimally difficult. Application deadline: rolling. Notification: continuous.
Costs Per Year: Application fee: $25. Comprehensive fee: $23,980 includes

full-time tuition ($15,940), mandatory fees ($1000), and college room and board ($7040). College room only: $6000. Room and board charges vary according to housing facility. Part-time tuition: $630 per credit hour. Part-time mandatory fees: $550 per year.
Collegiate Environment: Orientation program. Drama-theater group, choral group, student-run newspaper. Social organizations: 7 open to all. Most popular organizations: Student Government Association, Professional Management Association, National Society for Leadership and Success. Major annual events: Homecoming, Fall Harvest Festival, Spring Fling. Student services: personal-psychological counseling. Campus security: late night transport-escort service, controlled dormitory access, evening security guards. Thomas University Library plus 1 other. Weekly public service hours: 60. 80 computers available on campus for general student use. A campuswide network can be accessed from student residence rooms and from off campus. Students can access the following: online class registration. Staffed computer lab on campus provides training in use of computers, software, and the Internet.

■ **TOCCOA FALLS COLLEGE**
107 Kincaid Dr.
Toccoa Falls, GA 30598
Tel: (706)886-6831; Free: 888-785-5624
Fax: (706)282-6012
E-mail: rstewart@tfc.edu
Web Site: www.tfc.edu
Description: Independent interdenominational, 4-year, coed. Awards associate and bachelor's degrees. Founded 1907. Setting: 1,100-acre small town campus with easy access to Atlanta, GA metro area. Endowment: $2.8 million. Educational spending for the previous fiscal year: $4823 per student. Total enrollment: 1,656. Faculty: 138 (47 full-time, 91 part-time). Student-undergrad faculty ratio is 15:1. 962 applied, 59% were admitted. 13% from top 10% of their high school class, 31% from top quarter, 64% from top half. Full-time: 890 students, 55% women, 45% men. Part-time: 766 students, 61% women, 39% men. Students come from 33 states and territories, 8 other countries, 35% from out-of-state. 0.2% American Indian or Alaska Native, non-Hispanic/Latino; 5% Hispanic/Latino; 11% Black or African American, non-Hispanic/Latino; 5% Asian, non-Hispanic/Latino; 0.1% Native Hawaiian or other Pacific Islander, non-Hispanic/Latino; 0.5% international. 18% 25 or older, 51% live on campus, 3% transferred in. Retention: 60% of full-time freshmen returned the following year. Academic areas with the most degrees conferred: theology and religious vocations; business/marketing; psychology. Core. Calendar: 4-1-4. Services for LD students, advanced placement, independent study, distance learning, double major, summer session for credit, part-time degree program, internships. Study abroad program.
Entrance Requirements: Options: electronic application, early admission, deferred admission, international baccalaureate accepted. Required: essay, high school transcript, minimum 2 high school GPA, 1 recommendation, SAT or ACT. Required for some: interview. Entrance: moderately difficult. Application deadline: rolling. Notification: continuous. SAT Reasoning Test deadline: 8/1. Transfer credits accepted: Yes.
Costs Per Year: Application fee: $30. Comprehensive fee: $31,680 includes full-time tuition ($22,414), mandatory fees ($770), and college room and board ($8496). Part-time tuition: $934. Part-time mandatory fees: $770 per year.
Collegiate Environment: Orientation program. Drama-theater group, choral group, student-run newspaper, radio station. Social organizations: 17 open to all. Most popular organizations: Outdoor Club, Hmong Student Fellowship, The Justice Campaign, Toccoa Falls for Life, Theatrical Society. Major annual events: Back to School Bash, Christmas Banquet, World Outreach Conference. Student services: health clinic, personal-psychological counseling. Campus security: student patrols. 588 college housing spaces available; 450 were occupied in 2018-19. Freshmen guaranteed college housing. On-campus residence required through junior year. Options: men-only, women-only housing available. Seby Jones Library plus 1 other. Books: 52,639 (physical), 719,908 (digital/electronic); Serial titles: 33 (physical), 73,000 (digital/electronic); Databases: 279. Weekly public service hours: 83; students can reserve study rooms. Operations spending for the previous fiscal year: $265,987. 47 computers available on campus for general student use. A campuswide network can be accessed from student residence rooms and from off campus. Students can access the following: online class registration. Staffed computer lab on campus.
Community Environment: Toccoa is in a rural area in the foothills of the Blue Ridge Mountains. The Southern Railway and Greyhound Bus provide

public transportation. Industries located here are the manufacturing of machinery, garments, furniture and thread. Toccoa has a municipal recreation center and golf course. Mountain lakes and resorts are within a short distance, providing fishing, hunting, water sports, and picnicking.

■ **TRUETT MCCONNELL UNIVERSITY**
100 Alumni Dr.
Cleveland, GA 30528
Tel: (706)865-2134; Free: 800-226-8621
Fax: (706)219-3339
Web Site: www.truett.edu
Description: Independent Baptist, comprehensive, coed. Awards bachelor's and master's degrees. Founded 1946. Setting: 200-acre rural campus with easy access to Atlanta. Total enrollment: 2,187. Faculty: (52 full-time). Student-undergrad faculty ratio is 15:1. 543 applied, 91% were admitted. 9% from top 10% of their high school class, 32% from top quarter, 60% from top half. Full-time: 740 students, 55% women, 45% men. Part-time: 1,412 students, 56% women, 44% men. Students come from 17 states and territories, 15 other countries, 9% from out-of-state. 0.1% American Indian or Alaska Native, non-Hispanic/Latino; 6% Hispanic/Latino; 8% Black or African American, non-Hispanic/Latino; 0.4% Asian, non-Hispanic/Latino; 2% international. 10% 25 or older, 2% transferred in. Retention: 63% of full-time freshmen returned the following year. Academic areas with the most degrees conferred: health professions and related sciences; theology and religious vocations; business/marketing. Core. Calendar: semesters. Academic remediation for entering students, services for LD students, advanced placement, accelerated degree program, distance learning, double major, summer session for credit.
Entrance Requirements: Options: electronic application, early admission, deferred admission. Required: high school transcript, minimum 2 high school GPA, SAT or ACT. Required for some: essay, 1 recommendation, interview. Entrance: minimally difficult. Application deadline: 8/1. Notification: continuous. Transfer credits accepted: Yes.
Costs Per Year: Application fee: $0. Comprehensive fee: $27,780 includes full-time tuition ($19,320), mandatory fees ($910), and college room and board ($7550). Full-time tuition and fees vary according to course load, degree level, location, and program. Room and board charges vary according to housing facility. Part-time tuition: $805 per credit hour. Part-time mandatory fees: $455 per term. Part-time tuition and fees vary according to course load, degree level, location, and program.
Collegiate Environment: Orientation program. Choral group. Campus security: 24-hour weekday patrols, 10-hour weekend patrols by trained security personnel. Cofer Library. 40 computers available on campus for general student use. A campuswide network can be accessed from student residence rooms. Students can access the following: online class registration.
Community Environment: Cleveland is in the mountains of north Georgia, a few miles south of the famous Vogel State Park. Bus service is available. The community, with its inspiring mountain scenery, provides a wholesome environment for young people. The Chattahoochee National Forest is 10 miles away.

■ **UNIVERSITY OF GEORGIA**
Athens, GA 30602
Tel: (706)542-3000
E-mail: admproc@uga.edu
Web Site: www.uga.edu
Description: State-supported, university, coed. Part of University System of Georgia. Awards bachelor's, master's, and doctoral degrees and post-master's certificates. Founded 1785. Setting: 767-acre suburban campus with easy access to Atlanta. Endowment: $1.3 billion. Research spending for the previous fiscal year: $432 million. Educational spending for the previous fiscal year: $9147 per student. Total enrollment: 38,652. Faculty: 2,371 (2,095 full-time, 276 part-time). Student-undergrad faculty ratio is 17:1. 26,027 applied, 49% were admitted. 60% from top 10% of their high school class, 92% from top quarter, 99% from top half. Full-time: 27,947 students, 57% women, 43% men. Part-time: 1,664 students, 50% women, 50% men. Students come from 52 states and territories, 124 other countries, 11% from out-of-state. 0.1% American Indian or Alaska Native, non-Hispanic/Latino; 6% Hispanic/Latino; 8% Black or African American, non-Hispanic/Latino; 10% Asian, non-Hispanic/Latino; 0.1% Native Hawaiian or other Pacific Islander, non-Hispanic/Latino; 1% international. 2% 25 or older, 34% live on campus, 5% transferred in. Retention: 95% of full-time freshmen returned the following year. Academic areas with the most degrees conferred:

business/marketing; biological/life sciences; communication/journalism. Core. Calendar: semesters. Academic remediation for entering students, services for LD students, advanced placement, accelerated degree program, self-designed majors, honors program, independent study, distance learning, double major, summer session for credit, part-time degree program, external degree program, adult/continuing education programs, co-op programs and internships, graduate courses open to undergrads. Off campus study at National Student Exchange. Study abroad program. ROTC: Army, Air Force.
Entrance Requirements: Options: electronic application, early admission, early action, deferred admission, international baccalaureate accepted. Required: high school transcript, counselor evaluation, SAT or ACT. Recommended: essay, minimum 2 high school GPA. Entrance: moderately difficult. Application deadlines: 1/8, 10/15 for early action. Notification: 4/1, 12/1 for early action. SAT Reasoning Test deadline: 1/15. SAT Subject Test deadline: 1/15. Transfer credits accepted: Yes. Applicants placed on waiting list: 1,257. Wait-listed applicants offered admission: 32. Early action applicants: 14,686. Early action applicants admitted: 9,436.
Costs Per Year: Application fee: $70. State resident tuition: $9552 full-time. Nonresident tuition: $28,126 full-time. Mandatory fees: $2278 full-time. Full-time tuition and fees vary according to course load, location, and program. College room and board: $10,038. College room only: $6042. Room and board charges vary according to board plan and housing facility.
Collegiate Environment: Orientation program. Drama-theater group, choral group, marching band, student-run newspaper, radio station. Social organizations: 765 open to all; national fraternities, national sororities, local fraternities, local sororities; 20% of eligible men and 31% of eligible women are members. Most popular organizations: Intramural Sports, Recreational sports program, Tate Movie Screening, University Union, Red Coat Band. Major annual events: Concerts at Legion Field, Homecoming, UGA Health Fair. Student services: legal services, health clinic, personal-psychological counseling, women's center. Campus security: 24-hour emergency response devices and patrols, late night transport-escort service, controlled dormitory access. 10,068 college housing spaces available; 9,928 were occupied in 2018-19. Freshmen guaranteed college housing. On-campus residence required in freshman year. Options: coed, women-only housing available. Ilah Dunlap Little Memorial Library plus 4 others. Books: 5.3 million (digital/electronic). Students can reserve study rooms. Operations spending for the previous fiscal year: $27.8 million.
Community Environment: Athens, the largest city in the rolling Piedmont area of northeast Georgia, is 70 miles northeast of Atlanta. Many of its building exemplify Greek Revival architecture characteristic of the Old South. It enjoys a mild climate, with an annual mean temperature of 60 degrees. Recreational facilities include parks, golf courses, swimming pools, tennis courts, baseball parks, a bowling center, and skating rinks, as well as areas for hunting, fishing and boating. Athens, serviced by buses and an airline, has numerous lodging accommodations and restaurants both in town and on campus. Its manufactured products include textiles, plastics, metals, electrical equipment, dairy products, and paper goods.

■ **UNIVERSITY OF NORTH GEORGIA**
82 College Cir.
Dahlonega, GA 30597
Tel: (706)864-1400; Free: 800-498-9581
Fax: (706)864-1478
E-mail: molly.potts@ung.edu
Web Site: www.ung.edu
Description: State-supported, comprehensive, coed. Part of University System of Georgia. Awards associate, bachelor's, master's, and doctoral degrees and post-master's certificates. Founded 1873. Setting: 1,077-acre small town campus with easy access to Atlanta. Endowment: $58.4 million. Research spending for the previous fiscal year: $1.7 million. Educational spending for the previous fiscal year: $4975 per student. Total enrollment: 18,782. Faculty: 984 (678 full-time, 306 part-time). Student-undergrad faculty ratio is 19:1. 4,392 applied. 23% from top 10% of their high school class, 62% from top quarter, 92% from top half. Full-time: 12,712 students, 56% women, 44% men. Part-time: 5,461 students, 57% women, 43% men. Students come from 46 states and territories, 96 other countries, 4% from out-of-state. 0.2% American Indian or Alaska Native, non-Hispanic/Latino; 12% Hispanic/Latino; 4% Black or African American, non-Hispanic/Latino; 3% Asian, non-Hispanic/Latino; 0.2% Native Hawaiian or other Pacific Islander, non-Hispanic/Latino; 2% international. 12% 25 or older, 22% live on campus, 3% transferred in. Retention: 81% of full-time freshmen returned the following year. Academic areas with the most degrees conferred: business/marketing; education; health professions and related sciences.

Core. Calendar: semesters. Academic remediation for entering students, ESL program, services for LD students, advanced placement, accelerated degree program, freshman honors college, honors program, independent study, distance learning, double major, summer session for credit, part-time degree program, co-op programs and internships. Study abroad program. ROTC: Army.

Entrance Requirements: Options: electronic application, early admission, international baccalaureate accepted. Required: high school transcript, minimum 2 high school GPA, proof of immunization, SAT or ACT. Entrance: moderately difficult. Application deadline: 7/1. Notification: continuous. SAT Reasoning Test deadline: 2/2. SAT Subject Test deadline: 7/1. Transfer credits accepted: Yes.

Costs Per Year: Application fee: $30. State resident tuition: $5460 full-time, $182 per credit hour part-time. Nonresident tuition: $19,272 full-time, $642.40 per credit hour part-time. Mandatory fees: $1876 full-time. Full-time tuition and fees vary according to course load, degree level, and location. Part-time tuition varies according to course load, degree level, and location. College room and board: $10,800. College room only: $5726. Room and board charges vary according to board plan and housing facility.

Collegiate Environment: Orientation program. Drama-theater group, choral group, marching band, student-run newspaper, radio station. Social organizations: 352 open to all; national fraternities, national sororities, local fraternities; 6% of eligible men and 10% of eligible women are members. Most popular organizations: Student Government Association, Commuter Council, Graduate Student Senate, Student Activities Board, Greek organizations. Major annual events: Parents'/Alumni Weekend, Homecoming, Fall Jam. Student services: health clinic, personal-psychological counseling. Campus security: 24-hour emergency response devices and patrols, late night transport-escort service, controlled dormitory access. Library Technology Center plus 4 others. Books: 195,525 (physical), 433,929 (digital/electronic); Serial titles: 168 (physical); Databases: 298. Weekly public service hours: 94; students can reserve study rooms. Operations spending for the previous fiscal year: $3.1 million. 3,500 computers available on campus for general student use. A campuswide network can be accessed from student residence rooms and from off campus. Students can access the following: online class registration. Staffed computer lab on campus provides training in use of computers, software, and the Internet.

■ **UNIVERSITY OF WEST GEORGIA**
1601 Maple St.
Carrollton, GA 30118
Tel: (678)839-5000
Web Site: www.westga.edu

Description: State-supported, comprehensive, coed. Part of University System of Georgia. Awards bachelor's, master's, and doctoral degrees and post-master's certificates. Founded 1933. Setting: 645-acre rural campus with easy access to Atlanta. System endowment: $32.6 million. Research spending for the previous fiscal year: $1.6 million. Educational spending for the previous fiscal year: $7213 per student. Total enrollment: 13,733. Faculty: 737 (459 full-time, 278 part-time). Student-undergrad faculty ratio is 20:1. 7,924 applied, 59% were admitted. Full-time: 8,728 students, 63% women, 37% men. Part-time: 2,407 students, 64% women, 36% men. Students come from 38 states and territories, 72 other countries, 7% from out-of-state. 0.1% American Indian or Alaska Native, non-Hispanic/Latino; 8% Hispanic/Latino; 37% Black or African American, non-Hispanic/Latino; 1% Asian, non-Hispanic/Latino; 0.2% Native Hawaiian or other Pacific Islander, non-Hispanic/Latino; 1% international. 10% 25 or older, 28% live on campus, 6% transferred in. Retention: 69% of full-time freshmen returned the following year. Academic areas with the most degrees conferred: business/marketing; social sciences; health professions and related sciences. Core. Calendar: semesters. Services for LD students, advanced placement, accelerated degree program, freshman honors college, honors program, independent study, distance learning, double major, summer session for credit, part-time degree program, external degree program, co-op programs and internships, graduate courses open to undergrads. Off campus study at UWG Newnan, UWG Douglasville, Georgia Highlands College, Piedmont-South Atlantic Coast Cooperative Ecosystem Studies Unit (PSAC-CESU), Atlanta Regional Council for Higher Education (ARCHE) Cross Registration members. Study abroad program. ROTC: Air Force (c).

Entrance Requirements: Options: electronic application, early admission, deferred admission, international baccalaureate accepted. Required: minimum 2.5 high school GPA, proof of immunization, SAT or ACT. Required for some: high school transcript. Entrance: moderately difficult. Application deadline: rolling. Notification: continuous. SAT Reasoning Test deadline: 6/1. Transfer credits accepted: Yes.

Costs Per Year: Application fee: $40. State resident tuition: $5330 full-time, $177.67 per semester hour part-time. Nonresident tuition: $18,812 full-time, $627.07 per semester hour part-time. Mandatory fees: $2024 full-time. College room and board: $10,488. College room only: $5600.

Collegiate Environment: Orientation program. Drama-theater group, choral group, marching band, student-run newspaper, radio station. Social organizations: 150 open to all; national fraternities, national sororities, local fraternities. Most popular organizations: Black Student Alliance, Student Activities Council, Baptist Collegiate Ministries, Campus Outreach, United Voices Gospel Choir. Major annual events: Homecoming, Annual Campus Awards Program, Welcome Back Blast. Student services: health clinic, personal-psychological counseling. Campus security: 24-hour emergency response devices and patrols, student patrols, late night transport-escort service, controlled dormitory access. 3,313 college housing spaces available; 3,160 were occupied in 2018-19. Freshmen guaranteed college housing. On-campus residence required in freshman year. Options: coed, women-only housing available. Irvine Sullivan Ingram Library plus 1 other. Weekly public service hours: 109; study areas open 24 hours, 5-7 days a week; students can reserve study rooms. Operations spending for the previous fiscal year: $4.5 million. 1,200 computers available on campus for general student use. A campuswide network can be accessed from student residence rooms and from off campus. Students can access the following: online class registration. Staffed computer lab on campus (open 24 hours a day) provides training in use of computers, software, and the Internet.

Community Environment: Located in northwest Georgia, 48 miles southwest of the state capital, Atlanta, Carrollton has a mild climate with an average temperature of 63 degrees. Part-time employment is available. The benefits of this unique area include a safe, peaceful small town atmosphere, offering educational excellence in a personal environment, within 45 minutes of the cultural and social diversities of Atlanta. Private housing is available.

■ **VALDOSTA STATE UNIVERSITY**
1500 N Patterson St.
Valdosta, GA 31698
Tel: (229)333-5800; Free: 800-618-1878
Fax: (229)333-5482
E-mail: admissions@valdosta.edu
Web Site: www.valdosta.edu

Description: State-supported, university, coed. Part of University System of Georgia. Awards associate, bachelor's, master's, and doctoral degrees and post-master's certificates. Founded 1906. Setting: 180-acre small town campus. Endowment: $7.5 million. Research spending for the previous fiscal year: $329,077. Educational spending for the previous fiscal year: $5965 per student. Total enrollment: 11,341. Faculty: 559 (419 full-time, 140 part-time). Student-undergrad faculty ratio is 20:1. 5,303 applied, 74% were admitted. Full-time: 7,166 students, 62% women, 38% men. Part-time: 1,612 students, 61% women, 39% men. Students come from 46 states and territories, 54 other countries, 14% from out-of-state. 0.2% American Indian or Alaska Native, non-Hispanic/Latino; 6% Hispanic/Latino; 38% Black or African American, non-Hispanic/Latino; 1% Asian, non-Hispanic/Latino; 0.1% Native Hawaiian or other Pacific Islander, non-Hispanic/Latino; 2% international. 16% 25 or older, 28% live on campus, 8% transferred in. Retention: 69% of full-time freshmen returned the following year. Academic areas with the most degrees conferred: business/marketing; health professions and related sciences; education. Core. Calendar: semesters. ESL program, services for LD students, advanced placement, accelerated degree program, honors program, independent study, distance learning, double major, summer session for credit, part-time degree program, external degree program, adult/continuing education programs, co-op programs and internships, graduate courses open to undergrads. Off campus study at Abraham Baldwin Agricultural/ABAC on the Square-Moultrie, Albany Technical, Altamaha Technical, Central Texas, Georgia Technical, Darton State, Georgia Military, Gwinnett Technical, Lanier Technical, Middle Georgia State, North Florida Community, Okefenokee Technical, Savannah Technical, South Georgia State, South Georgia Technical, SW Georgia RESA, SW Georgia Technical, Wiregrass Georgia Technical Colleges; Columbus State University, Community College of Air Force. Study abroad program. ROTC: Air Force.

Entrance Requirements: Options: electronic application, deferred admission, international baccalaureate accepted. Required: high school transcript, SAT or ACT. Entrance: moderately difficult. Application deadlines: 6/15, rolling for nonresidents. Notification: continuous until 9/1, continuous until 8/1 for nonresidents. SAT Reasoning Test deadline: 7/15. Transfer credits accepted: Yes.

Costs Per Year: Application fee: $40. State resident tuition: $4,264 full-time,

$177.67 per credit hour part-time. Nonresident tuition: $15,050 full-time, $627.07 per credit hour part-time. Mandatory fees: $2146 full-time, $1073 per term part-time. Full-time tuition and fees vary according to course load, location, program, and reciprocity agreements. Part-time tuition and fees vary according to course load, location, program, and reciprocity agreements. College room and board: $7900. College room only: $4060. Room and board charges vary according to board plan and housing facility.

Collegiate Environment: Orientation program. Drama-theater group, choral group, marching band, student-run newspaper, radio station. Social organizations: 225 open to all; national fraternities, national sororities; 6% of eligible men and 10% of eligible women are members. Most popular organizations: Black Student League, Enactus, Psychology Club, Collegiate women of VSU, College Republican Society. Major annual events: The Happening, Homecoming Activities, Fall Explosion. Student services: health clinic, personal-psychological counseling. Campus security: 24-hour emergency response devices and patrols, late night transport-escort service, controlled dormitory access, bicycle patrols, security cameras, mobile security app. Odum Library. Books: 579,774 (physical), 408,139 (digital/electronic); Serial titles: 10,877 (physical), 39,852 (digital/electronic); Databases: 237. Students can reserve study rooms. Operations spending for the previous fiscal year: $4.5 million. 1,691 computers available on campus for general student use. Computer purchase/lease plans available. A campuswide network can be accessed from student residence rooms and from off campus. Students can access the following: online class registration. Staffed computer lab on campus (open 24 hours a day) provides training in use of computers and the Internet.

Community Environment: Valdosta, located in the south-central section of Georgia, is the largest city of the 16-county area that it serves. Buses and railroads serve the area, and airlines are available in Valdosta, Tallahassee, Jacksonville and Atlanta. Average temperature for the year is 67 degrees. Valdosta is the largest inland naval stores market in the world. Industries are tobacco, lumber, mobile homes, cotton, paper and metal goods. Valdosta Entertainment Association brings outstanding cultural events to the city. The Gulf of Mexico and the Atlantic Ocean are within 125 miles. Near the city are numerous freshwater lakes that provide fishing, boating, water skiing, beaches for swimming and picnic areas. Valdosta boasts a congenial atmosphere and friendly spirit. Newcomers and visitors are welcomed. Part-time employment is available.

■ WESLEYAN COLLEGE
4760 Forsyth Rd.
Macon, GA 31210-4462
Tel: (478)477-1110; Free: 800-447-6610
Fax: (478)757-4030
E-mail: admissions@wesleyancollege.edu
Web Site: www.wesleyancollege.edu

Description: Independent United Methodist, comprehensive. Awards bachelor's and master's degrees. Founded 1836. Setting: 200-acre suburban campus with easy access to Atlanta. Endowment: $60 million. Educational spending for the previous fiscal year: $12,438 per student. Total enrollment: 707. Faculty: 104 (56 full-time, 48 part-time). Student-undergrad faculty ratio is 15:1. 890 applied, 48% were admitted. 19% from top 10% of their high school class, 49% from top quarter, 73% from top half. Full-time: 490 students, 100% women. Part-time: 235 students, 75% women, 25% men. Students come from 15 states and territories, 17 other countries, 9% from out-of-state. 0.2% American Indian or Alaska Native, non-Hispanic/Latino; 6% Hispanic/Latino; 34% Black or African American, non-Hispanic/Latino; 2% Asian, non-Hispanic/Latino; 9% international. 23% 25 or older, 60% live on campus, 7% transferred in. Retention: 78% of full-time freshmen returned the following year. Academic areas with the most degrees conferred: business/marketing; health professions and related sciences; visual and performing arts; biological/life sciences. Core. Calendar: semesters. Services for LD students, advanced placement, self-designed majors, honors program, independent study, distance learning, double major, summer session for credit, part-time degree program, adult/continuing education programs, co-op programs and internships. Off campus study at Mercer University, College Consortium. Study abroad program. ROTC: Army (c).

Entrance Requirements: Options: electronic application, early admission, deferred admission, international baccalaureate accepted. Required: high school transcript, minimum 2 high school GPA, SAT or ACT. Recommended: essay, 2 recommendations. Required for some: interview. Entrance: moderately difficult. Application deadlines: rolling, rolling for nonresidents, 11/15 for early decision. Notification: continuous, continuous for nonresidents. SAT Reasoning Test deadline: 8/31. Transfer credits accepted: Yes.

Costs Per Year: Application fee: $30. One-time mandatory fee: $200. Comprehensive fee: $33,830 includes full-time tuition ($22,770), mandatory fees ($1000), and college room and board ($10,060). Part-time tuition: $540 per semester hour. Part-time mandatory fees: $40 per semester hour.

Collegiate Environment: Orientation program. Drama-theater group, choral group, student-run newspaper. Social organizations: 28 open to all. Most popular organizations: Student Government Association (SGA), Black Student Alliance (BSA), A.X.I.S. (Association of eXemplary International Students), GLBAL (Gay, Lesbian, Bi-sexual Alliance), Campus Activities Board (CAB). Major annual events: Homecoming, Stunt, Holiday Banquet. Student services: health clinic, personal-psychological counseling, women's center. Campus security: 24-hour emergency response devices and patrols, late night transport-escort service, controlled dormitory access. 567 college housing spaces available; 339 were occupied in 2018-19. Freshmen guaranteed college housing. Option: women-only housing available. Willet Memorial Library. Books: 88,108 (physical), 260,161 (digital/electronic); Serial titles: 646 (physical), 24,701 (digital/electronic); Databases: 294. Study areas open 24 hours, 5-7 days a week; students can reserve study rooms. Operations spending for the previous fiscal year: $337,600. 63 computers available on campus for general student use. A computer is required for all students. A campuswide network can be accessed from student residence rooms and from off campus. Students can access the following: online class registration, online payment.

Community Environment: The college is located in suburban Macon. There are 5 other coed colleges within a 60-mile radius of Macon.

■ WEST GEORGIA TECHNICAL COLLEGE
176 Murphy Campus Blvd.
Waco, GA 30182
Tel: (770)537-6000
Web Site: www.westgatech.edu

Description: State-supported, 2-year, coed. Part of Technical College System of Georgia. Awards certificates, diplomas, and terminal associate degrees. Founded 1966. Total enrollment: 6,743. Full-time: 1,931 students, 61% women, 39% men. Part-time: 4,812 students, 66% women, 34% men. 2% from out-of-state. 0.4% American Indian or Alaska Native, non-Hispanic/Latino; 5% Hispanic/Latino; 32% Black or African American, non-Hispanic/Latino; 1% Asian, non-Hispanic/Latino; 0.1% Native Hawaiian or other Pacific Islander, non-Hispanic/Latino. Retention: 59% of full-time freshmen returned the following year. Calendar: quarters. Distance learning.

Entrance Requirements: Open admission selective admission to some programs. Option: early admission. Required: high school transcript. Entrance: noncompetitive.

■ WIREGRASS GEORGIA TECHNICAL COLLEGE
4089 Val Tech Rd.
Valdosta, GA 31602
Tel: (229)333-2100
Fax: (229)333-2129
Web Site: www.wiregrass.edu

Description: State-supported, 2-year, coed. Part of Technical College System of Georgia. Awards certificates, diplomas, and terminal associate degrees. Founded 1963. Setting: suburban campus. Total enrollment: 3,939. Full-time: 947 students, 63% women, 37% men. Part-time: 2,993 students, 63% women, 37% men. 1% from out-of-state. 0.4% American Indian or Alaska Native, non-Hispanic/Latino; 5% Hispanic/Latino; 32% Black or African American, non-Hispanic/Latino; 0.8% Asian, non-Hispanic/Latino; 0.2% Native Hawaiian or other Pacific Islander, non-Hispanic/Latino. Retention: 59% of full-time freshmen returned the following year. Calendar: quarters. Distance learning.

Entrance Requirements: Open admission selective admission to some programs. Option: early admission. Required: high school transcript. Entrance: noncompetitive.

■ YOUNG HARRIS COLLEGE
1 College St.
Young Harris, GA 30582
Tel: (706)379-3111
Fax: (706)379-4306
E-mail: admissions@yhc.edu
Web Site: www.yhc.edu

Description: Independent United Methodist, 4-year, coed. Awards bachelor's degrees. Founded 1886. Setting: 800-acre small town campus. Endowment: $93.7 million. Educational spending for the previous fiscal year:

$8823 per student. Total enrollment: 1,034. Faculty: 105 (77 full-time, 28 part-time). Student-undergrad faculty ratio is 12:1. 2,061 applied, 48% were admitted. Full-time: 999 students, 53% women, 47% men. Part-time: 35 students, 74% women, 26% men. Students come from 24 states and territories, 26 other countries, 14% from out-of-state. 0.2% American Indian or Alaska Native, non-Hispanic/Latino; 6% Hispanic/Latino; 6% Black or African American, non-Hispanic/Latino; 0.8% Asian, non-Hispanic/Latino; 0.4% Native Hawaiian or other Pacific Islander, non-Hispanic/Latino. 1% 25 or older, 87% live on campus, 3% transferred in. Retention: 65% of full-time freshmen returned the following year. Core. Calendar: semesters. Services for LD students, advanced placement, honors program, double major, summer session for credit, part-time degree program, adult/continuing education programs, co-op programs and internships. Study abroad program.

Entrance Requirements: Option: electronic application. Required: high school transcript, SAT or ACT. Entrance: moderately difficult. Application deadline: rolling. Notification: continuous. Transfer credits accepted: Yes.

Collegiate Environment: Orientation program. Drama-theater group, choral group, student-run newspaper. Social organizations: 58 open to all; national fraternities, national sororities, local fraternities, local sororities; 13% of eligible men and 15% of eligible women are members. Most popular organizations: Greek life, religious organizations/Bible study, intramural sports, Student Government Association, Campus Activities Board. Major annual events: Spring Formal, Organizational Fair, Fall Fest. Student services: health clinic, personal-psychological counseling. Campus security: 24-hour emergency response devices and patrols, student patrols, late night transport-escort service, controlled dormitory access. Duckworth Library. Databases: 72. Study areas open 24 hours, 5-7 days a week. Operations spending for the previous fiscal year: $768,687. 99 computers available on campus for general student use. A campuswide network can be accessed from student residence rooms and from off campus. Students can access the following: online class registration. Staffed computer lab on campus.

Community Environment: Young Harris is situated in the Blue Ridge Mountains of northeast Georgia where the climate is moderate. Atlanta, Asheville, Chattanooga, and Greenville, South Carolina, are all within one hundred miles. Various religious denominations, a Lions Club, a clinic, and two hospitals serve the community. As part of a resort area the recreational activities include fishing, boating, hiking, horseback riding, picnicking, swimming, tennis, and golf. The county fair is an annual event.

■ ARGOSY UNIVERSITY, HAWAI'I

1001 Bishop St., Ste. 400
Honolulu, HI 96813
Tel: (808)536-5555; Free: 888-323-2777
Fax: (808)536-5505
Web Site: www.argosy.edu/locations/hawaii
Description: Proprietary, university, coed. Part of Education Management Corporation. Awards associate, bachelor's, master's, and doctoral degrees. Founded 1994. Calendar: semesters.

■ BRIGHAM YOUNG UNIVERSITY-HAWAII

55-220 Kulanui St.
Laie, HI 96762-1294
Tel: (808)293-3211
E-mail: admissions@byuh.edu
Web Site: www.byuh.edu
Description: Independent Latter-day Saints, 4-year, coed. Administratively affiliated with Brigham Young University. Awards associate and bachelor's degrees. Founded 1955. Setting: 60-acre small town campus with easy access to Honolulu. Total enrollment: 2,555. Faculty: 228 (121 full-time, 107 part-time). Student-undergrad faculty ratio is 15:1. 1,295 applied, 58% were admitted. Full-time: 2,380 students, 54% women, 46% men. Part-time: 175 students, 57% women, 43% men. Students come from 48 states and territories, 71 other countries, 75% from out-of-state. 26% 25 or older, 57% live on campus, 10% transferred in. Retention: 62% of full-time freshmen returned the following year. Academic areas with the most degrees conferred: business/marketing; education; interdisciplinary studies. Core. Calendar: semesters 2 semesters and 3 terms. Academic remediation for entering students, ESL program, services for LD students, advanced placement, accelerated degree program, freshman honors college, honors program, double major, summer session for credit, part-time degree program, adult/continuing education programs, co-op programs and internships. Off campus study. ROTC: Army (c), Naval (c), Air Force (c).
Entrance Requirements: Options: electronic application, early admission, deferred admission, international baccalaureate accepted. Required: essay, high school transcript, minimum 3 high school GPA, resume of activities, ecclesiastical endorsement, SAT or ACT. Recommended: ACT. Entrance: moderately difficult. Application deadline: 2/15. Notification: continuous. Preference given to Latter-Day Saints Church members. Transfer credits accepted: Yes.
Collegiate Environment: Orientation program. Drama-theater group, choral group, student-run newspaper. Social organizations: 46 open to all. Most popular organizations: Tonga Club, Samoa Club, Hawaiian Club, Hong Kong Club, Japanese Club. Major annual events: Culture Night, Foodfest, Songfest. Student services: health clinic, personal-psychological counseling. Campus security: 24-hour patrols, late night transport-escort service. Joseph F. Smith Library plus 1 other. 640 computers available on campus for general student use. A campuswide network can be accessed from student residence rooms. Students can access the following: online class registration. Staffed computer lab on campus provides training in use of computers, software, and the Internet.

■ CHAMINADE UNIVERSITY OF HONOLULU

3140 Waialae Ave.
Honolulu, HI 96816-1578

Tel: (808)735-4711; Free: 800-735-3733
Fax: (808)739-4647
E-mail: admissions@chaminade.edu
Web Site: www.chaminade.edu
Description: Independent Roman Catholic, comprehensive, coed. Awards associate, bachelor's, and master's degrees and post-master's certificates. Founded 1955. Setting: 62-acre urban campus with easy access to Honolulu. Endowment: $19.1 million. Educational spending for the previous fiscal year: $9076 per student. Total enrollment: 1,719. Faculty: 138 (91 full-time, 47 part-time). Student-undergrad faculty ratio is 11:1. 742 applied, 91% were admitted. 19% from top 10% of their high school class, 46% from top quarter, 81% from top half. Full-time: 1,125 students, 71% women, 29% men. Part-time: 32 students, 66% women, 34% men. Students come from 39 states and territories, 11 other countries, 29% from out-of-state. 0.4% American Indian or Alaska Native, non-Hispanic/Latino; 4% Hispanic/Latino; 3% Black or African American, non-Hispanic/Latino; 37% Asian, non-Hispanic/Latino; 26% Native Hawaiian or other Pacific Islander, non-Hispanic/Latino; 1% international. 15% 25 or older, 23% live on campus, 10% transferred in. Retention: 77% of full-time freshmen returned the following year. Academic areas with the most degrees conferred: homeland security, law enforcement, firefighting, and protective services; health professions and related sciences; business/marketing. Core. Calendar: semesters. Academic remediation for entering students, advanced placement, accelerated degree program, independent study, distance learning, double major, summer session for credit, part-time degree program, adult/continuing education programs, internships, graduate courses open to undergrads. Off campus study at University of Hawaii at Manoa, Brigham Young University, Hawaii Pacific University. Study abroad program. ROTC: Army (c), Air Force (c).
Entrance Requirements: Options: electronic application, deferred admission, international baccalaureate accepted. Required: essay, high school transcript, minimum 2.5 high school GPA, SAT or ACT, TOEFL for international students. Recommended: minimum 3 high school GPA. Required for some: minimum 2.75 high school GPA, 2 recommendations, interview. Entrance: moderately difficult. Application deadline: rolling. Notification: continuous. Transfer credits accepted: Yes.
Costs Per Year: Application fee: $50. One-time mandatory fee: $180. Comprehensive fee: $39,004 includes full-time tuition ($25,260), mandatory fees ($114), and college room and board ($13,630). Full-time tuition and fees vary according to course load, location, and program. Room and board charges vary according to board plan and housing facility. Part-time tuition: $842 per credit. Part-time tuition varies according to course load, location, and program.
Collegiate Environment: Orientation program. Drama-theater group, choral group, student-run newspaper, radio station. Social organizations: 43 open to all. Most popular organizations: Lumana O Samoa (Samoan Club), Kaimi Lalakea (Hawaiian Club), Rotaract, Residence Hall Association, Chaminade Student Government Association. Major annual events: International Extravaganza, Campus Ministry Awakening Retreats, Club Fest. Student services: personal-psychological counseling. Campus security: 24-hour emergency response devices and patrols, late night transport-escort service, controlled dormitory access. Sullivan Library. Books: 47,508 (physical), 133,757 (digital/electronic); Serial titles: 142 (physical), 36,441 (digital/electronic); Databases: 99. Operations spending for the previous fiscal year: $43,966. 200 computers available on campus for general student use. A campuswide network can be accessed from student residence rooms and

from off campus. Students can access the following: online class registration. Staffed computer lab on campus provides training in use of computers, software, and the Internet.
Community Environment: See University of Hawaii - Manoa.

■ **HAWAII COMMUNITY COLLEGE**
1175 Manono St.
Hilo, HI 96720-5096
Tel: (808)974-7611
Fax: (808)974-7692
Web Site: www.hawcc.hawaii.edu
Description: State-supported, 2-year, coed. Part of University of Hawaii System. Awards certificates, diplomas, transfer associate, and terminal associate degrees. Founded 1954. Setting: small town campus. Total enrollment: 2,603. 34% 25 or older. Calendar: semesters. ESL program, services for LD students, advanced placement, honors program, summer session for credit, part-time degree program, co-op programs.
Entrance Requirements: Open admission. Option: early admission. Entrance: noncompetitive. Application deadline: 8/1.
Collegiate Environment: Orientation program. Campus security: 24-hour patrols. Edwin H. Mookini Library plus 1 other.

■ **HAWAI'I PACIFIC UNIVERSITY**
1 Aloha Twr. Dr.
Honolulu, HI 96813
Tel: (808)544-0200; Free: 866-225-5478
Fax: (808)544-1136
E-mail: admissions@hpu.edu
Web Site: www.hpu.edu
Description: Independent, comprehensive, coed. Awards associate, bachelor's, master's, and doctoral degrees and post-master's certificates. Founded 1965. Setting: 140-acre urban campus. System endowment: $44.4 million. Research spending for the previous fiscal year: $4.9 million. Educational spending for the previous fiscal year: $7117 per student. Total enrollment: 4,146. Faculty: 359 (152 full-time, 207 part-time). Student-undergrad faculty ratio is 12:1. 6,551 applied, 75% were admitted. Full-time: 2,411 students, 65% women, 35% men. Part-time: 1,149 students, 49% women, 51% men. Students come from 54 states and territories, 55 other countries, 42% from out-of-state. 0.6% American Indian or Alaska Native, non-Hispanic/Latino; 14% Hispanic/Latino; 5% Black or African American, non-Hispanic/Latino; 15% Asian, non-Hispanic/Latino; 2% Native Hawaiian or other Pacific Islander, non-Hispanic/Latino; 10% international. 38% 25 or older, 14% live on campus, 9% transferred in. Retention: 65% of full-time freshmen returned the following year. Academic areas with the most degrees conferred: business/marketing; health professions and related sciences; biological/life sciences. Core. Calendar: semesters. Academic remediation for entering students, ESL program, services for LD students, advanced placement, accelerated degree program, self-designed majors, freshman honors college, honors program, independent study, distance learning, double major, summer session for credit, part-time degree program, adult/continuing education programs, co-op programs and internships, graduate courses open to undergrads. Off campus study at Carroll College, Creighton University, Samuel Merritt College, Southern California University of Health Sciences. Study abroad program. ROTC: Army (c), Air Force (c).
Entrance Requirements: Options: electronic application, early action, deferred admission, international baccalaureate accepted. Required: high school transcript, minimum 2.5 high school GPA, SAT or ACT. Recommended: essay, 2 recommendations. Required for some: interview, TOEFL or IELTS. Entrance: moderately difficult. Application deadline: rolling. SAT Reasoning Test deadline: 8/27. SAT Subject Test deadline: 8/27. Transfer credits accepted: Yes.
Costs Per Year: Application fee: $50. Comprehensive fee: $40,780 includes full-time tuition ($25,630), mandatory fees ($350), and college room and board ($14,800). Full-time tuition and fees vary according to course level, course load, degree level, location, program, and student level. Room and board charges vary according to board plan, housing facility, and location. Part-time tuition: $855 per credit. Part-time mandatory fees: $25 per term. Part-time tuition and fees vary according to course level, course load, degree level, location, program, and student level.
Collegiate Environment: Orientation program. Drama-theater group, choral group, student-run newspaper. Social organizations: 45 open to all; 30% of eligible men and 70% of eligible women are members. Most popular organizations: Student Government Association, Campus Activities Board, Student Nurses Association, Travel Industry Management Student Organiza-

tion, Christian Student Organization. Major annual events: Spring Talent Show, Club Carnival, Paina at the Pier. Student services: health clinic, personal-psychological counseling. Campus security: 24-hour emergency response devices and patrols, late night transport-escort service, controlled dormitory access, emergency notification, patrol system and emergency exit alarms in residence halls. Meader Library plus 2 others. Books: 103,021 (physical), 191,075 (digital/electronic); Serial titles: 64 (physical), 4,520 (digital/electronic); Databases: 101. Students can reserve study rooms. Operations spending for the previous fiscal year: $1.6 million. 200 computers available on campus for general student use. A campuswide network can be accessed from student residence rooms and from off campus. Students can access the following: online class registration. Staffed computer lab on campus provides training in use of computers, software, and the Internet.
Community Environment: Honolulu, the travel capital of the world and nexus of the Pacific Basin, is a cosmopolitan city of some 800,000. Its leading industries are the travel industry, agriculture, and government-related services. Positions are available for HPU students in a wide variety of fields via the university's Cooperative Education and Internship Program. Such cultural institutions as the Bishop Museum, the Honolulu Academy of Arts, and the Honolulu Symphony are located within two to four miles of the campus. Recreation facilities, most of them free, are widely available throughout Hawaii and are among the finest in the world; also among the world's finest are Hawaii's many major restaurants and hotels.

■ **HAWAII TOKAI INTERNATIONAL COLLEGE**
91-971 Farrington Hwy.
Kapolei, HI 96707
Tel: (808)983-4100
Fax: (808)983-4107
E-mail: admissions@tokai.edu
Web Site: www.htic.edu
Description: Independent, 2-year, coed. Part of Tokai University Educational System. Awards certificates, diplomas, transfer associate, and terminal associate degrees. Founded 1992. Setting: 7-acre suburban campus with easy access to Honolulu. Research spending for the previous fiscal year: $14,000. Educational spending for the previous fiscal year: $17,675 per student. Total enrollment: 85. Faculty: 22 (7 full-time, 15 part-time). Student-undergrad faculty ratio is 7:1. 35 applied, 86% were admitted. 13% from top 10% of their high school class, 63% from top quarter, 88% from top half. 1 valedictorian. Full-time: 85 students, 35% women, 65% men. Students come from 2 states and territories, 2 other countries, 5% from out-of-state. 2% Hispanic/Latino; 6% Asian, non-Hispanic/Latino; 4% Native Hawaiian or other Pacific Islander, non-Hispanic/Latino; 81% international. 1% 25 or older, 30% live on campus. Retention: 86% of full-time freshmen returned the following year. Core. Calendar: quarters. Academic remediation for entering students, ESL program, services for LD students, advanced placement, summer session for credit, part-time degree program, internships. Study abroad program.
Entrance Requirements: Options: electronic application, deferred admission, international baccalaureate accepted. Required: essay, high school transcript, minimum 2.5 high school GPA. Recommended: recommendations. Required for some: interview. Entrance: minimally difficult. Application deadline: rolling. Notification: continuous. Transfer credits accepted: Yes.
Costs Per Year: Application fee: $50. One-time mandatory fee: $20. Comprehensive fee: $22,485 includes full-time tuition ($12,750), mandatory fees ($735), and college room and board ($9000). Room and board charges vary according to board plan.
Collegiate Environment: Orientation program. Social organizations: 10 open to all. Most popular organizations: Basketball Club, International Friendship Association, Hiking Club, Hula Club, Phi Theta Kappa International Honor Society. Major annual events: Convocation, Student Presentation Day, Town Hall. Student services: health clinic, personal-psychological counseling. Campus security: 24-hour emergency response devices and patrols, controlled dormitory access. Library and Learning Center plus 1 other. Books: 7,807 (physical); Serial titles: 30 (physical); Databases: 48. Weekly public service hours: 68; students can reserve study rooms. Operations spending for the previous fiscal year: $113,000. 45 computers available on campus for general student use. A campuswide network can be accessed. Students can access the following: online class registration. Staffed computer lab on campus provides training in use of computers, software, and the Internet.

■ **HONOLULU COMMUNITY COLLEGE**
874 Dillingham Blvd.
Honolulu, HI 96817-4598

Tel: (808)845-9211
E-mail: honcc@hawaii.edu
Web Site: www.honolulu.hawaii.edu
Description: State-supported, 2-year, coed. Part of University of Hawaii System. Awards certificates, transfer associate, and terminal associate degrees. Founded 1920. Setting: 20-acre urban campus. Total enrollment: 4,368. Faculty: 216 (131 full-time, 85 part-time). Student-undergrad faculty ratio is 16:1. Full-time: 1,632 students, 36% women, 64% men. Part-time: 2,736 students, 44% women, 56% men. Students come from 26 states and territories, 12 other countries, 2% from out-of-state. 0.2% American Indian or Alaska Native, non-Hispanic/Latino; 9% Hispanic/Latino; 2% Black or African American, non-Hispanic/Latino; 42% Asian, non-Hispanic/Latino; 9% Native Hawaiian or other Pacific Islander, non-Hispanic/Latino; 1% international. 10% transferred in. Retention: 61% of full-time freshmen returned the following year. Core. Calendar: semesters. Academic remediation for entering students, ESL program, services for LD students, advanced placement, accelerated degree program, self-designed majors, distance learning, summer session for credit, part-time degree program, co-op programs and internships. ROTC: Army (c), Air Force (c).
Entrance Requirements: Open admission. Option: early admission. Required for some: TOEFL for international applicants. Entrance: noncompetitive. Application deadline: 8/15. Notification: continuous until 8/15.
Collegiate Environment: Orientation program. Student-run newspaper. Most popular organizations: Phi Theta Kappa, Hui 'Oiwi, Fashion Society. Major annual events: Campus Awareness Day, HCC Week. Student services: health clinic, personal-psychological counseling. Campus security: 24-hour emergency response devices. Honolulu Community College Library plus 1 other. 120 computers available on campus for general student use. A campuswide network can be accessed from off-campus. Students can access the following: online class registration. Staffed computer lab on campus.
Community Environment: See University of Hawaii - Manoa.

■ **KAPIOLANI COMMUNITY COLLEGE**
4303 Diamond Head Rd.
Honolulu, HI 96816-4421
Tel: (808)734-9111
Web Site: www.kapiolani.hawaii.edu
Description: State-supported, 2-year, coed. Part of University of Hawaii System. Awards certificates, transfer associate, and terminal associate degrees. Founded 1957. Setting: 52-acre urban campus. Total enrollment: 9,102. Student-undergrad faculty ratio is 21:1. 3% from out-of-state. 34% 25 or older. Core. Calendar: semesters. Academic remediation for entering students, ESL program, services for LD students, advanced placement, self-designed majors, honors program, distance learning, summer session for credit, part-time degree program, adult/continuing education programs, co-op programs and internships. Off campus study at other units of the University of Hawaii System. ROTC: Army (c), Air Force (c).
Entrance Requirements: Open admission except for nursing, health sciences, paralegal programs. Option: early admission. Entrance: noncompetitive. Application deadline: 7/15. Notification: continuous until 8/15. Preference given to state residents.
Collegiate Environment: Orientation program. Choral group, student-run newspaper. Campus security: 24-hour patrols. Lama Library.
Community Environment: See University of Hawaii - Manoa.

■ **KAUAI COMMUNITY COLLEGE**
3-1901 Kaumualii Hwy.
Lihue, HI 96766
Tel: (808)245-8311
Fax: (808)245-8297
E-mail: arkauai@hawaii.edu
Web Site: kauai.hawaii.edu
Description: State-supported, 2-year, coed. Part of University of Hawaii System. Awards certificates and transfer associate degrees. Founded 1965. Setting: 100-acre small town campus. Total enrollment: 1,345. Core. Calendar: semesters. ESL program, services for LD students, advanced placement, accelerated degree program, distance learning, summer session for credit, part-time degree program, co-op programs and internships.
Entrance Requirements: Open admission except for nursing, electrical installation and maintenance, electronics technology, facilities engineering programs. Option: early admission. Recommended: high school transcript. Required for some: high school transcript. Entrance: noncompetitive. Application deadline: 8/1. Notification: continuous until 8/1. Preference given to state residents.

Collegiate Environment: Choral group, student-run newspaper. Social organizations: 8 open to all. Most popular organizations: Food Service Club, Hui O Hana Po'okela (Hoper Club), Nursing Club, Phi Theta Kappa, Pamantasan Club. Student services: health clinic, personal-psychological counseling. Campus security: student patrols, 6-hour evening patrols by trained security personnel. S. W. Wilcox II Learning Resource Center plus 1 other. 173 computers available on campus for general student use. A campuswide network can be accessed. Staffed computer lab on campus.
Community Environment: Kauai is known as the"Garden Island," offering magnificent scenery and lush vegetation, beautiful waterfalls, the spectacular Waimea Canyon, the great"hidden" valley of Kalalau, and colorful tropical plants and flowers. Airlines and boats serve the area. Honolulu is 100 nautical miles away. Industries are sugar and tourism; oceanography research and development is conducted here. Community facilities include five public libraries and many churches of all denominations. Several county beach parks and one major state park provide recreation facilities for boating, swimming, scuba diving, deepsea and surf fishing. Wild boar, goat and pheasant hunting are favorite sports.

■ **LEEWARD COMMUNITY COLLEGE**
96-045 Ala Ike
Pearl City, HI 96782-3393
Tel: (808)455-0011
Fax: (808)455-0471
Web Site: www.leeward.hawaii.edu
Description: State-supported, 2-year, coed. Part of University of Hawaii System. Awards certificates, transfer associate, and terminal associate degrees. Founded 1968. Setting: 49-acre suburban campus with easy access to Honolulu. Total enrollment: 7,942. Faculty: 283 (178 full-time, 105 part-time). Student-undergrad faculty ratio is 23:1. 2,013 applied, 100% were admitted. Full-time: 3,296 students, 56% women, 44% men. Part-time: 4,646 students, 63% women, 37% men. Students come from 13 other countries, 1% from out-of-state. 0.3% American Indian or Alaska Native, non-Hispanic/Latino; 11% Hispanic/Latino; 2% Black or African American, non-Hispanic/Latino; 37% Asian, non-Hispanic/Latino; 12% Native Hawaiian or other Pacific Islander, non-Hispanic/Latino; 0.5% international. 29% 25 or older, 7% transferred in. Retention: 65% of full-time freshmen returned the following year. Core. Calendar: semesters. Academic remediation for entering students, ESL program, services for LD students, advanced placement, honors program, independent study, distance learning, summer session for credit, part-time degree program, co-op programs and internships. Off campus study at University of Hawaii - Manoa, University of Hawaii - Hilo, University of Hawaii - West Oahu, University of Hawaii Community Colleges (Hawaii Community College, Honolulu Community College, Kapiolani Community College, Kauai Community College, Maui College, Windward Community College). Study abroad program. ROTC: Air Force (c).
Entrance Requirements: Open admission except for Running Start, early admission. Options: electronic application, early admission, international baccalaureate accepted. Required for some: high school transcript. Entrance: noncompetitive. Application deadline: 7/15. Notification: continuous. Preference given to state residents. Transfer credits accepted: Yes.
Costs Per Year: Application fee: $25. State resident tuition: $2892 full-time, $128.50 per credit hour part-time. Nonresident tuition: $8220 full-time, $342.50 per credit hour part-time. Mandatory fees: $40 full-time, $1 per credit hour part-time, $20 per term part-time. Full-time tuition and fees vary according to course level and course load. Part-time tuition and fees vary according to course level and course load.
Collegiate Environment: Orientation program. Drama-theater group, choral group, student-run newspaper. Social organizations: 19 open to all. Most popular organizations: Soccer Club, Japan Circle, Future Teachers Club, Campus Crusade For Christ, 4n Tongues (Hip Hop). Major annual events: College Bash, Leeward Discovery Fair, Career, College and Job Fair. Student services: health clinic, personal-psychological counseling. Campus security: 24-hour emergency response devices and patrols, late night transport-escort service. 1,160 computers available on campus for general student use. A campuswide network can be accessed from off-campus. Students can access the following: online class registration, degree planning. Staffed computer lab on campus provides training in use of computers, software, and the Internet.
Community Environment: See University of Hawaii - Manoa.

■ **PACIFIC RIM CHRISTIAN UNIVERSITY**
2223 Ho'one'e Pl.
Honolulu, HI 96819

Tel: (808)518-4791
Fax: (808)670-3957
Web Site: www.pacrim.edu
Description: Independent Christian, comprehensive, coed. Awards associate, bachelor's, and master's degrees.

■ **REMINGTON COLLEGE-HONOLULU CAMPUS**
1111 Bishop St.
Ste. 400
Honolulu, HI 96813
Tel: (808)942-1000; Free: 800-323-8122
Fax: (808)533-3064
Web Site: www.remingtoncollege.edu
Description: Independent, primarily 2-year, coed. Awards diplomas, transfer associate, terminal associate, and bachelor's degrees.

■ **UNIVERSITY OF HAWAII AT HILO**
200 W Kawili St.
Hilo, HI 96720-4091
Tel: (808)932-7446; Free: 800-897-4456
Fax: (808)933-0861
E-mail: uhhadm@hawaii.edu
Web Site: hilo.hawaii.edu
Description: State-supported, comprehensive, coed. Part of University of Hawaii System. Awards bachelor's, master's, and doctoral degrees. Founded 1970. Setting: 115-acre small town campus. Total enrollment: 3,924. Faculty: 338 (241 full-time, 97 part-time). Student-undergrad faculty ratio is 13:1. 1,679 applied, 71% were admitted. 23% from top 10% of their high school class, 53% from top quarter, 88% from top half. Full-time: 2,726 students, 59% women, 41% men. Part-time: 636 students, 65% women, 35% men. 28% from out-of-state. 0.6% American Indian or Alaska Native, non-Hispanic/Latino; 13% Hispanic/Latino; 1% Black or African American, non-Hispanic/Latino; 17% Asian, non-Hispanic/Latino; 11% Native Hawaiian or other Pacific Islander, non-Hispanic/Latino; 5% international. 27% 25 or older, 18% transferred in. Retention: 66% of full-time freshmen returned the following year. Academic areas with the most degrees conferred: health professions and related sciences; social sciences; psychology. Core. Calendar: semesters. ESL program, services for LD students, advanced placement, self-designed majors, honors program, independent study, distance learning, double major, summer session for credit, part-time degree program, internships. Off campus study at members of the National Student Exchange. Study abroad program. ROTC: Army.
Entrance Requirements: Options: electronic application, deferred admission, international baccalaureate accepted. Required: high school transcript, SAT or ACT. Recommended: minimum 3 high school GPA. Entrance: moderately difficult. Application deadline: 7/1. Notification: 7/31. SAT Reasoning Test deadline: 7/1.
Collegiate Environment: Orientation program. Drama-theater group, choral group, student-run newspaper, radio station. Social organizations: 60 open to all; national fraternities, national sororities. Most popular organizations: International Student Association, Hawaiian Leadership and Development, Delta Sigma Pi Business Fraternity, University Canoe Club, Samoan Club. Major annual events: International Night, UH Hilo Ho'olaule'a, UH Hilo Earth Fair. Student services: health clinic, personal-psychological counseling, women's center. Campus security: 24-hour emergency response devices and patrols, controlled dormitory access. Edwin H. Mookini Library.

■ **UNIVERSITY OF HAWAII AT MANOA**
2500 Campus Rd.
Honolulu, HI 96822
Tel: (808)956-8111; Free: 800-823-9771
E-mail: uhmanoa.admissions@hawaii.edu
Web Site: manoa.hawaii.edu
Description: State-supported, university, coed. Part of University of Hawaii System. Awards bachelor's, master's, and doctoral degrees. Founded 1907. Setting: 320-acre urban campus with easy access to Honolulu. Research spending for the previous fiscal year: $295.1 million. Total enrollment: 17,710. Faculty: 1,416 (1,149 full-time, 267 part-time). Student-undergrad faculty ratio is 10:1. 9,350 applied, 83% were admitted. 25% from top 10% of their high school class, 54% from top quarter, 86% from top half. Full-time: 10,739 students, 57% women, 43% men. Part-time: 2,229 students, 55% women, 45% men. Students come from 51 states and territories, 64 other countries, 28% from out-of-state. 0.4% American Indian or Alaska Native, non-Hispanic/Latino; 2% Hispanic/Latino; 2% Black or African American,

non-Hispanic/Latino; 40% Asian, non-Hispanic/Latino; 17% Native Hawaiian or other Pacific Islander, non-Hispanic/Latino; 3% international. 16% 25 or older, 23% live on campus, 12% transferred in. Retention: 79% of full-time freshmen returned the following year. Academic areas with the most degrees conferred: business/marketing; social sciences; engineering. Core. Calendar: semesters. ESL program, services for LD students, advanced placement, self-designed majors, honors program, independent study, distance learning, double major, summer session for credit, part-time degree program, co-op programs and internships, graduate courses open to undergrads. Off campus study at members of the National Student Exchange. Study abroad program. ROTC: Army, Air Force.
Entrance Requirements: Options: electronic application, international baccalaureate accepted. Required: high school transcript, minimum 2.8 high school GPA, SAT or ACT. Recommended: SAT, ACT. Entrance: moderately difficult. Notification: continuous. Preference given to state residents. SAT Reasoning Test deadline: 3/1. Transfer credits accepted: Yes.
Costs Per Year: Application fee: $70. Area resident tuition: $462 part-time. State resident tuition: $11,088 full-time, $462 per credit hour part-time. Nonresident tuition: $33,120 full-time, $1380 per credit hour part-time. Mandatory fees: $882 full-time, $436 per term part-time. College room and board: $12,686. College room only: $7110.
Collegiate Environment: Orientation program. Drama-theater group, choral group, marching band, student-run newspaper, radio station. Social organizations: 280 open to all; national fraternities, national sororities, local fraternities, local sororities, business, engineering, and honor fraternities; 1% of eligible men and 1% of eligible women are members. Most popular organizations: Biology Club, Pre-Medical Association, International Student Association, Katipunan, Timpuyog. Major annual events: Taste of Manoa, Aloha Bash, UH Manoa Earth Day Festival. Student services: health clinic, personal-psychological counseling, women's center. Campus security: 24-hour emergency response devices and patrols, student patrols, late night transport-escort service, controlled dormitory access. 3,900 college housing spaces available; 2,840 were occupied in 2018-19. Freshmen given priority for college housing. Option: coed housing available. Hamilton Library plus 6 others. Books: 2.3 million (physical), 261,550 (digital/electronic); Serial titles: 25,284 (physical), 65,122 (digital/electronic); Databases: 395. Weekly public service hours: 89; study areas open 24 hours, 5-7 days a week; students can reserve study rooms. 117 computers available on campus for general student use. Computer purchase/lease plans available. A campuswide network can be accessed from student residence rooms and from off campus. Students can access the following: online class registration. Staffed computer lab on campus provides training in use of computers, software, and the Internet.

■ **UNIVERSITY OF HAWAII MAUI COLLEGE**
310 Kaahumanu Ave.
Kahului, HI 96732
Tel: (808)984-3500; Free: 800-479-6692
Fax: (808)242-9618
E-mail: skameda@hawaii.edu
Web Site: maui.hawaii.edu
Description: State-supported, primarily 2-year, coed. Part of University of Hawaii System. Awards certificates, transfer associate, terminal associate, and bachelor's degrees. Founded 1967. Setting: 77-acre rural campus. Total enrollment: 4,071. Faculty: 117 (116 full-time, 1 part-time). Full-time: 1,446 students, 62% women, 38% men. Part-time: 2,625 students, 66% women, 34% men. 1% live on campus. Core. Calendar: semesters. Academic remediation for entering students, ESL program, services for LD students, summer session for credit, part-time degree program, external degree program, adult/continuing education programs, co-op programs.
Entrance Requirements: Open admission. Options: electronic application, early admission. Required for some: high school transcript. Entrance: noncompetitive. Application deadline: rolling.
Collegiate Environment: Student-run newspaper. Student services: health clinic, personal-psychological counseling. Campus security: 24-hour emergency response devices and patrols. Maui Community College Library plus 1 other. Operations spending for the previous fiscal year: $412,000. 487 computers available on campus for general student use. A campuswide network can be accessed from off-campus. Staffed computer lab on campus.
Community Environment: Kahului is an urban community on the Island of Maui enjoying an average temperature of 74.9 degrees. Both airlines and boats serve the area. The community facilities include churches of most denominations, hospital, clinic and shopping center. The pineapple and sugar industries provide work during the summer. Recreational activities are

mainly surfing and swimming. The Island of Maui has three golf courses; the Maui Country Club, Royal Kaanapali Golf Course and the Waiehu Golf Course.

■ UNIVERSITY OF HAWAII-WEST OAHU

91-1001 Farrington Hwy.
Kapolei, HI 96707
Tel: (808)689-2800; Free: 866-299-8656
E-mail: uhwoadm@hawaii.edu
Web Site: www.uhwo.hawaii.edu

Description: State-supported, 4-year, coed. Part of University of Hawaii System. Awards bachelor's degrees. Founded 1976. Setting: small town campus with easy access to Honolulu. Total enrollment: 2,692. Faculty: 77 (all full-time). Student-undergrad faculty ratio is 24:1. 892 applied, 70% were admitted. 13% from top 10% of their high school class, 40% from top quarter, 79% from top half. Full-time: 1,438 students, 65% women, 35% men. Part-time: 1,254 students, 61% women, 39% men. 3% from out-of-state. 0.5% American Indian or Alaska Native, non-Hispanic/Latino; 1% Hispanic/Latino; 2% Black or African American, non-Hispanic/Latino; 39% Asian, non-Hispanic/Latino; 30% Native Hawaiian or other Pacific Islander, non-Hispanic/Latino; 0.4% international. 43% 25 or older, 22% transferred in. Retention: 67% of full-time freshmen returned the following year. Academic areas with the most degrees conferred: business/marketing; public administration and social services; social sciences. Calendar: semesters. Part-time degree program. ROTC: Army (c), Air Force (c).

Entrance Requirements: Option: deferred admission. Required: minimum 2.7 high school GPA. Required for some: high school transcript, 2 recommendations, college transcripts, SAT or ACT. Entrance: moderately difficult. Application deadline: 8/1. Notification: continuous until 12/15. Preference given to state residents. SAT Reasoning Test deadline: 8/1. SAT Subject Test deadline: 8/1.

Costs Per Year: Application fee: $50. State resident tuition: $7272 full-time, $303 per credit part-time. Nonresident tuition: $20,232 full-time, $843 per credit part-time. Mandatory fees: $240 full-time, $120 per term part-time.

Collegiate Environment: Orientation program. Student services: personal-psychological counseling. Campus security: 24-hour emergency response devices and patrols, late night transport-escort service. University of Hawaii-West Oahu Library.

■ UNIVERSITY OF PHOENIX-HAWAII CAMPUS

745 Fort St.
Honolulu, HI 96813-3800

Tel: (808)536-2686; Free: 866-766-0766
Web Site: www.phoenix.edu

Description: Proprietary, comprehensive, coed. Awards bachelor's and master's degrees (courses conducted at 121 campuses and learning centers in 25 states). Setting: urban campus. Total enrollment: 955. Faculty: 178 (20 full-time, 158 part-time). Full-time: 743 students, 71% women, 29% men. 75% 25 or older. Academic areas with the most degrees conferred: business/marketing; health professions and related sciences; computer and information sciences. Core. Calendar: continuous. Services for LD students, advanced placement, accelerated degree program, independent study, distance learning, external degree program, adult/continuing education programs, graduate courses open to undergrads.

Entrance Requirements: Open admission. Options: electronic application, deferred admission. Required: 1 recommendation. Required for some: high school transcript. Entrance: noncompetitive. Application deadline: rolling.

Collegiate Environment: Campus security: late night transport-escort service. University Library. Operations spending for the previous fiscal year: $6.8 million.

■ WINDWARD COMMUNITY COLLEGE

45-720 Keaahala Rd.
Kaneohe, HI 96744-3528
Tel: (808)235-7400
Web Site: www.windward.hawaii.edu

Description: State-supported, 2-year, coed. Part of University of Hawaii System. Awards certificates, transfer associate, and terminal associate degrees. Founded 1972. Setting: 78-acre small town campus with easy access to Honolulu. Total enrollment: 1,959. Student-undergrad faculty ratio is 15:1. 1% from out-of-state. 31% 25 or older. Retention: 57% of full-time freshmen returned the following year. Calendar: semesters. Academic remediation for entering students, advanced placement, distance learning, summer session for credit, part-time degree program, adult/continuing education programs. ROTC: Army (c), Air Force (c).

Entrance Requirements: Open admission. Option: early admission. Entrance: noncompetitive. Application deadline: rolling. Notification: continuous until 8/1. Preference given to state residents.

Costs Per Year: Application fee: $25. State resident tuition: $3084 full-time, $128.50 per credit hour part-time. Nonresident tuition: $8220 full-time, $342.50 per credit hour part-time. Mandatory fees: $54 full-time, $1 per credit hour part-time, $15 per term part-time.

Collegiate Environment: Orientation program. Library.

■ BOISE BIBLE COLLEGE

8695 W Marigold St.
Boise, ID 83714-1220
Tel: (208)376-7731; Free: 800-893-7755
Fax: (208)376-7743
E-mail: rgrove@boisebible.edu
Web Site: www.boisebible.edu

Description: Independent nondenominational, 4-year, coed. Awards associate and bachelor's degrees. Founded 1945. Setting: 17-acre suburban campus. Total enrollment: 174. Student-undergrad faculty ratio is 15:1. 77 applied, 100% were admitted. 56% from out-of-state. 16% 25 or older. Retention: 53% of full-time freshmen returned the following year. Core. Calendar: semesters. Academic remediation for entering students, advanced placement, independent study, distance learning, double major, part-time degree program, adult/continuing education programs, internships.
Entrance Requirements: Option: deferred admission. Required: essay, high school transcript, minimum 2.0 high school GPA, SAT or ACT. Entrance: minimally difficult. Application deadline: 8/1. Notification: continuous.
Collegiate Environment: Orientation program. Choral group. Student services: personal-psychological counseling. Campus security: controlled dormitory access, patrols by police officers. Boise Bible College Library.

■ BOISE STATE UNIVERSITY

1910 University Dr.
Boise, ID 83725-0399
Tel: (208)426-1011; Free: 800-824-7017
E-mail: bsuinfo@boisestate.edu
Web Site: www.boisestate.edu

Description: State-supported, university, coed. Part of Idaho System of Higher Education. Awards associate, bachelor's, master's, and doctoral degrees. Founded 1932. Setting: 287-acre urban campus. Total enrollment: 24,154. Faculty: 1,526 (757 full-time, 769 part-time). 8,330 applied, 82% were admitted. 15% from top 10% of their high school class, 39% from top quarter, 75% from top half. Full-time: 12,477 students, 54% women, 46% men. Part-time: 8,290 students, 58% women, 42% men. Students come from 50 states and territories, 58 other countries. 0.4% American Indian or Alaska Native, non-Hispanic/Latino; 13% Hispanic/Latino; 2% Black or African American, non-Hispanic/Latino; 2% Asian, non-Hispanic/Latino; 0.4% Native Hawaiian or other Pacific Islander, non-Hispanic/Latino; 2% international. 25% 25 or older, 31% live on campus, 7% transferred in. Retention: 80% of full-time freshmen returned the following year. Academic areas with the most degrees conferred: health professions and related sciences; business/marketing; engineering. Core. Calendar: semesters. Academic remediation for entering students, ESL program, services for LD students, advanced placement, self-designed majors, freshman honors college, honors program, independent study, distance learning, double major, summer session for credit, part-time degree program, adult/continuing education programs, co-op programs and internships, graduate courses open to undergrads. Off campus study at National Student Exchange. Study abroad program. ROTC: Army.
Entrance Requirements: Option: electronic application. Required for some: high school transcript, SAT or ACT. Entrance: moderately difficult. Application deadline: rolling. Notification: continuous. SAT Reasoning Test deadline: 5/15. SAT Subject Test deadline: 5/15. Transfer credits accepted: Yes.
Costs Per Year: Application fee: $50. State resident tuition: $5259 full-time, $350 per credit hour part-time. Nonresident tuition: $21,341 full-time, $689 per credit hour part-time. Mandatory fees: $2435 full-time, $111 per term part-time. Full-time tuition and fees vary according to course load and reciprocity agreements. Part-time tuition and fees vary according to course load. College room and board: $8994. Room and board charges vary according to board plan and housing facility.
Collegiate Environment: Orientation program. Drama-theater group, choral group, marching band, student-run newspaper, radio station. Social organizations: 300 open to all; national fraternities, national sororities, local fraternities, local sororities. Major annual events: Homecoming, Student Organizational Fair, Spring Fling. Student services: legal services, health clinic, personal-psychological counseling, women's center. Campus security: 24-hour emergency response devices and patrols, late night transport-escort service, controlled dormitory access. Albertson's Library plus 1 other. Books: 644,899 (physical), 60,977 (digital/electronic); Serial titles: 112,213 (digital/electronic); Databases: 303. Weekly public service hours: 115; study areas open 24 hours, 5-7 days a week; students can reserve study rooms. 900 computers available on campus for general student use. A campuswide network can be accessed from student residence rooms and from off campus. Students can access the following: online class registration. Staffed computer lab on campus provides training in use of computers, software, and the Internet.
Community Environment: Boise, the capital of Idaho and its largest city, is located on the Boise River at the upper end of the Boise Valley. It enjoys mild winters with very little snow and temperate summers with cool nights. Community facilities include hospitals and libraries. The Idaho Concert and Artists Association features artists of national and international fame. Points of interest are the State Capitol, Ann Morrison and Julia Davis Parks, Platt Gardens, State Historical Museum, Pioneer Village, Urquides Village, Boise Heights, Idaho City, and Silver City. The latter two are pioneer gold rush communities. Year-round recreational opportunities are available in and around Boise.

■ BRIGHAM YOUNG UNIVERSITY-IDAHO

525 S Ctr. St.
Rexburg, ID 83460
Tel: (208)496-2011
Fax: (208)496-1220
Web Site: www.byui.edu

Description: Independent, 4-year, coed, affiliated with The Church of Jesus Christ of Latter-day Saints. Awards associate and bachelor's degrees. Founded 1888. Setting: 255-acre small town campus. Total enrollment: 32,458. Faculty: 792 (481 full-time, 311 part-time). Student-undergrad faculty ratio is 25:1. 8,034 applied, 96% were admitted. Full-time: 16,538 students, 54% women, 46% men. Part-time: 15,920 students, 61% women, 39% men. Students come from 53 states and territories, 116 other countries, 78% from out-of-state. 0.3% American Indian or Alaska Native, non-Hispanic/Latino; 3% Hispanic/Latino; 0.6% Black or African American, non-Hispanic/Latino; 1% Asian, non-Hispanic/Latino; 0.7% Native Hawaiian or other Pacific Islander, non-Hispanic/Latino; 9% international. 15% 25 or older, 8% transferred in. Retention: 71% of full-time freshmen returned the following year. Academic areas with the most degrees conferred: business/marketing; health professions and related sciences; liberal arts/general studies. Core. Calendar: semesters. Academic remediation for entering students, services for LD students, advanced placement, accelerated degree program, honors program, summer session for credit, part-time degree program, adult/continuing education programs, internships. ROTC: Army.

Entrance Requirements: Option: electronic application. Required: essay, high school transcript, interview, SAT or ACT. Entrance: moderately difficult. Application deadline: 2/15. Notification: 4/1. Preference given to Latter-Day Saints Church members. SAT Reasoning Test deadline: 2/1. SAT Subject Test deadline: 2/1.

Collegiate Environment: Orientation program. Drama-theater group, choral group, student-run newspaper, radio station. Social organizations: national fraternities, national sororities. Student services: legal services, health clinic, personal-psychological counseling. Campus security: 24-hour emergency response devices and patrols, late night transport-escort service. David O. McKay Library. Students can reserve study rooms.

■ CARRINGTON COLLEGE-BOISE
1122 N Liberty St.
Boise, ID 83704
Tel: (208)377-8080
Web Site: www.carrington.edu
Description: Proprietary, 2-year, coed. Part of Carrington Colleges Group, Inc. Awards certificates and terminal associate degrees. Founded 1980. Total enrollment: 440. Faculty: 52 (18 full-time, 34 part-time). Student-undergrad faculty ratio is 14:1. Full-time: 395 students, 85% women, 15% men. Part-time: 51 students, 80% women, 20% men. 16% from out-of-state. 0.9% American Indian or Alaska Native, non-Hispanic/Latino; 17% Hispanic/Latino; 4% Black or African American, non-Hispanic/Latino; 7% Asian, non-Hispanic/Latino; 0.2% Native Hawaiian or other Pacific Islander, non-Hispanic/Latino. 60% 25 or older, 18% transferred in.
Entrance Requirements: Required: essay, high school transcript, interview, institutional entrance exam. Entrance: minimally difficult. Notification: continuous.
Collegiate Environment: Orientation program.

■ COLLEGE OF EASTERN IDAHO
1600 S 25th E
Idaho Falls, ID 83404-5788
Tel: (208)524-3000; Free: 800-662-0261
Fax: (208)524-3007
E-mail: hailey.mack@cei.edu
Web Site: www.eitc.edu
Description: State-supported, 2-year, coed. Awards certificates, transfer associate, and terminal associate degrees. Founded 1969. Setting: 60-acre small town campus. Educational spending for the previous fiscal year: $12,270 per student. Total enrollment: 791. Student-undergrad faculty ratio is 8:1. Students come from 7 states and territories, 1% from out-of-state. 0.6% American Indian or Alaska Native, non-Hispanic/Latino; 15% Hispanic/Latino; 0.1% Black or African American, non-Hispanic/Latino; 0.6% Asian, non-Hispanic/Latino; 0.3% Native Hawaiian or other Pacific Islander, non-Hispanic/Latino. 52% 25 or older. Retention: 40% of full-time freshmen returned the following year. Core. Calendar: semesters. Academic remediation for entering students, ESL program, services for LD students, advanced placement, summer session for credit, part-time degree program, adult/continuing education programs.
Entrance Requirements: Open admission. Options: electronic application, deferred admission. Required: high school transcript. Required for some: essay, interview, ACT Compass, ACT ASSET, or CPT. Entrance: noncompetitive. Application deadline: rolling. Transfer credits accepted: Yes.
Costs Per Year: Application fee: $0. Area resident tuition: $3096 full-time, $129 per credit hour part-time. State resident tuition: $4096 full-time, $179 per credit hour part-time. Nonresident tuition: $6192 full-time, $258 per credit hour part-time. Mandatory fees: $30 full-time. Full-time tuition and fees vary according to class time, course level, course load, degree level, location, program, and student level. Part-time tuition varies according to class time, course level, course load, degree level, location, program, and student level.
Collegiate Environment: Orientation program. Campus security: 24-hour emergency response devices and patrols, late night transport-escort service. Richard and Lila Jordan Library plus 1 other.

■ THE COLLEGE OF IDAHO
2112 Cleveland Blvd.
Caldwell, ID 83605
Tel: (208)459-5011; Free: 800-244-3246
Fax: (208)454-2077
E-mail: admission@collegeofidaho.edu
Web Site: www.collegeofidaho.edu
Description: Independent, comprehensive, coed. Awards bachelor's and master's degrees. Founded 1891. Setting: 50-acre suburban campus. Total enrollment: 964. Faculty: 139 (81 full-time, 58 part-time). Student-undergrad faculty ratio is 9:1. 2,754 applied, 49% were admitted. Full-time: 919 students, 52% women, 48% men. Part-time: 27 students, 63% women, 37% men. 36% from out-of-state. 0.3% American Indian or Alaska Native, non-Hispanic/Latino; 14% Hispanic/Latino; 2% Black or African American, non-Hispanic/Latino; 2% Asian, non-Hispanic/Latino; 1% Native Hawaiian or other Pacific Islander, non-Hispanic/Latino; 13% international. 4% 25 or older, 68% live on campus, 5% transferred in. Retention: 79% of full-time freshmen returned the following year. Academic areas with the most degrees conferred: health professions and related sciences; business/marketing; psychology. Core. Calendar: 12-6-12 week calendar. Academic remediation for entering students, ESL program, services for LD students, advanced placement, honors program, independent study, double major, summer session for credit, part-time degree program, co-op programs and internships, graduate courses open to undergrads. Off campus study. Study abroad program. ROTC: Army (c).
Entrance Requirements: Options: electronic application, early admission, early action, deferred admission, international baccalaureate accepted. Required: essay, high school transcript, 1 recommendation. Recommended: interview, class rank, extracurricular resume. Required for some: SAT or ACT. Entrance: moderately difficult. Application deadline: 2/16. Notification: continuous. Transfer credits accepted: Yes.
Costs Per Year: Comprehensive fee: $41,543 includes full-time tuition ($31,000), mandatory fees ($755), and college room and board ($9788). Part-time tuition: $1285 per credit.
Collegiate Environment: Orientation program. Drama-theater group, choral group, marching band, student-run newspaper. Social organizations: national fraternities, national sororities, local sororities. Student services: health clinic, personal-psychological counseling, women's center. Campus security: 24-hour emergency response devices and patrols, student patrols, late night transport-escort service, controlled dormitory access. Freshmen guaranteed college housing. On-campus residence required through junior year. Option: coed housing available. Cruzen-Murray. 100 computers available on campus for general student use. A campuswide network can be accessed. Students can access the following: online class registration, online course syllabi, course assignments, course discussion.

■ COLLEGE OF SOUTHERN IDAHO
PO Box 1238
Twin Falls, ID 83303-1238
Tel: (208)733-9554; Free: 800-680-0274
Fax: (208)736-3014
Web Site: www.csi.edu
Description: State and locally supported, 2-year, coed. Awards certificates and terminal associate degrees. Founded 1964. Setting: 287-acre small town campus. Total enrollment: 8,473. Faculty: 332 (155 full-time, 177 part-time). Student-undergrad faculty ratio is 21:1. Full-time: 2,402 students, 58% women, 42% men. Part-time: 6,071 students, 66% women, 34% men. 4% from out-of-state. 0.9% American Indian or Alaska Native, non-Hispanic/Latino; 22% Hispanic/Latino; 0.8% Black or African American, non-Hispanic/Latino; 0.9% Asian, non-Hispanic/Latino; 0.5% Native Hawaiian or other Pacific Islander, non-Hispanic/Latino; 0.8% international. 43% 25 or older, 4% live on campus. Core. Calendar: semesters. Academic remediation for entering students, ESL program, services for LD students, advanced placement, honors program, independent study, distance learning, summer session for credit, part-time degree program, adult/continuing education programs, co-op programs and internships.
Entrance Requirements: Open admission except for nursing program. Required: high school transcript. Required for some: interview. Entrance: noncompetitive.
Costs Per Year: Application fee: $10. Area resident tuition: $4200 full-time, $140 per credit hour part-time. State resident tuition: $5200 full-time, $190 per credit hour part-time. Nonresident tuition: $8550 full-time, $285 per credit hour part-time. Full-time tuition varies according to course load. Part-time tuition varies according to course load. College room and board: $5750. College room only: $2500. Room and board charges vary according to board plan.
Collegiate Environment: Drama-theater group, choral group, student-run newspaper, radio station. Most popular organizations: BPA, Delta Epsilon Chi, Chi Alpha (Christian Group), Vet Tech Club, Equine Club. Major annual events: Lane of Trees, Halloween Carnival, Ski Day. Student services: legal services, health clinic, personal-psychological counseling, women's center. Campus security: 24-hour emergency response devices and patrols, controlled dormitory access. College of Southern Idaho Library.

Community Environment: Twin Falls, a pleasant residential town with a population of 38,600, is the county seat of Twin Falls County, the cultural and trade center of South Central Idaho's Magic Valley. The city is located at the junction of Transcontinental Highway 30 and International Highway 93. Buses, railroads, and airlines serve the area. Due to the climate, location, and natural surroundings, there are an unlimited variety of outdoor recreational facilities and activities. The city serves as headquarters for the Sawtooth National Forest.

■ COLLEGE OF WESTERN IDAHO

6056 Birch Ln.
Nampa, ID 83687
Tel: (208)562-3000
Web Site: cwidaho.cc

Description: State-supported, 2-year, coed. Awards certificates, transfer associate, and terminal associate degrees. Founded 2007. Setting: rural campus with easy access to Boise. Total enrollment: 9,204. Faculty: 408 (125 full-time, 283 part-time). Student-undergrad faculty ratio is 22:1. 1% American Indian or Alaska Native, non-Hispanic/Latino; 14% Hispanic/Latino; 2% Black or African American, non-Hispanic/Latino; 1% Asian, non-Hispanic/Latino; 0.7% Native Hawaiian or other Pacific Islander, non-Hispanic/Latino. Core. Calendar: semesters. Academic remediation for entering students, ESL program, services for LD students, advanced placement, honors program, summer session for credit, part-time degree program, co-op programs and internships.

Entrance Requirements: Open admission. Options: electronic application, international baccalaureate accepted. Required: high school transcript. Recommended: SAT or ACT, ACT Compass. Application deadline: rolling. Transfer credits accepted: Yes.

Collegiate Environment: Orientation program. Student-run newspaper.

■ IDAHO STATE UNIVERSITY

921 S 8th Ave.
Pocatello, ID 83209
Tel: (208)282-0211
Web Site: www.isu.edu

Description: State-supported, university, coed. Awards bachelor's, master's, and doctoral degrees and post-master's certificates. Founded 1901. Setting: 1,100-acre urban campus. Total enrollment: 12,387. Faculty: 806 (617 full-time, 189 part-time). Student-undergrad faculty ratio is 14:1. 3,253 applied, 99% were admitted. 11% from top 10% of their high school class, 30% from top quarter, 57% from top half. Full-time: 6,137 students, 55% women, 45% men. Part-time: 4,279 students, 58% women, 42% men. Students come from 40 states and territories, 49 other countries, 9% from out-of-state. 2% American Indian or Alaska Native, non-Hispanic/Latino; 13% Hispanic/Latino; 1% Black or African American, non-Hispanic/Latino; 1% Asian, non-Hispanic/Latino; 0.3% Native Hawaiian or other Pacific Islander, non-Hispanic/Latino; 5% international. 31% 25 or older, 16% live on campus, 4% transferred in. Retention: 64% of full-time freshmen returned the following year. Academic areas with the most degrees conferred: health professions and related sciences; business/marketing; education; engineering. Core. Calendar: semesters. Academic remediation for entering students, ESL program, services for LD students, advanced placement, accelerated degree program, self-designed majors, honors program, independent study, distance learning, double major, summer session for credit, part-time degree program, adult/continuing education programs, co-op programs and internships, graduate courses open to undergrads. Off campus study. Study abroad program. ROTC: Army.

Entrance Requirements: Options: electronic application, early admission, deferred admission, international baccalaureate accepted. Required: high school transcript, minimum 2 high school GPA, SAT or ACT. Recommended: ACT. Entrance: minimally difficult. Application deadlines: rolling, rolling for nonresidents. Notification: continuous, continuous for nonresidents. Transfer credits accepted: Yes.

Collegiate Environment: Orientation program. Drama-theater group, choral group, marching band, student-run newspaper, radio station. Social organizations: 160 open to all; national fraternities, national sororities. Major annual events: Football Games, CommUniversity Welcome Back Orange & Black, Choir, Music Performances. Student services: health clinic, personal-psychological counseling, women's center. Campus security: 24-hour emergency response devices and patrols, late night transport-escort service, controlled dormitory access. 1,219 college housing spaces available; 968 were occupied in 2018-19. No special consideration for freshman housing applicants. Options: coed, men-only, women-only housing available. Eli M.

Oboler Library. Books: 620,925 (physical), 211,589 (digital/electronic); Serial titles: 150,874 (physical), 15,214 (digital/electronic); Databases: 173. Weekly public service hours: 103; students can reserve study rooms. 155 computers available on campus for general student use. A campuswide network can be accessed from student residence rooms and from off campus. Students can access the following: online class registration. Staffed computer lab on campus (open 24 hours a day) provides training in use of computers, software, and the Internet.

Community Environment: Pocatello is located in a farming and industrial area of southeastern Idaho where the climate is dry and sunny. Planes and buses provide transportation. The community facilities include many churches, two hospitals, the district health department, hotels, motels, etc. The municipal park has facilities for archery, baseball, field games, and includes a swimming pool and a zoo. Other facilities outside of Pocatello are in the intermountain region, which offers some of the best hunting and fishing in the United States. Camping, hiking, snowmobiling, swimming, boating, horseback riding and skiing available for the outdoor life. Rodeos and the Indian Sun Dances are special annual events.

■ LEWIS-CLARK STATE COLLEGE

500 Eighth Ave.
Lewiston, ID 83501-2698
Tel: (208)792-5272; Free: 800-933-5272
Fax: (208)799-2063
E-mail: admissions@lcsc.edu
Web Site: www.lcsc.edu

Description: State-supported, 4-year, coed. Awards associate and bachelor's degrees. Founded 1893. Setting: 44-acre small town campus. Total enrollment: 3,633. Faculty: 253 (173 full-time, 80 part-time). Student-undergrad faculty ratio is 14:1. 1,117 applied, 99% were admitted. 6% from top 10% of their high school class, 23% from top quarter, 46% from top half. Full-time: 2,274 students, 60% women, 40% men. Part-time: 1,359 students, 68% women, 32% men. 22% from out-of-state. 3% American Indian or Alaska Native, non-Hispanic/Latino; 6% Hispanic/Latino; 1% Black or African American, non-Hispanic/Latino; 1% Asian, non-Hispanic/Latino; 0.3% Native Hawaiian or other Pacific Islander, non-Hispanic/Latino; 3% international. 36% 25 or older, 14% live on campus, 11% transferred in. Academic areas with the most degrees conferred: health professions and related sciences; business/marketing; public administration and social services. Calendar: semesters. Part-time degree program, adult/continuing education programs. Study abroad program. ROTC: Army (c), Naval (c), Air Force (c).

Entrance Requirements: Options: electronic application, deferred admission, international baccalaureate accepted. Required: high school transcript, minimum 2 high school GPA. Required for some: interview, SAT or ACT. Entrance: minimally difficult.

Costs Per Year: Application fee: $0. State resident tuition: $6618 full-time, $338 per credit hour part-time. Nonresident tuition: $19,236 full-time, $338 per credit hour part-time. Full-time tuition varies according to course load and reciprocity agreements. College room and board: $7580. Room and board charges vary according to board plan and housing facility.

Collegiate Environment: Orientation program. Campus security: 24-hour emergency response devices and patrols, student patrols, late night transport-escort service. Lewis-Clark State College Library.

Community Environment: Lewiston is a small urban area that is a major community in the Nez Perce National Park area; climate is temperate. It is the center of a vast lumbering, mining, farming and ranching territory. Planes, buses and trains serve the area. Community facilities include libraries, museums, YWCA, hospital, clinics, community concert series and shopping areas. Part-time employment opportunities are good. Facilities are good for boating, fishing and big game hunting. Boat trips up Hell's Canyon of the Snake River are spectacular journeys; shorter trips are available. The Lewiston Roundup and Dogwood festival are special events.

■ NEW SAINT ANDREWS COLLEGE

405 S Main St.
Moscow, ID 83843
Tel: (208)882-1566
Fax: (208)882-4293
E-mail: info@nsa.edu
Web Site: www.nsa.edu

Description: Independent Christian, comprehensive, coed. Awards associate, bachelor's, and master's degrees. Founded 1993. Setting: small town campus. Educational spending for the previous fiscal year: $4997 per student. Total enrollment: 158. Faculty: 18 (6 full-time, 12 part-time).

Student-undergrad faculty ratio is 12:1. 68 applied, 93% were admitted. Full-time: 128 students, 59% women, 41% men. Part-time: 12 students, 50% women, 50% men. Students come from 28 states and territories, 5 other countries, 93% from out-of-state. 0.8% American Indian or Alaska Native, non-Hispanic/Latino; 4% Hispanic/Latino; 2% Asian, non-Hispanic/Latino; 7% international. 5% 25 or older. Retention: 76% of full-time freshmen returned the following year. Academic area with the most degrees conferred: liberal arts/general studies. Core. Calendar: 4 8-week terms. Advanced placement, independent study, summer session for credit, part-time degree program, graduate courses open to undergrads.

Entrance Requirements: Options: electronic application, deferred admission, international baccalaureate accepted. Required: essay, high school transcript, 2 recommendations, SAT or ACT. Required for some: interview. Entrance: moderately difficult. Application deadline: 2/15. Notification: 3/15. SAT Reasoning Test deadline: 8/1. Transfer credits accepted: Yes. Applicants placed on waiting list: 0.

Costs Per Year: Application fee: $40. Tuition: $475 per credit hour part-time. Part-time tuition varies according to program.

Collegiate Environment: Orientation program. Drama-theater group, choral group. Most popular organizations: Students for the Relief of the Oppressed, Nursing Home Visits and Elderly Assistance (snow and leaf removal, firewood distribution), Blood Drives, Fall Carnival, St. Andrews Day Food Bank Drive. Major annual events: Dances and Banquets, Student-Organized Sports, Theater Events. Student services: personal-psychological counseling. Campus security: 24-hour emergency response devices. Tyndale Library plus 1 other. Students can reserve study rooms. Operations spending for the previous fiscal year: $93,518. 4 computers available on campus for general student use. A campuswide network can be accessed from off-campus. Students can access the following: online class registration.

■ NORTH IDAHO COLLEGE

1000 W Garden Ave.
Coeur d Alene, ID 83814-2199
Tel: (208)769-3300; Free: 877-404-4536
Fax: (208)769-3273
E-mail: admit@nic.edu
Web Site: www.nic.edu

Description: State and locally supported, 2-year, coed. Awards certificates, transfer associate, and terminal associate degrees. Founded 1933. Setting: 42-acre small town campus. Total enrollment: 5,723. Faculty: 447 (160 full-time, 287 part-time). Student-undergrad faculty ratio is 17:1. 2,684 applied, 58% were admitted. Full-time: 3,437 students, 54% women, 46% men. Part-time: 2,286 students, 67% women, 33% men. 2% American Indian or Alaska Native, non-Hispanic/Latino; 3% Hispanic/Latino; 0.9% Black or African American, non-Hispanic/Latino; 1% Asian, non-Hispanic/Latino; 0.3% Native Hawaiian or other Pacific Islander, non-Hispanic/Latino. Core. Calendar: semesters. Academic remediation for entering students, ESL program, services for LD students, advanced placement, independent study, distance learning, summer session for credit, part-time degree program, adult/continuing education programs, co-op programs and internships. Off campus study at Lewis-Clark State College, University of Idaho. ROTC: Army (c).

Entrance Requirements: Options: electronic application, early admission, deferred admission. Required for some: essay, high school transcript, county residency certificate. Entrance: noncompetitive. Application deadline: 8/20.

Collegiate Environment: Orientation program. Drama-theater group, choral group, student-run newspaper. Social organizations: 25 open to all. Most popular organizations: Ski Club, Fusion, Baptist student ministries, Journalism Club, Phi Theta Kappa. Student services: legal services, health clinic, personal-psychological counseling, women's center. Campus security: 24-hour emergency response devices and patrols, late night transport-escort service. Molstead Library Computer Center. 145 computers available on campus for general student use. A campuswide network can be accessed. Students can access the following: online student information, records. Staffed computer lab on campus.

Community Environment: Coeur d'Alene is located on the north shore of Lake Coeur d'Alene, 33 miles east of Spokane, Washington. The area is a popular resort for summer and winter events. Two major ski areas are only minutes away from downtown and the lake offers many water sports activities. Average summer high temperature is 82 degrees and average summer lows are 51 degrees, average winter high temperature is 38 degrees and the average low is 26 degrees. There is an average of 50 inches of snow each year and total average precipitation is 26 inches. Transportation facilities for the Spokane/Coeur d'Alene area include bus, train and airline. Facilities of the community include library, hospital, county health unit and active civic

clubs. The college hosts art and music programs for the community in its 1,200 seat Boswell Hall auditorium. Coeur d'Alene draws its industry from tourism, high tech, forestry products and agricultural. Outdoor sports are boating, biking, hunting, fishing, golfing, water and snow skiing, sailing, windsurfing, swimming, and mountain biking.

■ NORTHWEST NAZARENE UNIVERSITY

623 S University Blvd.
Nampa, ID 83686-5897
Tel: (208)467-8011; Free: 877-668-4968
Fax: (208)467-8645
Web Site: www.nnu.edu

Description: Independent, comprehensive, coed, affiliated with Church of the Nazarene. Awards associate, bachelor's, master's, and doctoral degrees and post-master's certificates. Founded 1913. Setting: 85-acre small town campus with easy access to Boise. Total enrollment: 2,223. Faculty: 119 (118 full-time, 1 part-time). Student-undergrad faculty ratio is 16:1. 818 applied, 96% were admitted. 24% from top 10% of their high school class, 51% from top quarter, 80% from top half. Full-time: 1,154 students, 59% women, 41% men. Part-time: 376 students, 56% women, 44% men. 42% from out-of-state. 0.5% American Indian or Alaska Native, non-Hispanic/Latino; 7% Hispanic/Latino; 2% Black or African American, non-Hispanic/Latino; 2% Asian, non-Hispanic/Latino; 0.1% Native Hawaiian or other Pacific Islander, non-Hispanic/Latino; 4% international. 22% 25 or older, 71% live on campus, 5% transferred in. Retention: 76% of full-time freshmen returned the following year. Academic areas with the most degrees conferred: business/marketing; health professions and related sciences; education. Core. Calendar: semesters. Academic remediation for entering students, ESL program, services for LD students, advanced placement, accelerated degree program, self-designed majors, freshman honors college, honors program, independent study, distance learning, double major, summer session for credit, part-time degree program, adult/continuing education programs, co-op programs and internships, graduate courses open to undergrads. Off campus study at CCCU Exchange programs. Study abroad program. ROTC: Army.

Entrance Requirements: Options: electronic application, early action, deferred admission, international baccalaureate accepted. Required: essay, high school transcript, minimum 2.5 high school GPA, 2 recommendations, SAT or ACT. Required for some: interview. Entrance: moderately difficult. Application deadlines: 8/15, 12/15 for early action. Notification: continuous, 1/15 for early action. Transfer credits accepted: Yes.

Costs Per Year: Comprehensive fee: $37,200 includes full-time tuition ($29,300), mandatory fees ($500), and college room and board ($7400). College room only: $3550. Full-time tuition and fees vary according to class time, course load, degree level, location, program, and reciprocity agreements. Room and board charges vary according to board plan. Part-time tuition: $1200 per credit hour. Part-time mandatory fees: $250 per term. Part-time tuition and fees vary according to class time, location, and program.

Collegiate Environment: Orientation program. Drama-theater group, choral group, student-run newspaper. Social organizations: 40 open to all. Most popular organizations: Students in Free Enterprise (SIFE), Student Government Association, Fellowship of Christian Athletes, The Crusader newspaper, The Oasis yearbook. Major annual events: Fresheree Talent Show, TWIRP (The Woman is Required to Pay), Mr. NNU Pageant. Student services: health clinic, personal-psychological counseling. Campus security: 24-hour emergency response devices and patrols, student patrols, late night transport-escort service, controlled dormitory access, residence hall check-in system, on-campus police hub. John E. Riley Library.

Community Environment: Nampa, located in southwestern Idaho, has a mild climate with an average mean temperature of 51 degrees and average rainfall of 13 inches. It is the agricultural, industrial and transportation center of southwest Idaho. Industries are processing and packing food, building mobile homes, feed mills, and seed houses; Zilog, a computer chip manufacturer is located here. Community facilities include excellent library, churches representing 22 denominations, hospitals, motels and hotels. One hundred fifty civic, fraternal, and veterans organizations are active. Part-time employment is available. Recreational facilities consist of a state-of-the-art recreation center, six parks, softball and baseball fields, horseshoe courts, tennis courts, roller skating rink and bowling alleys; other facilities are Lake Lowell for swimming, boating, fishing and hunting. A ski run is within 35 miles. Points of interest are the Deer Flat National Wildlife Refuge, Givens' Hot Springs, Lakeview Park and Silver City and De Lamar, old mining towns. The Snake River Stampede, a rodeo, is an annual event held in July.

■ **STEVENS-HENAGER COLLEGE (BOISE)**

1444 S Entertainment Ave.
Boise, ID 83709
Tel: (208)336-7671; Free: 800-622-2640
Web Site: www.stevenshenager.edu
Description: Independent, 4-year, coed. Awards associate and bachelor's degrees. Founded 2004.

■ **STEVENS-HENAGER COLLEGE (IDAHO FALLS)**

901 Pier View Dr.
Ste. 105
Idaho Falls, ID 83402
Tel: (208)522-0887; Free: 800-622-2640
Web Site: www.stevenshenager.edu
Description: Independent, 4-year, coed. Awards associate and bachelor's degrees.

■ **UNIVERSITY OF IDAHO**

875 Perimeter Dr.
Moscow, ID 83844-2282
Tel: (208)885-6111; Free: 888-884-3246
Fax: (208)885-6911
E-mail: admissions@uidaho.edu
Web Site: www.uidaho.edu
Description: State-supported, university, coed. Awards bachelor's, master's, and doctoral degrees and post-master's certificates. Founded 1889. Setting: 810-acre small town campus. Endowment: $279.9 million. Research spending for the previous fiscal year: $111.6 million. Educational spending for the previous fiscal year: $6981 per student. Total enrollment: 11,841. Faculty: 715 (600 full-time, 115 part-time). Student-undergrad faculty ratio is 14:1. 7,938 applied, 77% were admitted. 18% from top 10% of their high school class, 40% from top quarter, 72% from top half. Full-time: 7,039 students, 48% women, 52% men. Part-time: 2,529 students, 54% women, 46% men. Students come from 51 states and territories, 45 other countries, 22% from out-of-state. 0.9% American Indian or Alaska Native, non-Hispanic/Latino; 10% Hispanic/Latino; 1% Black or African American, non-Hispanic/Latino; 1% Asian, non-Hispanic/Latino; 0.4% Native Hawaiian or other Pacific Islander, non-Hispanic/Latino; 4% international. 11% 25 or older, 37% live on campus, 6% transferred in. Retention: 81% of full-time freshmen returned the following year. Academic areas with the most degrees conferred: business/marketing; engineering; social sciences. Core. Calendar: semesters. Academic remediation for entering students, ESL program, services for LD students, advanced placement, accelerated degree program, honors program, independent study, distance learning, double major, summer session for credit, part-time degree program, adult/continuing education programs, co-op programs and internships, graduate courses open to undergrads. Off campus study at National Student Exchange. Study abroad program. ROTC: Army, Naval, Air Force (c).

Entrance Requirements: Options: electronic application, deferred admission, international baccalaureate accepted. Required: high school transcript, minimum 2.2 high school GPA, SAT or ACT. Required for some: essay, SAT and SAT Subject Tests or ACT. Entrance: moderately difficult. Application deadline: 8/1. Notification: continuous. Transfer credits accepted: Yes.

Costs Per Year: Application fee: $60. State resident tuition: $5778 full-time, $348 per credit hour part-time. Nonresident tuition: $23,414 full-time, $1230 per credit hour part-time. Mandatory fees: $2086 full-time, $46 per credit hour part-time. Full-time tuition and fees vary according to course load, program, and reciprocity agreements. Part-time tuition and fees vary according to program and reciprocity agreements. College room and board: $8880. Room and board charges vary according to board plan and housing facility.

Collegiate Environment: Orientation program. Drama-theater group, choral group, marching band, student-run newspaper, radio station. Social organizations: 140 open to all; national fraternities, national sororities; 18% of eligible men and 21% of eligible women are members. Most popular organizations: Student Alumni Relations Board (SARB), Associate Students University of Idaho (ASUI), Vandal Volunteers Club, Earth Club, Gender and Sexuality Alliance. Major annual events: Palousafest, UIdaho Bound, Cruise the World. Student services: health clinic, personal-psychological counseling, women's center. Campus security: 24-hour emergency response devices and patrols, late night transport-escort service, controlled dormitory access. 2,138 college housing spaces available; 1,868 were occupied in 2018-19. Freshmen guaranteed college housing. On-campus residence required in freshman year. Options: coed, men-only, women-only housing available. University of Idaho Library plus 1 other. Books: 1.5 million (physical), 1.3 million (digital/electronic); Serial titles: 109,553 (physical), 177,970 (digital/electronic). Operations spending for the previous fiscal year: $8.2 million. 510 computers available on campus for general student use. A campuswide network can be accessed from student residence rooms and from off campus. Students can access the following: online class registration. Staffed computer lab on campus provides training in use of computers, software, and the Internet.

Community Environment: The location is rural, combining the peace, calm, and simplicity of the country with the intellectual atmosphere of a progressive college town. Moscow is in Idaho's Palouse Hill country and leads the nation in the production and processing of seed peas and lentils. Community facilities include a library, churches, clinics, hospital, hotels and motels and 2 shopping malls. Air, bus and railroads serve the area. Part-time work is available. Apartments and rooms may be rented. Eight miles away is Washington State University, the land grant institution for the state of Washington. There is an active faculty exchange, cross registration, and multiple library resources.

■ **AMBRIA COLLEGE OF NURSING**

5210 Trillium Blvd.

Hoffman Estates, IL 60192

Tel: (847)397-0300

Web Site: www.ambria.edu

Description: Proprietary, primarily 2-year, coed. Awards transfer associate, terminal associate, and bachelor's degrees.

■ **AMERICAN ACADEMY OF ART**

332 S Michigan Ave.

Chicago, IL 60604-4302

Tel: (312)461-0600; Free: 888-461-0600

E-mail: srosenbloom@aaart.edu

Web Site: www.aaart.edu

Description: Independent, 4-year, coed. Awards bachelor's degrees. Founded 1923. Setting: urban campus with easy access to Chicago. Total enrollment: 260. Faculty: 26 (all full-time). Student-undergrad faculty ratio is 14:1. Full-time: 193 students, 65% women, 35% men. Part-time: 67 students, 54% women, 46% men. Students come from 7 states and territories, 18% from out-of-state. 0.4% American Indian or Alaska Native, non-Hispanic/Latino; 36% Hispanic/Latino; 10% Black or African American, non-Hispanic/Latino; 4% Asian, non-Hispanic/Latino; 0.8% Native Hawaiian or other Pacific Islander, non-Hispanic/Latino. 3% 25 or older, 2% transferred in. Retention: 75% of full-time freshmen returned the following year. Academic areas with the most degrees conferred: visual and performing arts; communication technologies. Core. Calendar: semesters. Academic remediation for entering students, accelerated degree program, independent study, summer session for credit, part-time degree program, adult/continuing education programs, internships. Study abroad program.

Entrance Requirements: Option: electronic application. Required: high school transcript, interview. Entrance: moderately difficult. Application deadline: rolling. Transfer credits accepted: Yes.

Costs Per Year: Application fee: $25. Tuition: $33,800 full-time. Mandatory fees: $720 full-time. Full-time tuition and fees vary according to course load.

Collegiate Environment: Orientation program. Campus security: 24-hour emergency response devices. Irving Shapiro Library.

Community Environment: See University of Chicago.

■ **AMERICAN INTERCONTINENTAL UNIVERSITY ONLINE**

231 N Martingale Rd.

6th Fl.

Schaumburg, IL 60173

Tel: (847)851-5000; Free: 877-701-3800

Fax: (847)851-6002

Web Site: www.aiuniv.edu

Description: Proprietary, comprehensive, coed. Administratively affiliated with American InterContinental University. Awards associate, bachelor's, and master's degrees (offers online degree programs only). Founded 1970. Setting: 1-acre suburban campus. Total enrollment: 22,424. Faculty: 396. Full-time: 20,341 students, 67% women, 33% men. 78% 25 or older, 20% transferred in. Academic areas with the most degrees conferred: business/marketing; computer and information sciences; homeland security, law enforcement, firefighting, and protective services. Core. Calendar: 5 10-week terms. Academic remediation for entering students, advanced place-

ment, accelerated degree program, distance learning, part-time degree program, adult/continuing education programs.

Entrance Requirements: Options: electronic application, deferred admission, international baccalaureate accepted. Required: essay, high school transcript, interview. Entrance: minimally difficult. Application deadline: rolling. Notification: continuous.

Collegiate Environment: Orientation program.

■ **ARGOSY UNIVERSITY, CHICAGO**

225 N Michigan Ave., Ste. 1300

Chicago, IL 60601

Tel: (312)777-7600; Free: 800-626-4123

Fax: (312)201-1907

Web Site: www.argosy.edu/chicago-illinois/default.aspx

Description: Proprietary, university, coed. Awards bachelor's, master's, and doctoral degrees. Founded 1976. Setting: urban campus. Calendar: semesters.

■ **AUGUSTANA COLLEGE**

639 38th St.

Rock Island, IL 61201-2296

Tel: (309)794-7000; Free: 800-798-8100

Fax: (309)794-7431

E-mail: admissions@augustana.edu

Web Site: www.augustana.edu

Description: Independent, 4-year, coed, affiliated with Evangelical Lutheran Church in America. Awards bachelor's degrees. Founded 1860. Setting: 115-acre suburban campus. Endowment: $168.8 million. Research spending for the previous fiscal year: $255,494. Educational spending for the previous fiscal year: $9903 per student. Total enrollment: 2,647. Faculty: 264 (195 full-time, 69 part-time). Student-undergrad faculty ratio is 12:1. 6,739 applied, 59% were admitted. 36% from top 10% of their high school class, 64% from top quarter, 90% from top half. Full-time: 2,637 students, 58% women, 42% men. Part-time: 10 students, 40% women, 60% men. Students come from 32 states and territories, 42 other countries, 15% from out-of-state. 10% Hispanic/Latino; 4% Black or African American, non-Hispanic/Latino; 2% Asian, non-Hispanic/Latino; 0.2% Native Hawaiian or other Pacific Islander, non-Hispanic/Latino; 7% international. 1% 25 or older, 71% live on campus, 2% transferred in. Retention: 87% of full-time freshmen returned the following year. Academic areas with the most degrees conferred: business/marketing; biological/life sciences; social sciences. Core. Calendar: quarters. ESL program, services for LD students, advanced placement, self-designed majors, honors program, independent study, double major, summer session for credit, part-time degree program, internships. Off campus study. Study abroad program.

Entrance Requirements: Options: electronic application, early admission, early decision, early action, deferred admission, international baccalaureate accepted. Required: high school transcript. Recommended: essay, 1 recommendation, interview. Required for some: essay, interview. Entrance: moderately difficult. Application deadlines: rolling, 11/1 for early decision, 11/1 for early action. Notification: continuous, 11/15 for early decision, 12/1 for early action. Transfer credits accepted: Yes. Early decision applicants: 33. Early decision applicants admitted: 32. Early action applicants: 0. Early action applicants admitted: 0.

Costs Per Year: Application fee: $0. Comprehensive fee: $52,707 includes

full-time tuition ($42,135) and college room and board ($10,572). College room only: $5079. Room and board charges vary according to board plan and housing facility. Part-time tuition: $1808 per credit. Part-time tuition varies according to course load.

Collegiate Environment: Orientation program. Drama-theater group, choral group, student-run newspaper, radio station. Social organizations: 208 open to all; local fraternities, local sororities; 26% of eligible men and 39% of eligible women are members. Most popular organizations: College Union Board of Managers, Student Government Association, student newspaper, student radio station, service organizations (APO, Dance Marathon committee). Major annual events: Symposium Day (alternate day of learning), All Campus Volunteer Day, Homecoming. Student services: personal-psychological counseling. Campus security: 24-hour emergency response devices and patrols, late night transport-escort service, controlled dormitory access. Thomas Tredway Library plus 1 other. Books: 128,238 (physical), 4,470 (digital/electronic); Serial titles: 233 (physical), 120,219 (digital/electronic); Databases: 106. Weekly public service hours: 100. Operations spending for the previous fiscal year: $1.3 million. 600 computers available on campus for general student use. A campuswide network can be accessed. Students can access the following: online class registration. Staffed computer lab on campus provides training in use of computers, software, and the Internet.

■ AURORA UNIVERSITY

347 S Gladstone Ave.
Aurora, IL 60506-4892
Tel: (630)892-6431; Free: 800-742-5281
Fax: (630)844-5535
E-mail: admission@aurora.edu
Web Site: www.aurora.edu

Description: Independent, comprehensive, coed. Awards bachelor's, master's, and doctoral degrees and post-master's certificates. Founded 1893. Setting: 70-acre suburban campus with easy access to Chicago. Endowment: $41.2 million. Educational spending for the previous fiscal year: $5530 per student. Total enrollment: 6,005. Faculty: 447 (139 full-time, 308 part-time). Student-undergrad faculty ratio is 18:1. 3,296 applied, 81% were admitted. Full-time: 3,537 students, 64% women, 36% men. Part-time: 483 students, 72% women, 28% men. Students come from 38 states and territories, 3 other countries, 11% from out-of-state. 0.2% American Indian or Alaska Native, non-Hispanic/Latino; 31% Hispanic/Latino; 7% Black or African American, non-Hispanic/Latino; 2% Asian, non-Hispanic/Latino; 0.1% Native Hawaiian or other Pacific Islander, non-Hispanic/Latino; 0.3% international. 17% 25 or older, 16% live on campus, 14% transferred in. Retention: 75% of full-time freshmen returned the following year. Academic areas with the most degrees conferred: business/marketing; health professions and related sciences; public administration and social services. Core. Calendar: semesters. Academic remediation for entering students, services for LD students, advanced placement, accelerated degree program, self-designed majors, independent study, distance learning, double major, summer session for credit, part-time degree program, adult/continuing education programs, internships, graduate courses open to undergrads. Off campus study at 3 members of the Council of West Suburban Colleges. Study abroad program. ROTC: Army (c).

Entrance Requirements: Options: electronic application, deferred admission. Required: high school transcript, minimum 2 high school GPA, SAT or ACT. Required for some: essay, 2 recommendations, interview. Entrance: moderately difficult. Application deadline: rolling. Notification: continuous. Transfer credits accepted: Yes.

Costs Per Year: Application fee: $0. Comprehensive fee: $36,760 includes full-time tuition ($24,800), mandatory fees ($260), and college room and board ($11,700). College room only: $6500. Part-time tuition: $710 per semester hour.

Collegiate Environment: Orientation program. Drama-theater group, choral group, student-run newspaper, radio station. Social organizations: 60 open to all; national fraternities, national sororities, local fraternities, local sororities; 1% of eligible men and 1% of eligible women are members. Most popular organizations: Latin American Student Organization, American Marketing Association, Student Nursing Association, Phi Eta Sigma, Spartan Athletic Training Student Organization. Major annual events: Fall Involvement Fair, Spring Fling Carnival, Pancake Night. Student services: health clinic, personal-psychological counseling. Campus security: 24-hour emergency response devices and patrols, late night transport-escort service, controlled dormitory access. 720 college housing spaces available; 679 were occupied in 2018-19. Freshmen given priority for college housing. Option:

coed housing available. Charles B. Phillips Library plus 1 other. Books: 24,587 (physical), 178,780 (digital/electronic); Serial titles: 2 (physical), 71,529 (digital/electronic); Databases: 63. Weekly public service hours: 96; students can reserve study rooms. Operations spending for the previous fiscal year: $736,686. 193 computers available on campus for general student use. A campuswide network can be accessed from student residence rooms and from off campus. Students can access the following: online class registration, learning management system. Staffed computer lab on campus.

Community Environment: Aurora is a large suburb in the Chicago metropolitan area but retains its own distinctive community life and atmosphere. The city is located in the Fox River Valley, 40 miles west of Chicago. Aurora is a city of schools, churches, libraries, and beautiful homes. Phillips Park provides facilities for tennis, swimming and golf.

■ BENEDICTINE UNIVERSITY

5700 College Rd.
Lisle, IL 60532
Tel: (630)829-6000; Free: 888-829-6363
Fax: (630)960-1126
E-mail: admissions@ben.edu
Web Site: www.ben.edu

Description: Independent Roman Catholic, comprehensive, coed. Awards bachelor's, master's, and doctoral degrees. Founded 1887. Setting: 108-acre suburban campus with easy access to Chicago. Endowment: $36.4 million. Research spending for the previous fiscal year: $251,492. Educational spending for the previous fiscal year: $7387 per student. Total enrollment: 4,940. Faculty: 436 (152 full-time, 284 part-time). Student-undergrad faculty ratio is 12:1. 5,257 applied, 65% were admitted. 14% from top 10% of their high school class, 40% from top quarter, 74% from top half. Full-time: 2,372 students, 55% women, 45% men. Part-time: 346 students, 53% women, 47% men. Students come from 49 states and territories, 11 other countries, 10% from out-of-state. 0.7% American Indian or Alaska Native, non-Hispanic/Latino; 17% Hispanic/Latino; 8% Black or African American, non-Hispanic/Latino; 14% Asian, non-Hispanic/Latino; 0.4% Native Hawaiian or other Pacific Islander, non-Hispanic/Latino; 1% international. 14% 25 or older, 22% live on campus, 11% transferred in. Retention: 72% of full-time freshmen returned the following year. Academic areas with the most degrees conferred: business/marketing; health professions and related sciences; psychology. Core. Calendar: semesters. Academic remediation for entering students, ESL program, services for LD students, advanced placement, accelerated degree program, honors program, independent study, distance learning, double major, summer session for credit, part-time degree program, adult/continuing education programs, internships, graduate courses open to undergrads. Off campus study. Study abroad program. ROTC: Army (c).

Entrance Requirements: Options: electronic application, deferred admission. Required: essay, high school transcript, SAT or ACT. Recommended: rank in upper 50% of high school class. Required for some: interview. Entrance: moderately difficult. Application deadline: rolling. Notification: continuous. SAT Reasoning Test deadline: 8/28. SAT Subject Test deadline: 8/28. Transfer credits accepted: Yes.

Costs Per Year: Application fee: $40. Tuition: $34,290 full-time, $1090 per credit hour part-time. Mandatory fees: $1590 full-time, $60 per credit hour part-time.

Collegiate Environment: Orientation program. Choral group, student-run newspaper, radio station. Social organizations: 50 open to all. Most popular organizations: Student Senate, MSA-Muslim Student Association, AMSA-American Medical Student Association, The Candor-Student Newspaper, Programming Board. Major annual events: Thanksgiving and Christmas Dinner, Quad Day, Homecoming. Student services: health clinic, personal-psychological counseling. Campus security: 24-hour emergency response devices and patrols, late night transport-escort service, controlled dormitory access. 782 college housing spaces available; 604 were occupied in 2018-19. Freshmen guaranteed college housing. Options: coed, men-only, women-only housing available. Benedictine Library. Books: 90,762 (physical), 187,960 (digital/electronic); Serial titles: 1,498 (physical), 51,758 (digital/electronic); Databases: 61. Students can reserve study rooms. Operations spending for the previous fiscal year: $1.2 million. 275 computers available on campus for general student use. A campuswide network can be accessed from student residence rooms and from off campus. Students can access the following: online class registration. Staffed computer lab on campus.

Community Environment: Lisle (population 23,000) is a suburban city located in Greater Chicago between Downers Grove and Naperville; it enjoys a temperate climate. Trains and buses serve the area. Ten shopping centers are located within 10 miles of the campus. Part-time employment is available for students. Recreational activities include varsity and intramural sports. Lisle is the home of the world famous Morton Arboretum. Benedictine University is located in DuPage County, one of the fastest growing areas in the Midwest.

■ **BLACK HAWK COLLEGE**
6600 34th Ave.
Moline, IL 61265-5899
Tel: (309)796-5000; Free: 800-334-1311
E-mail: ghurtado@bhc.edu
Web Site: www.bhc.edu
Description: State and locally supported, 2-year, coed. Awards certificates, transfer associate, and terminal associate degrees. Founded 1946. Setting: 232-acre urban campus. Educational spending for the previous fiscal year: $4754 per student. Total enrollment: 4,333. Faculty: 202 (101 full-time, 101 part-time). Student-undergrad faculty ratio is 20:1. 859 applied, 100% were admitted. 8% from top 10% of their high school class, 23% from top quarter, 53% from top half. Full-time: 1,625 students, 55% women, 45% men. Part-time: 2,708 students, 64% women, 36% men. Students come from 9 states and territories, 10 other countries, 11% from out-of-state. 0.2% American Indian or Alaska Native, non-Hispanic/Latino; 15% Hispanic/Latino; 11% Black or African American, non-Hispanic/Latino; 2% Asian, non-Hispanic/Latino. 28% 25 or older, 4% transferred in. Core. Calendar: semesters. Academic remediation for entering students, ESL program, services for LD students, advanced placement, independent study, distance learning, summer session for credit, part-time degree program, internships.
Entrance Requirements: Open admission. Options: electronic application, early admission, deferred admission. Recommended: high school transcript. Entrance: noncompetitive. Application deadlines: rolling, rolling for nonresidents, rolling for early decision plan 1, rolling for early decision plan 2, rolling for early action. Notification: continuous, continuous for nonresidents, rolling for early decision plan 1, rolling for early decision plan 2, rolling for early action. Transfer credits accepted: Yes.
Costs Per Year: Application fee: $20. Area resident tuition: $4470 full-time, $149 per credit hour part-time. State resident tuition: $7500 full-time, $250 per credit hour part-time. Nonresident tuition: $7650 full-time, $255 per credit hour part-time.
Collegiate Environment: Orientation program. Drama-theater group, choral group, student-run newspaper. Social organizations: 22 open to all. Most popular organizations: National Student Nurses Association, Wellness Club, Student Ambassadors, Association of Lation American Students, Clean Sphere. Major annual events: Fall Festival, Club and Organization Fair, Spring Fling. Student services: personal-psychological counseling. Campus security: 24-hour patrols. College housing not available. Quad City Campus Library plus 1 other. Books: 28,441 (physical), 181,568 (digital/electronic); Serial titles: 136 (physical), 50,357 (digital/electronic); Databases: 39. Weekly public service hours: 51; students can reserve study rooms. Operations spending for the previous fiscal year: $438,783. 950 computers available on campus for general student use. Computer purchase/lease plans available. A campuswide network can be accessed. Students can access the following: online class registration, college portal called myBlackHawk. Staffed computer lab on campus.

■ **BLACKBURN COLLEGE**
700 College Ave.
Carlinville, IL 62626-1498
Tel: (217)854-3231; Free: 800-233-3550
Fax: (217)854-3713
E-mail: justin.norwood@blackburn.edu
Web Site: www.blackburn.edu
Description: Independent Presbyterian, 4-year, coed. Awards bachelor's degrees. Founded 1837. Setting: 80-acre small town campus with easy access to St. Louis. Endowment: $23.4 million. Educational spending for the previous fiscal year: $6657 per student. Total enrollment: 566. Faculty: 75 (38 full-time, 37 part-time). Student-undergrad faculty ratio is 13:1. 869 applied, 54% were admitted. 10% from top 10% of their high school class, 32% from top quarter, 67% from top half. 5 valedictorians. Full-time: 548 students, 60% women, 40% men. Part-time: 18 students, 67% women, 33% men. Students come from 20 states and territories, 8 other countries, 10% from out-of-state. 4% Hispanic/Latino; 12% Black or African American, non-Hispanic/Latino; 1% Asian, non-Hispanic/Latino; 0.2% Native Hawaiian or other Pacific Islander, non-Hispanic/Latino; 2% international. 4% 25 or older,

69% live on campus, 5% transferred in. Retention: 70% of full-time freshmen returned the following year. Academic areas with the most degrees conferred: biological/life sciences; business/marketing; homeland security, law enforcement, firefighting, and protective services; visual and performing arts; psychology; education. Core. Calendar: semesters. Services for LD students, advanced placement, self-designed majors, honors program, independent study, double major, summer session for credit, co-op programs and internships. Off campus study. Study abroad program.
Entrance Requirements: Options: electronic application, deferred admission. Required: high school transcript, minimum 2 high school GPA, SAT or ACT. Recommended: minimum 2.5 high school GPA. Required for some: essay, 3 recommendations, interview. Entrance: moderately difficult. Application deadlines: rolling, rolling for nonresidents. Notification: continuous, continuous for nonresidents. Transfer credits accepted: Yes.
Costs Per Year: Application fee: $0. Comprehensive fee: $31,610 includes full-time tuition ($23,510) and college room and board ($8100). College room only: $4800. Part-time tuition: $765 per credit hour.
Collegiate Environment: Orientation program. Drama-theater group, choral group, student-run newspaper, radio station. Social organizations: 30 open to all. Most popular organizations: Habitat for Humanity, Pre-Health Professions, Running Club, Trading Card Games, Spectrum. Major annual events: Homecoming Dance, Mission Improvable, Platinum Bingo. Student services: personal-psychological counseling. Campus security: student patrols, late night transport-escort service. 454 college housing spaces available; 409 were occupied in 2018-19. Freshmen guaranteed college housing. On-campus residence required through junior year. Options: coed, men-only, women-only housing available. Lumpkin Learning Commons. Books: 62,000 (physical); Serial titles: 40 (physical); Databases: 21. Weekly public service hours: 80; students can reserve study rooms. Operations spending for the previous fiscal year: $194,549. 202 computers available on campus for general student use. A campuswide network can be accessed from student residence rooms and from off campus. Students can access the following: online class registration. Staffed computer lab on campus provides training in use of computers, software, and the Internet.

■ **BLESSING-RIEMAN COLLEGE OF NURSING & HEALTH SCIENCES**
11th and Oak
Quincy, IL 62305-7005
Tel: (217)228-5520; Free: 800-877-9140
Fax: (217)223-6400
E-mail: admissions@brcn.edu
Web Site: www.brcn.edu
Description: Independent, comprehensive, coed. Awards bachelor's and master's degrees. Founded 1985. Setting: 1-acre small town campus. Endowment: $7 million. Educational spending for the previous fiscal year: $8583 per student. Total enrollment: 251. Faculty: 18 (all full-time). Student-undergrad faculty ratio is 12:1. 546 applied, 66% were admitted. Full-time: 192 students, 88% women, 12% men. Part-time: 41 students, 83% women, 17% men. Students come from 10 states and territories, 30% from out-of-state. 0.9% Hispanic/Latino; 5% Black or African American, non-Hispanic/Latino; 2% Asian, non-Hispanic/Latino. 33% 25 or older, 82% live on campus, 12% transferred in. Academic area with the most degrees conferred: health professions and related sciences. Core. Calendar: semesters. Academic remediation for entering students, advanced placement, honors program, distance learning, double major, summer session for credit, part-time degree program, adult/continuing education programs, internships.
Entrance Requirements: Options: electronic application, deferred admission. Required: high school transcript, minimum 3 high school GPA, SAT or ACT. Recommended: essay, interview. Entrance: moderately difficult. Application deadline: rolling.
Collegiate Environment: Orientation program. Drama-theater group, choral group, student-run newspaper, radio station. Social organizations: national fraternities, national sororities; 40% of women are members. Most popular organization: Student Nurses Organization. Major annual events: Teddy Bear Clinic, Health Fair, Convocation. Student services: health clinic, personal-psychological counseling. Campus security: 24-hour patrols, late night transport-escort service, controlled dormitory access. Blessing Health Professions Library plus 1 other. Operations spending for the previous fiscal year: $431,748. 28 computers available on campus for general student use. A campuswide network can be accessed. Staffed computer lab on campus provides training in use of computers, software, and the Internet.

■ BRADLEY UNIVERSITY

1501 W Bradley Ave.
Peoria, IL 61625-0002
Tel: (309)676-7611; Free: 800-447-6460
E-mail: admissions@bradley.edu
Web Site: www.bradley.edu

Description: Independent, comprehensive, coed. Awards bachelor's, master's, and doctoral degrees and post-master's certificates. Founded 1897. Setting: 85-acre suburban campus. Endowment: $312.5 million. Research spending for the previous fiscal year: $3.1 million. Educational spending for the previous fiscal year: $16,047 per student. Total enrollment: 5,882. Faculty: 589 (354 full-time, 235 part-time). Student-undergrad faculty ratio is 12:1. 11,209 applied, 67% were admitted. 32% from top 10% of their high school class, 64% from top quarter, 92% from top half. Full-time: 4,462 students, 51% women, 49% men. Part-time: 144 students, 44% women, 56% men. Students come from 47 states and territories, 42 other countries, 18% from out-of-state. 10% Hispanic/Latino; 7% Black or African American, non-Hispanic/Latino; 3% Asian, non-Hispanic/Latino; 2% international. 3% 25 or older, 67% live on campus, 4% transferred in. Retention: 82% of full-time freshmen returned the following year. Academic areas with the most degrees conferred: business/marketing; engineering; health professions and related sciences. Core. Calendar: semesters. Services for LD students, advanced placement, accelerated degree program, self-designed majors, honors program, independent study, distance learning, double major, summer session for credit, part-time degree program, co-op programs and internships, graduate courses open to undergrads. Off campus study at Washington Semester; Hollywood Semester. Study abroad program. ROTC: Army.

Entrance Requirements: Options: electronic application, deferred admission, international baccalaureate accepted. Required: essay, high school transcript, SAT or ACT. Recommended: minimum 2.75 high school GPA, 1 recommendation, interview. Required for some: audition required of music majors and recommended for theatre majors, portfolio recommended for art majors. Entrance: moderately difficult. Application deadline: rolling. Notification: continuous. SAT Reasoning Test deadline: 7/1. Transfer credits accepted: Yes. Applicants placed on waiting list: 0. Wait-listed applicants offered admission: 0.

Costs Per Year: One-time mandatory fee: $200. Comprehensive fee: $44,380 includes full-time tuition ($33,360), mandatory fees ($400), and college room and board ($10,620). College room only: $6140. Full-time tuition and fees vary according to course load and program. Room and board charges vary according to board plan and housing facility. Part-time tuition: $890 per credit hour. Part-time mandatory fees: $400 per year. Part-time tuition and fees vary according to course load and program.

Collegiate Environment: Orientation program. Drama-theater group, choral group, student-run newspaper, radio station. Social organizations: 245 open to all; national fraternities, national sororities; 32% of eligible men and 31% of eligible women are members. Most popular organizations: Activities Council of Bradley University, CRU (Campus Christian group), Fraternity/Sorority Life, Service on Saturday, Alpha Phi Omega (Coed Service). Major annual events: Late Night BU, Student Organization Fair, Taste of Bradley. Student services: health clinic, personal-psychological counseling. Campus security: 24-hour emergency response devices and patrols, student patrols, late night transport-escort service, controlled dormitory access, emergency text messaging, mass notification/emergency communication system in 20 academic buildings. 3,290 college housing spaces available; 2,975 were occupied in 2018-19. Freshmen guaranteed college housing. On-campus residence required through sophomore year. Option: coed housing available. Cullom-Davis Library. Books: 545,721 (physical), 5,632 (digital/electronic); Serial titles: 1,557 (physical), 54,082 (digital/electronic); Databases: 54. Weekly public service hours: 129; students can reserve study rooms. Operations spending for the previous fiscal year: $2.5 million. 80 computers available on campus for general student use. Computer purchase/lease plans available. A campuswide network can be accessed from student residence rooms and from off campus. Students can access the following: online class registration, Online directory, catalog, library materials and other resources. Staffed computer lab on campus provides training in use of computers, software, and the Internet.

Community Environment: Bradley benefits tremendously from its location in Peoria, the state's second largest metropolitan area. (350,000) Students find manifold opportunities in terms of professional internships, cooperative education programs, research opportunities, social and cultural life and employment, and they also benefit from adjunct professors employed in various professors employed in various Peoria area businesses, professions, and other organizations. Peoria is a mecca for the arts and medical sciences. The city's three major health care facilities and the University of Illinois School of Medicine are known collectively as the Downstate Medical Center of Illinois. Together they have built one of the most modern, comprehensive health systems in the Midwest. With a symphony orchestra, civic opera, ballet company and a rich theater and gallery life, Peoria is the center of arts activity in central Illinois. Peoria is blessed with natural beauty, clean air and water, numerous parks, an all-season sports arena and a wealth of recreational opportunities. Peoria is within easy driving distance of two great cities: Three hours from Chicago and from St. Louis.

■ CARL SANDBURG COLLEGE

2400 Tom L. Wilson Blvd.
Galesburg, IL 61401-9576
Tel: (309)344-2518
Fax: (309)344-1395
Web Site: www.sandburg.edu

Description: State and locally supported, 2-year, coed. Part of Illinois Community College Board. Awards certificates, transfer associate, and terminal associate degrees. Founded 1967. Setting: 105-acre small town campus. Total enrollment: 2,693. 40% 25 or older. Calendar: semesters. Academic remediation for entering students, ESL program, services for LD students, advanced placement, self-designed majors, summer session for credit, part-time degree program, adult/continuing education programs, co-op programs and internships. ROTC: Army (c).

Entrance Requirements: Open admission for district residents. Options: early admission, deferred admission. Required: high school transcript. Entrance: noncompetitive. Application deadline: rolling.

Collegiate Environment: Drama-theater group, choral group. Student services: personal-psychological counseling. Campus security: 24-hour emergency response devices and patrols. Learning Resource Center plus 1 other. 110 computers available on campus for general student use. Staffed computer lab on campus.

Community Environment: Galesburg (population 32,000), once selected as one of the four ideal American cities by noted editor and author, Edward Bok, is located 180 miles southwest of Chicago on the main lines of the Burlington and Santa Fe Railroads. The Carl Sandburg birthplace preserves the early home of the poet and contains interesting Sandburg and Lincoln memoirs.

■ CHAMBERLAIN COLLEGE OF NURSING (ADDISON)

1221 N Swift Rd.
Addison, IL 60101
Tel: (630)953-3660; Free: 877-751-5783
Fax: (630)628-1154
Web Site: www.chamberlain.edu

Description: Proprietary, comprehensive, coed. Awards bachelor's, master's, and doctoral degrees and post-master's certificates. Total enrollment: 23,964. Faculty: 1,055 (75 full-time, 980 part-time). Student-undergrad faculty ratio is 24:1. Full-time: 2,183 students, 88% women, 12% men. Part-time: 12,076 students, 91% women, 9% men. 86% from out-of-state. 0.2% American Indian or Alaska Native, non-Hispanic/Latino; 10% Hispanic/Latino; 10% Black or African American, non-Hispanic/Latino; 5% Asian, non-Hispanic/Latino; 0.4% Native Hawaiian or other Pacific Islander, non-Hispanic/Latino; 0.3% international. 92% 25 or older, 40% transferred in. Calendar: semesters.

Entrance Requirements: Option: deferred admission. Required: SAT or ACT. Application deadline: rolling. Notification: continuous.

■ CHAMBERLAIN COLLEGE OF NURSING (CHICAGO)

3300 N Campbell Ave.
Chicago, IL 60618
Tel: (773)961-3000; Free: 877-751-5783
Fax: (773)961-3190
Web Site: www.chamberlain.edu

Description: Proprietary, 4-year, coed. Awards bachelor's degrees. Total enrollment: 940. Faculty: 91 (23 full-time, 68 part-time). Student-undergrad faculty ratio is 11:1. Full-time: 296 students, 88% women, 12% men. Part-time: 644 students, 83% women, 17% men. 2% from out-of-state. 0.1% American Indian or Alaska Native, non-Hispanic/Latino; 21% Hispanic/Latino; 9% Black or African American, non-Hispanic/Latino; 17% Asian, non-Hispanic/Latino; 0.2% Native Hawaiian or other Pacific Islander, non-Hispanic/Latino; 1% international. 64% 25 or older, 27% transferred in.

Academic area with the most degrees conferred: health professions and related sciences. Calendar: semesters. Accelerated degree program, distance learning.

Entrance Requirements: Option: deferred admission. Required: SAT or ACT. Application deadline: rolling. Notification: continuous.

■ CHAMBERLAIN COLLEGE OF NURSING (TINLEY PARK)

18624 W Creek Dr.
Tinley Park, IL 60477
Tel: (708)560-2000; Free: 877-751-5783
Fax: (708)560-2099
Web Site: www.chamberlain.edu

Description: Proprietary, 4-year, coed. Awards bachelor's degrees. Total enrollment: 665. Faculty: 76 (17 full-time, 59 part-time). Student-undergrad faculty ratio is 11:1. Full-time: 263 students, 88% women, 12% men. Part-time: 402 students, 89% women, 11% men. 6% from out-of-state. 19% Hispanic/Latino; 15% Black or African American, non-Hispanic/Latino; 4% Asian, non-Hispanic/Latino; 0.5% Native Hawaiian or other Pacific Islander, non-Hispanic/Latino. 54% 25 or older, 31% transferred in. Academic area with the most degrees conferred: health professions and related sciences. Accelerated degree program, distance learning.

Entrance Requirements: Option: deferred admission. Required: SAT or ACT. Application deadline: rolling. Notification: continuous.

■ CHICAGO STATE UNIVERSITY

9501 S King Dr.
Chicago, IL 60628
Tel: (773)995-2000
E-mail: jmarti21@csu.edu
Web Site: www.csu.edu

Description: State-supported, comprehensive, coed. Awards bachelor's, master's, and doctoral degrees. Founded 1867. Setting: 161-acre urban campus. Total enrollment: 5,211. Faculty: 366 (269 full-time, 97 part-time). Student-undergrad faculty ratio is 13:1. 5,517 applied, 30% were admitted. Full-time: 2,498 students, 70% women, 30% men. Part-time: 1,414 students, 73% women, 27% men. Students come from 25 states and territories, 23 other countries, 3% from out-of-state. 7% Hispanic/Latino; 74% Black or African American, non-Hispanic/Latino; 0.6% Asian, non-Hispanic/Latino; 4% international. 58% 25 or older, 13% transferred in. Retention: 53% of full-time freshmen returned the following year. Academic areas with the most degrees conferred: liberal arts/general studies; business/marketing; psychology. Core. Calendar: semesters. Academic remediation for entering students, services for LD students, advanced placement, accelerated degree program, self-designed majors, freshman honors college, honors program, independent study, distance learning, double major, summer session for credit, part-time degree program, external degree program, adult/continuing education programs, co-op programs and internships, graduate courses open to undergrads. Off campus study. Study abroad program. ROTC: Army, Naval (c), Air Force (c).

Entrance Requirements: Option: electronic application. Required: high school transcript, minimum 2.5 high school GPA, SAT or ACT. Required for some: essay, interview. Entrance: minimally difficult. Notification: continuous.

Collegiate Environment: Orientation program. Drama-theater group, choral group, student-run newspaper, radio station. Social organizations: 82 open to all; national fraternities, national sororities, local fraternities, local sororities. Student services: health clinic, personal-psychological counseling, women's center. Campus security: 24-hour emergency response devices and patrols, student patrols, late night transport-escort service, controlled dormitory access. New Academic Library. 75 computers available on campus for general student use. Computer purchase/lease plans available. A campuswide network can be accessed from student residence rooms and from off campus. Students can access the following: online class registration. Staffed computer lab on campus provides training in use of computers, software, and the Internet.

Community Environment: See University of Chicago.

■ CITY COLLEGES OF CHICAGO, HAROLD WASHINGTON COLLEGE

30 E Lake St.
Chicago, IL 60601-2449
Tel: (312)553-5600
Fax: (312)553-6077
Web Site: hwashington.ccc.edu

Description: State and locally supported, 2-year, coed. Part of City Colleges of Chicago. Awards certificates, transfer associate, and terminal associate degrees. Founded 1962. Setting: 1-acre urban campus. Total enrollment: 8,464. Student-undergrad faculty ratio is 33:1. 42% 25 or older. Core. Calendar: semesters. Academic remediation for entering students, ESL program, services for LD students, advanced placement, accelerated degree program, independent study, distance learning, double major, summer session for credit, part-time degree program, adult/continuing education programs, co-op programs and internships. Off campus study at Governors State University, Roosevelt University.

Entrance Requirements: Open admission. Options: early admission, deferred admission. Entrance: noncompetitive. Application deadline: rolling. Notification: continuous.

Collegiate Environment: Orientation program. Drama-theater group, choral group, student-run newspaper. Student services: personal-psychological counseling, women's center. Campus security: 24-hour emergency response devices and patrols. Harold Washington College Library plus 1 other.

Community Environment: See University of Chicago.

■ CITY COLLEGES OF CHICAGO, HARRY S. TRUMAN COLLEGE

1145 W Wilson Ave.
Chicago, IL 60640-5616
Tel: (773)907-4000
Fax: (773)907-4464
Web Site: www.trumancollege.edu

Description: State and locally supported, 2-year, coed. Part of City Colleges of Chicago. Awards certificates, diplomas, transfer associate, and terminal associate degrees. Founded 1956. Setting: 5-acre urban campus. Total enrollment: 13,174. Student-undergrad faculty ratio is 34:1. 65% 25 or older. Core. Calendar: semesters. Academic remediation for entering students, ESL program, services for LD students, advanced placement, honors program, distance learning, summer session for credit, part-time degree program, adult/continuing education programs, co-op programs and internships.

Entrance Requirements: Open admission. Options: early admission, deferred admission. Entrance: noncompetitive. Application deadline: rolling. Notification: continuous until 9/8.

Collegiate Environment: Orientation program. Drama-theater group. Student services: personal-psychological counseling. Campus security: 24-hour patrols, late night transport-escort service.

Community Environment: See University of Chicago.

■ CITY COLLEGES OF CHICAGO, KENNEDY-KING COLLEGE

6301 S Halstead St.
Chicago, IL 60621
Tel: (773)602-5000
E-mail: nambrose1@ccc.edu
Web Site: www.ccc.edu/colleges/kennedy

Description: State and locally supported, 2-year, coed. Part of City Colleges of Chicago. Awards certificates, transfer associate, and terminal associate degrees. Founded 1935. Setting: 40-acre urban campus with easy access to Chicago. Research spending for the previous fiscal year: $61,500. Educational spending for the previous fiscal year: $522 per student. Total enrollment: 2,825. Student-undergrad faculty ratio is 30:1. Full-time: 1,584 students, 58% women, 42% men. Part-time: 1,234 students, 63% women, 37% men. Students come from 20 states and territories, 8 other countries, 1% from out-of-state. 0.1% American Indian or Alaska Native, non-Hispanic/Latino; 14% Hispanic/Latino; 78% Black or African American, non-Hispanic/Latino; 1% Asian, non-Hispanic/Latino. 48% 25 or older, 1% transferred in. Retention: 34% of full-time freshmen returned the following year. Core. Calendar: semesters. Academic remediation for entering students, ESL program, advanced placement, honors program, distance learning, summer session for credit, part-time degree program, adult/continuing education programs, co-op programs and internships.

Entrance Requirements: Open admission. Option: electronic application. Required: high school transcript. Entrance: noncompetitive. Application deadline: rolling. Preference given to city residents.

Costs Per Year: Application fee: $0. Area resident tuition: $3504 full-time, $146 per credit hour part-time. State resident tuition: $9216 full-time, $384 per credit hour part-time. Nonresident tuition: $11,544 full-time, $481 per credit hour part-time. Full-time tuition varies according to course load and program. Part-time tuition varies according to course load and program.

Collegiate Environment: Orientation program. Social organizations: 15 open to all; 35% of eligible men and 65% of eligible women are members. Most popular organizations: Dynamic Movement Dance Club, African

American Studies Club, Access Ability Alliance Club, Phi Theta Kappa, Student Government Association. Major annual events: Open Mic Night, Black History Month, Student Engagement/Appreciation Days. Student services: personal-psychological counseling. Campus security: late night transport-escort service. Harold Washington College Library. Operations spending for the previous fiscal year: $516,620. 100 computers available on campus for general student use. A campuswide network can be accessed. Students can access the following: online class registration. Staffed computer lab on campus.

Community Environment: See University of Chicago.

■ **CITY COLLEGES OF CHICAGO, MALCOLM X COLLEGE**
1900 W Van Buren St.
Chicago, IL 60612-3145
Tel: (312)850-7000
Fax: (312)850-7092
E-mail: khollingsworth@ccc.edu
Web Site: malcolmx.ccc.edu

Description: State and locally supported, 2-year, coed. Part of City Colleges of Chicago. Awards certificates, transfer associate, and terminal associate degrees. Founded 1911. Setting: 20-acre urban campus. Total enrollment: 6,031. Faculty: 240 (75 full-time, 165 part-time). Student-undergrad faculty ratio is 25:1. Full-time: 2,522 students, 69% women, 31% men. Part-time: 3,509 students, 64% women, 36% men. 60% 25 or older. Core. Calendar: semesters. Academic remediation for entering students, ESL program, services for LD students, advanced placement, distance learning, summer session for credit, part-time degree program, adult/continuing education programs, co-op programs.

Entrance Requirements: Open admission except for allied health programs. Option: electronic application. Required: high school transcript, minimum 2 high school GPA. Required for some: essay, interview. Entrance: noncompetitive. Application deadline: rolling. Notification: continuous. Preference given to state residents. Transfer credits accepted: Yes.

Collegiate Environment: Orientation program. Student-run newspaper. Social organizations: 11 open to all. Most popular organizations: Student Government Association, Phi Theta Kappa, Phi Beta Lambda, Chess Club, Latino Leadership Council. Major annual events: Homecoming Parade, African-American History Month, Hispanic Heritage Month. Student services: personal-psychological counseling. Campus security: 24-hour emergency response devices and patrols. The Carter G. Woodson Library. 275 computers available on campus for general student use. A campuswide network can be accessed. Students can access the following: online class registration. Staffed computer lab on campus provides training in use of computers and the Internet.

Community Environment: See University of Chicago.

■ **CITY COLLEGES OF CHICAGO, OLIVE-HARVEY COLLEGE**
10001 S Woodlawn Ave.
Chicago, IL 60628-1645
Tel: (773)291-6100
Fax: (773)291-6304
E-mail: nalexander17@ccc.edu
Web Site: oliveharvey.ccc.edu

Description: State and locally supported, 2-year, coed. Part of City Colleges of Chicago. Awards certificates, transfer associate, and terminal associate degrees. Founded 1970. Setting: 67-acre urban campus with easy access to Chicago. Educational spending for the previous fiscal year: $7054 per student. Total enrollment: 2,882. Faculty: 126 (49 full-time, 77 part-time). Student-undergrad faculty ratio is 22:1. 0.2% American Indian or Alaska Native, non-Hispanic/Latino; 24% Hispanic/Latino; 69% Black or African American, non-Hispanic/Latino; 1% Asian, non-Hispanic/Latino; 0.3% international. Retention: 52% of full-time freshmen returned the following year. Core. Calendar: semesters. Academic remediation for entering students, ESL program, services for LD students, advanced placement, accelerated degree program, independent study, distance learning, summer session for credit, part-time degree program, adult/continuing education programs, co-op programs and internships.

Entrance Requirements: Open admission. Options: electronic application, early admission, deferred admission. Required for some: high school transcript. Entrance: noncompetitive. Application deadlines: rolling, rolling for nonresidents. Notification: continuous, continuous for nonresidents. Preference given to city residents. Transfer credits accepted: Yes.

Costs Per Year: Application fee: $0. Area resident tuition: $3504 full-time, $146 per credit hour part-time. State resident tuition: $9216 full-time, $384 per credit hour part-time. Nonresident tuition: $11,444 full-time, $481 per credit hour part-time. Full-time tuition varies according to program. Part-time tuition varies according to program.

Collegiate Environment: Orientation program. Drama-theater group. Social organizations: 8 open to all. Student services: personal-psychological counseling, women's center. Campus security: 24-hour emergency response devices and patrols. Olga-Haley Library-Learning Resource Center. Books: 70,820 (physical), 447,725 (digital/electronic); Serial titles: 50 (physical), 23,684 (digital/electronic); Databases: 81. Students can reserve study rooms. Operations spending for the previous fiscal year: $272,139.

Community Environment: See University of Chicago.

■ **CITY COLLEGES OF CHICAGO, RICHARD J. DALEY COLLEGE**
7500 S Pulaski Rd.
Chicago, IL 60652-1242
Tel: (773)838-7500
Fax: (773)838-7524
Web Site: daley.ccc.edu

Description: State and locally supported, 2-year, coed. Part of City Colleges of Chicago. Awards certificates, transfer associate, and terminal associate degrees. Founded 1960. Setting: 25-acre urban campus. Research spending for the previous fiscal year: $50,000. Educational spending for the previous fiscal year: $3469 per student. Total enrollment: 9,711. Faculty: 162 (56 full-time, 106 part-time). 837 applied, 100% were admitted. Full-time: 3,507 students, 59% women, 41% men. Part-time: 6,204 students, 61% women, 39% men. Students come from 2 states and territories. 53% 25 or older. Retention: 52% of full-time freshmen returned the following year. Core. Calendar: semesters. Academic remediation for entering students, ESL program, services for LD students, advanced placement, honors program, distance learning, summer session for credit, part-time degree program, adult/continuing education programs. Off campus study at Governors State University, Chicago State University. Study abroad program. ROTC: Air Force (c).

Entrance Requirements: Open admission except for nursing program. Options: early admission, deferred admission. Required: high school transcript. Recommended: interview. Required for some: essay. Entrance: noncompetitive. Application deadline: rolling. Preference given to city residents. Transfer credits accepted: Yes.

Collegiate Environment: Drama-theater group. Most popular organizations: Latin Student Organization, Student Government Association, African-American Culture Club. Campus security: 24-hour emergency response devices and patrols. Learning Resource Center plus 1 other. Operations spending for the previous fiscal year: $550,000. 325 computers available on campus for general student use. A campuswide network can be accessed. Students can access the following: online class registration. Staffed computer lab on campus provides training in use of software.

Community Environment: See University of Chicago.

■ **CITY COLLEGES OF CHICAGO, WILBUR WRIGHT COLLEGE**
4300 N Narragansett Ave.
Chicago, IL 60634-1591
Tel: (773)777-7900
E-mail: aaiello@ccc.edu
Web Site: wright.ccc.edu

Description: State and locally supported, 2-year, coed. Part of City Colleges of Chicago. Awards certificates, transfer associate, and terminal associate degrees. Founded 1934. Setting: 20-acre urban campus. Educational spending for the previous fiscal year: $2375 per student. Total enrollment: 6,826. Faculty: 262 (112 full-time, 150 part-time). Student-undergrad faculty ratio is 23:1. 2,550 applied, 100% were admitted. 5% from top 10% of their high school class, 20% from top quarter, 50% from top half. 45% 25 or older. Core. Calendar: semesters. Academic remediation for entering students, ESL program, accelerated degree program, distance learning, summer session for credit, part-time degree program, adult/continuing education programs.

Entrance Requirements: Open admission. Options: electronic application, early admission, deferred admission. Entrance: noncompetitive. Application deadline: rolling. Notification: continuous. Preference given to city residents.

Collegiate Environment: Orientation program. Drama-theater group, choral group, student-run newspaper. Social organizations: 23 open to all. Most popular organizations: Student Government, Circle K, Phi Theta Kappa, Black Student Union. Major annual events: Ethnic Food Fair, Hispanic-American History Month, Graduation. Student services: legal services. Campus security: 24-hour emergency response devices and patrols, student patrols, late night transport-escort service. Learning Resource Center plus 1 other. Operations spending for the previous fiscal year: $822,000. 700 computers available on campus for general student use. A campuswide network can be accessed. Students can access the following: online class registration. Staffed computer lab on campus provides training in use of computers, software, and the Internet.

■ COLLEGE OF DUPAGE
425 Fawell Blvd.
Glen Ellyn, IL 60137-6599
Tel: (630)942-2800
Fax: (630)790-2686
E-mail: admissions@cod.edu
Web Site: www.cod.edu

Description: State and locally supported, 2-year, coed. Awards certificates, transfer associate, and terminal associate degrees. Founded 1967. Setting: 297-acre suburban campus with easy access to Chicago. Endowment: $7.4 million. Total enrollment: 26,209. Faculty: 1,134 (273 full-time, 861 part-time). Student-undergrad faculty ratio is 21:1. 3,360 applied, 87% were admitted. Full-time: 9,464 students, 46% women, 54% men. Part-time: 16,745 students, 57% women, 43% men. Students come from 24 states and territories, 1% from out-of-state. 0.2% American Indian or Alaska Native, non-Hispanic/Latino; 22% Hispanic/Latino; 7% Black or African American, non-Hispanic/Latino; 9% Asian, non-Hispanic/Latino; 0.4% international. 13% transferred in. Retention: 60% of full-time freshmen returned the following year. Core. Calendar: semesters. Academic remediation for entering students, ESL program, services for LD students, advanced placement, accelerated degree program, self-designed majors, honors program, independent study, distance learning, double major, summer session for credit, part-time degree program, external degree program, adult/continuing education programs, co-op programs and internships. Off campus study at other colleges of the Illinois Community College System. Study abroad program.

Entrance Requirements: Open admission except for allied health programs. Options: early admission, deferred admission. Recommended: ACT. Entrance: noncompetitive. Application deadline: rolling. Notification: continuous. Transfer credits accepted: Yes.

Collegiate Environment: Orientation program. Drama-theater group, choral group, student-run newspaper. Social organizations: 37 open to all. Most popular organizations: Latino Ethnic Awareness Association, The Christian Group, Phi Theta Kappa, International Students Organization, Muslim Student Association. Major annual events: International Students' Year-End Cruise, Annual Pool Tournament, Street Fair. Student services: health clinic, personal-psychological counseling. Campus security: 24-hour emergency response devices and patrols, student patrols, late night transport-escort service. College of DuPage Library. 3,058 computers available on campus for general student use. A campuswide network can be accessed from off-campus. Students can access the following: online class registration. Staffed computer lab on campus.

Community Environment: Glen Ellyn is an attractive residential village with trees, rolling terrain, and well-landscaped dwellings; a suburban area near Wheaton, served by the regional commuter rail system, the shopping facilities are excellent. Glen Ellyn also has a library, YMCA, clinic in town, and hospitals nearby. Lake Ellyn is nearby for recreation, boating, swimming, etc.

■ COLLEGE OF LAKE COUNTY
19351 W Washington St.
Grayslake, IL 60030-1198
Tel: (847)543-2000
Fax: (847)223-1017
Web Site: www.clcillinois.edu

Description: District-supported, 2-year, coed. Part of Illinois Community College Board. Awards certificates, transfer associate, and terminal associate degrees. Founded 1967. Setting: 226-acre suburban campus with easy access to Chicago, Milwaukee. Total enrollment: 17,577. Faculty: 1,032 (210 full-time, 822 part-time). Student-undergrad faculty ratio is 17:1. Full-time: 4,945 students, 49% women, 51% men. Part-time: 12,632 students, 58% women, 42% men. Students come from 42 other countries, 1% from out-of-state. 0.2% American Indian or Alaska Native, non-Hispanic/Latino; 29% Hispanic/Latino; 9% Black or African American, non-Hispanic/Latino; 5% Asian, non-Hispanic/Latino; 0.1% Native Hawaiian or other Pacific Islander, non-Hispanic/Latino. 43% 25 or older. Core. Calendar: semesters. Academic remediation for entering students, ESL program, services for LD students, advanced placement, self-designed majors, honors program, independent

study, distance learning, double major, summer session for credit, part-time degree program, adult/continuing education programs, co-op programs and internships. Off campus study at McHenry County College, Gateway Technical College, Oakton Community College, William Rainey Harper College, Elgin Community College, College of DuPage. Study abroad program.

Entrance Requirements: Open admission except for health programs. Options: electronic application, early admission, deferred admission. Required for some: high school transcript, interview. Entrance: noncompetitive. Application deadline: rolling. Notification: continuous. Preference given to district residents.

Collegiate Environment: Orientation program. Drama-theater group, choral group, student-run newspaper, radio station. Social organizations: 40 open to all. Most popular organizations: Latino Alliance, Men of Vision, Asian Student Alliance, Student Government Association, Anime. Major annual events: Welcome Week activities, Spring Fling, New Student Orientation. Student services: health clinic, personal-psychological counseling, women's center. Campus security: 24-hour emergency response devices and patrols, late night transport-escort service. College of Lake County Library plus 1 other. 1,500 computers available on campus for general student use. A campuswide network can be accessed from off-campus. Students can access the following: online class registration. Staffed computer lab on campus.

Community Environment: The college has 2 campuses. The main campus centrally located in Grayslake (population 21,100), and the second campus situated in Waukegan (population 91,396). Waukegan is situated in the northeast corner of Illinois on the scenic shores of Lake Michigan. Excellent transportation facilities are available. Waukegan is an industrial city and is part of the metropolitan area of Chicago. Two of the principal industrial products are pharmaceutical supplies and outboard motors. Community facilities include over 50 churches of various denominations and municipal libraries. Recreation and sports include fishing, swimming, skiing, and hunting in the forest preserves. There are more than 60 lakes located in the county.

■ COLUMBIA COLLEGE CHICAGO
600 S Michigan Ave.
Chicago, IL 60605-1996
Tel: (312)663-1600
Web Site: www.colum.edu

Description: Independent, comprehensive, coed. Awards bachelor's and master's degrees. Founded 1890. Setting: urban campus with easy access to Chicago. Total enrollment: 6,825. Faculty: 926 (278 full-time, 648 part-time). Student-undergrad faculty ratio is 14:1. 8,088 applied, 87% were admitted. 12% from top 10% of their high school class, 35% from top quarter, 72% from top half. Full-time: 6,073 students, 58% women, 42% men. Part-time: 495 students, 54% women, 46% men. Students come from 58 states and territories, 28 other countries, 44% from out-of-state. 0.2% American Indian or Alaska Native, non-Hispanic/Latino; 16% Hispanic/Latino; 13% Black or African American, non-Hispanic/Latino; 4% Asian, non-Hispanic/Latino; 0.1% Native Hawaiian or other Pacific Islander, non-Hispanic/Latino; 5% international. 9% 25 or older, 34% live on campus, 11% transferred in. Retention: 68% of full-time freshmen returned the following year. Academic areas with the most degrees conferred: visual and performing arts; communication/journalism; business/marketing. Core. Calendar: semesters. Academic remediation for entering students, ESL program, services for LD students, advanced placement, honors program, independent study, distance learning, double major, summer session for credit, part-time degree program, adult/continuing education programs, co-op programs and internships. Off campus study at Second City Training Center. Study abroad program.

Entrance Requirements: Options: electronic application, deferred admission, international baccalaureate accepted. Required: high school transcript. Recommended: minimum 2 high school GPA, Work samples aren't required for admission, but we do invite you to upload any creative work you feel strengthens your application. Portfolios may also be submitted for scholarship and award consideration. Guidelines for portfolio submission by field of study can be found on our website. Entrance: minimally difficult. Application deadline: 8/15. Notification: continuous until 11/1. Transfer credits accepted: Yes.

Costs Per Year: Application fee: $50. Tuition: $26,610 full-time, $919 per credit hour part-time.

Collegiate Environment: Orientation program. Drama-theater group, choral group, student-run newspaper, radio station. Social organizations: 75 open to all. Most popular organizations: Black Student Union, Columbia Pride,

Muggles Association of Columbia, Improv Club, Student Athletics Association. Major annual events: Manifest Urban Arts Festival, New Student Convocation, Wicked Week. Student services: health clinic, personal-psychological counseling. Campus security: 24-hour emergency response devices and patrols, late night transport-escort service, controlled dormitory access. Option: coed housing available. Columbia College Chicago Library. Books: 295,362 (physical), 61,291 (digital/electronic); Serial titles: 553 (physical); Databases: 180. Students can reserve study rooms.

Community Environment: The college is located in the dynamic South Loop neighborhood. It is within walking distance of the Art Institute of Chicago, the Shedd Aquarium, major theaters, and the Orchestra Hall. Across the street from the campus are beautiful Grant Park and Lake Michigan.

■ **CONCORDIA UNIVERSITY CHICAGO**
7400 Augusta St.
River Forest, IL 60305-1499
Tel: (708)771-8300; Free: 800-285-2668
Fax: (708)209-3176
E-mail: gwen.kanelos@cuchicago.edu
Web Site: www.cuchicago.edu

Description: Independent, comprehensive, coed, affiliated with Lutheran Church-Missouri Synod. Part of Concordia University System. Awards associate, bachelor's, master's, and doctoral degrees and post-master's certificates. Founded 1864. Setting: 40-acre suburban campus with easy access to Chicago. Total enrollment: 5,971. Faculty: 529 (188 full-time, 341 part-time). Student-undergrad faculty ratio is 10:1. 5,024 applied, 76% were admitted. Full-time: 1,366 students, 58% women, 42% men. Part-time: 111 students, 64% women, 36% men. 27% from out-of-state. 0.1% American Indian or Alaska Native, non-Hispanic/Latino; 32% Hispanic/Latino; 13% Black or African American, non-Hispanic/Latino; 2% Asian, non-Hispanic/Latino; 0.2% Native Hawaiian or other Pacific Islander, non-Hispanic/Latino; 3% international. 19% 25 or older, 38% live on campus, 9% transferred in. Retention: 73% of full-time freshmen returned the following year. Academic areas with the most degrees conferred: business/marketing; education; parks and recreation. Core. Calendar: semesters. Accelerated degree program, self-designed majors, honors program, independent study, distance learning, double major, part-time degree program, adult/continuing education programs, internships. Study abroad program.

Entrance Requirements: Options: electronic application, early admission, deferred admission, international baccalaureate accepted. Required: high school transcript, minimum 2 high school GPA, 1 recommendation, general college preparatory program for degree seeking students, SAT or ACT. Required for some: essay, interview. Entrance: moderately difficult. Application deadline: rolling.

Costs Per Year: Application fee: $0. Comprehensive fee: $42,876 includes full-time tuition ($31,926), mandatory fees ($954), and college room and board ($9996). College room only: $6280. Part-time tuition: $956 per credit hour.

Collegiate Environment: Orientation program. Drama-theater group, choral group, student-run newspaper, radio station. Social organizations: 42 open to all. Most popular organizations: Campus Ministry, College Life, Student Government Association, Campus Activities Board, Art Club. Major annual events: Opening Service BBQ, Midnight Breakfast (fall and spring), Homecoming Carnival. Student services: health clinic, personal-psychological counseling. Campus security: 24-hour emergency response devices and patrols, student patrols, late night transport-escort service, controlled dormitory access, emergency call boxes. Freshmen guaranteed college housing. Option: coed housing available. Klinck Memorial Library. Books: 160,000 (physical); Databases: 80. Weekly public service hours: 89; students can reserve study rooms.

■ **COYNE COLLEGE**
1 N State St.
Ste. 400
Chicago, IL 60602
Tel: (773)577-8100; Free: 800-707-1922
Web Site: www.coynecollege.edu

Description: Proprietary, 2-year, coed. Awards certificates, diplomas, transfer associate, and terminal associate degrees. Setting: urban campus. Total enrollment: 522. Full-time: 522 students, 25% women, 75% men. Students come from 2 states and territories, 2% from out-of-state. 0.8% American Indian or Alaska Native, non-Hispanic/Latino; 44% Hispanic/Latino; 36% Black or African American, non-Hispanic/Latino; 0.8% Asian,

non-Hispanic/Latino. 59% 25 or older. Calendar: continuous. Academic remediation for entering students, accelerated degree program, co-op programs and internships. Off campus study.

Entrance Requirements: Required: interview, minimum Wonderlic Assessment score of 13, ACT score of 15, SAT score of 1800, or a degree from an accredited institution. Required for some: essay, high school transcript, 1 recommendation, SAT or ACT, Wonderlic aptitude test.

Collegiate Environment: Orientation program. Campus security: security guard during class times. Coyne College Resource Center plus 1 other. Books: 2,500 (physical), 200 (digital/electronic). 3 computers available on campus for general student use. A campuswide network can be accessed. Staffed computer lab on campus provides training in use of computers, software, and the Internet.

■ **DANVILLE AREA COMMUNITY COLLEGE**
2000 E Main St.
Danville, IL 61832-5199
Tel: (217)443-3222
Fax: (217)443-8560
E-mail: ncatlett@dacc.edu
Web Site: www.dacc.edu

Description: State and locally supported, 2-year, coed. Part of Illinois Community College Board. Awards certificates, transfer associate, and terminal associate degrees. Founded 1946. Setting: 50-acre small town campus. Endowment: $14.8 million. Total enrollment: 2,645. Faculty: 128 (64 full-time, 64 part-time). Student-undergrad faculty ratio is 18:1. Full-time: 1,013 students, 60% women, 40% men. Part-time: 1,632 students, 55% women, 45% men. Students come from 5 states and territories, 3 other countries, 7% from out-of-state. 0.3% American Indian or Alaska Native, non-Hispanic/Latino; 5% Hispanic/Latino; 15% Black or African American, non-Hispanic/Latino; 1% Asian, non-Hispanic/Latino; 0.1% Native Hawaiian or other Pacific Islander, non-Hispanic/Latino. 32% 25 or older, 26% transferred in. Retention: 52% of full-time freshmen returned the following year. Core. Calendar: semesters. Academic remediation for entering students, ESL program, services for LD students, advanced placement, independent study, distance learning, double major, summer session for credit, part-time degree program, adult/continuing education programs, co-op programs and internships. Off campus study.

Entrance Requirements: Open admission. Options: early admission, deferred admission. Required: high school transcript. Entrance: noncompetitive. Application deadline: rolling. Transfer credits accepted: Yes.

Costs Per Year: Application fee: $0. Area resident tuition: $4500 full-time, $140 per credit hour part-time. State resident tuition: $7500 full-time, $250 per credit hour part-time. Nonresident tuition: $7500 full-time, $250 per credit hour part-time. Mandatory fees: $675 full-time, $50 per credit hour part-time. Full-time tuition and fees vary according to program. Part-time tuition and fees vary according to program.

Collegiate Environment: Orientation program. Drama-theater group, choral group, student-run newspaper. Social organizations: 14 open to all. Most popular organizations: Phi Theta Kappa International Honor Society, The Guild, Powerhouse Campus Ministry, Rad Tech Club, Ag Club. Major annual event: Welcome Back to Campus (Quad Day). Student services: personal-psychological counseling. Campus security: 24-hour emergency response devices and patrols. Operations spending for the previous fiscal year: $428,055. 698 computers available on campus for general student use. A campuswide network can be accessed from off-campus. Students can access the following: online class registration, Scholarship Applications, Tuition Payments, Schedule Planning. Staffed computer lab on campus provides training in use of computers, software, and the Internet.

Community Environment: Danville, population 33,000, is the county seat of Vermillion County situated in the eastern part of the state, four miles from the Indiana border, and 124 miles south of Chicago. Four railroads serve the area which is in the middle of the cornbelt. The city is the site of the large radio telescope used by the University of Illinois for studying signals a billion light years away. Community facilities include many churches, a newspaper, TV station, YMCA, YWCA, radio stations, and hospitals. Within the city are ten city parks. Nearby is Lake Vermillion for boating, swimming and fishing; Kickapoo State Park is also available for camping and fishing. Annual events are the All Breed Dog Show, boat races, and auto races.

■ **DEPAUL UNIVERSITY**
1 E Jackson Blvd.
Chicago, IL 60604-2287
Tel: (312)362-8000; Free: 800-4DE-PAUL

Fax: (312)362-3322

E-mail: admission@depaul.edu

Web Site: www.depaul.edu

Description: Independent Roman Catholic, university, coed. Awards bachelor's, master's, and doctoral degrees and post-master's certificates. Founded 1898. Setting: 38-acre urban campus with easy access to Chicago. Endowment: $593.4 million. Research spending for the previous fiscal year: $9.6 million. Educational spending for the previous fiscal year: $12,598 per student. Total enrollment: 22,437. Faculty: 1,850 (909 full-time, 941 part-time). Student-undergrad faculty ratio is 16:1. 26,169 applied, 68% were admitted. Full-time: 12,795 students, 54% women, 46% men. Part-time: 1,712 students, 48% women, 52% men. Students come from 51 states and territories, 113 other countries, 25% from out-of-state. 0.2% American Indian or Alaska Native, non-Hispanic/Latino; 19% Hispanic/Latino; 8% Black or African American, non-Hispanic/Latino; 10% Asian, non-Hispanic/Latino; 0.2% Native Hawaiian or other Pacific Islander, non-Hispanic/Latino; 3% international. 15% 25 or older, 19% live on campus, 9% transferred in. Retention: 86% of full-time freshmen returned the following year. Academic areas with the most degrees conferred: business/marketing; communication/journalism; liberal arts/general studies; visual and performing arts. Core. Calendar: quarters College of Law on semester system. ROTC: Army.

Entrance Requirements: Options: electronic application, early action, deferred admission, international baccalaureate accepted. Required: high school transcript, minimum 2.3 high school GPA, 1 recommendation. Recommended: essay, minimum 2.75 high school GPA, SAT or ACT. Required for some: minimum 3 high school GPA, interview, Audition/Interviews required for the School of Music and Theatre School applicants. Animation majors must submit portfolio and creative statement. Entrance: moderately difficult. Application deadlines: 2/1, 11/15 for early action. Notification: 3/15, 1/15 for early action. SAT Reasoning Test deadline: 2/1. Transfer credits accepted: Yes. Early action applicants: 12,199. Early action applicants admitted: 9,801.

Costs Per Year: Application fee: $0. Comprehensive fee: $54,210 includes full-time tuition ($39,369), mandatory fees ($606), and college room and board ($14,235). College room only: $10,224. Full-time tuition and fees vary according to course load, program, and student level. Room and board charges vary according to board plan, housing facility, and location. Part-time tuition: $630 per credit hour. Part-time tuition varies according to course load, program, and student level.

Collegiate Environment: Drama-theater group, choral group, student-run newspaper, radio station. Social organizations: 271 open to all; national fraternities, national sororities; 5% of eligible men and 10% of eligible women are members. Most popular organizations: DePaul Community Service Association (DCSA), Black Student Union, DemonTHON, Panhellenic Council, DePaul Activities Board. Major annual events: FEST (University festival), Blue Demon Week, Welcome Week. Student services: legal services, health clinic, personal-psychological counseling, women's center. Campus security: 24-hour emergency response devices and patrols, late night transport-escort service, controlled dormitory access. 2,826 college housing spaces available; 2,667 were occupied in 2018-19. Freshmen guaranteed college housing. Option: coed housing available. John T. Richardson Library plus 2 others. Books: 572,086 (physical), 550,015 (digital/electronic); Serial titles: 20,100 (physical), 79,967 (digital/electronic). Students can reserve study rooms. Operations spending for the previous fiscal year: $11.8 million. 1,500 computers available on campus for general student use. A campuswide network can be accessed from student residence rooms and from off campus. Students can access the following: online class registration, tuition payments, degree progress, financial aid, transcript requests, housing services, student employment information. Staffed computer lab on campus provides training in use of computers, software, and the Internet.

Community Environment: DePaul is located in a culturally and academically rich urban environment. The downtown campus is minutes away from the Art Institute, Orchestra Hall, Lake Michigan, and the LaSalle Street business district. Because 75% of DePaul's students work to help finance their education, they find that the downtown location provides many employment opportunities. Facilities of the Colleges of Law and Commerce have undergone extensive remodeling, and further renovations are in progress, thus ensuring DePaul's continuing commitment to the growth and development of downtown Chicago. At the Lincoln Park campus, restoration of the community has paralleled the expansion of University facilities. The potpourri of stores, theaters, musical groups, and events reflects the broad spectrum of interests of the people who live and work in the area. A short walk or local bus ride enables students to browse through neighborhoods of craft shops and fine old Victorian homes or visit the area's conservatory, zoo, and two museums.

■ **DEVRY UNIVERSITY-ADDISON CAMPUS**

1221 N Swift Rd.

Addison, IL 60101

Tel: (630)953-1300; Free: 866-338-7934

Fax: (630)953-1236

Web Site: www.devry.edu

Description: Proprietary, 4-year, coed. Part of DeVry University. Awards associate and bachelor's degrees. Founded 1982. Setting: suburban campus with easy access to Chicago. Calendar: semesters.

Entrance Requirements: Application deadline: rolling. Notification: continuous.

■ **DEVRY UNIVERSITY-CHICAGO CAMPUS**

3300 N Campbell Ave.

Chicago, IL 60618

Tel: (773)929-8500; Free: 866-338-7934

Web Site: www.devry.edu

Description: Proprietary, comprehensive, coed. Part of DeVry University. Awards associate, bachelor's, and master's degrees. Founded 1931. Setting: urban campus. Total enrollment: 939. Faculty: 84 (14 full-time, 70 part-time). Student-undergrad faculty ratio is 16:1. Full-time: 373 students, 41% women, 59% men. Part-time: 411 students, 41% women, 59% men. 4% from out-of-state. 0.3% American Indian or Alaska Native, non-Hispanic/Latino; 43% Hispanic/Latino; 19% Black or African American, non-Hispanic/Latino; 11% Asian, non-Hispanic/Latino; 0.3% Native Hawaiian or other Pacific Islander, non-Hispanic/Latino; 4% international. 58% 25 or older, 11% transferred in. Calendar: semesters. Part-time degree program, adult/continuing education programs.

Entrance Requirements: Required: high school transcript, interview. Entrance: minimally difficult. Application deadline: rolling. Notification: continuous.

Collegiate Environment: Orientation program. Learning Resource Center.

■ **DEVRY UNIVERSITY-CHICAGO LOOP CAMPUS**

225 W Washington St., Ste. 100

Chicago, IL 60606

Tel: (312)372-4900; Free: 866-338-7934

Fax: (312)372-4870

Web Site: www.devry.edu

Description: Proprietary, comprehensive, coed.

■ **DEVRY UNIVERSITY ONLINE**

1221 N Swift Rd.

Addison, IL 60101

Free: 866-338-7934

Web Site: www.devry.edu

Description: Proprietary, comprehensive, coed. Awards associate, bachelor's, and master's degrees. Founded 2000. Total enrollment: 15,551. Faculty: 1,513 (70 full-time, 1,443 part-time). Student-undergrad faculty ratio is 14:1. Full-time: 3,429 students, 61% women, 39% men. Part-time: 8,597 students, 64% women, 36% men. 90% from out-of-state. 0.5% American Indian or Alaska Native, non-Hispanic/Latino; 12% Hispanic/Latino; 19% Black or African American, non-Hispanic/Latino; 3% Asian, non-Hispanic/Latino; 0.4% Native Hawaiian or other Pacific Islander, non-Hispanic/Latino; 0.8% international. 84% 25 or older, 31% transferred in. Calendar: semesters.

Entrance Requirements: Option: deferred admission. Required: high school transcript, interview. Application deadline: rolling. Notification: continuous.

■ **DEVRY UNIVERSITY-TINLEY PARK CAMPUS**

18624 W Creek Dr.

Tinley Park, IL 60477

Tel: (708)342-3300; Free: 866-338-7934

Web Site: www.devry.edu

Description: Proprietary, comprehensive, coed. Part of DeVry University. Awards associate, bachelor's, and master's degrees. Founded 2000. Setting: suburban campus. Calendar: semesters.

Entrance Requirements: Application deadline: rolling. Notification: continuous.

■ **DOMINICAN UNIVERSITY**
7900 W Division St.
River Forest, IL 60305-1099
Tel: (708)366-2490; Free: 800-828-8475
Fax: (708)366-5360
E-mail: domadmis@dom.edu
Web Site: www.dom.edu
Description: Independent Roman Catholic, comprehensive, coed. Awards bachelor's, master's, and doctoral degrees and post-master's certificates. Founded 1901. Setting: 30-acre suburban campus with easy access to Chicago. Endowment: $35.3 million. Educational spending for the previous fiscal year: $11,631 per student. Total enrollment: 2,990. Faculty: 394 (158 full-time, 236 part-time). Student-undergrad faculty ratio is 11:1. 4,813 applied, 64% were admitted. 22% from top 10% of their high school class, 52% from top quarter, 86% from top half. Full-time: 1,974 students, 68% women, 32% men. Part-time: 132 students, 72% women, 28% men. Students come from 30 states and territories, 9 other countries, 7% from out-of-state. 0.3% American Indian or Alaska Native, non-Hispanic/Latino; 79% Hispanic/Latino; 6% Black or African American, non-Hispanic/Latino; 3% Asian, non-Hispanic/Latino; 0.1% Native Hawaiian or other Pacific Islander, non-Hispanic/Latino; 2% international. 9% 25 or older, 26% live on campus, 8% transferred in. Retention: 83% of full-time freshmen returned the following year. Academic areas with the most degrees conferred: business/marketing; health professions and related sciences; interdisciplinary studies. Core. Calendar: semesters. Academic remediation for entering students, ESL program, services for LD students, advanced placement, accelerated degree program, self-designed majors, honors program, independent study, distance learning, double major, summer session for credit, part-time degree program, adult/continuing education programs, internships, graduate courses open to undergrads. Off campus study at Concordia University (IL), Elmhurst College, Illinois Institute of Technology. Study abroad program.
Entrance Requirements: Options: electronic application, deferred admission, international baccalaureate accepted. Required: high school transcript, SAT or ACT. Recommended: essay, minimum 2.5 high school GPA. Required for some: interview. Entrance: moderately difficult. Application deadlines: rolling, rolling for nonresidents. Notification: continuous, continuous for nonresidents. SAT Reasoning Test deadline: 8/20. SAT Subject Test deadline: 8/20. Transfer credits accepted: Yes.
Costs Per Year: Application fee: $25. One-time mandatory fee: $150. Comprehensive fee: $44,969 includes full-time tuition ($33,950), mandatory fees ($470), and college room and board ($10,549). Part-time tuition: $1133 per credit hour. Part-time mandatory fees: $90 per term.
Collegiate Environment: Orientation program. Drama-theater group, choral group, student-run newspaper. Social organizations: 32 open to all; 38% of eligible men and 38% of eligible women are members. Most popular organizations: Polish Club, Commuter Student Association, Nutrition Club, Organization of Latin American Students, Fashion Club. Major annual events: DUfest, Homecoming, Caritas Veritas. Student services: health clinic, personal-psychological counseling. Campus security: 24-hour emergency response devices and patrols, student patrols, late night transport-escort service, controlled dormitory access. 601 college housing spaces available; 543 were occupied in 2018-19. Freshmen given priority for college housing. Options: coed, women-only housing available. Rebecca Crown Library. Books: 247,967 (physical), 9,389 (digital/electronic); Serial titles: 280 (physical), 53,047 (digital/electronic); Databases: 114. Weekly public service hours: 100; students can reserve study rooms. Operations spending for the previous fiscal year: $1.9 million. 550 computers available on campus for general student use. Computer purchase/lease plans available. A campuswide network can be accessed from student residence rooms and from off campus. Students can access the following: online class registration. Staffed computer lab on campus provides training in use of computers, software, and the Internet.
Community Environment: The university is located in River Forest, a quiet, tree-lined residential suburb of Chicago; public transportation is easily accessible to downtown Chicago.

■ **EAST-WEST UNIVERSITY**
816 S Michigan Ave.
Chicago, IL 60605-2103
Tel: (312)939-0111
Fax: (312)939-0083
Web Site: www.eastwest.edu
Description: Independent, 4-year, coed. Awards associate and bachelor's degrees. Founded 1978. Setting: 1-acre urban campus with easy access to

Chicago. Endowment: $56.1 million. Educational spending for the previous fiscal year: $9379 per student. Total enrollment: 755. Faculty: 67 (18 full-time, 49 part-time). Student-undergrad faculty ratio is 15:1. 1,008 applied, 89% were admitted. 14% from top 10% of their high school class, 23% from top quarter, 70% from top half. Full-time: 737 students, 55% women, 45% men. Part-time: 18 students, 17% women, 83% men. Students come from 7 states and territories, 14 other countries, 7% from out-of-state. 0.5% American Indian or Alaska Native, non-Hispanic/Latino; 15% Hispanic/Latino; 65% Black or African American, non-Hispanic/Latino; 12% Asian, non-Hispanic/Latino; 0.7% Native Hawaiian or other Pacific Islander, non-Hispanic/Latino. 31% 25 or older, 12% transferred in. Retention: 71% of full-time freshmen returned the following year. Academic areas with the most degrees conferred: business/marketing; social sciences; computer and information sciences. Core. Calendar: quarters. Academic remediation for entering students, ESL program, advanced placement, honors program, double major, summer session for credit, part-time degree program, external degree program, co-op programs and internships.
Entrance Requirements: Options: electronic application, early decision. Required: essay, high school transcript, minimum 2 high school GPA, interview, ACT. Required for some: 1 recommendation. Entrance: minimally difficult. Application deadlines: rolling, 7/1 for early decision.
Collegiate Environment: Orientation program. Drama-theater group, choral group, student-run newspaper. Social organizations: 9 open to all. Most popular organizations: Student Government, performing arts, Black Student Union, Latino Student Association, Multicultural Student Association. Major annual events: Holiday Revue, Black History Month Events, International Day. Student services: personal-psychological counseling. East-West University Library. Operations spending for the previous fiscal year: $278,850. 144 computers available on campus for general student use. A campuswide network can be accessed from off-campus. Students can access the following: online class registration. Staffed computer lab on campus provides training in use of computers, software, and the Internet.
Community Environment: Located in Chicago's South Loop (Burnham Park) District, East-West overlooks scenic Grant Park and is within walking distance of the Field Museum, Shedd Aquarium, Adler Planetarium, Art Institute and Buckingham Fountain. Also within walking distance of the University is the"Loop" (Chicago's main business and banking district) and the historic Printer's Row area. The accessibility of such cultural landmarks adds to the overall education of the students.

■ **EASTERN ILLINOIS UNIVERSITY**
600 Lincoln Ave.
Charleston, IL 61920
Tel: (217)581-5000; Free: 877-581-2348
Fax: (217)581-7060
E-mail: dalee@eiu.edu
Web Site: www.eiu.edu
Description: State-supported, comprehensive, coed. Awards bachelor's and master's degrees and post-master's certificates. Founded 1895. Setting: 320-acre small town campus. Endowment: $88.6 million. Research spending for the previous fiscal year: $1.1 million. Educational spending for the previous fiscal year: $19,545 per student. Total enrollment: 7,526. Faculty: 506 (381 full-time, 125 part-time). Student-undergrad faculty ratio is 14:1. 8,420 applied, 47% were admitted. 11% from top 10% of their high school class, 34% from top quarter, 71% from top half. Full-time: 4,091 students, 59% women, 41% men. Part-time: 1,921 students, 54% women, 46% men. Students come from 34 states and territories, 38 other countries, 7% from out-of-state. 0.2% American Indian or Alaska Native, non-Hispanic/Latino; 12% Hispanic/Latino; 17% Black or African American, non-Hispanic/Latino; 2% Asian, non-Hispanic/Latino; 0.1% Native Hawaiian or other Pacific Islander, non-Hispanic/Latino; 2% international. 15% 25 or older, 30% live on campus, 32% transferred in. Retention: 70% of full-time freshmen returned the following year. Academic areas with the most degrees conferred: business/marketing; parks and recreation; liberal arts/general studies. Core. Calendar: semesters. Academic remediation for entering students, ESL program, services for LD students, advanced placement, accelerated degree program, freshman honors college, honors program, independent study, distance learning, double major, summer session for credit, part-time degree program, adult/continuing education programs, internships, graduate courses open to undergrads. Off campus study at Olney Central College, Kaskaskia College, Parkland College, Danville Area Community College, Lake Land College, Triton College, University Center of Lake County, Harper College, Rend Lake College, Richland Community College. Study abroad program. ROTC: Army.

Entrance Requirements: Options: electronic application, deferred admission, international baccalaureate accepted. Required: high school transcript, minimum 2.25 high school GPA, SAT or ACT. Required for some: essay, 1 recommendation, audition for music program. Entrance: moderately difficult. Application deadline: rolling. Notification: continuous. SAT Reasoning Test deadline: 8/15. Transfer credits accepted: Yes.

Costs Per Year: Application fee: $30. State resident tuition: $8880 full-time, $296 per credit hour part-time. Nonresident tuition: $11,100 full-time, $370 per credit hour part-time. Mandatory fees: $2923 full-time, $111 per credit hour part-time. Full-time tuition and fees vary according to course load and student level. Part-time tuition and fees vary according to course load and student level. College room and board: $9882. Room and board charges vary according to board plan and housing facility. Tuition guaranteed not to increase for student's term of enrollment.

Collegiate Environment: Orientation program. Drama-theater group, choral group, marching band, student-run newspaper, radio station. Social organizations: 196 open to all; national fraternities, national sororities; 16% of eligible men and 14% of eligible women are members. Most popular organizations: Greek Organizations, Religious Student Organizations, Intramural Sports, University Board, Civic Engagement & Volunteerism. Major annual events: Homecoming, Celebration: A Festival of the Arts, Family Weekend. Student services: legal services, health clinic, personal-psychological counseling, women's center. Campus security: 24-hour emergency response devices and patrols, student patrols, controlled dormitory access. 5,385 college housing spaces available; 1,837 were occupied in 2018-19. Freshmen guaranteed college housing. On-campus residence required in freshman year. Options: coed, men-only, women-only housing available. Booth Library. Books: 1 million (physical), 1.3 million (digital/electronic); Serial titles: 55 (physical), 55,520 (digital/electronic); Databases: 217. Weekly public service hours: 98. Operations spending for the previous fiscal year: $3.4 million. 900 computers available on campus for general student use. Computer purchase/lease plans available. A campuswide network can be accessed from student residence rooms and from off campus. Students can access the following: online class registration. Staffed computer lab on campus provides training in use of computers, software, and the Internet.

Community Environment: Located in east central Illinois, 50 miles south of the University of Illinois at Urbana-Champaign, Charleston (population 20,000) is second only to Springfield in Lincoln Lore. Airline service is available at the county airport. Within the community are churches of all denominations, medical facilities, library, and motels. Part-time employment is available. Fox Ridge and Lincoln Log Cabin State Parks nearby are of historical, scenic, and recreational interest.

■ ELGIN COMMUNITY COLLEGE

1700 Spartan Dr.
Elgin, IL 60123-7193
Tel: (847)697-1000
E-mail: admissions@elgin.edu
Web Site: www.elgin.edu

Description: State and locally supported, 2-year, coed. Part of Illinois Community College Board. Awards certificates, diplomas, transfer associate, and terminal associate degrees. Founded 1949. Setting: 145-acre suburban campus with easy access to Chicago. Total enrollment: 9,949. 7% from top 10% of their high school class, 17% from top quarter, 47% from top half. Full-time: 3,209 students, 49% women, 51% men. Part-time: 6,740 students, 56% women, 44% men. Students come from 4 states and territories, 15 other countries, 0.2% from out-of-state. 0.8% American Indian or Alaska Native, non-Hispanic/Latino; 42% Hispanic/Latino; 4% Black or African American, non-Hispanic/Latino; 7% Asian, non-Hispanic/Latino; 0.1% Native Hawaiian or other Pacific Islander, non-Hispanic/Latino; 0.5% international. 26% 25 or older, 4% transferred in. Retention: 77% of full-time freshmen returned the following year. Core. Calendar: semesters. Academic remediation for entering students, ESL program, services for LD students, advanced placement, accelerated degree program, honors program, independent study, distance learning, double major, summer session for credit, part-time degree program, co-op programs and internships. Off campus study at McHenry County College, Waubonsee Community College, College of DuPage, William Rainey Harper College, Rock Valley College, Illinois Valley Community College, College of Lake County. Study abroad program.

Entrance Requirements: Open admission except for nursing, selected health programs. Option: electronic application. Required for some: high school transcript, specific departmental requirements. Entrance: noncompetitive. Application deadline: rolling. Notification: continuous. Transfer credits accepted: Yes.

Collegiate Environment: Orientation program. Drama-theater group, choral group, student-run newspaper. Social organizations: 33 open to all. Most popular organizations: Phi Theta Kappa Honor Society, Organization of Latin American Students, Asian Filipino Club, Amnesty International, Student Government. Major annual events: Relay for Life, PB Jam (service event), ChiliRama (club involvement expo). Student services: legal services, personal-psychological counseling. Campus security: grounds patrolled daily 7 am-11 pm during the academic year. Renner Academic Library & Learning Resources. 1,145 computers available on campus for general student use. A campuswide network can be accessed from off-campus. Students can access the following: online class registration. Staffed computer lab on campus provides training in use of computers, software, and the Internet.

Community Environment: See Judson College.

■ ELMHURST COLLEGE

190 Prospect Ave.
Elmhurst, IL 60126-3296
Tel: (630)617-3500; Free: 800-697-1871
Fax: (630)617-5501
E-mail: admit@elmhurst.edu
Web Site: www.elmhurst.edu

Description: Independent, comprehensive, coed, affiliated with United Church of Christ. Awards bachelor's and master's degrees. Founded 1871. Setting: 38-acre suburban campus with easy access to Chicago. Endowment: $94.8 million. Total enrollment: 3,483. Faculty: 381 (153 full-time, 228 part-time). Student-undergrad faculty ratio is 14:1. 3,645 applied, 71% were admitted. 21% from top 10% of their high school class, 49% from top quarter, 77% from top half. Full-time: 2,732 students, 61% women, 39% men. Part-time: 143 students, 64% women, 36% men. Students come from 33 states and territories, 25 other countries, 9% from out-of-state. 0.1% American Indian or Alaska Native, non-Hispanic/Latino; 21% Hispanic/Latino; 5% Black or African American, non-Hispanic/Latino; 5% Asian, non-Hispanic/Latino; 0.1% Native Hawaiian or other Pacific Islander, non-Hispanic/Latino. 12% 25 or older, 32% live on campus, 13% transferred in. Retention: 75% of full-time freshmen returned the following year. Academic areas with the most degrees conferred: business/marketing; health professions and related sciences; psychology. Core. Calendar: 4-1-4. Academic remediation for entering students, services for LD students, advanced placement, accelerated degree program, honors program, independent study, double major, summer session for credit, part-time degree program, adult/continuing education programs, co-op programs and internships. Off campus study. Study abroad program. ROTC: Army (c), Air Force (c).

Entrance Requirements: Options: electronic application, early action, deferred admission, international baccalaureate accepted. Required: high school transcript, SAT or ACT. Recommended: essay, interview. Required for some: essay, interview. Entrance: moderately difficult. Application deadline: rolling. Notification: continuous. Transfer credits accepted: Yes. Early action applicants: 1,162. Early action applicants admitted: 1,067.

Costs Per Year: Application fee: $0. Comprehensive fee: $47,421 includes full-time tuition ($36,755), mandatory fees ($300), and college room and board ($10,366). College room only: $6244. Room and board charges vary according to board plan and housing facility. Part-time tuition: $1045 per semester hour. Part-time tuition varies according to course load.

Collegiate Environment: Orientation program. Drama-theater group, choral group, student-run newspaper, radio station. Social organizations: 100 open to all; national fraternities, national sororities, local sororities; 7% of eligible men and 11% of eligible women are members. Most popular organizations: Programming Board and Student Government, theater and music groups, Black Student Union, residence life groups, Hablamos. Major annual events: Homecoming, Orientation/Welcome Week, Relay For Life. Student services: health clinic, personal-psychological counseling. Campus security: 24-hour emergency response devices and patrols, late night transport-escort service, controlled dormitory access. Buehler Library. 800 computers available on campus for general student use. A campuswide network can be accessed. Students can access the following: online class registration. Staffed computer lab on campus.

Community Environment: A beautiful residential suburb of Chicago, 16 miles west of the Loop, Elmhurst has a population of approximately 45,000. Residents enjoy the advantages of life in a small city and the resources of a large city with its social and cultural facilities.

■ **EUREKA COLLEGE**

300 E College Ave.
Eureka, IL 61530
Tel: (309)467-3721; Free: 888-4-EUREKA
Fax: (309)467-6576
E-mail: mmurtagh@eureka.edu
Web Site: www.eureka.edu

Description: Independent, 4-year, coed, affiliated with Christian Church (Disciples of Christ). Awards bachelor's degrees. Founded 1855. Setting: 64-acre small town campus. Endowment: $25.3 million. Educational spending for the previous fiscal year: $6948 per student. Total enrollment: 672. Faculty: 74 (41 full-time, 33 part-time). Student-undergrad faculty ratio is 13:1. 1,046 applied, 65% were admitted. 8% from top 10% of their high school class, 25% from top quarter, 66% from top half. Full-time: 645 students, 52% women, 48% men. Part-time: 27 students, 33% women, 67% men. Students come from 8 states and territories, 2 other countries, 6% from out-of-state. 0.6% American Indian or Alaska Native, non-Hispanic/Latino; 3% Hispanic/Latino; 5% Black or African American, non-Hispanic/Latino; 0.6% Asian, non-Hispanic/Latino; 1% international. 6% 25 or older, 66% live on campus, 13% transferred in. Retention: 69% of full-time freshmen returned the following year. Academic areas with the most degrees conferred: business/marketing; education; psychology. Core. Calendar: semesters 4 8-week terms. Services for LD students, advanced placement, self-designed majors, honors program, independent study, double major, summer session for credit, co-op programs and internships. Study abroad program.

Entrance Requirements: Options: electronic application, international baccalaureate accepted. Required: high school transcript, minimum 2.3 high school GPA, 1 recommendation, SAT or ACT. Recommended: essay, interview. Required for some: essay. Entrance: minimally difficult. Application deadline: 8/1. Notification: continuous. SAT Reasoning Test deadline: 8/15. Transfer credits accepted: Yes.

Costs Per Year: Application fee: $0. Comprehensive fee: $35,010 includes full-time tuition ($25,150), mandatory fees ($240), and college room and board ($9620). College room only: $4620. Full-time tuition and fees vary according to course load and program. Room and board charges vary according to board plan and housing facility. Part-time tuition: $615 per semester hour. Part-time mandatory fees: $120 per term. Part-time tuition and fees vary according to course load and program.

Collegiate Environment: Orientation program. Drama-theater group, choral group, student-run newspaper. Social organizations: 41 open to all; national fraternities, national sororities, local fraternities, local sororities; 39% of eligible men and 31% of eligible women are members. Most popular organizations: Student Senate, Campus Activities Board (CAB), Alpha Phi Omega, Student Alliance for Greener Environments (SAGE), Multicultural Student Union (MCSU). Major annual events: Opening Convocation, Homecoming, Late Night Programming. Student services: health clinic, personal-psychological counseling. Campus security: 24-hour emergency response devices, late night transport-escort service, controlled dormitory access, late night patrols. Melick Library. Books: 81,371 (physical), 7,171 (digital/electronic); Serial titles: 532 (physical), 919 (digital/electronic); Databases: 11. Weekly public service hours: 70; students can reserve study rooms. Operations spending for the previous fiscal year: $325,659. 82 computers available on campus for general student use. A campuswide network can be accessed from student residence rooms and from off campus. Students can access the following: online class registration, bill payments, tax information. Staffed computer lab on campus provides training in use of computers, software, and the Internet.

Community Environment: A small community in central Illinois, between Bloomington and Peoria, Eureka, population 5,000, is 140 miles southwest of Chicago. The community provides a public library, churches, and a hospital. A lake more than a mile long offers boating and fishing. Part-time employment is available.

■ **FOX COLLEGE**

6640 S Cicero
Bedford Park, IL 60638
Tel: (708)636-7700
Fax: (708)636-8078
Web Site: www.foxcollege.edu

Description: Private, 2-year, coed. Awards diplomas and terminal associate degrees. Founded 1932. Setting: suburban campus. Total enrollment: 360. 742 applied, 68% were admitted. Calendar: semesters. Accelerated degree program, internships.

■ **GOVERNORS STATE UNIVERSITY**

One University Pky.
University Park, IL 60484
Tel: (708)534-5000; Free: 800-478-8478
Fax: (708)534-1640
E-mail: pmcguinness@govst.edu
Web Site: www.govst.edu

Description: State-supported, university, coed. Awards bachelor's, master's, and doctoral degrees and post-master's certificates. Founded 1969. Setting: 742-acre suburban campus with easy access to Chicago. Endowment: $2.1 million. Research spending for the previous fiscal year: $791,635. Educational spending for the previous fiscal year: $6340 per student. Total enrollment: 5,185. Faculty: 470 (230 full-time, 240 part-time). 1,305 applied, 43% were admitted. 8% from top 10% of their high school class, 33% from top quarter, 67% from top half. Full-time: 1,879 students, 62% women, 38% men. Part-time: 1,447 students, 66% women, 34% men. Students come from 16 states and territories, 35 other countries, 2% from out-of-state. 0.1% American Indian or Alaska Native, non-Hispanic/Latino; 13% Hispanic/Latino; 40% Black or African American, non-Hispanic/Latino; 2% Asian, non-Hispanic/Latino; 0.1% Native Hawaiian or other Pacific Islander, non-Hispanic/Latino; 1% international. 51% 25 or older, 7% live on campus, 23% transferred in. Retention: 54% of full-time freshmen returned the following year. Academic areas with the most degrees conferred: liberal arts/general studies; business/marketing; health professions and related sciences. Core. Calendar: semesters. ESL program, services for LD students, advanced placement, self-designed majors, honors program, independent study, distance learning, double major, summer session for credit, part-time degree program, external degree program, adult/continuing education programs, internships. Off campus study. Study abroad program. ROTC: Air Force (c).

Entrance Requirements: Options: electronic application, early admission, early decision, deferred admission, international baccalaureate accepted. Required: high school transcript, minimum 2.75 high school GPA, SAT and SAT Subject Tests or ACT. Required for some: essay, interview. Entrance: moderately difficult. Application deadline: 11/15 for early decision. Notification: 12/15 for early decision. SAT Reasoning Test deadline: 8/1. SAT Subject Test deadline: 8/1. Transfer credits accepted: Yes.

Costs Per Year: Application fee: $25. State resident tuition: $9390 full-time, $313 per credit hour part-time. Nonresident tuition: $18,780 full-time, $626 per credit hour part-time. Mandatory fees: $2806 full-time, $91 per credit hour part-time, $38 per term part-time. Full-time tuition and fees vary according to course load and reciprocity agreements. Part-time tuition and fees vary according to course load and reciprocity agreements. College room and board: $9945. College room only: $7945. Room and board charges vary according to board plan and housing facility. Tuition guaranteed not to increase for student's term of enrollment.

Collegiate Environment: Orientation program. Choral group, student-run newspaper. Student services: health clinic, personal-psychological counseling. Campus security: 24-hour emergency response devices and patrols, late night transport-escort service, controlled dormitory access. University Library. Books: 284,377 (physical), 339,176 (digital/electronic); Serial titles: 2,438 (physical), 11,484 (digital/electronic); Databases: 176. Weekly public service hours: 75; students can reserve study rooms. Operations spending for the previous fiscal year: $1.9 million.

Community Environment: Located in University Park, Illinois, on 750 acres, the University is in a suburban/rural setting. However, it is about 35 miles from downtown Chicago and thirty miles from Kankakee or Joliet, Illinois, in the Southern metropolitan area of Chicago. The campus is accessible via public transportation, from the city and most of the southern suburbs. Governors State University is a commuter institution. There is no student housing available.

■ **GREENVILLE UNIVERSITY**

315 E College Ave.
Greenville, IL 62246-0159
Tel: (618)664-2800; Free: 800-345-4440
Fax: (618)664-9841
E-mail: admissions@greenville.edu
Web Site: www.greenville.edu

Description: Independent Free Methodist, comprehensive, coed. Awards bachelor's and master's degrees. Founded 1892. Setting: 50-acre small town campus with easy access to St. Louis. Endowment: $16.3 million. Total enrollment: 1,132. Faculty: 165 (58 full-time, 107 part-time). Student-undergrad faculty ratio is 13:1. 2,245 applied, 48% were admitted. Full-time: 872 students, 46% women, 54% men. Part-time: 92 students, 61% women,

39% men. Students come from 37 states and territories, 19 other countries, 33% from out-of-state. 6% Hispanic/Latino; 15% Black or African American, non-Hispanic/Latino; 0.5% Asian, non-Hispanic/Latino; 6% international. 12% 25 or older, 69% live on campus, 9% transferred in. Retention: 70% of full-time freshmen returned the following year. Academic areas with the most degrees conferred: business/marketing; education; psychology. Core. Calendar: 4-1-4. Academic remediation for entering students, advanced placement, accelerated degree program, self-designed majors, honors program, independent study, distance learning, double major, summer session for credit, part-time degree program, external degree program, adult/continuing education programs, co-op programs and internships. Off campus study at 13 members of the Christian College Consortium, 100 members of the Council for Christian Colleges and Universities. Study abroad program. **Entrance Requirements:** Options: electronic application, early admission, deferred admission, international baccalaureate accepted. Required: essay, high school transcript, minimum 2.25 high school GPA, agreement to lifestyle statement, SAT or ACT. Required for some: interview. Entrance: moderately difficult. Application deadline: rolling. Notification: continuous. SAT Reasoning Test deadline: 8/1. SAT Subject Test deadline: 8/1. Transfer credits accepted: Yes.

Costs Per Year: Comprehensive fee: $37,502 includes full-time tuition ($27,580), mandatory fees ($374), and college room and board ($9548). College room only: $4698. Part-time tuition: $434 per credit hour.

Collegiate Environment: Orientation program. Drama-theater group, choral group, marching band, student-run newspaper, radio station. Social organizations: 25 open to all. Most popular organizations: Campus Activity Board, Panther Corps Marching Band, Greenville College Student Association, Habitat for Humanity, Music and Entertainment Industry Student Association. Major annual events: Homecoming, All-College Hike, Midnight Breakfast. Student services: personal-psychological counseling. Campus security: 24-hour emergency response devices and patrols, late night transport-escort service, controlled dormitory access. 826 college housing spaces available; 664 were occupied in 2018-19. Freshmen guaranteed college housing. On-campus residence required through senior year. Options: men-only, women-only housing available. Ruby E. Dare Library. Books: 131,047 (physical), 7,408 (digital/electronic). Students can reserve study rooms. Operations spending for the previous fiscal year: $392,283. 50 computers available on campus for general student use. A campuswide network can be accessed from student residence rooms and from off campus. Students can access the following: online class registration. Staffed computer lab on campus provides training in use of computers, software, and the Internet.

■ HARPER COLLEGE

1200 W Algonquin Rd.
Palatine, IL 60067-7398
Tel: (847)925-6000
Fax: (847)925-6044
Web Site: goforward.harpercollege.edu

Description: State and locally supported, 2-year, coed. Part of Illinois Community College Board. Awards certificates, transfer associate, and terminal associate degrees. Founded 1965. Setting: 200-acre suburban campus with easy access to Chicago. Total enrollment: 13,530. Faculty: 646 (205 full-time, 441 part-time). Student-undergrad faculty ratio is 19:1. Full-time: 4,606 students, 48% women, 52% men. Part-time: 8,924 students, 58% women, 42% men. 1% from out-of-state. 0.2% American Indian or Alaska Native, non-Hispanic/Latino; 27% Hispanic/Latino; 4% Black or African American, non-Hispanic/Latino; 13% Asian, non-Hispanic/Latino; 0.7% international. 29% 25 or older, 5% transferred in. Retention: 74% of full-time freshmen returned the following year. Core. Calendar: semesters. Academic remediation for entering students, ESL program, services for LD students, advanced placement, accelerated degree program, freshman honors college, honors program, independent study, distance learning, summer session for credit, part-time degree program, adult/continuing education programs, co-op programs and internships. Study abroad program.

Entrance Requirements: Open admission Open admission policy as described above for all students and selective admission to some programs. Option: electronic application. Required: high school transcript. Entrance: noncompetitive. Application deadline: rolling. Notification: continuous.

Costs Per Year: Application fee: $25. Area resident tuition: $3,892 full-time, $129.75 per credit hour part-time. State resident tuition: $11,602 full-time, $386.75 per credit hour part-time. Nonresident tuition: $13,868 full-time, $462.25 per credit hour part-time. Mandatory fees: $684 full-time, $19 per credit hour part-time. Full-time tuition and fees vary according to course load

and program. Part-time tuition and fees vary according to course load and program. Tuition guaranteed not to increase for student's term of enrollment. **Collegiate Environment:** Orientation program. Drama-theater group, choral group, student-run newspaper, radio station. Social organizations: 54 open to all. Most popular organizations: Student Radio Station, Program Board, Student Senate, Nursing Club, Phi Theta Kappa. Major annual events: Transfer Information Week, Wellness Week, Career Expo. Student services: legal services, health clinic, personal-psychological counseling, women's center. Campus security: 24-hour emergency response devices and patrols, late night transport-escort service. College housing not available. Harper College Library.

Community Environment: Palatine, population 67,200, is a suburban community located 30 miles northwest of Chicago. It enjoys a temperate Midwestern climate. Rail and bus services are available. Community facilities include churches of major denominations, a public library, and hospitals nearby. Many active organizations provide social, recreational, and cultural programs and functions.

■ HEARTLAND COMMUNITY COLLEGE

1500 W Raab Rd.
Normal, IL 61761
Tel: (309)268-8000
Fax: (309)268-7984
E-mail: Amanda.Rambo@heartland.edu
Web Site: www.heartland.edu

Description: State and locally supported, 2-year, coed. Part of Illinois Community College Board. Awards certificates, transfer associate, and terminal associate degrees. Founded 1990. Setting: 145-acre urban campus. Educational spending for the previous fiscal year: $6889 per student. Total enrollment: 4,722. Faculty: 299 (84 full-time, 215 part-time). Student-undergrad faculty ratio is 19:1. 2,735 applied, 100% were admitted. Full-time: 1,816 students, 51% women, 49% men. Part-time: 2,906 students, 57% women, 43% men. Students come from 27 states and territories, 13 other countries, 1% from out-of-state. 0.1% American Indian or Alaska Native, non-Hispanic/Latino; 7% Hispanic/Latino; 9% Black or African American, non-Hispanic/Latino; 2% Asian, non-Hispanic/Latino; 1% international. 27% 25 or older, 10% transferred in. Retention: 55% of full-time freshmen returned the following year. Core. Calendar: semesters. Academic remediation for entering students, ESL program, services for LD students, advanced placement, honors program, independent study, distance learning, double major, summer session for credit, part-time degree program, adult/continuing education programs, co-op programs and internships. Study abroad program.

Entrance Requirements: Open admission. Option: electronic application. Recommended: high school transcript. Entrance: noncompetitive. Application deadlines: rolling, rolling for nonresidents. Notification: continuous, continuous for nonresidents. Transfer credits accepted: Yes.

Costs Per Year: Application fee: $0. Area resident tuition: $4500 full-time, $150 per credit hour part-time. State resident tuition: $9000 full-time, $300 per credit hour part-time. Nonresident tuition: $13,500 full-time, $450 per credit hour part-time. Mandatory fees: $240 full-time, $8 per credit hour part-time.

Collegiate Environment: Orientation program. Drama-theater group, choral group, student-run newspaper. Social organizations: 21 open to all; Academic/professional, arts/cultural, ethnic group. Most popular organizations: Student Government, PRIDE, Game Club, Black Student Union, International Student Association. Major annual events: Fall Fest, Spring Fest, Hawkapalooza. Student services: personal-psychological counseling. Campus security: 24-hour emergency response devices and patrols. College housing not available. Heartland Community College Library. Books: 19,860 (physical); Serial titles: 22,933 (physical), 99,327 (digital/electronic); Databases: 20. Weekly public service hours: 61. Operations spending for the previous fiscal year: $349,445. 100 computers available on campus for general student use. A campuswide network can be accessed. Students can access the following: online class registration. Staffed computer lab on campus provides training in use of computers, software, and the Internet.

■ HEBREW THEOLOGICAL COLLEGE

7135 N Carpenter Rd.
Skokie, IL 60077-3263
Tel: (847)982-2500
Web Site: www.htc.edu

Description: Independent Jewish, 4-year. Awards bachelor's degrees. Founded 1922. Setting: 13-acre suburban campus with easy access to

Chicago. Total enrollment: 422. 331 applied. 2% 25 or older. Core. Calendar: semesters. Academic remediation for entering students, advanced placement, accelerated degree program, independent study, double major, summer session for credit, part-time degree program, internships. Study abroad program.

Entrance Requirements: Required: essay, high school transcript, 2 recommendations, interview, SAT or ACT. Entrance: moderately difficult. Application deadline: 8/15.

Collegiate Environment: Orientation program. Campus security: controlled dormitory access. Saul Silber Memorial Library plus 2 others.

Community Environment: A suburb of Chicago and adjacent to Evanston, Skokie has all the usual community facilities as well as good shopping areas.

■ **HIGHLAND COMMUNITY COLLEGE**
2998 W Pearl City Rd.
Freeport, IL 61032-9341
Tel: (815)235-6121
Fax: (815)235-6130
E-mail: jeremy.bradt@highland.edu
Web Site: www.highland.edu

Description: State and locally supported, 2-year, coed. Part of Illinois Community College Board. Awards certificates, transfer associate, and terminal associate degrees. Founded 1962. Setting: 240-acre rural campus. Total enrollment: 1,678. Faculty: 123 (47 full-time, 76 part-time). Student-undergrad faculty ratio is 15:1. 655 applied, 100% were admitted. 7% from top 10% of their high school class, 21% from top quarter, 47% from top half. Full-time: 828 students, 57% women, 43% men. Part-time: 850 students, 65% women, 35% men. 3% from out-of-state. 0.7% American Indian or Alaska Native, non-Hispanic/Latino; 3% Hispanic/Latino; 8% Black or African American, non-Hispanic/Latino; 1% Asian, non-Hispanic/Latino; 0.1% Native Hawaiian or other Pacific Islander, non-Hispanic/Latino; 0.7% international. 30% 25 or older, 3% transferred in. Core. Calendar: semesters. Academic remediation for entering students, ESL program, services for LD students, advanced placement, self-designed majors, honors program, independent study, distance learning, summer session for credit, part-time degree program, external degree program, adult/continuing education programs, co-op programs and internships.

Entrance Requirements: Open admission nursing. Options: electronic application, early admission, deferred admission, international baccalaureate accepted. Recommended: high school transcript. Required for some: high school transcript, 1 recommendation. Entrance: noncompetitive. Application deadline: rolling. Transfer credits accepted: Yes.

Costs Per Year: Application fee: $0. Area resident tuition: $4230 full-time, $141 per credit hour part-time. State resident tuition: $7170 full-time, $239 per credit hour part-time. Nonresident tuition: $7170 full-time, $239 per credit hour part-time. Mandatory fees: $990 full-time. Full-time tuition and fees vary according to program and reciprocity agreements. Part-time tuition varies according to program and reciprocity agreements.

Collegiate Environment: Orientation program. Drama-theater group, choral group, student-run newspaper, radio station. Most popular organizations: Phi Theta Kappa, Royal Scots, Prairie Wind, Intramurals, Collegiate Choir. Student services: personal-psychological counseling. Campus security: 24-hour emergency response devices and patrols. Clarence Mitchell Library. Operations spending for the previous fiscal year: $286,694. 426 computers available on campus for general student use. Computer purchase/lease plans available. A campuswide network can be accessed. Students can access the following: online class registration. Staffed computer lab on campus provides training in use of computers, software, and the Internet.

■ **ILLINOIS CENTRAL COLLEGE**
1 College Dr.
East Peoria, IL 61635-0001
Tel: (309)694-5422
Fax: (309)694-5450
E-mail: emily.points@icc.edu
Web Site: www.icc.edu

Description: State and locally supported, 2-year, coed. Part of Illinois Community College Board. Awards certificates, transfer associate, and terminal associate degrees. Founded 1967. Setting: 430-acre suburban campus. Educational spending for the previous fiscal year: $5381 per student. Total enrollment: 9,266. Faculty: 531 (166 full-time, 365 part-time). Student-undergrad faculty ratio is 18:1. 1,844 applied, 100% were admitted. Full-time: 3,115 students, 49% women, 51% men. Part-time: 6,151 students, 60% women, 40% men. Students come from 20 states and territories, 13

other countries, 1% from out-of-state. 0.3% American Indian or Alaska Native, non-Hispanic/Latino; 4% Hispanic/Latino; 12% Black or African American, non-Hispanic/Latino; 2% Asian, non-Hispanic/Latino; 0.1% Native Hawaiian or other Pacific Islander, non-Hispanic/Latino; 1% international. 26% 25 or older, 3% live on campus, 2% transferred in. Retention: 66% of full-time freshmen returned the following year. Core. Calendar: semesters. Academic remediation for entering students, ESL program, services for LD students, advanced placement, honors program, independent study, distance learning, summer session for credit, part-time degree program, adult/continuing education programs, internships. Study abroad program.

Entrance Requirements: Open admission except for college transfer associate degree, health applied science programs. Options: electronic application, early admission. Required: high school transcript. Entrance: noncompetitive. Application deadline: rolling. Notification: continuous. Transfer credits accepted: Yes.

Collegiate Environment: Orientation program. Drama-theater group, choral group, student-run newspaper, radio station. Social organizations: 48 open to all. Student services: health clinic, personal-psychological counseling. Campus security: 24-hour emergency response devices and patrols, late night transport-escort service, controlled dormitory access. Illinois Central College Library plus 1 other. Books: 45,000 (physical), 67,809 (digital/electronic); Serial titles: 101 (physical), 11,251 (digital/electronic); Databases: 186. Weekly public service hours: 72. Operations spending for the previous fiscal year: $1.1 million. 1,200 computers available on campus for general student use. Computer purchase/lease plans available. A campuswide network can be accessed from off-campus. Students can access the following: online class registration. Staffed computer lab on campus.

Community Environment: Illinois Central College is located in rural Tazewell County on the outskirts of East Peoria, IL. Primarily a commuter college, adequate bus transportation is available from the city of Peoria. The large rolling campus of 434 acres provides an open feeling for attending students. With the surrounding wooded areas, the beautiful campus provides easy access to classrooms, laboratories, bookstore, cafeteria, and other student services. Illinois Central faculty and staff are committed to student learning and take pride in the large number of successful graduates. Over the 25-year history of the college, approximately 225,000 different individuals have taken classes, and more than 20,000 have received degrees and certificates. Illinois Central College offers a diverse curriculum including college transfer, career education, developmental assistance and continuing community education.

■ **ILLINOIS COLLEGE**
1101 W College Ave.
Jacksonville, IL 62650-2299
Tel: (217)245-3000; Free: 866-464-5265
Fax: (217)245-3034
E-mail: admissions@ic.edu
Web Site: www.ic.edu

Description: Independent interdenominational, comprehensive, coed. Awards bachelor's and master's degrees. Founded 1829. Setting: 62-acre small town campus with easy access to St. Louis. Total enrollment: 983. Faculty: 90 (66 full-time, 24 part-time). Student-undergrad faculty ratio is 12:1. 3,378 applied, 76% were admitted. 15% from top 10% of their high school class, 43% from top quarter, 78% from top half. Full-time: 976 students, 51% women, 49% men. Part-time: 7 students, 86% women, 14% men. 12% from out-of-state. 0.3% American Indian or Alaska Native, non-Hispanic/Latino; 7% Hispanic/Latino; 10% Black or African American, non-Hispanic/Latino; 0.5% Asian, non-Hispanic/Latino; 0.1% Native Hawaiian or other Pacific Islander, non-Hispanic/Latino; 6% international. 2% 25 or older, 84% live on campus, 3% transferred in. Retention: 77% of full-time freshmen returned the following year. Academic areas with the most degrees conferred: business/marketing; biological/life sciences; social sciences. Calendar: semesters.

Entrance Requirements: Options: electronic application, early admission, deferred admission. Required: essay, high school transcript. Recommended: minimum 2.5 high school GPA. Required for some: essay, 1 recommendation. Entrance: moderately difficult. Notification: continuous until 9/1, continuous until 9/1 for nonresidents. Transfer credits accepted: Yes.

Costs Per Year: Application fee: $0. Comprehensive fee: $42,370 includes full-time tuition ($32,540), mandatory fees ($550), and college room and board ($9280). Room and board charges vary according to board plan and housing facility. Part-time tuition: $1015 per credit hour. Part-time mandatory fees: $137.50 per term. Part-time tuition and fees vary according to course load.

Collegiate Environment: Orientation program. Campus security: 24-hour emergency response devices and patrols, late night transport-escort service, controlled dormitory access. Freshmen guaranteed college housing. On-campus residence required through junior year. Options: coed, men-only, women-only housing available. Schewe Library.

Community Environment: Jacksonville, population 19,470, is located in the west-central part of Illinois. It is the home of the only ferris wheel factory in the United States. Within the community are a library, many churches, hospitals, movie theaters, golf courses, and lakes for boating and fishing. Part-time jobs are available.

■ **ILLINOIS EASTERN COMMUNITY COLLEGES, FRONTIER COMMUNITY COLLEGE**
2 Frontier Dr.
Fairfield, IL 62837
Tel: (618)842-3711; Free: 877-464-3687
Fax: (618)842-4425
E-mail: lossa@iecc.edu
Web Site: www.iecc.edu/fcc

Description: State and locally supported, 2-year, coed. Part of Illinois Eastern Community Colleges System. Awards certificates, transfer associate, and terminal associate degrees. Founded 1976. Setting: 8-acre rural campus. Total enrollment: 1,791. Faculty: 143 (6 full-time, 137 part-time). Student-undergrad faculty ratio is 27:1. Full-time: 290 students, 57% women, 43% men. Part-time: 1,501 students, 62% women, 38% men. 1% from out-of-state. 0.2% American Indian or Alaska Native, non-Hispanic/Latino; 1% Hispanic/Latino; 1% Black or African American, non-Hispanic/Latino; 0.3% Asian, non-Hispanic/Latino. 51% 25 or older. Core. Calendar: semesters. Academic remediation for entering students, ESL program, services for LD students, advanced placement, self-designed majors, independent study, distance learning, double major, summer session for credit, part-time degree program, external degree program, adult/continuing education programs, co-op programs.

Entrance Requirements: Open admission. Options: electronic application, early admission, deferred admission. Required: high school transcript. Entrance: noncompetitive. Application deadline: rolling. Notification: continuous. Preference given to district residents.

Costs Per Year: Area resident tuition: $2816 full-time, $88 per semester hour part-time. State resident tuition: $8589 full-time, $268.41 per semester hour part-time. Nonresident tuition: $10,580 full-time, $330.61 per semester hour part-time. Mandatory fees: $1154 full-time, $32 per semester hour part-time, $65 per term part-time.

Collegiate Environment: Learning Resource Center plus 1 other. Operations spending for the previous fiscal year: $114,176. 42 computers available on campus for general student use. Staffed computer lab on campus.

■ **ILLINOIS EASTERN COMMUNITY COLLEGES, LINCOLN TRAIL COLLEGE**
11220 State Hwy. 1
Robinson, IL 62454
Tel: (618)544-8657; Free: 866-582-4322
Fax: (618)544-4705
E-mail: scottm@iecc.edu
Web Site: www.iecc.edu/ltc

Description: State and locally supported, 2-year, coed. Part of Illinois Eastern Community Colleges System. Awards certificates, transfer associate, and terminal associate degrees. Founded 1969. Setting: 120-acre rural campus. Total enrollment: 933. Faculty: 82 (14 full-time, 68 part-time). Student-undergrad faculty ratio is 19:1. Full-time: 399 students, 48% women, 52% men. Part-time: 534 students, 59% women, 41% men. 6% from out-of-state. 0.6% American Indian or Alaska Native, non-Hispanic/Latino; 1% Hispanic/Latino; 5% Black or African American, non-Hispanic/Latino; 1% Asian, non-Hispanic/Latino; 0.1% Native Hawaiian or other Pacific Islander, non-Hispanic/Latino. 35% 25 or older. Core. Calendar: semesters. Academic remediation for entering students, ESL program, services for LD students, advanced placement, self-designed majors, independent study, distance learning, double major, summer session for credit, part-time degree program, external degree program, adult/continuing education programs, co-op programs and internships.

Entrance Requirements: Open admission. Options: electronic application, early admission, deferred admission. Required: high school transcript. Entrance: noncompetitive. Application deadline: rolling. Notification: continuous. Preference given to district residents.

Costs Per Year: Area resident tuition: $2816 full-time, $88 per semester

hour part-time. State resident tuition: $8589 full-time, $268.41 per semester hour part-time. Nonresident tuition: $10,580 full-time, $330.61 per semester hour part-time. Mandatory fees: $1154 full-time, $32 per semester hour part-time, $65 per term part-time.

Collegiate Environment: Drama-theater group, choral group. Social organizations: national fraternities. Eagleton Learning Resource Center plus 1 other. Operations spending for the previous fiscal year: $75,000. 96 computers available on campus for general student use. Staffed computer lab on campus.

■ **ILLINOIS EASTERN COMMUNITY COLLEGES, OLNEY CENTRAL COLLEGE**
305 NW St.
Olney, IL 62450
Tel: (618)395-7777; Free: 866-622-4322
Fax: (618)395-1261
E-mail: pampea@iecc.edu
Web Site: www.iecc.edu/occ

Description: State and locally supported, 2-year, coed. Part of Illinois Eastern Community Colleges System. Awards certificates, transfer associate, and terminal associate degrees. Founded 1962. Setting: 128-acre rural campus. Total enrollment: 1,142. Faculty: 101 (41 full-time, 60 part-time). Student-undergrad faculty ratio is 12:1. Full-time: 522 students, 55% women, 45% men. Part-time: 620 students, 62% women, 38% men. 0.2% American Indian or Alaska Native, non-Hispanic/Latino; 1% Hispanic/Latino; 2% Black or African American, non-Hispanic/Latino; 1% Asian, non-Hispanic/Latino. 47% 25 or older. Core. Calendar: semesters. Academic remediation for entering students, ESL program, services for LD students, advanced placement, self-designed majors, independent study, distance learning, double major, summer session for credit, part-time degree program, external degree program, adult/continuing education programs, co-op programs and internships.

Entrance Requirements: Open admission. Options: electronic application, early admission, deferred admission. Required: high school transcript. Entrance: noncompetitive. Application deadline: rolling. Notification: continuous. Preference given to district residents.

Costs Per Year: Area resident tuition: $2816 full-time, $88 per semester hour part-time. State resident tuition: $8589 full-time, $268.41 per semester hour part-time. Nonresident tuition: $10,580 full-time, $330.61 per semester hour part-time. Mandatory fees: $1154 full-time, $32 per semester hour part-time, $65 per term part-time.

Collegiate Environment: Drama-theater group, choral group, student-run newspaper. Anderson Learning Resources Center plus 1 other. Operations spending for the previous fiscal year: $115,825. 125 computers available on campus for general student use. Staffed computer lab on campus.

■ **ILLINOIS EASTERN COMMUNITY COLLEGES, WABASH VALLEY COLLEGE**
2200 College Dr.
Mount Carmel, IL 62863
Tel: (618)262-8641; Free: 866-982-4322
Fax: (618)262-8841
E-mail: cowgert@iecc.edu
Web Site: www.iecc.edu/wvc

Description: State and locally supported, 2-year, coed. Part of Illinois Eastern Community Colleges System. Awards certificates, transfer associate, and terminal associate degrees. Founded 1960. Setting: 40-acre rural campus. Total enrollment: 3,662. Faculty: 129 (31 full-time, 98 part-time). Student-undergrad faculty ratio is 33:1. Full-time: 458 students, 56% women, 44% men. Part-time: 3,204 students, 33% women, 67% men. 7% from out-of-state. 0.2% American Indian or Alaska Native, non-Hispanic/Latino; 0.7% Hispanic/Latino; 5% Black or African American, non-Hispanic/Latino; 1% Asian, non-Hispanic/Latino. 39% 25 or older. Core. Calendar: semesters. Academic remediation for entering students, ESL program, services for LD students, advanced placement, self-designed majors, independent study, distance learning, double major, summer session for credit, part-time degree program, external degree program, adult/continuing education programs, co-op programs and internships.

Entrance Requirements: Open admission. Options: electronic application, early admission, deferred admission. Required: high school transcript. Entrance: noncompetitive. Application deadline: rolling. Notification: continuous. Preference given to district residents.

Costs Per Year: Area resident tuition: $2816 full-time, $88 per semester hour part-time. State resident tuition: $8589 full-time, $268.41 per semester hour part-time. Nonresident tuition: $10,580 full-time, $330.61 per semester hour part-time. Mandatory fees: $1154 full-time, $32 per semester hour part-time, $65 per term part-time.

Collegiate Environment: Drama-theater group, choral group, student-run newspaper, radio station. Bauer Media Center plus 1 other. Operations spending for the previous fiscal year: $104,266. 100 computers available on campus for general student use. Staffed computer lab on campus.

■ **ILLINOIS INSTITUTE OF TECHNOLOGY**
10 W 35th St.
Chicago, IL 60616
Tel: (312)567-3000; Free: 800-448-2329
Fax: (312)567-6939
E-mail: admission@iit.edu
Web Site: www.iit.edu

Description: Independent, university, coed. Awards bachelor's, master's, and doctoral degrees and post-master's certificates. Founded 1890. Setting: 120-acre urban campus with easy access to Chicago. Endowment: $235.5 million. Research spending for the previous fiscal year: $77.1 million. Educational spending for the previous fiscal year: $11,145 per student. Total enrollment: 7,792. Faculty: 800 (423 full-time, 377 part-time). Student-undergrad faculty ratio is 13:1. 4,403 applied, 53% were admitted. 56% from top 10% of their high school class, 70% from top quarter, 98% from top half. Full-time: 2,790 students, 30% women, 70% men. Part-time: 201 students, 28% women, 72% men. Students come from 47 states and territories, 84 other countries, 21% from out-of-state. 0.3% American Indian or Alaska Native, non-Hispanic/Latino; 15% Hispanic/Latino; 6% Black or African American, non-Hispanic/Latino; 13% Asian, non-Hispanic/Latino; 0.1% Native Hawaiian or other Pacific Islander, non-Hispanic/Latino; 26% international. 13% 25 or older, 64% live on campus, 7% transferred in. Retention: 92% of full-time freshmen returned the following year. Academic areas with the most degrees conferred: engineering; architecture; computer and information sciences. Core. Calendar: semesters. ESL program, services for LD students, advanced placement, independent study, distance learning, double major, summer session for credit, part-time degree program, co-op programs and internships, graduate courses open to undergrads. Off campus study at Shimer College, VanderCook College of Music. Study abroad program. ROTC: Army, Naval, Air Force.

Entrance Requirements: Options: electronic application, early admission, deferred admission, international baccalaureate accepted. Required: essay, high school transcript, 1 recommendation, SAT or ACT. Recommended: interview. Entrance: moderately difficult. Application deadline: 8/1. Notification: continuous. SAT Reasoning Test deadline: 8/1. SAT Subject Test deadline: 8/1. Transfer credits accepted: Yes.

Costs Per Year: Application fee: $0. One-time mandatory fee: $350. Comprehensive fee: $60,058 includes full-time tuition ($45,872), mandatory fees ($1424), and college room and board ($12,762). College room only: $6642. Full-time tuition and fees vary according to student level. Room and board charges vary according to board plan and housing facility. Part-time tuition: $1433 per credit hour. Part-time mandatory fees: $40 per course, $155 per term. Part-time tuition and fees vary according to course load and student level.

Collegiate Environment: Orientation program. Drama-theater group, choral group, student-run newspaper, radio station. Social organizations: 105 open to all; national fraternities, national sororities, local sororities; 10% of eligible men and 14% of eligible women are members. Most popular organizations: Union Board, International Students Association, Student Government Association, Greek Council, Commuter Student Associate. Major annual events: Homecoming, International Fest, Spring Formal. Student services: legal services, health clinic, personal-psychological counseling, women's center. Campus security: 24-hour emergency response devices and patrols, late night transport-escort service, controlled dormitory access. Paul V. Galvin Library plus 5 others. Books: 1.7 million (physical), 99,658 (digital/electronic); Serial titles: 895 (physical); Databases: 464. Study areas open 24 hours, 5-7 days a week; students can reserve study rooms. Operations spending for the previous fiscal year: $7.3 million. 586 computers available on campus for general student use. A campuswide network can be accessed from student residence rooms and from off campus. Students can access the following: online class registration. Staffed computer lab on campus provides training in use of computers, software, and the Internet.

Community Environment: See University of Chicago.

■ **ILLINOIS STATE UNIVERSITY**
Normal, IL 61790
Tel: (309)438-2111; Free: 800-366-2478

Fax: (309)438-3932
E-mail: admissions@ilstu.edu
Web Site: www.illinoisstate.edu

Description: State-supported, university, coed. Awards bachelor's, master's, and doctoral degrees and post-master's certificates. Founded 1857. Setting: 1,111-acre suburban campus. Endowment: $112.7 million. Total enrollment: 20,784. Faculty: 1,290 (878 full-time, 412 part-time). Student-undergrad faculty ratio is 17:1. 12,078 applied, 89% were admitted. Full-time: 17,165 students, 56% women, 44% men. Part-time: 1,165 students, 46% women, 54% men. Students come from 47 states and territories, 69 other countries, 2% from out-of-state. 0.2% American Indian or Alaska Native, non-Hispanic/Latino; 10% Hispanic/Latino; 9% Black or African American, non-Hispanic/Latino; 2% Asian, non-Hispanic/Latino; 0.1% Native Hawaiian or other Pacific Islander, non-Hispanic/Latino; 0.5% international. 4% 25 or older, 31% live on campus, 10% transferred in. Retention: 81% of full-time freshmen returned the following year. Academic areas with the most degrees conferred: business/marketing; education; health professions and related sciences. Core. Calendar: semesters. Academic remediation for entering students, ESL program, services for LD students, advanced placement, accelerated degree program, self-designed majors, honors program, independent study, distance learning, double major, summer session for credit, part-time degree program, adult/continuing education programs, co-op programs and internships, graduate courses open to undergrads. Off campus study at National Student Exchange. Study abroad program. ROTC: Army.

Entrance Requirements: Options: electronic application, international baccalaureate accepted. Required: SAT or ACT. Recommended: essay, high school transcript. Required for some: interview. Entrance: minimally difficult. Application deadline: 4/1. Notification: continuous, continuous for nonresidents. SAT Reasoning Test deadline: 7/15. SAT Subject Test deadline: 7/15. Transfer credits accepted: Yes.

Costs Per Year: Application fee: $50. State resident tuition: $11,524 full-time, $384.13 per credit hour part-time. Nonresident tuition: $23,048 full-time, $768.26 per credit hour part-time. Mandatory fees: $2,992 full-time, $82.28 per credit hour part-time. Full-time tuition and fees vary according to degree level. Part-time tuition and fees vary according to degree level. College room and board: $9850. College room only: $5334. Room and board charges vary according to board plan and housing facility. Tuition guaranteed not to increase for student's term of enrollment.

Collegiate Environment: Orientation program. Drama-theater group, choral group, marching band, student-run newspaper, radio station. Social organizations: 393 open to all; national fraternities, national sororities; 11% of eligible men and 17% of eligible women are members. Major annual events: Festival ISU, Passages/Welcome Weekend, Homecoming. Student services: legal services, health clinic, personal-psychological counseling, women's center. Campus security: 24-hour emergency response devices and patrols, student patrols, late night transport-escort service, controlled dormitory access. Milner Library. Books: 1.4 million (physical), 190,817 (digital/electronic); Serial titles: 97,570 (digital/electronic); Databases: 251. Students can reserve study rooms. 2,500 computers available on campus for general student use. Computer purchase/lease plans available. A computer is required for all students. A campuswide network can be accessed from student residence rooms and from off campus. Students can access the following: online class registration. Staffed computer lab on campus provides training in use of computers, software, and the Internet.

Community Environment: Bloomington-Normal, with a combined population of 119,676, has a strong agricultural base with many business and industrial affiliations. Located at the intersection of Interstates 55 and 74, it is 132 miles from Chicago, 65 miles from Springfield, and 168 miles from St. Louis. Winters are moderately cold, summers are warm, and spring and fall are delightful. Both the twin-cities offer business districts for shopping, banking, and professional services, as well as year-round municipal recreational programs.

■ **ILLINOIS VALLEY COMMUNITY COLLEGE**
815 N Orlando Smith Rd.
Oglesby, IL 61348-9692
Tel: (815)224-2720
Fax: (815)224-3033
E-mail: quintin_overocker@ivcc.edu
Web Site: www.ivcc.edu

Description: District-supported, 2-year, coed. Part of Illinois Community College Board. Awards certificates, transfer associate, and terminal associate degrees. Founded 1924. Setting: 410-acre rural campus with easy access to Chicago. Endowment: $3.7 million. Educational spending for the previous fiscal year: $3460 per student. Total enrollment: 3,241. Faculty: 270 (91 full-time, 179 part-time). Student-undergrad faculty ratio is 16:1. 1,435 applied, 47% were admitted. Full-time: 1,259 students, 52% women, 48% men. Part-time: 1,982 students, 60% women, 40% men. Students come from 1 other country. 0.3% American Indian or Alaska Native, non-Hispanic/Latino; 5% Hispanic/Latino; 2% Black or African American, non-Hispanic/Latino; 1% Asian, non-Hispanic/Latino. 27% 25 or older, 3% transferred in. Retention: 59% of full-time freshmen returned the following year. Core. Calendar: semesters. Academic remediation for entering students, ESL program, services for LD students, advanced placement, self-designed majors, honors program, independent study, distance learning, summer session for credit, part-time degree program, internships. Off campus study at Sauk Valley Community College, Kishwaukee College, Kankakee Community College, Joliet Junior College, Rock Valley College, Elgin Community College, Waubonsee Community College, Illinois Central College. Study abroad program.

Entrance Requirements: Open admission except for nursing, dental assistant, therapeutic massage programs. Options: electronic application, early admission, deferred admission. Required: high school transcript. Recommended: ACT. Entrance: noncompetitive. Application deadline: rolling. Notification: continuous. Transfer credits accepted: Yes.

Costs Per Year: Application fee: $0. Area resident tuition: $125.60 per credit hour part-time. State resident tuition: $355.78 per credit hour part-time. Nonresident tuition: $384.88 per credit hour part-time. Mandatory fees: $7.40 per credit hour part-time, $5 per term part-time. Part-time tuition and fees vary according to course load and reciprocity agreements.

Collegiate Environment: Orientation program. Drama-theater group, choral group, student-run newspaper. Social organizations: 40 open to all. Most popular organizations: Chemistry Club, Student Embassadors, Phi Theta Kappa, Illinois Valley Leaders for Service, Student Veterans Association. Major annual events: New Student Convocation, Spirit Day. Student services: personal-psychological counseling. Campus security: 24-hour emergency response devices and patrols, late night transport-escort service. Jacobs Library. Operations spending for the previous fiscal year: $374,611. 242 computers available on campus for general student use. A campuswide network can be accessed. Students can access the following: online class registration, bookstore, transcripts, payments, scholarship application, career assessment. Staffed computer lab on campus provides training in use of computers, software, and the Internet.

Community Environment: Oglesby (population 3,621) is almost 75 miles southwest of Chicago, 50 miles northeast of Peoria.

■ ILLINOIS WESLEYAN UNIVERSITY

PO Box 2900
Bloomington, IL 61702-2900
Tel: (309)556-1000; Free: 800-332-2498
Fax: (309)556-3411
E-mail: iwuadmit@iwu.edu
Web Site: www.iwu.edu

Description: Independent, 4-year, coed. Awards bachelor's degrees. Founded 1850. Setting: 85-acre suburban campus. Endowment: $206.7 million. Total enrollment: 1,649. Faculty: 193 (142 full-time, 51 part-time). Student-undergrad faculty ratio is 10:1. 3,697 applied, 61% were admitted. 39% from top 10% of their high school class, 72% from top quarter, 95% from top half. Full-time: 1,646 students, 55% women, 45% men. Part-time: 3 students, 33% women, 67% men. Students come from 31 states and territories, 23 other countries, 14% from out-of-state. 8% Hispanic/Latino; 5% Black or African American, non-Hispanic/Latino; 6% Asian, non-Hispanic/Latino; 0.1% Native Hawaiian or other Pacific Islander, non-Hispanic/Latino; 8% international. 79% live on campus, 2% transferred in. Retention: 89% of full-time freshmen returned the following year. Academic areas with the most degrees conferred: business/marketing; social sciences; health professions and related sciences. Calendar: 4-4-1. ESL program, services for LD students, advanced placement, self-designed majors, honors program, independent study, distance learning, double major, internships. Off campus study. Study abroad program. ROTC: Army (c).

Entrance Requirements: Options: electronic application, early admission, early action, deferred admission, international baccalaureate accepted. Required: essay, high school transcript, minimum 2 high school GPA, 1 recommendation, SAT or ACT. Recommended: minimum 3 high school GPA, 2 recommendations, interview. Entrance: very difficult. Application deadline: 11/15 for early action. Notification: 12/15 for early action. SAT Reasoning

Test deadline: 4/1. SAT Subject Test deadline: 4/1. Transfer credits accepted: Yes. Applicants placed on waiting list: 42. Wait-listed applicants offered admission: 9.

Costs Per Year: Application fee: $0. Comprehensive fee: $58,620 includes full-time tuition ($47,434), mandatory fees ($202), and college room and board ($10,984). College room only: $6878. Room and board charges vary according to housing facility. Part-time tuition: $1482 per credit hour.

Collegiate Environment: Orientation program. Drama-theater group, choral group, student-run newspaper, radio station. Social organizations: 200 open to all; national fraternities, national sororities; 32% of eligible men and 34% of eligible women are members. Student services: health clinic, personal-psychological counseling. Campus security: 24-hour emergency response devices and patrols, late night transport-escort service, controlled dormitory access, emergency response team. The Ames Library. Books: 193,789 (physical), 35,089 (digital/electronic); Serial titles: 2,056 (physical), 80,933 (digital/electronic); Databases: 181. Students can reserve study rooms. 400 computers available on campus for general student use. Computer purchase/lease plans available. A campuswide network can be accessed from student residence rooms and from off campus. Students can access the following: online class registration. Staffed computer lab on campus provides training in use of computers, software, and the Internet.

Community Environment: Illinois Wesleyan University is located in Bloomington, Illinois, which is known as a research, insurance, retail, education and business center. Situated in a corporate community of 100,000 people, Bloomington is now one of the fastest growing communities in the country and is listed among the most desirable places to live in the nation.

■ JOHN A. LOGAN COLLEGE

700 Logan College Rd.
Carterville, IL 62918-9900
Tel: (618)985-3741
Fax: (618)985-2248
Web Site: www.jalc.edu

Description: State and locally supported, 2-year, coed. Part of Illinois Community College Board. Awards certificates and transfer associate degrees. Founded 1967. Setting: 160-acre rural campus. Total enrollment: 7,559. Faculty: 313 (103 full-time, 210 part-time). Student-undergrad faculty ratio is 24:1. Full-time: 2,368 students, 51% women, 49% men. Part-time: 5,191 students, 62% women, 38% men. 44% 25 or older. Core. Calendar: semesters. Academic remediation for entering students, services for LD students, advanced placement, distance learning, summer session for credit, part-time degree program, adult/continuing education programs, co-op programs and internships. Off campus study at Belleville Area College, Rend Lake College, Illinois Eastern Community Colleges, Shawnee Community College, Southern Illinois University Carbondale, Southeastern Illinois College. Study abroad program. ROTC: Army (c), Air Force (c).

Entrance Requirements: Open admission except for allied health, veterinary technology, and massage therapy programs. Option: early admission. Required: high school transcript. Entrance: noncompetitive. Application deadline: 8/25. Notification: continuous.

Collegiate Environment: Campus security: 24-hour emergency response devices and patrols. Learning Resource Center. 150 computers available on campus for general student use. A campuswide network can be accessed from off-campus. Students can access the following: online class registration. Staffed computer lab on campus provides training in use of computers, software, and the Internet.

■ JOHN WOOD COMMUNITY COLLEGE

1301 S 48th St.
Quincy, IL 62301-9147
Tel: (217)224-6500
Fax: (217)224-4208
E-mail: admissions@jwcc.edu
Web Site: www.jwcc.edu

Description: District-supported, 2-year, coed. Part of Illinois Community College Board. Awards certificates, transfer associate, and terminal associate degrees. Founded 1974. Setting: small town campus. Educational spending for the previous fiscal year: $4162 per student. Total enrollment: 2,390. Faculty: 258 (56 full-time, 202 part-time). Student-undergrad faculty ratio is 13:1. 5% from top 10% of their high school class, 9% from top quarter, 35% from top half. Full-time: 1,178 students, 53% women, 47% men. Part-time: 1,212 students, 66% women, 34% men. Students come from 18 states and territories, 7% from out-of-state. 0.4% American Indian or Alaska Native, non-Hispanic/Latino; 0.8% Hispanic/Latino; 4% Black or

African American, non-Hispanic/Latino; 0.6% Asian, non-Hispanic/Latino; 0.1% Native Hawaiian or other Pacific Islander, non-Hispanic/Latino. 37% 25 or older, 9% transferred in. Core. Calendar: semesters. Academic remediation for entering students, ESL program, services for LD students, advanced placement, accelerated degree program, self-designed majors, independent study, distance learning, summer session for credit, part-time degree program, external degree program, adult/continuing education programs, co-op programs and internships. Off campus study at members of the Quincy Area Education Consortium, Southeastern Community College (IA), Blessing Hospital, Quincy Area Vocational Technical Center. Study abroad program.

Entrance Requirements: Open admission except for nursing (ADN). Options: electronic application, early admission. Required: high school transcript. Recommended: ACT. Entrance: noncompetitive. Application deadline: rolling. Notification: continuous. Preference given to district residents. Transfer credits accepted: Yes.

Collegiate Environment: Orientation program. Choral group. Social organizations: 12 open to all; Phi Theta Kappa. Most popular organizations: Phi Theta Kappa, Agriculture Club, BACCHUS, Music Educators National Conference, Student Nurses Organization. Major annual events: Welcome Back Barbeque, Community College Month, including Student Appreciation Week, United Way events, including student-staff competitions. Campus security: 24-hour emergency response devices, late night transport-escort service, campus police department, 911-enhanced phone system. Academic Support Center. Operations spending for the previous fiscal year: $228,402. 400 computers available on campus for general student use. A campuswide network can be accessed. Students can access the following: online class registration. Staffed computer lab on campus provides training in use of computers, software, and the Internet.

Community Environment: See Quincy University.

■ JOLIET JUNIOR COLLEGE

1215 Houbolt Rd.
Joliet, IL 60431-8938
Tel: (815)729-9020
E-mail: admission@jjc.edu
Web Site: www.jjc.edu

Description: State and locally supported, 2-year, coed. Part of Illinois Community College Board. Awards certificates, diplomas, transfer associate, and terminal associate degrees. Founded 1901. Setting: 463-acre suburban campus with easy access to Chicago. Total enrollment: 15,288. Student-undergrad faculty ratio is 25:1. 1% from out-of-state. 38% 25 or older. Core. Calendar: semesters. Academic remediation for entering students, ESL program, services for LD students, advanced placement, honors program, independent study, distance learning, summer session for credit, part-time degree program, adult/continuing education programs, internships.

Entrance Requirements: Open admission except for nursing program. Options: early admission, deferred admission. Required: high school transcript. Entrance: noncompetitive. Application deadline: rolling. Preference given to district residents.

Collegiate Environment: Orientation program. Drama-theater group, choral group, student-run newspaper. Social organizations: national fraternities. Student services: personal-psychological counseling, women's center. Campus security: 24-hour emergency response devices and patrols, student patrols, late night transport-escort service. Learning Resource Center.

Community Environment: Joliet is a leading industrial area 38 miles southwest of Chicago's Loop. Railroads and buses are accessible; Midway and O'Hare Airports serve the area. Industries are steel, petroleum products, chemicals, wallpaper, machinery, and greeting cards. Shipping is also a major industry. Community facilities include excellent libraries, churches of almost every denomination, hospitals, YMCA, hotels and private rooming houses. Outdoor sports include hunting, boating, fishing, golf, and other sports.

■ JUDSON UNIVERSITY

1151 N State St.
Elgin, IL 60123-1498
Tel: (847)628-2500; Free: 800-879-5376
Fax: (847)695-0712
E-mail: molly.smith@judsonu.edu
Web Site: www.judsonu.edu

Description: Independent Baptist, comprehensive, coed. Awards associate, bachelor's, master's, and doctoral degrees. Founded 1963. Setting: 90-acre suburban campus with easy access to Chicago. Endowment: $11.2 million.

Research spending for the previous fiscal year: $33,005. Educational spending for the previous fiscal year: $10,576 per student. Total enrollment: 1,256. Faculty: 194 (59 full-time, 135 part-time). Student-undergrad faculty ratio is 10:1. 512 applied, 75% were admitted. 8% from top 10% of their high school class, 21% from top quarter, 56% from top half. Full-time: 679 students, 51% women, 49% men. Part-time: 355 students, 76% women, 24% men. Students come from 35 states and territories, 33 other countries, 14% from out-of-state. 21% Hispanic/Latino; 12% Black or African American, non-Hispanic/Latino; 2% Asian, non-Hispanic/Latino; 0.3% Native Hawaiian or other Pacific Islander, non-Hispanic/Latino; 5% international. 31% 25 or older, 60% live on campus, 17% transferred in. Retention: 69% of full-time freshmen returned the following year. Academic areas with the most degrees conferred: business/marketing; visual and performing arts; education. Core. Calendar: semesters. Academic remediation for entering students, services for LD students, advanced placement, accelerated degree program, self-designed majors, honors program, independent study, distance learning, double major, summer session for credit, part-time degree program, adult/continuing education programs, internships, graduate courses open to undergrads. Off campus study at Council for Christian Colleges & Universities, Chicago Semester, AuSable Institute, New York Center for Art & Media Studies and Associated Colleges of the Chicago Area. Study abroad program. ROTC: Army (c).

Entrance Requirements: Options: electronic application, international baccalaureate accepted. Required: high school transcript, minimum 2 high school GPA, minimum ACT score of 21, lifestyle statement, SAT or ACT. Recommended: essay. Required for some: essay. Entrance: moderately difficult. Application deadlines: rolling, rolling for nonresidents. Notification: continuous, continuous for nonresidents. SAT Reasoning Test deadline: 8/16. SAT Subject Test deadline: 8/16. Transfer credits accepted: Yes.

Costs Per Year: Application fee: $50. One-time mandatory fee: $100. Comprehensive fee: $40,160 includes full-time tuition ($28,840), mandatory fees ($1030), and college room and board ($10,290). Part-time tuition: $1185 per credit hour.

Collegiate Environment: Orientation program. Drama-theater group, choral group. Social organizations: 36 open to all. Most popular organizations: Judson Student Organization, University Ministries, Judson Choir, Fellowship of Christian Athletes, Judson Business Society. Major annual events: Homecoming, Spiritual Enrichment Week, Spring Dance. Student services: health clinic, personal-psychological counseling. Campus security: 24-hour emergency response devices and patrols, controlled dormitory access. 569 college housing spaces available; 414 were occupied in 2018-19. Freshmen guaranteed college housing. On-campus residence required through senior year. Options: coed, men-only, women-only housing available. Benjamin P. Browne Library. Books: 120,765 (physical), 6,280 (digital/electronic); Serial titles: 158 (physical), 48,401 (digital/electronic); Databases: 53. Weekly public service hours: 76; students can reserve study rooms. Operations spending for the previous fiscal year: $414,586. 140 computers available on campus for general student use. A campuswide network can be accessed from student residence rooms and from off campus. Students can access the following: online class registration. Staffed computer lab on campus.

■ KANKAKEE COMMUNITY COLLEGE

100 College Dr.
Kankakee, IL 60901
Tel: (815)802-8100
Fax: (815)933-0217
E-mail: kharpin@kcc.edu
Web Site: www.kcc.edu

Description: State and locally supported, 2-year, coed. Part of Illinois Community College Board. Awards certificates, diplomas, transfer associate, and terminal associate degrees (also offers continuing education program with significant enrollment not reflected in profile). Founded 1966. Setting: 185-acre small town campus with easy access to Chicago. Endowment: $6.5 million. Educational spending for the previous fiscal year: $437 per student. Total enrollment: 3,306. Faculty: 245 (59 full-time, 186 part-time). Student-undergrad faculty ratio is 14:1. 1,260 applied, 100% were admitted. 11% from top 10% of their high school class, 26% from top quarter, 57% from top half. Full-time: 1,222 students, 55% women, 45% men. Part-time: 2,084 students, 65% women, 35% men. Students come from 17 states and territories, 7 other countries, 1% from out-of-state. 0.5% American Indian or Alaska Native, non-Hispanic/Latino; 12% Hispanic/Latino; 14% Black or African American, non-Hispanic/Latino; 1% Asian, non-Hispanic/Latino; 0.1% Native Hawaiian or other Pacific Islander, non-Hispanic/Latino; 0.2% international. 35% 25 or older, 2% transferred in. Retention: 68% of full-time freshmen returned the following year. Core. Calendar: semesters. Academic remediation for entering students, ESL program, services for LD students, advanced placement, self-designed majors, honors program, independent study, distance learning, summer session for credit, part-time degree program, internships. Off campus study at Olivet Nazarene University, University of Illinois-Urbana (Agriculture program only), Franklin University. Study abroad program. ROTC: Army (c).

Entrance Requirements: Open admission except for health occupations programs. Options: electronic application, early admission, international baccalaureate accepted. Required: high school transcript. Entrance: noncompetitive. Application deadline: rolling. Notification: continuous. Preference given to district residents for health occupations programs. Transfer credits accepted: Yes.

Collegiate Environment: Orientation program. Drama-theater group. Social organizations: 17 open to all. Most popular organizations: Phi Theta Kappa, Hort, Student Nursing, Gay-Straight Alliance, Student Advisory Council. Major annual events: Fall Club Rush, National Coming Out Day, Wealth Watchers. Campus security: 24-hour patrols, late night transport-escort service. Kankakee Community College Learning Resource Center. Operations spending for the previous fiscal year: $119,370. 1,100 computers available on campus for general student use. A campuswide network can be accessed. Students can access the following: online class registration, online transcripts. Staffed computer lab on campus provides training in use of computers, software, and the Internet.

Community Environment: Kankakee (population 26,600), one of the fastest growing cities of Illinois and the U.S., has beautiful residential sections along the banks of the picturesque Kankakee River. Kankakee is located 60 miles southwest of Chicago and is the seat of Kankakee County. Some of the world's largest gladiolus fields are nearby. The manufacturing plants offer ample opportunity for employment. Nearby Chicago provides the cultural facilities for the outlying area. Kankakee County Fair and Championship Rodeo is an annual event in August.

■ **KASKASKIA COLLEGE**
27210 College Rd.
Centralia, IL 62801-7878
Tel: (618)545-3000; Free: 800-642-0859
Fax: (618)532-1135
E-mail: jlammers@kaskaskia.edu
Web Site: www.kaskaskia.edu

Description: State and locally supported, 2-year, coed. Part of Illinois Community College Board. Awards certificates, transfer associate, and terminal associate degrees. Founded 1966. Setting: 195-acre rural campus with easy access to St. Louis. System endowment: $7.7 million. Total enrollment: 3,164. Faculty: 158 (65 full-time, 93 part-time). Student-undergrad faculty ratio is 19:1. 236 applied, 100% were admitted. Full-time: 1,229 students, 60% women, 40% men. Part-time: 1,935 students, 62% women, 38% men. Students come from 12 states and territories, 0.4% from out-of-state. 0.3% American Indian or Alaska Native, non-Hispanic/Latino; 2% Hispanic/Latino; 5% Black or African American, non-Hispanic/Latino; 0.6% Asian, non-Hispanic/Latino. 21% 25 or older, 11% transferred in. Core. Calendar: semesters. Academic remediation for entering students, ESL program, services for LD students, accelerated degree program, honors program, independent study, distance learning, double major, summer session for credit, part-time degree program, adult/continuing education programs, co-op programs and internships. Off campus study at University Alliance. ROTC: Army (c).

Entrance Requirements: Open admission except for allied health programs. Options: electronic application, early admission, deferred admission. Required: high school transcript. Recommended: SAT or ACT. Required for some: interview. Entrance: noncompetitive. Application deadline: rolling. Notification: continuous. Preference given to district residents. Transfer credits accepted: Yes.

Costs Per Year: Application fee: $0. Area resident tuition: $4080 full-time, $136 per credit hour part-time. State resident tuition: $7050 full-time, $235 per credit hour part-time. Nonresident tuition: $11,850 full-time, $395 per credit hour part-time. Mandatory fees: $480 full-time, $16 per credit hour part-time.

Collegiate Environment: Orientation program. Drama-theater group, choral group. Social organizations: 31 open to all; 5% of eligible men and 9% of eligible women are members. Most popular organizations: Phi Theta Kappa, Student Radiography Club, LPN Club, Physical Therapy Club, Fellowship of Christian Athletes. Major annual event: Student Picnic. Student services: personal-psychological counseling. Campus security: 24-hour emergency

response devices and patrols, late night transport-escort service. College housing not available. Kaskaskia College Library. Books: 17,285 (physical), 24,433 (digital/electronic); Serial titles: 24 (physical); Databases: 86. Weekly public service hours: 47. Operations spending for the previous fiscal year: $56,053. 130 computers available on campus for general student use. A campuswide network can be accessed from off-campus. Students can access the following: online class registration. Staffed computer lab on campus.

Community Environment: Centralia, located 60 miles east of St. Louis, has mild winters and warm summers. Buses and planes serve the area. Community facilities include a hospital, library, hotels, motels, rooming houses, and a good shopping area. Three lakes are located nearby, for hunting and fishing, and there are three golf courses. The local merchants and civic organizations sponsor a Halloween Parade each year.

■ **KENDALL COLLEGE AT NATIONAL LOUIS UNIVERSITY**
900 N N Branch St.
Chicago, IL 60642
Tel: (312)752-2000; Free: 888-90-KENDALL
E-mail: info@kendall.edu
Web Site: www.kendall.edu

Description: Independent, 4-year, coed. Part of Laureate International Universities. Awards associate and bachelor's degrees. Founded 1934. Setting: urban campus with easy access to Chicago. Educational spending for the previous fiscal year: $1515 per student. Total enrollment: 1,200. Faculty: 279 (33 full-time, 246 part-time). Student-undergrad faculty ratio is 8:1. 154 applied, 84% were admitted. Full-time: 717 students, 66% women, 34% men. Part-time: 483 students, 87% women, 13% men. Students come from 34 states and territories, 39 other countries, 13% from out-of-state. 0.2% American Indian or Alaska Native, non-Hispanic/Latino; 16% Hispanic/Latino; 16% Black or African American, non-Hispanic/Latino; 3% Asian, non-Hispanic/Latino; 0.4% Native Hawaiian or other Pacific Islander, non-Hispanic/Latino; 19% international. 50% 25 or older, 12% transferred in. Retention: 54% of full-time freshmen returned the following year. Core. Calendar: quarters. Academic remediation for entering students, ESL program, services for LD students, advanced placement, accelerated degree program, independent study, distance learning, summer session for credit, part-time degree program, internships. Off campus study. Study abroad program.

Entrance Requirements: Options: electronic application, deferred admission, international baccalaureate accepted. Required: essay, high school transcript, interview. Recommended: minimum 2 high school GPA. Required for some: SAT or ACT. Entrance: minimally difficult. Application deadline: rolling. Notification: continuous. Transfer credits accepted: Yes.

Collegiate Environment: Orientation program. Social organizations: 6 open to all; 7% of eligible men and 7% of eligible women are members. Most popular organizations: International Club, SEED Club, Soccer Club, Meditation Club, Kendall Cares Community Service. Major annual events: International Fashion Show, Career Fairs, International Fair. Student services: personal-psychological counseling. Campus security: 24-hour emergency response devices and patrols, controlled dormitory access, 24-hour security at dorms. Iva Freeman Library. Books: 11,484 (physical); Serial titles: 56 (physical); Databases: 23. Weekly public service hours: 61. Operations spending for the previous fiscal year: $202,554. 60 computers available on campus for general student use. A campuswide network can be accessed from student residence rooms and from off campus. Students can access the following: online class registration. Staffed computer lab on campus provides training in use of computers, software, and the Internet.

Community Environment: See Northwestern University.

■ **KISHWAUKEE COLLEGE**
21193 Malta Rd.
Malta, IL 60150
Tel: (815)825-2086
Fax: (815)825-2306
E-mail: ghorta@kish.edu
Web Site: www.kish.edu

Description: State and locally supported, 2-year, coed. Part of Illinois Community College Board. Awards certificates, diplomas, transfer associate, and terminal associate degrees. Founded 1967. Setting: 120-acre rural campus with easy access to Chicago. Total enrollment: 3,775. Faculty: 236 (76 full-time, 160 part-time). Student-undergrad faculty ratio is 16:1. Full-time: 1,634 students, 52% women, 48% men. Part-time: 2,141 students, 53% women, 47% men. 0.5% American Indian or Alaska Native, non-Hispanic/Latino; 15%

Hispanic/Latino; 15% Black or African American, non-Hispanic/Latino; 2% Asian, non-Hispanic/Latino; 0.1% Native Hawaiian or other Pacific Islander, non-Hispanic/Latino. 26% 25 or older. Retention: 59% of full-time freshmen returned the following year. Core. Calendar: semesters. Academic remediation for entering students, ESL program, services for LD students, advanced placement, freshman honors college, honors program, independent study, distance learning, double major, summer session for credit, part-time degree program, external degree program, adult/continuing education programs, co-op programs and internships. Off campus study at Cooperative Agreements. Study abroad program.

Entrance Requirements: Open admission except for nursing and radiological technology programs. Options: electronic application, early admission, deferred admission. Recommended: high school transcript, transcripts from all other colleges or universities previously attended. Required for some: high school transcript. Entrance: noncompetitive. Application deadline: rolling. Notification: continuous. Transfer credits accepted: Yes.

Costs Per Year: Application fee: $0. Area resident tuition: $4260 full-time, $142 per credit hour part-time. State resident tuition: $8520 full-time, $284 per credit hour part-time. Nonresident tuition: $12,780 full-time, $426 per credit hour part-time. Mandatory fees: $570 full-time, $17 per credit hour part-time. Full-time tuition and fees vary according to program and reciprocity agreements. Part-time tuition and fees vary according to program and reciprocity agreements.

Collegiate Environment: Orientation program. Drama-theater group, choral group, student-run newspaper. Student services: health clinic, personal-psychological counseling. Campus security: 24-hour emergency response devices and patrols. Kishwaukee College Library. Students can reserve study rooms.

Community Environment: See Northern Illinois University.

■ **KNOX COLLEGE**
2 E S St.
Galesburg, IL 61401
Tel: (309)341-7000; Free: 800-678-KNOX
Fax: (309)341-7070
E-mail: admission@knox.edu
Web Site: www.knox.edu

Description: Independent, 4-year, coed. Awards bachelor's degrees. Founded 1837. Setting: 82-acre small town campus with easy access to Peoria, Quad Cities. Endowment: $160.1 million. Research spending for the previous fiscal year: $1.5 million. Educational spending for the previous fiscal year: $15,074 per student. Total enrollment: 1,333. Faculty: 136 (112 full-time, 24 part-time). Student-undergrad faculty ratio is 11:1. 2,738 applied, 74% were admitted. 32% from top 10% of their high school class, 62% from top quarter, 90% from top half. Full-time: 1,310 students, 56% women, 44% men. Part-time: 23 students, 61% women, 39% men. Students come from 43 states and territories, 48 other countries, 45% from out-of-state. 15% Hispanic/Latino; 8% Black or African American, non-Hispanic/Latino; 5% Asian, non-Hispanic/Latino; 0.2% Native Hawaiian or other Pacific Islander, non-Hispanic/Latino; 17% international. 1% 25 or older, 86% live on campus, 3% transferred in. Retention: 81% of full-time freshmen returned the following year. Academic areas with the most degrees conferred: social sciences; biological/life sciences; English. Core. Calendar: trimesters. ESL program, services for LD students, advanced placement, self-designed majors, honors program, independent study, double major, part-time degree program, internships. Off campus study at Argonne National Laboratory, Associated Colleges of the Midwest Newberry Library Program in the Humanities, Oak Ridge National Laboratory, American University Washington Semester Program. Study abroad program.

Entrance Requirements: Options: electronic application, early admission, early decision, early action, deferred admission, international baccalaureate accepted. Required: essay, high school transcript, 2 recommendations. Recommended: interview. Required for some: SAT or ACT. Entrance: very difficult. Application deadlines: 11/1 for early decision, 12/1 for early action. Notification: 3/15, 11/15 for early decision, 1/15 for early action. SAT Reasoning Test deadline: 1/15. Transfer credits accepted: Yes. Applicants placed on waiting list: 16. Wait-listed applicants offered admission: 0. Early decision applicants: 28. Early decision applicants admitted: 19. Early action applicants: 1,340. Early action applicants admitted: 1,097.

Costs Per Year: Application fee: $50. Comprehensive fee: $58,236 includes full-time tuition ($47,385), mandatory fees ($783), and college room and board ($10,068). College room only: $5040.

Collegiate Environment: Orientation program. Drama-theater group, choral group, student-run newspaper, radio station. Social organizations: 90 open

to all; national fraternities, national sororities, local fraternities; 19% of eligible men and 12% of eligible women are members. Most popular organizations: International Club, Best Buddies (Assistance and Friendship for Individuals with Intellectual Disabilities), Blessings in a Backpack, Alpha Phi Omega (APO, Co-ed Service Fraternity), Improv Club. Major annual events: International Fair, Pumphandle, Fresh Check Day. Student services: health clinic, personal-psychological counseling. Campus security: 24-hour emergency response devices and patrols, late night transport-escort service. 1,134 college housing spaces available; 1,056 were occupied in 2018-19. Freshmen guaranteed college housing. On-campus residence required through junior year. Options: coed, men-only, women-only housing available. Henry M. Seymour Library plus 1 other. Books: 331,297 (physical), 15,164 (digital/electronic); Serial titles: 152 (physical), 87,337 (digital/electronic); Databases: 200. Weekly public service hours: 106; students can reserve study rooms. Operations spending for the previous fiscal year: $2.1 million. 275 computers available on campus for general student use. A campuswide network can be accessed from student residence rooms and from off campus. Students can access the following: online class registration, transcripts, learning management system, streaming video, print billing. Staffed computer lab on campus provides training in use of computers, software, and the Internet.

Community Environment: Knox College is situated in the small city of Galesburg, Illinois, with a population of 32,017. It is 180 miles west of Chicago and easily accessible by Amtrak, Interstate Highway 74, and Greyhound bus lines.

■ **LAKE FOREST COLLEGE**
555 N Sheridan Rd.
Lake Forest, IL 60045
Tel: (847)234-3100; Free: 800-828-4751
Fax: (847)735-6271
E-mail: admissions@lakeforest.edu
Web Site: www.lakeforest.edu

Description: Independent, comprehensive, coed. Awards bachelor's and master's degrees. Founded 1857. Setting: 107-acre suburban campus with easy access to Chicago. Endowment: $90.6 million. Research spending for the previous fiscal year: $458,712. Educational spending for the previous fiscal year: $12,256 per student. Total enrollment: 1,512. Faculty: 178 (102 full-time, 76 part-time). Student-undergrad faculty ratio is 12:1. 4,147 applied, 58% were admitted. 27% from top 10% of their high school class, 62% from top quarter, 89% from top half. Full-time: 1,472 students, 57% women, 43% men. Part-time: 20 students, 40% women, 60% men. Students come from 41 states and territories, 77 other countries, 38% from out-of-state. 0.3% American Indian or Alaska Native, non-Hispanic/Latino; 14% Hispanic/Latino; 5% Black or African American, non-Hispanic/Latino; 5% Asian, non-Hispanic/Latino; 0.1% Native Hawaiian or other Pacific Islander, non-Hispanic/Latino; 11% international. 2% 25 or older, 78% live on campus, 5% transferred in. Retention: 83% of full-time freshmen returned the following year. Academic areas with the most degrees conferred: business/marketing; social sciences; biological/life sciences. Core. Calendar: semesters. Services for LD students, advanced placement, accelerated degree program, self-designed majors, honors program, independent study, double major, summer session for credit, part-time degree program, internships. Off campus study at 14 members of the Associated Colleges of the Midwest (ACM), The Washington Center, Webster University's Geneva (Switzerland), Athens (Greece), Vienna (Austria), and Leiden (Netherlands) international campuses, and Loyola University's Rome campus. Study abroad program.

Entrance Requirements: Options: electronic application, early decision, early action, deferred admission, international baccalaureate accepted. Required: essay, high school transcript, 1 recommendation. Recommended: interview, SAT or ACT. Entrance: moderately difficult. Application deadlines: 2/15, 11/15 for early decision, 11/15 for early action. Notification: continuous until 3/10, 12/15 for early decision. SAT Reasoning Test deadline: 3/15. Transfer credits accepted: Yes. Early decision applicants: 18. Early decision applicants admitted: 11. Early action applicants: 2,406. Early action applicants admitted: 1,607.

Costs Per Year: Application fee: $0. Comprehensive fee: $59,100 includes full-time tuition ($47,680), mandatory fees ($744), and college room and board ($10,676). College room only: $5140.

Collegiate Environment: Orientation program. Drama-theater group, choral group, student-run newspaper, radio station. Social organizations: 85 open to all; national fraternities, national sororities; 15% of eligible men and 15% of eligible women are members. Most popular organizations: Athletic Council, Student Government, United Black Association, PRIDE, Alpha Tau

Omega. Major annual events: Forester Day of Service, Homecoming Events, Spring Concert. Student services: health clinic, personal-psychological counseling. Campus security: 24-hour emergency response devices and patrols, student patrols, late night transport-escort service, controlled dormitory access. 1,286 college housing spaces available; 1,109 were occupied in 2018-19. Freshmen given priority for college housing. On-campus residence required through junior year. Option: coed housing available. Donnelley and Lee Library. Study areas open 24 hours, 5-7 days a week; students can reserve study rooms. Operations spending for the previous fiscal year: $1.4 million. 400 computers available on campus for general student use. Computer purchase/lease plans available. A campuswide network can be accessed from student residence rooms and from off campus. Students can access the following: online class registration, file storage. Staffed computer lab on campus (open 24 hours a day) provides training in use of computers, software, and the Internet.

■ **LAKE LAND COLLEGE**
5001 Lake Land Blvd.
Mattoon, IL 61938-9366
Tel: (217)234-5253
E-mail: admissions@lakeland.cc.il.us
Web Site: www.lakelandcollege.edu
Description: State and locally supported, 2-year, coed. Part of Illinois Community College Board. Awards certificates, transfer associate, and terminal associate degrees. Founded 1966. Setting: 308-acre rural campus. Endowment: $2.7 million. Educational spending for the previous fiscal year: $2016 per student. Total enrollment: 6,351. Faculty: 191 (116 full-time, 75 part-time). Student-undergrad faculty ratio is 21:1. Full-time: 2,809 students, 55% women, 45% men. Part-time: 3,542 students, 51% women, 49% men. 1% from out-of-state. 1% transferred in. Retention: 89% of full-time freshmen returned the following year. Core. Calendar: semesters. Academic remediation for entering students, ESL program, services for LD students, accelerated degree program, honors program, distance learning, summer session for credit, part-time degree program, external degree program, adult/continuing education programs, co-op programs and internships.
Entrance Requirements: Open admission except for dental services, nursing, physical therapy, civil engineering technology, and agricultural technology programs. Options: electronic application, early admission. Recommended: high school transcript, ACT. Entrance: noncompetitive. Application deadline: rolling. Notification: continuous.
Costs Per Year: Application fee: $0. Area resident tuition: $3165 full-time, $105.50 per credit hour part-time. State resident tuition: $6,999 full-time, $232.96 per credit hour part-time. Nonresident tuition: $12,790 full-time, $426.36 per credit hour part-time. Mandatory fees: $945 full-time, $31.50 per credit hour part-time.
Collegiate Environment: Orientation program. Choral group, student-run newspaper, radio station. Social organizations: 25 open to all. Most popular organizations: Agriculture Production and Management Club, Cosmetology Club, Agriculture Transfer Club, Phi Theta Kappa, Civil Engineering Technology Club. Major annual events: Spring Carnival, Alcohol Awareness Week, Blood Drives. Student services: personal-psychological counseling. Campus security: 24-hour patrols. Virgil H. Judge Learning Resource Center plus 1 other. Operations spending for the previous fiscal year: $439,600. 1,800 computers available on campus for general student use. A campuswide network can be accessed. Students can access the following: online class registration. Staffed computer lab on campus provides training in use of software.
Community Environment: Mattoon (population 17,000) is an agricultural, commercial, industrial, oil, and transportation center with an average temperature of 53 degrees and an annual rainfall of 39 inches. Bus, train, and air service is available. Community facilities include churches of all denominations, many civic, service, and fraternal organizations, a civic center, hospital, nursing center, clinic, and excellent shopping facilities. Recreational facilities include golf courses, swimming pools, bowling lanes, theatres, skating rinks, and Lakes Paradise and Mattoon with swimming, boating, fishing, and an amusement park. Mattoon is located in the heart of the Lincoln-Lore Lane with many historic points of interest in the area. Part-time employment is available.

■ **LAKEVIEW COLLEGE OF NURSING**
903 N Logan Ave.
Danville, IL 61832
Tel: (217)709-0920
E-mail: admission@lakeviewcol.edu

Web Site: www.lakeviewcol.edu
Description: Independent, upper-level, coed. Awards bachelor's degrees. Founded 1987. Setting: 1-acre small town campus. Total enrollment: 236. Faculty: 29 (20 full-time, 9 part-time). Student-undergrad faculty ratio is 12:1. Full-time: 199 students, 83% women, 17% men. Part-time: 37 students, 76% women, 24% men. 3% Hispanic/Latino; 9% Black or African American, non-Hispanic/Latino; 6% Asian, non-Hispanic/Latino; 0.4% Native Hawaiian or other Pacific Islander, non-Hispanic/Latino. 34% 25 or older. Academic area with the most degrees conferred: health professions and related sciences. Core. Calendar: semesters. Academic remediation for entering students, services for LD students, accelerated degree program, summer session for credit, part-time degree program. Off campus study at Lakeview College of Nursing, Charleston, IL Branch Location. ROTC: Army (c), Air Force (c).
Entrance Requirements: Transfer credits accepted: Yes.
Costs Per Year: Application fee: $100. Tuition: $13,500 full-time, $450 per credit hour part-time. Mandatory fees: $1950 full-time, $65 per credit hour part-time. Full-time tuition and fees vary according to course level, course load, and location. Part-time tuition and fees vary according to course level, course load, and location.
Collegiate Environment: Orientation program. Campus security: 24-hour emergency response devices and patrols. Lakeview College of Nursing Library plus 1 other. 61 computers available on campus for general student use. A computer is required for all students. A campuswide network can be accessed from off-campus. Staffed computer lab on campus provides training in use of software.

■ **LEWIS AND CLARK COMMUNITY COLLEGE**
5800 Godfrey Rd.
Godfrey, IL 62035-2466
Tel: (618)466-7000; Free: 800-YES-LCCC
Fax: (618)466-2798
Web Site: www.lc.edu
Description: District-supported, 2-year, coed. Part of Illinois Community College Board. Awards certificates, transfer associate, and terminal associate degrees. Founded 1970. Setting: 275-acre small town campus with easy access to St. Louis. Total enrollment: 8,179. Core. Calendar: semesters. Academic remediation for entering students, ESL program, services for LD students, advanced placement, independent study, distance learning, double major, summer session for credit, part-time degree program, adult/continuing education programs, co-op programs and internships. Off campus study at Blackburn College. ROTC: Army.
Entrance Requirements: Open admission except for nursing, dental assisting, dental hygiene, occupational therapy, paramedicine, and therapeutic massage. Options: early admission, deferred admission. Recommended: high school transcript. Required for some: interview. Entrance: noncompetitive. Application deadline: rolling. Notification: continuous.
Collegiate Environment: Orientation program. Choral group, student-run newspaper, radio station. Student services: health clinic, personal-psychological counseling. Campus security: 24-hour emergency response devices and patrols. Reid Memorial Library. Books: 50,000 (physical), 123 (digital/electronic); Serial titles: 65 (physical), 12,000 (digital/electronic); Databases: 44. Weekly public service hours: 56; students can reserve study rooms.
Community Environment: Godfrey (population 16,996) is near Alton (population 29,433), an industrial city just north of St. Louis. Industries include glass production, oil refineries, and manufacturing of steel products, brass, bronze, and copper goods. Railroads serve the area and air service is available at St. Louis airport, approximately 17 miles away. Alton has a community concert association, civic orchestra, little theater, and other similar facilities at nearby colleges. Recreational activities include golf, water sports, tennis, and spectator sports. Hunting and fishing opportunities are outstanding. Part-time work is available in industrial and commercial establishments.

■ **LEWIS UNIVERSITY**
One University Pky.
Romeoville, IL 60446
Tel: (815)838-0500; Free: 800-897-9000
Fax: (815)838-9456
E-mail: cockerry@lewisu.edu
Web Site: www.lewisu.edu
Description: Independent, comprehensive, coed, affiliated with Roman Catholic Church. Awards associate, bachelor's, master's, and doctoral degrees and post-master's certificates. Founded 1932. Setting: 410-acre suburban campus with easy access to Chicago. Total enrollment: 6,506.

Faculty: 675 (223 full-time, 452 part-time). Student-undergrad faculty ratio is 13:1. 5,447 applied, 54% were admitted. 20% from top 10% of their high school class, 49% from top quarter, 77% from top half. 4 valedictorians. Full-time: 3,687 students, 53% women, 47% men. Part-time: 819 students, 49% women, 51% men. Students come from 33 states and territories, 26 other countries, 9% from out-of-state. 0.2% American Indian or Alaska Native, non-Hispanic/Latino; 20% Hispanic/Latino; 5% Black or African American, non-Hispanic/Latino; 4% Asian, non-Hispanic/Latino; 0.1% Native Hawaiian or other Pacific Islander, non-Hispanic/Latino; 2% international. 21% 25 or older, 22% live on campus, 12% transferred in. Retention: 80% of full-time freshmen returned the following year. Academic areas with the most degrees conferred: business/marketing; health professions and related sciences; homeland security, law enforcement, firefighting, and protective services. Core. Calendar: semesters. Academic remediation for entering students, ESL program, services for LD students, advanced placement, accelerated degree program, self-designed majors, honors program, independent study, distance learning, double major, summer session for credit, part-time degree program, adult/continuing education programs, internships, graduate courses open to undergrads. Off campus study. Study abroad program. ROTC: Army (c), Air Force (c).

Entrance Requirements: Options: electronic application, deferred admission, international baccalaureate accepted. Required: high school transcript, minimum 2 high school GPA, SAT or ACT. Required for some: interview. Entrance: moderately difficult. Application deadline: 8/1. Notification: continuous. SAT Reasoning Test deadline: 8/1. Transfer credits accepted: Yes.

Costs Per Year: Application fee: $40. Comprehensive fee: $43,028 includes full-time tuition ($32,300), mandatory fees ($150), and college room and board ($10,578). Full-time tuition and fees vary according to course load, location, and program. Room and board charges vary according to board plan and housing facility. Part-time tuition: $948 per credit hour. Part-time mandatory fees: $75 per term. Part-time tuition and fees vary according to course load, location, and program.

Collegiate Environment: Orientation program. Drama-theater group, choral group, student-run newspaper, radio station. Social organizations: 120 open to all; national fraternities, national sororities, local fraternities, local sororities. Most popular organizations: Student Governing Board, Student Nurses Association, Latin American Student Organization, Theta Kappa Pi Sorority, Delta Sigma Pi (business fraternity). Major annual events: Homecoming and Family Day, Fall/Spring Formal, International Student Festival. Student services: health clinic, personal-psychological counseling. Campus security: 24-hour emergency response devices and patrols, late night transport-escort service, controlled dormitory access, Emergency notification system. Lewis University Library. Books: 120,468 (physical), 527,534 (digital/electronic); Serial titles: 1,622 (physical), 151,185 (digital/electronic); Databases: 115. Weekly public service hours: 102; students can reserve study rooms. 350 computers available on campus for general student use. A campuswide network can be accessed from student residence rooms and from off campus. Students can access the following: online class registration, online help desk, online billing, online financial aid, online payments, online admission application, online housing application, online application for graduation, online Blackboard course management system, online tutoring. Staffed computer lab on campus provides training in use of computers, software, and the Internet.

Community Environment: Romeoville, located 35 miles southwest of Chicago, enjoys a seasonal climate. The Regional Transportation Authority between Chicago and Joliet serves the area, as well as Amtrak. Romeoville has the usual civic, fraternal, and veterans' organizations. Part-time employment is available.

■ LINCOLN CHRISTIAN UNIVERSITY
100 Campus View Dr.
Lincoln, IL 62656-2167
Tel: (217)732-3168; Free: 888-522-5228
Fax: (217)732-5914
E-mail: enroll@lincolnchristian.edu
Web Site: www.lincolnchristian.edu

Description: Independent, comprehensive, coed, affiliated with Christian Churches and Churches of Christ. Awards associate, bachelor's, master's, and doctoral degrees. Founded 1944. Setting: 100-acre small town campus. Endowment: $5.2 million. Educational spending for the previous fiscal year: $5721 per student. Total enrollment: 732. Faculty: 69 (33 full-time, 36 part-time). Student-undergrad faculty ratio is 12:1. 301 applied, 62% were admitted. Full-time: 337 students, 48% women, 52% men. Part-time: 78 students, 60% women, 40% men. Students come from 27 states and territories, 2

other countries, 26% from out-of-state. 1% Hispanic/Latino; 7% Black or African American, non-Hispanic/Latino; 0.7% Asian, non-Hispanic/Latino; 0.2% Native Hawaiian or other Pacific Islander, non-Hispanic/Latino; 5% international. 20% 25 or older, 22% live on campus, 5% transferred in. Retention: 82% of full-time freshmen returned the following year. Academic areas with the most degrees conferred: theology and religious vocations; business/marketing; psychology. Core. Calendar: semesters. Academic remediation for entering students, services for LD students, advanced placement, honors program, independent study, distance learning, double major, summer session for credit, part-time degree program, external degree program, adult/continuing education programs, co-op programs and internships. Off campus study at Greenville College. Study abroad program.

Entrance Requirements: Options: electronic application, deferred admission. Required: essay, 3 recommendations, SAT or ACT. Required for some: high school transcript, interview. Entrance: moderately difficult. Application deadline: rolling. Notification: continuous. Preference given to Christian applicants interested in religious studies. SAT Reasoning Test deadline: 8/1. SAT Subject Test deadline: 8/1. Transfer credits accepted: Yes.

Costs Per Year: Application fee: $0. Comprehensive fee: $20,764 includes full-time tuition ($13,200) and college room and board ($7564). College room only: $3600. Room and board charges vary according to housing facility. Part-time tuition: $440 per credit hour.

Collegiate Environment: Orientation program. Drama-theater group, choral group. Social organizations: 4 open to all. Most popular organizations: Chorale, Student Cabinet, American Association of Christian Counselors (AACC) - Student Chapter, Cheerleading. Major annual events: Christmas in the Chapel, Lectureships, Convocation. Student services: personal-psychological counseling. Campus security: 24-hour emergency response devices, student patrols, controlled dormitory access. 486 college housing spaces available; 278 were occupied in 2018-19. Freshmen guaranteed college housing. On-campus residence required through senior year. Options: men-only, women-only housing available. Jessie Eury Library. Books: 92,813 (physical), 55,082 (digital/electronic); Serial titles: 719 (physical), 15,442 (digital/electronic); Databases: 52. Weekly public service hours: 82; students can reserve study rooms. Operations spending for the previous fiscal year: $550,242. 51 computers available on campus for general student use. A campuswide network can be accessed from student residence rooms and from off campus. Students can access the following: online class registration. Staffed computer lab on campus provides training in use of software.

Community Environment: See Lincoln College.

■ LINCOLN COLLEGE
300 Keokuk St.
Lincoln, IL 62656-1699
Tel: (217)732-3155; Free: 800-569-0558
Fax: (217)732-8859
Web Site: www.lincolncollege.edu

Description: Independent, 4-year, coed. Awards associate and bachelor's degrees. Founded 1865. Setting: 42-acre small town campus. Endowment: $20.5 million. Educational spending for the previous fiscal year: $5121 per student. Total enrollment: 1,120. Faculty: 114 (35 full-time, 79 part-time). Student-undergrad faculty ratio is 14:1. 1,537 applied, 68% were admitted. Full-time: 754 students, 49% women, 51% men. Part-time: 366 students, 69% women, 31% men. Students come from 18 states and territories, 8 other countries, 7% from out-of-state. 0.1% American Indian or Alaska Native, non-Hispanic/Latino; 7% Hispanic/Latino; 44% Black or African American, non-Hispanic/Latino; 0.4% Asian, non-Hispanic/Latino; 1% international. 26% 25 or older, 7% transferred in. Retention: 65% of full-time freshmen returned the following year. Academic areas with the most degrees conferred: business/marketing; health professions and related sciences; homeland security, law enforcement, firefighting, and protective services. Core. Calendar: semesters. Academic remediation for entering students, services for LD students, accelerated degree program, freshman honors college, honors program, independent study, summer session for credit, part-time degree program, internships.

Entrance Requirements: Options: electronic application, early admission, deferred admission. Required: high school transcript, minimum 2 high school GPA, SAT or ACT. Required for some: essay, 2 recommendations, interview. Entrance: minimally difficult. Application deadlines: rolling, rolling for nonresidents. Transfer credits accepted: Yes.

Costs Per Year: One-time mandatory fee: $50. Comprehensive fee: $26,300 includes full-time tuition ($17,500), mandatory fees ($1100), and college room and board ($7700). College room only: $3000. Room and board charges vary according to housing facility. Part-time tuition: $310 per credit hour. Tuition guaranteed not to increase for student's term of enrollment.

Collegiate Environment: Orientation program. Drama-theater group, choral group, student-run radio station. Social organizations: 21 open to all. Most popular organizations: Black Student Union, Phi Theta Kappa, Purple Pulse, Student Activities Board, Woment of Worth. Major annual events: Week of Welcome, Lynxfest, Homecoming. Student services: health clinic, personal-psychological counseling. Campus security: 24-hour emergency response devices and patrols, controlled dormitory access. McKinstry Library. Books: 23,449 (physical), 182,420 (digital/electronic); Serial titles: 3 (physical); Databases: 38. Students can reserve study rooms. Operations spending for the previous fiscal year: $237,243.

Community Environment: Lincoln (population 14,971) was founded in 1852, the only one of 24 similarly named cities of the United States that was named for Abraham Lincoln before he became famous. He assisted in planning the city and performed law work necessary for its incorporation. Lincoln christened the town with the juice of a watermelon when the first lots were sold in 1853. Lincoln is midway between Chicago and St. Louis on the main line of Alton route of GM & O Railroad. Churches of many denominations are located here.

■ **LINCOLN COLLEGE OF TECHNOLOGY**
8317 W N Ave.
Melrose Park, IL 60160
Tel: (708)344-4700; Free: 844-215-1513
Web Site: www.lincolntech.edu
Description: Proprietary, 2-year, coed. Awards certificates, transfer associate, and terminal associate degrees. Founded 1946.

■ **LINCOLN LAND COMMUNITY COLLEGE**
5250 Shepherd Rd.
Springfield, IL 62794-9256
Tel: (217)786-2200; Free: 800-727-4161
Fax: (217)786-2492
E-mail: ron.gregoire@llcc.edu
Web Site: www.llcc.edu
Description: District-supported, 2-year, coed. Part of Illinois Community College Board. Awards certificates, transfer associate, and terminal associate degrees. Founded 1967. Setting: 441-acre suburban campus. Endowment: $3.5 million. Educational spending for the previous fiscal year: $4399 per student. Total enrollment: 7,020. Faculty: 371 (129 full-time, 242 part-time). Student-undergrad faculty ratio is 21:1. 5% from top 10% of their high school class, 17% from top quarter, 48% from top half. Full-time: 2,985 students, 52% women, 48% men. Part-time: 4,035 students, 62% women, 38% men. Students come from 4 states and territories. 0.3% American Indian or Alaska Native, non-Hispanic/Latino; 2% Hispanic/Latino; 11% Black or African American, non-Hispanic/Latino; 1% Asian, non-Hispanic/Latino; 0.1% Native Hawaiian or other Pacific Islander, non-Hispanic/Latino. 32% 25 or older, 3% transferred in. Retention: 56% of full-time freshmen returned the following year. Core. Calendar: semesters. Academic remediation for entering students, ESL program, services for LD students, advanced placement, accelerated degree program, honors program, independent study, distance learning, summer session for credit, part-time degree program, external degree program, adult/continuing education programs, internships. Off campus study at Foreign Language/International Studies Consortium. Study abroad program.
Entrance Requirements: Open admission except for allied health programs. Options: electronic application, early admission, deferred admission. Recommended: high school transcript. Entrance: noncompetitive. Application deadline: rolling. Notification: continuous. Transfer credits accepted: Yes.
Collegiate Environment: Orientation program. Drama-theater group, choral group, student-run newspaper. Social organizations: 34 open to all. Most popular organizations: Student Government Association, Epicurean Club, Environmental Club, Chemistry Club, Agricultural Club. Major annual events: Graduation, New Student Welcome Lunch, Loggerpalooza. Student services: health clinic, personal-psychological counseling. Campus security: 24-hour emergency response devices and patrols, late night transport-escort service. Learning Resource Center. Operations spending for the previous fiscal year: $917,017. 525 computers available on campus for general student use. A campuswide network can be accessed from off-campus. Students can access the following: online class registration. Staffed computer lab on campus.

■ **LOYOLA UNIVERSITY CHICAGO**
1032 W Sheridan Rd.
Chicago, IL 60660
Tel: (773)274-3000; Free: 800-262-2373
Fax: (773)915-6414
E-mail: admission@luc.edu
Web Site: www.luc.edu
Description: Independent Roman Catholic (Jesuit), university, coed. Awards associate, bachelor's, master's, and doctoral degrees and post-master's certificates (also offers adult part-time program with significant enrollment not reflected in profile). Founded 1870. Setting: 105-acre urban campus. Endowment: $640.3 million. Research spending for the previous fiscal year: $41.3 million. Educational spending for the previous fiscal year: $12,795 per student. Total enrollment: 17,007. Faculty: 1,682 (840 full-time, 842 part-time). Student-undergrad faculty ratio is 14:1. 25,122 applied, 68% were admitted. 37% from top 10% of their high school class, 72% from top quarter, 95% from top half. 14 valedictorians. Full-time: 11,189 students, 67% women, 33% men. Part-time: 730 students, 63% women, 37% men. Students come from 52 states and territories, 106 other countries, 37% from out-of-state. 0.1% American Indian or Alaska Native, non-Hispanic/Latino; 16% Hispanic/Latino; 5% Black or African American, non-Hispanic/Latino; 13% Asian, non-Hispanic/Latino; 0.3% Native Hawaiian or other Pacific Islander, non-Hispanic/Latino; 5% international. 8% 25 or older, 40% live on campus, 4% transferred in. Retention: 85% of full-time freshmen returned the following year. Academic areas with the most degrees conferred: business/marketing; biological/life sciences; health professions and related sciences. Core. Calendar: semesters. ESL program, services for LD students, advanced placement, accelerated degree program, freshman honors college, honors program, independent study, distance learning, double major, summer session for credit, part-time degree program, adult/continuing education programs, co-op programs and internships, graduate courses open to undergrads. Off campus study. Study abroad program. ROTC: Army, Naval (c), Air Force (c).
Entrance Requirements: Options: electronic application, international baccalaureate accepted. Required: SAT or ACT. Entrance: moderately difficult. SAT Reasoning Test deadline: 2/1. Transfer credits accepted: Yes.
Costs Per Year: Application fee: $0. Comprehensive fee: $60,323 includes full-time tuition ($44,105), mandatory fees ($1438), and college room and board ($14,780). College room only: $9260. Part-time tuition: $814 per credit hour. Part-time mandatory fees: $230 per year.
Collegiate Environment: Orientation program. Drama-theater group, choral group, student-run newspaper, radio station. Social organizations: 230 open to all; national fraternities, national sororities; 10% of eligible men and 20% of eligible women are members. Most popular organizations: Panhellenic Council, National Society of Collegiate Scholars, Vegetarian and Vegan Society, Interfraternity Council, American Medical Student Association. Major annual events: Welcome Week, Senior Send-Off, Finals Breakfast. Student services: health clinic, personal-psychological counseling, women's center. Campus security: 24-hour emergency response devices, late night transport-escort service, controlled dormitory access. 4,816 college housing spaces available; 4,720 were occupied in 2018-19. Freshmen guaranteed college housing. On-campus residence required through sophomore year. Option: coed housing available. Cudahy Library plus 7 others. Books: 1.9 million (physical), 568,720 (digital/electronic); Serial titles: 2,245 (physical), 58,389 (digital/electronic); Databases: 545. Weekly public service hours: 144; study areas open 24 hours, 5-7 days a week; students can reserve study rooms. Operations spending for the previous fiscal year: $15.9 million. 1,300 computers available on campus for general student use. Computer purchase/lease plans available. A campuswide network can be accessed from student residence rooms and from off campus. Students can access the following: online class registration. Staffed computer lab on campus provides training in use of computers, software, and the Internet.
Community Environment: See University of Chicago.

■ **MACCORMAC COLLEGE**
506 S Wabash Ave.
Chicago, IL 60605-1667
Tel: (312)922-1884
Fax: (312)922-3196
Web Site: www.maccormac.edu
Description: Independent, 2-year, coed. Awards certificates, diplomas, transfer associate, and terminal associate degrees. Founded 1904. Setting: urban campus. Total enrollment: 377. Faculty: 34 (4 full-time, 30 part-time). Student-undergrad faculty ratio is 9:1. Full-time: 159 students, 86% women,

14% men. Part-time: 218 students, 89% women, 11% men. Students come from 7 states and territories, 8 other countries, 1% from out-of-state. 20% 25 or older. Core. Calendar: semesters. Academic remediation for entering students, ESL program, advanced placement, honors program, summer session for credit, part-time degree program, adult/continuing education programs, internships.

Entrance Requirements: Option: deferred admission. Required: high school transcript, ACT. Recommended: interview, SAT. Entrance: moderately difficult. Application deadline: rolling. Notification: continuous.

Collegiate Environment: Orientation program. Social organizations: 2 open to all. Major annual events: Halloween Party, Christmas Dance, All-College Picnic. Student services: personal-psychological counseling. Campus security: late night transport-escort service. MacCormac College Library. 180 computers available on campus for general student use. A campuswide network can be accessed.

Community Environment: See University of Chicago.

■ MACMURRAY COLLEGE

447 E College Ave.
Jacksonville, IL 62650
Tel: (217)479-7000; Free: 800-252-7485
Fax: (217)245-0405
E-mail: kristen.chenoweth@mac.edu
Web Site: www.mac.edu

Description: Independent United Methodist, 4-year, coed. Awards associate and bachelor's degrees. Founded 1846. Setting: 60-acre small town campus. Endowment: $13.5 million. Educational spending for the previous fiscal year: $7491 per student. Total enrollment: 552. 1,076 applied, 54% were admitted. 10% from top 10% of their high school class, 32% from top quarter, 68% from top half. 1 valedictorian. Full-time: 536 students, 50% women, 50% men. Part-time: 16 students, 63% women, 37% men. Students come from 25 states and territories, 15% from out-of-state. 6% Hispanic/Latino; 10% Black or African American, non-Hispanic/Latino; 0.2% Asian, non-Hispanic/Latino; 0.4% Native Hawaiian or other Pacific Islander, non-Hispanic/Latino; 0.2% international. 11% 25 or older, 56% live on campus, 7% transferred in. Retention: 67% of full-time freshmen returned the following year. Academic areas with the most degrees conferred: homeland security, law enforcement, firefighting, and protective services; health professions and related sciences; business/marketing. Core. Calendar: semesters. Academic remediation for entering students, services for LD students, advanced placement, accelerated degree program, independent study, distance learning, double major, summer session for credit, part-time degree program, internships. Off campus study. Study abroad program.

Entrance Requirements: Options: electronic application, early admission. Required: high school transcript, minimum 2.5 high school GPA, SAT or ACT. Required for some: essay. Entrance: moderately difficult. Application deadline: rolling. Notification: continuous. SAT Reasoning Test deadline: 8/1. SAT Subject Test deadline: 8/1. Transfer credits accepted: Yes.

Costs Per Year: Application fee: $0. Comprehensive fee: $37,150 includes full-time tuition ($26,930), mandatory fees ($780), and college room and board ($9440). Full-time tuition and fees vary according to course load and location. Room and board charges vary according to housing facility. Part-time tuition: $835 per credit hour. Part-time mandatory fees: $40 per credit hour, $10 per term. Part-time tuition and fees vary according to course load and location.

Collegiate Environment: Orientation program. Drama-theater group, choral group. Social organizations: 24 open to all; local fraternities, local sororities; 8% of eligible men and 15% of eligible women are members. Most popular organizations: Campus Activity Board, MacMurray Student Association, Helping Hands, Belles Lettres, Phi Nu. Major annual events: Homecoming, Highlander Games, Casino Night. Student services: health clinic, personal-psychological counseling. Campus security: 24-hour emergency response devices and patrols, student patrols, late night transport-escort service, controlled dormitory access. Henry Pfeiffer Library. Books: 87,300 (physical), 4,591 (digital/electronic); Serial titles: 893 (physical), 13,638 (digital/electronic); Databases: 42. Weekly public service hours: 85. Operations spending for the previous fiscal year: $509,158. 100 computers available on campus for general student use. A campuswide network can be accessed from student residence rooms and from off campus. Students can access the following: online class registration. Staffed computer lab on campus provides training in use of computers, software, and the Internet.

Community Environment: See Illinois College.

■ MCHENRY COUNTY COLLEGE

8900 US Hwy. 14
Crystal Lake, IL 60012-2761
Tel: (815)455-3700
E-mail: admissions@mchenry.edu
Web Site: www.mchenry.edu

Description: State and locally supported, 2-year, coed. Part of Illinois Community College Board. Awards certificates, transfer associate, and terminal associate degrees. Founded 1967. Setting: 168-acre suburban campus with easy access to Chicago. Educational spending for the previous fiscal year: $6543 per student. Total enrollment: 6,843. Faculty: 338 (92 full-time, 246 part-time). Student-undergrad faculty ratio is 21:1. 1,739 applied, 100% were admitted. Full-time: 2,112 students, 47% women, 53% men. Part-time: 4,731 students, 56% women, 44% men. 1% from out-of-state. 0.1% American Indian or Alaska Native, non-Hispanic/Latino; 18% Hispanic/Latino; 2% Black or African American, non-Hispanic/Latino; 2% Asian, non-Hispanic/Latino; 0.1% Native Hawaiian or other Pacific Islander, non-Hispanic/Latino; 0.1% international. 27% 25 or older, 9% transferred in. Core. Calendar: semesters. Academic remediation for entering students, ESL program, services for LD students, advanced placement, accelerated degree program, independent study, distance learning, summer session for credit, part-time degree program, adult/continuing education programs, co-op programs and internships. Study abroad program.

Entrance Requirements: Open admission. Options: electronic application, early admission, deferred admission. Recommended: high school transcript. Entrance: noncompetitive. Application deadlines: rolling, rolling for nonresidents. Notification: continuous, continuous for nonresidents. Transfer credits accepted: Yes.

Costs Per Year: Application fee: $15. Area resident tuition: $3210 full-time, $107 per credit hour part-time. State resident tuition: $11,862 full-time, $395.40 per credit hour part-time. Nonresident tuition: $14,319 full-time, $477.27 per credit hour part-time. Mandatory fees: $284 full-time, $9 per credit hour part-time, $7 per term part-time. Full-time tuition and fees vary according to course load. Part-time tuition and fees vary according to course load.

Collegiate Environment: Orientation program. Drama-theater group, choral group, student-run newspaper, radio station. Social organizations: 31 open to all. Most popular organizations: Phi Theta Kappa, Student Senate, Equality Club, Writer's Block, Latinos Unidos. Major annual events: Welcome Week Picnic and Convocation, Student Organization Fair, Spring Fling Week. Campus security: 24-hour emergency response devices and patrols, late night transport-escort service. College housing not available. McHenry County College Library. Books: 38,157 (physical), 1,272 (digital/electronic); Serial titles: 52 (physical), 42,334 (digital/electronic); Databases: 113. Operations spending for the previous fiscal year: $776,916. 113 computers available on campus for general student use. A campuswide network can be accessed from off-campus. Students can access the following: online class registration. Staffed computer lab on campus provides training in use of computers, software, and the Internet.

Community Environment: Crystal Lake after which the city (population 40,900) was named, is the only natural spring-fed lake between Chicago and Wisconsin. Within the city are 27 large industrial firms and 45 smaller ones, churches, library, medical center, hospitals, and 350 apartment units ranging from small to luxury townhouses. Recreational facilities include the 400 acres of parks and beaches along the lake for all types of water sports and other recreation.

■ MCKENDREE UNIVERSITY

701 College Rd.
Lebanon, IL 62254-1299
Tel: (618)537-4481; Free: 800-232-7228
Fax: (618)537-6259
E-mail: jlblasdel@mckendree.edu
Web Site: www.mckendree.edu

Description: Independent, university, coed, affiliated with United Methodist Church. Awards associate, bachelor's, master's, and doctoral degrees and post-master's certificates. Founded 1828. Setting: 235-acre suburban campus with easy access to St. Louis, MO; Belleville, IL. Total enrollment: 2,676. Faculty: 278 (97 full-time, 181 part-time). Student-undergrad faculty ratio is 14:1. 2,206 applied, 62% were admitted. 13% from top 10% of their high school class, 39% from top quarter, 77% from top half. Full-time: 1,692 students, 51% women, 49% men. Part-time: 412 students, 66% women, 34% men. Students come from 40 states and territories, 38 other countries, 27% from out-of-state. 0.3% American Indian or Alaska Native, non-

Hispanic/Latino; 4% Hispanic/Latino; 13% Black or African American, non-Hispanic/Latino; 0.6% Asian, non-Hispanic/Latino; 0.1% Native Hawaiian or other Pacific Islander, non-Hispanic/Latino; 3% international. 4% 25 or older, 77% live on campus, 5% transferred in. Retention: 75% of full-time freshmen returned the following year. Academic areas with the most degrees conferred: business/marketing; health professions and related sciences; psychology; social sciences. Core. Calendar: semesters. Academic remediation for entering students, services for LD students, advanced placement, accelerated degree program, self-designed majors, freshman honors college, honors program, independent study, distance learning, double major, summer session for credit, part-time degree program, adult/continuing education programs, co-op programs and internships, graduate courses open to undergrads. Off campus study. Study abroad program. ROTC: Army (c), Air Force (c).

Entrance Requirements: Options: electronic application, deferred admission. Required: essay, high school transcript, minimum 2.5 high school GPA, 1 recommendation, rank in upper 50% of high school class, minimum ACT score of 20, SAT or ACT. Required for some: interview. Entrance: moderately difficult. Application deadline: rolling. Notification: continuous. SAT Reasoning Test deadline: 8/14. Transfer credits accepted: Yes.

Costs Per Year: Comprehensive fee: $40,440 includes full-time tuition ($29,420), mandatory fees ($1100), and college room and board ($9920). College room only: $5120. Full-time tuition and fees vary according to course load, degree level, and location. Room and board charges vary according to board plan and housing facility. Part-time tuition: $960 per credit hour. Part-time tuition varies according to course load, degree level, and location.

Collegiate Environment: Orientation program. Drama-theater group, choral group, marching band, student-run newspaper, radio station. Social organizations: 60 open to all; national fraternities, national sororities, local fraternities, local sororities; 3% of eligible men and 15% of eligible women are members. Most popular organizations: Center for Public Service, Wonders of Wellness, Campus Ministries, APO, Debate. Major annual events: Academic Excellence Celebration, Involvement Fair, Homecoming. Student services: health clinic, personal-psychological counseling. Campus security: 24-hour emergency response devices and patrols, student patrols, late night transport-escort service, controlled dormitory access. Holman Library. Books: 76,806 (physical), 11,853 (digital/electronic); Serial titles: 5,099 (physical), 7,229 (digital/electronic); Databases: 59. Students can reserve study rooms. 380 computers available on campus for general student use. A campuswide network can be accessed from student residence rooms and from off campus. Students can access the following: online class registration. Staffed computer lab on campus provides training in use of computers, software, and the Internet.

Community Environment: Lebanon, population 3,700, is 23 miles east of St. Louis. The city has the usual Mississippi Valley climate, neither too hot nor too cold but unpredictable. Scott Air Force Base is six miles from downtown. Employment is available in Belleville, 12 miles away, Fairview Heights, 12 miles away, and in St. Louis proper. Hospital facilities are in Belleville, Highland, Breese and St. Louis. Local recreational activities are tennis, hunting, fishing, golfing, picnicking, and community theater.

■ **METHODIST COLLEGE**
415 St. Mark Ct.
Peoria, IL 61603
Tel: (309)672-5513
Fax: (309)671-8303
Web Site: www.methodistcol.edu
Description: Independent, 4-year, coed. Awards associate and bachelor's degrees.

■ **MIDSTATE COLLEGE**
411 W Northmoor Rd.
Peoria, IL 61614
Tel: (309)692-4092; Free: 800-251-4299
Fax: (309)692-3893
E-mail: jhancock2@midstate.edu
Web Site: www.midstate.edu
Description: Proprietary, 4-year, coed. Awards associate and bachelor's degrees. Founded 1888. Setting: 1-acre urban campus. Total enrollment: 641. 49 applied. 82% 25 or older. Core. Calendar: quarters. Academic remediation for entering students, freshman honors college, honors program, summer session for credit, part-time degree program, co-op programs and internships.

Entrance Requirements: Options: early admission, deferred admission. Required: high school transcript, Wonderlic aptitude test. Recommended: interview. Entrance: moderately difficult. Application deadline: rolling.
Collegiate Environment: Social organizations: national sororities, local fraternities. Campus security: late night transport-escort service. Barbara Fields Library.

Community Environment: Peoria is the third largest city of downstate Illinois. All modes of transportation are available. It is the hub of the central area of the state for cultural, business and professional activities. Peoria is a manufacturing and shipping center located in the heart of the farm belt. Community facilities include good shopping areas and recreational opportunities. Job opportunities are good, particularly for summer work. Points of interest are Fort Creve Coer, Indian burial mounds, Peoria Historical Society Museum, Lakeview Center for Arts Sciences, the Planetarium, the Peoria Civic Center, and Wildlife Prairie Park.

■ **MIDWESTERN CAREER COLLEGE**
20 N Wacker Dr. No.3800
Chicago, IL 60606
Tel: (312)236-9000
Web Site: www.mccollege.edu
Description: Proprietary, 2-year, coed. Awards certificates, diplomas, transfer associate, and terminal associate degrees. Founded 2004.

■ **MILLIKIN UNIVERSITY**
1184 W Main St.
Decatur, IL 62522-2084
Tel: (217)424-6211; Free: 800-373-7733
Fax: (217)425-4669
E-mail: admis@millikin.edu
Web Site: www.millikin.edu
Description: Independent, comprehensive, coed, affiliated with Presbyterian Church (U.S.A.). Awards bachelor's, master's, and doctoral degrees. Founded 1901. Setting: 75-acre suburban campus. Endowment: $110.5 million. Educational spending for the previous fiscal year: $21,548 per student. Total enrollment: 2,068. Faculty: 292 (153 full-time, 139 part-time). Student-undergrad faculty ratio is 10:1. 4,512 applied, 61% were admitted. 14% from top 10% of their high school class, 38% from top quarter, 71% from top half. Full-time: 1,894 students, 57% women, 43% men. Part-time: 91 students, 71% women, 29% men. Students come from 37 states and territories, 30 other countries, 19% from out-of-state. 0.2% American Indian or Alaska Native, non-Hispanic/Latino; 7% Hispanic/Latino; 14% Black or African American, non-Hispanic/Latino; 1% Asian, non-Hispanic/Latino; 0.1% Native Hawaiian or other Pacific Islander, non-Hispanic/Latino; 5% international. 8% 25 or older, 58% live on campus, 5% transferred in. Retention: 78% of full-time freshmen returned the following year. Academic areas with the most degrees conferred: business/marketing; visual and performing arts; health professions and related sciences. Core. Calendar: semesters. Academic remediation for entering students, ESL program, services for LD students, advanced placement, accelerated degree program, self-designed majors, honors program, independent study, distance learning, double major, summer session for credit, part-time degree program, adult/continuing education programs, internships, graduate courses open to undergrads. Off campus study at Drew University, American University, Urban Life Center. Study abroad program.

Entrance Requirements: Options: electronic application, deferred admission, international baccalaureate accepted. Required: high school transcript, minimum 2 high school GPA, 2 recommendations, SAT or ACT. Recommended: interview. Required for some: audition for music/theatre, art portfolio review. Entrance: moderately difficult. Application deadline: rolling. Notification: continuous. SAT Reasoning Test deadline: 5/1. SAT Subject Test deadline: 5/1. Transfer credits accepted: Yes.

Costs Per Year: Application fee: $0. Comprehensive fee: $48,848 includes full-time tuition ($36,262), mandatory fees ($792), and college room and board ($11,794). College room only: $9038. Part-time tuition: $511 per credit hour. Part-time mandatory fees: $22 per credit hour.

Collegiate Environment: Orientation program. Drama-theater group, choral group, student-run newspaper, radio station. Social organizations: 90 open to all; national fraternities, national sororities; 19% of eligible men and 23% of eligible women are members. Most popular organizations: University Center Board, Multicultural Student Council, Student Housing Council, Panhellenic Council, Interfraternity Council. Major annual events: Homecoming, Fall Family Weekend, Performing Arts Series. Student services: health clinic, personal-psychological counseling, women's center. Campus security:

24-hour emergency response devices and patrols, late night transport-escort service, controlled dormitory access. 1,131 college housing spaces available; 973 were occupied in 2018-19. Freshmen guaranteed college housing. On-campus residence required through junior year. Option: coed housing available. Staley Library. Books: 122,725 (physical), 23,745 (digital/electronic); Serial titles: 543 (physical), 49 (digital/electronic); Databases: 49. Weekly public service hours: 113; students can reserve study rooms. Operations spending for the previous fiscal year: $612,965. 135 computers available on campus for general student use. A campuswide network can be accessed from student residence rooms. Students can access the following: online class registration, online degree audit, online financials (view and pay bills, financial aid). Staffed computer lab on campus provides training in use of computers, software, and the Internet.

Community Environment: Decatur is a diversified industrial community. Bus and air service are available. Many part-time jobs are available. A well-developed park system provides varied recreational opportunities. South of Decatur is the Lincoln Trail Homestead State Park, which marks the first homestead site of the Lincoln family in Illinois.

■ **MONMOUTH COLLEGE**
700 E Broadway
Monmouth, IL 61462-1998
Tel: (309)457-2311; Free: 800-747-2687
Fax: (309)457-2141
E-mail: admissions@monmouthcollege.edu
Web Site: www.monmouthcollege.edu
Description: Independent, 4-year, coed, affiliated with Presbyterian Church. Awards bachelor's degrees. Founded 1853. Setting: 112-acre small town campus. Endowment: $113.8 million. Educational spending for the previous fiscal year: $12,731 per student. Total enrollment: 1,033. Faculty: 125 (91 full-time, 34 part-time). Student-undergrad faculty ratio is 11:1. 2,428 applied, 67% were admitted. 17% from top 10% of their high school class, 42% from top quarter, 71% from top half. Students come from 32 states and territories, 33 other countries, 11% from out-of-state. 0.2% American Indian or Alaska Native, non-Hispanic/Latino; 10% Hispanic/Latino; 11% Black or African American, non-Hispanic/Latino; 1% Asian, non-Hispanic/Latino; 7% international. 2% 25 or older, 91% live on campus. Retention: 71% of full-time freshmen returned the following year. Academic areas with the most degrees conferred: business/marketing; education; social sciences; psychology. Core. Calendar: semesters. Academic remediation for entering students, ESL program, services for LD students, advanced placement, self-designed majors, honors program, independent study, double major, part-time degree program, internships. Off campus study at American University - Washington Semester. Study abroad program. ROTC: Army (c).
Entrance Requirements: Options: electronic application, deferred admission, international baccalaureate accepted. Required: high school transcript, SAT or ACT. Recommended: essay, minimum 2.7 high school GPA, recommendations, interview. Required for some: interview. Entrance: moderately difficult. Application deadline: rolling. Notification: continuous. SAT Reasoning Test deadline: 5/1. SAT Subject Test deadline: 5/1. Transfer credits accepted: Yes.
Costs Per Year: Application fee: $0. One-time mandatory fee: $195. Comprehensive fee: $46,640 includes full-time tuition ($37,674) and college room and board ($8966). College room only: $5054. Room and board charges vary according to housing facility. Part-time tuition: $4709 per course.
Collegiate Environment: Orientation program. Drama-theater group, choral group, marching band, student-run newspaper, radio station. Social organizations: 72 open to all; national fraternities, national sororities; 18% of eligible men and 34% of eligible women are members. Most popular organizations: Fighting Scots Marching Band and Jazz Band, Associated Students of Monmouth College, Crimson Masque (theatre), Alternative Spring Break, Coalition for Ethnic Awareness. Major annual events: Homecoming, Scots Day (Founders' Day), Family Weekend. Student services: personal-psychological counseling. Campus security: 24-hour emergency response devices and patrols, late night transport-escort service, controlled dormitory access, full-time Director of Campus Security. Hewes Library. Books: 206,954 (physical), 33,996 (digital/electronic); Serial titles: 3,400 (physical), 28,190 (digital/electronic); Databases: 115. Weekly public service hours: 96; students can reserve study rooms. Operations spending for the previous fiscal year: $1.5 million. 140 computers available on campus for general student use. A campuswide network can be accessed from student residence rooms and from off campus. Students can access the fol-

lowing: online class registration. Staffed computer lab on campus (open 24 hours a day) provides training in use of computers, software, and the Internet.
Community Environment: Monmouth is located about 180 miles southwest of Chicago and 180 miles north of St. Louis in the heart of the rich corn belt of the Midwest. Although agriculture is the backbone of the economy in the area, numerous small businesses and light industry firms are located here. As a region noted for beef cattle feeding, Monmouth holds a three-day Prime Beef Festival in September. Monmouth Park, a natural forest at the outskirts of the city, has playground equipment, picnic facilities, and an 18-hole municipal golf course.

■ **MOODY BIBLE INSTITUTE**
820 N LaSalle Blvd.
Chicago, IL 60610-3284
Tel: (312)329-4000; Free: 800-967-4MBI
Fax: (312)329-8987
E-mail: admissions@moody.edu
Web Site: www.moody.edu
Description: Independent nondenominational, comprehensive, coed. Awards associate, bachelor's, and master's degrees. Founded 1886. Setting: 25-acre urban campus with easy access to Chicago. Endowment: $27.8 million. Educational spending for the previous fiscal year: $10,100 per student. Total enrollment: 3,349. Faculty: 211 (90 full-time, 121 part-time). Student-undergrad faculty ratio is 20:1. 816 applied, 89% were admitted. Full-time: 2,275 students, 47% women, 53% men. Part-time: 653 students, 36% women, 64% men. Students come from 24 other countries. Retention: 78% of full-time freshmen returned the following year. Academic areas with the most degrees conferred: theology and religious vocations; communication/journalism; visual and performing arts. Core. Calendar: semesters. ESL program, advanced placement, independent study, distance learning, double major, summer session for credit, part-time degree program, external degree program, adult/continuing education programs, internships, graduate courses open to undergrads. Off campus study at Roosevelt University, University of Illinois at Chicago, City Colleges of Chicago, Harold Washington College. Study abroad program.
Entrance Requirements: Options: electronic application, early admission, early decision, international baccalaureate accepted. Required: essay, high school transcript, minimum 2 high school GPA, 4 recommendations, Christian testimony, SAT and SAT Subject Tests or ACT. Required for some: interview. Entrance: moderately difficult. Application deadlines: 3/1, 12/1 for early decision. Notification: continuous until 4/1, 1/15 for early decision. SAT Reasoning Test deadline: 3/1. SAT Subject Test deadline: 3/1. Transfer credits accepted: Yes. Applicants placed on waiting list: 68. Wait-listed applicants offered admission: 0. Early decision applicants: 734. Early decision applicants admitted: 262.
Collegiate Environment: Orientation program. Drama-theater group, choral group, student-run newspaper, radio station. Student services: health clinic, personal-psychological counseling. Campus security: 24-hour emergency response devices and patrols, student patrols, late night transport-escort service, controlled dormitory access. Henry Crowell Learning Center plus 1 other. Operations spending for the previous fiscal year: $640,660.
Community Environment: See University of Chicago.

■ **MORAINE VALLEY COMMUNITY COLLEGE**
9000 W College Pky.
Palos Hills, IL 60465
Tel: (708)974-4300
Fax: (708)974-0681
E-mail: saratala@morainevalley.edu
Web Site: www.morainevalley.edu
Description: State and locally supported, 2-year, coed. Part of Illinois Community College Board. Awards certificates and transfer associate degrees. Founded 1967. Setting: 294-acre suburban campus with easy access to Chicago. Endowment: $13.3 million. Research spending for the previous fiscal year: $407,824. Educational spending for the previous fiscal year: $3744 per student. Total enrollment: 15,016. Faculty: 959 (196 full-time, 763 part-time). Student-undergrad faculty ratio is 21:1. Full-time: 6,393 students, 49% women, 51% men. Part-time: 8,623 students, 54% women, 46% men. 0.2% from out-of-state. 0.3% American Indian or Alaska Native, non-Hispanic/Latino; 23% Hispanic/Latino; 9% Black or African American, non-Hispanic/Latino; 3% Asian, non-Hispanic/Latino; 0.1% Native Hawaiian or other Pacific Islander, non-Hispanic/Latino; 2% international. 23% 25 or older, 3% transferred in. Retention: 66% of full-time freshmen returned the following

year. Core. Calendar: semesters. Academic remediation for entering students, ESL program, services for LD students, advanced placement, accelerated degree program, honors program, independent study, distance learning, double major, summer session for credit, part-time degree program, adult/continuing education programs, co-op programs and internships. Off campus study. Study abroad program.

Entrance Requirements: Open admission except for allied health, nursing programs. Options: electronic application, early admission, deferred admission. Recommended: high school transcript. Entrance: noncompetitive. Application deadline: rolling. Notification: continuous. Preference given to district residents for allied health, nursing programs. Transfer credits accepted: Yes.

Collegiate Environment: Orientation program. Drama-theater group, choral group, student-run newspaper. Social organizations: 44 open to all. Most popular organizations: Student Newspaper, Speech Team, Alliance of Latin American Students, Phi Theta Kappa, Arab Student Union. Major annual events: Back to School Fest, Phi Theta Kappa initiation, Student Activities Awards Banquet. Student services: personal-psychological counseling, women's center. Campus security: 24-hour emergency response devices and patrols, late night transport-escort service, campus police department, safety and security programs. Books: 64,610 (physical), 493 (digital/electronic); Serial titles: 314 (physical), 55 (digital/electronic); Databases: 63. Operations spending for the previous fiscal year: $1.9 million. 1,751 computers available on campus for general student use. A campuswide network can be accessed from off-campus. Students can access the following: online class registration. Staffed computer lab on campus provides training in use of computers, software, and the Internet.

Community Environment: Palos Hills is located 20 miles south of downtown Chicago near Oak Lawn, a suburban area that has access to all the cultural, educational, and recreational opportunities of Chicago. All major forms of transportation are available. The climate is seasonal. Part-time employment is available.

■ **MORRISON INSTITUTE OF TECHNOLOGY**

701 Portland Ave.
Morrison, IL 61270-0410
Tel: (815)772-7218
Fax: (815)772-7584
Web Site: www.morrisontech.edu

Description: Independent, 2-year, coed. Awards transfer associate and terminal associate degrees. Founded 1973. Setting: 17-acre small town campus. Endowment: $76,000. Total enrollment: 144. Faculty: 15 (14 full-time, 1 part-time). Student-undergrad faculty ratio is 13:1. 94 applied, 100% were admitted. 3% from top 10% of their high school class, 16% from top quarter, 38% from top half. 1 National Merit Scholar, 4 student government officers. Full-time: 142 students, 8% women, 92% men. Part-time: 2 students, 50% women, 50% men. Students come from 4 states and territories, 5% from out-of-state. 11% 25 or older, 55% live on campus, 7% transferred in. Core. Calendar: semesters. Academic remediation for entering students, double major, part-time degree program, internships.

Entrance Requirements: Open admission. Option: deferred admission. Required: high school transcript, proof of immunization. Entrance: noncompetitive. Application deadline: rolling. Notification: continuous until 9/1.

Collegiate Environment: Major annual events: Turkey Day, Harvest Hammer, Hunger and Homelessness Awareness Week. Campus security: late night transport-escort service, controlled dormitory access. Morrison Tech Learning Center plus 1 other. Study areas open 24 hours, 5-7 days a week. Operations spending for the previous fiscal year: $22,000. 60 computers available on campus for general student use. A campuswide network can be accessed. Staffed computer lab on campus provides training in use of computers, software, and the Internet.

Community Environment: Morrison is located 130 miles west of Chicago and 10 miles east of the Mississippi River. It is close to the Chestnut Lodge Winter Ski Area. Students are welcome in the local Theater Association and recreation leagues. Morrison also has two city parks and a state park with a lake. Community facilities include shopping areas, 16 churches, a public library, and two medical centers. A very safe campus environment.

■ **MORTON COLLEGE**

3801 S Central Ave.
Cicero, IL 60804-4398
Tel: (708)656-8000
Fax: (708)656-9592

Web Site: www.morton.edu

Description: State and locally supported, 2-year, coed. Part of Illinois Community College Board. Awards certificates, transfer associate, and terminal associate degrees. Founded 1924. Setting: 25-acre suburban campus with easy access to Chicago. Total enrollment: 4,387. Faculty: 240 (53 full-time, 187 part-time). Student-undergrad faculty ratio is 17:1. Full-time: 1,344 students, 52% women, 48% men. Part-time: 3,043 students, 60% women, 40% men. Students come from 15 states and territories, 1% from out-of-state. 0.1% American Indian or Alaska Native, non-Hispanic/Latino; 84% Hispanic/Latino; 3% Black or African American, non-Hispanic/Latino; 1% Asian, non-Hispanic/Latino. 25% 25 or older, 36% transferred in. Core. Calendar: semesters. Academic remediation for entering students, ESL program, services for LD students, advanced placement, self-designed majors, distance learning, summer session for credit, part-time degree program, adult/continuing education programs, internships.

Entrance Requirements: Open admission except for nursing, physical therapy assistant, therapeutic massage programs. Option: electronic application. Required: high school transcript. Entrance: noncompetitive. Application deadline: rolling. Preference given to district residents for nursing, physical therapy assistant programs, therapeutic massage. Transfer credits accepted: Yes.

Costs Per Year: Application fee: $10. Area resident tuition: $2112 full-time, $88 per credit hour part-time. State resident tuition: $5184 full-time, $216 per credit hour part-time. Nonresident tuition: $6720 full-time, $280 per credit hour part-time. Mandatory fees: $980 full-time, $40 per credit hour part-time, $10 per term part-time.

Collegiate Environment: Orientation program. Drama-theater group, student-run newspaper, radio station. Most popular organizations: Morton Ambassador Program, Campus Activities Board, Student Government Association, Nursing Club. Major annual events: Welcome Week, Success Workshop Series, Club Day. Campus security: 24-hour patrols, security cameras. Learning Resource Center. Students can reserve study rooms. 250 computers available on campus for general student use. Computer purchase/lease plans available. A campuswide network can be accessed from off-campus. Students can access the following: online class registration. Staffed computer lab on campus provides training in use of computers.

Community Environment: Cicero, (population 82,700), is a residential and industrial suburb on the west side of the greater Chicago area.

■ **NATIONAL LOUIS UNIVERSITY**

122 S Michigan Ave.
Chicago, IL 60603
Tel: (312)621-9650; Free: 888-658-8632
Fax: (312)261-3057
Web Site: www.nl.edu

Description: Independent, university, coed. Awards bachelor's, master's, and doctoral degrees and post-master's certificates. Founded 1886. Setting: 12-acre urban campus. Total enrollment: 4,918. Faculty: 290 (137 full-time, 153 part-time). Student-undergrad faculty ratio is 17:1. 2,713 applied, 86% were admitted. Full-time: 1,250 students, 69% women, 31% men. Part-time: 635 students, 79% women, 21% men. Students come from 20 states and territories, 3% from out-of-state. 0.2% American Indian or Alaska Native, non-Hispanic/Latino; 47% Hispanic/Latino; 29% Black or African American, non-Hispanic/Latino; 2% Asian, non-Hispanic/Latino; 0.2% Native Hawaiian or other Pacific Islander, non-Hispanic/Latino; 0.6% international. 45% 25 or older, 15% transferred in. Retention: 68% of full-time freshmen returned the following year. Core. Calendar: quarters. Academic remediation for entering students, ESL program, services for LD students, advanced placement, accelerated degree program, independent study, distance learning, summer session for credit, part-time degree program, adult/continuing education programs, internships, graduate courses open to undergrads.

Entrance Requirements: Options: electronic application, deferred admission, international baccalaureate accepted. Required: high school transcript, minimum 2 high school GPA. Recommended: interview, SAT or ACT. Entrance: moderately difficult. Application deadline: rolling. Notification: continuous. Transfer credits accepted: Yes.

Collegiate Environment: Orientation program. Student services: personal-psychological counseling. Campus security: 24-hour emergency response devices and patrols. NLU Library.

Community Environment: See Northwestern University.

■ **NORTH CENTRAL COLLEGE**

30 N Brainard St.
Naperville, IL 60566-7063

Tel: (630)637-5100; Free: 800-411-1861

E-mail: admissions@noctrl.edu

Web Site: www.northcentralcollege.edu

Description: Independent United Methodist, comprehensive, coed. Awards bachelor's and master's degrees. Founded 1861. Setting: 68-acre suburban campus with easy access to Chicago. Endowment: $110 million. Educational spending for the previous fiscal year: $10,502 per student. Total enrollment: 2,965. Faculty: 283 (151 full-time, 132 part-time). Student-undergrad faculty ratio is 14:1. 7,220 applied, 54% were admitted. 28% from top 10% of their high school class, 55% from top quarter, 85% from top half. 6 valedictorians. Full-time: 2,634 students, 54% women, 46% men. Part-time: 135 students, 54% women, 46% men. Students come from 27 states and territories, 45 other countries, 7% from out-of-state. 0.1% American Indian or Alaska Native, non-Hispanic/Latino; 15% Hispanic/Latino; 4% Black or African American, non-Hispanic/Latino; 3% Asian, non-Hispanic/Latino; 0.1% Native Hawaiian or other Pacific Islander, non-Hispanic/Latino. 4% 25 or older, 49% live on campus, 9% transferred in. Retention: 79% of full-time freshmen returned the following year. Academic areas with the most degrees conferred: business/marketing; social sciences; parks and recreation. Core. Calendar: quarters. Academic remediation for entering students, ESL program, services for LD students, advanced placement, accelerated degree program, self-designed majors, honors program, independent study, distance learning, double major, summer session for credit, part-time degree program, internships, graduate courses open to undergrads. Off campus study at Aurora University, Benedictine University, Northwestern Memorial Hospital, Hooke College of Applied Sciences. Study abroad program. ROTC: Army (c), Air Force (c).

Entrance Requirements: Options: electronic application, deferred admission, international baccalaureate accepted. Required: high school transcript, minimum 2.5 high school GPA, SAT or ACT. Recommended: essay, 1 recommendation, ACT. Required for some: interview. Entrance: moderately difficult. Application deadline: rolling. Notification: continuous. SAT Reasoning Test deadline: 6/1. SAT Subject Test deadline: 6/1. Transfer credits accepted: Yes.

Costs Per Year: Application fee: $25. Comprehensive fee: $49,899 includes full-time tuition ($38,700), mandatory fees ($180), and college room and board ($11,019). Room and board charges vary according to housing facility. Part-time tuition: $1075 per credit hour. Part-time tuition varies according to course load.

Collegiate Environment: Orientation program. Drama-theater group, choral group, marching band, student-run newspaper, radio station. Social organizations: 69 open to all. Most popular organizations: College Union Activities Board, WONC (student radio station), Cardinals in Action (service group), ENACTUS (Students in Free Enterprise SIFE), Residence Hall Association. Major annual events: Jim Wand (hypnotist show), Taste of Asia, Springfest. Student services: health clinic, personal-psychological counseling. Campus security: 24-hour emergency response devices and patrols, late night transport-escort service, controlled dormitory access. Oesterle Library. Books: 135,388 (physical), 74,330 (digital/electronic); Databases: 137. Operations spending for the previous fiscal year: $1.4 million. 450 computers available on campus for general student use. A campuswide network can be accessed from student residence rooms and from off campus. Students can access the following: online class registration, software packages. Staffed computer lab on campus provides training in use of computers.

Community Environment: Naperville, population 141,500, is a suburban community 29 miles west of Chicago on the Burlington Northern Railroad route. It has a moderate, temperate climate, is the site of many corporate and scientific research installations, and is in the "Research and Development Corridor of Illinois." The community facilities include public and college libraries, a YMCA, hospital, many churches, motels, restaurants, shopping, entertainment, and numerous civic organizations. Many parks and attractive natural surroundings provide for outdoor sports and recreation. Part-time employment for students is generally available.

■ **NORTH PARK UNIVERSITY**

3225 W Foster Ave.

Chicago, IL 60625-4895

Tel: (773)244-6200; Free: 800-888-NPC8

Fax: (773)583-0858

E-mail: afao@northpark.edu

Web Site: www.northpark.edu

Description: Independent, comprehensive, coed, affiliated with Evangelical Covenant Church. Awards bachelor's, master's, and doctoral degrees and

post-master's certificates. Founded 1891. Setting: 30-acre urban campus. Total enrollment: 3,138. Faculty: 305 (118 full-time, 187 part-time). Student-undergrad faculty ratio is 13:1. 3,961 applied, 52% were admitted. Full-time: 1,824 students, 63% women, 37% men. Part-time: 381 students, 65% women, 35% men. Students come from 42 states and territories, 30% from out-of-state. 0.4% American Indian or Alaska Native, non-Hispanic/Latino; 18% Hispanic/Latino; 9% Black or African American, non-Hispanic/Latino; 5% Asian, non-Hispanic/Latino; 0.4% Native Hawaiian or other Pacific Islander, non-Hispanic/Latino; 4% international. 22% 25 or older, 47% live on campus, 10% transferred in. Retention: 81% of full-time freshmen returned the following year. Academic areas with the most degrees conferred: health professions and related sciences; business/marketing; education. Core. Calendar: semesters. Academic remediation for entering students, ESL program, services for LD students, advanced placement, accelerated degree program, self-designed majors, freshman honors college, honors program, independent study, double major, summer session for credit, part-time degree program, adult/continuing education programs, internships, graduate courses open to undergrads. Off campus study at Christian College Coalition. Study abroad program. ROTC: Army (c).

Entrance Requirements: Options: electronic application, early admission, international baccalaureate accepted. Required: essay, high school transcript, minimum 2.75 high school GPA, 2 recommendations, SAT or ACT. Recommended: minimum 3 high school GPA. Required for some: interview. Entrance: moderately difficult. Application deadline: rolling. Notification: continuous. Transfer credits accepted: Yes.

Collegiate Environment: Orientation program. Drama-theater group, choral group, student-run newspaper. Student services: health clinic, personal-psychological counseling. Campus security: 24-hour emergency response devices and patrols, late night transport-escort service, controlled dormitory access. Brandel Library.

Community Environment: See University of Chicago.

■ **NORTHEASTERN ILLINOIS UNIVERSITY**

5500 N St. Louis Ave.

Chicago, IL 60625-4699

Tel: (773)583-4050

Fax: (773)794-6243

E-mail: admrec@neiu.edu

Web Site: www.neiu.edu

Description: State-supported, comprehensive, coed. Awards bachelor's and master's degrees. Founded 1961. Setting: 67-acre urban campus with easy access to Chicago. Endowment: $768,031. Research spending for the previous fiscal year: $1.6 million. Total enrollment: 9,538. Faculty: 623 (349 full-time, 274 part-time). Student-undergrad faculty ratio is 14:1. 6,203 applied, 71% were admitted. 4% from top 10% of their high school class, 18% from top quarter, 45% from top half. Full-time: 4,321 students, 56% women, 44% men. Part-time: 3,344 students, 57% women, 43% men. 0.2% American Indian or Alaska Native, non-Hispanic/Latino; 38% Hispanic/Latino; 11% Black or African American, non-Hispanic/Latino; 9% Asian, non-Hispanic/Latino; 0.3% Native Hawaiian or other Pacific Islander, non-Hispanic/Latino; 5% international. 3% live on campus, 17% transferred in. Retention: 55% of full-time freshmen returned the following year. Academic areas with the most degrees conferred: liberal arts/general studies; interdisciplinary studies; public administration and social services. Core. Calendar: semesters. Academic remediation for entering students, ESL program, services for LD students, advanced placement, honors program, independent study, distance learning, double major, summer session for credit, part-time degree program, external degree program, adult/continuing education programs, co-op programs and internships. Off campus study at National Student Exchange. Study abroad program. ROTC: Army (c), Air Force (c).

Entrance Requirements: Options: electronic application, deferred admission, international baccalaureate accepted. Required: high school transcript, SAT or ACT. Entrance: minimally difficult. SAT Reasoning Test deadline: 8/1. Transfer credits accepted: Yes.

Costs Per Year: Application fee: $30. State resident tuition: $10,415 full-time, $396 per credit hour part-time. Nonresident tuition: $20,830 full-time, $792 per credit hour part-time. Mandatory fees: $2136 full-time, $71 per credit hour part-time. Full-time tuition and fees vary according to course load, degree level, and program. Part-time tuition and fees vary according to course load, degree level, and program. College room and board: $11,424. College room only: $8424. Room and board charges vary according to housing facility. Tuition guaranteed not to increase for student's term of enrollment.

Collegiate Environment: Orientation program. Drama-theater group, choral

group, student-run newspaper, radio station. Social organizations: national fraternities, national sororities, local fraternities, local sororities. Most popular organizations: Student Government Association, United Greek Council, ASSW - Association of Student Social Workers, Accounting Associates, Computer Science Society. Major annual events: Talent Show, Student Organization Fair, Welcome Week. Student services: health clinic, personal-psychological counseling, women's center. Campus security: 24-hour emergency response devices and patrols, late night transport-escort service, controlled dormitory access. Ronald Williams Library plus 3 others. Books: 688,147 (physical), 156,705 (digital/electronic); Serial titles: 742 (physical), 86,898 (digital/electronic); Databases: 188. Weekly public service hours: 92. Operations spending for the previous fiscal year: $3.1 million.

Community Environment: See University of Chicago.

■ NORTHERN ILLINOIS UNIVERSITY

1425 W Lincoln Hwy.
DeKalb, IL 60115-2828
Tel: (815)753-1000; Free: 800-892-3050
E-mail: admissions@niu.edu
Web Site: www.niu.edu

Description: State-supported, university, coed. Awards bachelor's, master's, and doctoral degrees. Founded 1895. Setting: 650-acre small town campus with easy access to Chicago. Endowment: $6.5 million. Research spending for the previous fiscal year: $16 million. Educational spending for the previous fiscal year: $8353 per student. Total enrollment: 17,169. Faculty: 1,090 (832 full-time, 258 part-time). Student-undergrad faculty ratio is 14:1. 14,154 applied, 54% were admitted. 12% from top 10% of their high school class, 38% from top quarter, 75% from top half. Full-time: 11,190 students, 51% women, 49% men. Part-time: 1,598 students, 44% women, 56% men. Students come from 47 states and territories, 47 other countries, 3% from out-of-state. 0.1% American Indian or Alaska Native, non-Hispanic/Latino; 19% Hispanic/Latino; 17% Black or African American, non-Hispanic/Latino; 6% Asian, non-Hispanic/Latino; 0.1% Native Hawaiian or other Pacific Islander, non-Hispanic/Latino; 2% international. 16% 25 or older, 28% live on campus, 12% transferred in. Retention: 73% of full-time freshmen returned the following year. Academic areas with the most degrees conferred: business/marketing; health professions and related sciences; communication/journalism; social sciences; engineering. Core. Calendar: semesters. Services for LD students, advanced placement, accelerated degree program, self-designed majors, honors program, independent study, double major, summer session for credit, part-time degree program, adult/continuing education programs, co-op programs and internships, graduate courses open to undergrads. Off campus study at Rockford Regional Academic Center. Study abroad program. ROTC: Army, Air Force (c).

Entrance Requirements: Option: electronic application. Required: high school transcript, high school class rank, SAT or ACT. Entrance: moderately difficult. Notification: continuous. Transfer credits accepted: Yes.

Collegiate Environment: Orientation program. Drama-theater group, choral group, marching band, student-run newspaper, radio station. Social organizations: 327 open to all; national fraternities, national sororities; 4% of eligible men and 3% of eligible women are members. Most popular organizations: American Marketing Association, Delta Sigma Pi, Pi Sigma Epsilon, Black Choir, Student Volunteer Choir. Major annual events: Homecoming, NIU Cares Day, Welcome Day. Student services: legal services, health clinic, personal-psychological counseling, women's center. Campus security: 24-hour emergency response devices and patrols, student patrols, late night transport-escort service, controlled dormitory access. 4,587 college housing spaces available; 3,588 were occupied in 2018-19. Freshmen given priority for college housing. On-campus residence required through senior year. Option: coed housing available. Founders Memorial Library plus 4 others. Books: 1.8 million (physical), 595,551 (digital/electronic); Serial titles: 1,206 (physical), 82,960 (digital/electronic); Databases: 311. Weekly public service hours: 100; students can reserve study rooms. Operations spending for the previous fiscal year: $8.3 million. 1,500 computers available on campus for general student use. A campuswide network can be accessed from student residence rooms and from off campus. Students can access the following: online class registration. Staffed computer lab on campus.

■ NORTHWESTERN COLLEGE-BRIDGEVIEW CAMPUS

7725 S Harlem Ave.
Bridgeview, IL 60455
Tel: (708)237-5000; Free: 888-205-2283
Web Site: www.nc.edu/locations/bridgeview-campus

Description: Proprietary, 2-year, coed. Awards terminal associate degrees. Total enrollment: 1,060. 450 applied, 98% were admitted. Calendar: quarters.

■ NORTHWESTERN COLLEGE-CHICAGO CAMPUS

4829 N Lipps Ave.
Chicago, IL 60630
Tel: (847)233-7700; Free: 888-205-2283
Web Site: www.nc.edu/locations/chicago-campus

Description: Proprietary, 2-year, coed. Awards certificates, transfer associate, and terminal associate degrees (profile includes branch campuses in Bridgeview and Naperville, IL). Founded 1902. Setting: 3-acre urban campus with easy access to Chicago, IL. Educational spending for the previous fiscal year: $5000 per student. Total enrollment: 1,082. Faculty: 92 (35 full-time, 57 part-time). 555 applied, 95% were admitted. Full-time: 472 students, 82% women, 18% men. Part-time: 610 students, 84% women, 16% men. 2% from out-of-state. 2% American Indian or Alaska Native, non-Hispanic/Latino; 21% Hispanic/Latino; 40% Black or African American, non-Hispanic/Latino; 1% Asian, non-Hispanic/Latino; 0.2% Native Hawaiian or other Pacific Islander, non-Hispanic/Latino. 61% 25 or older. Core. Calendar: quarters. Academic remediation for entering students, honors program, independent study, summer session for credit, part-time degree program, co-op programs and internships.

Entrance Requirements: Option: electronic application. Required: high school transcript. Recommended: SAT or ACT. Entrance: minimally difficult. Application deadline: rolling. Transfer credits accepted: Yes.

Collegiate Environment: Student services: personal-psychological counseling. Edward G. Schumacher Memorial Library. Operations spending for the previous fiscal year: $500,000.

■ NORTHWESTERN UNIVERSITY

633 Clark St.
Evanston, IL 60208
Tel: (847)491-3741
E-mail: ug-admission@northwestern.edu
Web Site: www.northwestern.edu

Description: Independent, university, coed. Awards bachelor's, master's, and doctoral degrees and post-master's certificates. Founded 1851. Setting: 250-acre suburban campus with easy access to Chicago. Total enrollment: 21,591. Faculty: 1,772 (1,529 full-time, 243 part-time). Student-undergrad faculty ratio is 7:1. 40,425 applied, 8% were admitted. 91% from top 10% of their high school class. Full-time: 8,077 students, 51% women, 49% men. Part-time: 179 students, 51% women, 49% men. Students come from 75 other countries, 68% from out-of-state. 0.1% American Indian or Alaska Native, non-Hispanic/Latino; 13% Hispanic/Latino; 6% Black or African American, non-Hispanic/Latino; 18% Asian, non-Hispanic/Latino; 9% international. 60% live on campus, 2% transferred in. Retention: 98% of full-time freshmen returned the following year. Academic areas with the most degrees conferred: social sciences; communication/journalism; engineering. Core. Calendar: quarters. Services for LD students, advanced placement, accelerated degree program, self-designed majors, honors program, independent study, double major, summer session for credit, part-time degree program, adult/continuing education programs, co-op programs and internships, graduate courses open to undergrads. Study abroad program. ROTC: Army (c), Naval, Air Force (c).

Entrance Requirements: Options: electronic application, early admission, early decision, deferred admission. Required: essay, high school transcript, 1 recommendation, SAT or ACT. Required for some: audition for music program, SAT Subject Tests. Entrance: most difficult. Application deadlines: 1/1, 11/1 for early decision. Notification: 4/1, 12/15 for early decision. SAT Reasoning Test deadline: 1/15. SAT Subject Test deadline: 1/15. Transfer credits accepted: Yes. Applicants placed on waiting list: 2,861. Wait-listed applicants offered admission: 24. Early decision applicants: 4,047. Early decision applicants admitted: 1,072.

Costs Per Year: Application fee: $75. Comprehensive fee: $71,193 includes full-time tuition ($54,120), mandatory fees ($447), and college room and board ($16,626). Room and board charges vary according to board plan and housing facility.

Collegiate Environment: Orientation program. Drama-theater group, choral group, marching band, student-run newspaper, radio station. Social organizations: national fraternities, national sororities, local fraternities, local sororities; 34% of eligible men and 39% of eligible women are members. Major annual events: Dillo Day Music Festival, Dance Marathon, Wildcat Welcome. Student services: health clinic, personal-psychological counseling, women's center. Campus security: 24-hour emergency response devices and patrols, late night transport-escort service, controlled dormitory access. 60 undergraduates lived in college housing during 2018-19. Freshmen guaranteed college housing. Options: coed, men-only, women-only housing available. University Library plus 6 others.

Community Environment: Evanston is a residential city on Lake Michigan, adjoining the northern limits of the city of Chicago. With Lake Michigan forming an impressive backdrop, an abundance of oak, elm, and maple trees enhance the beauty of the community. Situated 12 miles from the center of Chicago, Evanston offers the advantages of a quiet, modern community close to a great thriving city. Excellent shopping facilities are available.

■ OAKTON COMMUNITY COLLEGE

1600 E Golf Rd.
Des Plaines, IL 60016-1268
Tel: (847)635-1600
Fax: (847)635-1706
E-mail: rcampbel@oakton.edu
Web Site: www.oakton.edu

Description: District-supported, 2-year, coed. Part of Illinois Community College Board. Awards certificates, transfer associate, and terminal associate degrees. Founded 1969. Setting: 193-acre suburban campus with easy access to Chicago. Total enrollment: 7,942. 0.5% American Indian or Alaska Native, non-Hispanic/Latino; 17% Hispanic/Latino; 8% Black or African American, non-Hispanic/Latino; 23% Asian, non-Hispanic/Latino. 36% 25 or older. Core. Calendar: semesters. Academic remediation for entering students, ESL program, services for LD students, advanced placement, honors program, independent study, distance learning, summer session for credit, part-time degree program, adult/continuing education programs, internships. Off campus study. Study abroad program.

Entrance Requirements: Open admission except for health care programs. Option: electronic application. Recommended: high school transcript. Required for some: interview. Entrance: noncompetitive. Application deadline: rolling. Notification: continuous.

Costs Per Year: Application fee: $25. Area resident tuition: $3270 full-time. State resident tuition: $8808 full-time. Nonresident tuition: $10,536 full-time.

Collegiate Environment: Orientation program. Drama-theater group, choral group, student-run newspaper. Student services: health clinic, personal-psychological counseling. Campus security: 24-hour emergency response devices and patrols, student patrols, late night transport-escort service. College housing not available. Oakton Community College Library plus 1 other.

Community Environment: Des Plaines, population 56,551, is a suburban community situated about 12 miles from the center of Chicago, the third largest city in the nation. Cultural facilities of Chicago include museums which cover a wide variety of fields, art galleries, research libraries, theaters, opera, and symphony orchestra.

■ OLIVET NAZARENE UNIVERSITY

One University Ave.
Bourbonnais, IL 60914
Tel: (815)939-5011; Free: 800-648-1463
Web Site: www.olivet.edu

Description: Independent, comprehensive, coed, affiliated with Church of the Nazarene. Awards bachelor's, master's, and doctoral degrees. Founded 1907. Setting: 275-acre small town campus with easy access to Chicago. Endowment: $33.2 million. Total enrollment: 4,986. Faculty: 453 (125 full-time, 328 part-time). Student-undergrad faculty ratio is 19:1. 3,964 applied, 66% were admitted. Full-time: 3,113 students, 58% women, 42% men. Part-time: 258 students, 72% women, 28% men. Students come from 46 states and territories, 19 other countries, 36% from out-of-state. 0.2% American Indian or Alaska Native, non-Hispanic/Latino; 8% Hispanic/Latino; 8% Black or African American, non-Hispanic/Latino; 3% Asian, non-Hispanic/Latino; 0.1% Native Hawaiian or other Pacific Islander, non-Hispanic/Latino; 1% international. 15% 25 or older, 77% live on campus, 9% transferred in. Retention: 78% of full-time freshmen returned the following year. Academic areas with the most degrees conferred: health professions and related sciences; business/marketing; education. Core. Calendar: semesters. Academic remediation for entering students, services for LD students, advanced placement, self-designed majors, honors program, independent study, distance learning, double major, summer session for credit, part-time degree program, adult/continuing education programs, co-op programs and internships, graduate courses open to undergrads. Off campus study at Contemporary Music Center, located in Nashville, Tennessee; Los Angeles

Film Studies Center operates in Burbank, California; New York City Semester - The King's College. Study abroad program. ROTC: Army.

Entrance Requirements: Options: electronic application, deferred admission, international baccalaureate accepted. Required: high school transcript, minimum 2 high school GPA, SAT or ACT. Recommended: essay, interview. Required for some: 2 recommendations. Entrance: moderately difficult. Application deadline: rolling. Notification: continuous. Transfer credits accepted: Yes.

Costs Per Year: Application fee: $25. Comprehensive fee: $43,970 includes full-time tuition ($35,080), mandatory fees ($990), and college room and board ($7900). Room and board charges vary according to board plan. Part-time tuition: $1462 per semester hour. Part-time tuition varies according to course load.

Collegiate Environment: Orientation program. Drama-theater group, choral group, marching band, student-run newspaper, radio station. Most popular organizations: Fellowship of Christian Athletes, C.A.U.S.E. (College and University Serving and Enabling), Diakonia, Student Education Association, Women's Residence Association. Major annual events: All-School Christmas Banquet, Junior/Senior Banquet, Homecoming Coronation. Student services: health clinic, personal-psychological counseling. Campus security: 24-hour patrols, late night transport-escort service. Benner Library. Books: 127,535 (physical), 215,890 (digital/electronic); Serial titles: 627 (physical), 65,313 (digital/electronic); Databases: 263. Students can reserve study rooms.

Community Environment: The campus is in the historic village of Bourbonnais (16,000) on the north edge of Kankakee, Illinois (100,000). This is the growing edge of the community, with excellent schools and small businesses. A shopping mall and numerous stores provide shopping convenience and employment opportunities. Major industries in the area include Armour Pharmaceutical, Armstrong Tile, Quaker Oats, General Foods, and a variety of metal working plants. The proximity to the Chicago metropolitan area is a definite asset.

■ PARKLAND COLLEGE

2400 W Bradley Ave.
Champaign, IL 61821-1899
Tel: (217)351-2200; Free: 800-346-8089
Fax: (217)351-7640
E-mail: admissions@parkland.edu
Web Site: www.parkland.edu

Description: District-supported, 2-year, coed. Part of Illinois Community College Board. Awards certificates, transfer associate, and terminal associate degrees. Founded 1967. Setting: 233-acre suburban campus. Total enrollment: 7,291. Faculty: 489. Student-undergrad faculty ratio is 15:1. 6,780 applied, 100% were admitted. 2% from out-of-state. 0.5% American Indian or Alaska Native, non-Hispanic/Latino; 4% Hispanic/Latino; 16% Black or African American, non-Hispanic/Latino; 3% Asian, non-Hispanic/Latino; 0.1% Native Hawaiian or other Pacific Islander, non-Hispanic/Latino; 1% international. 34% 25 or older. Core. Calendar: semesters. Academic remediation for entering students, ESL program, services for LD students, advanced placement, accelerated degree program, self-designed majors, honors program, independent study, distance learning, double major, summer session for credit, part-time degree program, adult/continuing education programs, co-op programs and internships. Off campus study at University of Illinois at Urbana-Champaign. Study abroad program. ROTC: Army (c), Naval (c), Air Force (c).

Entrance Requirements: Open admission except for allied health, nursing programs. Option: deferred admission. Recommended: high school transcript. Required for some: ACT. Entrance: noncompetitive. Application deadline: rolling. Notification: continuous.

Collegiate Environment: Orientation program. Drama-theater group, choral group, student-run newspaper, radio station. Student services: personal-psychological counseling. Campus security: 24-hour emergency response devices and patrols, late night transport-escort service. Parkland College Library. 1,200 computers available on campus for general student use. A campuswide network can be accessed. Students can access the following: online class registration. Staffed computer lab on campus.

Community Environment: See University of Illinois at Urbana-Champaign.

■ PRAIRIE STATE COLLEGE

202 S Halsted St.
Chicago Heights, IL 60411-8226
Tel: (708)709-3500
E-mail: jmmiller@prairiestate.edu

Web Site: www.prairiestate.edu

Description: State and locally supported, 2-year, coed. Part of Illinois Community College Board. Awards certificates, transfer associate, and terminal associate degrees. Founded 1958. Setting: 68-acre suburban campus with easy access to Chicago. Total enrollment: 5,854. Student-undergrad faculty ratio is 17:1. 5% from out-of-state. 45% 25 or older. Core. Calendar: semesters. Academic remediation for entering students, ESL program, services for LD students, advanced placement, self-designed majors, honors program, distance learning, summer session for credit, part-time degree program, adult/continuing education programs, internships.

Entrance Requirements: Open admission except for nursing, dental hygiene programs. Option: deferred admission. Required: high school transcript. Entrance: noncompetitive. Application deadline: rolling.

Collegiate Environment: Orientation program. Drama-theater group, choral group, student-run newspaper. Student services: personal-psychological counseling. Campus security: 24-hour emergency response devices and patrols, student patrols, late night transport-escort service. Learning Resource Center.

Community Environment: Chicago Heights is a metropolitan area located 25 miles south of the Chicago loop. Railroads and buses serve the area. Within the city are shopping centers, many churches, a library, and a hospital. For recreation, there are many parks, a community center with an educational, recreational and social service program, and a Forest Preserve of 1,350 acres.

■ **PRINCIPIA COLLEGE**

One Maybeck Pl.

Elsah, IL 62028-9799

Tel: (618)374-2131; Free: 800-277-4648

Fax: (618)374-4000

Web Site: www.principiacollege.edu

Description: Independent Christian Science, 4-year, coed. Awards bachelor's degrees. Founded 1910. Setting: 2,600-acre rural campus with easy access to St. Louis. Endowment: $377.5 million. Educational spending for the previous fiscal year: $24,387 per student. Total enrollment: 455. Faculty: 78 (68 full-time, 10 part-time). Student-undergrad faculty ratio is 6:1. 134 applied, 91% were admitted. 44% from top 10% of their high school class, 50% from top quarter, 61% from top half. Full-time: 441 students, 49% women, 51% men. Part-time: 14 students, 50% women, 50% men. Students come from 37 states and territories, 30 other countries, 88% from out-of-state. 0.2% American Indian or Alaska Native, non-Hispanic/Latino; 2% Hispanic/Latino; 2% Black or African American, non-Hispanic/Latino; 2% Asian, non-Hispanic/Latino; 0.4% Native Hawaiian or other Pacific Islander, non-Hispanic/Latino; 18% International. 5% 25 or older, 97% live on campus, 2% transferred in. Retention: 87% of full-time freshmen returned the following year. Academic areas with the most degrees conferred: education; business/marketing; social sciences. Core. Calendar: semesters. Advanced placement, self-designed majors, independent study, double major, summer session for credit, part-time degree program, internships. Off campus study. Study abroad program.

Entrance Requirements: Options: electronic application, deferred admission, international baccalaureate accepted. Required: essay, high school transcript, minimum 2.4 high school GPA, 3 recommendations, Christian Science commitment, SAT or ACT. Recommended: interview. Required for some: interview. Entrance: moderately difficult. Application deadline: rolling. Notification: continuous. SAT Reasoning Test deadline: 3/1. SAT Subject Test deadline: 7/1. Transfer credits accepted: Yes.

Costs Per Year: Application fee: $0. Comprehensive fee: $41,080 includes full-time tuition ($28,770), mandatory fees ($700), and college room and board ($11,610). College room only: $5510. Full-time tuition and fees vary according to course load. Room and board charges vary according to board plan. Part-time tuition: $959 per credit hour. Part-time tuition varies according to course load.

Collegiate Environment: Orientation program. Drama-theater group, choral group, student-run newspaper, radio station. Social organizations: 34 open to all. Most popular organizations: Christian Science Organization, Community Service Team, Solidarity (Multi-club group), Rugby Club, Student Government. Major annual events: Whole World Festival, Public Affairs Conference, Convocation Speaker Series. Student services: health clinic. Campus security: 24-hour emergency response devices and patrols, controlled dormitory access. Marshall Brooks Library plus 1 other. Books: 168,085 (physical), 338,122 (digital/electronic); Serial titles: 237 (physical), 99,238 (digital/electronic); Databases: 96. Weekly public service hours: 90; students can reserve study rooms. Operations spending for the previous fis-

cal year: $267,937. 100 computers available on campus for general student use. Computer purchase/lease plans available. A campuswide network can be accessed from student residence rooms and from off campus. Students can access the following: online class registration. Staffed computer lab on campus (open 24 hours a day) provides training in use of computers, software, and the Internet.

Community Environment: Principia College is located on 2,600 acres of the highest and loveliest section of the Piasa Bluffs above the Mississippi River. In a setting rich in beauty and historical significance, three great rivers may be seen from the bluffs: the Mississippi below, the Missouri to the southeast, and the Illinois, which joins the Mississippi to the west several miles upstream. Mean temperatures are 28-78 degrees, and rainfall averages 35 inches. Recreation, entertainment, and shopping are found in Alton and St. Louis. Part-time student employment is available at the college.

■ **QUINCY UNIVERSITY**

1800 College Ave.

Quincy, IL 62301-2699

Tel: (217)222-8020; Free: 800-688-4295

Fax: (217)228-5479

E-mail: admissions@quincy.edu

Web Site: www.quincy.edu

Description: Independent Roman Catholic, comprehensive, coed. Awards associate, bachelor's, and master's degrees. Founded 1860. Setting: 70-acre small town campus. Endowment: $18.1 million. Educational spending for the previous fiscal year: $5919 per student. Total enrollment: 1,293. Faculty: 114 (52 full-time, 62 part-time). Student-undergrad faculty ratio is 14:1. 1,553 applied, 63% were admitted. 8% from top 10% of their high school class, 32% from top quarter, 75% from top half. Full-time: 1,024 students, 53% women, 47% men. Part-time: 116 students, 66% women, 34% men. Students come from 32 states and territories, 6 other countries, 32% from out-of-state. 0.2% American Indian or Alaska Native, non-Hispanic/Latino; 4% Hispanic/Latino; 11% Black or African American, non-Hispanic/Latino; 1% Asian, non-Hispanic/Latino; 0.4% international. 10% 25 or older, 54% live on campus, 8% transferred in. Retention: 69% of full-time freshmen returned the following year. Academic areas with the most degrees conferred: business/marketing; health professions and related sciences; biological/life sciences; education; psychology. Core. Calendar: semesters. Academic remediation for entering students, advanced placement, accelerated degree program, self-designed majors, honors program, independent study, distance learning, double major, summer session for credit, part-time degree program, adult/continuing education programs, internships, graduate courses open to undergrads. Off campus study at American University (Washington Semester Program). Study abroad program.

Entrance Requirements: Options: electronic application, deferred admission, international baccalaureate accepted. Required: essay, high school transcript, minimum 2.5 high school GPA, SAT or ACT. Recommended: interview. Required for some: 1 recommendation, audition for music majors, portfolio recommended for art majors. Entrance: moderately difficult. Application deadline: rolling. Notification: continuous. SAT Reasoning Test deadline: 8/15. Transfer credits accepted: Yes.

Collegiate Environment: Orientation program. Drama-theater group, choral group, marching band, student-run newspaper. Social organizations: 50 open to all; national fraternities, national sororities; 6% of eligible men and 8% of eligible women are members. Most popular organizations: Student Senate, Kappa Kappa Psi, Student Programming Board, Minority Student Association, Students in Free Enterprise (SIFE). Major annual events: Homecoming, Hawk Wild Weekend, Hawk Back Weekend. Student services: health clinic, personal-psychological counseling. Campus security: 24-hour emergency response devices and patrols, student patrols, late night transport-escort service, controlled dormitory access, self-defense education, shuttle buses, lighted pathways/sidewalks. Brenner Library. Operations spending for the previous fiscal year: $367,891. 221 computers available on campus for general student use. A campuswide network can be accessed from student residence rooms and from off campus. Students can access the following: online class registration.

Community Environment: The University is located in a residential section of Quincy, a city of 50,000, located on the bluffs of the Mississippi River. It is within easy traveling distance of St. Louis (2 1/2 hours), Kansas City (4 hours), and Chicago (4 hours).

■ **RASMUSSEN COLLEGE AURORA**

2363 Sequoia Dr.

Aurora, IL 60506

Tel: (630)888-3500; Free: 888-549-6755
Fax: (630)888-3501
E-mail: susan.hammerstrom@rasmussen.edu
Web Site: www.rasmussen.edu
Description: Proprietary, 4-year, coed. Part of Rasmussen College System. Awards associate and bachelor's degrees. Setting: suburban campus. Total enrollment: 410. Faculty: 15 (3 full-time, 12 part-time). Student-undergrad faculty ratio is 22:1. 23 applied, 96% were admitted. Full-time: 273 students, 77% women, 23% men. Part-time: 137 students, 76% women, 24% men. 72% 25 or older. Core. Calendar: quarters. Academic remediation for entering students, accelerated degree program, distance learning, double major, summer session for credit, part-time degree program, adult/continuing education programs, internships.
Entrance Requirements: Options: electronic application, early admission, deferred admission. Required: high school transcript, minimum 2 high school GPA, institutional exam. Required for some: interview. Entrance: minimally difficult. Application deadline: rolling. Transfer credits accepted: Yes.
Collegiate Environment: Orientation program. Rasmussen College Library - Aurora. 87 computers available on campus for general student use. A campuswide network can be accessed from off-campus.

■ **RASMUSSEN COLLEGE MOKENA/TINLEY PARK**
8650 W Spring Lake Rd.
Mokena, IL 60448
Tel: (815)534-3300; Free: 888-549-6755
Web Site: www.rasmussen.edu
Description: Proprietary, 4-year, coed. Part of Rasmussen College System. Awards associate and bachelor's degrees. Setting: suburban campus. Total enrollment: 396. Faculty: 25 (1 full-time, 24 part-time). Student-undergrad faculty ratio is 22:1. 26 applied, 96% were admitted. Full-time: 195 students, 91% women, 9% men. Part-time: 201 students, 77% women, 23% men. 73% 25 or older. Core. Calendar: quarters. Academic remediation for entering students, accelerated degree program, distance learning, double major, summer session for credit, part-time degree program, adult/continuing education programs, internships.
Entrance Requirements: Options: electronic application, early admission, deferred admission. Required: high school transcript, minimum 2 high school GPA, institutional exam. Required for some: interview. Entrance: minimally difficult. Application deadline: rolling. Transfer credits accepted: Yes.
Collegiate Environment: Orientation program. Rasmussen College Library - Mokena. 73 computers available on campus for general student use. A campuswide network can be accessed from off-campus.

■ **RASMUSSEN COLLEGE ROCKFORD**
6000 E State St.
Fourth Fl.
Rockford, IL 61108
Tel: (815)316-4800; Free: 888-549-6755
Fax: (815)316-4801
E-mail: dwayne.bertotto@rasmussen.edu
Web Site: www.rasmussen.edu
Description: Proprietary, 4-year, coed. Part of Rasmussen College System. Awards associate and bachelor's degrees. Setting: suburban campus. Total enrollment: 630. Faculty: 54 (12 full-time, 42 part-time). Student-undergrad faculty ratio is 22:1. 33 applied, 94% were admitted. Full-time: 525 students, 86% women, 14% men. Part-time: 105 students, 87% women, 13% men. 71% 25 or older. Core. Calendar: quarters. Academic remediation for entering students, accelerated degree program, distance learning, double major, summer session for credit, part-time degree program, adult/continuing education programs, internships.
Entrance Requirements: Options: electronic application, early admission, deferred admission. Required: high school transcript, minimum 2 high school GPA, institutional exam. Required for some: interview. Entrance: minimally difficult. Application deadline: rolling. Transfer credits accepted: Yes.
Collegiate Environment: Orientation program. Rasmussen College Library - Rockford. 103 computers available on campus for general student use. A campuswide network can be accessed from off-campus.

■ **RASMUSSEN COLLEGE ROMEOVILLE/JOLIET**
1400 W Normantown Rd.
Romeoville, IL 60446
Tel: (815)306-2600; Free: 888-549-6755
E-mail: susan.hammerstrom@rasmussen.edu
Web Site: www.rasmussen.edu

Description: Proprietary, 4-year, coed. Part of Rasmussen College System. Awards associate and bachelor's degrees. Setting: suburban campus. Total enrollment: 542. Faculty: 58 (13 full-time, 45 part-time). Student-undergrad faculty ratio is 22:1. 35 applied, 91% were admitted. Full-time: 262 students, 85% women, 15% men. Part-time: 280 students, 74% women, 26% men. 65% 25 or older. Core. Calendar: quarters. Academic remediation for entering students, accelerated degree program, distance learning, double major, summer session for credit, part-time degree program, adult/continuing education programs, internships.
Entrance Requirements: Options: electronic application, early admission, deferred admission. Required: high school transcript, minimum 2 high school GPA, institutional exam. Required for some: interview. Entrance: minimally difficult. Application deadline: rolling. Transfer credits accepted: Yes.
Collegiate Environment: Orientation program. Rasmussen College Library - Romeoville. 87 computers available on campus for general student use. A campuswide network can be accessed from off-campus.

■ **REND LAKE COLLEGE**
468 N Ken Gray Pky.
Ina, IL 62846-9801
Tel: (618)437-5321; Free: 800-369-5321
Fax: (618)437-5677
E-mail: jensikj@rlc.edu
Web Site: www.rlc.edu
Description: State-supported, 2-year, coed. Part of Illinois Community College Board. Awards certificates, transfer associate, and terminal associate degrees. Founded 1967. Setting: 350-acre rural campus. Educational spending for the previous fiscal year: $3477 per student. Total enrollment: 2,486. Faculty: 133 (59 full-time, 79 part-time). Student-undergrad faculty ratio is 18:1. Full-time: 1,213 students, 54% women, 46% men. Part-time: 1,273 students, 52% women, 48% men. Students come from 5 states and territories, 7 other countries. 0.3% American Indian or Alaska Native, non-Hispanic/Latino; 1% Hispanic/Latino; 5% Black or African American, non-Hispanic/Latino; 0.9% Asian, non-Hispanic/Latino; 0.1% Native Hawaiian or other Pacific Islander, non-Hispanic/Latino; 0.1% international. 25% 25 or older, 3% transferred in. Core. Calendar: semesters. Academic remediation for entering students, ESL program, services for LD students, advanced placement, honors program, independent study, distance learning, double major, summer session for credit, part-time degree program, adult/continuing education programs, co-op programs and internships. Off campus study at Rend Lake College is part of an interdistrict Comprehensive Agreement Regarding the Expansion of Educational Resources (CAREER). This agreement among several Illinois community colleges allows students to take a career technical program at another college if their sending college does not offer that program. Study abroad program.
Entrance Requirements: Open admission. Options: electronic application, deferred admission. Required: high school transcript. Entrance: noncompetitive. Application deadlines: 8/24, 8/24 for nonresidents. Transfer credits accepted: Yes.
Costs Per Year: Application fee: $0. Area resident tuition: $3300 full-time, $110 per credit hour part-time. State resident tuition: $5250 full-time, $175 per credit hour part-time. Nonresident tuition: $6000 full-time, $200 per credit hour part-time. Mandatory fees: $750 full-time, $25 per credit hour part-time.
Collegiate Environment: Orientation program. Drama-theater group, choral group. Social organizations: 22 open to all. Most popular organizations: Collegiate FFA, Automotive Club, Art League, Thespians Club, Phi Theta Kappa. Major annual events: Fun Fest, Student Appreciation Days, Welcome Days. Student services: personal-psychological counseling. Campus security: 24-hour emergency response devices and patrols, late night transport-escort service. College housing not available. Learning Resource Center. Books: 12,708 (physical), 36,511 (digital/electronic); Serial titles: 48 (physical), 24,174 (digital/electronic); Databases: 33. Weekly public service hours: 54; students can reserve study rooms. Operations spending for the previous fiscal year: $197,890. 669 computers available on campus for general student use. A campuswide network can be accessed from off-campus. Staffed computer lab on campus.
Community Environment: The college is located in a rural area with all forms of transportation available. Industries in nearby Mount Vernon, population 16,344, include the manufacture of electric equipment, radiators, women's wear, shoes, forest products, boats, automobile tires, and chemicals. Oil production and agriculture are important in the surrounding areas. Cultural opportunities offered by the State Law Library and Museum. Community facilities include 40 churches of major denominations, hospitals,

a clinic, and major civic and service organizations. Recreational activities are boating, fishing, swimming, bowling, and golf. Du Quoin State Fair is an annual event.

■ **RESURRECTION UNIVERSITY**
1431 N Claremont Ave.
Chicago, IL 60622
Tel: (773)252-6464
Fax: (773)227-3838
Web Site: www.resu.edu

Description: Independent, upper-level, coed. Awards bachelor's, master's, and doctoral degrees. Founded 1982. Setting: 10-acre urban campus with easy access to Chicago. Endowment: $1.5 million. Educational spending for the previous fiscal year: $8848 per student. Total enrollment: 709. Faculty: 59 (26 full-time, 33 part-time). Student-undergrad faculty ratio is 7:1. Full-time: 499 students, 81% women, 19% men. Part-time: 103 students, 81% women, 19% men. Students come from 6 states and territories, 1% from out-of-state. 0.6% American Indian or Alaska Native, non-Hispanic/Latino; 25% Hispanic/Latino; 16% Black or African American, non-Hispanic/Latino; 13% Asian, non-Hispanic/Latino; 0.3% Native Hawaiian or other Pacific Islander, non-Hispanic/Latino. 72% 25 or older, 40% transferred in. Academic area with the most degrees conferred: health professions and related sciences. Calendar: semesters. Academic remediation for entering students, advanced placement, accelerated degree program, independent study, summer session for credit, part-time degree program, graduate courses open to undergrads.

Entrance Requirements: Transfer credits accepted: Yes.

Costs Per Year: Application fee: $50. One-time mandatory fee: $150. Tuition: $37,578 full-time. Mandatory fees: $870 full-time. Full-time tuition and fees vary according to course load, degree level, and program.

Collegiate Environment: Student services: personal-psychological counseling. Campus security: 24-hour emergency response devices and patrols, late night transport-escort service. Resurrection University Library. Operations spending for the previous fiscal year: $122,930. 36 computers available on campus for general student use. A computer is required for all students. A campuswide network can be accessed. Students can access the following: online class registration. Staffed computer lab on campus provides training in use of computers, software, and the Internet.

■ **RICHLAND COMMUNITY COLLEGE**
One College Park
Decatur, IL 62521-8513
Tel: (217)875-7200
Fax: (217)875-6991
E-mail: csebok@richland.edu
Web Site: www.richland.edu

Description: District-supported, 2-year, coed. Part of Illinois Community College Board. Awards certificates, transfer associate, and terminal associate degrees. Founded 1971. Setting: 117-acre small town campus. Total enrollment: 3,005. Faculty: 203 (75 full-time, 128 part-time). Student-undergrad faculty ratio is 15:1. 602 applied, 66% were admitted. 8% from top 10% of their high school class, 26% from top quarter, 48% from top half. Full-time: 951 students, 58% women, 42% men. Part-time: 2,054 students, 61% women, 39% men. Students come from 25 states and territories, 2% from out-of-state. 0.6% American Indian or Alaska Native, non-Hispanic/Latino; 1% Hispanic/Latino; 16% Black or African American, non-Hispanic/Latino; 1% Asian, non-Hispanic/Latino; 0.2% Native Hawaiian or other Pacific Islander, non-Hispanic/Latino. 57% 25 or older, 1% transferred in. Retention: 57% of full-time freshmen returned the following year. Core. Calendar: semesters. Academic remediation for entering students, ESL program, services for LD students, advanced placement, self-designed majors, freshman honors college, honors program, distance learning, summer session for credit, part-time degree program, adult/continuing education programs.

Entrance Requirements: Open admission. Option: early admission. Required: high school transcript. Recommended: ACT. Entrance: noncompetitive. Application deadline: rolling.

Collegiate Environment: Orientation program. Student-run newspaper. Social organizations: 35 open to all. Most popular organizations: Phi Theta Kappa, Media Club, InterVarsity Christian Fellowship, X-Ray Vision, Practical Nursing Club. Major annual events: Holiday Cookie Celebration, Soul Food Luncheon, Student Awards and Recognition Reception. Student services: personal-psychological counseling. Campus security: 24-hour emergency response devices and patrols. Kitty Lindsay Library. Books:

29,388 (physical), 15 (digital/electronic); Serial titles: 975 (physical); Databases: 28. Students can reserve study rooms. 65 computers available on campus for general student use. A campuswide network can be accessed from off-campus. Students can access the following: online class registration. Staffed computer lab on campus provides training in use of computers, software, and the Internet.

Community Environment: See Millikin University.

■ **ROBERT MORRIS UNIVERSITY ILLINOIS**
401 S State St.
Chicago, IL 60605
Tel: (312)935-6800; Free: 800-762-5960
Fax: (312)836-4599
E-mail: enroll@robertmorris.edu
Web Site: www.robertmorris.edu

Description: Independent, comprehensive, coed. Awards associate, bachelor's, and master's degrees. Founded 1913. Setting: urban campus with easy access to Chicago. Endowment: $17.9 million. Educational spending for the previous fiscal year: $3360 per student. Total enrollment: 2,307. Faculty: 184 (52 full-time, 132 part-time). Student-undergrad faculty ratio is 21:1. 2,705 applied, 16% were admitted. 3% from top 10% of their high school class, 10% from top quarter, 40% from top half. Full-time: 1,895 students, 43% women, 57% men. Part-time: 108 students, 65% women, 35% men. Students come from 39 states and territories, 10 other countries, 13% from out-of-state. 0.1% American Indian or Alaska Native, non-Hispanic/Latino; 31% Hispanic/Latino; 25% Black or African American, non-Hispanic/Latino; 3% Asian, non-Hispanic/Latino; 0.2% Native Hawaiian or other Pacific Islander, non-Hispanic/Latino; 0.9% international. 19% 25 or older, 11% live on campus, 15% transferred in. Retention: 49% of full-time freshmen returned the following year. Academic areas with the most degrees conferred: business/marketing; interdisciplinary studies; computer and information sciences. Core. Calendar: 5 10-week academic sessions per year. Services for LD students, advanced placement, accelerated degree program, honors program, double major, summer session for credit, part-time degree program, adult/continuing education programs, internships, graduate courses open to undergrads. Study abroad program. ROTC: Army (c).

Entrance Requirements: Options: electronic application, deferred admission. Recommended: interview. Required for some: high school transcript, SAT or ACT, ACT for nursing and surgical technology programs. Entrance: minimally difficult. Application deadline: rolling. Notification: continuous. Transfer credits accepted: Yes. Applicants placed on waiting list: 0. Wait-listed applicants offered admission: 0.

Costs Per Year: Application fee: $20. Comprehensive fee: $43,338 includes full-time tuition ($28,050), mandatory fees ($480), and college room and board ($14,808). Part-time tuition: $775 per quarter hour. Part-time tuition varies according to course load.

Collegiate Environment: Orientation program. Drama-theater group, choral group, marching band, student-run newspaper. Social organizations: 20 open to all; Honor Societies. Most popular organizations: UNA-USA, Eagles United for a Cause, Eagles Soaring for a Change, Cooks for a Cause, Eagle Newspaper. Major annual events: Welcome Week, Homecoming, Constitution Day. Student services: personal-psychological counseling. Campus security: late night transport-escort service, controlled dormitory access, Urban campus has multiple security officers at all times who are off-duty Chicago police officers. Information Technology Library. Books: 165,268 (physical), 58,182 (digital/electronic); Databases: 37. Weekly public service hours: 74; students can reserve study rooms. Operations spending for the previous fiscal year: $435,643. 1,307 computers available on campus for general student use. A campuswide network can be accessed from student residence rooms. Students can access the following: online class registration, online credentials, online payments, online student accounts, online degree audit. Staffed computer lab on campus provides training in use of computers and the Internet.

Community Environment: Located in Chicago's Loop, the main campus is in the heart of the downtown business and financial district.

■ **ROCK VALLEY COLLEGE**
3301 N Mulford Rd.
Rockford, IL 61114-5699
Tel: (815)921-7821; Free: 800-973-7821
Fax: (815)654-5568
E-mail: s.morgan@rockvalleycollege.edu
Web Site: www.rockvalleycollege.edu

Description: District-supported, 2-year, coed. Part of Illinois Community College Board. Awards certificates, diplomas, and transfer associate degrees. Founded 1964. Setting: 217-acre suburban campus with easy access to Chicago. Total enrollment: 6,244. Student-undergrad faculty ratio is 17:1. Full-time: 2,710 students, 54% women, 46% men. Part-time: 3,482 students, 57% women, 43% men. 0.3% American Indian or Alaska Native, non-Hispanic/Latino; 21% Hispanic/Latino; 9% Black or African American, non-Hispanic/Latino; 3% Asian, non-Hispanic/Latino; 0.1% Native Hawaiian or other Pacific Islander, non-Hispanic/Latino; 0.4% international. 27% 25 or older, 3% transferred in. Core. Calendar: semesters. Academic remediation for entering students, ESL program, services for LD students, advanced placement, self-designed majors, honors program, independent study, distance learning, summer session for credit, part-time degree program, adult/continuing education programs, co-op programs and internships. Study abroad program.

Entrance Requirements: Open admission. Required: high school transcript. Entrance: noncompetitive.

Costs Per Year: Application fee: $0. Area resident tuition: $3450 full-time. State resident tuition: $8610 full-time. Nonresident tuition: $15,000 full-time. Mandatory fees: $314 full-time.

Collegiate Environment: Orientation program. Drama-theater group, choral group, student-run newspaper. Social organizations: 12 open to all. Most popular organizations: Black Student Alliance, Phi Theta Kappa, Adults on Campus, Inter-Varsity Club, Christian Fellowship. Major annual events: New Student Week, Homecoming Week, May Fest. Student services: personal-psychological counseling. Campus security: 24-hour emergency response devices and patrols, late night transport-escort service. College housing not available. Educational Resource Center plus 1 other.

Community Environment: See Rockford College.

■ **ROCKFORD CAREER COLLEGE**
1130 S Alpine Rd.
Ste. 100
Rockford, IL 61108
Tel: (815)965-8616
Fax: (815)965-0360
Web Site: www.rockfordcareercollege.edu

Description: Independent, 2-year, coed. Awards certificates, diplomas, and terminal associate degrees. Founded 1862. Setting: urban campus with easy access to Chicago. Total enrollment: 428. Faculty: 26 (8 full-time, 18 part-time). Student-undergrad faculty ratio is 15:1. 125 applied. Full-time: 243 students, 90% women, 10% men. Part-time: 185 students, 87% women, 13% men. Students come from 2 states and territories, 1% from out-of-state. 65% 25 or older, 8% transferred in. Core. Calendar: quarters. Academic remediation for entering students, services for LD students, advanced placement, honors program, independent study, summer session for credit, part-time degree program, adult/continuing education programs, co-op programs and internships.

Entrance Requirements: Open admission. Options: electronic application, early admission. Required: high school transcript, interview. Required for some: essay. Entrance: minimally difficult. Application deadline: 9/4.

Collegiate Environment: Orientation program. Student-run newspaper. Most popular organization: International Students Club. Student services: personal-psychological counseling. Campus security: 24-hour patrols, late night transport-escort service. Rockford Business College Library plus 1 other. 65 computers available on campus for general student use. A campuswide network can be accessed. Staffed computer lab on campus.

Community Environment: See Rockford College.

■ **ROCKFORD UNIVERSITY**
5050 E State St.
Rockford, IL 61108-2393
Tel: (815)226-4000; Free: 800-892-2984
Fax: (815)226-4119
E-mail: admissions@rockford.edu
Web Site: www.rockford.edu

Description: Independent, comprehensive, coed. Awards bachelor's and master's degrees. Founded 1847. Setting: 150-acre suburban campus with easy access to Chicago. Total enrollment: 1,211. Faculty: 156 (76 full-time, 80 part-time). Student-undergrad faculty ratio is 10:1. 2,682 applied, 49% were admitted. Full-time: 888 students, 55% women, 45% men. Part-time: 114 students, 61% women, 39% men. 15% from out-of-state. 0.2% American Indian or Alaska Native, non-Hispanic/Latino; 17% Hispanic/Latino; 10% Black or African American, non-Hispanic/Latino; 2% Asian, non-Hispanic/

Latino; 7% international. 35% live on campus, 15% transferred in. Retention: 66% of full-time freshmen returned the following year. Academic areas with the most degrees conferred: business/marketing; health professions and related sciences; education. Core. Calendar: semesters. Academic remediation for entering students, ESL program, services for LD students, advanced placement, accelerated degree program, honors program, independent study, distance learning, double major, summer session for credit, part-time degree program, adult/continuing education programs, internships, graduate courses open to undergrads. Off campus study. Study abroad program.

Entrance Requirements: Options: electronic application, early admission, international baccalaureate accepted. Required: high school transcript, SAT or ACT. Recommended: minimum 2.65 high school GPA. Required for some: essay, minimum 2.65 high school GPA, 2 recommendations. Entrance: minimally difficult. Notification: continuous, continuous for nonresidents. Transfer credits accepted: Yes.

Costs Per Year: Application fee: $0. Comprehensive fee: $39,590 includes full-time tuition ($30,800), mandatory fees ($130), and college room and board ($8660). College room only: $4700. Full-time tuition and fees vary according to course load. Room and board charges vary according to board plan and housing facility. Part-time tuition: $795 per credit hour. Part-time tuition varies according to course load.

Collegiate Environment: Orientation program. Drama-theater group, choral group, student-run newspaper, radio station. Social organizations: 21 open to all. Most popular organizations: Campus Activities Board, Multicultural Club, Student Government Association, Nursing Student Organization, Alpha Helix. Major annual events: Homecoming, April Weekend, Casino Night. Student services: health clinic, personal-psychological counseling. Campus security: 24-hour emergency response devices and patrols, student patrols, late night transport-escort service, controlled dormitory access. 396 college housing spaces available; 286 were occupied in 2018-19. No special consideration for freshman housing applicants. Option: coed housing available. Howard Colman Library. Books: 134,831 (physical), 140,140 (digital/electronic); Serial titles: 157 (physical), 23,000 (digital/electronic); Databases: 27. Weekly public service hours: 85; students can reserve study rooms. 94 computers available on campus for general student use. A campuswide network can be accessed from student residence rooms and from off campus. Students can access the following: online class registration, online bill payment. Staffed computer lab on campus provides training in use of computers, software, and the Internet.

Community Environment: Rockford, population 152,916, is the second largest city in the state. It is 75 miles northwest of Chicago, and is situated in the historic and attractive Rock River Valley close to the Wisconsin border. Rockford is also an important industrial city that produces machine tools, furniture, hardware and automobile accessories.

■ **ROOSEVELT UNIVERSITY**
430 S Michigan Ave.
Chicago, IL 60605
Tel: (312)341-3500; Free: 877-APPLYRU
E-mail: anunez13@roosevelt.edu
Web Site: www.roosevelt.edu

Description: Independent, comprehensive, coed. Awards bachelor's, master's, and doctoral degrees. Founded 1945. Setting: urban campus with easy access to Chicago. Endowment: $109.6 million. Research spending for the previous fiscal year: $1 million. Educational spending for the previous fiscal year: $10,915 per student. Total enrollment: 4,457. Faculty: 622 (238 full-time, 384 part-time). Student-undergrad faculty ratio is 10:1. 4,018 applied, 70% were admitted. 2% from top 10% of their high school class, 6% from top quarter, 31% from top half. Full-time: 2,115 students, 63% women, 37% men. Part-time: 399 students, 64% women, 36% men. Students come from 39 states and territories, 44 other countries, 17% from out-of-state. 0.4% American Indian or Alaska Native, non-Hispanic/Latino; 25% Hispanic/Latino; 17% Black or African American, non-Hispanic/Latino; 6% Asian, non-Hispanic/Latino; 0.2% Native Hawaiian or other Pacific Islander, non-Hispanic/Latino; 4% international. 24% 25 or older, 20% live on campus, 16% transferred in. Retention: 64% of full-time freshmen returned the following year. Academic areas with the most degrees conferred: business/marketing; psychology; visual and performing arts. Core. Calendar: semesters. Academic remediation for entering students, ESL program, services for LD students, advanced placement, accelerated degree program, self-designed majors, honors program, independent study, distance learning, double major, summer session for credit, part-time degree program, adult/

continuing education programs, co-op programs and internships, graduate courses open to undergrads. Off campus study at School of the Art Institute of Chicago. Study abroad program.

Entrance Requirements: Options: electronic application, deferred admission, international baccalaureate accepted. Required: high school transcript, minimum 2.5 high school GPA, audition for music and theater programs, SAT or ACT. Recommended: essay. Required for some: essay, interview. Entrance: moderately difficult. Application deadline: 8/15. Notification: continuous. SAT Reasoning Test deadline: 8/15. SAT Subject Test deadline: 8/15. Transfer credits accepted: Yes.

Costs Per Year: Application fee: $25. Comprehensive fee: $43,055 includes full-time tuition ($29,832) and college room and board ($13,223). College room only: $9412. Full-time tuition varies according to program. Room and board charges vary according to board plan and housing facility. Part-time tuition: $797 per credit hour. Part-time mandatory fees: $303 per term. Part-time tuition and fees vary according to program.

Collegiate Environment: Orientation program. Student-run newspaper, radio station. Social organizations: 51 open to all; national fraternities, national sororities, local fraternities, local sororities; 1% of eligible men and 2% of eligible women are members. Most popular organizations: SPEED Programming Board, Student Government Association, Roosevelt Black Student Union, Alpha Phi Omega Co-ed Service Fraternity, Alpha Gamma Delta Sorority Inc. Major annual events: SPEED-Homecoming Week events, SPEED-Homecoming Week, SPEED-Social Justice Week. Student services: personal-psychological counseling. Campus security: 24-hour emergency response devices and patrols, late night transport-escort service, controlled dormitory access. Murray-Green Library plus 4 others. Books: 152,557 (physical), 43,963 (digital/electronic); Serial titles: 174 (physical), 41,406 (digital/electronic); Databases: 198. Operations spending for the previous fiscal year: $1.8 million. 646 computers available on campus for general student use. A campuswide network can be accessed from student residence rooms and from off campus. Students can access the following: online class registration. Staffed computer lab on campus provides training in use of computers, software, and the Internet.

Community Environment: Roosevelt University's downtown location places students only blocks away from such cultural and educational resources as the Art Institute, Orchestra Hall, the Opera House, the Field Museum of Natural History, the Grant Park Band Shell, the Shedd Aquarium and the Adler Planetarium. Roosevelt University is also located in the hub of the city's mercantile and financial districts - the Board of Trade, the State Street department stores, the LaSalle and Dearborn Streets banking houses, law offices, and government buildings all being within easy walking distance of the university. The Schauburg campus is located across from the Chicago area's largest shopping mall and only 15 minutes from O'Hare International Airport. The two campuses are linked by regularly scheduled van service and all academic programs are available at both locations except the Performing Arts (Chicago only).

■ RUSH UNIVERSITY

600 S Paulina
Chicago, IL 60612-3832
Tel: (312)942-5000
Fax: (312)942-2100
Web Site: www.rushu.rush.edu

Description: Independent, upper-level, coed. Awards bachelor's, master's, and doctoral degrees and post-master's certificates. Founded 1969. Setting: 35-acre urban campus. Endowment: $340.2 million. Research spending for the previous fiscal year: $41.6 million. Educational spending for the previous fiscal year: $20,780 per student. Total enrollment: 1,566. Faculty: 796 (all full-time). Student-undergrad faculty ratio is 8:1. 398 applied, 37% were admitted. Full-time: 159 students, 87% women, 13% men. Part-time: 7 students, 71% women, 29% men. Students come from 14 states and territories, 4 other countries, 19% from out-of-state. 60% 25 or older, 10% live on campus, 12% transferred in. Academic area with the most degrees conferred: health professions and related sciences. Calendar: quarters. Distance learning.

Collegiate Environment: Most popular organization: Service project to Belize. Major annual events: Octoberfest, TGIFs, Music Recital. Student services: health clinic, personal-psychological counseling. Campus security: 24-hour emergency response devices and patrols, late night transport-escort service, controlled dormitory access. Library of Rush University Medical Center. Operations spending for the previous fiscal year: $2.8 million. 150 computers available on campus for general student use. Computer purchase/lease plans available. A campuswide network can be accessed

from student residence rooms and from off campus. Staffed computer lab on campus provides training in use of computers, software, and the Internet.

Community Environment: See University of Chicago.

■ SAE INSTITUTE CHICAGO

820 N Orleans St. No.125
Chicago, IL 60610
Tel: (312)300-5685
Web Site: www.sae.edu

Description: Proprietary, 2-year, coed. Awards diplomas, transfer associate, and terminal associate degrees.

■ SAINT ANTHONY COLLEGE OF NURSING

3301 N Mulford Rd.
Rock Valley Campus
Rockford, IL 61114
Tel: (815)282-7900
E-mail: admissions@sacn.edu
Web Site: www.sacn.edu

Description: Independent Roman Catholic, upper-level, coed. Awards bachelor's, master's, and doctoral degrees and post-master's certificates. Founded 1915. Setting: 7-acre suburban campus with easy access to Chicago. Total enrollment: 321. Faculty: 39 (23 full-time, 16 part-time). Student-undergrad faculty ratio is 7:1. Full-time: 167 students, 89% women, 11% men. Part-time: 71 students, 90% women, 10% men. Students come from 2 states and territories, 10% from out-of-state. 13% Hispanic/Latino; 2% Black or African American, non-Hispanic/Latino; 5% Asian, non-Hispanic/Latino; 0.4% Native Hawaiian or other Pacific Islander, non-Hispanic/Latino. 53% 25 or older, 24% transferred in. Retention: 100% of full-time entering class returned the following year. Academic area with the most degrees conferred: health professions and related sciences. Core. Calendar: semesters. Services for LD students, advanced placement, independent study, summer session for credit, part-time degree program, internships.

Entrance Requirements: Transfer credits accepted: Yes.

Collegiate Environment: Orientation program. Social organizations: 1 open to all. Most popular organization: Student Organization. Major annual events: Opening Mass and Breakfast, Welcome Party for New Students, Student Organization Activities. Student services: legal services, health clinic, personal-psychological counseling. Campus security: 24-hour patrols. Sister Mary Linus Learning Resource Center. Students can reserve study rooms. 104 computers available on campus for general student use. A campuswide network can be accessed from off-campus. Students can access the following: online class registration. Staffed computer lab on campus provides training in use of computers, software, and the Internet.

■ ST. AUGUSTINE COLLEGE

1333-1345 W Argyle
Chicago, IL 60640-3501
Tel: (773)878-8756
E-mail: info@staugustine.edu
Web Site: www.staugustine.edu

Description: Independent, 4-year, coed. Awards associate and bachelor's degrees (offers bilingual Spanish/English degree programs). Founded 1980. Setting: 4-acre urban campus. Endowment: $501,935. Educational spending for the previous fiscal year: $2514 per student. Total enrollment: 1,430. Faculty: 154 (20 full-time, 134 part-time). Student-undergrad faculty ratio is 20:1. Full-time: 1,218 students, 76% women, 24% men. Part-time: 212 students, 74% women, 26% men. Students come from 2 states and territories, 5 other countries. 69% 25 or older, 3% transferred in. Retention: 68% of full-time freshmen returned the following year. Core. Calendar: semesters. Academic remediation for entering students, ESL program, services for LD students, independent study, double major, summer session for credit, part-time degree program, adult/continuing education programs, co-op programs and internships.

Entrance Requirements: Open admission. Entrance: noncompetitive. Application deadline: rolling. Notification: continuous. Transfer credits accepted: Yes.

Costs Per Year: Application fee: $0. Tuition: $11,400 full-time, $475 per semester hour part-time.

Collegiate Environment: Orientation program. Major annual events: Student Alliance Week, Hispanic History Week, Mexican Fiesta. Student services: personal-psychological counseling. Campus security: 24-hour patrols, late night transport-escort service. St. Augustine College Library. Operations spending for the previous fiscal year: $121,000. 292 computers available on campus for general student use. A campuswide network can be accessed. Staffed computer lab on campus provides training in use of computers, software, and the Internet.

■ SAINT FRANCIS MEDICAL CENTER COLLEGE OF NURSING
511 NE Greenleaf St.
Peoria, IL 61603-3783
Tel: (309)655-2201
Web Site: www.sfmccon.edu

Description: Independent Roman Catholic, upper-level, coed. Administratively affiliated with OSF Saint Francis Medical Center. Awards bachelor's, master's, and doctoral degrees and post-master's certificates. Founded 1986. Setting: urban campus. Educational spending for the previous fiscal year: $11,668 per student. Total enrollment: 645. Faculty: 54 (37 full-time, 17 part-time). Student-undergrad faculty ratio is 10:1. 90 applied, 84% were admitted. Full-time: 311 students, 87% women, 13% men. Part-time: 91 students, 90% women, 10% men. Students come from 3 states and territories, 4 other countries, 1% from out-of-state. 5% Hispanic/Latino; 5% Black or African American, non-Hispanic/Latino; 2% Asian, non-Hispanic/Latino; 1% international. 36% 25 or older, 20% live on campus, 30% transferred in. Academic area with the most degrees conferred: health professions and related sciences. Core. Calendar: semesters. Academic remediation for entering students, advanced placement, accelerated degree program, independent study, distance learning, summer session for credit, part-time degree program, adult/continuing education programs.

Entrance Requirements: Transfer credits accepted: Yes.

Costs Per Year: Application fee: $50. Tuition: $20,020 full-time, $616 per semester hour part-time. Mandatory fees: $1037 full-time, $215 per term part-time. Full-time tuition and fees vary according to course load, degree level, program, and student level. Part-time tuition and fees vary according to course load, degree level, program, and student level. College room only: $1850.

Collegiate Environment: Orientation program. Social organizations: 4 open to all. Most popular organizations: Student Senate, SNAI, Minority Student Association, Tau Omicron. Major annual events: Open House, Christmas Dinner, Spring Formal. Student services: health clinic, personal-psychological counseling. Campus security: 24-hour emergency response devices and patrols, late night transport-escort service, controlled dormitory access. Sister Mary Ludgera Pieperbeck Learning and Resource Center plus 1 other. Books: 4,054 (physical), 298 (digital/electronic); Serial titles: 126 (physical); Databases: 57. Students can reserve study rooms. Operations spending for the previous fiscal year: $30,876. 62 computers available on campus for general student use. A campuswide network can be accessed from student residence rooms and from off campus. Students can access the following: online class registration. Staffed computer lab on campus provides training in use of computers, software, and the Internet.

■ ST. JOHN'S COLLEGE
729 E Carpenter St.
Springfield, IL 62702
Tel: (217)525-5628
Web Site: www.sjcs.edu

Description: Independent Roman Catholic, upper-level, coed. Awards bachelor's degrees. Founded 1886. Setting: urban campus. Total enrollment: 122. Student-undergrad faculty ratio is 6:1. 90 applied, 68% were admitted. Full-time: 113 students, 89% women, 11% men. Part-time: 9 students, 100% women. 0.8% Hispanic/Latino; 0.8% international. 32% 25 or older, 53% transferred in. Retention: 87% of full-time entering class returned the following year. Calendar: semesters. Part-time degree program.

Entrance Requirements: Transfer credits accepted: Yes. Applicants placed on waiting list: 30. Wait-listed applicants offered admission: 0.

Collegiate Environment: Orientation program. Campus security: 24-hour emergency response devices and patrols, late night transport-escort service. St. John's Health Science Library.

■ SAINT XAVIER UNIVERSITY
3700 W 103rd St.
Chicago, IL 60655-3105
Tel: (773)298-3000; Free: 800-462-9288
Fax: (773)298-3076
E-mail: carlson@sxu.edu
Web Site: www.sxu.edu

Description: Independent Roman Catholic, comprehensive, coed. Awards bachelor's and master's degrees and post-master's certificates. Founded

1847. Setting: 70-acre urban campus. Endowment: $7.1 million. Total enrollment: 4,709. Faculty: 431 (173 full-time, 258 part-time). Student-undergrad faculty ratio is 14:1. 5,520 applied, 83% were admitted. 22% from top 10% of their high school class, 50% from top quarter, 84% from top half. Full-time: 2,537 students, 68% women, 32% men. Part-time: 456 students, 69% women, 31% men. 5% from out-of-state. 0.5% American Indian or Alaska Native, non-Hispanic/Latino; 17% Hispanic/Latino; 17% Black or African American, non-Hispanic/Latino; 2% Asian, non-Hispanic/Latino; 0.3% international. 19% 25 or older, 29% live on campus, 13% transferred in. Retention: 72% of full-time freshmen returned the following year. Academic areas with the most degrees conferred: education; business/marketing; health professions and related sciences. Core. Calendar: semesters. Academic remediation for entering students, ESL program, services for LD students, advanced placement, accelerated degree program, self-designed majors, honors program, independent study, double major, summer session for credit, part-time degree program, adult/continuing education programs, co-op programs and internships, graduate courses open to undergrads. Study abroad program. ROTC: Air Force (c).

Entrance Requirements: Options: electronic application, deferred admission, international baccalaureate accepted. Required: high school transcript, SAT or ACT. Recommended: essay, minimum 2.5 high school GPA, interview. Entrance: moderately difficult. Application deadline: rolling. Notification: continuous. Transfer credits accepted: Yes.

Collegiate Environment: Orientation program. Drama-theater group, choral group, marching band, student-run newspaper, radio station. Social organizations: 37 open to all. Most popular organizations: Student Activities Board, Black Student Union, UNIDOS (Hispanic Organization), Student Nurses Association, Business Students Association. Major annual events: Homecoming Celebrations, Boat Bash. Student services: health clinic, personal-psychological counseling, women's center. Campus security: 24-hour emergency response devices and patrols, late night transport-escort service. Byrne Memorial Library. 500 computers available on campus for general student use. A campuswide network can be accessed from student residence rooms and from off campus. Students can access the following: online class registration. Staffed computer lab on campus provides training in use of computers, software, and the Internet.

Community Environment: See University of Chicago.

■ SAUK VALLEY COMMUNITY COLLEGE
173 Illinois Rte. 2
Dixon, IL 61021
Tel: (815)288-5511
Web Site: www.svcc.edu

Description: District-supported, 2-year, coed. Part of Illinois Community College Board. Awards certificates, transfer associate, and terminal associate degrees. Founded 1965. Setting: 165-acre rural campus. Endowment: $2 million. Research spending for the previous fiscal year: $91,425. Educational spending for the previous fiscal year: $1357 per student. Total enrollment: 2,220. Faculty: 145 (44 full-time, 101 part-time). Student-undergrad faculty ratio is 21:1. 585 applied, 100% were admitted. Full-time: 998 students, 57% women, 43% men. Part-time: 1,222 students, 62% women, 38% men. 0.3% American Indian or Alaska Native, non-Hispanic/Latino; 8% Hispanic/Latino; 4% Black or African American, non-Hispanic/Latino; 0.7% Asian, non-Hispanic/Latino; 0.2% Native Hawaiian or other Pacific Islander, non-Hispanic/Latino. 37% 25 or older. Retention: 59% of full-time freshmen returned the following year. Core. Calendar: semesters. Academic remediation for entering students, ESL program, services for LD students, accelerated degree program, honors program, independent study, distance learning, summer session for credit, part-time degree program, adult/continuing education programs, co-op programs and internships. Off campus study at Highland Community College, Illinois Valley Community College, Rock Valley College, Kishwaukee College.

Entrance Requirements: Open admission except for health programs. Options: electronic application, early admission, deferred admission. Recommended: high school transcript, ACT. Entrance: noncompetitive. Application deadline: rolling. Notification: continuous. Transfer credits accepted: Yes.

Costs Per Year: Application fee: $0. Area resident tuition: $3556 full-time, $127 per credit hour part-time. State resident tuition: $9184 full-time, $328 per credit hour part-time. Nonresident tuition: $9968 full-time, $356 per credit hour part-time. Mandatory fees: $336 full-time, $12 per credit hour part-time.

Collegiate Environment: Orientation program. Drama-theater group, choral group, student-run newspaper. Social organizations: 21 open to all. Most popular organizations: Phi Theta Kappa, Criminal Justice Club, Health Careers Club, Association of Latin American Students. Student services:

personal-psychological counseling. Campus security: 24-hour emergency response devices and patrols, late night transport-escort service. Learning Resource Center plus 1 other. Operations spending for the previous fiscal year: $233,487. 100 computers available on campus for general student use. A campuswide network can be accessed from student residence rooms and from off campus. Students can access the following: online class registration. Staffed computer lab on campus provides training in use of computers, software, and the Internet.

Community Environment: Dixon has a population of 15,372; Sterling (population 15,381) is a small industrial city, enjoying a seasonal climate. Ozark Airlines and Greyhound buses serve the area. Community facilities include a public library, hospital, YMCA, YWCA, many churches, and all the major civic and service groups. Recreational opportunities abound in the many city parks providing swimming, tennis, picnic areas, boating and fishing, along with access to golf, bowling, roller skating, miniature golf and go-carting. Jobs are plentiful in this highly industrialized area.

■ **SCHOOL OF THE ART INSTITUTE OF CHICAGO**
37 S Wabash
Chicago, IL 60603-3103
Tel: (312)899-5100; Free: 800-232-SAIC
Fax: (312)263-0141
E-mail: ugadmiss@saic.edu
Web Site: www.saic.edu
Description: Independent, comprehensive, coed. Awards bachelor's and master's degrees. Founded 1866. Setting: 1-acre urban campus with easy access to Chicago. Total enrollment: 3,570. Faculty: 731 (172 full-time, 559 part-time). Student-undergrad faculty ratio is 11:1. 5,244 applied, 59% were admitted. Full-time: 2,681 students, 73% women, 27% men. Part-time: 168 students, 77% women, 23% men. Students come from 48 other countries. 0.2% American Indian or Alaska Native, non-Hispanic/Latino; 11% Hispanic/Latino; 3% Black or African American, non-Hispanic/Latino; 11% Asian, non-Hispanic/Latino; 0.1% Native Hawaiian or other Pacific Islander, non-Hispanic/Latino; 32% international. 17% live on campus, 7% transferred in. Retention: 81% of full-time freshmen returned the following year. Academic areas with the most degrees conferred: visual and performing arts; architecture. Core. Calendar: semesters. Academic remediation for entering students, ESL program, services for LD students, advanced placement, self-designed majors, independent study, double major, summer session for credit, part-time degree program, co-op programs and internships, graduate courses open to undergrads. Off campus study. Study abroad program.
Entrance Requirements: Options: electronic application, early action, deferred admission, international baccalaureate accepted. Required: essay, high school transcript, SAT or ACT. Recommended: interview. Entrance: very difficult. Application deadline: 11/15. Notification: continuous until 1/30. SAT Reasoning Test deadline: August. Transfer credits accepted: Yes.
Costs Per Year: Application fee: $65. Comprehensive fee: $65,200 includes full-time tuition ($48,390), mandatory fees ($920), and college room and board ($15,890). College room only: $12,300. Full-time tuition and fees vary according to course load, degree level, and program. Room and board charges vary according to board plan and housing facility. Part-time tuition: $1613 per credit hour. Part-time mandatory fees: $305 per term. Part-time tuition and fees vary according to course load, degree level, and program.
Collegiate Environment: Orientation program. Drama-theater group, student-run newspaper, radio station. Social organizations: 45 open to all. Most popular organizations: Student Association/Student Union Galleries, Korean Student Association, InterVarsity, Curatorial Community, Good 'Ol Futbol. Major annual events: Exhibition Openings, Holiday Art Sale, All School BBQ. Student services: health clinic, personal-psychological counseling. Campus security: 24-hour emergency response devices and patrols, late night transport-escort service, controlled dormitory access. The John M. Flaxman Library plus 1 other. Books: 110,287 (physical), 203,725 (digital/electronic); Serial titles: 19,541 (physical), 204,634 (digital/electronic); Databases: 177. 300 computers available on campus for general student use. Computer purchase/lease plans available. A computer is required for all students. A campuswide network can be accessed from student residence rooms and from off campus. Students can access the following: online class registration. Staffed computer lab on campus (open 24 hours a day) provides training in use of computers, software, and the Internet.
Community Environment: See University of Chicago.

■ **SHAWNEE COMMUNITY COLLEGE**
8364 Shawnee College Rd.
Ullin, IL 62992

Tel: (618)634-3200
Fax: (618)634-3300
E-mail: erink@shawneecc.edu
Web Site: www.shawneecc.edu
Description: State and locally supported, 2-year, coed. Part of Illinois Community College Board. Awards certificates, diplomas, transfer associate, and terminal associate degrees. Founded 1967. Setting: 163-acre rural campus. Total enrollment: 1,505. Faculty: 90 (33 full-time, 57 part-time). Student-undergrad faculty ratio is 19:1. 992 applied, 100% were admitted. Full-time: 680 students, 67% women, 33% men. Part-time: 825 students, 61% women, 39% men. Students come from 3 states and territories, 2% from out-of-state. 0.1% American Indian or Alaska Native, non-Hispanic/Latino; 4% Hispanic/Latino; 14% Black or African American, non-Hispanic/Latino; 0.5% Asian, non-Hispanic/Latino; 0.1% Native Hawaiian or other Pacific Islander, non-Hispanic/Latino. 22% 25 or older, 4% transferred in. Retention: 55% of full-time freshmen returned the following year. Core. Calendar: semesters. Academic remediation for entering students, ESL program, services for LD students, advanced placement, accelerated degree program, independent study, distance learning, double major, summer session for credit, part-time degree program, external degree program, adult/continuing education programs, co-op programs and internships. Off campus study.
Entrance Requirements: Open admission except for health programs. Options: electronic application, early admission, deferred admission. Required: high school transcript. Recommended: SAT. Required for some: SAT. Entrance: noncompetitive. Application deadline: rolling. Notification: continuous, rolling for early decision. Preference given to district residents. Transfer credits accepted: Yes.
Costs Per Year: Application fee: $0. Area resident tuition: $2760 full-time, $115 per credit hour part-time. State resident tuition: $4224 full-time, $176 per credit hour part-time. Nonresident tuition: $4608 full-time, $192 per credit hour part-time. Mandatory fees: $240 full-time, $10 per credit hour part-time.
Collegiate Environment: Orientation program. Drama-theater group, choral group. Social organizations: 14 open to all. Most popular organizations: Phi Theta Kappa, Phi Beta Lambda, Music Club, Student Senate, Future Teachers Organization. Major annual events: Homecoming, Fall Fest, Spring Fest. Student services: personal-psychological counseling. Campus security: 24-hour patrols. Shawnee Community College Library. Students can reserve study rooms.

■ **SOUTH SUBURBAN COLLEGE**
15800 S State St.
South Holland, IL 60473-1270
Tel: (708)596-2000
E-mail: admissionsquestions@ssc.edu
Web Site: www.ssc.edu
Description: State and locally supported, 2-year, coed. Part of Illinois Community College Board. Awards certificates, transfer associate, and terminal associate degrees. Founded 1927. Setting: 5-acre suburban campus with easy access to Chicago. Educational spending for the previous fiscal year: $15,623 per student. Total enrollment: 4,115. Faculty: 513 (114 full-time, 399 part-time). Student-undergrad faculty ratio is 13:1. 15% from top 10% of their high school class, 29% from top quarter. 3% from out-of-state. 0.3% American Indian or Alaska Native, non-Hispanic/Latino; 20% Hispanic/Latino; 54% Black or African American, non-Hispanic/Latino; 1% Asian, non-Hispanic/Latino; 0.2% Native Hawaiian or other Pacific Islander, non-Hispanic/Latino; 0.9% international. 52% 25 or older. Retention: 20% of full-time freshmen returned the following year. Core. Calendar: semesters. Academic remediation for entering students, ESL program, services for LD students, advanced placement, honors program, distance learning, summer session for credit, part-time degree program, adult/continuing education programs, co-op programs and internships. Off campus study at other colleges of the Illinois Community College System. Study abroad program.
Entrance Requirements: Open admission except for nursing, occupational therapy, court reporting, practical nursing, radiological technology programs. Options: early admission, deferred admission. Required: high school transcript. Recommended: essay, minimum 2 high school GPA. Required for some: essay. Entrance: noncompetitive. Application deadline: rolling. Notification: continuous. Preference given to district residents for nursing program. Transfer credits accepted: Yes.
Costs Per Year: Area resident tuition: $4560 full-time, $152 per credit hour part-time. State resident tuition: $10,500 full-time, $350 per credit hour part-time. Nonresident tuition: $12,150 full-time, $405 per credit hour part-time. Mandatory fees: $533 full-time, $17.75 per credit hour part-time. Full-time

tuition and fees vary according to course load and reciprocity agreements. Part-time tuition and fees vary according to course load and reciprocity agreements.

Collegiate Environment: Drama-theater group, choral group. Campus security: 24-hour emergency response devices and patrols. South Suburban College Library plus 1 other. Books: 25,563 (physical); Serial titles: 56 (physical); Databases: 25. Weekly public service hours: 60; students can reserve study rooms. 137 computers available on campus for general student use. A campuswide network can be accessed from off-campus. Students can access the following: online class registration. Staffed computer lab on campus provides training in use of computers, software, and the Internet.

■ **SOUTHEASTERN ILLINOIS COLLEGE**
3575 College Rd.
Harrisburg, IL 62946-4925
Tel: (618)252-5400; Free: 866-338-2742
Web Site: www.sic.edu

Description: State-supported, 2-year, coed. Part of Illinois Community College Board. Awards certificates, transfer associate, and terminal associate degrees. Founded 1960. Setting: 140-acre rural campus. Educational spending for the previous fiscal year: $4188 per student. Total enrollment: 2,941. 7% from out-of-state. 40% 25 or older. Core. Calendar: semesters. Academic remediation for entering students, services for LD students, advanced placement, self-designed majors, independent study, distance learning, summer session for credit, part-time degree program, adult/continuing education programs, internships. Off campus study at Southern Illinois Collegiate Common Market.

Entrance Requirements: Open admission except for nursing, medical records technology, medical lab technology, operating room technology, game management, occupational therapy programs, health information technology. Options: electronic application, early admission, deferred admission. Required: high school transcript. Entrance: noncompetitive. Application deadline: 9/1. Notification: continuous. Preference given to district residents.

Collegiate Environment: Drama-theater group, choral group. Social organizations: 13 open to all. Most popular organizations: Math and Science Club, Phi Theta Kappa, Forestry Club, Phi Beta Lambda, BASIC. Student services: personal-psychological counseling. Campus security: student patrols, evening security guard. Melba Patton Library plus 2 others. Operations spending for the previous fiscal year: $277,328.

Community Environment: Harrisburg is an important coal mining, dairying, agricultural, and commercial center. Community facilities include a library, hospital, churches, an historical museum, and TV and radio stations. Recreational facilities are unlimited with Shawnee National Forest and other federal and state recreation areas within five to ten miles, and many large lakes in the area. The Saline County Fair is an annual event each July. Some part-time work is available.

■ **SOUTHERN ILLINOIS UNIVERSITY CARBONDALE**
Carbondale, IL 62901-4701
Tel: (618)453-2121
Fax: (618)453-3250
E-mail: regstrar@siu.edu
Web Site: www.siu.edu

Description: State-supported, university, coed. Part of Southern Illinois University. Awards associate, bachelor's, master's, and doctoral degrees. Founded 1869. Setting: 1,136-acre rural campus with easy access to St. Louis. Research spending for the previous fiscal year: $37.8 million. Educational spending for the previous fiscal year: $7599 per student. Total enrollment: 12,776. Faculty: 940 (784 full-time, 156 part-time). Student-undergrad faculty ratio is 14:1. 6,219 applied, 72% were admitted. 15% from top 10% of their high school class, 44% from top quarter, 74% from top half. Full-time: 8,070 students, 47% women, 53% men. Part-time: 1,442 students, 41% women, 59% men. 20% from out-of-state. 0.3% American Indian or Alaska Native, non-Hispanic/Latino; 9% Hispanic/Latino; 15% Black or African American, non-Hispanic/Latino; 2% Asian, non-Hispanic/Latino; 0.1% Native Hawaiian or other Pacific Islander, non-Hispanic/Latino; 4% international. 21% 25 or older, 22% live on campus, 13% transferred in. Retention: 71% of full-time freshmen returned the following year. Academic areas with the most degrees conferred: business/marketing; education; engineering technologies. Core. Calendar: semesters plus 8-week summer session. Academic remediation for entering students, ESL program, services for LD students, advanced placement, accelerated degree program, self-designed majors, honors program, independent study, distance learning,

double major, summer session for credit, part-time degree program, adult/continuing education programs, co-op programs and internships, graduate courses open to undergrads. Off campus study. Study abroad program. ROTC: Army, Air Force.

Entrance Requirements: Options: electronic application, deferred admission, international baccalaureate accepted. Required: high school transcript, SAT or ACT. Entrance: moderately difficult. Application deadline: rolling. Notification: continuous. Transfer credits accepted: Yes.

Costs Per Year: Application fee: $40. State resident tuition: $9638 full-time, $321.25 per credit hour part-time. Nonresident tuition: $9638 full-time, $803.13 per credit hour part-time. Mandatory fees: $5066 full-time, $2960 per year part-time. Full-time tuition and fees vary according to course load, location, program, reciprocity agreements, and student level. Part-time tuition and fees vary according to course load, location, program, reciprocity agreements, and student level. College room and board: $10,622. Room and board charges vary according to board plan and housing facility. Part time fees are based on a student taking 6 credit hours per semester. Tuition guaranteed not to increase for student's term of enrollment.

Collegiate Environment: Orientation program. Drama-theater group, choral group, marching band, student-run newspaper, radio station. Social organizations: 258 open to all; national fraternities, national sororities, local fraternities, local sororities; 8% of eligible men and 8% of eligible women are members. Most popular organizations: Undergraduate Student Government, Greek Councils, International Student Council, Black Affairs Council, Dawg Pound. Major annual events: Homecoming, International Student Festival, Theta Xi Variety Show. Student services: legal services, health clinic, personal-psychological counseling, women's center. Campus security: 24-hour emergency response devices and patrols, student patrols, late night transport-escort service, controlled dormitory access, well-lit pathways, night safety vans, student transit system and extensive video security camera system. Freshmen guaranteed college housing. On-campus residence required in freshman year. Options: coed, men-only, women-only housing available. Morris Library plus 1 other. Books: 2.6 million (physical), 243,170 (digital/electronic); Serial titles: 286 (physical), 65,075 (digital/electronic); Databases: 175. Weekly public service hours: 100; students can reserve study rooms. Operations spending for the previous fiscal year: $8.9 million. 1,900 computers available on campus for general student use. Computer purchase/lease plans available. A campuswide network can be accessed from student residence rooms and from off campus. Students can access the following: online class registration. Staffed computer lab on campus provides training in use of computers, software, and the Internet.

Community Environment: Carbondale, an economic center of Southern Illinois, is only a few hours from Chicago, St. Louis, and Memphis. It sits amid rolling hills, farmlands, and orchards just 60 miles above the confluence of the Mississippi and Ohio Rivers. The area from Carbondale south is ruggedly scenic and suitable for a wide range of year-round outdoor activities. Within minutes are four large recreational lakes, the two great rivers, and spectacular 270,000-acre Shawnee National Forest. A large number of smaller lakes, state parks, and recreational areas are within easy driving distance.

■ **SOUTHERN ILLINOIS UNIVERSITY EDWARDSVILLE**
Edwardsville, IL 62026
Tel: (618)650-2000; Free: 800-447-SIUE
Fax: (618)692-2081
E-mail: admissions@siue.edu
Web Site: www.siue.edu

Description: State-supported, university, coed. Part of Southern Illinois University. Awards bachelor's, master's, and doctoral degrees and post-master's certificates. Founded 1957. Setting: 2,660-acre suburban campus with easy access to St. Louis. Endowment: $23.1 million. Research spending for the previous fiscal year: $10.3 million. Educational spending for the previous fiscal year: $13,522 per student. Total enrollment: 13,281. Faculty: 862 (611 full-time, 251 part-time). Student-undergrad faculty ratio is 19:1. 6,410 applied, 87% were admitted. 19% from top 10% of their high school class, 44% from top quarter, 76% from top half. Full-time: 8,979 students, 52% women, 48% men. Part-time: 1,854 students, 58% women, 42% men. Students come from 52 states and territories, 34 other countries, 14% from out-of-state. 0.3% American Indian or Alaska Native, non-Hispanic/Latino; 5% Hispanic/Latino; 13% Black or African American, non-Hispanic/Latino; 2% Asian, non-Hispanic/Latino; 0.1% Native Hawaiian or other Pacific Islander, non-Hispanic/Latino; 1% international. 15% 25 or older, 25% live on campus, 11% transferred in. Retention: 75% of full-time freshmen returned the following year. Academic areas with the most degrees conferred: health professions and related sciences; business/marketing; engineering. Core. Calendar: semesters. Academic remediation for entering students, ESL program, services for LD students, advanced placement, accelerated degree program, self-designed majors, honors program, independent study, distance learning, double major, summer session for credit, part-time degree program, external degree program, co-op programs and internships, graduate courses open to undergrads. Off campus study at Illinois Eastern Community College, Kaskaskia College, Lake Land College, Lewis and Clark Community College, Lincoln Land Community College, Rend Lake College, Shawnee Community College, Southeastern Illinois College, St. Charles Community College, St. Louis Community College, and Southwestern Illinois College. Participate in the Illinois Articulation Initiative and Transferology. Study abroad program. ROTC: Army, Air Force (c).

Entrance Requirements: Options: electronic application, early admission, deferred admission, international baccalaureate accepted. Required: high school transcript, minimum 2 high school GPA, college transcript(s), SAT or ACT. Required for some: essay. Entrance: moderately difficult. Application deadline: 5/1. Notification: continuous. SAT Reasoning Test deadline: 5/1. SAT Subject Test deadline: 8/1. Transfer credits accepted: Yes.

Costs Per Year: Application fee: $40. State resident tuition: $9123 full-time. Nonresident tuition: $9123 full-time. Mandatory fees: $3096 full-time. College room and board: $10,701. College room only: $7110. Tuition guaranteed not to increase for student's term of enrollment.

Collegiate Environment: Orientation program. Drama-theater group, choral group, student-run newspaper, radio station. Social organizations: 244 open to all; national fraternities, national sororities; 7% of eligible men and 12% of eligible women are members. Most popular organizations: Fraternity and Sorority Life, Campus Activities Board, Sports Clubs/Intramurals, Dance Marathon, Student Government. Major annual events: Cougar Welcome, Homecoming, Springfest. Student services: health clinic, personal-psychological counseling. Campus security: 24-hour emergency response devices and patrols, late night transport-escort service, controlled dormitory access. 3,572 college housing spaces available; 2,761 were occupied in 2018-19. Freshmen given priority for college housing. Option: coed housing available. Lovejoy Library. Books: 522,502 (physical), 91,353 (digital/electronic); Serial titles: 35,778 (physical), 35,637 (digital/electronic). Students can reserve study rooms. Operations spending for the previous fiscal year: $3.6 million. 315 computers available on campus for general student use. Computer purchase/lease plans available. A campuswide network can be accessed from student residence rooms and from off campus. Students can access the following: online class registration, online job finder. Staffed computer lab on campus provides training in use of computers, software, and the Internet.

Community Environment: Edwardsville/Glen Carbon (population more than 24,000) is a suburban St. Louis community with a public library, many churches, museum, YMCA, and hospital facilities nearby. It is located only 30 minutes from Lambert St. Louis International Airport.

■ **SOUTHWESTERN ILLINOIS COLLEGE**
2500 Carlyle Ave.
Belleville, IL 62221-5899
Tel: (618)235-2700
Fax: (618)235-1578
Web Site: www.swic.edu
Description: District-supported, 2-year, coed. Part of Illinois Community College Board. Awards certificates, diplomas, transfer associate, and terminal associate degrees. Founded 1946. Setting: suburban campus with easy access to St. Louis. Calendar: semesters.

■ **SPOON RIVER COLLEGE**
23235 N County 22
Canton, IL 61520-9801
Tel: (309)647-4645; Free: 800-334-7337
Fax: (309)649-6235
E-mail: info@src.edu
Web Site: www.src.edu
Description: State-supported, 2-year, coed. Part of Illinois Community College Board. Awards certificates, transfer associate, and terminal associate degrees. Founded 1959. Setting: 160-acre rural campus. Endowment: $2.4 million. Educational spending for the previous fiscal year: $3754 per student. Total enrollment: 1,560. Faculty: 121 (33 full-time, 88 part-time). Student-undergrad faculty ratio is 13:1. 914 applied, 35% were admitted. Full-time: 751 students, 56% women, 44% men. Part-time: 809 students, 64% women, 36% men. Students come from 10 states and territories, 1% from out-of-

state. 1% American Indian or Alaska Native, non-Hispanic/Latino; 2% Hispanic/Latino; 11% Black or African American, non-Hispanic/Latino; 0.8% Asian, non-Hispanic/Latino; 0.1% international. 22% 25 or older, 4% transferred in. Retention: 47% of full-time freshmen returned the following year. Core. Calendar: semesters. Academic remediation for entering students, ESL program, services for LD students, advanced placement, accelerated degree program, independent study, distance learning, summer session for credit, part-time degree program, adult/continuing education programs, internships. ROTC: Army (c).

Entrance Requirements: Open admission except for nursing program. Options: electronic application, early admission, deferred admission. Required: high school transcript. Entrance: noncompetitive. Application deadline: rolling. Notification: continuous. Transfer credits accepted: Yes.

Costs Per Year: Application fee: $0. Area resident tuition: $4480 full-time, $140 per semester hour part-time. State resident tuition: $10,176 full-time, $318 per semester hour part-time. Nonresident tuition: $11,328 full-time, $354 per semester hour part-time. Mandatory fees: $800 full-time, $25 per semester hour part-time. Full-time tuition and fees vary according to location. Part-time tuition and fees vary according to location.

Collegiate Environment: Orientation program. Drama-theater group, student-run newspaper. Social organizations: 11 open to all. Most popular organizations: Student Government Association, PEEPS, Intramural Athletics, Habitat for Humanity, Drama Club. Major annual events: Graduation, Snapper Bash. Student services: personal-psychological counseling. Campus security: 24-hour emergency response devices, night patrol by trained security personnel. Library/Learning Resource Center. Books: 12,647 (physical), 135,000 (digital/electronic); Serial titles: 4,560 (digital/electronic); Databases: 31. Weekly public service hours: 40. Operations spending for the previous fiscal year: $117,516. 600 computers available on campus for general student use. A campuswide network can be accessed from off-campus. Students can access the following: online class registration. Staffed computer lab on campus.

Community Environment: Canton is situated in an extremely fertile agricultural district with a seasonal climate. Planes and buses are available. Air service at Peoria some 30 miles distant. Industries are coal mining and the manufacture of farm implements. The city has a library, YMCA, YWCA, concert association, hospital, a downtown shopping area with over 100 retail outlets. Additional shopping facilities in Peoria. Recreational activities are boating, fishing, hunting, bowling, and golf. At least 12 retail and community-sponsored events are conducted each year.

■ **TAYLOR BUSINESS INSTITUTE**
318 W Adams
Chicago, IL 60606
Tel: (312)658-5100
Fax: (312)658-0867
Web Site: www.tbiil.edu
Description: Proprietary, 2-year, coed. Awards terminal associate degrees. Founded 1964. Total enrollment: 95. 131 applied, 78% were admitted.

■ **TELSHE YESHIVA-CHICAGO**
3535 W Foster Ave.
Chicago, IL 60625-5598
Tel: (773)463-7738
Description: Independent Jewish, comprehensive, men only. Awards bachelor's and master's degrees. Founded 1960. Total enrollment: 77. 8 applied, 100% were admitted. Core. Calendar: semesters. Summer session for credit, part-time degree program.
Entrance Requirements: Required: interview.
Collegiate Environment: Student services: health clinic, personal-psychological counseling.

■ **TRIBECA FLASHPOINT COLLEGE**
28 N Clark St.
Chicago, IL 60602
Tel: (312)332-0707
Web Site: www.tribecaflashpoint.edu
Description: Proprietary, 2-year, coed. Awards terminal associate degrees.

■ **TRINITY CHRISTIAN COLLEGE**
6601 W College Dr.
Palos Heights, IL 60463-0929
Tel: (708)597-3000; Free: 866-TRIN-4-ME
Fax: (708)239-3995

E-mail: brittany.minnesma@trnty.edu

Web Site: www.trnty.edu

Description: Independent Christian Reformed, comprehensive, coed. Part of n/a. Administratively affiliated with n/a. Awards bachelor's and master's degrees. Founded 1959. Setting: 53-acre suburban campus with easy access to Chicago. Endowment: $10.8 million. Educational spending for the previous fiscal year: $10,395 per student. Total enrollment: 1,131. Faculty: 142 (70 full-time, 72 part-time). Student-undergrad faculty ratio is 10:1. 768 applied, 80% were admitted. 15% from top 10% of their high school class, 30% from top quarter, 73% from top half. Full-time: 883 students, 67% women, 33% men. Part-time: 180 students, 66% women, 34% men. Students come from 29 states and territories, 10 other countries, 33% from out-of-state. 0.2% American Indian or Alaska Native, non-Hispanic/Latino; 12% Hispanic/Latino; 8% Black or African American, non-Hispanic/Latino; 1% Asian, non-Hispanic/Latino; 0.1% Native Hawaiian or other Pacific Islander, non-Hispanic/Latino; 12% international. 21% 25 or older, 42% live on campus, 8% transferred in. Retention: 80% of full-time freshmen returned the following year. Academic areas with the most degrees conferred: business/marketing; education; psychology. Core. Calendar: semesters plus 2 week interim term. Academic remediation for entering students, ESL program, services for LD students, advanced placement, accelerated degree program, honors program, independent study, distance learning, double major, summer session for credit, part-time degree program, adult/continuing education programs, co-op programs and internships. Off campus study. Study abroad program.

Entrance Requirements: Options: electronic application, deferred admission, international baccalaureate accepted. Required: essay, high school transcript, minimum 2.5 high school GPA, interview, SAT or ACT. Required for some: 1 recommendation, ACT Composite score of 19 or combined SAT score of 980. Entrance: moderately difficult. Application deadline: rolling. Notification: continuous. SAT Reasoning Test deadline: 8/1. SAT Subject Test deadline: 8/1. Transfer credits accepted: Yes.

Costs Per Year: Application fee: $0. One-time mandatory fee: $225. Comprehensive fee: $40,900 includes full-time tuition ($30,700), mandatory fees ($250), and college room and board ($9950). Part-time tuition: $992 per credit hour.

Collegiate Environment: Orientation program. Drama-theater group, choral group, student-run newspaper. Social organizations: 15 open to all. Most popular organizations: Student Association, Student ministries, Campus newspaper, Pro-Life Task Force, PACE (prison tutoring program). Major annual events: OPUS, Trollstock Talent Show, Fall Festival. Student services: personal-psychological counseling. Campus security: 24-hour emergency response devices and patrols, student patrols, late night transport-escort service, controlled dormitory access, security cameras, Code Blue Emergency Phones. 633 college housing spaces available; 507 were occupied in 2018-19. Freshmen guaranteed college housing. Option: coed housing available. Jennie Huizenga Memorial Library plus 1 other. Books: 60,951 (physical), 6,449 (digital/electronic); Serial titles: 20 (physical), 45,797 (digital/electronic); Databases: 61. Weekly public service hours: 84; students can reserve study rooms. Operations spending for the previous fiscal year: $389,255. 170 computers available on campus for general student use. A campuswide network can be accessed from student residence rooms. Students can access the following: online class registration. Staffed computer lab on campus provides training in use of computers, software, and the Internet.

Community Environment: Palos Heights is residential area located 25 miles from downtown Chicago.

■ **TRINITY COLLEGE OF NURSING AND HEALTH SCIENCES**

2122 25th Ave.

Rock Island, IL 61201

Tel: (309)779-7700

Fax: (309)779-7796

E-mail: perezlj@ihs.org

Web Site: www.trinitycollegeqc.edu

Description: Independent, 4-year, coed. Administratively affiliated with Trinity Medical Center. Awards associate and bachelor's degrees (general education requirements are taken off campus, usually at Black Hawk College, Eastern Iowa Community College District and Western Illinois University). Founded 1994. Setting: 2-acre urban campus. Endowment: $1.3 million. Educational spending for the previous fiscal year: $13,341 per student. Total enrollment: 232. Faculty: 26 (16 full-time, 10 part-time). Student-undergrad faculty ratio is 9:1. 4 applied, 50% were admitted. Full-time: 119 students, 93% women, 7% men. Part-time: 113 students, 91%

women, 9% men. 46% from out-of-state. 5% Hispanic/Latino; 4% Black or African American, non-Hispanic/Latino; 2% Asian, non-Hispanic/Latino; 0.4% Native Hawaiian or other Pacific Islander, non-Hispanic/Latino. 56% 25 or older, 17% transferred in. Retention: 100% of full-time freshmen returned the following year. Calendar: semesters. Services for LD students, advanced placement, accelerated degree program, independent study, distance learning, summer session for credit, part-time degree program, adult/continuing education programs, internships. Off campus study. Study abroad program.

Entrance Requirements: Options: electronic application, early admission, early decision. Required: minimum 2.5 high school GPA. Required for some: essay, high school transcript, minimum 3 high school GPA, interview, SAT or ACT. Entrance: moderately difficult. Application deadlines: rolling, 12/1 for early decision. Notification: continuous until 2/1, 12/15 for early decision. Transfer credits accepted: Yes. Applicants placed on waiting list: 33. Waitlisted applicants offered admission: 13. Early decision applicants admitted: 14.

Collegiate Environment: Orientation program. Social organizations: 3 open to all. Most popular organizations: Student Government Association, Phi Theta Kappa, BSN Honor Society. Major annual events: Alumni Weekend, Graduation, Orientation. Student services: personal-psychological counseling. Campus security: 24-hour emergency response devices. Trinity Medical Center Library - Rock Island Campus. Operations spending for the previous fiscal year: $377,031. 20 computers available on campus for general student use. A campuswide network can be accessed from off-campus.

■ **TRINITY INTERNATIONAL UNIVERSITY**

2065 Half Day Rd.

Deerfield, IL 60015-1284

Tel: (847)945-8800; Free: 800-822-3225

Fax: (847)317-7081

E-mail: tcadmissions@tiu.edu

Web Site: www.tiu.edu

Description: Independent, university, coed, affiliated with Evangelical Free Church of America. Administratively affiliated with Evangelical Free Church of America. Awards bachelor's, master's, and doctoral degrees. Founded 1897. Setting: 108-acre suburban campus with easy access to Chicago. Endowment: $28.7 million. Educational spending for the previous fiscal year: $5205 per student. Total enrollment: 2,671. Faculty: 82 (43 full-time, 39 part-time). Student-undergrad faculty ratio is 12:1. 548 applied, 63% were admitted. 37% from top 10% of their high school class, 43% from top quarter, 68% from top half. 6 valedictorians. Full-time: 841 students, 57% women, 43% men. Part-time: 127 students, 61% women, 39% men. Students come from 38 states and territories, 19 other countries, 41% from out-of-state. 2% 25 or older, 70% live on campus, 8% transferred in. Retention: 66% of full-time freshmen returned the following year. Academic areas with the most degrees conferred: education; business/marketing; theology and religious vocations. Core. Calendar: semesters. Academic remediation for entering students, advanced placement, honors program, independent study, double major, part-time degree program, adult/continuing education programs, internships, graduate courses open to undergrads. Off campus study at 13 members of the Christian College Consortium. Study abroad program.

Entrance Requirements: Options: electronic application, deferred admission, international baccalaureate accepted. Required: essay, high school transcript, minimum 2.5 high school GPA, 1 recommendation, SAT or ACT. Recommended: minimum 3.0 high school GPA. Required for some: interview. Entrance: moderately difficult. Application deadline: rolling. Notification: continuous until 9/1.

Collegiate Environment: Orientation program. Drama-theater group, choral group, student-run newspaper. Social organizations: 15 open to all. Most popular organizations: Student Government, College Union, Trinity Summer Mission, student newspaper, yearbook. Major annual events: Homecoming, Santa Lucia, Parents' Weekend. Student services: health clinic, personal-psychological counseling. Campus security: 24-hour patrols, controlled dormitory access. Rolfing Memorial Library. Operations spending for the previous fiscal year: $1.6 million. 130 computers available on campus for general student use. A campuswide network can be accessed from student residence rooms and from off campus. Students can access the following: online class registration. Staffed computer lab on campus provides training in use of computers, software, and the Internet.

Community Environment: Deerfield, population 19,400, is located 25 miles north of Chicago.

■ **TRITON COLLEGE**

2000 5th Ave.

River Grove, IL 60171

Tel: (708)456-0300
Fax: (708)583-3121
E-mail: mpatrice@triton.edu
Web Site: www.triton.edu
Description: State-supported, 2-year, coed. Part of Illinois Community College Board. Awards certificates, transfer associate, and terminal associate degrees. Founded 1964. Setting: 100-acre suburban campus with easy access to Chicago. Total enrollment: 15,658. Faculty: 644 (123 full-time, 521 part-time). Student-undergrad faculty ratio is 24:1. Full-time: 3,893 students, 51% women, 49% men. Part-time: 11,765 students, 56% women, 44% men. 40% 25 or older. Retention: 56% of full-time freshmen returned the following year. Core. Calendar: semesters. Academic remediation for entering students, ESL program, advanced placement, self-designed majors, freshman honors college, honors program, distance learning, summer session for credit, part-time degree program, adult/continuing education programs, co-op programs and internships.
Entrance Requirements: Open admission except for some allied health programs. Option: deferred admission. Required: high school transcript. Entrance: noncompetitive. Application deadline: rolling. Preference given to district residents.
Collegiate Environment: Orientation program. Drama-theater group, choral group, student-run newspaper, radio station. Social organizations: 34 open to all. Most popular organizations: Student Government, Program Board. Major annual events: Triton Spirit Week, World's Largest Sober Party. Student services: health clinic, personal-psychological counseling. Campus security: 24-hour emergency response devices and patrols. Learning Resource Center. 500 computers available on campus for general student use. A campuswide network can be accessed. Students can access the following: online class registration. Staffed computer lab on campus provides training in use of computers, software, and the Internet.
Community Environment: Triton college district is in the near west suburbs of Chicago. The college is approximately 15 miles from downtown Chicago.

■ **UNIVERSITY OF CHICAGO**
5801 S Ellis Ave.
Chicago, IL 60637-1513
Tel: (773)702-1234
Fax: (773)702-4199
E-mail: collegeadmissions@uchicago.edu
Web Site: www.uchicago.edu
Description: Independent, university, coed. Awards bachelor's, master's, and doctoral degrees. Founded 1890. Setting: 217-acre urban campus with easy access to Chicago. Total enrollment: 14,347. Faculty: 1,720 (1,461 full-time, 259 part-time). Student-undergrad faculty ratio is 5:1. 32,283 applied, 7% were admitted. 99% from top 10% of their high school class, 100% from top quarter, 100% from top half. Full-time: 6,551 students, 49% women, 51% men. Part-time: 1 student, 100% men. Students come from 52 states and territories, 77 other countries, 81% from out-of-state. 0.1% American Indian or Alaska Native, non-Hispanic/Latino; 14% Hispanic/Latino; 5% Black or African American, non-Hispanic/Latino; 19% Asian, non-Hispanic/Latino; 14% international. 55% live on campus, 1% transferred in. Retention: 99% of full-time freshmen returned the following year. Academic areas with the most degrees conferred: social sciences; mathematics and statistics; biological/life sciences. Core. Calendar: quarters. ESL program, services for LD students, advanced placement, accelerated degree program, self-designed majors, independent study, double major, summer session for credit, internships, graduate courses open to undergrads. Off campus study. Study abroad program. ROTC: Army (c), Air Force (c).
Entrance Requirements: Options: electronic application, early admission, early decision, early action, deferred admission, international baccalaureate accepted. Required: essay, high school transcript, 2 recommendations. Entrance: most difficult. Application deadline: 1/1. Notification: 4/1.
Costs Per Year: Application fee: $75. One-time mandatory fee: $1224. Comprehensive fee: $73,356 includes full-time tuition ($55,425), mandatory fees ($1581), and college room and board ($16,350). College room only: $9819. Room and board charges vary according to board plan, housing facility, and student level.
Collegiate Environment: Orientation program. Drama-theater group, choral group, student-run newspaper, radio station. Social organizations: 388 open to all; national fraternities, national sororities, local fraternities. Most popular organizations: University Theatre, Model United Nations, Council on University Programming, South Asian Students Association, Splash. Major annual events: Summer Breeze, Scavenger Hunt, Homecoming. Student services: health clinic, personal-psychological counseling, women's center.

Campus security: 24-hour emergency response devices and patrols, student patrols, late night transport-escort service, controlled dormitory access. 3,532 college housing spaces available; 3,514 were occupied in 2018-19. Freshmen guaranteed college housing. On-campus residence required in freshman year. Option: coed housing available. Joseph Regenstein Library plus 5 others. Students can reserve study rooms.
Community Environment: Chicago, with a population of nearly 3 million and the third largest city in the nation, is a metropolitan area extending along the southern end of Lake Michigan. It is a leading industrial, medical, educational, and cultural center. The University's campus is located in a residential neighborhood along the lake shore fifteen minutes away from the central downtown area. Cultural facilities include museums that cover a wide variety of fields, art galleries, research libraries, public libraries, theaters, opera, and a symphony orchestra. Numerous recreational activities and points of interest exist.

■ **UNIVERSITY OF ILLINOIS AT CHICAGO**
601 S Morgan St.
Chicago, IL 60607-7128
Tel: (312)996-7000
E-mail: uic.admit@uic.edu
Web Site: www.uic.edu
Description: State-supported, university, coed. Part of University of Illinois System. Awards bachelor's, master's, and doctoral degrees and post-master's certificates. Founded 1946. Setting: 240-acre urban campus with easy access to Chicago. Endowment: $321.6 million. Research spending for the previous fiscal year: $259.3 million. Educational spending for the previous fiscal year: $21,342 per student. Total enrollment: 30,538. Faculty: 1,613 (1,200 full-time, 413 part-time). Student-undergrad faculty ratio is 17:1. 18,768 applied, 77% were admitted. 25% from top 10% of their high school class, 58% from top quarter, 89% from top half. Full-time: 17,961 students, 51% women, 49% men. Part-time: 1,486 students, 44% women, 56% men. Students come from 65 other countries, 3% from out-of-state. 0.1% American Indian or Alaska Native, non-Hispanic/Latino; 33% Hispanic/Latino; 8% Black or African American, non-Hispanic/Latino; 22% Asian, non-Hispanic/Latino; 0.1% Native Hawaiian or other Pacific Islander, non-Hispanic/Latino; 4% international. 10% 25 or older, 15% live on campus, 11% transferred in. Retention: 80% of full-time freshmen returned the following year. Academic areas with the most degrees conferred: business/marketing; biological/life sciences; engineering; psychology. Core. Calendar: semesters. Academic remediation for entering students, services for LD students, advanced placement, accelerated degree program, self-designed majors, freshman honors college, honors program, independent study, distance learning, double major, summer session for credit, part-time degree program, co-op programs and internships, graduate courses open to undergrads. Off campus study. Study abroad program. ROTC: Army, Naval (c), Air Force (c).
Entrance Requirements: Options: electronic application, early admission, early action, international baccalaureate accepted. Required: essay, high school transcript, SAT or ACT. Required for some: audition for music and theater majors, portfolio for art majors. Entrance: moderately difficult. Application deadline: 1/15. Notification: continuous until 11/30. SAT Reasoning Test deadline: 2/1. SAT Subject Test deadline: 2/1. Transfer credits accepted: Yes.
Costs Per Year: Application fee: $50. State resident tuition: $10,584 full-time, $394.16 per credit hour part-time. Nonresident tuition: $23,440 full-time, $803.14 per credit hour part-time. Mandatory fees: $3030 full-time. Full-time tuition and fees vary according to degree level and program. Part-time tuition varies according to course load, degree level, and program. College room and board: $10,960. College room only: $7930. Room and board charges vary according to board plan and housing facility. Tuition guaranteed not to increase for student's term of enrollment.
Collegiate Environment: Orientation program. Drama-theater group, choral group, student-run newspaper, radio station. Social organizations: 287 open to all; national fraternities, national sororities, local fraternities, local sororities; 4% of eligible men and 5% of eligible women are members. Most popular organizations: Muslim Student Association, Alternative Spring Break, Filipinos in Alliance, Society of Future Physicians, Ski and Snowboard Club. Major annual events: Involvement Fair, Spark in the Park (annual fall concert), LOL@UIC (annual comedy show). Student services: legal services, health clinic, personal-psychological counseling, women's center. Campus security: 24-hour emergency response devices and patrols, student patrols, late night transport-escort service, controlled dormitory access, housing ID stickers, guest escort policy, 24-hour closed circuit videos for

exits and entrances, security screen for first floor. Richard J. Daley Library plus 2 others. Books: 1.6 million (physical), 617,614 (digital/electronic); Serial titles: 61,000 (digital/electronic); Databases: 100. Weekly public service hours: 140; study areas open 24 hours, 5-7 days a week; students can reserve study rooms. Operations spending for the previous fiscal year: $18.2 million. 1,052 computers available on campus for general student use. Computer purchase/lease plans available. A campuswide network can be accessed from student residence rooms and from off campus. Students can access the following: online class registration. Staffed computer lab on campus (open 24 hours a day) provides training in use of computers, software, and the Internet.

■ **UNIVERSITY OF ILLINOIS AT SPRINGFIELD**
One University Plz.
Springfield, IL 62703-5407
Tel: (217)206-6600; Free: 888-977-4847
Fax: (217)206-7279
E-mail: admissions@uis.edu
Web Site: www.uis.edu
Description: State-supported, comprehensive, coed. Part of University of Illinois System. Awards bachelor's, master's, and doctoral degrees and post-master's certificates. Founded 1969. Setting: 746-acre suburban campus. Endowment: $19.2 million. Total enrollment: 4,575. Faculty: 372 (212 full-time, 160 part-time). Student-undergrad faculty ratio is 13:1. 2,374 applied, 53% were admitted. 24% from top 10% of their high school class, 49% from top quarter, 78% from top half. Full-time: 1,799 students, 53% women, 47% men. Part-time: 1,015 students, 43% women, 57% men. Students come from 47 states and territories, 34 other countries, 12% from out-of-state. 0.2% American Indian or Alaska Native, non-Hispanic/Latino; 9% Hispanic/Latino; 14% Black or African American, non-Hispanic/Latino; 3% Asian, non-Hispanic/Latino; 3% international. 39% 25 or older, 31% live on campus, 17% transferred in. Retention: 77% of full-time freshmen returned the following year. Academic areas with the most degrees conferred: business/marketing; computer and information sciences; psychology. Core. Calendar: semesters. Academic remediation for entering students, ESL program, services for LD students, advanced placement, honors program, independent study, distance learning, summer session for credit, part-time degree program, co-op programs and internships, graduate courses open to undergrads. Off campus study. Study abroad program.
Entrance Requirements: Options: electronic application, deferred admission, international baccalaureate accepted. Required: high school transcript, SAT or ACT. Recommended: SAT and SAT Subject Tests or ACT. Entrance: moderately difficult. Application deadline: rolling. Transfer credits accepted: Yes.
Costs Per Year: Application fee: $50. State resident tuition: $9405 full-time, $313.50 per credit hour part-time. Nonresident tuition: $18,930 full-time, $631 per credit hour part-time. Mandatory fees: $2408 full-time. College room and board: $11,660. College room only: $7460.
Collegiate Environment: Orientation program. Drama-theater group, choral group, student-run newspaper, radio station. Social organizations: 86 open to all; national fraternities, national sororities. Most popular organizations: Christian Student Fellowship, Sigma Sigma Sigma, Delta Kappa Epsilon, International Student Organization, Alternative Spring Break. Major annual events: First Week, Homecoming, Spring Fest. Student services: health clinic, personal-psychological counseling, women's center. Campus security: 24-hour emergency response devices and patrols, late night transport-escort service, controlled dormitory access. 1,200 college housing spaces available; 844 were occupied in 2018-19. Freshmen guaranteed college housing. On-campus residence required in freshman year. Option: coed housing available. Norris L Brookens Library plus 1 other. Books: 352,668 (physical), 215,723 (digital/electronic); Serial titles: 9,513 (physical), 14,928 (digital/electronic); Databases: 176. Weekly public service hours: 90; students can reserve study rooms. 560 computers available on campus for general student use. A campuswide network can be accessed from student residence rooms and from off campus. Students can access the following: online class registration. Staffed computer lab on campus provides training in use of computers, software, and the Internet.

■ **UNIVERSITY OF ILLINOIS AT URBANA-CHAMPAIGN**
601 E John St.
Champaign, IL 61820
Tel: (217)333-1000
Fax: (217)244-7278
E-mail: ugradadmissions@uiuc.edu

Web Site: www.illinois.edu
Description: State-supported, university, coed. Part of University of Illinois System. Awards bachelor's, master's, and doctoral degrees and post-master's certificates. Founded 1867. Setting: 1,783-acre urban campus. Total enrollment: 44,942. Student-undergrad faculty ratio is 18:1. 33,203 applied, 62% were admitted. 55% from top 10% of their high school class, 87% from top quarter, 99% from top half. Full-time: 31,516 students, 44% women, 56% men. Part-time: 1,179 students, 35% women, 65% men. Students come from 52 states and territories, 119 other countries, 10% from out-of-state. 0.1% American Indian or Alaska Native, non-Hispanic/Latino; 8% Hispanic/Latino; 5% Black or African American, non-Hispanic/Latino; 15% Asian, non-Hispanic/Latino; 0.1% Native Hawaiian or other Pacific Islander, non-Hispanic/Latino; 15% international, 1% 25 or older, 50% live on campus, 4% transferred in. Retention: 93% of full-time freshmen returned the following year. Academic areas with the most degrees conferred: engineering; business/marketing; communication/journalism. Core. Calendar: semesters. Academic remediation for entering students, ESL program, services for LD students, advanced placement, accelerated degree program, self-designed majors, honors program, independent study, distance learning, double major, summer session for credit, co-op programs and internships, graduate courses open to undergrads. Off campus study at members of the Committee on Institutional Cooperation, Midwest Universities Consortium for International Activities. Study abroad program. ROTC: Army, Naval, Air Force.
Entrance Requirements: Options: electronic application, early admission, deferred admission, international baccalaureate accepted. Required: essay, high school transcript, SAT or ACT. Required for some: audition or portfolio. Entrance: very difficult. Application deadline: 1/2. Notification: 2/15. SAT Reasoning Test deadline: 12/30. Transfer credits accepted: Yes. Applicants placed on waiting list: 1,535. Wait-listed applicants offered admission: 0.
Collegiate Environment: Orientation program. Drama-theater group, choral group, marching band, student-run newspaper, radio station. Social organizations: 1,000 open to all; national fraternities, national sororities, local fraternities, local sororities; 21% of eligible men and 21% of eligible women are members. Most popular organizations: Volunteer Illini Project, October Lovers, Illini Pride Student Board, National Society of Collegiate Scholars, Phi Eta Sigma Freshman Honor Society. Major annual events: Homecoming, Moms' Weekend/Dads' Weekend, Quad Day. Student services: legal services, health clinic, personal-psychological counseling, women's center. Campus security: 24-hour emergency response devices and patrols, student patrols, late night transport-escort service, controlled dormitory access, safety training classes, ID cards with safety numbers. University Library plus 20 others.

■ **UNIVERSITY OF ST. FRANCIS**
500 Wilcox St.
Joliet, IL 60435-6169
Tel: (815)740-3400; Free: 800-735-7500
Fax: (815)740-4285
E-mail: eruiz@stfrancis.edu
Web Site: www.stfrancis.edu
Description: Independent Roman Catholic, comprehensive, coed. Awards bachelor's, master's, and doctoral degrees and post-master's certificates. Founded 1920. Setting: 18-acre suburban campus with easy access to Chicago. Endowment: $16.5 million. Research spending for the previous fiscal year: $50,764. Educational spending for the previous fiscal year: $5563 per student. Total enrollment: 2,479. Faculty: 266 (95 full-time, 171 part-time). Student-undergrad faculty ratio is 12:1. 1,560 applied, 52% were admitted. 12% from top 10% of their high school class, 41% from top quarter, 74% from top half. Full-time: 1,273 students, 62% women, 38% men. Part-time: 98 students, 71% women, 29% men. Students come from 20 states and territories, 7 other countries, 5% from out-of-state. 0.3% American Indian or Alaska Native, non-Hispanic/Latino; 22% Hispanic/Latino; 8% Black or African American, non-Hispanic/Latino; 2% Asian, non-Hispanic/Latino; 0.2% Native Hawaiian or other Pacific Islander, non-Hispanic/Latino; 4% international. 13% 25 or older, 25% live on campus, 13% transferred in. Retention: 80% of full-time freshmen returned the following year. Academic areas with the most degrees conferred: health professions and related sciences; business/marketing; education. Core. Calendar: semesters. Academic remediation for entering students, ESL program, services for LD students, advanced placement, accelerated degree program, self-designed majors, honors program, independent study, distance learning, double major, summer session for credit, part-time degree program, adult/continuing education programs, internships, graduate courses open to undergrads. Off campus study. Study abroad program. ROTC: Army (c).

Entrance Requirements: Options: electronic application, deferred admission, international baccalaureate accepted. Required: high school transcript, minimum 2.5 high school GPA, SAT or ACT. Required for some: essay, 2 recommendations, interview. Entrance: moderately difficult. Application deadline: 8/1. Notification: continuous. SAT Reasoning Test deadline: 8/1. Transfer credits accepted: Yes.

Costs Per Year: Application fee: $0. Comprehensive fee: $42,250 includes full-time tuition ($32,000), mandatory fees ($320), and college room and board ($9930). Full-time tuition and fees vary according to degree level, location, and program. Room and board charges vary according to housing facility. Part-time tuition: $825 per credit hour. Part-time mandatory fees: $75 per term. Part-time tuition and fees vary according to degree level and program.

Collegiate Environment: Orientation program. Drama-theater group, choral group, student-run newspaper, radio station. Social organizations: 65 open to all; national sororities; 1% of eligible men and 2% of eligible women are members. Most popular organizations: Student Nurses Association, Student Business Association, Justice League, Student Athletic Advisory Committee, Unidos Vamos a Alcanzar (UVA). Major annual events: Homecoming Competition, Glow Paint Party, Outdoor Activities. Student services: health clinic, personal-psychological counseling. Campus security: 24-hour emergency response devices and patrols, student patrols, late night transport-escort service, controlled dormitory access, First Response trained security personnel. Brown Library. Books: 113,077 (physical), 4,118 (digital/electronic); Serial titles: 605 (physical), 113 (digital/electronic); Databases: 76. Weekly public service hours: 74; students can reserve study rooms. Operations spending for the previous fiscal year: $832,841. 560 computers available on campus for general student use. A campuswide network can be accessed from student residence rooms and from off campus. Students can access the following: online class registration, billing/payment. Staffed computer lab on campus.

■ **VANDERCOOK COLLEGE OF MUSIC**
3140 S Federal St.
Chicago, IL 60616-3731
Tel: (312)225-6288
Fax: (312)225-5211
E-mail: admissions@vandercook.edu
Web Site: www.vandercook.edu

Description: Independent, comprehensive, coed. Awards bachelor's and master's degrees. Founded 1909. Setting: 1-acre urban campus with easy access to Chicago. Endowment: $514,572. Total enrollment: 262. Faculty: 37 (13 full-time, 24 part-time). Student-undergrad faculty ratio is 3:1. 38 applied, 100% were admitted. 100% from top half of their high school class. Full-time: 88 students, 47% women, 53% men. Part-time: 34 students, 38% women, 62% men. Students come from 12 states and territories, 2 other countries, 20% from out-of-state. 24% Hispanic/Latino; 3% Black or African American, non-Hispanic/Latino; 1% Native Hawaiian or other Pacific Islander, non-Hispanic/Latino; 2% international. 7% 25 or older, 18% live on campus, 2% transferred in. Retention: 73% of full-time freshmen returned the following year. Academic area with the most degrees conferred: education. Core. Calendar: semesters. Academic remediation for entering students, advanced placement, independent study.

Entrance Requirements: Options: electronic application, early admission, international baccalaureate accepted. Required: essay, high school transcript, 3 recommendations, interview, audition on the applicant's primary instrument or voice, SAT or ACT. Recommended: minimum 3 high school GPA. Required for some: minimum 3 high school GPA. Entrance: moderately difficult. Notification: continuous, continuous for nonresidents. Transfer credits accepted: Yes.

Costs Per Year: Application fee: $35. Comprehensive fee: $40,508 includes full-time tuition ($26,548), mandatory fees ($1886), and college room and board ($12,074). College room only: $6150. Full-time tuition and fees vary according to course level, course load, and program. Part-time tuition: $1115 per semester hour. Part-time tuition varies according to course level, course load, and program.

Collegiate Environment: Orientation program. Choral group, student-run radio station. Social organizations: 4 open to all; national fraternities, national sororities, local fraternities, local sororities. Most popular organizations: NAfME (National Association for Music Education), ACDA (American Choral Directors Association), NBA (National Band Association), ASTA (American String Teachers Association). Major annual events: Prism Concert, A Night of the Pops Benefit Concert, The Midwest Clinic (Symphonic Band only). Student services: health clinic, personal-

psychological counseling. Campus security: 24-hour emergency response devices and patrols, late night transport-escort service, controlled dormitory access. Harry Ruppel Memorial Library plus 1 other. Books: 16,985 (physical), 6,827 (digital/electronic); Serial titles: 200 (physical), 100 (digital/electronic); Databases: 28. Weekly public service hours: 54; students can reserve study rooms. Operations spending for the previous fiscal year: $28,464. 21 computers available on campus for general student use. A campuswide network can be accessed from student residence rooms and from off campus. Students can access the following: Dedicated WiFi network. Staffed computer lab on campus provides training in use of computers, software, and the Internet.

Community Environment: Urban.

■ **VET TECH INSTITUTE AT FOX COLLEGE**
18020 S Oak Park Ave.
Tinley Park, IL 60477
Tel: (708)444-4500; Free: 888-884-3694
Web Site: chicago.vettechinstitute.edu

Description: Private, 2-year, coed. Awards terminal associate degrees. Founded 2006. Setting: suburban campus. Total enrollment: 164. 349 applied, 65% were admitted. Calendar: semesters. Accelerated degree program, internships.

■ **WAUBONSEE COMMUNITY COLLEGE**
Rte. 47 at Waubonsee Dr.
Sugar Grove, IL 60554-9799
Tel: (630)466-7900
Fax: (630)466-4964
E-mail: admissions@waubonsee.edu
Web Site: www.waubonsee.edu

Description: District-supported, 2-year, coed. Part of Illinois Community College Board. Awards certificates, transfer associate, and terminal associate degrees. Founded 1966. Setting: 243-acre small town campus with easy access to Chicago. Total enrollment: 10,721. 2,431 applied, 100% were admitted. Full-time: 3,469 students, 49% women, 51% men. Part-time: 7,252 students, 59% women, 41% men. 0.1% American Indian or Alaska Native, non-Hispanic/Latino; 33% Hispanic/Latino; 7% Black or African American, non-Hispanic/Latino; 3% Asian, non-Hispanic/Latino; 0.1% Native Hawaiian or other Pacific Islander, non-Hispanic/Latino. Calendar: semesters. Academic remediation for entering students, ESL program, services for LD students, advanced placement, accelerated degree program, honors program, independent study, distance learning, summer session for credit, part-time degree program, internships. Off campus study at Emergency Medical Technician/Paramedic A.A.S. Program is based at Delnor Community Hospital in Geneva, IL is offered as a collaboration with the Southern Fox Valley Emergency Medical Services System (SFVEMSS) Paramedic Training Program. Study abroad program. ROTC: Army (c).

Entrance Requirements: Open admission except for nursing, interpreter training, auto body, certified nurse assistant programs, medical assistant, health care interpreting, therapeutic massage, phlebotomy, translation. Option: electronic application. Entrance: noncompetitive. Application deadline: rolling. Notification: continuous. Preference given to in-district residents for some health programs. Transfer credits accepted: Yes.

Costs Per Year: Application fee: $0. Area resident tuition: $3840 full-time, $128 per credit hour part-time. State resident tuition: $10,177 full-time, $339.24 per credit hour part-time. Nonresident tuition: $11,056 full-time, $368.52 per credit hour part-time. Mandatory fees: $240 full-time, $8 per credit hour part-time. Full-time tuition and fees vary according to reciprocity agreements. Part-time tuition and fees vary according to reciprocity agreements.

Collegiate Environment: Orientation program. Drama-theater group, choral group. Social organizations: 35 open to all; honor societies. Major annual events: College Night, Club Fair, Cinco de Mayo Celebration/Party Smart. Campus security: 24-hour emergency response devices and patrols, late night transport-escort service. Todd Library plus 3 others. 160 computers available on campus for general student use. A campuswide network can be accessed. Students can access the following: online class registration. Staffed computer lab on campus provides training in use of computers.

Community Environment: See Aurora University.

■ **WESTERN ILLINOIS UNIVERSITY**
1 University Cir.
Macomb, IL 61455-1390
Tel: (309)298-1414; Free: 877-742-5948

Fax: (309)298-3111

Web Site: www.wiu.edu

Description: State-supported, comprehensive, coed. Awards bachelor's, master's, and doctoral degrees and post-master's certificates. Founded 1899. Setting: 1,050-acre small town campus with easy access to Quad Cities; Peoria, IL; Springfield, IL. Endowment: $55.8 million. Research spending for the previous fiscal year: $3.7 million. Total enrollment: 8,294. Faculty: 587 (527 full-time, 60 part-time). Student-undergrad faculty ratio is 14:1. 9,151 applied, 59% were admitted. 11% from top 10% of their high school class, 32% from top quarter, 69% from top half. Full-time: 5,949 students, 52% women, 48% men. Part-time: 805 students, 49% women, 51% men. Students come from 43 states and territories, 61 other countries, 11% from out-of-state. 0.1% American Indian or Alaska Native, non-Hispanic/Latino; 13% Hispanic/Latino; 21% Black or African American, non-Hispanic/Latino; 1% Asian, non-Hispanic/Latino; 1% international. 15% 25 or older, 42% live on campus, 11% transferred in. Retention: 65% of full-time freshmen returned the following year. Academic areas with the most degrees conferred: homeland security, law enforcement, firefighting, and protective services; business/marketing; liberal arts/general studies. Core. Calendar: semesters. Academic remediation for entering students, ESL program, services for LD students, advanced placement, self-designed majors, freshman honors college, honors program, independent study, distance learning, double major, summer session for credit, part-time degree program, external degree program, adult/continuing education programs, internships, graduate courses open to undergrads. Off campus study at Western Illinois Education Consortium WIU currently has consortium agreements with the following community colleges: Black Hawk Community College Eastern Iowa Community College District (EICCD): Scott Community College Clinton Community College Muscatine Community College. Study abroad program. ROTC: Army.

Entrance Requirements: Options: electronic application, deferred admission. Required: high school transcript, minimum 2.5 high school GPA, SAT or ACT. Entrance: moderately difficult. Application deadlines: rolling, rolling for nonresidents. Notification: continuous, continuous for nonresidents. SAT Reasoning Test deadline: 5/15. Transfer credits accepted: Yes.

Costs Per Year: Application fee: $30. One-time mandatory fee: $200. State resident tuition: $8541 full-time, $284.70 per credit hour part-time. Nonresident tuition: $8541 full-time, $284.70 per credit hour part-time. Mandatory fees: $2726 full-time, $90.85 per credit hour part-time. Full-time tuition and fees vary according to course load, location, and student level. Part-time tuition and fees vary according to course load, location, and student level. College room and board: $9630. College room only: $5880. Room and board charges vary according to board plan, housing facility, and student level. Student Health Insurance $1684/year for students with 9 or more credit hours. Can be waived. Tuition guaranteed not to increase for student's term of enrollment.

Collegiate Environment: Orientation program. Drama-theater group, choral group, marching band, student-run newspaper, radio station. Social organizations: 274 open to all; national fraternities, national sororities, local fraternities, local sororities; 19% of eligible men and 15% of eligible women are members. Most popular organizations: Student Government Association, Black Student Association, University Union Board, Western's All Volunteer Effort (WAVE), Inter Hall Council. Major annual events: Family Weekend, Homecoming, Rocky After Dark/First Night. Student services: legal services, health clinic, personal-psychological counseling, women's center. Campus security: 24-hour emergency response devices and patrols, student patrols, late night transport-escort service, controlled dormitory access. 4,400 college housing spaces available; 2,675 were occupied in 2018-19. Freshmen guaranteed college housing. On-campus residence required through sophomore year. Options: coed, men-only, women-only housing available. Leslie Malpass Library plus 4 others. Books: 765,987 (physical), 149,419 (digital/electronic); Serial titles: 154,171 (physical), 77,503 (digital/electronic); Databases: 116. 632 computers available on campus for general student use. A campuswide network can be accessed from student residence rooms and from off campus. Students can access the following: online class registration. Staffed computer lab on campus (open 24 hours a day) provides training in use of computers, software, and the Internet.

Community Environment: Macomb is located 240 miles southwest of Chicago and 150 miles north of St. Louis on the main line of the Burlington Railroad. Besides agriculture, Macomb's industries produce ball bearings, plastic bags, porcelain insulators, and pottery. This is a friendly, Midwest community balanced by the youthfulness and creativity of the rapidly expanding university. The community facilities include a hospital, library, hotels, motels, and many clubs and organizations in the city. Recreational facilities include a swimming pool, bowling alleys, parks, and movie theaters.

■ **WHEATON COLLEGE**

501 College Ave.

Wheaton, IL 60187-5593

Tel: (630)752-5000; Free: 800-222-2419

Fax: (630)752-5285

E-mail: admissions@wheaton.edu

Web Site: www.wheaton.edu

Description: Independent nondenominational, comprehensive, coed. Awards bachelor's, master's, and doctoral degrees. Founded 1860. Setting: 80-acre suburban campus with easy access to Chicago. Endowment: $489.1 million. Research spending for the previous fiscal year: $1.8 million. Educational spending for the previous fiscal year: $15,601 per student. Total enrollment: 2,944. Faculty: 352 (222 full-time, 130 part-time). Student-undergrad faculty ratio is 11:1. 1,850 applied, 83% were admitted. 45% from top 10% of their high school class, 77% from top quarter, 94% from top half. 12 National Merit Scholars. Full-time: 2,326 students, 55% women, 45% men. Part-time: 75 students, 45% women, 55% men. Students come from 51 states and territories, 43 other countries, 73% from out-of-state. 0.1% American Indian or Alaska Native, non-Hispanic/Latino; 6% Hispanic/Latino; 3% Black or African American, non-Hispanic/Latino; 9% Asian, non-Hispanic/Latino; 3% international. 1% 25 or older, 89% live on campus, 2% transferred in. Retention: 92% of full-time freshmen returned the following year. Academic areas with the most degrees conferred: social sciences; business/marketing; communication/journalism; visual and performing arts. Core. Calendar: semesters. Services for LD students, advanced placement, self-designed majors, independent study, double major, summer session for credit, internships, graduate courses open to undergrads. Off campus study at members of the Christian College Consortium, Council for Christian Colleges and Universities. Study abroad program. ROTC: Army, Air Force (c).

Entrance Requirements: Options: electronic application, early action, deferred admission, international baccalaureate accepted. Required: essay, high school transcript, 2 recommendations, SAT or ACT. Recommended: interview. Entrance: very difficult. Application deadlines: 1/10, 11/1 for early action. Notification: 4/1, 12/31 for early action. Preference given to Christians. SAT Reasoning Test deadline: 1/10. Transfer credits accepted: Yes. Applicants placed on waiting list: 257. Wait-listed applicants offered admission: 19. Early action applicants: 975. Early action applicants admitted: 806.

Costs Per Year: Application fee: $50. Comprehensive fee: $48,330 includes full-time tuition ($37,700) and college room and board ($10,630). College room only: $6300. Part-time tuition: $1571 per credit hour.

Collegiate Environment: Orientation program. Drama-theater group, choral group, student-run newspaper. Social organizations: 96 open to all. Most popular organizations: Discipleship small groups, intramurals, Club Sports, Christian Service Council, New Student Orientation. Major annual events: Mastodon March, Talent Show, President's Ball. Student services: health clinic, personal-psychological counseling. Campus security: 24-hour emergency response devices and patrols, student patrols, late night transport-escort service, controlled dormitory access. 2,170 college housing spaces available; 2,104 were occupied in 2018-19. Freshmen guaranteed college housing. On-campus residence required through senior year. Options: coed, men-only, women-only housing available. Buswell Memorial Library. Books: 357,263 (physical), 162,503 (digital/electronic); Serial titles: 371 (physical), 6,140 (digital/electronic); Databases: 214. Weekly public service hours: 94; students can reserve study rooms. Operations spending for the previous fiscal year: $3.1 million. 325 computers available on campus for general student use. A campuswide network can be accessed from student residence rooms and from off campus. Students can access the following: online class registration, financial information, degree requirements evaluation. Staffed computer lab on campus provides training in use of software and the Internet.

■ **WORSHAM COLLEGE OF MORTUARY SCIENCE**

495 Northgate Pky.

Wheeling, IL 60090-2646

Tel: (847)808-8444

Fax: (847)808-8493

Web Site: www.worsham.edu

Description: Independent, 2-year, coed. Awards terminal associate degrees. Founded 1911. Total enrollment: 91. Student-undergrad faculty ratio is 21:1. 54% 25 or older. Calendar: quarters.

■ ANCILLA COLLEGE
9601 S Union Rd.
Donaldson, IN 46513
Tel: (574)936-8898; Free: 866-ANCILLA
Fax: (574)935-1773
E-mail: admissions@ancilla.edu
Web Site: www.ancilla.edu
Description: Independent Roman Catholic, 2-year, coed. Awards transfer associate and terminal associate degrees. Founded 1937. Setting: 63-acre rural campus. Endowment: $5.8 million. Educational spending for the previous fiscal year: $5453 per student. Total enrollment: 548. Faculty: 54 (19 full-time, 35 part-time). Student-undergrad faculty ratio is 16:1. 1,125 applied, 69% were admitted. 2% from top 10% of their high school class, 8% from top quarter, 30% from top half. Full-time: 451 students, 51% women, 49% men. Part-time: 97 students, 64% women, 36% men. Students come from 19 states and territories, 7 other countries, 12% from out-of-state. 0.4% American Indian or Alaska Native, non-Hispanic/Latino; 10% Hispanic/Latino; 18% Black or African American, non-Hispanic/Latino; 3% international. 11% 25 or older, 35% live on campus, 11% transferred in. Retention: 41% of full-time freshmen returned the following year. Core. Calendar: semesters. Academic remediation for entering students, services for LD students, advanced placement, self-designed majors, independent study, distance learning, double major, summer session for credit, part-time degree program, adult/continuing education programs, co-op programs and internships.
Entrance Requirements: Open admission. Options: electronic application, international baccalaureate accepted. Required: high school transcript. Entrance: noncompetitive. Application deadline: rolling. Transfer credits accepted: Yes.
Costs Per Year: Application fee: $0. Comprehensive fee: $26,930 includes full-time tuition ($17,100), mandatory fees ($230), and college room and board ($9600). Full-time tuition and fees vary according to course load and program. Part-time tuition: $570 per credit hour. Part-time mandatory fees: $115 per term. Part-time tuition and fees vary according to course load and program.
Collegiate Environment: Orientation program. Social organizations: 12 open to all. Most popular organizations: Student Government Association, Ancilla Student Ambassadors, FFA, Phi Theta Kappa, Leaders for Life. Major annual events: Convocation, Welcome Week, Fall Festival Day. Student services: personal-psychological counseling. Campus security: 24-hour emergency response devices and patrols, late night transport-escort service, controlled dormitory access. Gerald J. Ball Library. Books: 15,692 (physical), 3,767 (digital/electronic); Serial titles: 39 (physical); Databases: 84. Weekly public service hours: 66. Operations spending for the previous fiscal year: $164,060. 100 computers available on campus for general student use. A campuswide network can be accessed from student residence rooms. Students can access the following: network data storage, math lab, tutoring, free academic software. Staffed computer lab on campus provides training in use of computers, software, and the Internet.
Community Environment: Situated in a rural area with a temperate climate.

■ ANDERSON UNIVERSITY
1100 E Fifth St.
Anderson, IN 46012-3495
Tel: (765)649-9071; Free: 800-428-6414
Fax: (765)641-3851
E-mail: info@anderson.edu
Web Site: www.anderson.edu
Description: Independent, comprehensive, coed, affiliated with Church of God. Awards associate, bachelor's, master's, and doctoral degrees. Founded 1917. Setting: 163-acre suburban campus with easy access to Indianapolis. Endowment: $33.7 million. Educational spending for the previous fiscal year: $12,077 per student. Total enrollment: 1,877. Faculty: 252 (105 full-time, 147 part-time). Student-undergrad faculty ratio is 10:1. 2,236 applied, 65% were admitted. 20% from top 10% of their high school class, 50% from top quarter, 74% from top half. 10 valedictorians. Full-time: 1,431 students, 59% women, 41% men. Part-time: 135 students, 60% women, 40% men. Students come from 39 states and territories, 18 other countries, 24% from out-of-state. 1% American Indian or Alaska Native, non-Hispanic/Latino; 2% Hispanic/Latino; 9% Black or African American, non-Hispanic/Latino; 1% Asian, non-Hispanic/Latino; 0.3% Native Hawaiian or other Pacific Islander, non-Hispanic/Latino; 2% international. 8% 25 or older, 65% live on campus, 4% transferred in. Retention: 73% of full-time freshmen returned the following year. Academic areas with the most degrees conferred: business/marketing; education; health professions and related sciences. Core. Calendar: semesters. Academic remediation for entering students, services for LD students, advanced placement, accelerated degree program, self-designed majors, honors program, independent study, distance learning, double major, summer session for credit, part-time degree program, adult/continuing education programs, internships. Off campus study. Study abroad program.
Entrance Requirements: Options: electronic application, deferred admission, international baccalaureate accepted. Required: high school transcript, minimum 2 high school GPA, 2 recommendations, lifestyle statement, SAT or ACT. Recommended: essay. Required for some: interview. Entrance: moderately difficult. Application deadline: 7/1. Notification: 9/1. SAT Reasoning Test deadline: 7/1. Transfer credits accepted: Yes.
Costs Per Year: Application fee: $25. Comprehensive fee: $40,340 includes full-time tuition ($29,950), mandatory fees ($500), and college room and board ($9890). College room only: $6180. Room and board charges vary according to board plan and housing facility. Part-time tuition: $1249 per semester hour. Part-time tuition varies according to course load.
Collegiate Environment: Orientation program. Drama-theater group, choral group, student-run newspaper, radio station. Social organizations: 41 open to all. Most popular organizations: Adult and Continuing Education Students Association, Multicultural Student Union, Campus Ministries. Major annual events: Homecoming, Vision/Revision, Impact Your World Week. Student services: health clinic, personal-psychological counseling. Campus security: 24-hour emergency response devices and patrols, student patrols, late night transport-escort service, controlled dormitory access, 24-hour crime line. Robert A. Nicholson Library. Books: 318,141 (physical), 261,900 (digital/electronic); Serial titles: 7,348 (physical), 53,279 (digital/electronic); Databases: 136. Weekly public service hours: 95; study areas open 24 hours, 5-7 days a week; students can reserve study rooms. Operations spending for the previous fiscal year: $904,893. 300 computers available on campus for general student use. A campuswide network can be accessed from student residence rooms and from off campus. Students can access the following: online class registration, microcomputer software. Staffed computer lab on campus.
Community Environment: Anderson (population 57,500) is located 35 miles northeast of Indianapolis, and is known for the automotive electrical

systems and lighting equipment produced by Delco-Remy Division America. Other industries located here manufacture recreation equipment, files, copper wire, corrugated paper boxes, dairy products and agricultural products. Railroads, buses and airports serve the area. The community has a library, churches, and hospitals. Recreational facilities include five 18-hole golf courses and 17 city parks. Mounds State Park is nearby. Employment opportunities are available.

■ **BALL STATE UNIVERSITY**
2000 W University Ave.
Muncie, IN 47306
Tel: (765)289-1241; Free: 800-482-4BSU
Fax: (765)285-1632
Web Site: www.bsu.edu
Description: State-supported, university, coed. Awards bachelor's, master's, and doctoral degrees and post-master's certificates. Founded 1918. Setting: 1,140-acre suburban campus with easy access to Indianapolis. Endowment: $201.8 million. Research spending for the previous fiscal year: $9.8 million. Educational spending for the previous fiscal year: $10,014 per student. Total enrollment: 22,513. Faculty: 1,291 (1,022 full-time, 269 part-time). Student-undergrad faculty ratio is 17:1. 24,191 applied, 62% were admitted. 18% from top 10% of their high school class, 48% from top quarter, 86% from top half. Full-time: 15,203 students, 59% women, 41% men. Part-time: 1,801 students, 63% women, 37% men. Students come from 44 states and territories, 33 other countries, 15% from out-of-state. 5% Hispanic/Latino; 8% Black or African American, non-Hispanic/Latino; 1% Asian, non-Hispanic/Latino; 0.1% Native Hawaiian or other Pacific Islander, non-Hispanic/Latino; 1% international. 6% 25 or older, 44% live on campus, 5% transferred in. Retention: 79% of full-time freshmen returned the following year. Academic areas with the most degrees conferred: business/marketing; communication/journalism; health professions and related sciences. Core. Calendar: semesters. ESL program, services for LD students, advanced placement, accelerated degree program, self-designed majors, freshman honors college, honors program, independent study, distance learning, double major, summer session for credit, part-time degree program, external degree program, adult/continuing education programs, co-op programs and internships, graduate courses open to undergrads. Study abroad program. ROTC: Army.
Entrance Requirements: Option: electronic application. Required: high school transcript. Required for some: essay, SAT or ACT. SAT Reasoning Test deadline: 8/1. SAT Subject Test deadline: 8/1. Transfer credits accepted: Yes.
Costs Per Year: Application fee: $55. State resident tuition: $9234 full-time, $304 per credit hour part-time. Nonresident tuition: $25,806 full-time, $1023 per credit hour part-time. Mandatory fees: $662 full-time. Full-time tuition and fees vary according to program and reciprocity agreements. Part-time tuition varies according to course load, program, and reciprocity agreements. College room and board: $10,234. Room and board charges vary according to board plan and housing facility.
Collegiate Environment: Orientation program. Drama-theater group, choral group, marching band, student-run newspaper, radio station. Social organizations: 428 open to all; national fraternities, national sororities; 15% of eligible men and 15% of eligible women are members. Most popular organizations: Student Voluntary Services, National Society of Collegiate Scholars, Dance Marathon, Cardinal Catholic, National Society of Leadership and Success. Major annual events: Late Nite Carnival, Homecoming, Dance Mrathon. Student services: legal services, health clinic, personal-psychological counseling, women's center. Campus security: 24-hour emergency response devices and patrols, late night transport-escort service, controlled dormitory access. Bracken Library plus 2 others. Books: 822,983 (physical), 15,244 (digital/electronic); Serial titles: 13,599 (physical), 103,640 (digital/electronic); Databases: 296. Weekly public service hours: 123; students can reserve study rooms. Operations spending for the previous fiscal year: $11.2 million. 578 computers available on campus for general student use. Computer purchase/lease plans available. A campuswide network can be accessed from student residence rooms and from off campus. Students can access the following: online class registration, room reservations, testing and test results, manage and pay tuition, order/buy textbooks, request room repairs, order transcripts, manage meal plan, manage and prepay long distance service, undergraduate degree progress report. Staffed computer lab on campus provides training in use of computers, software, and the Internet.
Community Environment: Muncie is the county seat and the largest city in east-central Indiana. It is located on the White River, 66 miles northeast of Indianapolis. All forms of commercial transportation are available.

■ **BETHEL COLLEGE**
1001 Bethel Cir.
Mishawaka, IN 46545-5591
Tel: (574)259-8511; Free: 800-422-4101
Fax: (574)257-3326
E-mail: admissions@bethelcollege.edu
Web Site: www.bethelcollege.edu
Description: Independent, comprehensive, coed, affiliated with Missionary Church. Awards associate, bachelor's, and master's degrees. Founded 1947. Setting: 80-acre suburban campus. Endowment: $9.3 million. Educational spending for the previous fiscal year: $9414 per student. Total enrollment: 1,513. Faculty: 183 (67 full-time, 116 part-time). Student-undergrad faculty ratio is 12:1. 1,065 applied, 90% were admitted. 14% from top 10% of their high school class, 41% from top quarter, 72% from top half. 2 valedictorians. Full-time: 1,033 students, 60% women, 40% men. Part-time: 261 students, 76% women, 24% men. Students come from 29 states and territories, 15 other countries, 27% from out-of-state. 0.1% American Indian or Alaska Native, non-Hispanic/Latino; 8% Hispanic/Latino; 10% Black or African American, non-Hispanic/Latino; 2% Asian, non-Hispanic/Latino; 2% international. 26% 25 or older, 52% live on campus, 10% transferred in. Retention: 78% of full-time freshmen returned the following year. Academic areas with the most degrees conferred: business/marketing; health professions and related sciences; education. Core. Calendar: semesters. Academic remediation for entering students, services for LD students, advanced placement, accelerated degree program, self-designed majors, honors program, independent study, distance learning, double major, summer session for credit, part-time degree program, external degree program, adult/continuing education programs, internships, graduate courses open to undergrads. Off campus study at Northern Indiana Consortium for Education, Council for Christian Colleges and Universities. Study abroad program. ROTC: Army (c), Air Force (c).
Entrance Requirements: Options: electronic application, early admission, deferred admission, international baccalaureate accepted. Required: high school transcript, minimum 2 high school GPA, SAT or ACT. Recommended: essay, minimum 2.5 high school GPA, interview. Entrance: minimally difficult. Application deadline: 8/15. Notification: continuous. SAT Reasoning Test deadline: 8/15. SAT Subject Test deadline: 8/15. Transfer credits accepted: Yes.
Costs Per Year: Application fee: $0. Comprehensive fee: $37,590 includes full-time tuition ($28,140), mandatory fees ($450), and college room and board ($9000). College room only: $4280. Full-time tuition and fees vary according to program. Room and board charges vary according to board plan and housing facility. Part-time tuition: $895 per credit hour. Part-time mandatory fees: $250 per year. Part-time tuition and fees vary according to course load and program.
Collegiate Environment: Orientation program. Drama-theater group, choral group, student-run newspaper, radio station. Social organizations: 11 open to all. Most popular organizations: Student Government, Psychology Club, America Sign Language Club. Major annual events: Community Service Day, Midnight Breakfast, Spiritual Emphasis Weeks. Student services: health clinic, personal-psychological counseling. Campus security: 24-hour emergency response devices and patrols, late night transport-escort service, controlled dormitory access. Otis and Elizabeth Bowen Library. Books: 80,904 (physical), 174,107 (digital/electronic); Serial titles: 473 (physical), 58,644 (digital/electronic); Databases: 89. Weekly public service hours: 79. Operations spending for the previous fiscal year: $440,000. 160 computers available on campus for general student use. A campuswide network can be accessed from student residence rooms. Staffed computer lab on campus provides training in use of computers, software, and the Internet.

■ **BUTLER UNIVERSITY**
4600 Sunset Ave.
Indianapolis, IN 46208-3485
Tel: (317)940-8000; Free: 888-940-8100
Fax: (317)940-8150
E-mail: admission@butler.edu
Web Site: www.butler.edu
Description: Independent, comprehensive, coed. Awards bachelor's, master's, and doctoral degrees. Founded 1855. Setting: 295-acre suburban campus with easy access to Indianapolis. Endowment: $216.1 million. Research spending for the previous fiscal year: $948,000. Educational spending for the previous fiscal year: $14,249 per student. Total enrollment: 5,506. Faculty: 595 (377 full-time, 218 part-time). Student-undergrad faculty ratio is 11:1. 16,418 applied, 68% were admitted. 45% from top 10% of their

high school class, 76% from top quarter, 96% from top half. 5 National Merit Scholars, 83 valedictorians. Full-time: 4,520 students, 59% women, 41% men. Part-time: 178 students, 70% women, 30% men. Students come from 48 states and territories, 42 other countries, 55% from out-of-state. 0.2% American Indian or Alaska Native, non-Hispanic/Latino; 4% Hispanic/Latino; 4% Black or African American, non-Hispanic/Latino; 3% Asian, non-Hispanic/Latino; 1% international. 2% 25 or older, 67% live on campus, 2% transferred in. Retention: 89% of full-time freshmen returned the following year. Academic areas with the most degrees conferred: business/marketing; education; communication/journalism. Core. Calendar: semesters. Services for LD students, advanced placement, accelerated degree program, self-designed majors, honors program, independent study, distance learning, double major, summer session for credit, co-op programs and internships, graduate courses open to undergrads. Off campus study at Butler is a member of the Consortium for Urban Education in the Indianapolis area. Participants in addition to Butler University include: Franklin College, Marian College, IUPUI, Martin University, Ivy Tech State College, and University of Indianapolis. Butler University also participates in an exchange program with partner universities and also in the International Student Exchange Program network. Study abroad program. ROTC: Army (c), Air Force (c).

Entrance Requirements: Options: electronic application, early action, deferred admission, international baccalaureate accepted. Required: SAT or ACT. Entrance: moderately difficult. Application deadline: 2/1. Notification: continuous. Transfer credits accepted: Yes. Applicants placed on waiting list: 313. Wait-listed applicants offered admission: 3. Early action applicants: 11,149. Early action applicants admitted: 9,546.

Costs Per Year: Application fee: $0. Comprehensive fee: $57,900 includes full-time tuition ($41,370), mandatory fees ($990), and college room and board ($15,540). College room only: $8300. Part-time tuition: $1720 per credit hour.

Collegiate Environment: Orientation program. Drama-theater group, choral group, marching band, student-run newspaper, radio station. Social organizations: 128 open to all; national fraternities, national sororities; 12% of eligible men and 28% of eligible women are members. Most popular organizations: Pre-Pharmacy Club, American Chemical Society Students Affiliate, Answers for Autism (Butler University Chapter), Delta Delta Delta, Kappa Psi Pharmaceutical Fraternity. Major annual events: Homecoming, Butler University Dance Marathon, Spring Sports Spectacular. Student services: health clinic, personal-psychological counseling. Campus security: 24-hour emergency response devices and patrols, late night transport-escort service, controlled dormitory access. 3,307 undergraduates lived in college housing during 2018-19. Freshmen guaranteed college housing. On-campus residence required through junior year. Options: coed, women-only housing available. Irwin Library plus 2 others. Books: 195,698 (physical), 821,771 (digital/electronic); Serial titles: 13,168 (physical), 99,038 (digital/electronic); Databases: 323. Weekly public service hours: 106; students can reserve study rooms. Operations spending for the previous fiscal year: $3.7 million. 490 computers available on campus for general student use. Computer purchase/lease plans available. A campuswide network can be accessed from student residence rooms and from off campus. Students can access the following: online class registration. Staffed computer lab on campus (open 24 hours a day) provides training in use of computers, software, and the Internet.

Community Environment: Indianapolis is the capital city, located in the exact center of the state, enjoying a fine climate. All modes of transportation are available. Excellent city facilities include a library with 21 branches, a museum, churches of all denominations, and 17 hospitals. Recreational facilities consist of 32 parks and eight golf courses with additional facilities for auto races, boating, baseball, basketball, football, riding, swimming, roller skating, boxing, wrestling, and ice skating.

■ **CALUMET COLLEGE OF SAINT JOSEPH**
2400 New York Ave.
Whiting, IN 46394-2195
Tel: (219)473-7770; Free: 877-700-9100
Fax: (219)473-4259
E-mail: admissions@ccsj.edu
Web Site: www.ccsj.edu
Description: Independent Roman Catholic, comprehensive, coed. Awards associate, bachelor's, and master's degrees. Founded 1951. Setting: 25-acre urban campus with easy access to Chicago. Endowment: $4.3 million. Total enrollment: 772. Faculty: 85 (28 full-time, 57 part-time). Student-undergrad faculty ratio is 10:1. 655 applied, 22% were admitted. 1% from top 10% of their high school class, 9% from top quarter, 46% from top half. Full-

time: 285 students, 45% women, 55% men. Part-time: 299 students, 39% women, 61% men. Students come from 15 states and territories, 15 other countries, 50% from out-of-state. 0.2% American Indian or Alaska Native, non-Hispanic/Latino; 25% Hispanic/Latino; 21% Black or African American, non-Hispanic/Latino; 0.9% Asian, non-Hispanic/Latino; 0.2% Native Hawaiian or other Pacific Islander, non-Hispanic/Latino. 34% 25 or older, 3% transferred in. Retention: 54% of full-time freshmen returned the following year. Academic areas with the most degrees conferred: homeland security, law enforcement, firefighting, and protective services; business/marketing; interdisciplinary studies. Core. Calendar: semesters. Academic remediation for entering students, services for LD students, advanced placement, accelerated degree program, honors program, independent study, distance learning, double major, summer session for credit, part-time degree program, external degree program, adult/continuing education programs, co-op programs and internships.

Entrance Requirements: Open admission. Options: electronic application, deferred admission, international baccalaureate accepted. Required: high school transcript, ACCUPLACER. Recommended: minimum 2 high school GPA, interview, SAT or ACT. Required for some: essay, 1 recommendation. Entrance: noncompetitive. Application deadline: rolling. Notification: continuous. SAT Reasoning Test deadline: 9/1. Transfer credits accepted: Yes.

Costs Per Year: Application fee: $0. Tuition: $19,400 full-time, $620 per credit hour part-time. Mandatory fees: $970 full-time, $135 per term part-time. Tuition guaranteed not to increase for student's term of enrollment.

Collegiate Environment: Orientation program. Drama-theater group, student-run newspaper. Social organizations: 11 open to all; local fraternities, city-wide national Greek letter sororities. Most popular organizations: Student Government, Los Amigos Hispanic Club, Criminal Justice Club, Drama Club, GIVE. Major annual events: Welcome Back Week, Homecoming, Spirit Week. Student services: personal-psychological counseling. College housing not available. Mary Gorman Specker Memorial Library. Books: 10,000 (physical), 7,128 (digital/electronic); Serial titles: 2 (physical); Databases: 62. Weekly public service hours: 59. Operations spending for the previous fiscal year: $175,488. 241 computers available on campus for general student use. A campuswide network can be accessed.

Community Environment: Hammond-Whiting, facing Lake Michigan, is one of the greatest industrial regions in the world. Industries produce pig iron, rolled, forged and casted steel products, petroleum, lead and aluminum products, chemicals, railroad freight cars and building materials. Part-time employment is available.

■ **CHAMBERLAIN COLLEGE OF NURSING**
9100 Keystone Crossing
Indianapolis, IN 46240
Tel: (317)816-7335; Free: 877-751-5783
Fax: (317)815-3066
Web Site: www.chamberlain.edu
Description: Proprietary, 4-year, coed. Awards bachelor's degrees. Total enrollment: 265. Faculty: 28 (7 full-time, 21 part-time). Student-undergrad faculty ratio is 10:1. Full-time: 83 students, 92% women, 8% men. Part-time: 182 students, 92% women, 8% men. 2% from out-of-state. 5% Hispanic/Latino; 28% Black or African American, non-Hispanic/Latino; 2% Asian, non-Hispanic/Latino. 64% 25 or older, 32% transferred in. Academic area with the most degrees conferred: health professions and related sciences. Accelerated degree program, distance learning.
Entrance Requirements: Option: deferred admission. Required: SAT or ACT. Application deadline: rolling. Notification: continuous.

■ **COLLEGE OF COURT REPORTING**
455 W Lincolnway
Valparaiso, IN 46385
Tel: (219)942-1459; Free: 866-294-3974
Fax: (219)942-1631
E-mail: nrodriquez@ccr.edu
Web Site: www.ccr.edu
Description: Proprietary, 2-year, coed. Awards certificates, diplomas, transfer associate, and terminal associate degrees. Total enrollment: 275. Student-undergrad faculty ratio is 17:1. 86% from out-of-state. 89% 25 or older.

■ **CROSSROADS BIBLE COLLEGE**
601 N Shortridge Rd.
Indianapolis, IN 46219
Tel: (317)352-8736; Free: 800-822-3119

Fax: (317)352-9145

E-mail: admissions@crossroads.edu

Web Site: www.crossroads.edu

Description: Independent Baptist, 4-year, coed. Awards associate and bachelor's degrees. Founded 1980. Setting: 6-acre urban campus with easy access to Indianapolis. Educational spending for the previous fiscal year: $10,767 per student. Total enrollment: 232. Faculty: 35 (6 full-time, 29 part-time). Student-undergrad faculty ratio is 7:1. 42 applied, 95% were admitted. Full-time: 127 students, 53% women, 47% men. Part-time: 105 students, 59% women, 41% men. Students come from 12 states and territories, 7 other countries, 9% from out-of-state. 0.4% American Indian or Alaska Native, non-Hispanic/Latino; 2% Hispanic/Latino; 55% Black or African American, non-Hispanic/Latino; 0.4% Asian, non-Hispanic/Latino; 0.4% Native Hawaiian or other Pacific Islander, non-Hispanic/Latino. 79% 25 or older, 5% live on campus, 22% transferred in. Retention: 45% of full-time freshmen returned the following year. Core. Calendar: semesters. Academic remediation for entering students, accelerated degree program, independent study, distance learning, double major, summer session for credit, part-time degree program, external degree program, adult/continuing education programs, co-op programs and internships.

Entrance Requirements: Open admission. Options: electronic application, deferred admission. Required: essay, high school transcript. Required for some: interview. Entrance: noncompetitive. Application deadlines: 8/8, rolling for nonresidents. Notification: continuous, continuous for nonresidents. Transfer credits accepted: Yes.

Collegiate Environment: Orientation program. Choral group. Major annual events: Diversity/International Food Fair, Chapel, Move/Game Nights/Discussions. Student services: personal-psychological counseling. Campus security: 24-hour emergency response devices, student patrols, late night transport-escort service. Kathryn Ulmer Library plus 1 other. Operations spending for the previous fiscal year: $4621. 15 computers available on campus for general student use. A campuswide network can be accessed from student residence rooms. Students can access the following: online class registration.

■ **DEPAUW UNIVERSITY**

313 S Locust St.

Greencastle, IN 46135

Tel: (765)658-4800; Free: 800-447-2495

Fax: (765)658-4007

E-mail: rachelschmidtke@depauw.edu

Web Site: www.depauw.edu

Description: Independent, 4-year, coed, affiliated with United Methodist Church. Awards bachelor's degrees. Founded 1837. Setting: 655-acre small town campus with easy access to Indianapolis. Endowment: $614.6 million. Total enrollment: 2,158. Faculty: 264 (228 full-time, 36 part-time). Student-undergrad faculty ratio is 9:1. 5,173 applied, 67% were admitted. 45% from top 10% of their high school class, 70% from top quarter, 95% from top half. Full-time: 2,140 students, 52% women, 48% men. Part-time: 18 students, 50% women, 50% men. 0.4% American Indian or Alaska Native, non-Hispanic/Latino; 7% Hispanic/Latino; 5% Black or African American, non-Hispanic/Latino; 4% Asian, non-Hispanic/Latino; 10% international. 0.1% 25 or older, 96% live on campus, 1% transferred in. Retention: 89% of full-time freshmen returned the following year. Academic areas with the most degrees conferred: social sciences; communication/journalism; biological/life sciences. Core. Calendar: 4-1-4. ESL program, services for LD students, advanced placement, self-designed majors, honors program, independent study, double major, part-time degree program, co-op programs and internships. Off campus study. Study abroad program. ROTC: Army (c), Air Force (c).

Entrance Requirements: Options: electronic application, early admission, early decision, early action, deferred admission, international baccalaureate accepted. Required: essay, high school transcript, 1 recommendation, SAT or ACT. Recommended: interview. Entrance: moderately difficult. Application deadlines: 2/1, 11/1 for early decision, 12/1 for early action. Notification: continuous until 12/15, continuous for nonresidents, 12/1 for early decision, 1/15 for early action. SAT Reasoning Test deadline: 2/1. Transfer credits accepted: Yes.

Costs Per Year: Comprehensive fee: $62,724 includes full-time tuition ($48,860), mandatory fees ($844), and college room and board ($13,020). Room and board charges vary according to board plan.

Collegiate Environment: Orientation program. Drama-theater group, choral group, student-run newspaper, radio station. Social organizations: national fraternities, national sororities; 75% of eligible men and 65% of eligible women are members. Major annual events: Monon Bell, Little 5, DePauw Dialogue. Student services: health clinic, personal-psychological counseling, women's center. Campus security: 24-hour emergency response devices and patrols, student patrols, late night transport-escort service, controlled dormitory access. Roy O. West Library plus 2 others. Study areas open 24 hours, 5-7 days a week; students can reserve study rooms.

Community Environment: Greencastle is located 40 miles west of Indianapolis, and within a 4-hour drive of Chicago, Cincinnati, Columbus, Louisville, and St. Louis. Community facilities include churches and a county hospital. The resort areas of Cataract Lake and Mansfield Lake are within 15 miles, and provide facilities for water sports and fishing.

■ **EARLHAM COLLEGE**

801 National Rd. W

Richmond, IN 47374-4095

Tel: (765)983-1200; Free: 800-327-5426

Fax: (765)983-1560

E-mail: admission@earlham.edu

Web Site: www.earlham.edu

Description: Independent, comprehensive, coed, affiliated with Society of Friends. Awards bachelor's and master's degrees. Founded 1847. Setting: 800-acre small town campus with easy access to Cincinnati, Indianapolis, Dayton. System endowment: $425.4 million. Research spending for the previous fiscal year: $430,885. Educational spending for the previous fiscal year: $25,840 per student. Total enrollment: 1,087. Faculty: 115 (107 full-time, 8 part-time). Student-undergrad faculty ratio is 10:1. 2,799 applied, 52% were admitted. 40% from top 10% of their high school class, 70% from top quarter, 91% from top half. 1 valedictorian. Full-time: 1,043 students, 54% women, 46% men. Part-time: 7 students, 29% women, 71% men. Students come from 47 states and territories, 72 other countries, 90% from out-of-state. 0.4% American Indian or Alaska Native, non-Hispanic/Latino; 7% Hispanic/Latino; 9% Black or African American, non-Hispanic/Latino; 4% Asian, non-Hispanic/Latino; 0.1% Native Hawaiian or other Pacific Islander, non-Hispanic/Latino; 21% international. 95% live on campus, 1% transferred in. Retention: 82% of full-time freshmen returned the following year. Academic areas with the most degrees conferred: interdisciplinary studies; biological/life sciences; social sciences; visual and performing arts. Core. Calendar: semesters. ESL program, services for LD students, self-designed majors, honors program, independent study, double major, co-op programs and internships, graduate courses open to undergrads. Off campus study at members of the Great Lakes Colleges Association. Study abroad program.

Entrance Requirements: Options: electronic application, early admission, early decision, early action, deferred admission, international baccalaureate accepted. Required: essay, high school transcript, 2 recommendations. Recommended: minimum 3 high school GPA, interview. Required for some: SAT or ACT. Entrance: very difficult. Application deadlines: 2/15, 11/15 for early decision, 12/1 for early action. Notification: 4/1, 12/15 for early decision, 1/15 for early action. Preference given to Quakers, children of alumni, state residents, minorities. SAT Reasoning Test deadline: 2/15. Transfer credits accepted: Yes. Applicants placed on waiting list: 364. Wait-listed applicants offered admission: 100. Early decision applicants: 56. Early decision applicants admitted: 45.

Costs Per Year: Application fee: $0. Comprehensive fee: $58,265 includes full-time tuition ($46,410), mandatory fees ($970), and college room and board ($10,885). College room only: $5775. Part-time tuition: $1547 per credit hour.

Collegiate Environment: Orientation program. Drama-theater group, choral group, student-run newspaper, radio station. Social organizations: 70 open to all. Most popular organizations: Gospel Revelations Chorus, Dance Alloy, club sports, Student Government, Black Student Union. Major annual events: Homecoming Dance, International Festival, Convocation. Student services: health clinic, personal-psychological counseling, women's center. Campus security: 24-hour emergency response devices and patrols, student patrols, late night transport-escort service, controlled dormitory access. 1,063 college housing spaces available; 891 were occupied in 2018-19. Freshmen guaranteed college housing. On-campus residence required through senior year. Options: coed, men-only, women-only housing available. Lilly Library plus 1 other. Books: 329,649 (physical), 1.9 million (digital/electronic); Databases: 169. Students can reserve study rooms. Operations spending for the previous fiscal year: $683,742. 266 computers available on campus for general student use. Computer purchase/lease plans available. A campuswide network can be accessed from student residence rooms and from off campus. Students can access the following: online class registration. Staffed computer lab on campus provides training in use of computers, software, and the Internet.

Community Environment: The campus lies at the southwest edge of Richmond, IN, a city of 40,000 people. Richmond is 70 miles from Cincinnati, OH, and Indianapolis, IN, and 40 miles from Dayton, OH. Local activities include auctions, the city's arboretum, the pedestrian shopping mall downtown, the symphony orchestra, civic theater and opera companies, a historical museum and the art association. The city is served by buses. Airline service is available in Dayton, OH.

■ **FORTIS COLLEGE**
9001 N Wesleyan Rd.
Ste. 101
Indianapolis, IN 46268
Tel: (317)808-4800; Free: 855-4-FORTIS
E-mail: kbennett@edaff.com
Web Site: www.fortis.edu
Description: Proprietary, 2-year, coed. Awards certificates, diplomas, transfer associate, and terminal associate degrees.

■ **FRANKLIN COLLEGE**
101 Branigin Blvd.
Franklin, IN 46131
Tel: (317)738-8000; Free: 800-852-0232
Fax: (317)738-8274
E-mail: admissions@franklincollege.edu
Web Site: www.franklincollege.edu
Description: Independent, comprehensive, coed, affiliated with American Baptist Churches in the U.S.A. Awards bachelor's and master's degrees. Founded 1834. Setting: 207-acre suburban campus with easy access to Indianapolis. Endowment: $84.6 million. Educational spending for the previous fiscal year: $8297 per student. Total enrollment: 1,034. Faculty: 123 (75 full-time, 48 part-time). Student-undergrad faculty ratio is 11:1. 2,301 applied, 62% were admitted. 18% from top 10% of their high school class, 48% from top quarter, 85% from top half. Full-time: 962 students, 52% women, 48% men. Part-time: 54 students, 57% women, 43% men. Students come from 17 states and territories, 3 other countries, 8% from out-of-state. 0.3% American Indian or Alaska Native, non-Hispanic/Latino; 3% Hispanic/Latino; 4% Black or African American, non-Hispanic/Latino; 0.8% Asian, non-Hispanic/Latino; 0.3% international. 1% 25 or older, 69% live on campus, 3% transferred in. Retention: 75% of full-time freshmen returned the following year. Academic areas with the most degrees conferred: social sciences; parks and recreation; communication/journalism; education. Core. Calendar: 4-1-4. Academic remediation for entering students, ESL program, services for LD students, advanced placement, self-designed majors, independent study, double major, summer session for credit, part-time degree program, co-op programs and internships. Off campus study at Consortium for Urban Education. Study abroad program. ROTC: Army (c).
Entrance Requirements: Options: electronic application, deferred admission, international baccalaureate accepted. Required: high school transcript, SAT or ACT. Recommended: essay. Required for some: interview. Entrance: moderately difficult. Application deadline: rolling. Notification: continuous. Transfer credits accepted: Yes.
Costs Per Year: Application fee: $40. Comprehensive fee: $41,529 includes full-time tuition ($31,810), mandatory fees ($200), and college room and board ($9519). College room only: $5682. Full-time tuition and fees vary according to course load and degree level. Room and board charges vary according to board plan. Part-time tuition: $460 per credit hour. Part-time mandatory fees: $7 per credit hour. Part-time tuition and fees vary according to course load and degree level.
Collegiate Environment: Orientation program. Drama-theater group, choral group, student-run newspaper, radio station. Social organizations: 66 open to all; national fraternities, national sororities; 25% of eligible men and 45% of eligible women are members. Most popular organizations: Student Entertainment Board, Student Congress, FC Volunteers. Major annual events: Homecoming, Grizzly Grand Prix Festival, Bell Game Against Hanover College. Student services: health clinic, personal-psychological counseling. Campus security: 24-hour emergency response devices and patrols, student patrols, late night transport-escort service, controlled dormitory access. Hamilton Library. Books: 104,767 (physical), 1.5 million (digital/electronic); Serial titles: 33,498 (physical), 136,773 (digital/electronic); Databases: 78. Weekly public service hours: 83; students can reserve study rooms. Operations spending for the previous fiscal year: $195,644. 150 computers available on campus for general student use. Computer purchase/lease plans available. A campuswide network can be accessed from student residence rooms and from off campus. Students can access

the following: online class registration. Staffed computer lab on campus (open 24 hours a day) provides training in use of computers, software, and the Internet.
Community Environment: Franklin (population 21,700) is situated 20 miles south of Indianapolis with facilities that include a library, hospital, 15 churches representing major denominations, and various service, fraternal, and veteran's organizations. Recreational activities are fishing, swimming, tennis, and bowling. Part-time job opportunities are available.

■ **GOSHEN COLLEGE**
1700 S Main St.
Goshen, IN 46526-4794
Tel: (574)535-7000; Free: 800-348-7422
Fax: (574)535-7060
E-mail: admissions@goshen.edu
Web Site: www.goshen.edu
Description: Independent Mennonite, comprehensive, coed. Awards bachelor's, master's, and doctoral degrees. Founded 1894. Setting: 135-acre small town campus. Endowment: $112.2 million. Research spending for the previous fiscal year: $41,010. Educational spending for the previous fiscal year: $9771 per student. Total enrollment: 927. Faculty: 100 (62 full-time, 38 part-time). Student-undergrad faculty ratio is 11:1. 1,219 applied, 68% were admitted. 32% from top 10% of their high school class, 70% from top quarter, 90% from top half. Full-time: 798 students, 62% women, 38% men. Part-time: 47 students, 60% women, 40% men. Students come from 37 states and territories, 27 other countries, 41% from out-of-state. 0.1% American Indian or Alaska Native, non-Hispanic/Latino; 23% Hispanic/Latino; 4% Black or African American, non-Hispanic/Latino; 2% Asian, non-Hispanic/Latino; 0.1% Native Hawaiian or other Pacific Islander, non-Hispanic/Latino; 8% international. 12% 25 or older, 57% live on campus, 9% transferred in. Retention: 73% of full-time freshmen returned the following year. Academic areas with the most degrees conferred: health professions and related sciences; business/marketing; visual and performing arts. Core. Calendar: semesters. Academic remediation for entering students, services for LD students, advanced placement, accelerated degree program, self-designed majors, independent study, distance learning, double major, summer session for credit, part-time degree program, adult/continuing education programs, internships, graduate courses open to undergrads. Off campus study at Northern Indiana Consortium for Education. Study abroad program.
Entrance Requirements: Options: electronic application, deferred admission, international baccalaureate accepted. Required: minimum 2 high school GPA, SAT or ACT. Recommended: minimum 2.75 high school GPA, 1 recommendation, interview, rank in upper 50% of high school class. Required for some: essay, high school transcript. Entrance: moderately difficult. Application deadline: 7/15. Notification: continuous. SAT Reasoning Test deadline: 8/15. Transfer credits accepted: Yes.
Costs Per Year: Application fee: $25. Comprehensive fee: $45,300 includes full-time tuition ($34,540) and college room and board ($10,760). College room only: $5810. Part-time tuition: $1425 per credit hour.
Collegiate Environment: Orientation program. Drama-theater group, choral group, student-run newspaper, radio station. Social organizations: 30 open to all. Most popular organizations: International Student Club, Latino Student Union, PAX - Peace Club, Goshen Student Women's Organization, Business Club. Major annual events: Kickoff, Martin Luther King Jr. Day, International Student Coffeehouse. Student services: health clinic, personal-psychological counseling. Campus security: 24-hour emergency response devices and patrols, late night transport-escort service, controlled dormitory access. 846 college housing spaces available; 472 were occupied in 2018-19. Freshmen guaranteed college housing. On-campus residence required through junior year. Options: coed, men-only, women-only housing available. The Harold and Wilma Good Library plus 1 other. Books: 189,524 (physical), 201,282 (digital/electronic); Serial titles: 3,203 (physical), 21,953 (digital/electronic); Databases: 72. Weekly public service hours: 89; students can reserve study rooms. Operations spending for the previous fiscal year: $483,238. 160 computers available on campus for general student use. A campuswide network can be accessed. Students can access the following: online class registration. Staffed computer lab on campus provides training in use of computers, software, and the Internet.
Community Environment: Goshen,"The Maple City" is a diversified small industry center, situated ten miles south of the Michigan state line. Annual mean temperature is 55 degrees, and the annual rainfall is 34 inches. All forms of transportation are available, and the airport is five miles southeast. Community facilities include a public library, hospital, 24 churches and many civic, service and social organizations. Goshen is noted for its large number of Amish farmers, and hundreds of lakes are within a 40-mile radius.

■ GRACE COLLEGE

200 Seminary Dr.
Winona Lake, IN 46590-1294
Tel: (574)372-5100; Free: 800-54-GRACE
Fax: (574)372-5139
E-mail: enroll@grace.edu
Web Site: www.grace.edu

Description: Independent, comprehensive, coed, affiliated with Fellowship of Grace Brethren Churches. Administratively affiliated with Grace Theological Seminary. Awards associate, bachelor's, master's, and doctoral degrees. Founded 1948. Setting: 160-acre small town campus. Endowment: $12.3 million. Total enrollment: 2,333. Faculty: 184 (49 full-time, 135 part-time). Student-undergrad faculty ratio is 22:1. 4,204 applied, 78% were admitted. 22% from top 10% of their high school class, 54% from top quarter, 80% from top half. Full-time: 1,521 students, 58% women, 42% men. Part-time: 413 students, 47% women, 53% men. Students come from 33 states and territories, 7 other countries, 26% from out-of-state. 5% Hispanic/Latino; 6% Black or African American, non-Hispanic/Latino; 1% Asian, non-Hispanic/Latino; 0.6% international. 15% 25 or older, 51% live on campus, 3% transferred in. Retention: 80% of full-time freshmen returned the following year. Academic areas with the most degrees conferred: business/marketing; psychology; education. Core. Calendar: semesters. Academic remediation for entering students, services for LD students, advanced placement, accelerated degree program, honors program, independent study, distance learning, double major, summer session for credit, part-time degree program, adult/continuing education programs, co-op programs and internships, graduate courses open to undergrads. Off campus study at Coalition for Christian Colleges and Universities. Study abroad program.

Entrance Requirements: Options: electronic application, early admission, early action, deferred admission, international baccalaureate accepted. Required: essay, high school transcript, minimum 2.3 high school GPA, 2 recommendations, personal statement of faith, SAT or ACT. Required for some: interview. Entrance: moderately difficult. Application deadlines: 8/1, 12/1 for early action. Notification: 8/15.

Costs Per Year: Application fee: $30. Comprehensive fee: $33,902 includes full-time tuition ($24,768) and college room and board ($9134). Full-time tuition varies according to degree level, location, and student level. Room and board charges vary according to board plan and housing facility. Part-time tuition: $882 per credit hour. Part-time tuition varies according to degree level and location.

Collegiate Environment: Orientation program. Drama-theater group, choral group, student-run newspaper. Social organizations: 30 open to all. Most popular organizations: Grace Ministries in Action, Student Activities Board, Funfest, women's ministries, Breakout. Major annual events: Homecoming, Heart of the Holidays, Halloween Fun Fest. Student services: health clinic, personal-psychological counseling. Campus security: 24-hour emergency response devices and patrols, student patrols, late night transport-escort service, controlled dormitory access. Morgan Library. Operations spending for the previous fiscal year: $467,960. 150 computers available on campus for general student use. A campuswide network can be accessed from student residence rooms and from off campus. Students can access the following: online class registration.

Community Environment: One of the outstanding Christian summer resorts in America, Winona Lake, population 4,000, is situated two miles from Warsaw, Indiana, on the main line of Amtrack Railroad. This is a resort area for the entire family.

■ HANOVER COLLEGE

517 Ball Dr.
Hanover, IN 47243
Tel: (812)866-7000; Free: 800-213-2178
Fax: (812)866-7098
E-mail: admission@hanover.edu
Web Site: www.hanover.edu

Description: Independent Presbyterian, 4-year, coed. Awards bachelor's degrees. Founded 1827. Setting: 630-acre rural campus with easy access to Louisville. Endowment: $136.2 million. Research spending for the previous fiscal year: $91,435. Educational spending for the previous fiscal year: $15,353 per student. Total enrollment: 1,104. Faculty: 100 (84 full-time, 16 part-time). Student-undergrad faculty ratio is 12:1. 3,229 applied, 79% were admitted. 27% from top 10% of their high school class, 54% from top quarter, 88% from top half. Full-time: 1,097 students, 55% women, 45% men. Part-time: 7 students, 71% women, 29% men. Students come from 22 states and territories, 18 other countries, 33% from out-of-state. 0.3% American Indian or Alaska Native, non-Hispanic/Latino; 3% Hispanic/Latino; 6% Black or African American, non-Hispanic/Latino; 0.7% Asian, non-Hispanic/Latino; 0.3% Native Hawaiian or other Pacific Islander, non-Hispanic/Latino; 3% international. 93% live on campus, 1% transferred in. Retention: 75% of full-time freshmen returned the following year. Academic areas with the most degrees conferred: biological/life sciences; social sciences; communication/journalism. Core. Calendar: 4-4-1. Services for LD students, advanced placement, self-designed majors, independent study, distance learning, double major, summer session for credit, co-op programs and internships. Off campus study at Philadelphia Center (Hope College), The Washington Center, Associated Colleges of the Midwest. Study abroad program.

Entrance Requirements: Options: electronic application, early admission, early action, deferred admission, international baccalaureate accepted. Required: essay, high school transcript, 1 recommendation. Recommended: interview, SAT or ACT. Entrance: moderately difficult. Application deadline: rolling. Notification: continuous until 9/1. SAT Reasoning Test deadline: 4/30. Transfer credits accepted: Yes. Applicants placed on waiting list: 0. Wait-listed applicants offered admission: 0. Early action applicants: 3,977. Early action applicants admitted: 1,711.

Costs Per Year: Application fee: $0. One-time mandatory fee: $350. Comprehensive fee: $50,700 includes full-time tuition ($37,980), mandatory fees ($770), and college room and board ($11,950). College room only: $5950. Part-time tuition: $1055 per unit.

Collegiate Environment: Orientation program. Drama-theater group, choral group, marching band, student-run newspaper, radio station. Social organizations: 70 open to all; national fraternities, national sororities; 60% of eligible men and 39% of eligible women are members. Most popular organizations: Delight Ministries, Alpha Lambda Delta, Love Out Loud, Art Club, International Club. Major annual events: Homecoming, Parents' Day, Wiffleball Tournament. Student services: health clinic, personal-psychological counseling. Campus security: 24-hour emergency response devices and patrols, late night transport-escort service, controlled dormitory access. 1,250 college housing spaces available; 1,005 were occupied in 2018-19. Freshmen guaranteed college housing. On-campus residence required through senior year. Options: coed, men-only, women-only housing available. Duggan Library. Books: 196,284 (physical), 213,376 (digital/electronic); Serial titles: 6,584 (physical), 183,744 (digital/electronic); Databases: 117. Students can reserve study rooms. Operations spending for the previous fiscal year: $815,053. 120 computers available on campus for general student use. A campuswide network can be accessed from student residence rooms and from off campus. Students can access the following: online class registration. Staffed computer lab on campus provides training in use of computers, software, and the Internet.

Community Environment: Hanover is located four and one-half miles from Madison, Indiana (population 12,400), overlooking the beautiful Ohio River valley from a hilltop nearly 400 feet above the river. Community facilities include a modern hospital. The Hanover/Madison area is rich in historic lore and antiques. Clifty Falls, a large State Park, well known for its rugged scenery, serves this community.

■ HOLY CROSS COLLEGE

54515 State Rd. 933 N
Notre Dame, IN 46556-0308
Tel: (574)239-8400
Fax: (574)239-8323
E-mail: admissions@hcc-nd.edu
Web Site: www.hcc-nd.edu

Description: Independent Roman Catholic, 4-year, coed. Awards associate and bachelor's degrees. Founded 1966. Setting: 150-acre suburban campus with easy access to Chicago, Indianapolis. Total enrollment: 601. Faculty: 73 (23 full-time, 50 part-time). Student-undergrad faculty ratio is 14:1. 638 applied, 91% were admitted. Full-time: 541 students, 39% women, 61% men. Part-time: 60 students, 87% women, 13% men. Students come from 32 states and territories, 12 other countries, 50% from out-of-state. 0.7% American Indian or Alaska Native, non-Hispanic/Latino; 9% Hispanic/Latino; 10% Black or African American, non-Hispanic/Latino; 2% Asian, non-Hispanic/Latino; 0.2% Native Hawaiian or other Pacific Islander, non-Hispanic/Latino; 4% international. 5% 25 or older, 67% live on campus, 5% transferred in. Retention: 65% of full-time freshmen returned the following year. Academic areas with the most degrees conferred: business/marketing; psychology; communication/journalism. Core. Calendar: semesters. Academic remediation for entering students, services for LD students, self-designed majors, honors program, independent study, double major, summer session for credit, part-time degree program, internships. Study abroad program. ROTC: Army (c), Air Force (c).

Entrance Requirements: Options: electronic application, deferred admission, international baccalaureate accepted. Required: high school transcript, SAT or ACT. Recommended: essay, 2 recommendations, interview. Required for some: essay. Entrance: moderately difficult. Application deadline: rolling. Notification: continuous. SAT Reasoning Test deadline: 8/15. SAT Subject Test deadline: 8/15. Transfer credits accepted: Yes.

Collegiate Environment: Orientation program. Drama-theater group, choral group, marching band. Social organizations: 30 open to all. Most popular organizations: Student Government Association, Campus Ministry, Intramural athletics, Commuter Student Organization, SAGE. Major annual events: Martin Luther King Jr. Day Events, Fall Fest, Winter Formal. Student services: health clinic, personal-psychological counseling. Campus security: 24-hour emergency response devices, late night transport-escort service, controlled dormitory access. McKenna Library. Books: 21,257 (physical), 10,401 (digital/electronic); Serial titles: 74 (physical); Databases: 55. Weekly public service hours: 86. 60 computers available on campus for general student use. Computer purchase/lease plans available. A campuswide network can be accessed from student residence rooms and from off campus. Students can access the following: online class registration. Staffed computer lab on campus provides training in use of computers, software, and the Internet.

Community Environment: See University of Notre Dame.

■ **HORIZON UNIVERSITY**
7700 Indian Lake Rd.
Indianapolis, IN 46236
Tel: (858)695-8587; Free: 800-553-HORIZON
Web Site: www.horizonuniversity.edu

Description: Independent, 4-year, coed. Awards associate and bachelor's degrees. Founded 1993. Setting: 100-acre suburban campus with easy access to Indianapolis, IN. Student-undergrad faculty ratio is 2:1. Core. Calendar: semesters. Advanced placement, distance learning, summer session for credit, part-time degree program, adult/continuing education programs.

Entrance Requirements: Open admission. Options: electronic application, international baccalaureate accepted. Required: essay, high school transcript, minimum 2 high school GPA, 2 recommendations, interview. Entrance: noncompetitive. Transfer credits accepted: Yes.

Costs Per Year: Tuition: $9000 full-time, $250 per semester hour part-time. Mandatory fees: $300 full-time, $100 per term part-time.

Collegiate Environment: Orientation program.

■ **HUNTINGTON UNIVERSITY**
2303 College Ave.
Huntington, IN 46750-1299
Tel: (260)356-6000; Free: 800-642-6493
Fax: (260)356-9448
Web Site: www.huntington.edu

Description: Independent, comprehensive, coed, affiliated with Church of the United Brethren in Christ. Administratively affiliated with Church of the United Brethren in Christ. Awards associate, bachelor's, master's, and doctoral degrees. Founded 1897. Setting: 170-acre small town campus with easy access to Fort Wayne. Endowment: $25.2 million. Total enrollment: 1,295. Faculty: 112 (65 full-time, 47 part-time). Student-undergrad faculty ratio is 13:1. 789 applied, 90% were admitted. 20% from top 10% of their high school class, 45% from top quarter, 78% from top half. Full-time: 871 students, 56% women, 44% men. Part-time: 125 students, 52% women, 48% men. Students come from 32 states and territories, 24 other countries, 31% from out-of-state. 0.2% American Indian or Alaska Native, non-Hispanic/Latino; 5% Hispanic/Latino; 2% Black or African American, non-Hispanic/Latino; 0.2% Asian, non-Hispanic/Latino; 5% international. 1% 25 or older, 72% live on campus, 4% transferred in. Academic areas with the most degrees conferred: business/marketing; visual and performing arts; education. Core. Calendar: 4-1-4. Academic remediation for entering students, ESL program, services for LD students, advanced placement, accelerated degree program, independent study, distance learning, double major, summer session for credit, part-time degree program, adult/continuing education programs, internships, graduate courses open to undergrads. Off campus study at American Studies Program in Washington, D.C.; Contemporary Music Center in Nashville; Focus Leadership Institute in Colorado; Los Angeles Film Studies Center; Washington Journalism Center in Washington, DC. Study abroad program.

Entrance Requirements: Options: electronic application, deferred admission. Required: essay, high school transcript, minimum 2.3 high school GPA,

SAT or ACT. Recommended: interview. Entrance: moderately difficult. Application deadline: 8/1. Notification: continuous, continuous for nonresidents. SAT Reasoning Test deadline: 8/15. Transfer credits accepted: Yes.

Costs Per Year: Application fee: $20. Comprehensive fee: $34,848 includes full-time tuition ($25,312), mandatory fees ($868), and college room and board ($8668). Full-time tuition and fees vary according to course load, degree level, and program. Room and board charges vary according to board plan. Part-time tuition: $762 per credit hour. Part-time mandatory fees: $360 per year. Part-time tuition and fees vary according to course load, degree level, and program.

Collegiate Environment: Orientation program. Drama-theater group, choral group, student-run newspaper, radio station. Social organizations: 22 open to all. Most popular organizations: Friesen Center for Volunteer Service, Student Government Association, Multicultural Activities Council, Student Activities Board, Intramural Sports. Major annual events: Olympiad, Forester Night, Homecoming Weekend. Campus security: 24-hour emergency response devices, late night transport-escort service, campus police on duty from 6 pm to 6 am. RichLyn Library. Operations spending for the previous fiscal year: $228,373. 209 computers available on campus for general student use. A campuswide network can be accessed from student residence rooms and from off campus. Students can access the following: online class registration. Staffed computer lab on campus provides training in use of computers, software, and the Internet.

Community Environment: Huntington (population 17,011) is located 24 miles southwest of Fort Wayne and is 90 miles north of Indianapolis. It is in a grain and industrial region. City facilities include museums, library, many churches, YMCA, hospital and numerous civic organizations. The retail and industrial organizations and citizens of the community appreciate the importance of the college students in the overall well being of the community. Salamonie Reservoir, six miles southwest has facilities for camping, picnicking, fishing, and boating.

■ **INDIANA STATE UNIVERSITY**
210 N Seventh St.
Terre Haute, IN 47809
Tel: (812)237-6311; Free: 800-468-6478
Fax: (812)237-8023
E-mail: admissions@indstate.edu
Web Site: www.indstate.edu

Description: State-supported, university, coed. Awards bachelor's, master's, and doctoral degrees and post-master's certificates. Founded 1865. Setting: 435-acre small town campus with easy access to Indianapolis. Endowment: $48 million. Research spending for the previous fiscal year: $8.8 million. Educational spending for the previous fiscal year: $6201 per student. Total enrollment: 13,045. Faculty: 703 (467 full-time, 236 part-time). Student-undergrad faculty ratio is 21:1. 12,861 applied, 90% were admitted. 11% from top 10% of their high school class, 28% from top quarter, 62% from top half. Full-time: 8,891 students, 55% women, 45% men. Part-time: 2,159 students, 61% women, 39% men. Students come from 51 states and territories, 62 other countries, 25% from out-of-state. 0.4% American Indian or Alaska Native, non-Hispanic/Latino; 5% Hispanic/Latino; 18% Black or African American, non-Hispanic/Latino; 1% Asian, non-Hispanic/Latino; 0.1% Native Hawaiian or other Pacific Islander, non-Hispanic/Latino; 3% international. 18% 25 or older, 32% live on campus, 7% transferred in. Retention: 62% of full-time freshmen returned the following year. Academic areas with the most degrees conferred: health professions and related sciences; business/marketing; engineering technologies. Core. Calendar: semesters. Academic remediation for entering students, ESL program, services for LD students, advanced placement, accelerated degree program, freshman honors college, honors program, independent study, distance learning, double major, summer session for credit, part-time degree program, adult/continuing education programs, co-op programs and internships, graduate courses open to undergrads. Off campus study at Saint Mary-of-the-Woods College, Rose-Hulman Institute of Technology. Study abroad program. ROTC: Army, Air Force.

Entrance Requirements: Options: electronic application, deferred admission. Required: high school transcript, SAT or ACT. Recommended: minimum 2.5 high school GPA. Required for some: interview. Entrance: moderately difficult. Application deadline: 8/15. Notification: continuous. SAT Reasoning Test deadline: 8/15. SAT Subject Test deadline: 8/15. Transfer credits accepted: Yes.

Costs Per Year: Application fee: $25. State resident tuition: $8890 full-time, $322 per credit hour part-time. Nonresident tuition: $19,636 full-time, $695 per credit hour part-time. Mandatory fees: $200 full-time, $100 per term part-time. Full-time tuition and fees vary according to reciprocity agreements. Part-time tuition and fees vary according to course load and reciprocity agreements. College room and board: $10,590. College room only: $6706. Room and board charges vary according to board plan, housing facility, and student level.

Collegiate Environment: Orientation program. Drama-theater group, choral group, marching band, student-run newspaper, radio station. Social organizations: 243 open to all; national fraternities, national sororities; 12% of eligible men and 11% of eligible women are members. Most popular organizations: Union Board, Student Government Association, Panhellenic Council (sororities), Interfraternity Council (fraternities), Residence Hall Association. Major annual events: Homecoming, Club Week, Spring Week. Student services: health clinic, personal-psychological counseling, women's center. Campus security: 24-hour emergency response devices and patrols, student patrols, late night transport-escort service, RAVE Campus Alert Emails/Texts; Workshops and Video Training; Motorist Assistance; Other Education Opportunities;. 4,985 college housing spaces available; 4,742 were occupied in 2018-19. Freshmen guaranteed college housing. On-campus residence required in freshman year. Options: coed, men-only, women-only housing available. Cunningham Memorial Library plus 1 other. Books: 952,660 (physical), 825,318 (digital/electronic); Serial titles: 64,989 (physical), 83,801 (digital/electronic); Databases: 357. Weekly public service hours: 132; study areas open 24 hours, 5-7 days a week; students can reserve study rooms. Operations spending for the previous fiscal year: $5.1 million. 170 computers available on campus for general student use. Computer purchase/lease plans available. A computer is required for all students. A campuswide network can be accessed from student residence rooms and from off campus. Students can access the following: online class registration. Staffed computer lab on campus provides training in use of computers, software, and the Internet.

Community Environment: Indiana State is located in Terre Haute, a city of 60,000, on the banks of the Wabash River. Terre Haute is within a 500-mile radius of more than half the population of the United States. Chicago, St. Louis, Cincinnati, Louisville, and Nashville are within a half-day drive, and Indianapolis is only an hour and a half away. Terre Haute's cultural attractions include the Terre Haute Symphony Orchestra, Community Theater, the Sheldon Swope Art Museum, the Eugene V. Debs. Museum, and the Vigo County Historical Museum. The educational atmosphere of the city is enhanced by Saint Mary-of-the-Woods College, Rose-Hulman Institute of Technology, and Indiana Vocational-Tech College.

■ INDIANA TECH

1600 E Washington Blvd.
Fort Wayne, IN 46803-1297
Tel: (260)422-5561; Free: 800-937-2448
Fax: (260)422-7696
E-mail: admissions@indianatech.edu
Web Site: www.indianatech.edu

Description: Independent, comprehensive, coed. Awards associate, bachelor's, master's, and doctoral degrees. Founded 1930. Setting: 42-acre urban campus. Endowment: $123.2 million. Educational spending for the previous fiscal year: $3640 per student. Total enrollment: 7,996. Faculty: 530 (57 full-time, 473 part-time). Student-undergrad faculty ratio is 20:1. 3,059 applied, 70% were admitted. 8% from top 10% of their high school class, 28% from top quarter, 59% from top half. Full-time: 4,247 students, 58% women, 42% men. Part-time: 2,923 students, 65% women, 35% men. Students come from 49 states and territories, 57 other countries, 48% from out-of-state. 0.4% American Indian or Alaska Native, non-Hispanic/Latino; 4% Hispanic/Latino; 35% Black or African American, non-Hispanic/Latino; 0.5% Asian, non-Hispanic/Latino; 0.1% Native Hawaiian or other Pacific Islander, non-Hispanic/Latino; 5% international. 49% 25 or older, 55% live on campus, 7% transferred in. Retention: 60% of full-time freshmen returned the following year. Academic areas with the most degrees conferred: engineering; business/marketing; homeland security, law enforcement, firefighting, and protective services. Core. Calendar: semesters. Academic remediation for entering students, ESL program, services for LD students, advanced placement, accelerated degree program, self-designed majors, freshman honors college, honors program, independent study, distance learning, double major, summer session for credit, part-time degree program, external degree program, adult/continuing education programs, co-op programs and internships, graduate courses open to undergrads. Study abroad program. ROTC: Army (c).

Entrance Requirements: Options: electronic application, international baccalaureate accepted. Required: high school transcript, minimum 2 high

school GPA, SAT or ACT. Recommended: AP Exam Results. Required for some: essay, minimum 3 high school GPA, 2 recommendations, interview, interview. Entrance: moderately difficult. Application deadline: 8/15. Notification: continuous until 8/15. SAT Reasoning Test deadline: 8/15. Transfer credits accepted: Yes.

Costs Per Year: Application fee: $0. Comprehensive fee: $36,920 includes full-time tuition ($26,460), mandatory fees ($440), and college room and board ($10,020). Full-time tuition and fees vary according to course load and program. Room and board charges vary according to board plan and housing facility. Part-time tuition: $520 per credit hour. Part-time mandatory fees: $165 per term. Part-time tuition and fees vary according to course load and program. Tuition guaranteed not to increase for student's term of enrollment.

Collegiate Environment: Orientation program. Social organizations: 28 open to all; national fraternities, local sororities. Most popular organizations: Multicultural Club, NSBE, Indiana Tech Gaming Society, Tech LOL, Cyber Defense Club of Indiana Tech. Major annual events: Spring Bling Fling, Homecoming, Graduation. Student services: personal-psychological counseling. Campus security: 24-hour emergency response devices and patrols, student patrols, late night transport-escort service, controlled dormitory access. McMillen Library. Books: 15,633 (physical), 60,903 (digital/electronic); Serial titles: 182 (physical), 500,000 (digital/electronic); Databases: 10. Weekly public service hours: 72; students can reserve study rooms. Operations spending for the previous fiscal year: $418,740. 460 computers available on campus for general student use. A campuswide network can be accessed from student residence rooms and from off campus. Students can access the following: online class registration.

Community Environment: Fort Wayne is the hub of the great north central industrial and agricultural America and gateway to the northern Indiana lake region. Gasoline tank and pump manufacturing originated here, and industries now include a General Motors truck plant, electronics, automotive, and agriculture. The city has 147 churches, a civic theatre, and Philharmonic Symphony. Points of interest are the Allen County War Memorial Coliseum, Cathedral of the Immaculate Conception, Concordia Senior College, Fort Wayne Art School and Museum, Lincoln Museum, Lincoln Tower Building, Historical Fort Wayne, and many city parks.

■ INDIANA UNIVERSITY BLOOMINGTON

107 S Indiana Ave.
Bloomington, IN 47405-7000
Tel: (812)855-4848
Fax: (812)855-1871
E-mail: iuadmit@indiana.edu
Web Site: www.iub.edu

Description: State-supported, university, coed. Part of Indiana University System. Awards associate, bachelor's, master's, and doctoral degrees and post-master's certificates. Founded 1820. Setting: 1,939-acre small town campus with easy access to Indianapolis. Endowment: $1.3 billion. Research spending for the previous fiscal year: $100 million. Educational spending for the previous fiscal year: $14,714 per student. Total enrollment: 43,503. Faculty: 2,495 (2,156 full-time, 339 part-time). Student-undergrad faculty ratio is 17:1. 44,169 applied, 77% were admitted. 35% from top 10% of their high school class, 69% from top quarter, 95% from top half. Full-time: 32,109 students, 50% women, 50% men. Part-time: 1,192 students, 50% women, 50% men. Students come from 52 states and territories, 115 other countries, 35% from out-of-state. 0.1% American Indian or Alaska Native, non-Hispanic/Latino; 6% Hispanic/Latino; 5% Black or African American, non-Hispanic/Latino; 6% Asian, non-Hispanic/Latino; 9% international. 2% 25 or older, 37% live on campus, 2% transferred in. Retention: 91% of full-time freshmen returned the following year. Academic areas with the most degrees conferred: business/marketing; computer and information sciences; parks and recreation; public administration and social services. Core. Calendar: semesters plus summer sessions. Academic remediation for entering students, ESL program, services for LD students, advanced placement, accelerated degree program, self-designed majors, freshman honors college, honors program, independent study, distance learning, double major, summer session for credit, part-time degree program, external degree program, adult/continuing education programs, co-op programs and internships, graduate courses open to undergrads. Off campus study. Study abroad program. ROTC: Army, Air Force.

Entrance Requirements: Options: electronic application, early action, deferred admission, international baccalaureate accepted. Required: essay, high school transcript, SAT or ACT. Recommended: SAT Subject Tests. Entrance: moderately difficult. Application deadlines: rolling, 11/1 for early action. Notification: 1/15 for early action. SAT Reasoning Test deadline: 4/1.

SAT Subject Test deadline: 4/1. Transfer credits accepted: Yes. Applicants placed on waiting list: 2,835. Wait-listed applicants offered admission: 427.

Costs Per Year: Application fee: $65. State resident tuition: $9,342 full-time, $291.89 per credit hour part-time. Nonresident tuition: $34,117 full-time, $1,066.15 per credit hour part-time. Mandatory fees: $1,339 full-time. Full-time tuition and fees vary according to program. Part-time tuition varies according to course load and program. College room and board: $10,466. Room and board charges vary according to board plan and housing facility.

Collegiate Environment: Orientation program. Drama-theater group, choral group, marching band, student-run newspaper, radio station. Social organizations: 814 open to all; national fraternities, national sororities, local fraternities, local sororities; 23% of eligible men and 20% of eligible women are members. Most popular organizations: Union Board, Student Association, Student Foundation, Habitat for Humanity, Student Athletic Board. Major annual events: Homecoming, Little 500 Bike Race, Welcome Week Block Party. Student services: legal services, health clinic, personal-psychological counseling, women's center. Campus security: 24-hour emergency response devices and patrols, late night transport-escort service. 12,872 college housing spaces available; 12,563 were occupied in 2018-19. Freshmen guaranteed college housing. On-campus residence required in freshman year. Options: coed, men-only, women-only housing available. Indiana University Library plus 16 others. Books: 4.6 million (physical), 1.6 million (digital/electronic); Serial titles: 153,297 (physical), 111,600 (digital/electronic); Databases: 2,011. Study areas open 24 hours, 5-7 days a week; students can reserve study rooms. Operations spending for the previous fiscal year: $46.6 million. 2,150 computers available on campus for general student use. A campuswide network can be accessed from student residence rooms and from off campus. Students can access the following: online class registration. Staffed computer lab on campus (open 24 hours a day) provides training in use of computers, software, and the Internet.

Community Environment: The 1,900-acre main campus is located in a community of 66,000 in southern Indiana. Indianapolis, site of the I.U. Medical Center, is 50 miles away. Places of worship are located in the immediate community for all faiths. The city is served by air and bus.

■ **INDIANA UNIVERSITY EAST**
2325 Chester Blvd.
Richmond, IN 47374-1289
Tel: (765)973-8200; Free: 800-959-EAST
Fax: (765)973-8288
E-mail: applynow@iue.edu
Web Site: www.iue.edu

Description: State-supported, comprehensive, coed. Part of Indiana University System. Awards bachelor's and master's degrees. Founded 1971. Setting: 182-acre small town campus with easy access to Indianapolis. Endowment: $5.6 million. Research spending for the previous fiscal year: $424. Educational spending for the previous fiscal year: $6018 per student. Total enrollment: 3,722. Faculty: 274 (114 full-time, 160 part-time). Student-undergrad faculty ratio is 14:1. 1,979 applied, 65% were admitted. 11% from top 10% of their high school class, 34% from top quarter, 67% from top half. Full-time: 1,986 students, 68% women, 32% men. Part-time: 1,393 students, 59% women, 41% men. Students come from 46 states and territories, 51 other countries, 27% from out-of-state. 0.3% American Indian or Alaska Native, non-Hispanic/Latino; 4% Hispanic/Latino; 5% Black or African American, non-Hispanic/Latino; 1% Asian, non-Hispanic/Latino; 2% international. 41% 25 or older, 12% transferred in. Retention: 65% of full-time freshmen returned the following year. Academic areas with the most degrees conferred: business/marketing; health professions and related sciences; psychology. Core. Calendar: semesters. Academic remediation for entering students, services for LD students, advanced placement, accelerated degree program, honors program, independent study, distance learning, double major, summer session for credit, part-time degree program, external degree program, adult/continuing education programs, co-op programs and internships, graduate courses open to undergrads. Off campus study at Earlham College. Study abroad program.

Entrance Requirements: Options: electronic application, early admission, deferred admission. Required: high school transcript. Required for some: 1 recommendation, SAT or ACT. Entrance: moderately difficult. Application deadline: rolling. Notification: continuous. Transfer credits accepted: Yes.

Costs Per Year: Application fee: $35. State resident tuition: $6,727 full-time, $224.23 per credit hour part-time. Nonresident tuition: $18,783 full-time, $626.08 per credit hour part-time. Mandatory fees: $617 full-time. Full-time tuition and fees vary according to program and reciprocity agreements. Part-time tuition varies according to course load, program, and reciprocity agreements.

Collegiate Environment: Orientation program. Drama-theater group, choral group, student-run newspaper. Social organizations: 25 open to all. Most popular organization: Student Government Association. Major annual event: Homecoming. Student services: personal-psychological counseling. Campus security: 24-hour emergency response devices, late night transport-escort service. College housing not available. IU East Campus Library. Books: 21,911 (physical), 185,438 (digital/electronic); Serial titles: 2 (physical), 94,601 (digital/electronic); Databases: 524. Students can reserve study rooms. Operations spending for the previous fiscal year: $717,432. 196 computers available on campus for general student use. A campuswide network can be accessed from off-campus. Students can access the following: online class registration. Staffed computer lab on campus.

Community Environment: The school is located in an outlying area of Richmond, which has a population of about 37,500.

■ **INDIANA UNIVERSITY KOKOMO**
2300 S Washington St.
Kokomo, IN 46902-9003
Tel: (765)453-2000; Free: 888-875-4485
Fax: (765)455-9537
E-mail: iuadmis@iuk.edu
Web Site: www.iuk.edu

Description: State-supported, comprehensive, coed. Part of Indiana University System. Awards associate, bachelor's, and master's degrees. Founded 1945. Setting: 51-acre small town campus with easy access to Indianapolis. Endowment: $6.6 million. Research spending for the previous fiscal year: $211,106. Educational spending for the previous fiscal year: $6152 per student. Total enrollment: 3,123. Faculty: 265 (133 full-time, 132 part-time). Student-undergrad faculty ratio is 16:1. 2,499 applied, 80% were admitted. 6% from top 10% of their high school class, 29% from top quarter, 69% from top half. Full-time: 2,259 students, 63% women, 37% men. Part-time: 653 students, 65% women, 35% men. Students come from 17 states and territories, 25 other countries, 2% from out-of-state. 0.4% American Indian or Alaska Native, non-Hispanic/Latino; 5% Hispanic/Latino; 4% Black or African American, non-Hispanic/Latino; 1% Asian, non-Hispanic/Latino; 1% international. 22% 25 or older, 9% transferred in. Retention: 60% of full-time freshmen returned the following year. Academic areas with the most degrees conferred: health professions and related sciences; business/marketing; liberal arts/general studies. Core. Calendar: semesters. Academic remediation for entering students, ESL program, services for LD students, advanced placement, accelerated degree program, freshman honors college, honors program, independent study, distance learning, double major, summer session for credit, part-time degree program, external degree program, adult/continuing education programs, internships, graduate courses open to undergrads. Study abroad program.

Entrance Requirements: Options: electronic application, deferred admission, international baccalaureate accepted. Required: high school transcript. Required for some: SAT or ACT. Entrance: minimally difficult. Application deadline: rolling. Notification: continuous. SAT Reasoning Test deadline: 8/21. SAT Subject Test deadline: 8/21. Transfer credits accepted: Yes.

Costs Per Year: Application fee: $35. State resident tuition: $6,727 full-time, $224.23 per credit hour part-time. Nonresident tuition: $18,783 full-time, $626.08 per credit hour part-time. Mandatory fees: $617 full-time. Full-time tuition and fees vary according to program and reciprocity agreements. Part-time tuition varies according to course load, program, and reciprocity agreements.

Collegiate Environment: Orientation program. Drama-theater group, choral group, student-run newspaper. Social organizations: 44 open to all; national sororities, local sororities. Major annual events: Homecoming, Campus Fall Kick-off BBQ. Student services: personal-psychological counseling. Campus security: late night transport-escort service. College housing not available. IU Kokomo Library. Books: 92,259 (physical), 1.4 million (digital/electronic); Serial titles: 1,849 (physical), 116,559 (digital/electronic); Databases: 393. Students can reserve study rooms. Operations spending for the previous fiscal year: $1.2 million. 325 computers available on campus for general student use. A campuswide network can be accessed from off-campus. Students can access the following: online class registration. Staffed computer lab on campus.

Community Environment: Kokomo (population 46,178) is an urban area, enjoying a temperate climate, with excellent community facilities; shopping areas, library, museum, 71 churches and two hospitals. All forms of transportation are available. The General Motors Corp. and Chrysler Corp. plants in Kokomo manufacture car radios, transistors, transmissions, and aluminum die castings. Kokomo is the home of Elwood Haynes who invented one of the first American automobiles in 1893. Part-time employment is available.

■ **INDIANA UNIVERSITY NORTHWEST**

3400 Broadway
Gary, IN 46408-1197
Tel: (219)980-6500; Free: 800-968-7486
Fax: (219)981-4219
Web Site: www.iun.edu

Description: State-supported, comprehensive, coed. Part of Indiana University System. Awards associate, bachelor's, and master's degrees. Founded 1959. Setting: 43-acre suburban campus with easy access to Chicago. Endowment: $10.3 million. Research spending for the previous fiscal year: $502,859. Educational spending for the previous fiscal year: $7219 per student. Total enrollment: 3,959. Faculty: 346 (168 full-time, 178 part-time). Student-undergrad faculty ratio is 14:1. 2,182 applied, 80% were admitted. 10% from top 10% of their high school class, 30% from top quarter, 64% from top half. Full-time: 2,515 students, 69% women, 31% men. Part-time: 1,019 students, 73% women, 27% men. Students come from 12 states and territories, 34 other countries, 3% from out-of-state. 0.2% American Indian or Alaska Native, non-Hispanic/Latino; 24% Hispanic/Latino; 16% Black or African American, non-Hispanic/Latino; 3% Asian, non-Hispanic/Latino; 0.5% international. 27% 25 or older, 8% transferred in. Retention: 66% of full-time freshmen returned the following year. Academic areas with the most degrees conferred: health professions and related sciences; business/marketing; liberal arts/general studies. Core. Calendar: semesters. Academic remediation for entering students, services for LD students, advanced placement, accelerated degree program, self-designed majors, honors program, independent study, distance learning, double major, summer session for credit, part-time degree program, external degree program, adult/continuing education programs, co-op programs and internships, graduate courses open to undergrads. Off campus study. Study abroad program. ROTC: Army.

Entrance Requirements: Options: electronic application, deferred admission, international baccalaureate accepted. Required: high school transcript, minimum 2 high school GPA, SAT or ACT. Entrance: minimally difficult. Application deadline: rolling. Notification: continuous. Transfer credits accepted: Yes.

Costs Per Year: Application fee: $35. State resident tuition: $6,727 full-time, $224.23 per credit hour part-time. Nonresident tuition: $18,783 full-time, $626.08 per credit hour part-time. Mandatory fees: $617 full-time. Full-time tuition and fees vary according to program and reciprocity agreements. Part-time tuition varies according to course load, program, and reciprocity agreements.

Collegiate Environment: Orientation program. Drama-theater group, student-run newspaper, radio station. Social organizations: 62 open to all; national fraternities, national sororities, local fraternities, local sororities; 1% of eligible men and 1% of eligible women are members. Most popular organizations: Student Government Association, Student Ambassadors, Art Club, Modern Languages Club. Major annual events: Back2School Week, Communication Week, Health Fair. Student services: health clinic, personal-psychological counseling. Campus security: 24-hour emergency response devices and patrols, late night transport-escort service. College housing not available. John W. Anderson Library. Books: 252,605 (physical), 837,493 (digital/electronic); Serial titles: 2,342 (physical), 136,256 (digital/electronic); Databases: 539. Students can reserve study rooms. Operations spending for the previous fiscal year: $1.4 million. 682 computers available on campus for general student use. A campuswide network can be accessed from off-campus. Students can access the following: online class registration. Staffed computer lab on campus provides training in use of computers, software, and the Internet.

Community Environment: Gary (population 98,715) is the second largest city in Indiana, a metropolitan area, and is in one of the country's outstanding steel production areas. The United States Steel Corp. is located here on Lake Michigan. All forms of transportation are available. Community facilities include libraries, churches, hospitals, and shopping areas. Part-time employment is available. Marquette Park nearby has a four-mile beach, a pavilion, piers, and a picnic area.

■ **INDIANA UNIVERSITY-PURDUE UNIVERSITY INDIANAPOLIS**

420 University Blvd.
Indianapolis, IN 46202
Tel: (317)274-5555

Fax: (317)278-1862
Web Site: www.iupui.edu

Description: State-supported, university, coed. Part of Indiana University System. Awards associate, bachelor's, master's, and doctoral degrees and post-master's certificates. Founded 1969. Setting: 536-acre urban campus with easy access to Indianapolis. Endowment: $1 billion. Research spending for the previous fiscal year: $209.1 million. Educational spending for the previous fiscal year: $16,407 per student. Total enrollment: 29,579. Faculty: 3,687 (2,523 full-time, 1,164 part-time). Student-undergrad faculty ratio is 17:1. 13,339 applied, 81% were admitted. 15% from top 10% of their high school class, 42% from top quarter, 85% from top half. Full-time: 17,555 students, 59% women, 41% men. Part-time: 3,691 students, 54% women, 46% men. Students come from 46 states and territories, 135 other countries, 5% from out-of-state. 0.1% American Indian or Alaska Native, non-Hispanic/Latino; 8% Hispanic/Latino; 9% Black or African American, non-Hispanic/Latino; 5% Asian, non-Hispanic/Latino; 4% international. 17% 25 or older, 12% live on campus, 6% transferred in. Retention: 72% of full-time freshmen returned the following year. Academic areas with the most degrees conferred: business/marketing; health professions and related sciences; engineering. Core. Calendar: semesters. Academic remediation for entering students, ESL program, services for LD students, advanced placement, accelerated degree program, self-designed majors, freshman honors college, honors program, independent study, distance learning, double major, summer session for credit, part-time degree program, external degree program, adult/continuing education programs, co-op programs and internships, graduate courses open to undergrads. Off campus study at Consortium for Urban Education. Study abroad program. ROTC: Army, Air Force (c).

Entrance Requirements: Options: electronic application, international baccalaureate accepted. Required: essay, high school transcript, SAT or ACT. Required for some: portfolio for art program. Entrance: moderately difficult. Notification: continuous. SAT Reasoning Test deadline: 5/1. Transfer credits accepted: Yes.

Costs Per Year: Application fee: $65. State resident tuition: $8371 full-time, $279.03 per credit hour part-time. Nonresident tuition: $28,727 full-time, $957.58 per credit hour part-time. Mandatory fees: $1,094 full-time. Full-time tuition and fees vary according to location, program, and reciprocity agreements. Part-time tuition varies according to course load, location, program, and reciprocity agreements. College room and board: $9730. Room and board charges vary according to board plan and housing facility.

Collegiate Environment: Orientation program. Drama-theater group, choral group, student-run newspaper. Social organizations: 539 open to all; national fraternities, national sororities, local fraternities, local sororities; 1% of eligible men and 2% of eligible women are members. Major annual events: Weeks of Welcome, Jagathon, IUPUI Regatta. Student services: health clinic, personal-psychological counseling, women's center. Campus security: 24-hour emergency response devices and patrols, late night transport-escort service, controlled dormitory access. College housing designed to accommodate 2,398 students; 2,455 undergraduates lived in college housing during 2018-19. No special consideration for freshman housing applicants. Option: coed housing available. University Library plus 4 others. Books: 1.6 million (physical), 613,573 (digital/electronic); Serial titles: 10,792 (physical), 282,617 (digital/electronic); Databases: 902. Study areas open 24 hours, 5-7 days a week; students can reserve study rooms. Operations spending for the previous fiscal year: $20.5 million. 1,158 computers available on campus for general student use. A campuswide network can be accessed from student residence rooms and from off campus. Students can access the following: online class registration. Staffed computer lab on campus (open 24 hours a day) provides training in use of computers, software, and the Internet.

Community Environment: See Butler University.

■ **INDIANA UNIVERSITY SOUTH BEND**

1700 Mishawaka Ave.
South Bend, IN 46615
Tel: (574)520-4872; Free: 877-GO-2-IUSB
Fax: (574)520-4834
E-mail: admissions@iusb.edu
Web Site: www.iusb.edu

Description: State-supported, comprehensive, coed. Part of Indiana University System. Awards associate, bachelor's, and master's degrees. Founded 1922. Setting: 105-acre suburban campus with easy access to Chicago. Endowment: $19.1 million. Research spending for the previous fiscal year: $580,307. Educational spending for the previous fiscal year: $7653 per student. Total enrollment: 5,214. Faculty: 439 (249 full-time, 190 part-time). Student-undergrad faculty ratio is 13:1. 3,011 applied, 82% were admitted. 7% from top 10% of their high school class, 29% from top quarter, 65% from top half. Full-time: 3,614 students, 64% women, 36% men. Part-time: 1,093 students, 62% women, 38% men. Students come from 16 states and territories, 26 other countries, 5% from out-of-state. 0.2% American Indian or Alaska Native, non-Hispanic/Latino; 12% Hispanic/Latino; 8% Black or African American, non-Hispanic/Latino; 2% Asian, non-Hispanic/Latino; 0.1% Native Hawaiian or other Pacific Islander, non-Hispanic/Latino; 3% international. 21% 25 or older, 8% live on campus, 7% transferred in. Retention: 63% of full-time freshmen returned the following year. Academic areas with the most degrees conferred: health professions and related sciences; business/marketing; liberal arts/general studies; education. Core. Calendar: semesters. ESL program, services for LD students, advanced placement, accelerated degree program, freshman honors college, honors program, independent study, distance learning, double major, summer session for credit, part-time degree program, external degree program, adult/continuing education programs, internships, graduate courses open to undergrads. Off campus study. Study abroad program. ROTC: Army (c), Air Force (c).

Entrance Requirements: Options: electronic application, deferred admission, international baccalaureate accepted. Required: high school transcript, minimum 2 high school GPA, SAT or ACT. Entrance: moderately difficult. Application deadline: rolling. Notification: continuous. Transfer credits accepted: Yes.

Costs Per Year: Application fee: $35. State resident tuition: $6,727 full-time, $224.23 per credit hour part-time. Nonresident tuition: $18,783 full-time, $626.08 per credit hour part-time. Mandatory fees: $617 full-time. Full-time tuition and fees vary according to program and reciprocity agreements. Part-time tuition varies according to course load, program, and reciprocity agreements. College room only: $9034. Room charges vary according to housing facility.

Collegiate Environment: Orientation program. Drama-theater group, choral group, student-run newspaper. Social organizations: 95 open to all; national fraternities, national sororities, local fraternities, local sororities. Major annual events: Red and White Dance, Riverfest, International Food Festival. Student services: health clinic, personal-psychological counseling, women's center. Campus security: 24-hour emergency response devices and patrols, late night transport-escort service. 396 college housing spaces available; 378 were occupied in 2018-19. No special consideration for freshman housing applicants. Option: coed housing available. Franklin D. Schurz Library plus 1 other. Books: 356,495 (physical), 942,808 (digital/electronic); Serial titles: 7,253 (physical), 112,145 (digital/electronic); Databases: 408. Students can reserve study rooms. Operations spending for the previous fiscal year: $2.4 million. 730 computers available on campus for general student use. A campuswide network can be accessed from student residence rooms and from off campus. Students can access the following: online class registration. Staffed computer lab on campus provides training in use of computers, software, and the Internet.

Community Environment: See University of Notre Dame.

■ **INDIANA UNIVERSITY SOUTHEAST**
4201 Grant Line Rd.
New Albany, IN 47150-6405
Tel: (812)941-2000; Free: 800-852-8835
E-mail: admissions@ius.edu
Web Site: www.ius.edu
Description: State-supported, comprehensive, coed. Part of Indiana University System. Awards bachelor's and master's degrees. Founded 1941. Setting: 179-acre suburban campus with easy access to Louisville. Endowment: $15 million. Research spending for the previous fiscal year: $119,961. Educational spending for the previous fiscal year: $7630 per student. Total enrollment: 5,144. Faculty: 431 (207 full-time, 224 part-time). Student-undergrad faculty ratio is 14:1. 2,794 applied, 85% were admitted. 8% from top 10% of their high school class, 33% from top quarter, 68% from top half. Full-time: 3,204 students, 62% women, 38% men. Part-time: 1,455 students, 58% women, 42% men. Students come from 23 states and territories, 43 other countries, 30% from out-of-state. 0.1% American Indian or Alaska Native, non-Hispanic/Latino; 5% Hispanic/Latino; 7% Black or African American, non-Hispanic/Latino; 2% Asian, non-Hispanic/Latino; 0.7% international. 24% 25 or older, 8% live on campus, 7% transferred in. Retention: 59% of full-time freshmen returned the following year. Academic areas with the most degrees conferred: business/marketing; health professions and related sciences; education. Core. Calendar: semesters. Academic remediation for entering students, ESL program, services for LD students,

advanced placement, accelerated degree program, self-designed majors, honors program, independent study, distance learning, double major, summer session for credit, part-time degree program, external degree program, adult/continuing education programs, internships, graduate courses open to undergrads. Off campus study at Kentuckiana Metroversity. Study abroad program. ROTC: Army (c), Air Force (c).

Entrance Requirements: Options: electronic application, early admission, deferred admission, international baccalaureate accepted. Required: high school transcript, SAT or ACT. Entrance: minimally difficult. Application deadline: rolling. Notification: continuous. SAT Reasoning Test deadline: 8/1. Transfer credits accepted: Yes.

Costs Per Year: Application fee: $35. State resident tuition: $6,727 full-time, $224.23 per credit hour part-time. Nonresident tuition: $18,783 full-time, $626.08 per credit hour part-time. Mandatory fees: $617 full-time. Full-time tuition and fees vary according to program and reciprocity agreements. Part-time tuition varies according to course load, program, and reciprocity agreements. College room only: $9906. Room charges vary according to housing facility.

Collegiate Environment: Orientation program. Drama-theater group, choral group, student-run newspaper. Social organizations: 144 open to all; national fraternities, national sororities, local fraternities, local sororities; 6% of eligible men and 5% of eligible women are members. Major annual events: Homecoming, Wares of the World, International Festival. Student services: personal-psychological counseling. Campus security: 24-hour emergency response devices and patrols, late night transport-escort service. 399 college housing spaces available; 378 were occupied in 2018-19. No special consideration for freshman housing applicants. IU Southeast Library. Books: 350,569 (physical), 948,599 (digital/electronic); Serial titles: 199 (physical), 184,000 (digital/electronic); Databases: 338. Students can reserve study rooms. Operations spending for the previous fiscal year: $1.1 million. 890 computers available on campus for general student use. A campuswide network can be accessed from student residence rooms and from off campus. Students can access the following: online class registration. Staffed computer lab on campus provides training in use of computers, software, and the Internet.

Community Environment: New Albany (population 37,000), a highly industrialized area, enjoys a temperate climate. It is one of the Falls Cities, the others being Louisville, Kentucky and Jeffersonville, Indiana. Buses and railroads serve the area with airlines available at Louisville, Kentucky, Airport. The American Commercial Barge Line, one of the largest, has a terminal there. Community facilities include many churches, Steamboat Museum, hospital and parks. Some part-time employment is available. Ohio River provides facilities for all water sports. Derby Week is an annual event.

■ **INDIANA WESLEYAN UNIVERSITY**
4201 S Washington St.
Marion, IN 46953-4974
Tel: (765)674-6901; Free: 866-468-6498
Fax: (765)677-2333
E-mail: admissions@indwes.edu
Web Site: www.indwes.edu
Description: Independent Wesleyan, comprehensive, coed. Awards associate, bachelor's, master's, and doctoral degrees and post-master's certificates (also offers adult program with significant enrollment not reflected in profile). Founded 1920. Setting: 300-acre small town campus with easy access to Indianapolis. Total enrollment: 3,071. Faculty: 267 (160 full-time, 107 part-time). Student-undergrad faculty ratio is 13:1. 3,796 applied, 72% were admitted. 30% from top 10% of their high school class, 57% from top quarter, 88% from top half. Full-time: 2,634 students, 65% women, 35% men. Part-time: 165 students, 61% women, 39% men. 0.2% American Indian or Alaska Native, non-Hispanic/Latino; 4% Hispanic/Latino; 4% Black or African American, non-Hispanic/Latino; 2% Asian, non-Hispanic/Latino; 1% international. 3% 25 or older, 82% live on campus, 4% transferred in. Retention: 82% of full-time freshmen returned the following year. Core. Calendar: semesters. Academic remediation for entering students, services for LD students, advanced placement, freshman honors college, honors program, independent study, distance learning, double major, summer session for credit, part-time degree program, internships. Off campus study at Taylor University, Council for Christian Colleges and Universities. Study abroad program. ROTC: Army.

Entrance Requirements: Options: electronic application, deferred admission, international baccalaureate accepted. Required: essay, high school transcript, minimum 2.5 high school GPA, 2 recommendations, SAT or ACT.

Required for some: TOEFL for non-English speaking and some non-resident alien students. Entrance: moderately difficult. SAT Reasoning Test deadline: 8/15. Transfer credits accepted: Yes.

Costs Per Year: Comprehensive fee: $34,292 includes full-time tuition ($25,980) and college room and board ($8312). College room only: $4154. Full-time tuition varies according to course load and degree level. Room and board charges vary according to board plan. Part-time tuition: $555 per credit hour. Part-time tuition varies according to course load and degree level.

Collegiate Environment: Orientation program. Drama-theater group, choral group, student-run newspaper, radio station. Most popular organizations: Student Government Organization, Student Activities Council, University Players, World Christian Fellowship, Sixth Man Club. Major annual events: Homecoming, Friday Night Live, Spotted Cow Music Festival. Student services: health clinic, personal-psychological counseling. Campus security: 24-hour emergency response devices and patrols, late night transport-escort service, controlled dormitory access. Lewis A. Jackson Library. Students can reserve study rooms.

Community Environment: Marion is an industrial city in a farming and fruit raising region, located 70 miles northeast of Indianapolis and 50 miles southwest of Ft. Wayne in Grant County. Bus service is available. Major industries located here are Thompson Electronics, BICC Cables, General Motors, Gencorp., Foster-Forbes Glass, and General Plastics. Part-time employment is abundant. Mississinewa Lake and Salamonie Reservoir and Dam are nearby, providing facilities for many outdoor sports; also the city has facilities for tennis, swimming, and picnics. The Easter Pageant and Christmas Walkway of Lights are an annual event.

■ **INTERNATIONAL BUSINESS COLLEGE (FORT WAYNE)**
5699 Coventry Ln.
Fort Wayne, IN 46804
Tel: (260)459-4500; Free: 800-589-6363
Fax: (260)436-1896
Web Site: www.ibcfortwayne.edu
Description: Proprietary, 4-year, coed. Awards associate and bachelor's degrees. Founded 1889. Setting: suburban campus. Total enrollment: 372. 764 applied, 75% were admitted. Calendar: semesters. Accelerated degree program, internships.

■ **INTERNATIONAL BUSINESS COLLEGE (INDIANAPOLIS)**
7205 Shadeland Station
Indianapolis, IN 46256
Tel: (317)813-2300; Free: 800-589-6500
Fax: (317)841-6419
Web Site: www.ibcindianapolis.edu
Description: Proprietary, 2-year, coed. Awards diplomas and terminal associate degrees. Founded 1889. Setting: suburban campus. Total enrollment: 354. 825 applied, 71% were admitted. Calendar: semesters. Accelerated degree program, internships.

■ **IVY TECH COMMUNITY COLLEGE-BLOOMINGTON**
200 Daniels Way
Bloomington, IN 47404
Tel: (812)332-1559; Free: 888-IVY-LINE
Fax: (812)332-8147
E-mail: nfrederi@ivytech.edu
Web Site: www.ivytech.edu
Description: State-supported, 2-year, coed. Part of Ivy Tech Community College System. Awards certificates, transfer associate, and terminal associate degrees. Founded 2001. Total enrollment: 6,198. Faculty: 318 (99 full-time, 219 part-time). Student-undergrad faculty ratio is 19:1. 2,141 applied, 100% were admitted. Full-time: 1,656 students, 56% women, 44% men. Part-time: 4,542 students, 64% women, 36% men. 1% from out-of-state. 0.2% American Indian or Alaska Native, non-Hispanic/Latino; 1% Hispanic/ Latino; 3% Black or African American, non-Hispanic/Latino; 2% Asian, non-Hispanic/Latino; 0.2% Native Hawaiian or other Pacific Islander, non-Hispanic/Latino. 41% 25 or older, 5% transferred in. Retention: 50% of full-time freshmen returned the following year. Core. Calendar: semesters. Academic remediation for entering students, services for LD students, advanced placement, distance learning, summer session for credit, part-time degree program, external degree program, adult/continuing education programs, internships.
Entrance Requirements: Open admission. Options: electronic application, deferred admission. Required: high school transcript. Required for some:

interview. Entrance: noncompetitive. Application deadline: rolling. Notification: continuous. Preference given to state residents.
Collegiate Environment: Orientation program. Most popular organizations: Student Government, Phi Theta Kappa. Campus security: late night transport-escort service. 221 computers available on campus for general student use. Students can access the following: online class registration.

■ **IVY TECH COMMUNITY COLLEGE-CENTRAL INDIANA**
50 W Fall Creek Pky. N Dr.
Indianapolis, IN 46206-1763
Tel: (317)921-4800; Free: 888-IVYLINE
E-mail: tfunk@ivytech.edu
Web Site: www.ivytech.edu
Description: State-supported, 2-year, coed. Part of Ivy Tech Community College System. Awards certificates, transfer associate, and terminal associate degrees. Founded 1963. Setting: 10-acre urban campus. Total enrollment: 18,062. Faculty: 946 (187 full-time, 759 part-time). Student-undergrad faculty ratio is 23:1. Full-time: 4,604 students, 52% women, 48% men. Part-time: 13,458 students, 53% women, 47% men. 1% from out-of-state. 0.2% American Indian or Alaska Native, non-Hispanic/Latino; 5% Hispanic/Latino; 22% Black or African American, non-Hispanic/Latino; 4% Asian, non-Hispanic/Latino; 0.2% Native Hawaiian or other Pacific Islander, non-Hispanic/Latino. 46% 25 or older, 7% transferred in. Retention: 46% of full-time freshmen returned the following year. Core. Calendar: semesters. Academic remediation for entering students, ESL program, services for LD students, advanced placement, distance learning, summer session for credit, part-time degree program, adult/continuing education programs, co-op programs and internships. Off campus study at Indiana University-Purdue University at Indianapolis, Butler University, Marian College, University of Indianapolis, Martin University, Franklin College of Indiana.
Entrance Requirements: Open admission except for human services and health technology programs. Options: electronic application, early admission, deferred admission. Required: high school transcript. Required for some: interview. Entrance: noncompetitive. Application deadline: rolling. Notification: continuous. Preference given to state residents.
Collegiate Environment: Orientation program. Student-run newspaper. Most popular organizations: Student Government, Phi Theta Kappa, Human Services Club, Administrative Office Assistants Club, Radiology Club. Student services: personal-psychological counseling. Campus security: 24-hour emergency response devices and patrols, late night transport-escort service. 407 computers available on campus for general student use. Students can access the following: online class registration. Staffed computer lab on campus.

■ **IVY TECH COMMUNITY COLLEGE-COLUMBUS**
4475 Central Ave.
Columbus, IN 47203
Tel: (812)372-9925; Free: 888-IVY-LINE
Fax: (812)372-0311
E-mail: adeck@ivytech.edu
Web Site: www.ivytech.edu
Description: State-supported, 2-year, coed. Part of Ivy Tech Community College System. Awards certificates, transfer associate, and terminal associate degrees. Founded 1963. Setting: small town campus with easy access to Indianapolis. Total enrollment: 2,653. Faculty: 196 (53 full-time, 143 part-time). Student-undergrad faculty ratio is 15:1. Full-time: 652 students, 60% women, 40% men. Part-time: 2,001 students, 60% women, 40% men. 1% from out-of-state. 0.2% American Indian or Alaska Native, non-Hispanic/ Latino; 3% Hispanic/Latino; 2% Black or African American, non-Hispanic/ Latino; 1% Asian, non-Hispanic/Latino; 0.1% Native Hawaiian or other Pacific Islander, non-Hispanic/Latino. 45% 25 or older, 5% transferred in. Core. Calendar: semesters. Academic remediation for entering students, services for LD students, advanced placement, distance learning, summer session for credit, part-time degree program, adult/continuing education programs, internships.
Entrance Requirements: Open admission except for human services and health technology programs. Options: electronic application, early admission, deferred admission. Required: high school transcript. Required for some: interview. Entrance: noncompetitive. Application deadline: rolling. Notification: continuous. Preference given to state residents.
Collegiate Environment: Orientation program. Most popular organizations: Student Government, Phi Theta Kappa, LPN Club. Campus security: late night transport-escort service, trained evening security personnel, escort

service. 185 computers available on campus for general student use. Students can access the following: online class registration. Staffed computer lab on campus.

■ IVY TECH COMMUNITY COLLEGE-EAST CENTRAL
4301 S Cowan Rd.
Muncie, IN 47302
Tel: (765)289-2291; Free: 888-IVY-LINE
E-mail: mlewelle@ivytech.edu
Web Site: www.ivytech.edu
Description: State-supported, 2-year, coed. Part of Ivy Tech Community College System. Awards certificates, transfer associate, and terminal associate degrees. Founded 1968. Setting: 15-acre suburban campus with easy access to Indianapolis. Total enrollment: 5,462. Faculty: 468 (116 full-time, 352 part-time). Student-undergrad faculty ratio is 15:1. Full-time: 2,030 students, 60% women, 40% men. Part-time: 3,432 students, 61% women, 39% men. 1% from out-of-state. 0.3% American Indian or Alaska Native, non-Hispanic/Latino; 2% Hispanic/Latino; 7% Black or African American, non-Hispanic/Latino; 0.7% Asian, non-Hispanic/Latino; 0.1% Native Hawaiian or other Pacific Islander, non-Hispanic/Latino. 41% 25 or older, 6% transferred in. Retention: 48% of full-time freshmen returned the following year. Core. Calendar: semesters. Academic remediation for entering students, services for LD students, advanced placement, distance learning, part-time degree program, adult/continuing education programs, internships.
Entrance Requirements: Open admission except for allied health programs in human services and health technology. Options: electronic application, early admission, deferred admission. Required: high school transcript. Required for some: interview. Entrance: noncompetitive. Application deadline: rolling. Notification: continuous. Preference given to state residents.
Collegiate Environment: Orientation program. Most popular organizations: Business Professionals of America, SkillsUSA-VICA, Student Government, Phi Theta Kappa, Human Services Club. 270 computers available on campus for general student use. A campuswide network can be accessed from off-campus. Students can access the following: online class registration. Staffed computer lab on campus.

■ IVY TECH COMMUNITY COLLEGE-KOKOMO
1815 E Morgan St.
Kokomo, IN 46903-1373
Tel: (765)459-0561; Free: 888-IVY-LINE
E-mail: mfedersp@ivytech.edu
Web Site: www.ivytech.edu
Description: State-supported, 2-year, coed. Part of Ivy Tech Community College System. Awards certificates, transfer associate, and terminal associate degrees. Founded 1968. Setting: 20-acre small town campus with easy access to Indianapolis. Total enrollment: 2,422. Faculty: 221 (59 full-time, 162 part-time). Student-undergrad faculty ratio is 12:1. Full-time: 804 students, 56% women, 44% men. Part-time: 1,618 students, 60% women, 40% men. 0.7% American Indian or Alaska Native, non-Hispanic/Latino; 4% Hispanic/Latino; 6% Black or African American, non-Hispanic/Latino; 2% Asian, non-Hispanic/Latino. 49% 25 or older, 5% transferred in. Retention: 55% of full-time freshmen returned the following year. Core. Calendar: semesters. Academic remediation for entering students, services for LD students, advanced placement, distance learning, summer session for credit, part-time degree program, adult/continuing education programs, internships.
Entrance Requirements: Open admission except for allied health programs in human services and health technology. Options: electronic application, early admission. Required: high school transcript. Required for some: interview. Entrance: noncompetitive. Application deadline: rolling. Notification: continuous. Preference given to state residents.
Collegiate Environment: Student-run newspaper. Most popular organizations: Student Government, Collegiate Secretaries International, Licensed Practical Nursing Club, Phi Theta Kappa. Student services: personal-psychological counseling. Campus security: 24-hour emergency response devices, late night transport-escort service. 320 computers available on campus for general student use. A campuswide network can be accessed from off-campus. Students can access the following: online class registration. Staffed computer lab on campus.

■ IVY TECH COMMUNITY COLLEGE-LAFAYETTE
3101 S Creasy Ln.
Lafayette, IN 47905
Tel: (765)772-9100; Free: 888-IVY-LINE

E-mail: ihernand@ivytech.edu
Web Site: www.ivytech.edu
Description: State-supported, 2-year, coed. Part of Ivy Tech Community College System. Awards certificates, transfer associate, and terminal associate degrees. Founded 1968. Setting: suburban campus with easy access to Indianapolis. Total enrollment: 4,517. Faculty: 397 (89 full-time, 308 part-time). Student-undergrad faculty ratio is 15:1. Full-time: 1,698 students, 53% women, 47% men. Part-time: 2,819 students, 56% women, 44% men. 1% from out-of-state. 0.4% American Indian or Alaska Native, non-Hispanic/Latino; 6% Hispanic/Latino; 5% Black or African American, non-Hispanic/Latino; 2% Asian, non-Hispanic/Latino; 0.2% Native Hawaiian or other Pacific Islander, non-Hispanic/Latino. 36% 25 or older, 7% transferred in. Retention: 53% of full-time freshmen returned the following year. Core. Calendar: semesters. Academic remediation for entering students, services for LD students, advanced placement, distance learning, summer session for credit, part-time degree program, internships.
Entrance Requirements: Open admission except for allied health programs in human services and health technology. Option: electronic application. Required: high school transcript. Required for some: interview. Entrance: noncompetitive. Application deadline: rolling. Notification: continuous. Preference given to state residents.
Collegiate Environment: Orientation program. Student-run newspaper. Most popular organizations: Student Government, Phi Theta Kappa, LPN Club, Accounting Club, Student Computer Technology Association. Student services: personal-psychological counseling. 267 computers available on campus for general student use. A campuswide network can be accessed. Students can access the following: online class registration. Staffed computer lab on campus.

■ IVY TECH COMMUNITY COLLEGE-NORTH CENTRAL
220 Dean Johnson Blvd.
South Bend, IN 46601
Tel: (574)289-7001; Free: 888-IVY-LINE
Fax: (574)236-7181
E-mail: dwilliams770@ivytech.edu
Web Site: www.ivytech.edu
Description: State-supported, 2-year, coed. Part of Ivy Tech Community College System. Awards certificates, transfer associate, and terminal associate degrees. Founded 1968. Setting: 4-acre suburban campus. Total enrollment: 4,805. Faculty: 374 (106 full-time, 268 part-time). Student-undergrad faculty ratio is 14:1. Full-time: 1,407 students, 61% women, 39% men. Part-time: 3,398 students, 63% women, 37% men. 2% from out-of-state. 0.4% American Indian or Alaska Native, non-Hispanic/Latino; 11% Hispanic/Latino; 14% Black or African American, non-Hispanic/Latino; 1% Asian, non-Hispanic/Latino; 0.2% Native Hawaiian or other Pacific Islander, non-Hispanic/Latino. 49% 25 or older, 8% transferred in. Retention: 47% of full-time freshmen returned the following year. Core. Calendar: semesters. Academic remediation for entering students, ESL program, services for LD students, advanced placement, distance learning, summer session for credit, part-time degree program, adult/continuing education programs, internships. Off campus study at other members of the Northern Indiana Consortium for Education.
Entrance Requirements: Open admission except for allied health programs, in human services and health technology. Options: electronic application, early admission, deferred admission. Required: high school transcript. Required for some: interview. Entrance: noncompetitive. Application deadline: rolling. Notification: continuous. Preference given to state residents.
Collegiate Environment: Orientation program. Most popular organizations: Phi Theta Kappa, Student Government, LPN Club. Student services: personal-psychological counseling, women's center. Campus security: 24-hour emergency response devices and patrols, late night transport-escort service, security during hours of operation. 426 computers available on campus for general student use. Students can access the following: online class registration. Staffed computer lab on campus.

■ IVY TECH COMMUNITY COLLEGE-NORTHEAST
3800 N Anthony Blvd.
Fort Wayne, IN 46805
Tel: (260)482-9171; Free: 888-IVY-LINE
Fax: (260)480-4177
E-mail: rboss1@ivytech.edu
Web Site: www.ivytech.edu
Description: State-supported, 2-year, coed. Part of Ivy Tech Community

College System. Awards certificates, transfer associate, and terminal associate degrees. Founded 1969. Setting: 22-acre urban campus. Total enrollment: 6,795. Faculty: 449 (137 full-time, 312 part-time). Student-undergrad faculty ratio is 16:1. Full-time: 1,869 students, 55% women, 45% men. Part-time: 4,926 students, 54% women, 46% men. 1% from out-of-state. 0.5% American Indian or Alaska Native, non-Hispanic/Latino; 5% Hispanic/Latino; 11% Black or African American, non-Hispanic/Latino; 3% Asian, non-Hispanic/Latino; 0.2% Native Hawaiian or other Pacific Islander, non-Hispanic/Latino. 45% 25 or older, 7% transferred in. Retention: 50% of full-time freshmen returned the following year. Core. Calendar: semesters. ESL program, services for LD students, advanced placement, distance learning, summer session for credit, part-time degree program, adult/continuing education programs, internships.

Entrance Requirements: Open admission except for allied health programs in human services and health technology. Option: early admission. Required: high school transcript. Required for some: interview. Entrance: noncompetitive. Application deadline: rolling. Notification: continuous. Preference given to state residents.

Collegiate Environment: Orientation program. Student-run newspaper. Most popular organizations: Student Government, LPN Club, Phi Theta Kappa. Campus security: 24-hour emergency response devices and patrols, late night transport-escort service. 382 computers available on campus for general student use. Students can access the following: online class registration. Staffed computer lab on campus.

■ IVY TECH COMMUNITY COLLEGE-NORTHWEST

1440 E 35th Ave.
Gary, IN 46409
Tel: (219)981-1111; Free: 888-IVY-LINE
E-mail: dwilliams770@ivytech.edu
Web Site: www.ivytech.edu

Description: State-supported, 2-year, coed. Part of Ivy Tech Community College System. Awards certificates, transfer associate, and terminal associate degrees. Founded 1963. Setting: 13-acre urban campus with easy access to Chicago. Total enrollment: 8,314. Faculty: 495 (131 full-time, 364 part-time). Student-undergrad faculty ratio is 18:1. Full-time: 2,399 students, 59% women, 41% men. Part-time: 5,915 students, 56% women, 44% men. 1% from out-of-state. 0.4% American Indian or Alaska Native, non-Hispanic/Latino; 10% Hispanic/Latino; 21% Black or African American, non-Hispanic/Latino; 0.9% Asian, non-Hispanic/Latino; 0.2% Native Hawaiian or other Pacific Islander, non-Hispanic/Latino. 48% 25 or older, 9% transferred in. Core. Calendar: semesters. Academic remediation for entering students, services for LD students, advanced placement, distance learning, summer session for credit, part-time degree program, adult/continuing education programs, internships.

Entrance Requirements: Open admission except for allied health programs in human services and health technology. Options: electronic application, deferred admission. Required: high school transcript. Required for some: interview. Entrance: noncompetitive. Application deadline: rolling. Notification: continuous. Preference given to state residents.

Collegiate Environment: Orientation program. Most popular organizations: Phi Theta Kappa, LPN Club, Computer Club, Student Government, Business Club. Campus security: 24-hour emergency response devices, late night transport-escort service. 267 computers available on campus for general student use. Students can access the following: online class registration. Staffed computer lab on campus.

■ IVY TECH COMMUNITY COLLEGE-RICHMOND

2357 Chester Blvd.
Richmond, IN 47374
Tel: (765)966-2656; Free: 888-IVY-LINE
E-mail: lprzybys@ivytech.edu
Web Site: www.ivytech.edu

Description: State-supported, 2-year, coed. Part of Ivy Tech Community College System. Awards certificates, transfer associate, and terminal associate degrees. Founded 1963. Setting: 23-acre small town campus with easy access to Indianapolis. Total enrollment: 1,527. Faculty: 127 (40 full-time, 87 part-time). Student-undergrad faculty ratio is 13:1. Full-time: 415 students, 64% women, 36% men. Part-time: 1,112 students, 64% women, 36% men. 1% from out-of-state. 0.6% American Indian or Alaska Native, non-Hispanic/Latino; 0.6% Hispanic/Latino; 4% Black or African American, non-Hispanic/Latino; 0.5% Asian, non-Hispanic/Latino; 0.1% Native Hawaiian or other Pacific Islander, non-Hispanic/Latino. 53% 25 or older, 7% transferred in. Retention: 50% of full-time freshmen returned the following year. Core.

Calendar: semesters. Academic remediation for entering students, services for LD students, advanced placement, independent study, distance learning, summer session for credit, part-time degree program, adult/continuing education programs, internships. Off campus study at Indiana University East.

Entrance Requirements: Open admission except for human services and health technology programs. Options: electronic application, early admission. Required: high school transcript. Required for some: interview. Entrance: noncompetitive. Application deadline: rolling. Notification: continuous. Preference given to state residents.

Collegiate Environment: Orientation program. Student-run newspaper. Most popular organizations: Student Government, Phi Theta Kappa, LPN Club, CATS 2000, Business Professionals of America. Student services: personal-psychological counseling. Campus security: 24-hour emergency response devices, late night transport-escort service. 169 computers available on campus for general student use. A campuswide network can be accessed. Students can access the following: online class registration. Staffed computer lab on campus.

■ IVY TECH COMMUNITY COLLEGE-SELLERSBURG

8204 Hwy. 311
Sellersburg, IN 47172
Tel: (812)246-3301; Free: 888-IVY-LINE
E-mail: bharris88@ivytech.edu
Web Site: www.ivytech.edu

Description: State-supported, 2-year, coed. Part of Ivy Tech Community College System. Awards certificates, transfer associate, and terminal associate degrees. Founded 1968. Setting: 63-acre small town campus with easy access to Louisville. Total enrollment: 4,684. Faculty: 203 (54 full-time, 149 part-time). Student-undergrad faculty ratio is 20:1. Full-time: 867 students, 63% women, 37% men. Part-time: 3,817 students, 49% women, 51% men. 9% from out-of-state. 0.3% American Indian or Alaska Native, non-Hispanic/Latino; 2% Hispanic/Latino; 7% Black or African American, non-Hispanic/Latino; 0.8% Asian, non-Hispanic/Latino; 0.1% Native Hawaiian or other Pacific Islander, non-Hispanic/Latino. 51% 25 or older, 8% transferred in. Retention: 55% of full-time freshmen returned the following year. Core. Calendar: semesters. Academic remediation for entering students, services for LD students, advanced placement, distance learning, summer session for credit, part-time degree program, adult/continuing education programs, co-op programs and internships.

Entrance Requirements: Open admission except for human services and health programs. Options: electronic application, early admission, deferred admission. Required: high school transcript. Required for some: interview. Entrance: noncompetitive. Application deadline: rolling. Notification: continuous. Preference given to state residents.

Collegiate Environment: Orientation program. Most popular organizations: Phi Theta Kappa, Practical Nursing Club, Medical Assistant Club, Accounting Club, Student Government. Campus security: late night transport-escort service. 187 computers available on campus for general student use. A campuswide network can be accessed. Students can access the following: online class registration. Staffed computer lab on campus.

■ IVY TECH COMMUNITY COLLEGE-SOUTHEAST

590 Ivy Tech Dr.
Madison, IN 47250
Tel: (812)265-4028; Free: 888-IVY-LINE
E-mail: sgrubbs5@ivytech.edu
Web Site: www.ivytech.edu

Description: State-supported, 2-year, coed. Part of Ivy Tech Community College System. Awards certificates, transfer associate, and terminal associate degrees. Founded 1963. Setting: 5-acre small town campus with easy access to Louisville. Total enrollment: 2,334. Faculty: 183 (54 full-time, 129 part-time). Student-undergrad faculty ratio is 13:1. Full-time: 635 students, 63% women, 37% men. Part-time: 1,699 students, 64% women, 36% men. 1% from out-of-state. 0.4% American Indian or Alaska Native, non-Hispanic/Latino; 0.7% Hispanic/Latino; 1% Black or African American, non-Hispanic/Latino; 0.5% Asian, non-Hispanic/Latino. 40% 25 or older, 5% transferred in. Retention: 63% of full-time freshmen returned the following year. Core. Calendar: semesters. Academic remediation for entering students, services for LD students, advanced placement, distance learning, summer session for credit, part-time degree program, internships.

Entrance Requirements: Open admission except for human services and health technology programs. Option: electronic application. Required: high school transcript. Required for some: interview. Entrance: noncompetitive. Application deadline: rolling. Notification: continuous. Preference given to state residents.

Collegiate Environment: Orientation program. Most popular organizations: Student Government, Phi Theta Kappa, LPN Club. Campus security: 24-hour emergency response devices. 123 computers available on campus for general student use. A campuswide network can be accessed. Students can access the following: online class registration. Staffed computer lab on campus.

■ IVY TECH COMMUNITY COLLEGE-SOUTHWEST

3501 N First Ave.
Evansville, IN 47710
Tel: (812)426-2865; Free: 888-IVY-LINE
E-mail: ajohnson@ivytech.edu
Web Site: www.ivytech.edu

Description: State-supported, 2-year, coed. Part of Ivy Tech Community College System. Awards certificates, transfer associate, and terminal associate degrees. Founded 1963. Setting: 15-acre suburban campus. Total enrollment: 4,076. Faculty: 290 (77 full-time, 213 part-time). Student-undergrad faculty ratio is 17:1. Full-time: 928 students, 57% women, 43% men. Part-time: 3,148 students, 57% women, 43% men. 1% from out-of-state. 0.3% American Indian or Alaska Native, non-Hispanic/Latino; 0.9% Hispanic/Latino; 7% Black or African American, non-Hispanic/Latino; 0.9% Asian, non-Hispanic/Latino; 0.1% Native Hawaiian or other Pacific Islander, non-Hispanic/Latino. 53% 25 or older, 7% transferred in. Retention: 52% of full-time freshmen returned the following year. Core. Calendar: semesters. Academic remediation for entering students, services for LD students, advanced placement, independent study, distance learning, summer session for credit, part-time degree program, co-op programs and internships.

Entrance Requirements: Open admission except for human services and health technology programs. Options: electronic application, early admission, deferred admission. Required: high school transcript. Required for some: interview. Entrance: noncompetitive. Application deadline: rolling. Notification: continuous. Preference given to state residents.

Collegiate Environment: Orientation program. Most popular organizations: Student Government, Phi Theta Kappa, LPN Club, National Association of Industrial Technology, Design Club. Campus security: late night transport-escort service. 362 computers available on campus for general student use. Students can access the following: online class registration. Staffed computer lab on campus.

■ IVY TECH COMMUNITY COLLEGE-WABASH VALLEY

8000 S Education Dr.
Terre Haute, IN 47802
Tel: (812)299-1121; Free: 888-IVY-LINE
E-mail: nstorey@ivytech.edu
Web Site: www.ivytech.edu

Description: State-supported, 2-year, coed. Part of Ivy Tech Community College System. Awards certificates, transfer associate, and terminal associate degrees. Founded 1966. Setting: 55-acre suburban campus with easy access to Indianapolis. Total enrollment: 3,637. Faculty: 287 (98 full-time, 189 part-time). Student-undergrad faculty ratio is 19:1. Full-time: 1,216 students, 62% women, 38% men. Part-time: 2,421 students, 53% women, 47% men. 1% from out-of-state. 0.4% American Indian or Alaska Native, non-Hispanic/Latino; 0.7% Hispanic/Latino; 4% Black or African American, non-Hispanic/Latino; 0.5% Asian, non-Hispanic/Latino. 45% 25 or older, 7% transferred in. Retention: 55% of full-time freshmen returned the following year. Core. Calendar: semesters. Academic remediation for entering students, services for LD students, advanced placement, distance learning, summer session for credit, part-time degree program, adult/continuing education programs, internships.

Entrance Requirements: Open admission except for allied health programs in human services and health technology. Options: electronic application, early admission, deferred admission. Required: high school transcript. Required for some: interview. Entrance: noncompetitive. Application deadline: rolling. Notification: continuous. Preference given to state residents.

Collegiate Environment: Orientation program. Most popular organizations: Student Government, Phi Theta Kappa, LPN Club, National Association of Industrial Technology. Student services: personal-psychological counseling, women's center. Campus security: 24-hour emergency response devices. 305 computers available on campus for general student use. A campuswide

network can be accessed. Students can access the following: online class registration. Staffed computer lab on campus.

■ LINCOLN COLLEGE OF TECHNOLOGY

7225 Winton Dr.
Bldg. 128
Indianapolis, IN 46268
Tel: (317)632-5553; Free: 844-215-1513
Web Site: www.lincolntech.edu

Description: Proprietary, 2-year, coed. Part of Lincoln Technical Institute, Inc. Awards certificates and terminal associate degrees. Founded 1946. Setting: urban campus. Total enrollment: 1,650. 17% 25 or older. Calendar: modular. Summer session for credit.

Entrance Requirements: Required: high school transcript, interview. Entrance: minimally difficult. Application deadline: rolling.

Collegiate Environment: Orientation program. Student services: personal-psychological counseling.

■ MANCHESTER UNIVERSITY

604 E College Ave.
North Manchester, IN 46962-1225
Tel: (260)982-5000; Free: 800-852-3648
Fax: (260)982-5043
E-mail: bcchauncey@manchester.edu
Web Site: www.manchester.edu

Description: Independent, comprehensive, coed, affiliated with Church of the Brethren. Awards associate, bachelor's, master's, and doctoral degrees. Founded 1889. Setting: 125-acre small town campus. Endowment: $60.2 million. Research spending for the previous fiscal year: $551,000. Educational spending for the previous fiscal year: $9839 per student. Total enrollment: 1,530. Faculty: 140 (73 full-time, 67 part-time). Student-undergrad faculty ratio is 14:1. 4,253 applied, 59% were admitted. 13% from top 10% of their high school class, 40% from top quarter, 77% from top half. Full-time: 1,176 students, 53% women, 47% men. Part-time: 15 students, 53% women, 47% men. Students come from 26 states and territories, 20 other countries, 17% from out-of-state. 0.1% American Indian or Alaska Native, non-Hispanic/Latino; 7% Hispanic/Latino; 8% Black or African American, non-Hispanic/Latino; 1% Asian, non-Hispanic/Latino; 4% international. 1% 25 or older, 74% live on campus, 2% transferred in. Retention: 60% of full-time freshmen returned the following year. Academic areas with the most degrees conferred: business/marketing; health professions and related sciences; parks and recreation. Core. Calendar: 4-1-4. Services for LD students, advanced placement, accelerated degree program, self-designed majors, honors program, independent study, distance learning, double major, summer session for credit, part-time degree program, internships. Off campus study. Study abroad program.

Entrance Requirements: Options: electronic application, deferred admission, international baccalaureate accepted. Required: high school transcript, 1 recommendation, rank in upper 50% of high school class. Recommended: minimum 2.3 high school GPA. Required for some: minimum 3 high school GPA. Entrance: moderately difficult. Application deadline: rolling. Notification: continuous. Transfer credits accepted: Yes.

Costs Per Year: Application fee: $25. One-time mandatory fee: $250. Comprehensive fee: $43,674 includes full-time tuition ($32,366), mandatory fees ($1258), and college room and board ($10,050). College room only: $5350. Part-time tuition: $745 per credit hour. Part-time mandatory fees: $35 per credit hour.

Collegiate Environment: Orientation program. Drama-theater group, choral group, student-run newspaper, radio station. Social organizations: 61 open to all. Most popular organizations: College of Business Club, Fellowship of Christian Athletes, Student Education Association, African Student Association, Asian Awareness Association. Major annual events: Homecoming/Family Weekend, Lil' Sibs Weekends, May Day Weekend. Student services: health clinic, personal-psychological counseling. Campus security: 24-hour patrols, student patrols, late night transport-escort service. 1,000 college housing spaces available; 910 were occupied in 2018-19. Freshmen guaranteed college housing. On-campus residence required through junior year. Option: coed housing available. Funderburg Library. Study areas open 24 hours, 5-7 days a week. Operations spending for the previous fiscal year: $421,330. 226 computers available on campus for general student use. Computer purchase/lease plans available. A campuswide network can be accessed from student residence rooms and from off campus. Students can access the following: online class registration.

Community Environment: North Manchester (population 6,000) is situated in north central Indiana, 35 miles west of Ft. Wayne, and 100 miles north of Indianapolis, and 3 hours from Chicago, enjoying a favorable climate. Bus facilities and airlines are within 30 miles. Community facilities include a library, indoor swimming pool, churches of many denominations, a medical clinic across the street from campus and a hospital within 20 minutes.

■ MARIAN UNIVERSITY

3200 Cold Spring Rd.
Indianapolis, IN 46222-1997
Tel: (317)955-6000
E-mail: admissions@marian.edu
Web Site: www.marian.edu

Description: Independent Roman Catholic, comprehensive, coed. Awards associate, bachelor's, master's, and doctoral degrees. Founded 1851. Setting: 114-acre suburban campus with easy access to Indianapolis. Endowment: $63.7 million. Research spending for the previous fiscal year: $136,807. Educational spending for the previous fiscal year: $11,560 per student. Total enrollment: 3,592. Faculty: 316 (155 full-time, 161 part-time). Student-undergrad faculty ratio is 14:1. 2,325 applied, 61% were admitted. 20% from top 10% of their high school class, 48% from top quarter, 76% from top half. Full-time: 1,995 students, 61% women, 39% men. Part-time: 433 students, 73% women, 27% men. Students come from 35 states and territories, 34 other countries, 23% from out-of-state. 6% Hispanic/Latino; 11% Black or African American, non-Hispanic/Latino; 3% Asian, non-Hispanic/Latino; 0.1% Native Hawaiian or other Pacific Islander, non-Hispanic/Latino; 1% international. 25% 25 or older, 49% live on campus, 2% transferred in. Retention: 77% of full-time freshmen returned the following year. Academic areas with the most degrees conferred: health professions and related sciences; business/marketing; parks and recreation. Core. Calendar: semesters. Academic remediation for entering students, services for LD students, advanced placement, accelerated degree program, honors program, independent study, distance learning, double major, summer session for credit, part-time degree program, adult/continuing education programs, co-op programs and internships. Off campus study at Indiana University-Purdue University at Indianapolis, University of Indianapolis, Christian Theological Seminary, Butler University. Study abroad program. ROTC: Army (c).

Entrance Requirements: Options: electronic application, deferred admission, international baccalaureate accepted. Required: high school transcript, college transcripts for transfer students, SAT or ACT. Required for some: essay, 1 recommendation, interview. Entrance: moderately difficult. Notification: continuous. SAT Reasoning Test deadline: 8/1. Transfer credits accepted: Yes.

Costs Per Year: Application fee: $0. Comprehensive fee: $14,460 includes full-time tuition ($3500) and college room and board ($10,960). Part-time tuition: $1500 per credit hour.

Collegiate Environment: Orientation program. Drama-theater group, choral group, marching band, student-run newspaper. Social organizations: 40 open to all. Most popular organizations: Student Government Association, College Mentors for Kids, Best Buddies, Knight Nation, Sophia Club. Major annual events: Homecoming, Fall and Spring Formal, Monthly Coffeehouse and Open Mic Series. Student services: health clinic, personal-psychological counseling. Campus security: 24-hour emergency response devices and patrols, student patrols, late night transport-escort service, controlled dormitory access. College housing designed to accommodate 887 students; 918 undergraduates lived in college housing during 2018-19. Freshmen guaranteed college housing. On-campus residence required through junior year. Option: coed housing available. Mother Theresa Hackelmeier Memorial Library. Books: 80,118 (physical); Serial titles: 150 (physical), 44,749 (digital/electronic). Weekly public service hours: 95. Operations spending for the previous fiscal year: $1.2 million. 201 computers available on campus for general student use. Computer purchase/lease plans available. A campuswide network can be accessed from student residence rooms. Students can access the following: online class registration. Staffed computer lab on campus provides training in use of computers, software, and the Internet.

Community Environment: See Butler University.

■ MARTIN UNIVERSITY

2171 Avondale Pl.
Indianapolis, IN 46218-3867
Tel: (317)543-3235
Fax: (317)543-3257
Web Site: www.martin.edu

Description: Independent, comprehensive, coed. Awards bachelor's and master's degrees. Founded 1977. Setting: 5-acre urban campus. Endowment: $128,101. Educational spending for the previous fiscal year: $2759 per student. Total enrollment: 1,236. Faculty: 43 (26 full-time, 17 part-time). Student-undergrad faculty ratio is 21:1. 243 applied, 96% were admitted. Full-time: 336 students, 77% women, 23% men. Part-time: 738 students, 64% women, 36% men. Students come from 2 other countries. 93% 25 or older. Retention: 75% of full-time freshmen returned the following year. Academic areas with the most degrees conferred: liberal arts/general studies; psychology; business/marketing. Core. Calendar: semesters. Academic remediation for entering students, advanced placement, accelerated degree program, self-designed majors, honors program, independent study, double major, summer session for credit, part-time degree program, external degree program, adult/continuing education programs, internships, graduate courses open to undergrads. Off campus study at Consortium for Urban Education (CUE).

Entrance Requirements: Open admission. Options: electronic application, early admission, deferred admission. Required: essay, high school transcript, interview, writing sample. Entrance: noncompetitive. Application deadline: rolling. Notification: continuous.

Collegiate Environment: Orientation program. Major annual events: Orientation, Honors Program, Constitution Day. Campus security: building security, security personnel from 7 am to 9:30 pm. 20 computers available on campus for general student use. Computer purchase/lease plans available. A campuswide network can be accessed. Staffed computer lab on campus provides training in use of computers, software, and the Internet.

■ MID-AMERICA COLLEGE OF FUNERAL SERVICE

3111 Hamburg Pke.
Jeffersonville, IN 47130-9630
Tel: (812)288-8878; Free: 800-221-6158
Fax: (812)288-5942
E-mail: macfs@mindspring.com
Web Site: www.mid-america.edu

Description: Independent, primarily 2-year, coed. Awards terminal associate and bachelor's degrees. Founded 1905. Setting: 3-acre small town campus with easy access to Louisville. Total enrollment: 120. Faculty: 7 (6 full-time, 1 part-time). Student-undergrad faculty ratio is 13:1. Students come from 6 states and territories. 13% 25 or older. Core. Calendar: quarters. Academic remediation for entering students.

Entrance Requirements: Open admission. Option: deferred admission. Required: high school transcript. Entrance: minimally difficult. Application deadline: rolling.

Collegiate Environment: Orientation program. 15 computers available on campus for general student use. Staffed computer lab on campus.

■ NATIONAL AMERICAN UNIVERSITY

3600 Woodview Trace
Ste. 200
Indianapolis, IN 46268
Tel: (317)810-8100; Free: 800-609-1430
Web Site: www.national.edu

Description: Proprietary, 4-year, coed. Awards associate and bachelor's degrees.

■ OAKLAND CITY UNIVERSITY

138 N Lucretia St.
Oakland City, IN 47660-1099
Tel: (812)749-4781; Free: 800-737-5125
Fax: (812)749-1233
E-mail: jcates@oak.edu
Web Site: www.oak.edu

Description: Independent General Baptist, comprehensive, coed. Awards associate, bachelor's, master's, and doctoral degrees. Founded 1885. Setting: 20-acre rural campus. Endowment: $5.2 million. Total enrollment: 1,419. Faculty: 155 (35 full-time, 120 part-time). Student-undergrad faculty ratio is 12:1. 1,010 applied, 50% were admitted. 5% from top 10% of their high school class, 34% from top quarter, 55% from top half. Full-time: 597 students, 52% women, 48% men. Part-time: 634 students, 54% women, 46% men. Students come from 17 states and territories, 12 other countries, 19% from out-of-state. 0.5% American Indian or Alaska Native, non-Hispanic/Latino; 4% Hispanic/Latino; 7% Black or African American, non-Hispanic/Latino; 0.2% Asian, non-Hispanic/Latino; 3% international. 39% 25 or older, 61% live on campus, 5% transferred in. Retention: 62% of full-time freshmen returned the following year. Academic areas with the most degrees conferred: business/marketing; homeland security, law enforcement, firefighting, and protective services; biological/life sciences; education. Core. Calendar: semesters. Academic remediation for entering students, services for LD students, advanced placement, accelerated degree program, distance learning, summer session for credit, part-time degree program, external degree program, adult/continuing education programs.

Entrance Requirements: Options: electronic application, early admission, deferred admission. Required: high school transcript, minimum 2 high school GPA. Recommended: essay, interview. Required for some: SAT or ACT. Entrance: minimally difficult. SAT Reasoning Test deadline: 8/1. Transfer credits accepted: Yes.

Costs Per Year: Application fee: $35. Comprehensive fee: $34,700 includes full-time tuition ($24,300) and college room and board ($10,400). College room only: $3600. Part-time tuition: $810 per credit hour.

Collegiate Environment: Orientation program. Drama-theater group, choral group, student-run newspaper. Most popular organizations: Student Government Association, Good News Players, Art Guild, FOCUS, intramural sports. Major annual events: Founder's Day, Formal Tea, Homecoming. Student services: personal-psychological counseling. Campus security: 24-hour patrols, student patrols. Freshmen guaranteed college housing. Options: men-only, women-only housing available. Barger-Richardson Library. Books: 84,412 (physical), 17,690 (digital/electronic); Serial titles: 79 (physical), 50,255 (digital/electronic); Databases: 52. 200 computers available on campus for general student use. A campuswide network can be accessed from student residence rooms and from off campus. Students can access the following: online class registration. Staffed computer lab on campus provides training in use of computers, software, and the Internet.

Community Environment: Oakland City is a friendly rural-suburban community with a Midwest climate, temperatures ranging from a high of 98 degrees to a low of ten degrees. Average rainfall is over 40 inches annually. Community facilities include six churches, both Protestant and Catholic, numerous civic and service groups, library, individual stores, and a shopping center 15 miles away. Some part time jobs are available for students.

■ **PURDUE UNIVERSITY**

West Lafayette, IN 47907
Tel: (765)494-4600
Fax: (765)494-0544
E-mail: admissions@purdue.edu
Web Site: www.purdue.edu

Description: State-supported, university, coed. Part of Purdue University System. Awards associate, bachelor's, master's, and doctoral degrees and post-master's certificates. Founded 1869. Setting: 2,660-acre suburban campus with easy access to Indianapolis. Endowment: $2.5 billion. Research spending for the previous fiscal year: $622.8 million. Total enrollment: 43,411. Faculty: 2,700 (2,354 full-time, 346 part-time). Student-undergrad faculty ratio is 13:1. 53,439 applied, 58% were admitted. 32% from top 10% of their high school class, 69% from top quarter, 96% from top half. Full-time: 31,217 students, 43% women, 57% men. Part-time: 1,455 students, 48% women, 52% men. Students come from 47 states and territories, 111 other countries, 39% from out-of-state. 0.1% American Indian or Alaska Native, non-Hispanic/Latino; 5% Hispanic/Latino; 3% Black or African American, non-Hispanic/Latino; 9% Asian, non-Hispanic/Latino; 0.1% Native Hawaiian or other Pacific Islander, non-Hispanic/Latino; 14% international. 2% 25 or older, 41% live on campus, 2% transferred in. Retention: 92% of full-time freshmen returned the following year. Academic areas with the most degrees conferred: engineering; business/marketing; computer and information sciences. Core. Calendar: semesters. ESL program, services for LD students, accelerated degree program, honors program, independent study, distance learning, double major, summer session for credit, part-time degree program, adult/continuing education programs, co-op programs, graduate courses open to undergrads. Study abroad program. ROTC: Army, Naval, Air Force.

Entrance Requirements: Options: electronic application, early admission, early action, deferred admission. Required: essay, high school transcript, SAT or ACT. Entrance: moderately difficult. Application deadline: rolling. Notification: 12/12. SAT Reasoning Test deadline: 2/1. Transfer credits accepted: Yes. Applicants placed on waiting list: 5,276. Wait-listed applicants offered admission: 565.

Costs Per Year: Application fee: $60. State resident tuition: $9208 full-time, $330 per credit hour part-time. Nonresident tuition: $28,010 full-time, $930 per credit hour part-time. Mandatory fees: $784 full-time, $18 per credit hour part-time, $18. College room and board: $10,030. College room only: $4860.

Collegiate Environment: Orientation program. Drama-theater group, choral group, marching band, student-run newspaper, radio station. Social organizations: 968 open to all; national fraternities, national sororities, cooperative housing; 18% of eligible men and 20% of eligible women are members. Most popular organizations: Purdue Student Government, FSCL Councils, RHA, Purdue Engineering Student Council, AG Council. Major annual events: PESC Roundtable, Homecoming, Purdue Dance Marathon. Student services: legal services, health clinic, personal-psychological counseling, women's center. Campus security: 24-hour emergency response devices and patrols, student patrols, late night transport-escort service, controlled dormitory access. 13,950 college housing spaces available; 13,468 were occupied in 2018-19. Freshmen given priority for college housing. Options: coed, men-only, women-only housing available. Purdue University Libraries plus 9 others. Books: 946,376 (physical), 2.5 million (digital/electronic); Serial titles: 44,788 (physical), 136,167 (digital/electronic); Databases: 580. Weekly public service hours: 168; study areas open 24 hours, 5-7 days a week; students can reserve study rooms. Operations spending for the previous fiscal year: $28.8 million. 5,237 computers available on campus for general student use. Computer purchase/lease plans available. A campuswide network can be accessed from student residence rooms and from off campus. Students can access the following: online class registration. Staffed computer lab on campus (open 24 hours a day) provides training in use of computers, software, and the Internet.

Community Environment: Lafayette is located 65 miles northwest of Indianapolis and 120 miles southeast of Chicago. It is located on the Wabash River, in a rich grain-growing county where livestock and dairying are principal agricultural industries. All forms of commercial transportation are available. The community facilities include libraries, churches that represent 34 denominations, Lafayette Symphony Orchestra, Civic Theatre, museums, hospitals, a TV station, and good shopping at downtown locations and 8 other shopping centers. Many hotel and motel accommodations are available for the conventions at Lafayette.

■ **PURDUE UNIVERSITY FORT WAYNE**

2101 E Coliseum Blvd.
Fort Wayne, IN 46805-1499
Tel: (260)481-6100; Free: 800-324-4739
E-mail: morrena@ipfw.edu
Web Site: www.ipfw.edu

Description: State-supported, comprehensive, coed. Part of Indiana University System and Purdue University System. Awards associate, bachelor's, and master's degrees. Founded 1917. Setting: 683-acre urban campus. Endowment: $57.1 million. Research spending for the previous fiscal year: $1.3 million. Educational spending for the previous fiscal year: $6952 per student. Total enrollment: 13,214. Faculty: 801 (403 full-time, 398 part-time). Student-undergrad faculty ratio is 17:1. 3,386 applied, 91% were admitted. 14% from top 10% of their high school class, 38% from top quarter, 75% from top half. 12 valedictorians. Full-time: 6,971 students, 54% women, 46% men. Part-time: 5,703 students, 57% women, 43% men. Students come from 37 states and territories, 45 other countries, 5% from out-of-state. 0.3% American Indian or Alaska Native, non-Hispanic/Latino; 5% Hispanic/Latino; 5% Black or African American, non-Hispanic/Latino; 2% Asian, non-Hispanic/Latino; 1% international. 25% 25 or older, 8% live on campus, 5% transferred in. Retention: 68% of full-time freshmen returned the following year. Academic areas with the most degrees conferred: business/marketing; liberal arts/general studies; health professions and related sciences. Core. Calendar: semesters. Academic remediation for entering students, ESL program, services for LD students, advanced placement, accelerated degree program, self-designed majors, honors program, independent study, distance learning, double major, summer session for credit, part-time degree program, adult/continuing education programs, co-op programs and internships, graduate courses open to undergrads. Off campus study at National Student Exchange. Study abroad program. ROTC: Army.

Entrance Requirements: Options: electronic application, deferred admission, international baccalaureate accepted. Required: high school transcript, minimum 2.8 high school GPA, SAT or ACT. Recommended: rank in upper 50% of high school class. Entrance: minimally difficult. Application deadline: 8/1. Notification: continuous, continuous for nonresidents. SAT Reasoning Test deadline: 8/1. Transfer credits accepted: Yes.

Costs Per Year: Application fee: $50. State resident tuition: $8,450 full-time, $281.65 per credit hour part-time. Nonresident tuition: $20,298 full-time, $676.25 per credit hour part-time. Full-time tuition varies according to course load. Part-time tuition varies according to course load.

Collegiate Environment: Orientation program. Drama-theater group, choral

group, student-run newspaper. Social organizations: 120 open to all. Most popular organizations: Live Action Combat Club, Active Minds, InterVarsity Christian Fellowship, Student Athlete Leadership Team, League of Legends (LOL). Major annual events: PIT Theater Performances, Kids' Carnival, IPFW Health Fair. Student services: health clinic, personal-psychological counseling, women's center. Campus security: 24-hour emergency response devices and patrols, late night transport-escort service, controlled dormitory access. Helmke Library. Operations spending for the previous fiscal year: $2.1 million. 642 computers available on campus for general student use. Computer purchase/lease plans available. A campuswide network can be accessed from student residence rooms and from off campus. Students can access the following: online class registration, student academic records. Staffed computer lab on campus provides training in use of computers, software, and the Internet.

Community Environment: See Indiana Institute of Technology.

■ PURDUE UNIVERSITY GLOBAL
9000 Keystone Crossing
Ste. 800
Indianapolis, IN 46240
Description: Independent, comprehensive, coed.

■ PURDUE UNIVERSITY NORTHWEST
2200 169th St.
Hammond, IN 46323-2094
Tel: (219)989-2400; Free: 800-447-8738
Fax: (219)989-2775
Web Site: www.pnw.edu
Description: State-supported, comprehensive, coed. Part of Purdue University System. Awards associate, bachelor's, master's, and doctoral degrees and post-master's certificates. Founded 2016. Setting: 454-acre urban campus with easy access to Chicago. Endowment: $25.1 million. Research spending for the previous fiscal year: $3.6 million. Educational spending for the previous fiscal year: $9363 per student. Total enrollment: 10,473. Faculty: 699 (372 full-time, 327 part-time). Student-undergrad faculty ratio is 16:1. 1,686 applied, 97% were admitted. 10% from top 10% of their high school class, 33% from top quarter, 53% from top half. Full-time: 5,806 students, 50% women, 50% men. Part-time: 3,767 students, 66% women, 34% men. Students come from 29 states and territories, 37 other countries, 10% from out-of-state. 0.3% American Indian or Alaska Native, non-Hispanic/Latino; 20% Hispanic/Latino; 10% Black or African American, non-Hispanic/Latino; 3% Asian, non-Hispanic/Latino; 0.1% Native Hawaiian or other Pacific Islander, non-Hispanic/Latino; 3% international. 22% 25 or older, 7% live on campus, 9% transferred in. Retention: 69% of full-time freshmen returned the following year. Academic areas with the most degrees conferred: health professions and related sciences; business/marketing; engineering. Core. Calendar: semesters. Academic remediation for entering students, ESL program, services for LD students, advanced placement, accelerated degree program, freshman honors college, honors program, independent study, distance learning, double major, summer session for credit, part-time degree program, adult/continuing education programs, co-op programs and internships, graduate courses open to undergrads. Study abroad program. ROTC: Army.

Entrance Requirements: Option: electronic application. Required: high school transcript, minimum 2 high school GPA, SAT or ACT. Entrance: moderately difficult. Application deadlines: 8/1, 8/1 for nonresidents. Notification: continuous, continuous for nonresidents. SAT Reasoning Test deadline: 8/1. SAT Subject Test deadline: 8/1. Transfer credits accepted: Yes.

Costs Per Year: Application fee: $25. State resident tuition: $7686 full-time, $231.10 per credit hour part-time. Nonresident tuition: $17,368 full-time, $553.80 per credit hour part-time. Mandatory fees: $753 full-time, $25.10 per credit hour part-time. Full-time tuition and fees vary according to course level and program. Part-time tuition and fees vary according to program. College room and board: $7640. College room only: $2790. Room and board charges vary according to housing facility.

Collegiate Environment: Orientation program. Drama-theater group, choral group, student-run newspaper. Social organizations: 99 open to all; national fraternities, national sororities, local fraternities, local sororities; 1% of eligible men and 1% of eligible women are members. Most popular organizations: Black Student Union, Women in Business, National Society of Black Engineers, American Sign Language Club, Student Athlete Advisory Committee. Major annual events: Welcome Rally, Halloween Party, Pancake Study Break. Student services: health clinic, personal-psychological counseling. Campus security: 24-hour emergency response devices and

patrols, student patrols, late night transport-escort service, controlled dormitory access. 749 college housing spaces available; 678 were occupied in 2018-19. No special consideration for freshman housing applicants. Option: coed housing available. Purdue University Northwest Libraries plus 2 others. Books: 200,372 (physical), 428,023 (digital/electronic); Serial titles: 1,735 (physical), 80,832 (digital/electronic); Databases: 180. Weekly public service hours: 138. Operations spending for the previous fiscal year: $1.8 million. 1,700 computers available on campus for general student use. A campuswide network can be accessed from student residence rooms. Students can access the following: online class registration. Staffed computer lab on campus provides training in use of computers, software, and the Internet.
Community Environment: Purdue University - Calumet primarily serves the communities located in the northwestern part of the state, adjacent to metropolitan Chicago. It is situated in the southeastern section of Hammond, just off the Borman Expressway and Indianapolis Boulevard.

■ PURDUE UNIVERSITY PATTI & RUSTY RUEFF SCHOOL OF DESIGN, ART, AND PERFORMANCE (WEST LAFAYETTE)
Pao Hall of Visual & Performing Arts
552 W Wood St.
West Lafayette, IN 47907
E-mail: admissions@purdue.edu
Web Site: www.cla.purdue.edu/academic/rueffschool/index.html

■ PURDUE UNIVERSITY SCHOOL OF LANGUAGES AND CULTURES
640 Oval Dr.
West Lafayette, IN 47907-2039
Tel: (765)494-3828

■ RADIOLOGICAL TECHNOLOGIES UNIVERSITY VT
100 E Wayne St.
Ste. 140
South Bend, IN 46601
Description: Proprietary, comprehensive, coed.

■ ROSE-HULMAN INSTITUTE OF TECHNOLOGY
5500 Wabash Ave.
Terre Haute, IN 47803-3999
Tel: (812)877-1511; Free: 800-248-7448
Fax: (812)877-8941
E-mail: admissions@rose-hulman.edu
Web Site: www.rose-hulman.edu
Description: Independent, comprehensive, coed. Awards bachelor's and master's degrees. Founded 1874. Setting: 200-acre suburban campus with easy access to Indianapolis. Endowment: $206.2 million. Research spending for the previous fiscal year: $3.2 million. Educational spending for the previous fiscal year: $16,093 per student. Total enrollment: 2,245. Faculty: 202 (190 full-time, 12 part-time). Student-undergrad faculty ratio is 11:1. 4,473 applied, 61% were admitted. 64% from top 10% of their high school class, 91% from top quarter, 100% from top half. 14 National Merit Scholars, 35 valedictorians, 22 student government officers. Full-time: 2,147 students, 25% women, 75% men. Part-time: 21 students, 14% women, 86% men. Students come from 49 states and territories, 11 other countries, 64% from out-of-state. 0.1% American Indian or Alaska Native, non-Hispanic/Latino; 5% Hispanic/Latino; 3% Black or African American, non-Hispanic/Latino; 5% Asian, non-Hispanic/Latino; 0.1% Native Hawaiian or other Pacific Islander, non-Hispanic/Latino; 15% international. 0.7% 25 or older, 58% live on campus, 1% transferred in. Retention: 91% of full-time freshmen returned the following year. Academic areas with the most degrees conferred: engineering; computer and information sciences; physical sciences. Core. Calendar: quarters. ESL program, services for LD students, advanced placement, accelerated degree program, independent study, double major, summer session for credit, adult/continuing education programs, co-op programs, graduate courses open to undergrads. Off campus study at Indiana State University, St. Mary-of-the-Woods College. Study abroad program. ROTC: Army, Air Force.

Entrance Requirements: Options: electronic application, early action, deferred admission, international baccalaureate accepted. Required: essay, high school transcript, 1 recommendation, curricular prerequisites, SAT or ACT. Entrance: very difficult. Application deadlines: 2/1, 11/1 for early action. Notification: 3/15, 12/16 for early action. SAT Reasoning Test deadline: 2/1. Transfer credits accepted: Yes. Applicants placed on waiting list: 379. Waitlisted applicants offered admission: 39. Early action applicants: 2,319. Early action applicants admitted: 1,994.

Costs Per Year: Application fee: $50. One-time mandatory fee: $2300. Comprehensive fee: $62,337 includes full-time tuition ($46,641), mandatory fees ($930), and college room and board ($14,766). College room only: $8988. Full-time tuition and fees vary according to course load. Room and board charges vary according to board plan. Part-time tuition: $1361 per credit hour. Part-time tuition varies according to course load.

Collegiate Environment: Orientation program. Drama-theater group, choral group, student-run newspaper, radio station. Social organizations: 100 open to all; national fraternities, national sororities; 36% of eligible men and 34% of eligible women are members. Most popular organizations: Residence Hall Association, Student Activities Board, Branam Innovation Center competition teams, Drama Club, Diversity organizations. Major annual events: Day of Service, Greatest Floor Competition, Homecoming. Student services: health clinic, personal-psychological counseling. Campus security: 24-hour emergency response devices and patrols, late night transport-escort service, controlled dormitory access. John A. Logan Library. Books: 29,406 (physical), 301,291 (digital/electronic); Serial titles: 42 (physical), 41,278 (digital/electronic); Databases: 33. Weekly public service hours: 101; students can reserve study rooms. Operations spending for the previous fiscal year: $966,314. 48 computers available on campus for general student use. Computer purchase/lease plans available. A computer is required for all students. A campuswide network can be accessed from student residence rooms and from off campus. Students can access the following: online class registration.

Community Environment: See Indiana State University.

■ **SAINT MARY-OF-THE-WOODS COLLEGE**

Saint Mary of the Woods, IN 47876

Tel: (812)535-5151; Free: 800-926-SMWC

Fax: (812)535-5215

E-mail: rmcdonald@smwc.edu

Web Site: www.smwc.edu

Description: Independent Roman Catholic, comprehensive, coed. Awards associate, bachelor's, and master's degrees (also offers external degree program with significant enrollment not reflected in profile). Founded 1840. Setting: 67-acre rural campus with easy access to Indianapolis. Total enrollment: 952. Faculty: 142 (49 full-time, 93 part-time). Student-undergrad faculty ratio is 7:1. 578 applied, 75% were admitted. Full-time: 397 students, 90% women, 10% men. Part-time: 359 students, 90% women, 10% men. 28% from out-of-state. 0.6% American Indian or Alaska Native, non-Hispanic/Latino; 2% Hispanic/Latino; 4% Black or African American, non-Hispanic/Latino; 1% Asian, non-Hispanic/Latino; 0.3% Native Hawaiian or other Pacific Islander, non-Hispanic/Latino; 0.8% international. 54% 25 or older, 42% live on campus, 12% transferred in. Retention: 66% of full-time freshmen returned the following year. Core. Calendar: semesters. Academic remediation for entering students, services for LD students, advanced placement, accelerated degree program, self-designed majors, honors program, independent study, distance learning, double major, summer session for credit, part-time degree program, external degree program, adult/continuing education programs, internships. Off campus study at College Consortium of Western Indiana - Indiana State University, Rose-Hulman Institute of Technology, Saint Mary-of-the-Woods; Indiana College Network (ICN). Study abroad program. ROTC: Army (c), Naval (c), Air Force (c).

Entrance Requirements: Open admission. Options: electronic application, early admission, deferred admission, international baccalaureate accepted. Required: high school transcript, minimum 2 high school GPA, SAT or ACT. Recommended: essay. Required for some: essay, minimum 1 high school GPA, official transcripts from all previous institutions for transfers; proof of RN license, valid driver's license, and background check for RN-to-BSN program; background check and Praxis II scores for teacher licensure. Entrance: minimally difficult. Transfer credits accepted: Yes.

Costs Per Year: Application fee: $0. Comprehensive fee: $40,874 includes full-time tuition ($29,510), mandatory fees ($450), and college room and board ($10,914). College room only: $6614. Full-time tuition and fees vary according to location, program, and student level. Room and board charges vary according to board plan and housing facility. Part-time tuition: $496 per credit hour. Part-time tuition varies according to course load, location, program, and student level. Tuition guaranteed not to increase for student's term of enrollment.

Collegiate Environment: Orientation program. Drama-theater group, choral group, student-run newspaper. Student services: health clinic, personal-psychological counseling. Campus security: 24-hour emergency response devices and patrols, late night transport-escort service, Resident Assistants (RAs) patrol the residence hall 3-4 times per night. Rooney Library.

■ **SAINT MARY'S COLLEGE**

Notre Dame, IN 46556

Tel: (574)284-4000; Free: 800-551-7621

Fax: (574)284-4713

E-mail: sdvorak@saintmarys.edu

Web Site: www.saintmarys.edu

Description: Independent Roman Catholic, comprehensive, women only. Awards bachelor's, master's, and doctoral degrees. Founded 1844. Setting: 100-acre suburban campus. Endowment: $164.9 million. Educational spending for the previous fiscal year: $18,355 per student. Total enrollment: 1,701. Faculty: 210 (140 full-time, 70 part-time). Student-undergrad faculty ratio is 10:1. 1,771 applied, 82% were admitted. 18% from top 10% of their high school class, 54% from top quarter, 89% from top half. 2 class presidents, 3 valedictorians, 5 student government officers. Full-time: 1,569 students. Part-time: 56 students. Students come from 43 states and territories, 10 other countries, 73% from out-of-state. 0.1% American Indian or Alaska Native, non-Hispanic/Latino; 11% Hispanic/Latino; 2% Black or African American, non-Hispanic/Latino; 2% Asian, non-Hispanic/Latino; 0.1% Native Hawaiian or other Pacific Islander, non-Hispanic/Latino; 2% international. 1% 25 or older, 86% live on campus, 2% transferred in. Retention: 86% of full-time freshmen returned the following year. Academic areas with the most degrees conferred: health professions and related sciences; business/marketing; biological/life sciences. Core. Calendar: semesters. ESL program, services for LD students, advanced placement, self-designed majors, independent study, distance learning, double major, summer session for credit, part-time degree program, internships, graduate courses open to undergrads. Off campus study at University of Notre Dame, members of the Northern Indiana Consortium for Education. Study abroad program. ROTC: Army (c), Naval (c), Air Force (c).

Entrance Requirements: Options: electronic application, early admission, early decision, deferred admission, international baccalaureate accepted. Required: essay, high school transcript, 1 recommendation, 16 high school academic units, minimum two years of study of the same foreign language, SAT or ACT. Recommended: interview. Entrance: moderately difficult. Application deadlines: 2/15, 11/15 for early decision. Notification: continuous, 12/15 for early decision. SAT Reasoning Test deadline: 3/1. Transfer credits accepted: Yes. Early decision applicants: 64. Early decision applicants admitted: 51.

Costs Per Year: Application fee: $0. One-time mandatory fee: $150. Comprehensive fee: $54,800 includes full-time tuition ($41,380), mandatory fees ($840), and college room and board ($12,580). College room only: $7800. Room and board charges vary according to board plan and housing facility. Part-time tuition: $1640 per credit hour.

Collegiate Environment: Orientation program. Drama-theater group, choral group, marching band, student-run newspaper, radio station. Social organizations: 76 open to all. Most popular organizations: Student Government Association, Dance Marathon, Class Boards, Residence Hall Association, Student Diversity Board. Major annual events: Back to School Dance, All School Formal, Diverse Student Leadership Conference. Student services: health clinic, personal-psychological counseling, women's center. Campus security: 24-hour emergency response devices and patrols, late night transport-escort service, controlled dormitory access. Cushwa-Leighton Library. Books: 260,077 (physical), 140,170 (digital/electronic); Serial titles: 4,136 (physical), 205,506 (digital/electronic); Databases: 74. Weekly public service hours: 54; study areas open 24 hours, 5-7 days a week; students can reserve study rooms. Operations spending for the previous fiscal year: $279,259. 291 computers available on campus for general student use. Computer purchase/lease plans available. A campuswide network can be accessed from student residence rooms and from off campus. Students can access the following: online class registration. Staffed computer lab on campus provides training in use of computers, software, and the Internet.

■ **TAYLOR UNIVERSITY**

236 W Reade Ave.

Upland, IN 46989-1001

Tel: (765)998-2751; Free: 800-882-3456

Fax: (765)998-4925

E-mail: admissions@taylor.edu

Web Site: www.taylor.edu

Description: Independent interdenominational, comprehensive, coed. Awards bachelor's and master's degrees. Founded 1846. Setting: 950-acre rural campus with easy access to Indianapolis. Endowment: $95.9 million. Research spending for the previous fiscal year: $263,000. Educational spending for the previous fiscal year: $11,882 per student. Total enrollment: 2,195. Faculty: 201 (135 full-time, 66 part-time). Student-undergrad faculty ratio is 13:1. 2,165 applied, 78% were admitted. 36% from top 10% of their high school class, 60% from top quarter, 87% from top half. Full-time: 1,846 students, 54% women, 46% men. Part-time: 321 students, 61% women, 39% men. Students come from 42 states and territories, 31 other countries, 45% from out-of-state. 0.6% American Indian or Alaska Native, non-Hispanic/Latino; 4% Hispanic/Latino; 3% Black or African American, non-Hispanic/Latino; 3% Asian, non-Hispanic/Latino; 0.3% Native Hawaiian or other Pacific Islander, non-Hispanic/Latino; 5% international. 1% 25 or older, 89% live on campus, 2% transferred in. Retention: 86% of full-time freshmen returned the following year. Academic areas with the most degrees conferred: education; business/marketing; biological/life sciences. Core. Calendar: 4-1-4. Academic remediation for entering students, ESL program, services for LD students, advanced placement, self-designed majors, honors program, independent study, distance learning, double major, summer session for credit, part-time degree program, co-op programs and internships, graduate courses open to undergrads. Off campus study at Christian College Consortium and the Council for Christian Colleges & Universities. Study abroad program.

Entrance Requirements: Options: electronic application, early action, deferred admission. Required: essay, high school transcript, 2 recommendations, interview, SAT or ACT. Recommended: minimum 2.8 high school GPA. Entrance: moderately difficult. Application deadline: rolling. Notification: continuous. Preference given to Evangelical Christians. SAT Reasoning Test deadline: 6/1. Transfer credits accepted: Yes.

Costs Per Year: Application fee: $25. Comprehensive fee: $45,255 includes full-time tuition ($35,050), mandatory fees ($255), and college room and board ($9950). College room only: $5230. Part-time tuition: $1235 per credit hour. Part-time mandatory fees: $45 per term.

Collegiate Environment: Orientation program. Drama-theater group, choral group, student-run newspaper, radio station. Social organizations: 76 open to all. Most popular organizations: Spring Break Missions, Lighthouse, Alpha Pi Iota, Encounter, Kappa Delta Pi. Major annual events: Airband, Sing Noel, Silent Night and Holidays with the Haines. Student services: health clinic, personal-psychological counseling. Campus security: 24-hour patrols, student patrols, late night transport-escort service, controlled dormitory access. 1,754 college housing spaces available; 1,689 were occupied in 2018-19. Freshmen guaranteed college housing. On-campus residence required through junior year. Options: men-only, women-only housing available. Zondervan Library. Books: 128,733 (physical), 228,315 (digital/electronic); Serial titles: 631 (physical); Databases: 115. Weekly public service hours: 96; study areas open 24 hours, 5-7 days a week. Operations spending for the previous fiscal year: $1 million. 375 computers available on campus for general student use. Computer purchase/lease plans available. A campuswide network can be accessed from student residence rooms and from off campus. Students can access the following: online class registration. Staffed computer lab on campus provides training in use of computers, software, and the Internet.

Community Environment: Upland (population 3,700) has all the advantages of quiet, country life with the nearby cities for activities. It is located 14 miles southeast of Marion and 23 miles north of Muncie. Buses and trains are accessible. The communities have churches of many denominations, health services and hospitals. Recreational activities are hunting, tennis, boating, fishing, golf and other sports.

■ TRINE UNIVERSITY

1 University Ave.
Angola, IN 46703-1764
Tel: (260)665-4100; Free: 800-347-4878
Fax: (260)665-4292
E-mail: admit@trine.edu
Web Site: www.trine.edu

Description: Independent, comprehensive, coed. Awards associate, bachelor's, master's, and doctoral degrees. Founded 1884. Setting: 400-acre small town campus. Endowment: $32 million. Educational spending for the previous fiscal year: $6937 per student. Total enrollment: 4,302. Faculty: 165 (113 full-time, 52 part-time). Student-undergrad faculty ratio is 16:1. 3,597 applied, 66% were admitted. 23% from top 10% of their high school class, 51% from top quarter, 84% from top half. Full-time: 1,920 students, 30% women, 70% men. Part-time: 2,184 students, 58% women, 42% men. Students come from 37 states and territories, 26 other countries, 20% from out-of-state. 0.3% American Indian or Alaska Native, non-Hispanic/Latino; 8% Hispanic/Latino; 6% Black or African American, non-Hispanic/Latino; 2%

Asian, non-Hispanic/Latino; 0.2% Native Hawaiian or other Pacific Islander, non-Hispanic/Latino; 5% international. 5% 25 or older, 71% live on campus, 2% transferred in. Retention: 80% of full-time freshmen returned the following year. Academic areas with the most degrees conferred: engineering; business/marketing; parks and recreation. Core. Calendar: semesters. Academic remediation for entering students, ESL program, services for LD students, advanced placement, self-designed majors, honors program, independent study, distance learning, double major, summer session for credit, part-time degree program, adult/continuing education programs, co-op programs and internships, graduate courses open to undergrads. Study abroad program. ROTC: Air Force (c).

Entrance Requirements: Options: electronic application, deferred admission, international baccalaureate accepted. Required: high school transcript, minimum 2.5 high school GPA, SAT or ACT. Recommended: essay, 2 recommendations, interview. Entrance: moderately difficult. Application deadline: 8/1. Notification: 8/15. SAT Reasoning Test deadline: 8/1. Transfer credits accepted: Yes.

Costs Per Year: Application fee: $0. Comprehensive fee: $42,986 includes full-time tuition ($31,700), mandatory fees ($476), and college room and board ($10,810). College room only: $6370. Full-time tuition and fees vary according to course load and program. Room and board charges vary according to board plan and housing facility. Part-time tuition: $990 per credit hour. Part-time tuition varies according to course load and program.

Collegiate Environment: Orientation program. Drama-theater group, choral group, marching band, student-run radio station. Social organizations: 51 open to all; national fraternities, national sororities, local sororities; 23% of eligible men and 24% of eligible women are members. Most popular organizations: Campus Christian House, Society of Women Engineers, Multicultural Student Organization, SPEAK, Trine Disc Golf Collective. Major annual events: Homecoming, Bingo for Bucks, Moonlight Breakfast. Student services: health clinic, personal-psychological counseling. Campus security: 24-hour emergency response devices and patrols, late night transport-escort service, controlled dormitory access. Sponsel Library plus 1 other. Books: 23,523 (physical), 225,584 (digital/electronic); Serial titles: 19 (physical), 21,141 (digital/electronic); Databases: 87. Operations spending for the previous fiscal year: $447,698. 400 computers available on campus for general student use. Computer purchase/lease plans available. A campuswide network can be accessed from student residence rooms. Students can access the following: online class registration, online campus billing accounts, course management system. Staffed computer lab on campus provides training in use of computers, software, and the Internet.

Community Environment: Angola, population 7,890, is situated at the intersection of U.S. Highways 20, 27, I-69 and the Indiana Toll Road. The city has a small airport. Recreational facilities include three golf courses, including one located on the Tri-State campus, Pokagon State Park five miles north, and many miles of shoreline surrounding more than 100 spring-fed lakes.

■ UNIVERSITY OF EVANSVILLE

1800 Lincoln Ave.
Evansville, IN 47722
Tel: (812)488-2000; Free: 800-423-8633
Fax: (812)474-4076
E-mail: kh88@evansville.edu
Web Site: www.evansville.edu

Description: Independent, comprehensive, coed, affiliated with United Methodist Church. Awards associate, bachelor's, master's, and doctoral degrees. Founded 1854. Setting: 75-acre urban campus. Endowment: $127.8 million. Research spending for the previous fiscal year: $184,343. Educational spending for the previous fiscal year: $11,476 per student. Total enrollment: 2,516. Faculty: 262 (173 full-time, 89 part-time). Student-undergrad faculty ratio is 11:1. 3,825 applied, 70% were admitted. 37% from top 10% of their high school class, 67% from top quarter, 92% from top half. Full-time: 2,024 students, 56% women, 44% men. Part-time: 318 students, 56% women, 44% men. Students come from 44 states and territories, 55 other countries, 35% from out-of-state. 0.1% American Indian or Alaska Native, non-Hispanic/Latino; 3% Hispanic/Latino; 3% Black or African American, non-Hispanic/Latino; 2% Asian, non-Hispanic/Latino; 14% international. 5% 25 or older, 51% live on campus, 3% transferred in. Retention: 84% of full-time freshmen returned the following year. Academic areas with the most degrees conferred: business/marketing; health professions and related sciences; parks and recreation. Core. Calendar: semesters. ESL program, services for LD students, advanced placement, accelerated degree program, self-designed majors, honors program, independent study, distance learning, double major, summer session for credit, part-time degree program, adult/continuing education programs, co-op programs and internships, graduate courses open to undergrads. Study abroad program. ROTC: Army (c).

Entrance Requirements: Options: electronic application, early admission, early action, deferred admission, international baccalaureate accepted. Required: high school transcript. Recommended: minimum 3 high school GPA, 1 recommendation, interview. Required for some: essay, interview, SAT and/or ACT scores, SAT or ACT. Entrance: moderately difficult. Application deadline: 12/1 for early action. Transfer credits accepted: Yes.

Costs Per Year: Application fee: $0. Comprehensive fee: $48,876 includes full-time tuition ($35,300), mandatory fees ($1116), and college room and board ($12,460). College room only: $6540. Full-time tuition and fees vary according to location and program. Room and board charges vary according to board plan, housing facility, and location. Part-time tuition: $990 per credit hour. Part-time mandatory fees: $148 per term. Part-time tuition and fees vary according to course load and program.

Collegiate Environment: Orientation program. Drama-theater group, choral group, student-run newspaper, radio station. Social organizations: 115 open to all; national fraternities, national sororities, local sororities; 25% of eligible men and 24% of eligible women are members. Most popular organizations: Resident Students Association, International Club, PT Club, Newman Club, Venturing. Major annual events: Student Organization Fair, International Bazaar, Musical Madness. Student services: health clinic, personal-psychological counseling. Campus security: 24-hour emergency response devices and patrols, student patrols, late night transport-escort service, controlled dormitory access. University of Evansville Libraries. Books: 235,259 (physical), 222,903 (digital/electronic); Serial titles: 56,159 (digital/electronic); Databases: 128. Weekly public service hours: 97; students can reserve study rooms. Operations spending for the previous fiscal year: $1.9 million. 219 computers available on campus for general student use. A campuswide network can be accessed from student residence rooms and from off campus. Students can access the following: online class registration. Staffed computer lab on campus provides training in use of computers, software, and the Internet.

Community Environment: Evansville, population 115,900, is the fourth largest city in Indiana, and the largest in Southern Indiana. Cultural activities include a philharmonic orchestra, art museum, planetarium, zoo, civic and repertory theaters, and the remains of early Indian settlement.

■ UNIVERSITY OF INDIANAPOLIS

1400 E Hanna Ave.
Indianapolis, IN 46227-3697
Tel: (317)788-3368; Free: 800-232-8634
Fax: (317)788-3300
E-mail: admissions@uindy.edu
Web Site: www.uindy.edu

Description: Independent, comprehensive, coed, affiliated with United Methodist Church. Awards associate, bachelor's, master's, and doctoral degrees. Founded 1902. Setting: 65-acre urban campus with easy access to Indianapolis. Total enrollment: 5,711. Student-undergrad faculty ratio is 12:1. 7,301 applied, 86% were admitted. 21% from top 10% of their high school class, 51% from top quarter, 85% from top half. Full-time: 3,589 students, 62% women, 38% men. Part-time: 757 students, 72% women, 28% men. 10% from out-of-state. 0.2% American Indian or Alaska Native, non-Hispanic/Latino; 5% Hispanic/Latino; 9% Black or African American, non-Hispanic/Latino; 2% Asian, non-Hispanic/Latino; 0.1% Native Hawaiian or other Pacific Islander, non-Hispanic/Latino; 8% international. 17% 25 or older, 36% live on campus, 5% transferred in. Retention: 77% of full-time freshmen returned the following year. Academic areas with the most degrees conferred: health professions and related sciences; business/marketing; parks and recreation. Core. Calendar: semesters. Academic remediation for entering students, ESL program, services for LD students, advanced placement, accelerated degree program, self-designed majors, freshman honors college, honors program, independent study, distance learning, double major, summer session for credit, part-time degree program, adult/continuing education programs, co-op programs and internships, graduate courses open to undergrads. Off campus study at 7 members of the Consortium for Urban Education, 10 members of the May Term Consortium. Study abroad program. ROTC: Army (c).

Entrance Requirements: Options: electronic application, deferred admission, international baccalaureate accepted. Required: high school transcript, minimum 2 high school GPA, SAT or ACT. Required for some: interview. Entrance: moderately difficult. Application deadline: rolling. Notification: continuous. SAT Reasoning Test deadline: 8/1. Transfer credits accepted: Yes. Applicants placed on waiting list: 57.

Costs Per Year: Application fee: $25. Comprehensive fee: $39,976 includes full-time tuition ($28,836), mandatory fees ($852), and college room and board ($10,288). College room only: $5280. Full-time tuition and fees vary according to class time and program. Room and board charges vary according to board plan and housing facility. Part-time tuition: $1200 per credit hour. Part-time mandatory fees: $256 per term. Part-time tuition and fees vary according to class time, course load, and program.

Collegiate Environment: Orientation program. Drama-theater group, choral group, student-run newspaper, radio station. Social organizations: 37 open to all. Most popular organizations: Fellowship of Christian Athletes, Intercultural Association, Circle K, Indianapolis Student Government, Residence Hall Association. Major annual events: Late Nights, Winter Formal Dance, Cyclerama. Student services: health clinic, personal-psychological counseling. Campus security: 24-hour emergency response devices and patrols, student patrols, late night transport-escort service, controlled dormitory access, emergency call boxes. Krannert Memorial Library. Students can reserve study rooms. 255 computers available on campus for general student use. A campuswide network can be accessed from student residence rooms and from off campus. Students can access the following: online class registration. Staffed computer lab on campus (open 24 hours a day).

Community Environment: The university is located in the southern, residential suburb of Indianapolis known as University Heights. Indianapolis is the nation's third largest capital city and is known as the "Amateur Sports Capital of the World." The metropolitan area has a population of more than one million. Recreational, cultural, and social opportunities abound. Bus, train, and airline services are within minutes of the campus. There are also numerous shops, restaurants, hotels, and a major shopping mall nearby.

■ UNIVERSITY OF NOTRE DAME

Notre Dame, IN 46556
Tel: (574)631-5000
Fax: (574)631-8865
Web Site: www.nd.edu

Description: Independent Roman Catholic, university, coed. Awards bachelor's, master's, and doctoral degrees. Founded 1842. Setting: 1,250-acre suburban campus. Endowment: $13.4 billion. Total enrollment: 12,607. Faculty: 1,386 (1,216 full-time, 170 part-time). Student-undergrad faculty ratio is 10:1. 20,371 applied, 18% were admitted. 89% from top 10% of their high school class, 98% from top quarter, 100% from top half. Full-time: 8,607 students, 48% women, 52% men. Part-time: 10 students, 20% women, 80% men. Students come from 54 states and territories, 71 other countries, 92% from out-of-state. 0.2% American Indian or Alaska Native, non-Hispanic/Latino; 11% Hispanic/Latino; 4% Black or African American, non-Hispanic/Latino; 5% Asian, non-Hispanic/Latino; 7% international. 78% live on campus, 2% transferred in. Retention: 98% of full-time freshmen returned the following year. Academic areas with the most degrees conferred: business/marketing; engineering; social sciences. Core. Calendar: semesters. Services for LD students, advanced placement, self-designed majors, honors program, independent study, distance learning, double major, summer session for credit, internships, graduate courses open to undergrads. Off campus study at Saint Mary's College (IN). Study abroad program. ROTC: Army, Naval, Air Force.

Entrance Requirements: Options: electronic application, early action, deferred admission, international baccalaureate accepted. Required: essay, high school transcript, 1 recommendation, SAT or ACT. Required for some: SAT Subject Tests. Entrance: most difficult. Application deadlines: 12/1, 11/1 for early action. Notification: 4/10. SAT Reasoning Test deadline: 3/1. SAT Subject Test deadline: 3/1. Transfer credits accepted: Yes. Applicants placed on waiting list: 1,450. Wait-listed applicants offered admission: 20. Early action applicants: 4,926. Early action applicants admitted: 1,473.

Costs Per Year: Application fee: $75. Comprehensive fee: $68,801 includes full-time tuition ($52,884), mandatory fees ($507), and college room and board ($15,410). Part-time tuition: $2201 per credit hour.

Collegiate Environment: Orientation program. Drama-theater group, choral group, marching band, student-run newspaper, radio station. Social organizations: 440 open to all. Most popular organizations: marching band, Circle K, Finance Club, Notre Dame/St. Mary's Right to Life. Major annual events: Home Football Weekends, Bookstore Basketball Tournament, Junior Parents' Weekend. Student services: health clinic, personal-psychological counseling, women's center. Campus security: 24-hour emergency response devices and patrols, student patrols, late night transport-escort service, controlled dormitory access. 6,415 undergraduates lived in college housing during 2018-19. Freshmen guaranteed college housing. On-campus residence required in freshman year. Options: men-only, women-only housing available. Hesburgh Library plus 11 others. 782 computers available on campus for general student use. Computer purchase/lease plans available. A campuswide network can be accessed from student residence rooms and from off campus. Students can access the following: online class registration. Staffed computer lab on campus (open 24 hours a day).

Community Environment: The South Bend area has a population of over 100,000. The downtown district, located 3 miles south of the campus, has enjoyed a complete urban renewal and offers attractive services to the students. A world-class water raceway provides excellent opportunities for challenging kayaking, tubing and canoeing. Home of the College Football Hall of Fame. Several major shopping malls with direct bus service to campus are less than 15 minutes away.

■ UNIVERSITY OF SAINT FRANCIS

2701 Spring St.
Fort Wayne, IN 46808-3994
Tel: (260)399-7700; Free: 800-729-4732
E-mail: admis@sf.edu
Web Site: www.sf.edu

Description: Independent Roman Catholic, comprehensive, coed. Awards associate, bachelor's, master's, and doctoral degrees and post-master's certificates. Founded 1890. Setting: 100-acre urban campus. Endowment: $34.1 million. Educational spending for the previous fiscal year: $10,166 per student. Total enrollment: 2,199. Faculty: 301 (136 full-time, 165 part-time). Student-undergrad faculty ratio is 10:1. 1,490 applied, 93% were admitted. 22% from top 10% of their high school class, 42% from top quarter, 75% from top half. Full-time: 1,511 students, 68% women, 32% men. Part-time: 267 students, 90% women, 10% men. Students come from 18 states and territories, 6 other countries, 11% from out-of-state. 0.1% American Indian or Alaska Native, non-Hispanic/Latino; 8% Hispanic/Latino; 7% Black or African American, non-Hispanic/Latino; 2% Asian, non-Hispanic/Latino; 0.1% Native Hawaiian or other Pacific Islander, non-Hispanic/Latino; 0.9% international. 20% 25 or older, 23% live on campus, 10% transferred in. Retention: 74% of full-time freshmen returned the following year. Academic areas with the most degrees conferred: health professions and related sciences; business/marketing; visual and performing arts. Core. Calendar: semesters. Academic remediation for entering students, services for LD students, advanced placement, self-designed majors, honors program, independent study, distance learning, double major, summer session for credit, part-time degree program, co-op programs and internships, graduate courses open to undergrads. Off campus study at Fort Wayne Higher Education Consortium. ROTC: Army (c).

Entrance Requirements: Options: electronic application, deferred admission, international baccalaureate accepted. Required: high school transcript, minimum 2.3 high school GPA, SAT or ACT. Recommended: essay. Required for some: essay, interview. Entrance: noncompetitive. Application deadline: rolling. Notification: continuous. Transfer credits accepted: Yes.

Costs Per Year: One-time mandatory fee: $100. Comprehensive fee: $41,660 includes full-time tuition ($30,380), mandatory fees ($1100), and college room and board ($10,180). Part-time tuition: $965 per semester hour. Part-time mandatory fees: $30 per semester hour, $155 per term.

Collegiate Environment: Orientation program. Drama-theater group, choral group, marching band, student-run newspaper. Social organizations: 37 open to all. Most popular organizations: Student Activities Council, Student Government Association, Intramural Sports, Residence Hall Association, Ultimate Frisbee. Major annual events: Homecoming, Spring Fling, Casino Night. Student services: personal-psychological counseling. Campus security: 24-hour emergency response devices and patrols, late night transport-escort service, controlled dormitory access. 431 college housing spaces available; 406 were occupied in 2018-19. Freshmen given priority for college housing. On-campus residence required through junior year. Options: coed, men-only, women-only housing available. Lee and Jim Vann Library. Books: 64,241 (physical), 163,451 (digital/electronic); Serial titles: 798 (physical), 41,820 (digital/electronic); Databases: 110. Weekly public service hours: 86; study areas open 24 hours, 5-7 days a week; students can reserve study rooms. Operations spending for the previous fiscal year: $878,841. 120 computers available on campus for general student use. Computer purchase/lease plans available. A campuswide network can be accessed from student residence rooms and from off campus. Students can access the following: online class registration. Staffed computer lab on campus provides training in use of computers, software, and the Internet.

■ UNIVERSITY OF SOUTHERN INDIANA

8600 University Blvd.
Evansville, IN 47712-3590
Tel: (812)464-8600; Free: 800-467-1965
Fax: (812)465-7154
E-mail: enroll@usi.edu
Web Site: www.usi.edu

Description: State-supported, comprehensive, coed. Part of Indiana Commission for Higher Education. Awards associate, bachelor's, master's, and doctoral degrees and post-master's certificates. Founded 1965. Setting: 1,400-acre suburban campus. Research spending for the previous fiscal year: $267,036. Educational spending for the previous fiscal year: $5892 per student. Total enrollment: 8,962. Faculty: 651 (362 full-time, 289 part-time). Student-undergrad faculty ratio is 17:1. 4,461 applied, 95% were admitted. 14% from top 10% of their high school class, 34% from top quarter, 69% from top half. Full-time: 6,422 students, 62% women, 38% men. Part-time: 1,091 students, 62% women, 38% men. 15% from out-of-state. 0.2% American Indian or Alaska Native, non-Hispanic/Latino; 4% Hispanic/Latino; 4% Black or African American, non-Hispanic/Latino; 1% Asian, non-Hispanic/Latino; 0.1% Native Hawaiian or other Pacific Islander, non-Hispanic/Latino; 2% international. 14% 25 or older, 32% live on campus, 7% transferred in. Retention: 72% of full-time freshmen returned the following year. Academic areas with the most degrees conferred: health professions and related sciences; business/marketing; education. Core. Calendar: semesters. Academic remediation for entering students, ESL program, services for LD students, advanced placement, accelerated degree program, honors program, independent study, distance learning, double major, summer session for credit, part-time degree program, adult/continuing education programs, co-op programs and internships, graduate courses open to undergrads. Study abroad program. ROTC: Army.

Entrance Requirements: Options: electronic application, international baccalaureate accepted. Required: high school transcript, SAT or ACT. Recommended: minimum 2.5 high school GPA. Required for some: interview. Entrance: moderately difficult. Notification: continuous. Transfer credits accepted: Yes.

Collegiate Environment: Orientation program. Drama-theater group, choral group, student-run newspaper, radio station. Social organizations: 144 open to all; national fraternities, national sororities; 8% of eligible men and 9% of eligible women are members. Most popular organizations: Sororities, Fraternities, Riley Dance Marathon, Activities Programming Board, Student Government Association. Major annual events: SpringFest, Welcome Week, Dance Marathon. Student services: health clinic, personal-psychological counseling. Campus security: 24-hour emergency response devices and patrols, student patrols, late night transport-escort service, controlled dormitory access. No special consideration for freshman housing applicants. Option: coed housing available. David L. Rice Library. Books: 241,710 (physical), 230,844 (digital/electronic); Serial titles: 1,075 (physical), 141,229 (digital/electronic); Databases: 168. Weekly public service hours: 114; students can reserve study rooms. Operations spending for the previous fiscal year: $2.7 million. 1,165 computers available on campus for general student use. A campuswide network can be accessed from student residence rooms and from off campus. Students can access the following: online class registration. Staffed computer lab on campus provides training in use of computers and software.

Community Environment: See University of Evansville.

■ VALPARAISO UNIVERSITY

1700 Chapel Dr.
Valparaiso, IN 46383
Tel: (219)464-5000; Free: 888-GO-VALPO
Fax: (219)464-6898
E-mail: undergrad.admission@valpo.edu
Web Site: www.valpo.edu

Description: Independent, comprehensive, coed, affiliated with Lutheran Church. Awards associate, bachelor's, master's, and doctoral degrees and post-master's certificates. Founded 1859. Setting: 350-acre small town campus with easy access to Chicago. Endowment: $250.4 million. Research spending for the previous fiscal year: $1.2 million. Educational spending for the previous fiscal year: $11,920 per student. Total enrollment: 3,804. Faculty: 414 (308 full-time, 106 part-time). Student-undergrad faculty ratio is 11:1. 7,062 applied, 89% were admitted. 29% from top 10% of their high school class, 63% from top quarter, 93% from top half. 2 National Merit Scholars, 16 valedictorians. Full-time: 3,138 students, 56% women, 44% men. Part-time: 79 students, 58% women, 42% men. Students come from

44 states and territories, 35 other countries, 54% from out-of-state. 0.1% American Indian or Alaska Native, non-Hispanic/Latino; 9% Hispanic/Latino; 5% Black or African American, non-Hispanic/Latino; 2% Asian, non-Hispanic/Latino; 4% international. 5% 25 or older, 62% live on campus, 6% transferred in. Retention: 80% of full-time freshmen returned the following year. Academic areas with the most degrees conferred: health professions and related sciences; engineering; business/marketing. Core. Calendar: semesters. ESL program, services for LD students, advanced placement, accelerated degree program, self-designed majors, freshman honors college, honors program, independent study, distance learning, double major, summer session for credit, part-time degree program, adult/continuing education programs, co-op programs and internships, graduate courses open to undergrads. Off campus study at Associated Colleges of the Midwest and Lutheran College Washington Consortium. Study abroad program. ROTC: Army (c), Air Force (c).

Entrance Requirements: Options: electronic application, deferred admission, international baccalaureate accepted. Required: essay, high school transcript, SAT or ACT. Recommended: 2 recommendations, interview. Entrance: moderately difficult. Application deadline: rolling. Notification: continuous. Transfer credits accepted: Yes.

Costs Per Year: Comprehensive fee: $54,080 includes full-time tuition ($40,520), mandatory fees ($1300), and college room and board ($12,260). College room only: $7580. Part-time tuition: $1785 per credit hour.

Collegiate Environment: Orientation program. Drama-theater group, choral group, student-run newspaper, radio station. Social organizations: 91 open to all; national fraternities, national sororities, Alpha Phi Omega, Phi Mu Alpha; 28% of eligible men and 27% of eligible women are members. Most popular organizations: Student Government, Student Volunteer Organization, Chapel Programs, Union Board. Major annual events: Homecoming, Family Weekend, Martin Luther King, Jr. Day. Student services: legal services, health clinic, personal-psychological counseling. Campus security: 24-hour emergency response devices and patrols, late night transport-escort service, controlled dormitory access. 2,400 college housing spaces available; 1,998 were occupied in 2018-19. Freshmen guaranteed college housing. On-campus residence required through junior year. Options: coed, women-only housing available. Christopher Center for Library and Information Resources plus 1 other. Books: 614,267 (physical), 160,863 (digital/electronic); Serial titles: 123 (physical), 310,054 (digital/electronic); Databases: 200. Weekly public service hours: 113. Operations spending for the previous fiscal year: $3.3 million. 500 computers available on campus for general student use. A campuswide network can be accessed from student residence rooms and from off campus. Students can access the following: online class registration, Web Academic Information, Degree Audit, Online Course Evaluations. Staffed computer lab on campus provides training in use of computers, software, and the Internet.

Community Environment: Valparaiso University is located 50 miles southeast of Chicago. For those interested in off-campus recreation and entertainment, it is a 20-minute drive to the Indiana Dunes National Lakeshore and less than an hour to the many theaters, museums, restaurants and athletic events of Chicago.

■ VET TECH INSTITUTE AT INTERNATIONAL BUSINESS COLLEGE (FORT WAYNE)
5699 Coventry Ln.
Fort Wayne, IN 46804
Tel: (260)459-4500; Free: 800-589-6363
Web Site: ftwayne.vettechinstitute.edu
Description: Private, 2-year, coed. Awards terminal associate degrees. Founded 2005. Setting: suburban campus. Total enrollment: 147. 317 applied, 54% were admitted. Calendar: semesters. Accelerated degree program, internships.

■ VET TECH INSTITUTE AT INTERNATIONAL BUSINESS COLLEGE (INDIANAPOLIS)
7205 Shadeland Station
Indianapolis, IN 46256
Tel: (317)813-2300; Free: 800-589-6500
Fax: (317)841-6419
Web Site: indianapolis.vettechinstitute.edu
Description: Private, 2-year, coed. Awards terminal associate degrees. Founded 2007. Setting: suburban campus. Total enrollment: 147. 390 applied, 51% were admitted. Calendar: semesters. Accelerated degree program, internships.

■ VINCENNES UNIVERSITY
1002 N First St.
Vincennes, IN 47591
Tel: (812)888-8888; Free: 800-742-9198
Fax: (812)888-5868
Web Site: www.vinu.edu
Description: State-supported, primarily 2-year, coed. Awards certificates, transfer associate, and bachelor's degrees. Founded 1801. Setting: 160-acre small town campus. Total enrollment: 17,481. Faculty: 817 (180 full-time, 637 part-time). Student-undergrad faculty ratio is 16:1. 4,728 applied, 77% were admitted. Full-time: 4,970 students, 47% women, 53% men. Part-time: 12,511 students, 45% women, 55% men. 17% from out-of-state. 0.4% American Indian or Alaska Native, non-Hispanic/Latino; 15% Hispanic/Latino; 10% Black or African American, non-Hispanic/Latino; 2% Asian, non-Hispanic/Latino; 0.2% Native Hawaiian or other Pacific Islander, non-Hispanic/Latino; 0.2% international. 32% 25 or older, 37% live on campus, 1% transferred in. Retention: 56% of full-time freshmen returned the following year. Academic areas with the most degrees conferred: health professions and related sciences; homeland security, law enforcement, firefighting, and protective services; engineering technologies. Core. Calendar: semesters. Academic remediation for entering students, ESL program, services for LD students, advanced placement, accelerated degree program, self-designed majors, freshman honors college, honors program, independent study, distance learning, double major, summer session for credit, part-time degree program, external degree program, adult/continuing education programs, internships. Off campus study. ROTC: Army (c).

Entrance Requirements: Open admission. Options: electronic application, deferred admission. Required: high school transcript. Required for some: interview. Entrance: noncompetitive. Application deadline: rolling. Notification: continuous until 8/1. Transfer credits accepted: Yes.

Collegiate Environment: Orientation program. Drama-theater group, choral group, student-run newspaper, radio station. Social organizations: national fraternities, national sororities, local fraternities, local sororities. Student services: health clinic, personal-psychological counseling. Campus security: 24-hour emergency response devices and patrols, student patrols, late night transport-escort service, controlled dormitory access. Freshmen guaranteed college housing. On-campus residence required in freshman year. Options: coed, men-only, women-only housing available. Shake Learning Resource Center. Books: 85,614 (physical), 104,859 (digital/electronic); Serial titles: 1,377 (physical); Databases: 99. 1,500 computers available on campus for general student use. A campuswide network can be accessed from student residence rooms and from off campus. Staffed computer lab on campus.

Community Environment: Vincennes (population 18,000) is the oldest city in the state and was the capital of the Old Northwest. On the banks of the Wabash River, Vincennes is the distribution point for this area, which produces peaches, apples, cantaloupes, watermelons, sweet potatoes and wheat. Points of interest are the Cathedral Library, George Rogers Clark National Historic Park, Harrison Mansion, Indiana Territory State Memorial and the Old Cathedral.

■ WABASH COLLEGE
PO Box 352
Crawfordsville, IN 47933-0352
Tel: (765)361-6100; Free: 800-345-5385
Fax: (765)361-6437
E-mail: timmonsc@wabash.edu
Web Site: www.wabash.edu
Description: Independent, 4-year, men only. Awards bachelor's degrees. Founded 1832. Setting: 94-acre small town campus with easy access to Indianapolis. Endowment: $349.7 million. Research spending for the previous fiscal year: $1.7 million. Educational spending for the previous fiscal year: $12,542 per student. Total enrollment: 882. Faculty: 99 (83 full-time, 16 part-time). Student-undergrad faculty ratio is 10:1. 1,336 applied, 65% were admitted. 29% from top 10% of their high school class, 64% from top quarter, 92% from top half. Full-time: 881 students. Part-time: 1 student. Students come from 27 states and territories, 17 other countries, 21% from out-of-state. 9% Hispanic/Latino; 6% Black or African American, non-Hispanic/Latino; 0.9% Asian, non-Hispanic/Latino; 6% international. 0.1% 25 or older, 98% live on campus, 1% transferred in. Retention: 86% of full-time freshmen returned the following year. Academic areas with the most degrees conferred: social sciences; mathematics and statistics; biological/life sciences. Core. Calendar: semesters. Services for LD students, advanced placement, self-designed majors, independent study, double major, internships. Off campus study at Members of the Great Lakes Colleges Association. Study abroad program.

Entrance Requirements: Options: electronic application, early admission, early decision, early action, deferred admission, international baccalaureate accepted. Required: high school transcript, 1 recommendation, General college-preparatory program, SAT or ACT. Required for some: essay, interview. Entrance: moderately difficult. Application deadlines: 11/1 for early decision, 12/1 for early action. Notification: continuous until 1/28, continuous until 1/28 for nonresidents, 12/5 for early decision, 12/31 for early action. SAT Reasoning Test deadline: 5/1. Transfer credits accepted: Yes. Early decision applicants: 29. Early decision applicants admitted: 27.

Costs Per Year: Application fee: $50. Comprehensive fee: $55,220 includes full-time tuition ($43,870), mandatory fees ($850), and college room and board ($10,500). College room only: $5700. Part-time tuition: $1828 per credit hour.

Collegiate Environment: Orientation program. Drama-theater group, choral group, student-run newspaper, radio station. Social organizations: 64 open to all; national fraternities. Most popular organizations: Inter-Fraternity Council, Malcolm X Institute for Black Studies, Sphinx Club, Student Government, Independent Men's Association. Major annual events: Midnight Munch, Monon Bell Football Game, Chapel Sing. Student services: health clinic, personal-psychological counseling. Campus security: 24-hour

emergency response devices and patrols. 924 college housing spaces available; 873 were occupied in 2018-19. Freshmen guaranteed college housing. On-campus residence required through senior year. Option: men-only housing available. Lilly Library. Books: 254,041 (physical), 351,882 (digital/electronic); Serial titles: 81 (physical), 400,768 (digital/electronic); Databases: 82. Weekly public service hours: 105. Operations spending for the previous fiscal year: $1.2 million. 321 computers available on campus for general student use. Computer purchase/lease plans available. A campuswide network can be accessed from student residence rooms and from off campus. Students can access the following: online class registration, online course management, degree audit, expenses. Staffed computer lab on campus provides training in use of computers, software, and the Internet.

Community Environment: Crawfordsville (population 15,155), is located 45 miles northwest of Indianapolis. It is an historic small town community, and has many churches, a hospital, and motels. Recreational facilities include golf courses and swimming pools. Shades State Park is 14 miles away, and Turkey Run State Park is approximately 25 miles distant. Points of interest are the Lane Place Museum and Lew Wallace"Ben Hur" Museum.

ALLEN COLLEGE

1825 Logan Ave.
Waterloo, IA 50703
Tel: (319)226-2000
Fax: (319)226-2020
E-mail: admissions@allencollege.edu
Web Site: www.allencollege.edu

Description: Independent, comprehensive, coed. Awards associate, bachelor's, master's, and doctoral degrees and post-master's certificates (liberal arts and general education courses offered at either University of North Iowa or Wartburg College). Founded 1989. Setting: 20-acre suburban campus. Endowment: $7.5 million. Educational spending for the previous fiscal year: $10,944 per student. Total enrollment: 682. Faculty: 57 (41 full-time, 16 part-time). Student-undergrad faculty ratio is 17:1. Full-time: 302 students, 93% women, 7% men. Part-time: 39 students, 85% women, 15% men. Students come from 7 states and territories, 2 other countries, 4% from out-of-state. 0.3% American Indian or Alaska Native, non-Hispanic/Latino; 1% Hispanic/Latino; 0.9% Black or African American, non-Hispanic/Latino; 1% Asian, non-Hispanic/Latino; 0.6% international. 19% 25 or older, 36% transferred in. Retention: 95% of full-time freshmen returned the following year. Academic area with the most degrees conferred: health professions and related sciences. Core. Calendar: semesters. Advanced placement, accelerated degree program, honors program, independent study, distance learning, part-time degree program, co-op programs and internships, graduate courses open to undergrads. Off campus study. ROTC: Army (c).

Entrance Requirements: Option: electronic application. Required for some: essay, high school transcript, 1 recommendation, interview, SAT or ACT, ATI, TEAS for undergraduate pre-licensure students. Entrance: moderately difficult. Application deadline: 2/1. Notification: continuous until 3/1. Transfer credits accepted: Yes.

Costs Per Year: Application fee: $50. Comprehensive fee: $26,332 includes full-time tuition ($17,612), mandatory fees ($1440), and college room and board ($7280). College room only: $3640. Part-time tuition: $629 per credit hour. Part-time mandatory fees: $86 per credit hour.

Collegiate Environment: Orientation program. Choral group. Social organizations: 4 open to all. Most popular organizations: Allen Student Nurses's Association, Nurses'; Christian Fellowship. Student services: health clinic, personal-psychological counseling. Campus security: 24-hour patrols, late night transport-escort service, controlled dormitory access. College housing not available. Barrett Library plus 1 other. Books: 13,280 (physical), 9,138 (digital/electronic); Serial titles: 208 (physical), 3,610 (digital/electronic); Databases: 47. Weekly public service hours: 50; study areas open 24 hours, 5-7 days a week; students can reserve study rooms. Operations spending for the previous fiscal year: $360,766. 32 computers available on campus for general student use. A campuswide network can be accessed from off-campus. Students can access the following: online proctoring exams. Staffed computer lab on campus provides training in use of computers, software, and the Internet.

BRIAR CLIFF UNIVERSITY

3303 Rebecca St.
Sioux City, IA 51104-0100
Tel: (712)279-5321; Free: 800-662-3303
Fax: (712)279-5410
E-mail: admissions@briarcliff.edu
Web Site: www.briarcliff.edu

Description: Independent Roman Catholic, comprehensive, coed. Awards associate, bachelor's, master's, and doctoral degrees and post-master's certificates. Founded 1930. Setting: 75-acre suburban campus. Total enrollment: 1,316. Faculty: 122 (64 full-time, 58 part-time). Student-undergrad faculty ratio is 14:1. 1,491 applied, 60% were admitted. 11% from top 10% of their high school class, 25% from top quarter, 72% from top half. Full-time: 797 students, 48% women, 52% men. Part-time: 320 students, 75% women, 25% men. 32% from out-of-state. 2% American Indian or Alaska Native, non-Hispanic/Latino; 15% Hispanic/Latino; 9% Black or African American, non-Hispanic/Latino; 1% Asian, non-Hispanic/Latino; 0.8% Native Hawaiian or other Pacific Islander, non-Hispanic/Latino; 5% international. 20% 25 or older, 30% live on campus, 14% transferred in. Retention: 79% of full-time freshmen returned the following year. Core. Calendar: 3 10-week terms plus two 5-week summer sessions. Academic remediation for entering students, services for LD students, advanced placement, accelerated degree program, self-designed majors, honors program, independent study, distance learning, double major, summer session for credit, part-time degree program, adult/continuing education programs, internships. Off campus study at Colleges of Mid-America. Study abroad program. ROTC: Army (c).

Entrance Requirements: Options: electronic application, early admission, deferred admission. Required: high school transcript, minimum 2 high school GPA, SAT or ACT. Required for some: essay, 3 recommendations, interview. Entrance: moderately difficult.

Collegiate Environment: Orientation program. Drama-theater group, choral group, student-run newspaper, radio station. Most popular organizations: Residence Hall Association, Briar Cliff Student Government, Choices, Blue Crew, Catholic Daughters of America. Major annual events: Glo-Fest, Homecoming Dance, Winterfest Dance. Student services: health clinic, personal-psychological counseling. Campus security: 24-hour emergency response devices and patrols, student patrols, late night transport-escort service, controlled dormitory access. Bishop Mueller Library.

BUENA VISTA UNIVERSITY

610 W Fourth St.
Storm Lake, IA 50588
Tel: (712)749-2400; Free: 800-383-9600
Fax: (712)749-2037
E-mail: BooneN@bvu.edu
Web Site: www.bvu.edu

Description: Independent, comprehensive, coed, affiliated with Presbyterian Church (U.S.A.). Awards bachelor's and master's degrees. Founded 1891. Setting: 60-acre small town campus. Endowment: $138.1 million. Educational spending for the previous fiscal year: $7783 per student. Total enrollment: 820. Faculty: 101 (82 full-time, 19 part-time). Student-undergrad faculty ratio is 9:1. 2,055 applied, 57% were admitted. 11% from top 10% of their high school class, 42% from top quarter, 75% from top half. 9 valedictorians. Full-time: 719 students, 49% women, 51% men. Part-time: 13 students, 54% women, 46% men. Students come from 25 states and territories, 12 other countries, 29% from out-of-state. 0.4% American Indian or Alaska Native, non-Hispanic/Latino; 9% Hispanic/Latino; 6% Black or African American, non-Hispanic/Latino; 0.6% Asian, non-Hispanic/Latino; 0.1% Native Hawaiian or other Pacific Islander, non-Hispanic/Latino; 3% international. 3% 25 or older, 90% live on campus, 5% transferred in. Retention: 60% of full-time freshmen returned the following year. Academic areas with the most degrees conferred: business/marketing; education; communication/journalism. Core. Calendar: 4-1-4. Academic remediation for entering students, ESL program, services for LD students, advanced placement, self-designed majors, honors program, independent study, distance learning, double major, summer session for credit, part-time degree program, external degree program, adult/continuing education programs, internships, graduate courses open to undergrads. Off campus study at Washington University in St. Louis. Study abroad program. ROTC: Army.

Entrance Requirements: Options: electronic application, deferred admission, international baccalaureate accepted. Required: high school transcript, SAT or ACT. Recommended: minimum 3 high school GPA, ACT. Required for some: essay, interview. Entrance: moderately difficult. Notification: continuous. SAT Reasoning Test deadline: 8/1. Transfer credits accepted: Yes.

Costs Per Year: Comprehensive fee: $45,066 includes full-time tuition ($35,194) and college room and board ($9872). College room only: $4941. Part-time tuition: $1184 per credit hour.

Collegiate Environment: Orientation program. Drama-theater group, choral group, student-run newspaper, radio station. Social organizations: 65 open to all. Most popular organizations: Student Activities Board, Orientation Team, Esprit De Corps, Student Senate, Student Mobilizing Outreach and Volunteer Efforts. Major annual events: Homecoming, All Campus Christmas Dinner, Buenafication Day. Student services: health clinic, personal-psychological counseling. Campus security: 24-hour emergency response devices, late night transport-escort service, controlled dormitory access, night security patrols. 1,012 college housing spaces available; 657 were occupied in 2018-19. Freshmen guaranteed college housing. On-campus residence required through senior year. Option: coed housing available. BVU Library. Books: 107,288 (physical), 164,907 (digital/electronic); Serial titles: 842 (physical), 23,059 (digital/electronic); Databases: 104. Weekly public service hours: 94; students can reserve study rooms. Operations spending for the previous fiscal year: $857,838.

Community Environment: Storm Lake (population 10,000) is the county seat of Buena Vista County, and is located 75 miles east of Sioux City and 160 miles northwest of Des Moines. Bus lines and nearby airport facilities provide adequate transportation. Several churches of various Christian denominations are represented in the community.

■ **CENTRAL COLLEGE**

812 University St.
Pella, IA 50219
Tel: (641)628-9000; Free: 877-462-3687
Fax: (641)628-5316
E-mail: freiburgerc@central.edu
Web Site: www.central.edu

Description: Independent, 4-year, coed, affiliated with Reformed Church in America. Awards bachelor's degrees. Founded 1853. Setting: 169-acre small town campus with easy access to Des Moines. Endowment: $79.9 million. Educational spending for the previous fiscal year: $14,085 per student. Total enrollment: 1,274. Faculty: 105 (100 full-time, 5 part-time). Student-undergrad faculty ratio is 12:1. 3,071 applied, 64% were admitted. 23% from top 10% of their high school class, 54% from top quarter, 85% from top half. Full-time: 1,230 students, 52% women, 48% men. Part-time: 44 students, 61% women, 39% men. Students come from 27 states and territories, 3 other countries, 27% from out-of-state. 0.2% American Indian or Alaska Native, non-Hispanic/Latino; 4% Hispanic/Latino; 2% Black or African American, non-Hispanic/Latino; 1% Asian, non-Hispanic/Latino; 0.1% Native Hawaiian or other Pacific Islander, non-Hispanic/Latino; 1% international. 1% 25 or older, 91% live on campus, 3% transferred in. Retention: 78% of full-time freshmen returned the following year. Academic areas with the most degrees conferred: biological/life sciences; business/marketing; social sciences. Core. Calendar: semesters. Services for LD students, advanced placement, self-designed majors, honors program, independent study, double major, summer session for credit, part-time degree program, co-op programs and internships. Off campus study. Study abroad program.

Entrance Requirements: Options: electronic application, deferred admission, international baccalaureate accepted. Required: high school transcript, SAT or ACT. Recommended: minimum 2.7 high school GPA. Required for some: essay, 3 recommendations, interview. Entrance: moderately difficult. Application deadline: 8/15. Notification: continuous. SAT Reasoning Test deadline: 7/1. SAT Subject Test deadline: 7/1. Transfer credits accepted: Yes.

Costs Per Year: Application fee: $25. Comprehensive fee: $47,555 includes full-time tuition ($37,275) and college room and board ($10,280). College room only: $4892. Room and board charges vary according to board plan. Part-time tuition: $1554 per credit hour. Part-time tuition varies according to course load.

Collegiate Environment: Orientation program. Drama-theater group, choral group. Social organizations: 80 open to all; local fraternities, local sororities; 3% of eligible men and 2% of eligible women are members. Most popular organizations: Academic Honorary Associations and Health Professions Club, Music Ensembles, Campus Ministries, Student Senate, Students Concerned About the Environment (SCATE). Major annual events: Annual Lemming Race, Breakfast of Champions, Candlelight Christmas Concert. Student services: personal-psychological counseling. Campus security: 24-hour emergency response devices and patrols, late night transport-escort service, controlled dormitory access. Geisler Library plus 2 others. Books: 180,617 (physical), 977 (digital/electronic); Databases: 26. Students can reserve study rooms. Operations spending for the previous fiscal year: $502,835. 200 computers available on campus for general student use. A campuswide network can be accessed from student residence rooms and from off campus. Students can access the following: online class registration. Staffed computer lab on campus provides training in use of computers, software, and the Internet.

Community Environment: Pella (population 10,300), a rapidly growing agricultural and industrial community, is located 43 miles southeast of Des Moines. Active churches, libraries, and a community hospital serve the area. Pella is widely known for its attractive homes, gardens, and fine community spirit. Red Rock Dam and Lake is located four miles south. Tulip Time is an annual event here dedicated to preserving the Dutch heritage of the town.

■ **CLARKE UNIVERSITY**

1550 Clarke Dr.
Dubuque, IA 52001-3198
Tel: (563)588-6300; Free: 800-383-2345
Fax: (563)588-6789
E-mail: admissions@clarke.edu
Web Site: www.clarke.edu

Description: Independent Roman Catholic, comprehensive, coed. Awards associate, bachelor's, master's, and doctoral degrees. Founded 1843. Setting: 55-acre urban campus. Endowment: $31.3 million. Educational spending for the previous fiscal year: $9178 per student. Total enrollment: 1,032. Faculty: 90 (88 full-time, 2 part-time). Student-undergrad faculty ratio is 8:1. 1,149 applied, 63% were admitted. 15% from top 10% of their high school class, 47% from top quarter, 78% from top half. Full-time: 708 students, 64% women, 36% men. Part-time: 53 students, 64% women, 36% men. Students come from 32 states and territories, 8 other countries, 50% from out-of-state. 0.5% American Indian or Alaska Native, non-Hispanic/Latino; 7% Hispanic/Latino; 6% Black or African American, non-Hispanic/Latino; 1% Asian, non-Hispanic/Latino; 0.7% Native Hawaiian or other Pacific Islander, non-Hispanic/Latino; 1% international. 15% 25 or older, 55% live on campus, 9% transferred in. Retention: 75% of full-time freshmen returned the following year. Academic areas with the most degrees conferred: health professions and related sciences; psychology; business/marketing. Core. Calendar: semesters. Services for LD students, advanced placement, accelerated degree program, self-designed majors, honors program, independent study, distance learning, double major, summer session for credit, part-time degree program, adult/continuing education programs, co-op programs and internships. Off campus study. Study abroad program. ROTC: Army (c).

Entrance Requirements: Options: electronic application, deferred admission, international baccalaureate accepted. Required: high school transcript, minimum 2 high school GPA, SAT or ACT. Entrance: moderately difficult. Application deadline: rolling. Notification: 7/15. SAT Reasoning Test deadline: 8/18. SAT Subject Test deadline: 8/18. Transfer credits accepted: Yes.

Costs Per Year: Application fee: $25. Comprehensive fee: $42,950 includes full-time tuition ($32,300), mandatory fees ($1050), and college room and board ($9600). College room only: $4600. Room and board charges vary according to board plan. Part-time tuition: $720 per credit hour.

Collegiate Environment: Orientation program. Drama-theater group, choral group. Social organizations: 26 open to all. Most popular organizations: Admissions Student Team, Student Multicultural Organization, Concert Choir, Campus Ministry, Student Government. Major annual events: Homecoming, May Daze, Christmas Dinner. Student services: health clinic, personal-psychological counseling. Campus security: 24-hour emergency response devices and patrols, late night transport-escort service, controlled dormitory access. Nicholas J. Schrupp Library. Books: 76,525 (physical), 136,800 (digital/electronic); Serial titles: 150 (physical), 53,000 (digital/electronic); Databases: 60. Weekly public service hours: 90. Operations spending for the previous fiscal year: $559,393. 237 computers available on campus for general student use. A campuswide network can be accessed from student residence rooms and from off campus. Students can access

the following: online class registration. Staffed computer lab on campus provides training in use of computers, software, and the Internet.

Community Environment: The small city of Dubuque is located on the Mississippi River where Iowa, Illinois and Wisconsin meet. The oldest city in Iowa, it features rugged bluffs and Victorian architecture. Excellent air connections with Chicago's O'Hare Airport and the Minneapolis-St. Paul Airport are available. The city is the cultural, recreational and commercial center of the tristate area, and offers theater, symphony, art galleries, museums, dog racing, riverboat gambling, and concerts as well as facilities for boating, skiing, golf and tennis.

■ CLINTON COMMUNITY COLLEGE

1000 Lincoln Blvd.
Clinton, IA 52732-6299
Tel: (563)244-7001; Free: 800-462-3255
Fax: (563)244-7107
E-mail: gmohr@eicc.edu
Web Site: www.eicc.edu/about-eicc/colleges-and-centers/clinton -community-college.aspx
Description: State and locally supported, 2-year, coed. Part of Eastern Iowa Community College District. Awards certificates, diplomas, transfer associate, and terminal associate degrees. Founded 1946. Setting: 20-acre small town campus. Total enrollment: 1,240. Faculty: 43 (30 full-time, 13 part-time). Student-undergrad faculty ratio is 23:1. 254 applied, 100% were admitted. Full-time: 571 students, 63% women, 37% men. Part-time: 669 students, 68% women, 32% men. Students come from 8 states and territories, 5 other countries, 8% from out-of-state. 30% 25 or older. Retention: 58% of full-time freshmen returned the following year. Core. Calendar: semesters. Academic remediation for entering students, ESL program, services for LD students, advanced placement, self-designed majors, independent study, distance learning, double major, summer session for credit, part-time degree program, adult/continuing education programs, co-op programs and internships. Study abroad program.
Entrance Requirements: Open admission except for nursing program. Options: electronic application, early admission, deferred admission. Entrance: noncompetitive. Application deadline: rolling. Notification: continuous.
Collegiate Environment: Orientation program. Drama-theater group. Social organizations: Greek honors society. Campus security: 24-hour emergency response devices. Clinton Community College Library. 37 computers available on campus for general student use. A campuswide network can be accessed from off-campus. Students can access the following: online class registration. Staffed computer lab on campus provides training in use of computers, software, and the Internet.

■ COE COLLEGE

1220 1st Ave., NE
Cedar Rapids, IA 52402-5092
Tel: (319)399-8000; Free: 877-225-5263
Fax: (319)399-8816
E-mail: admission@coe.edu
Web Site: www.coe.edu
Description: Independent, 4-year, coed, affiliated with Presbyterian Church. Awards bachelor's degrees. Founded 1851. Setting: 53-acre urban campus. Endowment: $85.6 million. Research spending for the previous fiscal year: $546,065. Educational spending for the previous fiscal year: $12,809 per student. Total enrollment: 1,394. Faculty: 177 (101 full-time, 76 part-time). Student-undergrad faculty ratio is 11:1. 7,002 applied, 56% were admitted. 27% from top 10% of their high school class, 54% from top quarter, 88% from top half. 11 valedictorians. Full-time: 1,369 students, 56% women, 44% men. Part-time: 25 students, 48% women, 52% men. Students come from 37 states and territories, 20 other countries, 58% from out-of-state. 0.4% American Indian or Alaska Native, non-Hispanic/Latino; 10% Hispanic/Latino; 8% Black or African American, non-Hispanic/Latino; 4% Asian, non-Hispanic/Latino; 0.1% Native Hawaiian or other Pacific Islander, non-Hispanic/Latino; 2% international. 2% 25 or older, 86% live on campus, 3% transferred in. Retention: 81% of full-time freshmen returned the following year. Academic areas with the most degrees conferred: business/marketing; biological/life sciences; psychology. Core. Calendar: 4-4-1. ESL program, services for LD students, advanced placement, self-designed majors, honors program, independent study, double major, summer session for credit, part-time degree program, internships. Off campus study at University of Iowa, Mount Mercy College, Associated Colleges of the Midwest, Washington University in St. Louis. Study abroad program. ROTC: Army, Air Force (c).
Entrance Requirements: Options: electronic application, early admission,

early action, deferred admission, international baccalaureate accepted. Required: essay, high school transcript, 1 recommendation, SAT or ACT. Recommended: minimum 3 high school GPA, interview. Entrance: moderately difficult. Application deadlines: 3/1, 12/10 for early action. Notification: 3/15. SAT Reasoning Test deadline: 3/1. SAT Subject Test deadline: 3/1. Transfer credits accepted: Yes. Early action applicants: 5,605. Early action applicants admitted: 3,467.
Costs Per Year: Application fee: $30. Comprehensive fee: $54,480 includes full-time tuition ($44,700), mandatory fees ($300), and college room and board ($9480). Room and board charges vary according to board plan and housing facility. Part-time tuition: $5587 per course. Part-time tuition varies according to course load.
Collegiate Environment: Orientation program. Drama-theater group, choral group, student-run newspaper, radio station. Social organizations: 70 open to all; national fraternities, national sororities; 25% of eligible men and 25% of eligible women are members. Most popular organizations: Multicultural Fusion, Coe Alliance, Student Senate, Habitat for Humanity, International Club. Major annual events: Homecoming Dance, Presidential Ball, Drag Show. Student services: health clinic, personal-psychological counseling. Campus security: 24-hour emergency response devices and patrols, late night transport-escort service, controlled dormitory access. Stewart Memorial Library plus 1 other. Books: 238,645 (physical), 289,126 (digital/electronic); Serial titles: 751 (physical), 3,630 (digital/electronic); Databases: 140. Weekly public service hours: 106. Operations spending for the previous fiscal year: $1.6 million. 450 computers available on campus for general student use. Computer purchase/lease plans available. A campuswide network can be accessed from student residence rooms and from off campus. Students can access the following: online class registration. Staffed computer lab on campus provides training in use of computers, software, and the Internet.
Community Environment: Cedar Rapids, a metropolitan community of 150,000 is located just 225 miles west of Chicago in east-central Iowa. All forms of commercial transportation are available. Community facilities include over 100 churches, a symphony orchestra, library, hospital, and shopping in the downtown area, plus three shopping centers. Part time employment is available. Cedar Rapids has over 59 city parks which offer a variety of recreational facilities. Points of interest are the Cedar Rapids Art Center, Iowa Masonic Library, Paramount Theater of Performing Arts, Five Seasons Civic Center, and Theatre Cedar Rapids.

■ CORNELL COLLEGE

600 First St. SW
Mount Vernon, IA 52314-1098
Tel: (319)895-4000; Free: 800-747-1112
Fax: (319)895-4492
E-mail: admission@cornellcollege.edu
Web Site: www.cornellcollege.edu
Description: Independent Methodist, 4-year, coed. Awards bachelor's degrees. Founded 1853. Setting: 129-acre small town campus. Endowment: $77.7 million. Research spending for the previous fiscal year: $88,723. Educational spending for the previous fiscal year: $10,068 per student. Total enrollment: 1,028. Faculty: 114 (74 full-time, 40 part-time). Student-undergrad faculty ratio is 11:1. 2,532 applied, 61% were admitted. 22% from top 10% of their high school class, 46% from top quarter, 82% from top half. 9 valedictorians. Full-time: 1,007 students, 49% women, 51% men. Part-time: 8 students, 38% women, 62% men. Students come from 48 states and territories, 19 other countries, 76% from out-of-state. 2% American Indian or Alaska Native, non-Hispanic/Latino; 8% Hispanic/Latino; 6% Black or African American, non-Hispanic/Latino; 4% Asian, non-Hispanic/Latino; 0.1% Native Hawaiian or other Pacific Islander, non-Hispanic/Latino; 7% international. 2% 25 or older, 88% live on campus, 3% transferred in. Retention: 82% of full-time freshmen returned the following year. Academic areas with the most degrees conferred: biological/life sciences; education; social sciences. Core. Calendar: 8 3.5 week terms. ESL program, services for LD students, advanced placement, self-designed majors, independent study, double major, internships. Off campus study at Associated Colleges of the Midwest, Audubon Center of the North Woods, Oak Ridge National Laboratory. Study abroad program.
Entrance Requirements: Options: electronic application, early admission, early decision, early action, deferred admission, international baccalaureate accepted. Required: essay, high school transcript. Entrance: moderately difficult. Application deadlines: rolling for nonresidents, 11/1 for early decision. Notification: 3/20, continuous for nonresidents, rolling for early action. SAT

Reasoning Test deadline: 3/1. Transfer credits accepted: Yes. Applicants placed on waiting list: 0. Early action applicants: 80. Early action applicants admitted: 27.

Costs Per Year: Comprehensive fee: $53,736 includes full-time tuition ($43,550), mandatory fees ($426), and college room and board ($9760). College room only: $4500. Part-time tuition: $3141 per course.

Collegiate Environment: Orientation program. Drama-theater group, choral group, student-run newspaper, radio station. Social organizations: 78 open to all; local fraternities, local sororities; 21% of eligible men and 32% of eligible women are members. Most popular organizations: Student-initiated Living-Learning Community, Chess and Games, Environmental Club, Performing Arts and Activities Council, Alliance. Major annual events: Homecoming, Music, Cultural events, and Theatre Productions, Interactive Entertainment. Student services: health clinic, personal-psychological counseling. Campus security: 24-hour emergency response devices and patrols, late night transport-escort service, controlled dormitory access. 1,124 college housing spaces available; 985 were occupied in 2018-19. Freshmen guaranteed college housing. On-campus residence required through senior year. Options: coed, women-only housing available. Cole Library plus 1 other. Books: 232,914 (physical); Serial titles: 491 (digital/electronic). Weekly public service hours: 70; students can reserve study rooms. Operations spending for the previous fiscal year: $883,825. 259 computers available on campus for general student use. A campuswide network can be accessed from student residence rooms and from off campus. Students can access the following: online class registration. Staffed computer lab on campus.

Community Environment: Mount Vernon is a small town located 15 miles east of Cedar Rapids and 22 miles north of Iowa City. Bus and airline service are available in Cedar Rapids. The community and college share many facilities. Community facilities include churches and various civic, fraternal and veteran's organizations. Opportunities for student employment off campus are limited. Excellent recreational facilities are available at the Palisades State Park, MacBride State Park and Coralville Reservoir, for fishing and boating, golf, bowling, swimming, and cross-country skiing. Downhill skiing facilities are available within 70 miles.

■ DES MOINES AREA COMMUNITY COLLEGE
2006 S Ankeny Blvd.
Ankeny, IA 50021-8995
Tel: (515)964-6200; Free: 800-362-2127
E-mail: mjleutsch@dmacc.edu
Web Site: www.dmacc.edu

Description: State and locally supported, 2-year, coed. Part of Iowa Area Community Colleges System. Awards certificates, diplomas, transfer associate, and terminal associate degrees (profile also includes information from the Boone, Carroll, Des Moines, and Newton campuses). Founded 1966. Setting: 362-acre small town campus. Endowment: $7 million. Total enrollment: 22,982. Faculty: 1,145 (343 full-time, 802 part-time). Student-undergrad faculty ratio is 20:1. Full-time: 6,476 students, 51% women, 49% men. Part-time: 16,506 students, 56% women, 44% men. Students come from 52 states and territories, 12 other countries, 7% from out-of-state. 0.3% American Indian or Alaska Native, non-Hispanic/Latino; 8% Hispanic/Latino; 6% Black or African American, non-Hispanic/Latino; 4% Asian, non-Hispanic/Latino; 0.1% Native Hawaiian or other Pacific Islander, non-Hispanic/Latino; 0.9% international. 35% 25 or older, 9% transferred in. Retention: 59% of full-time freshmen returned the following year. Core. Calendar: semesters. Academic remediation for entering students, ESL program, services for LD students, advanced placement, self-designed majors, honors program, distance learning, summer session for credit, part-time degree program, adult/continuing education programs, co-op programs. Off campus study at Drake University, Grand View College, Iowa State University of Science and Technology, University of Northern Iowa.

Entrance Requirements: Open admission. Options: electronic application, early admission, deferred admission. Required for some: high school transcript, interview, SAT or ACT, ACT Compass. Entrance: noncompetitive. Application deadline: rolling.

Costs Per Year: Application fee: $0. State resident tuition: $4680 full-time, $156 per credit hour part-time. Nonresident tuition: $9360 full-time, $312 per credit hour part-time. Full-time tuition varies according to course load and reciprocity agreements. Part-time tuition varies according to course load and reciprocity agreements. College room and board: $7302. College room only: $4800. Room and board charges vary according to location.

Collegiate Environment: Drama-theater group, choral group, student-run newspaper. Social organizations: 30 open to all. Most popular organizations:

Agri-Business Club, Horticulture Club, Hospitality Arts Club, Iowa Delta Epsilon Chi, Dental Hygienist Club. Major annual events: Orientation, Drive Into DMACC Days. Student services: health clinic, personal-psychological counseling. Campus security: 24-hour emergency response devices and patrols, late night transport-escort service. DMACC District Library plus 4 others. Operations spending for the previous fiscal year: $1.6 million. 400 computers available on campus for general student use. A campuswide network can be accessed. Students can access the following: online class registration, online classes. Staffed computer lab on campus provides training in use of software.

■ DIVINE WORD COLLEGE
102 Jacoby Dr. SW
Epworth, IA 52045-0380
Tel: (563)876-3353; Free: 800-553-3321
Fax: (563)876-3407
Web Site: www.dwci.edu

Description: Independent Roman Catholic, 4-year, coed. Awards associate and bachelor's degrees. Founded 1912. Setting: 35-acre rural campus. Total enrollment: 133. Core. Calendar: semesters. Academic remediation for entering students, ESL program, advanced placement, independent study, double major, co-op programs and internships. Study abroad program.

Entrance Requirements: Option: early admission. Required: essay, high school transcript, 3 recommendations, interview. Recommended: SAT or ACT. Application deadline: 7/15. Notification: continuous until 8/1. Transfer credits accepted: Yes.

Collegiate Environment: Orientation program. Choral group. Student services: personal-psychological counseling. Campus security: controlled dormitory access. Matthew Jacoby Library.

■ DORDT COLLEGE
498 4th Ave., NE
Sioux Center, IA 51250-1697
Tel: (712)722-6000; Free: 800-343-6738
Fax: (712)722-1967
E-mail: admissions@dordt.edu
Web Site: www.dordt.edu

Description: Independent Christian Reformed, comprehensive, coed. Awards associate, bachelor's, and master's degrees. Founded 1955. Setting: 110-acre small town campus. Endowment: $26 million. Educational spending for the previous fiscal year: $8328 per student. Total enrollment: 1,405. Faculty: 105 (80 full-time, 25 part-time). Student-undergrad faculty ratio is 15:1. 1,355 applied, 75% were admitted. 17% from top 10% of their high school class, 35% from top quarter, 75% from top half. 6 National Merit Scholars. Full-time: 1,345 students, 46% women, 54% men. Part-time: 31 students, 39% women, 61% men. Students come from 38 states and territories, 26 other countries, 63% from out-of-state. 0.1% American Indian or Alaska Native, non-Hispanic/Latino; 2% Hispanic/Latino; 2% Black or African American, non-Hispanic/Latino; 0.9% Asian, non-Hispanic/Latino; 9% international. 5% 25 or older, 90% live on campus, 4% transferred in. Retention: 80% of full-time freshmen returned the following year. Core. Calendar: semesters. Academic remediation for entering students, ESL program, services for LD students, advanced placement, self-designed majors, freshman honors college, honors program, independent study, distance learning, double major, part-time degree program, internships. Off campus study at Christian College Coalition, Chicago Metro Program, American Studies Program, Los Angeles Film Studies Program, European Studies program, Nicaragua Studies Program. Study abroad program.

Entrance Requirements: Options: electronic application, deferred admission, international baccalaureate accepted. Required: high school transcript, minimum 2.25 high school GPA, SAT or ACT. Required for some: essay, interview. Entrance: moderately difficult. Application deadline: 8/1. Notification: 8/1.

Collegiate Environment: Orientation program. Drama-theater group, choral group, student-run newspaper, radio station. Social organizations: 50 open to all. Most popular organizations: PLIA, Future Teachers, Ag Club, Lacrosse Club, Defenders of Life. Major annual events: Talent Extravaganza, Homecoming, Parents' Weekend. Student services: health clinic, personal-psychological counseling. Campus security: 24-hour emergency response devices, student patrols, late night transport-escort service, controlled dormitory access. Dordt College Library plus 1 other. Operations spending for the previous fiscal year: $514,075. 200 computers available on campus for general student use. A campuswide network can be accessed from student residence rooms and from off campus. Students can access the following:

online class registration. Staffed computer lab on campus provides training in use of computers, software, and the Internet.

Community Environment: Sioux Center, population 6,500 is a rural area with a temperate climate. College transportation serves the area. A public library, hospital, churches, clinics and shopping facilities are all available within the community. Recreational activities include swimming, golf, and fishing. Part-time employment may be found.

■ **DRAKE UNIVERSITY**
2507 University Ave.
Des Moines, IA 50311-4516
Tel: (515)271-2011
Fax: (515)271-2831
Web Site: www.drake.edu

Description: Independent, university, coed. Awards bachelor's, master's, and doctoral degrees and post-master's certificates. Founded 1881. Setting: 120-acre urban campus. Endowment: $210.6 million. Research spending for the previous fiscal year: $1.1 million. Educational spending for the previous fiscal year: $11,724 per student. Total enrollment: 4,869. Faculty: 472 (305 full-time, 167 part-time). 6,886 applied, 68% were admitted. 39% from top 10% of their high school class, 68% from top quarter, 92% from top half. Full-time: 2,834 students, 59% women, 41% men. Part-time: 181 students, 45% women, 55% men. 65% from out-of-state. 6% Hispanic/Latino; 5% Black or African American, non-Hispanic/Latino; 4% Asian, non-Hispanic/Latino; 4% international. 3% 25 or older, 70% live on campus, 4% transferred in. Retention: 89% of full-time freshmen returned the following year. Academic areas with the most degrees conferred: business/marketing; communication/journalism; social sciences. Core. Calendar: semesters. ESL program, services for LD students, advanced placement, accelerated degree program, self-designed majors, honors program, independent study, distance learning, double major, summer session for credit, part-time degree program, co-op programs and internships, graduate courses open to undergrads. Off campus study at Des Moines Consortium. Study abroad program. ROTC: Army (c), Air Force (c).

Entrance Requirements: Options: electronic application, early admission, deferred admission, international baccalaureate accepted. Required: high school transcript, minimum X high school GPA. Recommended: essay, recommendations, interview. Required for some: SAT or ACT. Entrance: moderately difficult. Application deadline: 3/1. Notification: continuous. SAT Reasoning Test deadline: 4/1. Transfer credits accepted: Yes.

Costs Per Year: Comprehensive fee: $51,924 includes full-time tuition ($41,250), mandatory fees ($146), and college room and board ($10,528). College room only: $4692. Full-time tuition and fees vary according to course load, degree level, program, and student level. Room and board charges vary according to board plan and housing facility. Part-time tuition: $845 per credit hour. Part-time tuition varies according to class time, degree level, and program. Tuition guaranteed not to increase for student's term of enrollment.

Collegiate Environment: Orientation program. Drama-theater group, choral group, marching band, student-run newspaper, radio station. Social organizations: 120 open to all; national fraternities, national sororities. Most popular organizations: Student Activities Board, Drake Magazine, Dog Pound Pep Squad, Alpha Phi Omega, Residence Hall Association. Major annual events: Drake Relays, Parent/Family Weekend, Homecoming. Student services: legal services, health clinic, personal-psychological counseling. Campus security: 24-hour emergency response devices and patrols, late night transport-escort service, controlled dormitory access. Freshmen guaranteed college housing. On-campus residence required through sophomore year. Option: coed housing available. Cowles Library plus 1 other. Study areas open 24 hours, 5-7 days a week; students can reserve study rooms. Operations spending for the previous fiscal year: $5.3 million.

Community Environment: Des Moines is Iowa's capital city, and its metropolitan population of 456,000 is the largest in the state. The downtown area includes the Convention Center, a skywalk system linking office buildings and shops, and a major restoration and conversion of historic buildings in the former city market area. A Civic Center offers plays, concerts and other entertainment. The Art Center, in a park setting of trees and gardens, houses a permanent collection of paintings and sculpture, in addition to traveling exhibits. Major business interests include a concentration of home offices of insurance companies and the pivotal operation of a large publishing firm.

■ **ELLSWORTH COMMUNITY COLLEGE**
1100 College Ave.
Iowa Falls, IA 50126-1199

Tel: (641)648-4611; Free: 800-ECC-9235
Fax: (641)648-3128
Web Site: ecc.iavalley.edu

Description: State and locally supported, 2-year, coed. Part of Iowa Valley Community College District System. Awards diplomas, transfer associate, and terminal associate degrees. Founded 1890. Setting: 10-acre small town campus. Total enrollment: 916. 17% 25 or older. Core. Calendar: semesters. Academic remediation for entering students, services for LD students, advanced placement, self-designed majors, honors program, distance learning, summer session for credit, part-time degree program, adult/continuing education programs, co-op programs and internships.

Entrance Requirements: Open admission for state residents. Options: electronic application, early admission, deferred admission. Required: high school transcript. Entrance: noncompetitive. Application deadlines: rolling, 8/1 for nonresidents. Notification: continuous.

Costs Per Year: State resident tuition: $5190 full-time, $173 per credit hour part-time. Nonresident tuition: $6360 full-time, $212 per credit hour part-time. Mandatory fees: $780 full-time, $26 per credit hour part-time. Full-time tuition and fees vary according to course load. Part-time tuition and fees vary according to course load. College room and board: $5970. College room only: $3780. Room and board charges vary according to housing facility.

Collegiate Environment: Orientation program. Drama-theater group, choral group, student-run newspaper. Student services: personal-psychological counseling. Campus security: 24-hour emergency response devices and patrols. Osgood Learning Resource Center.

Community Environment: Iowa Falls (population 5,112) is a rural area situated on the Iowa River. Community facilities include 18 churches of all denominations, a hospital, library, motels, hotels, and various civic and service organizations. Part-time jobs are available. Recreational facilities include a theater, hunting, fishing, water skiing, swimming and two nine-hole golf courses.

■ **EMMAUS BIBLE COLLEGE**
2570 Asbury Rd.
Dubuque, IA 52001-3097
Tel: (563)588-8000; Free: 800-397-2425
Fax: (563)588-1216
Web Site: www.emmaus.edu

Description: Independent nondenominational, 4-year, coed. Awards associate and bachelor's degrees. Founded 1941. Setting: 22-acre small town campus. Total enrollment: 269. Faculty: 39 (20 full-time, 19 part-time). Student-undergrad faculty ratio is 10:1. 193 applied, 58% were admitted. 15% from top 10% of their high school class, 44% from top quarter, 77% from top half. Full-time: 248 students, 55% women, 45% men. Part-time: 21 students, 62% women, 38% men. 57% from out-of-state. 2% American Indian or Alaska Native, non-Hispanic/Latino; 6% Hispanic/Latino; 4% Black or African American, non-Hispanic/Latino; 5% Asian, non-Hispanic/Latino. 10% 25 or older, 90% live on campus, 8% transferred in. Retention: 70% of full-time freshmen returned the following year. Academic areas with the most degrees conferred: theology and religious vocations; education; psychology. Core. Calendar: semesters. Services for LD students, advanced placement, independent study, distance learning, double major, summer session for credit, part-time degree program, internships. Off campus study.

Entrance Requirements: Open admission. Options: electronic application, deferred admission. Required: essay, high school transcript, minimum 2 high school GPA, 1 recommendation, SAT or ACT. Entrance: noncompetitive. Application deadline: 8/1. Notification: continuous. SAT Reasoning Test deadline: 8/1. Transfer credits accepted: Yes.

Costs Per Year: Comprehensive fee: $26,900 includes full-time tuition ($18,400) and college room and board ($8500). Full-time tuition varies according to course load. Part-time tuition: $765 per credit hour.

Collegiate Environment: Orientation program. Choral group. Student services: personal-psychological counseling. Campus security: 24-hour emergency response devices, student patrols, controlled dormitory access. The Emmaus Bible College Library plus 1 other. Weekly public service hours: 130.

Community Environment: Emmaus Bible College is located in Dubuque, Iowa, a Mississippi River City, of 60,000 people. It serves as the metropolitan center of 300,000 residents in the tri-state trading area. It is a city of traditional values and loyalties reflecting the past with a progressive spirit toward the future. Dubuque provides many wholesome activities for the Emmaus student. The Dubuque Symphony Orchestra performs regularly at the Five Flags Center. The Spirit of Dubuque, a paddlewheeler, plies the Mississippi and provides dining en route. Fall brings out the beauty of the variety of trees and foliage along the river and its tributaries. Dubuque is also a center for education, boasting three colleges in addition to Emmaus, as well as two seminaries. This healthy environment is a suitable setting for the Emmaus education and for the community outreach of Christian service and evangelism.

■ FAITH BAPTIST BIBLE COLLEGE AND THEOLOGICAL SEMINARY
1900 NW 4th St.
Ankeny, IA 50023
Tel: (515)964-0601; Free: 888-FAITH 4U
Fax: (515)964-1638
E-mail: admissions@faith.edu
Web Site: www.faith.edu
Description: Independent, comprehensive, coed, affiliated with General Association of Regular Baptist Churches. Awards associate, bachelor's, and master's degrees. Founded 1921. Setting: 52-acre suburban campus. Endowment: $4 million. Educational spending for the previous fiscal year: $3060 per student. Total enrollment: 274. Faculty: 30 (17 full-time, 13 part-time). Student-undergrad faculty ratio is 11:1. 133 applied. 15% from top 10% of their high school class, 33% from top quarter, 63% from top half. Full-time: 194 students, 55% women, 45% men. Part-time: 32 students, 59% women, 41% men. Students come from 33 states and territories, 4 other countries, 62% from out-of-state. 0.9% American Indian or Alaska Native, non-Hispanic/Latino; 0.9% Hispanic/Latino; 0.4% Black or African American, non-Hispanic/Latino; 1% Asian, non-Hispanic/Latino; 0.4% international. 3% 25 or older, 5% transferred in. Retention: 73% of full-time freshmen returned the following year. Academic areas with the most degrees conferred: theology and religious vocations; education; business/marketing. Core. Calendar: semesters. Academic remediation for entering students, advanced placement, independent study, distance learning, double major, summer session for credit, part-time degree program, adult/continuing education programs, internships, graduate courses open to undergrads. Study abroad program.
Entrance Requirements: Options: electronic application, deferred admission. Required: essay, high school transcript, 2 recommendations, SAT or ACT. Recommended: minimum 2 high school GPA. Required for some: interview. Entrance: minimally difficult. Application deadline: 8/1. Notification: 9/1. SAT Reasoning Test deadline: 8/1. SAT Subject Test deadline: 8/1. Transfer credits accepted: Yes.
Costs Per Year: Application fee: $45. One-time mandatory fee: $50. Comprehensive fee: $23,676 includes full-time tuition ($16,274), mandatory fees ($602), and college room and board ($6800). College room only: $3230. Full-time tuition and fees vary according to course load. Part-time tuition: $595 per credit hour. Part-time mandatory fees: $301 per term.
Collegiate Environment: Orientation program. Drama-theater group, choral group. Social organizations: 6 open to all; 70% of eligible men and 70% of eligible women are members. Most popular organizations: Student Association, Student Missionary Fellowship, Intramural Sports, Photo Club, Chapel Orchestra. Major annual events: Homecoming Week, Student Appreciation Night, Spring Banquet. Student services: personal-psychological counseling. Campus security: 24-hour emergency response devices and patrols, late night transport-escort service. John L. Patten Library. Operations spending for the previous fiscal year: $116,053. 45 computers available on campus for general student use. A campuswide network can be accessed from student residence rooms and from off campus. Students can access the following: online class registration. Staffed computer lab on campus provides training in use of computers, software, and the Internet.

■ GRACELAND UNIVERSITY
1 University Pl.
Lamoni, IA 50140
Tel: (641)784-5000; Free: 866-GRACELAND
Fax: (641)784-5480
E-mail: admissions@graceland.edu
Web Site: www.graceland.edu
Description: Independent Community of Christ, comprehensive, coed. Awards bachelor's, master's, and doctoral degrees and post-master's certificates. Founded 1895. Setting: 170-acre rural campus with easy access to Des Moines. Endowment: $53.3 million. Educational spending for the previous fiscal year: $7684 per student. Total enrollment: 1,992. Faculty: 156 (67 full-time, 89 part-time). Student-undergrad faculty ratio is 17:1. 3,004 applied, 58% were admitted. 12% from top 10% of their high school class, 27% from top quarter, 65% from top half. Full-time: 1,023 students, 55% women, 45% men. Part-time: 157 students, 76% women, 24% men. Students come from 40 states and territories, 20 other countries, 73% from out-of-state.

0.5% American Indian or Alaska Native, non-Hispanic/Latino; 10% Hispanic/Latino; 9% Black or African American, non-Hispanic/Latino; 1% Asian, non-Hispanic/Latino; 2% Native Hawaiian or other Pacific Islander, non-Hispanic/Latino; 5% international. 16% 25 or older, 74% live on campus, 8% transferred in. Retention: 59% of full-time freshmen returned the following year. Academic areas with the most degrees conferred: health professions and related sciences; business/marketing; education; parks and recreation. Core. Calendar: 4-1-4. Academic remediation for entering students, services for LD students, advanced placement, accelerated degree program, self-designed majors, freshman honors college, honors program, independent study, distance learning, double major, summer session for credit, part-time degree program, adult/continuing education programs, co-op programs and internships, graduate courses open to undergrads. Study abroad program.
Entrance Requirements: Options: electronic application, international baccalaureate accepted. Required: high school transcript, 2 of the following: minimum high school GPA of 2.5, rank in top half of class, or minimum SAT score of 960/ACT of 21, SAT or ACT, TOEFL or IELTS for all students whose first language is not English. Required for some: essay, 2 recommendations, interview. Entrance: moderately difficult. Application deadline: rolling. Notification: continuous. Transfer credits accepted: Yes.
Costs Per Year: Application fee: $0. Comprehensive fee: $39,520 includes full-time tuition ($29,750), mandatory fees ($670), and college room and board ($9100). College room only: $3490. Part-time tuition: $800 per semester hour.
Collegiate Environment: Orientation program. Drama-theater group, choral group, marching band, student-run newspaper, radio station. Social organizations: 43 open to all. Most popular organizations: Black Student Union, Latin Club, Enactus, Social Equality Alliance, Communication Club. Major annual events: New Year's in November, Final Fling, Air Band Competition at Homecoming. Student services: health clinic, personal-psychological counseling. Campus security: 24-hour emergency response devices, controlled dormitory access. 810 college housing spaces available; 647 were occupied in 2018-19. Freshmen guaranteed college housing. On-campus residence required through senior year. Options: men-only, women-only housing available. F. M. Smith Library. Books: 80,000 (physical), 350,000 (digital/electronic); Serial titles: 130 (physical), 60 (digital/electronic); Databases: 50. Weekly public service hours: 80; students can reserve study rooms. Operations spending for the previous fiscal year: $502,579. 178 computers available on campus for general student use. A campuswide network can be accessed from student residence rooms and from off campus. Students can access the following: online class registration. Staffed computer lab on campus provides training in use of computers, software, and the Internet.
Community Environment: Lamoni (population 2,470), a picturesque town in the rolling hills of south central Iowa, is within easy driving distance of Des Moines, Omaha, Council Bluffs, and Kansas City. Bus transportation is available to these urban centers. The city has an excellent library and shopping area including several antique malls. Churches play an important part in the life of the community and a county hospital is located in nearby Leon. Citizens enjoy world-renowned artists in concert and theater productions at the college fine arts center, movies, sports, clubs, and lodges. Nine Eagles State Park (12 miles southeast), Central Park, and Foreman Park provide facilities for recreation.

■ GRAND VIEW UNIVERSITY
1200 Grandview Ave.
Des Moines, IA 50316-1599
Tel: (515)263-2800; Free: 800-444-6083
Fax: (515)263-2974
E-mail: admissions@grandview.edu
Web Site: www.grandview.edu
Description: Independent, comprehensive, coed, affiliated with Evangelical Lutheran Church in America. Awards bachelor's and master's degrees. Founded 1896. Setting: 25-acre urban campus. Endowment: $22.6 million. Educational spending for the previous fiscal year: $6472 per student. Total enrollment: 1,836. Faculty: 222 (89 full-time, 133 part-time). Student-undergrad faculty ratio is 13:1. 820 applied, 93% were admitted. 15% from top 10% of their high school class, 36% from top quarter, 69% from top half. 7 valedictorians. Full-time: 1,574 students, 55% women, 45% men. Part-time: 214 students, 64% women, 36% men. Students come from 38 states and territories, 38 other countries, 7% from out-of-state. 0.4% American Indian or Alaska Native, non-Hispanic/Latino; 5% Hispanic/Latino; 7% Black or African American, non-Hispanic/Latino; 3% Asian, non-Hispanic/Latino; 0.2% Native Hawaiian or other Pacific Islander, non-Hispanic/Latino; 3%

international. 20% 25 or older, 55% live on campus, 14% transferred in. Retention: 67% of full-time freshmen returned the following year. Academic areas with the most degrees conferred: business/marketing; health professions and related sciences; parks and recreation. Core. Calendar: semesters. Academic remediation for entering students, ESL program, services for LD students, advanced placement, accelerated degree program, self-designed majors, freshman honors college, honors program, independent study, distance learning, double major, summer session for credit, part-time degree program, adult/continuing education programs, co-op programs and internships, graduate courses open to undergrads. Off campus study at Drake University, Des Moines Area Community College. Study abroad program. ROTC: Army (c), Air Force (c).

Entrance Requirements: Option: electronic application. Required: high school transcript, SAT or ACT. Recommended: minimum 2 high school GPA. Entrance: minimally difficult. Application deadline: 8/15. Notification: 9/15. Transfer credits accepted: Yes.

Costs Per Year: Application fee: $0. Comprehensive fee: $36,786 includes full-time tuition ($26,922), mandatory fees ($686), and college room and board ($9178). Full-time tuition and fees vary according to class time and course load. Room and board charges vary according to board plan and housing facility. Part-time tuition: $669 per credit hour. Part-time tuition varies according to class time and course load.

Collegiate Environment: Orientation program. Drama-theater group, choral group, student-run newspaper, radio station. Social organizations: 43 open to all. Most popular organizations: Nursing Student Association, Art Club, Science Club, Education Club, Business Club. Major annual event: Homecoming. Student services: health clinic, personal-psychological counseling. Campus security: 24-hour emergency response devices and patrols, late night transport-escort service, controlled dormitory access, night security patrols. Grand View University Library plus 1 other. Books: 88,382 (physical), 45,490 (digital/electronic); Serial titles: 514 (physical), 75,889 (digital/electronic); Databases: 29. Weekly public service hours: 86. Operations spending for the previous fiscal year: $537,745. 336 computers available on campus for general student use. A campuswide network can be accessed from student residence rooms and from off campus. Students can access the following: online class registration. Staffed computer lab on campus provides training in use of computers.

Community Environment: See Drake University.

■ **GRINNELL COLLEGE**
1103 Park St.
Grinnell, IA 50112-1690
Tel: (641)269-4000; Free: 800-247-0113
Fax: (641)269-3408
E-mail: askgrin@grinnell.edu
Web Site: www.grinnell.edu
Description: Independent, 4-year, coed. Awards bachelor's degrees. Founded 1846. Setting: 120-acre small town campus. Endowment: $1.9 billion. Educational spending for the previous fiscal year: $26,256 per student. Total enrollment: 1,712. Faculty: 209 (177 full-time, 32 part-time). Student-undergrad faculty ratio is 9:1. 5,850 applied, 29% were admitted. 69% from top 10% of their high school class, 91% from top quarter, 99% from top half. Full-time: 1,662 students, 54% women, 46% men. Part-time: 50 students, 34% women, 66% men. Students come from 52 states and territories, 51 other countries, 92% from out-of-state. 7% Hispanic/Latino; 6% Black or African American, non-Hispanic/Latino; 8% Asian, non-Hispanic/Latino; 19% international. 88% live on campus, 1% transferred in. Retention: 96% of full-time freshmen returned the following year. Academic areas with the most degrees conferred: social sciences; biological/life sciences; physical sciences. Calendar: semesters. Services for LD students, advanced placement, accelerated degree program, self-designed majors, independent study, double major, internships. Off campus study. Study abroad program.

Entrance Requirements: Options: electronic application, early admission, early decision, deferred admission, international baccalaureate accepted. Required: essay, high school transcript, 3 recommendations, SAT or ACT. Recommended: interview. Entrance: very difficult. Application deadlines: 1/15, 11/15 for early decision plan 1, 1/1 for early decision plan 2. Notification: 4/1, 12/15 for early decision plan 1, 2/1 for early decision plan 2. SAT Reasoning Test deadline: 1/15. Transfer credits accepted: Yes. Applicants placed on waiting list: 1,126. Wait-listed applicants offered admission: 12. Early decision applicants: 322. Early decision applicants admitted: 197.

Costs Per Year: Application fee: $0. Comprehensive fee: $65,202 includes full-time tuition ($51,924), mandatory fees ($468), and college room and

board ($12,810). College room only: $6050. Room and board charges vary according to board plan and housing facility. Part-time tuition: $1571 per credit hour.

Collegiate Environment: Orientation program. Drama-theater group, choral group, student-run newspaper, radio station. Social organizations: 114 open to all. Most popular organizations: Concerned Black Students, International Student Organization, Student Organization of Latinas/Latinos, Campus Democrats, Ultimate Frisbee. Major annual events: Titular Head Student Film Festival, Mary B. James, Grinnell Relays. Student services: health clinic, personal-psychological counseling. Campus security: 24-hour emergency response devices and patrols, student patrols, late night transport-escort service, controlled dormitory access. Burling Library plus 2 others. Books: 488,334 (physical), 474,326 (digital/electronic); Serial titles: 6,491 (physical), 11,577 (digital/electronic); Databases: 346. Weekly public service hours: 109. Operations spending for the previous fiscal year: $3.8 million. 200 computers available on campus for general student use. A campuswide network can be accessed from student residence rooms and from off campus. Students can access the following: online class registration. Staffed computer lab on campus provides training in use of computers, software, and the Internet.

Community Environment: Grinnell, population 9,332, is located 1 hour east of Des Moines and 1 hour west of Iowa City, on Interstate 80 and is within a five-hour drive from Chicago, St. Louis, Kansas City, and Minneapolis.

■ **HAMILTON TECHNICAL COLLEGE**
1011 E 53rd St.
Davenport, IA 52807-2653
Tel: (563)386-3570; Free: 866-966-4825
Fax: (563)386-6756
Web Site: www.hamiltontechcollege.edu
Description: Proprietary, 4-year, coed. Awards associate and bachelor's degrees. Founded 1969. Setting: urban campus. Faculty: 12 (11 full-time, 1 part-time). Student-undergrad faculty ratio is 20:1. 95 applied. Academic area with the most degrees conferred: engineering technologies. Calendar: continuous.

Entrance Requirements: Open admission. Option: deferred admission. Required: high school transcript, interview. Entrance: noncompetitive. Application deadline: rolling.

Collegiate Environment: Campus security: 24-hour emergency response devices. Hamilton Technical College Library.

■ **HAWKEYE COMMUNITY COLLEGE**
PO Box 8015
Waterloo, IA 50704-8015
Tel: (319)296-2320; Free: 800-670-4769
Fax: (319)296-2874
E-mail: holly.grimm-see@hawkeyecollege.edu
Web Site: www.hawkeyecollege.edu
Description: State and locally supported, 2-year, coed. Awards certificates, diplomas, transfer associate, and terminal associate degrees. Founded 1966. Setting: 320-acre rural campus. Endowment: $2.3 million. Research spending for the previous fiscal year: $214,478. Educational spending for the previous fiscal year: $7388 per student. Total enrollment: 5,259. Faculty: 296 (110 full-time, 186 part-time). Student-undergrad faculty ratio is 17:1. 1,562 applied, 95% were admitted. Full-time: 2,256 students, 52% women, 48% men. Part-time: 3,003 students, 58% women, 42% men. Students come from 9 states and territories, 17 other countries, 1% from out-of-state. 0.2% American Indian or Alaska Native, non-Hispanic/Latino; 4% Hispanic/Latino; 7% Black or African American, non-Hispanic/Latino; 2% Asian, non-Hispanic/Latino; 0.3% Native Hawaiian or other Pacific Islander, non-Hispanic/Latino; 0.5% international. 25% 25 or older, 5% transferred in. Calendar: semesters. Academic remediation for entering students, ESL program, services for LD students, advanced placement, accelerated degree program, distance learning, summer session for credit, part-time degree program, external degree program, adult/continuing education programs, co-op programs. Study abroad program. ROTC: Army (c).

Entrance Requirements: Open admission. Options: electronic application, deferred admission. Required: high school transcript, ACT ACCUPLACER or the equivalent from ACT or accredited college course(s). Required for some: ACT. Entrance: noncompetitive. Application deadline: rolling. Notification: continuous. Transfer credits accepted: Yes.

Costs Per Year: Application fee: $0. State resident tuition: $5012 full-time, $179 per credit hour part-time. Nonresident tuition: $5712 full-time, $204 per credit hour part-time. Mandatory fees: $224 full-time, $8 per credit hour part-time.

Collegiate Environment: Orientation program. Drama-theater group, choral group. Social organizations: 29 open to all; academic fraternities; 40% of eligible men and 60% of eligible women are members. Most popular organizations: Student Leadership, Phi Theta Kappa, Student Ambassadors, Student American Dental Hygienist Association, Photography. Major annual events: Fall Fest, Culture Fest, Intramurals. Student services: health clinic, personal-psychological counseling, women's center. Campus security: 24-hour patrols. College housing not available. Hawkeye Community College Library. Books: 29,911 (physical), 201,941 (digital/electronic); Serial titles: 85 (physical), 39 (digital/electronic); Databases: 62. Weekly public service hours: 70; students can reserve study rooms. Operations spending for the previous fiscal year: $493,990. 2,466 computers available on campus for general student use. A campuswide network can be accessed. Students can access the following: online class registration. Staffed computer lab on campus provides training in use of computers, software, and the Internet.

Community Environment: Waterloo, population 66,500, is an industrial city. The manufacture of tractors, and the horse racing cart known as the Sulky by the Jerald Sulky Company. Highlights of interest are the Museum of History and Science.

■ **INDIAN HILLS COMMUNITY COLLEGE**
525 Grandview Ave., Bldg. No.1
Ottumwa, IA 52501-1398
Tel: (641)683-5111; Free: 800-726-2585
Web Site: www.ihcc.cc.ia.us

Description: State and locally supported, 2-year, coed. Part of Iowa Area Community Colleges System. Awards certificates, diplomas, transfer associate, and terminal associate degrees. Founded 1966. Setting: 400-acre small town campus. Total enrollment: 4,174. 28% 25 or older. Calendar: quarters. Academic remediation for entering students, ESL program, services for LD students, self-designed majors, honors program, summer session for credit, part-time degree program, adult/continuing education programs, co-op programs and internships.

Entrance Requirements: Open admission except for nursing, technology programs. Option: early admission. Required for some: high school transcript. Entrance: noncompetitive. Application deadline: rolling.

Collegiate Environment: Orientation program. Drama-theater group. Student services: personal-psychological counseling, women's center. Campus security: 24-hour emergency response devices and patrols. Indian Hills Community College Library plus 2 others.

Community Environment: The population of Ottumwa is 25,000. This community is located about 85 miles southwest of Des Moines. Recreational activities are available at Lake Rathbun, about six miles northwest of Centerville.

■ **INSTE BIBLE COLLEGE**
2302 SW 3rd St.
Ankeny, IA 50023
Tel: (515)289-9200
Fax: (515)289-9201
Web Site: www.inste.edu

Description: Proprietary, 4-year, coed. Awards bachelor's degrees.

■ **IOWA CENTRAL COMMUNITY COLLEGE**
One Triton Cir.
Fort Dodge, IA 50501
Tel: (515)576-7201; Free: 800-362-2793
Fax: (515)576-7724
E-mail: flattery@iowacentral.com
Web Site: www.iowacentral.edu

Description: State and locally supported, 2-year, coed. Awards certificates, diplomas, transfer associate, and terminal associate degrees. Founded 1966. Setting: 110-acre small town campus. Total enrollment: 5,489. Faculty: 427 (99 full-time, 328 part-time). Student-undergrad faculty ratio is 18:1. 1,186 applied. Students come from 40 states and territories, 34 other countries, 8% from out-of-state. 1% American Indian or Alaska Native, non-Hispanic/Latino; 9% Hispanic/Latino; 9% Black or African American, non-Hispanic/Latino; 2% Asian, non-Hispanic/Latino; 0.2% Native Hawaiian or other Pacific Islander, non-Hispanic/Latino; 2% international. 14% 25 or older, 18% live on campus. Core. Calendar: semesters. Academic remediation for entering students, ESL program, services for LD students, advanced placement, independent study, summer session for credit, part-time degree program, adult/continuing education programs, co-op programs and internships. Study abroad program.

Entrance Requirements: Open admission We have an open admission policy to the college. The Health Science programs have established criteria for admittance into those specific programs that is separate from the college policy. Options: electronic application, early admission, deferred admission. Recommended: high school transcript. Required for some: high school transcript, recommendations, interview. Entrance: noncompetitive. Application deadline: rolling. Notification: continuous. Transfer credits accepted: Yes.

Costs Per Year: Application fee: $0. State resident tuition: $4392 full-time, $168 per credit hour part-time. Nonresident tuition: $6312 full-time, $249 per credit hour part-time. Mandatory fees: $336 full-time, $14 per credit hour part-time. Full-time tuition and fees vary according to course load and program. Part-time tuition and fees vary according to course load and program. College room and board: $6850.

Collegiate Environment: Orientation program. Drama-theater group, choral group, marching band, student-run newspaper, radio station. Social organizations: 1 open to all. Most popular organizations: Student Senate, BPA, Phi Beta Lambda. Major annual events: First Week of Fall Semester Activities, Hypnotist, Theater Productions. Student services: health clinic, personal-psychological counseling. Campus security: 24-hour emergency response devices and patrols, student patrols, late night transport-escort service, controlled dormitory access. Iowa Central Community College Library plus 1 other. Students can reserve study rooms. 1,300 computers available on campus for general student use. A campuswide network can be accessed from student residence rooms and from off campus. Staffed computer lab on campus.

■ **IOWA LAKES COMMUNITY COLLEGE**
19 S 7th St.
Estherville, IA 51334-2295
Tel: (712)362-2604; Free: 800-521-5054
E-mail: info@iowalakes.edu
Web Site: www.iowalakes.edu

Description: State and locally supported, 2-year, coed. Part of Iowa Community College System. Awards certificates, diplomas, transfer associate, and terminal associate degrees. Founded 1967. Setting: 20-acre small town campus. Endowment: $6.5 million. Educational spending for the previous fiscal year: $4619 per student. Total enrollment: 2,340. Faculty: 177 (91 full-time, 86 part-time). Student-undergrad faculty ratio is 18:1. 1,425 applied, 92% were admitted. Full-time: 1,090 students, 45% women, 55% men. Students come from 37 states and territories, 10 other countries. 1% American Indian or Alaska Native, non-Hispanic/Latino; 7% Hispanic/Latino; 6% Black or African American, non-Hispanic/Latino; 0.6% Asian, non-Hispanic/Latino; 0.3% Native Hawaiian or other Pacific Islander, non-Hispanic/Latino; 2% international. 25% 25 or older, 37% live on campus. Retention: 54% of full-time freshmen returned the following year. Core. Calendar: semesters. Academic remediation for entering students, ESL program, services for LD students, advanced placement, accelerated degree program, honors program, independent study, distance learning, summer session for credit, part-time degree program, adult/continuing education programs, co-op programs and internships.

Entrance Requirements: Open admission except for allied health, aviation and wind energy programs. Option: electronic application. Required for some: interview. Entrance: noncompetitive. Application deadline: rolling. Transfer credits accepted: Yes.

Collegiate Environment: Orientation program. Drama-theater group, choral group. Social organizations: 42 open to all. Most popular organizations: music, Criminal Justice, nursing clubs, Environmental Studies, Business. Major annual events: Homecoming, Convocations, Coffee Houses/Concerts. Campus security: 24-hour emergency response devices, student patrols. Iowa Lakes Community College Library plus 2 others. Operations spending for the previous fiscal year: $483,141. 1,316 computers available on campus for general student use. A campuswide network can be accessed from student residence rooms and from off campus. Students can access the following: online class registration. Staffed computer lab on campus provides training in use of software and the Internet.

■ **IOWA STATE UNIVERSITY OF SCIENCE AND TECHNOLOGY**
Ames, IA 50011
Tel: (515)294-4111; Free: 800-262-3810
Fax: (515)294-2592
E-mail: pbcaffr@iastate.edu
Web Site: www.iastate.edu

Description: State-supported, university, coed. Awards bachelor's, master's, and doctoral degrees and post-master's certificates. Founded 1858. Setting: 1,795-acre suburban campus with easy access to Des Moines. Endowment: $838.9 million. Research spending for the previous fiscal year: $179.5 million. Educational spending for the previous fiscal year: $8381 per student. Total enrollment: 34,992. Faculty: 1,851 (1,550 full-time, 301 part-time). Student-undergrad faculty ratio is 19:1. 18,855 applied, 91% were admitted. 27% from top 10% of their high school class, 59% from top quarter, 91% from top half. Full-time: 27,929 students, 43% women, 57% men. Part-time: 1,692 students, 39% women, 61% men. Students come from 52 states and territories, 123 other countries, 37% from out-of-state. 0.2% American Indian or Alaska Native, non-Hispanic/Latino; 6% Hispanic/Latino; 3% Black or African American, non-Hispanic/Latino; 3% Asian, non-Hispanic/Latino; 0.1% Native Hawaiian or other Pacific Islander, non-Hispanic/Latino; 6% international. 4% 25 or older, 41% live on campus, 5% transferred in. Retention: 88% of full-time freshmen returned the following year. Academic areas with the most degrees conferred: engineering; business/marketing; agriculture. Calendar: semesters. Academic remediation for entering students, ESL program, services for LD students, advanced placement, accelerated degree program, self-designed majors, freshman honors college, honors program, independent study, distance learning, double major, summer session for credit, part-time degree program, external degree program, adult/continuing education programs, co-op programs and internships, graduate courses open to undergrads. Off campus study at Iowa Regents' Universities Student Exchange, National Student Exchange. Study abroad program. ROTC: Army, Naval, Air Force.

Entrance Requirements: Options: electronic application, early admission, deferred admission, international baccalaureate accepted. Required: high school transcript, minimum Regent Admission Index (RAI) of245, high school course requirements, SAT or ACT. Entrance: moderately difficult. Application deadline: rolling. Notification: continuous. SAT Reasoning Test deadline: 7/15. SAT Subject Test deadline: 7/15. Transfer credits accepted: Yes.

Costs Per Year: Application fee: $40. State resident tuition: $7740 full-time, $323 per credit hour part-time. Nonresident tuition: $22,144 full-time, $923 per credit hour part-time. Mandatory fees: $1,248 full-time. Full-time tuition and fees vary according to class time, course level, degree level, program, and student level. Part-time tuition varies according to class time, course level, course load, degree level, program, and student level. College room and board: $8720. College room only: $4694. Room and board charges vary according to board plan and housing facility.

Collegiate Environment: Orientation program. Drama-theater group, choral group, marching band, student-run newspaper, radio station. Social organizations: 898 open to all; national fraternities, national sororities, local fraternities; 13% of eligible men and 21% of eligible women are members. Most popular organizations: Greek Life, Intramural Sports Activities, Club Sports. Major annual events: Homecoming, Family Weekend. Student services: legal services, health clinic, personal-psychological counseling, women's center. Campus security: 24-hour emergency response devices and patrols, late night transport-escort service, controlled dormitory access. 12,854 college housing spaces available; 11,378 were occupied in 2018-19. No special consideration for freshman housing applicants. Options: coed, men-only, women-only housing available. Parks Library (University Library) plus 1 other. Books: 2.8 million (physical), 460,516 (digital/electronic); Serial titles: 32,462 (physical), 110,162 (digital/electronic); Databases: 287. Weekly public service hours: 113; students can reserve study rooms. Operations spending for the previous fiscal year: $21.5 million. 2,557 computers available on campus for general student use. Computer purchase/lease plans available. A campuswide network can be accessed from student residence rooms and from off campus. Students can access the following: online class registration, network services. Staffed computer lab on campus provides training in use of computers, software, and the Internet.

■ IOWA WESLEYAN UNIVERSITY

601 N Main St.
Mount Pleasant, IA 52641-1398
Tel: (319)385-8021; Free: 800-582-2383
Fax: (319)385-6296
E-mail: julie.duplessis@iw.edu
Web Site: www.iw.edu

Description: Independent United Methodist, comprehensive, coed. Awards bachelor's degrees. Founded 1842. Setting: 60-acre small town campus. Endowment: $9.7 million. Educational spending for the previous fiscal year: $13,544 per student. Total enrollment: 473. Faculty: 84 (36 full-time, 48 part-time). Student-undergrad faculty ratio is 10:1. 1,696 applied, 41% were admitted. 9% from top 10% of their high school class, 27% from top quarter,

55% from top half. Full-time: 386 students, 58% women, 42% men. Part-time: 87 students, 71% women, 29% men. Students come from 26 states and territories, 2 other countries, 36% from out-of-state. 0.8% American Indian or Alaska Native, non-Hispanic/Latino; 4% Hispanic/Latino; 6% Black or African American, non-Hispanic/Latino; 1% Asian, non-Hispanic/Latino; 0.2% Native Hawaiian or other Pacific Islander, non-Hispanic/Latino; 5% international. 30% 25 or older, 68% live on campus, 11% transferred in. Retention: 58% of full-time freshmen returned the following year. Academic areas with the most degrees conferred: education; health professions and related sciences; business/marketing. Core. Calendar: semesters. Academic remediation for entering students, services for LD students, advanced placement, self-designed majors, honors program, independent study, distance learning, double major, summer session for credit, part-time degree program, adult/continuing education programs, co-op programs and internships. Off campus study at Southeastern Community College, Muscatine Community College. Study abroad program.

Entrance Requirements: Options: electronic application, early admission, deferred admission. Required: high school transcript, minimum 2.5 high school GPA, minimum ACT score of 19 or SAT of 890, SAT or ACT. Required for some: essay, 1 recommendation, interview. Entrance: moderately difficult. Application deadline: 8/15. SAT Reasoning Test deadline: 8/15. SAT Subject Test deadline: 8/15. Transfer credits accepted: Yes.

Collegiate Environment: Orientation program. Choral group. Social organizations: 32 open to all; local fraternities, local sororities; 13% of eligible men and 11% of eligible women are members. Most popular organizations: Student Union Board, Student Government Association, Behavioral Science Club, Student Nurses Association, Homecoming Committee. Major annual events: Homecoming, Spring Thing, Chris Jones (hypnotist). Student services: personal-psychological counseling. Campus security: late night transport-escort service, controlled dormitory access, evening patrols by trained security personnel. Chadwick Library plus 1 other. Books: 93,754 (physical), 3,338 (digital/electronic); Serial titles: 2,169 (physical), 4,827 (digital/electronic); Databases: 32. Weekly public service hours: 80; students can reserve study rooms. Operations spending for the previous fiscal year: $254,046. 97 computers available on campus for general student use. A campuswide network can be accessed from student residence rooms. Staffed computer lab on campus provides training in use of computers, software, and the Internet.

Community Environment: Mount Pleasant (population 8,700) is located at the intersection of U.S. Highways 218 and 34; Amtrak and a municipal airport serve the area. Community facilities include many churches, libraries, a hospital, motels, and civic and fraternal organizations. Part time employment is available. Two state parks are nearby which provide facilities for boating and fishing.

■ IOWA WESTERN COMMUNITY COLLEGE

2700 College Rd., Box 4-C
Council Bluffs, IA 51502
Tel: (712)325-3200; Free: 800-432-5852
Fax: (712)325-3720
E-mail: admissions@iwcc.edu
Web Site: www.iwcc.edu

Description: District-supported, 2-year, coed. Part of Iowa Department of Education Division of Community Colleges. Awards certificates, diplomas, transfer associate, and terminal associate degrees. Founded 1966. Setting: 282-acre suburban campus with easy access to Omaha. Total enrollment: 5,300. 22% 25 or older. Core. Calendar: semesters. Academic remediation for entering students, ESL program, services for LD students, independent study, distance learning, summer session for credit, part-time degree program, adult/continuing education programs, co-op programs and internships. ROTC: Army (c), Air Force (c).

Entrance Requirements: Open admission except for nursing, technical programs. Options: early admission, deferred admission. Required: high school transcript. Entrance: noncompetitive. Application deadline: rolling.

Collegiate Environment: Orientation program. Drama-theater group, choral group, student-run newspaper, radio station. Student services: personal-psychological counseling. Campus security: 24-hour patrols, late night transport-escort service.

■ KIRKWOOD COMMUNITY COLLEGE

PO Box 2068
Cedar Rapids, IA 52406-2068
Tel: (319)398-5411; Free: 800-332-2055
Fax: (319)398-1244

Web Site: www.kirkwood.edu

Description: State and locally supported, 2-year, coed. Part of Iowa Department of Education Division of Community Colleges. Awards certificates, diplomas, transfer associate, and terminal associate degrees. Founded 1966. Setting: 630-acre suburban campus. Endowment: $16 million. Total enrollment: 17,841. Faculty: 968 (288 full-time, 680 part-time). Student-undergrad faculty ratio is 24:1. Students come from 94 other countries, 3% from out-of-state. 35% 25 or older. Core. Calendar: semesters. Academic remediation for entering students, ESL program, services for LD students, advanced placement, accelerated degree program, self-designed majors, honors program, independent study, distance learning, summer session for credit, part-time degree program, external degree program, adult/continuing education programs, co-op programs and internships. Off campus study at Iowa State University of Science and Technology, University of Northern Iowa, St. Ambrose University.

Entrance Requirements: Open admission. Options: electronic application, early admission. Required: high school transcript. Entrance: noncompetitive. Application deadline: rolling. Notification: continuous.

Collegiate Environment: Orientation program. Drama-theater group, choral group, student-run newspaper. Social organizations: 45 open to all. Major annual events: Homecoming, Fall Orientation, Graduation. Student services: legal services, health clinic, personal-psychological counseling. Campus security: 24-hour emergency response devices and patrols. Library. 1,000 computers available on campus for general student use. A campuswide network can be accessed. Students can access the following: online class registration. Staffed computer lab on campus.

Community Environment: Cedar Rapids/Marion is a dynamic community of 130,000, and Kirkwood students enjoy its many options for recreation, entertainment, and shopping. Located just five minutes north of the campus, downtown Cedar Rapids features Five Seasons Center, which holds an arena accommodating 8,000 persons for rock concerts, sports events, auto and ice shows, and more. Numerous restaurants, night spots, and movie theaters round out the entertainment scene. There are 62 parks for swimming, golfing, tennis, boating, and camping, and there is shopping in two large malls and the thriving downtown business districts of Cedar Rapids and Marion. Cultural activity centers around the Cedar Rapids Symphony, Art Museum, and Community Theater, as well as the area's four colleges. Religious activity is based in more than 125 congregations of all faiths. Apartment and condominium housing is available in all price ranges, and more new units are being built. Cedar Rapids/Marion is an attractive and stimulating place to live as well as learn. In addition to the Cedar Rapids campus, there are Kirkwood learning centers in each of the seven counties in the College's service area.

■ **LORAS COLLEGE**

1450 Alta Vista

Dubuque, IA 52004-0178

Tel: (563)588-7100; Free: 800-245-6727

Fax: (563)588-7964

Web Site: www.loras.edu

Description: Independent Roman Catholic, comprehensive, coed. Awards bachelor's and master's degrees. Founded 1839. Setting: 64-acre suburban campus. Endowment: $39.8 million. Research spending for the previous fiscal year: $721,042. Educational spending for the previous fiscal year: $6579 per student. Total enrollment: 1,470. Faculty: 144 (99 full-time, 45 part-time). Student-undergrad faculty ratio is 12:1. 1,312 applied, 93% were admitted. Full-time: 1,345 students, 46% women, 54% men. Part-time: 48 students, 44% women, 56% men. Students come from 26 states and territories, 10 other countries, 58% from out-of-state. 0.1% American Indian or Alaska Native, non-Hispanic/Latino; 8% Hispanic/Latino; 3% Black or African American, non-Hispanic/Latino; 0.7% Asian, non-Hispanic/Latino; 0.1% Native Hawaiian or other Pacific Islander, non-Hispanic/Latino; 2% international. 2% 25 or older, 65% live on campus, 4% transferred in. Retention: 81% of full-time freshmen returned the following year. Academic areas with the most degrees conferred: business/marketing; parks and recreation; communication/journalism. Core. Calendar: semesters plus January term. Academic remediation for entering students, services for LD students, advanced placement, self-designed majors, honors program, independent study, distance learning, double major, summer session for credit, part-time degree program, co-op programs and internships, graduate courses open to undergrads. Off campus study at Off-campus study options: Washington Center Program, Disney Semester, Semester at Sea; Cross-registration: With Clarke University (Dubuque, IA) and University of Dubuque (Dubuque, IA). Study abroad program. ROTC: Army (c).

Entrance Requirements: Options: electronic application, deferred admission, international baccalaureate accepted. Required: high school transcript, minimum 2.5 high school GPA, SAT or ACT. Recommended: 1 recommendation. Required for some: essay, 1 recommendation, interview. Entrance: moderately difficult. Application deadline: rolling. Notification: continuous. SAT Reasoning Test deadline: 8/31. SAT Subject Test deadline: 8/31. Transfer credits accepted: Yes.

Costs Per Year: Application fee: $0. Comprehensive fee: $43,643 includes full-time tuition ($33,500), mandatory fees ($1718), and college room and board ($8425). College room only: $4000. Part-time tuition: $750 per credit hour. Part-time mandatory fees: $45 per credit hour.

Collegiate Environment: Orientation program. Drama-theater group, choral group, student-run newspaper, radio station. Social organizations: 55 open to all; national fraternities, national sororities. Most popular organizations: Dance Marathon, Campus Activities Board, DuBuddies, Social Work Club, American Chemical Society. Major annual events: Campus Fest, Homecoming, Family Weekend. Student services: health clinic, personal-psychological counseling. Campus security: 24-hour emergency response devices and patrols, late night transport-escort service, controlled dormitory access. 1,067 college housing spaces available; 884 were occupied in 2018-19. Freshmen guaranteed college housing. On-campus residence required through junior year. Options: coed, men-only, women-only housing available. Loras College Library. Books: 212,063 (physical), 357,608 (digital/electronic); Serial titles: 37 (physical), 37,834 (digital/electronic); Databases: 123. Weekly public service hours: 91; students can reserve study rooms. Operations spending for the previous fiscal year: $526,158. 5 computers available on campus for general student use. A computer is required for all students. A campuswide network can be accessed from student residence rooms and from off campus. Students can access the following: online class registration.

Community Environment: The small city of Dubuque is located on the Mississippi River where Iowa, Illinois, and Wisconsin meet. The oldest city in Iowa, it features rugged bluffs and Victorian architecture. Excellent air connections with Chicago's O'Hare Airport and with the Minneapolis-St. Paul Airport are available. The city is the commercial, cultural, and recreational center of the tri-state area. It offers concerts, theater, symphony, art galleries, museums, and riverboat gambling. Facilities are available for boating, skiing, golf, and tennis.

■ **LUTHER COLLEGE**

700 College Dr.

Decorah, IA 52101

Tel: (563)387-2000; Free: 800-458-8437

Fax: (563)387-2159

E-mail: hartde01@luther.edu

Web Site: www.luther.edu

Description: Independent, 4-year, coed, affiliated with Evangelical Lutheran Church in America. Awards bachelor's degrees. Founded 1861. Setting: 200-acre small town campus. Endowment: $161.8 million. Research spending for the previous fiscal year: $734,639. Educational spending for the previous fiscal year: $14,224 per student. Total enrollment: 2,053. Faculty: 208 (168 full-time, 40 part-time). Student-undergrad faculty ratio is 11:1. 4,288 applied, 65% were admitted. 26% from top 10% of their high school class, 54% from top quarter, 86% from top half. 7 National Merit Scholars, 19 class presidents, 17 valedictorians, 167 student government officers. Full-time: 2,014 students, 56% women, 44% men. Part-time: 39 students, 44% women, 56% men. Students come from 39 states and territories, 74 other countries, 71% from out-of-state. 0.4% American Indian or Alaska Native, non-Hispanic/Latino; 5% Hispanic/Latino; 2% Black or African American, non-Hispanic/Latino; 1% Asian, non-Hispanic/Latino; 0.1% Native Hawaiian or other Pacific Islander, non-Hispanic/Latino; 8% international. 0.5% 25 or older, 93% live on campus, 1% transferred in. Retention: 83% of full-time freshmen returned the following year. Academic areas with the most degrees conferred: business/marketing; visual and performing arts; biological/life sciences. Core. Calendar: 4-1-4. Academic remediation for entering students, services for LD students, advanced placement, self-designed majors, honors program, independent study, double major, summer session for credit, part-time degree program, internships. Off campus study. Study abroad program.

Entrance Requirements: Options: electronic application, deferred admission, international baccalaureate accepted. Required: essay, high school transcript, 1 recommendation, SAT or ACT. Recommended: interview. Entrance: moderately difficult. Notification: continuous. Transfer credits accepted: Yes.

Costs Per Year: Comprehensive fee: $51,750 includes full-time tuition

($41,950), mandatory fees ($340), and college room and board ($9460). College room only: $4420. Full-time tuition and fees vary according to course load. Room and board charges vary according to board plan and housing facility. Part-time tuition: $1498 per credit hour. Part-time tuition varies according to course load.

Collegiate Environment: Orientation program. Drama-theater group, choral group, student-run newspaper, radio station. Social organizations: 99 open to all; local fraternities, local sororities, Alpha Phi Omega; 1% of eligible men and 2% of eligible women are members. Most popular organizations: Alpha Phi Omega, college ministries, recreational sports, Student Activities Council, Diversity groups. Major annual events: Open Mic, Jazz Night, Flamingo Ball, Family Weekend/SAC Soda Shoppe, Christmas at Luther Weekend. Student services: health clinic, personal-psychological counseling, women's center. Campus security: 24-hour emergency response devices and patrols, late night transport-escort service, controlled dormitory access. Preus Library. Books: 202,938 (physical), 292,640 (digital/electronic); Serial titles: 17,086 (physical), 17,086 (digital/electronic); Databases: 99. Weekly public service hours: 104; students can reserve study rooms. Operations spending for the previous fiscal year: $1.7 million. 592 computers available on campus for general student use. A campuswide network can be accessed from student residence rooms and from off campus. Students can access the following: online class registration. Staffed computer lab on campus provides training in use of computers, software, and the Internet.

Community Environment: Decorah (population 8,000) is on the banks of the Upper Iowa River, in an area known as Little Switzerland, in northeast Iowa. Twin Springs and Siewer Springs state fish hatcheries are nearby. Decorah has set aside more than 328 acres for recreation. Outdoor activities include golf, skiing, hiking, hunting and fishing.

■ **MAHARISHI UNIVERSITY OF MANAGEMENT**
1000 N 4th St.
Fairfield, IA 52557
Tel: (641)472-7000; Free: 800-369-6480
Fax: (641)472-1189
E-mail: admissions@mum.edu
Web Site: www.mum.edu

Description: Independent, university, coed. Awards bachelor's, master's, and doctoral degrees. Founded 1971. Setting: 242-acre small town campus. Total enrollment: 1,599. Faculty: 156 (111 full-time, 45 part-time). Student-undergrad faculty ratio is 9:1. 42 applied, 64% were admitted. Full-time: 173 students, 57% women, 43% men. Part-time: 151 students, 70% women, 30% men. 88% from out-of-state. 0.8% American Indian or Alaska Native, non-Hispanic/Latino; 10% Hispanic/Latino; 11% Black or African American, non-Hispanic/Latino; 2% Asian, non-Hispanic/Latino; 0.8% Native Hawaiian or other Pacific Islander, non-Hispanic/Latino; 5% international. 50% 25 or older, 58% live on campus, 8% transferred in. Retention: 53% of full-time freshmen returned the following year. Academic areas with the most degrees conferred: business/marketing; interdisciplinary studies; communication/journalism. Core. Calendar: semesters. ESL program, self-designed majors, independent study, double major, adult/continuing education programs. Off campus study.

Entrance Requirements: Options: electronic application, early admission, deferred admission, international baccalaureate accepted. Required: essay, high school transcript, minimum 2.5 high school GPA, 2 recommendations. Recommended: interview. Entrance: moderately difficult. Preference given to graduates of the Maharishi School of the Age of Enlightenment. Transfer credits accepted: Yes.

Costs Per Year: Application fee: $20. Comprehensive fee: $23,930 includes full-time tuition ($16,000), mandatory fees ($530), and college room and board ($7400). Part-time tuition: $500 per unit.

Collegiate Environment: Orientation program. Student services: health clinic, personal-psychological counseling. Campus security: 24-hour emergency response devices and patrols, late night transport-escort service, controlled dormitory access. Freshmen guaranteed college housing. On-campus residence required through senior year. Options: men-only, women-only housing available. Maharishi University of Management Library. Weekly public service hours: 55.

Community Environment: The University is located in the Fairfield, Iowa, 50 miles west of the Mississippi River in the heartland of the central United States. A thirty percent growth in the population and the appearance of numerous new businesses in Fairfield in recent years have spurred an unprecedented level of economic and cultural growth in the community. Fairfield is viewed as one of the great success stories in Iowa, and is recognized throughout the state for its creativity in business, the arts, and education. Located within easy access of Chicago, St. Louis, and Kansas City, it is only one hour south of Iowa City, home of the University of Iowa.

■ **MARSHALLTOWN COMMUNITY COLLEGE**
3700 S Ctr. St.
Marshalltown, IA 50158-4760
Tel: (641)752-7106; Free: 866-622-4748
Fax: (641)752-8149
Web Site: mcc.iavalley.edu

Description: District-supported, 2-year, coed. Part of Iowa Valley Community College District System. Awards certificates, diplomas, transfer associate, and terminal associate degrees. Founded 1927. Setting: 200-acre small town campus. Total enrollment: 1,701. 28% 25 or older. Core. Calendar: semesters. Academic remediation for entering students, ESL program, services for LD students, advanced placement, self-designed majors, freshman honors college, honors program, independent study, distance learning, summer session for credit, part-time degree program, adult/continuing education programs, co-op programs and internships. Study abroad program. ROTC: Air Force (c).

Entrance Requirements: Open admission. Options: electronic application, early admission. Required: high school transcript, ACT Compass. Recommended: ACT. Required for some: interview. Entrance: noncompetitive. Application deadline: rolling. Notification: continuous.

Collegiate Environment: Drama-theater group, choral group, student-run newspaper, radio station. Student services: personal-psychological counseling. Learning Resource Center.

Community Environment: Marshalltown, an industrial city in central Iowa, is an important bus and truck terminal. The community facilities include 32 churches, hospitals, a library and many civic service clubs, as well as a Chamber of Commerce. Opportunities for part time or seasonal employment are excellent. Recreational facilities include an expanding park system; three golf courses; YMCA; two swimming pools; large youth soccer, football, and Little League complexes; a five-mile in-city walk/jog/bike path with greenbelt environment; new playgrounds; two bowling alleys; and three theaters.

■ **MERCY COLLEGE OF HEALTH SCIENCES**
928 Sixth Ave.
Des Moines, IA 50309-1239
Tel: (515)643-3180; Free: 800-637-2994
Fax: (515)643-6698
E-mail: hgaumer@mercydesmoines.org
Web Site: www.mchs.edu

Description: Independent, 4-year, coed, affiliated with Roman Catholic Church. Administratively affiliated with Catholic Health Initiatives, Mercy Medial Center. Awards associate and bachelor's degrees. Founded 1995. Setting: 5-acre urban campus with easy access to Des Moines, IA. Total enrollment: 771. Faculty: 92 (43 full-time, 49 part-time). Student-undergrad faculty ratio is 10:1. Students come from 5 states and territories, 2% from out-of-state. 4% Hispanic/Latino; 7% Black or African American, non-Hispanic/Latino; 3% Asian, non-Hispanic/Latino. 44% 25 or older. Retention: 100% of full-time freshmen returned the following year. Academic area with the most degrees conferred: health professions and related sciences. Core. Calendar: semesters. Academic remediation for entering students, ESL program, services for LD students, advanced placement, accelerated degree program, independent study, distance learning, summer session for credit, part-time degree program, adult/continuing education programs. Off campus study. Study abroad program.

Entrance Requirements: Required: high school transcript, minimum 2.25 high school GPA. Recommended: ACT.

Costs Per Year: Tuition: $17,952 full-time, $659 per credit hour part-time. Full-time tuition varies according to program. Part-time tuition varies according to course load.

Collegiate Environment: Orientation program. Most popular organizations: student senate, Campus Ministry, Science Club, Mercy College Association of Nursing Students, Zeta Chi—At Large Chapter. Major annual events: President's Luncheons, Career Fair, Cultural Fair. Student services: personal-psychological counseling. Campus security: 24-hour emergency response devices and patrols, late night transport-escort service. Mercy College Library plus 1 other. Students can reserve study rooms. 46 computers available on campus for general student use. A campuswide network can be accessed from off-campus. Students can access the following: online class registration.

Community Environment: Des Moines is the setting for MCHS's four-acre campus, which is located just south of Interstate 235 and three blocks south of Mercy Medical Center.

■ **MORNINGSIDE COLLEGE**
1501 Morningside Ave.
Sioux City, IA 51106
Tel: (712)274-5000; Free: 800-831-0806
E-mail: mscadm@morningside.edu
Web Site: www.morningside.edu
Description: Independent, comprehensive, coed, affiliated with United Methodist Church. Awards bachelor's and master's degrees and post-master's certificates. Founded 1894. Setting: 69-acre suburban campus with easy access to Omaha, NE. Endowment: $47.1 million. Total enrollment: 2,684. Faculty: 240 (78 full-time, 162 part-time). Student-undergrad faculty ratio is 14:1. 4,385 applied, 58% were admitted. 14% from top 10% of their high school class, 36% from top quarter, 70% from top half. Full-time: 1,212 students, 50% women, 50% men. Part-time: 69 students, 48% women, 52% men. Students come from 26 states and territories, 19 other countries, 45% from out-of-state. 0.5% American Indian or Alaska Native, non-Hispanic/Latino; 7% Hispanic/Latino; 2% Black or African American, non-Hispanic/Latino; 1% Asian, non-Hispanic/Latino; 0.2% Native Hawaiian or other Pacific Islander, non-Hispanic/Latino; 5% international. 8% 25 or older, 55% live on campus, 4% transferred in. Retention: 71% of full-time freshmen returned the following year. Academic areas with the most degrees conferred: business/marketing; education; biological/life sciences. Core. Calendar: semesters. Academic remediation for entering students, ESL program, services for LD students, advanced placement, self-designed majors, honors program, independent study, distance learning, double major, summer session for credit, part-time degree program, adult/continuing education programs, internships, graduate courses open to undergrads. Off campus study at American University, Drew University. Study abroad program. ROTC: Army (c).
Entrance Requirements: Options: electronic application, deferred admission, international baccalaureate accepted. Required: high school transcript, minimum 2.5 high school GPA, minimum ACT score of 20 or SAT of 1410 and either rank in top half of class or 2.5 GPA, SAT or ACT. Recommended: interview. Entrance: moderately difficult. Application deadline: rolling. Notification: continuous. SAT Reasoning Test deadline: 8/15. Transfer credits accepted: Yes.
Costs Per Year: Application fee: $0. Comprehensive fee: $42,560 includes full-time tuition ($31,220), mandatory fees ($1500), and college room and board ($9840). College room only: $5320. Part-time tuition: $570 per credit hour.
Collegiate Environment: Orientation program. Drama-theater group, choral group, marching band, student-run newspaper, radio station. Social organizations: 45 open to all; national fraternities, national sororities; 4% of eligible men and 2% of eligible women are members. Most popular organizations: Student Government/Activities Council, Student Ambassadors, Homecoming Committee. Major annual events: Homecoming, Honors Assembly, Christmas at Morningside. Student services: health clinic, personal-psychological counseling, women's center. Campus security: 24-hour emergency response devices and patrols, student patrols, late night transport-escort service, controlled dormitory access. 858 college housing spaces available; 673 were occupied in 2018-19. Freshmen guaranteed college housing. On-campus residence required through junior year. Option: coed housing available. Hickman-Johnson-Furrow Learning Center. Books: 40,458 (physical), 325 (digital/electronic); Serial titles: 516 (physical), 74 (digital/electronic); Databases: 46. Weekly public service hours: 93. Operations spending for the previous fiscal year: $226,143.
Community Environment: See Briar Cliff College.

■ **MOUNT MERCY UNIVERSITY**
1330 Elmhurst Dr., NE
Cedar Rapids, IA 52402-4797
Tel: (319)363-8213; Free: 800-248-4504
Fax: (319)368-6492
E-mail: tcrumley@mtmercy.edu
Web Site: www.mtmercy.edu
Description: Independent Roman Catholic, comprehensive, coed. Awards bachelor's, master's, and doctoral degrees. Founded 1928. Setting: 40-acre suburban campus with easy access to Iowa City. Endowment: $26.4 million. Educational spending for the previous fiscal year: $5469 per student. Total enrollment: 1,848. Faculty: 160 (83 full-time, 77 part-time). Student-

undergrad faculty ratio is 15:1. 1,457 applied, 57% were admitted. 17% from top 10% of their high school class, 44% from top quarter, 82% from top half. Full-time: 1,083 students, 66% women, 34% men. Part-time: 434 students, 73% women, 27% men. Students come from 28 states and territories, 33 other countries, 10% from out-of-state. 2% American Indian or Alaska Native, non-Hispanic/Latino; 1% Hispanic/Latino; 7% Black or African American, non-Hispanic/Latino; 2% Asian, non-Hispanic/Latino; 0.5% Native Hawaiian or other Pacific Islander, non-Hispanic/Latino; 4% international. 36% 25 or older, 40% live on campus, 15% transferred in. Retention: 73% of full-time freshmen returned the following year. Academic areas with the most degrees conferred: business/marketing; health professions and related sciences; education. Core. Calendar: 4-1-4. Academic remediation for entering students, services for LD students, advanced placement, accelerated degree program, honors program, independent study, double major, summer session for credit, part-time degree program, external degree program, adult/continuing education programs, internships. Off campus study at Coe College. Study abroad program.
Entrance Requirements: Options: electronic application, deferred admission. Required: high school transcript, minimum 2.5 high school GPA, SAT or ACT. Required for some: 1 recommendation. Entrance: moderately difficult. Application deadline: 8/15. Notification: continuous. Transfer credits accepted: Yes.
Costs Per Year: Application fee: $0. Comprehensive fee: $41,532 includes full-time tuition ($31,598), mandatory fees ($400), and college room and board ($9534). Full-time tuition and fees vary according to course load. Room and board charges vary according to board plan and housing facility. Part-time tuition: $958 per credit hour. Part-time mandatory fees: $180 per year. Part-time tuition and fees vary according to course load.
Collegiate Environment: Orientation program. Drama-theater group, choral group, student-run newspaper. Social organizations: 35 open to all. Most popular organizations: Student Ambassadors, Mount Mercy University Association of Nursing Students, Cheerleaders, Black Student Union, Student Government Association. Major annual events: Vegas Night, Christmas Club Friday, Spring Fling Week. Student services: health clinic, personal-psychological counseling. Campus security: 24-hour emergency response devices and patrols, student patrols, late night transport-escort service, controlled dormitory access, Department of Public Safety operational 24-hours a day, 7 days a week. Busse Library. Books: 124,017 (physical), 191,793 (digital/electronic); Serial titles: 3,972 (physical). Students can reserve study rooms. Operations spending for the previous fiscal year: $587,719. 120 computers available on campus for general student use. A campuswide network can be accessed from student residence rooms and from off campus. Students can access the following: online class registration. Staffed computer lab on campus provides training in use of computers and software.
Community Environment: See Kirkwood Community College.

■ **MUSCATINE COMMUNITY COLLEGE**
152 Colorado St.
Muscatine, IA 52761-5396
Tel: (563)288-6001; Free: 800-351-4669
Fax: (563)288-6074
E-mail: gmohr@eicc.edu
Web Site: www.eicc.edu/about-eicc/colleges-and-centers/muscatine-community-college.aspx
Description: State-supported, 2-year, coed. Part of Eastern Iowa Community College District. Awards diplomas, transfer associate, and terminal associate degrees. Founded 1929. Setting: 25-acre small town campus. Educational spending for the previous fiscal year: $2249 per student. Total enrollment: 1,624. Faculty: 91 (32 full-time, 59 part-time). 311 applied, 100% were admitted. Full-time: 608 students, 56% women, 44% men. Part-time: 1,016 students, 53% women, 47% men. Students come from 6 states and territories, 8 other countries, 3% from out-of-state. 26% 25 or older, 4% live on campus. Retention: 55% of full-time freshmen returned the following year. Core. Calendar: semesters. Academic remediation for entering students, ESL program, services for LD students, advanced placement, self-designed majors, honors program, independent study, distance learning, double major, summer session for credit, part-time degree program, adult/continuing education programs, co-op programs and internships. Off campus study at Black Hawk College, Carl Sandburg Community College, Kirkwood Community College, Northeast Iowa Community College. Study abroad program.
Entrance Requirements: Open admission except for nursing program and vet tech. Option: electronic application. Entrance: noncompetitive. Application deadline: rolling. Notification: continuous.

Collegiate Environment: Orientation program. Drama-theater group, choral group, student-run newspaper. Campus security: 24-hour emergency response devices. Muscatine Community College Library. 57 computers available on campus for general student use. A campuswide network can be accessed from off-campus. Students can access the following: online class registration. Staffed computer lab on campus provides training in use of computers, software, and the Internet.

Community Environment: Muscatine, an industrial center, is located on the Mississippi River, and has an annual mean temperature of 50 degrees, and an average rainfall of 34 inches. Vegetables and melons are raised in the vicinity; over three million bushels of grain are shipped from here each year. Community facilities include many churches and a library. Parks, a golf course, a bowling alley and skating rink offer recreation. The Mississippi River and nearby Cedar and Iowa rivers provide excellent picnicking, fishing and boat launching facilities. Points of interest are the Laura Musser Art Gallery and Museum, and Weed Park.

■ **NORTH IOWA AREA COMMUNITY COLLEGE**
500 College Dr.
Mason City, IA 50401-7299
Tel: (641)423-1264; Free: 888-GO NIACC
Fax: (641)423-1711
E-mail: request@niacc.edu
Web Site: www.niacc.edu

Description: State and locally supported, 2-year, coed. Part of Iowa Community College System. Awards certificates, diplomas, and transfer associate degrees. Founded 1918. Setting: 500-acre rural campus. Total enrollment: 2,947. Faculty: 127 (68 full-time, 59 part-time). Student-undergrad faculty ratio is 10:1. 5% from top 10% of their high school class, 17% from top quarter, 41% from top half. Full-time: 1,346 students, 51% women, 49% men. Part-time: 1,601 students, 58% women, 42% men. 0.2% American Indian or Alaska Native, non-Hispanic/Latino; 5% Hispanic/Latino; 4% Black or African American, non-Hispanic/Latino; 1% Asian, non-Hispanic/Latino; 2% international. 18% 25 or older, 12% live on campus. Core. Calendar: semesters. Academic remediation for entering students, ESL program, services for LD students, advanced placement, self-designed majors, honors program, distance learning, summer session for credit, part-time degree program, co-op programs and internships.

Entrance Requirements: Open admission. Option: electronic application. Required: high school transcript. Entrance: noncompetitive. Application deadline: rolling. Notification: continuous. Transfer credits accepted: Yes.

Costs Per Year: Application fee: $0. State resident tuition: $4,628 full-time, $154.25 per semester hour part-time. Nonresident tuition: $6,941 full-time, $231.38 per semester hour part-time. Mandatory fees: $780 full-time, $26 per semester hour part-time. Full-time tuition and fees vary according to course load. Part-time tuition and fees vary according to course load. College room and board: $7128. Room and board charges vary according to housing facility.

Collegiate Environment: Orientation program. Drama-theater group, choral group, student-run newspaper. Social organizations: 35 open to all. Most popular organizations: Ski and Snowboard Club, intramurals, Student Senate, Education Club, Women in Learning and Leadership. Major annual events: Quodlibet, Homecoming, Pack the Gym. Student services: health clinic, personal-psychological counseling. Campus security: student patrols, late night transport-escort service, controlled dormitory access.

Community Environment: Mason City (population 27,909) is located in the north center of the state midway between Des Moines and Minneapolis - St. Paul, and has an average winter temperature of 28 degrees, summer average 63 degrees. One bus line and an airline offer transportation. The community facilities include hospitals, a library, Art Center, hotels and motels. Brick, tile and Portland cement are manufactured from the deposits of clay, limestone and sand in this area. Part-time work is available. Recreation activities include golf, water sports in summer, ice boating and fishing in winter, ice skating, pheasant deer and duck hunting.

■ **NORTHEAST IOWA COMMUNITY COLLEGE**
Box 400
Calmar, IA 52132-0480
Tel: (563)562-3263; Free: 800-728-CALMAR
Fax: (563)562-3719
E-mail: mcconnellb@nicc.edu
Web Site: www.nicc.edu

Description: State and locally supported, 2-year, coed. Part of Iowa Area Community Colleges System. Awards certificates, diplomas, transfer associ-

ate, and terminal associate degrees. Founded 1966. Setting: 210-acre rural campus. Total enrollment: 4,545. Faculty: 293 (111 full-time, 182 part-time). Student-undergrad faculty ratio is 13:1. 1,976 applied, 99% were admitted. Full-time: 1,221 students, 55% women, 45% men. Part-time: 3,324 students, 58% women, 42% men. 12% from out-of-state. 0.4% American Indian or Alaska Native, non-Hispanic/Latino; 3% Hispanic/Latino; 5% Black or African American, non-Hispanic/Latino; 0.7% Asian, non-Hispanic/Latino; 0.4% Native Hawaiian or other Pacific Islander, non-Hispanic/Latino; 0.8% international. 32% 25 or older, 4% transferred in. Retention: 52% of full-time freshmen returned the following year. Core. Calendar: semesters. Academic remediation for entering students, services for LD students, advanced placement, honors program, distance learning, double major, summer session for credit, part-time degree program, external degree program, adult/continuing education programs, co-op programs and internships. Off campus study at Upper Iowa University, Clarke College, University of Dubuque, Loras College.

Entrance Requirements: Open admission. Option: electronic application. Recommended: high school transcript. Entrance: noncompetitive. Transfer credits accepted: Yes. Applicants placed on waiting list: 1. Wait-listed applicants offered admission: 1.

Costs Per Year: Application fee: $0. State resident tuition: $5100 full-time, $170 per credit hour part-time. Nonresident tuition: $5700 full-time, $190 per credit hour part-time. Mandatory fees: $720 full-time, $24 per credit hour part-time. Full-time tuition and fees vary according to course load and program. Part-time tuition and fees vary according to course load and program.

Collegiate Environment: Orientation program. Choral group, student-run newspaper. Social organizations: national fraternities, national sororities. Student services: personal-psychological counseling. Campus security: security personnel on weeknights. Wilder Resource Center and Burton Payne Library plus 2 others.

Community Environment: Calmar is located 10 miles from Decorah, 25 miles from Cresco, 17 miles from Postville, and 24 miles from New Hampton. The town's primary business is agriculture and related fields. Two firms here manufacture furniture and truck racks. Recreational facilities are provided by Calmar Lake, Upper Iowa River, and Turkey River, which furnish great opportunity for fishing and hunting. Northeast Iowa operates a second campus at Peosta, Iowa, which is located approximately ten miles west of the city of Dubuque. The rural area of Peosta is similar to that of Calmar, except that it is close to the metropolitan area of Dubuque, which has a population of nearly 70,000. It offers a wide range of cultural and recreational activities and is situated on the Mississippi River. The popularity of Northeast Iowa is pointed out by the growing numbers of tourists who travel to the area from all over the Midwest.

■ **NORTHWEST IOWA COMMUNITY COLLEGE**
603 W Park St.
Sheldon, IA 51201-1046
Tel: (712)324-5061; Free: 800-352-4907
Fax: (712)324-4136
Web Site: www.nwicc.edu

Description: State-supported, 2-year, coed. Part of Iowa Department of Education Division of Community Colleges. Awards certificates, diplomas, transfer associate, and terminal associate degrees. Founded 1966. Setting: 263-acre small town campus with easy access to Sioux City, IA and Sioux Falls, SD. Total enrollment: 1,288. Faculty: 139 (40 full-time, 99 part-time). Student-undergrad faculty ratio is 11:1. 22% 25 or older. Retention: 93% of full-time freshmen returned the following year. Calendar: semesters. Academic remediation for entering students, ESL program, services for LD students, distance learning, double major, part-time degree program, adult/continuing education programs, co-op programs. Off campus study. Study abroad program.

Entrance Requirements: Open admission. Option: electronic application. Required: high school transcript, ACT Compass. Required for some: minimum 2.0 high school GPA. Entrance: noncompetitive. Application deadline: rolling. Notification: continuous.

Collegiate Environment: Orientation program. Student-run newspaper. Social organizations: 3 open to all. Major annual events: Fall Kick-off BBQ, Free Holiday Meals, SGA Special Entertainment. Student services: personal-psychological counseling. Campus security: 24-hour emergency response devices. Northwest Iowa Community College Library plus 1 other. 358 computers available on campus for general student use. A campuswide network can be accessed. Staffed computer lab on campus provides training in use of computers, software, and the Internet.

Community Environment: Sheldon (population 4,800) is the trading center for a rich, five-county farmland area. Bus and train transportation are available, airline service is within 55 miles at Sioux City. Local parks and a golf club provide facilities for recreation. The Iowa Lakes Region is a 50 mile drive. Community facilities include public libraries, churches, a modern hospital, and an indoor swimming pool.

■ NORTHWESTERN COLLEGE

101 Seventh St., SW
Orange City, IA 51041-1996
Tel: (712)707-7000; Free: 800-747-4757
Fax: (712)707-7247
E-mail: admissions@nwciowa.edu
Web Site: www.nwciowa.edu

Description: Independent, comprehensive, coed, affiliated with Reformed Church in America. Awards bachelor's and master's degrees. Founded 1882. Setting: 100-acre small town campus. Endowment: $49.4 million. Educational spending for the previous fiscal year: $8476 per student. Total enrollment: 1,251. Faculty: 141 (82 full-time, 59 part-time). Student-undergrad faculty ratio is 11:1. 1,959 applied, 68% were admitted. 25% from top 10% of their high school class, 59% from top quarter, 83% from top half. 18 valedictorians. Full-time: 997 students, 56% women, 44% men. Part-time: 52 students, 63% women, 37% men. Students come from 31 states and territories, 20 other countries, 42% from out-of-state. 0.2% American Indian or Alaska Native, non-Hispanic/Latino; 4% Hispanic/Latino; 1% Black or African American, non-Hispanic/Latino; 1% Asian, non-Hispanic/Latino; 3% international. 2% 25 or older, 92% live on campus, 1% transferred in. Retention: 77% of full-time freshmen returned the following year. Academic areas with the most degrees conferred: education; business/marketing; health professions and related sciences. Core. Calendar: semesters. Academic remediation for entering students, ESL program, services for LD students, advanced placement, self-designed majors, honors program, independent study, distance learning, double major, summer session for credit, co-op programs and internships. Off campus study at 5 members of the Mid-America States Universities Association, Council for Christian Colleges and Universities. Study abroad program.

Entrance Requirements: Options: electronic application, early admission, deferred admission, international baccalaureate accepted. Required: essay, high school transcript, minimum 2 high school GPA, SAT or ACT. Recommended: minimum 2.5 high school GPA, 1 recommendation, interview. Entrance: moderately difficult. Application deadline: rolling. Notification: continuous. SAT Reasoning Test deadline: 8/15. SAT Subject Test deadline: 8/15. Transfer credits accepted: Yes.

Costs Per Year: Application fee: $0. Comprehensive fee: $40,300 includes full-time tuition ($30,900), mandatory fees ($200), and college room and board ($9200). Room and board charges vary according to board plan and housing facility. Part-time tuition: $650 per credit hour. Part-time mandatory fees: $75 per term. Part-time tuition and fees vary according to course load.

Collegiate Environment: Orientation program. Drama-theater group, choral group, student-run newspaper. Social organizations: 50 open to all. Most popular organizations: Drama Ministries Ensemble, A cappella Choir, Discipleship Groups, Fellowship of Christian Athletes, International Club. Major annual events: Clash of the Classes, RUSH (student dance exhibition), Colenbrander Hall Christmas Bash. Student services: health clinic, personal-psychological counseling. Campus security: 24-hour emergency response devices, controlled dormitory access. DeWitt Learning Commons plus 1 other. Books: 80,887 (physical), 151,137 (digital/electronic); Serial titles: 2,286 (physical), 80,593 (digital/electronic); Databases: 65. Weekly public service hours: 98; students can reserve study rooms. 250 computers available on campus for general student use. A campuswide network can be accessed from student residence rooms and from off campus. Students can access the following: online class registration, online degree audits. Staffed computer lab on campus provides training in use of computers, software, and the Internet.

■ PALMER COLLEGE OF CHIROPRACTIC

1000 Brady St.
Davenport, IA 52803-5287
Tel: (563)884-5000; Free: 800-722-3648
Fax: (563)884-5897
E-mail: lisa.gisel@palmer.edu
Web Site: www.palmer.edu

Description: Independent, comprehensive, coed. Awards associate, incidental bachelor's, master's, and doctoral degrees. Founded 1897. Set-ting: 31-acre urban campus. Total enrollment: 2,310. Faculty: 15 (2 full-time, 13 part-time). Student-undergrad faculty ratio is 3:1. 24 applied, 83% were admitted. Full-time: 39 students, 54% women, 46% men. Part-time: 10 students, 40% women, 60% men. Students come from 16 states and territories, 1 other country, 63% from out-of-state. 2% Hispanic/Latino; 2% Black or African American, non-Hispanic/Latino; 2% Asian, non-Hispanic/Latino. 45% 25 or older, 59% transferred in. Retention: 50% of full-time freshmen returned the following year. Academic area with the most degrees conferred: biological/life sciences. Core. Calendar: trimesters. Academic remediation for entering students, services for LD students, summer session for credit, internships.

Entrance Requirements: Open admission. Options: electronic application, deferred admission. Required: high school transcript, minimum 2 high school GPA, minimum 2.0 in math, science, and English courses. Required for some: essay, interview. Entrance: noncompetitive. Application deadline: rolling. Notification: continuous. Transfer credits accepted: Yes.

Collegiate Environment: Orientation program. Student-run newspaper. Social organizations: 60 open to all; national fraternities, local fraternities, local sororities. Most popular organizations: Gonstead Club, intramural sports, campus guides, Student International Chiropractic Association, Palmer Student Alumni Foundation. Major annual events: Homecoming, Chili Cook-off, Student Holiday Dance. Student services: health clinic, personal-psychological counseling. Campus security: 24-hour emergency response devices and patrols, late night transport-escort service. David D. Palmer Health Sciences Library. Operations spending for the previous fiscal year: $1.3 million. 94 computers available on campus for general student use. A campuswide network can be accessed. Staffed computer lab on campus provides training in use of computers, software, and the Internet.

Community Environment: The Quad-Cities area, a community of about 400,000, offers a wide variety of entertainment options including more than 275 restaurants; professional basketball and ice hockey; Class A baseball; arena football; 60 miles of bike trails; theater, museums and the art galleries.

■ PURDUE UNIVERSITY GLOBAL (CEDAR FALLS)

7009 Nordic Dr.
Cedar Falls, IA 50613
Tel: (319)277-0220; Free: 844-PURDUE-G
Web Site: www.purdueglobal.edu

Description: Independent, comprehensive, coed. Awards associate, bachelor's, and master's degrees. Founded 2000. Calendar: quarters.

Entrance Requirements: Application deadline: rolling.

■ PURDUE UNIVERSITY GLOBAL (CEDAR RAPIDS)

3165 Edgewood Pky., SW
Cedar Rapids, IA 52404
Tel: (319)363-0481; Free: 844-PURDUE-G
Web Site: www.purdueglobal.edu

Description: Independent, comprehensive, coed. Administratively affiliated with Kaplan University - Davenport Campus. Awards associate, bachelor's, and master's degrees. Founded 1900. Setting: suburban campus. Calendar: quarters.

■ PURDUE UNIVERSITY GLOBAL (DAVENPORT)

1801 E Kimberly Rd.
Ste. 1
Davenport, IA 52807
Tel: (563)355-3500; Free: 844-PURDUE-G
Web Site: www.purdueglobal.edu

Description: Independent, comprehensive, coed. Awards associate, bachelor's, and master's degrees (profile includes both traditional and on-line students). Founded 1937. Setting: suburban campus. Calendar: quarters.

■ PURDUE UNIVERSITY GLOBAL (MASON CITY)

2570 4th St., SW
Mason City, IA 50401
Tel: (641)423-2530; Free: 844-PURDUE-G
Web Site: www.purdueglobal.edu

Description: Independent, comprehensive, coed. Awards associate, bachelor's, and master's degrees. Founded 1900.

■ PURDUE UNIVERSITY GLOBAL (URBANDALE)

4655 121st St.
Urbandale, IA 50323

Tel: (515)727-2100; Free: 844-PURDUE-G

Web Site: www.purdueglobal.edu

Description: Independent, comprehensive, coed. Awards associate, bachelor's, and master's degrees.

■ **ROSS COLLEGE**

2119 E Kimberly Rd.

Bettendorf, IA 52722

Tel: (563)344-1500; Free: 866-815-5578

Web Site: www.rosseducation.edu

Description: Proprietary, 2-year, coed. Part of Education Management Corporation. Awards diplomas and terminal associate degrees.

■ **ST. AMBROSE UNIVERSITY**

518 W Locust St.

Davenport, IA 52803-2898

Tel: (563)333-6000; Free: 800-383-2627

Fax: (563)383-8791

E-mail: conklinallisonj@sau.edu

Web Site: www.sau.edu

Description: Independent Roman Catholic, comprehensive, coed. Awards bachelor's, master's, and doctoral degrees and post-master's certificates. Founded 1882. Setting: 118-acre urban campus. Endowment: $139.8 million. Educational spending for the previous fiscal year: $8865 per student. Total enrollment: 3,118. Faculty: 346 (204 full-time, 142 part-time). Student-undergrad faculty ratio is 12:1. 5,351 applied, 61% were admitted. 14% from top 10% of their high school class, 42% from top quarter, 76% from top half. Full-time: 2,215 students, 56% women, 44% men. Part-time: 155 students, 60% women, 40% men. Students come from 28 states and territories, 24 other countries, 62% from out-of-state. 0.1% American Indian or Alaska Native, non-Hispanic/Latino; 8% Hispanic/Latino; 5% Black or African American, non-Hispanic/Latino; 1% Asian, non-Hispanic/Latino; 0.2% Native Hawaiian or other Pacific Islander, non-Hispanic/Latino; 5% international. 12% 25 or older, 66% live on campus, 9% transferred in. Retention: 78% of full-time freshmen returned the following year. Academic areas with the most degrees conferred: business/marketing; psychology; parks and recreation; health professions and related sciences. Core. Calendar: semesters. Academic remediation for entering students, ESL program, services for LD students, advanced placement, accelerated degree program, self-designed majors, honors program, independent study, distance learning, double major, summer session for credit, part-time degree program, adult/continuing education programs, co-op programs and internships, graduate courses open to undergrads. Off campus study at Eastern Iowa Community Colleges, Black Hawk Community College, Kirkwood Community College, community colleges in Iowa and Illinois, Iowa State University, University of Iowa School of Law, Palmer College of Chiropractic Medicine. Study abroad program.

Entrance Requirements: Options: electronic application, deferred admission, international baccalaureate accepted. Required: high school transcript, minimum 2.5 high school GPA, SAT or ACT. Recommended: interview. Required for some: interview. Entrance: moderately difficult. Application deadline: rolling. Notification: 10/1. SAT Reasoning Test deadline: 8/1. SAT Subject Test deadline: 8/1. Transfer credits accepted: Yes.

Costs Per Year: Application fee: $0. Comprehensive fee: $41,364 includes full-time tuition ($30,614), mandatory fees ($280), and college room and board ($10,470). College room only: $6384. Full-time tuition and fees vary according to course load and location. Room and board charges vary according to board plan and housing facility. Part-time tuition: $942 per credit hour. Part-time mandatory fees: $280 per term. Part-time tuition and fees vary according to course load and location.

Collegiate Environment: Orientation program. Drama-theater group, choral group, marching band, student-run newspaper, radio station. Social organizations: 93 open to all. Most popular organizations: Dance Marathon, Habitat for Humanity, Biology Club, Ambrosians for Peace and Justice, SPTO - Student Physical Therapy Organization. Major annual events: Midnight Breakfast, Last Blast, Dance Marathon Big Event. Student services: health clinic, personal-psychological counseling. Campus security: 24-hour emergency response devices and patrols, student patrols, late night transport-escort service, controlled dormitory access, off-duty officer available three nights/week for 4.5 hours per night, twelve cameras record various public areas on campus. SAU Library plus 1 other. Books: 172,923 (physical), 13,678 (digital/electronic); Serial titles: 502 (physical); Databases: 85. Weekly public service hours: 95; students can reserve study rooms. Operations spending for the previous fiscal year: $1.6 million. 507 computers available on campus for general student use. A campuswide network can be accessed from student residence rooms and from off campus. Students can access the following: online class registration, online course syllabi, online payments. Staffed computer lab on campus provides training in use of computers, software, and the Internet.

■ **ST. LUKE'S COLLEGE**

2800 Pierce St.

Sioux City, IA 51104

Tel: (712)279-3149; Free: 800-352-4660

Fax: (712)233-8017

E-mail: sherry.mccarthy@stlukescollege.edu

Web Site: stlukescollege.edu

Description: Independent, primarily 2-year, coed. Administratively affiliated with UnityPoint Health. Awards certificates, transfer associate, terminal associate, and bachelor's degrees. Founded 1967. Setting: 3-acre rural campus with easy access to Omaha. System endowment: $1.2 million. Educational spending for the previous fiscal year: $18,493 per student. Total enrollment: 270. Faculty: 36 (22 full-time, 14 part-time). Student-undergrad faculty ratio is 6:1. 15 applied, 100% were admitted. 30% from top quarter of their high school class, 80% from top half. Full-time: 127 students, 89% women, 11% men. Part-time: 143 students, 92% women, 8% men. Students come from 15 states and territories, 1 other country, 41% from out-of-state. 2% American Indian or Alaska Native, non-Hispanic/Latino; 8% Hispanic/Latino; 3% Black or African American, non-Hispanic/Latino; 3% Asian, non-Hispanic/Latino; 0.4% Native Hawaiian or other Pacific Islander, non-Hispanic/Latino. 53% 25 or older, 13% transferred in. Retention: 100% of full-time freshmen returned the following year. Academic area with the most degrees conferred: health professions and related sciences. Core. Calendar: semesters. Services for LD students, advanced placement, distance learning, summer session for credit, internships.

Entrance Requirements: Option: electronic application. Required: essay, high school transcript, minimum 2.5 high school GPA, interview, SAT or ACT. Entrance: minimally difficult. Notification: continuous, continuous for nonresidents, rolling for early decision plan 1, rolling for early decision plan 2, rolling for early action. SAT Reasoning Test deadline: 8/15. SAT Subject Test deadline: 8/15. Transfer credits accepted: Yes.

Costs Per Year: Application fee: $0. Tuition: $18,900 full-time, $525 part-time. Mandatory fees: $1560 full-time, $1560 per year part-time.

Collegiate Environment: Orientation program. Major annual events: Phone-a-Thon, CMN Radio Thon. Student services: health clinic, personal-psychological counseling. Campus security: 24-hour emergency response devices and patrols, late night transport-escort service. College housing not available. St. Luke's College Library. Books: 2,205 (physical); Serial titles: 63 (physical); Databases: 5. Weekly public service hours: 56. Operations spending for the previous fiscal year: $297,686. 9 computers available on campus for general student use. A campuswide network can be accessed. Students can access the following: online class registration. Staffed computer lab on campus provides training in use of computers, software, and the Internet.

■ **SCOTT COMMUNITY COLLEGE**

500 Belmont Rd.

Bettendorf, IA 52722-6804

Tel: (563)441-4001; Free: 800-895-0811

Fax: (563)441-4066

E-mail: gmohr@eicc.edu

Web Site: www.eicc.edu/about-eicc/colleges-and-centers/scott-community-college.aspx

Description: State and locally supported, 2-year, coed. Part of Eastern Iowa Community College District. Awards certificates, diplomas, transfer associate, and terminal associate degrees. Founded 1966. Setting: urban campus. Total enrollment: 4,111. Faculty: 250 (86 full-time, 164 part-time). Student-undergrad faculty ratio is 20:1. 904 applied, 100% were admitted. Full-time: 2,059 students, 62% women, 38% men. Part-time: 2,052 students, 63% women, 37% men. Students come from 26 states and territories, 23 other countries, 9% from out-of-state. 40% 25 or older, 1% transferred in. Retention: 48% of full-time freshmen returned the following year. Core. Calendar: semesters. Academic remediation for entering students, ESL program, services for LD students, advanced placement, self-designed majors, honors program, independent study, distance learning, double major, summer session for credit, part-time degree program, adult/continuing education programs, co-op programs and internships. Off campus study at Black Hawk College, Carl Sandburg College, Northeast Iowa Community College, Kirkwood Community College. Study abroad program.

Entrance Requirements: Open admission except for nursing program. Option: electronic application. Entrance: noncompetitive. Application deadline: rolling. Notification: continuous.

Collegiate Environment: Orientation program. Drama-theater group. Social organizations: Greek honor society. Most popular organizations: Student Government, Campus Activities Board. Campus security: 24-hour emergency response devices. Scott Community College Library. 200 computers available on campus for general student use. A campuswide network can be accessed from off-campus. Students can access the following: online class registration. Staffed computer lab on campus provides training in use of computers, software, and the Internet.

Community Environment: Davenport (population 98,845), part of the Iowa-Illinois Quad Cities (pop. 375,000), is situated on the north bank of the Mississippi River and has an average temperature of 57 degrees and average rainfall of 50 inches. Commercial transportation is available. Community facilities are excellent and include 91 churches, hotels, hospitals, four local radio stations, four TV stations, a public library, and numerous civic and service organizations. Some of its industries' products are brooms, clothing, food, machinery, foundry products, and aircraft instruments. The 27 city parks offer varied recreational facilities. Vandeer Veer Park has gardens with approximately 2,500 species of roses.

■ **SHILOH UNIVERSITY**
100 Shiloh Dr.
Kalona, IA 52247
Tel: (319)656-2447
E-mail: admissions@shilohuniversity.edu
Web Site: www.shilohuniversity.edu

Description: Independent, comprehensive, coed. Awards associate, bachelor's, master's, and doctoral degrees. Founded 2007. Setting: 200-acre small town campus. Educational spending for the previous fiscal year: $4579 per student. Total enrollment: 42. Faculty: 34 (7 full-time, 27 part-time). Student-undergrad faculty ratio is 1:1. 3 applied, 33% were admitted. Part-time: 14 students, 64% women, 36% men. Students come from 16 states and territories, 2 other countries, 88% from out-of-state. 7% Hispanic/Latino; 7% Black or African American, non-Hispanic/Latino; 7% Asian, non-Hispanic/Latino. 39% 25 or older, 271% transferred in. Retention: 60% of full-time freshmen returned the following year. Academic area with the most degrees conferred: theology and religious vocations. Core. Services for LD students, distance learning, summer session for credit, part-time degree program. Off campus study.

Entrance Requirements: Options: electronic application, early admission, deferred admission, international baccalaureate accepted. Required: essay, high school transcript, minimum 2 high school GPA. Required for some: 1 recommendation. Entrance: noncompetitive. Application deadlines: 7/5, 7/1 for nonresidents. Notification: 7/19, continuous for nonresidents. Transfer credits accepted: Yes.

Costs Per Year: Application fee: $0. Tuition: $4725 full-time, $175 per credit hour part-time.

Collegiate Environment: University e-Library. Databases: 2. Operations spending for the previous fiscal year: $16,141.

■ **SIMPSON COLLEGE**
701 N C St.
Indianola, IA 50125-1297
Tel: (515)961-6251; Free: 800-362-2454
Fax: (515)961-1498
Web Site: www.simpson.edu

Description: Independent United Methodist, comprehensive, coed. Awards bachelor's and master's degrees. Founded 1860. Setting: 85-acre suburban campus with easy access to Des Moines. Endowment: $84.6 million. Educational spending for the previous fiscal year: $12,184 per student. Total enrollment: 1,479. Faculty: 194 (104 full-time, 90 part-time). Student-undergrad faculty ratio is 10:1. 1,265 applied, 83% were admitted. 23% from top 10% of their high school class, 58% from top quarter, 82% from top half. Full-time: 1,280 students, 54% women, 46% men. Part-time: 152 students, 57% women, 43% men. Students come from 29 states and territories, 6 other countries, 19% from out-of-state. 0.1% American Indian or Alaska Native, non-Hispanic/Latino; 4% Hispanic/Latino; 2% Black or African American, non-Hispanic/Latino; 2% Asian, non-Hispanic/Latino; 0.2% Native Hawaiian or other Pacific Islander, non-Hispanic/Latino; 1% international. 13% 25 or older, 77% live on campus, 5% transferred in. Retention: 80% of full-time freshmen returned the following year. Academic areas with the most degrees conferred: business/marketing; education; social sciences; parks

and recreation. Core. Calendar: 4-4-1. Services for LD students, advanced placement, accelerated degree program, self-designed majors, honors program, independent study, distance learning, double major, summer session for credit, part-time degree program, adult/continuing education programs, co-op programs and internships. Off campus study at Allen College, Drake University. Study abroad program.

Entrance Requirements: Options: electronic application, deferred admission, international baccalaureate accepted. Required: high school transcript, guidance counselor recommendation form, SAT or ACT. Recommended: minimum 3 high school GPA, interview. Entrance: moderately difficult. Application deadline: 8/15. Notification: continuous. SAT Reasoning Test deadline: 7/1. SAT Subject Test deadline: 7/1. Transfer credits accepted: Yes.

Costs Per Year: Application fee: $0. One-time mandatory fee: $200. Comprehensive fee: $47,524 includes full-time tuition ($38,412), mandatory fees ($732), and college room and board ($8380). College room only: $4062. Full-time tuition and fees vary according to class time, course load, degree level, and program. Room and board charges vary according to board plan and housing facility. Part-time tuition: $375 per credit hour. Part-time mandatory fees: $6 per credit hour. Part-time tuition and fees vary according to class time, course load, degree level, and program.

Collegiate Environment: Orientation program. Drama-theater group, choral group, student-run newspaper, radio station. Social organizations: 70 open to all; national fraternities, national sororities, local fraternities, local sororities; 24% of eligible men and 24% of eligible women are members. Most popular organizations: Religious Life Community, Campus Activities Board, Student Government Association, Residence Hall Association, intramurals. Major annual events: Homecoming Week, Campus Day (campus beautification/volunteer service day), Back to School Stand-Around. Student services: health clinic, personal-psychological counseling, women's center. Campus security: 24-hour emergency response devices and patrols, student patrols, late night transport-escort service, controlled dormitory access, SAFE (Simpson Alert for Emergencies) provides phone calls in case of campus security/weather emergencies. Dunn Library. Books: 116,870 (physical), 168,359 (digital/electronic); Serial titles: 234 (physical), 278,513 (digital/electronic); Databases: 38. Weekly public service hours: 95. Operations spending for the previous fiscal year: $838,172. 425 computers available on campus for general student use. A campuswide network can be accessed from student residence rooms and from off campus. Students can access the following: online class registration. Staffed computer lab on campus provides training in use of computers, software, and the Internet.

Community Environment: Indianola (population 14,000) is located 20 minutes from Des Moines, the state capital, and enjoys the advantages of both a charming small town and a metropolitan center. Major transportation facilities are found in Des Moines, including the Des Moines International Airport. While Des Moines is known as a commercial and industrial city in the heart of a great agricultural state, it is also known for its educational, cultural, philanthropic, and religious institutions.

■ **SOUTHEASTERN COMMUNITY COLLEGE**
1500 W Agency Rd.
West Burlington, IA 52655-0180
Tel: (319)752-2731; Free: 866-722-4692
Fax: (319)752-4957
E-mail: admoff@scciowa.edu
Web Site: www.scciowa.edu

Description: State and locally supported, 2-year, coed. Part of Iowa Department of Education Division of Community Colleges. Awards certificates, diplomas, and transfer associate degrees. Founded 1968. Setting: 160-acre small town campus. Total enrollment: 3,167. Faculty: 120 (67 full-time, 53 part-time). Student-undergrad faculty ratio is 17:1. 1,008 applied, 77% were admitted. 7% from top 10% of their high school class, 23% from top quarter, 52% from top half. Full-time: 1,312 students, 56% women, 44% men. Part-time: 1,532 students, 57% women, 43% men. 12% from out-of-state. 0.7% American Indian or Alaska Native, non-Hispanic/Latino; 5% Hispanic/Latino; 5% Black or African American, non-Hispanic/Latino; 1% Asian, non-Hispanic/Latino; 0.1% Native Hawaiian or other Pacific Islander, non-Hispanic/Latino; 0.9% international. 29% 25 or older, 2% live on campus, 2% transferred in. Calendar: semesters. Part-time degree program, adult/continuing education programs.

Entrance Requirements: Open admission except for computer programming, nursing, electronics, medical assistant, medical laboratory technology, manufacturing technology, engineering design, occupational therapy assistant, physical therapy assistant programs. Options: early admission, deferred admission. Entrance: noncompetitive.

Costs Per Year: Application fee: $0. State resident tuition: $5430 full-time, $181 per credit hour part-time. Nonresident tuition: $5580 full-time, $186 per credit hour part-time. Mandatory fees: $150 full-time. College room and board: $8600. Room and board charges vary according to housing facility and location.

Collegiate Environment: Campus security: controlled dormitory access, night patrols by trained security personnel. Yohe Memorial Library.

■ **SOUTHWESTERN COMMUNITY COLLEGE**
1501 W Townline St.
Creston, IA 50801
Tel: (641)782-7081; Free: 800-247-4023
Fax: (641)782-3312
E-mail: maitlen@swcciowa.edu
Web Site: www.swcciowa.edu

Description: State-supported, 2-year, coed. Part of Iowa Department of Education Division of Community Colleges. Awards certificates, diplomas, transfer associate, and terminal associate degrees. Founded 1966. Setting: 406-acre rural campus. Total enrollment: 1,547. Faculty: 123 (43 full-time, 80 part-time). Student-undergrad faculty ratio is 16:1. 5% from top 10% of their high school class, 19% from top quarter, 48% from top half. Full-time: 683 students, 53% women, 47% men. Part-time: 864 students, 64% women, 36% men. Students come from 21 states and territories, 8 other countries, 5% from out-of-state. 29% 25 or older, 6% live on campus, 6% transferred in. Retention: 57% of full-time freshmen returned the following year. Calendar: semesters. Academic remediation for entering students, advanced placement, independent study, distance learning, double major, summer session for credit, part-time degree program, adult/continuing education programs.

Entrance Requirements: Open admission except for allied health programs. Options: electronic application, early admission. Required: high school transcript. Required for some: SAT or ACT, ACT Compass/ACCUPLACER. Entrance: noncompetitive. Notification: continuous. Transfer credits accepted: Yes.

Collegiate Environment: Drama-theater group, choral group. Major annual events: All-School Picnic, Job Fair, Orientation. Student services: personal-psychological counseling. Campus security: 24-hour emergency response devices, controlled dormitory access. 280 college housing spaces available; all were occupied in 2018-19. No special consideration for freshman housing applicants. Options: coed, men-only, women-only housing available. Learning Resource Center. Books: 15,796 (physical), 28,886 (digital/electronic); Databases: 60. Weekly public service hours: 58. 200 computers available on campus for general student use. A campuswide network can be accessed from off-campus. Students can access the following: online class registration. Staffed computer lab on campus.

■ **UNIVERSITY OF DUBUQUE**
2000 University Ave.
Dubuque, IA 52001-5099
Tel: (563)589-3000; Free: 800-722-5583
Fax: (563)589-3690
E-mail: admissns@dbq.edu
Web Site: www.dbq.edu

Description: Independent Presbyterian, comprehensive, coed. Awards associate, bachelor's, master's, and doctoral degrees. Founded 1852. Setting: 77-acre suburban campus. Endowment: $132.6 million. Educational spending for the previous fiscal year: $6890 per student. Total enrollment: 2,340. Faculty: 385 (105 full-time, 280 part-time). Student-undergrad faculty ratio is 13:1. 1,761 applied, 74% were admitted. 4% from top 10% of their high school class, 20% from top quarter, 50% from top half. Full-time: 1,710 students, 40% women, 60% men. Part-time: 255 students, 53% women, 47% men. Students come from 42 states and territories, 28 other countries, 54% from out-of-state. 0.2% American Indian or Alaska Native, non-Hispanic/Latino; 9% Hispanic/Latino; 15% Black or African American, non-Hispanic/Latino; 2% Asian, non-Hispanic/Latino; 0.4% Native Hawaiian or other Pacific Islander, non-Hispanic/Latino; 6% international. 18% 25 or older, 45% live on campus, 8% transferred in. Retention: 58% of full-time freshmen returned the following year. Academic areas with the most degrees conferred: business/marketing; education; transportation and materials moving. Core. Calendar: 4-1-4. Academic remediation for entering students, services for LD students, advanced placement, accelerated degree program, self-designed majors, honors program, independent study, distance learning, double major, summer session for credit, part-time degree program, adult/continuing education programs, internships, graduate courses open to undergrads. Off campus study at Clarke University, Loras College. Study abroad program. ROTC: Army.

Entrance Requirements: Options: electronic application, deferred admission, international baccalaureate accepted. Required: essay, high school transcript, 2 recommendations, SAT or ACT. Recommended: interview. Entrance: moderately difficult. Application deadline: rolling. Notification: continuous. SAT Reasoning Test deadline: 8/1. SAT Subject Test deadline: 8/1. Transfer credits accepted: Yes.

Costs Per Year: Application fee: $25. Comprehensive fee: $43,890 includes full-time tuition ($32,670), mandatory fees ($1440), and college room and board ($9780). College room only: $4930. Room and board charges vary according to board plan and housing facility. Part-time tuition: $880 per credit hour.

Collegiate Environment: Orientation program. Drama-theater group, choral group, student-run newspaper. Social organizations: 59 open to all; local fraternities, local sororities; 2% of eligible men and 5% of eligible women are members. Most popular organizations: Greek Council, Saudi Student Organization, Student Nurses Association, Accounting Club, ROTC. Major annual events: Homecoming, Involvement Fair, Finals Feast. Student services: health clinic, personal-psychological counseling. Campus security: 24-hour patrols, late night transport-escort service, controlled dormitory access. Charles C. Myers Library. Books: 134,278 (physical), 178,036 (digital/electronic); Serial titles: 180 (physical), 30,070 (digital/electronic); Databases: 58. Weekly public service hours: 109. Operations spending for the previous fiscal year: $221,104. 244 computers available on campus for general student use. A campuswide network can be accessed from student residence rooms and from off campus. Students can access the following: online class registration. Staffed computer lab on campus provides training in use of software.

■ **THE UNIVERSITY OF IOWA**
Iowa City, IA 52242-1316
Tel: (319)335-3500; Free: 800-553-4692
Fax: (319)335-1535
E-mail: admissions@uiowa.edu
Web Site: www.uiowa.edu

Description: State-supported, university, coed. Awards bachelor's, master's, and doctoral degrees and post-master's certificates. Founded 1847. Setting: 1,700-acre small town campus. Endowment: $1.3 billion. Research spending for the previous fiscal year: $353.3 million. Educational spending for the previous fiscal year: $14,593 per student. Total enrollment: 31,387. Faculty: 1,616 (1,484 full-time, 132 part-time). Student-undergrad faculty ratio is 16:1. 24,097 applied, 81% were admitted. 24% from top 10% of their high school class, 57% from top quarter, 90% from top half. 26 National Merit Scholars. Full-time: 19,546 students, 52% women, 48% men. Part-time: 2,808 students, 50% women, 50% men. Students come from 53 states and territories, 61 other countries, 34% from out-of-state. 0.1% American Indian or Alaska Native, non-Hispanic/Latino; 6% Hispanic/Latino; 3% Black or African American, non-Hispanic/Latino; 3% Asian, non-Hispanic/Latino; 0.1% Native Hawaiian or other Pacific Islander, non-Hispanic/Latino; 11% international. 8% 25 or older, 26% live on campus, 5% transferred in. Retention: 89% of full-time freshmen returned the following year. Academic areas with the most degrees conferred: business/marketing; parks and recreation; social sciences. Core. Calendar: semesters. ESL program, services for LD students, advanced placement, accelerated degree program, self-designed majors, honors program, independent study, distance learning, double major, summer session for credit, part-time degree program, external degree program, adult/continuing education programs, co-op programs and internships, graduate courses open to undergrads. Off campus study at Iowa State University of Science and Technology, University of Northern Iowa, Committee on Institutional Cooperation. Study abroad program. ROTC: Army, Air Force.

Entrance Requirements: Options: electronic application, early admission, deferred admission, international baccalaureate accepted. Required: high school transcript, minimum Regent Admission Index (RAI) requirement of 245 for residents, 255 for nonresidents, SAT or ACT. Entrance: moderately difficult. Application deadline: 4/1. Notification: continuous. SAT Reasoning Test deadline: 4/1. SAT Subject Test deadline: 4/1. Transfer credits accepted: Yes. Applicants placed on waiting list: 0.

Costs Per Year: Application fee: $40. State resident tuition: $9492 full-time. Nonresident tuition: $31,458 full-time. Full-time tuition varies according to course level, course load, degree level, program, and student level. College room and board: $11,172. Room and board charges vary according to board plan and housing facility.

Collegiate Environment: Orientation program. Drama-theater group, choral group, marching band, student-run newspaper, radio station. Social

organizations: 512 open to all; national fraternities, national sororities; 14% of eligible men and 19% of eligible women are members. Most popular organizations: Association of Residence Halls, Graduate Student Senate, National Society of Collegiate Scholars, Organization for the Active Support of International Students (OASIS), Dance Marathon. Major annual events: River Fest Annual Spring Festival, Homecoming, Dance Marathon. Student services: legal services, health clinic, personal-psychological counseling, women's center. Campus security: 24-hour emergency response devices and patrols, late night transport-escort service, controlled dormitory access. Main Library plus 8 others. Operations spending for the previous fiscal year: $25.7 million. 1,468 computers available on campus for general student use. Computer purchase/lease plans available. A campuswide network can be accessed from student residence rooms and from off campus. Students can access the following: online class registration, online degree process, financial aid summary, university bill. Staffed computer lab on campus (open 24 hours a day) provides training in use of computers, software, and the Internet.

Community Environment: Greater Iowa City (population 62,887) is located in eastern Iowa. Major transportation facilities are accessible. The university hospital and medical and scientific research departments make Iowa City an important medical center for the area and state. Public and historical libraries and museums, churches of most denominations, hospitals, and civic, fraternal, and veterans' organizations are a part of the community.

■ UNIVERSITY OF NORTHERN IOWA

1227 W 27th St.
Cedar Falls, IA 50614
Tel: (319)273-2311; Free: 800-772-2037
Fax: (319)273-2885
E-mail: admissions@uni.edu
Web Site: www.uni.edu

Description: State-supported, comprehensive, coed. Part of Board of Regents, State of Iowa. Awards bachelor's, master's, and doctoral degrees. Founded 1876. Setting: 908-acre suburban campus. Endowment: $137.5 million. Research spending for the previous fiscal year: $2.5 million. Educational spending for the previous fiscal year: $15,145 per student. Total enrollment: 11,212. Faculty: 655 (496 full-time, 189 part-time). Student-undergrad faculty ratio is 18:1. 5,217 applied, 81% were admitted. 20% from top 10% of their high school class, 51% from top quarter, 86% from top half. Full-time: 8,745 students, 59% women, 41% men. Part-time: 816 students, 49% women, 51% men. Students come from 32 states and territories, 60 other countries, 6% from out-of-state. 0.4% American Indian or Alaska Native, non-Hispanic/Latino; 4% Hispanic/Latino; 3% Black or African American, non-Hispanic/Latino; 1% Asian, non-Hispanic/Latino; 0.1% Native Hawaiian or other Pacific Islander, non-Hispanic/Latino; 3% international. 7% 25 or older, 32% live on campus, 8% transferred in. Retention: 84% of full-time freshmen returned the following year. Academic areas with the most degrees conferred: business/marketing; education; communication/journalism. Core. Calendar: semesters. Academic remediation for entering students, ESL program, services for LD students, advanced placement, accelerated degree program, self-designed majors, honors program, independent study, distance learning, double major, summer session for credit, part-time degree program, external degree program, adult/continuing education programs, co-op programs and internships, graduate courses open to undergrads. Off campus study at Iowa Regents' Universities Student Exchange, National Student Exchange. Study abroad program. ROTC: Army.

Entrance Requirements: Options: electronic application, deferred admission, international baccalaureate accepted. Required: high school transcript, 4 years of English; 3 years each of math, science and social studies; 2 or more years of electives, which may include foreign language and fine arts, SAT or ACT. Recommended: SAT, ACT. Required for some: interview. Entrance: moderately difficult. Notification: 7/1. SAT Reasoning Test deadline: 8/15. SAT Subject Test deadline: 8/15. Transfer credits accepted: Yes.

Costs Per Year: Application fee: $40. State resident tuition: $7665 full-time, $320 per credit hour part-time. Nonresident tuition: $18,207 full-time, $759 per credit hour part-time. Mandatory fees: $1273 full-time. Full-time tuition and fees vary according to course load and program. Part-time tuition varies according to course load and program. College room and board: $8948. College room only: $4540. Room and board charges vary according to board plan and housing facility.

Collegiate Environment: Orientation program. Drama-theater group, choral group, marching band, student-run newspaper, radio station. Social

organizations: 278 open to all; national fraternities, national sororities; 4% of eligible men and 5% of eligible women are members. Most popular organizations: Dance Marathon, Colleges Against Cancer/Relay for Life, Accounting Club, Phi Eta Sigma, Students Today Alumni Tomorrow. Major annual events: Homecoming, Dance Marathon, Welcome Week. Student services: health clinic, personal-psychological counseling. Campus security: 24-hour emergency response devices and patrols, student patrols, late night transport-escort service, controlled dormitory access. 4,401 college housing spaces available; 3,558 were occupied in 2018-19. Freshmen guaranteed college housing. Options: coed, men-only, women-only housing available. Rod Library plus 1 other. Books: 746,500 (physical), 338,651 (digital/electronic); Serial titles: 20,207 (physical), 64,588 (digital/electronic); Databases: 191. Weekly public service hours: 97; students can reserve study rooms. Operations spending for the previous fiscal year: $6.9 million. 1,900 computers available on campus for general student use. Computer purchase/lease plans available. A campuswide network can be accessed from student residence rooms and from off campus. Students can access the following: online class registration, student account, degree audit, program of study. Staffed computer lab on campus (open 24 hours a day) provides training in use of computers, software, and the Internet.

Community Environment: Cedar Falls is an active industrial community on the Cedar River, situated in northeast Iowa. Along with nearby Waterloo, the area population is well over 100,000. All forms of commercial transportation are available. Recreational facilities include many parks, Cedar River for fishing and boating, and two public golf courses. Part-time work is available.

■ UPPER IOWA UNIVERSITY

605 Washington St., Box 1857
Fayette, IA 52142-1857
Tel: (563)425-5200; Free: 800-553-4150
Fax: (563)425-5277
E-mail: frankenk@uiu.edu
Web Site: www.uiu.edu

Description: Independent, comprehensive, coed. Awards associate, bachelor's, and master's degrees (enrollment figures include extended learning centers and online and distance education programs). Founded 1857. Setting: 100-acre rural campus with easy access to Minneapolis-St. Paul, Chicago. Endowment: $17.1 million. Educational spending for the previous fiscal year: $4521 per student. Total enrollment: 4,944. Faculty: 518 (72 full-time, 446 part-time). Student-undergrad faculty ratio is 17:1. 1,901 applied, 56% were admitted. 16% from top 10% of their high school class, 35% from top quarter, 65% from top half. Full-time: 2,110 students, 62% women, 38% men. Part-time: 2,165 students, 62% women, 38% men. Students come from 50 states and territories, 46 other countries, 55% from out-of-state. 0.4% American Indian or Alaska Native, non-Hispanic/Latino; 5% Hispanic/Latino; 18% Black or African American, non-Hispanic/Latino; 2% Asian, non-Hispanic/Latino; 0.2% Native Hawaiian or other Pacific Islander, non-Hispanic/Latino; 12% international. 64% 25 or older, 56% live on campus, 12% transferred in. Retention: 60% of full-time freshmen returned the following year. Academic areas with the most degrees conferred: business/marketing; psychology; health professions and related sciences. Core. Calendar: 6 8-week terms. Academic remediation for entering students, ESL program, services for LD students, advanced placement, accelerated degree program, self-designed majors, freshman honors college, honors program, independent study, distance learning, double major, summer session for credit, part-time degree program, external degree program, adult/continuing education programs, co-op programs and internships. Off campus study at North Iowa Community College (agribusiness), North Iowa Community College (industrial technology). Study abroad program.

Entrance Requirements: Open admission. Option: electronic application. Required: high school transcript, minimum 2 high school GPA, SAT or ACT. Entrance: moderately difficult. Application deadline: rolling. SAT Reasoning Test deadline: 8/23. SAT Subject Test deadline: 8/23. Transfer credits accepted: Yes.

Costs Per Year: Comprehensive fee: $38,910 includes full-time tuition ($29,700), mandatory fees ($750), and college room and board ($8460). College room only: $3900. Full-time tuition and fees vary according to degree level, location, and program. Room and board charges vary according to board plan, housing facility, and location. Part-time tuition: $454 per credit hour.

Collegiate Environment: Orientation program. Drama-theater group, choral group, student-run newspaper. Social organizations: 34 open to all; local fraternities, local sororities; 15% of eligible men and 24% of eligible women are members. Most popular organizations: Student Athlete Advisory Committee, Peacock Alumni for Student Traditions, UIU Science and Environment Club, Student Government Association, Peacocks for Progress. Major annual events: Winter Formal, Homecoming, Backyard BBQ. Student services: personal-psychological counseling. Campus security: late night transport-escort service, controlled dormitory access. Henderson Wilder Library. Books: 68,870 (physical), 7,450 (digital/electronic); Serial titles: 211 (physical), 83,993 (digital/electronic); Databases: 40. Weekly public service hours: 85. Operations spending for the previous fiscal year: $423,241. 360 computers available on campus for general student use. Computer purchase/lease plans available. A campuswide network can be accessed. Students can access the following: online class registration.

Community Environment: Fayette (population 1,340) is a rural area in northeastern Iowa, 50 miles from the Mississippi River. Community facilities include five churches and hospital service in the county seat 8 miles away. The city has a Chamber of Commerce and other civic and fraternal organizations. Part-time work is available for students and families. Outdoor sports include hiking, cross-country skiing, hunting, fishing, and golf.

■ WALDORF UNIVERSITY
106 S 6th St.
Forest City, IA 50436
Tel: (641)585-2450; Free: 800-292-1903
Fax: (641)585-8194
Web Site: www.waldorf.edu

Description: Independent Lutheran, comprehensive, coed. Part of Columbia Southern Education Group. Awards associate, bachelor's, and master's degrees. Founded 1903. Setting: 51-acre rural campus. Total enrollment: 2,487. Faculty: 171 (47 full-time, 124 part-time). Student-undergrad faculty ratio is 19:1. 771 applied, 72% were admitted. 4% from top 10% of their high school class, 17% from top quarter, 57% from top half. Full-time: 1,517 students, 39% women, 61% men. Part-time: 609 students, 32% women, 68% men. Students come from 50 states and territories, 24 other countries, 83% from out-of-state. 0.8% American Indian or Alaska Native, non-Hispanic/Latino; 9% Hispanic/Latino; 12% Black or African American, non-Hispanic/Latino; 2% Asian, non-Hispanic/Latino; 0.2% Native Hawaiian or other Pacific Islander, non-Hispanic/Latino; 1% international. 56% 25 or older, 70% live on campus, 4% transferred in. Retention: 46% of full-time freshmen returned the following year. Core. Calendar: semesters. Academic remediation for entering students, services for LD students, advanced placement, freshman honors college, honors program, independent study, distance learning, double major, summer session for credit, part-time degree program, adult/continuing education programs, co-op programs and internships.

Entrance Requirements: Option: electronic application. Required: high school transcript, SAT or ACT. Recommended: minimum 2 high school GPA. Required for some: 1 recommendation, interview. Entrance: moderately difficult. Application deadline: rolling. Notification: continuous. SAT Reasoning Test deadline: 8/11. SAT Subject Test deadline: 8/11. Transfer credits accepted: Yes.

Costs Per Year: Application fee: $0. Comprehensive fee: $29,600 includes full-time tuition ($20,934), mandatory fees ($1142), and college room and board ($7524). Full-time tuition and fees vary according to class time, course load, and program. Room and board charges vary according to board plan and housing facility. Part-time tuition: $295 per credit hour.

Collegiate Environment: Orientation program. Drama-theater group, choral group, student-run newspaper, radio station. Social organizations: 30 open to all; music and theatre honor societies; 6% of eligible men and 6% of eligible women are members. Most popular organizations: Student Activities Team, Education Club, Campus Ministry groups, intramurals, Radio/TV/Newspaper. Major annual events: Homecoming Week, De-Stress Weeks, Christmas Festival. Student services: health clinic, personal-psychological counseling. Campus security: 24-hour emergency response devices, student patrols, late night transport-escort service, controlled dormitory access, evening and night patrols by trained security personnel, camera surveillance system. Luise V. Hanson Library. Books: 55,884 (physical), 152,040 (digital/electronic); Serial titles: 394 (physical); Databases: 87. Weekly public service hours: 97; students can reserve study rooms. 621 computers available on campus for general student use. Computer purchase/lease plans available. A campuswide network can be accessed from student residence rooms.

Community Environment: Forest City (population 4,250), so named for the numerous trees covering the slopes of the rolling hills surrounding the city, is in north-central Iowa on the Winnebago River, near Mason City (population 27,900) and midway between Minneapolis and Des Moines. It is also the county seat and serves as both the manufacturing and administrative center for Winnebago Industries. A few miles to the east is Pilot Knob State Park, offering hiking and winter sports. Also available for recreation is the YMCA.

■ WARTBURG COLLEGE
100 Wartburg Blvd.
Waverly, IA 50677-0903
Tel: (319)352-8200; Free: 800-772-2085
Fax: (319)352-8279
E-mail: admissions@wartburg.edu
Web Site: www.wartburg.edu

Description: Independent Lutheran, 4-year, coed. Awards bachelor's and master's degrees. Founded 1852. Setting: 170-acre small town campus. Endowment: $76.7 million. Educational spending for the previous fiscal year: $9871 per student. Total enrollment: 1,505. Faculty: 158 (93 full-time, 65 part-time). Student-undergrad faculty ratio is 11:1. 4,298 applied, 76% were admitted. 22% from top 10% of their high school class, 51% from top quarter, 79% from top half. Full-time: 1,456 students, 54% women, 46% men. Part-time: 42 students, 36% women, 64% men. Students come from 35 states and territories, 53 other countries, 31% from out-of-state. 0.1% American Indian or Alaska Native, non-Hispanic/Latino; 5% Hispanic/Latino; 4% Black or African American, non-Hispanic/Latino; 1% Asian, non-Hispanic/Latino; 0.1% Native Hawaiian or other Pacific Islander, non-Hispanic/Latino; 7% international. 1% 25 or older, 87% live on campus, 2% transferred in. Retention: 79% of full-time freshmen returned the following year. Academic areas with the most degrees conferred: business/marketing; biological/life sciences; education. Core. Calendar: 4-4-1. Academic remediation for entering students, services for LD students, advanced placement, accelerated degree program, self-designed majors, honors program, independent study, double major, summer session for credit, part-time degree program, internships. Off campus study at members of the May Term Consortium. Study abroad program.

Entrance Requirements: Options: electronic application, early action, deferred admission, international baccalaureate accepted. Required: high school transcript, minimum 2.5 high school GPA, SAT or ACT. Recommended: secondary school report. Entrance: moderately difficult. Application deadline: rolling. Notification: continuous. Transfer credits accepted: Yes. Applicants placed on waiting list: 0. Wait-listed applicants offered admission: 0.

Costs Per Year: Application fee: $0. Comprehensive fee: $53,210 includes full-time tuition ($41,830), mandatory fees ($2100), and college room and board ($9280). College room only: $5290. Part-time tuition: $2200 per course. Part-time mandatory fees: $125 per term.

Collegiate Environment: Orientation program. Drama-theater group, choral group, student-run newspaper, radio station. Social organizations: 86 open to all. Most popular organizations: Entertainment To Knight (ETK), Student Senate, Wartburg College Dance Marathon (WCDM), Symphonic Band, Wartburg Choir. Major annual events: Outfly, Homecoming, Christmas with Wartburg. Student services: health clinic, personal-psychological counseling. Campus security: 24-hour emergency response devices and patrols, late night transport-escort service, controlled dormitory access. 1,409 college housing spaces available; 1,260 were occupied in 2018-19. Freshmen guaranteed college housing. On-campus residence required through senior year. Options: coed, men-only, women-only housing available. Vogel Library. Books: 144,314 (physical), 164,971 (digital/electronic); Serial titles: 2,993 (physical), 68,512 (digital/electronic); Databases: 176. Weekly public service hours: 91. Operations spending for the previous fiscal year: $729,850. 349 computers available on campus for general student use. A campuswide network can be accessed from student residence rooms and from off campus. Students can access the following: online class registration, billing, satellite. Staffed computer lab on campus provides training in use of computers, software, and the Internet.

Community Environment: Waverly is a rural Iowa community (population 9,290), within 15 minutes of the Waterloo-Cedar Falls metro area (population 101,000). A variety of cultural events are available. The community provides libraries, a museum, a hospital, churches, clinics, shopping facilities and a community symphony. Part-time employment opportunities are limited.

■ WESTERN IOWA TECH COMMUNITY COLLEGE
4647 Stone Ave.
Sioux City, IA 51102-5199
Tel: (712)274-6400; Free: 800-352-4649
Fax: (712)274-6412
Web Site: www.witcc.edu

Description: State-supported, 2-year, coed. Part of Iowa Department of

Education Division of Community Colleges. Awards certificates, diplomas, transfer associate, and terminal associate degrees. Founded 1966. Setting: 143-acre suburban campus. Endowment: $1.7 million. Research spending for the previous fiscal year: $169,266. Educational spending for the previous fiscal year: $3766 per student. Total enrollment: 6,152. Faculty: 518 (80 full-time, 438 part-time). Student-undergrad faculty ratio is 16:1. Full-time: 2,292 students, 53% women, 47% men. Part-time: 3,860 students, 60% women, 40% men. Students come from 30 states and territories, 8 other countries, 10% from out-of-state. 2% American Indian or Alaska Native, non-Hispanic/Latino; 15% Hispanic/Latino; 3% Black or African American, non-Hispanic/Latino; 2% Asian, non-Hispanic/Latino; 0.2% Native Hawaiian or other Pacific Islander, non-Hispanic/Latino; 0.7% international. 21% 25 or older, 5% live on campus, 4% transferred in. Retention: 52% of full-time freshmen returned the following year. Core. Calendar: semesters. Academic remediation for entering students, ESL program, services for LD students, advanced placement, accelerated degree program, self-designed majors, honors program, independent study, distance learning, double major, summer session for credit, part-time degree program, co-op programs and internships. Off campus study. Study abroad program.

Entrance Requirements: Open admission except for health occupations programs. Options: electronic application, early admission, deferred admission. Recommended: high school transcript, ACT, SAT or ACT. Entrance: noncompetitive. Application deadline: rolling. Notification: continuous. Transfer credits accepted: Yes.

Collegiate Environment: Orientation program. Drama-theater group, choral group. Social organizations: 27 open to all. Most popular organizations: Shakespeare Overseas Traveling Club, Habitat for Humanity, Anime Club, Leadership Academy, Police Science Club. Major annual event: WITStock. Student services: personal-psychological counseling. Campus security: 24-hour emergency response devices and patrols, controlled dormitory access. Western Iowa Tech Community College Library Services plus 1 other. Books: 17,232 (physical), 12,438 (digital/electronic). Weekly public service hours: 60. Operations spending for the previous fiscal year: $84,600.

Community Environment: See Briar Cliff University.

■ **WILLIAM PENN UNIVERSITY**
201 Trueblood Ave.
Oskaloosa, IA 52577-1799
Tel: (641)673-1001
Fax: (641)673-1396
E-mail: admissions@wmpenn.edu
Web Site: www.wmpenn.edu
Description: Independent, comprehensive, coed, affiliated with Society of Friends. Awards bachelor's and master's degrees. Founded 1873. Setting: 60-acre rural campus with easy access to Des Moines. Endowment: $4.7 million. Educational spending for the previous fiscal year: $4802 per student.

Total enrollment: 1,372. Faculty: 134 (46 full-time, 88 part-time). Student-undergrad faculty ratio is 18:1. 1,219 applied, 56% were admitted. Students come from 46 states and territories, 22 other countries, 47% from out-of-state. 0.9% American Indian or Alaska Native, non-Hispanic/Latino; 10% Hispanic/Latino; 22% Black or African American, non-Hispanic/Latino; 1% Asian, non-Hispanic/Latino; 0.3% Native Hawaiian or other Pacific Islander, non-Hispanic/Latino; 5% international. 22% 25 or older, 55% live on campus. Retention: 51% of full-time freshmen returned the following year. Academic areas with the most degrees conferred: business/marketing; education; parks and recreation. Core. Calendar: semesters. Academic remediation for entering students, services for LD students, advanced placement, honors program, independent study, distance learning, double major, summer session for credit, part-time degree program, adult/continuing education programs, co-op programs and internships. Study abroad program.

Entrance Requirements: Options: electronic application, deferred admission. Required: high school transcript, minimum 2 high school GPA, SAT or ACT. Required for some: essay, recommendations, interview. Entrance: moderately difficult. Application deadline: rolling. Notification: continuous. SAT Reasoning Test deadline: 8/15. SAT Subject Test deadline: 8/15. Transfer credits accepted: Yes.

Costs Per Year: Application fee: $0. Comprehensive fee: $32,552 includes full-time tuition ($24,870), mandatory fees ($730), and college room and board ($6952). College room only: $3102. Full-time tuition and fees vary according to class time, course load, degree level, location, and program. Room and board charges vary according to housing facility. Part-time tuition: $380 per credit hour. Part-time mandatory fees: $19 per credit hour. Part-time tuition and fees vary according to class time, course load, degree level, location, and program.

Collegiate Environment: Orientation program. Drama-theater group, choral group, marching band, student-run newspaper, radio station. Social organizations: 20 open to all; local fraternities, local sororities; 6% of eligible men and 6% of eligible women are members. Most popular organizations: Greek Council, Biology Club, Education Club, Student Government Association, Computer Club. Major annual events: Homecoming, Campus Beautification Day, PennStock. Student services: health clinic, personal-psychological counseling. Campus security: 24-hour emergency response devices and patrols, late night transport-escort service, controlled dormitory access. Wilcox Library plus 1 other. Books: 61,804 (physical), 162,694 (digital/electronic); Serial titles: 54 (physical), 48,768 (digital/electronic); Databases: 38. Weekly public service hours: 92; students can reserve study rooms. Operations spending for the previous fiscal year: $229,606. 200 computers available on campus for general student use. A campuswide network can be accessed from student residence rooms and from off campus. Staffed computer lab on campus provides training in use of computers, software, and the Internet.

■ **ALLEN COMMUNITY COLLEGE**
1801 N Cottonwood St.
Iola, KS 66749-1607
Tel: (620)365-5116
Fax: (620)365-7406
E-mail: bilderback@allencc.edu
Web Site: www.allencc.edu
Description: State and locally supported, 2-year, coed. Part of Kansas State Board of Regents. Awards certificates, transfer associate, and terminal associate degrees. Founded 1923. Setting: 88-acre small town campus. Total enrollment: 2,379. Student-undergrad faculty ratio is 18:1. 20% 25 or older. Core. Calendar: semesters. Academic remediation for entering students, ESL program, services for LD students, self-designed majors, independent study, distance learning, summer session for credit, part-time degree program, adult/continuing education programs, co-op programs and internships.
Entrance Requirements: Open admission. Options: electronic application, early admission, deferred admission. Required: high school transcript. Entrance: noncompetitive. Application deadline: 8/24. Notification: continuous. Transfer credits accepted: Yes.
Collegiate Environment: Drama-theater group, choral group, student-run newspaper. Social organizations: Phi Theta Kappa. Most popular organizations: Intramurals, Student Senate, Theatre, Phi Theta Kappa. Major annual events: Homecoming, Welcome Week. Student services: personal-psychological counseling. Learning Resource Center plus 1 other. 80 computers available on campus for general student use. A campuswide network can be accessed from student residence rooms. Students can access the following: online class registration. Staffed computer lab on campus provides training in use of computers and the Internet.
Community Environment: Iola is a rural area with community facilities that provide a library, hospital, many churches and a fine arts center. Part-time employment is available. Fishing, boating, golf and bowling are some of the recreational activities. The County 4-H Fair is an annual event as is the Farm-City Day Celebration.

■ **BAKER UNIVERSITY**
PO Box 65
Baldwin City, KS 66006-0065
Tel: (785)594-6451; Free: 800-873-4282
Fax: (785)594-6721
E-mail: admissions@bakeru.edu
Web Site: www.bakeru.edu
Description: Independent United Methodist, comprehensive, coed. Awards bachelor's, master's, and doctoral degrees (profile includes information primarily for undergraduate residential campus in Baldwin City, KS). Founded 1858. Setting: 26-acre small town campus with easy access to Kansas City. Endowment: $38.6 million. Educational spending for the previous fiscal year: $5670 per student. Total enrollment: 1,214. Faculty: 99 (59 full-time, 40 part-time). Student-undergrad faculty ratio is 13:1. 804 applied, 88% were admitted. 19% from top 10% of their high school class, 41% from top quarter, 83% from top half. 10 valedictorians. Full-time: 850 students, 49% women, 51% men. Part-time: 364 students, 53% women, 47% men. Students come from 27 states and territories, 15 other countries, 28% from out-of-state. 0.8% American Indian or Alaska Native, non-Hispanic/Latino; 9% Hispanic/Latino; 9% Black or African American, non-Hispanic/Latino; 0.9% Asian, non-Hispanic/Latino; 0.6% Native Hawaiian or other Pacific Islander, non-Hispanic/Latino; 3% international. 0.7% 25 or older, 83% live on campus, 5% transferred in. Retention: 81% of full-time freshmen returned the following year. Academic areas with the most degrees conferred: business/marketing; parks and recreation; psychology; education. Core. Calendar: 4-1-4 semesters for nursing program. Services for LD students, advanced placement, self-designed majors, honors program, independent study, double major, summer session for credit, internships. Study abroad program. ROTC: Army (c), Air Force (c).
Entrance Requirements: Options: electronic application, deferred admission, international baccalaureate accepted. Required: high school transcript, SAT or ACT. Required for some: essay, 1 recommendation, interview, ACT or SAT scores. Entrance: moderately difficult. Application deadline: rolling. SAT Reasoning Test deadline: 8/15. Transfer credits accepted: Yes.
Costs Per Year: Application fee: $0. One-time mandatory fee: $100. Comprehensive fee: $39,130 includes full-time tuition ($29,300), mandatory fees ($580), and college room and board ($9250). Part-time tuition: $945 per credit hour. Part-time mandatory fees: $200 per year.
Collegiate Environment: Orientation program. Drama-theater group, choral group, student-run newspaper, radio station. Social organizations: 75 open to all; national fraternities, national sororities, local fraternities; 36% of eligible men and 45% of eligible women are members. Most popular organizations: Exercise Science Student Alliance, Baker University Speech Choir, Mungano, Student Senate, Student Activities Council. Major annual events: Homecoming, Springfest Week, International Education Week. Student services: health clinic, personal-psychological counseling. Campus security: 24-hour emergency response devices and patrols, controlled dormitory access. 576 college housing spaces available; 504 were occupied in 2018-19. Freshmen guaranteed college housing. On-campus residence required through senior year. Options: coed, men-only, women-only housing available. Baker University Library. Books: 66,909 (physical), 186,955 (digital/electronic); Serial titles: 4,188 (physical), 35,698 (digital/electronic); Databases: 50. Weekly public service hours: 73; study areas open 24 hours, 5-7 days a week; students can reserve study rooms. Operations spending for the previous fiscal year: $415,574. 140 computers available on campus for general student use. A campuswide network can be accessed from student residence rooms. Students can access the following: online class registration. Staffed computer lab on campus provides training in use of computers, software, and the Internet.
Community Environment: A rural town located 30 miles southwest of Kansas City and 15 miles south of Lawrence. The city is 10 miles from Lone Star Lake, which provides recreational facilities. Churches of many denominations are represented here. Shopping, a public library, and a clinic all serve the community. The larger shopping centers of Kansas City and Topeka are excellent as are the cultural advantages of these two cities, which contribute to the enjoyment of the smaller surrounding areas.

■ **BARCLAY COLLEGE**
607 N Kingman
Haviland, KS 67059-0288
Tel: (620)862-5252; Free: 800-862-0226
Fax: (620)862-5403
E-mail: jkendall@barclaycollege.edu
Web Site: www.barclaycollege.edu
Description: Independent, comprehensive, coed, affiliated with Society of Friends. Awards associate, bachelor's, and master's degrees. Founded 1917. Setting: 17-acre rural campus. Endowment: $1.5 million. Educational

spending for the previous fiscal year: $6367 per student. Total enrollment: 259. Faculty: 42 (25 full-time, 17 part-time). Student-undergrad faculty ratio is 10:1. 109 applied, 67% were admitted. Full-time: 178 students, 53% women, 47% men. Part-time: 51 students, 39% women, 61% men. Students come from 34 states and territories, 7 other countries, 56% from out-of-state. 2% American Indian or Alaska Native, non-Hispanic/Latino; 6% Hispanic/Latino; 16% Black or African American, non-Hispanic/Latino; 0.9% Asian, non-Hispanic/Latino; 2% international. 25% 25 or older, 78% live on campus, 11% transferred in. Retention: 65% of full-time freshmen returned the following year. Academic areas with the most degrees conferred: theology and religious vocations; business/marketing; education. Core. Calendar: semesters. Academic remediation for entering students, advanced placement, independent study, distance learning, double major, part-time degree program, external degree program, adult/continuing education programs, internships. Off campus study at Pratt County Community College, Nursing; Fort Hays State University, Education and Nursing; Hutchinson Community College, Nursing.

Entrance Requirements: Options: electronic application, early admission, deferred admission. Required: essay, high school transcript, minimum 2.3 high school GPA, 2 recommendations, interview, SAT or ACT. Entrance: minimally difficult. Application deadline: 9/1. Notification: continuous. Transfer credits accepted: Yes.

Collegiate Environment: Drama-theater group, choral group. Social organizations: 3 open to all. Major annual events: Homecoming, Christmas Banquet. Student services: personal-psychological counseling. Campus security: student patrols. Worden Memorial Library. Books: 44,420 (physical), 23 (digital/electronic); Serial titles: 410 (physical), 4 (digital/electronic); Databases: 48. Weekly public service hours: 95. Operations spending for the previous fiscal year: $75,000. 28 computers available on campus for general student use. A campuswide network can be accessed from student residence rooms and from off campus. Students can access the following: online class registration. Staffed computer lab on campus provides training in use of computers, software, and the Internet.

Community Environment: Haviland is a small town in a rural area with a friendly and supportive atmosphere. Especially welcoming to young families.

■ **BARTON COUNTY COMMUNITY COLLEGE**
245 NE 30 Rd.
Great Bend, KS 67530
Tel: (620)792-2701; Free: 800-722-6842
Fax: (620)792-3238
E-mail: admissions@bartonccc.edu
Web Site: www.bartonccc.edu

Description: State and locally supported, 2-year, coed. Part of Kansas Board of Regents. Awards certificates, transfer associate, and terminal associate degrees. Founded 1969. Setting: 140-acre rural campus. Total enrollment: 4,131. Faculty: 215 (71 full-time, 144 part-time). Student-undergrad faculty ratio is 20:1. Full-time: 875 students, 50% women, 50% men. Part-time: 3,256 students, 49% women, 51% men. 1% American Indian or Alaska Native, non-Hispanic/Latino; 12% Hispanic/Latino; 13% Black or African American, non-Hispanic/Latino; 2% Asian, non-Hispanic/Latino; 0.7% Native Hawaiian or other Pacific Islander, non-Hispanic/Latino; 0.3% international. 8% live on campus. Calendar: semesters. Academic remediation for entering students, ESL program, services for LD students, advanced placement, accelerated degree program, honors program, independent study, distance learning, double major, summer session for credit, part-time degree program, external degree program, adult/continuing education programs, co-op programs and internships. ROTC: Army.

Entrance Requirements: Open admission. Options: electronic application, early admission. Recommended: high school transcript. Entrance: noncompetitive. Application deadline: rolling. Transfer credits accepted: Yes.

Costs Per Year: Application fee: $0. State resident tuition: $2368 full-time, $74 per credit hour part-time. Nonresident tuition: $2368 full-time, $74 per credit hour part-time. Mandatory fees: $1216 full-time, $38 per credit hour part-time. Full-time tuition and fees vary according to course load. Part-time tuition and fees vary according to course load. College room and board: $8400. Room and board charges vary according to board plan.

Collegiate Environment: Orientation program. Drama-theater group, choral group, student-run newspaper. Social organizations: 20 open to all. Most popular organizations: Danceline, Business Professionals, Psychology Club, Agriculture Club, Cougarettes. Major annual events: Homecoming, Parents' Day, Orientation/Welcome Back Days. Student services: health clinic, personal-psychological counseling. Campus security: 24-hour emergency response devices and patrols. Barton County Community College Library.

350 computers available on campus for general student use. A campuswide network can be accessed from student residence rooms and from off campus. Students can access the following: online class registration. Staffed computer lab on campus provides training in use of computers and the Internet.

Community Environment: An urban area, Great Bend (population 15,500) is in the wheat belt and is a large oil producing area. Thirty churches, a library, a hospital and good shopping facilities are a part of the community. Brit Spaugh Park has recreational facilities for tennis, baseball, swimming, and picnicking. Cheyenne Bottoms, nearby, is a wildlife and waterfowl refuge of more than 18,000 acres of which 15,000 acres are covered by water. All forms of commercial transportation are available.

■ **BENEDICTINE COLLEGE**
1020 N 2nd St.
Atchison, KS 66002-1499
Tel: (913)367-5340; Free: 800-467-5340
Fax: (913)367-3673
E-mail: phelgesen@benedictine.edu
Web Site: www.benedictine.edu

Description: Independent Roman Catholic, comprehensive, coed. Awards associate, bachelor's, and master's degrees. Founded 1859. Setting: 225-acre small town campus with easy access to Kansas City. Endowment: $24.3 million. Research spending for the previous fiscal year: $26,295. Educational spending for the previous fiscal year: $8125 per student. Total enrollment: 2,167. Faculty: 200 (116 full-time, 84 part-time). Student-undergrad faculty ratio is 13:1. 2,367 applied, 97% were admitted. 19% from top 10% of their high school class, 42% from top quarter, 67% from top half. Full-time: 1,806 students, 54% women, 46% men. Part-time: 265 students, 60% women, 40% men. Students come from 49 states and territories, 16 other countries, 76% from out-of-state. 0.6% American Indian or Alaska Native, non-Hispanic/Latino; 7% Hispanic/Latino; 3% Black or African American, non-Hispanic/Latino; 0.8% Asian, non-Hispanic/Latino; 0.3% Native Hawaiian or other Pacific Islander, non-Hispanic/Latino; 2% international. 2% 25 or older, 82% live on campus, 4% transferred in. Retention: 79% of full-time freshmen returned the following year. Academic areas with the most degrees conferred: business/marketing; education; theology and religious vocations. Core. Calendar: semesters. Academic remediation for entering students, ESL program, services for LD students, advanced placement, self-designed majors, honors program, independent study, distance learning, double major, summer session for credit, part-time degree program, co-op programs and internships, graduate courses open to undergrads. Off campus study. Study abroad program. ROTC: Army (c).

Entrance Requirements: Options: electronic application, deferred admission, international baccalaureate accepted. Required: high school transcript, minimum 2 high school GPA, 1 recommendation, SAT or ACT. Required for some: interview. Entrance: minimally difficult. Application deadline: rolling. Notification: continuous. SAT Reasoning Test deadline: 8/15. SAT Subject Test deadline: 8/15. Transfer credits accepted: Yes.

Costs Per Year: Application fee: $50. Comprehensive fee: $39,530 includes full-time tuition ($28,730), mandatory fees ($800), and college room and board ($10,000). College room only: $5340. Full-time tuition and fees vary according to course load and degree level. Room and board charges vary according to board plan and housing facility. Part-time tuition: $825 per credit hour. Part-time tuition varies according to course load and degree level.

Collegiate Environment: Orientation program. Drama-theater group, choral group, marching band, student-run newspaper. Social organizations: 43 open to all; 45% of eligible men and 55% of eligible women are members. Most popular organizations: Student Government, ENACTUS, Knights of Columbus, Concert Chorale/Chamber Singers, Ravens Respect Life. Major annual events: Oktoberfest, Homecoming, Family Weekend. Student services: health clinic, personal-psychological counseling. Campus security: 24-hour emergency response devices and patrols, late night transport-escort service, controlled dormitory access. Benedictine College Library. Books: 198,277 (physical), 139,987 (digital/electronic); Serial titles: 45,794 (physical), 400 (digital/electronic); Databases: 88. Weekly public service hours: 85. Operations spending for the previous fiscal year: $572,678. 100 computers available on campus for general student use. Computer purchase/lease plans available. A campuswide network can be accessed from student residence rooms and from off campus. Students can access the following: online class registration. Staffed computer lab on campus provides training in use of computers, software, and the Internet.

Community Environment: Atchison is located on the Kansas-Missouri border, within 30-50 miles of St. Joseph and Kansas City, Missouri, and Topeka and Kansas City, Kansas.

■ BETHANY COLLEGE

335 E Swensson St.
Lindsborg, KS 67456-1897
Tel: (785)227-3311; Free: 800-826-2281
Fax: (785)227-2860
E-mail: admissions@bethanylb.edu
Web Site: www.bethanylb.edu

Description: Independent Lutheran, 4-year, coed. Awards bachelor's degrees. Founded 1881. Setting: 80-acre small town campus. Endowment: $24.1 million. Educational spending for the previous fiscal year: $6502 per student. Total enrollment: 665. Faculty: 74 (39 full-time, 35 part-time). Student-undergrad faculty ratio is 12:1. 1,139 applied, 59% were admitted. 8% from top 10% of their high school class, 20% from top quarter, 63% from top half. Full-time: 603 students, 40% women, 60% men. Part-time: 62 students, 42% women, 58% men. Students come from 21 states and territories, 19 other countries, 45% from out-of-state. 0.8% American Indian or Alaska Native, non-Hispanic/Latino; 11% Hispanic/Latino; 12% Black or African American, non-Hispanic/Latino; 1% Asian, non-Hispanic/Latino; 6% international. 4% 25 or older, 67% live on campus, 11% transferred in. Retention: 64% of full-time freshmen returned the following year. Core. Calendar: 4-1-4. Academic remediation for entering students, services for LD students, advanced placement, accelerated degree program, self-designed majors, honors program, independent study, double major, summer session for credit, internships. Off campus study at 6 members of the Associated Colleges of Central Kansas. Study abroad program.

Entrance Requirements: Options: electronic application, deferred admission, international baccalaureate accepted. Required: high school transcript, minimum 2 high school GPA, SAT or ACT. Required for some: essay, recommendations. Entrance: moderately difficult. Application deadline: rolling. Notification: continuous. SAT Reasoning Test deadline: 8/15. SAT Subject Test deadline: 8/15. Transfer credits accepted: Yes.

Costs Per Year: Application fee: $0. Comprehensive fee: $39,265 includes full-time tuition ($26,960), mandatory fees ($890), and college room and board ($11,415). College room only: $6615. Full-time tuition and fees vary according to program. Room and board charges vary according to board plan and housing facility. Part-time tuition: $560 per credit hour. Part-time mandatory fees: $200 per term. Part-time tuition and fees vary according to course load and program.

Collegiate Environment: Orientation program. Drama-theater group, choral group, student-run newspaper. Social organizations: 35 open to all; local fraternities, local sororities; 11% of eligible men and 21% of eligible women are members. Most popular organizations: Student Activities Board (SAB), Alpha Theta Chi, Alpha Sigma Nu, Fellowship of Christian Athletes (FCA), Bethany Youth Ministries Team. Major annual events: Handel's Messiah by the Bethany Oratorio Society, Homecoming Events/Talent Show, Midnight Movie and Bowling. Student services: health clinic, personal-psychological counseling. Campus security: 24-hour emergency response devices, controlled dormitory access, night patrols by security personnel. Wallerstedt Library plus 1 other. Operations spending for the previous fiscal year: $179,726. 65 computers available on campus for general student use. A campuswide network can be accessed from student residence rooms and from off campus. Students can access the following: online class registration. Staffed computer lab on campus provides training in use of computers and software.

■ BETHEL COLLEGE

300 E 27th St.
North Newton, KS 67117
Tel: (316)283-2500; Free: 800-522-1887
Fax: (316)284-5286
E-mail: admissions@bethelks.edu
Web Site: www.bethelks.edu

Description: Independent, 4-year, coed, affiliated with Mennonite Church USA. Awards bachelor's degrees. Founded 1887. Setting: 90-acre small town campus with easy access to Wichita. Endowment: $18.9 million. Educational spending for the previous fiscal year: $7696 per student. Total enrollment: 444. Faculty: 73 (40 full-time, 33 part-time). Student-undergrad faculty ratio is 10:1. 1,093 applied, 44% were admitted. 15% from top 10% of their high school class, 31% from top quarter, 66% from top half. Full-time: 430 students, 53% women, 47% men. Part-time: 14 students, 93% women, 7% men. Students come from 25 states and territories, 6 other countries, 33% from out-of-state. 0.9% American Indian or Alaska Native, non-Hispanic/Latino; 9% Hispanic/Latino; 15% Black or African American, non-Hispanic/Latino; 2% Asian, non-Hispanic/Latino; 2% international. 7% 25 or

older, 66% live on campus, 11% transferred in. Retention: 56% of full-time freshmen returned the following year. Academic areas with the most degrees conferred: business/marketing; health professions and related sciences; parks and recreation. Core. Calendar: 4-1-4. Services for LD students, advanced placement, self-designed majors, honors program, independent study, double major, summer session for credit, part-time degree program, adult/continuing education programs, co-op programs and internships. Study abroad program.

Entrance Requirements: Options: electronic application, deferred admission, international baccalaureate accepted. Required: high school transcript, SAT or ACT. Recommended: interview. Required for some: essay, minimum 2.5 high school GPA, 2 recommendations. Entrance: moderately difficult. Application deadlines: rolling, rolling for early decision plan 1, rolling for early decision plan 2, rolling for early action. Notification: continuous, rolling for early decision plan 1, rolling for early decision plan 2, rolling for early action. SAT Reasoning Test deadline: 8/1. Transfer credits accepted: Yes.

Costs Per Year: Application fee: $0. Comprehensive fee: $38,370 includes full-time tuition ($29,150), mandatory fees ($240), and college room and board ($8980). College room only: $4340.

Collegiate Environment: Orientation program. Drama-theater group, choral group, student-run newspaper, radio station. Social organizations: 21 open to all. Most popular organizations: FEMCORE, Fellowship of Christian Athletes, Rock-climbing Club, Social Work Student Organization, We-Belong or Business Club. Major annual events: Fall Festival, Winter Gala, Bubbert Awards. Student services: health clinic, personal-psychological counseling. Campus security: 24-hour emergency response devices and patrols, controlled dormitory access, SMS Alert System. 492 college housing spaces available; 293 were occupied in 2018-19. Freshmen guaranteed college housing. On-campus residence required through senior year. Option: coed housing available. Mantz Library plus 1 other. Books: 120,875 (physical), 155,552 (digital/electronic); Serial titles: 2,990 (physical), 109,552 (digital/electronic); Databases: 97. Weekly public service hours: 91; students can reserve study rooms. Operations spending for the previous fiscal year: $290,079. 47 computers available on campus for general student use. A campuswide network can be accessed from student residence rooms and from off campus. Students can access the following: online class registration. Staffed computer lab on campus.

■ BUTLER COMMUNITY COLLEGE

901 S Haverhill Rd.
El Dorado, KS 67042-3280
Tel: (316)321-2222
Fax: (316)322-3109
E-mail: admissions@butlercc.edu
Web Site: www.butlercc.edu

Description: State and locally supported, 2-year, coed. Part of Kansas State Board of Education. Awards transfer associate and terminal associate degrees. Founded 1927. Setting: 80-acre small town campus. Endowment: $5.4 million. Educational spending for the previous fiscal year: $2799 per student. Total enrollment: 8,096. Faculty: 582 (151 full-time, 431 part-time). Student-undergrad faculty ratio is 17:1. Full-time: 3,543 students, 54% women, 46% men. Part-time: 4,553 students, 63% women, 37% men. Students come from 19 states and territories, 34 other countries, 3% from out-of-state. 37% 25 or older, 4% live on campus, 6% transferred in. Retention: 59% of full-time freshmen returned the following year. Core. Calendar: semesters. Academic remediation for entering students, ESL program, services for LD students, advanced placement, accelerated degree program, self-designed majors, honors program, independent study, distance learning, double major, summer session for credit, part-time degree program, adult/continuing education programs, co-op programs.

Entrance Requirements: Open admission. Options: early admission, deferred admission. Required: high school transcript. Entrance: noncompetitive. Application deadline: 8/19. Notification: continuous.

Collegiate Environment: Orientation program. Drama-theater group, choral group, student-run newspaper, radio station. Social organizations: 21 open to all. Most popular organizations: Phi Theta Kappa, HALO (Hispanic American Leadership Organization), Student Nurses Association, Kansas Gaming Association, Colleges Against Cancer. Major annual events: Welcome Week Orientation, Homecoming, Spring Fling. Student services: health clinic, personal-psychological counseling. Campus security: 24-hour emergency response devices and patrols, controlled dormitory access, video cameras at dormitory entrances and parking lot. L. W. Nixon Library. Operations spending for the previous fiscal year: $114,734. 1,200 computers available on campus for general student use. A campuswide network can be accessed from off-campus. Students can access the following: online class registration. Staffed computer lab on campus.

Community Environment: Butler County attracts visitors because of its location near the scenic Flint Hills in Kansas and the El Dorado Lake, a federal Corps of Engineers Project covering approximately 4,500 acres. Butler County has an approximate population of 63,000 persons in nine communities. Butler County communities offers good schools, numerous musical, writing and civic clubs with an emphasis toward educational and cultural opportunities. Located just 30 minutes east of Wichita, a city of approximately 355,000 residents, Butler County residents and BCCC students are also offered all the advantages of a major metropolitan city.

■ **CENTRAL CHRISTIAN COLLEGE OF KANSAS**

1200 S Main
McPherson, KS 67460-5799
Tel: (620)241-0723; Free: 800-835-0078
Fax: (620)241-6032
Web Site: www.centralchristian.edu

Description: Independent Free Methodist, 4-year, coed. Awards associate and bachelor's degrees. Founded 1884. Setting: 16-acre small town campus. Endowment: $6.9 million. Educational spending for the previous fiscal year: $6116 per student. Total enrollment: 466. Faculty: 46 (19 full-time, 27 part-time). Student-undergrad faculty ratio is 14:1. 402 applied, 99% were admitted. 7% from top 10% of their high school class, 28% from top quarter, 67% from top half. 3 valedictorians. Full-time: 328 students, 44% women, 56% men. Part-time: 138 students, 60% women, 40% men. Students come from 26 states and territories, 4 other countries, 47% from out-of-state. 5% 25 or older, 85% live on campus, 6% transferred in. Retention: 72% of full-time freshmen returned the following year. Academic areas with the most degrees conferred: business/marketing; theology and religious vocations; liberal arts/general studies. Core. Calendar: 4-1-4. Academic remediation for entering students, services for LD students, advanced placement, self-designed majors, independent study, distance learning, double major, part-time degree program, adult/continuing education programs, co-op programs and internships. Off campus study at McPherson College, Christian Center for Urban Studies, Focus on the Family Institute, CCCU. Study abroad program.

Entrance Requirements: Options: electronic application, deferred admission, international baccalaureate accepted. Required: high school transcript, minimum 2.5 high school GPA, 2 recommendations, SAT or ACT. Recommended: essay, interview. Entrance: minimally difficult. Application deadline: rolling. Notification: continuous. Transfer credits accepted: Yes.

Costs Per Year: Application fee: $20. Comprehensive fee: $35,060 includes full-time tuition ($28,500), mandatory fees ($200), and college room and board ($6360). Full-time tuition and fees vary according to course load and program. Room and board charges vary according to board plan and gender. Part-time tuition: $425 per credit hour. Part-time tuition varies according to course load and program.

Collegiate Environment: Orientation program. Drama-theater group, choral group, student-run newspaper. Social organizations: 9 open to all. Most popular organizations: Student Government, Outreach Central, Student Activities Committee, Social Awareness Board, Phi Beta Lambda Business Club. Major annual events: All College Picnic, Community Service Day, Christmas Banquet. Student services: health clinic, personal-psychological counseling. Briner Library. Operations spending for the previous fiscal year: $81,762. 28 computers available on campus for general student use. A campuswide network can be accessed from student residence rooms. Staffed computer lab on campus provides training in use of computers, software, and the Internet.

Community Environment: The community of McPherson, Kansas is an attractive Midwestern agricultural and petroleum based city of 14,000. Located 50 miles north of Wichita, the community is rated the thirty-third best small town in the United States.

■ **CLEVELAND UNIVERSITY-KANSAS CITY**

10850 Lowell Ave.
Overland Park, KS 66210
Tel: (913)234-0600; Free: 800-467-2252
Fax: (913)234-0912
E-mail: kc.admissions@cleveland.edu
Web Site: www.cleveland.edu

Description: Independent, comprehensive, coed. Awards associate, bachelor's, master's, and doctoral degrees. Founded 1922. Setting: 34-acre suburban campus with easy access to Kansas City. Total enrollment: 455.

Faculty: 53 (43 full-time, 10 part-time). Student-undergrad faculty ratio is 10:1. 3 applied. Full-time: 33 students, 52% women, 48% men. Part-time: 10 students, 40% women, 60% men. Students come from 15 states and territories, 47% from out-of-state. 2% Hispanic/Latino; 2% Black or African American, non-Hispanic/Latino; 2% international. 54% 25 or older, 42% transferred in. Retention: 50% of full-time freshmen returned the following year. Academic area with the most degrees conferred: biological/life sciences. Core. Calendar: trimesters. Academic remediation for entering students, services for LD students, advanced placement, accelerated degree program, summer session for credit, co-op programs and internships.

Entrance Requirements: Open admission except for BS degree transfer students. Options: electronic application, deferred admission, international baccalaureate accepted. Required: high school transcript, minimum 2.5 high school GPA. Required for some: interview, cumulative college GPA of 2.0 for BS degree transfer students, SAT or ACT. Entrance: noncompetitive. Application deadline: rolling. Notification: continuous. Transfer credits accepted: Yes.

Collegiate Environment: Orientation program. Major annual events: Homecoming, Winter Formal, Fun and Sun day. Student services: health clinic, personal-psychological counseling. Campus security: 24-hour patrols. Ruth R. Cleveland Memorial Library. 30 computers available on campus for general student use. A campuswide network can be accessed. Students can access the following: educational software.

■ **CLOUD COUNTY COMMUNITY COLLEGE**

2221 Campus Dr.
Concordia, KS 66901-1002
Tel: (785)243-1435; Free: 800-729-5101
Fax: (785)243-1043
E-mail: solson@cloud.edu
Web Site: www.cloud.edu

Description: State and locally supported, 2-year, coed. Part of Kansas Community College System. Awards certificates, diplomas, transfer associate, and terminal associate degrees. Founded 1965. Setting: 35-acre rural campus. Total enrollment: 1,873. Faculty: 237 (44 full-time, 193 part-time). Student-undergrad faculty ratio is 11:1. Full-time: 814 students, 49% women, 51% men. Part-time: 1,059 students, 62% women, 38% men. Students come from 26 states and territories, 33 other countries, 7% from out-of-state. 0.8% American Indian or Alaska Native, non-Hispanic/Latino; 7% Hispanic/Latino; 6% Black or African American, non-Hispanic/Latino; 1% Asian, non-Hispanic/Latino; 0.2% Native Hawaiian or other Pacific Islander, non-Hispanic/Latino; 5% international. 25% 25 or older, 7% transferred in. Retention: 64% of full-time freshmen returned the following year. Core. Calendar: semesters. Academic remediation for entering students, ESL program, services for LD students, advanced placement, freshman honors college, honors program, distance learning, summer session for credit, part-time degree program, adult/continuing education programs, co-op programs and internships.

Entrance Requirements: Open admission. Options: early admission, deferred admission. Required: high school transcript. Entrance: noncompetitive. Application deadline: 9/11. Notification: continuous. Transfer credits accepted: Yes.

Costs Per Year: Application fee: $0. Area resident tuition: $2130 full-time, $71 per credit hour part-time. State resident tuition: $2340 full-time, $78 per credit hour part-time. Nonresident tuition: $2520 full-time, $84 per credit hour part-time. Mandatory fees: $960 full-time, $25 per credit hour part-time. Full-time tuition and fees vary according to course level, course load, location, program, reciprocity agreements, and student level. Part-time tuition and fees vary according to course level, course load, location, program, reciprocity agreements, and student level. College room and board: $5800. Room and board charges vary according to board plan and housing facility.

Collegiate Environment: Orientation program. Drama-theater group, choral group, student-run newspaper, radio station. Social organizations: Phi Theta Kappa Honor Society. Student services: health clinic. Campus security: 24-hour emergency response devices. Cloud County Community College Library. Books: 16,807 (physical), 9,784 (digital/electronic); Databases: 45. Weekly public service hours: 40. 250 computers available on campus for general student use. A campuswide network can be accessed from student residence rooms and from off campus. Students can access the following: online class registration. Staffed computer lab on campus provides training in use of computers, software, and the Internet.

Community Environment: Located in the Republican River Valley, Concordia is a central shopping, industrial and medical district for the citizens of North Central Kansas. The city of approximately 7,000 is home to

St. Joseph Hospital, which is operated by the Sisters of St. Joseph. The city features a large municipal swimming complex, a vigorous summer recreational program, tennis courts and spacious parks. Concordia hosts the annual North Central Kansas Rodeo and the annual Fall Fest Celebration, and is the home of the Cloud County Fair. The Brown Grand Theater, which is on the National Register of Historic Sites, features many cultural events throughout the year.

■ **COFFEYVILLE COMMUNITY COLLEGE**
400 W 11th St.
Coffeyville, KS 67337-5063
Tel: (620)251-7700; Free: 877-51-RAVEN
Fax: (620)252-7098
E-mail: staciam@coffeyville.edu
Web Site: www.coffeyville.edu
Description: State and locally supported, 2-year, coed. Part of Kansas State Board of Education. Awards certificates, transfer associate, and terminal associate degrees. Founded 1923. Setting: 39-acre small town campus with easy access to Tulsa. Total enrollment: 2,056. Student-undergrad faculty ratio is 22:1. 29% from out-of-state. 31% 25 or older. Core. Calendar: semesters. Academic remediation for entering students, ESL program, services for LD students, advanced placement, self-designed majors, honors program, distance learning, double major, summer session for credit, part-time degree program, adult/continuing education programs, co-op programs and internships.
Entrance Requirements: Open admission. Options: early admission, deferred admission. Required: high school transcript. Entrance: noncompetitive. Application deadline: rolling. Notification: continuous.
Collegiate Environment: Drama-theater group, choral group, marching band. Student services: health clinic, personal-psychological counseling, women's center. Campus security: 24-hour patrols, late night transport-escort service, controlled dormitory access. Russell H. Graham Learning Resource Center plus 1 other.
Community Environment: A town of diversified industries, Coffeyville has churches of many denominations, a hospital and numerous civic, service and social organizations. A municipal airport, railroads and bus lines provide transportation. A significant point of interest is the Dalton Defenders Museum. Coffeyville was once the home of the famous baseball pitcher, Walter Johnson; a memorial to Johnson may be seen in Walter Johnson Park.

■ **COLBY COMMUNITY COLLEGE**
1255 S Range
Colby, KS 67701-4099
Tel: (785)462-3984; Free: 888-634-9350
Fax: (785)462-4600
E-mail: admissions@colbycc.edu
Web Site: www.colbycc.edu
Description: State and locally supported, 2-year, coed. Part of Kansas State Board of Education. Awards certificates, diplomas, transfer associate, and terminal associate degrees. Founded 1964. Setting: 80-acre small town campus. Endowment: $3.4 million. Educational spending for the previous fiscal year: $3780 per student. Total enrollment: 1,451. Faculty: 153 (58 full-time, 95 part-time). Student-undergrad faculty ratio is 11:1. 1,016 applied, 100% were admitted. 3% from top 10% of their high school class, 15% from top quarter, 42% from top half. Full-time: 723 students, 60% women, 40% men. Part-time: 728 students, 69% women, 31% men. Students come from 15 states and territories, 5 other countries, 30% from out-of-state. 0.6% American Indian or Alaska Native, non-Hispanic/Latino; 7% Hispanic/Latino; 7% Black or African American, non-Hispanic/Latino; 2% Asian, non-Hispanic/Latino; 0.5% Native Hawaiian or other Pacific Islander, non-Hispanic/Latino; 5% international. 12% 25 or older, 30% live on campus, 6% transferred in. Core. Calendar: semesters. Academic remediation for entering students, services for LD students, advanced placement, self-designed majors, honors program, distance learning, double major, summer session for credit, part-time degree program, adult/continuing education programs, co-op programs and internships.
Entrance Requirements: Open admission except for animal science, health-related programs. Options: electronic application, early admission, deferred admission. Required: high school transcript, ACT Compass or ACT ASSET. Recommended: SAT or ACT. Required for some: interview. Entrance: noncompetitive. Application deadline: rolling. Notification: continuous. Transfer credits accepted: Yes.
Collegiate Environment: Orientation program. Drama-theater group, choral

group, student-run newspaper, radio station. Social organizations: 16 open to all. Most popular organizations: KSNEA, Physical Therapist Assistants Club, Block and Bridle, SVTA, COPNS. Major annual events: Fall Formal, Spring Formal, End of Year Event. Student services: health clinic, personal-psychological counseling. Campus security: 24-hour emergency response devices and patrols. Davis Library. Operations spending for the previous fiscal year: $116,000. 125 computers available on campus for general student use. Computer purchase/lease plans available. A campuswide network can be accessed from student residence rooms and from off campus. Students can access the following: online class registration. Staffed computer lab on campus provides training in use of computers, software, and the Internet.
Community Environment: Colby is in the state's leading wheat-producing area, the northwest corner of the state. Population 5,030. Community facilities include a fine hospital, library and churches of most faiths. Job opportunities are open with the city and community providing employment for students wherever possible.

■ **COWLEY COUNTY COMMUNITY COLLEGE AND AREA VOCATIONAL-TECHNICAL SCHOOL**
125 S Second
Arkansas City, KS 67005-1147
Tel: (620)442-0430; Free: 800-593-CCCC
Fax: (620)441-5350
E-mail: admissions@cowley.edu
Web Site: www.cowley.edu
Description: State and locally supported, 2-year, coed. Part of Kansas State Board of Education. Awards certificates, diplomas, transfer associate, and terminal associate degrees. Founded 1922. Setting: 19-acre small town campus. Endowment: $4.7 million. Educational spending for the previous fiscal year: $1173 per student. Total enrollment: 4,328. Faculty: 253 (48 full-time, 205 part-time). Student-undergrad faculty ratio is 26:1. 1,010 applied, 100% were admitted. 6% from top 10% of their high school class, 23% from top quarter, 50% from top half. 13 valedictorians. Full-time: 2,328 students, 59% women, 41% men. Part-time: 2,000 students, 65% women, 35% men. 10% from out-of-state. 13% 25 or older, 12% live on campus. Retention: 58% of full-time freshmen returned the following year. Core. Calendar: semesters. Academic remediation for entering students, services for LD students, advanced placement, accelerated degree program, independent study, distance learning, summer session for credit, part-time degree program, external degree program, adult/continuing education programs, co-op programs. Off campus study.
Entrance Requirements: Open admission. Options: electronic application, early admission. Required: high school transcript. Recommended: ACT. Entrance: noncompetitive. Application deadline: rolling. Notification: continuous. Transfer credits accepted: Yes.
Collegiate Environment: Orientation program. Drama-theater group, choral group, student-run newspaper. Social organizations: 25 open to all. Most popular organizations: Cowley Activity Awareness Team (CAAT), Academic Civic Engagement through Service (ACES), Phi Theta Kappa, Cowley College Student Senate, Creative Claws. Major annual events: Mr. Cinderfella, Spring Break Awareness Week, Homecoming. Student services: health clinic, personal-psychological counseling. Campus security: 24-hour emergency response devices and patrols, student patrols, late night transport-escort service, controlled dormitory access, residence hall entrances are locked at night. Renn Memorial Library. Operations spending for the previous fiscal year: $162,117. 100 computers available on campus for general student use. A campuswide network can be accessed from student residence rooms and from off campus. Students can access the following: online class registration. Staffed computer lab on campus provides training in use of computers, software, and the Internet.

■ **DODGE CITY COMMUNITY COLLEGE**
2501 N 14th Ave.
Dodge City, KS 67801-2399
Tel: (620)225-1321
Fax: (620)225-0918
Web Site: www.dc3.edu
Description: State and locally supported, 2-year, coed. Part of Kansas State Board of Regents. Awards certificates, transfer associate, and terminal associate degrees. Founded 1935. Setting: 143-acre small town campus. Total enrollment: 1,804. Faculty: 195 (52 full-time, 143 part-time). Student-undergrad faculty ratio is 12:1. 1% American Indian or Alaska Native, non-Hispanic/Latino; 40% Hispanic/Latino; 9% Black or African American, non-Hispanic/Latino; 1% Asian, non-Hispanic/Latino; 0.2% Native Hawaiian or

other Pacific Islander, non-Hispanic/Latino. Core. Calendar: semesters. Academic remediation for entering students, ESL program, services for LD students, advanced placement, distance learning, summer session for credit, part-time degree program, external degree program, adult/continuing education programs, co-op programs and internships. Off campus study.

Entrance Requirements: Open admission. Options: electronic application, early admission, deferred admission, international baccalaureate accepted. Required: high school transcript. Entrance: noncompetitive. Application deadline: rolling. Notification: continuous, Transfer credits accepted: Yes.

Costs Per Year: Application fee: $0. Area resident tuition: $930 full-time, $31 per credit hour part-time. State resident tuition: $1470 full-time, $49 per credit hour part-time. Nonresident tuition: $1770 full-time, $59 per credit hour part-time. Mandatory fees: $1670 full-time, $52 per credit hour part-time, $30 per term part-time. College room and board: $6650. Room and board charges vary according to board plan and housing facility.

Collegiate Environment: Choral group, student-run radio station. Major annual events: Homecoming, Spring Fling, Multicultural Day. Student services: personal-psychological counseling. Campus security: 24-hour emergency response devices and patrols, late night transport-escort service, controlled dormitory access. Learning Resource Center. Students can reserve study rooms. 125 computers available on campus for general student use. A campuswide network can be accessed from student residence rooms. Students can access the following: online class registration. Staffed computer lab on campus provides training in use of computers, software, and the Internet.

Community Environment: Dodge City serves as a supply and trade center for a large agricultural area. It is located on the plains of western Kansas. All modes of transportation are accessible. Community facilities include a library, hospitals, churches of all major denominations, community concert association, and many fraternal, civic and veteran's organizations. Sports include golf, bowling, fishing, hunting and boating. Points of interest are Boot Hill, Fort Dodge and Point Rocks. Special events are Dodge City Days rodeo and the Square Dance Festival.

■ DONNELLY COLLEGE
608 N 18th St.
Kansas City, KS 66102-4298
Tel: (913)621-8700
Fax: (913)621-0354
E-mail: admissions@donnelly.edu
Web Site: www.donnelly.edu

Description: Independent Roman Catholic, primarily 2-year, coed. Awards certificates, transfer associate, terminal associate, and bachelor's degrees. Founded 1949. Setting: 4-acre urban campus. Total enrollment: 294. Student-undergrad faculty ratio is 11:1. 349 applied, 100% were admitted. Full-time: 179 students, 80% women, 20% men. Part-time: 115 students, 65% women, 35% men. Students come from 2 states and territories, 24 other countries, 31% from out-of-state. 2% American Indian or Alaska Native, non-Hispanic/Latino; 39% Hispanic/Latino; 33% Black or African American, non-Hispanic/Latino; 6% Asian, non-Hispanic/Latino; 0.7% Native Hawaiian or other Pacific Islander, non-Hispanic/Latino; 1% international. 44% 25 or older, 16% transferred in. Retention: 55% of full-time freshmen returned the following year. Academic areas with the most degrees conferred: business/marketing; education; computer and information sciences. Core. Calendar: semesters. Academic remediation for entering students, ESL program, services for LD students, advanced placement, honors program, independent study, distance learning, summer session for credit, part-time degree program, external degree program.

Entrance Requirements: Open admission. Options: electronic application, early admission, deferred admission, international baccalaureate accepted. Recommended: high school transcript. Entrance: noncompetitive. Application deadline: rolling. Transfer credits accepted: Yes.

Costs Per Year: Application fee: $0. Tuition: $7080 full-time, $295 per credit hour part-time. Mandatory fees: $180 full-time, $5 per credit hour part-time, $30 per term part-time. Full-time tuition and fees vary according to course load, degree level, and program. Part-time tuition and fees vary according to course load, degree level, and program.

Collegiate Environment: Orientation program. Most popular organizations: Organization of Student Leadership, Student Ambassadors, Healthy Student Task Force, Men's Soccer Club, Women's Soccer Club. Major annual events: Convocation Day, Thanks and Giving Celebration, Multicultural Festival. Student services: personal-psychological counseling. Campus security: 24-hour emergency response devices. Trant Memorial Library plus 1 other.

■ EMPORIA STATE UNIVERSITY
1 Kellogg Cir.
Emporia, KS 66801-5415
Tel: (620)341-1200; Free: 877-468-6378
E-mail: go2esu@emporia.edu
Web Site: www.emporia.edu

Description: State-supported, comprehensive, coed. Part of Kansas State Board of Regents. Awards bachelor's, master's, and doctoral degrees and post-master's certificates. Founded 1863. Setting: 207-acre small town campus with easy access to Wichita. Endowment: $74.4 million. Research spending for the previous fiscal year: $441,227. Educational spending for the previous fiscal year: $3216 per student. Total enrollment: 5,732. Faculty: 278 (247 full-time, 31 part-time). Student-undergrad faculty ratio is 17:1. 1,693 applied, 83% were admitted. 14% from top 10% of their high school class, 38% from top quarter, 73% from top half. Full-time: 3,340 students, 62% women, 38% men. Part-time: 265 students, 62% women, 38% men. Students come from 20 states and territories, 50 other countries, 10% from out-of-state. 0.4% American Indian or Alaska Native, non-Hispanic/Latino; 7% Hispanic/Latino; 5% Black or African American, non-Hispanic/Latino; 0.9% Asian, non-Hispanic/Latino; 0.1% Native Hawaiian or other Pacific Islander, non-Hispanic/Latino; 7% international. 1% 25 or older, 17% live on campus, 10% transferred in. Retention: 73% of full-time freshmen returned the following year. Academic areas with the most degrees conferred: education; business/marketing; health professions and related sciences. Core. Calendar: semesters. Academic remediation for entering students, ESL program, services for LD students, advanced placement, accelerated degree program, freshman honors college, honors program, independent study, distance learning, double major, summer session for credit, part-time degree program, adult/continuing education programs, co-op programs and internships, graduate courses open to undergrads. Off campus study. Study abroad program.

Entrance Requirements: Options: electronic application, early admission, deferred admission. Required: high school transcript, minimum ACT score of 21, or rank in the top 1/3 and completed QA core classes with cum 2.0 GPA, 22 Math subscore, or completed 4th year of math, SAT or ACT. Recommended: minimum 2 high school GPA. Entrance: noncompetitive. Application deadline: rolling. Notification: continuous. SAT Reasoning Test deadline: 12/15. Transfer credits accepted: Yes.

Costs Per Year: Application fee: $30. State resident tuition: $5,154 full-time, $171.81 per credit hour part-time. Nonresident tuition: $19,071 full-time, $635.69 per credit hour part-time. Mandatory fees: $1,604 full-time, $88.98 per credit hour part-time. Full-time tuition and fees vary according to course load, degree level, and location. Part-time tuition and fees vary according to course load, degree level, and location. College room and board: $8912. College room only: $5280. Room and board charges vary according to board plan, housing facility, and location.

Collegiate Environment: Orientation program. Drama-theater group, choral group, marching band, student-run newspaper, radio station. Social organizations: 125 open to all; national fraternities, national sororities; 11% of eligible men and 10% of eligible women are members. Most popular organizations: Phi Eta Sigma, Student Chapter of the American Library Association of ESU, TradPlus Student Organization, Arabic Culture Student Organization, Emporia Kansas Association of Nursing Students. Major annual events: Homecoming, Flintstock, Family Day. Student services: legal services, health clinic, personal-psychological counseling, women's center. Campus security: 24-hour emergency response devices and patrols, student patrols, late night transport-escort service, controlled dormitory access, 24-hour residence hall monitoring, safety and self-awareness programs. William Allen White Library plus 1 other. Books: 389,595 (physical), 153,016 (digital/electronic); Serial titles: 35,153 (physical), 278 (digital/electronic); Databases: 97. Weekly public service hours: 79; study areas open 24 hours, 5-7 days a week; students can reserve study rooms. Operations spending for the previous fiscal year: $1.7 million. 410 computers available on campus for general student use. A campuswide network can be accessed from student residence rooms and from off campus. Students can access the following: online class registration. Staffed computer lab on campus provides training in use of computers, software, and the Internet.

Community Environment: Emporia, close to the nation's geographical center, is an industrial city as well as a "university town." From this agricultural area more than 100,000 cattle are sent to market each year. The community facilities include a hospital, libraries, an auditorium and many civic, social and veteran's organizations. All forms of commercial transportation are available. Parks, golf courses, a skating rink, tennis courts, ball fields, bowling alley, and swimming pools are some of the facilities for recreation.

■ FLINT HILLS TECHNICAL COLLEGE
3301 W 18th Ave.
Emporia, KS 66801
Tel: (620)343-4600; Free: 800-711-6947
Web Site: www.fhtc.edu
Description: State-supported, 2-year, coed. Awards certificates and terminal associate degrees. Founded 1963. Total enrollment: 481. Faculty: 72 (27 full-time, 45 part-time). Student-undergrad faculty ratio is 15:1. Full-time: 259 students, 54% women, 46% men. Part-time: 222 students, 46% women, 54% men. 39% from out-of-state. Retention: 88% of full-time freshmen returned the following year. Calendar: semesters.
Entrance Requirements: Required: high school transcript, SAT or ACT. Recommended: interview. Entrance: noncompetitive.
Collegiate Environment: Orientation program. 86 computers available on campus for general student use. A campuswide network can be accessed from off-campus. Staffed computer lab on campus provides training in use of computers, software, and the Internet.

■ FORT HAYS STATE UNIVERSITY
600 Park St.
Hays, KS 67601-4099
Tel: (785)628-4000; Free: 800-628-FHSU
Fax: (785)628-4014
E-mail: tcline@fhsu.edu
Web Site: www.fhsu.edu
Description: State-supported, comprehensive, coed. Awards associate, bachelor's, and master's degrees and post-master's certificates. Founded 1902. Setting: 200-acre small town campus. Total enrollment: 14,210. Faculty: 544 (315 full-time, 229 part-time). Student-undergrad faculty ratio is 16:1. 13% from top 10% of their high school class, 32% from top quarter, 64% from top half. Full-time: 5,705 students, 59% women, 41% men. Part-time: 6,126 students, 63% women, 37% men. 31% from out-of-state. 0.4% American Indian or Alaska Native, non-Hispanic/Latino; 7% Hispanic/Latino; 4% Black or African American, non-Hispanic/Latino; 1% Asian, non-Hispanic/Latino; 0.1% Native Hawaiian or other Pacific Islander, non-Hispanic/Latino; 29% international. 32% 25 or older, 11% live on campus, 20% transferred in. Retention: 69% of full-time freshmen returned the following year. Academic areas with the most degrees conferred: business/marketing; education; liberal arts/general studies. Core. Calendar: semesters. Academic remediation for entering students, ESL program, self-designed majors, honors program, independent study, distance learning, double major, part-time degree program, internships. Study abroad program.
Entrance Requirements: Required: high school transcript. Required for some: SAT or ACT.
Collegiate Environment: Orientation program. Drama-theater group, choral group, marching band, student-run newspaper, radio station. Social organizations: 125 open to all. Most popular organizations: Students for Life, Honors Society, Panhellenic Council, Residents Hall Association, Catholic Disciples. Student services: health clinic. Campus security: 24-hour emergency response devices and patrols. Forsyth Library.
Community Environment: Fort Hays, a military post on the old frontier, gave this railroad town its name of Hays. Known as an agricultural, educational, and regional medical center Hays has vast interests in oil and livestock as well. Ellis county, the county in which Hays is located, is the largest oil producing county in the State of Kansas. Fort Hays Experiment Station, one of the largest dryland experiment stations in the world, is located here.

■ FORT SCOTT COMMUNITY COLLEGE
2108 S Horton
Fort Scott, KS 66701
Tel: (316)223-2700; Free: 800-874-3722
Fax: (316)223-4927
Web Site: www.fortscott.edu
Description: State and locally supported, 2-year, coed. Awards certificates, transfer associate, and terminal associate degrees. Founded 1919. Setting: 147-acre small town campus. Total enrollment: 1,696. 25% 25 or older. Core. Calendar: semesters. Academic remediation for entering students, ESL program, services for LD students, advanced placement, self-designed majors, independent study, distance learning, summer session for credit,

part-time degree program, external degree program, adult/continuing education programs, co-op programs and internships. Study abroad program. ROTC: Army (c).
Entrance Requirements: Open admission. Options: early admission, deferred admission. Entrance: minimally difficult. Application deadline: 8/15.
Collegiate Environment: Orientation program. Drama-theater group, choral group, marching band. Student services: personal-psychological counseling. Campus security: controlled dormitory access, evening security from 9 pm to 6 am. Learning Resource Center.
Community Environment: FSCC is located in Fort Scott, Kansas, a thriving agricultural-industrial town at the intersection of U.S. highways 69 and 54 in southeast Kansas. About 9,000 persons live in Fort Scott and an additional 6,000 live in the surrounding Bourbon County area. Fort Scott citizens continue to value their historic background, dating from the time the town was established as a military outpost in 1842. The original army post on the Indian frontier, restored and operated by the National Park Service as the Fort Scott National Historic Site, draws thousands of tourists annually. The city is served by major highways and bus lines and has a municipal airport. Superb medical facilities, including a 164-bed hospital, provide medical services for much of southeast Kansas. Numerous cultural opportunities include an active arts council and civic symphony. Outstanding community recreational programs and facilities, 180 acres of parks and several area lakes enhance the college experience for FSCC students.

■ FRIENDS UNIVERSITY
2100 W University Ave.
Wichita, KS 67213
Tel: (316)295-5000; Free: 800-794-6945
Fax: (316)262-5027
E-mail: learn@friends.edu
Web Site: www.friends.edu
Description: Independent, comprehensive, coed, affiliated with Christian non-denominational. Awards bachelor's and master's degrees. Founded 1898. Setting: 55-acre urban campus. Endowment: $49.1 million. Educational spending for the previous fiscal year: $5835 per student. Total enrollment: 1,698. Faculty: 282 (61 full-time, 221 part-time). Student-undergrad faculty ratio is 10:1. 881 applied, 48% were admitted. 22% from top 10% of their high school class, 48% from top quarter, 80% from top half. Full-time: 906 students, 54% women, 46% men. Part-time: 240 students, 64% women, 36% men. Students come from 38 states and territories, 15 other countries, 20% from out-of-state. 2% American Indian or Alaska Native, non-Hispanic/Latino; 11% Hispanic/Latino; 9% Black or African American, non-Hispanic/Latino; 0.9% Asian, non-Hispanic/Latino; 0.2% Native Hawaiian or other Pacific Islander, non-Hispanic/Latino. 34% 25 or older, 25% live on campus, 16% transferred in. Retention: 74% of full-time freshmen returned the following year. Academic areas with the most degrees conferred: business/marketing; biological/life sciences; computer and information sciences. Core. Calendar: semesters. Academic remediation for entering students, services for LD students, advanced placement, accelerated degree program, self-designed majors, honors program, independent study, distance learning, double major, summer session for credit, part-time degree program, adult/continuing education programs, co-op programs and internships, graduate courses open to undergrads. Off campus study at Friends University students at Newman University, Wichita, Kansas on a space-available basis. The courses are counted as resident credit at Friends University. Most courses are available on both campuses to all students without separate registrations or added costs. The student exchange program is designed to enrich the educational opportunities of Friends and Newman students. Study abroad program.
Entrance Requirements: Options: electronic application, international baccalaureate accepted. Recommended: ACT, SAT and SAT Subject Tests or ACT. Required for some: high school transcript, minimum 2 high school GPA, interview, audition for music, dance and theater programs; portfolio for art program, SAT or ACT. Entrance: moderately difficult. Application deadline: rolling. Notification: continuous. SAT Reasoning Test deadline: 9/30. SAT Subject Test deadline: 9/30. Transfer credits accepted: Yes.
Costs Per Year: Application fee: $0. Comprehensive fee: $36,387 includes full-time tuition ($27,965), mandatory fees ($450), and college room and board ($7972). College room only: $3800. Full-time tuition and fees vary according to class time, course load, degree level, and location. Room and board charges vary according to board plan and housing facility. Part-time tuition: $932 per credit hour. Part-time tuition varies according to class time, course load, degree level, and location.
Collegiate Environment: Orientation program. Drama-theater group, choral

group. Social organizations: 24 open to all. Most popular organizations: Concert Choir, Singing Quakers, Zoo Science Club, Psychology Club, Spanish Club. Major annual events: Late Night Breakfast, Homecoming Week, Cherry Carnival Week. Student services: health clinic, personal-psychological counseling. Campus security: 24-hour emergency response devices and patrols, late night transport-escort service, controlled dormitory access. Edmund Stanley Library plus 1 other. Books: 88,223 (physical), 141,741 (digital/electronic); Serial titles: 202 (physical); Databases: 102. Operations spending for the previous fiscal year: $443,199. 360 computers available on campus for general student use. A campuswide network can be accessed from student residence rooms and from off campus. Students can access the following: online class registration. Staffed computer lab on campus provides training in use of computers, software, and the Internet.

■ GARDEN CITY COMMUNITY COLLEGE

801 Campus Dr.
Garden City, KS 67846-6399
Tel: (316)276-7611; Free: 800-658-1696
E-mail: admissions@gcccks.edu
Web Site: www.gcccks.edu

Description: County-supported, 2-year, coed. Part of Kansas Board of Regents. Awards certificates, transfer associate, and terminal associate degrees. Founded 1919. Setting: 63-acre rural campus. Endowment: $5.9 million. Total enrollment: 1,997. Faculty: (62 full-time). 558 applied, 100% were admitted. 3% from top 10% of their high school class, 18% from top quarter, 46% from top half. Full-time: 1,069 students, 49% women, 51% men. Part-time: 928 students, 60% women, 40% men. Students come from 5 other countries, 17% from out-of-state. 0.8% American Indian or Alaska Native, non-Hispanic/Latino; 39% Hispanic/Latino; 7% Black or African American, non-Hispanic/Latino; 3% Asian, non-Hispanic/Latino; 0.1% Native Hawaiian or other Pacific Islander, non-Hispanic/Latino; 0.4% international. 20% 25 or older, 3% transferred in. Core: Calendar: semesters. Academic remediation for entering students, ESL program, services for LD students, advanced placement, self-designed majors, distance learning, summer session for credit, part-time degree program, external degree program, adult/continuing education programs.

Entrance Requirements: Open admission except for transfer students. Required: high school transcript, ACT Compass. Recommended: ACT. Entrance: noncompetitive. Application deadline: rolling. Transfer credits accepted: Yes.

Collegiate Environment: Orientation program. Drama-theater group, choral group, student-run newspaper. Social organizations: 19 open to all. Most popular organizations: HALO (Hispanic Student Leadership Organization), GC3 Media, Criminal Justice/Tau Epsilon Lambda, SGA (Student Government Association), PTK (Phi Theta Kappa). Major annual events: HALO/SSS Campus Fiesta, SGA Casino Night, Constitution Day Demonstration. Student services: health clinic, personal-psychological counseling. Campus security: 24-hour emergency response devices and patrols, student patrols, late night transport-escort service, controlled dormitory access. Saffell Library. 400 computers available on campus for general student use. A campuswide network can be accessed from student residence rooms. Students can access the following: online class registration. Staffed computer lab on campus provides training in use of software.

Community Environment: Garden City is on the Arkansas River in a fertile agricultural area. Predominant crops are corn, alfalfa, wheat and grain sorgums, with beef cattle production very strong. Shopping facilities are good. Finnup Park, a large recreational development, contains a swimming pool, picnic sites, museum and zoo. Other facilities for recreation are golf courses and local parks. One of the largest buffalo herds is located at Garden City on the Buffalo Preserve. All forms of commercial transportation are available.

■ GRANTHAM UNIVERSITY

16025 W 113th St.
Lenexa, KS 66219
Free: 800-955-2527
Fax: (816)595-5757
E-mail: admissions@grantham.edu
Web Site: www.grantham.edu

Description: Proprietary, comprehensive, coed. Awards associate, bachelor's, and master's degrees (offers only external degree programs). Founded 1951. Setting: urban campus with easy access to Kansas City. Total enrollment: 9,463. Faculty: 10 (all full-time). Student-undergrad faculty ratio is 17:1. Core. Calendar: continuous. Academic remediation for entering

students, advanced placement, accelerated degree program, self-designed majors, independent study, distance learning, part-time degree program, external degree program, adult/continuing education programs.

Entrance Requirements: Open admission. Options: electronic application, international baccalaureate accepted. Entrance: noncompetitive. Application deadline: rolling. Notification: continuous. Transfer credits accepted: Yes.

Collegiate Environment: Orientation program. Grantham Online Library. Operations spending for the previous fiscal year: $106,602.

■ HASKELL INDIAN NATIONS UNIVERSITY

155 Indian Ave., No.5031
Lawrence, KS 66046-4800
Tel: (785)749-8404
Fax: (785)749-8429
Web Site: www.haskell.edu

Description: Federally supported, 4-year, coed. Awards associate and bachelor's degrees. Founded 1884. Setting: 320-acre suburban campus. Total enrollment: 894. 544 applied. 24% 25 or older. Core. Calendar: semesters. Academic remediation for entering students, services for LD students, advanced placement, self-designed majors, independent study, distance learning, summer session for credit, part-time degree program, internships. Off campus study at members of the American Indian Higher Education Consortium, Kansas City Regional Council for Higher Education, University of Kansas. ROTC: Air Force (c).

Entrance Requirements: Option: electronic application. Required: high school transcript, minimum 2.0 high school GPA, ACT. Required for some: 2 recommendations. Entrance: minimally difficult. Application deadline: 7/30. Notification: continuous. Preference given to applicants with at least one-fourth Native American ancestry or tribal membership.

Collegiate Environment: Orientation program. Drama-theater group, student-run newspaper. Student services: health clinic, personal-psychological counseling. Campus security: night patrol only.

Community Environment: See University of Kansas.

■ HESSTON COLLEGE

Box 3000
Hesston, KS 67062-2093
Tel: (620)327-4221; Free: 800-995-2757
Fax: (620)327-8300
E-mail: admissions@hesston.edu
Web Site: www.hesston.edu

Description: Independent Mennonite, primarily 2-year, coed. Awards transfer associate, terminal associate, and bachelor's degrees. Founded 1909. Setting: 50-acre small town campus with easy access to Wichita. Endowment: $12.9 million. Educational spending for the previous fiscal year: $9905 per student. Total enrollment: 442. Faculty: 53 (38 full-time, 15 part-time). Student-undergrad faculty ratio is 8:1. 562 applied, 56% were admitted. Full-time: 403 students, 59% women, 41% men. Part-time: 39 students, 62% women, 38% men. Students come from 29 states and territories, 15 other countries, 43% from out-of-state. 0.2% American Indian or Alaska Native, non-Hispanic/Latino; 12% Hispanic/Latino; 5% Black or African American, non-Hispanic/Latino; 2% Asian, non-Hispanic/Latino; 13% international. 16% 25 or older, 69% live on campus, 8% transferred in. Retention: 77% of full-time freshmen returned the following year. Academic area with the most degrees conferred: health professions and related sciences. Core. Calendar: semesters. Academic remediation for entering students, ESL program, services for LD students, advanced placement, independent study, double major, summer session for credit, part-time degree program, adult/continuing education programs, co-op programs and internships.

Entrance Requirements: Open admission except for nursing programs. Options: electronic application, early admission, deferred admission. Required: high school transcript, SAT or ACT. Required for some: 2 recommendations, interview. Entrance: noncompetitive. Application deadline: rolling. Transfer credits accepted: Yes.

Costs Per Year: Application fee: $0. Comprehensive fee: $35,700 includes full-time tuition ($26,460), mandatory fees ($440), and college room and board ($8800). Full-time tuition and fees vary according to course load and program. Part-time tuition: $1102 per credit hour. Part-time mandatory fees: $110 per term. Part-time tuition and fees vary according to course load.

Collegiate Environment: Orientation program. Drama-theater group, choral group, student-run newspaper. Most popular organizations: Peace and Service Club, Intramural Sports, Ministry Assistants. Major annual events: Commencement, Feast of Carols, Mod Olympics. Student services:

personal-psychological counseling. Campus security: 24-hour emergency response devices, controlled dormitory access. Mary Miller Library. Students can reserve study rooms. Operations spending for the previous fiscal year: $147,685. 115 computers available on campus for general student use. A campuswide network can be accessed from student residence rooms and from off campus. Students can access the following: online class registration. Staffed computer lab on campus provides training in use of computers, software, and the Internet.

Community Environment: Hesston is a small, progressive, south central Kansas town with a population of 3,600. It is located 35 miles north of Wichita, and has ready access to air, rail, and bus transportation. Part-time employment for students is available in the area and is coordinated through the Cooperative Education office on campus. A temperate climate allows considerable outside activity. Recreational facilities located in or near Hesston include an 18-hole golf course, bike trails, tennis courts, year-round swimming pool, and numerous county and state parks and lakes.

■ HIGHLAND COMMUNITY COLLEGE
606 W Main St.
Highland, KS 66035
Tel: (785)442-6000
Fax: (785)442-6100
Web Site: www.highlandcc.edu

Description: State and locally supported, 2-year, coed. Part of Kansas Community College System. Awards certificates, transfer associate, and terminal associate degrees. Founded 1858. Setting: 20-acre rural campus. Total enrollment: 2,810. 21% 25 or older. Core. Calendar: semesters. Academic remediation for entering students, services for LD students, advanced placement, self-designed majors, summer session for credit, part-time degree program, adult/continuing education programs, co-op programs and internships. Off campus study. ROTC: Army (c).

Entrance Requirements: Open admission for state residents. Option: early admission. Required: high school transcript. Entrance: minimally difficult. Application deadline: 8/20. Notification: continuous. Preference given to state residents.

Collegiate Environment: Drama-theater group, student-run newspaper.

■ HUTCHINSON COMMUNITY COLLEGE
1300 N Plum St.
Hutchinson, KS 67501-5894
Tel: (620)665-3500; Free: 888-GO-HUTCH
Fax: (620)665-3310
E-mail: strobelc@hutchcc.edu
Web Site: www.hutchcc.edu

Description: State and locally supported, 2-year, coed. Part of Kansas Board of Regents. Awards certificates, transfer associate, and terminal associate degrees. Founded 1928. Setting: 47-acre small town campus with easy access to Wichita. Total enrollment: 5,574. Faculty: 318 (109 full-time, 209 part-time). Student-undergrad faculty ratio is 18:1. 2,452 applied, 100% were admitted. Full-time: 2,055 students, 51% women, 49% men. Part-time: 3,519 students, 57% women, 43% men. Students come from 43 states and territories, 10 other countries, 8% from out-of-state. 1% American Indian or Alaska Native, non-Hispanic/Latino; 12% Hispanic/Latino; 6% Black or African American, non-Hispanic/Latino; 0.7% Asian, non-Hispanic/Latino; 0.1% Native Hawaiian or other Pacific Islander, non-Hispanic/Latino; 0.6% international. 25% 25 or older, 10% live on campus, 8% transferred in. Core. Calendar: semesters. Academic remediation for entering students, ESL program, services for LD students, advanced placement, honors program, independent study, distance learning, double major, summer session for credit, part-time degree program, co-op programs and internships.

Entrance Requirements: Open admission. Options: electronic application, early admission, deferred admission, international baccalaureate accepted. Required: high school transcript. Required for some: interview. Entrance: noncompetitive. Application deadline: rolling. Notification: continuous. Transfer credits accepted: Yes.

Costs Per Year: Application fee: $0. Area resident tuition: $2592 full-time, $81 per credit hour part-time. State resident tuition: $2912 full-time, $91 per credit hour part-time. Nonresident tuition: $3904 full-time, $122 per credit hour part-time. Mandatory fees: $736 full-time, $23 per credit hour part-time. College room and board: $6000.

Collegiate Environment: Drama-theater group, choral group, student-run newspaper. Social organizations: 50 open to all. Most popular organizations: CKI (Circle K), Honors Club, DragonLAN (Computer/technology club), HutchCC Bigs (Big Brothres/Big Sisters), Collegiate 4-H. Major annual events: Fall & Spring Homecoming, Spring Fling, HutchCC Career Fair. Student services: health clinic, personal-psychological counseling. Campus security: 24-hour emergency response devices and patrols, late night transport-escort service, controlled dormitory access. 530 college housing spaces available; all were occupied in 2018-19. No special consideration for freshman housing applicants. Options: men-only, women-only housing available. John F. Kennedy Library plus 1 other. Books: 33,604 (physical), 14,281 (digital/electronic); Serial titles: 101 (physical); Databases: 98. Weekly public service hours: 65. 500 computers available on campus for general student use. A campuswide network can be accessed from student residence rooms and from off campus. Students can access the following: online class registration. Staffed computer lab on campus provides training in use of computers, software, and the Internet.

■ INDEPENDENCE COMMUNITY COLLEGE
1057 W College Ave.
Independence, KS 67301-0708
Tel: (620)331-4100; Free: 800-842-6063
Fax: (620)331-5344
E-mail: bthornton@indycc.edu
Web Site: www.indycc.edu

Description: State-supported, 2-year, coed. Part of Kansas Board of Regents. Awards certificates, transfer associate, and terminal associate degrees. Founded 1925. Setting: 68-acre rural campus. Educational spending for the previous fiscal year: $1742 per student. Total enrollment: 897. Faculty: 94 (36 full-time, 58 part-time). Student-undergrad faculty ratio is 12:1. Full-time: 510 students, 43% women, 57% men. Part-time: 387 students, 63% women, 37% men. Students come from 31 states and territories, 6 other countries, 44% from out-of-state. 2% American Indian or Alaska Native, non-Hispanic/Latino; 5% Hispanic/Latino; 16% Black or African American, non-Hispanic/Latino; 0.6% Asian, non-Hispanic/Latino; 0.6% Native Hawaiian or other Pacific Islander, non-Hispanic/Latino; 2% international. 17% 25 or older, 3% transferred in. Retention: 39% of full-time freshmen returned the following year. Core. Calendar: semesters. Academic remediation for entering students, ESL program, services for LD students, advanced placement, independent study, distance learning, summer session for credit, part-time degree program, external degree program, co-op programs.

Entrance Requirements: Required: high school transcript. Required for some: essay, minimum 2.5 high school GPA, 2 recommendations, interview.

Collegiate Environment: Drama-theater group, choral group, marching band. Social organizations: 8 open to all. Most popular organizations: Phi Theta Kappa, Ambassadors, International Student Organization. Major annual events: Homecoming, International Flag Ceremony. Campus security: controlled dormitory access, night patrol. Independence Community College Library plus 1 other. Operations spending for the previous fiscal year: $122,341.

Community Environment: Independence, is in a predominately agricultural region that also produces oil. The community includes a number of churches, a hospital and numerous civic, fraternal and veteran's organizations. An airport is within a ten-minute drive. Montgomery County State Lake and the Elk City Reservoir provide facilities for all water sports. Other recreational activities are golf, tennis and bowling.

■ JOHNSON COUNTY COMMUNITY COLLEGE
12345 College Blvd.
Overland Park, KS 66210-1299
Tel: (913)469-8500
Web Site: www.jccc.edu

Description: State and locally supported, 2-year, coed. Part of Kansas State Board of Education. Awards certificates, transfer associate, and terminal associate degrees. Founded 1967. Setting: 220-acre suburban campus with easy access to Kansas City. Endowment: $20 million. Total enrollment: 19,139. Faculty: 871 (310 full-time, 561 part-time). Student-undergrad faculty ratio is 20:1. Full-time: 6,059 students, 50% women, 50% men. Part-time: 13,051 students, 54% women, 46% men. Students come from 40 states and territories, 88 other countries, 9% from out-of-state. 0.6% American Indian or Alaska Native, non-Hispanic/Latino; 9% Hispanic/Latino; 6% Black or African American, non-Hispanic/Latino; 4% Asian, non-Hispanic/Latino; 0.2% Native Hawaiian or other Pacific Islander, non-Hispanic/Latino; 3% international. 37% 25 or older, 5% transferred in. Retention: 64% of full-time freshmen returned the following year. Core. Calendar: semesters. Academic remediation for entering students, ESL program, services for LD students, advanced placement, self-designed majors, honors program, independent study, distance learning, double major, summer session for credit, part-time degree program, adult/continuing education programs, co-op programs and internships. Off campus study. Study abroad program.

Entrance Requirements: Open admission except for nursing, dental hygiene, paralegal, respiratory care, interpreter training, emergency medical technology programs. Options: electronic application, early admission, international baccalaureate accepted. Required for some: high school transcript. Entrance: noncompetitive. Application deadline: rolling. Notification: continuous. Transfer credits accepted: Yes.

Costs Per Year: Application fee: $0. Area resident tuition: $2310 full-time, $77 per credit hour part-time. State resident tuition: $2820 full-time, $94 per credit hour part-time. Nonresident tuition: $6120 full-time, $204 per credit hour part-time. Mandatory fees: $480 full-time, $16 per credit hour part-time. Full-time tuition and fees vary according to course load and program. Part-time tuition and fees vary according to course load and program.

Collegiate Environment: Orientation program. Drama-theater group, student-run newspaper, radio station. Student services: personal-psychological counseling. Campus security: 24-hour emergency response devices and patrols, late night transport-escort service. Johnson County Community College Library. Books: 75,947 (physical); Databases: 137.

■ KANSAS CITY KANSAS COMMUNITY COLLEGE

7250 State Ave.
Kansas City, KS 66112-3003
Tel: (913)334-1100
Fax: (913)696-9646
E-mail: dmcdowell@kckcc.edu
Web Site: www.kckcc.edu

Description: State and locally supported, 2-year, coed. Awards certificates, diplomas, transfer associate, and terminal associate degrees. Founded 1923. Setting: 148-acre urban campus. Endowment: $1.1 million. Research spending for the previous fiscal year: $200,072. Educational spending for the previous fiscal year: $3920 per student. Total enrollment: 7,555. Faculty: 480 (148 full-time, 332 part-time). Student-undergrad faculty ratio is 17:1. Full-time: 2,903 students, 58% women, 42% men. Part-time: 4,652 students, 67% women, 33% men. Students come from 27 states and territories, 13 other countries, 5% from out-of-state. 0.6% American Indian or Alaska Native, non-Hispanic/Latino; 10% Hispanic/Latino; 29% Black or African American, non-Hispanic/Latino; 2% Asian, non-Hispanic/Latino; 0.2% Native Hawaiian or other Pacific Islander, non-Hispanic/Latino; 2% international. 59% 25 or older, 4% transferred in. Core. Calendar: semesters. Academic remediation for entering students, ESL program, services for LD students, advanced placement, freshman honors college, honors program, independent study, distance learning, summer session for credit, part-time degree program, external degree program, adult/continuing education programs, co-op programs and internships.

Entrance Requirements: Open admission except for nursing program. Options: electronic application, international baccalaureate accepted. Required: high school transcript. Entrance: noncompetitive. Application deadline: rolling. Notification: continuous.

Collegiate Environment: Drama-theater group, choral group, student-run newspaper. Social organizations: 25 open to all. Most popular organizations: Student Senate, Phi Theta Kappa, Drama Club, The African American Student Union, Collegiate Educators Music Club. Major annual events: Last Class Bash, Candle Lighting Program, First Class Bash. Student services: health clinic, personal-psychological counseling, women's center. Campus security: 24-hour emergency response devices and patrols, student patrols, late night transport-escort service. Kansas City Kansas Community College Library plus 1 other. Operations spending for the previous fiscal year: $776,088. 775 computers available on campus for general student use. A campuswide network can be accessed from off-campus. Students can access the following: online class registration. Staffed computer lab on campus.

■ KANSAS STATE UNIVERSITY

Manhattan, KS 66506
Tel: (785)532-6011; Free: 800-432-8270
Fax: (785)532-6393
E-mail: k-state@k-state.edu
Web Site: www.k-state.edu

Description: State-supported, university, coed. Part of Kansas Board of Regents. Awards associate, bachelor's, master's, and doctoral degrees. Founded 1863. Setting: 668-acre suburban campus. Endowment: $506.4 million. Research spending for the previous fiscal year: $157.4 million.

Educational spending for the previous fiscal year: $10,681 per student. Total enrollment: 22,795. Faculty: 1,281 (1,104 full-time, 177 part-time). Student-undergrad faculty ratio is 18:1. 8,310 applied, 95% were admitted. 25% from top 10% of their high school class, 51% from top quarter, 80% from top half. 241 valedictorians. Full-time: 16,770 students, 47% women, 53% men. Part-time: 1,718 students, 52% women, 48% men. Students come from 52 states and territories, 81 other countries, 18% from out-of-state. 0.5% American Indian or Alaska Native, non-Hispanic/Latino; 7% Hispanic/Latino; 3% Black or African American, non-Hispanic/Latino; 1% Asian, non-Hispanic/Latino; 0.1% Native Hawaiian or other Pacific Islander, non-Hispanic/Latino; 5% international. 9% 25 or older, 24% live on campus, 7% transferred in. Retention: 84% of full-time freshmen returned the following year. Academic areas with the most degrees conferred: business/marketing; agriculture; engineering. Core. Calendar: semesters. Academic remediation for entering students, ESL program, services for LD students, advanced placement, accelerated degree program, freshman honors college, honors program, independent study, distance learning, double major, summer session for credit, part-time degree program, adult/continuing education programs, co-op programs and internships, graduate courses open to undergrads. Off campus study at Manhattan Christian College, University of Missouri-Kansas City, 19 Kansas community colleges. Study abroad program. ROTC: Army, Air Force.

Entrance Requirements: Options: electronic application, early admission. Required: high school transcript, minimum 2 high school GPA, minimum ACT composite of 21 or top third of high school graduating class. Recommended: SAT or ACT. Required for some: SAT or ACT. Entrance: minimally difficult. Application deadline: rolling. Notification: continuous. Transfer credits accepted: Yes.

Costs Per Year: Application fee: $40. State resident tuition: $9375 full-time. Nonresident tuition: $24,879 full-time. Mandatory fees: $1008 full-time. Full-time tuition and fees vary according to course level, course load, degree level, location, program, and reciprocity agreements. College room and board: $9680. Room and board charges vary according to board plan, housing facility, and location.

Collegiate Environment: Orientation program. Drama-theater group, choral group, marching band, student-run newspaper, radio station. Social organizations: national fraternities, national sororities. Most popular organizations: athletic department groups, marching band, Union Governing Board, theater productions, debate team. Major annual events: Homecoming, Multicultural Week, open house. Student services: legal services, health clinic, personal-psychological counseling, women's center. Campus security: 24-hour emergency response devices and patrols, late night transport-escort service, controlled dormitory access. Hale Library plus 3 others. Books: 1.3 million (physical), 1.5 million (digital/electronic); Serial titles: 51,881 (physical), 114,285 (digital/electronic); Databases: 278. Weekly public service hours: 80; study areas open 24 hours, 5-7 days a week; students can reserve study rooms. Operations spending for the previous fiscal year: $14.4 million.

Community Environment: Manhattan, a beautiful city, situated on the Blue River and Kansas River, enjoys the excellent recreational facilities of Tuttle Creek Dam. The community offers libraries, churches, hospitals, hotels, motels, rooming houses and four attractive shopping centers including Manhattan Town Center. Numerous civic, service and social organizations exist. Part-time work is available. Historic Fort Riley is eight miles away.

■ KANSAS STATE UNIVERSITY POLYTECHNIC CAMPUS

2310 Centennial Rd.
Salina, KS 67401
Tel: (785)826-2672
Web Site: www.polytechnic.k-state.edu

Description: State-supported, comprehensive, coed. Awards associate, bachelor's, and master's degrees. Total enrollment: 682. Faculty: 43 (all full-time). Student-undergrad faculty ratio is 13:1. Full-time: 470 students, 22% women, 78% men. Part-time: 157 students, 30% women, 70% men. Students come from 22 states and territories. 0.5% American Indian or Alaska Native, non-Hispanic/Latino; 7% Hispanic/Latino; 3% Black or African American, non-Hispanic/Latino; 2% Asian, non-Hispanic/Latino; 0.3% Native Hawaiian or other Pacific Islander, non-Hispanic/Latino; 3% international. 35% 25 or older. Retention: 80% of full-time freshmen returned the following year. Academic areas with the most degrees conferred: transportation and materials moving; business/marketing; engineering technologies. Calendar: semesters. ESL program, independent study, distance learning, double major, co-op programs and internships. Study abroad program. ROTC: Army, Air Force.

Entrance Requirements: Notification: continuous, rolling for early action. SAT Reasoning Test deadline: 8/1.

Costs Per Year: Application fee: $30. State resident tuition: $9506 full-time. Nonresident tuition: $24,040 full-time. Full-time tuition varies according to program. College room and board: $7170.

■ **KANSAS WESLEYAN UNIVERSITY**
100 E Claflin Ave.
Salina, KS 67401-6196
Tel: (785)827-5541; Free: 800-874-1154
Fax: (785)827-0927
E-mail: esteban.paredes@kwu.edu
Web Site: www.kwu.edu
Description: Independent United Methodist, comprehensive, coed. Awards associate, bachelor's, and master's degrees. Founded 1886. Setting: 28-acre small town campus. Endowment: $12.2 million. Educational spending for the previous fiscal year: $5631 per student. Total enrollment: 742. Faculty: 87 (47 full-time, 40 part-time). Student-undergrad faculty ratio is 13:1. 860 applied, 47% were admitted. 18% from top 10% of their high school class, 37% from top quarter, 74% from top half. Full-time: 606 students, 40% women, 60% men. Part-time: 62 students, 44% women, 56% men. Students come from 34 states and territories, 10 other countries, 57% from out-of-state. 0.3% American Indian or Alaska Native, non-Hispanic/Latino; 16% Hispanic/Latino; 13% Black or African American, non-Hispanic/Latino; 0.5% Asian, non-Hispanic/Latino; 0.3% Native Hawaiian or other Pacific Islander, non-Hispanic/Latino; 2% international. 7% 25 or older, 60% live on campus, 12% transferred in. Retention: 58% of full-time freshmen returned the following year. Academic areas with the most degrees conferred: business/marketing; parks and recreation; health professions and related sciences; education. Core. Calendar: semesters plus summer term. Academic remediation for entering students, services for LD students, advanced placement, self-designed majors, honors program, independent study, distance learning, double major, summer session for credit, part-time degree program, internships, graduate courses open to undergrads. Off campus study at The Washington Center. Study abroad program.
Entrance Requirements: Options: electronic application, deferred admission, international baccalaureate accepted. Required: high school transcript, minimum 2.5 high school GPA, SAT or ACT. Required for some: essay, interview. Entrance: moderately difficult. Application deadline: rolling. Notification: continuous. SAT Reasoning Test deadline: 8/20. SAT Subject Test deadline: 8/20. Transfer credits accepted: Yes.
Costs Per Year: Application fee: $20. One-time mandatory fee: $200. Comprehensive fee: $39,300 includes full-time tuition ($29,500) and college room and board ($9800). Part-time tuition: $3000 per term.
Collegiate Environment: Orientation program. Drama-theater group, choral group, student-run newspaper, radio station. Social organizations: 30 open to all. Most popular organizations: Fellowship of Christian Athletes, Student Government, Wesleyan Chorale, Coyote Gaming Club, Coyote Activities Board. Major annual events: Homecoming, Project Hero, Spring Fling. Student services: personal-psychological counseling. Campus security: 24-hour emergency response devices, student patrols, late night transport-escort service, controlled dormitory access. 490 college housing spaces available; 404 were occupied in 2018-19. Freshmen guaranteed college housing. On-campus residence required through sophomore year. Options: coed, men-only, women-only housing available. Memorial Library. Books: 63,237 (physical), 7,273 (digital/electronic); Serial titles: 402 (physical); Databases: 69. Weekly public service hours: 86; students can reserve study rooms. Operations spending for the previous fiscal year: $260,933. 195 computers available on campus for general student use. A campuswide network can be accessed from student residence rooms. Students can access the following: online class registration. Staffed computer lab on campus.
Community Environment: Salina (pop. 45,956), situated in the central part of the state, is the fifth largest city in Kansas. Major forms of transportation are available. Community facilities include a public library, municipal shopping center, museum, community theater, and numerous churches. Points of interest include Kanapolis Lake and Rock City.

■ **LABETTE COMMUNITY COLLEGE**
200 S 14th St.
Parsons, KS 67357-4299
Tel: (620)421-6700; Free: 888-522-3883
Web Site: www.labette.edu
Description: State and locally supported, 2-year, coed. Part of Kansas State Board of Education. Awards certificates, transfer associate, and terminal associate degrees. Founded 1923. Setting: 4-acre small town campus. Total

enrollment: 1,401. Faculty: 208 (31 full-time, 177 part-time). 212 applied, 100% were admitted. 20% from top 10% of their high school class, 59% from top half. Full-time: 466 students, 58% women, 42% men. Part-time: 935 students, 69% women, 31% men. Students come from 7 states and territories, 4 other countries. 40% 25 or older. Calendar: semesters. Academic remediation for entering students, services for LD students, advanced placement, accelerated degree program, independent study, distance learning, double major, summer session for credit, part-time degree program, adult/continuing education programs, co-op programs and internships. Off campus study. ROTC: Army (c).
Entrance Requirements: Open admission except for nursing program. Option: early admission. Recommended: high school transcript. Required for some: interview. Entrance: noncompetitive. Application deadline: rolling. Notification: continuous.
Collegiate Environment: Choral group. Social organizations: 18 open to all. Most popular organizations: Adult Women Who Are Returning to Education (AWARE), Phi Beta Lambda. Student services: personal-psychological counseling. Labette Community College Library. 66 computers available on campus for general student use. Staffed computer lab on campus.
Community Environment: This is an agricultural and industrial area, dairying being the principal source of income. Lake Parsons, which is municipally owned, provides facilities for picnicking, fishing and boating. Camping is available at Marvel Park and the Neosho Water Fowl Management Area, 12 miles north of the city, affords fishing and hunting as well.

■ **MANHATTAN AREA TECHNICAL COLLEGE**
3136 Dickens Ave.
Manhattan, KS 66503
Tel: (785)587-2800; Free: 800-352-7575
E-mail: neilross@manhattantech.edu
Web Site: www.manhattantech.edu
Description: State and locally supported, 2-year, coed. Awards certificates, transfer associate, and terminal associate degrees. Founded 1965. Setting: 18-acre rural campus. Educational spending for the previous fiscal year: $10,538 per student. Total enrollment: 825. Faculty: 80 (29 full-time, 51 part-time). Student-undergrad faculty ratio is 11:1. Full-time: 349 students, 45% women, 55% men. Part-time: 476 students, 54% women, 46% men. Students come from 10 states and territories, 1% from out-of-state. 0.6% American Indian or Alaska Native, non-Hispanic/Latino; 8% Hispanic/Latino; 6% Black or African American, non-Hispanic/Latino; 2% Asian, non-Hispanic/Latino; 0.1% Native Hawaiian or other Pacific Islander, non-Hispanic/Latino; 0.1% international. 47% 25 or older, 16% transferred in. Retention: 26% of full-time freshmen returned the following year. Core. Calendar: semesters. Academic remediation for entering students, services for LD students, advanced placement, self-designed majors, honors program, distance learning, double major, summer session for credit, part-time degree program, adult/continuing education programs, co-op programs and internships.
Entrance Requirements: Open admission. Option: electronic application. Required: high school transcript. Required for some: essay, 3 recommendations, interview, specific admission criteria for pre-allied health programs, Class A CDL for electric power and distribution program. Entrance: minimally difficult. Application deadline: rolling. Transfer credits accepted: Yes.
Collegiate Environment: Orientation program. Social organizations: SkillsUSA, Phi Theta Kappa. Major annual events: Annual Open House, Blood Drives. Campus security: late night transport-escort service, evening security guards. MATC Library. Books: 2,031 (physical), 3,665 (digital/electronic); Databases: 42. Weekly public service hours: 50. Operations spending for the previous fiscal year: $19,106. 140 computers available on campus for general student use. A campuswide network can be accessed from off-campus. Students can access the following: online class registration. Staffed computer lab on campus provides training in use of computers, software, and the Internet.

■ **MANHATTAN CHRISTIAN COLLEGE**
1415 Anderson Ave.
Manhattan, KS 66502-4081
Tel: (785)539-3571; Free: 877-246-4622
Fax: (785)539-0832
E-mail: teka.wilson@mccks.edu
Web Site: www.mccks.edu
Description: Independent, 4-year, coed, affiliated with Christian Churches and Churches of Christ. Awards associate and bachelor's degrees. Founded 1927. Setting: 10-acre small town campus. Total enrollment: 327. Faculty: 34 (24 full-time, 10 part-time). Student-undergrad faculty ratio is 12:1. 162 ap-

plied, 60% were admitted. 1% from out-of-state. 0.9% American Indian or Alaska Native, non-Hispanic/Latino; 4% Hispanic/Latino; 2% Black or African American, non-Hispanic/Latino; 5% international. 16% 25 or older. Retention: 75% of full-time freshmen returned the following year. Core. Calendar: semesters. Academic remediation for entering students, advanced placement, independent study, distance learning, double major, summer session for credit, part-time degree program, adult/continuing education programs, co-op programs and internships. ROTC: Army (c), Air Force (c).

Entrance Requirements: Options: electronic application, international baccalaureate accepted. Required: essay, high school transcript, minimum 2 high school GPA, 2 recommendations, ACT of 18, SAT of 1290, SAT or ACT. Entrance: minimally difficult. Application deadline: 8/11. Notification: continuous, continuous for nonresidents. SAT Reasoning Test deadline: 8/11. SAT Subject Test deadline: 8/11.

Collegiate Environment: Orientation program. Drama-theater group, choral group, student-run newspaper. Most popular organizations: Campus Planning Committee, Drama Club, Nursing Home Ministry. Student services: personal-psychological counseling. Jolliffe Hall Library.

Community Environment: See Kansas State University.

■ **MCPHERSON COLLEGE**
1600 E Euclid
McPherson, KS 67460-1402
Tel: (620)242-0400; Free: 800-365-7402
Fax: (620)241-8443
E-mail: admiss@mcpherson.edu
Web Site: www.mcpherson.edu
Description: Independent, comprehensive, coed, affiliated with Church of the Brethren. Awards bachelor's and master's degrees. Founded 1887. Setting: 26-acre small town campus. Endowment: $39.1 million. Educational spending for the previous fiscal year: $773 per student. Total enrollment: 733. Faculty: 47 (43 full-time, 4 part-time). Student-undergrad faculty ratio is 13:1. 759 applied, 27% were admitted. 7% from top 10% of their high school class, 29% from top quarter, 63% from top half. Full-time: 673 students, 34% women, 66% men. Part-time: 52 students, 58% women, 42% men. Students come from 34 states and territories, 16 other countries, 53% from out-of-state. 2% American Indian or Alaska Native, non-Hispanic/Latino; 14% Hispanic/Latino; 13% Black or African American, non-Hispanic/Latino; 1% Asian, non-Hispanic/Latino; 0.1% Native Hawaiian or other Pacific Islander, non-Hispanic/Latino; 1% international. 5% 25 or older, 66% live on campus, 12% transferred in. Retention: 63% of full-time freshmen returned the following year. Academic areas with the most degrees conferred: business/marketing; engineering technologies; parks and recreation; biological/life sciences. Core. Calendar: 4-1-4. Academic remediation for entering students, ESL program, services for LD students, self-designed majors, independent study, double major, summer session for credit, part-time degree program, internships. Off campus study. Study abroad program.

Entrance Requirements: Options: electronic application, deferred admission. Required: high school transcript, minimum 2 high school GPA, SAT or ACT. Entrance: moderately difficult. Application deadline: 8/12. Notification: continuous. SAT Reasoning Test deadline: 8/1. SAT Subject Test deadline: 8/1. Transfer credits accepted: Yes.

Costs Per Year: Application fee: $0. Comprehensive fee: $37,740 includes full-time tuition ($28,161), mandatory fees ($790), and college room and board ($8789). Full-time tuition and fees vary according to course load. Room and board charges vary according to board plan and housing facility. Part-time tuition: $430 per credit hour. Part-time mandatory fees: $50 per term. Part-time tuition and fees vary according to course load.

Collegiate Environment: Orientation program. Drama-theater group, choral group, student-run newspaper. Social organizations: 25 open to all; 50% of eligible men and 75% of eligible women are members. Most popular organizations: Student Activities Board, Student Government Association, CARS Club, Business Club, Multicultural Student Association. Major annual events: Campus Blowout, Bingo Nights, Classic Car Show. Student services: health clinic, personal-psychological counseling. Campus security: student patrols, controlled dormitory access, Security cameras. Miller Library. Books: 42,629 (physical), 164,814 (digital/electronic); Serial titles: 681 (physical), 92,937 (digital/electronic); Databases: 65. Weekly public service hours: 86; students can reserve study rooms. Operations spending for the previous fiscal year: $166,154. 190 computers available on campus for general student use. A campuswide network can be accessed from student residence rooms and from off campus. Students can access the following: online class registration.

Community Environment: McPherson is a small city of 14,000 located

near Highway I-135. The county seat, as well as the business center for the surrounding agricultural area, McPherson's principal industries include oil refining, insulation, plastic pipe, pharmaceuticals, mobile homes, and farm equipment. The community supports many cultural activities such as activities symphony, theatre guild, chorale, and art festival. Air transportation is available at nearby Wichita, Salina and Hutchinson, as well as churches, motels, and several parks.

■ **MIDAMERICA NAZARENE UNIVERSITY**
2030 E College Way
Olathe, KS 66062-1899
Tel: (913)782-3750; Free: 800-800-8887
Fax: (913)791-3481
E-mail: mvluoma@mnu.edu
Web Site: www.mnu.edu
Description: Independent, comprehensive, coed, affiliated with Church of the Nazarene. Awards associate, bachelor's, and master's degrees and post-master's certificates. Founded 1966. Setting: 105-acre suburban campus with easy access to Kansas City. Endowment: $10.6 million. Educational spending for the previous fiscal year: $8088 per student. Total enrollment: 1,888. Faculty: 270 (88 full-time, 182 part-time). Student-undergrad faculty ratio is 7:1. 957 applied, 66% were admitted. 16% from top 10% of their high school class, 36% from top quarter, 64% from top half. Full-time: 998 students, 57% women, 43% men. Part-time: 310 students, 64% women, 36% men. Students come from 43 states and territories, 17 other countries, 40% from out-of-state. 1% American Indian or Alaska Native, non-Hispanic/Latino; 8% Hispanic/Latino; 12% Black or African American, non-Hispanic/Latino; 2% Asian, non-Hispanic/Latino; 0.8% Native Hawaiian or other Pacific Islander, non-Hispanic/Latino. 28% 25 or older, 56% live on campus, 7% transferred in. Retention: 63% of full-time freshmen returned the following year. Academic areas with the most degrees conferred: health professions and related sciences; business/marketing; parks and recreation; education. Core. Calendar: semesters. Academic remediation for entering students, ESL program, services for LD students, advanced placement, accelerated degree program, self-designed majors, freshman honors college, honors program, independent study, distance learning, double major, summer session for credit, part-time degree program, adult/continuing education programs, co-op programs and internships, graduate courses open to undergrads. Off campus study at Coalition for Christian Colleges and Universities. Study abroad program. ROTC: Army (c), Air Force (c).

Entrance Requirements: Open admission. Options: electronic application, deferred admission, international baccalaureate accepted. Required: high school transcript, minimum 2 high school GPA. Recommended: TOEFL for international applicants. Required for some: SAT or ACT. Entrance: minimally difficult. Application deadline: 8/1. Notification: continuous. SAT Reasoning Test deadline: 8/15. SAT Subject Test deadline: 8/15. Transfer credits accepted: Yes.

Costs Per Year: Comprehensive fee: $39,444 includes full-time tuition ($29,986), mandatory fees ($750), and college room and board ($8708). College room only: $4834. Full-time tuition and fees vary according to course load, degree level, program, and reciprocity agreements. Room and board charges vary according to board plan and housing facility. Part-time tuition: $1119 per credit hour. Part-time tuition varies according to course load, degree level, program, and reciprocity agreements.

Collegiate Environment: Orientation program. Drama-theater group, choral group, student-run newspaper, radio station. Most popular organizations: LOL - Loving on Littles, S.M.I.L.E. - Students Ministering in the Lives of Elderly, Center for Grace, Freedom Fire, Students for Social Justice. Major annual events: White Light Event, Homecoming Hoe Down, Root Beer Fest. Student services: personal-psychological counseling. Campus security: 24-hour emergency response devices and patrols, student patrols, late night transport-escort service, controlled dormitory access. Mabee Library. Books: 88,000 (physical), 249,000 (digital/electronic); Serial titles: 397 (physical), 25 (digital/electronic); Databases: 35. Weekly public service hours: 81; study areas open 24 hours, 5-7 days a week; students can reserve study rooms. Operations spending for the previous fiscal year: $799,836. 85 computers available on campus for general student use. A campuswide network can be accessed. Students can access the following: online class registration. Staffed computer lab on campus provides training in use of computers, software, and the Internet.

■ **NATIONAL AMERICAN UNIVERSITY (GARDEN CITY)**
801 Campus Dr.
Garden City, KS 67846

Description: Proprietary, 4-year, coed.

■ **NATIONAL AMERICAN UNIVERSITY (OVERLAND PARK)**
10310 Mastin St.
Overland Park, KS 66212
Tel: (913)981-8700; Free: 866-628-1288
Web Site: www.national.edu
Description: Independent, 4-year, coed. Awards associate degrees. Total enrollment: 156.
Entrance Requirements: Entrance: noncompetitive.

■ **NATIONAL AMERICAN UNIVERSITY (WICHITA)**
7309 E 21st St.
Ste. G40
Wichita, KS 67206
Tel: (316)681-3050; Free: 877-628-9424
Web Site: www.national.edu
Description: Proprietary, 4-year, coed.

■ **NATIONAL AMERICAN UNIVERSITY (WICHITA)**
8428 W 13th St. N
Ste. 120
Wichita, KS 67212
Free: 877-628-9424
Web Site: www.national.edu
Description: Proprietary, 4-year, coed.

■ **NEOSHO COUNTY COMMUNITY COLLEGE**
800 W 14th St.
Chanute, KS 66720-2699
Tel: (620)431-6222
Fax: (620)431-0082
E-mail: llast@neosho.edu
Web Site: www.neosho.edu
Description: State and locally supported, 2-year, coed. Part of Kansas State Board of Education. Awards certificates, diplomas, transfer associate, and terminal associate degrees. Founded 1936. Setting: 50-acre small town campus. Endowment: $370,000. Total enrollment: 1,826. Faculty: 126 (40 full-time, 86 part-time). 573 applied, 100% were admitted. Full-time: 615 students, 61% women, 39% men. Part-time: 1,211 students, 69% women, 31% men. Students come from 15 states and territories. 58% 25 or older, 5% live on campus. Core. Calendar: semesters. Academic remediation for entering students, services for LD students, advanced placement, self-designed majors, summer session for credit, part-time degree program, adult/continuing education programs.
Entrance Requirements: Open admission. Option: early admission. Required: high school transcript. Entrance: noncompetitive. Application deadline: 9/15. Notification: continuous.
Collegiate Environment: Drama-theater group, choral group, student-run newspaper. Most popular organizations: Business Club, Science Club, Student Nurses Association, Fellowship of Christian Athletes, Nontraditional Student Organization. Major annual events: Homecoming, Fun-in-the-Sun Week, Halloween Dance. Student services: personal-psychological counseling. Campus security: controlled dormitory access. Chapman Library. 100 computers available on campus for general student use. Staffed computer lab on campus.
Community Environment: An industrial city with rural and urban sections, Chanute is the girlhood home of Osa Johnson, famous African and South Seas explorer. Oil production, manufacturing and agriculture are important to the city's economy. The varied industries include a cement plant, an oil field equipment manufacturing company, a garment factory and machine shops. Some part-time employment is available. Chanute has good shopping facilities, a hospital, many churches, a theater, a skating rink, commercial family recreation, a lake and a municipal golf course. A Mexican Fiesta, the Fall Festival, and a Horse Show are special annual events.

■ **NEWMAN UNIVERSITY**
3100 McCormick Ave.
Wichita, KS 67213-2097
Tel: (316)942-4291; Free: 877-NEWMANU
Fax: (316)942-4483
E-mail: englishk@newmanu.edu
Web Site: www.newmanu.edu
Description: Independent Roman Catholic, comprehensive, coed. Awards associate, bachelor's, and master's degrees. Founded 1933. Setting: 61-acre urban campus with easy access to Sedgwick County. Total enrollment: 1,766. Faculty: 202 (83 full-time, 119 part-time). Student-undergrad faculty ratio is 11:1. 1,084 applied, 64% were admitted. 23% from top 10% of their high school class, 48% from top quarter, 76% from top half. Full-time: 1,013 students, 67% women, 33% men. Part-time: 185 students, 60% women, 40% men. 17% from out-of-state. 1% American Indian or Alaska Native, non-Hispanic/Latino; 15% Hispanic/Latino; 6% Black or African American, non-Hispanic/Latino; 5% Asian, non-Hispanic/Latino; 8% international. 25% 25 or older, 23% live on campus, 12% transferred in. Retention: 80% of full-time freshmen returned the following year. Academic areas with the most degrees conferred: education; health professions and related sciences; biological/life sciences. Core. Calendar: semesters. Academic remediation for entering students, services for LD students, advanced placement, accelerated degree program, self-designed majors, honors program, independent study, distance learning, double major, summer session for credit, part-time degree program, adult/continuing education programs, co-op programs and internships. Off campus study at Friends University. Study abroad program.
Entrance Requirements: Options: electronic application, early admission, deferred admission. Required: high school transcript, minimum 2 high school GPA. Recommended: interview. Required for some: SAT or ACT. Entrance: minimally difficult. Application deadline: rolling. Notification: continuous. SAT Reasoning Test deadline: 8/15. SAT Subject Test deadline: 8/15. Transfer credits accepted: Yes.
Costs Per Year: Application fee: $0. Comprehensive fee: $38,970 includes full-time tuition ($29,260), mandatory fees ($1304), and college room and board ($8406). College room only: $4484. Room and board charges vary according to board plan and housing facility. Part-time tuition: $976 per credit hour. Part-time tuition varies according to course load.
Collegiate Environment: Orientation program. Drama-theater group, choral group, student-run newspaper. Social organizations: 32 open to all. Most popular organizations: Newman University Medical Professionals Club (NUMPC), National Society of Leadership and Success, Student Athlete Advisory Committee, Swing Dance Club, Hispanic American Leadership Organization (HALO). Major annual events: Orientation/Welcome Back Bash, Homecoming, Spring Fling. Student services: personal-psychological counseling. Campus security: 24-hour emergency response devices and patrols, student patrols, late night transport-escort service, controlled dormitory access. Dugan Library. Students can reserve study rooms.
Community Environment: See Wichita State University.

■ **NORTH CENTRAL KANSAS TECHNICAL COLLEGE**
PO Box 507, 3033 US Hwy. 24
Beloit, KS 67420
Tel: (913)738-2276; Free: 800-658-4655
E-mail: jheidrick@ncktc.tec.ks.us
Web Site: www.ncktc.edu
Description: State-supported, 2-year, coed. Awards terminal associate degrees. Founded 1963. Total enrollment: 513. Calendar: semesters.
Entrance Requirements: Entrance: noncompetitive.

■ **NORTHWEST KANSAS TECHNICAL COLLEGE**
PO Box 668, 1209 Harrison St.
Goodland, KS 67735
Tel: (785)899-3641; Free: 800-316-4127
Fax: (785)899-5711
Web Site: www.nwktc.edu
Description: State-supported, 2-year, coed. Awards terminal associate degrees. Founded 1964. Total enrollment: 281. Calendar: semesters.
Entrance Requirements: Entrance: noncompetitive.

■ **OTTAWA UNIVERSITY**
1001 S Cedar
Ottawa, KS 66067-3399
Tel: (785)242-5200; Free: 800-755-5200
Fax: (785)242-7429
E-mail: andy.stiles@ottawa.edu
Web Site: www.ottawa.edu
Description: Independent American Baptist Churches in the USA, comprehensive, coed. Awards bachelor's and master's degrees (also offers master's, adult, international and on-line education programs with significant enrollment not reflected in profile). Founded 1865. Setting: 64-acre small town campus with easy access to Kansas City. Endowment: $17.6 million. Total enrollment: 2,319. Faculty: 68 (26 full-time, 42 part-time). Student-

undergrad faculty ratio is 18:1. 1,168 applied, 26% were admitted. 27% from top 10% of their high school class, 37% from top quarter, 52% from top half. Full-time: 673 students, 44% women, 56% men. Part-time: 1,081 students, 71% women, 29% men. Students come from 44 states and territories, 3 other countries, 33% from out-of-state. 3% American Indian or Alaska Native, non-Hispanic/Latino; 12% Hispanic/Latino; 12% Black or African American, non-Hispanic/Latino; 2% Asian, non-Hispanic/Latino; 0.3% Native Hawaiian or other Pacific Islander, non-Hispanic/Latino. 53% 25 or older, 63% live on campus, 80% transferred in. Retention: 57% of full-time freshmen returned the following year. Core. Calendar: semesters. Advanced placement, self-designed majors, independent study, distance learning, double major, summer session for credit, part-time degree program, internships, graduate courses open to undergrads. Study abroad program.

Entrance Requirements: Options: electronic application, international baccalaureate accepted. Required: high school transcript, minimum 2.5 high school GPA, rank in upper 50% of high school class. Recommended: 2 recommendations, interview, SAT or ACT, SAT and SAT Subject Tests or ACT. Required for some: essay. Entrance: moderately difficult. Application deadline: rolling. Notification: continuous. Transfer credits accepted: Yes.

Costs Per Year: Application fee: $25. Comprehensive fee: $35,690 includes full-time tuition ($28,410), mandatory fees ($1280), and college room and board ($6000). College room only: $5000. Full-time tuition and fees vary according to course load and program. Room and board charges vary according to board plan and housing facility. Part-time tuition: $1185 per credit hour. Part-time mandatory fees: $531 per year. Part-time tuition and fees vary according to course load and program.

Collegiate Environment: Orientation program. Drama-theater group, choral group, student-run newspaper, radio station. Social organizations: 20 open to all; Greek Life social clubs. Most popular organizations: Christian Faith In Action, Student Activities Force, Education Club, Whole Earth Club, Fellowship of Christian Athletes. Major annual events: Welcome Week, Casino Night, Late Night Finals Breakfast. Student services: health clinic, personal-psychological counseling. Campus security: 24-hour emergency response devices and patrols, controlled dormitory access. 386 college housing spaces available; 335 were occupied in 2018-19. Freshmen guaranteed college housing. On-campus residence required through junior year. Options: coed, women-only housing available. Gangwish Library. Books: 47,152 (physical), 290,000 (digital/electronic); Serial titles: 5 (physical), 424,464 (digital/electronic); Databases: 124. Students can reserve study rooms. Operations spending for the previous fiscal year: $225,494. 40 computers available on campus for general student use. Computer purchase/lease plans available. A campuswide network can be accessed. Students can access the following: online class registration. Staffed computer lab on campus provides training in use of computers and the Internet.

Community Environment: The city is named for the Indians who established a new reservation here in 1834. Pomona Dam and Reservoir, fifteen miles northwest, provides facilities for picnicking, camping, trailering, swimming, boating, fishing and hunting. Forest Park on the Marais des Cygnes River provides additional outdoor recreational facilities. Community facilities include libraries, municipal airport and trains and buses for transportation. Other cultural and recreational activities are enjoyed in Kansas City, which is an hour's drive away.

■ **PITTSBURG STATE UNIVERSITY**
1701 S Broadway
Pittsburg, KS 66762
Tel: (620)231-7000; Free: 800-854-7488
Fax: (620)235-4080
E-mail: psuadmit@pittstate.edu
Web Site: www.pittstate.edu

Description: State-supported, comprehensive, coed. Part of Kansas State Board of Regents. Awards associate, bachelor's, master's, and doctoral degrees and post-master's certificates. Founded 1903. Setting: 30-acre small town campus. Total enrollment: 6,907. Faculty: 382 (292 full-time, 90 part-time). Student-undergrad faculty ratio is 18:1. 2,486 applied, 87% were admitted. 40% from top 10% of their high school class, 55% from top quarter, 79% from top half. Full-time: 5,109 students, 47% women, 53% men. Part-time: 597 students, 55% women, 45% men. 31% from out-of-state. 1% American Indian or Alaska Native, non-Hispanic/Latino; 6% Hispanic/Latino; 4% Black or African American, non-Hispanic/Latino; 0.9% Asian, non-Hispanic/Latino; 0.2% Native Hawaiian or other Pacific Islander, non-Hispanic/Latino; 3% international. 11% 25 or older, 9% transferred in. Retention: 74% of full-time freshmen returned the following year. Academic areas with the most degrees conferred: business/marketing; engineering technolo-

gies; education. Core. Calendar: semesters. Services for LD students, accelerated degree program, self-designed majors, freshman honors college, honors program, independent study, distance learning, double major, summer session for credit, part-time degree program, adult/continuing education programs, internships, graduate courses open to undergrads. Off campus study at Southside Education Center, Wichita, KS, Kansas City Metro Center, Lenexa, KS. Study abroad program. ROTC: Army.

Entrance Requirements: Options: electronic application, deferred admission, international baccalaureate accepted. Required: high school transcript, ACT. Required for some: minimum 2 high school GPA. Entrance: minimally difficult. Application deadline: rolling. Transfer credits accepted: Yes.

Costs Per Year: Application fee: $30. State resident tuition: $5694 full-time, $190 per credit hour part-time. Nonresident tuition: $17,038 full-time, $568 per credit hour part-time. Mandatory fees: $1604 full-time, $72 per credit hour part-time. College room and board: $7700. Room and board charges vary according to board plan.

Collegiate Environment: Orientation program. Drama-theater group, choral group, marching band, student-run newspaper, radio station. Social organizations: national fraternities, national sororities. Most popular organizations: Student Government Association, student yearbook, student newspaper, Student Activities Council, Students in Free Enterprise (SIFE). Major annual events: Homecoming, Family Day, Visit the Campus Day. Student services: legal services, health clinic, personal-psychological counseling. Campus security: 24-hour emergency response devices and patrols, late night transport-escort service, controlled dormitory access. Leonard H. Axe Library plus 2 others.

Community Environment: Pittsburg is the largest city in southeast Kansas. It is widely known for its fine homes, large churches, excellent schools, and many municipal facilities. Much of the coal mining in Kansas was done in this area. Some of the abandoned open pits have been flooded and stocked for fishing, swimming, boating, and water skiing. Other recreational activities within the city are bowling, tennis, and golf. Part-time employment opportunities are good.

■ **PRATT COMMUNITY COLLEGE**
348 NE State Rd. 61
Pratt, KS 67124-8317
Tel: (620)672-9800
Fax: (620)450-2285
E-mail: theresaz@prattcc.edu
Web Site: www.prattcc.edu

Description: State and locally supported, 2-year, coed. Part of Kansas State Board of Education. Awards certificates, transfer associate, and terminal associate degrees. Founded 1938. Setting: 80-acre rural campus with easy access to Wichita. Endowment: $3 million. Educational spending for the previous fiscal year: $3481 per student. Total enrollment: 1,664. Faculty: 45. Student-undergrad faculty ratio is 15:1. Full-time: 751 students, 48% women, 52% men. Part-time: 913 students, 59% women, 41% men. Students come from 14 other countries, 14% from out-of-state. 20% 25 or older, 35% live on campus, 8% transferred in. Retention: 60% of full-time freshmen returned the following year. Core. Calendar: semesters. Academic remediation for entering students, advanced placement, distance learning, summer session for credit, part-time degree program, adult/continuing education programs, co-op programs and internships.

Entrance Requirements: Open admission. Options: electronic application, early admission. Required: high school transcript. Required for some: ACT ASSET. Entrance: noncompetitive. Application deadline: rolling. Transfer credits accepted: Yes.

Collegiate Environment: Drama-theater group, choral group, student-run newspaper. Social organizations: 14 open to all. Most popular organizations: Phi Theta Kappa, Rotaract, Christian Challenge, Block and Bridle, Kappa Beta Delta. Major annual events: Mr. Cinderfella, Beaver Fever Week, Rodeo Week. Student services: health clinic, personal-psychological counseling. Campus security: 24-hour patrols, late night transport-escort service, controlled dormitory access. The Linda Hunt Memorial Library. Operations spending for the previous fiscal year: $139,228. 120 computers available on campus for general student use. A campuswide network can be accessed from off-campus. Students can access the following: online class registration. Staffed computer lab on campus provides training in use of computers, software, and the Internet.

■ **RASMUSSEN COLLEGE KANSAS CITY/OVERLAND PARK**
11600 College Blvd.
Overland Park, KS 66210

Tel: (913)491-7870; Free: 888-549-6755
E-mail: susan.hammerstrom@rasmussen.edu
Web Site: www.rasmussen.edu
Description: Proprietary, 4-year, coed. Part of Rasmussen College System. Awards associate and bachelor's degrees. Founded 2013. Setting: suburban campus. Total enrollment: 169. Faculty: 6 (1 full-time, 5 part-time). Student-undergrad faculty ratio is 22:1. 21 applied, 76% were admitted. Full-time: 98 students, 78% women, 22% men. Part-time: 71 students, 85% women, 15% men. 80% 25 or older. Core. Calendar: quarters. Academic remediation for entering students, accelerated degree program, distance learning, double major, summer session for credit, part-time degree program, adult/continuing education programs, internships.
Entrance Requirements: Options: electronic application, early admission, deferred admission. Required: high school transcript, minimum 2 high school GPA, institutional exam. Required for some: interview. Entrance: minimally difficult. Application deadline: rolling. Transfer credits accepted: Yes.
Collegiate Environment: Orientation program. Rasmussen College Library - Kansas City/Overland Park.

■ **RASMUSSEN COLLEGE TOPEKA**
620 SW Governor View
Topeka, KS 66606
Tel: (785)228-7320; Free: 888-549-6755
E-mail: susan.hammerstrom@rasmussen.edu
Web Site: www.rasmussen.edu
Description: Proprietary, 4-year, coed. Part of Rasmussen College System. Awards associate and bachelor's degrees. Founded 2013. Setting: suburban campus. Total enrollment: 141. Faculty: 46 (3 full-time, 43 part-time). Student-undergrad faculty ratio is 22:1. 15 applied, 93% were admitted. Full-time: 83 students, 72% women, 28% men. Part-time: 58 students, 67% women, 33% men. 75% 25 or older. Core. Calendar: quarters. Academic remediation for entering students, accelerated degree program, distance learning, double major, summer session for credit, part-time degree program, adult/continuing education programs, internships.
Entrance Requirements: Options: electronic application, early admission, deferred admission. Required: high school transcript, minimum 2 high school GPA, institutional exam. Required for some: interview. Entrance: minimally difficult. Application deadline: rolling. Transfer credits accepted: Yes.
Collegiate Environment: Orientation program. Rasmussen College Library - Topeka.

■ **SALINA AREA TECHNICAL COLLEGE**
2562 Centennial Rd.
Salina, KS 67401
Tel: (785)309-3100
Fax: (785)309-3101
E-mail: rebekah.ohlde@salinatech.edu
Web Site: www.salinatech.edu
Description: State and locally supported, 2-year, coed. Awards certificates, transfer associate, and terminal associate degrees. Founded 1965. Setting: small town campus. Total enrollment: 582. Full-time: 216 students, 29% women, 71% men. Part-time: 366 students, 58% women, 42% men. 1% American Indian or Alaska Native, non-Hispanic/Latino; 7% Hispanic/Latino; 2% Black or African American, non-Hispanic/Latino; 0.9% Asian, non-Hispanic/Latino; 0.2% Native Hawaiian or other Pacific Islander, non-Hispanic/Latino; 0.2% international. Core. Academic remediation for entering students, services for LD students, advanced placement, self-designed majors, independent study, distance learning, summer session for credit, part-time degree program, adult/continuing education programs, co-op programs and internships.
Entrance Requirements: Option: electronic application. Required: high school transcript, ACCUPLACER. Required for some: essay, 1 recommendation. Application deadline: rolling. Notification: continuous. Transfer credits accepted: Yes.
Collegiate Environment: Orientation program. Social organizations: 1 open to all. Most popular organization: Student Government Association. Major annual events: SATC Car Show (Vehicle Extravaganza), Thanksgiving Luncheon/Potluck, Student Appreciation Luncheons.

■ **SEWARD COUNTY COMMUNITY COLLEGE AND AREA TECHNICAL SCHOOL**
PO Box 1137
Liberal, KS 67905-1137
Tel: (620)624-1951; Free: 800-373-9951

Fax: (620)629-2725
Web Site: www.sccc.edu
Description: State and locally supported, 2-year, coed. Part of Kansas State Board of Regents. Awards certificates, diplomas, transfer associate, and terminal associate degrees. Founded 1969. Setting: 120-acre rural campus. Total enrollment: 1,656. 39% 25 or older. Core. Calendar: semesters. Academic remediation for entering students, ESL program, self-designed majors, distance learning, summer session for credit, part-time degree program, external degree program, adult/continuing education programs, co-op programs and internships.
Entrance Requirements: Open admission. Options: early admission, deferred admission. Required: high school transcript. Required for some: minimum 2.0 high school GPA, 1 recommendation, interview. Entrance: noncompetitive. Application deadline: 8/15. Notification: continuous.
Collegiate Environment: Orientation program. Drama-theater group, choral group, student-run newspaper. Campus security: 24-hour patrols, late night transport-escort service. Learning Resource Center plus 1 other.
Community Environment: Liberal is the county seat of Seward County. Oil discoveries have added significantly to the economic importance of Liberal. Southwestern Kansas is rich in wheat, oil and gas, and growing agri-related industries such as cattle/swine feed operations and meat packing. Part time employment is available. All forms of commercial transportation are available. A golf course, parks and swimming pools are some of the recreational facilities. Shopping facilities are excellent.

■ **SOUTHWESTERN COLLEGE**
100 College St.
Winfield, KS 67156-2499
Tel: (620)229-6000; Free: 800-846-1543
Fax: (620)229-6224
Web Site: www.sckans.edu
Description: Independent United Methodist, comprehensive, coed. Awards bachelor's, master's, and doctoral degrees. Founded 1885. Setting: 70-acre small town campus with easy access to Wichita. Endowment: $26.5 million. Research spending for the previous fiscal year: $118,266. Educational spending for the previous fiscal year: $6760 per student. Total enrollment: 1,306. Faculty: 167 (43 full-time, 124 part-time). Student-undergrad faculty ratio is 10:1. 512 applied, 97% were admitted. 11% from top 10% of their high school class, 33% from top quarter, 65% from top half. 4 valedictorians. Full-time: 577 students, 37% women, 63% men. Part-time: 570 students, 36% women, 64% men. Students come from 43 states and territories, 18 other countries, 61% from out-of-state. 1% American Indian or Alaska Native, non-Hispanic/Latino; 9% Hispanic/Latino; 11% Black or African American, non-Hispanic/Latino; 1% Asian, non-Hispanic/Latino; 0.3% Native Hawaiian or other Pacific Islander, non-Hispanic/Latino; 5% international. 46% 25 or older, 37% live on campus, 15% transferred in. Retention: 62% of full-time freshmen returned the following year. Academic areas with the most degrees conferred: business/marketing; health professions and related sciences; computer and information sciences. Core. Calendar: semesters. Academic remediation for entering students, ESL program, services for LD students, advanced placement, accelerated degree program, self-designed majors, honors program, independent study, distance learning, double major, summer session for credit, part-time degree program, adult/continuing education programs, internships. Off campus study at Urban Life Center, Chicago; Washington Internship Institute, Washington, DC. Study abroad program.
Entrance Requirements: Options: electronic application, international baccalaureate accepted. Required: high school transcript, minimum 2.6 high school GPA, SAT or ACT. Required for some: essay, 2 recommendations. Entrance: minimally difficult. Application deadline: 8/25. Notification: continuous, continuous for nonresidents. SAT Reasoning Test deadline: 8/25. SAT Subject Test deadline: 8/25. Transfer credits accepted: Yes.
Costs Per Year: Application fee: $25. Comprehensive fee: $37,910 includes full-time tuition ($30,000), mandatory fees ($150), and college room and board ($7760). College room only: $3620. Full-time tuition and fees vary according to course load, degree level, location, and program. Room and board charges vary according to board plan and housing facility. Part-time tuition: $1250 per credit hour. Part-time tuition varies according to course load, degree level, location, and program.
Collegiate Environment: Orientation program. Drama-theater group, choral group, student-run newspaper, radio station. Social organizations: 25 open to all. Most popular organizations: Discipleship SC, Leadership SC, Student Foundation, Student Government Association, Gaming Club. Major annual events: Moundbuilding Ceremony, Homecoming, Christmas Bingo. Student

services: personal-psychological counseling. Campus security: 24-hour emergency response devices and patrols, late night transport-escort service, controlled dormitory access. Harold and Mary Ellen Deets Library. Books: 49,349 (physical), 479,970 (digital/electronic); Serial titles: 10 (physical), 21,560 (digital/electronic); Databases: 84. Weekly public service hours: 91; students can reserve study rooms. Operations spending for the previous fiscal year: $275,631. 45 computers available on campus for general student use. Computer purchase/lease plans available. A campuswide network can be accessed from student residence rooms and from off campus. Students can access the following: online class registration, everything in Self-Service and BlackBoard.

■ **STERLING COLLEGE**

125 W Cooper
Sterling, KS 67579-0098
Tel: (620)278-2173; Free: 800-346-1017
Fax: (620)278-3690
E-mail: admissions@sterling.edu
Web Site: www.sterling.edu
Description: Independent Presbyterian, 4-year, coed. Awards bachelor's degrees. Founded 1887. Setting: 46-acre rural campus. Endowment: $16 million. Total enrollment: 650. 1,033 applied, 37% were admitted. 9% from top 10% of their high school class, 16% from top quarter, 33% from top half. 8 valedictorians. Full-time: 574 students, 48% women, 52% men. Part-time: 76 students, 64% women, 36% men. Students come from 36 states and territories, 7 other countries, 53% from out-of-state. 3% American Indian or Alaska Native, non-Hispanic/Latino; 12% Hispanic/Latino; 11% Black or African American, non-Hispanic/Latino; 0.9% Asian, non-Hispanic/Latino; 2% international. 6% 25 or older, 80% live on campus, 9% transferred in. Retention: 61% of full-time freshmen returned the following year. Core. Calendar: 4-1-4. Services for LD students, advanced placement, self-designed majors, honors program, independent study, distance learning, double major, summer session for credit, internships. Off campus study at 6 members of the Associated Colleges of Central Kansas. Study abroad program.
Entrance Requirements: Options: electronic application, deferred admission. Required: high school transcript, minimum 2.2 high school GPA, SAT or ACT. Recommended: essay, interview. Required for some: 2 recommendations. Entrance: minimally difficult. Application deadline: rolling. Notification: continuous. SAT Reasoning Test deadline: 8/1. SAT Subject Test deadline: 8/1. Transfer credits accepted: Yes.
Costs Per Year: Application fee: $25. Comprehensive fee: $33,866 includes full-time tuition ($25,000), mandatory fees ($1000), and college room and board ($7866). Full-time tuition and fees vary according to course load. Room and board charges vary according to board plan and housing facility. Part-time tuition: $466 per credit hour. Part-time tuition varies according to course load.
Collegiate Environment: Orientation program. Drama-theater group, choral group, student-run newspaper, radio station. Social organizations: 18 open to all. Most popular organizations: Fellowship of Christian Athletes, Student Activities Council, Bible study groups, theatre, Mission teams. Major annual events: Homecoming, Last Blast (end of year outdoor party), Convocations. Student services: health clinic, personal-psychological counseling. Campus security: controlled dormitory access, late night security patrol. Mabee Library. Books: 50,908 (physical), 80,159 (digital/electronic); Serial titles: 74 (physical); Databases: 28. Weekly public service hours: 75; students can reserve study rooms. Operations spending for the previous fiscal year: $146,112. 50 computers available on campus for general student use. A campuswide network can be accessed from student residence rooms and from off campus. Students can access the following: online class registration. Staffed computer lab on campus.
Community Environment: Sterling is in a rich wheat-growing, oil producing area with community facilities that include churches, Medical Center and many businesses. Opportunities for part time work are good. Train and bus service are available as well as an airport in Hutchinson, 25 miles away. Recreational activities are baseball, fishing, picnicking, and swimming at the municipal lake and college swimming pool.

■ **TABOR COLLEGE**

400 S Jefferson
Hillsboro, KS 67063
Tel: (620)947-3121; Free: 800-822-6799
Fax: (620)947-2607
E-mail: kellydugger@tabor.edu
Web Site: www.tabor.edu
Description: Independent Mennonite Brethren, comprehensive, coed. Awards associate, bachelor's, and master's degrees. Founded 1908. Setting: 87-acre small town campus with easy access to Wichita. Endowment: $9.4 million. Educational spending for the previous fiscal year: $5497 per student. Total enrollment: 712. Faculty: 106 (31 full-time, 75 part-time). Student-undergrad faculty ratio is 10:1. 937 applied, 58% were admitted. 11% from top 10% of their high school class, 21% from top quarter, 31% from top half. Full-time: 541 students, 42% women, 58% men. Part-time: 114 students, 55% women, 45% men. Students come from 39 states and territories, 14 other countries, 54% from out-of-state. 0.8% American Indian or Alaska Native, non-Hispanic/Latino; 12% Hispanic/Latino; 11% Black or African American, non-Hispanic/Latino; 0.6% Native Hawaiian or other Pacific Islander, non-Hispanic/Latino; 3% international. 9% 25 or older, 92% live on campus, 9% transferred in. Retention: 60% of full-time freshmen returned the following year. Academic areas with the most degrees conferred: business/marketing; health professions and related sciences; parks and recreation. Core. Calendar: 4-1-4 (adult and graduate studies programs run by cohort groups). Academic remediation for entering students, services for LD students, advanced placement, accelerated degree program, self-designed majors, honors program, independent study, distance learning, double major, part-time degree program, adult/continuing education programs, co-op programs and internships. Off campus study at Associated Colleges of Central Kansas, Focus on the Family Institute, Au Sable Institute, American Studies Program, Contemporary Music Center, Los Angeles Film Studies Center, Washington Journalism Center, International Semester Programs, Oxford Summer Programme. Study abroad program.
Entrance Requirements: Options: electronic application, deferred admission, international baccalaureate accepted. Required: essay, high school transcript, minimum 2 high school GPA, validation of high school graduation date for transfers, SAT or ACT. Recommended: interview. Entrance: moderately difficult. Application deadline: rolling. Notification: continuous. SAT Reasoning Test deadline: 9/1. Transfer credits accepted: Yes.
Costs Per Year: Application fee: $50. Comprehensive fee: $39,350 includes full-time tuition ($28,400), mandatory fees ($975), and college room and board ($9975). Part-time tuition: $570 per hour. Part-time mandatory fees: $20 per hour.
Collegiate Environment: Orientation program. Drama-theater group, choral group, student-run newspaper. Social organizations: 13 open to all. Most popular organizations: Student Activities Board, CHUMS (Challenging, Helping and Understanding through Mentorship), Intramurals, WUMP (Wichita Urban Ministries Plunge), Multi-Cultural Student Union. Major annual events: Homecoming, Sadie Hawkins Weekend, Christmas Banquet. Student services: personal-psychological counseling. 595 college housing spaces available; 508 were occupied in 2018-19. On-campus residence required through senior year. Options: men-only, women-only housing available. Tabor College Library. Books: 61,550 (physical), 225,000 (digital/electronic); Serial titles: 148 (physical), 5,000 (digital/electronic); Databases: 41. Weekly public service hours: 85; students can reserve study rooms. Operations spending for the previous fiscal year: $199,334. 35 computers available on campus for general student use. A campuswide network can be accessed. Students can access the following: online registration for Hillsboro undergraduate students.
Community Environment: Situated in the wheat and dairy area of central Kansas, Hillsboro is the leading trade center of western Marion County. Community facilities include a hospital, park, swimming pool and golf course.

■ **THE UNIVERSITY OF KANSAS**

1450 Jayhawk Blvd.
Lawrence, KS 66045
Tel: (785)864-2700
Fax: (785)864-5006
E-mail: adm@ku.edu
Web Site: www.ku.edu
Description: State-supported, university, coed. Part of Kansas Board of Regents. Awards bachelor's, master's, and doctoral degrees and post-master's certificates (University of Kansas is a single institution with academic programs and facilities at two primary locations: Lawrence and Kansas City). Founded 1866. Setting: 1,000-acre suburban campus with easy access to Kansas City. Endowment: $1.6 billion. Research spending for the previous fiscal year: $303.3 million. Total enrollment: 27,625. Faculty: 1,625 (1,359 full-time, 266 part-time). Student-undergrad faculty ratio is 17:1. 14,538 applied, 93% were admitted. 26% from top 10% of their high school class, 58% from top quarter, 88% from top half. 36 National Merit Scholars. Full-time: 17,151 students, 51% women, 49% men. Part-time: 2,187

students, 52% women, 48% men. Students come from 53 states and territories, 76 other countries, 28% from out-of-state. 0.3% American Indian or Alaska Native, non-Hispanic/Latino; 8% Hispanic/Latino; 4% Black or African American, non-Hispanic/Latino; 5% Asian, non-Hispanic/Latino; 0.1% Native Hawaiian or other Pacific Islander, non-Hispanic/Latino; 6% international. 8% 25 or older, 26% live on campus, 6% transferred in. Retention: 83% of full-time freshmen returned the following year. Academic areas with the most degrees conferred: business/marketing; health professions and related sciences; communication/journalism. Core. Calendar: semesters. Academic remediation for entering students, ESL program, services for LD students, advanced placement, accelerated degree program, freshman honors college, honors program, independent study, distance learning, double major, summer session for credit, part-time degree program, adult/continuing education programs, co-op programs and internships, graduate courses open to undergrads. Study abroad program. ROTC: Army, Naval, Air Force.
Entrance Requirements: Options: electronic application, international baccalaureate accepted. Required: high school transcript, minimum 3 high school GPA, Kansas Qualified Admissions Curriculum with minimum 2.0 GPA for state residents and 2.5 for nonresidents and minimum 3.0 overall GPA and ACT score of 24/SAT of 1160 or minimum 3.25 overall GPA and ACT score of 21/SAT of 1060, SAT or ACT. Entrance: moderately difficult. Application deadline: 8/13. Notification: continuous. SAT Reasoning Test deadline: 5/1. Transfer credits accepted: Yes.
Costs Per Year: Application fee: $40. State resident tuition: $10,092 full-time, $336.40 per credit hour part-time. Nonresident tuition: $26,302 full-time, $876.75 per credit hour part-time. Mandatory fees: $1056 full-time, $83.49 per credit hour part-time. Full-time tuition and fees vary according to reciprocity agreements. Part-time tuition and fees vary according to reciprocity agreements. College room and board: $10,350. College room only: $6084. Room and board charges vary according to board plan and housing facility.
Collegiate Environment: Orientation program. Drama-theater group, choral group, marching band, student-run newspaper, radio station. Social organizations: 560 open to all; national fraternities, national sororities; 20% of eligible men and 28% of eligible women are members. Most popular organizations: KU Adventure Club, Panhellenic Association, Center for Community Outreach, Pre-Nursing Club, American Red Cross Club. Major annual events: Graduation, Home Basketball Games, Home Football Games. Student services: legal services, health clinic, personal-psychological counseling, women's center. Campus security: 24-hour emergency response devices and patrols, late night transport-escort service, controlled dormitory access, University police department. Watson Library plus 11 others. Books: 4.7 million (physical), 1 million (digital/electronic). Weekly public service hours: 168; study areas open 24 hours, 5-7 days a week; students can reserve study rooms. Operations spending for the previous fiscal year: $21.9 million. 1,500 computers available on campus for general student use. A campuswide network can be accessed from student residence rooms and from off campus. Students can access the following: online class registration, online payments. Staffed computer lab on campus (open 24 hours a day) provides training in use of computers, software, and the Internet.
Community Environment: Lawrence, a town about 70,000, is set among the rolling hills of northeast Kansas. The cosmopolitan quality of the campus extends to the community, making a wide variety of cultural, ethnic, and recreational opportunities available to university students. Lawrence offers shopping areas, restaurants, entertainment, and recreational facilities that are either within easy walking distance of the campus or served by the university bus service. Near Lawrence there are several lakes for boating, fishing, and swimming. Metropolitan Kansas City, with its professional sports, ballet, opera, concerts, night spots, galleries, museums, festivals, and international airport, is about 40 miles east of Lawrence. Topeka, the state capital, is 30 miles west.

■ UNIVERSITY OF SAINT MARY
4100 S Fourth St. Trafficway
Leavenworth, KS 66048-5082
Tel: (913)682-5151; Free: 800-752-7043
Fax: (913)758-6140
E-mail: admiss@stmary.edu
Web Site: www.stmary.edu
Description: Independent Roman Catholic, comprehensive, coed. Awards associate, bachelor's, master's, and doctoral degrees. Founded 1923. Setting: 240-acre small town campus with easy access to Kansas City. Endowment: $20.9 million. Educational spending for the previous fiscal year: $7245 per student. Total enrollment: 1,254. Faculty: 151 (67 full-time, 84 part-time). Student-undergrad faculty ratio is 9:1. 996 applied, 61% were admitted. 9% from top 10% of their high school class, 30% from top quarter, 63% from top half. Full-time: 675 students, 45% women, 55% men. Part-time: 57 students, 86% women, 14% men. Students come from 40 states and territories, 5

other countries, 49% from out-of-state. 1% American Indian or Alaska Native, non-Hispanic/Latino; 16% Hispanic/Latino; 12% Black or African American, non-Hispanic/Latino; 1% Asian, non-Hispanic/Latino; 1% Native Hawaiian or other Pacific Islander, non-Hispanic/Latino; 1% international. 13% 25 or older, 39% live on campus, 16% transferred in. Retention: 62% of full-time freshmen returned the following year. Academic areas with the most degrees conferred: health professions and related sciences; psychology; biological/life sciences. Core. Calendar: semesters. Academic remediation for entering students, services for LD students, advanced placement, self-designed majors, honors program, independent study, distance learning, double major, summer session for credit, part-time degree program, adult/continuing education programs, co-op programs and internships, graduate courses open to undergrads. Off campus study at University of Kansas, members of the Council of Independent Colleges. Study abroad program. ROTC: Army (c).
Entrance Requirements: Options: electronic application, international baccalaureate accepted. Required: high school transcript, minimum 2.5 high school GPA, SAT and ACT. Recommended: ACT. Entrance: moderately difficult. Application deadline: rolling. Notification: continuous. SAT Reasoning Test deadline: 9/1. SAT Subject Test deadline: 9/1. Transfer credits accepted: Yes.
Costs Per Year: Application fee: $25. Comprehensive fee: $38,070 includes full-time tuition ($28,860), mandatory fees ($1070), and college room and board ($8140). Part-time tuition: $665 per credit hour.
Collegiate Environment: Orientation program. Drama-theater group, choral group. Social organizations: 25 open to all. Most popular organizations: Student Government Association, BACCHUS, Theatrical Union, campus ministry. Major annual events: Family Weekend, Heritage Day, Spring Honors Convocation. Student services: personal-psychological counseling. Campus security: 24-hour patrols, late night transport-escort service, controlled dormitory access. 325 college housing spaces available; 282 were occupied in 2018-19. Freshmen guaranteed college housing. On-campus residence required through sophomore year. Option: coed housing available. Keleher Learning Commons/DePaul Library plus 1 other. Books: 75,000 (physical), 10,500 (digital/electronic); Serial titles: 15 (physical), 38,459 (digital/electronic); Databases: 63. Weekly public service hours: 68; students can reserve study rooms. Operations spending for the previous fiscal year: $301,023. 30 computers available on campus for general student use. A computer is required for all students. A campuswide network can be accessed from student residence rooms and from off campus. Students can access the following: online class registration.
Community Environment: Leavenworth is 26 miles northwest of Kansas City, which contributes to the economic and recreational interest of the community.

■ WASHBURN UNIVERSITY
1700 SW College Ave.
Topeka, KS 66621
Tel: (785)670-1010; Free: 800-332-0291
Fax: (785)231-1089
E-mail: admissions@washburn.edu
Web Site: www.washburn.edu
Description: City-supported, comprehensive, coed. Awards associate, bachelor's, master's, and doctoral degrees and post-master's certificates. Founded 1865. Setting: 160-acre urban campus with easy access to Kansas City. Endowment: $172.4 million. Research spending for the previous fiscal year: $133,050. Total enrollment: 6,615. Faculty: 512 (248 full-time, 264 part-time). Student-undergrad faculty ratio is 12:1. 1,458 applied, 99% were admitted. 13% from top 10% of their high school class, 34% from top quarter, 67% from top half. 22 valedictorians. Full-time: 3,767 students, 58% women, 42% men. Part-time: 2,026 students, 62% women, 38% men. Students come from 38 states and territories, 38 other countries, 7% from out-of-state. 0.5% American Indian or Alaska Native, non-Hispanic/Latino; 7% Hispanic/Latino; 5% Black or African American, non-Hispanic/Latino; 1% Asian, non-Hispanic/Latino; 0.1% Native Hawaiian or other Pacific Islander, non-Hispanic/Latino; 4% international. 28% 25 or older, 18% live on campus, 9% transferred in. Retention: 68% of full-time freshmen returned the following year. Academic areas with the most degrees conferred: health professions and related sciences; business/marketing; communication/journalism; education. Core. Calendar: semesters. Academic remediation for entering students, ESL program, services for LD students, advanced placement, self-designed majors, honors program, independent study, distance learning, double major, summer session for credit, part-time degree program, adult/continuing education programs, co-op programs and internships, graduate courses open to undergrads. Off campus study. Study abroad program. ROTC: Army, Naval (c), Air Force (c).
Entrance Requirements: Open admission except select programs. Option: electronic application. Required: high school transcript, ACT. Entrance:

noncompetitive. Application deadline: 8/1. Notification: continuous. SAT Reasoning Test deadline: 8/1. Transfer credits accepted: Yes.

Costs Per Year: Application fee: $20. State resident tuition: $8760 full-time, $292 per credit hour part-time. Nonresident tuition: $19,830 full-time, $661 per credit hour part-time. Mandatory fees: $110 full-time, $55 per term part-time. Full-time tuition and fees vary according to program. Part-time tuition and fees vary according to program. College room and board: $9144. Room and board charges vary according to board plan and housing facility.

Collegiate Environment: Orientation program. Drama-theater group, choral group, marching band, student-run newspaper. Social organizations: 120 open to all; national fraternities, national sororities, local fraternities; 9% of eligible men and 9% of eligible women are members. Major annual events: Theatre, Family Day, Homecoming. Student services: legal services, health clinic, personal-psychological counseling. Campus security: 24-hour emergency response devices and patrols, student patrols, late night transport-escort service. Mabee Library plus 1 other. Books: 441,448 (physical), 292,840 (digital/electronic); Serial titles: 93,914 (physical); Databases: 182. Weekly public service hours: 104; students can reserve study rooms. 542 computers available on campus for general student use. A campuswide network can be accessed from student residence rooms and from off campus. Students can access the following: online class registration. Staffed computer lab on campus provides training in use of computers, software, and the Internet.

Community Environment: Topeka, the state capital of Kansas, is situated on the edge of the wheat belt approximately 60 miles from Kansas City. The leading industries are meat packing, tire manufacturing, grain milling, printing and publishing, and the manufacture of steel products. Excellent community facilities include libraries, museums, many churches, and outstanding medical facilities. The Topeka Civic Theatre and Topeka Community Concert group provide the citizens with unusual cultural activities. Lake Shawnee is a popular recreation spot; Gage Park is a beautiful park within the city that has the finest facilities for picnicking and swimming, as well as lovely rose gardens. All major forms of commercial transportation are available. The Menninger Clinic located here is one of the world's largest psychiatric research and training centers.

■ WICHITA AREA TECHNICAL COLLEGE

4004 N Webb Rd., Ste. 100
Wichita, KS 67226
Tel: (316)677-9400
E-mail: info@watc.edu
Web Site: www.watc.edu

Description: District-supported, 2-year, coed. Awards certificates, diplomas, transfer associate, and terminal associate degrees. Founded 1963. Setting: urban campus. Endowment: $1.1 million. Educational spending for the previous fiscal year: $5518 per student. Total enrollment: 2,934. Faculty: 167 (54 full-time, 113 part-time). Student-undergrad faculty ratio is 19:1. Full-time: 1,087 students, 50% women, 50% men. Part-time: 1,849 students, 56% women, 44% men. Students come from 11 states and territories, 1% from out-of-state. 2% American Indian or Alaska Native, non-Hispanic/Latino; 10% Hispanic/Latino; 16% Black or African American, non-Hispanic/Latino; 4% Asian, non-Hispanic/Latino; 0.3% Native Hawaiian or other Pacific Islander, non-Hispanic/Latino; 0.1% international. 59% 25 or older, 3% transferred in. Retention: 58% of full-time freshmen returned the following year. Calendar: semesters. Academic remediation for entering students, services for LD students, distance learning, summer session for credit, part-time degree program, internships.

Entrance Requirements: Required for some: high school transcript, WorkKeys, ACT Compass, TEAS.

Collegiate Environment: Most popular organizations: SkillsUSA, Shooting Club. Campus security: 24-hour emergency response devices and patrols, late night transport-escort service. WATC Library. Operations spending for the previous fiscal year: $103,703. 130 computers available on campus for general student use. A campuswide network can be accessed from off-campus. Students can access the following: online class registration. Staffed computer lab on campus provides training in use of computers, software, and the Internet.

■ WICHITA STATE UNIVERSITY

1845 N Fairmount
Wichita, KS 67260
Tel: (316)978-3456; Free: 800-362-2594
Fax: (316)978-3795
Web Site: www.wichita.edu

Description: State-supported, university, coed. Part of Kansas Board of Regents. Awards associate, bachelor's, master's, and doctoral degrees and post-master's certificates. Founded 1895. Setting: 335-acre urban campus. Endowment: $302 million. Total enrollment: 15,081. Faculty: 771 (505 full-

time, 266 part-time). Student-undergrad faculty ratio is 20:1. 5,469 applied, 97% were admitted. 20% from top 10% of their high school class, 44% from top quarter, 80% from top half. Full-time: 8,749 students, 53% women, 47% men. Part-time: 3,649 students, 56% women, 44% men. Students come from 48 states and territories, 96 other countries, 9% from out-of-state. 0.6% American Indian or Alaska Native, non-Hispanic/Latino; 12% Hispanic/Latino; 6% Black or African American, non-Hispanic/Latino; 7% Asian, non-Hispanic/Latino; 0.1% Native Hawaiian or other Pacific Islander, non-Hispanic/Latino; 8% international. 25% 25 or older, 11% live on campus, 10% transferred in. Retention: 73% of full-time freshmen returned the following year. Academic areas with the most degrees conferred: business/marketing; health professions and related sciences; engineering. Core. Calendar: semesters. Academic remediation for entering students, ESL program, services for LD students, advanced placement, accelerated degree program, freshman honors college, honors program, independent study, distance learning, double major, summer session for credit, part-time degree program, adult/continuing education programs, co-op programs and internships, graduate courses open to undergrads. Off campus study at National Student Exchange, Midwest Student Exchange. Study abroad program.

Entrance Requirements: Open admission for those who already have a previous bachelor degree. Options: electronic application, deferred admission, international baccalaureate accepted. Required: high school transcript. Recommended: minimum X high school GPA, SAT or ACT. Required for some: minimum 2.5 high school GPA, rank in upper one-third of high school class or complete the pre-college curriculum with a minimum 2.0 GPA (2.5 GPA for nonresidents), SAT or ACT. Entrance: minimally difficult. Application deadline: rolling. Notification: continuous. Transfer credits accepted: Yes.

Costs Per Year: Application fee: $30. State resident tuition: $6,709 full-time, $223.62 per credit hour part-time. Nonresident tuition: $15,890 full-time, $529.68 per credit hour part-time. Mandatory fees: $1,562 full-time, $7.75 per credit hour part-time, $443.30 per term part-time. Full-time tuition and fees vary according to course level, course load, degree level, and program. Part-time tuition and fees vary according to course level, course load, degree level, and program. College room and board: $11,252. Room and board charges vary according to board plan and housing facility.

Collegiate Environment: Orientation program. Drama-theater group, choral group, student-run newspaper, radio station. Social organizations: 200 open to all; national fraternities, national sororities, local fraternities, local sororities. Major annual events: Shocktoberfest, Welcome Fest, Convocation. Student services: health clinic, personal-psychological counseling, women's center. Campus security: 24-hour emergency response devices and patrols, student patrols, late night transport-escort service, controlled dormitory access, bicycle patrols by campus security. Ablah Library plus 2 others. Books: 1.9 million (physical), 475,186 (digital/electronic); Serial titles: 460 (physical), 94,566 (digital/electronic); Databases: 269. Study areas open 24 hours, 5-7 days a week; students can reserve study rooms. 1,500 computers available on campus for general student use. A campuswide network can be accessed from student residence rooms and from off campus. Students can access the following: online class registration, learning management system. Staffed computer lab on campus.

Community Environment: Wichita, population 354,800, is the largest city in Kansas. It is located 161 miles southeast of the center of the U.S. Primary economic factors contributing to the growth and development of the city have been aircraft manufacturing, oil and natural gas, air conditioners, heating and lighting units, as well as camping equipment and agriculture. It is the Aviation Center of the World. WSU is an important resource to the Wichita area business community. The university supports research and development through programs such as the Center for Productivity Enhancement and the National Institute for Aviation Research. The corporate community utilizes programs offered by the University's Center for Management for continuing professional development. The Center for Entrepreneurship and Small Business Management encourages development of small businesses, while the Hugo Wall Center for Urban Studies supports local and state government facilities for canoeing, boating, and water skiing. Several theater groups stage productions throughout the year and the Wichita Symphony has provided more than 30 years of professional music. The city's civic and cultural complex offers an outstanding library in addition to a modern convention and performing arts center.

■ WICHITA TECHNICAL INSTITUTE

2051 S Meridian Ave.
Wichita, KS 67213
Tel: (316)943-2241
Fax: (316)943-2241
Web Site: www.wti.edu

Description: Proprietary, 2-year, coed. Awards certificates, transfer associate, and terminal associate degrees.

■ ALICE LLOYD COLLEGE

100 Purpose Rd.
Pippa Passes, KY 41844
Tel: (606)368-2101; Free: 888-280-4252
Fax: (606)368-2125
E-mail: jdcornett@alc.edu
Web Site: www.alc.edu

Description: Independent, 4-year, coed. Awards bachelor's degrees. Founded 1923. Setting: 175-acre rural campus. Endowment: $40.8 million. Educational spending for the previous fiscal year: $4350 per student. Total enrollment: 598. Faculty: 47 (29 full-time, 18 part-time). Student-undergrad faculty ratio is 17:1. 5,599 applied, 6% were admitted. 12% from top 10% of their high school class, 40% from top quarter, 73% from top half. Full-time: 578 students, 53% women, 47% men. Part-time: 20 students, 55% women, 45% men. Students come from 7 states and territories, 4 other countries, 16% from out-of-state. 1% Hispanic/Latino; 2% Black or African American, non-Hispanic/Latino; 0.2% Asian, non-Hispanic/Latino; 0.3% Native Hawaiian or other Pacific Islander, non-Hispanic/Latino; 0.7% international. 2% 25 or older, 70% live on campus, 4% transferred in. Retention: 60% of full-time freshmen returned the following year. Academic areas with the most degrees conferred: biological/life sciences; parks and recreation; social sciences. Core. Calendar: semesters. Academic remediation for entering students, advanced placement, independent study, double major, part-time degree program, internships. Study abroad program.

Entrance Requirements: Option: electronic application. Required: high school transcript, minimum 2.25 high school GPA, interview, SAT or ACT. Required for some: essay, 2 recommendations. Entrance: minimally difficult. Application deadlines: rolling, rolling for nonresidents, rolling for early decision plan 1, rolling for early decision plan 2, rolling for early action. Transfer credits accepted: Yes.

Costs Per Year: Application fee: $0. Comprehensive fee: $9030 includes full-time tuition ($0), mandatory fees ($2150), and college room and board ($6880). College room only: $3300. Part-time mandatory fees: $225 per credit. The cost of tuition is covered by a combination of scholarships and other financial aid.

Collegiate Environment: Orientation program. Drama-theater group, choral group, student-run newspaper, radio station. Social organizations: 23 open to all; 10% of eligible men and 10% of eligible women are members. Most popular organizations: Voices of Appalachia, Intramurals, Baptist Collegiate Ministries, Allied Health Sciences Club, Alpha Chi National Honor Society. Major annual events: Religious Emphasis Week, Alcohol Awareness Week, Appalachia Day Homecoming. Student services: health clinic, personal-psychological counseling. Campus security: 24-hour emergency response devices and patrols, late night transport-escort service, controlled dormitory access, video cameras. McGaw Library and Learning Center. Books: 63,050 (physical), 170,956 (digital/electronic); Serial titles: 57 (physical), 23,210 (digital/electronic); Databases: 105. Weekly public service hours: 74; students can reserve study rooms. Operations spending for the previous fiscal year: $251,900. 146 computers available on campus for general student use. A campuswide network can be accessed from student residence rooms. Staffed computer lab on campus provides training in use of software.

Community Environment: Located in a small, rural town, the primary industries being coal mining and farming.

■ AMERICAN NATIONAL UNIVERSITY (DANVILLE)

115 E Lexington Ave.
Danville, KY 40422
Tel: (859)236-6991; Free: 888-9-JOBREADY
Web Site: www.an.edu

Description: Proprietary, 2-year, coed. Part of National College of Business and Technology. Awards diplomas and terminal associate degrees. Founded 1962. Core. Calendar: quarters. Services for LD students, advanced placement, honors program, double major, summer session for credit, part-time degree program, internships.

Entrance Requirements: Open admission. Option: electronic application. Required: high school transcript. Entrance: noncompetitive. Application deadline: rolling. Notification: continuous.

Collegiate Environment: Orientation program.

■ AMERICAN NATIONAL UNIVERSITY (FLORENCE)

8095 Connector Dr.
Florence, KY 41042
Tel: (859)525-6510; Free: 888-9-JOBREADY
Fax: (859)525-8961
Web Site: www.an.edu

Description: Proprietary, 2-year, coed. Part of National College of Business and Technology. Awards diplomas and terminal associate degrees. Founded 1941. Setting: suburban campus. Core. Calendar: quarters. Services for LD students, advanced placement, honors program, double major, summer session for credit, part-time degree program, internships.

Entrance Requirements: Open admission. Option: electronic application. Recommended: interview. Required for some: high school transcript. Entrance: noncompetitive. Application deadline: rolling. Notification: continuous.

Collegiate Environment: Orientation program. Campus security: 24-hour emergency response devices.

■ AMERICAN NATIONAL UNIVERSITY (LEXINGTON)

2376 Sir Barton Way
Lexington, KY 40509
Tel: (859)253-0621; Free: 888-9-JOBREADY
Web Site: www.an.edu

Description: Proprietary, primarily 2-year, coed. Part of National College of Business and Technology. Awards diplomas, terminal associate, and bachelor's degrees. Founded 1947. Setting: urban campus. Core. Calendar: quarters. Advanced placement, honors program, double major, summer session for credit, part-time degree program, internships.

Entrance Requirements: Open admission. Option: electronic application. Required: high school transcript. Entrance: noncompetitive. Application deadline: rolling. Notification: continuous.

Collegiate Environment: Orientation program.

■ AMERICAN NATIONAL UNIVERSITY (LOUISVILLE)

4205 Dixie Hwy.
Louisville, KY 40216
Tel: (502)447-7634; Free: 888-9-JOBREADY
Web Site: www.an.edu

Description: Proprietary, primarily 2-year, coed. Part of National College of Business and Technology. Awards diplomas, terminal associate, and bachelor's degrees. Founded 1990. Core. Calendar: quarters. Services for LD students, advanced placement, honors program, double major, summer session for credit, part-time degree program, internships.

Entrance Requirements: Open admission. Option: electronic application. Recommended: interview. Required for some: high school transcript. Entrance: noncompetitive. Application deadline: rolling. Notification: continuous.

Collegiate Environment: Orientation program.

■ **AMERICAN NATIONAL UNIVERSITY (PIKEVILLE)**
50 National College Blvd.
Pikeville, KY 41501
Tel: (606)478-7200; Free: 888-9-JOBREADY
Fax: (606)437-4952
Web Site: www.an.edu
Description: Proprietary, 2-year, coed. Part of National College of Business and Technology. Awards diplomas and terminal associate degrees. Founded 1976. Setting: rural campus. Core. Calendar: quarters. Services for LD students, advanced placement, honors program, double major, summer session for credit, part-time degree program, internships.
Entrance Requirements: Open admission. Recommended: interview. Required for some: high school transcript. Entrance: noncompetitive. Application deadline: rolling. Notification: continuous.
Collegiate Environment: Orientation program.

■ **AMERICAN NATIONAL UNIVERSITY (RICHMOND)**
125 S Killarney Ln.
Richmond, KY 40475
Tel: (859)623-8956; Free: 888-9-JOBREADY
Fax: (859)624-5544
Web Site: www.an.edu
Description: Proprietary, 2-year, coed. Part of National College of Business and Technology. Awards diplomas and terminal associate degrees. Founded 1951. Setting: suburban campus. Core. Calendar: quarters. Advanced placement, honors program, double major, summer session for credit, part-time degree program, internships.
Entrance Requirements: Open admission. Option: electronic application. Recommended: interview. Required for some: high school transcript. Entrance: noncompetitive. Application deadline: rolling. Notification: continuous.
Collegiate Environment: Orientation program.

■ **ASBURY UNIVERSITY**
1 Macklem Dr.
Wilmore, KY 40390-1198
Tel: (859)858-3511; Free: 800-888-1818
Fax: (859)858-3921
E-mail: admissions@asbury.edu
Web Site: www.asbury.edu
Description: Independent nondenominational, comprehensive, coed. Awards associate, bachelor's, and master's degrees. Founded 1890. Setting: 400-acre small town campus with easy access to Lexington, KY. Endowment: $47.8 million. Educational spending for the previous fiscal year: $5377 per student. Total enrollment: 1,973. Faculty: 204 (94 full-time, 110 part-time). Student-undergrad faculty ratio is 13:1. 1,105 applied, 70% were admitted. 28% from top 10% of their high school class, 59% from top quarter, 84% from top half. Full-time: 1,323 students, 61% women, 39% men. Part-time: 394 students, 59% women, 41% men. Students come from 41 states and territories, 35 other countries, 47% from out-of-state. 0.6% American Indian or Alaska Native, non-Hispanic/Latino; 6% Hispanic/Latino; 4% Black or African American, non-Hispanic/Latino; 2% Asian, non-Hispanic/Latino; 0.2% Native Hawaiian or other Pacific Islander, non-Hispanic/Latino; 4% international. 3% 25 or older, 85% live on campus, 3% transferred in. Retention: 85% of full-time freshmen returned the following year. Academic areas with the most degrees conferred: communication/journalism; business/marketing; theology and religious vocations. Core. Calendar: semesters. Services for LD students, advanced placement, distance learning, double major, summer session for credit, adult/continuing education programs, internships, graduate courses open to undergrads. Off campus study at Exchange program with Consortium of Christian Colleges, Best Semester Programs of the Council for Christian Colleges and Universities, Semester in Spain through Trinity Christian College. Study abroad program. ROTC: Army (c), Air Force (c).
Entrance Requirements: Options: electronic application, early admission,

deferred admission, international baccalaureate accepted. Required: essay, high school transcript, minimum 2.5 high school GPA, 1 recommendation, SAT or ACT. Entrance: moderately difficult. Application deadline: rolling. Notification: continuous. Transfer credits accepted: Yes.
Costs Per Year: Application fee: $0. Comprehensive fee: $37,358 includes full-time tuition ($29,900), mandatory fees ($298), and college room and board ($7160). Full-time tuition and fees vary according to course load and program. Room and board charges vary according to board plan and housing facility. Part-time tuition: $1150 per credit hour. Part-time tuition varies according to course load and program.
Collegiate Environment: Orientation program. Drama-theater group, choral group, student-run newspaper, radio station. Social organizations: 30 open to all. Most popular organizations: Asbury Student Congress, Spiritual Life Board, Summer Ministry Teams, Asbury Outdoors, WGM Global Cafe. Major annual events: Legacy Games Event, High Bridge Film Festival, Fall Variety Show. Student services: health clinic, personal-psychological counseling. Campus security: 24-hour emergency response devices, late night transport-escort service, controlled dormitory access, late night security personnel. Kinlaw Library. Books: 157,131 (physical), 168,625 (digital/electronic); Serial titles: 442 (physical), 37,780 (digital/electronic); Databases: 60. Weekly public service hours: 88; students can reserve study rooms. Operations spending for the previous fiscal year: $648,254. 250 computers available on campus for general student use. Computer purchase/lease plans available. A campuswide network can be accessed from student residence rooms and from off campus. Students can access the following: online class registration. Staffed computer lab on campus provides training in use of computers, software, and the Internet.
Community Environment: This is rural town with air and bus service available in nearby Lexington, Kentucky. There are several natural and historic points of interest located nearby: High Bridge, Shakertown, Fort Harrod, Boone's Tavern, National Cemetery at Camp Nelson, Kentucky Horse Park, world famous thoroughbred farms and Natural Bridge.

■ **ASHLAND COMMUNITY AND TECHNICAL COLLEGE**
1400 College Dr.
Ashland, KY 41101-3683
Tel: (606)329-2999; Free: 800-928-4256
Fax: (606)325-8124
Web Site: www.ashland.kctcs.edu
Description: State-supported, 2-year, coed. Part of Kentucky Community and Technical College System. Awards certificates, diplomas, transfer associate, and terminal associate degrees. Founded 1937. Setting: 47-acre small town campus. Total enrollment: 4,419. Student-undergrad faculty ratio is 17:1. 9% from out-of-state. 37% 25 or older. Core. Calendar: semesters. Academic remediation for entering students, services for LD students, advanced placement, honors program, distance learning, summer session for credit, part-time degree program, adult/continuing education programs, co-op programs and internships. Off campus study at University of Kentucky, other area colleges.
Entrance Requirements: Open admission except for nursing program. Options: early admission, deferred admission. Required: high school transcript. Entrance: noncompetitive. Application deadline: 8/20.
Collegiate Environment: Orientation program. Drama-theater group, choral group, student-run newspaper. Student services: personal-psychological counseling. Campus security: 24-hour emergency response devices and patrols, late night transport-escort service, electronic surveillance of bookstore and business office. Joseph and Sylvia Mansbach Memorial Library.
Community Environment: On the Ohio River, Ashland has a temperate climate with an average annual temperature of 55 degrees. This city has 25 industries including steel, oil refining, a coal and coke-processing plant and a firebrick factory. More than 21 million tons of barge traffic on the river passes the city annually. The Greenup Locks and Dam complex consist of two adjacent chambers which elevate 1,100 foot modern tows in 20 minutes as opposed to the six hours previously required. Transportation is provided by bus and railroad. Part time work is available. City services include a public library, churches of 15 denominations, Y's (no overnight facilities), and hospitals. Recreational facilities easily accessible are indoor theatres, several drive-ins, golf courses, boating, fishing, two state parks, bowling alleys, municipal swimming pool and private swim club, baseball, tennis, and croquet.

■ **ATA COLLEGE**
10180 Linn Station Rd.
Ste. A200

Louisville, KY 40223
Tel: (502)371-8330
Web Site: www.ata.edu
Description: Proprietary, 2-year, coed. Awards terminal associate degrees. Total enrollment: 450. Student-undergrad faculty ratio is 14:1. 73 applied, 78% were admitted. 16% from out-of-state. 66% 25 or older. Retention: 74% of full-time freshmen returned the following year.
Entrance Requirements: Open admission.

■ BECKFIELD COLLEGE

16 Spiral Dr.
Florence, KY 41042
Tel: (859)371-9393
Fax: (859)371-5096
E-mail: lboerger@beckfield.edu
Web Site: www.beckfield.edu
Description: Proprietary, primarily 2-year, coed. Awards certificates, diplomas, terminal associate, and bachelor's degrees. Founded 1984. Setting: suburban campus. Total enrollment: 605. 69% 25 or older. Calendar: quarters.
Entrance Requirements: Open admission.

■ BELLARMINE UNIVERSITY

2001 Newburg Rd.
Louisville, KY 40205
Tel: (502)272-8000; Free: 800-274-4723
E-mail: admissions@bellarmine.edu
Web Site: www.bellarmine.edu
Description: Independent Roman Catholic, comprehensive, coed. Awards bachelor's, master's, and doctoral degrees. Founded 1950. Setting: 175-acre suburban campus with easy access to Louisville. Endowment: $66.9 million. Educational spending for the previous fiscal year: $10,917 per student. Total enrollment: 3,369. Faculty: 418 (176 full-time, 242 part-time). Student-undergrad faculty ratio is 12:1. 5,535 applied, 86% were admitted. Full-time: 2,401 students, 64% women, 36% men. Part-time: 151 students, 60% women, 40% men. Students come from 41 states and territories, 22 other countries, 29% from out-of-state. 0.2% American Indian or Alaska Native, non-Hispanic/Latino; 4% Hispanic/Latino; 5% Black or African American, non-Hispanic/Latino; 2% Asian, non-Hispanic/Latino; 0.1% Native Hawaiian or other Pacific Islander, non-Hispanic/Latino; 1% international. 6% 25 or older, 40% live on campus, 2% transferred in. Retention: 79% of full-time freshmen returned the following year. Academic areas with the most degrees conferred: health professions and related sciences; business/marketing; parks and recreation. Core. Calendar: semesters. Services for LD students, advanced placement, accelerated degree program, self-designed majors, freshman honors college, honors program, independent study, distance learning, double major, summer session for credit, part-time degree program, adult/continuing education programs, co-op programs and internships, graduate courses open to undergrads. Study abroad program. ROTC: Army (c), Air Force (c).
Entrance Requirements: Options: electronic application, early admission, early action, deferred admission, international baccalaureate accepted. Required: high school transcript, minimum 2.5 high school GPA, 1 recommendation, SAT or ACT. Recommended: interview. Required for some: essay. Entrance: moderately difficult. Application deadline: 8/15. Notification: continuous until 9/1. SAT Reasoning Test deadline: 8/15. SAT Subject Test deadline: 8/15. Transfer credits accepted: Yes.
Costs Per Year: Application fee: $25. One-time mandatory fee: $400. Comprehensive fee: $51,850 includes full-time tuition ($40,880), mandatory fees ($1550), and college room and board ($9420). College room only: $4800. Part-time tuition: $950 per credit hour.
Collegiate Environment: Orientation program. Drama-theater group, choral group, student-run newspaper, radio station. Social organizations: 75 open to all; national fraternities, national sororities; 1% of eligible men and 1% of eligible women are members. Most popular organizations: Student Government, Bellarmine Activities Council, Knights Nation, Fellowship of Christian Athletes, Delta Sigma Pi. Major annual events: Ball on the Belle, Homecoming, Late Night Breakfast. Student services: health clinic, personal-psychological counseling. Campus security: 24-hour emergency response devices and patrols, student patrols, late night transport-escort service, controlled dormitory access, 24-hour locked residence hall entrances, security cameras. 1,112 college housing spaces available; 1,050 were occupied in 2018-19. Freshmen guaranteed college housing. On-campus residence required through junior year. Options: coed, men-only, women-

only housing available. W. L. Lyons Brown Library. Books: 130,534 (physical), 288,828 (digital/electronic); Serial titles: 189 (physical), 88,144 (digital/electronic); Databases: 145. Weekly public service hours: 140; study areas open 24 hours, 5-7 days a week. Operations spending for the previous fiscal year: $1.5 million. 440 computers available on campus for general student use. A campuswide network can be accessed from student residence rooms and from off campus. Students can access the following: online class registration, mobile app. Staffed computer lab on campus (open 24 hours a day) provides training in use of computers, software, and the Internet.

■ BEREA COLLEGE

Berea, KY 40404
Tel: (859)985-3000; Free: 800-326-5948
E-mail: admissions@berea.edu
Web Site: www.berea.edu
Description: Independent, 4-year, coed. Awards bachelor's degrees. Founded 1855. Setting: 140-acre small town campus. Endowment: $1.2 billion. Educational spending for the previous fiscal year: $16,327 per student. Total enrollment: 1,673. Faculty: 191 (137 full-time, 54 part-time). Student-undergrad faculty ratio is 10:1. 1,575 applied, 38% were admitted. 22% from top 10% of their high school class, 69% from top quarter, 96% from top half. Full-time: 1,631 students, 57% women, 43% men. Part-time: 42 students, 62% women, 38% men. Students come from 42 states and territories, 74 other countries, 55% from out-of-state. 0.1% American Indian or Alaska Native, non-Hispanic/Latino; 12% Hispanic/Latino; 16% Black or African American, non-Hispanic/Latino; 3% Asian, non-Hispanic/Latino; 0.1% Native Hawaiian or other Pacific Islander, non-Hispanic/Latino; 8% international. 4% 25 or older, 87% live on campus, 3% transferred in. Retention: 83% of full-time freshmen returned the following year. Academic areas with the most degrees conferred: biological/life sciences; business/marketing; social sciences. Core. Calendar: semesters. Academic remediation for entering students, ESL program, services for LD students, advanced placement, self-designed majors, honors program, independent study, double major, summer session for credit, internships. Off campus study. Study abroad program.
Entrance Requirements: Option: electronic application. Required: essay, high school transcript, SAT or ACT. Recommended: 2 recommendations, interview. Entrance: moderately difficult. Application deadlines: 3/31, 3/31 for nonresidents. Notification: continuous until 11/1, continuous until 11/1 for nonresidents. Preference given to Appalachian residents with high ability and limited economic resources. SAT Reasoning Test deadline: 4/30. SAT Subject Test deadline: 4/30.
Costs Per Year: Application fee: $0. Comprehensive fee: $7566 includes full-time tuition ($0), mandatory fees ($600), and college room and board ($6966).
Collegiate Environment: Orientation program. Drama-theater group, choral group, student-run newspaper. Social organizations: 70 open to all. Most popular organizations: Campus Activities Board, Cosmopolitan Club, CELTS (Center for Excellence in Learning through Service), Black Cultural Center, African Student Association. Major annual events: Mountain Day, Graduation, Labor Day. Student services: health clinic, personal-psychological counseling, women's center. Campus security: 24-hour emergency response devices and patrols, late night transport-escort service, controlled dormitory access. 1,390 college housing spaces available. Freshmen guaranteed college housing. On-campus residence required through senior year. Options: men-only, women-only housing available. Hutchins Library plus 1 other. Books: 325,660 (physical), 242,958 (digital/electronic); Serial titles: 99,454 (physical), 8,958 (digital/electronic). Weekly public service hours: 94; students can reserve study rooms. Operations spending for the previous fiscal year: $1.6 million.
Community Environment: Nestled in the foothills of the Cumberland Mountains, Berea draws 80% of its students from the Appalachian regions of nine southern states. Excellent motels are found in the community as well as the college hotel. The Churchill Weavers, one of the largest hand-weaving companies in the country, is located here.

■ BIG SANDY COMMUNITY AND TECHNICAL COLLEGE

One Bert T. Combs Dr.
Prestonsburg, KY 41653-1815
Tel: (606)886-3863; Free: 888-641-4132
Fax: (606)886-6943
Web Site: www.bigsandy.kctcs.edu
Description: State-supported, 2-year, coed. Part of Kentucky Community and Technical College System. Awards transfer associate and terminal associate degrees. Founded 1964. Setting: 50-acre rural campus. Total enroll-

ment: 4,856. 36% 25 or older. Core. Calendar: semesters. Academic remediation for entering students, services for LD students, advanced placement, independent study, distance learning, summer session for credit, part-time degree program, adult/continuing education programs, co-op programs. Off campus study at Morehead State University.

Entrance Requirements: Open admission except for nursing program. Options: early admission, deferred admission. Required: high school transcript. Entrance: noncompetitive. Application deadline: rolling.

Collegiate Environment: Orientation program. Choral group. Student services: health clinic, personal-psychological counseling. Campus security: 24-hour emergency response devices. Magoffin Learning Resource Center.

Community Environment: Prestonsburg is the site of a revolutionary war battle and General Garfield's headquarters in 1862. Surrounding the city are eastern Kentucky's coal, oil and gas fields. The urban area has transportation provided by bus and car. The city has hospitals, churches of all denominations, average shopping facilities, and good opportunities for part-time employment. Recreational facilities are available at a state park with boating, fishing, swimming, water skiing, horseback riding, and high lift. Locally are a public park, bowling alley, golf course, swimming pool and tennis courts. The Kentucky Highland Folk Festival, The Jenny Wiley Festival and Horse Show are annual events.

■ **BLUEGRASS COMMUNITY AND TECHNICAL COLLEGE**
470 Cooper Dr.
Lexington, KY 40506-0235
Tel: (859)246-0235; Free: 866-744-4872
E-mail: shelbie.hugle@kctcs.edu
Web Site: www.bluegrass.kctcs.edu

Description: State-supported, 2-year, coed. Part of Kentucky Community and Technical College System. Awards certificates, diplomas, transfer associate, and terminal associate degrees. Founded 1965. Setting: 10-acre urban campus. Endowment: $967,117. Educational spending for the previous fiscal year: $6021 per student. Total enrollment: 11,596. Faculty: 846 (260 full-time, 586 part-time). Student-undergrad faculty ratio is 18:1. Full-time: 5,539 students, 57% women, 43% men. Part-time: 6,057 students, 56% women, 44% men. Students come from 16 states and territories, 26 other countries. 3% live on campus, 4% transferred in. Core. Calendar: semesters. Academic remediation for entering students, ESL program, services for LD students, advanced placement, accelerated degree program, honors program, distance learning, double major, summer session for credit, part-time degree program, adult/continuing education programs, co-op programs. ROTC: Army (c), Air Force (c).

Entrance Requirements: Open admission. Options: electronic application, early admission. Recommended: high school transcript. Required for some: high school transcript. Entrance: noncompetitive. Application deadline: 8/2. Transfer credits accepted: Yes.

Collegiate Environment: Orientation program. Drama-theater group, choral group, student-run newspaper. Social organizations: 21 open to all. Most popular organizations: Student Nursing Association, intramural sports, Enlace (Latino Student Association), International Students' Association, Student American Dental Hygienists Association. Major annual events: Spring Fling, Fall Fest, Welcome Back Ice Cream Special. Student services: personal-psychological counseling. Campus security: 24-hour emergency response devices and patrols, late night transport-escort service. Bluegrass Community and Technical College Library. Operations spending for the previous fiscal year: $185,767. 300 computers available on campus for general student use. A campuswide network can be accessed. Students can access the following: online class registration. Staffed computer lab on campus provides training in use of computers, software, and the Internet.

■ **BRESCIA UNIVERSITY**
717 Frederica St.
Owensboro, KY 42301-3023
Tel: (270)685-3131; Free: 877-273-7242
Fax: (270)686-6422
Web Site: www.brescia.edu

Description: Independent Roman Catholic, comprehensive, coed. Awards associate, bachelor's, and master's degrees. Founded 1950. Setting: 9-acre urban campus. Endowment: $12.4 million. Total enrollment: 1,338. Faculty: 124 (48 full-time, 76 part-time). Student-undergrad faculty ratio is 12:1. 4,158 applied, 42% were admitted. Full-time: 709 students, 73% women, 27% men. Part-time: 563 students, 56% women, 44% men. Students come from 48 states and territories, 7 other countries, 56% from out-of-state. 0.3% American Indian or Alaska Native, non-Hispanic/Latino; 7% Hispanic/Latino;

15% Black or African American, non-Hispanic/Latino; 1% Asian, non-Hispanic/Latino; 0.2% Native Hawaiian or other Pacific Islander, non-Hispanic/Latino; 1% international. 33% 25 or older, 41% live on campus, 8% transferred in. Retention: 64% of full-time freshmen returned the following year. Academic areas with the most degrees conferred: public administration and social services; business/marketing; health professions and related sciences. Core. Calendar: semesters. Academic remediation for entering students, services for LD students, advanced placement, self-designed majors, honors program, independent study, distance learning, double major, summer session for credit, part-time degree program, adult/continuing education programs, internships. Off campus study at Kentucky Wesleyan College, Owensboro Community and Technical College. Study abroad program.

Entrance Requirements: Options: electronic application, deferred admission. Required: high school transcript, SAT or ACT. Required for some: essay, 1 recommendation, interview. Entrance: moderately difficult. Application deadline: rolling. Notification: continuous. SAT Reasoning Test deadline: 8/23. SAT Subject Test deadline: 8/23. Transfer credits accepted: Yes.

Costs Per Year: Application fee: $25. One-time mandatory fee: $200. Comprehensive fee: $31,450 includes full-time tuition ($21,500), mandatory fees ($600), and college room and board ($9350). Full-time tuition and fees vary according to course load, degree level, and location. Room and board charges vary according to board plan and housing facility. Part-time tuition: $590 per credit hour. Part-time tuition varies according to course load, degree level, and location.

Collegiate Environment: Orientation program. Drama-theater group, choral group, student-run newspaper. Social organizations: 15 open to all; 30% of eligible men and 70% of eligible women are members. Most popular organizations: Student Government, Alpha Chi, Kentucky Education Association, National Society for Speech Language and Hearing Association, ZEST. Major annual events: Orientation, Homecoming, Founder's Day Convocation. Student services: personal-psychological counseling. Campus security: 24-hour emergency response devices, late night transport-escort service, controlled dormitory access. Fr. Leonard Alvey Library. Books: 72,970 (physical), 1,245 (digital/electronic); Databases: 75. Students can reserve study rooms. Operations spending for the previous fiscal year: $407,154. 90 computers available on campus for general student use. Computer purchase/lease plans available. A campuswide network can be accessed from student residence rooms and from off campus. Staffed computer lab on campus provides training in use of computers, software, and the Internet.

Community Environment: Brescia University is located in Owensboro, Kentucky, on the Ohio River. With a metropolitan population of 55,500, Owensboro is easily accessible from any direction. The college campus is within walking distance of the revitalized downtown area, the performing arts center, public library, art museum, natural science and history museum, as well as numerous restaurants, churches, and parks. Many Owensboro industries and professional organizations cooperate with Brescia in providing enriching off-campus learning opportunities for students, particularly in the areas of business, education, psychology, social work, speech and hearing, and special education.

■ **CAMPBELLSVILLE UNIVERSITY**
1 University Dr.
Campbellsville, KY 42718-2799
Tel: (270)789-5000; Free: 800-264-6014
Fax: (270)789-5071
E-mail: admissions@campbellsville.edu
Web Site: www.campbellsville.edu

Description: Independent, comprehensive, coed, affiliated with Kentucky Baptist Convention. Awards associate, bachelor's, master's, and doctoral degrees and post-master's certificates. Founded 1906. Setting: 90-acre small town campus. Endowment: $21 million. Educational spending for the previous fiscal year: $4619 per student. Total enrollment: 12,629. Faculty: 463 (170 full-time, 293 part-time). Student-undergrad faculty ratio is 23:1. 3,542 applied, 83% were admitted. 15% from top 10% of their high school class, 36% from top quarter, 67% from top half. Full-time: 2,263 students, 57% women, 43% men. Part-time: 2,876 students, 63% women, 37% men. Students come from 42 states and territories, 46 other countries, 16% from out-of-state. 0.4% American Indian or Alaska Native, non-Hispanic/Latino; 3% Hispanic/Latino; 13% Black or African American, non-Hispanic/Latino; 0.5% Asian, non-Hispanic/Latino; 0.2% Native Hawaiian or other Pacific Islander, non-Hispanic/Latino; 6% international. 25% 25 or older, 56% live on campus, 5% transferred in. Retention: 64% of full-time freshmen returned the following year. Academic areas with the most degrees conferred: business/marketing; education; homeland security, law enforcement, firefighting, and protective services. Core. Calendar: semesters. Academic remediation for entering students, ESL program, services for LD students, advanced placement, accelerated degree program, honors program, independent study, distance learning, double major, summer session for credit, part-time degree program, adult/continuing education programs, co-op programs and internships, graduate courses open to undergrads. Off campus study at Western Kentucky University (ROTC). Study abroad program. ROTC: Army (c).

Entrance Requirements: Options: electronic application, deferred admission. Required: high school transcript, minimum 2 high school GPA. Recommended: essay, minimum 3 high school GPA, interview, SAT or ACT. Entrance: moderately difficult. Application deadline: rolling. Notification: continuous. SAT Reasoning Test deadline: 8/15. Transfer credits accepted: Yes.

Costs Per Year: Application fee: $20. Comprehensive fee: $33,400 includes full-time tuition ($24,900), mandatory fees ($500), and college room and board ($8000). Part-time tuition: $1038 per credit hour. Part-time mandatory fees: $250 per year.

Collegiate Environment: Orientation program. Drama-theater group, choral group, marching band, student-run newspaper, radio station. Social organizations: 34 open to all. Most popular organizations: Baptist Campus Ministries, Student Government Association, International Student Association, Black Student Association, KANS (Nursing Society). Major annual events: Welcome Week Events (concert), Homecoming, Midnight Breakfast. Student services: health clinic, personal-psychological counseling. Campus security: 24-hour emergency response devices and patrols, student patrols, late night transport-escort service, controlled dormitory access. 1,185 college housing spaces available; 1,052 were occupied in 2018-19. Freshmen guaranteed college housing. On-campus residence required through sophomore year. Options: men-only, women-only housing available. Montgomery Library. Books: 125,057 (physical), 351,230 (digital/electronic); Serial titles: 7,762 (digital/electronic); Databases: 94. Weekly public service hours: 77; students can reserve study rooms. Operations spending for the previous fiscal year: $462,651. 220 computers available on campus for general student use. A campuswide network can be accessed from student residence rooms and from off campus. Students can access the following: online class registration. Staffed computer lab on campus provides training in use of computers, software, and the Internet.

Community Environment: The 70-acre Campbellsville campus is situated precisely in the center of Kentucky, one-half mile from downtown Campbellsville (population 10,900), 40 minutes southeast of Elizabethtown, one and one-half hours from Louisville and Lexington, and just over two hours from Nashville. The college is located on KY55 and can be reached from the north by way of the Bluegrass Parkway and from the south by way of the Cumberland Parkway.

■ **CENTRE COLLEGE**
600 W Walnut St.
Danville, KY 40422-1394
Tel: (859)238-5200; Free: 800-423-6236
Fax: (859)238-5456
E-mail: admission@centre.edu
Web Site: www.centre.edu

Description: Independent, 4-year, coed, affiliated with Presbyterian Church (U.S.A.). Awards bachelor's degrees. Founded 1819. Setting: 160-acre small town campus. System endowment: $269.4 million. Research spending for the previous fiscal year: $497,459. Educational spending for the previous fiscal year: $14,216 per student. Total enrollment: 1,450. Faculty: 137 (129 full-time, 8 part-time). Student-undergrad faculty ratio is 10:1. 2,454 applied, 76% were admitted. 64% from top 10% of their high school class, 86% from top quarter, 99% from top half. Full-time: 1,449 students, 51% women, 49% men. Part-time: 1 student, 100% men. Students come from 46 states and territories, 17 other countries, 44% from out-of-state. 0.2% American Indian or Alaska Native, non-Hispanic/Latino; 5% Hispanic/Latino; 5% Black or African American, non-Hispanic/Latino; 5% Asian, non-Hispanic/Latino; 0.1% Native Hawaiian or other Pacific Islander, non-Hispanic/Latino; 7% international. 98% live on campus, 1% transferred in. Retention: 91% of full-time freshmen returned the following year. Academic areas with the most degrees conferred: social sciences; psychology; biological/life sciences. Core. Calendar: 4-1-4. Services for LD students, advanced placement, self-designed majors, honors program, independent study, double major, co-op programs and internships. Off campus study at Associated Colleges of the South. Study abroad program. ROTC: Army (c), Air Force (c).

Entrance Requirements: Options: electronic application, early admission, early decision, early action, deferred admission, international baccalaureate accepted. Required: essay, high school transcript, 1 recommendation, SAT or ACT. Recommended: interview. Entrance: very difficult. Application deadlines: 1/15, 11/15 for early decision, 12/1 for early action. Notification: 3/31, 12/15 for early decision, 1/15 for early action. SAT Reasoning Test deadline: 1/15. Transfer credits accepted: Yes. Applicants placed on waiting list: 107. Wait-listed applicants offered admission: 4. Early decision applicants: 88. Early decision applicants admitted: 67. Early action applicants: 1,423. Early action applicants admitted: 1,230.

Costs Per Year: Application fee: $0. Comprehensive fee: $52,180 includes full-time tuition ($41,700) and college room and board ($10,480). College room only: $5240. Room and board charges vary according to housing facility. Part-time tuition: $1489 per credit hour.

Collegiate Environment: Orientation program. Drama-theater group, choral group, student-run newspaper, radio station. Social organizations: 70 open to all; national fraternities, national sororities, local fraternities; 36% of eligible men and 40% of eligible women are members. Most popular organizations: Student Government Association, Centre Action Reaches Everyone, Student Activities Council, Christian fellowship group, Diversity Student Union. Major annual events: Homecoming, Spring Carnival, Family Weekend. Student services: health clinic, personal-psychological counseling. Campus security: 24-hour emergency response devices and patrols, late night transport-escort service, controlled dormitory access. Doherty Library. Books: 231,820 (physical), 33,042 (digital/electronic); Serial titles: 536 (physical), 27,570 (digital/electronic); Databases: 530. Weekly public service hours: 113; study areas open 24 hours, 5-7 days a week; students can reserve study rooms. Operations spending for the previous fiscal year: $1.4 million. 425 computers available on campus for general student use. Computer purchase/lease plans available. A campuswide network can be accessed from student residence rooms and from off campus. Students can access the following: online class registration. Staffed computer lab on campus provides training in use of computers, software, and the Internet.

Community Environment: Danville is a prosperous community located on the southern edge of Kentucky's famous bluegrass region. The town has a rich historical heritage. It was the first seat of government west of the Alleghenies, and is also known for its early contributions in medicine, education, and government. Today, Danville is a model in Kentucky and the region as a center for light industry, with more than a dozen major employers. Midwinter days average 35 degrees; midsummer temperatures average 80 degrees. There is sunshine 60% of the time. Transportation is provided by a bus line and three main highways. Danville has fine horse farms, many churches, a library, a Regional Arts Center, bowling alley, fishing, boating, waterskiing, golf, and theaters. Part-time jobs are available.

■ **CLEAR CREEK BAPTIST BIBLE COLLEGE**
300 Clear Creek Rd.
Pineville, KY 40977-9754
Tel: (606)337-3196
E-mail: bhowell@ccbbc.edu
Web Site: www.ccbbc.edu

Description: Independent Southern Baptist, 4-year, coed. Awards associate and bachelor's degrees. Founded 1926. Setting: 700-acre rural campus. Total enrollment: 172. Faculty: 16 (8 full-time, 8 part-time). Student-undergrad faculty ratio is 13:1. 52 applied, 88% were admitted. 72% 25 or older. Retention: 88% of full-time freshmen returned the following year. Core. Calendar: semesters. Summer session for credit, part-time degree program.

Entrance Requirements: Open admission. Options: electronic application, deferred admission. Required: essay, 4 recommendations. Recommended: high school transcript, interview. Entrance: noncompetitive. Application deadline: 7/15. Notification: continuous.

Collegiate Environment: Orientation program. Choral group. Student services: health clinic, personal-psychological counseling. Campus security: 24-hour emergency response devices, student patrols. Carolyn Boatman Brooks Memorial Library. 15 computers available on campus for general student use. A campuswide network can be accessed. Staffed computer lab on campus.

Community Environment: The campus bounds Pine Mountain State Park. Pineville, founded in 1799, is located in a rural area 16 miles north of Cumberland Gap, and is served by the Greyhound bus line. Churches, a small shopping area and some part-time employment are available.

■ **DAYMAR COLLEGE**
2421 Fitzgerald Industrial Dr.
Bowling Green, KY 42101

Tel: (270)843-6750; Free: 877-258-7796
Fax: (270)843-6976
E-mail: thenderson@daymarcollege.edu
Web Site: www.daymarcollege.edu
Description: Proprietary, 2-year, coed. Awards diplomas and transfer associate degrees. Founded 1989. Setting: suburban campus with easy access to Nashville. Total enrollment: 499. Student-undergrad faculty ratio is 18:1. 6% from out-of-state. 67% 25 or older. Core. Calendar: semesters. Part-time degree program, adult/continuing education programs.
Entrance Requirements: Open admission. Required: high school transcript. Entrance: noncompetitive.
Collegiate Environment: Orientation program. Student-run newspaper. Student services: personal-psychological counseling. Campus security: 24-hour emergency response devices.

■ EASTERN KENTUCKY UNIVERSITY
521 Lancaster Ave.
Richmond, KY 40475-3102
Tel: (859)622-1000; Free: 800-465-9191
Fax: (859)622-1020
E-mail: admissions@eku.edu
Web Site: www.eku.edu
Description: State-supported, comprehensive, coed. Awards associate, bachelor's, master's, and doctoral degrees and post-master's certificates. Founded 1906. Setting: 500-acre small town campus with easy access to Lexington. Endowment: $60.2 million. Research spending for the previous fiscal year: $1 million. Educational spending for the previous fiscal year: $6979 per student. Total enrollment: 16,844. Faculty: 1,144 (637 full-time, 507 part-time). Student-undergrad faculty ratio is 17:1. 10,215 applied, 71% were admitted. 10% from top 10% of their high school class, 25% from top quarter, 49% from top half. 34 valedictorians, 274 student government officers. Full-time: 11,332 students, 57% women, 43% men. Part-time: 2,995 students, 59% women, 41% men. Students come from 53 states and territories, 44 other countries, 13% from out-of-state. 0.3% American Indian or Alaska Native, non-Hispanic/Latino; 2% Hispanic/Latino; 6% Black or African American, non-Hispanic/Latino; 0.8% Asian, non-Hispanic/Latino; 0.1% Native Hawaiian or other Pacific Islander, non-Hispanic/Latino; 2% international. 23% 25 or older, 32% live on campus, 7% transferred in. Retention: 74% of full-time freshmen returned the following year. Academic areas with the most degrees conferred: health professions and related sciences; homeland security, law enforcement, firefighting, and protective services; education. Core. Calendar: semesters. Academic remediation for entering students, ESL program, services for LD students, advanced placement, accelerated degree program, self-designed majors, honors program, independent study, distance learning, double major, summer session for credit, part-time degree program, external degree program, adult/continuing education programs, co-op programs and internships, graduate courses open to undergrads. Study abroad program. ROTC: Army, Air Force (c).
Entrance Requirements: Open admission. Options: electronic application, deferred admission, international baccalaureate accepted. Required: high school transcript, minimum 2 high school GPA, SAT or ACT. Recommended: minimum 2.5 high school GPA. Required for some: SAT and SAT Subject Tests or ACT. Entrance: minimally difficult. Application deadline: 8/1. Notification: continuous, continuous for nonresidents. SAT Reasoning Test deadline: 8/1. SAT Subject Test deadline: 8/1. Transfer credits accepted: Yes.
Costs Per Year: Application fee: $35. State resident tuition: $8996 full-time, $365 per credit hour part-time. Nonresident tuition: $18,774 full-time, $782.25 per credit hour part-time. Full-time tuition varies according to degree level and location. Part-time tuition varies according to course load. College room and board: $9788. College room only: $4918. Room and board charges vary according to board plan and housing facility.
Collegiate Environment: Orientation program. Drama-theater group, choral group, marching band, student-run newspaper, radio station. Social organizations: 160 open to all; national fraternities, national sororities, local fraternities; 8% of eligible men and 6% of eligible women are members. Most popular organizations: Honor Society, Regular Society. Major annual events: Homecoming, Fall Festival, Spring Fling. Student services: health clinic, personal-psychological counseling. Campus security: 24-hour emergency response devices and patrols, student patrols, late night transport-escort service, controlled dormitory access. John Grant Crabbe Library plus 2 others. Operations spending for the previous fiscal year: $5.5 million. 1,800 computers available on campus for general student use. A campuswide network can be accessed from student residence rooms and from off

campus. Students can access the following: online class registration. Staffed computer lab on campus provides training in use of computers, software, and the Internet.
Community Environment: Local industries are a miniature lamp plant and tool and die manufacturing. Richmond is located in the famous Bluegrass Region, 26 miles southeast of Lexington, and 55 miles to the State Capital of Frankfort on the Kentucky River. Recreational facilities are available at nearby parks and lakes. There are part-time work opportunities available.

■ ELIZABETHTOWN COMMUNITY AND TECHNICAL COLLEGE
620 College St. Rd.
Elizabethtown, KY 42701
Tel: (270)769-2371; Free: 877-246-2322
Fax: (270)769-0736
Web Site: www.elizabethtown.kctcs.edu
Description: State-supported, 2-year, coed. Part of Kentucky Community and Technical College System. Awards certificates, diplomas, transfer associate, and terminal associate degrees. Founded 1966. Setting: 80-acre small town campus. Endowment: $655,000. Educational spending for the previous fiscal year: $3762 per student. Total enrollment: 7,353. Faculty: 302 (141 full-time, 161 part-time). Student-undergrad faculty ratio is 22:1. Full-time: 2,822 students, 56% women, 44% men. Part-time: 4,531 students, 51% women, 49% men. Students come from 17 states and territories, 1% from out-of-state. 0.4% American Indian or Alaska Native, non-Hispanic/Latino; 3% Hispanic/Latino; 7% Black or African American, non-Hispanic/Latino; 0.9% Asian, non-Hispanic/Latino; 0.2% Native Hawaiian or other Pacific Islander, non-Hispanic/Latino. 46% 25 or older, 3% transferred in. Calendar: semesters. Academic remediation for entering students, services for LD students, advanced placement, distance learning, summer session for credit, part-time degree program, co-op programs and internships. Off campus study.
Entrance Requirements: Option: electronic application. Recommended: ACT. Required for some: high school transcript. Entrance: noncompetitive. Application deadline: rolling. Notification: continuous.
Collegiate Environment: Orientation program. Student-run newspaper. Campus security: late night transport-escort service. ECTC Media Center. Operations spending for the previous fiscal year: $467,009. 150 computers available on campus for general student use. A campuswide network can be accessed. Students can access the following: online class registration, online bill payment. Staffed computer lab on campus provides training in use of computers, software, and the Internet.

■ GALEN COLLEGE OF NURSING (HAZARD)
100 Airport Gardens Dr.
Hazard, KY 41701
Description: Proprietary, 2-year, coed.

■ GALEN COLLEGE OF NURSING (LOUISVILLE)
1031 Zorn Ave.
Ste. 400
Louisville, KY 40207
Tel: (502)410-6200; Free: 877-223-7040
Web Site: www.galencollege.edu
Description: Proprietary, primarily 2-year, coed. Awards certificates, transfer associate, terminal associate, and bachelor's degrees. Founded 1990.

■ GATEWAY COMMUNITY AND TECHNICAL COLLEGE
500 Technology Way
Florence, KY 41042
Tel: (859)441-4500
Fax: (859)292-6415
E-mail: andre.washington@kctcs.edu
Web Site: www.gateway.kctcs.edu
Description: State-supported, 2-year, coed. Part of Kentucky Community and Technical College System. Awards certificates, diplomas, transfer associate, and terminal associate degrees. Founded 1961. Setting: suburban campus with easy access to Cincinnati. Total enrollment: 4,215. Faculty: 234 (84 full-time, 150 part-time). Student-undergrad faculty ratio is 18:1. 1,872 applied, 98% were admitted. 5% from out-of-state. 0.2% American Indian or Alaska Native, non-Hispanic/Latino; 4% Hispanic/Latino; 7% Black or African American, non-Hispanic/Latino; 0.7% Asian, non-Hispanic/Latino. 40% 25 or older. Core. Calendar: semesters. Academic remediation for entering students, services for LD students, distance learning, summer session for credit, part-time degree program, co-op programs and internships.

Entrance Requirements: Open admission. Options: electronic application, early admission, deferred admission. Required: high school transcript, ACT or SAT; KYOTE (Math); TABE-Advanced (Reading and Writing). Entrance: minimally difficult. Application deadline: rolling. Notification: continuous. Transfer credits accepted: Yes.

Costs Per Year: State resident tuition: $4056 full-time, $169 per credit part-time. Nonresident tuition: $14,208 full-time, $592 per credit part-time. Mandatory fees: $8 per credit part-time, $40 per term part-time. Full-time tuition varies according to course load. Part-time tuition and fees vary according to course load.

Collegiate Environment: Orientation program. Social organizations: Phi Theta Kappa, National Technical Honor Society. Most popular organizations: National Technical Honor Society, Student Government Association, Speech Team, Phi Theta Kappa. Student services: personal-psychological counseling. Campus security: 24-hour emergency response devices, campus security during hours of operation. Main library plus 3 others. 881 computers available on campus for general student use. A campuswide network can be accessed. Students can access the following: online class registration.

■ **GEORGETOWN COLLEGE**
400 E College St.
Georgetown, KY 40324-1696
Tel: (502)863-8000; Free: 800-788-9985
Fax: (502)868-8891
E-mail: admissions@georgetowncollege.edu
Web Site: www.georgetowncollege.edu

Description: Independent, comprehensive, coed, affiliated with Baptist Church. Awards bachelor's and master's degrees. Founded 1829. Setting: 104-acre suburban campus with easy access to Cincinnati, OH; Louisville, KY. Endowment: $41.7 million. Educational spending for the previous fiscal year: $6353 per student. Total enrollment: 1,608. Faculty: 159 (78 full-time, 81 part-time). Student-undergrad faculty ratio is 11:1. 2,498 applied, 67% were admitted. 17% from top 10% of their high school class, 40% from top quarter, 68% from top half. Full-time: 912 students, 56% women, 44% men. Part-time: 49 students, 47% women, 53% men. Students come from 31 states and territories, 9 other countries, 25% from out-of-state. 0.2% American Indian or Alaska Native, non-Hispanic/Latino; 4% Hispanic/Latino; 10% Black or African American, non-Hispanic/Latino; 0.7% Asian, non-Hispanic/Latino; 0.4% international. 2% 25 or older, 90% live on campus, 6% transferred in. Retention: 63% of full-time freshmen returned the following year. Academic areas with the most degrees conferred: business/marketing; biological/life sciences; parks and recreation. Core. Calendar: semesters. ESL program, services for LD students, advanced placement, self-designed majors, honors program, independent study, distance learning, double major, summer session for credit, part-time degree program, co-op programs and internships, graduate courses open to undergrads. Off campus study. Study abroad program. ROTC: Army (c), Air Force (c).

Entrance Requirements: Options: electronic application, deferred admission, international baccalaureate accepted. Required: high school transcript, minimum 2 high school GPA, SAT or ACT. Required for some: interview. Entrance: moderately difficult. Application deadline: rolling. Notification: continuous. SAT Reasoning Test deadline: 8/15. Transfer credits accepted: Yes.

Costs Per Year: Application fee: $0. Comprehensive fee: $49,970 includes full-time tuition ($39,810) and college room and board ($10,160). College room only: $4900. Part-time tuition: $1230 per credit hour.

Collegiate Environment: Orientation program. Drama-theater group, choral group, student-run newspaper, radio station. Social organizations: national fraternities, national sororities, local fraternities, local sororities; 25% of eligible men and 34% of eligible women are members. Major annual events: Homecoming, Hanging of the Green, Midnight Brunch during Finals Weeks. Student services: health clinic, personal-psychological counseling. Campus security: 24-hour patrols, late night transport-escort service, controlled dormitory access. Freshmen guaranteed college housing. On-campus residence required through senior year. Options: men-only, women-only housing available. Anna Ashcraft Ensor Learning Resource Center. Books: 129,442 (physical), 256,326 (digital/electronic); Serial titles: 20 (physical), 41,920 (digital/electronic); Databases: 133. Weekly public service hours: 92. 120 computers available on campus for general student use. Computer purchase/lease plans available. A campuswide network can be accessed from student residence rooms and from off campus. Students can access the following: online class registration, Library apps for smartphones. Staffed computer lab on campus provides training in use of computers, software, and the Internet.

Community Environment: This town was the site of McClelland's Fort, a log stockade that was completed about 1776. Today the city is a residential and educational community located 12 miles north of Lexington and 75 miles east of Louisville, and can be reached by several major highways. Recently identified as one of Kentucky's two"safest cities," Georgetown is also the site of the Toyota Corporation's manufacturing plant. The Kentucky State Horse Park is only 5 miles south of the campus.

■ **HAZARD COMMUNITY AND TECHNICAL COLLEGE**
1 Community College Dr.
Hazard, KY 41701-2403
Tel: (606)436-5721; Free: 800-246-7521
Fax: (606)439-2988
Web Site: www.hazard.kctcs.edu

Description: State-supported, 2-year, coed. Part of Kentucky Community and Technical College System. Awards certificates, diplomas, transfer associate, and terminal associate degrees. Founded 1968. Setting: 34-acre rural campus. Total enrollment: 4,714. Faculty: 170 (80 full-time, 90 part-time). Student-undergrad faculty ratio is 25:1. 7% from top 10% of their high school class, 26% from top quarter, 55% from top half. Full-time: 1,806 students, 62% women, 38% men. Part-time: 2,908 students, 37% women, 63% men. 2% from out-of-state. 43% 25 or older. Calendar: semesters. Honors program, independent study, distance learning, co-op programs.

Entrance Requirements: Open admission for state residents. Option: early admission. Required: high school transcript. Entrance: noncompetitive. Application deadline: rolling. Notification: continuous.

Community Environment: Hazard, the County Seat of Perry County, is the retail and cultural center of southeastern Kentucky. The college serves an 8-county (Breathitt, Knott, Leslie, Letcher, Wolfe, Lee, Owsley, and Perry) all rural area. The College's service area is also in the heart of the state's coal country, in the Cumberland Mountains of Kentucky.

■ **HENDERSON COMMUNITY COLLEGE**
2660 S Green St.
Henderson, KY 42420-4623
Tel: (270)827-1867; Free: 800-696-9958
E-mail: chad.phillips@kctcs.edu
Web Site: www.henderson.kctcs.edu

Description: State-supported, 2-year, coed. Part of Kentucky Community and Technical College System. Awards certificates, diplomas, transfer associate, and terminal associate degrees. Founded 1963. Setting: 120-acre small town campus. Total enrollment: 1,586. Full-time: 506 students, 61% women, 39% men. Part-time: 1,080 students, 71% women, 29% men. Students come from 9 states and territories, 9% from out-of-state. 0.1% American Indian or Alaska Native, non-Hispanic/Latino; 4% Hispanic/Latino; 10% Black or African American, non-Hispanic/Latino; 0.4% Asian, non-Hispanic/Latino; 0.1% Native Hawaiian or other Pacific Islander, non-Hispanic/Latino. 41% 25 or older, 3% transferred in. Retention: 52% of full-time freshmen returned the following year. Core. Calendar: semesters. Academic remediation for entering students, ESL program, advanced placement, accelerated degree program, independent study, distance learning, double major, summer session for credit, part-time degree program, external degree program, adult/continuing education programs, co-op programs and internships. Off campus study.

Entrance Requirements: Open admission. Required: high school transcript. Required for some: essay, interview. Entrance: noncompetitive.

Costs Per Year: Area resident tuition: $169 full-time. State resident tuition: $169 full-time. Nonresident tuition: $592 full-time.

Collegiate Environment: Orientation program. Drama-theater group, student-run radio station. Student services: personal-psychological counseling. Campus security: 24-hour emergency response devices. College housing not available. Hartfield Learning Resource Center plus 1 other.

Community Environment: An industrial city, Henderson is on the Ohio River in an important oil-producing and agricultural area. Principal crops are corn, soybeans and tobacco. Part-time employment is available. Transportation provided by rail and bus lines within the city and airlines located in Evansville, Indiana, nine miles away. Ellis Park Racetrack, three miles north, offers thoroughbred racing August through Labor Day and harness racing from in late May to late July. 95 organizations embrace all types of activities. There is a hospital and clinics, public library, YMCA, and 36 churches offering community service. This is the home of Audubon Museum which houses the world's finest collection of Audubon items. The city has one of the finest summer recreational programs in the state of Kentucky. the finest summer recreational programs in the state of Kentucky.

■ HOPKINSVILLE COMMUNITY COLLEGE

PO Box 2100
Hopkinsville, KY 42241-2100
Tel: (270)707-3700; Free: 866-534-2224
Web Site: hopkinsville.kctcs.edu

Description: State-supported, 2-year, coed. Part of Kentucky Community and Technical College System. Awards certificates, diplomas, transfer associate, and terminal associate degrees. Founded 1965. Setting: 69-acre small town campus with easy access to Nashville. Total enrollment: 3,120. Faculty: 158 (57 full-time, 101 part-time). Student-undergrad faculty ratio is 12:1. Full-time: 1,245 students, 66% women, 34% men. Part-time: 1,875 students, 62% women, 38% men. 0.5% American Indian or Alaska Native, non-Hispanic/Latino; 9% Hispanic/Latino; 22% Black or African American, non-Hispanic/Latino; 1% Asian, non-Hispanic/Latino; 0.8% Native Hawaiian or other Pacific Islander, non-Hispanic/Latino; 0.2% international. 7% transferred in. Retention: 43% of full-time freshmen returned the following year. Core. Calendar: semesters. Academic remediation for entering students, services for LD students, advanced placement, honors program, independent study, distance learning, summer session for credit, part-time degree program, co-op programs.

Entrance Requirements: Open admission except for nursing program. Options: electronic application, deferred admission. Recommended: high school transcript. Entrance: noncompetitive. Application deadline: rolling. Notification: continuous. Transfer credits accepted: Yes.

Costs Per Year: Application fee: $0. State resident tuition: $5070 full-time, $169 per credit hour part-time. Nonresident tuition: $17,760 full-time, $592 per credit hour part-time. Mandatory fees: $340 full-time, $8 per credit hour part-time. Full-time tuition and fees vary according to reciprocity agreements. Part-time tuition and fees vary according to reciprocity agreements.

Collegiate Environment: Orientation program. Student-run newspaper. Social organizations: 25 open to all. Most popular organizations: Ag Tech, Amateur Radio, Ballroom Dance, Baptist Campus Ministries, Black Men United. Major annual events: Fun Day, Appreciation Day, Circle of Love. Campus security: 24-hour emergency response devices, late night transport-escort service, security provided by trained security personnel during hours of normal operation. Learning Resource Center. 400 computers available on campus for general student use. Computer purchase/lease plans available. A campuswide network can be accessed. Students can access the following: online class registration. Staffed computer lab on campus.

Community Environment: Hopkinsville is noted as an agricultural and industrial center with important livestock, grain, and dark tobacco markets, flour and feed production, and the manufacturing of shoes, clothing, hardwood flooring, lighting fixtures, industrial springs, and automotive products. The city is served by rail, bus, and air lines via nearby Clarksville and Nashville, Tennessee.

■ INTERACTIVE COLLEGE OF TECHNOLOGY

76 Carothers Rd.
Newport, KY 41071
Tel: (859)282-8989
Fax: (859)282-8475
E-mail: dmamas@ict.edu
Web Site: ict.edu

Description: Proprietary, 2-year, coed. Part of Interactive Learning Systems. Awards certificates, diplomas, and terminal associate degrees. Founded 1980. Setting: small town campus with easy access to Cincinnati. Core. Calendar: semesters. Academic remediation for entering students, distance learning, part-time degree program, internships.

■ JEFFERSON COMMUNITY AND TECHNICAL COLLEGE

109 E Broadway
Louisville, KY 40202-2005
Tel: (502)213-5333
Fax: (502)213-2115
Web Site: www.jefferson.kctcs.edu

Description: State-supported, 2-year, coed. Part of Kentucky Community and Technical College System. Awards certificates, diplomas, transfer associate, and terminal associate degrees. Founded 1968. Setting: 10-acre urban campus. Endowment: $2.2 million. Educational spending for the previous fiscal year: $1982 per student. Total enrollment: 15,475. Faculty: 652 (292 full-time, 360 part-time). Student-undergrad faculty ratio is 19:1. Full-time: 4,879 students, 56% women, 44% men. Part-time: 10,596 students, 51% women, 49% men. Students come from 10 states and territories, 5% from out-of-state. 39% 25 or older, 14% transferred in. Core. Calendar:

semesters. Academic remediation for entering students, ESL program, services for LD students, advanced placement, honors program, independent study, distance learning, summer session for credit, part-time degree program, external degree program, adult/continuing education programs, co-op programs and internships. Off campus study at members of the Kentuckiana Metroversity. ROTC: Army (c).

Entrance Requirements: Open admission except for high school students in early admissions programs. Option: early admission. Entrance: noncompetitive. Application deadline: rolling. Notification: continuous.

Collegiate Environment: Drama-theater group, student-run newspaper. Student services: personal-psychological counseling. Campus security: 24-hour emergency response devices and patrols, late night transport-escort service. John T. Smith Learning Resource Center plus 3 others. Operations spending for the previous fiscal year: $282,102. 895 computers available on campus for general student use. A campuswide network can be accessed from off-campus. Students can access the following: online class registration. Staffed computer lab on campus provides training in use of computers and the Internet.

Community Environment: See University of Louisville.

■ KENTUCKY CHRISTIAN UNIVERSITY

100 Academic Pky.
Grayson, KY 41143-2205
Tel: (606)474-3000; Free: 800-522-3181
Fax: (606)474-3155
E-mail: sgreer@kcu.edu
Web Site: www.kcu.edu

Description: Independent, comprehensive, coed, affiliated with Christian Churches and Churches of Christ. Awards bachelor's and master's degrees. Founded 1919. Setting: 121-acre small town campus. Endowment: $6.2 million. Educational spending for the previous fiscal year: $5343 per student. Total enrollment: 637. Faculty: 64 (34 full-time, 30 part-time). Student-undergrad faculty ratio is 12:1. 886 applied, 48% were admitted. 15% from top 10% of their high school class, 33% from top quarter, 64% from top half. 1 valedictorian. Full-time: 497 students, 42% women, 58% men. Part-time: 105 students, 79% women, 21% men. Students come from 29 states and territories, 3 other countries, 51% from out-of-state. 0.2% American Indian or Alaska Native, non-Hispanic/Latino; 1% Hispanic/Latino; 10% Black or African American, non-Hispanic/Latino; 0.7% Asian, non-Hispanic/Latino; 2% international. 13% 25 or older, 68% live on campus, 5% transferred in. Retention: 73% of full-time freshmen returned the following year. Academic areas with the most degrees conferred: public administration and social services; health professions and related sciences; interdisciplinary studies. Core. Calendar: semesters. Academic remediation for entering students, services for LD students, advanced placement, accelerated degree program, independent study, distance learning, double major, summer session for credit, part-time degree program, external degree program, adult/continuing education programs, co-op programs and internships, graduate courses open to undergrads. Off campus study at The Contemporary Music Center (sponsored by the Christian Coalition of Colleges and Universities), Knowledge Elements Education Network. Study abroad program.

Entrance Requirements: Options: electronic application, international baccalaureate accepted. Required: essay, high school transcript, minimum 2 high school GPA, 2 recommendations, SAT or ACT. Required for some: 3 recommendations, interview. Entrance: moderately difficult. Application deadline: rolling. Notification: continuous. Preference given to students with a Christian background. SAT Reasoning Test deadline: 8/1. SAT Subject Test deadline: 8/1. Transfer credits accepted: Yes.

Collegiate Environment: Orientation program. Drama-theater group, choral group, marching band. Social organizations: 21 open to all. Most popular organizations: Congressional Award Society, Laos Protos (Social Work), Herodotus Society (History), Elevate (Musical Touring Group), Student Council. Major annual event: Weekly Chapels. Student services: health clinic, personal-psychological counseling. Campus security: 24-hour emergency response devices, late night transport-escort service, controlled dormitory access. L. Palmer Young Library. Operations spending for the previous fiscal year: $254,970. 72 computers available on campus for general student use. A campuswide network can be accessed from student residence rooms. Students can access the following: online class registration. Staffed computer lab on campus provides training in use of computers and software.

Community Environment: Grayson can be accessed via bus. It has many Protestant churches and several organizations, including the Creative Arts Club and Chamber of Commerce. Health services are provided by two clinic and two hospitals within 20 miles. Recreation available includes hunting, fishing, boating, bowling, swimming, horseback riding and miniature golf with three state parks in the area. Grayson is a friendly town with complete up-to-date modern stores comparable to a city twice its size.

■ KENTUCKY MOUNTAIN BIBLE COLLEGE

855 Hwy. 541
Jackson, KY 41339
Tel: (606)693-5000; Free: 800-879-KMBC
Fax: (606)693-7744
E-mail: dlorimer@kmbc.edu
Web Site: www.kmbc.edu

Description: Independent interdenominational, 4-year, coed. Awards associate and bachelor's degrees. Founded 1931. Setting: 500-acre rural campus with easy access to Lexington. Total enrollment: 83. Faculty: 14 (1 full-time, 13 part-time). Student-undergrad faculty ratio is 13:1. 72 applied, 50% were admitted. 11% from top 10% of their high school class, 44% from top quarter, 66% from top half. Full-time: 67 students, 39% women, 61% men. Part-time: 16 students, 19% women, 81% men. Students come from 16 states and territories, 3 other countries, 70% from out-of-state. 17% 25 or older, 92% live on campus, 11% transferred in. Retention: 66% of full-time freshmen returned the following year. Academic area with the most degrees conferred: theology and religious vocations. Core. Calendar: semesters. Academic remediation for entering students, independent study, distance learning, part-time degree program, co-op programs and internships.

Entrance Requirements: Required: essay, high school transcript, minimum 2 high school GPA, testimony of Christian belief and practice, ACT. Recommended: minimum 2 high school GPA, interview. Entrance: minimally difficult. Application deadline: rolling. Notification: continuous. Transfer credits accepted: Yes.

Costs Per Year: Application fee: $25. One-time mandatory fee: $640. Comprehensive fee: $14,510 includes full-time tuition ($8550), mandatory fees ($910), and college room and board ($5050). College room only: $1900. Full-time tuition and fees vary according to program. Room and board charges vary according to housing facility. Part-time tuition: $285 per credit hour. Part-time mandatory fees: $290 per term. Part-time tuition and fees vary according to program.

Collegiate Environment: Orientation program. Drama-theater group, choral group, student-run newspaper. Social organizations: 3 open to all. Most popular organizations: Missionary Involvement, Class Organizations. Major annual events: Convocation, Holiness Convention, Constitution Day Celebration. Student services: personal-psychological counseling. Campus security: student patrols. Gibson Library plus 1 other. Books: 34,770 (physical), 52 (digital/electronic); Serial titles: 111 (physical). Weekly public service hours: 70. 4 computers available on campus for general student use. A campuswide network can be accessed from student residence rooms. Students can access the following: online class registration. Staffed computer lab on campus.

Community Environment: Vancleve is a rural town located 7 miles northwest of Jackson just off State Highway 15. Radio Station WMTC is located here. Part-time employment found on campus.

■ KENTUCKY STATE UNIVERSITY

400 E Main St.
Frankfort, KY 40601
Tel: (502)597-6000; Free: 877-367-5978
Fax: (502)597-6239
E-mail: admissions@kysu.edu
Web Site: www.kysu.edu

Description: State-related, comprehensive, coed. Awards associate, bachelor's, master's, and doctoral degrees. Founded 1886. Setting: 916-acre small town campus with easy access to Louisville. Endowment: $16.6 million. Research spending for the previous fiscal year: $15.2 million. Educational spending for the previous fiscal year: $3739 per student. Total enrollment: 1,925. Faculty: 130 (106 full-time, 24 part-time). Student-undergrad faculty ratio is 11:1. 2,078 applied, 45% were admitted. 6 student government officers. Full-time: 1,122 students, 55% women, 45% men. Part-time: 635 students, 67% women, 33% men. Students come from 39 states and territories, 14 other countries, 31% from out-of-state. 0.5% American Indian or Alaska Native, non-Hispanic/Latino; 16% Hispanic/Latino; 53% Black or African American, non-Hispanic/Latino; 0.9% Asian, non-Hispanic/Latino; 1% Native Hawaiian or other Pacific Islander, non-Hispanic/Latino; 1% international. 23% 25 or older, 36% live on campus, 9% transferred in. Retention: 68% of full-time freshmen returned the following year. Academic

areas with the most degrees conferred: liberal arts/general studies; business/marketing; public administration and social services. Core. Calendar: semesters. Academic remediation for entering students, services for LD students, advanced placement, self-designed majors, freshman honors college, honors program, independent study, distance learning, double major, summer session for credit, part-time degree program, external degree program, adult/continuing education programs, co-op programs and internships. Study abroad program. ROTC: Army (c), Air Force (c).

Entrance Requirements: Required: high school transcript, minimum 2.5 high school GPA, minimum ACT score of 18, SAT or ACT.

Costs Per Year: State resident tuition: $7406 full-time, $325 per credit hour part-time. Nonresident tuition: $18,314 full-time, $802 per credit hour part-time. Mandatory fees: $390 full-time. Full-time tuition and fees vary according to course load. Part-time tuition varies according to course load. College room and board: $6690. College room only: $3340. Room and board charges vary according to board plan and housing facility.

Collegiate Environment: Orientation program. Drama-theater group, choral group, marching band, student-run newspaper. Social organizations: 46 open to all; national fraternities, national sororities, local fraternities; 6% of eligible men and 5% of eligible women are members. Most popular organizations: Collegiate100, Alpha Phi Omega, Drive Our Peer's Education DOPE, Student Ambassador's, Alpha Phi Alpha. Major annual events: Homecoming Step Show, Homecoming Fashion Shows, Central State Basketball Games. Student services: health clinic, personal-psychological counseling. Campus security: 24-hour emergency response devices and patrols, student patrols, late night transport-escort service, controlled dormitory access. Paul G. Blazer Library. Books: 170,726 (physical), 23,417 (digital/electronic); Serial titles: 1,894 (physical), 38,647 (digital/electronic); Databases: 56. Weekly public service hours: 101; study areas open 24 hours, 5-7 days a week. Operations spending for the previous fiscal year: $1.4 million. 142 computers available on campus for general student use. A campuswide network can be accessed from student residence rooms and from off campus. Students can access the following: online class registration, student bill-pay, address verification, ability to accept financial aid awards. Staffed computer lab on campus provides training in use of computers, software, and the Internet.

Community Environment: Founded in 1786, Frankfort was selected as Kentucky's capital in 1792. Located at the western edge of the Bluegrass region, Frankfort, population 27,000, is home to several plants which manufacture electronic equipment, shoes, underwear, metal auto trim, precision parts and screws. There is access to rail and bus lines. The city has a public library, hospital, Y's, shopping facilities, theatres, and swimming. Organizations including major civic, fraternal, and veterans' are located in the area.

■ KENTUCKY WESLEYAN COLLEGE

3000 Frederica St.
Owensboro, KY 42301
Tel: (270)926-3111; Free: 800-990-0592
Fax: (270)926-3196
Web Site: www.kwc.edu

Description: Independent Methodist, 4-year, coed. Awards bachelor's degrees. Founded 1858. Setting: 52-acre suburban campus. Endowment: $34.3 million. Total enrollment: 785. Faculty: 92 (47 full-time, 45 part-time). Student-undergrad faculty ratio is 11:1. 995 applied, 67% were admitted. Full-time: 663 students, 48% women, 52% men. Part-time: 122 students, 66% women, 34% men. Students come from 14 states and territories, 5 other countries, 29% from out-of-state. 0.1% American Indian or Alaska Native, non-Hispanic/Latino; 1% Hispanic/Latino; 16% Black or African American, non-Hispanic/Latino; 1% Asian, non-Hispanic/Latino. 5% 25 or older, 46% live on campus, 6% transferred in. Retention: 67% of full-time freshmen returned the following year. Core. Calendar: semesters. Academic remediation for entering students, services for LD students, advanced placement, accelerated degree program, independent study, distance learning, double major, summer session for credit, part-time degree program, adult/continuing education programs, co-op programs and internships. Off campus study at Brescia University, Owensboro Community and Technical College, University of Louisville School of Law. Study abroad program. ROTC: Army (c).

Entrance Requirements: Options: electronic application, early admission, deferred admission, international baccalaureate accepted. Required: high school transcript, SAT or ACT. Entrance: moderately difficult. Notification: continuous. SAT Reasoning Test deadline: 8/31. SAT Subject Test deadline: 8/31. Transfer credits accepted: Yes.

Costs Per Year: Application fee: $0. Comprehensive fee: $35,844 includes

full-time tuition ($25,260), mandatory fees ($820), and college room and board ($9764). Full-time tuition and fees vary according to course load. Room and board charges vary according to board plan and housing facility. Part-time tuition: $730 per credit hour. Part-time mandatory fees: $70 per term. Part-time tuition and fees vary according to course load.

Collegiate Environment: Orientation program. Drama-theater group, choral group, student-run newspaper, radio station. Social organizations: 42 open to all; national fraternities, national sororities, local sororities. Most popular organizations: Student Government Association, Student Activities Programming Board, Campus Ministries, Pre Professional, St Jude Up 'Til Dawn Executive Board. Major annual events: Homecoming, Annual Thanksgiving Dinner/Lessons in Carols, K-Dub Idol. Student services: health clinic, personal-psychological counseling, women's center. Campus security: 24-hour emergency response devices, late night transport-escort service, 12-hour patrols by trained security personnel. Library Learning Center. Students can reserve study rooms. Operations spending for the previous fiscal year: $324,928. 125 computers available on campus for general student use. Computer purchase/lease plans available. A campuswide network can be accessed from student residence rooms and from off campus. Students can access the following: online class registration. Staffed computer lab on campus provides training in use of computers, software, and the Internet.

Community Environment: Owensboro, population 55,500, with sunshine 52-60 percent of the year is the largest city in western Kentucky. There are good commercial bus and air transportation facilities. The city has public libraries, many churches, a hospital, three medical centers and a public health center. Recreation facilities include theaters, drive-ins, bowling alleys, golf courses as well as fishing, boating, swimming, indoor athletics and other activities.

■ LINDSEY WILSON COLLEGE
210 Lindsey Wilson St.
Columbia, KY 42728
Tel: (270)384-2126; Free: 800-264-0138
Fax: (270)384-8200
Web Site: www.lindsey.edu
Description: Independent United Methodist, comprehensive, coed. Awards associate, bachelor's, master's, and doctoral degrees. Founded 1903. Setting: 225-acre rural campus. Endowment: $24.3 million. Research spending for the previous fiscal year: $235,340. Educational spending for the previous fiscal year: $4585 per student. Total enrollment: 2,565. Faculty: 239 (107 full-time, 132 part-time). Student-undergrad faculty ratio is 13:1. 2,090 applied, 92% were admitted. 15% from top 10% of their high school class, 36% from top quarter, 71% from top half. 10 valedictorians. Full-time: 1,919 students, 60% women, 40% men. Part-time: 149 students, 68% women, 32% men. Students come from 30 states and territories, 35 other countries, 20% from out-of-state. 0.3% American Indian or Alaska Native, non-Hispanic/Latino; 0.8% Hispanic/Latino; 8% Black or African American, non-Hispanic/Latino; 0.4% Asian, non-Hispanic/Latino; 0.1% Native Hawaiian or other Pacific Islander, non-Hispanic/Latino. 18% 25 or older, 52% live on campus, 12% transferred in. Retention: 57% of full-time freshmen returned the following year. Academic areas with the most degrees conferred: public administration and social services; business/marketing; homeland security, law enforcement, firefighting, and protective services. Core. Calendar: semesters. Academic remediation for entering students, ESL program, services for LD students, advanced placement, accelerated degree program, self-designed majors, independent study, double major, summer session for credit, part-time degree program, adult/continuing education programs, co-op programs and internships, graduate courses open to undergrads. Off campus study. Study abroad program.

Entrance Requirements: Open admission. Option: electronic application. Required: high school transcript. Recommended: interview. Required for some: SAT or ACT. Entrance: minimally difficult. Application deadline: rolling. Notification: continuous.

Costs Per Year: Application fee: $0. Comprehensive fee: $34,235 includes full-time tuition ($24,600), mandatory fees ($250), and college room and board ($9385). College room only: $3400. Full-time tuition and fees vary according to class time, degree level, and location. Part-time tuition: $1025 per credit hour. Part-time mandatory fees: $50 per term. Part-time tuition and fees vary according to class time, degree level, and location.

Collegiate Environment: Orientation program. Drama-theater group, choral group, marching band, student-run newspaper. Social organizations: 27 open to all. Major annual events: Homecoming, Founder' Day, Malvina Farkie Day. Student services: health clinic, personal-psychological counseling, women's center. Campus security: 24-hour emergency response

devices and patrols. Katie Murrell Library. Operations spending for the previous fiscal year: $413,271. 120 computers available on campus for general student use. A campuswide network can be accessed from student residence rooms and from off campus. Students can access the following: online class registration. Staffed computer lab on campus.

Community Environment: Columbia is the seat of Adair County. The climate is moderate. The city is located 8 miles from Green River Lake State Park and 20 miles from Cumberland Lake State Park, both known for their boating, fishing, water skiing and other water activities. Community services include seven churches, a modern hospital, and adequate shopping. There are several service clubs, and an excellent relationship exists between the local population and the college.

■ MADISONVILLE COMMUNITY COLLEGE
2000 College Dr.
Madisonville, KY 42431-9185
Tel: (270)821-2250
Fax: (270)824-1866
Web Site: www.madisonville.kctcs.edu
Description: State-supported, 2-year, coed. Part of Kentucky Community and Technical College System. Awards certificates, diplomas, transfer associate, and terminal associate degrees. Founded 1968. Setting: 150-acre small town campus. Endowment: $2.4 million. Educational spending for the previous fiscal year: $4341 per student. Total enrollment: 3,500. Faculty: 184 (95 full-time, 89 part-time). 0.2% from out-of-state. 42% 25 or older. Core. Calendar: semesters. Academic remediation for entering students, services for LD students, advanced placement, independent study, distance learning, summer session for credit, part-time degree program, external degree program, adult/continuing education programs, co-op programs and internships. Off campus study.

Entrance Requirements: Open admission. Options: electronic application, early admission, deferred admission. Required: high school transcript. Entrance: noncompetitive. Application deadline: rolling. Notification: continuous.

Collegiate Environment: Orientation program. Drama-theater group, choral group, student-run newspaper. Most popular organizations: Student Government, Baptist Student Union, Socratic Society, Student Ambassadors, Academic Team. Student services: personal-psychological counseling. Campus security: 24-hour emergency response devices, late night transport-escort service, evening patrols. Loman C. Trover Library plus 1 other. Operations spending for the previous fiscal year: $211,216. 35 computers available on campus for general student use. A campuswide network can be accessed from off-campus. Staffed computer lab on campus.

Community Environment: Centered on a plateau between the Pond and Tradewater Rivers, Madisonville is one of the principal loose leaf tobacco markets in western Kentucky. Underground coal mining operations are in the vicinity. Good shopping facilities are available. The city has several churches, a public library, and one theatre. The climate is moderate and part-time employment is available.

■ MAYSVILLE COMMUNITY AND TECHNICAL COLLEGE (MAYSVILLE)
1755 US 68
Maysville, KY 41056
Tel: (606)759-7141
Web Site: www.maysville.kctcs.edu
Description: State-supported, 2-year, coed. Part of Kentucky Community and Technical College System. Awards certificates, diplomas, transfer associate, and terminal associate degrees. Founded 1967. Setting: 12-acre rural campus. Total enrollment: 3,495. 0.1% American Indian or Alaska Native, non-Hispanic/Latino; 2% Hispanic/Latino; 2% Black or African American, non-Hispanic/Latino; 0.2% Asian, non-Hispanic/Latino; 0.1% Native Hawaiian or other Pacific Islander, non-Hispanic/Latino. Core. Calendar: semesters. Academic remediation for entering students, ESL program, services for LD students, advanced placement, honors program, independent study, distance learning, summer session for credit, part-time degree program, external degree program, adult/continuing education programs, co-op programs and internships. Off campus study.

Entrance Requirements: Open admission except for nursing, early childhood education, respiratory care, surgical technologist programs. Options: electronic application, early admission. Required: high school transcript. Entrance: noncompetitive. Application deadline: rolling. Notification: continuous.

Costs Per Year: Application fee: $0. One-time mandatory fee: $8. State resident tuition: $169 per credit hour part-time. Nonresident tuition: $592 per credit hour part-time. Part-time tuition varies according to reciprocity agreements.

Collegiate Environment: Orientation program. Student services: personal-psychological counseling. Campus security: 24-hour emergency response devices, student patrols, evening parking lot security. Finch Library.

Community Environment: From 1786 to 1789, Daniel Boone and his wife operated a tavern in Maysville, one of the first incorporated towns in Kentucky. Today this is a metropolitan city. The average temperature is 55.3 degrees with an average rainfall of 43.58 inches. Known as one of the largest burley tobacco markets in the world, the city has three large redrying plants and 18 loose-leaf sale warehouses. These warehouses are open daily from 10 to 2 during the tobacco sale and auction season. The manufacturer of power driven pulleys and bicycle parts are also among Maysville's chief industries. There is a hospital and clinic in town, and various civic, fraternal and veteran's organizations are represented. There are excellent shopping facilities. Cinema 4, boating, golf courses, and several private clubs are easily accessible for recreation. Part-time employment is available.

■ MAYSVILLE COMMUNITY AND TECHNICAL COLLEGE (MOREHEAD)

609 Viking Dr.
Morehead, KY 40351
Tel: (606)783-1538
Fax: (606)784-9876
Web Site: www.maysville.kctcs.edu
Description: State-supported, 2-year, coed. Awards certificates, diplomas, and terminal associate degrees. Founded 1984. Calendar: semesters.

■ MIDWAY UNIVERSITY

512 E Stephens St.
Midway, KY 40347-1120
Tel: (859)846-4421; Free: 800-755-0031
Fax: (859)846-5823
Web Site: www.midway.edu
Description: Independent, comprehensive, coed, affiliated with Christian Church (Disciples of Christ). Awards associate, bachelor's, master's, and doctoral degrees. Founded 1847. Setting: 110-acre small town campus with easy access to Louisville, Lexington. Total enrollment: 1,600. Faculty: 118 (57 full-time, 61 part-time). Student-undergrad faculty ratio is 16:1. 1,572 applied. 14% from top 10% of their high school class, 38% from top quarter, 68% from top half. 1 valedictorian, 32 student government officers. Full-time: 1,022 students, 88% women, 12% men. Part-time: 491 students, 78% women, 22% men. Students come from 27 states and territories, 2 other countries, 8% from out-of-state. 0.7% American Indian or Alaska Native, non-Hispanic/Latino; 0.9% Hispanic/Latino; 9% Black or African American, non-Hispanic/Latino; 0.5% Asian, non-Hispanic/Latino; 0.7% Native Hawaiian or other Pacific Islander, non-Hispanic/Latino; 0.1% international. 40% 25 or older, 14% live on campus, 15% transferred in. Retention: 75% of full-time freshmen returned the following year. Academic areas with the most degrees conferred: business/marketing; education; agriculture. Core. Calendar: semesters. Academic remediation for entering students, services for LD students, advanced placement, honors program, independent study, distance learning, summer session for credit, part-time degree program, external degree program, adult/continuing education programs, internships. Off campus study at Kentucky Institute of International Studies. Study abroad program. ROTC: Army (c), Air Force (c).

Entrance Requirements: Options: electronic application, early admission, deferred admission. Required: high school transcript, SAT or ACT. Recommended: minimum 2.2 high school GPA. Required for some: essay, interview. Entrance: minimally difficult. Application deadline: rolling. Notification: continuous.

Costs Per Year: Application fee: $25. Comprehensive fee: $33,100 includes full-time tuition ($24,500) and college room and board ($8600). College room only: $4400. Full-time tuition varies according to class time, location, and program. Room and board charges vary according to board plan and housing facility. Part-time tuition: $910 per credit hour. Part-time tuition varies according to class time, location, and program.

Collegiate Environment: Orientation program. Choral group. Social organizations: 21 open to all. Most popular organizations: Student Government, Midway Chorale, Midway Association of Nursing Students, Kentucky Education Association-Student Program, Midway Horse Women's Association. Major annual events: Christmas Vespers, Last Supper, Night of Lights. Student services: health clinic, personal-psychological counseling, women's

center. Campus security: 24-hour emergency response devices and patrols, late night transport-escort service. Little Memorial Library. 50 computers available on campus for general student use. A campuswide network can be accessed from student residence rooms and from off campus. Students can access the following: online class registration. Staffed computer lab on campus provides training in use of computers, software, and the Internet.

Community Environment: Appropriately named, Midway is located halfway between Lexington and Frankfort in Woodford County. The climate is moderate. Midway has seven churches of various denominations and several large horse farms.

■ MOREHEAD STATE UNIVERSITY

150 University Blvd.
Morehead, KY 40351
Tel: (606)783-2221; Free: 800-585-6781
Fax: (606)783-5038
E-mail: admissions@moreheadstate.edu
Web Site: www.moreheadstate.edu
Description: State-supported, comprehensive, coed. Awards associate, bachelor's, master's, and doctoral degrees and post-master's certificates. Founded 1922. Setting: 1,187-acre small town campus. Endowment: $43 million. Research spending for the previous fiscal year: $3.7 million. Educational spending for the previous fiscal year: $6658 per student. Total enrollment: 10,584. Faculty: 411 (316 full-time, 95 part-time). Student-undergrad faculty ratio is 15:1. 5,392 applied, 80% were admitted. 23% from top 10% of their high school class, 51% from top quarter, 83% from top half. Full-time: 5,835 students, 59% women, 41% men. Part-time: 3,830 students, 61% women, 39% men. Students come from 44 states and territories, 24 other countries, 13% from out-of-state. 0.2% American Indian or Alaska Native, non-Hispanic/Latino; 2% Hispanic/Latino; 3% Black or African American, non-Hispanic/Latino; 0.6% Asian, non-Hispanic/Latino; 0.1% Native Hawaiian or other Pacific Islander, non-Hispanic/Latino; 2% international. 17% 25 or older, 42% live on campus, 5% transferred in. Retention: 72% of full-time freshmen returned the following year. Academic areas with the most degrees conferred: business/marketing; liberal arts/general studies; education. Core. Calendar: semesters. Academic remediation for entering students, ESL program, services for LD students, advanced placement, accelerated degree program, self-designed majors, honors program, independent study, distance learning, double major, summer session for credit, part-time degree program, adult/continuing education programs, co-op programs and internships, graduate courses open to undergrads. Off campus study at KCTCS, University Center of the Mountains, University of Kentucky. Study abroad program. ROTC: Army.

Entrance Requirements: Options: electronic application, early admission, deferred admission, international baccalaureate accepted. Required: high school transcript, SAT or ACT. Required for some: essay, 1 recommendation, interview. Entrance: minimally difficult. Application deadline: rolling. Notification: continuous. SAT Reasoning Test deadline: 8/1. SAT Subject Test deadline: 8/1. Transfer credits accepted: Yes.

Costs Per Year: Application fee: $30. State resident tuition: $8750 full-time, $365 per credit hour part-time. Nonresident tuition: $13,226 full-time, $552 per credit hour part-time. Mandatory fees: $320 full-time, $14 per credit hour part-time. Full-time tuition and fees vary according to course load, degree level, location, reciprocity agreements, and student level. Part-time tuition and fees vary according to course load, degree level, location, reciprocity agreements, and student level. College room and board: $9730. College room only: $5480. Room and board charges vary according to board plan and housing facility.

Collegiate Environment: Orientation program. Drama-theater group, choral group, marching band, student-run newspaper, radio station. Social organizations: 158 open to all; national fraternities, national sororities. Most popular organizations: Delta Tau Delta Fraternity, Delta Gamma, Phi Sigma Pi (Honors), Baptist Campus Ministries (BCM), Collegiate Future Farmers of America (FFA). Major annual events: Black-Out Game (men's basketball), President's Lecture Series, Homecoming. Student services: health clinic, personal-psychological counseling. Campus security: 24-hour emergency response devices and patrols, student patrols, late night transport-escort service, controlled dormitory access, LiveSafe app—a two-way communication safety app between students and University Police. Camden Carroll Library. Books: 339,640 (physical), 121,456 (digital/electronic); Serial titles: 29,191 (physical), 72,511 (digital/electronic); Databases: 152. Weekly public service hours: 95; students can reserve study rooms. Operations spending for the previous fiscal year: $3.6 million. 950 computers available on campus for general student use. A campuswide network can be accessed from student residence rooms and from off campus. Students can access the following: online class registration. Staffed computer lab on campus provides training in use of computers, software, and the Internet.

Community Environment: The city of Morehead is located between Lexington, KY, and Huntington, WV. Community services include a hospital, several churches, five motels, several restaurants and 2 shopping centers. Area recreation includes the Daniel Boone National Forest. The campus is a 1-hour drive from several state parks, and 20 minutes from swimming, boating, fishing, and water skiing. The campus also has Eagle Lake for recreation with a golf course and horseback riding. Several annual local festivals and university-sponsored Appalachia celebrations provide further entertainment.

■ MURRAY STATE UNIVERSITY
102 Curris Ctr.
Murray, KY 42071
Tel: (270)762-3011; Free: 800-272-4678
Fax: (270)762-3413
E-mail: msu.admissions@murraystate.edu
Web Site: www.murraystate.edu

Description: State-supported, university, coed. Awards bachelor's, master's, and doctoral degrees. Founded 1922. Setting: 261-acre small town campus. Total enrollment: 9,465. Faculty: 593 (446 full-time, 147 part-time). Student-undergrad faculty ratio is 15:1. 8,256 applied, 81% were admitted, 27% from top 10% of their high school class, 54% from top quarter, 82% from top half. Full-time: 6,276 students, 59% women, 41% men. Part-time: 1,872 students, 61% women, 39% men. Students come from 44 states and territories, 39 other countries, 32% from out-of-state. 0.2% American Indian or Alaska Native, non-Hispanic/Latino; 2% Hispanic/Latino; 6% Black or African American, non-Hispanic/Latino; 0.8% Asian, non-Hispanic/Latino; 3% international. 11% 25 or older, 33% live on campus, 7% transferred in. Retention: 79% of full-time freshmen returned the following year. Academic areas with the most degrees conferred: health professions and related sciences; business/marketing; education. Core. Calendar: semesters. Academic remediation for entering students, ESL program, services for LD students, advanced placement, self-designed majors, freshman honors college, honors program, independent study, distance learning, double major, summer session for credit, part-time degree program, external degree program, adult/continuing education programs, co-op programs and internships, graduate courses open to undergrads. Off campus study at Academic Common Market, National Student Exchange. Study abroad program. ROTC: Army.

Entrance Requirements: Options: electronic application, early admission, international baccalaureate accepted. Required: high school transcript, minimum 3 high school GPA, minimum ACT composite score of 18 or SAT score of 870, rank in the top half of high school class or minimum 3.0 GPA; high school curriculum criteria, SAT or ACT. Recommended: ACT. Entrance: moderately difficult. Application deadline: rolling. Notification: continuous. SAT Reasoning Test deadline: 8/15. SAT Subject Test deadline: 8/15. Transfer credits accepted: Yes.

Costs Per Year: Application fee: $40. State resident tuition: $9084 full-time, $378.50 per credit hour part-time. Nonresident tuition: $24,540 full-time, $1,023 per credit hour part-time. Full-time tuition varies according to course load and reciprocity agreements. Part-time tuition varies according to reciprocity agreements. College room and board: $9190. College room only: $5424. Room and board charges vary according to board plan and housing facility.

Collegiate Environment: Orientation program. Drama-theater group, choral group, marching band, student-run newspaper. Social organizations: 184 open to all; national fraternities, national sororities; 16% of eligible men and 15% of eligible women are members. Most popular organizations: Racer Band, Student Government Association, National Panhellenic Council, International Student Organization, MSU Student Ambassadors. Major annual events: Homecoming, All Campus Sing, Campus Lights. Student services: health clinic, personal-psychological counseling, women's center. Campus security: 24-hour emergency response devices and patrols, student patrols, late night transport-escort service, controlled dormitory access. 3,106 college housing spaces available; 2,321 were occupied in 2018-19. Freshmen given priority for college housing. On-campus residence required through sophomore year. Options: coed, women-only housing available. Waterfield Library plus 4 others. Books: 330,959 (physical), 51,049 (digital/electronic); Serial titles: 1,305 (physical), 64,102 (digital/electronic); Databases: 127. Weekly public service hours: 107; students can reserve study rooms.

Community Environment: The area around Munas has a hospital and several churches. Recreation is available at nearby Kentucky Lake, the largest lake created by the Tennessee Valley Authority, Lake Barkley, and Land Between Lakes, a recreation area of 177,000 acres. Part-time employment is available.

■ NORTHERN KENTUCKY UNIVERSITY
Louie B Nunn Dr.
Highland Heights, KY 41099
Tel: (859)572-5100; Free: 800-637-9948
E-mail: beanorse@nku.edu
Web Site: www.nku.edu

Description: State-supported, comprehensive, coed. Awards bachelor's, master's, and doctoral degrees and post-master's certificates. Founded 1968. Setting: 428-acre suburban campus with easy access to Cincinnati. Endowment: $106.2 million. Research spending for the previous fiscal year: $1.4 million. Educational spending for the previous fiscal year: $5945 per student. Total enrollment: 14,783. Faculty: 1,004 (560 full-time, 444 part-time). 5,995 applied, 89% were admitted. Full-time: 8,570 students, 58% women, 42% men. Part-time: 3,363 students, 60% women, 40% men. Students come from 41 states and territories, 56 other countries, 30% from out-of-state. 0.2% American Indian or Alaska Native, non-Hispanic/Latino; 3% Hispanic/Latino; 7% Black or African American, non-Hispanic/Latino; 1% Asian, non-Hispanic/Latino; 0.1% Native Hawaiian or other Pacific Islander, non-Hispanic/Latino; 3% international. 20% 25 or older, 15% live on campus, 7% transferred in. Retention: 67% of full-time freshmen returned the following year. Academic areas with the most degrees conferred: business/marketing; health professions and related sciences; computer and information sciences. Calendar: semesters. Academic remediation for entering students, ESL program, services for LD students, advanced placement, accelerated degree program, self-designed majors, honors program, independent study, distance learning, double major, summer session for credit, part-time degree program, adult/continuing education programs, co-op programs and internships, graduate courses open to undergrads. Off campus study at Gateway Community and Technical College, Jefferson Community and Technical College, Greater Cincinnati Consortium of Colleges and Universities. Study abroad program. ROTC: Army (c), Air Force (c).

Entrance Requirements: Open admission NKU has specific GPA and test score requirements for general admissions and additional requirements for special programs. Options: electronic application, international baccalaureate accepted. Required: high school transcript, minimum 2 high school GPA, SAT or ACT. Required for some: Some programs require separate applications. Entrance: moderately difficult. Application deadlines: 8/20, 8/15 for nonresidents. Notification: continuous, continuous for nonresidents. SAT Reasoning Test deadline: 8/22. SAT Subject Test deadline: 8/22. Transfer credits accepted: Yes.

Costs Per Year: Application fee: $40. State resident tuition: $9648 full-time, $402 per credit hour part-time. Nonresident tuition: $19,296 full-time, $804 per credit hour part-time. Mandatory fees: $384 full-time, $16 per credit hour part-time. Full-time tuition and fees vary according to course load, program, and reciprocity agreements. Part-time tuition and fees vary according to course load, program, and reciprocity agreements. College room and board: $10,022. Room and board charges vary according to board plan and housing facility.

Collegiate Environment: Orientation program. Drama-theater group, choral group, student-run newspaper, radio station. Social organizations: 195 open to all; national fraternities, national sororities; 9% of eligible men and 13% of eligible women are members. Most popular organizations: Sororities, Fraternities, Freshmen Service Leadership Committee, Student Alumni Association, Activities Programming Board. Major annual events: Fresh Fusion, Homecoming, Victorfest. Student services: legal services, health clinic, personal-psychological counseling, women's center. Campus security: 24-hour emergency response devices and patrols, late night transport-escort service, controlled dormitory access. 2,060 college housing spaces available; 1,665 were occupied in 2018-19. Freshmen given priority for college housing. On-campus residence required in freshman year. Option: coed housing available. W. Frank Steely Library plus 1 other. Books: 326,648 (physical), 39,448 (digital/electronic); Serial titles: 56,176 (digital/electronic); Databases: 108. Weekly public service hours: 104; students can reserve study rooms. Operations spending for the previous fiscal year: $6.3 million. 200 computers available on campus for general student use. A campuswide network can be accessed from student residence rooms and from off campus. Students can access the following: online class registration. Staffed computer lab on campus provides training in use of computers, software, and the Internet.

Community Environment: Located in the largest metropolitan area of any state university in Kentucky, NKU is seven miles southeast of Cincinnati, Ohio.

■ **OWENSBORO COMMUNITY AND TECHNICAL COLLEGE**
4800 New Hartford Rd.
Owensboro, KY 42303-1899
Tel: (270)686-4400; Free: 866-755-6282
Fax: (270)686-4496
E-mail: barb.tipmore@kctcs.edu
Web Site: www.owensboro.kctcs.edu
Description: State-supported, 2-year, coed. Part of Kentucky Community and Technical College System. Awards certificates, diplomas, transfer associate, and terminal associate degrees. Founded 1986. Setting: 102-acre suburban campus. Total enrollment: 3,947. Faculty: 142 (76 full-time, 66 part-time). Student-undergrad faculty ratio is 24:1. Full-time: 1,519 students, 54% women, 46% men. Part-time: 2,428 students, 53% women, 47% men. Students come from 31 states and territories, 1 other country, 6% from out-of-state. 0.2% American Indian or Alaska Native, non-Hispanic/Latino; 3% Hispanic/Latino; 4% Black or African American, non-Hispanic/Latino; 1% Asian, non-Hispanic/Latino; 0.1% Native Hawaiian or other Pacific Islander, non-Hispanic/Latino. 37% 25 or older, 4% transferred in. Retention: 61% of full-time freshmen returned the following year. Core. Calendar: semesters. Academic remediation for entering students, ESL program, services for LD students, advanced placement, self-designed majors, honors program, independent study, distance learning, summer session for credit, part-time degree program, external degree program, adult/continuing education programs, co-op programs. Off campus study. Study abroad program. ROTC: Army.
Entrance Requirements: Open admission. Option: electronic application. Required: high school transcript. Recommended: SAT or ACT. Entrance: noncompetitive. Application deadline: rolling. Notification: continuous. Transfer credits accepted: Yes.
Costs Per Year: Application fee: $0. State resident tuition: $5070 full-time, $169 per credit hour part-time. Nonresident tuition: $17,760 full-time, $592 per credit hour part-time. Mandatory fees: $240 full-time, $8 per credit hour part-time. Full-time tuition and fees vary according to course load and reciprocity agreements. Part-time tuition and fees vary according to course load and reciprocity agreements.
Collegiate Environment: Orientation program. Drama-theater group, choral group. Social organizations: 5 open to all. Most popular organization: Student Government Association. Major annual events: Fall Fling, Spring Fling, Hanging of the Greens. Campus security: 24-hour emergency response devices, late night transport-escort service. College housing not available. Main Campus Library plus 1 other. Books: 24,843 (physical), 131,593 (digital/electronic); Serial titles: 19 (physical); Databases: 52. Weekly public service hours: 48. 350 computers available on campus for general student use. A campuswide network can be accessed from off-campus. Students can access the following: online class registration. Staffed computer lab on campus provides training in use of computers and the Internet.
Community Environment: A myriad of items including bread, soybean oil, paper, plastics, and electronic components are made in the Owensboro area. Thirty manufacturers have forty or more employees, including such national firms as Baskin-Robbins, General Electric, and Kimberly Clark. Eight percent of the land is used for farming. The fifth largest city in the state, population 55,459, it is home to the International Barbecue Festival, the International Bluegrass Museum Association, and the world's largest sassafras tree.

■ **ROSS COLLEGE**
4001 Fort Cambell Blvd.
Hopkinsville, KY 42240
Tel: (270)886-1302; Free: 866-815-5578
Fax: (270)886-3544
Web Site: www.rosseducation.edu
Description: Proprietary, 2-year, coed. Part of Education Management Corporation. Awards diplomas and terminal associate degrees. Setting: small town campus. Calendar: quarters.

■ **SIMMONS COLLEGE OF KENTUCKY**
1018 S 7th St.
Louisville, KY 40203

Tel: (502)776-1443
Web Site: www.simmonscollegeky.edu
Description: Independent, 4-year, coed, affiliated with Baptist Church. Awards associate and bachelor's degrees. Founded 1873.

■ **SOMERSET COMMUNITY COLLEGE**
808 Monticello St.
Somerset, KY 42501-2973
Tel: (606)679-8501; Free: 877-629-9722
E-mail: somerset-admissions@kctcs.edu
Web Site: www.somerset.kctcs.edu
Description: State-supported, 2-year, coed. Part of Kentucky Community and Technical College System. Awards certificates, diplomas, transfer associate, and terminal associate degrees. Founded 1965. Setting: 70-acre small town campus. Total enrollment: 5,900. Faculty: 222 (141 full-time, 81 part-time). Student-undergrad faculty ratio is 24:1. 38% 25 or older. Retention: 58% of full-time freshmen returned the following year. Calendar: semesters. Academic remediation for entering students, services for LD students, advanced placement, distance learning, summer session for credit, part-time degree program, adult/continuing education programs.
Entrance Requirements: Open admission except for nursing, clinical laboratory technology, physical therapy assistant, surgical technology, radiography programs. Options: electronic application, early admission. Required: high school transcript. Entrance: noncompetitive. Application deadline: 8/14. Notification: continuous. Transfer credits accepted: Yes.
Costs Per Year: Application fee: $0. State resident tuition: $4860 full-time, $162 per credit hour part-time. Nonresident tuition: $17,010 full-time, $567 per credit hour part-time. Mandatory fees: $240 full-time, $8 per credit hour part-time. Full-time tuition and fees vary according to course load. Part-time tuition and fees vary according to course load.
Collegiate Environment: Orientation program. Drama-theater group, student-run newspaper. Somerset Community College Library.
Community Environment: Located in an urban area in south central Kentucky, railroad and bus service are available to Somerset. It has a local YMCA, library, hospital and other health services and various organizations including Rotary, Kiwanis, Jaycees, and a Chamber of Commerce. Recreation is provided with 3 theatres, drive-ins, golf, tennis, and Lake Cumberland with 1,225 miles of shoreline.

■ **SOUTHCENTRAL KENTUCKY COMMUNITY AND TECHNICAL COLLEGE**
1845 Loop Dr.
Bowling Green, KY 42101
Tel: (270)901-1000; Free: 800-790-0990
Fax: (270)746-7466
Web Site: southcentral.kctcs.edu
Description: State-supported, 2-year, coed. Part of Kentucky Community and Technical College System. Awards certificates, diplomas, transfer associate, and terminal associate degrees. Founded 1938. Total enrollment: 4,953. 54% 25 or older. Calendar: semesters.
Entrance Requirements: Open admission.

■ **SOUTHEAST KENTUCKY COMMUNITY AND TECHNICAL COLLEGE**
700 College Rd.
Cumberland, KY 40823-1099
Tel: (606)589-2145; Free: 888-274-SECC
Fax: (606)589-5423
Web Site: www.southeast.kctcs.edu
Description: State-supported, 2-year, coed. Part of Kentucky Community and Technical College System. Awards certificates, diplomas, transfer associate, and terminal associate degrees. Founded 1960. Setting: 150-acre rural campus. Educational spending for the previous fiscal year: $5481 per student. Total enrollment: 3,125. Faculty: 139 (91 full-time, 48 part-time). Student-undergrad faculty ratio is 20:1. 698 applied, 95% were admitted. 20% from top 10% of their high school class, 30% from top quarter, 40% from top half. 4 valedictorians. Full-time: 1,480 students, 57% women, 43% men. Part-time: 1,645 students, 44% women, 56% men. Students come from 21 states and territories, 1 other country, 6% from out-of-state. 0.6% American Indian or Alaska Native, non-Hispanic/Latino; 0.5% Hispanic/Latino; 2% Black or African American, non-Hispanic/Latino; 0.2% Asian, non-Hispanic/Latino; 0.3% Native Hawaiian or other Pacific Islander, non-Hispanic/Latino. 32% 25 or older, 2% transferred in. Retention: 64% of full-time freshmen returned the following year. Core. Calendar: semesters.

Academic remediation for entering students, advanced placement, accelerated degree program, independent study, distance learning, summer session for credit, part-time degree program, adult/continuing education programs. Study abroad program.

Entrance Requirements: Open admission except for allied health programs. Required: high school transcript. Recommended: ACT. Entrance: noncompetitive. Application deadline: 8/20. Notification: continuous until 9/3.

Costs Per Year: Application fee: $0. State resident tuition: $162 per credit hour part-time. Nonresident tuition: $567 per credit hour part-time. Mandatory fees: $8 per credit hour part-time. Tuition guaranteed not to increase for student's term of enrollment.

Collegiate Environment: Orientation program. Drama-theater group, choral group, student-run newspaper. Social organizations: 10 open to all. Most popular organizations: Professional Business Leaders, Student Government Association, Phi Theta Kappa, Black Student Union, Nursing Club. Major annual events: Octoberfest, Swappin' Meetin', Spring on Cloverlick. Gertrude Dale Library plus 4 others. 96 computers available on campus for general student use. A campuswide network can be accessed. Students can access the following: online class registration, online admissions. Staffed computer lab on campus.

Community Environment: Cumberland is a rural town in Harlan County of southeastern Kentucky. The city has Protestant and Catholic churches, and a community hospital and other medical services. Recreation is provided by movie theaters, fishing at Kingdom Come State Park Lake, picnic areas, a lodge and trailer park and a city park. Local merchants employ college students since the town serves an area of approximately 20,000 persons. Various civic, service, fraternal and veteran's organizations, including a Chamber of Commerce, enhance the community spirit.

■ **THE SOUTHERN BAPTIST THEOLOGICAL SEMINARY**
2825 Lexington Rd.
Louisville, KY 40280-0004
Tel: (502)897-4011
Web Site: www.sbts.edu

Description: Independent Southern Baptist, comprehensive, coed. Awards associate, bachelor's, master's, and doctoral degrees. Founded 1858. Total enrollment: 3,190. 110 applied, 71% were admitted. Full-time: 412 students, 28% women, 72% men. Part-time: 256 students, 31% women, 69% men. 63% 25 or older, 12% transferred in. Retention: 78% of full-time freshmen returned the following year. Core. Graduate courses open to undergrads.

Entrance Requirements: Open admission. Option: international baccalaureate accepted. Required: essay, high school transcript, minimum 2.0 high school GPA. Required for some: SAT or ACT. Application deadline: 7/15.

Collegiate Environment: Orientation program. Choral group. Student services: health clinic, personal-psychological counseling.

Community Environment: See University of Louisville.

■ **SPALDING UNIVERSITY**
845 S Third St.
Louisville, KY 40203-2188
Tel: (502)585-9911; Free: 800-896-8941
Fax: (502)585-7158
E-mail: melder@spalding.edu
Web Site: www.spalding.edu

Description: Independent, comprehensive, coed, affiliated with Roman Catholic Church. Awards associate, bachelor's, master's, and doctoral degrees and post-master's certificates. Founded 1814. Setting: 24-acre urban campus with easy access to Louisville. Endowment: $16.6 million. Research spending for the previous fiscal year: $180,318. Educational spending for the previous fiscal year: $6692 per student. Total enrollment: 2,322. Faculty: 170 (99 full-time, 71 part-time). Student-undergrad faculty ratio is 12:1. 990 applied, 51% were admitted. Full-time: 920 students, 72% women, 28% men. Part-time: 396 students, 67% women, 33% men. Students come from 2 other countries, 20% from out-of-state. 0.1% American Indian or Alaska Native, non-Hispanic/Latino; 3% Hispanic/Latino; 17% Black or African American, non-Hispanic/Latino; 2% Asian, non-Hispanic/Latino; 0.1% Native Hawaiian or other Pacific Islander, non-Hispanic/Latino; 0.2% international. 46% 25 or older, 5% live on campus, 11% transferred in. Academic areas with the most degrees conferred: health professions and related sciences; psychology; communication/journalism. Core. Academic remediation for entering students, services for LD students, advanced placement, accelerated degree program, independent study, distance learning, double major, summer session for credit, part-time degree

program, adult/continuing education programs, co-op programs and internships, graduate courses open to undergrads. Off campus study at other institutions in the Kentuckiana Metroversity (University of Louisville, Bellarmine University, Indiana University Southeast, Southern Baptist Theological Seminary, Louisville Presbyterian Theological Seminary, and Jefferson Community College) and the Regis Online Consortium. Study abroad program. ROTC: Army (c), Air Force (c).

Entrance Requirements: Options: electronic application, early admission, deferred admission, international baccalaureate accepted. Required: high school transcript, minimum 2.5 high school GPA, SAT or ACT. Recommended: interview. Required for some: essay. Entrance: moderately difficult. Application deadline: rolling. Notification: continuous. Transfer credits accepted: Yes.

Costs Per Year: Application fee: $20. Comprehensive fee: $31,900 includes full-time tuition ($24,500) and college room and board ($7400). College room only: $4600. Full-time tuition varies according to course load, degree level, and program. Room and board charges vary according to board plan. Part-time tuition: $815 per credit hour. Part-time tuition varies according to course load, degree level, and program.

Collegiate Environment: Orientation program. Choral group, student-run radio station. Social organizations: 23 open to all; local fraternities, local sororities. Most popular organizations: Egan Service Learning Program, Student Occupational Therapy Association, Spalding University Nursing Students, Campus Activities Board, Best Buddies. Major annual events: Rat Race- Run for the Rodents, Welcome Week, Career Expo. Student services: personal-psychological counseling. Campus security: 24-hour emergency response devices and patrols, late night transport-escort service, controlled dormitory access. Spalding Library. Books: 70,000 (physical), 425,638 (digital/electronic); Serial titles: 102 (physical), 100,000 (digital/electronic); Databases: 70. Students can reserve study rooms. Operations spending for the previous fiscal year: $308,000. 259 computers available on campus for general student use. A campuswide network can be accessed from student residence rooms and from off campus. Students can access the following: online class registration. Staffed computer lab on campus provides training in use of computers, software, and the Internet.

Community Environment: See University of Louisville.

■ **SULLIVAN UNIVERSITY**
3101 Bardstown Rd.
Louisville, KY 40205
Tel: (502)456-6504; Free: 800-844-1354
Fax: (502)456-0040
E-mail: admissions@sullivan.edu
Web Site: www.sullivan.edu

Description: Proprietary, comprehensive, coed. Part of The Sullivan University System, Inc. Awards associate, bachelor's, master's, and doctoral degrees. Founded 1962. Setting: 15-acre suburban campus. Total enrollment: 3,574. Faculty: 276 (106 full-time, 170 part-time). Student-undergrad faculty ratio is 19:1. 1,377 applied, 84% were admitted. Full-time: 1,652 students, 62% women, 38% men. Part-time: 1,032 students, 63% women, 37% men. Students come from 32 states and territories, 5 other countries, 18% from out-of-state. 0.4% American Indian or Alaska Native, non-Hispanic/Latino; 16% Black or African American, non-Hispanic/Latino; 2% Asian, non-Hispanic/Latino; 0.3% Native Hawaiian or other Pacific Islander, non-Hispanic/Latino. 41% 25 or older, 6% live on campus, 5% transferred in. Calendar: quarters. Academic remediation for entering students, services for LD students, accelerated degree program, self-designed majors, independent study, distance learning, double major, part-time degree program, adult/continuing education programs, co-op programs and internships.

Entrance Requirements: Options: electronic application, deferred admission, international baccalaureate accepted. Recommended: SAT or ACT. Required for some: essay, high school transcript, interview, criminal background check and no felony convictions, drug testing, and immunizations. Entrance: minimally difficult. Application deadlines: rolling, rolling for nonresidents. Notification: continuous, continuous for nonresidents. SAT Reasoning Test deadline: 9/20. SAT Subject Test deadline: 9/20. Transfer credits accepted: Yes.

Collegiate Environment: Orientation program. Social organizations: 13 open to all. Most popular organizations: Housing and Residence Life, Student Veterans Association, Sigma Beta Delta, Phi Beta Lambda, Game Club. Major annual events: Welcome Week, Blood Drive, Title IX. Student services: personal-psychological counseling. Campus security: 24-hour patrols, late night transport-escort service, controlled dormitory access. 505 college housing spaces available; 201 were occupied in 2018-19. Freshmen guaranteed college housing. Options: coed, men-only, women-only housing available. Sullivan University Library and Learning Resource Center. Books: 31,224 (physical), 67,291 (digital/electronic); Serial titles: 29 (physical), 134,525 (digital/electronic); Databases: 166. Weekly public service hours: 82. Operations spending for the previous fiscal year: $724,776. 93 computers available on campus for general student use. A campuswide network can be accessed from student residence rooms and from off campus. Students can access the following: online class registration. Staffed computer lab on campus provides training in use of computers, software, and the Internet.

■ THOMAS MORE UNIVERSITY

333 Thomas More Pky.

Crestview Hills, KY 41017-3495

Tel: (859)341-5800; Free: 800-825-4557

Fax: (859)344-3638

E-mail: admissions@thomasmore.edu

Web Site: www.thomasmore.edu

Description: Independent Roman Catholic, comprehensive, coed. Awards associate, bachelor's, and master's degrees. Founded 1921. Setting: 100-acre suburban campus with easy access to Cincinnati. Endowment: $20.7 million. Total enrollment: 1,959. Faculty: 139 (79 full-time, 60 part-time). Student-undergrad faculty ratio is 16:1. 2,401 applied, 89% were admitted. Full-time: 1,369 students, 49% women, 51% men. Part-time: 452 students, 63% women, 37% men. Students come from 25 states and territories, 3 other countries, 47% from out-of-state. 0.1% American Indian or Alaska Native, non-Hispanic/Latino; 3% Hispanic/Latino; 7% Black or African American, non-Hispanic/Latino; 0.7% Asian, non-Hispanic/Latino; 0.3% Native Hawaiian or other Pacific Islander, non-Hispanic/Latino; 0.6% international. 21% 25 or older, 31% live on campus, 4% transferred in. Retention: 70% of full-time freshmen returned the following year. Academic areas with the most degrees conferred: business/marketing; health professions and related sciences; biological/life sciences. Core. Calendar: semesters. Academic remediation for entering students, services for LD students, advanced placement, accelerated degree program, self-designed majors, honors program, independent study, distance learning, double major, summer session for credit, part-time degree program, adult/continuing education programs, co-op programs and internships. Off campus study at members of the Greater Cincinnati Consortium of Colleges and Universities. Study abroad program. ROTC: Army (c), Air Force (c).

Entrance Requirements: Options: electronic application, deferred admission, international baccalaureate accepted. Required: high school transcript, minimum 2.5 high school GPA, SAT or ACT. Entrance: moderately difficult. Application deadline: 8/1. Notification: continuous. SAT Reasoning Test deadline: 8/15. Transfer credits accepted: Yes.

Costs Per Year: Application fee: $25. One-time mandatory fee: $250. Comprehensive fee: $39,850 includes full-time tuition ($29,700), mandatory fees ($1500), and college room and board ($8650). Room and board charges vary according to board plan and housing facility. Part-time tuition: $650 per credit hour. Part-time mandatory fees: $75 per credit hour.

Collegiate Environment: Orientation program. Drama-theater group, choral group, marching band. Social organizations: 40 open to all; national fraternities, national sororities; 2% of eligible men and 3% of eligible women are members. Most popular organizations: Student Government Association, Student Activities Board, More Ministry, Outdoors Adventure Club, Education Club. Major annual events: Winter Wonderland, Welcome Carnival, Relay for Life. Student services: health clinic, personal-psychological counseling. Campus security: 24-hour emergency response devices and patrols, late night transport-escort service, controlled dormitory access. Thomas More College Library plus 1 other. Books: 87,667 (physical), 3,056 (digital/electronic); Serial titles: 329 (physical); Databases: 65. Weekly public service hours: 76. Operations spending for the previous fiscal year: $391,586. 96 computers available on campus for general student use. A campuswide network can be accessed from student residence rooms and from off campus. Students can access the following: online class registration. Staffed computer lab on campus provides training in use of computers, software, and the Internet.

Community Environment: The campus is located just 10 minutes south of downtown Cincinnati. The Greater Cincinnati International Airport is a five-minute drive from campus. Numerous activities and faculties include the Cincinnati Symphony Orchestra, jazz clubs, restaurants, shops, live theater and ballet, the Cincinnati Zoo, the annual Riverfest, Oktoberfest and Taste of Cincinnati. Teams include the Cincinnati Reds and the Bengals.

■ TRANSYLVANIA UNIVERSITY

300 N Broadway

Lexington, KY 40508-1797

Tel: (859)233-8300; Free: 800-872-6798

Fax: (859)233-8797

E-mail: admissions@transy.edu

Web Site: www.transy.edu

Description: Independent, 4-year, coed, affiliated with Christian Church (Disciples of Christ). Awards bachelor's degrees. Founded 1780. Setting: 40-acre urban campus with easy access to Cincinnati, Louisville. Endowment: $179.2 million. Educational spending for the previous fiscal year: $11,920 per student. Total enrollment: 963. Faculty: 103 (82 full-time, 21 part-time). Student-undergrad faculty ratio is 11:1. 1,567 applied, 95% were admitted. 34% from top 10% of their high school class, 65% from top quarter, 87% from top half. Full-time: 959 students, 60% women, 40% men. Part-time: 4 students, 25% women, 75% men. Students come from 30 states and territories, 7 other countries, 22% from out-of-state. 0.1% American Indian or Alaska Native, non-Hispanic/Latino; 5% Hispanic/Latino; 4% Black or African American, non-Hispanic/Latino; 1% Asian, non-Hispanic/Latino; 3% international. 74% live on campus, 1% transferred in. Retention: 82% of full-time freshmen returned the following year. Academic areas with the most degrees conferred: business/marketing; biological/life sciences; parks and recreation. Core. Calendar: 4-4-1. Services for LD students, advanced placement, self-designed majors, independent study, double major, summer session for credit, part-time degree program, internships. Off campus study at Kentucky Institute for International Studies. Study abroad program. ROTC: Army (c), Air Force (c).

Entrance Requirements: Options: electronic application, early admission, early action, deferred admission, international baccalaureate accepted. Required: essay, high school transcript, minimum 2.75 high school GPA, 2 recommendations. Recommended: interview. Required for some: interview. Entrance: very difficult. Application deadlines: 11/15, 11/1 for early action. Notification: 12/1, 12/1 for early action. SAT Reasoning Test deadline: 2/1. Transfer credits accepted: Yes.

Costs Per Year: Application fee: $0. Comprehensive fee: $49,210 includes full-time tuition ($37,170), mandatory fees ($1580), and college room and board ($10,460). College room only: $5920. Room and board charges vary according to board plan and housing facility. Part-time tuition: $4130 per course. Part-time tuition varies according to course load.

Collegiate Environment: Orientation program. Drama-theater group, choral group, student-run newspaper, radio station. Social organizations: 71 open to all; national fraternities, national sororities; 57% of eligible men and 56% of eligible women are members. Most popular organizations: Student Government Association, Delta Sigma Phi, Phi Mu, Delta Delta Delta, Chi Omega. Major annual events: Campus Sing, Crimson Affair, Transy's Got Talent. Student services: health clinic, personal-psychological counseling. Campus security: 24-hour emergency response devices and patrols, late night transport-escort service, controlled dormitory access. J. Douglas Gay Jr./Frances Carrick Thomas Library. Books: 124,199 (physical), 170,342 (digital/electronic); Serial titles: 530 (physical), 23,600 (digital/electronic); Databases: 70. Weekly public service hours: 102; students can reserve study rooms. Operations spending for the previous fiscal year: $803,808. 90 computers available on campus for general student use. A campuswide network can be accessed from student residence rooms and from off campus. Students can access the following: online class registration.

Community Environment: See University of Kentucky.

■ UNION COLLEGE

310 College St.

Barbourville, KY 40906-1499

Tel: (606)546-4151; Free: 800-489-8646

Fax: (606)546-1667

E-mail: enrollme@unionky.edu

Web Site: www.unionky.edu

Description: Independent United Methodist, comprehensive, coed. Awards bachelor's and master's degrees and post-master's certificates. Founded 1879. Setting: 100-acre small town campus. Endowment: $22.7 million. Research spending for the previous fiscal year: $2168. Total enrollment: 1,329. Faculty: 131 (53 full-time, 78 part-time). Student-undergrad faculty ratio is 12:1. 1,539 applied, 56% were admitted. Full-time: 912 students, 49% women, 51% men. Part-time: 203 students, 65% women, 35% men. Students come from 34 states and territories, 16 other countries, 29% from out-of-state. 0.6% American Indian or Alaska Native, non-Hispanic/Latino; 2% Hispanic/Latino; 14% Black or African American, non-Hispanic/Latino;

0.2% Asian, non-Hispanic/Latino; 0.2% Native Hawaiian or other Pacific Islander, non-Hispanic/Latino; 9% international. 17% 25 or older, 47% live on campus, 9% transferred in. Retention: 65% of full-time freshmen returned the following year. Academic areas with the most degrees conferred: health professions and related sciences; business/marketing; education. Core. Calendar: semesters. Academic remediation for entering students, ESL program, services for LD students, advanced placement, accelerated degree program, self-designed majors, honors program, independent study, double major, summer session for credit, part-time degree program, graduate courses open to undergrads. Off campus study. Study abroad program.

Entrance Requirements: Options: electronic application, deferred admission. Required: high school transcript, minimum 2 high school GPA, SAT or ACT. Required for some: interview, Non-refundable application fee of $100 for international students only. Entrance: moderately difficult. Application deadline: rolling. Notification: continuous, 9/1 for nonresidents. Transfer credits accepted: Yes.

Costs Per Year: Comprehensive fee: $1620. College room only: $3300. Part-time tuition: $345 per credit hour.

Collegiate Environment: Orientation program. Drama-theater group, choral group. Social organizations: 26 open to all. Most popular organizations: Student Ambassadors, Student Government Association, Union Singers, International Club, Spiritual Life Team. Major annual events: Welcome Weekend, Homecoming Week, Convocations. Student services: health clinic, personal-psychological counseling. Campus security: 24-hour emergency response devices and patrols, late night transport-escort service, controlled dormitory access. 447 college housing spaces available. Freshmen guaranteed college housing. On-campus residence required through sophomore year. Options: men-only, women-only housing available. Weeks-Townsend Memorial Library plus 1 other. Books: 121,623 (physical), 386,171 (digital/electronic); Serial titles: 42,795 (physical); Databases: 124,060. Operations spending for the previous fiscal year: $443,361. 290 computers available on campus for general student use. A campuswide network can be accessed from student residence rooms and from off campus. Students can access the following: online class registration. Staffed computer lab on campus provides training in use of computers, software, and the Internet.

■ **UNIVERSITY OF THE CUMBERLANDS**
6178 College Station Dr.
Williamsburg, KY 40769-1372
Tel: (606)549-2200; Free: 800-343-1609
Fax: (606)539-4303
E-mail: admiss@ucumberlands.edu
Web Site: www.ucumberlands.edu
Description: Independent Kentucky Baptist, university, coed. Awards associate, bachelor's, master's, and doctoral degrees and post-master's certificates. Founded 1889. Setting: 150-acre rural campus with easy access to Knoxville. Total enrollment: 7,693. Faculty: 378 (162 full-time, 216 part-time). Student-undergrad faculty ratio is 15:1. 2,326 applied, 71% were admitted. 15% from top 10% of their high school class, 42% from top quarter, 72% from top half. 8 valedictorians. Full-time: 1,780 students, 54% women, 46% men. Part-time: 1,302 students, 57% women, 43% men. Students come from 38 states and territories, 26 other countries, 32% from out-of-state. 0.4% American Indian or Alaska Native, non-Hispanic/Latino; 2% Hispanic/Latino; 5% Black or African American, non-Hispanic/Latino; 0.4% Asian, non-Hispanic/Latino; 0.1% Native Hawaiian or other Pacific Islander, non-Hispanic/Latino; 4% international. 27% 25 or older, 80% live on campus, 5% transferred in. Retention: 65% of full-time freshmen returned the following year. Academic areas with the most degrees conferred: business/marketing; psychology; homeland security, law enforcement, firefighting, and protective services. Core. Calendar: semesters. Academic remediation for entering students, advanced placement, accelerated degree program, self-designed majors, honors program, independent study, distance learning, double major, summer session for credit, part-time degree program, adult/continuing education programs, co-op programs and internships, graduate courses open to undergrads. Study abroad program.

Entrance Requirements: Options: electronic application, deferred admission, international baccalaureate accepted. Required: high school transcript, minimum 2 high school GPA, SAT or ACT. Entrance: moderately difficult. Application deadline: 8/31. Notification: 8/31. SAT Reasoning Test deadline: 8/15. Transfer credits accepted: Yes.

Costs Per Year: Comprehensive fee: $32,000 includes full-time tuition ($22,640), mandatory fees ($360), and college room and board ($9000).

Collegiate Environment: Orientation program. Drama-theater group, choral group, marching band, student-run newspaper, radio station. Social

organizations: 28 open to all. Most popular organizations: Campus Activity Board, Baptist Campus Ministries, Mountain Outreach, Appalachian Ministries, Student Government Association. Major annual events: Homecoming, Spotlight, Spring Fever. Student services: health clinic, personal-psychological counseling. Campus security: 24-hour emergency response devices and patrols, student patrols, late night transport-escort service. Norma Perkins Hagan Memorial Library plus 1 other. Books: 127,545 (physical), 325,906 (digital/electronic); Serial titles: 428 (physical), 63,756 (digital/electronic); Databases: 83. Weekly public service hours: 79. Operations spending for the previous fiscal year: $312,762. 171 computers available on campus for general student use. A campuswide network can be accessed from student residence rooms and from off campus. Students can access the following: online class registration, online housing requests. Staffed computer lab on campus provides training in use of computers, software, and the Internet.

Community Environment: Located in the southeastern part of Kentucky, Williamsburg is accessible via bus service and interstate highway. The city offers facilities that include 14 churches of various denominations, 4 medical clinics, civic organizations and city parks. Recreation is found at Cumberland Falls State Park, Cumberland Lake, Laurel Lake, cinemas and theaters. There is adequate modern housing available and motels nearby. Part-time employment opportunities are available for students.

■ **UNIVERSITY OF KENTUCKY**
Lexington, KY 40506-0032
Tel: (859)257-9000; Free: 866-900-GO-UK
Fax: (859)257-4000
E-mail: admission@uky.edu
Web Site: www.uky.edu
Description: State-supported, university, coed. Part of Kentucky does not have a state system. Awards bachelor's, master's, and doctoral degrees and post-master's certificates. Founded 1865. Setting: 813-acre urban campus with easy access to Cincinnati, Louisville. Endowment: $1.3 billion. Research spending for the previous fiscal year: $311.3 million. Educational spending for the previous fiscal year: $12,568 per student. Total enrollment: 29,182. Faculty: 2,149 (1,437 full-time, 712 part-time). 19,324 applied, 94% were admitted. 32% from top 10% of their high school class, 59% from top quarter, 86% from top half. Full-time: 20,484 students, 56% women, 44% men. Part-time: 1,652 students, 51% women, 49% men. Students come from 54 states and territories, 67 other countries, 31% from out-of-state. 0.1% American Indian or Alaska Native, non-Hispanic/Latino; 5% Hispanic/Latino; 8% Black or African American, non-Hispanic/Latino; 3% Asian, non-Hispanic/Latino; 0.1% Native Hawaiian or other Pacific Islander, non-Hispanic/Latino; 2% international. 6% 25 or older, 31% live on campus, 4% transferred in. Retention: 85% of full-time freshmen returned the following year. Academic areas with the most degrees conferred: business/marketing; education; communication/journalism. Core. Calendar: semesters. Academic remediation for entering students, ESL program, services for LD students, advanced placement, accelerated degree program, self-designed majors, honors program, independent study, distance learning, double major, summer session for credit, part-time degree program, adult/continuing education programs, co-op programs and internships, graduate courses open to undergrads. Off campus study at National Student Exchange. Study abroad program. ROTC: Army, Air Force.

Entrance Requirements: Options: electronic application, early admission, early action, deferred admission, international baccalaureate accepted. Required: essay, high school transcript, SAT or ACT. Required for some: Audition required of music and dance majors. Entrance: moderately difficult. Application deadlines: 2/15, 2/15 for nonresidents, 12/1 for early action. Notification: continuous until 3/15, continuous until 3/15 for nonresidents, rolling for early action. SAT Reasoning Test deadline: 8/1. SAT Subject Test deadline: 8/1. Transfer credits accepted: Yes. Applicants placed on waiting list: 484. Wait-listed applicants offered admission: 45.

Costs Per Year: Application fee: $50. State resident tuition: $10,896 full-time, $490 per credit hour part-time. Nonresident tuition: $27,750 full-time, $1189 per credit hour part-time. Mandatory fees: $1349 full-time, $42.50 per credit hour part-time. Full-time tuition and fees vary according to location, program, reciprocity agreements, and student level. Part-time tuition and fees vary according to course load, location, program, reciprocity agreements, and student level. College room and board: $12,982. College room only: $8832. Room and board charges vary according to board plan and housing facility.

Collegiate Environment: Orientation program. Drama-theater group, choral group, marching band, student-run newspaper, radio station. Social

organizations: 506 open to all; national fraternities, national sororities, local fraternities, local sororities; 19% of eligible men and 32% of eligible women are members. Most popular organizations: Student Activities Board, Student Government Association, Campus Progressive Coalition, Ski and Snowboard Club, Society of Women Engineers. Major annual events: Homecoming, Student Center Night, Cultural Diversity Festival. Student services: legal services, health clinic, personal-psychological counseling, women's center. Campus security: 24-hour emergency response devices and patrols, late night transport-escort service, controlled dormitory access. 6,824 undergraduates lived in college housing during 2018-19. Freshmen given priority for college housing. Options: coed, men-only housing available. William T. Young Library plus 10 others. Books: 2.5 million (physical), 1.7 million (digital/electronic); Serial titles: 56,959 (physical), 175,865 (digital/electronic); Databases: 435. Study areas open 24 hours, 5-7 days a week; students can reserve study rooms. Operations spending for the previous fiscal year: $28 million. 1,000 computers available on campus for general student use. Computer purchase/lease plans available. A campuswide network can be accessed from student residence rooms and from off campus. Students can access the following: online class registration. Staffed computer lab on campus (open 24 hours a day) provides training in use of computers and software.

Community Environment: Lexington is located in the famous Bluegrass area of Kentucky. It is centrally located with Louisville 80 miles to the west and Cincinnati 90 miles to the north. Travel is made easier with close access to Interstates 75 and 64. The Mountain Parkway connects the Bluegrass with eastern Kentucky, and the Bluegrass Parkway links the western part of the State and Interstate 65. Lexington, known throughout the world as the home of the thoroughbred, attracts thousands of horse fans and buyers each year. Keeneland, a thoroughbred race track, and the famous trotting track, the Red Mile draw racing fans. The thoroughbred is not Lexington's only equine citizen; the standardbred, the quarterhorse, the saddle horse, and the Arabian are some of the many other breeds that live on some of the world's most famous farms in the Bluegrass. Since 1974, Lexington has been governed by an urban county form of government. The Lexington-Fayette County population is approximately 268,000, and this second largest city in Kentucky has seen steady growth in population. Lexington is very proud of its quality of life which can be attributed to the rich history of the area, and this quality is carefully monitored so that expansion and growth will enhance rather than hinder that lifestyle. Its economy is diverse in its job opportunities with the University of Kentucky and LexMark being the major employers. Employment can also be found in equine related businesses, tobacco, medicine, and retail and service industries. Among the many products manufactured in this area are electric typewriters and computer printers, peanut butter, tobacco processing and by-products, paper goods, and various equine-related products. Lexington's climate includes a mean annual temperature of 55 degrees Fahrenheit, and annual precipitation is 44 inches. The Bluegrass area has four distinct seasons with no prolonged periods of extreme temperatures or precipitation.

■ UNIVERSITY OF LOUISVILLE

2301 S Third St.
Louisville, KY 40292-0001
Tel: (502)852-5555; Free: 800-334-8635
Fax: (502)852-4776
E-mail: admitme@louisville.edu
Web Site: www.louisville.edu

Description: State-supported, university, coed. Awards associate, bachelor's, master's, and doctoral degrees and post-master's certificates. Founded 1798. Setting: 640-acre urban campus with easy access to Louisville. Endowment: $792.2 million. Research spending for the previous fiscal year: $49.4 million. Educational spending for the previous fiscal year: $17,018 per student. Total enrollment: 21,431. Faculty: 1,511 (919 full-time, 592 part-time). Student-undergrad faculty ratio is 15:1. 13,570 applied, 73% were admitted. 25 National Merit Scholars. Full-time: 11,930 students, 54% women, 46% men. Part-time: 3,712 students, 48% women, 52% men. Students come from 52 states and territories, 63 other countries, 17% from out-of-state. 0.1% American Indian or Alaska Native, non-Hispanic/Latino; 5% Hispanic/Latino; 12% Black or African American, non-Hispanic/Latino; 4% Asian, non-Hispanic/Latino; 1% international. 15% 25 or older, 23% live on campus, 6% transferred in. Retention: 80% of full-time freshmen returned the following year. Academic areas with the most degrees conferred: business/marketing; engineering; health professions and related sciences. Core. Calendar: semesters. Academic remediation for entering students, ESL program, services for LD students, advanced placement, accelerated degree program, honors program, independent study, distance learning, double major, summer session for credit, part-time degree program, adult/continuing education programs, co-op programs and internships, graduate

courses open to undergrads. Off campus study at Kentuckiana Metroversity. Study abroad program. ROTC: Army, Air Force.

Entrance Requirements: Options: electronic application, deferred admission, international baccalaureate accepted. Required: high school transcript, minimum 2.5 high school GPA. Required for some: SAT or ACT, TOEFL for students whose primary language is not English. Entrance: moderately difficult. Application deadline: 8/1. SAT Reasoning Test deadline: 7/18. Transfer credits accepted: Yes.

Costs Per Year: Application fee: $25. State resident tuition: $11,460 full-time, $478 per credit hour part-time. Nonresident tuition: $27,082 full-time, $1129 per credit hour part-time. Mandatory fees: $196 full-time. College room and board: $9058. College room only: $5282.

Collegiate Environment: Orientation program. Drama-theater group, choral group, marching band, student-run newspaper. Social organizations: 458 open to all; national fraternities, national sororities; 15% of eligible men and 16% of eligible women are members. Most popular organizations: Baptist Campus Ministry, Society of Porter Scholars, Association of Black Students, Common Ground, Raise Red Dance Marathon. Major annual events: Homecoming Events, Fryberger Sing, Welcome Weekend. Student services: health clinic, personal-psychological counseling, women's center. Campus security: 24-hour emergency response devices and patrols, late night transport-escort service, controlled dormitory access. 6,918 college housing spaces available; 5,440 were occupied in 2018-19. Freshmen guaranteed college housing. On-campus residence required in freshman year. Options: coed, men-only, women-only housing available. William F. Ekstrom Library plus 6 others. Books: 1.6 million (physical), 367,856 (digital/electronic); Serial titles: 2,158 (physical), 90,689 (digital/electronic); Databases: 345. Weekly public service hours: 97; study areas open 24 hours, 5-7 days a week; students can reserve study rooms. Operations spending for the previous fiscal year: $17.4 million. 400 computers available on campus for general student use. Computer purchase/lease plans available. A campuswide network can be accessed from student residence rooms and from off campus. Students can access the following: online class registration. Staffed computer lab on campus (open 24 hours a day) provides training in use of computers, software, and the Internet.

Community Environment: Louisville is known as the Derby City for the annual running of the Kentucky Derby at Churchill Downs. The city was the base of supplies for Clark's expeditions, which culminated in the conquest of the northwest. U.S. river boats pass through the locks around 25-foot falls in the Ohio River. Louisville is an important distilling center and one of the largest tobacco product manufacturing centers in the world. There are many other local manufacturing firms in the area, and part-time employment is available. There is a community-wide fund for music, drama, and art, and the city has resident opera, ballet, orchestra, and theater companies.

■ UNIVERSITY OF PIKEVILLE

147 Sycamore St.
Pikeville, KY 41501
Tel: (606)218-5250; Free: 866-232-7700
Fax: (606)218-5269
E-mail: wewantyou@pc.edu
Web Site: www.upike.edu

Description: Independent, comprehensive, coed, affiliated with Presbyterian Church (U.S.A.). Awards associate, bachelor's, master's, and doctoral degrees. Founded 1889. Setting: 25-acre small town campus. Endowment: $15.4 million. Research spending for the previous fiscal year: $97,032. Educational spending for the previous fiscal year: $6752 per student. Total enrollment: 2,335. Faculty: 105 (65 full-time, 40 part-time). Student-undergrad faculty ratio is 14:1. 2,299 applied, 100% were admitted. 15% from top 10% of their high school class, 35% from top quarter, 59% from top half. 14 valedictorians. Full-time: 1,049 students, 51% women, 49% men. Part-time: 510 students, 62% women, 38% men. Students come from 29 states and territories, 13 other countries, 20% from out-of-state. 0.8% American Indian or Alaska Native, non-Hispanic/Latino; 0.8% Hispanic/Latino; 6% Black or African American, non-Hispanic/Latino; 0.8% Asian, non-Hispanic/Latino; 0.1% Native Hawaiian or other Pacific Islander, non-Hispanic/Latino; 2% international. 10% 25 or older, 50% live on campus, 7% transferred in. Retention: 57% of full-time freshmen returned the following year. Academic areas with the most degrees conferred: business/marketing; biological/life sciences; psychology. Core. Calendar: semesters. Academic remediation for entering students, ESL program, services for LD students, advanced placement, self-designed majors, distance learning, double major, summer session for credit, part-time degree program, internships. Study abroad program. ROTC: Army.

Entrance Requirements: Open admission open admission for most students except for nursing, education, and social work programs. Options: electronic application, deferred admission. Required: high school transcript,

SAT or ACT. Entrance: noncompetitive. Application deadline: 8/15. Notification: continuous. SAT Reasoning Test deadline: 8/15. Transfer credits accepted: Yes.

Costs Per Year: Application fee: $0. Comprehensive fee: $28,750 includes full-time tuition ($20,800), mandatory fees ($150), and college room and board ($7800). Full-time tuition and fees vary according to course load. Room and board charges vary according to housing facility. Part-time tuition: $867 per semester hour. Part-time tuition varies according to course load.

Collegiate Environment: Orientation program. Drama-theater group, choral group, student-run newspaper. Social organizations: 30 open to all; local fraternities, local sororities; 8% of eligible men and 9% of eligible women are members. Most popular organizations: Student Government, Phi Beta Lambda, Lambda Sigma, Concert Choir, Student Nurses at UPIKE. Major annual events: Homecoming, Founder' Day. Student services: health clinic. Campus security: 24-hour patrols, controlled dormitory access. Allara Library plus 2 others. Books: 73,924 (physical), 214,499 (digital/electronic); Serial titles: 1,437 (physical), 88,386 (digital/electronic); Databases: 73. Weekly public service hours: 105; students can reserve study rooms. Operations spending for the previous fiscal year: $1.1 million. 308 computers available on campus for general student use. A campuswide network can be accessed from student residence rooms and from off campus. Staffed computer lab on campus.

Community Environment: Located in the heart of Big Sandy Valley, Pikeville is an important mining and trade center in the midst of Elkhorn coalfield. Breaks Park, southeast of town and Jenny Wiley State Park north of town, provides recreational facilities. Part-time employment is available.

■ WEST KENTUCKY COMMUNITY AND TECHNICAL COLLEGE
4810 Alben Barkley Dr.
Paducah, KY 42001
Tel: (270)554-9200
Fax: (270)554-6217
E-mail: trent.johnson@kctcs.edu
Web Site: www.westkentucky.kctcs.edu

Description: State-supported, 2-year, coed. Part of Kentucky Community and Technical College System. Awards certificates, diplomas, transfer associate, and terminal associate degrees. Founded 1932. Setting: 117-acre small town campus. Total enrollment: 6,259. Faculty: (121 full-time, 166 part-time). Student-undergrad faculty ratio is 18:1. Students come from 25 states and territories. 0.3% American Indian or Alaska Native, non-Hispanic/Latino; 4% Hispanic/Latino; 8% Black or African American, non-Hispanic/Latino; 0.6% Asian, non-Hispanic/Latino; 0.1% international. 35% 25 or older. Retention: 57% of full-time freshmen returned the following year. Core. Calendar: semesters. Academic remediation for entering students, ESL program, accelerated degree program, honors program, independent study, distance learning, summer session for credit, part-time degree program, external degree program, adult/continuing education programs, co-op programs. Study abroad program.

Entrance Requirements: Open admission There are a few selective admission programs including some allied health programs like Nursing, Surgical Technology, Radiography, Sonography, and Dental Assisting. Options: electronic application, early admission. Required: high school transcript. Entrance: noncompetitive. Application deadline: rolling. Notification: continuous. Transfer credits accepted: Yes.

Costs Per Year: Application fee: $0. State resident tuition: $5070 full-time, $169 per credit hour part-time. Nonresident tuition: $17,760 full-time, $592 per credit hour part-time. Mandatory fees: $240 full-time, $8 per credit hour part-time.

Collegiate Environment: Orientation program. Campus security: 24-hour patrols. College housing not available. WKCTC Matheson Library. 160 computers available on campus for general student use. A campuswide network can be accessed. Staffed computer lab on campus.

Community Environment: A busy town with a leisurely atmosphere, Paducah was named for Indian Chief, Paduke, who is buried on the bank of the river. It is an important market for burley and dark tobacco. Diversified industries include boat and barge builders, electronics and chemicals plants. Part-time work is available. Located at the confluence of the Tennessee and Ohio Rivers, average winter temperature is 46.2 degrees, summer, 73.4 degrees. Highways, airlines, and bus lines serve the community. A public library, churches, two hospitals, hotels and motels and many civic organizations are available. Recreation areas include nearby Kentucky and Barkley Lakes and the"Land Between Lakes" area as well as three state parks, several public parks, a swimming pool, golf courses and theatres.

■ WESTERN KENTUCKY UNIVERSITY
1906 College Heights Blvd.
Bowling Green, KY 42101

Tel: (270)745-0111; Free: 800-495-8463
Fax: (270)745-6133
Web Site: www.wku.edu

Description: State-supported, comprehensive, coed. Awards associate, bachelor's, master's, and doctoral degrees and post-master's certificates. Founded 1906. Setting: 235-acre suburban campus with easy access to Nashville. Endowment: $163.2 million. Research spending for the previous fiscal year: $7.5 million. Educational spending for the previous fiscal year: $6935 per student. Total enrollment: 19,456. Faculty: 1,116 (709 full-time, 407 part-time). Student-undergrad faculty ratio is 18:1. 9,250 applied, 97% were admitted. 22% from top 10% of their high school class, 46% from top quarter, 75% from top half. 117 valedictorians. Full-time: 12,393 students, 58% women, 42% men. Part-time: 4,637 students, 64% women, 36% men. Students come from 47 states and territories, 58 other countries, 22% from out-of-state. 0.3% American Indian or Alaska Native, non-Hispanic/Latino; 4% Hispanic/Latino; 8% Black or African American, non-Hispanic/Latino; 2% Asian, non-Hispanic/Latino; 0.1% Native Hawaiian or other Pacific Islander, non-Hispanic/Latino; 3% international. 15% 25 or older, 35% live on campus, 6% transferred in. Retention: 72% of full-time freshmen returned the following year. Academic areas with the most degrees conferred: business/marketing; health professions and related sciences; liberal arts/general studies. Core. Calendar: semesters. Academic remediation for entering students, ESL program, services for LD students, advanced placement, accelerated degree program, self-designed majors, freshman honors college, honors program, independent study, distance learning, double major, summer session for credit, part-time degree program, adult/continuing education programs, co-op programs and internships, graduate courses open to undergrads. Off campus study. Study abroad program. ROTC: Army, Air Force (c).

Entrance Requirements: Options: electronic application, deferred admission, international baccalaureate accepted. Required: high school transcript, minimum ACT composite score of 20 or greater, SAT combined score of 1020 or greater (940 or greater for tests taken prior to March 2016), unweighted high school GPA of 2.50 or higher, or minimum on Composite Admission Index score, SAT or ACT. Entrance: minimally difficult. Notification: continuous. SAT Reasoning Test deadline: 8/1. SAT Subject Test deadline: 8/1. Transfer credits accepted: Yes.

Costs Per Year: Application fee: $45. State resident tuition: $10,602 full-time, $442 per credit hour part-time. Nonresident tuition: $26,496 full-time, $1104 per credit hour part-time. Full-time tuition varies according to reciprocity agreements. Part-time tuition varies according to reciprocity agreements. College room and board: $8343. College room only: $4768. Room and board charges vary according to board plan and housing facility.

Collegiate Environment: Orientation program. Drama-theater group, choral group, marching band, student-run newspaper, radio station. Social organizations: 347 open to all; national fraternities, national sororities; 15% of eligible men and 18% of eligible women are members. Most popular organizations: Student Government Association, Campus Activities Board, Campus Crusade for Christ, Campus Ministries, Residence Hall Association. Major annual events: Big Red's Roar (homecoming pep rally), CAB-OOM Spring Festival, Football Tailgating. Student services: legal services, health clinic, personal-psychological counseling, women's center. Campus security: 24-hour emergency response devices and patrols, student patrols, late night transport-escort service, controlled dormitory access. 5,650 college housing spaces available; 4,831 were occupied in 2018-19. Freshmen given priority for college housing. On-campus residence required through sophomore year. Options: coed, men-only, women-only housing available. Helm-Cravens Library plus 2 others. Books: 848,646 (physical), 112,090 (digital/electronic); Serial titles: 10,834 (physical), 48,911 (digital/electronic); Databases: 48,893. Weekly public service hours: 95; students can reserve study rooms. Operations spending for the previous fiscal year: $6 million. 312 computers available on campus for general student use. Computer purchase/lease plans available. A campuswide network can be accessed from student residence rooms and from off campus. Students can access the following: online class registration. Staffed computer lab on campus (open 24 hours a day) provides training in use of computers, software, and the Internet.

Community Environment: The city of Bowling Green is located on the Barrer River in Warren County in southern Kentucky. Situated 60 miles north of Nashville, and 103 miles south of Louisville, Bowling Green has about 80 churches of 26 denominations, a public library, and two hospitals. Recreation is provided by local theaters and parks, including nearby Mammoth Cave National Park.

■ **BATON ROUGE COMMUNITY COLLEGE**
201 Community College Dr.
Baton Rouge, LA 70806
Tel: (225)216-8000; Free: 800-601-4558
Fax: (225)216-8100
Web Site: www.mybrcc.edu
Description: State-supported, 2-year, coed. Awards transfer associate and terminal associate degrees. Founded 1995. Total enrollment: 7,031. 24% 25 or older. Calendar: semesters.
Entrance Requirements: Open admission.

■ **BATON ROUGE SCHOOL OF COMPUTERS**
9352 Interline Ave.
Baton Rouge, LA 70809
Tel: (225)923-2524; Free: 888-920-2772
Fax: (504)923-2979
E-mail: admissions@brsc.net
Web Site: www.brsc.edu
Description: Proprietary, 2-year, coed. Awards certificates and terminal associate degrees. Founded 1979. Total enrollment: 56. Student-undergrad faculty ratio is 25:1. 64% 25 or older.
Entrance Requirements: Required: interview, Wonderlic aptitude test. Entrance: noncompetitive.

■ **BOSSIER PARISH COMMUNITY COLLEGE**
6220 E Texas St.
Bossier City, LA 71111
Tel: (318)678-6000
Web Site: www.bpcc.edu
Description: State-supported, 2-year, coed. Part of Louisiana Community and Technical College System. Awards certificates, diplomas, and transfer associate degrees. Founded 1967. Setting: 64-acre urban campus with easy access to Shreveport. Total enrollment: 6,042. Faculty: 229 (117 full-time, 112 part-time). Student-undergrad faculty ratio is 22:1. 3,208 applied, 99% were admitted. 1% from top 10% of their high school class, 21% from top quarter, 37% from top half. Full-time: 2,310 students, 63% women, 37% men. Part-time: 3,732 students, 67% women, 33% men. 3% from out-of-state. 1% American Indian or Alaska Native, non-Hispanic/Latino; 1% Hispanic/Latino; 42% Black or African American, non-Hispanic/Latino; 0.7% Asian, non-Hispanic/Latino; 0.2% Native Hawaiian or other Pacific Islander, non-Hispanic/Latino; 0.1% international. 43% 25 or older, 13% transferred in. Retention: 42% of full-time freshmen returned the following year. Core. Calendar: semesters. Academic remediation for entering students, services for LD students, advanced placement, distance learning, double major, summer session for credit, part-time degree program, adult/continuing education programs.
Entrance Requirements: Open admission. Option: early admission. Entrance: noncompetitive.
Costs Per Year: Application fee: $0. State resident tuition: $3335 full-time, $139 per credit hour part-time. Nonresident tuition: $8012 full-time, $334 per credit hour part-time. Mandatory fees: $948 full-time, $37 per credit hour part-time, $30 per term part-time. Full-time tuition and fees vary according to course load, location, and program. Part-time tuition and fees vary according to course load, location, and program.
Collegiate Environment: Orientation program. Drama-theater group, choral group, student-run newspaper. Student services: personal-psychological counseling. Campus security: student patrols. Bossier Parish Community College Library.

■ **CAMERON COLLEGE**
2740 Canal St.
New Orleans, LA 70119
Tel: (504)821-5881
Web Site: www.cameroncollege.com
Description: Proprietary, 2-year, coed. Awards terminal associate degrees. Founded 1981. 29% 25 or older.
Entrance Requirements: Open admission.

■ **CENTENARY COLLEGE OF LOUISIANA**
2911 Centenary Blvd.
Shreveport, LA 71104
Tel: (318)869-5011; Free: 800-234-4448
Fax: (318)869-5005
E-mail: lcarlton@centenary.edu
Web Site: www.centenary.edu
Description: Independent United Methodist, comprehensive, coed. Awards bachelor's and master's degrees. Founded 1825. Setting: 65-acre urban campus with easy access to Shreveport. Total enrollment: 585. Faculty: 83 (55 full-time, 28 part-time). Student-undergrad faculty ratio is 9:1. 893 applied, 60% were admitted. Full-time: 539 students, 58% women, 42% men. Part-time: 13 students, 15% women, 85% men. 0.5% American Indian or Alaska Native, non-Hispanic/Latino; 10% Hispanic/Latino; 14% Black or African American, non-Hispanic/Latino; 2% Asian, non-Hispanic/Latino; 0.2% Native Hawaiian or other Pacific Islander, non-Hispanic/Latino; 3% international. Retention: 76% of full-time freshmen returned the following year. Academic areas with the most degrees conferred: biological/life sciences; business/marketing; visual and performing arts. Core. Calendar: 4-4-1. Services for LD students, advanced placement, self-designed majors, honors program, independent study, double major, summer session for credit, part-time degree program, internships, graduate courses open to undergrads. Off campus study. Study abroad program.
Entrance Requirements: Options: electronic application, early admission, early action, deferred admission, international baccalaureate accepted. Required: SAT or ACT. Entrance: moderately difficult. Application deadline: rolling. Notification: continuous. Transfer credits accepted: Yes.
Costs Per Year: Application fee: $0. One-time mandatory fee: $250. Comprehensive fee: $50,980 includes full-time tuition ($37,310) and college room and board ($13,670). Part-time tuition: $1554 per credit hour.
Collegiate Environment: Orientation program. Drama-theater group, choral group, student-run newspaper, radio station. Social organizations: national fraternities, national sororities, local fraternities. Most popular organizations: Intramural sports, Residence Life (Centenary Activities Board), Fellowship of Christian Athletes, Christian Leadership Center, Media Group. Major annual events: CAB Spring Fling, CAB Fall Fest, Homecoming. Student services: health clinic, personal-psychological counseling. Campus security: 24-hour emergency response devices and patrols, late night transport-escort service, controlled dormitory access. Freshmen guaranteed college housing. On-campus residence required through senior year. Option: coed housing available. Magale Library plus 1 other. Students can reserve study rooms.
Community Environment: See Louisiana State University Shreveport.

■ **CENTRAL LOUISIANA TECHNICAL COMMUNITY COLLEGE**
4311 S MacArthur Dr.
Alexandria, LA 71302
Tel: (318)487-5439
E-mail: meredithclark@cltcc.edu
Web Site: www.cltcc.edu
Description: State-supported, 2-year, coed. Part of Louisiana Technical Community College System. Awards certificates, diplomas, and transfer associate degrees. Setting: small town campus. Endowment: $289,536. Educational spending for the previous fiscal year: $5193 per student. Total enrollment: 2,432. Faculty: 130 (85 full-time, 45 part-time). Student-undergrad faculty ratio is 24:1. 1,687 applied, 100% were admitted. Full-time: 1,107 students, 52% women, 48% men. Part-time: 1,325 students, 40% women, 60% men. Students come from 3 states and territories, 2% from out-of-state. 3% American Indian or Alaska Native, non-Hispanic/Latino; 29% Black or African American, non-Hispanic/Latino; 0.4% Asian, non-Hispanic/Latino. 25% 25 or older, 9% transferred in. Retention: 69% of full-time freshmen returned the following year. Core. Calendar: semesters. Academic remediation for entering students, ESL program, services for LD students, advanced placement, honors program, independent study, distance learning, double major, summer session for credit, part-time degree program, internships.
Entrance Requirements: Open admission. Option: electronic application. Required: high school transcript. Entrance: noncompetitive. Notification: continuous. Transfer credits accepted: Yes.
Costs Per Year: Application fee: $5. State resident tuition: $3335 full-time, $175 per credit hour part-time. Nonresident tuition: $8053 full-time, $346 per credit hour part-time. Mandatory fees: $754 full-time, $377 per term part-time. Full-time tuition and fees vary according to course load, location, and program. Part-time tuition and fees vary according to course load, location, and program.
Collegiate Environment: Orientation program. Social organizations: 2 open to all; 2% of eligible men and 2% of eligible women are members. Most popular organizations: Skills USA, Student Government Association. Student services: personal-psychological counseling. Campus security: 24-hour emergency response devices. Books: 1,484 (physical), 5,331 (digital/electronic); Databases: 86. Weekly public service hours: 40. 100 computers available on campus for general student use. A campuswide network can be accessed. Students can access the following: online class registration. Staffed computer lab on campus provides training in use of computers, software, and the Internet.

■ **DELGADO COMMUNITY COLLEGE**
615 City Park Ave.
New Orleans, LA 70119
Tel: (504)671-5000
Fax: (504)483-1986
E-mail: enroll@dcc.edu
Web Site: www.dcc.edu
Description: State-supported, 2-year, coed. Part of Louisiana Community and Technical College System. Awards certificates, transfer associate, and terminal associate degrees. Founded 1921. Setting: 57-acre urban campus. Endowment: $2 million. Research spending for the previous fiscal year: $60,000. Total enrollment: 18,698. Faculty: 600 (380 full-time, 220 part-time). Student-undergrad faculty ratio is 42:1. Full-time: 7,906 students, 62% women, 38% men. Part-time: 10,792 students, 68% women, 32% men. Students come from 20 states and territories. 0.4% American Indian or Alaska Native, non-Hispanic/Latino; 8% Hispanic/Latino; 45% Black or African American, non-Hispanic/Latino; 3% Asian, non-Hispanic/Latino; 0.1% Native Hawaiian or other Pacific Islander, non-Hispanic/Latino; 0.8% international. 59% 25 or older. Retention: 57% of full-time freshmen returned the following year. Core. Calendar: semesters. Academic remediation for entering students, ESL program, services for LD students, advanced placement, honors program, distance learning, double major, summer session for credit, part-time degree program, co-op programs. Off campus study at University of New Orleans, Southern University at New Orleans. ROTC: Army (c), Air Force (c).
Entrance Requirements: Open admission except for allied health, nursing, culinary arts programs. Option: electronic application. Recommended: high school transcript, proof of immunization. Required for some: high school transcript. Entrance: noncompetitive. Application deadline: rolling.
Collegiate Environment: Orientation program. Drama-theater group, student-run newspaper, radio station. Social organizations: 50 open to all. Most popular organizations: Student Government, Circle K, International

Club, Phi Theta Kappa, Lambda Phi Nu. Major annual events: Homecoming Week, Spring Fest, International Week. Student services: legal services, health clinic, personal-psychological counseling, women's center. Campus security: 24-hour patrols, late night transport-escort service. Moss Memorial Library. Operations spending for the previous fiscal year: $1 million. 950 computers available on campus for general student use. A campuswide network can be accessed from off-campus. Staffed computer lab on campus.
Community Environment: See Tulane University.

■ **DILLARD UNIVERSITY**
2601 Gentilly Blvd.
New Orleans, LA 70122-3097
Tel: (504)283-8822; Free: 800-216-8094
Fax: (504)286-4895
E-mail: acyprian@dillard.edu
Web Site: www.dillard.edu
Description: Independent interdenominational, 4-year, coed. Awards bachelor's degrees. Founded 1869. Setting: 55-acre urban campus. Endowment: $58.4 million. Educational spending for the previous fiscal year: $12,378 per student. Total enrollment: 1,185. Faculty: 139 (72 full-time, 67 part-time). Student-undergrad faculty ratio is 12:1. 4,615 applied, 48% were admitted. 10% from top 10% of their high school class, 35% from top quarter, 69% from top half. Full-time: 1,133 students, 73% women, 27% men. Part-time: 52 students, 69% women, 31% men. Students come from 29 states and territories, 10 other countries, 36% from out-of-state. 0.4% Hispanic/Latino; 91% Black or African American, non-Hispanic/Latino; 2% international. 8% 25 or older, 40% live on campus, 5% transferred in. Retention: 75% of full-time freshmen returned the following year. Academic areas with the most degrees conferred: health professions and related sciences; social sciences; psychology. Core. Calendar: semesters. Academic remediation for entering students, ESL program, services for LD students, advanced placement, honors program, independent study, double major, summer session for credit, part-time degree program, external degree program, co-op programs and internships. Study abroad program. ROTC: Army (c), Naval (c), Air Force (c).
Entrance Requirements: Options: electronic application, early admission, international baccalaureate accepted. Required: high school transcript, minimum 2.5 high school GPA, SAT or ACT, minimum SAT score of 870 (math and verbal) or minimum ACT composite score of 18. Required for some: essay, 2 recommendations. Entrance: moderately difficult. Application deadline: rolling. Notification: continuous. SAT Reasoning Test deadline: 8/15. SAT Subject Test deadline: 8/15. Transfer credits accepted: Yes.
Costs Per Year: Application fee: $35. Comprehensive fee: $28,018 includes full-time tuition ($16,580), mandatory fees ($1338), and college room and board ($10,100). College room only: $6156. Part-time tuition: $691 per credit hour.
Collegiate Environment: Orientation program. Drama-theater group, choral group, student-run newspaper, radio station. Social organizations: 45 open to all; national fraternities, national sororities; 25% of eligible men and 40% of eligible women are members. Most popular organizations: Student Government Association, Student Activities Board, National Pan-Hellenic Council, Collegiate 100, Class Councils. Major annual events: Coronation, Spring Fest, MLK Week for Peace and Justice. Student services: legal services, health clinic, personal-psychological counseling. Campus security: 24-hour emergency response devices and patrols, late night transport-escort service, controlled dormitory access. Will W. Alexander Library plus 1 other. 75 computers available on campus for general student use. A campuswide network can be accessed from student residence rooms and from off campus. Students can access the following: online class registration. Staffed computer lab on campus provides training in use of computers, software, and the Internet.
Community Environment: See Tulane University.

■ **FLETCHER TECHNICAL COMMUNITY COLLEGE**
1407 Hwy. 311
Schriever, LA 70395
Tel: (985)448-7900
Fax: (985)446-3308
Web Site: www.fletcher.edu
Description: State-supported, 2-year, coed. Awards certificates, diplomas, transfer associate, and terminal associate degrees. Total enrollment: 788. Faculty: 61 (26 full-time, 35 part-time). Calendar: semesters.

■ **FORTIS COLLEGE**
9255 Interline Ave.
Baton Rouge, LA 70809

Tel: (225)248-1015; Free: 855-4-FORTIS
Fax: (225)248-9571
Web Site: www.fortis.edu
Description: Proprietary, 2-year, coed. Awards certificates, diplomas, transfer associate, and terminal associate degrees. Founded 1970. Setting: 4-acre urban campus. Total enrollment: 327. 198 applied. 51% 25 or older. Core. Calendar: quarters. Internships.
Entrance Requirements: Required: high school transcript, interview, Wonderlic aptitude test. Recommended: minimum 2.0 high school GPA, 2 recommendations. Entrance: noncompetitive. Application deadline: rolling. Notification: continuous.

■ FRANCISCAN MISSIONARIES OF OUR LADY UNIVERSITY
5414 Brittany Dr.
Baton Rouge, LA 70808
Tel: (225)768-1700
Fax: (225)768-1726
E-mail: admissions@franu.edu
Web Site: www.franu.edu
Description: Independent Roman Catholic, comprehensive, coed. Awards associate, bachelor's, master's, and doctoral degrees. Founded 1990. Setting: 5-acre urban campus with easy access to New Orleans. Total enrollment: 1,362. 291 applied, 48% were admitted. Full-time: 566 students, 86% women, 14% men. Part-time: 619 students, 87% women, 13% men. 10% from out-of-state. 0.8% American Indian or Alaska Native, non-Hispanic/Latino; 9% Hispanic/Latino; 18% Black or African American, non-Hispanic/Latino; 3% Asian, non-Hispanic/Latino; 0.4% Native Hawaiian or other Pacific Islander, non-Hispanic/Latino. Retention: 75% of full-time freshmen returned the following year. Core. Calendar: semesters. Services for LD students, advanced placement, distance learning, summer session for credit, part-time degree program. Off campus study. ROTC: Army (c), Air Force (c).
Entrance Requirements: Options: electronic application, early admission, deferred admission. Required: high school transcript, minimum 2.5 high school GPA, SAT or ACT. Entrance: minimally difficult. Application deadline: 8/1. Notification: continuous. SAT Reasoning Test deadline: 7/1. SAT Subject Test deadline: 7/1. Transfer credits accepted: Yes.
Costs Per Year: Application fee: $35. Tuition: $12,161 full-time, $506.72 per credit hour part-time. Mandatory fees: $1126 full-time. Full-time tuition and fees vary according to course load, degree level, and program. Part-time tuition varies according to course load, degree level, and program.
Collegiate Environment: Orientation program. Most popular organizations: Student Government Association, Cultural Arts Association, Christian Fellowship Association, Mathematics/Science Association. Major annual events: Welcome Week, Spring Crawfish Boil, Fall Festival. Student services: health clinic, personal-psychological counseling. Campus security: 24-hour patrols. Students can reserve study rooms. 150 computers available on campus for general student use. A campuswide network can be accessed. Students can access the following: online class registration.

■ GRAMBLING STATE UNIVERSITY
403 Main St.
Grambling, LA 71245
Tel: (318)247-3811; Free: 800-569-4714
Fax: (318)274-6172
E-mail: hudsond@gram.edu
Web Site: www.gram.edu
Description: State-supported, university, coed. Part of University of Louisiana System. Awards bachelor's, master's, and doctoral degrees and post-master's certificates. Founded 1901. Setting: 590-acre small town campus with easy access to Shreveport. Endowment: $6.8 million. Research spending for the previous fiscal year: $3.4 million. Educational spending for the previous fiscal year: $4760 per student. Total enrollment: 5,188. Faculty: 176 (160 full-time, 16 part-time). Student-undergrad faculty ratio is 26:1. 6,340 applied, 45% were admitted. 6% from top 10% of their high school class, 15% from top quarter, 32% from top half. Full-time: 3,732 students, 58% women, 42% men. Part-time: 357 students, 59% women, 41% men. Students come from 42 states and territories, 25 other countries, 33% from out-of-state. 0.2% American Indian or Alaska Native, non-Hispanic/Latino; 1% Hispanic/Latino; 89% Black or African American, non-Hispanic/Latino; 0.1% Asian, non-Hispanic/Latino; 5% international. 17% 25 or older, 6% transferred in. Retention: 68% of full-time freshmen returned the following year. Academic areas with the most degrees conferred: public administration and social services; education; parks and recreation. Core. Calendar: semesters. Academic remediation for entering students, services for LD

students, advanced placement, honors program, distance learning, double major, summer session for credit, part-time degree program, adult/continuing education programs, co-op programs and internships, graduate courses open to undergrads. Off campus study at Louisiana Tech University. ROTC: Army, Air Force (c).
Entrance Requirements: Options: electronic application, early admission. Required: high school transcript, minimum 2 high school GPA, 19 units from Required Core 4 Curriculum including no more than one developmental course, SAT or ACT. Entrance: noncompetitive. Application deadline: 8/15. Notification: 4/1. SAT Reasoning Test deadline: 8/15. SAT Subject Test deadline: 8/15. Transfer credits accepted: Yes.
Costs Per Year: Application fee: $20. State resident tuition: $5140 full-time, $215 per credit hour part-time. Nonresident tuition: $14,163 full-time, $591 per credit hour part-time. Mandatory fees: $2295 full-time, $1845 per year part-time. Full-time tuition and fees vary according to program. Part-time tuition and fees vary according to program. College room and board: $10,406. College room only: $6728. Room and board charges vary according to housing facility.
Collegiate Environment: Orientation program. Drama-theater group, choral group, marching band, student-run newspaper, radio station. Social organizations: national fraternities, national sororities, local fraternities, local sororities; 35% of eligible men and 65% of eligible women are members. Most popular organizations: Tiger Marching Band, Black Dynasty Modeling Troupe, Academic and Professional Clubs, sororities, fraternities. Major annual events: Bayou Classic Football Game, Homecoming Festivities, Springfest. Student services: health clinic, personal-psychological counseling. Campus security: 24-hour emergency response devices and patrols, student patrols, late night transport-escort service, controlled dormitory access. A. C. Lewis Memorial Library. Books: 127,508 (physical), 205,483 (digital/electronic); Serial titles: 835 (physical), 51,728 (digital/electronic); Databases: 101. Weekly public service hours: 49; students can reserve study rooms. Operations spending for the previous fiscal year: $1.7 million. 500 computers available on campus for general student use. A campuswide network can be accessed from student residence rooms and from off campus. Students can access the following: online class registration. Staffed computer lab on campus provides training in use of computers, software, and the Internet.
Community Environment: Grambling is in a suburban location five miles from Ruston, 35 miles from Monroe, and 70 miles from Shreveport. There is easy access to several major air and bus lines. The town has many fraternal, athletic, social, and civic organizations, and there are theatres in nearby Ruston. Excellent hunting, fishing, and boating facilities in the area. This is the home of the annual North Louisiana Broiler Show and Fair, and an annual Housing Clinic.

■ HERZING UNIVERSITY
2500 Williams Blvd.
Kenner, LA 70062
Tel: (504)733-0074; Free: 800-596-0724
Fax: (504)733-0020
Web Site: www.herzing.edu/new-orleans
Description: Independent, 4-year, coed. Awards associate and bachelor's degrees. Founded 1996. Calendar: semesters.

■ ITI TECHNICAL COLLEGE
13944 Airline Hwy.
Baton Rouge, LA 70817
Tel: (225)752-4233; Free: 888-211-7165
Fax: (225)756-0903
E-mail: snorris@iticollege.edu
Web Site: www.iticollege.edu
Description: Proprietary, 2-year, coed. Awards certificates and terminal associate degrees. Founded 1973. Setting: 10-acre suburban campus. Total enrollment: 622. Full-time: 622 students, 15% women, 85% men. Students come from 2 states and territories. 0.5% American Indian or Alaska Native, non-Hispanic/Latino; 1% Hispanic/Latino; 45% Black or African American, non-Hispanic/Latino; 0.3% Asian, non-Hispanic/Latino. 47% 25 or older. Calendar: quarters. Internships.
Entrance Requirements: Required: high school transcript, interview.
Collegiate Environment: Orientation program. Campus security: electronic alarm devices during non-business hours, security cameras 24-hours. ITI Technical College Library. 8 computers available on campus for general student use. A campuswide network can be accessed. Staffed computer lab on campus provides training in use of computers, software, and the Internet.

■ LOUISIANA COLLEGE

1140 College Dr.
Pineville, LA 71359-0001
Tel: (318)487-7011; Free: 800-487-1906
Fax: (318)487-7550
E-mail: admissions@lacollege.edu
Web Site: www.lacollege.edu

Description: Independent Southern Baptist, comprehensive, coed. Awards associate, bachelor's, and master's degrees. Founded 1906. Setting: 81-acre small town campus. Endowment: $37.9 million. Educational spending for the previous fiscal year: $20,167 per student. Total enrollment: 1,245. Faculty: 119 (75 full-time, 44 part-time). Student-undergrad faculty ratio is 12:1. 808 applied, 78% were admitted. Full-time: 893 students, 47% women, 53% men. Part-time: 111 students, 52% women, 48% men. Students come from 14 states and territories, 15 other countries, 10% from out-of-state. 0.8% American Indian or Alaska Native, non-Hispanic/Latino; 4% Hispanic/Latino; 24% Black or African American, non-Hispanic/Latino; 1% Asian, non-Hispanic/Latino; 0.2% Native Hawaiian or other Pacific Islander, non-Hispanic/Latino; 2% international. 13% 25 or older, 54% live on campus, 7% transferred in. Retention: 65% of full-time freshmen returned the following year. Academic areas with the most degrees conferred: health professions and related sciences; parks and recreation; business/marketing. Core. Calendar: semesters. Academic remediation for entering students, ESL program, services for LD students, advanced placement, accelerated degree program, self-designed majors, honors program, independent study, distance learning, double major, summer session for credit, part-time degree program, adult/continuing education programs, internships. Off campus study.

Entrance Requirements: Open admission. Options: electronic application, early action. Required: high school transcript, minimum 2 high school GPA, SAT or ACT. Recommended: ACT. Required for some: essay. Entrance: moderately difficult. Application deadline: rolling. Notification: continuous. SAT Reasoning Test deadline: 8/15. SAT Subject Test deadline: 8/15. Transfer credits accepted: Yes.

Costs Per Year: Application fee: $25. Comprehensive fee: $22,618 includes full-time tuition ($17,000) and college room and board ($5618). College room only: $2226. Full-time tuition varies according to course load, degree level, and student level. Room and board charges vary according to board plan and housing facility. Part-time tuition: $531 per credit hour. Part-time tuition varies according to course load, degree level, and student level.

Collegiate Environment: Orientation program. Drama-theater group, choral group, marching band, student-run radio station. Social organizations: 12 open to all. Most popular organizations: Baptist Collegiate Ministry, Delta Xi Omega, Student Government Association, Union Board, Lambda Chi Beta. Major annual events: Gala Christmas, Homecoming, Cochon de Lait. Student services: health clinic, personal-psychological counseling. Campus security: 24-hour emergency response devices and patrols, student patrols, late night transport-escort service, controlled dormitory access. 703 college housing spaces available; 540 were occupied in 2018-19. Freshmen guaranteed college housing. On-campus residence required through sophomore year. Options: men-only, women-only housing available. Richard W. Norton Memorial Library. Books: 81,432 (physical), 301,231 (digital/electronic); Serial titles: 84 (physical), 86,957 (digital/electronic); Databases: 138. Weekly public service hours: 70; students can reserve study rooms. Operations spending for the previous fiscal year: $192,520. 323 computers available on campus for general student use. A campuswide network can be accessed from student residence rooms and from off campus. Students can access the following: online class registration. Staffed computer lab on campus provides training in use of computers, software, and the Internet.

Community Environment: Alexandria-Pineville is in the geographic heart of the state. The urban population of 64,000 has access to several major shopping malls, movie theaters, cultural attractions, fine restaurants, historical landmarks and churches representing nearly every denomination. The area is particularly noted for outdoor recreation opportunities, including year-round water sports and public hunting land. Part-time job opportunities in the community are numerous for college students.

■ LOUISIANA CULINARY INSTITUTE

10550 Airline Hwy.
Baton Rouge, LA 70816
Tel: (225)769-8820; Free: 877-533-3198
Fax: (225)769-8792
Web Site: www.lci.edu

Description: Proprietary, primarily 2-year, coed. Awards transfer associate, terminal associate, and bachelor's degrees. Calendar: quarters.

■ LOUISIANA DELTA COMMUNITY COLLEGE

7500 Millhaven Rd.
Monroe, LA 71203
Tel: (318)345-9000; Free: 866-500-LDCC
Web Site: www.ladelta.edu

Description: State-supported, 2-year, coed. Part of Louisiana Community and Technical College System. Awards certificates, diplomas, transfer associate, and terminal associate degrees. Setting: 70-acre rural campus with easy access to Monroe, LA. Total enrollment: 4,933. Faculty: 197 (91 full-time, 106 part-time). Student-undergrad faculty ratio is 19:1. 13% from top 10% of their high school class, 19% from top quarter, 44% from top half. Full-time: 2,259 students, 59% women, 41% men. Part-time: 2,674 students, 62% women, 38% men. Students come from 23 states and territories, 2% from out-of-state. 0.2% American Indian or Alaska Native, non-Hispanic/Latino; 4% Hispanic/Latino; 36% Black or African American, non-Hispanic/Latino; 0.4% Asian, non-Hispanic/Latino; 0.1% Native Hawaiian or other Pacific Islander, non-Hispanic/Latino; 0.1% international. 40% 25 or older, 5% transferred in. Calendar: semesters. Academic remediation for entering students, services for LD students, advanced placement, accelerated degree program, distance learning, double major, summer session for credit, part-time degree program, internships.

Entrance Requirements: Required: high school transcript, SAT or ACT, ACT Compass.

Collegiate Environment: Orientation program. Drama-theater group. Student services: personal-psychological counseling.

■ LOUISIANA STATE UNIVERSITY AND AGRICULTURAL & MECHANICAL COLLEGE

Baton Rouge, LA 70803
Tel: (225)578-3202
Fax: (225)578-4433
E-mail: cbrow63@lsu.edu
Web Site: www.lsu.edu

Description: State-supported, university, coed. Part of Louisiana State University System. Awards bachelor's, master's, and doctoral degrees and post-master's certificates. Founded 1860. Setting: 2,000-acre urban campus with easy access to New Orleans. Endowment: $457.7 million. Research spending for the previous fiscal year: $151.1 million. Educational spending for the previous fiscal year: $9921 per student. Total enrollment: 30,985. Faculty: 1,501 (1,326 full-time, 175 part-time). Student-undergrad faculty ratio is 20:1. 24,280 applied, 74% were admitted. 23% from top 10% of their high school class, 47% from top quarter, 77% from top half. 24 National Merit Scholars, 283 valedictorians. Full-time: 22,433 students, 53% women, 47% men. Part-time: 2,928 students, 49% women, 51% men. Students come from 52 states and territories, 71 other countries, 18% from out-of-state. 0.4% American Indian or Alaska Native, non-Hispanic/Latino; 7% Hispanic/Latino; 13% Black or African American, non-Hispanic/Latino; 4% Asian, non-Hispanic/Latino; 0.1% Native Hawaiian or other Pacific Islander, non-Hispanic/Latino; 2% international. 4% 25 or older, 30% live on campus, 3% transferred in. Retention: 84% of full-time freshmen returned the following year. Academic areas with the most degrees conferred: business/marketing; engineering; education. Core. Calendar: semesters. ESL program, services for LD students, advanced placement, accelerated degree program, self-designed majors, freshman honors college, honors program, independent study, distance learning, double major, summer session for credit, part-time degree program, adult/continuing education programs, co-op programs and internships, graduate courses open to undergrads. Off campus study at Southern University and Agricultural and Mechanical College, members of the National Student Exchange, Baton Rouge Community College. Study abroad program. ROTC: Army, Naval (c), Air Force.

Entrance Requirements: Options: electronic application, early admission, deferred admission, international baccalaureate accepted. Required: high school transcript, minimum 3 high school GPA, 1 recommendation, ACT Composite score of 22 (18 in English and 19 in Math) or SAT Total Score of 1100 (500 in English and 510 in Math), SAT or ACT. Required for some: essay. Entrance: moderately difficult. Notification: continuous. SAT Reasoning Test deadline: 8/1. Transfer credits accepted: Yes.

Costs Per Year: Application fee: $50. State resident tuition: $8038 full-time. Nonresident tuition: $24,715 full-time. Mandatory fees: $3912 full-time. Full-time tuition and fees vary according to course load. College room and board: $11,830. College room only: $7740. Room and board charges vary according to board plan and housing facility.

Collegiate Environment: Orientation program. Drama-theater group, choral group, marching band, student-run newspaper, radio station. Social

organizations: 517 open to all; national fraternities, national sororities; 16% of eligible men and 27% of eligible women are members. Most popular organizations: intramural athletics, student political organizations, student professional organizations, religious organizations, cultural organizations. Major annual events: Fall Fest, Student Disability Week, Homecoming Week activities. Student services: legal services, health clinic, personal-psychological counseling, women's center. Campus security: 24-hour emergency response devices and patrols, late night transport-escort service, controlled dormitory access. 8,842 college housing spaces available; 7,476 were occupied in 2018-19. Freshmen guaranteed college housing. On-campus residence required in freshman year. Options: coed, men-only, women-only housing available. Troy H. Middleton Library plus 4 others. Books: 3 million (physical), 601,314 (digital/electronic); Serial titles: 627,726 (physical), 336,271 (digital/electronic); Databases: 300. Study areas open 24 hours, 5-7 days a week; students can reserve study rooms. Operations spending for the previous fiscal year: $14.2 million. 1,314 computers available on campus for general student use. A campuswide network can be accessed. Students can access the following: online class registration, free software for download, storage, discounts on hardware, virtual computer lab. Staffed computer lab on campus provides training in use of computers, software, and the Internet.

Community Environment: Baton Rouge, with a metropolitan-area population of more than 600,000, is the capital of Louisiana, the state's second largest port for ocean-going vessels, and the fifth largest inland port in the nation. A rich mixture of French, Spanish, and English cultures reflects Baton Rouge's history. Geographically, Baton Rouge is the center of South Louisiana's main cultural and recreational attractions. New Orleans is 80 miles to the southeast; the Feliciana parishes, noted for their antebellum homes, are less than an hour's drive to the north; and to the west lies the Acadian-French country of bayous, lakes, and marshes. Baton Rouge's industry is widely diversified. It is a major petrochemical center, as well as a center for banking and financial services and a major retail center. Cultural organizations include the Baton Rouge Symphony, the Baton Rouge Ballet, and community theater groups. Baton Rouge has many recreation centers, golf courses, and parks. Mild temperatures make outdoor activities possible and enjoyable throughout the year.

■ **LOUISIANA STATE UNIVERSITY AT ALEXANDRIA**
8100 Hwy. 71 S
Alexandria, LA 71302-9121
Tel: (318)445-3672; Free: 888-473-6417
Fax: (318)473-6418
E-mail: admissions@lsua.edu
Web Site: www.lsua.edu
Description: State-supported, 4-year, coed. Part of Louisiana State University System. Awards associate and bachelor's degrees. Founded 1960. Setting: 3,114-acre rural campus. System endowment: $15.3 million. Educational spending for the previous fiscal year: $5744 per student. Total enrollment: 3,277. Faculty: 172 (90 full-time, 82 part-time). Student-undergrad faculty ratio is 18:1. 2,102 applied, 31% were admitted. 11% from top 10% of their high school class, 33% from top quarter, 71% from top half. Full-time: 1,850 students, 64% women, 36% men. Part-time: 1,427 students, 71% women, 29% men. Students come from 27 states and territories, 30 other countries, 4% from out-of-state. 7% American Indian or Alaska Native, non-Hispanic/Latino; 2% Hispanic/Latino; 17% Black or African American, non-Hispanic/Latino; 2% Asian, non-Hispanic/Latino; 3% international. 28% 25 or older, 9% live on campus, 16% transferred in. Retention: 56% of full-time freshmen returned the following year. Academic areas with the most degrees conferred: liberal arts/general studies; business/marketing; homeland security, law enforcement, firefighting, and protective services. Core. Calendar: semesters. Services for LD students, advanced placement, accelerated degree program, honors program, independent study, distance learning, double major, summer session for credit, part-time degree program, adult/continuing education programs, co-op programs and internships. ROTC: Army.
Entrance Requirements: Options: electronic application, early admission. Required: high school transcript, SAT or ACT. Required for some: minimum 2 high school GPA. Entrance: moderately difficult. Application deadline: rolling. Notification: continuous. SAT Reasoning Test deadline: 8/15. SAT Subject Test deadline: 8/15. Transfer credits accepted: Yes.
Collegiate Environment: Orientation program. Drama-theater group, choral group, student-run newspaper. Social organizations: 15 open to all. Most popular organization: Student Government Association. Major annual events: SGA Crawfish Boil, Trick or Treat Street, Mardi Gras Parade.

Student services: health clinic, personal-psychological counseling. Campus security: 24-hour emergency response devices and patrols. James C. Bolton Library. Books: 123,993 (physical), 224,774 (digital/electronic); Serial titles: 505 (physical), 501,390 (digital/electronic); Databases: 85. Students can reserve study rooms. Operations spending for the previous fiscal year: $301,732. 325 computers available on campus for general student use. A campuswide network can be accessed from student residence rooms. Students can access the following: online class registration. Staffed computer lab on campus provides training in use of computers, software, and the Internet.

■ **LOUISIANA STATE UNIVERSITY AT EUNICE**
PO Box 1129
Eunice, LA 70535-1129
Tel: (337)457-7311
Fax: (337)457-7311
E-mail: admissions@lsue.edu
Web Site: www.lsue.edu
Description: State-supported, 2-year, coed. Part of Louisiana State University System. Awards certificates, transfer associate, and terminal associate degrees. Founded 1967. Setting: 199-acre small town campus. Endowment: $2.1 million. Educational spending for the previous fiscal year: $2911 per student. Total enrollment: 2,906. Faculty: 140 (76 full-time, 64 part-time). Student-undergrad faculty ratio is 21:1. 1,483 applied, 99.9% were admitted. Full-time: 1,388 students, 67% women, 33% men. Part-time: 1,518 students, 73% women, 27% men. Students come from 16 states and territories, 6 other countries, 2% from out-of-state. 0.5% American Indian or Alaska Native, non-Hispanic/Latino; 2% Hispanic/Latino; 25% Black or African American, non-Hispanic/Latino; 0.7% Asian, non-Hispanic/Latino; 0.3% international. 25% 25 or older, 6% live on campus, 25% transferred in. Core. Calendar: semesters. Academic remediation for entering students, services for LD students, advanced placement, honors program, distance learning, summer session for credit, part-time degree program, adult/continuing education programs, co-op programs. Off campus study.
Entrance Requirements: Open admission. Options: electronic application, early admission. Required: high school transcript. Entrance: noncompetitive. Application deadline: 8/7. Transfer credits accepted: Yes.
Costs Per Year: Application fee: $25. State resident tuition: $2868 full-time, $197.10 per credit hour part-time. Nonresident tuition: $8232 full-time, $420.60 per credit hour part-time. Mandatory fees: $1,862 full-time, $77.60 per credit hour part-time. Full-time tuition and fees vary according to class time, course load, location, and program. Part-time tuition and fees vary according to class time, location, and program. College room and board: $11,238. Room and board charges vary according to board plan and housing facility.
Collegiate Environment: Orientation program. Choral group. Social organizations: 14 open to all; local fraternities, local sororities. Most popular organizations: Student Government Association, Students in Free Enterprise (SIFE), Criminal Justice Society, Student Nurses Association, Phi Theta Kappa. Major annual events: Festival of the Arts, Annual Blood Drive, End of Semester Bash. Student services: personal-psychological counseling. Campus security: 24-hour emergency response devices and patrols, controlled dormitory access. Arnold LeDoux Library. Books: 65,807 (physical), 90 (digital/electronic). Weekly public service hours: 90. 160 computers available on campus for general student use. A campuswide network can be accessed from student residence rooms. Students can access the following: online class registration, Online Learning Management System. Staffed computer lab on campus provides training in use of computers and the Internet.

■ **LOUISIANA STATE UNIVERSITY HEALTH SCIENCES CENTER**
433 Bolivar St.
New Orleans, LA 70112-2223
Tel: (504)568-4808
Web Site: www.lsuhsc.edu
Description: State-supported, university, coed. Part of Louisiana State University System. Awards associate, bachelor's, master's, and doctoral degrees. Founded 1931. Setting: 80-acre urban campus with easy access to New Orleans. Endowment: $120.1 million. Research spending for the previous fiscal year: $40.8 million. Educational spending for the previous fiscal year: $80,973 per student. Total enrollment: 2,777. Faculty: 897 (682 full-time, 215 part-time). Student-undergrad faculty ratio is 4:1. Full-time: 696 students, 88% women, 12% men. Part-time: 225 students, 86% women, 14% men. Students come from 19 states and territories, 10 other countries,

6% from out-of-state. 0.4% American Indian or Alaska Native, non-Hispanic/Latino; 6% Hispanic/Latino; 10% Black or African American, non-Hispanic/Latino; 5% Asian, non-Hispanic/Latino; 0.1% international. 30% 25 or older, 10% live on campus, 25% transferred in. Academic area with the most degrees conferred: health professions and related sciences. Calendar: varies by academic program. Academic remediation for entering students, services for LD students, advanced placement, accelerated degree program, independent study, distance learning, double major, summer session for credit, adult/continuing education programs, co-op programs and internships, graduate courses open to undergrads. ROTC: Army (c), Naval (c), Air Force (c).

Entrance Requirements: Option: electronic application. Transfer credits accepted: Yes.

Costs Per Year: Application fee: $50. State resident tuition: $5612 full-time, $357 per semester hour part-time. Nonresident tuition: $12,394 full-time, $424 per semester hour part-time. Mandatory fees: $2696 full-time, $158 per semester hour part-time. Full-time tuition and fees vary according to degree level, program, and reciprocity agreements. Part-time tuition and fees vary according to course load, degree level, program, and reciprocity agreements. College room only: $5598. Room charges vary according to housing facility.

Collegiate Environment: Orientation program. Student services: health clinic, personal-psychological counseling. Campus security: 24-hour emergency response devices and patrols, late night transport-escort service, controlled dormitory access. John P. Ische Library plus 2 others. Books: 61,199 (physical); Serial titles: 4,968 (physical), 3,068 (digital/electronic); Databases: 204. Weekly public service hours: 97; study areas open 24 hours, 5-7 days a week. Operations spending for the previous fiscal year: $3.8 million. 120 computers available on campus for general student use. Computer purchase/lease plans available. A campuswide network can be accessed from student residence rooms and from off campus. Students can access the following: online class registration. Staffed computer lab on campus (open 24 hours a day) provides training in use of computers, software, and the Internet.

■ LOUISIANA STATE UNIVERSITY IN SHREVEPORT

1 University Pl.
Shreveport, LA 71115-2399
Tel: (318)797-5000; Free: 800-229-5957
Fax: (318)797-5286
Web Site: www.lsus.edu

Description: State-supported, comprehensive, coed. Part of Louisiana State University System. Awards bachelor's, master's, and doctoral degrees and post-master's certificates. Founded 1965. Setting: 250-acre urban campus. Endowment: $16.7 million. Research spending for the previous fiscal year: $584,684. Educational spending for the previous fiscal year: $5187 per student. Total enrollment: 4,428. Faculty: 178 (117 full-time, 61 part-time). Student-undergrad faculty ratio is 21:1. 602 applied, 81% were admitted. Full-time: 1,826 students, 61% women, 39% men. Part-time: 950 students, 60% women, 40% men. Students come from 43 states and territories, 12 other countries, 7% from out-of-state. 0.6% American Indian or Alaska Native, non-Hispanic/Latino; 4% Hispanic/Latino; 21% Black or African American, non-Hispanic/Latino; 2% Asian, non-Hispanic/Latino; 0.1% Native Hawaiian or other Pacific Islander, non-Hispanic/Latino; 2% international. 28% 25 or older. Retention: 65% of full-time freshmen returned the following year. Academic areas with the most degrees conferred: business/marketing; liberal arts/general studies; biological/life sciences. Core. Calendar: semesters plus 8-week and two 4-week summer terms. Academic remediation for entering students, ESL program, services for LD students, advanced placement, accelerated degree program, self-designed majors, honors program, independent study, distance learning, double major, summer session for credit, part-time degree program, adult/continuing education programs, co-op programs and internships, graduate courses open to undergrads. Off campus study. ROTC: Army.

Entrance Requirements: Options: electronic application, international baccalaureate accepted. Required: high school transcript, minimum 2 high school GPA, SAT or ACT. Entrance: moderately difficult. Application deadline: rolling. Transfer credits accepted: Yes.

Collegiate Environment: Orientation program. Drama-theater group, student-run newspaper. Social organizations: national fraternities, national sororities, local fraternities; 1% of eligible men and 1% of eligible women are members. Student services: personal-psychological counseling. Campus security: 24-hour emergency response devices and patrols, student patrols, controlled dormitory access. Noel Memorial Library. Databases: 142. Weekly

public service hours: 71; students can reserve study rooms. Operations spending for the previous fiscal year: $1.5 million.

■ LOUISIANA TECH UNIVERSITY

PO Box 3168
Ruston, LA 71272
Tel: (318)257-0211; Free: 800-528-3241
E-mail: bulldog@latech.edu
Web Site: www.latech.edu

Description: State-supported, university, coed. Part of University of Louisiana System. Awards associate, bachelor's, master's, and doctoral degrees and post-master's certificates. Founded 1894. Setting: 247-acre small town campus. Total enrollment: 12,672. Faculty: 432 (356 full-time, 76 part-time). Student-undergrad faculty ratio is 26:1. 7,227 applied, 62% were admitted. 25% from top 10% of their high school class, 50% from top quarter, 81% from top half. Full-time: 7,850 students, 44% women, 56% men. Part-time: 3,431 students, 57% women, 43% men. 11% from out-of-state. 0.4% American Indian or Alaska Native, non-Hispanic/Latino; 4% Hispanic/Latino; 14% Black or African American, non-Hispanic/Latino; 1% Asian, non-Hispanic/Latino; 2% international. 10% 25 or older, 15% live on campus, 3% transferred in. Retention: 81% of full-time freshmen returned the following year. Academic areas with the most degrees conferred: business/marketing; engineering; liberal arts/general studies. Core. Calendar: quarters. Academic remediation for entering students, advanced placement, honors program, independent study, distance learning, double major, summer session for credit, part-time degree program, adult/continuing education programs, internships, graduate courses open to undergrads. Off campus study at Grambling State University. Study abroad program. ROTC: Army (c), Air Force.

Entrance Requirements: Option: early admission. Required: high school transcript, minimum 2.2 high school GPA, SAT or ACT. Recommended: ACT. Entrance: moderately difficult. SAT Reasoning Test deadline: 7/1.

Costs Per Year: Application fee: $20. State resident tuition: $6114 full-time, $322 per credit hour part-time. Nonresident tuition: $15,027 full-time, $619 per credit hour part-time. Mandatory fees: $3531 full-time. Full-time tuition and fees vary according to course load, location, and program. Part-time tuition varies according to course load, location, and program. College room and board: $6495. College room only: $2940. Room and board charges vary according to board plan and housing facility.

Collegiate Environment: Orientation program. Drama-theater group, choral group, marching band, student-run newspaper, radio station. Social organizations: national fraternities, national sororities. Most popular organizations: Student Government Association, Association of Women's Studies, Union Board. Major annual events: Homecoming, Spring Fling, Little Las Vegas Night. Student services: legal services, health clinic, personal-psychological counseling. Campus security: 24-hour emergency response devices and patrols, student patrols, late night transport-escort service, controlled dormitory access. Prescott Memorial Library.

Community Environment: This is an urban area with bus service available. City has a public library, several churches, its own hospital, medical clinics, and good shopping facilities. Theatres, drive-in, golf, fishing, boating, and a campus olympic swimming pool provide recreation opportunities. There is also a concert association.

■ LOYOLA UNIVERSITY NEW ORLEANS

6363 Saint Charles Ave.
New Orleans, LA 70118-6195
Tel: (504)865-2011; Free: 800-4-LOYOLA
Fax: (504)865-3383
E-mail: nament@loyno.edu
Web Site: www.loyno.edu

Description: Independent Roman Catholic (Jesuit), comprehensive, coed. Awards bachelor's, master's, and doctoral degrees and post-master's certificates. Founded 1912. Setting: 26-acre suburban campus with easy access to New Orleans. Endowment: $234 million. Research spending for the previous fiscal year: $1.1 million. Educational spending for the previous fiscal year: $13,808 per student. Total enrollment: 4,261. Faculty: 406 (234 full-time, 172 part-time). Student-undergrad faculty ratio is 11:1. 4,514 applied, 94% were admitted. 25% from top 10% of their high school class, 51% from top quarter, 76% from top half. Full-time: 2,691 students, 63% women, 37% men. Part-time: 291 students, 68% women, 32% men. Students come from 50 states and territories, 37 other countries, 57% from out-of-state. 0.5% American Indian or Alaska Native, non-Hispanic/Latino; 18% Hispanic/Latino; 17% Black or African American, non-Hispanic/Latino; 3% Asian, non-

Hispanic/Latino; 0.1% Native Hawaiian or other Pacific Islander, non-Hispanic/Latino; 2% international. 3% 25 or older, 54% live on campus, 7% transferred in. Retention: 85% of full-time freshmen returned the following year. Academic areas with the most degrees conferred: visual and performing arts; business/marketing; social sciences. Core. Calendar: semesters. ESL program, services for LD students, advanced placement, accelerated degree program, self-designed majors, honors program, independent study, distance learning, double major, summer session for credit, part-time degree program, external degree program, adult/continuing education programs, co-op programs and internships, graduate courses open to undergrads. Off campus study at Tulane University, Dillard, Xavier University of Louisiana, Notre Dame Seminary. Study abroad program. ROTC: Army (c), Naval (c), Air Force (c).

Entrance Requirements: Options: electronic application, early admission, early action, international baccalaureate accepted. Required: essay, high school transcript, 1 recommendation, SAT or ACT. Recommended: interview. Entrance: moderately difficult. Application deadlines: rolling, rolling for nonresidents. Notification: continuous, continuous for nonresidents. SAT Reasoning Test deadline: 8/1. Transfer credits accepted: Yes.

Costs Per Year: Application fee: $0. One-time mandatory fee: $250. Comprehensive fee: $54,140 includes full-time tuition ($38,926), mandatory fees ($1666), and college room and board ($13,548). College room only: $7430. Part-time tuition: $1094 per credit hour.

Collegiate Environment: Orientation program. Drama-theater group, choral group, student-run newspaper, radio station. Social organizations: 126 open to all; national fraternities, national sororities, local fraternities; 6% of eligible men and 20% of eligible women are members. Most popular organizations: Panhellenic Council, Black Student Union, Loyola University Community Action Plan, Quidditch, Interfraternity Council. Major annual events: Take Back the Night, Maroon and Gold Senior Crawfish Boil, Family Weekend. Student services: health clinic, personal-psychological counseling, women's center. Campus security: 24-hour emergency response devices and patrols, student patrols, late night transport-escort service, controlled dormitory access. College housing designed to accommodate 1,332 students; 1,340 undergraduates lived in college housing during 2018-19. Freshmen guaranteed college housing. On-campus residence required through sophomore year. Option: coed housing available. Monroe Library plus 1 other. Books: 353,685 (physical), 42,981 (digital/electronic); Serial titles: 1,385 (physical), 250,962 (digital/electronic); Databases: 129. Weekly public service hours: 114; students can reserve study rooms. Operations spending for the previous fiscal year: $3.9 million. 525 computers available on campus for general student use. Computer purchase/lease plans available. A campuswide network can be accessed from student residence rooms and from off campus. Students can access the following: online class registration. Staffed computer lab on campus provides training in use of computers, software, and the Internet.

Community Environment: See Tulane University.

■ **MCCANN SCHOOL OF BUSINESS & TECHNOLOGY**

2319 Louisville Ave.

Monroe, LA 71201

Tel: (318)537-8099; Free: 866-865-8065

Fax: (318)324-9883

E-mail: susan.boudreaux@careertc.edu

Web Site: www.mccann.edu

Description: Proprietary, 2-year, coed. Part of Delta Career Education Corporation. Awards diplomas and terminal associate degrees. Founded 1985. Setting: small town campus with easy access to Shreveport. Total enrollment: 576. Faculty: 35 (19 full-time, 16 part-time). Student-undergrad faculty ratio is 20:1. Full-time: 450 students, 84% women, 16% men. Part-time: 126 students, 83% women, 17% men. Students come from 2 states and territories, 1% from out-of-state. 0.3% American Indian or Alaska Native, non-Hispanic/Latino; 0.7% Hispanic/Latino; 71% Black or African American, non-Hispanic/Latino; 0.2% Asian, non-Hispanic/Latino. 56% 25 or older. Retention: 80% of full-time freshmen returned the following year. Core. Calendar: quarters. Academic remediation for entering students, advanced placement, independent study, double major, adult/continuing education programs, co-op programs and internships.

Entrance Requirements: Options: deferred admission, international baccalaureate accepted. Required: high school transcript, interview, SLE-Wonderlic Scholastic Level Exam; Math Proficiency Exam; English Proficiency Exam. Entrance: moderately difficult. Application deadline: rolling. Notification: continuous. Transfer credits accepted: Yes.

Collegiate Environment: Orientation program. Social organizations: 10

open to all; 2% of eligible men and 20% of eligible women are members. Most popular organizations: Medical Assisting Club, Surgical Technology Club, Criminal Justice Club, Rad Tech Club, Management/Information Processing Club. Major annual events: Awards Day, Job Fair, Student Appreciation Day/Week. Campus security: 24-hour emergency response devices, late night transport-escort service, evening security guard. Library & Information Resources Network. 78 computers available on campus for general student use. A campuswide network can be accessed. Staffed computer lab on campus provides training in use of computers, software, and the Internet.

■ **MCNEESE STATE UNIVERSITY**

4205 Ryan St.

Lake Charles, LA 70609

Tel: (337)475-5000; Free: 800-622-3352

E-mail: kistre@mcneese.edu

Web Site: www.mcneese.edu

Description: State-supported, comprehensive, coed. Part of University of Louisiana System. Awards associate, bachelor's, and master's degrees and post-master's certificates. Founded 1939. Setting: 766-acre suburban campus. Total enrollment: 7,649. Faculty: 440 (263 full-time, 177 part-time). Student-undergrad faculty ratio is 21:1. 3,224 applied, 43% were admitted. Full-time: 5,641 students, 59% women, 41% men. Part-time: 1,392 students, 63% women, 37% men. Students come from 37 states and territories, 54 other countries, 7% from out-of-state. 0.5% American Indian or Alaska Native, non-Hispanic/Latino; 4% Hispanic/Latino; 16% Black or African American, non-Hispanic/Latino; 1% Asian, non-Hispanic/Latino; 0.1% Native Hawaiian or other Pacific Islander, non-Hispanic/Latino; 5% international. 15% 25 or older, 5% transferred in. Retention: 70% of full-time freshmen returned the following year. Core. Calendar: semesters. Academic remediation for entering students, ESL program, services for LD students, advanced placement, accelerated degree program, freshman honors college, honors program, independent study, distance learning, double major, summer session for credit, part-time degree program, co-op programs and internships, graduate courses open to undergrads. Off campus study at Council of Intercollegiate Nursing Consortium, Health Systems Management Program. Study abroad program.

Entrance Requirements: Options: electronic application, early admission, deferred admission, international baccalaureate accepted. Required: high school transcript, minimum 2.35 high school GPA, Louisiana Board of Regents high school Core 4 curriculum, no more than one developmental course, SAT or ACT. Entrance: moderately difficult. Application deadline: rolling. Notification: continuous. Transfer credits accepted: Yes.

Costs Per Year: Application fee: $20. State resident tuition: $7668 full-time. Nonresident tuition: $12,667 full-time. Mandatory fees: $2,535 full-time. Full-time tuition and fees vary according to course load. College room and board: $7524. College room only: $4150. Room and board charges vary according to board plan and housing facility.

Collegiate Environment: Orientation program. Drama-theater group, choral group, marching band, student-run newspaper. Social organizations: national fraternities, national sororities. Most popular organizations: Student Government Association, International Students Association, Resident Student Association. Major annual events: Homecoming, Spring Fling. Student services: health clinic, personal-psychological counseling, women's center. Campus security: 24-hour emergency response devices and patrols, late night transport-escort service, controlled dormitory access. Option: coed housing available. Frazar Memorial Library plus 1 other.

Community Environment: The city owes its development to the combination of Capt. J. B. Watkins, a variety of natural resources and a deepwater port. In 1887 Captain Watkins of New York moved his newspaper to Lake Charles and started an overwhelming advertising program, which, with the terminus of a railroad at New Orleans, resulted in the development of a 17-mill lumber industry. The discovery of oil in the early 1900s and a new process of mining sulfur further enriched the city. Forests are presently nearly depleted and the sulfur supply is no longer industrially profitable. This city with its vast oil companies in southwest Louisiana is a leader in the petrochemical industry. A deepwater port since 1926, it is currently the nation's leading rice port. Docks also handle general cargo, the output of chemical and petrochemical plants and products of the city's two large rice mills. Student employment is available. Transportation is provided by commercial passenger air lines, rail, and bus service. There are libraries, YMCA, a great number of churches, and three hospitals easily accessible. Recreation includes fishing, hunting, theatres, and an annual rodeo.

■ **NEW ORLEANS BAPTIST THEOLOGICAL SEMINARY**
3939 Gentilly Blvd.
New Orleans, LA 70126-4858
Tel: (504)282-4455; Free: 800-662-8701
Web Site: www.nobts.edu
Description: Independent Southern Baptist, comprehensive, coed. Awards associate, bachelor's, master's, and doctoral degrees. Founded 1917. Setting: 81-acre suburban campus. Total enrollment: 2,036. Core. Calendar: semesters. Academic remediation for entering students, ESL program, independent study, summer session for credit, part-time degree program, adult/continuing education programs, internships. Off campus study.
Entrance Requirements: Open admission. Option: deferred admission. Recommended: minimum 2.0 high school GPA. Entrance: minimally difficult. Application deadline: 8/9. Notification: continuous.
Collegiate Environment: Orientation program. Choral group, student-run radio station. Student services: health clinic, personal-psychological counseling. Campus security: 24-hour emergency response devices and patrols. John Christian Library plus 1 other.
Community Environment: See Tulane University.

■ **NICHOLLS STATE UNIVERSITY**
906 E First St.
Thibodaux, LA 70310
Tel: (985)446-8111; Free: 877-NICHOLLS
Fax: (985)448-4929
E-mail: nicholls@nicholls.edu
Web Site: www.nicholls.edu
Description: State-supported, comprehensive, coed. Part of University of Louisiana System. Awards associate, bachelor's, and master's degrees and post-master's certificates. Founded 1948. Setting: 210-acre small town campus with easy access to New Orleans. Research spending for the previous fiscal year: $393,750. Total enrollment: 6,298. Faculty: 311 (257 full-time, 54 part-time). Student-undergrad faculty ratio is 20:1. 2,424 applied, 88% were admitted. 16% from top 10% of their high school class, 42% from top quarter, 74% from top half. 38 valedictorians. Full-time: 4,769 students, 62% women, 38% men. Part-time: 926 students, 62% women, 38% men. Students come from 36 states and territories, 38 other countries, 5% from out-of-state. 2% American Indian or Alaska Native, non-Hispanic/Latino; 3% Hispanic/Latino; 20% Black or African American, non-Hispanic/Latino; 1% Asian, non-Hispanic/Latino; 0.1% Native Hawaiian or other Pacific Islander, non-Hispanic/Latino; 2% international. 18% 25 or older, 18% live on campus, 5% transferred in. Retention: 67% of full-time freshmen returned the following year. Academic areas with the most degrees conferred: business/marketing; health professions and related sciences; liberal arts/general studies. Core. Calendar: semesters. Academic remediation for entering students, ESL program, services for LD students, advanced placement, accelerated degree program, honors program, independent study, distance learning, double major, summer session for credit, part-time degree program, adult/continuing education programs, co-op programs and internships, graduate courses open to undergrads. Off campus study. Study abroad program.
Entrance Requirements: Options: electronic application, early admission, deferred admission. Required: high school transcript, minimum 2 high school GPA, minimum state core curriculum (19 units), minimum overall GPA of 2.0, SAT or ACT. Entrance: noncompetitive. Application deadline: rolling. Notification: 9/1. SAT Reasoning Test deadline: 8/15. SAT Subject Test deadline: 8/15.
Collegiate Environment: Orientation program. Drama-theater group, choral group, marching band, student-run newspaper, radio station. Social organizations: 78 open to all; national fraternities, national sororities, local fraternities; 8% of eligible men and 8% of eligible women are members. Most popular organizations: Student Government Association, Student Programming Association, Residence Hall Association, Food Advisory Association. Major annual events: Homecoming, Spring Fest, Family Day. Student services: legal services, health clinic, personal-psychological counseling, women's center. Campus security: 24-hour emergency response devices and patrols, student patrols, late night transport-escort service. Allen J. Ellender Memorial Library plus 3 others. 285 computers available on campus for general student use. A campuswide network can be accessed from student residence rooms and from off campus. Students can access the following: online class registration, course management system. Staffed computer lab on campus.
Community Environment: The campus is located in a sugar-belt town on the banks of picturesque Bayou Lafourche. Incorporated in 1838, this was the first trading post established between New Orleans and the country

along Bayou Teche in southeastern Louisiana. There are many beautiful plantations in the vicinity. Thibodaux presents a small town atmosphere. It is a quick 45 miles from historic New Orleans by rail or bus. The year-round climate is mild to moderate. The city has a public library, churches representing all denominations, and a hospital. Recreation includes movies, theater, hunting, boating, fishing, golf, bowling, swimming, and tennis. Student employment is available in the area and on campus.

■ **NORTHSHORE TECHNICAL COMMUNITY COLLEGE**
1710 Sullivan Dr.
Bogalusa, LA 70427
Tel: (504)732-6640
Web Site: www.northshorecollege.edu
Description: State-supported, 2-year, coed. Awards certificates, diplomas, transfer associate, and terminal associate degrees. Total enrollment: 717. Faculty: 80 (41 full-time, 39 part-time). Calendar: semesters.

■ **NORTHWEST LOUISIANA TECHNICAL COLLEGE**
9500 Industrial Dr.
Minden, LA 71055
Tel: (318)371-3035
Web Site: www.nwltc.edu
Description: State-supported, 2-year, coed. Awards certificates, diplomas, and terminal associate degrees. Founded 1952. Total enrollment: 810. Faculty: 82 (34 full-time, 48 part-time). 40% 25 or older. Calendar: semesters.

■ **NORTHWESTERN STATE UNIVERSITY OF LOUISIANA**
715 University Pky.
Natchitoches, LA 71497
Tel: (318)357-6361; Free: 800-327-1903
E-mail: recruiting@nsula.edu
Web Site: www.nsula.edu
Description: State-supported, comprehensive, coed. Part of University of Louisiana System. Awards associate, bachelor's, master's, and doctoral degrees and post-master's certificates. Founded 1884. Setting: 916-acre small town campus. Endowment: $15.4 million. Research spending for the previous fiscal year: $404,841. Educational spending for the previous fiscal year: $6061 per student. Total enrollment: 10,572. Faculty: 469 (303 full-time, 166 part-time). Student-undergrad faculty ratio is 19:1. 5,494 applied, 62% were admitted. 14% from top 10% of their high school class, 40% from top quarter, 71% from top half. Full-time: 5,471 students, 67% women, 33% men. Part-time: 3,981 students, 73% women, 27% men. Students come from 56 states and territories, 27 other countries, 8% from out-of-state. 2% American Indian or Alaska Native, non-Hispanic/Latino; 6% Hispanic/Latino; 28% Black or African American, non-Hispanic/Latino; 0.8% Asian, non-Hispanic/Latino; 0.2% Native Hawaiian or other Pacific Islander, non-Hispanic/Latino; 1% international. 31% 25 or older, 8% transferred in. Retention: 75% of full-time freshmen returned the following year. Academic areas with the most degrees conferred: health professions and related sciences; business/marketing; liberal arts/general studies. Core. Calendar: semesters. Services for LD students, advanced placement, freshman honors college, honors program, independent study, distance learning, double major, summer session for credit, part-time degree program, adult/continuing education programs, co-op programs and internships, graduate courses open to undergrads. Study abroad program. ROTC: Army, Air Force (c).
Entrance Requirements: Options: electronic application, deferred admission. Required: high school transcript, minimum 2.35 high school GPA, college preparatory curriculum, SAT or ACT. Entrance: moderately difficult. Application deadline: 7/6. Notification: continuous, continuous for nonresidents. SAT Reasoning Test deadline: 7/27. Transfer credits accepted: Yes.
Costs Per Year: Application fee: $20. State resident tuition: $5180 full-time. Nonresident tuition: $15,968 full-time. Mandatory fees: $3400 full-time. Full-time tuition and fees vary according to course load and location. College room and board: $9230. College room only: $5850. Room and board charges vary according to board plan and housing facility.
Collegiate Environment: Orientation program. Drama-theater group, choral group, marching band, student-run newspaper, radio station. Social organizations: 114 open to all; national fraternities, national sororities. Most popular organizations: Student Activities Board, Student Government Associate, College Panhellenic Council. Major annual events: Spring Fling Week, Homecoming Week, Welcome Week. Student services: health clinic, personal-psychological counseling. Campus security: 24-hour emergency response devices and patrols, student patrols, late night transport-escort

service, controlled dormitory access. Eugene P. Watson Memorial Library plus 1 other. Books: 310,849 (physical), 38,166 (digital/electronic); Serial titles: 329 (physical), 230 (digital/electronic); Databases: 111. Weekly public service hours: 87; students can reserve study rooms. Operations spending for the previous fiscal year: $1.6 million. 1,500 computers available on campus for general student use. A campuswide network can be accessed from student residence rooms and from off campus. Students can access the following: online class registration. Staffed computer lab on campus provides training in use of computers, software, and the Internet.

■ NUNEZ COMMUNITY COLLEGE

3710 Paris Rd.
Chalmette, LA 70043
Tel: (504)278-6200
Fax: (504)680-2243
E-mail: bmaillet@nunez.edu
Web Site: www.nunez.edu

Description: State-supported, 2-year, coed. Part of Louisiana Community and Technical College System. Awards certificates, diplomas, transfer associate, and terminal associate degrees. Founded 1992. Setting: 20-acre suburban campus with easy access to New Orleans. Endowment: $1.2 million. Total enrollment: 2,599. Faculty: 106 (46 full-time, 60 part-time). Student-undergrad faculty ratio is 23:1. Full-time: 986 students, 60% women, 40% men. Part-time: 1,613 students, 69% women, 31% men. Students come from 15 states and territories, 9 other countries, 1% from out-of-state. 0.7% American Indian or Alaska Native, non-Hispanic/Latino; 7% Hispanic/Latino; 40% Black or African American, non-Hispanic/Latino; 2% Asian, non-Hispanic/Latino; 0.2% Native Hawaiian or other Pacific Islander, non-Hispanic/Latino; 0.6% international. 34% 25 or older, 16% transferred in. Core. Calendar: semesters. Academic remediation for entering students, services for LD students, advanced placement, accelerated degree program, self-designed majors, independent study, distance learning, double major, summer session for credit, part-time degree program, adult/continuing education programs, co-op programs and internships. Off campus study at University of New Orleans, Southeastern Louisiana University, Delgado Community College.

Entrance Requirements: Open admission. Options: electronic application, early admission, deferred admission, international baccalaureate accepted. Required for some: high school transcript. Entrance: noncompetitive. Application deadline: rolling. Transfer credits accepted: Yes.

Collegiate Environment: Orientation program. Major annual events: Spring Fling, Fall Fest, Job Fair. Student services: health clinic, personal-psychological counseling. Campus security: late night transport-escort service, security cameras. Nunez Community College Library. Operations spending for the previous fiscal year: $216,157. 200 computers available on campus for general student use. A campuswide network can be accessed. Students can access the following: online class registration. Staffed computer lab on campus provides training in use of computers, software, and the Internet.

■ REMINGTON COLLEGE-BATON ROUGE CAMPUS

4520 S Sherwood Forrest Blvd.
Baton Rouge, LA 70816
Tel: (225)240-7049; Free: 800-323-8122
Fax: (225)922-6569
Web Site: www.remingtoncollege.edu

Description: Independent, 2-year, coed. Awards terminal associate degrees. Calendar: continuous.

■ REMINGTON COLLEGE-LAFAYETTE CAMPUS

303 Rue Louis XIV
Lafayette, LA 70508
Tel: (337)981-4010; Free: 800-323-8122
Fax: (337)983-7130
Web Site: www.remingtoncollege.edu

Description: Independent, 2-year, coed. Awards terminal associate degrees. Founded 1940. Setting: 4-acre urban campus. Calendar: continuous. Honors program, independent study.

Entrance Requirements: Entrance: noncompetitive.

Collegiate Environment: Campus security: 24-hour emergency response devices. Remington College Library.

■ REMINGTON COLLEGE-SHREVEPORT

2106 W Bert Kouns Industrial Loop
Shreveport, LA 71118

Tel: (318)239-4309; Free: 800-323-8122
Web Site: www.remingtoncollege.edu

Description: Independent, 2-year, coed. Awards terminal associate degrees.

■ RIVER PARISHES COMMUNITY COLLEGE

925 W Edenborne Pky.
Gonzales, LA 70737
Tel: (225)675-8270
Fax: (225)675-5478
Web Site: www.rpcc.edu

Description: State-supported, 2-year, coed. Awards certificates, diplomas, and transfer associate degrees. Founded 1997. Total enrollment: 1,163. 28% 25 or older. Calendar: semesters.

■ SAINT JOSEPH SEMINARY COLLEGE

Saint Benedict, LA 70457
Tel: (985)867-2299
E-mail: registrar@sjasc.edu
Web Site: www.sjasc.edu

Description: Independent Roman Catholic, 4-year, men only. Awards bachelor's degrees (Religious Studies Institute is coed). Founded 1891. Setting: 1,800-acre rural campus with easy access to New Orleans. Endowment: $1.1 million. Educational spending for the previous fiscal year: $6430 per student. Total enrollment: 107. Faculty: 22 (10 full-time, 12 part-time). Student-undergrad faculty ratio is 3:1. Full-time: 104 students. Part-time: 3 students. Students come from 8 states and territories, 5 other countries, 45% from out-of-state. 19% Hispanic/Latino; 5% Asian, non-Hispanic/Latino. 28% 25 or older, 100% live on campus, 37% transferred in. Retention: 50% of full-time freshmen returned the following year. Core. Calendar: semesters. Academic remediation for entering students, ESL program, services for LD students, advanced placement, adult/continuing education programs.

Entrance Requirements: Options: early admission, deferred admission. Required: high school transcript, minimum 2 high school GPA, ACT. Entrance: minimally difficult. Application deadline: rolling. Notification: continuous. Preference given to candidates for the priesthood. Transfer credits accepted: Yes.

Collegiate Environment: Orientation program. Drama-theater group, choral group, student-run newspaper. Social organizations: 5 open to all. Most popular organizations: Student Government, yearbook. Major annual events: Annual Bonfire, Saint Joseph Day Celebration, Abbey Youth Festival. Student services: health clinic, personal-psychological counseling. Campus security: 24-hour emergency response devices, controlled dormitory access, entrance gate. Pere Rouquette Library plus 1 other. Operations spending for the previous fiscal year: $65,900. 14 computers available on campus for general student use. A campuswide network can be accessed from student residence rooms and from off campus. Staffed computer lab on campus provides training in use of computers, software, and the Internet.

Community Environment: Saint Benedict is located four miles north of Covington and 50 miles north of New Orleans. There is bus service available to Covington from New Orleans, Baton Rouge, and Hammond.

■ SOUTH CENTRAL LOUISIANA TECHNICAL COLLEGE

900 Youngs Rd.
Morgan City, LA 70380
Tel: (985)380-2957
Web Site: www.scl.edu

Description: State-supported, 2-year, coed. Awards certificates, diplomas, and terminal associate degrees. Total enrollment: 734. Faculty: 63 (39 full-time, 24 part-time). Calendar: semesters.

■ SOUTH LOUISIANA COMMUNITY COLLEGE

1101 Bertrand Dr.
Lafayette, LA 70506
Tel: (337)521-9000
E-mail: admissions@solacc.edu
Web Site: www.solacc.edu

Description: State-supported, 2-year, coed. Part of Louisiana Community and Technical College System. Awards certificates, diplomas, transfer associate, and terminal associate degrees. Setting: small town campus. Endowment: $846,166. Educational spending for the previous fiscal year: $3791 per student. Total enrollment: 6,332. Faculty: 257 (133 full-time, 124 part-time). Student-undergrad faculty ratio is 25:1. Full-time: 3,436 students, 57% women, 43% men. Part-time: 2,896 students, 56% women, 44% men.

Students come from 12 states and territories, 17 other countries, 1% from out-of-state. 0.5% American Indian or Alaska Native, non-Hispanic/Latino; 3% Hispanic/Latino; 35% Black or African American, non-Hispanic/Latino; 2% Asian, non-Hispanic/Latino; 0.1% Native Hawaiian or other Pacific Islander, non-Hispanic/Latino; 0.8% international. 23% 25 or older, 7% transferred in. Retention: 55% of full-time freshmen returned the following year. Calendar: semesters. Academic remediation for entering students, ESL program, services for LD students, advanced placement, independent study, distance learning, double major, summer session for credit, part-time degree program, internships.

Entrance Requirements: Open admission. Option: electronic application. Required: high school transcript. Entrance: minimally difficult. Transfer credits accepted: Yes.

Collegiate Environment: Orientation program. Operations spending for the previous fiscal year: $538,131.

■ SOUTHEASTERN LOUISIANA UNIVERSITY

548 Ned McGehee Dr.

Hammond, LA 70402

Tel: (985)549-2000; Free: 800-222-7358

Fax: (985)549-5095

Web Site: www.southeastern.edu

Description: State-supported, comprehensive, coed. Part of University of Louisiana System. Awards associate, bachelor's, master's, and doctoral degrees and post-master's certificates. Founded 1925. Setting: 375-acre small town campus with easy access to New Orleans. Endowment: $52.6 million. Research spending for the previous fiscal year: $438,837. Educational spending for the previous fiscal year: $5670 per student. Total enrollment: 14,327. Faculty: 611 (501 full-time, 110 part-time). Student-undergrad faculty ratio is 19:1. 4,248 applied, 90% were admitted. 12% from top 10% of their high school class, 34% from top quarter, 68% from top half. Full-time: 9,194 students, 62% women, 38% men. Part-time: 4,166 students, 62% women, 38% men. Students come from 44 states and territories, 56 other countries, 4% from out-of-state. 0.3% American Indian or Alaska Native, non-Hispanic/Latino; 7% Hispanic/Latino; 20% Black or African American, non-Hispanic/Latino; 2% Asian, non-Hispanic/Latino; 0.1% Native Hawaiian or other Pacific Islander, non-Hispanic/Latino; 1% international. 11% 25 or older, 24% live on campus, 5% transferred in. Retention: 67% of full-time freshmen returned the following year. Academic areas with the most degrees conferred: business/marketing; health professions and related sciences; liberal arts/general studies. Core. Calendar: semesters. Academic remediation for entering students, ESL program, services for LD students, advanced placement, accelerated degree program, honors program, independent study, distance learning, double major, summer session for credit, part-time degree program, adult/continuing education programs, internships, graduate courses open to undergrads. Off campus study at Connect to Success program, a joint venture between NTCC(North shore Technical Community College) and Southeastern that expands access and preparation of NTCC students who have the opportunity to eventually transfer to a baccalaureate program at Southeastern or some other university. Study abroad program. ROTC: Army.

Entrance Requirements: Options: electronic application, early admission, deferred admission, international baccalaureate accepted. Required: high school transcript, minimum 2.35 high school GPA, proof of immunization; college transcripts and statement of good standing required for some, SAT or ACT. Entrance: moderately difficult. Application deadline: 8/1. Notification: continuous until 10/15. SAT Reasoning Test deadline: 8/1. Transfer credits accepted: Yes.

Costs Per Year: Application fee: $20. State resident tuition: $5777 full-time, $340 per credit hour part-time. Nonresident tuition: $18,255 full-time, $860 per credit hour part-time. Mandatory fees: $2388 full-time. Full-time tuition and fees vary according to course load. Part-time tuition varies according to course load. College room and board: $8420. College room only: $4940. Room and board charges vary according to board plan and housing facility.

Collegiate Environment: Orientation program. Drama-theater group, choral group, marching band, student-run newspaper, radio station. Social organizations: 105 open to all; national fraternities, national sororities; 5% of eligible men and 12% of eligible women are members. Most popular organizations: Baptist Collegiate Ministry, Catholic Student Association, Gamma Beta Phi, Phi Mu, Alpha Omicron Pi / Sigma Sigma Sigma. Major annual events: Homecoming, Gumbo Ya Ya, Strawberry Jubilee. Student services: health clinic, personal-psychological counseling. Campus security: 24-hour emergency response devices and patrols, student patrols, late night transport-escort service, controlled dormitory access. 2,742 college housing

spaces available; 2,589 were occupied in 2018-19. No special consideration for freshman housing applicants. Options: coed, women-only housing available. Linus A. Sims Memorial Library plus 1 other. Books: 1.3 million (physical), 428,672 (digital/electronic); Serial titles: 338 (physical), 561 (digital/electronic). Students can reserve study rooms. 1,031 computers available on campus for general student use. A campuswide network can be accessed from student residence rooms and from off campus. Students can access the following: online class registration, campus Webmail, student newspaper, transcripts, bookstore. Staffed computer lab on campus (open 24 hours a day) provides training in use of computers, software, and the Internet.

Community Environment: City is located in the Southeastern section of the state. Climate is subtropical. Transportation to and from city available via Illinois Central Railroad and Greyhound Bus Co. There are five libraries, six local theatres, golf, hunting, fishing, boating at Lake Poncharlain for recreation. Two hospitals, six motels and numerous apartments are available. Part-time employment for students is limited. There are 35 civic, fraternal, and veteran's organizations in Hammond.

■ SOUTHERN UNIVERSITY AND AGRICULTURAL AND MECHANICAL COLLEGE

Baton Rouge, LA 70813

Tel: (225)771-4500

E-mail: manicia_finch@subr.edu

Web Site: www.subr.edu

Description: State-supported, university, coed. Part of Southern University System. Awards bachelor's, master's, and doctoral degrees and post-master's certificates. Founded 1880. Setting: 964-acre suburban campus. Endowment: $12.9 million. Total enrollment: 6,693. Faculty: 423 (309 full-time, 114 part-time). Student-undergrad faculty ratio is 16:1. 8,482 applied, 53% were admitted. 3% from top 10% of their high school class, 17% from top quarter, 41% from top half. 12 valedictorians, 5 student government officers. Full-time: 4,868 students, 64% women, 36% men. Part-time: 970 students, 67% women, 33% men. Students come from 38 states and territories, 15 other countries, 18% from out-of-state. 0.2% American Indian or Alaska Native, non-Hispanic/Latino; 0.7% Hispanic/Latino; 93% Black or African American, non-Hispanic/Latino; 0.3% Asian, non-Hispanic/Latino; 0.7% international. 13% 25 or older, 31% live on campus, 6% transferred in. Retention: 68% of full-time freshmen returned the following year. Academic areas with the most degrees conferred: health professions and related sciences; business/marketing; homeland security, law enforcement, firefighting, and protective services. Core. Calendar: semesters. Academic remediation for entering students, services for LD students, advanced placement, honors program, distance learning, summer session for credit, part-time degree program, adult/continuing education programs, co-op programs and internships, graduate courses open to undergrads. Off campus study at Louisiana State University and Agricultural and Mechanical College, Southeastern Louisiana University, Southern University at New Orleans, Baton Rouge Community College. Study abroad program. ROTC: Army, Naval, Air Force (c).

Entrance Requirements: Options: electronic application, early admission. Required: high school transcript, minimum 2 high school GPA, Louisiana Board of Regents Core curriculum of 16.5 units of selected courses, SAT or ACT. Entrance: moderately difficult. Notification: continuous.

Collegiate Environment: Orientation program. Drama-theater group, choral group, marching band, student-run newspaper. Social organizations: 66 open to all; national fraternities, national sororities, local fraternities, local sororities; 2% of eligible men and 0.3% of eligible women are members. Most popular organizations: Student Government Association, Association for Women Students, Men's Federation, Collegiate 100 Black Men, Southern University Pan Hellenic Council. Major annual events: Homecoming, Founder's Day, Springfest. Student services: legal services, health clinic, personal-psychological counseling, women's center. Campus security: 24-hour emergency response devices and patrols, late night transport-escort service, controlled dormitory access. 2,606 college housing spaces available; 2,135 were occupied in 2018-19. Freshmen given priority for college housing. On-campus residence required in freshman year. Options: men-only, women-only housing available. John B. Cade Library plus 2 others. 1,500 computers available on campus for general student use. A campuswide network can be accessed from student residence rooms and from off campus. Students can access the following: online class registration. Staffed computer lab on campus (open 24 hours a day) provides training in use of computers, software, and the Internet.

■ **SOUTHERN UNIVERSITY AT NEW ORLEANS**
6400 Press Dr.
New Orleans, LA 70126-1009
Tel: (504)286-5000
Web Site: www.suno.edu
Description: State-supported, comprehensive, coed. Part of Southern University System. Awards associate, bachelor's, and master's degrees. Founded 1959. Setting: 66-acre urban campus with easy access to New Orleans. Endowment: $3.9 million. Research spending for the previous fiscal year: $365,398. Total enrollment: 3,141. Faculty: 102 (100 full-time, 2 part-time). 801 applied, 79% were admitted. Full-time: 2,048 students, 69% women, 31% men. Part-time: 542 students, 77% women, 23% men. Students come from 21 states and territories, 10 other countries, 3% from out-of-state. 49% 25 or older, 13% transferred in. Retention: 43% of full-time freshmen returned the following year. Academic areas with the most degrees conferred: liberal arts/general studies; business/marketing; homeland security, law enforcement, firefighting, and protective services; public administration and social services. Core. Calendar: semesters. Academic remediation for entering students, services for LD students, self-designed majors, distance learning, double major, summer session for credit, part-time degree program, adult/continuing education programs, co-op programs and internships, graduate courses open to undergrads. Off campus study at University of New Orleans, Delgado Community College. ROTC: Army (c), Air Force (c).
Entrance Requirements: Options: electronic application, early admission, early decision, early action, deferred admission. Required: high school transcript, health forms, SAT or ACT. Recommended: ACT. Entrance: noncompetitive. Application deadline: 7/1. Transfer credits accepted: Yes.
Collegiate Environment: Social organizations: 4 open to all; national fraternities, national sororities, local fraternities, local sororities; 10% of eligible men and 10% of eligible women are members. Most popular organizations: Student Government Association, First 50 Knights, Psychology Club, Communication Club. Major annual events: International Week, Black History Month, Wellness Week. Student services: health clinic, personal-psychological counseling. Campus security: 24-hour emergency response devices and patrols, late night transport-escort service. Leonard Washington Library. Operations spending for the previous fiscal year: $600,775. 100 computers available on campus for general student use. A campuswide network can be accessed. Students can access the following: online class registration. Staffed computer lab on campus provides training in use of computers, software, and the Internet.

■ **SOUTHERN UNIVERSITY AT SHREVEPORT**
3050 Martin Luther King, Jr. Dr.
Shreveport, LA 71107
Tel: (318)670-6000; Free: 800-458-1472
Fax: (318)674-3489
E-mail: danderson@susla.edu
Web Site: www.susla.edu
Description: State-supported, 2-year, coed. Part of Southern University System. Awards certificates, transfer associate, and terminal associate degrees. Founded 1964. Setting: 103-acre urban campus. Endowment: $619,644. Research spending for the previous fiscal year: $540,780. Educational spending for the previous fiscal year: $2487 per student. Total enrollment: 2,651. Faculty: 129 (69 full-time, 60 part-time). Student-undergrad faculty ratio is 21:1. 1 applied, 99.9% were admitted. 10% from top 10% of their high school class, 30% from top quarter. 15 student government officers. Full-time: 1,511 students, 68% women, 32% men. Part-time: 1,140 students, 74% women, 26% men. Students come from 25 states and territories, 3 other countries, 3% from out-of-state. 0.3% American Indian or Alaska Native, non-Hispanic/Latino; 0.2% Hispanic/Latino; 91% Black or African American, non-Hispanic/Latino; 0.4% Asian, non-Hispanic/Latino; 3% international. 35% 25 or older, 7% live on campus, 7% transferred in. Retention: 41% of full-time freshmen returned the following year. Core. Calendar: semesters. Academic remediation for entering students, ESL program, services for LD students, advanced placement, self-designed majors, honors program, distance learning, double major, summer session for credit, part-time degree program, adult/continuing education programs, co-op programs and internships. ROTC: Army (c).
Entrance Requirements: Open admission. Recommended: high school transcript, ACT. Required for some: SAT or ACT. Application deadline: rolling.
Costs Per Year: Application fee: $25. One-time mandatory fee: $125. State resident tuition: $2618 full-time. Nonresident tuition: $5919 full-time. Mandatory fees: $1549 full-time. Full-time tuition and fees vary according to

program. College room and board: $11,330. College room only: $8460. Room and board charges vary according to board plan and housing facility.
Collegiate Environment: Orientation program. Choral group, marching band, student-run newspaper. Social organizations: 14 open to all; local fraternities, local sororities; 2% of eligible men and 3% of eligible women are members. Most popular organizations: Afro-American Society, SUSLA Gospel Choir, Student Center Board, Allied Health, Engineering Club. Major annual events: Career Day, Homecoming, Springfest. Student services: personal-psychological counseling. Campus security: 24-hour emergency response devices and patrols, controlled dormitory access. 240 college housing spaces available; 205 were occupied in 2018-19. No special consideration for freshman housing applicants. Option: coed housing available. Library/Learning Resources Center plus 1 other. Books: 56,043 (physical), 11,097 (digital/electronic); Serial titles: 164 (physical); Databases: 86. Students can reserve study rooms. Operations spending for the previous fiscal year: $424,082. 150 computers available on campus for general student use. Computer purchase/lease plans available. A campuswide network can be accessed from student residence rooms. Students can access the following: online class registration. Staffed computer lab on campus provides training in use of computers, software, and the Internet.

■ **SOUTHWEST UNIVERSITY**
2200 Veterans Memorial Blvd.
Kenner, LA 70062
Tel: (504)468-2900; Free: 800-433-5923
E-mail: admissions@southwest.edu
Web Site: www.southwest.edu
Description: Proprietary, comprehensive, coed. Awards associate, bachelor's, and master's degrees. Total enrollment: 425. Core. Accelerated degree program, distance learning, double major.
Entrance Requirements: Required: high school transcript, resume.

■ **SOWELA TECHNICAL COMMUNITY COLLEGE**
3820 Senator J. Bennett Johnston Ave.
Lake Charles, LA 70615
Tel: (337)421-6565; Free: 800-256-0483
Web Site: www.sowela.edu
Description: State-supported, 2-year, coed. Part of Louisiana Community and Technical College System. Awards certificates, diplomas, transfer associate, and terminal associate degrees. Founded 1938. Setting: 84-acre urban campus. Endowment: $1 million. Educational spending for the previous fiscal year: $3652 per student. Total enrollment: 3,459. Faculty: 159 (83 full-time, 76 part-time). Student-undergrad faculty ratio is 24:1. 762 applied, 100% were admitted. 10% from top 10% of their high school class, 22% from top quarter, 41% from top half. Full-time: 1,796 students, 51% women, 49% men. Part-time: 1,663 students, 48% women, 52% men. Students come from 21 states and territories, 15 other countries, 2% from out-of-state. 1% American Indian or Alaska Native, non-Hispanic/Latino; 4% Hispanic/Latino; 24% Black or African American, non-Hispanic/Latino; 0.7% Asian, non-Hispanic/Latino; 0.8% Native Hawaiian or other Pacific Islander, non-Hispanic/Latino; 0.5% international. 29% 25 or older, 12% transferred in. Retention: 54% of full-time freshmen returned the following year. Core. Calendar: semesters. Academic remediation for entering students, services for LD students, advanced placement, accelerated degree program, distance learning, double major, summer session for credit, part-time degree program, external degree program, adult/continuing education programs, internships. Off campus study at Senior Technical Education Program at Sowela; Dual-Enrollment within the 5 parish area: Calcasieu, Jeff Davis, Beauregard, Allen, Cameron.
Entrance Requirements: Open admission Open admission for all programs with the exception of Practical Nursing, Registered Nurse, and Process Technology programs. Options: electronic application, early admission, international baccalaureate accepted. Required: proof of immunization, proof of Selective Service status. Required for some: high school transcript. Application deadline: rolling. Notification: continuous. Transfer credits accepted: Yes.
Costs Per Year: Application fee: $0. Area resident tuition: $3335 full-time, $138.96 per credit hour part-time. State resident tuition: $3335 full-time, $138.96 per credit hour part-time. Nonresident tuition: $7672 full-time, $351.75 per credit hour part-time. Mandatory fees: $1210 full-time, $40 per credit hour part-time, $30.
Collegiate Environment: Orientation program. Choral group, student-run newspaper. Social organizations: 10 open to all; Phi Theta Kappa. Most popular organizations: SkillsUSA, Student Government Association (SGA),

Graphic Arts, Nursing Association, Phi Theta Kappa. Major annual events: Spring Fest, Welcome Week, Career Fair. Student services: personal-psychological counseling. Campus security: security guard on duty. College housing not available. Library and Learning Resource Center plus 3 others. Books: 7,767 (physical), 11,150 (digital/electronic); Serial titles: 21 (physical), 32,295 (digital/electronic); Databases: 64. Weekly public service hours: 50; students can reserve study rooms. Operations spending for the previous fiscal year: $326,538. 800 computers available on campus for general student use. A campuswide network can be accessed. Students can access the following: online class registration, Wireless Internet access. Staffed computer lab on campus provides training in use of computers, software, and the Internet.

■ TULANE UNIVERSITY

6823 St. Charles Ave.
New Orleans, LA 70118-5669
Tel: (504)865-5000; Free: 800-873-9283
Fax: (504)862-8715
E-mail: undergrad.admission@tulane.edu
Web Site: www.tulane.edu

Description: Independent, university, coed. Awards bachelor's, master's, and doctoral degrees. Founded 1834. Setting: 110-acre urban campus. Endowment: $1.7 billion. Research spending for the previous fiscal year: $148.2 million. Educational spending for the previous fiscal year: $26,849 per student. Total enrollment: 11,722. Faculty: 1,271 (792 full-time, 479 part-time). Student-undergrad faculty ratio is 8:1. 38,816 applied, 17% were admitted. 63% from top 10% of their high school class, 88% from top quarter, 96% from top half. Full-time: 6,747 students, 60% women, 40% men. Part-time: 26 students, 50% women, 50% men. Students come from 53 states and territories, 93 other countries, 79% from out-of-state. 0.1% American Indian or Alaska Native, non-Hispanic/Latino; 7% Hispanic/Latino; 4% Black or African American, non-Hispanic/Latino; 5% Asian, non-Hispanic/Latino; 0.2% Native Hawaiian or other Pacific Islander, non-Hispanic/Latino; 5% international. 8% 25 or older, 48% live on campus, 2% transferred in. Retention: 94% of full-time freshmen returned the following year. Academic areas with the most degrees conferred: business/marketing; social sciences; biological/life sciences. Core. Calendar: semesters plus 3 summer sessions. ESL program, services for LD students, advanced placement, accelerated degree program, self-designed majors, freshman honors college, honors program, independent study, distance learning, double major, summer session for credit, part-time degree program, adult/continuing education programs, co-op programs and internships, graduate courses open to undergrads. Off campus study at Xavier University of Louisiana, Loyola University New Orleans. Study abroad program. ROTC: Army, Naval, Air Force.

Entrance Requirements: Options: electronic application, early decision, early action, deferred admission, international baccalaureate accepted. Required: essay, high school transcript, 1 recommendation, SAT or ACT. Entrance: very difficult. Application deadlines: 11/15, 11/1 for early decision plan 1, 1/7 for early decision plan 2, 11/15 for early action. Notification: 4/1, 12/15 for early decision plan 1, 1/28 for early decision plan 2, 1/15 for early action. SAT Reasoning Test deadline: 1/15. SAT Subject Test deadline: 1/15. Applicants placed on waiting list: 10,384. Wait-listed applicants offered admission: 2. Early decision applicants: 1,659. Early decision applicants admitted: 535. Early action applicants: 24,057. Early action applicants admitted: 1,326.

Costs Per Year: Application fee: $0. Comprehensive fee: $73,264 includes full-time tuition ($52,760), mandatory fees ($4040), and college room and board ($16,464). College room only: $9700.

Collegiate Environment: Orientation program. Drama-theater group, choral group, marching band, student-run newspaper, radio station. Social organizations: 250 open to all; national fraternities, national sororities; 30% of eligible men and 50% of eligible women are members. Most popular organizations: Community Action Council of Tulane Students (CACTUS), Associated Student Body, Tulane University Campus Programming (TUCP), Association of Club Sports (ACS), National Pan-Hellenic Council. Major annual events: Outreach Tulane (community service day for freshmen), Student Activities Expo, Homecoming. Student services: legal services, health clinic, personal-psychological counseling, women's center. Campus security: 24-hour emergency response devices and patrols, student patrols, late night transport-escort service, controlled dormitory access, on and off-campus shuttle service, crime prevention programs, lighted pathways, TUPD patrols 24 hrs a day 365 days a year, virtual. 4,056 college housing spaces available; 4,000 were occupied in 2018-19. Freshmen guaranteed college

housing. On-campus residence required through sophomore year. Options: coed, women-only housing available. Howard Tilton Memorial Library plus 8 others. Books: 4.6 million (physical); Serial titles: 77,251 (physical). Study areas open 24 hours, 5-7 days a week. Operations spending for the previous fiscal year: $25.3 million. 556 computers available on campus for general student use. A campuswide network can be accessed from student residence rooms and from off campus. Students can access the following: online class registration. Staffed computer lab on campus (open 24 hours a day) provides training in use of computers, software, and the Internet.

Community Environment: Year-round New Orleans offers festivals and jazz bands, symphonies and operas, Broadway shows and concerts. But the City that Care Forgot also blends its unique French and Spanish heritage to offer quiet entertainment in museums, galleries, quaint restaurants or strolls through the European ambiance of the French Quarter. The 1.3 million people living in the metropolitan area succeed as well in running Louisiana's business, banking, judicial and cultural capital. Many students find the city to be as much a place of learning and intellectual challenge as the classroom. Moderate temperatures can be enjoyed year-round. New Orleans is one of the greatest distributing points in the South, and one of the largest ports in the United States; it is a marketing center for cotton, oil, salt, sulfur, natural gas, agricultural and forest products. Good transportation facilities are available. This is a paradise for those who fish or hunt. Since the city is a tourist attraction, there are many recreational facilities and community services available. Work opportunities are available for students.

■ UNIVERSITY OF HOLY CROSS

4123 Woodland Dr.
New Orleans, LA 70131-7399
Tel: (504)394-7744; Free: 800-259-7744
Fax: (504)391-2421
Web Site: www.uhcno.edu

Description: Independent Roman Catholic, comprehensive, coed. Awards associate, bachelor's, and master's degrees. Founded 1916. Setting: 40-acre suburban campus. Total enrollment: 1,298. 42% 25 or older. Core. Calendar: semesters plus summer sessions. Academic remediation for entering students, services for LD students, advanced placement, independent study, distance learning, double major, summer session for credit, part-time degree program, adult/continuing education programs, co-op programs and internships, graduate courses open to undergrads. Off campus study at Delgado Community College, St. Joseph Seminary College, Notre Dame Seminary, Ochsner Clinical Foundation, Louisiana Universities Marine Consortium, Gulf Coast Research Laboratories. Study abroad program. ROTC: Army (c), Air Force (c).

Entrance Requirements: Open admission. Options: electronic application, deferred admission, international baccalaureate accepted. Required: high school transcript. Recommended: minimum 2.0 high school GPA. Entrance: minimally difficult. Application deadline: 7/20. Notification: continuous.

Costs Per Year: Application fee: $15. Tuition: $12,480 full-time, $520 per credit hour part-time. Mandatory fees: $1700 full-time, $850 per term part-time. Full-time tuition and fees vary according to course load, degree level, and program. Part-time tuition and fees vary according to course load, degree level, and program.

Collegiate Environment: Orientation program. Drama-theater group, student-run newspaper. Student services: personal-psychological counseling. Campus security: 24-hour patrols. Blaine Kern Library.

Community Environment: See Tulane University.

■ UNIVERSITY OF LOUISIANA AT LAFAYETTE

104 University Cir.
PO Drawer 41008
Lafayette, LA 70504
Tel: (337)482-1000; Free: 800-752-6553
Fax: (337)482-6195
E-mail: admissions@louisiana.edu
Web Site: www.louisiana.edu

Description: State-supported, university, coed. Part of University of Louisiana System. Awards bachelor's, master's, and doctoral degrees and post-master's certificates. Founded 1898. Setting: 1,375-acre urban campus. Endowment: $143.1 million. Research spending for the previous fiscal year: $48.8 million. Educational spending for the previous fiscal year: $5354 per student. Total enrollment: 17,508. Faculty: 793 (601 full-time, 192 part-time). Student-undergrad faculty ratio is 23:1. 10,899 applied, 55% were admitted. 21% from top 10% of their high school class, 46% from top quarter, 77% from top half. Full-time: 12,867 students, 54% women, 46% men. Part-time: 3,003 students, 65% women, 35% men. Students come from 49 states and territories, 68 other countries, 8% from out-of-state. 0.4% American Indian or Alaska Native, non-Hispanic/Latino; 4% Hispanic/Latino; 22% Black or African American, non-Hispanic/Latino; 2% Asian, non-Hispanic/Latino; 0.1% Native Hawaiian or other Pacific Islander, non-Hispanic/Latino; 2% international. 16% 25 or older, 20% live on campus, 6% transferred in. Retention: 76% of full-time freshmen returned the following year. Core. Calendar: semesters. Academic remediation for entering students, services for LD students, advanced placement, accelerated degree program, self-designed majors, honors program, independent study, distance learning, double major, summer session for credit, part-time degree program, adult/continuing education programs, co-op programs and internships. Study abroad program. ROTC: Army.

Entrance Requirements: Options: electronic application, early admission, deferred admission, international baccalaureate accepted. Required: high school transcript, minimum 2 high school GPA, core requirements, SAT or ACT. Entrance: moderately difficult. Application deadline: rolling.

Collegiate Environment: Orientation program. Drama-theater group, choral group, marching band, student-run newspaper, radio station. Social organizations: 200 open to all; national fraternities, national sororities; 9% of eligible men and 8% of eligible women are members. Most popular organizations: Union Program Council, Chi Alpha, Student Government Association, Greek Council, Newman Club. Major annual events: Homecoming, Lagniappe Day, Mardi Gras. Student services: legal services, health clinic, personal-psychological counseling, women's center. Campus security: 24-hour emergency response devices and patrols, late night transport-escort service, controlled dormitory access. Edith Garland Dupre Library. Books: 1.4 million (physical); Serial titles: 20,881 (physical); Databases: 149. Students can reserve study rooms. Operations spending for the previous fiscal year: $4 million. 413 computers available on campus for general student use. A campuswide network can be accessed from off-campus. Students can access the following: online class registration. Staffed computer lab on campus provides training in use of computers, software, and the Internet.

■ UNIVERSITY OF LOUISIANA AT MONROE
700 University Ave.
Monroe, LA 71209-0001
Tel: (318)342-1000; Free: 800-372-5127
Fax: (318)342-1049
E-mail: peterson@ulm.edu
Web Site: www.ulm.edu

Description: State-supported, university, coed. Part of University of Louisiana System. Awards associate, bachelor's, master's, and doctoral degrees and post-master's certificates. Founded 1931. Setting: 238-acre urban campus. Endowment: $50.6 million. Research spending for the previous fiscal year: $3 million. Educational spending for the previous fiscal year: $5598 per student. Total enrollment: 9,181. Faculty: 480 (324 full-time, 156 part-time). Student-undergrad faculty ratio is 19:1. 3,969 applied, 72% were admitted. 20% from top 10% of their high school class, 49% from top quarter, 79% from top half. Full-time: 5,212 students, 63% women, 37% men. Part-time: 2,736 students, 63% women, 37% men. Students come from 45 states and territories, 48 other countries, 9% from out-of-state. 0.4% American Indian or Alaska Native, non-Hispanic/Latino; 2% Hispanic/Latino; 23% Black or African American, non-Hispanic/Latino; 2% Asian, non-Hispanic/Latino; 0.1% Native Hawaiian or other Pacific Islander, non-Hispanic/Latino; 3% international. 14% 25 or older, 30% live on campus, 6% transferred in. Academic areas with the most degrees conferred: health professions and related sciences; business/marketing; psychology. Core. Calendar: semesters. Academic remediation for entering students, ESL program, services for LD students, advanced placement, accelerated degree program, honors program, independent study, distance learning, double major, summer session for credit, part-time degree program, external degree program, adult/continuing education programs, co-op programs and internships, graduate courses open to undergrads. Off campus study. Study abroad program. ROTC: Army (c).

Entrance Requirements: Options: electronic application, early admission, international baccalaureate accepted. Required: high school transcript, minimum 2.35 high school GPA, SAT or ACT. Entrance: moderately difficult. Application deadline: rolling. Notification: continuous. Transfer credits accepted: Yes.

Costs Per Year: Application fee: $20. State resident tuition: $8,734 full-time, $685.53 per credit hour part-time. Nonresident tuition: $20,834 full-time, $685.53 per credit hour part-time. Full-time tuition varies according to course load, degree level, and program. Part-time tuition varies according to course

load, degree level, and program. College room and board: $7868. Room and board charges vary according to board plan and housing facility.

Collegiate Environment: Orientation program. Drama-theater group, choral group, marching band, student-run newspaper, radio station. Social organizations: 140 open to all; national fraternities, national sororities. Most popular organizations: Maroon Platoon, Alpha Lambda Delta, Louisiana Pharmacist Alliance, Association for Students in Kinesiology, Pre-Pharmacy Organization/Sound of Today. Major annual events: Homecoming, Spring Fever Week, Casino Night. Student services: health clinic, personal-psychological counseling. Campus security: 24-hour emergency response devices and patrols, student patrols, late night transport-escort service, controlled dormitory access. University Library. Books: 150,255 (physical), 293,246 (digital/electronic); Serial titles: 245 (physical), 93,407 (digital/electronic); Databases: 101. Students can reserve study rooms. Operations spending for the previous fiscal year: $1.2 million.

■ UNIVERSITY OF NEW ORLEANS
2000 Lakeshore Dr.
New Orleans, LA 70148
Tel: (504)280-6000; Free: 888-514-4275
Fax: (504)280-5522
E-mail: bjhornsb@uno.edu
Web Site: www.uno.edu

Description: State-supported, university, coed. Part of University of Louisiana System. Awards bachelor's, master's, and doctoral degrees. Founded 1958. Setting: 345-acre urban campus. Total enrollment: 7,964. Faculty: 387 (243 full-time, 144 part-time). Student-undergrad faculty ratio is 22:1. 3,739 applied, 57% were admitted. 15% from top 10% of their high school class, 34% from top quarter, 64% from top half. Full-time: 4,737 students, 49% women, 51% men. Part-time: 1,735 students, 51% women, 49% men. 0.3% American Indian or Alaska Native, non-Hispanic/Latino; 13% Hispanic/Latino; 15% Black or African American, non-Hispanic/Latino; 9% Asian, non-Hispanic/Latino; 0.1% Native Hawaiian or other Pacific Islander, non-Hispanic/Latino; 4% international. 10% transferred in. Retention: 62% of full-time freshmen returned the following year. Academic areas with the most degrees conferred: business/marketing; interdisciplinary studies; visual and performing arts. Core. Calendar: semesters. ESL program, services for LD students, advanced placement, honors program, independent study, distance learning, double major, summer session for credit, part-time degree program, co-op programs and internships, graduate courses open to undergrads. Study abroad program. ROTC: Army (c), Naval (c), Air Force (c).

Entrance Requirements: Options: electronic application, deferred admission, international baccalaureate accepted. Required: high school transcript, SAT or ACT. SAT Reasoning Test deadline: 9/1. Transfer credits accepted: Yes.

Costs Per Year: Application fee: $25. State resident tuition: $6090 full-time. Nonresident tuition: $10,926 full-time. Mandatory fees: $2682 full-time. Full-time tuition and fees vary according to course load, degree level, program, and reciprocity agreements. College room and board: $10,712. Room and board charges vary according to board plan and housing facility.

Collegiate Environment: Orientation program. Drama-theater group, choral group, student-run newspaper. Social organizations: 100 open to all; national fraternities, national sororities. Most popular organizations: Student Activities Council, Student Government, International Student Organization, Vietnamese American Student Association, Greek Life. Major annual events: Annual Crawfish Boil, Annual International Night, Welcome Week Events. Student services: legal services, health clinic, personal-psychological counseling, women's center. Campus security: 24-hour emergency response devices and patrols, late night transport-escort service, controlled dormitory access. Earl K. Long Library. Books: 1 million (physical), 220,863 (digital/electronic); Serial titles: 25,831 (physical), 55,551 (digital/electronic); Databases: 154. Students can reserve study rooms. 1,050 computers available on campus for general student use. A campuswide network can be accessed from student residence rooms and from off campus. Students can access the following: online class registration, learning management system. Staffed computer lab on campus provides training in use of computers, software, and the Internet.

Community Environment: See Tulane University.

■ XAVIER UNIVERSITY OF LOUISIANA
1 Drexel Dr.
New Orleans, LA 70125
Tel: (504)486-7411; Free: 877-XAVIERU

E-mail: apply@xula.edu
Web Site: www.xula.edu
Description: Independent Roman Catholic, comprehensive, coed. Awards bachelor's, master's, and doctoral degrees. Founded 1925. Setting: 23-acre urban campus. Total enrollment: 3,044. Faculty: 243 (219 full-time, 24 part-time). Student-undergrad faculty ratio is 14:1. 7,164 applied, 64% were admitted. 28% from top 10% of their high school class, 54% from top quarter, 78% from top half. Full-time: 2,155 students, 74% women, 26% men. Part-time: 138 students, 58% women, 42% men. 46% from out-of-state. 0.1% American Indian or Alaska Native, non-Hispanic/Latino; 3% Hispanic/Latino; 78% Black or African American, non-Hispanic/Latino; 7% Asian, non-Hispanic/Latino; 0.1% Native Hawaiian or other Pacific Islander, non-Hispanic/Latino; 2% international. 2% 25 or older, 48% live on campus, 4% transferred in. Retention: 70% of full-time freshmen returned the following year. Academic areas with the most degrees conferred: biological/life sciences; physical sciences; psychology. Core. Calendar: semesters. Academic remediation for entering students, services for LD students, advanced placement, accelerated degree program, freshman honors college, honors program, independent study, distance learning, double major, summer session for credit, part-time degree program, adult/continuing education programs, co-op programs and internships, graduate courses open to

undergrads. Off campus study at 2 members of the New Orleans Consortium, St. Michael's College, University of Notre Dame. Study abroad program. ROTC: Army (c), Naval (c), Air Force (c).
Entrance Requirements: Options: electronic application, deferred admission. Required: high school transcript, minimum 2 high school GPA, 1 recommendation, SAT or ACT. Required for some: interview. Entrance: moderately difficult. Application deadline: 7/1. Notification: continuous. SAT Reasoning Test deadline: 7/15. SAT Subject Test deadline: 7/15.
Costs Per Year: Application fee: $0. One-time mandatory fee: $150. Comprehensive fee: $33,522 includes full-time tuition ($21,954), mandatory fees ($2465), and college room and board ($9103). Room and board charges vary according to housing facility. Part-time tuition: $915 per credit hour. Part-time mandatory fees: $250 per term. Part-time tuition and fees vary according to course load.
Collegiate Environment: Orientation program. Drama-theater group, choral group, student-run newspaper. Social organizations: national fraternities, national sororities. Student services: health clinic, personal-psychological counseling. Campus security: 24-hour emergency response devices and patrols, student patrols, bicycle patrols. Xavier Library.
Community Environment: See Tulane University.

■ BATES COLLEGE

2 Andrews Rd.
Lewiston, ME 04240-6028
Tel: (207)786-6255; Free: 855-228-3755
Fax: (207)786-6025
E-mail: admission@bates.edu
Web Site: www.bates.edu

Description: Independent, 4-year, coed. Awards bachelor's degrees. Founded 1855. Setting: 133-acre small town campus. Endowment: $293.8 million. Research spending for the previous fiscal year: $1.8 million. Educational spending for the previous fiscal year: $22,470 per student. Total enrollment: 1,787. Faculty: 195 (179 full-time, 16 part-time). Student-undergrad faculty ratio is 10:1. 5,316 applied, 22% were admitted. 63% from top 10% of their high school class. Full-time: 1,787 students, 51% women, 49% men. Students come from 43 states and territories, 59 other countries, 90% from out-of-state. 0.1% American Indian or Alaska Native, non-Hispanic/Latino; 9% Hispanic/Latino; 5% Black or African American, non-Hispanic/Latino; 4% Asian, non-Hispanic/Latino; 0.1% Native Hawaiian or other Pacific Islander, non-Hispanic/Latino; 7% international. 92% live on campus, 1% transferred in. Retention: 95% of full-time freshmen returned the following year. Academic areas with the most degrees conferred: social sciences; biological/life sciences; psychology. Core. Calendar: 4-4-1. Services for LD students, advanced placement, accelerated degree program, self-designed majors, honors program, independent study, double major, co-op programs and internships. Off campus study at American University, Williams College (Mystic Seaport Program), Morehouse College, Spelman College. Study abroad program.

Entrance Requirements: Options: electronic application, early admission, early decision, deferred admission, international baccalaureate accepted. Required: essay, high school transcript, 3 recommendations. Recommended: interview. Entrance: very difficult. Application deadlines: 1/1, 11/15 for early decision plan 1, 1/1 for early decision plan 2. Notification: 4/1, 12/20 for early decision plan 1, 2/15 for early decision plan 2. SAT Reasoning Test deadline: 1/1. SAT Subject Test deadline: 1/1. Transfer credits accepted: Yes. Applicants placed on waiting list: 1,640. Wait-listed applicants offered admission: 7. Early decision applicants: 721. Early decision applicants admitted: 349.

Costs Per Year: Application fee: $60. Comprehensive fee: $69,018 includes full-time tuition ($53,794) and college room and board ($15,224).

Collegiate Environment: Orientation program. Drama-theater group, choral group, student-run newspaper, radio station. Social organizations: 110 open to all. Most popular organizations: Outing Club (outdoor recreation), International Club, Chase Hall Committee (student activities planning), Representative Assembly, WRBC (student radio station). Major annual events: All College Gala, Winter Carnival, Mount David Summit. Student services: health clinic, personal-psychological counseling, women's center. Campus security: 24-hour emergency response devices and patrols, student patrols, late night transport-escort service, controlled dormitory access, emergency contact/notification system. Ladd Library plus 1 other. Books: 602,011 (physical), 725,335 (digital/electronic); Databases: 371. 400 computers available on campus for general student use. Computer purchase/lease plans available. A campuswide network can be accessed from student residence rooms and from off campus. Students can access the following: online class registration, course Web pages; course management system; software applications for learning, teaching and research; online course evaluation, transcripts, major declaration, degree audit,

financial records. Staffed computer lab on campus provides training in use of computers, software, and the Internet.

Community Environment: The second largest city in state, Lewiston is Maine's leading textile center. It is located on the Androscoggin River at Twin Falls, directly opposite the city of Auburn. Minimum-maximum temperatures are 0-50 degrees in the winter and 50-90 degrees in the summer. Commercial transportation is available via air and bus. The city has several churches, Ys, a public library, two hospitals, several movie theaters, and hotels and motels.

■ BEAL COLLEGE

99 Farm Rd.
Bangor, ME 04401
Tel: (207)947-4591; Free: 800-660-7351
E-mail: admissions@bealcollege.edu
Web Site: www.bealcollege.edu

Description: Proprietary, 2-year, coed. Awards certificates, diplomas, and terminal associate degrees. Founded 1891. Setting: 4-acre small town campus. Total enrollment: 464. Faculty: 40 (8 full-time, 32 part-time). Student-undergrad faculty ratio is 30:1. Full-time: 363 students, 63% women, 37% men. Part-time: 101 students, 79% women, 21% men. 2% American Indian or Alaska Native, non-Hispanic/Latino; 1% Hispanic/Latino; 0.9% Black or African American, non-Hispanic/Latino; 0.6% Asian, non-Hispanic/Latino; 0.2% Native Hawaiian or other Pacific Islander, non-Hispanic/Latino. 53% 25 or older, 10% transferred in. Retention: 60% of full-time freshmen returned the following year. Core. Calendar: modular. Advanced placement, accelerated degree program, summer session for credit, part-time degree program, adult/continuing education programs, internships.

Entrance Requirements: Open admission. Option: deferred admission. Required: essay, high school transcript, 1 recommendation, interview, immunizations, entrance exam. Entrance: noncompetitive. Application deadline: rolling. Transfer credits accepted: Yes.

Costs Per Year: Application fee: $30. Tuition: $10,440 full-time, $290 per credit hour part-time. Mandatory fees: $1185 full-time, $25 per credit hour part-time. Full-time tuition and fees vary according to course load and program. Part-time tuition and fees vary according to course load and program.

Collegiate Environment: Orientation program. Student-run newspaper. Beal College Library. Books: 4,256 (physical); Serial titles: 28 (physical). Weekly public service hours: 40. 42 computers available on campus for general student use. Students can access the following: online class registration.

■ BOWDOIN COLLEGE

255 Maine St.
Brunswick, ME 04011
Tel: (207)725-3000
Fax: (207)725-3003
E-mail: admissions@bowdoin.edu
Web Site: www.bowdoin.edu

Description: Independent, 4-year, coed. Awards bachelor's degrees. Founded 1794. Setting: 207-acre small town campus with easy access to Portland. Endowment: $1.5 billion. Research spending for the previous fiscal year: $2.4 million. Educational spending for the previous fiscal year: $30,767 per student. Total enrollment: 1,816. Faculty: 228 (194 full-time, 34 part-time). Student-undergrad faculty ratio is 9:1. 7,251 applied, 14% were admitted. 86% from top 10% of their high school class, 96% from top quarter, 100% from top half. 23 National Merit Scholars, 29 valedictorians. Full-time: 1,813 students, 50% women, 50% men. Part-time: 3 students, 67% women, 33% men. Students come from 46 states and territories, 35 other countries, 89% from out-of-state. 0.3% American Indian or Alaska Native, non-Hispanic/Latino; 11% Hispanic/Latino; 6% Black or African American, non-Hispanic/Latino; 7% Asian, non-Hispanic/Latino; 0.1% Native Hawaiian or other Pacific Islander, non-Hispanic/Latino; 5% international. 90% live on campus, 1% transferred in. Retention: 96% of full-time freshmen returned the following year. Academic areas with the most degrees conferred: social sciences; biological/life sciences; area and ethnic studies. Core. Calendar: semesters. Services for LD students, advanced placement, accelerated degree program, self-designed majors, independent study, double major. Off campus study at Twelve College Exchange Program; American University, Washington Semester; Bowdoin Marine Science Semester, Brunswick and Harpswell, ME; SEA Semester, Woods Hole; Williams College Mystic Seaport Maritime Studies Program; National Theater Institute. Study abroad program.

Entrance Requirements: Options: electronic application, early admission, early decision, deferred admission, international baccalaureate accepted. Required: essay, high school transcript, 3 recommendations. Recommended: interview. Entrance: most difficult. Application deadlines: 1/1, 11/15 for early decision plan 1, 1/1 for early decision plan 2. Notification: 3/20, 12/15 for early decision plan 1, 2/15 for early decision plan 2. SAT Reasoning Test deadline: 1/1. SAT Subject Test deadline: 1/1. Transfer credits accepted: Yes. Early decision applicants: 870. Early decision applicants admitted: 246.

Costs Per Year: Application fee: $65. Comprehensive fee: $68,620 includes full-time tuition ($53,418), mandatory fees ($504), and college room and board ($14,698). College room only: $6868. Room and board charges vary according to board plan. Part-time tuition: $1043 per credit hour.

Collegiate Environment: Orientation program. Drama-theater group, choral group, student-run newspaper, radio station. Social organizations: 120 open to all. Most popular organizations: Outing Club, Intramural sports, Community Service Volunteer Programs, WBOR 91.1 FM Radio, Bowdoin Orient Student Newspaper. Major annual events: Common Good Day, Ivies Weekend, Museum Receptions. Student services: health clinic, personal-psychological counseling, women's center. Campus security: 24-hour emergency response devices and patrols, late night transport-escort service, controlled dormitory access, self-defense education, safe ride service, emergency notification system. Hawthorne-Longfellow Library plus 3 others. Books: 1.2 million (physical), 1.1 million (digital/electronic); Serial titles: 7,146 (physical), 80,997 (digital/electronic); Databases: 515. Weekly public service hours: 112; students can reserve study rooms. Operations spending for the previous fiscal year: $6.2 million. 500 computers available on campus for general student use. Computer purchase/lease plans available. A campuswide network can be accessed from student residence rooms and from off campus. Students can access the following: online class registration, computer repair; training classes; 24/7 software support; free equipment loaner pool: laptops, video and digital cameras, sound and lighting systems, iPads; movie streaming service; free office software; digital media lab. Staffed computer lab on campus provides training in use of computers, software, and the Internet.

Community Environment: Brunswick, a community of 20,500, is located within brief driving distance of several fine beaches and summer resort areas; skiing is available in winter. There are excellent highways and airline service to Portland, only 26 miles away. The area has several excellent motels. The town has a public library, Maine State Music Theatre, which features Broadway musicals each summer, and churches of many denominations, shopping centers and movie theaters; good restaurants. Recreational facilities include golf, hunting, boating, fishing, skiing, biking, backpacking, and other sports.

■ **CENTRAL MAINE COMMUNITY COLLEGE**
1250 Turner St.
Auburn, ME 04210-6498
Tel: (207)755-5100; Free: 800-891-2002
Fax: (207)755-5491
E-mail: enroll@cmcc.edu
Web Site: www.cmcc.edu
Description: State-supported, 2-year, coed. Part of Maine Community College System. Awards certificates, transfer associate, and terminal associate degrees. Founded 1964. Setting: 135-acre small town campus. Endowment:

$975,000. Educational spending for the previous fiscal year: $4818 per student. Total enrollment: 2,900. Faculty: 203 (54 full-time, 149 part-time). Student-undergrad faculty ratio is 17:1. Full-time: 1,095 students, 46% women, 54% men. Part-time: 1,805 students, 57% women, 43% men. Students come from 12 states and territories, 3 other countries, 5% from out-of-state. 0.5% American Indian or Alaska Native, non-Hispanic/Latino; 2% Hispanic/Latino; 8% Black or African American, non-Hispanic/Latino; 0.7% Asian, non-Hispanic/Latino; 0.1% Native Hawaiian or other Pacific Islander, non-Hispanic/Latino; 0.7% international. 34% 25 or older, 8% live on campus, 7% transferred in. Core. Calendar: semesters. Academic remediation for entering students, ESL program, services for LD students, advanced placement, accelerated degree program, honors program, independent study, distance learning, summer session for credit, part-time degree program, adult/continuing education programs, co-op programs and internships.

Entrance Requirements: Options: electronic application, deferred admission. Required: high school transcript. Recommended: essay, SAT and SAT Subject Tests or ACT. Entrance: minimally difficult. Application deadline: rolling. Notification: continuous. Transfer credits accepted: Yes.

Costs Per Year: Application fee: $20. State resident tuition: $2820 full-time, $94 per credit hour part-time. Nonresident tuition: $5640 full-time, $188 per credit hour part-time. Mandatory fees: $1080 full-time, $35 per credit hour part-time. Full-time tuition and fees vary according to course load, program, and reciprocity agreements. Part-time tuition and fees vary according to course load, program, and reciprocity agreements. College room and board: $9340. Room and board charges vary according to housing facility.

Collegiate Environment: Orientation program. Campus security: 24-hour emergency response devices, student patrols, controlled dormitory access, night patrols by police. Central Maine Community College Library. Books: 7,810 (physical); Serial titles: 44 (physical); Databases: 92. Weekly public service hours: 53; students can reserve study rooms. Operations spending for the previous fiscal year: $264,087. 700 computers available on campus for general student use. A campuswide network can be accessed from student residence rooms and from off campus. Students can access the following: online class registration, online request for academic transcripts. Staffed computer lab on campus provides training in use of computers and the Internet.

Community Environment: See Bates College.

■ **COLBY COLLEGE**
4000 Mayflower Hill
Waterville, ME 04901-8840
Tel: (207)859-4000; Free: 800-723-3032
Fax: (207)872-3474
E-mail: admissions@colby.edu
Web Site: www.colby.edu
Description: Independent, 4-year, coed. Awards bachelor's degrees. Founded 1813. Setting: 714-acre small town campus with easy access to Portland, ME. Endowment: $775.1 million. Research spending for the previous fiscal year: $2.3 million. Educational spending for the previous fiscal year: $24,820 per student. Total enrollment: 1,917. 11,190 applied, 16% were admitted. 78% from top 10% of their high school class, 94% from top quarter, 100% from top half. Full-time: 1,917 students, 52% women, 48% men. Students come from 47 states and territories, 52 other countries, 89% from out-of-state. 0.4% American Indian or Alaska Native, non-Hispanic/Latino; 7% Hispanic/Latino; 4% Black or African American, non-Hispanic/Latino; 7% Asian, non-Hispanic/Latino; 0.2% Native Hawaiian or other Pacific Islander, non-Hispanic/Latino; 10% international. 95% live on campus, 1% transferred in. Retention: 94% of full-time freshmen returned the following year. Academic areas with the most degrees conferred: social sciences; biological/life sciences; interdisciplinary studies. Core. Calendar: 4-1-4. Services for LD students, advanced placement, self-designed majors, honors program, independent study, double major, internships. Off campus study at Pomona College, Pitzer College, Howard University, Claremont McKenna College, Scripps College, Boston University (SEA Semester), Williams College (Mystic Seaport Program), Clark Atlanta University, Semester in Environmental Science-Woods Hole, The Washington Center, Bigelow Laboratory for Ocean Sciences, Dartmouth Dual Degree program in Engineering, Columbia University Engineering program. Study abroad program. ROTC: Army (c).

Entrance Requirements: Options: electronic application, early admission, early decision, deferred admission, international baccalaureate accepted. Required: essay, high school transcript, 2 recommendations. Recommended: interview. Required for some: SAT or ACT, SAT and SAT Subject

Tests or ACT. Entrance: most difficult. Application deadlines: 1/1, 11/15 for early decision plan 1, 1/1 for early decision plan 2. Notification: 4/1, 4/1 for nonresidents, 12/15 for early decision plan 1, 2/15 for early decision plan 2. SAT Reasoning Test deadline: 2/15. SAT Subject Test deadline: 2/15. Transfer credits accepted: Yes. Applicants placed on waiting list: 2,242. Waitlisted applicants offered admission: 32. Early decision applicants: 678. Early decision applicants admitted: 256.

Costs Per Year: Application fee: $0. Comprehensive fee: $69,400 includes full-time tuition ($52,890), mandatory fees ($2320), and college room and board ($14,190). Part-time tuition: $2030 per credit hour. Part-time tuition varies according to course load.

Collegiate Environment: Orientation program. Drama-theater group, choral group, student-run newspaper, radio station. Social organizations: 110 open to all. Most popular organizations: Outing Club, volunteer center, WMHB-FM (College Radio Station), Student Government, Powder and Wig (theater). Major annual events: Family Weekend, Spring Concert, SHOUT (Speaking, Hearing, Opening Up Together) Speaker. Student services: health clinic, personal-psychological counseling, women's center. Campus security: 24-hour emergency response devices and patrols, student patrols, late night transport-escort service, controlled dormitory access, campus lighting, student emergency response team, self-defense class, property ID program, party monitors. Miller Library plus 3 others. Books: 545,763 (physical), 595,720 (digital/electronic); Serial titles: 22,931 (physical), 100,911 (digital/electronic); Databases: 701. Weekly public service hours: 119; study areas open 24 hours, 5-7 days a week. Operations spending for the previous fiscal year: $8 million. 158 computers available on campus for general student use. A campuswide network can be accessed from student residence rooms and from off campus. Students can access the following: online class registration, software license for every student computer, unlimited technology training, video editing lab, high performance natural science research computing, GIS lab. Staffed computer lab on campus (open 24 hours a day) provides training in use of computers, software, and the Internet.

Community Environment: Colby, located in the Kennebec River Valley, is one mile from downtown Waterville, a regional center for industry, professional, and retail trade. Major employers in the area include Maine General Medical Center, L.L. Bean, SAPPI Fine Paper, the Chinet Co., and The State of Maine. Transportation is available to Waterville by bus from Portland or Boston. Commercial airports serve Portland, Bangor, and Augusta.

■ **COLLEGE OF THE ATLANTIC**
105 Eden St.
Bar Harbor, ME 04609-1198
Tel: (207)288-5015; Free: 800-528-0025
Fax: (207)288-4126
E-mail: inquiry@coa.edu
Web Site: www.coa.edu
Description: Independent, comprehensive, coed. Awards bachelor's and master's degrees. Founded 1969. Setting: 35-acre small town campus. Endowment: $53 million. Research spending for the previous fiscal year: $2 million. Educational spending for the previous fiscal year: $18,228 per student. Total enrollment: 354. Faculty: 53 (26 full-time, 27 part-time). Student-undergrad faculty ratio is 10:1. 474 applied, 68% were admitted. 22% from top 10% of their high school class, 50% from top quarter, 97% from top half. Full-time: 330 students, 77% women, 23% men. Part-time: 19 students, 37% women, 63% men. Students come from 33 states and territories, 41 other countries, 78% from out-of-state. 0.3% American Indian or Alaska Native, non-Hispanic/Latino; 3% Hispanic/Latino; 1% Black or African American, non-Hispanic/Latino; 3% Asian, non-Hispanic/Latino; 21% international. 4% 25 or older, 46% live on campus, 6% transferred in. Retention: 76% of full-time freshmen returned the following year. Academic area with the most degrees conferred: interdisciplinary studies. Core. Calendar: trimesters. Academic remediation for entering students, services for LD students, advanced placement, accelerated degree program, self-designed majors, independent study, summer session for credit, part-time degree program, co-op programs and internships, graduate courses open to undergrads. Off campus study at University of Maine; Ecoleague consortium: Alaska Pacific University, Dickinson College, Green Mountain College, Northland College and Prescott College; The New School; National Outdoor Leadership School. Study abroad program.

Entrance Requirements: Options: electronic application, early admission, early decision, deferred admission, international baccalaureate accepted. Required: essay, high school transcript, 3 recommendations. Recommended: minimum 3 high school GPA, interview. Entrance: very difficult. Application deadlines: 2/1, 12/1 for early decision plan 1, 1/15 for early decision

plan 2. Notification: 4/1, 12/15 for early decision plan 1, 1/30 for early decision plan 2. Transfer credits accepted: Yes. Early decision applicants: 30. Early decision applicants admitted: 27.

Costs Per Year: Application fee: $50. Comprehensive fee: $53,289 includes full-time tuition ($42,993), mandatory fees ($549), and college room and board ($9747). College room only: $6210. Full-time tuition and fees vary according to course load and degree level. Room and board charges vary according to board plan. Part-time tuition: $4777 per credit. Part-time mandatory fees: $183 per term. Part-time tuition and fees vary according to course load and degree level.

Collegiate Environment: Orientation program. Drama-theater group, choral group, student-run newspaper. Social organizations: 20 open to all. Most popular organizations: Earth in Brackets earth, Outing Club, Campus Committee for Sustainability, Spectrum (LGBTQ+), Futbol (soccer) Club. Major annual events: Bar Island Swim, Earth Day, Aurora Ball-ealis (midwinter semi-formal). Student services: health clinic, personal-psychological counseling. Campus security: 24-hour emergency response devices and patrols, late night transport-escort service. Thorndike Library. Books: 45,700 (physical), 15,500 (digital/electronic); Serial titles: 400 (physical), 62,600 (digital/electronic); Databases: 76. Weekly public service hours: 101; students can reserve study rooms. Operations spending for the previous fiscal year: $539,316. 45 computers available on campus for general student use. A campuswide network can be accessed from student residence rooms. Students can access the following: online class registration, online billing, transcript, financial aid, course management system. Staffed computer lab on campus provides training in use of computers, software, and the Internet.

Community Environment: Bar Harbor and Mount Desert Island's natural environment provide excellent opportunities for environmental studies. Cooperative resource sharing is available with the Jackson Laboratory, Mount Desert Island Biological Laboratory, Acadia National Park and the local school system. In the summer, Bar Harbor is supported by the tourist trade. Other businesses which provide for the local economy are boatbuilding, fishing, and lobstering. Bar Harbor is easily accessible by Bar Harbor Airlines, Greyhound Bus or automobile via State Routes 1 and 3.

■ **EASTERN MAINE COMMUNITY COLLEGE**
354 Hogan Rd.
Bangor, ME 04401-4206
Tel: (207)974-4600
Fax: (207)974-4683
E-mail: admissions@emcc.edu
Web Site: www.emcc.edu
Description: State-supported, 2-year, coed. Part of Maine Community College System. Awards certificates, diplomas, transfer associate, and terminal associate degrees. Founded 1966. Setting: 72-acre small town campus. Total enrollment: 1,923. 1,823 applied. 33% 25 or older. Calendar: semesters. Academic remediation for entering students, advanced placement, summer session for credit, part-time degree program, adult/continuing education programs.

Entrance Requirements: Option: deferred admission. Required: essay, high school transcript, ACCUPLACER. Recommended: minimum 2.0 high school GPA. Required for some: interview, SAT. Entrance: minimally difficult. Application deadline: rolling. Notification: continuous. Preference given to state residents.

Costs Per Year: Application fee: $20. One-time mandatory fee: $70. State resident tuition: $2820 full-time, $94 per credit hour part-time. Nonresident tuition: $5640 full-time, $188 per credit hour part-time. Mandatory fees: $642 full-time, $21.40 per credit hour part-time. Full-time tuition and fees vary according to course load and program. Part-time tuition and fees vary according to course load and program.

Collegiate Environment: Orientation program. Student-run newspaper. Student services: health clinic, personal-psychological counseling. Campus security: late night transport-escort service, controlled dormitory access. Eastern Maine Technical College Library plus 1 other.

■ **HUSSON UNIVERSITY**
1 College Cir.
Bangor, ME 04401-2999
Tel: (207)941-7000; Free: 800-4-HUSSON
Fax: (207)941-7935
E-mail: smithad@husson.edu
Web Site: www.husson.edu
Description: Independent, comprehensive, coed. Awards associate, bachelor's, master's, and doctoral degrees and post-master's certificates.

Founded 1898. Setting: 208-acre suburban campus. Endowment: $17.3 million. Educational spending for the previous fiscal year: $6350 per student. Total enrollment: 3,640. Faculty: 341 (141 full-time, 200 part-time). Student-undergrad faculty ratio is 15:1. 2,460 applied, 80% were admitted. 11% from top 10% of their high school class, 37% from top quarter, 69% from top half. 28 class presidents, 5 valedictorians, 92 student government officers. Full-time: 2,298 students, 53% women, 47% men. Part-time: 465 students, 66% women, 34% men. Students come from 29 states and territories, 28 other countries, 28% from out-of-state. 0.3% American Indian or Alaska Native, non-Hispanic/Latino; 2% Hispanic/Latino; 4% Black or African American, non-Hispanic/Latino; 1% Asian, non-Hispanic/Latino; 0.2% Native Hawaiian or other Pacific Islander, non-Hispanic/Latino; 3% international. 18% 25 or older, 39% live on campus, 5% transferred in. Retention: 76% of full-time freshmen returned the following year. Academic areas with the most degrees conferred: business/marketing; health professions and related sciences; homeland security, law enforcement, firefighting, and protective services. Core. Calendar: semesters. Academic remediation for entering students, ESL program, services for LD students, advanced placement, self-designed majors, independent study, distance learning, double major, summer session for credit, part-time degree program, adult/continuing education programs, co-op programs and internships, graduate courses open to undergrads. Off campus study at Eastern Maine Community College, Central Maine Community College, Kennebec Valley Community College, Northern Maine Community College, Southern Maine Community College Washington County Community College, York County Community College, Andover College, University College of Bangor, Dean Junior College, Community College of Rhode Island. Study abroad program. ROTC: Army, Naval (c).

Entrance Requirements: Options: electronic application, deferred admission, international baccalaureate accepted. Required: essay, high school transcript, 1 recommendation, SAT or ACT. Recommended: minimum 3 high school GPA, interview. Entrance: moderately difficult. Application deadline: 8/15. Notification: continuous. SAT Reasoning Test deadline: 8/15. SAT Subject Test deadline: 8/15. Transfer credits accepted: Yes.

Costs Per Year: Application fee: $40. One-time mandatory fee: $150. Comprehensive fee: $27,430 includes full-time tuition ($17,100), mandatory fees ($500), and college room and board ($9830). College room only: $4950. Full-time tuition and fees vary according to class time and location. Room and board charges vary according to board plan and housing facility. Part-time tuition: $570 per credit. Part-time mandatory fees: $120 per year. Part-time tuition and fees vary according to class time, course load, and location.

Collegiate Environment: Orientation program. Drama-theater group, choral group, student-run radio station. Social organizations: 51 open to all; national fraternities, national sororities, local fraternities, local sororities; 3% of eligible men and 5% of eligible women are members. Most popular organizations: Organization of Student Nurses, Organization of Physical Therapy Students, Outdoors Club, International Student Association, Habitat for Humanity. Major annual events: Winter Week, Spring Week, Homecoming. Student services: health clinic, personal-psychological counseling. Campus security: 24-hour emergency response devices and patrols, late night transport-escort service, controlled dormitory access. Sawyer Library. Books: 41,659 (physical), 5,539 (digital/electronic); Serial titles: 74 (physical), 151 (digital/electronic); Databases: 91. Weekly public service hours: 98; study areas open 24 hours, 5-7 days a week; students can reserve study rooms. Operations spending for the previous fiscal year: $549,583. 131 computers available on campus for general student use. A campuswide network can be accessed from student residence rooms and from off campus. Students can access the following: online class registration. Staffed computer lab on campus provides training in use of computers, software, and the Internet.

■ KENNEBEC VALLEY COMMUNITY COLLEGE
92 Western Ave.
Fairfield, ME 04937-1367
Tel: (207)453-5000; Free: 800-528-5882
E-mail: admissions@kvcc.me.edu
Web Site: www.kvcc.me.edu
Description: State-supported, 2-year, coed. Part of Maine Community College System. Awards certificates, diplomas, transfer associate, and terminal associate degrees. Founded 1970. Setting: small town campus. Endowment: $3.1 million. Total enrollment: 2,554. Faculty: 163 (40 full-time, 123 part-time). Full-time: 565 students, 55% women, 45% men. Part-time: 1,989 students, 65% women, 35% men. Students come from 13 states and territories, 2% from out-of-state. 0.7% American Indian or Alaska Native, non-

Hispanic/Latino; 1% Hispanic/Latino; 1% Black or African American, non-Hispanic/Latino; 0.7% Asian, non-Hispanic/Latino; 0.1% Native Hawaiian or other Pacific Islander, non-Hispanic/Latino; 0.2% international. 50% 25 or older, 8% transferred in. Core. Calendar: semesters. Academic remediation for entering students, services for LD students, advanced placement, accelerated degree program, independent study, distance learning, summer session for credit, part-time degree program, external degree program, adult/continuing education programs, internships.

Entrance Requirements: Open admission except for nursing, radiologic technology, physical therapist assistant, and occupational therapist assistant programs. Options: electronic application, deferred admission. Required: essay, high school transcript. Recommended: SAT or ACT. Required for some: interview, HESI nursing exam, HOBET for allied health programs, ACCUPLACER. Entrance: noncompetitive. Application deadline: rolling. Notification: continuous. Transfer credits accepted: Yes.

Costs Per Year: State resident tuition: $2820 full-time, $94 per credit hour part-time. Nonresident tuition: $5640 full-time, $188 per credit hour part-time. Mandatory fees: $997 full-time. Full-time tuition and fees vary according to course load and program. Part-time tuition varies according to course load and program.

Collegiate Environment: Orientation program. Choral group. Social organizations: 26 open to all. Most popular organizations: Phi Theta Kappa, National Society for Leadership and Success, Student Senate, KV Federal Nurses Association. Major annual events: Welcome Week Activities, Week of Eek, Valentine's Week. Student services: personal-psychological counseling. Campus security: evening security patrol. Lunder Library plus 2 others. Operations spending for the previous fiscal year: $286,674.

Community Environment: See Colby College.

■ THE LANDING SCHOOL
286 River Rd.
Arundel, ME 04046
Tel: (207)985-7976
Fax: (207)985-7942
E-mail: info@landingschool.edu
Web Site: www.landingschool.edu
Description: Independent, 2-year, coed. Awards diplomas, transfer associate, and terminal associate degrees. Founded 1978. Setting: 4-acre rural campus with easy access to Portland, ME and Boston, MA. Total enrollment: 81. Faculty: (10 full-time). Student-undergrad faculty ratio is 9:1. 120 applied, 68% were admitted. Full-time: 81 students, 2% women, 98% men. Students come from 41 states and territories, 8 other countries, 75% from out-of-state. 2% Hispanic/Latino; 1% Black or African American, non-Hispanic/Latino; 2% international. 80% 25 or older. Retention: 84% of full-time freshmen returned the following year. Core. Calendar: continuous. Academic remediation for entering students, services for LD students, adult/continuing education programs, co-op programs and internships.

Entrance Requirements: Open admission. Options: electronic application, early admission, deferred admission. Required: essay, high school transcript, 3 recommendations, interview. Application deadlines: rolling, rolling for early decision plan 1, rolling for early decision plan 2. Notification: continuous, rolling for early decision plan 1, rolling for early decision plan 2. Transfer credits accepted: Yes. Applicants placed on waiting list: 0.

Collegiate Environment: Social organizations: 3 open to all. Most popular organizations: Jam Band, Hockey Club, Surf Club. Major annual events: Launch Day, Career Fair, Holiday Dinners. Student services: personal-psychological counseling. Campus security: 24-hour emergency response devices. S/V Patience Learning Resource Center. 8 computers available on campus for general student use. Staffed computer lab on campus provides training in use of computers and the Internet.

■ MAINE COLLEGE OF ART
522 Congress St.
Portland, ME 04101
Tel: (207)775-3052; Free: 800-699-1509
Fax: (207)772-5069
Web Site: www.meca.edu
Description: Independent, comprehensive, coed. Awards bachelor's and master's degrees. Founded 1882. Setting: urban campus. Total enrollment: 405. Full-time: 353 students, 71% women, 29% men. Part-time: 16 students, 56% women, 44% men. Students come from 24 states and territories, 1 other country, 41% from out-of-state. 0.8% American Indian or Alaska Native, non-Hispanic/Latino; 3% Hispanic/Latino; 1% Black or African American, non-Hispanic/Latino; 2% Asian, non-Hispanic/Latino. 10% 25 or

older, 44% live on campus, 11% transferred in. Retention: 75% of full-time freshmen returned the following year. Core. Calendar: semesters. Services for LD students, advanced placement, double major, part-time degree program, co-op programs and internships. Off campus study at Association of Independent Colleges of Art and Design Mobility Program, Greater Portland Alliance of Colleges and Universities. Study abroad program.

Entrance Requirements: Required: essay, minimum 2 high school GPA, 2 recommendations, portfolio of 15-20 pieces of recent artwork. Recommended: interview. Required for some: high school transcript.

Collegiate Environment: Orientation program. Student services: personal-psychological counseling. Campus security: 24-hour emergency response devices and patrols, controlled dormitory access. Joanne Waxman Library. 85 computers available on campus for general student use. A campuswide network can be accessed from student residence rooms and from off campus. Students can access the following: invoices, transcripts.

■ **MAINE COLLEGE OF HEALTH PROFESSIONS**
70 Middle St.
Lewiston, ME 04240-0305
Tel: (207)795-2840
Fax: (207)795-2849
E-mail: watsoner@mchp.edu
Web Site: www.mchp.edu

Description: Independent, primarily 2-year, coed. Awards certificates, terminal associate, and bachelor's degrees. Founded 1891. Setting: urban campus. Total enrollment: 188. Faculty: 19 (17 full-time, 2 part-time). Student-undergrad faculty ratio is 5:1. 13 applied. 25% from top 10% of their high school class, 75% from top half. Full-time: 44 students, 80% women, 20% men. Part-time: 144 students, 90% women, 10% men. 0.5% American Indian or Alaska Native, non-Hispanic/Latino; 1% Hispanic/Latino; 2% Black or African American, non-Hispanic/Latino; 2% Asian, non-Hispanic/Latino. 44% 25 or older, 4% live on campus, 50% transferred in. Core. Calendar: semesters. Services for LD students, advanced placement, summer session for credit. Off campus study.

Entrance Requirements: Option: electronic application. Required: essay, high school transcript, high school or college-level algebra, second math, biology, chemistry. Required for some: SAT or ACT, HESI Entrance Exam for nursing, ACCUPLACER. Entrance: moderately difficult. Application deadline: 4/14. Notification: 5/1. SAT Reasoning Test deadline: 4/14. Transfer credits accepted: Yes.

Costs Per Year: Application fee: $50. Tuition: $10,720 full-time, $5360 per year part-time. Mandatory fees: $1525 full-time. Full-time tuition and fees vary according to course load and program. Part-time tuition varies according to course load and program. College room only: $2350.

Collegiate Environment: Orientation program. Social organizations: 1 open to all. Most popular organization: Student Government. Major annual events: Community Service Day, Alumni Graduation Breakfast, Alumni Hosted Holiday Party. Student services: health clinic, personal-psychological counseling. Campus security: 24-hour emergency response devices and patrols, late night transport-escort service, controlled dormitory access. Gerrish True Health Sciences Library plus 1 other. Books: 2,816 (physical), 172 (digital/electronic); Databases: 17. Study areas open 24 hours, 5-7 days a week. 30 computers available on campus for general student use.

■ **MAINE MARITIME ACADEMY**
1 Pleasant St.
Castine, ME 04420
Tel: (207)326-4311; Free: 800-227-8465
Fax: (207)326-2515
Web Site: www.mainemaritime.edu

Description: State-supported, comprehensive, coed. Awards associate, bachelor's, and master's degrees. Founded 1941. Setting: 35-acre small town campus. Endowment: $17.7 million. Research spending for the previous fiscal year: $551,707. Educational spending for the previous fiscal year: $6366 per student. Total enrollment: 1,066. Faculty: 93 (65 full-time, 28 part-time). Student-undergrad faculty ratio is 13:1. 805 applied, 79% were admitted. Full-time: 1,024 students, 13% women, 87% men. Part-time: 13 students, 15% women, 85% men. Students come from 32 states and territories, 3 other countries, 27% from out-of-state. 0.3% American Indian or Alaska Native, non-Hispanic/Latino; 0.8% Hispanic/Latino; 0.5% Black or African American, non-Hispanic/Latino; 0.8% Asian, non-Hispanic/Latino; 0.2% Native Hawaiian or other Pacific Islander, non-Hispanic/Latino. 8% 25 or older, 78% live on campus, 6% transferred in. Retention: 79% of full-time freshmen returned the following year. Academic areas with the most degrees

conferred: engineering technologies; transportation and materials moving; engineering. Core. Calendar: semesters. Academic remediation for entering students, advanced placement, self-designed majors, honors program, independent study, double major, adult/continuing education programs, co-op programs and internships. Off campus study at International Association of Maritime Universities. Study abroad program. ROTC: Army (c), Naval.

Entrance Requirements: Options: electronic application, early admission, early action, deferred admission, international baccalaureate accepted. Required: high school transcript, 1 recommendation, SAT or ACT. Recommended: interview. Entrance: moderately difficult. Application deadline: rolling, 10/30 for early action. Notification: 2/1 for early action. SAT Reasoning Test deadline: 3/1. Transfer credits accepted: Yes. Applicants placed on waiting list: 12. Wait-listed applicants offered admission: 0. Early action applicants: 420. Early action applicants admitted: 318.

Collegiate Environment: Orientation program. Drama-theater group, choral group, marching band. Social organizations: 30 open to all. Most popular organizations: Rugby Club, yacht club, Alpha Phi Omega (community service), Chess Club, Drill Team. Major annual events: Parents' Weekends, Ring Dance, Ship jump. Student services: health clinic, personal-psychological counseling, women's center. Campus security: 24-hour emergency response devices and patrols, late night transport-escort service, controlled dormitory access. Nutting Memorial Library. Operations spending for the previous fiscal year: $993,558.

Community Environment: The French erected the first fort here in 1613, but the first permanent settlement was made by the English in 1760. Fort George, partially restored, is maintained as a memorial today. Castine is on south central coast of Maine, 35 miles south of Bangor.

■ **NORTHERN MAINE COMMUNITY COLLEGE**
33 Edgemont Dr.
Presque Isle, ME 04769-2016
Tel: (207)768-2700; Free: 800-535-6682
Fax: (207)768-2831
E-mail: nnpoulin@nmcc.edu
Web Site: www.nmcc.edu

Description: State-supported, 2-year, coed. Part of Maine Community College System. Awards certificates, transfer associate, and terminal associate degrees. Founded 1963. Setting: 86-acre small town campus. Educational spending for the previous fiscal year: $3456 per student. Total enrollment: 955. Faculty: 77 (45 full-time, 32 part-time). Student-undergrad faculty ratio is 15:1. 761 applied, 53% were admitted. Students come from 4 states and territories, 4% from out-of-state. 40% 25 or older, 50% live on campus. Retention: 57% of full-time freshmen returned the following year. Core. Calendar: semesters. Academic remediation for entering students, services for LD students, advanced placement, independent study, double major, summer session for credit, part-time degree program, adult/continuing education programs, co-op programs and internships. Off campus study at University of Maine at Presque Isle.

Entrance Requirements: Open admission. Options: electronic application, early admission, deferred admission. Required: high school transcript, interview. Recommended: essay, minimum 2 high school GPA. Entrance: minimally difficult. Application deadline: rolling. Notification: continuous.

Costs Per Year: Application fee: $20. One-time mandatory fee: $66. State resident tuition: $2820 full-time, $94 per credit hour part-time. Nonresident tuition: $5640 full-time, $188 per credit hour part-time. Mandatory fees: $1000 full-time. Full-time tuition and fees vary according to course load, program, and reciprocity agreements. Part-time tuition varies according to course load, program, and reciprocity agreements. College room and board: $7818. Room and board charges vary according to board plan and housing facility.

Collegiate Environment: Orientation program. Social organizations: Phi Theta Kappa honor society. Most popular organizations: Student Senate, Alpha Beta Gamma, Phi Theta Kappa, Student Nurses Association. Major annual events: Casino & Mocktails Night, Bingo, Senior Send-Off BBQ. Student services: health clinic. Campus security: 24-hour emergency response devices and patrols, controlled dormitory access. Northern Maine Community College Library. Weekly public service hours: 40; students can reserve study rooms. Operations spending for the previous fiscal year: $163,430. 233 computers available on campus for general student use. Computer purchase/lease plans available. A campuswide network can be accessed. Students can access the following: online class registration, forms and student account information. Staffed computer lab on campus provides training in use of computers, software, and the Internet.

Community Environment: See University of Maine - Presque Isle.

■ PURDUE UNIVERSITY GLOBAL (AUGUSTA)
14 Marketplace Dr.
Augusta, ME 04330
Tel: (207)213-2500; Free: 844-PURDUE-G
Web Site: www.purdueglobal.edu
Description: Independent, comprehensive, coed. Awards associate, bachelor's, master's, and doctoral degrees.

■ PURDUE UNIVERSITY GLOBAL (LEWISTON)
475 Lisbon St.
Lewiston, ME 04240
Tel: (207)333-3300; Free: 844-PURDUE-G
Web Site: www.purdueglobal.edu
Description: Independent, comprehensive, coed. Awards associate and master's degrees.

■ SAINT JOSEPH'S COLLEGE OF MAINE
278 Whites Bridge Rd.
Standish, ME 04084
Tel: (207)892-6766; Free: 800-338-7057
Fax: (207)893-7862
E-mail: admission@sjcme.edu
Web Site: www.sjcme.edu
Description: Independent, comprehensive, coed, affiliated with Roman Catholic Church. Awards bachelor's and master's degrees and post-master's certificates (profile does not include enrollment in distance learning master's program). Founded 1912. Setting: 350-acre small town campus. Endowment: $9.2 million. Research spending for the previous fiscal year: $114,734. Total enrollment: 3,355. Faculty: 126 (68 full-time, 58 part-time). Student-undergrad faculty ratio is 14:1. 1,321 applied, 88% were admitted. 2 valedictorians. Full-time: 1,728 students, 69% women, 31% men. Part-time: 656 students, 79% women, 21% men. Students come from 15 states and territories, 1 other country, 45% from out-of-state. 2% Hispanic/Latino; 3% Black or African American, non-Hispanic/Latino; 1% Asian, non-Hispanic/Latino. 38% 25 or older, 74% live on campus, 1% transferred in. Retention: 76% of full-time freshmen returned the following year. Academic areas with the most degrees conferred: health professions and related sciences; business/marketing; education. Core. Calendar: semesters. Services for LD students, advanced placement, self-designed majors, honors program, independent study, distance learning, double major, summer session for credit, part-time degree program, adult/continuing education programs, co-op programs and internships. Off campus study at Greater Portland Alliance of Colleges and Universities, a consortium that includes University of Southern Maine, Maine College of Art, University of New England, Southern Maine Technical College, and Saint Joseph's College. Study abroad program. ROTC: Army (c).
Entrance Requirements: Options: electronic application, early action, deferred admission. Required: essay, high school transcript, minimum 2 high school GPA, 2 recommendations, SAT or ACT. Recommended: interview. Entrance: moderately difficult. Application deadlines: rolling, 11/15 for early action. Notification: continuous, 12/17 for early action. Transfer credits accepted: Yes. Early action applicants: 464. Early action applicants admitted: 436.
Costs Per Year: Application fee: $0. Comprehensive fee: $49,330 includes full-time tuition ($35,650) and college room and board ($13,680). Room and board charges vary according to board plan. Part-time tuition: $1050 per credit hour. Part-time tuition varies according to course load.
Collegiate Environment: Orientation program. Drama-theater group, student-run newspaper. Social organizations: 25 open to all. Most popular organizations: Campus ministry, Superkids, Student Government Association and Senate, Business Club, Inter-Hall Council. Major annual events: Family Weekend, Spring Fling, Welcome Back Weekends. Student services: health clinic, personal-psychological counseling. Campus security: 24-hour emergency response devices and patrols, late night transport-escort service, controlled dormitory access. Wellehan Library. Operations spending for the previous fiscal year: $403,893. 102 computers available on campus for general student use. Computer purchase/lease plans available. A campuswide network can be accessed from student residence rooms. Students can access the following: online class registration. Staffed computer lab on campus provides training in use of computers, software, and the Internet.

■ SOUTHERN MAINE COMMUNITY COLLEGE
2 Fort Rd.
South Portland, ME 04106

Tel: (207)741-5500; Free: 877-282-2182
Fax: (207)741-5751
E-mail: alee@smccme.edu
Web Site: www.smccme.edu
Description: State-supported, 2-year, coed. Part of Maine Community College System. Awards certificates, transfer associate, and terminal associate degrees. Founded 1946. Setting: 80-acre suburban campus. Total enrollment: 8,491. Faculty: 446 (96 full-time, 350 part-time). Student-undergrad faculty ratio is 18:1. Full-time: 3,424 students, 66% women, 34% men. Part-time: 4,064 students, 64% women, 36% men. Students come from 15 states and territories, 10 other countries. 0.3% American Indian or Alaska Native, non-Hispanic/Latino; 4% Hispanic/Latino; 7% Black or African American, non-Hispanic/Latino; 2% Asian, non-Hispanic/Latino; 0.2% Native Hawaiian or other Pacific Islander, non-Hispanic/Latino; 0.7% international. 5% live on campus. Retention: 55% of full-time freshmen returned the following year. Calendar: semesters. Academic remediation for entering students, ESL program, services for LD students, advanced placement, honors program, independent study, distance learning, double major, summer session for credit, part-time degree program, internships. Off campus study at Great Portland Alliance of Colleges and Universities. Study abroad program.
Entrance Requirements: Open admission. Option: electronic application. Required: high school transcript. Entrance: noncompetitive. Application deadlines: rolling, rolling for nonresidents. Notification: continuous, continuous for nonresidents. Transfer credits accepted: Yes.
Costs Per Year: Application fee: $20. State resident tuition: $2820 full-time, $94 per credit hour part-time. Nonresident tuition: $5640 full-time, $188 per credit hour part-time. Mandatory fees: $1000 full-time. College room and board: $9488.
Collegiate Environment: Orientation program. Drama-theater group, choral group, student-run newspaper. Most popular organization: Student Senate. Major annual events: Welcome Back Barbecue, Winter Carnival, Spring Fest. Student services: personal-psychological counseling. Campus security: 24-hour patrols, student patrols, late night transport-escort service, controlled dormitory access. 450 college housing spaces available; all were occupied in 2018-19. No special consideration for freshman housing applicants. Options: coed, men-only housing available. Southern Maine Community College Library. Books: 20,586 (physical), 30,783 (digital/electronic); Serial titles: 1,026 (physical), 23,074 (digital/electronic); Databases: 34. Weekly public service hours: 68; students can reserve study rooms. 128 computers available on campus for general student use. A campuswide network can be accessed from student residence rooms and from off campus. Students can access the following: online class registration; additional 550 computers in classrooms. Staffed computer lab on campus.

■ THOMAS COLLEGE
180 W River Rd.
Waterville, ME 04901-5097
Tel: (207)859-1111; Free: 800-339-7001
Fax: (207)859-1114
E-mail: admiss@thomas.edu
Web Site: www.thomas.edu
Description: Independent, comprehensive, coed. Awards associate, bachelor's, and master's degrees. Founded 1894. Setting: 70-acre small town campus. Endowment: $10.5 million. Educational spending for the previous fiscal year: $5256 per student. Total enrollment: 1,367. Faculty: 87 (33 full-time, 54 part-time). Student-undergrad faculty ratio is 19:1. Full-time: 808 students, 48% women, 52% men. Part-time: 404 students, 61% women, 39% men. Students come from 24 states and territories, 5 other countries, 14% from out-of-state. 0.7% American Indian or Alaska Native, non-Hispanic/Latino; 2% Hispanic/Latino; 3% Black or African American, non-Hispanic/Latino; 0.7% Asian, non-Hispanic/Latino; 2% international. 6% 25 or older, 64% live on campus, 4% transferred in. Retention: 71% of full-time freshmen returned the following year. Core. Calendar: semesters. Academic remediation for entering students, services for LD students, advanced placement, accelerated degree program, double major, summer session for credit, part-time degree program, adult/continuing education programs, co-op programs and internships. Off campus study at Colby College, Kennebec Valley Community College, Unity College. Study abroad program.
Entrance Requirements: Required: essay, high school transcript, 1 recommendation. Recommended: minimum 2 high school GPA, interview, rank in upper 50% of high school class.
Costs Per Year: Comprehensive fee: $37,750 includes full-time tuition ($25,960), mandatory fees ($940), and college room and board ($10,850). College room only: $5290. Room and board charges vary according to board plan and housing facility.

Collegiate Environment: Orientation program. Drama-theater group. Social organizations: 21 open to all; national fraternities; 2% of men are members. Most popular organizations: Phi Beta Lambda, Music Club, Gaming Club, Otherwise, Education Club. Major annual events: Deep Freeze Week, Student Appreciation Day and Casino Night, Welcome Week. Student services: health clinic, personal-psychological counseling. Campus security: 24-hour emergency response devices and patrols, student patrols, controlled dormitory access. Marriner Library. Books: 17,925 (physical), 5,600 (digital/electronic); Serial titles: 30 (physical), 6 (digital/electronic); Databases: 80. Weekly public service hours: 90; study areas open 24 hours, 5-7 days a week; students can reserve study rooms. Operations spending for the previous fiscal year: $294,905. 120 computers available on campus for general student use. A campuswide network can be accessed from student residence rooms and from off campus. Students can access the following: online class registration. Staffed computer lab on campus provides training in use of computers, software, and the Internet.

■ UNITY COLLEGE

90 Quaker Hill Rd.
Unity, ME 04988
Tel: (207)509-7100
Fax: (207)948-6277
E-mail: jsalty@unity.edu
Web Site: www.unity.edu

Description: Independent, comprehensive, coed. Awards bachelor's and master's degrees. Founded 1965. Setting: 300-acre rural campus. Endowment: $14 million. Educational spending for the previous fiscal year: $8000 per student. Total enrollment: 733. Student-undergrad faculty ratio is 14:1. 915 applied, 89% were admitted. Full-time: 694 students, 51% women, 49% men. Part-time: 10 students, 40% women, 60% men. Students come from 32 states and territories, 1 other country, 74% from out-of-state. 2% American Indian or Alaska Native, non-Hispanic/Latino; 1% Hispanic/Latino; 0.7% Black or African American, non-Hispanic/Latino; 0.9% Asian, non-Hispanic/Latino. 5% 25 or older, 70% live on campus, 8% transferred in. Retention: 64% of full-time freshmen returned the following year. Academic areas with the most degrees conferred: natural resources/environmental science; biological/life sciences; communication/journalism; engineering technologies; law/legal studies; health professions and related sciences. Core. Calendar: semesters. Academic remediation for entering students, services for LD students, advanced placement, accelerated degree program, honors program, independent study, double major, summer session for credit, part-time degree program, co-op programs and internships. Off campus study at The Washington Center, Washington DC. Study abroad program.

Entrance Requirements: Options: electronic application, early action, deferred admission, international baccalaureate accepted. Required: essay, high school transcript. Recommended: minimum 2.5 high school GPA, interview, SAT or ACT. Required for some: interview. Entrance: moderately difficult. Application deadlines: rolling, 12/15 for early action. Notification: continuous, 12/31 for early action. Transfer credits accepted: Yes. Early action applicants: 708. Early action applicants admitted: 521.

Costs Per Year: Application fee: $0. Comprehensive fee: $39,870 includes full-time tuition ($27,960), mandatory fees ($1200), and college room and board ($10,710). Room and board charges vary according to board plan and housing facility. Part-time tuition: $1010 per credit.

Collegiate Environment: Orientation program. Drama-theater group, choral group. Social organizations: 32 open to all. Most popular organizations: Woodsmen Team, Ultimate Frisbee, Outing Club. Major annual events: Earth Day, Winter Carnival, Community Weekend. Student services: health clinic, personal-psychological counseling. Campus security: 24-hour emergency response devices and patrols, security cameras in certain areas. Dorothy Webb Quimby Library. Books: 52,723 (physical), 15,329 (digital/electronic); Databases: 72. Weekly public service hours: 40. Operations spending for the previous fiscal year: $184,000. 140 computers available on campus for general student use. A campuswide network can be accessed from student residence rooms and from off campus. Students can access the following: online class registration. Staffed computer lab on campus provides training in use of computers, software, and the Internet.

Community Environment: Located on Lake Winnecook, which is three miles long and has excellent fishing, canoeing, and sailing, Unity has several small businesses, two churches, a public library, and several fraternal organizations. Transportation is provided by air and bus lines. The climate is cool.

■ UNIVERSITY OF MAINE

Orono, ME 04469
Tel: (207)581-1865; Free: 877-486-2364
Fax: (207)581-1213
E-mail: um-admit@maine.edu
Web Site: www.umaine.edu

Description: State-supported, university, coed. Part of University of Maine System. Awards bachelor's, master's, and doctoral degrees and post-master's certificates. Founded 1865. Setting: 660-acre small town campus. Endowment: $323 million. Research spending for the previous fiscal year: $77 million. Educational spending for the previous fiscal year: $10,095 per student. Total enrollment: 11,404. Faculty: 878 (533 full-time, 345 part-time). Student-undergrad faculty ratio is 16:1. 12,457 applied, 92% were admitted. 18% from top 10% of their high school class, 40% from top quarter, 73% from top half. 28 valedictorians. Full-time: 8,158 students, 47% women, 53% men. Part-time: 1,207 students, 49% women, 51% men. Students come from 50 states and territories, 36 other countries, 37% from out-of-state. 0.8% American Indian or Alaska Native, non-Hispanic/Latino; 4% Hispanic/Latino; 2% Black or African American, non-Hispanic/Latino; 1% Asian, non-Hispanic/Latino; 2% international. 6% 25 or older, 38% live on campus, 4% transferred in. Retention: 78% of full-time freshmen returned the following year. Academic areas with the most degrees conferred: business/marketing; engineering; education. Calendar: semesters. ESL program, services for LD students, advanced placement, accelerated degree program, self-designed majors, freshman honors college, honors program, independent study, distance learning, double major, summer session for credit, part-time degree program, internships, graduate courses open to undergrads. Off campus study at Other institutions of the University of Maine System. Study abroad program. ROTC: Army, Naval.

Entrance Requirements: Options: electronic application, early admission, early action, deferred admission, international baccalaureate accepted. Required: 1 recommendation, SAT or ACT. Entrance: moderately difficult. Application deadlines: 2/1, 2/1 for nonresidents, 12/1 for early action. Notification: continuous, continuous for nonresidents, 1/15 for early action. SAT Reasoning Test deadline: 5/1. Transfer credits accepted: Yes. Applicants placed on waiting list: 0. Wait-listed applicants offered admission: 0. Early action applicants: 7,189. Early action applicants admitted: 6,582.

Collegiate Environment: Orientation program. Drama-theater group, choral group, marching band, student-run newspaper, radio station. Social organizations: 160 open to all; national fraternities, national sororities, local fraternities, local sororities. Most popular organizations: Fraternity and Sorority Life, Alternative Breaks, UMaine Student Government, Campus Activities Board, Wilde Stein. Major annual events: Maine Day, Homecoming, Family and Friends Weekend. Student services: legal services, health clinic, personal-psychological counseling, women's center. Campus security: 24-hour emergency response devices and patrols, late night transport-escort service, controlled dormitory access, area emergency text and email message system. 3,650 college housing spaces available; 3,433 were occupied in 2018-19. Freshmen guaranteed college housing. On-campus residence required in freshman year. Option: coed housing available. Fogler Library. Books: 3.6 million (physical), 1.1 million (digital/electronic); Serial titles: 66,214 (physical), 142,082 (digital/electronic); Databases: 364. Weekly public service hours: 103; students can reserve study rooms. Operations spending for the previous fiscal year: $10.1 million. 600 computers available on campus for general student use. Computer purchase/lease plans available. A campuswide network can be accessed from student residence rooms and from off campus. Students can access the following: online class registration, online housing and financial aid information. Staffed computer lab on campus provides training in use of computers, software, and the Internet.

■ UNIVERSITY OF MAINE AT AUGUSTA

46 University Dr.
Augusta, ME 04330-9410
Tel: (207)621-3000; Free: 877-862-1234
Fax: (207)621-3116
E-mail: umaadm@maine.edu
Web Site: www.uma.edu

Description: State-supported, 4-year, coed. Part of University of Maine System. Awards associate and bachelor's degrees (also offers some graduate courses and continuing education programs with significant enrollment not reflected in profile). Founded 1965. Setting: 159-acre small town campus. Endowment: $7.3 million. Research spending for the previous fiscal year: $107,000. Educational spending for the previous fiscal year: $5893 per student. Total enrollment: 4,683. Faculty: 260 (87 full-time, 173 part-time). Student-undergrad faculty ratio is 16:1. 1,025 applied, 98% were admitted. Full-time: 1,663 students, 70% women, 30% men. Part-time: 3,020 students, 74% women, 26% men. 4% from out-of-state. 2% American Indian or Alaska Native, non-Hispanic/Latino; 2% Hispanic/Latino; 1% Black or African American, non-Hispanic/Latino; 0.6% Asian, non-Hispanic/Latino; 0.1% Native Hawaiian or other Pacific Islander, non-Hispanic/Latino; 0.4% international. 72% 25 or older, 13% transferred in. Retention: 56% of full-time freshmen returned the following year. Academic areas with the most degrees conferred: health professions and related sciences; liberal arts/ general studies; business/marketing. Core. Calendar: semesters. Academic remediation for entering students, services for LD students, advanced placement, self-designed majors, honors program, independent study, distance learning, double major, summer session for credit, part-time degree program, adult/continuing education programs, internships. Off campus study at other campuses of the University of Maine System. Study abroad program. ROTC: Army (c).

Entrance Requirements: Options: electronic application, early admission, deferred admission. Recommended: essay. Required for some: high school transcript, interview, music audition. Entrance: noncompetitive. Transfer credits accepted: Yes.

Costs Per Year: Application fee: $40. State resident tuition: $6990 full-time, $233 per credit hour part-time. Nonresident tuition: $16,920 full-time, $564 per credit hour part-time. Mandatory fees: $998 full-time, $33.25 per credit hour part-time. Full-time tuition and fees vary according to course load, location, program, and reciprocity agreements. Part-time tuition and fees vary according to course load, location, program, and reciprocity agreements.

Collegiate Environment: Orientation program. Drama-theater group, student-run newspaper. Most popular organizations: Honors Program Student Association, Arts and Architecture Students of UMA, Student Nurse Association, Student American Dental Hygiene Association, International Student Club. Major annual events: UMA Day, Jazz Week, Poetry Festival. Student services: personal-psychological counseling. Campus security: 24-hour emergency response devices, late night transport-escort service. The Bennett D. Katz Library. Operations spending for the previous fiscal year: $554,104.

■ UNIVERSITY OF MAINE AT FARMINGTON

111 S St.
Farmington, ME 04938
Tel: (207)778-7000
Fax: (207)778-8182
E-mail: ellrich@maine.edu
Web Site: www.umf.maine.edu

Description: State-supported, comprehensive, coed. Part of University of Maine System. Awards bachelor's and master's degrees. Founded 1863. Setting: 55-acre small town campus. Endowment: $13.1 million. Total enrollment: 2,040. Faculty: 195 (119 full-time, 76 part-time). Student-undergrad faculty ratio is 13:1. 1,905 applied, 81% were admitted. 16% from top 10% of their high school class, 44% from top quarter, 74% from top half. Full-time: 1,564 students, 66% women, 34% men. Part-time: 172 students, 69% women, 31% men. 17% from out-of-state. 0.6% American Indian or Alaska Native, non-Hispanic/Latino; 3% Hispanic/Latino; 2% Black or African American, non-Hispanic/Latino; 0.9% Asian, non-Hispanic/Latino; 0.4% international. 7% 25 or older, 51% live on campus, 5% transferred in. Retention: 71% of full-time freshmen returned the following year. Academic areas with the most degrees conferred: education; health professions and related sciences; business/marketing. Core. Calendar: semesters 3 summer sessions: one of 5 weeks and two of 4 weeks each. Academic remediation for entering students, services for LD students, advanced placement, accelerated degree program, self-designed majors, honors program, independent study, distance learning, double major, summer session for credit, part-time degree program, internships. Off campus study at National Student Exchange, other institutions of the University of Maine System; Chiropractic 3+3: BS in Biology at UMF to Doctor of Chiropractic at Logan University; Counseling 3+2: BA in Psychology at UMF to MS in Counseling at University of Southern Maine and BS in Rehabilitation Services at UMF to MS in Counseling at University of Southern Maine; Social Work 3+2: BA in Psychology at UMF to MSW at University of Southern Maine. Study abroad program.

Entrance Requirements: Options: electronic application, early admission, early action, deferred admission, international baccalaureate accepted. Required: high school transcript, 1 recommendation. Recommended: interview. Required for some: essay, Minimum 2.75 GPA for College of

Education transfers, 2.5 for Health and Rehabilitation, 2.0 for all others. Entrance: moderately difficult. Application deadline: 11/15 for early action. SAT Reasoning Test deadline: 8/15. SAT Subject Test deadline: 8/15. Transfer credits accepted: Yes.

Costs Per Year: State resident tuition: $9118 full-time, $303.93 per credit hour part-time. Nonresident tuition: $18,598 full-time, $619.93 per credit hour part-time. Mandatory fees: $898 full-time. Full-time tuition and fees vary according to course load and reciprocity agreements. Part-time tuition varies according to course load and reciprocity agreements. College room and board: $9626. College room only: $5180. Room and board charges vary according to board plan and housing facility.

Collegiate Environment: Orientation program. Drama-theater group, choral group, student-run newspaper, radio station. Social organizations: 56 open to all; 10% of eligible men and 25% of eligible women are members. Most popular organizations: Bust-A-Move Beavers, Commuter Council, Intervarsity Christian Fellowship, Student Senate, Campus Residence Council. Major annual events: Relay for Life, Spring Fling, Alumni, Family, & Friends Fall Fest. Student services: health clinic, personal-psychological counseling. Campus security: 24-hour emergency response devices and patrols, student patrols, late night transport-escort service, controlled dormitory access, safety whistles, security cameras. Freshmen guaranteed college housing. On-campus residence required in freshman year. Options: coed, women-only housing available. Mantor Library plus 1 other. Weekly public service hours: 88; students can reserve study rooms. Operations spending for the previous fiscal year: $559,089. 220 computers available on campus for general student use. Computer purchase/lease plans available. A campuswide network can be accessed from student residence rooms and from off campus. Students can access the following: online class registration. Staffed computer lab on campus (open 24 hours a day) provides training in use of computers, software, and the Internet.

■ UNIVERSITY OF MAINE AT FORT KENT

23 University Dr.
Fort Kent, ME 04743-1292
Tel: (207)834-7500; Free: 888-TRY-UMFK
Fax: (207)834-7609
Web Site: www.umfk.maine.edu

Description: State-supported, 4-year, coed. Part of University of Maine System. Awards associate and bachelor's degrees. Founded 1878. Setting: 52-acre rural campus. Endowment: $3.1 million. Research spending for the previous fiscal year: $4188. Educational spending for the previous fiscal year: $6357 per student. Total enrollment: 1,760. Faculty: 93 (34 full-time, 59 part-time). Student-undergrad faculty ratio is 14:1. 572 applied, 97% were admitted. 3% from top 10% of their high school class, 11% from top quarter, 38% from top half. Full-time: 582 students, 65% women, 35% men. Part-time: 1,178 students, 74% women, 26% men. Students come from 26 states and territories, 26 other countries, 14% from out-of-state. 0.9% American Indian or Alaska Native, non-Hispanic/Latino; 3% Hispanic/Latino; 3% Black or African American, non-Hispanic/Latino; 0.7% Asian, non-Hispanic/Latino; 0.2% Native Hawaiian or other Pacific Islander, non-Hispanic/Latino; 7% international. 43% 25 or older, 29% live on campus, 13% transferred in. Retention: 61% of full-time freshmen returned the following year. Academic areas with the most degrees conferred: health professions and related sciences; business/marketing; public administration and social services; biological/life sciences; social sciences. Core. Calendar: semesters. Academic remediation for entering students, ESL program, services for LD students, advanced placement, accelerated degree program, self-designed majors, honors program, independent study, distance learning, double major, summer session for credit, part-time degree program, external degree program, co-op programs and internships.

Entrance Requirements: Options: electronic application, deferred admission. Required: essay, high school transcript. Required for some: interview, SAT or ACT. Entrance: minimally difficult. Application deadline: rolling. Notification: continuous. Transfer credits accepted: Yes.

Costs Per Year: Application fee: $40. State resident tuition: $6990 full-time, $233 per credit hour part-time. Nonresident tuition: $11,190 full-time, $373 per credit hour part-time. Mandatory fees: $1125 full-time, $37.50 per credit hour part-time. College room and board: $8220. College room only: $4250. Room and board charges vary according to board plan and housing facility.

Collegiate Environment: Orientation program. Drama-theater group. Social organizations: 9 open to all; national fraternities, national sororities; 3% of eligible men and 3% of eligible women are members. Most popular organizations: Student Nurses Organization, Student Teachers Educational Professional Society, Student Senate, Student Activities Board, Dorm Council.

Major annual events: Quebec City Carnival Field Trip, Scarecrow Festival, Spring Formal. Student services: health clinic, personal-psychological counseling. Campus security: controlled dormitory access, night patrols by security personnel 11pm-7am. Waneta Blake Library. Books: 44,058 (physical), 9,361 (digital/electronic); Serial titles: 92 (physical), 61,183 (digital/electronic); Databases: 106. Weekly public service hours: 88; students can reserve study rooms. Operations spending for the previous fiscal year: $296,895. 100 computers available on campus for general student use. A campuswide network can be accessed from student residence rooms and from off campus. Students can access the following: online class registration. Staffed computer lab on campus provides training in use of computers, software, and the Internet.

■ **UNIVERSITY OF MAINE AT MACHIAS**

116 O'Brien Ave.
Machias, ME 04654
Tel: (207)255-1200; Free: 888-468-6866
Fax: (207)255-1363
Web Site: www.machias.edu
Description: State-supported, 4-year, coed. Part of University of Maine System. Awards associate and bachelor's degrees. Founded 1909. Setting: 42-acre rural campus. Endowment: $2.5 million. Research spending for the previous fiscal year: $753,000. Educational spending for the previous fiscal year: $9800 per student. Total enrollment: 675. Faculty: 66 (28 full-time, 38 part-time). Student-undergrad faculty ratio is 12:1. 596 applied, 98% were admitted. Full-time: 345 students, 64% women, 36% men. Part-time: 330 students, 78% women, 22% men. 11% from out-of-state. 4% American Indian or Alaska Native, non-Hispanic/Latino; 4% Hispanic/Latino; 3% Black or African American, non-Hispanic/Latino; 0.6% Asian, non-Hispanic/Latino; 0.2% Native Hawaiian or other Pacific Islander, non-Hispanic/Latino; 0.4% international. 36% 25 or older, 56% live on campus, 5% transferred in. Retention: 55% of full-time freshmen returned the following year. Academic areas with the most degrees conferred: biological/life sciences; liberal arts/general studies; psychology. Core. Calendar: semesters. Academic remediation for entering students, services for LD students, advanced placement, self-designed majors, independent study, distance learning, double major, summer session for credit, part-time degree program, co-op programs and internships. Off campus study. Study abroad program.
Entrance Requirements: Options: electronic application, early admission, early action, deferred admission. Required: essay, high school transcript, 1 recommendation. Recommended: minimum 2.5 high school GPA, 2 recommendations, interview. Required for some: minimum 2 high school GPA. Entrance: moderately difficult. Transfer credits accepted: Yes.
Collegiate Environment: Orientation program. No special consideration for freshman housing applicants. On-campus residence required through sophomore year. Option: coed housing available. Merrill Library. Operations spending for the previous fiscal year: $252,886.

■ **UNIVERSITY OF MAINE AT PRESQUE ISLE**

181 Main St.
Presque Isle, ME 04769-2888
Tel: (207)768-9400
Fax: (207)768-9608
E-mail: patricia.armstrong@umpi.edu
Web Site: www.umpi.edu
Description: State-supported, 4-year, coed. Part of University of Maine System. Awards associate and bachelor's degrees. Founded 1903. Setting: 150-acre small town campus. Endowment: $1.3 million. Research spending for the previous fiscal year: $101,000. Educational spending for the previous fiscal year: $7716 per student. Total enrollment: 1,554. Faculty: 93 (40 full-time, 53 part-time). Student-undergrad faculty ratio is 13:1. 801 applied, 92% were admitted. 7% from top 10% of their high school class, 27% from top quarter, 57% from top half. Full-time: 673 students, 61% women, 39% men. Part-time: 881 students, 61% women, 39% men. Students come from 32 states and territories, 8 other countries, 14% from out-of-state. 2% American Indian or Alaska Native, non-Hispanic/Latino; 2% Hispanic/Latino; 3% Black or African American, non-Hispanic/Latino; 0.8% Asian, non-Hispanic/Latino; 0.1% Native Hawaiian or other Pacific Islander, non-Hispanic/Latino; 2% international. 31% 25 or older, 34% live on campus, 7% transferred in. Retention: 62% of full-time freshmen returned the following year. Academic areas with the most degrees conferred: business/marketing; liberal arts/general studies; education. Core. Calendar: semesters. Academic remediation for entering students, services for LD students, advanced placement, accelerated degree program, self-designed majors, honors program, independent study, distance learning, double major, summer session for credit, part-time degree program, adult/continuing education programs, co-op programs and internships. Off campus study. Study abroad program.
Entrance Requirements: Options: electronic application, early admission,

deferred admission, international baccalaureate accepted. Required: essay, high school transcript, 1 recommendation. Recommended: minimum 2 high school GPA. Required for some: interview. Entrance: minimally difficult. Application deadlines: rolling, rolling for nonresidents, rolling for early decision plan 1, rolling for early decision plan 2, rolling for early action. Notification: continuous, continuous for nonresidents, rolling for early decision plan 1, rolling for early decision plan 2, rolling for early action. Transfer credits accepted: Yes.
Costs Per Year: Application fee: $40. State resident tuition: $7170 full-time, $239 per credit hour part-time. Nonresident tuition: $11,460 full-time, $382 per credit hour part-time. Mandatory fees: $1194 full-time, $25 per credit hour part-time, $53.75 per term part-time. College room and board: $8406. College room only: $4850.
Collegiate Environment: Orientation program. Student-run newspaper, radio station. Social organizations: 13 open to all; national fraternities, national sororities, national honor societies. Major annual events: University Day, Convocation. Student services: health clinic, personal-psychological counseling. Campus security: student patrols, late night transport-escort service, controlled dormitory access. 380 college housing spaces available; 269 were occupied in 2018-19. Freshmen given priority for college housing. Option: coed housing available. Center for Innovative Learning plus 1 other. Books: 63,527 (physical), 159,418 (digital/electronic); Serial titles: 8 (physical), 75,843 (digital/electronic); Databases: 153. Weekly public service hours: 72. Operations spending for the previous fiscal year: $188,718.

■ **UNIVERSITY OF NEW ENGLAND**

11 Hills Beach Rd.
Biddeford, ME 04005-9526
Tel: (207)283-0171; Free: 800-477-4863
E-mail: admissions@une.edu
Web Site: www.une.edu
Description: Independent, comprehensive, coed. Awards bachelor's, master's, and doctoral degrees and post-master's certificates. Founded 1831. Setting: 540-acre small town campus. Endowment: $35.5 million. Research spending for the previous fiscal year: $6.1 million. Educational spending for the previous fiscal year: $10,373 per student. Total enrollment: 8,291. Faculty: 599 (285 full-time, 314 part-time). Student-undergrad faculty ratio is 13:1. 5,087 applied, 81% were admitted. Full-time: 2,361 students, 71% women, 29% men. Part-time: 2,062 students, 80% women, 20% men. Students come from 39 states and territories, 6 other countries, 70% from out-of-state. 0.5% American Indian or Alaska Native, non-Hispanic/Latino; 0.1% Hispanic/Latino; 2% Black or African American, non-Hispanic/Latino; 5% Asian, non-Hispanic/Latino; 0.1% Native Hawaiian or other Pacific Islander, non-Hispanic/Latino; 0.3% international. 3% 25 or older, 65% live on campus, 2% transferred in. Retention: 78% of full-time freshmen returned the following year. Academic areas with the most degrees conferred: health professions and related sciences; biological/life sciences; parks and recreation. Core. Calendar: semesters. Academic remediation for entering students, services for LD students, advanced placement, accelerated degree program, honors program, independent study, distance learning, double major, summer session for credit, part-time degree program, adult/continuing education programs, co-op programs and internships, graduate courses open to undergrads. Off campus study at Greater Portland Alliance of Colleges and Universities. Study abroad program. ROTC: Army (c).
Entrance Requirements: Options: electronic application, early admission, early action, deferred admission, international baccalaureate accepted. Required: essay, high school transcript, SAT or ACT. Recommended: 1 recommendation. Entrance: moderately difficult. Application deadlines: 2/15, 12/1 for early action. Notification: continuous, rolling for early action. Transfer credits accepted: Yes. Early action applicants: 2,505. Early action applicants admitted: 2,015.
Costs Per Year: Application fee: $40. Comprehensive fee: $51,610 includes full-time tuition ($36,300), mandatory fees ($1320), and college room and board ($13,990). Full-time tuition and fees vary according to course load and program. Room and board charges vary according to board plan and housing facility. Part-time tuition: $1280 per credit hour. Part-time mandatory fees: $1320 per year. Part-time tuition and fees vary according to course load and program.
Collegiate Environment: Orientation program. Drama-theater group, choral group, student-run newspaper. Social organizations: 70 open to all. Most popular organizations: Student Government, Outing Club, Campus Programming Board, Earth's Eco, Dance Team. Major annual events: Homecoming, Jam Fest, Winter Fest. Student services: health clinic, personal-psychological counseling. Campus security: 24-hour emergency response devices and patrols, late night transport-escort service, controlled dormitory access. Jack S. Ketchum Library plus 1 other. Books: 135,000 (physical), 1.2 million (digital/electronic); Serial titles: 140,000 (digital/electronic); Databases: 200. Weekly public service hours: 146; study areas open 24 hours, 5-7 days a week; students can reserve study rooms. Operations

spending for the previous fiscal year: $3.5 million. 91 computers available on campus for general student use. Computer purchase/lease plans available. A campuswide network can be accessed from student residence rooms and from off campus. Students can access the following: online class registration. Staffed computer lab on campus (open 24 hours a day) provides training in use of software.

Community Environment: On the Saco River, the University of New England is located outside the small City of Biddeford (pop. 22,072) on the coast of Southern Maine, two hours from Boston and 25 minutes from Portland, Maine's largest city. Part-time work is available for students. Biddeford city services include hospital, churches, library, and Chamber of commerce. Recreational facilities good, with beaches of Biddeford Pool, Kennebunk, and Old Orchard; golf, fishing, swimming, skiing, are within easy reach.

■ UNIVERSITY OF SOUTHERN MAINE

96 Falmouth St.
Portland, ME 04103
Tel: (207)780-4141; Free: 800-800-4USM
Fax: (207)780-5640
E-mail: admitusm@maine.edu
Web Site: www.usm.maine.edu

Description: State-supported, comprehensive, coed. Part of University of Maine System. Awards bachelor's, master's, and doctoral degrees and postmaster's certificates. Founded 1878. Setting: 144-acre urban campus. Endowment: $38.5 million. Total enrollment: 7,855. Faculty: 662 (265 full-time, 397 part-time). Student-undergrad faculty ratio is 14:1. 4,111 applied, 80% were admitted. 11% from top 10% of their high school class, 37% from top quarter, 75% from top half. Full-time: 3,750 students, 58% women, 42% men. Part-time: 2,439 students, 57% women, 43% men. Students come from 38 states and territories, 16 other countries, 12% from out-of-state. 0.7% American Indian or Alaska Native, non-Hispanic/Latino; 2% Hispanic/Latino; 4% Black or African American, non-Hispanic/Latino; 2% Asian, non-Hispanic/Latino; 1% international. 32% 25 or older, 24% live on campus, 11% transferred in. Retention: 63% of full-time freshmen returned the following year. Core. Calendar: semesters. Academic remediation for entering students, ESL program, services for LD students, advanced placement, accelerated degree program, self-designed majors, honors program, independent study, distance learning, double major, summer session for credit, part-time degree program, adult/continuing education programs, co-op programs and internships, graduate courses open to undergrads. Off campus study at National Student Exchange. Study abroad program. ROTC: Army (c), Air Force (c).

Entrance Requirements: Options: electronic application, early admission, deferred admission, international baccalaureate accepted. Required: essay, high school transcript, SAT. Recommended: 1 recommendation, interview. Required for some: interview, audition for music majors. Entrance: moderately difficult. Notification: continuous. SAT Reasoning Test deadline: 8/2. Transfer credits accepted: Yes.

Costs Per Year: Application fee: $40. State resident tuition: $8130 full-time, $271 per credit hour part-time. Nonresident tuition: $21,390 full-time, $713 per credit hour part-time. Mandatory fees: $1390 full-time, $30 per credit hour part-time, $100 per term part-time. Full-time tuition and fees vary according to course load, degree level, and reciprocity agreements. Part-time tuition and fees vary according to course load, degree level, and reciprocity agreements. College room and board: $9450. College room only: $5000. Room and board charges vary according to board plan and housing facility.

Collegiate Environment: Orientation program. Drama-theater group, choral group, student-run newspaper, radio station. Social organizations: national fraternities, national sororities, local fraternities, local sororities. Most popular organizations: Outing and Ski Clubs, Gorham Events Board, Commuter Student Group, Circle K. Major annual events: Spring Fling, Husky Fest, Theatre and Music Performers. Student services: legal services, health clinic, personal-psychological counseling, women's center. Campus security: 24-hour emergency response devices and patrols, late night transport-escort service, controlled dormitory access, security lighting, preventive programs within residence halls. Glickman Library plus 3 others. 219 computers available on campus for general student use. Computer purchase/lease plans available. A campuswide network can be accessed from student residence rooms and from off campus. Students can access the following: online class registration. Staffed computer lab on campus provides training in use of computers, software, and the Internet.

■ WASHINGTON COUNTY COMMUNITY COLLEGE

One College Dr.
Calais, ME 04619
Tel: (207)454-1000
Fax: (207)454-1026
Web Site: www.wccc.me.edu

Description: State-supported, 2-year, coed. Part of Maine Community College System. Awards certificates, diplomas, transfer associate, and terminal associate degrees. Founded 1969. Setting: 40-acre rural campus. Total enrollment: 374. Student-undergrad faculty ratio is 11:1. Students come from 4 states and territories, 1 other country, 3% from out-of-state. 40% 25 or older. Retention: 63% of full-time freshmen returned the following year. Calendar: semesters. Academic remediation for entering students, services for LD students, advanced placement, independent study, distance learning, double major, part-time degree program, external degree program, adult/continuing education programs, co-op programs and internships. Off campus study. Study abroad program.

Entrance Requirements: Open admission. Option: deferred admission. Required: essay, high school transcript, interview. Recommended: minimum 2 high school GPA. Entrance: noncompetitive. Application deadline: rolling. Notification: continuous.

Costs Per Year: Application fee: $20. State resident tuition: $2820 full-time, $94 per credit hour part-time. Nonresident tuition: $5640 full-time, $188 per credit hour part-time. Mandatory fees: $902 full-time. Full-time tuition and fees vary according to course load and program. Part-time tuition varies according to course load and program. College room and board: $5340. College room only: $3620.

Collegiate Environment: Orientation program. Choral group. Student services: personal-psychological counseling. Campus security: 24-hour emergency response devices. Washington County Technical College Library.

■ YORK COUNTY COMMUNITY COLLEGE

112 College Dr.
Wells, ME 04090
Tel: (207)646-9282; Free: 800-580-3820
Fax: (207)641-0837
Web Site: www.yccc.edu

Description: State-supported, 2-year, coed. Part of Maine Community College System. Awards certificates, transfer associate, and terminal associate degrees. Founded 1994. Setting: 84-acre small town campus with easy access to Boston. Total enrollment: 1,708. Faculty: 149 (23 full-time, 126 part-time). Student-undergrad faculty ratio is 13:1. 488 applied, 99% were admitted. Full-time: 399 students, 61% women, 39% men. Part-time: 1,309 students, 62% women, 38% men. Students come from 8 states and territories, 3% from out-of-state. 0.3% American Indian or Alaska Native, non-Hispanic/Latino; 2% Hispanic/Latino; 0.9% Black or African American, non-Hispanic/Latino; 2% Asian, non-Hispanic/Latino; 0.3% international. 31% 25 or older, 14% transferred in. Retention: 64% of full-time freshmen returned the following year. Calendar: semesters. Academic remediation for entering students, services for LD students, advanced placement, distance learning, summer session for credit, part-time degree program, adult/continuing education programs, co-op programs and internships. Off campus study.

Entrance Requirements: Open admission. Options: electronic application, deferred admission. Required: high school transcript. Recommended: interview, SAT or ACT. Entrance: noncompetitive. Application deadline: rolling. Notification: continuous. Transfer credits accepted: Yes.

Costs Per Year: Application fee: $20. State resident tuition: $2760 full-time, $92 per credit part-time. Nonresident tuition: $5520 full-time, $184 per credit part-time. Mandatory fees: $810 full-time. Full-time tuition and fees vary according to course level, course load, and reciprocity agreements. Part-time tuition varies according to course level, course load, and reciprocity agreements.

Collegiate Environment: Orientation program. Most popular organizations: Student Senate, Phi Theta Kappa, Criminal Justice Club. Major annual events: Spring Fling, Welcome Back Cookout, End of the Year Celebration. Student services: personal-psychological counseling. Campus security: full-time College Safety and Security Manager. Library and Learning Resource Center plus 1 other. Books: 12,399 (physical); Serial titles: 1,625 (physical); Databases: 28. Weekly public service hours: 57; students can reserve study rooms. 35 computers available on campus for general student use. A campuswide network can be accessed. Students can access the following: online class registration. Staffed computer lab on campus provides training in use of computers, software, and the Internet.

■ ALLEGANY COLLEGE OF MARYLAND

12401 Willowbrook Rd., SE
Cumberland, MD 21502-2596
Tel: (301)784-5000
Fax: (301)784-5024
E-mail: cnolan@allegany.edu
Web Site: www.allegany.edu

Description: State and locally supported, 2-year, coed. Part of Maryland State Community Colleges System. Awards certificates, transfer associate, and terminal associate degrees. Founded 1961. Setting: 311-acre small town campus. Total enrollment: 4,913. Faculty: 232 (114 full-time, 118 part-time). Student-undergrad faculty ratio is 16:1. 7% live on campus. Calendar: semesters. Academic remediation for entering students, ESL program, advanced placement, honors program, independent study, distance learning, double major, summer session for credit, part-time degree program, adult/continuing education programs, internships. ROTC: Army (c).

Entrance Requirements: Open admission except for allied health programs. Options: electronic application, early admission. Required: high school transcript. Required for some: ACT. Entrance: noncompetitive. Application deadline: rolling.

Collegiate Environment: Orientation program. Choral group. Social organizations: 24 open to all. Most popular organizations: SAHDA, Honors Club, EMT Club, Forestry Club. Major annual events: All College Awards Banquet, Welcome Back Picnic, Spring Fling Tension Breaker. Student services: personal-psychological counseling, women's center. Campus security: 24-hour emergency response devices and patrols, late night transport-escort service. Allegany College of Maryland Library. 700 computers available on campus for general student use. A campuswide network can be accessed from off-campus. Students can access the following: online class registration. Staffed computer lab on campus.

■ ANNE ARUNDEL COMMUNITY COLLEGE

101 College Pky.
Arnold, MD 21012-1895
Tel: (410)647-7100
Fax: (410)541-2245
E-mail: 4info@aacc.edu
Web Site: www.aacc.edu

Description: State and locally supported, 2-year, coed. Awards certificates, transfer associate, and terminal associate degrees. Founded 1961. Setting: 230-acre suburban campus with easy access to Baltimore and Washington, DC. Total enrollment: 13,354. Faculty: 1,226 (252 full-time, 974 part-time). Student-undergrad faculty ratio is 12:1. 2,660 applied, 100% were admitted. Full-time: 3,815 students, 51% women, 49% men. Part-time: 9,539 students, 62% women, 38% men. Students come from 28 states and territories, 87 other countries, 1% from out-of-state. 4% American Indian or Alaska Native, non-Hispanic/Latino; 8% Hispanic/Latino; 58% Black or African American, non-Hispanic/Latino; 0.3% Asian, non-Hispanic/Latino; 0.2% Native Hawaiian or other Pacific Islander, non-Hispanic/Latino; 2% international. 35% 25 or older, 29% transferred in. Retention: 63% of full-time freshmen returned the following year. Core. Calendar: semesters. Academic remediation for entering students, ESL program, services for LD students, advanced placement, honors program, independent study, distance learning, summer session for credit, part-time degree program, co-op programs and internships. ROTC: Army (c), Air Force (c).

Entrance Requirements: Open admission. Options: electronic application, early admission, international baccalaureate accepted. Required: high school transcript. Required for some: minimum X high school GPA, recommendations. Entrance: noncompetitive. Application deadline: rolling. Notification: continuous. Preference given to health professions programs. Transfer credits accepted: Yes.

Costs Per Year: Application fee: $0. Area resident tuition: $3360 full-time, $112 per credit hour part-time. State resident tuition: $6570 full-time, $219 per credit hour part-time. Nonresident tuition: $11,430 full-time, $381 per credit hour part-time. Mandatory fees: $800 full-time, $25 per credit hour part-time, $25 per term part-time. Full-time tuition and fees vary according to program. Part-time tuition and fees vary according to program.

Collegiate Environment: Orientation program. Drama-theater group, choral group, student-run newspaper. Social organizations: 45 open to all. Most popular organizations: Adventure Society, Entrepreneurs Club, Christian Coalition Organization, Gay/Straight Alliance, History Club. Major annual events: Food Truck Festival, Wingsfest, Breakfast with Santa. Student services: health clinic, personal-psychological counseling. Campus security: 24-hour emergency response devices and patrols, student patrols, late night transport-escort service. Andrew G. Truxal Library plus 1 other. Books: 152,186 (physical), 114,000 (digital/electronic); Serial titles: 135 (physical), 15,000 (digital/electronic); Databases: 60. Weekly public service hours: 77.

■ BAIS HAMEDRASH AND MESIVTA OF BALTIMORE

6823 Old Pimlico Rd.
Baltimore, MD 21209
Tel: (410)486-0006
Web Site: www.bhmb.edu

Description: Independent Jewish, 4-year, coed. Awards bachelor's degrees.

■ BALTIMORE CITY COMMUNITY COLLEGE

2901 Liberty Heights Ave.
Baltimore, MD 21215-7893
Tel: (410)462-8300
Fax: (410)462-7677
Web Site: www.bccc.edu

Description: State-supported, 2-year, coed. Awards certificates, transfer associate, and terminal associate degrees. Founded 1947. Setting: 19-acre urban campus. Total enrollment: 6,953. Student-undergrad faculty ratio is 18:1. 1% from out-of-state. 56% 25 or older. Core. Calendar: semesters. Academic remediation for entering students, ESL program, services for LD students, advanced placement, honors program, distance learning, double major, summer session for credit, part-time degree program, adult/continuing education programs, co-op programs and internships. Study abroad program.

Entrance Requirements: Open admission except for allied health programs. Options: early admission, deferred admission. Required: high school transcript, ACCUPLACER. Recommended: interview. Entrance: noncompetitive. Application deadline: 8/9. Notification: continuous.

Collegiate Environment: Orientation program. Choral group, student-run newspaper, radio station. Student services: health clinic, personal-psychological counseling. Bard Library.

Community Environment: See University of Baltimore.

■ BOWIE STATE UNIVERSITY

14000 Jericho Park Rd.
Bowie, MD 20715-9465

Tel: (301)860-4000; Free: 877-772-6943
Fax: (301)860-3510
E-mail: sholt@bowiestate.edu
Web Site: www.bowiestate.edu

Description: State-supported, comprehensive, coed. Part of University System of Maryland. Awards bachelor's, master's, and doctoral degrees. Founded 1865. Setting: 295-acre small town campus with easy access to Baltimore and Washington, DC. Total enrollment: 5,669. Faculty: 414 (216 full-time, 198 part-time). Student-undergrad faculty ratio is 16:1. 6,720 applied, 41% were admitted. 3% from top 10% of their high school class. Full-time: 3,939 students, 61% women, 39% men. Part-time: 772 students, 65% women, 35% men. Students come from 31 states and territories, 9% from out-of-state. 0.1% American Indian or Alaska Native, non-Hispanic/Latino; 3% Hispanic/Latino; 86% Black or African American, non-Hispanic/Latino; 1% Asian, non-Hispanic/Latino; 0.1% Native Hawaiian or other Pacific Islander, non-Hispanic/Latino; 1% international. 32% 25 or older, 35% live on campus. Retention: 70% of full-time freshmen returned the following year. Core. Calendar: semesters. Academic remediation for entering students, services for LD students, advanced placement, honors program, independent study, distance learning, double major, summer session for credit, part-time degree program, external degree program, adult/continuing education programs, co-op programs and internships, graduate courses open to undergrads. Off campus study at other units of the University System of Maryland. Study abroad program. ROTC: Army.

Entrance Requirements: Options: electronic application, international baccalaureate accepted. Required: high school transcript, minimum 2.5 high school GPA, SAT or ACT. Entrance: minimally difficult. Application deadline: 4/1. Notification: continuous. Preference given to state residents. Transfer credits accepted: Yes.

Costs Per Year: Application fee: $40. State resident tuition: $5536 full-time, $243.50 per credit hour part-time. Nonresident tuition: $16,176 full-time, $680 per credit hour part-time. Mandatory fees: $2698 full-time, $121.56 per credit hour part-time. College room and board: $10,904. Room and board charges vary according to board plan and housing facility.

Collegiate Environment: Orientation program. Drama-theater group, choral group, marching band, student-run newspaper, radio station. Social organizations: 52 open to all; national fraternities, national sororities; 6% of eligible men and 10% of eligible women are members. Most popular organization: Honda Campus All-Star Challenge. Major annual events: Fall Convocation, Homecoming Events, Honors Convocation. Student services: health clinic, personal-psychological counseling. Campus security: 24-hour emergency response devices and patrols, student patrols, late night transport-escort service, controlled dormitory access. Thurgood Marshall Library. Students can reserve study rooms. 3,950 computers available on campus for general student use. A campuswide network can be accessed from student residence rooms and from off campus. Students can access the following: online class registration. Staffed computer lab on campus (open 24 hours a day).

Community Environment: A suburban community with good transportation facilities. Baltimore-Washington Airport at Baltimore is 14 miles. Student employment is available in many commercial establishments and private homes. Bowie is near beaches and many recreation centers.

■ CAPITOL TECHNOLOGY UNIVERSITY

11301 Springfield Rd.
Laurel, MD 20708-9759
Tel: (301)369-2800; Free: 800-950-1992
Web Site: www.captechu.edu

Description: Independent, comprehensive, coed. Awards associate, bachelor's, master's, and doctoral degrees. Founded 1964. Setting: 52-acre suburban campus with easy access to Baltimore and Washington, DC. Total enrollment: 699. Student-undergrad faculty ratio is 12:1. 384 applied. Students come from 11 states and territories. 41% 25 or older. Core. Calendar: semesters. Academic remediation for entering students, ESL program, advanced placement, accelerated degree program, summer session for credit, part-time degree program, adult/continuing education programs, co-op programs. ROTC: Army (c).

Entrance Requirements: Options: electronic application, deferred admission, international baccalaureate accepted. Required: high school transcript, SAT or ACT. Recommended: minimum 2.2 high school GPA, interview. Required for some: essay, 2 recommendations, interview. Entrance: minimally difficult. Application deadline: rolling.

Costs Per Year: Application fee: $25. Tuition: $24,708 full-time, $813 per credit part-time. Mandatory fees: $832 full-time, $32 per credit part-time.

Collegiate Environment: Orientation program. Student-run newspaper. Student services: personal-psychological counseling. Campus security: night security patrols.

Community Environment: The town is in Prince George's County, a suburban area within easy reach of Washington, DC, and Baltimore, MD. Much of Washington's electronic industry is located in this area. The Capital Beltway is only four minutes from the school, providing easy access to the metropolitan area.

■ CARROLL COMMUNITY COLLEGE

1601 Washington Rd.
Westminster, MD 21157
Tel: (410)386-8000; Free: 888-221-9748
Fax: (410)876-8855
E-mail: cedwards@carrollcc.edu
Web Site: www.carrollcc.edu

Description: State and locally supported, 2-year, coed. Part of Maryland Higher Education Commission. Awards certificates, transfer associate, and terminal associate degrees. Founded 1993. Setting: 80-acre suburban campus with easy access to Baltimore. Endowment: $7.7 million. Total enrollment: 3,020. Faculty: 225 (75 full-time, 150 part-time). Student-undergrad faculty ratio is 13:1. 567 applied, 100% were admitted. Full-time: 997 students, 50% women, 50% men. Part-time: 2,023 students, 65% women, 35% men. Students come from 6 states and territories, 20 other countries, 2% from out-of-state. 0.1% American Indian or Alaska Native, non-Hispanic/Latino; 5% Hispanic/Latino; 4% Black or African American, non-Hispanic/Latino; 3% Asian, non-Hispanic/Latino; 0.1% Native Hawaiian or other Pacific Islander, non-Hispanic/Latino; 0.2% international. 24% 25 or older, 7% transferred in. Core. Calendar: semesters plus winter and summer sessions. Academic remediation for entering students, ESL program, services for LD students, advanced placement, honors program, independent study, distance learning, summer session for credit, part-time degree program, internships.

Entrance Requirements: Open admission except for selective admissions programs; registered nurse track; physical therapist assistant; Hill Scholars cohort; STEM Scholars cohort. Option: electronic application. Required: high school transcript. Entrance: noncompetitive. Application deadline: rolling. Notification: continuous. Transfer credits accepted: Yes.

Costs Per Year: Application fee: $0. Area resident tuition: $5160 full-time, $172 per credit hour part-time. State resident tuition: $7485 full-time, $249.50 per credit hour part-time. Nonresident tuition: $10,448 full-time, $348.25 per credit hour part-time.

Collegiate Environment: Orientation program. Drama-theater group. Social organizations: 22 open to all. Most popular organizations: Student Government Organization, S.T.E.M. Club, Campus Activities Board, Service Learning Club, Early Childhood Education Club. Major annual events: Crab Feast, Health Fair, Get Out-of-Town Trips to New York City. Campus security: 24-hour emergency response devices, late night security escort to vehicle in parking lot. Carroll Community College Library. Books: 39,451 (physical), 150,490 (digital/electronic); Serial titles: 152 (physical), 18,508 (digital/electronic); Databases: 42. 1,082 computers available on campus for general student use. A campuswide network can be accessed. Students can access the following: online class registration, learning management systems. Staffed computer lab on campus provides training in use of computers, software, and the Internet.

■ CECIL COLLEGE

One Seahawk Dr.
North East, MD 21901-1999
Tel: (410)287-6060
Fax: (410)287-1026
E-mail: cdryer@cecil.edu
Web Site: www.cecil.edu

Description: County-supported, primarily 2-year, coed. Awards certificates, transfer associate, and bachelor's degrees. Founded 1968. Setting: 159-acre small town campus with easy access to Baltimore. Total enrollment: 2,468. Faculty: 295 (50 full-time, 245 part-time). Student-undergrad faculty ratio is 11:1. Full-time: 867 students, 56% women, 44% men. Part-time: 1,601 students, 68% women, 32% men. Students come from 9 states and territories, 21 other countries, 16% from out-of-state. 0.3% American Indian or Alaska Native, non-Hispanic/Latino; 6% Hispanic/Latino; 10% Black or African American, non-Hispanic/Latino; 1% Asian, non-Hispanic/Latino; 0.1% Native Hawaiian or other Pacific Islander, non-Hispanic/Latino; 0.6% international. 20% 25 or older, 4% transferred in. Retention: 56% of full-time freshmen returned the following year. Core. Calendar: semesters. Academic remediation for entering students, ESL program, services for LD students, advanced placement, accelerated degree program, independent study, distance learning, double major, summer session for credit, part-time degree program, adult/continuing education programs, co-op programs and internships. Off campus study.

Entrance Requirements: Open admission except for nursing program. Options: electronic application, early admission, deferred admission. Required: high school transcript. Entrance: noncompetitive. Application deadline: rolling. Notification: continuous. Transfer credits accepted: Yes.

Costs Per Year: Area resident tuition: $3570 full-time, $119 per credit hour part-time. State resident tuition: $6780 full-time, $226 per credit hour part-time. Nonresident tuition: $8280 full-time, $276 per credit hour part-time. Mandatory fees: $735 full-time, $8 per credit hour part-time, $90 per term part-time.

Collegiate Environment: Orientation program. Drama-theater group. Social organizations: 14 open to all; national fraternities; 4% of eligible men and 4% of eligible women are members. Most popular organizations: Student Government, Non-Traditional Student Organization, Student Nurses Association. Major annual events: Welcome Back Event, Spring Fling, Chautauqua Festival. Student services: personal-psychological counseling, women's center. Campus security: 24-hour emergency response devices, late night transport-escort service, armed patrols from 6:30 am-7:00 pm. Cecil County Veterans Memorial Library. 105 computers available on campus for general student use. A campuswide network can be accessed from off-campus. Students can access the following: online class registration. Staffed computer lab on campus provides training in use of computers, software, and the Internet.

Community Environment: North East is approximately 5 miles west of Elkton, which is nestled in the valley where the Chesapeake Bay begins. It is within easy reach of the major cities on the East Coast with all forms of major commercial transportation available. Three interchanges on the John F. Kennedy Turnpike and super highways make New York or Washington, D.C., an easy two-hour drive. Elkton, rich in historical sites, has churches, health centers, and good shopping. The area offers hunting, fishing, camping, yachting, and racing and, with its beaches, parks, and marinas, is an ideal spot for vacationing.

■ **CHESAPEAKE COLLEGE**
1000 College Cir.
Wye Mills, MD 21679
Tel: (410)822-5400
Fax: (410)827-9466
E-mail: adenherder@chesapeake.edu
Web Site: www.chesapeake.edu

Description: State and locally supported, 2-year, coed. Awards certificates, transfer associate, and terminal associate degrees. Founded 1965. Setting: 170-acre rural campus with easy access to Baltimore and Washington, DC. Total enrollment: 2,189. Core. Calendar: semesters. Academic remediation for entering students, ESL program, services for LD students, advanced placement, honors program, independent study, distance learning, summer session for credit, part-time degree program, adult/continuing education programs, internships.

Entrance Requirements: Open admission except for nursing, radiological technology and physical therapy assistant programs. Options: electronic application, international baccalaureate accepted. Required: high school transcript. Entrance: noncompetitive. Application deadline: rolling. Notification: continuous. Transfer credits accepted: Yes.

Costs Per Year: Application fee: $0. Area resident tuition: $3660 full-time, $122 per credit hour part-time. State resident tuition: $5700 full-time, $190 per credit hour part-time. Nonresident tuition: $8010 full-time, $267 per credit hour part-time. Mandatory fees: $1100 full-time, $35 per credit hour part-time, $25 per term part-time. Full-time tuition and fees vary according to location. Part-time tuition and fees vary according to location.

Collegiate Environment: Orientation program. Drama-theater group. Social organizations: 12 open to all. Most popular organizations: Student Senate, Geek club, Green Team, Phi Theta Kappa, UHURU. Major annual events: Halloween Rave, Field Day, Chesapeake Choice Awards. Campus security: 24-hour emergency response devices. Learning Resource Center. Books: 44,000 (physical), 300,000 (digital/electronic); Serial titles: 38 (physical), 25,500 (digital/electronic); Databases: 56. Weekly public service hours: 56. 62 computers available on campus for general student use. A campuswide network can be accessed from off-campus. Students can access the following: online class registration. Staffed computer lab on campus provides training in use of computers, software, and the Internet.

■ **COLLEGE OF SOUTHERN MARYLAND**
8730 Mitchell Rd.
La Plata, MD 20646-0910
Tel: (301)934-2251; Free: 800-933-9177
Fax: (301)934-5255
E-mail: askme@csmd.edu
Web Site: www.csmd.edu

Description: State and locally supported, 2-year, coed. Awards certificates, transfer associate, and terminal associate degrees. Founded 1958. Setting: 175-acre rural campus with easy access to Washington, DC. Total enrollment: 8,411. Faculty: 513 (125 full-time, 388 part-time). Student-undergrad faculty ratio is 19:1. Full-time: 3,087 students, 54% women, 46% men. Part-time: 5,324 students, 65% women, 35% men. 0.5% American Indian or Alaska Native, non-Hispanic/Latino; 6% Hispanic/Latino; 26% Black or African American, non-Hispanic/Latino; 3% Asian, non-Hispanic/Latino; 0.3% Native Hawaiian or other Pacific Islander, non-Hispanic/Latino; 0.4% international. 33% 25 or older, 7% transferred in. Calendar: semesters. Academic remediation for entering students, services for LD students, advanced placement, accelerated degree program, honors program, independent study, distance learning, summer session for credit, part-time degree program, adult/continuing education programs, co-op programs. Study abroad program.

Entrance Requirements: Open admission except for nursing program. Options: electronic application, early admission, deferred admission. Recommended: high school transcript. Entrance: noncompetitive. Application deadline: rolling. Notification: continuous. Transfer credits accepted: Yes.

Collegiate Environment: Orientation program. Drama-theater group, choral group, student-run newspaper. Most popular organizations: Spanish Club, Nursing Student Association, Science Club, Black Student Union, BACCHUS. Major annual events: Spring Fling Week, Fall Picnic, Transfer Day. Student services: personal-psychological counseling. Campus security: 24-hour emergency response devices and patrols. College of Southern Maryland Library.

Community Environment: Southern Maryland is within a short distance of Washington, D.C. Community recreational activities include bowling, hunting, swimming, boating, camping, fishing, water sports, and fox hunting. Some of the special events are the annual county fair, and the Maryland Garden Tours.

■ **COMMUNITY COLLEGE OF BALTIMORE COUNTY**
7201 Rossville Blvd.
Baltimore, MD 21237-3899
Tel: (443)840-2222
E-mail: ddrake@ccbcmd.edu
Web Site: www.ccbcmd.edu

Description: County-supported, 2-year, coed. Awards certificates, transfer associate, and terminal associate degrees. Founded 1957. Setting: 350-acre suburban campus with easy access to Baltimore. Total enrollment: 18,830. Faculty: 1,132 (422 full-time, 710 part-time). Full-time: 5,081 students, 52% women, 48% men. Part-time: 13,752 students, 66% women, 34% men. 0.3% American Indian or Alaska Native, non-Hispanic/Latino; 5% Hispanic/Latino; 39% Black or African American, non-Hispanic/Latino; 6% Asian, non-Hispanic/Latino; 0.2% Native Hawaiian or other Pacific Islander, non-Hispanic/Latino; 6% international. Calendar: semesters. Academic remediation for entering students, ESL program, services for LD students, advanced placement, honors program, independent study, distance learning, summer session for credit, part-time degree program, co-op programs and internships. Off campus study. Study abroad program.

Entrance Requirements: Open admission. Option: electronic application. Required: high school transcript. Entrance: noncompetitive. Application deadline: rolling.

Costs Per Year: Area resident tuition: $3660 full-time, $122 per credit hour part-time. State resident tuition: $6930 full-time, $231 per credit hour part-time. Nonresident tuition: $10,500 full-time, $350 per credit hour part-time. Mandatory fees: $1236 full-time. Full-time tuition and fees vary according to course load. Part-time tuition varies according to course load.

Collegiate Environment: Orientation program. Drama-theater group, choral group, student-run newspaper. Campus security: 24-hour emergency response devices and patrols, late night transport-escort service. College housing not available.

■ **COPPIN STATE UNIVERSITY**
2500 W N Ave.
Baltimore, MD 21216-3698

Tel: (410)951-3000; Free: 800-635-3674
Fax: (410)523-7238
E-mail: mgross@coppin.edu
Web Site: www.coppin.edu
Description: State-supported, comprehensive, coed. Part of University System of Maryland. Awards bachelor's and master's degrees. Founded 1900. Setting: 33-acre urban campus. Total enrollment: 3,800. Faculty: 312 (157 full-time, 155 part-time). Student-undergrad faculty ratio is 15:1. 3,767 applied, 54% were admitted. Full-time: 2,599 students, 75% women, 25% men. Part-time: 699 students, 80% women, 20% men. Students come from 25 states and territories, 7% from out-of-state. 41% 25 or older, 8% transferred in. Retention: 61% of full-time freshmen returned the following year. Core. Calendar: semesters. Academic remediation for entering students, ESL program, services for LD students, advanced placement, freshman honors college, honors program, double major, summer session for credit, part-time degree program, external degree program, adult/continuing education programs, co-op programs and internships, graduate courses open to undergrads. Off campus study at 6 members of the Cooperative Education Program. ROTC: Army.
Entrance Requirements: Options: electronic application, early admission, deferred admission. Required: high school transcript, SAT or ACT. Recommended: minimum 2.5 high school GPA, interview. Required for some: 2 recommendations. Entrance: moderately difficult. Application deadline: 7/15. Notification: continuous.
Costs Per Year: Application fee: $35. State resident tuition: $4557 full-time, $194 per credit hour part-time. Nonresident tuition: $10,828 full-time, $603 per credit hour part-time. Mandatory fees: $2068 full-time. Full-time tuition and fees vary according to course load. Part-time tuition varies according to course load. College room and board: $10,396. College room only: $5985. Room and board charges vary according to board plan.
Collegiate Environment: Orientation program. Drama-theater group, choral group, student-run newspaper. Social organizations: national fraternities, national sororities, local fraternities, local sororities. Student services: health clinic, personal-psychological counseling. Campus security: 24-hour emergency response devices and patrols, late night transport-escort service, controlled dormitory access. Parlett L. Moore Library.
Community Environment: See University of Baltimore.

■ **FAITH THEOLOGICAL SEMINARY**
529 Walker Ave.
Baltimore, MD 21212
Tel: (410)323-6211
Fax: (410)323-6331
Web Site: www.fts.edu
Description: Independent, comprehensive, coed, affiliated with Christian non-denominational. Awards bachelor's, master's, and doctoral degrees. Setting: urban campus. Academic area with the most degrees conferred: theology and religious vocations.
Entrance Requirements: Required: essay, high school transcript, 2 recommendations, photos. Recommended: interview. Required for some: interview.
Collegiate Environment: John Norris Library.

■ **FORTIS COLLEGE**
4351 Garden City Dr.
Landover, MD 20785
Tel: (301)459-3650; Free: 855-4-FORTIS
Web Site: www.fortis.edu
Description: Proprietary, 2-year, coed. Awards certificates, diplomas, transfer associate, and terminal associate degrees.

■ **FREDERICK COMMUNITY COLLEGE**
7932 Opossumtown Pke.
Frederick, MD 21702-2097
Tel: (301)846-2400
E-mail: admissions@frederick.edu
Web Site: www.frederick.edu
Description: State and locally supported, 2-year, coed. Awards certificates, transfer associate, and terminal associate degrees. Founded 1957. Setting: 100-acre small town campus with easy access to Baltimore and Washington, DC. System endowment: $13.8 million. Educational spending for the previous fiscal year: $8195 per student. Total enrollment: 6,220. Faculty: 409 (102 full-time, 307 part-time). Student-undergrad faculty ratio is 15:1. Full-time: 2,027 students, 50% women, 50% men. Part-time: 4,193 students, 59%

women, 41% men. 0.2% American Indian or Alaska Native, non-Hispanic/Latino; 13% Hispanic/Latino; 15% Black or African American, non-Hispanic/Latino; 4% Asian, non-Hispanic/Latino; 0.1% Native Hawaiian or other Pacific Islander, non-Hispanic/Latino; 1% international. 25% 25 or older, 3% transferred in. Retention: 46% of full-time freshmen returned the following year. Academic areas with the most degrees conferred: liberal arts/general studies; business/marketing; health professions and related sciences. Core. Calendar: semesters. Academic remediation for entering students, ESL program, services for LD students, advanced placement, freshman honors college, honors program, independent study, distance learning, summer session for credit, part-time degree program, external degree program, adult/continuing education programs, co-op programs and internships. Off campus study at Hood College, Mount Saint Mary's College. Study abroad program.
Entrance Requirements: Open admission except for allied health program clinical portions. Option: electronic application. Recommended: high school transcript. Entrance: noncompetitive. Application deadline: rolling. Notification: continuous. Transfer credits accepted: Yes.
Costs Per Year: Application fee: $0. Area resident tuition: $4,457 full-time, $122 per credit hour part-time. State resident tuition: $8,777 full-time, $266 per credit hour part-time. Nonresident tuition: $11,627 full-time, $361 per credit hour part-time. Mandatory fees: $797 full-time, $27.64 per credit hour part-time. Full-time tuition and fees vary according to course load. Part-time tuition and fees vary according to course load.
Collegiate Environment: Orientation program. Drama-theater group, student-run newspaper. Social organizations: 30 open to all. Major annual events: Spring Fling, Welcome Back Lunch/Activities, Free Food Events. Student services: personal-psychological counseling, women's center. Campus security: 24-hour emergency response devices and patrols, late night transport-escort service. FCC Library. Books: 11,831 (physical), 52,846 (digital/electronic); Serial titles: 19 (physical); Databases: 25. Students can reserve study rooms. Operations spending for the previous fiscal year: $338,464. 816 computers available on campus for general student use. A campuswide network can be accessed from off-campus. Students can access the following: online class registration. Staffed computer lab on campus provides training in use of computers, software, and the Internet.
Community Environment: See Hood College.

■ **FROSTBURG STATE UNIVERSITY**
101 Braddock Rd.
Frostburg, MD 21532-1099
Tel: (301)687-4000
Fax: (301)687-7074
Web Site: www.frostburg.edu
Description: State-supported, comprehensive, coed. Part of University System of Maryland. Awards bachelor's, master's, and doctoral degrees. Founded 1898. Setting: 260-acre small town campus with easy access to Baltimore and Washington, DC. Endowment: $25.1 million. Educational spending for the previous fiscal year: $7284 per student. Total enrollment: 5,396. Faculty: 390 (249 full-time, 141 part-time). Student-undergrad faculty ratio is 15:1. 3,436 applied, 72% were admitted. 10% from top 10% of their high school class, 39% from top quarter, 65% from top half. Full-time: 3,849 students, 47% women, 53% men. Part-time: 876 students, 73% women, 27% men. Students come from 31 states and territories, 41 other countries, 7% from out-of-state. 0.1% American Indian or Alaska Native, non-Hispanic/Latino; 6% Hispanic/Latino; 31% Black or African American, non-Hispanic/Latino; 2% Asian, non-Hispanic/Latino; 4% international. 15% 25 or older, 28% live on campus, 10% transferred in. Retention: 74% of full-time freshmen returned the following year. Academic areas with the most degrees conferred: health professions and related sciences; business/marketing; liberal arts/general studies. Core. Calendar: semesters. Services for LD students, advanced placement, freshman honors college, honors program, independent study, distance learning, double major, summer session for credit, part-time degree program, adult/continuing education programs, co-op programs and internships, graduate courses open to undergrads. Off campus study at Cooperative Education Program, Frostburg Programs at USM Hagerstown. Study abroad program.
Entrance Requirements: Options: electronic application, early admission. Required: high school transcript, minimum 2 high school GPA, SAT or ACT. Recommended: interview. Required for some: essay. Entrance: moderately difficult. Application deadlines: 2/15, 2/30 for nonresidents. Transfer credits accepted: Yes.
Costs Per Year: Application fee: $30. State resident tuition: $6600 full-time, $272 per credit hour part-time. Nonresident tuition: $20,320 full-time, $570 per credit hour part-time. Mandatory fees: $2572 full-time, $121 per credit

hour part-time, $27 per term part-time. Full-time tuition and fees vary according to location. Part-time tuition and fees vary according to course load and location. College room and board: $9398. College room only: $4882. Room and board charges vary according to board plan and housing facility.

Collegiate Environment: Drama-theater group, choral group, marching band, student-run newspaper, radio station. Social organizations: 80 open to all; national fraternities, national sororities; 10% of eligible men and 10% of eligible women are members. Most popular organizations: Student Government Association, Black Student Association, Campus Activities Board, Residence Hall Association, University Programming Council. Major annual events: Homecoming, Parents' Weekend, Greek Week. Student services: health clinic, personal-psychological counseling, women's center. Campus security: 24-hour emergency response devices and patrols, student patrols, late night transport-escort service, controlled dormitory access, bicycle patrols. Lewis J. Ort Library. Operations spending for the previous fiscal year: $842,483. 577 computers available on campus for general student use. Computer purchase/lease plans available. A campuswide network can be accessed from student residence rooms and from off campus. Students can access the following: online class registration. Staffed computer lab on campus (open 24 hours a day) provides training in use of computers, software, and the Internet.

Community Environment: The state university, in the City of Frostburg (population 7,958) is located in the mountains of western Maryland at an elevation of 2,200 feet. There are nearby state parks and winter sports activities including ice skating, skiing, and sleighing.

■ **GARRETT COLLEGE**
687 Mosser Rd.
McHenry, MD 21541
Tel: (301)387-3000; Free: 866-55-GARRETT
Fax: (301)387-3055
E-mail: admissions@garrettcollege.edu
Web Site: www.garrettcollege.edu

Description: State and locally supported, 2-year, coed. Awards certificates, transfer associate, and terminal associate degrees. Founded 1966. Setting: 62-acre rural campus. Educational spending for the previous fiscal year: $7919 per student. Total enrollment: 754. Faculty: 55 (20 full-time, 35 part-time). Student-undergrad faculty ratio is 19:1. 1,159 applied, 71% were admitted. 8% from top 10% of their high school class, 21% from top quarter, 48% from top half. Full-time: 523 students, 47% women, 53% men. Part-time: 231 students, 60% women, 40% men. Students come from 12 states and territories, 6 other countries, 19% from out-of-state. 0.3% American Indian or Alaska Native, non-Hispanic/Latino; 1% Hispanic/Latino; 25% Black or African American, non-Hispanic/Latino; 1% international. 13% 25 or older, 24% live on campus, 4% transferred in. Core. Calendar: semesters. Academic remediation for entering students, services for LD students, advanced placement, honors program, independent study, distance learning, double major, summer session for credit, part-time degree program, external degree program, adult/continuing education programs, co-op programs and internships.

Entrance Requirements: Open admission. Options: electronic application, early admission, deferred admission. Required: high school transcript. Entrance: noncompetitive. Application deadline: rolling. Notification: continuous. Transfer credits accepted: Yes.

Costs Per Year: Application fee: $0. Area resident tuition: $2996 full-time, $107 per credit hour part-time. State resident tuition: $6720 full-time, $240 per credit hour part-time. Nonresident tuition: $8120 full-time, $290 per credit hour part-time. Mandatory fees: $1092 full-time, $39 per credit hour part-time, $25 per term part-time. Full-time tuition and fees vary according to program and reciprocity agreements. Part-time tuition and fees vary according to program and reciprocity agreements. College room and board: $8275. College room only: $5775. Room and board charges vary according to board plan and housing facility.

Collegiate Environment: Orientation program. Social organizations: 2 open to all. Most popular organizations: SGA, International Students Club, CRU, SING (Students in Need Group), Rock Climbing Wall (open sessions). Major annual events: Orientation, Spring Fling, Spirit Week. Student services: health clinic, personal-psychological counseling. Campus security: 24-hour emergency response devices and patrols, controlled dormitory access. Learning Resource Center. Books: 31,225 (physical), 35,243 (digital/electronic); Serial titles: 119 (physical); Databases: 21. Weekly public service hours: 64. Operations spending for the previous fiscal year: $257,447. 48 computers available on campus for general student use. A campuswide network can be accessed from off-campus. Staffed computer lab on campus.

Community Environment: Garrett County is a rural area of approximately 30,000 year-round inhabitants, most of whom are employed in small business, education, agriculture and tourism. It is also a four-season resort area with seasonal swells in population. The natural resources of the region are conducive to the college's three signature programs: Adventure sports, Agricultural Management, and Natural Resources and Wildlife Technology.

■ **GOUCHER COLLEGE**
1021 Dulaney Valley Rd.
Baltimore, MD 21204-2794
Tel: (410)337-6000; Free: 800-468-2437
Fax: (410)337-6236
E-mail: admissions@goucher.edu
Web Site: www.goucher.edu

Description: Independent, comprehensive, coed. Awards bachelor's and master's degrees. Founded 1885. Setting: 287-acre suburban campus with easy access to Baltimore and Washington, DC. Endowment: $201.5 million. Research spending for the previous fiscal year: $191,000. Educational spending for the previous fiscal year: $16,537 per student. Total enrollment: 2,172. Faculty: 175 (129 full-time, 46 part-time). Student-undergrad faculty ratio is 10:1. 3,443 applied, 79% were admitted. 13% from top 10% of their high school class, 47% from top quarter, 76% from top half. 31 student government officers. Full-time: 1,444 students, 68% women, 32% men. Part-time: 29 students, 52% women, 48% men. Students come from 48 states and territories, 26 other countries, 72% from out-of-state. 6% Hispanic/Latino; 13% Black or African American, non-Hispanic/Latino; 4% Asian, non-Hispanic/Latino; 0.3% Native Hawaiian or other Pacific Islander, non-Hispanic/Latino; 3% international. 2% 25 or older, 84% live on campus, 2% transferred in. Retention: 79% of full-time freshmen returned the following year. Academic areas with the most degrees conferred: social sciences; psychology; visual and performing arts. Core. Calendar: semesters. Services for LD students, advanced placement, accelerated degree program, self-designed majors, independent study, distance learning, double major, summer session for credit, part-time degree program, adult/continuing education programs, internships, graduate courses open to undergrads. Off campus study at Johns Hopkins University; Morgan State University; Maryland Institute College of Art; Loyola University, MD; Towson University; Notre Dame of Maryland University; Coppin State; Stevenson University; Community College of Baltimore County; University of Baltimore; University of Maryland, Baltimore. Study abroad program. ROTC: Army (c), Air Force (c).

Entrance Requirements: Options: electronic application, early admission, early decision, early action, deferred admission, international baccalaureate accepted. Required: essay, a short video, digital application, signed statement of academic integrity, two works from high school career (one of which must be a graded writing assignment) for Goucher Video Application. Recommended: 3 recommendations, interview. Required for some: high school transcript. Entrance: moderately difficult. Application deadlines: 2/1, 11/15 for early decision, 12/1 for early action. Notification: 4/1, 12/15 for early decision, 2/1 for early action. SAT Reasoning Test deadline: 2/1. Transfer credits accepted: Yes. Applicants placed on waiting list: 102. Wait-listed applicants offered admission: 20. Early decision applicants: 33. Early decision applicants admitted: 22. Early action applicants: 1,682. Early action applicants admitted: 1,432.

Costs Per Year: Application fee: $55. Comprehensive fee: $58,758 includes full-time tuition ($43,412), mandatory fees ($840), and college room and board ($14,506). Room and board charges vary according to board plan and housing facility.

Collegiate Environment: Orientation program. Drama-theater group, choral group, student-run newspaper, radio station. Social organizations: 65 open to all. Most popular organizations: Ultimate Frisbee, Yoga Club, Hip Hop Team, Umoja: The Black Student Union, Model Senate. Major annual events: Opening Celebration, GIG (Get Into Goucher Day), Gala. Student services: health clinic, personal-psychological counseling. Campus security: 24-hour emergency response devices and patrols, late night transport-escort service, controlled dormitory access, E2 campus alerts. Goucher College Library plus 1 other. Books: 250,000 (physical), 300,000 (digital/electronic); Serial titles: 96,000 (digital/electronic); Databases: 120. Weekly public service hours: 168; study areas open 24 hours, 5-7 days a week. Operations spending for the previous fiscal year: $2.5 million. 130 computers available on campus for general student use. Computer purchase/lease plans available. A computer is required for all students. A campuswide network can be accessed from student residence rooms and from off campus. Students can access the following: online class registration, transcripts, financial aid information, billing, ePortfolios, academic progress reports, study abroad plans. Staffed computer lab on campus (open 24 hours a day) provides training in use of computers, software, and the Internet.

Community Environment: Goucher is located on 287 wooded acres in suburban Towson, seat of Baltimore County. The college is 20 minutes away from downtown Baltimore, an hour's drive from Washington, D.C., and 25 miles from the state capital of Annapolis, on the Chesapeake Bay. There are extensive walking, riding, and running trails that help create a small college atmosphere.

■ **HAGERSTOWN COMMUNITY COLLEGE**
11400 Robinwood Dr.
Hagerstown, MD 21742
Tel: (240)500-2000
Fax: (301)739-0737
Web Site: www.hagerstowncc.edu

Description: State and locally supported, 2-year, coed. Awards certificates, transfer associate, and terminal associate degrees. Founded 1946. Setting: 319-acre suburban campus with easy access to Baltimore and Washington, DC. Total enrollment: 4,069. Faculty: 221 (78 full-time, 143 part-time). Student-undergrad faculty ratio is 17:1. Full-time: 999 students, 50% women, 50% men. Part-time: 3,070 students, 67% women, 33% men. 0.3% American Indian or Alaska Native, non-Hispanic/Latino; 6% Hispanic/Latino; 10% Black or African American, non-Hispanic/Latino; 2% Asian, non-Hispanic/Latino; 0.1% Native Hawaiian or other Pacific Islander, non-Hispanic/Latino; 1% international. 30% 25 or older, 8% transferred in. Core. Calendar: semesters. Academic remediation for entering students, ESL program, services for LD students, advanced placement, accelerated degree program, honors program, independent study, distance learning, summer session for credit, part-time degree program, adult/continuing education programs, co-op programs and internships. Off campus study.

Entrance Requirements: Open admission except for nursing (RN), radiography, paramedic emergency services (EMT), practical nursing (LPN), and dental hygiene programs. Options: electronic application, deferred admission. Required for some: high school transcript. Entrance: noncompetitive. Application deadline: rolling. Notification: continuous. Transfer credits accepted: Yes.

Costs Per Year: Application fee: $0. Area resident tuition: $3146 full-time, $121 per credit hour part-time. State resident tuition: $4940 full-time, $190 per credit hour part-time. Nonresident tuition: $6500 full-time, $250 per credit hour part-time. Mandatory fees: $398 full-time, $13 per credit hour part-time, $30 per term part-time. Full-time tuition and fees vary according to course load, program, and reciprocity agreements. Part-time tuition and fees vary according to course load, program, and reciprocity agreements.

Collegiate Environment: Orientation program. Drama-theater group, choral group, student-run newspaper. Social organizations: 34 open to all; Phi Theta Kappa. Most popular organizations: Phi Theta Kappa, Robinwood Players Theater Club, Association of Nursing Students, Radiography Club, Art and Design Club. Student services: personal-psychological counseling. Campus security: 24-hour patrols, student patrols. William Brish Library. 650 computers available on campus for general student use. Computer purchase/lease plans available. A campuswide network can be accessed. Students can access the following: online class registration. Staffed computer lab on campus.

Community Environment: In the heart of Cumberland Valley, Hagerstown is manufacturing city nestled at an intersection of highway interstates and rail transportation. All forms of commercial transportation are available. Recreational facilities are numerous. Points of interest are Antietam Battlefield, Old Ft. Frederick State Park, Hager House, and Washington County Museum of Fine Arts. Special events include the annual Halloween Mummer's Parade.

■ **HARFORD COMMUNITY COLLEGE**
401 Thomas Run Rd.
Bel Air, MD 21015-1698
Tel: (443)412-2000
Web Site: www.harford.edu

Description: State and locally supported, 2-year, coed. Awards certificates, diplomas, transfer associate, and terminal associate degrees. Founded 1957. Setting: 352-acre small town campus with easy access to Baltimore. Total enrollment: 6,100. Faculty: 319 (99 full-time, 220 part-time). Student-undergrad faculty ratio is 21:1. 1,191 applied, 100% were admitted. Students come from 23 states and territories, 51 other countries, 4% from out-of-state. 0.3% American Indian or Alaska Native, non-Hispanic/Latino; 5% Hispanic/Latino; 16% Black or African American, non-Hispanic/Latino; 2% Asian, non-

Hispanic/Latino; 0.2% Native Hawaiian or other Pacific Islander, non-Hispanic/Latino; 1% international. 28% 25 or older. Core. Calendar: semesters. Academic remediation for entering students, ESL program, services for LD students, advanced placement, self-designed majors, honors program, independent study, distance learning, double major, summer session for credit, part-time degree program, adult/continuing education programs, co-op programs and internships. Study abroad program.

Entrance Requirements: Open admission except for nursing program. Options: electronic application, international baccalaureate accepted. Entrance: noncompetitive. Application deadline: rolling. Notification: continuous. Transfer credits accepted: Yes.

Costs Per Year: Application fee: $0. Area resident tuition: $3870 full-time, $129 per credit hour part-time. State resident tuition: $6,586 full-time, $219.52 per credit hour part-time. Nonresident tuition: $9,301 full-time, $310.04 per credit hour part-time. Mandatory fees: $774 full-time, $25.80 per credit hour part-time.

Collegiate Environment: Orientation program. Drama-theater group, choral group, student-run newspaper, radio station. Social organizations: 33 open to all. Most popular organizations: Phi Theta Kappa, Student Nurses Association, Gamers Guild, Actor's Guild, Future Educators of America. Major annual events: OwlFest, Club Row, Thanksgiving Dinner. Student services: personal-psychological counseling. Campus security: 24-hour patrols, late night transport-escort service. Harford Community College Library. Books: 43,126 (physical), 324,718 (digital/electronic); Serial titles: 828 (physical), 75 (digital/electronic); Databases: 79. 267 computers available on campus for general student use. A campuswide network can be accessed. Students can access the following: online class registration. Staffed computer lab on campus provides training in use of computers, software, and the Internet.

■ **HOOD COLLEGE**
401 Rosemont Ave.
Frederick, MD 21701-8575
Tel: (301)663-3131; Free: 800-922-1599
E-mail: admission@hood.edu
Web Site: www.hood.edu

Description: Independent, comprehensive, coed. Awards bachelor's, master's, and doctoral degrees (also offers adult program with significant enrollment not reflected in profile). Founded 1893. Setting: 50-acre suburban campus with easy access to Baltimore and Washington, DC. Endowment: $99.7 million. Research spending for the previous fiscal year: $232,220. Educational spending for the previous fiscal year: $10,088 per student. Total enrollment: 2,052. Faculty: 240 (105 full-time, 135 part-time). Student-undergrad faculty ratio is 10:1. 1,562 applied, 71% were admitted. 24% from top 10% of their high school class, 44% from top quarter, 76% from top half. 3 valedictorians. Full-time: 1,014 students, 63% women, 37% men. Part-time: 78 students, 67% women, 33% men. Students come from 25 states and territories, 14 other countries, 25% from out-of-state. 0.2% American Indian or Alaska Native, non-Hispanic/Latino; 11% Hispanic/Latino; 18% Black or African American, non-Hispanic/Latino; 3% Asian, non-Hispanic/Latino; 0.1% Native Hawaiian or other Pacific Islander, non-Hispanic/Latino; 2% international. 10% 25 or older, 51% live on campus, 10% transferred in. Retention: 71% of full-time freshmen returned the following year. Academic areas with the most degrees conferred: business/marketing; education; communication/journalism. Core. Calendar: semesters. Academic remediation for entering students, services for LD students, advanced placement, self-designed majors, honors program, independent study, double major, summer session for credit, part-time degree program, internships, graduate courses open to undergrads. Off campus study at Washington Semester Program, The Washington Center, Public Leadership Education Network (PLEN), Council of International Education Exchange (CIEE). Study abroad program. ROTC: Army.

Entrance Requirements: Options: electronic application, international baccalaureate accepted. Required: essay, high school transcript, minimum 2 high school GPA. Recommended: 2 recommendations, interview. Entrance: moderately difficult. Application deadline: rolling. Notification: continuous. Transfer credits accepted: Yes.

Costs Per Year: Application fee: $0. Comprehensive fee: $53,940 includes full-time tuition ($40,460), mandatory fees ($600), and college room and board ($12,880). College room only: $6600. Part-time tuition: $1180 per credit hour.

Collegiate Environment: Orientation program. Drama-theater group, choral group, student-run newspaper, radio station. Social organizations: 60 open to all. Most popular organizations: Black Student Union (BSU), Campus Activities Board (CAB), La Comunida, Queer Student Union (QSU),

Enactus. Major annual events: Late Night Breakfast, Spring Fest and Crabfest, Homecoming and Fall Family Weekend. Student services: health clinic, personal-psychological counseling. Campus security: 24-hour emergency response devices and patrols, late night transport-escort service, controlled dormitory access. 663 college housing spaces available; 565 were occupied in 2018-19. Freshmen guaranteed college housing. On-campus residence required through junior year. Option: coed housing available. Beneficial-Hodson Library and Information Technology Center plus 1 other. Books: 113,587 (physical), 367,563 (digital/electronic); Serial titles: 1,546 (physical), 2,440 (digital/electronic); Databases: 148. Students can reserve study rooms. Operations spending for the previous fiscal year: $702,209. 470 computers available on campus for general student use. Computer purchase/lease plans available. A campuswide network can be accessed from student residence rooms and from off campus. Students can access the following: online class registration, Virtual Computer Lab (VCL), wireless printing. Staffed computer lab on campus provides training in use of computers, software, and the Internet.

Community Environment: Hood College is located on almost 50 acres near downtown Frederick, Maryland, a community of approximately 49,000. The campus is 45 miles west of Baltimore and an equal distance northwest of Washington D.C. The proximity of the Hood campus to these major metropolitan areas increases the opportunities open to students to participate in social and cultural activities, to complete internships, and to explore prominent research facilities.

■ HOWARD COMMUNITY COLLEGE

10901 Little Patuxent Pky.
Columbia, MD 21044-3197
Tel: (443)518-1200
E-mail: admissions@howardcc.edu
Web Site: www.howardcc.edu

Description: State and locally supported, 2-year, coed. Awards certificates, transfer associate, and terminal associate degrees. Founded 1966. Setting: 122-acre suburban campus with easy access to Baltimore and Washington, DC. Total enrollment: 9,726. Faculty: 801 (199 full-time, 602 part-time). Student-undergrad faculty ratio is 14:1. 2,661 applied, 100% were admitted. Students come from 13 states and territories, 110 other countries, 1% from out-of-state. 0.3% American Indian or Alaska Native, non-Hispanic/Latino; 11% Hispanic/Latino; 31% Black or African American, non-Hispanic/Latino; 13% Asian, non-Hispanic/Latino; 0.3% Native Hawaiian or other Pacific Islander, non-Hispanic/Latino. 36% 25 or older. Core. Calendar: semesters. Academic remediation for entering students, ESL program, services for LD students, advanced placement, freshman honors college, honors program, distance learning, double major, summer session for credit, part-time degree program, external degree program, adult/continuing education programs, co-op programs and internships. Off campus study. Study abroad program.

Entrance Requirements: Open admission except for nursing/allied health programs, Rouse, STEM, Schoenbrodt Scholars, Silas Craft, early entrance, dual enrollment, and STARTALK, F1 applicants. Options: electronic application, early admission, deferred admission, international baccalaureate accepted. Required for some: essay, high school transcript, minimum 3.2 high school GPA, 2 recommendations, SAT or ACT. Entrance: noncompetitive. Application deadline: rolling. Notification: continuous. Transfer credits accepted: Yes.

Costs Per Year: Application fee: $25. Area resident tuition: $4140 full-time, $138 per semester hour part-time. State resident tuition: $6780 full-time, $226 per semester hour part-time. Nonresident tuition: $8280 full-time, $276 per semester hour part-time. Mandatory fees: $779 full-time, $25.97 per semester hour part-time. Full-time tuition and fees vary according to course load. Part-time tuition and fees vary according to course load.

Collegiate Environment: Orientation program. Drama-theater group, choral group, student-run newspaper, radio station. Social organizations: 25 open to all. Most popular organizations: Phi Theta Kappa, Nursing Club, Black Leadership Organization, Student Newspaper, Student Government Association. Major annual events: Welcome Carnival, Club Rush, Transfer/Career Fairs. Student services: personal-psychological counseling. Campus security: 24-hour emergency response devices and patrols, late night transport-escort service. Howard Community College Library. Students can reserve study rooms.

Community Environment: Columbia, a planned city of 100,000, was designed as a community of village centers. Small lakes, parks, and bicycle paths add charm and access to the outdoors. Situated between two major cities, Baltimore and Washington, there is quick access to transportation facilities at airports and rail stations. The Columbia Mall provides major

shopping facilities, and each village center complements the mall with supermarkets and convenience stores. The college serves as a cultural center in the county and hosts a variety of concerts, stage productions and cultural activities in its theatre.

■ JOHNS HOPKINS UNIVERSITY

3400 N Charles St.
Baltimore, MD 21218
Tel: (410)516-8000
Fax: (410)516-6025
Web Site: www.jhu.edu

Description: Independent, university, coed. Awards bachelor's, master's, and doctoral degrees. Founded 1876. Setting: 140-acre urban campus with easy access to Baltimore and Washington, DC. System endowment: $4.9 billion. Total enrollment: 7,920. Faculty: 741 (710 full-time, 31 part-time). Student-undergrad faculty ratio is 8:1. 29,129 applied, 11% were admitted. 96% from top 10% of their high school class, 99% from top quarter, 100% from top half. Full-time: 5,325 students, 52% women, 48% men. Part-time: 49 students, 29% women, 71% men. Students come from 54 states and territories, 51 other countries, 90% from out-of-state. 0.1% American Indian or Alaska Native, non-Hispanic/Latino; 15% Hispanic/Latino; 7% Black or African American, non-Hispanic/Latino; 27% Asian, non-Hispanic/Latino; 0.2% Native Hawaiian or other Pacific Islander, non-Hispanic/Latino; 10% international. 1% 25 or older, 51% live on campus, 1% transferred in. Retention: 98% of full-time freshmen returned the following year. Academic areas with the most degrees conferred: engineering; biological/life sciences; social sciences. Core. Calendar: 4-1-4. Services for LD students, advanced placement, self-designed majors, independent study, double major, summer session for credit, internships, graduate courses open to undergrads. Off campus study at Academic Cooperative Program: University of Maryland, Baltimore County; Loyola College; Towson University; Morgan State University; College of Notre Dame of Maryland; Stevenson University; Goucher College; and Maryland Institute College of Art. Study abroad program. ROTC: Army, Air Force (c).

Entrance Requirements: Options: electronic application, early decision, deferred admission. Required: essay, high school transcript, 2 recommendations, SAT or ACT. Application deadlines: 1/1, 11/1 for early decision. Notification: 4/1, 12/15 for early decision. SAT Reasoning Test deadline: 1/1. SAT Subject Test deadline: 1/1. Transfer credits accepted: Yes. Applicants placed on waiting list: 3,555. Wait-listed applicants offered admission: 207. Early decision applicants: 2,023. Early decision applicants admitted: 610.

Costs Per Year: Application fee: $70. One-time mandatory fee: $500. Comprehensive fee: $69,576 includes full-time tuition ($53,740) and college room and board ($15,836). College room only: $9178. Room and board charges vary according to board plan and housing facility. Part-time tuition: $1791 per credit hour.

Collegiate Environment: Orientation program. Drama-theater group, choral group, student-run newspaper, radio station. Social organizations: 422 open to all; national fraternities, national sororities; 18% of eligible men and 27% of eligible women are members. Major annual events: Spring Fair, Hoptoberfest, Lighting of the Quad. Student services: health clinic, personal-psychological counseling, women's center. Campus security: 24-hour emergency response devices and patrols, student patrols, late night transport-escort service, controlled dormitory access, CCTV monitoring of public areas. 2,751 college housing spaces available; 2,724 were occupied in 2018-19. Freshmen guaranteed college housing. On-campus residence required through sophomore year. Option: coed housing available. The Sheridan Libraries plus 2 others. Books: 2.4 million (physical), 1.8 million (digital/electronic); Serial titles: 51,824 (physical), 154,044 (digital/electronic); Databases: 836. Study areas open 24 hours, 5-7 days a week; students can reserve study rooms. 200 computers available on campus for general student use. Computer purchase/lease plans available. A campuswide network can be accessed from student residence rooms and from off campus. Students can access the following: online class registration. Staffed computer lab on campus (open 24 hours a day) provides training in use of computers, software, and the Internet.

Community Environment: See University of Baltimore.

■ LINCOLN COLLEGE OF TECHNOLOGY

9325 Snowden River Pky.
Columbia, MD 21046
Tel: (410)290-7100; Free: 844-215-1513
Web Site: www.lincolntech.edu

Description: Proprietary, 2-year, coed. Awards certificates, transfer associate, and terminal associate degrees. Founded 1946.

■ LOYOLA UNIVERSITY MARYLAND

4501 N Charles St.
Baltimore, MD 21210-2699
Tel: (410)617-2000; Free: 800-221-9107
Fax: (410)323-2768
Web Site: www.loyola.edu
Description: Independent Roman Catholic (Jesuit), university, coed. Awards bachelor's, master's, and doctoral degrees and post-master's certificates. Founded 1852. Setting: 89-acre urban campus with easy access to Washington, DC. Endowment: $193.8 million. Research spending for the previous fiscal year: $197.8 million. Educational spending for the previous fiscal year: $38,052 per student. Total enrollment: 6,084. Faculty: 553 (369 full-time, 184 part-time). Student-undergrad faculty ratio is 12:1. 12,727 applied, 66% were admitted. 29% from top 10% of their high school class, 68% from top quarter, 93% from top half. Full-time: 4,050 students, 57% women, 43% men. Part-time: 54 students, 54% women, 46% men. 82% from out-of-state. 0.1% American Indian or Alaska Native, non-Hispanic/Latino; 10% Hispanic/Latino; 5% Black or African American, non-Hispanic/Latino; 4% Asian, non-Hispanic/Latino; 0.1% Native Hawaiian or other Pacific Islander, non-Hispanic/Latino; 1% international. 1% 25 or older, 83% live on campus, 1% transferred in. Retention: 87% of full-time freshmen returned the following year. Academic areas with the most degrees conferred: business/marketing; social sciences; communication/journalism. Core. Calendar: semesters. Services for LD students, advanced placement, accelerated degree program, honors program, independent study, double major, summer session for credit, part-time degree program, co-op programs and internships, graduate courses open to undergrads. Off campus study at Johns Hopkins University; College of Notre Dame of Maryland; Goucher College; Towson State University; Morgan State University; Peabody Conservatory of Music of The Johns Hopkins University; Maryland Institute, College of Art. Study abroad program. ROTC: Army, Air Force (c).
Entrance Requirements: Options: electronic application, early admission, early decision, early action, deferred admission, international baccalaureate accepted. Required: essay, high school transcript. Entrance: moderately difficult. Application deadlines: 1/15, 11/1 for early decision, 11/15 for early action. Notification: 4/1, 4/1 for nonresidents, 1/15 for early action. Transfer credits accepted: Yes. Applicants placed on waiting list: 1,673. Wait-listed applicants offered admission: 29. Early decision applicants: 122. Early decision applicants admitted: 65.
Costs Per Year: Application fee: $60. Comprehensive fee: $63,515 includes full-time tuition ($47,520), mandatory fees ($1565), and college room and board ($14,430). Full-time tuition and fees vary according to course load. Room and board charges vary according to board plan and housing facility. Part-time tuition: $765 per credit. Part-time tuition varies according to course load.
Collegiate Environment: Orientation program. Drama-theater group, choral group, student-run newspaper, radio station. Social organizations: 213 open to all. Most popular organizations: Student Government Association, Resident Affairs Council (RAC), Relay for Life, Resident Assistants (RA), The Evergreens. Major annual events: Loyolapalooza, Relay for Life. Student services: health clinic, personal-psychological counseling, women's center. Campus security: 24-hour emergency response devices and patrols, late night transport-escort service, controlled dormitory access. Loyola/Notre Dame Library plus 1 other. Operations spending for the previous fiscal year: $3.4 million. 690 computers available on campus for general student use. Computer purchase/lease plans available. A campuswide network can be accessed from student residence rooms and from off campus. Students can access the following: online class registration. Staffed computer lab on campus provides training in use of computers, software, and the Internet.

■ MAPLE SPRINGS BAPTIST BIBLE COLLEGE AND SEMINARY

4130 Belt Rd.
Capitol Heights, MD 20743
Tel: (301)736-3631
Fax: (301)735-6507
Web Site: www.msbbcs.edu
Description: Independent Baptist, comprehensive, coed. Awards associate, bachelor's, master's, and doctoral degrees. Founded 1986. Setting: 1-acre suburban campus with easy access to Washington, DC. Research spending for the previous fiscal year: $4370. Total enrollment: 99. Faculty: 23 (3 full-time, 20 part-time). 2 applied, 100% were admitted. Full-time: 3 students, 67% women, 33% men. Part-time: 71 students, 55% women, 45% men. Students come from 3 states and territories, 32% from out-of-state. 4% Hispanic/Latino; 96% Black or African American, non-Hispanic/Latino. 100%

25 or older. Retention: 75% of full-time freshmen returned the following year. Core. Calendar: semesters. Academic remediation for entering students, accelerated degree program, independent study, part-time degree program, external degree program, adult/continuing education programs, internships, graduate courses open to undergrads.
Entrance Requirements: Open admission. Option: deferred admission. Required: essay, high school transcript, 2 recommendations, interview. Entrance: minimally difficult. Application deadline: rolling. Notification: continuous. Transfer credits accepted: Yes.
Collegiate Environment: Orientation program. Student-run newspaper. Campus security: 24-hour emergency response devices, part-time security personnel. Maple Springs Baptist Bible College and Seminary Library plus 1 other. Operations spending for the previous fiscal year: $45,900.

■ MARYLAND INSTITUTE COLLEGE OF ART

1300 Mount Royal Ave.
Baltimore, MD 21217
Tel: (410)669-9200
Fax: (410)225-2337
E-mail: admissions@mica.edu
Web Site: www.mica.edu
Description: Independent, comprehensive, coed. Awards bachelor's and master's degrees. Founded 1826. Setting: 16-acre urban campus with easy access to Washington, DC. Endowment: $90.8 million. Total enrollment: 2,110. Faculty: 352 (157 full-time, 195 part-time). Student-undergrad faculty ratio is 8:1. 3,702 applied, 64% were admitted. Full-time: 1,689 students, 75% women, 25% men. Part-time: 25 students, 64% women, 36% men. Students come from 44 states and territories, 42 other countries, 74% from out-of-state. 3% Hispanic/Latino; 8% Black or African American, non-Hispanic/Latino; 11% Asian, non-Hispanic/Latino; 0.1% Native Hawaiian or other Pacific Islander, non-Hispanic/Latino; 27% international. 5% 25 or older, 88% live on campus, 5% transferred in. Retention: 88% of full-time freshmen returned the following year. Academic areas with the most degrees conferred: visual and performing arts; education; architecture. Core. Calendar: semesters. ESL program, services for LD students, advanced placement, accelerated degree program, self-designed majors, independent study, distance learning, double major, summer session for credit, adult/continuing education programs, internships. Off campus study at Association of Independent Colleges of Art and Design, Johns Hopkins University, Goucher College, University of Baltimore, Loyola University, Notre Dame College, Peabody Conservatory of Music of the Johns Hopkins University, and Towson University. Study abroad program. ROTC: Army (c).
Entrance Requirements: Options: electronic application, early admission, early decision, early action, deferred admission, international baccalaureate accepted. Required: essay, high school transcript, 3 recommendations, art portfolio, test scores, and a list of activities and interests, SAT or ACT. Recommended: interview. Entrance: very difficult. Application deadlines: 2/1, 2/1 for nonresidents, 11/1 for early decision, 12/1 for early action. Notification: 2/26, 3/6 for nonresidents, 12/1 for early decision, 1/11 for early action. SAT Reasoning Test deadline: 2/1. Transfer credits accepted: Yes.
Costs Per Year: Application fee: $70. One-time mandatory fee: $190. Comprehensive fee: $61,910 includes full-time tuition ($46,870), mandatory fees ($1760), and college room and board ($13,280). College room only: $10,010. Room and board charges vary according to board plan and housing facility. Part-time tuition: $1950 per credit hour. Part-time mandatory fees: $880 per term.
Collegiate Environment: Orientation program. Drama-theater group, choral group, student-run radio station. Social organizations: 49 open to all. Most popular organizations: Haunted House, Urban Gaming Club, Oy, Korean International Student Association, MICA Design League. Major annual events: Halloween Party, Fashion Show, Last Blast. Student services: health clinic, personal-psychological counseling. Campus security: 24-hour emergency response devices and patrols, student patrols, late night transport-escort service, controlled dormitory access, self-defense education, 24-hour building security, safety awareness programs, campus patrols by city police, Rave Guardian mobile app. 997 college housing spaces available; 922 were occupied in 2018-19. Freshmen guaranteed college housing. On-campus residence required through sophomore year. Option: coed housing available. Decker Library. Books: 76,337 (physical), 191,873 (digital/electronic); Serial titles: 407 (physical); Databases: 41. Weekly public service hours: 70; students can reserve study rooms. Operations spending for the previous fiscal year: $863,457. 750 computers available on campus for general student use. A campuswide network can be accessed from student residence rooms and from off campus. Students can access the fol-

lowing: online class registration, Campus Portal, online gallery space, Behance image portfolio system, Google Apps, Lynda.com web-based training, network storage space, personal websites, online software training tutorials, Canvas learning management system, printing services.
Community Environment: See University of Baltimore.

■ MCDANIEL COLLEGE

2 College Hill
Westminster, MD 21157-4390
Tel: (410)848-7000; Free: 800-638-5005
Fax: (410)857-2729
E-mail: admissions@mcdaniel.edu
Web Site: www.mcdaniel.edu

Description: Independent, comprehensive, coed. Awards bachelor's and master's degrees. Founded 1867. Setting: 160-acre suburban campus with easy access to Baltimore and Washington, DC. Endowment: $132 million. Research spending for the previous fiscal year: $180,017. Educational spending for the previous fiscal year: $13,133 per student. Total enrollment: 2,729. Faculty: 564 (133 full-time, 431 part-time). Student-undergrad faculty ratio is 11:1. 2,814 applied, 85% were admitted. 26% from top 10% of their high school class, 51% from top quarter, 84% from top half. Full-time: 1,529 students, 51% women, 49% men. Part-time: 29 students, 55% women, 45% men. Students come from 39 states and territories, 35 other countries, 34% from out-of-state. 0.3% American Indian or Alaska Native, non-Hispanic/Latino; 6% Hispanic/Latino; 14% Black or African American, non-Hispanic/Latino; 3% Asian, non-Hispanic/Latino; 0.1% Native Hawaiian or other Pacific Islander, non-Hispanic/Latino; 4% international. 3% 25 or older, 82% live on campus, 4% transferred in. Retention: 81% of full-time freshmen returned the following year. Academic areas with the most degrees conferred: parks and recreation; social sciences; business/marketing; psychology. Core. Calendar: 4-1-4. Academic remediation for entering students, services for LD students, advanced placement, self-designed majors, honors program, independent study, distance learning, double major, summer session for credit, part-time degree program, adult/continuing education programs, internships, graduate courses open to undergrads. Off campus study at Gallaudet, Washington Semester, Washington Center, Washington Institute, Philadelphia Center. Study abroad program. ROTC: Army.

Entrance Requirements: Options: electronic application, early admission, early decision, early action, deferred admission, international baccalaureate accepted. Required: essay, high school transcript, minimum 2.5 high school GPA, 2 recommendations, SAT or ACT. Recommended: interview. Entrance: moderately difficult. Application deadlines: rolling, rolling for nonresidents, 11/1 for early decision plan 1, 1/15 for early decision plan 2, 12/15 for early action. Notification: continuous, continuous for nonresidents, 12/1 for early decision plan 1, 2/1 for early decision plan 2, 1/15 for early action. Transfer credits accepted: Yes. Applicants placed on waiting list: 81. Wait-listed applicants offered admission: 1. Early decision applicants: 18. Early decision applicants admitted: 17.

Costs Per Year: Application fee: $50. Comprehensive fee: $54,690 includes full-time tuition ($43,260) and college room and board ($11,430). College room only: $5250. Full-time tuition varies according to course load. Room and board charges vary according to board plan and housing facility. Part-time tuition: $1352 per credit hour. Part-time tuition varies according to course load.

Collegiate Environment: Orientation program. Drama-theater group, choral group, student-run newspaper, radio station. Social organizations: 90 open to all; national fraternities, national sororities, local fraternities, local sororities; 15% of eligible men and 19% of eligible women are members. Most popular organizations: Student Government Association, Black Student Union, International Club, Maryland State Legislature, McDaniel Allies. Major annual events: Homecoming, Spring Fling. Student services: health clinic, personal-psychological counseling. Campus security: 24-hour emergency response devices and patrols, late night transport-escort service. 1,384 college housing spaces available; 1,330 were occupied in 2018-19. Freshmen guaranteed college housing. On-campus residence required through junior year. Option: coed housing available. Hoover Library. Books: 181,489 (physical), 193,549 (digital/electronic); Serial titles: 1,440 (physical), 83,076 (digital/electronic); Databases: 87. Weekly public service hours: 103; study areas open 24 hours, 5-7 days a week; students can reserve study rooms. Operations spending for the previous fiscal year: $1.7 million. 138 computers available on campus for general student use. A campuswide network can be accessed from student residence rooms and from off campus. Students can access the following: online class registration, online billing summaries,

financial aid letter, tax information. Staffed computer lab on campus (open 24 hours a day) provides training in use of computers, software, and the Internet.

■ MONTGOMERY COLLEGE

51 Mannakee St.
Rockville, MD 20850
Tel: (240)567-5000
Web Site: www.montgomerycollege.edu

Description: State and locally supported, 2-year, coed. Awards certificates, diplomas, transfer associate, and terminal associate degrees. Founded 1946. Setting: 333-acre suburban campus with easy access to Washington, DC. Endowment: $26.1 million. Research spending for the previous fiscal year: $277,575. Educational spending for the previous fiscal year: $7757 per student. Total enrollment: 22,875. Faculty: 1,331 (481 full-time, 850 part-time). Student-undergrad faculty ratio is 17:1. 10,976 applied, 100% were admitted. Full-time: 8,060 students, 50% women, 50% men. Part-time: 14,815 students, 55% women, 45% men. Students come from 24 states and territories, 163 other countries, 3% from out-of-state. 0.3% American Indian or Alaska Native, non-Hispanic/Latino; 25% Hispanic/Latino; 26% Black or African American, non-Hispanic/Latino; 12% Asian, non-Hispanic/Latino; 0.2% Native Hawaiian or other Pacific Islander, non-Hispanic/Latino; 10% international. 29% 25 or older, 65% transferred in. Core. Calendar: semesters. Academic remediation for entering students, ESL program, services for LD students, advanced placement, honors program, independent study, distance learning, double major, summer session for credit, part-time degree program, external degree program, adult/continuing education programs, co-op programs and internships. Off campus study at International Education & Study Abroad Program. Study abroad program. ROTC: Air Force (c).

Entrance Requirements: Open admission. Options: electronic application, early admission, deferred admission, international baccalaureate accepted. Recommended: high school transcript, interview. Entrance: noncompetitive. Application deadline: rolling. Notification: continuous. Transfer credits accepted: Yes.

Costs Per Year: Application fee: $25. Area resident tuition: $3072 full-time, $128 per credit hour part-time. State resident tuition: $6264 full-time, $261 per credit hour part-time. Nonresident tuition: $8688 full-time, $362 per credit hour part-time. Mandatory fees: $1,070 full-time, $69 per credit hour part-time. Full-time tuition and fees vary according to course load. Part-time tuition and fees vary according to course load.

Collegiate Environment: Orientation program. Drama-theater group, choral group, student-run newspaper, radio station. Social organizations: 141 open to all. Most popular organizations: Math Club, Engineers without Borders (EWB), STEM Education Community Club, Cyber Security Club, Animation and Drone Club. Major annual events: Student Academic Excellence Awards, Student Transfer Fair, Student Jobs Fair. Campus security: 24-hour emergency response devices and patrols. Montgomery College Library plus 3 others. Books: 211,641 (physical), 57,782 (digital/electronic); Serial titles: 9,356 (physical), 104,416 (digital/electronic); Databases: 176. Weekly public service hours: 73; students can reserve study rooms. Operations spending for the previous fiscal year: $6 million. 4,600 computers available on campus for general student use. Computer purchase/lease plans available. A campuswide network can be accessed. Students can access the following: online class registration, 2600 laptops and tablets for academic areas; Access to Office 365; Collaboration tools; Online Training. Staffed computer lab on campus provides training in use of computers, software, and the Internet.

■ MORGAN STATE UNIVERSITY

1700 E Cold Spring Ln.
Baltimore, MD 21251
Tel: (443)885-3333; Free: 800-332-6674
Web Site: www.morgan.edu

Description: State-supported, university, coed. Awards bachelor's, master's, and doctoral degrees. Founded 1867. Setting: 143-acre urban campus with easy access to Washington, DC. Total enrollment: 7,005. Faculty: 558 (436 full-time, 122 part-time). Student-undergrad faculty ratio is 13:1. 9,166 applied, 43% were admitted. Full-time: 5,472 students, 55% women, 45% men. Part-time: 642 students, 54% women, 46% men. Students come from 35 states and territories, 50 other countries, 24% from out-of-state. 12% 25 or older, 46% live on campus, 4% transferred in. Retention: 68% of full-time freshmen returned the following year. Academic areas with the most degrees conferred: family and consumer sciences; business/marketing; communication/journalism. Core. Calendar: semesters. Academic remediation for entering students, services for LD students, advanced placement, accelerated degree program, honors program, independent study, summer session for credit, part-time degree program, co-op programs and internships, graduate courses open to undergrads. Off campus study at Towson University, Coppin State College, University of Maryland. ROTC: Army.

Entrance Requirements: Options: electronic application, early admission, deferred admission, international baccalaureate accepted. Required: high school transcript, minimum 2.0 high school GPA, SAT or ACT. Recommended: essay. Required for some: 2 recommendations, interview, SAT Subject Tests. Entrance: moderately difficult. Application deadline: 4/15. Notification: 6/30. Preference given to state residents.

Costs Per Year: Application fee: $35. State resident tuition: $5369 full-time, $245 per credit part-time. Nonresident tuition: $15,636 full-time, $616 per credit part-time. Mandatory fees: $2530 full-time, $81.50 per credit part-time. College room and board: $10,862. College room only: $6564. Room and board charges vary according to board plan and housing facility.

Collegiate Environment: Orientation program. Drama-theater group, choral group, marching band, student-run newspaper, radio station. Social organizations: 11 open to all; national fraternities, national sororities; 10% of eligible men and 10% of eligible women are members. Most popular organizations: Student Government Association, Greek Life, choir, band, cultural organizations. Major annual events: Homecoming, I Love Morgan Day. Student services: health clinic, personal-psychological counseling. Campus security: 24-hour emergency response devices and patrols, late night transport-escort service, controlled dormitory access. Soper Library. 285 computers available on campus for general student use. A campuswide network can be accessed from student residence rooms and from off campus. Students can access the following: online class registration, engineering lab supercomputer. Staffed computer lab on campus.

Community Environment: See University of Baltimore.

■ **MOUNT ST. MARY'S UNIVERSITY**
16300 Old Emmitsburg Rd.
Emmitsburg, MD 21727-7799
Tel: (301)447-6122; Free: 800-448-4347
E-mail: admissions@msmary.edu
Web Site: www.msmary.edu

Description: Independent Roman Catholic, comprehensive, coed. Awards bachelor's and master's degrees and post-master's certificates. Founded 1808. Setting: 1,500-acre rural campus with easy access to Baltimore and Washington, DC. Endowment: $50.3 million. Educational spending for the previous fiscal year: $9701 per student. Total enrollment: 2,323. Faculty: 208 (129 full-time, 79 part-time). Student-undergrad faculty ratio is 13:1. 6,130 applied, 64% were admitted. 8% from top 10% of their high school class, 30% from top quarter, 64% from top half. Full-time: 1,696 students, 53% women, 47% men. Part-time: 121 students, 46% women, 54% men. Students come from 43 states and territories, 10 other countries, 43% from out-of-state. 0.5% American Indian or Alaska Native, non-Hispanic/Latino; 11% Hispanic/Latino; 17% Black or African American, non-Hispanic/Latino; 3% Asian, non-Hispanic/Latino; 0.2% Native Hawaiian or other Pacific Islander, non-Hispanic/Latino; 0.7% international. 2% 25 or older, 80% live on campus, 3% transferred in. Retention: 76% of full-time freshmen returned the following year. Academic areas with the most degrees conferred: business/marketing; social sciences; biological/life sciences. Core. Calendar: semesters. Academic remediation for entering students, services for LD students, advanced placement, accelerated degree program, self-designed majors, honors program, independent study, double major, summer session for credit, part-time degree program, adult/continuing education programs, internships, graduate courses open to undergrads. Off campus study. Study abroad program. ROTC: Army (c).

Entrance Requirements: Options: electronic application, early action, deferred admission, international baccalaureate accepted. Required: high school transcript, minimum 2 high school GPA, 1 recommendation, SAT or ACT. Recommended: essay, minimum 3 high school GPA, interview. Entrance: moderately difficult. Application deadlines: 3/1, 12/1 for early action. Notification: continuous, 12/25 for early action. SAT Reasoning Test deadline: 3/1. Transfer credits accepted: Yes. Applicants placed on waiting list: 0. Wait-listed applicants offered admission: 0. Early action applicants: 143. Early action applicants admitted: 123.

Costs Per Year: Application fee: $45. Comprehensive fee: $54,425 includes full-time tuition ($39,975), mandatory fees ($1375), and college room and board ($13,075). College room only: $6650. Full-time tuition and fees vary according to location and program. Room and board charges vary according to housing facility. Part-time tuition: $1300 per credit hour. Part-time tuition varies according to location and program.

Collegiate Environment: Orientation program. Drama-theater group, choral group, student-run newspaper, radio station. Social organizations: 70 open to all. Most popular organizations: Mount Students for Life, CRUX - Outdoor Adventures, Campus Ministry Student Organization, FOCUS, Mount Chorale. Major annual events: Homecoming, Christmas Dance, Family Fest. Student services: health clinic, personal-psychological counseling. Campus security: 24-hour emergency response devices and patrols, late night transport-escort service, controlled dormitory access. Phillips Library. Books: 149,657 (physical), 280,598 (digital/electronic); Serial titles: 1,207 (physical), 26,497 (digital/electronic); Databases: 157. Operations spending for the previous fiscal year: $777,621. 80 computers available on campus for general student use. A campuswide network can be accessed from student residence rooms. Students can access the following: online class registration, tuition payment, course management system.

■ **NER ISRAEL RABBINICAL COLLEGE**
400 Mount Wilson Ln.
Baltimore, MD 21208
Tel: (410)484-7200
Fax: (410)484-3060

Description: Independent Jewish, comprehensive, men only. Awards bachelor's, master's, and doctoral degrees. Founded 1933. Setting: 54-acre suburban campus. Total enrollment: 574. 67 applied. 7% 25 or older. Core. Calendar: semesters. Academic remediation for entering students, ESL program, honors program, summer session for credit, graduate courses open to undergrads. Study abroad program.

Entrance Requirements: Options: early admission, deferred admission. Required: high school transcript. Recommended: interview. Entrance: moderately difficult. Application deadline: rolling.

Collegiate Environment: Student services: health clinic.

Community Environment: See University of Baltimore.

■ **NOTRE DAME OF MARYLAND UNIVERSITY**
4701 N Charles St.
Baltimore, MD 21210-2476
Tel: (410)435-0100; Free: 800-435-0200
Fax: (410)532-6287
E-mail: abaumler@ndm.edu
Web Site: www.ndm.edu

Description: Independent Roman Catholic, comprehensive, coed. Awards bachelor's, master's, and doctoral degrees and post-master's certificates (offers coed undergraduate program for adult students). Founded 1873. Setting: 58-acre urban campus with easy access to Baltimore and Washington, DC. Total enrollment: 2,764. Faculty: 136 (126 full-time, 10 part-time). Student-undergrad faculty ratio is 11:1. 827 applied, 49% were admitted. 24% from top 10% of their high school class, 49% from top quarter, 85% from top half. Full-time: 538 students, 99% women, 1% men. Part-time: 631 students, 92% women, 8% men. Students come from 18 states and territories, 12 other countries, 7% from out-of-state. 3% American Indian or Alaska Native, non-Hispanic/Latino; 6% Hispanic/Latino; 27% Black or African American, non-Hispanic/Latino; 5% Asian, non-Hispanic/Latino; 0.3% Native Hawaiian or other Pacific Islander, non-Hispanic/Latino; 1% international. 57% 25 or older, 5% transferred in. Retention: 85% of full-time freshmen returned the following year. Academic areas with the most degrees conferred: health professions and related sciences; liberal arts/general studies; interdisciplinary studies. Core. Calendar: 4-1-4. ESL program, services for LD students, advanced placement, accelerated degree program, self-designed majors, honors program, independent study, distance learning, double major, summer session for credit, part-time degree program, adult/continuing education programs, internships, graduate courses open to undergrads. Off campus study at Loyola College, Johns Hopkins University, Towson University, Goucher College, Morgan State University, Coppin State College, Maryland Institute College of Art. Study abroad program. ROTC: Army (c).

Entrance Requirements: Options: electronic application, early admission, early action, deferred admission, international baccalaureate accepted. Required: essay, high school transcript, minimum 2.5 high school GPA, 2 recommendations, SAT or ACT. Recommended: minimum 3 high school GPA, interview, resume. Entrance: moderately difficult. Application deadline: rolling. Notification: continuous. SAT Reasoning Test deadline: 2/15. Transfer credits accepted: Yes.

Collegiate Environment: Orientation program. Drama-theater group, choral group, student-run newspaper, radio station. Most popular organizations: Omega Phi Alpha Service Sorority, Maryland Student Legislature, Business and Economics Society, Sigma Tau Delta Honor Society, Residence Hall Council. Major annual events: Winterfest, Bachelor Ball, Family Weekend. Student services: health clinic, personal-psychological counseling, women's center. Campus security: 24-hour emergency response devices and patrols, late night transport-escort service, controlled dormitory access, emergency call boxes. Loyola/Notre Dame Library. 100 computers available on campus for general student use. A campuswide network can be accessed from student residence rooms and from off campus. Students can access the following: online class registration, online classroom assignments and information. Staffed computer lab on campus provides training in use of computers, software, and the Internet.

Community Environment: Like Boston, Baltimore is a college town. There are nine nearby colleges and universities and over 60,000 students in the Baltimore metropolitan area which enhances academic and social opportunities. The Notre Dame campus is located 15 minutes from the nationally known Inner Harbor area where concerts, fairs and ethnic festivals are sponsored. Both mountains and ocean are only a few hours from Notre Dame, providing opportunities for skiing in the winter and relaxing on the beach in the summer. Annapolis, home of the U. S. Naval Academy, is about 45 minutes from Notre Dame, and Washington, D. C., with all of its resources, is less than an hour's drive from the college.

■ **PEABODY CONSERVATORY OF THE JOHNS HOPKINS UNIVERSITY**
1 E Mount Vernon Pl.
Baltimore, MD 21202-2397
Tel: (410)659-8150; Free: 800-368-2521
Web Site: www.peabody.jhu.edu
Description: Independent, comprehensive, coed. Administratively affiliated with Johns Hopkins University. Awards bachelor's, master's, and doctoral degrees and post-master's certificates. Founded 1857. Setting: 1-acre urban campus with easy access to Washington, DC. Endowment: $106.2 million. Educational spending for the previous fiscal year: $19,778 per student. Total enrollment: 567. Faculty: 178 (82 full-time, 96 part-time). Student-undergrad faculty ratio is 6:1. 711 applied, 52% were admitted. Full-time: 262 students, 51% women, 49% men. Part-time: 7 students, 100% men. Students come from 33 states and territories, 16 other countries, 72% from out-of-state. 1% American Indian or Alaska Native, non-Hispanic/Latino; 4% Hispanic/Latino; 5% Black or African American, non-Hispanic/Latino; 27% Asian, non-Hispanic/Latino; 18% international. 2% 25 or older, 40% live on campus, 5% transferred in. Retention: 87% of full-time freshmen returned the following year. Academic areas with the most degrees conferred: visual and performing arts; education. Core. Calendar: semesters. Academic remediation for entering students, ESL program, services for LD students, advanced placement, accelerated degree program, honors program, independent study, double major, internships, graduate courses open to undergrads. Off campus study at Johns Hopkins University; Loyola College; Maryland Institute, College of Art.
Entrance Requirements: Required: essay, high school transcript, 3 recommendations, interview, audition. Recommended: minimum 3 high school GPA. Required for some: SAT or ACT. Entrance: very difficult. Application deadline: 12/1. Notification: 4/1. Transfer credits accepted: Yes.
Collegiate Environment: Orientation program. Choral group. Major annual events: Beginning of the Year Events, Relaxation Day, End of Year Party. Student services: health clinic, personal-psychological counseling. Campus security: 24-hour emergency response devices and patrols, late night transport-escort service, controlled dormitory access. Arthur Friedheim Library plus 1 other. Operations spending for the previous fiscal year: $674,568. 40 computers available on campus for general student use. A campuswide network can be accessed from student residence rooms and from off campus. Students can access the following: online class registration, word processing, music processing. Staffed computer lab on campus provides training in use of computers, software, and the Internet.

■ **PRINCE GEORGE'S COMMUNITY COLLEGE**
301 Largo Rd.
Largo, MD 20774-2199
Tel: (301)336-6000
E-mail: enrollmentservices@pgcc.edu
Web Site: www.pgcc.edu
Description: County-supported, 2-year, coed. Awards certificates, transfer associate, and terminal associate degrees. Founded 1958. Setting: 150-acre suburban campus with easy access to Washington, DC. Total enrollment: 11,861. Faculty: 695 (244 full-time, 451 part-time). Student-undergrad faculty

ratio is 15:1. 4,178 applied, 100% were admitted. Full-time: 3,007 students, 55% women, 45% men. Part-time: 8,854 students, 67% women, 33% men. Students come from 20 states and territories, 98 other countries, 4% from out-of-state. 47% 25 or older, 8% transferred in. Retention: 58% of full-time freshmen returned the following year. Core. Calendar: semesters plus 2 summer sessions. Academic remediation for entering students, ESL program, services for LD students, advanced placement, honors program, distance learning, summer session for credit, part-time degree program, external degree program, adult/continuing education programs, co-op programs. ROTC: Army (c).
Entrance Requirements: Open admission. Option: early admission. Recommended: minimum 2.0 high school GPA. Required for some: high school transcript. Entrance: noncompetitive. Application deadline: rolling. Notification: continuous.
Collegiate Environment: Orientation program. Drama-theater group, choral group, student-run newspaper. Social organizations: 40 open to all. Most popular organizations: Crusaders for Christ, Student Program Board, Union of Black Scholars, International Student Groups. Major annual events: International Festival, Bluebird Blues Jazz Festival, Jook Joint Saturday Night. Student services: health clinic, personal-psychological counseling. Campus security: 24-hour emergency response devices and patrols, late night transport-escort service. Accokeek Hall. 450 computers available on campus for general student use. A campuswide network can be accessed from off-campus. Students can access the following: online class registration. Staffed computer lab on campus.

■ **PURDUE UNIVERSITY GLOBAL**
18618 Crestwood Dr.
Hagerstown, MD 21742
Tel: (301)766-3600; Free: 844-PURDUE-G
Web Site: www.purdueglobal.edu
Description: Independent, comprehensive, coed. Administratively affiliated with Kaplan Higher Education. Awards associate, bachelor's, and master's degrees. Founded 1938. Setting: 8-acre small town campus. 3% live on campus. Calendar: quarters.

■ **ST. JOHN'S COLLEGE**
60 College Ave.
Annapolis, MD 21401
Tel: (410)263-2371; Free: 800-727-9238
E-mail: annapolis.admissions@sjc.edu
Web Site: www.sjc.edu
Description: Independent, comprehensive, coed. Administratively affiliated with St. John's College - Santa Fe. Awards bachelor's and master's degrees. Founded 1696. Setting: 36-acre small town campus with easy access to Washington, D.C. and Baltimore, MD. Endowment: $120.9 million. Educational spending for the previous fiscal year: $18,219 per student. Total enrollment: 527. Faculty: 70 (63 full-time, 7 part-time). Student-undergrad faculty ratio is 7:1. 913 applied, 58% were admitted. 22% from top 10% of their high school class, 44% from top quarter, 67% from top half. Full-time: 474 students, 48% women, 52% men. Students come from 43 states and territories, 30 other countries, 60% from out-of-state. 5% Hispanic/Latino; 2% Black or African American, non-Hispanic/Latino; 4% Asian, non-Hispanic/Latino; 23% international. 6% 25 or older, 96% live on campus, 4% transferred in. Retention: 91% of full-time freshmen returned the following year. Academic area with the most degrees conferred: liberal arts/general studies. Core. Calendar: semesters. Services for LD students, internships. Off campus study at St. John's College in Santa Fe, New Mexico. Study abroad program.
Entrance Requirements: Options: electronic application, early admission, early action, deferred admission, international baccalaureate accepted. Required: essay, high school transcript, 2 recommendations. Recommended: interview, SAT/ACT, TOEFL/IELTS or interview for international applicants; SAT/ACT/CLT for homeschooled students and applicants who have not and will not graduate high school. Required for some: outline of curriculum for home-schooled applicants, SAT or ACT. Entrance: very difficult. Application deadlines: rolling, 11/15 for early action. Notification: continuous, 12/15 for early action. Transfer credits accepted: No. Applicants placed on waiting list: 30. Wait-listed applicants offered admission: 2. Early action applicants: 344. Early action applicants admitted: 260.
Costs Per Year: Application fee: $0. One-time mandatory fee: $100. Comprehensive fee: $49,271 includes full-time tuition ($35,000), mandatory fees ($635), and college room and board ($13,636). College room only: $7000. Room and board charges vary according to board plan and housing facility.

Collegiate Environment: Orientation program. Drama-theater group, choral group, student-run newspaper. Social organizations: 40 open to all. Most popular organizations: King William's Players (drama), Reality (social), Delegate Council (student government), Waltz (social), Student Committee on Instruction (advisory). Major annual events: Convocation, Annual Croquet Match Against the USNA (Annapolis Cup), Reality (year-end festival). Student services: health clinic, personal-psychological counseling. Campus security: 24-hour emergency response devices and patrols, late night transport-escort service, controlled dormitory access. 354 college housing spaces available; 321 were occupied in 2018-19. Freshmen guaranteed college housing. On-campus residence required in freshman year. Option: coed housing available. Greenfield Library plus 1 other. Books: 111,240 (physical), 538 (digital/electronic); Serial titles: 128 (physical), 2,410 (digital/electronic); Databases: 14. Weekly public service hours: 94; students can reserve study rooms. Operations spending for the previous fiscal year: $448,632. 26 computers available on campus for general student use. A campuswide network can be accessed from student residence rooms and from off campus. Students can access the following: free wi-fi access throughout the campus; support for bring-your-own mobile devices. Staffed computer lab on campus (open 24 hours a day) provides training in use of computers, software, and the Internet.

■ **ST. MARY'S COLLEGE OF MARYLAND**
47645 College Dr.
Saint Marys City, MD 20686-3001
Tel: (240)895-2000; Free: 800-492-7181
Fax: (240)895-5001
E-mail: admissions@smcm.edu
Web Site: www.smcm.edu

Description: State-supported, comprehensive, coed. Awards bachelor's and master's degrees. Founded 1840. Setting: 361-acre rural campus. Endowment: $36.4 million. Research spending for the previous fiscal year: $306,294. Educational spending for the previous fiscal year: $12,831 per student. Total enrollment: 1,602. Faculty: 209 (135 full-time, 74 part-time). Student-undergrad faculty ratio is 10:1. 1,700 applied, 80% were admitted. Full-time: 1,521 students, 58% women, 42% men. Part-time: 51 students, 43% women, 57% men. Students come from 26 states and territories, 7 other countries, 6% from out-of-state. 0.1% American Indian or Alaska Native, non-Hispanic/Latino; 7% Hispanic/Latino; 9% Black or African American, non-Hispanic/Latino; 4% Asian, non-Hispanic/Latino; 0.1% Native Hawaiian or other Pacific Islander, non-Hispanic/Latino; 0.8% international. 3% 25 or older, 80% live on campus, 7% transferred in. Retention: 82% of full-time freshmen returned the following year. Academic areas with the most degrees conferred: social sciences; biological/life sciences; psychology. Core. Calendar: semesters. Services for LD students, advanced placement, self-designed majors, freshman honors college, independent study, double major, summer session for credit, part-time degree program, co-op programs and internships. Study abroad program.

Entrance Requirements: Options: electronic application, early decision, early action, deferred admission, international baccalaureate accepted. Required: essay, high school transcript, 2 recommendations, SAT or ACT. Recommended: interview. Entrance: moderately difficult. Application deadlines: 1/15, 1/15 for nonresidents, 11/1 for early decision, 11/1 for early action. Notification: continuous until 4/1, continuous for nonresidents, 12/1 for early decision, 1/1 for early action. SAT Reasoning Test deadline: 2/15. SAT Subject Test deadline: 2/15. Transfer credits accepted: Yes. Early action applicants: 943. Early action applicants admitted: 860.

Costs Per Year: Application fee: $50. State resident tuition: $11,646 full-time, $200 per credit hour part-time. Nonresident tuition: $27,097 full-time, $200 per credit hour part-time. Mandatory fees: $2850 full-time. Full-time tuition and fees vary according to course load. Part-time tuition varies according to course load. College room and board: $12,816. College room only: $7400. Room and board charges vary according to board plan and housing facility.

Collegiate Environment: Orientation program. Drama-theater group, choral group, student-run newspaper, radio station. Social organizations: 99 open to all. Most popular organizations: Dance Club, Humans vs. Zombies, InterVarsity Christian Fellowship, Habitat for Humanity, Programs Board. Major annual events: World Carnival, Dance Shows, Relay for Life. Student services: health clinic, personal-psychological counseling. Campus security: 24-hour emergency response devices and patrols, late night transport-escort service, controlled dormitory access. 1,507 college housing spaces available; 1,252 were occupied in 2018-19. Freshmen guaranteed college housing. Options: coed, men-only, women-only housing available. Library,

Archives, and Media Center. Books: 123,704 (physical), 12,593 (digital/electronic); Serial titles: 1,193 (physical), 90,283 (digital/electronic); Databases: 112. Weekly public service hours: 106; study areas open 24 hours, 5-7 days a week; students can reserve study rooms. Operations spending for the previous fiscal year: $2.1 million. 340 computers available on campus for general student use. Computer purchase/lease plans available. A campuswide network can be accessed from student residence rooms and from off campus. Students can access the following: online class registration, learning management system. Staffed computer lab on campus provides training in use of computers, software, and the Internet.

■ **SALISBURY UNIVERSITY**
1101 Camden Ave.
Salisbury, MD 21801-6837
Tel: (410)543-6000; Free: 888-543-0148
Fax: (410)548-2587
E-mail: admissions@salisbury.edu
Web Site: www.salisbury.edu

Description: State-supported, comprehensive, coed. Part of University System of Maryland. Awards bachelor's, master's, and doctoral degrees and post-master's certificates. Founded 1925. Setting: 201-acre small town campus. Endowment: $71.3 million. Research spending for the previous fiscal year: $1.5 million. Educational spending for the previous fiscal year: $7966 per student. Total enrollment: 8,567. Faculty: 669 (444 full-time, 225 part-time). Student-undergrad faculty ratio is 16:1. 8,983 applied, 62% were admitted. 15% from top 10% of their high school class, 45% from top quarter, 86% from top half. Full-time: 7,081 students, 56% women, 44% men. Part-time: 569 students, 51% women, 49% men. Students come from 31 states and territories, 37 other countries, 13% from out-of-state. 0.7% American Indian or Alaska Native, non-Hispanic/Latino; 4% Hispanic/Latino; 14% Black or African American, non-Hispanic/Latino; 4% Asian, non-Hispanic/Latino; 0.2% Native Hawaiian or other Pacific Islander, non-Hispanic/Latino; 1% international. 7% 25 or older, 29% live on campus, 10% transferred in. Retention: 83% of full-time freshmen returned the following year. Academic areas with the most degrees conferred: business/marketing; education; communication/journalism; parks and recreation. Core. Calendar: 4-1-4. ESL program, services for LD students, advanced placement, accelerated degree program, self-designed majors, freshman honors college, honors program, independent study, distance learning, double major, summer session for credit, part-time degree program, co-op programs and internships, graduate courses open to undergrads. Off campus study at Applicable to all other units of the University System of Maryland. Study abroad program. ROTC: Army, Air Force (c).

Entrance Requirements: Options: electronic application, early admission, early decision, early action, deferred admission, international baccalaureate accepted. Required: essay, minimum 2 high school GPA, 1 recommendation. Required for some: high school transcript, SAT or ACT. Entrance: moderately difficult. Application deadlines: 1/15, 1/15 for nonresidents, 11/15 for early decision, 12/1 for early action. Notification: 3/15, 3/15 for nonresidents, 12/15 for early decision, 1/15 for early action. SAT Reasoning Test deadline: 1/15. Transfer credits accepted: Yes. Early decision applicants: 358. Early decision applicants admitted: 200. Early action applicants: 4,048. Early action applicants admitted: 3,160.

Costs Per Year: Application fee: $50. State resident tuition: $7122 full-time, $292 per credit hour part-time. Nonresident tuition: $16,824 full-time, $695 per credit hour part-time. Mandatory fees: $2702 full-time, $100 per credit hour part-time. Full-time tuition and fees vary according to location. Part-time tuition and fees vary according to location. College room and board: $11,950. College room only: $6950. Room and board charges vary according to board plan and housing facility.

Collegiate Environment: Orientation program. Drama-theater group, choral group, student-run newspaper, radio station. Social organizations: 100 open to all; national fraternities, national sororities, local fraternities, local sororities, Academic, Art/Music, Cultural, Dance, Drama, Etc. Most popular organizations: Student Government Association, Radio (WXSU) / SU TV / The Flyer Newspaper, Student Organization for Activity Planning (SOAP), Campus Crusade for Christ, Black Student Union. Major annual events: Relay for Life, Homecoming Week, Big Event Community Service. Student services: health clinic, personal-psychological counseling. Campus security: 24-hour emergency response devices and patrols, student patrols, late night transport-escort service, controlled dormitory access. 3,136 college housing spaces available; 3,097 were occupied in 2018-19. Freshmen given priority for college housing. On-campus residence required through sophomore year. Option: coed housing available. Guerreri Academic Commons plus 2 others. Books: 269,531 (physical), 347 (digital/electronic); Serial titles: 694 (physical), 150 (digital/electronic); Databases: 106. Weekly public service hours: 112; study areas open 24 hours, 5-7 days a week; students can reserve study rooms. Operations spending for the previous fiscal year: $3.9 million. 1,000 computers available on campus for general student use. A campuswide network can be accessed from student residence rooms and from off campus. Students can access the following: online class registration, university accounts, student web hosting. Staffed computer lab on campus provides training in use of software and the Internet.

■ **STEVENSON UNIVERSITY**
1525 Greenspring Valley Rd.
Stevenson, MD 21153
Tel: (410)486-7000; Free: 877-468-3852
E-mail: admissions@stevenson.edu
Web Site: www.stevenson.edu
Description: Independent, comprehensive, coed. Awards bachelor's and master's degrees. Founded 1952. Setting: 163-acre suburban campus with easy access to Baltimore. Endowment: $82.7 million. Research spending for the previous fiscal year: $110,271. Educational spending for the previous fiscal year: $11,605 per student. Total enrollment: 3,876. Faculty: 462 (132 full-time, 330 part-time). Student-undergrad faculty ratio is 16:1. 5,533 applied, 61% were admitted. 20% from top 10% of their high school class, 45% from top quarter, 81% from top half. Full-time: 2,926 students, 64% women, 36% men. Part-time: 471 students, 78% women, 22% men. Students come from 32 states and territories, 5 other countries, 23% from out-of-state. 0.1% American Indian or Alaska Native, non-Hispanic/Latino; 6% Hispanic/Latino; 28% Black or African American, non-Hispanic/Latino; 4% Asian, non-Hispanic/Latino; 0.1% Native Hawaiian or other Pacific Islander, non-Hispanic/Latino; 0.4% international. 15% 25 or older, 52% live on campus, 5% transferred in. Retention: 81% of full-time freshmen returned the following year. Academic areas with the most degrees conferred: health professions and related sciences; business/marketing; education. Core. Calendar: semesters. Academic remediation for entering students, services for LD students, advanced placement, accelerated degree program, self-designed majors, honors program, independent study, distance learning, double major, summer session for credit, part-time degree program, adult/continuing education programs, co-op programs and internships, graduate courses open to undergrads. Off campus study at Chesapeake Community College, Anne Arundel Community College, Howard Community College, Carroll Community College, Prince George's Community College, Baltimore City Community College. Study abroad program. ROTC: Army (c), Air Force (c).
Entrance Requirements: Options: electronic application, deferred admission, international baccalaureate accepted. Required: essay, high school transcript, 1 recommendation, SAT or ACT. Required for some: interview. Entrance: moderately difficult. Application deadline: rolling. Notification: continuous. SAT Reasoning Test deadline: 3/1. Transfer credits accepted: Yes.
Costs Per Year: Application fee: $40. Comprehensive fee: $49,488 includes full-time tuition ($33,690), mandatory fees ($2552), and college room and board ($13,246). College room only: $8446. Full-time tuition and fees vary according to course load and degree level. Room and board charges vary according to board plan and housing facility. Part-time tuition: $850 per credit hour. Part-time mandatory fees: $75 per term. Part-time tuition and fees vary according to degree level.
Collegiate Environment: Orientation program. Drama-theater group, choral group, marching band, student-run newspaper, radio station. Social organizations: national fraternities, national sororities, local fraternities. Most popular organizations: Relay for Life, Mustang Activities Programming, Black Student Union, American Chemical Society, Phi Sigma Sigma. Major annual events: Welcome Picnic, Homecoming Weekend, Football Events. Student services: health clinic, personal-psychological counseling. Campus security: 24-hour emergency response devices and patrols, late night transport-escort service, controlled dormitory access, patrols by trained security personnel during campus hours. Stevenson University Learning Resource Center-Greenspring Campus plus 2 others. Books: 67,987 (physical), 342,648 (digital/electronic); Serial titles: 476 (physical), 72,885 (digital/electronic); Databases: 88. Weekly public service hours: 136; students can reserve study rooms. Operations spending for the previous fiscal year: $1.6 million. 515 computers available on campus for general student use. Computer purchase/lease plans available. A campuswide network can be accessed from student residence rooms and from off campus. Students can access the following: online class registration. Staffed computer lab on campus provides training in use of computers, software, and the Internet.

Community Environment: Located in the open countryside of Baltimore County, 20 minutes from the center of urban Baltimore, the college offers a country setting with city conveniences.

■ **STRATFORD UNIVERSITY**
210 S Central Ave.
Baltimore, MD 21202
Tel: (410)752-4710; Free: 800-624-9926
Fax: (410)752-3730
E-mail: baadmissions@stratford.edu
Web Site: www.stratford.edu
Description: Proprietary, comprehensive, coed. Awards associate, bachelor's, and master's degrees. Founded 1972. Setting: 6-acre urban campus with easy access to Baltimore and Washington, DC. Total enrollment: 323. Faculty: 41 (15 full-time, 26 part-time). Full-time: 30 students, 47% women, 53% men. Part-time: 288 students, 61% women, 39% men. 0.3% American Indian or Alaska Native, non-Hispanic/Latino; 2% Hispanic/Latino; 78% Black or African American, non-Hispanic/Latino; 1% Asian, non-Hispanic/Latino. Core. Calendar: quarters. Academic remediation for entering students, services for LD students, accelerated degree program, independent study, summer session for credit, part-time degree program, adult/continuing education programs, co-op programs and internships. Off campus study.
Entrance Requirements: Open admission. Option: electronic application. Required: high school transcript, interview. Recommended: essay. Required for some: 1 recommendation. Entrance: minimally difficult. Application deadline: rolling. Notification: continuous. Transfer credits accepted: Yes.
Costs Per Year: Application fee: $50. One-time mandatory fee: $100. Tuition: $24,975 full-time, $1665 per course part-time. Full-time tuition varies according to course level, course load, degree level, and program. Part-time tuition varies according to course level, course load, degree level, and program.
Collegiate Environment: Orientation program. Learning Resource Center.

■ **STRAYER UNIVERSITY-ANNE ARUNDEL CAMPUS**
1520 Jabez Run
Ste. 100
Millersville, MD 21108
Tel: (410)923-4500; Free: 888-311-0355
Web Site: www.strayer.edu
Description: Proprietary, comprehensive, coed. Awards associate, bachelor's, and master's degrees.

■ **STRAYER UNIVERSITY-OWINGS MILLS CAMPUS**
500 Redland Ct.
Ste. 100
Owings Mills, MD 21117
Tel: (443)394-3339; Free: 888-311-0355
Web Site: www.strayer.edu
Description: Proprietary, comprehensive, coed. Awards associate, bachelor's, and master's degrees.

■ **STRAYER UNIVERSITY-PRINCE GEORGE'S CAMPUS**
5110 Auth Way
Suitland, MD 20746
Tel: (301)505-3300; Free: 888-311-0355
Web Site: www.strayer.edu
Description: Proprietary, comprehensive, coed. Awards associate, bachelor's, and master's degrees.

■ **STRAYER UNIVERSITY-ROCKVILLE CAMPUS**
1803 Research Blvd.
Ste. 110
Rockville, MD 20850
Tel: (301)838-4700; Free: 888-311-0355
Web Site: www.strayer.edu
Description: Proprietary, comprehensive, coed. Awards associate, bachelor's, and master's degrees.

■ **STRAYER UNIVERSITY-WHITE MARSH CAMPUS**
9920 Franklin Sq. Dr.
Ste. 200
Baltimore, MD 21236
Tel: (410)238-9000; Free: 888-311-0355

Web Site: www.strayer.edu

Description: Proprietary, comprehensive, coed. Awards associate, bachelor's, and master's degrees. Founded 1892.

■ **TOWSON UNIVERSITY**
8000 York Rd.
Towson, MD 21252-0001
Tel: (410)704-2000
Fax: (410)704-3030
E-mail: admissions@towson.edu
Web Site: www.towson.edu

Description: State-supported, university, coed. Part of University System of Maryland. Awards bachelor's, master's, and doctoral degrees and post-master's certificates. Founded 1866. Setting: 329-acre suburban campus with easy access to Baltimore and Washington, DC. System endowment: $83.5 million. Research spending for the previous fiscal year: $5 million. Educational spending for the previous fiscal year: $6622 per student. Total enrollment: 22,923. Faculty: 1,743 (903 full-time, 840 part-time). Student-undergrad faculty ratio is 17:1. 11,933 applied, 79% were admitted. 14% from top 10% of their high school class, 39% from top quarter, 78% from top half. Full-time: 17,350 students, 60% women, 40% men. Part-time: 2,468 students, 54% women, 46% men. Students come from 45 states and territories, 73 other countries, 12% from out-of-state. 0.1% American Indian or Alaska Native, non-Hispanic/Latino; 8% Hispanic/Latino; 23% Black or African American, non-Hispanic/Latino; 6% Asian, non-Hispanic/Latino; 0.1% Native Hawaiian or other Pacific Islander, non-Hispanic/Latino; 2% international. 10% 25 or older, 28% live on campus, 11% transferred in. Retention: 85% of full-time freshmen returned the following year. Academic areas with the most degrees conferred: business/marketing; health professions and related sciences; social sciences. Core. Calendar: semesters. Academic remediation for entering students, ESL program, services for LD students, advanced placement, self-designed majors, freshman honors college, honors program, independent study, distance learning, double major, summer session for credit, part-time degree program, adult/continuing education programs, co-op programs and internships, graduate courses open to undergrads. Off campus study at all state colleges in Maryland, other institutions of higher education in the Baltimore metropolitan area, members of the National Student Exchange. Study abroad program. ROTC: Army (c), Air Force (c).

Entrance Requirements: Options: electronic application, early admission, early action, deferred admission, international baccalaureate accepted. Required: essay, high school transcript, SAT or ACT. Recommended: minimum 3 high school GPA, 2 recommendations, resume or activity list. Required for some: interview. Entrance: moderately difficult. Notification: continuous. SAT Reasoning Test deadline: 2/15. Transfer credits accepted: Yes. Early action applicants: 9,198. Early action applicants admitted: 6,222.

Costs Per Year: Application fee: $45. State resident tuition: $6962 full-time, $299 per credit hour part-time. Nonresident tuition: $210,898 full-time, $888 per credit hour part-time. Mandatory fees: $3344 full-time, $147 per credit hour part-time. College room and board: $13,034. College room only: $7446.

Collegiate Environment: Orientation program. Drama-theater group, choral group, marching band, student-run newspaper, radio station. Social organizations: 300 open to all; national fraternities, national sororities, local fraternities, local sororities; 10% of eligible men and 12% of eligible women are members. Most popular organizations: University Residence Government, Latin American Student Organization, Black Student Union, Hillel, African Diaspora Club. Major annual events: Tiger Fest (spring festival), Homecoming Weekend, Summer Orientation. Student services: health clinic, personal-psychological counseling, women's center. Campus security: 24-hour emergency response devices and patrols, late night transport-escort service, controlled dormitory access. 5,716 college housing spaces available; 5,592 were occupied in 2018-19. Freshmen guaranteed college housing. Option: coed housing available. Cook Library. Books: 396,754 (physical), 520,928 (digital/electronic); Serial titles: 288 (physical), 79,916 (digital/electronic); Databases: 312. Weekly public service hours: 108; study areas open 24 hours, 5-7 days a week; students can reserve study rooms. Operations spending for the previous fiscal year: $6.8 million. 3,800 computers available on campus for general student use. A campuswide network can be accessed from student residence rooms and from off campus. Students can access the following: online class registration. Staffed computer lab on campus provides training in use of computers, software, and the Internet.

■ **UNITED STATES NAVAL ACADEMY**
121 Blake Rd.
Annapolis, MD 21402-5000

Tel: (410)293-1000; Free: 888-249-7707
Fax: (410)293-4348
E-mail: webmail@usna.edu
Web Site: www.usna.edu

Description: Federally supported, 4-year, coed. Awards bachelor's degrees. Founded 1845. Setting: 338-acre small town campus with easy access to Baltimore and Washington, DC. Endowment: $223.3 million. Research spending for the previous fiscal year: $9.8 million. Educational spending for the previous fiscal year: $41,275 per student. Total enrollment: 4,525. Faculty: 592 (554 full-time, 38 part-time). Student-undergrad faculty ratio is 8:1. 16,101 applied, 9% were admitted. 58% from top 10% of their high school class, 83% from top quarter, 94% from top half. Full-time: 4,525 students, 25% women, 75% men. Students come from 54 states and territories, 28 other countries, 94% from out-of-state. 0.3% American Indian or Alaska Native, non-Hispanic/Latino; 11% Hispanic/Latino; 7% Black or African American, non-Hispanic/Latino; 7% Asian, non-Hispanic/Latino; 0.5% Native Hawaiian or other Pacific Islander, non-Hispanic/Latino; 1% international. 1% 25 or older, 100% live on campus. Retention: 98% of full-time freshmen returned the following year. Academic areas with the most degrees conferred: engineering; social sciences; physical sciences. Core. Calendar: semesters. Academic remediation for entering students, advanced placement, honors program, independent study, double major, summer session for credit. Off campus study. Study abroad program.

Entrance Requirements: Options: electronic application, early action. Required: essay, high school transcript, 2 recommendations, interview, age 17-22, medical exam, authorized nomination, candidate fitness test, SAT or ACT. Entrance: very difficult. Application deadline: 1/31. Notification: continuous until 4/15. SAT Reasoning Test deadline: 1/31. Applicants placed on waiting list: 187. Wait-listed applicants offered admission: 4.

Costs Per Year: Application fee: $0. Comprehensive fee: $0. The Navy pays for the tuition, room and board, medical and dental care of Naval Academy midshipmen.

Collegiate Environment: Orientation program. Drama-theater group, choral group, marching band, student-run radio station. Social organizations: 100 open to all. Most popular organizations: Mountaineering Club, Semper Fi, Black Studies Club, Midshipmen Action Club, Martial Arts Club. Major annual events: Parents' Weekend, Army-Navy Football Game, Commissioning Week. Student services: legal services, health clinic, personal-psychological counseling, women's center. Campus security: 24-hour emergency response devices and patrols, campus gate security. Nimitz Library. Books: 580,342 (physical), 425,564 (digital/electronic); Serial titles: 4,594 (physical), 71,757 (digital/electronic); Databases: 170. Weekly public service hours: 100. Operations spending for the previous fiscal year: $4.6 million. 1,000 computers available on campus for general student use. Computer purchase/lease plans available. A computer is required for all students. A campuswide network can be accessed from student residence rooms and from off campus. Students can access the following: online class registration. Staffed computer lab on campus provides training in use of computers, software, and the Internet.

■ **UNIVERSITY OF BALTIMORE**
1420 N Charles St.
Baltimore, MD 21201-5779
Tel: (410)837-4200
Fax: (410)837-4793
E-mail: admission@ubalt.edu
Web Site: www.ubalt.edu

Description: State-supported, comprehensive, coed. Part of University System of Maryland. Awards bachelor's, master's, and doctoral degrees. Founded 1925. Setting: 49-acre urban campus. Total enrollment: 3,526. Faculty: 405 (199 full-time, 206 part-time). Student-undergrad faculty ratio is 19:1. 806 applied, 60% were admitted. Students come from 14 states and territories, 62 other countries, 1% from out-of-state. 0.4% American Indian or Alaska Native, non-Hispanic/Latino; 3% Hispanic/Latino; 42% Black or African American, non-Hispanic/Latino; 4% Asian, non-Hispanic/Latino; 0.1% Native Hawaiian or other Pacific Islander, non-Hispanic/Latino; 1% international. 50% 25 or older. Retention: 78% of full-time freshmen returned the following year. Core. Calendar: semesters. Academic remediation for entering students, services for LD students, advanced placement, accelerated degree program, freshman honors college, honors program, independent study, distance learning, summer session for credit, part-time degree program, adult/continuing education programs, co-op programs and internships, graduate courses open to undergrads. Off campus study at University of Maryland Baltimore County, Coppin State College, Morgan State

University, Towson University, Bowie State College, Maryland Institute, College of Art. Study abroad program. ROTC: Army (c), Air Force (c).

Entrance Requirements: Options: electronic application, deferred admission, international baccalaureate accepted. Required: essay, high school transcript, SAT or ACT. Recommended: minimum 3 high school GPA, 2 recommendations, interview. Entrance: minimally difficult. Application deadline: rolling. Notification: continuous. SAT Reasoning Test deadline: 7/31. Transfer credits accepted: Yes.

Collegiate Environment: Orientation program. Drama-theater group, choral group, student-run newspaper. Social organizations: 65 open to all; local fraternities, local sororities. Most popular organizations: Psi Chi, APALSA, International Student Association, African Student Association, Forensics Student Association. Major annual events: Semi-Annual Block Party, Speaker Series, Access UB. Student services: health clinic, personal-psychological counseling. Campus security: 24-hour emergency response devices and patrols, late night transport-escort service. Langsdale Library plus 1 other. 135 computers available on campus for general student use. Computer purchase/lease plans available. A campuswide network can be accessed from off-campus. Students can access the following: online class registration. Staffed computer lab on campus (open 24 hours a day) provides training in use of computers, software, and the Internet.

Community Environment: Baltimore is an important industrial and educational center for the state of Maryland and the regional northeastern United States. The port has an active international market and foreign trade. Downtown Baltimore has become a popular tourist site; the Inner Harbor complex, including Harborplace and the National Aquarium, is recognized internationally. New stadiums to house the Baltimore Orioles and Baltimore Ravens have been completed at Camden Yards in downtown Baltimore. Pimlico Race Course is the home of the annual Preakness race. University of Baltimore is located in the cultural center of the city, adjacent to the Lyric Opera House, Meyerhoff Symphony Hall and the Maryland Institute of Art.

■ **UNIVERSITY OF MARYLAND, BALTIMORE COUNTY**
1000 Hilltop Cir.
Baltimore, MD 21250
Tel: (410)455-1000; Free: 800-862-2402
Fax: (410)455-1210
E-mail: admissions@umbc.edu
Web Site: www.umbc.edu

Description: State-supported, university, coed. Part of University System of Maryland. Awards bachelor's, master's, and doctoral degrees. Founded 1963. Setting: 530-acre suburban campus with easy access to Washington, DC. Endowment: $105.2 million. Research spending for the previous fiscal year: $63.9 million. Educational spending for the previous fiscal year: $11,208 per student. Total enrollment: 13,767. Faculty: 830 (538 full-time, 292 part-time). Student-undergrad faculty ratio is 18:1. 11,720 applied, 58% were admitted. 23% from top 10% of their high school class, 50% from top quarter, 84% from top half. Full-time: 10,834 students, 51% women, 49% men. Part-time: 1,637 students, 44% women, 56% men. Students come from 42 states and territories, 81 other countries, 5% from out-of-state. 0.2% American Indian or Alaska Native, non-Hispanic/Latino; 8% Hispanic/Latino; 18% Black or African American, non-Hispanic/Latino; 22% Asian, non-Hispanic/Latino; 0.2% Native Hawaiian or other Pacific Islander, non-Hispanic/Latino; 4% international. 14% 25 or older, 35% live on campus, 9% transferred in. Retention: 87% of full-time freshmen returned the following year. Academic areas with the most degrees conferred: computer and information sciences; biological/life sciences; psychology. Core. Calendar: 4-1-4. Academic remediation for entering students, ESL program, services for LD students, advanced placement, self-designed majors, freshman honors college, honors program, independent study, distance learning, double major, summer session for credit, part-time degree program, external degree program, adult/continuing education programs, co-op programs and internships, graduate courses open to undergrads. Off campus study at Johns Hopkins University, University System of Maryland. Study abroad program. ROTC: Army (c), Naval, Air Force (c).

Entrance Requirements: Options: electronic application, early admission, early action, deferred admission, international baccalaureate accepted. Required: essay, high school transcript, SAT or ACT. Recommended: minimum 3 high school GPA, 2 recommendations. Entrance: moderately difficult. Application deadlines: 2/1, 11/1 for early action. Notification: continuous, 12/15 for early action. SAT Reasoning Test deadline: 2/1. Transfer credits accepted: Yes. Applicants placed on waiting list: 443. Wait-listed applicants offered admission: 74. Early action applicants: 6,280. Early action applicants admitted: 2,940.

Costs Per Year: Application fee: $75. One-time mandatory fee: $225. State resident tuition: $8534 full-time, $354 per credit hour part-time. Nonresident tuition: $23,628 full-time, $981 per credit hour part-time. Mandatory fees: $3244 full-time, $140 per credit hour part-time. Full-time tuition and fees vary according to location and program. Part-time tuition and fees vary according to location and program. College room and board: $11,696. College room only: $7050. Room and board charges vary according to board plan and housing facility.

Collegiate Environment: Orientation program. Drama-theater group, choral group, student-run newspaper, radio station. Social organizations: 260 open to all; national fraternities, national sororities; 3% of eligible men and 5% of eligible women are members. Most popular organizations: Student Government Association, Student Events Board, Retriever Weekly, Resident Student Association, WMBC, Campus Radio. Major annual events: Quadmania (spring festival), Welcome Week, Homecoming. Student services: health clinic, personal-psychological counseling, women's center. Campus security: 24-hour emergency response devices and patrols, late night transport-escort service. 4,000 college housing spaces available; 3,979 were occupied in 2018-19. Freshmen guaranteed college housing. Option: coed housing available. Albin O. Kuhn Library and Gallery. Books: 700,265 (physical), 175,405 (digital/electronic); Serial titles: 18,354 (physical), 134,280 (digital/electronic); Databases: 388. Weekly public service hours: 94; study areas open 24 hours, 5-7 days a week; students can reserve study rooms. Operations spending for the previous fiscal year: $9.7 million. 1,065 computers available on campus for general student use. Computer purchase/lease plans available. A computer is required for all students. A campuswide network can be accessed from student residence rooms and from off campus. Students can access the following: online class registration, billing, housing, parking, degree audit and advising. Staffed computer lab on campus (open 24 hours a day) provides training in use of software and the Internet.

Community Environment: The ultramodern 500-acre campus is in an open-country setting in Catonsville, only minutes from the heart of Baltimore and less than an hour from the nation's capital. Baltimore, just six miles from the campus, is a rich resource for university students. Opportunities for musical, athletic, theatrical, and cultural events abound. The dynamic and dramatic Inner Harbor area features a convention center, the Maryland Science Center, Pier 7 Performing Arts Pavilion, the National Aquarium, and the lively collection of shops and restaurants called Harborplace. The Morris Mechanic Theatre brings Broadway to Baltimore, while the Baltimore Symphony Orchestra and internationally acclaimed artists perform in the striking Meyerhoff Concert Hall. The Walters Art Gallery, the Enoch Pratt Library, and Oriole Park at Camden Yards are also part of the city's rich tradition. Washington, only 32 miles from the campus, offers the student a wealth of academic, cultural, political, and leisure activities.

■ **UNIVERSITY OF MARYLAND, COLLEGE PARK**
College Park, MD 20742
Tel: (301)405-1000; Free: 800-422-5867
Fax: (301)314-9693
E-mail: ApplyMaryland@umd.edu
Web Site: www.maryland.edu

Description: State-supported, university, coed. Part of University System of Maryland. Awards bachelor's, master's, and doctoral degrees and post-master's certificates. Founded 1856. Setting: 1,335-acre suburban campus with easy access to Baltimore and Washington, DC. Endowment: $531.2 million. Research spending for the previous fiscal year: $549 million. Educational spending for the previous fiscal year: $17,199 per student. Total enrollment: 41,200. Faculty: 2,615 (1,843 full-time, 772 part-time). Student-undergrad faculty ratio is 18:1. 33,461 applied, 47% were admitted. 75% from top 10% of their high school class, 93% from top quarter, 99% from top half. Full-time: 28,501 students, 47% women, 53% men. Part-time: 2,261 students, 43% women, 57% men. Students come from 49 states and territories, 66 other countries, 23% from out-of-state. 0.1% American Indian or Alaska Native, non-Hispanic/Latino; 10% Hispanic/Latino; 12% Black or African American, non-Hispanic/Latino; 17% Asian, non-Hispanic/Latino; 0.1% Native Hawaiian or other Pacific Islander, non-Hispanic/Latino; 5% international. 6% 25 or older, 41% live on campus, 7% transferred in. Retention: 95% of full-time freshmen returned the following year. Academic areas with the most degrees conferred: social sciences; engineering; business/marketing. Core. Calendar: semesters. Academic remediation for entering students, ESL program, services for LD students, advanced placement, accelerated degree program, self-designed majors, honors program, independent study, distance learning, double major, summer session for credit, part-time degree program, external degree program, adult/continuing education programs, co-op programs and internships, graduate courses open to undergrads. Off campus study at Consortium of Universities of the Washington, DC Area. Study abroad program. ROTC: Army, Naval (c), Air Force.

Entrance Requirements: Options: electronic application, early admission, early action, deferred admission, international baccalaureate accepted. Required: essay, high school transcript, SAT or ACT. Recommended: 2 recommendations. Required for some: Resume of activities, audition for music applicants, drawing requirement for architecture applicants. Entrance: moderately difficult. Application deadlines: 1/20, 1/20 for nonresidents, 11/1 for early action. Notification: 4/1, 4/1 for nonresidents, 1/31 for early action. Preference given to state residents. SAT Reasoning Test deadline: 11/1. Transfer credits accepted: Yes.

Costs Per Year: Application fee: $75. State resident tuition: $8651 full-time, $360 per credit hour part-time. Nonresident tuition: $33,272 full-time, $1387 per credit hour part-time. Mandatory fees: $1944 full-time, $453 per term part-time. Full-time tuition and fees vary according to location, program, and student level. Part-time tuition and fees vary according to course load, location, program, and student level. College room and board: $12,429. College room only: $7425. Room and board charges vary according to board plan and housing facility.

Collegiate Environment: Orientation program. Drama-theater group, choral group, marching band, student-run newspaper, radio station. Social organizations: 762 open to all; national fraternities, national sororities; 15% of eligible men and 19% of eligible women are members. Most popular organizations: Student Government Association, Residence Hall Association, Black Student Union, Asian-American Student Union/Jewish Student Union, Commuter Students Association. Major annual events: First Look Fair, All-Niter, Art Attack. Student services: legal services, health clinic, personal-psychological counseling, women's center. Campus security: 24-hour emergency response devices and patrols, student patrols, late night transport-escort service, controlled dormitory access. 12,537 college housing spaces available; 12,439 were occupied in 2018-19. Freshmen given priority for college housing. Options: coed, women-only housing available. McKeldin Library plus 6 others. Books: 2.1 million (physical), 2.8 million (digital/electronic); Serial titles: 2,759 (physical), 63,891 (digital/electronic); Databases: 164. Weekly public service hours: 140; study areas open 24 hours, 5-7 days a week; students can reserve study rooms. Operations spending for the previous fiscal year: $29.9 million.

■ UNIVERSITY OF MARYLAND EASTERN SHORE
11868 Academic Oval
Princess Anne, MD 21853
Tel: (410)651-2200
Fax: (410)651-7922
Web Site: www.umes.edu
Description: State-supported, university, coed. Part of University System of Maryland. Awards bachelor's, master's, and doctoral degrees. Founded 1886. Setting: 745-acre rural campus. Endowment: $27.9 million. Research spending for the previous fiscal year: $10.2 million. Educational spending for the previous fiscal year: $13,660 per student. Total enrollment: 3,199. Faculty: 288 (204 full-time, 84 part-time). Student-undergrad faculty ratio is 13:1. 4,923 applied, 54% were admitted. Full-time: 2,360 students, 56% women, 44% men. Part-time: 243 students, 52% women, 48% men. Students come from 31 states and territories, 31 other countries, 19% from out-of-state. 0.2% American Indian or Alaska Native, non-Hispanic/Latino; 4% Hispanic/Latino; 71% Black or African American, non-Hispanic/Latino; 2% Asian, non-Hispanic/Latino; 0.1% Native Hawaiian or other Pacific Islander, non-Hispanic/Latino; 3% international. 10% 25 or older, 58% live on campus, 6% transferred in. Retention: 63% of full-time freshmen returned the following year. Academic areas with the most degrees conferred: business/marketing; homeland security, law enforcement, firefighting, and protective services; parks and recreation. Core. Calendar: semesters. Part-time degree program. ROTC: Army (c).
Entrance Requirements: Options: electronic application, deferred admission. Required: essay, high school transcript, minimum 2.5 high school GPA, 3 recommendations, SAT or ACT. Required for some: interview. Entrance: moderately difficult. SAT Reasoning Test deadline: 7/15. Transfer credits accepted: Yes.
Costs Per Year: Application fee: $35. Area resident tuition: $5418 full-time, $224 per credit hour part-time. State resident tuition: $5418 full-time, $224 per credit hour part-time. Nonresident tuition: $15,828 full-time, $583 per credit hour part-time. Mandatory fees: $3140 full-time, $84 per credit hour part-time. College room and board: $11,189. College room only: $6730.

Collegiate Environment: Orientation program. Social organizations: 72 open to all. Campus security: 24-hour emergency response devices and patrols, student patrols, late night transport-escort service, controlled dormitory access. 1,798 college housing spaces available; 1,481 were occupied in 2018-19. Options: coed, men-only, women-only housing available. Frederick Douglass Library. Books: 131,714 (physical), 28,157 (digital/electronic); Serial titles: 170 (physical), 1,152 (digital/electronic); Databases: 149. Study areas open 24 hours, 5-7 days a week; students can reserve study rooms. Operations spending for the previous fiscal year: $1.8 million. 1,097 computers available on campus for general student use. A campuswide network can be accessed. Students can access the following: online class registration. Staffed computer lab on campus.

■ UNIVERSITY OF MARYLAND UNIVERSITY COLLEGE
3501 University Blvd. E
Adelphi, MD 20783
Tel: (301)985-7000; Free: 800-888-8682
Fax: (301)985-7678
Web Site: www.umuc.edu
Description: State-supported, comprehensive, coed. Part of University System of Maryland. Awards associate, bachelor's, master's, and doctoral degrees (offers primarily part-time evening and weekend degree programs at more than 30 off-campus locations in Maryland and the Washington, DC area, and more than 180 military communities in Europe and Asia with military enrollment not reflected in this profile; associate of arts program available to military students only). Founded 1947. Setting: suburban campus with easy access to Washington, DC. Total enrollment: 60,603. Faculty: 3,846 (193 full-time, 3,653 part-time). Student-undergrad faculty ratio is 19:1. 2,592 applied, 100% were admitted. Full-time: 9,607 students, 48% women, 52% men. Part-time: 37,646 students, 44% women, 56% men. Students come from 52 states and territories, 58 other countries, 62% from out-of-state. 0.5% American Indian or Alaska Native, non-Hispanic/Latino; 14% Hispanic/Latino; 27% Black or African American, non-Hispanic/Latino; 5% Asian, non-Hispanic/Latino; 0.6% Native Hawaiian or other Pacific Islander, non-Hispanic/Latino; 1% international. 75% 25 or older, 23% transferred in. Academic areas with the most degrees conferred: computer and information sciences; business/marketing; psychology. Core. Calendar: semesters. Academic remediation for entering students, services for LD students, advanced placement, accelerated degree program, independent study, distance learning, double major, summer session for credit, part-time degree program, external degree program, co-op programs and internships. Off campus study.
Entrance Requirements: Open admission. Options: electronic application, early decision, deferred admission, international baccalaureate accepted. Required: high school transcript. Entrance: noncompetitive. Application deadline: rolling. Notification: continuous. Transfer credits accepted: Yes.
Costs Per Year: Application fee: $50. State resident tuition: $6936 full-time, $289 per credit hour part-time. Nonresident tuition: $11,976 full-time, $499 per credit hour part-time. Mandatory fees: $360 full-time.
Collegiate Environment: Orientation program. Campus security: 24-hour emergency response devices and patrols, late night transport-escort service. College housing not available. Library plus 1 other. Books: 1,234 (physical), 129,937 (digital/electronic); Serial titles: 1 (physical), 161,585 (digital/electronic); Databases: 96. Weekly public service hours: 95. 510 computers available on campus for general student use. Computer purchase/lease plans available. A campuswide network can be accessed from off-campus. Students can access the following: online class registration. Staffed computer lab on campus provides training in use of computers, software, and the Internet.
Community Environment: The administrative site is located at College Park, a small town of 25,000. Programs are offered at more than 30 locations throughout Maryland, Northern Virginia, and the Washington, D.C. area.

■ WASHINGTON ADVENTIST UNIVERSITY
7600 Flower Ave.
Takoma Park, MD 20912
Tel: (301)891-4000; Free: 800-835-4212
Fax: (301)891-4230
E-mail: enroll@cuc.edu
Web Site: www.wau.edu
Description: Independent Seventh-day Adventist, comprehensive, coed. Awards associate, bachelor's, and master's degrees. Founded 1904. Setting: suburban campus. Total enrollment: 1,493. Faculty: 134 (52 full-time, 82

part-time). Student-undergrad faculty ratio is 14:1. Full-time: 1,058 students, 68% women, 32% men. Part-time: 269 students, 67% women, 33% men. 34% from out-of-state. 0.5% American Indian or Alaska Native, non-Hispanic/Latino; 10% Hispanic/Latino; 60% Black or African American, non-Hispanic/Latino; 7% Asian, non-Hispanic/Latino. 27% 25 or older. Retention: 69% of full-time freshmen returned the following year. Academic areas with the most degrees conferred: health professions and related sciences; business/marketing; psychology. Calendar: semesters. Part-time degree program, external degree program, adult/continuing education programs.

Entrance Requirements: Options: electronic application, early admission, deferred admission. Required: essay, high school transcript, minimum 2.5 high school GPA, 2 recommendations, SAT or ACT. Required for some: interview. Entrance: moderately difficult. Application deadline: 8/1. Notification: continuous. SAT Subject Test deadline: 8/1.

Collegiate Environment: Orientation program. Campus security: 24-hour emergency response devices and patrols, late night transport-escort service. Theofield G. Weis Library.

Community Environment: A suburb of Washington, D.C., the residents of Takoma Park enjoy the cultural and recreational facilities of that city. There are many opportunities for part-time employment. Shopping facilities are excellent.

■ WASHINGTON COLLEGE
300 Washington Ave.
Chestertown, MD 21620-1197
Tel: (410)778-2800; Free: 800-422-1782
Fax: (410)778-7287
E-mail: wc_admissions@washcoll.edu
Web Site: www.washcoll.edu

Description: Independent, 4-year, coed. Awards bachelor's degrees. Founded 1782. Setting: 140-acre small town campus with easy access to Baltimore and Washington, DC. Endowment: $220 million. Educational spending for the previous fiscal year: $15,000 per student. Total enrollment: 1,484. Faculty: 175 (116 full-time, 59 part-time). Student-undergrad faculty ratio is 11:1. 5,515 applied, 48% were admitted. 38% from top 10% of their high school class, 70% from top quarter, 91% from top half. Full-time: 1,456 students, 58% women, 42% men. Part-time: 28 students, 50% women, 50% men. Students come from 38 states and territories, 26 other countries, 54% from out-of-state. 0.7% American Indian or Alaska Native, non-Hispanic/Latino; 6% Hispanic/Latino; 8% Black or African American, non-Hispanic/Latino; 3% Asian, non-Hispanic/Latino; 0.1% Native Hawaiian or other Pacific Islander, non-Hispanic/Latino; 10% international. 1% 25 or older, 85% live on campus, 2% transferred in. Retention: 85% of full-time freshmen returned the following year. Academic areas with the most degrees conferred: social sciences; business/marketing; biological/life sciences. Core. Calendar: semesters. ESL program, services for LD students, accelerated degree program, self-designed majors, honors program, independent study, double major, summer session for credit, part-time degree program, internships. Off campus study. Study abroad program.

Entrance Requirements: Options: electronic application, early admission, early decision, early action, deferred admission, international baccalaureate accepted. Required: essay, high school transcript, 1 recommendation, SAT or ACT. Recommended: interview. Required for some: interview. Entrance: moderately difficult. Application deadlines: 2/15, 11/15 for early decision plan 1, 12/15 for early decision plan 2, 12/1 for early action. Notification: continuous, 12/15 for early decision plan 1, 1/15 for early decision plan 2, 1/15 for early action. SAT Reasoning Test deadline: 2/15. Transfer credits accepted: Yes. Applicants placed on waiting list: 0.

Costs Per Year: Application fee: $0. Comprehensive fee: $59,420 includes full-time tuition ($45,888), mandatory fees ($1118), and college room and board ($12,414). College room only: $6000. Room and board charges vary according to board plan, housing facility, and location. Part-time tuition: $1912 per credit hour. Part-time tuition varies according to course load. Tuition guaranteed not to increase for student's term of enrollment.

Collegiate Environment: Orientation program. Drama-theater group, choral group, student-run newspaper, radio station. Social organizations: 90 open to all; national fraternities, national sororities, local fraternities; 15% of eligible men and 17% of eligible women are members. Most popular organizations: Presidential Fellows, Dance Club, Habitat for Humanity, Peer Mentor, Animal Impact Club. Major annual events: Fall Family Weekend,

George Washington's Birthday Ball, Spring Fling. Student services: health clinic, personal-psychological counseling. Campus security: 24-hour emergency response devices and patrols, student patrols, late night transport-escort service, controlled dormitory access, LiveSafe mobile app. Clifton M. Miller Library. 100 computers available on campus for general student use. Computer purchase/lease plans available. A campuswide network can be accessed from student residence rooms and from off campus. Students can access the following: online class registration. Staffed computer lab on campus provides training in use of computers, software, and the Internet.

Community Environment: Chestertown is on the eastern shore of Maryland, 40 miles from Chesapeake Bay Bridge. The community facilities include churches and numerous civic and service organizations. Boating, fishing and hunting are some of the outdoor sports of the area.

■ WOR-WIC COMMUNITY COLLEGE
32000 Campus Dr.
Salisbury, MD 21804
Tel: (410)334-2800
E-mail: admissions@worwic.edu
Web Site: www.worwic.edu

Description: State and locally supported, 2-year, coed. Awards certificates, transfer associate, and terminal associate degrees. Founded 1976. Setting: 202-acre small town campus. Endowment: $19 million. Educational spending for the previous fiscal year: $4372 per student. Total enrollment: 3,025. Faculty: 161 (65 full-time, 96 part-time). Student-undergrad faculty ratio is 16:1. 943 applied, 100% were admitted. Full-time: 786 students, 57% women, 43% men. Part-time: 2,239 students, 67% women, 33% men. Students come from 11 states and territories, 5 other countries, 3% from out-of-state. 0.4% American Indian or Alaska Native, non-Hispanic/Latino; 6% Hispanic/Latino; 28% Black or African American, non-Hispanic/Latino; 2% Asian, non-Hispanic/Latino; 0.1% Native Hawaiian or other Pacific Islander, non-Hispanic/Latino; 0.7% international. 42% 25 or older, 6% transferred in. Calendar: semesters. Academic remediation for entering students, ESL program, services for LD students, advanced placement, accelerated degree program, honors program, independent study, distance learning, double major, summer session for credit, part-time degree program, adult/continuing education programs, internships.

Entrance Requirements: Open admission. Options: electronic application, early admission. Recommended: high school transcript. Entrance: noncompetitive. Application deadline: rolling. Transfer credits accepted: Yes.

Costs Per Year: Application fee: $0. Area resident tuition: $3480 full-time, $116 per credit part-time. State resident tuition: $7230 full-time, $241 per credit part-time. Nonresident tuition: $9060 full-time, $302 per credit part-time. Mandatory fees: $570 full-time, $19 per credit part-time.

Collegiate Environment: Orientation program. Social organizations: 15 open to all. Most popular organizations: Nursing Student Organization, Criminal Justice Club, The Gaming Association, Veterans - Military Association, Phi Theta Kappa (PTK): Alpha Nu Omicron. Major annual events: Family Fun Day, National Pizza Day, Health Fair. Student services: personal-psychological counseling. Campus security: 24-hour emergency response devices, late night transport-escort service. College housing not available. Patricia M. Hazel Resource Center plus 4 others. Databases: 55. Weekly public service hours: 70. Operations spending for the previous fiscal year: $469,329. 835 computers available on campus for general student use. A campuswide network can be accessed from off-campus. Students can access the following: online class registration. Staffed computer lab on campus provides training in use of computers, software, and the Internet.

■ YESHIVA COLLEGE OF THE NATION'S CAPITAL
1216 Arcola Ave.
Silver Spring, MD 20902
Tel: (301)593-2534
Fax: (301)949-7040
Web Site: www.yeshiva.edu

Description: Independent Jewish, 4-year, men only. Part of Yeshiva of Greater Washington. Awards bachelor's degrees. Founded 1963. Setting: suburban campus. Total enrollment: 43. Full-time: 45 students. 30% 25 or older.

Entrance Requirements: Open admission.

■ AMERICAN INTERNATIONAL COLLEGE

1000 State St.
Springfield, MA 01109-3189
Tel: (413)737-7000; Free: 800-242-3142
Fax: (413)737-2803
E-mail: jonathan.scully@aic.edu
Web Site: www.aic.edu

Description: Independent, comprehensive, coed. Awards associate, bachelor's, master's, and doctoral degrees and post-master's certificates. Founded 1885. Setting: 58-acre urban campus. Endowment: $15 million. Educational spending for the previous fiscal year: $6080 per student. Total enrollment: 3,283. Faculty: 320 (72 full-time, 248 part-time). Student-undergrad faculty ratio is 18:1. 1,988 applied, 72% were admitted. Full-time: 1,254 students, 58% women, 42% men. Part-time: 118 students, 71% women, 29% men. Students come from 30 states and territories, 20 other countries, 62% from out-of-state. 0.5% American Indian or Alaska Native, non-Hispanic/Latino; 19% Hispanic/Latino; 24% Black or African American, non-Hispanic/Latino; 1% Asian, non-Hispanic/Latino; 0.4% Native Hawaiian or other Pacific Islander, non-Hispanic/Latino; 3% international. 15% 25 or older, 49% live on campus, 10% transferred in. Retention: 62% of full-time freshmen returned the following year. Academic areas with the most degrees conferred: health professions and related sciences; business/marketing; social sciences. Core. Calendar: semesters. Academic remediation for entering students, services for LD students, advanced placement, accelerated degree program, honors program, independent study, distance learning, double major, summer session for credit, part-time degree program, adult/continuing education programs, internships, graduate courses open to undergrads. Off campus study at Cooperating Colleges of Greater Springfield. Study abroad program. ROTC: Army (c), Air Force (c).

Entrance Requirements: Options: electronic application, deferred admission, international baccalaureate accepted. Required: high school transcript. Recommended: essay, 1 recommendation. Entrance: minimally difficult. Application deadline: 9/7. Notification: continuous. Transfer credits accepted: Yes.

Costs Per Year: Application fee: $0. Comprehensive fee: $49,780 includes full-time tuition ($35,680) and college room and board ($14,100). College room only: $7140. Full-time tuition varies according to course load and program. Room and board charges vary according to board plan and housing facility. Part-time tuition: $735 per credit hour. Part-time mandatory fees: $30 per term. Part-time tuition and fees vary according to course load.

Collegiate Environment: Orientation program. Drama-theater group, choral group, student-run newspaper. Social organizations: 40 open to all; local fraternities, local sororities; 1% of men are members. Most popular organizations: Student Activities Committee, Model Congress, PRIDE (Persons Ready in Defense of Ebony), Student Government, School newspaper. Major annual events: Homecoming, Model Congress, 3.0 Club (student athlete recognition). Student services: health clinic, personal-psychological counseling. Campus security: 24-hour emergency response devices and patrols, late night transport-escort service, controlled dormitory access. James J. Shea Sr. Library. Books: 56,511 (physical), 179,160 (digital/electronic); Serial titles: 183 (physical), 962 (digital/electronic); Databases: 64. Weekly public service hours: 100; students can reserve study rooms. Operations spending for the previous fiscal year: $753,059. 230 computers available on campus for general student use. Computer purchase/lease plans available. A campuswide network can be accessed from student residence rooms and from off campus. Students can access the following: online class registration. Staffed computer lab on campus provides training in use of computers, software, and the Internet.

Community Environment: Springfield is a city of 152,000 that offers a multitude of activities for college students, including a quadrangle of museums, the Stage West Theater Company, and the Springfield Civic Center.

■ AMHERST COLLEGE

PO Box 5000
Amherst, MA 01002-5000
Tel: (413)542-2000
Fax: (413)542-2040
E-mail: admission@amherst.edu
Web Site: www.amherst.edu

Description: Independent, 4-year, coed. Awards bachelor's degrees. Founded 1821. Setting: 1,020-acre small town campus. Total enrollment: 1,836. Faculty: 291 (223 full-time, 68 part-time). Student-undergrad faculty ratio is 8:1. 9,285 applied, 13% were admitted. 83% from top 10% of their high school class, 94% from top quarter, 100% from top half. Full-time: 1,836 students, 49% women, 51% men. Students come from 48 states and territories, 58 other countries, 86% from out-of-state. 0.6% American Indian or Alaska Native, non-Hispanic/Latino; 13% Hispanic/Latino; 11% Black or African American, non-Hispanic/Latino; 14% Asian, non-Hispanic/Latino; 0.1% Native Hawaiian or other Pacific Islander, non-Hispanic/Latino; 9% international. 1% 25 or older, 97% live on campus, 1% transferred in. Retention: 96% of full-time freshmen returned the following year. Academic areas with the most degrees conferred: social sciences; biological/life sciences; mathematics and statistics. Calendar: semesters. Services for LD students, self-designed majors, independent study, double major, internships. Off campus study at Five Colleges, Inc., Twelve College Exchange Program, Dual-degree Engineering program with Dartmouth Thayer School of Engineering. Study abroad program. ROTC: Army (c), Air Force (c).

Entrance Requirements: Options: electronic application, early admission, early decision, deferred admission. Required: essay, high school transcript, 3 recommendations, Amherst College Supplement, SAT or ACT. Entrance: most difficult. Application deadlines: 1/1, 11/1 for early decision. Notification: 4/1, 12/15 for early decision. SAT Reasoning Test deadline: 1/1. SAT Subject Test deadline: 1/1. Transfer credits accepted: Yes. Applicants placed on waiting list: 1,144. Wait-listed applicants offered admission: 60. Early decision applicants: 502. Early decision applicants admitted: 173.

Costs Per Year: Application fee: $65. Comprehensive fee: $71,166 includes full-time tuition ($55,520), mandatory fees ($906), and college room and board ($14,740). College room only: $7990.

Collegiate Environment: Orientation program. Drama-theater group, choral group, student-run newspaper, radio station. Social organizations: 150 open to all. Most popular organizations: Association of Amherst Students, Black Students Union, Student Publications (e.g., Amherst Student, Indicator), A Capella Groups (e.g., Zumbye's, Bluestockings), Amherst Dance. Major annual events: Homecoming, Fall/Winter/Spring Carnivals, Spring Concert. Student services: health clinic, personal-psychological counseling, women's center. Campus security: 24-hour emergency response devices and patrols, late night transport-escort service, controlled dormitory access. Robert Frost Library plus 3 others.

Community Environment: Well-known American poets Emily Dickinson, Robert Frost and Eugene Field, and author Ray Stannard Baker (David Grayson) all lived in Amherst. Located on eastern edge of Connecticut Valley, the town has mean winter temperature of 25.2 degrees, and summer, 72 degrees. Annual rainfall is 43.8 inches. Rail and bus service is available. Free 5-college bus system connects all five institutions. Recreation provided at Mt. Sugarloaf and Mt. Tom Reservation nearby. Town has theatres, golf, tennis, fishing, and ice skating. Community opera performs annually. Nearby are the Pelham Hills, where Daniel Shays organized his rebellion; Deerfield, with its Bloody Brook, so named after a 17th-century clash between Indians and settlers; the Holyoke Range; and byways reminiscent of colonial days. Tobacco farms and apple orchards dot the Connecticut River valley, and throughout the neighboring hills are many opportunities for hiking, canoeing, and skiing amid the small villages, farms, and abandoned factories of another age. An exciting community lies in the midst of this bucolic setting. Amherst students and townspeople alike thrive on the contemporary vitality of a major academic center, since both Hampshire College and the University of Massachusetts are also located in Amherst, with Smith and Mount Holyoke Colleges nearby. The resulting concentration of students, teachers, practicing artists, and visiting speakers makes the area a hub of scholarship and creativity. It has even been said that, after Boston, the Pioneer Valley offers the richest array of cultural events in New England.

■ ANNA MARIA COLLEGE
50 Sunset Ln.
Paxton, MA 01612
Tel: (508)849-3300
E-mail: admissions@annamaria.edu
Web Site: www.annamaria.edu

Description: Independent Roman Catholic, comprehensive, coed. Awards bachelor's, master's, and doctoral degrees and post-master's certificates. Founded 1946. Setting: 192-acre rural campus with easy access to Boston. System endowment: $4.3 million. Total enrollment: 1,468. Faculty: (38 full-time). Student-undergrad faculty ratio is 11:1. 1,785 applied, 80% were admitted. Full-time: 811 students, 62% women, 38% men. Part-time: 317 students, 56% women, 44% men. Students come from 32 states and territories, 27% from out-of-state. 0.4% American Indian or Alaska Native, non-Hispanic/Latino; 8% Hispanic/Latino; 10% Black or African American, non-Hispanic/Latino; 2% Asian, non-Hispanic/Latino; 0.3% Native Hawaiian or other Pacific Islander, non-Hispanic/Latino; 0.4% international. 60% live on campus, 6% transferred in. Retention: 65% of full-time freshmen returned the following year. Academic areas with the most degrees conferred: health professions and related sciences; homeland security, law enforcement, firefighting, and protective services; public administration and social services. Core. Calendar: semesters. Academic remediation for entering students, services for LD students, advanced placement, accelerated degree program, self-designed majors, honors program, independent study, distance learning, double major, summer session for credit, part-time degree program, adult/continuing education programs, co-op programs and internships, graduate courses open to undergrads. Off campus study at Colleges of Worcester Consortium. Study abroad program. ROTC: Army (c), Air Force (c).
Entrance Requirements: Options: electronic application, deferred admission, international baccalaureate accepted. Required: high school transcript, minimum 2 high school GPA. Recommended: 1 recommendation, interview. Required for some: essay, audition for music programs, portfolio for art programs. Entrance: minimally difficult. Application deadline: rolling. Notification: continuous. Transfer credits accepted: Yes.
Costs Per Year: Application fee: $25. Comprehensive fee: $52,090 includes full-time tuition ($35,480), mandatory fees ($2380), and college room and board ($14,230). Full-time tuition and fees vary according to course load, degree level, and program. Room and board charges vary according to board plan and housing facility. Part-time tuition: $1478 per credit. Part-time mandatory fees: $89.17 per credit. Part-time tuition and fees vary according to course load, degree level, and program.
Collegiate Environment: Orientation program. Drama-theater group, choral group, marching band. Social organizations: 15 open to all. Most popular organizations: Habitat for Humanity, Social Action Group, Chorus Club, Alana, Programming Board - AMCAB. Major annual events: President's Christmas Dinner, Semi-Formal, Spring Weekend. Student services: health clinic, personal-psychological counseling. Campus security: 24-hour emergency response devices and patrols, late night transport-escort service, controlled dormitory access. Mondor-Eagen Library. Books: 59,659 (physical), 132,939 (digital/electronic); Databases: 98. Operations spending for the previous fiscal year: $130,355. 86 computers available on campus for general student use. A campuswide network can be accessed from student residence rooms. Students can access the following: online class registration, student account information.

Community Environment: Paxton is located in the geographical center of Massachusetts, eight miles northwest of Worcester and a one-hour drive from Boston or Providence. Summer and winter sports are available in the area. Excellent job opportunities are available in the immediate area.

■ ASSUMPTION COLLEGE
500 Salisbury St.
Worcester, MA 01609-1296
Tel: (508)767-7000; Free: 866-477-7776
Fax: (508)799-4412
Web Site: www.assumption.edu

Description: Independent Roman Catholic, comprehensive, coed. Awards bachelor's and master's degrees and post-master's certificates. Founded 1904. Setting: 180-acre suburban campus with easy access to Boston. Endowment: $109.7 million. Educational spending for the previous fiscal year: $9582 per student. Total enrollment: 2,329. Faculty: 336 (135 full-time, 91 part-time). Student-undergrad faculty ratio is 11:1. 4,178 applied, 81% were admitted. 12% from top 10% of their high school class, 39% from top quarter, 73% from top half. Full-time: 1,917 students, 57% women, 43% men. Part-time: 21 students, 38% women, 62% men. Students come from 30 states and territories, 14 other countries, 35% from out-of-state. 0.1% American Indian or Alaska Native, non-Hispanic/Latino; 8% Hispanic/Latino; 5% Black or African American, non-Hispanic/Latino; 3% Asian, non-Hispanic/Latino; 0.1% Native Hawaiian or other Pacific Islander, non-Hispanic/Latino; 2% international. 1% 25 or older, 84% live on campus, 1% transferred in. Retention: 83% of full-time freshmen returned the following year. Academic areas with the most degrees conferred: business/marketing; health professions and related sciences; social sciences. Core. Calendar: semesters. ROTC: Army (c), Air Force (c).
Entrance Requirements: Options: electronic application, early decision, early action, deferred admission, international baccalaureate accepted. Required: essay, high school transcript, 1 recommendation. Recommended: interview. Entrance: moderately difficult. Application deadlines: 2/15, 11/1 for early decision. Notification: continuous, 12/8 for early decision. SAT Reasoning Test deadline: 2/15. Transfer credits accepted: Yes. Applicants placed on waiting list: 139. Wait-listed applicants offered admission: 5. Early decision applicants: 34. Early decision applicants admitted: 31. Early action applicants: 2,309. Early action applicants admitted: 2,134.
Costs Per Year: Application fee: $50. Comprehensive fee: $55,444 includes full-time tuition ($41,516), mandatory fees ($800), and college room and board ($13,128). College room only: $8310. Part-time tuition: $1384 per credit hour.
Collegiate Environment: Drama-theater group, choral group, student-run newspaper. Social organizations: 60 open to all. Most popular organizations: Volunteer center, Campus Activities Board, Student Government, Campus Ministry, intramural sports. Major annual events: Family Weekend, Spring Concert, Midnight Breakfast. Student services: health clinic, personal-psychological counseling. Campus security: 24-hour emergency response devices and patrols, student patrols, late night transport-escort service, controlled dormitory access, front gate security, well-lit pathways. 1,859 college housing spaces available; 1,624 were occupied in 2018-19. Freshmen guaranteed college housing. Options: coed, women-only housing available. Emmanuel d'Alzon Library. Books: 119,254 (physical), 155,116 (digital/electronic); Serial titles: 1,915 (physical), 43,143 (digital/electronic); Databases: 75. Weekly public service hours: 102; students can reserve study rooms. Operations spending for the previous fiscal year: $1.4 million. 361 computers available on campus for general student use. Computer purchase/lease plans available. A campuswide network can be accessed from student residence rooms and from off campus. Students can access the following: online class registration. Staffed computer lab on campus provides training in use of computers, software, and the Internet.
Community Environment: 175-acre park-like campus situated in residential section of city. See Clark University for area details.

■ BABSON COLLEGE
231 Forest St.
Babson Park, MA 02457-0310
Tel: (781)235-1200; Free: 800-488-3696
Fax: (781)239-5614
E-mail: ugradadmission@babson.edu
Web Site: www.babson.edu

Description: Independent, comprehensive, coed. Awards bachelor's and master's degrees. Founded 1919. Setting: 370-acre suburban campus with easy access to Boston. Endowment: $348.6 million. Total enrollment: 3,357.

Faculty: 263 (180 full-time, 83 part-time). Student-undergrad faculty ratio is 11:1. 6,383 applied, 24% were admitted. Full-time: 2,361 students, 48% women, 52% men. Students come from 49 states and territories, 80 other countries, 76% from out-of-state. 0.1% American Indian or Alaska Native, non-Hispanic/Latino; 11% Hispanic/Latino; 4% Black or African American, non-Hispanic/Latino; 12% Asian, non-Hispanic/Latino; 0.1% Native Hawaiian or other Pacific Islander, non-Hispanic/Latino; 28% international. 1% 25 or older, 79% live on campus, 2% transferred in. Retention: 94% of full-time freshmen returned the following year. Academic area with the most degrees conferred: business/marketing. Core. Calendar: semesters. Services for LD students, advanced placement, self-designed majors, freshman honors college, honors program, independent study, summer session for credit, internships. Off campus study at Brandeis University, Wellesley College, Olin College of Engineering. Study abroad program. ROTC: Army (c).

Entrance Requirements: Options: electronic application, early decision, early action, deferred admission, international baccalaureate accepted. Required: essay, high school transcript, 2 recommendations, SAT or ACT. Recommended: interview, TOEFL or IELTS for non-native English speakers. Entrance: very difficult. Application deadlines: 1/3, 11/1 for early decision plan 1, 1/2 for early decision plan 2. Notification: 4/1, 12/15 for early decision plan 1. SAT Reasoning Test deadline: 1/2. Transfer credits accepted: Yes. Applicants placed on waiting list: 1,852. Wait-listed applicants offered admission: 5. Early decision applicants: 431. Early decision applicants admitted: 170. Early action applicants: 2,494. Early action applicants admitted: 614.

Costs Per Year: Application fee: $75. Comprehensive fee: $69,384 includes full-time tuition ($52,608) and college room and board ($16,776).

Collegiate Environment: Orientation program. Drama-theater group, choral group, student-run newspaper, radio station. Social organizations: 143 open to all; national fraternities, national sororities; 13% of eligible men and 26% of eligible women are members. Major annual events: Midnight Breakfast, Spring Weekend, Homecoming. Student services: health clinic, personal-psychological counseling, women's center. Campus security: 24-hour emergency response devices and patrols, late night transport-escort service, controlled dormitory access. Freshmen guaranteed college housing. On-campus residence required in freshman year. Options: coed, men-only housing available. Horn Library plus 1 other.

Community Environment: Breadth distinguishes Babson from other undergraduate management programs. The focus of the Babson education blends professional (50%) and liberal arts (50%) courses with campus and field experiences in a small college setting where both halves of the faculty work together to help students perform well and to grow in response to change. Babson is located 30 minutes by car from Boston.

■ BARD COLLEGE AT SIMON'S ROCK

84 Alford Rd.
Great Barrington, MA 01230-9702
Tel: (413)644-4400; Free: 800-235-7186
Fax: (413)528-7334
E-mail: admit@simons-rock.edu
Web Site: www.simons-rock.edu

Description: Independent, 4-year, coed. Administratively affiliated with Bard College. Awards associate and bachelor's degrees. Founded 1964. Setting: 210-acre small town campus with easy access to Boston, New York City. Total enrollment: 329. Faculty: 70 (46 full-time, 24 part-time). Student-undergrad faculty ratio is 6:1. 199 applied, 89% were admitted. 60% from top 10% of their high school class, 81% from top quarter, 96% from top half. Full-time: 323 students, 61% women, 39% men. Part-time: 6 students, 33% women, 67% men. Students come from 38 states and territories, 14 other countries, 82% from out-of-state. 0.3% American Indian or Alaska Native, non-Hispanic/Latino; 3% Hispanic/Latino; 4% Black or African American, non-Hispanic/Latino; 10% Asian, non-Hispanic/Latino; 14% international. 92% live on campus. Retention: 76% of full-time freshmen returned the following year. Academic areas with the most degrees conferred: visual and performing arts; interdisciplinary studies; liberal arts/general studies. Core. Calendar: semesters. ESL program, services for LD students, self-designed majors, independent study, double major, co-op programs and internships. Off campus study at Columbia University, Vermont Law School, International Center of Photography, Eugene O'Neill Theater Center. Study abroad program.

Entrance Requirements: Option: electronic application. Required: essay, high school transcript, 3 recommendations, interview, school report, parent supplement. Entrance: moderately difficult. Application deadlines: 5/1, rolling for nonresidents. Notification: continuous, continuous for nonresidents. SAT

Reasoning Test deadline: 5/1. SAT Subject Test deadline: 5/1. Transfer credits accepted: Yes. Applicants placed on waiting list: 0. Wait-listed applicants offered admission: 0.

Costs Per Year: Application fee: $50. Comprehensive fee: $69,998 includes full-time tuition ($53,682), mandatory fees ($1400), and college room and board ($14,916). Full-time tuition and fees vary according to course load.

Collegiate Environment: Orientation program. Drama-theater group, choral group, student-run newspaper. Social organizations: 35 open to all. Most popular organizations: Black Student Union, QueerSA, Student Action Service Learning, U.S.O. (Untitled Student Organization), Boffing. Major annual events: MayFest, Prom, Dance Concert. Student services: health clinic, personal-psychological counseling, women's center. Campus security: 24-hour emergency response devices and patrols, controlled dormitory access, security escorts, late night transport. Alumni Library. Books: 68,511 (physical), 3,850 (digital/electronic); Serial titles: 120 (physical), 41,033 (digital/electronic); Databases: 22. Weekly public service hours: 106. 50 computers available on campus for general student use. A campuswide network can be accessed from student residence rooms and from off campus. Staffed computer lab on campus provides training in use of computers, software, and the Internet.

■ BAY PATH UNIVERSITY

588 Longmeadow St.
Longmeadow, MA 01106-2292
Tel: (413)565-1000; Free: 800-782-7284
Fax: (413)567-0501
E-mail: dbryden@baypath.edu
Web Site: www.baypath.edu

Description: Independent, comprehensive. Awards associate, bachelor's, master's, and doctoral degrees and post-master's certificates. Founded 1897. Setting: 48-acre suburban campus with easy access to Hartford, CT and Boston, MA. Endowment: $41.5 million. Educational spending for the previous fiscal year: $10,315 per student. Total enrollment: 3,298. Faculty: 478 (73 full-time, 405 part-time). Student-undergrad faculty ratio is 13:1. 1,470 applied, 63% were admitted. 19% from top 10% of their high school class, 47% from top quarter, 76% from top half. Full-time: 1,367 students, 100% women. Part-time: 580 students, 100% women. Students come from 8 states and territories, 5 other countries, 42% from out-of-state. 0.3% American Indian or Alaska Native, non-Hispanic/Latino; 19% Hispanic/Latino; 13% Black or African American, non-Hispanic/Latino; 2% Asian, non-Hispanic/Latino; 0.1% Native Hawaiian or other Pacific Islander, non-Hispanic/Latino; 0.6% international. 9% 25 or older, 45% live on campus, 4% transferred in. Retention: 70% of full-time freshmen returned the following year. Academic areas with the most degrees conferred: business/marketing; psychology; health professions and related sciences. Core. Calendar: semesters. Academic remediation for entering students, ESL program, services for LD students, advanced placement, accelerated degree program, self-designed majors, honors program, independent study, distance learning, double major, summer session for credit, part-time degree program, external degree program, adult/continuing education programs, co-op programs and internships, graduate courses open to undergrads. Off campus study at Cooperating Colleges of Greater Springfield. Study abroad program. ROTC: Army (c), Air Force (c).

Entrance Requirements: Options: electronic application, early action, deferred admission, international baccalaureate accepted. Recommended: minimum 2 high school GPA, interview. Required for some: essay, high school transcript, interview. Entrance: moderately difficult. Application deadline: 8/1. Transfer credits accepted: Yes.

Collegiate Environment: Orientation program. Drama-theater group, choral group. Social organizations: 32 open to all. Most popular organizations: Habitat for Humanity, Tactical Team, Wellness Wildcats, Women of Culture, Alliance Club. Major annual events: Women's Leadership Conference, Campus Awakening, Academic Achievement Day. Student services: health clinic, personal-psychological counseling. Campus security: 24-hour emergency response devices and patrols, late night transport-escort service, controlled dormitory access. Hatch Library. Books: 52,565 (physical), 408,000 (digital/electronic); Serial titles: 80 (physical), 55,000 (digital/electronic); Databases: 110. Weekly public service hours: 86; students can reserve study rooms. Operations spending for the previous fiscal year: $877,400. 235 computers available on campus for general student use. A campuswide network can be accessed from student residence rooms and from off campus. Students can access the following: online class registration.

Community Environment: Longmeadow is a small, residential, historic town located on the Connecticut/Massachusetts border. Its location near two major cities provides cultural and social advantages.

■ BAY STATE COLLEGE
122 Commonwealth Ave.
Boston, MA 02116-2975
Tel: (617)217-9000; Free: 800-81-LEARN
Fax: (617)536-1735
E-mail: admissions@baystate.edu
Web Site: www.baystate.edu
Description: Independent, primarily 2-year, coed. Awards certificates, diplomas, transfer associate, terminal associate, and bachelor's degrees. Founded 1946. Setting: urban campus. Total enrollment: 1,098. Student-undergrad faculty ratio is 20:1. 1,988 applied, 53% were admitted. 13% from out-of-state. 48% 25 or older, 26% live on campus. Retention: 76% of full-time freshmen returned the following year. Core. Calendar: semesters. Academic remediation for entering students, ESL program, advanced placement, accelerated degree program, independent study, distance learning, summer session for credit, part-time degree program, adult/continuing education programs, co-op programs and internships. Study abroad program.
Entrance Requirements: Options: electronic application, early admission. Required: high school transcript, minimum 2.3 high school GPA. Recommended: interview, SAT or ACT. Entrance: minimally difficult. Application deadline: rolling. Transfer credits accepted: Yes.
Collegiate Environment: Orientation program. Student-run radio station. Student services: personal-psychological counseling. Campus security: late night transport-escort service, controlled dormitory access, 14-hour patrols by trained security personnel. Bay State College Library.
Community Environment: See Boston University.

■ BECKER COLLEGE
61 Sever St.
Worcester, MA 01609
Tel: (508)791-9241; Free: 877-5BECKER
Fax: (508)831-7505
E-mail: admissions@becker.edu
Web Site: www.becker.edu
Description: Independent, comprehensive, coed. Awards associate, bachelor's, and master's degrees (also includes Leicester, MA small town campus). Founded 1784. Setting: 100-acre urban campus with easy access to Boston, MA; Providence, RI; Hartford, CT. Total enrollment: 1,892. Faculty: 267 (48 full-time, 219 part-time). Student-undergrad faculty ratio is 14:1. 4,972 applied, 69% were admitted. Full-time: 1,530 students, 52% women, 48% men. Part-time: 352 students, 84% women, 16% men. Students come from 37 states and territories, 29 other countries, 38% from out-of-state. 0.7% American Indian or Alaska Native, non-Hispanic/Latino; 8% Hispanic/Latino; 7% Black or African American, non-Hispanic/Latino; 2% Asian, non-Hispanic/Latino; 0.1% Native Hawaiian or other Pacific Islander, non-Hispanic/Latino; 0.8% international. 18% 25 or older, 55% live on campus, 7% transferred in. Retention: 73% of full-time freshmen returned the following year. Academic areas with the most degrees conferred: visual and performing arts; health professions and related sciences; psychology. Core. Calendar: semesters. Academic remediation for entering students, services for LD students, advanced placement, accelerated degree program, independent study, distance learning, double major, summer session for credit, part-time degree program, adult/continuing education programs, co-op programs and internships, graduate courses open to undergrads. Off campus study at Becker College is a member of the Higher Education Consortium of Central Massachusetts (HECCMA). Students may take courses for free at the following institutions: Worcester Polytechnic Institute, Cummings School of Veterinary Medicine at Tufts University, UMass Medical School, MCPHS University, College of the Holy Cross, Clark University, Worcester State University, Assumption College, Anna Maria College, Quinsigamond Community College. Study abroad program. ROTC: Army (c), Naval (c), Air Force (c).
Entrance Requirements: Options: electronic application, early admission, early decision, early action, international baccalaureate accepted. Required: high school transcript, minimum 2 high school GPA, SAT or ACT. Recommended: essay, recommendations, interview. Entrance: moderately difficult. Application deadlines: rolling, 11/15 for early decision, 11/15 for early action. Notification: continuous, 12/15 for early decision, 12/15 for early action. SAT Reasoning Test deadline: 8/15. Transfer credits accepted: Yes. Early deci-

sion applicants: 20. Early decision applicants admitted: 15. Early action applicants: 800. Early action applicants admitted: 707.
Costs Per Year: One-time mandatory fee: $275. Comprehensive fee: $53,000 includes full-time tuition ($35,600), mandatory fees ($3600), and college room and board ($13,800). Full-time tuition and fees vary according to class time, course load, and program. Room and board charges vary according to housing facility. Part-time tuition: $1483 per credit. Part-time tuition varies according to class time, course load, and program.
Collegiate Environment: Orientation program. Drama-theater group, choral group, student-run newspaper. Social organizations: 30 open to all. Most popular organizations: Campus Activities Board (CAB), Animal Health Club/Pre-Veterinary Club, International Game Developers Association (IGDA), Dance Club, Marine Wildlife Conversation Club. Major annual events: Family Weekend, Winter Welcome Back Week, Spring Weekend. Student services: health clinic, personal-psychological counseling. Campus security: 24-hour emergency response devices and patrols, late night transport-escort service, controlled dormitory access. Ruska Library plus 1 other. Books: 14,869 (physical), 46,845 (digital/electronic); Serial titles: 15 (physical), 74 (digital/electronic); Databases: 68. Weekly public service hours: 168; study areas open 24 hours, 5-7 days a week; students can reserve study rooms. 404 computers available on campus for general student use. A campuswide network can be accessed from student residence rooms and from off campus. Students can access the following: online class registration, Portal, 24X7 Library Chat, 24X7 online Tutoring. Staffed computer lab on campus provides training in use of computers, software, and the Internet.

■ BENJAMIN FRANKLIN INSTITUTE OF TECHNOLOGY
41 Berkeley St.
Boston, MA 02116-6296
Tel: (617)423-4630; Free: 877-400-BFIT
Fax: (617)482-3706
E-mail: bjohnson@bfit.edu
Web Site: www.bfit.edu
Description: Independent, primarily 2-year, coed. Awards certificates, transfer associate, terminal associate, and bachelor's degrees. Founded 1908. Setting: 3-acre urban campus. Total enrollment: 493. 635 applied, 64% were admitted. Full-time: 428 students, 10% women, 90% men. Part-time: 65 students, 9% women, 91% men. 0.4% American Indian or Alaska Native, non-Hispanic/Latino; 21% Hispanic/Latino; 29% Black or African American, non-Hispanic/Latino; 9% Asian, non-Hispanic/Latino; 0.2% Native Hawaiian or other Pacific Islander, non-Hispanic/Latino; 0.8% international. Core. Calendar: semesters. Academic remediation for entering students, ESL program, services for LD students, advanced placement, summer session for credit, part-time degree program, adult/continuing education programs, co-op programs and internships. Off campus study at University of Massachusetts - Dartmouth, Boston Architectural College, Wentworth Institute of Technology.
Entrance Requirements: Open admission. Options: electronic application, deferred admission, international baccalaureate accepted. Required: high school transcript. Recommended: essay, minimum 2 high school GPA, interview, SAT or ACT. Entrance: minimally difficult.
Collegiate Environment: Orientation program. Most popular organizations: Phi Theta Kappa, Student Government and Leadership, yearbook and video club, Green Technology Club, Women's Forum. Major annual events: Technology Olympics, Multicultural Feast, Spring Carnival. Student services: personal-psychological counseling. Campus security: 24-hour emergency response devices. Lufkin Memorial Library.

■ BENTLEY UNIVERSITY
175 Forest St.
Waltham, MA 02452-4705
Tel: (781)891-2000; Free: 800-523-2354
Fax: (781)891-3414
Web Site: www.bentley.edu
Description: Independent, comprehensive, coed. Awards bachelor's, master's, and doctoral degrees and post-master's certificates. Founded 1917. Setting: 163-acre suburban campus with easy access to Boston. Endowment: $289.6 million. Research spending for the previous fiscal year: $2.9 million. Educational spending for the previous fiscal year: $15,208 per student. Total enrollment: 5,460. Faculty: 463 (291 full-time, 172 part-time). Student-undergrad faculty ratio is 11:1. 9,252 applied, 43% were admitted. 50% from top 10% of their high school class, 89% from top quarter, 98% from top half. Full-time: 4,185 students, 40% women, 60% men. Part-time: 68 students, 40% women, 60% men. Students come from 44 states and ter-

ritories, 76 other countries, 58% from out-of-state. 7% Hispanic/Latino; 4% Black or African American, non-Hispanic/Latino; 8% Asian, non-Hispanic/Latino; 0.1% Native Hawaiian or other Pacific Islander, non-Hispanic/Latino; 16% international. 2% 25 or older, 78% live on campus, 2% transferred in. Retention: 93% of full-time freshmen returned the following year. Academic areas with the most degrees conferred: business/marketing; computer and information sciences; mathematics and statistics. Core. Calendar: semesters. ESL program, services for LD students, advanced placement, honors program, independent study, double major, summer session for credit, part-time degree program, internships, graduate courses open to undergrads. Off campus study at Brandeis. Study abroad program.

Entrance Requirements: Options: electronic application, early admission, early decision, deferred admission, international baccalaureate accepted. Required: essay, high school transcript, 2 recommendations, SAT or ACT, TOEFL or IELTS is required for non-native English speakers. Recommended: interview. Entrance: very difficult. Application deadlines: 1/7, 1/7 for nonresidents, 11/15 for early decision. Notification: 3/31, 3/31 for nonresidents, 12/21 for early decision. SAT Reasoning Test deadline: 2/15. Transfer credits accepted: Yes. Applicants placed on waiting list: 1,659. Wait-listed applicants offered admission: 1. Early decision applicants: 356. Early decision applicants admitted: 244.

Costs Per Year: Application fee: $75. Comprehensive fee: $68,790 includes full-time tuition ($50,060), mandatory fees ($1770), and college room and board ($16,960). College room only: $10,290.

Collegiate Environment: Orientation program. Drama-theater group, choral group, student-run newspaper, radio station. Social organizations: 115 open to all; national fraternities, national sororities, local fraternities; 4% of eligible men and 7% of eligible women are members. Most popular organizations: South Asian Student Association, Campus Activities Board, Delta Sigma Pi, Bentley Investment Group, National Association of Black Accountants. Major annual events: Spring Day, Relay for Life, Breakfast by Moonlight. Student services: health clinic, personal-psychological counseling, women's center. Campus security: 24-hour emergency response devices and patrols, late night transport-escort service, controlled dormitory access. 3,228 undergraduates lived in college housing during 2018-19. Freshmen guaranteed college housing. Option: coed housing available. Bentley Library. Books: 184,868 (physical), 217,175 (digital/electronic); Serial titles: 2,781 (physical), 116,336 (digital/electronic); Databases: 144. Weekly public service hours: 110; students can reserve study rooms. Operations spending for the previous fiscal year: $4.1 million. 4,620 computers available on campus for general student use. Computer purchase/lease plans available. A computer is required for all students. A campuswide network can be accessed from student residence rooms and from off campus. Students can access the following: online class registration, grade checking; online admission; blackboard; resume review; student employment; interlibary loan; free software. Staffed computer lab on campus provides training in use of computers, software, and the Internet.

Community Environment: The college represents the best of New England college campuses and provides an inviting atmosphere for study and socializing. Located in Waltham, Massachusetts, just 10 miles from Boston, Bentley's 163-acre suburban campus puts the city's many resources within easy reach. Boston is the country's ultimate college town. From theater to art exhibits, dance clubs to alternative rock concerts, championship sports to championship shopping, Boston has the proverbial "something for everyone." The college offers a shuttle service into Cambridge at Harvard Square, and from there, the entire city of Boston is accessible via public transportation.

■ BERKLEE COLLEGE OF MUSIC

1140 Boylston St.
Boston, MA 02215-3693
Tel: (617)266-1400; Free: 800-BERKLEE
Fax: (617)747-2047
E-mail: admissions@berklee.edu
Web Site: www.berklee.edu

Description: Independent, comprehensive, coed. Awards bachelor's and master's degrees. Founded 1945. Setting: urban campus. Total enrollment: 5,272. Faculty: 692 (266 full-time, 426 part-time). Student-undergrad faculty ratio is 11:1. 7,682 applied, 26% were admitted. Full-time: 4,291 students, 33% women, 67% men. Part-time: 821 students, 33% women, 67% men. 85% from out-of-state. 0.1% American Indian or Alaska Native, non-Hispanic/Latino; 8% Hispanic/Latino; 5% Black or African American, non-Hispanic/Latino; 4% Asian, non-Hispanic/Latino; 0.4% Native Hawaiian or other Pacific Islander, non-Hispanic/Latino; 33% international. 19% 25 or

older, 27% live on campus, 7% transferred in. Retention: 85% of full-time freshmen returned the following year. Academic areas with the most degrees conferred: visual and performing arts; health professions and related sciences; education. Calendar: semesters. ESL program, self-designed majors, independent study, distance learning, double major, co-op programs and internships. Study abroad program.

Entrance Requirements: Options: electronic application, early action, deferred admission, international baccalaureate accepted. Required: essay, high school transcript, 2 recommendations, interview, 2 years of formal music study, audition. Entrance: moderately difficult. Application deadlines: 1/15, 11/1 for early action. Notification: 3/31, 1/31 for early action. Applicants placed on waiting list: 232. Wait-listed applicants offered admission: 23.

Costs Per Year: Application fee: $150. Comprehensive fee: $62,500 includes full-time tuition ($42,880), mandatory fees ($1260), and college room and board ($18,360). Part-time tuition: $1560 per credit.

Collegiate Environment: Orientation program. Drama-theater group, choral group, student-run newspaper, radio station. Campus security: 24-hour patrols. The Stan Getz Media Center and Library.

Community Environment: See Boston University.

■ BERKSHIRE COMMUNITY COLLEGE

1350 W St.
Pittsfield, MA 01201-5786
Tel: (413)499-4660
Fax: (606)224-7744
E-mail: tschetti@berkshirecc.edu
Web Site: www.berkshirecc.edu

Description: State-supported, 2-year, coed. Part of Massachusetts Public Higher Education System. Awards certificates, transfer associate, and terminal associate degrees. Founded 1960. Setting: 180-acre rural campus with easy access to Hartford, CT; Albany, NY. Educational spending for the previous fiscal year: $6598 per student. Total enrollment: 1,959. Faculty: 176 (56 full-time, 120 part-time). Student-undergrad faculty ratio is 10:1. 752 applied, 99% were admitted. Full-time: 635 students, 52% women, 48% men. Part-time: 1,324 students, 67% women, 33% men. 8% from out-of-state. 0.6% American Indian or Alaska Native, non-Hispanic/Latino; 9% Hispanic/Latino; 7% Black or African American, non-Hispanic/Latino; 2% Asian, non-Hispanic/Latino; 0.2% Native Hawaiian or other Pacific Islander, non-Hispanic/Latino; 0.2% international. 42% 25 or older, 4% transferred in. Core. Calendar: semesters. Academic remediation for entering students, ESL program, services for LD students, advanced placement, accelerated degree program, freshman honors college, honors program, independent study, distance learning, summer session for credit, part-time degree program, adult/continuing education programs, co-op programs and internships. Off campus study at Massachusetts College of Liberal Arts, Williams College, Springfield Technical Community College, Greenfield Community College, Mount Wachusetts Community College.

Entrance Requirements: Open admission except for nursing and allied health programs. Options: electronic application, deferred admission. Required: high school transcript. Entrance: noncompetitive. Application deadline: rolling. Notification: continuous. Transfer credits accepted: Yes.

Collegiate Environment: Orientation program. Drama-theater group, choral group. Social organizations: 17 open to all. Most popular organizations: Mass PIRG, Student Nurse Organization, Student Senate, Diversity Club, LPN Organization. Major annual events: Concerts, Speakers, Film Presentations. Student services: personal-psychological counseling. Campus security: 24-hour emergency response devices and patrols, late night transport-escort service. Jonathan Edwards Library. Books: 52,501 (physical), 45,753 (digital/electronic); Serial titles: 983 (physical), 88 (digital/electronic); Databases: 88. Weekly public service hours: 52; students can reserve study rooms. Operations spending for the previous fiscal year: $390,647. 259 computers available on campus for general student use. A campuswide network can be accessed from off-campus. Students can access the following: online class registration, Web advisor. Staffed computer lab on campus provides training in use of computers, software, and the Internet.

Community Environment: Set in the cultural mecca of the rolling Berkshire hills, this attractive area is also the home to long established plastics and paper industries. The city has three libraries, numerous churches, two hospitals, a museum, YMCA, and good shopping facilities. Regular transportation is available by rail bus and air. Theatres, bowling, three golf courses, two large lakes, many parks, and closeness to area festivals and summer attractions make this city a favorite recreation spot. Part-time employment is available.

■ BOSTON ARCHITECTURAL COLLEGE

320 Newbury St.
Boston, MA 02115-2795
Tel: (617)262-5000
Fax: (617)585-0111
E-mail: admissions@the-bac.edu
Web Site: www.the-bac.edu

Description: Independent, comprehensive, coed. Awards bachelor's and master's degrees. Founded 1889. Setting: 1-acre urban campus with easy access to Boston. Endowment: $10.1 million. Total enrollment: 878. Faculty: 264 (26 full-time, 238 part-time). Student-undergrad faculty ratio is 4:1. 178 applied, 15% were admitted. Full-time: 354 students, 35% women, 65% men. Part-time: 118 students, 65% women, 35% men. 0.3% American Indian or Alaska Native, non-Hispanic/Latino; 17% Hispanic/Latino; 6% Black or African American, non-Hispanic/Latino; 9% Asian, non-Hispanic/Latino; 0.3% Native Hawaiian or other Pacific Islander, non-Hispanic/Latino; 5% international. Retention: 75% of full-time freshmen returned the following year. Academic area with the most degrees conferred: architecture. Core. Calendar: semesters. Services for LD students, advanced placement, independent study, distance learning, summer session for credit, adult/continuing education programs, internships. Off campus study at Art Institute of Boston at Lesley College, ProArts Consortium - Berklee, Boston Conservatory, Emerson College, MassArt, New England Conservatory, SFMA at Tufts.

Entrance Requirements: Open admission. Option: electronic application. Required: essay, high school transcript, resume and creative exercise. Recommended: interview. Entrance: noncompetitive. Transfer credits accepted: Yes.

Costs Per Year: Tuition: $21,144 full-time, $1762 per credit hour part-time. Mandatory fees: $750 full-time, $225 per term part-time. Full-time tuition and fees vary according to course load and program. Part-time tuition and fees vary according to course load and program.

Collegiate Environment: Orientation program. Social organizations: 7 open to all. Most popular organizations: Student Government Association, Student American Society of Landscape Architects, BAC Interior Design Society (IIDA and ASID), National Organization of Minority Architecture Students (NOMAS), American Institute of Architectural Students. Major annual events: First Fridays, PARTI, Food for Finals and Extended Hours. Student services: legal services, personal-psychological counseling. Campus security: 24-hour emergency response devices and patrols, late night transport-escort service, electronically operated building access, closed-circuit TV systems. Shaw and Stone Library. Books: 42,224 (physical), 117,108 (digital/electronic); Serial titles: 613 (physical), 313,728 (digital/electronic); Databases: 73. Weekly public service hours: 71. Operations spending for the previous fiscal year: $695,303. 84 computers available on campus for general student use. A campuswide network can be accessed from off-campus. Students can access the following: online class registration. Staffed computer lab on campus provides training in use of computers, software, and the Internet.

■ BOSTON BAPTIST COLLEGE

950 Metropolitan Ave.
Boston, MA 02136
Tel: (617)364-3510; Free: 888-235-2014
Fax: (617)364-0723
E-mail: kmelton@boston.edu
Web Site: www.boston.edu

Description: Independent Baptist, 4-year, coed. Awards associate and bachelor's degrees. Founded 1976. Setting: 8-acre suburban campus with easy access to Boston, Providence. Total enrollment: 96. Full-time: 73 students, 37% women, 63% men. Part-time: 23 students, 70% women, 30% men. Students come from 15 states and territories, 57% from out-of-state. 8% Hispanic/Latino; 7% Black or African American, non-Hispanic/Latino. 20% 25 or older, 65% live on campus, 11% transferred in. Retention: 74% of full-time freshmen returned the following year. Academic area with the most degrees conferred: theology and religious vocations. Core. Calendar: semesters. Academic remediation for entering students, advanced placement, honors program, distance learning, summer session for credit, part-time degree program, adult/continuing education programs. Off campus study.

Entrance Requirements: Option: deferred admission. Required: essay, high school transcript, 1 recommendation. Recommended: 1 recommendation. Required for some: SAT or ACT. Entrance: moderately difficult. Application deadline: rolling. Transfer credits accepted: Yes.

Collegiate Environment: Orientation program. Choral group. Social organizations: 3 open to all; local fraternities, local sororities; 90% of eligible men and 90% of eligible women are members. Most popular organizations: Community Service Organization, Recruitment, Campus Life. Student services: personal-psychological counseling. Campus security: 24-hour emergency response devices, student patrols, late night transport-escort service, controlled dormitory access. Boston Baptist College Library plus 1 other. 10 computers available on campus for general student use. A campuswide network can be accessed from student residence rooms and from off campus. Staffed computer lab on campus provides training in use of computers, software, and the Internet.

■ BOSTON COLLEGE

140 Commonwealth Ave.
Chestnut Hill, MA 02467-3800
Tel: (617)552-8000; Free: 800-360-2522
Fax: (617)552-0798
Web Site: www.bc.edu

Description: Independent Roman Catholic (Jesuit), university, coed. Awards bachelor's, master's, and doctoral degrees and post-master's certificates (also offers continuing education program with significant enrollment not reflected in profile). Founded 1863. Setting: 227-acre suburban campus with easy access to Boston. Endowment: $2.6 billion. Research spending for the previous fiscal year: $44 million. Total enrollment: 14,107. Faculty: 1,664 (834 full-time, 830 part-time). Student-undergrad faculty ratio is 12:1. 31,084 applied, 28% were admitted. 78% from top 10% of their high school class, 94% from top quarter, 98% from top half. Full-time: 9,377 students, 53% women, 47% men. Students come from 54 states and territories, 68 other countries, 72% from out-of-state. 11% Hispanic/Latino; 4% Black or African American, non-Hispanic/Latino; 10% Asian, non-Hispanic/Latino; 8% international. 84% live on campus, 2% transferred in. Retention: 95% of full-time freshmen returned the following year. Academic areas with the most degrees conferred: business/marketing; social sciences; biological/life sciences; psychology. Core. Calendar: semesters. Services for LD students, advanced placement, accelerated degree program, self-designed majors, honors program, independent study, double major, summer session for credit, part-time degree program, internships, graduate courses open to undergrads. Off campus study at Boston University, Brandeis University, Hebrew College, Pine Manor College, Regis College, Tufts University. Study abroad program. ROTC: Army (c), Naval (c), Air Force (c).

Entrance Requirements: Options: electronic application, early admission, early decision, deferred admission, international baccalaureate accepted. Required: essay, high school transcript, 2 recommendations, SAT or ACT. Entrance: very difficult. Application deadlines: 1/1, 11/1 for early decision plan 1, 1/1 for early decision plan 2. Notification: 4/1, 12/15 for early decision plan 1, 2/15 for early decision plan 2. SAT Reasoning Test deadline: 1/1. SAT Subject Test deadline: 1/1. Transfer credits accepted: Yes. Applicants placed on waiting list: 7,566. Wait-listed applicants offered admission: 273.

Collegiate Environment: Orientation program. Drama-theater group, choral group, marching band, student-run newspaper, radio station. Social organizations: 225 open to all. Most popular organizations: UGBC and individual School Senates, Asian Caucus, Appalachia Volunteers, Dance Marathon, 4Boston. Major annual events: Homecoming, Middlemarch Ball, Sporting Events. Student services: health clinic, personal-psychological counseling, women's center. Campus security: 24-hour emergency response devices and patrols, late night transport-escort service, controlled dormitory access. 7,689 college housing spaces available; all were occupied in 2018-19. Freshmen guaranteed college housing. Options: coed, women-only housing available. O'Neill Library plus 8 others. Books: 3.3 million (physical), 875,636 (digital/electronic); Serial titles: 3,545 (physical), 44,846 (digital/electronic). Study areas open 24 hours, 5-7 days a week; students can reserve study rooms. 1,000 computers available on campus for general student use. Computer purchase/lease plans available. A campuswide network can be accessed from student residence rooms and from off campus. Students can access the following: online class registration. Staffed computer lab on campus provides training in use of computers, software, and the Internet.

Community Environment: Boston College considers, and the students concur, that the suburban location of the campus six miles from Boston is the ideal setting for a University. The campus boasts superior academic, residential, and recreational facilities, and the dynamic Greater Boston area offers unlimited cultural, educational, and personal opportunities for individual development within a cosmopolitan atmosphere.

■ BOSTON UNIVERSITY

One Silber Way
Boston, MA 02215
Tel: (617)353-2000
Fax: (617)353-9695
E-mail: admissions@bu.edu
Web Site: www.bu.edu

Description: Independent, university, coed. Awards bachelor's, master's, and doctoral degrees and post-master's certificates. Founded 1839. Setting: 169-acre urban campus with easy access to Boston. System endowment: $2.2 billion. Research spending for the previous fiscal year: $175.3 million. Educational spending for the previous fiscal year: $37,601 per student. Total enrollment: 34,657. Faculty: 2,665 (1,873 full-time, 792 part-time). Student-undergrad faculty ratio is 10:1. 64,481 applied, 22% were admitted. 65% from top 10% of their high school class, 93% from top quarter, 100% from top half. 25 National Merit Scholars, 59 valedictorians. Full-time: 17,396 students, 60% women, 40% men. Part-time: 1,119 students, 54% women, 46% men. Students come from 52 states and territories, 121 other countries, 72% from out-of-state. 11% Hispanic/Latino; 4% Black or African American, non-Hispanic/Latino; 15% Asian, non-Hispanic/Latino; 0.1% Native Hawaiian or other Pacific Islander, non-Hispanic/Latino; 21% international. 2% 25 or older, 75% live on campus, 4% transferred in. Retention: 94% of full-time freshmen returned the following year. Academic areas with the most degrees conferred: business/marketing; social sciences; communication/journalism. Core. Calendar: semesters. ESL program, services for LD students, advanced placement, accelerated degree program, self-designed majors, freshman honors college, honors program, independent study, distance learning, double major, summer session for credit, part-time degree program, adult/continuing education programs, co-op programs and internships, graduate courses open to undergrads. Off campus study at Boston College, Brandeis University, Hebrew College, Tufts University. Study abroad program. ROTC: Army, Naval, Air Force.

Entrance Requirements: Options: electronic application, early admission, early decision, deferred admission, international baccalaureate accepted. Required: essay, high school transcript, 2 recommendations. Required for some: interview, audition, portfolio, SAT or ACT, SAT Subject Tests. Entrance: very difficult. Application deadlines: 1/6, 11/1 for early decision plan 1, 1/6 for early decision plan 2. Notification: 4/1, 12/15 for early decision plan 1, 2/7 for early decision plan 2. SAT Reasoning Test deadline: 1/6. SAT Subject Test deadline: 1/6. Transfer credits accepted: Yes. Applicants placed on waiting list: 5,441. Wait-listed applicants offered admission: 1. Early decision applicants: 4,474. Early decision applicants admitted: 1,267.

Costs Per Year: Application fee: $80. Comprehensive fee: $72,052 includes full-time tuition ($54,720), mandatory fees ($1172), and college room and board ($16,160). College room only: $10,680. Part-time tuition: $1710 per credit.

Collegiate Environment: Orientation program. Drama-theater group, choral group, marching band, student-run newspaper, radio station. Social organizations: 450 open to all; national fraternities, national sororities; 2% of women are members. Most popular organizations: performing and Acappella groups, cultural organizations, service organizations, Student Government, residence hall associations. Major annual events: Head of the Charles River Regatta, Beanpot Tournament, SPLASH. Student services: health clinic, personal-psychological counseling, women's center. Campus security: 24-hour emergency response devices and patrols, late night transport-escort service, controlled dormitory access. 11,732 college housing spaces available; 11,691 were occupied in 2018-19. Freshmen guaranteed college housing. On-campus residence required in freshman year. Options: coed, women-only housing available. Mugar Memorial Library plus 20 others. Books: 1.2 million (physical), 2.1 million (digital/electronic); Serial titles: 248,885 (physical), 111,406 (digital/electronic); Databases: 721. Weekly public service hours: 123; students can reserve study rooms. Operations spending for the previous fiscal year: $25.6 million. 250 computers available on campus for general student use. Computer purchase/lease plans available. A campuswide network can be accessed from student residence rooms and from off campus. Students can access the following: online class registration, research and educational networks. Staffed computer lab on campus provides training in use of computers, software, and the Internet.

Community Environment: Historic capital of Massachusetts, Boston is a contrast of past and present with broad avenues disappearing into crooked, narrow streets of colonial Boston. Modern stores and buildings stand next to Revolutionary shrines. With one in every five residents a college student, Boston is America's ultimate college town.

■ BRANDEIS UNIVERSITY

415 S St.
Waltham, MA 02454-9110
Tel: (781)736-2000; Free: 800-622-0622
Fax: (781)736-3536
E-mail: admissions@brandeis.edu
Web Site: www.brandeis.edu

Description: Independent, university, coed. Awards bachelor's, master's, and doctoral degrees and post-master's certificates. Founded 1948. Setting: 235-acre suburban campus with easy access to Boston. Endowment: $1 billion. Research spending for the previous fiscal year: $50.1 million. Educational spending for the previous fiscal year: $23,290 per student. Total enrollment: 5,801. Faculty: 541 (366 full-time, 175 part-time). Student-undergrad faculty ratio is 10:1. 11,798 applied, 31% were admitted. 56% from top 10% of their high school class, 91% from top quarter, 99% from top half. 14 National Merit Scholars, 14 valedictorians. Full-time: 3,619 students, 61% women, 39% men. Part-time: 20 students, 60% women, 40% men. Students come from 49 states and territories, 56 other countries, 70% from out-of-state. 0.1% American Indian or Alaska Native, non-Hispanic/Latino; 8% Hispanic/Latino; 5% Black or African American, non-Hispanic/Latino; 14% Asian, non-Hispanic/Latino; 0.2% Native Hawaiian or other Pacific Islander, non-Hispanic/Latino; 20% international. 76% live on campus, 1% transferred in. Retention: 92% of full-time freshmen returned the following year. Academic areas with the most degrees conferred: social sciences; biological/life sciences; business/marketing. Core. Calendar: semesters. Services for LD students, advanced placement, self-designed majors, independent study, double major, summer session for credit, internships, graduate courses open to undergrads. Off campus study at Tufts University, Babson College, Bentley College, Boston University, Wellesley College, Boston College, Olin College of Engineering. Study abroad program. ROTC: Army (c), Air Force (c).

Entrance Requirements: Options: electronic application, early admission, early decision, deferred admission, international baccalaureate accepted. Required: essay, high school transcript, 1 recommendation, SAT or ACT. Recommended: interview. Entrance: most difficult. Application deadlines: 1/1, 11/1 for early decision plan 1, 1/1 for early decision plan 2. Notification: 4/1, 12/15 for early decision plan 1, 2/1 for early decision plan 2. SAT Reasoning Test deadline: 1/1. SAT Subject Test deadline: 1/1. Transfer credits accepted: Yes. Applicants placed on waiting list: 1,844. Wait-listed applicants offered admission: 1. Early decision applicants: 851. Early decision applicants admitted: 333.

Costs Per Year: Application fee: $80. Comprehensive fee: $73,641 includes full-time tuition ($55,340), mandatory fees ($2221), and college room and board ($16,080). Part-time tuition: $1729 per credit. Part-time mandatory fees: $2221 per year.

Collegiate Environment: Orientation program. Drama-theater group, choral group, student-run newspaper, radio station. Social organizations: 201 open to all. Most popular organizations: Waltham Group, Undergraduate Theater Collective, Mountain Club, Student Union, BEMCo - student EMTs. Major annual events: Spring Fest, Brandeis Korean Student Association K-Nite, Liquid Latex. Student services: health clinic, personal-psychological counseling, women's center. Campus security: 24-hour emergency response devices and patrols, late night transport-escort service, controlled dormitory access. 2,960 college housing spaces available; 2,800 were occupied in 2018-19. Freshmen guaranteed college housing. On-campus residence required in freshman year. Option: coed housing available. Brandeis Library plus 1 other. Books: 1 million (physical), 1.1 million (digital/electronic); Serial titles: 11,941 (physical), 37,330 (digital/electronic); Databases: 445. Students can reserve study rooms. Operations spending for the previous fiscal year: $7.9 million. 130 computers available on campus for general student use. Computer purchase/lease plans available. A campuswide network can be accessed from student residence rooms and from off campus. Students can access the following: online class registration, educational software. Staffed computer lab on campus provides training in use of computers, software, and the Internet.

Community Environment: Waltham is a city of 58,000, ten miles west of Boston on the Charles River. It is a traditional manufacturing community that now hosts extensive high-tech industries. The City is served by commuter railroad and excellent bus lines for easy access to Boston and Cambridge. The locale has two colleges, four hospitals, a wide range of religious institutions, public library, Federal Archives and Records Center, parks, and a variety of ethnic restaurants. Good job and community service opportunities for students are available.

■ **BRIDGEWATER STATE UNIVERSITY**
131 Summer St.
Bridgewater, MA 02325
Tel: (508)531-1000
Fax: (508)531-1707
E-mail: admission@bridgew.edu
Web Site: www.bridgew.edu
Description: State-supported, comprehensive, coed. Part of Massachusetts Department of Higher Education. Awards bachelor's and master's degrees and post-master's certificates. Founded 1840. Setting: 278-acre suburban campus with easy access to Boston. Endowment: $41.6 million. Total enrollment: 10,990. Faculty: 789 (355 full-time, 434 part-time). Student-undergrad faculty ratio is 19:1. 6,806 applied, 90% were admitted. Full-time: 7,877 students, 59% women, 41% men. Part-time: 1,627 students, 57% women, 43% men. Students come from 28 states and territories, 34 other countries, 4% from out-of-state. 0.1% American Indian or Alaska Native, non-Hispanic/Latino; 7% Hispanic/Latino; 9% Black or African American, non-Hispanic/Latino; 2% Asian, non-Hispanic/Latino; 0.1% Native Hawaiian or other Pacific Islander, non-Hispanic/Latino; 0.5% international. 9% 25 or older, 40% live on campus, 11% transferred in. Retention: 78% of full-time freshmen returned the following year. Academic areas with the most degrees conferred: education; business/marketing; psychology. Core. Calendar: semesters. Academic remediation for entering students, ESL program, services for LD students, advanced placement, accelerated degree program, honors program, independent study, distance learning, double major, summer session for credit, part-time degree program, adult/continuing education programs, internships. Off campus study at Southeastern Association for Cooperation in Higher Education, the College Academic Program Sharing, National Student Exchange. Study abroad program. ROTC: Army (c), Air Force (c).
Entrance Requirements: Options: electronic application, early action, deferred admission, international baccalaureate accepted. Recommended: SAT. Entrance: moderately difficult. Application deadlines: 2/15, 11/15 for early action. Notification: continuous until 4/15. Transfer credits accepted: Yes. Early action applicants: 2,372. Early action applicants admitted: 2,379.
Costs Per Year: Application fee: $50. State resident tuition: $910 full-time, $38 per credit hour part-time. Nonresident tuition: $7050 full-time, $294 per credit hour part-time. Mandatory fees: $9457 full-time, $386.96 per credit hour part-time. College room and board: $12,750. College room only: $8400.
Collegiate Environment: Orientation program. Drama-theater group, choral group, student-run newspaper, radio station. Social organizations: 80 open to all; national fraternities, national sororities, co-ed fraternity; 4% of eligible men and 6% of eligible women are members. Most popular organizations: BSU Chapter of the Student Education Association of Massachusetts, Residence Hall Association, Best Buddies, Alpha Sigma Tau Sorority, Delta Phi Epsilon Sorority. Major annual events: Carnival, Greek Life Lip Sync, Homecoming and Family Day Fair. Student services: health clinic, personal-psychological counseling. Campus security: 24-hour emergency response devices and patrols, late night transport-escort service, controlled dormitory access. 3,294 college housing spaces available; 3,215 were occupied in 2018-19. Freshmen given priority for college housing. Option: coed housing available. Clement C. Maxwell Library. Books: 214,839 (physical), 54,656 (digital/electronic); Serial titles: 2,287 (physical), 31,407 (digital/electronic); Databases: 205. Weekly public service hours: 93. Operations spending for the previous fiscal year: $1.2 million. 780 computers available on campus for general student use. A computer is required for all students. A campuswide network can be accessed from student residence rooms and from off campus. Students can access the following: online class registration, student account information, application software. Staffed computer lab on campus provides training in use of computers, software, and the Internet.
Community Environment: This largely residential, colonial town, 30 miles southeast of Boston, has among its manufactures, shoes, leatherboard, nails, and bricks. Extensive excavations by archaeologists have revealed the remains of two Indian civilizations in the area. Boston provides the area with all the cultural, and recreational advantages of a large city.

■ **BRISTOL COMMUNITY COLLEGE**
777 Elsbree St.
Fall River, MA 02720-7395
Tel: (508)678-2811
Fax: (508)674-8838
E-mail: john.mclaughlin2@bristolcc.edu
Web Site: www.bristolcc.edu
Description: State-supported, 2-year, coed. Part of Massachusetts Com-

munity College System. Awards certificates, transfer associate, and terminal associate degrees. Founded 1965. Setting: 102-acre urban campus with easy access to Boston. Endowment: $9.5 million. Total enrollment: 7,637. Faculty: 653 (129 full-time, 524 part-time). Student-undergrad faculty ratio is 16:1. Students come from 7 other countries, 13% from out-of-state. 0.2% American Indian or Alaska Native, non-Hispanic/Latino; 9% Hispanic/Latino; 8% Black or African American, non-Hispanic/Latino; 2% Asian, non-Hispanic/Latino; 0.1% Native Hawaiian or other Pacific Islander, non-Hispanic/Latino. 38% 25 or older. Core. Calendar: semesters. Academic remediation for entering students, ESL program, services for LD students, advanced placement, accelerated degree program, self-designed majors, honors program, independent study, distance learning, summer session for credit, part-time degree program, adult/continuing education programs, co-op programs and internships. Off campus study at Southeastern Association for Cooperation in Higher Education in Massachusetts.
Entrance Requirements: Open admission except for health science and culinary arts programs. Options: electronic application, deferred admission. Required: high school transcript. Entrance: noncompetitive. Notification: continuous. Applicants placed on waiting list: 103. Wait-listed applicants offered admission: 14.
Costs Per Year: Application fee: $10. State resident tuition: $576 full-time, $24 per credit part-time. Nonresident tuition: $5520 full-time, $230 per credit part-time. Mandatory fees: $5088 full-time, $212 per credit part-time. Full-time tuition and fees vary according to course load. Part-time tuition and fees vary according to course load.
Collegiate Environment: Orientation program. Drama-theater group, student-run newspaper. Social organizations: 35 open to all. Most popular organizations: International Club, STEM, Dental Hygiene, Medical Assisting, Seeds of Sustainability (SOS). Major annual events: Harvest Festival, Club Fair, Welcome Week Activities. Student services: health clinic, personal-psychological counseling, women's center. Campus security: 24-hour emergency response devices and patrols, late night transport-escort service. Learning Resources Center plus 3 others. Books: 53,650 (physical), 47,790 (digital/electronic); Serial titles: 98 (physical); Databases: 83. Weekly public service hours: 73; students can reserve study rooms. 956 computers available on campus for general student use. A campuswide network can be accessed from off-campus. Students can access the following: online class registration. Staffed computer lab on campus provides training in use of computers, software, and the Internet.
Community Environment: Located approximately 50 miles south of Boston, Massachusetts and 18 miles southeast of Providence, Rhode Island on the New England Coast, the City is easily accessible by train, bus and air. Fall River's major industries include textiles, needlecrafts, and rubber and chemicals. The city, the factory outlet capital of New England, is experiencing a revitalization in its business and residential districts. Many opportunities exist for part-time and full-time work for students.

■ **BUNKER HILL COMMUNITY COLLEGE**
250 New Rutherford Ave.
Boston, MA 02129
Tel: (617)228-2000
Fax: (617)228-2120
Web Site: www.bhcc.mass.edu
Description: State-supported, 2-year, coed. Awards certificates and transfer associate degrees. Founded 1973. Setting: 21-acre urban campus. Endowment: $4.6 million. Total enrollment: 12,657. Faculty: 780 (149 full-time, 639 part-time). Student-undergrad faculty ratio is 22:1. 7,383 applied, 89% were admitted. Full-time: 4,185 students, 52% women, 48% men. Part-time: 8,472 students, 61% women, 39% men. 0.3% American Indian or Alaska Native, non-Hispanic/Latino; 27% Hispanic/Latino; 26% Black or African American, non-Hispanic/Latino; 11% Asian, non-Hispanic/Latino; 0.1% Native Hawaiian or other Pacific Islander, non-Hispanic/Latino; 5% international. Core. Calendar: semesters. Academic remediation for entering students, ESL program, services for LD students, advanced placement, accelerated degree program, honors program, independent study, distance learning, summer session for credit, part-time degree program, external degree program, co-op programs and internships. Study abroad program.
Entrance Requirements: Open admission. Options: electronic application, international baccalaureate accepted. Required: high school transcript. Application deadline: rolling. Notification: continuous. Transfer credits accepted: Yes.
Costs Per Year: State resident tuition: $576 full-time, $24 per credit hour part-time. Nonresident tuition: $5520 full-time, $230 per credit hour part-time. Mandatory fees: $4128 full-time, $172 per credit hour part-time.

Collegiate Environment: Orientation program. Drama-theater group, choral group, student-run radio station. Social organizations: 40 open to all. Most popular organizations: Alpha Kappa Mu Honor Society, Asian-Pacific Students Association, Music Club, Latinos Unidos Club, Christian Fellowship. Major annual events: Holiday Stroll, Family Day, Spring Day. Student services: health clinic, personal-psychological counseling. Campus security: 24-hour emergency response devices and patrols, late night transport-escort service. College housing not available. Bunker Hill Community College Library. Books: 40,964 (physical), 80,596 (digital/electronic); Serial titles: 92 (physical), 39 (digital/electronic); Databases: 105. Operations spending for the previous fiscal year: $847,411. 1,749 computers available on campus for general student use. A campuswide network can be accessed from off-campus. Students can access the following: online class registration, academic support services. Staffed computer lab on campus provides training in use of computers, software, and the Internet.

Community Environment: The college is located on a 21-acre site in the Charlestown District of Boston. The campus is very near the Bunker Hill Monument and the U.S.S. Constitution. The school is within immediate access to Boston's bus-streetcar-subway system.

■ CAMBRIDGE COLLEGE

500 Rutherford Ave.
Boston, MA 02129
Tel: (617)868-1000; Free: 800-877-4723
Fax: (617)349-3545
E-mail: denise.haile@cambridgecollege.edu
Web Site: www.cambridgecollege.edu

Description: Independent, comprehensive, coed. Awards bachelor's, master's, and doctoral degrees and post-master's certificates. Founded 1971. Setting: urban campus with easy access to Boston. Endowment: $11.4 million. Total enrollment: 3,757. Faculty: 453 (19 full-time, 434 part-time). Student-undergrad faculty ratio is 13:1. 107 applied, 64% were admitted. Full-time: 270 students, 71% women, 29% men. Part-time: 820 students, 66% women, 34% men. Students come from 7 states and territories, 13% from out-of-state. 0.3% American Indian or Alaska Native, non-Hispanic/Latino; 24% Hispanic/Latino; 32% Black or African American, non-Hispanic/Latino; 3% Asian, non-Hispanic/Latino; 0.3% Native Hawaiian or other Pacific Islander, non-Hispanic/Latino; 5% international. 85% 25 or older, 7% transferred in. Retention: 41% of full-time freshmen returned the following year. Academic areas with the most degrees conferred: liberal arts/general studies; business/marketing; public administration and social services. Core. Calendar: trimesters. Services for LD students, advanced placement, accelerated degree program, independent study, distance learning, summer session for credit, part-time degree program, adult/continuing education programs, internships, graduate courses open to undergrads.

Entrance Requirements: Open admission. Options: electronic application, deferred admission, international baccalaureate accepted. Required: essay, high school transcript, 1 recommendation, resume, health insurance, immunizations form, application form. Recommended: interview. Entrance: noncompetitive. Application deadline: rolling. Notification: continuous. Transfer credits accepted: Yes.

Collegiate Environment: Orientation program. Cambridge College Online Library. Operations spending for the previous fiscal year: $246,380.

■ CAPE COD COMMUNITY COLLEGE

2240 Iyannough Rd.
West Barnstable, MA 02668-1599
Tel: (508)362-2131; Free: 877-846-3672
E-mail: admiss@capecod.edu
Web Site: www.capecod.edu

Description: State-supported, 2-year, coed. Part of Massachusetts Public Higher Education System. Awards certificates, transfer associate, and terminal associate degrees. Founded 1961. Setting: 120-acre rural campus with easy access to Boston. Total enrollment: 4,657. Student-undergrad faculty ratio is 18:1. 1% from out-of-state. 39% 25 or older. Core. Calendar: semesters. Academic remediation for entering students, ESL program, services for LD students, advanced placement, freshman honors college, honors program, independent study, distance learning, summer session for credit, part-time degree program, adult/continuing education programs, co-op programs and internships. Off campus study at Bridgewater State College, Bristol Community College, Dean College, Massasoit Community College, Stonehill College, University of Massachusetts Dartmouth. Study abroad program.

Entrance Requirements: Open admission except for nursing, dental hygiene, physical therapy programs. Options: deferred admission, international baccalaureate accepted. Required: high school transcript. Required for some: essay. Entrance: noncompetitive. Application deadline: 8/10. Notification: continuous. Preference given to state residents.

Collegiate Environment: Orientation program. Drama-theater group, choral group, student-run newspaper, radio station. Student services: health clinic, personal-psychological counseling, women's center. Campus security: 24-hour patrols. Cape Cod Community College Learning Resource Center.

Community Environment: A rural village in the town of Barnstable on Cape Cod with several museums dedicated to early Americana in the area. The community has excellent facilities for all sports, yacht races and tournaments, and many historic celebrations. Part-time employment is available with exceptional opportunities in the summer. Transportation provided by air and bus. Shopping facilities are excellent.

■ CLARK UNIVERSITY

950 Main St.
Worcester, MA 01610-1477
Tel: (508)793-7711; Free: 800-GO-CLARK
Fax: (508)793-8821
E-mail: admissions@clarku.edu
Web Site: www.clarku.edu

Description: Independent, university, coed. Awards bachelor's, master's, and doctoral degrees and post-master's certificates. Founded 1887. Setting: 50-acre urban campus with easy access to Boston. Endowment: $436.9 million. Research spending for the previous fiscal year: $7.9 million. Educational spending for the previous fiscal year: $14,034 per student. Total enrollment: 3,122. Faculty: 298 (207 full-time, 92 part-time). Student-undergrad faculty ratio is 9:1. 7,687 applied, 59% were admitted. 39% from top 10% of their high school class, 71% from top quarter, 95% from top half. Full-time: 2,263 students, 61% women, 39% men. Part-time: 41 students, 46% women, 54% men. Students come from 43 states and territories, 56 other countries, 61% from out-of-state. 9% Hispanic/Latino; 4% Black or African American, non-Hispanic/Latino; 8% Asian, non-Hispanic/Latino; 12% international. 1% 25 or older, 66% live on campus, 2% transferred in. Retention: 87% of full-time freshmen returned the following year. Academic areas with the most degrees conferred: social sciences; psychology; biological/life sciences. Core. Calendar: semesters. ESL program, services for LD students, advanced placement, accelerated degree program, self-designed majors, honors program, independent study, distance learning, double major, summer session for credit, part-time degree program, adult/continuing education programs, internships, graduate courses open to undergrads. Off campus study at Worcester Consortium for Higher Education. Study abroad program. ROTC: Army (c), Air Force (c).

Entrance Requirements: Options: electronic application, early admission, early decision, early action, deferred admission, international baccalaureate accepted. Required: essay, high school transcript, 2 recommendations. Recommended: interview. Entrance: moderately difficult. Application deadlines: 1/15, 11/1 for early decision plan 1, 1/15 for early decision plan 2, 11/1 for early action. Notification: 4/1, 12/15 for early decision plan 1, 2/15 for early decision plan 2, 1/15 for early action. Transfer credits accepted: Yes. Applicants placed on waiting list: 710. Wait-listed applicants offered admission: 5. Early decision applicants: 54. Early decision applicants admitted: 34.

Costs Per Year: Application fee: $60. Comprehensive fee: $56,680 includes full-time tuition ($46,850), mandatory fees ($350), and college room and board ($9480). Part-time tuition: $1464 per unit.

Collegiate Environment: Orientation program. Drama-theater group, choral group, marching band, student-run newspaper, radio station. Social organizations: 130 open to all. Most popular organizations: International Students Association, Science Fiction People of Clark, Outing Club, Hillel, Clark Musical Theater. Major annual events: Spree Day, International Gala, Fall Major Event (comedy show or concert). Student services: health clinic, personal-psychological counseling, women's center. Campus security: 24-hour emergency response devices and patrols, student patrols, late night transport-escort service, controlled dormitory access. Freshmen guaranteed college housing. On-campus residence required through sophomore year. Options: coed, women-only housing available. Robert Hutchings Goddard Library plus 8 others. Students can reserve study rooms. Operations spending for the previous fiscal year: $2.8 million.

Community Environment: An industrial center and state center for biotechnology and related research, Worcester is the second largest city in all of New England. Good transportation facilities make area easily accessible. Located 38 miles west of Boston, city has several religious groups of all denominations, as well as significant libraries, museums, parks, theatre, and music facilities and municipal recreation opportunities and the Centrum (seating 13,000) houses concerts, sport events, and exhibits. Many students take advantage of the city's offerings through paid and unpaid internships with area corporations and institutions.

■ COLLEGE OF THE HOLY CROSS

1 College St.
Worcester, MA 01610-2395
Tel: (508)793-2011; Free: 800-442-2421
Fax: (508)793-3888
Web Site: www.holycross.edu
Description: Independent Roman Catholic (Jesuit), 4-year, coed. Awards bachelor's degrees. Founded 1843. Setting: 174-acre suburban campus with easy access to Boston. Endowment: $783.2 million. Research spending for the previous fiscal year: $941,893. Educational spending for the previous fiscal year: $21,608 per student. Total enrollment: 3,128. Faculty: 328 (290 full-time, 38 part-time). Student-undergrad faculty ratio is 10:1. 7,054 applied, 38% were admitted. 58% from top 10% of their high school class, 88% from top quarter, 100% from top half. 12 valedictorians. Full-time: 3,102 students, 52% women, 48% men. Part-time: 26 students, 69% women, 31% men. Students come from 50 states and territories, 24 other countries, 58% from out-of-state. 0.1% American Indian or Alaska Native, non-Hispanic/Latino; 10% Hispanic/Latino; 4% Black or African American, non-Hispanic/Latino; 4% Asian, non-Hispanic/Latino; 0.1% Native Hawaiian or other Pacific Islander, non-Hispanic/Latino; 3% international. 90% live on campus, 1% transferred in. Retention: 95% of full-time freshmen returned the following year. Academic areas with the most degrees conferred: social sciences; psychology; foreign languages and literature. Core. Calendar: semesters. Services for LD students, advanced placement, accelerated degree program, self-designed majors, honors program, independent study, double major, summer session for credit, internships. Off campus study at Higher Education Consortium of Central Massachusetts, which includes the University of Massachusetts Medical School, Worcester Polytechnic Institute and Clark University. Study abroad program. ROTC: Army (c), Naval, Air Force (c).
Entrance Requirements: Options: electronic application, early admission, early decision, deferred admission, international baccalaureate accepted. Required: essay, high school transcript, 2 recommendations. Recommended: interview. Entrance: very difficult. Application deadlines: 1/15, 12/15 for early decision. Notification: 4/1, rolling for early decision. SAT Reasoning Test deadline: 2/1. SAT Subject Test deadline: 2/1. Transfer credits accepted: Yes. Applicants placed on waiting list: 1,581. Wait-listed applicants offered admission: 0. Early decision applicants: 471. Early decision applicants admitted: 383.
Costs Per Year: Application fee: $60. Comprehensive fee: $69,810 includes full-time tuition ($54,050), mandatory fees ($690), and college room and board ($15,070). College room only: $8250.
Collegiate Environment: Orientation program. Drama-theater group, choral group, marching band, student-run newspaper, radio station. Social organizations: 103 open to all. Most popular organizations: SPUD (community service organization), choral and music groups, Campus Activities Board, Student Government Association, Purple Key Society. Major annual events: Homecoming, Family Weekend, Purple Pride Day. Student services: health clinic, personal-psychological counseling. Campus security: 24-hour emergency response devices and patrols, late night transport-escort service, controlled dormitory access. College housing designed to accommodate 2,507 students; 2,615 undergraduates lived in college housing during 2018-19. Freshmen guaranteed college housing. On-campus residence required through sophomore year. Option: coed housing available. Dinand Library plus 4 others. Books: 651,508 (physical), 292,776 (digital/electronic); Serial titles: 441 (physical), 24,739 (digital/electronic); Databases: 312. Study areas open 24 hours, 5-7 days a week; students can reserve study rooms. Operations spending for the previous fiscal year: $4.4 million. 298 computers available on campus for general student use. Computer purchase/lease plans available. A campuswide network can be accessed from student residence rooms and from off campus. Students can access the following: online class registration. Staffed computer lab on campus provides training in use of software and the Internet.
Community Environment: See Clark University.

■ CURRY COLLEGE

1071 Blue Hill Ave.
Milton, MA 02186-9984
Tel: (617)333-0500; Free: 800-669-0686
Fax: (617)333-6860
E-mail: curryadm@curry.edu
Web Site: www.curry.edu
Description: Independent, comprehensive, coed. Awards bachelor's and master's degrees and post-master's certificates. Founded 1879. Setting: 131-acre suburban campus with easy access to Boston. Endowment: $99.4 million. Educational spending for the previous fiscal year: $12,491 per student. Total enrollment: 2,799. Faculty: 361 (129 full-time, 232 part-time). Student-undergrad faculty ratio is 13:1. 5,733 applied, 93% were admitted. 3% from top 10% of their high school class, 16% from top quarter, 40% from top half. Full-time: 1,989 students, 54% women, 46% men. Part-time: 367 students, 78% women, 22% men. Students come from 29 states and territories, 21 other countries, 26% from out-of-state. 0.3% American Indian or Alaska Native, non-Hispanic/Latino; 8% Hispanic/Latino; 12% Black or African American, non-Hispanic/Latino; 3% Asian, non-Hispanic/Latino; 0.2% Native Hawaiian or other Pacific Islander, non-Hispanic/Latino; 2% international. 19% 25 or older, 83% live on campus, 3% transferred in. Retention: 68% of full-time freshmen returned the following year. Academic areas with the most degrees conferred: health professions and related sciences; business/marketing; homeland security, law enforcement, firefighting, and protective services. Core. Calendar: semesters. Academic remediation for entering students, ESL program, services for LD students, advanced placement, accelerated degree program, self-designed majors, honors program, independent study, double major, summer session for credit, part-time degree program, adult/continuing education programs, internships. Off campus study. Study abroad program. ROTC: Army (c).
Entrance Requirements: Options: electronic application, early admission, early action, deferred admission, international baccalaureate accepted. Required: essay, high school transcript, minimum 2 high school GPA, 1 recommendation, Common Application Supplement and Program for Advancement of Learning (PAL), Cognitive and Achievement Testing for PAL. Required for some: interview, SAT or ACT, TOEFL for international applicants whose native language is not English. Entrance: moderately difficult. Notification: continuous. SAT Reasoning Test deadline: 4/1. Transfer credits accepted: Yes. Applicants placed on waiting list: 67. Wait-listed applicants offered admission: 0. Early action applicants: 1,976. Early action applicants admitted: 1,596.
Costs Per Year: Application fee: $50. One-time mandatory fee: $360. Comprehensive fee: $57,210 includes full-time tuition ($38,950), mandatory fees ($1920), and college room and board ($16,340). College room only: $8780. Part-time tuition: $1248 per credit.
Collegiate Environment: Orientation program. Drama-theater group, choral group, student-run newspaper, radio station. Social organizations: 40 open to all. Most popular organizations: Students Entertainment and Events (SEE), Black Student Union (BSU), Latino Student Union (LSU), Multicultural Student Union (MSU), Student Government Association (SGA). Major annual events: Homecoming, Big Bang, Spring Weekend. Student services: health clinic, personal-psychological counseling. Campus security: 24-hour emergency response devices and patrols, late night transport-escort service, controlled dormitory access, campus safety office. 1,591 college housing spaces available; 1,387 were occupied in 2018-19. No special consideration for freshman housing applicants. Options: coed, men-only, women-only housing available. Levin Library. Books: 71,564 (physical), 141,518 (digital/electronic); Serial titles: 66 (physical), 109,694 (digital/electronic); Databases: 101. Weekly public service hours: 98; students can reserve study rooms. Operations spending for the previous fiscal year: $1.9 million. 245 computers available on campus for general student use. A campuswide network can be accessed from student residence rooms and from off campus. Students can access the following: online class registration. Staffed computer lab on campus provides training in use of computers, software, and the Internet.
Community Environment: Suburban location about seven miles south of Boston near the Neponset River in the town of Milton. All forms of transportation easily accessible. Shuttle bus to Boston, rapid transit. Blue Hills Reservation, a summer and winter sports center with golf course, ice rink, ski slopes, is located nearby. Job opportunities, community services, and cultural advantages will be found in neighboring Boston, as well as on campus.

■ DEAN COLLEGE

99 Main St.
Franklin, MA 02038-1994
Tel: (508)541-1900; Free: 877-TRY-DEAN
Fax: (508)541-8726

E-mail: igodes@dean.edu

Web Site: www.dean.edu

Description: Independent, 4-year, coed. Awards associate and bachelor's degrees. Founded 1865. Setting: 100-acre suburban campus with easy access to Boston, MA and Providence, RI. Endowment: $47.1 million. Educational spending for the previous fiscal year: $9369 per student. Total enrollment: 1,323. Faculty: 150 (29 full-time, 121 part-time). Student-undergrad faculty ratio is 17:1. 4,854 applied, 83% were admitted. Full-time: 1,152 students, 51% women, 49% men. Part-time: 171 students, 60% women, 40% men. Students come from 35 states and territories, 19 other countries, 44% from out-of-state. 0.4% American Indian or Alaska Native, non-Hispanic/Latino; 10% Hispanic/Latino; 13% Black or African American, non-Hispanic/Latino; 1% Asian, non-Hispanic/Latino; 0.2% Native Hawaiian or other Pacific Islander, non-Hispanic/Latino; 4% international. 8% 25 or older, 90% live on campus, 3% transferred in. Retention: 70% of full-time freshmen returned the following year. Academic areas with the most degrees conferred: visual and performing arts; business/marketing; psychology. Core. Calendar: semesters. ESL program, services for LD students, advanced placement, accelerated degree program, self-designed majors, honors program, independent study, distance learning, double major, summer session for credit, part-time degree program, adult/continuing education programs, internships. Off campus study at Washington Center for Internships and Academic Seminars Disney College Program. Study abroad program.

Entrance Requirements: Options: electronic application, early admission, early action, deferred admission, international baccalaureate accepted. Required: high school transcript. Recommended: essay, minimum 2 high school GPA, 1 recommendation, interview. Required for some: audition for performing arts majors. Entrance: moderately difficult. Application deadlines: rolling, 12/1 for early action. Notification: continuous, 1/15 for early action. SAT Reasoning Test deadline: 8/15. Transfer credits accepted: Yes. Early action applicants: 2,396. Early action applicants admitted: 1,665.

Costs Per Year: Application fee: $0. One-time mandatory fee: $300. Comprehensive fee: $57,672 includes full-time tuition ($40,214), mandatory fees ($200), and college room and board ($17,258). College room only: $10,900. Part-time tuition: $365 per credit hour. Part-time mandatory fees: $25 per term.

Collegiate Environment: Orientation program. Drama-theater group, choral group, student-run radio station. Social organizations: 35 open to all. Most popular organizations: National Society of Leadership and Success, Student Activities Committee, Residence Hall Association, International Student Association, Dean Community Outreach. Major annual events: Spring Fling, Homecoming, Bulldog Bash. Student services: health clinic, personal-psychological counseling. Campus security: 24-hour emergency response devices and patrols, student patrols, late night transport-escort service, controlled dormitory access. 1,000 college housing spaces available; all were occupied in 2018-19. Freshmen guaranteed college housing. On-campus residence required through senior year. Options: coed, men-only, women-only housing available. E. Ross Anderson Library. Books: 35,672 (physical), 49,661 (digital/electronic); Serial titles: 100,000 (digital/electronic); Databases: 42. Weekly public service hours: 77. Operations spending for the previous fiscal year: $296,500. 36 computers available on campus for general student use. A computer is required for all students. A campuswide network can be accessed from student residence rooms. Students can access the following: online class registration. Staffed computer lab on campus provides training in use of computers, software, and the Internet.

Community Environment: Franklin is located 30 miles southwest of Boston and is the birthplace of Horace Mann. This is a rapidly growing area easily accessible by bus and rail. The community has swimming pools, tennis courts, ski facilities, riding, golf, movies, bowling, and dancing. There are many shopping centers nearby. Some part-time employment is available for students.

■ **EASTERN NAZARENE COLLEGE**

23 E Elm Ave.

Quincy, MA 02170

Tel: (617)745-3000; Free: 800-88-ENC88

Fax: (617)745-3907

E-mail: ashley.rudeen@enc.edu

Web Site: www.enc.edu

Description: Independent, comprehensive, coed, affiliated with Church of the Nazarene. Awards associate, bachelor's, and master's degrees. Founded 1900. Setting: 17-acre urban campus with easy access to Boston.

Total enrollment: 848. 1,157 applied, 68% were admitted. Full-time: 571 students, 55% women, 45% men. Part-time: 123 students, 67% women, 33% men. Students come from 37 states and territories, 15 other countries, 40% from out-of-state. 0.1% American Indian or Alaska Native, non-Hispanic/Latino; 13% Hispanic/Latino; 21% Black or African American, non-Hispanic/Latino; 2% Asian, non-Hispanic/Latino; 0.4% Native Hawaiian or other Pacific Islander, non-Hispanic/Latino; 4% international. 27% 25 or older, 50% live on campus, 5% transferred in. Retention: 67% of full-time freshmen returned the following year. Academic areas with the most degrees conferred: education; business/marketing; psychology. Core. Calendar: semesters. Academic remediation for entering students, services for LD students, advanced placement, accelerated degree program, honors program, independent study, double major, summer session for credit, part-time degree program, adult/continuing education programs, co-op programs and internships, graduate courses open to undergrads. Off campus study. Study abroad program.

Entrance Requirements: Options: electronic application, early admission, deferred admission. Required: high school transcript, minimum 2 high school GPA, 1 recommendation, SAT or ACT. Recommended: essay, minimum 3 high school GPA, 2 recommendations, interview. Entrance: moderately difficult. Application deadline: rolling. Notification: continuous. SAT Reasoning Test deadline: 9/1. SAT Subject Test deadline: 9/1. Transfer credits accepted: Yes.

Costs Per Year: Comprehensive fee: $35,222 includes full-time tuition ($24,698), mandatory fees ($900), and college room and board ($9624). Full-time tuition and fees vary according to class time, course load, degree level, location, program, and reciprocity agreements. Room and board charges vary according to board plan and housing facility. Part-time tuition: $1338 per credit hour. Part-time tuition varies according to class time, degree level, location, program, and reciprocity agreements.

Collegiate Environment: Orientation program. Drama-theater group, choral group, student-run newspaper. Social organizations: 50 open to all. Most popular organizations: Gospel Choir, A cappella Choir, Germantown Tutoring, ALANA, Spirit Team. Major annual events: Welcome Week, Homecoming, Spring Fever Day. Student services: health clinic, personal-psychological counseling. Campus security: 24-hour emergency response devices and patrols, student patrols, late night transport-escort service, controlled dormitory access. Nease Library. Books: 113,825 (physical), 314,187 (digital/electronic); Serial titles: 748 (physical), 295,387 (digital/electronic); Databases: 90. Weekly public service hours: 95; study areas open 24 hours, 5-7 days a week; students can reserve study rooms. 140 computers available on campus for general student use. Computer purchase/lease plans available. A campuswide network can be accessed from student residence rooms and from off campus. Students can access the following: online class registration. Staffed computer lab on campus provides training in use of computers, software, and the Internet.

Community Environment: See Quincy College.

■ **ELMS COLLEGE**

291 Springfield St.

Chicopee, MA 01013-2839

Tel: (413)594-2761; Free: 800-255-ELMS

Fax: (413)594-2781

E-mail: admissions@elms.edu

Web Site: www.elms.edu

Description: Independent Roman Catholic, comprehensive, coed. Awards associate, bachelor's, master's, and doctoral degrees and post-master's certificates. Founded 1928. Setting: 32-acre suburban campus. Total enrollment: 1,580. Faculty: 187 (66 full-time, 121 part-time). Student-undergrad faculty ratio is 12:1. 868 applied, 79% were admitted. Full-time: 973 students, 74% women, 26% men. Part-time: 201 students, 75% women, 25% men. Students come from 28 states and territories, 21 other countries, 23% from out-of-state. 0.3% American Indian or Alaska Native, non-Hispanic/Latino; 14% Hispanic/Latino; 9% Black or African American, non-Hispanic/Latino; 2% Asian, non-Hispanic/Latino; 0.5% international. 32% 25 or older, 33% live on campus, 4% transferred in. Retention: 84% of full-time freshmen returned the following year. Academic areas with the most degrees conferred: health professions and related sciences; business/marketing; public administration and social services. Core. Calendar: semesters. ESL program, services for LD students, advanced placement, accelerated degree program, independent study, distance learning, double major, summer session for credit, part-time degree program, adult/continuing education programs, co-op programs and internships, graduate courses open to undergrads. Off campus study at Cooperating Colleges of Greater

Springfield, Sisters of Saint Joseph Colleges Consortium. Study abroad program. ROTC: Army (c), Air Force (c).

Entrance Requirements: Options: early admission, deferred admission, international baccalaureate accepted. Required: essay, high school transcript, 2 recommendations, SAT or ACT. Recommended: interview. Entrance: moderately difficult. Application deadline: rolling. Notification: continuous. SAT Reasoning Test deadline: 9/1. Transfer credits accepted: Yes.

Costs Per Year: Comprehensive fee: $48,894 includes full-time tuition ($34,114), mandatory fees ($1674), and college room and board ($13,106). Room and board charges vary according to board plan. Part-time tuition: $691 per credit hour. Part-time tuition varies according to location and program.

Collegiate Environment: Orientation program. Choral group. Social organizations: 21 open to all. Student services: health clinic, personal-psychological counseling. Campus security: 24-hour emergency response devices and patrols, controlled dormitory access. Alumnae Library. 175 computers available on campus for general student use. A campuswide network can be accessed from student residence rooms and from off campus. Students can access the following: online class registration. Staffed computer lab on campus.

Community Environment: Elms is located in western Massachusetts, two and one half miles from Springfield, near the junction of I-91 and I-90 (Mass. Turnpike). The climate is temperate. The community has several churches, museums, a library, theatre, sports center, cultural and social events at many of the nearby colleges, shopping, and major civic, fraternal, and veteran's organizations. Part-time employment is available.

■ **EMERSON COLLEGE**
120 Boylston St.
Boston, MA 02116-4624
Tel: (617)824-8500
Fax: (617)824-8609
Web Site: www.emerson.edu

Description: Independent, comprehensive, coed. Awards bachelor's, master's, and doctoral degrees. Founded 1880. Setting: urban campus with easy access to Boston, MA. Endowment: $171.6 million. Research spending for the previous fiscal year: $3.7 million. Total enrollment: 4,582. Faculty: 459 (206 full-time, 253 part-time). Student-undergrad faculty ratio is 13:1. 12,941 applied, 36% were admitted. 29% from top 10% of their high school class, 70% from top quarter, 94% from top half. Full-time: 3,779 students, 60% women, 40% men. Part-time: 76 students, 71% women, 29% men. 78% from out-of-state. 0.1% American Indian or Alaska Native, non-Hispanic/Latino; 13% Hispanic/Latino; 3% Black or African American, non-Hispanic/Latino; 5% Asian, non-Hispanic/Latino; 0.1% Native Hawaiian or other Pacific Islander, non-Hispanic/Latino; 11% international. 1% 25 or older, 52% live on campus, 5% transferred in. Retention: 87% of full-time freshmen returned the following year. Academic areas with the most degrees conferred: visual and performing arts; communication/journalism; business/marketing. Core. Calendar: semesters. Services for LD students, advanced placement, self-designed majors, honors program, independent study, double major, summer session for credit, part-time degree program, adult/continuing education programs, internships, graduate courses open to undergrads. Off campus study. Study abroad program.

Entrance Requirements: Options: electronic application, early admission, early action, deferred admission, international baccalaureate accepted. Required: essay, high school transcript, 1 recommendation. Required for some: interview. Entrance: very difficult. Application deadlines: 1/15, 11/1 for early action. Notification: continuous until 4/1, 12/15 for early action. SAT Reasoning Test deadline: 1/5. Transfer credits accepted: Yes. Applicants placed on waiting list: 1,490. Wait-listed applicants offered admission: 0.

Costs Per Year: Application fee: $65. Comprehensive fee: $67,128 includes full-time tuition ($47,856), mandatory fees ($872), and college room and board ($18,400).

Collegiate Environment: Orientation program. Drama-theater group, choral group, student-run newspaper, radio station. Social organizations: 85 open to all; national fraternities, national sororities, local fraternities, local sororities; 2% of eligible men and 3% of eligible women are members. Most popular organizations: EIV (Emerson Independent Video), National Broadcasting Society (student chapter), SPEC (Screenwriting), Entertainment Monthly (entertainment news), Emerson International (international student group). Major annual events: EVVY's (award show), Spring Musical, Emerson Recognition and Achievement Awards (student government). Student services: health clinic, personal-psychological counseling. Campus

security: 24-hour emergency response devices and patrols, late night transport-escort service, controlled dormitory access. 2,692 college housing spaces available; all were occupied in 2018-19. Freshmen guaranteed college housing. On-campus residence required through junior year. Option: coed housing available. Iwasaki Library plus 1 other. Books: 336,669 (physical), 2,484 (digital/electronic); Serial titles: 67,760 (digital/electronic); Databases: 125. Weekly public service hours: 93; students can reserve study rooms. 480 computers available on campus for general student use. Computer purchase/lease plans available. A campuswide network can be accessed from student residence rooms and from off campus. Students can access the following: online class registration. Staffed computer lab on campus provides training in use of computers, software, and the Internet.

Community Environment: See Boston University.

■ **EMMANUEL COLLEGE**
400 The Fenway
Boston, MA 02115
Tel: (617)735-9715
Fax: (617)735-9801
E-mail: enroll@emmanuel.edu
Web Site: www.emmanuel.edu

Description: Independent Roman Catholic, comprehensive, coed. Awards bachelor's and master's degrees and post-master's certificates. Founded 1919. Setting: 17-acre urban campus. Endowment: $137.3 million. Research spending for the previous fiscal year: $373,419. Educational spending for the previous fiscal year: $9634 per student. Total enrollment: 2,209. Faculty: 199 (94 full-time, 105 part-time). Student-undergrad faculty ratio is 13:1. 5,770 applied, 77% were admitted. 16% from top 10% of their high school class, 27% from top quarter, 77% from top half. Full-time: 1,935 students, 75% women, 25% men. Part-time: 154 students, 85% women, 15% men. Students come from 34 states and territories, 53 other countries, 40% from out-of-state. 0.2% American Indian or Alaska Native, non-Hispanic/Latino; 11% Hispanic/Latino; 6% Black or African American, non-Hispanic/Latino; 4% Asian, non-Hispanic/Latino; 1% international. 1% 25 or older, 72% live on campus, 2% transferred in. Retention: 78% of full-time freshmen returned the following year. Academic areas with the most degrees conferred: biological/life sciences; psychology; business/marketing. Core. Calendar: semesters. Services for LD students, advanced placement, self-designed majors, honors program, independent study, distance learning, double major, summer session for credit, part-time degree program, internships, graduate courses open to undergrads. Off campus study at Colleges of the Fenway. Study abroad program. ROTC: Army (c).

Entrance Requirements: Options: electronic application, early admission, early action, deferred admission. Required: essay, high school transcript, 2 recommendations. Recommended: interview. Application deadlines: 2/15, 11/1 for early action. Notification: continuous until 1/15, 12/15 for early action. SAT Reasoning Test deadline: 2/15. Transfer credits accepted: Yes. Early action applicants: 2,847. Early action applicants admitted: 2,593.

Costs Per Year: Application fee: $60. One-time mandatory fee: $350. Comprehensive fee: $56,892 includes full-time tuition ($41,028), mandatory fees ($420), and college room and board ($15,444). Part-time tuition: $1,282.13 per credit hour.

Collegiate Environment: Orientation program. Drama-theater group, choral group, student-run newspaper, radio station. Social organizations: 69 open to all. Most popular organizations: Student Government Association, Biology Club, Emmanuel College Programming Team, Black Student Union, EMS Club. Major annual events: Emmanuel College Dance Marathon, Big Man On Campus, Day of Service. Student services: health clinic, personal-psychological counseling. Campus security: 24-hour emergency response devices and patrols, late night transport-escort service, controlled dormitory access. 1,395 college housing spaces available. Freshmen guaranteed college housing. Option: coed housing available. Cardinal Cushing Library/Learning Commons. Books: 63,542 (physical), 191,776 (digital/electronic); Serial titles: 70 (physical), 2,855 (digital/electronic); Databases: 61. Weekly public service hours: 108; students can reserve study rooms. Operations spending for the previous fiscal year: $1.9 million. 284 computers available on campus for general student use. A campuswide network can be accessed from student residence rooms. Students can access the following: online class registration. Staffed computer lab on campus provides training in use of computers, software, and the Internet.

■ **ENDICOTT COLLEGE**
376 Hale St.
Beverly, MA 01915-2096

Tel: (978)927-0585; Free: 800-325-1114

Fax: (978)927-0084

E-mail: admissio@endicott.edu

Web Site: www.endicott.edu

Description: Independent, comprehensive, coed. Awards associate, bachelor's, master's, and doctoral degrees and post-master's certificates. Founded 1939. Setting: 235-acre suburban campus with easy access to Boston. Endowment: $88.7 million. Educational spending for the previous fiscal year: $11,953 per student. Total enrollment: 5,131. Faculty: 581 (110 full-time, 471 part-time). Student-undergrad faculty ratio is 14:1. 3,598 applied, 80% were admitted. 16% from top 10% of their high school class, 40% from top quarter, 78% from top half. Full-time: 3,029 students, 61% women, 39% men. Part-time: 356 students, 69% women, 31% men. Students come from 33 states and territories, 37 other countries, 50% from out-of-state. 0.2% American Indian or Alaska Native, non-Hispanic/Latino; 5% Hispanic/Latino; 2% Black or African American, non-Hispanic/Latino; 1% Asian, non-Hispanic/Latino; 0.1% Native Hawaiian or other Pacific Islander, non-Hispanic/Latino; 2% international. 91% live on campus, 4% transferred in. Retention: 83% of full-time freshmen returned the following year. Academic areas with the most degrees conferred: business/marketing; health professions and related sciences; parks and recreation. Core. Calendar: semesters. ESL program, services for LD students, advanced placement, accelerated degree program, self-designed majors, honors program, independent study, distance learning, double major, summer session for credit, part-time degree program, adult/continuing education programs, co-op programs and internships, graduate courses open to undergrads. Off campus study at 10 members of the Northeast Consortium of Colleges and Universities in Massachusetts. Study abroad program. ROTC: Army (c).

Entrance Requirements: Options: electronic application, international baccalaureate accepted. Required: essay, high school transcript, minimum 2.5 high school GPA, 1 recommendation. Recommended: interview. Required for some: SAT or ACT. Entrance: moderately difficult. Application deadline: 2/15. Notification: continuous. SAT Reasoning Test deadline: 2/15. SAT Subject Test deadline: 2/15. Transfer credits accepted: Yes. Applicants placed on waiting list: 42. Wait-listed applicants offered admission: 15.

Costs Per Year: Application fee: $50. Comprehensive fee: $49,664 includes full-time tuition ($33,304), mandatory fees ($700), and college room and board ($15,660). College room only: $10,794. Part-time tuition: $1024 per credit hour.

Collegiate Environment: Orientation program. Drama-theater group, choral group, student-run newspaper, radio station. Social organizations: 62 open to all. Major annual events: Homecoming/Family Weekend, Spring Week, Gullabration. Student services: health clinic, personal-psychological counseling. Campus security: 24-hour emergency response devices and patrols, student patrols, late night transport-escort service, controlled dormitory access. 2,547 college housing spaces available; 2,493 were occupied in 2018-19. Freshmen guaranteed college housing. Options: coed, women-only housing available. Diane M. Halle Library. Books: 112,262 (physical), 176,762 (digital/electronic); Serial titles: 47 (physical), 145,447 (digital/electronic); Databases: 175. Weekly public service hours: 97; students can reserve study rooms. Operations spending for the previous fiscal year: $926,988. 285 computers available on campus for general student use. Computer purchase/lease plans available. A campuswide network can be accessed from student residence rooms and from off campus. Students can access the following: online class registration. Staffed computer lab on campus provides training in use of computers, software, and the Internet.

Community Environment: Suburban.

■ **FINE MORTUARY COLLEGE, LLC**

150 Kerry Pl.

Norwood, MA 02062

Tel: (781)762-1211

Fax: (781)762-7177

Web Site: www.fmc.edu

Description: Proprietary, 2-year, coed. Awards terminal associate degrees. Founded 1996. Setting: suburban campus with easy access to Boston. Total enrollment: 99. Faculty: 17 (2 full-time, 15 part-time). Student-undergrad faculty ratio is 8:1. 14 applied, 86% were admitted. Full-time: 15 students, 40% women, 60% men. Part-time: 84 students, 71% women, 29% men. Students come from 6 states and territories, 23% from out-of-state. 1% American Indian or Alaska Native, non-Hispanic/Latino; 4% Hispanic/Latino; 8% Black or African American, non-Hispanic/Latino. 68% 25 or older, 1% transferred in. Core. Calendar: continuous. Academic remediation for enter-

ing students, distance learning, summer session for credit, part-time degree program, adult/continuing education programs, co-op programs and internships. Off campus study.

Entrance Requirements: Required: essay, high school transcript, 1 recommendation. Recommended: interview. Entrance: noncompetitive. Application deadline: rolling. Notification: continuous, rolling for early decision. Transfer credits accepted: Yes.

Costs Per Year: Application fee: $75. Tuition: $20,520 full-time, $760 per credit hour part-time.

Collegiate Environment: Orientation program. FINE Multimedia Center. Books: 550 (physical); Serial titles: 3 (physical). 7 computers available on campus for general student use. A computer is required for all students. A campuswide network can be accessed. Staffed computer lab on campus provides training in use of computers, software, and the Internet.

■ **FISHER COLLEGE**

118 Beacon St.

Boston, MA 02116-1500

Tel: (617)236-8800

Fax: (617)236-8858

E-mail: admissions@fisher.edu

Web Site: www.fisher.edu

Description: Independent, comprehensive, coed. Awards associate, bachelor's, and master's degrees. Founded 1903. Setting: 1-acre urban campus with easy access to Boston. Endowment: $34 million. Educational spending for the previous fiscal year: $7605 per student. Total enrollment: 1,923. Faculty: 188 (35 full-time, 153 part-time). Student-undergrad faculty ratio is 16:1. 2,792 applied, 66% were admitted. Full-time: 748 students, 50% women, 50% men. Part-time: 1,134 students, 89% women, 11% men. Students come from 38 states and territories, 40 other countries, 21% from out-of-state. 0.1% American Indian or Alaska Native, non-Hispanic/Latino; 10% Hispanic/Latino; 11% Black or African American, non-Hispanic/Latino; 0.9% Asian, non-Hispanic/Latino; 0.1% Native Hawaiian or other Pacific Islander, non-Hispanic/Latino; 9% international. 43% 25 or older, 22% live on campus, 3% transferred in. Retention: 60% of full-time freshmen returned the following year. Academic areas with the most degrees conferred: business/marketing; public administration and social services; homeland security, law enforcement, firefighting, and protective services. Core. Calendar: semesters. Academic remediation for entering students, ESL program, services for LD students, advanced placement, accelerated degree program, honors program, independent study, distance learning, summer session for credit, part-time degree program, adult/continuing education programs, internships, graduate courses open to undergrads. Off campus study. Study abroad program. ROTC: Army (c).

Entrance Requirements: Option: electronic application. Required: high school transcript. Recommended: minimum 2 high school GPA. Required for some: essay, interview, SAT or ACT. Transfer credits accepted: Yes.

Costs Per Year: Application fee: $50. Comprehensive fee: $47,310 includes full-time tuition ($30,389), mandatory fees ($995), and college room and board ($15,926). Room and board charges vary according to housing facility. Part-time tuition: $1172 per course. Part-time mandatory fees: $95 per course. Part-time tuition and fees vary according to course load.

Collegiate Environment: Orientation program. Drama-theater group, choral group. Social organizations: 25 open to all. Most popular organizations: National Society of Leadership and Success (NSLS), Psychology Club, Criminal Justice Club, Fashion Club, Multi-Cultural Club. Major annual events: Bingo, Clubs and Organizations Fair, Lessons Learned. Student services: health clinic, personal-psychological counseling, women's center. Campus security: 24-hour emergency response devices and patrols, student patrols, controlled dormitory access. Fisher College Library. Books: 23,902 (physical), 105,119 (digital/electronic); Serial titles: 40 (physical); Databases: 104. Weekly public service hours: 72; study areas open 24 hours, 5-7 days a week; students can reserve study rooms. Operations spending for the previous fiscal year: $400,953. 208 computers available on campus for general student use. A campuswide network can be accessed from student residence rooms and from off campus. Students can access the following: online class registration. Staffed computer lab on campus provides training in use of computers, software, and the Internet.

Community Environment: See Boston University.

■ **FITCHBURG STATE UNIVERSITY**

160 Pearl St.

Fitchburg, MA 01420-2697

Tel: (978)345-2151; Free: 800-705-9692

Fax: (978)665-4540

E-mail: admissions@fitchburgstate.edu

Web Site: www.fitchburgstate.edu

Description: State-supported, comprehensive, coed. Part of Massachusetts Public Higher Education System. Awards bachelor's and master's degrees and post-master's certificates. Founded 1894. Setting: 78-acre suburban campus with easy access to Boston. Endowment: $20 million. Research spending for the previous fiscal year: $12,339. Educational spending for the previous fiscal year: $19,111 per student. Total enrollment: 7,200. Faculty: 318 (210 full-time, 90 part-time). Student-undergrad faculty ratio is 13:1. 3,234 applied, 87% were admitted. Full-time: 3,320 students, 52% women, 48% men. Part-time: 844 students, 56% women, 44% men. Students come from 26 states and territories, 5 other countries, 8% from out-of-state. 0.1% American Indian or Alaska Native, non-Hispanic/Latino; 12% Hispanic/Latino; 11% Black or African American, non-Hispanic/Latino; 2% Asian, non-Hispanic/Latino; 0.3% international. 15% 25 or older, 39% live on campus, 9% transferred in. Retention: 73% of full-time freshmen returned the following year. Academic areas with the most degrees conferred: visual and performing arts; business/marketing; biological/life sciences. Core. Calendar: semesters. Academic remediation for entering students, services for LD students, advanced placement, accelerated degree program, self-designed majors, honors program, independent study, distance learning, double major, summer session for credit, part-time degree program, adult/continuing education programs, internships. Off campus study. Study abroad program. ROTC: Army.

Entrance Requirements: Options: electronic application, deferred admission. Required: essay, high school transcript, minimum 2 high school GPA, 16 core courses. Recommended: SAT or ACT, SAT and SAT Subject Tests or ACT. Entrance: moderately difficult. Application deadline: rolling. Notification: continuous. SAT Reasoning Test deadline: 5/1. Transfer credits accepted: Yes. Applicants placed on waiting list: 0. Wait-listed applicants offered admission: 0.

Costs Per Year: Application fee: $50. State resident tuition: $970 full-time, $40.42 per credit hour part-time. Nonresident tuition: $7050 full-time, $293.75 per credit hour part-time. Mandatory fees: $9385 full-time, $391.05 per credit hour part-time. Full-time tuition and fees vary according to class time and reciprocity agreements. Part-time tuition and fees vary according to class time and reciprocity agreements. College room and board: $11,073. College room only: $7583. Room and board charges vary according to board plan and housing facility.

Collegiate Environment: Orientation program. Drama-theater group, choral group, student-run newspaper, radio station. Social organizations: 60 open to all; national fraternities, national sororities; 1% of eligible men and 3% of eligible women are members. Most popular organizations: Student Government Association, Dance Club, Activities Board, Greek Council, MASSPIRG. Major annual events: Rock the Block, Student Convocations, Family Weekend. Student services: health clinic, personal-psychological counseling. Campus security: 24-hour emergency response devices and patrols, student patrols, late night transport-escort service, controlled dormitory access. 1,732 college housing spaces available; 1,553 were occupied in 2018-19. Freshmen given priority for college housing. Option: coed housing available. Amelia V. Galucci-Cirio Library. Books: 222,517 (physical); Databases: 150. Weekly public service hours: 77. 500 computers available on campus for general student use. A computer is required for all students. A campuswide network can be accessed from student residence rooms and from off campus. Students can access the following: online class registration. Staffed computer lab on campus (open 24 hours a day).

Community Environment: The college is located in an urban setting, 50 miles from Boston.

■ **FRAMINGHAM STATE UNIVERSITY**

100 State St.

Framingham, MA 01701-9101

Tel: (508)620-1220

Fax: (508)626-4017

E-mail: admissions@framingham.edu

Web Site: www.framingham.edu

Description: State-supported, comprehensive, coed. Part of Massachusetts Public Higher Education System. Awards bachelor's and master's degrees. Founded 1839. Setting: 77-acre suburban campus with easy access to Boston. Endowment: $41.8 million. Research spending for the previous fiscal year: $2.1 million. Educational spending for the previous fiscal year: $7501 per student. Total enrollment: 5,565. Faculty: 327 (200 full-time, 127 part-time). Student-undergrad faculty ratio is 14:1. 5,706 applied, 73% were

admitted. Full-time: 3,421 students, 58% women, 42% men. Part-time: 516 students, 60% women, 40% men. Students come from 12 other countries, 7% from out-of-state. 0.1% American Indian or Alaska Native, non-Hispanic/Latino; 16% Hispanic/Latino; 12% Black or African American, non-Hispanic/Latino; 3% Asian, non-Hispanic/Latino; 0.4% international. 16% 25 or older, 47% live on campus, 9% transferred in. Retention: 70% of full-time freshmen returned the following year. Academic areas with the most degrees conferred: business/marketing; social sciences; family and consumer sciences. Core. Calendar: semesters. ESL program, services for LD students, advanced placement, self-designed majors, honors program, independent study, distance learning, double major, summer session for credit, part-time degree program, co-op programs and internships. Off campus study at College Academic Program Sharing, 8 members of the other Massachusetts State colleges. Study abroad program.

Entrance Requirements: Options: electronic application, early action, deferred admission. Required: high school transcript, minimum 2 high school GPA, minimum of 16 college preparatory courses in specified areas, SAT or ACT. Recommended: minimum 3 high school GPA. Entrance: moderately difficult. Application deadlines: 2/15, 11/15 for early action. Notification: continuous. Preference given to state residents. SAT Reasoning Test deadline: 2/15. Transfer credits accepted: Yes. Early action applicants: 1,519. Early action applicants admitted: 1,266.

Costs Per Year: Application fee: $50. State resident tuition: $970 full-time, $162 per course part-time. Nonresident tuition: $7050 full-time, $1175 per course part-time. Mandatory fees: $9365 full-time, $1561 per course part-time. College room and board: $11,820.

Collegiate Environment: Orientation program. Drama-theater group, choral group, student-run newspaper, radio station. Social organizations: 56 open to all. Most popular organizations: Dance Club, Student Union Activities Board, Gatepost (student newspaper), Student Government Association, Hilltop Players (theater group). Major annual events: Homecoming, The Sandbox Festival, Semi-Formal. Student services: legal services, health clinic, personal-psychological counseling. Campus security: 24-hour emergency response devices and patrols, student patrols, late night transport-escort service, controlled dormitory access. 1,978 college housing spaces available; 1,829 were occupied in 2018-19. Freshmen given priority for college housing. Options: coed, women-only housing available. Henry Whittemore Library. Books: 156,090 (physical), 28,774 (digital/electronic); Serial titles: 120 (physical); Databases: 65. Weekly public service hours: 100. Operations spending for the previous fiscal year: $621,000. 216 computers available on campus for general student use. Computer purchase/lease plans available. A computer is required for all students. A campuswide network can be accessed from student residence rooms and from off campus. Students can access the following: online class registration. Staffed computer lab on campus.

Community Environment: Area is located 20 miles west of Boston and has transportation facilities. Part-time job opportunities are available for students. This diversified community offers many opportunities in the areas of high technology, retailing, and manufacturing, as well as being a major residential center.

■ **FRANKLIN W. OLIN COLLEGE OF ENGINEERING**

1000 Olin Way

Needham, MA 02492-1200

Tel: (781)292-2300

Web Site: www.olin.edu

Description: Independent, 4-year, coed. Awards bachelor's degrees. Founded 1997. Setting: 75-acre suburban campus with easy access to Boston. Endowment: $384.3 million. Research spending for the previous fiscal year: $3.4 million. Educational spending for the previous fiscal year: $31,912 per student. Total enrollment: 390. Faculty: 58 (42 full-time, 16 part-time). Student-undergrad faculty ratio is 8:1. 878 applied, 16% were admitted. 15 National Merit Scholars, 3 class presidents, 9 valedictorians, 7 student government officers. Full-time: 347 students, 50% women, 50% men. Part-time: 43 students, 53% women, 47% men. Students come from 43 states and territories, 7 other countries, 89% from out-of-state. 9% Hispanic/Latino; 2% Black or African American, non-Hispanic/Latino; 13% Asian, non-Hispanic/Latino; 11% international. 100% live on campus, 1% transferred in. Retention: 100% of full-time freshmen returned the following year. Academic area with the most degrees conferred: engineering. Core. Calendar: semesters. Services for LD students, self-designed majors, independent study, internships. Off campus study at Babson College, Brandeis University, Wellesley College. Study abroad program.

Entrance Requirements: Options: electronic application, deferred admis-

sion, international baccalaureate accepted. Required: essay, high school transcript, 3 recommendations, interview, SAT or ACT. Entrance: most difficult. Application deadline: 1/1. Notification: 4/1. SAT Reasoning Test deadline: 1/1. SAT Subject Test deadline: 1/1. Transfer credits accepted: No. Applicants placed on waiting list: 47. Wait-listed applicants offered admission: 3.

Costs Per Year: Application fee: $85. One-time mandatory fee: $2656. Comprehensive fee: $69,716 includes full-time tuition ($52,164), mandatory fees ($680), and college room and board ($16,872). Part-time tuition: $1630 per credit hour.

Collegiate Environment: Orientation program. Drama-theater group, choral group, student-run newspaper. Social organizations: 79 open to all. Most popular organizations: Council of Olin Representatives, Stay Late and Create, Support, Encourage and Recognize Volunteerism (SERV), Mini Baja, Olin Fire Arts Club. Major annual events: Candidates' Weekend, Expo, Fall Career Fair. Student services: health clinic, personal-psychological counseling. Campus security: 24-hour emergency response devices and patrols, controlled dormitory access. 354 college housing spaces available; 340 were occupied in 2018-19. Freshmen guaranteed college housing. On-campus residence required through senior year. Option: coed housing available. Franklin W. Olin Library. Books: 24,500 (physical), 414,224 (digital/electronic); Serial titles: 35 (physical), 159,537 (digital/electronic); Databases: 112. Study areas open 24 hours, 5-7 days a week; students can reserve study rooms. Operations spending for the previous fiscal year: $713,884.

■ **GORDON COLLEGE**
255 Grapevine Rd.
Wenham, MA 01984-1899
Tel: (978)927-2300; Free: 866-464-6736
Fax: (978)524-3704
E-mail: admissions@gordon.edu
Web Site: www.gordon.edu

Description: Independent nondenominational, comprehensive, coed. Awards bachelor's and master's degrees. Founded 1889. Setting: 485-acre suburban campus with easy access to Boston. Endowment: $56.8 million. Research spending for the previous fiscal year: $344,267. Educational spending for the previous fiscal year: $12,488 per student. Total enrollment: 1,955. Faculty: 243 (93 full-time, 150 part-time). Student-undergrad faculty ratio is 11:1. 3,062 applied, 75% were admitted. 23% from top 10% of their high school class, 51% from top quarter, 83% from top half. 4 National Merit Scholars. Full-time: 1,555 students, 64% women, 36% men. Part-time: 63 students, 56% women, 44% men. Students come from 44 states and territories, 48 other countries, 67% from out-of-state. 0.1% American Indian or Alaska Native, non-Hispanic/Latino; 9% Hispanic/Latino; 5% Black or African American, non-Hispanic/Latino; 5% Asian, non-Hispanic/Latino; 9% international. 2% 25 or older, 89% live on campus, 2% transferred in. Retention: 83% of full-time freshmen returned the following year. Academic areas with the most degrees conferred: business/marketing; education; biological/life sciences. Core. Calendar: semesters. Services for LD students, advanced placement, self-designed majors, honors program, independent study, double major, summer session for credit, part-time degree program, co-op programs and internships, graduate courses open to undergrads. Off campus study at Member of the Christian College Consortium (CCC), Consortium of Christian Colleges and Universities (CCCU), Northeast Consortium of Colleges and Universities in Massachusetts (NECCUM), and the Annapolis Group. Study abroad program. ROTC: Army (c), Air Force (c).

Entrance Requirements: Options: electronic application, early admission, early action, deferred admission, international baccalaureate accepted. Required: essay, high school transcript, 1 recommendation, interview, pastoral recommendation and statement of Christian faith, SAT or ACT. Recommended: minimum 3 high school GPA. Entrance: moderately difficult. Application deadline: rolling for nonresidents. Notification: continuous until 8/15, continuous for nonresidents. SAT Reasoning Test deadline: 8/1. SAT Subject Test deadline: 8/1. Transfer credits accepted: Yes. Applicants placed on waiting list: 0. Wait-listed applicants offered admission: 0. Early action applicants: 1,348. Early action applicants admitted: 1,305.

Costs Per Year: Application fee: $50. Comprehensive fee: $49,900 includes full-time tuition ($37,000), mandatory fees ($1650), and college room and board ($11,250). College room only: $7100. Part-time tuition: $925 per credit.

Collegiate Environment: Orientation program. Drama-theater group, choral group, student-run newspaper, radio station. Social organizations: 120 open to all. Most popular organizations: Student Government Association, Student

ministries and volunteer programs, Diverse music ensembles, Intramural sports, Short-term missions. Major annual events: Golden Goose, Gordon Globes, Senior Formal. Student services: health clinic, personal-psychological counseling. Campus security: 24-hour emergency response devices and patrols, late night transport-escort service, controlled dormitory access. 1,448 college housing spaces available; 1,397 were occupied in 2018-19. Freshmen guaranteed college housing. Options: coed, men-only, women-only housing available. Jenks Learning Resource Center. Books: 131,441 (physical), 199,117 (digital/electronic); Serial titles: 1,849 (physical). Weekly public service hours: 103; students can reserve study rooms. Operations spending for the previous fiscal year: $823,874. 100 computers available on campus for general student use. Computer purchase/lease plans available. A campuswide network can be accessed from student residence rooms and from off campus. Students can access the following: online class registration. Staffed computer lab on campus provides training in use of computers, software, and the Internet.

■ **GREENFIELD COMMUNITY COLLEGE**
1 College Dr.
Greenfield, MA 01301-9739
Tel: (413)775-1000
Fax: (413)773-5129
E-mail: admission@gcc.mass.edu
Web Site: www.gcc.mass.edu

Description: State-supported, 2-year, coed. Part of Commonwealth of Massachusetts Department of Higher Education. Awards certificates, transfer associate, and terminal associate degrees. Founded 1962. Setting: 120-acre small town campus. Research spending for the previous fiscal year: $11,077. Educational spending for the previous fiscal year: $8125 per student. Total enrollment: 2,127. Student-undergrad faculty ratio is 13:1. Full-time: 758 students, 56% women, 44% men. Part-time: 1,369 students, 63% women, 37% men. 8% from out-of-state. 0.6% American Indian or Alaska Native, non-Hispanic/Latino; 7% Hispanic/Latino; 3% Black or African American, non-Hispanic/Latino; 4% Asian, non-Hispanic/Latino. 42% 25 or older, 11% transferred in. Retention: 60% of full-time freshmen returned the following year. Core. Calendar: semesters. Academic remediation for entering students, ESL program, services for LD students, advanced placement, independent study, distance learning, double major, summer session for credit, part-time degree program, adult/continuing education programs, co-op programs and internships.

Entrance Requirements: Open admission except for allied health, outdoor leadership programs. Option: electronic application. Required for some: high school transcript, interview, Psychological Corporation Practical Nursing Entrance Examination. Entrance: noncompetitive. Application deadline: rolling. Preference given to state residents.

Costs Per Year: Application fee: $0. State resident tuition: $624 full-time, $26 per credit hour part-time. Nonresident tuition: $6744 full-time, $281 per credit hour part-time. Mandatory fees: $4946 full-time, $262 per credit hour part-time. Full-time tuition and fees vary according to class time, course load, and program. Part-time tuition and fees vary according to class time, course load, and program.

Collegiate Environment: Orientation program. Drama-theater group, choral group. Social organizations: 11 open to all. Most popular organizations: Student Senate, Art Club, Business Club, Active Minds Club, International Students Club. Major annual events: Spring Weekend, End of Semester Celebration. Student services: legal services, personal-psychological counseling, women's center. Campus security: 24-hour emergency response devices and patrols, late night transport-escort service. Greenfield Community College Library. Operations spending for the previous fiscal year: $544,210. 130 computers available on campus for general student use. A campuswide network can be accessed from off-campus. Staffed computer lab on campus provides training in use of computers, software, and the Internet.

Community Environment: The world's largest producer of taps and dies, Greenfield is a center for winter sports, and hunting and fishing in season. This is a combined rural and suburban area with bus service and limited rail service available. Climate is temperate. Recreational facilities include excellent ski area, 13 movie theatres, and all water sports on Connecticut River. Limited part-time employment for students. County fair held annually in September; Winter Carnival in February; Spring Farmers' Market.

■ **HAMPSHIRE COLLEGE**
893 W St.
Amherst, MA 01002

Tel: (413)549-4600; Free: 877-937-4267
Fax: (413)582-5631
E-mail: admissions@hampshire.edu
Web Site: www.hampshire.edu

Description: Independent, 4-year, coed. Awards bachelor's degrees. Founded 1965. Setting: 800-acre small town campus. Endowment: $48.5 million. Research spending for the previous fiscal year: $4.7 million. Educational spending for the previous fiscal year: $16,253 per student. Total enrollment: 1,268. Faculty: 162 (114 full-time, 48 part-time). Student-undergrad faculty ratio is 10:1. 2,305 applied, 63% were admitted. Full-time: 1,268 students, 63% women, 37% men. 78% from out-of-state. 0.1% American Indian or Alaska Native, non-Hispanic/Latino; 12% Hispanic/Latino; 7% Black or African American, non-Hispanic/Latino; 2% Asian, non-Hispanic/Latino; 5% international. 3% 25 or older, 84% live on campus, 4% transferred in. Retention: 77% of full-time freshmen returned the following year. Academic areas with the most degrees conferred: visual and performing arts; English; social sciences. Core. Calendar: semesters. Services for LD students, advanced placement, self-designed majors, independent study, internships. Off campus study at Five Colleges. Study abroad program. ROTC: Army (c).

Entrance Requirements: Options: electronic application, early admission, early decision, early action, deferred admission, international baccalaureate accepted. Required: essay, high school transcript, 1 recommendation. Recommended: interview. Entrance: moderately difficult. Application deadlines: 1/15, 11/15 for early decision plan 1, 1/1 for early decision plan 2, 12/1 for early action. Notification: 4/1, 12/15 for early decision plan 1, 2/1 for early decision plan 2, 2/1 for early action. SAT Subject Test deadline: 2/1. Transfer credits accepted: Yes. Applicants placed on waiting list: 153. Wait-listed applicants offered admission: 56. Early decision applicants: 116. Early decision applicants admitted: 90.

Costs Per Year: Application fee: $0. Comprehensive fee: $63,636 includes full-time tuition ($50,030) and college room and board ($13,606). College room only: $8520. Room and board charges vary according to board plan.

Collegiate Environment: Orientation program. Drama-theater group, choral group, student-run newspaper, radio station. Social organizations: 125 open to all. Most popular organizations: Red Scare Frisbee, Queer Community Alliance, Excalibur (fantasy/role playing), Sports Coop, Circus Folks Unite. Major annual events: Spring Jam, Hampshire Halloween, Family and Friends Weekend. Student services: health clinic, personal-psychological counseling, women's center. Campus security: 24-hour emergency response devices and patrols. Harold F. Johnson Library. Books: 125,971 (physical), 194,919 (digital/electronic); Serial titles: 753 (physical), 37,716 (digital/electronic); Databases: 133. Weekly public service hours: 102; study areas open 24 hours, 5-7 days a week; students can reserve study rooms. Operations spending for the previous fiscal year: $1.6 million. 205 computers available on campus for general student use. Computer purchase/lease plans available. A campuswide network can be accessed. Students can access the following: online class registration. Staffed computer lab on campus provides training in use of computers, software, and the Internet.

Community Environment: See Amherst College.

■ HARVARD UNIVERSITY
Cambridge, MA 02138
Tel: (617)495-1000
Web Site: www.harvard.edu

Description: Independent, university, coed. Awards bachelor's, master's, and doctoral degrees. Founded 1636. Setting: 380-acre urban campus with easy access to Boston. Endowment: $39.2 billion. Total enrollment: 11,365. Faculty: 1,154 (981 full-time, 173 part-time). Student-undergrad faculty ratio is 6:1. 39,506 applied, 5% were admitted. 94% from top 10% of their high school class, 99% from top quarter, 100% from top half. Full-time: 6,785 students, 49% women, 51% men. Part-time: 3 students, 67% women, 33% men. Students come from 56 states and territories, 106 other countries, 84% from out-of-state. 0.2% American Indian or Alaska Native, non-Hispanic/Latino; 11% Hispanic/Latino; 8% Black or African American, non-Hispanic/Latino; 20% Asian, non-Hispanic/Latino; 13% international. 0.5% 25 or older, 97% live on campus, 1% transferred in. Retention: 98% of full-time freshmen returned the following year. Academic areas with the most degrees conferred: social sciences; biological/life sciences; mathematics and statistics. Core. Calendar: semesters. Services for LD students, advanced placement, accelerated degree program, self-designed majors, honors program, independent study, double major, summer session for credit, internships, graduate courses open to undergrads. Off campus study at Massachusetts Institute of Technology. Study abroad program. ROTC: Army, Naval, Air Force.

Entrance Requirements: Options: electronic application, early admission, early action, deferred admission, international baccalaureate accepted. Required: essay, high school transcript, SAT or ACT, SAT Subject Tests. Recommended: 2 recommendations, interview. Entrance: most difficult. Application deadline: 1/1. Notification: 4/1. SAT Reasoning Test deadline: 3/6. SAT Subject Test deadline: 2/23. Early action applicants: 6,472. Early action applicants admitted: 922.

Costs Per Year: Application fee: $75. Comprehensive fee: $67,580 includes full-time tuition ($46,340), mandatory fees ($4080), and college room and board ($17,160). College room only: $10,609.

Collegiate Environment: Orientation program. Drama-theater group, choral group, marching band, student-run newspaper, radio station. Social organizations: 447 open to all; house system. Most popular organizations: Phillips Brooks House Association, Asian-American Association, International Relations Council, Harvard Crimson (newspaper), Harvard/Radcliffe Chorus. Major annual events: Commencement, Welcome Back Event, Yardfest. Student services: health clinic, personal-psychological counseling, women's center. Campus security: 24-hour emergency response devices and patrols, late night transport-escort service, controlled dormitory access, required and optional safety courses. 6,570 college housing spaces available; 6,439 were occupied in 2018-19. Freshmen guaranteed college housing. On-campus residence required in freshman year. Option: coed housing available. Widener Library. 605 computers available on campus for general student use. Computer purchase/lease plans available. A campuswide network can be accessed from student residence rooms and from off campus. Students can access the following: online class registration. Staffed computer lab on campus provides training in use of computers, software, and the Internet.

Community Environment: Settled in 1630, Cambridge has been the home of such famous writers as Henry Wadsworth Longfellow, James Russell Lowell, and Oliver Wendell Holmes. It is also the birthplace in Massachusetts of high technology industry. With a population of about 100,100 concentrated in 6.25 square miles, Cambridge today is the sixth largest city in the state. A vital university town, Cambridge is also a city of long-established neighborhoods with strong ethnic roots and traditions. Just across the Charles River and connected by an efficient transit system, Boston offers historical landmarks, professional sports, cosmopolitan shopping, world-famous hospitals and outstanding cultural opportunities.

■ HELLENIC COLLEGE
50 Goddard Ave.
Brookline, MA 02445-7496
Tel: (617)731-3500; Free: 866-424-2338
Fax: (617)232-7819
E-mail: admissions@hchc.edu
Web Site: www.hchc.edu

Description: Independent Greek Orthodox, comprehensive, coed. Awards bachelor's and master's degrees (also offers graduate degree programs through Holy Cross Greek Orthodox School of Theology). Founded 1937. Setting: 52-acre suburban campus with easy access to Boston. System endowment: $24.4 million. Educational spending for the previous fiscal year: $21,485 per student. Total enrollment: 193. Faculty: 50 (20 full-time, 30 part-time). Student-undergrad faculty ratio is 9:1. 68 applied, 65% were admitted. Full-time: 91 students, 40% women, 60% men. Part-time: 1 student, 100% women. Students come from 22 states and territories, 2 other countries, 80% from out-of-state. 4% Hispanic/Latino; 1% Asian, non-Hispanic/Latino; 7% international. 13% 25 or older, 71% live on campus, 5% transferred in. Retention: 81% of full-time freshmen returned the following year. Core. Calendar: semesters. Academic remediation for entering students, services for LD students, advanced placement, honors program, independent study, summer session for credit, part-time degree program, adult/continuing education programs, internships. Off campus study at Boston Theological Institute, Boston College, Newbury College. Study abroad program.

Entrance Requirements: Options: electronic application, early action, deferred admission. Required: essay, high school transcript, minimum 2 high school GPA, interview, SAT or ACT, TOEFL for international students. Entrance: minimally difficult. Application deadlines: rolling, 12/1 for early action. Notification: continuous. SAT Reasoning Test deadline: 8/1. Transfer credits accepted: Yes.

Collegiate Environment: Orientation program. Choral group, student-run newspaper. Most popular organizations: Campus Activities Board, Student Government Association, Intramural sports. Major annual events: Chamby Awards, Annual Graduation Dinner Dance, Festivals. Student services: personal-psychological counseling. Campus security: 24-hour patrols, controlled dormitory access. Archbishop Iakovos Library. Books: 63,725 (physical), 246 (digital/electronic); Serial titles: 414 (physical); Databases: 80. Weekly public service hours: 76; students can reserve study rooms. Operations spending for the previous fiscal year: $846,893. 35 computers available on campus for general student use. A campuswide network can be accessed from student residence rooms. Staffed computer lab on campus provides training in use of computers, software, and the Internet.

■ HOLYOKE COMMUNITY COLLEGE

303 Homestead Ave.
Holyoke, MA 01040-1099
Tel: (413)538-7000
E-mail: admissions@hcc.edu
Web Site: www.hcc.edu

Description: State-supported, 2-year, coed. Part of Massachusetts Public Higher Education System. Awards certificates, transfer associate, and terminal associate degrees. Founded 1946. Setting: 135-acre small town campus. System endowment: $13 million. Total enrollment: 5,565. Faculty: 449 (128 full-time, 321 part-time). Student-undergrad faculty ratio is 15:1. 3,380 applied, 87% were admitted. Full-time: 2,506 students, 55% women, 45% men. Part-time: 3,059 students, 67% women, 33% men. Students come from 18 states and territories, 1% from out-of-state. 0.4% American Indian or Alaska Native, non-Hispanic/Latino; 27% Hispanic/Latino; 6% Black or African American, non-Hispanic/Latino; 3% Asian, non-Hispanic/Latino; 0.8% international. 33% 25 or older, 7% transferred in. Core. Calendar: semesters. Academic remediation for entering students, ESL program, services for LD students, advanced placement, self-designed majors, honors program, independent study, distance learning, double major, summer session for credit, part-time degree program, adult/continuing education programs, co-op programs and internships. Off campus study at Cooperating Colleges of Greater Springfield. Study abroad program. ROTC: Army (c), Air Force (c).

Entrance Requirements: Open admission except for nursing and radiological science programs. Options: electronic application, early admission, deferred admission. Required: high school transcript. Recommended: interview. Entrance: noncompetitive. Application deadline: rolling. Notification: continuous.

Costs Per Year: Application fee: $0. One-time mandatory fee: $70. State resident tuition: $576 full-time, $193 per credit hour part-time. Nonresident tuition: $5520 full-time, $399 per credit hour part-time. Mandatory fees: $4206 full-time, $135 per term part-time. Full-time tuition and fees vary according to course load. Part-time tuition and fees vary according to course load.

Collegiate Environment: Orientation program. Drama-theater group, student-run newspaper, radio station. Social organizations: 40 open to all. Most popular organizations: Drama Club, Japanese Anime Club, Student Senate, LISA Club, STRIVE. Major annual events: Spring Fling Week, Welcome Week, Black History Month. Student services: health clinic, personal-psychological counseling, women's center. Campus security: 24-hour emergency response devices and patrols, late night transport-escort service. Holyoke Community College Library plus 1 other. Books: 40,127 (physical), 62,355 (digital/electronic); Serial titles: 22 (physical), 32,539 (digital/electronic); Databases: 183. Weekly public service hours: 65; students can reserve study rooms. Operations spending for the previous fiscal year: $168,241. 1,218 computers available on campus for general student use. Computer purchase/lease plans available. A campuswide network can be accessed from off-campus. Students can access the following: online class registration. Staffed computer lab on campus provides training in use of computers, software, and the Internet.

Community Environment: Holyoke is located 87 miles west of Boston on the shores of the Connecticut River and was the first planned industrial center in the country. Industries include the production of fine writing paper and various mills. The game of volleyball, first known as minonette, was invented here in 1895. The city has historical points of interest, museums, three movie theatres, public beaches and marinas, a community concert series featuring nationally known artists, and Mt. Tom Ski area. Westover Air Force Base is five miles from town. Part-time employment is available.

■ HULT INTERNATIONAL BUSINESS SCHOOL

1 Education St.
Cambridge, MA 02141
Tel: (617)746-1990
Fax: (617)746-1991
Web Site: www.hult.edu

Description: Independent, comprehensive, coed. Awards bachelor's and master's degrees. Founded 1964. Calendar: trimesters.

■ LABOURÉ COLLEGE

303 Adams St.
Milton, MA 02186
Tel: (617)322-3575
Web Site: www.laboure.edu

Description: Independent Roman Catholic, 2-year, coed. Awards certificates, transfer associate, and terminal associate degrees. Founded 1971. Setting: urban campus. Total enrollment: 548. 119 applied. 73% 25 or older. Core. Calendar: semesters. Academic remediation for entering students, services for LD students, accelerated degree program, independent study, summer session for credit, part-time degree program, adult/continuing education programs.

Entrance Requirements: Option: deferred admission. Required: high school transcript. Entrance: minimally difficult. Application deadline: rolling.

Collegiate Environment: Orientation program. Student-run newspaper. Student services: health clinic, personal-psychological counseling. Campus security: 24-hour emergency response devices. Helen Stubblefield Law Library.

■ LASELL COLLEGE

1844 Commonwealth Ave.
Newton, MA 02466-2709
Tel: (617)243-2000; Free: 888-LASELL-4
Fax: (617)796-4343
E-mail: info@lasell.edu
Web Site: www.lasell.edu

Description: Independent, comprehensive, coed. Awards bachelor's and master's degrees. Founded 1851. Setting: 53-acre suburban campus with easy access to Boston. Endowment: $41.4 million. Research spending for the previous fiscal year: $182,399. Educational spending for the previous fiscal year: $8427 per student. Total enrollment: 2,116. Faculty: 248 (85 full-time, 163 part-time). Student-undergrad faculty ratio is 13:1. 3,180 applied, 80% were admitted. 10% from top 10% of their high school class, 30% from top quarter, 67% from top half. Full-time: 1,624 students, 64% women, 36% men. Part-time: 50 students, 50% women, 50% men. Students come from 28 states and territories, 22 other countries, 40% from out-of-state. 0.1% American Indian or Alaska Native, non-Hispanic/Latino; 10% Hispanic/Latino; 7% Black or African American, non-Hispanic/Latino; 2% Asian, non-Hispanic/Latino; 0.1% Native Hawaiian or other Pacific Islander, non-Hispanic/Latino; 6% international. 3% 25 or older, 73% live on campus, 9% transferred in. Retention: 68% of full-time freshmen returned the following year. Academic areas with the most degrees conferred: business/marketing; communication/journalism; parks and recreation. Core. Calendar: semesters. ESL program, services for LD students, advanced placement, accelerated degree program, self-designed majors, honors program, independent study, distance learning, double major, summer session for credit, part-time degree program, co-op programs and internships, graduate courses open to undergrads. Off campus study at Washington Semester, Regis College. Study abroad program.

Entrance Requirements: Options: electronic application, early action, deferred admission, international baccalaureate accepted. Required: essay, high school transcript, 2 recommendations, college preparatory program. Recommended: interview. Required for some: SAT or ACT. Entrance: moderately difficult. Application deadlines: rolling, 11/15 for early action. Transfer credits accepted: Yes.

Costs Per Year: Application fee: $40. Comprehensive fee: $53,000 includes full-time tuition ($35,700), mandatory fees ($1300), and college room and board ($16,000). Part-time tuition: $1155 per credit hour. Part-time mandatory fees: $325 per term.

Collegiate Environment: Orientation program. Drama-theater group, choral group, student-run newspaper, radio station. Social organizations: 69 open to all. Most popular organizations: 19851 Chronicle, Campus Activities Board, Hope for Humanity, Lasell College Drama Club, Lasell College Radio (Marathon Monday). Major annual events: River Day/Family and Friends Weekend, Torchlight Parade, Spring/Winter Fest Week. Student services: health clinic, personal-psychological counseling. Campus security: 24-hour emergency response devices and patrols, late night transport-escort service, controlled dormitory access. 1,325 college housing spaces available; 1,188 were occupied in 2018-19. Freshmen guaranteed college housing. Options: coed, women-only housing available. Brennan Library. Books: 35,093 (physical), 59,782 (digital/electronic); Serial titles: 63 (physical), 113,658 (digital/electronic); Databases: 88. Weekly public service hours: 83; students can reserve study rooms. Operations spending for the previous fiscal year: $569,359. 219 computers available on campus for general student use.

Computer purchase/lease plans available. A campuswide network can be accessed from student residence rooms and from off campus. Students can access the following: online class registration, online tutoring. Staffed computer lab on campus provides training in use of computers, software, and the Internet.

Community Environment: See Boston University.

■ LAWRENCE MEMORIAL/REGIS COLLEGE

170 Governors Ave.
Medford, MA 02155
Description: Private, 2-year, coed.

■ LESLEY UNIVERSITY

29 Everett St.
Cambridge, MA 02138-2790
Tel: (617)868-9600; Free: 800-999-1959
Fax: (617)349-8150
Web Site: www.lesley.edu
Description: Independent, comprehensive, coed. Awards associate, bachelor's, master's, and doctoral degrees and post-master's certificates. Founded 1909. Setting: urban campus with easy access to Boston. Total enrollment: 4,838. Faculty: 665 (147 full-time, 518 part-time). Student-undergrad faculty ratio is 12:1. 3,171 applied, 76% were admitted. 13% from top 10% of their high school class, 39% from top quarter, 74% from top half. Full-time: 1,699 students, 79% women, 21% men. Part-time: 509 students, 77% women, 23% men. 33% from out-of-state. 0.2% American Indian or Alaska Native, non-Hispanic/Latino; 15% Hispanic/Latino; 7% Black or African American, non-Hispanic/Latino; 5% Asian, non-Hispanic/Latino; 4% international. 19% 25 or older, 43% live on campus, 6% transferred in. Retention: 80% of full-time freshmen returned the following year. Academic areas with the most degrees conferred: psychology; visual and performing arts; liberal arts/general studies; health professions and related sciences. Core. Calendar: semesters. Academic remediation for entering students, services for LD students, advanced placement, accelerated degree program, self-designed majors, freshman honors college, honors program, independent study, distance learning, double major, summer session for credit, part-time degree program, adult/continuing education programs, internships, graduate courses open to undergrads. Off campus study. Study abroad program.

Entrance Requirements: Options: electronic application, early action, deferred admission, international baccalaureate accepted. Required: essay, high school transcript. Recommended: interview. Required for some: SAT or ACT. Notification: continuous until 1/15, rolling for early action. SAT Reasoning Test deadline: 3/1.

Costs Per Year: Comprehensive fee: $44,730 includes full-time tuition ($28,500) and college room and board ($16,230). College room only: $9830. Part-time tuition: $920 per credit hour.

Collegiate Environment: Orientation program. Drama-theater group, choral group, student-run newspaper. Major annual event: Quad Fest. Student services: health clinic, personal-psychological counseling. Campus security: 24-hour emergency response devices and patrols, late night transport-escort service, controlled dormitory access. Freshmen given priority for college housing. Options: coed, women-only housing available. Sherrill Library.

■ MASSACHUSETTS BAY COMMUNITY COLLEGE

50 Oakland St.
Wellesley Hills, MA 02481
Tel: (781)239-3000
Fax: (781)239-1047
E-mail: amccarty1@massbay.edu
Web Site: www.massbay.edu
Description: State-supported, 2-year, coed. Awards certificates, transfer associate, and terminal associate degrees. Founded 1961. Setting: 84-acre suburban campus with easy access to Boston. Total enrollment: 4,368. Faculty: 341 (72 full-time, 269 part-time). Student-undergrad faculty ratio is 17:1. 2,589 applied, 80% were admitted. Full-time: 1,471 students, 42% women, 58% men. Part-time: 2,897 students, 59% women, 41% men. Students come from 10 states and territories, 73 other countries, 1% from out-of-state. 0.4% American Indian or Alaska Native, non-Hispanic/Latino; 21% Hispanic/Latino; 16% Black or African American, non-Hispanic/Latino; 4% Asian, non-Hispanic/Latino; 0.1% Native Hawaiian or other Pacific Islander, non-Hispanic/Latino; 2% international. 37% 25 or older, 6% transferred in. Retention: 57% of full-time freshmen returned the following year. Core. Calendar: semesters. Academic remediation for entering

students, ESL program, services for LD students, advanced placement, honors program, independent study, distance learning, double major, summer session for credit, part-time degree program, adult/continuing education programs, co-op programs and internships. Study abroad program.

Entrance Requirements: Open admission except for nursing, selective allied health and automotive programs. Options: electronic application, deferred admission, international baccalaureate accepted. Required for some: high school transcript. Entrance: noncompetitive. Application deadline: rolling. Notification: continuous. Transfer credits accepted: Yes.

Costs Per Year: Application fee: $0. State resident tuition: $576 full-time, $24 per credit part-time. Nonresident tuition: $5520 full-time, $230 per credit part-time. Mandatory fees: $4512 full-time, $188 per credit part-time. Full-time tuition and fees vary according to class time, course load, program, and reciprocity agreements. Part-time tuition and fees vary according to class time, course load, program, and reciprocity agreements.

Collegiate Environment: Orientation program. Drama-theater group, choral group. Social organizations: 21 open to all. Most popular organizations: Veterans Club, Gamer's Guild, Nursing Club, Student Government Association, International Club. Major annual events: Mobile Market, Transfer Fair, Club Fair. Student services: personal-psychological counseling. Campus security: 24-hour emergency response devices and patrols. College housing not available. Perkins Library plus 1 other. Books: 20,790 (physical), 6,806 (digital/electronic); Serial titles: 27 (physical), 322,824 (digital/electronic); Databases: 117. Weekly public service hours: 66. Operations spending for the previous fiscal year: $441,597. 91 computers available on campus for general student use. A campuswide network can be accessed. Students can access the following: online class registration. Staffed computer lab on campus provides training in use of software.

Community Environment: See Wellesley College.

■ MASSACHUSETTS COLLEGE OF ART AND DESIGN

621 Huntington Ave.
Boston, MA 02115-5882
Tel: (617)879-7000
Fax: (617)879-7250
E-mail: admissions@massart.edu
Web Site: www.massart.edu
Description: State-supported, comprehensive, coed. Part of Massachusetts Public Higher Education System. Awards bachelor's and master's degrees. Founded 1873. Setting: 5-acre urban campus. Endowment: $16 million. Educational spending for the previous fiscal year: $39,383 per student. Total enrollment: 2,065. Faculty: 290 (117 full-time, 173 part-time). Student-undergrad faculty ratio is 9:1. 2,386 applied, 71% were admitted. Full-time: 1,662 students, 71% women, 29% men. Part-time: 269 students, 64% women, 36% men. Students come from 32 states and territories, 45 other countries, 32% from out-of-state. 0.2% American Indian or Alaska Native, non-Hispanic/Latino; 11% Hispanic/Latino; 5% Black or African American, non-Hispanic/Latino; 8% Asian, non-Hispanic/Latino; 0.1% Native Hawaiian or other Pacific Islander, non-Hispanic/Latino; 4% international. 6% 25 or older, 41% live on campus, 6% transferred in. Retention: 87% of full-time freshmen returned the following year. Academic areas with the most degrees conferred: visual and performing arts; education. Core. Calendar: semesters. Self-designed majors, independent study, double major, summer session for credit, part-time degree program, internships, graduate courses open to undergrads. Off campus study at members of the Pro Arts Consortium, Association of Independent Colleges of Art and Design, CAPS, Colleges of the Fenway. Study abroad program.

Entrance Requirements: Options: electronic application, early action, deferred admission. Required: essay, high school transcript, 2 recommendations, portfolio of 15-20 pieces of artwork completed in the last 2 years. Recommended: minimum 3 high school GPA. Entrance: moderately difficult. Application deadlines: 2/1, 12/1 for early action. Notification: 1/5 for early action. Preference given to state residents. Transfer credits accepted: Yes. Applicants placed on waiting list: 4. Wait-listed applicants offered admission: 4. Early action applicants: 588. Early action applicants admitted: 472.

Costs Per Year: Application fee: $70. State resident tuition: $13,200 full-time. Nonresident tuition: $36,400 full-time. College room and board: $13,500. Room and board charges vary according to board plan and housing facility.

Collegiate Environment: Orientation program. Drama-theater group, choral group, student-run newspaper, radio station. Social organizations: 30 open to all. Most popular organizations: International Students' Club, Design Research Unit, Spectrum, film society, Event Works. Major annual events: All School Show, Annual Holiday Sale, Service Learning Day. Student services:

health clinic, personal-psychological counseling, women's center. Campus security: 24-hour emergency response devices and patrols, late night transport-escort service, controlled dormitory access, security lighting, self-defense workshops. Morton R. Godine Library. Books: 106,885 (physical), 173,498 (digital/electronic); Databases: 75. Operations spending for the previous fiscal year: $240,910. 370 computers available on campus for general student use. Computer purchase/lease plans available. A campuswide network can be accessed from student residence rooms and from off campus. Students can access the following: online class registration. Staffed computer lab on campus provides training in use of computers, software, and the Internet.

Community Environment: See Boston University.

■ **MASSACHUSETTS COLLEGE OF LIBERAL ARTS**
375 Church St.
North Adams, MA 01247-4100
Tel: (413)662-5000; Free: 800-989-MCLA
Fax: (413)662-5179
E-mail: kayla.kollins@mcla.edu
Web Site: www.mcla.edu
Description: State-supported, comprehensive, coed. Part of Massachusetts State University System. Awards bachelor's and master's degrees and post-master's certificates. Founded 1894. Setting: 105-acre small town campus with easy access to Albany-Schenectady-Troy New York Metro Area. Total enrollment: 1,452. Faculty: 172 (90 full-time, 82 part-time). Student-undergrad faculty ratio is 12:1. 1,931 applied, 74% were admitted. Full-time: 1,109 students, 61% women, 39% men. Part-time: 168 students, 67% women, 33% men. 25% from out-of-state. 0.3% American Indian or Alaska Native, non-Hispanic/Latino; 10% Hispanic/Latino; 8% Black or African American, non-Hispanic/Latino; 2% Asian, non-Hispanic/Latino; 0.1% Native Hawaiian or other Pacific Islander, non-Hispanic/Latino; 0.5% international. 14% 25 or older, 58% live on campus, 9% transferred in. Retention: 70% of full-time freshmen returned the following year. Academic areas with the most degrees conferred: business/marketing; interdisciplinary studies; English. Core. Calendar: semesters. Academic remediation for entering students, services for LD students, advanced placement, accelerated degree program, self-designed majors, honors program, independent study, distance learning, double major, summer session for credit, part-time degree program, adult/continuing education programs, co-op programs and internships, graduate courses open to undergrads. Off campus study at College Academic Program Sharing, Williams College, Berkshire Community College. Study abroad program.
Entrance Requirements: Options: electronic application, early admission, early action, deferred admission, international baccalaureate accepted. Required: essay, high school transcript, minimum 3 high school GPA, 1 recommendation, SAT or ACT. Required for some: interview, sliding scale applies (GPA and SAT) if below 3.0. Entrance: moderately difficult. Application deadline: rolling. Notification: continuous, 12/15 for early action. SAT Reasoning Test deadline: 6/30. Transfer credits accepted: Yes.
Costs Per Year: Application fee: $0. State resident tuition: $1030 full-time, $42.92 per credit part-time. Nonresident tuition: $9975 full-time, $415.63 per credit part-time. Mandatory fees: $9529 full-time, $322.88 per credit part-time. Full-time tuition and fees vary according to reciprocity agreements. Part-time tuition and fees vary according to course load and reciprocity agreements. College room and board: $10,980. Room and board charges vary according to board plan and housing facility.
Collegiate Environment: Orientation program. Drama-theater group, choral group, student-run newspaper, radio station. Social organizations: 50 open to all; local fraternities, local sororities. Most popular organizations: Student Activities Council, Student Government Association, The Beacon (Student Newspaper), Harlequin-Musical Theatre Company, Dance Company. Major annual events: Summer Reading Program, Midnight Madness, Midnight Breakfast. Student services: health clinic, personal-psychological counseling, women's center. Campus security: 24-hour emergency response devices and patrols, late night transport-escort service, controlled dormitory access. 1,020 college housing spaces available; 745 were occupied in 2018-19. Freshmen guaranteed college housing. On-campus residence required through junior year. Option: coed housing available. Eugene L. Freel Library. Books: 125,000 (physical), 229,000 (digital/electronic); Serial titles: 1,000 (physical), 43,000 (digital/electronic); Databases: 82. 140 computers available on campus for general student use. Computer purchase/lease plans available. A computer is required for all students. A campuswide network can be accessed from student residence rooms and from off campus. Students can access the following: online class registration. Staffed computer lab on campus provides training in use of computers, software, and the Internet.

Community Environment: In the northwestern corner of state, this Berkshire town produces a diversity of small business establishments and cultural activities. Bus lines are accessible. A regional hospital, Sterling and Francine Clark Art Institute, Massachusetts Museum of Contemporary Art, and numerous civic and service organizations are found here. There are 6 major ski areas within 25 miles and Mohawk and Taconic Trails. Part-time employment is seasonal for students. The city has an annual Fall Festival.

■ **MASSACHUSETTS INSTITUTE OF TECHNOLOGY**
77 Massachusetts Ave.
Cambridge, MA 02139-4307
Tel: (617)253-1000
Fax: (617)258-8304
Web Site: www.mit.edu
Description: Independent, university, coed. Awards bachelor's, master's, and doctoral degrees. Founded 1861. Setting: 166-acre urban campus with easy access to Boston. Endowment: $16.4 billion. Research spending for the previous fiscal year: $731.5 million. Educational spending for the previous fiscal year: $91,260 per student. Total enrollment: 11,574. Faculty: 1,617 (1,312 full-time, 305 part-time). Student-undergrad faculty ratio is 3:1. 20,247 applied, 7% were admitted. 97% from top 10% of their high school class, 100% from top quarter, 100% from top half. 175 valedictorians. Full-time: 4,557 students, 47% women, 53% men. Part-time: 45 students, 33% women, 67% men. 91% from out-of-state. 0.1% American Indian or Alaska Native, non-Hispanic/Latino; 15% Hispanic/Latino; 6% Black or African American, non-Hispanic/Latino; 28% Asian, non-Hispanic/Latino; 10% international. 1% 25 or older, 92% live on campus, 1% transferred in. Retention: 99% of full-time freshmen returned the following year. Academic areas with the most degrees conferred: engineering; computer and information sciences; mathematics and statistics. Core. Calendar: 4-1-4. ESL program, services for LD students, advanced placement, independent study, double major, co-op programs and internships, graduate courses open to undergrads. Off campus study at Wellesley College, Harvard University, and Massachusetts College of Art and Design. Study abroad program. ROTC: Army, Naval, Air Force.
Entrance Requirements: Options: electronic application, early admission, early action, deferred admission, international baccalaureate accepted. Required: essay, high school transcript, 2 recommendations, SAT or ACT, SAT Subject Tests. Recommended: interview. Entrance: most difficult. Application deadlines: 1/1, 11/1 for early action. Notification: 3/20, 12/20 for early action. SAT Reasoning Test deadline: 2/15. SAT Subject Test deadline: 2/15. Transfer credits accepted: Yes. Applicants placed on waiting list: 527. Wait-listed applicants offered admission: 14. Early action applicants: 8,394. Early action applicants admitted: 657.
Costs Per Year: Application fee: $75. Comprehensive fee: $70,180 includes full-time tuition ($53,450), mandatory fees ($340), and college room and board ($16,390). College room only: $10,430. Part-time mandatory fees: $830 per credit hour.
Collegiate Environment: Orientation program. Drama-theater group, choral group, marching band, student-run newspaper, radio station. Social organizations: 450 open to all; national fraternities, national sororities, local fraternities; 43% of eligible men and 28% of eligible women are members. Most popular organizations: Educational Studies Program, Dance Troupe, Science Fiction Society, The Tech (student newspaper), Anime Club. Major annual events: Independent Activities Period (IAP), Brass Rat (Class Ring) Premiere, Campus Preview Weekend. Student services: health clinic, personal-psychological counseling. Campus security: 24-hour emergency response devices and patrols, late night transport-escort service, controlled dormitory access. Freshmen guaranteed college housing. On-campus residence required in freshman year. Options: coed, women-only housing available. MIT Libraries plus 5 others. Books: 1.3 million (physical), 758,981 (digital/electronic); Serial titles: 50,139 (physical), 58,996 (digital/electronic); Databases: 336. Weekly public service hours: 95; study areas open 24 hours, 5-7 days a week; students can reserve study rooms. 1,050 computers available on campus for general student use. Computer purchase/lease plans available. A campuswide network can be accessed from student residence rooms and from off campus. Students can access the following: online class registration. Staffed computer lab on campus (open 24 hours a day) provides training in use of computers, software, and the Internet.
Community Environment: See Harvard University.

■ **MASSACHUSETTS MARITIME ACADEMY**
101 Academy Dr.
Buzzards Bay, MA 02532-1803

Tel: (508)830-5000; Free: 800-544-3411
Fax: (508)830-5077
E-mail: jtefft@maritime.edu
Web Site: www.maritime.edu
Description: State-supported, comprehensive, coed. Part of Massachusetts State University System. Awards bachelor's and master's degrees. Founded 1891. Setting: 54-acre small town campus with easy access to Boston, Providence. Total enrollment: 1,802. Faculty: 141 (88 full-time, 53 part-time). Student-undergrad faculty ratio is 16:1. 758 applied, 89% were admitted. Full-time: 1,614 students, 13% women, 87% men. Part-time: 95 students, 41% women, 59% men. 19% from out-of-state. 0.1% American Indian or Alaska Native, non-Hispanic/Latino; 4% Hispanic/Latino; 1% Black or African American, non-Hispanic/Latino; 1% Asian, non-Hispanic/Latino; 0.6% international. 2% 25 or older, 97% live on campus, 2% transferred in. Retention: 86% of full-time freshmen returned the following year. Academic areas with the most degrees conferred: engineering; transportation and materials moving; business/marketing. Core. Calendar: 4-1-4 plus sea term. Services for LD students, advanced placement, independent study, distance learning, double major, summer session for credit, part-time degree program, co-op programs and internships. Off campus study. Study abroad program. ROTC: Army (c).
Entrance Requirements: Options: electronic application, early action, deferred admission, international baccalaureate accepted. Required: essay, high school transcript, minimum 2 high school GPA, 2 recommendations, minimum college GPA 2.5 if transferring 12-23 credits, minimum college GPA 2.0 for more than 24 transferable credits, SAT or ACT. Recommended: interview. Entrance: moderately difficult. Application deadlines: rolling, 11/1 for early action. Notification: continuous, 12/31 for early action. Transfer credits accepted: Yes. Applicants placed on waiting list: 1. Wait-listed applicants offered admission: 1. Early action applicants: 129. Early action applicants admitted: 129.
Costs Per Year: Application fee: $50. State resident tuition: $1782 full-time, $74.25 per credit part-time. Nonresident tuition: $18,160 full-time, $756.67 per credit part-time. Mandatory fees: $7946 full-time, $320.25 per credit part-time. Full-time tuition and fees vary according to reciprocity agreements. Part-time tuition and fees vary according to course load and reciprocity agreements. College room and board: $12,675. College room only: $7560.
Collegiate Environment: Orientation program. Drama-theater group, marching band. Social organizations: 20 open to all. Most popular organizations: Student Government, Intramurals, Regimental Leadership, Band/Honor Guard, NCAA Division 3 Athletics. Major annual events: Emery Rice Day, Homecoming/Ring Dance, Change of Command. Student services: health clinic, personal-psychological counseling, women's center. Campus security: 24-hour emergency response devices and patrols, late night transport-escort service, controlled dormitory access. 1,615 college housing spaces available; 1,598 were occupied in 2018-19. Freshmen guaranteed college housing. On-campus residence required through senior year. Option: coed housing available. American Bureau of Shipping Information Commons plus 1 other. Databases: 124. 130 computers available on campus for general student use. A computer is required for all students. A campuswide network can be accessed from student residence rooms and from off campus. Students can access the following: online class registration, course-supported e-learning. Staffed computer lab on campus provides training in use of computers, software, and the Internet.
Community Environment: Bourne is the second largest town on Cape Cod and has a New England climate. It is located 60 miles from Boston, and bus service and air service from Hyannis are available. The Trading Post, located here, is a replica of the trading post built in 1627. Bourne Scenic Park is a good area for picnics and camping. Boating, fishing, swimming and golf are available for recreation in this resort community.

■ **MASSASOIT COMMUNITY COLLEGE**
1 Massasoit Blvd.
Brockton, MA 02302-3996
Tel: (508)588-9100; Free: 800-CAREERS
Fax: (508)427-1220
Web Site: www.massasoit.mass.edu
Description: State-supported, 2-year, coed. Awards certificates, transfer associate, and terminal associate degrees. Founded 1966. Setting: 100-acre suburban campus with easy access to Boston. Total enrollment: 7,941. Faculty: 503 (119 full-time, 384 part-time). Full-time: 3,631 students, 49% women, 51% men. Part-time: 4,310 students, 62% women, 38% men. Students come from 13 states and territories, 6 other countries, 1% from out-of-state. 38% 25 or older, 6% transferred in. Core. Calendar: semesters.

Academic remediation for entering students, ESL program, services for LD students, accelerated degree program, independent study, distance learning, summer session for credit, part-time degree program, adult/continuing education programs, co-op programs and internships. Off campus study at 9 members of the Southeastern Association for Cooperation in Higher Education in Massachusetts.
Entrance Requirements: Open admission except for allied health programs. Entrance: noncompetitive. Application deadline: rolling. Notification: continuous. Preference given to state residents.
Collegiate Environment: Drama-theater group, student-run newspaper, radio station. Social organizations: 32 open to all. Most popular organizations: Drama Club, student newspaper, Phi Theta Kappa, International Student Association, Student Senate. Student services: health clinic, personal-psychological counseling, women's center. Campus security: 24-hour patrols.
Community Environment: Brockton is located 20 miles south of downtown Boston and the center of the second fastest growing area of the State. The college service area encompasses one million people in 51 cities and towns south of Boston and includes the city of Quincy.

■ **MCPHS UNIVERSITY**
179 Longwood Ave.
Boston, MA 02115-5896
Tel: (617)732-2800
Fax: (617)732-2801
E-mail: admissions@mcphs.edu
Web Site: www.mcphs.edu
Description: Independent, university, coed. Awards bachelor's, master's, and doctoral degrees and post-master's certificates. Founded 1823. Setting: 3-acre urban campus. Endowment: $847.8 million. Total enrollment: 7,208. Faculty: 738 (310 full-time, 428 part-time). 5,526 applied, 84% were admitted. Full-time: 3,624 students, 71% women, 29% men. Part-time: 258 students, 79% women, 21% men. Students come from 42 states and territories, 52 other countries, 40% from out-of-state. 0.2% American Indian or Alaska Native, non-Hispanic/Latino; 7% Hispanic/Latino; 7% Black or African American, non-Hispanic/Latino; 22% Asian, non-Hispanic/Latino; 0.1% Native Hawaiian or other Pacific Islander, non-Hispanic/Latino; 15% international. 14% 25 or older, 7% transferred in. Retention: 82% of full-time freshmen returned the following year. Academic areas with the most degrees conferred: health professions and related sciences; biological/life sciences; psychology. Core. Calendar: semesters. Services for LD students, advanced placement, accelerated degree program, independent study, distance learning, double major, summer session for credit, part-time degree program, adult/continuing education programs, co-op programs and internships, graduate courses open to undergrads. Off campus study at Colleges of the Fenway. Study abroad program.
Entrance Requirements: Open admission. Options: electronic application, early action, deferred admission, international baccalaureate accepted. Required: essay, 1 recommendation, SAT or ACT. Required for some: high school transcript, interview. Application deadlines: rolling, 11/1 for early action. Notification: continuous until 2/15, 12/1 for early action. Applicants placed on waiting list: 0. Wait-listed applicants offered admission: 0.
Costs Per Year: Application fee: $0. Comprehensive fee: $49,105 includes full-time tuition ($31,600), mandatory fees ($1105), and college room and board ($16,400). College room only: $13,126. Full-time tuition and fees vary according to course load, degree level, location, program, and student level. Room and board charges vary according to board plan, housing facility, and location.
Collegiate Environment: Orientation program. Drama-theater group, choral group, student-run newspaper. Social organizations: 100 open to all; national fraternities. Most popular organizations: Residence Hall Council, Vietnamese Student Association, Student Government Association, Campus Activities Board, Student Indian Organization. Major annual events: Fall Harvest Ball, Culture Fest, Activities Fair. Student services: health clinic, personal-psychological counseling. Campus security: 24-hour emergency response devices and patrols, late night transport-escort service, controlled dormitory access, electronically operated academic area entrances, security guards at entrance. Henrietta DeBenedictis Library plus 2 others. 507 computers available on campus for general student use. A campuswide network can be accessed from student residence rooms and from off campus. Students can access the following: online class registration. Staffed computer lab on campus.

■ **MERRIMACK COLLEGE**
315 Tpke. St.
North Andover, MA 01845-5800
Tel: (978)837-5000
Fax: (978)837-5222
Web Site: www.merrimack.edu
Description: Independent Roman Catholic, comprehensive, coed. Awards bachelor's and master's degrees and post-master's certificates. Founded 1947. Setting: 220-acre suburban campus with easy access to Boston. Endowment: $58.5 million. Research spending for the previous fiscal year: $663,215. Educational spending for the previous fiscal year: $8930 per student. Total enrollment: 4,516. Faculty: 451 (197 full-time, 254 part-time). Student-undergrad faculty ratio is 14:1. 8,668 applied, 83% were admitted. Full-time: 3,587 students, 50% women, 50% men. Part-time: 139 students, 40% women, 60% men. Students come from 33 states and territories, 28 other countries, 29% from out-of-state. 7% Hispanic/Latino; 3% Black or African American, non-Hispanic/Latino; 2% Asian, non-Hispanic/Latino; 0.1% Native Hawaiian or other Pacific Islander, non-Hispanic/Latino; 2% international. 1% 25 or older, 71% live on campus, 2% transferred in. Retention: 85% of full-time freshmen returned the following year. Academic areas with the most degrees conferred: business/marketing; family and consumer sciences; health professions and related sciences. Core. Calendar: semesters. Academic remediation for entering students, services for LD students, advanced placement, accelerated degree program, self-designed majors, honors program, independent study, double major, summer session for credit, part-time degree program, adult/continuing education programs, co-op programs and internships, graduate courses open to undergrads. Off campus study at Northeast Consortium of Colleges and Universities in Massachusetts, American University Washington Semester. Study abroad program. ROTC: Air Force (c).
Entrance Requirements: Options: electronic application, early admission, early decision, early action, deferred admission, international baccalaureate accepted. Required: essay, high school transcript, 1 recommendation, first quarter senior grades. Recommended: interview. Entrance: moderately difficult. Application deadlines: 2/15, 11/15 for early decision, 1/15 for early action. Notification: continuous until 3/15, 12/15 for early decision, 2/15 for early action. SAT Reasoning Test deadline: 2/15. Transfer credits accepted: Yes. Applicants placed on waiting list: 0. Wait-listed applicants offered admission: 0. Early decision applicants: 76. Early decision applicants admitted: 69. Early action applicants: 4,369. Early action applicants admitted: 4,064.
Costs Per Year: Application fee: $0. Comprehensive fee: $58,150 includes full-time tuition ($39,330), mandatory fees ($2370), and college room and board ($16,450). Full-time tuition and fees vary according to degree level. Room and board charges vary according to board plan and housing facility. Part-time tuition: $1415 per credit. Part-time tuition varies according to class time, course load, and degree level.
Collegiate Environment: Orientation program. Drama-theater group, choral group, student-run newspaper, radio station. Social organizations: 59 open to all; national fraternities, national sororities, local fraternities, local sororities; 4% of eligible men and 10% of eligible women are members. Most popular organizations: Onstagers, Live to Give (Relay for Life), Zeta Tau Alpha, WMCK, Young Athletes Program/Special Olympics. Major annual events: Spring Concert, Block Party, Relay for Life. Student services: health clinic, personal-psychological counseling. Campus security: 24-hour emergency response devices and patrols, late night transport-escort service, controlled dormitory access. 2,613 college housing spaces available; 2,521 were occupied in 2018-19. Freshmen guaranteed college housing. Option: coed housing available. McQuade Library. Books: 90,940 (physical), 179,938 (digital/electronic); Serial titles: 56 (physical), 155,880 (digital/electronic); Databases: 231.
Community Environment: North Andover is approximately 25 miles north of Boston and has rail and bus service to the city. Andover is used extensively for relaxation, shopping and eating. The local area is rich in cultural and historic attractions.

■ **MIDDLESEX COMMUNITY COLLEGE**
591 Springs Rd.
Bedford, MA 01730-1655
Tel: (781)280-3200; Free: 800-818-3434
Fax: (978)656-3322
Web Site: www.middlesex.mass.edu
Description: State-supported, 2-year, coed. Part of Massachusetts Public Higher Education System. Awards certificates, transfer associate, and terminal associate degrees. Founded 1970. Setting: 200-acre suburban

campus with easy access to Boston. Total enrollment: 8,617. Full-time: 3,155 students, 53% women, 47% men. Part-time: 5,590 students, 62% women, 38% men. 0.2% American Indian or Alaska Native, non-Hispanic/Latino; 19% Hispanic/Latino; 7% Black or African American, non-Hispanic/Latino; 13% Asian, non-Hispanic/Latino; 2% international. 36% 25 or older. Core. Calendar: semesters. Academic remediation for entering students, ESL program, services for LD students, advanced placement, accelerated degree program, honors program, independent study, distance learning, summer session for credit, part-time degree program, adult/continuing education programs, co-op programs and internships. Off campus study at members of the Northeast Consortium of Colleges and Universities in Massachusetts. Study abroad program. ROTC: Air Force (c).
Entrance Requirements: Open admission for most programs. Options: electronic application, early admission. Required for some: high school transcript, 3 recommendations, interview, ACCUPLACER, TEAS. Entrance: noncompetitive. Application deadline: rolling. Notification: continuous. Preference given to state residents.
Costs Per Year: Application fee: $0. State resident tuition: $5160 full-time. Nonresident tuition: $11,112 full-time. Mandatory fees: $950 full-time. Full-time tuition and fees vary according to course load, program, and reciprocity agreements.
Collegiate Environment: Orientation program. Drama-theater group. Student services: legal services, health clinic, personal-psychological counseling. Campus security: 24-hour emergency response devices and patrols. Main library plus 1 other.

■ **MONTSERRAT COLLEGE OF ART**
23 Essex St.
Beverly, MA 01915
Tel: (978)922-8222; Free: 800-836-0487
Fax: (978)922-4268
E-mail: jeffrey.newell@montserrat.edu
Web Site: www.montserrat.edu
Description: Independent, 4-year, coed. Awards bachelor's degrees. Founded 1970. Setting: 10-acre suburban campus with easy access to Boston. Endowment: $670,985. Research spending for the previous fiscal year: $4452. Educational spending for the previous fiscal year: $6389 per student. Total enrollment: 397. Faculty: 77 (19 full-time, 58 part-time). Student-undergrad faculty ratio is 12:1. 404 applied, 79% were admitted. Full-time: 389 students, 73% women, 27% men. Part-time: 8 students, 75% women, 25% men. Students come from 23 states and territories, 1 other country, 52% from out-of-state. 0.3% American Indian or Alaska Native, non-Hispanic/Latino; 4% Hispanic/Latino; 2% Black or African American, non-Hispanic/Latino; 2% Native Hawaiian or other Pacific Islander, non-Hispanic/Latino; 0.5% international. 5% 25 or older, 63% live on campus, 5% transferred in. Retention: 79% of full-time freshmen returned the following year. Academic area with the most degrees conferred: visual and performing arts. Core. Calendar: semesters. Academic remediation for entering students, services for LD students, advanced placement, self-designed majors, independent study, double major, part-time degree program, adult/continuing education programs, co-op programs and internships. Off campus study at Northeast Consortium of Colleges and Universities in Massachusetts, Association of Independent Colleges of Art and Design. Study abroad program.
Entrance Requirements: Options: electronic application, early action, deferred admission, international baccalaureate accepted. Required: essay, high school transcript, minimum 2 high school GPA, 2 recommendations, portfolio. Recommended: minimum 2 high school GPA, interview. Required for some: SAT or ACT. Entrance: moderately difficult. Application deadlines: 8/15, rolling for nonresidents, 12/1 for early action. Notification: continuous until 12/15, continuous until 12/15 for nonresidents, 12/15 for early action. Transfer credits accepted: Yes. Applicants placed on waiting list: 10. Wait-listed applicants offered admission: 1. Early action applicants: 125. Early action applicants admitted: 50.
Costs Per Year: Application fee: $50. Tuition: $31,900 full-time, $1329 per credit hour part-time. Mandatory fees: $1500 full-time, $60 per credit hour part-time. Full-time tuition and fees vary according to course load and student level. Part-time tuition and fees vary according to course load and student level. College room only: $9900.
Collegiate Environment: Orientation program. Drama-theater group, student-run newspaper. Most popular organizations: Student Voice, Theatre Club, Bear Gallery, Dance Club, InterVarsity. Major annual events: Kwanahunakmas, Halloween Party, Drag Show. Student services: health clinic, personal-psychological counseling. Campus security: 24-hour

emergency response devices and patrols, student patrols, late night transport-escort service, controlled dormitory access. Paul Scott Library plus 1 other. Operations spending for the previous fiscal year: $115,583. 98 computers available on campus for general student use. A campuswide network can be accessed from student residence rooms and from off campus. Staffed computer lab on campus provides training in use of computers, software, and the Internet.

Community Environment: Just 30 minutes north of Boston, Beverly is a residential city with a population of 39,800. The historic rocky coast of the north shore of Boston offers a contemplative setting with its harborside parks and beaches, access to the nearby fishing and yachting harbors of Gloucester, Marblehead and Rockport, and to the historic city of Salem, immediately adjacent to Beverly. The environment of the north shore is offset by the accessibility to a large metropolitan city with galleries, museums, cultural events, and nightlife.

■ MOUNT HOLYOKE COLLEGE

50 College St.
South Hadley, MA 01075
Tel: (413)538-2000
Fax: (413)538-2409
E-mail: admission@mtholyoke.edu
Web Site: www.mtholyoke.edu

Description: Independent, comprehensive, women only. Awards bachelor's and master's degrees. Founded 1837. Setting: 800-acre small town campus with easy access to Springfield. Endowment: $729.4 million. Research spending for the previous fiscal year: $3.2 million. Educational spending for the previous fiscal year: $24,641 per student. Total enrollment: 2,334. Faculty: 264 (213 full-time, 51 part-time). Student-undergrad faculty ratio is 9:1. 3,446 applied, 51% were admitted. 54% from top 10% of their high school class, 91% from top quarter, 98% from top half. 6 class presidents, 108 valedictorians, 40 student government officers. Full-time: 2,161 students. Part-time: 49 students. Students come from 46 states and territories, 57 other countries, 53% from out-of-state. 0.2% American Indian or Alaska Native, non-Hispanic/Latino; 7% Hispanic/Latino; 5% Black or African American, non-Hispanic/Latino; 10% Asian, non-Hispanic/Latino; 27% international. 4% 25 or older, 95% live on campus, 2% transferred in. Retention: 91% of full-time freshmen returned the following year. Academic areas with the most degrees conferred: social sciences; biological/life sciences; psychology. Core. Calendar: semesters. Services for LD students, advanced placement, self-designed majors, independent study, distance learning, double major, summer session for credit, part-time degree program, adult/continuing education programs, internships. Off campus study at member of the Twelve College Exchange Program, Five Colleges, Inc., Spelman College, Mills College. Study abroad program. ROTC: Army (c), Air Force (c).

Entrance Requirements: Options: electronic application, early admission, early decision, deferred admission, international baccalaureate accepted. Required: essay, high school transcript, 2 recommendations. Recommended: interview. Entrance: very difficult. Application deadlines: 1/15, 11/15 for early decision plan 1, 1/1 for early decision plan 2. Notification: 4/1, 1/1 for early decision plan 1, 2/1 for early decision plan 2. SAT Subject Test deadline: 1/15. Transfer credits accepted: Yes. Applicants placed on waiting list: 437. Wait-listed applicants offered admission: 1. Early decision applicants: 311. Early decision applicants admitted: 172.

Costs Per Year: Application fee: $60. Comprehensive fee: $64,658 includes full-time tuition ($49,780), mandatory fees ($218), and college room and board ($14,660). College room only: $7160.

Collegiate Environment: Orientation program. Drama-theater group, choral group, student-run newspaper, radio station. Social organizations: 120 open to all. Most popular organizations: Student Government Association, C.A.U. S.E. (Creating Awareness and Unity for Social Equality), MHC Outing Club, Mount Holyoke Symphony Orchestra, Mount Holyoke News. Major annual events: Convocation, Pangy (Pangynaskeia) Day, Spring Weekend. Student services: health clinic, personal-psychological counseling. Campus security: 24-hour emergency response devices and patrols, student patrols, late night transport-escort service, controlled dormitory access, police officers on-campus. Williston Memorial Library plus 2 others. Books: 662,010 (physical), 853,290 (digital/electronic); Serial titles: 603 (physical), 8,098 (digital/electronic); Databases: 227. Weekly public service hours: 115; students can reserve study rooms. Operations spending for the previous fiscal year: $10.8 million. 392 computers available on campus for general student use. Computer purchase/lease plans available. A campuswide network can be accessed from student residence rooms and from off campus. Students can

access the following: online class registration, personal Web pages. Staffed computer lab on campus provides training in use of computers, software, and the Internet.

Community Environment: Across from campus in South Hadley Center is the Village Commons, apartments, movie theaters, a restaurant, an ice cream shop, a pub, a video rental shop, clothing stores, and offices, all attract people from across the five college areas. South Hadley is approximately 3 hours from the city of New York and only an hour and 30 minutes away from Boston. The Bradley International Airport is 40 minutes away and serves the Hartford and Springfield areas. Springfield, only 12 miles away, is accessible by Amtrak. There are buses running from Boston, Hartford, and Springfield to the campus gates. A free bus runs every half hour, taking students to the four other schools (Smith, Amherst, Hampshire, and The University of Massachusetts at Amherst).

■ MOUNT WACHUSETT COMMUNITY COLLEGE

444 Green St.
Gardner, MA 01440
Tel: (978)632-6600
Fax: (978)632-8925
E-mail: admissions@mwcc.mass.edu
Web Site: www.mwcc.edu

Description: State-supported, 2-year, coed. Part of Massachusetts Public Higher Education System. Awards certificates, diplomas, transfer associate, and terminal associate degrees. Founded 1963. Setting: 270-acre small town campus with easy access to Boston. Endowment: $399,545. Educational spending for the previous fiscal year: $5332 per student. Total enrollment: 3,854. Faculty: 419 (74 full-time, 345 part-time). Student-undergrad faculty ratio is 12:1. 1,627 applied, 98% were admitted. Full-time: 1,345 students, 58% women, 42% men. Part-time: 2,509 students, 68% women, 32% men. Students come from 9 states and territories, 7 other countries. 0.4% American Indian or Alaska Native, non-Hispanic/Latino; 16% Hispanic/Latino; 7% Black or African American, non-Hispanic/Latino; 2% Asian, non-Hispanic/Latino; 0.1% Native Hawaiian or other Pacific Islander, non-Hispanic/Latino; 0.3% international. 7% transferred in. Core. Calendar: semesters. Academic remediation for entering students, ESL program, services for LD students, advanced placement, accelerated degree program, honors program, independent study, distance learning, double major, summer session for credit, part-time degree program, adult/continuing education programs, co-op programs and internships. Study abroad program. ROTC: Army (c).

Entrance Requirements: Open admission except for registered nursing, LPN Bridge to Nursing, dental hygiene, medical lab technology, physical therapist assistant, health information management, PN, dental assistant, Pre-Healthcare Academy, and STEM Starter Academy programs. Options: electronic application, early admission. Required for some: high school transcript. Entrance: noncompetitive. Application deadline: 9/11. Notification: continuous. Preference given to state residents. Transfer credits accepted: Yes.

Costs Per Year: Application fee: $0. State resident tuition: $600 full-time, $25 per credit hour part-time. Nonresident tuition: $5520 full-time, $230 per credit hour part-time. Mandatory fees: $4948 full-time, $187 per credit hour part-time, $125 per term part-time. Full-time tuition and fees vary according to program and reciprocity agreements. Part-time tuition and fees vary according to program and reciprocity agreements.

Collegiate Environment: Orientation program. Drama-theater group, student-run newspaper. Social organizations: 37 open to all; The National Society of Leadership and Success. Most popular organizations: Otaku Anime Club, Dental Hygienist Club, Parent Support Group, Student Government Association, Student Nurses Association. Major annual events: Orientation, Fall Fest, Commencement Dinner/Awards Ceremony. Student services: health clinic, personal-psychological counseling. Campus security: 24-hour emergency response devices and patrols, late night transport-escort service, security cameras, access cards for laboratory access. LaChance Library. Books: 36,000 (physical), 43,164 (digital/electronic); Serial titles: 24 (physical), 1 (digital/electronic); Databases: 67. Weekly public service hours: 57; students can reserve study rooms. Operations spending for the previous fiscal year: $501,880. 696 computers available on campus for general student use. A campuswide network can be accessed. Students can access the following: online class registration, portal.

Community Environment: City has airport and bus service. Community services include three libraries, many churches of most denominations, the Henry Heywood Memorial Hospital, and a downtown shopping center. Recreational facilities are swimming pool, golf course, lakes, bowling and theatre. Excellent opportunities for part-time employment.

■ NEW ENGLAND COLLEGE OF BUSINESS AND FINANCE

10 High St.
Ste. 204
Boston, MA 02111-2645
Tel: (617)951-2350; Free: 800-997-1673
Fax: (617)951-2533
Web Site: necb.edu

Description: Independent, comprehensive, coed. Part of Whitney International University. Awards associate, bachelor's, and master's degrees (offers primarily part-time evening degree programs; bachelor's degree offered jointly with Bentley College, Assumption College, Providence College, University of Hartford, and University System College for Lifelong Learning). Founded 1909. Setting: urban campus. Total enrollment: 412. Faculty: 29 (1 full-time, 28 part-time). Students come from 8 states and territories, 39% from out-of-state. 78% 25 or older. Retention: 79% of full-time freshmen returned the following year. Core. Calendar: 8-week terms (6 per academic year). Academic remediation for entering students, independent study, distance learning, summer session for credit, part-time degree program, adult/continuing education programs, internships.

Entrance Requirements: Open admission. Option: electronic application. Required: essay, high school transcript, interview. Entrance: noncompetitive. Application deadline: rolling. Notification: continuous. Transfer credits accepted: Yes.

Collegiate Environment: Campus security: reception desk in lobby of building. 5 computers available on campus for general student use. A computer is required for all students. Students can access the following: online class registration.

■ NEW ENGLAND CONSERVATORY OF MUSIC

290 Huntington Ave.
Boston, MA 02115-5000
Tel: (617)585-1100
Fax: (617)585-1115
Web Site: necmusic.edu

Description: Independent, comprehensive, coed. Awards bachelor's, master's, and doctoral degrees and post-master's certificates. Founded 1867. Setting: 2-acre urban campus. Endowment: $120.3 million. Educational spending for the previous fiscal year: $21,766 per student. Total enrollment: 788. Faculty: 235 (102 full-time, 133 part-time). Student-undergrad faculty ratio is 5:1. 1,170 applied, 32% were admitted. Full-time: 371 students, 44% women, 56% men. Part-time: 38 students, 37% women, 63% men. Students come from 34 states and territories, 19 other countries, 87% from out-of-state. 3% Hispanic/Latino; 3% Black or African American, non-Hispanic/Latino; 10% Asian, non-Hispanic/Latino; 34% international. 3% 25 or older, 30% live on campus, 4% transferred in. Retention: 86% of full-time freshmen returned the following year. Academic area with the most degrees conferred: visual and performing arts. Core. Calendar: semesters. ESL program, services for LD students, advanced placement, independent study, double major, summer session for credit, internships, graduate courses open to undergrads. Off campus study at Tufts University, Northeastern University. Study abroad program.

Entrance Requirements: Options: electronic application, deferred admission. Required: essay, high school transcript, minimum 2.75 high school GPA, 2 recommendations, audition recording, repertoire list. Entrance: very difficult. Application deadline: 12/1. Notification: 4/1. Transfer credits accepted: Yes. Applicants placed on waiting list: 114. Wait-listed applicants offered admission: 21.

Costs Per Year: Application fee: $115. Comprehensive fee: $64,650 includes full-time tuition ($47,900), mandatory fees ($850), and college room and board ($15,900). Room and board charges vary according to board plan. Part-time tuition: $1535 per credit hour. Part-time mandatory fees: $850 per year.

Collegiate Environment: Orientation program. Drama-theater group, choral group, student-run newspaper. Social organizations: 1 open to all. Most popular organization: The Penguin (newspaper). Major annual events: Spring and Fall Barbecues, Prom at the Colonnade, Commencement. Student services: health clinic, personal-psychological counseling. Campus security: 24-hour patrols, late night transport-escort service. Spaulding Library plus 3 others. Books: 103,097 (physical), 248,432 (digital/electronic); Serial titles: 161 (physical), 98 (digital/electronic); Databases: 109. Weekly public service hours: 85. Operations spending for the previous fiscal year: $873,977. 70 computers available on campus for general student use. A campuswide network can be accessed. Students can access the following: online class registration. Staffed computer lab on campus provides training in use of computers, software, and the Internet.

Community Environment: See Boston University.

■ NICHOLS COLLEGE

PO Box 5000
Dudley, MA 01571-5000
Tel: (508)213-1560; Free: 800-470-3379
Fax: (508)213-9885
E-mail: paul.brower@nichols.edu
Web Site: www.nichols.edu

Description: Independent, comprehensive, coed. Awards bachelor's and master's degrees. Founded 1815. Setting: 250-acre small town campus with easy access to Boston. Endowment: $15.4 million. Educational spending for the previous fiscal year: $4703 per student. Total enrollment: 1,592. Faculty: 137 (51 full-time, 86 part-time). Student-undergrad faculty ratio is 17:1. 2,435 applied, 82% were admitted. Full-time: 1,224 students, 37% women, 63% men. Part-time: 98 students, 52% women, 48% men. Students come from 23 states and territories, 15 other countries, 40% from out-of-state. 0.2% American Indian or Alaska Native, non-Hispanic/Latino; 8% Hispanic/Latino; 7% Black or African American, non-Hispanic/Latino; 1% Asian, non-Hispanic/Latino; 0.1% Native Hawaiian or other Pacific Islander, non-Hispanic/Latino; 2% international. 7% 25 or older, 77% live on campus, 16% transferred in. Retention: 74% of full-time freshmen returned the following year. Academic areas with the most degrees conferred: business/marketing; parks and recreation; homeland security, law enforcement, firefighting, and protective services. Core. Calendar: semesters. Services for LD students, advanced placement, accelerated degree program, honors program, independent study, distance learning, double major, summer session for credit, part-time degree program, adult/continuing education programs, co-op programs and internships, graduate courses open to undergrads. Off campus study at Washington Center: Washington, DC. Study abroad program.

Entrance Requirements: Options: electronic application, early action, deferred admission, international baccalaureate accepted. Required: essay, high school transcript, 1 recommendation. Recommended: 2 recommendations. Required for some: interview, SAT or ACT. Entrance: minimally difficult. Application deadlines: rolling, rolling for nonresidents. Notification: continuous for nonresidents. Transfer credits accepted: Yes. Early action applicants: 1,009. Early action applicants admitted: 685.

Costs Per Year: Comprehensive fee: $49,965 includes full-time tuition ($34,615), mandatory fees ($1100), and college room and board ($14,250). Part-time tuition: $1130 per credit.

Collegiate Environment: Orientation program. Student-run radio station. Social organizations: 40 open to all. Most popular organizations: Campus Activities Board, Institute for Women's Leadership, Student Government Association, Student Athletic Advisory Council, Student Alumni Association. Major annual events: Homecoming, Spring Weekend (BisonFest), Welcome Week. Student services: health clinic, personal-psychological counseling, women's center. Campus security: 24-hour emergency response devices and patrols, student patrols, late night transport-escort service, controlled dormitory access. 1,000 college housing spaces available; 954 were occupied in 2018-19. Freshmen guaranteed college housing. Options: coed, men-only, women-only housing available. Conant Library. Books: 27,627 (physical), 150,177 (digital/electronic); Serial titles: 42 (physical); Databases: 35. Weekly public service hours: 102; study areas open 24 hours, 5-7 days a week; students can reserve study rooms. Operations spending for the previous fiscal year: $401,498. 154 computers available on campus for general student use. A campuswide network can be accessed from student residence rooms and from off campus. Students can access the following: online class registration. Staffed computer lab on campus provides training in use of computers, software, and the Internet.

■ NORTH SHORE COMMUNITY COLLEGE

1 Ferncroft Rd.
Danvers, MA 01923-4093
Tel: (978)762-4000
Fax: (978)762-4021
E-mail: gilopez@northshore.edu
Web Site: www.northshore.edu

Description: State-supported, 2-year, coed. Awards certificates, transfer associate, and terminal associate degrees. Founded 1965. Setting: suburban campus with easy access to Boston. Endowment: $7.4 million. Educational spending for the previous fiscal year: $4683 per student. Total enrollment: 6,087. Faculty: 486 (135 full-time, 351 part-time). Student-undergrad faculty ratio is 17:1. 3,870 applied, 92% were admitted. Students come from 14 states and territories, 7 other countries, 2% from out-of-state. 0.1% American

Indian or Alaska Native, non-Hispanic/Latino; 24% Hispanic/Latino; 10% Black or African American, non-Hispanic/Latino; 4% Asian, non-Hispanic/Latino; 0.2% Native Hawaiian or other Pacific Islander, non-Hispanic/Latino; 0.1% international. 39% 25 or older. Core. Calendar: semesters. Academic remediation for entering students, ESL program, services for LD students, advanced placement, accelerated degree program, honors program, independent study, distance learning, summer session for credit, part-time degree program, adult/continuing education programs, co-op programs and internships.

Entrance Requirements: Open admission except for nursing, engineering, health-related programs. Options: electronic application, early admission, deferred admission. Required for some: essay, high school transcript, interview. Entrance: noncompetitive. Application deadline: rolling. Notification: continuous. Preference given to state residents.

Collegiate Environment: Orientation program. Drama-theater group, student-run newspaper. Social organizations: 23 open to all; national fraternities. Most popular organizations: Program Council, Student Government, Performing Arts, Student Newspaper, Phi Theta Kappa. Major annual events: Multicultural Fair, Spring Fling, Alcohol Awareness Week. Student services: health clinic, personal-psychological counseling, women's center. Campus security: 24-hour emergency response devices and patrols, late night transport-escort service. Learning Resource Center plus 2 others. 160 computers available on campus for general student use. A campuswide network can be accessed from off-campus. Students can access the following: online class registration, online bill pay, shared network storage, online advising, personal Web space, mobile printing from personally-owned devices. Staffed computer lab on campus provides training in use of computers, software, and the Internet.

Community Environment: Suburban.

■ **NORTHEASTERN UNIVERSITY**
360 Huntington Ave.
Boston, MA 02115-5096
Tel: (617)373-2000
Fax: (617)373-8780
E-mail: admissions@northeastern.edu
Web Site: www.northeastern.edu

Description: Independent, university, coed. Awards bachelor's, master's, and doctoral degrees and post-master's certificates. Founded 1898. Setting: 73-acre urban campus. Total enrollment: 26,660. Faculty: 1,743 (1,310 full-time, 433 part-time). Student-undergrad faculty ratio is 14:1. 54,209 applied, 27% were admitted. 75% from top 10% of their high school class, 93% from top quarter, 99% from top half. Full-time: 18,230 students, 51% women, 49% men. Part-time: 39 students, 64% women, 36% men. Students come from 124 other countries, 73% from out-of-state. 8% Hispanic/Latino; 4% Black or African American, non-Hispanic/Latino; 13% Asian, non-Hispanic/Latino; 18% international. 1% 25 or older, 49% live on campus, 2% transferred in. Retention: 97% of full-time freshmen returned the following year. Academic areas with the most degrees conferred: business/marketing; engineering; health professions and related sciences; social sciences. Calendar: semesters. Services for LD students, accelerated degree program, self-designed majors, honors program, independent study, double major, summer session for credit, co-op programs and internships. Off campus study at New England Conservatory of Music, Hebrew College, Roxbury Community College, School of the Museum of Fine Arts. Study abroad program. ROTC: Army, Naval (c), Air Force (c).

Entrance Requirements: Options: electronic application, early admission, early decision, early action, deferred admission, international baccalaureate accepted. Required: SAT or ACT. Entrance: very difficult. Application deadlines: 1/1, 11/1 for early decision plan 1, 1/1 for early decision plan 2, 11/1 for early action. Notification: continuous until 4/1, 12/15 for early decision plan 1, 2/15 for early decision plan 2, 12/31 for early action. SAT Reasoning Test deadline: 1/1. Transfer credits accepted: Yes. Early decision applicants: 953. Early decision applicants admitted: 361.

Costs Per Year: Application fee: $75. Comprehensive fee: $67,792 includes full-time tuition ($50,450), mandatory fees ($1072), and college room and board ($16,270). Room and board charges vary according to board plan and housing facility.

Collegiate Environment: Orientation program. Drama-theater group, choral group, student-run newspaper, radio station. Social organizations: 400 open to all; national fraternities, national sororities, local fraternities, local sororities; 10% of eligible men and 16% of eligible women are members. Most popular organizations: Student Government Association, Council for University Programs, Resident Student Association, Downhillers Ski and

Snowboard Club, Northeastern University Huskiers and Outing Club. Major annual events: Welcome Week, Springfest, Carnevale. Student services: health clinic, personal-psychological counseling. Campus security: 24-hour emergency response devices and patrols, student patrols, late night transport-escort service, controlled dormitory access, public safety website. Snell Library plus 3 others. Books: 530,566 (physical), 589,334 (digital/electronic). Study areas open 24 hours, 5-7 days a week; students can reserve study rooms.

Community Environment: Students at Northeastern University have access to the full range of cultural, educational, historical, and recreational offerings of Boston, the higher education capital of the world. The cultural opportunities include the Museum of Fine Arts, Symphony Hall, and the Boston Public Library. The University is adjacent to the Fenway, a spacious park that includes a beautiful rose garden and paths.

■ **NORTHERN ESSEX COMMUNITY COLLEGE**
100 Elliott St.
Haverhill, MA 01830
Tel: (978)556-3000
Web Site: www.necc.mass.edu

Description: State-supported, 2-year, coed. Awards certificates, transfer associate, and terminal associate degrees. Founded 1960. Setting: 106-acre suburban campus with easy access to Boston. Endowment: $3.8 million. Educational spending for the previous fiscal year: $7237 per student. Total enrollment: 5,726. Faculty: 528 (112 full-time, 416 part-time). Full-time: 1,943 students, 53% women, 47% men. Part-time: 3,783 students, 65% women, 35% men. Students come from 9 states and territories, 1 other country, 13% from out-of-state. 0.2% American Indian or Alaska Native, non-Hispanic/Latino; 42% Hispanic/Latino; 4% Black or African American, non-Hispanic/Latino; 2% Asian, non-Hispanic/Latino; 0.3% Native Hawaiian or other Pacific Islander, non-Hispanic/Latino; 0.6% international. 35% 25 or older, 5% transferred in. Retention: 58% of full-time freshmen returned the following year. Core. Calendar: semesters. Academic remediation for entering students, ESL program, services for LD students, advanced placement, freshman honors college, honors program, independent study, distance learning, double major, summer session for credit, part-time degree program, adult/continuing education programs, co-op programs and internships. Off campus study. Study abroad program. ROTC: Air Force (c).

Entrance Requirements: Open admission except for health, human services, technology programs. Option: early admission. Required: high school transcript. Required for some: Psychological Corporation Aptitude Test for practical nursing. Entrance: noncompetitive. Application deadline: rolling. Notification: continuous. Preference given to state residents. Transfer credits accepted: Yes.

Costs Per Year: Application fee: $0. State resident tuition: $600 full-time, $25 per credit hour part-time. Nonresident tuition: $6384 full-time, $266 per credit hour part-time. Mandatory fees: $4536 full-time, $189 per credit hour part-time. Full-time tuition and fees vary according to program and reciprocity agreements. Part-time tuition and fees vary according to program and reciprocity agreements.

Collegiate Environment: Drama-theater group, choral group, student-run newspaper. Social organizations: 17 open to all. Major annual events: Campus Classic 5K, Spring Jam. Campus security: 24-hour emergency response devices and patrols. Bentley Library. Books: 41,604 (physical), 11,287 (digital/electronic); Serial titles: 3,440 (physical), 27,741 (digital/electronic); Databases: 68. Operations spending for the previous fiscal year: $887,094. 750 computers available on campus for general student use. A campuswide network can be accessed from off-campus. Students can access the following: online class registration. Staffed computer lab on campus provides training in use of computers.

■ **NORTHPOINT BIBLE COLLEGE**
320 S Main St.
Haverhill, MA 01835
Tel: (978)478-3400; Free: 800-356-4014
Web Site: northpoint.edu

Description: Independent, 4-year, coed, affiliated with Assembly of God Church. Awards bachelor's degrees. Founded 1924. Total enrollment: 265. 35% 25 or older. Calendar: semesters.

Entrance Requirements: Open admission.

■ **PINE MANOR COLLEGE**
400 Heath St.
Chestnut Hill, MA 02467

Tel: (617)731-7000; Free: 800-762-1357
Fax: (617)731-7199
Web Site: www.pmc.edu

Description: Independent, comprehensive, coed. Awards associate, bachelor's, and master's degrees. Founded 1911. Setting: 50-acre suburban campus. Endowment: $11 million. Educational spending for the previous fiscal year: $6875 per student. Total enrollment: 450. Faculty: 56 (20 full-time, 36 part-time). Student-undergrad faculty ratio is 8:1. 588 applied, 51% were admitted. Full-time: 417 students, 48% women, 52% men. Part-time: 2 students, 100% women. Students come from 25 states and territories, 16 other countries, 52% from out-of-state. 1% American Indian or Alaska Native, non-Hispanic/Latino; 15% Hispanic/Latino; 24% Black or African American, non-Hispanic/Latino; 2% Asian, non-Hispanic/Latino; 40% international. 5% 25 or older, 5% transferred in. Retention: 59% of full-time freshmen returned the following year. Academic areas with the most degrees conferred: biological/life sciences; psychology; business/marketing. Core. Calendar: semesters. Academic remediation for entering students, ESL program, services for LD students, advanced placement, self-designed majors, honors program, independent study, double major, summer session for credit, part-time degree program, external degree program, adult/continuing education programs, internships. Off campus study. Study abroad program.

Entrance Requirements: Options: electronic application, deferred admission, international baccalaureate accepted. Required: essay, high school transcript, recommendations. Recommended: minimum 2 high school GPA, interview. Entrance: moderately difficult. Application deadline: rolling. Notification: continuous. SAT Reasoning Test deadline: 8/1. Transfer credits accepted: Yes.

Costs Per Year: Application fee: $25. Comprehensive fee: $45,706 includes full-time tuition ($30,666), mandatory fees ($1210), and college room and board ($13,830). Full-time tuition and fees vary according to course load. Room and board charges vary according to housing facility. Part-time tuition: $955 per credit hour. Part-time mandatory fees: $1000 per year. Part-time tuition and fees vary according to course load.

Collegiate Environment: Orientation program. Drama-theater group, choral group, student-run newspaper, radio station. Most popular organizations: African American, Latina, Asian, Native American and All (ALANA), Community Service Committee, International Student Club, The Model UN, Student Government Association (SGA). Major annual event: Community Learning Day. Student services: health clinic, personal-psychological counseling, women's center. Campus security: 24-hour emergency response devices and patrols, student patrols, late night transport-escort service, controlled dormitory access. Annenberg Library plus 1 other. Books: 63,939 (physical), 46,446 (digital/electronic); Serial titles: 38 (physical), 8 (digital/electronic); Databases: 43. Weekly public service hours: 73; students can reserve study rooms. Operations spending for the previous fiscal year: $256,299. 85 computers available on campus for general student use. Computer purchase/lease plans available. A campuswide network can be accessed from student residence rooms and from off campus. Staffed computer lab on campus.

■ **QUINCY COLLEGE**
1250 Hancock St.
Quincy, MA 02169
Tel: (617)984-1700; Free: 800-698-1700
Fax: (617)984-1669
Web Site: www.quincycollege.edu

Description: City-supported, 2-year, coed. Awards certificates, transfer associate, and terminal associate degrees. Founded 1958. Setting: 2-acre suburban campus with easy access to Boston. Endowment: $112,021. Educational spending for the previous fiscal year: $6032 per student. Total enrollment: 4,732. Faculty: 352 (68 full-time, 284 part-time). Student-undergrad faculty ratio is 18:1. Full-time: 1,844 students, 60% women, 40% men. Part-time: 2,888 students, 72% women, 28% men. Students come from 18 states and territories, 1% from out-of-state. 0.3% American Indian or Alaska Native, non-Hispanic/Latino; 7% Hispanic/Latino; 25% Black or African American, non-Hispanic/Latino; 6% Asian, non-Hispanic/Latino; 0.1% Native Hawaiian or other Pacific Islander, non-Hispanic/Latino; 8% international. 47% 25 or older, 1% transferred in. Retention: 53% of full-time freshmen returned the following year. Core. Calendar: semesters. Academic remediation for entering students, ESL program, services for LD students, advanced placement, independent study, distance learning, summer session for credit, part-time degree program, external degree program, adult/continuing education programs, internships.

Entrance Requirements: Open admission except for nursing, surgical technology programs, phlebotomy, medical laboratory technician and physical therapy assistant. Options: electronic application, early admission, deferred admission. Required: high school transcript. Entrance: noncompetitive. Application deadline: rolling. Notification: continuous. Transfer credits accepted: Yes.

Collegiate Environment: Orientation program. Drama-theater group, student-run newspaper. Social organizations: 24 open to all; Gamma and Phi Theta Kappa honor societies. Most popular organizations: Student Government Association, Computer Club, Campus Newspaper, Drama Club, Chess Club. Campus security: 24-hour emergency response devices. Anselmo Library plus 1 other. Books: 10,543 (physical), 240,593 (digital/electronic); Serial titles: 12 (physical), 1,922 (digital/electronic); Databases: 52. Operations spending for the previous fiscal year: $160,000. 312 computers available on campus for general student use. Computer purchase/lease plans available. A campuswide network can be accessed from off-campus. Students can access the following: online class registration. Staffed computer lab on campus.

Community Environment: An important business and industrial city today, Quincy has given the nation some of its most important patriots. Quincy was the birthplace of two presidents, John Adams and his son, John Quincy Adams. This South Shore suburb is located about seven miles from downtown Boston, a 15-minute ride by public transportation. There is easy access to all Boston facilities.

■ **QUINSIGAMOND COMMUNITY COLLEGE**
670 W Boylston St.
Worcester, MA 01606-2092
Tel: (508)853-2300
Fax: (508)852-6943
Web Site: www.qcc.edu

Description: State-supported, 2-year, coed. Part of Massachusetts System of Higher Education. Awards certificates, transfer associate, and terminal associate degrees. Founded 1963. Setting: 57-acre urban campus with easy access to Boston. Endowment: $473,714. Educational spending for the previous fiscal year: $7315 per student. Total enrollment: 7,265. Faculty: 567 (134 full-time, 433 part-time). Student-undergrad faculty ratio is 16:1. 4,052 applied, 65% were admitted. Full-time: 2,541 students, 53% women, 47% men. Part-time: 4,724 students, 61% women, 39% men. Students come from 19 states and territories, 35 other countries, 1% from out-of-state. 0.4% American Indian or Alaska Native, non-Hispanic/Latino; 20% Hispanic/Latino; 13% Black or African American, non-Hispanic/Latino; 5% Asian, non-Hispanic/Latino; 0.1% Native Hawaiian or other Pacific Islander, non-Hispanic/Latino; 0.5% international. 39% 25 or older, 10% transferred in. Core. Calendar: semesters. Academic remediation for entering students, ESL program, services for LD students, advanced placement, accelerated degree program, honors program, independent study, distance learning, double major, summer session for credit, part-time degree program, co-op programs and internships. Off campus study at member of Higher Education Consortium of Central Massachusetts (HECCMA) comprised of twelve (12) colleges in Central Massachusetts. ROTC: Army (c).

Entrance Requirements: Open admission. Option: electronic application. Required: high school transcript. Required for some: interview. Entrance: noncompetitive. Application deadline: rolling. Notification: continuous. Transfer credits accepted: Yes.

Costs Per Year: Application fee: $20. State resident tuition: $720 full-time, $24 per credit part-time. Nonresident tuition: $6900 full-time, $230 per credit part-time. Mandatory fees: $6060 full-time, $173 per credit part-time, $350 per term part-time.

Collegiate Environment: Orientation program. Drama-theater group, student-run newspaper. Social organizations: 45 open to all. Most popular organizations: Academic-Related Clubs, Phi Theta Kappa, Student Senate, Anime Club, Psi Beta Club. Major annual events: Spring Fling, Honors and Awards Banquet, Welcome Week. Student services: personal-psychological counseling. Campus security: 24-hour emergency response devices and patrols, late night transport-escort service. College housing not available. Alden Library plus 1 other. Books: 43,862 (physical), 83,063 (digital/electronic); Serial titles: 12 (physical), 62,000 (digital/electronic); Databases: 61. Weekly public service hours: 67; students can reserve study rooms. Operations spending for the previous fiscal year: $760,367. 1,298 computers available on campus for general student use. A campuswide network can be accessed from off-campus. Students can access the following: online class registration, Portal. Staffed computer lab on campus provides training in use of computers, software, and the Internet.

Community Environment: See Clark University.

■ **REGIS COLLEGE**
235 Wellesley St.
Weston, MA 02493
Tel: (781)768-7000; Free: 866-438-7344
Fax: (781)768-8339
E-mail: admission@regiscollege.edu
Web Site: www.regiscollege.edu

Description: Independent Roman Catholic, comprehensive, coed. Awards associate, bachelor's, master's, and doctoral degrees and post-master's certificates. Founded 1927. Setting: 131-acre small town campus with easy access to Boston. Endowment: $33.7 million. Educational spending for the previous fiscal year: $11,581 per student. Total enrollment: 1,954. Faculty: 210 (96 full-time, 114 part-time). Student-undergrad faculty ratio is 11:1. 2,023 applied, 84% were admitted. 10% from top 10% of their high school class, 35% from top quarter, 66% from top half. Full-time: 958 students, 76% women, 24% men. Part-time: 277 students, 88% women, 12% men. Students come from 22 states and territories, 10 other countries, 19% from out-of-state. 0.2% American Indian or Alaska Native, non-Hispanic/Latino; 11% Hispanic/Latino; 19% Black or African American, non-Hispanic/Latino; 4% Asian, non-Hispanic/Latino; 0.1% Native Hawaiian or other Pacific Islander, non-Hispanic/Latino; 2% international. 20% 25 or older, 60% live on campus, 2% transferred in. Retention: 82% of full-time freshmen returned the following year. Academic areas with the most degrees conferred: health professions and related sciences; business/marketing; biological/life sciences. Core. Calendar: semesters. Academic remediation for entering students, ESL program, services for LD students, advanced placement, accelerated degree program, self-designed majors, honors program, independent study, double major, summer session for credit, part-time degree program, adult/continuing education programs, internships, graduate courses open to undergrads. Off campus study at Babson College, Bentley College, Boston College, American University, National Federation of Carondolet Colleges. Study abroad program. ROTC: Army (c).
Entrance Requirements: Options: electronic application, early admission, early action, deferred admission, international baccalaureate accepted. Required: essay, high school transcript, minimum 2 high school GPA, 2 recommendations. Recommended: minimum 3 high school GPA, interview, rank in upper 50% of high school class. Required for some: interview, SAT or ACT. Entrance: moderately difficult. Application deadlines: rolling, 12/1 for early action. Notification: 12/23 for early action. SAT Reasoning Test deadline: 8/1. Transfer credits accepted: Yes. Early action applicants: 759. Early action applicants admitted: 738.
Costs Per Year: Application fee: $50. Comprehensive fee: $56,195 includes full-time tuition ($41,015) and college room and board ($15,180).
Collegiate Environment: Orientation program. Drama-theater group, choral group, student-run newspaper, radio station. Social organizations: 27 open to all. Most popular organizations: Campus Ministry, SGA-Student Government Association, Asian American Student Organization, Dynasty Step Squad, Black Student Organization. Major annual events: Spring Weekend/Week, AAA Fear Factor, Christmas Tree Lighting. Student services: health clinic, personal-psychological counseling. Campus security: 24-hour emergency response devices and patrols, late night transport-escort service, controlled dormitory access. Regis College Library. Books: 108,313 (physical), 421,975 (digital/electronic); Serial titles: 126 (physical), 153 (digital/electronic); Databases: 58. Weekly public service hours: 108. Operations spending for the previous fiscal year: $767,211. 196 computers available on campus for general student use. A campuswide network can be accessed from student residence rooms and from off campus. Students can access the following: online class registration, online bills, financial aid award letters and check-in requirements. Staffed computer lab on campus provides training in use of computers and software.
Community Environment: Regis College is in a suburban community located approximately 12 miles west of Boston. Community services, cultural, and recreational facilities are located in Boston.

■ **ROXBURY COMMUNITY COLLEGE**
1234 Columbus Ave.
Roxbury Crossing, MA 02120-3400
Tel: (617)427-0060
Web Site: www.rcc.mass.edu

Description: State-supported, 2-year, coed. Part of Massachusetts Public Higher Education System. Awards certificates, transfer associate, and terminal associate degrees. Founded 1973. Setting: 12-acre urban campus with easy access to Boston. Total enrollment: 2,382. Faculty: 120 (65 full-time, 55 part-time). Student-undergrad faculty ratio is 16:1. 1,290 applied, 83% were admitted. Full-time: 1,124 students, 62% women, 38% men. Part-time: 1,258 students, 65% women, 35% men. Students come from 14 states and territories. 61% 25 or older, 1% transferred in. Core. Calendar: semesters. Academic remediation for entering students, ESL program, services for LD students, self-designed majors, honors program, summer session for credit, part-time degree program, adult/continuing education programs, internships. Off campus study.
Entrance Requirements: Open admission except for nursing program. Option: deferred admission. Required: high school transcript. Entrance: noncompetitive. Application deadline: rolling. Notification: continuous. Preference given to local residents.
Collegiate Environment: Drama-theater group, choral group, student-run newspaper. Student services: personal-psychological counseling. Campus security: 24-hour emergency response devices and patrols, late night transport-escort service. Roxbury Community College Library. 100 computers available on campus for general student use. A campuswide network can be accessed from off-campus. Staffed computer lab on campus.

■ **SALEM STATE UNIVERSITY**
352 Lafayette St.
Salem, MA 01970-5353
Tel: (978)542-6000
Fax: (978)542-6126
E-mail: admissions@salemstate.edu
Web Site: www.salemstate.edu

Description: State-supported, comprehensive, coed. Part of Massachusetts Public Higher Education System. Awards bachelor's and master's degrees and post-master's certificates. Founded 1854. Setting: 62-acre urban campus with easy access to Boston. Total enrollment: 9,301. Student-undergrad faculty ratio is 15:1. 5,216 applied, 72% were admitted. Full-time: 5,834 students, 60% women, 40% men. Part-time: 1,830 students, 62% women, 38% men. Students come from 57 other countries, 3% from out-of-state. 0.3% American Indian or Alaska Native, non-Hispanic/Latino; 10% Hispanic/Latino; 8% Black or African American, non-Hispanic/Latino; 3% Asian, non-Hispanic/Latino; 0.1% Native Hawaiian or other Pacific Islander, non-Hispanic/Latino; 4% international. 23% 25 or older, 28% live on campus, 10% transferred in. Retention: 78% of full-time freshmen returned the following year. Academic areas with the most degrees conferred: business/marketing; health professions and related sciences; homeland security, law enforcement, firefighting, and protective services. Core. Calendar: semesters. Academic remediation for entering students, ESL program, services for LD students, advanced placement, accelerated degree program, self-designed majors, honors program, independent study, distance learning, double major, summer session for credit, part-time degree program, adult/continuing education programs, internships, graduate courses open to undergrads. Off campus study at other Massachusetts state colleges, Northeast Consortium of Colleges and Universities in Massachusetts. Study abroad program. ROTC: Army (c), Air Force (c).
Entrance Requirements: Options: electronic application, early action, international baccalaureate accepted. Required: high school transcript, SAT or ACT. Required for some: interview. Entrance: minimally difficult. Application deadline: 5/1. Notification: continuous. SAT Reasoning Test deadline: 4/15. Transfer credits accepted: Yes.
Costs Per Year: Application fee: $40. State resident tuition: $910 full-time, $37.92 per credit part-time. Nonresident tuition: $7050 full-time, $293.75 per credit part-time. Mandatory fees: $9974 full-time, $415.60 per term part-time. Full-time tuition and fees vary according to class time and course load. Part-time tuition and fees vary according to class time and course load. College room and board: $12,896. Room and board charges vary according to board plan and housing facility.
Collegiate Environment: Orientation program. Drama-theater group, choral group, student-run newspaper, radio station. Social organizations: 70 open to all; national fraternities, national sororities. Most popular organizations: Student Government Association, Program Council, Residence Hall Association, Multicultural Student Association, International Student Association. Major annual events: Student Involvement and Activities Block Party, Multicultural Student Association Back to School Party, SSUphoria Electronic Dance Music Concert. Student services: legal services, health clinic, personal-psychological counseling, women's center. Campus security: 24-hour emergency response devices and patrols, late night transport-escort service, controlled dormitory access. Salem State University Library. 255 computers available on campus for general student use. Computer

purchase/lease plans available. A computer is required for all students. A campuswide network can be accessed from student residence rooms and from off campus. Students can access the following: online class registration. Staffed computer lab on campus provides training in use of computers, software, and the Internet.

Community Environment: Salem State College is located in Salem, Massachusetts. Salem was founded in 1626, and is one of the oldest cities in the country. It was one of the most active seaports in the New World, and was the capital of the Massachusetts Bay Colony until 1630. Salem was the site of the witchcraft trials in which the accusations of group of children and women caused 19 people to be hanged and one pressed to death. Many handsome old houses reminiscent of the days when sea captains and China merchants grew rich from importing are still to be seen. Marblehead harbor, one of the yachting capitals of the world, is only three miles away. The city is located approximately 14 miles north of Boston, is suburban in nature and has good bus and train service.

■ **SALTER COLLEGE (CHICOPEE)**
645 Shawinigan Dr.
Chicopee, MA 01020
Tel: (413)206-0300
Web Site: www.saltercollege.com
Description: Proprietary, 2-year, coed. Awards certificates and transfer associate degrees.

■ **SALTER COLLEGE (WEST BOYLSTON)**
184 W Boylston St.
West Boylston, MA 01583
Web Site: www.saltercollege.com
Description: Proprietary, 2-year, coed. Awards certificates, transfer associate, and terminal associate degrees.

■ **SIMMONS UNIVERSITY**
300 The Fenway
Boston, MA 02115
Tel: (617)521-2000; Free: 800-345-8468
Fax: (617)521-3199
E-mail: danielle.navarro@simmons.edu
Web Site: www.simmons.edu
Description: Independent, university. Awards bachelor's, master's, and doctoral degrees and post-master's certificates. Founded 1899. Setting: 12-acre urban campus with easy access to Boston. Endowment: $188.2 million. Research spending for the previous fiscal year: $307,126. Educational spending for the previous fiscal year: $17,475 per student. Total enrollment: 6,402. Faculty: 1,071 (245 full-time, 826 part-time). Student-undergrad faculty ratio is 12:1. 3,483 applied, 60% were admitted. 36% from top 10% of their high school class, 70% from top quarter, 94% from top half. Full-time: 1,553 students, 99% women, 1% men. Part-time: 210 students, 97% women, 3% men. Students come from 33 states and territories, 51 other countries, 40% from out-of-state. 0.1% American Indian or Alaska Native, non-Hispanic/Latino; 6% Hispanic/Latino; 6% Black or African American, non-Hispanic/Latino; 10% Asian, non-Hispanic/Latino; 0.2% Native Hawaiian or other Pacific Islander, non-Hispanic/Latino; 5% international. 12% 25 or older, 63% live on campus, 3% transferred in. Retention: 84% of full-time freshmen returned the following year. Academic areas with the most degrees conferred: health professions and related sciences; social sciences; business/marketing. Core. Calendar: semesters. Services for LD students, advanced placement, accelerated degree program, self-designed majors, honors program, independent study, distance learning, double major, summer session for credit, part-time degree program, external degree program, adult/continuing education programs, internships, graduate courses open to undergrads. Off campus study at Exchange program with Mills College, Spelman College, Colleges of the Fenway, double degree programs with Massachusetts College of Pharmacy. Study abroad program. ROTC: Army (c).
Entrance Requirements: Options: electronic application, early action, deferred admission, international baccalaureate accepted. Required: essay, high school transcript, 2 recommendations, SAT or ACT. Recommended: minimum 3 high school GPA, interview. Entrance: moderately difficult. Application deadlines: 2/1, 12/1 for early action. Notification: continuous until 3/15, 3/15 for nonresidents, 1/15 for early action. SAT Reasoning Test deadline: 2/1. SAT Subject Test deadline: 2/1. Transfer credits accepted: Yes. Applicants placed on waiting list: 0. Wait-listed applicants offered admission: 0. Early action applicants: 1,755. Early action applicants admitted: 1,312.

Costs Per Year: Application fee: $55. Comprehensive fee: $56,000 includes full-time tuition ($39,660), mandatory fees ($1140), and college room and board ($15,200). Full-time tuition and fees vary according to course load and program. Room and board charges vary according to board plan and location. Part-time tuition: $1360 per credit hour. Part-time mandatory fees: $260 per term. Part-time tuition and fees vary according to course load and program.

Collegiate Environment: Orientation program. Drama-theater group, choral group, student-run newspaper, radio station. Social organizations: 71 open to all. Most popular organizations: Simmons College Dance Company, Student Government Association, Simmons Student Nursing Association, Sexuality Women and Gender (SWAG), Class Councils (2018, 2019, 2020, 2021). Major annual events: Winter Wonderland, Spring Carnival, Soiree. Student services: health clinic, personal-psychological counseling, women's center. Campus security: 24-hour emergency response devices and patrols, late night transport-escort service, controlled dormitory access. Beatley Library. Books: 154,852 (physical), 37,362 (digital/electronic); Serial titles: 13 (physical), 278,000 (digital/electronic); Databases: 137. Weekly public service hours: 105; students can reserve study rooms. Operations spending for the previous fiscal year: $2.5 million. 570 computers available on campus for general student use. Computer purchase/lease plans available. A campuswide network can be accessed from student residence rooms and from off campus. Students can access the following: online class registration. Staffed computer lab on campus provides training in use of computers, software, and the Internet.

Community Environment: Simmons College is next door to the Isabella Stewart Gardner Museum and two blocks away from the Museum of Fine Arts. Other nearby attractions are Fenway Park, the Charles River, Beacon Hill, Back Bay, Cambridge and the North End. Complete intercity transportation is available.

■ **SMITH COLLEGE**
Northampton, MA 01063
Tel: (413)584-2700; Free: 800-383-3232
Fax: (413)585-2123
E-mail: admission@smith.edu
Web Site: www.smith.edu
Description: Independent, comprehensive. Awards bachelor's, master's, and doctoral degrees and post-master's certificates. Founded 1871. Setting: 147-acre small town campus with easy access to Hartford. Total enrollment: 2,918. 5,432 applied, 32% were admitted. 72% from top 10% of their high school class, 96% from top quarter, 100% from top half. Full-time: 2,505 students, 99% women, 1% men. Part-time: 16 students, 100% women. 79% from out-of-state. 0.1% American Indian or Alaska Native, non-Hispanic/Latino; 10% Hispanic/Latino; 7% Black or African American, non-Hispanic/Latino; 11% Asian, non-Hispanic/Latino; 0.1% Native Hawaiian or other Pacific Islander, non-Hispanic/Latino; 14% international. 4% 25 or older, 95% live on campus, 2% transferred in. Retention: 93% of full-time freshmen returned the following year. Academic areas with the most degrees conferred: social sciences; biological/life sciences; psychology. Calendar: semesters. Accelerated degree program, self-designed majors, honors program, independent study, double major, part-time degree program, adult/continuing education programs, internships. Study abroad program. ROTC: Army (c), Air Force (c).
Entrance Requirements: Options: electronic application, early admission, early decision, deferred admission, international baccalaureate accepted. Required: essay, high school transcript, 3 recommendations. Recommended: interview. Required for some: SAT or ACT. Entrance: very difficult. SAT Reasoning Test deadline: 1/15. SAT Subject Test deadline: 1/15. Transfer credits accepted: Yes. Applicants placed on waiting list: 931. Wait-listed applicants offered admission: 19. Early decision applicants: 538. Early decision applicants admitted: 293.
Costs Per Year: Application fee: $0. Comprehensive fee: $69,924 includes full-time tuition ($52,120), mandatory fees ($284), and college room and board ($17,520). College room only: $8800. Part-time tuition: $1630 per credit hour.
Collegiate Environment: Drama-theater group, choral group, student-run newspaper, radio station. Campus security: 24-hour emergency response devices and patrols, late night transport-escort service, self-defense workshops, emergency telephones, programs in crime and sexual assault prevention. Neilson Library.
Community Environment: The early frontier town of Northampton, settled in 1654, has been transformed over the intervening three-and-one-half centuries into a lively and sophisticated center of culture, commerce, and

entertainment. Northampton has been named the Number 1 small town for the arts in the country by writer John Villani. Today there is a population of over 28,000. Located in the western-central part of state, about 18 miles north of Springfield, the area is easily accessible to good recreational sites. The city has a community hospital, theatres, art galleries, parks, and several hotels and motels. Part-time work is available for students.

■ SPRINGFIELD COLLEGE

263 Alden St.
Springfield, MA 01109-3797
Tel: (413)748-3000; Free: 800-343-1257
Fax: (413)748-3764
E-mail: admissions@spfldcol.edu
Web Site: www.springfield.edu

Description: Independent, comprehensive, coed. Awards bachelor's, master's, and doctoral degrees. Founded 1885. Setting: 150-acre suburban campus. Total enrollment: 3,254. Faculty: 211. 4,112 applied, 64% were admitted. 16% from top 10% of their high school class, 33% from top quarter, 74% from top half. Full-time: 2,129 students, 51% women, 49% men. Part-time: 31 students, 45% women, 55% men. Students come from 24 states and territories, 57% from out-of-state. 0.3% American Indian or Alaska Native, non-Hispanic/Latino; 6% Hispanic/Latino; 5% Black or African American, non-Hispanic/Latino; 1% Asian, non-Hispanic/Latino; 0.1% Native Hawaiian or other Pacific Islander, non-Hispanic/Latino; 3% international. 2% 25 or older, 83% live on campus, 4% transferred in. Retention: 87% of full-time freshmen returned the following year. Academic areas with the most degrees conferred: health professions and related sciences; business/marketing; psychology. Core. Calendar: semesters. ESL program, services for LD students, advanced placement, independent study, double major, summer session for credit, part-time degree program, adult/continuing education programs, internships, graduate courses open to undergrads. Off campus study. Study abroad program. ROTC: Army (c), Air Force (c).

Entrance Requirements: Options: electronic application, early decision, deferred admission. Required: high school transcript, 1 recommendation, SAT or ACT. Recommended: interview. Required for some: portfolio. Entrance: moderately difficult. Application deadlines: 4/1, 12/1 for early decision plan 1, 1/15 for early decision plan 2. Notification: continuous, 2/1 for early decision plan 1, 3/1 for early decision plan 2. Preference given to children of alumni. SAT Reasoning Test deadline: 4/15. Transfer credits accepted: Yes.

Costs Per Year: Application fee: $50. One-time mandatory fee: $240. Comprehensive fee: $49,995 includes full-time tuition ($36,920), mandatory fees ($525), and college room and board ($12,550). College room only: $6830. Full-time tuition and fees vary according to class time, course load, location, and program. Room and board charges vary according to board plan and housing facility. Part-time tuition: $1109 per credit. Part-time tuition varies according to class time, course load, location, and program.

Collegiate Environment: Orientation program. Drama-theater group, choral group, student-run newspaper, radio station. Student services: health clinic, personal-psychological counseling. Babson Library.

Community Environment: Established as a trading post in 1636, Springfield is located on the Connecticut River in Southwestern part of the state. City is noted today for its diversified industries including the manufacture of firearms, plastics, chemicals, radio equipment, tires, paper, and electrical equipment. Ample part-time job opportunities available. Several movie theatres, municipal auditorium, drive-ins, summer theatre, two municipal golf courses, 150 parks, civic center, and playgrounds, swimming, skating, quadrangle of museums, public libraries, provide excellent recreational and cultural opportunities. Easy access to commercial, bus and rail service.

■ SPRINGFIELD TECHNICAL COMMUNITY COLLEGE

1 Armory Sq.
Ste. 1
Springfield, MA 01102
Tel: (413)781-7822
Fax: (413)781-5805
E-mail: lapierce@stcc.edu
Web Site: www.stcc.edu

Description: State-supported, 2-year, coed. Awards certificates, transfer associate, and terminal associate degrees. Founded 1967. Setting: 34-acre urban campus. Educational spending for the previous fiscal year: $18,332 per student. Total enrollment: 5,343. Faculty: 366 (146 full-time, 220 part-time). Student-undergrad faculty ratio is 15:1. 3,295 applied, 80% were

admitted. Full-time: 2,287 students, 55% women, 45% men. Part-time: 3,056 students, 61% women, 39% men. Students come from 16 states and territories, 41 other countries, 2% from out-of-state. 0.3% American Indian or Alaska Native, non-Hispanic/Latino; 29% Hispanic/Latino; 16% Black or African American, non-Hispanic/Latino; 3% Asian, non-Hispanic/Latino; 0.1% Native Hawaiian or other Pacific Islander, non-Hispanic/Latino. 39% 25 or older, 6% transferred in. Retention: 55% of full-time freshmen returned the following year. Core. Calendar: semesters. Academic remediation for entering students, ESL program, services for LD students, advanced placement, honors program, independent study, distance learning, summer session for credit, part-time degree program, adult/continuing education programs, co-op programs and internships. Off campus study at Cooperating Colleges of Greater Springfield.

Entrance Requirements: Open admission except some vocational programs. Option: electronic application. Required: high school transcript. Required for some: interview, SAT. Entrance: noncompetitive. Application deadline: rolling. Notification: continuous. Transfer credits accepted: Yes.

Costs Per Year: Application fee: $0. State resident tuition: $750 full-time, $25 per credit part-time. Nonresident tuition: $7260 full-time, $242 per credit part-time. Mandatory fees: $5556 full-time, $178 per credit part-time, $108 per term part-time. Full-time tuition and fees vary according to course load and reciprocity agreements. Part-time tuition and fees vary according to course load and reciprocity agreements. Tuition guaranteed not to increase for student's term of enrollment.

Collegiate Environment: Orientation program. Drama-theater group, student-run newspaper. Social organizations: 41 open to all. Most popular organizations: Gay Lesbian Bisexual Transgender Alliance (GLBTA), Respiratory Care Club, Cosmetology Club, Anime Club, Dental Hygiene Club. Major annual events: Multicultural Luncheon, Spring Fling, Opening Picnic. Student services: legal services, health clinic, personal-psychological counseling. Campus security: 24-hour emergency response devices and patrols, late night transport-escort service. Springfield Technical Community College Library. Books: 45,975 (physical), 9,270 (digital/electronic); Serial titles: 159 (physical), 12 (digital/electronic); Databases: 93. Weekly public service hours: 61. 1,743 computers available on campus for general student use. A campuswide network can be accessed from off-campus. Students can access the following: online class registration. Staffed computer lab on campus.

Community Environment: See Springfield College.

■ STONEHILL COLLEGE

320 Washington St.
North Easton, MA 02357
Tel: (508)565-1000
Fax: (508)565-1500
Web Site: www.stonehill.edu

Description: Independent Roman Catholic, comprehensive, coed. Awards bachelor's and master's degrees. Founded 1948. Setting: 384-acre suburban campus with easy access to Boston. Endowment: $211.4 million. Research spending for the previous fiscal year: $581,809. Educational spending for the previous fiscal year: $13,888 per student. Total enrollment: 2,556. Faculty: 280 (170 full-time, 110 part-time). Student-undergrad faculty ratio is 12:1. 6,609 applied, 70% were admitted. 20% from top 10% of their high school class, 54% from top quarter, 87% from top half. Full-time: 2,513 students, 60% women, 40% men. Part-time: 22 students, 45% women, 55% men. Students come from 36 states and territories, 14 other countries, 36% from out-of-state. 0.1% American Indian or Alaska Native, non-Hispanic/Latino; 5% Hispanic/Latino; 4% Black or African American, non-Hispanic/Latino; 2% Asian, non-Hispanic/Latino; 0.8% international. 86% live on campus, 2% transferred in. Retention: 87% of full-time freshmen returned the following year. Academic areas with the most degrees conferred: business/marketing; social sciences; biological/life sciences. Core. Calendar: semesters. Services for LD students, advanced placement, self-designed majors, honors program, independent study, double major, summer session for credit, part-time degree program, internships. Off campus study at Eight members of the Southeastern Association for Cooperation of Higher Education in Massachusetts (SACHEM Exchange): Bridgewater State University, Bristol Community College, Cape Cod Community College, Dean College, Massasoit Community College, University of Massachusetts at Dartmouth, Wheaton College and Massachusetts Maritime Academy. University of Portland (Oregon) Exchange. Study abroad program. ROTC: Army.

Entrance Requirements: Options: electronic application, early decision, early action, deferred admission, international baccalaureate accepted.

Required: essay, high school transcript, 2 recommendations. Recommended: interview. Entrance: very difficult. Application deadlines: 1/15, 12/1 for early decision. Notification: 3/15, 12/31 for early decision. SAT Reasoning Test deadline: 1/15. Transfer credits accepted: Yes. Applicants placed on waiting list: 960. Wait-listed applicants offered admission: 53. Early decision applicants: 79. Early decision applicants admitted: 73. Early action applicants: 2,989. Early action applicants admitted: 1,811.

Costs Per Year: Application fee: $60. Comprehensive fee: $58,746 includes full-time tuition ($42,746) and college room and board ($16,000). College room only: $9992. Part-time tuition: $1425 per credit hour. Part-time tuition varies according to course load.

Collegiate Environment: Orientation program. Drama-theater group, choral group, student-run newspaper, radio station. Social organizations: 90 open to all. Most popular organizations: Community Engagement, Recreation/ Intramural Sports Teams, Dance Club, Student Government Association, Financial Management Association. Major annual events: Spring Concert, Skyhawk Madness, Dances and Outdoor Festivals. Student services: health clinic, personal-psychological counseling. Campus security: 24-hour emergency response devices and patrols, late night transport-escort service, controlled dormitory access, restricted access on weekends. 2,191 college housing spaces available; 2,125 were occupied in 2018-19. No special consideration for freshman housing applicants. Options: coed, women-only housing available. MacPhaidin Library plus 2 others. Books: 163,838 (physical), 302,839 (digital/electronic); Serial titles: 3,788 (physical), 79,489 (digital/electronic); Databases: 67. Weekly public service hours: 110; students can reserve study rooms. Operations spending for the previous fiscal year: $1.9 million. 407 computers available on campus for general student use. A campuswide network can be accessed from student residence rooms and from off campus. Students can access the following: online class registration, Learning Management System, online degree evaluation/planning, add funds to ID, use at off campus locations, housing contracts and room lottery, financial aid awards, time sheets and payments for campus jobs, ebill. Staffed computer lab on campus (open 24 hours a day) provides training in use of computers, software, and the Internet.

Community Environment: The College is in Easton, adjoining Brockton and 20 miles south of Boston. Transportation is available to Brockton, and the Boston subway system. Cultural, recreational and community services are all quite accessible.

■ SUFFOLK UNIVERSITY

8 Ashburton Pl.
Boston, MA 02108-2770
Tel: (617)573-8000; Free: 800-6-SUFFOLK
Fax: (617)742-4291
E-mail: admission@suffolk.edu
Web Site: www.suffolk.edu

Description: Independent, comprehensive, coed. Awards associate, bachelor's, master's, and doctoral degrees and post-master's certificates (doctoral degree in law). Founded 1906. Setting: 2-acre urban campus with easy access to Boston, MA. Endowment: $231.7 million. Research spending for the previous fiscal year: $3.8 million. Educational spending for the previous fiscal year: $8351 per student. Total enrollment: 7,288. Faculty: 685 (346 full-time, 339 part-time). Student-undergrad faculty ratio is 13:1. 8,237 applied, 83% were admitted. 12% from top 10% of their high school class, 39% from top quarter, 69% from top half. Full-time: 4,849 students, 55% women, 45% men. Part-time: 268 students, 49% women, 51% men. Students come from 45 states and territories, 115 other countries, 32% from out-of-state. 0.1% American Indian or Alaska Native, non-Hispanic/Latino; 12% Hispanic/ Latino; 5% Black or African American, non-Hispanic/Latino; 8% Asian, non-Hispanic/Latino; 0.1% Native Hawaiian or other Pacific Islander, non-Hispanic/Latino; 22% international. 5% 25 or older, 25% live on campus, 6% transferred in. Retention: 77% of full-time freshmen returned the following year. Academic areas with the most degrees conferred: business/marketing; social sciences; communication/journalism. Core. Calendar: semesters. Academic remediation for entering students, ESL program, services for LD students, advanced placement, accelerated degree program, honors program, independent study, distance learning, double major, summer session for credit, part-time degree program, adult/continuing education programs, co-op programs and internships, graduate courses open to undergrads. Off campus study. Study abroad program. ROTC: Army (c).

Entrance Requirements: Options: electronic application, early action, deferred admission, international baccalaureate accepted. Required: essay, high school transcript, 2 recommendations. Required for some: interview. Entrance: moderately difficult. Application deadlines: 2/15, 11/15 for early ac-

tion. Notification: continuous until 3/20, 12/15 for early action. SAT Subject Test deadline: 4/15. Transfer credits accepted: Yes. Early action applicants: 2,349. Early action applicants admitted: 2,236.

Costs Per Year: Application fee: $50. One-time mandatory fee: $240. Comprehensive fee: $56,412 includes full-time tuition ($38,420), mandatory fees ($146), and college room and board ($17,846). College room only: $14,484. Full-time tuition and fees vary according to course level and reciprocity agreements. Room and board charges vary according to board plan and housing facility. Part-time tuition: $1130 per credit hour. Part-time mandatory fees: $19 per term. Part-time tuition and fees vary according to course level, course load, and reciprocity agreements.

Collegiate Environment: Orientation program. Drama-theater group, choral group, student-run newspaper, radio station. Social organizations: 78 open to all; national fraternities, national sororities; 1% of eligible men and 1% of eligible women are members. Most popular organizations: Student Government Association, Program Committee, Suffolk Free Radio, Black Student Union, Journey Leadership Program. Major annual events: Plazapalooza (Student Organization Fair), Unity Week, Winter/Spring Ball. Student services: health clinic, personal-psychological counseling, women's center. Campus security: 24-hour emergency response devices, late night transport-escort service, controlled dormitory access. Mildred Sawyer Library plus 3 others. Books: 128,945 (physical), 249,567 (digital/electronic); Serial titles: 307 (physical), 65,782 (digital/electronic); Databases: 174. Weekly public service hours: 103; students can reserve study rooms. Operations spending for the previous fiscal year: $3.9 million. 675 computers available on campus for general student use. Computer purchase/lease plans available. A campuswide network can be accessed from student residence rooms and from off campus. Students can access the following: online class registration. Staffed computer lab on campus provides training in use of computers, software, and the Internet.

Community Environment: Suffolk University is located in the heart of Boston, a city rich in history and culture. In addition to being an international center for high-technology, finance, architecture, and medicine, Boston boasts over 50 of the finest colleges and universities in the nation. Founded in 1630, ten years after the Pilgrims landed at Plymouth, Boston is the capital of the Commonwealth of Massachusetts and is the largest city in New England. The city of Boston has a population of over 559,000 people whose heritage is drawn worldwide. The Freedom Trail includes 16 landmarks significant to our nation's history, including Faneuil Hall, the Old North Church, Paul Revere's house, Old Ironsides and the Bunker Hill Monument. Hidden throughout Boston are treasures such as the Isabella Stewart Gardner Museum and the African Meeting House, which is the oldest black church building still standing in this country. There is various entertainment such as the Boston Ballet, the Boston Symphony Orchestra, and the theatre, as well as comedy clubs and clubs featuring many different types of music. In addition, Boston offers some of the finest shopping and dining facilities in the country. Boston is also the home of four professional sports teams — the Boston Bruins, the Boston Celtics, the Boston Red Sox, and the New England Patriots. The city is accessible by public transportation, commuter rail, bus service, air service, and taxi service. Due to its size, Boston is also an excellent walking city. At the hub of the transportation system is Suffolk University, on the edge of Beacon Hill, a maze of brick sidewalks and cobblestone streets, 18th and 19th century townhouses and mansions. The area was settled by the Boston Brahmins and is still one of the most desirable addresses.

■ TUFTS UNIVERSITY

Medford, MA 02155
Tel: (617)628-5000
Fax: (617)627-3860
E-mail: undergraduate.admissions@tufts.edu
Web Site: www.tufts.edu

Description: Independent, university, coed. Awards bachelor's, master's, and doctoral degrees and post-master's certificates. Founded 1852. Setting: 150-acre suburban campus with easy access to Boston. Total enrollment: 11,449. Faculty: 1,077 (681 full-time, 396 part-time). Student-undergrad faculty ratio is 9:1. 21,101 applied, 15% were admitted. Full-time: 5,483 students, 51% women, 49% men. Part-time: 58 students, 59% women, 41% men. Students come from 51 states and territories, 74 other countries, 75% from out-of-state. 7% Hispanic/Latino; 4% Black or African American, non-Hispanic/Latino; 12% Asian, non-Hispanic/Latino; 10% international. 1% 25 or older, 63% live on campus, 1% transferred in. Retention: 97% of full-time freshmen returned the following year. Academic areas with the most degrees conferred: social sciences; engineering; computer and information sciences.

Core. Calendar: semesters. Academic remediation for entering students, services for LD students, advanced placement, self-designed majors, independent study, double major, summer session for credit, adult/continuing education programs, co-op programs and internships, graduate courses open to undergrads. Off campus study at Boston College, Boston University, Brandeis University, Swarthmore College, Spelman College, American University. Study abroad program. ROTC: Army (c), Naval (c), Air Force (c).

Entrance Requirements: Options: electronic application, early admission, early decision, deferred admission, international baccalaureate accepted. Required: essay, high school transcript, 2 recommendations, Common Application or Coalition Application or QuestBridge Application, the Tufts Supplement, SAT or ACT. Recommended: interview. Required for some: art portfolio in lieu of Subject Tests for applicants to the School of Museum of Fine Arts. Entrance: most difficult. Application deadlines: 1/1, 11/1 for early decision plan 1, 1/1 for early decision plan 2. Notification: 4/1, 12/15 for early decision plan 1, 2/15 for early decision plan 2. SAT Reasoning Test deadline: 2/1. SAT Subject Test deadline: 2/1. Transfer credits accepted: Yes. Applicants placed on waiting list: 1,504. Wait-listed applicants offered admission: 0.

Costs Per Year: Application fee: $75. Comprehensive fee: $70,942 includes full-time tuition ($55,172), mandatory fees ($1210), and college room and board ($14,560). College room only: $7934. Room and board charges vary according to board plan. Part-time tuition: $2298 per credit hour.

Collegiate Environment: Orientation program. Drama-theater group, choral group, student-run newspaper, radio station. Social organizations: 325 open to all; national fraternities, national sororities, local fraternities, local sororities; 16% of eligible men and 17% of eligible women are members. Most popular organizations: Leonard Carmichael Society (community service), Tufts Dance Collective, intramural sports, Tufts Daily (newspaper), Tufts Mountain Club. Major annual events: Homecoming, Spring Fling, Supershow. Student services: legal services, health clinic, personal-psychological counseling, women's center. Campus security: 24-hour emergency response devices and patrols, late night transport-escort service, controlled dormitory access, security lighting, call boxes to campus police. Tisch Library plus 3 others. Books: 1.3 million (physical), 432,877 (digital/electronic); Serial titles: 1,012 (physical); Databases: 83,216. Weekly public service hours: 110; students can reserve study rooms. Operations spending for the previous fiscal year: $20.1 million. 1,039 computers available on campus for general student use. Computer purchase/lease plans available. A campuswide network can be accessed from student residence rooms and from off campus. Students can access the following: online class registration, Cloud storage for all students, staff, and faculty. Staffed computer lab on campus provides training in use of computers, software, and the Internet.

Community Environment: Medford is a residential suburb of Boston, located approximately five miles northwest of the city. One of the oldest settlements in the Commonwealth and in the United States, Medford was founded in 1630 and has many historical points of interest. Beautiful Mystic Lakes are located on the northwest border of the city, and further recreational opportunities are provided by the Middlesex Fells, a mountainous reservation of approximately 4,000 acres. Part-time employment is available in Boston.

■ **UNIVERSITY OF MASSACHUSETTS AMHERST**

Amherst, MA 01003

Tel: (413)545-0111

Fax: (413)545-4312

E-mail: mail@admissions.umass.edu

Web Site: www.umass.edu

Description: State-supported, university, coed. Part of University of Massachusetts. Awards associate, bachelor's, master's, and doctoral degrees and post-master's certificates. Founded 1863. Setting: 1,463-acre small town campus with easy access to Springfield, MA and Hartford, CT. Endowment: $347 million. Research spending for the previous fiscal year: $211.1 million. Educational spending for the previous fiscal year: $16,928 per student. Total enrollment: 30,593. Faculty: 1,745 (1,417 full-time, 328 part-time). Student-undergrad faculty ratio is 17:1. 41,612 applied, 60% were admitted. 32% from top 10% of their high school class, 71% from top quarter, 97% from top half. Full-time: 21,784 students, 49% women, 51% men. Part-time: 1,731 students, 61% women, 39% men. Students come from 49 states and territories, 81 other countries, 18% from out-of-state. 0.1% American Indian or Alaska Native, non-Hispanic/Latino; 7% Hispanic/Latino; 5% Black or African American, non-Hispanic/Latino; 10% Asian, non-Hispanic/Latino; 0.1% Native Hawaiian or other Pacific Islander, non-Hispanic/Latino; 7% international. 8% 25 or older, 62% live on campus, 5% transferred in. Reten-

tion: 91% of full-time freshmen returned the following year. Academic areas with the most degrees conferred: business/marketing; social sciences; biological/life sciences. Core. Calendar: semesters. ESL program, services for LD students, advanced placement, accelerated degree program, self-designed majors, freshman honors college, honors program, independent study, distance learning, double major, summer session for credit, part-time degree program, adult/continuing education programs, co-op programs and internships, graduate courses open to undergrads. Off campus study at Members of the 5-College Consortium (Hampshire College, Smith College, Mount Holyoke College, Amherst College, and University of Massachusetts Amherst), National Student Exchange, and other units of the University of Massachusetts System. Study abroad program. ROTC: Army, Air Force.

Entrance Requirements: Options: electronic application, early action, deferred admission, international baccalaureate accepted. Required: essay, high school transcript, 1 recommendation, SAT or ACT. Entrance: moderately difficult. Application deadlines: 1/15, 11/1 for early action. Notification: continuous, 12/15 for early action. SAT Reasoning Test deadline: 2/1. Transfer credits accepted: Yes. Applicants placed on waiting list: 6,250. Wait-listed applicants offered admission: 8. Early action applicants: 17,781. Early action applicants admitted: 13,503.

Costs Per Year: Application fee: $80. One-time mandatory fee: $185. State resident tuition: $15,406 full-time, $5395 per term part-time. Nonresident tuition: $34,089 full-time, $12,036 per term part-time. Mandatory fees: $481 full-time, $240.50 per term part-time. Full-time tuition and fees vary according to class time, location, program, reciprocity agreements, and student level. Part-time tuition and fees vary according to class time, course load, location, program, reciprocity agreements, and student level. College room and board: $13,202. College room only: $7068. Room and board charges vary according to board plan and housing facility.

Collegiate Environment: Orientation program. Drama-theater group, choral group, marching band, student-run newspaper, radio station. Social organizations: 500 open to all; national fraternities, national sororities, local fraternities, local sororities; 8% of eligible men and 8% of eligible women are members. Most popular organizations: Minutemen Marching Band, Ski and Board Club, Outing Club, University Programming Council, Student Government Association. Major annual events: First Week, Homecoming Weekend, Spring Concert. Student services: legal services, health clinic, personal-psychological counseling, women's center. Campus security: 24-hour emergency response devices and patrols, student patrols, late night transport-escort service, controlled dormitory access. 13,666 college housing spaces available; 13,551 were occupied in 2018-19. Freshmen guaranteed college housing. On-campus residence required in freshman year. Option: coed housing available. W. E. B. Du Bois Library plus 1 other. Books: 2.8 million (physical), 1.6 million (digital/electronic); Serial titles: 2,297 (physical), 126,215 (digital/electronic); Databases: 558. Weekly public service hours: 142; study areas open 24 hours, 5-7 days a week; students can reserve study rooms. Operations spending for the previous fiscal year: $20.1 million. 539 computers available on campus for general student use. Computer purchase/lease plans available. A campuswide network can be accessed. Students can access the following: online class registration, online housing assignments, bill payment, Learning Management System, file storage, Web hosting, blogs. Staffed computer lab on campus provides training in use of computers, software, and the Internet.

Community Environment: See Amherst College.

■ **UNIVERSITY OF MASSACHUSETTS BOSTON**

100 Morrissey Blvd.

Boston, MA 02125-3393

Tel: (617)287-5000

E-mail: enrollment.info@umb.edu

Web Site: www.umb.edu

Description: State-supported, university, coed. Part of University of Massachusetts. Awards bachelor's, master's, and doctoral degrees and post-master's certificates. Founded 1964. Setting: 120-acre urban campus. Endowment: $74.4 million. Research spending for the previous fiscal year: $43.7 million. Educational spending for the previous fiscal year: $13,068 per student. Total enrollment: 16,155. Faculty: 1,163 (718 full-time, 445 part-time). Student-undergrad faculty ratio is 17:1. 11,907 applied, 78% were admitted. 23% from top 10% of their high school class, 17% from top quarter, 18% from top half. Full-time: 10,017 students, 54% women, 46% men. Part-time: 2,697 students, 54% women, 46% men. 5% from out-of-state. 0.1% American Indian or Alaska Native, non-Hispanic/Latino; 17% Hispanic/Latino; 17% Black or African American, non-Hispanic/Latino; 14% Asian, non-Hispanic/Latino; 11% international. 23% 25 or older, 9% live on campus,

10% transferred in. Retention: 76% of full-time freshmen returned the following year. Academic areas with the most degrees conferred: business/marketing; social sciences; health professions and related sciences. Core. Calendar: semesters. Academic remediation for entering students, ESL program, services for LD students, advanced placement, accelerated degree program, self-designed majors, freshman honors college, honors program, independent study, distance learning, double major, summer session for credit, part-time degree program, adult/continuing education programs, co-op programs and internships, graduate courses open to undergrads. Off campus study at members of the National Student Exchange, New England Regional Student Exchange. Study abroad program. ROTC: Army (c), Naval (c), Air Force (c).

Entrance Requirements: Options: electronic application, early admission, early action, deferred admission, international baccalaureate accepted. Required: high school transcript, minimum 2.5 high school GPA, 1 recommendation. Required for some: essay, minimum 2.75 high school GPA, SAT or ACT. Entrance: moderately difficult. Notification: continuous until 4/30. SAT Reasoning Test deadline: 3/15. Transfer credits accepted: Yes.

Costs Per Year: Application fee: $60. State resident tuition: $13,841 full-time, $576.80 per credit hour part-time. Nonresident tuition: $33,640 full-time, $1,402 per credit hour part-time. Mandatory fees: $326 full-time, $13.70 per credit hour part-time. Full-time tuition and fees vary according to program. Part-time tuition and fees vary according to program.

Collegiate Environment: Orientation program. Drama-theater group, choral group, student-run newspaper, radio station. Social organizations: 100 open to all. Most popular organizations: Student Arts and Events Council, Haitian Student Association, Golden Key Honor Society, Campus Kitchens, Mass Media. Major annual events: Convocation, Commencement, Fall and Spring Festivals. Student services: health clinic, personal-psychological counseling, women's center. Campus security: 24-hour emergency response devices and patrols, late night transport-escort service, crime prevention program, bicycle patrols. College housing not available. Joseph P. Healey Library. Books: 459,163 (physical), 547,086 (digital/electronic); Databases: 124. Operations spending for the previous fiscal year: $5.4 million. 350 computers available on campus for general student use. A campuswide network can be accessed from off-campus. Students can access the following: online class registration. Staffed computer lab on campus provides training in use of computers, software, and the Internet.

Community Environment: See Boston University.

■ **UNIVERSITY OF MASSACHUSETTS DARTMOUTH**

285 Old Westport Rd.
North Dartmouth, MA 02747-2300
Tel: (508)999-8000
Fax: (508)999-8755
Web Site: www.umassd.edu

Description: State-supported, university, coed. Part of University of Massachusetts. Awards bachelor's, master's, and doctoral degrees and post-master's certificates. Founded 1895. Setting: 710-acre suburban campus with easy access to Boston, Providence. Endowment: $56.4 million. Research spending for the previous fiscal year: $12.2 million. Educational spending for the previous fiscal year: $7782 per student. Total enrollment: 8,513. Faculty: 584 (402 full-time, 182 part-time). Student-undergrad faculty ratio is 16:1. 8,697 applied, 78% were admitted. 14% from top 10% of their high school class, 34% from top quarter, 68% from top half. Full-time: 5,895 students, 48% women, 52% men. Part-time: 946 students, 57% women, 43% men. Students come from 38 states and territories, 39 other countries, 9% from out-of-state. 0.2% American Indian or Alaska Native, non-Hispanic/Latino; 10% Hispanic/Latino; 16% Black or African American, non-Hispanic/Latino; 4% Asian, non-Hispanic/Latino; 2% international. 15% 25 or older, 52% live on campus, 11% transferred in. Retention: 71% of full-time freshmen returned the following year. Academic areas with the most degrees conferred: business/marketing; health professions and related sciences; social sciences; engineering. Core. Calendar: semesters. Academic remediation for entering students, ESL program, services for LD students, advanced placement, accelerated degree program, self-designed majors, honors program, independent study, distance learning, double major, summer session for credit, part-time degree program, co-op programs and internships, graduate courses open to undergrads. Off campus study at Members of the Southeastern Association for Cooperation in Higher Education in Massachusetts (SACHEM). Study abroad program. ROTC: Army (c).

Entrance Requirements: Options: electronic application, early admission, early action, deferred admission. Required: high school transcript, minimum 2 high school GPA, SAT or ACT. Recommended: essay, 1 recommendation.

Entrance: moderately difficult. Application deadlines: rolling, rolling for nonresidents, rolling for early action. Notification: continuous, continuous for nonresidents, rolling for early action. SAT Reasoning Test deadline: 8/21. SAT Subject Test deadline: 8/21. Transfer credits accepted: Yes. Early action applicants: 2,510. Early action applicants admitted: 2,267.

Costs Per Year: Application fee: $60. One-time mandatory fee: $100. State resident tuition: $13,496 full-time, $562.33 per credit part-time. Nonresident tuition: $28,716 full-time, $1,197 per credit part-time. Mandatory fees: $425 full-time, $26.71 per credit part-time. Full-time tuition and fees vary according to class time, program, and reciprocity agreements. Part-time tuition and fees vary according to class time, course load, program, and reciprocity agreements. College room and board: $13,582. College room only: $4982. Room and board charges vary according to board plan and housing facility.

Collegiate Environment: Orientation program. Drama-theater group, choral group, student-run newspaper. Social organizations: 171 open to all; national fraternities, national sororities, local fraternities, local sororities. Most popular organizations: Outdoor Club, Ski and Snowboard Club, 20 Cent Fiction, Relay for Life, American Red Cross. Major annual events: Homecoming Weekend, Welcome Back Week, Moonlight Breakfast. Student services: health clinic, personal-psychological counseling, women's center. Campus security: 24-hour emergency response devices and patrols, student patrols, late night transport-escort service, controlled dormitory access. 4,406 college housing spaces available; 3,535 were occupied in 2018-19. No special consideration for freshman housing applicants. Option: coed housing available. Claire T. Carney Library. Books: 242,682 (physical), 80,828 (digital/electronic); Serial titles: 1,348 (physical), 110,141 (digital/electronic); Databases: 142. Students can reserve study rooms. Operations spending for the previous fiscal year: $5.2 million. 400 computers available on campus for general student use. Computer purchase/lease plans available. A campuswide network can be accessed from student residence rooms and from off campus. Students can access the following: online class registration. Staffed computer lab on campus provides training in use of computers, software, and the Internet.

Community Environment: North Dartmouth is located near the larger city of New Bedford, MA. This city, on Buzzard's Bay, was once the greatest whaling port in the world. Fishing fleets and allied industries contribute one-fifth of New Bedford's income. The city is also known for the manufacture of fine textile goods, plastics, tire fabrics, boats, golf balls, cut glass, and other products. The area is easily accessible by rail, bus, and air. The city has a library and whaling museum. Major community services are located in the immediate area. Part-time jobs opportunities are available.

■ **UNIVERSITY OF MASSACHUSETTS LOWELL**

1 University Ave.
Lowell, MA 01854
Tel: (978)934-4000
Fax: (978)934-3000
Web Site: www.uml.edu

Description: State-supported, university, coed. Part of University of Massachusetts. Awards associate, bachelor's, master's, and doctoral degrees and post-master's certificates. Founded 1894. Setting: 100-acre urban campus with easy access to Boston. Endowment: $91.7 million. Research spending for the previous fiscal year: $49.1 million. Educational spending for the previous fiscal year: $9085 per student. Total enrollment: 18,244. Faculty: 1,110 (637 full-time, 473 part-time). Student-undergrad faculty ratio is 17:1. 12,117 applied, 72% were admitted. 25% from top 10% of their high school class, 56% from top quarter, 88% from top half. 8 valedictorians. Full-time: 10,651 students, 38% women, 62% men. Part-time: 3,354 students, 40% women, 60% men. Students come from 51 states and territories, 64 other countries, 8% from out-of-state. 0.1% American Indian or Alaska Native, non-Hispanic/Latino; 11% Hispanic/Latino; 6% Black or African American, non-Hispanic/Latino; 11% Asian, non-Hispanic/Latino; 4% international. 11% 25 or older, 61% live on campus, 8% transferred in. Retention: 85% of full-time freshmen returned the following year. Academic areas with the most degrees conferred: business/marketing; engineering; computer and information sciences. Core. Calendar: semesters. Services for LD students, advanced placement, accelerated degree program, honors program, independent study, distance learning, double major, summer session for credit, part-time degree program, adult/continuing education programs, co-op programs and internships, graduate courses open to undergrads. Off campus study at Northeast Consortium of Colleges and Universities in Massachusetts. Study abroad program. ROTC: Army, Air Force.

Entrance Requirements: Options: electronic application, early action, deferred admission, international baccalaureate accepted. Required: essay, high school transcript, minimum 3 high school GPA, 1 recommendation, SAT or ACT. Required for some: audition for music students, art portfolio for art majors, three additional short answer questions for No Test option, short answer questions for No Test option. Entrance: moderately difficult. Application deadlines: 2/1, 11/1 for early action. Notification: 3/10, 12/10 for early action. SAT Reasoning Test deadline: 3/1. Transfer credits accepted: Yes. Applicants placed on waiting list: 1,190. Wait-listed applicants offered admission: 642. Early action applicants: 3,985. Early action applicants admitted: 3,568.

Costs Per Year: Application fee: $60. State resident tuition: $14,710 full-time, $613 per credit hour part-time. Nonresident tuition: $32,357 full-time, $1348 per credit hour part-time. Mandatory fees: $470 full-time, $20 per credit hour part-time. Part-time tuition and fees vary according to course load. College room and board: $12,748. College room only: $8400. Room and board charges vary according to board plan and housing facility.

Collegiate Environment: Orientation program. Drama-theater group, choral group, marching band, student-run newspaper, radio station. Social organizations: 250 open to all; national fraternities, national sororities, local fraternities, local sororities. Most popular organizations: Student Government Association, Recreational Sports Clubs, Association of Students of African Origin, WUML (radio station), Campus Activities Programming Association. Major annual events: Spring Carnival, Family Day, Culture Shock. Student services: health clinic, personal-psychological counseling. Campus security: 24-hour emergency response devices and patrols, controlled dormitory access, police and security patrols. 4,797 college housing spaces available; 4,500 were occupied in 2018-19. No special consideration for freshman housing applicants. Option: coed housing available. O'Leary Library and Learning Commons plus 2 others. Books: 224,700 (physical), 192,900 (digital/electronic); Serial titles: 5,641 (physical), 127,540 (digital/electronic); Databases: 180. Weekly public service hours: 118; students can reserve study rooms. Operations spending for the previous fiscal year: $4.8 million. 2,145 computers available on campus for general student use. Computer purchase/lease plans available. A campuswide network can be accessed from student residence rooms and from off campus. Students can access the following: online class registration. Staffed computer lab on campus provides training in use of computers, software, and the Internet.

Community Environment: in the metropolitan area, the cotton and woolen plants once caused city to be known as"the spindle city." Today, textile manufacture has been de-emphasized and industry is diversified with electronics paramount. Lowell is the home of the only federal Urban National Park. Part-time employment available for students. Commercial air, rail, and bus service is easily accessible. Community has public library, churches of all denominations, YMCA, YWCA, art gallery, and hospitals. All sports facilities are available as well as beaches, theatres, and famous ski area within a short distance.

■ **URBAN COLLEGE OF BOSTON**
2 Boylston St.
2nd Fl.
Boston, MA 02116
Tel: (617)449-7070
Web Site: www.urbancollege.edu
Description: Independent, 2-year, coed. Awards certificates and terminal associate degrees. Founded 1993. Setting: urban campus with easy access to Boston. Total enrollment: 812. Student-undergrad faculty ratio is 12:1. Full-time: 59 students, 88% women, 12% men. Part-time: 753 students, 93% women, 7% men. 85% 25 or older, 1% transferred in. Retention: 33% of full-time freshmen returned the following year. Calendar: semesters. Part-time degree program.
Entrance Requirements: Open admission. Required for some: high school transcript. Transfer credits accepted: Yes.
Collegiate Environment: Campus security: 24-hour emergency response devices.

■ **WELLESLEY COLLEGE**
106 Central St.
Wellesley, MA 02481
Tel: (781)283-1000
Fax: (781)283-3678
E-mail: admission@wellesley.edu
Web Site: www.wellesley.edu
Description: Independent, 4-year, women only. Awards bachelor's degrees (double bachelor's degree with Massachusetts Institute of Technology).

Founded 1870. Setting: 500-acre suburban campus with easy access to Boston. Endowment: $1.9 billion. Research spending for the previous fiscal year: $11.2 million. Educational spending for the previous fiscal year: $33,887 per student. Total enrollment: 2,508. Faculty: 359 (309 full-time, 50 part-time). Student-undergrad faculty ratio is 7:1. 5,666 applied, 22% were admitted. 81% from top 10% of their high school class, 96% from top quarter, 99% from top half. Full-time: 2,374 students. Part-time: 134 students. Students come from 50 states and territories, 84 other countries, 87% from out-of-state. 0.2% American Indian or Alaska Native, non-Hispanic/Latino; 12% Hispanic/Latino; 6% Black or African American, non-Hispanic/Latino; 23% Asian, non-Hispanic/Latino; 13% international. 2% 25 or older, 98% live on campus, 1% transferred in. Retention: 95% of full-time freshmen returned the following year. Academic areas with the most degrees conferred: social sciences; biological/life sciences; area and ethnic studies. Core. Calendar: semesters. Services for LD students, advanced placement, self-designed majors, honors program, independent study, double major, summer session for credit, part-time degree program, adult/continuing education programs, co-op programs and internships. Off campus study at Brandeis University, Babson College, Massachusetts Institute of Technology, members of the Twelve College Exchange Program, Spelman College, Mills College. Study abroad program. ROTC: Army (c), Air Force (c).

Entrance Requirements: Options: electronic application, early admission, early decision, deferred admission, international baccalaureate accepted. Required: essay, high school transcript, 3 recommendations, first senior marking period grades and mid-year report, SAT or ACT. Recommended: interview. Required for some: interview. Entrance: most difficult. Application deadlines: 1/15, 11/1 for early decision plan 1, 1/1 for early decision plan 2. Notification: 4/1, 12/15 for early decision plan 1, 2/28 for early decision plan 2. SAT Reasoning Test deadline: 12/31. SAT Subject Test deadline: 12/31. Transfer credits accepted: Yes. Applicants placed on waiting list: 2,032. Wait-listed applicants offered admission: 36. Early decision applicants: 714. Early decision applicants admitted: 248.

Costs Per Year: Application fee: $0. Comprehensive fee: $70,200 includes full-time tuition ($53,408), mandatory fees ($324), and college room and board ($16,468). College room only: $8468. Part-time tuition: $6676 per course. Part-time mandatory fees: $40.50 per course. Part-time tuition and fees vary according to course load.

Collegiate Environment: Orientation program. Drama-theater group, choral group, student-run newspaper, radio station. Social organizations: 160 open to all. Most popular organizations: Student Government, community service organizations, cultural clubs, societies, theater groups. Major annual events: Marathon Monday/Scream Tunnel, Spring Concert, Lake Day. Student services: health clinic, personal-psychological counseling, women's center. Campus security: 24-hour emergency response devices and patrols, late night transport-escort service, controlled dormitory access. Margaret Clapp Library plus 5 others. Books: 717,924 (physical), 770,553 (digital/electronic); Serial titles: 319,932 (physical), 94,450 (digital/electronic). Students can reserve study rooms. Operations spending for the previous fiscal year: $6.4 million. 468 computers available on campus for general student use. Computer purchase/lease plans available. A campuswide network can be accessed from student residence rooms and from off campus. Students can access the following: online class registration. Staffed computer lab on campus (open 24 hours a day) provides training in use of computers, software, and the Internet.

Community Environment: The campus is located in a suburb of Boston 15 miles from the heart of the city. Railroad and bus transportation is available. Community services, and cultural and recreational facilities are found in adjacent Boston.

■ **WENTWORTH INSTITUTE OF TECHNOLOGY**
550 Huntington Ave.
Boston, MA 02115-5998
Tel: (617)989-4590; Free: 800-556-0610
Fax: (617)989-4010
E-mail: dufoura@wit.edu
Web Site: www.wit.edu
Description: Independent, comprehensive, coed. Awards associate, bachelor's, and master's degrees. Founded 1904. Setting: 31-acre urban campus with easy access to Boston, MA. Endowment: $94.1 million. Educational spending for the previous fiscal year: $9719 per student. Total enrollment: 4,454. Faculty: 354 (158 full-time, 196 part-time). Student-undergrad faculty ratio is 17:1. 6,172 applied, 92% were admitted. Full-time: 3,904 students, 21% women, 79% men. Part-time: 358 students, 19% women, 81% men. Students come from 29 states and territories, 60 other

countries, 34% from out-of-state. 0.1% American Indian or Alaska Native, non-Hispanic/Latino; 10% Hispanic/Latino; 4% Black or African American, non-Hispanic/Latino; 7% Asian, non-Hispanic/Latino; 8% international. 9% 25 or older, 49% live on campus, 4% transferred in. Retention: 84% of full-time freshmen returned the following year. Academic areas with the most degrees conferred: engineering; business/marketing; computer and information sciences. Calendar: semesters for freshmen and sophomores, trimesters for juniors and seniors. Academic remediation for entering students, services for LD students, advanced placement, distance learning, summer session for credit, part-time degree program, co-op programs and internships. Off campus study at Emmanuel College (MA), Massachusetts College of Art, Massachusetts College of Pharmacy and Allied Health Sciences, Simmons College, Wheelock College. Study abroad program. ROTC: Army (c), Air Force (c).

Entrance Requirements: Options: electronic application, deferred admission, international baccalaureate accepted. Required: essay, high school transcript, 1 recommendation, SAT or ACT. Recommended: minimum 2 high school GPA, interview. Entrance: moderately difficult. Application deadlines: 2/15, rolling for nonresidents. Notification: continuous. SAT Reasoning Test deadline: 2/15. Transfer credits accepted: Yes.

Costs Per Year: Application fee: $50. Comprehensive fee: $48,140 includes full-time tuition ($33,950) and college room and board ($14,190). College room only: $11,090. Full-time tuition varies according to class time, course load, and program. Room and board charges vary according to board plan and housing facility. Part-time tuition: $1060 per credit hour. Part-time tuition varies according to class time, course load, and program.

Collegiate Environment: Orientation program. Student-run radio station. Social organizations: 58 open to all. Most popular organizations: Intramural Sports, Wentworth Events Board, Multicultural Student Association, Phi Sigma Pi, Major Particular Professional Student Associations. Major annual events: Beaux Arts Ball, Family Weekend, Design Lecture Series. Student services: health clinic, personal-psychological counseling, women's center. Campus security: 24-hour emergency response devices and patrols, student patrols, late night transport-escort service, controlled dormitory access. Douglas D. Schumann Library & Learning Commons plus 1 other. Books: 51,754 (physical), 244,116 (digital/electronic); Serial titles: 210 (physical), 77,225 (digital/electronic); Databases: 75. Weekly public service hours: 100. Operations spending for the previous fiscal year: $2.6 million. 320 computers available on campus for general student use. Computer purchase/lease plans available. A computer is required for all students. A campuswide network can be accessed from student residence rooms and from off campus. Students can access the following: online class registration. Staffed computer lab on campus provides training in use of computers.

Community Environment: See Boston University.

■ WESTERN NEW ENGLAND UNIVERSITY

1215 Wilbraham Rd.
Springfield, MA 01119
Tel: (413)782-3111; Free: 800-325-1122
Fax: (413)782-1777
E-mail: learn@wne.edu
Web Site: www.wne.edu

Description: Independent, university, coed. Awards associate, bachelor's, master's, and doctoral degrees. Founded 1919. Setting: 215-acre suburban campus. Endowment: $73 million. Research spending for the previous fiscal year: $516,739. Total enrollment: 3,813. Faculty: 367 (241 full-time, 126 part-time). Student-undergrad faculty ratio is 12:1. 6,645 applied, 81% were admitted. 14% from top 10% of their high school class, 40% from top quarter, 76% from top half. Full-time: 2,613 students, 37% women, 63% men. Part-time: 123 students, 39% women, 61% men. Students come from 26 states and territories, 22 other countries, 49% from out-of-state. 0.3% American Indian or Alaska Native, non-Hispanic/Latino; 9% Hispanic/Latino; 6% Black or African American, non-Hispanic/Latino; 3% Asian, non-Hispanic/Latino; 0.3% Native Hawaiian or other Pacific Islander, non-Hispanic/Latino; 3% international. 4% 25 or older, 61% live on campus, 4% transferred in. Retention: 75% of full-time freshmen returned the following year. Academic areas with the most degrees conferred: engineering; business/marketing; health professions and related sciences. Core. Calendar: semesters. Services for LD students, advanced placement, accelerated degree program, honors program, independent study, distance learning, double major, summer session for credit, part-time degree program, adult/continuing education programs, internships, graduate courses open to undergrads. Off campus study at Cooperating Colleges of Greater Springfield. Study abroad program. ROTC: Army, Air Force (c).

Entrance Requirements: Options: electronic application, early admission, deferred admission, international baccalaureate accepted. Required: high school transcript, 1 recommendation. Recommended: essay, interview. Required for some: SAT or ACT. Entrance: moderately difficult. Application deadline: rolling. Notification: continuous. SAT Reasoning Test deadline: 8/15. Transfer credits accepted: Yes.

Costs Per Year: Application fee: $40. Comprehensive fee: $50,394 includes full-time tuition ($34,338), mandatory fees ($2466), and college room and board ($13,590). Full-time tuition and fees vary according to course load and program. Room and board charges vary according to board plan and housing facility. Part-time tuition: $647 per credit. Part-time tuition varies according to course load and program.

Collegiate Environment: Orientation program. Drama-theater group, choral group, student-run newspaper, radio station. Social organizations: 70 open to all. Most popular organizations: Student Senate, Residence Hall Association, Campus Activities Board, student radio station, The Westerner (student newspaper). Major annual events: Homecoming, Family Weekend, Spring Concert. Student services: health clinic, personal-psychological counseling. Campus security: 24-hour emergency response devices and patrols, student patrols, late night transport-escort service, controlled dormitory access, security cameras. D'Amour Library plus 1 other. Books: 106,500 (physical), 31,912 (digital/electronic); Serial titles: 46 (physical), 109,440 (digital/electronic); Databases: 128. Weekly public service hours: 97; study areas open 24 hours, 5-7 days a week. Operations spending for the previous fiscal year: $708,495. 530 computers available on campus for general student use. A campuswide network can be accessed from student residence rooms and from off campus. Students can access the following: online class registration.

Community Environment: The College is located in a residential section of Springfield, Massachusetts, about four miles from the city's downtown area. Because Springfield is a city of 157,000 people, there are a variety of social, cultural, and athletic activities from which to choose. Some of the city's special features are live theater ant City Stage; the Springfield Symphony; the Quadrangle, a complex of museums; the Basketball Hall of Fame; the Springfield Falcons hockey team; Six Flags New England Amusement Park; the Eastern States Exposition fairgrounds; and many activities, shows, and concerts held in the Springfield Civic Center. Public transportation is available to locations throughout the greater Springfield area. The College is also a member of the Cooperating Colleges of Greater Springfield, a group of 8 private and public colleges in the immediate area.

■ WESTFIELD STATE UNIVERSITY

577 Western Ave.
Westfield, MA 01086
Tel: (413)572-5300
E-mail: admission@westfield.ma.edu
Web Site: www.westfield.ma.edu

Description: State-supported, comprehensive, coed. Part of Massachusetts Public Higher Education System. Awards bachelor's and master's degrees. Founded 1839. Setting: 256-acre suburban campus. Endowment: $5.5 million. Educational spending for the previous fiscal year: $7747 per student. Total enrollment: 6,237. Faculty: 524 (229 full-time, 295 part-time). Student-undergrad faculty ratio is 16:1. 4,381 applied, 85% were admitted. 5% from top 10% of their high school class, 20% from top quarter, 55% from top half. Full-time: 4,791 students, 54% women, 46% men. Part-time: 761 students, 50% women, 50% men. Students come from 21 states and territories, 18 other countries, 7% from out-of-state. 0.3% American Indian or Alaska Native, non-Hispanic/Latino; 10% Hispanic/Latino; 5% Black or African American, non-Hispanic/Latino; 2% Asian, non-Hispanic/Latino; 0.1% Native Hawaiian or other Pacific Islander, non-Hispanic/Latino; 0.4% international. 10% 25 or older, 51% live on campus, 8% transferred in. Retention: 79% of full-time freshmen returned the following year. Academic areas with the most degrees conferred: homeland security, law enforcement, firefighting, and protective services; liberal arts/general studies; business/marketing. Core. Calendar: semesters. Services for LD students, advanced placement, self-designed majors, honors program, independent study, distance learning, double major, summer session for credit, part-time degree program, adult/continuing education programs, internships, graduate courses open to undergrads. Off campus study at National Student Exchange, College Academic Program Sharing (MA State Colleges), Cooperating Colleges of Greater Springfield. Study abroad program. ROTC: Army (c), Air Force (c).

Entrance Requirements: Options: electronic application, deferred admission. Required: high school transcript, minimum 3 high school GPA, SAT or ACT. Required for some: interview, audition for music majors, portfolio for art majors, essay and interview for nursing majors, sliding scale minimum high school GPA using SAT/ACT scores for GPAs between 2.0 and 3.0. Entrance: moderately difficult. Application deadline: 3/1. Notification: continuous until 3/15. SAT Reasoning Test deadline: 3/1. Transfer credits accepted: Yes.

Costs Per Year: Application fee: $50. State resident tuition: $970 full-time, $315 per credit hour part-time. Nonresident tuition: $7050 full-time, $315 per credit hour part-time. Mandatory fees: $9459 full-time, $75 per term part-time. Full-time tuition and fees vary according to program and reciprocity agreements. Part-time tuition and fees vary according to course load. College room and board: $10,948. Room and board charges vary according to board plan and housing facility.

Collegiate Environment: Orientation program. Drama-theater group, choral group, student-run newspaper, radio station. Social organizations: 94 open to all. Most popular organizations: Student National Education Association, Student Government Association, Campus Activities Board, The Dance Company, Multicultural Student Association. Major annual events: Spring Weekend, Opening Day Picnic, Homecoming Weekend. Student services: legal services, health clinic, personal-psychological counseling. Campus security: 24-hour emergency response devices and patrols, student patrols, late night transport-escort service, controlled dormitory access. Governor Joseph B. Ely Library. Books: 129,289 (physical), 160,388 (digital/electronic); Serial titles: 5,137 (physical), 25,808 (digital/electronic); Databases: 138. Weekly public service hours: 92; students can reserve study rooms. Operations spending for the previous fiscal year: $626,666. 814 computers available on campus for general student use. A campuswide network can be accessed from student residence rooms and from off campus. Students can access the following: online class registration, online transcripts and billing information, Web portal.

Community Environment: Founded in 1669, city is located in southwestern part of state approximately nine miles northwest of Springfield. This is an industrial city manufacturing paper, machinery, and toys. Part-time employment is available for students. Several historical sites are found in the immediate area, including Grandmother's Garden, a municipally owned garden of old-fashioned flowers and herbs. Nearby Stanley Park offers 85 acres of floral gardens, arboretum, concerts, 96-foot high Carillon, covered bridge, old mill, blacksmith shop, and multicolored fountain. Adjacent cities offer many community services.

■ WHEATON COLLEGE

26 E Main St.
Norton, MA 02766
Tel: (508)286-8200; Free: 800-394-6003
E-mail: admission@wheatoncollege.edu
Web Site: www.wheatoncollege.edu

Description: Independent, 4-year, coed. Awards bachelor's degrees. Founded 1834. Setting: 478-acre suburban campus with easy access to Boston, MA. Endowment: $211.9 million. Research spending for the previous fiscal year: $184,595. Educational spending for the previous fiscal year: $17,767 per student. Total enrollment: 1,760. Faculty: 185 (132 full-time, 53 part-time). Student-undergrad faculty ratio is 10:1. 3,674 applied, 70% were admitted. 21% from top 10% of their high school class, 52% from top quarter, 84% from top half. Full-time: 1,751 students, 61% women, 39% men. Part-time: 9 students, 89% women, 11% men. Students come from 39 states and territories, 67 other countries, 61% from out-of-state. 0.2% American Indian or Alaska Native, non-Hispanic/Latino; 8% Hispanic/Latino; 5% Black or African American, non-Hispanic/Latino; 5% Asian, non-Hispanic/Latino; 10% international. 0.2% 25 or older, 96% live on campus, 1% transferred in. Retention: 87% of full-time freshmen returned the following year. Academic areas with the most degrees conferred: social sciences; visual and performing arts; business/marketing. Core. Calendar: semesters. Services for LD students, advanced placement, accelerated degree program, self-designed majors, honors program, independent study, double major, summer session for credit, co-op programs and internships. Off campus study at Salt Institute for Documentary Studies (SALT); Marine Biological Lab (Woods Hole, MA); O'Neill National Theater Institute (Waterford, CT); Twelve College Exchange; Semester at American University (Washington, D.C.); Williams-Mystic Maritime Studies Program; Semester in Boston; Sea Semester; Wheaton in Hawaii; cross registration with Brown University; Southeastern Association for Cooperation in Higher Education in Massachusetts (SACHEM); Boston Marine Studies Consortium. Study abroad program. ROTC: Army (c).

Entrance Requirements: Options: electronic application, early admission, early decision, early action, deferred admission, international baccalaureate accepted. Required: essay, high school transcript, 2 recommendations. Recommended: interview. Entrance: very difficult. Application deadlines: 1/1,

1/1 for nonresidents, 11/1 for early decision plan 1, 1/1 for early decision plan 2, 11/1 for early action. Notification: 3/31, 3/31 for nonresidents, 12/3 for early decision plan 1, 2/1 for early decision plan 2, 1/15 for early action. SAT Reasoning Test deadline: 2/1. SAT Subject Test deadline: 2/1. Transfer credits accepted: Yes. Applicants placed on waiting list: 73. Wait-listed applicants offered admission: 0. Early decision applicants: 147. Early decision applicants admitted: 108. Early action applicants: 1,252. Early action applicants admitted: 1,018.

Costs Per Year: Application fee: $60. One-time mandatory fee: $50. Comprehensive fee: $68,364 includes full-time tuition ($54,118), mandatory fees ($350), and college room and board ($13,896). College room only: $7412. Part-time tuition: $6764 per course.

Collegiate Environment: Orientation program. Drama-theater group, choral group, student-run newspaper, radio station. Social organizations: 110 open to all. Most popular organizations: Student Government Association, Performance Groups (a capella, dance and improv), Black Student Association (BSA), Programming Activities Council, Feminist Association of Wheaton (FAW). Major annual events: Spring Weekend, Head of the Peacock, Holi. Student services: health clinic, personal-psychological counseling. Campus security: 24-hour emergency response devices and patrols, student patrols, late night transport-escort service, controlled dormitory access. 1,631 college housing spaces available; 1,507 were occupied in 2018-19. Freshmen guaranteed college housing. Options: coed, women-only housing available. Madeleine Clark Wallace Library. Books: 297,992 (physical), 167,919 (digital/electronic); Serial titles: 4,504 (physical), 33,166 (digital/electronic); Databases: 157. Weekly public service hours: 114; students can reserve study rooms. Operations spending for the previous fiscal year: $2.8 million. 196 computers available on campus for general student use. Computer purchase/lease plans available. A campuswide network can be accessed from student residence rooms and from off campus. Students can access the following: online class registration, assistive technology, online software training, media equipment loan program. Staffed computer lab on campus (open 24 hours a day) provides training in use of computers, software, and the Internet.

■ WILLIAM JAMES COLLEGE

One Wells Ave.
Newton, MA 02459
Tel: (617)327-6777; Free: 888-664-MSPP
Fax: (617)327-4447

Description: Independent, upper-level, coed. Awards bachelor's, master's, and doctoral degrees and post-master's certificates. Founded 1974. Setting: suburban campus with easy access to Boston, Mass. Total enrollment: 765. Faculty: 7 (1 full-time, 6 part-time). Part-time: 14 students, 71% women, 29% men. 7% American Indian or Alaska Native, non-Hispanic/Latino; 14% Hispanic/Latino; 14% Black or African American, non-Hispanic/Latino. Calendar: semesters.

■ WILLIAMS COLLEGE

880 Main St.
Williamstown, MA 01267
Tel: (413)597-3131
Fax: (413)597-4018
E-mail: admission@williams.edu
Web Site: www.williams.edu

Description: Independent, comprehensive, coed. Awards bachelor's and master's degrees. Founded 1793. Setting: 450-acre small town campus with easy access to Albany NY. Endowment: $2.8 billion. Total enrollment: 2,127. Faculty: 357 (296 full-time, 61 part-time). Student-undergrad faculty ratio is 7:1. 9,560 applied, 13% were admitted. 89% from top 10% of their high school class, 97% from top quarter, 100% from top half. Full-time: 2,020 students, 48% women, 52% men. Part-time: 53 students, 40% women, 60% men. Students come from 45 states and territories, 90 other countries, 86% from out-of-state. 0.1% American Indian or Alaska Native, non-Hispanic/Latino; 13% Hispanic/Latino; 8% Black or African American, non-Hispanic/Latino; 13% Asian, non-Hispanic/Latino; 8% international. 0.4% 25 or older, 93% live on campus, 1% transferred in. Retention: 99% of full-time freshmen returned the following year. Academic areas with the most degrees conferred: social sciences; mathematics and statistics; biological/life sciences. Core. Calendar: 4-1-4. Services for LD students, self-designed majors, independent study, double major, internships. Off campus study. Study abroad program. ROTC: Air Force (c).

Entrance Requirements: Options: electronic application, early admission, early decision, deferred admission. Required: essay, high school transcript,

2 recommendations, SAT or ACT. Entrance: most difficult. Application deadlines: 1/1, 11/15 for early decision. Notification: 4/7, 12/15 for early decision. SAT Reasoning Test deadline: 1/1. Transfer credits accepted: Yes. Applicants placed on waiting list: 1,772. Wait-listed applicants offered admission: 76. Early decision applicants: 748. Early decision applicants admitted: 258.

Costs Per Year: Application fee: $65. Comprehensive fee: $72,270 includes full-time tuition ($56,970), mandatory fees ($310), and college room and board ($14,990). College room only: $7600.

Collegiate Environment: Orientation program. Drama-theater group, choral group, marching band, student-run newspaper, radio station. Social organizations: 150 open to all. Major annual events: Mountain Day, Winter Carnival, Claiming Williams. Student services: health clinic, personal-psychological counseling. Campus security: 24-hour emergency response devices and patrols, student patrols, late night transport-escort service, controlled dormitory access. 2,020 college housing spaces available. Freshmen guaranteed college housing. On-campus residence required through junior year. Option: coed housing available. Sawyer Library plus 2 others. Books: 1 million (physical); Serial titles: 737 (physical), 90,227 (digital/electronic). Weekly public service hours: 118; study areas open 24 hours, 5-7 days a week; students can reserve study rooms. 1,000 computers available on campus for general student use. A campuswide network can be accessed from student residence rooms and from off campus. Students can access the following: online class registration. Staffed computer lab on campus provides training in use of computers and software.

Community Environment: This pleasant colonial town was named for its founder, Col. Ephraim Williams. It is located in the Berkshire Mountains within easy commuting distance of Albany, Boston, and New York. Heavy tourist trade is found here, and the area is known as"Village Beautiful." Excellent facilities are available for skiing, horseback riding, hunting in season, fishing, hiking, and golf. The town has several art museum and its own symphony orchestra. The Tanglewood Music Festival is held nearby annually.

■ **WORCESTER POLYTECHNIC INSTITUTE**
100 Institute Rd.
Worcester, MA 01609-2280
Tel: (508)831-5000
Fax: (508)831-5875
E-mail: admissions@wpi.edu
Web Site: www.wpi.edu
Description: Independent, university, coed. Awards bachelor's, master's, and doctoral degrees. Founded 1865. Setting: 95-acre suburban campus with easy access to Boston. Endowment: $519.6 million. Total enrollment: 6,874. Faculty: 508 (420 full-time, 88 part-time). Student-undergrad faculty ratio is 13:1. 10,584 applied, 42% were admitted. 64% from top 10% of their high school class, 93% from top quarter, 100% from top half. 33 valedictorians. Full-time: 4,527 students, 39% women, 61% men. Part-time: 144 students, 26% women, 74% men. Students come from 44 states and territories, 66 other countries, 55% from out-of-state. 0.3% American Indian or Alaska Native, non-Hispanic/Latino; 9% Hispanic/Latino; 3% Black or African American, non-Hispanic/Latino; 5% Asian, non-Hispanic/Latino; 9% international. 1% 25 or older, 49% live on campus, 1% transferred in. Retention: 96% of full-time freshmen returned the following year. Academic areas with the most degrees conferred: engineering; computer and information sciences; biological/life sciences. Core. Calendar: 4 7-week terms. ESL program, services for LD students, advanced placement, accelerated degree program, self-designed majors, independent study, distance learning, double major, summer session for credit, part-time degree program, co-op programs and internships, graduate courses open to undergrads. Off campus study. Study abroad program. ROTC: Army, Naval (c), Air Force.
Entrance Requirements: Options: electronic application, early admission, early action, deferred admission, international baccalaureate accepted. Required: essay, high school transcript, 2 recommendations. Required for some: interview, IELTS or TOEFL. Entrance: very difficult. Application deadlines: 2/1, 1/1 for early action. Notification: 4/1, 2/1 for early action. SAT Reasoning Test deadline: 3/1. SAT Subject Test deadline: 3/1. Transfer credits accepted: Yes. Applicants placed on waiting list: 3,202. Wait-listed applicants offered admission: 153. Early action applicants: 6,468. Early action applicants admitted: 4,194.
Costs Per Year: Application fee: $65. One-time mandatory fee: $200. Comprehensive fee: $65,304 includes full-time tuition ($49,860), mandatory fees ($670), and college room and board ($14,774). College room only:

$8440. Room and board charges vary according to board plan and housing facility. Part-time tuition: $1385 per credit hour. Part-time tuition varies according to course load.

Collegiate Environment: Orientation program. Drama-theater group, choral group, student-run newspaper, radio station. Social organizations: 227 open to all; national fraternities, national sororities. Most popular organizations: Student Government Association, Panhellenic, Interfraternity Council, Intramural and Club Sports, Music Association. Major annual events: Relay for Life, Spring Concert, Black Student Union Fashion Show. Student services: health clinic, personal-psychological counseling. Campus security: 24-hour emergency response devices and patrols, student patrols, late night transport-escort service, controlled dormitory access. 2,240 college housing spaces available; 2,207 were occupied in 2018-19. Freshmen guaranteed college housing. Option: coed housing available. George C. Gordon Library plus 1 other. Books: 192,701 (physical), 750,858 (digital/electronic); Serial titles: 5,371 (physical), 143,312 (digital/electronic); Databases: 215. Weekly public service hours: 107; students can reserve study rooms. 860 computers available on campus for general student use. Computer purchase/lease plans available. A campuswide network can be accessed from student residence rooms and from off campus. Students can access the following: online class registration, online course content. Staffed computer lab on campus provides training in use of computers, software, and the Internet.
Community Environment: See Clark University.

■ **WORCESTER STATE UNIVERSITY**
486 Chandler St.
Worcester, MA 01602-2597
Tel: (508)929-8000
Fax: (508)929-8131
Web Site: www.worcester.edu
Description: State-supported, comprehensive, coed. Part of Massachusetts Public Higher Education System. Awards bachelor's and master's degrees and post-master's certificates. Founded 1874. Setting: 58-acre urban campus with easy access to Boston. Endowment: $17.4 million. Educational spending for the previous fiscal year: $6718 per student. Total enrollment: 6,217. Faculty: 465 (208 full-time, 257 part-time). Student-undergrad faculty ratio is 17:1. 4,076 applied, 78% were admitted. Full-time: 4,164 students, 60% women, 40% men. Part-time: 1,216 students, 58% women, 42% men. Students come from 23 states and territories, 22 other countries, 4% from out-of-state. 0.4% American Indian or Alaska Native, non-Hispanic/Latino; 13% Hispanic/Latino; 9% Black or African American, non-Hispanic/Latino; 5% Asian, non-Hispanic/Latino; 0.1% Native Hawaiian or other Pacific Islander, non-Hispanic/Latino; 1% international. 16% 25 or older, 31% live on campus, 10% transferred in. Retention: 79% of full-time freshmen returned the following year. Academic areas with the most degrees conferred: health professions and related sciences; business/marketing; homeland security, law enforcement, firefighting, and protective services. Core. Calendar: semesters. Academic remediation for entering students, ESL program, services for LD students, advanced placement, accelerated degree program, self-designed majors, honors program, independent study, distance learning, double major, summer session for credit, part-time degree program, adult/continuing education programs, internships, graduate courses open to undergrads. Off campus study at Higher Education Consortium of Central Massachusetts. Study abroad program. ROTC: Army (c), Naval (c), Air Force (c).
Entrance Requirements: Options: electronic application, early action, deferred admission. Required: high school transcript, minimum 2 high school GPA. Required for some: essay, SAT or ACT. Entrance: moderately difficult. Application deadline: 11/15 for early action. Notification: 1/2. Transfer credits accepted: Yes.
Costs Per Year: Application fee: $50. State resident tuition: $970 full-time, $40.42 per credit hour part-time. Nonresident tuition: $7050 full-time, $293.75 per credit hour part-time. Mandatory fees: $9191 full-time, $382.96 per credit hour part-time. Full-time tuition and fees vary according to class time, course load, degree level, and reciprocity agreements. Part-time tuition and fees vary according to class time, course load, degree level, and reciprocity agreements. College room and board: $12,262. College room only: $8428. Room and board charges vary according to board plan and housing facility.
Collegiate Environment: Orientation program. Drama-theater group, choral group, student-run radio station. Social organizations: 40 open to all. Most popular organizations: Senate, SEC (Student Events Committee), TWA (Third World Alliance), WSCW (radio station), Dance Company/Club. Major

annual events: Multicultural Festival, Homecoming, SGA Auction to Benefit the Homeless. Student services: health clinic, personal-psychological counseling. Campus security: 24-hour emergency response devices and patrols, late night transport-escort service, controlled dormitory access, well-lit campus, limited access to campus at night. College housing designed to accommodate 1,500 students; 1,538 undergraduates lived in college housing during 2018-19. No special consideration for freshman housing applicants. Options: coed, men-only, women-only housing available. Learning Resource Center. Books: 128,798 (physical), 1.6 million (digital/electronic); Serial titles: 202 (physical), 144,391 (digital/electronic); Databases: 273. Weekly public service hours: 100. Operations spending for the previous fiscal year: $1.5 million.

Community Environment: The Worcester State College location has the advantages of a suburban setting in the west side of Worcester, while less than two miles from downtown Worcester. A shuttle service provides free student transportation to the other nine college in the Colleges of Worcester Consortium and to City Hall, the Worcester Public Library, and several cultural centers. Worcester, the"Heart of New England," is about 40 miles from Boston, 45 miles from Providence, Rhode Island and 60 miles from Hartford, Connecticut. More than 700,000 people live within an hour's drive. The Worcester Centrum and Convention Center, with a seating capacity of 15,500, hosts a variety of sports and entertainment events. Lakes, rivers, city parks and beaches make fishing and boating, and a variety of activities, available. Hiking and skiing are available in nearby Mt. Wachusett.

■ ADRIAN COLLEGE

110 S Madison St.
Adrian, MI 49221-2575
Tel: (517)265-5161; Free: 800-877-2246
Fax: (517)265-3331
E-mail: admissions@adrian.edu
Web Site: www.adrian.edu

Description: Independent, comprehensive, coed, affiliated with United Methodist Church. Awards associate, bachelor's, and master's degrees. Founded 1859. Setting: 100-acre small town campus with easy access to Detroit, Toledo. Endowment: $27.4 million. Educational spending for the previous fiscal year: $7520 per student. Total enrollment: 1,656. Faculty: 195 (94 full-time, 101 part-time). Student-undergrad faculty ratio is 10:1. 4,675 applied, 56% were admitted. Full-time: 1,553 students, 49% women, 51% men. Part-time: 94 students, 40% women, 60% men. Students come from 29 states and territories, 5 other countries, 21% from out-of-state. 0.4% American Indian or Alaska Native, non-Hispanic/Latino; 2% Hispanic/Latino; 10% Black or African American, non-Hispanic/Latino; 0.5% Asian, non-Hispanic/Latino; 0.1% Native Hawaiian or other Pacific Islander, non-Hispanic/Latino; 0.1% international. 92% live on campus, 4% transferred in. Retention: 70% of full-time freshmen returned the following year. Academic areas with the most degrees conferred: business/marketing; visual and performing arts; biological/life sciences. Core. Calendar: semesters. Academic remediation for entering students, ESL program, services for LD students, advanced placement, self-designed majors, honors program, independent study, double major, summer session for credit, part-time degree program, adult/continuing education programs, internships, graduate courses open to undergrads. Off campus study at Urban Life Center (Chicago), The Washington Center, ROTC credit at University of Toledo. Study abroad program. ROTC: Army (c).

Entrance Requirements: Options: electronic application, deferred admission, international baccalaureate accepted. Required: high school transcript, SAT or ACT. Recommended: ACT. Required for some: essay, interview. Entrance: moderately difficult. Application deadline: 8/1. Notification: continuous. SAT Reasoning Test deadline: 8/1. SAT Subject Test deadline: 8/1. Transfer credits accepted: Yes.

Collegiate Environment: Orientation program. Drama-theater group, choral group, marching band, student-run newspaper, radio station. Social organizations: 75 open to all; national fraternities, national sororities, local sororities; 25% of eligible men and 19% of eligible women are members. Most popular organizations: Student Government Association, Adrian College Business Club, Circle K, Campus Activities Network, Adrian College Mortar Board. Major annual events: Homecoming, The Annual Spring Concert, Crazy C.A.N. Friday. Student services: health clinic, personal-psychological counseling. Campus security: 24-hour patrols, student patrols, late night transport-escort service, controlled dormitory access. Shipman Library. Operations spending for the previous fiscal year: $678,829. 120 computers available on campus for general student use. A campuswide network can be accessed from student residence rooms. Students can access the following: online class registration. Staffed computer lab on campus (open 24 hours a day).

Community Environment: Adrian is 35 miles southwest of Ann Arbor and 35 miles northwest of Toledo, Ohio, located in the center of a large industrial, agricultural and recreational area. Leading manufactured products include aircraft, automobile, and refrigerator parts, paper, wood cabinetry, plastics, tools, and chemicals. Water sports and fishing are easily accessible with many lakes within a 25-mile radius. Part-time job opportunities are available.

■ ALBION COLLEGE

611 E Porter St.
Albion, MI 49224-1831
Tel: (517)629-1000; Free: 800-858-6770
Fax: (517)629-0569
E-mail: ssanders@albion.edu
Web Site: www.albion.edu

Description: Independent Methodist, 4-year, coed. Awards bachelor's degrees. Founded 1835. Setting: 574-acre small town campus with easy access to Detroit. Endowment: $173.6 million. Research spending for the previous fiscal year: $1.1 million. Educational spending for the previous fiscal year: $15,517 per student. Total enrollment: 1,533. Faculty: 168 (117 full-time, 51 part-time). Student-undergrad faculty ratio is 12:1. 4,226 applied, 68% were admitted. 1 National Merit Scholar, 10 valedictorians. Full-time: 1,509 students, 54% women, 46% men. Part-time: 24 students, 54% women, 46% men. Students come from 31 states and territories, 11 other countries, 26% from out-of-state. 0.3% American Indian or Alaska Native, non-Hispanic/Latino; 10% Hispanic/Latino; 15% Black or African American, non-Hispanic/Latino; 2% Asian, non-Hispanic/Latino; 2% international. 95% live on campus, 2% transferred in. Retention: 75% of full-time freshmen returned the following year. Academic areas with the most degrees conferred: social sciences; business/marketing; biological/life sciences. Core. Calendar: semesters. Services for LD students, advanced placement, self-designed majors, honors program, independent study, distance learning, double major, summer session for credit, part-time degree program, internships. Off campus study at Great Lakes Colleges Association. Study abroad program. ROTC: Army (c).

Entrance Requirements: Options: electronic application, early admission, early action, deferred admission, international baccalaureate accepted. Required: high school transcript, 1 recommendation, SAT or ACT. Recommended: essay, interview. Application deadlines: rolling, 12/1 for early action. Notification: continuous until 10/15, 11/1 for early action. SAT Reasoning Test deadline: 3/1. SAT Subject Test deadline: 3/1. Transfer credits accepted: Yes. Early action applicants: 1,907. Early action applicants admitted: 1,422.

Costs Per Year: Application fee: $0. One-time mandatory fee: $185. Comprehensive fee: $60,470 includes full-time tuition ($47,570), mandatory fees ($520), and college room and board ($12,380). College room only: $6080.

Collegiate Environment: Orientation program. Drama-theater group, choral group, marching band, student-run newspaper, radio station. Social organizations: 110 open to all; national fraternities, national sororities; 35% of eligible men and 28% of eligible women are members. Most popular organizations: Greek Life (Fraternities and Sororities), Student Senate (Student Government), Union Board (programming Board), Student Volunteer Bureau, Umbrella. Major annual events: Briton Bash, Day of Woden, Big Show. Student services: health clinic, personal-psychological counseling, women's center. Campus security: 24-hour emergency response devices and patrols, late night transport-escort service, controlled dormitory access. 1,729 college housing spaces available; 1,513 were occupied in 2018-19. Freshmen guaranteed college housing. On-campus residence required through senior year. Options: coed, men-only, women-only housing available. Stockwell Mudd Libraries. Books: 345,123 (physical), 292,100 (digital/electronic); Serial titles: 752 (physical), 77,172 (digital/electronic); Databases: 205. Weekly public service hours: 110. Operations spending for the previous fiscal year: $1.3 million. 250 computers available on campus for general student use. A campuswide network can be accessed from student residence rooms and from off campus. Students can access the following: online class registration, online student account and financial aid. Staffed computer lab on campus provides training in use of computers, software, and the Internet.

Community Environment: Located one and one-half hours west of Detroit and three hours east of Chicago, the city of Albion combines small town life, a strong industrial base, and the amenities of a college town to form a unique community for its citizens. Albion boasts a rich history of educational and industrial accomplishment and prides itself on its ethnic and cultural diversity. Part-time employment is available. The area is served by Greyhound Bus and Amtrak and has a library, hospital, parks, and several civic and service organizations. Facilities are provided for tennis, golf, skating, and water sports.

■ **ALMA COLLEGE**
614 W Superior St.
Alma, MI 48801-1599
Tel: (989)463-7111; Free: 800-321-ALMA
Fax: (989)463-7057
E-mail: admissions@alma.edu
Web Site: www.alma.edu
Description: Independent Presbyterian, 4-year, coed. Awards bachelor's degrees. Founded 1886. Setting: 128-acre small town campus with easy access to Lansing. Endowment: $120.2 million. Research spending for the previous fiscal year: $190,378. Educational spending for the previous fiscal year: $11,691 per student. Total enrollment: 1,426. Faculty: 158 (99 full-time, 59 part-time). Student-undergrad faculty ratio is 12:1. 4,728 applied, 64% were admitted. 18% from top 10% of their high school class, 25% from top quarter, 84% from top half. 8 valedictorians. Full-time: 1,376 students, 57% women, 43% men. Part-time: 50 students, 52% women, 48% men. Students come from 29 states and territories, 10 other countries, 9% from out-of-state. 0.4% American Indian or Alaska Native, non-Hispanic/Latino; 5% Hispanic/Latino; 3% Black or African American, non-Hispanic/Latino; 1% Asian, non-Hispanic/Latino; 0.1% Native Hawaiian or other Pacific Islander, non-Hispanic/Latino; 2% international. 1% 25 or older, 95% live on campus, 3% transferred in. Retention: 77% of full-time freshmen returned the following year. Academic areas with the most degrees conferred: health professions and related sciences; business/marketing; education. Core. Calendar: 4-4-1. Services for LD students, self-designed majors, honors program, independent study, double major, co-op programs and internships. Off campus study at Philadelphia Center Internship, Urban Life Center, Washington Semester. Study abroad program. ROTC: Army (c).
Entrance Requirements: Options: electronic application, international baccalaureate accepted. Required: essay, high school transcript, SAT or ACT. Required for some: interview. Entrance: moderately difficult. Application deadline: rolling. Notification: continuous. SAT Reasoning Test deadline: 9/1. Transfer credits accepted: Yes.
Costs Per Year: Application fee: $25. Comprehensive fee: $51,256 includes full-time tuition ($39,998), mandatory fees ($260), and college room and board ($10,998). Room and board charges vary according to board plan and housing facility. Part-time tuition: $1195 per credit hour. Part-time tuition varies according to course load.
Collegiate Environment: Orientation program. Drama-theater group, choral group, marching band, student-run newspaper. Social organizations: 80 open to all; national fraternities, national sororities, local fraternities, local sororities; 22% of eligible men and 18% of eligible women are members. Most popular organizations: Alma Ambassadors, Alma College Union Board, Alma College Otaku Gamers (ACOG), Student Congress, Alpha Phi Omega. Major annual events: Homecoming, Throwdown in A Town, Orientation Hypnotist. Student services: health clinic, personal-psychological counseling. Campus security: 24-hour emergency response devices, late night transport-escort service, controlled dormitory access. Kerhl Building-Monteith Library. Books: 245,135 (physical), 150,135 (digital/electronic); Serial titles: 1,000 (physical). Weekly public service hours: 100; students can reserve study rooms. Operations spending for the previous fiscal year: $1.2 million. 410 computers available on campus for general student use. A campuswide network can be accessed from student residence rooms. Students can access the following: online class registration. Staffed computer lab on campus provides training in use of computers, software, and the Internet.

Community Environment: Alma is located in a rural area in the center of Michigan's lower peninsula. Major industries include manufacturing of automotive parts, plastic extrusions, drainage and metal products. Some part-time work available for students. Area has access to rail service and airport. Alma has its own public library, hospital and motels. Recreation facilities include golf, Community Center, swimming pool, parks and the Pine River for boating and fishing. Alma College is within two hours of Michigan's beaches and ski resorts.

■ **ALPENA COMMUNITY COLLEGE**
665 Johnson St.
Alpena, MI 49707-1495
Tel: (989)356-9021
Fax: (989)358-7553
E-mail: kollienm@alpenacc.edu
Web Site: www.alpenacc.edu
Description: State and locally supported, 2-year, coed. Awards certificates, transfer associate, and terminal associate degrees. Founded 1952. Setting: 700-acre small town campus. Endowment: $3.3 million. Educational spending for the previous fiscal year: $7628 per student. Total enrollment: 1,950. Faculty: 125 (55 full-time, 70 part-time). Student-undergrad faculty ratio is 17:1. 1,050 applied, 100% were admitted. 10% from top 10% of their high school class, 25% from top quarter, 50% from top half. Students come from 4 states and territories, 0.01% from out-of-state. 40% 25 or older, 2% live on campus. Retention: 55% of full-time freshmen returned the following year. Core. Calendar: semesters. Academic remediation for entering students, services for LD students, advanced placement, distance learning, double major, summer session for credit, part-time degree program, internships.
Entrance Requirements: Open admission except for nursing, utility technician programs. Options: electronic application, early admission, deferred admission. Recommended: high school transcript. Entrance: noncompetitive. Application deadline: rolling. Notification: continuous.
Collegiate Environment: Orientation program. Drama-theater group, choral group. Social organizations: 8 open to all. Most popular organizations: Nursing Association, Student Senate, Phi Theta Kappa, Law Enforcement Club. Major annual events: Awards Night, Spring Fling. Student services: personal-psychological counseling. Campus security: 24-hour emergency response devices. Stephen Fletcher Library. Operations spending for the previous fiscal year: $324,807. 75 computers available on campus for general student use. A campuswide network can be accessed from off-campus. Staffed computer lab on campus.
Community Environment: Located on Thunder Bay, 94 miles south of the Straits of Mackinac and 235 miles north of Detroit, Alpena is the largest port on northern Lake Huron. Industries include a cement plant, paper mill, and shale quarry. The mean annual temperature is 42.2 degrees. Air and bus service are available. The community has several churches, theatres, a hospital, museum, and planetarium. Alpena is well known for fine fishing, hunting, and winter sports. There are five city parks and over 240,000 acres of public land within a one-hour drive. Recreation facilities include golf, sailboat racing, tennis, and skating. Part-time employment is available for students.

■ **ANDREWS UNIVERSITY**
8975 US 31
Berrien Springs, MI 49104
Tel: (269)471-7771; Free: 800-253-2874
Fax: (269)471-3228
E-mail: enroll@andrews.edu
Web Site: www.andrews.edu
Description: Independent Seventh-day Adventist, university, coed. Awards associate, bachelor's, master's, and doctoral degrees and post-master's certificates. Founded 1874. Setting: 1,650-acre small town campus. Endowment: $53.1 million. Research spending for the previous fiscal year: $1.3 million. Educational spending for the previous fiscal year: $12,746 per student. Total enrollment: 3,348. Faculty: 276 (219 full-time, 57 part-time). Student-undergrad faculty ratio is 10:1. 1,554 applied, 58% were admitted. 19% from top 10% of their high school class, 42% from top quarter, 69% from top half. 20 National Merit Scholars. Full-time: 1,344 students, 56% women, 44% men. Part-time: 360 students, 54% women, 46% men. Students come from 51 states and territories, 67 other countries, 64% from out-of-state. 0.3% American Indian or Alaska Native, non-Hispanic/Latino; 14% Hispanic/Latino; 19% Black or African American, non-Hispanic/Latino; 14% Asian, non-Hispanic/Latino; 0.4% Native Hawaiian or other Pacific Islander, non-Hispanic/Latino; 18% international. 14% 25 or older, 57% live

on campus, 7% transferred in. Retention: 87% of full-time freshmen returned the following year. Academic areas with the most degrees conferred: visual and performing arts; business/marketing; agriculture; biological/life sciences; health professions and related sciences. Core. Calendar: semesters. Academic remediation for entering students, ESL program, advanced placement, accelerated degree program, self-designed majors, freshman honors college, honors program, distance learning, double major, summer session for credit, part-time degree program, adult/continuing education programs, co-op programs and internships, graduate courses open to undergrads. Off campus study. Study abroad program.

Entrance Requirements: Options: electronic application, deferred admission, international baccalaureate accepted. Required: high school transcript, minimum 2.25 high school GPA, 2 recommendations, SAT or ACT. Entrance: moderately difficult. Application deadline: rolling. Notification: continuous.

Costs Per Year: Application fee: $30. Comprehensive fee: $38,366 includes full-time tuition ($28,272), mandatory fees ($1016), and college room and board ($9078). College room only: $4778. Full-time tuition and fees vary according to course load. Room and board charges vary according to board plan. Part-time tuition: $1178 per credit hour. Part-time mandatory fees: $124 per term. Part-time tuition and fees vary according to course load.

Collegiate Environment: Orientation program. Drama-theater group, choral group, student-run newspaper, radio station. Social organizations: 30 open to all. Major annual events: College Days, Feast of Lights, homecoming. Student services: health clinic, personal-psychological counseling. Campus security: 24-hour emergency response devices and patrols, controlled dormitory access. James White Library plus 2 others. Books: 950,014 (physical), 394,023 (digital/electronic); Serial titles: 1,229 (physical), 198,545 (digital/electronic); Databases: 187. Operations spending for the previous fiscal year: $3.1 million. 100 computers available on campus for general student use. Computer purchase/lease plans available. A campuswide network can be accessed from student residence rooms and from off campus. Students can access the following: online class registration, degree audit. Staffed computer lab on campus.

Community Environment: Andrews is located in a small town in the southwest part of Michigan. The area is accessible by bus, airplane, or Amtrak. Shopping and cultural activities are located in South Bend, Indiana, which is 25 miles away, and St. Joseph/Benton Harbor, Michigan, which is 10 miles away, and are approximately 30 minutes away. Lake Michigan, with its 200-foot high sand dunes and water activities, is less than 30 minutes distant. Chicago is less than two hours distant.

■ **AQUINAS COLLEGE**
1700 Fulton St. E
Grand Rapids, MI 49506
Tel: (616)632-8900; Free: 800-678-9593
Fax: (616)459-2563
E-mail: admissions@aquinas.edu
Web Site: www.aquinas.edu
Description: Independent Roman Catholic, comprehensive, coed. Awards associate, bachelor's, and master's degrees. Founded 1886. Setting: 117-acre suburban campus with easy access to Grand Rapids. Endowment: $40.8 million. Educational spending for the previous fiscal year: $7588 per student. Total enrollment: 1,716. Faculty: 210 (84 full-time, 126 part-time). Student-undergrad faculty ratio is 12:1. 1,875 applied, 75% were admitted. Full-time: 1,317 students, 61% women, 39% men. Part-time: 234 students, 59% women, 41% men. Students come from 25 states and territories, 22 other countries, 5% from out-of-state. 0.4% American Indian or Alaska Native, non-Hispanic/Latino; 7% Hispanic/Latino; 4% Black or African American, non-Hispanic/Latino; 1% Asian, non-Hispanic/Latino; 0.1% Native Hawaiian or other Pacific Islander, non-Hispanic/Latino; 2% international. 8% 25 or older, 46% live on campus, 4% transferred in. Retention: 74% of full-time freshmen returned the following year. Academic areas with the most degrees conferred: business/marketing; biological/life sciences; social sciences. Core. Calendar: semesters. Academic remediation for entering students, ESL program, services for LD students, advanced placement, self-designed majors, honors program, independent study, distance learning, double major, summer session for credit, part-time degree program, adult/continuing education programs, co-op programs and internships, graduate courses open to undergrads. Off campus study at Dominican College Interchange. Study abroad program.
Entrance Requirements: Options: electronic application, deferred admission, international baccalaureate accepted. Required: high school transcript, minimum 2.5 high school GPA, SAT or ACT. Required for some: essay, interview. Entrance: moderately difficult. Application deadline: rolling. SAT Reasoning Test deadline: 8/1. Transfer credits accepted: Yes.

Costs Per Year: Application fee: $0. Comprehensive fee: $41,906 includes full-time tuition ($31,976), mandatory fees ($598), and college room and board ($9332). College room only: $4376. Full-time tuition and fees vary according to course load. Room and board charges vary according to board plan and housing facility. Part-time tuition: $498 per credit hour. Part-time mandatory fees: $60 per term. Part-time tuition and fees vary according to course load.

Collegiate Environment: Orientation program. Drama-theater group, choral group, student-run newspaper, radio station. Social organizations: 72 open to all. Most popular organizations: Community Senate Programming Board, The Saint (newspaper), Insignis Honors Group, Community Action Volunteers of Aquinas (CAVA), Residence Hall Association. Major annual events: Homecoming, St. Thomas Aquinas Celebration Week, Refresh Yourself. Student services: health clinic, personal-psychological counseling, women's center. Campus security: 24-hour emergency response devices and patrols, student patrols, late night transport-escort service, controlled dormitory access. Grace Hauenstein Library plus 1 other. Books: 85,348 (physical), 196,003 (digital/electronic); Serial titles: 231 (physical); Databases: 85. Weekly public service hours: 90; students can reserve study rooms. Operations spending for the previous fiscal year: $1.1 million. 210 computers available on campus for general student use. Computer purchase/lease plans available. A campuswide network can be accessed from student residence rooms and from off campus. Students can access the following: online class registration. Staffed computer lab on campus provides training in use of computers and the Internet.

Community Environment: Grand Rapids is an urban setting. The greater Grand Rapids area has a population of over 1,000,000, and is one of the fastest growing areas in the nation. It is the commercial, medical and cultural center of west Michigan.

■ **BAKER COLLEGE**
Baker College System Headquarters
1050 W Bristol Rd.
Flint, MI 48507
Tel: (810)766-4000; Free: 800-964-4299
Fax: (810)766-4049
E-mail: mark.heaton@baker.edu
Web Site: www.baker.edu
Description: Independent, comprehensive, coed. Part of The Baker College System. Awards associate, bachelor's, master's, and doctoral degrees. Founded 1911. Setting: suburban campus with easy access to Detroit. Total enrollment: 24,677. Faculty: (2,170 full-time). Student-undergrad faculty ratio is 13:1. 8,662 applied, 100% were admitted. Students come from 40 states and territories, 6 other countries, 1% from out-of-state. 0.7% American Indian or Alaska Native, non-Hispanic/Latino; 3% Hispanic/Latino; 18% Black or African American, non-Hispanic/Latino; 0.5% Asian, non-Hispanic/Latino. 8% live on campus. Core. Calendar: quarters. Academic remediation for entering students, services for LD students, advanced placement, accelerated degree program, independent study, distance learning, double major, summer session for credit, part-time degree program, external degree program, co-op programs and internships.
Entrance Requirements: Open admission. Options: electronic application, early admission, deferred admission, international baccalaureate accepted. Required: high school transcript. Recommended: SAT or ACT. Entrance: minimally difficult. Application deadline: 9/19. Transfer credits accepted: Yes.
Collegiate Environment: Orientation program. Most popular organizations: Occupational Therapy Club, Interior Design Society, Medical Assistants Student Organization, Physical Therapist Assistant Club, Cyber Defense Team. Major annual events: Campus Spirit Day, Student Club Day. Student services: personal-psychological counseling. Campus security: 24-hour emergency response devices, late night transport-escort service, video monitoring of high traffic areas. Marianne Jewell Library. 412 computers available on campus for general student use. A campuswide network can be accessed from student residence rooms and from off campus. Students can access the following: online class registration. Staffed computer lab on campus provides training in use of computers, software, and the Internet.

■ **BAY MILLS COMMUNITY COLLEGE**
12214 W Lakeshore Dr.
Brimley, MI 49715
Tel: (906)248-3354; Free: 800-844-BMCC
Fax: (906)248-3351
Web Site: www.bmcc.edu
Description: District-supported, 2-year, coed. Awards certificates, diplomas,

and transfer associate degrees. Founded 1984. Setting: rural campus. Total enrollment: 427. 67% 25 or older. Calendar: semesters. Academic remediation for entering students, part-time degree program, internships.
Entrance Requirements: Open admission. Option: early admission. Required: high school transcript. Entrance: noncompetitive. Application deadline: rolling.
Collegiate Environment: Student services: personal-psychological counseling. Campus security: 24-hour emergency response devices.

■ **BAY DE NOC COMMUNITY COLLEGE**
2001 N Lincoln Rd.
Escanaba, MI 49829-2511
Tel: (906)786-5802; Free: 800-221-2001
Fax: (906)786-6555
E-mail: jessica.lamarch@baycollege.edu
Web Site: www.baycollege.edu
Description: County-supported, 2-year, coed. Part of Michigan Department of Education. Awards certificates, transfer associate, and terminal associate degrees. Founded 1963. Setting: 150-acre rural campus. Endowment: $6.9 million. Educational spending for the previous fiscal year: $7878 per student. Total enrollment: 1,853. Faculty: 120 (47 full-time, 73 part-time). Student-undergrad faculty ratio is 15:1. Full-time: 711 students, 51% women, 49% men. Part-time: 1,142 students, 68% women, 32% men. Students come from 2 states and territories, 3% from out-of-state. 3% American Indian or Alaska Native, non-Hispanic/Latino; 2% Hispanic/Latino; 0.3% Black or African American, non-Hispanic/Latino; 0.6% Asian, non-Hispanic/Latino; 0.1% Native Hawaiian or other Pacific Islander, non-Hispanic/Latino. 31% 25 or older, 4% live on campus, 16% transferred in. Retention: 58% of full-time freshmen returned the following year. Core. Calendar: semesters. Academic remediation for entering students, services for LD students, advanced placement, honors program, independent study, distance learning, double major, summer session for credit, part-time degree program, adult/continuing education programs, co-op programs and internships.
Entrance Requirements: Open admission. Options: electronic application, early admission, deferred admission. Required: high school transcript. Entrance: noncompetitive. Application deadline: rolling. Notification: continuous.
Costs Per Year: Area resident tuition: $3472 full-time, $124 per contact hour part-time. State resident tuition: $5964 full-time, $213 per contact hour part-time. Nonresident tuition: $7280 full-time, $260 per contact hour part-time. Mandatory fees: $1036 full-time, $37 per contact hour part-time. Full-time tuition and fees vary according to course load, location, and reciprocity agreements. Part-time tuition and fees vary according to course load, location, and reciprocity agreements.
Collegiate Environment: Orientation program. Drama-theater group. Social organizations: 19 open to all. Most popular organizations: Phi Theta Kappa, Art Club, Bay Area Water Tech Association (BAWA), Gaming Galaxy, Bay Business Professionals in America (BPA). Major annual events: Welcome Week Cookout, Student Organization Fair, Hypnotist. Student services: personal-psychological counseling. Campus security: resident assistants in housing. Library/Learning Resources Center. Books: 31,671 (physical), 46 (digital/electronic); Serial titles: 9 (physical), 2,576 (digital/electronic). Weekly public service hours: 52; students can reserve study rooms. Operations spending for the previous fiscal year: $306,968. 535 computers available on campus for general student use. A campuswide network can be accessed from student residence rooms and from off campus. Students can access the following: online class registration. Staffed computer lab on campus.
Community Environment: An industrial city, Escanaba has an excellent deepwater harbor and mammoth ore docks from which about six million tons of iron ore are shipped annually. Local manufactures include paper, welding machines and lumber products. Part-time employment is available for students. City services include a library, hospital, and major transportation facilities. Recreation includes swimming, boating, golf, tennis, fishing and winter sports.

■ **CALVIN COLLEGE**
3201 Burton St., SE
Grand Rapids, MI 49546-4388
Tel: (616)526-6000; Free: 800-688-0122
Fax: (616)526-8551
E-mail: admissions@calvin.edu
Web Site: www.calvin.edu
Description: Independent Christian Reformed, comprehensive, coed. Awards associate, bachelor's, and master's degrees. Founded 1876. Set-

ting: 400-acre suburban campus with easy access to Grand Rapids, MI. Endowment: $160.8 million. Research spending for the previous fiscal year: $3 million. Educational spending for the previous fiscal year: $12,106 per student. Total enrollment: 3,732. Faculty: 339 (232 full-time, 107 part-time). Student-undergrad faculty ratio is 13:1. 3,847 applied, 79% were admitted. 31% from top 10% of their high school class, 58% from top quarter, 83% from top half. 5 National Merit Scholars, 13 valedictorians. Full-time: 3,417 students, 54% women, 46% men. Part-time: 208 students, 33% women, 67% men. Students come from 46 states and territories, 64 other countries, 42% from out-of-state. 0.1% American Indian or Alaska Native, non-Hispanic/Latino; 5% Hispanic/Latino; 3% Black or African American, non-Hispanic/Latino; 5% Asian, non-Hispanic/Latino; 12% international. 2% 25 or older, 58% live on campus, 2% transferred in. Retention: 87% of full-time freshmen returned the following year. Academic areas with the most degrees conferred: education; health professions and related sciences; business/marketing. Core. Calendar: 4-1-4. Academic remediation for entering students, services for LD students, advanced placement, accelerated degree program, self-designed majors, honors program, independent study, distance learning, double major, summer session for credit, part-time degree program, internships, graduate courses open to undergrads. Off campus study at Council for Christian Colleges and Universities, Central College, Trinity Christian College, Au Sable Institute. Study abroad program. ROTC: Army (c).
Entrance Requirements: Options: electronic application, deferred admission, international baccalaureate accepted. Required: essay, high school transcript, 1 recommendation, SAT or ACT, or CLT. Recommended: interview. Entrance: moderately difficult. Application deadlines: 8/15, 8/15 for nonresidents. Notification: continuous. SAT Reasoning Test deadline: 8/15. Transfer credits accepted: Yes.
Costs Per Year: Application fee: $35. Comprehensive fee: $46,900 includes full-time tuition ($36,100), mandatory fees ($200), and college room and board ($10,600). Part-time tuition: $867 per credit hour.
Collegiate Environment: Orientation program. Drama-theater group, choral group, student-run newspaper. Social organizations: 73 open to all. Most popular organizations: Dance Guild, Pre-Health Professionals, Calvin Outdoor Recreation, National Student Speech, Language, and Hearing Association, African Students Association. Major annual events: Rangeela (international student talent showcase), Fall and Spring Music and Arts Festivals, Chaos Day. Student services: health clinic, personal-psychological counseling. Campus security: 24-hour emergency response devices and patrols, student patrols, late night transport-escort service, controlled dormitory access. 2,534 college housing spaces available; 2,124 were occupied in 2018-19. Freshmen guaranteed college housing. On-campus residence required through sophomore year. Options: men-only, women-only housing available. Hekman Library. Books: 524,139 (physical), 381,981 (digital/electronic); Serial titles: 6,139 (physical), 36,320 (digital/electronic); Databases: 120. Weekly public service hours: 90; students can reserve study rooms. Operations spending for the previous fiscal year: $2.7 million. 1,025 computers available on campus for general student use. Computer purchase/lease plans available. A campuswide network can be accessed from student residence rooms and from off campus. Students can access the following: online class registration. Staffed computer lab on campus provides training in use of computers, software, and the Internet.
Community Environment: The city of Grand Rapids provides additional service, internship, recreational, and employment opportunities for students in the area's six colleges. It has a lively interest in the arts, as evidenced by an active symphony orchestra, civic theatre, ballet association, and art museum. Recreational opportunities abound with professional hockey, basketball, baseball, and arena football or concerts at DeVos Hall or Van Andel Arena.

■ **CAREER QUEST LEARNING CENTER-JACKSON**
209 E Washington Ave.
Ste. 241
Jackson, MI 49201
Tel: (517)990-9595
Web Site: www.careerquest.edu
Description: Proprietary, 2-year, coed.

■ **CAREER QUEST LEARNING CENTER-LANSING**
3215 S Pennsylvania Ave.
Lansing, MI 48910
Tel: (517)318-3330
Web Site: www.careerquest.edu

Description: Proprietary, 2-year, coed.

■ **CAREER QUEST LEARNING CENTER-MT. PLEASANT**
2116 S Mission St.
Mount Pleasant, MI 48858
Description: Proprietary, 2-year, coed.

■ **CENTRAL MICHIGAN UNIVERSITY**
1200 S Franklin St.
Mount Pleasant, MI 48859
Tel: (989)774-4000; Free: 888-292-5366
Fax: (989)774-3537
Web Site: www.cmich.edu
Description: State-supported, university, coed. Awards bachelor's, master's, and doctoral degrees and post-master's certificates. Founded 1892. Setting: 854-acre small town campus. Endowment: $130.7 million. Research spending for the previous fiscal year: $13.1 million. Educational spending for the previous fiscal year: $7500 per student. Total enrollment: 21,705. Faculty: 1,218 (754 full-time, 464 part-time). Student-undergrad faculty ratio is 20:1. 17,858 applied, 69% were admitted. 22% from top 10% of their high school class, 52% from top quarter, 70% from top half. Full-time: 14,270 students, 57% women, 43% men. Part-time: 2,162 students, 59% women, 41% men. Students come from 53 states and territories, 61 other countries, 7% from out-of-state. 0.8% American Indian or Alaska Native, non-Hispanic/Latino; 5% Hispanic/Latino; 9% Black or African American, non-Hispanic/Latino; 1% Asian, non-Hispanic/Latino; 3% international. 5% 25 or older, 36% live on campus, 6% transferred in. Retention: 77% of full-time freshmen returned the following year. Academic areas with the most degrees conferred: business/marketing; communication/journalism; parks and recreation. Core. Calendar: semesters. ROTC: Army, Air Force (c).
Entrance Requirements: Options: electronic application, early admission, early action, deferred admission, international baccalaureate accepted. Required: high school transcript, SAT or ACT. Required for some: essay, interview. Entrance: moderately difficult. Application deadlines: rolling, 5/1 for early action. Notification: continuous, 5/8 for early action. Transfer credits accepted: Yes.
Costs Per Year: Application fee: $35. State resident tuition: $12,510 full-time, $417 per credit hour part-time. Nonresident tuition: $23,670 full-time, $789 per credit hour part-time. Full-time tuition varies according to location. Part-time tuition varies according to location. College room and board: $9736. College room only: $4868. Room and board charges vary according to board plan and housing facility.
Collegiate Environment: Drama-theater group, choral group, marching band, student-run newspaper, radio station. Social organizations: 260 open to all; national fraternities, national sororities, local fraternities; 8% of eligible men and 9% of eligible women are members. Major annual events: Homecoming, Siblings' Weekend, Mainstage. Student services: health clinic, personal-psychological counseling, women's center. Campus security: 24-hour emergency response devices and patrols, late night transport-escort service, controlled dormitory access. 6,958 college housing spaces available; 5,085 were occupied in 2018-19. Freshmen guaranteed college housing. On-campus residence required in freshman year. Option: coed housing available. Charles V. Park Library. Books: 895,460 (physical), 709,885 (digital/electronic); Serial titles: 2,156 (physical), 114,678 (digital/electronic); Databases: 336. Weekly public service hours: 101; students can reserve study rooms. Operations spending for the previous fiscal year: $10.2 million. 490 computers available on campus for general student use. Computer purchase/lease plans available. A campuswide network can be accessed from student residence rooms and from off campus. Students can access the following: online class registration, learning management system. Staffed computer lab on campus (open 24 hours a day) provides training in use of computers, software, and the Internet.
Community Environment: Located in the approximate center of the state, Mount Pleasant is the largest city in the county. Average temperature is 45.6 degrees; rainfall, 26.14; snowfall, 45.7 inches. The area has a hospital, auditoriums, theatres, motels, a public stadium, and its own airport. Ten lakes and a ski range nearby offer excellent recreational facilities. An Indian reservation is located four miles east of the city.

■ **CHAMBERLAIN COLLEGE OF NURSING**
200 Kirts Blvd.
Troy, MI 48084
Tel: (248)817-4140; Free: 877-751-5783
Fax: (248)817-4237

Web Site: www.chamberlain.edu
Description: Proprietary, 4-year, coed. Awards bachelor's degrees. Total enrollment: 304. Faculty: 34 (8 full-time, 26 part-time). Student-undergrad faculty ratio is 11:1. Full-time: 113 students, 83% women, 17% men. Part-time: 191 students, 92% women, 8% men. 2% from out-of-state. 4% Hispanic/Latino; 13% Black or African American, non-Hispanic/Latino; 7% Asian, non-Hispanic/Latino; 0.3% international. 52% 25 or older, 31% transferred in. Accelerated degree program, distance learning.
Entrance Requirements: Option: deferred admission. Required: SAT or ACT. Application deadline: rolling. Notification: continuous.

■ **CLEARY UNIVERSITY**
3750 Cleary Dr.
Howell, MI 48843
Tel: (517)548-3670; Free: 800-686-1883
E-mail: admissions@cleary.edu
Web Site: www.cleary.edu
Description: Independent, comprehensive, coed. Awards associate, bachelor's, and master's degrees. Founded 1883. Setting: 32-acre suburban campus with easy access to Detroit, Ann Arbor. Endowment: $998,704. Educational spending for the previous fiscal year: $3309 per student. Total enrollment: 704. Faculty: 78 (all part-time). Student-undergrad faculty ratio is 15:1. 81 applied, 48% were admitted. Full-time: 268 students, 60% women, 40% men. Part-time: 350 students, 55% women, 45% men. Students come from 11 states and territories, 2% from out-of-state. 0.2% American Indian or Alaska Native, non-Hispanic/Latino; 1% Hispanic/Latino; 7% Black or African American, non-Hispanic/Latino; 1% Asian, non-Hispanic/Latino. 78% 25 or older, 14% transferred in. Retention: 75% of full-time freshmen returned the following year. Academic area with the most degrees conferred: business/marketing. Core. Calendar: semesters. Advanced placement, accelerated degree program, honors program, independent study, distance learning, double major, summer session for credit, part-time degree program, adult/continuing education programs, co-op programs and internships. Off campus study at Consortium agreements with Mott Community College (Flint), Henry Ford Community College, Montcalm Community College, and Concordia University (Ann Arbor).
Entrance Requirements: Options: electronic application, early admission, deferred admission, international baccalaureate accepted. Required: high school transcript, minimum 2.5 high school GPA, SAT or ACT. Recommended: interview. Required for some: essay, minimum ACT score of 19 for freshmen, minimum high school GPA of 2.0 for non-traditional and transfer students, SAT Subject Tests. Entrance: moderately difficult. Application deadline: 7/15. Transfer credits accepted: Yes.
Collegiate Environment: Orientation program. Social organizations: 6 open to all; 1% of eligible men and 1% of eligible women are members. Most popular organizations: Cleary Professional Accounting Associates, Human Resources and Organizational Leadership Association, Event and Meeting Planning Student Association, Veterans Club, Accounting/Fraud Examiners Club. Major annual events: Cleary University Auction, Cleary Classic Alumni and Friends Gold Outing, Livingston Economic Club Speaker Series. Student services: personal-psychological counseling. Campus security: 24-hour emergency response devices, access to facilities limited to authorized persons. Cleary Online Library. Operations spending for the previous fiscal year: $34,496. 26 computers available on campus for general student use. A computer is required for all students. A campuswide network can be accessed from student residence rooms and from off campus. Staffed computer lab on campus.

■ **COLLEGE FOR CREATIVE STUDIES**
201 E Kirby
Detroit, MI 48202-4034
Tel: (313)664-7400; Free: 800-952-ARTS
Fax: (313)872-2739
E-mail: admissions@collegeforcreativestudies.edu
Web Site: www.collegeforcreativestudies.edu
Description: Independent, comprehensive, coed. Awards bachelor's and master's degrees. Founded 1926. Setting: urban campus. Total enrollment: 1,459. Faculty: 289 (48 full-time, 241 part-time). Student-undergrad faculty ratio is 9:1. 1,388 applied, 46% were admitted. Full-time: 1,120 students, 47% women, 53% men. Part-time: 281 students, 60% women, 40% men. 8% from out-of-state. 0.2% American Indian or Alaska Native, non-Hispanic/Latino; 4% Hispanic/Latino; 9% Black or African American, non-Hispanic/Latino; 4% Asian, non-Hispanic/Latino; 0.3% Native Hawaiian or other Pacific Islander, non-Hispanic/Latino; 7% international. 16% 25 or older, 38%

live on campus, 9% transferred in. Retention: 82% of full-time freshmen returned the following year. Academic area with the most degrees conferred: visual and performing arts. Calendar: semesters. Part-time degree program.
Entrance Requirements: Options: electronic application, early action, deferred admission. Required: essay, high school transcript, portfolio, SAT or ACT. Recommended: minimum 2.5 high school GPA. Required for some: interview. Entrance: moderately difficult. Applicants placed on waiting list: 0.
Collegiate Environment: Orientation program. Campus security: 24-hour patrols, late night transport-escort service, controlled dormitory access. Center for Creative Studies Library.

■ COMPASS COLLEGE OF CINEMATIC ARTS

41 Sheldon Blvd. SE
Grand Rapids, MI 49503
Tel: (616)988-1000
Web Site: www.compass.edu
Description: Independent, 4-year, coed. Awards associate and bachelor's degrees. Setting: urban campus. Total enrollment: 130. Core. Academic remediation for entering students, advanced placement, accelerated degree program, internships.
Entrance Requirements: Required: essay, high school transcript, minimum 2 high school GPA, 2 recommendations, interview, Portfolio of 2 film pieces and 2 non-film pieces. Recommended: SAT or ACT. Entrance: minimally difficult. Application deadline: rolling. Notification: continuous. Transfer credits accepted: Yes.
Collegiate Environment: Orientation program.

■ CONCORDIA UNIVERSITY ANN ARBOR

4090 Geddes Rd.
Ann Arbor, MI 48105-2797
Tel: (734)995-7300; Free: 877-955-7520
Fax: (734)995-4610
E-mail: admissions@cuaa.edu
Web Site: www.cuaa.edu
Description: Independent, comprehensive, coed, affiliated with Lutheran Church-Missouri Synod. Part of Concordia University System. Awards associate, bachelor's, and master's degrees. Founded 1963. Setting: 187-acre suburban campus with easy access to Detroit. Endowment: $7.6 million. Educational spending for the previous fiscal year: $6014 per student. Total enrollment: 711. Faculty: 124 (28 full-time, 96 part-time). Student-undergrad faculty ratio is 11:1. 837 applied, 56% were admitted. Full-time: 474 students, 43% women, 57% men. Part-time: 35 students, 46% women, 54% men. 4% Hispanic/Latino; 10% Black or African American, non-Hispanic/Latino; 1% Asian, non-Hispanic/Latino; 2% international. 9% 25 or older, 79% live on campus, 9% transferred in. Retention: 58% of full-time freshmen returned the following year. Core. Calendar: semesters. Academic remediation for entering students, ESL program, services for LD students, advanced placement, accelerated degree program, self-designed majors, independent study, distance learning, double major, summer session for credit, part-time degree program, co-op programs and internships, graduate courses open to undergrads. Off campus study at Concordia University System. Study abroad program. ROTC: Army (c), Air Force (c).
Entrance Requirements: Options: electronic application, deferred admission, international baccalaureate accepted. Required: high school transcript, SAT or ACT. Recommended: minimum 2.5 high school GPA, ACT. Required for some: essay, 1 recommendation, interview. Entrance: moderately difficult. Application deadline: rolling. SAT Reasoning Test deadline: 8/15. SAT Subject Test deadline: 8/15.
Collegiate Environment: Orientation program. Drama-theater group, choral group. Social organizations: 16 open to all. Most popular organizations: Student Activities Committee, Athletes in Action, Student Senate, Spiritual Life Committee, Off-campus ministries. Major annual events: Boar's Head Christmas Festival, Homecoming, Spring Formal. Student services: personal-psychological counseling. Campus security: 24-hour emergency response devices and patrols, late night transport-escort service, controlled dormitory access. Zimmerman Library. Operations spending for the previous fiscal year: $266,548. 60 computers available on campus for general student use. A campuswide network can be accessed from student residence rooms and from off campus. Students can access the following: online class registration, online billing information. Staffed computer lab on campus provides training in use of computers, software, and the Internet.

■ CORNERSTONE UNIVERSITY

1001 E Beltline Ave., NE
Grand Rapids, MI 49525-5897

Tel: (616)949-5300; Free: 800-787-9778
Fax: (616)222-1540
E-mail: admissions@cornerstone.edu
Web Site: www.cornerstone.edu
Description: Independent nondenominational, comprehensive, coed. Awards associate, bachelor's, master's, and doctoral degrees. Founded 1941. Setting: 132-acre suburban campus with easy access to Grand Rapids. Endowment: $9.2 million. Educational spending for the previous fiscal year: $6071 per student. Total enrollment: 2,361. Faculty: 374 (63 full-time, 311 part-time). Student-undergrad faculty ratio is 15:1. 2,737 applied, 67% were admitted. 19% from top 10% of their high school class, 43% from top quarter, 80% from top half. 5 valedictorians. Full-time: 1,260 students, 60% women, 40% men. Part-time: 495 students, 67% women, 33% men. Students come from 26 states and territories, 30 other countries, 20% from out-of-state. 0.3% American Indian or Alaska Native, non-Hispanic/Latino; 5% Hispanic/Latino; 12% Black or African American, non-Hispanic/Latino; 2% Asian, non-Hispanic/Latino; 0.1% Native Hawaiian or other Pacific Islander, non-Hispanic/Latino; 4% international. 3% 25 or older, 63% live on campus, 6% transferred in. Retention: 77% of full-time freshmen returned the following year. Academic areas with the most degrees conferred: business/marketing; theology and religious vocations; psychology. Core. Calendar: semesters. Academic remediation for entering students, ESL program, services for LD students, advanced placement, accelerated degree program, self-designed majors, honors program, independent study, distance learning, double major, summer session for credit, part-time degree program, adult/continuing education programs, internships, graduate courses open to undergrads. Off campus study at Aquinas College, Au Sable, Calvin College, Grand Valley State University, Chicago Semester (program of Trinity Christian College), Washington Journalism Institute (Best Semester program). Contemporary Music Center (Best Semester program), L.A. Film Studies (Best Semester program), American Studies (Best Semester program). Study abroad program. ROTC: Army (c).
Entrance Requirements: Option: electronic application. Required: essay, high school transcript, minimum 2.5 high school GPA, 1 recommendation, pastoral letter, SAT or ACT. Entrance: minimally difficult. Application deadline: rolling. Notification: continuous. Transfer credits accepted: Yes.
Costs Per Year: Application fee: $0. Comprehensive fee: $33,800 includes full-time tuition ($24,500) and college room and board ($9300). Full-time tuition varies according to course load and reciprocity agreements. Room and board charges vary according to board plan and housing facility. Part-time tuition: $942 per credit hour. Part-time tuition varies according to course load.
Collegiate Environment: Orientation program. Drama-theater group, choral group. Social organizations: 15 open to all. Most popular organizations: Student Government, Student Education Association, Intramural Sports, Student Activities Council, International Justice Mission. Major annual events: Homecoming, Mudbowl, Mock Rock (lip sync contest). Student services: health clinic, personal-psychological counseling. Campus security: 24-hour emergency response devices and patrols, student patrols, late night transport-escort service, controlled dormitory access. Miller Library. Books: 102,008 (physical), 198,380 (digital/electronic); Serial titles: 522 (physical), 46,267 (digital/electronic); Databases: 176. Weekly public service hours: 85; students can reserve study rooms. Operations spending for the previous fiscal year: $1 million. 43 computers available on campus for general student use. Computer purchase/lease plans available. A computer is required for all students. A campuswide network can be accessed from student residence rooms and from off campus. Students can access the following: online class registration. Staffed computer lab on campus provides training in use of computers, software, and the Internet.

■ DAVENPORT UNIVERSITY

6191 Kraft Ave. SE
Grand Rapids, MI 49512
Tel: (616)698-7111; Free: 866-686-1600
Fax: (616)554-5214
E-mail: david.lawrence@davenport.edu
Web Site: www.davenport.edu
Description: Independent, comprehensive, coed. Awards associate, bachelor's, and master's degrees and post-master's certificates. Founded 1866. Setting: 77-acre suburban campus with easy access to Grand Rapids. Endowment: $26 million. Educational spending for the previous fiscal year: $5720 per student. Total enrollment: 6,534. Faculty: 678 (139 full-time, 539 part-time). Student-undergrad faculty ratio is 12:1. 2,184 applied, 89% were admitted. Full-time: 2,518 students, 47% women, 53% men. Part-time: 2,648

students, 63% women, 37% men. Students come from 30 states and territories, 20 other countries, 2% from out-of-state. 0.6% American Indian or Alaska Native, non-Hispanic/Latino; 6% Hispanic/Latino; 13% Black or African American, non-Hispanic/Latino; 3% Asian, non-Hispanic/Latino; 0.2% Native Hawaiian or other Pacific Islander, non-Hispanic/Latino; 3% international. 50% 25 or older, 6% live on campus. Retention: 73% of full-time freshmen returned the following year. Academic areas with the most degrees conferred: business/marketing; health professions and related sciences; computer and information sciences. Core. Calendar: semesters. Academic remediation for entering students, ESL program, services for LD students, advanced placement, accelerated degree program, independent study, distance learning, summer session for credit, part-time degree program, adult/continuing education programs, co-op programs and internships. Study abroad program. ROTC: Army (c).

Entrance Requirements: Options: electronic application, deferred admission. Required: high school transcript. Recommended: interview, SAT, ACT. Entrance: minimally difficult. Application deadline: rolling. Notification: continuous. Transfer credits accepted: Yes.

Costs Per Year: Application fee: $25. Tuition: $17,544 full-time, $731 per credit hour part-time. Mandatory fees: $700 full-time, $350 per term part-time. Full-time tuition and fees vary according to location and program. Part-time tuition and fees vary according to location and program.

Collegiate Environment: Orientation program. Marching band. Social organizations: 26 open to all. Most popular organizations: Business Professionals of America, Delta Epsilon Chi, Student Government, Health Occupations Students of America, Connect. Major annual events: Pantherpalooza, Homecoming, MLK Volunteer Day. Student services: personal-psychological counseling. Campus security: 24-hour emergency response devices and patrols, late night transport-escort service, controlled dormitory access. 811 college housing spaces available; all were occupied in 2018-19. Freshmen given priority for college housing. Option: coed housing available. Margaret D. Sneden Library Information Commons plus 3 others. Students can reserve study rooms. 3,098 computers available on campus for general student use. Computer purchase/lease plans available. A campuswide network can be accessed from student residence rooms and from off campus. Students can access the following: online class registration. Staffed computer lab on campus provides training in use of computers.

■ **DELTA COLLEGE**
1961 Delta Rd.
University Center, MI 48710
Tel: (989)686-9000
Fax: (989)686-8736
E-mail: admit@delta.edu
Web Site: www.delta.edu

Description: District-supported, 2-year, coed. Awards certificates, transfer associate, and terminal associate degrees. Founded 1961. Setting: 640-acre rural campus. Endowment: $20.1 million. Educational spending for the previous fiscal year: $6690 per student. Total enrollment: 9,132. Faculty: 539 (204 full-time, 335 part-time). Student-undergrad faculty ratio is 16:1. 1,692 applied, 100% were admitted. Full-time: 3,312 students, 53% women, 47% men. Part-time: 5,820 students, 57% women, 43% men. Students come from 5 states and territories, 1 other country. 0.5% American Indian or Alaska Native, non-Hispanic/Latino; 6% Hispanic/Latino; 8% Black or African American, non-Hispanic/Latino; 0.7% Asian, non-Hispanic/Latino; 0.6% international. 30% 25 or older, 3% transferred in. Core. Calendar: semesters. Academic remediation for entering students, services for LD students, advanced placement, freshman honors college, honors program, independent study, distance learning, double major, summer session for credit, part-time degree program, adult/continuing education programs, co-op programs and internships. Off campus study. Study abroad program.

Entrance Requirements: Open admission except for international applicants. Options: electronic application, early admission, deferred admission, international baccalaureate accepted. Recommended: high school transcript. Required for some: essay. Entrance: noncompetitive. Application deadline: rolling. Notification: continuous. Transfer credits accepted: Yes.

Costs Per Year: Application fee: $0. Area resident tuition: $3360 full-time, $112 per credit hour part-time. State resident tuition: $5760 full-time, $192 per credit hour part-time. Nonresident tuition: $10,830 full-time, $361 per credit hour part-time. Mandatory fees: $650 full-time, $17 per credit hour part-time, $40 per term part-time. Full-time tuition and fees vary according to course load. Part-time tuition and fees vary according to course load.

Collegiate Environment: Orientation program. Drama-theater group, choral group, student-run newspaper. Social organizations: 35 open to all; 40% of

eligible men and 60% of eligible women are members. Most popular organizations: DECA, Phi Theta Kappa, DCSNA (student nursing association), Physical Therapy Assistant (PTA) Club, Honors. Major annual events: Student Success Fair, Employment Fair, Financial Literacy Week. Student services: personal-psychological counseling. Campus security: 24-hour emergency response devices, student patrols, late night transport-escort service. Library Learning Information Center. Books: 55,653 (physical); Serial titles: 292 (physical); Databases: 35. Weekly public service hours: 71. Operations spending for the previous fiscal year: $982,909. 145 computers available on campus for general student use. A campuswide network can be accessed from off-campus. Students can access the following: online class registration. Staffed computer lab on campus provides training in use of computers and the Internet.

Community Environment: University Center encompasses the tri-county area of Bay, Midland and Saginaw counties. The area has good shopping, commuter bus service and very active churches. Saginaw Arts Council promotes and encourages the area's cultural and educational organizations. There are excellent part-time employment opportunities for students. Summer and winter sports resort areas are located nearby. Some areas are highly industrialized.

■ **EASTERN MICHIGAN UNIVERSITY**
Ypsilanti, MI 48197
Tel: (734)487-1849; Free: 800-GO TO EMU
Fax: (734)487-1484
Web Site: www.emich.edu

Description: State-supported, comprehensive, coed. Awards bachelor's, master's, and doctoral degrees and post-master's certificates. Founded 1849. Setting: 460-acre suburban campus with easy access to Detroit. Endowment: $67.2 million. Research spending for the previous fiscal year: $4.1 million. Educational spending for the previous fiscal year: $6545 per student. Total enrollment: 20,313. Faculty: 1,319 (760 full-time, 559 part-time). Student-undergrad faculty ratio is 17:1. 16,012 applied, 73% were admitted. 14% from top 10% of their high school class, 38% from top quarter, 74% from top half. Full-time: 12,395 students, 59% women, 41% men. Part-time: 4,602 students, 59% women, 41% men. 10% from out-of-state. 0.3% American Indian or Alaska Native, non-Hispanic/Latino; 5% Hispanic/Latino; 18% Black or African American, non-Hispanic/Latino; 3% Asian, non-Hispanic/Latino; 0.1% Native Hawaiian or other Pacific Islander, non-Hispanic/Latino; 2% international. 22% 25 or older, 22% live on campus, 9% transferred in. Retention: 72% of full-time freshmen returned the following year. Academic areas with the most degrees conferred: business/marketing; health professions and related sciences; education. Core. Calendar: semesters. Academic remediation for entering students, ESL program, services for LD students, advanced placement, accelerated degree program, self-designed majors, honors program, independent study, distance learning, double major, summer session for credit, part-time degree program, external degree program, co-op programs and internships, graduate courses open to undergrads. Study abroad program. ROTC: Army, Naval (c), Air Force (c).

Entrance Requirements: Options: electronic application, deferred admission, international baccalaureate accepted. Required: high school transcript, minimum 2 high school GPA, SAT or ACT. Required for some: 1 recommendation, interview. Entrance: moderately difficult. Application deadline: rolling. Notification: continuous. Transfer credits accepted: Yes.

Collegiate Environment: Orientation program. Drama-theater group, choral group, marching band, student-run newspaper, radio station. Social organizations: 300 open to all; national fraternities, national sororities, local fraternities, local sororities; 4% of eligible men and 4% of eligible women are members. Most popular organizations: International Student Association, Golden Key International Honor Society, Psychology Club, Indian Student Association, GREEN (Gathering Resources to Educate about our Environment and Nature). Major annual events: Homecoming, Family Weekend, Campus-Wide Picnic. Student services: legal services, health clinic, personal-psychological counseling, women's center. Campus security: 24-hour emergency response devices and patrols, student patrols, late night transport-escort service, controlled dormitory access, bicycle patrols, local police in dormitories, self-defense education, lighted pathways, bike lock lease program. Bruce T. Halle Library. Operations spending for the previous fiscal year: $7.9 million. 1,600 computers available on campus for general student use. A campuswide network can be accessed from student residence rooms. Students can access the following: online class registration. Staffed computer lab on campus (open 24 hours a day) provides training in use of computers, software, and the Internet.

Community Environment: Named for the Greek general of the 1820s

Demetrius Ypsilanti, the community became a city in 1858. Ypsilanti is located in southeastern Michigan, approximately 40 miles west of Detroit and 7 miles from Ann Arbor. In addition to the extensive cultural opportunities at Eastern, the resources of the University of Michigan are 15 minutes away and downtown Detroit is a 45 minute drive. Regular bus service is available. Ypsilanti has an impressive historic district (Depot Town) and hosts a Heritage Festival annually in late August.

■ **FERRIS STATE UNIVERSITY**
1201 S State St.
Big Rapids, MI 49307
Tel: (231)591-2000; Free: 800-433-7747
Fax: (231)591-2978
E-mail: dadayja@ferris.edu
Web Site: www.ferris.edu
Description: State-supported, comprehensive, coed. Awards associate, bachelor's, master's, and doctoral degrees. Founded 1884. Setting: 941-acre small town campus with easy access to Grand Rapids. Endowment: $73.8 million. Research spending for the previous fiscal year: $727,570. Educational spending for the previous fiscal year: $8418 per student. Total enrollment: 13,798. Faculty: 916 (551 full-time, 365 part-time). Student-undergrad faculty ratio is 16:1. 9,926 applied, 74% were admitted. Full-time: 8,469 students, 49% women, 51% men. Part-time: 4,035 students, 59% women, 41% men. Students come from 46 states and territories, 49 other countries, 6% from out-of-state. 0.5% American Indian or Alaska Native, non-Hispanic/Latino; 5% Hispanic/Latino; 8% Black or African American, non-Hispanic/Latino; 2% Asian, non-Hispanic/Latino; 0.1% Native Hawaiian or other Pacific Islander, non-Hispanic/Latino; 0.7% international. 22% 25 or older, 21% live on campus, 10% transferred in. Retention: 79% of full-time freshmen returned the following year. Academic areas with the most degrees conferred: business/marketing; health professions and related sciences; homeland security, law enforcement, firefighting, and protective services. Core. Calendar: semesters. Academic remediation for entering students, ESL program, services for LD students, advanced placement, accelerated degree program, self-designed majors, freshman honors college, honors program, independent study, distance learning, double major, summer session for credit, part-time degree program, external degree program, adult/continuing education programs, co-op programs and internships, graduate courses open to undergrads. Off campus study at Delta College, Henry Ford Community College (CC), Lansing CC, Mott CC, Macomb CC, Macomb CC, St. Clair County CC, North Central Michigan College, Northwestern Michigan College, University Center, Gaylord, Westshore Community College, Muskegon CC, Southwestern Michigan College, Alpena CC, Bay Mills CC, Bay College, Grand Rapids CC, Mid-Michigan CC, Montcalm CC, Oakland CC, Schoolcraft College, Wayne CC District, Kirtland CC. Study abroad program. ROTC: Army (c).
Entrance Requirements: Options: electronic application, international baccalaureate accepted. Required: high school transcript, minimum 2.5 high school GPA. Required for some: essay, interview, SAT or ACT. Entrance: minimally difficult. Application deadline: 8/1. Notification: continuous. SAT Reasoning Test deadline: 8/1. Transfer credits accepted: Yes.
Costs Per Year: Application fee: $0. State resident tuition: $12,630 full-time, $421 per credit hour part-time. Nonresident tuition: $12,630 full-time, $421 per credit hour part-time. Full-time tuition varies according to location, program, and student level. Part-time tuition varies according to location and student level. College room and board: $9894. Room and board charges vary according to board plan and housing facility.
Collegiate Environment: Orientation program. Drama-theater group, choral group, student-run newspaper, radio station. Social organizations: 234 open to all; national fraternities, national sororities, local fraternities, local sororities; 1% of eligible men and 1% of eligible women are members. Most popular organizations: Student American Dental Hygiene Association, Pre-Pharm D, American Pharmacist Association, Student Nurses Association, American Marketing Association. Major annual events: Homecoming, Music Takes Action, The Big Event. Student services: health clinic, personal-psychological counseling. Campus security: 24-hour emergency response devices, student patrols, late night transport-escort service, controlled dormitory access. Ferris Library for Information, Technology and Education. Books: 267,897 (physical), 214,655 (digital/electronic); Serial titles: 161 (physical), 160,936 (digital/electronic); Databases: 183. Weekly public service hours: 93; study areas open 24 hours, 5-7 days a week; students can reserve study rooms. Operations spending for the previous fiscal year: $4.2 million. 1,723 computers available on campus for general student use. A campuswide network can be accessed from student residence rooms and

from off campus. Students can access the following: online class registration. Staffed computer lab on campus (open 24 hours a day) provides training in use of computers.
Community Environment: Home for Ferris is Big Rapids, a city of approximately 15,000 residents. The county seat of Mecosta County, Big Rapids is at the junction of U.S. 131 and M-20, 54 miles north of Michigan's second-largest city, Grand Rapids, and within approximately 200 miles of Detroit and Chicago. As one might guess from its name, Big Rapids' primary natural feature is a river, the Muskegon, whose wooded banks wind through town and form the eastern border of the Ferris campus. The former logging community is located in the heart of an extensive recreation area of which Mecosta County, with its 101 lakes and four county parks is a significant part. The city is served by a daily newspaper, one AM and two FM radio stations, a cable television system, a movie theater, roller skating and ice skating rinks, 18-hole college golf course, community pool, diverse commercial districts, four banks, three motels, Holiday Inn Hotel and Conference center, bus lines, 24 churches, a 74-bed hospital, and a community library holding nearly 50,000 volumes.

■ **FINLANDIA UNIVERSITY**
601 Quincy St.
Hancock, MI 49930-1882
Tel: (906)482-5300; Free: 877-202-5491
Fax: (906)487-7300
E-mail: admissions@finlandia.edu
Web Site: www.finlandia.edu
Description: Independent, 4-year, coed, affiliated with Evangelical Lutheran Church in America. Awards associate and bachelor's degrees. Founded 1896. Setting: 25-acre small town campus. Endowment: $2.5 million. Educational spending for the previous fiscal year: $7441 per student. Total enrollment: 545. Faculty: 70 (42 full-time, 28 part-time). Student-undergrad faculty ratio is 10:1. 646 applied, 67% were admitted. 3 class presidents, 6 valedictorians, 3 student government officers. Full-time: 485 students, 63% women, 37% men. Part-time: 60 students, 80% women, 20% men. Students come from 13 states and territories, 3 other countries, 10% from out-of-state. 26% 25 or older, 24% live on campus, 10% transferred in. Retention: 61% of full-time freshmen returned the following year. Academic areas with the most degrees conferred: business/marketing; health professions and related sciences; visual and performing arts. Core. Calendar: semesters. Academic remediation for entering students, ESL program, services for LD students, advanced placement, accelerated degree program, independent study, distance learning, summer session for credit, part-time degree program, adult/continuing education programs, co-op programs and internships. Off campus study. Study abroad program. ROTC: Army (c), Air Force (c).
Entrance Requirements: Options: electronic application, early admission, international baccalaureate accepted. Required: essay, high school transcript, minimum 2.0 high school GPA. Recommended: SAT or ACT. Required for some: interview. Entrance: minimally difficult. Application deadline: 8/25. Notification: continuous, continuous for nonresidents.
Collegiate Environment: Orientation program. Drama-theater group, choral group, student-run newspaper. Social organizations: 12 open to all. Most popular organizations: Student Senate, Campus Ministry, student newspaper, International Club, Artists Coalition. Major annual events: Homecoming, Arts and Music Festival, Campus Play. Campus security: 24-hour emergency response devices, student patrols. Sulo and Aileen Maki Library. Operations spending for the previous fiscal year: $169,206. 80 computers available on campus for general student use. A campuswide network can be accessed from student residence rooms and from off campus. Students can access the following: online class registration, home directory/network. Staffed computer lab on campus provides training in use of computers.
Community Environment: The campus is located near downtown Hancock, within a day's drive of Detroit, Chicago, Milwaukee, Duluth, and Minneapolis. The city, in "Copper County" sprang up amid the region's copper mining industry at the turn of the century. The area still has historical remnants of the mining but it is also know for its autumn when the expansive forests are ablaze with color. Community services include two hospitals, four theaters, and all major civic, fraternal, and service organizations. Recreational activities include fishing, camping, skiing, hunting, golf, hockey, and basketball, as well as the cold water and clean beaches of Lake Superior. Limited off-campus employment is available.

■ **GLEN OAKS COMMUNITY COLLEGE**
62249 Shimmel Rd.
Centreville, MI 49032-9719

Tel: (269)467-9945; Free: 888-994-7818
Fax: (269)467-9068
E-mail: thowden@glenoaks.edu
Web Site: www.glenoaks.edu
Description: State and locally supported, 2-year, coed. Awards certificates, transfer associate, and terminal associate degrees. Founded 1965. Setting: 300-acre rural campus. Total enrollment: 1,221. Student-undergrad faculty ratio is 16:1. Full-time: 531 students, 60% women, 40% men. Part-time: 690 students, 62% women, 38% men. 0.4% American Indian or Alaska Native, non-Hispanic/Latino; 6% Hispanic/Latino; 6% Black or African American, non-Hispanic/Latino; 1% Asian, non-Hispanic/Latino; 0.1% international. 4% transferred in. Core. Calendar: semesters. Academic remediation for entering students, services for LD students, advanced placement, distance learning, summer session for credit, part-time degree program, internships.
Entrance Requirements: Open admission. Option: electronic application. Required: high school transcript. Entrance: noncompetitive. Application deadline: rolling. Transfer credits accepted: Yes.
Collegiate Environment: Orientation program. Student services: personal-psychological counseling. Campus security: 24-hour emergency response devices. E. J. Shaheen Library.
Community Environment: Glen Oaks is located in the center of St. Joseph County, almost equidistant between Three Rivers and Sturgis, the county's two largest cities. Nestled in the hills of Sherman Township, it has a population of approximately 1,180 people. The area is primarily agricultural, with heavy-to-light industry focused in Sturgis and Three Rivers. Located midway between Chicago and Detroit on the"Chicago Trail," it has the potential for vast economic and population growth. The area also abounds in lakes and rolling hills, affording many opportunities for a variety of recreational activities throughout the year. The citizens are fortunate to be served by modern medical facilities and by well-supported public educational facilities. An energetic civic outreach program provides support for the educational, cultural, civil and economic community and assures its growth and progress.

■ **GOGEBIC COMMUNITY COLLEGE**
E-4946 Jackson Rd.
Ironwood, MI 49938
Tel: (906)932-4231; Free: 800-682-5910
Fax: (906)932-5541
E-mail: jeanneg@gogebic.edu
Web Site: www.gogebic.edu
Description: State and locally supported, 2-year, coed. Part of Michigan Department of Education. Awards certificates, transfer associate, and terminal associate degrees. Founded 1932. Setting: 195-acre small town campus. Total enrollment: 1,199. Full-time: 647 students, 55% women, 45% men. Part-time: 552 students, 59% women, 41% men. Students come from 5 states and territories, 1 other country. 40% 25 or older. Core. Calendar: semesters. Academic remediation for entering students, services for LD students, advanced placement, honors program, distance learning, summer session for credit, part-time degree program, adult/continuing education programs, co-op programs and internships. Study abroad program.
Entrance Requirements: Open admission except for LPN and ADN nursing. Options: electronic application, early admission, deferred admission. Required: high school transcript. Entrance: noncompetitive. Application deadlines: rolling, 8/15 for nonresidents. Notification: continuous. Transfer credits accepted: Yes.
Costs Per Year: Application fee: $10. Area resident tuition: $3720 full-time, $120 per credit hour part-time. State resident tuition: $5270 full-time, $170 per credit hour part-time. Nonresident tuition: $6669 full-time, $199 per credit hour part-time. Mandatory fees: $1204 full-time. Full-time tuition and fees vary according to course load, program, and reciprocity agreements. Part-time tuition varies according to course load and reciprocity agreements. College room only: $3800.
Collegiate Environment: Orientation program. Drama-theater group, choral group. Most popular organizations: Chieftain Student Newspaper, Phi Theta Kappa, Student Senate, Alcohol and Drug Prevention Team (ADAPT), Intramural sports. Major annual events: Halloween Costume Party and Dance, Annual Formal Dance, Zombie Run. Student services: personal-psychological counseling. Campus security: controlled dormitory access. Alex D. Chisholm Learning Resources Center.
Community Environment: On the Michigan-Wisconsin border, in the heart of the Midwest ski area, Ironwood is the trading center and lumbering headquarters of the Gogebic Range. The area has refreshing summers and snowy invigorating winters. The city has a library, churches, a hospital, and passenger transportation via air and bus lines. The community has two theatres, hunting, boating, fishing, and excellent skiing for recreation.

■ **GRACE BIBLE COLLEGE**
1011 Aldon St. SW
Grand Rapids, MI 49509-0910
Tel: (616)538-2330; Free: 800-968-1887
Fax: (616)538-0599
E-mail: gbc@gbcol.edu
Web Site: www.gbcol.edu
Description: Independent, 4-year, coed, affiliated with Grace Gospel Fellowship. Awards associate and bachelor's degrees. Founded 1945. Setting: 21-acre suburban campus. Endowment: $319,000. Educational spending for the previous fiscal year: $5262 per student. Total enrollment: 207. Faculty: 21 (7 full-time, 14 part-time). Student-undergrad faculty ratio is 17:1. 158 applied, 34% were admitted. 17% from top 10% of their high school class, 27% from top quarter, 47% from top half. Full-time: 192 students, 42% women, 58% men. Part-time: 15 students, 47% women, 53% men. Students come from 15 states and territories, 3 other countries, 19% from out-of-state. 2% Hispanic/Latino; 4% Black or African American, non-Hispanic/Latino; 1% Asian, non-Hispanic/Latino; 0.5% Native Hawaiian or other Pacific Islander, non-Hispanic/Latino; 0.5% international. 8% 25 or older, 53% live on campus, 11% transferred in. Retention: 80% of full-time freshmen returned the following year. Academic areas with the most degrees conferred: theology and religious vocations; public administration and social services; interdisciplinary studies. Core. Calendar: semesters. Academic remediation for entering students, advanced placement, independent study, internships. Off campus study at Grand Rapids Community College, Davenport University, Cornerstone University. ROTC: Army (c).
Entrance Requirements: Options: electronic application, early admission, deferred admission. Required: high school transcript, 2 recommendations, SAT and SAT Subject Tests or ACT. Recommended: minimum 2.5 high school GPA. Required for some: interview. Entrance: minimally difficult. Application deadline: 7/15. Notification: 8/1.
Collegiate Environment: Orientation program. Choral group. Social organizations: 4 open to all. Most popular organizations: Student Missionary Fellowship, Student Activities Committee, Student Council, Campus Ministry Team. Major annual events: Campus Clean-Up Days, Fridays at Grace, Winter Formal. Student services: personal-psychological counseling. Campus security: student patrols, controlled dormitory access. Bultema Memorial Library. Operations spending for the previous fiscal year: $69,656. 27 computers available on campus for general student use. A campuswide network can be accessed from student residence rooms. Staffed computer lab on campus provides training in use of computers, software, and the Internet.

■ **GRAND RAPIDS COMMUNITY COLLEGE**
143 Bostwick Ave., NE
Grand Rapids, MI 49503-3201
Tel: (616)234-4000
Fax: (616)234-4005
E-mail: lcook@grcc.edu
Web Site: www.grcc.edu
Description: District-supported, 2-year, coed. Part of Michigan Department of Education. Awards certificates, transfer associate, and terminal associate degrees. Founded 1914. Setting: 35-acre urban campus. Endowment: $31.2 million. Educational spending for the previous fiscal year: $4835 per student. Total enrollment: 13,767. Faculty: 705 (222 full-time, 483 part-time). Student-undergrad faculty ratio is 21:1. 8,687 applied. Full-time: 4,104 students, 51% women, 49% men. Part-time: 9,663 students, 53% women, 47% men. Students come from 3 states and territories, 6 other countries, 1% from out-of-state. 0.5% American Indian or Alaska Native, non-Hispanic/Latino; 14% Hispanic/Latino; 9% Black or African American, non-Hispanic/Latino; 4% Asian, non-Hispanic/Latino; 0.1% Native Hawaiian or other Pacific Islander, non-Hispanic/Latino; 0.4% international. 30% 25 or older, 8% transferred in. Core. Calendar: semesters. Academic remediation for entering students, ESL program, services for LD students, advanced placement, honors program, independent study, distance learning, summer session for credit, part-time degree program, adult/continuing education programs, co-op programs and internships. Off campus study. Study abroad program.
Entrance Requirements: Open admission. Options: electronic application, deferred admission. Required: high school transcript. Entrance: noncompetitive. Notification: continuous. Transfer credits accepted: Yes.
Costs Per Year: Application fee: $0. Area resident tuition: $3420 full-time, $114 per contact hour part-time. State resident tuition: $7320 full-time, $244 per contact hour part-time. Nonresident tuition: $10,860 full-time, $362 per contact hour part-time. Mandatory fees: $459 full-time, $15 per contact hour

part-time, $90 per term part-time. Full-time tuition and fees vary according to course load and program. Part-time tuition and fees vary according to course load and program.

Collegiate Environment: Orientation program. Drama-theater group, choral group, student-run newspaper. Social organizations: 32 open to all. Most popular organizations: Student Alliance, Phi Theta Kappa, Hispanic Student Organization, Student Gamers Association, Foreign Affairs Club. Major annual events: Finals Relaxer, Welcome Week, Homecoming. Student services: personal-psychological counseling. Campus security: 24-hour emergency response devices, late night transport-escort service. College housing not available. Arthur Andrews Memorial Library. Books: 67,050 (physical), 168,882 (digital/electronic); Serial titles: 357 (physical), 25,196 (digital/electronic); Databases: 100. Students can reserve study rooms. Operations spending for the previous fiscal year: $1.9 million. 1,500 computers available on campus for general student use. A campuswide network can be accessed from off-campus. Students can access the following: online class registration. Staffed computer lab on campus provides training in use of computers, software, and the Internet.

Community Environment: See Calvin College.

■ GRAND VALLEY STATE UNIVERSITY

1 Campus Dr.
Allendale, MI 49401-9403
Tel: (616)331-5000; Free: 800-748-0246
Fax: (616)331-2000
E-mail: go2gvsu@gvsu.edu
Web Site: www.gvsu.edu

Description: State-supported, comprehensive, coed. Awards bachelor's, master's, and doctoral degrees and post-master's certificates. Founded 1960. Setting: 1,391-acre small town campus with easy access to Grand Rapids. Endowment: $126.8 million. Research spending for the previous fiscal year: $6.9 million. Total enrollment: 24,677. Faculty: 1,783 (1,188 full-time, 595 part-time). Student-undergrad faculty ratio is 17:1. 17,133 applied, 83% were admitted. 20% from top 10% of their high school class, 47% from top quarter, 83% from top half. Full-time: 19,233 students, 60% women, 40% men. Part-time: 2,447 students, 52% women, 48% men. Students come from 47 states and territories, 73 other countries, 7% from out-of-state. 0.3% American Indian or Alaska Native, non-Hispanic/Latino; 6% Hispanic/Latino; 5% Black or African American, non-Hispanic/Latino; 2% Asian, non-Hispanic/Latino; 0.1% Native Hawaiian or other Pacific Islander, non-Hispanic/Latino; 1% international. 7% 25 or older, 29% live on campus, 7% transferred in. Retention: 85% of full-time freshmen returned the following year. Academic areas with the most degrees conferred: business/marketing; health professions and related sciences; communication/journalism. Core. Calendar: semesters. Academic remediation for entering students, ESL program, services for LD students, advanced placement, accelerated degree program, freshman honors college, honors program, independent study, distance learning, double major, summer session for credit, part-time degree program, adult/continuing education programs, co-op programs and internships, graduate courses open to undergrads. Study abroad program.

Entrance Requirements: Option: electronic application. Required: high school transcript, SAT or ACT. Required for some: essay, interview. Entrance: moderately difficult. Notification: 5/1.

Costs Per Year: Application fee: $30. State resident tuition: $12,484 full-time, $521 per credit hour part-time. Nonresident tuition: $17,762 full-time, $742 per credit hour part-time. Full-time tuition varies according to course level, course load, program, and student level. Part-time tuition varies according to course level, course load, program, and student level. College room and board: $8690. College room only: $4345. Room and board charges vary according to board plan and housing facility.

Collegiate Environment: Orientation program. Drama-theater group, choral group, marching band, student-run newspaper, radio station. Social organizations: 486 open to all; national fraternities, national sororities, local fraternities, local sororities. Most popular organizations: Habitat for Humanity, Alternative Breaks, Hospitality and tourism Management Club, Dance Troupe, Colleges Against Cancer. Major annual events: Campus Life Night, Homecoming, President's Ball. Student services: health clinic, personal-psychological counseling, women's center. Campus security: 24-hour emergency response devices and patrols, student patrols, late night transport-escort service, controlled dormitory access. 6,012 college housing spaces available; all were occupied in 2018-19. Freshmen guaranteed college housing. Option: coed housing available. Mary Idema Pew Library Learning and Information Commons plus 5 others. Books: 567,197 (physical), 1 million (digital/electronic). Students can reserve study rooms. Opera-

tions spending for the previous fiscal year: $12 million. 2,600 computers available on campus for general student use. A campuswide network can be accessed from student residence rooms and from off campus. Students can access the following: online class registration, transcript, degree audit, credit card payments. Staffed computer lab on campus provides training in use of computers, software, and the Internet.

Community Environment: This is a rural community that has Protestant and Catholic churches and a small library. Many part-time job opportunities are available for students. Allendale has facilities for bowling, water sports, and winter sports. The area features an annual winter carnival and spring arts festival.

■ GREAT LAKES CHRISTIAN COLLEGE

6211 W Willow Hwy.
Lansing, MI 48917-1299
Tel: (517)321-0242; Free: 800-YES-GLCC
Fax: (517)321-5902
E-mail: jcarter@glcc.edu
Web Site: www.glcc.edu

Description: Independent, 4-year, coed, affiliated with Christian Churches and Churches of Christ. Awards associate and bachelor's degrees. Founded 1949. Setting: 47-acre suburban campus. Endowment: $514,831. Educational spending for the previous fiscal year: $5560 per student. Total enrollment: 225. Faculty: 23 (10 full-time, 13 part-time). Student-undergrad faculty ratio is 10:1. Students come from 4 states and territories, 3 other countries, 2% from out-of-state. 0.5% American Indian or Alaska Native, non-Hispanic/Latino; 2% Hispanic/Latino; 23% Black or African American, non-Hispanic/Latino; 0.5% Asian, non-Hispanic/Latino; 3% international. Retention: 53% of full-time freshmen returned the following year. Academic area with the most degrees conferred: theology and religious vocations. Core. Calendar: semesters. Academic remediation for entering students, services for LD students, advanced placement, independent study, double major, part-time degree program, internships. Off campus study.

Entrance Requirements: Option: electronic application. Required: essay, high school transcript, minimum 2.25 high school GPA, 3 recommendations, SAT or ACT. Entrance: minimally difficult. Application deadline: 8/1. Notification: 8/15. Transfer credits accepted: Yes.

Collegiate Environment: Orientation program. Drama-theater group, choral group, student-run newspaper. Major annual events: Madrigal Dinner Theater, Concerts. Student services: personal-psychological counseling. Campus security: controlled dormitory access, evening security patrols. Louis M. Detro Memorial Library. Operations spending for the previous fiscal year: $122,477. 24 computers available on campus for general student use. A campuswide network can be accessed from student residence rooms and from off campus. Staffed computer lab on campus provides training in use of computers, software, and the Internet.

Community Environment: See Lansing Community College.

■ HENRY FORD COLLEGE

5101 Evergreen Rd.
Dearborn, MI 48128-1495
Tel: (313)845-9615; Free: 800-585-HFCC
Fax: (313)845-9658
E-mail: enroll@hfcc.edu
Web Site: www.hfcc.edu

Description: District-supported, 2-year, coed. Awards certificates, transfer associate, and terminal associate degrees. Founded 1938. Setting: 75-acre suburban campus with easy access to Detroit. Total enrollment: 17,542. Student-undergrad faculty ratio is 24:1. 39% 25 or older. Core. Calendar: semesters. Academic remediation for entering students, ESL program, advanced placement, freshman honors college, honors program, independent study, distance learning, summer session for credit, part-time degree program, adult/continuing education programs, co-op programs and internships. Study abroad program.

Entrance Requirements: Open admission except for nursing, allied health, honors programs. Options: early admission, deferred admission. Recommended: high school transcript. Entrance: noncompetitive. Application deadline: rolling. Notification: continuous.

Collegiate Environment: Drama-theater group, choral group, student-run newspaper, radio station. Student services: personal-psychological counseling, women's center. Campus security: 24-hour emergency response devices and patrols, late night transport-escort service. Eshleman Library.

Community Environment: Dearborn's boundaries have been extended to join those of Detroit, and it is difficult to discern where one city ends and the other begins. Dearborn is a distinct entity with history, government and industries of its own. The area is called the city with no slums. There are limited job opportunities within the immediate area, though Detroit offers good part-time employment. Camp Dearborn 35 miles northwest offers 6 lakes, a trout stream, picnic groves, a 1/2 mile beach, and camping facilities. Community services include two general hospitals, five public libraries, and limited access to all major forms of public transportation. The city has outstanding public recreation facilities.

■ **HILLSDALE COLLEGE**
33 E College St.
Hillsdale, MI 49242-1298
Tel: (517)437-7341
Fax: (517)437-0190
E-mail: admissions@hillsdale.edu
Web Site: www.hillsdale.edu

Description: Independent, comprehensive, coed. Awards bachelor's, master's, and doctoral degrees. Founded 1844. Setting: 400-acre small town campus. Endowment: $597.9 million. Educational spending for the previous fiscal year: $30,220 per student. Total enrollment: 1,521. Faculty: 227 (143 full-time, 84 part-time). Student-undergrad faculty ratio is 10:1. 2,209 applied, 36% were admitted. Full-time: 1,434 students, 48% women, 52% men. Part-time: 34 students, 47% women, 53% men. Students come from 51 states and territories, 12 other countries, 67% from out-of-state. 2% 25 or older, 66% live on campus, 1% transferred in. Retention: 91% of full-time freshmen returned the following year. Academic areas with the most degrees conferred: public administration and social services; business/marketing; foreign languages and literature; English. Core. Calendar: semesters. Advanced placement, self-designed majors, honors program, independent study, double major, summer session for credit, part-time degree program, internships. Off campus study. Study abroad program.

Entrance Requirements: Options: electronic application, early admission, early decision, international baccalaureate accepted. Required: essay, high school transcript, 2 recommendations, SAT or ACT. Recommended: minimum 3.5 high school GPA, interview, campus visit, college prep courses. Entrance: most difficult. Application deadlines: 4/1, 4/1 for nonresidents, 11/1 for early decision. Notification: continuous, continuous for nonresidents, 12/1 for early decision. SAT Reasoning Test deadline: 4/1. SAT Subject Test deadline: 4/1. Transfer credits accepted: Yes. Applicants placed on waiting list: 151. Wait-listed applicants offered admission: 30. Early decision applicants: 284. Early decision applicants admitted: 120.

Costs Per Year: Application fee: $35. One-time mandatory fee: $325. Comprehensive fee: $38,578 includes full-time tuition ($26,300), mandatory fees ($1278), and college room and board ($11,000). College room only: $5440. Full-time tuition and fees vary according to degree level. Room and board charges vary according to board plan and housing facility. Part-time tuition: $1050 per credit hour. Part-time mandatory fees: $85 per credit hour, $1278 per year. Part-time tuition and fees vary according to degree level.

Collegiate Environment: Orientation program. Drama-theater group, choral group, student-run newspaper, radio station. Social organizations: 147 open to all; national fraternities, national sororities; 24% of eligible men and 33% of eligible women are members. Most popular organizations: GOAL Volunteer Program, Greek Life, College Republicans, Intervarsity, Students for Life. Major annual events: Centralhallapalooza, President's Ball, Homecoming Spirit Week. Student services: health clinic, personal-psychological counseling. Campus security: 24-hour emergency response devices and patrols, student patrols, late night transport-escort service, controlled dormitory access. 1,032 college housing spaces available; 950 were occupied in 2018-19. Freshmen guaranteed college housing. On-campus residence required through sophomore year. Options: men-only, women-only housing available. Michael Alex Mossey Library. Books: 275,174 (physical), 2 million (digital/electronic); Serial titles: 570 (physical), 30,000 (digital/electronic); Databases: 235. Operations spending for the previous fiscal year: $1.8 million. 359 computers available on campus for general student use. A campuswide network can be accessed from student residence rooms and from off campus. Students can access the following: online class registration. Staffed computer lab on campus provides training in use of computers, software, and the Internet.

Community Environment: Hillsdale is a county seat located in the south central part of the lower peninsula. In an agricultural region, it is a resort and industrial community, manufacturing automobile parts and accessories, and tool and die products. The area has bus service and a municipal airport.

■ **HOPE COLLEGE**
141 E 12th St.
Holland, MI 49422-9000
Tel: (616)395-7000; Free: 800-968-7850
Fax: (616)395-7130
E-mail: admissions@hope.edu
Web Site: www.hope.edu

Description: Independent, 4-year, coed, affiliated with Reformed Church in America. Awards bachelor's degrees. Founded 1866. Setting: 91-acre suburban campus with easy access to Grand Rapids. Endowment: $208 million. Research spending for the previous fiscal year: $6 million. Educational spending for the previous fiscal year: $11,387 per student. Total enrollment: 3,150. Faculty: 348 (238 full-time, 110 part-time). Student-undergrad faculty ratio is 11:1. 3,899 applied, 84% were admitted. 32% from top 10% of their high school class, 66% from top quarter, 93% from top half. Full-time: 3,018 students, 61% women, 39% men. Part-time: 132 students, 56% women, 44% men. Students come from 36 states and territories, 35 other countries, 28% from out-of-state. 8% Hispanic/Latino; 3% Black or African American, non-Hispanic/Latino; 2% Asian, non-Hispanic/Latino; 3% international. 0.5% 25 or older, 88% live on campus, 2% transferred in. Retention: 91% of full-time freshmen returned the following year. Academic areas with the most degrees conferred: business/marketing; education; psychology. Core. Calendar: semesters. ESL program, services for LD students, advanced placement, self-designed majors, independent study, double major, summer session for credit, part-time degree program, external degree program, internships. Off campus study at members of the Great Lakes Colleges Association, Associated Colleges of the Midwest, Institute of European Studies, Council for International Educational Exchange. Study abroad program. ROTC: Army (c).

Entrance Requirements: Options: electronic application, early admission, deferred admission, international baccalaureate accepted. Required: essay, high school transcript, SAT or ACT. Recommended: interview. Required for some: 1 recommendation. Entrance: moderately difficult. Application deadline: rolling. Notification: continuous. SAT Reasoning Test deadline: 3/31. Transfer credits accepted: Yes. Applicants placed on waiting list: 409. Wait-listed applicants offered admission: 19.

Costs Per Year: Application fee: $35. Comprehensive fee: $44,320 includes full-time tuition ($33,700), mandatory fees ($310), and college room and board ($10,310). College room only: $4730. Room and board charges vary according to board plan.

Collegiate Environment: Orientation program. Drama-theater group, choral group, student-run newspaper, radio station. Social organizations: 78 open to all; national fraternities, national sororities, local fraternities, local sororities; 6% of eligible men and 11% of eligible women are members. Most popular organizations: Social Activities Committee, Greek Life, Dance Marathon, Hockey Club, Relay for Life. Major annual events: Homecoming Weekend Events, Nykerk Cup Competition, Spring Fling. Student services: health clinic, personal-psychological counseling. Campus security: 24-hour emergency response devices and patrols, late night transport-escort service, controlled dormitory access. Van Wylen Library plus 2 others. Books: 247,002 (physical), 242,414 (digital/electronic); Serial titles: 2,530 (physical), 41,509 (digital/electronic); Databases: 166. Weekly public service hours: 96. Operations spending for the previous fiscal year: $2.9 million. 300 computers available on campus for general student use. A campuswide network can be accessed from student residence rooms and from off campus. Students can access the following: online class registration. Staffed computer lab on campus provides training in use of computers, software, and the Internet.

Community Environment: Settled by the Dutch in 1847, the city still has many of the characteristics of a Dutch town. This is the tulip center of America, and millions of these flowers bloom in the parks and residential sections during May. Located on Lake Macatawa and Lake Michigan, the area offers many opportunities for water and other outdoor sports activities. Holland is surrounded by a large fruit-growing and farming area, and is also an industrial and resort town. The city has bus and train service, two airports, a public library, several churches, a hospital and several parks. Holland has a population of approximately 34,400; it is a very friendly, safe and clean community.

■ **JACKSON COLLEGE**
2111 Emmons Rd.
Jackson, MI 49201-8399
Tel: (517)787-0800; Free: 888-522-7344
E-mail: admissions@jccmi.edu
Web Site: www.jccmi.edu

Description: County-supported, 2-year, coed. Awards certificates, transfer associate, and terminal associate degrees. Founded 1928. Setting: 580-acre suburban campus with easy access to Detroit. Total enrollment: 5,665. Faculty: 407 (87 full-time, 320 part-time). Student-undergrad faculty ratio is 18:1. Full-time: 2,389 students, 60% women, 40% men. Part-time: 3,276 students, 64% women, 36% men. 2% from out-of-state. 39% 25 or older. Retention: 57% of full-time freshmen returned the following year. Core. Calendar: semesters. Academic remediation for entering students, ESL program, services for LD students, advanced placement, accelerated degree program, freshman honors college, honors program, independent study, distance learning, double major, summer session for credit, part-time degree program, adult/continuing education programs, co-op programs and internships.

Entrance Requirements: Open admission except for nursing and allied health programs. Options: electronic application, international baccalaureate accepted. Required: minimum ACT of 16 for housing admission. Required for some: minimum 16 high school GPA. Entrance: noncompetitive. Transfer credits accepted: Yes.

Collegiate Environment: Orientation program. Drama-theater group, choral group. Student services: health clinic. Campus security: 24-hour emergency response devices and patrols, student patrols, late night transport-escort service, controlled dormitory access. Atkinson Learning Resources Center.

Community Environment: The college is located seven miles south of Jackson, an important industrial city that manufactures mainly automobile and airplane parts and supplies. Major highways provide access to Chicago and Detroit. The county has numerous lakes, golf courses and parks. Cultural activities include a symphony orchestra, music, and dance and theater groups. Also located in the area are the Illuminated Cascades, the Ella Sharp Museum and the Michigan Space and Science Center.

■ **KALAMAZOO COLLEGE**
1200 Academy St.
Kalamazoo, MI 49006-3295
Tel: (269)337-7000; Free: 800-253-3602
Fax: (269)337-7251
E-mail: gabriela.lovell@kzoo.edu
Web Site: www.kzoo.edu

Description: Independent, 4-year, coed, affiliated with American Baptist Churches in the U.S.A. Awards bachelor's degrees. Founded 1833. Setting: 60-acre urban campus with easy access to Grand Rapids. Endowment: $227 million. Total enrollment: 1,467. Faculty: 141 (105 full-time, 36 part-time). Student-undergrad faculty ratio is 13:1. 3,371 applied, 73% were admitted. 54% from top 10% of their high school class, 84% from top quarter, 99% from top half. Full-time: 1,457 students, 58% women, 42% men. Part-time: 10 students, 20% women, 80% men. 33% from out-of-state. 0.1% American Indian or Alaska Native, non-Hispanic/Latino; 14% Hispanic/Latino; 8% Black or African American, non-Hispanic/Latino; 7% Asian, non-Hispanic/Latino; 6% international. 60% live on campus, 1% transferred in. Retention: 22% of full-time freshmen returned the following year. Academic areas with the most degrees conferred: social sciences; biological/life sciences; business/marketing. Core. Calendar: quarters. Services for LD students, advanced placement, self-designed majors, independent study, double major, internships. Off campus study at Western Michigan University. Study abroad program. ROTC: Army (c).

Entrance Requirements: Options: electronic application, early decision, early action, deferred admission, international baccalaureate accepted. Required: essay, high school transcript, 2 recommendations. Recommended: minimum 3 high school GPA, interview. Entrance: very difficult. Application deadlines: 1/15, 11/1 for early decision. Notification: 4/1, 12/1 for early decision. SAT Reasoning Test deadline: 2/15. Transfer credits accepted: Yes. Applicants placed on waiting list: 291. Wait-listed applicants offered admission: 148. Early decision applicants: 59. Early decision applicants admitted: 50.

Costs Per Year: Application fee: $0. Comprehensive fee: $60,546 includes full-time tuition ($50,046), mandatory fees ($366), and college room and board ($10,134). College room only: $4929.

Collegiate Environment: Orientation program. Drama-theater group, choral group, student-run newspaper, radio station. Social organizations: 70 open to all. Most popular organizations: Cirque du K, A cappella groups, Food Recovery Network, Women of Color, Swing Club. Major annual events: Monte Carlo Night, Spring Fling, K Fest (student involvement fair). Student services: health clinic, personal-psychological counseling. Campus security: 24-hour emergency response devices and patrols, late night transport-escort service, controlled dormitory access. Freshmen guaranteed college housing.

On-campus residence required through junior year. Option: coed housing available. Upjohn Library Commons. Books: 272,425 (physical), 162,857 (digital/electronic); Serial titles: 2,660 (physical), 176,641 (digital/electronic); Databases: 517. Weekly public service hours: 114. Operations spending for the previous fiscal year: $1 million. 250 computers available on campus for general student use. A campuswide network can be accessed. Students can access the following: online class registration, residential computer consultant. Staffed computer lab on campus (open 24 hours a day) provides training in use of computers, software, and the Internet.

Community Environment: Kalamazoo is a college-centered community, 130 miles from Detroit and Chicago. The airport serves nine major airlines. Locally, many companies, hospitals and local governments make internships available to students.

■ **KALAMAZOO VALLEY COMMUNITY COLLEGE**
PO Box 4070
Kalamazoo, MI 49003-4070
Tel: (269)488-4400
Fax: (269)448-4555
Web Site: www.kvcc.edu

Description: State and locally supported, 2-year, coed. Awards certificates, transfer associate, and terminal associate degrees. Founded 1966. Setting: 187-acre suburban campus. Educational spending for the previous fiscal year: $311 per student. Total enrollment: 11,113. 1% from out-of-state. 37% 25 or older. Core. Calendar: semesters. Academic remediation for entering students, ESL program, services for LD students, advanced placement, self-designed majors, honors program, independent study, distance learning, summer session for credit, part-time degree program, co-op programs and internships. Off campus study at 5 members of the Kalamazoo Consortium. ROTC: Army (c).

Entrance Requirements: Open admission. Required: high school transcript, ACT. Entrance: noncompetitive. Application deadline: rolling. Notification: continuous. Transfer credits accepted: Yes.

Costs Per Year: Application fee: $0. Area resident tuition: $3210 full-time, $107 per contact hour part-time. State resident tuition: $5520 full-time, $184 per contact hour part-time. Nonresident tuition: $7410 full-time, $247 per contact hour part-time. Mandatory fees: $256 full-time, $128 per term part-time.

Collegiate Environment: Orientation program. Choral group. Student services: personal-psychological counseling. Campus security: 24-hour emergency response devices and patrols. Kalamazoo Valley Community College Library.

Community Environment: See Western Michigan University.

■ **KELLOGG COMMUNITY COLLEGE**
450 N Ave.
Battle Creek, MI 49017-3397
Tel: (616)965-3931
Fax: (616)965-4133
E-mail: jewelln@kellogg.edu
Web Site: www.kellogg.edu

Description: State and locally supported, 2-year, coed. Part of Michigan Department of Education. Awards certificates, transfer associate, and terminal associate degrees. Founded 1956. Setting: 120-acre urban campus. Educational spending for the previous fiscal year: $7147 per student. Total enrollment: 4,814. Student-undergrad faculty ratio is 17:1. Full-time: 1,160 students, 60% women, 40% men. Part-time: 3,654 students, 69% women, 31% men. Students come from 3 other countries. 1% American Indian or Alaska Native, non-Hispanic/Latino; 5% Hispanic/Latino; 9% Black or African American, non-Hispanic/Latino; 2% Asian, non-Hispanic/Latino; 0.1% Native Hawaiian or other Pacific Islander, non-Hispanic/Latino; 0.4% international. 5% transferred in. Core. Calendar: semesters. Academic remediation for entering students, ESL program, services for LD students, advanced placement, accelerated degree program, freshman honors college, honors program, independent study, distance learning, double major, summer session for credit, part-time degree program, adult/continuing education programs, co-op programs and internships. Off campus study.

Entrance Requirements: Open admission except for allied health and nursing programs. Options: electronic application, early admission. Required for some: high school transcript, minimum 2 high school GPA. Entrance: noncompetitive. Application deadline: rolling. Notification: continuous. Transfer credits accepted: Yes.

Costs Per Year: Application fee: $0. Area resident tuition: $3683 full-time. State resident tuition: $5693 full-time. Nonresident tuition: $7950 full-time.

Collegiate Environment: Orientation program. Drama-theater group, choral group, student-run newspaper. Social organizations: 25 open to all. Most popular organizations: Tech Club, Phi Theta Kappa, Student Nurses Association, Crude Arts Club, Art League. Major annual events: KCC Bruin Boost and KCC Bruin Blast, Leadership Conference, Blood Drive. Campus security: 24-hour emergency response devices and patrols, late night transport-escort service. Emory W. Morris Learning Resource Center. Books: 51,629 (physical), 20,975 (digital/electronic); Serial titles: 62 (physical), 74,000 (digital/electronic); Databases: 67. Weekly public service hours: 81; students can reserve study rooms. Operations spending for the previous fiscal year: $698,772. 1,000 computers available on campus for general student use. Computer purchase/lease plans available. A campuswide network can be accessed from off-campus. Students can access the following: online class registration. Staffed computer lab on campus provides training in use of computers and software.

Community Environment: This is the home of cereal manufacturers. Other manufacturers produce packaging machines and auto parts. Commercial passenger facilities include bus, rail, and air. Some part-time employment is available for students. The city has good recreational areas for picnicking, golf, camping, tobogganing and skiing. All are easily accessible. The American Amateur Baseball Series is held here annually.

■ KETTERING UNIVERSITY
1700 University Ave.
Flint, MI 48504
Tel: (810)762-9500; Free: 800-955-4464
Fax: (810)762-9837
E-mail: kdarcy@kettering.edu
Web Site: www.kettering.edu
Description: Independent, comprehensive, coed. Awards bachelor's and master's degrees. Founded 1919. Setting: 85-acre urban campus with easy access to Detroit. Endowment: $81.3 million. Research spending for the previous fiscal year: $3.8 million. Educational spending for the previous fiscal year: $10,576 per student. Total enrollment: 2,311. Faculty: 146 (114 full-time, 32 part-time). Student-undergrad faculty ratio is 15:1. 1,931 applied, 70% were admitted. 32% from top 10% of their high school class, 60% from top quarter, 91% from top half. Full-time: 1,807 students, 19% women, 81% men. Part-time: 82 students, 20% women, 80% men. 15% from out-of-state. 0.3% American Indian or Alaska Native, non-Hispanic/Latino; 5% Hispanic/Latino; 3% Black or African American, non-Hispanic/Latino; 4% Asian, non-Hispanic/Latino; 4% international. 3% 25 or older, 9% live on campus, 2% transferred in. Retention: 93% of full-time freshmen returned the following year. Academic areas with the most degrees conferred: engineering; computer and information sciences; business/marketing. Core. Calendar: semesters (11 weeks of full-time study plus 12 weeks of paid co-op experience per semester). Services for LD students, advanced placement, independent study, distance learning, double major, summer session for credit, external degree program, co-op programs and internships, graduate courses open to undergrads. Study abroad program.
Entrance Requirements: Options: electronic application, early action, deferred admission, international baccalaureate accepted. Required: high school transcript, SAT or ACT. Recommended: minimum 3 high school GPA, interview. Required for some: essay. Entrance: very difficult. Application deadline: rolling. Notification: continuous. Transfer credits accepted: Yes.
Costs Per Year: Application fee: $0. Comprehensive fee: $51,730 includes full-time tuition ($43,490) and college room and board ($8240). College room only: $5000. Part-time tuition: $1459 per credit hour.
Collegiate Environment: Orientation program. Choral group, student-run newspaper, radio station. Social organizations: national fraternities, national sororities. Most popular organizations: Student Government, Dance Club, Firebirds, Outdoors Club, International Club. Major annual events: Greek Week, Relay for Life, Midnight Breakfast. Student services: health clinic, personal-psychological counseling, women's center. Campus security: 24-hour emergency response devices and patrols, late night transport-escort service, controlled dormitory access, security card access to all campus buildings 24/7 except the campus center main entrance which is secure 11pm-7am. Kettering University Library. Operations spending for the previous fiscal year: $1.2 million.
Community Environment: A pioneer in the early days of the automobile industry, Flint is located about one hour north of Detroit and within an hour of Ann Arbor and East Lansing. Commercial transportation is provided by air, bus, and rail lines. The Flint area has several hospitals, churches of most faiths, the Flint Cultural Center with museums and institutes of arts and

music, and shopping. Recreational facilities are abundant, from the university Recreation Center and playing fields, to nearby golf courses, ski slopes, lakes, theatres, and more.

■ KEWEENAW BAY OJIBWA COMMUNITY COLLEGE
111 Beartown Rd.
Baraga, MI 49908
Tel: (906)524-8400
Fax: (906)524-8106
E-mail: megan@kbocc.org
Web Site: www.kbocc.edu
Description: County-supported, 2-year, coed. Awards transfer associate and terminal associate degrees. Setting: rural campus. Total enrollment: 77. Full-time: 43 students, 67% women, 33% men. Part-time: 34 students, 71% women, 29% men. Calendar: semesters.
Entrance Requirements: Required: high school transcript.

■ KIRTLAND COMMUNITY COLLEGE
10775 N St. Helen Rd.
Roscommon, MI 48653-9699
Tel: (989)275-5000
Fax: (989)275-8210
E-mail: registrar@kirtland.edu
Web Site: www.kirtland.edu
Description: District-supported, 2-year, coed. Awards certificates, transfer associate, and terminal associate degrees. Founded 1966. Setting: 180-acre rural campus. Educational spending for the previous fiscal year: $5799 per student. Total enrollment: 1,528. Faculty: 124 (33 full-time, 91 part-time). Student-undergrad faculty ratio is 17:1. 564 applied, 100% were admitted. 3% from top 10% of their high school class, 12% from top quarter, 47% from top half. Full-time: 499 students, 62% women, 38% men. Part-time: 1,029 students, 58% women, 42% men. Students come from 7 states and territories. 1% American Indian or Alaska Native, non-Hispanic/Latino; 2% Hispanic/Latino; 1% Black or African American, non-Hispanic/Latino; 0.7% Asian, non-Hispanic/Latino. 37% 25 or older. Core. Calendar: semesters. Academic remediation for entering students, services for LD students, advanced placement, honors program, independent study, distance learning, summer session for credit, part-time degree program, adult/continuing education programs, co-op programs and internships.
Entrance Requirements: Open admission. Option: electronic application. Required: high school transcript. Recommended: SAT or ACT. Entrance: noncompetitive. Application deadline: rolling. Notification: continuous until 8/15. Transfer credits accepted: Yes.
Costs Per Year: Application fee: $0. Area resident tuition: $3540 full-time, $118 per contact hour part-time. State resident tuition: $5250 full-time, $175 per contact hour part-time. Nonresident tuition: $7500 full-time, $250 per contact hour part-time. Mandatory fees: $630 full-time, $21 per contact hour part-time.
Collegiate Environment: Orientation program. Social organizations: Phi Theta Kappa. Campus security: 24-hour emergency response devices, student patrols, late night transport-escort service, campus warning siren, uniformed armed police officers, RAVE alert system (text, email, voice). Kirtland Community College Library plus 1 other. Books: 27,089 (physical), 180,843 (digital/electronic); Serial titles: 105 (physical); Databases: 55. Weekly public service hours: 40; students can reserve study rooms. 35 computers available on campus for general student use. A campuswide network can be accessed from off-campus. Students can access the following: online class registration.
Community Environment: The college is located in the heart of Michigan's four-season vacationland amidst excellent hunting, fishing, swimming, boating, skiing and snowmobiling lands and lakes. Interstate Route I-75 provides the most direct means of approach to within twelve miles of the campus, which is located at the juncture of Roscommon, Ogemaw, Oscoda and Crawford counties on County Road F-97.

■ KUYPER COLLEGE
3333 E Beltline, NE
Grand Rapids, MI 49525-9749
Tel: (616)222-3000
Fax: (616)222-3045
Web Site: www.kuyper.edu
Description: Independent Christian, 4-year, coed. Awards associate, bachelor's, and master's degrees. Founded 1939. Setting: 34-acre suburban campus with easy access to Grand Rapids. Total enrollment: 160. Faculty:

24 (8 full-time, 16 part-time). Student-undergrad faculty ratio is 12:1. 119 applied, 68% were admitted. Full-time: 130 students, 60% women, 40% men. Part-time: 30 students, 70% women, 30% men. Students come from 10 states and territories, 8 other countries, 8% from out-of-state. 0.6% American Indian or Alaska Native, non-Hispanic/Latino; 3% Hispanic/Latino; 3% Black or African American, non-Hispanic/Latino; 4% Asian, non-Hispanic/Latino; 6% international. 7% 25 or older, 42% live on campus, 9% transferred in. Retention: 75% of full-time freshmen returned the following year. Academic areas with the most degrees conferred: public administration and social services; theology and religious vocations; liberal arts/general studies. Core. Calendar: semesters. Academic remediation for entering students, services for LD students, advanced placement, self-designed majors, independent study, double major, summer session for credit, part-time degree program, co-op programs and internships. Off campus study at Grand Rapids Community College, Cornerstone University, Davenport University. Study abroad program. ROTC: Army (c).

Entrance Requirements: Options: electronic application, deferred admission, international baccalaureate accepted. Required: essay, high school transcript, minimum 2.25 high school GPA, SAT or ACT. Recommended: interview. Entrance: moderately difficult. Application deadline: rolling. Notification: continuous. Transfer credits accepted: Yes.

Costs Per Year: Application fee: $0. Comprehensive fee: $29,274 includes full-time tuition ($21,314), mandatory fees ($675), and college room and board ($7285). Full-time tuition and fees vary according to course load and reciprocity agreements. Room and board charges vary according to board plan, housing facility, and student level. Part-time tuition: $950 per credit hour. Part-time mandatory fees: $335 per year. Part-time tuition and fees vary according to course load and reciprocity agreements.

Collegiate Environment: Orientation program. Drama-theater group, choral group. Social organizations: 10 open to all. Most popular organizations: intramurals, Student Activities Club, Helping and Nurturing During Service, Yearbook, Roots. Major annual events: Christmas Banquet, Variety Show, All Campus Retreat. Student services: health clinic, personal-psychological counseling. Campus security: 24-hour emergency response devices, student patrols, late night transport-escort service, controlled dormitory access. 160 college housing spaces available; 109 were occupied in 2018-19. Freshmen guaranteed college housing. On-campus residence required through sophomore year. Option: coed housing available. Zondervan Library plus 1 other. Books: 78,702 (physical), 14,199 (digital/electronic); Databases: 101. Weekly public service hours: 72; students can reserve study rooms. 70 computers available on campus for general student use. A campuswide network can be accessed from student residence rooms and from off campus. Students can access the following: online class registration. Staffed computer lab on campus provides training in use of computers, software, and the Internet.

Community Environment: See Calvin College.

■ LAKE MICHIGAN COLLEGE

2755 E Napier Ave.
Benton Harbor, MI 49022-1899
Tel: (269)927-8100; Free: 800-252-1LMC
E-mail: thomas@lakemichigancollege.edu
Web Site: www.lakemichigancollege.edu

Description: District-supported, 2-year, coed. Part of Michigan Department of Education. Awards certificates, transfer associate, and terminal associate degrees. Founded 1946. Setting: 260-acre small town campus. Endowment: $6.4 million. Educational spending for the previous fiscal year: $4368 per student. Total enrollment: 4,548. Faculty: 327 (58 full-time, 269 part-time). Student-undergrad faculty ratio is 17:1. 1,580 applied, 94% were admitted. 5% from top 10% of their high school class, 18% from top quarter, 47% from top half. Full-time: 1,508 students, 57% women, 43% men. Part-time: 3,040 students, 61% women, 39% men. Students come from 5 states and territories, 50 other countries, 2% from out-of-state. 0.8% American Indian or Alaska Native, non-Hispanic/Latino; 6% Hispanic/Latino; 21% Black or African American, non-Hispanic/Latino; 1% Asian, non-Hispanic/Latino; 0.4% Native Hawaiian or other Pacific Islander, non-Hispanic/Latino. 37% 25 or older, 6% transferred in. Retention: 42% of full-time freshmen returned the following year. Core. Calendar: semesters. Academic remediation for entering students, ESL program, services for LD students, self-designed majors, honors program, independent study, distance learning, summer session for credit, part-time degree program, adult/continuing education programs, co-op programs. Off campus study at Western Michigan University.

Entrance Requirements: Open admission. Option: electronic application.

Required: high school transcript. Required for some: interview. Entrance: noncompetitive. Application deadline: rolling. Notification: continuous. Transfer credits accepted: Yes.

Collegiate Environment: Orientation program. Drama-theater group, choral group. Social organizations: 20 open to all. Most popular organizations: Cheer Team, Phi Theta Kappa, Student Senate, Movie Club, LMC Sky Kings (Sky Diving Club). Major annual events: Welcome Week, Spring Fling, Honors Convocation. Campus security: 24-hour emergency response devices, contracted campus security force. William Hessel Library. Operations spending for the previous fiscal year: $348,404. 120 computers available on campus for general student use. A campuswide network can be accessed. Students can access the following: online class registration, online financial aid information. Staffed computer lab on campus provides training in use of computers, software, and the Internet.

■ LAKE SUPERIOR STATE UNIVERSITY

650 W Easterday Ave.
Sault Sainte Marie, MI 49783
Tel: (906)632-6841; Free: 888-800-LSSU
Fax: (906)635-6669
Web Site: www.lssu.edu

Description: State-supported, comprehensive, coed. Awards associate, bachelor's, and master's degrees. Founded 1946. Setting: 115-acre small town campus. Endowment: $9 million. Research spending for the previous fiscal year: $443,045. Educational spending for the previous fiscal year: $6342 per student. Total enrollment: 2,438. Faculty: 178 (119 full-time, 59 part-time). Student-undergrad faculty ratio is 15:1. 1,465 applied, 90% were admitted. 14% from top 10% of their high school class, 40% from top quarter, 76% from top half. Full-time: 1,966 students, 49% women, 51% men. Part-time: 466 students, 57% women, 43% men. Students come from 16 states and territories, 8 other countries, 7% from out-of-state. 9% American Indian or Alaska Native, non-Hispanic/Latino; 3% Hispanic/Latino; 2% Black or African American, non-Hispanic/Latino; 0.5% Asian, non-Hispanic/Latino; 6% international. 10% 25 or older, 35% live on campus, 9% transferred in. Retention: 68% of full-time freshmen returned the following year. Academic areas with the most degrees conferred: homeland security, law enforcement, firefighting, and protective services; business/marketing; health professions and related sciences. Core. Calendar: semesters. Services for LD students, advanced placement, self-designed majors, freshman honors college, honors program, independent study, distance learning, double major, summer session for credit, part-time degree program, co-op programs and internships. Off campus study at Regional campus locations in Dearborn, MI; Gaylord, MI; Petosky, MI; and Escanaba, MI. Study abroad program.

Entrance Requirements: Options: electronic application, deferred admission, international baccalaureate accepted. Required: high school transcript, SAT or ACT. Entrance: moderately difficult. Application deadline: rolling. Notification: continuous. SAT Reasoning Test deadline: 7/31. SAT Subject Test deadline: 7/31. Transfer credits accepted: Yes.

Collegiate Environment: Orientation program. Drama-theater group, choral group, student-run newspaper, radio station. Social organizations: 65 open to all; national fraternities, national sororities, local fraternities, local sororities. Most popular organizations: Activities Board, SAILS - Student Alumni Involved in Lake State, Fisheries and Wildlife, Enactus (Formally known as SIFE), Chemistry and Environmental Science Club. Major annual events: Winter Carnival, Laker Week, Lakerpalooza. Student services: health clinic, personal-psychological counseling. Campus security: 24-hour emergency response devices and patrols, student patrols, late night transport-escort service. Kenneth Shouldice Library. Operations spending for the previous fiscal year: $926,678. 325 computers available on campus for general student use. A campuswide network can be accessed from student residence rooms and from off campus. Students can access the following: online class registration. Staffed computer lab on campus provides training in use of software.

■ LANSING COMMUNITY COLLEGE

PO Box 40010
Lansing, MI 48901-7210
Tel: (517)483-1957; Free: 800-644-4LCC
Fax: (517)483-9668
E-mail: grossbt@lcc.edu
Web Site: www.lcc.edu

Description: State and locally supported, 2-year, coed. Part of Michigan Department of Education. Awards certificates, transfer associate, and terminal associate degrees. Founded 1957. Setting: 28-acre urban campus.

Endowment: $7.3 million. Educational spending for the previous fiscal year: $3542 per student. Total enrollment: 13,583. Full-time: 5,088 students, 52% women, 48% men. Part-time: 8,495 students, 55% women, 45% men. 0.5% American Indian or Alaska Native, non-Hispanic/Latino; 8% Hispanic/Latino; 10% Black or African American, non-Hispanic/Latino; 3% Asian, non-Hispanic/Latino; 0.2% Native Hawaiian or other Pacific Islander, non-Hispanic/Latino; 1% international. Core. Calendar: semesters. Academic remediation for entering students, ESL program, services for LD students, advanced placement, honors program, independent study, distance learning, double major, summer session for credit, part-time degree program, external degree program, adult/continuing education programs, co-op programs and internships. Study abroad program. ROTC: Army (c), Air Force (c).

Entrance Requirements: Open admission except for international students or allied health, fire science, automotive technologies, law enforcement programs. Options: electronic application, early admission, deferred admission, international baccalaureate accepted. Required for some: essay, high school transcript, 2 recommendations, interview, specific additional requirements for health, aviation, music, police academy, and fire academy program admissions. Entrance: noncompetitive. Application deadline: 8/7. Preference given to district residents. Transfer credits accepted: Yes.

Collegiate Environment: Orientation program. Drama-theater group, choral group, student-run newspaper. Social organizations: national fraternities, national sororities. Most popular organizations: American Marketing Association, Phi Theta Kappa, Future Teachers' Club, Health Career Related Clubs (Dental Hygiene, Nurses), Gay-Straight Alliance. Major annual events: Graduation, Student Recognition Banquet, Welcome Week/Spring Fling. Student services: personal-psychological counseling, women's center. Campus security: 24-hour emergency response devices and patrols, student patrols, late night transport-escort service. Lansing Community College Library. Operations spending for the previous fiscal year: $499,174.

Community Environment: Named capital of the state in 1847, Lansing is well-known for its automotive industries. Over two-thirds of its products are gas engines, automobile parts, drop forgings and castings. The State Historical Museum is located here. The area has golf courses, theatres, a baseball team, museums, parks, and a riverfront walk. Excellent part-time employment is available for students.

■ **LAWRENCE TECHNOLOGICAL UNIVERSITY**
21000 W Ten Mile Rd.
Southfield, MI 48075-1058
Tel: (248)204-4000; Free: 800-225-5588
Fax: (248)204-3727
E-mail: admissions@ltu.edu
Web Site: www.ltu.edu

Description: Independent, university, coed. Awards associate, bachelor's, master's, and doctoral degrees. Founded 1932. Setting: 107-acre suburban campus with easy access to Detroit. Endowment: $50.4 million. Research spending for the previous fiscal year: $410,460. Educational spending for the previous fiscal year: $10,460 per student. Total enrollment: 2,915. Faculty: 352 (120 full-time, 232 part-time). Student-undergrad faculty ratio is 11:1. 2,347 applied, 78% were admitted. Full-time: 1,693 students, 26% women, 74% men. Part-time: 479 students, 27% women, 73% men. Students come from 38 states and territories, 36 other countries, 9% from out-of-state. 0.2% American Indian or Alaska Native, non-Hispanic/Latino; 3% Hispanic/Latino; 8% Black or African American, non-Hispanic/Latino; 3% Asian, non-Hispanic/Latino; 12% international. 13% 25 or older, 39% live on campus, 7% transferred in. Retention: 81% of full-time freshmen returned the following year. Academic areas with the most degrees conferred: engineering; architecture; computer and information sciences. Core. Calendar: semesters. Academic remediation for entering students, ESL program, services for LD students, advanced placement, accelerated degree program, honors program, independent study, distance learning, double major, summer session for credit, part-time degree program, adult/continuing education programs, co-op programs and internships, graduate courses open to undergrads. Off campus study. Study abroad program. ROTC: Army (c).

Entrance Requirements: Options: electronic application, deferred admission, international baccalaureate accepted. Required: high school transcript, minimum 2.5 high school GPA, SAT or ACT. Required for some: essay, minimum 2.75 high school GPA, 1 recommendation, interview. Entrance: moderately difficult. Notification: continuous until 8/26. Transfer credits accepted: Yes.

Costs Per Year: Application fee: $30. Comprehensive fee: $43,520 includes full-time tuition ($32,370), mandatory fees ($1200), and college room and board ($9950). College room only: $7050. Full-time tuition and fees vary ac-

cording to course level, degree level, location, program, and student level. Room and board charges vary according to board plan and housing facility. Part-time tuition: $1079 per credit hour. Part-time tuition varies according to course level, degree level, location, program, and student level.

Collegiate Environment: Orientation program. Drama-theater group, student-run newspaper. Social organizations: 44 open to all; national fraternities, national sororities, local fraternities, local sororities; 9% of eligible men and 20% of eligible women are members. Most popular organizations: American Institute of Architecture Students, American Society of Mechanical Engineers, Sigma Phi Epsilon, American Society of Civil Engineers, Student Government. Major annual events: Discovery Days, New Student Convocation, Welcome Back Picnic. Student services: personal-psychological counseling. Campus security: 24-hour emergency response devices and patrols, late night transport-escort service, controlled dormitory access. 750 college housing spaces available; all were occupied in 2018-19. Freshmen given priority for college housing. Option: coed housing available. Lawrence Technological University Library plus 1 other. Books: 54,776 (physical), 427,400 (digital/electronic); Serial titles: 51,210 (digital/electronic); Databases: 171. Weekly public service hours: 73; students can reserve study rooms. Operations spending for the previous fiscal year: $960,881. 1,887 computers available on campus for general student use. Computer purchase/lease plans available. A computer is required for all students. A campuswide network can be accessed from student residence rooms and from off campus. Students can access the following: online class registration, degree audit, Canvas/Blackboard, Banner (student information), personal websites, document collection, Handshake, Placement, Mapworks advising. Staffed computer lab on campus (open 24 hours a day) provides training in use of computers, software, and the Internet.

Community Environment: The city is a northern suburb of Detroit, with excellent full-time and part-time employment opportunities for students. Good recreational facilities are nearby. Southfield has excellent shopping areas and a Civic Center that includes a 166-acre park. Transportation and other facilities of Detroit are easily accessible.

■ **MACOMB COMMUNITY COLLEGE**
14500 E Twelve Mile Rd.
Warren, MI 48088-3896
Tel: (586)445-7999; Free: 866-MACOMB1
Fax: (586)445-7140
E-mail: stevensr@macomb.edu
Web Site: www.macomb.edu

Description: District-supported, 2-year, coed. Part of Michigan Public Community College System. Awards certificates, transfer associate, and terminal associate degrees. Founded 1954. Setting: 384-acre suburban campus with easy access to Detroit. Endowment: $20.4 million. Educational spending for the previous fiscal year: $4660 per student. Total enrollment: 21,014. Faculty: 971 (202 full-time, 769 part-time). Student-undergrad faculty ratio is 24:1. Full-time: 6,116 students, 51% women, 49% men. Part-time: 14,898 students, 54% women, 46% men. Students come from 4 states and territories. 0.5% American Indian or Alaska Native, non-Hispanic/Latino; 3% Hispanic/Latino; 11% Black or African American, non-Hispanic/Latino; 5% Asian, non-Hispanic/Latino; 0.1% Native Hawaiian or other Pacific Islander, non-Hispanic/Latino; 2% international. 36% 25 or older. Retention: 56% of full-time freshmen returned the following year. Calendar: semesters. Academic remediation for entering students, ESL program, services for LD students, advanced placement, self-designed majors, honors program, summer session for credit, part-time degree program, adult/continuing education programs, co-op programs and internships. Off campus study at Wayne State University, Wayne County Community College, Benjamin Davis Vocational Technical Center, Oakland Community College.

Entrance Requirements: Open admission except for nursing, occupational therapy, respiratory therapy, veterinary technician, physical therapy programs. Options: early admission, deferred admission. Entrance: noncompetitive. Application deadline: rolling.

Costs Per Year: Application fee: $0. Area resident tuition: $3100 full-time, $100 per credit hour part-time. State resident tuition: $5766 full-time, $186 per credit hour part-time. Nonresident tuition: $7347 full-time, $237 per credit hour part-time. Mandatory fees: $275 full-time, $5 per credit hour part-time, $60 per term part-time. Full-time tuition and fees vary according to course load. Part-time tuition and fees vary according to course load.

Collegiate Environment: Orientation program. Drama-theater group. Social organizations: 20 open to all. Most popular organizations: Phi Beta Kappa, Adventure Unlimited, Alpha Rho Rho, SADD. Major annual events: Welcome Back Picnic, Spring Fling, Bandemonium. Student services: health clinic, personal-psychological counseling. Campus security: 24-hour emergency response devices and patrols, late night transport-escort service, security phones in parking lots, surveillance cameras. Library of South Campus. Books: 181,121 (physical), 51,203 (digital/electronic); Serial titles: 51,079 (physical), 97,750 (digital/electronic). Students can reserve study rooms. Operations spending for the previous fiscal year: $1.6 million. 2,000 computers available on campus for general student use. A campuswide network can be accessed from off-campus. Students can access the following: online class registration. Staffed computer lab on campus.

Community Environment: Community has many libraries, churches of various denominations, hospitals, and excellent shopping facilities. Some part-time work is available for students. City has major recreational facilities, and borders Lake St. Clair.

■ MADONNA UNIVERSITY
36600 Schoolcraft Rd.
Livonia, MI 48150-1173
Tel: (734)432-5300; Free: 800-852-4951
Fax: (734)432-5393
E-mail: mschroeder@madonna.edu
Web Site: www.madonna.edu

Description: Independent Roman Catholic, comprehensive, coed. Awards associate, bachelor's, master's, and doctoral degrees and post-master's certificates. Founded 1947. Setting: 85-acre suburban campus with easy access to Detroit. Endowment: $41.1 million. Educational spending for the previous fiscal year: $8839 per student. Total enrollment: 3,044. Faculty: 324 (99 full-time, 225 part-time). Student-undergrad faculty ratio is 13:1. 985 applied, 78% were admitted. 8% from top 10% of their high school class, 24% from top quarter, 42% from top half. Full-time: 1,431 students, 67% women, 33% men. Part-time: 1,009 students, 63% women, 37% men. Students come from 20 states and territories, 5 other countries, 2% from out-of-state. 0.1% American Indian or Alaska Native, non-Hispanic/Latino; 4% Hispanic/Latino; 11% Black or African American, non-Hispanic/Latino; 2% Asian, non-Hispanic/Latino; 0.2% Native Hawaiian or other Pacific Islander, non-Hispanic/Latino; 13% international. 33% 25 or older, 12% live on campus, 20% transferred in. Retention: 76% of full-time freshmen returned the following year. Academic areas with the most degrees conferred: business/marketing; health professions and related sciences; homeland security, law enforcement, firefighting, and protective services. Core. Calendar: semesters. ESL program, services for LD students, advanced placement, accelerated degree program, self-designed majors, independent study, distance learning, double major, summer session for credit, part-time degree program, adult/continuing education programs, co-op programs and internships, graduate courses open to undergrads. Off campus study at 4 members of the Detroit Area Consortium of Catholic Colleges. Study abroad program. ROTC: Army (c).

Entrance Requirements: Options: electronic application, early decision, deferred admission, international baccalaureate accepted. Required: SAT or ACT. Recommended: minimum 2.8 high school GPA. Required for some: essay, high school transcript, 2 recommendations, Music performance and dance majors require auditions before selection to the program. Entrance: moderately difficult. Application deadlines: rolling, rolling for nonresidents, 12/1 for early decision. Notification: continuous, continuous for nonresidents, 1/15 for early decision. SAT Reasoning Test deadline: 7/1. SAT Subject Test deadline: 7/1. Transfer credits accepted: Yes. Early decision applicants: 0. Early decision applicants admitted: 0.

Costs Per Year: Application fee: $0. Comprehensive fee: $34,550 includes full-time tuition ($23,100) and college room and board ($11,450). College room only: $5500. Part-time tuition: $770 per credit hour.

Collegiate Environment: Orientation program. Drama-theater group, choral group, student-run newspaper, radio station. Social organizations: 55 open to all. Most popular organizations: Campus Ministry, Madonna University Nursing Student Association, Broadcast and Film Club, Society of Future Teachers, Michigan Blood Club. Major annual events: Welcome Weekend, Spirit Week/Founder's Day Activities, Homecoming. Student services: personal-psychological counseling. Campus security: 24-hour emergency response devices and patrols, late night transport-escort service, controlled dormitory access. 406 college housing spaces available; 306 were occupied in 2018-19. Freshmen guaranteed college housing. Options: men-only, women-only housing available. Madonna University Library. Books: 71,562 (physical), 181,927 (digital/electronic); Serial titles: 190 (physical), 70,781 (digital/electronic); Databases: 130. Weekly public service hours: 100; students can reserve study rooms. Operations spending for the previous fiscal year: $1.4 million. 205 computers available on campus for general

student use. Computer purchase/lease plans available. A campuswide network can be accessed from student residence rooms and from off campus. Students can access the following: online class registration, online payments, online statements, online unofficial transcripts. Staffed computer lab on campus provides training in use of computers, software, and the Internet.

Community Environment: See Schoolcraft College.

■ MIAT COLLEGE OF TECHNOLOGY
2955 S Haggerty Rd.
Canton, MI 48188
Tel: (734)483-3758
Web Site: www.miat.edu

Description: Proprietary, 2-year, coed. Awards certificates, transfer associate, and terminal associate degrees.

■ MICHIGAN STATE UNIVERSITY
East Lansing, MI 48824
Tel: (517)355-1855
E-mail: admis@msu.edu
Web Site: www.msu.edu

Description: State-supported, university, coed. Awards bachelor's, master's, and doctoral degrees and post-master's certificates. Founded 1855. Setting: 5,192-acre suburban campus with easy access to Detroit. Endowment: $3.3 billion. Research spending for the previous fiscal year: $457.7 million. Total enrollment: 50,351. Faculty: 2,926 (2,551 full-time, 375 part-time). Student-undergrad faculty ratio is 16:1. 33,129 applied, 78% were admitted. 29% from top 10% of their high school class, 67% from top quarter, 95% from top half. Full-time: 35,744 students, 51% women, 49% men. Part-time: 3,679 students, 45% women, 55% men. Students come from 54 states and territories, 104 other countries, 14% from out-of-state. 0.2% American Indian or Alaska Native, non-Hispanic/Latino; 5% Hispanic/Latino; 7% Black or African American, non-Hispanic/Latino; 6% Asian, non-Hispanic/Latino; 0.1% Native Hawaiian or other Pacific Islander, non-Hispanic/Latino; 10% international. 3% 25 or older, 39% live on campus, 4% transferred in. Retention: 92% of full-time freshmen returned the following year. Academic areas with the most degrees conferred: business/marketing; communication/journalism; biological/life sciences. Core. Calendar: semesters. Academic remediation for entering students, ESL program, services for LD students, advanced placement, accelerated degree program, self-designed majors, freshman honors college, honors program, independent study, distance learning, double major, summer session for credit, part-time degree program, adult/continuing education programs, co-op programs and internships, graduate courses open to undergrads. Off campus study at Great Plains Interactive Distance Education Alliance. Study abroad program. ROTC: Army, Air Force.

Entrance Requirements: Options: electronic application, early action, deferred admission, international baccalaureate accepted. Required: essay, high school transcript, SAT or ACT. Entrance: moderately difficult. Application deadlines: rolling, rolling for nonresidents. Notification: continuous, continuous for nonresidents. SAT Reasoning Test deadline: 6/15. Transfer credits accepted: Yes.

Costs Per Year: Application fee: $65. State resident tuition: $14,460 full-time, $482 per credit hour part-time. Nonresident tuition: $39,765 full-time, $1,326 per credit hour part-time. Full-time tuition varies according to course load, program, and student level. Part-time tuition varies according to course load, program, and student level. College room and board: $10,322. College room only: $4292. Room and board charges vary according to board plan and housing facility.

Collegiate Environment: Orientation program. Drama-theater group, choral group, marching band, student-run newspaper, radio station. Social organizations: 700 open to all; national fraternities, national sororities, local fraternities; 12% of eligible men and 11% of eligible women are members. Major annual events: Football Games in Spartan Stadium, Basketball Games in Breslin Center, Homecoming Festivities. Student services: legal services, health clinic, personal-psychological counseling, women's center. Campus security: 24-hour emergency response devices and patrols, late night transport-escort service, controlled dormitory access. 16,620 college housing spaces available; 15,316 were occupied in 2018-19. Freshmen guaranteed college housing. On-campus residence required in freshman year. Options: coed, women-only housing available. Main Library plus 2 others. Books: 3.6 million (physical), 3 million (digital/electronic); Serial titles: 136,425 (physical), 194,857 (digital/electronic). Weekly public service hours: 142. Operations spending for the previous fiscal year: $34.4 million.

Community Environment: Located in a metropolitan area adjacent to

Lansing, the state capital of Michigan. There are four hospitals, access to houses of worship, various entertainment venues, and good shopping facilities within the immediate area.

■ MICHIGAN TECHNOLOGICAL UNIVERSITY

1400 Townsend Dr.
Houghton, MI 49931
Tel: (906)487-1885; Free: 888-MTU-1885
Fax: (906)487-3343
E-mail: mtu4u@mtu.edu
Web Site: www.mtu.edu

Description: State-supported, university, coed. Awards associate, bachelor's, master's, and doctoral degrees. Founded 1885. Setting: 925-acre small town campus. Endowment: $106.4 million. Research spending for the previous fiscal year: $56.8 million. Educational spending for the previous fiscal year: $10,109 per student. Total enrollment: 7,319. Faculty: 450 (416 full-time, 34 part-time). Student-undergrad faculty ratio is 12:1. 5,469 applied, 74% were admitted. 32% from top 10% of their high school class, 65% from top quarter, 91% from top half. 5 National Merit Scholars, 64 valedictorians. Full-time: 5,517 students, 27% women, 73% men. Part-time: 400 students, 30% women, 70% men. Students come from 45 states and territories, 35 other countries, 22% from out-of-state. 0.3% American Indian or Alaska Native, non-Hispanic/Latino; 2% Hispanic/Latino; 0.9% Black or African American, non-Hispanic/Latino; 1% Asian, non-Hispanic/Latino; 0.1% Native Hawaiian or other Pacific Islander, non-Hispanic/Latino; 3% international. 3% 25 or older, 45% live on campus, 3% transferred in. Retention: 83% of full-time freshmen returned the following year. Academic areas with the most degrees conferred: engineering; business/marketing; computer and information sciences. Core. Calendar: semesters. ESL program, services for LD students, advanced placement, accelerated degree program, honors program, independent study, distance learning, double major, summer session for credit, part-time degree program, co-op programs and internships, graduate courses open to undergrads. Off campus study. Study abroad program. ROTC: Army, Air Force.

Entrance Requirements: Options: electronic application, deferred admission, international baccalaureate accepted. Required: high school transcript, SAT or ACT. Recommended: minimum 2.75 high school GPA. Required for some: essay, examples of creative work for some majors in Visual and Performing Arts Department. Entrance: moderately difficult. Application deadline: rolling. Notification: continuous. SAT Reasoning Test deadline: 8/25. Transfer credits accepted: Yes.

Costs Per Year: State resident tuition: $15,346 full-time, $579 per credit hour part-time. Nonresident tuition: $33,426 full-time, $1238 per credit hour part-time. Mandatory fees: $300 full-time, $150 per term part-time. Full-time tuition and fees vary according to program and student level. Part-time tuition and fees vary according to course load, program, and student level. College room and board: $10,756. College room only: $5982. Room and board charges vary according to board plan and housing facility.

Collegiate Environment: Orientation program. Drama-theater group, choral group, student-run newspaper, radio station. Social organizations: 229 open to all; national fraternities, national sororities, local fraternities, local sororities; 11% of eligible men and 15% of eligible women are members. Most popular organizations: Indian Students Associate, Society of Women Engineers, Huskies Pep Band, Fishing Club, WMTU. Major annual events: K-Day (Keweenaw Day), Winter Carnival, Parade of Nations. Student services: health clinic, personal-psychological counseling, women's center. Campus security: 24-hour emergency response devices and patrols, late night transport-escort service, controlled dormitory access. J. R. Van Pelt and John and Ruanne Opie Library. Books: 362,342 (physical), 142,603 (digital/electronic); Serial titles: 14,050 (physical), 124,764 (digital/electronic); Databases: 347. Weekly public service hours: 105; study areas open 24 hours, 5-7 days a week; students can reserve study rooms. 1,079 computers available on campus for general student use. A campuswide network can be accessed from student residence rooms and from off campus. Students can access the following: online class registration. Staffed computer lab on campus provides training in use of computers, software, and the Internet.

Community Environment: The main campus is located in Houghton, at the heart of the colorful Keweenaw Peninsula in Upper Michigan. Houghton is part of the Houghton-Hancock twin-city center of approximately 12,000. Numerous water and winter sports are available. The community has public libraries, churches for all major religions, a hospital, and opportunities for a variety of recreational and cultural activities. Part-time employment is available.

■ MID MICHIGAN COMMUNITY COLLEGE

1375 S Clare Ave.
Harrison, MI 48625-9447
Tel: (989)386-6622
Fax: (989)386-9088
E-mail: apply@midmich.edu
Web Site: www.midmich.edu

Description: State and locally supported, 2-year, coed. Part of Michigan Department of Education. Awards certificates, transfer associate, and terminal associate degrees. Founded 1965. Setting: 560-acre rural campus. Educational spending for the previous fiscal year: $903 per student. Total enrollment: 4,885. Faculty: 264 (46 full-time, 218 part-time). Student-undergrad faculty ratio is 26:1. 785 applied, 100% were admitted. Full-time: 2,193 students, 53% women, 47% men. Part-time: 2,692 students, 63% women, 37% men. 1% from out-of-state. 2% American Indian or Alaska Native, non-Hispanic/Latino; 3% Hispanic/Latino; 3% Black or African American, non-Hispanic/Latino; 0.2% Asian, non-Hispanic/Latino; 0.4% Native Hawaiian or other Pacific Islander, non-Hispanic/Latino; 0.6% international. 29% 25 or older, 4% transferred in. Retention: 43% of full-time freshmen returned the following year. Core. Calendar: semesters. Academic remediation for entering students, services for LD students, advanced placement, honors program, independent study, distance learning, summer session for credit, part-time degree program, adult/continuing education programs, co-op programs and internships.

Entrance Requirements: Open admission except for allied health programs. Options: electronic application, early admission. Recommended: high school transcript. Entrance: noncompetitive. Application deadline: rolling. Notification: continuous. Transfer credits accepted: Yes.

Collegiate Environment: Orientation program. Drama-theater group. Social organizations: 35 open to all. Most popular organizations: MC2, Phi Theta Kappa, Art Club, ECHO, Japan Culture Club. Major annual events: Spring Picnic, Fall Festival, Christmas Canned Food Drive and Coats for Kids Programs. Student services: personal-psychological counseling. Campus security: 24-hour emergency response devices. Charles A. Amble Library. 175 computers available on campus for general student use. Computer purchase/lease plans available. A campuswide network can be accessed from off-campus. Students can access the following: online class registration. Staffed computer lab on campus provides training in use of computers.

■ MONROE COUNTY COMMUNITY COLLEGE

1555 S Raisinville Rd.
Monroe, MI 48161-9047
Tel: (734)242-7300
Fax: (734)242-9711
E-mail: mhall@monroeccc.edu
Web Site: www.monroeccc.edu

Description: County-supported, 2-year, coed. Part of Michigan Department of Education. Awards certificates, transfer associate, and terminal associate degrees. Founded 1964. Setting: 150-acre small town campus with easy access to Detroit, Toledo. Total enrollment: 3,144. Faculty: 170 (40 full-time, 130 part-time). 2,500 applied, 100% were admitted. Students come from 2 other countries, 4% from out-of-state. 0.3% American Indian or Alaska Native, non-Hispanic/Latino; 3% Hispanic/Latino; 3% Black or African American, non-Hispanic/Latino; 0.8% Asian, non-Hispanic/Latino; 0.1% Native Hawaiian or other Pacific Islander, non-Hispanic/Latino; 0.1% international. 25% 25 or older. Core. Calendar: semesters. Academic remediation for entering students, services for LD students, advanced placement, honors program, independent study, distance learning, summer session for credit, part-time degree program. Study abroad program.

Entrance Requirements: Open admission except for allied health, culinary arts programs. Options: early admission, deferred admission. Required: high school transcript, ACT, ACT Compass, SAT, ACCUPLACER. Recommended: SAT, ACT. Entrance: noncompetitive. Notification: continuous.

Costs Per Year: Application fee: $0. Area resident tuition: $3048 full-time. State resident tuition: $5040 full-time. Nonresident tuition: $5556 full-time. Mandatory fees: $80 full-time. Full-time tuition and fees vary according to reciprocity agreements.

Collegiate Environment: Orientation program. Drama-theater group, choral group, student-run newspaper. Most popular organizations: Student Government, Society of Auto Engineers, Oasis, Nursing Students Organization, Respiratory Therapy. Major annual events: Family Fun Night, Fall Welcome Back Barbeque, Honors Reception. Campus security: police patrols during open hours. Campbell Learning Resource Center. 210 computers available on campus for general student use. A campuswide network can be accessed from off-campus. Students can access the following: online class registration. Staffed computer lab on campus.

Community Environment: The third oldest community in the state, Monroe was founded in 1780 by the French. This early settlement, called Frenchtown, was the scene of the River Raisin Massacre in 1813. The only Michigan port on Lake Erie, Monroe includes among its industries large nurseries, paper mills, a limestone quarry, recreation, and a branch automotive factory. It is a suburban city with a community airport and bus lines easily accessible. There are many civic, fraternal and veteran's organizations in this area. Community has a library, YMCA, museum, hospital, theater, 9 golf courses, many public parks and 6 shopping centers.

■ **MONTCALM COMMUNITY COLLEGE**
2800 College Dr.
Sidney, MI 48885
Tel: (989)328-2111; Free: 877-328-2111
Fax: (989)328-2950
E-mail: admissions@montcalm.edu
Web Site: www.montcalm.edu

Description: State and locally supported, 2-year, coed. Part of Michigan Department of Education. Awards certificates, transfer associate, and terminal associate degrees. Founded 1965. Setting: 240-acre rural campus with easy access to Grand Rapids. Total enrollment: 1,832. Faculty: 118 (29 full-time, 89 part-time). Student-undergrad faculty ratio is 16:1. Full-time: 538 students, 66% women, 34% men. Part-time: 1,294 students, 65% women, 35% men. 0.6% American Indian or Alaska Native, non-Hispanic/Latino; 1% Hispanic/Latino; 0.4% Black or African American, non-Hispanic/Latino; 0.2% Asian, non-Hispanic/Latino; 0.1% international. 55% 25 or older, 15% transferred in. Core. Calendar: semesters. Academic remediation for entering students, services for LD students, advanced placement, independent study, distance learning, double major, summer session for credit, part-time degree program, adult/continuing education programs, co-op programs and internships. Off campus study. Study abroad program.

Entrance Requirements: Open admission except for nursing program. Options: electronic application, early admission, deferred admission. Recommended: high school transcript. Entrance: noncompetitive.

Collegiate Environment: Orientation program. Drama-theater group, choral group. Most popular organizations: Nursing Club, Native American Club, Phi Theta Kappa, Business Club, Judo Club. Student services: personal-psychological counseling. Montcalm Community College Library.

Community Environment: Located in a rural area, air transportation is accessible within a one-hour drive. A neighboring city has theatres, libraries and hospitals. There are 104 lakes in the county providing excellent recreational opportunities. Some part-time employment is available for students.

■ **MOTT COMMUNITY COLLEGE**
1401 E Ct. St.
Flint, MI 48503-2089
Tel: (810)762-0200; Free: 800-852-8614
Fax: (810)762-0292
E-mail: regina.broomfield@mcc.edu
Web Site: www.mcc.edu

Description: District-supported, 2-year, coed. Awards certificates, transfer associate, and terminal associate degrees. Founded 1923. Setting: 32-acre urban campus with easy access to Detroit. Endowment: $40.1 million. Educational spending for the previous fiscal year: $5229 per student. Total enrollment: 7,689. Faculty: 410 (157 full-time, 253 part-time). Student-undergrad faculty ratio is 16:1. Full-time: 2,022 students, 54% women, 46% men. Part-time: 5,667 students, 60% women, 40% men. 0.4% American Indian or Alaska Native, non-Hispanic/Latino; 5% Hispanic/Latino; 16% Black or African American, non-Hispanic/Latino; 0.6% Asian, non-Hispanic/Latino; 0.1% Native Hawaiian or other Pacific Islander, non-Hispanic/Latino; 0.3% international. 40% 25 or older, 2% transferred in. Core. Calendar: semesters. Academic remediation for entering students, ESL program, services for LD students, advanced placement, accelerated degree program, honors program, independent study, distance learning, double major, summer session for credit, part-time degree program, adult/continuing education programs, co-op programs and internships.

Entrance Requirements: Open admission. Options: electronic application, early admission, deferred admission. Required: high school transcript. Entrance: noncompetitive. Application deadline: 8/31. Transfer credits accepted: Yes.

Costs Per Year: Application fee: $0. Area resident tuition: $4215 full-time,

$140.49 per contact hour part-time. State resident tuition: $5502 full-time, $183.40 per contact hour part-time. Nonresident tuition: $7842 full-time, $261.40 per contact hour part-time. Mandatory fees: $17.79 per contact hour part-time, $140.49 per term part-time. Full-time tuition varies according to course load. Part-time tuition and fees vary according to course load.

Collegiate Environment: Orientation program. Choral group. Social organizations: national fraternities, national sororities. Most popular organizations: Otaku Club, Respiratory Care Student Society, Physical Therapist Assistants, Occupational Therapist Assistants, Transitions Cosmetology. Major annual events: Fall Rally, College Night, Annual Tree Lighting. Student services: health clinic, personal-psychological counseling. Campus security: 24-hour emergency response devices and patrols, student patrols, late night transport-escort service, closed-circuit TV surveillance, whistle alert program, 3P Campaign: Prevent, Protect, and Prosecute Violence Against Women. Charles Stewart Mott Library. Students can reserve study rooms. Operations spending for the previous fiscal year: $904,863.

■ **MUSKEGON COMMUNITY COLLEGE**
221 S Quarterline Rd.
Muskegon, MI 49442-1493
Tel: (231)773-9131; Free: 866-711-4622
Fax: (231)777-0255
E-mail: johnathon.skidmore@muskegoncc.edu
Web Site: www.muskegoncc.edu

Description: State and locally supported, 2-year, coed. Part of Michigan Department of Education. Awards transfer associate and terminal associate degrees. Founded 1926. Setting: 112-acre small town campus with easy access to Grand Rapids. Total enrollment: 4,506. Faculty: 324 (83 full-time, 241 part-time). Student-undergrad faculty ratio is 19:1. 802 applied, 100% were admitted. Full-time: 1,488 students, 52% women, 48% men. Part-time: 3,018 students, 58% women, 42% men. Students come from 4 states and territories, 0.01% from out-of-state. 0.9% American Indian or Alaska Native, non-Hispanic/Latino; 3% Hispanic/Latino; 9% Black or African American, non-Hispanic/Latino; 0.8% Asian, non-Hispanic/Latino; 0.1% Native Hawaiian or other Pacific Islander, non-Hispanic/Latino; 0.4% international. Retention: 59% of full-time freshmen returned the following year. Core. Calendar: semesters. Academic remediation for entering students, self-designed majors, honors program, summer session for credit, part-time degree program, adult/continuing education programs, co-op programs.

Entrance Requirements: Open admission. Options: electronic application, early admission, deferred admission. Required: high school transcript. Entrance: noncompetitive. Application deadline: rolling. Notification: continuous. Transfer credits accepted: Yes.

Collegiate Environment: Orientation program. Drama-theater group, choral group, student-run newspaper. Social organizations: 30 open to all. Most popular organizations: Respiratory Therapy, Hispanic Student Organization, Black Student Alliance, International Club, Rotaract. Major annual events: Taste of Tomorrow, College Open House, Welcome Days. Student services: personal-psychological counseling. Campus security: 24-hour emergency response devices, on-campus security officer. Hendrik Meijer and Technology Center. 135 computers available on campus for general student use. A campuswide network can be accessed. Students can access the following: online class registration. Staffed computer lab on campus provides training in use of computers, software, and the Internet.

Community Environment: Formerly known as the Lumber Queen of the World, cutting 800 million board feet of lumber in 1888, Muskegon is the largest city on the east bank of Lake Michigan. Today it is an important lake port and a manufacturing and resort center. Numerous industries produce automotive parts, foundry products, paper, oil, chemicals and recreational equipment. Area has an international airport and a seaway-depth port. There are art galleries, museums, and historical sites located within the immediate vicinity. The nearby Muskegon River offers excellent fishing, boating, and canoeing.

■ **NORTH CENTRAL MICHIGAN COLLEGE**
1515 Howard St.
Petoskey, MI 49770-8717
Tel: (231)348-6600; Free: 888-298-6605
Web Site: www.ncmich.edu

Description: County-supported, 2-year, coed. Awards certificates, transfer associate, and terminal associate degrees. Founded 1958. Setting: 270-acre small town campus. Total enrollment: 2,770. Faculty: 133 (31 full-time, 102 part-time). Student-undergrad faculty ratio is 17:1. 55% 25 or older.

Calendar: semesters. Academic remediation for entering students, services for LD students, advanced placement, independent study, distance learning, double major, summer session for credit, part-time degree program, co-op programs and internships.

Entrance Requirements: Open admission except for nursing program. Required: high school transcript, ACT. Entrance: noncompetitive. Application deadline: rolling. Notification: continuous.

Collegiate Environment: Orientation program. Student services: personal-psychological counseling. Campus security: 24-hour emergency response devices. North Central Michigan College Library. 133 computers available on campus for general student use. A campuswide network can be accessed. Students can access the following: online class registration. Staffed computer lab on campus.

Community Environment: A resort and health center, the city is located on Little Traverse Bay. Within a 30-minute drive are 6 major ski resorts. Other recreational facilities include water sports on Lake Michigan, summer concerts, golf and tennis. The area has good transportation provided by air and bus service. There is some part-time employment available for students. Community services include a library, an arts center, many churches, 2 hospitals, and a clinic.

■ **NORTHERN MICHIGAN UNIVERSITY**

1401 Presque Isle Ave.
Marquette, MI 49855-5301
Tel: (906)227-1000; Free: 800-682-9797
Fax: (906)227-1747
E-mail: admissions@nmu.edu
Web Site: www.nmu.edu

Description: State-supported, comprehensive, coed. Awards associate, bachelor's, master's, and doctoral degrees and post-master's certificates. Founded 1899. Setting: 360-acre small town campus. Total enrollment: 7,612. Faculty: 419 (288 full-time, 131 part-time). Student-undergrad faculty ratio is 20:1. 6,173 applied, 74% were admitted. Full-time: 6,207 students, 54% women, 46% men. Part-time: 811 students, 57% women, 43% men. 19% from out-of-state. 1% American Indian or Alaska Native, non-Hispanic/Latino; 3% Hispanic/Latino; 2% Black or African American, non-Hispanic/Latino; 0.5% Asian, non-Hispanic/Latino; 1% international. 10% 25 or older, 42% live on campus, 6% transferred in. Retention: 78% of full-time freshmen returned the following year. Academic areas with the most degrees conferred: business/marketing; health professions and related sciences; biological/life sciences. Calendar: semesters. ESL program, services for LD students, accelerated degree program, self-designed majors, honors program, independent study, distance learning, double major, summer session for credit, part-time degree program, adult/continuing education programs, co-op programs and internships. Study abroad program. ROTC: Army.

Entrance Requirements: Options: electronic application, deferred admission, international baccalaureate accepted. Required: high school transcript, SAT or ACT. Application deadline: rolling. Notification: continuous. SAT Reasoning Test deadline: 8/21. SAT Subject Test deadline: 8/21. Transfer credits accepted: Yes.

Costs Per Year: Application fee: $35. One-time mandatory fee: $254. State resident tuition: $9984 full-time, $427 per credit hour part-time. Nonresident tuition: $15,864 full-time, $661 per credit hour part-time. Mandatory fees: $745 full-time, $118 per term part-time. Full-time tuition and fees vary according to student level. Part-time tuition and fees vary according to student level. College room and board: $10,666. College room only: $5692. Room and board charges vary according to board plan, housing facility, and student level.

Collegiate Environment: Orientation program. Drama-theater group, choral group, marching band, student-run newspaper, radio station. Social organizations: 350 open to all; national fraternities, national sororities. Major annual events: Homecoming, Fall Fest, Winter Fest. Student services: health clinic, personal-psychological counseling. Campus security: 24-hour emergency response devices and patrols, student patrols, late night transport-escort service, controlled dormitory access. Lydia M. Olson Library.

Community Environment: Located on Lake Superior, Marquette is a day's driving distance from Chicago, Minneapolis, Duluth and Milwaukee. It is an important service and distribution center.

■ **NORTHWESTERN MICHIGAN COLLEGE**

1701 E Front St.
Traverse City, MI 49686-3061
Tel: (231)995-1000; Free: 800-748-0566

Fax: (231)995-1680
E-mail: c.claerhout@nmc.edu
Web Site: www.nmc.edu

Description: State and locally supported, primarily 2-year, coed. Awards certificates, transfer associate, terminal associate, and bachelor's degrees. Founded 1951. Setting: 180-acre small town campus. Total enrollment: 4,609. Faculty: 280 (91 full-time, 189 part-time). Student-undergrad faculty ratio is 18:1. 1,909 applied, 55% were admitted. Full-time: 2,011 students, 53% women, 47% men. Part-time: 2,598 students, 64% women, 36% men. Students come from 19 states and territories, 21 other countries, 2% from out-of-state. 37% 25 or older, 11% transferred in. Retention: 61% of full-time freshmen returned the following year. Academic area with the most degrees conferred: transportation and materials moving. Core. Calendar: semesters. Academic remediation for entering students, services for LD students, advanced placement, honors program, independent study, distance learning, summer session for credit, part-time degree program, adult/continuing education programs, co-op programs and internships.

Entrance Requirements: Open admission for residents of sponsoring counties. Options: electronic application, early admission, deferred admission. Recommended: minimum 2 high school GPA. Required for some: high school transcript. Entrance: noncompetitive. Application deadline: rolling. Notification: continuous until 8/22. Transfer credits accepted: Yes.

Collegiate Environment: Orientation program. Drama-theater group, choral group, student-run newspaper, radio station. Social organizations: 17 open to all. Most popular organizations: Residence Hall Council, Honors fraternity, student newspaper, student magazine, NMC I-dance. Major annual events: Campus Clean-Up Day, Annual Barbecue, Sweet Earth Arts and Music Festival. Student services: health clinic, personal-psychological counseling. Campus security: 24-hour emergency response devices and patrols, student patrols, late night transport-escort service, controlled dormitory access, well-lit campus. Mark and Helen Osterlin Library plus 1 other. 553 computers available on campus for general student use. A campuswide network can be accessed from student residence rooms and from off campus. Students can access the following: online class registration. Staffed computer lab on campus provides training in use of computers, software, and the Internet.

Community Environment: The Grand Traverse region is the center of Michigan's cherry-growing belt, with Traverse City marketing more cherries than any other city in the country. This is also an important year-round resort area. The temperature averages about 70 degrees in summer. Bus and air transportation are easily accessible. There are many churches, 2 hospitals, 2 libraries, 2 museums, and other major community services. Recreational activities include sailing, golf, hunting, tennis, swimming, water skiing, fishing, bowling, skating, and all winter sports. Concerts and travel lectures are given here, and the National Cherry Festival is an annual event.

■ **NORTHWOOD UNIVERSITY, MICHIGAN CAMPUS**

4000 Whiting Dr.
Midland, MI 48640-2398
Tel: (989)837-4200; Free: 800-457-7878
Fax: (989)837-4490
E-mail: miadmit@northwood.edu
Web Site: www.northwood.edu

Description: Independent, comprehensive, coed. Awards associate, bachelor's, and master's degrees. Founded 1959. Setting: 468-acre small town campus. Endowment: $99.5 million. Educational spending for the previous fiscal year: $6967 per student. Total enrollment: 1,594. Faculty: 141 (49 full-time, 92 part-time). Student-undergrad faculty ratio is 20:1. 1,445 applied, 68% were admitted. 7% from top 10% of their high school class, 20% from top quarter, 52% from top half. Full-time: 1,178 students, 33% women, 67% men. Part-time: 67 students, 46% women, 54% men. Students come from 27 states and territories, 22 other countries, 12% from out-of-state. 0.1% American Indian or Alaska Native, non-Hispanic/Latino; 4% Hispanic/Latino; 6% Black or African American, non-Hispanic/Latino; 0.4% Asian, non-Hispanic/Latino; 0.1% Native Hawaiian or other Pacific Islander, non-Hispanic/Latino; 6% international. 4% 25 or older, 43% live on campus, 10% transferred in. Retention: 78% of full-time freshmen returned the following year. Academic areas with the most degrees conferred: business/marketing; parks and recreation; health professions and related sciences. Core. Calendar: semesters. Academic remediation for entering students, ESL program, services for LD students, advanced placement, accelerated degree program, honors program, distance learning, double major, summer session for credit, part-time degree program, external degree program, adult/continuing education programs, co-op programs and internships. Off campus study. Study abroad program.

Entrance Requirements: Options: electronic application, early admission, deferred admission, international baccalaureate accepted. Required: essay, high school transcript, minimum 2 high school GPA, SAT or ACT. Recommended: 1 recommendation, interview. Entrance: moderately difficult. Notification: continuous, continuous for nonresidents. SAT Reasoning Test deadline: 8/1. Transfer credits accepted: Yes.

Costs Per Year: Application fee: $30. Comprehensive fee: $37,540 includes full-time tuition ($25,710), mandatory fees ($1350), and college room and board ($10,480). College room only: $5460. Full-time tuition and fees vary according to course load and location. Room and board charges vary according to board plan. Part-time tuition: $989 per credit hour. Part-time tuition varies according to course load and location.

Collegiate Environment: Orientation program. Drama-theater group, student-run newspaper. Social organizations: 60 open to all; national fraternities, national sororities, local fraternities, local sororities; 10% of eligible men and 15% of eligible women are members. Most popular organizations: Student Government Association, intramural sports/club sports, United Way, Northwood University International Auto Show (NUTAS), Student Alumni Network. Major annual events: Auto Show/Homecoming, Values Emphasis Week, Go MAD Day. Student services: health clinic, personal-psychological counseling. Campus security: 24-hour emergency response devices and patrols, late night transport-escort service, controlled dormitory access. 868 college housing spaces available; 543 were occupied in 2018-19. Freshmen guaranteed college housing. On-campus residence required in freshman year. Options: coed, men-only, women-only housing available. Strosacker Library. Books: 30,504 (physical); Databases: 26. Weekly public service hours: 89; students can reserve study rooms. Operations spending for the previous fiscal year: $798,500. 215 computers available on campus for general student use. A campuswide network can be accessed from student residence rooms and from off campus. Students can access the following: online class registration. Staffed computer lab on campus.

■ OAKLAND COMMUNITY COLLEGE

2480 Opdyke Rd.
Bloomfield Hills, MI 48304-2266
Tel: (248)341-2000
Fax: (248)341-2099
E-mail: smlinden@oaklandcc.edu
Web Site: www.oaklandcc.edu

Description: State and locally supported, 2-year, coed. Awards certificates, transfer associate, and terminal associate degrees. Founded 1964. Setting: 540-acre suburban campus with easy access to Detroit. Endowment: $1.2 million. Research spending for the previous fiscal year: $1. Educational spending for the previous fiscal year: $3242 per student. Total enrollment: 26,405. Faculty: 1,458 (243 full-time, 1,215 part-time). Student-undergrad faculty ratio is 22:1. 7,672 applied, 100% were admitted. Full-time: 8,058 students, 52% women, 48% men. Part-time: 18,347 students, 59% women, 41% men. Students come from 11 states and territories, 47 other countries, 0.1% from out-of-state. 0.5% American Indian or Alaska Native, non-Hispanic/Latino; 3% Hispanic/Latino; 30% Black or African American, non-Hispanic/Latino; 2% Asian, non-Hispanic/Latino; 0.1% Native Hawaiian or other Pacific Islander, non-Hispanic/Latino; 4% international. 46% 25 or older, 5% transferred in. Retention: 48% of full-time freshmen returned the following year. Core. Calendar: semesters. Academic remediation for entering students, ESL program, services for LD students, advanced placement, independent study, distance learning, summer session for credit, part-time degree program, adult/continuing education programs, co-op programs and internships. Off campus study at Macomb Community College. Study abroad program.

Entrance Requirements: Open admission. Options: electronic application, deferred admission. Entrance: noncompetitive. Application deadline: rolling. Notification: continuous. Transfer credits accepted: Yes.

Costs Per Year: Application fee: $0. Area resident tuition: $2760 full-time, $92 per credit hour part-time. State resident tuition: $5340 full-time, $178 per credit hour part-time. Nonresident tuition: $5340 full-time, $178 per credit hour part-time. Mandatory fees: $200 full-time, $100 per term part-time.

Collegiate Environment: Orientation program. Drama-theater group, choral group. Social organizations: Phi Theta Kappa, Alpha Beta Gamma. Most popular organizations: Phi Theta Kappa, Gamers Guild, BELIEVERS, Criminal Justice Student Organization, Student Government. Major annual events: Welcome Week Resource Fair, Welcome Week Student Organization Fair, Student Life Speaker Series. Student services: personal-psychological counseling, women's center. Campus security: 24-hour

emergency response devices, late night transport-escort service. Main library plus 5 others. Operations spending for the previous fiscal year: $4.1 million. 2,501 computers available on campus for general student use. A campuswide network can be accessed from off-campus. Students can access the following: online class registration. Staffed computer lab on campus provides training in use of computers, software, and the Internet.

Community Environment: Oakland County is composed of both rural and urban towns and has all types of public transportation. Average temperature in winter is 20 degrees, with 70 degrees in summer. The average precipitation is 30 inches. There are good summer and winter sports facilities within the immediate area, with more than 400 lakes nearby. Extensive health services are available.

■ OAKLAND UNIVERSITY

201 Meadow Brook Rd.
Rochester, MI 48309-4401
Tel: (248)370-2100; Free: 800-OAK-UNIV
Fax: (248)370-4462
Web Site: www.oakland.edu

Description: State-supported, university, coed. Awards bachelor's, master's, and doctoral degrees and post-master's certificates. Founded 1957. Setting: 1,444-acre suburban campus with easy access to Detroit. Endowment: $87.1 million. Research spending for the previous fiscal year: $9.8 million. Educational spending for the previous fiscal year: $6765 per student. Total enrollment: 19,333. Faculty: (589 full-time). Student-undergrad faculty ratio is 21:1. 10,296 applied, 84% were admitted. 20% from top 10% of their high school class, 46% from top quarter, 79% from top half. Full-time: 12,549 students, 57% women, 43% men. Part-time: 3,352 students, 52% women, 48% men. Students come from 38 states and territories, 46 other countries, 1% from out-of-state. 0.3% American Indian or Alaska Native, non-Hispanic/Latino; 4% Hispanic/Latino; 7% Black or African American, non-Hispanic/Latino; 5% Asian, non-Hispanic/Latino; 0.1% Native Hawaiian or other Pacific Islander, non-Hispanic/Latino; 2% international. 17% 25 or older, 16% live on campus, 9% transferred in. Retention: 77% of full-time freshmen returned the following year. Academic areas with the most degrees conferred: health professions and related sciences; business/marketing; engineering. Core. Calendar: semesters. Academic remediation for entering students, ESL program, services for LD students, advanced placement, accelerated degree program, self-designed majors, freshman honors college, honors program, independent study, distance learning, double major, summer session for credit, part-time degree program, co-op programs and internships, graduate courses open to undergrads. Off campus study. Study abroad program. ROTC: Air Force (c).

Entrance Requirements: Options: electronic application, deferred admission, international baccalaureate accepted. Required: high school transcript, minimum 2.5 high school GPA, SAT or ACT. Required for some: interview, audition for music, theatre, and dance. Entrance: moderately difficult. Application deadline: rolling. Notification: continuous until 9/1. SAT Reasoning Test deadline: 9/1. SAT Subject Test deadline: 9/1. Transfer credits accepted: Yes.

Collegiate Environment: Orientation program. Drama-theater group, choral group, student-run newspaper, radio station. Social organizations: 322 open to all; national fraternities, national sororities; 3% of eligible men and 5% of eligible women are members. Most popular organizations: Alternative Break, Beta Alpha Psi, Grizz Gang, Meadow Brook Ball Committee, Student Program Board. Major annual events: Welcome Week, Homecoming & Reunion Weekend, WinterFest. Student services: health clinic, personal-psychological counseling. Campus security: 24-hour emergency response devices and patrols, student patrols, late night transport-escort service, controlled dormitory access, state certified police officers, security lighting, extensive camera system, self-defense/alcohol abuse classes. Kresge Library plus 1 other. Books: 499,352 (physical), 648,059 (digital/electronic); Serial titles: 3,674 (physical), 59,485 (digital/electronic); Databases: 234. Weekly public service hours: 168; study areas open 24 hours, 5-7 days a week; students can reserve study rooms. Operations spending for the previous fiscal year: $8.7 million.

Community Environment: This is a suburban community with access to nearby Detroit via Interstate 75, and Michigan Highway 59. The immediate area has a hospital, shopping facilities, Oakland Technology Park, and several churches. Recreation is extensive both on and off campus. On campus cultural opportunities include Meadow Brook Theater, Meadow Brook Music Festival, Meadow Brook Art Gallery, and the Oakland University Center for Performing Arts. In addition, roller rinks, bowling centers, golf courses, Silverdome, the Palace (Home of the Detroit Pistons), theatres, and the local Avon Players offer recreational and cultural activities off campus. There is seasonal part-time employment for students. Special events held annually include Meadowbrook Music Festival in summer and the Christmas Parade; the annual Arts and Apples Festival is in September.

■ OLIVET COLLEGE
320 S Main St.
Olivet, MI 49076-9701
Tel: (269)749-7000; Free: 800-456-7189
Fax: (616)749-3821
E-mail: admissions@olivetcollege.edu
Web Site: www.olivetcollege.edu
Description: Independent, comprehensive, coed, affiliated with Congregational Christian Church. Awards bachelor's and master's degrees. Founded 1844. Setting: 92-acre small town campus with easy access to Lansing, Battle Creek. Endowment: $16.8 million. Educational spending for the previous fiscal year: $5986 per student. Total enrollment: 1,078. Faculty: 90 (44 full-time, 46 part-time). Student-undergrad faculty ratio is 16:1. 2,654 applied, 50% were admitted. Full-time: 951 students, 40% women, 60% men. Part-time: 94 students, 51% women, 49% men. Students come from 17 states and territories, 6 other countries, 6% from out-of-state. 0.3% American Indian or Alaska Native, non-Hispanic/Latino; 5% Hispanic/Latino; 16% Black or African American, non-Hispanic/Latino; 0.5% Asian, non-Hispanic/Latino; 1% international. 2% 25 or older, 71% live on campus, 5% transferred in. Retention: 67% of full-time freshmen returned the following year. Academic areas with the most degrees conferred: business/marketing; homeland security, law enforcement, firefighting, and protective services; biological/life sciences. Core. Calendar: 4-4-1. Advanced placement, self-designed majors, honors program, independent study, double major, summer session for credit, part-time degree program, co-op programs and internships. ROTC: Air Force (c).
Entrance Requirements: Options: electronic application, deferred admission, international baccalaureate accepted. Required: high school transcript, SAT or ACT. Recommended: minimum 2.6 high school GPA. Required for some: essay, interview. Entrance: minimally difficult. Application deadline: rolling. Notification: continuous. Transfer credits accepted: Yes.
Collegiate Environment: Orientation program. Choral group, marching band, student-run newspaper, radio station. Social organizations: 24 open to all; local fraternities, local sororities, Theme houses. Most popular organizations: Minority Association of Premedical Students, Gay-Straight Alliance, Mathletes, OC Association Computing Machinery, Black Student Union. Major annual events: Lecture and Symposium Speakers Series, Service Day, Midnight breakfast. Student services: women's center. Campus security: 24-hour patrols, late night transport-escort service, security cameras in all dorms and campus surveillance. Burrage Library plus 1 other. Books: 61,268 (physical); Serial titles: 211 (physical), 68,401 (digital/electronic); Databases: 14. Students can reserve study rooms. Operations spending for the previous fiscal year: $244,767. 125 computers available on campus for general student use. A campuswide network can be accessed from student residence rooms and from off campus. Students can access the following: online class registration. Staffed computer lab on campus.
Community Environment: Olivet, population 1,789, is located 30 miles south of Lansing and 125 miles west of Detroit.

■ ROCHESTER COLLEGE
800 W Avon Rd.
Rochester Hills, MI 48307-2764
Tel: (248)218-2000; Free: 800-521-6010
Fax: (248)218-2005
E-mail: ssamuels@rc.edu
Web Site: www.rc.edu
Description: Independent, comprehensive, coed, affiliated with Church of Christ. Awards associate, bachelor's, and master's degrees. Founded 1959. Setting: 81-acre suburban campus with easy access to Detroit. Total enrollment: 1,098. Faculty: 167 (38 full-time, 129 part-time). Student-undergrad faculty ratio is 6:1. 361 applied, 100% were admitted. Full-time: 697 students, 57% women, 43% men. Part-time: 368 students, 73% women, 27% men. Students come from 21 states and territories, 5 other countries, 3% from out-of-state. 0.5% American Indian or Alaska Native, non-Hispanic/Latino; 2% Hispanic/Latino; 16% Black or African American, non-Hispanic/Latino; 1% Asian, non-Hispanic/Latino; 2% international. 35% 25 or older, 24% live on campus, 12% transferred in. Retention: 66% of full-time freshmen returned the following year. Academic areas with the most degrees conferred: business/marketing; education; health professions and related

sciences. Core. Calendar: semesters. Academic remediation for entering students, advanced placement, accelerated degree program, independent study, distance learning, double major, summer session for credit, part-time degree program, external degree program, adult/continuing education programs, internships. Off campus study at Macomb Community College, Oakland Community College, Mott Community College, Specs Howard School of Broadcast Arts. Study abroad program.
Entrance Requirements: Options: electronic application, early admission, deferred admission. Required: high school transcript, minimum 2.25 high school GPA, SAT or ACT. Recommended: SAT. Required for some: essay, interview. Entrance: minimally difficult. Application deadlines: rolling, rolling for nonresidents. Notification: continuous, continuous for nonresidents. Transfer credits accepted: Yes.
Costs Per Year: Comprehensive fee: $32,576 includes full-time tuition ($23,996) and college room and board ($8580). Part-time tuition: $730 per semester hour.
Collegiate Environment: Orientation program. Drama-theater group, choral group, student-run newspaper. Social organizations: 3 open to all; local fraternities, local sororities. Most popular organizations: Theatre, Shield Magazine and Shield Online, Image, Student Government. Major annual events: Homecoming, Student Emmys, Ice Cream Olympics. Student services: personal-psychological counseling. Campus security: 24-hour emergency response devices, late night transport-escort service, controlled dormitory access. 338 college housing spaces available; 222 were occupied in 2018-19. Freshmen guaranteed college housing. On-campus residence required through sophomore year. Options: men-only, women-only housing available. Ennis and Nancy Ham Library. Books: 46,238 (physical), 9,510 (digital/electronic); Serial titles: 37 (physical), 30,672 (digital/electronic); Databases: 74. Weekly public service hours: 69. 40 computers available on campus for general student use. A campuswide network can be accessed from student residence rooms and from off campus. Students can access the following: online class registration. Staffed computer lab on campus.
Community Environment: See Oakland University.

■ SACRED HEART MAJOR SEMINARY
2701 Chicago Blvd.
Detroit, MI 48206-1799
Tel: (313)883-8500
Web Site: www.shms.edu
Description: Independent Roman Catholic, comprehensive, coed. Awards associate, bachelor's, and master's degrees. Founded 1919. Setting: 24-acre urban campus. Total enrollment: 466. Faculty: 75 (29 full-time, 46 part-time). Student-undergrad faculty ratio is 6:1. 4 applied, 100% were admitted. 33% from top quarter of their high school class. Full-time: 57 students, 4% women, 96% men. Part-time: 207 students, 53% women, 47% men. 4% from out-of-state. 1% American Indian or Alaska Native, non-Hispanic/Latino; 5% Hispanic/Latino; 4% Black or African American, non-Hispanic/Latino; 3% international. 82% 25 or older, 17% live on campus, 10% transferred in. Retention: 100% of full-time freshmen returned the following year. Academic areas with the most degrees conferred: liberal arts/general studies; theology and religious vocations. Calendar: semesters. Part-time degree program.
Entrance Requirements: Options: early admission, deferred admission. Required: essay, high school transcript, minimum 2 high school GPA, 1 recommendation, interview, SAT or ACT. Entrance: moderately difficult. Application deadline: 8/15. Notification: 8/22. Preference given to candidates for the priesthood. SAT Reasoning Test deadline: 8/15. SAT Subject Test deadline: 8/15.
Collegiate Environment: Orientation program. Choral group. Student services: personal-psychological counseling. Szoka Library.
Community Environment: At the turn of the 20th century, Detroit was a quiet, tree-shaded community brewing beer and producing comfortable carriages and comforting stoves. The serenity was broken by Henry Ford's creation, a vehicle "propelled by power generated from within itself." Today it is the greatest automobile-manufacturing city in the world. It is also rapidly becoming a steel center and a leader in the manufacturing of pharmaceuticals, office equipment, rubber products, salt, television components, synthetic resins and paints, meat products, marine engines, and more than half the garden seed used throughout the country. Annual mean temperature is 49.3 degrees, and annual rainfall is 31.03 inches. Definitely an industrial city, Detroit has a civic center complex on the riverfront, an excellent park system, and numerous museums and art galleries.

■ SAGINAW CHIPPEWA TRIBAL COLLEGE
2274 Enterprise Dr.
Mount Pleasant, MI 48858

Tel: (989)775-4123
Fax: (989)775-4528
E-mail: aflaugher@sagchip.edu
Web Site: www.sagchip.edu
Description: Independent, 2-year, coed. Awards transfer associate and terminal associate degrees. Founded 1998. Setting: small town campus. Total enrollment: 140. Faculty: 22 (8 full-time, 14 part-time). Student-undergrad faculty ratio is 6:1. Full-time: 36 students, 72% women, 28% men. Part-time: 104 students, 67% women, 33% men. 72% American Indian or Alaska Native, non-Hispanic/Latino; 6% Hispanic/Latino; 2% Black or African American, non-Hispanic/Latino. 58% 25 or older. Core. Calendar: semesters. Summer session for credit, part-time degree program.
Entrance Requirements: Open admission. Option: electronic application. Required: high school transcript. Transfer credits accepted: Yes.
Costs Per Year: One-time mandatory fee: $25. Tuition: $1560 full-time, $60 per credit hour part-time. Mandatory fees: $25 per credit hour part-time. Full-time tuition varies according to class time, course level, course load, degree level, location, program, and student level. Part-time tuition and fees vary according to class time, course level, course load, degree level, location, program, and student level.
Collegiate Environment: Orientation program. Saginaw Chippewa Tribal College Library. Books: 2,134 (physical), 12,155 (digital/electronic); Serial titles: 4 (physical); Databases: 1. Students can reserve study rooms. 60 computers available on campus for general student use. A campuswide network can be accessed. Staffed computer lab on campus provides training in use of computers and the Internet.

■ **SAGINAW VALLEY STATE UNIVERSITY**
7400 Bay Rd.
University Center, MI 48710
Tel: (989)964-4000; Free: 800-968-9500
Fax: (989)964-0180
E-mail: admissions@svsu.edu
Web Site: www.svsu.edu
Description: State-supported, comprehensive, coed. Awards bachelor's, master's, and doctoral degrees and post-master's certificates. Founded 1963. Setting: 782-acre small town campus. Endowment: $76.5 million. Research spending for the previous fiscal year: $1.3 million. Educational spending for the previous fiscal year: $5826 per student. Total enrollment: 8,535. Faculty: 721 (288 full-time, 433 part-time). Student-undergrad faculty ratio is 17:1. 7,329 applied, 77% were admitted. 18% from top 10% of their high school class, 43% from top quarter, 76% from top half. Full-time: 6,483 students, 60% women, 40% men. Part-time: 1,256 students, 58% women, 42% men. Students come from 27 states and territories, 36 other countries, 2% from out-of-state. 0.2% American Indian or Alaska Native, non-Hispanic/Latino; 5% Hispanic/Latino; 8% Black or African American, non-Hispanic/Latino; 0.8% Asian, non-Hispanic/Latino; 6% international. 15% 25 or older, 31% live on campus, 6% transferred in. Retention: 77% of full-time freshmen returned the following year. Academic areas with the most degrees conferred: health professions and related sciences; business/marketing; public administration and social services. Core. Calendar: semesters plus summer session. Academic remediation for entering students, ESL program, services for LD students, advanced placement, accelerated degree program, self-designed majors, honors program, independent study, distance learning, double major, summer session for credit, part-time degree program, adult/continuing education programs, co-op programs and internships, graduate courses open to undergrads. Study abroad program.
Entrance Requirements: Options: electronic application, deferred admission, international baccalaureate accepted. Required: high school transcript, minimum 2.5 high school GPA, SAT or ACT. Entrance: moderately difficult. Application deadline: rolling. Notification: continuous. Transfer credits accepted: Yes.
Costs Per Year: Application fee: $30. State resident tuition: $9870 full-time, $329 per credit hour part-time. Nonresident tuition: $23,777 full-time, $792.55 per credit hour part-time. Mandatory fees: $438 full-time, $14.60 per credit hour part-time. Full-time tuition and fees vary according to course level, degree level, location, and program. Part-time tuition and fees vary according to course level, degree level, location, and program. College room and board: $10,186. College room only: $4380. Room and board charges vary according to board plan and housing facility.
Collegiate Environment: Orientation program. Drama-theater group, choral group, marching band, student-run newspaper, radio station. Social organizations: 166 open to all; national fraternities, national sororities, local fraternities, local sororities; 3% of eligible men and 3% of eligible women are

members. Most popular organizations: His House Christian Fellowship, Criminal Justice Society, Delta Sigma Pi, Alpha Phi Omega, International Students Club. Major annual events: Card's Party, Homecoming Week, Battle of the Valleys. Student services: health clinic, personal-psychological counseling. Campus security: 24-hour emergency response devices and patrols, student patrols, late night transport-escort service, controlled dormitory access, Sexual Assault Prevention Program. 2,714 college housing spaces available; 2,667 were occupied in 2018-19. Freshmen given priority for college housing. Option: coed housing available. Zahnow Library. Books: 217,900 (physical), 107,479 (digital/electronic); Serial titles: 127 (physical), 50,164 (digital/electronic); Databases: 63. Weekly public service hours: 92. Operations spending for the previous fiscal year: $2.3 million. 424 computers available on campus for general student use. Computer purchase/lease plans available. A campuswide network can be accessed from student residence rooms and from off campus. Students can access the following: online class registration.
Community Environment: The college has a 782-acre campus located 3 miles south of I-75 on M-84. Combined with this rural atmosphere are urban advantages available in neighboring Saginaw, Bay City and Midland, where tri-county populations total 325,000.

■ **ST. CLAIR COUNTY COMMUNITY COLLEGE**
323 Erie St.
Port Huron, MI 48061-5015
Tel: (810)984-3881; Free: 800-553-2427
Fax: (810)984-4730
Web Site: www.sc4.edu
Description: State and locally supported, 2-year, coed. Part of Michigan Department of Education. Awards certificates, transfer associate, and terminal associate degrees. Founded 1923. Setting: 25-acre small town campus with easy access to Detroit. Total enrollment: 3,625. Faculty: 254 (74 full-time, 180 part-time). Student-undergrad faculty ratio is 19:1. Full-time: 1,415 students, 60% women, 40% men. Part-time: 2,210 students, 62% women, 38% men. Retention: 58% of full-time freshmen returned the following year. Core. Calendar: semesters. Academic remediation for entering students, services for LD students, advanced placement, honors program, independent study, distance learning, summer session for credit, part-time degree program, adult/continuing education programs, co-op programs.
Entrance Requirements: Open admission nursing, radiologic technology and health information technology programs require a secondary application and competitive admissions. Options: electronic application, early admission. Required: high school transcript. Entrance: noncompetitive. Application deadline: rolling. Transfer credits accepted: Yes.
Collegiate Environment: Orientation program. Drama-theater group, student-run newspaper, radio station. Social organizations: 15 open to all; Phi Theta Kappa, International Honor Society. Most popular organizations: Phi Theta Kappa, Business Club, Gay-Straight Alliance, Criminal Justice Club. Major annual events: StressBreaker, Club Awareness Day, Paczki Day. Student services: personal-psychological counseling. Campus security: 24-hour emergency response devices, late night transport-escort service, patrols by security until 10 pm. Main library plus 1 other.

■ **SCHOOLCRAFT COLLEGE**
18600 Haggerty Rd.
Livonia, MI 48152-2696
Tel: (734)462-4400
Fax: (734)462-4553
E-mail: admissions@schoolcraft.edu
Web Site: www.schoolcraft.edu
Description: District-supported, primarily 2-year, coed. Part of Michigan Department of Education. Awards certificates, transfer associate, terminal associate, and bachelor's degrees. Founded 1961. Setting: suburban campus with easy access to Detroit. Total enrollment: 10,558. Faculty: 515 (101 full-time, 414 part-time). Student-undergrad faculty ratio is 23:1. Full-time: 2,955 students, 47% women, 53% men. Part-time: 7,603 students, 56% women, 44% men. 0.6% American Indian or Alaska Native, non-Hispanic/Latino; 5% Hispanic/Latino; 14% Black or African American, non-Hispanic/Latino; 4% Asian, non-Hispanic/Latino; 0.1% Native Hawaiian or other Pacific Islander, non-Hispanic/Latino; 2% international. 31% 25 or older, 23% transferred in. Retention: 62% of full-time freshmen returned the following year. Core. Calendar: semesters. Academic remediation for entering students, ESL program, services for LD students, advanced placement,

honors program, independent study, distance learning, summer session for credit, part-time degree program, internships. Study abroad program.

Entrance Requirements: Open admission. Options: electronic application, early admission, deferred admission. Recommended: high school transcript. Required for some: high school transcript. Entrance: noncompetitive. Application deadline: rolling. Transfer credits accepted: Yes.

Costs Per Year: Application fee: $0. Area resident tuition: $3450 full-time, $115 per credit hour part-time. State resident tuition: $4980 full-time, $166 per credit hour part-time. Nonresident tuition: $7350 full-time, $245 per credit hour part-time. Mandatory fees: $952 full-time, $23 per credit hour part-time, $43 per term part-time.

Collegiate Environment: Orientation program. Drama-theater group, choral group, student-run newspaper. Social organizations: 30 open to all. Most popular organizations: Phi Theta Kappa, The Schoolcraft Connection Newspaper, Student Activities Board, Project Playhem Gaming Club, Otaku Anime Japanese Animation Club. Major annual events: School Daze, Soup Kitchen, Multi-Cultural Fair. Student services: health clinic, personal-psychological counseling, women's center. Campus security: 24-hour emergency response devices and patrols, late night transport-escort service. Bradner Library plus 1 other. Books: 67,778 (physical), 74,201 (digital/electronic); Databases: 147. Students can reserve study rooms.

Community Environment: Livonia is in a suburban area, population 97,977, located 20 miles west of Detroit and is convenient to airports. Good part-time employment opportunities are available for students.

■ **SIENA HEIGHTS UNIVERSITY**
1247 E Siena Heights Dr.
Adrian, MI 49221-1796
Tel: (517)263-0731; Free: 800-521-0009
Fax: (517)264-7745
E-mail: tmohre@sienaheights.edu
Web Site: www.sienaheights.edu

Description: Independent Roman Catholic, comprehensive, coed. Awards associate, bachelor's, and master's degrees. Founded 1919. Setting: 140-acre small town campus with easy access to Detroit, Toledo. Total enrollment: 2,642. Faculty: 268 (85 full-time, 183 part-time). Student-undergrad faculty ratio is 12:1. 1,545 applied, 74% were admitted. 11% from top 10% of their high school class, 38% from top quarter, 66% from top half. Full-time: 1,245 students, 51% women, 49% men. Part-time: 1,157 students, 62% women, 38% men. Students come from 39 states and territories, 30 other countries, 16% from out-of-state. 0.5% American Indian or Alaska Native, non-Hispanic/Latino; 4% Hispanic/Latino; 12% Black or African American, non-Hispanic/Latino; 1% Asian, non-Hispanic/Latino; 0.2% Native Hawaiian or other Pacific Islander, non-Hispanic/Latino; 3% international. 50% 25 or older, 25% live on campus, 5% transferred in. Retention: 63% of full-time freshmen returned the following year. Academic areas with the most degrees conferred: health professions and related sciences; business/marketing; homeland security, law enforcement, firefighting, and protective services. Core. Calendar: semesters. Academic remediation for entering students, ESL program, services for LD students, advanced placement, accelerated degree program, self-designed majors, independent study, distance learning, double major, summer session for credit, part-time degree program, adult/continuing education programs, co-op programs and internships. Off campus study. Study abroad program.

Entrance Requirements: Options: electronic application, deferred admission, international baccalaureate accepted. Required: high school transcript, SAT or ACT. Entrance: moderately difficult. Application deadline: rolling. SAT Reasoning Test deadline: 8/1. Transfer credits accepted: Yes.

Costs Per Year: Comprehensive fee: $37,744 includes full-time tuition ($26,558), mandatory fees ($566), and college room and board ($10,620). Full-time tuition and fees vary according to course load, location, and program. Room and board charges vary according to board plan, housing facility, and location. Part-time tuition: $530 per semester hour. Part-time mandatory fees: $283 per term. Part-time tuition and fees vary according to course load, location, and program.

Collegiate Environment: Orientation program. Drama-theater group, choral group, marching band, student-run newspaper. Social organizations: national fraternities, national sororities. Major annual events: Football Games, Midnight breakfast during exam weeks, Theatre Productions. Student services: health clinic, personal-psychological counseling. Campus security: 24-hour emergency response devices and patrols, student patrols, late night transport-escort service. Siena Heights University Library plus 1 other. 180 computers available on campus for general student use. A campuswide network can be accessed from student residence rooms and

from off campus. Students can access the following: online class registration. Staffed computer lab on campus provides training in use of computers, software, and the Internet.

Community Environment: See Adrian College.

■ **SOUTHWESTERN MICHIGAN COLLEGE**
58900 Cherry Grove Rd.
Dowagiac, MI 49047-9793
Tel: (269)782-1000; Free: 800-456-8675
Fax: (269)782-8414
E-mail: lleone@swmich.edu
Web Site: www.swmich.edu

Description: State and locally supported, 2-year, coed. Awards certificates, transfer associate, and terminal associate degrees. Founded 1964. Setting: 240-acre rural campus. Total enrollment: 2,130. Faculty: 123 (59 full-time, 64 part-time). Student-undergrad faculty ratio is 20:1. 1,928 applied, 99.9% were admitted. Full-time: 880 students, 56% women, 44% men. Part-time: 1,250 students, 62% women, 38% men. Students come from 10 states and territories, 1 other country, 18% from out-of-state. 1% American Indian or Alaska Native, non-Hispanic/Latino; 5% Hispanic/Latino; 12% Black or African American, non-Hispanic/Latino; 2% Asian, non-Hispanic/Latino; 0.1% Native Hawaiian or other Pacific Islander, non-Hispanic/Latino; 0.1% international. 22% 25 or older, 22% live on campus, 5% transferred in. Retention: 48% of full-time freshmen returned the following year. Core. Calendar: semesters. Academic remediation for entering students, ESL program, services for LD students, advanced placement, accelerated degree program, honors program, independent study, summer session for credit, part-time degree program, adult/continuing education programs, co-op programs and internships.

Entrance Requirements: Open admission. Options: electronic application, deferred admission. Required: high school transcript. Required for some: interview. Entrance: noncompetitive. Application deadlines: rolling, rolling for nonresidents. Notification: continuous, continuous for nonresidents. Transfer credits accepted: Yes.

Costs Per Year: Area resident tuition: $3698 full-time, $123.25 per contact hour part-time. State resident tuition: $4845 full-time, $161.50 per contact hour part-time. Nonresident tuition: $5280 full-time, $176 per contact hour part-time. Mandatory fees: $1560 full-time, $52 per contact hour part-time. College room and board: $9450. College room only: $6500.

Collegiate Environment: Orientation program. Drama-theater group, choral group. Social organizations: 20 open to all. Most popular organizations: Agriscience Club, Business Club, Criminal Justice Club, Rock Climbing Club, STEM Club. Major annual events: Campus Bash (fall and spring), Off Campus Student Activities/Trips. Student services: personal-psychological counseling. Campus security: 24-hour emergency response devices and patrols, controlled dormitory access. 402 college housing spaces available; 345 were occupied in 2018-19. No special consideration for freshman housing applicants. Option: coed housing available. Fred L. Mathews Library. Books: 23,473 (physical), 725 (digital/electronic); Serial titles: 4 (physical), 37,873 (digital/electronic); Databases: 49. Weekly public service hours: 61; students can reserve study rooms. 100 computers available on campus for general student use. A campuswide network can be accessed from student residence rooms and from off campus. Students can access the following: online class registration. Staffed computer lab on campus provides training in use of computers, software, and the Internet.

■ **SPRING ARBOR UNIVERSITY**
106 E Main St.
Spring Arbor, MI 49283-9799
Tel: (517)750-1200; Free: 800-968-0011
Fax: (517)750-1604
E-mail: admissions@arbor.edu
Web Site: www.arbor.edu

Description: Independent Free Methodist, comprehensive, coed. Awards associate, bachelor's, and master's degrees. Founded 1873. Setting: 100-acre rural campus. Endowment: $13.3 million. Educational spending for the previous fiscal year: $8125 per student. Total enrollment: 3,404. Faculty: 138 (84 full-time, 54 part-time). Student-undergrad faculty ratio is 13:1. 1,546 applied, 69% were admitted. 23% from top 10% of their high school class, 49% from top quarter, 75% from top half. Full-time: 1,703 students, 66% women, 34% men. Part-time: 732 students, 72% women, 28% men. Students come from 25 states and territories, 10 other countries, 12% from out-of-state. 0.5% American Indian or Alaska Native, non-Hispanic/Latino; 3% Hispanic/Latino; 10% Black or African American, non-Hispanic/Latino; 0.8% Asian, non-Hispanic/Latino; 0.2% Native Hawaiian or other Pacific Islander, non-Hispanic/Latino; 0.6% international. 5% 25 or older, 70% live on campus, 2% transferred in. Retention: 79% of full-time freshmen returned the following year. Academic areas with the most degrees conferred: business/marketing; public administration and social services; health professions and related sciences. Core. Calendar: 4-1-4. Academic remediation for entering students, ESL program, services for LD students, advanced placement, accelerated degree program, self-designed majors, honors program, independent study, distance learning, double major, summer session for credit, part-time degree program, adult/continuing education programs, internships, graduate courses open to undergrads. Off campus study at Christian College Consortium. Study abroad program. ROTC: Army, Air Force (c).

Entrance Requirements: Options: electronic application, early admission, deferred admission. Required: high school transcript, SAT or ACT. Recommended: minimum 2.6 high school GPA, guidance counselor's form, minimum ACT score of 20 or SAT score of 930, ACT. Required for some: essay, interview. Entrance: moderately difficult. Application deadline: 8/1. Notification: continuous, continuous for nonresidents. SAT Reasoning Test deadline: 8/1. Transfer credits accepted: Yes.

Costs Per Year: Application fee: $30. Comprehensive fee: $38,820 includes full-time tuition ($28,210), mandatory fees ($600), and college room and board ($10,010). Full-time tuition and fees vary according to course load, degree level, and program. Room and board charges vary according to board plan and housing facility. Part-time tuition: $685 per credit hour. Part-time tuition varies according to course load, degree level, program, and reciprocity agreements.

Collegiate Environment: Orientation program. Drama-theater group, choral group, student-run newspaper, radio station. Social organizations: 50 open to all. Most popular organizations: Inter-faith Shelter Ministries, Band of Brothers, Action Jackson, Circle of Sisters, Heartside Homeless. Major annual events: Arbor Games, Porchfest, Midnight Breakfast. Student services: health clinic, personal-psychological counseling. Campus security: 24-hour emergency response devices and patrols, student patrols, late night transport-escort service, controlled dormitory access. Hugh A. White Library. Books: 95,739 (physical), 142,749 (digital/electronic); Databases: 49. Students can reserve study rooms. Operations spending for the previous fiscal year: $237,529. 251 computers available on campus for general student use. A campuswide network can be accessed from student residence rooms and from off campus. Students can access the following: online class registration. Staffed computer lab on campus provides training in use of computers, software, and the Internet.

■ UNIVERSITY OF DETROIT MERCY

4001 W McNichols Rd.
Detroit, MI 48221
Tel: (313)993-1000; Free: 800-635-5020
Fax: (313)993-3326
Web Site: www.udmercy.edu
Description: Independent Roman Catholic (Jesuit), university, coed. Awards bachelor's, master's, and doctoral degrees and post-master's certificates. Founded 1877. Setting: 70-acre urban campus with easy access to Detroit, MI. Endowment: $43.9 million. Research spending for the previous fiscal year: $1.3 million. Educational spending for the previous fiscal year: $15,106 per student. Total enrollment: 5,111. Faculty: 770 (337 full-time, 433 part-time). Student-undergrad faculty ratio is 10:1. 3,760 applied, 83% were admitted. 19% from top 10% of their high school class, 47% from top quarter, 81% from top half. Full-time: 2,494 students, 62% women, 38% men. Part-time: 386 students, 63% women, 37% men. 6% from out-of-state. 0.5% American Indian or Alaska Native, non-Hispanic/Latino; 6% Hispanic/Latino; 13% Black or African American, non-Hispanic/Latino; 6% Asian, non-Hispanic/Latino; 0.1% Native Hawaiian or other Pacific Islander, non-Hispanic/Latino; 8% international. 14% 25 or older, 30% live on campus, 8% transferred in. Retention: 83% of full-time freshmen returned the following year. Academic areas with the most degrees conferred: health professions and related sciences; engineering; biological/life sciences. Core. Calendar: semesters. Academic remediation for entering students, ESL program, services for LD students, advanced placement, accelerated degree program, honors program, independent study, distance learning, double major, summer session for credit, part-time degree program, co-op programs and internships, graduate courses open to undergrads. Off campus study at Madonna University, Marygrove College, Sacred Heart Seminary. Study abroad program.

Entrance Requirements: Options: electronic application, early decision, deferred admission, international baccalaureate accepted. Required: essay,

high school transcript, minimum 2.5 high school GPA, SAT or ACT. Recommended: 1 recommendation, interview. Entrance: moderately difficult. Application deadline: rolling. Notification: continuous. SAT Reasoning Test deadline: 8/1. SAT Subject Test deadline: 8/1. Transfer credits accepted: Yes. Early decision applicants: 489. Early decision applicants admitted: 251.

Costs Per Year: Application fee: $0. Comprehensive fee: $38,620 includes full-time tuition ($28,840) and college room and board ($9780). Part-time tuition: $1080 per credit hour.

Collegiate Environment: Orientation program. Drama-theater group, choral group, student-run newspaper, radio station. Social organizations: 74 open to all; national fraternities, national sororities; 3% of eligible men and 4% of eligible women are members. Most popular organizations: Alpha Phi Omega, Biology Club, Chemistry Club, Pre-Dentistry Club, Greek Organizations - NPC, NIC, and NPHC. Major annual events: Midnight Bike Ride, Ultimate Talent Show, Homecoming Casino Night. Student services: health clinic, personal-psychological counseling. Campus security: 24-hour emergency response devices and patrols, student patrols, late night transport-escort service. Freshmen guaranteed college housing. Option: coed housing available. McNichols Campus Library. Books: 468,257 (physical), 175,312 (digital/electronic); Serial titles: 107,735 (digital/electronic); Databases: 84. Weekly public service hours: 80. Operations spending for the previous fiscal year: $1.2 million. 157 computers available on campus for general student use. A campuswide network can be accessed from student residence rooms. Students can access the following: online class registration. Staffed computer lab on campus provides training in use of computers, software, and the Internet.

Community Environment: See Wayne State University.

■ UNIVERSITY OF MICHIGAN

Ann Arbor, MI 48109
Tel: (734)764-1817
Fax: (734)936-0740
Web Site: www.umich.edu
Description: State-supported, university, coed. Awards bachelor's, master's, and doctoral degrees and post-master's certificates. Founded 1817. Setting: 3,207-acre urban campus with easy access to Detroit. Endowment: $11.7 billion. Research spending for the previous fiscal year: $919.7 million. Educational spending for the previous fiscal year: $26,520 per student. Total enrollment: 46,716. Faculty: 3,527 (2,888 full-time, 639 part-time). Student-undergrad faculty ratio is 15:1. 64,917 applied, 23% were admitted. Full-time: 29,245 students, 50% women, 50% men. Part-time: 1,073 students, 38% women, 62% men. Students come from 54 states and territories, 92 other countries, 41% from out-of-state. 0.1% American Indian or Alaska Native, non-Hispanic/Latino; 6% Hispanic/Latino; 4% Black or African American, non-Hispanic/Latino; 15% Asian, non-Hispanic/Latino; 7% international. 2% 25 or older, 31% live on campus, 4% transferred in. Retention: 97% of full-time freshmen returned the following year. Academic areas with the most degrees conferred: engineering; social sciences; computer and information sciences. Calendar: trimesters. ESL program, services for LD students, advanced placement, accelerated degree program, self-designed majors, honors program, independent study, distance learning, double major, summer session for credit, part-time degree program, external degree program, adult/continuing education programs, co-op programs and internships, graduate courses open to undergrads. Off campus study. Study abroad program. ROTC: Army, Naval, Air Force.

Entrance Requirements: Options: electronic application, early action, deferred admission, international baccalaureate accepted. Required: essay, high school transcript, 1 recommendation, SAT or ACT. Required for some: interview, audition for School of Music, Theatre and Dance; portfolio for School of Art and Design, SAT Subject Tests. Entrance: very difficult. Application deadlines: 2/1, 2/1 for nonresidents, 11/1 for early action. Notification: continuous, 12/24 for early action. SAT Reasoning Test deadline: 2/1. Transfer credits accepted: Yes. Applicants placed on waiting list: 14,783. Wait-listed applicants offered admission: 415.

Costs Per Year: Application fee: $75. State resident tuition: $14,934 full-time. Nonresident tuition: $49,022 full-time. Mandatory fees: $328 full-time. College room and board: $11,534.

Collegiate Environment: Orientation program. Drama-theater group, choral group, marching band, student-run newspaper, radio station. Social organizations: 1,300 open to all; national fraternities, national sororities; 12% of eligible men and 25% of eligible women are members. Most popular organizations: Hillel Society, K-Grams (Kids'; Program), M-Powered Entrepreneurial Club, Dance Marathon, Alternative Spring Break. Major annual events: Martin Luther King Day Symposium, FestiFall and Escapade,

Dance Marathon. Student services: legal services, health clinic, personal-psychological counseling, women's center. Campus security: 24-hour emergency response devices and patrols, student patrols, late night transport-escort service, controlled dormitory access. 9,690 college housing spaces available; 9,518 were occupied in 2018-19. Freshmen guaranteed college housing. Options: coed, women-only housing available. Shapiro Undergraduate Library plus 9 others. Books: 12 million (physical), 3.7 million (digital/electronic); Serial titles: 320,457 (physical), 221,979 (digital/electronic); Databases: 4,091. Weekly public service hours: 168; study areas open 24 hours, 5-7 days a week; students can reserve study rooms. Operations spending for the previous fiscal year: $82.2 million. 4,000 computers available on campus for general student use. Computer purchase/lease plans available. A campuswide network can be accessed from student residence rooms and from off campus. Students can access the following: online class registration, file storage, personal Web pages, printing. Staffed computer lab on campus (open 24 hours a day) provides training in use of computers, software, and the Internet.

Community Environment: Predominantly a college community, Ann Arbor also serves as a center for scientific and industrial research and development. Products manufactured in the area include precision instruments, automotive parts, ball bearings, computer components and machine tools. Part-time employment is available for students. Average summer temperature is 79 degrees; winter, 27.8 degrees; average rainfall is 30.7 inches. Average snowfall is 35.3 inches. City has excellent transportation facilities including rail, bus, air service, and expressways out of Detroit. Area offers many cultural and recreational advantages usually found only in a large metropolis. For instance, the Ann Arbor Musical Society provides classical concerts of major world orchestras, chamber music groups and soloists. The Ann Arbor May Festival is an additional musical attraction each year.

■ **UNIVERSITY OF MICHIGAN-DEARBORN**
4901 Evergreen Rd.
Dearborn, MI 48128
Tel: (313)593-5000
E-mail: umd-admissions@umich.edu
Web Site: www.umdearborn.edu
Description: State-supported, comprehensive, coed. Part of University of Michigan System. Awards bachelor's, master's, and doctoral degrees. Founded 1959. Setting: 202-acre suburban campus with easy access to Detroit. Total enrollment: 9,468. Faculty: 546 (355 full-time, 191 part-time). Student-undergrad faculty ratio is 17:1. 7,669 applied, 78% were admitted. Full-time: 5,238 students, 45% women, 55% men. Part-time: 1,947 students, 50% women, 50% men. Students come from 20 states and territories, 26 other countries, 3% from out-of-state. 0.3% American Indian or Alaska Native, non-Hispanic/Latino; 6% Hispanic/Latino; 8% Black or African American, non-Hispanic/Latino; 8% Asian, non-Hispanic/Latino; 0.1% Native Hawaiian or other Pacific Islander, non-Hispanic/Latino; 2% international. 18% 25 or older, 10% transferred in. Retention: 78% of full-time freshmen returned the following year. Academic areas with the most degrees conferred: business/marketing; engineering; psychology. Core. Calendar: semesters. Academic remediation for entering students, ESL program, services for LD students, advanced placement, self-designed majors, honors program, independent study, distance learning, double major, summer session for credit, part-time degree program, adult/continuing education programs, co-op programs and internships, graduate courses open to undergrads. Off campus study. Study abroad program. ROTC: Army, Naval (c), Air Force.
Entrance Requirements: Options: electronic application, deferred admission, international baccalaureate accepted. Required: high school transcript, SAT or ACT. Recommended: minimum 2.5 high school GPA. Entrance: moderately difficult. Application deadline: rolling. Notification: continuous. SAT Reasoning Test deadline: 9/4. Transfer credits accepted: Yes.
Collegiate Environment: Orientation program. Student-run newspaper, radio station. Social organizations: 155 open to all; national fraternities, national sororities. Major annual events: Week of Welcome, MLK Service Day, Homecoming events. Student services: personal-psychological counseling, women's center. Campus security: 24-hour emergency response devices and patrols, late night transport-escort service. College housing not available. Mardigian Library. Books: 189,907 (physical), 662,503 (digital/electronic); Serial titles: 387 (physical), 103,160 (digital/electronic); Databases: 795. Weekly public service hours: 95; students can reserve study rooms. 1,060 computers available on campus for general student use. Computer purchase/lease plans available. A campuswide network can be accessed from off-campus. Students can access the following: online class

registration, tuition and application payments accepted online. Staffed computer lab on campus provides training in use of computers and the Internet.
Community Environment: The university is situated in the middle of a rapidly expanding industrial, residential and social area. Nearby is the Ford Motor Company World Headquarters Complex, the Fairlane Town Center, the Hyatt Regency Hotel and several new apartment and townhouse complexes. Within one hour's driving distance are the cultural opportunities available in Ann Arbor, Meadow Brook Theatre in Rochester, the Michigan Opera Theatre and the Fisher Theatre of Detroit and the various social and cultural events in the city of Dearborn.

■ **UNIVERSITY OF MICHIGAN-FLINT**
303 E Kearsley St.
Flint, MI 48502-1950
Tel: (810)762-3300; Free: 800-942-5636
E-mail: admissions@umflint.edu
Web Site: www.umflint.edu
Description: State-supported, comprehensive, coed. Part of University of Michigan System. Awards bachelor's, master's, and doctoral degrees and post-master's certificates. Founded 1956. Setting: 76-acre urban campus with easy access to Detroit, Lansing. Endowment: $106.3 million. Research spending for the previous fiscal year: $1.2 million. Educational spending for the previous fiscal year: $10,181 per student. Total enrollment: 7,836. Faculty: 573 (326 full-time, 247 part-time). Student-undergrad faculty ratio is 13:1. 4,558 applied, 65% were admitted. 18% from top 10% of their high school class, 43% from top quarter, 80% from top half. Full-time: 3,809 students, 59% women, 41% men. Part-time: 2,625 students, 64% women, 36% men. Students come from 21 states and territories, 27 other countries, 2% from out-of-state. 0.7% American Indian or Alaska Native, non-Hispanic/Latino; 4% Hispanic/Latino; 13% Black or African American, non-Hispanic/Latino; 2% Asian, non-Hispanic/Latino; 0.1% Native Hawaiian or other Pacific Islander, non-Hispanic/Latino; 4% international. 37% 25 or older, 6% live on campus, 11% transferred in. Retention: 77% of full-time freshmen returned the following year. Academic areas with the most degrees conferred: health professions and related sciences; business/marketing; psychology. Core. Calendar: semesters. Academic remediation for entering students, ESL program, services for LD students, advanced placement, accelerated degree program, self-designed majors, honors program, independent study, distance learning, double major, summer session for credit, part-time degree program, adult/continuing education programs, co-op programs and internships, graduate courses open to undergrads. Off campus study at National Student Exchange (NSE). Study abroad program. ROTC: Army (c), Naval (c), Air Force (c).
Entrance Requirements: Options: electronic application, deferred admission. Required: high school transcript, minimum 2.7 high school GPA, SAT or ACT. Entrance: moderately difficult. Application deadline: 8/18. Notification: continuous. SAT Reasoning Test deadline: 6/30. SAT Subject Test deadline: 6/30. Transfer credits accepted: Yes.
Costs Per Year: Application fee: $30. State resident tuition: $11,388 full-time, $450 per credit hour part-time. Nonresident tuition: $22,146 full-time, $895 per credit hour part-time. Mandatory fees: $432 full-time, $216 per term part-time. Full-time tuition and fees vary according to course level, course load, degree level, program, and student level. Part-time tuition and fees vary according to course level, course load, degree level, program, and student level. College room and board: $8769. College room only: $5709. Room and board charges vary according to housing facility.
Collegiate Environment: Orientation program. Drama-theater group, choral group, student-run newspaper. Social organizations: 120 open to all; national fraternities, national sororities, local fraternities, local sororities; 3% of eligible men and 4% of eligible women are members. Most popular organizations: Fraternity and Sorority Life, National Society for Leadership and Success, Psychology Club, Baccalaureate Student Nurses Organization, Student Nurse Practitioner Association. Major annual events: Maize & Blue Days, Campus Activities Board Mega Vegas Night, Family Day. Student services: personal-psychological counseling, women's center. Campus security: 24-hour emergency response devices and patrols, student patrols, late night transport-escort service, controlled dormitory access. Frances Willson Thompson Library plus 1 other. Books: 251,483 (physical), 981,065 (digital/electronic); Serial titles: 1,862 (physical), 163,338 (digital/electronic); Databases: 1,387. Weekly public service hours: 96; students can reserve study rooms. Operations spending for the previous fiscal year: $2.5 million. 512 computers available on campus for general student use. Computer purchase/lease plans available. A campuswide network can be accessed

from student residence rooms and from off campus. Students can access the following: online class registration. Staffed computer lab on campus provides training in use of computers, software, and the Internet.

Community Environment: See Kettering University.

■ **WALSH COLLEGE OF ACCOUNTANCY AND BUSINESS ADMINISTRATION**
3838 Livernois Rd.
Troy, MI 48083
Tel: (248)689-8282; Free: 800-925-7401
Fax: (248)524-2520
Web Site: www.walshcollege.edu

Description: Independent, upper-level, coed. Awards bachelor's and master's degrees. Founded 1922. Setting: 29-acre suburban campus with easy access to Detroit. Endowment: $8.4 million. Research spending for the previous fiscal year: $108,298. Educational spending for the previous fiscal year: $5307 per student. Total enrollment: 2,299. Faculty: 113 (23 full-time, 90 part-time). Student-undergrad faculty ratio is 15:1. Full-time: 78 students, 42% women, 58% men. Part-time: 815 students, 49% women, 51% men. Students come from 8 states and territories, 35 other countries, 0.01% from out-of-state. 2% Hispanic/Latino; 5% Black or African American, non-Hispanic/Latino; 5% Asian, non-Hispanic/Latino; 0.1% Native Hawaiian or other Pacific Islander, non-Hispanic/Latino; 2% international. 59% 25 or older, 99% transferred in. Academic areas with the most degrees conferred: business/marketing; computer and information sciences. Calendar: 4 11-week semesters. Academic remediation for entering students, services for LD students, advanced placement, independent study, distance learning, double major, summer session for credit, part-time degree program, adult/continuing education programs, internships, graduate courses open to undergrads. Off campus study.

Entrance Requirements: Transfer credits accepted: Yes.

Collegiate Environment: Orientation program. Social organizations: 8 open to all. Most popular organizations: Delta Mu Delta, Accounting and Taxation Student Organization, International Student Organization, MBA Association, Walsh College Marketing Association. Major annual events: ISO International Day, Oktoberfest, Welcome Week. Campus security: 24-hour emergency response devices. Vollbrecht Library plus 1 other. Books: 27,985 (physical), 18,425 (digital/electronic); Serial titles: 2,262 (physical), 71,676 (digital/electronic); Databases: 79. Weekly public service hours: 113. Operations spending for the previous fiscal year: $572,708. 400 computers available on campus for general student use. A campuswide network can be accessed from off-campus. Students can access the following: online class registration, Campus Wifi. Staffed computer lab on campus provides training in use of computers, software, and the Internet.

Community Environment: The college is located north of Detroit in the city of Troy, population 81,168. The city serves as headquarters for many large corporations.

■ **WASHTENAW COMMUNITY COLLEGE**
4800 E Huron River Dr.
Ann Arbor, MI 48106
Tel: (734)973-3300
Fax: (734)677-5408
Web Site: www.wccnet.edu

Description: State and locally supported, 2-year, coed. Awards certificates, transfer associate, and terminal associate degrees. Founded 1965. Setting: 235-acre suburban campus with easy access to Detroit. Total enrollment: 12,912. Student-undergrad faculty ratio is 16:1. 1% from out-of-state. 45% 25 or older. Retention: 65% of full-time freshmen returned the following year. Core. Calendar: semesters. Academic remediation for entering students, advanced placement, distance learning, summer session for credit, part-time degree program, external degree program, adult/continuing education programs, internships. Study abroad program. ROTC: Army (c), Naval (c), Air Force (c).

Entrance Requirements: Open admission except for health occupations programs. Options: electronic application, early admission, deferred admission, international baccalaureate accepted. Recommended: SAT or ACT. Required for some: high school transcript. Entrance: noncompetitive. Application deadline: rolling. Notification: continuous. Preference given to county residents for over-subscribed programs.

Collegiate Environment: Orientation program. Campus security: 24-hour emergency response devices and patrols, late night transport-escort service. Media Resource Center.

Community Environment: See University of Michigan.

■ **WAYNE COUNTY COMMUNITY COLLEGE DISTRICT**
801 W Fort St.
Detroit, MI 48226-3010
Tel: (313)496-2600
Fax: (313)961-2791
E-mail: aphilli1@wcccd.edu
Web Site: www.wcccd.edu

Description: State and locally supported, 2-year, coed. Awards certificates, transfer associate, and terminal associate degrees. Founded 1967. Setting: urban campus. Total enrollment: 14,957. Student-undergrad faculty ratio is 17:1. Full-time: 2,005 students, 57% women, 43% men. Part-time: 12,952 students, 66% women, 34% men. 0.2% American Indian or Alaska Native, non-Hispanic/Latino; 2% Hispanic/Latino; 69% Black or African American, non-Hispanic/Latino; 0.6% Asian, non-Hispanic/Latino; 0.1% Native Hawaiian or other Pacific Islander, non-Hispanic/Latino; 0.6% international. 57% 25 or older, 10% transferred in. Core. Calendar: semesters. Academic remediation for entering students, ESL program, services for LD students, advanced placement, honors program, distance learning, summer session for credit, part-time degree program, adult/continuing education programs, co-op programs and internships. Study abroad program.

Entrance Requirements: Open admission. Options: electronic application, early admission, deferred admission. Required: high school transcript. Application deadline: rolling. Transfer credits accepted: Yes.

Collegiate Environment: Orientation program. Campus security: 24-hour emergency response devices. College housing not available. Learning Resource Center.

■ **WAYNE STATE UNIVERSITY**
656 W Kirby St.
Detroit, MI 48202
Tel: (313)577-2424; Free: 877-WSU-INFO
Fax: (313)577-7536
E-mail: admissions@wayne.edu
Web Site: www.wayne.edu

Description: State-supported, university, coed. Awards bachelor's, master's, and doctoral degrees and post-master's certificates. Founded 1868. Setting: 195-acre urban campus with easy access to Detroit. Endowment: $366.7 million. Research spending for the previous fiscal year: $192 million. Educational spending for the previous fiscal year: $12,570 per student. Total enrollment: 27,089. Faculty: 1,740 (1,034 full-time, 706 part-time). Student-undergrad faculty ratio is 16:1. 15,331 applied, 67% were admitted. 19% from top 10% of their high school class, 47% from top quarter, 79% from top half. Full-time: 12,409 students, 56% women, 44% men. Part-time: 4,913 students, 53% women, 47% men. Students come from 39 states and territories, 40 other countries, 2% from out-of-state. 0.2% American Indian or Alaska Native, non-Hispanic/Latino; 5% Hispanic/Latino; 17% Black or African American, non-Hispanic/Latino; 10% Asian, non-Hispanic/Latino; 0.1% Native Hawaiian or other Pacific Islander, non-Hispanic/Latino; 2% international. 21% 25 or older, 13% live on campus, 11% transferred in. Retention: 81% of full-time freshmen returned the following year. Academic areas with the most degrees conferred: business/marketing; psychology; health professions and related sciences. Core. Calendar: semesters. Academic remediation for entering students, ESL program, services for LD students, advanced placement, accelerated degree program, freshman honors college, honors program, independent study, distance learning, double major, summer session for credit, part-time degree program, co-op programs and internships, graduate courses open to undergrads. Off campus study. Study abroad program. ROTC: Army, Air Force (c).

Entrance Requirements: Options: electronic application, deferred admission, international baccalaureate accepted. Required: high school transcript, SAT or ACT. Entrance: moderately difficult. Application deadline: 8/1. SAT Reasoning Test deadline: 8/1. SAT Subject Test deadline: 8/1. Transfer credits accepted: Yes.

Collegiate Environment: Orientation program. Drama-theater group, choral group, marching band, student-run newspaper, radio station. Social organizations: 548 open to all; national fraternities, national sororities, local fraternities, local sororities. Major annual events: Festifall, Late Night Breakfast, International Fair. Student services: legal services, health clinic, personal-psychological counseling. Campus security: 24-hour emergency response devices and patrols, late night transport-escort service, controlled dormitory access, VIN etching, bike patrol, safety and defense classes, K-9 unit, victim assistance, confidential tip line. David Adamany Undergraduate Library plus 5 others. Books: 1.7 million (physical), 1.1 million (digital/electronic); Serial titles: 60,832 (physical), 112,521 (digital/electronic);

Databases: 700. Weekly public service hours: 138; study areas open 24 hours, 5-7 days a week. Operations spending for the previous fiscal year: $19.1 million.

Community Environment: At the turn of the 20th Century, Detroit was a quiet, tree-shaded community brewing beer and producing comfortable carriages and comforting stoves. The serenity was broken by Henry Ford's creation, a vehicle "propelled by power generated from within itself." Today, it is the greatest automobile-manufacturing city in the world. It is also rapidly becoming a steel center and a leader in the manufacturing of pharmaceuticals, office equipment, rubber products, salt, television components, synthetic resins and paints, meat products, marine engines and more than half the garden seed used throughout the country. Annual mean temperature is 49.3 degrees, and annual rainfall is 31.03 inches. Definitely an industrial city, Detroit has a civic center complex on the riverfront, an excellent park system and numerous museums and art galleries.

■ **WEST SHORE COMMUNITY COLLEGE**
PO Box 277, 3000 N Stiles Rd.
Scottville, MI 49454-0277
Tel: (231)845-6211
Fax: (231)845-0207
E-mail: admissions@westshore.edu
Web Site: www.westshore.edu

Description: District-supported, 2-year, coed. Part of Michigan Department of Education. Awards certificates, transfer associate, and terminal associate degrees. Founded 1967. Setting: 375-acre rural campus. Total enrollment: 1,372. Faculty: 100 (28 full-time, 72 part-time). 245 applied, 100% were admitted. Full-time: 658 students, 56% women, 44% men. Part-time: 895 students, 67% women, 33% men. 39% 25 or older, 3% transferred in. Core. Calendar: semesters. Academic remediation for entering students, services for LD students, advanced placement, self-designed majors, independent study, distance learning, summer session for credit, part-time degree program, adult/continuing education programs, co-op programs and internships. Off campus study.

Entrance Requirements: Open admission except for applicants under 18 or nursing program. Options: early admission, deferred admission. Required: high school transcript. Entrance: noncompetitive. Application deadline: rolling. Notification: continuous.

Collegiate Environment: Orientation program. Drama-theater group, choral group, student-run newspaper. Social organizations: 13 open to all. Most popular organizations: Art Club, Student Senate, Phi Theta Kappa, Science Club, Law Enforcement Club. Student services: personal-psychological counseling. Campus security: 24-hour emergency response devices and patrols. West Shore Library plus 1 other. 185 computers available on campus for general student use. A campuswide network can be accessed from off-campus. Students can access the following: e-mail. Staffed computer lab on campus.

Community Environment: Scottville is a rural city located 80 miles northwest of Grand Rapids. Agriculture is the main economic feature of the city with a Stokley canning factory second. Recreation is provided by local Riverside Park, with camping, boating and fishing. In addition, duck and small game hunting is available in the surrounding area. Community services include a library, and five churches. Bus, rail and air transportation are easily accessible.

■ **WESTERN MICHIGAN UNIVERSITY**
1903 W Michigan Ave.
Kalamazoo, MI 49008
Tel: (269)387-1000
Fax: (269)387-2096
E-mail: ask-wmu@wmich.edu
Web Site: www.wmich.edu

Description: State-supported, university, coed. Awards bachelor's, master's, and doctoral degrees and post-master's certificates. Founded 1903. Setting: 1,289-acre urban campus. Endowment: $386.6 million. Research spending for the previous fiscal year: $21 million. Educational spending for the previous fiscal year: $9806 per student. Total enrollment: 22,894. Faculty: 1,451 (926 full-time, 525 part-time). Student-undergrad faculty ratio is 17:1. 14,263 applied, 82% were admitted. 11% from top 10% of their high school class, 33% from top quarter, 70% from top half. Full-time: 15,063 students, 49% women, 51% men. Part-time: 2,873 students, 52% women, 48% men.

Students come from 43 states and territories, 57 other countries, 10% from out-of-state. 0.4% American Indian or Alaska Native, non-Hispanic/Latino; 6% Hispanic/Latino; 12% Black or African American, non-Hispanic/Latino; 2% Asian, non-Hispanic/Latino; 0.1% Native Hawaiian or other Pacific Islander, non-Hispanic/Latino; 4% international. 12% 25 or older, 28% live on campus, 9% transferred in. Retention: 78% of full-time freshmen returned the following year. Academic areas with the most degrees conferred: business/marketing; health professions and related sciences; interdisciplinary studies. Core. Calendar: semesters. Academic remediation for entering students, ESL program, services for LD students, advanced placement, accelerated degree program, self-designed majors, freshman honors college, honors program, independent study, distance learning, double major, summer session for credit, part-time degree program, adult/continuing education programs, co-op programs and internships, graduate courses open to undergrads. Off campus study at Kalamazoo College, Kalamazoo Valley Community College. Study abroad program. ROTC: Army.

Entrance Requirements: Options: electronic application, international baccalaureate accepted. Required: high school transcript, minimum 2.5 high school GPA, SAT or ACT. Entrance: moderately difficult. Application deadline: rolling. Notification: continuous. SAT Reasoning Test deadline: 9/1. SAT Subject Test deadline: 9/1. Transfer credits accepted: Yes.

Costs Per Year: Application fee: $40. State resident tuition: $11,560 full-time, $463.55 per credit hour part-time. Nonresident tuition: $14,450 full-time, $579.44 per credit hour part-time. Mandatory fees: $923 full-time, $258.50 per term part-time. Full-time tuition and fees vary according to course load, location, program, reciprocity agreements, and student level. Part-time tuition and fees vary according to course load, location, program, reciprocity agreements, and student level. College room and board: $10,143. College room only: $5231. Room and board charges vary according to board plan and housing facility.

Collegiate Environment: Orientation program. Drama-theater group, choral group, marching band, student-run newspaper, radio station. Social organizations: 385 open to all; national fraternities, national sororities, local fraternities, local sororities; 6% of eligible men and 8% of eligible women are members. Most popular organizations: Campus Activities Board, Western Student Association, Young Black Male Support Network, Drive Safe Kalamazoo, Alternative Spring Break. Major annual events: Bronco Bash, Homecoming, International Festival. Student services: health clinic, personal-psychological counseling, women's center. Campus security: 24-hour emergency response devices and patrols, student patrols, late night transport-escort service, controlled dormitory access, residence hall security system, engravers for identification of items, free bicycle registration. Waldo Library plus 4 others. Books: 1.8 million (physical), 661,724 (digital/electronic); Serial titles: 936 (physical), 80,141 (digital/electronic); Databases: 638. Weekly public service hours: 106; students can reserve study rooms. Operations spending for the previous fiscal year: $15.6 million. 2,250 computers available on campus for general student use. Computer purchase/lease plans available. A campuswide network can be accessed from student residence rooms and from off campus. Students can access the following: online class registration. Staffed computer lab on campus provides training in use of computers, software, and the Internet.

Community Environment: At one time a gathering place of the Potawatomies, the city received its name from the Indian word meaning "place where the water boils." Today the city is an important paper-manufacturing center with an annual production of over three million tons. The city is also prominent in the manufacture of pharmaceutical drugs. Part-time work is available for students. The largest city in southwest Michigan, Kalamazoo has many parks and picnic areas, 9 golf courses, ski areas, sandy beaches, and good hunting in season. Community service is provided by several churches, 2 hospitals, and shopping malls. The municipal library, art center, civic players, and symphony orchestra provide cultural outlets.

■ **YESHIVA BETH YEHUDA-YESHIVA GEDOLAH OF GREATER DETROIT**
24600 Greenfield
Oak Park, MI 48237-1544
Tel: (248)968-3360

Description: Independent Jewish, comprehensive, men only. Awards bachelor's and master's degrees. Founded 1985. Setting: 1-acre campus with easy access to Detroit. Total enrollment: 64. 27 applied, 100% were admitted. 2% 25 or older.

■ ACADEMY COLLEGE

1600 W 82nd St., Ste. 100
Bloomington, MN 55431
Tel: (952)851-0066; Free: 800-292-9149
Fax: (952)851-0094
E-mail: admissions@academycollege.edu
Web Site: www.academycollege.edu

Description: Proprietary, 4-year, coed. Awards associate and bachelor's degrees. Founded 1936. Setting: urban campus. Total enrollment: 65. Student-undergrad faculty ratio is 8:1. Students come from 4 states and territories, 5% from out-of-state. 2% Hispanic/Latino; 8% Black or African American, non-Hispanic/Latino; 12% Asian, non-Hispanic/Latino. 32% 25 or older. Retention: 100% of full-time freshmen returned the following year. Academic areas with the most degrees conferred: business/marketing; computer and information sciences; transportation and materials moving. Core. Calendar: quarters. Academic remediation for entering students, advanced placement, accelerated degree program, distance learning, summer session for credit, part-time degree program, adult/continuing education programs, co-op programs and internships.

Entrance Requirements: Open admission. Options: electronic application, early admission, deferred admission, international baccalaureate accepted. Required: high school transcript, interview. Entrance: noncompetitive. Notification: continuous.

Collegiate Environment: Orientation program. Learning Resource Center plus 1 other. 25 computers available on campus for general student use. A campuswide network can be accessed. Students can access the following: online class registration. Staffed computer lab on campus.

■ ALEXANDRIA TECHNICAL AND COMMUNITY COLLEGE

1601 Jefferson St.
Alexandria, MN 56308-3707
Tel: (320)762-0221; Free: 888-234-1222
Fax: (320)762-4430
E-mail: info@alextech.edu
Web Site: www.alextech.edu

Description: State-supported, 2-year, coed. Part of Minnesota State Colleges and Universities System. Awards certificates, diplomas, transfer associate, and terminal associate degrees. Founded 1961. Setting: 98-acre small town campus. Total enrollment: 2,483. Faculty: 95 (62 full-time, 32 part-time). Student-undergrad faculty ratio is 20:1. Students come from 18 states and territories, 3% from out-of-state. 2% American Indian or Alaska Native, non-Hispanic/Latino; 2% Hispanic/Latino; 2% Black or African American, non-Hispanic/Latino; 1% Asian, non-Hispanic/Latino. 17% 25 or older. Calendar: semesters. Academic remediation for entering students, services for LD students, advanced placement, self-designed majors, independent study, distance learning, double major, summer session for credit, part-time degree program, internships.

Entrance Requirements: Open admission. Options: electronic application, early admission, deferred admission. Recommended: interview. Required for some: high school transcript, interview. Entrance: minimally difficult. Application deadlines: rolling, rolling for nonresidents. Notification: continuous, continuous for nonresidents. Transfer credits accepted: Yes.

Costs Per Year: Application fee: $20. State resident tuition: $4,816 full-time, $160.53 per credit part-time. Nonresident tuition: $4,816 full-time, $160.53 per credit part-time. Mandatory fees: $600 full-time, $20 per credit part-time.

Collegiate Environment: Orientation program. Social organizations: 5 open to all; Phi Theta Kappa Honor society. Most popular organizations: Student Senate, Intercultural Club, Trapshooting League, GAT (Gamers of Alex Tech), Book Club. Major annual events: Kick Off, Open House, Graduation. Student services: personal-psychological counseling. Campus security: student patrols, late night transport-escort service. College housing not available. Learning Resource Center. Books: 7,582 (physical), 13,367 (digital/electronic); Serial titles: 24 (physical); Databases: 14. Weekly public service hours: 51; students can reserve study rooms. 172 computers available on campus for general student use. Computer purchase/lease plans available. A campuswide network can be accessed from off-campus. Students can access the following: online class registration. Staffed computer lab on campus provides training in use of computers, software, and the Internet.

■ ANOKA-RAMSEY COMMUNITY COLLEGE

11200 Mississippi Blvd. NW
Coon Rapids, MN 55433-3470
Tel: (763)433-1100
Fax: (763)576-5944
E-mail: admissions@anokaramsey.edu
Web Site: www.anokaramsey.edu

Description: State-supported, 2-year, coed. Part of Minnesota State Colleges and Universities System. Awards certificates, transfer associate, and terminal associate degrees. Founded 1965. Setting: 230-acre suburban campus with easy access to Minneapolis-St. Paul. Educational spending for the previous fiscal year: $5013 per student. Total enrollment: 8,874. Faculty: 248 (126 full-time, 122 part-time). Student-undergrad faculty ratio is 32:1. Full-time: 3,386 students, 60% women, 40% men. Part-time: 5,488 students, 61% women, 39% men. 0.5% American Indian or Alaska Native, non-Hispanic/Latino; 5% Hispanic/Latino; 9% Black or African American, non-Hispanic/Latino; 4% Asian, non-Hispanic/Latino; 0.1% Native Hawaiian or other Pacific Islander, non-Hispanic/Latino; 0.5% international. 25% transferred in. Retention: 54% of full-time freshmen returned the following year. Core. Calendar: semesters. Academic remediation for entering students, ESL program, services for LD students, advanced placement, accelerated degree program, honors program, independent study, distance learning, double major, summer session for credit, part-time degree program, co-op programs and internships. Off campus study at other colleges in the Minnesota State Colleges and Universities System; evening courses at area community centers and high schools. Study abroad program. ROTC: Air Force (c).

Entrance Requirements: Open admission for state residents if not in the nursing, pharmacy technology, or physical therapy assistant programs. Options: electronic application, early admission, deferred admission, international baccalaureate accepted. Required for some: high school transcript. Entrance: noncompetitive. Application deadline: rolling. Notification: continuous. Transfer credits accepted: Yes.

Costs Per Year: Application fee: $0. State resident tuition: $4349 full-time, $144.95 per credit part-time. Nonresident tuition: $4349 full-time, $144.95 per credit part-time. Mandatory fees: $724 full-time, $24.12 per credit part-time. Full-time tuition and fees vary according to course load and program. Part-time tuition and fees vary according to course load and program.

Collegiate Environment: Orientation program. Drama-theater group, choral group, student-run newspaper. Social organizations: 50 open to all. Most popular organizations: Student Senate, Swing Dance Club, Concert Choir, Anime Association, Concert Band. Major annual events: Fall Picnic, Spring Picnic, Plays. Student services: health clinic, personal-psychological counseling. Campus security: 24-hour emergency response devices, late night transport-escort service. Coon Rapids Campus Library plus 1 other. Books: 56,573 (physical), 15,450 (digital/electronic); Serial titles: 176 (physical), 71 (digital/electronic); Databases: 30. Weekly public service hours: 63. 728 computers available on campus for general student use. A campuswide network can be accessed from off-campus. Students can access the following: online class registration. Staffed computer lab on campus provides training in use of computers, software, and the Internet.

Community Environment: A suburban area with a temperate climate, Coon Rapids (population 53,000) enjoys all the recreational, social and cultural advantages of the Twin Cities. All forms of commercial transportation are available. Community facilities include churches, a public library and a community hospital nearby.

■ ANOKA TECHNICAL COLLEGE
1355 W Hwy. 10
Anoka, MN 55303
Tel: (763)433-1100
E-mail: enrollmentservices@anokatech.edu
Web Site: www.anokatech.edu

Description: State-supported, 2-year, coed. Part of Minnesota State Colleges and Universities System. Awards certificates, diplomas, transfer associate, and terminal associate degrees. Founded 1967. Setting: 23-acre small town campus with easy access to Minneapolis-St. Paul. Educational spending for the previous fiscal year: $7186 per student. Total enrollment: 1,814. Faculty: 88 (53 full-time, 35 part-time). Student-undergrad faculty ratio is 18:1. Full-time: 832 students, 43% women, 57% men. Part-time: 977 students, 69% women, 31% men. 0.4% American Indian or Alaska Native, non-Hispanic/Latino; 4% Hispanic/Latino; 9% Black or African American, non-Hispanic/Latino; 4% Asian, non-Hispanic/Latino; 0.1% Native Hawaiian or other Pacific Islander, non-Hispanic/Latino; 0.1% international. 55% transferred in. Retention: 49% of full-time freshmen returned the following year. Calendar: semesters. Academic remediation for entering students, ESL program, services for LD students, advanced placement, distance learning, double major, part-time degree program, co-op programs and internships.

Entrance Requirements: Open admission. Options: electronic application, deferred admission, international baccalaureate accepted. Required: high school transcript. Required for some: interview. Entrance: noncompetitive. Transfer credits accepted: Yes.

Costs Per Year: Application fee: $0. State resident tuition: $5009 full-time, $166.97 per credit part-time. Nonresident tuition: $5009 full-time, $166.97 per credit part-time. Mandatory fees: $575 full-time, $19.15 per credit part-time. Full-time tuition and fees vary according to course load, program, and reciprocity agreements. Part-time tuition and fees vary according to course load, program, and reciprocity agreements.

Collegiate Environment: Orientation program. Social organizations: 10 open to all. Student services: personal-psychological counseling. Campus security: 24-hour emergency response devices, late night transport-escort service. Anoka Technical College Library. Books: 7,402 (physical), 8,635 (digital/electronic); Serial titles: 17 (physical), 2 (digital/electronic); Databases: 41. Weekly public service hours: 59; students can reserve study rooms.

■ ARGOSY UNIVERSITY, TWIN CITIES
1515 Central Pky.
Eagan, MN 55121
Tel: (651)846-2882; Free: 888-844-2004
Fax: (952)844-0472
Web Site: www.argosy.edu/locations/twin-cities

Description: Proprietary, university, coed. Part of Education Management Corporation. Awards associate, bachelor's, master's, and doctoral degrees and post-master's certificates. Founded 1961. Setting: suburban campus. Calendar: semesters.

■ AUGSBURG UNIVERSITY
2211 Riverside Ave.
Minneapolis, MN 55454-1351
Tel: (612)330-1000; Free: 800-788-5678
Fax: (612)330-1649
E-mail: vanovers@augsburg.edu
Web Site: www.augsburg.edu

Description: Independent Lutheran, comprehensive, coed. Awards bachelor's, master's, and doctoral degrees. Founded 1869. Setting: 23-acre urban campus with easy access to Minneapolis-St. Paul. Total enrollment:

3,562. Faculty: 369 (174 full-time, 195 part-time). Student-undergrad faculty ratio is 13:1. 3,163 applied, 45% were admitted. Full-time: 2,033 students, 52% women, 48% men. Part-time: 394 students, 65% women, 35% men. 11% from out-of-state. 1% American Indian or Alaska Native, non-Hispanic/Latino; 8% Hispanic/Latino; 13% Black or African American, non-Hispanic/Latino; 9% Asian, non-Hispanic/Latino; 0.1% Native Hawaiian or other Pacific Islander, non-Hispanic/Latino; 3% international. 19% 25 or older, 36% live on campus, 11% transferred in. Retention: 77% of full-time freshmen returned the following year. Academic areas with the most degrees conferred: business/marketing; health professions and related sciences; education. Core. Calendar: semesters for undergraduate programs; trimesters for graduate programs and weekend college. Academic remediation for entering students, ESL program, services for LD students, advanced placement, self-designed majors, freshman honors college, honors program, independent study, double major, summer session for credit, part-time degree program, adult/continuing education programs, co-op programs and internships. Off campus study at Associated Colleges of the Twin Cities. Study abroad program. ROTC: Army (c), Naval (c), Air Force (c).

Entrance Requirements: Options: electronic application, deferred admission, international baccalaureate accepted. Required: essay, high school transcript, 1 recommendation, letter of recommendation from an academic teacher, SAT or ACT. Recommended: minimum 2.75 high school GPA, interview. Entrance: moderately difficult. Application deadline: 8/1. Notification: continuous. SAT Reasoning Test deadline: 8/1. SAT Subject Test deadline: 8/1. Transfer credits accepted: Yes.

Costs Per Year: Application fee: $0. Comprehensive fee: $49,080 includes full-time tuition ($38,150), mandatory fees ($650), and college room and board ($10,280). College room only: $5350. Full-time tuition and fees vary according to class time and location. Room and board charges vary according to board plan and housing facility. Part-time tuition: $1192 per credit hour. Part-time mandatory fees: $174.75 per term. Part-time tuition and fees vary according to class time and location.

Collegiate Environment: Orientation program. Drama-theater group, choral group, student-run newspaper, radio station. Most popular organizations: Pan-Afrikan Student Union, Augsburg Business Organization, Queer Pride Alliance, Students for Racial Justice, Augsburg Asian Student Association. Major annual events: Homecoming, The Snow Show, Advent Vespers/Velkommen Jul. Student services: health clinic, personal-psychological counseling, women's center. Campus security: 24-hour emergency response devices and patrols, student patrols, late night transport-escort service, controlled dormitory access. James G. Lindell Library. Students can reserve study rooms.

Community Environment: Augsburg's campus is located in the heart of the Twin Cities, surrounding Murphy Square, the first of 155 parks in the"City of Lakes." The University of Minnesota West Bank campus and two of the city's largest hospitals, Fairview and St. Mary's, are adjacent to the campus. Downtown Minneapolis and St. Paul are minutes west and east via Interstate 94 which forms the southern border of the campus, or on bus routes that also connect with the suburbs.

■ BEMIDJI STATE UNIVERSITY
1500 Birchmont Dr., NE
Bemidji, MN 56601-2699
Tel: (218)755-2000; Free: 800-475-2001
Fax: (218)755-2074
Web Site: www.bemidjistate.edu

Description: State-supported, comprehensive, coed. Part of Minnesota State Colleges and Universities System. Awards associate, bachelor's, and master's degrees. Founded 1919. Setting: 89-acre small town campus. Total enrollment: 5,189. Faculty: 241 (158 full-time, 83 part-time). Student-undergrad faculty ratio is 21:1. 4,033 applied, 66% were admitted. 11% from top 10% of their high school class, 30% from top quarter, 73% from top half. Full-time: 3,351 students, 55% women, 45% men. Part-time: 1,482 students, 65% women, 35% men. 12% from out-of-state. 3% American Indian or Alaska Native, non-Hispanic/Latino; 2% Hispanic/Latino; 2% Black or African American, non-Hispanic/Latino; 1% Asian, non-Hispanic/Latino; 0.1% Native Hawaiian or other Pacific Islander, non-Hispanic/Latino; 2% international. 27% 25 or older, 28% live on campus, 9% transferred in. Academic areas with the most degrees conferred: business/marketing; health professions and related sciences; education. Calendar: semesters. Part-time degree program, external degree program, adult/continuing education programs.

Entrance Requirements: Options: electronic application, early action, deferred admission, international baccalaureate accepted. Required: high school transcript, SAT or ACT. Required for some: essay, interview. Entrance: moderately difficult. SAT Reasoning Test deadline: 9/1. SAT Subject Test deadline: 9/1.

Costs Per Year: Application fee: $20. State resident tuition: $7630 full-time, $266.45 per credit part-time. Nonresident tuition: $7630 full-time, $266.45 per credit part-time. Mandatory fees: $1066 full-time, $18.11 per credit part-time. College room and board: $8408.

Collegiate Environment: Orientation program. Campus security: 24-hour emergency response devices and patrols, late night transport-escort service, controlled dormitory access. A. C. Clark Library.

Community Environment: A regional home for outdoor sports and cultural arts activities, Bemidji (population 13,000) lies in Minnesota North Country on the shores of Lake Bemidji. This area is noted for its scenic forests and lakes that are enjoyed by recreational enthusiasts during all seasons. From excellent fishing in the summer to cross-country and downhill skiing in the winter, residents and visitors alike have found Bemidji to be a community that satisfies a great diversity of interests.

■ **BETHANY GLOBAL UNIVERSITY**
6820 Auto Club Rd.
Ste. C
Bloomington, MN 55438
Tel: (952)944-2121; Free: 800-323-3417
Web Site: www.bethanygu.edu
Description: Independent Christian, comprehensive, coed. Awards associate, bachelor's, and master's degrees. Founded 1948.

■ **BETHANY LUTHERAN COLLEGE**
700 Luther Dr.
Mankato, MN 56001-6163
Tel: (507)344-7000; Free: 800-944-3066
Fax: (507)344-7376
E-mail: jeff.lemke@blc.edu
Web Site: www.blc.edu
Description: Independent Lutheran, 4-year, coed. Awards bachelor's degrees. Founded 1927. Setting: 50-acre small town campus with easy access to Minneapolis-St. Paul. System endowment: $43.3 million. Educational spending for the previous fiscal year: $13,137 per student. Total enrollment: 739. Faculty: 69 (41 full-time, 28 part-time). Student-undergrad faculty ratio is 9:1. 497 applied, 78% were admitted. 4% from top 10% of their high school class, 40% from top quarter, 71% from top half. Full-time: 593 students, 52% women, 48% men. Part-time: 146 students, 55% women, 45% men. Students come from 25 states and territories, 19 other countries, 24% from out-of-state. 4% Hispanic/Latino; 3% Black or African American, non-Hispanic/Latino; 2% Asian, non-Hispanic/Latino; 10% international. 3% 25 or older, 72% live on campus, 7% transferred in. Retention: 80% of full-time freshmen returned the following year. Academic areas with the most degrees conferred: business/marketing; communication/journalism; biological/life sciences. Core. Calendar: semesters. Academic remediation for entering students, ESL program, services for LD students, advanced placement, self-designed majors, independent study, distance learning, double major, summer session for credit, adult/continuing education programs, co-op programs and internships. Study abroad program. ROTC: Army (c).

Entrance Requirements: Options: electronic application, international baccalaureate accepted. Required: high school transcript, minimum 2.4 high school GPA, SAT or ACT. Recommended: essay, minimum 3.2 high school GPA, interview. Required for some: interview. Entrance: moderately difficult. Application deadlines: 7/1, 7/1 for nonresidents. Notification: continuous, continuous for nonresidents. SAT Reasoning Test deadline: 8/15. SAT Subject Test deadline: 8/15. Transfer credits accepted: Yes.

Costs Per Year: Application fee: $0. One-time mandatory fee: $130. Comprehensive fee: $36,170 includes full-time tuition ($27,400), mandatory fees ($680), and college room and board ($8090). Part-time tuition: $1155. Part-time mandatory fees: $340 per term.

Collegiate Environment: Orientation program. Drama-theater group, choral group, student-run newspaper. Social organizations: 19 open to all. Most popular organizations: Bethany Activities Committee, Student Senate, Scholastic Leadership Society, PAMA (Promoting Awareness, spurring Motivation, and encouraging Action), Bethany Society of Royal Scientists. Major annual events: Spring Formal, Fall Festival, Luthapalooza. Student services: health clinic, personal-psychological counseling. Campus security: 24-hour emergency response devices and patrols, late night transport-escort service, controlled dormitory access. 534 college housing spaces available;

415 were occupied in 2018-19. Freshmen guaranteed college housing. On-campus residence required through sophomore year. Options: men-only, women-only housing available. Memorial Library plus 1 other. Books: 65,787 (physical), 27,706 (digital/electronic); Serial titles: 649 (physical), 224 (digital/electronic); Databases: 90. Weekly public service hours: 88. Operations spending for the previous fiscal year: $284,927. 100 computers available on campus for general student use. A campuswide network can be accessed from student residence rooms and from off campus. Students can access the following: online class registration. Staffed computer lab on campus provides training in use of computers, software, and the Internet.

Community Environment: See Minnesota State University-Mankato.

■ **BETHEL UNIVERSITY**
3900 Bethel Dr.
Saint Paul, MN 55112-6999
Tel: (651)638-6400; Free: 800-255-8706
Web Site: www.bethel.edu
Description: Independent, comprehensive, coed, affiliated with Baptist General Conference. Awards associate, bachelor's, master's, and doctoral degrees and post-master's certificates. Founded 1871. Setting: 289-acre suburban campus with easy access to Minneapolis-St. Paul. Endowment: $47.9 million. Total enrollment: 4,493. Faculty: 287 (168 full-time, 119 part-time). Student-undergrad faculty ratio is 11:1. 2,184 applied, 71% were admitted. 25% from top 10% of their high school class, 55% from top quarter, 84% from top half. Full-time: 2,417 students, 62% women, 38% men. Part-time: 440 students, 63% women, 37% men. Students come from 37 states and territories, 10 other countries, 21% from out-of-state. 0.4% American Indian or Alaska Native, non-Hispanic/Latino; 5% Hispanic/Latino; 5% Black or African American, non-Hispanic/Latino; 4% Asian, non-Hispanic/Latino; 0.1% Native Hawaiian or other Pacific Islander, non-Hispanic/Latino; 0.8% international. 2% 25 or older, 66% live on campus, 3% transferred in. Retention: 85% of full-time freshmen returned the following year. Academic areas with the most degrees conferred: business/marketing; health professions and related sciences; education. Core. Calendar: 4-1-4. Academic remediation for entering students, services for LD students, advanced placement, self-designed majors, honors program, independent study, distance learning, double major, summer session for credit, part-time degree program, adult/continuing education programs, internships. Off campus study at Council for Christian Colleges and Universities. Study abroad program. ROTC: Army (c), Air Force (c).

Entrance Requirements: Options: electronic application, early admission, international baccalaureate accepted. Required: essay, high school transcript, rank in upper 50% of high school class, SAT or ACT. Recommended: minimum 2.5 high school GPA, interview. Required for some: 2 recommendations. Entrance: moderately difficult. Application deadline: rolling. Notification: continuous. Transfer credits accepted: Yes.

Costs Per Year: Application fee: $0. Comprehensive fee: $49,240 includes full-time tuition ($38,300), mandatory fees ($160), and college room and board ($10,780). College room only: $5900. Part-time tuition: $1600 per credit.

Collegiate Environment: Orientation program. Drama-theater group, choral group, student-run newspaper, radio station. Social organizations: 55 open to all. Most popular organizations: Bethel Student Government, Bethel Business and Economics Association, Bethel Rec Sports, Welcome Week. Major annual events: Christmas Formal and Dance, Homecoming Week Events, Airband Competition (annual lip sync competition). Student services: health clinic, personal-psychological counseling. Campus security: 24-hour emergency response devices and patrols, student patrols, late night transport-escort service, controlled dormitory access, video surveillance for residence halls, academic buildings, and parking lots. 1,858 college housing spaces available; 1,610 were occupied in 2018-19. Freshmen guaranteed college housing. On-campus residence required through sophomore year. Bethel University Library plus 1 other. Books: 131,467 (physical), 207,567 (digital/electronic); Serial titles: 748 (physical), 56,439 (digital/electronic); Databases: 126. Weekly public service hours: 96; students can reserve study rooms. Operations spending for the previous fiscal year: $2.4 million. 203 computers available on campus for general student use. Computer purchase/lease plans available. A campuswide network can be accessed from student residence rooms and from off campus. Students can access the following: online class registration. Staffed computer lab on campus provides training in use of computers, software, and the Internet.

■ **BETHLEHEM COLLEGE & SEMINARY**
720 13th Ave. S
Minneapolis, MN 55415

Web Site: www.bcsmn.edu
Description: Independent Baptist, comprehensive, coed.

■ **CAPELLA UNIVERSITY**
225 S 6th St., 9th Fl.
Minneapolis, MN 55402
Tel: (612)252-4200; Free: 866-283-7921
Fax: (612)337-5396
E-mail: info@capella.edu
Web Site: www.capella.edu
Description: Proprietary, upper-level, coed. Awards bachelor's, master's, and doctoral degrees and post-master's certificates (offers only distance learning degree programs). Founded 1993. Setting: urban campus. Total enrollment: 36,375. Full-time: 1,156 students, 57% women, 43% men. Part-time: 6,331 students, 67% women, 33% men. 0.5% American Indian or Alaska Native, non-Hispanic/Latino; 5% Hispanic/Latino; 28% Black or African American, non-Hispanic/Latino; 1% Asian, non-Hispanic/Latino; 0.4% Native Hawaiian or other Pacific Islander, non-Hispanic/Latino; 0.2% international. Academic areas with the most degrees conferred: business/marketing; computer and information sciences; homeland security, law enforcement, firefighting, and protective services. Core. Calendar: quarters. Services for LD students, advanced placement, accelerated degree program, independent study, distance learning, double major, summer session for credit, part-time degree program, adult/continuing education programs, internships. Off campus study.
Entrance Requirements: Transfer credits accepted: Yes.
Collegiate Environment: Orientation program. Capella University Library.

■ **CARLETON COLLEGE**
One N College St.
Northfield, MN 55057-4001
Tel: (507)646-4000; Free: 800-995-2275
Fax: (507)646-4526
Web Site: www.carleton.edu
Description: Independent, 4-year, coed. Awards bachelor's degrees. Founded 1866. Setting: 955-acre small town campus with easy access to Minneapolis-St. Paul. Endowment: $828.2 million. Research spending for the previous fiscal year: $4.2 million. Educational spending for the previous fiscal year: $29,313 per student. Total enrollment: 2,078. Faculty: 261 (212 full-time, 49 part-time). Student-undergrad faculty ratio is 9:1. 6,499 applied, 21% were admitted. 86% from top 10% of their high school class, 98% from top quarter, 100% from top half. 51 National Merit Scholars. Full-time: 2,055 students, 51% women, 49% men. Part-time: 23 students, 65% women, 35% men. Students come from 50 states and territories, 42 other countries, 85% from out-of-state. 8% Hispanic/Latino; 5% Black or African American, non-Hispanic/Latino; 8% Asian, non-Hispanic/Latino; 10% international. 100% live on campus, 1% transferred in. Retention: 96% of full-time freshmen returned the following year. Academic areas with the most degrees conferred: social sciences; physical sciences; computer and information sciences. Core. Calendar: 3 courses for each of three terms. Services for LD students, advanced placement, accelerated degree program, self-designed majors, independent study, double major, internships. Off campus study at Associated Colleges of the Midwest, Higher Education Consortium for Urban Affairs, cooperative programs/St. Olaf College. Study abroad program.
Entrance Requirements: Options: electronic application, early admission, early decision, deferred admission, international baccalaureate accepted. Required: essay, high school transcript, 2 recommendations, Common Application Supplement, SAT or ACT. Recommended: interview, SAT Subject Tests. Entrance: very difficult. Application deadlines: 1/15, 11/15 for early decision plan 1, 1/15 for early decision plan 2. Notification: 3/31, 12/15 for early decision plan 1, 2/15 for early decision plan 2. SAT Reasoning Test deadline: 2/1. SAT Subject Test deadline: 2/1. Transfer credits accepted: Yes. Applicants placed on waiting list: 1,315. Wait-listed applicants offered admission: 41. Early decision applicants: 725. Early decision applicants admitted: 215.
Costs Per Year: Application fee: $30. Comprehensive fee: $68,844 includes full-time tuition ($54,438), mandatory fees ($321), and college room and board ($14,085). College room only: $7398. Room and board charges vary according to board plan.
Collegiate Environment: Orientation program. Drama-theater group, choral group, student-run newspaper, radio station. Social organizations: 328 open to all. Most popular organizations: CANOE (Carleton Association of Nature and Outdoor Enthusiasts), Farm Club, Ebony II, WHIMS (Women in Math and Science), Amnesty International. Major annual events: Halloween

Concert and Masquerade Ball, Spring Concert, Mid-Winter Ball. Student services: health clinic, personal-psychological counseling, women's center. Campus security: 24-hour emergency response devices and patrols, student patrols, late night transport-escort service, controlled dormitory access, Emergency Notification Service (cell phone text and email alerts). Laurence McKinley Gould Library plus 1 other. Books: 499,801 (physical), 640,539 (digital/electronic); Serial titles: 82,879 (digital/electronic); Databases: 31,508. Weekly public service hours: 118. Operations spending for the previous fiscal year: $6.3 million. 250 computers available on campus for general student use. Computer purchase/lease plans available. A campuswide network can be accessed from student residence rooms and from off campus. Students can access the following: online class registration. Staffed computer lab on campus (open 24 hours a day) provides training in use of computers, software, and the Internet.
Community Environment: Northfield (population 18,671), a two-college town, located 40 miles south of Minneapolis and St. Paul, is the home of several major industries that contribute to the prosperity of the community. Part-time employment is limited. Good shopping facilities, library, churches, a hospital and an arts guild are a part of the community. A Carleton - St. Olaf bus also makes round trips daily to the Twin Cities. The Defeat of Jesse James Days in September is a special annual event.

■ **CENTRAL LAKES COLLEGE**
501 W College Dr.
Brainerd, MN 56401-3904
Tel: (218)855-8000; Free: 800-933-0346
Fax: (218)855-8220
E-mail: rtretter@clcmn.edu
Web Site: www.clcmn.edu
Description: State-supported, 2-year, coed. Part of Minnesota State Colleges and Universities System. Awards certificates, diplomas, transfer associate, and terminal associate degrees. Founded 1938. Setting: small town campus. Endowment: $7.3 million. Educational spending for the previous fiscal year: $2993 per student. Total enrollment: 3,715. Faculty: 135 (93 full-time, 42 part-time). Student-undergrad faculty ratio is 20:1. Students come from 26 states and territories, 2% from out-of-state. 21% 25 or older. Retention: 58% of full-time freshmen returned the following year. Core. Calendar: semesters. Academic remediation for entering students, ESL program, services for LD students, advanced placement, independent study, distance learning, summer session for credit, part-time degree program, external degree program, internships. Off campus study at other colleges in the Minnesota State Colleges and Universities System.
Entrance Requirements: Open admission except for nonresidents. Options: electronic application, deferred admission. Required: high school transcript. Entrance: noncompetitive. Application deadline: rolling. Transfer credits accepted: Yes.
Costs Per Year: Application fee: $20. State resident tuition: $4773 full-time, $159 per credit hour part-time. Nonresident tuition: $4773 full-time, $159 per credit hour part-time. Mandatory fees: $675 full-time, $22.50 per credit hour part-time. Full-time tuition and fees vary according to course load and program. Part-time tuition and fees vary according to course load and program.
Collegiate Environment: Orientation program. Drama-theater group, choral group, student-run newspaper. Major annual events: Homecoming, Snow Daze Festival. Student services: health clinic, personal-psychological counseling. Campus security: 24-hour emergency response devices and patrols, student patrols, late night transport-escort service. Learning Resource Center. 100 computers available on campus for general student use. A campuswide network can be accessed. Students can access the following: online class registration. Staffed computer lab on campus provides training in use of computers, software, and the Internet.
Community Environment: One of the state's best developed vacation areas, Brainerd (population 13,684) is on the Mississippi River near the center of the state. The town is the supply point for resorts along 464 lakes within a 25-mile radius of the town. There are opportunities for varied types of sports activities such as fishing, golfing, skiing, snowmobiling and water sports. Other activities include summer theatre, yacht club regatta, antique shows and concerts. Shopping areas, churches, a public library, a hospital and a YMCA are available. Transportation is provided by bus, railway and airlines.

■ **CENTURY COLLEGE**
3300 Century Ave. N
White Bear Lake, MN 55110

Tel: (651)779-3200; Free: 800-228-1978
Fax: (651)779-5810
E-mail: admissions@century.edu
Web Site: www.century.edu

Description: State-supported, 2-year, coed. Part of Minnesota State Colleges and Universities System. Awards certificates, diplomas, transfer associate, and terminal associate degrees. Founded 1970. Setting: 170-acre suburban campus with easy access to Minneapolis-St. Paul. Total enrollment: 8,442. Faculty: 362 (182 full-time, 180 part-time). Student-undergrad faculty ratio is 22:1. 2,807 applied, 100% were admitted. Full-time: 3,641 students, 51% women, 49% men. Part-time: 4,801 students, 59% women, 41% men. Students come from 37 states and territories, 50 other countries, 6% from out-of-state. 0.3% American Indian or Alaska Native, non-Hispanic/Latino; 8% Hispanic/Latino; 10% Black or African American, non-Hispanic/Latino; 18% Asian, non-Hispanic/Latino; 0.1% Native Hawaiian or other Pacific Islander, non-Hispanic/Latino; 2% international. 38% 25 or older, 42% transferred in. Calendar: semesters. Academic remediation for entering students, ESL program, services for LD students, advanced placement, self-designed majors, honors program, independent study, distance learning, double major, summer session for credit, part-time degree program, internships. ROTC: Air Force (c).

Entrance Requirements: Open admission except for dental assistant, dental hygiene, medical assistant, nursing, orthotic and prosthetic clinical applications, paramedic, radiology technology which require special applications and course requirements. Options: electronic application, deferred admission, international baccalaureate accepted. Required: high school transcript. Entrance: noncompetitive. Application deadline: rolling. Transfer credits accepted: Yes.

Costs Per Year: Application fee: $20. State resident tuition: $4,817 full-time, $160.58 per semester hour part-time. Nonresident tuition: $4,817 full-time, $160.58 per semester hour part-time. Mandatory fees: $618 full-time, $20.61 per semester hour part-time. Full-time tuition and fees vary according to class time, program, and reciprocity agreements. Part-time tuition and fees vary according to class time, program, and reciprocity agreements.

Collegiate Environment: Orientation program. Drama-theater group, choral group, student-run newspaper. Social organizations: 47 open to all. Most popular organizations: Anime Club, Phi Theta Kappa, Planning Activities Committee, Spanish Club, Nursing. Major annual events: Student Success Day (fall/spring), Wood Duck Days, Welcome Week. Student services: health clinic, personal-psychological counseling. Campus security: late night transport-escort service, day patrols. Century College Library. Books: 58,410 (physical), 180,870 (digital/electronic); Serial titles: 285 (physical), 39,784 (digital/electronic); Databases: 61. Weekly public service hours: 65; students can reserve study rooms. Operations spending for the previous fiscal year: $1.1 million. 1,570 computers available on campus for general student use. A campuswide network can be accessed from off-campus. Students can access the following: online class registration, D2L. Staffed computer lab on campus provides training in use of computers, software, and the Internet.

■ COLLEGE OF SAINT BENEDICT

37 S College Ave.
Saint Joseph, MN 56374
Tel: (320)363-5011; Free: 800-544-1489
Fax: (320)363-5010
E-mail: admissions@csbsju.edu
Web Site: www.csbsju.edu

Description: Independent Roman Catholic, 4-year, women only. Awards bachelor's degrees (coordinate with Saint John's University for men). Founded 1913. Setting: 300-acre small town campus with easy access to Minneapolis-St. Paul. Endowment: $78.1 million. Research spending for the previous fiscal year: $1.1 million. Educational spending for the previous fiscal year: $12,456 per student. Total enrollment: 1,782. Faculty: 169 (141 full-time, 28 part-time). Student-undergrad faculty ratio is 12:1. 1,931 applied, 83% were admitted. 34% from top 10% of their high school class, 62% from top quarter, 91% from top half. 3 National Merit Scholars. Full-time: 1,764 students. Part-time: 18 students. Students come from 31 states and territories, 9 other countries, 17% from out-of-state. 0.7% American Indian or Alaska Native, non-Hispanic/Latino; 8% Hispanic/Latino; 3% Black or African American, non-Hispanic/Latino; 5% Asian, non-Hispanic/Latino; 0.1% Native Hawaiian or other Pacific Islander, non-Hispanic/Latino; 4% international. 1% 25 or older, 93% live on campus, 1% transferred in. Retention: 89% of full-time freshmen returned the following year. Academic areas with the most degrees conferred: English; psychology; business/marketing. Core. Calendar: semesters. ESL program, services for LD students, advanced

placement, self-designed majors, honors program, independent study, double major, internships. Off campus study at Saint John's University (MN), Saint Cloud State University. Study abroad program. ROTC: Army (c).

Entrance Requirements: Options: electronic application, early action, deferred admission, international baccalaureate accepted. Required: high school transcript, college preparatory program, SAT or ACT. Recommended: minimum 3 high school GPA. Entrance: moderately difficult. Application deadline: 12/15 for early action. Notification: continuous until 10/1, 1/15 for early action. Transfer credits accepted: Yes. Early action applicants: 1,656. Early action applicants admitted: 1,432.

Costs Per Year: Application fee: $0. Comprehensive fee: $56,168 includes full-time tuition ($44,184), mandatory fees ($1080), and college room and board ($10,904). College room only: $5356. Room and board charges vary according to board plan and housing facility. Part-time tuition: $1841 per credit hour. Part-time tuition varies according to course load.

Collegiate Environment: Orientation program. Drama-theater group, choral group, student-run newspaper, radio station. Social organizations: 100 open to all. Most popular organizations: Joint Events Council, Outdoor Leadership Center, Magis Ministries, Enactus, Archipelago Caribbean Association. Major annual events: Involvement Fair, Festival of Cultures, Pines Concert in Spring. Student services: health clinic, personal-psychological counseling, women's center. Campus security: 24-hour emergency response devices and patrols, student patrols, late night transport-escort service, controlled dormitory access. 1,665 college housing spaces available; 1,651 were occupied in 2018-19. Freshmen guaranteed college housing. On-campus residence required through senior year. Option: women-only housing available. Clemens Library plus 2 others. Books: 659,802 (physical), 741,067 (digital/electronic); Serial titles: 798 (physical), 35,878 (digital/electronic); Databases: 226. Weekly public service hours: 104; students can reserve study rooms. Operations spending for the previous fiscal year: $1.5 million. 248 computers available on campus for general student use. Students can access the following: online class registration, online student accounts. Staffed computer lab on campus provides training in use of computers, software, and the Internet.

■ THE COLLEGE OF ST. SCHOLASTICA

1200 Kenwood Ave.
Duluth, MN 55811-4199
Tel: (218)723-6000; Free: 800-249-6412
Fax: (218)723-6290
E-mail: bkarl@css.edu
Web Site: www.css.edu

Description: Independent, comprehensive, coed, affiliated with Roman Catholic Church. Awards bachelor's, master's, and doctoral degrees and post-master's certificates. Founded 1912. Setting: 186-acre suburban campus. Endowment: $89.6 million. Educational spending for the previous fiscal year: $8966 per student. Total enrollment: 4,043. Faculty: 407 (207 full-time, 200 part-time). Student-undergrad faculty ratio is 14:1. 3,808 applied, 66% were admitted. 17% from top 10% of their high school class, 47% from top quarter, 79% from top half. 12 valedictorians. Full-time: 2,062 students, 69% women, 31% men. Part-time: 417 students, 82% women, 18% men. Students come from 49 states and territories, 20 other countries, 13% from out-of-state. 0.8% American Indian or Alaska Native, non-Hispanic/Latino; 4% Hispanic/Latino; 3% Black or African American, non-Hispanic/Latino; 3% Asian, non-Hispanic/Latino; 2% international. 28% 25 or older, 51% live on campus, 15% transferred in. Retention: 80% of full-time freshmen returned the following year. Academic areas with the most degrees conferred: health professions and related sciences; business/marketing; public administration and social services. Core. Calendar: semesters. Services for LD students, advanced placement, accelerated degree program, self-designed majors, honors program, independent study, distance learning, double major, summer session for credit, part-time degree program, adult/continuing education programs, internships, graduate courses open to undergrads. Off campus study at University of Wisconsin-Superior, University of Minnesota, Duluth. Study abroad program. ROTC: Air Force (c).

Entrance Requirements: Options: electronic application, deferred admission, international baccalaureate accepted. Entrance: moderately difficult. Application deadline: rolling. Notification: continuous. SAT Reasoning Test deadline: 9/1. Transfer credits accepted: Yes.

Costs Per Year: Application fee: $0. Comprehensive fee: $48,370 includes full-time tuition ($37,622), mandatory fees ($660), and college room and board ($10,088). College room only: $5602. Part-time tuition: $1175 per credit.

Collegiate Environment: Orientation program. Drama-theater group, choral group, student-run newspaper. Social organizations: 68 open to all. Most popular organizations: Campus Activity Board, Inter-Varsity, Habitat for Humanity, SHIMA, Volunteers Involved Through Action. Major annual events: Mayfest, Fallfest, Homecoming. Student services: health clinic, personal-psychological counseling. Campus security: 24-hour emergency response devices and patrols, late night transport-escort service, controlled dormitory access, student door monitor at night. 961 college housing spaces available; 900 were occupied in 2018-19. Freshmen given priority for college housing. On-campus residence required through sophomore year. Option: coed housing available. College of St. Scholastica Library. Books: 110,578 (physical), 10,442 (digital/electronic); Serial titles: 122 (physical), 208 (digital/electronic); Databases: 227. Weekly public service hours: 91. Operations spending for the previous fiscal year: $357,913. 614 computers available on campus for general student use. A campuswide network can be accessed from student residence rooms and from off campus. Students can access the following: online class registration, student account information, transcripts. Staffed computer lab on campus provides training in use of computers, software, and the Internet.

■ CONCORDIA COLLEGE

901 S 8th St.
Moorhead, MN 56562
Tel: (218)299-4000; Free: 800-699-9897
Fax: (218)299-3947
E-mail: cthorson@cord.edu
Web Site: www.concordiacollege.edu

Description: Independent, comprehensive, coed, affiliated with Evangelical Lutheran Church in America. Awards bachelor's and master's degrees. Founded 1891. Setting: 113-acre suburban campus. Endowment: $111.3 million. Research spending for the previous fiscal year: $319,363. Educational spending for the previous fiscal year: $12,287 per student. Total enrollment: 2,132. Faculty: 246 (167 full-time, 79 part-time). Student-undergrad faculty ratio is 11:1. 3,741 applied, 65% were admitted. 27% from top 10% of their high school class, 55% from top quarter, 82% from top half. Full-time: 2,066 students, 58% women, 42% men. Part-time: 48 students, 71% women, 29% men. Students come from 38 states and territories, 26 other countries, 30% from out-of-state. 0.8% American Indian or Alaska Native, non-Hispanic/Latino; 2% Hispanic/Latino; 2% Black or African American, non-Hispanic/Latino; 1% Asian, non-Hispanic/Latino; 4% international. 1% 25 or older, 62% live on campus, 2% transferred in. Retention: 84% of full-time freshmen returned the following year. Academic areas with the most degrees conferred: education; business/marketing; biological/life sciences. Core. Calendar: semesters. Services for LD students, advanced placement, accelerated degree program, self-designed majors, honors program, independent study, distance learning, double major, summer session for credit, part-time degree program, co-op programs and internships, graduate courses open to undergrads. Off campus study at Tri-College University, Superior Studies Consortium. Study abroad program. ROTC: Army (c), Air Force (c).
Entrance Requirements: Options: electronic application, early admission, deferred admission, international baccalaureate accepted. Required: high school transcript, 2 recommendations, SAT or ACT. Entrance: moderately difficult. Application deadline: rolling. Notification: continuous. SAT Reasoning Test deadline: 8/1. Transfer credits accepted: Yes.
Costs Per Year: Application fee: $20. Comprehensive fee: $48,272 includes full-time tuition ($39,650), mandatory fees ($392), and college room and board ($8230). College room only: $3520. Full-time tuition and fees vary according to course load and degree level. Room and board charges vary according to board plan and housing facility.
Collegiate Environment: Orientation program. Drama-theater group, choral group, student-run newspaper, radio station. Social organizations: 110 open to all. Most popular organizations: Campus Entertainment Commission, Habitat for Humanity, Dance Marathon, Student Government Association, Campus Ministry Commission. Major annual events: Family Weekend, Homecoming, Faith, Reason and World Affairs Symposium. Student services: health clinic, personal-psychological counseling, women's center. Campus security: 24-hour emergency response devices and patrols, controlled dormitory access, well-lighted campus; outdoor campus emergency phones. Carl B. Ylvisaker Library. Books: 347,087 (physical), 134,773 (digital/electronic); Databases: 148. Weekly public service hours: 93; students can reserve study rooms. Operations spending for the previous fiscal year: $1.1 million. 570 computers available on campus for general student use. Computer purchase/lease plans available. A campuswide

network can be accessed from student residence rooms and from off campus. Students can access the following: online class registration, online degree audit. Staffed computer lab on campus provides training in use of software.

■ CONCORDIA UNIVERSITY, ST. PAUL

1282 Concordia Ave.
Saint Paul, MN 55104-5494
Tel: (651)641-8278; Free: 800-333-4705
Fax: (651)659-0207
E-mail: admission@csp.edu
Web Site: www.csp.edu

Description: Independent, comprehensive, coed, affiliated with Lutheran Church-Missouri Synod. Awards associate, bachelor's, master's, and doctoral degrees and post-master's certificates. Founded 1893. Setting: 37-acre urban campus with easy access to Minneapolis-St. Paul. Endowment: $48.3 million. Educational spending for the previous fiscal year: $4561 per student. Total enrollment: 4,792. Faculty: 441 (96 full-time, 345 part-time). Student-undergrad faculty ratio is 18:1. 1,500 applied, 55% were admitted. Full-time: 1,444 students, 54% women, 46% men. Part-time: 1,407 students, 63% women, 37% men. Students come from 50 states and territories, 10 other countries, 26% from out-of-state. 0.4% American Indian or Alaska Native, non-Hispanic/Latino; 4% Hispanic/Latino; 12% Black or African American, non-Hispanic/Latino; 8% Asian, non-Hispanic/Latino; 0.3% Native Hawaiian or other Pacific Islander, non-Hispanic/Latino; 4% international. 49% 25 or older, 26% live on campus, 24% transferred in. Retention: 65% of full-time freshmen returned the following year. Academic areas with the most degrees conferred: business/marketing; parks and recreation; health professions and related sciences. Core. Calendar: semesters. Academic remediation for entering students, services for LD students, advanced placement, accelerated degree program, self-designed majors, independent study, distance learning, double major, summer session for credit, part-time degree program, adult/continuing education programs, internships, graduate courses open to undergrads. Off campus study at University of Minnesota-Twin Cities Campus. Study abroad program. ROTC: Army (c), Air Force (c).
Entrance Requirements: Options: electronic application, early admission, deferred admission, international baccalaureate accepted. Required: high school transcript, 2 recommendations, SAT or ACT. Recommended: minimum 2 high school GPA. Required for some: essay. Entrance: minimally difficult. Application deadline: 8/1. Notification: continuous. Transfer credits accepted: Yes.
Costs Per Year: Comprehensive fee: $31,775 includes full-time tuition ($22,775) and college room and board ($9000). Full-time tuition varies according to degree level and program. Room and board charges vary according to board plan and housing facility. Part-time tuition: $600 per credit. Part-time tuition varies according to course load, degree level, and program.
Collegiate Environment: Orientation program. Drama-theater group, choral group, student-run newspaper. Social organizations: 45 open to all. Most popular organizations: Southeast Asian Student Organization, United Minds of Joint Action. Major annual events: Homecoming, Festival of Beginnings, Christmas Concert. Student services: personal-psychological counseling. Campus security: 24-hour emergency response devices and patrols, student patrols, late night transport-escort service, controlled dormitory access. Library Technology Center. Books: 108,345 (physical), 226,902 (digital/electronic); Serial titles: 917 (physical), 98,931 (digital/electronic); Databases: 178. Weekly public service hours: 74; students can reserve study rooms. Operations spending for the previous fiscal year: $1.1 million. 10 computers available on campus for general student use. A campuswide network can be accessed from student residence rooms and from off campus. Students can access the following: online class registration.

■ CROWN COLLEGE

8700 College View Dr.
Saint Bonifacius, MN 55375-9001
Tel: (952)446-4100; Free: 800-68-CROWN
Fax: (952)446-4149
E-mail: admissions@crown.edu
Web Site: www.crown.edu

Description: Independent, comprehensive, coed, affiliated with The Christian and Missionary Alliance. Awards associate, bachelor's, and master's degrees. Founded 1916. Setting: 215-acre small town campus with easy access to Minneapolis-St. Paul. Endowment: $6.5 million. Educational spending for the previous fiscal year: $3444 per student. Total enrollment: 1,269. Faculty: 160 (33 full-time, 127 part-time). Student-undergrad faculty ratio is 15:1. 838 applied, 56% were admitted. Full-time: 885 students, 55% women, 45% men. Part-time: 203 students, 64% women, 36% men. Students come from 34 states and territories, 11 other countries, 39% from out-of-state. 0.6% American Indian or Alaska Native, non-Hispanic/Latino; 4% Hispanic/Latino; 3% Black or African American, non-Hispanic/Latino; 7% Asian, non-Hispanic/Latino; 3% international. 6% 25 or older, 79% live on campus, 5% transferred in. Retention: 79% of full-time freshmen returned the following year. Core. Calendar: semesters. Academic remediation for entering students, ESL program, services for LD students, advanced placement, accelerated degree program, honors program, independent study, distance learning, double major, summer session for credit, part-time degree program, external degree program, adult/continuing education programs, internships, graduate courses open to undergrads. Study abroad program. ROTC: Army (c).

Entrance Requirements: Options: electronic application, early admission, deferred admission, international baccalaureate accepted. Required: essay, high school transcript, minimum 2 high school GPA, SAT or ACT. Required for some: interview. Entrance: minimally difficult. Application deadline: rolling. Notification: continuous. SAT Reasoning Test deadline: 8/15. SAT Subject Test deadline: 8/15. Transfer credits accepted: Yes.

Collegiate Environment: Orientation program. Drama-theater group, choral group, student-run newspaper, radio station. Most popular organizations: Hmong Student Fellowship, Global Impact Team, Student Activities Board, Student Senate, Storm Chaser Newspaper. Major annual events: Homecoming and Following Regatta, Christmas Dinner/Advent service, Spring Banquet. Student services: health clinic, personal-psychological counseling. Campus security: 24-hour emergency response devices, student patrols, late night transport-escort service, controlled dormitory access. Peter Watne Memorial Library. Operations spending for the previous fiscal year: $362,834. 95 computers available on campus for general student use. A campuswide network can be accessed from student residence rooms and from off campus. Students can access the following: online class registration. Staffed computer lab on campus provides training in use of the Internet.

Community Environment: The College is located in a small community about 20 miles west of Minneapolis.

■ **DAKOTA COUNTY TECHNICAL COLLEGE**
1300 E 145th St.
Rosemount, MN 55068
Tel: (651)423-8000; Free: 877-YES-DCTC
E-mail: admissions@dctc.mnscu.edu
Web Site: www.dctc.edu

Description: State-supported, 2-year, coed. Part of Minnesota State Colleges and Universities System. Awards certificates, diplomas, transfer associate, and terminal associate degrees. Founded 1970. Setting: 100-acre suburban campus with easy access to Minneapolis-St. Paul. Endowment: $3.2 million. Research spending for the previous fiscal year: $193,000. Educational spending for the previous fiscal year: $2670 per student. Total enrollment: 3,672. Faculty: 141 (93 full-time, 48 part-time). Student-undergrad faculty ratio is 30:1. Full-time: 1,690 students, 40% women, 60% men. Part-time: 1,982 students, 40% women, 60% men. Students come from 8 states and territories, 28 other countries, 3% from out-of-state. 0.8% American Indian or Alaska Native, non-Hispanic/Latino; 3% Hispanic/Latino; 7% Black or African American, non-Hispanic/Latino; 3% Asian, non-Hispanic/Latino; 0.8% international. 46% 25 or older, 17% transferred in. Core. Calendar: semesters. Academic remediation for entering students, ESL program, services for LD students, self-designed majors, independent study, distance learning, double major, summer session for credit, part-time degree program, co-op programs and internships.

Entrance Requirements: Open admission. Option: electronic application. Required for some: high school transcript. Entrance: noncompetitive. Application deadline: rolling. Transfer credits accepted: Yes. Applicants placed on waiting list: 250. Wait-listed applicants offered admission: 113.

Collegiate Environment: Orientation program. Social organizations: 16 open to all. Most popular organizations: Phi Theta Kappa International Honor Society, SkillsUSA Minnesota, Multicultural Student Leadership Association, Veterans Club, Automotive Club. Major annual events: Multicultural Day, Spring Fling, College Showcase. Student services: personal-psychological counseling. Campus security: 24-hour emergency response devices, late night transport-escort service. DCTC Library. Operations spending for the previous fiscal year: $427,000. 600 computers available on campus for general student use. A campuswide network can be accessed. Students can access the following: online class registration. Staffed computer lab on campus provides training in use of the Internet.

■ **DUNWOODY COLLEGE OF TECHNOLOGY**
818 Dunwoody Blvd.
Minneapolis, MN 55403
Tel: (612)374-5800; Free: 800-292-4625
Fax: (612)374-4128
E-mail: kobrien@dunwoody.edu
Web Site: www.dunwoody.edu

Description: Independent, primarily 2-year, coed. Awards certificates, terminal associate, and bachelor's degrees. Founded 1914. Setting: 11-acre urban campus with easy access to Minneapolis-St. Paul. Endowment: $22.6 million. Research spending for the previous fiscal year: $85,000. Total enrollment: 1,305. Faculty: 155 (89 full-time, 66 part-time). Student-undergrad faculty ratio is 10:1. 614 applied, 62% were admitted. 8% from top 10% of their high school class, 31% from top quarter, 66% from top half. Full-time: 1,053 students, 15% women, 85% men. Part-time: 252 students, 22% women, 78% men. Students come from 3 other countries, 3% from out-of-state. 0.3% American Indian or Alaska Native, non-Hispanic/Latino; 3% Hispanic/Latino; 5% Black or African American, non-Hispanic/Latino; 7% Asian, non-Hispanic/Latino; 0.2% international. 42% 25 or older, 1% live on campus, 18% transferred in. Retention: 100% of full-time freshmen returned the following year. Academic areas with the most degrees conferred: engineering; business/marketing; visual and performing arts. Core. Calendar: semesters. Academic remediation for entering students, independent study, distance learning, summer session for credit, adult/continuing education programs, co-op programs and internships. Study abroad program.

Entrance Requirements: Options: electronic application, international baccalaureate accepted. Required: interview. Recommended: minimum 2.5 high school GPA. Required for some: 1 recommendation, ACT scores and Resumes, ACT. Entrance: minimally difficult. Application deadline: rolling. Notification: continuous. SAT Reasoning Test deadline: 8/1. SAT Subject Test deadline: 8/1. Transfer credits accepted: Yes.

Costs Per Year: Application fee: $50. Comprehensive fee: $28,753 includes full-time tuition ($21,394), mandatory fees ($1725), and college room and board ($5634).

Collegiate Environment: Orientation program. Social organizations: 22 open to all; Phi Theta Kappa Honor Society. Most popular organizations: Phi Theta Kappa, Historic Green, Dunwoody Motorsports Club, Architectural Institute of America Student Chapter, Professional Association for Design. Major annual events: Fall Fling, Spring Fling, Chili Bowl Cook-off. Student services: women's center. Campus security: 24-hour emergency response devices, late night transport-escort service. College housing not available. Learning Resource Center plus 1 other. Books: 8,000 (physical), 188,153 (digital/electronic); Serial titles: 136 (physical); Databases: 26. Weekly public service hours: 55. Operations spending for the previous fiscal year: $197,263. 300 computers available on campus for general student use. Computer purchase/lease plans available. A computer is required for all students. A campuswide network can be accessed from off-campus. Students can access the following: online class registration.

■ **FOND DU LAC TRIBAL AND COMMUNITY COLLEGE**
2101 14th St.
Cloquet, MN 55720
Tel: (218)879-0800; Free: 800-657-3712
Fax: (218)879-0814
E-mail: admissions@fdltcc.edu
Web Site: www.fdltcc.edu

Description: State-supported, 2-year, coed. Part of Minnesota State Colleges and Universities System. Awards certificates, transfer associate, and terminal associate degrees. Founded 1987. Setting: 31-acre rural campus. Total enrollment: 2,305. Student-undergrad faculty ratio is 29:1. 9% from out-of-state. 21% 25 or older. Core. Calendar: semesters. Academic remediation for entering students, services for LD students, advanced placement, independent study, distance learning, double major, summer session for credit, part-time degree program, external degree program, adult/continuing education programs, co-op programs and internships. Off campus study.

Entrance Requirements: Open admission. Options: electronic application, early admission, deferred admission. Required for some: high school transcript. Entrance: noncompetitive. Notification: continuous until 8/20.

Costs Per Year: Application fee: $20. State resident tuition: $4767 full-time, $158.90 per credit part-time. Nonresident tuition: $4767 full-time, $158.90 per credit part-time. Mandatory fees: $550 full-time, $18.35 per credit part-time. Full-time tuition and fees vary according to program and reciprocity agreements. Part-time tuition and fees vary according to program and reciprocity agreements. College room only: $3458.

Collegiate Environment: Orientation program. Drama-theater group, choral group, student-run newspaper. Student services: personal-psychological counseling. Campus security: 24-hour emergency response devices, late night transport-escort service, controlled dormitory access, video surveillance system. Ruth Meyers Library.

■ **GUSTAVUS ADOLPHUS COLLEGE**
800 W College Ave.
Saint Peter, MN 56082-1498
Tel: (507)933-8000
E-mail: admission@gac.edu
Web Site: www.gustavus.edu

Description: Independent, 4-year, coed, affiliated with Evangelical Lutheran Church in America. Awards bachelor's degrees. Founded 1862. Setting: 340-acre small town campus with easy access to Minneapolis-St. Paul. Endowment: $166.8 million. Research spending for the previous fiscal year: $137,394. Educational spending for the previous fiscal year: $15,909 per student. Total enrollment: 2,201. Faculty: 224 (184 full-time, 40 part-time). Student-undergrad faculty ratio is 11:1. 4,834 applied, 68% were admitted. 33% from top 10% of their high school class, 65% from top quarter, 93% from top half. Full-time: 2,170 students, 56% women, 44% men. Part-time: 31 students, 61% women, 39% men. Students come from 45 states and territories, 26 other countries, 17% from out-of-state. 5% Hispanic/Latino; 2% Black or African American, non-Hispanic/Latino; 5% Asian, non-Hispanic/Latino; 0.1% Native Hawaiian or other Pacific Islander, non-Hispanic/Latino; 5% international. 1% 25 or older, 97% live on campus, 1% transferred in. Retention: 88% of full-time freshmen returned the following year. Academic areas with the most degrees conferred: business/marketing; social sciences; biological/life sciences. Core. Calendar: 4-1-4. Services for LD students, advanced placement, accelerated degree program, self-designed majors, honors program, independent study, double major, co-op programs and internships. Off campus study. Study abroad program. ROTC: Army (c).

Entrance Requirements: Options: electronic application, early admission, early action, deferred admission, international baccalaureate accepted. Required: essay, high school transcript, 1 recommendation. Recommended: interview. Entrance: very difficult. Application deadlines: 4/1, rolling for early action. Notification: continuous, rolling for early action. SAT Reasoning Test deadline: 5/1. Early action applicants: 1,805. Early action applicants admitted: 1,558.

Costs Per Year: Application fee: $0. One-time mandatory fee: $490. Comprehensive fee: $55,010 includes full-time tuition ($44,900), mandatory fees ($200), and college room and board ($9910). College room only: $6300. Room and board charges vary according to board plan and housing facility. Part-time tuition: $7680 per course.

Collegiate Environment: Orientation program. Drama-theater group, choral group, student-run newspaper, radio station. Social organizations: 120 open to all; national fraternities, national sororities, local fraternities, local sororities; 17% of eligible men and 13% of eligible women are members. Most popular organizations: Proclaim, Big Partner/Little Partner, Study Buddies, I am...We are, Pound Pals. Major annual events: Nobel Conference, Christmas in Christ Chapel, Mayday. Student services: health clinic, personal-psychological counseling, women's center. Campus security: 24-hour emergency response devices and patrols, late night transport-escort service, controlled dormitory access. Folke Bernadotte Memorial Library. Books: 326,681 (physical), 53,368 (digital/electronic); Serial titles: 1,126 (physical); Databases: 108. Students can reserve study rooms. Operations spending for the previous fiscal year: $1.8 million. 400 computers available on campus for general student use. A campuswide network can be accessed from student residence rooms and from off campus. Students can access the following: online class registration. Staffed computer lab on campus provides training in use of computers and software.

Community Environment: St. Peter is located 68 miles south of Minneapolis with the usual community facilities. Bus transportation is convenient.

■ **HAMLINE UNIVERSITY**
1536 Hewitt Ave.
Saint Paul, MN 55104-1284
Tel: (651)523-2800; Free: 800-753-9753
Fax: (651)523-2458
Web Site: www.hamline.edu

Description: Independent, comprehensive, coed, affiliated with United Methodist Church. Awards bachelor's, master's, and doctoral degrees and post-master's certificates. Founded 1854. Setting: 60-acre urban campus with easy access to Minneapolis-St. Paul. Total enrollment: 3,526. Faculty: 290 (151 full-time, 139 part-time). Student-undergrad faculty ratio is 13:1. 4,794 applied, 67% were admitted. 17% from top 10% of their high school class, 49% from top quarter, 83% from top half. Full-time: 2,028 students, 62% women, 38% men. Part-time: 78 students, 53% women, 47% men. Students come from 35 states and territories, 34 other countries, 18% from out-of-state. 0.2% American Indian or Alaska Native, non-Hispanic/Latino; 9% Hispanic/Latino; 9% Black or African American, non-Hispanic/Latino; 7% Asian, non-Hispanic/Latino; 0.9% international. 5% 25 or older, 38% live on campus, 6% transferred in. Retention: 74% of full-time freshmen returned the following year. Academic areas with the most degrees conferred: social sciences; business/marketing; interdisciplinary studies. Core. Calendar: 4-1-4. ESL program, services for LD students, advanced placement, self-designed majors, honors program, independent study, distance learning, double major, summer session for credit, part-time degree program, internships, graduate courses open to undergrads. Off campus study at Member of the Associated Colleges of the Twin Cities, American University, and Higher Education Consortium for Urban Affairs. Study abroad program. ROTC: Army (c), Air Force (c).

Entrance Requirements: Options: electronic application, early admission, early decision, early action, deferred admission, international baccalaureate accepted. Required: essay, high school transcript, SAT or ACT. Recommended: 1 recommendation, interview. Entrance: moderately difficult. Application deadlines: rolling, rolling for nonresidents, 11/1 for early decision, 12/1 for early action. Notification: continuous, continuous for nonresidents, 11/15 for early decision, rolling for early action. SAT Reasoning Test deadline: 6/30. SAT Subject Test deadline: 6/30. Transfer credits accepted: Yes. Early decision applicants: 19. Early decision applicants admitted: 18.

Costs Per Year: Application fee: $0. Comprehensive fee: $53,366 includes full-time tuition ($41,734), mandatory fees ($1040), and college room and board ($10,592). College room only: $5150. Part-time tuition: $1304 per credit hour. Part-time mandatory fees: $806 per year.

Collegiate Environment: Orientation program. Drama-theater group, choral group, student-run newspaper, radio station. Social organizations: 65 open to all; national fraternities, national sororities. Most popular organizations: Hamline Undergraduate Student Congress (HUSC), Hamline University Programming Board (HUPB), Black Student Collective (BSC), Feed Your Brain Campaign (FYB), Asian Pacific American Coalition (APAC). Major annual events: Annual Lip Sync Competition, Late Night Study Break, End of the Year Party. Student services: health clinic, personal-psychological counseling, women's center. Campus security: 24-hour emergency response devices and patrols, student patrols, late night transport-escort service, controlled dormitory access. 847 college housing spaces available; 725 were occupied in 2018-19. Freshmen guaranteed college housing. Option: coed housing available. Bush Library. Books: 125,914 (physical), 476,812 (digital/electronic); Serial titles: 807 (physical), 67,981 (digital/electronic); Databases: 113. Students can reserve study rooms. 300 computers available on campus for general student use. A campuswide network can be accessed from student residence rooms and from off campus. Students can access the following: online class registration. Staffed computer lab on campus provides training in use of computers, software, and the Internet.

■ **HENNEPIN TECHNICAL COLLEGE**
9000 Brooklyn Blvd.
Brooklyn Park, MN 55445
Tel: (952)995-1300; Free: 800-645-4655
Fax: (763)488-2944
E-mail: info@hennepintech.edu
Web Site: www.hennepintech.edu

Description: State-supported, 2-year, coed. Part of Minnesota State Colleges and Universities System. Awards certificates, diplomas, transfer associate, and terminal associate degrees. Founded 1972. Setting: 100-acre suburban campus with easy access to Minneapolis-St. Paul. Endowment: $942,735. Educational spending for the previous fiscal year: $6930 per student. Total enrollment: 5,299. Faculty: 235 (116 full-time, 119 part-time). Student-undergrad faculty ratio is 21:1. 1,987 applied, 100% were admitted. 4% from out-of-state. 0.5% American Indian or Alaska Native, non-Hispanic/Latino; 8% Hispanic/Latino; 23% Black or African American, non-Hispanic/Latino; 10% Asian, non-Hispanic/Latino; 0.1% Native Hawaiian or other Pacific Islander, non-Hispanic/Latino; 0.3% international. 57% 25 or older. Core. Calendar: semesters. Academic remediation for entering students, ESL program, services for LD students, advanced placement, self-designed majors, independent study, distance learning, double major, summer session for credit, part-time degree program, adult/continuing education programs, co-op programs and internships.

Entrance Requirements: Open admission. Options: electronic application, international baccalaureate accepted. Recommended: high school transcript. Entrance: noncompetitive. Application deadline: rolling. Notification: continuous. Transfer credits accepted: Yes.

Collegiate Environment: Orientation program. Most popular organizations: Student Senate, SkillsUSA, Student Nurses Who Care, Veterans. Major annual events: International Festival, College Success Day. Student services: personal-psychological counseling. Campus security: late night transport-escort service, security service. Hennepin Technical College Library plus 1 other. Books: 10,784 (physical), 215,854 (digital/electronic); Serial titles: 30 (physical); Databases: 48. Weekly public service hours: 60. Operations spending for the previous fiscal year: $252,378. 100 computers available on campus for general student use. A campuswide network can be accessed. Students can access the following: online class registration. Staffed computer lab on campus provides training in use of computers, software, and the Internet.

■ **HERZING UNIVERSITY**
5700 W Broadway
Minneapolis, MN 55428
Tel: (763)535-3000; Free: 800-596-0724
Fax: (763)535-9205
E-mail: info@mpls.herzing.edu
Web Site: www.herzing.edu/minneapolis
Description: Independent, primarily 2-year, coed. Part of Herzing College. Awards certificates, diplomas, terminal associate, and bachelor's degrees. Founded 1961. Setting: 1-acre suburban campus. Total enrollment: 270. Faculty: 32 (21 full-time, 11 part-time). Student-undergrad faculty ratio is 14:1. 128 applied, 75% were admitted. Full-time: 242 students, 93% women, 7% men. Part-time: 28 students, 89% women, 11% men. Students come from 3 states and territories, 1% from out-of-state. 43% 25 or older. Core. Calendar: semesters. Distance learning, part-time degree program, adult/continuing education programs, internships.
Entrance Requirements: Open admission. Required: high school transcript, interview, ACCUPLACER.
Collegiate Environment: Orientation program. Major annual event: Dental Assistants State Convention. Student services: personal-psychological counseling. Campus security: 24-hour emergency response devices. Main library plus 1 other. Operations spending for the previous fiscal year: $53,173. 50 computers available on campus for general student use. Staffed computer lab on campus.

■ **HIBBING COMMUNITY COLLEGE**
1515 E 25th St.
Hibbing, MN 55746-3300
Tel: (218)262-7200; Free: 800-224-4HCC
E-mail: admissions@hibbing.edu
Web Site: www.hcc.mnscu.edu
Description: State-supported, 2-year, coed. Part of Minnesota State Colleges and Universities System. Awards certificates, diplomas, transfer associate, and terminal associate degrees. Founded 1916. Setting: 100-acre small town campus. Total enrollment: 1,596. Student-undergrad faculty ratio is 17:1. 3% from out-of-state. 44% 25 or older. Core. Calendar: semesters. Academic remediation for entering students, services for LD students, advanced placement, distance learning, summer session for credit, part-time degree program, adult/continuing education programs, co-op programs and internships. Off campus study at other colleges in the Minnesota State Colleges and Universities System. Study abroad program.
Entrance Requirements: Open admission except for nursing, law enforcement programs. Options: early admission, deferred admission. Required: high school transcript. Entrance: noncompetitive. Application deadline: rolling. Notification: continuous.
Collegiate Environment: Orientation program. Drama-theater group, choral group, marching band. Student services: personal-psychological counseling. Campus security: late night transport-escort service. Hibbing Community College Library.
Community Environment: Hibbing (population 16,500) is the largest of the Mesabi Range towns where there are many open pits for mining ore. Located 70 miles from Duluth, plants in the area mine taconite, an ore-bearing rock that yields a rich iron ore concentrate when processed. The community facilities include a library, churches of major denominations, a

hospital, 3 clinics, and shopping areas. Some part-time employment is available. Recreational activities include bowling, hunting, skiing, snowmobiling, fishing, tennis, water sports and curling. Points of interest are the Hibbing-Chisholm Pit Crossing Route and the Hull-Rust-Mahoning Mine. The Last Chance International Curling Bonspeil and the Winter Carnival are annual events.

■ **THE INSTITUTE OF PRODUCTION AND RECORDING**
300 N 1st Ave.
Ste. 500
Minneapolis, MN 55401
Tel: (612)244-2800
Web Site: www.ipr.edu
Description: Proprietary, 2-year, coed. Part of Globe Education Network (GEN). Awards terminal associate degrees. Setting: 4-acre urban campus with easy access to Minneapolis-St. Paul. Total enrollment: 242. Faculty: 40 (15 full-time, 25 part-time). Full-time: 153 students, 10% women, 90% men. Part-time: 89 students, 11% women, 89% men. Students come from 20 states and territories, 24% from out-of-state. 0.4% American Indian or Alaska Native, non-Hispanic/Latino; 5% Hispanic/Latino; 10% Black or African American, non-Hispanic/Latino; 2% Asian, non-Hispanic/Latino; 0.4% Native Hawaiian or other Pacific Islander, non-Hispanic/Latino; 0.4% international. 27% 25 or older, 15% transferred in. Core. Academic remediation for entering students, services for LD students, advanced placement, accelerated degree program, independent study, summer session for credit, part-time degree program, adult/continuing education programs, internships. Off campus study at Globe Education Network, including Broadview University, Duluth Business University, Globe University, Minnesota School of Business, Minnesota School of Cosmetology, and The Institute of Production and Recording.
Entrance Requirements: Option: electronic application. Required: high school transcript, interview, ACCUPLACER is required of most applicants unless documentation of a minimum ACT composite score of 21 or documentation of a minimum composite score of 1485 on the SAT is presented. Application deadline: rolling. Notification: continuous. Transfer credits accepted: Yes.
Collegiate Environment: Orientation program. Campus security: 24-hour emergency response devices. Institute of Production and Recording Campus Library.

■ **INVER HILLS COMMUNITY COLLEGE**
2500 E 80th St.
Inver Grove Heights, MN 55076-3224
Tel: (651)450-8500
Fax: (651)450-8677
E-mail: admissions@inverhills.edu
Web Site: www.inverhills.edu
Description: State-supported, 2-year, coed. Part of Minnesota State Colleges and Universities System. Awards certificates, transfer associate, and terminal associate degrees. Founded 1969. Setting: 100-acre suburban campus with easy access to Minneapolis-St. Paul. Total enrollment: 6,342. Faculty: 226 (105 full-time, 121 part-time). 1,002 applied, 98% were admitted. Full-time: 2,502 students, 53% women, 47% men. Part-time: 3,840 students, 64% women, 36% men. Students come from 19 states and territories, 2% from out-of-state. 1% American Indian or Alaska Native, non-Hispanic/Latino; 5% Hispanic/Latino; 11% Black or African American, non-Hispanic/Latino; 6% Asian, non-Hispanic/Latino; 0.3% Native Hawaiian or other Pacific Islander, non-Hispanic/Latino; 0.6% international. 43% 25 or older, 5% transferred in. Core. Calendar: semesters. Academic remediation for entering students, ESL program, services for LD students, advanced placement, accelerated degree program, honors program, independent study, distance learning, summer session for credit, part-time degree program, external degree program, co-op programs and internships. Off campus study at other colleges in the Minnesota State Colleges and Universities System. ROTC: Army (c), Air Force (c).
Entrance Requirements: Open admission except for nursing, emergency medical technology programs. Options: electronic application, international baccalaureate accepted. Recommended: high school transcript. Required for some: high school transcript. Entrance: noncompetitive. Application deadline: 8/15. Notification: continuous. Transfer credits accepted: Yes.
Collegiate Environment: Orientation program. Drama-theater group, choral group. Most popular organizations: VIBE, Student Senate, Health Service Student Association, Phi Theta Kappa, Nursing Club. Major annual events: Student Success Day, Spring Fling, Kick-Off Day. Student services: health

clinic, personal-psychological counseling. Campus security: late night transport-escort service, evening police patrol. 1,400 computers available on campus for general student use. A campuswide network can be accessed. Students can access the following: online class registration. Staffed computer lab on campus (open 24 hours a day) provides training in use of computers, software, and the Internet.

Community Environment: See Bethel College.

■ **ITASCA COMMUNITY COLLEGE**
1851 Hwy. 169 E
Grand Rapids, MN 55744
Tel: (218)322-2300; Free: 800-996-6422
Fax: (218)327-4350
E-mail: iccinfo@itascacc.edu
Web Site: www.itascacc.edu

Description: State-supported, 2-year, coed. Part of Minnesota State Colleges and Universities System, Northeastern Higher Education District. Awards certificates, diplomas, transfer associate, and terminal associate degrees. Founded 1922. Setting: 24-acre rural campus. Endowment: $4 million. Total enrollment: 1,299. Faculty: 77 (43 full-time, 34 part-time). Student-undergrad faculty ratio is 17:1. 946 applied, 100% were admitted. Students come from 2 other countries, 4% from out-of-state. 4% American Indian or Alaska Native, non-Hispanic/Latino; 0.4% Hispanic/Latino; 3% Black or African American, non-Hispanic/Latino; 0.5% Asian, non-Hispanic/Latino; 0.2% Native Hawaiian or other Pacific Islander, non-Hispanic/Latino. 28% 25 or older, 10% live on campus. Retention: 53% of full-time freshmen returned the following year. Core. Calendar: semesters. Academic remediation for entering students, services for LD students, advanced placement, independent study, double major, summer session for credit, part-time degree program, adult/continuing education programs, co-op programs and internships. Off campus study. Study abroad program.

Entrance Requirements: Open admission. Options: electronic application, international baccalaureate accepted. Required: high school transcript. Entrance: noncompetitive. Application deadline: 8/20. Notification: continuous.

Costs Per Year: Application fee: $0. State resident tuition: $5,324 full-time, $177.47 per credit hour part-time. Nonresident tuition: $6,506 full-time, $216.87 per credit hour part-time. Mandatory fees: $596 full-time, $19.85 per credit hour part-time. Full-time tuition and fees vary according to course load, program, and reciprocity agreements. Part-time tuition and fees vary according to course load, program, and reciprocity agreements. College room and board: $5920. College room only: $4520. Room and board charges vary according to board plan.

Collegiate Environment: Orientation program. Social organizations: 20 open to all. Most popular organizations: Student Association, Circle K, Student Ambassadors, Minority Student Club, Psychology Club. Major annual events: Free Christmas Dinner, Marker Dance, Rock and Bowl. Campus security: student patrols, late night transport-escort service, controlled dormitory access, evening patrols by trained security personnel. Itasca Community College Library. 250 computers available on campus for general student use. A campuswide network can be accessed from student residence rooms and from off campus. Students can access the following: online class registration. Staffed computer lab on campus.

Community Environment: A rural community beautifully situated on the Mississippi River and 5 lakes, Grand Rapids (population 8,000) is the county seat of Itasca County, a bustling community with a strong tourist trade. Over 1,000 lakes in the county provide the facilities for all water sports; fishing, hunting, bowling and golf are some of the other recreational activities available. Quadna Mt. ski resort is nearby. Part-time employment opportunities are good.

■ **LAKE SUPERIOR COLLEGE**
2101 Trinity Rd.
Duluth, MN 55811
Tel: (218)733-7600; Free: 800-432-2884
E-mail: enroll@lsc.edu
Web Site: www.lsc.edu

Description: State-supported, 2-year, coed. Part of Minnesota State. Awards certificates, diplomas, transfer associate, and terminal associate degrees. Founded 1995. Setting: 105-acre urban campus. Total enrollment: 4,690. Faculty: 249 (102 full-time, 147 part-time). Student-undergrad faculty ratio is 18:1. 1,310 applied, 100% were admitted. Full-time: 1,849 students, 50% women, 50% men. Part-time: 2,841 students, 61% women, 39% men. Students come from 34 states and territories, 13 other countries, 13% from

out-of-state. 2% American Indian or Alaska Native, non-Hispanic/Latino; 3% Hispanic/Latino; 3% Black or African American, non-Hispanic/Latino; 2% Asian, non-Hispanic/Latino; 0.1% Native Hawaiian or other Pacific Islander, non-Hispanic/Latino; 2% international. 36% 25 or older, 34% transferred in. Calendar: semesters. Academic remediation for entering students, services for LD students, advanced placement, independent study, distance learning, double major, summer session for credit, part-time degree program, internships. Study abroad program.

Entrance Requirements: Open admission. Option: electronic application. Required: high school transcript. Entrance: noncompetitive. Application deadline: rolling. Notification: continuous. Transfer credits accepted: Yes.

Costs Per Year: Application fee: $20. State resident tuition: $4,417 full-time, $147.24 per credit part-time. Nonresident tuition: $5,522 full-time, $184.05 per credit part-time. Mandatory fees: $749 full-time. Full-time tuition and fees vary according to program and reciprocity agreements. Part-time tuition varies according to program and reciprocity agreements.

Collegiate Environment: Orientation program. Choral group. Social organizations: 30 open to all. Student services: personal-psychological counseling. Campus security: 24-hour emergency response devices, late night transport-escort service. College housing not available. Harold P. Erickson Library. Students can reserve study rooms.

■ **LEECH LAKE TRIBAL COLLEGE**
6945 Littlewolf Rd. NW
Cass Lake, MN 56633
Tel: (218)335-4200
Fax: (218)335-4282
E-mail: shelly.braford@lltc.edu
Web Site: www.lltc.edu

Description: Public, 2-year, coed. Awards certificates, diplomas, transfer associate, and terminal associate degrees. Founded 1992. Setting: rural campus. Total enrollment: 243. Faculty: 28 (9 full-time, 19 part-time). Student-undergrad faculty ratio is 16:1. Full-time: 190 students, 46% women, 54% men. Part-time: 53 students, 79% women, 21% men. 20% 25 or older. Core. Calendar: semesters. Academic remediation for entering students, services for LD students, advanced placement, independent study, double major, summer session for credit, part-time degree program, internships.

Entrance Requirements: Open admission. Required: high school transcript. Notification: continuous until 8/22. Transfer credits accepted: Yes.

Collegiate Environment: Orientation program. Student services: personal-psychological counseling. Agindaasoowigamig. 50 computers available on campus for general student use. A campuswide network can be accessed. Staffed computer lab on campus provides training in use of computers, software, and the Internet.

■ **MACALESTER COLLEGE**
1600 Grand Ave.
Saint Paul, MN 55105-1899
Tel: (651)696-6000; Free: 800-231-7974
Fax: (651)696-6500
E-mail: admissions@macalester.edu
Web Site: www.macalester.edu

Description: Independent, 4-year, coed. Awards bachelor's degrees. Founded 1874. Setting: 53-acre urban campus. Endowment: $767.5 million. Research spending for the previous fiscal year: $1.9 million. Educational spending for the previous fiscal year: $19,815 per student. Total enrollment: 2,174. Faculty: 264 (188 full-time, 76 part-time). Student-undergrad faculty ratio is 10:1. 5,985 applied, 41% were admitted. 63% from top 10% of their high school class, 91% from top quarter, 99% from top half. 15 National Merit Scholars. Full-time: 2,140 students, 59% women, 41% men. Part-time: 34 students, 65% women, 35% men. Students come from 54 states and territories, 96 other countries, 82% from out-of-state. 0.2% American Indian or Alaska Native, non-Hispanic/Latino; 8% Hispanic/Latino; 3% Black or African American, non-Hispanic/Latino; 8% Asian, non-Hispanic/Latino; 16% international. 1% 25 or older, 72% live on campus, 1% transferred in. Retention: 96% of full-time freshmen returned the following year. Academic areas with the most degrees conferred: social sciences; biological/life sciences; foreign languages and literature. Core. Calendar: semesters. Services for LD students, advanced placement, self-designed majors, honors program, independent study, double major, summer session for credit, part-time degree program, internships. Off campus study at Associated Colleges of the Twin Cities, also referred to as ACTC, is a consortium of five liberal arts colleges in Saint Paul and Minneapolis, formed to develop cooperative programs and offer cross-registration to their students. The five participating schools are: Macalester College, University of St. Thomas, St. Catherine University, Hamline University, and Augsburg College. Macalester College also takes part in an exchange with the Minneapolis College of Art and Design, in which students can cross-register for classes. Study abroad program. ROTC: Army (c), Naval (c), Air Force (c).

Entrance Requirements: Options: electronic application, early admission, early decision, deferred admission, international baccalaureate accepted. Required: essay, high school transcript, 2 recommendations, SAT or ACT. Recommended: interview. Entrance: very difficult. Application deadlines: 1/15, 11/15 for early decision plan 1, 1/1 for early decision plan 2. Notification: 3/30, 12/15 for early decision plan 1, 2/1 for early decision plan 2. SAT Reasoning Test deadline: 1/15. Transfer credits accepted: Yes. Applicants placed on waiting list: 426. Wait-listed applicants offered admission: 0. Early decision applicants: 309. Early decision applicants admitted: 161.

Costs Per Year: Application fee: $40. Comprehensive fee: $68,884 includes full-time tuition ($56,062), mandatory fees ($230), and college room and board ($12,592). College room only: $6762. Part-time tuition: $1752 per credit.

Collegiate Environment: Orientation program. Drama-theater group, choral group, student-run newspaper, radio station. Social organizations: 107 open to all. Most popular organizations: Program Board, WMCN - Macalester College Radio, The Mac Weekly, Outing Club, Climbing Club. Major annual events: Winter Ball, Springfest, Founders Day. Student services: health clinic, personal-psychological counseling. Campus security: 24-hour emergency response devices and patrols, late night transport-escort service, controlled dormitory access. 1,300 college housing spaces available; all were occupied in 2018-19. Freshmen guaranteed college housing. On-campus residence required through sophomore year. Options: coed, men-only, women-only housing available. DeWitt Wallace Library. Books: 326,620 (physical), 179,946 (digital/electronic); Serial titles: 2,412 (physical), 76,659 (digital/electronic); Databases: 202. Weekly public service hours: 109; study areas open 24 hours, 5-7 days a week; students can reserve study rooms. Operations spending for the previous fiscal year: $3 million. 375 computers available on campus for general student use. Computer purchase/lease plans available. A campuswide network can be accessed from student residence rooms and from off campus. Students can access the following: online class registration, wireless networking, free printing, specialized tools, 3D printing, scanning, A/V equipment checkout (cameras, microphones, etc.). Staffed computer lab on campus (open 24 hours a day) provides training in use of computers, software, and the Internet.

Community Environment: The Twin Cities, Minneapolis and St. Paul, with their suburbs, comprise a metropolitan area with a population of 3 million people. The area is the cultural and economic gateway to the northwest and it abounds in cultural advantages of every sort for students. Great art galleries, theaters for the performing arts, notable choral and instrumental music organizations as well as parks, lakes, and professional sports enrich community life.

■ **MARTIN LUTHER COLLEGE**
1995 Luther Ct.
New Ulm, MN 56073
Tel: (507)354-8221; Free: 877-MLC-1995
Fax: (507)354-8225
E-mail: steinma@mlc-wels.edu
Web Site: www.mlc-wels.edu

Description: Independent, comprehensive, coed, affiliated with Wisconsin Evangelical Lutheran Synod. Awards bachelor's and master's degrees. Founded 1995. Setting: 50-acre small town campus. Total enrollment: 972. Faculty: 79 (55 full-time, 24 part-time). Student-undergrad faculty ratio is 12:1. 270 applied, 89% were admitted. 13% from top 10% of their high school class, 28% from top quarter, 60% from top half. Full-time: 751 students, 48% women, 52% men. Part-time: 134 students, 62% women, 38% men. 82% from out-of-state. 0.1% American Indian or Alaska Native, non-Hispanic/Latino; 2% Hispanic/Latino; 1% Black or African American, non-Hispanic/Latino; 0.7% Asian, non-Hispanic/Latino; 0.2% Native Hawaiian or other Pacific Islander, non-Hispanic/Latino; 2% international. 3% 25 or older, 91% live on campus, 2% transferred in. Retention: 85% of full-time freshmen returned the following year. Academic areas with the most degrees conferred: education; theology and religious vocations. Calendar: semesters. Advanced placement, distance learning, double major, summer session for credit.

Entrance Requirements: Option: deferred admission. Required: high school transcript, minimum 2 high school GPA, SAT or ACT. Entrance: moderately difficult. SAT Reasoning Test deadline: 6/30. SAT Subject Test deadline: 6/30.

Costs Per Year: Application fee: $0. Comprehensive fee: $22,130 includes full-time tuition ($15,870) and college room and board ($6260).

Collegiate Environment: Orientation program. Drama-theater group, choral group. Student services: health clinic, personal-psychological counseling. Freshmen guaranteed college housing. On-campus residence required in freshman year. Options: men-only, women-only housing available. Martin Luther College Library.

Community Environment: New Ulm (population 13,600), a rural area 100 miles from Minneapolis and St. Paul, is a city where German immigrants carefully planned wide streets and numerous park areas in such a way that it has not been necessary to change the original plan. Part-time employment opportunities are good. Historical points of interest include the Brown County Historical Museum, Hermann's Monument, and Glockenspiel.

■ **MESABI RANGE COLLEGE**
1001 W Chestnut St.
Virginia, MN 55792-3448
Tel: (218)741-3095; Free: 800-657-3860
E-mail: b.kochevar@mesabirange.edu
Web Site: www.mesabirange.edu

Description: State-supported, 2-year, coed. Part of Minnesota State. Awards certificates, diplomas, transfer associate, and terminal associate degrees. Founded 1918. Setting: 30-acre small town campus. Total enrollment: 1,089. Faculty: 165. Student-undergrad faculty ratio is 24:1. Students come from 6 states and territories, 2 other countries. 3% American Indian or Alaska Native, non-Hispanic/Latino; 2% Hispanic/Latino; 8% Black or African American, non-Hispanic/Latino; 0.3% Asian, non-Hispanic/Latino; 0.2% Native Hawaiian or other Pacific Islander, non-Hispanic/Latino. 10% live on campus. Core. Calendar: semesters. Academic remediation for entering students, services for LD students, advanced placement, self-designed majors, independent study, distance learning, summer session for credit, part-time degree program, adult/continuing education programs, co-op programs and internships. Off campus study at other colleges in the Minnesota State System. Study abroad program.

Entrance Requirements: Open admission. Options: electronic application, early admission, deferred admission. Required: high school transcript. Entrance: noncompetitive. Application deadline: rolling. Notification: continuous. Transfer credits accepted: Yes.

Costs Per Year: Application fee: $20. State resident tuition: $4,729 full-time, $157.62 per credit part-time. Nonresident tuition: $5,911 full-time, $197.02 per credit part-time. Mandatory fees: $600 full-time, $20 per credit part-time.

Collegiate Environment: Orientation program. Drama-theater group. Social organizations: 20 open to all; Phi Theta Kappa Honor Society. Most popular organizations: Student Senate, Human Services Club, Career Program Clubs, Student Life Club, Gaming Club. Major annual events: Homecoming, Thanksgiving Dinner, Deep Freeze Activities Week. Student services: personal-psychological counseling. Mesabi Library. 120 computers available on campus for general student use. Students can access the following: online class registration. Staffed computer lab on campus.

Community Environment: The hub of Minnesota Arrowhead country and Taconite capital of the world, Virginia offers ready access to countless waterways and forestland, including Voyageurs National Park and the Boundary Waters Canoe Area. The Giants Ridge Ski Area features excellent alpine and cross country skiing. The city also has 2 municipal parks, 2 lakes and an 18-hole golf course. Part-time employment is available.

■ **METROPOLITAN STATE UNIVERSITY**
700 E 7th St.
Saint Paul, MN 55106-5000
Tel: (651)793-1212
Fax: (651)772-7632
E-mail: daryl.johnson@metrostate.edu
Web Site: www.metrostate.edu

Description: State-supported, comprehensive, coed. Part of Minnesota State Colleges and Universities System. Awards bachelor's, master's, and doctoral degrees (offers primarily part-time evening degree programs). Founded 1971. Setting: urban campus with easy access to Minneapolis-St. Paul. Total enrollment: 8,354. 376 applied, 100% were admitted. Full-time: 2,714 students, 54% women, 46% men. Part-time: 4,879 students, 57% women, 43% men. 0.7% American Indian or Alaska Native, non-Hispanic/Latino; 5% Hispanic/Latino; 19% Black or African American, non-Hispanic/Latino; 12% Asian, non-Hispanic/Latino; 0.1% Native Hawaiian or other Pacific Islander, non-Hispanic/Latino; 2% international. 72% 25 or older, 91% transferred in. Retention: 60% of full-time freshmen returned the following year. Academic areas with the most degrees conferred: business/marketing; interdisciplinary studies; health professions and related sciences; homeland security, law enforcement, firefighting, and protective services. Core. Calendar: semesters. ESL program, advanced placement, self-designed majors, independent study, distance learning, double major, summer session for credit, part-time degree program, external degree program, adult/continuing education programs, internships. Off campus study at other colleges in the Minnesota State College and University System. Study abroad program.

Entrance Requirements: Options: electronic application, deferred admission, international baccalaureate accepted. Required: high school transcript, minimum 2 high school GPA. Recommended: SAT or ACT. Entrance: minimally difficult. Application deadline: 6/15.

Costs Per Year: Application fee: $20. State resident tuition: $6,826 full-time, $227.53 per credit part-time. Nonresident tuition: $13,927 full-time, $464.23 per credit part-time. Mandatory fees: $1,053 full-time, $35.11 per credit part-time.

Collegiate Environment: Orientation program. Drama-theater group, student-run newspaper. Social organizations: 33 open to all. Student services: personal-psychological counseling. Campus security: 24-hour emergency response devices, late night transport-escort service. Library and Learning Center.

Community Environment: See Bethel College.

■ **MINNEAPOLIS BUSINESS COLLEGE**
1711 W County Rd. B
Roseville, MN 55113
Tel: (612)636-7406; Free: 800-279-5200
Fax: (612)636-8185
Web Site: www.minneapolisbusinesscollege.edu
Description: Proprietary, 2-year, coed. Awards diplomas and terminal associate degrees. Founded 1874. Setting: suburban campus with easy access to Minneapolis-St. Paul. Total enrollment: 231. 379 applied, 87% were admitted. Calendar: semesters. Accelerated degree program, internships.

■ **MINNEAPOLIS COLLEGE OF ART AND DESIGN**
2501 Stevens Ave.
Minneapolis, MN 55404-4347
Tel: (612)874-3700; Free: 800-874-6223
Fax: (612)874-3704
Web Site: www.mcad.edu
Description: Independent, comprehensive, coed. Awards bachelor's and master's degrees. Founded 1886. Setting: 3-acre urban campus. Endowment: $47.9 million. Educational spending for the previous fiscal year: $27,242 per student. Total enrollment: 727. Faculty: 139 (42 full-time, 97 part-time). Student-undergrad faculty ratio is 10:1. 692 applied, 59% were admitted. Full-time: 664 students, 69% women, 31% men. Part-time: 11 students, 45% women, 55% men. Students come from 13 other countries, 47% from out-of-state. 2% American Indian or Alaska Native, non-Hispanic/Latino; 7% Hispanic/Latino; 6% Black or African American, non-Hispanic/Latino; 8% Asian, non-Hispanic/Latino; 0.1% Native Hawaiian or other Pacific Islander, non-Hispanic/Latino; 2% international. 11% 25 or older, 9% transferred in. Retention: 83% of full-time freshmen returned the following year. Academic areas with the most degrees conferred: visual and performing arts; communication technologies; business/marketing. Core. Calendar: semesters. Services for LD students, advanced placement, independent study, distance learning, summer session for credit, part-time degree program, adult/continuing education programs, co-op programs and internships. Off campus study at Members of the Association of Independent Colleges of Art and Design, Macalester College. Study abroad program.

Entrance Requirements: Options: electronic application, early action, international baccalaureate accepted. Required: essay, high school transcript. Recommended: interview. Required for some: SAT or ACT. Entrance: moderately difficult. Application deadlines: 5/1, 12/1 for early action. Notification: continuous, 12/15 for early action. SAT Reasoning Test deadline: 5/1. Transfer credits accepted: Yes.

Costs Per Year: Application fee: $50. Tuition: $38,670 full-time, $1612 per credit hour part-time. Mandatory fees: $450 full-time, $225 per term part-time. Part-time tuition and fees vary according to course load. College room only: $5610. Room charges vary according to housing facility.

Collegiate Environment: Orientation program. Social organizations: 30 open to all. Most popular organizations: Peoples Library, Black Artist Student Union, Animation Study Group, Comic Club, Kinda Midnight Movies Club. Major annual events: Black and White Ball, Thanksgiving Dinner. Student

services: personal-psychological counseling. Campus security: 24-hour emergency response devices and patrols, late night transport-escort service, controlled dormitory access. MCAD Library. Books: 50,000 (physical), 145,000 (digital/electronic); Serial titles: 329 (physical); Databases: 8.

Community Environment: See University of Minnesota - Twin Cities.

■ **MINNEAPOLIS COMMUNITY AND TECHNICAL COLLEGE**
1501 Hennepin Ave.
Minneapolis, MN 55403-1779
Tel: (612)659-6000; Free: 800-247-0911
Fax: (612)659-6825
E-mail: admissions.office@minneapolis.edu
Web Site: www.minneapolis.edu
Description: State-supported, 2-year, coed. Part of Minnesota State Colleges and Universities System. Awards certificates, diplomas, transfer associate, and terminal associate degrees. Founded 1965. Setting: 22-acre urban campus. Total enrollment: 9,465. Faculty: 397 (178 full-time, 219 part-time). Full-time: 3,210 students, 49% women, 51% men. Part-time: 6,255 students, 58% women, 42% men. 2% American Indian or Alaska Native, non-Hispanic/Latino; 10% Hispanic/Latino; 31% Black or African American, non-Hispanic/Latino; 6% Asian, non-Hispanic/Latino; 0.1% Native Hawaiian or other Pacific Islander, non-Hispanic/Latino; 1% international. Core. Calendar: semesters. Academic remediation for entering students, ESL program, services for LD students, advanced placement, accelerated degree program, honors program, independent study, distance learning, summer session for credit, part-time degree program, adult/continuing education programs, internships. Off campus study at other colleges in the Minnesota State Colleges and Universities System. Study abroad program.

Entrance Requirements: Open admission except for students in the Cinema Division; students in the air traffic control, law enforcement and nursing programs; and international students. Options: electronic application, early admission, deferred admission, international baccalaureate accepted. Required: high school transcript. Entrance: noncompetitive. Application deadline: rolling. Notification: continuous.

Collegiate Environment: Orientation program. Drama-theater group, choral group, student-run newspaper. Social organizations: 44 open to all. Most popular organizations: Student Senate, College Choirs, Student African American Brotherhood /B2B, Science Club, Phi Theta Kappa. Major annual events: Sustainability Fair, Science, Technology, Engineering, and Math Fair, MCTC College Transfer Fairs. Student services: legal services, health clinic, personal-psychological counseling. Campus security: 24-hour emergency response devices and patrols, late night transport-escort service. Minneapolis Community and Technical College Library plus 1 other. 279 computers available on campus for general student use. A campuswide network can be accessed from off-campus. Students can access the following: online class registration. Staffed computer lab on campus provides training in use of computers, software, and the Internet.

Community Environment: Minneapolis Community College's beautiful campus borders a city park and is within walking distance of cultural centers (Guthrie Theatre, Walker Art Center) and downtown Minneapolis.

■ **MINNESOTA STATE COLLEGE-SOUTHEAST TECHNICAL**
1250 Homer Rd.
Winona, MN 55987
Tel: (507)453-2700; Free: 800-372-8164
Fax: (507)453-2715
Web Site: www.southeastmn.edu
Description: State-supported, 2-year, coed. Part of Minnesota State Colleges and Universities System. Awards certificates, diplomas, transfer associate, and terminal associate degrees. Founded 1992. Setting: 132-acre small town campus with easy access to Minneapolis-St. Paul. Total enrollment: 1,814. Faculty: 102 (50 full-time, 52 part-time). Student-undergrad faculty ratio is 15:1. 1,666 applied, 35% were admitted. 5% from top quarter of their high school class, 24% from top half. Full-time: 710 students, 48% women, 52% men. Part-time: 1,104 students, 60% women, 40% men. 26% from out-of-state. 0.5% American Indian or Alaska Native, non-Hispanic/Latino; 4% Hispanic/Latino; 4% Black or African American, non-Hispanic/Latino; 3% Asian, non-Hispanic/Latino; 0.1% Native Hawaiian or other Pacific Islander, non-Hispanic/Latino; 0.4% international. 45% 25 or older, 10% transferred in. Calendar: semesters. Distance learning, double major, internships.

Entrance Requirements: Open admission except for nursing, radiography, and truck driving programs. Option: electronic application. Required: high school transcript. Recommended: interview. Entrance: noncompetitive. Application deadline: rolling. Notification: continuous.

Costs Per Year: Application fee: $20.

Collegiate Environment: Orientation program. Student-run newspaper. Campus security: 24-hour emergency response devices, late night transport-escort service. College housing not available. Learning Resource Center.

■ MINNESOTA STATE COMMUNITY AND TECHNICAL COLLEGE

1414 College Way
Fergus Falls, MN 56537-1009
Tel: (218)736-1500; Free: 877-450-3322
Fax: (218)739-7475
Web Site: www.minnesota.edu

Description: State-supported, 2-year, coed. Part of Minnesota State Colleges and Universities System. Awards certificates, diplomas, transfer associate, and terminal associate degrees. Founded 1960. Setting: rural campus. Total enrollment: 6,303. 34% 25 or older, 2% live on campus. Core. Calendar: semesters. Academic remediation for entering students, ESL program, services for LD students, advanced placement, accelerated degree program, freshman honors college, honors program, independent study, distance learning, double major, summer session for credit, part-time degree program, co-op programs and internships. Off campus study at other online courses from colleges in the Minnesota State Colleges and Universities System. Study abroad program.

Entrance Requirements: Open admission except for heath care programs. Options: electronic application, early admission, deferred admission. Entrance: noncompetitive. Transfer credits accepted: Yes.

Costs Per Year: Application fee: $20. One-time mandatory fee: $20. State resident tuition: $4821 full-time, $160.70 per credit hour part-time. Nonresident tuition: $4821 full-time, $160.70 per credit hour part-time. Mandatory fees: $514 full-time. Full-time tuition and fees vary according to location and program. Part-time tuition varies according to location and program. College room and board: $6724. Room and board charges vary according to board plan and housing facility.

Collegiate Environment: Orientation program. Drama-theater group, choral group. Most popular organizations: Student Senate, Students In Free Enterprise (SIFE), Phi Theta Kappa, Business Professionals of America, SkillsUSA-VICA. Major annual events: Homecoming, Minnesota Meltdown, Health Awareness Week. Student services: personal-psychological counseling, women's center. Campus security: 24-hour emergency response devices, late night transport-escort service, security for special events. Minnesota State Community and Technical College - Fergus Falls Library plus 4 others.

Community Environment: One of the largest dairy products and poultry shipping points in the northwest, Fergus Falls (population 13,722) also has the largest cooperative creamery in this region. Trains and buses are convenient for transportation. There are 1,000 lakes in the area which are within a 10 minute drive to an hour's drive. A fine park system, public golf course, municipal swimming beach, trap-shooting facilities, tennis courts, archery range, ice skating rinks, skiing facilities and rope tows provide the recreational activities. The hunting and fishing opportunities are unsurpassed.

■ MINNESOTA STATE COMMUNITY AND TECHNICAL COLLEGE-DETROIT LAKES

900 Hwy. 34, E
Detroit Lakes, MN 56501
Tel: (218)846-7444; Free: 800-492-4836
Fax: (218)847-7170
Web Site: www.minnesota.edu

Description: State-supported, 2-year, coed. Part of Minnesota State Colleges and Universities System. Awards certificates, transfer associate, and terminal associate degrees. Founded 1966. Setting: small town campus. Total enrollment: 6,391. Faculty: 276 (154 full-time, 122 part-time). Full-time: 2,658 students, 51% women, 49% men. Part-time: 3,733 students, 66% women, 34% men. 1% American Indian or Alaska Native, non-Hispanic/Latino; 7% Hispanic/Latino; 18% Black or African American, non-Hispanic/Latino; 4% Asian, non-Hispanic/Latino; 0.2% Native Hawaiian or other Pacific Islander, non-Hispanic/Latino; 0.3% international. Calendar: semesters.

Entrance Requirements: Required: high school transcript, immunization record.

Costs Per Year: Application fee: $20. One-time mandatory fee: $20. State resident tuition: $4821 full-time, $160.70 per credit hour part-time.

Nonresident tuition: $4821 full-time, $160.70 per credit hour part-time. Mandatory fees: $514 full-time. Full-time tuition and fees vary according to location and program. Part-time tuition varies according to location and program.

■ MINNESOTA STATE COMMUNITY AND TECHNICAL COLLEGE-MOORHEAD

1900 28th Ave., S
Moorhead, MN 56560
Tel: (218)236-6277; Free: 800-426-5603
Fax: (218)299-6584
Web Site: www.minnesota.edu

Description: State-supported, 2-year, coed. Part of Minnesota State Colleges and Universities System. Awards certificates, diplomas, and transfer associate degrees. Setting: rural campus. Total enrollment: 6,303. Faculty: 276 (154 full-time, 122 part-time). Full-time: 2,581 students, 50% women, 50% men. Part-time: 3,722 students, 66% women, 34% men. Calendar: semesters.

Entrance Requirements: Required: high school transcript, immunization record.

Costs Per Year: Application fee: $20. One-time mandatory fee: $20. State resident tuition: $4821 full-time, $160.70 per credit hour part-time. Nonresident tuition: $4821 full-time, $160.70 per credit hour part-time. Mandatory fees: $514 full-time. Full-time tuition and fees vary according to location and program. Part-time tuition varies according to location and program.

■ MINNESOTA STATE COMMUNITY AND TECHNICAL COLLEGE-WADENA

405 Colfax Ave., SW
Wadena, MN 56482
Tel: (218)631-7800; Free: 800-247-2007
Fax: (218)631-7901
Web Site: www.minnesota.edu

Description: State-supported, 2-year, coed. Awards certificates, transfer associate, and terminal associate degrees. Setting: small town campus. Total enrollment: 6,303. Faculty: 276 (154 full-time, 122 part-time). Full-time: 2,581 students, 50% women, 50% men. Part-time: 3,719 students, 66% women, 34% men. 0.3% American Indian or Alaska Native, non-Hispanic/Latino; 3% Hispanic/Latino; 0.5% Black or African American, non-Hispanic/Latino. Calendar: semesters.

Entrance Requirements: Required: high school transcript, immunization record.

Costs Per Year: Application fee: $20. One-time mandatory fee: $20. State resident tuition: $4821 full-time, $160.70 per credit hour part-time. Nonresident tuition: $4821 full-time, $160.70 per credit hour part-time. Mandatory fees: $514 full-time. Full-time tuition and fees vary according to location and program. Part-time tuition varies according to location and program.

■ MINNESOTA STATE UNIVERSITY MANKATO

228 Wiecking Ctr.
Mankato, MN 56001
Tel: (507)389-2463; Free: 800-722-0544
E-mail: admissions@mnsu.edu
Web Site: mankato.mnsu.edu

Description: State-supported, university, coed. Part of Minnesota State Colleges and Universities System. Awards associate, bachelor's, master's, and doctoral degrees and post-master's certificates. Founded 1868. Setting: 303-acre small town campus with easy access to Minneapolis-St. Paul. Research spending for the previous fiscal year: $978,730. Educational spending for the previous fiscal year: $3812 per student. Total enrollment: 15,407. Faculty: 754 (436 full-time, 318 part-time). Student-undergrad faculty ratio is 20:1. 6% from top 10% of their high school class, 23% from top quarter, 64% from top half. Full-time: 11,412 students, 50% women, 50% men. Part-time: 2,047 students, 61% women, 39% men. Students come from 91 other countries, 12% from out-of-state. 0.2% American Indian or Alaska Native, non-Hispanic/Latino; 3% Hispanic/Latino; 5% Black or African American, non-Hispanic/Latino; 3% Asian, non-Hispanic/Latino; 5% international. 12% 25 or older, 25% live on campus, 8% transferred in. Retention: 81% of full-time freshmen returned the following year. Academic areas with the most degrees conferred: business/marketing; health professions and related sciences; education. Core. Calendar: semesters. Academic remediation for entering students, ESL program, services for LD students, advanced placement, accelerated degree program, self-designed majors, honors program, independent study, distance learning, double major, summer session for credit, part-time degree program, external degree program, adult/continuing education programs, co-op programs and internships, graduate courses open to undergrads. Off campus study at other colleges in the Minnesota State College and University System. Study abroad program. ROTC: Army.

Entrance Requirements: Required: high school transcript, SAT or ACT. Required for some: essay, minimum X high school GPA, 1 recommendation, personal statement, letter and senior grades.

Collegiate Environment: Orientation program. Drama-theater group, choral group, marching band, student-run newspaper, radio station. Social organizations: 300 open to all; national fraternities, national sororities, local fraternities, local sororities. Major annual events: Homecoming Events, Welcome Week Activities, Mavericks After Dark. Student services: legal services, health clinic, personal-psychological counseling, women's center. Campus security: 24-hour emergency response devices and patrols, student patrols, late night transport-escort service, controlled dormitory access, Night Owl security program in residence halls, closed circuit cameras in parking lots. Memorial Library. Operations spending for the previous fiscal year: $4.6 million. 900 computers available on campus for general student use. Computer purchase/lease plans available. A campuswide network can be accessed from student residence rooms and from off campus. Students can access the following: online class registration. Staffed computer lab on campus provides training in use of computers, software, and the Internet.

Community Environment: Mankato (population 35,000), on a great bend in the Minnesota River, is the trade and distributing center for agricultural southwestern Minnesota. Bus and air service is available. Community facilities include a number of churches, hospitals, and the usual civic and service organizations. About 30 lakes within a 25-mile area provide facilities for all water sports and fishing; other activities include golf, hunting and skiing. Points of interest are the Blue Earth County Historical Society Museum, Minneopa State Park and Sibley Park.

■ **MINNESOTA STATE UNIVERSITY MOORHEAD**

1104 7th Ave. S
Moorhead, MN 56563
Tel: (218)477-2161; Free: 800-593-7246
Fax: (218)236-2168
Web Site: www.mnstate.edu

Description: State-supported, comprehensive, coed. Part of Minnesota State Colleges and Universities System. Awards bachelor's, master's, and doctoral degrees and post-master's certificates. Founded 1885. Setting: 119-acre urban campus. Endowment: $24.5 million. Research spending for the previous fiscal year: $220,000. Educational spending for the previous fiscal year: $7891 per student. Total enrollment: 5,860. Faculty: 309 (220 full-time, 81 part-time). Student-undergrad faculty ratio is 19:1. 4,204 applied, 60% were admitted. 11% from top 10% of their high school class, 31% from top quarter, 66% from top half. Full-time: 3,895 students, 61% women, 39% men. Part-time: 933 students, 61% women, 39% men. Students come from 35 states and territories, 46 other countries, 33% from out-of-state. 0.6% American Indian or Alaska Native, non-Hispanic/Latino; 3% Hispanic/Latino; 4% Black or African American, non-Hispanic/Latino; 2% Asian, non-Hispanic/Latino; 0.1% Native Hawaiian or other Pacific Islander, non-Hispanic/Latino; 6% international. 20% 25 or older, 25% live on campus, 8% transferred in. Retention: 72% of full-time freshmen returned the following year. Academic areas with the most degrees conferred: education; business/marketing; health professions and related sciences. Core. Calendar: semesters. Academic remediation for entering students, ESL program, services for LD students, advanced placement, self-designed majors, honors program, independent study, distance learning, double major, summer session for credit, part-time degree program, adult/continuing education programs, internships, graduate courses open to undergrads. Off campus study at North Dakota State University, Concordia College (Moorhead, MN), Minnesota State Community and Technical College, and North Dakota State College of Science, as well as other colleges of the Minnesota State Colleges and Universities System. Study abroad program. ROTC: Army (c), Air Force (c).

Entrance Requirements: Options: electronic application, deferred admission, international baccalaureate accepted. Required: high school transcript, SAT or ACT. Recommended: ACT. Entrance: moderately difficult. Application deadlines: rolling, rolling for nonresidents. Notification: continuous, continuous for nonresidents. SAT Reasoning Test deadline: 8/1. Transfer credits accepted: Yes.

Costs Per Year: Application fee: $20. One-time mandatory fee: $90. State

resident tuition: $7410 full-time, $239 per credit hour part-time. Nonresident tuition: $14,820 full-time, $478 per credit hour part-time. Mandatory fees: $1162 full-time, $48.40 per credit hour part-time, $581 per term part-time. Full-time tuition and fees vary according to course load and reciprocity agreements. Part-time tuition and fees vary according to reciprocity agreements. College room and board: $9280. College room only: $5950. Room and board charges vary according to board plan and housing facility.

Collegiate Environment: Orientation program. Drama-theater group, choral group, student-run newspaper, radio station. Social organizations: 120 open to all; national fraternities, national sororities; 1% of eligible men and 2% of eligible women are members. Most popular organizations: NSSLHA / Collegiate SERTOMA, Cinethusiasts, Student Council for Exceptional Children, Education Minnesota Student Program, National Society of Leadership and Success. Major annual events: Homecoming, Welcome Week, Opening Football Game. Student services: health clinic, personal-psychological counseling, women's center. Campus security: 24-hour emergency response devices and patrols, student patrols, late night transport-escort service, controlled dormitory access. 1,930 college housing spaces available; 1,229 were occupied in 2018-19. Freshmen guaranteed college housing. Option: coed housing available. Livingston Lord Library plus 1 other. Books: 326,187 (physical), 20,401 (digital/electronic); Serial titles: 1,634 (physical), 18,041 (digital/electronic); Databases: 84. Weekly public service hours: 79. Operations spending for the previous fiscal year: $1.9 million. 1,500 computers available on campus for general student use. Computer purchase/lease plans available. A campuswide network can be accessed from student residence rooms and from off campus. Students can access the following: online class registration. Staffed computer lab on campus (open 24 hours a day) provides training in use of computers, software, and the Internet.

Community Environment: Consistently ranked as one of the best places to live in the country by leading publications, the cities of Moorhead, Minn., and Fargo, N.D. boast a high quality of life based on excellent schools and hospitals, booming business and job growth, superior educational, professional and recreational opportunities, and a safe, clean environment. In 2000 Fargo/Moorhead was awarded The prestigious All-American City Award. More than 20,000 students attend six educational institutions in Fargo-Moorhead. With a metro population of 157,000, the community is a regional center for education, business, communication, finance, health care and entertainment. MSU is just 4 hours from Minneapolis-St. Paul, 3 1/2 hours from Winnipeg, 3 hours from Bismarck, N.D., and 45 minutes from some of the best lake country in Minnesota.

■ **MINNESOTA WEST COMMUNITY AND TECHNICAL COLLEGE**

1314 N Hiawatha Ave.
Pipestone, MN 56164
Tel: (507)825-6800; Free: 800-658-2330
Fax: (507)825-4656
E-mail: crystal.strouth@mnwest.edu
Web Site: www.mnwest.edu

Description: State-supported, 2-year, coed. Part of Minnesota State Colleges and Universities System. Awards certificates, diplomas, transfer associate, and terminal associate degrees (profile contains information from Canby, Granite Falls, Jackson, and Worthington campuses). Founded 1967. Setting: rural campus. Total enrollment: 3,182. Faculty: 151 (69 full-time, 82 part-time). Student-undergrad faculty ratio is 21:1. 11% from out-of-state. 0.9% American Indian or Alaska Native, non-Hispanic/Latino; 6% Hispanic/Latino; 5% Black or African American, non-Hispanic/Latino; 3% Asian, non-Hispanic/Latino; 0.1% Native Hawaiian or other Pacific Islander, non-Hispanic/Latino. Retention: 60% of full-time freshmen returned the following year. Core. Calendar: semesters. Academic remediation for entering students, services for LD students, advanced placement, honors program, independent study, distance learning, double major, summer session for credit, part-time degree program, external degree program, co-op programs and internships.

Entrance Requirements: Open admission. Option: electronic application. Required: high school transcript. Entrance: noncompetitive. Application deadline: rolling. Notification: continuous. Transfer credits accepted: Yes.

Costs Per Year: Application fee: $20. One-time mandatory fee: $20. State resident tuition: $5146 full-time, $171.53 per credit part-time. Nonresident tuition: $5146 full-time, $171.53 per credit part-time. Mandatory fees: $546 full-time, $18.20 per credit part-time. Full-time tuition and fees vary according to program and reciprocity agreements. Part-time tuition and fees vary according to program and reciprocity agreements.

Collegiate Environment: Orientation program. Choral group. Library and Academic Resource Center plus 4 others.

■ **NATIONAL AMERICAN UNIVERSITY (BLOOMINGTON)**
7801 Metro Pky.
Ste. 200
Bloomington, MN 55425
Tel: (952)356-3600; Free: 866-628-6387
E-mail: jmichaelson@national.edu
Web Site: www.national.edu
Description: Proprietary, 4-year, coed. Awards associate degrees. Setting: urban campus. Total enrollment: 474. Faculty: 46 (15 full-time, 31 part-time). Student-undergrad faculty ratio is 19:1. 36 applied, 100% were admitted. Full-time: 311 students, 64% women, 36% men. Part-time: 163 students, 61% women, 39% men. Students come from 25 states and territories, 7 other countries, 24% from out-of-state. 51% 25 or older, 18% live on campus, 4% transferred in. Retention: 46% of full-time freshmen returned the following year. ESL program, services for LD students, advanced placement, honors program, independent study, distance learning, double major, summer session for credit, part-time degree program, external degree program, adult/continuing education programs, co-op programs and internships. ROTC: Air Force.
Entrance Requirements: Recommended: high school transcript, interview. Required for some: high school transcript.
Collegiate Environment: Jefferson Library.

■ **NATIONAL AMERICAN UNIVERSITY (BROOKLYN CENTER)**
6200 Shingle Creek Pky.
Ste. 130
Brooklyn Center, MN 55430
Tel: (763)852-7500; Free: 866-628-6387
Fax: (763)549-9955
Web Site: www.national.edu
Description: Proprietary, 4-year, coed. Awards associate degrees.

■ **NATIONAL AMERICAN UNIVERSITY (BURNSVILLE)**
513 W Travelers Trl.
Burnsville, MN 55337
Tel: (952)563-1250; Free: 866-628-6387
Web Site: www.national.edu
Description: Proprietary, 4-year, coed. Awards associate and bachelor's degrees.

■ **NATIONAL AMERICAN UNIVERSITY (ROSEVILLE)**
1550 W Hwy. 36
Roseville, MN 55113
Tel: (651)855-6300; Free: 866-628-6387
Fax: (651)644-0690
Web Site: www.national.edu
Description: Proprietary, 4-year, coed. Part of National American University. Awards associate and bachelor's degrees. Setting: 1-acre urban campus. Faculty: 32 (5 full-time, 27 part-time). Student-undergrad faculty ratio is 10:1. 259 applied, 100% were admitted. Students come from 5 states and territories. 50% 25 or older. Retention: 52% of full-time freshmen returned the following year. Calendar: quarters.
Entrance Requirements: Required: high school transcript. Recommended: minimum 2.0 high school GPA, interview. Required for some: essay. Application deadline: rolling. Notification: continuous.
Collegiate Environment: Student-run newspaper. Social organizations: 3 open to all. Most popular organizations: Southeast Asian Student Organization, Phi Beta Lambda/Lambda Beta Omicron, Student Government Association, International Student Organization. Major annual event: Grad Fest. Campus security: late night transport-escort service.

■ **NORMANDALE COMMUNITY COLLEGE**
9700 France Ave. S
Bloomington, MN 55431-4399
Tel: (952)358-8200; Free: 800-481-5412
Fax: (612)487-8101
E-mail: information@normandale.edu
Web Site: www.normandale.edu
Description: State-supported, 2-year, coed. Part of Minnesota State Colleges and Universities System. Awards certificates, transfer associate, and terminal associate degrees. Founded 1968. Setting: 90-acre suburban campus with easy access to Minneapolis-St. Paul. Faculty: 358 (193 full-time, 165 part-time). 2,311 applied, 87% were admitted. Core. Calendar: semesters. Academic remediation for entering students, ESL program,

services for LD students, advanced placement, self-designed majors, independent study, distance learning, summer session for credit, part-time degree program, external degree program, adult/continuing education programs, co-op programs and internships. Off campus study at other colleges in the Minnesota State Colleges and Universities System. Study abroad program.
Entrance Requirements: Open admission except for specific health science degree programs. Options: electronic application, deferred admission, international baccalaureate accepted. Required for some: high school transcript. Entrance: noncompetitive. Application deadline: 8/10. Notification: 8/10. Transfer credits accepted: Yes.
Collegiate Environment: Orientation program. Drama-theater group, choral group, student-run newspaper. Social organizations: 30 open to all. Most popular organizations: Program Board (NPB), Student Senate, Phi Theta Kappa, Inter-Varsity Christian Fellowship, Latino Student Club. Major annual events: Spring Fling, Winter Festival Breakfast, CultureFest. Student services: personal-psychological counseling. Campus security: 24-hour emergency response devices, student patrols, late night transport-escort service. Library plus 1 other. 900 computers available on campus for general student use. Computer purchase/lease plans available. A campuswide network can be accessed from off-campus. Students can access the following: online class registration, online school catalog. Staffed computer lab on campus provides training in use of computers, software, and the Internet.
Community Environment: The college is located in Bloomington, a suburb of 85,000 people located 10 miles south of Minneapolis and 7 miles west of the Minneapolis/St. Paul Airport.

■ **NORTH CENTRAL UNIVERSITY**
910 Elliot Ave.
Minneapolis, MN 55404-1322
Tel: (612)332-3491; Free: 800-289-6222
Fax: (612)343-4778
E-mail: admissions@northcentral.edu
Web Site: www.northcentral.edu
Description: Independent, 4-year, coed, affiliated with Assemblies of God. Awards associate and bachelor's degrees. Founded 1930. Setting: 9-acre urban campus. Total enrollment: 1,125. Faculty: 102 (40 full-time, 62 part-time). Student-undergrad faculty ratio is 19:1. 450 applied. Students come from 42 states and territories, 6 other countries, 55% from out-of-state. 10% 25 or older, 80% live on campus. Core. Calendar: semesters plus January and May terms. Academic remediation for entering students, services for LD students, advanced placement, self-designed majors, independent study, double major, summer session for credit, part-time degree program, co-op programs and internships. Off campus study. ROTC: Army (c), Air Force (c).
Entrance Requirements: Open admission. Options: electronic application, deferred admission, international baccalaureate accepted. Required: essay, high school transcript, minimum 2.2 high school GPA, Christian testimony, SAT or ACT. Required for some: interview. Entrance: noncompetitive. Application deadline: 6/1. Notification: 6/15.
Costs Per Year: Application fee: $25. Comprehensive fee: $31,640 includes full-time tuition ($23,540), mandatory fees ($700), and college room and board ($7400). College room only: $4130. Full-time tuition and fees vary according to course load. Room and board charges vary according to board plan and housing facility.
Collegiate Environment: Orientation program. Drama-theater group, choral group, student-run newspaper, radio station. Most popular organizations: Residence Life, Discipleship Leaders, Orientation Leaders, Student Ministries Board, Student Activities Committee. Major annual events: The Week, Battle of the Floors, Holy Convocation. Student services: personal-psychological counseling. Campus security: 24-hour emergency response devices and patrols, late night transport-escort service, controlled dormitory access. T. J. Jones Information Resource Center. 40 computers available on campus for general student use. A campuswide network can be accessed from student residence rooms. Students can access the following: online class registration. Staffed computer lab on campus.
Community Environment: See University of Minnesota - Twin Cities.

■ **NORTH HENNEPIN COMMUNITY COLLEGE**
7411 85th Ave. N
Brooklyn Park, MN 55445
Tel: (763)488-0391; Free: 800-818-0395
Fax: (763)424-0929
E-mail: solson2@nhcc.edu
Web Site: www.nhcc.edu

Description: State-supported, 2-year, coed. Part of Minnesota State Colleges and Universities system. Awards certificates, transfer associate, and terminal associate degrees. Founded 1966. Setting: 80-acre suburban campus with easy access to Minneapolis-St. Paul. Endowment: $761,415. Research spending for the previous fiscal year: $2798. Educational spending for the previous fiscal year: $4948 per student. Total enrollment: 6,509. Faculty: 222 (118 full-time, 104 part-time). Core. Calendar: semesters. Academic remediation for entering students, ESL program, services for LD students, advanced placement, accelerated degree program, self-designed majors, honors program, independent study, distance learning, double major, summer session for credit, part-time degree program, external degree program, adult/continuing education programs, internships. Off campus study at Hennepin Technical College. Study abroad program. ROTC: Army (c), Naval (c), Air Force (c).

Entrance Requirements: Open admission except for nursing, medical laboratory technology (MLT), and paralegal programs. Options: electronic application, early admission, deferred admission, international baccalaureate accepted. Recommended: high school transcript. Entrance: noncompetitive. Application deadline: rolling. Notification: continuous. Transfer credits accepted: Yes.

Costs Per Year: Application fee: $20. State resident tuition: $3,961 full-time, $165.06 per credit part-time. Nonresident tuition: $3,961 full-time, $165.06 per credit part-time. Mandatory fees: $472 full-time, $19.68 per credit part-time. Full-time tuition and fees vary according to location and program. Part-time tuition and fees vary according to location and program.

Collegiate Environment: Orientation program. Drama-theater group, choral group. Social organizations: 25 open to all; Phi Theta Kappa. Most popular organizations: Hmong Student Club, Student Nurses Association, Student Senate, Badminton Club, Students Serving Our Community. Major annual events: Great NHCC Get-Together, Student Appreciation Celebration, Halloween Costume & Office Decorating Contest. Student services: health clinic, personal-psychological counseling. Campus security: 24-hour emergency response devices, student patrols, late night transport-escort service. Learning Resource Center. Operations spending for the previous fiscal year: $557,247. 1,060 computers available on campus for general student use. A campuswide network can be accessed from off-campus. Students can access the following: online class registration. Staffed computer lab on campus provides training in use of computers, software, and the Internet.

■ **NORTHLAND COMMUNITY AND TECHNICAL COLLEGE**
1101 Hwy. One E
Thief River Falls, MN 56701
Tel: (218)683-8800; Free: 800-959-6282
Fax: (218)681-6405
E-mail: nicki.carlson@northlandcollege.edu
Web Site: www.northlandcollege.edu

Description: State-supported, 2-year, coed. Part of Minnesota State Colleges and Universities System. Awards certificates, diplomas, transfer associate, and terminal associate degrees. Founded 1949. Setting: 239-acre small town campus. Total enrollment: 3,599. Faculty: 150 (92 full-time, 58 part-time). Student-undergrad faculty ratio is 19:1. 1,200 applied, 100% were admitted. Full-time: 1,375 students, 49% women, 51% men. Part-time: 2,224 students, 61% women, 39% men. Students come from 24 states and territories, 1 other country, 7% from out-of-state. 2% American Indian or Alaska Native, non-Hispanic/Latino; 4% Hispanic/Latino; 7% Black or African American, non-Hispanic/Latino; 3% Asian, non-Hispanic/Latino; 0.1% Native Hawaiian or other Pacific Islander, non-Hispanic/Latino; 0.5% international. 11% transferred in. Retention: 56% of full-time freshmen returned the following year. Calendar: semesters. Academic remediation for entering students, services for LD students, advanced placement, distance learning, double major, summer session for credit, part-time degree program, adult/continuing education programs, co-op programs and internships. Off campus study at other colleges in the Minnesota State Colleges and Universities System.

Entrance Requirements: Open admission. Options: electronic application, early admission, deferred admission, international baccalaureate accepted. Required: high school transcript. Entrance: noncompetitive. Application deadline: 8/24. Notification: continuous. Transfer credits accepted: Yes.

Costs Per Year: Application fee: $20. State resident tuition: $4950 full-time, $165 per credit hour part-time. Nonresident tuition: $4950 full-time, $165 per credit hour part-time. Mandatory fees: $598 full-time, $299.50 per term part-time. Full-time tuition and fees vary according to course load and program. Part-time tuition and fees vary according to course load and program.

Collegiate Environment: Orientation program. Choral group, student-run radio station. Social organizations: 31 open to all; Phi Theta Kappa. Most popular organizations: Student Senate, PAMA, AD Nursing, PN Nursing, Fire Tech. Major annual events: Earth Day Campus Clean-Up, Rock n' Bowl, Black History Month's Soul Food Feed. Student services: personal-psychological counseling, women's center. Campus security: student patrols, late night transport-escort service. Northland Community and Technical College Library plus 1 other. Books: 24,000 (physical), 19,000 (digital/electronic); Serial titles: 55 (physical); Databases: 47. Weekly public service hours: 82; students can reserve study rooms. 800 computers available on campus for general student use. A campuswide network can be accessed. Students can access the following: online class registration. Staffed computer lab on campus provides training in use of computers, software, and the Internet.

Community Environment: Thief River Falls (population 8,300) is in northwest Minnesota. The facilities for outdoor recreation are numerous. Commercial transportation is available. The community provides a complete downtown shopping center, a public library, hospitals and an employment office.

■ **NORTHWEST TECHNICAL COLLEGE**
905 Grant Ave., SE
Bemidji, MN 56601
Tel: (218)333-6600; Free: 800-942-8324
E-mail: kari.kantack@ntcmn.edu
Web Site: www.ntcmn.edu

Description: State-supported, 2-year, coed. Part of Minnesota State Colleges and Universities System. Administratively affiliated with Bemidji State University. Awards certificates, diplomas, and terminal associate degrees. Founded 1993. Setting: small town campus. Total enrollment: 1,114. Faculty: 73 (28 full-time, 45 part-time). Student-undergrad faculty ratio is 14:1. Full-time: 336 students, 55% women, 45% men. Part-time: 778 students, 75% women, 25% men. 7% from out-of-state. 8% American Indian or Alaska Native, non-Hispanic/Latino; 2% Hispanic/Latino; 2% Black or African American, non-Hispanic/Latino; 0.4% Asian, non-Hispanic/Latino; 0.3% Native Hawaiian or other Pacific Islander, non-Hispanic/Latino; 0.3% international. 56% 25 or older, 4% live on campus, 13% transferred in. Retention: 49% of full-time freshmen returned the following year. Calendar: semesters. Part-time degree program.

Entrance Requirements: Option: electronic application. Required: high school transcript. Entrance: noncompetitive.

Collegiate Environment: Orientation program. Northwest Technical College Learning Enrichment Center.

■ **OAK HILLS CHRISTIAN COLLEGE**
1600 Oak Hills Rd., SW
Bemidji, MN 56601-8832
Tel: (218)751-8670; Free: 888-751-8670
Fax: (218)751-8825
E-mail: admissions@oakhills.edu
Web Site: www.oakhills.edu

Description: Independent interdenominational, 4-year, coed. Awards associate and bachelor's degrees. Founded 1946. Setting: 180-acre rural campus. Endowment: $371,108. Educational spending for the previous fiscal year: $2700 per student. Total enrollment: 140. Faculty: 19 (6 full-time, 13 part-time). Student-undergrad faculty ratio is 13:1. 70 applied, 56% were admitted. 5% from top 10% of their high school class, 5% from top quarter, 47% from top half. Full-time: 134 students, 51% women, 49% men. Part-time: 6 students, 67% women, 33% men. Students come from 16 states and territories, 1 other country, 33% from out-of-state. 1% American Indian or Alaska Native, non-Hispanic/Latino; 0.7% Hispanic/Latino; 4% Black or African American, non-Hispanic/Latino; 1% Asian, non-Hispanic/Latino; 0.7% international. 14% 25 or older, 85% live on campus, 11% transferred in. Retention: 55% of full-time freshmen returned the following year. Academic areas with the most degrees conferred: theology and religious vocations; liberal arts/general studies. Core. Calendar: semesters. Academic remediation for entering students, services for LD students, advanced placement, independent study, double major, part-time degree program, internships. Off campus study.

Entrance Requirements: Options: electronic application, deferred admission. Required: essay, high school transcript, minimum 2 high school GPA, 2 recommendations, SAT or ACT. Required for some: interview. Entrance: minimally difficult. Application deadline: rolling. Notification: continuous. SAT Reasoning Test deadline: 9/1. SAT Subject Test deadline: 9/1. Transfer credits accepted: Yes.

Collegiate Environment: Choral group. Most popular organizations: Student Council (SALT), Students Older Than Average, Student Activity Team, Outreach Program. Major annual events: Spring Banquet, Christmas Festival, Spiritual Enrichment Days and Campus Clean-Up. Student services: health clinic, personal-psychological counseling. Campus security: controlled dormitory access, evening patrols by trained security personnel. Cummings Library. Operations spending for the previous fiscal year: $56,924. 8 computers available on campus for general student use. A campuswide network can be accessed from student residence rooms. Students can access the following: online class registration. Staffed computer lab on campus.

■ **PINE TECHNICAL AND COMMUNITY COLLEGE**
900 4th St. SE
Pine City, MN 55063
Tel: (320)629-5100; Free: 800-521-7463
Fax: (320)629-5101
Web Site: www.pine.edu
Description: State-supported, 2-year, coed. Part of Minnesota State Colleges and Universities System. Awards certificates, diplomas, transfer associate, and terminal associate degrees. Founded 1965. Setting: 6-acre small town campus with easy access to Minneapolis-St. Paul. Total enrollment: 812. Faculty: 39 (18 full-time, 21 part-time). Student-undergrad faculty ratio is 18:1. Full-time: 296 students, 60% women, 40% men. Part-time: 516 students, 72% women, 28% men. Students come from 5 states and territories, 10% from out-of-state. 45% 25 or older, 11% transferred in. Core. Calendar: semesters. Academic remediation for entering students, services for LD students, advanced placement, independent study, distance learning, double major, summer session for credit, part-time degree program, internships.
Entrance Requirements: Open admission except for gunsmithing. Option: early admission. Required: high school transcript. Entrance: noncompetitive. Application deadline: rolling.
Collegiate Environment: Orientation program. Student services: personal-psychological counseling, women's center. Campus security: late night transport-escort service. Learning Resource Technology Center plus 1 other. 150 computers available on campus for general student use. A campuswide network can be accessed from off-campus. Students can access the following: online class registration. Staffed computer lab on campus.

■ **RAINY RIVER COMMUNITY COLLEGE**
1501 Hwy. 71
International Falls, MN 56649
Tel: (218)285-7722; Free: 800-456-3996
Fax: (218)285-2239
E-mail: berta.wilcox@rainyriver.edu
Web Site: www.rainyriver.edu
Description: State-supported, 2-year, coed. Part of Minnesota State Colleges and Universities System. Awards certificates, diplomas, transfer associate, and terminal associate degrees. Founded 1967. Setting: 80-acre small town campus. Total enrollment: 241. Faculty: 25 (10 full-time, 15 part-time). Student-undergrad faculty ratio is 15:1. Students come from 16 states and territories, 2 other countries. 8% American Indian or Alaska Native, non-Hispanic/Latino; 9% Hispanic/Latino; 19% Black or African American, non-Hispanic/Latino; 1% Asian, non-Hispanic/Latino; 7% international. 54% 25 or older. Core. Calendar: semesters. Academic remediation for entering students, services for LD students, advanced placement, honors program, independent study, summer session for credit, part-time degree program, adult/continuing education programs, co-op programs and internships.
Entrance Requirements: Open admission. Options: electronic application, early admission, deferred admission. Recommended: high school transcript. Entrance: noncompetitive. Application deadline: rolling. Notification: continuous. Transfer credits accepted: Yes.
Costs Per Year: Application fee: $20. State resident tuition: $5,324 full-time, $177.47 per credit part-time. Nonresident tuition: $6,506 full-time, $216.87 per credit part-time. Full-time tuition varies according to course load and reciprocity agreements. Part-time tuition varies according to course load and reciprocity agreements. College room and board: $4280. College room only: $3480.
Collegiate Environment: Orientation program. Drama-theater group. Social organizations: 3 open to all. Most popular organizations: Anishinaabe Student Coalition, Student Senate, Black Student Association. Major annual events: Awareness Week, Diversity Week, Rainy Experience Giving. Student

services: personal-psychological counseling. Campus security: 24-hour emergency response devices, late night transport-escort service, controlled dormitory access. Rainy River Community College Library. 70 computers available on campus for general student use. A campuswide network can be accessed. Students can access the following: online class registration. Staffed computer lab on campus provides training in use of computers, software, and the Internet.
Community Environment: Located on the Rainy River, which is the Minnesota-Ontario border. International Falls (population 6,332) is the supply point for an immense wilderness region famous for hunting, fishing and canoe trips. It is also an important port of entry from Ontario vacation country. Community facilities include complete church representation, good medical services, downtown and mall shopping areas, and numerous service organizations. Because of the great influx of summer tourists, many part-time jobs are available. Millions of acres are in the wilderness including Voyageurs National Park, which is close to International Falls. Rainy Lake, the biggest tourist attraction in the area, is 3 miles from town and features year-round good fishing. Other sports are swimming, water skiing, camping, hunting, boating and winter sports.

■ **RASMUSSEN COLLEGE BLAINE**
3629 95th Ave. NE
Blaine, MN 55014
Tel: (763)795-4720; Free: 888-549-6755
E-mail: susan.hammerstrom@rasmussen.edu
Web Site: www.rasmussen.edu
Description: Proprietary, 4-year, coed. Part of Rasmussen College System. Awards associate and bachelor's degrees. Setting: suburban campus with easy access to Minneapolis-St. Paul. Total enrollment: 393. Faculty: 34 (8 full-time, 26 part-time). Student-undergrad faculty ratio is 22:1. 28 applied, 93% were admitted. Full-time: 228 students, 77% women, 23% men. Part-time: 165 students, 66% women, 34% men. 72% 25 or older. Core. Calendar: quarters. Academic remediation for entering students, accelerated degree program, distance learning, double major, summer session for credit, part-time degree program, adult/continuing education programs, internships.
Entrance Requirements: Options: electronic application, early admission, deferred admission. Required: high school transcript, minimum 2 high school GPA, institutional exam. Required for some: interview. Entrance: minimally difficult. Application deadline: rolling. Transfer credits accepted: Yes.
Collegiate Environment: Orientation program. Rasmussen College Library - Blaine. 81 computers available on campus for general student use. A campuswide network can be accessed from off-campus.

■ **RASMUSSEN COLLEGE BLOOMINGTON**
4400 W 78th St.
Bloomington, MN 55435
Tel: (952)545-2000; Free: 888-549-6755
E-mail: dwayne.bertotto@rasmussen.edu
Web Site: www.rasmussen.edu
Description: Proprietary, 4-year, coed. Part of Rasmussen College System. Awards associate and bachelor's degrees. Founded 1904. Setting: suburban campus with easy access to Minneapolis-St. Paul. Total enrollment: 997. Student-undergrad faculty ratio is 22:1. 26 applied, 92% were admitted. Full-time: 923 students, 82% women, 18% men. Part-time: 74 students, 69% women, 31% men. 71% 25 or older. Core. Calendar: quarters. Academic remediation for entering students, accelerated degree program, distance learning, double major, summer session for credit, part-time degree program, adult/continuing education programs, internships.
Entrance Requirements: Options: electronic application, early admission, deferred admission. Required: high school transcript, minimum 2 high school GPA, institutional exam. Required for some: interview. Entrance: minimally difficult. Application deadline: rolling. Transfer credits accepted: Yes.
Collegiate Environment: Orientation program. Rasmussen College Library - Bloomington. 68 computers available on campus for general student use. A campuswide network can be accessed from off-campus. Staffed computer lab on campus.

■ **RASMUSSEN COLLEGE BROOKLYN PARK**
8301 93rd Ave. N
Brooklyn Park, MN 55445
Tel: (763)493-4500; Free: 888-549-6755
Fax: (763)425-4344
E-mail: dwayne.bertotto@rasmussen.edu
Web Site: www.rasmussen.edu

Description: Proprietary, 4-year, coed. Part of Rasmussen College System. Awards associate and bachelor's degrees. Setting: suburban campus with easy access to Minneapolis-St. Paul. Total enrollment: 568. Faculty: 53 (12 full-time, 41 part-time). Student-undergrad faculty ratio is 22:1. 47 applied, 79% were admitted. Full-time: 458 students, 78% women, 22% men. Part-time: 110 students, 85% women, 15% men. 75% 25 or older. Core. Calendar: quarters. Academic remediation for entering students, accelerated degree program, distance learning, double major, summer session for credit, part-time degree program, adult/continuing education programs, internships.
Entrance Requirements: Options: electronic application, early admission, deferred admission. Required: high school transcript, minimum 2 high school GPA, institutional exam. Required for some: interview. Entrance: minimally difficult. Application deadline: rolling. Transfer credits accepted: Yes.
Collegiate Environment: Orientation program. Rasmussen College Library - Brooklyn Park. 80 computers available on campus for general student use. A campuswide network can be accessed from off-campus.

■ **RASMUSSEN COLLEGE EAGAN**
3500 Federal Dr.
Eagan, MN 55122
Tel: (651)687-9000; Free: 888-549-6755
Fax: (651)687-0507
E-mail: dwayne.bertotto@rasmussen.edu
Web Site: www.rasmussen.edu
Description: Proprietary, 4-year, coed. Part of Rasmussen College System. Awards associate and bachelor's degrees. Founded 1904. Setting: suburban campus with easy access to Minneapolis-St. Paul. Total enrollment: 506. Faculty: 83 (11 full-time, 72 part-time). Student-undergrad faculty ratio is 22:1. 27 applied, 93% were admitted. Full-time: 389 students, 72% women, 28% men. Part-time: 117 students, 74% women, 26% men. Core. Calendar: quarters. Academic remediation for entering students, accelerated degree program, distance learning, double major, summer session for credit, part-time degree program, adult/continuing education programs, internships.
Entrance Requirements: Options: electronic application, early admission, deferred admission. Required: high school transcript, minimum 2 high school GPA, institutional exam. Required for some: interview. Entrance: minimally difficult. Application deadline: rolling. Transfer credits accepted: Yes.
Collegiate Environment: Orientation program. Rasmussen College Library - Eagan. 93 computers available on campus for general student use. A campuswide network can be accessed from off-campus.

■ **RASMUSSEN COLLEGE LAKE ELMO/WOODBURY**
8565 Eagle Point Cir.
Lake Elmo, MN 55042
Tel: (651)259-6600; Free: 888-549-6755
Fax: (651)259-6601
E-mail: susan.hammerstrom@rasmussen.edu
Web Site: www.rasmussen.edu
Description: Proprietary, 4-year, coed. Part of Rasmussen College System. Awards associate and bachelor's degrees. Setting: suburban campus with easy access to Minneapolis-St. Paul. Total enrollment: 2,169. Faculty: 23 (6 full-time, 17 part-time). Student-undergrad faculty ratio is 22:1. Full-time: 269 students, 82% women, 18% men. Part-time: 1,900 students, 85% women, 15% men. 73% 25 or older. Core. Calendar: quarters. Academic remediation for entering students, accelerated degree program, distance learning, double major, summer session for credit, part-time degree program, adult/continuing education programs, internships.
Entrance Requirements: Options: electronic application, early admission, deferred admission. Required: high school transcript, minimum 2 high school GPA, institutional exam. Required for some: interview. Entrance: minimally difficult. Application deadline: rolling. Transfer credits accepted: Yes.
Collegiate Environment: Orientation program. Rasmussen College Library - Lake Elmo. 85 computers available on campus for general student use. A campuswide network can be accessed from off-campus.

■ **RASMUSSEN COLLEGE MANKATO**
1400 Madison Ave.
Mankato, MN 56001
Tel: (507)625-6556; Free: 888-549-6755
Fax: (507)625-6557
E-mail: dwayne.bertto@rasmussen.edu
Web Site: www.rasmussen.edu
Description: Proprietary, 4-year, coed. Part of Rasmussen College System. Awards associate and bachelor's degrees. Founded 1904. Setting: suburban

campus with easy access to Minneapolis-St. Paul. Total enrollment: 682. Faculty: 62 (18 full-time, 44 part-time). Student-undergrad faculty ratio is 22:1. 37 applied, 86% were admitted. Full-time: 597 students, 83% women, 17% men. Part-time: 85 students, 74% women, 26% men. Core. Calendar: quarters. Academic remediation for entering students, accelerated degree program, distance learning, double major, summer session for credit, part-time degree program, adult/continuing education programs, internships.
Entrance Requirements: Options: electronic application, early admission, deferred admission. Required: high school transcript, minimum 2 high school GPA, institutional exam. Required for some: interview. Entrance: minimally difficult. Application deadline: rolling. Transfer credits accepted: Yes.
Collegiate Environment: Orientation program. Rasmussen College Library - Mankato. 116 computers available on campus for general student use. A campuswide network can be accessed from off-campus.

■ **RASMUSSEN COLLEGE MOORHEAD**
1250 29th Ave. S
Moorhead, MN 56560
Tel: (218)304-6200; Free: 888-549-6755
Fax: (218)304-2601
E-mail: susan.hammerstrom@rasmussen.edu
Web Site: www.rasmussen.edu
Description: Proprietary, 4-year, coed. Part of Rasmussen College System. Awards associate and bachelor's degrees. Setting: suburban campus. Total enrollment: 190. Faculty: 55 (8 full-time, 47 part-time). Student-undergrad faculty ratio is 22:1. 10 applied, 100% were admitted. Full-time: 114 students, 75% women, 25% men. Part-time: 76 students, 82% women, 18% men. 61% 25 or older. Core. Calendar: quarters. Academic remediation for entering students, accelerated degree program, distance learning, double major, summer session for credit, part-time degree program, adult/continuing education programs, internships.
Entrance Requirements: Options: electronic application, early admission, deferred admission. Required: high school transcript, minimum 2 high school GPA, institutional exam. Required for some: interview. Entrance: minimally difficult. Application deadline: rolling. Transfer credits accepted: Yes.
Collegiate Environment: Orientation program. Rasmussen College Library - Moorhead. 31 computers available on campus for general student use. A campuswide network can be accessed from off-campus.

■ **RASMUSSEN COLLEGE ST. CLOUD**
226 Park Ave. S
Saint Cloud, MN 56301
Tel: (320)251-5600; Free: 888-549-6755
Fax: (320)251-3702
E-mail: dwayne.bertotto@rasmussen.edu
Web Site: www.rasmussen.edu
Description: Proprietary, 4-year, coed. Part of Rasmussen College System. Awards associate and bachelor's degrees. Founded 1904. Setting: suburban campus. Total enrollment: 765. Faculty: 62 (16 full-time, 46 part-time). Student-undergrad faculty ratio is 22:1. 37 applied, 92% were admitted. Full-time: 665 students, 84% women, 16% men. Part-time: 100 students, 89% women, 11% men. 68% 25 or older. Core. Calendar: quarters. Academic remediation for entering students, accelerated degree program, distance learning, double major, summer session for credit, part-time degree program, adult/continuing education programs, internships.
Entrance Requirements: Options: electronic application, early admission, deferred admission. Required: high school transcript, minimum 2 high school GPA, institutional exam. Required for some: interview. Entrance: minimally difficult. Application deadline: rolling. Transfer credits accepted: Yes.
Collegiate Environment: Orientation program. Rasmussen College Library - St. Cloud. 91 computers available on campus for general student use. A campuswide network can be accessed from off-campus.

■ **RIDGEWATER COLLEGE**
2101 15th Ave. NW
Willmar, MN 56201
Tel: (320)222-5200; Free: 800-722-1151
E-mail: linda.duering@ridgewater.edu
Web Site: www.ridgewater.edu
Description: State-supported, 2-year, coed. Part of Minnesota State Colleges and Universities System. Awards certificates, diplomas, transfer associate, and terminal associate degrees. Founded 1961. Setting: 83-acre small town campus. Total enrollment: 4,385. Faculty: 186 (110 full-time, 76 part-time). Calendar: semesters. Academic remediation for entering

students, services for LD students, advanced placement, self-designed majors, distance learning, summer session for credit, part-time degree program, co-op programs and internships. Off campus study at other colleges in the Minnesota State Colleges and Universities System. Study abroad program.

Entrance Requirements: Open admission except for nursing, chemical dependency practitioner, and veterinary technology programs. Option: electronic application. Required: high school transcript. Required for some: interview. Entrance: noncompetitive.

Costs Per Year: Application fee: $20. State resident tuition: $5760 full-time, $161.29 per credit hour part-time. Nonresident tuition: $5760 full-time, $161.29 per credit hour part-time. Mandatory fees: $579 full-time, $19.45 per credit hour part-time. Full-time tuition and fees vary according to course load and reciprocity agreements. Part-time tuition and fees vary according to course load and reciprocity agreements.

Collegiate Environment: Orientation program. Student services: personal-psychological counseling. Campus security: 24-hour emergency response devices. College housing not available.

Community Environment: Greater Willmar, with a population of approximately 18,000, is the largest city within a 60-mile radius. It is an important shipping point for grain and livestock. The division headquarters of the Burlington Northern Railway and a large Hormel turkey-processing plant are located here. Other products manufactured here are plastics, furniture, sheet metal, concrete, clothing, machinery, cookies, and dairy products. The many lakes in the area provide good fishing and recreation. The campus is located in prime hunting country. The community offers a semirural setting with many cultural opportunities and, at the same time, is two hours from the Twin Cities of Minneapolis and St. Paul. The city of Hutchinson is a population center of approximately 13,700 and is located 60 miles west of the Twin Cities on Highway 7. Hutchinson has the second oldest park system in the United States and takes pride in its adaptation to the local environment, such as the Crow River, which flows through the community. In addition, there are a dozen lakes within 15 minutes which are ideal for boating and fishing. Major employers in Hutchinson include 3M Company, Hutchinson Technology, Inc., Hutchinson Manufacturing, and Mid-America Dairymen, Inc. A small town atmosphere with a high-tech future.

■ RIVERLAND COMMUNITY COLLEGE

1900 8th Ave., NW
Austin, MN 55912
Tel: (507)433-0600; Free: 800-247-5039
Fax: (507)433-0515
Web Site: www.riverland.edu

Description: State-supported, 2-year, coed. Part of Minnesota State Colleges and Universities System. Awards certificates, diplomas, transfer associate, and terminal associate degrees. Founded 1940. Setting: 187-acre small town campus. Total enrollment: 3,014. Students come from 16 states and territories, 23 other countries, 3% from out-of-state. 0.3% American Indian or Alaska Native, non-Hispanic/Latino; 11% Hispanic/Latino; 5% Black or African American, non-Hispanic/Latino; 1% Asian, non-Hispanic/Latino; 0.2% Native Hawaiian or other Pacific Islander, non-Hispanic/Latino; 1% international. 39% 25 or older, 2% live on campus. Retention: 52% of full-time freshmen returned the following year. Core. Calendar: semesters. Academic remediation for entering students, ESL program, services for LD students, advanced placement, independent study, distance learning, double major, summer session for credit, part-time degree program, adult/continuing education programs, internships. Off campus study at Minnesota State Colleges and Universities System. Study abroad program.

Entrance Requirements: Open admission except for nursing, human services, occupational therapy assistant, physical therapy assistant, law enforcement programs. Options: electronic application, early admission. Required: high school transcript. Entrance: noncompetitive. Application deadline: rolling.

Collegiate Environment: Orientation program. Drama-theater group, choral group, student-run newspaper. Social organizations: 8 open to all. Most popular organizations: College Choir, student newspaper, Student Activities Board, Phi Theta Kappa, Theater Club. Major annual events: Multicultural Week, College Fair, Technology Day. Student services: personal-psychological counseling, women's center. Campus security: late night transport-escort service. Riverland Community College Library plus 2 others. 175 computers available on campus for general student use. A campuswide network can be accessed from student residence rooms. Students can access the following: online class registration. Staffed computer lab on campus provides training in use of computers, software, and the Internet.

■ ROCHESTER COMMUNITY AND TECHNICAL COLLEGE

851 30th Ave., SE
Rochester, MN 55904-4999
Tel: (507)285-7210
Fax: (507)285-7496
Web Site: www.rctc.edu

Description: State-supported, 2-year, coed. Part of Minnesota State Colleges and Universities System. Awards certificates, diplomas, transfer associate, and terminal associate degrees (also offers 13 programs that lead to a bachelor's degree with Winona State University or University of Minnesota). Founded 1915. Setting: 460-acre small town campus. Total enrollment: 5,898. 34% 25 or older. Core. Calendar: semesters. Academic remediation for entering students, ESL program, services for LD students, advanced placement, honors program, independent study, distance learning, summer session for credit, part-time degree program, internships. Off campus study at other colleges in the Minnesota State Colleges and Universities System, Winona State University-Rochester Center.

Entrance Requirements: Open admission except for allied health, technology programs. Option: early admission. Required: high school transcript. Entrance: noncompetitive. Application deadline: 8/24. Notification: continuous.

Collegiate Environment: Orientation program. Drama-theater group, choral group, student-run newspaper. Student services: health clinic, personal-psychological counseling. Campus security: student patrols, late night transport-escort service. Goddard Library plus 1 other.

Community Environment: The Mayo Clinic, founded by Drs. William and Charles Mayo, has made Rochester (population 94,950) world famous. The transient population is estimated at 8,000 to 10,000 at any given time. Visitors are estimated at 550,000 annually. All forms of commercial transportation are available. Community cultural facilities include the Rochester Symphony Orchestra, Rochester Municipal Band, Oratorio Society, summer open-air concerts, Carillon concerts 3 times a week, and a civic theater with a full-time director.

■ ST. CATHERINE UNIVERSITY

2004 Randolph Ave.
Saint Paul, MN 55105
Tel: (651)690-6000; Free: 800-945-4599
Fax: (651)690-6042
E-mail: stkate@stkate.edu
Web Site: www.stkate.edu

Description: Independent Roman Catholic, comprehensive. Awards associate, bachelor's, master's, and doctoral degrees. Founded 1905. Setting: 110-acre urban campus with easy access to Minneapolis-St. Paul. Total enrollment: 4,724. Faculty: 536 (292 full-time, 244 part-time). Student-undergrad faculty ratio is 10:1. 2,682 applied, 70% were admitted. 24% from top 10% of their high school class, 62% from top quarter, 94% from top half. Full-time: 2,124 students, 99% women, 1% men. Part-time: 1,034 students, 92% women, 8% men. 12% from out-of-state. 0.4% American Indian or Alaska Native, non-Hispanic/Latino; 9% Hispanic/Latino; 10% Black or African American, non-Hispanic/Latino; 11% Asian, non-Hispanic/Latino; 0.2% Native Hawaiian or other Pacific Islander, non-Hispanic/Latino; 0.7% international. 6% 25 or older, 38% live on campus, 19% transferred in. Retention: 81% of full-time freshmen returned the following year. Academic areas with the most degrees conferred: health professions and related sciences; business/marketing; public administration and social services. Calendar: 4-1-4. Self-designed majors, honors program, independent study, distance learning, double major, part-time degree program, adult/continuing education programs, internships. Study abroad program. ROTC: Army (c), Air Force (c).

Entrance Requirements: Options: deferred admission, international baccalaureate accepted. Required: high school transcript, 1 recommendation, SAT or ACT. Recommended: interview. Required for some: essay, interview. Entrance: moderately difficult. SAT Reasoning Test deadline: 8/15.

Costs Per Year: Application fee: $0. Comprehensive fee: $51,523 includes full-time tuition ($41,504), mandatory fees ($759), and college room and board ($9260). Full-time tuition and fees vary according to degree level. Room and board charges vary according to board plan and housing facility. Part-time tuition: $1297 per credit hour. Part-time mandatory fees: $322 per term. Part-time tuition and fees vary according to degree level.

Collegiate Environment: Orientation program. Drama-theater group, choral group, student-run newspaper, radio station. Campus security: 24-hour emergency response devices and patrols, student patrols, late night transport-escort service, controlled dormitory access. St. Catherine Library.

■ ST. CLOUD STATE UNIVERSITY

720 4th Ave. S
Saint Cloud, MN 56301-4498
Tel: (320)308-0121; Free: 877-654-7278
E-mail: scsu4u@stcloudstate.edu
Web Site: www.stcloudstate.edu

Description: State-supported, comprehensive, coed. Part of Minnesota State Colleges and Universities System. Awards associate, bachelor's, master's, and doctoral degrees and post-master's certificates. Founded 1869. Setting: 100-acre suburban campus with easy access to Minneapolis-St. Paul. Endowment: $24.7 million. Research spending for the previous fiscal year: $3.1 million. Educational spending for the previous fiscal year: $7195 per student. Total enrollment: 15,092. Faculty: 744 (501 full-time, 243 part-time). Student-undergrad faculty ratio is 20:1. 6,986 applied, 85% were admitted. 5% from top 10% of their high school class, 19% from top quarter, 46% from top half. Full-time: 8,837 students, 52% women, 48% men. Part-time: 4,399 students, 55% women, 45% men. Students come from 48 states and territories, 95 other countries, 8% from out-of-state. 0.3% American Indian or Alaska Native, non-Hispanic/Latino; 3% Hispanic/Latino; 6% Black or African American, non-Hispanic/Latino; 6% Asian, non-Hispanic/Latino; 7% international. 19% 25 or older, 8% transferred in. Retention: 69% of full-time freshmen returned the following year. Academic areas with the most degrees conferred: business/marketing; health professions and related sciences; education. Core. Calendar: semesters. Academic remediation for entering students, ESL program, services for LD students, advanced placement, accelerated degree program, self-designed majors, honors program, independent study, distance learning, double major, summer session for credit, part-time degree program, adult/continuing education programs, co-op programs and internships, graduate courses open to undergrads. Off campus study at members of the Tri-College Exchange Program, other colleges in the Minnesota State Colleges and University System. Study abroad program. ROTC: Army.

Entrance Requirements: Options: electronic application, deferred admission, international baccalaureate accepted. Required: high school transcript, SAT or ACT. Entrance: moderately difficult. Application deadline: 8/1. Notification: continuous, continuous for nonresidents. SAT Reasoning Test deadline: 8/1. SAT Subject Test deadline: 8/1. Transfer credits accepted: Yes.

Costs Per Year: Application fee: $20. State resident tuition: $7094 full-time, $241 per credit hour part-time. Nonresident tuition: $15,328 full-time, $520.75 per credit hour part-time. Mandatory fees: $1166 full-time, $50.75 per credit hour part-time, $65 per term part-time. Full-time tuition and fees vary according to course load, location, and reciprocity agreements. Part-time tuition and fees vary according to course load, location, and reciprocity agreements. College room and board: $8900. College room only: $5526. Room and board charges vary according to board plan and housing facility.

Collegiate Environment: Orientation program. Drama-theater group, choral group, student-run newspaper, radio station. Social organizations: 202 open to all; national fraternities, national sororities, local sororities. Most popular organizations: Nepalese Student Association, Residence Hall Association, International Student Association, College Panhellenic Council, KVSC - Campus Radio Station. Major annual events: Huskies First Four Weeks, Mainstreet, Atwood After Dark. Student services: legal services, health clinic, personal-psychological counseling, women's center. Campus security: 24-hour emergency response devices and patrols, student patrols, late night transport-escort service. James W. Miller Learning Resources Center. Operations spending for the previous fiscal year: $3.8 million.

■ ST. CLOUD TECHNICAL & COMMUNITY COLLEGE

1540 Northway Dr.
Saint Cloud, MN 56303-1240
Tel: (320)654-5000; Free: 800-222-1009
Fax: (320)654-5981
E-mail: jelness@sctcc.edu
Web Site: www.sctcc.edu

Description: State-supported, 2-year, coed. Part of Minnesota State Colleges and Universities System. Awards certificates, diplomas, transfer associate, and terminal associate degrees. Founded 1948. Setting: 35-acre urban campus with easy access to Minneapolis-St. Paul. Research spending for the previous fiscal year: $5476. Educational spending for the previous fiscal year: $4900 per student. Total enrollment: 4,751. Faculty: 259 (96 full-time, 163 part-time). Student-undergrad faculty ratio is 22:1. 1,866 applied, 98% were admitted. Full-time: 2,230 students, 49% women, 51% men. Part-time: 2,521 students, 58% women, 42% men. Students come from 7 states

and territories, 1 other country, 3% from out-of-state. 0.5% American Indian or Alaska Native, non-Hispanic/Latino; 3% Hispanic/Latino; 6% Black or African American, non-Hispanic/Latino; 1% Asian, non-Hispanic/Latino; 0.3% international. 35% 25 or older, 37% transferred in. Retention: 49% of full-time freshmen returned the following year. Calendar: semesters. Academic remediation for entering students, ESL program, services for LD students, advanced placement, independent study, distance learning, summer session for credit, part-time degree program, adult/continuing education programs, co-op programs and internships.

Entrance Requirements: Open admission except for dental hygiene, echocardiography, sonography, nursing, invasive cardiovascular technology. Options: electronic application, early admission, deferred admission. Required: high school transcript. Required for some: essay, interview. Entrance: noncompetitive. Application deadline: rolling. Notification: continuous until 8/1. Transfer credits accepted: Yes.

Collegiate Environment: Orientation program. Drama-theater group. Social organizations: 18 open to all. Most popular organizations: Student Senate, Distributive Education Club of America, Phi Theta Kappa Honor Society, SkillsUSA, Central Minnesota Builders Association. Major annual events: Graduation, Annual Job Fair, Fall Welcome Back Activities. Student services: personal-psychological counseling. Campus security: late night transport-escort service. Learning Resource Center plus 1 other. Operations spending for the previous fiscal year: $240,130. 690 computers available on campus for general student use. Computer purchase/lease plans available. A computer is required for all students. A campuswide network can be accessed. Students can access the following: online class registration. Staffed computer lab on campus provides training in use of computers, software, and the Internet.

■ SAINT JOHN'S UNIVERSITY

2850 Abbey Plz.
Collegeville, MN 56321
Tel: (320)363-2011; Free: 800-544-1489
Fax: (320)363-3206
E-mail: admissions@csbsju.edu
Web Site: www.csbsju.edu

Description: Independent Roman Catholic, comprehensive. Awards bachelor's and master's degrees (coordinate with College of Saint Benedict for women). Founded 1857. Setting: 2,500-acre rural campus with easy access to Minneapolis-St. Paul. Endowment: $196.8 million. Research spending for the previous fiscal year: $1.2 million. Educational spending for the previous fiscal year: $15,108 per student. Total enrollment: 1,777. Faculty: 157 (131 full-time, 26 part-time). Student-undergrad faculty ratio is 12:1. 1,552 applied, 80% were admitted. 16% from top 10% of their high school class, 44% from top quarter, 74% from top half. 1 National Merit Scholar. Full-time: 1,646 students, 100% men. Part-time: 21 students, 100% men. Students come from 37 states and territories, 13 other countries, 20% from out-of-state. 0.7% American Indian or Alaska Native, non-Hispanic/Latino; 8% Hispanic/Latino; 5% Black or African American, non-Hispanic/Latino; 3% Asian, non-Hispanic/Latino; 0.3% Native Hawaiian or other Pacific Islander, non-Hispanic/Latino; 5% international. 1% 25 or older, 88% live on campus, 1% transferred in. Retention: 87% of full-time freshmen returned the following year. Academic areas with the most degrees conferred: business/marketing; social sciences; English. Core. Calendar: semesters. ESL program, services for LD students, advanced placement, self-designed majors, honors program, independent study, double major, internships, graduate courses open to undergrads. Off campus study at College of Saint Benedict, Saint Cloud State University. Study abroad program. ROTC: Army.

Entrance Requirements: Options: electronic application, early action, deferred admission, international baccalaureate accepted. Required: high school transcript, college preparatory program, SAT or ACT. Recommended: minimum 3 high school GPA. Entrance: moderately difficult. Application deadline: 12/15 for early action. Notification: 1/15 for early action. Transfer credits accepted: Yes. Early action applicants: 1,149. Early action applicants admitted: 981.

Costs Per Year: Application fee: $0. Comprehensive fee: $55,309 includes full-time tuition ($44,184), mandatory fees ($806), and college room and board ($10,319). College room only: $5171. Room and board charges vary according to board plan and housing facility. Part-time tuition: $1841 per credit hour. Part-time tuition varies according to course load.

Collegiate Environment: Orientation program. Drama-theater group, choral group, student-run newspaper, radio station. Social organizations: 100 open to all. Most popular organizations: Joint Events Council, Outdoor Leadership Center, Magis Ministries, Enactus, Archipelago Caribbean Association. Major annual events: Involvement Fair, Festival of Cultures, Pines Concert in Spring. Student services: health clinic, personal-psychological counseling. Campus security: 24-hour emergency response devices and patrols, student patrols, late night transport-escort service, controlled dormitory access. 1,529 college housing spaces available; 1,474 were occupied in 2018-19. Freshmen guaranteed college housing. On-campus residence required through senior year. Option: men-only housing available. Alcuin Library plus 2 others. Books: 659,802 (physical), 741,067 (digital/electronic); Serial titles: 798 (physical), 35,878 (digital/electronic); Databases: 226. Weekly public service hours: 104; students can reserve study rooms. Operations spending for the previous fiscal year: $1.7 million. 248 computers available on campus for general student use. A campuswide network can be accessed from student residence rooms and from off campus. Students can access the following: online class registration, online student accounts. Staffed computer lab on campus provides training in use of computers, software, and the Internet.

■ SAINT MARY'S UNIVERSITY OF MINNESOTA

700 Ter. Heights
Winona, MN 55987-1399
Tel: (507)452-4430; Free: 800-635-5987
Fax: (507)457-1722
E-mail: dmeyer@smumn.edu
Web Site: www.smumn.edu

Description: Independent Roman Catholic, comprehensive, coed. Awards bachelor's, master's, and doctoral degrees and post-master's certificates. Founded 1912. Setting: 350-acre small town campus. Total enrollment: 5,560. Faculty: 524 (100 full-time, 424 part-time). Student-undergrad faculty ratio is 18:1. 1,641 applied, 92% were admitted. Full-time: 1,118 students, 55% women, 45% men. Part-time: 324 students, 63% women, 37% men. Students come from 33 states and territories, 18 other countries, 48% from out-of-state. 0.4% American Indian or Alaska Native, non-Hispanic/Latino; 8% Hispanic/Latino; 9% Black or African American, non-Hispanic/Latino; 3% Asian, non-Hispanic/Latino; 0.1% Native Hawaiian or other Pacific Islander, non-Hispanic/Latino; 3% international. 1% 25 or older, 85% live on campus, 7% transferred in. Retention: 82% of full-time freshmen returned the following year. Academic areas with the most degrees conferred: business/marketing; health professions and related sciences; education. Core. Calendar: semesters. Academic remediation for entering students, ESL program, services for LD students, advanced placement, accelerated degree program, self-designed majors, honors program, independent study, distance learning, double major, summer session for credit, part-time degree program, adult/continuing education programs, co-op programs and internships, graduate courses open to undergrads. Off campus study at Winona State University, Lasallian International Programs Consortium. Study abroad program. ROTC: Army (c).

Entrance Requirements: Options: electronic application, early admission, deferred admission, international baccalaureate accepted. Required: essay, high school transcript, minimum 2.5 high school GPA, SAT or ACT. Recommended: 2 recommendations. Required for some: interview. Entrance: moderately difficult. Notification: continuous. Transfer credits accepted: Yes.

Costs Per Year: Application fee: $25. Comprehensive fee: $45,940 includes full-time tuition ($36,050), mandatory fees ($540), and college room and board ($9350). College room only: $5230. Part-time tuition: $1200 per credit.

Collegiate Environment: Orientation program. Drama-theater group, choral group, student-run newspaper, radio station. Social organizations: 85 open to all; national fraternities, national sororities; 4% of eligible men and 3% of eligible women are members. Most popular organizations: Student Activity Committee, PR Business Club, Serving Others United in Love (Soul) - Mission Trips, Colleges Against Cancer, Club Hockey. Major annual events: BLUE Angel, Gaslight, Taylor Richmond Benefit Dance. Student services: health clinic, personal-psychological counseling. Campus security: 24-hour emergency response devices and patrols, late night transport-escort service, controlled dormitory access. 1,158 college housing spaces available; 887 were occupied in 2018-19. Freshmen guaranteed college housing. On-campus residence required through sophomore year. Options: coed, men-only, women-only housing available. Fitzgerald Library plus 1 other. Books: 210,639 (physical), 10,144 (digital/electronic); Serial titles: 169 (physical), 82,154 (digital/electronic); Databases: 77. Weekly public service hours: 97; students can reserve study rooms. 200 computers available on campus for general student use. A campuswide network can be accessed from student residence rooms and from off campus. Students can access the following: online class registration. Staffed computer lab on campus provides training in use of computers, software, and the Internet.

■ ST. OLAF COLLEGE

1520 St. Olaf Ave.
Northfield, MN 55057-1098
Tel: (507)786-2222; Free: 800-800-3025
Fax: (507)646-3832
E-mail: admissions@stolaf.edu
Web Site: www.stolaf.edu

Description: Independent Lutheran, 4-year, coed. Awards bachelor's degrees. Founded 1874. Setting: 300-acre small town campus with easy access to Minneapolis-St. Paul. Endowment: $536.1 million. Research spending for the previous fiscal year: $1.5 million. Total enrollment: 3,048. Faculty: 326 (209 full-time, 117 part-time). Student-undergrad faculty ratio is 12:1. 5,496 applied, 50% were admitted. 41% from top 10% of their high school class, 72% from top quarter, 96% from top half. 10 National Merit Scholars. Full-time: 3,023 students, 57% women, 43% men. Part-time: 25 students, 76% women, 24% men. Students come from 49 states and territories, 85 other countries, 53% from out-of-state. 7% Hispanic/Latino; 3% Black or African American, non-Hispanic/Latino; 7% Asian, non-Hispanic/Latino; 0.1% Native Hawaiian or other Pacific Islander, non-Hispanic/Latino; 10% international. 95% live on campus, 1% transferred in. Retention: 91% of full-time freshmen returned the following year. Academic areas with the most degrees conferred: social sciences; biological/life sciences; visual and performing arts. Core. Calendar: 4-1-4. ESL program, services for LD students, advanced placement, self-designed majors, independent study, double major, summer session for credit, part-time degree program, internships. Off campus study at Oak Ridge Science semester, HECUA programs, Washington Semester-American University, Oregon Extension. Study abroad program.

Entrance Requirements: Options: electronic application, early decision, deferred admission, international baccalaureate accepted. Required: essay, high school transcript, 1 recommendation, SAT or ACT. Recommended: 2 recommendations, interview. Entrance: very difficult. Application deadlines: 1/15, 11/15 for early decision. Notification: 3/20, 12/15 for early decision. SAT Reasoning Test deadline: 1/15. Transfer credits accepted: Yes. Applicants placed on waiting list: 911. Wait-listed applicants offered admission: 51. Early decision applicants: 368. Early decision applicants admitted: 279.

Costs Per Year: Application fee: $0. Comprehensive fee: $53,040 includes full-time tuition ($47,840) and college room and board ($5200). College room only: $5650. Room and board charges vary according to board plan. Part-time tuition: $5980 per course. Part-time tuition varies according to course load.

Collegiate Environment: Orientation program. Drama-theater group, choral group, student-run newspaper, radio station. Social organizations: 214 open to all. Most popular organizations: Student Government Association, Ultimate Frisbee Teams, Ole Spring Relief, Alpha Phi Omega, SARN: Sexual Assault Resource Network. Major annual events: Homecoming/Family Weekend, Christmas Festival, Co-Curricular Extravaganza. Student services: health clinic, personal-psychological counseling. Campus security: 24-hour emergency response devices and patrols, late night transport-escort service, controlled dormitory access. 2,750 college housing spaces available; 2,728 were occupied in 2018-19. Freshmen guaranteed college housing. On-campus residence required through senior year. Option: coed housing available. Rolvaag Memorial Library plus 1 other. Books: 610,051 (physical), 606,055 (digital/electronic); Serial titles: 3,347 (physical), 119,677 (digital/electronic); Databases: 349. Weekly public service hours: 112. 840 computers available on campus for general student use. A campuswide network can be accessed from student residence rooms and from off campus. Students can access the following: online class registration. Staffed computer lab on campus provides training in use of computers, software, and the Internet.

■ SAINT PAUL COLLEGE-A COMMUNITY & TECHNICAL COLLEGE

235 Marshall Ave.
Saint Paul, MN 55102-1800
Tel: (651)846-1600; Free: 800-227-6029
Fax: (651)221-1416
E-mail: admissions@saintpaul.edu
Web Site: www.saintpaul.edu

Description: State-related, 2-year, coed. Part of Minnesota State Colleges and Universities System. Awards certificates, diplomas, transfer associate, and terminal associate degrees. Founded 1919. Setting: urban campus. Research spending for the previous fiscal year: $200,000. Total enrollment: 5,928. Faculty: 316 (107 full-time, 209 part-time). Student-undergrad faculty ratio is 18:1. 4,454 applied, 100% were admitted. Full-time: 2,454 students,

50% women, 50% men. Part-time: 3,474 students, 54% women, 46% men. 8% from out-of-state. 54% 25 or older, 13% transferred in. Calendar: semesters. Academic remediation for entering students, ESL program, honors program, distance learning, summer session for credit, part-time degree program, adult/continuing education programs, internships. Off campus study.

Entrance Requirements: Open admission. Options: electronic application, early admission. Required: ACCUPLACER. Required for some: high school transcript, interview. Entrance: noncompetitive. Application deadline: rolling.

Collegiate Environment: Most popular organization: Student Senate. Student services: personal-psychological counseling, women's center. Campus security: late night transport-escort service. Saint Paul College Library. Operations spending for the previous fiscal year: $200,000.

■ **SOUTH CENTRAL COLLEGE**
1920 Lee Blvd.
North Mankato, MN 56003
Tel: (507)389-7200
Web Site: southcentral.edu

Description: State-supported, 2-year, coed. Part of Minnesota State Colleges and Universities System. Awards certificates, diplomas, transfer associate, and terminal associate degrees. Founded 1946. Setting: urban campus. Total enrollment: 3,839. Student-undergrad faculty ratio is 12:1. 1% from out-of-state. 42% 25 or older. Retention: 60% of full-time freshmen returned the following year. Calendar: semesters. Academic remediation for entering students, advanced placement, distance learning, part-time degree program.

Entrance Requirements: Open admission. Required: high school transcript. Application deadline: 8/1. Notification: continuous.

Collegiate Environment: Orientation program.

■ **SOUTHWEST MINNESOTA STATE UNIVERSITY**
1501 State St.
Marshall, MN 56258
Tel: (507)537-7021; Free: 800-642-0684
Fax: (507)537-7154
E-mail: andrew.hlubek@smsu.edu
Web Site: www.smsu.edu

Description: State-supported, comprehensive, coed. Part of Minnesota State Colleges and Universities System. Awards associate, bachelor's, and master's degrees. Founded 1963. Setting: 216-acre small town campus. Research spending for the previous fiscal year: $251. Educational spending for the previous fiscal year: $4176 per student. Total enrollment: 6,896. Faculty: 194 (108 full-time, 86 part-time). Student-undergrad faculty ratio is 16:1. 1,839 applied. 7% from top 10% of their high school class, 24% from top quarter, 59% from top half. Full-time: 2,080 students, 56% women, 44% men. Part-time: 4,371 students, 59% women, 41% men. Students come from 26 states and territories, 25 other countries, 21% from out-of-state. 0.9% American Indian or Alaska Native, non-Hispanic/Latino; 2% Hispanic/Latino; 4% Black or African American, non-Hispanic/Latino; 2% Asian, non-Hispanic/Latino; 4% international. 19% 25 or older, 40% live on campus, 4% transferred in. Retention: 69% of full-time freshmen returned the following year. Academic areas with the most degrees conferred: business/marketing; education; parks and recreation. Core. Calendar: semesters. Academic remediation for entering students, ESL program, services for LD students, advanced placement, accelerated degree program, self-designed majors, freshman honors college, honors program, independent study, distance learning, double major, summer session for credit, part-time degree program, external degree program, adult/continuing education programs, internships, graduate courses open to undergrads. Off campus study at other colleges in the Minnesota State College and University System. Study abroad program.

Entrance Requirements: Options: electronic application, early admission, deferred admission. Required: high school transcript, minimum 3 high school GPA, top half of graduating class or 21 ACT, SAT or ACT. Recommended: ACT. Required for some: interview. Entrance: minimally difficult. Application deadline: 9/1. SAT Reasoning Test deadline: 8/23. SAT Subject Test deadline: 8/23. Transfer credits accepted: Yes.

Collegiate Environment: Orientation program. Drama-theater group, choral group, marching band, student-run newspaper, radio station. Social organizations: 100 open to all. Most popular organizations: Students in Free Enterprise (SIFE), Society of Leadership and Success, Family and Child Educators (FACE), Habitat for Humanity, Education Minnesota Student Program. Major annual events: Red Cross Blood Drive, Fall Fest (homecom-

ing), Hawaiian Night. Student services: health clinic, personal-psychological counseling, women's center. Campus security: 24-hour emergency response devices and patrols, student patrols, late night transport-escort service, controlled dormitory access. Southwest Minnesota State University. Operations spending for the previous fiscal year: $922,260. 420 computers available on campus for general student use. A campuswide network can be accessed from student residence rooms and from off campus. Students can access the following: online class registration. Staffed computer lab on campus provides training in use of computers, software, and the Internet.

Community Environment: Marshall (population 12,200) is in the heart of rural, southwestern Minnesota. Air service, bus service and major highways make it accessible to parks, Minneapolis-St. Paul, Duluth and Sioux Falls, S.D. Marshall is a "college town" with restaurants, a shopping mall, churches, 3 movie theaters and a modern downtown area. It is also an expanding commercial center with a large industrial park and is the headquarters for several national agribusinesses and related firms. Marshall has a new, multimillion dollar hospital and health care facility. 5 city parks, a county park and 2 state parks are within a short drive. The community and university combine to offer concerts, theater and art/craft exhibits. Part-time job opportunities are available for students.

■ **UNIVERSITY OF MINNESOTA, CROOKSTON**
2900 University Ave.
Crookston, MN 56716-5001
Tel: (218)281-6510; Free: 800-862-6466
Fax: (218)281-8050
E-mail: mchristo@crk.umn.edu
Web Site: www.umcrookston.edu

Description: State-supported, 4-year, coed. Part of University of Minnesota System. Awards bachelor's degrees. Founded 1966. Setting: 237-acre rural campus. Endowment: $15.2 million. Research spending for the previous fiscal year: $133,182. Educational spending for the previous fiscal year: $9618 per student. Total enrollment: 2,823. Faculty: 116 (71 full-time, 45 part-time). Student-undergrad faculty ratio is 16:1. 1,073 applied, 78% were admitted. 11% from top 10% of their high school class, 37% from top quarter, 68% from top half. Full-time: 1,281 students, 51% women, 49% men. Part-time: 1,542 students, 55% women, 45% men. Students come from 45 states and territories, 17 other countries, 30% from out-of-state. 0.4% American Indian or Alaska Native, non-Hispanic/Latino; 4% Hispanic/Latino; 7% Black or African American, non-Hispanic/Latino; 2% Asian, non-Hispanic/Latino; 0.2% Native Hawaiian or other Pacific Islander, non-Hispanic/Latino; 5% international. 46% 25 or older, 9% transferred in. Retention: 65% of full-time freshmen returned the following year. Academic areas with the most degrees conferred: business/marketing; agriculture; natural resources/environmental science. Core. Calendar: semesters. Academic remediation for entering students, ESL program, services for LD students, advanced placement, self-designed majors, honors program, independent study, distance learning, double major, summer session for credit, part-time degree program, co-op programs and internships. Off campus study at the five campuses of the University of Minnesota System. Study abroad program. ROTC: Air Force (c).

Entrance Requirements: Options: electronic application, deferred admission, international baccalaureate accepted. Required: high school transcript, minimum 2 high school GPA, minimum ACT composite score of 21 or SAT of 980, SAT or ACT. Recommended: ACT. Entrance: minimally difficult. Application deadline: rolling. Notification: continuous. SAT Reasoning Test deadline: 8/1. Transfer credits accepted: Yes.

Collegiate Environment: Orientation program. Drama-theater group, choral group. Social organizations: 42 open to all; national fraternities, local fraternities; 2% of eligible men and 1% of eligible women are members. Most popular organizations: National Society for Leadership and Success, Archery Club, Crookston Futbol Club, Choir, Student Athletic Advisory Council. Major annual events: Homecoming, Sno-Daze, Ag Arama. Student services: health clinic, personal-psychological counseling, women's center. Campus security: 24-hour emergency response devices, student patrols, controlled dormitory access. UMC Library. Books: 47,423 (physical), 336,375 (digital/electronic); Serial titles: 412 (physical), 8,500 (digital/electronic); Databases: 152. Weekly public service hours: 76. Operations spending for the previous fiscal year: $311,117. 25 computers available on campus for general student use. Computer purchase/lease plans available. A campuswide network can be accessed from student residence rooms and from off campus. Students can access the following: online class registration, personal Web pages. Staffed computer lab on campus provides training in use of computers, software, and the Internet.

Community Environment: Crookston (population 7,929) is the county seat of Polk County, one of the largest rural counties in the state. It is an agricultural processing center for the Red River Valley that produces wheat, barley, and sugar beets. Trains and buses are convenient for transportation. Recreational activities include swimming, camping, roller skating, ice skating, golf and bowling. The Old Crossing Treaty State Historic Park and the Polk County Pioneer Museum are some of the points of interest.

■ **UNIVERSITY OF MINNESOTA, DULUTH**

1049 University Dr.

Duluth, MN 55812-2496

Tel: (218)726-8000; Free: 800-232-1339

Fax: (218)726-6394

Web Site: www.d.umn.edu

Description: State-supported, comprehensive, coed. Part of University of Minnesota System. Awards bachelor's, master's, and doctoral degrees. Founded 1947. Setting: 250-acre suburban campus. Endowment: $170.8 million. Research spending for the previous fiscal year: $27.3 million. Educational spending for the previous fiscal year: $7382 per student. Total enrollment: 11,040. Faculty: 599 (489 full-time, 110 part-time). Student-undergrad faculty ratio is 18:1. 9,204 applied, 74% were admitted. 20% from top 10% of their high school class, 47% from top quarter, 87% from top half. Full-time: 8,799 students, 48% women, 52% men. Part-time: 1,178 students, 51% women, 49% men. Students come from 38 states and territories, 35 other countries, 12% from out-of-state. 0.5% American Indian or Alaska Native, non-Hispanic/Latino; 3% Hispanic/Latino; 2% Black or African American, non-Hispanic/Latino; 4% Asian, non-Hispanic/Latino; 0.1% Native Hawaiian or other Pacific Islander, non-Hispanic/Latino; 2% international. 4% 25 or older, 33% live on campus, 4% transferred in. Retention: 79% of full-time freshmen returned the following year. Academic areas with the most degrees conferred: business/marketing; engineering; biological/life sciences; social sciences. Core. Calendar: semesters. Academic remediation for entering students, ESL program, services for LD students, advanced placement, self-designed majors, honors program, independent study, distance learning, double major, summer session for credit, part-time degree program, adult/continuing education programs, internships, graduate courses open to undergrads. Off campus study at University of Wisconsin-Superior, College of St. Scholastica, Lake Superior College. Study abroad program. ROTC: Air Force.

Entrance Requirements: Options: electronic application, international baccalaureate accepted. Required: high school transcript, SAT or ACT. Recommended: essay. Required for some: interview. Entrance: moderately difficult. Application deadlines: 6/15, 6/15 for nonresidents. Notification: continuous until 9/15, continuous until 9/15 for nonresidents. Transfer credits accepted: Yes.

Costs Per Year: Application fee: $40. State resident tuition: $12,016 full-time, $462 per credit hour part-time. Nonresident tuition: $17,134 full-time, $659 per credit hour part-time. Mandatory fees: $1351 full-time. Full-time tuition and fees vary according to course load, program, and reciprocity agreements. Part-time tuition varies according to course load, program, and reciprocity agreements. College room and board: $7760. College room only: $3668. Room and board charges vary according to board plan and housing facility.

Collegiate Environment: Orientation program. Drama-theater group, choral group, marching band, student-run newspaper, radio station. Social organizations: 252 open to all; national fraternities, national sororities, local fraternities, local sororities; 5% of eligible men and 5% of eligible women are members. Most popular organizations: UMD Student Association, Newman Catholic Campus Ministries, Panhellenic Council, Coloring Club, Rod and Gun Club at UMD. Major annual events: Kirby Program Board Annual Spring Concert, Queer and Allied Student Union Drag Show, International Club Feast of Nations. Student services: health clinic, personal-psychological counseling, women's center. Campus security: 24-hour emergency response devices and patrols, late night transport-escort service. 2,992 college housing spaces available; all were occupied in 2018-19. Freshmen given priority for college housing. Options: coed, men-only, women-only housing available. Kathryn A. Martin Library. Books: 319,423 (physical), 611,335 (digital/electronic); Serial titles: 7,397 (physical), 130,550 (digital/electronic); Databases: 150. Weekly public service hours: 94; students can reserve study rooms. Operations spending for the previous fiscal year: $3.5 million. 548 computers available on campus for general student use. Computer purchase/lease plans available. A computer is required for all students. A campuswide network can be accessed from student residence rooms and

from off campus. Students can access the following: online class registration. Staffed computer lab on campus provides training in use of computers, software, and the Internet.

Community Environment: On picturesque slopes, Duluth (population 84,800) commands splendid views of the St. Louis River, the harbor and Lake Superior. The city is headquarters for the Superior National Forest, which is the largest in the nation.

■ **UNIVERSITY OF MINNESOTA, MORRIS**

600 E 4th St.

Morris, MN 56267-2134

Tel: (320)589-6035; Free: 888-866-3382

Fax: (320)589-6399

Web Site: www.morris.umn.edu

Description: State-supported, 4-year, coed. Part of University of Minnesota System. Awards bachelor's degrees. Founded 1959. Setting: 130-acre rural campus. Endowment: $15.4 million. Research spending for the previous fiscal year: $939,174. Educational spending for the previous fiscal year: $9634 per student. Total enrollment: 1,554. Faculty: 158 (125 full-time, 33 part-time). Student-undergrad faculty ratio is 11:1. 3,139 applied, 63% were admitted. 31% from top 10% of their high school class, 57% from top quarter, 90% from top half. 1 National Merit Scholar, 11 valedictorians. Full-time: 1,463 students, 57% women, 43% men. Part-time: 91 students, 57% women, 43% men. Students come from 32 states and territories, 23 other countries, 17% from out-of-state. 8% American Indian or Alaska Native, non-Hispanic/Latino; 5% Hispanic/Latino; 2% Black or African American, non-Hispanic/Latino; 3% Asian, non-Hispanic/Latino; 11% international. 3% 25 or older, 52% live on campus, 5% transferred in. Retention: 77% of full-time freshmen returned the following year. Academic areas with the most degrees conferred: biological/life sciences; psychology; social sciences. Core. Calendar: semesters. ESL program, services for LD students, advanced placement, self-designed majors, freshman honors college, honors program, independent study, distance learning, double major, summer session for credit, part-time degree program, internships. Off campus study at other units of the University of Minnesota System, National Student Exchange. Study abroad program.

Entrance Requirements: Options: electronic application, deferred admission, international baccalaureate accepted. Required: high school transcript, SAT or ACT. Required for some: essay, 1 recommendation, interview. Entrance: moderately difficult. Application deadline: 8/1. Notification: continuous. SAT Reasoning Test deadline: 3/15. SAT Subject Test deadline: 3/15. Transfer credits accepted: Yes.

Costs Per Year: Application fee: $35. State resident tuition: $12,142 full-time, $467 per credit hour part-time. Nonresident tuition: $14,170 full-time, $545 per credit hour part-time. Mandatory fees: $1172 full-time. Full-time tuition and fees vary according to reciprocity agreements. Part-time tuition varies according to course load and reciprocity agreements. College room and board: $8342. College room only: $3942. Room and board charges vary according to board plan and housing facility.

Collegiate Environment: Orientation program. Drama-theater group, choral group, student-run newspaper, radio station. Social organizations: 125 open to all. Most popular organizations: Student Radio Station, Inter-Varsity Christian Fellowship, Jazz Ensemble/Concert Choir, Big Friend, Little Friend, Student Newspaper. Major annual events: Homecoming, Jazz Fest, The Great Finals Pancake Breakfast. Student services: legal services, health clinic, personal-psychological counseling, women's center. Campus security: 24-hour emergency response devices and patrols, late night transport-escort service, controlled dormitory access. 1,032 college housing spaces available; 832 were occupied in 2018-19. Freshmen guaranteed college housing. Option: coed housing available. Rodney A. Briggs Library plus 1 other. Books: 218,848 (physical), 800,000 (digital/electronic); Serial titles: 140 (physical), 121,380 (digital/electronic); Databases: 112. Weekly public service hours: 99. Operations spending for the previous fiscal year: $1.1 million. 350 computers available on campus for general student use. Computer purchase/lease plans available. A campuswide network can be accessed from student residence rooms and from off campus. Students can access the following: online class registration. Staffed computer lab on campus provides training in use of computers, software, and the Internet.

Community Environment: The rural setting of Morris (population 5,091) is ideal for outdoor activities year round. Students participate in the community through the many churches, the library, hospital and ambulance service, nursing home, community education, and parks. Employment is available for students that seek work.

■ UNIVERSITY OF MINNESOTA ROCHESTER

111 S Broadway
Ste. 300
Rochester, MN 55904
Tel: (877)280-4699
Web Site: www.r.umn.edu
Description: State-supported, comprehensive, coed. Awards bachelor's and master's degrees. Founded 2006.

■ UNIVERSITY OF MINNESOTA, TWIN CITIES CAMPUS

100 Church St., SE
Minneapolis, MN 55455-0213
Tel: (612)625-5000; Free: 800-752-1000
Fax: (612)626-1693
E-mail: admissions@tc.umn.edu
Web Site: www.twin-cities.umn.edu
Description: State-supported, university, coed. Part of University of Minnesota System. Awards bachelor's, master's, and doctoral degrees and post-master's certificates. Founded 1851. Setting: 2,000-acre urban campus with easy access to Minneapolis-St. Paul. Total enrollment: 50,943. Faculty: 3,785 (2,630 full-time, 1,155 part-time). Student-undergrad faculty ratio is 17:1. 43,444 applied, 52% were admitted. 50% from top 10% of their high school class, 85% from top quarter, 100% from top half. Full-time: 30,001 students, 54% women, 46% men. Part-time: 4,632 students, 51% women, 49% men. Students come from 51 states and territories, 98 other countries, 28% from out-of-state. 0.3% American Indian or Alaska Native, non-Hispanic/Latino; 4% Hispanic/Latino; 5% Black or African American, non-Hispanic/Latino; 10% Asian, non-Hispanic/Latino; 0.1% Native Hawaiian or other Pacific Islander, non-Hispanic/Latino; 8% international. 7% 25 or older, 22% live on campus, 6% transferred in. Retention: 93% of full-time freshmen returned the following year. Academic areas with the most degrees conferred: biological/life sciences; social sciences; engineering. Core. Calendar: semesters. Academic remediation for entering students, ESL program, services for LD students, advanced placement, accelerated degree program, self-designed majors, freshman honors college, honors program, independent study, distance learning, double major, summer session for credit, part-time degree program, external degree program, adult/continuing education programs, co-op programs and internships, graduate courses open to undergrads. Off campus study at National Student Exchange, Minnesota Community College System. Study abroad program. ROTC: Army, Naval, Air Force.
Entrance Requirements: Options: electronic application, early admission, deferred admission, international baccalaureate accepted. Required: high school transcript, SAT or ACT. Recommended: minimum 2 high school GPA. Entrance: moderately difficult. Application deadlines: rolling, rolling for nonresidents. Notification: continuous, continuous for nonresidents. SAT Reasoning Test deadline: 12/15. SAT Subject Test deadline: 12/15. Transfer credits accepted: Yes.
Costs Per Year: Application fee: $55. State resident tuition: $13,058 full-time, $502 per credit part-time. Nonresident tuition: $28,736 full-time, $933 per credit part-time. Mandatory fees: $1635 full-time. Full-time tuition and fees vary according to program and reciprocity agreements. Part-time tuition varies according to course load, program, and reciprocity agreements. College room and board: $10,312. College room only: $5922. Room and board charges vary according to board plan, housing facility, and location.
Collegiate Environment: Orientation program. Drama-theater group, choral group, marching band, student-run newspaper, radio station. Social organizations: 350 open to all; national fraternities, national sororities, local sororities; 3% of eligible men and 3% of eligible women are members. Most popular organization: Student Government. Major annual event: Homecoming. Student services: legal services, health clinic, personal-psychological counseling, women's center. Campus security: 24-hour emergency response devices and patrols, student patrols, late night transport-escort service, controlled dormitory access. 7,294 college housing spaces available; 7,241 were occupied in 2018-19. Freshmen guaranteed college housing. Option: coed housing available. Wilson Library plus 17 others. Books: 4.1 million (physical), 1.2 million (digital/electronic); Serial titles: 153,056 (physical), 290,349 (digital/electronic); Databases: 947. Students can reserve study rooms.

■ UNIVERSITY OF NORTHWESTERN-ST. PAUL

3003 Snelling Ave. N
Saint Paul, MN 55113-1598
Tel: (651)631-5100; Free: 800-827-6827

Fax: (651)631-5680
Web Site: www.unwsp.edu
Description: Independent nondenominational, comprehensive, coed. Awards associate, bachelor's, and master's degrees. Founded 1902. Setting: 107-acre suburban campus with easy access to Minneapolis-St. Paul. Endowment: $17.9 million. Educational spending for the previous fiscal year: $7598 per student. Total enrollment: 3,623. Faculty: 313 (82 full-time, 231 part-time). Student-undergrad faculty ratio is 18:1. 930 applied, 90% were admitted. 22% from top 10% of their high school class, 45% from top quarter, 68% from top half. 12 valedictorians. Full-time: 2,097 students, 62% women, 38% men. Part-time: 1,346 students, 63% women, 37% men. Students come from 32 states and territories, 9 other countries, 22% from out-of-state. 0.3% American Indian or Alaska Native, non-Hispanic/Latino; 6% Hispanic/Latino; 4% Black or African American, non-Hispanic/Latino; 4% Asian, non-Hispanic/Latino; 0.8% international. 11% 25 or older, 56% live on campus, 5% transferred in. Retention: 79% of full-time freshmen returned the following year. Academic areas with the most degrees conferred: theology and religious vocations; business/marketing; psychology; health professions and related sciences. Core. Calendar: semesters. Academic remediation for entering students, services for LD students, advanced placement, self-designed majors, honors program, independent study, distance learning, double major, summer session for credit, part-time degree program, adult/continuing education programs, internships. Off campus study at Council for Christian Colleges and Universities, EduVenture, Focus on the Family Institute, William Mitchell College of Law, Jerusalem University College, Au Sable Institute. Study abroad program. ROTC: Army (c), Air Force (c).
Entrance Requirements: Options: electronic application, early admission, early action, deferred admission, international baccalaureate accepted. Required: essay, high school transcript, minimum 2 high school GPA, 2 recommendations, lifestyle agreement, statement of Christian faith, SAT or ACT. Recommended: minimum 3 high school GPA. Required for some: interview. Entrance: moderately difficult. Application deadlines: 8/1, 8/1 for nonresidents, rolling for early action. Notification: continuous, continuous for nonresidents, rolling for early action. SAT Reasoning Test deadline: 8/1. SAT Subject Test deadline: 8/1. Transfer credits accepted: Yes. Early action applicants: 275. Early action applicants admitted: 182.
Costs Per Year: Application fee: $25. Comprehensive fee: $41,870 includes full-time tuition ($31,580), mandatory fees ($630), and college room and board ($9660). College room only: $5810. Part-time tuition: $1345 per credit.
Collegiate Environment: Orientation program. Drama-theater group, choral group, student-run newspaper, radio station. Social organizations: 40 open to all. Most popular organizations: Northwestern Student Association (student government), The Gathering (religious group), Student Missions Fellowship, Guardian Angels, Outreach Ministries. Major annual events: Variety Shows, Christmas at Northwestern, Day of Prayer and Service. Student services: health clinic, personal-psychological counseling. Campus security: 24-hour emergency response devices and patrols, late night transport-escort service, controlled dormitory access. 1,279 college housing spaces available; 1,002 were occupied in 2018-19. Freshmen guaranteed college housing. On-campus residence required through junior year. Options: coed, men-only, women-only housing available. Berntsen Resource Center. Books: 87,336 (physical), 377,241 (digital/electronic); Serial titles: 408 (physical), 49,850 (digital/electronic); Databases: 102. Operations spending for the previous fiscal year: $1.1 million. 200 computers available on campus for general student use. Computer purchase/lease plans available. A computer is required for all students. A campuswide network can be accessed from student residence rooms and from off campus. Students can access the following: online class registration, network file space, personal website, integrated student portal, b/w and color printing, virtual labs. Staffed computer lab on campus provides training in use of computers, software, and the Internet.

■ UNIVERSITY OF ST. THOMAS

2115 Summit Ave.
Saint Paul, MN 55105-1096
Tel: (651)962-5000; Free: 800-328-6819
Fax: (651)962-6160
Web Site: www.stthomas.edu
Description: Independent Roman Catholic, university, coed. Awards associate, bachelor's, master's, and doctoral degrees and post-master's certificates. Founded 1885. Setting: 78-acre urban campus with easy access to Minneapolis-St. Paul. Endowment: $494 million. Total enrollment: 10,035. Faculty: 826 (452 full-time, 374 part-time). Student-undergrad faculty ratio is 14:1. 6,819 applied, 82% were admitted. 21% from top 10% of their high

school class, 51% from top quarter, 85% from top half. Full-time: 6,162 students, 47% women, 53% men. Part-time: 233 students, 46% women, 54% men. 0.2% American Indian or Alaska Native, non-Hispanic/Latino; 5% Hispanic/Latino; 3% Black or African American, non-Hispanic/Latino; 4% Asian, non-Hispanic/Latino; 3% international. 3% 25 or older, 40% live on campus, 3% transferred in. Retention: 86% of full-time freshmen returned the following year. Academic areas with the most degrees conferred: engineering; biological/life sciences; social sciences. Core. Calendar: 4-1-4. ESL program, services for LD students, advanced placement, accelerated degree program, self-designed majors, honors program, independent study, distance learning, double major, summer session for credit, part-time degree program, co-op programs and internships, graduate courses open to undergrads. Off campus study at Associated Colleges of the Twin Cities (ACTC) Augsburg; Hamline; Macalester; St. Catherine; UST Catholic College Cooperative Tuition Exchange Program (CCCTE). Study abroad program. ROTC: Army (c), Naval (c), Air Force.

Entrance Requirements: Options: electronic application, early action, deferred admission, international baccalaureate accepted. Required: essay, high school transcript, SAT or ACT. Recommended: interview. Entrance: moderately difficult. Application deadline: rolling. Notification: continuous. Transfer credits accepted: Yes.

Costs Per Year: Comprehensive fee: $56,942 includes full-time tuition ($44,780), mandatory fees ($1000), and college room and board ($11,162). College room only: $6812.

Collegiate Environment: Orientation program. Drama-theater group, choral group, student-run newspaper, radio station. Social organizations: 141 open to all. Major annual events: Mid-Winter Week, World Series of Wiffle Ball, Tommies Together Day of Service. Student services: health clinic, personal-psychological counseling, women's center. Campus security: 24-hour emergency response devices and patrols, late night transport-escort service, controlled dormitory access. 2,720 college housing spaces available; 2,292 were occupied in 2018-19. Freshmen given priority for college housing. Options: coed, men-only, women-only housing available. O'Shaughnessy-Frey Library plus 7 others. Books: 399,594 (physical), 1.2 million (digital/electronic); Serial titles: 1,701 (physical), 76,726 (digital/electronic); Databases: 308. Students can reserve study rooms.

■ **VERMILION COMMUNITY COLLEGE**
1900 E Camp St.
Ely, MN 55731-1996
Tel: (218)365-7200; Free: 800-657-3608
Web Site: www.vcc.edu

Description: State-supported, 2-year, coed. Part of Minnesota State Colleges and Universities System. Awards certificates, diplomas, transfer associate, and terminal associate degrees. Founded 1922. Setting: 5-acre rural campus. Total enrollment: 745. Faculty: 85 (25 full-time, 60 part-time). Student-undergrad faculty ratio is 13:1. 595 applied, 57% were admitted. Students come from 3 other countries. 10% 25 or older, 50% live on campus. Core. Calendar: semesters. Academic remediation for entering students, services for LD students, advanced placement, honors program, summer session for credit, part-time degree program, adult/continuing education programs, co-op programs and internships. Off campus study at other colleges in the Minnesota State Colleges and Universities System.

Entrance Requirements: Open admission. Options: electronic application, early admission, deferred admission. Required: high school transcript. Entrance: noncompetitive. Application deadline: rolling. Notification: continuous.

Collegiate Environment: Orientation program. Most popular organizations: Student Life Committee, student government, Drama Club. Major annual events: New Student Week, New Year's Dance, Karaoke Night. Student services: personal-psychological counseling, women's center. Campus security: student patrols, late night transport-escort service, controlled dormitory access. Vermilion Community College Library. 60 computers available on campus for general student use. A campuswide network can be accessed from student residence rooms and from off campus. Staffed computer lab on campus.

Community Environment: Located on the edge of the Boundary Waters Canoe Area, Vermilion offers its students one of the most beautiful wilderness areas in America for a college setting. The town of Ely, with a population of about 3,600, provides nearby shopping facilities, churches, a golf course, tennis courts, restaurants and an excellent hospital. Limited part-time work is available in the community. The area provides exceptional opportunities for camping, canoeing, fishing, hunting, snowmobiling, cross-country skiing, downhill skiing, and even dog sledding.

■ **WALDEN UNIVERSITY**
100 Washington S, Ste. 900
Minneapolis, MN 55401
Free: 866-492-5336
Web Site: www.waldenu.edu

Description: Proprietary, university, coed. Part of Laureate International Universities. Awards bachelor's, master's, and doctoral degrees and post-master's certificates. Founded 1970. Total enrollment: 52,799. Faculty: 2,754 (210 full-time, 2,544 part-time). 479 applied, 98% were admitted. Full-time: 784 students, 82% women, 18% men. Part-time: 7,455 students, 76% women, 24% men. Students come from 52 states and territories, 70 other countries, 97% from out-of-state. 0.5% American Indian or Alaska Native, non-Hispanic/Latino; 6% Hispanic/Latino; 30% Black or African American, non-Hispanic/Latino; 2% Asian, non-Hispanic/Latino; 0.3% Native Hawaiian or other Pacific Islander, non-Hispanic/Latino; 0.9% international. 84% 25 or older, 14% transferred in. Academic areas with the most degrees conferred: health professions and related sciences; business/marketing; psychology. Core. Calendar: quarter/semester depending on program. Academic remediation for entering students, services for LD students, accelerated degree program, self-designed majors, honors program, distance learning, summer session for credit, part-time degree program, internships, graduate courses open to undergrads. Off campus study. Study abroad program.

Entrance Requirements: Options: electronic application, deferred admission, international baccalaureate accepted. Required: high school transcript. Application deadline: rolling. Notification: continuous. Transfer credits accepted: Yes.

Collegiate Environment: Orientation program. Major annual event: Global Days of Service. Student services: legal services, personal-psychological counseling. Walden University Library. Books: 206,177 (digital/electronic); Serial titles: 69,602 (digital/electronic); Databases: 106. Weekly public service hours: 69.

■ **WHITE EARTH TRIBAL AND COMMUNITY COLLEGE**
102 3rd St. NE
Mahnomen, MN 56557
Tel: (218)935-0417
Web Site: www.wetcc.edu

Description: Independent, 2-year, coed. Awards transfer associate and terminal associate degrees. Calendar: semesters.

■ **WINONA STATE UNIVERSITY**
175 W Mark St.
Winona, MN 55987
Tel: (507)457-5000; Free: 800-DIAL WSU
Fax: (507)457-5620
E-mail: admissions@winona.edu
Web Site: www.winona.edu

Description: State-supported, comprehensive, coed. Part of Minnesota State Colleges and Universities System. Awards associate, bachelor's, master's, and doctoral degrees and post-master's certificates. Founded 1858. Setting: 125-acre small town campus with easy access to Minneapolis-St.Paul. Endowment: $22.6 million. Research spending for the previous fiscal year: $506,000. Educational spending for the previous fiscal year: $7086 per student. Total enrollment: 7,953. Faculty: 526 (338 full-time, 188 part-time). Student-undergrad faculty ratio is 18:1. 7,468 applied, 66% were admitted. 10% from top 10% of their high school class, 31% from top quarter, 70% from top half. Full-time: 6,501 students, 63% women, 37% men. Part-time: 936 students, 66% women, 34% men. Students come from 37 states and territories, 45 other countries, 29% from out-of-state. 0.2% American Indian or Alaska Native, non-Hispanic/Latino; 3% Hispanic/Latino; 3% Black or African American, non-Hispanic/Latino; 2% Asian, non-Hispanic/Latino; 0.1% Native Hawaiian or other Pacific Islander, non-Hispanic/Latino; 2% international. 15% 25 or older, 29% live on campus, 8% transferred in. Retention: 78% of full-time freshmen returned the following year. Academic areas with the most degrees conferred: business/marketing; health professions and related sciences; education. Core. Calendar: semesters. Academic remediation for entering students, ESL program, services for LD students, advanced placement, self-designed majors, independent study, distance learning, double major, summer session for credit, part-time degree program, adult/continuing education programs, internships, graduate courses open to undergrads. Off campus study at Saint Mary's University of Minnesota, other colleges in the Minnesota State Colleges and Universities System. Study abroad program. ROTC: Army (c).

Entrance Requirements: Options: electronic application, deferred admis-

sion, international baccalaureate accepted. Required: high school transcript, 16 high school preparation requirements and either minimum composite ACT of 21 with top two-thirds of high school class rank or minimum cumulative GPA of 2.75 or, minimum composite ACT of 18 with either top half of high school class rank or minimum cumulative high school GPA of 3.0, SAT or ACT. Entrance: moderately difficult. Application deadlines: 7/1, 7/4 for nonresidents. Notification: continuous, continuous for nonresidents. SAT Reasoning Test deadline: 7/1. SAT Subject Test deadline: 7/1. Transfer credits accepted: Yes.

Costs Per Year: Application fee: $20. State resident tuition: $7377 full-time, $243.98 per credit hour part-time. Nonresident tuition: $13,298 full-time, $442.95 per credit hour part-time. Mandatory fees: $2049 full-time, $40.79 per credit hour part-time, $485 per term part-time. Full-time tuition and fees vary according to location, program, and reciprocity agreements. Part-time tuition and fees vary according to course load, location, program, and reciprocity agreements. College room and board: $8746. College room only: $5750. Room and board charges vary according to board plan, housing facility, and location.

Collegiate Environment: Orientation program. Drama-theater group, choral group, student-run newspaper, radio station. Social organizations: 180 open to all; national fraternities, national sororities, local fraternities, local sororities. Most popular organizations: University Program Activities Committee, Student Senate, Residence Hall Association, Inter Varsity. Major annual events: Homecoming, Family Weekend, Club Fair. Student services: health clinic, personal-psychological counseling. Campus security: 24-hour emergency response devices and patrols, student patrols, late night transport-escort service, controlled dormitory access, security cameras. Darrel W. Krueger Library. Books: 242,347 (physical), 59,498 (digital/electronic); Serial titles: 2,097 (physical), 34,000 (digital/electronic); Databases: 138. Weekly public service hours: 99; students can reserve study rooms. Operations spending for the previous fiscal year: $246,505. 50 computers available on campus for general student use. Computer purchase/lease plans available. A computer is required for all students. A campuswide network can be accessed from student residence rooms and from off campus. Students can access the following: online class registration. Staffed computer lab on campus provides training in use of computers, software, and the Internet.

Community Environment: Winona (population 26,500) is a large town in southeastern Minnesota, in a sector known as Hiawatha Valley. Limestone from the quarries here is comparable to much of Italy's finest travertine. Winona is headquarters for the Upper Mississippi River Wildlife and Fish Refuge. Trains and buses provide commercial transportation. Community facilities include many churches, a public library, a hospital, hotels and motels. Part-time employment is available. Recreational activities include fishing, golf, swimming, hunting, boating and skiing.

■ ALCORN STATE UNIVERSITY

1000 ASU Dr.

Lorman, MS 39096-7500

Tel: (601)877-6100; Free: 800-222-6790

Fax: (601)877-6347

E-mail: ksampson@alcorn.edu

Web Site: www.alcorn.edu

Description: State-supported, comprehensive, coed. Part of Mississippi Institutions of Higher Learning. Awards associate, bachelor's, and master's degrees and post-master's certificates. Founded 1871. Setting: 1,756-acre rural campus. System endowment: $17.3 million. Research spending for the previous fiscal year: $6.8 million. Educational spending for the previous fiscal year: $7244 per student. Total enrollment: 3,716. Faculty: 221 (150 full-time, 71 part-time). Student-undergrad faculty ratio is 19:1. 3,464 applied, 79% were admitted. Full-time: 2,893 students, 64% women, 36% men. Part-time: 279 students, 68% women, 32% men. Students come from 35 states and territories, 31 other countries, 28% from out-of-state. 0.2% American Indian or Alaska Native, non-Hispanic/Latino; 0.5% Hispanic/Latino; 91% Black or African American, non-Hispanic/Latino; 0.1% Asian, non-Hispanic/Latino; 3% international. 11% 25 or older, 63% live on campus, 5% transferred in. Retention: 75% of full-time freshmen returned the following year. Academic areas with the most degrees conferred: liberal arts/general studies; biological/life sciences; agriculture. Core. Calendar: semesters. Academic remediation for entering students, advanced placement, accelerated degree program, honors program, independent study, distance learning, double major, summer session for credit, part-time degree program, adult/continuing education programs, co-op programs and internships, graduate courses open to undergrads. Off campus study at Pennsylvania State University. Study abroad program. ROTC: Army.

Entrance Requirements: Options: electronic application, deferred admission, international baccalaureate accepted. Required: high school transcript, minimum 2 high school GPA, SAT or ACT. Entrance: moderately difficult. Application deadline: rolling. Notification: continuous. Transfer credits accepted: Yes.

Costs Per Year: Application fee: $0. State resident tuition: $7084 full-time, $592 per credit hour part-time. Nonresident tuition: $7084 full-time, $592 per credit hour part-time. Full-time tuition varies according to course load. Part-time tuition varies according to course load. College room and board: $10,374. College room only: $7078. Room and board charges vary according to board plan and housing facility.

Collegiate Environment: Orientation program. Drama-theater group, choral group, marching band, student-run newspaper, radio station. Social organizations: 85 open to all; national fraternities, national sororities. Most popular organizations: marching band, Gospel Choir, inter-faith choir. Major annual events: Greek Step Show, Concerts, Homecoming. Student services: health clinic, personal-psychological counseling. Campus security: 24-hour emergency response devices and patrols, late night transport-escort service, controlled dormitory access. John Dewey Boyd Library plus 1 other. Books: 412,321 (physical), 441,114 (digital/electronic); Serial titles: 312 (physical), 75,805 (digital/electronic); Databases: 91. Weekly public service hours: 88; study areas open 24 hours, 5-7 days a week; students can reserve study rooms. Operations spending for the previous fiscal year: $746,144. 500 computers available on campus for general student use. A campuswide network can be accessed from student residence rooms and from off campus. Students can access the following: online class registration, online payment; online transcript request. Staffed computer lab on campus provides training in use of computers, software, and the Internet.

Community Environment: This rural community has a population of less than 3,900. Multidenominational churches serve the area. It is an ideal place for hiking, camping and other outdoor recreational activities. The university is located in Claiborne County, seven miles west of Lorman, seventeen miles southwest of Poet Gibson, and forty-five miles south of Vicksburg.

■ ANTONELLI COLLEGE (HATTIESBURG)

1500 N 31st Ave.

Hattiesburg, MS 39401

Tel: (601)583-4100

Fax: (601)583-0839

E-mail: admissionsh@antonellicollege.edu

Web Site: www.antonellicollege.edu

Description: Proprietary, 2-year, coed. Awards certificates and transfer associate degrees. Total enrollment: 354. Calendar: quarters.

Entrance Requirements: Entrance: noncompetitive.

■ ANTONELLI COLLEGE (JACKSON)

2323 Lakeland Dr.

Jackson, MS 39232

Tel: (601)362-9991

Fax: (601)362-2333

Web Site: www.antonellicollege.edu

Description: Proprietary, 2-year, coed. Awards diplomas, transfer associate, and terminal associate degrees. Total enrollment: 240. 67% 25 or older. Calendar: quarters.

Entrance Requirements: Open admission.

■ BELHAVEN UNIVERSITY

1500 Peachtree St.

Jackson, MS 39202-1789

Tel: (601)968-5928; Free: 800-960-5940

Fax: (601)968-9998

E-mail: admission@belhaven.edu

Web Site: www.belhaven.edu

Description: Independent Presbyterian, comprehensive, coed. Awards associate, bachelor's, master's, and doctoral degrees. Founded 1883. Setting: 46-acre urban campus. Endowment: $5.6 million. Educational spending for the previous fiscal year: $5432 per student. Total enrollment: 4,458. Faculty: 456 (95 full-time, 361 part-time). Student-undergrad faculty ratio is 15:1. 2,324 applied, 59% were admitted. 4% from top 10% of their high school class, 28% from top quarter, 68% from top half. Full-time: 1,248 students, 59% women, 41% men. Part-time: 1,234 students, 72% women, 28% men. Students come from 47 states and territories, 25 other countries, 33% from out-of-state. 0.4% American Indian or Alaska Native, non-Hispanic/Latino; 5% Hispanic/Latino; 45% Black or African American, non-Hispanic/Latino; 0.9% Asian, non-Hispanic/Latino; 2% international. 51% 25 or older, 22% live on campus, 15% transferred in. Retention: 63% of full-time freshmen returned the following year. Academic areas with the most degrees conferred: business/marketing; health professions and related sciences; social sciences; parks and recreation. Core. Calendar: semesters. Academic remediation for entering students, ESL program, advanced placement, accelerated degree program, self-designed majors, honors program, independent study, distance learning, double major, summer session for credit, part-time degree program, adult/continuing education programs, internships. Off campus study at Coalition for Christian Colleges and Universities. Study abroad program. ROTC: Army (c), Air Force (c).

Entrance Requirements: Options: electronic application, early admission, deferred admission, international baccalaureate accepted. Required: high school transcript, minimum 2 high school GPA, 1 recommendation, SAT or ACT. Required for some: essay, interview. Entrance: moderately difficult. Application deadline: rolling. Notification: continuous. Transfer credits accepted: Yes.

Costs Per Year: Application fee: $25. Comprehensive fee: $33,800 includes full-time tuition ($24,950), mandatory fees ($350), and college room and board ($8500). Full-time tuition and fees vary according to location and program. Room and board charges vary according to housing facility. Part-time tuition: $425 per credit hour. Part-time mandatory fees: $25 per credit hour. Part-time tuition and fees vary according to course load, location, and program.

Collegiate Environment: Orientation program. Drama-theater group, choral group, marching band, student-run newspaper. Social organizations: 30 open to all. Most popular organizations: Belhaven Activities Team, Fellowship of Christian Athletes, Reformed University Fellowship, Phi Beta Lambda, Belhaven University New Music Society. Major annual events: Martin Luther King Jr. Service Day, Luau, Singing Christmas Tree. Student services: health clinic, personal-psychological counseling. Campus security: 24-hour emergency response devices and patrols, late night transport-escort service, controlled dormitory access. Warren A. Hood Library plus 1 other. Books: 42,425 (physical), 106,114 (digital/electronic); Serial titles: 160 (physical), 75,718 (digital/electronic); Databases: 96. Weekly public service hours: 104. Operations spending for the previous fiscal year: $17,904. 36 computers available on campus for general student use. A campuswide network can be accessed from student residence rooms and from off campus. Students can access the following: online class registration.

Community Environment: See Jackson State University.

■ **BLUE MOUNTAIN COLLEGE**
201 W Main St.
Blue Mountain, MS 38610
Tel: (662)685-4771; Free: 800-235-0136
Fax: (662)685-4776
E-mail: lgibson@bmc.edu
Web Site: www.bmc.edu
Description: Independent Southern Baptist, comprehensive, coed. Awards bachelor's and master's degrees. Founded 1873. Setting: 190-acre rural campus with easy access to Memphis. Endowment: $15.6 million. Educational spending for the previous fiscal year: $1841 per student. Total enrollment: 601. Faculty: 54 (35 full-time, 19 part-time). Student-undergrad faculty ratio is 14:1. 207 applied, 99% were admitted. 13% from top 10% of their high school class, 40% from top quarter, 70% from top half. Full-time: 531 students, 52% women, 48% men. Part-time: 57 students, 75% women, 25% men. Students come from 14 states and territories, 11 other countries, 19% from out-of-state. 0.5% American Indian or Alaska Native, non-Hispanic/Latino; 2% Hispanic/Latino; 12% Black or African American, non-Hispanic/Latino; 0.3% Asian, non-Hispanic/Latino; 2% international. 15% 25 or older, 59% live on campus, 21% transferred in. Retention: 65% of full-time freshmen returned the following year. Academic areas with the most degrees conferred: education; theology and religious vocations; business/marketing. Core. Calendar: semesters. Academic remediation for entering students, services for LD students, advanced placement, accelerated degree program, honors program, distance learning, double major, summer session for credit, part-time degree program, adult/continuing education programs, internships, graduate courses open to undergrads.

Entrance Requirements: Options: electronic application, early decision, deferred admission. Required: SAT or ACT. Recommended: minimum 2 high school GPA. Required for some: high school transcript. Entrance: moderately difficult. Application deadline: rolling. Notification: continuous. SAT Reasoning Test deadline: 8/15. SAT Subject Test deadline: 8/15. Transfer credits accepted: Yes.

Costs Per Year: Application fee: $0. Comprehensive fee: $19,054 includes full-time tuition ($10,690), mandatory fees ($1894), and college room and board ($6470). Full-time tuition and fees vary according to course load, degree level, and program. Room and board charges vary according to housing facility and location. Part-time tuition: $356 per semester hour. Part-time mandatory fees: $54 per semester hour. Part-time tuition and fees vary according to course load, degree level, and program.

Collegiate Environment: Orientation program. Drama-theater group, choral group, marching band, student-run newspaper. Social organizations: 35 open to all; societies for men and women; 31% of eligible men and 63% of eligible women are members. Most popular organizations: Baptist Student Union, Student Body Association, Intramural Association, Ministerial Association, Mississippi Association of Educators/Student Program. Major annual events: BSU/SBA Welcome Back Parties, Society Rush, Track Meet. Campus security: 24-hour emergency response devices and patrols, controlled dormitory access. Guyton Library plus 1 other. Books: 41,725 (physical), 35,897 (digital/electronic); Serial titles: 143 (physical); Databases: 24. Weekly public service hours: 70. Operations spending for the previous fiscal year: $145,928. 95 computers available on campus for general student use. A campuswide network can be accessed from student residence rooms. Staffed computer lab on campus provides training in use of computers, software, and the Internet.

Community Environment: A rural community, Blue Mountain has a warm and pleasant climate with an average temperature of 68 degrees. Blue Mountain is about 70 miles from Memphis. Recreational facilities include a swimming pool, golf course, athletic field, physical education center, tennis courts, student center and 2 auditoriums for productions.

■ **COAHOMA COMMUNITY COLLEGE**
3240 Friars Point Rd.
Clarksdale, MS 38614-9799
Tel: (662)627-2571; Free: 866-470-1CCC
Web Site: www.coahomacc.edu
Description: State and locally supported, 2-year, coed. Part of Mississippi State Board for Community and Junior Colleges. Awards certificates, transfer associate, and terminal associate degrees. Founded 1949. Setting: 29-acre rural campus with easy access to Memphis. Total enrollment: 2,216. Faculty: 117 (53 full-time, 64 part-time). Student-undergrad faculty ratio is 19:1. Full-time: 1,962 students, 69% women, 31% men. Part-time: 254 students, 80% women, 20% men. 41% 25 or older, 22% live on campus. Retention: 58% of full-time freshmen returned the following year. Core. Calendar: semesters. Academic remediation for entering students, advanced placement, accelerated degree program, self-designed majors, distance learning, part-time degree program, adult/continuing education programs, co-op programs. Off campus study.

Entrance Requirements: Open admission. Required: high school transcript. Required for some: interview. Entrance: noncompetitive. Application deadline: rolling. Notification: continuous.

Collegiate Environment: Orientation program. Drama-theater group, choral group, marching band, student-run newspaper. Most popular organizations: Student Government Association, VICA (Vocational Industrial Clubs of America), Phi Theta Kappa Honor Society. Major annual events: High School Day, Coronation of Miss Coahoma Community College, Graduation. Student services: health clinic, personal-psychological counseling. Campus security: 24-hour patrols, controlled dormitory access. Dickerson-Johnson Library. 25 computers available on campus for general student use. A campuswide network can be accessed from student residence rooms. Students can access the following: online class registration. Staffed computer lab on campus provides training in use of computers and the Internet.

Community Environment: Clarksdale, an important distributing outlet in an agricultural region, is a prime example of the state's"Balance Agriculture with Industry" program. The city gins large amounts of cotton and manufactures conveyor equipment, corrugated boxes, farm machinery, tire tubes, agricultural chemicals and fertilizers, builder's hardware, electronic equipment and furniture. The Greyhound Bus line serves the city. The area has a public library, hospital, churches of all major denominations and movie theatres.

■ **CONCORDE CAREER COLLEGE**
7900 Airways Blvd.
Ste. 103
Southaven, MS 38671
Web Site: www.concorde.edu
Description: Proprietary, 2-year, coed.

■ **COPIAH-LINCOLN COMMUNITY COLLEGE**
PO Box 649
Wesson, MS 39191
Tel: (601)643-5101
Fax: (601)643-8212
E-mail: gay.langham@colin.edu

Web Site: www.colin.edu

Description: State and locally supported, 2-year, coed. Part of Mississippi Community College Board. Awards certificates, transfer associate, and terminal associate degrees. Founded 1928. Setting: 525-acre rural campus with easy access to Jackson. Endowment: $2.5 million. Total enrollment: 3,100. Faculty: 197 (102 full-time, 95 part-time). Full-time: 2,128 students, 59% women, 41% men. Part-time: 972 students, 67% women, 33% men. Students come from 8 states and territories, 1 other country, 1% from out-of-state. 0.9% Hispanic/Latino; 40% Black or African American, non-Hispanic/Latino; 0.1% Asian, non-Hispanic/Latino. 5% 25 or older, 30% live on campus, 5% transferred in. Core. Calendar: semesters. Academic remediation for entering students, services for LD students, advanced placement, accelerated degree program, self-designed majors, honors program, distance learning, summer session for credit, part-time degree program, adult/continuing education programs. Study abroad program.

Entrance Requirements: Open admission. Option: early admission. Required: high school transcript. Application deadline: rolling. Preference given to state residents. Transfer credits accepted: Yes.

Costs Per Year: Application fee: $0. State resident tuition: $1400 full-time, $140 per credit hour part-time. Nonresident tuition: $2400 full-time, $240 per credit hour part-time. Mandatory fees: $190 full-time, $19 per credit hour part-time. College room and board: $1825. College room only: $800. Room and board charges vary according to board plan and housing facility.

Collegiate Environment: Orientation program. Drama-theater group, choral group, marching band, student-run newspaper, radio station. Major annual events: Homecoming, Spring Fling, Graduation. Student services: health clinic, personal-psychological counseling. Campus security: 24-hour patrols. Oswalt Memorial Library. Operations spending for the previous fiscal year: $396,208. 300 computers available on campus for general student use. A campuswide network can be accessed from student residence rooms. Students can access the following: online class registration. Staffed computer lab on campus provides training in use of computers and software.

Community Environment: Wesson is located on U.S. Highway 51, approximately 150 miles north of New Orleans. The climate is pleasant. Transportation is provided by the Illinois Central railroad. Some part-time employment is available for students.

■ DELTA STATE UNIVERSITY

Hwy. 8 W
Cleveland, MS 38733-0001
Tel: (662)846-3000; Free: 800-468-6378
Fax: (662)846-4016
E-mail: admissions@deltastate.edu
Web Site: www.deltastate.edu

Description: State-supported, comprehensive, coed. Part of Mississippi Institutions of Higher Learning. Awards bachelor's, master's, and doctoral degrees and post-master's certificates. Founded 1924. Setting: 332-acre small town campus. Endowment: $32.9 million. Research spending for the previous fiscal year: $498,170. Educational spending for the previous fiscal year: $6184 per student. Total enrollment: 3,715. Faculty: 275 (157 full-time, 118 part-time). Student-undergrad faculty ratio is 14:1. 905 applied, 85% were admitted. 17% from top 10% of their high school class, 39% from top quarter, 71% from top half. 8 valedictorians. Full-time: 1,989 students, 56% women, 44% men. Part-time: 1,086 students, 63% women, 37% men. Students come from 31 states and territories, 47 other countries, 17% from out-of-state. 0.2% American Indian or Alaska Native, non-Hispanic/Latino; 3% Hispanic/Latino; 28% Black or African American, non-Hispanic/Latino; 1% Asian, non-Hispanic/Latino; 0.1% Native Hawaiian or other Pacific Islander, non-Hispanic/Latino; 4% international. 13% 25 or older, 39% live on campus, 14% transferred in. Retention: 67% of full-time freshmen returned the following year. Academic areas with the most degrees conferred: business/marketing; education; health professions and related sciences. Core. Calendar: semesters. Academic remediation for entering students, services for LD students, advanced placement, freshman honors college, honors program, independent study, distance learning, double major, summer session for credit, part-time degree program, adult/continuing education programs, co-op programs and internships.

Entrance Requirements: Options: electronic application, deferred admission. Required: minimum 2 high school GPA, ACT, SAT or ACT. Required for some: high school transcript, interview for art, music majors. Entrance: noncompetitive. Application deadlines: rolling, 4/15 for early action. Notification: continuous. Transfer credits accepted: Yes. Early action applicants: 657. Early action applicants admitted: 260.

Costs Per Year: Application fee: $25. State resident tuition: $7076 full-time,

$295 per credit hour part-time. Nonresident tuition: $7076 full-time, $295 per credit hour part-time. Mandatory fees: $170 full-time, $7.08 per credit hour part-time. Full-time tuition and fees vary according to course load. Part-time tuition and fees vary according to course load. College room and board: $7722. College room only: $4442. Room and board charges vary according to board plan and housing facility.

Collegiate Environment: Orientation program. Drama-theater group, choral group, marching band, student-run newspaper. Social organizations: 39 open to all; national fraternities, national sororities; 20% of eligible men and 25% of eligible women are members. Most popular organizations: Student Government Association, Okra Patch, Baptist Student Union, Union Program Council, Wesley Foundation. Major annual events: Homecoming, Pig Pickin', Springfest. Student services: health clinic, personal-psychological counseling. Campus security: 24-hour emergency response devices and patrols, late night transport-escort service, controlled dormitory access. 1,320 college housing spaces available; 799 were occupied in 2018-19. Freshmen guaranteed college housing. On-campus residence required in freshman year. Options: coed, men-only, women-only housing available. Roberts-LaForge Library plus 1 other. Books: 326,317 (physical), 72,046 (digital/electronic); Serial titles: 1,174 (physical), 25,014 (digital/electronic); Databases: 83. Weekly public service hours: 75. Operations spending for the previous fiscal year: $80,250.

Community Environment: Located midway between Memphis, Tennessee and Vicksburg, Mississippi, the city has a public library, several churches representing the major denominations, and a hospital. Bus lines are accessible to the area and a regional airport is located 30 miles from campus in Greenville. Recreation is provided in the community through a local Little Theatre, movies, swimming pools, 4 municipal parks, a nine-hole golf course, bowling, and fishing and hunting in the nearby lake region. Average living facilities are provided by a hotel, motel, several apartments, rooming houses and dormitories. The city has over 35 civic, fraternal and business organizations. Some part-time employment is available for students.

■ EAST CENTRAL COMMUNITY COLLEGE

PO Box 129
Decatur, MS 39327-0129
Tel: (601)635-2111; Free: 877-462-3222
Fax: (601)635-2150
Web Site: www.eccc.edu

Description: State and locally supported, 2-year, coed. Part of Mississippi State Board for Community and Junior Colleges. Awards certificates, transfer associate, and terminal associate degrees. Founded 1928. Setting: 200-acre rural campus. Total enrollment: 2,281. 31% 25 or older. Core. Calendar: semesters. Academic remediation for entering students, services for LD students, advanced placement, honors program, summer session for credit, part-time degree program, adult/continuing education programs.

Entrance Requirements: Open admission. Option: early admission. Required: high school transcript. Entrance: noncompetitive. Application deadline: rolling. Notification: continuous.

Collegiate Environment: Orientation program. Drama-theater group, choral group, marching band, student-run newspaper. Student services: health clinic, personal-psychological counseling. Campus security: 24-hour patrols. Burton Library.

Community Environment: Located in a rural area with a healthful atmosphere, Decatur has 2 churches and very active civic, fraternal and veteran's organizations. Hunting in the local area, fishing and swimming provide recreation for the city.

■ EAST MISSISSIPPI COMMUNITY COLLEGE

PO Box 158
Scooba, MS 39358-0158
Tel: (662)476-8442
Web Site: www.eastms.edu

Description: State and locally supported, 2-year, coed. Part of Mississippi State Board for Community and Junior Colleges. Awards certificates, transfer associate, and terminal associate degrees. Founded 1927. Setting: 25-acre rural campus. Total enrollment: 4,012. 36% 25 or older. Core. Calendar: semesters. Academic remediation for entering students, services for LD students, advanced placement, honors program, distance learning, double major, summer session for credit, part-time degree program, adult/continuing education programs, co-op programs.

Entrance Requirements: Open admission. Options: electronic application, deferred admission. Required: high school transcript. Entrance: noncompetitive. Application deadline: rolling.

Costs Per Year: Application fee: $0. State resident tuition: $3200 full-time, $150 per credit hour part-time. Nonresident tuition: $6200 full-time, $250 per credit hour part-time. Mandatory fees: $390 full-time, $5 per credit hour part-time, $120 per term part-time. Full-time tuition and fees vary according to course load and program. Part-time tuition and fees vary according to course load and program. College room and board: $4300. College room only: $2550. Room and board charges vary according to board plan.

Collegiate Environment: Orientation program. Drama-theater group, choral group, marching band, student-run newspaper. Social organizations: local fraternities. Student services: personal-psychological counseling. Campus security: 24-hour emergency response devices and patrols. Tubb-May Library.

Community Environment: Scooba is located in the east central part of Mississippi, 35 miles north of Meridian. The area is accessible by railroad and U.S. Highway 45. There are excellent bus, train and air facilities in nearby Meridian.

■ HINDS COMMUNITY COLLEGE

PO Box 1100
Raymond, MS 39154-1100
Tel: (601)857-5261; Free: 800-HINDSCC
Web Site: www.hindscc.edu

Description: State and locally supported, 2-year, coed. Part of Mississippi Community College Board. Awards certificates, transfer associate, and terminal associate degrees (profile includes Raymond, Jackson Academic and Technical Center, Jackson Nursing-Allied Health Center, Rankin, Utica, and Vicksburg campus locations). Founded 1917. Setting: 671-acre small town campus with easy access to Jackson. Total enrollment: 12,061. Student-undergrad faculty ratio is 17:1. Full-time: 7,196 students, 58% women, 42% men. Part-time: 4,865 students, 63% women, 37% men. Students come from 23 states and territories, 15 other countries, 3% from out-of-state. 0.2% American Indian or Alaska Native, non-Hispanic/Latino; 2% Hispanic/Latino; 56% Black or African American, non-Hispanic/Latino; 0.9% Asian, non-Hispanic/Latino. 27% 25 or older, 8% transferred in. Retention: 57% of full-time freshmen returned the following year. Core. Calendar: semesters. Academic remediation for entering students, services for LD students, advanced placement, accelerated degree program, honors program, independent study, distance learning, double major, summer session for credit, part-time degree program, adult/continuing education programs, co-op programs and internships. Study abroad program. ROTC: Army.

Entrance Requirements: Open admission. Option: electronic application. Transfer credits accepted: Yes.

Costs Per Year: Application fee: $0. State resident tuition: $2880 full-time, $120 per credit hour part-time. Nonresident tuition: $5920 full-time, $240 per credit hour part-time. Mandatory fees: $250 full-time, $10 per credit hour part-time, $125 per term part-time. Part-time tuition and fees vary according to course load. College room and board: $4736. Room and board charges vary according to housing facility.

Collegiate Environment: Drama-theater group, choral group, marching band, student-run newspaper. Student services: personal-psychological counseling. Campus security: 24-hour emergency response devices and patrols, late night transport-escort service, controlled dormitory access. McLendon Library plus 5 others. Students can reserve study rooms.

Community Environment: Raymond is a suburban area 15 miles east of Jackson. The community has a regional library and a general hospital 8 miles east. There are several churches of various denominations in the immediate area. Local clubs include Lions, Business & Professional Women, and the Jaycees. Hinds Community College has a part-time employment agreement with a local industry.

■ HOLMES COMMUNITY COLLEGE

PO Box 369
Goodman, MS 39079-0369
Tel: (662)472-2312; Free: 800-HOLMES-4
Fax: (662)472-9156
Web Site: www.holmescc.edu

Description: State and locally supported, 2-year, coed. Part of Mississippi State Board for Community and Junior Colleges. Awards certificates, transfer associate, and terminal associate degrees. Founded 1928. Setting: 196-acre small town campus. Total enrollment: 5,107. 34% 25 or older. Core. Calendar: semesters. Academic remediation for entering students, services for LD students, advanced placement, distance learning, summer session for credit, adult/continuing education programs, co-op programs.

Entrance Requirements: Open admission. Option: early admission. Required: high school transcript. Entrance: noncompetitive. Application deadline: rolling. Notification: continuous.

Collegiate Environment: Drama-theater group, choral group, marching band, student-run newspaper. Student services: personal-psychological counseling. Campus security: 24-hour emergency response devices and patrols. McMorrough Library plus 2 others.

Community Environment: Located in a rural area, there is bus service to Goodman. The climate is mild and humid. Railroad service is available in nearby Durant, Mississippi. Several churches of various denominations are located here. Many cultural, recreational and community services available in Jackson, the State Capital, 48 miles away. There is some work available for students requiring financial assistance.

■ ITAWAMBA COMMUNITY COLLEGE

602 W Hill St.
Fulton, MS 38843
Tel: (662)862-8000
Fax: (662)862-8036
E-mail: laboggs@iccms.edu
Web Site: www.iccms.edu

Description: State and locally supported, 2-year, coed. Part of Mississippi State Board for Community and Junior Colleges. Awards certificates, transfer associate, and terminal associate degrees. Founded 1947. Setting: 300-acre small town campus. Total enrollment: 5,611. Faculty: 353 (167 full-time, 186 part-time). Student-undergrad faculty ratio is 19:1. Full-time: 3,605 students, 58% women, 42% men. Part-time: 2,006 students, 64% women, 36% men. 10% 25 or older. Retention: 70% of full-time freshmen returned the following year. Core. Calendar: semesters. Academic remediation for entering students, ESL program, services for LD students, honors program, distance learning, summer session for credit, part-time degree program, adult/continuing education programs, co-op programs. ROTC: Army.

Entrance Requirements: Open admission except for allied health programs. Options: electronic application, early admission. Required: high school transcript. Entrance: noncompetitive. Application deadline: rolling. Notification: continuous. Transfer credits accepted: Yes.

Collegiate Environment: Orientation program. Drama-theater group, choral group, marching band, student-run newspaper. 200 computers available on campus for general student use. A campuswide network can be accessed from student residence rooms and from off campus. Students can access the following: online class registration. Staffed computer lab on campus provides training in use of computers, software, and the Internet.

Community Environment: Fulton is a rural community in northeast Mississippi. The climate is moderate to warm. The area is accessible to bus and rail lines and has several churches of various denominations. Recreation is provided by local theatres, boating water skiing, fishing, and golf. Community services include the County Health Department, a hospital, and fine shopping facilities. There are many active civic and fraternal organizations within the immediate area.

■ JACKSON STATE UNIVERSITY

1400 John R Lynch St.
Jackson, MS 39217
Tel: (601)979-2121; Free: 800-848-6817
Fax: (601)979-2358
E-mail: keiona.miller@jsums.edu
Web Site: www.jsums.edu

Description: State-supported, university, coed. Part of Mississippi Institutions of Higher Learning. Awards bachelor's, master's, and doctoral degrees and post-master's certificates. Founded 1877. Setting: 250-acre urban campus. Research spending for the previous fiscal year: $170.5 million. Educational spending for the previous fiscal year: $8932 per student. Total enrollment: 7,250. Faculty: 527 (347 full-time, 180 part-time). Student-undergrad faculty ratio is 17:1. 7,680 applied, 69% were admitted. Full-time: 4,840 students, 64% women, 36% men. Part-time: 491 students, 68% women, 32% men. Students come from 58 other countries, 30% from out-of-state. 0.3% American Indian or Alaska Native, non-Hispanic/Latino; 0.8% Hispanic/Latino; 92% Black or African American, non-Hispanic/Latino; 0.2% Asian, non-Hispanic/Latino; 2% international. 26% 25 or older, 41% live on campus, 8% transferred in. Retention: 53% of full-time freshmen returned the following year. Academic areas with the most degrees conferred: business/marketing; biological/life sciences; education; interdisciplinary studies. Core. Calendar: semesters. Academic remediation for entering students, ESL program, services for LD students, advanced placement, accelerated degree program, honors program, independent study, distance learning, double major, summer session for credit, part-time degree program, adult/continuing education programs, co-op programs and internships, graduate courses open to undergrads. Off campus study at National Student Exchange. Study abroad program. ROTC: Army, Air Force.

Entrance Requirements: Options: electronic application, international baccalaureate accepted. Required: high school transcript, immunization record, minimum ACT Composite score of 16, SAT or ACT. Entrance: minimally difficult. Application deadline: rolling for early action. Notification: continuous. SAT Reasoning Test deadline: 9/5. SAT Subject Test deadline: 9/5. Transfer credits accepted: Yes.

Costs Per Year: Application fee: $0. State resident tuition: $7876 full-time, $329 per hour part-time. Nonresident tuition: $19,104 full-time, $797 per hour part-time. Mandatory fees: $70 full-time. Full-time tuition and fees vary according to course level, course load, degree level, and student level. Part-time tuition varies according to course level, degree level, and student level. College room and board: $9552. College room only: $5784. Room and board charges vary according to housing facility.

Collegiate Environment: Orientation program. Drama-theater group, choral group, marching band, student-run newspaper. Social organizations: 95 open to all; national fraternities, national sororities, local fraternities, local sororities; 74% of eligible men and 94% of eligible women are members. Most popular organizations: Student Government Association, Sonic Boom of the South, MADDRAMA, Interfaith, NAACP. Major annual events: Homecoming, Thee I Love Bash, New Student Welcome Week. Student services: health clinic, personal-psychological counseling. Campus security: 24-hour emergency response devices and patrols, controlled dormitory access. College housing designed to accommodate 2,279 students; 2,313 undergraduates lived in college housing during 2018-19. Freshmen given priority for college housing. Options: coed, men-only, women-only housing available. H. T. Sampson Library plus 4 others. Books: 374,387 (digital/electronic); Serial titles: 317,232 (digital/electronic); Databases: 70. Operations spending for the previous fiscal year: $858,378. 2,000 computers available on campus for general student use. A campuswide network can be accessed from student residence rooms and from off campus. Students can access the following: online class registration. Staffed computer lab on campus provides training in use of computers, software, and the Internet.

Community Environment: On the Pearl River, Jackson is the capital and largest city of Mississippi. It was first established as a trading post by the French. In the early days, many Virginians and Carolinians passed through here as they followed the Old Natchez Trace to the Southwest. The area enjoys year-round pleasant weather. Being a major city, there are good facilities for rail and air transportation. Community associations sponsoring cultural pursuits include Jackson Music Association, Little Theatre, Municipal Art Gallery and Symphony Orchestra. Local services are supplied by 5 hospitals, libraries and many churches. Recreation facilities include 12 parks, 4 municipal swimming pools, a zoo, golf courses, tennis courts, and fishing and hunting nearby.

■ **JONES COUNTY JUNIOR COLLEGE**
900 S Ct. St.
Ellisville, MS 39437-3901
Tel: (601)477-4000
Fax: (601)477-4017
Web Site: www.jcjc.edu

Description: State and locally supported, 2-year, coed. Part of Mississippi State Board for Community and Junior Colleges. Awards certificates, transfer associate, and terminal associate degrees. Founded 1928. Setting: 360-acre small town campus. Total enrollment: 5,640. Faculty: 175 (170 full-time, 5 part-time). Student-undergrad faculty ratio is 25:1. Students come from 9 states and territories. 22% 25 or older, 20% live on campus. Core. Calendar: semesters. Academic remediation for entering students, advanced placement, honors program, distance learning, summer session for credit, part-time degree program, co-op programs. ROTC: Army (c), Air Force (c).

Entrance Requirements: Open admission. Option: early admission. Required: high school transcript, SAT or ACT. Entrance: noncompetitive. Application deadline: 8/26. Notification: continuous. Preference given to district residents.

Collegiate Environment: Drama-theater group, choral group, marching band, student-run newspaper. Most popular organization: Student Government. Major annual events: Homecoming, Spring Fever Week. Student services: health clinic, personal-psychological counseling. Campus security: 24-hour patrols. Memorial Library. 600 computers available on campus for general student use. Staffed computer lab on campus.

Community Environment: The city is located 7 miles from Laurel. The climate is mild. Churches, libraries and museums all contribute to the pleasant living of the area. Transportation is provided by rail and air lines, and the town is easily accessible by highway. Fishing, hunting, and golf are the major recreational pastimes. There are some part-time job opportunities for students.

■ **MERIDIAN COMMUNITY COLLEGE**
910 Hwy. 19 N
Meridian, MS 39307
Tel: (601)483-8241; Free: 800-MCC-THE-1
E-mail: apayne@meridiancc.edu
Web Site: www.meridiancc.edu

Description: State and locally supported, 2-year, coed. Part of Mississippi Community College Board. Awards certificates, transfer associate, and terminal associate degrees. Founded 1937. Setting: 91-acre small town campus. Endowment: $12.7 million. Educational spending for the previous fiscal year: $6619 per student. Total enrollment: 3,555. Faculty: 213 (132 full-time, 81 part-time). Student-undergrad faculty ratio is 18:1. 2% American Indian or Alaska Native, non-Hispanic/Latino; 1% Hispanic/Latino; 43% Black or African American, non-Hispanic/Latino; 0.5% Asian, non-Hispanic/Latino. 12% live on campus. Retention: 55% of full-time freshmen returned the following year. Core. Calendar: semesters. Academic remediation for entering students, ESL program, services for LD students, advanced placement, accelerated degree program, freshman honors college, honors program, independent study, distance learning, double major, summer session for credit, part-time degree program, adult/continuing education programs, co-op programs and internships.

Entrance Requirements: Open admission. Option: early admission. Required: high school transcript, minimum 2 high school GPA. Entrance: noncompetitive. Application deadlines: rolling, rolling for nonresidents. Notification: continuous, continuous for nonresidents. Transfer credits accepted: Yes.

Costs Per Year: Application fee: $0. State resident tuition: $2800 full-time, $150 per credit hour part-time. Nonresident tuition: $3780 full-time, $177 per credit hour part-time. Mandatory fees: $300 full-time, $6 per credit hour part-time, $25 per term part-time. Full-time tuition and fees vary according to program. Part-time tuition and fees vary according to program.

Collegiate Environment: Orientation program. Drama-theater group, choral group, student-run radio station. Social organizations: 22 open to all. Most popular organizations: Phi Theta Kappa, VICA (Vocational Industrial Clubs of America), Health Occupations Students of America, Organization of Student Nurses, Distributive Education Clubs of America. Major annual events: Spring Fest, Fall Fest, My College Cares. Student services: personal-psychological counseling. Campus security: 24-hour patrols by law enforcement officers. L.O. Todd-Billy C. Beal Learning Resources Center. Books: 49,544 (physical), 174,022 (digital/electronic); Serial titles: 207 (physical), 11 (digital/electronic); Databases: 13. Operations spending for the previous fiscal year: $867,746. 85 computers available on campus for general student use. A campuswide network can be accessed from student residence rooms. Students can access the following: online class registration. Staffed computer lab on campus provides training in use of computers, software, and the Internet.

Community Environment: Neither destruction by fire during the Civil War, a riot in 1871, a yellow fever epidemic in 1878, nor a cyclone in 1906 could keep Meridian down. It survived these disasters to become the state's leading industrial city. In an area providing abundant raw agricultural and industrial materials, local industries produce wood products, clothing, clay pipes, metal windows, asphalt roofing, fabricated steel and dairy and meat products. The region also produces timber, corn, cotton and cattle. Passenger air, rail and bus service is available. The city has private hospitals. Cultural activities include Little Theatre, Symphony Orchestra, Meridian Chorale and Art Association. The economic base is evenly divided between agriculture, industry and military payrolls.

■ **MILLSAPS COLLEGE**
1701 N State St.
Jackson, MS 39210
Tel: (601)974-1000; Free: 800-352-1050
Fax: (601)974-1059
E-mail: admissions@millsaps.edu
Web Site: www.millsaps.edu

Description: Independent United Methodist, comprehensive, coed. Awards bachelor's and master's degrees. Founded 1890. Setting: 100-acre urban campus. Endowment: $100.8 million. Total enrollment: 864. Faculty: 111 (82 full-time, 29 part-time). Student-undergrad faculty ratio is 9:1. 4,161 applied, 59% were admitted. 100% from top quarter of their high school class, 100% from top half. Full-time: 790 students, 52% women, 48% men. Part-time: 8 students, 38% women, 62% men. 55% from out-of-state. 1% American Indian or Alaska Native, non-Hispanic/Latino; 5% Hispanic/Latino; 20% Black or African American, non-Hispanic/Latino; 4% Asian, non-Hispanic/Latino; 5% international. 1% 25 or older, 89% live on campus, 2% transferred in. Retention: 79% of full-time freshmen returned the following year. Academic areas with the most degrees conferred: business/marketing; biological/life sciences; psychology. Core. Calendar: semesters. Services for LD students, advanced placement, accelerated degree program, self-designed majors, honors program, independent study, double major, summer session for credit, part-time degree program, internships, graduate courses open to undergrads. Off campus study at AIFS (American Institute for Foreign Study), AustraLearn, AsiaLearn, EuroLearn (educational programs of GlobalLinks Learning Abroad), CIEE (Council on International Educational Exchange). Millsaps is a member institution of ISEP (International Student Exchange Programs) and IES Abroad Consortium. Millsaps also encourages students to participate in several other programs, including The Alliance for Global Education, Arcadia University, IFSA-Butler, GSE, ISA, Semester at Sea. Study abroad program. ROTC: Army (c), Air Force (c).

Entrance Requirements: Options: electronic application, early admission, early action, deferred admission, international baccalaureate accepted. Required: essay, high school transcript, minimum 2.5 high school GPA, 1 recommendation, secondary school report, SAT or ACT. Required for some: interview. Entrance: moderately difficult. Application deadlines: 2/1, rolling for nonresidents, 11/15 for early action. Notification: continuous until 3/15, continuous for nonresidents, 1/15 for early action. SAT Reasoning Test deadline: 7/1. SAT Subject Test deadline: 7/1. Transfer credits accepted: Yes.

Costs Per Year: Application fee: $0. Comprehensive fee: $55,524 includes full-time tuition ($38,600), mandatory fees ($2714), and college room and board ($14,210). College room only: $7950. Part-time tuition: $1190 per semester hour.

Collegiate Environment: Orientation program. Drama-theater group, choral group, student-run newspaper. Social organizations: 80 open to all; national fraternities, national sororities; 60% of eligible men and 64% of eligible women are members. Most popular organizations: Campus Ministry Team, Student Body Association, SAPS (Campus Programming Board), Interfraternity/Panhellenic Councils, intramural sports. Major annual events: Major Madness, Homecoming, Project Midtown. Student services: health clinic, personal-psychological counseling. Campus security: 24-hour emergency response devices and patrols, student patrols, late night transport-escort service, controlled dormitory access. Freshmen guaranteed college housing. On-campus residence required through sophomore year. Options: coed, men-only, women-only housing available. Millsaps-Wilson Library. 150 computers available on campus for general student use. Computer purchase/lease plans available. A campuswide network can be accessed from student residence rooms and from off campus. Students can access the following: online class registration, online transcripts. Staffed computer lab on campus provides training in use of computers, software, and the Internet.

Community Environment: See Jackson State University.

■ **MISSISSIPPI COLLEGE**
200 S Capitol St.
Clinton, MS 39058
Tel: (601)925-3000; Free: 800-738-1236
Fax: (601)925-3804
E-mail: enrollment-services@mc.edu
Web Site: www.mc.edu
Description: Independent Southern Baptist, comprehensive, coed. Part of Mississippi Baptist Convention. Awards bachelor's, master's, and doctoral degrees and post-master's certificates. Founded 1826. Setting: 140-acre suburban campus with easy access to Jackson. Endowment: $72.5 million. Educational spending for the previous fiscal year: $798 per student. Total enrollment: 5,036. Faculty: 433 (228 full-time, 205 part-time). Student-undergrad faculty ratio is 15:1. 1,958 applied, 82% were admitted. 34% from top 10% of their high school class, 56% from top quarter, 79% from top half. Full-time: 2,677 students, 60% women, 40% men. Part-time: 327 students, 56% women, 44% men. Students come from 42 states and territories, 36 other countries, 29% from out-of-state. 0.5% American Indian or Alaska Na-

tive, non-Hispanic/Latino; 3% Hispanic/Latino; 18% Black or African American, non-Hispanic/Latino; 2% Asian, non-Hispanic/Latino; 6% international. 15% 25 or older, 64% live on campus, 8% transferred in. Retention: 79% of full-time freshmen returned the following year. Academic areas with the most degrees conferred: business/marketing; parks and recreation; health professions and related sciences. Core. Calendar: semesters. Academic remediation for entering students, ESL program, services for LD students, advanced placement, accelerated degree program, honors program, independent study, distance learning, double major, summer session for credit, part-time degree program, adult/continuing education programs, co-op programs and internships, graduate courses open to undergrads. Study abroad program. ROTC: Army, Air Force.

Entrance Requirements: Options: electronic application, early admission, deferred admission, international baccalaureate accepted. Required: high school transcript, SAT or ACT. Recommended: minimum 2 high school GPA, interview. Required for some: 2 recommendations. Entrance: moderately difficult. Application deadline: rolling. Notification: continuous. Transfer credits accepted: Yes.

Costs Per Year: Application fee: $25. Comprehensive fee: $28,326 includes full-time tuition ($17,000), mandatory fees ($1026), and college room and board ($10,300). Full-time tuition and fees vary according to course load. Room and board charges vary according to housing facility. Part-time tuition: $532 per credit hour. Part-time mandatory fees: $210 per term.

Collegiate Environment: Orientation program. Drama-theater group, choral group, marching band, student-run newspaper, radio station. Social organizations: 74 open to all; local fraternities, local sororities; 10% of eligible men and 24% of eligible women are members. Most popular organizations: Baptist Student Union, Nenamoosha Social Tribe, Laguna Social Tribe, Civitan Service Club, Shawreth Service Club. Major annual events: Welcome Week, Homecoming, Spring Fever Week. Student services: health clinic, personal-psychological counseling. Campus security: 24-hour emergency response devices and patrols, late night transport-escort service, controlled dormitory access. Leland Speed Library plus 1 other. Books: 252,127 (physical), 1,634 (digital/electronic); Serial titles: 9,071 (physical), 21 (digital/electronic); Databases: 55. Operations spending for the previous fiscal year: $1.3 million. 492 computers available on campus for general student use. A campuswide network can be accessed from student residence rooms and from off campus. Students can access the following: online class registration. Staffed computer lab on campus provides training in use of computers, software, and the Internet.

Community Environment: This is a suburban community located adjacent to Jackson's city limits. The climate is warm. The area has a shopping center, and rapid expansion of businesses and residential areas is anticipated. Clinton has excellent highway, air, and rail connections.

■ **MISSISSIPPI DELTA COMMUNITY COLLEGE**
Hwy. 3 and Cherry St.
Moorhead, MS 38761-0668
Tel: (662)246-6322
Web Site: www.msdelta.edu
Description: District-supported, 2-year, coed. Part of Mississippi State Board for Community and Junior Colleges. Awards certificates, diplomas, transfer associate, and terminal associate degrees. Founded 1926. Setting: 425-acre small town campus. Educational spending for the previous fiscal year: $2372 per student. Total enrollment: 2,950. Faculty: 208 (112 full-time, 96 part-time). Student-undergrad faculty ratio is 18:1. 909 applied, 100% were admitted. Full-time: 2,305 students, 62% women, 38% men. Part-time: 645 students, 67% women, 33% men. Students come from 6 states and territories. 0.9% Hispanic/Latino; 64% Black or African American, non-Hispanic/Latino; 0.8% Asian, non-Hispanic/Latino. 20% 25 or older, 25% live on campus. Retention: 58% of full-time freshmen returned the following year. Calendar: semesters. Academic remediation for entering students, advanced placement, summer session for credit, part-time degree program, adult/continuing education programs.

Entrance Requirements: Option: deferred admission. Required: high school transcript. Required for some: ACT. Entrance: noncompetitive. Application deadlines: 7/27, rolling for nonresidents. Notification: continuous, continuous for nonresidents. Preference given to district residents. Transfer credits accepted: Yes.

Collegiate Environment: Choral group, marching band. Social organizations: 16 open to all. Most popular organizations: Phi Theta Kappa, SkillsUSA, Phi Beta Lambda, Student Government Association, Nursing Club. Major annual events: Homecoming, Springfest, Spring Fine Arts Show. Student services: personal-psychological counseling. Campus security: 24-

hour emergency response devices and patrols, late night transport-escort service, controlled dormitory access. Stanny Sanders Library. Operations spending for the previous fiscal year: $443,719. 80 computers available on campus for general student use. Staffed computer lab on campus.

Community Environment: This is a rural area with bus and air transportation 8 miles distant. The immediate area supports a clinic and small stores. There is some part-time employment for men over 18. Better employment opportunities for students are available in the neighboring community. The city has a theater, swimming pool and tennis courts. 5 local lakes provide hunting and fishing within the area.

■ MISSISSIPPI GULF COAST COMMUNITY COLLEGE

PO Box 609
Perkinston, MS 39573
Tel: (601)928-5211
Fax: (601)928-6299
Web Site: www.mgccc.edu

Description: District-supported, 2-year, coed. Awards certificates, diplomas, transfer associate, and terminal associate degrees. Founded 1911. Setting: 600-acre small town campus with easy access to New Orleans. Total enrollment: 10,074. Faculty: 488 (287 full-time, 201 part-time). Student-undergrad faculty ratio is 24:1. Full-time: 6,935 students, 59% women, 41% men. Part-time: 3,139 students, 60% women, 40% men. Students come from 15 states and territories, 4% from out-of-state. 0.5% American Indian or Alaska Native, non-Hispanic/Latino; 3% Hispanic/Latino; 24% Black or African American, non-Hispanic/Latino; 3% Asian, non-Hispanic/Latino; 0.1% Native Hawaiian or other Pacific Islander, non-Hispanic/Latino. 7% live on campus. Retention: 62% of full-time freshmen returned the following year. Core. Calendar: semesters. Academic remediation for entering students, ESL program, advanced placement, honors program, independent study, distance learning, summer session for credit, part-time degree program, adult/continuing education programs, co-op programs and internships. Study abroad program.

Entrance Requirements: Required: high school transcript.

Collegiate Environment: Orientation program. Drama-theater group, choral group, marching band, student-run newspaper. Social organizations: 33 open to all. Most popular organizations: Student Government Association, Students in Free Enterprise (SIFE), Reflections. Major annual events: Homecoming, Fall Bash, Spring Fling. Student services: personal-psychological counseling, women's center. Campus security: 24-hour emergency response devices and patrols. Main library plus 3 others. 435 computers available on campus for general student use. A campuswide network can be accessed from student residence rooms. Students can access the following: online class registration. Staffed computer lab on campus provides training in use of computers, software, and the Internet.

Community Environment: The city lies 25 miles north of Gulfport. Area is reached by Interstate 10 and Highway 49. Air service is available.

■ MISSISSIPPI STATE UNIVERSITY

75 B.S. Hood Dr.
Mississippi State, MS 39762
Tel: (662)325-2323
Fax: (662)325-3299
E-mail: admit@msstate.edu
Web Site: www.msstate.edu

Description: State-supported, university, coed. Part of Mississippi Institutions of Higher Learning. Awards associate, bachelor's, master's, and doctoral degrees and post-master's certificates. Founded 1878. Setting: 4,200-acre small town campus. Endowment: $472 million. Research spending for the previous fiscal year: $153.1 million. Educational spending for the previous fiscal year: $7360 per student. Total enrollment: 21,883. Faculty: 1,142 (970 full-time, 172 part-time). Student-undergrad faculty ratio is 20:1. 13,817 applied, 73% were admitted. 25% from top 10% of their high school class, 54% from top quarter, 82% from top half. 33 National Merit Scholars. Full-time: 16,803 students, 50% women, 50% men. Part-time: 1,509 students, 45% women, 55% men. Students come from 52 states and territories, 49 other countries, 30% from out-of-state. 0.5% American Indian or Alaska Native, non-Hispanic/Latino; 3% Hispanic/Latino; 20% Black or African American, non-Hispanic/Latino; 1% Asian, non-Hispanic/Latino; 0.1% Native Hawaiian or other Pacific Islander, non-Hispanic/Latino; 1% international. 9% 25 or older, 27% live on campus, 11% transferred in. Retention: 79% of full-time freshmen returned the following year. Academic areas with the most degrees conferred: business/marketing; engineering; interdisciplinary studies. Core. Calendar: semesters. Academic remediation

for entering students, ESL program, services for LD students, advanced placement, accelerated degree program, self-designed majors, freshman honors college, honors program, independent study, distance learning, double major, summer session for credit, part-time degree program, adult/continuing education programs, co-op programs and internships, graduate courses open to undergrads. Off campus study at Meridian Campus, Stennis Center (Hancock County). Study abroad program. ROTC: Army, Air Force.

Entrance Requirements: Options: electronic application, international baccalaureate accepted. Required: high school transcript, minimum 2 high school GPA, SAT or ACT. Entrance: moderately difficult. Application deadline: 8/1. Notification: continuous. SAT Reasoning Test deadline: 8/15. SAT Subject Test deadline: 8/15. Transfer credits accepted: Yes.

Costs Per Year: Application fee: $40. One-time mandatory fee: $55. State resident tuition: $8450 full-time, $360.59 per credit hour part-time. Nonresident tuition: $23,140 full-time, $969.09 per credit hour part-time. Mandatory fees: $110 full-time. Full-time tuition and fees vary according to degree level, location, and reciprocity agreements. Part-time tuition varies according to course load, degree level, location, and reciprocity agreements. College room and board: $9764. College room only: $5983. Room and board charges vary according to board plan, housing facility, and student level.

Collegiate Environment: Orientation program. Drama-theater group, choral group, marching band, student-run newspaper, radio station. Social organizations: 400 open to all; national fraternities, national sororities; 14% of eligible men and 17% of eligible women are members. Most popular organizations: Student Association, Black Student Alliance, Residence Hall Association, Fashion Board, Campus Activities Board. Major annual events: Bulldog Bash, Homecoming, Athletic Events. Student services: health clinic, personal-psychological counseling. Campus security: 24-hour emergency response devices and patrols, late night transport-escort service, controlled dormitory access, bicycle patrols, crime prevention program, RAD program, general law enforcement services. Mitchell Memorial Library plus 2 others. Books: 257,296 (physical), 56,456 (digital/electronic); Serial titles: 1,646 (physical), 231,031 (digital/electronic); Databases: 185. Weekly public service hours: 110; students can reserve study rooms. Operations spending for the previous fiscal year: $13.8 million. 1,000 computers available on campus for general student use. A campuswide network can be accessed from student residence rooms and from off campus. Students can access the following: online class registration. Staffed computer lab on campus provides training in use of computers, software, and the Internet.

■ MISSISSIPPI UNIVERSITY FOR WOMEN

1100 College St., MUW-1600
Columbus, MS 39701-9998
Tel: (662)329-4750; Free: 877-GO 2 THE W
Fax: (662)329-7297
Web Site: www.muw.edu

Description: State-supported, comprehensive, coed. Part of Mississippi Institutions of Higher Learning. Awards associate, bachelor's, master's, and doctoral degrees and post-master's certificates. Founded 1884. Setting: 110-acre small town campus. Endowment: $50.3 million. Research spending for the previous fiscal year: $532,706. Educational spending for the previous fiscal year: $5257 per student. Total enrollment: 2,673. Faculty: 201 (137 full-time, 64 part-time). Student-undergrad faculty ratio is 14:1. 671 applied, 96% were admitted. 24% from top 10% of their high school class, 54% from top quarter, 84% from top half. 9 valedictorians. Full-time: 1,976 students, 83% women, 17% men. Part-time: 494 students, 71% women, 29% men. Students come from 10 states and territories, 7 other countries, 12% from out-of-state. 0.3% American Indian or Alaska Native, non-Hispanic/Latino; 0.4% Hispanic/Latino; 36% Black or African American, non-Hispanic/Latino; 2% Asian, non-Hispanic/Latino; 0.1% Native Hawaiian or other Pacific Islander, non-Hispanic/Latino; 4% international. 33% 25 or older, 27% live on campus, 25% transferred in. Retention: 75% of full-time freshmen returned the following year. Academic areas with the most degrees conferred: health professions and related sciences; business/marketing; parks and recreation; liberal arts/general studies. Core. Calendar: semesters. Academic remediation for entering students, services for LD students, advanced placement, freshman honors college, honors program, independent study, distance learning, double major, summer session for credit, part-time degree program, adult/continuing education programs, internships, graduate courses open to undergrads. Off campus study at Mississippi State University. Study abroad program. ROTC: Air Force (c).

Entrance Requirements: Options: electronic application, early admission, international baccalaureate accepted. Required: high school transcript.

Recommended: SAT or ACT. Required for some: minimum 2 high school GPA, rank in upper 50% of high school class, SAT or ACT. Entrance: moderately difficult. Application deadline: rolling. Notification: continuous. SAT Reasoning Test deadline: 8/20. SAT Subject Test deadline: 8/20. Transfer credits accepted: Yes.

Collegiate Environment: Orientation program. Drama-theater group, choral group, student-run newspaper, radio station. Social organizations: 55 open to all; national fraternities, national sororities, local fraternities, local sororities; 10% of eligible men and 13% of eligible women are members. Most popular organizations: Student Government Association, Wesley Foundation, International Student Association, Baptist Student Union, International Justice Mission. Major annual events: Blues Week, Late Night Exam Breakfast, intramurals. Student services: health clinic, personal-psychological counseling, women's center. Campus security: 24-hour emergency response and patrols, late night transport-escort service, controlled dormitory access, tornado and voice-over sirens, voice mail and text messaging emergency notification system. John Clayton Fant Memorial Library plus 2 others. Books: 197,660 (physical); Serial titles: 4,889 (physical), 1,560 (digital/electronic); Databases: 74. Weekly public service hours: 76; students can reserve study rooms. Operations spending for the previous fiscal year: $1 million. 393 computers available on campus for general student use. A campuswide network can be accessed from student residence rooms and from off campus. Students can access the following: online class registration. Staffed computer lab on campus provides training in use of computers, software, and the Internet.

■ MISSISSIPPI VALLEY STATE UNIVERSITY
14000 Hwy. 82 W
Itta Bena, MS 38941-1400
Tel: (662)254-9041
Fax: (662)254-7900
Web Site: www.mvsu.edu

Description: State-supported, comprehensive, coed. Part of Mississippi Institutions of Higher Learning. Awards bachelor's and master's degrees. Founded 1946. Setting: 450-acre small town campus. Endowment: $1.6 million. Educational spending for the previous fiscal year: $5390 per student. Total enrollment: 2,455. Faculty: 172 (120 full-time, 52 part-time). Student-undergrad faculty ratio is 15:1. 2,605 applied, 84% were admitted. Full-time: 1,744 students, 58% women, 42% men. Part-time: 267 students, 72% women, 28% men. Students come from 33 states and territories, 11 other countries, 25% from out-of-state. 1% Hispanic/Latino; 91% Black or African American, non-Hispanic/Latino; 0.2% Asian, non-Hispanic/Latino; 0.2% Native Hawaiian or other Pacific Islander, non-Hispanic/Latino. 16% 25 or older, 46% live on campus, 10% transferred in. Retention: 60% of full-time freshmen returned the following year. Academic areas with the most degrees conferred: education; business/marketing; homeland security, law enforcement, firefighting, and protective services. Core. Calendar: semesters. Academic remediation for entering students, freshman honors college, honors program, distance learning, double major, summer session for credit, part-time degree program, co-op programs and internships, graduate courses open to undergrads. ROTC: Army.

Entrance Requirements: Option: deferred admission. Required: high school transcript, SAT or ACT. Recommended: interview. Required for some: 2.5 recommendations. Entrance: minimally difficult. Application deadline: rolling. Notification: continuous.

Costs Per Year: Application fee: $0. State resident tuition: $6530 full-time, $272 per credit hour part-time. Nonresident tuition: $6530 full-time, $272 per credit hour part-time. Mandatory fees: $20 full-time, $20 per year part-time. College room and board: $7764. College room only: $4258.

Collegiate Environment: Orientation program. Drama-theater group, choral group, marching band, student-run newspaper, radio station. Social organizations: 52 open to all; national fraternities, national sororities, local fraternities, local sororities; 5% of eligible men and 4% of eligible women are members. Most popular organizations: Student Government Association, Baptist Student Union, Black Student Fellowship, National Education Association. Major annual events: Homecoming, Black History Month, Founder's Day. Student services: health clinic, personal-psychological counseling. Campus security: 24-hour emergency response devices and patrols, controlled dormitory access. James Herbert White Library. Books: 127,541 (physical), 53,358 (digital/electronic); Databases: 62. Weekly public service hours: 84; students can reserve study rooms. Operations spending for the previous fiscal year: $794,980. 285 computers available on campus for general student use. A campuswide network can be accessed from student residence rooms and from off campus. Students can access the following: online class registration. Staffed computer lab on campus.

Community Environment: This is a rural community with a mild, temperate climate. Bus service provides transportation for the city and adjacent areas. Community services within the immediate area include churches of major denominations and a clinic. Shopping facilities are available within the surrounding communities. There is no part-time employment available for students.

■ NORTHEAST MISSISSIPPI COMMUNITY COLLEGE
101 Cunningham Blvd.
Booneville, MS 38829
Tel: (662)728-7751; Free: 800-555-2154
Fax: (662)728-1165
E-mail: admitme@nemcc.edu
Web Site: www.nemcc.edu

Description: State-supported, 2-year, coed. Part of Mississippi State Board for Community and Junior Colleges. Awards certificates, transfer associate, and terminal associate degrees. Founded 1948. Setting: 100-acre small town campus. Total enrollment: 3,339. 24% 25 or older. Core. Calendar: semesters. Academic remediation for entering students, services for LD students, advanced placement, self-designed majors, summer session for credit, part-time degree program, adult/continuing education programs, co-op programs.

Entrance Requirements: Open admission. Option: early admission. Required for some: SAT or ACT. Entrance: noncompetitive. Application deadline: rolling. Notification: continuous.

Collegiate Environment: Orientation program. Drama-theater group, choral group, marching band, student-run newspaper. Student services: personal-psychological counseling. Campus security: 24-hour patrols, student patrols, controlled dormitory access. Eula Dees Library.

Community Environment: The city is located in the northeast corner of Mississippi, 100 miles southeast of Memphis, Tennessee. It has a warm and pleasant climate.

■ NORTHWEST MISSISSIPPI COMMUNITY COLLEGE
4975 Hwy. 51 N
Senatobia, MS 38668-1701
Tel: (662)562-3200
Fax: (662)562-3911
Web Site: www.northwestms.edu

Description: State and locally supported, 2-year, coed. Part of Mississippi State Board for Community and Junior Colleges. Awards transfer associate and terminal associate degrees. Founded 1927. Setting: 75-acre rural campus with easy access to Memphis. Total enrollment: 7,700. Faculty: (200 full-time). Student-undergrad faculty ratio is 20:1. Retention: 60% of full-time freshmen returned the following year. Core. Calendar: semesters. Academic remediation for entering students, services for LD students, honors program, distance learning, summer session for credit, part-time degree program, adult/continuing education programs. ROTC: Air Force.

Entrance Requirements: Open admission. Options: electronic application, early admission, deferred admission. Required: high school transcript. Entrance: noncompetitive. Application deadline: 8/15. Notification: continuous. Transfer credits accepted: Yes.

Collegiate Environment: Drama-theater group, choral group, marching band, student-run newspaper. Major annual event: Homecoming. Student services: personal-psychological counseling. Campus security: 24-hour emergency response devices and patrols, late night transport-escort service, controlled dormitory access. R. C. Pugh Library. Study areas open 24 hours, 5-7 days a week. 50 computers available on campus for general student use. A campuswide network can be accessed. Students can access the following: online class registration. Staffed computer lab on campus.

Community Environment: Senatobia is the seat of Tate County, lying 40 miles south of Memphis, Tennessee. The area is served by Illinois Central Railroad. The city itself is located off Interstate Highway 55. Nearby is Arkabutla Reservoir and Dam, a well-known recreation facility.

■ PEARL RIVER COMMUNITY COLLEGE
101 Hwy. 11 N
Poplarville, MS 39470
Tel: (601)403-1000
Fax: (601)403-1135
E-mail: dford@prcc.edu
Web Site: www.prcc.edu

Description: State and locally supported, 2-year, coed. Part of Mississippi State Board for Community and Junior Colleges. Awards certificates, transfer associate, and terminal associate degrees. Founded 1909. Setting: 240-acre rural campus with easy access to New Orleans. Total enrollment: 3,700. Faculty: 225 (160 full-time, 65 part-time). Students come from 11 states and territories. 27% 25 or older, 20% live on campus. Core. Calendar: semesters. Academic remediation for entering students, advanced placement, self-designed majors, summer session for credit, part-time degree program, adult/continuing education programs, co-op programs.

Entrance Requirements: Open admission except for nursing, data processing programs. Options: early admission, deferred admission. Required: high school transcript. Entrance: minimally difficult. Application deadline: rolling. Notification: continuous until 8/15. Preference given to state residents.

Collegiate Environment: Drama-theater group, choral group, marching band, student-run newspaper. Social organizations: 4 open to all. Major annual events: Homecoming, Fall Fest, Spring Fest. Student services: health clinic, personal-psychological counseling, women's center. Campus security: 24-hour patrols. Pearl River Community College Library. 90 computers available on campus for general student use. Staffed computer lab on campus.

Community Environment: Poplarville is located in the southern portion of the state and has a temperate climate. New Orleans may be reached 70 miles southwest via Interstate Highway 59. Poplarville has its own hospital.

■ RUST COLLEGE
150 Rust Ave.
Holly Springs, MS 38635
Tel: (662)252-8000; Free: 888-886-8492
Fax: (662)252-6107
E-mail: btalley@rustcollege.edu
Web Site: www.rustcollege.edu

Description: Independent United Methodist, 4-year, coed. Awards associate and bachelor's degrees. Founded 1866. Setting: 126-acre small town campus with easy access to Memphis. Endowment: $41.7 million. Educational spending for the previous fiscal year: $3803 per student. Total enrollment: 1,004. Faculty: 51 (48 full-time, 3 part-time). Student-undergrad faculty ratio is 20:1. 5,337 applied, 7% were admitted. Full-time: 873 students, 60% women, 40% men. Part-time: 131 students, 63% women, 37% men. Students come from 22 states and territories, 6 other countries, 58% from out-of-state. 95% Black or African American, non-Hispanic/Latino; 0.1% Asian, non-Hispanic/Latino; 2% international. 9% 25 or older, 76% live on campus, 7% transferred in. Retention: 59% of full-time freshmen returned the following year. Academic areas with the most degrees conferred: biological/life sciences; social sciences; business/marketing; communication/journalism. Core. Calendar: semesters. Academic remediation for entering students, advanced placement, accelerated degree program, honors program, independent study, double major, summer session for credit, part-time degree program, adult/continuing education programs, internships. Study abroad program.

Entrance Requirements: Required: high school transcript, minimum 2.5 high school GPA, 2 recommendations, ACT. Entrance: minimally difficult. Application deadline: rolling. Notification: continuous. Transfer credits accepted: Yes.

Costs Per Year: Application fee: $10. Comprehensive fee: $14,200 includes full-time tuition ($9900) and college room and board ($4300). Full-time tuition varies according to course load. Part-time tuition: $421 per credit hour. Part-time tuition varies according to course load.

Collegiate Environment: Orientation program. Drama-theater group, choral group, marching band, student-run radio station. Social organizations: 32 open to all; national fraternities, national sororities; 20% of eligible men and 25% of eligible women are members. Most popular organizations: National Sororities, National Fraternities, Choral Group, Television Station, Radio Station. Major annual events: Founders Weekend, SGA Spring Fest, Greek Life Showcase. Student services: health clinic, women's center. Campus security: 24-hour emergency response devices and patrols, controlled dormitory access. Leontyne Price Library. Books: 126,854 (physical), 438 (digital/electronic); Serial titles: 279 (physical); Databases: 6. Weekly public service hours: 90; students can reserve study rooms. Operations spending for the previous fiscal year: $523,781. 339 computers available on campus for general student use. A campuswide network can be accessed from student residence rooms and from off campus. Staffed computer lab on campus.

Community Environment: A typical antebellum town, Holly Springs grew up during the great cotton boom before the Civil War. The fine old mansions and churches of the town reflect the prosperity of the cotton era. There are shopping areas in nearby Memphis. No part-time employment is available for students.

■ SOUTHEASTERN BAPTIST COLLEGE
4229 Hwy. 15 N
Laurel, MS 39440-1096
Tel: (601)426-6346
Web Site: www.southeasternbaptist.edu

Description: Independent Baptist, 4-year, coed. Awards associate and bachelor's degrees. Founded 1949. Setting: 23-acre small town campus. Total enrollment: 79. 20% from out-of-state. 51% 25 or older, 31% live on campus. Core. Calendar: semesters. Academic remediation for entering students, advanced placement, summer session for credit, part-time degree program, adult/continuing education programs.

Entrance Requirements: Open admission. Options: early admission, deferred admission. Required: high school transcript, 2 recommendations. Required for some: interview. Entrance: noncompetitive. Application deadline: rolling.

Collegiate Environment: Choral group. A. R. Reddin Memorial Library.

Community Environment: Laurel's growth from a small village in 1900 to its present metropolitan size has been due to its pine forests and oil development. Lumber represents an important industry, but other firms manufacture clothing, machines, doors, furniture, agricultural implements, distribution transformers, oil well drilling equipment, walk-in refrigerators, condiments and janitorial supplies. There is a complete recreation program in the city, and it is close to resorts and state parks. Railroad, bus and air transportation is available in the immediate area. Laurel is considered the medical center of the surrounding area.

■ SOUTHWEST MISSISSIPPI COMMUNITY COLLEGE
1156 College Dr.
Summit, MS 39666
Tel: (601)276-2000
Fax: (601)276-3888
E-mail: mattc@smcc.edu
Web Site: www.smcc.cc.ms.us

Description: State and locally supported, 2-year, coed. Part of Mississippi State Board for Community and Junior Colleges. Awards certificates, transfer associate, and terminal associate degrees. Founded 1918. Setting: 701-acre rural campus. Total enrollment: 2,053. Faculty: 90 (71 full-time, 19 part-time). Student-undergrad faculty ratio is 24:1. Full-time: 1,785 students, 63% women, 37% men. Part-time: 268 students, 75% women, 25% men. Students come from 8 states and territories, 1 other country, 6% from out-of-state. 0.4% American Indian or Alaska Native, non-Hispanic/Latino; 0.3% Hispanic/Latino; 43% Black or African American, non-Hispanic/Latino; 0.5% Asian, non-Hispanic/Latino. 29% 25 or older, 35% live on campus, 45% transferred in. Retention: 50% of full-time freshmen returned the following year. Core. Calendar: semesters. Academic remediation for entering students, advanced placement, distance learning, summer session for credit, part-time degree program, adult/continuing education programs.

Entrance Requirements: Open admission. Required: high school transcript. Entrance: noncompetitive. Application deadline: 8/1. Transfer credits accepted: Yes.

Collegiate Environment: Orientation program. Choral group, marching band, student-run newspaper. Campus security: 24-hour patrols. Library Learning Resources Center (LLRC). 300 computers available on campus for general student use. A campuswide network can be accessed from student residence rooms. Students can access the following: online class registration. Staffed computer lab on campus provides training in use of computers, software, and the Internet.

Community Environment: Summit is a suburban area near McComb, Mississippi. The city is served by bus and rail. Health services, a library, and churches, are to be found in the neighboring city. There are shopping facilities in the immediate area. Some part-time employment is available. Recreation in the area includes boating, fishing and camping.

■ STRAYER UNIVERSITY-JACKSON CAMPUS
460 Briarwood Dr.
Ste. 200
Jackson, MS 39206
Tel: (601)718-5900; Free: 888-311-0355
Web Site: www.strayer.edu

Description: Proprietary, comprehensive, coed. Awards associate, bachelor's, and master's degrees.

■ TOUGALOO COLLEGE
500 W County Line Rd.
Tougaloo, MS 39174

Tel: (601)977-7700; Free: 888-42GALOO
Fax: (601)977-7739
E-mail: jjacobs@tougaloo.edu
Web Site: www.tougaloo.edu
Description: Independent, 4-year, coed, affiliated with United Church of Christ. Awards associate and bachelor's degrees. Founded 1869. Setting: 500-acre suburban campus. Endowment: $4.7 million. Research spending for the previous fiscal year: $236,232. Total enrollment: 900. Faculty: 103 (70 full-time, 33 part-time). Student-undergrad faculty ratio is 13:1. 2,551 applied, 40% were admitted. 13% from top 10% of their high school class, 30% from top quarter, 57% from top half. Full-time: 872 students, 66% women, 34% men. Part-time: 28 students, 57% women, 43% men. Students come from 17 states and territories, 4 other countries, 19% from out-of-state. 0.1% American Indian or Alaska Native, non-Hispanic/Latino; 0.3% Hispanic/Latino; 99% Black or African American, non-Hispanic/Latino; 0.4% international. 5% 25 or older, 66% live on campus, 9% transferred in. Retention: 82% of full-time freshmen returned the following year. Academic areas with the most degrees conferred: social sciences; education; biological/life sciences. Core. Calendar: semesters. Academic remediation for entering students, advanced placement, accelerated degree program, self-designed majors, honors program, independent study, double major, summer session for credit, part-time degree program, adult/continuing education programs, co-op programs and internships. Off campus study at Brown University, New York University, Boston University. Study abroad program. ROTC: Army.
Entrance Requirements: Options: early admission, international baccalaureate accepted. Required: high school transcript, minimum 2 high school GPA, SAT or ACT. Entrance: minimally difficult. Application deadline: rolling. Notification: continuous. Transfer credits accepted: Yes.
Collegiate Environment: Orientation program. Drama-theater group, choral group, student-run newspaper. Social organizations: 8 open to all; national fraternities, national sororities, local fraternities; 30% of eligible men and 35% of eligible women are members. Most popular organizations: concert choir, Student Government Association, gospel choir, NAACP, Pre-Alumni Club. Major annual events: Founders' Weekend, Humanities Festival, Honor's Day. Student services: health clinic, personal-psychological counseling. Campus security: 24-hour emergency response devices and patrols. L. Zenobiz Coleman Library. 100 computers available on campus for general student use. A campuswide network can be accessed from student residence rooms and from off campus. Students can access the following: online class registration. Staffed computer lab on campus provides training in use of computers, software, and the Internet.
Community Environment: See Jackson State University.

■ **UNIVERSITY OF MISSISSIPPI**
University, MS 38677
Tel: (662)915-7211
Fax: (662)915-5869
E-mail: admissions@olemiss.edu
Web Site: www.olemiss.edu
Description: State-supported, university, coed. Part of Mississippi Institutions of Higher Learning. Awards bachelor's, master's, and doctoral degrees and post-master's certificates. Founded 1844. Setting: 34,977-acre small town campus with easy access to Memphis. Endowment: $670.6 million. Research spending for the previous fiscal year: $85.8 million. Educational spending for the previous fiscal year: $8911 per student. Total enrollment: 23,136. Faculty: 1,344 (1,045 full-time, 299 part-time). Student-undergrad faculty ratio is 18:1. 17,416 applied, 84% were admitted. 26% from top 10% of their high school class, 52% from top quarter, 80% from top half. Full-time: 17,511 students, 56% women, 44% men. Part-time: 1,226 students, 55% women, 45% men. Students come from 51 states and territories, 66 other countries, 44% from out-of-state. 0.3% American Indian or Alaska Native, non-Hispanic/Latino; 3% Hispanic/Latino; 13% Black or African American, non-Hispanic/Latino; 2% Asian, non-Hispanic/Latino; 0.1% Native Hawaiian or other Pacific Islander, non-Hispanic/Latino; 2% international. 7% 25 or older, 25% live on campus, 7% transferred in. Retention: 85% of full-time freshmen returned the following year. Academic areas with the most degrees conferred: business/marketing; health professions and related sciences; communication/journalism. Core. Calendar: semesters. Academic remediation for entering students, ESL program, services for LD students, advanced placement, accelerated degree program, freshman honors college, honors program, independent study, distance learning, double major, summer session for credit, part-time degree program, adult/continuing education programs, co-op programs and internships, graduate courses open to undergrads. Study abroad program. ROTC: Army, Naval, Air Force.

Entrance Requirements: Options: electronic application, deferred admission, international baccalaureate accepted. Required: high school transcript, minimum 2 high school GPA, SAT or ACT. Entrance: moderately difficult. Application deadline: rolling. Notification: continuous. SAT Reasoning Test deadline: 8/1. SAT Subject Test deadline: 8/1. Transfer credits accepted: Yes.
Collegiate Environment: Orientation program. Drama-theater group, choral group, marching band, student-run newspaper, radio station. Social organizations: 423 open to all; national fraternities, national sororities, local fraternities; 35% of eligible men and 44% of eligible women are members. Most popular organizations: Associated Student Body, Gospel Choir, sport clubs, Black Student Union, Student Programming Board. Major annual events: Welcome Week, Grove Bowl Week/Grove Bowl Game/Spring Concert, Awards of Distinction. Student services: health clinic, personal-psychological counseling, women's center. Campus security: 24-hour emergency response devices and patrols, late night transport-escort service, controlled dormitory access, crime prevention programs. J. D. Williams Library plus 1 other. Books: 3.3 million (physical), 814,143 (digital/electronic); Serial titles: 39,667 (physical), 135,210 (digital/electronic); Databases: 389. Weekly public service hours: 109. Operations spending for the previous fiscal year: $10.9 million. 259 computers available on campus for general student use. A campuswide network can be accessed from student residence rooms and from off campus. Students can access the following: online class registration. Staffed computer lab on campus provides training in use of computers, software, and the Internet.
Community Environment: University is a part of Oxford. Located in a cotton, corn and cattle region, Oxford is the seat of Lafayette County. Annual average temperature is 80 degrees in July and 40 degrees in January, with average rainfall 54.55 inches. Total snowfall yearly averages 1.2 inches. Bus service and shuttle service from Memphis Airport are available to the city. Area has 3 recreational parks, swimming pools, movie theaters, bowling and golf facilities. Oxford is near Holly Springs National Forest which encompasses over 90,000 acres and numerous lakes. The lakes provide excellent hunting, swimming, boating and vacation facilities.

■ **UNIVERSITY OF MISSISSIPPI MEDICAL CENTER**
2500 N State St.
Jackson, MS 39216-4505
Tel: (601)984-1000
Fax: (601)984-1080
Web Site: www.umc.edu
Description: State-supported, upper-level, coed. Administratively affiliated with University of Mississippi. Awards bachelor's, master's, and doctoral degrees. Founded 1955. Setting: 164-acre urban campus. Endowment: $33.5 million. Research spending for the previous fiscal year: $35.3 million. Educational spending for the previous fiscal year: $6579 per student. Total enrollment: 2,092. Faculty: 836 (698 full-time, 138 part-time). Student-undergrad faculty ratio is 2:1. Full-time: 383 students, 81% women, 19% men. Part-time: 129 students, 75% women, 25% men. 64% transferred in. Academic area with the most degrees conferred: health professions and related sciences. Calendar: semesters. Services for LD students, distance learning, internships. Study abroad program.
Collegiate Environment: Orientation program. Student-run newspaper. Student services: health clinic, personal-psychological counseling. Campus security: 24-hour emergency response devices and patrols, late night transport-escort service, controlled dormitory access. Rowland Medical Library. Operations spending for the previous fiscal year: $3.3 million. 90 computers available on campus for general student use. Computer purchase/lease plans available. A campuswide network can be accessed from off-campus. Staffed computer lab on campus.
Community Environment: See Jackson State University.

■ **UNIVERSITY OF SOUTHERN MISSISSIPPI**
118 College Dr.
Hattiesburg, MS 39406-0001
Tel: (601)266-1000
Web Site: www.usm.edu
Description: State-supported, university, coed. Part of Mississippi Institutions of Higher Learning. Awards bachelor's, master's, and doctoral degrees and post-master's certificates. Founded 1910. Setting: 1,090-acre suburban campus. Endowment: $82.7 million. Total enrollment: 14,478. Faculty: 899 (706 full-time, 193 part-time). Student-undergrad faculty ratio is 17:1. 6,405 applied, 98% were admitted. Full-time: 10,384 students, 64% women, 36% men. Part-time: 1,431 students, 55% women, 45% men. 18% from out-of-

state. 0.5% American Indian or Alaska Native, non-Hispanic/Latino; 3% Hispanic/Latino; 28% Black or African American, non-Hispanic/Latino; 1% Asian, non-Hispanic/Latino; 0.1% Native Hawaiian or other Pacific Islander, non-Hispanic/Latino; 2% international. 20% 25 or older, 28% live on campus, 15% transferred in. Retention: 72% of full-time freshmen returned the following year. Academic areas with the most degrees conferred: business/marketing; health professions and related sciences; education. Core. Calendar: semesters. Academic remediation for entering students, ESL program, services for LD students, advanced placement, accelerated degree program, honors program, independent study, distance learning, double major, summer session for credit, part-time degree program, adult/continuing education programs, co-op programs and internships, graduate courses open to undergrads. Off campus study at Gulf Coast Research Laboratory, Marine Science Laboratory, Stennis Space Center. Study abroad program. ROTC: Army (c), Air Force.

Entrance Requirements: Options: electronic application, early admission. Required: minimum 2 high school GPA, SAT or ACT. Required for some: high school transcript, statement of good standing from prior institutions, college transcripts. Entrance: moderately difficult. Application deadline: 6/30. SAT Subject Test deadline: 6/30. Transfer credits accepted: Yes.

Costs Per Year: Application fee: $40. State resident tuition: $8108 full-time, $338 per credit hour part-time. Nonresident tuition: $10,108 full-time. Part-time tuition varies according to course load and degree level. College room and board: $10,638. College room only: $6598. Room and board charges vary according to board plan and housing facility.

Collegiate Environment: Orientation program. Drama-theater group, choral group, marching band, student-run newspaper, radio station. Social organizations: 239 open to all; national fraternities, national sororities, local fraternities, local sororities; 10% of eligible men and 14% of eligible women are members. Major annual events: Crawfish Festival, Friday Night at the Fountain Pep Rally, Homecoming. Student services: legal services, health clinic, personal-psychological counseling, women's center. Campus security: 24-hour emergency response devices and patrols, late night transport-escort service, controlled dormitory access. Cook Memorial Library plus 4 others. Books: 1.4 million (physical), 331,932 (digital/electronic); Serial titles: 27,243 (physical), 118,798 (digital/electronic); Databases: 200. Weekly public service hours: 117; students can reserve study rooms. 436 computers available on campus for general student use. Computer purchase/lease plans available. A campuswide network can be accessed from student residence rooms and from off campus. Students can access the following: online class registration. Staffed computer lab on campus provides training in use of computers, software, and the Internet.

Community Environment: Primarily a thriving industrial city, Hattiesburg produces chemicals, clothing, concrete and corrugated containers, and has food processing plants, lumber mills and an oil refinery. Passenger bus, rail and air service is accessible. The city is a well-rounded community with a splendid balance among agriculture, commerce and industry. There are a public library and two hospitals located within the city limits. Each year, the Hattiesburg Concert Association brings concerts, symphonies and choral groups to the city. A full-time recreation department is operated, with both indoor and outdoor programs year-round. There is good hunting and fishing in the general area.

■ WILLIAM CAREY UNIVERSITY

710 William Carey Pky.
Hattiesburg, MS 39401
Tel: (601)318-6051; Free: 800-962-5991
Fax: (601)318-6454
E-mail: admissions@wmcarey.edu
Web Site: www.wmcarey.edu

Description: Independent Southern Baptist, comprehensive, coed. Awards bachelor's and master's degrees. Founded 1906. Setting: 110-acre small town campus with easy access to New Orleans. Total enrollment: 3,248. Student-undergrad faculty ratio is 19:1. 465 applied, 93% were admitted. 11% from out-of-state. 45% 25 or older. Retention: 74% of full-time freshmen returned the following year. Core. Calendar: trimesters. Academic remediation for entering students, services for LD students, advanced placement, accelerated degree program, honors program, independent study, distance learning, double major, summer session for credit, part-time degree program, adult/continuing education programs, internships, graduate courses open to undergrads. Off campus study. ROTC: Army (c), Air Force (c).

Entrance Requirements: Options: early admission, deferred admission, international baccalaureate accepted. Required: high school transcript, SAT or ACT. Recommended: minimum 2.0 high school GPA. Entrance: moderately difficult. Application deadline: rolling. Notification: continuous until 8/15.

Collegiate Environment: Orientation program. Drama-theater group, choral group, student-run newspaper. Social organizations: local fraternities, local sororities. Student services: personal-psychological counseling. Campus security: 24-hour patrols, controlled dormitory access. Smith-Rouse Library.

Community Environment: See University of Southern Mississippi.

■ AMERICAN BUSINESS & TECHNOLOGY UNIVERSITY
1018 W St.Maartens Dr.
Saint Joseph, MO 64506
Tel: (816)279-7000; Free: 800-804-1388
Fax: (888)890-8190
Web Site: www.abtu.edu
Description: Proprietary, comprehensive, coed. Awards associate, bachelor's, and master's degrees. Founded 2001.

■ AMERICAN TRADE SCHOOL
3925 Industrial Dr.
Saint Ann, MO 63074
Web Site: www.americantradeschool.edu
Description: Proprietary, 2-year, coed. Awards diplomas, transfer associate, and terminal associate degrees.

■ AVILA UNIVERSITY
11901 Wornall Rd.
Kansas City, MO 64145-1698
Tel: (816)942-8400; Free: 800-GO-AVILA
Fax: (816)942-3362
E-mail: josh.parisse@avila.edu
Web Site: www.avila.edu
Description: Independent Roman Catholic, comprehensive, coed. Administratively affiliated with The Sisters of Saint Joseph of Carondelet, St. Louis Province. Awards bachelor's and master's degrees. Founded 1916. Setting: 50-acre suburban campus. Endowment: $10.8 million. Educational spending for the previous fiscal year: $8176 per student. Total enrollment: 1,671. Faculty: 238 (73 full-time, 165 part-time). Student-undergrad faculty ratio is 13:1. 2,302 applied, 41% were admitted. 19% from top 10% of their high school class, 20% from top quarter, 73% from top half. Full-time: 1,042 students, 56% women, 44% men. Part-time: 204 students, 82% women, 18% men. Students come from 29 states and territories, 17 other countries, 33% from out-of-state. 0.5% American Indian or Alaska Native, non-Hispanic/Latino; 10% Hispanic/Latino; 23% Black or African American, non-Hispanic/Latino; 2% Asian, non-Hispanic/Latino; 0.5% Native Hawaiian or other Pacific Islander, non-Hispanic/Latino; 9% international. 26% 25 or older, 31% live on campus, 11% transferred in. Retention: 68% of full-time freshmen returned the following year. Academic areas with the most degrees conferred: health professions and related sciences; business/marketing; computer and information sciences. Core. Calendar: semesters. Academic remediation for entering students, ESL program, services for LD students, advanced placement, accelerated degree program, independent study, distance learning, double major, summer session for credit, part-time degree program, adult/continuing education programs, co-op programs and internships. Off campus study at Sisters of St. Joseph Consortium, Council of Independent Colleges Exchange Program, The Tuition Exchange. Study abroad program. ROTC: Army (c).
Entrance Requirements: Options: electronic application, early admission, international baccalaureate accepted. Required: high school transcript, minimum 2.5 high school GPA, secondary school report, SAT or ACT. Recommended: interview. Required for some: essay. Entrance: minimally difficult. Notification: 8/15. SAT Reasoning Test deadline: 9/1. SAT Subject Test deadline: 9/1. Transfer credits accepted: Yes.
Costs Per Year: Comprehensive fee: $27,500 includes full-time tuition ($20,500) and college room and board ($7000). College room only: $3400. Part-time tuition: $778 per credit hour. Tuition guaranteed not to increase for student's term of enrollment.
Collegiate Environment: Orientation program. Drama-theater group, choral group, student-run newspaper. Social organizations: 42 open to all. Most popular organizations: Avila Ambassadors, Avila Student Nurses Association, Campus Ministries, Saudi Arabian Student Association, Avila University Theatre Company. Major annual events: Homecoming Week, Spring Fling Week, AU Kick Off Celebration. Student services: health clinic, personal-psychological counseling. Campus security: 24-hour emergency response devices and patrols, student patrols, late night transport-escort service, controlled dormitory access. 360 college housing spaces available; 332 were occupied in 2018-19. Freshmen guaranteed college housing. On-campus residence required through sophomore year. Options: coed, men-only, women-only housing available. Hooley-Bundshu Library plus 1 other. Books: 39,963 (physical), 309,288 (digital/electronic); Serial titles: 205 (physical), 389,497 (digital/electronic); Databases: 72. Weekly public service hours: 91; students can reserve study rooms. Operations spending for the previous fiscal year: $404,124. 141 computers available on campus for general student use. A campuswide network can be accessed from student residence rooms and from off campus. Students can access the following: online class registration, laptop checkout through library. Staffed computer lab on campus (open 24 hours a day) provides training in use of computers, software, and the Internet.
Community Environment: See University of Missouri - Kansas City.

■ BAPTIST BIBLE COLLEGE
628 E Kearney St.
Springfield, MO 65803-3498
Tel: (417)268-6000; Free: 800-228-5754
Fax: (417)831-8029
Web Site: www.gobbc.edu
Description: Independent Baptist, comprehensive, coed. Awards associate, bachelor's, master's, and doctoral degrees. Founded 1950. Setting: 38-acre suburban campus. Total enrollment: 636. Faculty: 53 (26 full-time, 27 part-time). 264 applied, 76% were admitted. Full-time: 444 students, 50% women, 50% men. Part-time: 100 students, 34% women, 66% men. Students come from 36 states and territories, 6 other countries, 57% from out-of-state. 17% 25 or older, 61% live on campus, 6% transferred in. Retention: 57% of full-time freshmen returned the following year. Core. Calendar: semesters. Academic remediation for entering students, summer session for credit, part-time degree program, internships, graduate courses open to undergrads. ROTC: Army (c).
Entrance Requirements: Options: electronic application, early admission, deferred admission. Required: high school transcript, 1 recommendation, SAT or ACT. Entrance: noncompetitive. Application deadline: rolling. Notification: continuous. Preference given to members of supporting churches.
Collegiate Environment: Orientation program. Drama-theater group, choral group, student-run radio station. Student services: health clinic, personal-psychological counseling. G. B. Vick Memorial Library plus 1 other. 50 computers available on campus for general student use. Staffed computer lab on campus.
Community Environment: See Southwest Missouri State University.

■ BOLIVAR TECHNICAL COLLEGE
1135 N Oakland Ave.
Bolivar, MO 65613

Description: Independent, 2-year, coed.

■ **BRYAN UNIVERSITY**
4255 S Nature Ctr. Way
Springfield, MO 65804
Tel: (417)862-5700; Free: 855-566-0650
Web Site: www.bryanu.edu
Description: Proprietary, comprehensive, coed. Awards associate, bachelor's, and master's degrees.

■ **CALVARY UNIVERSITY**
15800 Calvary Rd.
Kansas City, MO 64147
Tel: (816)322-0110; Free: 800-326-3960
E-mail: ann.rogers@cavalry.edu
Web Site: www.calvary.edu
Description: Independent nondenominational, comprehensive, coed. Awards associate, bachelor's, and master's degrees. Founded 1932. Setting: 55-acre suburban campus with easy access to Kansas City. Endowment: $1.2 million. Educational spending for the previous fiscal year: $5960 per student. Total enrollment: 271. Faculty: 44 (11 full-time, 33 part-time). Student-undergrad faculty ratio is 7:1. 44 applied, 98% were admitted. 29% from top 10% of their high school class, 43% from top quarter, 57% from top half. Full-time: 138 students, 48% women, 52% men. Part-time: 93 students, 47% women, 53% men. Students come from 18 states and territories, 1 other country, 49% from out-of-state. 1% American Indian or Alaska Native, non-Hispanic/Latino; 1% Hispanic/Latino; 10% Black or African American, non-Hispanic/Latino; 3% Asian, non-Hispanic/Latino; 0.4% Native Hawaiian or other Pacific Islander, non-Hispanic/Latino. 35% 25 or older, 41% live on campus, 12% transferred in. Retention: 53% of full-time freshmen returned the following year. Academic areas with the most degrees conferred: theology and religious vocations; business/marketing; visual and performing arts; interdisciplinary studies. Core. Calendar: semesters. Services for LD students, advanced placement, accelerated degree program, self-designed majors, independent study, distance learning, double major, summer session for credit, part-time degree program, adult/continuing education programs, co-op programs and internships, graduate courses open to undergrads. Off campus study at Johnson County Community College, Kansas City Kansas Community College, Metropolitan Community College, University of Central Missouri, University of Missouri-Kansas City, Graduate Institute of Applied Linguistics, School of Missionary Aviation Technology, Children's Ministries Institute, U.S. Army Training and Doctrine Command. ROTC: Army (c).
Entrance Requirements: Option: electronic application. Required: essay, minimum 2 high school GPA, 2 recommendations, SAT or ACT. Recommended: interview. Required for some: high school transcript. Entrance: noncompetitive. Application deadlines: rolling, rolling for early action. Notification: continuous. Transfer credits accepted: Yes.
Costs Per Year: Application fee: $0. One-time mandatory fee: $100. Comprehensive fee: $19,387 includes full-time tuition ($10,276), mandatory fees ($876), and college room and board ($8235). College room only: $3900. Full-time tuition and fees vary according to location and program. Room and board charges vary according to board plan and housing facility. Part-time tuition: $367 per credit hour. Part-time mandatory fees: $63 per credit hour, $438 per term. Part-time tuition and fees vary according to location and program.
Collegiate Environment: Orientation program. Drama-theater group, choral group. Most popular organizations: Missions Encounter, Masterworks (Fine Arts). Major annual events: Fall Theater production, Spring Banquet, All-Calvary Workday. Student services: personal-psychological counseling. Campus security: 24-hour emergency response devices and patrols, late night transport-escort service, controlled dormitory access, night patrols by trained security personnel, monitored closed circuit cameras. Hilda Kroeker Library. Books: 41,841 (physical), 420 (digital/electronic); Serial titles: 268 (physical); Databases: 4. Operations spending for the previous fiscal year: $108,883. 32 computers available on campus for general student use. A campuswide network can be accessed from student residence rooms. Students can access the following: online class registration. Staffed computer lab on campus provides training in use of computers, software, and the Internet.
Community Environment: See University of Missouri Kansas City.

■ **CENTRAL CHRISTIAN COLLEGE OF THE BIBLE**
911 Urbandale Dr. E
Moberly, MO 65270-1997

Tel: (660)263-3900; Free: 888-263-3900
Fax: (660)263-3936
E-mail: admissions@cccb.edu
Web Site: www.cccb.edu
Description: Independent, 4-year, coed, affiliated with Christian Churches and Churches of Christ. Awards associate and bachelor's degrees. Founded 1957. Setting: 40-acre small town campus. Total enrollment: 417. Student-undergrad faculty ratio is 19:1. 354 applied, 65% were admitted. 56% from out-of-state. 18% 25 or older. Retention: 57% of full-time freshmen returned the following year. Core. Calendar: semesters. Academic remediation for entering students, self-designed majors, part-time degree program, internships. Off campus study at Fort Hays State University, Tabor College, Johnson Bible College, Moberly Area Community College.
Entrance Requirements: Options: early admission, deferred admission. Required: high school transcript, 3 recommendations, SAT or ACT. Entrance: noncompetitive. Application deadline: rolling. Preference given to Christians.
Costs Per Year: Application fee: $25. Comprehensive fee: $20,700 includes full-time tuition ($7500), mandatory fees ($6600), and college room and board ($6600). Room and board charges vary according to board plan. Part-time tuition: $300 per credit hour. Part-time mandatory fees: $3300 per term. Part-time tuition and fees vary according to course load. All students receive a full tuition scholarship.
Collegiate Environment: Orientation program. Choral group. Student services: personal-psychological counseling.

■ **CENTRAL METHODIST UNIVERSITY**
411 Central Methodist Sq.
Fayette, MO 65248-1198
Tel: (660)248-3391; Free: 877-CMU-1854
Fax: (660)248-2287
Web Site: www.centralmethodist.edu
Description: Independent Methodist, comprehensive, coed. Administratively affiliated with Central Methodist University - College of Graduate and Extended Studies. Awards associate, bachelor's, and master's degrees. Founded 1854. Setting: 80-acre small town campus. Endowment: $45.5 million. Educational spending for the previous fiscal year: $5337 per student. Total enrollment: 1,060. Faculty: 118 (69 full-time, 49 part-time). Student-undergrad faculty ratio is 12:1. 1,357 applied, 63% were admitted. 17% from top 10% of their high school class, 42% from top quarter, 73% from top half. Full-time: 1,034 students, 53% women, 47% men. Part-time: 26 students, 50% women, 50% men. Students come from 24 states and territories, 29 other countries, 15% from out-of-state. 0.5% American Indian or Alaska Native, non-Hispanic/Latino; 4% Hispanic/Latino; 8% Black or African American, non-Hispanic/Latino; 0.3% Asian, non-Hispanic/Latino; 0.1% Native Hawaiian or other Pacific Islander, non-Hispanic/Latino; 6% international. 6% 25 or older, 60% live on campus, 8% transferred in. Retention: 68% of full-time freshmen returned the following year. Academic areas with the most degrees conferred: health professions and related sciences; computer and information sciences; business/marketing. Core. Calendar: semesters. Academic remediation for entering students, services for LD students, advanced placement, self-designed majors, honors program, independent study, double major, summer session for credit, part-time degree program, co-op programs and internships. Study abroad program. ROTC: Army (c), Air Force (c).
Entrance Requirements: Options: electronic application, deferred admission. Required: high school transcript, minimum 2.5 high school GPA, SAT or ACT. Required for some: 2 recommendations. Entrance: moderately difficult. Application deadline: rolling. Notification: continuous. SAT Reasoning Test deadline: 8/15. SAT Subject Test deadline: 8/15. Transfer credits accepted: Yes.
Costs Per Year: Application fee: $0. One-time mandatory fee: $100. Comprehensive fee: $32,360 includes full-time tuition ($23,650), mandatory fees ($770), and college room and board ($7940). College room only: $3890. Full-time tuition and fees vary according to program and reciprocity agreements. Room and board charges vary according to board plan and housing facility. Part-time tuition: $210 per credit hour. Part-time mandatory fees: $31 per credit hour. Part-time tuition and fees vary according to course load and program.
Collegiate Environment: Orientation program. Drama-theater group, choral group, marching band, student-run newspaper, radio station. Social organizations: 66 open to all; national fraternities, national sororities, local fraternities, local sororities; 20% of eligible men and 27% of eligible women are members. Most popular organizations: Student Government Association, Enactus, Alpha Phi Omega, Beta Beta Beta, Campus Ministries. Major an-

nual events: Family Day, Homecoming, Service Day. Student services: health clinic, personal-psychological counseling. Campus security: 24-hour emergency response devices, late night transport-escort service, controlled dormitory access. Smiley Library. Books: 67,581 (physical), 127,545 (digital/electronic); Serial titles: 96 (physical), 38,528 (digital/electronic); Databases: 35. Students can reserve study rooms. Operations spending for the previous fiscal year: $113,500. 100 computers available on campus for general student use. A campuswide network can be accessed from student residence rooms and from off campus. Students can access the following: online class registration. Staffed computer lab on campus.

Community Environment: Fayette (population 2,700) is the county seat of Howard County and is in an area that is noted for the production of purebred cattle. Both Kansas City and St. Louis are about a two-hour drive away. The cultural facilities of both large cities are available and add charm to the community.

■ **CHAMBERLAIN COLLEGE OF NURSING**
11830 Westline Industrial Dr.
Ste. 106
Saint Louis, MO 63146
Tel: (314)991-6200; Free: 877-751-5783
Fax: (314)991-6283
Web Site: www.chamberlain.edu

Description: Proprietary, 4-year, coed. Part of DeVry University. Awards bachelor's degrees. Founded 1889. Setting: urban campus. Total enrollment: 543. Faculty: 79 (20 full-time, 59 part-time). Student-undergrad faculty ratio is 7:1. Full-time: 145 students, 88% women, 12% men. Part-time: 398 students, 92% women, 8% men. 25% from out-of-state. 0.4% American Indian or Alaska Native, non-Hispanic/Latino; 2% Hispanic/Latino; 11% Black or African American, non-Hispanic/Latino; 2% Asian, non-Hispanic/Latino; 0.2% Native Hawaiian or other Pacific Islander, non-Hispanic/Latino. 45% 25 or older, 24% transferred in. Academic area with the most degrees conferred: health professions and related sciences. Calendar: semesters. Accelerated degree program, distance learning, part-time degree program.

Entrance Requirements: Option: deferred admission. Required: essay, high school transcript, SAT or ACT. Required for some: interview. Entrance: moderately difficult. Application deadline: rolling. Notification: continuous.

Collegiate Environment: Orientation program. Campus security: 24-hour patrols, late night transport-escort service, controlled dormitory access.

■ **CITY VISION UNIVERSITY**
3101 Troost Ave., Ste. 200
Kansas City, MO 64109-1845
Tel: (816)960-2008
Fax: (816)569-0223
E-mail: newstudents@cityvision.edu
Web Site: www.cityvision.edu

Description: Independent Christian, comprehensive, coed. Awards associate, bachelor's, and master's degrees. Founded 1998. Educational spending for the previous fiscal year: $529 per student. Total enrollment: 106. Faculty: 21 (all part-time). Student-undergrad faculty ratio is 5:1. Full-time: 24 students, 54% women, 46% men. Part-time: 72 students, 60% women, 40% men. Students come from 31 states and territories, 3 other countries, 94% from out-of-state. 86% 25 or older, 16% transferred in. Academic areas with the most degrees conferred: health professions and related sciences; business/marketing; theology and religious vocations. Core. Calendar: 5 terms that are 8 week long course offerings. Services for LD students, independent study, distance learning, double major, summer session for credit, part-time degree program, adult/continuing education programs, internships, graduate courses open to undergrads.

Entrance Requirements: Open admission. Option: electronic application. Required: high school transcript. Entrance: noncompetitive. Application deadline: rolling. Notification: continuous. Transfer credits accepted: Yes.

Collegiate Environment: Orientation program.

■ **COLLEGE OF THE OZARKS**
PO Box 17
Point Lookout, MO 65726
Tel: (417)334-6411; Free: 800-222-0525
Fax: (417)335-2618
E-mail: admissions@cofo.edu
Web Site: www.cofo.edu

Description: Independent Presbyterian, 4-year, coed. Awards bachelor's degrees. Founded 1906. Setting: 1,000-acre rural campus. Endowment:

$509.1 million. Educational spending for the previous fiscal year: $10,643 per student. Total enrollment: 1,565. Faculty: 133 (92 full-time, 41 part-time). Student-undergrad faculty ratio is 14:1. 2,874 applied, 12% were admitted. 23% from top 10% of their high school class, 46% from top quarter, 95% from top half. 8 valedictorians. Full-time: 1,533 students, 55% women, 45% men. Part-time: 32 students, 53% women, 47% men. Students come from 33 states and territories, 20 other countries, 25% from out-of-state. 0.4% American Indian or Alaska Native, non-Hispanic/Latino; 3% Hispanic/Latino; 0.6% Black or African American, non-Hispanic/Latino; 0.8% Asian, non-Hispanic/Latino; 0.2% Native Hawaiian or other Pacific Islander, non-Hispanic/Latino; 2% international. 2% 25 or older, 90% live on campus, 2% transferred in. Retention: 75% of full-time freshmen returned the following year. Academic areas with the most degrees conferred: business/marketing; agriculture; education. Core. Calendar: semesters. Academic remediation for entering students, ESL program, services for LD students, advanced placement, self-designed majors, independent study, double major, summer session for credit, internships. Off campus study.

Entrance Requirements: Option: electronic application. Required: high school transcript, 2 recommendations, interview, medical history, financial statement, SAT or ACT. Recommended: minimum 3 high school GPA, ACT. Entrance: moderately difficult. Application deadlines: 12/31, 12/31 for nonresidents. Notification: continuous, 1/15 for nonresidents. Preference given to financially needy students. SAT Reasoning Test deadline: 2/15. SAT Subject Test deadline: 2/15. Transfer credits accepted: Yes. Applicants placed on waiting list: 437. Wait-listed applicants offered admission: 13.

Costs Per Year: Application fee: $0. Comprehensive fee: $8060 includes full-time tuition ($0), mandatory fees ($460), and college room and board ($7600). College room only: $3800. Part-time tuition: $310 per credit hour. Part-time mandatory fees: $230 per term.

Collegiate Environment: Orientation program. Drama-theater group, choral group, student-run newspaper, radio station. Social organizations: 48 open to all. Most popular organizations: Young Americans for Freedom, Chi Alpha, Baptist Student Union, Agriculture Club, FCA. Major annual events: Homecoming, Mud Fest, Spring Formal. Student services: health clinic, personal-psychological counseling. Campus security: 24-hour emergency response devices and patrols, student patrols, late night transport-escort service, controlled dormitory access, front gate closed 6 pm to 5 am, security checks cars for proper credentials for entry. 1,447 college housing spaces available; 1,359 were occupied in 2018-19. No special consideration for freshman housing applicants. On-campus residence required through senior year. Options: men-only, women-only housing available. Lyons Memorial Library. Books: 96,874 (physical), 500,000 (digital/electronic); Serial titles: 77 (physical), 52,500 (digital/electronic); Databases: 52. Weekly public service hours: 80. Operations spending for the previous fiscal year: $462,460. 402 computers available on campus for general student use. A campuswide network can be accessed from student residence rooms and from off campus. Students can access the following: online class registration. Staffed computer lab on campus provides training in use of computers, software, and the Internet.

Community Environment: Point Lookout is a rural area near Branson, 38 miles south of Springfield. Bus service is available and air travel is a little more than 60 minutes away. Shopping areas, a library, and churches of major denominations are part of the community. A great deal of part-time employment is available especially during the April-December tourist season. All recreational facilities are available in the summer resort area.

■ **COLUMBIA COLLEGE**
1001 Rogers St.
Columbia, MO 65216-0002
Tel: (573)875-8700; Free: 800-231-2391
Fax: (573)875-7506
Web Site: www.ccis.edu

Description: Independent, comprehensive, coed, affiliated with Christian Church (Disciples of Christ). Awards associate, bachelor's, and master's degrees (offers continuing education program with significant enrollment not reflected in profile). Founded 1851. Setting: 33-acre urban campus with easy access to St. Louis and Kansas City. Endowment: $171.7 million. Educational spending for the previous fiscal year: $5973 per student. Total enrollment: 1,152. Faculty: 150 (74 full-time, 76 part-time). Student-undergrad faculty ratio is 11:1. 1,796 applied, 48% were admitted. 25% from top 10% of their high school class, 30% from top quarter, 80% from top half. Full-time: 865 students, 55% women, 45% men. Part-time: 158 students, 65% women, 35% men. Students come from 28 states and territories, 30 other countries, 12% from out-of-state. 0.3% American Indian or Alaska Native, non-Hispanic/Latino; 4% Hispanic/Latino; 4% Black or African American, non-Hispanic/Latino; 0.7% Asian, non-Hispanic/Latino; 0.1% Native Hawaiian or other Pacific Islander, non-Hispanic/Latino; 7% international. 18% 25 or older, 37% live on campus, 12% transferred in. Retention: 71% of full-time freshmen returned the following year. Academic areas with the most degrees conferred: business/marketing; liberal arts/general studies; visual and performing arts. Core. Calendar: semesters. ESL program, services for LD students, advanced placement, self-designed majors, honors program, independent study, distance learning, double major, summer session for credit, part-time degree program, adult/continuing education programs, co-op programs and internships, graduate courses open to undergrads. Off campus study at Cooperative cross-enrollment with the University of Missouri-Columbia and Stephens College (MO) and a study abroad consortium with Central College (IA). Study abroad program. ROTC: Army (c), Naval (c), Air Force (c).

Entrance Requirements: Options: electronic application, deferred admission, international baccalaureate accepted. Required: high school transcript, minimum 2.5 high school GPA, SAT or ACT. Required for some: essay, interview. Entrance: minimally difficult. Notification: continuous. SAT Reasoning Test deadline: 8/15. SAT Subject Test deadline: 8/15. Transfer credits accepted: Yes.

Costs Per Year: Comprehensive fee: $30,512 includes full-time tuition ($22,704) and college room and board ($7808). College room only: $4674. Full-time tuition varies according to class time, course load, program, reciprocity agreements, and student level. Room and board charges vary according to housing facility. Part-time tuition: $487 per credit hour. Part-time tuition varies according to class time, course load, location, and reciprocity agreements. Tuition guaranteed not to increase for student's term of enrollment.

Collegiate Environment: Orientation program. Drama-theater group, choral group. Social organizations: 35 open to all. Most popular organizations: International Club, Honor Student Association, Black Student Coalition, Pre-Healthcare Professionals, Commited and Serving Together. Major annual events: Hey Day, Homecoming/Family Day, Storm the Gate. Student services: health clinic, personal-psychological counseling. Campus security: 24-hour emergency response devices and patrols, late night transport-escort service, controlled dormitory access, building monitor patrols off-campus site. 391 college housing spaces available; 384 were occupied in 2018-19. Freshmen guaranteed college housing. On-campus residence required through sophomore year. Options: coed, women-only housing available. J. W. and Lois Stafford Library. Books: 61,752 (physical), 225,968 (digital/electronic); Serial titles: 104 (physical), 63,429 (digital/electronic); Databases: 70. Weekly public service hours: 94; students can reserve study rooms. Operations spending for the previous fiscal year: $795,603. 220 computers available on campus for general student use. Computer purchase/lease plans available. A campuswide network can be accessed from student residence rooms and from off campus. Students can access the following: online class registration. Staffed computer lab on campus provides training in use of computers, software, and the Internet.

■ **CONCEPTION SEMINARY COLLEGE**
37174 State Hwy. VV
Conception, MO 64433
Tel: (660)944-3105
Fax: (660)944-2829
E-mail: admissions@conception.edu
Web Site: www.conception.edu
Description: Independent Roman Catholic, 4-year, men only. Awards bachelor's degrees. Founded 1886. Setting: 30-acre rural campus. Total enrollment: 67. Student-undergrad faculty ratio is 4:1. 28 applied, 100% were admitted. Full-time: 67 students. Students come from 58 states and territories, 4 other countries, 76% from out-of-state. 18% Hispanic/Latino; 7% Asian, non-Hispanic/Latino. 22% 25 or older, 21% transferred in. Retention: 45% of full-time freshmen returned the following year. Core. Calendar: semesters. Academic remediation for entering students, ESL program, services for LD students, advanced placement, independent study, co-op programs. Off campus study at Northwest Missouri State University.
Entrance Requirements: Options: early admission, deferred admission. Required: essay, high school transcript, minimum 2 high school GPA, 2 recommendations, church certificate, medical history, SAT or ACT. Entrance: noncompetitive. Preference given to Catholic seminarians. Transfer credits accepted: Yes.
Costs Per Year: Application fee: $0. Comprehensive fee: $34,385 includes

full-time tuition ($21,326), mandatory fees ($250), and college room and board ($12,809). College room only: $5358. Part-time tuition: $200 per credit hour.
Collegiate Environment: Orientation program. Drama-theater group, choral group. Social organizations: national fraternities, local fraternities. Student services: health clinic, personal-psychological counseling. Campus security: 24-hour emergency response devices. Conception Seminary College Library. 20 computers available on campus for general student use. A campuswide network can be accessed from student residence rooms and from off campus. Staffed computer lab on campus.
Community Environment: Conception is located in northwest Missouri, 85 miles north of Kansas City. The Abbey contains a collection of rare manuscripts dating back to the 10th century. See also Missouri Western State College for information about St. Joseph, the nearest large city.

■ **CONCORDE CAREER COLLEGE**
3239 Broadway St.
Kansas City, MO 64111
Tel: (816)531-5223
Fax: (816)756-3231
E-mail: dcrow@concorde.edu
Web Site: www.concorde.edu
Description: Proprietary, 2-year, coed. Awards certificates and terminal associate degrees. Founded 1983. Total enrollment: 821. Student-undergrad faculty ratio is 29:1. 261 applied, 100% were admitted. 20% from out-of-state. 62% 25 or older.
Entrance Requirements: Required: high school transcript.

■ **COTTEY COLLEGE**
1000 W Austin
Nevada, MO 64772
Tel: (417)667-8181; Free: 888-526-8839
Fax: (417)667-8103
E-mail: amoore@cottey.edu
Web Site: www.cottey.edu
Description: Independent, primarily 2-year, women only. Awards transfer associate and bachelor's degrees. Founded 1884. Setting: 51-acre small town campus. Endowment: $108.8 million. Educational spending for the previous fiscal year: $24,890 per student. Total enrollment: 265. Faculty: 52 (41 full-time, 11 part-time). Student-undergrad faculty ratio is 7:1. 525 applied, 64% were admitted. 12% from top 10% of their high school class, 34% from top quarter, 60% from top half. 2 class presidents, 3 valedictorians, 20 student government officers. Full-time: 260 students. Part-time: 5 students. Students come from 32 states and territories, 18 other countries, 85% from out-of-state. 2% American Indian or Alaska Native, non-Hispanic/Latino; 8% Hispanic/Latino; 5% Black or African American, non-Hispanic/Latino; 0.4% Asian, non-Hispanic/Latino; 0.4% Native Hawaiian or other Pacific Islander, non-Hispanic/Latino; 15% international. 15% 25 or older, 90% live on campus, 4% transferred in. Retention: 70% of full-time freshmen returned the following year. Academic areas with the most degrees conferred: psychology; English; business/marketing. Core. Calendar: semesters. Services for LD students, advanced placement, independent study, distance learning, part-time degree program, internships. Study abroad program.
Entrance Requirements: Options: electronic application, early admission, deferred admission, international baccalaureate accepted. Required: essay, high school transcript, 1 recommendation, SAT or ACT. Recommended: minimum 2.6 high school GPA, interview. Required for some: TOEFL, IELTS. Entrance: moderately difficult. Application deadline: rolling. Notification: continuous. Transfer credits accepted: Yes. Applicants placed on waiting list: 0.
Costs Per Year: Application fee: $20. Comprehensive fee: $28,850 includes full-time tuition ($19,900), mandatory fees ($1250), and college room and board ($7700). College room only: $4200. Room and board charges vary according to housing facility. Part-time tuition: $125 per credit hour. Part-time mandatory fees: $22 per credit hour, $87.50 per term. Part-time tuition and fees vary according to course load.
Collegiate Environment: Orientation program. Drama-theater group, choral group. Social organizations: 30 open to all. Most popular organizations: Inter-Society, Golden Key, French Club, Student Government, Global Citizens. Major annual events: Hanging of the Greens, Assessment Day. Student services: health clinic, personal-psychological counseling. Campus security: 24-hour emergency response devices and patrols, late night transport-escort service, controlled dormitory access. Blanche Skiff Ross Memorial Library plus 1 other. Weekly public service hours: 88. Operations

spending for the previous fiscal year: $194,423. 70 computers available on campus for general student use. A campuswide network can be accessed from student residence rooms and from off campus. Staffed computer lab on campus provides training in use of computers, software, and the Internet.

Community Environment: Located 100 miles south of Kansas City, 60 miles north of Joplin, and 90 miles north of Springfield, Nevada has a population of 8,500 and is the county seat of Vernon County. Although historically an agricultural community, Nevada has a diverse economic base. The Jefferson Bus Lines connect Nevada to the International Airport in Kansas City and the municipal airport in Joplin. The community facilities include 27 churches, a number of civic, fraternal, and veterans' organizations, a municipal hospital, and a community center. Part-time employment for students is available. Recreational activities are hunting, fishing, golf, and bowling. The Chamber of Commerce holds a number of special events during the year.

■ **COX COLLEGE**
1423 N Jefferson
Springfield, MO 65802
Tel: (417)269-3401
Web Site: www.coxcollege.edu

Description: Independent, comprehensive, coed. Awards associate, bachelor's, and master's degrees and post-master's certificates. Founded 1907. Setting: urban campus. Total enrollment: 899. Faculty: 190 (102 full-time, 88 part-time). Student-undergrad faculty ratio is 9:1. 27 applied, 59% were admitted. 6% from out-of-state. 0.5% American Indian or Alaska Native, non-Hispanic/Latino; 2% Hispanic/Latino; 2% Black or African American, non-Hispanic/Latino; 2% Asian, non-Hispanic/Latino. Retention: 100% of full-time freshmen returned the following year. Academic area with the most degrees conferred: health professions and related sciences. Core. Calendar: semesters. Academic remediation for entering students, accelerated degree program, distance learning, summer session for credit, part-time degree program, graduate courses open to undergrads.

Entrance Requirements: Options: electronic application, early decision. Required: high school transcript, minimum 2.5 high school GPA. Recommended: SAT or ACT. Application deadlines: 1/15, 11/1 for early decision. Notification: 3/1, 12/1 for early decision. Transfer credits accepted: Yes.

Collegiate Environment: Orientation program. Student services: personal-psychological counseling. Campus security: 24-hour emergency response devices and patrols, late night transport-escort service, controlled dormitory access. The Cox Health Systems Libraries plus 2 others. Weekly public service hours: 60. 75 computers available on campus for general student use. A campuswide network can be accessed from off-campus. Students can access the following: online class registration.

■ **CROWDER COLLEGE**
601 Laclede Ave.
Neosho, MO 64850-9160
Tel: (417)451-3223; Free: 866-238-7788
Fax: (417)451-4280
E-mail: jamesdickey@crowder.edu
Web Site: www.crowder.edu

Description: State and locally supported, 2-year, coed. Part of Missouri Coordinating Board for Higher Education. Awards certificates, transfer associate, and terminal associate degrees. Founded 1963. Setting: 608-acre rural campus. Total enrollment: 4,960. Faculty: 454 (104 full-time, 350 part-time). Student-undergrad faculty ratio is 11:1. Students come from 12 states and territories, 6% from out-of-state. 2% American Indian or Alaska Native, non-Hispanic/Latino; 9% Hispanic/Latino; 1% Black or African American, non-Hispanic/Latino; 2% Asian, non-Hispanic/Latino; 0.4% Native Hawaiian or other Pacific Islander, non-Hispanic/Latino; 1% international. 30% 25 or older, 10% live on campus. Retention: 64% of full-time freshmen returned the following year. Core. Calendar: semesters. Academic remediation for entering students, ESL program, advanced placement, self-designed majors, freshman honors college, honors program, independent study, summer session for credit, part-time degree program, adult/continuing education programs, co-op programs. Study abroad program.

Entrance Requirements: Open admission except for nursing program. Required: high school transcript. Entrance: noncompetitive. Application deadline: rolling. Notification: continuous.

Costs Per Year: Application fee: $25. Area resident tuition: $2640 full-time, $88 per credit hour part-time. State resident tuition: $4140 full-time, $138 per credit hour part-time. Nonresident tuition: $4140 full-time, $138 per credit hour part-time. Mandatory fees: $900 full-time, $30 per credit hour part-time.

Full-time tuition and fees vary according to program. Part-time tuition and fees vary according to program. College room and board: $3300. College room only: $2300. Room and board charges vary according to board plan and housing facility.

Collegiate Environment: Orientation program. Drama-theater group, choral group, student-run newspaper. Social organizations: 15 open to all. Most popular organizations: Phi Theta Kappa, Students in Free Enterprise (SIFE), Baptist Student Union, Student Senate, Student Ambassadors. Major annual events: Homecoming, Welcome Back Dance, Halloween Dance. Campus security: 24-hour patrols. Bill & Margot Lee Library. 1,100 computers available on campus for general student use. A campuswide network can be accessed. Students can access the following: online class registration. Staffed computer lab on campus provides training in use of computers, software, and the Internet.

Community Environment: Neosho (population 11,000) is the birthplace of Thomas Hart Benton, 18 miles from Joplin. All forms of commercial transportation are available. Churches of most of the major denominations, two libraries, a museum, two hospitals and numerous civic and fraternal organizations are represented. Part time jobs are available in Neosho and the two county districts. Neosho provides the area with a full time recreation director and planned activities for the community. The Government Fish Hatchery is nearby.

■ **CULVER-STOCKTON COLLEGE**
1 College Hill
Canton, MO 63435-1299
Tel: (573)288-6000; Free: 800-537-1883
Fax: (217)231-6611
E-mail: admission@culver.edu
Web Site: www.culver.edu

Description: Independent, comprehensive, coed, affiliated with Christian Church (Disciples of Christ). Awards bachelor's and master's degrees. Founded 1853. Setting: 143-acre rural campus. Endowment: $24.8 million. Educational spending for the previous fiscal year: $4947 per student. Total enrollment: 1,068. Faculty: 102 (53 full-time, 49 part-time). Student-undergrad faculty ratio is 15:1. 4,784 applied, 46% were admitted. 7% from top 10% of their high school class, 27% from top quarter, 58% from top half. 4 valedictorians. Full-time: 919 students, 48% women, 52% men. Part-time: 103 students, 63% women, 37% men. Students come from 39 states and territories, 18 other countries, 45% from out-of-state. 0.5% American Indian or Alaska Native, non-Hispanic/Latino; 5% Hispanic/Latino; 13% Black or African American, non-Hispanic/Latino; 0.5% Asian, non-Hispanic/Latino; 0.1% Native Hawaiian or other Pacific Islander, non-Hispanic/Latino; 5% international. 2% 25 or older, 74% live on campus, 4% transferred in. Retention: 67% of full-time freshmen returned the following year. Academic areas with the most degrees conferred: business/marketing; homeland security, law enforcement, firefighting, and protective services; education. Core. Calendar: semesters. Academic remediation for entering students, services for LD students, advanced placement, accelerated degree program, self-designed majors, honors program, independent study, distance learning, double major, summer session for credit, part-time degree program, adult/continuing education programs, internships. Study abroad program.

Entrance Requirements: Options: electronic application, deferred admission, international baccalaureate accepted. Required: high school transcript, minimum 2 high school GPA, SAT or ACT. Recommended: essay, 1 recommendation, interview. Entrance: moderately difficult. Application deadline: rolling. Notification: continuous. SAT Reasoning Test deadline: 8/15. Transfer credits accepted: Yes.

Costs Per Year: Application fee: $0. One-time mandatory fee: $210. Comprehensive fee: $35,900 includes full-time tuition ($26,780), mandatory fees ($425), and college room and board ($8695). College room only: $3895. Part-time tuition: $610 per credit hour. Part-time mandatory fees: $17.71 per credit hour.

Collegiate Environment: Orientation program. Drama-theater group, choral group, student-run newspaper, radio station. Social organizations: 50 open to all; national fraternities, national sororities; 39% of eligible men and 45% of eligible women are members. Most popular organizations: Campus Programming Council (CPC), The Black Student Union (BSU), Student Government Association (SGA), Health Outreach Peer Educators (HOPE), Institute of Management Accountants (IMA). Major annual events: Hillstock, Wildcat Welcome, Greek Week. Student services: personal-psychological counseling. Campus security: 24-hour emergency response devices and patrols, late night transport-escort service, controlled dormitory access. 850 college housing spaces available; 794 were occupied in 2018-19. Freshmen guaranteed college housing. On-campus residence required through senior year. Options: coed, men-only, women-only housing available. Carl Johann Memorial Library. Books: 106,810 (physical), 368,101 (digital/electronic); Serial titles: 755 (physical), 229,284 (digital/electronic); Databases: 26. Weekly public service hours: 65; students can reserve study rooms. Operations spending for the previous fiscal year: $260,802. 100 computers available on campus for general student use. A campuswide network can be accessed from student residence rooms and from off campus. Students can access the following: online class registration. Staffed computer lab on campus.

Community Environment: Canton, population 2,502, is 20 miles north of Quincy, IL, 30 miles south of Keokuk, IA, and approximately two hours north of St. Louis, MO. On the Mississippi River, it is the site of the U.S. Lock and Dam No. 20, which is one of the series of navigation dams built between Minneapolis and St. Louis. Libraries, museums, many churches, and good shopping facilities all provide service to the community. A state park is nearby for recreational and outdoor play. The college homecoming is a community affair. Part-time employment is available.

▪ DEVRY UNIVERSITY-KANSAS CITY CAMPUS
1310 E 104th St., 2nd Fl.
Kansas City, MO 64131
Tel: (816)943-7300; Free: 866-338-7934
Web Site: www.devry.edu
Description: Proprietary, comprehensive, coed. Part of DeVry University. Awards associate, bachelor's, and master's degrees. Founded 1931. Setting: urban campus. Total enrollment: 348. Faculty: 35 (2 full-time, 33 part-time). Student-undergrad faculty ratio is 14:1. Full-time: 90 students, 30% women, 70% men. Part-time: 141 students, 40% women, 60% men. 29% from out-of-state. 1% American Indian or Alaska Native, non-Hispanic/Latino; 8% Hispanic/Latino; 19% Black or African American, non-Hispanic/Latino; 1% Asian, non-Hispanic/Latino. 77% 25 or older, 20% transferred in. Calendar: semesters. Accelerated degree program, honors program, distance learning. Study abroad program.
Entrance Requirements: Option: deferred admission. Entrance: minimally difficult. Application deadline: rolling. Notification: continuous.

▪ DRURY UNIVERSITY
900 N Benton Ave.
Springfield, MO 65802
Tel: (417)873-7879; Free: 800-922-2274
Fax: (417)873-7529
E-mail: druryad@drury.edu
Web Site: www.drury.edu
Description: Independent, comprehensive, coed. Awards bachelor's and master's degrees (also offers evening program with significant enrollment not reflected in profile). Founded 1873. Setting: 90-acre urban campus. Endowment: $97.5 million. Research spending for the previous fiscal year: $49,934. Educational spending for the previous fiscal year: $8817 per student. Total enrollment: 1,728. Faculty: 141 (111 full-time, 30 part-time). Student-undergrad faculty ratio is 13:1. 1,575 applied, 73% were admitted. 30% from top 10% of their high school class, 63% from top quarter, 88% from top half. 3 National Merit Scholars, 19 valedictorians. Full-time: 1,462 students, 58% women, 42% men. Part-time: 27 students, 56% women, 44% men. Students come from 33 states and territories, 57 other countries, 25% from out-of-state. 1% American Indian or Alaska Native, non-Hispanic/Latino; 2% Hispanic/Latino; 3% Black or African American, non-Hispanic/Latino; 1% Asian, non-Hispanic/Latino; 0.2% Native Hawaiian or other Pacific Islander, non-Hispanic/Latino; 7% international. 61% live on campus, 6% transferred in. Retention: 83% of full-time freshmen returned the following year. Academic areas with the most degrees conferred: biological/life sciences; business/marketing; visual and performing arts. Core. Calendar: semesters. Academic remediation for entering students, ESL program, services for LD students, advanced placement, accelerated degree program, self-designed majors, freshman honors college, honors program, independent study, distance learning, double major, summer session for credit, part-time degree program, adult/continuing education programs, co-op programs and internships, graduate courses open to undergrads. Off campus study. Study abroad program.
Entrance Requirements: Options: electronic application, deferred admission, international baccalaureate accepted. Required: essay, high school transcript, minimum 2.7 high school GPA, 1 recommendation, SAT or ACT. Recommended: interview. Entrance: moderately difficult. Application deadline: rolling. Notification: continuous. SAT Reasoning Test deadline: 1/15. Transfer credits accepted: Yes.

Costs Per Year: Application fee: $0. One-time mandatory fee: $150. Comprehensive fee: $38,561 includes full-time tuition ($28,500), mandatory fees ($1015), and college room and board ($9046). College room only: $5830. Part-time tuition: $959 per credit hour.
Collegiate Environment: Orientation program. Drama-theater group, choral group, student-run newspaper, radio station. Social organizations: 74 open to all; national fraternities, national sororities, honor societies and clubs; 22% of eligible men and 27% of eligible women are members. Most popular organizations: Drury Volunteer Corps (DVC), International Student Association, Fanthers, Drury Allies, Commuter Student Association. Major annual events: May Ball, Late Night Breakfast, Fireworks on Sunderland Field. Student services: health clinic, personal-psychological counseling. Campus security: 24-hour emergency response devices and patrols, student patrols, late night transport-escort service, controlled dormitory access. 1,029 college housing spaces available; 934 were occupied in 2018-19. Freshmen guaranteed college housing. On-campus residence required through junior year. Options: coed, men-only, women-only housing available. F. W. Olin Library plus 1 other. Books: 154,247 (physical), 234,110 (digital/electronic); Serial titles: 354 (digital/electronic); Databases: 44. Weekly public service hours: 92; students can reserve study rooms. Operations spending for the previous fiscal year: $778,181. 385 computers available on campus for general student use. A campuswide network can be accessed from student residence rooms and from off campus. Students can access the following: online class registration, digital imaging lab, online bill payment/student information. Staffed computer lab on campus provides training in use of computers, software, and the Internet.
Community Environment: See Southwest Missouri State University.

▪ EAST CENTRAL COLLEGE
1964 Prairie Dell Rd.
Union, MO 63084
Tel: (636)584-6500
Fax: (636)583-1897
E-mail: jc.crane@eastcentral.edu
Web Site: www.eastcentral.edu
Description: District-supported, 2-year, coed. Awards certificates, transfer associate, and terminal associate degrees. Founded 1959. Setting: 207-acre rural campus with easy access to St. Louis. Total enrollment: 2,629. Full-time: 1,219 students, 59% women, 41% men. Part-time: 1,410 students, 62% women, 38% men. 0.5% American Indian or Alaska Native, non-Hispanic/Latino; 2% Hispanic/Latino; 1% Black or African American, non-Hispanic/Latino; 0.9% Asian, non-Hispanic/Latino; 0.5% international. Core. Calendar: semesters. Academic remediation for entering students, ESL program, services for LD students, advanced placement, honors program, independent study, distance learning, summer session for credit, part-time degree program, adult/continuing education programs, internships. Off campus study at Occupational Therapy Assistant Program - University of Missouri Columbia. Study abroad program.
Entrance Requirements: Open admission. Options: electronic application, early admission, deferred admission. Required: high school transcript. Entrance: noncompetitive. Application deadline: rolling. Transfer credits accepted: Yes.
Costs Per Year: Application fee: $0. Area resident tuition: $2040 full-time, $85 per credit hour part-time. State resident tuition: $2928 full-time, $122 per credit hour part-time. Nonresident tuition: $4344 full-time, $181 per credit hour part-time. Mandatory fees: $552 full-time, $23 per credit hour part-time. Full-time tuition and fees vary according to course load and program. Part-time tuition and fees vary according to course load and program.
Collegiate Environment: Orientation program. Drama-theater group, choral group, student-run newspaper. Social organizations: 20 open to all. Most popular organizations: Student Nurse Association - Union Campus, Rolla Student Nurse Organization, R&R Club, Art Club, Engineering Club. Major annual events: Falcon Fest, Transfer and Career Fair, International Education Week. Student services: personal-psychological counseling. Campus security: 24-hour emergency response devices, late night transport-escort service. College housing not available. East Central College Library. Students can reserve study rooms. 900 computers available on campus for general student use. A campuswide network can be accessed from off-campus. Students can access the following: online class registration. Staffed computer lab on campus provides training in use of computers, software, and the Internet.
Community Environment: Union (population 9,000) is the county seat of Franklin County, and is located 40 miles west of St. Louis; see Washington University for information about St. Louis.

■ EVANGEL UNIVERSITY

1111 N Glenstone
Springfield, MO 65802
Tel: (417)865-2815; Free: 800-382-6435
Fax: (417)865-9599
E-mail: admissions@evangel.edu
Web Site: www.evangel.edu

Description: Independent, comprehensive, coed, affiliated with Assemblies of God. Awards associate, bachelor's, master's, and doctoral degrees. Founded 1955. Setting: 80-acre urban campus. Total enrollment: 2,112. Student-undergrad faculty ratio is 14:1. 918 applied. Full-time: 1,461 students, 56% women, 44% men. Part-time: 170 students, 48% women, 52% men. 0.6% American Indian or Alaska Native, non-Hispanic/Latino; 5% Hispanic/Latino; 4% Black or African American, non-Hispanic/Latino; 2% Asian, non-Hispanic/Latino; 0.2% Native Hawaiian or other Pacific Islander, non-Hispanic/Latino; 0.8% international. 5% transferred in. Retention: 79% of full-time freshmen returned the following year. Academic areas with the most degrees conferred: business/marketing; theology and religious vocations; education. Calendar: semesters. ROTC: Army (c).

Entrance Requirements: Options: electronic application, deferred admission, international baccalaureate accepted. Required: essay, high school transcript, interview, SAT or ACT. Recommended: minimum 2 high school GPA. Entrance: moderately difficult.

Costs Per Year: Application fee: $0. Tuition: $22,146 full-time, $896 per credit hour part-time. Mandatory fees: $1275 full-time. Full-time tuition and fees vary according to course load. Part-time tuition varies according to course load. College room only: $4304.

Collegiate Environment: Orientation program. Drama-theater group, choral group, marching band, student-run newspaper, radio station. Most popular organizations: Activities Board, student government, CrossWalk Student Ministries, Honor Societies, Music Ensembles. Student services: health clinic, personal-psychological counseling. Campus security: 24-hour emergency response devices and patrols, student patrols, late night transport-escort service, controlled dormitory access. Claude Kendrick Library.

Community Environment: See Southwest Missouri State University.

■ FONTBONNE UNIVERSITY

6800 Wydown Blvd.
Saint Louis, MO 63105-3098
Tel: (314)862-3456; Free: 800-205-5862
Fax: (314)719-8021
E-mail: fbyou@fontbonne.edu
Web Site: www.fontbonne.edu

Description: Independent Roman Catholic, comprehensive, coed. Awards bachelor's and master's degrees and post-master's certificates. Founded 1917. Setting: 13-acre suburban campus with easy access to St. Louis. Endowment: $19.2 million. Educational spending for the previous fiscal year: $7779 per student. Total enrollment: 1,713. Faculty: 201 (75 full-time, 126 part-time). Student-undergrad faculty ratio is 11:1. 494 applied, 97% were admitted. Full-time: 902 students, 66% women, 34% men. Part-time: 197 students, 81% women, 19% men. Students come from 23 states and territories, 13 other countries, 15% from out-of-state. 0.4% American Indian or Alaska Native, non-Hispanic/Latino; 2% Hispanic/Latino; 15% Black or African American, non-Hispanic/Latino; 1% Asian, non-Hispanic/Latino; 0.1% Native Hawaiian or other Pacific Islander, non-Hispanic/Latino; 7% international. 30% 25 or older, 1% transferred in. Retention: 79% of full-time freshmen returned the following year. Academic areas with the most degrees conferred: business/marketing; education; health professions and related sciences. Core. Calendar: semesters. Academic remediation for entering students, ESL program, services for LD students, advanced placement, accelerated degree program, self-designed majors, honors program, independent study, distance learning, double major, summer session for credit, part-time degree program, adult/continuing education programs, co-op programs and internships, graduate courses open to undergrads. Off campus study at Webster University, Maryville College, Lindenwood College, Missouri Baptist College. Study abroad program. ROTC: Army (c), Air Force (c).

Entrance Requirements: Options: electronic application, deferred admission. Required: high school transcript, minimum 2.5 high school GPA, SAT or ACT. Recommended: 2 recommendations, interview. Required for some: essay. Entrance: moderately difficult. Application deadline: rolling. Notification: continuous. SAT Reasoning Test deadline: 5/1.

Costs Per Year: Application fee: $25. Comprehensive fee: $36,885 includes

full-time tuition ($25,980), mandatory fees ($360), and college room and board ($10,545). Full-time tuition and fees vary according to degree level. Room and board charges vary according to board plan and housing facility. Part-time tuition: $694 per credit hour. Part-time tuition varies according to degree level.

Collegiate Environment: Orientation program. Drama-theater group, choral group, student-run newspaper. Social organizations: 28 open to all. Most popular organizations: Future Teachers Association, Students for the Enhancement of Black Awareness, Fontbonne Athletic Association, Fontbonne in Service and Humility, Student Government Association. Major annual events: Late Night, Christmas Ball, Springfest. Student services: health clinic, personal-psychological counseling. Campus security: 24-hour patrols, late night transport-escort service, controlled dormitory access. The Jack C. Taylor Library at Fontbonne University plus 1 other. Books: 87,793 (physical), 210,611 (digital/electronic); Databases: 38. Operations spending for the previous fiscal year: $85,313. 215 computers available on campus for general student use. A campuswide network can be accessed from student residence rooms and from off campus. Students can access the following: online class registration. Staffed computer lab on campus provides training in use of computers, software, and the Internet.

■ GLOBAL UNIVERSITY

1211 S Glenstone Ave.
Springfield, MO 65804
Tel: (417)862-9533; Free: 800-443-1083
Fax: (417)862-5318
E-mail: twaggoner@globaluniversity.edu
Web Site: www.globaluniversity.edu

Description: Independent, comprehensive, coed, affiliated with Assemblies of God. Awards associate, bachelor's, master's, and doctoral degrees (offers only external degree programs). Founded 1948. Setting: small town campus. Total enrollment: 4,551. Faculty: 633 (81 full-time, 552 part-time). Student-undergrad faculty ratio is 11:1. Students come from 50 states and territories, 127 other countries, 98% from out-of-state. 91% 25 or older. Academic area with the most degrees conferred: theology and religious vocations. Core. Calendar: continuous. Advanced placement, independent study, distance learning, double major, part-time degree program, external degree program, adult/continuing education programs, graduate courses open to undergrads. Off campus study.

Entrance Requirements: Open admission. Option: international baccalaureate accepted. Required: high school transcript. Recommended: essay. Required for some: 1 recommendation. Entrance: noncompetitive. Application deadline: rolling. Transfer credits accepted: Yes.

Collegiate Environment: Orientation program. Campus security: 24-hour emergency response devices. Global University Library.

■ GOLDFARB SCHOOL OF NURSING AT BARNES-JEWISH COLLEGE

4483 Duncan Ave.
Saint Louis, MO 63110
Tel: (314)454-7055; Free: 800-832-9009
Fax: (314)454-5239
Web Site: www.barnesjewishcollege.edu

Description: Independent, comprehensive, coed. Administratively affiliated with Barnes Jewish Hospital. Awards bachelor's, master's, and doctoral degrees and post-master's certificates. Founded 1902. Setting: 2-acre urban campus with easy access to St. Louis, Missouri. Endowment: $25.2 million. Research spending for the previous fiscal year: $1.4 million. Educational spending for the previous fiscal year: $14,242 per student. Total enrollment: 695. Faculty: 97 (46 full-time, 51 part-time). Student-undergrad faculty ratio is 11:1. 429 applied, 84% were admitted. Full-time: 569 students, 90% women, 10% men. Part-time: 61 students, 92% women, 8% men. Students come from 11 states and territories, 2 other countries, 27% from out-of-state. 0.5% American Indian or Alaska Native, non-Hispanic/Latino; 3% Hispanic/Latino; 7% Black or African American, non-Hispanic/Latino; 2% Asian, non-Hispanic/Latino; 0.3% Native Hawaiian or other Pacific Islander, non-Hispanic/Latino; 0.3% international. 39% 25 or older, 100% transferred in. Academic area with the most degrees conferred: health professions and related sciences. Core. Calendar: trimesters. Services for LD students, advanced placement, accelerated degree program, independent study, summer session for credit, graduate courses open to undergrads. Off campus study.

Entrance Requirements: Options: electronic application, deferred admission, international baccalaureate accepted. Entrance: moderately difficult.

Transfer credits accepted: Yes. Applicants placed on waiting list: 216. Waitlisted applicants offered admission: 72.

Costs Per Year: Application fee: $50. Tuition: $20,020 full-time, $770 per credit hour part-time. Mandatory fees: $1320 full-time, $615 per term part-time. Full-time tuition and fees vary according to course load and degree level. Part-time tuition and fees vary according to course load and degree level.

Collegiate Environment: Orientation program. Student-run newspaper. Social organizations: 6 open to all. Most popular organizations: Student Nurses Association, Student Council, GSON Men Excelling in Nursing, Veterans and Supporters Together. Major annual events: Fall Ice Cream Social, Homecoming. Student services: legal services, personal-psychological counseling. Campus security: 24-hour patrols, late night transport-escort service. Goldfarb School of Nursing Library plus 2 others. Books: 1,100 (physical), 20,000 (digital/electronic); Serial titles: 62 (digital/electronic); Databases: 14. Operations spending for the previous fiscal year: $364,641. 160 computers available on campus for general student use. A campuswide network can be accessed from off-campus. Students can access the following: software, research databases. Staffed computer lab on campus provides training in use of computers, software, and the Internet.

■ GRACELAND UNIVERSITY
1401 W Truman Rd.
Independence, MO 64050-3434
Tel: (816)833-0524; Free: 866-GRACELAND
E-mail: gic@graceland.edu
Web Site: www.graceland.edu
Description: Independent Community of Christ, comprehensive, coed. Awards bachelor's and master's degrees and post-master's certificates. Calendar: 4-1-4.

■ HANNIBAL-LAGRANGE UNIVERSITY
2800 Palmyra Rd.
Hannibal, MO 63401-1999
Tel: (573)221-3675; Free: 800-HLG-1119
Fax: (573)221-6594
E-mail: admissions@hlg.edu
Web Site: www.hlg.edu
Description: Independent Southern Baptist, comprehensive, coed. Awards associate, bachelor's, and master's degrees. Founded 1858. Setting: 110-acre small town campus. Endowment: $8.4 million. Total enrollment: 974. Faculty: 138 (62 full-time, 76 part-time). Student-undergrad faculty ratio is 14:1. Students come from 26 states and territories, 25 other countries, 16% from out-of-state. 0.3% American Indian or Alaska Native, non-Hispanic/Latino; 3% Hispanic/Latino; 4% Black or African American, non-Hispanic/Latino; 0.4% Asian, non-Hispanic/Latino; 0.3% Native Hawaiian or other Pacific Islander, non-Hispanic/Latino; 6% international. 59% live on campus. Core. Calendar: semesters. Academic remediation for entering students, ESL program, services for LD students, advanced placement, accelerated degree program, self-designed majors, honors program, independent study, distance learning, double major, summer session for credit, part-time degree program, adult/continuing education programs, internships. Off campus study. Study abroad program.

Entrance Requirements: Open admission. Options: electronic application, early admission, deferred admission. Required: high school transcript, minimum 2 high school GPA, SAT or ACT. Entrance: minimally difficult. Application deadlines: rolling, 8/10 for nonresidents. Notification: continuous until 9/10, 9/10 for nonresidents. SAT Reasoning Test deadline: 9/10. SAT Subject Test deadline: 9/10. Transfer credits accepted: Yes.

Costs Per Year: Application fee: $25. One-time mandatory fee: $150. Comprehensive fee: $30,858 includes full-time tuition ($21,450), mandatory fees ($1300), and college room and board ($8108). Full-time tuition and fees vary according to course load, degree level, location, program, and student level. Room and board charges vary according to housing facility. Part-time tuition: $715 per credit hour. Part-time mandatory fees: $325 per term. Part-time tuition and fees vary according to course load, degree level, location, program, and student level.

Collegiate Environment: Orientation program. Drama-theater group, choral group, student-run newspaper. Social organizations: 17 open to all; local fraternities, local sororities; 45% of eligible men and 60% of eligible women are members. Most popular organizations: Phi Beta Lambda, Student Nursing Association, Student Teachers Organization, Phi Beta Delta, Alpha Tau Beta. Major annual events: Homecoming, Booster Banquet, Experience HLGU Day. Campus security: 24-hour emergency response devices and patrols, student patrols, late night transport-escort service, controlled dormitory access, camera surveillance, alert system. Roland Library plus 1 other. Books: 113,238 (physical), 11,053 (digital/electronic); Databases: 77. Students can reserve study rooms. Operations spending for the previous fiscal year: $684,591. 258 computers available on campus for general student use. A campuswide network can be accessed from student residence rooms. Students can access the following: online class registration. Staffed computer lab on campus provides training in use of computers and the Internet.

Community Environment: The boyhood home of Mark Twain, Hannibal (population 17,649), is located on the west bank of the Mississippi River, 120 miles north of St. Louis. Buses and trains are the principal forms of transportation as well as a municipal airport that serves the area. A public library, YMCA, churches, a music association, and numerous civic and service organizations are a part of the community. Some recreational activities include swimming, bowling, and fishing.

■ HARRIS-STOWE STATE UNIVERSITY
3026 Laclede Ave.
Saint Louis, MO 63103-2136
Tel: (314)340-3366
Fax: (314)340-3322
E-mail: admissions@hssu.edu
Web Site: www.hssu.edu
Description: State-supported, 4-year, coed. Part of Missouri Coordinating Board for Higher Education. Awards bachelor's degrees. Founded 1857. Setting: 22-acre urban campus with easy access to St. Louis. Total enrollment: 1,442. Faculty: 170 (29 full-time, 141 part-time). Student-undergrad faculty ratio is 16:1. 4,414 applied, 40% were admitted. 5% from top 10% of their high school class, 26% from top quarter, 52% from top half. Full-time: 1,163 students, 64% women, 36% men. Part-time: 279 students, 74% women, 26% men. 24% from out-of-state. 0.1% American Indian or Alaska Native, non-Hispanic/Latino; 3% Hispanic/Latino; 80% Black or African American, non-Hispanic/Latino; 0.5% Asian, non-Hispanic/Latino; 1% international. 28% 25 or older, 29% live on campus, 12% transferred in. Retention: 55% of full-time freshmen returned the following year. Academic areas with the most degrees conferred: business/marketing; education; homeland security, law enforcement, firefighting, and protective services. Core. Calendar: semesters. Academic remediation for entering students, services for LD students, advanced placement, accelerated degree program, self-designed majors, honors program, distance learning, summer session for credit, part-time degree program, co-op programs and internships. Off campus study at Saint Louis University, University of Missouri-St. Louis. Study abroad program. ROTC: Army (c).

Entrance Requirements: Options: electronic application, early admission, deferred admission. Required: high school transcript, SAT or ACT. Entrance: noncompetitive. Notification: continuous. Transfer credits accepted: Yes.

Costs Per Year: Application fee: $20. State resident tuition: $4944 full-time, $206 per credit hour part-time. Nonresident tuition: $9576 full-time, $399 per credit hour part-time. Mandatory fees: $444 full-time, $222 per term part-time. Full-time tuition and fees vary according to course load. College room and board: $9491. College room only: $6741. Room and board charges vary according to housing facility.

Collegiate Environment: Orientation program. Drama-theater group, choral group. Social organizations: national fraternities, national sororities, local fraternities, local sororities. Most popular organizations: Drama Club, Concert chorale, Student Government Association, Multicultural Council, Student Ambassadors. Major annual events: Homecoming, Commencement, Organization Day. Student services: health clinic, personal-psychological counseling. Campus security: 24-hour emergency response devices and patrols, late night transport-escort service, controlled dormitory access. AT&T Library and Technology Center plus 1 other.

■ JEFFERSON COLLEGE
1000 Viking Dr.
Hillsboro, MO 63050-2441
Tel: (636)797-3000
Fax: (636)789-4012
E-mail: admissions@jeffco.edu
Web Site: www.jeffco.edu
Description: District-supported, 2-year, coed. Awards certificates, diplomas, transfer associate, and terminal associate degrees. Founded 1963. Setting: 455-acre rural campus with easy access to St. Louis. System endowment: $689,969. Educational spending for the previous fiscal year: $3254 per

student. Total enrollment: 4,705. Faculty: 353 (100 full-time, 253 part-time). Student-undergrad faculty ratio is 17:1. Full-time: 2,287 students, 57% women, 43% men. Part-time: 2,418 students, 62% women, 38% men. 0.6% American Indian or Alaska Native, non-Hispanic/Latino; 0.4% Hispanic/Latino; 2% Black or African American, non-Hispanic/Latino; 0.8% Asian, non-Hispanic/Latino; 0.1% Native Hawaiian or other Pacific Islander, non-Hispanic/Latino; 0.3% international. Core. Calendar: semesters. Academic remediation for entering students, ESL program, services for LD students, advanced placement, freshman honors college, honors program, distance learning, summer session for credit, part-time degree program, adult/continuing education programs, internships. Off campus study.

Entrance Requirements: Open admission except for veterinary technology, nursing, emergency medical technician programs, law enforcement academy, and health and occupational therapy programs. Options: electronic application, early admission. Required: high school transcript. Entrance: noncompetitive. Application deadline: rolling. Transfer credits accepted: Yes.

Costs Per Year: Application fee: $25. Area resident tuition: $3180 full-time, $106 per credit hour part-time. State resident tuition: $4770 full-time, $159 per credit hour part-time. Nonresident tuition: $6360 full-time, $212 per credit hour part-time. Mandatory fees: $300 full-time, $10 per credit hour part-time. Full-time tuition and fees vary according to course load and program. Part-time tuition and fees vary according to course load and program.

Collegiate Environment: Orientation program. Drama-theater group, choral group, student-run newspaper. Social organizations: 15 open to all; national sororities. Most popular organizations: Student Senate, Nursing Associations, Baptist Student Unit, Phi Theta Kappa, National Technical Honors Society. Major annual events: Special Olympics, Shocktober Night, Spring Fling. Student services: health clinic, personal-psychological counseling. Campus security: 24-hour patrols, campus police department. Jefferson College Library plus 1 other. Books: 75,216 (physical), 183,744 (digital/electronic); Serial titles: 54 (physical), 31,939 (digital/electronic); Databases: 62. Weekly public service hours: 66; students can reserve study rooms. Operations spending for the previous fiscal year: $620,200. 1,700 computers available on campus for general student use. A campuswide network can be accessed from student residence rooms and from off campus. Students can access the following: online class registration. Staffed computer lab on campus provides training in use of computers, software, and the Internet.

Community Environment: Hillsboro (population 1,784) is a rural community with a temperate climate. It is located within a 30-minute drive of metropolitan St. Louis. The town is situated near several small lakes, which are excellent for fishing and boating. Hillsboro is the headquarters for the county health unit. The community facilities include civic clubs, a shopping center, churches of major denominations, and a college library. The recreational, social and cultural facilities of St. Louis are accessible. Opportunities for part-time employment are good. See also Washington University for information on St. Louis.

■ **KANSAS CITY ART INSTITUTE**
4415 Warwick Blvd.
Kansas City, MO 64111-1874
Tel: (816)472-4852; Free: 800-522-5224
Fax: (816)531-6296
E-mail: admiss@kcai.edu
Web Site: www.kcai.edu

Description: Independent, 4-year, coed. Awards bachelor's degrees. Founded 1885. Setting: 18-acre urban campus with easy access to Kansas City, MO. Total enrollment: 663. Faculty: (56 full-time, 52 part-time). Student-undergrad faculty ratio is 9:1. 669 applied, 67% were admitted. 12% from top 10% of their high school class, 33% from top quarter, 68% from top half. Full-time: 656 students, 72% women, 28% men. Part-time: 7 students, 57% women, 43% men. 64% from out-of-state. 0.4% American Indian or Alaska Native, non-Hispanic/Latino; 8% Hispanic/Latino; 5% Black or African American, non-Hispanic/Latino; 3% Asian, non-Hispanic/Latino; 1% international. 7% 25 or older, 37% live on campus, 8% transferred in. Retention: 77% of full-time freshmen returned the following year. Academic area with the most degrees conferred: visual and performing arts. Core. Calendar: semesters. Services for LD students, independent study, double major, summer session for credit, part-time degree program, internships. Off campus study at New York Studio Program, AICAD School Exchange. Study abroad program.

Entrance Requirements: Options: electronic application, early admission, deferred admission, international baccalaureate accepted. Required: essay, high school transcript, 1 recommendation, portfolio, SAT or ACT. Recom-

mended: minimum 2.5 high school GPA, interview. Required for some: TOEFL. Entrance: moderately difficult. Application deadline: 8/15. Transfer credits accepted: Yes.

Costs Per Year: Application fee: $45. Comprehensive fee: $48,800 includes full-time tuition ($37,900), mandatory fees ($500), and college room and board ($10,400). Full-time tuition and fees vary according to reciprocity agreements. Part-time tuition: $1510 per credit hour. Part-time tuition varies according to reciprocity agreements.

Collegiate Environment: Orientation program. Student-run radio station. Student services: personal-psychological counseling. Campus security: 24-hour emergency response devices and patrols, late night transport-escort service, controlled dormitory access. Jannes Library. Weekly public service hours: 84; students can reserve study rooms.

Community Environment: See University of Missouri - Kansas City.

■ **LINCOLN UNIVERSITY**
820 Chestnut St.
Jefferson City, MO 65101
Tel: (573)681-5000
Fax: (573)681-6074
E-mail: admissions@lincolnu.edu
Web Site: www.lincolnu.edu

Description: State-supported, comprehensive, coed. Awards associate, bachelor's, and master's degrees. Founded 1866. Setting: 174-acre small town campus. Endowment: $1.6 million. Research spending for the previous fiscal year: $4.9 million. Educational spending for the previous fiscal year: $5954 per student. Total enrollment: 2,619. Faculty: 153 (105 full-time, 48 part-time). Student-undergrad faculty ratio is 17:1. 3,423 applied, 52% were admitted. 5% from top 10% of their high school class, 15% from top quarter, 39% from top half. Full-time: 1,804 students, 55% women, 45% men. Part-time: 708 students, 64% women, 36% men. Students come from 30 states and territories, 4 other countries, 30% from out-of-state. 0.3% American Indian or Alaska Native, non-Hispanic/Latino; 2% Hispanic/Latino; 57% Black or African American, non-Hispanic/Latino; 0.6% Asian, non-Hispanic/Latino; 0.1% Native Hawaiian or other Pacific Islander, non-Hispanic/Latino; 2% international. 16% 25 or older, 48% live on campus, 5% transferred in. Retention: 53% of full-time freshmen returned the following year. Academic areas with the most degrees conferred: health professions and related sciences; education; liberal arts/general studies. Core. Calendar: semesters. Services for LD students, advanced placement, accelerated degree program, freshman honors college, honors program, independent study, distance learning, double major, summer session for credit, part-time degree program, adult/continuing education programs, co-op programs and internships, graduate courses open to undergrads. Off campus study at Mid-Missouri Associated Colleges and Universities (MMACU) consortium. Study abroad program. ROTC: Army.

Entrance Requirements: Open admission for first-time freshmen who reside in Missouri. Options: electronic application, deferred admission, international baccalaureate accepted. Required: high school transcript, SAT or ACT. Required for some: minimum 2 high school GPA. Entrance: noncompetitive. Application deadline: rolling. Notification: continuous. Transfer credits accepted: Yes.

Costs Per Year: Application fee: $0. State resident tuition: $6270 full-time, $209 per credit hour part-time. Nonresident tuition: $12,810 full-time, $427 per credit hour part-time. Mandatory fees: $1,362 full-time, $10 per credit hour part-time, $381.10 per term part-time. Full-time tuition and fees vary according to course load, location, and reciprocity agreements. Part-time tuition and fees vary according to course load, location, and reciprocity agreements. College room and board: $7068. College room only: $3618. Room and board charges vary according to board plan and housing facility.

Collegiate Environment: Orientation program. Choral group, marching band, student-run newspaper. Social organizations: 32 open to all; national fraternities, national sororities, local fraternities, local sororities. Most popular organizations: Student Government Association (SGA), Lincoln University Band, Alpha Kappa Mu, Army ROTC, International Student Association. Major annual events: Homecoming, Springfest, Founder's Day. Student services: health clinic, personal-psychological counseling, women's center. Campus security: 24-hour emergency response devices and patrols, student patrols, late night transport-escort service, controlled dormitory access, Rape Aggression Defense class upon request, Operation ID, timely warnings, text message safety alerts, Webpage with helpful tips. Inman E. Page Library. Books: 99,126 (physical), 197,476 (digital/electronic); Serial titles: 1,194 (physical), 19,000 (digital/electronic); Databases: 39. Weekly public service hours: 88. Operations spending for the previous fiscal year:

$816,243. 365 computers available on campus for general student use. Computer purchase/lease plans available. A campuswide network can be accessed from student residence rooms and from off campus. Students can access the following: online class registration. Staffed computer lab on campus.

■ LINDENWOOD UNIVERSITY

209 S Kingshighway
Saint Charles, MO 63301-1695
Tel: (636)949-2000
Fax: (636)949-4910
E-mail: KSchilli@lindenwood.edu
Web Site: www.lindenwood.edu

Description: Independent Presbyterian, comprehensive, coed. Awards bachelor's, master's, and doctoral degrees and post-master's certificates. Founded 1827. Setting: 285-acre suburban campus with easy access to St. Louis. Endowment: $160.3 million. Educational spending for the previous fiscal year: $6034 per student. Total enrollment: 9,468. Faculty: 1,223 (283 full-time, 940 part-time). Student-undergrad faculty ratio is 13:1. 3,416 applied, 88% were admitted. Full-time: 5,969 students, 54% women, 46% men. Part-time: 560 students, 57% women, 43% men. Students come from 48 states and territories, 86 other countries, 40% from out-of-state. 0.3% American Indian or Alaska Native, non-Hispanic/Latino; 5% Hispanic/Latino; 13% Black or African American, non-Hispanic/Latino; 0.9% Asian, non-Hispanic/Latino; 0.5% Native Hawaiian or other Pacific Islander, non-Hispanic/Latino; 12% international. 25% 25 or older, 55% live on campus, 11% transferred in. Retention: 70% of full-time freshmen returned the following year. Academic areas with the most degrees conferred: business/marketing; computer and information sciences; homeland security, law enforcement, firefighting, and protective services. Core. Calendar: 4-1-4 for daytime programs; quarters and trimesters for evening programs. Academic remediation for entering students, ESL program, services for LD students, advanced placement, accelerated degree program, self-designed majors, freshman honors college, honors program, independent study, distance learning, double major, summer session for credit, part-time degree program, external degree program, adult/continuing education programs, internships, graduate courses open to undergrads. Off campus study at St. Louis Private College Consortium, Washington University in St. Louis, University of Missouri-Columbia. Study abroad program. ROTC: Army (c), Air Force (c).

Entrance Requirements: Options: electronic application, deferred admission, international baccalaureate accepted. Required: minimum 2.5 high school GPA, personal resume indicating community service, youth leadership, clubs, organizations, and non-academic experience. Recommended: 3 recommendations, interview. Required for some: essay, high school transcript, SAT or ACT. Entrance: moderately difficult. Application deadline: rolling. Notification: continuous. SAT Reasoning Test deadline: 8/10. SAT Subject Test deadline: 8/10. Transfer credits accepted: Yes. Applicants placed on waiting list: 0. Wait-listed applicants offered admission: 0.

Costs Per Year: Application fee: $0. Comprehensive fee: $27,300 includes full-time tuition ($18,000), mandatory fees ($100), and college room and board ($9200). Part-time tuition: $495 per credit hour.

Collegiate Environment: Orientation program. Drama-theater group, choral group, marching band, student-run newspaper, radio station. Social organizations: 89 open to all; national fraternities, national sororities, local fraternities, local sororities. Most popular organizations: Kappa Delta Pi, Athletes in Action, Black Student Union, Lindenwood Gender Sexualities Alliance, Psychology Interest Club. Major annual events: Dark Carnival, Evans Unlocked, Late Night Breakfast. Student services: health clinic, personal-psychological counseling. Campus security: 24-hour emergency response devices and patrols, late night transport-escort service, controlled dormitory access. 4,033 college housing spaces available; 3,874 were occupied in 2018-19. Freshmen given priority for college housing. Options: coed, men-only, women-only housing available. Library and Academic Resource Center plus 1 other. Books: 74,836 (physical), 278,834 (digital/electronic); Serial titles: 193 (physical), 97 (digital/electronic); Databases: 141. Students can reserve study rooms. Operations spending for the previous year: $1.9 million. 231 computers available on campus for general student use. A campuswide network can be accessed from student residence rooms and from off campus. Students can access the following: online class registration. Staffed computer lab on campus provides training in use of computers and the Internet.

Community Environment: St. Charles was one of the first settlements on the Missouri River. It is located 20 miles from St. Louis. An airport is located ten miles away. Community facilities include restaurants, shopping, churches, hospital, hotels, motels, and recreation centers. Swimming, boating, and skating are some of the recreational activities found in St. Charles County.

■ LOGAN UNIVERSITY

1851 Schoettler Rd.
Chesterfield, MO 63017
Tel: (636)227-2100; Free: 800-533-9210
Fax: (636)227-9338
E-mail: admissions@logan.edu
Web Site: www.logan.edu

Description: Independent, upper-level, coed. Awards bachelor's, master's, and doctoral degrees. Founded 1935. Setting: 112-acre suburban campus with easy access to St. Louis. Endowment: $15.6 million. Research spending for the previous fiscal year: $643,738. Educational spending for the previous fiscal year: $13,309 per student. Total enrollment: 1,371. Faculty: 114 (49 full-time, 65 part-time). Student-undergrad faculty ratio is 9:1. 8 applied, 100% were admitted. Full-time: 51 students, 59% women, 41% men. Part-time: 75 students, 67% women, 33% men. Students come from 2 other countries, 61% from out-of-state. 3% Hispanic/Latino; 0.8% Asian, non-Hispanic/Latino; 0.8% international. 49% 25 or older, 25% transferred in. Academic areas with the most degrees conferred: interdisciplinary studies; biological/life sciences. Core. Calendar: trimesters. Services for LD students, advanced placement, accelerated degree program, independent study, distance learning, summer session for credit, part-time degree program, external degree program, adult/continuing education programs, co-op programs, graduate courses open to undergrads.

Entrance Requirements: Transfer credits accepted: Yes.

Costs Per Year: Application fee: $25. Tuition: $8250 full-time, $275 per credit hour part-time. Mandatory fees: $100 full-time, $50 per term part-time. Full-time tuition and fees vary according to course load, degree level, and program. Part-time tuition and fees vary according to course load, degree level, and program.

Collegiate Environment: Orientation program. Social organizations: 36 open to all; national fraternities, national sororities, Chi Rho Sigma, a coed fraternal organization. Most popular organizations: Chiropractic on Purpose, SOT Club, Rehab2Performance, Family Wellness, Gonstead Club. Major annual events: Arthritis Walk, Graduation Celebrations, Club Day. Student services: health clinic, personal-psychological counseling. Campus security: 24-hour patrols, late night transport-escort service. Learning Resources Center. Books: 11,773 (physical), 3,679 (digital/electronic); Serial titles: 23 (physical), 64 (digital/electronic); Databases: 94. Weekly public service hours: 84. Operations spending for the previous fiscal year: $506,195. 100 computers available on campus for general student use. A campuswide network can be accessed. Students can access the following: online class registration, student portal, learning management system, online storage, specialty health care software, high-speed printing. Staffed computer lab on campus.

■ MARYVILLE UNIVERSITY OF SAINT LOUIS

650 Maryville University Dr.
Saint Louis, MO 63141-7299
Tel: (314)529-9300; Free: 800-627-9855
Fax: (314)529-9927
E-mail: admissions@maryville.edu
Web Site: www.maryville.edu

Description: Independent, university, coed. Awards bachelor's, master's, and doctoral degrees and post-master's certificates. Founded 1872. Setting: 130-acre suburban campus with easy access to St. Louis. Endowment: $55.2 million. Educational spending for the previous fiscal year: $7355 per student. Total enrollment: 9,139. Faculty: 824 (156 full-time, 668 part-time). Student-undergrad faculty ratio is 14:1. 2,074 applied, 95% were admitted. 24% from top 10% of their high school class, 56% from top quarter, 89% from top half. Full-time: 2,594 students, 62% women, 38% men. Part-time: 1,084 students, 75% women, 25% men. Students come from 46 states and territories, 45 other countries, 31% from out-of-state. 0.5% American Indian or Alaska Native, non-Hispanic/Latino; 5% Hispanic/Latino; 10% Black or African American, non-Hispanic/Latino; 3% Asian, non-Hispanic/Latino; 0.1% Native Hawaiian or other Pacific Islander, non-Hispanic/Latino; 4% international. 26% 25 or older, 26% live on campus, 19% transferred in. Retention: 86% of full-time freshmen returned the following year. Academic areas with the most degrees conferred: health professions and related sciences; business/marketing; psychology. Core. Calendar: semesters. ESL program, services for LD students, advanced placement, accelerated degree program, honors program, independent study, distance learning, double major, summer session for credit, part-time degree program, external degree program, adult/continuing education programs, co-op programs and internships, graduate courses open to undergrads. Off campus study at Fontbonne University, Lindenwood University, Webster University, Missouri Baptist University. Study abroad program. ROTC: Army (c).

Entrance Requirements: Options: electronic application, deferred admission, international baccalaureate accepted. Required: high school transcript, minimum 2.5 high school GPA. Required for some: essay, interview, audition, portfolio. Entrance: moderately difficult. Application deadline: rolling for nonresidents. Notification: continuous, continuous for nonresidents. Transfer credits accepted: Yes.

Costs Per Year: Application fee: $0. Comprehensive fee: $38,558 includes full-time tuition ($26,070), mandatory fees ($2400), and college room and board ($10,088). Part-time tuition: $781 per credit hour.

Collegiate Environment: Orientation program. Drama-theater group, choral group, student-run newspaper. Social organizations: 100 open to all. Most popular organizations: Campus Activities Board, Physical Therapy Club, Student Nurses Association, Community Service Club, Green Maryville Student Association. Major annual events: Fall Festival, End of the Year Bash, Involvement Fair. Student services: health clinic, personal-psychological counseling. Campus security: 24-hour emergency response devices and patrols, late night transport-escort service, controlled dormitory access, video security system in residence halls, self-defense and education programs. 1,047 college housing spaces available; 980 were occupied in 2018-19. No special consideration for freshman housing applicants. Option: coed housing available. University Library. Books: 57,027 (physical), 252,154 (digital/electronic); Serial titles: 78,331 (digital/electronic); Databases: 138. Weekly public service hours: 103; study areas open 24 hours, 5-7 days a week. Operations spending for the previous fiscal year: $941,638. 563 computers available on campus for general student use. A campuswide network can be accessed from student residence rooms and from off campus. Students can access the following: online class registration, specialized software, university catalog. Staffed computer lab on campus (open 24 hours a day) provides training in use of computers, software, and the Internet.

Community Environment: The campus is located at Highway 40/I-64 and Woods Mill Road, 2 miles west of I-270 in West St. Louis County. The campus is nestled on 130 acres of rolling hills, with wooded areas, creeks, and two lakes. It is within 20 minutes of downtown St. Louis which provides many social, cultural, athletic, and entertainment facilities including, the St. Louis Art Museum, St. Louis Symphony Orchestra, St. Louis Science Center, Missouri Botanical Garden, Municipal Opera, ballet, rock performances, theaters, restaurants, a world renown zoo, a large park system, as well as professional baseball, hockey, soccer, and football, and an International airport.

■ **METRO BUSINESS COLLEGE (CAPE GIRARDEAU)**
1732 N Kingshighway
Cape Girardeau, MO 63701
Tel: (573)334-9181; Free: 888-206-4545
Fax: (573)334-0617
Web Site: www.metrobusinesscollege.edu
Description: Proprietary, primarily 2-year, coed. Awards certificates, diplomas, terminal associate, and bachelor's degrees. Total enrollment: 396. 57% 25 or older. Calendar: quarters.
Entrance Requirements: Entrance: minimally difficult.

■ **METRO BUSINESS COLLEGE (JEFFERSON CITY)**
210 El Mercado Plz.
Jefferson City, MO 65109
Tel: (573)635-6600; Free: 888-206-4545
Fax: (573)635-6999
E-mail: cheri@metrobusinesscollege.edu
Web Site: www.metrobusinesscollege.edu
Description: Proprietary, 2-year, coed. Awards certificates and terminal associate degrees. Founded 1979. Setting: suburban campus. Total enrollment: 142. Faculty: 11 (6 full-time, 5 part-time). Student-undergrad faculty ratio is 11:1. 0.7% American Indian or Alaska Native, non-Hispanic/Latino; 18% Black or African American, non-Hispanic/Latino; 2% Asian, non-Hispanic/Latino. 62% 25 or older. Core. Calendar: continuous. Academic remediation for entering students, services for LD students, advanced placement, independent study, summer session for credit, part-time degree program, adult/continuing education programs, internships.

Entrance Requirements: Required: essay, high school transcript, interview, Wonderlic aptitude test.
Collegiate Environment: Orientation program. Student-run newspaper. Social organizations: 1 open to all; 50% of eligible men and 65% of eligible women are members. Most popular organization: Student Council. Major annual events: School Picnic, Graduation, Academic Olympics. Student services: personal-psychological counseling. Databases: 1. 92 computers available on campus for general student use. Computer purchase/lease plans available. A campuswide network can be accessed. Staffed computer lab on campus provides training in use of computers and software.

■ **METRO BUSINESS COLLEGE (ROLLA)**
1202 E Hwy. 72
Rolla, MO 65401
Tel: (573)364-8464; Free: 888-206-4545
Fax: (573)364-8077
E-mail: inforolla@metrobusinesscollege.edu
Web Site: www.metrobusinesscollege.edu
Description: Proprietary, 2-year, coed. Awards certificates and terminal associate degrees. Founded 1979. Calendar: quarters.
Entrance Requirements: Required: interview.

■ **METROPOLITAN COMMUNITY COLLEGE-KANSAS CITY**
3200 Broadway
Kansas City, MO 64111
Tel: (816)604-1000
E-mail: tuesday.stanley@mcckc.edu
Web Site: www.mcckc.edu
Description: State and locally supported, 2-year, coed. Part of Metropolitan Community Colleges System. Awards certificates, transfer associate, and terminal associate degrees. Founded 1969. Setting: 420-acre suburban campus with easy access to Kansas City. System endowment: $4.5 million. Total enrollment: 19,234. Faculty: 904 (218 full-time, 686 part-time). Student-undergrad faculty ratio is 26:1. 4,160 applied, 100% were admitted. Full-time: 7,734 students, 53% women, 47% men. Part-time: 11,500 students, 59% women, 41% men. Students come from 19 states and territories, 74 other countries, 1% from out-of-state. 0.3% American Indian or Alaska Native, non-Hispanic/Latino; 9% Hispanic/Latino; 17% Black or African American, non-Hispanic/Latino; 3% Asian, non-Hispanic/Latino; 0.3% Native Hawaiian or other Pacific Islander, non-Hispanic/Latino. 37% 25 or older, 4% transferred in. Retention: 52% of full-time freshmen returned the following year. Core. Calendar: semesters. Academic remediation for entering students, ESL program, services for LD students, advanced placement, accelerated degree program, honors program, independent study, distance learning, summer session for credit, part-time degree program, adult/continuing education programs, co-op programs and internships. Off campus study at Johnson County Community College.

Entrance Requirements: Open admission except for automotive, veterinary technology, and the allied health fields. Options: electronic application, early admission, deferred admission. Recommended: ACT. Entrance: noncompetitive. Application deadline: rolling. Notification: continuous.
Collegiate Environment: Orientation program. Drama-theater group, choral group, student-run newspaper. Social organizations: national fraternities. Most popular organizations: student newspaper, student government, Phi Theta Kappa, Metropolitan Chorale of KC, Student Ambassadors. Major annual events: Panache Fashion Show, Flights of Fancy, Day of Service. Student services: personal-psychological counseling. Campus security: 24-hour emergency response devices and patrols, late night transport-escort service. College Library. Operations spending for the previous fiscal year: $2.2 million. 2,778 computers available on campus for general student use. A campuswide network can be accessed from off-campus. Students can access the following: online class registration. Staffed computer lab on campus provides training in use of computers, software, and the Internet.
Community Environment: See University of Missouri Kansas City.

■ **MIDWEST INSTITUTE (EARTH CITY)**
4260 Shoreline Dr.
Earth City, MO 63045
Tel: (314)344-4440; Free: 800-695-5550
Fax: (314)344-0495
Web Site: www.midwestinstitute.com
Description: Proprietary, 2-year, coed. Awards terminal associate degrees.

■ **MIDWEST INSTITUTE (FENTON)**
964 S Hwy. Dr.
Fenton, MO 63026
Tel: (314)965-8363; Free: 800-695-5550
Fax: (314)965-1558
Web Site: www.midwestinstitute.com
Description: Proprietary, 2-year, coed. Awards terminal associate degrees. Founded 1963. Total enrollment: 162. 150 applied, 99% were admitted.
Entrance Requirements: Recommended: high school transcript.

■ **MIDWEST UNIVERSITY**
851 Parr Rd.
Wentzville, MO 63385
Tel: (636)327-4645
Fax: (636)327-4715
Web Site: www.midwest.edu
Description: Independent interdenominational, university, coed. Awards bachelor's, master's, and doctoral degrees. Founded 1986. Total enrollment: 300. Student-undergrad faculty ratio is 24:1. 94% 25 or older. Calendar: semesters. Distance learning.
Entrance Requirements: Required: 1 recommendation.

■ **MINERAL AREA COLLEGE**
PO Box 1000
Park Hills, MO 63601-1000
Tel: (573)431-4593
E-mail: preeder@mineralarea.edu
Web Site: www.mineralarea.edu
Description: District-supported, 2-year, coed. Part of Missouri Coordinating Board for Higher Education. Awards certificates, transfer associate, and terminal associate degrees. Founded 1922. Setting: 240-acre rural campus with easy access to St. Louis. Total enrollment: 4,508. Faculty: 316 (73 full-time, 243 part-time). Student-undergrad faculty ratio is 14:1. Full-time: 2,869 students, 54% women, 46% men. Part-time: 1,639 students, 63% women, 37% men. Students come from 14 states and territories, 2 other countries, 1% from out-of-state. 0.6% American Indian or Alaska Native, non-Hispanic/Latino; 1% Hispanic/Latino; 2% Black or African American, non-Hispanic/Latino; 0.4% Asian, non-Hispanic/Latino; 0.1% Native Hawaiian or other Pacific Islander, non-Hispanic/Latino; 0.1% international. 23% 25 or older, 4% transferred in. Retention: 68% of full-time freshmen returned the following year. Core. Calendar: semesters. Academic remediation for entering students, services for LD students, advanced placement, honors program, distance learning, summer session for credit, part-time degree program, internships. Off campus study at East Central College, Jefferson College.
Entrance Requirements: Open admission except for allied health and law enforcement programs. Options: electronic application, early admission. Required: high school transcript. Entrance: noncompetitive. Application deadline: rolling. Notification: continuous.
Collegiate Environment: Orientation program. Drama-theater group, choral group. Student services: personal-psychological counseling. Campus security: 24-hour patrols. C. H. Cozen Learning Resource Center. 125 computers available on campus for general student use. A campuswide network can be accessed from student residence rooms and from off campus. Students can access the following: online class registration. Staffed computer lab on campus provides training in use of computers and software.
Community Environment: Park Hills (population 8,525) is located in east-central Missouri, 60 miles south of St. Louis. Kentucky, Illinois and Arkansas are not too distant. District facilities include most denominations of churches, four newspapers, four radio station and parks. Outdoor activities are hunting and fishing, tennis, golf.

■ **MISSOURI BAPTIST UNIVERSITY**
One College Park Dr.
Saint Louis, MO 63141-8660
Tel: (314)434-1115; Free: 877-434-1115
Fax: (314)434-7596
E-mail: admissions@mobap.edu
Web Site: www.mobap.edu
Description: Independent Southern Baptist, comprehensive, coed. Awards associate, bachelor's, master's, and doctoral degrees and post-master's certificates. Founded 1964. Setting: 65-acre suburban campus with easy access to St. Louis. Total enrollment: 5,313. Faculty: 528 (76 full-time, 452 part-time). Student-undergrad faculty ratio is 19:1. 807 applied, 52% were admitted. 10% from top 10% of their high school class, 33% from top quarter, 64% from top half. Full-time: 1,469 students, 55% women, 45% men. Part-time: 2,944 students, 64% women, 36% men. Students come from 37 states and territories, 20 other countries, 25% from out-of-state. 1% American Indian or Alaska Native, non-Hispanic/Latino; 1% Hispanic/Latino; 6% Black or African American, non-Hispanic/Latino; 2% Asian, non-Hispanic/Latino; 0.2% Native Hawaiian or other Pacific Islander, non-Hispanic/Latino; 1% international. 14% 25 or older, 28% live on campus, 8% transferred in. Retention: 70% of full-time freshmen returned the following year. Core. Calendar: semesters. Academic remediation for entering students, services for LD students, advanced placement, accelerated degree program, self-designed majors, honors program, independent study, distance learning, double major, summer session for credit, part-time degree program, adult/continuing education programs, internships, graduate courses open to undergrads. Off campus study at Maryville University of Saint Louis, Lindenwood University, Fontbonne University, Webster University. Study abroad program. ROTC: Army (c).
Entrance Requirements: Options: electronic application, international baccalaureate accepted. Required: high school transcript, minimum 2 high school GPA, 1 recommendation, SAT or ACT. Entrance: moderately difficult. Application deadline: rolling. Notification: continuous. SAT Reasoning Test deadline: 8/13. SAT Subject Test deadline: 8/13. Transfer credits accepted: Yes.
Costs Per Year: Application fee: $35. Comprehensive fee: $37,290 includes full-time tuition ($26,860), mandatory fees ($1360), and college room and board ($9070). Part-time tuition: $929 per credit hour. Part-time mandatory fees: $29 per credit hour.
Collegiate Environment: Orientation program. Drama-theater group, choral group, student-run radio station. Social organizations: 25 open to all; national fraternities, national sororities. Most popular organizations: Enactus; Students in Free Enterprise, Amp Ministries, Student Missouri State Teacher's Association, Gamma Delta Sigma, Ministerial Alliance. Major annual events: Homecoming, The Perk, Welcome Weekend. Student services: health clinic, personal-psychological counseling. Campus security: 24-hour emergency response devices and patrols, late night transport-escort service, controlled dormitory access. 420 college housing spaces available; 345 were occupied in 2018-19. Freshmen given priority for college housing. Options: men-only, women-only housing available. Jung-Kellogg Library. Books: 48,169 (physical), 222,044 (digital/electronic); Serial titles: 512 (physical), 104 (digital/electronic); Databases: 92. Weekly public service hours: 76. 100 computers available on campus for general student use. A campuswide network can be accessed from student residence rooms and from off campus. Students can access the following: online class registration.
Community Environment: See Washington University.

■ **MISSOURI SOUTHERN STATE UNIVERSITY**
3950 E Newman Rd.
Joplin, MO 64801-1595
Tel: (417)625-9300; Free: 866-818-MSSU
Fax: (417)659-4429
E-mail: admissions@mssu.edu
Web Site: www.mssu.edu
Description: State-supported, comprehensive, coed. Awards associate, bachelor's, and master's degrees. Founded 1937. Setting: 365-acre small town campus. Educational spending for the previous fiscal year: $15,376 per student. Total enrollment: 5,783. Faculty: 350 (202 full-time, 148 part-time). Student-undergrad faculty ratio is 18:1. 2,333 applied, 94% were admitted. 14% from top 10% of their high school class, 39% from top quarter, 70% from top half. Full-time: 4,210 students, 57% women, 43% men. Part-time: 1,522 students, 51% women, 49% men. Students come from 41 states and territories, 31 other countries, 18% from out-of-state. 3% American Indian or Alaska Native, non-Hispanic/Latino; 5% Hispanic/Latino; 6% Black or African American, non-Hispanic/Latino; 2% Asian, non-Hispanic/Latino; 0.2% Native Hawaiian or other Pacific Islander, non-Hispanic/Latino; 4% international. 28% 25 or older, 14% live on campus, 10% transferred in. Retention: 65% of full-time freshmen returned the following year. Academic areas with the most degrees conferred: business/marketing; education; homeland security, law enforcement, firefighting, and protective services. Core. Calendar: semesters. Academic remediation for entering students, ESL program, services for LD students, advanced placement, accelerated degree program, honors program, independent study, distance learning, double major, summer session for credit, part-time degree program, adult/continuing education programs, co-op programs and internships. Off campus study. Study abroad program.
Entrance Requirements: Options: electronic application, deferred admis-

sion, international baccalaureate accepted. Required: high school transcript, minimum 2.25 high school GPA, class rank of at least 50%, minimum recommended ACT score of at 21, SAT and SAT Subject Tests or ACT. Recommended: ACT. Required for some: 2 recommendations. Entrance: moderately difficult. Application deadline: rolling. Notification: continuous until 9/1. SAT Reasoning Test deadline: 8/1.

Collegiate Environment: Orientation program. Drama-theater group, choral group, marching band, student-run newspaper, radio station. Social organizations: 84 open to all; national fraternities, national sororities, local fraternities. Major annual events: Welcome Week, International Studies, Spring Fling. Student services: health clinic, personal-psychological counseling. Campus security: 24-hour emergency response devices and patrols, late night transport-escort service, controlled dormitory access, security at campus events, emergency vehicle assistance, safety awareness information to students. George A. Spiva Library. Books: 262,310 (physical), 362,170 (digital/electronic); Serial titles: 6,081 (physical); Databases: 221. Operations spending for the previous fiscal year: $969,594. 550 computers available on campus for general student use. A campuswide network can be accessed from student residence rooms and from off campus. Students can access the following: online class registration. Staffed computer lab on campus provides training in use of computers, software, and the Internet.

Community Environment: Located in southwest Missouri at the northern gateway of the Ozark Resort area, Joplin (population 47,000) is surrounded by numerous spring fed fishing streams in scenic hill country. The city has many manufacturing and wholesale firms as well as industry involving the mining and processing of zinc ore. All forms of commercial transportation are available. Part-time employment is available. There are over 100 churches, 14 elementary schools, 1 junior high school, 1 high school, 2 four-year colleges, and 2 hospitals.

■ MISSOURI STATE UNIVERSITY

901 S National
Springfield, MO 65897
Tel: (417)836-5000; Free: 800-492-7900
Fax: (417)836-6334
E-mail: info@missouristate.edu
Web Site: www.missouristate.edu

Description: State-supported, comprehensive, coed. Awards bachelor's, master's, and doctoral degrees and post-master's certificates. Founded 1905. Setting: 225-acre suburban campus. Total enrollment: 23,697. Faculty: 1,123 (753 full-time, 370 part-time). Student-undergrad faculty ratio is 21:1. 9,453 applied, 84% were admitted. 21% from top 10% of their high school class, 49% from top quarter, 83% from top half. Full-time: 15,363 students, 58% women, 42% men. Part-time: 5,001 students, 57% women, 43% men. 11% from out-of-state. 0.4% American Indian or Alaska Native, non-Hispanic/Latino; 4% Hispanic/Latino; 5% Black or African American, non-Hispanic/Latino; 1% Asian, non-Hispanic/Latino; 0.1% Native Hawaiian or other Pacific Islander, non-Hispanic/Latino; 4% international. 15% 25 or older, 23% live on campus, 8% transferred in. Retention: 77% of full-time freshmen returned the following year. Academic areas with the most degrees conferred: business/marketing; education; health professions and related sciences. Core. Calendar: semesters. ESL program, services for LD students, advanced placement, accelerated degree program, self-designed majors, freshman honors college, honors program, independent study, distance learning, double major, summer session for credit, part-time degree program, co-op programs and internships, graduate courses open to undergrads. Off campus study at National Student Exchange. Study abroad program. ROTC: Army.

Entrance Requirements: Options: electronic application, international baccalaureate accepted. Required: high school transcript, SAT or ACT. Required for some: essay, interview. Entrance: moderately difficult. Transfer credits accepted: Yes.

Costs Per Year: Application fee: $35. State resident tuition: $6360 full-time, $212 per credit hour part-time. Nonresident tuition: $14,310 full-time, $477 per credit hour part-time. Mandatory fees: $1016 full-time. Full-time tuition and fees vary according to course level, course load, and program. Part-time tuition varies according to course level, course load, and program. College room and board: $8755. Room and board charges vary according to board plan, housing facility, and location.

Collegiate Environment: Orientation program. Drama-theater group, choral group, marching band, student-run newspaper, radio station. Social organizations: national fraternities, national sororities. Most popular organizations: Residence Hall Association, Campus Ministries, Fraternity and Sorority Life, Student Government Association, Student Activities Council. Major annual events: New Student Festival, Homecoming, Bear Bash. Student services: legal services, health clinic, personal-psychological counseling. Campus security: 24-hour emergency response devices and patrols, late night transport-escort service, controlled dormitory access, on-campus police substation. Meyer Library.

Community Environment: Springfield (population 150,290) is Missouri's third largest city and is within one hour's drive from many of the popular resort and vacation areas of the southwest Missouri Ozark region. Springfield has become a major health care center for the region and is home to several major businesses and industries including Bass Pro Shops, General Electric, Kraft, and Associated Wholesale Grocers.

■ MISSOURI STATE UNIVERSITY-WEST PLAINS

128 Garfield
West Plains, MO 65775
Tel: (417)255-7255; Free: 888-466-7897
E-mail: melissajett@missouristate.edu
Web Site: wp.missouristate.edu

Description: State-supported, 2-year, coed. Part of Missouri State University. Awards certificates, transfer associate, and terminal associate degrees. Founded 1963. Setting: 20-acre small town campus. Endowment: $8.3 million. Research spending for the previous fiscal year: $1744. Educational spending for the previous fiscal year: $4720 per student. Total enrollment: 1,869. Faculty: 106 (36 full-time, 70 part-time). Student-undergrad faculty ratio is 20:1. 947 applied, 39% were admitted. 6% from top 10% of their high school class, 21% from top quarter, 51% from top half. Full-time: 806 students, 64% women, 36% men. Part-time: 1,103 students, 66% women, 34% men. Students come from 18 states and territories, 15 other countries, 3% from out-of-state. 5% American Indian or Alaska Native, non-Hispanic/Latino; 3% Hispanic/Latino; 1% Black or African American, non-Hispanic/Latino; 0.1% Asian, non-Hispanic/Latino; 84% Native Hawaiian or other Pacific Islander, non-Hispanic/Latino; 0.7% international. 28% 25 or older, 10% live on campus, 4% transferred in. Core. Calendar: semesters. Academic remediation for entering students, services for LD students, advanced placement, honors program, distance learning, summer session for credit, part-time degree program, adult/continuing education programs, co-op programs and internships. Off campus study at Missouri State University - Mountain Grove. Study abroad program.

Entrance Requirements: Open admission All open with additional requirements for Nursing program. Options: electronic application, international baccalaureate accepted. Required for some: high school transcript. Entrance: noncompetitive. Application deadlines: rolling, rolling for nonresidents. Notification: continuous, continuous for nonresidents. Transfer credits accepted: Yes.

Costs Per Year: State resident tuition: $3900 full-time, $130 per credit hour part-time. Nonresident tuition: $7800 full-time, $260 per credit hour part-time. Mandatory fees: $555 full-time, $555 per year part-time. Full-time tuition and fees vary according to program and reciprocity agreements. Part-time tuition and fees vary according to program and reciprocity agreements. College room and board: $6118. Room and board charges vary according to housing facility.

Collegiate Environment: Orientation program. Social organizations: 30 open to all; Phi Beta Lambda (FBLA), Phi Theta Kappa (NHS). Most popular organizations: Student Government Association, Student Nurses Association, Student Ambassadors, Christian Campus House, Grizzly Cheer Team. Major annual events: Homecoming, Athletic Events, Welcome Week. Student services: legal services, personal-psychological counseling. Campus security: 24-hour emergency response devices, student patrols, late night transport-escort service, controlled dormitory access, access only with key, agreement with city police for patrols. 334 college housing spaces available; 190 were occupied in 2018-19. No special consideration for freshman housing applicants. On-campus residence required in freshman year. Option: coed housing available. Garnett Library. Books: 42,808 (physical), 234,677 (digital/electronic); Serial titles: 118 (physical), 5,877 (digital/electronic); Databases: 239. Weekly public service hours: 67. Operations spending for the previous fiscal year: $4408. 150 computers available on campus for general student use. A campuswide network can be accessed from student residence rooms and from off campus. Students can access the following: online class registration, Portal, learning management system, online account review and bill pay. Staffed computer lab on campus provides training in use of computers, software, and the Internet.

■ MISSOURI UNIVERSITY OF SCIENCE AND TECHNOLOGY

1870 Miner Cir.
Rolla, MO 65409

Tel: (573)341-4111; Free: 800-522-0938

E-mail: admissions@mst.edu

Web Site: www.mst.edu

Description: State-supported, university, coed. Part of University of Missouri System. Awards bachelor's, master's, and doctoral degrees. Founded 1870. Setting: 284-acre small town campus. Endowment: $160.2 million. Research spending for the previous fiscal year: $23.2 million. Educational spending for the previous fiscal year: $11,577 per student. Total enrollment: 8,884. Faculty: 453 (373 full-time, 80 part-time). Student-undergrad faculty ratio is 20:1. 3,876 applied, 84% were admitted. 39% from top 10% of their high school class, 72% from top quarter, 94% from top half. Full-time: 6,128 students, 24% women, 76% men. Part-time: 792 students, 23% women, 77% men. Students come from 50 states and territories, 38 other countries, 17% from out-of-state. 0.3% American Indian or Alaska Native, non-Hispanic/Latino; 4% Hispanic/Latino; 3% Black or African American, non-Hispanic/Latino; 4% Asian, non-Hispanic/Latino; 3% international. 6% 25 or older, 30% live on campus, 6% transferred in. Retention: 81% of full-time freshmen returned the following year. Academic areas with the most degrees conferred: engineering; computer and information sciences; engineering technologies. Core. Calendar: semesters. ESL program, services for LD students, advanced placement, accelerated degree program, freshman honors college, honors program, independent study, distance learning, double major, summer session for credit, part-time degree program, adult/continuing education programs, co-op programs and internships, graduate courses open to undergrads. Off campus study at University of Missouri-Columbia. Study abroad program. ROTC: Army, Air Force.

Entrance Requirements: Options: electronic application, deferred admission, international baccalaureate accepted. Required: high school transcript, SAT or ACT. Recommended: ACT. Required for some: essay, interview. Entrance: very difficult. Application deadlines: 7/1, rolling for nonresidents. Notification: continuous until 10/1, continuous until 10/1 for nonresidents. SAT Reasoning Test deadline: 5/1. SAT Subject Test deadline: 5/1. Transfer credits accepted: Yes.

Costs Per Year: Application fee: $50. State resident tuition: $8460 full-time, $282 per credit hour part-time. Nonresident tuition: $26,322 full-time, $877.40 per credit hour part-time. Full-time tuition varies according to course load, degree level, program, and student level. Part-time tuition varies according to course load, degree level, program, and student level. College room and board: $10,094. Room and board charges vary according to board plan, housing facility, and location.

Collegiate Environment: Orientation program. Drama-theater group, choral group, marching band, student-run newspaper, radio station. Social organizations: 222 open to all; national fraternities, national sororities, local fraternities, local sororities; 20% of eligible men and 24% of eligible women are members. Most popular organizations: Academic Organizations, Honor Society, Special Interest Group, Greek Organizations, Recreational and Sports Club. Major annual events: Involvement Fair, St. Patrick's Celebration, Block Party. Student services: health clinic, personal-psychological counseling, women's center. Campus security: 24-hour emergency response devices and patrols, student patrols, late night transport-escort service, controlled dormitory access, crime prevention programs. Curtis Laws Wilson Library. Books: 305,834 (physical), 447,868 (digital/electronic); Serial titles: 14,178 (physical), 79,586 (digital/electronic); Databases: 180. Weekly public service hours: 112; students can reserve study rooms. Operations spending for the previous fiscal year: $2.9 million. 980 computers available on campus for general student use. Computer purchase/lease plans available. A campuswide network can be accessed from student residence rooms and from off campus. Students can access the following: online class registration. Staffed computer lab on campus (open 24 hours a day) provides training in use of computers, software, and the Internet.

Community Environment: Rolla, population 17,717, is one of the most scenic sections of the Ozarks, where excellent fishing and hunting are available. Situated in the center of Missouri, on Interstate 44. A number of churches of most denominations, a hospital, clinics, a library and civic organizations are all a part of the community services. Lake and river recreation available, caves to explore, tennis courts, baseball diamonds, golf courses, and bowling alleys provide recreation. Part time employment for students is available. Rolla originally was an Ozarks farm trade center. After the establishment of the university campus, several large and important federal and state government agencies located here. Today the community is unusual in its concentration of about 1,000 professional engineers, geologists, cartographers, mathematicians, and technicians who are employed by these offices.

■ **MISSOURI VALLEY COLLEGE**

500 E College

Marshall, MO 65340-3197

Tel: (660)831-4000

Fax: (660)831-4039

E-mail: admissions@moval.edu

Web Site: www.moval.edu

Description: Independent, comprehensive, coed, affiliated with Presbyterian Church. Awards associate, bachelor's, and master's degrees. Founded 1889. Setting: 140-acre small town campus with easy access to Kansas City. Total enrollment: 1,820. Faculty: 147 (87 full-time, 60 part-time). Student-undergrad faculty ratio is 14:1. 2,300 applied, 54% were admitted. 3% from top 10% of their high school class, 16% from top quarter, 31% from top half. Full-time: 1,296 students, 38% women, 62% men. Part-time: 502 students, 63% women, 37% men. 53% from out-of-state. 0.8% American Indian or Alaska Native, non-Hispanic/Latino; 10% Hispanic/Latino; 20% Black or African American, non-Hispanic/Latino; 0.8% Asian, non-Hispanic/Latino; 0.5% Native Hawaiian or other Pacific Islander, non-Hispanic/Latino; 16% international. 8% 25 or older, 75% live on campus, 9% transferred in. Retention: 45% of full-time freshmen returned the following year. Academic areas with the most degrees conferred: business/marketing; parks and recreation; psychology. Core. Calendar: semesters plus 2 summer sessions. Academic remediation for entering students, ESL program, services for LD students, advanced placement, self-designed majors, honors program, independent study, distance learning, double major, summer session for credit, part-time degree program, adult/continuing education programs, co-op programs and internships. Study abroad program. ROTC: Army (c).

Entrance Requirements: Options: electronic application, early admission, deferred admission. Required: high school transcript, SAT or ACT. Recommended: minimum 2 high school GPA, interview. Required for some: essay, 3 recommendations, interview. Entrance: minimally difficult. Application deadline: 9/1. Notification: continuous. Transfer credits accepted: Yes.

Costs Per Year: Application fee: $0. Comprehensive fee: $29,750 includes full-time tuition ($19,300), mandatory fees ($1300), and college room and board ($9150). College room only: $4850. Full-time tuition and fees vary according to program. Room and board charges vary according to board plan, gender, housing facility, location, and student level. Part-time tuition: $350 per credit hour. Part-time tuition varies according to program.

Collegiate Environment: Orientation program. Drama-theater group, choral group, student-run newspaper, radio station. Social organizations: national fraternities, national sororities. Student services: health clinic, personal-psychological counseling. Campus security: 24-hour emergency response devices, student patrols, late night transport-escort service, evening to 4 am patrol by trained security personnel. Murrell Memorial Library plus 1 other. Databases: 37. 300 computers available on campus for general student use. A campuswide network can be accessed from student residence rooms and from off campus. Students can access the following: online class registration. Staffed computer lab on campus provides training in use of computers, software, and the Internet.

Community Environment: Marshall, population 12,400, is located 80 miles east of Kansas City and bus transportation is available. Community recreational facilities include a bowling alley, skating rink, and a philharmonic orchestra. The Indian Foothills Park, at the eastern city limits, provides tennis courts, ball fields, a golf course, swimming, fishing, and picnic grounds.

■ **MISSOURI WESTERN STATE UNIVERSITY**

4525 Downs Dr.

Saint Joseph, MO 64507-2294

Tel: (816)271-4200; Free: 800-662-7041

Fax: (816)271-5833

E-mail: admission@missouriwestern.edu

Web Site: www.missouriwestern.edu

Description: State-supported, comprehensive, coed. Awards associate, bachelor's, and master's degrees. Founded 1915. Setting: 744-acre suburban campus with easy access to Kansas City. Total enrollment: 5,533. Faculty: 343 (207 full-time, 136 part-time). Student-undergrad faculty ratio is 17:1. 5,390 applied, 74% were admitted. 10% from top 10% of their high school class, 30% from top quarter, 63% from top half. Full-time: 3,498 students, 59% women, 41% men. Part-time: 1,794 students, 58% women, 42% men. Students come from 37 states and territories, 27 other countries, 14% from out-of-state. 0.5% American Indian or Alaska Native, non-Hispanic/Latino; 1% Hispanic/Latino; 11% Black or African American, non-Hispanic/Latino; 1% Asian, non-Hispanic/Latino; 0.3% Native Hawaiian or other Pacific Islander, non-Hispanic/Latino; 1% international. 19% 25 or older, 21% live on campus, 6% transferred in. Retention: 66% of full-time freshmen returned the following year. Academic areas with the most degrees conferred: health professions and related sciences; business/marketing; education. Core. Calendar: semesters. Academic remediation for entering students, ESL program, services for LD students, advanced placement, accelerated degree program, self-designed majors, freshman honors college, honors program, independent study, distance learning, double major, summer session for credit, part-time degree program, adult/continuing education programs, internships, graduate courses open to undergrads. Off campus study at Metropolitan Community College Penn Valley Campus, Kansas City Northland Campus. Study abroad program. ROTC: Army.

Entrance Requirements: Open admission. Options: electronic application, international baccalaureate accepted. Required: high school transcript, SAT or ACT. Entrance: noncompetitive. Application deadline: 5/1. Notification: continuous. Transfer credits accepted: Yes.

Costs Per Year: Application fee: $0. State resident tuition: $6,191 full-time, $206.37 per credit hour part-time. Nonresident tuition: $12,782 full-time, $426.05 per credit hour part-time. Mandatory fees: $718 full-time, $99.10 per credit hour part-time. Full-time tuition and fees vary according to course load, location, and program. Part-time tuition and fees vary according to course load, location, and program. College room and board: $8348. College room only: $4690. Room and board charges vary according to board plan and housing facility.

Collegiate Environment: Orientation program. Drama-theater group, choral group, marching band, student-run newspaper. Social organizations: 66 open to all; national fraternities, national sororities, local fraternities. Major annual events: Homecoming, Family Day, Springfest. Student services: health clinic, personal-psychological counseling, women's center. Campus security: 24-hour patrols, student patrols, late night transport-escort service, controlled dormitory access. Missouri Western State University Library. Books: 166,649 (physical), 215,083 (digital/electronic); Serial titles: 1,585 (physical), 57,298 (digital/electronic); Databases: 65.

Community Environment: Located in America's heartland, St. Joseph was one of only 10 cities nationwide to receive the prestigious 1997 All-America City Award. A thriving business community has seen St. Joseph grow from a booming frontier town to the market place for the four-state area of Missouri, Iowa, Kansas, and Nebraska. With a population of 72,600, St. Joseph boasts metropolitan advantages blended with small town flavor. The city offers 26-miles of parkway system, Olympic-size ice rink, YMCA and YWCA, St. Joseph Symphony, Performing Arts Association Arts Association, Robidoux Resident Theatre, and 13 museums, including the Albrecht-Kemper Museum of Art; Jesse James House; Pony Express Stables and the St. Joseph Museum.

■ MOBERLY AREA COMMUNITY COLLEGE
101 College Ave.
Moberly, MO 65270-1304
Tel: (660)263-4110; Free: 800-622-2070
Fax: (660)263-6252
E-mail: info@macc.edu
Web Site: www.macc.edu

Description: State and locally supported, 2-year, coed. Awards certificates, transfer associate, and terminal associate degrees. Founded 1927. Setting: 32-acre small town campus. Total enrollment: 4,009. Faculty: 233 (67 full-time, 166 part-time). Student-undergrad faculty ratio is 21:1. 25% from top quarter of their high school class, 60% from top half. Full-time: 2,023 students, 57% women, 43% men. Part-time: 1,986 students, 63% women, 37% men. Students come from 21 states and territories, 9 other countries, 1% from out-of-state. 23% 25 or older, 1% live on campus, 5% transferred in. Retention: 44% of full-time freshmen returned the following year. Core. Calendar: semesters. Academic remediation for entering students, services for LD students, advanced placement, honors program, distance learning, summer session for credit, part-time degree program, adult/continuing education programs, co-op programs and internships. Study abroad program.

Entrance Requirements: Open admission except for nursing, law enforcement, and medical laboratory technician programs. Options: electronic application, international baccalaureate accepted. Required: high school transcript. Recommended: ACT. Required for some: ACT. Entrance: noncompetitive. Application deadline: rolling. Notification: continuous until 9/1.

Collegiate Environment: Orientation program. Drama-theater group, choral group, student-run newspaper. Social organizations: 9 open to all; local fraternities, local sororities; 10% of eligible men and 10% of eligible women

are members. Most popular organizations: Phi Theta Kappa, Student Nurses Association, Affiliate of the Missouri Association for the Education of Young Children, Delta Epsilon Chi, Multicultural Club. Major annual events: Theatrical Production, Fall Picnic, Spring Picnic. Campus security: student patrols, controlled dormitory access, extensive surveillance. Kate Stamper Wilhite Library. 750 computers available on campus for general student use. A campuswide network can be accessed from student residence rooms and from off campus. Students can access the following: online class registration. Staffed computer lab on campus provides training in use of computers, software, and the Internet.

Community Environment: Moberly (population 13,900) is the county seat of Randolph County, in central Missouri. The town is served by one major railroad and the Omar Bradley Airport. Community facilities include churches of all denominations, a regional hospital, and Little Dixie Regional Library. A moderately large shopping district is available. Student employment is available in retail, restaurants, filling stations, and warehouses. Housing may be found in hotels, motels, and apartments. Outdoor activities are golf, boating, fishing, hunting, baseball, and tennis.

■ NATIONAL AMERICAN UNIVERSITY (INDEPENDENCE)
3620 Arowhead Ave.
Independence, MO 64057
Tel: (816)412-7700; Free: 866-628-1288
Web Site: www.national.edu
Description: Proprietary, 4-year, coed.

■ NATIONAL AMERICAN UNIVERSITY (KANSAS CITY)
7490 NW 87th St.
Kansas City, MO 64153
Tel: (816)412-5500; Free: 866-628-1288
Web Site: www.national.edu
Description: Proprietary, 4-year, coed. Part of National College. Awards associate and bachelor's degrees. Founded 1941. Setting: 1-acre urban campus. Total enrollment: 315. 77% 25 or older. Calendar: quarters. Independent study, distance learning, summer session for credit, part-time degree program, external degree program, co-op programs. Study abroad program.

Entrance Requirements: Open admission. Options: early admission, deferred admission, international baccalaureate accepted. Required: high school transcript, interview. Entrance: noncompetitive. Application deadline: rolling. Notification: continuous until 9/12.

Collegiate Environment: Campus security: 24-hour patrols. Learning Resource Center plus 1 other.

■ NATIONAL AMERICAN UNIVERSITY (LEES SUMMIT)
401 NW Murray Rd.
Lees Summit, MO 64081
Tel: (816)600-3900; Free: 866-628-1288
Web Site: www.national.edu
Description: Proprietary, 4-year, coed. Awards associate and bachelor's degrees.

■ NORTH CENTRAL MISSOURI COLLEGE
1301 Main St.
Trenton, MO 64683-1824
Tel: (660)359-3948
E-mail: jcunningham@mail.ncmissouri.edu
Web Site: www.ncmissouri.edu

Description: District-supported, 2-year, coed. Awards certificates, transfer associate, and terminal associate degrees. Founded 1925. Setting: 2-acre small town campus. Total enrollment: 1,505. Faculty: 94 (33 full-time, 61 part-time). Student-undergrad faculty ratio is 16:1. 708 applied, 88% were admitted. Full-time: 796 students, 72% women, 28% men. Part-time: 709 students, 70% women, 30% men. Students come from 10 states and territories, 1% from out-of-state. 28% 25 or older, 6% transferred in. Retention: 69% of full-time freshmen returned the following year. Calendar: semesters. Academic remediation for entering students, services for LD students, advanced placement, accelerated degree program, distance learning, summer session for credit, part-time degree program, adult/continuing education programs, co-op programs and internships.

Entrance Requirements: Open admission except for health occupations programs. Required: high school transcript. Recommended: SAT or ACT. Entrance: noncompetitive. Application deadline: rolling.

Costs Per Year: Application fee: $15. Area resident tuition: $2550 full-time,

$85 per credit hour part-time. State resident tuition: $4350 full-time, $145 per credit hour part-time. Nonresident tuition: $5250 full-time, $175 per credit hour part-time. Full-time tuition varies according to location and program. Part-time tuition varies according to location and program.

Collegiate Environment: Orientation program. Drama-theater group. Social organizations: local fraternities, local sororities. Most popular organizations: Student Nurses Association, Student Practical Nurses Association, Delta Epsilon Chi (business), Pre-med Club, Postsecondary Agriculture Students. Student services: personal-psychological counseling. Campus security: controlled dormitory access. North Central Missouri College Library. 159 computers available on campus for general student use. A campuswide network can be accessed. Students can access the following: online class registration. Staffed computer lab on campus provides training in use of computers, software, and the Internet.

Community Environment: A rural location in central north Missouri, Trenton (population 6,121) has 11 churches, libraries, a hospital, and numerous civic, fraternal, and veteran's organizations. Several lakes are nearby offering excellent fishing, swimming, and boating. City parks also provide facilities for recreation. Part-time employment is available.

■ NORTHWEST MISSOURI STATE UNIVERSITY

800 University Dr.
Maryville, MO 64468-6001
Tel: (660)562-1212; Free: 800-633-1175
Fax: (660)562-1121
E-mail: admissions@nwmissouri.edu
Web Site: www.nwmissouri.edu

Description: State-supported, comprehensive, coed. Part of Missouri Coordinating Board for Higher Education. Awards bachelor's and master's degrees and post-master's certificates. Founded 1905. Setting: 370-acre small town campus with easy access to Kansas City. Endowment: $29.8 million. Total enrollment: 6,857. Faculty: 324 (241 full-time, 83 part-time). Student-undergrad faculty ratio is 21:1. 6,048 applied, 79% were admitted. 14% from top 10% of their high school class, 38% from top quarter, 73% from top half. Full-time: 4,928 students, 57% women, 43% men. Part-time: 726 students, 59% women, 41% men. Students come from 34 states and territories, 30 other countries, 32% from out-of-state. 0.3% American Indian or Alaska Native, non-Hispanic/Latino; 4% Hispanic/Latino; 6% Black or African American, non-Hispanic/Latino; 0.8% Asian, non-Hispanic/Latino; 0.1% Native Hawaiian or other Pacific Islander, non-Hispanic/Latino; 3% international. 4% 25 or older, 33% live on campus, 6% transferred in. Retention: 78% of full-time freshmen returned the following year. Academic areas with the most degrees conferred: business/marketing; education; psychology; agriculture. Core. Calendar: trimesters. Academic remediation for entering students, services for LD students, advanced placement, honors program, independent study, distance learning, double major, summer session for credit, part-time degree program, internships, graduate courses open to undergrads. Off campus study at Allen County Community College, Black Hawk Community College, Butler County Community College, Central Community College, Colby Community College, Colorado Online Community College, Cottey College, Crowder College, Des Moines Area Community College, East Central College, Eastern Iowa Community College, Ellsworth Community College, North Central Missouri College, Fort Scott Community College, Hawkeye Community College, Highland Community College, Ozarks Technical Community College, Johnson County Community College. Study abroad program.

Entrance Requirements: Options: electronic application, deferred admission, international baccalaureate accepted. Required: high school transcript, minimum 2 high school GPA, minimum SAT score of 980 or ACT Composite of 21, SAT or ACT. Required for some: interview. Entrance: moderately difficult. Application deadline: rolling. Notification: continuous. Preference given to Missouri residents. SAT Reasoning Test deadline: 8/1. SAT Subject Test deadline: 8/1. Transfer credits accepted: Yes.

Costs Per Year: Application fee: $25. State resident tuition: $5,702 full-time, $190.08 per credit hour part-time. Nonresident tuition: $12,355 full-time, $411.83 per credit hour part-time. Mandatory fees: $4,102 full-time, $136.75 per credit hour part-time. Full-time tuition and fees vary according to course load, location, program, and reciprocity agreements. Part-time tuition and fees vary according to course load and location. College room and board: $10,016. College room only: $6356. Room and board charges vary according to board plan and housing facility.

Collegiate Environment: Orientation program. Drama-theater group, choral group, marching band, student-run newspaper, radio station. Social organizations: 192 open to all; national fraternities, national sororities; 12% of eligible men and 16% of eligible women are members. Most popular organizations: Indian Student Association, ACM, National Society of Leadership and Success, Student Senate, Resident Hall Association (RHA). Major annual events: Homecoming, Family Day, Northwest Week. Student services: health clinic, personal-psychological counseling, women's center. Campus security: 24-hour emergency response devices and patrols, student patrols, late night transport-escort service, controlled dormitory access. 2,963 college housing spaces available; 1,884 were occupied in 2018-19. Freshmen guaranteed college housing. On-campus residence required in freshman year. Option: coed housing available. Owens Library. Books: 165,794 (physical), 213,591 (digital/electronic). Weekly public service hours: 95; students can reserve study rooms. 260 computers available on campus for general student use. Computer purchase/lease plans available. A campuswide network can be accessed from student residence rooms and from off campus. Students can access the following: online class registration, online courses with library and databases. Staffed computer lab on campus provides training in use of computers, software, and the Internet.

Community Environment: Maryville (population 10,500) is a rural area in northwest Missouri. Dormitories, fraternity houses, and private homes provide housing. Community facilities include a library, 13 churches, a hospital, and several civic, national, and international branches of clubs and organizations are represented. Train and bus transportation is available. 90 miles from Kansas City, 45 from St. Joseph, 110 from Omaha and 125 from Des Moines.

■ OZARK CHRISTIAN COLLEGE

1111 N Main St.
Joplin, MO 64801-4804
Tel: (417)624-2518; Free: 800-299-4622
Fax: (417)624-0090
E-mail: occadmin@occ.edu
Web Site: www.occ.edu

Description: Independent Christian, 4-year, coed. Awards associate and bachelor's degrees. Founded 1942. Setting: 110-acre small town campus. Faculty: 60 (30 full-time, 30 part-time). Student-undergrad faculty ratio is 19:1. 63% live on campus. Calendar: semesters. Academic remediation for entering students, ESL program, services for LD students, distance learning, double major, summer session for credit, part-time degree program, adult/continuing education programs, internships.

Entrance Requirements: Option: electronic application. Required: essay, high school transcript, 2 recommendations, SAT or ACT. Required for some: interview. Entrance: noncompetitive. Application deadline: 8/5.

Collegiate Environment: Orientation program. Drama-theater group, choral group, student-run radio station. Social organizations: 3 open to all. Most popular organizations: Family Outreach Group, God's Spokesman, Imagine. Major annual events: Parents' Day, Living Christmas Tree, preaching/teaching convention. Student services: health clinic, personal-psychological counseling. Campus security: 24-hour emergency response devices, controlled dormitory access, 12-hour patrols by trained security personnel. Seth Wilson Library. 28 computers available on campus for general student use. Staffed computer lab on campus.

■ OZARKS TECHNICAL COMMUNITY COLLEGE

1001 E Chestnut Expy.
Springfield, MO 65802
Tel: (417)447-7500
Fax: (417)895-7161
Web Site: www.otc.edu

Description: District-supported, 2-year, coed. Part of Missouri Coordinating Board for Higher Education. Awards certificates, diplomas, transfer associate, and terminal associate degrees. Founded 1990. Setting: urban campus. Endowment: $2.8 million. Total enrollment: 13,260. Faculty: 994 (204 full-time, 790 part-time). Student-undergrad faculty ratio is 21:1. Students come from 31 states and territories, 2% from out-of-state. 0.5% American Indian or Alaska Native, non-Hispanic/Latino; 5% Hispanic/Latino; 3% Black or African American, non-Hispanic/Latino; 1% Asian, non-Hispanic/Latino; 0.2% Native Hawaiian or other Pacific Islander, non-Hispanic/Latino. Core. Calendar: semesters. Academic remediation for entering students, ESL program, services for LD students, honors program, distance learning, double major, summer session for credit, part-time degree program, adult/continuing education programs, co-op programs and internships. Off campus study at Missouri State University.

Entrance Requirements: Open admission except for allied health

programs. Option: electronic application. Required: high school transcript. Entrance: noncompetitive. Application deadline: rolling. Notification: continuous. Transfer credits accepted: Yes.

Costs Per Year: Application fee: $0. Area resident tuition: $2592 full-time, $108 per credit hour part-time. State resident tuition: $3840 full-time, $160.50 per credit hour part-time. Nonresident tuition: $4800 full-time, $200 per credit hour part-time. Mandatory fees: $700 full-time, $25 per credit hour part-time, $100 per term part-time. Full-time tuition and fees vary according to program. Part-time tuition and fees vary according to program.

Collegiate Environment: Orientation program. Choral group, student-run newspaper. Most popular organization: Phi Theta Kappa. Major annual event: Annual Student Picnic. Student services: personal-psychological counseling. Campus security: 24-hour emergency response devices. Main library plus 1 other. Operations spending for the previous fiscal year: $669,366. 150 computers available on campus for general student use. A campuswide network can be accessed. Students can access the following: online class registration. Staffed computer lab on campus.

■ PARK UNIVERSITY

8700 NW River Park Dr.
Parkville, MO 64152-3795
Tel: (816)741-2000; Free: 800-745-7275
Fax: (816)741-4462
E-mail: admissions@mail.park.edu
Web Site: www.park.edu

Description: Independent, comprehensive, coed. Awards associate, bachelor's, and master's degrees. Founded 1875. Setting: 800-acre suburban campus with easy access to Kansas City. Endowment: $52.3 million. Total enrollment: 9,800. Faculty: 174 (137 full-time, 37 part-time). Student-undergrad faculty ratio is 12:1. 576 applied. 16% from top 10% of their high school class, 33% from top quarter, 47% from top half. Full-time: 1,089 students, 56% women, 44% men. Part-time: 7,857 students, 46% women, 54% men. Students come from 50 states and territories, 101 other countries, 20% from out-of-state. 1% American Indian or Alaska Native, non-Hispanic/Latino; 3% Hispanic/Latino; 18% Black or African American, non-Hispanic/Latino; 4% Asian, non-Hispanic/Latino; 0.1% Native Hawaiian or other Pacific Islander, non-Hispanic/Latino; 5% international. 30% 25 or older, 20% live on campus, 3% transferred in. Retention: 58% of full-time freshmen returned the following year. Academic areas with the most degrees conferred: business/marketing; psychology; homeland security, law enforcement, firefighting, and protective services. Core. Calendar: semesters. Academic remediation for entering students, ESL program, services for LD students, advanced placement, self-designed majors, honors program, independent study, distance learning, double major, summer session for credit, part-time degree program, external degree program, adult/continuing education programs, internships, graduate courses open to undergrads. Off campus study at members of the Kansas City Professional Development Council. ROTC: Army.

Entrance Requirements: Options: electronic application, early admission, deferred admission, international baccalaureate accepted. Required: high school transcript, minimum 2 high school GPA, SAT or ACT. Required for some: 2 recommendations, SAT or ACT. Entrance: minimally difficult. Application deadline: 8/1. Notification: continuous. SAT Reasoning Test deadline: 8/1. SAT Subject Test deadline: 8/1. Transfer credits accepted: Yes.

Collegiate Environment: Orientation program. Drama-theater group, student-run newspaper, radio station. Social organizations: 15 open to all. Most popular organizations: World Student Union, Park Student Government Association, National Society of Leadership and Success, Student Nurses Association, Students in Interior Design. Major annual events: Harvest Fest, International Talk like a Pirate Day, Park Idol Competition. Student services: health clinic, personal-psychological counseling. Campus security: 24-hour patrols, student patrols, late night transport-escort service. McAfee Memorial Library. Operations spending for the previous fiscal year: $780,466. 1,240 computers available on campus for general student use. A campuswide network can be accessed from student residence rooms. Students can access the following: online class registration, virtual applications; electronic portfolios. Staffed computer lab on campus provides training in use of computers, software, and the Internet.

Community Environment: See University of Missouri - Kansas City.

■ PINNACLE CAREER INSTITUTE (KANSAS CITY)

11500 NW Ambassador Dr.
Ste. 221

Kansas City, MO 64153
Tel: (816)270-5300; Free: 877-241-3097
Web Site: www.pcitraining.edu

Description: Proprietary, 2-year, coed. Part of Pinnacle Career Institute. Awards certificates, diplomas, and terminal associate degrees. Setting: suburban campus with easy access to Kansas City. Total enrollment: 147. 0.7% American Indian or Alaska Native, non-Hispanic/Latino; 9% Hispanic/Latino; 14% Black or African American, non-Hispanic/Latino. Calendar: monthly modules.

Entrance Requirements: Open admission. Option: electronic application. Required: high school transcript, interview.

Collegiate Environment: Orientation program. 36 computers available on campus for general student use. A campuswide network can be accessed from off-campus. Staffed computer lab on campus provides training in use of computers, software, and the Internet.

■ PINNACLE CAREER INSTITUTE (KANSAS CITY)

10301 Hickman Mills Dr.
Kansas City, MO 64137
Tel: (816)331-5700; Free: 877-241-3097
Web Site: www.pcitraining.edu

Description: Proprietary, 2-year, coed. Awards certificates and transfer associate degrees. Founded 1953. Total enrollment: 437. 167 applied. 44% 25 or older.

Entrance Requirements: Application deadline: 6/1.

■ PURDUE UNIVERSITY GLOBAL

1807 Park 270 Dr.
Saint Louis, MO 63146
Description: Independent, comprehensive, coed.

■ RANKEN TECHNICAL COLLEGE

4431 Finney Ave.
Saint Louis, MO 63113
Tel: (314)371-0233; Free: 866-4-RANKEN
Fax: (314)371-0241
Web Site: www.ranken.edu

Description: Independent, primarily 2-year, coed. Awards certificates, transfer associate, terminal associate, and bachelor's degrees. Founded 1907. Setting: 10-acre urban campus. Total enrollment: 1,743. 34% 25 or older. Calendar: semesters. Academic remediation for entering students, services for LD students, advanced placement, independent study, distance learning, summer session for credit, part-time degree program, adult/continuing education programs, co-op programs and internships.

Entrance Requirements: Option: electronic application. Required: essay, high school transcript, interview. Entrance: moderately difficult. Application deadline: rolling.

Collegiate Environment: Orientation program. Student-run newspaper. Student services: personal-psychological counseling, women's center. Campus security: 24-hour emergency response devices and patrols. Ashley Gray, Jr. Learning Center.

■ RESEARCH COLLEGE OF NURSING

2525 E Meyer Blvd.
Kansas City, MO 64132
Tel: (816)995-2800
Fax: (816)276-3526
E-mail: kyle.johnson@rockhurst.edu
Web Site: www.researchcollege.edu

Description: Independent, comprehensive, coed. Part of Rockhurst University. Awards bachelor's and master's degrees and post-master's certificates (bachelor's degree offered jointly with Rockhurst College). Founded 1980. Setting: 66-acre urban campus with easy access to Kansas City. Total enrollment: 415. Faculty: 29 (26 full-time, 3 part-time). Student-undergrad faculty ratio is 7:1. 339 applied, 73% were admitted. 24% from top 10% of their high school class, 67% from top quarter, 95% from top half. Full-time: 264 students, 92% women, 8% men. Students come from 7 states and territories, 20% from out-of-state. 0.4% American Indian or Alaska Native, non-Hispanic/Latino; 4% Hispanic/Latino; 3% Black or African American, non-Hispanic/Latino; 2% Asian, non-Hispanic/Latino. 75% 25 or older, 2% transferred in. Academic area with the most degrees conferred: health professions and related sciences. Core. Calendar: semesters. Services for LD students, advanced placement, accelerated degree program, honors program, independent study, double major, summer session for credit, graduate courses open to undergrads. Study abroad program. ROTC: Army (c).

Entrance Requirements: Options: electronic application, deferred admission, international baccalaureate accepted. Required: high school transcript, 1 recommendation, SAT or ACT. Recommended: minimum 2.8 high school GPA, interview. Entrance: moderately difficult. Application deadline: 6/30. Notification: 8/15, 6/20 for nonresidents.

Costs Per Year: Application fee: $0. One-time mandatory fee: $150. Comprehensive fee: $47,840 includes full-time tuition ($36,800), mandatory fees ($950), and college room and board ($10,090). College room only: $6240. Room and board charges vary according to board plan, housing facility, and location. Part-time tuition: $1228 per credit hour. Part-time mandatory fees: $35 per credit hour. Part-time tuition and fees vary according to class time.

Collegiate Environment: Orientation program. Drama-theater group, choral group, student-run newspaper, radio station. Social organizations: 40 open to all; national fraternities, national sororities, local sororities; 75% of eligible men and 75% of eligible women are members. Major annual events: Mass of the Holy Spirit, Polar Walk, homecoming. Student services: health clinic, personal-psychological counseling. Campus security: 24-hour emergency response devices and patrols, late night transport-escort service, controlled dormitory access. Greenlease Library. 125 computers available on campus for general student use. A campuswide network can be accessed from student residence rooms and from off campus. Students can access the following: online class registration. Staffed computer lab on campus.

■ **ROCKHURST UNIVERSITY**
1100 Rockhurst Rd.
Kansas City, MO 64110-2561
Tel: (816)501-4000; Free: 800-842-6776
Fax: (816)501-4241
E-mail: admission@rockhurst.edu
Web Site: www.rockhurst.edu

Description: Independent Roman Catholic (Jesuit), comprehensive, coed. Awards bachelor's, master's, and doctoral degrees. Founded 1910. Setting: 35-acre urban campus. Endowment: $35.7 million. Research spending for the previous fiscal year: $12,226. Total enrollment: 3,043. Faculty: 239 (128 full-time, 111 part-time). Student-undergrad faculty ratio is 13:1. 3,115 applied, 72% were admitted. 25% from top 10% of their high school class, 56% from top quarter, 84% from top half. Full-time: 1,445 students, 56% women, 44% men. Part-time: 763 students, 70% women, 30% men. Students come from 39 states and territories, 17 other countries, 33% from out-of-state. 0.7% American Indian or Alaska Native, non-Hispanic/Latino; 9% Hispanic/Latino; 5% Black or African American, non-Hispanic/Latino; 3% Asian, non-Hispanic/Latino; 1% international. 7% 25 or older, 49% live on campus, 4% transferred in. Retention: 86% of full-time freshmen returned the following year. Academic areas with the most degrees conferred: health professions and related sciences; business/marketing; psychology; biological/life sciences. Core. Calendar: semesters. Academic remediation for entering students, services for LD students, advanced placement, accelerated degree program, freshman honors college, honors program, independent study, distance learning, double major, summer session for credit, part-time degree program, co-op programs and internships, graduate courses open to undergrads. Off campus study at Kansas City Area Student Exchange. Study abroad program. ROTC: Army (c).

Entrance Requirements: Options: electronic application, deferred admission, international baccalaureate accepted. Required: high school transcript, minimum 2 high school GPA, 1 recommendation, SAT or ACT. Required for some: essay, interview. Entrance: moderately difficult. Application deadline: 6/30. Notification: continuous. SAT Reasoning Test deadline: 8/1. SAT Subject Test deadline: 8/1. Transfer credits accepted: Yes.

Costs Per Year: Application fee: $0. Comprehensive fee: $47,160 includes full-time tuition ($36,800), mandatory fees ($790), and college room and board ($9570). College room only: $6240. Full-time tuition and fees vary according to class time and course load. Room and board charges vary according to board plan and housing facility. Part-time tuition: $614 per credit hour. Part-time mandatory fees: $25 per credit hour. Part-time tuition and fees vary according to class time and course load.

Collegiate Environment: Orientation program. Drama-theater group, choral group, student-run newspaper. Social organizations: 60 open to all; national fraternities, national sororities; 37% of eligible men and 47% of eligible women are members. Most popular organizations: Student Activities Board, Student Senate, Voices for Justice, Panhellenic Sororities, IFC Fraternities.

Major annual events: Rockstock Spring Concert, Homecoming Dance, Turkey Dinner. Student services: health clinic, personal-psychological counseling. Campus security: 24-hour emergency response devices and patrols, late night transport-escort service, controlled dormitory access, closed-circuit TV monitors. Greenlease Library. Books: 112,979 (physical), 180,624 (digital/electronic); Serial titles: 798 (physical), 103,252 (digital/electronic); Databases: 110. Weekly public service hours: 85. Operations spending for the previous fiscal year: $292,825. 235 computers available on campus for general student use. A campuswide network can be accessed from student residence rooms. Students can access the following: online class registration, campus portal.

Community Environment: See University of Missouri - Kansas City.

■ **ST. CHARLES COMMUNITY COLLEGE**
4601 Mid Rivers Mall Dr.
Cottleville, MO 63376
Tel: (636)922-8000
Fax: (636)922-8236
E-mail: cakins@stchas.edu
Web Site: www.stchas.edu

Description: State-supported, 2-year, coed. Part of Missouri Coordinating Board for Higher Education. Awards certificates, transfer associate, and terminal associate degrees. Founded 1986. Setting: 228-acre suburban campus with easy access to St. Louis. Endowment: $83,673. Educational spending for the previous fiscal year: $5550 per student. Total enrollment: 6,269. Faculty: 374 (109 full-time, 265 part-time). Student-undergrad faculty ratio is 20:1. 1,477 applied. Full-time: 3,167 students, 54% women, 46% men. Part-time: 3,102 students, 60% women, 40% men. Students come from 14 states and territories, 36 other countries. 0.3% American Indian or Alaska Native, non-Hispanic/Latino; 5% Hispanic/Latino; 7% Black or African American, non-Hispanic/Latino; 2% Asian, non-Hispanic/Latino; 0.1% Native Hawaiian or other Pacific Islander, non-Hispanic/Latino; 0.9% international. 23% 25 or older, 6% transferred in. Core. Calendar: semesters. Academic remediation for entering students, ESL program, services for LD students, advanced placement, honors program, independent study, distance learning, double major, summer session for credit, part-time degree program, adult/continuing education programs, co-op programs and internships. Study abroad program.

Entrance Requirements: Open admission except for nursing and allied health programs. Options: electronic application, early admission, deferred admission. Required for some: high school transcript, minimum 2.5 high school GPA. Entrance: noncompetitive. Application deadline: rolling. Notification: continuous. Transfer credits accepted: Yes.

Costs Per Year: Application fee: $10. Area resident tuition: $2472 full-time, $103 per credit hour part-time. State resident tuition: $3696 full-time, $154 per credit hour part-time. Nonresident tuition: $5184 full-time, $216 per credit hour part-time. Mandatory fees: $192 full-time, $8 per credit hour part-time. Full-time tuition and fees vary according to course load, location, and program. Part-time tuition and fees vary according to course load, location, and program.

Collegiate Environment: Orientation program. Drama-theater group, choral group, student-run newspaper. Social organizations: 50 open to all. Most popular organizations: Phi Theta Kappa, GAMES Club, Student Government Association, Cougar Activities Crew, International Club. Major annual events: Spring Fling, Fall Fun Blitz, Finals De-Stress Fest. Student services: personal-psychological counseling. Campus security: 24-hour emergency response devices and patrols, late night transport-escort service, campus police officers on duty during normal operating hours. Paul and Helen Schnare Library. Books: 56,851 (physical), 30,196 (digital/electronic); Serial titles: 349 (physical), 348,033 (digital/electronic); Databases: 43. Weekly public service hours: 72. Operations spending for the previous fiscal year: $974,180. 1,210 computers available on campus for general student use. Computer purchase/lease plans available. A campuswide network can be accessed from off-campus. Students can access the following: online class registration, online courses. Staffed computer lab on campus provides training in use of computers, software, and the Internet.

■ **SAINT LOUIS CHRISTIAN COLLEGE**
1360 Grandview Dr.
Florissant, MO 63033-6499
Tel: (314)837-6777; Free: 800-887-SLCC
Fax: (314)837-8291
E-mail: bfarrar@stlchristian.edu
Web Site: www.stlchristian.edu

Description: Independent Christian, 4-year, coed. Awards associate and bachelor's degrees. Founded 1956. Setting: 30-acre suburban campus with easy access to St. Louis. Endowment: $1.1 million. Educational spending for the previous fiscal year: $6262 per student. Total enrollment: 113. Faculty: 26 (6 full-time, 20 part-time). Student-undergrad faculty ratio is 9:1. 51 applied, 27% were admitted. 40% from top quarter of their high school class, 40% from top half. Full-time: 94 students, 43% women, 57% men. Part-time: 19 students, 37% women, 63% men. Students come from 9 states and territories, 2 other countries, 34% from out-of-state. 37% Black or African American, non-Hispanic/Latino; 2% international. 68% live on campus, 12% transferred in. Retention: 55% of full-time freshmen returned the following year. Academic area with the most degrees conferred: theology and religious vocations. Core. Calendar: semesters. Academic remediation for entering students, services for LD students, advanced placement, accelerated degree program, independent study, double major, summer session for credit, part-time degree program, adult/continuing education programs, internships. Study abroad program.

Entrance Requirements: Option: electronic application. Required: essay, high school transcript, 2 recommendations, minimum ACT score of 18 or SAT of 940, SAT or ACT. Recommended: minimum 2 high school GPA. Required for some: interview. Entrance: minimally difficult. Application deadline: 8/7. Notification: continuous. SAT Reasoning Test deadline: 8/7. SAT Subject Test deadline: 8/7. Transfer credits accepted: Yes.

Costs Per Year: Application fee: $30. Comprehensive fee $16,610 includes full-time tuition ($11,100), mandatory fees ($460), and college room and board ($5050). Room and board charges vary according to housing facility. Part-time tuition: $370 per credit hour.

Collegiate Environment: Orientation program. Drama-theater group, choral group. Social organizations: 3 open to all. Most popular organizations: World Christians Unlimited, Drama Club, pep band. Major annual events: Jam Fest, Jesus Encounter, Junior High Winterfest. Student services: personal-psychological counseling. Campus security: 24-hour emergency response devices and patrols, controlled dormitory access, night security. St. Louis Christian College Library. Books: 30,076 (physical); Serial titles: 332 (physical). Operations spending for the previous fiscal year: $113,018. 10 computers available on campus for general student use. A campuswide network can be accessed from student residence rooms and from off campus. Students can access the following: online class registration. Staffed computer lab on campus provides training in use of computers, software, and the Internet.

■ **ST. LOUIS COLLEGE OF HEALTH CAREERS (FENTON)**
1297 N Hwy. Dr.
Fenton, MO 63026
Tel: (636)529-0000; Free: 866-529-2070
Fax: (636)529-0430
Web Site: www.slchc.com
Description: Proprietary, primarily 2-year, coed. Awards transfer associate, terminal associate, and bachelor's degrees. Calendar: semesters.

■ **ST. LOUIS COLLEGE OF HEALTH CAREERS (SAINT LOUIS)**
909 S Taylor Ave.
Saint Louis, MO 63110
Tel: (314)652-0300; Free: 866-529-2070
Fax: (314)652-4825
Web Site: www.slchc.com
Description: Proprietary, 2-year, coed. Awards certificates and terminal associate degrees. Founded 1981. Total enrollment: 340. Student-undergrad faculty ratio is 12:1. 30% from out-of-state. 45% 25 or older.
Entrance Requirements: Required: high school transcript, interview.

■ **ST. LOUIS COLLEGE OF PHARMACY**
4588 Parkview Pl.
Saint Louis, MO 63110-1088
Tel: (314)367-8700; Free: 800-278-5267
Fax: (314)367-2784
E-mail: connie.horrall@stlcop.edu
Web Site: www.stlcop.edu
Description: Independent, comprehensive, coed. Awards bachelor's and doctoral degrees. Founded 1864. Setting: 9-acre urban campus with easy access to St. Louis. Endowment: $137.2 million. Research spending for the previous fiscal year: $420,516. Educational spending for the previous fiscal year: $18,415 per student. Total enrollment: 1,309. Faculty: 171 (111 full-time, 60 part-time). Student-undergrad faculty ratio is 8:1. 361 applied, 72% were admitted. 37% from top 10% of their high school class, 80% from top

quarter, 98% from top half. 7 valedictorians. Full-time: 435 students, 59% women, 41% men. Part-time: 13 students, 62% women, 38% men. Students come from 25 states and territories, 9 other countries, 46% from out-of-state. 0.4% American Indian or Alaska Native, non-Hispanic/Latino; 2% Hispanic/Latino; 10% Black or African American, non-Hispanic/Latino; 19% Asian, non-Hispanic/Latino; 0.2% Native Hawaiian or other Pacific Islander, non-Hispanic/Latino; 4% international. 6% 25 or older, 58% live on campus, 19% transferred in. Retention: 85% of full-time freshmen returned the following year. Academic areas with the most degrees conferred: biological/life sciences; liberal arts/general studies. Core. Calendar: semesters. Academic remediation for entering students, services for LD students, advanced placement, independent study, summer session for credit, internships. Study abroad program. ROTC: Army (c), Naval (c), Air Force (c).

Entrance Requirements: Options: electronic application, early admission, early decision, early action, deferred admission, international baccalaureate accepted. Required: essay, high school transcript, minimum 3 high school GPA, 3 recommendations, letter of reference from science teacher, SAT or ACT. Required for some: interview. Entrance: moderately difficult. Application deadlines: 3/1, 12/1 for early decision, 12/1 for early action. Notification: 4/1, 1/15 for early decision, 1/15 for early action. SAT Reasoning Test deadline: 3/1. SAT Subject Test deadline: 3/1. Transfer credits accepted: Yes. Early decision applicants: 70. Early decision applicants admitted: 68. Early action applicants: 139. Early action applicants admitted: 122.

Costs Per Year: Application fee: $55. Comprehensive fee: $41,900 includes full-time tuition ($28,451), mandatory fees ($1530), and college room and board ($11,919). College room only: $6489. Full-time tuition and fees vary according to degree level, program, and student level. Room and board charges vary according to board plan and housing facility. Part-time tuition: $948 per credit hour. Part-time mandatory fees: $1530 per year.

Collegiate Environment: Orientation program. Drama-theater group, choral group, student-run newspaper. Social organizations: 55 open to all; national fraternities, national sororities, professional fraternities; 40% of eligible men and 60% of eligible women are members. Most popular organizations: Student Government Association, Student Pharmacist Association, International Student Association, Women's Health Interest Group, Student Alumni Association. Major annual events: Homecoming, Organization Fair (Welcome Week), Holiday dance. Student services: personal-psychological counseling. Campus security: 24-hour emergency response devices and patrols, late night transport-escort service, controlled dormitory access. O. J. Cloughly Alumni Library. Books: 14,941 (physical), 180,979 (digital/electronic); Serial titles: 445 (physical), 43,334 (digital/electronic); Databases: 62. Weekly public service hours: 101; study areas open 24 hours, 5-7 days a week; students can reserve study rooms. Operations spending for the previous fiscal year: $565,379. 1,390 computers available on campus for general student use. Computer purchase/lease plans available. A computer is required for all students. A campuswide network can be accessed from student residence rooms and from off campus. Students can access the following: online class registration.

■ **ST. LOUIS COMMUNITY COLLEGE**
300 S Broadway
Saint Louis, MO 63102
Tel: (314)539-5000
Web Site: www.stlcc.edu
Description: Public, 2-year, coed. Part of St. Louis Community College. Awards certificates, transfer associate, and terminal associate degrees. Founded 1962. Setting: suburban campus with easy access to St. Louis. Total enrollment: 18,157. Faculty: 1,209 (342 full-time, 867 part-time). Student-undergrad faculty ratio is 17:1. Full-time: 6,580 students, 56% women, 44% men. Part-time: 11,577 students, 64% women, 36% men. Students come from 31 states and territories, 110 other countries, 2% from out-of-state. 0.2% American Indian or Alaska Native, non-Hispanic/Latino; 3% Hispanic/Latino; 33% Black or African American, non-Hispanic/Latino; 3% Asian, non-Hispanic/Latino; 0.1% Native Hawaiian or other Pacific Islander, non-Hispanic/Latino; 2% international. 38% 25 or older, 7% transferred in. Retention: 58% of full-time freshmen returned the following year. Calendar: semesters. Academic remediation for entering students, ESL program, services for LD students, advanced placement, accelerated degree program, honors program, independent study, distance learning, summer session for credit, part-time degree program, adult/continuing education programs, internships. Study abroad program.

Entrance Requirements: Open admission Open admissions except for select allied health programs (e.g., nursing, paramedic, occupational therapy, physical therapy). Option: electronic application. Required for some:

high school transcript, interview. Entrance: noncompetitive. Application deadline: rolling. Notification: continuous. Transfer credits accepted: Yes.

Costs Per Year: Application fee: $0. Area resident tuition: $2790 full-time, $93 per credit hour part-time. State resident tuition: $4200 full-time, $140 per credit hour part-time. Nonresident tuition: $5940 full-time, $198 per credit hour part-time. Mandatory fees: $495 full-time, $16.50 per credit hour part-time. Full-time tuition and fees vary according to course load. Part-time tuition and fees vary according to course load.

Collegiate Environment: Orientation program. Drama-theater group, student-run newspaper. Student services: personal-psychological counseling. Campus security: 24-hour emergency response devices, late night transport-escort service. College housing not available.

■ **SAINT LOUIS UNIVERSITY**
One N Grand Blvd.
Saint Louis, MO 63103
Tel: (314)977-2222; Free: 800-758-3678
Fax: (314)977-7136
E-mail: admission@slu.edu
Web Site: www.slu.edu
Description: Independent Roman Catholic (Jesuit), university, coed. Awards bachelor's, master's, and doctoral degrees and post-master's certificates. Founded 1818. Setting: 282-acre urban campus. Total enrollment: 11,823. Faculty: 1,166 (702 full-time, 464 part-time). Student-undergrad faculty ratio is 9:1. 15,120 applied, 58% were admitted. 48% from top 10% of their high school class, 77% from top quarter, 94% from top half. Full-time: 6,560 students, 60% women, 40% men. Part-time: 607 students, 57% women, 43% men. 59% from out-of-state. 0.1% American Indian or Alaska Native, non-Hispanic/Latino; 6% Hispanic/Latino; 6% Black or African American, non-Hispanic/Latino; 11% Asian, non-Hispanic/Latino; 5% international. 10% 25 or older, 53% live on campus, 5% transferred in. Retention: 90% of full-time freshmen returned the following year. Academic areas with the most degrees conferred: health professions and related sciences; business/marketing; engineering; parks and recreation. Core. Calendar: semesters. Academic remediation for entering students, ESL program, services for LD students, advanced placement, accelerated degree program, self-designed majors, honors program, independent study, distance learning, double major, summer session for credit, part-time degree program, adult/continuing education programs, co-op programs and internships, graduate courses open to undergrads. Study abroad program. ROTC: Army (c), Air Force.
Entrance Requirements: Options: electronic application, early admission, deferred admission, international baccalaureate accepted. Required: essay, high school transcript, SAT or ACT. Recommended: 2 recommendations, interview, Health exam. Entrance: very difficult. Application deadlines: rolling, rolling for nonresidents. Notification: continuous, continuous for nonresidents. SAT Reasoning Test deadline: 12/1. Transfer credits accepted: Yes. Applicants placed on waiting list: 251. Wait-listed applicants offered admission: 236.
Costs Per Year: Application fee: $0. One-time mandatory fee: $200. Comprehensive fee: $58,024 includes full-time tuition ($44,700), mandatory fees ($724), and college room and board ($12,600). Part-time tuition: $1560 per credit.
Collegiate Environment: Orientation program. Drama-theater group, choral group, student-run newspaper, radio station. Social organizations: national fraternities, national sororities. Student services: health clinic, personal-psychological counseling. Campus security: 24-hour emergency response devices and patrols, late night transport-escort service, controlled dormitory access. Freshmen guaranteed college housing. On-campus residence required through sophomore year. Option: coed housing available. Pius XII Memorial Library plus 2 others. Study areas open 24 hours, 5-7 days a week; students can reserve study rooms.
Community Environment: See Washington University.

■ **SAINT LUKE'S COLLEGE OF HEALTH SCIENCES**
624 Westport Rd.
Kansas City, MO 64111
Tel: (816)936-8700
Web Site: www.saintlukescollege.edu
Description: Independent Episcopal, upper-level, coed. Administratively affiliated with Saint Luke's Hospital. Awards bachelor's degrees. Founded 1903. Setting: 3-acre urban campus. Endowment: $2.8 million. Total enrollment: 113. Faculty: 15 (all full-time). Student-undergrad faculty ratio is 8:1. Full-time: 101 students, 91% women, 9% men. Part-time: 12 students, 83% women, 17% men. Students come from 5 states and territories. 51% 25 or

older, 46% transferred in. Core. Calendar: semesters. Summer session for credit, part-time degree program, co-op programs.
Entrance Requirements: Transfer credits accepted: Yes.
Collegiate Environment: Orientation program. Social organizations: 1 open to all. Most popular organization: Saint Luke's Student Nurse Association. Major annual events: College Picnic, College Spring Banquet. Student services: health clinic, personal-psychological counseling. Campus security: 24-hour emergency response devices and patrols. Health Sciences Library. 20 computers available on campus for general student use. Students can access the following: Evolve. Staffed computer lab on campus provides training in use of computers.

■ **SOUTHEAST MISSOURI HOSPITAL COLLEGE OF NURSING AND HEALTH SCIENCES**
2001 William St.
Cape Girardeau, MO 63701
Tel: (573)334-6825
Fax: (573)339-7805
Web Site: www.sehcollege.edu
Description: Independent, 2-year, coed. Awards certificates, transfer associate, and terminal associate degrees. Founded 1928. Setting: 1-acre rural campus. Total enrollment: 196. Faculty: 31 (22 full-time, 9 part-time). Student-undergrad faculty ratio is 5:1. 215 applied, 80% were admitted. Full-time: 25 students, 80% women, 20% men. Part-time: 171 students, 80% women, 20% men. Students come from 3 states and territories, 5% from out-of-state. 0.5% Hispanic/Latino; 3% Black or African American, non-Hispanic/Latino; 1% Asian, non-Hispanic/Latino; 0.5% Native Hawaiian or other Pacific Islander, non-Hispanic/Latino. 66% 25 or older, 96% transferred in. Retention: 100% of full-time freshmen returned the following year. Core. Calendar: 6 7-week terms per year. Advanced placement.
Entrance Requirements: Required: high school transcript, minimum 2 high school GPA, 1 recommendation, SAT or ACT. Required for some: minimum score of 75 on NLN exam for Bridge Program, minimum COMPASS scores of 75 in writing, 85 in reading, and 46 in Pre-Algebra for for associate degree programs, ACT Compass, NLN. Entrance: moderately difficult. Application deadline: rolling. Notification: continuous.
Collegiate Environment: Orientation program. Major annual events: Political Barbeque, Christmas Party, Professional Development Seminar. Campus security: 24-hour emergency response devices and patrols, late night transport-escort service, electronic campus access. 27 computers available on campus for general student use. A campuswide network can be accessed from off-campus.

■ **SOUTHEAST MISSOURI STATE UNIVERSITY**
One University Plz.
Cape Girardeau, MO 63701-4799
Tel: (573)651-2000
Web Site: www.semo.edu
Description: State-supported, comprehensive, coed. Part of Missouri Coordinating Board for Higher Education. Awards associate, bachelor's, and master's degrees and post-master's certificates. Founded 1873. Setting: 400-acre small town campus. Endowment: $79 million. Research spending for the previous fiscal year: $1.2 million. Educational spending for the previous fiscal year: $9369 per student. Total enrollment: 11,071. Faculty: 555 (396 full-time, 159 part-time). Student-undergrad faculty ratio is 20:1. 4,638 applied, 84% were admitted. 20% from top 10% of their high school class, 51% from top quarter, 71% from top half. 32 valedictorians. Full-time: 7,296 students, 58% women, 42% men. Part-time: 2,745 students, 61% women, 39% men. Students come from 43 states and territories, 56 other countries, 21% from out-of-state. 0.2% American Indian or Alaska Native, non-Hispanic/Latino; 2% Hispanic/Latino; 8% Black or African American, non-Hispanic/Latino; 1% Asian, non-Hispanic/Latino; 5% international. 14% 25 or older, 34% live on campus, 5% transferred in. Retention: 74% of full-time freshmen returned the following year. Academic areas with the most degrees conferred: business/marketing; education; liberal arts/general studies. Core. Calendar: semesters. Academic remediation for entering students, ESL program, services for LD students, advanced placement, accelerated degree program, self-designed majors, honors program, independent study, distance learning, double major, summer session for credit, part-time degree program, adult/continuing education programs, internships. Off campus study at Schools in the MACE initiative, including University of Central Missouri, Northwest Missouri State, Lincoln University, and Missouri State University. Study abroad program. ROTC: Air Force.
Entrance Requirements: Options: electronic application, deferred admis-

sion, international baccalaureate accepted. Required: high school transcript, minimum 2 high school GPA. Required for some: SAT or ACT. Entrance: moderately difficult. Application deadlines: 7/1, rolling for nonresidents. Notification: 9/1. Transfer credits accepted: Yes.

Costs Per Year: Application fee: $30. State resident tuition: $6,254 full-time, $208.45 per credit hour part-time. Nonresident tuition: $11,991 full-time, $399.70 per credit hour part-time. Mandatory fees: $1164 full-time, $38.80 per credit hour part-time. Full-time tuition and fees vary according to course load and location. Part-time tuition and fees vary according to course load and location. College room and board: $8935. Room and board charges vary according to board plan and housing facility.

Collegiate Environment: Orientation program. Drama-theater group, choral group, marching band, student-run newspaper, radio station. Social organizations: 262 open to all; national fraternities, national sororities, local fraternities; 19% of eligible men and 19% of eligible women are members. Most popular organizations: Student Government, Student Activities Council, Greek Life, Residence Hall Association, International Students Association. Major annual events: Ice Cream Pig-Out, Welcome Back Picnic, Late Night Breakfast. Student services: health clinic, personal-psychological counseling. Campus security: 24-hour emergency response devices and patrols, late night transport-escort service, controlled dormitory access. 3,112 college housing spaces available; 2,986 were occupied in 2018-19. Freshmen guaranteed college housing. On-campus residence required through sophomore year. Option: coed housing available. Kent Library. Books: 380,006 (physical), 263,780 (digital/electronic); Serial titles: 4,163 (physical), 58,594 (digital/electronic); Databases: 159. Weekly public service hours: 92. Operations spending for the previous fiscal year: $3.6 million. 1,550 computers available on campus for general student use. A campuswide network can be accessed from student residence rooms. Students can access the following: online class registration. Staffed computer lab on campus provides training in use of computers, software, and the Internet.

Community Environment: Cape Girardeau (population 36,200) was founded in 1793 as an Indian trading post. It is now a progressive industrial city. Commercial transportation is convenient; other community facilities include many churches, hospitals, shopping areas and a library. Part time employment is available.

■ **SOUTHWEST BAPTIST UNIVERSITY**
1600 University Ave.
Bolivar, MO 65613-2597
Tel: (417)326-5281; Free: 800-526-5859
Fax: (417)328-1514
E-mail: bvanstavern@sbuniv.edu
Web Site: www.sbuniv.edu

Description: Independent Southern Baptist, comprehensive, coed. Awards associate, bachelor's, master's, and doctoral degrees and post-master's certificates. Founded 1878. Setting: 152-acre small town campus. Endowment: $26.4 million. Educational spending for the previous fiscal year: $3429 per student. Total enrollment: 3,356. Faculty: 310 (156 full-time, 154 part-time). Student-undergrad faculty ratio is 11:1. 1,946 applied, 71% were admitted. 23% from top 10% of their high school class, 48% from top quarter, 80% from top half. Full-time: 1,780 students, 61% women, 39% men. Part-time: 883 students, 68% women, 32% men. Students come from 34 states and territories, 16 other countries, 21% from out-of-state. 0.8% American Indian or Alaska Native, non-Hispanic/Latino; 3% Hispanic/Latino; 4% Black or African American, non-Hispanic/Latino; 0.7% Asian, non-Hispanic/Latino; 0.2% Native Hawaiian or other Pacific Islander, non-Hispanic/Latino; 1% international. 21% 25 or older, 50% live on campus, 8% transferred in. Retention: 71% of full-time freshmen returned the following year. Academic areas with the most degrees conferred: health professions and related sciences; education; business/marketing. Core. Calendar: 4-1-4. Academic remediation for entering students, services for LD students, advanced placement, self-designed majors, honors program, independent study, distance learning, double major, summer session for credit, part-time degree program, co-op programs and internships, graduate courses open to undergrads. Off campus study at Mountain View Center, Salem Center, Springfield Center. Study abroad program. ROTC: Army (c).

Entrance Requirements: Options: electronic application, international baccalaureate accepted. Required: high school transcript, minimum 2.5 high school GPA, SAT or ACT. Recommended: essay, interview. Required for some: 3 recommendations. Entrance: moderately difficult. Application deadline: rolling. Notification: continuous. SAT Reasoning Test deadline: 8/25. SAT Subject Test deadline: 8/25. Transfer credits accepted: Yes.

Costs Per Year: Application fee: $30. Comprehensive fee: $32,330 includes full-time tuition ($23,600), mandatory fees ($910), and college room and board ($7820). College room only: $3400. Part-time tuition: $865 per credit hour.

Collegiate Environment: Orientation program. Drama-theater group, choral group, student-run newspaper. Social organizations: 27 open to all. Most popular organizations: Enactus, Student Government Association, Fellowship of Christian Athletes, Student Missouri State Teachers Association, PSY CHI. Major annual events: Homecoming, Bye Bash, Concerts and Sporting events. Student services: health clinic, personal-psychological counseling. Campus security: 24-hour emergency response devices and patrols, controlled dormitory access. 1,097 college housing spaces available; 893 were occupied in 2018-19. Freshmen guaranteed college housing. On-campus residence required through junior year. Options: men-only, women-only housing available. Harriett K. Hutchens Library. Weekly public service hours: 85; students can reserve study rooms. Operations spending for the previous fiscal year: $1.8 million. 351 computers available on campus for general student use. A campuswide network can be accessed from student residence rooms and from off campus. Students can access the following: online class registration. Staffed computer lab on campus provides training in use of computers, software, and the Internet.

Community Environment: The county seat of Polk County, Bolivar (population 10,100) is in the midst of a recreational area and is the center of a developing lake region. There is bus transportation to Springfield and Kansas City from Bolivar. A community concert association, allied with Columbia Artists Management of New York, brings quality musical attractions to Bolivar each season. The Southwest Regional Library which serves three counties is located here.

■ **STATE FAIR COMMUNITY COLLEGE**
3201 W 16th St.
Sedalia, MO 65301-2199
Tel: (660)530-5800; Free: 877-311-7322
Fax: (660)530-5820
Web Site: www.sfccmo.edu

Description: District-supported, 2-year, coed. Part of Missouri Coordinating Board for Higher Education. Awards certificates, transfer associate, and terminal associate degrees. Founded 1966. Setting: 128-acre small town campus. Endowment: $12.5 million. Educational spending for the previous fiscal year: $3560 per student. Total enrollment: 4,983. Faculty: 387 (79 full-time, 308 part-time). Student-undergrad faculty ratio is 32:1. Full-time: 2,506 students, 67% women, 33% men. Part-time: 2,477 students, 63% women, 37% men. Students come from 15 states and territories, 2 other countries. 0.7% American Indian or Alaska Native, non-Hispanic/Latino; 2% Hispanic/Latino; 4% Black or African American, non-Hispanic/Latino; 0.7% Asian, non-Hispanic/Latino; 0.2% Native Hawaiian or other Pacific Islander, non-Hispanic/Latino. 32% 25 or older, 7% transferred in. Retention: 59% of full-time freshmen returned the following year. Core. Calendar: semesters. Academic remediation for entering students, ESL program, services for LD students, advanced placement, distance learning, summer session for credit, part-time degree program, adult/continuing education programs, internships. Off campus study.

Entrance Requirements: Open admission except for allied health programs. Option: electronic application. Application deadline: rolling. Transfer credits accepted: Yes.

Costs Per Year: Area resident tuition: $3150 full-time, $105 per credit hour part-time. State resident tuition: $4800 full-time, $160 per credit hour part-time. Nonresident tuition: $6600 full-time, $220 per credit hour part-time. Mandatory fees: $600 full-time, $20 per credit hour part-time.

Collegiate Environment: Orientation program. Drama-theater group, choral group. Social organizations: 24 open to all. Student services: personal-psychological counseling. Campus security: 24-hour emergency response devices, controlled dormitory access, Campus Safety Officer on campus M-Th from 11 am - 10 pm, security during evening class hours. Donald C. Proctor Library. Operations spending for the previous fiscal year: $173,168. 520 computers available on campus for general student use. A campuswide network can be accessed from student residence rooms and from off campus. Students can access the following: online class registration. Staffed computer lab on campus provides training in use of computers, software, and the Internet.

Community Environment: Sedalia (population 20,430) is a rural community, and is the home of the Missouri State Fair. It is also an industrial area that produces truck bodies, brooms, mops, wheels, toolboxes, restaurant equipment, and fans. All forms of commercial transportation are available. Good shopping facilities, many churches, and various service clubs are a part of the community's facilities. Many part-time employment opportunities are available. Parks provide opportunities for recreation.

■ STATE TECHNICAL COLLEGE OF MISSOURI
One Technology Dr.
Linn, MO 65051-9606
Tel: (573)897-5000; Free: 800-743-TECH
Web Site: www.statetechmo.edu
Description: State-supported, 2-year, coed. Awards certificates and terminal associate degrees. Founded 1961. Setting: 350-acre rural campus. Total enrollment: 1,256. Faculty: 111 (88 full-time, 23 part-time). Student-undergrad faculty ratio is 11:1. Full-time: 1,041 students, 14% women, 86% men. Part-time: 215 students, 40% women, 60% men. Students come from 7 states and territories, 3% from out-of-state. 0.3% American Indian or Alaska Native, non-Hispanic/Latino; 2% Hispanic/Latino; 1% Black or African American, non-Hispanic/Latino; 0.2% Asian, non-Hispanic/Latino. 7% 25 or older, 11% live on campus, 10% transferred in. Retention: 86% of full-time freshmen returned the following year. Core. Calendar: semesters. Academic remediation for entering students, services for LD students, advanced placement, independent study, distance learning, double major, summer session for credit, part-time degree program, external degree program, adult/continuing education programs, co-op programs and internships. Off campus study.
Entrance Requirements: Options: electronic application, early admission, early decision, early action. Required: high school transcript, ACCUPLACER. Required for some: essay, 1 recommendation, interview, ACT. Application deadline: rolling. Notification: continuous. Transfer credits accepted: Yes.
Collegiate Environment: Orientation program. Social organizations: 16 open to all. Most popular organizations: SkillsUSA, Phi Theta Kappa, Student Government Association, Aviation Club, Electricity Club. Major annual events: Power Up, Casino Night, Family Day. Student services: health clinic, personal-psychological counseling. Campus security: 24-hour emergency response devices, student patrols, controlled dormitory access, indoor and outdoor surveillance cameras. State Technical College of Missouri Library plus 1 other. Weekly public service hours: 64; students can reserve study rooms.

■ STEPHENS COLLEGE
1200 E Broadway
Columbia, MO 65215-0002
Tel: (573)442-2211; Free: 800-876-7207
Fax: (573)876-7237
E-mail: apply@stephens.edu
Web Site: www.stephens.edu
Description: Independent, comprehensive. Awards associate, bachelor's, and master's degrees and post-master's certificates. Founded 1833. Setting: 48-acre urban campus. Endowment: $46.8 million. Educational spending for the previous fiscal year: $7221 per student. Total enrollment: 891. Faculty: 117 (54 full-time, 63 part-time). Student-undergrad faculty ratio is 8:1. 1,153 applied, 54% were admitted. 19% from top 10% of their high school class, 45% from top quarter, 81% from top half. Full-time: 595 students, 99% women, 1% men. Part-time: 111 students, 97% women, 3% men. Students come from 36 states and territories, 2 other countries, 43% from out-of-state. 1% American Indian or Alaska Native, non-Hispanic/Latino; 5% Hispanic/Latino; 15% Black or African American, non-Hispanic/Latino; 1% Asian, non-Hispanic/Latino; 0.6% Native Hawaiian or other Pacific Islander, non-Hispanic/Latino; 0.3% international. 71% live on campus, 8% transferred in. Retention: 72% of full-time freshmen returned the following year. Core. Calendar: semesters. Academic remediation for entering students, services for LD students, advanced placement, accelerated degree program, self-designed majors, freshman honors college, honors program, independent study, distance learning, double major, summer session for credit, part-time degree program, external degree program, adult/continuing education programs, co-op programs and internships. Graduate courses open to undergrads. Off campus study at University of Missouri, Washington University, Chatham University, Lincoln University, William Woods University, Westminster College, and Columbia College. Study abroad program. ROTC: Army (c), Naval (c), Air Force (c).
Entrance Requirements: Options: electronic application, deferred admission, international baccalaureate accepted. Required: essay, high school transcript, minimum 2 high school GPA, SAT or ACT. Recommended: minimum 2.5 high school GPA, interview. Required for some: 1 recommendation, audition for dance, audition recommended for theater. Entrance:

moderately difficult. Notification: continuous until 9/15. SAT Reasoning Test deadline: 8/1. SAT Subject Test deadline: 8/1. Transfer credits accepted: Yes.
Costs Per Year: Application fee: $25. Comprehensive fee: $39,440 includes full-time tuition ($30,750), mandatory fees ($200), and college room and board ($8490). College room only: $4610. Full-time tuition and fees vary according to course load, degree level, program, and reciprocity agreements. Room and board charges vary according to board plan and housing facility.
Collegiate Environment: Orientation program. Drama-theater group, choral group, student-run newspaper. Social organizations: 15 open to all; national sororities; 7% of women are members. Most popular organizations: Innovative Fashion Association, Warehouse Theatre, Student Government Association, American Marketing Association (AMA). Major annual events: Opening Convocation, Midnight Breakfast, Honors Convocation. Student services: health clinic, personal-psychological counseling. Campus security: 24-hour emergency response devices and patrols, student patrols, late night transport-escort service, controlled dormitory access. Hugh Stephens Library. Operations spending for the previous fiscal year: $330,810. 130 computers available on campus for general student use. A campuswide network can be accessed from student residence rooms and from off campus. Students can access the following: online class registration.
Community Environment: Stephens College is located in Columbia, Missouri. Situated between Kansas City and St. Louis, Columbia is the cultural, medical, and business center of mid-Missouri. Often called "College Town, USA", Columbia is also the home of Columbia College and the University of Missouri. Stephens students have easy access to Columbia's shopping, dining, and entertainment offerings.

■ STEVENS-THE INSTITUTE OF BUSINESS & ARTS
1521 Washington Ave.
Saint Louis, MO 63102
Tel: (314)421-0949; Free: 800-871-0949
Fax: (314)421-0304
E-mail: admission@siba.edu
Web Site: www.siba.edu
Description: Proprietary, 4-year, coed. Awards associate and bachelor's degrees. Founded 1947. Setting: urban campus. Educational spending for the previous fiscal year: $3700 per student. Total enrollment: 121. Faculty: 17 (5 full-time, 12 part-time). Student-undergrad faculty ratio is 9:1. 45 applied, 71% were admitted. Students come from 5 states and territories, 25% from out-of-state. 3% Hispanic/Latino; 65% Black or African American, non-Hispanic/Latino; 0.8% Asian, non-Hispanic/Latino. 49% 25 or older. Retention: 69% of full-time freshmen returned the following year. Core. Calendar: quarters. Academic remediation for entering students, accelerated degree program, independent study, summer session for credit, part-time degree program, adult/continuing education programs, internships.
Entrance Requirements: Options: electronic application, early admission, deferred admission. Required: essay, high school transcript, interview. Required for some: SAT or ACT. Entrance: moderately difficult. Application deadline: rolling. Notification: continuous, rolling for early decision. Transfer credits accepted: Yes.
Costs Per Year: Application fee: $25. Tuition: $12,720 full-time, $265 per credit hour part-time. Mandatory fees: $600 full-time, $200 per term part-time. Full-time tuition and fees vary according to course load and program. Part-time tuition and fees vary according to course load and program. Tuition guaranteed not to increase for student's term of enrollment.
Collegiate Environment: Orientation program. Social organizations: Student Government. Most popular organization: Student Government. Major annual events: Career Networking Seminar, Student Christmas Party, The Siba Scholarship Fund Trivia Night. Campus security: late night transport-escort service, 24-hour controlled entrances. St. Louis Public Library. Operations spending for the previous fiscal year: $16,500. 45 computers available on campus for general student use. A campuswide network can be accessed from student residence rooms and from off campus. Staffed computer lab on campus provides training in use of computers, software, and the Internet.

■ TEXAS COUNTY TECHNICAL COLLEGE
6915 S Hwy. 63
Houston, MO 65483
Tel: (417)967-5466
Web Site: www.texascountytech.edu
Description: Independent, 2-year, coed. Awards transfer associate degrees.

■ THREE RIVERS COLLEGE

2080 Three Rivers Blvd.
Poplar Bluff, MO 63901-2393
Tel: (573)840-9600; Free: 877-TRY-TRCC
Web Site: www.trcc.edu

Description: State and locally supported, 2-year, coed. Part of Missouri Coordinating Board for Higher Education. Awards certificates, transfer associate, and terminal associate degrees. Founded 1966. Setting: 80-acre rural campus. Educational spending for the previous fiscal year: $2989 per student. Total enrollment: 3,226. Faculty: 306 (67 full-time, 239 part-time). 818 applied, 100% were admitted. Full-time: 1,789 students, 64% women, 36% men. Part-time: 1,437 students, 70% women, 30% men. Students come from 14 states and territories, 1 other country, 3% from out-of-state. 0.5% American Indian or Alaska Native, non-Hispanic/Latino; 2% Hispanic/Latino; 10% Black or African American, non-Hispanic/Latino; 0.5% Asian, non-Hispanic/Latino; 0.1% Native Hawaiian or other Pacific Islander, non-Hispanic/Latino; 0.2% international. 29% 25 or older, 5% live on campus, 2% transferred in. Calendar: semesters. Academic remediation for entering students, ESL program, services for LD students, advanced placement, honors program, independent study, distance learning, double major, summer session for credit, part-time degree program, external degree program, adult/continuing education programs, co-op programs. Off campus study.

Entrance Requirements: Open admission. Options: electronic application, early admission. Recommended: high school transcript. Required for some: high school transcript. Entrance: noncompetitive. Application deadline: rolling. Notification: continuous. Transfer credits accepted: Yes.

Costs Per Year: Area resident tuition: $2760 full-time, $92 per credit hour part-time. State resident tuition: $4200 full-time, $140 per credit hour part-time. Nonresident tuition: $5340 full-time, $178 per credit hour part-time. Mandatory fees: $1200 full-time, $40 per credit hour part-time. College room only: $3440.

Collegiate Environment: Orientation program. Drama-theater group, choral group. Social organizations: 28 open to all; honors societies. Most popular organizations: Marketing Management Association, Phi Theta Kappa, Phi Beta Lambda, GO FAR, TRCC Aggies. Student services: personal-psychological counseling. Campus security: 24-hour emergency response devices, 24-hour Mass Notification and Storm Warning System. Rutland Library. Books: 15,286 (physical), 200,299 (digital/electronic); Serial titles: 40 (physical); Databases: 53. Weekly public service hours: 57; students can reserve study rooms. Operations spending for the previous fiscal year: $269,901. 500 computers available on campus for general student use. Computer purchase/lease plans available. A campuswide network can be accessed from student residence rooms. Students can access the following: online class registration. Staffed computer lab on campus (open 24 hours a day) provides training in use of computers, software, and the Internet.

Community Environment: Poplar Bluff, population 16,900, is a metropolitan area in southeast Missouri where the climate is temperate and living is pleasant. The community has two private general hospitals, one veteran's hospital, many churches, a library, and numerous civic organizations. Many natural streams and lakes within driving distance of the city provide excellent facilities for all outdoor sports. Part-time jobs are available.

■ TRUMAN STATE UNIVERSITY

100 E Normal Ave.
Kirksville, MO 63501-4221
Tel: (660)785-4000; Free: 800-892-7792
Fax: (660)785-7456
E-mail: dhowd@truman.edu
Web Site: www.truman.edu

Description: State-supported, comprehensive, coed. Awards bachelor's and master's degrees. Founded 1867. Setting: 140-acre small town campus. Endowment: $49.1 million. Research spending for the previous fiscal year: $737,389. Educational spending for the previous fiscal year: $11,420 per student. Total enrollment: 5,853. Faculty: 370 (301 full-time, 69 part-time). Student-undergrad faculty ratio is 16:1. 4,568 applied, 65% were admitted. 53% from top 10% of their high school class, 83% from top quarter, 98% from top half. 4 National Merit Scholars, 193 valedictorians. Full-time: 4,771 students, 59% women, 41% men. Part-time: 733 students, 57% women, 43% men. Students come from 40 states and territories, 48 other countries, 16% from out-of-state. 0.3% American Indian or Alaska Native, non-Hispanic/Latino; 3% Hispanic/Latino; 4% Black or African American, non-Hispanic/Latino; 3% Asian, non-Hispanic/Latino; 0.1% Native Hawaiian or other Pacific Islander, non-Hispanic/Latino; 7% international. 1% 25 or older, 40% live on campus, 2% transferred in. Retention: 84% of full-time freshmen

returned the following year. Academic areas with the most degrees conferred: business/marketing; health professions and related sciences; biological/life sciences. Core. Calendar: semesters. Services for LD students, advanced placement, accelerated degree program, self-designed majors, honors program, independent study, double major, summer session for credit, part-time degree program, co-op programs and internships, graduate courses open to undergrads. Off campus study. Study abroad program. ROTC: Army.

Entrance Requirements: Options: electronic application, deferred admission, international baccalaureate accepted. Required: essay, high school transcript. Recommended: minimum 3 high school GPA, interview, activities list/resume. Entrance: moderately difficult. Application deadline: rolling. Notification: continuous. Transfer credits accepted: Yes.

Costs Per Year: Application fee: $0.

Collegiate Environment: Orientation program. Drama-theater group, choral group, marching band, student-run newspaper, radio station. Social organizations: 253 open to all; national fraternities, national sororities, local fraternities, local sororities; 21% of eligible men and 18% of eligible women are members. Most popular organizations: Alpha Phi Omega (co-ed service fraternity), Nursing Students Association, Alpha Sigma Gamma (service sorority), Beta Beta Beta (biology honors), National Society of Collegiate Scholars. Major annual events: Homecoming, Final Blowout (spring carnival), BIG Event (one-day community service event). Student services: health clinic, personal-psychological counseling, women's center. Campus security: 24-hour emergency response devices and patrols, student patrols, late night transport-escort service, controlled dormitory access. 2,700 college housing spaces available; 2,289 were occupied in 2018-19. Freshmen guaranteed college housing. On-campus residence required in freshman year. Option: coed housing available. Pickler Memorial Library. Books: 495,980 (physical), 388,874 (digital/electronic); Serial titles: 355 (physical), 2,407 (digital/electronic); Databases: 107. Weekly public service hours: 105; students can reserve study rooms. Operations spending for the previous fiscal year: $3 million. 1,056 computers available on campus for general student use. A campuswide network can be accessed from student residence rooms and from off campus. Students can access the following: online class registration. Staffed computer lab on campus provides training in use of computers, software, and the Internet.

Community Environment: Kirksville, Missouri, is located in the northeastern part of the state, a 3 to 4-hour drive from Kansas City, St. Louis, and Des Moines, Iowa, and 80 miles west of historic Hannibal, Missouri, and Quincy, Illinois. The town is served by a direct Amtrak connection from Chicago and Quincy, IL. A municipal airport provides daily flights to and from Kansas City. Kirksville offers an environment for serious study in a community where higher education is the focal point. Besides University students, the community is home to 17,000 townspeople and nearly 250 medical students at the Kirksville College of Osteopathic Medicine.

■ UNIVERSITY OF CENTRAL MISSOURI

Warrensburg, MO 64093
Tel: (660)543-4111; Free: 800-729-8266
Fax: (660)543-8517
E-mail: admit@ucmo.edu
Web Site: www.ucmo.edu

Description: State-supported, comprehensive, coed. Awards bachelor's and master's degrees and post-master's certificates. Founded 1871. Setting: 1,561-acre small town campus with easy access to Kansas City. Total enrollment: 12,333. Faculty: 655 (494 full-time, 161 part-time). Student-undergrad faculty ratio is 18:1. 4,748 applied, 84% were admitted. 10% from top 10% of their high school class, 23% from top quarter, 29% from top half. Full-time: 7,701 students, 55% women, 45% men. Part-time: 2,100 students, 58% women, 42% men. Students come from 46 states and territories, 42 other countries, 11% from out-of-state. 0.3% American Indian or Alaska Native, non-Hispanic/Latino; 5% Hispanic/Latino; 10% Black or African American, non-Hispanic/Latino; 0.9% Asian, non-Hispanic/Latino; 0.3% Native Hawaiian or other Pacific Islander, non-Hispanic/Latino; 3% international. 13% 25 or older, 34% live on campus, 9% transferred in. Retention: 72% of full-time freshmen returned the following year. Academic areas with the most degrees conferred: education; health professions and related sciences; business/marketing. Core. Calendar: semesters. Academic remediation for entering students, ESL program, services for LD students, advanced placement, accelerated degree program, self-designed majors, honors program, distance learning, double major, summer session for credit, part-time degree program, adult/continuing education programs, internships, graduate courses open to undergrads. Off campus study. Study abroad program. ROTC: Army, Air Force (c).

Entrance Requirements: Options: electronic application, deferred admission, international baccalaureate accepted. Required: high school transcript, rank in upper two-thirds of high school class, SAT or ACT. Entrance: moderately difficult. Application deadline: rolling. Notification: continuous. Transfer credits accepted: Yes.

Costs Per Year: Application fee: $30. State resident tuition: $6,770 full-time, $225.65 per credit hour part-time. Nonresident tuition: $13,539 full-time, $451.30 per credit hour part-time. Mandatory fees: $903 full-time, $30.10 per credit hour part-time. Full-time tuition and fees vary according to course load and location. Part-time tuition and fees vary according to location. College room and board: $8766. College room only: $5502. Room and board charges vary according to board plan, housing facility, and student level.

Collegiate Environment: Orientation program. Drama-theater group, choral group, marching band, student-run newspaper, radio station. Social organizations: 225 open to all; national fraternities, national sororities; 11% of eligible men and 13% of eligible women are members. Most popular organizations: Roaring Red (Student Booster Club), Greek Organization, Campus Christian House, BSU (Baptist Student Union), International Student Organization. Major annual events: Homecoming, Greek Week Activities, Welcome Week. Student services: health clinic, personal-psychological counseling, women's center. Campus security: 24-hour emergency response devices and patrols, student patrols, late night transport-escort service, controlled dormitory access, canine patrol. James C. Kirkpatrick Library plus 1 other. Books: 499,982 (physical), 268,431 (digital/electronic); Serial titles: 1,579 (physical), 89,008 (digital/electronic); Databases: 97. Weekly public service hours: 96; students can reserve study rooms. 6,395 computers available on campus for general student use. A campuswide network can be accessed from student residence rooms and from off campus. Students can access the following: online class registration. Staffed computer lab on campus provides training in use of computers, software, and the Internet.

Community Environment: Surrounded by rolling prairie and scenic woodlands, Warrensburg is located just south of Interstate 70 at the junction of highways 50 and 13. An hour's drive southeast of Kansas City, it is directly en route to a number of popular Missouri attractions, including the Lake of the Ozarks and Branson. Warrensburg's 18,500 residents are in the enviable position of being close to a metropolitan area while able to enjoy the safety and advantages of small-town life. Bus and train lines serve the town. Employment and housing are available both on and off campus.

■ **UNIVERSITY OF MISSOURI**

Columbia, MO 65211

Tel: (573)882-2121

Fax: (573)882-7887

E-mail: mu4u@missouri.edu

Web Site: www.missouri.edu

Description: State-supported, university, coed. Part of University of Missouri System. Awards bachelor's, master's, and doctoral degrees and post-master's certificates. Founded 1839. Setting: 1,262-acre suburban campus. Endowment: $1 billion. Research spending for the previous fiscal year: $126.7 million. Total enrollment: 29,866. Faculty: 1,326 (1,258 full-time, 68 part-time). Student-undergrad faculty ratio is 18:1. 18,948 applied, 78% were admitted. 30% from top 10% of their high school class, 61% from top quarter, 90% from top half. Full-time: 20,720 students, 53% women, 47% men. Part-time: 1,783 students, 47% women, 53% men. Students come from 49 states and territories, 72 other countries, 20% from out-of-state. 8% American Indian or Alaska Native, non-Hispanic/Latino; 5% Hispanic/Latino; 0.2% Black or African American, non-Hispanic/Latino; 78% Asian, non-Hispanic/Latino; 3% international. 4% 25 or older, 21% live on campus, 4% transferred in. Retention: 87% of full-time freshmen returned the following year. Academic areas with the most degrees conferred: business/marketing; health professions and related sciences; communication/journalism. Core. Calendar: semesters. ESL program, services for LD students, advanced placement, accelerated degree program, self-designed majors, freshman honors college, honors program, independent study, distance learning, double major, summer session for credit, part-time degree program, external degree program, adult/continuing education programs, co-op programs and internships, graduate courses open to undergrads. Off campus study at Mid-Missouri Associated Colleges and Universities, Great Plains IDEA. Study abroad program. ROTC: Army, Naval, Air Force.

Entrance Requirements: Options: electronic application, deferred admission, international baccalaureate accepted. Required: high school transcript, specific high school curriculum, SAT or ACT. Recommended: SAT, ACT. Entrance: moderately difficult. Application deadlines: rolling, rolling for

nonresidents. Notification: continuous, continuous for nonresidents. SAT Reasoning Test deadline: 8/1. Transfer credits accepted: Yes.

Costs Per Year: Application fee: $55. State resident tuition: $8,590 full-time, $287.90 per credit hour part-time. Nonresident tuition: $25,707 full-time, $856.90 per credit hour part-time. Mandatory fees: $1335 full-time, $32.33 per credit hour part-time. Full-time tuition and fees vary according to course load, program, and reciprocity agreements. Part-time tuition and fees vary according to course load, program, and reciprocity agreements. College room and board: $10,380. College room only: $6620. Room and board charges vary according to board plan and housing facility.

Collegiate Environment: Orientation program. Drama-theater group, choral group, marching band, student-run newspaper, radio station. Social organizations: 542 open to all; national fraternities, national sororities; 24% of eligible men and 31% of eligible women are members. Most popular organizations: Alpha Kappa Psi Professional Business Fraternity (Academic), Pre-Medical Society (Academic), Alpha Phi Omega (Service), Mizzou Global Medical Training (Service), UM Investment Group (Academic). Major annual events: Homecoming, Midnight BBQ, International Welcome Party. Student services: legal services, health clinic, personal-psychological counseling, women's center. Campus security: 24-hour emergency response devices and patrols, late night transport-escort service, controlled dormitory access. 5,348 college housing spaces available; 4,924 were occupied in 2018-19. Freshmen guaranteed college housing. On-campus residence required in freshman year. Options: coed, men-only, women-only housing available. Ellis Library plus 9 others. Books: 2.1 million (physical), 953,740 (digital/electronic); Serial titles: 87,432 (physical), 94,920 (digital/electronic); Databases: 60. Students can reserve study rooms. Operations spending for the previous fiscal year: $16.9 million. 1,200 computers available on campus for general student use. Computer purchase/lease plans available. A campuswide network can be accessed from student residence rooms and from off campus. Students can access the following: online class registration. Staffed computer lab on campus (open 24 hours a day) provides training in use of computers, software, and the Internet.

Community Environment: The University rests in the heart of Columbia, a growing city of more than 76,000. Cited for its excellent educational opportunities and quality of life, Columbia has ranked among the top most livable cities in the United States for more than a decade, according to Money Magazine. Columbia combines the benefits of a large city - a wide selection of lodging, dining, shopping, cultural and sporting opportunities - with the friendly atmosphere and convenience of a small town. All forms of public transportation are available. Situated midway between St. Louis and Kansas City (each about two hours away), Columbia also is within a two-hour drive for the Lake of the Ozarks recreation area, which provides opportunities for many outdoor sports.

■ **UNIVERSITY OF MISSOURI-KANSAS CITY**

5100 Rockhill Rd.

Kansas City, MO 64110-2499

Tel: (816)235-1000; Free: 800-775-8652

Fax: (816)235-1717

E-mail: admit@umkc.edu

Web Site: www.umkc.edu

Description: State-supported, university, coed. Part of University of Missouri System. Awards bachelor's, master's, and doctoral degrees and post-master's certificates. Founded 1929. Setting: 191-acre urban campus with easy access to Kansas City. Endowment: $305.8 million. Total enrollment: 16,944. Faculty: 1,207 (745 full-time, 462 part-time). Student-undergrad faculty ratio is 14:1. 5,138 applied, 62% were admitted. 31% from top 10% of their high school class, 56% from top quarter, 84% from top half. Full-time: 6,669 students, 57% women, 43% men. Part-time: 5,039 students, 58% women, 42% men. Students come from 39 states and territories, 55 other countries, 24% from out-of-state. 0.4% American Indian or Alaska Native, non-Hispanic/Latino; 8% Hispanic/Latino; 12% Black or African American, non-Hispanic/Latino; 6% Asian, non-Hispanic/Latino; 0.2% Native Hawaiian or other Pacific Islander, non-Hispanic/Latino; 4% international. 1% 25 or older, 25% live on campus, 11% transferred in. Retention: 75% of full-time freshmen returned the following year. Core. Calendar: semesters. ESL program, services for LD students, advanced placement, accelerated degree program, self-designed majors, freshman honors college, honors program, independent study, distance learning, double major, summer session for credit, part-time degree program, adult/continuing education programs, co-op programs and internships, graduate courses open to undergrads. Off campus study at other campuses of the University of Missouri System. Study abroad program. ROTC: Army, Air Force (c).

Entrance Requirements: Options: electronic application, deferred admission, international baccalaureate accepted. Required: high school transcript, SAT or ACT. Required for some: essay, interview. Entrance: moderately difficult. Application deadline: rolling. Notification: continuous. SAT Reasoning Test deadline: 8/15. Transfer credits accepted: Yes.

Costs Per Year: Application fee: $45. State resident tuition: $8,423 full-time, $280.78 per credit hour part-time. Nonresident tuition: $23,550 full-time, $785 per credit hour part-time. Mandatory fees: $1,461 full-time, $104.52 per credit hour part-time. Full-time tuition and fees vary according to course load and program. Part-time tuition and fees vary according to course load and program.

Collegiate Environment: Orientation program. Drama-theater group, choral group, student-run newspaper, radio station. Social organizations: 266 open to all; national fraternities, national sororities, local fraternities, local sororities; 3% of eligible men and 4% of eligible women are members. Most popular organizations: Union Programming Board, International Student Council, Alpha Phi Omega, Omicron Delta Kappa, Greek Organizations. Major annual events: UPB's Big Event, UPB Talent Show, Roos Give Back Community Service Day. Student services: legal services, health clinic, personal-psychological counseling, women's center. Campus security: 24-hour emergency response devices and patrols, late night transport-escort service, controlled dormitory access. Miller-Nichols Library plus 3 others. Students can reserve study rooms. 400 computers available on campus for general student use. Computer purchase/lease plans available. A campuswide network can be accessed from student residence rooms and from off campus. Students can access the following: online class registration. Staffed computer lab on campus provides training in use of computers, software, and the Internet.

Community Environment: One of the country's largest railroad centers, Kansas City is also a great manufacturing city and an important distributing point located at the confluence of the Kansas and Missouri Rivers. All forms of commercial transportation are convenient. Extensive cultural activities are available. Recreational facilities are numerous. Swope Park is one the largest municipal playgrounds in the country that contains 1,705 acres, two golf courses, tennis courts, picnic grounds, a zoo, swimming pool and a lagoon for boating. Kansas City is the home of the Chiefs of the National Football League and Royals baseball team of the American League. The Country Club district in the southern part of the city has gained international attention as a model for city planning. Each home in this district is planned to harmonize with its surroundings, and careful selection of European art objects beautify street corners.

■ UNIVERSITY OF MISSOURI-ST. LOUIS

One University Blvd.
Saint Louis, MO 63121
Tel: (314)516-5000; Free: 888-GO2-USML
Fax: (314)516-5310
E-mail: askdrew@umsl.edu
Web Site: www.umsl.edu

Description: State-supported, university, coed. Part of University of Missouri System. Awards bachelor's, master's, and doctoral degrees and post-master's certificates. Founded 1963. Setting: 350-acre suburban campus with easy access to St. Louis. Endowment: $83.5 million. Research spending for the previous fiscal year: $8.5 million. Educational spending for the previous fiscal year: $8261 per student. Total enrollment: 16,740. Faculty: 825 (432 full-time, 393 part-time). Student-undergrad faculty ratio is 18:1. 1,970 applied, 76% were admitted. 27% from top 10% of their high school class, 58% from top quarter, 88% from top half. Full-time: 5,492 students, 55% women, 45% men. Part-time: 8,320 students, 58% women, 42% men. Students come from 34 states and territories, 44 other countries, 11% from out-of-state. 0.4% American Indian or Alaska Native, non-Hispanic/Latino; 3% Hispanic/Latino; 17% Black or African American, non-Hispanic/Latino; 5% Asian, non-Hispanic/Latino; 0.1% Native Hawaiian or other Pacific Islander, non-Hispanic/Latino; 3% international. 36% 25 or older, 9% live on campus, 10% transferred in. Retention: 74% of full-time freshmen returned the following year. Academic areas with the most degrees conferred: business/marketing; health professions and related sciences; education. Core. Calendar: semesters. ESL program, services for LD students, advanced placement, accelerated degree program, self-designed majors, freshman honors college, honors program, independent study, distance learning, double major, summer session for credit, part-time degree program, adult/continuing education programs, co-op programs and internships, graduate courses open to undergrads. Off campus study at Saint Louis University, Washington University in St. Louis, St. Charles Community

College, Mineral Area Community College, Jefferson College, St. Louis Community College - Wildwood, St. Louis Community College - Florissant Valley and South County Education University Center. Study abroad program. ROTC: Army, Air Force (c).

Entrance Requirements: Options: electronic application, international baccalaureate accepted. Required: high school transcript, minimum 2 high school GPA, CBHE core requirements, SAT or ACT. Required for some: essay, 2 recommendations, interview. Entrance: moderately difficult. Application deadline: rolling. Notification: continuous. SAT Reasoning Test deadline: 9/17. Transfer credits accepted: Yes.

Costs Per Year: Application fee: $35. State resident tuition: $349.70 per credit hour part-time. Nonresident tuition: $930 per credit hour part-time. Part-time tuition varies according to course level, course load, location, program, and reciprocity agreements.

Collegiate Environment: Orientation program. Drama-theater group, choral group, student-run newspaper, radio station. Social organizations: 120 open to all; national fraternities, national sororities; 1% of eligible men and 1% of eligible women are members. Most popular organizations: Student Government Association, Associated Black Collegians, Pierre laclede Honors College Student Association, Residence Hall Association, UMSL Radio Station. Major annual events: Pack the Stands, Mirth Week (spring carnival), Homecoming. Student services: health clinic, personal-psychological counseling, women's center. Campus security: 24-hour emergency response devices and patrols, late night transport-escort service, controlled dormitory access, criminal investigations. Thomas Jefferson Library plus 1 other. Books: 1.3 million (physical), 206,616 (digital/electronic); Serial titles: 990 (physical), 1,295 (digital/electronic); Databases: 195. Weekly public service hours: 82; students can reserve study rooms. Operations spending for the previous fiscal year: $5.5 million. 1,391 computers available on campus for general student use. Computer purchase/lease plans available. A campuswide network can be accessed from student residence rooms and from off campus. Students can access the following: online class registration. Staffed computer lab on campus provides training in use of computers, software, and the Internet.

■ WASHINGTON UNIVERSITY IN ST. LOUIS

One Brookings Dr.
Saint Louis, MO 63130-4899
Tel: (314)935-5000; Free: 800-638-0700
Fax: (314)935-4290
E-mail: admissions@wustl.edu
Web Site: www.wustl.edu

Description: Independent, university, coed. Awards bachelor's, master's, and doctoral degrees and post-master's certificates. Founded 1853. Setting: 169-acre urban campus with easy access to St. Louis. Endowment: $7.7 billion. Research spending for the previous fiscal year: $537.8 million. Educational spending for the previous fiscal year: $127,669 per student. Total enrollment: 15,852. Faculty: 1,466 (984 full-time, 482 part-time). Student-undergrad faculty ratio is 8:1. 31,320 applied, 15% were admitted. 80% from top 10% of their high school class, 97% from top quarter, 99% from top half. Full-time: 7,146 students, 53% women, 47% men. Part-time: 605 students, 64% women, 36% men. Students come from 53 states and territories, 50 other countries, 90% from out-of-state. 9% Hispanic/Latino; 9% Black or African American, non-Hispanic/Latino; 16% Asian, non-Hispanic/Latino; 0.1% Native Hawaiian or other Pacific Islander, non-Hispanic/Latino; 7% international. 3% 25 or older, 74% live on campus, 1% transferred in. Retention: 97% of full-time freshmen returned the following year. Academic areas with the most degrees conferred: engineering; business/marketing; social sciences. Core. Calendar: semesters. ESL program, services for LD students, advanced placement, accelerated degree program, self-designed majors, independent study, double major, summer session for credit, part-time degree program, adult/continuing education programs, co-op programs and internships, graduate courses open to undergrads. Off campus study at Consortium on Financing Higher Education. Study abroad program. ROTC: Army, Air Force (c).

Entrance Requirements: Options: electronic application, early admission, early decision, deferred admission, international baccalaureate accepted. Required: essay, high school transcript, 2 recommendations, SAT or ACT. Recommended: minimum 3.5 high school GPA. Required for some: portfolio for the College of Art and the College of Architecture. Entrance: most difficult. Application deadlines: 1/2, 11/1 for early decision plan 1, 1/2 for early decision plan 2. Notification: 4/1, 12/15 for early decision plan 1, 2/15 for early decision plan 2. SAT Reasoning Test deadline: 1/2. SAT Subject Test deadline: 1/2. Transfer credits accepted: Yes. Wait-listed applicants offered admission: 31. Early decision applicants: 1,840. Early decision applicants admitted: 772.

Costs Per Year: Application fee: $75. Comprehensive fee: $72,192 includes full-time tuition ($54,250), mandatory fees ($1042), and college room and board ($16,900). College room only: $11,650.

Collegiate Environment: Orientation program. Drama-theater group, choral group, student-run newspaper, radio station. Social organizations: 480 open to all; national fraternities, national sororities; 26% of eligible men and 38% of eligible women are members. Most popular organizations: Campus Kitchen, KWUR - Campus Radio Station, Culinary Arts, Catholic Student Union, Ashoka. Major annual events: Thurtene Carnival, WILD (concert festival), Black Anthology and Diwali. Student services: health clinic, personal-psychological counseling. Campus security: 24-hour emergency response devices and patrols, student patrols, late night transport-escort service, controlled dormitory access. 5,349 college housing spaces available; 5,220 were occupied in 2018-19. Freshmen guaranteed college housing. On-campus residence required in freshman year. Options: coed, men-only, women-only housing available. John M. Olin Library plus 12 others. Books: 2.8 million (physical), 2 million (digital/electronic); Serial titles: 704 (physical), 170,031 (digital/electronic); Databases: 955. Weekly public service hours: 120; study areas open 24 hours, 5-7 days a week; students can reserve study rooms. Operations spending for the previous fiscal year: $40.9 million. 2,500 computers available on campus for general student use. Computer purchase/lease plans available. A campuswide network can be accessed from student residence rooms and from off campus. Students can access the following: online class registration. Staffed computer lab on campus provides training in use of computers, software, and the Internet.

■ **WEBSTER UNIVERSITY**
470 E Lockwood Ave.
Saint Louis, MO 63119-3194
Tel: (314)968-6900; Free: 800-753-6765
Fax: (314)968-7115
Web Site: www.webster.edu
Description: Independent, comprehensive, coed. Awards bachelor's, master's, and doctoral degrees and post-master's certificates. Founded 1915. Setting: 47-acre suburban campus with easy access to St. Louis. Total enrollment: 4,090. Faculty: (198 full-time, 430 part-time). Student-undergrad faculty ratio is 9:1. 2,585 applied, 47% were admitted. 12% from top 10% of their high school class, 37% from top quarter, 75% from top half. Full-time: 2,212 students, 57% women, 43% men. Part-time: 332 students, 44% women, 56% men. 27% from out-of-state. 0.1% American Indian or Alaska Native, non-Hispanic/Latino; 6% Hispanic/Latino; 12% Black or African American, non-Hispanic/Latino; 2% Asian, non-Hispanic/Latino; 3% international. 17% 25 or older, 9% transferred in. Retention: 79% of full-time freshmen returned the following year. Academic areas with the most degrees conferred: business/marketing; visual and performing arts; communication/journalism. Core. Calendar: semesters. ESL program, services for LD students, advanced placement, accelerated degree program, self-designed majors, independent study, distance learning, double major, summer session for credit, part-time degree program, adult/continuing education programs, co-op programs and internships, graduate courses open to undergrads. Off campus study at Fontbonne University, Lindenwood University, Maryville University of Saint Louis, Eden Theological Seminary, Missouri Baptist University. Study abroad program. ROTC: Army (c), Air Force (c).
Entrance Requirements: Options: electronic application, early admission, deferred admission, international baccalaureate accepted. Required: essay, high school transcript, minimum 2.5 high school GPA, 1 recommendation, SAT or ACT. Recommended: minimum 3 high school GPA. Required for some: interview, audition, portfolio review, and/or interview. Entrance: moderately difficult. Application deadline: 8/1. Notification: continuous, continuous for nonresidents. SAT Reasoning Test deadline: 4/1. SAT Subject Test deadline: 4/1. Transfer credits accepted: Yes.
Costs Per Year: Application fee: $35. One-time mandatory fee: $125. Comprehensive fee: $38,950 includes full-time tuition ($27,700), mandatory fees ($200), and college room and board ($11,050). College room only: $6050. Full-time tuition and fees vary according to program. Room and board charges vary according to board plan and housing facility. Part-time tuition: $710 per credit hour.
Collegiate Environment: Orientation program. Drama-theater group, choral group, student-run newspaper, radio station. Social organizations: national sororities. Student services: health clinic, personal-psychological counseling. Campus security: 24-hour emergency response devices and patrols, student

patrols, late night transport-escort service, controlled dormitory access. Emerson Library. Study areas open 24 hours, 5-7 days a week; students can reserve study rooms.
Community Environment: A suburban area 10 miles from St. Louis, Webster Groves (population 22,896) has the convenience of all major forms of transportation. The shopping facilities here are excellent, numerous civic and service organizations are active. Webster Groves also enjoys the recreational and cultural advantages of St. Louis. Other facilities include a library, and churches of major denominations. Some part-time employment is available.

■ **WELLSPRING SCHOOL OF ALLIED HEALTH**
9140 Ward Pky.
Ste. 100
Kansas City, MO 64114
Tel: (816)523-9140
Web Site: www.wellspring.edu
Description: Proprietary, 2-year, coed. Awards certificates, transfer associate, and terminal associate degrees.

■ **WESTMINSTER COLLEGE**
501 Westminster Ave.
Fulton, MO 65251-1299
Tel: (573)642-3361; Free: 800-475-3361
Fax: (573)592-5227
E-mail: admissions@westminster-mo.edu
Web Site: www.westminster-mo.edu
Description: Independent, 4-year, coed, affiliated with Presbyterian Church. Awards bachelor's degrees. Founded 1851. Setting: 80-acre small town campus. Endowment: $56.6 million. Educational spending for the previous fiscal year: $7355 per student. Total enrollment: 940. Faculty: 96 (61 full-time, 35 part-time). Student-undergrad faculty ratio is 14:1. 1,789 applied, 64% were admitted. 21% from top 10% of their high school class, 40% from top quarter, 75% from top half. Full-time: 919 students, 43% women, 57% men. Part-time: 21 students, 24% women, 76% men. Students come from 29 states and territories, 70 other countries, 20% from out-of-state. 2% American Indian or Alaska Native, non-Hispanic/Latino; 3% Hispanic/Latino; 9% Black or African American, non-Hispanic/Latino; 0.4% Asian, non-Hispanic/Latino; 16% international. 3% 25 or older, 82% live on campus, 5% transferred in. Retention: 83% of full-time freshmen returned the following year. Academic areas with the most degrees conferred: business/marketing; biological/life sciences; education. Core. Calendar: semesters. Academic remediation for entering students, ESL program, services for LD students, advanced placement, self-designed majors, honors program, independent study, distance learning, double major, summer session for credit, part-time degree program, co-op programs and internships. Off campus study at Chicago Urban Studies Semester, American University. Study abroad program. ROTC: Army (c), Air Force (c).
Entrance Requirements: Options: electronic application, early admission, deferred admission, international baccalaureate accepted. Required: high school transcript, 1 recommendation, SAT or ACT. Recommended: essay, minimum 2.5 high school GPA. Required for some: interview. Entrance: moderately difficult. Notification: 8/1.
Costs Per Year: Application fee: $0. Comprehensive fee: $37,740 includes full-time tuition ($25,700), mandatory fees ($1900), and college room and board ($10,140). College room only: $5470. Full-time tuition and fees vary according to reciprocity agreements. Room and board charges vary according to board plan and housing facility. Part-time tuition: $800 per credit hour.
Collegiate Environment: Orientation program. Drama-theater group, choral group, student-run newspaper. Social organizations: 54 open to all; national fraternities, national sororities; 48% of eligible men and 35% of eligible women are members. Most popular organizations: Student Government Association, Environmentally Concerned Students, International Student Club, Habitat for Humanity, Little Brother/Little Sister. Major annual events: Leadership Challenge, Take Back the Night, Wellness Week. Student services: health clinic, personal-psychological counseling, women's center. Campus security: 24-hour emergency response devices and patrols, late night transport-escort service, controlled dormitory access, well-lit campus. Reeves Memorial Library plus 1 other. Books: 104,327 (physical), 156,300 (digital/electronic); Databases: 58. Students can reserve study rooms. Operations spending for the previous fiscal year: $238,407. 188 computers available on campus for general student use. A campuswide network can be accessed from student residence rooms and from off campus. Students can

access the following: online class registration. Staffed computer lab on campus provides training in use of computers, software, and the Internet.

■ **WILLIAM JEWELL COLLEGE**
500 College Hill
Liberty, MO 64068-1843
Tel: (816)781-7700; Free: 888-2JEWELL
Fax: (816)415-5027
E-mail: hainesb@william.jewell.edu
Web Site: www.jewell.edu

Description: Independent, comprehensive, coed. Awards bachelor's and master's degrees (also offers evening program with significant enrollment not reflected in profile). Founded 1849. Setting: 200-acre suburban campus with easy access to Kansas City. Endowment: $63.8 million. Educational spending for the previous fiscal year: $11,373 per student. Total enrollment: 808. Faculty: 96 (69 full-time, 27 part-time). Student-undergrad faculty ratio is 10:1. 1,316 applied, 46% were admitted. 31% from top 10% of their high school class, 56% from top quarter, 90% from top half. 6 valedictorians. Full-time: 779 students, 54% women, 46% men. Part-time: 24 students, 67% women, 33% men. Students come from 30 states and territories, 19 other countries, 38% from out-of-state. 0.1% American Indian or Alaska Native, non-Hispanic/Latino; 6% Hispanic/Latino; 5% Black or African American, non-Hispanic/Latino; 1% Asian, non-Hispanic/Latino; 0.4% Native Hawaiian or other Pacific Islander, non-Hispanic/Latino; 3% international. 7% 25 or older, 85% live on campus, 5% transferred in. Retention: 73% of full-time freshmen returned the following year. Academic areas with the most degrees conferred: health professions and related sciences; business/marketing; biological/life sciences. Core. Calendar: semesters. ESL program, services for LD students, advanced placement, accelerated degree program, self-designed majors, honors program, independent study, distance learning, double major, summer session for credit, co-op programs and internships, graduate courses open to undergrads. Off campus study. Study abroad program. ROTC: Army (c).
Entrance Requirements: Options: electronic application, deferred admission, international baccalaureate accepted. Required: essay, high school transcript. Recommended: SAT or ACT. Required for some: interview. Entrance: moderately difficult. Application deadline: rolling. Notification: 11/1. SAT Reasoning Test deadline: 8/1. SAT Subject Test deadline: 8/1. Transfer credits accepted: Yes.
Costs Per Year: Application fee: $0. Comprehensive fee: $44,580 includes full-time tuition ($33,500), mandatory fees ($950), and college room and board ($10,130). Part-time tuition: $980 per credit.
Collegiate Environment: Orientation program. Drama-theater group, choral group, student-run newspaper. Social organizations: 50 open to all; national fraternities, national sororities; 40% of eligible men and 40% of eligible women are members. Most popular organizations: College Union Activities, Intramurals, Mosaic, Student Senate, Black Student Association. Major annual events: Homecoming, Hanging of the Green/Lighting of the Quad, Undergraduate Research Colloquium. Student services: health clinic, personal-psychological counseling. Campus security: 24-hour emergency response devices and patrols, late night transport-escort service, controlled dormitory access. 1,009 college housing spaces available; 644 were occupied in 2018-19. Freshmen guaranteed college housing. On-campus residence required through senior year. Options: coed, men-only, women-only housing available. Charles F. Curry Library. Books: 129,403 (physical), 364,504 (digital/electronic); Serial titles: 71 (physical), 57,096 (digital/electronic); Databases: 63. Weekly public service hours: 90; study areas open 24 hours, 5-7 days a week; students can reserve study rooms. Operations spending for the previous fiscal year: $906,356. 25 computers available on campus for general student use. A computer is required for all students. A campuswide network can be accessed from student residence rooms and from off campus. Students can access the following: online class registration, all students provided with an iPad and support service.
Community Environment: A suburban community, Liberty is 13 miles northeast of Kansas City and enjoys all of the cultural and recreational advantages afforded by its proximity to a major metropolitan area of 1.5 million people. Several points of interest are the State Ballet of Missouri, the Kansas city Symphony, and the Nelson-Atkins Museum of Art. Kansas City also offers professional football and baseball. The Harriman Fine Arts

Program provides great performances from such artists as Itzhak Perlman, Paul Taylor Dance Company, and Yo Yo Ma.

■ **WILLIAM WOODS UNIVERSITY**
One University Ave.
Fulton, MO 65251-1098
Tel: (573)642-2251; Free: 800-995-3159
Fax: (573)592-1146
E-mail: ashley.sundin@williamwoods.edu
Web Site: www.williamwoods.edu

Description: Independent, comprehensive, coed, affiliated with Christian Church (Disciples of Christ). Awards associate, bachelor's, master's, and doctoral degrees and post-master's certificates. Founded 1870. Setting: 200-acre small town campus with easy access to St. Louis, Kansas City. Endowment: $18.5 million. Educational spending for the previous fiscal year: $4911 per student. Total enrollment: 2,281. Faculty: 240 (60 full-time, 180 part-time). Student-undergrad faculty ratio is 16:1. 892 applied, 75% were admitted. 10% from top 10% of their high school class, 37% from top quarter, 82% from top half. Full-time: 796 students, 72% women, 28% men. Part-time: 162 students, 78% women, 22% men. Students come from 31 states and territories, 19 other countries, 39% from out-of-state. 0.5% American Indian or Alaska Native, non-Hispanic/Latino; 3% Hispanic/Latino; 5% Black or African American, non-Hispanic/Latino; 0.7% Asian, non-Hispanic/Latino; 5% international. 15% 25 or older, 63% live on campus, 6% transferred in. Retention: 72% of full-time freshmen returned the following year. Academic areas with the most degrees conferred: foreign languages and literature; business/marketing; agriculture; education. Core. Calendar: semesters. Academic remediation for entering students, services for LD students, advanced placement, accelerated degree program, self-designed majors, honors program, independent study, distance learning, double major, summer session for credit, part-time degree program, internships, graduate courses open to undergrads. Off campus study at University of Missouri-Columbia, Westminster College (MO). Study abroad program. ROTC: Army (c), Naval (c), Air Force (c).
Entrance Requirements: Options: electronic application, deferred admission, international baccalaureate accepted. Required: high school transcript, minimum 2.5 high school GPA, 16 hours college preparatory units, SAT or ACT. Entrance: moderately difficult. Application deadline: 8/15. Notification: continuous. SAT Reasoning Test deadline: 8/15. SAT Subject Test deadline: 8/15. Transfer credits accepted: Yes.
Costs Per Year: Application fee: $0. Comprehensive fee: $33,885 includes full-time tuition ($23,230), mandatory fees ($955), and college room and board ($9700). College room only: $5050. Full-time tuition and fees vary according to course load and program. Room and board charges vary according to board plan and housing facility. Part-time tuition: $425 per credit hour. Part-time mandatory fees: $75 per term. Part-time tuition and fees vary according to course load and program.
Collegiate Environment: Orientation program. Drama-theater group, choral group, student-run radio station. Social organizations: 45 open to all; national fraternities, national sororities; 43% of eligible men and 45% of eligible women are members. Most popular organizations: DECA, Students of Social Work, Campus Activities Board, Hands Up, Campus Crusade for Christ. Major annual events: Student Activities Fair, President's Concert and Lecture Series Events. Student services: health clinic, personal-psychological counseling. Campus security: 24-hour emergency response devices and patrols, late night transport-escort service, controlled dormitory access. Dulany Library. Books: 75,506 (physical), 274,700 (digital/electronic); Serial titles: 821 (physical), 122,059 (digital/electronic); Databases: 57. Weekly public service hours: 87; students can reserve study rooms. Operations spending for the previous fiscal year: $523,255. 197 computers available on campus for general student use. A campuswide network can be accessed from student residence rooms and from off campus. Students can access the following: online class registration. Staffed computer lab on campus provides training in use of computers, software, and the Internet.
Community Environment: The wooded Missouri landscape provides a scenic setting for residents of the area. Colleges, state educational and health facilities and professional industries are primary employers. Part-time employment is available. The regional area provides major medical centers, churches, libraries, restaurants, and recreational and entertainment facilities.

■ AANIIIH NAKODA COLLEGE

PO Box 159
Harlem, MT 59526-0159
Tel: (406)353-2607
Fax: (406)353-2898
Web Site: www.ancollege.edu

Description: Federally supported, 2-year, coed. Awards certificates, transfer associate, and terminal associate degrees. Founded 1984. Setting: 3-acre rural campus. Total enrollment: 236. Student-undergrad faculty ratio is 11:1. 66% 25 or older. Core. Calendar: quarters. Academic remediation for entering students, part-time degree program, co-op programs.

Entrance Requirements: Open admission. Options: early admission, deferred admission. Required: high school transcript. Entrance: noncompetitive. Application deadline: rolling. Notification: continuous.

Collegiate Environment: Orientation program. Student-run radio station. Campus security: 24-hour patrols. Fort Belknap College Library.

■ BLACKFEET COMMUNITY COLLEGE

PO Box 819
Browning, MT 59417-0819
Tel: (406)338-5441; Free: 800-549-7457
Fax: (406)338-3272
Web Site: www.bfcc.edu

Description: Independent, 2-year, coed. Awards certificates, diplomas, transfer associate, and terminal associate degrees. Founded 1974. Setting: 5-acre small town campus. Total enrollment: 471. 55% 25 or older. Core. Calendar: semesters. Academic remediation for entering students, part-time degree program, adult/continuing education programs. Off campus study at members of the American Indian Higher Education Consortium.

Entrance Requirements: Open admission. Option: early admission. Required: high school transcript, immunization with second MMR, Certificate of Indian Blood. Entrance: noncompetitive. Application deadline: 8/29. Notification: continuous.

Collegiate Environment: Orientation program. Campus security: 16-hour patrols by security personnel.

■ CARROLL COLLEGE

1601 N Benton Ave.
Helena, MT 59625-0002
Tel: (406)447-4300; Free: 800-992-3648
Fax: (406)447-4533
E-mail: admission@carroll.edu
Web Site: www.carroll.edu

Description: Independent Roman Catholic, 4-year, coed. Awards associate and bachelor's degrees. Founded 1909. Setting: 61-acre small town campus. Endowment: $36 million. Total enrollment: 1,352. Faculty: 163 (91 full-time, 72 part-time). Student-undergrad faculty ratio is 12:1. 3,005 applied, 71% were admitted. 29% from top 10% of their high school class, 62% from top quarter, 87% from top half. Full-time: 1,287 students, 60% women, 40% men. Part-time: 65 students, 58% women, 42% men. Students come from 35 states and territories, 14 other countries, 5% from out-of-state. 0.6% American Indian or Alaska Native, non-Hispanic/Latino; 5% Hispanic/Latino; 0.7% Black or African American, non-Hispanic/Latino; 1% Asian, non-Hispanic/Latino; 0.2% Native Hawaiian or other Pacific Islander, non-Hispanic/Latino; 1% international. 4% 25 or older, 57% live on campus, 3%

transferred in. Retention: 79% of full-time freshmen returned the following year. Academic areas with the most degrees conferred: health professions and related sciences; biological/life sciences; business/marketing. Core. Calendar: semesters. ESL program, advanced placement, accelerated degree program, self-designed majors, freshman honors college, honors program, independent study, double major, summer session for credit, part-time degree program, adult/continuing education programs, co-op programs and internships. Study abroad program. ROTC: Army.

Entrance Requirements: Options: electronic application, deferred admission, international baccalaureate accepted. Required: essay, high school transcript, SAT or ACT. Recommended: interview. Required for some: interview, SAT Subject Tests. Entrance: moderately difficult. Application deadline: 2/15. Notification: continuous, continuous for nonresidents. SAT Reasoning Test deadline: 6/15. SAT Subject Test deadline: 6/15. Transfer credits accepted: Yes.

Costs Per Year: Application fee: $35. Comprehensive fee: $45,466 includes full-time tuition ($34,506), mandatory fees ($980), and college room and board ($9980). Full-time tuition and fees vary according to program. Room and board charges vary according to board plan. Part-time tuition: $1438 per credit hour. Part-time mandatory fees: $245 per year. Part-time tuition and fees vary according to program.

Collegiate Environment: Orientation program. Drama-theater group, choral group, student-run newspaper, radio station. Most popular organizations: Student Government, Carroll Outreach Team, Carroll Adventure and Mountaineering Program, Up 'Til Dawn, Engineers Without Borders. Major annual events: Homecoming, Casino Night, Spring Softball Tournament. Student services: health clinic, personal-psychological counseling. Campus security: 24-hour emergency response devices, late night transport-escort service, controlled dormitory access. Corette Library plus 1 other. Books: 76,993 (physical), 230,000 (digital/electronic); Databases: 79. Study areas open 24 hours, 5-7 days a week; students can reserve study rooms. Operations spending for the previous fiscal year: $671,484.

■ CHIEF DULL KNIFE COLLEGE

1 College Dr.
Lame Deer, MT 59043-0098
Tel: (406)477-6215
Fax: (406)477-6219
Web Site: www.cdkc.edu

Description: Independent, 2-year, coed. Awards certificates, transfer associate, and terminal associate degrees. Founded 1975. Setting: 3-acre rural campus. Total enrollment: 472. Student-undergrad faculty ratio is 13:1. 40% 25 or older. Core. Calendar: semesters. Academic remediation for entering students, services for LD students, summer session for credit, part-time degree program, adult/continuing education programs, co-op programs and internships. Off campus study at members of the American Indian Higher Education Consortium.

Entrance Requirements: Open admission. Option: early admission. Required: high school transcript. Entrance: noncompetitive. Application deadline: rolling. Notification: continuous.

Collegiate Environment: Student-run newspaper. Student services: personal-psychological counseling.

■ DAWSON COMMUNITY COLLEGE

300 College Dr.
Glendive, MT 59330-0421

Tel: (406)377-3396; Free: 800-821-8320
Fax: (406)377-8132
E-mail: jbrandt@dawson.edu
Web Site: www.dawson.edu

Description: State and locally supported, 2-year, coed. Part of Montana University System. Awards certificates, transfer associate, and terminal associate degrees. Founded 1940. Setting: 300-acre rural campus. Endowment: $3.5 million. Educational spending for the previous fiscal year: $6272 per student. Total enrollment: 329. Faculty: 32 (13 full-time, 19 part-time). Student-undergrad faculty ratio is 17:1. 326 applied, 100% were admitted. Full-time: 205 students, 42% women, 58% men. Part-time: 124 students, 64% women, 36% men. Students come from 19 states and territories, 2 other countries, 80% from out-of-state. 3% American Indian or Alaska Native, non-Hispanic/Latino; 3% Hispanic/Latino; 5% Black or African American, non-Hispanic/Latino; 0.9% Asian, non-Hispanic/Latino; 0.3% Native Hawaiian or other Pacific Islander, non-Hispanic/Latino; 2% international. 189% 25 or older, 11% transferred in. Core. Calendar: semesters. Academic remediation for entering students, services for LD students, independent study, distance learning, summer session for credit, part-time degree program, adult/continuing education programs, internships.

Entrance Requirements: Open admission. Options: electronic application, deferred admission, international baccalaureate accepted. Required: high school transcript. Entrance: noncompetitive. Application deadline: rolling. Notification: continuous. Transfer credits accepted: Yes.

Costs Per Year: Application fee: $30. Area resident tuition: $2100 full-time, $70 per credit hour part-time. State resident tuition: $3630 full-time, $121 per credit hour part-time. Nonresident tuition: $6150 full-time, $205 per credit hour part-time. Mandatory fees: $1620 full-time, $54 per credit hour part-time. College room and board: $7574. Room and board charges vary according to board plan.

Collegiate Environment: Orientation program. Drama-theater group, choral group. Social organizations: 18 open to all. Most popular organizations: Phi Theta Kappa, Associated Student Body, Rodeo Club, Intervarsity, FFA. Major annual events: Homecoming, International Night, Awards Ceremony. Campus security: 24-hour emergency response devices. Jane Carey Memorial Library plus 1 other. Books: 33,477 (physical), 13,359 (digital/electronic); Serial titles: 81 (physical); Databases: 118. Weekly public service hours: 40; students can reserve study rooms. Operations spending for the previous fiscal year: $110,529. 72 computers available on campus for general student use. A campuswide network can be accessed. Students can access the following: online class registration. Staffed computer lab on campus provides training in use of computers, software, and the Internet.

Community Environment: Dawson is located in Glendive, the county seat of Dawson County. It is a transportation, agricultural and energy resource center located on the Yellowstone River on I-94. The city has a library, Frontier Gateway Museum, several churches, a hospital, and most major civic, fraternal and veteran's organizations within the immediate area. Recreation facilities include indoor and outdoor theaters, good hunting, limited boating and fishing, golf, and other outdoor sports. Some part-time work is available for students.

■ FLATHEAD VALLEY COMMUNITY COLLEGE

777 Grandview Dr.
Kalispell, MT 59901-2622
Tel: (406)756-3822; Free: 800-313-3822
Fax: (406)756-3815
E-mail: mstoltz@fvcc.cc.mt.us
Web Site: www.fvcc.edu

Description: State and locally supported, 2-year, coed. Part of Montana University System. Awards certificates, transfer associate, and terminal associate degrees. Founded 1967. Setting: 209-acre small town campus. Endowment: $6.5 million. Educational spending for the previous fiscal year: $4133 per student. Total enrollment: 2,216. Faculty: 206 (54 full-time, 152 part-time). Student-undergrad faculty ratio is 16:1. Full-time: 1,082 students, 54% women, 46% men. Part-time: 1,134 students, 67% women, 33% men. Students come from 18 states and territories, 3% from out-of-state. 3% American Indian or Alaska Native, non-Hispanic/Latino; 2% Hispanic/Latino; 0.3% Black or African American, non-Hispanic/Latino; 0.9% Asian, non-Hispanic/Latino; 0.3% Native Hawaiian or other Pacific Islander, non-Hispanic/Latino; 0.1% international. 49% 25 or older, 1% live on campus, 8% transferred in. Retention: 52% of full-time freshmen returned the following year. Core. Calendar: semesters. Academic remediation for entering students, ESL program, services for LD students, advanced placement, honors program, independent study, distance learning, double major, sum-

mer session for credit, part-time degree program, adult/continuing education programs, co-op programs and internships. Study abroad program.

Entrance Requirements: Open admission. Options: electronic application, early admission, deferred admission, international baccalaureate accepted. Required: high school transcript. Recommended: ACT. Entrance: noncompetitive. Application deadline: rolling. Transfer credits accepted: Yes.

Collegiate Environment: Orientation program. Drama-theater group, choral group, student-run newspaper. Social organizations: 23 open to all. Most popular organizations: Forestry Club, Phi Theta Kappa. Student services: health clinic, personal-psychological counseling. Flathead Valley Community College Library. Operations spending for the previous fiscal year: $238,002. 230 computers available on campus for general student use. A campuswide network can be accessed. Students can access the following: online class registration. Staffed computer lab on campus.

Community Environment: The campus is located 3 miles north of Kalispell city center in the beautiful Flathead Valley, a region noted for the production of seed potatoes, wheat, cattle, Christmas trees, plywood, lumber and sweet cherries. The city is circled by dense forests, lakes, and mountains, with more than 2,000 miles of good fishing streams. Transportation for the area is provided by air, rail, and bus lines. There are 28 churches, one library, a hospital and a medical center. Convenient shopping is easily accessible. Although Kalispell is a resort area, the local industries include plywood production, camper and camp trailer manufacturing, log-skidding machinery, and chemical and concrete products. Part-time employment is available for students.

■ FORT PECK COMMUNITY COLLEGE

PO Box 398
Poplar, MT 59255-0398
Tel: (406)768-5551
Web Site: www.fpcc.edu

Description: District-supported, 2-year, coed. Awards certificates, transfer associate, and terminal associate degrees. Founded 1978. Setting: small town campus. Total enrollment: 422. 63% 25 or older. Core. Calendar: semesters. Summer session for credit, part-time degree program. Off campus study at members of the American Indian Higher Education Consortium.

Entrance Requirements: Open admission. Options: electronic application, early admission. Entrance: noncompetitive. Application deadline: rolling.

■ GREAT FALLS COLLEGE MONTANA STATE UNIVERSITY

2100 16th Ave., S
Great Falls, MT 59405
Tel: (406)771-4300; Free: 800-446-2698
Fax: (406)771-4317
E-mail: joe.simonsen@gfcmsu.edu
Web Site: www.gfcmsu.edu

Description: State-supported, 2-year, coed. Part of Montana University System. Awards certificates, transfer associate, and terminal associate degrees. Founded 1969. Setting: 40-acre small town campus. Endowment: $11,300. Educational spending for the previous fiscal year: $8052 per student. Total enrollment: 1,690. Faculty: 114 (44 full-time, 70 part-time). Student-undergrad faculty ratio is 15:1. 412 applied, 86% were admitted. Full-time: 646 students, 68% women, 32% men. Part-time: 1,044 students, 72% women, 28% men. Students come from 28 states and territories, 2 other countries, 4% from out-of-state. 5% American Indian or Alaska Native, non-Hispanic/Latino; 5% Hispanic/Latino; 2% Black or African American, non-Hispanic/Latino; 0.9% Asian, non-Hispanic/Latino; 0.1% Native Hawaiian or other Pacific Islander, non-Hispanic/Latino; 0.1% international. 53% 25 or older, 7% transferred in. Calendar: semesters. Academic remediation for entering students, services for LD students, advanced placement, independent study, distance learning, double major, summer session for credit, part-time degree program, internships. Off campus study.

Entrance Requirements: Open admission Open admissions policy except for dental assistant and hygiene, paramedic, medical assistant, practical nurse, registered nurse, surgical technology, respiratory care, physical therapist assistant, welding programs. Options: electronic application, early admission. Required: high school transcript, proof of immunization. Entrance: noncompetitive. Application deadline: rolling. Notification: continuous. Transfer credits accepted: Yes.

Costs Per Year: Application fee: $30. State resident tuition: $2752 full-time, $114.67 per credit hour part-time. Nonresident tuition: $9644 full-time, $401.84 per credit hour part-time. Mandatory fees: $634 full-time, $58.51 per credit hour part-time, $30 per term part-time. Full-time tuition and fees vary according to course load, location, and program. Part-time tuition and fees vary according to course load, location, and program.

Collegiate Environment: Orientation program. Choral group. Social organizations: 13 open to all. Most popular organizations: The Associated Students of Great Falls College Montana State University, Phi Theta Kappa, Medical Assistant Club, Dental Hygiene Club, Nursing Club. Major annual events: Trick or Treat Bash, No Smile Left Behind, Spring Fling/Picnic. Campus security: 24-hour emergency response devices, patrol by security personnel. Weaver Library plus 1 other. Books: 9,239 (physical), 266,102 (digital/electronic); Serial titles: 60 (physical), 121,995 (digital/electronic); Databases: 55. Students can reserve study rooms. Operations spending for the previous fiscal year: $320,766. 520 computers available on campus for general student use. A campuswide network can be accessed from off-campus. Students can access the following: online class registration. Staffed computer lab on campus provides training in use of computers, software, and the Internet.

■ HELENA COLLEGE UNIVERSITY OF MONTANA

1115 N Roberts St.
Helena, MT 59601
Tel: (406)444-6800; Free: 800-241-4882
Fax: (406)444-6892
Web Site: www.umhelena.edu

Description: State-supported, 2-year, coed. Part of Montana University System. Administratively affiliated with The University of Montana. Awards certificates, transfer associate, and terminal associate degrees. Founded 1939. Setting: small town campus. Endowment: $75,877. Educational spending for the previous fiscal year: $7473 per student. Total enrollment: 1,430. Faculty: 155 (40 full-time, 115 part-time). Student-undergrad faculty ratio is 12:1. 669 applied, 87% were admitted. Full-time: 670 students, 50% women, 50% men. Part-time: 760 students, 66% women, 34% men. Students come from 12 states and territories. 4% American Indian or Alaska Native, non-Hispanic/Latino; 2% Hispanic/Latino; 0.6% Black or African American, non-Hispanic/Latino; 1% Asian, non-Hispanic/Latino. 46% 25 or older, 7% transferred in. Retention: 53% of full-time freshmen returned the following year. Core. Calendar: semesters. Academic remediation for entering students, services for LD students, advanced placement, distance learning, double major, summer session for credit, part-time degree program, adult/continuing education programs, internships. Study abroad program.

Entrance Requirements: Open admission. Options: electronic application, early admission, deferred admission, international baccalaureate accepted. Required for some: high school transcript. Entrance: noncompetitive. Application deadline: rolling. Transfer credits accepted: Yes.

Collegiate Environment: Orientation program. Social organizations: 3 open to all. Most popular organizations: Student Government Association, Phi Theta Kappa, College Christian Fellowship, Aviation Club, Future Machinists of America. Major annual events: Fall and Spring BBQs, Community Fairs, HC SGA Christmas Party. Student services: personal-psychological counseling. Campus security: late night transport-escort service. Helena College. Operations spending for the previous fiscal year: $198,050. 200 computers available on campus for general student use. A campuswide network can be accessed from off-campus. Students can access the following: online class registration. Staffed computer lab on campus provides training in use of computers, software, and the Internet.

■ HIGHLANDS COLLEGE OF MONTANA TECH

25 Basin Creek Rd.
Butte, MT 59701
Tel: (406)496-3701
Fax: (406)496-3710
Web Site: www.mtech.edu/academics/highlands

Description: State-supported, 2-year, coed. Awards certificates, transfer associate, and terminal associate degrees. Founded 1969.

■ LITTLE BIG HORN COLLEGE

Box 370
1 Forest Ln.
Crow Agency, MT 59022-0370
Tel: (406)638-3104
Web Site: www.lbhc.edu

Description: Independent, 2-year, coed. Awards certificates, transfer associate, and terminal associate degrees. Founded 1980. Setting: 5-acre rural campus. Total enrollment: 317. Faculty: 12 (11 full-time, 1 part-time). Student-undergrad faculty ratio is 25:1. 50% 25 or older. Core. Calendar:

quarters. Part-time degree program. Off campus study at members of the American Indian Higher Education Consortium.

Entrance Requirements: Open admission. Required: high school transcript. Entrance: noncompetitive. Application deadline: rolling. Notification: continuous.

Collegiate Environment: Student-run newspaper. 30 computers available on campus for general student use. Staffed computer lab on campus.

■ MILES COMMUNITY COLLEGE

2715 Dickinson
Miles City, MT 59301-4799
Tel: (406)874-6100; Free: 800-541-9281
Fax: (406)874-6282
E-mail: andersonh@milescc.edu
Web Site: www.milescc.edu

Description: State and locally supported, 2-year, coed. Part of Montana University System. Awards certificates, transfer associate, and terminal associate degrees. Founded 1939. Setting: 8-acre small town campus. Total enrollment: 441. Faculty: 50 (24 full-time, 26 part-time). Student-undergrad faculty ratio is 10:1. 319 applied, 100% were admitted. Full-time: 280 students, 50% women, 50% men. Part-time: 161 students, 81% women, 19% men. Students come from 24 states and territories, 4 other countries, 14% from out-of-state. 4% American Indian or Alaska Native, non-Hispanic/Latino; 2% Hispanic/Latino; 2% Black or African American, non-Hispanic/Latino; 1% Asian, non-Hispanic/Latino; 2% international. 32% live on campus, 11% transferred in. Core. Calendar: semesters. Academic remediation for entering students, ESL program, services for LD students, advanced placement, accelerated degree program, honors program, independent study, distance learning, double major, summer session for credit, part-time degree program, adult/continuing education programs, co-op programs and internships.

Entrance Requirements: Open admission except for nursing program, heavy equipment operator program. Options: electronic application, early admission, deferred admission. Required: high school transcript. Entrance: noncompetitive. Application deadline: rolling. Transfer credits accepted: Yes. Applicants placed on waiting list: 0. Wait-listed applicants offered admission: 0.

Collegiate Environment: Orientation program. Drama-theater group. Student services: personal-psychological counseling. Campus security: 24-hour emergency response devices, manual dormitory entrances locked all the time, only accessible with key. Library Resource Center. 165 computers available on campus for general student use. A campuswide network can be accessed from student residence rooms and from off campus. Staffed computer lab on campus.

Community Environment: Vast livestock ranches around Miles City raise more than one-fourth of the cattle and sheep produced in Montana. Wheat is the primary crop grown in the dryland area. The city itself is a pleasant residential town with a mean annual temperature of 44.4 degrees, and an average rainfall of 13.79 inches. Local area is served by airlines and bus lines. The community has 17 churches, tennis courts, two theaters, bowling alley, golf course, radio and TV station and various civic and fraternal organizations. Local homes, apartments and rooms provide student housing in addition to dormitories. There are limited part-time work opportunities for students.

■ MONTANA BIBLE COLLEGE

3625 S 19th Ave.
Bozeman, MT 59718
Tel: (406)586-3585; Free: 888-462-2463
Web Site: www.montanabiblecollege.edu

Description: Independent Christian, 4-year, coed. Awards bachelor's degrees. Setting: urban campus. Calendar: semesters.

Entrance Requirements: Open admission. Options: electronic application, international baccalaureate accepted. Required: essay, 4 recommendations, SAT or ACT. Required for some: high school transcript, college transcript. Transfer credits accepted: Yes.

Costs Per Year: Tuition: $7680 full-time, $240 per credit hour part-time. Mandatory fees: $600 full-time. Full-time tuition and fees vary according to location. Part-time tuition varies according to course load and location. College room only: $3200. Room charges vary according to housing facility.

Collegiate Environment: Gail Horton Library plus 1 other.

■ MONTANA STATE UNIVERSITY

Bozeman, MT 59717
Tel: (406)994-0211; Free: 888-MSU-CATS

E-mail: admissions@montana.edu

Web Site: www.montana.edu

Description: State-supported, university, coed. Part of Montana University System. Awards associate, bachelor's, master's, and doctoral degrees and post-master's certificates. Founded 1893. Setting: 1,850-acre small town campus. Endowment: $126.5 million. Research spending for the previous fiscal year: $116 million. Educational spending for the previous fiscal year: $7521 per student. Total enrollment: 16,440. Faculty: 1,038 (600 full-time, 438 part-time). Student-undergrad faculty ratio is 19:1. 15,996 applied, 83% were admitted. 20% from top 10% of their high school class, 43% from top quarter, 74% from top half. Full-time: 12,248 students, 45% women, 55% men. Part-time: 2,152 students, 46% women, 54% men. 39% from out-of-state. 2% American Indian or Alaska Native, non-Hispanic/Latino; 4% Hispanic/Latino; 0.7% Black or African American, non-Hispanic/Latino; 0.9% Asian, non-Hispanic/Latino; 0.1% Native Hawaiian or other Pacific Islander, non-Hispanic/Latino; 3% international. 14% 25 or older, 25% live on campus, 6% transferred in. Retention: 76% of full-time freshmen returned the following year. Core. Calendar: semesters. Academic remediation for entering students, ESL program, services for LD students, advanced placement, self-designed majors, freshman honors college, honors program, independent study, distance learning, double major, summer session for credit, part-time degree program, adult/continuing education programs, co-op programs and internships, graduate courses open to undergrads. Off campus study at members of the National Student Exchange. Study abroad program. ROTC: Army, Air Force.

Entrance Requirements: Options: electronic application, early admission, deferred admission, international baccalaureate accepted. Required: high school transcript, minimum 2.5 high school GPA, SAT or ACT. Entrance: moderately difficult. Application deadlines: rolling, rolling for nonresidents. Notification: continuous, continuous for nonresidents. Transfer credits accepted: Yes.

Costs Per Year: Application fee: $30. State resident tuition: $5654 full-time, $236 per credit part-time. Nonresident tuition: $23,082 full-time, $962 per credit part-time. Mandatory fees: $1767 full-time, $113 per credit part-time. Full-time tuition and fees vary according to course load, degree level, location, and program. Part-time tuition and fees vary according to course load, degree level, location, and program. College room and board: $10,100. Room and board charges vary according to board plan and housing facility.

Collegiate Environment: Orientation program. Drama-theater group, choral group, marching band, student-run newspaper, radio station. Social organizations: national fraternities, national sororities. Most popular organizations: Spurs, Inter-Varsity Christian Fellowship, Campus Crusade for Christ, Fangs, Mortar Board. Major annual events: International Food Bazaar, Native American Pow-Wow, Day of Student Recognition. Student services: legal services, health clinic, personal-psychological counseling, women's center. Campus security: 24-hour emergency response devices and patrols, student patrols, late night transport-escort service, 24-hour residence hall monitoring. Renne Library plus 2 others. Students can reserve study rooms. Operations spending for the previous fiscal year: $8.8 million.

Community Environment: At the heart of the Gallatin Valley, known for its scenic beauty, the city is headquarters for Gallatin National Forest. The Bridger Bowl Ski Area, 18 miles northwest, and Big Sky, Inc. 33 miles south offer skiing from mid-November to mid-March. Immediately south of Bozeman, Highway 191 follows Gallatin River through the forest to Yellowstone National Park 90 miles away. The Gallatin Field airport is 8 miles from Bozeman and is served by Delta and Northwest. Community services include many churches, public library, one hospital, and many hotels and motels. Various service clubs, veteran's clubs, and many fraternal organizations are represented within the immediate area. Recreation other than skiing is provided by local picnic areas, swimming pools, five parks, tennis courts, dude ranches, golf courses, hunting, boating, and fishing. Bozeman is known for its year-round outdoor recreational opportunities.

■ MONTANA STATE UNIVERSITY BILLINGS

1500 University Dr.

Billings, MT 59101

Tel: (406)657-2011; Free: 800-565-6782

Fax: (406)657-2302

E-mail: tammi.watson@msubillings.edu

Web Site: www.msubillings.edu

Description: State-supported, comprehensive, coed. Part of Montana University System. Awards associate, bachelor's, and master's degrees. Founded 1927. Setting: 92-acre urban campus. Endowment: $24.7 million. Research spending for the previous fiscal year: $642,610. Educational

spending for the previous fiscal year: $7730 per student. Total enrollment: 4,401. Faculty: 325 (158 full-time, 167 part-time). Student-undergrad faculty ratio is 14:1. 1,423 applied, 99% were admitted. 7% from top 10% of their high school class, 26% from top quarter, 61% from top half. 11 valedictorians. Full-time: 2,400 students, 58% women, 42% men. Part-time: 1,621 students, 69% women, 31% men. Students come from 39 states and territories, 30 other countries, 5% from out-of-state. 4% American Indian or Alaska Native, non-Hispanic/Latino; 6% Hispanic/Latino; 1% Black or African American, non-Hispanic/Latino; 0.9% Asian, non-Hispanic/Latino; 0.3% Native Hawaiian or other Pacific Islander, non-Hispanic/Latino; 2% international. 35% 25 or older, 10% live on campus, 10% transferred in. Retention: 57% of full-time freshmen returned the following year. Academic areas with the most degrees conferred: business/marketing; education; psychology. Core. Calendar: semesters. Academic remediation for entering students, ESL program, services for LD students, advanced placement, accelerated degree program, self-designed majors, honors program, independent study, distance learning, double major, summer session for credit, part-time degree program, adult/continuing education programs, co-op programs and internships, graduate courses open to undergrads. Off campus study. Study abroad program. ROTC: Army.

Entrance Requirements: Open admission for the City College (two-year Community College). Option: electronic application. Required: high school transcript. Required for some: SAT or ACT. Entrance: minimally difficult. Application deadline: rolling. Notification: continuous. SAT Reasoning Test deadline: 9/1. SAT Subject Test deadline: 9/1. Transfer credits accepted: Yes.

Costs Per Year: Application fee: $30. State resident tuition: $4,485 full-time, $186.87 per credit hour part-time. Nonresident tuition: $17,678 full-time, $736.59 per credit hour part-time. Mandatory fees: $1436 full-time. Full-time tuition and fees vary according to course load, location, and program. Part-time tuition varies according to course load, location, and program. College room and board: $8186. College room only: $4450. Room and board charges vary according to board plan and housing facility.

Collegiate Environment: Orientation program. Drama-theater group, choral group, student-run newspaper, radio station. Social organizations: 60 open to all. Most popular organizations: Intervarsity Christian Fellowship, Accounting Club, HEROES, Multicultural Club, Art Student League. Major annual events: Welcome Week Events, Power of One Events, Freak Week Events. Student services: legal services, health clinic, personal-psychological counseling, women's center. Campus security: 24-hour emergency response devices and patrols, late night transport-escort service, controlled dormitory access. Montana State University Billings Library plus 2 others. Books: 138,650 (physical), 351,351 (digital/electronic); Serial titles: 1,368 (physical), 669,204 (digital/electronic); Databases: 170. Weekly public service hours: 82; students can reserve study rooms. Operations spending for the previous fiscal year: $967,827. 1,500 computers available on campus for general student use. Computer purchase/lease plans available. A campuswide network can be accessed from student residence rooms and from off campus. Students can access the following: online class registration, online degree programs. Staffed computer lab on campus provides training in use of computers, software, and the Internet.

Community Environment: Billings is an expanding city located in the Yellowstone River Valley between rugged mountains and sweeping plains. The city is the largest in Montana, and has a population of approximately 98,700 people living in the metropolitan area. The "Magic City" is a transportation, medical, agricultural, wholesale, and retail trade center. It is served by major air, bus, and rail lines, and excellent interstate highways. Community services include many churches representing most denominations, a city library, theatres, museums, art galleries, two hospitals, YMCA, YWCA, and various civic and fraternal organizations. Recreational sites are numerous and include opportunities for fishing, hunting, boating, bowling, golf, skiing, and hiking.

■ MONTANA STATE UNIVERSITY-NORTHERN

PO Box 7751

Havre, MT 59501-7751

Tel: (406)265-3700; Free: 800-662-6132

Fax: (406)265-3777

Web Site: www.msun.edu

Description: State-supported, comprehensive, coed. Part of Montana University System. Awards associate, bachelor's, and master's degrees. Founded 1929. Setting: 10-acre small town campus. Total enrollment: 1,273. Faculty: 96 (62 full-time, 34 part-time). Student-undergrad faculty ratio is 15:1. 378 applied, 64% were admitted. 4% from top 10% of their high school class, 14% from top quarter, 43% from top half. Full-time: 923 students, 43% women, 57% men. Part-time: 285 students, 74% women, 26% men. 89% from out-of-state. 13% American Indian or Alaska Native, non-Hispanic/Latino; 2% Hispanic/Latino; 0.9% Black or African American, non-Hispanic/Latino; 1% Asian, non-Hispanic/Latino; 1% international. 34% 25 or older, 22% live on campus, 15% transferred in. Retention: 58% of full-time freshmen returned the following year. Academic areas with the most degrees conferred: education; mechanic and repair technologies; health professions and related sciences. Calendar: semesters. Part-time degree program, adult/continuing education programs.

Entrance Requirements: Options: early admission, deferred admission. Required: high school transcript. Required for some: minimum 2 high school GPA. Entrance: moderately difficult. Application deadline: rolling. Notification: continuous.

Costs Per Year: Application fee: $30. State resident tuition: $5954 full-time, $289.27 per credit part-time. Nonresident tuition: $18,666 full-time, $818.85 per credit part-time.

Collegiate Environment: Orientation program. Vande Bogart Libraries.

Community Environment: Havre is the transportation hub of the Northern Great Plains, America's agricultural heartland. Montana's panoramic Big Sky meets a horizon of rolling foothills and abundant lakes and reservoirs. The community is easily accessible from all directions by highway, Amtrak, and a commuter airline with links to major international airports. Rugged environments such as Glacier National Park, the Cypress Hills of Canada, the Bears Paw Mountains and the Little Rockies, are only a few hours away. Picnicking, camping, abundant wildlife, lakes with great fishing, boating, and water skiing, and numerous winter and summer sports offer recreation for outdoor enthusiasts.

■ MONTANA TECH OF THE UNIVERSITY OF MONTANA
1300 W Park St.
Butte, MT 59701-8997
Tel: (406)496-4101; Free: 800-445-TECH
Fax: (406)496-4710
E-mail: scrowe@mtech.edu
Web Site: www.mtech.edu

Description: State-supported, comprehensive, coed. Part of Montana University System. Awards associate, bachelor's, master's, and doctoral degrees. Founded 1895. Setting: 56-acre small town campus. Endowment: $32.9 million. Research spending for the previous fiscal year: $11.4 million. Educational spending for the previous fiscal year: $7240 per student. Total enrollment: 2,678. Faculty: 213 (150 full-time, 63 part-time). Student-undergrad faculty ratio is 13:1. 981 applied, 92% were admitted. 25% from top 10% of their high school class, 56% from top quarter, 86% from top half. Full-time: 1,924 students, 34% women, 66% men. Part-time: 504 students, 54% women, 46% men. Students come from 39 states and territories, 10 other countries, 14% from out-of-state. 2% American Indian or Alaska Native, non-Hispanic/Latino; 2% Hispanic/Latino; 0.9% Black or African American, non-Hispanic/Latino; 0.5% Asian, non-Hispanic/Latino; 10% international. 24% 25 or older, 12% live on campus, 6% transferred in. Retention: 76% of full-time freshmen returned the following year. Academic areas with the most degrees conferred: engineering; health professions and related sciences; business/marketing. Core. Calendar: semesters. Academic remediation for entering students, services for LD students, advanced placement, self-designed majors, honors program, independent study, distance learning, double major, summer session for credit, part-time degree program, external degree program, adult/continuing education programs, co-op programs and internships, graduate courses open to undergrads.

Entrance Requirements: Open admission for Highlands College students. Options: electronic application, deferred admission, international baccalaureate accepted. Required: high school transcript, proof of immunization, SAT or ACT. Required for some: minimum 2.5 high school GPA. Entrance: moderately difficult. Application deadline: rolling. Notification: continuous.

Costs Per Year: Application fee: $30. State resident tuition: $5707 full-time, $238 per credit part-time. Nonresident tuition: $20,870 full-time, $886 per credit part-time. Mandatory fees: $1704 full-time, $69 per credit part-time. Full-time tuition and fees vary according to course load, degree level, location, and program. Part-time tuition and fees vary according to course load, degree level, location, and program. College room and board: $9828. College room only: $4366. Room and board charges vary according to board plan.

Collegiate Environment: Orientation program. Choral group, student-run newspaper, radio station. Social organizations: 30 open to all. Most popular organizations: Circle K, Ski/Snowboard Club, BSU, Hockey Club, Dance

Club. Major annual events: Homecoming, Mulletfest, Holiday Stroll. Student services: health clinic, personal-psychological counseling. Campus security: 24-hour patrols, controlled dormitory access. Montana Tech Library. Books: 80,864 (physical), 91,830 (digital/electronic); Serial titles: 1,859 (physical), 67,191 (digital/electronic); Databases: 148. Weekly public service hours: 80; students can reserve study rooms. Operations spending for the previous fiscal year: $275,293. 660 computers available on campus for general student use. A campuswide network can be accessed from student residence rooms and from off campus. Students can access the following: online class registration.

Community Environment: Known as the "richest hill on earth," Butte has the reputation of being the world's greatest mining city. Mine workings consist of more than 10,000 miles of underground excavation. They produce a substantial percentage of the total amount of copper mined in the United States and a quantity of zinc ore. The Butte mining district is on the edge of one of the broad, faulted valleys characteristic of western Montana. During the more than 100 years of its active existence, this district has yielded manganese, copper, zinc, silver, lead, gold, and minor amounts of other metals. Three mountain ranges surround the city from the Continental Divide. The area is served by two transcontinental railroads, airlines, and bus lines. Butte community service facilities include many churches, two hospitals, five radio stations, and two TV stations. The city has a wholesale and retail shopping center. Many civic, fraternal, and professional organizations meet regularly in the immediate area. Recreation in the forms of skiing, hiking, fishing, hunting, boating, and golf are within minutes of the city.

■ PIMA MEDICAL INSTITUTE
434 E Poindexter St.
Dillon, MT 59725
Web Site: www.pmi.edu
Description: Proprietary, 2-year, coed.

■ ROCKY MOUNTAIN COLLEGE
1511 Poly Dr.
Billings, MT 59102-1796
Tel: (406)657-1000; Free: 800-877-6259
Fax: (406)259-9751
E-mail: admissions@rocky.edu
Web Site: www.rocky.edu

Description: Independent interdenominational, comprehensive, coed. Awards associate, bachelor's, master's, and doctoral degrees. Founded 1878. Setting: 60-acre suburban campus. Endowment: $30.9 million. Educational spending for the previous fiscal year: $10,034 per student. Total enrollment: 997. Faculty: 112 (64 full-time, 48 part-time). Student-undergrad faculty ratio is 11:1. 1,521 applied, 58% were admitted. 17% from top 10% of their high school class, 46% from top quarter, 76% from top half. Full-time: 867 students, 49% women, 51% men. Part-time: 30 students, 37% women, 63% men. Students come from 43 states and territories, 16 other countries, 47% from out-of-state. 2% American Indian or Alaska Native, non-Hispanic/Latino; 6% Hispanic/Latino; 3% Black or African American, non-Hispanic/Latino; 0.6% Asian, non-Hispanic/Latino; 0.7% Native Hawaiian or other Pacific Islander, non-Hispanic/Latino; 4% international. 7% 25 or older, 51% live on campus, 5% transferred in. Retention: 67% of full-time freshmen returned the following year. Academic areas with the most degrees conferred: business/marketing; parks and recreation; biological/life sciences. Core. Calendar: semesters. Academic remediation for entering students, ESL program, services for LD students, advanced placement, accelerated degree program, self-designed majors, honors program, independent study, double major, summer session for credit, part-time degree program, adult/continuing education programs, internships. Off campus study. Study abroad program. ROTC: Army (c).

Entrance Requirements: Options: electronic application, deferred admission, international baccalaureate accepted. Required: high school transcript, minimum 2.5 high school GPA, SAT or ACT. Required for some: essay, 2 recommendations, interview. Entrance: moderately difficult. Application deadline: rolling. Notification: continuous. Transfer credits accepted: Yes.

Costs Per Year: Application fee: $35. Comprehensive fee: $38,004 includes full-time tuition ($28,962), mandatory fees ($590), and college room and board ($8452). College room only: $4140. Part-time tuition: $1207 per credit.

Collegiate Environment: Orientation program. Drama-theater group, choral group, student-run newspaper. Social organizations: 15 open to all. Most popular organizations: Outdoor Recreation, Enactus, Flight Team/Club, Environmental Club, InterVarsity Christian Fellowship. Major annual events: Homecoming, Yule Log Dinner, Academic Awards Banquet. Student services: health clinic, personal-psychological counseling. Campus security: 24-hour emergency response devices, student patrols, late night transport-escort service, controlled dormitory access. 570 college housing spaces available; 456 were occupied in 2018-19. Freshmen guaranteed college housing. On-campus residence required through sophomore year. Option: coed housing available. Paul M. Adams Memorial Library. Books: 46,877 (physical), 172,956 (digital/electronic); Serial titles: 379 (physical), 92,127 (digital/electronic); Databases: 119. Weekly public service hours: 89. Operations spending for the previous fiscal year: $350,033. 113 computers available on campus for general student use. A campuswide network can be accessed from student residence rooms and from off campus. Students can access the following: online class registration. Staffed computer lab on campus (open 24 hours a day) provides training in use of computers, software, and the Internet.

■ **SALISH KOOTENAI COLLEGE**
PO Box 70
Pablo, MT 59855-0117
Tel: (406)275-4800
Fax: (406)275-4801
E-mail: jackie_moran@skc.edu
Web Site: www.skc.edu
Description: Independent, primarily 2-year, coed. Awards certificates, transfer associate, terminal associate, and bachelor's degrees. Founded 1977. Setting: 4-acre rural campus. Total enrollment: 1,088. Faculty: 80 (45 full-time, 35 part-time). 344 applied, 64% were admitted. 50% from top half of their high school class. Full-time: 585 students, 63% women, 37% men. Part-time: 503 students, 58% women, 42% men. Students come from 3 states and territories. 48% 25 or older. Core. Calendar: quarters. Academic remediation for entering students, services for LD students, summer session for credit, part-time degree program, adult/continuing education programs, co-op programs. Off campus study at members of the American Indian Higher Education Consortium.
Entrance Requirements: Open admission. Option: deferred admission. Required: high school transcript, proof of immunization, tribal enrollment. Entrance: noncompetitive. Application deadline: rolling. Notification: continuous. Preference given to Native Americans.
Collegiate Environment: Drama-theater group. Student services: personal-psychological counseling. 30 computers available on campus for general student use.

■ **STONE CHILD COLLEGE**
8294 Upper Box Elder Rd.
Box Elder, MT 59521
Tel: (406)395-4313
Fax: (406)395-4836
Web Site: www.stonechild.edu
Description: Independent, 2-year, coed. Awards certificates, transfer associate, and terminal associate degrees. Founded 1984. Setting: rural campus. Total enrollment: 240. Faculty: 22 (10 full-time, 12 part-time). 11 applied, 100% were admitted. Calendar: semesters.
Entrance Requirements: Open admission. Required: high school transcript. Entrance: noncompetitive.
Collegiate Environment: 42 computers available on campus for general student use. Staffed computer lab on campus.

■ **UNIVERSITY OF MONTANA**
32 Campus Dr.
Missoula, MT 59812
Tel: (406)243-0211; Free: 800-462-8636
Fax: (406)243-5711
E-mail: admiss@umontana.edu
Web Site: www.umt.edu
Description: State-supported, university, coed. Part of Montana University System. Awards associate, bachelor's, master's, and doctoral degrees and post-master's certificates. Founded 1893. Setting: 220-acre urban campus. Endowment: $166.4 million. Research spending for the previous fiscal year: $56.7 million. Educational spending for the previous fiscal year: $10,478 per student. Total enrollment: 11,865. Faculty: 728 (521 full-time, 207 part-time). Student-undergrad faculty ratio is 17:1. 6,182 applied, 93% were admitted. 17% from top 10% of their high school class, 42% from top quarter, 73% from top half. Full-time: 7,444 students, 55% women, 45% men. Part-time: 1,879 students, 57% women, 43% men. Students come from 56 states and territories, 68 other countries, 28% from out-of-state. 3% American Indian or

Alaska Native, non-Hispanic/Latino; 5% Hispanic/Latino; 1% Black or African American, non-Hispanic/Latino; 1% Asian, non-Hispanic/Latino; 0.2% Native Hawaiian or other Pacific Islander, non-Hispanic/Latino; 2% international. 22% 25 or older, 35% live on campus, 9% transferred in. Retention: 69% of full-time freshmen returned the following year. Academic areas with the most degrees conferred: business/marketing; social sciences; education. Core. Calendar: semesters. Academic remediation for entering students, ESL program, services for LD students, advanced placement, freshman honors college, honors program, independent study, distance learning, double major, summer session for credit, part-time degree program, external degree program, co-op programs and internships, graduate courses open to undergrads. Off campus study at members of the National Student Exchange. Study abroad program. ROTC: Army.
Entrance Requirements: Options: electronic application, early admission, deferred admission, international baccalaureate accepted. Required: high school transcript, minimum 2.5 high school GPA, SAT or ACT. Entrance: moderately difficult. Application deadline: rolling. SAT Reasoning Test deadline: 8/28. Transfer credits accepted: Yes.
Costs Per Year: Application fee: $36. State resident tuition: $5347 full-time, $223 per credit hour part-time. Nonresident tuition: $23,062 full-time, $961 per credit hour part-time. Mandatory fees: $1897 full-time, $115 per credit hour part-time. Full-time tuition and fees vary according to degree level, location, program, reciprocity agreements, and student level. Part-time tuition and fees vary according to course load, degree level, location, and student level. College room and board: $9544. Room and board charges vary according to board plan and housing facility.
Collegiate Environment: Orientation program. Drama-theater group, choral group, marching band, student-run newspaper, radio station. Social organizations: national fraternities, national sororities; 6% of eligible men and 6% of eligible women are members. Student services: legal services, health clinic, personal-psychological counseling, women's center. Campus security: 24-hour emergency response devices and patrols, student patrols, late night transport-escort service, controlled dormitory access. Maureen and Mike Mansfield Library plus 2 others. Books: 139,763 (physical), 602,331 (digital/electronic); Serial titles: 15,019 (physical), 62,294 (digital/electronic); Databases: 202. Students can reserve study rooms. Operations spending for the previous fiscal year: $8.2 million.

■ **THE UNIVERSITY OF MONTANA WESTERN**
710 S Atlantic
Dillon, MT 59725-3598
Tel: (406)683-7011; Free: 877-683-7331
Fax: (406)683-7493
E-mail: janet.jones@umwestern.edu
Web Site: www.umwestern.edu
Description: State-supported, 4-year, coed. Part of Montana University System. Awards associate and bachelor's degrees. Founded 1893. Setting: 30-acre small town campus. Endowment: $5.1 million. Research spending for the previous fiscal year: $75,565. Educational spending for the previous fiscal year: $6741 per student. Total enrollment: 1,505. Faculty: 90 (62 full-time, 28 part-time). Student-undergrad faculty ratio is 17:1. 815 applied, 70% were admitted. 6% from top 10% of their high school class, 18% from top quarter, 51% from top half. Full-time: 1,232 students, 57% women, 43% men. Part-time: 273 students, 79% women, 21% men. Students come from 33 states and territories, 2 other countries, 27% from out-of-state. 4% American Indian or Alaska Native, non-Hispanic/Latino; 3% Hispanic/Latino; 1% Black or African American, non-Hispanic/Latino; 0.6% Asian, non-Hispanic/Latino; 0.6% Native Hawaiian or other Pacific Islander, non-Hispanic/Latino; 0.1% international. 25% 25 or older, 21% live on campus, 10% transferred in. Retention: 77% of full-time freshmen returned the following year. Academic areas with the most degrees conferred: education; business/marketing; agriculture. Core. Calendar: semesters. Academic remediation for entering students, services for LD students, advanced placement, honors program, independent study, distance learning, double major, summer session for credit, part-time degree program, co-op programs and internships. Off campus study. Study abroad program.
Entrance Requirements: Open admission for Associate Degree programs. Options: electronic application, deferred admission, international baccalaureate accepted. Required: high school transcript, MMR immunization record, SAT or ACT. Entrance: minimally difficult. Application deadlines: rolling, rolling for nonresidents. Notification: continuous, continuous for nonresidents. SAT Reasoning Test deadline: 8/25. SAT Subject Test deadline: 8/25. Transfer credits accepted: Yes.
Costs Per Year: Application fee: $30. State resident tuition: $4523 full-time.

Nonresident tuition: $15,913 full-time. Mandatory fees: $1,194 full-time. Full-time tuition and fees vary according to course load, location, program, reciprocity agreements, and student level. College room and board: $8090. College room only: $3290. Room and board charges vary according to housing facility.

Collegiate Environment: Orientation program. Drama-theater group, choral group, student-run radio station. Social organizations: 33 open to all. Most popular organizations: Biology Club, Rodeo Club, YoungLife Club, Education Club, Social Club. Major annual events: Athletic Events, Welcome Fair, Scholarship Luncheon. Student services: health clinic, personal-psychological counseling. Campus security: 24-hour emergency response devices and patrols, student patrols, late night transport-escort service. Lucy Carson Memorial Library. Books: 76,813 (physical), 697,448 (digital/electronic); Serial titles: 97 (physical); Databases: 146. Weekly public service hours: 85; students can reserve study rooms. 247 computers available on campus for general student use. A campuswide network can be accessed from student residence rooms and from off campus. Students can access the following: online class registration. Staffed computer lab on campus provides training in use of computers, software, and the Internet.

■ **UNIVERSITY OF PROVIDENCE**
1301 Twentieth St. S
Great Falls, MT 59405
Tel: (406)761-8210; Free: 800-856-9544
Fax: (406)791-5209
E-mail: admissions@uprovidence.edu
Web Site: www.uprovidence.edu

Description: Independent Roman Catholic, comprehensive, coed. Awards associate, bachelor's, and master's degrees. Founded 1932. Setting: 40-acre urban campus. Total enrollment: 1,039. Faculty: 127 (55 full-time, 72 part-time). Student-undergrad faculty ratio is 10:1. 845 applied, 72% were admitted. Full-time: 453 students, 53% women, 47% men. Part-time: 424 students, 80% women, 20% men. 65% from out-of-state. 1% American Indian or Alaska Native, non-Hispanic/Latino; 3% Hispanic/Latino; 4% Black or African American, non-Hispanic/Latino; 4% Asian, non-Hispanic/Latino; 0.4% Native Hawaiian or other Pacific Islander, non-Hispanic/Latino. 50% 25 or older, 30% live on campus, 17% transferred in. Retention: 52% of full-time freshmen returned the following year. Academic areas with the most degrees conferred: public administration and social services; law/legal studies. Calendar: semesters. Part-time degree program, adult/continuing education programs.

Entrance Requirements: Options: electronic application, early admission, deferred admission, international baccalaureate accepted. Required: high school transcript, SAT or ACT. Recommended: essay, interview, SAT and SAT Subject Tests or ACT, SAT Subject Tests. Entrance: noncompetitive. Notification: continuous. SAT Subject Test deadline: 8/1.

Costs Per Year: Application fee: $35. Comprehensive fee: $35,770 includes full-time tuition ($25,692), mandatory fees ($200), and college room and board ($9878). College room only: $5350. Part-time tuition: $838.

Collegiate Environment: Orientation program. Campus security: 24-hour emergency response devices and patrols, late night transport-escort service, controlled dormitory access. Freshmen guaranteed college housing. On-campus residence required through sophomore year. Option: coed housing available. University of Great Falls Library.

Community Environment: Montana's second largest city, Great Falls is an industrial, financial, wholesale and distributing center. Major agricultural pursuits in the area are livestock farming and wood production. Known as the city "between the parks," Great Falls is almost equidistant to Yellowstone and Glacier National Parks. The winters are moderate. Summer evenings are cool. The area is served by air, rail, and bus lines. Local attractions include dude and guest ranches, fishing, hunting, and skiing. Some employment opportunities are available in the area.

■ BELLEVUE UNIVERSITY

1000 Galvin Rd. S
Bellevue, NE 68005-3098
Tel: (402)291-8100; Free: 800-756-7920
Fax: (402)293-2020
E-mail: nick.baker@bellevue.edu
Web Site: www.bellevue.edu

Description: Independent, comprehensive, coed. Awards bachelor's, master's, and doctoral degrees. Founded 1965. Setting: 50-acre suburban campus with easy access to Omaha. Endowment: $43.6 million. Research spending for the previous fiscal year: $1.2 million. Educational spending for the previous fiscal year: $2696 per student. Total enrollment: 10,304. Faculty: 411 (89 full-time, 322 part-time). Student-undergrad faculty ratio is 40:1. Full-time: 4,978 students, 49% women, 51% men. Part-time: 1,850 students, 48% women, 52% men. Students come from 53 states and territories, 34 other countries, 50% from out-of-state. 0.7% American Indian or Alaska Native, non-Hispanic/Latino; 7% Hispanic/Latino; 13% Black or African American, non-Hispanic/Latino; 2% Asian, non-Hispanic/Latino; 0.4% Native Hawaiian or other Pacific Islander, non-Hispanic/Latino; 2% international. 80% 25 or older. Retention: 50% of full-time freshmen returned the following year. Academic areas with the most degrees conferred: business/marketing; social sciences; health professions and related sciences; computer and information sciences. Core. Calendar: semesters for day division, trimesters for evening division. Academic remediation for entering students, ESL program, services for LD students, advanced placement, accelerated degree program, independent study, distance learning, double major, summer session for credit, part-time degree program, external degree program, adult/continuing education programs, internships. Off campus study. Study abroad program. ROTC: Army (c), Air Force (c).

Entrance Requirements: Open admission. Options: electronic application, deferred admission. Required: high school transcript. Entrance: noncompetitive. Application deadline: rolling. Transfer credits accepted: Yes.

Costs Per Year: Application fee: $50. Tuition: $8940 full-time, $298 per credit hour part-time. Mandatory fees: $450 full-time, $225 per term part-time. Full-time tuition and fees vary according to course load. Part-time tuition and fees vary according to course load.

Collegiate Environment: Orientation program. Social organizations: 5 open to all. Most popular organizations: International Student Organization, Multicultural Club, Student Advisory Council, Student Veterans Organization, Institute of Management Accountants. Major annual events: Student Appreciation Day, BRUIN Week, Bowling Night. Campus security: 24-hour emergency response devices. Freeman/Lozier Library plus 1 other. Operations spending for the previous fiscal year: $1.3 million. 470 computers available on campus for general student use. A campuswide network can be accessed from off-campus. Students can access the following: online class registration. Staffed computer lab on campus provides training in use of computers, software, and the Internet.

Community Environment: The oldest continuous settlement in Nebraska, Bellevue is located on the bluffs of the Missouri River, just south of Omaha and adjoining Offutt Air Force Base, the headquarters of the Strategic Air Command. The Fontenelle Forest Nature Center between Bellevue and the Missouri River contains displays of regional habitats.

■ BRYAN COLLEGE OF HEALTH SCIENCES

1535 S 52nd St.
Lincoln, NE 68506
Tel: (402)481-3801
Web Site: www.bryanhealthcollege.edu

Description: Independent, comprehensive, coed. Awards associate, bachelor's, and master's degrees. 107 applied, 52% were admitted.

Entrance Requirements: Option: electronic application. Required: high school transcript, 2 recommendations, SAT or ACT. Required for some: essay, minimum 2.75 high school GPA, interview. Transfer credits accepted: Yes.

Costs Per Year: One-time mandatory fee: $175. Tuition: $17,370 full-time, $579 per credit hour part-time. Mandatory fees: $1050 full-time. Full-time tuition and fees vary according to course load. Part-time tuition varies according to course load.

■ CENTRAL COMMUNITY COLLEGE-COLUMBUS CAMPUS

4500 63rd St.
Columbus, NE 68602-1027
Tel: (402)564-7132; Free: 877-CCC-0780
Fax: (402)562-1201
E-mail: eleffler@cccneb.edu
Web Site: www.cccneb.edu

Description: State and locally supported, 2-year, coed. Part of Central Community College. Awards certificates, diplomas, transfer associate, and terminal associate degrees. Founded 1968. Setting: 90-acre small town campus. Total enrollment: 2,872. Faculty: 99 (46 full-time, 53 part-time). Full-time: 523 students, 53% women, 47% men. Part-time: 2,349 students, 61% women, 39% men. Students come from 24 other countries. 0.2% American Indian or Alaska Native, non-Hispanic/Latino; 13% Hispanic/Latino; 2% Black or African American, non-Hispanic/Latino; 0.8% Asian, non-Hispanic/Latino; 0.2% Native Hawaiian or other Pacific Islander, non-Hispanic/Latino. 39% 25 or older, 17% live on campus, 4% transferred in. Core. Calendar: semesters plus 6-week summer session. Academic remediation for entering students, ESL program, services for LD students, advanced placement, accelerated degree program, self-designed majors, independent study, distance learning, summer session for credit, part-time degree program, external degree program, adult/continuing education programs, co-op programs and internships. Off campus study.

Entrance Requirements: Open admission. Options: electronic application, early admission. Required: high school transcript. Required for some: 3 recommendations, interview. Entrance: noncompetitive. Application deadline: rolling. Notification: continuous. Transfer credits accepted: Yes.

Collegiate Environment: Orientation program. Drama-theater group, choral group. Social organizations: 12 open to all. Most popular organizations: Phi Theta Kappa, Drama Club, Art Club, Cantari, Chorale. Major annual events: East Central Nebraska College Fair, Ethnic Festival, Christmas Party. Student services: personal-psychological counseling, women's center. Campus security: 24-hour emergency response devices and patrols, controlled dormitory access, night security. Learning Resources Center.

Community Environment: Columbus was originally an agricultural area, but in the late 1940s, as the town was dying from the loss of young people to the larger cities, a concerted effort was begun to introduce industry to the community. This effort has been very successful, and to date the area has more industrial workers per capita than any other city in the Midwest. Products range from agricultural equipment to medical equipment. Commercial transportation is available. Pawnee Park offers swimming, tennis, picnic grounds, and athletic fields. Lake North offers swimming, water skiing, and boating. Lake Babcok offers fishing and boating, plus free camp grounds equipped with electrical outlets and tables. Columbus is 85 miles from Omaha and 80 miles from Lincoln. The community facilities include 22 churches and one library.

■ CENTRAL COMMUNITY COLLEGE-GRAND ISLAND CAMPUS
PO Box 4903
Grand Island, NE 68802-4903
Tel: (308)398-4222; Free: 877-CCC-0780
Fax: (308)398-7398
E-mail: mlubken@cccneb.edu
Web Site: www.cccneb.edu
Description: State and locally supported, 2-year, coed. Part of Central Community College. Awards certificates, diplomas, transfer associate, and terminal associate degrees. Founded 1976. Setting: 80-acre small town campus. Total enrollment: 3,469. Faculty: 112. Student-undergrad faculty ratio is 15:1. Full-time: 423 students, 57% women, 43% men. Part-time: 3,046 students, 68% women, 32% men. Students come from 24 other countries. 0.5% American Indian or Alaska Native, non-Hispanic/Latino; 13% Hispanic/Latino; 2% Black or African American, non-Hispanic/Latino; 1% Asian, non-Hispanic/Latino; 0.2% Native Hawaiian or other Pacific Islander, non-Hispanic/Latino. 46% 25 or older, 10% live on campus, 3% transferred in. Core. Calendar: semesters plus 6-week summer session. Academic remediation for entering students, ESL program, services for LD students, advanced placement, accelerated degree program, self-designed majors, independent study, distance learning, summer session for credit, part-time degree program, external degree program, adult/continuing education programs, co-op programs and internships. Off campus study.
Entrance Requirements: Open admission. Options: electronic application, early admission. Required: high school transcript. Required for some: 3 recommendations, interview. Entrance: noncompetitive. Application deadline: rolling. Notification: continuous. Transfer credits accepted: Yes.
Collegiate Environment: Orientation program. Social organizations: 7 open to all. Most popular organizations: Mid-Nebraska Users of Computers, Student Activities Organization, intramurals, TRIO, Phi Theta Kappa. Major annual events: Christmas Party, Spring Picnic, Halloween Party. Student services: personal-psychological counseling. Central Community College-Grand Island Campus Library.
Community Environment: Grand Island is located in Central Nebraska and is a leading agricultural center for retailing and industry. Due to agricultural production, industry has quickly expanded, with a resulting rapid population growth. There are many recreational opportunities available to residents and visitors, including swimming, golfing, horse racing, bowling, hunting, and a variety of health-related activities. A large museum complex is located at Grand Island and reflects the Old West tradition. More than 40 churches, two hospitals, a children's zoo and a major library are available.

■ CENTRAL COMMUNITY COLLEGE-HASTINGS CAMPUS
PO Box 1024
Hastings, NE 68902-1024
Tel: (402)463-9811; Free: 877-CCC-0780
E-mail: rglenn@ccneb.edu
Web Site: www.cccneb.edu
Description: State and locally supported, 2-year, coed. Part of Central Community College. Awards certificates, diplomas, transfer associate, and terminal associate degrees. Founded 1966. Setting: 644-acre small town campus. Total enrollment: 2,966. Faculty: 109 (49 full-time, 60 part-time). Student-undergrad faculty ratio is 15:1. Full-time: 1,001 students, 46% women, 54% men. Part-time: 1,965 students, 63% women, 37% men. Students come from 24 other countries. 0.4% American Indian or Alaska Native, non-Hispanic/Latino; 7% Hispanic/Latino; 0.7% Black or African American, non-Hispanic/Latino; 0.9% Asian, non-Hispanic/Latino; 0.1% Native Hawaiian or other Pacific Islander, non-Hispanic/Latino. 36% 25 or older, 5% transferred in. Core. Calendar: semesters plus 6-week summer session. Academic remediation for entering students, ESL program, services for LD students, advanced placement, accelerated degree program, self-designed majors, independent study, distance learning, summer session for credit, part-time degree program, external degree program, adult/continuing education programs, co-op programs and internships. Off campus study.
Entrance Requirements: Open admission. Options: electronic application, early admission. Required: high school transcript. Required for some: 3 recommendations, interview. Entrance: noncompetitive. Application deadline: rolling. Notification: continuous. Transfer credits accepted: Yes.
Collegiate Environment: Orientation program. Student-run radio station. Social organizations: 13 open to all. Most popular organizations: Student

Senate, Central Dormitory Council, Judicial Board, Seeds and Soils, Young Farmers and Ranchers. Major annual events: Back-to-School Week, Christmas Party. Student services: personal-psychological counseling, women's center. Campus security: 24-hour emergency response devices and patrols, controlled dormitory access. Nuckolls Library.
Community Environment: See Hastings College.

■ CHADRON STATE COLLEGE
1000 Main St.
Chadron, NE 69337
Tel: (308)432-6000; Free: 800-242-3766
Fax: (308)432-6229
E-mail: inquire@csc.edu
Web Site: www.csc.edu
Description: State-supported, comprehensive, coed. Part of Nebraska State College System. Awards bachelor's and master's degrees. Founded 1911. Setting: 281-acre small town campus. Total enrollment: 2,649. Student-undergrad faculty ratio is 19:1. 31% from out-of-state. 24% 25 or older. Retention: 64% of full-time freshmen returned the following year. Core. Calendar: semesters. Services for LD students, advanced placement, self-designed majors, honors program, independent study, distance learning, double major, summer session for credit, part-time degree program, external degree program, adult/continuing education programs, co-op programs and internships, graduate courses open to undergrads. Off campus study. Study abroad program.
Entrance Requirements: Open admission. Options: electronic application, early admission. Required: high school transcript, health forms. Entrance: noncompetitive. Application deadline: rolling. Notification: continuous.
Collegiate Environment: Orientation program. Drama-theater group, choral group, student-run newspaper, radio station. Student services: health clinic, personal-psychological counseling. Campus security: 24-hour emergency response devices and patrols, student patrols, late night transport-escort service. Reta King Library.
Community Environment: Chadron, located in northwestern Nebraska, is near the Nebraska National Forest where hunting is popular as well as trout fishing. Chadron is also a short drive from snow skiing, water skiing, and the Black Hills of South Dakota. The community facilities include a public library, hospital, churches, and numerous civic organizations.

■ CHI HEALTH SCHOOL OF RADIOLOGIC TECHNOLOGY
6911 N 68th Plz.
Omaha, NE 68122
Tel: (402)398-5527
Web Site: www.chihealth.com/school-of-radiologic-technology
Description: Independent, 2-year, coed. Awards terminal associate degrees. Setting: 1-acre urban campus with easy access to Omaha, NE. Educational spending for the previous fiscal year: $8000 per student. Total enrollment: 15. Faculty: (3 full-time). Student-undergrad faculty ratio is 7:1. Full-time: 15 students, 87% women, 13% men. Students come from 4 states and territories, 20% from out-of-state. 7% Black or African American, non-Hispanic/Latino. 27% 25 or older. Retention: 9% of full-time freshmen returned the following year. Academic remediation for entering students, services for LD students.
Entrance Requirements: Required: essay, high school transcript, minimum 2 high school GPA, 3 recommendations, interview, entrance exam. Required for some: interview. Entrance: moderately difficult. Application deadline: 2/1. Transfer credits accepted: Yes.
Costs Per Year: Application fee: $25. One-time mandatory fee: $25. Tuition: $6250 full-time. Tuition guaranteed not to increase for student's term of enrollment.
Collegiate Environment: Student services: legal services, health clinic, personal-psychological counseling. Campus security: 24-hour emergency response devices and patrols.

■ CLARKSON COLLEGE
101 S 42nd St.
Omaha, NE 68131-2739
Tel: (402)552-3100; Free: 800-647-5500
Fax: (402)552-6057
Web Site: www.clarksoncollege.edu
Description: Independent, comprehensive, coed. Awards associate, bachelor's, and master's degrees and post-master's certificates. Founded 1888. Setting: 3-acre urban campus. Endowment: $937,115. Educational spending for the previous fiscal year: $8259 per student. Total enrollment:

820. Faculty: 101 (48 full-time, 53 part-time). Student-undergrad faculty ratio is 8:1. 87 applied, 55% were admitted. 15% from top 10% of their high school class, 30% from top quarter, 85% from top half. Full-time: 39 students, 95% women, 5% men. Students come from 33 states and territories, 33% from out-of-state. 42% 25 or older, 14% live on campus, 438% transferred in. Retention: 85% of full-time freshmen returned the following year. Academic area with the most degrees conferred: health professions and related sciences. Core. Calendar: semesters. Advanced placement, accelerated degree program, independent study, distance learning, double major, summer session for credit, part-time degree program, external degree program, adult/continuing education programs, co-op programs and internships, graduate courses open to undergrads. Study abroad program. ROTC: Army (c), Air Force (c).

Entrance Requirements: Options: electronic application, deferred admission. Required: essay, high school transcript, minimum 2.5 high school GPA. Recommended: minimum 3 high school GPA. Required for some: minimum 3 high school GPA, 2 recommendations, SAT or ACT. Entrance: moderately difficult. Application deadline: rolling. Notification: continuous.

Collegiate Environment: Orientation program. Student-run newspaper. Social organizations: 10 open to all. Most popular organizations: Student Nurses Association, Radiology Student Association, Student Government Association, Student Ambassadors, Physical Therapist Assistant Student Association. Major annual events: Welcome Week, Talent Show, Casino Night. Student services: health clinic, personal-psychological counseling. Campus security: 24-hour emergency response devices and patrols, student patrols, late night transport-escort service, controlled dormitory access. Clarkson College Library. Operations spending for the previous fiscal year: $242,150. 40 computers available on campus for general student use. A campuswide network can be accessed from off-campus. Students can access the following: online class registration. Staffed computer lab on campus provides training in use of computers, software, and the Internet.

■ **COLLEGE OF SAINT MARY**
7000 Mercy Rd.
Omaha, NE 68106
Tel: (402)399-2400; Free: 800-926-5534
Fax: (402)399-2412
Web Site: www.csm.edu
Description: Independent Roman Catholic, comprehensive, women only. Awards associate, bachelor's, master's, and doctoral degrees. Founded 1923. Setting: 25-acre urban campus. Endowment: $19.8 million. Research spending for the previous fiscal year: $97,386. Educational spending for the previous fiscal year: $6244 per student. Total enrollment: 1,168. Faculty: 193 (72 full-time, 121 part-time). Student-undergrad faculty ratio is 10:1. 428 applied, 52% were admitted. 15% from top 10% of their high school class, 40% from top quarter, 72% from top half. Full-time: 794 students. Part-time: 67 students. Students come from 34 states and territories, 11 other countries, 24% from out-of-state. 0.7% American Indian or Alaska Native, non-Hispanic/Latino; 12% Hispanic/Latino; 8% Black or African American, non-Hispanic/Latino; 3% Asian, non-Hispanic/Latino; 0.4% Native Hawaiian or other Pacific Islander, non-Hispanic/Latino; 0.9% international. 29% 25 or older, 25% live on campus, 17% transferred in. Retention: 78% of full-time freshmen returned the following year. Academic areas with the most degrees conferred: health professions and related sciences; biological/life sciences; liberal arts/general studies; education. Calendar: semesters. Academic remediation for entering students, services for LD students, advanced placement, accelerated degree program, honors program, independent study, distance learning, double major, summer session for credit, part-time degree program, internships, graduate courses open to undergrads. Study abroad program. ROTC: Army (c), Air Force (c).

Entrance Requirements: Options: electronic application, international baccalaureate accepted. Required: high school transcript, minimum 2 high school GPA, SAT or ACT. Required for some: essay, 3 recommendations, interview, ACT. Entrance: minimally difficult. Application deadline: rolling. Notification: continuous. Transfer credits accepted: Yes. Applicants placed on waiting list: 0. Wait-listed applicants offered admission: 0.

Costs Per Year: Application fee: $30. Comprehensive fee: $28,600 includes full-time tuition ($20,750) and college room and board ($7850). Part-time tuition: $765 per credit.

Collegiate Environment: Orientation program. Drama-theater group, choral group. Social organizations: 22 open to all. Most popular organizations: Residence Hall Council, Campus Activities Board, Student Education Association of Nebraska, Student Occupational Therapy Club, Student Nurses Association. Major annual events: Senate Casino Night, Hypnotist/Mentalist,

The Heart of the Walking Woman Celebration. Student services: health clinic, personal-psychological counseling. Campus security: 24-hour emergency response devices and patrols, late night transport-escort service, controlled dormitory access. 309 college housing spaces available; 296 were occupied in 2018-19. Freshmen guaranteed college housing. On-campus residence required through sophomore year. Option: women-only housing available. College of Saint Mary Library. Books: 57,458 (physical), 23,434 (digital/electronic); Serial titles: 32 (physical), 108 (digital/electronic); Databases: 30. Weekly public service hours: 81; study areas open 24 hours, 5-7 days a week. Operations spending for the previous fiscal year: $378,505. 215 computers available on campus for general student use. A campuswide network can be accessed from student residence rooms. Students can access the following: online class registration. Staffed computer lab on campus provides training in use of computers, software, and the Internet.

■ **CONCORDIA UNIVERSITY, NEBRASKA**
800 N Columbia Ave.
Seward, NE 68434
Tel: (402)643-3651; Free: 800-535-5494
Fax: (402)643-4073
E-mail: admiss@cune.edu
Web Site: www.cune.edu
Description: Independent, comprehensive, coed, affiliated with Lutheran Church-Missouri Synod. Awards bachelor's and master's degrees. Founded 1894. Setting: 120-acre small town campus with easy access to Omaha. Endowment: $51 million. Educational spending for the previous fiscal year: $6285 per student. Total enrollment: 2,520. Faculty: 253 (61 full-time, 192 part-time). Student-undergrad faculty ratio is 14:1. 1,537 applied, 75% were admitted. 18% from top 10% of their high school class, 43% from top quarter, 72% from top half. Full-time: 1,231 students, 52% women, 48% men. Part-time: 453 students, 57% women, 43% men. Students come from 40 states and territories, 9 other countries, 52% from out-of-state. 0.2% American Indian or Alaska Native, non-Hispanic/Latino; 6% Hispanic/Latino; 4% Black or African American, non-Hispanic/Latino; 1% Asian, non-Hispanic/Latino; 0.2% Native Hawaiian or other Pacific Islander, non-Hispanic/Latino; 2% international. 3% 25 or older, 57% live on campus, 2% transferred in. Retention: 74% of full-time freshmen returned the following year. Academic areas with the most degrees conferred: education; business/marketing; biological/life sciences. Core. Calendar: 4-4-1. Academic remediation for entering students, services for LD students, advanced placement, accelerated degree program, independent study, distance learning, double major, summer session for credit, part-time degree program, adult/continuing education programs, internships, graduate courses open to undergrads. Off campus study at University of Nebraska-Lincoln. Study abroad program. ROTC: Army (c), Air Force (c).

Entrance Requirements: Options: electronic application, deferred admission, international baccalaureate accepted. Required: high school transcript, SAT or ACT. Required for some: essay, 2 recommendations. Entrance: moderately difficult. Application deadline: 8/1. Notification: continuous. SAT Reasoning Test deadline: 8/1. Transfer credits accepted: Yes.

Costs Per Year: Application fee: $0. Comprehensive fee: $40,690 includes full-time tuition ($31,620), mandatory fees ($600), and college room and board ($8470). College room only: $3570. Room and board charges vary according to board plan and housing facility. Part-time tuition: $925 per credit hour. Part-time mandatory fees: $150 per term.

Collegiate Environment: Orientation program. Drama-theater group, choral group, student-run newspaper. Social organizations: 30 open to all. Most popular organizations: Student Activities Council, Musical Groups, Curtain/Drama Club, Student Senate, Concordia Youth Ministry. Major annual events: Homecoming Weekend, Spring Weekend Events, Christmas at Concordia. Student services: health clinic, personal-psychological counseling. Campus security: 24-hour emergency response devices and patrols, controlled dormitory access. Link Library plus 1 other. Books: 124,354 (physical), 38,136 (digital/electronic); Serial titles: 711 (physical), 82 (digital/electronic); Databases: 22. Weekly public service hours: 89; students can reserve study rooms. 220 computers available on campus for general student use. A campuswide network can be accessed from student residence rooms and from off campus. Students can access the following: online class registration, academic plans, human resource data. Staffed computer lab on campus provides training in use of computers, software, and the Internet.

■ CREATIVE CENTER

10850 Emmet St.
Omaha, NE 68164
Tel: (402)898-1000; Free: 888-898-1789
Fax: (402)898-1301
E-mail: rich_c@creativecenter.edu
Web Site: www.creativecenter.edu
Description: Proprietary, 4-year, coed. Awards associate and bachelor's degrees. Founded 1993. Setting: 2-acre urban campus with easy access to Omaha. Total enrollment: 39. Faculty: 11 (2 full-time, 9 part-time). Student-undergrad faculty ratio is 10:1. Full-time: 38 students, 76% women, 24% men. Part-time: 1 student, 100% women. Academic area with the most degrees conferred: visual and performing arts. Core. Calendar: semesters. Services for LD students, advanced placement, accelerated degree program, part-time degree program.
Entrance Requirements: Required: essay, high school transcript, 1 recommendation, interview, portfolio. Recommended: minimum 2 high school GPA. Application deadlines: rolling, rolling for nonresidents. Notification: continuous, continuous for nonresidents. Transfer credits accepted: Yes.
Costs Per Year: Application fee: $100. One-time mandatory fee: $2800. Tuition: $25,600 full-time, $2560 per course part-time. Mandatory fees: $2055 full-time.
Collegiate Environment: Orientation program. College housing not available. Student Library plus 1 other. 8 computers available on campus for general student use. Computer purchase/lease plans available. A computer is required for all students. A campuswide network can be accessed. Students can access the following: all students own a laptop computer as part of tuition and fees.

■ CREIGHTON UNIVERSITY

2500 California Plz.
Omaha, NE 68178-0001
Tel: (402)280-2700; Free: 800-282-5835
Fax: (402)280-2685
E-mail: admissions@creighton.edu
Web Site: www.creighton.edu
Description: Independent Roman Catholic (Jesuit), university, coed. Awards associate, bachelor's, master's, and doctoral degrees and post-master's certificates. Founded 1878. Setting: 139-acre urban campus with easy access to Omaha. Endowment: $568.8 million. Research spending for the previous fiscal year: $17.2 million. Educational spending for the previous fiscal year: $15,453 per student. Total enrollment: 8,910. Faculty: 912 (587 full-time, 325 part-time). Student-undergrad faculty ratio is 11:1. 10,112 applied, 71% were admitted. 37% from top 10% of their high school class, 70% from top quarter, 93% from top half. 2 National Merit Scholars. Full-time: 4,291 students, 57% women, 43% men. Part-time: 155 students, 50% women, 50% men. Students come from 50 states and territories, 31 other countries, 78% from out-of-state. 0.4% American Indian or Alaska Native, non-Hispanic/Latino; 8% Hispanic/Latino; 2% Black or African American, non-Hispanic/Latino; 9% Asian, non-Hispanic/Latino; 0.5% Native Hawaiian or other Pacific Islander, non-Hispanic/Latino; 2% international. 5% 25 or older, 55% live on campus, 1% transferred in. Retention: 89% of full-time freshmen returned the following year. Academic areas with the most degrees conferred: business/marketing; health professions and related sciences; biological/life sciences. Core. Calendar: semesters. ESL program, services for LD students, advanced placement, accelerated degree program, honors program, independent study, distance learning, double major, summer session for credit, part-time degree program, adult/continuing education programs, internships, graduate courses open to undergrads. Off campus study at Art-Engineering Program (with University of Detroit Mercy; with Marquette University). Study abroad program. ROTC: Army, Air Force (c).
Entrance Requirements: Options: electronic application, early action, deferred admission, international baccalaureate accepted. Required: essay, high school transcript, 1 recommendation, SAT or ACT. Recommended: minimum 3 high school GPA. Entrance: moderately difficult. Application deadlines: 2/15, 11/1 for early action. Notification: continuous, rolling for early action. SAT Reasoning Test deadline: 3/1. Transfer credits accepted: Yes. Early action applicants: 2,888. Early action applicants admitted: 2,711.
Costs Per Year: Application fee: $40. Comprehensive fee: $52,674 includes full-time tuition ($39,630), mandatory fees ($1770), and college room and board ($11,274). Part-time tuition: $1240 per credit hour. Part-time mandatory fees: $175 per term.
Collegiate Environment: Orientation program. Drama-theater group, choral group, student-run newspaper, radio station. Social organizations: 252 open to all; national fraternities, national sororities, local fraternities, local sororities; 46% of eligible men and 30% of eligible women are members. Most popular organizations: Birdcage, Hui O Hawaii, Pre-Med Society, Partners Against Cancer, American Pharmacists Association Academy of Student Pharmacist. Major annual events: Skutt Shutdown, Fallapalooza Concert, Lip Sync. Student services: health clinic, personal-psychological counseling, women's center. Campus security: 24-hour emergency response devices and patrols, student patrols, late night transport-escort service, controlled dormitory access. 2,517 college housing spaces available. Freshmen guaranteed college housing. On-campus residence required through sophomore year. Option: coed housing available. Reinert Alumni Memorial Library plus 2 others. Study areas open 24 hours, 5-7 days a week. 565 computers available on campus for general student use. Computer purchase/lease plans available. A campuswide network can be accessed from student residence rooms and from off campus. Students can access the following: online class registration, financial aid information.
Community Environment: Metropolitan Omaha has a population of over 414,000 and serves as a communication and cultural center for the Plains States. Urban Omaha is in a period of rapid renewal through publicly and privately supported programs. It is a major insurance center of the nation, other industries such as railroads, telecommunications, creative enterprises, and health care institutions are well represented. It is best known, however, as a food processing center because of its location in the area known as the "bread basket of America". Cultural attractions include the Omaha Symphony Orchestra, Ballet and Opera Company, Community Playhouse, the Joslyn Art Museum, and the Henry Dvorly Zoo, rated the no. 1 family attraction in America by Family Life Magazine.

■ DOANE UNIVERSITY

1014 Boswell Ave.
Crete, NE 68333-2430
Tel: (402)826-2161; Free: 800-333-6263
Fax: (402)826-8600
E-mail: kyle.mcmurray@doane.edu
Web Site: www.doane.edu
Description: Independent, comprehensive, coed, affiliated with United Church of Christ. Awards bachelor's, master's, and doctoral degrees and post-master's certificates (non-traditional undergraduate programs and graduate programs offered at Lincoln campus). Founded 1872. Setting: 300-acre small town campus with easy access to Omaha. Endowment: $112.9 million. Research spending for the previous fiscal year: $389,710. Educational spending for the previous fiscal year: $17,417 per student. Total enrollment: 1,069. Faculty: 124 (88 full-time, 36 part-time). Student-undergrad faculty ratio is 11:1. 2,392 applied, 65% were admitted. 15% from top 10% of their high school class, 36% from top quarter, 71% from top half. Full-time: 1,062 students, 47% women, 53% men. Part-time: 7 students, 29% women, 71% men. Students come from 31 states and territories, 11 other countries, 23% from out-of-state. 0.4% American Indian or Alaska Native, non-Hispanic/Latino; 7% Hispanic/Latino; 2% Black or African American, non-Hispanic/Latino; 1% Asian, non-Hispanic/Latino; 0.2% Native Hawaiian or other Pacific Islander, non-Hispanic/Latino; 2% international. 2% 25 or older, 82% live on campus, 3% transferred in. Retention: 78% of full-time freshmen returned the following year. Academic areas with the most degrees conferred: education; business/marketing; biological/life sciences. Core. Calendar: 4-1-4. ESL program, advanced placement, self-designed majors, honors program, independent study, double major, summer session for credit, co-op programs and internships, graduate courses open to undergrads. Off campus study at Association of Nebraska Interterm Colleges. Study abroad program. ROTC: Army (c), Air Force (c).
Entrance Requirements: Option: electronic application. Required: high school transcript, 2 recommendations, SAT or ACT. Recommended: minimum 2 high school GPA. Required for some: interview.
Costs Per Year: Comprehensive fee: $43,200 includes full-time tuition ($33,000), mandatory fees ($800), and college room and board ($9400). Full-time tuition and fees vary according to location. Room and board charges vary according to board plan, housing facility, and location. Part-time tuition: $1100 per credit hour. Part-time tuition varies according to course load and location.
Collegiate Environment: Orientation program. Drama-theater group, choral group, marching band, student-run newspaper, radio station. Social organizations: 60 open to all; local fraternities, local sororities; 23% of eligible men and 24% of eligible women are members. Most popular organizations: Student Activities Council, Hansen Leadership Program, band/choir, Doane Ambassadors, Doane Art League. Major annual events:

Homecoming, Big Event, Stop Day. Student services: health clinic, personal-psychological counseling. Campus security: 24-hour emergency response devices and patrols, student patrols, late night transport-escort service, controlled dormitory access, evening patrols by trained security personnel. Perkins Library plus 1 other. Study areas open 24 hours, 5-7 days a week; students can reserve study rooms. Operations spending for the previous fiscal year: $689,771. 250 computers available on campus for general student use. Computer purchase/lease plans available. A campuswide network can be accessed from student residence rooms and from off campus. Students can access the following: online class registration. Staffed computer lab on campus provides training in use of computers, software, and the Internet.

Community Environment: Crete, a community of 5,000 persons, is located 25 miles southwest of Lincoln. The community includes nine churches of different denominations, a hospital, library, and numerous civic, fraternal and veterans' organizations. Recreation includes bowling, fishing, hunting, golf, and numerous other activities.

■ HASTINGS COLLEGE

710 N Turner Ave.
Hastings, NE 68901
Tel: (402)463-2402; Free: 800-532-7642
Fax: (402)463-3002
E-mail: cschukei@hastings.edu
Web Site: www.hastings.edu

Description: Independent Presbyterian, comprehensive, coed. Awards bachelor's and master's degrees. Founded 1882. Setting: 109-acre small town campus. Endowment: $87.2 million. Educational spending for the previous fiscal year: $8141 per student. Total enrollment: 1,212. Faculty: 119 (77 full-time, 42 part-time). Student-undergrad faculty ratio is 13:1. 1,688 applied, 71% were admitted. 20% from top 10% of their high school class, 45% from top quarter, 80% from top half. Full-time: 1,129 students, 49% women, 51% men. Part-time: 54 students, 48% women, 52% men. Students come from 21 states and territories, 8 other countries, 33% from out-of-state. 0.5% American Indian or Alaska Native, non-Hispanic/Latino; 6% Hispanic/Latino; 3% Black or African American, non-Hispanic/Latino; 1% Asian, non-Hispanic/Latino; 0.4% Native Hawaiian or other Pacific Islander, non-Hispanic/Latino; 2% international. 63% live on campus, 5% transferred in. Retention: 74% of full-time freshmen returned the following year. Academic areas with the most degrees conferred: education; business/marketing; social sciences. Core. Calendar: 4-1-4. Services for LD students, advanced placement, self-designed majors, independent study, double major, summer session for credit, part-time degree program, adult/continuing education programs, internships, graduate courses open to undergrads. Off campus study. Study abroad program.

Entrance Requirements: Options: electronic application, international baccalaureate accepted. Required: high school transcript, minimum 2 high school GPA, counselor's recommendation, SAT or ACT. Required for some: essay, 2 recommendations, interview. Entrance: moderately difficult. Application deadline: 8/1. Notification: continuous. SAT Reasoning Test deadline: 8/1. SAT Subject Test deadline: 8/1. Transfer credits accepted: Yes.

Costs Per Year: Application fee: $0. Comprehensive fee: $39,750 includes full-time tuition ($28,600), mandatory fees ($1450), and college room and board ($9700). College room only: $4700. Full-time tuition and fees vary according to course load. Room and board charges vary according to housing facility. Part-time tuition: $1180 per credit hour. Part-time tuition varies according to course load.

Collegiate Environment: Orientation program. Drama-theater group, choral group, marching band, student-run newspaper, radio station. Social organizations: 60 open to all; local fraternities, local sororities; 27% of eligible men and 27% of eligible women are members. Most popular organizations: Student Association, Student Alumni Ambassadors, Fellowship of Christian Athletes, Phi Mu Alpha Sinfonia, Hastings College Singers. Major annual events: Homecoming, Boar's Head Dinner, Greek Dinner Dance. Student services: health clinic, personal-psychological counseling. Campus security: 24-hour emergency response devices, student patrols, late night transport-escort service, controlled dormitory access, security cameras at entrances and in parking lots. Perkins Library. Books: 108,388 (physical), 126,378 (digital/electronic); Serial titles: 6,962 (physical), 21,582 (digital/electronic); Databases: 56. Weekly public service hours: 93; students can reserve study rooms. Operations spending for the previous fiscal year: $492,079. 240 computers available on campus for general student use. A campuswide network can be accessed from student residence rooms and from off campus. Students can access the following: online class registration, e-mail. Staffed computer lab on campus provides training in use of computers, software, and the Internet.

Community Environment: Located in the south central section of the state, Hastings is in the heart of an important irrigated agricultural and stock-raising area. All commercial transportation is available. Part-time jobs are available for students. Community facilities include a library, churches of all denominations and numerous fraternal organizations. Prospect Park contains the Aquacourt, an ultramodern swimming pool, fishing and skiing. A municipal pool is in Libs Park. Lake Hastings, one mile north, offers water sports and fishing. Points of interest are the Fisher Rainbow Fountain, the Hastings Museum, which includes the J.M. McDonald Planetarium, and the Imax theater.

■ LITTLE PRIEST TRIBAL COLLEGE

PO Box 270
Winnebago, NE 68071
Tel: (402)878-2380
Fax: (402)878-2355
Web Site: www.littlepriest.edu

Description: Independent, 2-year, coed. Awards transfer associate degrees. Founded 1996. Setting: 10-acre rural campus with easy access to Sioux City. Endowment: $1.5 million. Total enrollment: 122. Faculty: 34 (11 full-time, 23 part-time). Student-undergrad faculty ratio is 6:1. Full-time: 80 students, 64% women, 36% men. Part-time: 42 students, 83% women, 17% men. Students come from 10 states and territories, 10% from out-of-state. 93% American Indian or Alaska Native, non-Hispanic/Latino. 62% 25 or older. Core.

Entrance Requirements: Open admission. Options: electronic application, early admission. Required: high school transcript. Transfer credits accepted: Yes.

Collegiate Environment: Orientation program. Major annual event: Kick-Off Pow Wows (beginning of semester). Campus security: 24-hour emergency response devices. Little Priest Tribal College Library. Operations spending for the previous fiscal year: $171,500. 72 computers available on campus for general student use. Computer purchase/lease plans available. A campuswide network can be accessed. Students can access the following: online class registration. Staffed computer lab on campus provides training in use of computers, software, and the Internet.

■ METROPOLITAN COMMUNITY COLLEGE

PO Box 3777
Omaha, NE 68103-0777
Tel: (402)457-2400; Free: 800-228-9553
Fax: (402)457-2564
E-mail: mvazquez@mccneb.edu
Web Site: www.mccneb.edu

Description: State and locally supported, 2-year, coed. Part of Nebraska Coordinating Commission for Postsecondary Education. Awards certificates, diplomas, transfer associate, and terminal associate degrees. Founded 1974. Setting: 172-acre urban campus. Endowment: $1.4 million. Educational spending for the previous fiscal year: $2790 per student. Total enrollment: 17,003. Faculty: 877 (198 full-time, 679 part-time). Student-undergrad faculty ratio is 16:1. 4,141 applied, 100% were admitted. Full-time: 7,095 students, 55% women, 45% men. Part-time: 9,908 students, 58% women, 42% men. 3% from out-of-state. 44% 25 or older, 0.2% live on campus, 17% transferred in. Retention: 50% of full-time freshmen returned the following year. Core. Calendar: quarters. Academic remediation for entering students, ESL program, services for LD students, advanced placement, independent study, distance learning, summer session for credit, part-time degree program, adult/continuing education programs, co-op programs and internships. ROTC: Army (c).

Entrance Requirements: Open admission. Option: early admission. Recommended: high school transcript. Entrance: noncompetitive. Application deadline: rolling. Notification: continuous.

Collegiate Environment: Orientation program. Student services: personal-psychological counseling. Campus security: 24-hour emergency response devices and patrols, late night transport-escort service, controlled dormitory access, security on duty 9 pm to 6 am. Metropolitan Community College plus 2 others. Operations spending for the previous fiscal year: $891,473. 1,700 computers available on campus for general student use. A campuswide network can be accessed from student residence rooms and from off campus. Students can access the following: online class registration, online classes, e-mail. Staffed computer lab on campus provides training in use of computers and software.

Community Environment: See Creighton University.

■ MID-PLAINS COMMUNITY COLLEGE
1101 Halligan Dr.
North Platte, NE 69101
Tel: (308)535-3600; Free: 800-658-4348
Fax: (308)532-8590
E-mail: ablards@mpcc.edu
Web Site: www.mpcc.edu
Description: District-supported, 2-year, coed. Awards certificates, diplomas, transfer associate, and terminal associate degrees. Founded 1973. Setting: small town campus. Endowment: $6.6 million. Educational spending for the previous fiscal year: $6654 per student. Total enrollment: 2,222. Faculty: 384 (62 full-time, 322 part-time). Student-undergrad faculty ratio is 8:1. Students come from 30 states and territories, 13 other countries, 9% from out-of-state. 0.5% American Indian or Alaska Native, non-Hispanic/Latino; 8% Hispanic/Latino; 2% Black or African American, non-Hispanic/Latino; 0.6% Asian, non-Hispanic/Latino; 0.1% Native Hawaiian or other Pacific Islander, non-Hispanic/Latino; 2% international. 31% 25 or older, 20% live on campus. Core. Calendar: semesters. Academic remediation for entering students, ESL program, services for LD students, advanced placement, accelerated degree program, independent study, distance learning, double major, summer session for credit, part-time degree program, external degree program, adult/continuing education programs, co-op programs and internships.
Entrance Requirements: Open admission. Options: electronic application, deferred admission. Required: high school transcript. Recommended: ACT. Required for some: 2 recommendations, interview, ACCUPLACER. Entrance: minimally difficult. Application deadline: rolling. Notification: continuous. SAT Reasoning Test deadline: 8/19. SAT Subject Test deadline: 8/19. Transfer credits accepted: Yes.
Costs Per Year: Application fee: $0. State resident tuition: $2760 full-time, $92 per credit hour part-time. Nonresident tuition: $3600 full-time, $120 per credit hour part-time. Mandatory fees: $450 full-time, $15 per credit hour part-time. Full-time tuition and fees vary according to course load, program, and reciprocity agreements. Part-time tuition and fees vary according to course load, program, and reciprocity agreements. College room and board: $6500. College room only: $3020. Room and board charges vary according to board plan, housing facility, and location.
Collegiate Environment: Orientation program. Drama-theater group, choral group, student-run newspaper. Social organizations: 10 open to all; national fraternities, national sororities. Most popular organizations: Student Senate, Phi Theta Kappa, Phi Beta Lambda, Intercollegiate Athletics, MPCC Student Nurses Association. Major annual events: Annual Welcome Week Hypnotist, Annual Homecoming Week, Annual Chili Feed. Student services: personal-psychological counseling. Campus security: controlled dormitory access. von Riesen Library plus 1 other. Books: 17,993 (physical), 51,889 (digital/electronic); Serial titles: 50 (physical); Databases: 37. Weekly public service hours: 70; students can reserve study rooms. Operations spending for the previous fiscal year: $260,523. 723 computers available on campus for general student use. A campuswide network can be accessed. Students can access the following: online class registration.
Community Environment: A rural and agricultural community, North Platte is a railroad division point with extensive railroad shops. Important crops raised are corn, wheat, and alfalfa. Maloney Reservoir, six miles south of North Platte, offers boating, fishing and hunting. Community facilities include many churches, a regional medical center, shopping areas, a community playhouse, civic music association and numerous social and service organizations. Part-time employment opportunities are good.

■ MIDLAND UNIVERSITY
900 N Clarkson St.
Fremont, NE 68025-4200
Tel: (402)721-5480; Free: 800-642-8382
Fax: (402)721-0250
E-mail: oliver@midlandu.edu
Web Site: www.midlandu.edu
Description: Independent Lutheran, 4-year, coed. Awards associate and bachelor's degrees. Founded 1883. Setting: 27-acre small town campus with easy access to Omaha. Endowment: $21 million. Educational spending for the previous fiscal year: $5371 per student. Total enrollment: 827. Faculty: 81 (54 full-time, 27 part-time). Student-undergrad faculty ratio is 14:1. 920 applied, 88% were admitted. 9% from top 10% of their high school class, 26% from top quarter, 57% from top half. 1 class president, 17 valedictorians, 5 student government officers. Full-time: 808 students, 56% women, 44% men. Part-time: 19 students, 58% women, 42% men. Students come from 18 states and territories, 1 other country, 26% from out-of-state. 5% 25 or

older, 62% live on campus, 5% transferred in. Retention: 80% of full-time freshmen returned the following year. Core. Calendar: 4-1-4. Academic remediation for entering students, ESL program, services for LD students, advanced placement, accelerated degree program, self-designed majors, honors program, independent study, double major, summer session for credit, part-time degree program, co-op programs and internships. Off campus study at Concordia University, Doane College, Dana College, Hastings College, Central College. Study abroad program.
Entrance Requirements: Options: electronic application, early admission, international baccalaureate accepted. Required: high school transcript, SAT or ACT. Recommended: essay, minimum 3.0 high school GPA. Required for some: interview. Entrance: moderately difficult. Application deadline: rolling. Notification: continuous until 9/1.
Collegiate Environment: Orientation program. Drama-theater group, choral group, marching band, student-run newspaper. Social organizations: 48 open to all; local fraternities, local sororities; 40% of eligible men and 40% of eligible women are members. Most popular organizations: Student Nurses Association, Student Education Association, Phi Beta Lambda, Fellowship of Christian Athletes, Circle K. Major annual events: Homecoming, Snow Days, Spring Fling. Student services: health clinic, personal-psychological counseling. Campus security: 24-hour emergency response devices, student patrols, late night transport-escort service, controlled dormitory access. Luther Library. Operations spending for the previous fiscal year: $276,356. 190 computers available on campus for general student use. A campuswide network can be accessed from student residence rooms and from off campus. Students can access the following: online class registration. Staffed computer lab on campus provides training in use of computers, software, and the Internet.
Community Environment: Situated near the Platte River, Fremont, the trading center of a dairying and livestock area, is located 35 miles northwest of Omaha and 51 miles north of Lincoln, Nebraska. Fremont is also recognized as the hybrid seed corn center of the state. Some of the products of industry are poultry, butter, flour, soybeans, and animal food. Some nationally known manufacturers such as Campbell Soup, Fel-Tex Ammonia, Magnus Metal, and Hormel Meats have plants in the area. Part-time employment is available. Boating, fishing and hunting are some of the outdoor sports available.

■ MYOTHERAPY INSTITUTE
4001 Pioneers Woods Dr.
Lincoln, NE 68506
Tel: (402)421-7410
Fax: (402)421-6736
Web Site: www.myotherapy.edu
Description: Proprietary, 2-year, coed. Awards terminal associate degrees. Total enrollment: 52.
Entrance Requirements: Entrance: noncompetitive.

■ NATIONAL AMERICAN UNIVERSITY
3604 Summit Plz. Dr.
Bellevue, NE 68123
Tel: (402)972-4250
Web Site: www.national.edu
Description: Proprietary, 4-year, coed. Awards associate and bachelor's degrees.

■ NEBRASKA CHRISTIAN COLLEGE OF HOPE INTERNATIONAL UNIVERSITY
12550 S 114th St.
Papillion, NE 68046
Tel: (402)935-9400
E-mail: dj.parkey@nechristian.edu
Web Site: www.nechristian.edu
Description: Independent, comprehensive, coed, affiliated with Christian Churches and Churches of Christ. Awards associate, bachelor's, and master's degrees. Founded 1944. Setting: 85-acre small town campus with easy access to Omaha, NE. Endowment: $1.3 million. Total enrollment: 145. Faculty: 27 (5 full-time, 22 part-time). Student-undergrad faculty ratio is 12:1. 154 applied, 44% were admitted. 12% from top quarter of their high school class, 42% from top half. Full-time: 144 students, 41% women, 59% men. Part-time: 1 student, 100% men. 52% from out-of-state. 1% American Indian or Alaska Native, non-Hispanic/Latino; 14% Hispanic/Latino; 9% Black or African American, non-Hispanic/Latino; 1% Asian, non-Hispanic/Latino. 27% 25 or older, 73% live on campus, 19% transferred in. Retention: 63% of full-

time freshmen returned the following year. Core. Calendar: semesters. Academic remediation for entering students, independent study, distance learning, double major, part-time degree program, internships. Off campus study at Hope International University, Grace University, Northeast Community College, Wayne State College, York College (NE), Fort Hays State University. Study abroad program.

Entrance Requirements: Required: essay, high school transcript, 2 recommendations, ACT. Required for some: interview, minimum ACT score of 18 for recent high school graduates. SAT Reasoning Test deadline: 8/1. SAT Subject Test deadline: 8/1.

Costs Per Year: Application fee: $40. Comprehensive fee: $26,685 includes full-time tuition ($17,350), mandatory fees ($315), and college room and board ($9020). College room only: $5100. Full-time tuition and fees vary according to course load. Room and board charges vary according to board plan and housing facility. Part-time tuition: $760 per credit hour. Part-time mandatory fees: $315 per year. Part-time tuition and fees vary according to course load.

Collegiate Environment: Orientation program. Choral group. Most popular organizations: Global Gospel Group, Running Club, Minority Students Organization, Spiritual Life Group, Writing Club. Major annual events: Rush Week, Missions Emphasis Week, Spring Formal. Campus security: student patrols, controlled dormitory access. Swedberg Library.

Community Environment: Primarily a rural community, Norfolk depends very heavily on agriculture and the raising of beef as its primary industries. The livestock business is valued at almost a $40 million industry. Community facilities include a public library, 20 churches representing 16 denominations, a YMCA and civic organizations such as Rotary, Kiwanis and the Lions Club. Part-time employment is available. Lewis and Clark Lake and other facilities provide swimming, boating, fishing and golf. The Norfolk Historical Museum exhibits a collection of local historical relics.

■ NEBRASKA COLLEGE OF TECHNICAL AGRICULTURE

RR3, Box 23A
Curtis, NE 69025-9205
Tel: (308)367-4124; Free: 800-3CURTIS
Fax: (308)367-5203
Web Site: www.ncta.unl.edu

Description: State-supported, 2-year, coed. Part of University of Nebraska System. Administratively affiliated with Institute of Agriculture and Natural Resources - University of Nebraska. Awards certificates, transfer associate, and terminal associate degrees. Founded 1965. Setting: 634-acre rural campus. Research spending for the previous fiscal year: $2360. Total enrollment: 425. Faculty: 21 (13 full-time, 8 part-time). Student-undergrad faculty ratio is 13:1. Full-time: 246 students, 52% women, 48% men. Part-time: 179 students, 49% women, 51% men. Students come from 10 states and territories. 45% live on campus. Retention: 64% of full-time freshmen returned the following year. Core. Calendar: 8-week modular system. Academic remediation for entering students, independent study, distance learning, double major, part-time degree program, external degree program, adult/continuing education programs, internships. Study abroad program.

Entrance Requirements: Open admission. Option: early admission. Required: high school transcript, ACT. Recommended: interview. Entrance: noncompetitive. Application deadline: rolling. Transfer credits accepted: Yes.

Collegiate Environment: Orientation program. Student-run newspaper. Social organizations: 13 open to all. Most popular organizations: Aggie Livestock Association, Student Technicians Veterinary Medicine Association, Business Club, Phi Theta Kappa, Rodeo Club. Major annual events: Annual Open House, Step Ahead Days, Orientation. Student services: health clinic, personal-psychological counseling. Campus security: 24-hour emergency response devices, controlled dormitory access, night security. Nebraska College of Technical Agriculture Library. Operations spending for the previous fiscal year: $55,223. 45 computers available on campus for general student use. Computer purchase/lease plans available. A campuswide network can be accessed from student residence rooms and from off campus. Students can access the following: online class registration. Staffed computer lab on campus.

■ NEBRASKA INDIAN COMMUNITY COLLEGE

PO Box 428
Macy, NE 68039-0428
Tel: (402)494-2311; Free: 844-440-NICC
Fax: (402)878-2522
E-mail: tmunhofen@thenicc.edu
Web Site: www.thenicc.edu

Description: Federally supported, 2-year, coed. Awards certificates, transfer associate, and terminal associate degrees. Founded 1979. Setting: 22-acre rural campus with easy access to Omaha. Total enrollment: 180. Faculty: 22 (8 full-time, 14 part-time). Student-undergrad faculty ratio is 5:1. 57 applied, 100% were admitted. Full-time: 47 students, 60% women, 40% men. Part-time: 133 students, 73% women, 27% men. Students come from 3 states and territories, 13% from out-of-state. 44% 25 or older, 2% transferred in. Core. Calendar: semesters. Academic remediation for entering students, services for LD students, independent study, distance learning, double major, summer session for credit, part-time degree program, adult/continuing education programs, internships. Study abroad program.

Entrance Requirements: Open admission. Options: electronic application, early admission. Required: high school transcript. Required for some: certificate of tribal enrollment. Application deadlines: rolling, rolling for nonresidents. Transfer credits accepted: Yes.

Costs Per Year: One-time mandatory fee: $25. State resident tuition: $4080 full-time, $170 per credit hour part-time. Nonresident tuition: $4080 full-time, $170 per credit hour part-time. Full-time tuition varies according to course load. Part-time tuition varies according to course load.

Collegiate Environment: Orientation program. Social organizations: 2 open to all. Most popular organizations: Student Senate, AIHEC. Major annual events: Pow-wows, Movie Nights, Santa Claus. Macy Library plus 1 other. Books: 17,555 (physical), 370 (digital/electronic). Weekly public service hours: 40. 25 computers available on campus for general student use. Computer purchase/lease plans available. A campuswide network can be accessed. Staffed computer lab on campus provides training in use of computers, software, and the Internet.

■ NEBRASKA METHODIST COLLEGE

720 N 87th St.
Omaha, NE 68114
Tel: (402)354-7000; Free: 800-335-5510
Fax: (402)354-4819
E-mail: megan.maryott@methodistcollege.edu
Web Site: www.methodistcollege.edu

Description: Independent, comprehensive, coed, affiliated with United Methodist Church. Awards associate, bachelor's, master's, and doctoral degrees and post-master's certificates. Founded 1891. Setting: 8-acre urban campus. Total enrollment: 1,102. Faculty: 67 (62 full-time, 5 part-time). Student-undergrad faculty ratio is 12:1. 86 applied, 91% were admitted. 7% from top 10% of their high school class, 42% from top quarter, 80% from top half. Full-time: 419 students, 89% women, 11% men. Part-time: 376 students, 90% women, 10% men. Students come from 17 states and territories, 5 other countries, 14% from out-of-state. 0.3% American Indian or Alaska Native, non-Hispanic/Latino; 6% Hispanic/Latino; 4% Black or African American, non-Hispanic/Latino; 2% Asian, non-Hispanic/Latino; 0.1% Native Hawaiian or other Pacific Islander, non-Hispanic/Latino; 0.1% international. 41% 25 or older, 10% live on campus, 19% transferred in. Retention: 81% of full-time freshmen returned the following year. Academic area with the most degrees conferred: health professions and related sciences. Core. Calendar: semesters. Academic remediation for entering students, services for LD students, advanced placement, accelerated degree program, independent study, distance learning, summer session for credit, external degree program, adult/continuing education programs, co-op programs. ROTC: Air Force (c).

Entrance Requirements: Options: electronic application, deferred admission. Required: essay, high school transcript, minimum 2.5 high school GPA, SAT or ACT. Entrance: moderately difficult. Application deadline: rolling. SAT Reasoning Test deadline: 4/30. Transfer credits accepted: Yes.

Costs Per Year: Application fee: $25. Comprehensive fee: $25,894 includes full-time tuition ($15,660), mandatory fees ($648), and college room and board ($9586). Part-time tuition: $580 per credit hour.

Collegiate Environment: Orientation program. Social organizations: 12 open to all; 10% of eligible men and 90% of eligible women are members. Most popular organizations: Student Nurses Association, Methodist Allied Health Student Association, Student Government, Student Ambassadors, Residence Hall Council. Major annual events: Welcome Week, Study/Finals Week, Homecoming Week. Student services: health clinic, personal-psychological counseling. Campus security: 24-hour emergency response devices and patrols, late night transport-escort service, controlled dormitory access. 100 college housing spaces available; 86 were occupied in 2018-19. No special consideration for freshman housing applicants. Option: coed housing available. John Moritz Library. Books: 1,374 (physical), 15 (digital/electronic); Serial titles: 55 (physical), 13,033 (digital/electronic); Databases:

23. Weekly public service hours: 65. 50 computers available on campus for general student use. A campuswide network can be accessed from student residence rooms. Students can access the following: online class registration. Staffed computer lab on campus provides training in use of computers, software, and the Internet.

■ NEBRASKA WESLEYAN UNIVERSITY

5000 Saint Paul Ave.
Lincoln, NE 68504-2796
Tel: (402)466-2371; Free: 800-541-3818
Fax: (402)465-2179
E-mail: admissions@nebrwesleyan.edu
Web Site: www.nebrwesleyan.edu

Description: Independent United Methodist, comprehensive, coed. Awards bachelor's and master's degrees and post-master's certificates. Founded 1887. Setting: 50-acre suburban campus with easy access to Omaha. Endowment: $50.9 million. Educational spending for the previous fiscal year: $7694 per student. Total enrollment: 2,059. Faculty: (111 full-time). Student-undergrad faculty ratio is 12:1. 1,803 applied, 74% were admitted. 19% from top 10% of their high school class, 23% from top quarter, 81% from top half. Full-time: 1,586 students, 55% women, 45% men. Part-time: 230 students, 77% women, 23% men. Students come from 24 states and territories, 19 other countries, 14% from out-of-state. 0.2% American Indian or Alaska Native, non-Hispanic/Latino; 6% Hispanic/Latino; 3% Black or African American, non-Hispanic/Latino; 2% Asian, non-Hispanic/Latino; 0.1% Native Hawaiian or other Pacific Islander, non-Hispanic/Latino; 2% international. 16% 25 or older, 6% transferred in. Retention: 78% of full-time freshmen returned the following year. Academic areas with the most degrees conferred: health professions and related sciences; business/marketing; biological/life sciences. Core. Calendar: semesters. Services for LD students, advanced placement, accelerated degree program, self-designed majors, independent study, double major, summer session for credit, part-time degree program, adult/continuing education programs, internships, graduate courses open to undergrads. Off campus study. Study abroad program. ROTC: Army (c), Naval (c), Air Force (c).

Entrance Requirements: Options: electronic application, early decision, deferred admission, international baccalaureate accepted. Required: high school transcript, SAT or ACT. Required for some: essay. Entrance: moderately difficult. Application deadlines: 8/15, 12/1 for early decision. Notification: continuous. SAT Reasoning Test deadline: 7/1. SAT Subject Test deadline: 7/1. Transfer credits accepted: Yes. Early decision applicants: 200. Early decision applicants admitted: 183.

Costs Per Year: Application fee: $0. Comprehensive fee: $43,582 includes full-time tuition ($33,252), mandatory fees ($830), and college room and board ($9500). Room and board charges vary according to board plan and housing facility.

Collegiate Environment: Orientation program. Drama-theater group, choral group, marching band, student-run newspaper, radio station. Social organizations: 90 open to all; national fraternities, national sororities, local sororities; 15% of eligible men and 24% of eligible women are members. Major annual events: Jim Wand hypnotist show, Visions and Ventures Symposium, Homecoming. Student services: health clinic, personal-psychological counseling, women's center. Campus security: 24-hour emergency response devices and patrols, late night transport-escort service, controlled dormitory access. Cochrane Woods Library. Books: 316,222 (physical), 185,022 (digital/electronic); Serial titles: 1,711 (physical), 16,353 (digital/electronic); Databases: 69. Weekly public service hours: 91; students can reserve study rooms. Operations spending for the previous fiscal year: $720,269. 360 computers available on campus for general student use. A campuswide network can be accessed from student residence rooms and from off campus. Students can access the following: online class registration. Staffed computer lab on campus (open 24 hours a day) provides training in use of computers, software, and the Internet.

Community Environment: The capital, Lincoln, in southeastern Nebraska, is in a vast agricultural area where irrigation is an important factor. Many insurance firms have their home offices here. Major forms of transportation are available. Pershing Municipal Auditorium and the Bob Devaney Sports Center is used for conventions, concerts and athletic activities. Recreational facilities and sporting events are numerous. Some of the points of interest are Antelope Park, the Sunken Garden, Fairview, a home occupied by the William Jennings Bryan family for 15 years, Pioneer Park, Holmes Lake with bike trails, Sheldon Memorial Art Gallery, the University of Nebraska State Museum, and the Haymarket District. Part-time jobs are available on and off campus.

■ NORTHEAST COMMUNITY COLLEGE

801 E Benjamin Ave.
Norfolk, NE 68702-0469
Tel: (402)371-2020
Fax: (402)644-0650
E-mail: admission@northeast.edu
Web Site: www.northeast.edu

Description: State and locally supported, 2-year, coed. Part of Nebraska Coordinating Commission for Postsecondary Education. Awards certificates, diplomas, transfer associate, and terminal associate degrees. Founded 1973. Setting: 202-acre small town campus. Educational spending for the previous fiscal year: $3122 per student. Total enrollment: 5,075. Faculty: 300 (127 full-time, 173 part-time). Student-undergrad faculty ratio is 17:1. Full-time: 2,121 students, 49% women, 51% men. Part-time: 2,954 students, 44% women, 56% men. Students come from 12 states and territories, 5% from out-of-state. 1% American Indian or Alaska Native, non-Hispanic/Latino; 10% Hispanic/Latino; 1% Black or African American, non-Hispanic/Latino; 0.4% Asian, non-Hispanic/Latino; 1% international. 31% 25 or older, 20% live on campus, 5% transferred in. Retention: 70% of full-time freshmen returned the following year. Core. Calendar: semesters. Academic remediation for entering students, ESL program, services for LD students, advanced placement, independent study, distance learning, double major, summer session for credit, part-time degree program, adult/continuing education programs, co-op programs and internships. Off campus study. Study abroad program.

Entrance Requirements: Open admission. Options: electronic application, early admission, international baccalaureate accepted. Recommended: high school transcript. Required for some: essay, high school transcript, minimum X high school GPA, 3 recommendations, interview. Entrance: noncompetitive. Application deadline: rolling. Notification: continuous. Transfer credits accepted: Yes.

Costs Per Year: Application fee: $0. State resident tuition: $2880 full-time, $96 per credit hour part-time. Nonresident tuition: $4035 full-time, $134.50 per credit hour part-time. Mandatory fees: $600 full-time, $20 per credit hour part-time. College room and board: $8605. College room only: $5420. Room and board charges vary according to board plan and housing facility.

Collegiate Environment: Orientation program. Drama-theater group, choral group, student-run newspaper, radio station. Social organizations: 50 open to all. Most popular organizations: Phi Theta Kappa, Farm Bureau Club, Enactus, Christian Student Fellowship, Love Your Melon. Major annual events: Cheers to Leadership Root Beer Kegger, Welcome Back Picnic and Inflatables, Extreme Bowling. Student services: health clinic, personal-psychological counseling. Campus security: 24-hour emergency response devices and patrols, controlled dormitory access, building walk-throughs and parking lot patrols, door and dorm checks, armed security. Library Resource Center. Books: 20,648 (physical); Serial titles: 411 (physical); Databases: 70. Weekly public service hours: 78. Operations spending for the previous fiscal year: $354,366. 895 computers available on campus for general student use. A campuswide network can be accessed. Students can access the following: online class registration. Staffed computer lab on campus provides training in use of computers, software, and the Internet.

Community Environment: See Nebraska Christian College.

■ OMAHA SCHOOL OF MASSAGE AND HEALTHCARE OF HERZING UNIVERSITY

9748 Park Dr.
Omaha, NE 68127
Tel: (402)331-3694
Fax: (402)331-0280
Web Site: www.osmhc.com

Description: Independent, 2-year, coed. Awards diplomas and terminal associate degrees. Founded 1991.

■ PERU STATE COLLEGE

PO Box 10
Peru, NE 68421
Tel: (402)872-3815; Free: 800-741-4412
E-mail: mwillis@peru.edu
Web Site: www.peru.edu

Description: State-supported, comprehensive, coed. Part of Nebraska State College System. Awards bachelor's and master's degrees. Founded 1867. Setting: 104-acre rural campus. Total enrollment: 2,358. Faculty: 109 (47 full-time, 62 part-time). Student-undergrad faculty ratio is 24:1. 869 applied, 49% were admitted. 13% from top quarter of their high school class,

46% from top half. Full-time: 1,192 students, 58% women, 42% men. Part-time: 902 students, 60% women, 40% men. 1% American Indian or Alaska Native, non-Hispanic/Latino; 4% Hispanic/Latino; 5% Black or African American, non-Hispanic/Latino; 1% Asian, non-Hispanic/Latino; 0.1% Native Hawaiian or other Pacific Islander, non-Hispanic/Latino. 33% live on campus, 9% transferred in. Academic areas with the most degrees conferred: business/marketing; education; homeland security, law enforcement, firefighting, and protective services. Core. Calendar: semesters. Academic remediation for entering students, services for LD students, advanced placement, accelerated degree program, freshman honors college, honors program, distance learning, double major, summer session for credit, part-time degree program, external degree program, adult/continuing education programs, co-op programs and internships, graduate courses open to undergrads. Off campus study. ROTC: Army (c), Air Force (c).

Entrance Requirements: Open admission. Options: electronic application, international baccalaureate accepted. Required: high school transcript. Required for some: SAT or ACT. Entrance: noncompetitive. Application deadline: rolling. Notification: continuous. Transfer credits accepted: Yes.

Costs Per Year: Application fee: $0. State resident tuition: $5310 full-time, $177 per credit hour part-time. Nonresident tuition: $5310 full-time, $177 per credit hour part-time. Mandatory fees: $2142 full-time, $71.35 per credit hour part-time. Full-time tuition and fees vary according to course level, course load, and location. Part-time tuition and fees vary according to course level, course load, and location. College room and board: $8796. College room only: $4538. Room and board charges vary according to board plan and housing facility.

Collegiate Environment: Orientation program. Drama-theater group, choral group, marching band, student-run newspaper. Social organizations: 20 open to all. Most popular organizations: Campus Activities Board, Black Student Union, Peru Student Education Association (PSEA), Phi Beta Lambda (PBL), Pilot Club. Major annual events: Homecoming, Spring Fling, Oakstock. Student services: health clinic. Campus security: 24-hour emergency response devices and patrols, late night transport-escort service. Peru State College Library. Operations spending for the previous fiscal year: $144,370. 125 computers available on campus for general student use. A campuswide network can be accessed from student residence rooms. Students can access the following: online class registration. Staffed computer lab on campus.

Community Environment: Peru is situated in an agricultural region of southeast Nebraska on bluffs overlooking the Missouri River. Corn, wheat, apples, and many other crops are raised in the area. The town is 65 miles from Omaha and 75 miles from Lincoln.

■ PURDUE UNIVERSITY GLOBAL (LINCOLN)
1821 K St.
Lincoln, NE 68508
Tel: (402)474-5315; Free: 844-PURDUE-G
Web Site: www.purdueglobal.edu
Description: Independent, comprehensive, coed. Awards associate, bachelor's, and master's degrees. Founded 1884. Setting: urban campus. Calendar: quarters.

■ PURDUE UNIVERSITY GLOBAL (OMAHA)
5425 N 103rd St.
Omaha, NE 68134
Tel: (402)431-6100; Free: 844-PURDUE-G
Web Site: www.purdueglobal.edu
Description: Independent, comprehensive, coed. Awards associate, bachelor's, and master's degrees. Founded 1891. Setting: urban campus. Calendar: quarters.

■ ST. GREGORY THE GREAT SEMINARY
800 Fletcher Rd.
Seward, NE 68434-8145
Tel: (402)643-4052
Fax: (402)643-6964
E-mail: sggs@stgregoryseminary.edu
Web Site: www.sggs.edu
Description: Independent Roman Catholic, 4-year, men only. Awards bachelor's degrees. Setting: 60-acre small town campus. Total enrollment: 48. Faculty: 13 (7 full-time, 6 part-time). Student-undergrad faculty ratio is 5:1. 7 applied, 100% were admitted. Full-time: 48 students. Students come from 8 states and territories, 5 other countries, 50% from out-of-state. 10% Hispanic/Latino; 6% Asian, non-Hispanic/Latino; 8% international. 8% 25 or

older, 100% live on campus, 15% transferred in. Retention: 75% of full-time freshmen returned the following year. Core.

Entrance Requirements: Required: essay, high school transcript, 3 recommendations, interview, Church documents, letter of sponsorship from diocese, SAT or ACT. Transfer credits accepted: Yes.

Collegiate Environment: Orientation program. Our Lady Seat of Wisdom Library.

■ SOUTHEAST COMMUNITY COLLEGE, BEATRICE CAMPUS
4771 W Scott Rd.
Beatrice, NE 68310
Tel: (402)228-3468; Free: 800-233-5027
Fax: (402)228-2218
Web Site: www.southeast.edu
Description: District-supported, 2-year, coed. Part of Southeast Community College System. Awards certificates, diplomas, transfer associate, and terminal associate degrees. Founded 1976. Setting: 640-acre small town campus. Core. Calendar: semesters. Academic remediation for entering students, services for LD students, advanced placement, distance learning, summer session for credit, part-time degree program, adult/continuing education programs, co-op programs and internships. Off campus study at Peru State College.

Entrance Requirements: Open admission. Options: electronic application, early admission, deferred admission. Required: high school transcript. Recommended: minimum 2.0 high school GPA, SAT or ACT, ACT ASSET, ACT Compass. Required for some: ACT ASSET, ACT Compass. Entrance: noncompetitive. Application deadline: rolling.

Collegiate Environment: Orientation program. Drama-theater group, choral group, student-run newspaper, radio station. Student services: personal-psychological counseling. Campus security: controlled dormitory access, evening security. Learning Resource Center.

■ SOUTHEAST COMMUNITY COLLEGE, LINCOLN CAMPUS
8800 O St.
Lincoln, NE 68520-1299
Tel: (402)471-3333; Free: 800-642-4075
E-mail: admissions@southeast.edu
Web Site: www.southeast.edu
Description: District-supported, 2-year, coed. Part of Southeast Community College Area. Awards certificates, diplomas, transfer associate, and terminal associate degrees. Founded 1973. Setting: 115-acre suburban campus with easy access to Omaha. Total enrollment: 9,262. Faculty: 742 (370 full-time, 372 part-time). Student-undergrad faculty ratio is 12:1. Full-time: 3,942 students, 45% women, 55% men. Part-time: 5,320 students, 57% women, 43% men. 7% from out-of-state. 0.7% American Indian or Alaska Native, non-Hispanic/Latino; 8% Hispanic/Latino; 6% Black or African American, non-Hispanic/Latino; 3% Asian, non-Hispanic/Latino; 0.1% Native Hawaiian or other Pacific Islander, non-Hispanic/Latino. Core. Calendar: quarters. Academic remediation for entering students, ESL program, services for LD students, advanced placement, independent study, distance learning, summer session for credit, part-time degree program, co-op programs and internships. Off campus study at University of Nebraska-Lincoln.

Entrance Requirements: Open admission. Options: electronic application, early admission, deferred admission. Required: high school transcript. Recommended: ACT. Entrance: noncompetitive. Application deadline: rolling. Transfer credits accepted: Yes.

Costs Per Year: State resident tuition: $3,038 full-time, $67.50 per quarter hour part-time. Nonresident tuition: $3,668 full-time, $81.50 per quarter hour part-time. Mandatory fees: $90 full-time, $2 per quarter hour part-time. Full-time tuition and fees vary according to course load. Part-time tuition and fees vary according to course load.

Collegiate Environment: Orientation program. Campus security: late night transport-escort service. Lincoln Campus Learning Resource Center. Books: 26,473 (physical), 37,630 (digital/electronic); Serial titles: 338 (physical), 97 (digital/electronic); Databases: 67. Weekly public service hours: 68.

■ SOUTHEAST COMMUNITY COLLEGE, MILFORD CAMPUS
600 State St.
Milford, NE 68405
Tel: (402)761-2131; Free: 800-933-7223
E-mail: admissions@southeast.edu
Web Site: www.southeast.edu
Description: District-supported, 2-year, coed. Part of Southeast Community College System. Awards diplomas and terminal associate degrees. Founded

1941. Setting: 50-acre small town campus with easy access to Omaha. Total enrollment: 9,262. Faculty: 742 (370 full-time, 372 part-time). Student-undergrad faculty ratio is 12:1. Full-time: 3,942 students, 45% women, 55% men. Part-time: 5,320 students, 57% women, 43% men. 7% from out-of-state. 0.7% American Indian or Alaska Native, non-Hispanic/Latino; 8% Hispanic/Latino; 6% Black or African American, non-Hispanic/Latino; 3% Asian, non-Hispanic/Latino; 0.1% Native Hawaiian or other Pacific Islander, non-Hispanic/Latino. Core. Calendar: quarters. Academic remediation for entering students, services for LD students, advanced placement, distance learning, summer session for credit, part-time degree program, co-op programs and internships.

Entrance Requirements: Open admission. Options: electronic application, early admission, deferred admission. Required: high school transcript. Recommended: ACT. Entrance: noncompetitive. Application deadline: rolling. Notification: continuous. Transfer credits accepted: Yes.

Costs Per Year: State resident tuition: $3,038 full-time, $67.50 per quarter hour part-time. Nonresident tuition: $3,668 full-time, $81.50 per quarter hour part-time. Mandatory fees: $90 full-time, $2 per quarter hour part-time. Full-time tuition and fees vary according to course load. Part-time tuition and fees vary according to course load.

Collegiate Environment: Orientation program. Campus security: late night transport-escort service, controlled dormitory access. Milford Campus Learning Resource Center. Books: 26,473 (physical), 37,630 (digital/electronic); Serial titles: 338 (physical), 97 (digital/electronic); Databases: 67. Weekly public service hours: 51; students can reserve study rooms.

■ UNION COLLEGE

3800 S 48th St.
Lincoln, NE 68506-4300
Tel: (402)486-2600; Free: 800-228-4600
Fax: (402)486-2895
E-mail: enroll@ucollege.edu
Web Site: www.ucollege.edu

Description: Independent Seventh-day Adventist, comprehensive, coed. Awards associate, bachelor's, and master's degrees. Founded 1891. Setting: 26-acre suburban campus with easy access to Omaha. Total enrollment: 868. Faculty: 118 (64 full-time, 54 part-time). Student-undergrad faculty ratio is 9:1. 1,573 applied, 60% were admitted. Full-time: 707 students, 58% women, 42% men. Part-time: 74 students, 61% women, 39% men. Students come from 45 states and territories, 29 other countries, 80% from out-of-state. 0.4% American Indian or Alaska Native, non-Hispanic/Latino; 22% Hispanic/Latino; 8% Black or African American, non-Hispanic/Latino; 5% Asian, non-Hispanic/Latino; 0.5% Native Hawaiian or other Pacific Islander, non-Hispanic/Latino; 8% international. 9% 25 or older, 75% live on campus, 11% transferred in. Retention: 80% of full-time freshmen returned the following year. Academic areas with the most degrees conferred: health professions and related sciences; business/marketing; education. Core. Calendar: semesters. Services for LD students, advanced placement, accelerated degree program, self-designed majors, honors program, independent study, double major, summer session for credit, part-time degree program, adult/continuing education programs, co-op programs and internships. Off campus study at University of Nebraska, Southeast Community College. Study abroad program.

Entrance Requirements: Option: electronic application. Required: high school transcript, minimum 2.5 high school GPA, 3 recommendations, SAT or ACT. Required for some: essay, interview. Entrance: moderately difficult. SAT Reasoning Test deadline: 8/15. SAT Subject Test deadline: 8/15. Transfer credits accepted: Yes.

Costs Per Year: Application fee: $0. Comprehensive fee: $30,850 includes full-time tuition ($22,680), mandatory fees ($1100), and college room and board ($7070). College room only: $4020. Full-time tuition and fees vary according to course load, degree level, and program. Room and board charges vary according to board plan and housing facility. Part-time tuition: $945 per credit hour. Part-time mandatory fees: $550 per term. Part-time tuition and fees vary according to program.

Collegiate Environment: Orientation program. Drama-theater group, choral group, student-run newspaper. Most popular organizations: Business and Computer Science Club, Math and Science Club, Nursing Club, Amnesty International, International Club. Major annual events: Project Impact, ASB Handshake, Basketball Tournament. Student services: health clinic, personal-psychological counseling. Campus security: 24-hour emergency response devices, student patrols, late night transport-escort service. Ella Johnson Crandall Library. Books: 143,808 (physical), 187,159 (digital/electronic); Serial titles: 136 (physical), 136 (digital/electronic); Databases: 61. Students can reserve study rooms.

■ UNIVERSAL COLLEGE OF HEALING ARTS

8702 N 30th St.
Omaha, NE 68112-1810
Tel: (402)556-4456
Web Site: www.ucha.edu

Description: Proprietary, 2-year, coed. Awards diplomas, transfer associate, and terminal associate degrees.

■ UNIVERSITY OF NEBRASKA AT KEARNEY

905 W 25th St.
Kearney, NE 68849-0001
Tel: (308)865-8441; Free: 800-532-7639
Fax: (308)865-8987
E-mail: admissionsug@unk.edu
Web Site: www.unk.edu

Description: State-supported, comprehensive, coed. Part of University of Nebraska System. Awards bachelor's and master's degrees and post-master's certificates. Founded 1903. Setting: 235-acre small town campus. Total enrollment: 6,644. Faculty: 457 (323 full-time, 134 part-time). Student-undergrad faculty ratio is 14:1. 5,911 applied, 82% were admitted. 20% from top 10% of their high school class, 44% from top quarter, 79% from top half. Full-time: 4,063 students, 57% women, 43% men. Part-time: 780 students, 58% women, 42% men. 8% from out-of-state. 0.1% American Indian or Alaska Native, non-Hispanic/Latino; 11% Hispanic/Latino; 2% Black or African American, non-Hispanic/Latino; 0.8% Asian, non-Hispanic/Latino; 0.1% Native Hawaiian or other Pacific Islander, non-Hispanic/Latino; 5% international. 10% 25 or older, 35% live on campus, 6% transferred in. Retention: 79% of full-time freshmen returned the following year. Academic areas with the most degrees conferred: business/marketing; education; parks and recreation. Core. Calendar: semesters. Services for LD students, honors program, independent study, distance learning, double major, part-time degree program, internships, graduate courses open to undergrads. Study abroad program. ROTC: Army.

Entrance Requirements: Option: electronic application. Required: high school transcript, rank in upper 50% of high school class, SAT or ACT. Entrance: moderately difficult. Application deadline: 8/15. Notification: continuous until 9/1. Transfer credits accepted: Yes.

Costs Per Year: Application fee: $45. State resident tuition: $5940 full-time, $198 per credit hour part-time. Nonresident tuition: $12,930 full-time, $431 per credit hour part-time. Mandatory fees: $1573 full-time. Full-time tuition and fees vary according to course level, course load, degree level, location, and program. Part-time tuition varies according to course level, course load, degree level, location, and program. College room and board: $9878. College room only: $5058. Room and board charges vary according to board plan and housing facility.

Collegiate Environment: Orientation program. Drama-theater group, marching band, student-run newspaper, radio station. Social organizations: national fraternities, national sororities. Student services: health clinic, personal-psychological counseling. Campus security: 24-hour emergency response devices and patrols, late night transport-escort service. Calvin T. Ryan Library.

■ UNIVERSITY OF NEBRASKA-LINCOLN

14th and R Sts.
Lincoln, NE 68588
Tel: (402)472-7211; Free: 800-742-8800
Fax: (402)472-0670
E-mail: admissions@unl.edu
Web Site: www.unl.edu

Description: State-supported, university, coed. Part of University of Nebraska System. Awards bachelor's, master's, and doctoral degrees and post-master's certificates. Founded 1869. Setting: 856-acre urban campus with easy access to Omaha. System endowment: $1.7 billion. Research spending for the previous fiscal year: $208.2 million. Educational spending for the previous fiscal year: $11,067 per student. Total enrollment: 25,820. Faculty: 1,397 (1,300 full-time, 97 part-time). Student-undergrad faculty ratio is 21:1. 14,956 applied, 80% were admitted. 26% from top 10% of their high school class, 54% from top quarter, 86% from top half. 33 National Merit Scholars. Full-time: 19,466 students, 48% women, 52% men. Part-time: 1,364 students, 42% women, 58% men. Students come from 51 states and territories, 107 other countries, 24% from out-of-state. 0.2% American Indian or Alaska Native, non-Hispanic/Latino; 7% Hispanic/Latino; 3% Black or African American, non-Hispanic/Latino; 3% Asian, non-Hispanic/Latino; 0.1% Native Hawaiian or other Pacific Islander, non-Hispanic/Latino; 9%

international. 5% 25 or older, 34% live on campus, 4% transferred in. Retention: 83% of full-time freshmen returned the following year. Academic areas with the most degrees conferred: business/marketing; engineering; agriculture; communication/journalism; family and consumer sciences. Core. Calendar: semesters. ESL program, services for LD students, advanced placement, accelerated degree program, self-designed majors, honors program, independent study, distance learning, double major, summer session for credit, part-time degree program, adult/continuing education programs, co-op programs and internships, graduate courses open to undergrads. Off campus study at Great Plains Interactive Distance Education Alliance. Study abroad program. ROTC: Army, Naval, Air Force.

Entrance Requirements: Options: electronic application, international baccalaureate accepted. Required: high school transcript, minimum ACT score of 20 or combined total of 1030 or higher on the SAT Evidence-Based Reading and Writing and SAT Math sections or rank in upper 50% of high school class, SAT or ACT. Recommended: ACT. Entrance: moderately difficult. Application deadlines: 5/1, 5/1 for nonresidents. Notification: continuous, continuous for nonresidents. SAT Reasoning Test deadline: 7/15. Transfer credits accepted: Yes.

Costs Per Year: Application fee: $45. State resident tuition: $7350 full-time, $245 per credit hour part-time. Nonresident tuition: $23,145 full-time, $771.50 per credit hour part-time. Mandatory fees: $1804 full-time, $17.25 per credit hour part-time, $395 per term part-time. Full-time tuition and fees vary according to course load, location, program, and reciprocity agreements. Part-time tuition and fees vary according to course load, location, program, and reciprocity agreements. College room and board: $11,430. Room and board charges vary according to board plan and housing facility.

Collegiate Environment: Orientation program. Drama-theater group, choral group, marching band, student-run newspaper, radio station. Social organizations: 460 open to all; national fraternities, national sororities, local fraternities, local sororities, 4 historically African-American & 6 multi-cult; 18% of eligible men and 26% of eligible women are members. Most popular organizations: Student Alumni Association, Mexican American Student Association, University Program Council Nebraska, eSAB (Engineering Student Advisory Board), ASUN (Association of Students of the University of Nebraska, student body government). Major annual events: University Program Council Concerts, Big Red Welcome, Homecomming. Student services: legal services, health clinic, personal-psychological counseling, women's center. Campus security: 24-hour emergency response devices and patrols, late night transport-escort service, controlled dormitory access. 8,800 college housing spaces available; 7,064 were occupied in 2018-19. Freshmen guaranteed college housing. On-campus residence required in freshman year. Options: coed, women-only housing available. Love Memorial Library plus 7 others. Books: 1.8 million (physical), 727,811 (digital/electronic); Serial titles: 101,076 (physical), 74,949 (digital/electronic); Databases: 462. Weekly public service hours: 130; students can reserve study rooms. Operations spending for the previous fiscal year: $18.9 million. 455 computers available on campus for general student use. Computer purchase/lease plans available. A campuswide network can be accessed from student residence rooms and from off campus. Students can access the following: online class registration.

Community Environment: UNL is located in the capital city of Lincoln, a community of more than 209,000 that combines a college-town atmosphere with the entertainment and nightlife of a larger city. Lincoln boasts a thriving arts community with dozens of art galleries and the Lied Center for Performing Arts, which hosts major productions such as Les Miserables, Cats, and performances by the Russian Ballet, Celine Dion, and cellist Yo-yo Ma. Lincoln has more parks per capita than any other U.S. city and a growing network of bike paths that extend far beyond the city limits. There are 16 golf courses, hundreds of restaurants, more than 30 movie screens, major shopping malls, and a restored downtown historic district complete with specialty shops, coffeehouses, and a dinner theater. Major metropolitan cities like Omaha, Kansas City, Chicago, and Denver are within a day's driving distance, and Lincoln is easily accessible by plane, train, and bus.

■ **UNIVERSITY OF NEBRASKA MEDICAL CENTER**
Nebraska Medical Ctr.
Omaha, NE 68198
Tel: (402)559-4000; Free: 800-626-8431
Fax: (402)559-6796
Web Site: www.unmc.edu
Description: State-supported, upper-level, coed. Part of University of Nebraska System. Awards bachelor's, master's, and doctoral degrees and post-master's certificates. Founded 1869. Setting: 16-acre urban campus.

Endowment: $11.9 million. Research spending for the previous fiscal year: $101.5 million. Educational spending for the previous fiscal year: $42,076 per student. Total enrollment: 3,625. Faculty: 1,232 (1,023 full-time, 209 part-time). Student-undergrad faculty ratio is 3:1. Full-time: 895 students, 88% women, 12% men. Part-time: 118 students, 77% women, 23% men. Students come from 20 states and territories, 10 other countries, 10% from out-of-state. 0.6% American Indian or Alaska Native, non-Hispanic/Latino; 3% Hispanic/Latino; 1% Black or African American, non-Hispanic/Latino; 2% Asian, non-Hispanic/Latino; 0.1% Native Hawaiian or other Pacific Islander, non-Hispanic/Latino; 1% international. 38% 25 or older, 42% transferred in. Academic area with the most degrees conferred: health professions and related sciences. Calendar: semesters. Services for LD students, accelerated degree program, honors program, distance learning, summer session for credit, part-time degree program, graduate courses open to undergrads. Off campus study at University of Nebraska-Lincoln, University of Nebraska at Omaha, University of Nebraska at Kearney. ROTC: Army (c), Air Force (c).

Entrance Requirements: Transfer credits accepted: Yes.

Collegiate Environment: Orientation program. Social organizations: 5 open to all; national fraternities, national sororities. Most popular organizations: Student Government, Toastmasters, Student Alliance for Global Health, Christian Medical Society, Student Research Group. Major annual event: Spring Dance. Student services: health clinic, personal-psychological counseling. Campus security: 24-hour emergency response devices and patrols, late night transport-escort service. McGoogan Library of Medicine. Operations spending for the previous fiscal year: $2.9 million. 120 computers available on campus for general student use. A campuswide network can be accessed from off-campus. Students can access the following: online class registration.

Community Environment: See Creighton University.

■ **UNIVERSITY OF NEBRASKA AT OMAHA**
6001 Dodge St.
Omaha, NE 68182
Tel: (402)554-2200
Fax: (402)554-3472
Web Site: www.unomaha.edu
Description: State-supported, university, coed. Part of University of Nebraska System. Awards bachelor's, master's, and doctoral degrees and post-master's certificates. Founded 1908. Setting: 503-acre urban campus. Research spending for the previous fiscal year: $8.3 million. Educational spending for the previous fiscal year: $7490 per student. Total enrollment: 15,227. Faculty: 1,044 (520 full-time, 524 part-time). Student-undergrad faculty ratio is 17:1. 4,955 applied, 71% were admitted. 15% from top 10% of their high school class, 40% from top quarter, 75% from top half. Full-time: 9,511 students, 53% women, 47% men. Part-time: 2,824 students, 48% women, 52% men. Students come from 42 states and territories, 62 other countries, 7% from out-of-state. 0.4% American Indian or Alaska Native, non-Hispanic/Latino; 9% Hispanic/Latino; 6% Black or African American, non-Hispanic/Latino; 3% Asian, non-Hispanic/Latino; 0.1% Native Hawaiian or other Pacific Islander, non-Hispanic/Latino; 3% international. 22% 25 or older, 11% live on campus, 11% transferred in. Retention: 75% of full-time freshmen returned the following year. Academic areas with the most degrees conferred: business/marketing; education; homeland security, law enforcement, firefighting, and protective services. Core. Calendar: semesters. ESL program, services for LD students, advanced placement, self-designed majors, honors program, independent study, distance learning, double major, summer session for credit, part-time degree program, adult/continuing education programs, co-op programs and internships, graduate courses open to undergrads. Off campus study at other units of the University of Nebraska System. Study abroad program. ROTC: Army (c), Air Force.

Entrance Requirements: Options: electronic application, deferred admission. Required: high school transcript, SAT or ACT. Entrance: minimally difficult. Application deadline: 8/1. Notification: continuous.

Collegiate Environment: Orientation program. Drama-theater group, choral group, marching band, student-run newspaper, radio station. Social organizations: 153 open to all; national fraternities, national sororities; 2% of eligible men and 2% of eligible women are members. Most popular organizations: Student Programming Board-Maverick Productions, student government, Greek Life, Emerging Leaders, PRSSA - Public Relations student society of America. Major annual events: Homecoming, International Banquet, Welcome Week. Student services: legal services, health clinic, personal-psychological counseling, women's center. Campus security: 24-hour emergency response devices and patrols, late night transport-escort service, controlled dormitory access. Criss Library. Operations spending for the previous fiscal year: $6.3 million. 2,450 computers available on campus for general student use. Computer purchase/lease plans available. A campuswide network can be accessed from student residence rooms and from off campus. Students can access the following: online class registration. Staffed computer lab on campus (open 24 hours a day) provides training in use of the Internet.

■ WAYNE STATE COLLEGE
1111 Main St.
Wayne, NE 68787
Tel: (402)375-7000; Free: 866-WSC-CATS
Fax: (402)375-7204
E-mail: admit1@wsc.edu
Web Site: www.wsc.edu

Description: State-supported, comprehensive, coed. Part of Nebraska State College System. Awards bachelor's and master's degrees and post-master's certificates. Founded 1910. Setting: 128-acre small town campus. Endowment: $22 million. Total enrollment: 3,292. Faculty: 204 (118 full-time, 86 part-time). Student-undergrad faculty ratio is 19:1. 1,706 applied, 100% were admitted. 12% from top 10% of their high school class, 30% from top quarter, 59% from top half. Full-time: 2,404 students, 57% women, 43% men. Part-time: 353 students, 64% women, 36% men. Students come from 36 states and territories, 25 other countries, 15% from out-of-state. 1% American Indian or Alaska Native, non-Hispanic/Latino; 9% Hispanic/Latino; 3% Black or African American, non-Hispanic/Latino; 0.7% Asian, non-Hispanic/Latino; 0.1% Native Hawaiian or other Pacific Islander, non-Hispanic/Latino; 1% international. 9% 25 or older, 40% live on campus, 8% transferred in. Retention: 69% of full-time freshmen returned the following year. Academic areas with the most degrees conferred: education; business/marketing; homeland security, law enforcement, firefighting, and protective services. Core. Calendar: semesters. Services for LD students, advanced placement, self-designed majors, honors program, independent study, distance learning, double major, summer session for credit, part-time degree program, adult/continuing education programs, co-op programs and internships, graduate courses open to undergrads. Off campus study. Study abroad program. ROTC: Army.

Entrance Requirements: Open admission except for RHOP, Neihardt Scholar programs. Options: electronic application, deferred admission. Required: high school transcript. Entrance: noncompetitive. Application deadline: rolling. Notification: continuous. Transfer credits accepted: Yes.

Costs Per Year: State resident tuition: $5310 full-time, $177 per credit hour part-time. Nonresident tuition: $10,620 full-time, $354 per credit hour part-time. Mandatory fees: $1679 full-time, $64.75 per credit hour part-time. Full-time tuition and fees vary according to course level, course load, and location. Part-time tuition and fees vary according to course level, course load, and location. College room and board: $7668. College room only: $3870. Room and board charges vary according to board plan and housing facility.

Collegiate Environment: Orientation program. Drama-theater group, choral group, marching band, student-run newspaper, radio station. Social organizations: 110 open to all; national fraternities, national sororities, local fraternities, local sororities. Student services: health clinic, personal-psychological counseling. Campus security: 24-hour emergency response devices and patrols, student patrols, late night transport-escort service, controlled dormitory access. U. S. Conn Library. Books: 145,315 (physical), 290,865 (digital/electronic); Serial titles: 1,045 (physical), 66 (digital/electronic); Databases: 49. 365 computers available on campus for general student use. Computer purchase/lease plans available. A campuswide network can be accessed from student residence rooms and from off campus. Students can access the following: online class registration. Staffed computer lab on campus provides training in use of computers, software, and the Internet.

Community Environment: Located 45 miles southwest of Sioux City, Iowa, Wayne is the county seat. Bus transportation and chartered air service are available. Dormitories, motels, and rooming houses provide housing for students. Community facilities include churches of most denominations and a hospital. Hunting, swimming and golf are some of the outdoor activities available.

■ WESTERN NEBRASKA COMMUNITY COLLEGE
371 College Dr.
Sidney, NE 69162
Tel: (308)254-5450; Free: 800-222-9682
Fax: (308)254-7444

Web Site: www.wncc.net

Description: State and locally supported, 2-year, coed. Part of Western Community College Area System. Awards certificates, diplomas, transfer associate, and terminal associate degrees. Founded 1926. Setting: 20-acre rural campus. Total enrollment: 2,304. Student-undergrad faculty ratio is 11:1. 17% from out-of-state. 39% 25 or older. Retention: 56% of full-time freshmen returned the following year. Core. Calendar: semesters. Academic remediation for entering students, services for LD students, advanced placement, accelerated degree program, independent study, distance learning, summer session for credit, part-time degree program, adult/continuing education programs, co-op programs and internships.

Entrance Requirements: Open admission. Option: electronic application. Recommended: high school transcript. Entrance: noncompetitive. Application deadline: rolling. Notification: continuous until 8/21.

Collegiate Environment: Orientation program. Drama-theater group, choral group, student-run newspaper. Social organizations: national sororities. Student services: personal-psychological counseling. Campus security: 24-hour emergency response devices and patrols, late night transport-escort service, controlled dormitory access, patrols by trained security personnel from 12:30 am to 6 am. Western Nebraska Community College Library.

Community Environment: In the valley of the North Platte River, Scottsbluff is an agriculture center. It is also called the Capital of America's Valley of the Nile. This is the location of the largest continuous area of irrigated land in the country. Recreational activities include hunting, fishing, golf, swimming and winter sports nearby.

■ YORK COLLEGE
1125 E 8th St.
York, NE 68467
Tel: (402)363-5600; Free: 800-950-9675
Fax: (402)363-5666
E-mail: enroll@york.edu
Web Site: www.york.edu

Description: Independent, 4-year, coed, affiliated with Church of Christ. Awards associate and bachelor's degrees. Founded 1890. Setting: 44-acre small town campus. Endowment: $5.9 million. Educational spending for the previous fiscal year: $4440 per student. Total enrollment: 430. Faculty: 38 (22 full-time, 16 part-time). Student-undergrad faculty ratio is 11:1. 485 applied, 60% were admitted. 9% from top 10% of their high school class, 24% from top quarter, 47% from top half. 2 valedictorians. Full-time: 416 students, 44% women, 56% men. Part-time: 14 students, 64% women, 36% men. Students come from 23 states and territories, 4 other countries, 70% from out-of-state. 5% 25 or older, 80% live on campus, 14% transferred in. Retention: 58% of full-time freshmen returned the following year. Academic areas with the most degrees conferred: education; psychology; business/marketing. Core. Calendar: semesters. Academic remediation for entering students, services for LD students, advanced placement, honors program, independent study, double major, summer session for credit, part-time degree program, co-op programs and internships. Study abroad program. ROTC: Army (c), Naval (c), Air Force (c).

Entrance Requirements: Options: electronic application, early admission, deferred admission, international baccalaureate accepted. Required: high school transcript, minimum 2 high school GPA, SAT or ACT. Required for some: 1 recommendation. Entrance: moderately difficult. Application deadline: rolling. Notification: continuous. SAT Reasoning Test deadline: 8/1. Transfer credits accepted: Yes.

Collegiate Environment: Orientation program. Drama-theater group, choral group, student-run newspaper. Social organizations: 8 open to all; local fraternities, local sororities; 46% of eligible men and 64% of eligible women are members. Most popular organizations: concert choir, Student Association, Promethians, Marksmen. Major annual events: Homecoming, Songfest, All-School Banquet. Student services: personal-psychological counseling. Campus security: 24-hour patrols, student patrols, controlled dormitory access. Levitt Library. Operations spending for the previous fiscal year: $240,236. 57 computers available on campus for general student use. A campuswide network can be accessed from student residence rooms and from off campus. Staffed computer lab on campus provides training in use of computers, software, and the Internet.

Community Environment: York is located about 50 miles from Lincoln, where all forms of commercial transportation are available. Various civic and service organizations are active here as well as churches of many denominations. Recreational facilities include parks, playgrounds, a swimming pool, baseball park, basketball courts, and a community center.

■ ARIZONA COLLEGE-LAS VEGAS

2320 S Rancho Dr.
Las Vegas, NV 89102
Web Site: www.arizonacollege.edu
Description: Proprietary, 4-year, coed.

■ THE ART INSTITUTE OF LAS VEGAS

2350 Corporate Cir. Dr.
Henderson, NV 89074
Tel: (702)369-9944; Free: 800-833-2678
Fax: (702)992-8558
Web Site: www.artinstitutes.edu/lasvegas
Description: Proprietary, 4-year, coed. Part of Education Management Corporation. Awards associate and bachelor's degrees. Founded 2002. Setting: suburban campus. Calendar: quarters.

■ CAREER COLLEGE OF NORTHERN NEVADA

1421 Pullman Dr.
Sparks, NV 89434
Tel: (775)856-2266
E-mail: mclark@ccnn4u.com
Web Site: www.ccnn.edu
Description: Proprietary, 2-year, coed. Awards diplomas and terminal associate degrees. Founded 1984. Setting: 2-acre urban campus with easy access to Reno, NV. Educational spending for the previous fiscal year: $7882 per student. Total enrollment: 342. Faculty: 23 (11 full-time, 12 part-time). Student-undergrad faculty ratio is 20:1. 270 applied, 100% were admitted. Students come from 1 other country, 3% from out-of-state. 62% 25 or older. Core. Calendar: quarters 6-week terms. Academic remediation for entering students, accelerated degree program, double major, summer session for credit, co-op programs and internships.
Entrance Requirements: Open admission. Required: high school transcript, interview, Wonderlic aptitude test. Entrance: noncompetitive. Application deadline: rolling. Notification: continuous. Transfer credits accepted: Yes.
Collegiate Environment: Orientation program. Campus security: 24-hour emergency response devices. Library. Books: 1,200 (physical), 110,000 (digital/electronic). Weekly public service hours: 50. Operations spending for the previous fiscal year: $2598. 120 computers available on campus for general student use. Computer purchase/lease plans available. A campuswide network can be accessed. Staffed computer lab on campus provides training in use of computers, software, and the Internet.

■ CARRINGTON COLLEGE-LAS VEGAS

5740 S Eastern Ave.
Ste. 140
Las Vegas, NV 89119
Tel: (702)688-4300
Web Site: www.carrington.edu
Description: Proprietary, 2-year, coed. Part of Carrington Colleges Group, Inc. Awards certificates and terminal associate degrees. Total enrollment: 352. Faculty: 25 (10 full-time, 15 part-time). Student-undergrad faculty ratio is 21:1. Full-time: 299 students, 72% women, 28% men. Part-time: 53 students, 60% women, 40% men. 2% from out-of-state. 0.3% American Indian or Alaska Native, non-Hispanic/Latino; 32% Hispanic/Latino; 15%

Black or African American, non-Hispanic/Latino; 18% Asian, non-Hispanic/Latino; 6% Native Hawaiian or other Pacific Islander, non-Hispanic/Latino. 57% 25 or older, 23% transferred in.
Entrance Requirements: Required: essay, interview. Required for some: high school transcript. Notification: continuous.

■ CARRINGTON COLLEGE-RENO

5580 Kietzke Ln.
Reno, NV 89511
Tel: (775)335-2900
Web Site: www.carrington.edu
Description: Proprietary, 2-year, coed. Part of Carrington Colleges Group, Inc. Awards certificates and terminal associate degrees. Total enrollment: 360. Faculty: 152 (31 full-time, 121 part-time). Student-undergrad faculty ratio is 15:1. Full-time: 292 students, 80% women, 20% men. Part-time: 68 students, 90% women, 10% men. 12% from out-of-state. 0.3% American Indian or Alaska Native, non-Hispanic/Latino; 20% Hispanic/Latino; 1% Black or African American, non-Hispanic/Latino; 6% Asian, non-Hispanic/Latino; 0.6% Native Hawaiian or other Pacific Islander, non-Hispanic/Latino. 60% 25 or older, 17% transferred in.
Entrance Requirements: Required: essay, high school transcript, interview, institutional entrance exam. Notification: continuous.

■ CHAMBERLAIN COLLEGE OF NURSING

9901 Covington Cross Dr.
Las Vegas, NV 89144
Tel: (702)786-1660; Free: 877-751-5783
Fax: (702)786-1661
Web Site: www.chamberlain.edu
Description: Proprietary, 4-year, coed. Awards bachelor's degrees. Total enrollment: 258. Faculty: 25 (8 full-time, 17 part-time). Student-undergrad faculty ratio is 12:1. Full-time: 113 students, 80% women, 20% men. Part-time: 145 students, 83% women, 17% men. 8% from out-of-state. 16% Hispanic/Latino; 12% Black or African American, non-Hispanic/Latino; 33% Asian, non-Hispanic/Latino; 5% Native Hawaiian or other Pacific Islander, non-Hispanic/Latino. 64% 25 or older, 21% transferred in. Accelerated degree program, distance learning.
Entrance Requirements: Option: deferred admission. Required: SAT or ACT. Application deadline: rolling. Notification: continuous.

■ COLLEGE OF SOUTHERN NEVADA

6375 W Charleston Blvd.
Las Vegas, NV 89146
Tel: (702)651-5000
Web Site: www.csn.edu
Description: State-supported, primarily 2-year, coed. Part of University and Community College System of Nevada. Awards certificates, transfer associate, and bachelor's degrees. Founded 1971. Setting: 89-acre suburban campus with easy access to Las Vegas. Core. Calendar: semesters. Academic remediation for entering students, ESL program, services for LD students, advanced placement, accelerated degree program, honors program, independent study, distance learning, double major, summer session for credit, part-time degree program, adult/continuing education programs, co-op programs and internships. ROTC: Army.
Entrance Requirements: Open admission except for allied health

programs. Option: early admission. Required: student data form. Entrance: noncompetitive. Application deadline: rolling.

Collegiate Environment: Orientation program. Drama-theater group, choral group, student-run newspaper. Student services: legal services, health clinic, personal-psychological counseling, women's center. Campus security: 24-hour emergency response devices and patrols. Learning Assistance Center.

Community Environment: See University of Nevada - Las Vegas.

■ DEEP SPRINGS COLLEGE

HC 72, Box 45001
Dyer, NV 89010
Tel: (760)872-2000
E-mail: apcom@deepsprings.edu
Web Site: www.deepsprings.edu

Description: Independent, 2-year, men only. Awards transfer associate degrees. Founded 1917. Setting: 3,000-acre rural campus. Endowment: $18 million. Educational spending for the previous fiscal year: $14,230 per student. Total enrollment: 28. Faculty: 16 (3 full-time, 13 part-time). Student-undergrad faculty ratio is 4:1. 100% from top 10% of their high school class, 100% from top quarter, 100% from top half. Full-time: 28 students. Students come from 14 states and territories, 3 other countries, 83% from out-of-state. 4% Hispanic/Latino; 14% Asian, non-Hispanic/Latino; 14% international. 100% live on campus, 50% transferred in. Retention: 93% of full-time freshmen returned the following year. Calendar: 6 7-week terms. Services for LD students, independent study, distance learning, summer session for credit, internships.

Entrance Requirements: Required: essay, high school transcript, 2 recommendations, interview. Required for some: SAT or ACT.

Costs Per Year: Comprehensive fee: $0. Every student accepted to Deep Springs receives a scholarship covering tuition, room, and board.

Collegiate Environment: Orientation program. Drama-theater group, choral group. Most popular organizations: Student Self-Government, Labor Program, Applications Committee, Review Committee, Curriculum Committee. Major annual events: Trustees Weekend, Cattle Round-Up, Thanksgiving Celebration. Student services: legal services, personal-psychological counseling. Campus security: 24-hour emergency response devices, late night transport-escort service. Deep Springs College. Operations spending for the previous fiscal year: $5000. 6 computers available on campus for general student use.

■ DEVRY UNIVERSITY-HENDERSON CAMPUS

2490 Paseo Verde Pky., Ste. 150
Henderson, NV 89074
Tel: (702)933-9700; Free: 866-338-7934
Fax: (702)933-9717
Web Site: www.devry.edu

Description: Proprietary, comprehensive, coed. Awards associate, bachelor's, and master's degrees. Calendar: semesters.

Entrance Requirements: Application deadline: rolling. Notification: continuous.

■ GREAT BASIN COLLEGE

1500 College Pky.
Elko, NV 89801-3348
Tel: (775)738-8493
E-mail: jan.king@gbcnv.edu
Web Site: www.gbcnv.edu

Description: State-supported, primarily 2-year, coed. Part of Nevada System of Higher Education. Awards certificates, transfer associate, terminal associate, and bachelor's degrees. Founded 1967. Setting: 45-acre small town campus. Endowment: $6.7 million. Total enrollment: 3,362. 804 applied, 61% were admitted. Full-time: 903 students, 59% women, 41% men. Part-time: 2,459 students, 67% women, 33% men. Students come from 28 states and territories, 26 other countries, 6% from out-of-state. 3% American Indian or Alaska Native, non-Hispanic/Latino; 19% Hispanic/Latino; 2% Black or African American, non-Hispanic/Latino; 2% Asian, non-Hispanic/Latino; 0.6% Native Hawaiian or other Pacific Islander, non-Hispanic/Latino. 52% 25 or older, 4% live on campus, 7% transferred in. Retention: 65% of full-time freshmen returned the following year. Academic areas with the most degrees conferred: health professions and related sciences; business/marketing; engineering technologies. Core. Calendar: semesters. Academic remediation for entering students, ESL program, services for LD students, accelerated degree program, independent study, distance learning, double

major, summer session for credit, part-time degree program, external degree program, adult/continuing education programs, co-op programs. Off campus study at University of Nevada, Reno.

Entrance Requirements: Open admission except for nursing program. Options: electronic application, early admission, deferred admission. Entrance: noncompetitive. Application deadline: rolling. Notification: continuous. Transfer credits accepted: Yes.

Collegiate Environment: Orientation program. Student services: personal-psychological counseling. Campus security: late night transport-escort service, evening patrols by trained security personnel. Learning Resource Center. Books: 94,193 (physical), 250,157 (digital/electronic); Serial titles: 2,946 (physical), 230,872 (digital/electronic); Databases: 80. Weekly public service hours: 46; students can reserve study rooms. 95 computers available on campus for general student use. A campuswide network can be accessed from student residence rooms and from off campus. Students can access the following: online class registration. Staffed computer lab on campus provides training in use of computers, software, and the Internet.

Community Environment: Primarily involved in mining, ranching, and government business, Elko is the largest city in Elko County and is at the heart of the nation's finest hunting and fishing areas, along with such historic landmarks as old ghost towns and deserted mining camps. Located at the base of the Ruby Mountains, Elko is also near Jarbidge Wilderness area and Great Basin National Park.

■ NEVADA STATE COLLEGE

1300 Nevada State Dr.
Henderson, NV 89002
Tel: (702)992-2000
Fax: (702)992-2226
E-mail: admissions@nsc.edu
Web Site: www.nsc.edu

Description: State-supported, 4-year, coed. Part of Nevada System of Higher Education. Awards bachelor's degrees. Founded 2002. Setting: 520-acre suburban campus with easy access to Las Vegas. Endowment: $1 million. Research spending for the previous fiscal year: $91,068. Educational spending for the previous fiscal year: $2770 per student. Total enrollment: 3,747. Faculty: 267 (71 full-time, 196 part-time). Student-undergrad faculty ratio is 18:1. 924 applied, 76% were admitted. Full-time: 1,460 students, 74% women, 26% men. Part-time: 2,287 students, 77% women, 23% men. 2% from out-of-state. 0.6% American Indian or Alaska Native, non-Hispanic/Latino; 27% Hispanic/Latino; 9% Black or African American, non-Hispanic/Latino; 12% Asian, non-Hispanic/Latino; 2% Native Hawaiian or other Pacific Islander, non-Hispanic/Latino. 55% 25 or older, 10% transferred in. Retention: 72% of full-time freshmen returned the following year. Academic areas with the most degrees conferred: health professions and related sciences; psychology; education. Core. Calendar: semesters. Academic remediation for entering students, services for LD students, advanced placement, accelerated degree program, self-designed majors, independent study, distance learning, double major, summer session for credit, part-time degree program, adult/continuing education programs, co-op programs and internships. Study abroad program. ROTC: Army (c).

Entrance Requirements: Option: electronic application. Required: high school transcript, minimum 2 high school GPA. Entrance: minimally difficult. Application deadline: rolling. Notification: continuous. Transfer credits accepted: Yes.

Costs Per Year: Application fee: $30. State resident tuition: $5,138 full-time, $171.25 per credit part-time. Nonresident tuition: $12,020 full-time, $333 per credit part-time. Full-time tuition varies according to course load and program. Part-time tuition varies according to course load and program.

Collegiate Environment: Orientation program. Student-run newspaper. Social organizations: 10 open to all. Most popular organizations: Nevada State Student Alliance (Student Government), Pre-Professional Club, American Sign Language Club, Student Nurses Association, Circle K International. Major annual events: Scorpions' Calling, Spirit Week, Holiday Events. Student services: health clinic, personal-psychological counseling. Campus security: private contracted security patrols. Nevada State College Library plus 1 other. Books: 15,768 (physical), 206,855 (digital/electronic); Serial titles: 53,083 (digital/electronic); Databases: 98. Students can reserve study rooms. Operations spending for the previous fiscal year: $574,260. 140 computers available on campus for general student use. A campuswide network can be accessed from off-campus. Students can access the following: online class registration. Staffed computer lab on campus provides training in use of computers, software, and the Internet.

NORTHWEST CAREER COLLEGE

7398 Smoke Ranch Rd.
Ste. 100
Las Vegas, NV 89128
Tel: (702)254-7577
Web Site: www.northwestcareercollege.edu
Description: Proprietary, 2-year, coed. Awards certificates, transfer associate, and terminal associate degrees.

PIMA MEDICAL INSTITUTE

3333 E Flamingo Rd.
Las Vegas, NV 89121
Tel: (702)458-9650; Free: 800-477-PIMA
Web Site: www.pmi.edu
Description: Proprietary, primarily 2-year, coed. Part of Vocational Training Institutes, Inc. Awards certificates, terminal associate, and bachelor's degrees. Founded 2003. Setting: urban campus. Total enrollment: 820. 57% 25 or older. Core. Calendar: modular. Advanced placement, distance learning, internships.
Entrance Requirements: Required: interview, Wonderlic Scholastic Level Exam (SLE). Required for some: essay, high school transcript. Entrance: moderately difficult.
Collegiate Environment: Orientation program. E-Global.

SIERRA NEVADA COLLEGE

999 Tahoe Blvd.
Incline Village, NV 89451
Tel: (775)831-1314
Fax: (775)831-1347
E-mail: admissions@sierranevada.edu
Web Site: www.sierranevada.edu
Description: Independent, comprehensive, coed. Awards bachelor's and master's degrees. Founded 1969. Setting: 20-acre small town campus with easy access to Reno. Endowment: $4.3 million. Educational spending for the previous fiscal year: $6698 per student. Total enrollment: 950. Faculty: 130 (41 full-time, 89 part-time). Student-undergrad faculty ratio is 10:1. 735 applied, 69% were admitted. 10% from top 10% of their high school class, 20% from top quarter, 45% from top half. Full-time: 410 students, 43% women, 57% men. Part-time: 23 students, 48% women, 52% men. Students come from 19 states and territories, 7 other countries, 82% from out-of-state. 3% American Indian or Alaska Native, non-Hispanic/Latino; 4% Hispanic/Latino; 3% Black or African American, non-Hispanic/Latino; 3% Asian, non-Hispanic/Latino; 2% Native Hawaiian or other Pacific Islander, non-Hispanic/Latino. 13% 25 or older, 40% live on campus, 12% transferred in. Retention: 68% of full-time freshmen returned the following year. Academic areas with the most degrees conferred: business/marketing; interdisciplinary studies; psychology. Core. Calendar: semesters. Academic remediation for entering students, ESL program, services for LD students, advanced placement, accelerated degree program, self-designed majors, honors program, independent study, distance learning, double major, summer session for credit, part-time degree program, adult/continuing education programs, co-op programs and internships, graduate courses open to undergrads. Study abroad program.
Entrance Requirements: Options: electronic application, deferred admission, international baccalaureate accepted. Required: minimum 2.6 high school GPA, SAT or ACT. Recommended: essay, interview. Required for some: high school transcript, 1 recommendation. Entrance: moderately difficult. Application deadline: rolling. SAT Reasoning Test deadline: 8/26. SAT Subject Test deadline: 8/26. Transfer credits accepted: Yes.
Costs Per Year: Application fee: $0. Comprehensive fee: $47,598 includes full-time tuition ($33,158), mandatory fees ($1083), and college room and board ($13,357). College room only: $6711. Full-time tuition and fees vary according to course load, degree level, location, program, and reciprocity agreements. Room and board charges vary according to board plan. Part-time tuition: $1410 per credit hour. Part-time tuition varies according to course load, degree level, location, program, and reciprocity agreements.
Collegiate Environment: Orientation program. Choral group, student-run newspaper. Social organizations: 15 open to all. Most popular organizations: Film Club, International Club, Sustainability Club, Rock Climbing Club, First Generation Club. Major annual events: Spring Formal, Bohemia Night, Casino Night. Student services: personal-psychological counseling. Campus security: 24-hour emergency response devices and patrols, student patrols, controlled dormitory access. Prim Library. Books: 27,716 (physical), 7,520 (digital/electronic); Serial titles: 1,106 (physical); Databases: 35. Weekly

public service hours: 40. Operations spending for the previous fiscal year: $216,702. 50 computers available on campus for general student use. A computer is required for all students. A campuswide network can be accessed from student residence rooms and from off campus. Staffed computer lab on campus provides training in use of computers, software, and the Internet.

TRUCKEE MEADOWS COMMUNITY COLLEGE

7000 Dandini Blvd.
Reno, NV 89512-3901
Tel: (775)673-7000
Fax: (775)673-7028
Web Site: www.tmcc.edu
Description: State-supported, primarily 2-year, coed. Part of Nevada System of Higher Education. Awards certificates, transfer associate, terminal associate, and bachelor's degrees. Founded 1971. Setting: 63-acre suburban campus. Endowment: $11.1 million. Educational spending for the previous fiscal year: $5595 per student. Total enrollment: 10,861. Faculty: 716 (158 full-time, 558 part-time). Student-undergrad faculty ratio is 21:1. 3,290 applied, 100% were admitted. Full-time: 2,927 students, 54% women, 46% men. Part-time: 7,933 students, 53% women, 47% men. Students come from 23 states and territories, 20 other countries, 6% from out-of-state. 1% American Indian or Alaska Native, non-Hispanic/Latino; 30% Hispanic/Latino; 3% Black or African American, non-Hispanic/Latino; 6% Asian, non-Hispanic/Latino; 0.5% international. 36% 25 or older, 6% transferred in. Retention: 63% of full-time freshmen returned the following year. Academic area with the most degrees conferred: business/marketing. Calendar: semesters. Academic remediation for entering students, ESL program, services for LD students, advanced placement, accelerated degree program, independent study, distance learning, double major, summer session for credit, part-time degree program, adult/continuing education programs, co-op programs and internships. ROTC: Army (c).
Entrance Requirements: Open admission. Options: electronic application, early admission. Entrance: noncompetitive. Application deadline: rolling. Notification: continuous. Transfer credits accepted: Yes.
Costs Per Year: Application fee: $10. State resident tuition: $2370 full-time, $98.75 per credit part-time. Nonresident tuition: $9283 full-time, $207.50 per credit part-time. Mandatory fees: $300 full-time, $12.50 per credit part-time.
Collegiate Environment: Orientation program. Drama-theater group, student-run newspaper. Social organizations: 7 open to all. Most popular organizations: Entrepreneurship Club, International Club, Phi Theta Kappa, Student Government Association, Student Media and Broadcasting Club. Major annual events: Commencement, Welcome Back Fair, Spring Fling. Student services: personal-psychological counseling. Campus security: 24-hour emergency response devices and patrols, late night transport-escort service. College housing not available. Elizabeth Sturm Library plus 2 others. Books: 48,770 (physical); Serial titles: 36 (physical), 4 (digital/electronic); Databases: 93. Operations spending for the previous fiscal year: $883,296.
Community Environment: Reno/Sparks, cities of approximately 240,000, are bounded on the west by the majestic Sierra Nevada, and on the east by the rolling basin and range province. The climate is cool and dry, and is marked by the full pageant of the seasons. A mixture of metropolitan and quietly provincial, the area is noted on the one hand for its fashionable hotels and tourist attractions, and on the other for its beautiful parks, which line the Truckee River, and its modern residential areas. Recreational activities abound, both in Reno and its environs. Within a one-hour drive of the campus are the Lake Tahoe resort area in the high Sierra, and the unique prehistoric desert sea, Pyramid Lake. The adjoining Sierra is also the site of a number of nationally famed ski areas, including Squaw Valley, site of the 1960 Winter Olympics. Other scenic attractions include Virginia City, setting for one of the West's richest mining bonanzas, and Genoa, the state's first pioneer settlement.

UNIVERSITY OF NEVADA, LAS VEGAS

4505 S Maryland Pky.
Las Vegas, NV 89154
Tel: (702)895-3011
Fax: (702)895-1118
E-mail: kristine.shay@unlv.edu
Web Site: www.unlv.edu
Description: State-supported, university, coed. Part of Nevada System of Higher Education. Awards bachelor's, master's, and doctoral degrees and post-master's certificates. Founded 1957. Setting: 332-acre urban campus

with easy access to Las Vegas. Endowment: $55.4 million. Research spending for the previous fiscal year: $41.7 million. Educational spending for the previous fiscal year: $12,815 per student. Total enrollment: 30,457. Faculty: 1,820 (1,005 full-time, 815 part-time). Student-undergrad faculty ratio is 21:1. 11,613 applied, 82% were admitted. 22% from top 10% of their high school class, 52% from top quarter, 83% from top half. Full-time: 18,764 students, 57% women, 43% men. Part-time: 6,518 students, 55% women, 45% men. 12% from out-of-state. 0.3% American Indian or Alaska Native, non-Hispanic/Latino; 30% Hispanic/Latino; 8% Black or African American, non-Hispanic/Latino; 16% Asian, non-Hispanic/Latino; 0.9% Native Hawaiian or other Pacific Islander, non-Hispanic/Latino; 3% international. 20% 25 or older, 10% transferred in. Retention: 76% of full-time freshmen returned the following year. Academic areas with the most degrees conferred: business/marketing; psychology; social sciences; homeland security, law enforcement, firefighting, and protective services. Core. Calendar: semesters. Academic remediation for entering students, ESL program, services for LD students, advanced placement, honors program, independent study, distance learning, double major, summer session for credit, part-time degree program, adult/continuing education programs, co-op programs and internships, graduate courses open to undergrads. Study abroad program. ROTC: Army, Air Force.

Entrance Requirements: Options: electronic application, early admission, deferred admission, international baccalaureate accepted. Required: high school transcript, minimum 3 high school GPA, SAT or ACT. Entrance: moderately difficult. Notification: continuous. SAT Reasoning Test deadline: 8/15. Transfer credits accepted: Yes.

Costs Per Year: Application fee: $60. One-time mandatory fee: $120. State resident tuition: $7,169 full-time, $224 per credit hour part-time. Nonresident tuition: $22,316 full-time, $470.50 per credit hour part-time. Mandatory fees: $696 full-time, $14.97 per credit hour part-time, $348 per term part-time. Full-time tuition and fees vary according to course level, program, and reciprocity agreements. Part-time tuition and fees vary according to course level, program, and reciprocity agreements. College room and board: $10,780. College room only: $5880. Room and board charges vary according to board plan and housing facility.

Collegiate Environment: Orientation program. Drama-theater group, choral group, marching band, student-run newspaper, radio station. Social organizations: 383 open to all; national fraternities, national sororities, local fraternities, local sororities; 8% of eligible men and 8% of eligible women are members. Most popular organizations: Social Fraternities and Sororities, Psychology Club, Honors Student Council, Association of Pre-Health Professionals, UNLV Student Nurses Association. Major annual events: UNLV Creates, Premier UNLV, Rebel Homecoming Week. Student services: legal services, health clinic, personal-psychological counseling, women's center. Campus security: 24-hour emergency response devices and patrols, late night transport-escort service, controlled dormitory access. 1,750 college housing spaces available; 1,686 were occupied in 2018-19. Freshmen given priority for college housing. Option: coed housing available. Lied Library plus 4 others. Books: 1.2 million (physical), 1.4 million (digital/electronic); Serial titles: 16,265 (physical), 95,398 (digital/electronic); Databases: 430. Weekly public service hours: 101; students can reserve study rooms. Operations spending for the previous fiscal year: $2.9 million. 2,100 computers available on campus for general student use. A campuswide network can be accessed from student residence rooms and from off campus. Students can access the following: online class registration. Staffed computer lab on campus provides training in use of computers, software, and the Internet.

Community Environment: Situated in southeast Nevada, Las Vegas is a great vacation and convention center located near Lake Mead and the mountains. Las Vegas is one of the fastest growing cities in the United States; some 1.3 million people live in southern Nevada. Community facilities include churches of most denominations, hospitals and clinics, and good shopping centers. The hotels feature some of the best entertainers in America. Nearby Charleston Peak provides expert ski runs and other snow sports facilities.

■ **UNIVERSITY OF NEVADA, RENO**

Reno, NV 89557

Tel: (775)784-1110; Free: 866-263-8232

E-mail: asknevada@unr.edu

Web Site: www.unr.edu

Description: State-supported, university, coed. Part of Nevada System of Higher Education. Awards bachelor's, master's, and doctoral degrees and post-master's certificates. Founded 1874. Setting: 200-acre urban campus. Total enrollment: 21,463. Faculty: 1,274 (710 full-time, 564 part-time).

Student-undergrad faculty ratio is 20:1. 9,531 applied, 88% were admitted. 27% from top 10% of their high school class, 58% from top quarter, 87% from top half. Full-time: 15,200 students, 53% women, 47% men. Part-time: 2,730 students, 51% women, 49% men. Students come from 43 states and territories, 52 other countries, 27% from out-of-state. 0.7% American Indian or Alaska Native, non-Hispanic/Latino; 21% Hispanic/Latino; 3% Black or African American, non-Hispanic/Latino; 8% Asian, non-Hispanic/Latino; 0.6% Native Hawaiian or other Pacific Islander, non-Hispanic/Latino; 1% international. 10% 25 or older, 16% live on campus, 6% transferred in. Retention: 81% of full-time freshmen returned the following year. Academic areas with the most degrees conferred: business/marketing; health professions and related sciences; engineering. Core. Calendar: semesters. Academic remediation for entering students, ESL program, services for LD students, advanced placement, honors program, independent study, distance learning, double major, summer session for credit, part-time degree program, adult/continuing education programs, internships, graduate courses open to undergrads. Off campus study at National Student Exchange. Study abroad program. ROTC: Army.

Entrance Requirements: Options: electronic application, early admission, early action, deferred admission, international baccalaureate accepted. Required: high school transcript, minimum 3 high school GPA, SAT or ACT. Entrance: moderately difficult. Notification: continuous, continuous for nonresidents, rolling for early action. SAT Reasoning Test deadline: 4/7. Transfer credits accepted: Yes.

Costs Per Year: Application fee: $60. State resident tuition: $6990 full-time, $224 per credit part-time. Nonresident tuition: $21,462 full-time, $470 per credit part-time. Mandatory fees: $774 full-time, $282 per term part-time. Full-time tuition and fees vary according to course level, course load, degree level, and program. Part-time tuition and fees vary according to course level, course load, degree level, and program. College room and board: $10,868. College room only: $6100. Room and board charges vary according to board plan and housing facility.

Collegiate Environment: Orientation program. Drama-theater group, choral group, marching band, student-run newspaper, radio station. Social organizations: national fraternities, national sororities, local fraternities, local sororities. Most popular organizations: Intervarsity Christian Fellowship, Student Ambassadors, Young Democrats, Asian American Association, Blue Crew. Major annual events: Homecoming, MacKay Days, Night of All Nations. Student services: legal services, health clinic, personal-psychological counseling, women's center. Campus security: 24-hour emergency response devices and patrols, late night transport-escort service, controlled dormitory access. 3,045 college housing spaces available; 3,000 were occupied in 2018-19. Freshmen given priority for college housing. Options: coed, men-only, women-only housing available. Mathewson-IGT Knowledge Center plus 2 others. Books: 1.4 million (physical), 588,940 (digital/electronic). Students can reserve study rooms.

Community Environment: When Reno was laid out as a townsite in 1868, it was named in honor of Major General Jesse L. Reno, who died in the Battle of the South Mountain during the Civil War. Reno is situated on the Truckee River near the base of the Sierra Nevada and has a cool, dry climate. Mining, livestock raising, lumber products, agriculture and tourism are the important industries of the area. Part-time employment is available. The city has a number of parks with facilities for swimming, tennis and picnicking; within a 25 to 90 minute drive from Reno, winter sports are available at a number of major resorts. Annual events are the Reno Rodeo, Reno Balloon Race, Air Races, and Holiday Festival of Trees.

■ **UNIVERSITY OF PHOENIX-LAS VEGAS CAMPUS**

3755 Breakthrough Way

Las Vegas, NV 89135

Tel: (702)638-7279; Free: 866-766-0766

Fax: (702)638-8035

Web Site: www.phoenix.edu

Description: Proprietary, comprehensive, coed. Awards associate, bachelor's, and master's degrees and post-master's certificates. Founded 1994. Setting: urban campus. Total enrollment: 3,162. Faculty: 279 (35 full-time, 244 part-time). Full-time: 2,301 students, 67% women, 33% men. 83% 25 or older. Retention: 38% of full-time freshmen returned the following year. Academic areas with the most degrees conferred: business/marketing; computer and information sciences; homeland security, law enforcement, firefighting, and protective services. Core. Calendar: continuous. Services for LD students, advanced placement, accelerated degree program, independent study, distance learning, external degree program, adult/continuing education programs, graduate courses open to undergrads.

Entrance Requirements: Open admission. Options: electronic application, deferred admission. Required: 1 recommendation. Required for some: high school transcript. Entrance: noncompetitive. Application deadline: rolling.

Collegiate Environment: Campus security: late night transport-escort service. University Library. Operations spending for the previous fiscal year: $6.8 million.

■ WESTERN NEVADA COLLEGE

2201 W College Pky.
Carson City, NV 89703-7316
Tel: (775)445-3000
Fax: (775)887-3141
E-mail: wncc_aro@wncc.edu
Web Site: www.wnc.edu

Description: State-supported, primarily 2-year, coed. Part of Nevada System of Higher Education. Awards certificates, transfer associate, terminal associate, and bachelor's degrees. Founded 1971. Setting: 200-acre small town campus. Endowment: $250,000. Research spending for the previous fiscal year: $3000. Total enrollment: 3,567. Faculty: 241 (52 full-time, 189 part-time). Student-undergrad faculty ratio is 18:1. 804 applied, 81% were admitted. Full-time: 1,231 students, 55% women, 45% men. Part-time: 2,336 students, 56% women, 44% men. Students come from 6 states and territories, 21 other countries, 3% from out-of-state. 2% American Indian or Alaska Native, non-Hispanic/Latino; 22% Hispanic/Latino; 2% Black or African American, non-Hispanic/Latino; 2% Asian, non-Hispanic/Latino; 0.8% Native Hawaiian or other Pacific Islander, non-Hispanic/Latino; 0.3% international. 41% 25 or older, 6% transferred in. Retention: 55% of full-time freshmen returned the following year. Academic area with the most degrees conferred: construction trades. Core. Calendar: semesters. Academic remediation for entering students, ESL program, services for LD students, advanced placement, honors program, independent study, distance learning, double major, summer session for credit, part-time degree program, adult/continuing education programs, co-op programs and internships.

Entrance Requirements: Open admission. Options: electronic application, early admission. Recommended: high school transcript. Required for some: high school transcript. Entrance: noncompetitive. Application deadline: rolling. Transfer credits accepted: Yes.

Costs Per Year: Application fee: $15. State resident tuition: $3308 full-time. Nonresident tuition: $10,220 full-time. Full-time tuition varies according to degree level.

Collegiate Environment: Orientation program. Drama-theater group, choral group. Most popular organizations: Associated Students of Western Nevada, Soccer Club, Veterans Club, National Student Nurses Association, American Sign Language Club. Major annual events: Commencement Ceremony, Fall Welcome Back BBQ, Scholarship Reception. Student services: personal-psychological counseling. Campus security: late night transport-escort service. Western Nevada College Library and Media Services plus 1 other. Books: 35,923 (physical), 4,544 (digital/electronic); Serial titles: 2,725 (physical); Databases: 33. Weekly public service hours: 61; students can reserve study rooms. Operations spending for the previous fiscal year: $970,000. 669 computers available on campus for general student use. A campuswide network can be accessed. Students can access the following: online class registration. Staffed computer lab on campus provides training in use of computers and the Internet.

Community Environment: Carson City (pop. 56,062), the Capital of Nevada, is located near scenic Lake Tahoe and the Carson River. It is an agricultural region formerly important for silver production.

■ COLBY-SAWYER COLLEGE

541 Main St.
New London, NH 03257
Tel: (603)526-3000; Free: 800-272-1015
Fax: (603)526-3452
E-mail: admissions@colby-sawyer.edu
Web Site: www.colby-sawyer.edu

Description: Independent, 4-year, coed. Awards associate and bachelor's degrees. Founded 1837. Setting: 200-acre small town campus. Endowment: $36 million. Educational spending for the previous fiscal year: $9336 per student. Total enrollment: 1,106. Faculty: 101 (67 full-time, 34 part-time). Student-undergrad faculty ratio is 14:1. 1,989 applied, 87% were admitted. Full-time: 1,011 students, 70% women, 30% men. Part-time: 79 students, 68% women, 32% men. Students come from 29 states and territories, 25 other countries, 72% from out-of-state. 1% American Indian or Alaska Native, non-Hispanic/Latino; 3% Hispanic/Latino; 6% Black or African American, non-Hispanic/Latino; 2% Asian, non-Hispanic/Latino; 8% international. 1% 25 or older, 87% live on campus, 3% transferred in. Retention: 78% of full-time freshmen returned the following year. Academic areas with the most degrees conferred: health professions and related sciences; parks and recreation; business/marketing. Core. Calendar: semesters. Services for LD students, advanced placement, accelerated degree program, self-designed majors, honors program, independent study, distance learning, double major, part-time degree program, internships. Off campus study at The New Hampshire College and University Council, American University. Study abroad program. ROTC: Army (c).

Entrance Requirements: Options: electronic application, early admission, early action, deferred admission, international baccalaureate accepted. Required: essay, high school transcript, minimum 2.5 high school GPA, college preparatory courses: 4 years of English, 3 years of math, 3 years of lab science, 3 years of social science and 2 years of the same language. Recommended: 1 recommendation, interview. Entrance: moderately difficult. Application deadlines: 4/1, 12/1 for early action. Notification: continuous until 1/1. Transfer credits accepted: Yes. Early action applicants: 1,292. Early action applicants admitted: 1,014.

Costs Per Year: Application fee: $45. Comprehensive fee: $56,662 includes full-time tuition ($41,598), mandatory fees ($800), and college room and board ($14,264). Room and board charges vary according to board plan and housing facility. Part-time tuition: $1386 per credit. Part-time tuition varies according to course load.

Collegiate Environment: Orientation program. Drama-theater group, choral group, student-run newspaper. Social organizations: 60 open to all. Most popular organizations: Campus Activities Board, Student Government Association, Dance Club, Colby-Sawyer Players (Theater), Student Nurses Association. Major annual events: Welcome Back Weekend, Mountain Day, CSC Leadership Retreat. Student services: health clinic, personal-psychological counseling. Campus security: 24-hour emergency response devices and patrols, late night transport-escort service, controlled dormitory access, awareness seminars. Susan Colgate Cleveland Library Learning Center. Books: 83,409 (physical), 144,473 (digital/electronic); Serial titles: 486 (physical); Databases: 119. Weekly public service hours: 100; students can reserve study rooms. Operations spending for the previous fiscal year: $612,330. 180 computers available on campus for general student use. A campuswide network can be accessed from student residence rooms and from off campus. Students can access the following: online class registration, online bill payment, SmartCard (for use on campus and with selected local vendors), learning management systems, tutoring, reference librarians via chat, e-databases/e-journals, disk storage space. Staffed computer lab on campus (open 24 hours a day) provides training in use of computers, software, and the Internet.

Community Environment: Located in west central New Hampshire, New London enjoys a very agreeable climate and is a summer and winter tourist haven. Lake Sunapee is ten minutes west of New London and Mount Sunapee Ski Area is approximately twenty minutes away. There are excellent stores and specialty shops along with hotels, inns and lodges that are found in a resort area. Recreation includes winter skiing, hiking, biking, and seasonal fishing in lakes and streams.

■ DARTMOUTH COLLEGE

Hanover, NH 03755
Tel: (603)646-1110
Fax: (603)646-1216
E-mail: admissions.reply@dartmouth.edu
Web Site: www.dartmouth.edu

Description: Independent, university, coed. Awards bachelor's, master's, and doctoral degrees. Founded 1769. Setting: 269-acre small town campus. Endowment: $5.5 billion. Research spending for the previous fiscal year: $158.3 million. Educational spending for the previous fiscal year: $27,978 per student. Total enrollment: 6,571. Faculty: 784 (606 full-time, 178 part-time). Student-undergrad faculty ratio is 7:1. 22,033 applied, 9% were admitted. 95% from top 10% of their high school class, 99% from top quarter, 99% from top half. Full-time: 4,357 students, 49% women, 51% men. Part-time: 60 students, 47% women, 53% men. Students come from 53 states and territories, 95 other countries, 97% from out-of-state. 2% American Indian or Alaska Native, non-Hispanic/Latino; 10% Hispanic/Latino; 6% Black or African American, non-Hispanic/Latino; 15% Asian, non-Hispanic/Latino; 0.3% Native Hawaiian or other Pacific Islander, non-Hispanic/Latino; 9% international. 1% 25 or older, 87% live on campus, 1% transferred in. Retention: 97% of full-time freshmen returned the following year. Academic areas with the most degrees conferred: social sciences; biological/life sciences; engineering. Core. Calendar: quarters. Services for LD students, advanced placement, self-designed majors, honors program, independent study, double major, summer session for credit, internships, graduate courses open to undergrads. Off campus study at members of the Twelve College Exchange Program, University of California, San Diego, Morehouse College, Spelman College. Study abroad program. ROTC: Army (c).

Entrance Requirements: Options: electronic application, early admission, early decision, deferred admission, international baccalaureate accepted. Required: essay, high school transcript, 3 recommendations, peer evaluation, SAT or ACT, SAT and SAT Subject Tests or ACT. Recommended: interview. Entrance: most difficult. Application deadlines: 1/1, 11/1 for early decision. Notification: 4/10, 12/15 for early decision. SAT Reasoning Test deadline: 1/1. SAT Subject Test deadline: 1/1. Transfer credits accepted: Yes. Applicants placed on waiting list: 1,925. Wait-listed applicants offered admission: 0. Early decision applicants: 2,269. Early decision applicants admitted: 574.

Costs Per Year: Application fee: $80. One-time mandatory fee: $418. Comprehensive fee: $73,578 includes full-time tuition ($55,605), mandatory fees ($1599), and college room and board ($16,374). College room only: $9879.

Collegiate Environment: Orientation program. Drama-theater group, choral group, marching band, student-run newspaper, radio station. Social

organizations: 139 open to all; national fraternities, national sororities, local fraternities, local sororities; 35% of eligible men and 42% of eligible women are members. Most popular organizations: Dartmouth Student Assembly, Dartmouth Outing Club, Collis After Dark, Green Key Society, GLOS - Greek Letter Organizations and Societies. Major annual events: Dartmouth Night/ Homecoming, Winter Carnival, Green Key Weekend. Student services: health clinic, personal-psychological counseling, women's center. Campus security: 24-hour emergency response devices and patrols, late night transport-escort service, controlled dormitory access. 3,495 undergraduates lived in college housing during 2018-19. Freshmen guaranteed college housing. On-campus residence required in freshman year. Option: coed housing available. Baker-Berry Library plus 8 others. Books: 2.5 million (physical), 991,009 (digital/electronic); Serial titles: 15,595 (physical). Study areas open 24 hours, 5-7 days a week; students can reserve study rooms. Operations spending for the previous fiscal year: $12.1 million. 200 computers available on campus for general student use. Computer purchase/lease plans available. A computer is required for all students. A campuswide network can be accessed from student residence rooms and from off campus. Students can access the following: online class registration. Staffed computer lab on campus provides training in use of software.

Community Environment: The northern New England surroundings and the small town pleasantness of Hanover are very much a part of undergraduate life. Located in the central western part of New Hampshire, Hanover is bordered by the Connecticut River dividing New Hampshire and Vermont. The rural location provides unsurpassed facilities and opportunities for all forms of outdoor recreation. Hanover provides convenient student shopping facilities, and is easily accessible to all major transportation centers in New England and New York by interstate highway, bus and commuter airline service. Boston, two hours away by car, is the nearest large metropolitan area.

■ **FRANKLIN PIERCE UNIVERSITY**
40 University Dr.
Rindge, NH 03461-0060
Tel: (603)899-4000; Free: 800-437-0048
Fax: (603)899-4372
Web Site: www.franklinpierce.edu
Description: Independent, comprehensive, coed. Awards associate, bachelor's, master's, and doctoral degrees (profile does not reflect significant enrollment at 6 continuing education sites; master's degree is only offered at these sites). Founded 1962. Setting: 1,200-acre rural campus. Endowment: $13.2 million. Research spending for the previous fiscal year: $205,326. Educational spending for the previous fiscal year: $8216 per student. Total enrollment: 2,189. Faculty: 340 (93 full-time, 247 part-time). Student-undergrad faculty ratio is 13:1. 5,240 applied, 79% were admitted. 8% from top 10% of their high school class, 19% from top quarter, 56% from top half. Full-time: 1,413 students, 54% women, 46% men. Part-time: 216 students, 63% women, 37% men. Students come from 27 states and territories, 15 other countries, 81% from out-of-state. 0.4% American Indian or Alaska Native, non-Hispanic/Latino; 7% Hispanic/Latino; 7% Black or African American, non-Hispanic/Latino; 1% Asian, non-Hispanic/Latino; 0.1% Native Hawaiian or other Pacific Islander, non-Hispanic/Latino; 3% international. 2% 25 or older, 89% live on campus, 2% transferred in. Retention: 59% of full-time freshmen returned the following year. Academic areas with the most degrees conferred: health professions and related sciences; business/ marketing; homeland security, law enforcement, firefighting, and protective services. Core. Calendar: differs by branch and program. Academic remediation for entering students, ESL program, services for LD students, advanced placement, accelerated degree program, self-designed majors, freshman honors college, honors program, independent study, distance learning, double major, summer session for credit, part-time degree program, external degree program, adult/continuing education programs, internships, graduate courses open to undergrads. Off campus study. Study abroad program. ROTC: Army (c).
Entrance Requirements: Options: electronic application, early admission, deferred admission, international baccalaureate accepted. Required: essay, high school transcript, 1 recommendation. Recommended: minimum 2.2 high school GPA, interview. Required for some: minimum 2 high school GPA, SAT or ACT. Entrance: minimally difficult. Application deadlines: rolling, rolling for nonresidents. Notification: continuous, continuous for nonresidents. SAT Reasoning Test deadline: 8/31. Transfer credits accepted: Yes.
Costs Per Year: Application fee: $40. Comprehensive fee: $52,100 includes full-time tuition ($34,900), mandatory fees ($3300), and college room and board ($13,900). College room only: $8100. Part-time tuition: $1197 per credit hour.

Collegiate Environment: Orientation program. Drama-theater group, choral group, student-run newspaper, radio station. Social organizations: 40 open to all. Most popular organizations: Peer Leadership, Health Sciences Club, Student Government, Honors Program, Hope Happens Here. Major annual events: Grand Monadnock Climb, Academic Showcase, Block Party. Student services: health clinic, personal-psychological counseling. Campus security: 24-hour emergency response devices and patrols, student patrols, late night transport-escort service, controlled dormitory access. 1,364 college housing spaces available; 1,269 were occupied in 2018-19. Freshmen guaranteed college housing. On-campus residence required in freshman year. Option: coed housing available. Frank S. DiPietro Library plus 1 other. Books: 105,736 (physical), 246,080 (digital/electronic); Serial titles: 72 (physical), 70,000 (digital/electronic); Databases: 70. Weekly public service hours: 95. Operations spending for the previous fiscal year: $924,749. 100 computers available on campus for general student use. Computer purchase/lease plans available. A campuswide network can be accessed from student residence rooms and from off campus. Students can access the following: online class registration. Staffed computer lab on campus provides training in use of computers, software, and the Internet.

Community Environment: Rindge is a rural community with a temperate climate. Cathedral of the Pines, an outdoor international shrine for people of all faiths, is located here. Numerous lakes in the area provide facilities for boating and fishing. There is limited part-time work for students off campus.

■ **GRANITE STATE COLLEGE**
25 Hall St.
Concord, NH 03301
Tel: (603)228-3000; Free: 888-228-3000
Fax: (603)229-0964
E-mail: gsc.admissions@granite.edu
Web Site: www.granite.edu
Description: State and locally supported, comprehensive, coed. Part of University System of New Hampshire. Awards associate, bachelor's, and master's degrees (offers primarily part-time degree programs; courses offered at 50 locations in New Hampshire). Founded 1972. Setting: suburban campus. Endowment: $7.5 million. Total enrollment: 2,019. Faculty: 163 (14 full-time, 148 part-time). Student-undergrad faculty ratio is 11:1. 263 applied, 100% were admitted. Full-time: 807 students, 70% women, 30% men. Part-time: 951 students, 76% women, 24% men. Students come from 42 states and territories, 1 other country, 18% from out-of-state. 0.4% American Indian or Alaska Native, non-Hispanic/Latino; 4% Hispanic/Latino; 3% Black or African American, non-Hispanic/Latino; 1% Asian, non-Hispanic/Latino; 0.1% international. 78% 25 or older, 18% transferred in. Retention: 46% of full-time freshmen returned the following year. Academic areas with the most degrees conferred: business/marketing; interdisciplinary studies; health professions and related sciences; psychology. Core. Calendar: trimesters. Academic remediation for entering students, services for LD students, advanced placement, accelerated degree program, self-designed majors, independent study, distance learning, double major, summer session for credit, part-time degree program, adult/continuing education programs, co-op programs and internships, graduate courses open to undergrads. Off campus study at Other institutions within the University System of New Hampshire and the New Hampshire College and University Council.
Entrance Requirements: Open admission. Option: electronic application. Required for some: high school transcript, associate degree for some BS programs. Entrance: noncompetitive. Application deadline: rolling. Notification: continuous. Transfer credits accepted: Yes.
Costs Per Year: Application fee: $0. Area resident tuition: $7536 full-time, $314 per credit part-time. State resident tuition: $7536 full-time, $314 per credit part-time. Nonresident tuition: $8520 full-time, $355 per credit part-time. Mandatory fees: $225 full-time, $314 per credit part-time, $75 per term part-time.
Collegiate Environment: Orientation program. Social organizations: 2 open to all. Most popular organizations: Alumni Advisory Board, Student Advisory Board. Student services: personal-psychological counseling. No special consideration for freshman housing applicants. GSC Library and Information Commons. Books: 250,000 (digital/electronic); Databases: 29. Weekly public service hours: 126. Operations spending for the previous fiscal year: $168,565. 120 computers available on campus for general student use. A campuswide network can be accessed. Students can access the following: online class registration. Staffed computer lab on campus provides training in use of computers and the Internet.

■ GREAT BAY COMMUNITY COLLEGE

320 Corporate Dr.
Portsmouth, NH 03801
Tel: (603)427-7600
E-mail: askgreatbay@ccsnh.edu
Web Site: www.greatbay.edu
Description: State-supported, 2-year, coed. Awards certificates, diplomas, transfer associate, and terminal associate degrees. Total enrollment: 1,850. Student-undergrad faculty ratio is 10:1. 4% from out-of-state. 36% 25 or older.
Entrance Requirements: Open admission. Required: high school transcript.

■ HELLENIC AMERICAN UNIVERSITY

505 Amherst St.
Nashua, NH 03063
Tel: (603)577-8700
Web Site: www.hauniv.edu
Description: Independent, comprehensive, coed.

■ KEENE STATE COLLEGE

229 Main St.
Keene, NH 03435
Tel: (603)352-1909; Free: 800-KSC-1909
Fax: (603)358-2767
E-mail: mrichmon@keene.edu
Web Site: www.keene.edu
Description: State-supported, comprehensive, coed. Part of University System of New Hampshire. Awards bachelor's and master's degrees and post-master's certificates. Founded 1909. Setting: 150-acre small town campus. Total enrollment: 3,866. 5,580 applied, 83% were admitted. 6% from top 10% of their high school class, 21% from top quarter, 55% from top half. Full-time: 3,624 students, 55% women, 45% men. Part-time: 156 students, 44% women, 56% men. Students come from 27 states and territories, 8 other countries, 57% from out-of-state. 0.2% American Indian or Alaska Native, non-Hispanic/Latino; 4% Hispanic/Latino; 2% Black or African American, non-Hispanic/Latino; 1% Asian, non-Hispanic/Latino; 0.1% Native Hawaiian or other Pacific Islander, non-Hispanic/Latino; 0.1% international. 3% 25 or older, 55% live on campus, 3% transferred in. Retention: 71% of full-time freshmen returned the following year. Academic areas with the most degrees conferred: engineering technologies; health professions and related sciences; education. Core. Calendar: semesters. ESL program, services for LD students, advanced placement, accelerated degree program, self-designed majors, freshman honors college, honors program, independent study, distance learning, double major, summer session for credit, part-time degree program, adult/continuing education programs, co-op programs and internships, graduate courses open to undergrads. Off campus study. Study abroad program. ROTC: Army (c), Air Force (c).
Entrance Requirements: Options: electronic application, deferred admission. Required: essay, high school transcript. Recommended: 1 recommendation. Entrance: moderately difficult. Application deadline: 4/1. Notification: continuous. SAT Reasoning Test deadline: 4/1. Transfer credits accepted: Yes.
Costs Per Year: Application fee: $50. State resident tuition: $11,468 full-time, $478 per credit part-time. Nonresident tuition: $20,432 full-time, $852 per credit part-time. Mandatory fees: $2744 full-time, $111 per credit part-time. Part-time tuition and fees vary according to course load. College room and board: $11,026. Room and board charges vary according to board plan and housing facility.
Collegiate Environment: Orientation program. Drama-theater group, choral group, student-run newspaper, radio station. Social organizations: 100 open to all; national fraternities, national sororities; 6% of eligible men and 7% of eligible women are members. Most popular organizations: Environmental Outing Club, Social Activities Council, Student Government, Chock Full O Notes, The Equinox student newspaper. Major annual events: Winter Celebration, Spring Carnival, Spring Concert. Student services: health clinic, personal-psychological counseling, women's center. Campus security: 24-hour emergency response devices and patrols, late night transport-escort service, controlled dormitory access, Emergency Notification System. Mason Library. Books: 247,720 (physical), 319,081 (digital/electronic); Serial titles: 142 (physical), 73,114 (digital/electronic); Databases: 92. Weekly public service hours: 102; students can reserve study rooms. 600 computers available on campus for general student use. Computer purchase/lease plans available. A campuswide network can be accessed from student residence rooms and from off campus. Students can access the following: online class

registration. Staffed computer lab on campus provides training in use of computers, software, and the Internet.
Community Environment: Keene, population 22,700, is located in the southwest corner of New Hampshire, 90 miles from Boston. All forms of commercial transportation are available. Keene is a city of diversified industry with metal and machine industries the most important. There are a number of churches, a community hospital and library serving the area. One of the most popular resorts in the state, Keene has many lakes and ponds within a 20-mile radius as well as golf courses and facilities for winter sports. A number of covered bridges may be seen on side roads off State Highway 10 between Keene and Winchester.

■ LAKES REGION COMMUNITY COLLEGE

379 Belmont Rd.
Laconia, NH 03246
Tel: (603)524-3207
Fax: (603)524-8084
Web Site: www.lrcc.edu
Description: State-supported, 2-year, coed. Part of Community College System of New Hampshire. Awards certificates, transfer associate, and terminal associate degrees. Setting: small town campus. Total enrollment: 1,179. Student-undergrad faculty ratio is 9:1. Full-time: 490 students, 40% women, 60% men. Part-time: 689 students, 63% women, 37% men. Students come from 5 states and territories, 2 other countries, 3% from out-of-state. 0.5% American Indian or Alaska Native, non-Hispanic/Latino; 1% Hispanic/Latino; 0.5% Black or African American, non-Hispanic/Latino; 0.5% Asian, non-Hispanic/Latino; 0.1% Native Hawaiian or other Pacific Islander, non-Hispanic/Latino. 39% 25 or older. Core. Calendar: semesters accelerated terms also offered. Academic remediation for entering students, services for LD students, accelerated degree program, self-designed majors, independent study, distance learning, double major, summer session for credit, part-time degree program, external degree program, adult/continuing education programs, co-op programs and internships.
Entrance Requirements: Open admission except for nursing and automotive service education program. Options: electronic application, deferred admission, international baccalaureate accepted. Required: high school transcript. Notification: continuous. Transfer credits accepted: Yes.
Costs Per Year: State resident tuition: $5040 full-time, $210 per credit part-time. Nonresident tuition: $11,472 full-time, $478 per credit part-time. Mandatory fees: $6 per credit part-time.
Collegiate Environment: Orientation program. Student services: personal-psychological counseling. Campus security: 24-hour emergency response devices, late night transport-escort service, controlled dormitory access, Evening patrols by trained security personnel. Hugh Bennett Library plus 1 other. Students can reserve study rooms.

■ MANCHESTER COMMUNITY COLLEGE

1066 Front St.
Manchester, NH 03102-8518
Tel: (603)668-6706
E-mail: jpoirier@nhctc.edu
Web Site: www.mccnh.edu
Description: State-supported, 2-year, coed. Part of New Hampshire Community Technical College System. Awards certificates, diplomas, transfer associate, and terminal associate degrees. Founded 1945. Setting: 60-acre urban campus with easy access to Boston. Research spending for the previous fiscal year: $35,000. Total enrollment: 3,122. Faculty: 202 (52 full-time, 150 part-time). Student-undergrad faculty ratio is 14:1. Students come from 5 states and territories, 7% from out-of-state. 40% 25 or older. Core. Calendar: semesters. Academic remediation for entering students, ESL program, services for LD students, advanced placement, independent study, distance learning, double major, summer session for credit, part-time degree program, external degree program, adult/continuing education programs, co-op programs and internships.
Entrance Requirements: Options: early admission, deferred admission. Required: high school transcript. Required for some: interview. Entrance: minimally difficult. Application deadline: rolling. Notification: continuous.
Collegiate Environment: Orientation program. Social organizations: 4 open to all. Most popular organizations: Student Senate, Phi Theta Kappa, American Society of Welders, Student Nurses Association. Major annual events: Spring Formal, Graduation. Student services: personal-psychological counseling. Campus security: trained security personnel. New Hampshire Community Technical College Library plus 1 other. Operations spending for the previous fiscal year: $66,600. 210 computers available on campus for

general student use. A campuswide network can be accessed. Students can access the following: online class registration. Staffed computer lab on campus.

■ NASHUA COMMUNITY COLLEGE

505 Amherst St.
Nashua, NH 03063-1026
Tel: (603)882-6923
Fax: (603)882-8690
E-mail: pgoodman@ccsnh.edu
Web Site: www.nashuacc.edu

Description: State-supported, 2-year, coed. Part of Community College System of New Hampshire. Awards certificates, transfer associate, and terminal associate degrees. Founded 1967. Setting: 66-acre urban campus with easy access to Boston. Total enrollment: 2,100. Faculty: 108 (42 full-time, 66 part-time). 1 valedictorian. Core. Calendar: semesters. Academic remediation for entering students, ESL program, services for LD students, self-designed majors, distance learning, summer session for credit, part-time degree program, adult/continuing education programs, co-op programs and internships.

Entrance Requirements: Open admission. Option: deferred admission. Required: high school transcript, interview. Required for some: TEAS for pre-nursing. Entrance: noncompetitive. Application deadline: rolling. Notification: continuous. Transfer credits accepted: Yes.

Collegiate Environment: Orientation program. Drama-theater group, student-run newspaper. Social organizations: 11 open to all. Most popular organizations: Student Senate, Phi Theta Kappa, AmeriCorp, Paralegal Club, Athletics. Major annual event: Orientation. Student services: personal-psychological counseling. Campus security: 24-hour emergency response devices, late night transport-escort service. Walter B. Peterson Library and Media Center. 150 computers available on campus for general student use. A campuswide network can be accessed. Staffed computer lab on campus.

■ NEW ENGLAND COLLEGE

15 Main St.
Henniker, NH 03242-3293
Tel: (603)428-2211; Free: 800-521-7642
E-mail: elorentsen@nec.edu
Web Site: www.nec.edu

Description: Independent, comprehensive, coed. Awards associate, bachelor's, master's, and doctoral degrees. Founded 1946. Setting: 225-acre small town campus with easy access to Boston. Endowment: $11.9 million. Research spending for the previous fiscal year: $140,272. Educational spending for the previous fiscal year: $3785 per student. Total enrollment: 2,713. Faculty: 283 (42 full-time, 241 part-time). Student-undergrad faculty ratio is 16:1. 8,616 applied, 99.9% were admitted. 10% from top 10% of their high school class, 34% from top quarter, 58% from top half. 5 class presidents, 2 valedictorians, 26 student government officers. Full-time: 1,815 students, 59% women, 41% men. Part-time: 25 students, 56% women, 44% men. Students come from 41 states and territories, 21 other countries, 82% from out-of-state. 0.6% American Indian or Alaska Native, non-Hispanic/Latino; 8% Hispanic/Latino; 24% Black or African American, non-Hispanic/Latino; 2% Asian, non-Hispanic/Latino; 0.2% Native Hawaiian or other Pacific Islander, non-Hispanic/Latino; 4% international. 38% 25 or older, 41% live on campus, 8% transferred in. Retention: 58% of full-time freshmen returned the following year. Academic areas with the most degrees conferred: business/marketing; psychology; homeland security, law enforcement, firefighting, and protective services; health professions and related sciences. Core. Calendar: semesters for residential undergraduates; 7-week terms for online undergraduate and graduate programs. Academic remediation for entering students, ESL program, services for LD students, advanced placement, accelerated degree program, self-designed majors, freshman honors college, honors program, independent study, distance learning, double major, summer session for credit, part-time degree program, external degree program, adult/continuing education programs, internships, graduate courses open to undergrads. Off campus study at Members of the New Hampshire College and University Council. Study abroad program. ROTC: Army (c), Air Force (c).

Entrance Requirements: Options: electronic application, deferred admission, international baccalaureate accepted. Required: essay, high school transcript, 2 recommendations. Recommended: interview. Entrance: minimally difficult. Application deadline: rolling for nonresidents. Notification: continuous, continuous for nonresidents. Transfer credits accepted: Yes.

Costs Per Year: Comprehensive fee: $52,840 includes full-time tuition

($37,490), mandatory fees ($1180), and college room and board ($14,170). College room only: $7610. Part-time tuition: $405 per credit hour.

Collegiate Environment: Orientation program. Drama-theater group, student-run newspaper, radio station. Social organizations: 33 open to all; national fraternities, national sororities, local fraternities, local sororities, Honors Co-ed Greek Organization; 5% of eligible men and 8% of eligible women are members. Most popular organizations: Student Senate, Campus Activities Board, Criminal Justice Club, International Student Association, Political Science Club. Major annual events: Midnight Madness, Pancake Breakfast, River Day. Student services: health clinic, personal-psychological counseling, women's center. Campus security: 24-hour emergency response devices and patrols, student patrols, late night transport-escort service, controlled dormitory access, emergency text system. 731 college housing spaces available; 726 were occupied in 2018-19. Freshmen guaranteed college housing. On-campus residence required through junior year. Option: coed housing available. Danforth Library. Books: 98,000 (physical), 152,000 (digital/electronic); Serial titles: 101 (physical), 100,000 (digital/electronic); Databases: 22. Weekly public service hours: 126; study areas open 24 hours, 5-7 days a week; students can reserve study rooms. Operations spending for the previous fiscal year: $191,422. 212 computers available on campus for general student use. Computer purchase/lease plans available. A campuswide network can be accessed from student residence rooms and from off campus. Students can access the following: online class registration, financial aid, billing, advising, degree audit. Staffed computer lab on campus provides training in use of computers, software, and the Internet.

Community Environment: The campus is situated in an area abounding in natural beauty. Henniker, a village of 3,200, is located on the Contoocook River in a mountainous area of New Hampshire 85 miles from Boston and 15 miles from Concord, the capital. The campus facilities are located throughout Henniker allowing students easy walking access to stores and restaurants. Alpine skiing and snowboarding are available at Pat's Peak two miles from Henniker. Other outdoor recreational facilities abound in the surrounding area.

■ NEW HAMPSHIRE INSTITUTE OF ART

148 Concord St.
Manchester, NH 03104
Tel: (603)623-0313; Free: 866-241-4918
Fax: (603)641-1832
E-mail: admissions@nhia.edu
Web Site: www.nhia.edu

Description: Independent, comprehensive, coed. Awards bachelor's and master's degrees. Founded 1898. Setting: urban campus with easy access to Boston. Endowment: $22.8 million. Educational spending for the previous fiscal year: $12,401 per student. Total enrollment: 402. Faculty: 73 (18 full-time, 55 part-time). Student-undergrad faculty ratio is 10:1. 356 applied, 58% were admitted. Full-time: 316 students, 68% women, 32% men. Part-time: 26 students, 54% women, 46% men. Students come from 14 states and territories, 48% from out-of-state. 0.6% American Indian or Alaska Native, non-Hispanic/Latino; 9% Hispanic/Latino; 1% Black or African American, non-Hispanic/Latino; 1% Asian, non-Hispanic/Latino; 0.6% Native Hawaiian or other Pacific Islander, non-Hispanic/Latino. 7% 25 or older, 52% live on campus, 4% transferred in. Retention: 73% of full-time freshmen returned the following year. Academic areas with the most degrees conferred: visual and performing arts; liberal arts/general studies; education. Core. Calendar: semesters. Services for LD students, advanced placement, accelerated degree program, independent study, summer session for credit, part-time degree program, adult/continuing education programs, co-op programs and internships, graduate courses open to undergrads. Study abroad program.

Entrance Requirements: Options: electronic application, early action, deferred admission, international baccalaureate accepted. Required: essay, high school transcript, portfolio. Recommended: minimum 2 high school GPA, 2 recommendations. Required for some: SAT or ACT. Entrance: moderately difficult. Application deadlines: rolling, 12/15 for early action. Notification: continuous, 1/15 for early action. Transfer credits accepted: Yes.

Costs Per Year: Application fee: $30. Comprehensive fee: $40,140 includes full-time tuition ($25,990), mandatory fees ($2690), and college room and board ($11,460). Full-time tuition and fees vary according to degree level. Room and board charges vary according to board plan. Part-time tuition: $3285 per course. Part-time mandatory fees: $95 per credit hour, $100 per term. Part-time tuition and fees vary according to course load and degree level.

Collegiate Environment: Orientation program. Student-run newspaper, radio station. Social organizations: 10 open to all. Most popular organizations: Student Leadership Council, Comic/Arts Club, Neo-Victorian Club, Design Ink, Gay/Straight Alliance. Major annual events: Student Art Exhibitions, Student Affairs Events, Art Attack. Student services: health clinic, personal-psychological counseling. Campus security: late night transport-escort service, controlled dormitory access. Teti Library. Books: 17,000 (physical), 144,463 (digital/electronic); Serial titles: 80 (physical), 7,800 (digital/electronic); Databases: 30. Weekly public service hours: 63. Operations spending for the previous fiscal year: $329,467. 100 computers available on campus for general student use. A campuswide network can be accessed from student residence rooms and from off campus. Students can access the following: online class registration. Staffed computer lab on campus provides training in use of computers, software, and the Internet.

■ **NHTI, CONCORD'S COMMUNITY COLLEGE**
31 College Dr.
Concord, NH 03301-7412
Tel: (603)271-6484; Free: 800-247-0179
Fax: (603)271-7734
Web Site: www.nhti.edu
Description: State-supported, 2-year, coed. Part of Community College System of New Hampshire. Awards certificates, diplomas, and transfer associate degrees. Founded 1964. Setting: 225-acre small town campus with easy access to Boston. Total enrollment: 3,700. Faculty: 109. Student-undergrad faculty ratio is 15:1. 50% 25 or older, 23% live on campus. Calendar: semesters. Academic remediation for entering students, ESL program, services for LD students, advanced placement, distance learning, double major, summer session for credit, part-time degree program, external degree program, adult/continuing education programs.
Entrance Requirements: Option: electronic application. Required: high school transcript. Recommended: minimum 2 high school GPA, SAT or ACT. Required for some: essay, interview, National League of Nursing Exam. Entrance: moderately difficult. Application deadline: rolling. Notification: continuous. Preference given to state residents. Transfer credits accepted: Yes.
Collegiate Environment: Orientation program. Drama-theater group. Most popular organizations: Phi Theta Kappa, Student Senate, Student Nurses Association, Criminal Justice Club, Outing Club. Major annual events: Convocation, International Student Day, Awards Day. Student services: health clinic, personal-psychological counseling. Campus security: 24-hour emergency response devices and patrols, late night transport-escort service, controlled dormitory access, cameras in vital locations. Main library plus 1 other. 160 computers available on campus for general student use. Students can access the following: online class registration, electronic application. Staffed computer lab on campus.
Community Environment: Bisected by the Merrimack River, Concord is the capital of New Hampshire, and is the economic and political center of the state. It is a key city on the interstate highway system. Community facilities include three libraries, numerous churches, a YMCA, hospitals, and good shopping. Job opportunities are good.

■ **NORTHEAST CATHOLIC COLLEGE**
511 Kearsarge Mountain Rd.
Warner, NH 03278
Tel: (603)456-2656; Free: 877-498-1723
Fax: (603)456-2660
E-mail: admissions@magdalen.edu
Web Site: www.magdalen.edu
Description: Independent Roman Catholic, 4-year, coed. Awards associate and bachelor's degrees. Founded 1973. Setting: 135-acre small town campus. Total enrollment: 68. Student-undergrad faculty ratio is 11:1. 95% from out-of-state. 4% 25 or older, 100% live on campus. Retention: 86% of full-time freshmen returned the following year. Academic area with the most degrees conferred: liberal arts/general studies. Core. Calendar: semesters. Academic remediation for entering students, part-time degree program, co-op programs.
Entrance Requirements: Option: early decision. Required: essay, high school transcript, 2 recommendations, interview, medical examination form, SAT or ACT. Entrance: moderately difficult. Application deadline: rolling.
Collegiate Environment: Orientation program. Choral group. Student services: personal-psychological counseling. Campus security: 24-hour emergency response devices, student patrols. St. Augustine Learning Center.

■ **PLYMOUTH STATE UNIVERSITY**
17 High St.
Plymouth, NH 03264-1595

Tel: (603)535-5000; Free: 800-842-6900
Fax: (603)535-2714
E-mail: admissions@plymouth.edu
Web Site: www.plymouth.edu
Description: State-supported, comprehensive, coed. Part of University System of New Hampshire. Awards bachelor's, master's, and doctoral degrees and post-master's certificates. Founded 1871. Setting: 170-acre small town campus with easy access to Manchester. Endowment: $19.3 million. Research spending for the previous fiscal year: $2.3 million. Educational spending for the previous fiscal year: $6900 per student. Total enrollment: 5,050. Faculty: 426 (188 full-time, 238 part-time). Student-undergrad faculty ratio is 17:1. 6,864 applied, 79% were admitted. 5% from top 10% of their high school class, 20% from top quarter, 54% from top half. Full-time: 3,935 students, 50% women, 50% men. Part-time: 190 students, 42% women, 58% men. Students come from 44 states and territories, 18 other countries, 45% from out-of-state. 0.5% American Indian or Alaska Native, non-Hispanic/Latino; 1% Hispanic/Latino; 2% Black or African American, non-Hispanic/Latino; 2% Asian, non-Hispanic/Latino; 0.1% Native Hawaiian or other Pacific Islander, non-Hispanic/Latino; 2% international. 3% 25 or older, 56% live on campus, 5% transferred in. Retention: 70% of full-time freshmen returned the following year. Academic areas with the most degrees conferred: business/marketing; education; parks and recreation. Core. Calendar: semesters. Services for LD students, advanced placement, self-designed majors, honors program, independent study, distance learning, double major, summer session for credit, part-time degree program, adult/continuing education programs, internships, graduate courses open to undergrads. Off campus study at Members of the New Hampshire College and University Council, National Student Exchange. Study abroad program. ROTC: Army (c), Air Force (c).
Entrance Requirements: Options: electronic application, deferred admission, international baccalaureate accepted. Required: essay, 1 recommendation. Recommended: minimum 2.5 high school GPA. Required for some: high school transcript, minimum X high school GPA, interview. Entrance: moderately difficult. Application deadline: 4/1. Notification: continuous until 11/1. Transfer credits accepted: Yes.
Costs Per Year: Application fee: $50. State resident tuition: $11,580 full-time, $485 per credit hour part-time. Nonresident tuition: $20,250 full-time, $845 per credit hour part-time. Mandatory fees: $2519 full-time, $105 per credit hour part-time. Full-time tuition and fees vary according to reciprocity agreements. Part-time tuition and fees vary according to reciprocity agreements. College room and board: $11,100. College room only: $7300. Room and board charges vary according to board plan, housing facility, and student level.
Collegiate Environment: Orientation program. Drama-theater group, choral group, student-run newspaper, radio station. Social organizations: 85 open to all; national sororities; 3% of women are members. Most popular organizations: Pre Medical Professional Society, Student Nurse Association, Marketing Association of Plymouth State, Gaming Club, Programing Activities in a Campus Environment. Major annual events: Spring Fling, Ski Day, Student Activities Fair. Student services: health clinic, personal-psychological counseling, women's center. Campus security: 24-hour emergency response devices and patrols, late night transport-escort service, controlled dormitory access, shuttle bus service, crime prevention programs, self-defense education. Lamson Learning Commons. Books: 344,605 (physical), 155,000 (digital/electronic); Serial titles: 790 (physical), 1,500 (digital/electronic); Databases: 87. Weekly public service hours: 94. Operations spending for the previous fiscal year: $1.9 million. 600 computers available on campus for general student use. Computer purchase/lease plans available. A campuswide network can be accessed from student residence rooms and from off campus. Students can access the following: online class registration, degree audit, academic history, account status. Staffed computer lab on campus provides training in use of computers, software, and the Internet.
Community Environment: With the White Mountains to the north, the Lakes Region to the south, and the Pemigewasset Rivers bordering the town to the east, Plymouth, NH is home to some of the country's most spectacular wilderness. PSC students step outside every morning into a natural landscape that provides four seasons of recreational and educational adventure. Here, the outdoors offer a natural laboratory, a classroom, and a playground. The campus is nestled in the town of Plymouth, which has been ranked seventh in The 100 Best Small Towns in America. Plymouth is less than 2 hours' drive from Boston. Portland , Maine is 2 hours east; Burlington, Vermont, is 2 hours to the northwest; and Montreal, Canada is only 3 1/2 hours to the north. Recreational activities include skiing and other winter sports, hiking, fishing, boating, and hunting.

■ **RIVER VALLEY COMMUNITY COLLEGE**
1 College Pl.
Claremont, NH 03743
Tel: (603)542-7744
Fax: (603)543-1844
Web Site: www.rivervalley.edu
Description: State-supported, 2-year, coed. Part of Community College System of New Hampshire. Awards certificates, diplomas, transfer associate, and terminal associate degrees. Setting: 80-acre rural campus. Total enrollment: 1,009. Faculty: 112 (36 full-time, 76 part-time). Student-undergrad faculty ratio is 6:1. 664 applied, 77% were admitted. Full-time: 236 students, 56% women, 44% men. Part-time: 773 students, 73% women, 27% men. 6% from out-of-state. 1% American Indian or Alaska Native, non-Hispanic/Latino; 2% Hispanic/Latino; 0.7% Black or African American, non-Hispanic/Latino; 2% Asian, non-Hispanic/Latino. 53% 25 or older. Calendar: semesters. Academic remediation for entering students, services for LD students, independent study, distance learning, double major, summer session for credit, part-time degree program.
Entrance Requirements: Option: electronic application. Required: high school transcript. Required for some: 2 recommendations, interview. Transfer credits accepted: Yes.
Collegiate Environment: Orientation program. Social organizations: 1 open to all. Most popular organization: Student Government Association. Campus security: 24-hour emergency response devices, security personnel on campus 6:30 am to 10 pm. Charles Puksta Library plus 1 other. 30 computers available on campus for general student use. A campuswide network can be accessed. Students can access the following: online class registration. Staffed computer lab on campus provides training in use of computers, software, and the Internet.

■ **RIVIER UNIVERSITY**
420 S Main St.
Nashua, NH 03060
Tel: (603)888-1311; Free: 800-44RIVIER
Fax: (603)891-1799
E-mail: rivadmit@rivier.edu
Web Site: www.rivier.edu
Description: Independent Roman Catholic, comprehensive, coed. Awards associate, bachelor's, master's, and doctoral degrees and post-master's certificates. Founded 1933. Setting: 68-acre suburban campus with easy access to Boston. Total enrollment: 2,157. Faculty: 209 (61 full-time, 148 part-time). Student-undergrad faculty ratio is 13:1. 2,271 applied, 68% were admitted. Full-time: 863 students, 76% women, 24% men. Part-time: 486 students, 88% women, 12% men. Students come from 27 states and territories, 17 other countries, 45% from out-of-state. 0.4% American Indian or Alaska Native, non-Hispanic/Latino; 4% Hispanic/Latino; 4% Black or African American, non-Hispanic/Latino; 3% Asian, non-Hispanic/Latino; 0.2% Native Hawaiian or other Pacific Islander, non-Hispanic/Latino. 43% 25 or older, 48% live on campus, 9% transferred in. Retention: 73% of full-time freshmen returned the following year. Academic areas with the most degrees conferred: health professions and related sciences; business/marketing; education. Core. Calendar: semesters. Services for LD students, advanced placement, independent study, distance learning, double major, summer session for credit, part-time degree program, internships, graduate courses open to undergrads. Off campus study at members of the New Hampshire College and University Council. Study abroad program. ROTC: Army (c), Air Force (c).
Entrance Requirements: Options: electronic application, deferred admission. Required: essay, high school transcript, 1 recommendation. Recommended: minimum 2.3 high school GPA, interview, SAT or ACT. Required for some: SAT or ACT, nursing exam. Entrance: moderately difficult. Application deadline: rolling. Notification: continuous. Transfer credits accepted: Yes.
Collegiate Environment: Orientation program. Drama-theater group, choral group. Social organizations: 13 open to all. Most popular organizations: Student Government Association, Campus Activities Board, Campus Ministry, Student Nurses Association, Theater Club. Major annual events: Family Day, Spring Weekend, Semi-Formal. Student services: health clinic, personal-psychological counseling. Campus security: 24-hour emergency response devices and patrols, late night transport-escort service, controlled dormitory access. Regina Library plus 1 other. 175 computers available on campus for general student use. A campuswide network can be accessed from student residence rooms and from off campus. Students can access the following: online class registration. Staffed computer lab on campus provides training in use of computers, software, and the Internet.

Community Environment: Nashua is the second largest city in New Hampshire. It is conveniently located within an hour's drive of Boston, the White Mountains, and the seacoast, and is home to a large technology industry. Buses provide ample transportation to shopping malls, libraries, banking facilities, and many other services within just a few miles of the campus.

■ **SAINT ANSELM COLLEGE**
100 Saint Anselm Dr.
Manchester, NH 03102-1310
Tel: (603)641-7000; Free: 888-4ANSELM
Fax: (603)641-7550
Web Site: www.anselm.edu
Description: Independent Roman Catholic, 4-year, coed. Awards bachelor's degrees. Founded 1889. Setting: 380-acre suburban campus with easy access to Boston. Endowment: $134.6 million. Total enrollment: 2,050. Faculty: 233 (155 full-time, 78 part-time). Student-undergrad faculty ratio is 11:1. 3,896 applied, 77% were admitted. 27% from top 10% of their high school class, 55% from top quarter, 83% from top half. Full-time: 2,019 students, 61% women, 39% men. Part-time: 31 students, 68% women, 32% men. Students come from 30 states and territories, 9 other countries, 78% from out-of-state. 4% Hispanic/Latino; 2% Black or African American, non-Hispanic/Latino; 1% Asian, non-Hispanic/Latino; 0.8% international. 1% 25 or older, 91% live on campus, 1% transferred in. Retention: 91% of full-time freshmen returned the following year. Academic areas with the most degrees conferred: health professions and related sciences; business/marketing; social sciences. Core. Calendar: semesters. Services for LD students, advanced placement, accelerated degree program, honors program, independent study, double major, summer session for credit, part-time degree program, internships. Off campus study at Member Institution of the New Hampshire College and University Council. Study abroad program. ROTC: Army (c).
Entrance Requirements: Options: electronic application, early admission, early decision, early action, deferred admission, international baccalaureate accepted. Required: essay, high school transcript, 2 recommendations. Recommended: interview. Required for some: SAT or ACT. Entrance: moderately difficult. Application deadlines: 2/1, 12/1 for early decision, 11/15 for early action. Notification: 3/15, 12/31 for early decision, 1/15 for early action. SAT Reasoning Test deadline: 2/1. SAT Subject Test deadline: 2/1. Transfer credits accepted: Yes. Applicants placed on waiting list: 294. Wait-listed applicants offered admission: 1. Early decision applicants: 43. Early decision applicants admitted: 41. Early action applicants: 2,507. Early action applicants admitted: 1,943.
Costs Per Year: Application fee: $50. Comprehensive fee: $56,850 includes full-time tuition ($40,500), mandatory fees ($1600), and college room and board ($14,750). College room only: $8850. Part-time tuition: $1000 per credit. Part-time mandatory fees: $600 per term.
Collegiate Environment: Orientation program. Drama-theater group, choral group, student-run newspaper. Social organizations: 60 open to all. Most popular organizations: Meelia Center for Community Engagement, Anselmian Abbey Players, Club Sports, Service and Solidarity Mission Trips, Saint Anselm College Crier (School Newspaper). Major annual events: Homecoming, Spring Weekend, Family Weekend. Student services: health clinic, personal-psychological counseling. Campus security: 24-hour emergency response devices and patrols, student patrols, late night transport-escort service, controlled dormitory access. 1,775 college housing spaces available; 1,763 were occupied in 2018-19. Freshmen guaranteed college housing. Options: coed, men-only, women-only housing available. Geisel Library plus 2 others. Students can reserve study rooms. 400 computers available on campus for general student use. Computer purchase/lease plans available. A campuswide network can be accessed from student residence rooms and from off campus. Students can access the following: online class registration. Staffed computer lab on campus.
Community Environment: On the banks of Merrimack River, Manchester is the largest city in the state. The city is a retail, industrial, distribution and financial center. All means of commercial transportation are available. Community facilities include 54 churches, 8 hospitals, a public library, hotels and motels. The recreational activities are numerous. They include golf, swimming, bowling, tennis, roller skating, fishing, sailing, skiing, ice skating, and tobogganing. Points of interest are the Currier Gallery of Art, Manchester Historic Association and the Old Blodgett Canal.

■ **ST. JOSEPH SCHOOL OF NURSING**
5 Woodward Ave.
Nashua, NH 03060

Tel: (603)594-2567; Free: 800-370-3169
Fax: (603)594-2581
Web Site: www.sjson.edu

Description: Independent, 2-year, coed, affiliated with Roman Catholic Church. Administratively affiliated with St. Joseph Hospital. Awards transfer associate and terminal associate degrees. Founded 1964. Setting: urban campus with easy access to Boston, Portland. Educational spending for the previous fiscal year: $9973 per student. Total enrollment: 144. Faculty: 20 (11 full-time, 9 part-time). 5 applied, 40% were admitted. 1 student government officer. Full-time: 63 students, 92% women, 8% men. Part-time: 81 students, 88% women, 12% men. Students come from 3 states and territories, 9 other countries, 27% from out-of-state. 76% 25 or older, 24% transferred in. Core. Calendar: semesters. Academic remediation for entering students, services for LD students, advanced placement, summer session for credit.

Entrance Requirements: Option: electronic application. Required: essay, high school transcript, minimum 2.5 high school GPA, 3 recommendations, interview. Entrance: moderately difficult. Application deadline: 7/10. Transfer credits accepted: Yes. Applicants placed on waiting list: 5. Wait-listed applicants offered admission: 2.

Collegiate Environment: Orientation program. Campus security: 24-hour emergency response devices and patrols, late night transport-escort service. Operations spending for the previous fiscal year: $46,000. 25 computers available on campus for general student use. Staffed computer lab on campus provides training in use of computers, software, and the Internet.

■ **SOUTHERN NEW HAMPSHIRE UNIVERSITY**
2500 N River Rd.
Manchester, NH 03106-1045
Tel: (603)668-2211; Free: 888-327-7648
Fax: (603)645-9693
E-mail: t.whittum@snhu.edu
Web Site: www.snhu.edu

Description: Independent, university, coed. Awards associate, bachelor's, master's, and doctoral degrees and post-master's certificates. Founded 1932. Setting: 317-acre suburban campus with easy access to Boston. Educational spending for the previous fiscal year: $4809 per student. Total enrollment: 4,092. Faculty: 445 (133 full-time, 312 part-time). Student-undergrad faculty ratio is 13:1. 4,207 applied, 93% were admitted. 10% from top 10% of their high school class, 23% from top quarter, 54% from top half. Full-time: 2,935 students, 53% women, 47% men. Part-time: 85 students, 44% women, 56% men. Students come from 29 states and territories, 35 other countries, 53% from out-of-state. 0.4% American Indian or Alaska Native, non-Hispanic/Latino; 4% Hispanic/Latino; 3% Black or African American, non-Hispanic/Latino; 2% Asian, non-Hispanic/Latino; 0.1% Native Hawaiian or other Pacific Islander, non-Hispanic/Latino; 7% international. 7% 25 or older, 62% live on campus, 8% transferred in. Retention: 72% of full-time freshmen returned the following year. Academic areas with the most degrees conferred: business/marketing; education; computer and information sciences. Core. Calendar: semesters. Academic remediation for entering students, ESL program, services for LD students, advanced placement, accelerated degree program, honors program, independent study, distance learning, double major, summer session for credit, part-time degree program, adult/continuing education programs, co-op programs and internships, graduate courses open to undergrads. Off campus study at members of the New Hampshire College and University Council. Study abroad program. ROTC: Army (c), Air Force (c).

Entrance Requirements: Options: electronic application, early action, deferred admission, international baccalaureate accepted. Required: essay, high school transcript, minimum 2 high school GPA, 1 recommendation. Recommended: interview. Entrance: moderately difficult. Application deadlines: rolling, 11/15 for early action. Notification: continuous, 12/15 for early action. Transfer credits accepted: Yes.

Costs Per Year: Application fee: $40. Comprehensive fee: $44,256 includes full-time tuition ($30,756), mandatory fees ($380), and college room and board ($13,120). College room only: $9225. Full-time tuition and fees vary according to course load. Room and board charges vary according to board plan and housing facility.

Collegiate Environment: Orientation program. Drama-theater group, choral group, student-run newspaper, radio station. Social organizations: 62 open to all; national fraternities, national sororities, local fraternities, local sororities. Most popular organizations: Coordinators of Activities and Programming Events (CAPE), Psychology Club, Economics/Finance Association, Gaming Club, Outing Club. Major annual events: Late Night Breakfast, SNHU Stock

Concert/Festival, Homecoming Weekend. Student services: health clinic, women's center. Campus security: 24-hour emergency response devices and patrols, student patrols, late night transport-escort service, controlled dormitory access. Shapiro Library and Learning Commons. Students can reserve study rooms. Operations spending for the previous fiscal year: $2.8 million.

Community Environment: Combining the tradition of the past with the sophistication of the future, Manchester has everything to be expected in a city with a population of more than 100,000, offering a thriving business environment as well as numerous cultural facilities. It is also within an hour of Boston, many ski resorts, and beaches that provide opportunities for jobs and recreation.

■ **THOMAS MORE COLLEGE OF LIBERAL ARTS**
6 Manchester St.
Merrimack, NH 03054-4818
Tel: (603)880-8308; Free: 800-880-8308
Fax: (603)880-9280
Web Site: www.thomasmorecollege.edu

Description: Independent, 4-year, coed, affiliated with Roman Catholic Church. Awards bachelor's degrees. Founded 1978. Setting: 14-acre small town campus with easy access to Boston. Endowment: $551,325. Educational spending for the previous fiscal year: $9507 per student. Total enrollment: 90. Student-undergrad faculty ratio is 9:1. 32 applied, 41% were admitted. 2 National Merit Scholars. Full-time: 90 students, 53% women, 47% men. Students come from 23 states and territories, 1 other country, 89% from out-of-state. 1% American Indian or Alaska Native, non-Hispanic/Latino; 4% Hispanic/Latino; 1% Black or African American, non-Hispanic/Latino; 2% international. 4% 25 or older, 98% live on campus, 8% transferred in. Retention: 100% of full-time freshmen returned the following year. Academic area with the most degrees conferred: liberal arts/general studies. Core. Calendar: semesters. Independent study. Study abroad program.

Entrance Requirements: Option: electronic application. Required: essay, high school transcript, 2 recommendations. Recommended: SAT or ACT. Required for some: interview. Entrance: moderately difficult. Application deadline: rolling. Notification: continuous. Transfer credits accepted: No.

Costs Per Year: Application fee: $0. Comprehensive fee: $31,300 includes full-time tuition ($21,600) and college room and board ($9700). Full-time tuition varies according to course load, program, and reciprocity agreements. Room and board charges vary according to board plan. Part-time tuition: $900 per credit hour. Part-time tuition varies according to course load, program, and reciprocity agreements.

Collegiate Environment: Orientation program. Drama-theater group, choral group. Major annual events: Graduation, Convocation, visiting lectures. Campus security: 24-hour emergency response devices, student patrols, late night transport-escort service, on-site staff member. Warren Memorial Library plus 1 other. Books: 44,075 (physical); Serial titles: 43,515 (physical). Operations spending for the previous fiscal year: $8182. 4 computers available on campus for general student use. Students can access the following: online class registration. Staffed computer lab on campus.

■ **UNIVERSITY OF NEW HAMPSHIRE**
Durham, NH 03824
Tel: (603)862-1234
Web Site: www.unh.edu

Description: State-supported, university, coed. Part of University System of New Hampshire. Awards associate, bachelor's, master's, and doctoral degrees. Founded 1866. Setting: 2,600-acre small town campus with easy access to Boston. Endowment: $389.5 million. Research spending for the previous fiscal year: $122.2 million. Total enrollment: 15,305. Faculty: 1,008 (630 full-time, 378 part-time). Student-undergrad faculty ratio is 18:1. 20,096 applied, 77% were admitted. 20% from top 10% of their high school class, 48% from top quarter, 85% from top half. 20 valedictorians. Full-time: 12,477 students, 55% women, 45% men. Part-time: 305 students, 43% women, 57% men. Students come from 49 states and territories, 35 other countries, 52% from out-of-state. 0.1% American Indian or Alaska Native, non-Hispanic/Latino; 3% Hispanic/Latino; 1% Black or African American, non-Hispanic/Latino; 3% Asian, non-Hispanic/Latino; 4% international. 2% 25 or older, 56% live on campus, 4% transferred in. Retention: 85% of full-time freshmen returned the following year. Academic areas with the most degrees conferred: business/marketing; engineering; biological/life sciences. Core. Calendar: semesters. ESL program, services for LD students, advanced placement, accelerated degree program, self-designed majors, honors program, independent study, distance learning, double major, summer session for credit, part-time degree program, internships, graduate courses open to undergrads. Off campus study at National Student Exchange, New Hampshire College and University Council Exchange, New England Land Grant Universities Exchange, UC Santa Cruz Exchange. Study abroad program. ROTC: Army, Air Force.

Entrance Requirements: Options: electronic application, early action, deferred admission, international baccalaureate accepted. Required: high school transcript, 1 recommendation, Common Application, audition for some majors in music and theater, portfolio for art studio majors, SAT or ACT. Recommended: minimum 3 high school GPA. Entrance: moderately difficult. Application deadlines: 2/1, 2/1 for nonresidents, 11/15 for early action. Notification: continuous until 12/1, continuous for nonresidents, rolling for early action. SAT Reasoning Test deadline: 2/1. Transfer credits accepted: Yes. Early action applicants: 11,437. Early action applicants admitted: 9,929.

Costs Per Year: Application fee: $50. State resident tuition: $15,140 full-time, $630 per credit hour part-time. Nonresident tuition: $30,520 full-time, $1270 per credit hour part-time. Mandatory fees: $3359 full-time, $1,680 per year part-time. Full-time tuition and fees vary according to program. Part-time tuition and fees vary according to course load and program. College room and board: $11,588. College room only: $7220. Room and board charges vary according to board plan and housing facility.

Collegiate Environment: Orientation program. Drama-theater group, choral group, marching band, student-run newspaper, radio station. Social organizations: 271 open to all; national fraternities, national sororities; 14% of eligible men and 19% of eligible women are members. Most popular organizations: Campus Activity Board, The Outing Club, Resident Hall Association, Alpha Phi Omega, Memorial Union Student Organization. Major annual events: University Day Student Activities Fair, Jukebox, May Day Carnival. Student services: health clinic, personal-psychological counseling, women's center. Campus security: 24-hour emergency response devices, late night transport-escort service, controlled dormitory access, lighted sidewalks, emergency phones located across campus, campus-wide 24-hour emergency alert system, 24-hour police coverage. College housing designed to accommodate 7,000 students; 7,119 undergraduates lived in college housing during 2018-19. Freshmen guaranteed college housing. Option: coed housing available. Dimond Library plus 4 others. Books: 1.6 million (physical), 889,664 (digital/electronic); Serial titles: 749 (physical), 84,556 (digital/electronic); Databases: 430. Weekly public service hours: 117; students can reserve study rooms. Operations spending for the previous fiscal year: $18.9 million. 320 computers available on campus for general student use. Computer purchase/lease plans available. A campuswide network can be accessed from student residence rooms and from off campus. Students can access the following: online class registration. Staffed computer lab on campus provides training in use of computers, software, and the Internet.

Community Environment: Situated in southeastern New Hampshire, Durham is a quiet college town with many small restaurants, shops, and pubs located near the university. The cultural and recreational advantages of Portland to the northeast and nearby Boston to the south are both within one hour's drive. The University is 10 miles from the Atlantic coastline and historic Portsmouth. The White Mountains and ski areas are 60 miles to the northwest.

UNIVERSITY OF NEW HAMPSHIRE AT MANCHESTER

88 Commercial St.
Manchester, NH 03101-1113
Tel: (603)641-4321
Fax: (603)641-4125
E-mail: erika.couture@unh.edu
Web Site: manchester.unh.edu

Description: State-supported, comprehensive, coed. Part of University of New Hampshire. Awards associate, bachelor's, and master's degrees. Founded 1967. Setting: urban campus with easy access to Boston. Total enrollment: 1,045. Faculty: 103 (30 full-time, 73 part-time). Student-undergrad faculty ratio is 11:1. 205 applied, 73% were admitted. 3% from top 10% of their high school class, 29% from top quarter, 74% from top half. Full-time: 591 students, 54% women, 46% men. Part-time: 171 students, 45% women, 55% men. Students come from 8 states and territories, 2% from out-of-state. 0.1% American Indian or Alaska Native, non-Hispanic/Latino; 5% Hispanic/Latino; 1% Black or African American, non-Hispanic/Latino; 5% Asian, non-Hispanic/Latino; 0.4% international. 28% 25 or older,

19% transferred in. Retention: 81% of full-time freshmen returned the following year. Academic areas with the most degrees conferred: biological/life sciences; business/marketing; engineering technologies. Core. Calendar: semesters. Academic remediation for entering students, ESL program, services for LD students, advanced placement, self-designed majors, independent study, double major, summer session for credit, part-time degree program, adult/continuing education programs, co-op programs and internships. Off campus study at 12 members of the New Hampshire College and University Council. Study abroad program. ROTC: Army (c), Air Force (c).

Entrance Requirements: Options: electronic application, deferred admission. Required: essay, high school transcript, 1 recommendation, SAT or ACT. Recommended: interview. Entrance: moderately difficult. Application deadline: 4/1. Notification: continuous. Transfer credits accepted: Yes.

Collegiate Environment: Orientation program. Choral group, student-run newspaper. Social organizations: 14 open to all. Most popular organizations: Milling Around (A Cappella Group), Be Involved (Community Service), Common Ground (LGBT+), Our World (Environmental), Veterans and Allies Club. Campus security: 24-hour emergency response devices, late night transport-escort service. UNH Manchester Library plus 1 other. Books: 30,000 (physical). Students can reserve study rooms. 108 computers available on campus for general student use. A campuswide network can be accessed from off-campus. Students can access the following: online class registration. Staffed computer lab on campus (open 24 hours a day) provides training in use of computers, software, and the Internet.

WHITE MOUNTAINS COMMUNITY COLLEGE

2020 Riverside Dr.
Berlin, NH 03570
Tel: (603)752-1113; Free: 800-445-4525
Fax: (603)752-6335
E-mail: agaeb@ccsnh.edu
Web Site: www.wmcc.edu

Description: State-supported, 2-year, coed. Part of Community College System of New Hampshire. Awards certificates, transfer associate, and terminal associate degrees. Founded 1966. Setting: 325-acre rural campus. Total enrollment: 802. Faculty: 133 (24 full-time, 109 part-time). Student-undergrad faculty ratio is 8:1. 320 applied, 99% were admitted. Full-time: 299 students, 50% women, 50% men. Part-time: 503 students, 76% women, 24% men. Students come from 6 states and territories, 13% from out-of-state. 0.1% American Indian or Alaska Native, non-Hispanic/Latino; 1% Hispanic/Latino; 0.2% Black or African American, non-Hispanic/Latino; 0.4% Asian, non-Hispanic/Latino. 46% 25 or older, 4% transferred in. Core. Calendar: semesters. Academic remediation for entering students, services for LD students, advanced placement, self-designed majors, independent study, distance learning, double major, summer session for credit, part-time degree program, external degree program, adult/continuing education programs, co-op programs and internships.

Entrance Requirements: Open admission ALL PROGRAMS ARE OPEN ADMISSION EXCEPT FOR THE NURSING PROGRAM. Options: electronic application, deferred admission. Required: high school transcript. Required for some: recommendations, TEAS for associate's degree nursing program. Entrance: minimally difficult. Application deadlines: rolling, rolling for nonresidents. Notification: continuous, continuous for nonresidents. Transfer credits accepted: Yes.

Costs Per Year: Application fee: $20. One-time mandatory fee: $65. State resident tuition: $6400 full-time, $210 per credit hour part-time. Nonresident tuition: $14,960 full-time, $478 per credit hour part-time. Mandatory fees: $944 full-time, $17 per credit hour part-time. Full-time tuition and fees vary according to class time, location, and program. Part-time tuition and fees vary according to class time, location, and program.

Collegiate Environment: Orientation program. Social organizations: 1 open to all; Phi Theta Kappa Honor Society; 5% of eligible men and 10% of eligible women are members. Most popular organization: Student Senate. Major annual event: Job Networking Fair. Student services: personal-psychological counseling. Campus security: 24-hour emergency response devices, late night transport-escort service. Fortier Library. Books: 17,808 (physical); Serial titles: 35 (physical); Databases: 48. Weekly public service hours: 55; students can reserve study rooms. 65 computers available on campus for general student use. A campuswide network can be accessed. Students can access the following: online class registration, online access to business account details through Student Information System. Staffed computer lab on campus provides training in use of computers, software, and the Internet.

■ **ASSUMPTION COLLEGE FOR SISTERS**
200 A Morris Ave.
Denville, NJ 07834
Tel: (973)957-0188
Fax: (973)975-0190
E-mail: deanregistrar@acs350.org
Web Site: www.acs350.org
Description: Independent Roman Catholic, 2-year, women only. Awards certificates and transfer associate degrees. Founded 1953. Setting: 112-acre rural campus with easy access to New York City. Total enrollment: 33. Student-undergrad faculty ratio is 7:1. 91% 25 or older. Retention: 100% of full-time freshmen returned the following year. Core. Calendar: semesters. Academic remediation for entering students, ESL program, services for LD students, advanced placement, summer session for credit, part-time degree program.
Entrance Requirements: Required: high school transcript, 1 recommendation, women religious or women in religious formation. Entrance: noncompetitive.
Collegiate Environment: Orientation program. Choral group. Campus security: 24-hour emergency response devices. Assumption College for Sisters Library.

■ **ATLANTIC CAPE COMMUNITY COLLEGE**
5100 Black Horse Pke.
Mays Landing, NJ 08330-2699
Tel: (609)625-1111
Fax: (609)343-4921
E-mail: accadmit@atlantic.edu
Web Site: www.atlantic.edu
Description: County-supported, 2-year, coed. Awards certificates, diplomas, transfer associate, and terminal associate degrees. Founded 1964. Setting: 537-acre small town campus with easy access to Philadelphia. Total enrollment: 7,007. Student-undergrad faculty ratio is 21:1. 1% from out-of-state. 36% 25 or older. Retention: 60% of full-time freshmen returned the following year. Core. Calendar: semesters. Academic remediation for entering students, ESL program, services for LD students, advanced placement, independent study, distance learning, double major, summer session for credit, part-time degree program, adult/continuing education programs, co-op programs and internships.
Entrance Requirements: Open admission except for culinary arts, nursing, allied health, occupation therapy, physical therapy, respiratory therapy assistant programs. Options: electronic application, early admission, deferred admission. Recommended: high school transcript. Entrance: noncompetitive. Application deadline: 7/1.
Collegiate Environment: Orientation program. Drama-theater group, student-run newspaper, radio station. Student services: personal-psychological counseling. Campus security: 24-hour emergency response devices and patrols. William Spangler Library.
Community Environment: Population 2,321. Mays Landing is the county seat of Atlantic County, 18 miles from Atlantic City.

■ **BAIS MEDRASH MAYAN HATORAH**
101 Milton St.
Lakewood, NJ 08701
Description: Independent religious, 4-year, coed.

■ **BAIS MEDRASH TORAS CHESED**
910 Monmouth Ave.
Lakewood, NJ 08701
Web Site: www.bmtc.edu
Description: Independent Jewish, 4-year, men only. Awards bachelor's degrees.

■ **BERGEN COMMUNITY COLLEGE**
400 Paramus Rd.
Paramus, NJ 07652-1595
Tel: (201)447-7100
Fax: (201)444-7036
E-mail: admsoffice@bergen.edu
Web Site: www.bergen.edu
Description: County-supported, 2-year, coed. Awards certificates, transfer associate, and terminal associate degrees. Founded 1965. Setting: 167-acre suburban campus with easy access to New York City. Total enrollment: 16,469. Student-undergrad faculty ratio is 22:1. 1% from out-of-state. 30% 25 or older. Core. Calendar: semesters. Academic remediation for entering students, ESL program, services for LD students, honors program, distance learning, summer session for credit, part-time degree program, adult/continuing education programs, co-op programs and internships. Study abroad program.
Entrance Requirements: Open admission except for allied health programs. Entrance: noncompetitive. Notification: continuous. Preference given to county residents for nursing and dental hygiene programs.
Collegiate Environment: Orientation program. Drama-theater group, choral group, student-run newspaper. Student services: health clinic, personal-psychological counseling. Campus security: 24-hour patrols. Sidney Silverman Library and Learning Resources Center plus 1 other.
Community Environment: Bergen Community College is located in Paramus, which is the geographic center of Bergen County in northern New Jersey. With more than 300,000 households and nearly 1 million residents, Bergen County is one of the largest counties in the state. The college is located on a 167-acre campus that is bordered by two golf courses and a county park. There is convenient transportation to New York City by bus, train, and ferry. The college is approximately 20 minutes from the George Washington Bridge.

■ **BERKELEY COLLEGE-WOODLAND PARK CAMPUS**
44 Rifle Camp Rd.
Woodland Park, NJ 07424
Tel: (973)278-5400; Free: 800-446-5400
Fax: (973)278-2242
E-mail: info@berkeleycollege.edu
Web Site: www.berkeleycollege.edu
Description: Proprietary, comprehensive, coed. Administratively affiliated with Berkeley College - New York. Awards associate, bachelor's, and master's degrees. Founded 1931. Setting: 25-acre suburban campus with easy access to New York City. Educational spending for the previous fiscal year: $7487 per student. Total enrollment: 3,468. Faculty: 312 (125 full-time, 187 part-time). Student-undergrad faculty ratio is 14:1. 1,105 applied, 99% were admitted. Full-time: 2,431 students, 69% women, 31% men. Part-time: 893 students, 79% women, 21% men. Students come from 19 states and territories, 9 other countries, 3% from out-of-state. 0.2% American Indian or

Alaska Native, non-Hispanic/Latino; 41% Hispanic/Latino; 18% Black or African American, non-Hispanic/Latino; 1% Asian, non-Hispanic/Latino; 0.1% Native Hawaiian or other Pacific Islander, non-Hispanic/Latino; 0.5% international. 46% 25 or older, 14% transferred in. Retention: 61% of full-time freshmen returned the following year. Academic areas with the most degrees conferred: business/marketing; homeland security, law enforcement, firefighting, and protective services; health professions and related sciences. Core. Calendar: semesters. Academic remediation for entering students, advanced placement, accelerated degree program, honors program, independent study, distance learning, part-time degree program, adult/continuing education programs, co-op programs and internships, graduate courses open to undergrads. Off campus study at Berkeley College - New York. ROTC: Army (c).

Entrance Requirements: Open admission. Options: electronic application, deferred admission. Required: essay, high school transcript. Recommended: interview. Entrance: minimally difficult. Application deadlines: rolling, rolling for nonresidents. Notification: continuous, continuous for nonresidents. Transfer credits accepted: Yes.

Collegiate Environment: Orientation program. Student-run newspaper. Social organizations: 16 open to all. Most popular organizations: Student Veterans of America, Latino/Hispanic Club, Sister-2-Sister Group, Multicultural Club, Law and Justice Studies Club. Major annual events: Movie Knight, Chat'n'Chew with the President, Academic Awards Ceremonies. Student services: personal-psychological counseling. Campus security: 24-hour emergency response devices and patrols. Walter A. Brower Library. Books: 52,322 (physical), 168,797 (digital/electronic); Serial titles: 152 (physical), 72,544 (digital/electronic); Databases: 84. Students can reserve study rooms. Operations spending for the previous fiscal year: $1.3 million. 955 computers available on campus for general student use. A campuswide network can be accessed from off-campus. Students can access the following: online class registration. Staffed computer lab on campus provides training in use of computers, software, and the Internet.

■ **BETH MEDRASH GOVOHA**
617 Sixth St.
Lakewood, NJ 08701-2797
Tel: (732)367-1060
Description: Independent Jewish, comprehensive, men only. Awards bachelor's and master's degrees. Founded 1943. Setting: small town campus with easy access to New York City, Philadelphia. Total enrollment: 5,788. Calendar: semesters.
Entrance Requirements: Entrance: moderately difficult.
Community Environment: See Georgian Court College.

■ **BLOOMFIELD COLLEGE**
467 Franklin St.
Bloomfield, NJ 07003-9981
Tel: (973)748-9000; Free: 800-848-4555
Fax: (973)748-0916
E-mail: nicole_cibelli@bloomfield.edu
Web Site: www.bloomfield.edu
Description: Independent, comprehensive, coed, affiliated with Presbyterian Church (U.S.A.). Awards bachelor's and master's degrees. Founded 1868. Setting: 12-acre suburban campus with easy access to New York City. Endowment: $12.6 million. Educational spending for the previous fiscal year: $7902 per student. Total enrollment: 2,000. Faculty: 230 (70 full-time, 160 part-time). Student-undergrad faculty ratio is 15:1. 3,623 applied, 62% were admitted. 7% from top 10% of their high school class, 20% from top quarter, 50% from top half. Full-time: 1,767 students, 62% women, 38% men. Part-time: 180 students, 71% women, 29% men. Students come from 24 states and territories, 8 other countries, 6% from out-of-state. 0.3% American Indian or Alaska Native, non-Hispanic/Latino; 28% Hispanic/Latino; 50% Black or African American, non-Hispanic/Latino; 2% Asian, non-Hispanic/Latino; 0.6% Native Hawaiian or other Pacific Islander, non-Hispanic/Latino; 4% international. 16% 25 or older, 28% live on campus, 8% transferred in. Retention: 65% of full-time freshmen returned the following year. Academic areas with the most degrees conferred: visual and performing arts; business/marketing; social sciences. Core. Calendar: semesters. Academic remediation for entering students, ESL program, services for LD students, advanced placement, accelerated degree program, self-designed majors, freshman honors college, honors program, independent study, distance learning, double major, summer session for credit, part-time degree program, internships, graduate courses open to undergrads. Study abroad program. ROTC: Army (c).

Entrance Requirements: Options: electronic application, early action, deferred admission, international baccalaureate accepted. Required: essay, high school transcript, minimum 2.5 high school GPA, 2 recommendations, graded essay/term paper or personal essay, SAT or ACT. Recommended: interview. Entrance: moderately difficult. Application deadlines: 8/1, 12/1 for early action. Notification: continuous until 10/1, 12/24 for early action. SAT Reasoning Test deadline: 8/1. Transfer credits accepted: Yes. Early action applicants: 601. Early action applicants admitted: 473.

Costs Per Year: Application fee: $40. Comprehensive fee: $41,900 includes full-time tuition ($29,950) and college room and board ($11,950). Full-time tuition varies according to degree level. Room and board charges vary according to housing facility. Part-time tuition: $3760 per course. Part-time tuition varies according to course load and degree level.

Collegiate Environment: Orientation program. Drama-theater group, student-run radio station. Social organizations: 47 open to all; national fraternities, national sororities, Chi Phi Sigma (coed); 4% of eligible men and 2% of eligible women are members. Most popular organizations: First Ladies of Bloomfield, Green Hearts Environmental Club, Christian Fellowship, Team Infinite, Male Empowerment Network. Major annual events: Welcome Back BBQ, Springfest, Spring Formal. Student services: health clinic, personal-psychological counseling. Campus security: 24-hour emergency response devices and patrols, late night transport-escort service, controlled dormitory access, security cameras in high-traffic areas, controlled access to dormitories. Bloomfield College Library plus 1 other. Books: 63,000 (physical), 127,000 (digital/electronic); Serial titles: 45 (physical); Databases: 50. Weekly public service hours: 92. Operations spending for the previous fiscal year: $796,971. 390 computers available on campus for general student use. A campuswide network can be accessed from student residence rooms and from off campus. Students can access the following: online class registration. Staffed computer lab on campus provides training in use of computers, software, and the Internet.

Community Environment: Located between Newark and Montclair, Bloomfield, population 55,000, is a suburban, residential city. Excellent shopping facilities, libraries, churches, numerous civic and service organizations and hospitals are a part of the community. Part-time employment is available. Commercial transportation is convenient.

■ **BROOKDALE COMMUNITY COLLEGE**
765 Newman Springs Rd.
Lincroft, NJ 07738-1597
Tel: (732)842-1900
Fax: (732)576-1643
Web Site: www.brookdalecc.edu
Description: County-supported, 2-year, coed. Part of New Jersey Commission on Higher Education. Awards certificates, transfer associate, and terminal associate degrees. Founded 1967. Setting: 221-acre small town campus with easy access to New York City. Total enrollment: 14,025. 29% 25 or older. Core. Calendar: semesters plus 1 ten-week and 2 six-week summer terms. Academic remediation for entering students, ESL program, services for LD students, advanced placement, honors program, independent study, distance learning, summer session for credit, part-time degree program, adult/continuing education programs, co-op programs and internships. Study abroad program. ROTC: Army (c), Air Force (c).

Entrance Requirements: Open admission. Options: early admission, deferred admission. Required: high school transcript. Entrance: noncompetitive. Application deadline: rolling. Notification: continuous. Preference given to county residents.

Collegiate Environment: Orientation program. Drama-theater group, student-run newspaper, radio station. Student services: personal-psychological counseling, women's center. Campus security: 24-hour emergency response devices and patrols. Brookdale Community College Library.

Community Environment: Bounded by Sandy Hook Bay and the Navesink River, the Lincroft countryside area is located along the eastern shore of central New Jersey. The area abounds in orchards and horse farms. Community facilities include a library, churches of various faiths, above-average shopping facilities and many civic and service organizations. Railroads and buses furnish public transportation. Recreational facilities are very good including 7 miles of seashore for bay fishing, swimming and water sports.

■ **CALDWELL UNIVERSITY**
120 Bloomfield Ave.
Caldwell, NJ 07006-6195
Tel: (973)618-3000

E-mail: JJiras@caldwell.edu

Web Site: www.caldwell.edu

Description: Independent Roman Catholic, comprehensive, coed. Awards bachelor's, master's, and doctoral degrees and post-master's certificates. Founded 1939. Setting: 70-acre suburban campus with easy access to New York City. Endowment: $4.3 million. Educational spending for the previous fiscal year: $6431 per student. Total enrollment: 2,176. Faculty: 294 (79 full-time, 210 part-time). Student-undergrad faculty ratio is 12:1. 4,433 applied, 67% were admitted. 7% from top 10% of their high school class, 29% from top quarter, 67% from top half. Full-time: 1,515 students, 66% women, 34% men. Part-time: 129 students, 80% women, 20% men. Students come from 25 states and territories, 40 other countries, 6% from out-of-state. 0.1% American Indian or Alaska Native, non-Hispanic/Latino; 27% Hispanic/Latino; 14% Black or African American, non-Hispanic/Latino; 3% Asian, non-Hispanic/Latino; 0.2% Native Hawaiian or other Pacific Islander, non-Hispanic/Latino; 12% international. 10% 25 or older, 36% live on campus, 3% transferred in. Retention: 79% of full-time freshmen returned the following year. Academic areas with the most degrees conferred: health professions and related sciences; business/marketing; psychology. Core. Calendar: semesters. Academic remediation for entering students, services for LD students, advanced placement, accelerated degree program, self-designed majors, honors program, independent study, distance learning, double major, summer session for credit, part-time degree program, adult/continuing education programs, internships, graduate courses open to undergrads. Study abroad program. ROTC: Army (c).

Entrance Requirements: Options: electronic application, early admission, early decision, deferred admission, international baccalaureate accepted. Required: essay, high school transcript, 2 recommendations, SAT or ACT. Recommended: minimum 3 high school GPA, interview, 16 units of college preparatory coursework. Entrance: moderately difficult. Application deadlines: 4/1, 4/1 for nonresidents, 12/1 for early action. Notification: 4/15, 12/31 for early action. SAT Reasoning Test deadline: 8/1. SAT Subject Test deadline: 8/31. Transfer credits accepted: Yes. Early action applicants: 1,364. Early action applicants admitted: 1,263.

Costs Per Year: Application fee: $50. Comprehensive fee: $48,355 includes full-time tuition ($33,990), mandatory fees ($1950), and college room and board ($12,415). Part-time tuition: $950 per credit hour. Part-time mandatory fees: $235 per term.

Collegiate Environment: Orientation program. Drama-theater group, choral group, marching band, student-run newspaper. Social organizations: 40 open to all; national fraternities, national sororities; 1% of eligible men and 4% of eligible women are members. Most popular organizations: International Student Organization (ISO), Latino American Student Organization (LASO), Filipino Organization Rooted in Caldwell's Excellence (FORCE), Health Professions Club (HPC), Dance Team. Major annual events: Caldwell Fest, Homecoming Bonfire, Halloween Party. Student services: health clinic, personal-psychological counseling. Campus security: 24-hour emergency response devices and patrols, late night transport-escort service, controlled dormitory access. 611 college housing spaces available; 590 were occupied in 2018-19. Freshmen given priority for college housing. Option: coed housing available. Jennings Library plus 1 other. Books: 142,662 (physical), 166,014 (digital/electronic); Serial titles: 88 (physical), 66,812 (digital/electronic); Databases: 66. Students can reserve study rooms. Operations spending for the previous fiscal year: $871,716. 52 computers available on campus for general student use. A campuswide network can be accessed from student residence rooms. Students can access the following: online class registration. Staffed computer lab on campus.

Community Environment: The birthplace of President Grover Cleveland, Caldwell is situated in Western Essex County with bus lines serving the area, and New York City only 20 miles away. Community services include a number of churches, a public library, hospitals and various civic organizations. The Grover Cleveland County Park, golf courses and tennis courts provide facilities for recreation. Skiing and ice skating are available during the winter season.

■ **CAMDEN COUNTY COLLEGE**

PO Box 200

Blackwood, NJ 08012-0200

Tel: (856)227-7200

E-mail: ddelaney@camdencc.edu

Web Site: www.camdencc.edu

Description: State and locally supported, 2-year, coed. Part of New Jersey Office of the Secretary of Higher Education. Awards certificates, transfer associate, and terminal associate degrees. Founded 1967. Setting: 320-acre suburban campus with easy access to Philadelphia. Total enrollment: 10,492. Faculty: 678 (132 full-time, 546 part-time). 6,383 applied. Full-time: 5,041 students, 54% women, 46% men. Part-time: 5,451 students, 60% women, 40% men. Students come from 21 states and territories, 2% from out-of-state. 1% American Indian or Alaska Native, non-Hispanic/Latino; 17% Hispanic/Latino; 20% Black or African American, non-Hispanic/Latino; 6% Asian, non-Hispanic/Latino; 0.3% Native Hawaiian or other Pacific Islander, non-Hispanic/Latino; 3% international. 37% 25 or older, 8% transferred in. Core. Calendar: semesters. Academic remediation for entering students, ESL program, services for LD students, advanced placement, freshman honors college, honors program, independent study, distance learning, double major, summer session for credit, part-time degree program, external degree program, adult/continuing education programs, co-op programs and internships. Off campus study. Study abroad program.

Entrance Requirements: Open admission. Options: electronic application, early admission. Required for some: high school transcript. Entrance: noncompetitive. Application deadline: rolling. Transfer credits accepted: Yes.

Costs Per Year: Application fee: $0. Area resident tuition: $3210 full-time, $107 per credit hour part-time. State resident tuition: $3330 full-time, $111 per credit hour part-time. Nonresident tuition: $3330 full-time, $111 per credit hour part-time. Mandatory fees: $1110 full-time, $37 per credit hour part-time. Full-time tuition and fees vary according to course load and program. Part-time tuition and fees vary according to course load and program.

Collegiate Environment: Orientation program. Drama-theater group, choral group, student-run newspaper, radio station. Student services: health clinic. Campus security: 24-hour emergency response devices and patrols, late night transport-escort service. Wolverton Center Library.

Community Environment: Blackwood is located in Gloucester Township (population 66,539), near Philadelphia, PA.

■ **CENTENARY UNIVERSITY**

400 Jefferson St.

Hackettstown, NJ 07840-2100

Tel: (908)852-1400; Free: 800-236-8679

Fax: (908)852-3454

E-mail: yountj@centenaryuniversity.edu

Web Site: www.centenaryuniversity.edu

Description: Independent, comprehensive, coed, affiliated with United Methodist Church. Awards associate, bachelor's, master's, and doctoral degrees. Founded 1867. Setting: 105-acre suburban campus with easy access to New York City. Endowment: $10.7 million. Educational spending for the previous fiscal year: $7136 per student. Total enrollment: 2,203. Faculty: (82 full-time). 1,160 applied, 88% were admitted. Full-time: 1,444 students, 62% women, 38% men. Part-time: 74 students, 65% women, 35% men. 0.2% American Indian or Alaska Native, non-Hispanic/Latino; 12% Hispanic/Latino; 10% Black or African American, non-Hispanic/Latino; 2% Asian, non-Hispanic/Latino; 3% international. Retention: 87% of full-time freshmen returned the following year. Academic areas with the most degrees conferred: business/marketing; visual and performing arts; social sciences; education. Core. Calendar: semesters. ESL program, services for LD students, advanced placement, accelerated degree program, self-designed majors, independent study, distance learning, double major, summer session for credit, part-time degree program, adult/continuing education programs, internships. Off campus study. Study abroad program.

Entrance Requirements: Options: electronic application, deferred admission, international baccalaureate accepted. Required: essay, high school transcript, SAT or ACT. Recommended: interview. Required for some: interview. Entrance: moderately difficult. Application deadline: rolling. Notification: continuous. SAT Reasoning Test deadline: 8/1. Transfer credits accepted: Yes.

Costs Per Year: Application fee: $30. Comprehensive fee: $44,442 includes full-time tuition ($32,092), mandatory fees ($906), and college room and board ($11,444). College room only: $7680. Full-time tuition and fees vary according to program. Room and board charges vary according to board plan. Part-time tuition: $618 per credit hour. Part-time mandatory fees: $11 per credit hour, $19 per term. Part-time tuition and fees vary according to program.

Collegiate Environment: Orientation program. Drama-theater group, student-run newspaper. Social organizations: 35 open to all; national fraternities, national sororities, local fraternities, local sororities; 4% of eligible men and 3% of eligible women are members. Most popular organizations: First Year Leaders, Student Government, ENACTUS, Honor Societies, Fraternities and Sororities. Major annual events: President's Ball, Campus Picnic, Convocation. Student services: health clinic, personal-psychological counseling. Campus security: 24-hour emergency response devices and patrols, late night transport-escort service, controlled dormitory access. Taylor Memorial Library. Books: 45,025 (physical), 114 (digital/electronic); Serial titles: 2,710 (physical), 1,896 (digital/electronic); Databases: 85. Weekly public service hours: 82.

Community Environment: Population 9,375, Hackettstown is a suburban and residential community. The area industry has not destroyed the natural surroundings. There is easy access to New York City by bus and train. The ski resorts of the Pocono Mountains are only 30 minutes via Route 80 West. State parks maintained by New Jersey are minutes away.

■ **CHAMBERLAIN COLLEGE OF NURSING**
630 U.S. Hwy. 1
North Brunswick, NJ 08902
Tel: (732)875-1300; Free: 877-751-5783
Fax: (732)875-1394
Web Site: www.chamberlain.edu

Description: Proprietary, 4-year, coed. Awards bachelor's degrees. Total enrollment: 345. Faculty: 30 (9 full-time, 21 part-time). Student-undergrad faculty ratio is 12:1. Full-time: 122 students, 93% women, 7% men. Part-time: 223 students, 86% women, 14% men. 15% from out-of-state. 0.3% American Indian or Alaska Native, non-Hispanic/Latino; 15% Hispanic/Latino; 31% Black or African American, non-Hispanic/Latino; 12% Asian, non-Hispanic/Latino; 0.3% Native Hawaiian or other Pacific Islander, non-Hispanic/Latino; 0.6% international. 62% 25 or older, 48% transferred in. Accelerated degree program, distance learning.

Entrance Requirements: Option: deferred admission. Required: SAT or ACT. Application deadline: rolling. Notification: continuous.

■ **THE COLLEGE OF NEW JERSEY**
2000 Pennington Rd.
Ewing, NJ 08628
Tel: (609)771-1855
Web Site: www.tcnj.edu

Description: State-supported, comprehensive, coed. Awards bachelor's and master's degrees and post-master's certificates. Founded 1855. Setting: 255-acre suburban campus with easy access to Philadelphia. Research spending for the previous fiscal year: $18.3 million. Educational spending for the previous fiscal year: $11,142 per student. Total enrollment: 7,552. Faculty: 858 (365 full-time, 493 part-time). Student-undergrad faculty ratio is 13:1. 12,898 applied, 48% were admitted. 36% from top 10% of their high school class, 73% from top quarter, 98% from top half. Full-time: 6,728 students, 57% women, 43% men. Part-time: 227 students, 63% women, 37% men. Students come from 24 states and territories, 4 other countries, 6% from out-of-state. 0.1% American Indian or Alaska Native, non-Hispanic/Latino; 13% Hispanic/Latino; 6% Black or African American, non-Hispanic/Latino; 12% Asian, non-Hispanic/Latino; 0.2% Native Hawaiian or other Pacific Islander, non-Hispanic/Latino; 0.3% international. 4% 25 or older, 58% live on campus, 3% transferred in. Retention: 94% of full-time freshmen returned the following year. Academic areas with the most degrees conferred: business/marketing; education; communication/journalism. Core. Calendar: semesters. Academic remediation for entering students, ESL program, services for LD students, advanced placement, accelerated degree program, self-designed majors, honors program, independent study, double major, summer session for credit, part-time degree program, internships, graduate courses open to undergrads. Off campus study at members of the National Student Exchange, Philadelphia College of Pharmacy and Science, New Jersey Marine Sciences Consortium (Sandy Hook and Sea Isle City). Study abroad program. ROTC: Army (c), Air Force (c).

Entrance Requirements: Options: electronic application, early decision, deferred admission, international baccalaureate accepted. Required: essay, high school transcript, SAT or ACT. Recommended: minimum 2.5 high school GPA, 3 recommendations. Required for some: interview, art portfolio or music audition. Entrance: very difficult. Application deadlines: 2/1, 11/1 for early decision plan 1, 1/1 for early decision plan 2. Notification: continuous until 4/1; 12/1 for early decision plan 1, 2/1 for early decision plan 2. SAT Reasoning Test deadline: 3/1. Transfer credits accepted: Yes. Applicants placed on waiting list: 2,405. Wait-listed applicants offered admission: 20. Early decision applicants: 710. Early decision applicants admitted: 442.

Costs Per Year: Application fee: $75. State resident tuition: $12,947 full-time, $459.22 per credit hour part-time. Nonresident tuition: $24,662 full-time, $873.36 per credit hour part-time. Mandatory fees: $3,604 full-time, $149.69 per credit hour part-time. Full-time tuition and fees vary according to course load. Part-time tuition and fees vary according to course load. Col-

lege room and board: $13,648. College room only: $4408. Room and board charges vary according to board plan.

Collegiate Environment: Orientation program. Drama-theater group, choral group, student-run newspaper, radio station. Social organizations: 205 open to all; national fraternities, national sororities, local fraternities, local sororities; 14% of eligible men and 11% of eligible women are members. Most popular organizations: Student Government Association, College Union Board, Inter-Greek Council, The Signal. Major annual events: Homecoming Spirit Week, Funival, TCNJ Late Nighter. Student services: legal services, health clinic, personal-psychological counseling, women's center. Campus security: 24-hour emergency response devices and patrols, student patrols, late night transport-escort service, controlled dormitory access. The College of New Jersey Library. Books: 694,461 (physical), 6,455 (digital/electronic); Serial titles: 44,898 (physical), 8,859 (digital/electronic); Databases: 114. Weekly public service hours: 98; students can reserve study rooms. Operations spending for the previous fiscal year: $5.7 million. 631 computers available on campus for general student use. Computer purchase/lease plans available. A campuswide network can be accessed from student residence rooms and from off campus. Students can access the following: online class registration. Staffed computer lab on campus provides training in use of computers, software, and the Internet.

Community Environment: See Rider University.

■ **COLLEGE OF SAINT ELIZABETH**
2 Convent Rd.
Morristown, NJ 07960-6989
Tel: (973)290-4000; Free: 800-210-7900
Fax: (973)290-4710
E-mail: apply@cse.edu
Web Site: www.cse.edu

Description: Independent Roman Catholic, comprehensive, coed. Awards bachelor's, master's, and doctoral degrees (also offers coed adult undergraduate degree program and coed graduate programs). Founded 1899. Setting: 200-acre suburban campus with easy access to New York City. Endowment: $19.3 million. Educational spending for the previous fiscal year: $9744 per student. Total enrollment: 1,149. Faculty: 177 (49 full-time, 128 part-time). Student-undergrad faculty ratio is 10:1. 1,969 applied, 65% were admitted. Full-time: 587 students, 77% women, 23% men. Part-time: 178 students, 85% women, 15% men. Students come from 12 states and territories, 14 other countries, 6% from out-of-state. 0.4% American Indian or Alaska Native, non-Hispanic/Latino; 24% Hispanic/Latino; 32% Black or African American, non-Hispanic/Latino; 4% Asian, non-Hispanic/Latino; 0.3% Native Hawaiian or other Pacific Islander, non-Hispanic/Latino; 3% international. 32% 25 or older, 48% live on campus, 4% transferred in. Retention: 68% of full-time freshmen returned the following year. Academic areas with the most degrees conferred: health professions and related sciences; psychology; interdisciplinary studies; business/marketing. Core. Calendar: semesters. Academic remediation for entering students, ESL program, services for LD students, advanced placement, accelerated degree program, self-designed majors, honors program, independent study, distance learning, double major, summer session for credit, part-time degree program, external degree program, adult/continuing education programs, internships, graduate courses open to undergrads. Off campus study at Drew University, Madison, NJ; Fairleigh Dickinson University, Florham Park, NJ; Online Consortium of Independent Colleges and Universities (OCICU); County College of Morris (CCM)-CSE Justice Studies Program. Study abroad program.

Entrance Requirements: Options: electronic application, deferred admission, international baccalaureate accepted. Required: essay, high school transcript, minimum 2 high school GPA, 2 recommendations. Recommended: interview. Application deadline: rolling. Notification: continuous. SAT Reasoning Test deadline: 8/15. Transfer credits accepted: Yes.

Costs Per Year: Application fee: $35. Comprehensive fee: $45,875 includes full-time tuition ($31,000), mandatory fees ($2131), and college room and board ($12,744). Full-time tuition and fees vary according to course load and program. Room and board charges vary according to board plan. Part-time tuition: $800 per credit hour. Part-time tuition varies according to course load, location, and program.

Collegiate Environment: Orientation program. Drama-theater group, choral group. Social organizations: 20 open to all. Most popular organizations: Student Government Association (SGA), Students Take Action Committee (STAC) Volunteer Organization, International/Intercultural Clubs, College Activities Board (CAB), Campus Ministry. Major annual events: Oktoberfest/Parents' Day, International Night, Christmas Celebration. Student services:

health clinic, personal-psychological counseling. Campus security: 24-hour emergency response devices and patrols, late night transport-escort service, controlled dormitory access. Mahoney Library plus 1 other. Books: 113,292 (physical), 1.1 million (digital/electronic); Serial titles: 240 (physical), 26,767 (digital/electronic); Databases: 122. Weekly public service hours: 75. Operations spending for the previous fiscal year: $1.5 million. 127 computers available on campus for general student use. A campuswide network can be accessed from student residence rooms and from off campus. Students can access the following: online class registration, online course evaluations; online system for registering for student activities, clubs, and events. Staffed computer lab on campus provides training in use of computers, software, and the Internet.

Community Environment: Situated in northern New Jersey, two miles east of Morristown (population 18,851), the college is near enough to New York to enjoy the educational, cultural and social advantages of that city. All forms of commercial transportation are convenient.

■ **COUNTY COLLEGE OF MORRIS**
214 Ctr. Grove Rd.
Randolph, NJ 07869-2086
Tel: (973)328-5000
Fax: (973)328-1282
Web Site: www.ccm.edu
Description: County-supported, 2-year, coed. Awards certificates, transfer associate, and terminal associate degrees. Founded 1966. Setting: 218-acre suburban campus with easy access to New York City. Endowment: $5.4 million. Educational spending for the previous fiscal year: $4764 per student. Total enrollment: 7,949. 4,036 applied, 63% were admitted. Full-time: 3,819 students, 42% women, 58% men. Part-time: 4,130 students, 54% women, 46% men. Students come from 6 states and territories, 0.4% from out-of-state. 0.4% American Indian or Alaska Native, non-Hispanic/Latino; 21% Hispanic/Latino; 5% Black or African American, non-Hispanic/Latino; 6% Asian, non-Hispanic/Latino; 0.2% Native Hawaiian or other Pacific Islander, non-Hispanic/Latino; 2% international. 5% transferred in. Retention: 72% of full-time freshmen returned the following year. Core. Calendar: semesters. Academic remediation for entering students, ESL program, services for LD students, advanced placement, accelerated degree program, independent study, distance learning, double major, summer session for credit, co-op programs and internships. Study abroad program.
Entrance Requirements: Open admission. Options: electronic application, international baccalaureate accepted. Required: high school transcript. Entrance: noncompetitive. Application deadline: rolling. Notification: continuous. Transfer credits accepted: Yes.
Costs Per Year: Application fee: $30. Area resident tuition: $3840 full-time, $128 per credit hour part-time. State resident tuition: $7680 full-time, $256 per credit hour part-time. Nonresident tuition: $10,980 full-time, $366 per credit hour part-time. Mandatory fees: $1150 full-time, $29 per credit hour part-time, $28. Full-time tuition and fees vary according to course load, location, and program. Part-time tuition and fees vary according to course load, location, and program.
Collegiate Environment: Orientation program. Drama-theater group, choral group, student-run newspaper. Social organizations: 57 open to all; 4% of eligible men and 6% of eligible women are members. Most popular organizations: Phi Theta Kappa Honor Society, EOF Student Alliance, Student Nurses Association, New Social Engine, Cyber Security Club. Major annual events: Welcome Back Bash, Student Club Fair, Spring Picnic. Student services: health clinic, personal-psychological counseling, women's center. Campus security: 24-hour emergency response devices and patrols, late night transport-escort service. Learning Resource Center plus 1 other. Books: 38,594 (physical), 3,508 (digital/electronic); Serial titles: 26 (physical), 5 (digital/electronic); Databases: 123. Weekly public service hours: 68. Operations spending for the previous fiscal year: $1.3 million. 100 computers available on campus for general student use. A campuswide network can be accessed. Students can access the following: online class registration. Staffed computer lab on campus provides training in use of software and the Internet.
Community Environment: Morristown, population 18,851 is a suburban area 27 miles west of New York City, and was the winter encampment of General Washington's army during the winter of 1777 and 1779-80. Many historical events took place in Morristown. The sites have been restored and are incorporated in the Morristown National Historical Park. Commercial transportation is available. Excellent shopping and recreational facilities are available, including all water sports. Part-time employment opportunities are good.

■ **CUMBERLAND COUNTY COLLEGE**
3322 College Dr.
Vineland, NJ 08360
Tel: (856)691-8600
Fax: (856)691-6157
Web Site: www.cccnj.edu
Description: State and locally supported, 2-year, coed. Part of New Jersey Commission on Higher Education. Awards certificates, transfer associate, and terminal associate degrees. Founded 1963. Setting: 100-acre small town campus with easy access to Philadelphia. Total enrollment: 3,844. Faculty: 272 (43 full-time, 229 part-time). Student-undergrad faculty ratio is 23:1. 1% American Indian or Alaska Native, non-Hispanic/Latino; 28% Hispanic/Latino; 23% Black or African American, non-Hispanic/Latino; 0.8% Asian, non-Hispanic/Latino; 0.9% Native Hawaiian or other Pacific Islander, non-Hispanic/Latino; 0.1% international. 34% 25 or older. Retention: 66% of full-time freshmen returned the following year. Core. Calendar: semesters. Academic remediation for entering students, ESL program, services for LD students, advanced placement, honors program, independent study, distance learning, double major, summer session for credit, part-time degree program, co-op programs.
Entrance Requirements: Open admission except for nursing, radiography programs. Options: electronic application, early admission, deferred admission. Required: high school transcript. Entrance: noncompetitive. Application deadline: rolling. Notification: continuous. Transfer credits accepted: Yes.
Collegiate Environment: Orientation program. Drama-theater group, choral group, student-run newspaper. Student services: personal-psychological counseling. Campus security: 24-hour emergency response devices, late night transport-escort service. Cumberland County College Library.
Community Environment: Cumberland County's population lies mainly in the tri-city area of Vineland, Bridgeton, and Millville. Industries include glass production, clothing manufacturing, and food processing and canning. Most church denominations are represented, and a hospital, shopping facilities, and numerous service and civic groups all contribute to the general well-being of the Cumberland area. Golf, tennis, and water sports are the main recreational activities in the county.

■ **DEVRY UNIVERSITY-NORTH BRUNSWICK CAMPUS**
630 US Hwy. 1
North Brunswick, NJ 08902
Tel: (732)729-3960; Free: 866-338-7934
Web Site: www.devry.edu
Description: Proprietary, comprehensive, coed. Part of DeVry University. Awards associate, bachelor's, and master's degrees. Founded 1969. Setting: urban campus. Total enrollment: 681. Faculty: 65 (14 full-time, 51 part-time). Student-undergrad faculty ratio is 14:1. Full-time: 286 students, 28% women, 72% men. Part-time: 297 students, 25% women, 75% men. 4% from out-of-state. 0.2% American Indian or Alaska Native, non-Hispanic/Latino; 29% Hispanic/Latino; 18% Black or African American, non-Hispanic/Latino; 10% Asian, non-Hispanic/Latino; 0.5% Native Hawaiian or other Pacific Islander, non-Hispanic/Latino; 2% international. 52% 25 or older, 16% transferred in. Calendar: semesters. Part-time degree program, adult/continuing education programs.
Entrance Requirements: Option: deferred admission. Required: high school transcript, interview. Entrance: minimally difficult. Application deadline: rolling. Notification: continuous.
Collegiate Environment: Learning Resource Center.
Community Environment: North Brunswick is a suburban community within easy access to New York City, and Philadelphia and all their cultural and recreational resources. In addition, the 125-mile New Jersey Seacoast provides all forms of water sports.

■ **DREW UNIVERSITY**
36 Madison Ave.
Madison, NJ 07940-1493
Tel: (973)408-3000
Fax: (973)408-3939
Web Site: www.drew.edu
Description: Independent, university, coed, affiliated with United Methodist Church. Awards bachelor's, master's, and doctoral degrees and post-master's certificates. Founded 1867. Setting: 186-acre suburban campus with easy access to New York City. Total enrollment: 2,246. Faculty: 272 (150 full-time, 122 part-time). Student-undergrad faculty ratio is 10:1. 3,788 applied, 69% were admitted. 24% from top 10% of their high school class, 60% from top quarter, 84% from top half. Full-time: 1,634 students, 58%

women, 42% men. Part-time: 34 students, 50% women, 50% men. Students come from 37 states and territories, 47 other countries, 36% from out-of-state. 0.3% American Indian or Alaska Native, non-Hispanic/Latino; 15% Hispanic/Latino; 7% Black or African American, non-Hispanic/Latino; 5% Asian, non-Hispanic/Latino; 11% international. 3% 25 or older, 80% live on campus, 6% transferred in. Retention: 84% of full-time freshmen returned the following year. Academic areas with the most degrees conferred: social sciences; biological/life sciences; business/marketing. Core. Calendar: semesters. ESL program, services for LD students, advanced placement, accelerated degree program, self-designed majors, freshman honors college, honors program, independent study, double major, summer session for credit, part-time degree program, adult/continuing education programs, internships, graduate courses open to undergrads. Off campus study at College of Saint Elizabeth, Fairleigh Dickinson University. Study abroad program. ROTC: Army (c).

Entrance Requirements: Options: electronic application, early admission, early decision, early action, deferred admission, international baccalaureate accepted. Required: essay, high school transcript, 2 recommendations. Recommended: interview. Entrance: moderately difficult. Application deadlines: 2/1, 11/15 for early decision. Notification: 3/18, 12/15 for early decision. SAT Reasoning Test deadline: 2/1. Transfer credits accepted: Yes. Applicants placed on waiting list: 270. Wait-listed applicants offered admission: 0. Early decision applicants: 110. Early decision applicants admitted: 90.

Costs Per Year: Application fee: $40. Comprehensive fee: $53,608 includes full-time tuition ($38,668), mandatory fees ($832), and college room and board ($14,108). College room only: $8908. Room and board charges vary according to board plan and housing facility. Part-time tuition: $1612 per credit. Part-time tuition varies according to course load.

Collegiate Environment: Orientation program. Drama-theater group, choral group, student-run newspaper, radio station. Social organizations: 105 open to all. Most popular organizations: Drew Organization of Gaming, International Student Association, ARIEL Latin Culture Society, Drew University Chemistry Society, Drew African Students Association. Major annual events: Activities Fair, Holiday Ball, First Annual Picnic. Student services: health clinic, personal-psychological counseling. Campus security: 24-hour emergency response devices and patrols, late night transport-escort service, controlled dormitory access. 1,450 college housing spaces available; 1,350 were occupied in 2018-19. Freshmen guaranteed college housing. Option: coed housing available. Rose Memorial Library plus 1 other. Books: 446,142 (physical), 224,692 (digital/electronic); Serial titles: 7,192 (physical), 164,691 (digital/electronic); Databases: 196. Weekly public service hours: 108; students can reserve study rooms. 95 computers available on campus for general student use. Computer purchase/lease plans available. A computer is required for all students. A campuswide network can be accessed from student residence rooms and from off campus. Students can access the following: online class registration. Staffed computer lab on campus provides training in use of computers, software, and the Internet.

Community Environment: Madison, population approximately 16,000, is a suburban community in historical surroundings. Bordering a rural area that features numerous horse farms and a 6,000-acre national wildlife preserve, Madison is on a commuter rail line, just 30 miles from Manhattan. Some part-time employment is available.

■ **EASTERN INTERNATIONAL COLLEGE (BELLEVILLE)**
251 Washington Ave.
Belleville, NJ 07109
Tel: (973)751-9051
Web Site: www.eicollege.edu
Description: Proprietary, primarily 2-year, coed. Awards transfer associate, terminal associate, and bachelor's degrees. Setting: urban campus with easy access to Manhattan, New York.

■ **EASTERN INTERNATIONAL COLLEGE (JERSEY CITY)**
684 Newark Ave.
Jersey City, NJ 07306
Tel: (201)216-9901
Web Site: www.eicollege.edu
Description: Proprietary, primarily 2-year, coed. Awards transfer associate, terminal associate, and bachelor's degrees.

■ **EASTWICK COLLEGE (HACKENSACK)**
250 Moore St.
Hackensack, NJ 07601

Tel: (201)488-9400
Web Site: www.eastwickcollege.edu
Description: Proprietary, 2-year, coed. Awards certificates, diplomas, transfer associate, and terminal associate degrees. Founded 1969.

■ **EASTWICK COLLEGE (NUTLEY)**
103 Park Ave.
Nutley, NJ 07110
Tel: (973)661-0600
Web Site: www.eastwickcollege.edu
Description: Proprietary, 2-year, coed. Awards certificates, diplomas, transfer associate, and terminal associate degrees.

■ **EASTWICK COLLEGE (RAMSEY)**
10 S Franklin Tpke.
Ramsey, NJ 07446
Tel: (201)327-8877
Web Site: www.eastwickcollege.edu
Description: Proprietary, primarily 2-year, coed. Awards diplomas, transfer associate, terminal associate, and bachelor's degrees.

■ **ESSEX COUNTY COLLEGE**
303 University Ave.
Newark, NJ 07102-1798
Tel: (973)877-3000
Fax: (973)623-6449
Web Site: www.essex.edu
Description: County-supported, 2-year, coed. Part of New Jersey Commission on Higher Education. Awards certificates, transfer associate, and terminal associate degrees. Founded 1966. Setting: 22-acre urban campus with easy access to New York City. Total enrollment: 11,979. Faculty: 601 (118 full-time, 483 part-time). Student-undergrad faculty ratio is 29:1. 7,757 applied, 100% were admitted. Full-time: 6,569 students, 57% women, 43% men. Part-time: 5,410 students, 59% women, 41% men. Students come from 9 states and territories, 49 other countries, 1% from out-of-state. 0.2% American Indian or Alaska Native, non-Hispanic/Latino; 24% Hispanic/Latino; 48% Black or African American, non-Hispanic/Latino; 4% Asian, non-Hispanic/Latino; 0.1% Native Hawaiian or other Pacific Islander, non-Hispanic/Latino; 8% international. 41% 25 or older, 2% transferred in. Retention: 50% of full-time freshmen returned the following year. Core. Calendar: semesters. Academic remediation for entering students, ESL program, services for LD students, advanced placement, accelerated degree program, independent study, distance learning, double major, summer session for credit, part-time degree program, adult/continuing education programs, co-op programs and internships. Off campus study at New Jersey Institute of Technology; Rutgers, The State University of New Jersey; University of Medicine and Dentistry of New Jersey. ROTC: Army (c).

Entrance Requirements: Open admission except for allied health programs. Options: electronic application, deferred admission. Required: high school transcript. Entrance: noncompetitive. Application deadlines: 8/15, rolling for nonresidents. Notification: continuous, continuous for nonresidents.

Collegiate Environment: Orientation program. Drama-theater group, choral group, student-run newspaper. Social organizations: 20 open to all. Most popular organizations: Fashion Entertainment Board, Phi Theta Kappa, Latin Student Union, DECA, Black Student Association. Student services: personal-psychological counseling, women's center. Campus security: 24-hour emergency response devices and patrols. Martin Luther King, Jr. Library. 750 computers available on campus for general student use. A campuswide network can be accessed from off-campus. Staffed computer lab on campus.

Community Environment: See New Jersey Institute of Technology.

■ **FAIRLEIGH DICKINSON UNIVERSITY, FLORHAM CAMPUS**
285 Madison Ave.
Madison, NJ 07940-1099
Tel: (973)443-8500; Free: 800-338-8803
Web Site: www.fdu.edu
Description: Independent, comprehensive, coed. Awards bachelor's, master's, and doctoral degrees and post-master's certificates. Founded 1942. Setting: 178-acre suburban campus with easy access to New York City. Total enrollment: 3,512. Faculty: 453 (153 full-time, 300 part-time). Student-undergrad faculty ratio is 13:1. 4,175 applied, 84% were admitted. 19% from top 10% of their high school class, 49% from top quarter, 81%

from top half. Full-time: 2,640 students, 57% women, 43% men. Part-time: 107 students, 42% women, 58% men. Students come from 25 states and territories, 9 other countries, 17% from out-of-state. 0.2% American Indian or Alaska Native, non-Hispanic/Latino; 18% Hispanic/Latino; 8% Black or African American, non-Hispanic/Latino; 5% Asian, non-Hispanic/Latino; 0.1% Native Hawaiian or other Pacific Islander, non-Hispanic/Latino; 0.4% international. 3% 25 or older, 61% live on campus, 4% transferred in. Retention: 81% of full-time freshmen returned the following year. Academic areas with the most degrees conferred: business/marketing; visual and performing arts; psychology. Core. Calendar: semesters. Academic remediation for entering students, services for LD students, advanced placement, accelerated degree program, self-designed majors, honors program, independent study, distance learning, double major, summer session for credit, part-time degree program, adult/continuing education programs, co-op programs and internships, graduate courses open to undergrads. Off campus study at College of Saint Elizabeth, Drew University. Study abroad program. ROTC: Army (c), Air Force (c).

Entrance Requirements: Options: electronic application, international baccalaureate accepted. Required: high school transcript, 2 recommendations, SAT or ACT. Entrance: moderately difficult. Application deadlines: rolling, rolling for nonresidents. Notification: continuous, continuous for nonresidents. SAT Reasoning Test deadline: 7/1. SAT Subject Test deadline: 7/1. Transfer credits accepted: Yes.

Costs Per Year: Application fee: $40. One-time mandatory fee: $815. Comprehensive fee: $56,558 includes full-time tuition ($42,096), mandatory fees ($1046), and college room and board ($13,416). College room only: $8810. Full-time tuition and fees vary according to location and program. Room and board charges vary according to board plan, housing facility, and location. Part-time tuition: $997 per credit hour. Part-time mandatory fees: $422 per year. Part-time tuition and fees vary according to location and program.

Collegiate Environment: Orientation program. Drama-theater group, choral group, student-run newspaper. Social organizations: national fraternities, national sororities. Student services: health clinic, personal-psychological counseling. Campus security: 24-hour emergency response devices and patrols, late night transport-escort service, controlled dormitory access, trained law enforcement personnel on staff. Monninger Center for Learning and Research. Books: 131,212 (physical), 158,628 (digital/electronic); Serial titles: 1,423 (physical), 126,248 (digital/electronic); Databases: 144. Weekly public service hours: 83.

■ **FAIRLEIGH DICKINSON UNIVERSITY, METROPOLITAN CAMPUS**
1000 River Rd.
Teaneck, NJ 07666-1914
Tel: (201)692-2000; Free: 800-338-8803
Web Site: www.fdu.edu
Description: Independent, university, coed. Awards associate, bachelor's, master's, and doctoral degrees and post-master's certificates. Founded 1942. Setting: 88-acre suburban campus with easy access to New York City. Total enrollment: 7,846. Faculty: 682 (172 full-time, 510 part-time). Student-undergrad faculty ratio is 14:1. 3,777 applied, 88% were admitted. 19% from top 10% of their high school class, 48% from top quarter, 80% from top half. Full-time: 2,374 students, 59% women, 41% men. Part-time: 3,093 students, 55% women, 45% men. Students come from 31 states and territories, 50 other countries, 12% from out-of-state. 0.4% American Indian or Alaska Native, non-Hispanic/Latino; 31% Hispanic/Latino; 7% Black or African American, non-Hispanic/Latino; 6% Asian, non-Hispanic/Latino; 0.4% Native Hawaiian or other Pacific Islander, non-Hispanic/Latino; 4% international. 32% 25 or older, 22% live on campus, 5% transferred in. Retention: 74% of full-time freshmen returned the following year. Academic areas with the most degrees conferred: liberal arts/general studies; business/marketing; health professions and related sciences. Core. Calendar: semesters. Academic remediation for entering students, ESL program, services for LD students, advanced placement, accelerated degree program, self-designed majors, honors program, independent study, distance learning, double major, summer session for credit, part-time degree program, external degree program, adult/continuing education programs, co-op programs and internships, graduate courses open to undergrads. Off campus study at College of St. Elizabeth, Drew University. Study abroad program. ROTC: Army (c), Air Force (c).
Entrance Requirements: Options: electronic application, early admission. Required: high school transcript, 2 recommendations, SAT or ACT. Required for some: interview. Entrance: moderately difficult. Application deadline: rolling. Notification: continuous. SAT Reasoning Test deadline: 7/1. SAT Subject Test deadline: 7/1. Transfer credits accepted: Yes.

Costs Per Year: Application fee: $40. One-time mandatory fee: $815. Comprehensive fee: $54,102 includes full-time tuition ($39,686), mandatory fees ($1046), and college room and board ($13,370). College room only: $8764. Full-time tuition and fees vary according to location and program. Room and board charges vary according to board plan and housing facility. Part-time tuition: $997 per credit hour. Part-time mandatory fees: $422 per year. Part-time tuition and fees vary according to location and program.
Collegiate Environment: Orientation program. Drama-theater group, choral group, student-run newspaper, radio station. Social organizations: national fraternities, national sororities. Student services: health clinic, personal-psychological counseling, women's center. Campus security: 24-hour emergency response devices and patrols, late night transport-escort service, controlled dormitory access, trained law enforcement personnel on staff. Giovatto Library. Books: 157,566 (physical); Serial titles: 1,217 (physical), 126,248 (digital/electronic); Databases: 144. Weekly public service hours: 87.

■ **FELICIAN UNIVERSITY**
262 S Main St.
Lodi, NJ 07644-2117
Tel: (201)559-6000
Fax: (973)778-4111
E-mail: fullerc@felician.edu
Web Site: www.felician.edu
Description: Independent Roman Catholic, comprehensive, coed. Awards associate, bachelor's, master's, and doctoral degrees and post-master's certificates. Founded 1942. Setting: 37-acre small town campus with easy access to New York City. Endowment: $6.5 million. Educational spending for the previous fiscal year: $7627 per student. Total enrollment: 1,996. Faculty: 215 (79 full-time, 136 part-time). Student-undergrad faculty ratio is 14:1. 2,249 applied, 79% were admitted. 7% from top 10% of their high school class, 23% from top quarter, 56% from top half. Full-time: 1,430 students, 69% women, 31% men. Part-time: 196 students, 80% women, 20% men. Students come from 14 states and territories, 18 other countries, 8% from out-of-state. 0.4% American Indian or Alaska Native, non-Hispanic/Latino; 29% Hispanic/Latino; 24% Black or African American, non-Hispanic/Latino; 5% Asian, non-Hispanic/Latino; 0.4% Native Hawaiian or other Pacific Islander, non-Hispanic/Latino; 2% international. 27% 25 or older, 30% live on campus, 10% transferred in. Retention: 76% of full-time freshmen returned the following year. Academic areas with the most degrees conferred: health professions and related sciences; business/marketing; biological/life sciences. Core. Calendar: semesters. Academic remediation for entering students, ESL program, services for LD students, advanced placement, accelerated degree program, self-designed majors, honors program, independent study, distance learning, double major, summer session for credit, part-time degree program, external degree program, adult/continuing education programs, co-op programs and internships, graduate courses open to undergrads. Off campus study at Rutgers - SHRP; Sage Graduate School; NY College of Podiatric Medicine; NY Chiropractic College; Bloomsburg University of PA. Study abroad program. ROTC: Army (c), Air Force (c).
Entrance Requirements: Option: deferred admission. Required: essay, high school transcript, minimum 2 high school GPA, recommendations, SAT or ACT. Recommended: SAT and SAT Subject Tests or ACT. Required for some: interview, SAT, ACT, SAT Subject Tests. Entrance: moderately difficult. Application deadlines: 5/1, 2/15 for nonresidents. Notification: continuous, continuous for nonresidents. SAT Reasoning Test deadline: 7/1. SAT Subject Test deadline: 7/1. Transfer credits accepted: Yes.
Costs Per Year: Application fee: $30. Comprehensive fee: $47,200 includes full-time tuition ($31,915), mandatory fees ($2400), and college room and board ($12,885). Full-time tuition and fees vary according to program. Room and board charges vary according to housing facility. Part-time tuition: $1055 per credit hour. Part-time mandatory fees: $475 per term. Part-time tuition and fees vary according to course load and program.
Collegiate Environment: Orientation program. Drama-theater group, choral group, student-run radio station. Social organizations: 37 open to all; local fraternities, local sororities; 3% of eligible men and 1% of eligible women are members. Most popular organizations: Student Nurses Association, Zeta Alpha Zeta teaching sorority, Campus Activity Board, Students in Free Enterprise (SIFE), Student Government Association. Major annual events: Homecoming/College Festival, Midnight Madness, Springfest. Student services: health clinic, personal-psychological counseling. Campus security: 24-hour patrols, student patrols, late night transport-escort service. Felician University Library plus 1 other. Books: 68,565 (physical), 158,952 (digital/

electronic); Serial titles: 178 (physical), 51,874 (digital/electronic); Databases: 56. Weekly public service hours: 137; students can reserve study rooms. Operations spending for the previous fiscal year: $562,803. 190 computers available on campus for general student use. A campuswide network can be accessed from student residence rooms and from off campus. Students can access the following: online class registration. Staffed computer lab on campus provides training in use of computers and the Internet.

Community Environment: Felician is located on two campuses, in Lodi and in Rutherford, in Bergen County, New Jersey, 12 miles from New York City and 10 minutes from the Meadowlands Sports Complex.

■ GEORGIAN COURT UNIVERSITY

900 Lakewood Ave.
Lakewood, NJ 08701-2697
Tel: (732)987-2200; Free: 800-458-8422
Fax: (732)987-2000
E-mail: admissions@georgian.edu
Web Site: www.georgian.edu

Description: Independent Roman Catholic, comprehensive, coed. Awards bachelor's and master's degrees and post-master's certificates. Founded 1908. Setting: 156-acre suburban campus with easy access to New York City, Philadelphia. Endowment: $56 million. Total enrollment: 2,390. Faculty: 284 (87 full-time, 197 part-time). Student-undergrad faculty ratio is 12:1. 1,946 applied, 69% were admitted. 7% from top 10% of their high school class, 28% from top quarter, 57% from top half. Full-time: 1,343 students, 73% women, 27% men. Part-time: 270 students, 60% women, 40% men. Students come from 19 states and territories, 16 other countries, 6% from out-of-state. 0.5% American Indian or Alaska Native, non-Hispanic/Latino; 13% Hispanic/Latino; 12% Black or African American, non-Hispanic/Latino; 3% Asian, non-Hispanic/Latino; 0.1% Native Hawaiian or other Pacific Islander, non-Hispanic/Latino; 1% international. 17% 25 or older, 27% live on campus, 19% transferred in. Retention: 72% of full-time freshmen returned the following year. Academic areas with the most degrees conferred: psychology; health professions and related sciences; business/marketing. Core. Calendar: semesters. Academic remediation for entering students, ESL program, services for LD students, advanced placement, accelerated degree program, self-designed majors, honors program, independent study, distance learning, double major, summer session for credit, part-time degree program, adult/continuing education programs, internships, graduate courses open to undergrads. Off campus study. Study abroad program.

Entrance Requirements: Options: electronic application, early action, deferred admission. Required: high school transcript, minimum 2.5 high school GPA, SAT or ACT. Required for some: essay, 2 recommendations, interview. Entrance: moderately difficult. Application deadlines: 8/1, 12/1 for early action. SAT Reasoning Test deadline: 8/15. SAT Subject Test deadline: 8/15. Transfer credits accepted: Yes.

Costs Per Year: Application fee: $40. Comprehensive fee: $43,784 includes full-time tuition ($31,416), mandatory fees ($1560), and college room and board ($10,808). Full-time tuition and fees vary according to location, program, and reciprocity agreements. Part-time tuition: $718 per credit hour. Part-time mandatory fees: $365 per term. Part-time tuition and fees vary according to location, program, and reciprocity agreements.

Collegiate Environment: Orientation program. Student-run newspaper. Social organizations: 40 open to all. Most popular organizations: Basketball Club, Black Student Union, Math Club, Dance Theatre Club, History Club. Major annual events: Great Gatsby Party, Homecoming, GCU Step & Stroll Exhibition. Student services: health clinic, personal-psychological counseling. Campus security: 24-hour emergency response devices and patrols, late night transport-escort service, controlled dormitory access. The Sister Mary Joseph Cunningham Library. Books: 129,447 (physical), 117,590 (digital/electronic); Serial titles: 2,898 (physical), 33,651 (digital/electronic); Databases: 115. Weekly public service hours: 85; students can reserve study rooms. 221 computers available on campus for general student use. A campuswide network can be accessed from student residence rooms and from off campus. Students can access the following: online class registration. Staffed computer lab on campus provides training in use of computers, software, and the Internet.

Community Environment: Lakewood, population 36,000, is located in the central part of New Jersey and is convenient to the Route 9 corridor, Garden State Parkway, and Interstate 95. New York City, Philadelphia, and Atlantic City are each less than one and one-half hours from the college. Lakewood offers the services of a public library, hospital, various houses of worship, and numerous major civic and service organizations. The famous New Jersey shore is less than one-half hour away. Nearby are also the Naval Air Engineering Center, a sport parachuting center, and shopping centers.

■ HUDSON COUNTY COMMUNITY COLLEGE

70 Sip Ave.
Jersey City, NJ 07306
Tel: (201)714-7100
Fax: (201)714-2136
Web Site: www.hccc.edu

Description: State and locally supported, 2-year, coed. Awards certificates, transfer associate, and terminal associate degrees. Founded 1974. Setting: urban campus with easy access to New York City. Total enrollment: 8,864. Faculty: 661 (84 full-time, 577 part-time). Student-undergrad faculty ratio is 35:1. Full-time: 5,136 students, 57% women, 43% men. Part-time: 3,728 students, 62% women, 38% men. 0.3% American Indian or Alaska Native, non-Hispanic/Latino; 55% Hispanic/Latino; 14% Black or African American, non-Hispanic/Latino; 8% Asian, non-Hispanic/Latino; 0.5% Native Hawaiian or other Pacific Islander, non-Hispanic/Latino; 0.5% international. 33% 25 or older, 4% transferred in. Retention: 58% of full-time freshmen returned the following year. Core. Calendar: semesters. Academic remediation for entering students, ESL program, services for LD students, advanced placement, honors program, independent study, distance learning, summer session for credit, part-time degree program, internships.

Entrance Requirements: Open admission. Option: electronic application. Entrance: noncompetitive. Application deadline: 9/1. Notification: continuous until 9/1. Transfer credits accepted: Yes.

Costs Per Year: Application fee: $20. Area resident tuition: $4260 full-time, $142 per credit hour part-time. State resident tuition: $8520 full-time, $284 per credit hour part-time. Nonresident tuition: $12,570 full-time, $419 per credit hour part-time. Mandatory fees: $1,458 full-time, $47.75 per credit hour part-time, $25 per term part-time. Full-time tuition and fees vary according to course load and program. Part-time tuition and fees vary according to course load and program.

Collegiate Environment: Orientation program. Drama-theater group, student-run newspaper. Major annual events: College Transfer Fair, Major Exploration Fair, HCCC Pridefest. Student services: personal-psychological counseling. Campus security: 24-hour emergency response devices, late night transport-escort service. Hudson County Community College Library plus 1 other. Books: 49,853 (physical), 2,881 (digital/electronic); Serial titles: 1,269 (physical), 750 (digital/electronic); Databases: 74. Students can reserve study rooms.

■ JERSEY COLLEGE

546 US Hwy. 46
Teterboro, NJ 07608
Tel: (201)489-5836
Web Site: www.jerseycollege.edu

Description: Proprietary, 2-year, coed. Awards diplomas and transfer associate degrees. Founded 2003. Setting: 1-acre urban campus with easy access to New York City. Total enrollment: 2,743. Faculty: 217 (92 full-time, 125 part-time). Student-undergrad faculty ratio is 16:1. 204 applied, 71% were admitted. Full-time: 2,743 students, 91% women, 9% men. Students come from 14 states and territories, 28% from out-of-state. 0.3% American Indian or Alaska Native, non-Hispanic/Latino; 10% Hispanic/Latino; 63% Black or African American, non-Hispanic/Latino; 4% Asian, non-Hispanic/Latino; 0.5% Native Hawaiian or other Pacific Islander, non-Hispanic/Latino. 12% 25 or older, 15% transferred in. Core. Academic remediation for entering students, accelerated degree program, adult/continuing education programs.

Entrance Requirements: Option: international baccalaureate accepted. Required: essay, high school transcript, 2 recommendations, interview, proof of U.S. citizenship or Permanent Resident Card. Recommended: SAT or ACT. Required for some: math and reading entrance exams. Application deadline: rolling. Notification: continuous. Transfer credits accepted: Yes.

Collegiate Environment: Orientation program. Main Library. Books: 14,981 (physical), 145,557 (digital/electronic); Serial titles: 555 (physical); Databases: 3. Students can reserve study rooms. 274 computers available on campus for general student use. A campuswide network can be accessed. Staffed computer lab on campus provides training in use of computers and the Internet.

■ KEAN UNIVERSITY

1000 Morris Ave.
Union, NJ 07083

Tel: (908)737-5326

Fax: (908)737-3415

E-mail: admitme@kean.edu

Web Site: www.kean.edu

Description: State-supported, university, coed. Part of New Jersey State College System. Awards bachelor's, master's, and doctoral degrees and post-master's certificates. Founded 1855. Setting: 240-acre suburban campus with easy access to New York City. Total enrollment: 14,056. Faculty: 1,393 (357 full-time, 1,036 part-time). Student-undergrad faculty ratio is 17:1. 9,082 applied, 86% were admitted. Full-time: 9,609 students, 60% women, 40% men. Part-time: 2,215 students, 61% women, 39% men. Students come from 22 states and territories, 39 other countries, 2% from out-of-state. 0.2% American Indian or Alaska Native, non-Hispanic/Latino; 30% Hispanic/Latino; 21% Black or African American, non-Hispanic/Latino; 5% Asian, non-Hispanic/Latino; 0.3% Native Hawaiian or other Pacific Islander, non-Hispanic/Latino; 2% international. 25% 25 or older, 16% live on campus, 12% transferred in. Retention: 72% of full-time freshmen returned the following year. Academic areas with the most degrees conferred: business/marketing; psychology; education. Core. Calendar: semesters. Academic remediation for entering students, ESL program, services for LD students, advanced placement, accelerated degree program, independent study, distance learning, double major, summer session for credit, part-time degree program, external degree program, adult/continuing education programs, co-op programs and internships, graduate courses open to undergrads. Off campus study at Dual major in Psychology and Psychiatric Rehabilitation: This is a joint program that Kean University has established with Rutgers University, School of Health Related Professions. Students will take courses for the Psychology and General Education components of this major at Kean University. The B.S Health Information Management program is a joint program with Rutgers Newark. The undergraduate completes all the pre-professional coursework at Kean University including program prerequisites. B.S. Clinical Lab Science, Medi. Study abroad program. ROTC: Army (c), Air Force (c).

Entrance Requirements: Options: electronic application, early action, deferred admission. Required: high school transcript, SAT or ACT, SAT or ACT. Recommended: essay, 2 recommendations. Required for some: interview. Entrance: moderately difficult. Application deadlines: 8/15, 12/1 for early action. Notification: continuous until 11/1, 1/1 for early action. SAT Reasoning Test deadline: 8/15. Transfer credits accepted: Yes. Early action applicants: 3,790. Early action applicants admitted: 2,095.

Costs Per Year: Application fee: $75. State resident tuition: $9740 full-time, $381.50 per credit part-time. Nonresident tuition: $16,775 full-time, $601 per credit part-time. Mandatory fees: $2608 full-time, $89.50 per credit part-time. Part-time tuition and fees vary according to course load. College room and board: $14,470. Room and board charges vary according to board plan, housing facility, and location.

Collegiate Environment: Orientation program. Drama-theater group, choral group, student-run newspaper, radio station. Social organizations: 155 open to all; national fraternities, national sororities, local fraternities, local sororities. Most popular organizations: American Sign Language Club, Kean University Council for Exceptional Children, Kean University Rotaract Action Club, EEO Society, Pre-Medical Pre-Dental Association. Major annual events: Homecoming, Comedy Shows, Kean Day. Student services: health clinic, personal-psychological counseling. Campus security: 24-hour emergency response devices and patrols, student patrols, late night transport-escort service, controlled dormitory access. 2,128 college housing spaces available; 1,841 were occupied in 2018-19. Freshmen given priority for college housing. Option: coed housing available. Nancy Thompson Library. Books: 177,961 (physical), 12,121 (digital/electronic); Serial titles: 59,728 (digital/electronic); Databases: 244. Weekly public service hours: 102. Operations spending for the previous fiscal year: $2.7 million. 1,700 computers available on campus for general student use. A computer is required for all students. A campuswide network can be accessed from student residence rooms and from off campus. Students can access the following: online class registration. Staffed computer lab on campus (open 24 hours a day) provides training in use of computers and the Internet.

Community Environment: The township of Union, population 55,326, and its proximity to major automobile, bus, rail, and air transportation networks makes access to the university excellent. This provides continuous cultural, intellectual and social interchange between the cities and the university. Community facilities include library, numerous churches, hospitals and clinics, major civic and service organizations. A recreation center provides facilities for special activities.

■ **MERCER COUNTY COMMUNITY COLLEGE**

1200 Old Trenton Rd.

Trenton, NJ 08690-1004

Tel: (609)586-4800; Free: 800-392-MCCC

Fax: (609)586-6944

E-mail: admiss@mccc.edu

Web Site: www.mccc.edu

Description: State and locally supported, 2-year, coed. Awards certificates, transfer associate, and terminal associate degrees. Founded 1966. Setting: 292-acre suburban campus with easy access to New York City, Philadelphia. Educational spending for the previous fiscal year: $6061 per student. Total enrollment: 7,979. Faculty: 797. Student-undergrad faculty ratio is 18:1. Full-time: 3,077 students, 49% women, 51% men. Part-time: 4,902 students, 53% women, 47% men. Students come from 7 states and territories, 89 other countries, 1% from out-of-state. 0.2% American Indian or Alaska Native, non-Hispanic/Latino; 18% Hispanic/Latino; 22% Black or African American, non-Hispanic/Latino; 6% Asian, non-Hispanic/Latino; 0.2% Native Hawaiian or other Pacific Islander, non-Hispanic/Latino; 4% international. 30% 25 or older, 3% transferred in. Retention: 71% of full-time freshmen returned the following year. Core. Calendar: semesters. Academic remediation for entering students, ESL program, services for LD students, advanced placement, accelerated degree program, self-designed majors, independent study, distance learning, double major, summer session for credit, part-time degree program, external degree program, adult/continuing education programs, co-op programs and internships. ROTC: Army (c), Air Force (c).

Entrance Requirements: Open admission. Options: electronic application, deferred admission. Required: high school transcript. Recommended: interview. Entrance: noncompetitive. Application deadline: rolling. Notification: continuous. Preference given to county residents.

Costs Per Year: Application fee: $0. Area resident tuition: $3294 full-time, $137.25 per credit hour part-time. State resident tuition: $4482 full-time, $186.75 per credit hour part-time. Nonresident tuition: $6726 full-time, $280.25 per credit hour part-time. Mandatory fees: $912 full-time, $38 per credit hour part-time. Full-time tuition and fees vary according to program and reciprocity agreements. Part-time tuition and fees vary according to program and reciprocity agreements.

Collegiate Environment: Orientation program. Drama-theater group, choral group, student-run newspaper, radio station. Social organizations: 38 open to all. Most popular organizations: Student Government Association, Student Radio Station, African-American Student Organization, Student Activities Board, Phi Theta Kappa. Major annual events: NJCAA National Soccer Tournament, Club Day, Spring Day. Student services: personal-psychological counseling. Campus security: 24-hour emergency response devices and patrols. Mercer County Community College Library plus 1 other. Operations spending for the previous fiscal year: $555,239.

Community Environment: See Rider University.

■ **MIDDLESEX COUNTY COLLEGE**

2600 Woodbridge Ave.

Edison, NJ 08818-3050

Tel: (732)548-6000

Web Site: www.middlesexcc.edu

Description: County-supported, 2-year, coed. Awards certificates, transfer associate, and terminal associate degrees. Founded 1964. Setting: 200-acre suburban campus with easy access to New York City. Total enrollment: 11,673. Student-undergrad faculty ratio is 24:1. 0.4% American Indian or Alaska Native, non-Hispanic/Latino; 30% Hispanic/Latino; 11% Black or African American, non-Hispanic/Latino; 14% Asian, non-Hispanic/Latino; 0.5% Native Hawaiian or other Pacific Islander, non-Hispanic/Latino; 2% international. Retention: 62% of full-time freshmen returned the following year. Core. Calendar: semesters. Academic remediation for entering students, ESL program, services for LD students, advanced placement, independent study, distance learning, summer session for credit, part-time degree program, adult/continuing education programs, co-op programs and internships. Off campus study. Study abroad program. ROTC: Army (c).

Entrance Requirements: Open admission except for dental hygiene, nursing, radiography, medical laboratory technology, psychosocial rehabilitation, respiratory care and automotive technology programs. Options: early admission, deferred admission. Required: high school transcript. Entrance: noncompetitive. Application deadline: rolling. Notification: continuous. Preference given to county residents.

Collegiate Environment: Orientation program. Drama-theater group, choral group, student-run newspaper, radio station. Student services: health clinic, personal-psychological counseling. Campus security: 24-hour emergency response devices and patrols. Middlesex County College Library plus 1 other.

Community Environment: Edison (population, 97,687) is located in a major metropolitan area, and is both a residential and industrial city with train and bus service available. It is located 45 minutes from New York City. Community facilities include a library, churches of all denominations, several hospitals, museums and various civic and service organizations. Edison offers fine shopping facilities. Part-time jobs are available. Parks and the Raritan River provide for boating and swimming, etc.

■ **MONMOUTH UNIVERSITY**
400 Cedar Ave.
West Long Branch, NJ 07764-1898
Tel: (732)571-3400; Free: 800-543-9671
Fax: (732)263-5166
E-mail: admission@monmouth.edu
Web Site: www.monmouth.edu

Description: Independent, comprehensive, coed. Awards bachelor's, master's, and doctoral degrees and post-master's certificates. Founded 1933. Setting: 159-acre suburban campus with easy access to New York City, Philadelphia. Endowment: $77.8 million. Research spending for the previous fiscal year: $2.2 million. Educational spending for the previous fiscal year: $9673 per student. Total enrollment: 6,371. Faculty: 646 (284 full-time, 362 part-time). Student-undergrad faculty ratio is 13:1. 9,097 applied, 77% were admitted. 14% from top 10% of their high school class, 41% from top quarter, 75% from top half. Full-time: 4,490 students, 57% women, 43% men. Part-time: 217 students, 49% women, 51% men. Students come from 27 states and territories, 24 other countries, 21% from out-of-state. 0.1% American Indian or Alaska Native, non-Hispanic/Latino; 12% Hispanic/Latino; 5% Black or African American, non-Hispanic/Latino; 3% Asian, non-Hispanic/Latino; 0.7% international. 2% 25 or older, 41% live on campus, 5% transferred in. Retention: 79% of full-time freshmen returned the following year. Academic areas with the most degrees conferred: business/marketing; communication/journalism; education. Core. Calendar: semesters. Academic remediation for entering students, services for LD students, advanced placement, accelerated degree program, self-designed majors, honors program, independent study, distance learning, double major, summer session for credit, part-time degree program, co-op programs and internships, graduate courses open to undergrads. Off campus study. Study abroad program. ROTC: Army (c), Air Force (c).

Entrance Requirements: Options: electronic application, early action, deferred admission, international baccalaureate accepted. Required: essay, high school transcript, 1 recommendation, SAT or ACT. Recommended: resume of activities including community involvement and leadership positions. Required for some: interview. Entrance: moderately difficult. Application deadlines: 3/1, 12/1 for early action. Notification: 4/1, 1/15 for early action. SAT Reasoning Test deadline: 3/1. Transfer credits accepted: Yes. Early action applicants: 3,491. Early action applicants admitted: 3,258.

Costs Per Year: Application fee: $50. One-time mandatory fee: $200. Tuition: $37,438 full-time, $1084 per credit hour part-time. Mandatory fees: $700 full-time, $175 per term part-time. Part-time tuition and fees vary according to course load.

Collegiate Environment: Orientation program. Drama-theater group, choral group, student-run newspaper, radio station. Social organizations: 104 open to all; national fraternities, national sororities; 16% of eligible men and 15% of eligible women are members. Most popular organizations: Veterans Student Association, Student Government Association, Economics and Finance Club, Pre-Law Club, Colleges Against Cancer. Major annual events: Homecoming, The Big Event, Spring Fest. Student services: legal services, health clinic, personal-psychological counseling, women's center. Campus security: 24-hour emergency response devices and patrols, late night transport-escort service, controlled dormitory access. Monmouth University Library. Books: 275,000 (physical), 40,416 (digital/electronic); Serial titles: 1,622 (physical), 73,909 (digital/electronic); Databases: 189. Weekly public service hours: 111; students can reserve study rooms. Operations spending for the previous fiscal year: $894,658. 1,000 computers available on campus for general student use. Computer purchase/lease plans available. A campuswide network can be accessed from student residence rooms and from off campus. Students can access the following: online class registration. Staffed computer lab on campus provides training in use of computers, software, and the Internet.

Community Environment: The university is located in West Long Branch, a suburban community of 7,700 people. The campus is located just one mile from the Atlantic Ocean. Both New York and Philadelphia are about a one and a half hour trip away. Newark airport is 45 miles distant. Train and bus service are available 2 miles from campus.

■ **MONTCLAIR STATE UNIVERSITY**
1 Normal Ave.
Montclair, NJ 07043-1624
Tel: (973)655-4000
Fax: (973)893-5455
E-mail: undergraduate.admissions@montclair.edu
Web Site: www.montclair.edu

Description: State-supported, university, coed. Awards bachelor's, master's, and doctoral degrees. Founded 1908. Setting: 250-acre suburban campus with easy access to New York City. Total enrollment: 21,115. Faculty: 1,855 (636 full-time, 1,219 part-time). Student-undergrad faculty ratio is 17:1. 14,324 applied, 71% were admitted. 11% from top 10% of their high school class, 34% from top quarter, 75% from top half. Full-time: 15,133 students, 62% women, 38% men. Part-time: 1,855 students, 56% women, 44% men. Students come from 41 states and territories, 69 other countries, 3% from out-of-state. 0.1% American Indian or Alaska Native, non-Hispanic/Latino; 29% Hispanic/Latino; 13% Black or African American, non-Hispanic/Latino; 6% Asian, non-Hispanic/Latino; 0.2% Native Hawaiian or other Pacific Islander, non-Hispanic/Latino; 2% international. 11% 25 or older, 30% live on campus, 10% transferred in. Retention: 80% of full-time freshmen returned the following year. Academic areas with the most degrees conferred: business/marketing; psychology; family and consumer sciences. Core. Calendar: semesters. Academic remediation for entering students, ESL program, services for LD students, advanced placement, accelerated degree program, freshman honors college, honors program, independent study, double major, summer session for credit, part-time degree program, adult/continuing education programs, co-op programs and internships, graduate courses open to undergrads. Off campus study at New Jersey School of Conservation, New Jersey Marine Science Consortium. Study abroad program.

Entrance Requirements: Options: electronic application, deferred admission, international baccalaureate accepted. Required: essay, high school transcript. Required for some: interview. Entrance: moderately difficult. Notification: continuous. Transfer credits accepted: Yes. Applicants placed on waiting list: 507. Wait-listed applicants offered admission: 284.

Costs Per Year: Application fee: $65. State resident tuition: $11,132 full-time, $371 per credit part-time. Nonresident tuition: $18,920 full-time, $631 per credit part-time. Mandatory fees: $1658 full-time, $55 per credit part-time. College room and board: $15,564. Room and board charges vary according to board plan and housing facility.

Collegiate Environment: Orientation program. Drama-theater group, choral group, student-run newspaper, radio station. Social organizations: 160 open to all; national fraternities, national sororities, local fraternities, local sororities. Most popular organizations: Latin American Student Organization, Campus Recreation, MSU Players, Unified Asian American Student Organization, SLAM (Student Life At Montclair). Major annual events: Homecoming, Montclairfest/M-Glow, World's Fair. Student services: health clinic, personal-psychological counseling, women's center. Campus security: 24-hour emergency response devices and patrols, late night transport-escort service, controlled dormitory access, video surveillance, student escorts. 5,195 college housing spaces available; 5,061 were occupied in 2018-19. Freshmen guaranteed college housing. Option: coed housing available. Sprague Library. Books: 432,414 (physical), 157,098 (digital/electronic); Serial titles: 9,510 (physical), 62,084 (digital/electronic); Databases: 238. Weekly public service hours: 93; students can reserve study rooms. 800 computers available on campus for general student use. Computer purchase/lease plans available. A campuswide network can be accessed from student residence rooms and from off campus. Students can access the following: online class registration, online storage, online course delivery, online computing lab, student online portal. Staffed computer lab on campus provides training in use of computers, software, and the Internet.

Community Environment: Population about 37,700, the township of Montclair is a residential suburb about 14 miles west of New York City and about six miles northwest of Newark. Residents can commute to Manhattan by bus or railroad. An art museum, theater groups, music societies, and a library are provided by the community as well as two hospitals, several shopping areas and numerous active civic and social organizations.

■ **NEW JERSEY CITY UNIVERSITY**
2039 Kennedy Blvd.
Jersey City, NJ 07305-1597

Tel: (201)200-2000; Free: 888-441-NJCU
Fax: (201)200-2044
E-mail: admissions@nicu.edu
Web Site: www.njcu.edu

Description: State-supported, comprehensive, coed. Awards bachelor's, master's, and doctoral degrees and post-master's certificates. Founded 1927. Setting: 51-acre urban campus with easy access to New York City. Total enrollment: 7,991. Faculty: 808 (254 full-time, 554 part-time). Student-undergrad faculty ratio is 15:1. 4,315 applied, 96% were admitted. 9% from top 10% of their high school class, 25% from top quarter, 57% from top half. Full-time: 5,091 students, 58% women, 42% men. Part-time: 1,146 students, 63% women, 37% men. 1% from out-of-state. 0.4% American Indian or Alaska Native, non-Hispanic/Latino; 40% Hispanic/Latino; 23% Black or African American, non-Hispanic/Latino; 8% Asian, non-Hispanic/Latino; 0.5% Native Hawaiian or other Pacific Islander, non-Hispanic/Latino; 1% international. 30% 25 or older, 9% live on campus, 12% transferred in. Retention: 73% of full-time freshmen returned the following year. Academic areas with the most degrees conferred: health professions and related sciences; business/marketing; homeland security, law enforcement, firefighting, and protective services. Core. Calendar: semesters. Academic remediation for entering students, ESL program, services for LD students, advanced placement, accelerated degree program, honors program, independent study, distance learning, double major, summer session for credit, part-time degree program, adult/continuing education programs, co-op programs and internships, graduate courses open to undergrads. Off campus study. Study abroad program. ROTC: Army (c), Naval (c).

Entrance Requirements: Options: electronic application, deferred admission. Required: essay, high school transcript, minimum 2.75 high school GPA. Recommended: 1 recommendation, SAT. Required for some: interview. Entrance: moderately difficult. Notification: continuous. SAT Reasoning Test deadline: 7/31. Transfer credits accepted: Yes.

Costs Per Year: Application fee: $50. State resident tuition: $8518 full-time, $284 per credit hour part-time. Nonresident tuition: $17,932 full-time, $600 per credit hour part-time. Mandatory fees: $3482 full-time, $115 per credit hour part-time. Part-time tuition and fees vary according to course load. College room and board: $12,072. Room and board charges vary according to board plan and housing facility.

Collegiate Environment: Orientation program. Drama-theater group, choral group, student-run newspaper, radio station. Social organizations: national fraternities, national sororities, local fraternities, local sororities. Student services: legal services, health clinic, personal-psychological counseling, women's center. Campus security: 24-hour emergency response devices and patrols, late night transport-escort service. 650 college housing spaces available; 600 were occupied in 2018-19. No special consideration for freshman housing applicants. Option: coed housing available. Congressman Frank J. Guarini Library. Books: 300,000 (physical), 150,000 (digital/electronic); Serial titles: 150 (physical), 32,000 (digital/electronic); Databases: 152. Weekly public service hours: 82.

Community Environment: Jersey City, the second largest in the state with a population of 239,614, is just across the Hudson River (via the Holland Tunnel or PATH trains) from New York City. A manufacturing center, Jersey City is home to roughly 600 industrial plants. It is a major shipping port and the terminus for some of the nation's largest railroads and transcontinental motor freight lines. Transportation is convenient for all the entertainment, recreational, cultural, and historical offerings to be had in either New Jersey or throughout the tri-state area.

■ NEW JERSEY INSTITUTE OF TECHNOLOGY

University Heights
Newark, NJ 07102
Tel: (973)596-3000; Free: 800-925-NJIT
Fax: (973)802-1854
E-mail: admissions@njit.edu
Web Site: www.njit.edu

Description: State-supported, university, coed. Part of State of New Jersey Department of Education. Awards bachelor's, master's, and doctoral degrees. Founded 1881. Setting: 48-acre urban campus with easy access to New York City. Endowment: $113.6 million. Research spending for the previous fiscal year: $98.2 million. Educational spending for the previous fiscal year: $15,250 per student. Total enrollment: 11,423. Faculty: 785 (441 full-time, 344 part-time). Student-undergrad faculty ratio is 17:1. 8,123 applied, 64% were admitted. 34% from top 10% of their high school class, 62% from top quarter, 90% from top half. Full-time: 6,827 students, 24% women, 76% men. Part-time: 1,705 students, 30% women, 70% men. Students come from 23 states and territories, 64 other countries, 3% from out-of-state. 0.1% American Indian or Alaska Native, non-Hispanic/Latino; 22% Hispanic/Latino; 8% Black or African American, non-Hispanic/Latino; 22% Asian, non-Hispanic/Latino; 5% international. 15% 25 or older, 24% live on campus, 10% transferred in. Retention: 88% of full-time freshmen returned the following year. Academic areas with the most degrees conferred: engineering; computer and information sciences; engineering technologies. Core. Calendar: semesters. Academic remediation for entering students, ESL program, services for LD students, advanced placement, accelerated degree program, freshman honors college, honors program, independent study, distance learning, double major, summer session for credit, part-time degree program, adult/continuing education programs, co-op programs and internships, graduate courses open to undergrads. Off campus study at Essex County College; Rutgers, The State University of New Jersey; Camden County College. Study abroad program. ROTC: Army (c), Air Force.

Entrance Requirements: Options: electronic application, early admission, deferred admission, international baccalaureate accepted. Required: high school transcript, 1 recommendation, SAT or ACT. Required for some: essay, interview. Entrance: moderately difficult. Notification: continuous. Preference given to state residents. Transfer credits accepted: Yes.

Costs Per Year: Application fee: $75. State resident tuition: $14,174 full-time, $539 per credit part-time. Nonresident tuition: $29,586 full-time, $1265 per credit part-time. Mandatory fees: $3164 full-time, $186 per credit part-time. College room and board: $13,600.

Collegiate Environment: Orientation program. Drama-theater group, student-run newspaper, radio station. Social organizations: 85 open to all; national fraternities, national sororities, local fraternities, local sororities; 5% of eligible men and 3% of eligible women are members. Most popular organizations: Student Senate, Student Activities Council, Vector, Institute of Industrial Engineers, WJTB Geek Radio. Major annual events: Highlander's Homecoming, Renaissance Fair, NJIT L.E.A.D.S. Conference. Student services: health clinic, personal-psychological counseling, women's center. Campus security: 24-hour emergency response devices and patrols, student patrols, late night transport-escort service, controlled dormitory access. 2,000 college housing spaces available; 1,950 were occupied in 2018-19. No special consideration for freshman housing applicants. Option: coed housing available. Van Houten Library plus 1 other. Books: 138,456 (physical), 185,262 (digital/electronic); Serial titles: 50 (physical), 185,301 (digital/electronic); Databases: 35. Weekly public service hours: 111; students can reserve study rooms. Operations spending for the previous fiscal year: $1.8 million. 1,938 computers available on campus for general student use. Computer purchase/lease plans available. A campuswide network can be accessed from student residence rooms and from off campus. Students can access the following: online class registration. Staffed computer lab on campus provides training in use of computers, software, and the Internet.

Community Environment: Newark is the largest metropolis of New Jersey and contains some of the state's greatest cultural institutions: the Newark Museum, the Newark Public Library, and Symphony Hall. Construction has begun on the 12.5 acre New Jersey Center for the Performing Arts. Part-time employment opportunities are good.

■ OCEAN COUNTY COLLEGE

College Dr.
Toms River, NJ 08754-2001
Tel: (732)255-0400
E-mail: shartigan@ocean.edu
Web Site: www.ocean.edu

Description: County-supported, 2-year, coed. Awards certificates, diplomas, transfer associate, and terminal associate degrees. Founded 1964. Setting: 275-acre suburban campus with easy access to Philadelphia. Educational spending for the previous fiscal year: $2561 per student. Total enrollment: 8,663. Faculty: 490 (99 full-time, 391 part-time). Student-undergrad faculty ratio is 25:1. 1,842 applied, 100% were admitted. Full-time: 4,611 students, 51% women, 49% men. Part-time: 4,052 students, 62% women, 38% men. Students come from 36 states and territories, 1% from out-of-state. 0.3% American Indian or Alaska Native, non-Hispanic/Latino; 11% Hispanic/Latino; 5% Black or African American, non-Hispanic/Latino; 2% Asian, non-Hispanic/Latino; 0.2% Native Hawaiian or other Pacific Islander, non-Hispanic/Latino; 1% international. 21% 25 or older, 4% transferred in. Retention: 69% of full-time freshmen returned the following year. Core. Calendar: semesters. Academic remediation for entering students, ESL program, services for LD students, advanced placement, accelerated degree program, honors program, distance learning, summer session for credit, part-time degree program, adult/continuing education programs, co-op programs and internships. Study abroad program.

Entrance Requirements: Open admission except for nursing program. Option: electronic application. Required for some: high school transcript, ACCUPLACER or waiver for degree-seeking students. Entrance: noncompetitive. Application deadline: rolling. Notification: continuous. Preference given to county residents for nursing program. Transfer credits accepted: Yes.

Costs Per Year: Application fee: $0. Area resident tuition: $3570 full-time, $119 per credit part-time. State resident tuition: $4110 full-time, $137 per credit part-time. Nonresident tuition: $6750 full-time, $225 per credit part-time. Mandatory fees: $945 full-time, $31.50 per credit part-time. Full-time tuition and fees vary according to program. Part-time tuition and fees vary according to program.

Collegiate Environment: Orientation program. Drama-theater group, choral group, student-run newspaper, radio station. Social organizations: 63 open to all; academic, cultural, community service clubs. Most popular organizations: Student Activities Board, Student Government, OCC Vikings Cheerleaders, NJ STARS Club, Speech and Theater Club. Major annual events: Spring Dinner Dance, Welcome Back Picnic, Spring Day. Student services: personal-psychological counseling. Campus security: 24-hour emergency response devices and patrols, late night transport-escort service, security cameras in hallways and parking lots. Ocean County College Library. Books: 69,761 (physical), 170,000 (digital/electronic); Serial titles: 290 (physical); Databases: 42. Weekly public service hours: 68; students can reserve study rooms. Operations spending for the previous fiscal year: $1.1 million. 210 computers available on campus for general student use. Computer purchase/lease plans available. A campuswide network can be accessed from off-campus. Students can access the following: online class registration. Staffed computer lab on campus provides training in use of computers, software, and the Internet.

Community Environment: A principality in Dover Township, Toms River is the business, vacation, financial, and industrial hub of Ocean County. The city is located four miles inland from the New Jersey shoreline where buses and trains are convenient. An airport is within 20 miles. Community facilities include churches of the major denominations, hospitals, libraries, and civic and service organizations. Recreational activities offered are swimming, picnicking, hiking, camping and canoeing. Some part-time work is available.

■ **PASSAIC COUNTY COMMUNITY COLLEGE**
One College Blvd.
Paterson, NJ 07505-1179
Tel: (973)684-6800
Web Site: www.pccc.cc.nj.us
Description: County-supported, 2-year, coed. Awards certificates, transfer associate, and terminal associate degrees. Founded 1968. Setting: 6-acre urban campus with easy access to New York City. Endowment: $78,695. Research spending for the previous fiscal year: $97,474. Educational spending for the previous fiscal year: $3777 per student. Total enrollment: 6,308. Faculty: 357 (78 full-time, 279 part-time). 2,076 applied, 100% were admitted. 1% from out-of-state. 41% 25 or older. Core. Calendar: semesters. Academic remediation for entering students, ESL program, advanced placement, honors program, independent study, distance learning, double major, summer session for credit, part-time degree program, co-op programs and internships. Study abroad program. ROTC: Army (c).

Entrance Requirements: Open admission except for nursing, respiratory therapy, radiological technology programs. Options: early admission, deferred admission. Entrance: noncompetitive. Application deadline: rolling. Preference given to county residents.

Collegiate Environment: Choral group, student-run newspaper. Most popular organizations: Latin American Club, Christian Club, International Club, Soccer Club, Volleyball Club. Student services: personal-psychological counseling. Campus security: late night transport-escort service. Passaic County Community College Learning Resource Center plus 1 other. Operations spending for the previous fiscal year: $482,542. 150 computers available on campus for general student use. Staffed computer lab on campus.

Community Environment: See Bergen Community College.

■ **PILLAR COLLEGE**
60 Park Pl., Ste. 701
Newark, NJ 07102
Tel: (973)803-5000; Free: 800-234-9305
E-mail: info@pillar.edu
Web Site: www.pillar.edu
Description: Independent Pillar of Fire International, comprehensive, coed. Awards associate and bachelor's degrees. Founded 1908. Setting: rural

campus with easy access to New York City. Total enrollment: 240. Faculty: 8. Student-undergrad faculty ratio is 15:1. 126 applied, 48% were admitted. Full-time: 174 students, 55% women, 45% men. Part-time: 66 students, 62% women, 38% men. Students come from 3 states and territories. 75% 25 or older, 12% transferred in. Retention: 70% of full-time freshmen returned the following year. Core. Calendar: semesters plus 'FastTrack' semesters. Academic remediation for entering students, services for LD students, advanced placement, accelerated degree program, distance learning, double major, summer session for credit, part-time degree program, adult/continuing education programs, co-op programs and internships.

Entrance Requirements: Options: electronic application, deferred admission, international baccalaureate accepted. Required: essay. Required for some: high school transcript, minimum 2.5 high school GPA, interview, SAT or ACT. Entrance: minimally difficult. Application deadline: rolling. Notification: continuous. Transfer credits accepted: Yes.

Collegiate Environment: Orientation program. Social organizations: 3 open to all. Most popular organizations: Student Government Association, FYI (For Your Inspiration art club), LYF (Life Your Faith Community Service). Major annual events: Chapels, Convocation, Picnics. Student services: health clinic, personal-psychological counseling. Arthur K. White Library. 20 computers available on campus for general student use. A campuswide network can be accessed. Students can access the following: online class registration. Staffed computer lab on campus provides training in use of computers, software, and the Internet.

■ **PRINCETON UNIVERSITY**
Princeton, NJ 08544-1019
Tel: (609)258-3000
Web Site: www.princeton.edu
Description: Independent, university, coed. Awards bachelor's, master's, and doctoral degrees. Founded 1746. Setting: 600-acre suburban campus with easy access to New York City, Philadelphia. Total enrollment: 8,374. Faculty: 1,166 (985 full-time, 181 part-time). Student-undergrad faculty ratio is 5:1. 35,370 applied, 5% were admitted. Full-time: 5,321 students, 49% women, 51% men. Part-time: 107 students, 47% women, 53% men. Students come from 53 states and territories, 97 other countries, 82% from out-of-state. 0.2% American Indian or Alaska Native, non-Hispanic/Latino; 10% Hispanic/Latino; 8% Black or African American, non-Hispanic/Latino; 21% Asian, non-Hispanic/Latino; 0.1% Native Hawaiian or other Pacific Islander, non-Hispanic/Latino; 12% international. 0.3% 25 or older, 96% live on campus, 1% transferred in. Retention: 98% of full-time freshmen returned the following year. Academic areas with the most degrees conferred: social sciences; engineering; computer and information sciences. Core. Calendar: semesters. Services for LD students, advanced placement, self-designed majors, independent study, graduate courses open to undergrads. Off campus study at Rutgers, The State University of New Jersey, Westminster Choir College of Rider University, Princeton Theological Seminary. Study abroad program. ROTC: Army, Naval (c), Air Force (c).

Entrance Requirements: Options: electronic application, early action, deferred admission, international baccalaureate accepted. Required: high school transcript, 3 recommendations, graded written paper, SAT or ACT. Recommended: interview, SAT Subject Tests. Entrance: most difficult. Application deadline: 1/1. Notification: 4/1, 4/1 for nonresidents. SAT Reasoning Test deadline: 1/1. SAT Subject Test deadline: 1/1. Transfer credits accepted: Yes. Applicants placed on waiting list: 1,125. Wait-listed applicants offered admission: 0.

Costs Per Year: Application fee: $75. Comprehensive fee: $66,700 includes full-time tuition ($49,450), mandatory fees ($890), and college room and board ($16,360). College room only: $9520. Part-time tuition: $6166 per year. Part-time mandatory fees: $25 per term.

Collegiate Environment: Orientation program. Drama-theater group, choral group, marching band, student-run newspaper, radio station. Social organizations: 250 open to all; Eating clubs. Student services: legal services, health clinic, personal-psychological counseling, women's center. Campus security: 24-hour emergency response devices and patrols, student patrols, late night transport-escort service, controlled dormitory access. 5,113 college housing spaces available; 5,020 were occupied in 2018-19. Freshmen guaranteed college housing. On-campus residence required through sophomore year. Options: coed, men-only, women-only housing available. Harvey S. Firestone Memorial Library plus 9 others. Books: 7.3 million (physical), 2.1 million (digital/electronic); Serial titles: 159,820 (physical), 291,025 (digital/electronic); Databases: 1,899. Weekly public service hours: 105. 500 computers available on campus for general student use. Computer purchase/lease plans available. A campuswide network can be accessed from student residence rooms and from off campus. Students can access the following: online class registration, academic applications and courseware, printing, network file space, website hosting, media lab, broadcast center. Staffed computer lab on campus (open 24 hours a day) provides training in use of computers, software, and the Internet.

Community Environment: Numerous historical events have taken place at Princeton since the time of its founding in 1746. The first state legislature met here in 1776, as well as in 1873; the Continental Congress Sessions were held here. Princeton is 50 miles southwest of New York City and 45 miles northeast of Philadelphia. All forms of commercial transportation are available. Community facilities are excellent, housing is available for students. The James Forrestal Campus which adjoins Princeton University's campus is an integral part of the University's advanced training and research in the basic and engineering sciences. The largest single project at Forrestal is the Plasma Physics Laboratory, a long range effort to develop a controlled thermonuclear reactor which would provide an infinite energy source. Many of the facilities of the Department of Aerospace and Mechanical Sciences for the Aerospace Propulsion Sciences and the Gas Dynamics Laboratories are here. Rockingham, five miles north is also known as the Berrien Mansion which was used as General Washington's headquarters during 1783. His "Farewell Address to the Armies" was delivered here.

■ **RABBI JACOB JOSEPH SCHOOL**
One Plainfield Ave.
Edison, NJ 08817
Tel: (732)985-6533
Description: Independent Jewish, 4-year, men only. Awards bachelor's degrees. Total enrollment: 41. 17 applied, 100% were admitted.
Entrance Requirements: Recommended: high school transcript.

■ **RABBINICAL COLLEGE OF AMERICA**
226 Sussex Ave.
Morristown, NJ 07962-1996
Tel: (973)267-9404
Fax: (973)267-5208
Web Site: www.rca.edu
Description: Independent Jewish, 4-year, men only. Awards bachelor's degrees. Founded 1956. Setting: 81-acre small town campus with easy access to New York City. Total enrollment: 259. Faculty: 16 (all full-time). Student-undergrad faculty ratio is 12:1. 60 applied, 100% were admitted. Students come from 24 states and territories, 10 other countries. Core. Calendar: semesters. Academic remediation for entering students, accelerated degree program, summer session for credit, internships. Off campus study at Yeshivah Gedolah of New England, Yeshivah Gedolah of Miami. Study abroad program.
Entrance Requirements: Required: interview. Entrance: minimally difficult. Application deadline: rolling.
Collegiate Environment: Student services: health clinic, personal-psychological counseling.

■ **RAMAPO COLLEGE OF NEW JERSEY**
505 Ramapo Valley Rd.
Mahwah, NJ 07430-1680
Tel: (201)684-7500; Free: 800-9RAMAPO
Fax: (201)684-7508
E-mail: admissions@ramapo.edu
Web Site: www.ramapo.edu
Description: State-supported, comprehensive, coed. Part of New Jersey State College System. Awards bachelor's and master's degrees and post-master's certificates. Founded 1969. Setting: 300-acre suburban campus with easy access to New York City. Total enrollment: 6,120. Faculty: 491 (216 full-time, 275 part-time). Student-undergrad faculty ratio is 18:1. 6,695 applied, 57% were admitted. 16% from top 10% of their high school class, 41% from top quarter, 79% from top half. Full-time: 4,910 students, 54% women, 46% men. Part-time: 708 students, 63% women, 37% men. 6% from out-of-state. 0.5% American Indian or Alaska Native, non-Hispanic/Latino; 16% Hispanic/Latino; 5% Black or African American, non-Hispanic/Latino; 8% Asian, non-Hispanic/Latino; 0.1% Native Hawaiian or other Pacific Islander, non-Hispanic/Latino; 2% international. 11% 25 or older, 46% live on campus, 9% transferred in. Retention: 86% of full-time freshmen returned the following year. Academic areas with the most degrees conferred: business/marketing; psychology; communication/journalism. Core. Calendar: semesters. Academic remediation for entering students, services for LD students, advanced placement, accelerated degree program,

self-designed majors, freshman honors college, honors program, independent study, distance learning, double major, summer session for credit, part-time degree program, external degree program, adult/continuing education programs, co-op programs and internships, graduate courses open to undergrads. Off campus study at New Jersey Institute of Technology; SUNY State College of Optometry; University of Medical and Dentistry of NJ; NY Chiropractic College. Study abroad program. ROTC: Army (c), Air Force (c).
Entrance Requirements: Options: electronic application, early admission, early decision, deferred admission. Required: essay, high school transcript, SAT or ACT. Recommended: minimum 3 high school GPA. Entrance: moderately difficult. SAT Reasoning Test deadline: 3/1. Applicants placed on waiting list: 881. Wait-listed applicants offered admission: 224. Early decision applicants: 196. Early decision applicants admitted: 140.
Costs Per Year: Application fee: $65. State resident tuition: $11,902 full-time, $371.95 per credit part-time. Nonresident tuition: $21,243 full-time, $663.85 per credit part-time. Mandatory fees: $2472 full-time, $77.25 per credit part-time. Full-time tuition and fees vary according to reciprocity agreements. Part-time tuition and fees vary according to reciprocity agreements. College room and board: $12,450. College room only: $8650. Room and board charges vary according to board plan and housing facility.
Collegiate Environment: Orientation program. Drama-theater group, choral group, student-run newspaper, radio station. Social organizations: 112 open to all; national fraternities, national sororities. Most popular organizations: NORML, 1 Step, Biology & Biochemistry Club, Campus Crusade for Christ, Culture Club. Major annual events: Relay For Life, major concerts, Octoberfest and LollanoBooza. Student services: health clinic, personal-psychological counseling, women's center. Campus security: 24-hour emergency response devices and patrols, late night transport-escort service, controlled dormitory access, surveillance cameras, patrols by trained security personnel. George T. Potter Library.
Community Environment: Mahwah, population 24,600, is a suburban community near the foothills of the Ramapo Mountains on the New York-New Jersey border. Darlington County Park offers two lakes for swimming and a third for boating. Sports facilities, skiing, nature trails and picnic areas exist at nearby Campgaw Mountain.

■ **RARITAN VALLEY COMMUNITY COLLEGE**
118 Lamington Rd.
Branchburg, NJ 08876
Tel: (908)526-1200
Fax: (908)704-3442
E-mail: jwheeler@raritanval.edu
Web Site: www.raritanval.edu
Description: State and locally supported, 2-year, coed. Awards certificates, transfer associate, and terminal associate degrees. Founded 1965. Setting: 240-acre suburban campus with easy access to New York City, Philadelphia. Endowment: $139,462. Research spending for the previous fiscal year: $889,267. Educational spending for the previous fiscal year: $4076 per student. Total enrollment: 7,887. Faculty: 497 (126 full-time, 371 part-time). Student-undergrad faculty ratio is 20:1. 2,306 applied, 100% were admitted. Full-time: 3,089 students, 45% women, 55% men. Part-time: 4,798 students, 52% women, 48% men. Students come from 12 states and territories, 1% from out-of-state. 0.2% American Indian or Alaska Native, non-Hispanic/Latino; 24% Hispanic/Latino; 12% Black or African American, non-Hispanic/Latino; 5% Asian, non-Hispanic/Latino; 0.3% Native Hawaiian or other Pacific Islander, non-Hispanic/Latino; 2% international. 26% 25 or older, 5% transferred in. Retention: 69% of full-time freshmen returned the following year. Core. Calendar: semesters. Academic remediation for entering students, ESL program, services for LD students, advanced placement, freshman honors college, honors program, independent study, distance learning, double major, summer session for credit, part-time degree program, adult/continuing education programs, co-op programs and internships. Off campus study. ROTC: Army (c), Air Force (c).
Entrance Requirements: Open admission. Option: electronic application. Application deadline: rolling. Notification: continuous, continuous for nonresidents. Transfer credits accepted: Yes.
Costs Per Year: Application fee: $25. Area resident tuition: $4860 full-time, $162 per credit hour part-time. State resident tuition: $6360 full-time, $212 per credit hour part-time. Nonresident tuition: $6360 full-time, $212 per credit hour part-time. Mandatory fees: $1126 full-time, $27 per credit hour part-time, $113 per term part-time.
Collegiate Environment: Orientation program. Drama-theater group, choral group, student-run newspaper, radio station. Social organizations: 48 open to all. Most popular organizations: Phi Theta Kappa, Rotaract, Enactus,

Health Oriented Peer Educators (HOPE), Orgullo Latino (OLC). Major annual events: Fall Picnic, Spring Picnic, Student Awards Banquet. Student services: personal-psychological counseling. Campus security: 24-hour emergency response devices and patrols, late night transport-escort service. College housing not available. Evelyn S. Field Library. Books: 64,100 (physical), 130,487 (digital/electronic); Serial titles: 109 (physical), 58,888 (digital/electronic); Databases: 73. Operations spending for the previous fiscal year: $1.2 million.

Community Environment: Somerville is the county seat for Somerset County. It is a suburban community located ten miles west of Plainfield and ten miles northwest of New Brunswick.

■ RIDER UNIVERSITY

2083 Lawrenceville Rd.
Lawrenceville, NJ 08648-3001
Tel: (609)896-5000; Free: 800-257-9026
Fax: (609)895-6645
Web Site: www.rider.edu

Description: Independent, comprehensive, coed. Awards associate, bachelor's, master's, and doctoral degrees and post-master's certificates. Founded 1865. Setting: 280-acre suburban campus with easy access to New York City, Philadelphia. Endowment: $64.3 million. Research spending for the previous fiscal year: $1.4 million. Educational spending for the previous fiscal year: $13,149 per student. Total enrollment: 4,825. Faculty: 595 (234 full-time, 361 part-time). Student-undergrad faculty ratio is 11:1. 9,429 applied, 70% were admitted. 15% from top 10% of their high school class, 38% from top quarter, 71% from top half. Full-time: 3,534 students, 58% women, 42% men. Part-time: 364 students, 55% women, 45% men. Students come from 42 states and territories, 64 other countries, 25% from out-of-state. 0.2% American Indian or Alaska Native, non-Hispanic/Latino; 16% Hispanic/Latino; 13% Black or African American, non-Hispanic/Latino; 5% Asian, non-Hispanic/Latino; 3% international. 7% 25 or older, 53% live on campus, 5% transferred in. Retention: 78% of full-time freshmen returned the following year. Academic areas with the most degrees conferred: business/marketing; visual and performing arts; education. Core. Calendar: semesters. Academic remediation for entering students, ESL program, services for LD students, advanced placement, honors program, independent study, distance learning, double major, summer session for credit, part-time degree program, adult/continuing education programs, co-op programs and internships, graduate courses open to undergrads. Study abroad program. ROTC: Army (c).

Entrance Requirements: Options: electronic application, early admission, early action, deferred admission, international baccalaureate accepted. Required: essay, high school transcript, 1 recommendation. Required for some: interview. Entrance: moderately difficult. Application deadlines: rolling, 11/15 for early action. Notification: continuous, 12/15 for early action. Transfer credits accepted: Yes. Applicants placed on waiting list: 53. Waitlisted applicants offered admission: 41.

Costs Per Year: Application fee: $50. Comprehensive fee: $58,140 includes full-time tuition ($42,120), mandatory fees ($740), and college room and board ($15,280). College room only: $10,020.

Collegiate Environment: Orientation program. Drama-theater group, choral group, student-run newspaper, radio station. Social organizations: 126 open to all; national fraternities, national sororities; 5% of eligible men and 11% of eligible women are members. Most popular organizations: Student Government Association, Greek Council, Association of Commuter Students, Black Student Union, Residence Hall Association. Major annual events: Cranberry Fest, Scream Screen for Halloween, Midnight MAACness. Student services: health clinic, personal-psychological counseling. Campus security: 24-hour emergency response devices and patrols, student patrols, late night transport-escort service, controlled dormitory access. 2,718 college housing spaces available; 1,939 were occupied in 2018-19. Freshmen given priority for college housing. Options: coed, women-only housing available. Franklin F. Moore Library plus 1 other. Books: 311,713 (physical), 174,115 (digital/electronic); Serial titles: 723 (physical), 54,382 (digital/electronic); Databases: 171. Study areas open 24 hours, 5-7 days a week; students can reserve study rooms. 300 computers available on campus for general student use. Computer purchase/lease plans available. A campuswide network can be accessed. Students can access the following: online class registration. Staffed computer lab on campus (open 24 hours a day) provides training in use of computers, software, and the Internet.

Community Environment: The capital of the state, Trenton's slogan is"Trenton Makes-the World Takes" and more than 400 industries support this claim. Products include pottery, wire, rope, rubber and cigars. Situated midway between New York City and Philadelphia, all forms of commercial transportation are available. Along with the usual community facilities, Trenton supports a symphony orchestra and provides community concerts. There are many part-time job opportunities in the New York to Philadelphia corridor. The mountains and seashore are a short distance, providing excellent recreational facilities. Some of the numerous points of interest are the Friends Meetinghouse, New Jersey State Museum, Old Barracks, Trent House and Washington Crossing State Park.

■ ROWAN COLLEGE AT BURLINGTON COUNTY

601 Pemberton Browns Mills Rd.
Pemberton, NJ 08068
Tel: (609)894-9311
Fax: (609)894-0183
Web Site: www.rcbc.edu

Description: County-supported, 2-year, coed. Awards certificates, transfer associate, and terminal associate degrees. Founded 1966. Setting: 225-acre suburban campus with easy access to Philadelphia. Total enrollment: 8,762. Student-undergrad faculty ratio is 26:1. Students come from 23 states and territories, 1% from out-of-state. 0.2% American Indian or Alaska Native, non-Hispanic/Latino; 10% Hispanic/Latino; 20% Black or African American, non-Hispanic/Latino; 4% Asian, non-Hispanic/Latino; 0.2% Native Hawaiian or other Pacific Islander, non-Hispanic/Latino; 2% international. 33% 25 or older. Core. Calendar: semesters plus 2 summer terms. Academic remediation for entering students, ESL program, services for LD students, advanced placement, accelerated degree program, honors program, independent study, distance learning, double major, summer session for credit, part-time degree program, adult/continuing education programs, co-op programs and internships. Study abroad program.

Entrance Requirements: Open admission except for allied health program. Options: electronic application, early admission, deferred admission. Recommended: high school transcript. Entrance: noncompetitive. Application deadline: rolling. Notification: continuous. Transfer credits accepted: Yes.

Costs Per Year: Application fee: $20. Area resident tuition: $3330 full-time, $111 per credit hour part-time. State resident tuition: $3810 full-time, $127 per credit hour part-time. Nonresident tuition: $5760 full-time, $192 per credit hour part-time. Mandatory fees: $1425 full-time, $47.50 per credit hour part-time. Full-time tuition and fees vary according to program. Part-time tuition and fees vary according to program.

Collegiate Environment: Orientation program. Drama-theater group, choral group, student-run radio station. Social organizations: 23 open to all. Most popular organizations: Student Government Association, Phi Theta Kappa, Dental Hygiene Club, Student Nurses Association, Radiography Club. Major annual events: National Make a Difference Day, African American History Month Events, Drugs/Alcohol Awareness Week. Student services: personal-psychological counseling. Campus security: 24-hour emergency response devices and patrols, late night transport-escort service, electronic entrances to buildings and rooms, surveillance cameras. William K. McDaniel Integrated Learning Resource Center plus 1 other. 1,447 computers available on campus for general student use. A campuswide network can be accessed from off-campus. Students can access the following: online class registration. Staffed computer lab on campus provides training in use of computers, software, and the Internet.

Community Environment: The main campus is located in a rural setting where the principal agricultural pursuit is the raising of berries. Bus transportation is available. The campus is located 35 minutes from Center City Philadelphia and 90 minutes from New York City. Fort Dix and McGuire Air Force Base are nearby. Burlington County, the largest of New Jersey's 21 counties, has numerous churches and synagogues and excellent health care and recreational facilities.

■ ROWAN COLLEGE AT GLOUCESTER COUNTY

1400 Tanyard Rd.
Sewell, NJ 08080
Tel: (856)468-5000
Fax: (856)468-8498
E-mail: jatkinso@gccnj.edu
Web Site: www.rcgc.edu

Description: County-supported, 2-year, coed. Part of New Jersey Commission on Higher Education. Awards certificates, transfer associate, and terminal associate degrees. Founded 1967. Setting: 270-acre rural campus with easy access to Philadelphia. Total enrollment: 6,490. Student-undergrad faculty ratio is 28:1. 1% from out-of-state. 28% 25 or older. Core. Calendar: semesters. Academic remediation for entering students, services for LD students, advanced placement, distance learning, summer session for credit, part-time degree program, co-op programs.

Entrance Requirements: Open admission except for nursing, respiratory therapy, nuclear medicine, ultrasound, auto technology programs. Options: electronic application, deferred admission. Required: high school transcript. Required for some: SAT or ACT. Entrance: noncompetitive. Application deadline: rolling.

Collegiate Environment: Drama-theater group, choral group, student-run newspaper, radio station. Student services: health clinic, personal-psychological counseling, women's center. Campus security: 24-hour emergency response devices and patrols, late night transport-escort service. Gloucester County College Library.

Community Environment: See Rutgers, The State University of New Jersey - Camden College of Arts and Sciences.

■ **ROWAN UNIVERSITY**
201 Mullica Hill Rd.
Glassboro, NJ 08028-1701
Tel: (856)256-4500; Free: 800-447-1165N
Web Site: www.rowan.edu

Description: State-supported, comprehensive, coed. Part of New Jersey State College System. Awards bachelor's, master's, and doctoral degrees and post-master's certificates. Founded 1923. Setting: 921-acre suburban campus with easy access to Philadelphia. Endowment: $173.2 million. Research spending for the previous fiscal year: $11.9 million. Educational spending for the previous fiscal year: $34,943 per student. Total enrollment: 18,484. Faculty: 1,593 (465 full-time, 1,128 part-time). Student-undergrad faculty ratio is 17:1. 13,900 applied, 59% were admitted. Full-time: 13,635 students, 45% women, 55% men. Part-time: 1,766 students, 53% women, 47% men. Students come from 28 states and territories, 22 other countries, 5% from out-of-state. 0.1% American Indian or Alaska Native, non-Hispanic/Latino; 10% Hispanic/Latino; 10% Black or African American, non-Hispanic/Latino; 5% Asian, non-Hispanic/Latino; 0.1% Native Hawaiian or other Pacific Islander, non-Hispanic/Latino; 0.8% international. 11% 25 or older, 37% live on campus, 13% transferred in. Retention: 85% of full-time freshmen returned the following year. Academic areas with the most degrees conferred: business/marketing; education; psychology. Core. Calendar: semesters. Academic remediation for entering students, ESL program, services for LD students, advanced placement, accelerated degree program, freshman honors college, honors program, independent study, distance learning, double major, summer session for credit, part-time degree program, adult/continuing education programs, co-op programs and internships, graduate courses open to undergrads. Off campus study at Camden County College, Cumberland County College, Rowan College at Gloucester County, Rowan College at Burlington County. Study abroad program. ROTC: Army (c).

Entrance Requirements: Options: electronic application, early admission, deferred admission. Required: high school transcript, minimum 2 high school GPA, SAT or ACT. Required for some: interview. Entrance: moderately difficult. Application deadline: 3/1. Notification: continuous. SAT Reasoning Test deadline: January. SAT Subject Test deadline: October. Transfer credits accepted: Yes.

Costs Per Year: Application fee: $65. State resident tuition: $9858 full-time, $378.50 per credit hour part-time. Nonresident tuition: $18,500 full-time, $712.25 per credit hour part-time. Mandatory fees: $3839 full-time, $164 per credit hour part-time. Full-time tuition and fees vary according to course load, degree level, location, and program. Part-time tuition and fees vary according to course load, degree level, location, and program. College room and board: $12,552. College room only: $8072. Room and board charges vary according to board plan and housing facility.

Collegiate Environment: Orientation program. Drama-theater group, choral group, student-run newspaper, radio station. Social organizations: 140 open to all; national fraternities, national sororities, local fraternities; 6% of eligible men and 8% of eligible women are members. Most popular organizations: Kappa Delta Pi, Public Relations Student Society of America, Student University Programmes, Rowan Television Network, Elementary Education Club. Major annual events: Profstock (spring concert), Homecoming Week, Spring Festival Weekend. Student services: legal services, health clinic, personal-psychological counseling. Campus security: 24-hour emergency response devices and patrols, student patrols, late night transport-escort service, controlled dormitory access, EMS service including 2 ambulances, security and campus police trained as police officers in NJ. Keith and Shirley Campbell Library plus 4 others. Books: 328,891 (physical), 494,739 (digital/electronic); Serial titles: 129,972 (digital/electronic); Databases: 846.

Students can reserve study rooms. Operations spending for the previous fiscal year: $8 million. 836 computers available on campus for general student use. A campuswide network can be accessed. Students can access the following: online class registration. Staffed computer lab on campus provides training in use of computers, software, and the Internet.

Community Environment: Glassboro was established in 1775 when a German widow and her seven sons organized Stanger & Co., the first successful glass factory in North America. Hollybush, a mansion of a glass manufacturer, which formed part of the original campus, was the site of a summit conference between President Lyndon Johnson and Russian Premier Alexei Kosygin in 1967. Glassboro is near enough to large cities that all forms of commercial transportation are available. Philadelphia Airport is 35 minutes away. Part-time employment is available. Nearby lakes and beaches provide recreational facilities.

■ **RUTGERS UNIVERSITY-CAMDEN**
406 Penn St.
Camden, NJ 08102-1401
Tel: (856)225-1766
E-mail: admissions@camden.rutgers.edu
Web Site: www.camden.rutgers.edu

Description: State-supported, university, coed. Administratively affiliated with Rutgers, The State University of New Jersey. Awards bachelor's, master's, and doctoral degrees and post-master's certificates. Founded 1926. Setting: 29-acre urban campus with easy access to Philadelphia. System endowment: $1.2 million. Total enrollment: 6,853. Faculty: 700 (315 full-time, 385 part-time). Student-undergrad faculty ratio is 11:1. 11,338 applied, 69% were admitted. 12% from top 10% of their high school class, 37% from top quarter, 76% from top half. 2 valedictorians. Full-time: 4,493 students, 59% women, 41% men. Part-time: 996 students, 61% women, 39% men. Students come from 29 states and territories, 24 other countries, 2% from out-of-state. 0.1% American Indian or Alaska Native, non-Hispanic/Latino; 15% Hispanic/Latino; 18% Black or African American, non-Hispanic/Latino; 10% Asian, non-Hispanic/Latino; 0.1% Native Hawaiian or other Pacific Islander, non-Hispanic/Latino; 2% international. 29% 25 or older, 17% live on campus, 16% transferred in. Retention: 88% of full-time freshmen returned the following year. Academic areas with the most degrees conferred: business/marketing; health professions and related sciences; psychology. Core. Calendar: semesters. Academic remediation for entering students, ESL program, services for LD students, advanced placement, accelerated degree program, self-designed majors, freshman honors college, honors program, independent study, distance learning, double major, summer session for credit, part-time degree program, adult/continuing education programs, co-op programs and internships, graduate courses open to undergrads. Off campus study. Study abroad program. ROTC: Army (c), Air Force (c).

Entrance Requirements: Options: electronic application, early action, deferred admission, international baccalaureate accepted. Required: essay, SAT or ACT. Required for some: high school transcript, interview. Entrance: moderately difficult. Application deadline: 11/1 for early action. Notification: 1/31 for early action. Preference given to state residents. Transfer credits accepted: Yes.

Costs Per Year: Application fee: $70. State resident tuition: $11,886 full-time, $383 per credit hour part-time. Nonresident tuition: $27,664 full-time, $898 per credit hour part-time. Mandatory fees: $2949 full-time, $595 per term part-time. Full-time tuition and fees vary according to program. Part-time tuition and fees vary according to course load and program. College room and board: $12,336. College room only: $8582. Room and board charges vary according to board plan and housing facility.

Collegiate Environment: Orientation program. Drama-theater group, choral group, student-run newspaper, radio station. Social organizations: 75 open to all; national fraternities, national sororities. Major annual events: Rutgers Day, Cultural Activities, Spring Fest. Student services: legal services, health clinic, personal-psychological counseling, women's center. Campus security: 24-hour emergency response devices and patrols, student patrols, late night transport-escort service, controlled dormitory access. Paul Robeson Library plus 1 other. Weekly public service hours: 90; students can reserve study rooms.

■ **RUTGERS UNIVERSITY-NEW BRUNSWICK**
65 Davidson Rd.
Rm. 202
Piscataway, NJ 08854-8097
Tel: (732)445-4636

E-mail: admissions@ugadm.rutgers.edu

Web Site: newbrunswick.rutgers.edu

Description: State-supported, university, coed. Administratively affiliated with Rutgers, The State University of New Jersey. Awards associate, bachelor's, master's, and doctoral degrees and post-master's certificates. Founded 1766. Setting: 2,685-acre urban campus with easy access to New York City. System endowment: $1.2 million. Total enrollment: 49,577. Faculty: 4,525 (2,092 full-time, 2,433 part-time). Student-undergrad faculty ratio is 13:1. 38,384 applied, 58% were admitted. 38% from top 10% of their high school class, 75% from top quarter, 96% from top half. 52 valedictorians. Full-time: 33,677 students, 50% women, 50% men. Part-time: 1,964 students, 56% women, 44% men. Students come from 51 states and territories, 92 other countries, 6% from out-of-state. 13% Hispanic/Latino; 7% Black or African American, non-Hispanic/Latino; 27% Asian, non-Hispanic/Latino; 0.3% Native Hawaiian or other Pacific Islander, non-Hispanic/Latino; 9% international. 7% 25 or older, 43% live on campus, 8% transferred in. Retention: 93% of full-time freshmen returned the following year. Academic areas with the most degrees conferred: business/marketing; engineering; health professions and related sciences. Core. Calendar: semesters. Academic remediation for entering students, ESL program, services for LD students, advanced placement, accelerated degree program, self-designed majors, freshman honors college, honors program, independent study, distance learning, double major, summer session for credit, part-time degree program, adult/continuing education programs, co-op programs and internships, graduate courses open to undergrads. Off campus study. Study abroad program. ROTC: Army, Naval, Air Force.

Entrance Requirements: Options: electronic application, early action, deferred admission, international baccalaureate accepted. Required: essay, SAT or ACT. Required for some: high school transcript, interview. Entrance: moderately difficult. Application deadline: 11/1 for early action. Notification: 1/31 for early action. Preference given to state residents. Transfer credits accepted: Yes.

Costs Per Year: Application fee: $70. State resident tuition: $11,886 full-time, $383 per credit hour part-time. Nonresident tuition: $28,194 full-time, $915 per credit hour part-time. Mandatory fees: $3088 full-time, $445 per term part-time. Full-time tuition and fees vary according to program. Part-time tuition and fees vary according to course load and program. College room and board: $12,706. College room only: $7746. Room and board charges vary according to board plan and housing facility.

Collegiate Environment: Orientation program. Drama-theater group, choral group, marching band, student-run newspaper, radio station. Social organizations: 750 open to all; national fraternities, national sororities. Major annual events: Rutgers Day, Dance Marathon, Multicultural Programs. Student services: legal services, health clinic, personal-psychological counseling, women's center. Campus security: 24-hour emergency response devices and patrols, student patrols, late night transport-escort service, controlled dormitory access. Archibald S. Alexander Library plus 15 others. Study areas open 24 hours, 5-7 days a week; students can reserve study rooms.

■ RUTGERS UNIVERSITY-NEWARK

249 University Ave.

Newark, NJ 07102

Tel: (973)353-1766

Fax: (973)353-1048

E-mail: newarkadmissions@ugadm.rutgers.edu

Web Site: www.newark.rutgers.edu

Description: State-supported, university, coed. Administratively affiliated with Rutgers, The State University of New Jersey. Awards bachelor's, master's, and doctoral degrees and post-master's certificates. Founded 1908. Setting: 40-acre urban campus with easy access to New York City. System endowment: $1.2 million. Total enrollment: 12,768. Faculty: 1,023 (554 full-time, 469 part-time). Student-undergrad faculty ratio is 10:1. 13,435 applied, 64% were admitted. 21% from top 10% of their high school class, 53% from top quarter, 87% from top half. 5 valedictorians. Full-time: 7,162 students, 55% women, 45% men. Part-time: 1,389 students, 53% women, 47% men. Students come from 26 states and territories, 57 other countries, 1% from out-of-state. 0.1% American Indian or Alaska Native, non-Hispanic/Latino; 29% Hispanic/Latino; 20% Black or African American, non-Hispanic/Latino; 18% Asian, non-Hispanic/Latino; 0.3% Native Hawaiian or other Pacific Islander, non-Hispanic/Latino; 5% international. 20% 25 or older, 22% live on campus, 13% transferred in. Retention: 84% of full-time freshmen returned the following year. Academic areas with the most degrees conferred: business/marketing; psychology; homeland security, law enforce-

ment, firefighting, and protective services. Core. Calendar: semesters. Academic remediation for entering students, ESL program, services for LD students, advanced placement, accelerated degree program, self-designed majors, freshman honors college, honors program, independent study, distance learning, double major, summer session for credit, part-time degree program, adult/continuing education programs, co-op programs and internships, graduate courses open to undergrads. Off campus study at New Jersey Institute of Technology. Study abroad program. ROTC: Army, Naval, Air Force.

Entrance Requirements: Options: electronic application, early action, deferred admission, international baccalaureate accepted. Required: essay, SAT or ACT. Required for some: high school transcript. Entrance: moderately difficult. Application deadline: 11/1 for early action. Notification: 1/31 for early action. Preference given to state residents. Transfer credits accepted: Yes.

Costs Per Year: Application fee: $70. State resident tuition: $11,886 full-time, $383 per credit hour part-time. Nonresident tuition: $28,194 full-time, $915 per credit hour part-time. Mandatory fees: $2523 full-time, $487 per term part-time. Full-time tuition and fees vary according to program. Part-time tuition and fees vary according to course load and program. College room and board: $13,536. College room only: $8372. Room and board charges vary according to board plan and housing facility.

Collegiate Environment: Orientation program. Drama-theater group, choral group, marching band, student-run newspaper, radio station. Social organizations: 200 open to all; national fraternities, national sororities. Major annual events: Homecoming, Rutgers Day, Cultural Events. Student services: legal services, health clinic, personal-psychological counseling, women's center. Campus security: 24-hour emergency response devices and patrols, student patrols, late night transport-escort service, controlled dormitory access. John Cotton Dana Library plus 4 others. Weekly public service hours: 91; students can reserve study rooms.

■ SAINT PETER'S UNIVERSITY

2641 Kennedy Blvd.

Jersey City, NJ 07306-5997

Tel: (201)761-6000; Free: 888-SPC-9933

Fax: (201)432-5860

E-mail: ktillotson@saintpeters.edu

Web Site: www.saintpeters.edu

Description: Independent Roman Catholic (Jesuit), comprehensive, coed. Awards associate, bachelor's, master's, and doctoral degrees and post-master's certificates. Founded 1872. Setting: 15-acre urban campus with easy access to New York City. Total enrollment: 3,524. Faculty: 322 (119 full-time, 203 part-time). Student-undergrad faculty ratio is 13:1. 4,670 applied, 71% were admitted. 17% from top 10% of their high school class, 43% from top quarter, 76% from top half. Full-time: 2,387 students, 63% women, 37% men. Part-time: 250 students, 76% women, 24% men. 9% from out-of-state. 0.4% American Indian or Alaska Native, non-Hispanic/Latino; 45% Hispanic/Latino; 22% Black or African American, non-Hispanic/Latino; 7% Asian, non-Hispanic/Latino; 0.7% Native Hawaiian or other Pacific Islander, non-Hispanic/Latino; 2% international. 13% 25 or older, 31% live on campus, 5% transferred in. Retention: 82% of full-time freshmen returned the following year. Academic areas with the most degrees conferred: business/marketing; homeland security, law enforcement, firefighting, and protective services; health professions and related sciences. Core. Calendar: semesters. Academic remediation for entering students, ESL program, services for LD students, advanced placement, accelerated degree program, self-designed majors, honors program, independent study, distance learning, double major, summer session for credit, part-time degree program, adult/continuing education programs, co-op programs and internships, graduate courses open to undergrads. Off campus study at members of the Jesuit Student Exchange. Study abroad program. ROTC: Army (c).

Entrance Requirements: Options: early action, deferred admission, international baccalaureate accepted. Required: essay, high school transcript, minimum 2 high school GPA, 2 recommendations. Recommended: interview. Required for some: interview, SAT or ACT. Entrance: moderately difficult. Notification: continuous until 11/7. SAT Reasoning Test deadline: 8/17.

Collegiate Environment: Orientation program. Drama-theater group, choral group, student-run newspaper, radio station. Social organizations: 50 open to all. Student services: health clinic, personal-psychological counseling. Campus security: 24-hour emergency response devices and patrols, late night transport-escort service, controlled dormitory access, ID checks at residence halls and library. Theresa and Edward O'Toole Library plus 2 others.

■ SALEM COMMUNITY COLLEGE

460 Hollywood Ave.
Carneys Point, NJ 08069-2799
Tel: (856)299-2100
Fax: (856)299-9193
E-mail: kmcshay@salemcc.edu
Web Site: www.salemcc.edu

Description: County-supported, 2-year, coed. Awards certificates, transfer associate, and terminal associate degrees. Founded 1972. Setting: small town campus with easy access to Philadelphia. Total enrollment: 1,107. Faculty: 87 (17 full-time, 70 part-time). Student-undergrad faculty ratio is 19:1. Full-time: 602 students, 58% women, 42% men. Part-time: 505 students, 61% women, 39% men. 20% from out-of-state. 0.6% American Indian or Alaska Native, non-Hispanic/Latino; 5% Hispanic/Latino; 18% Black or African American, non-Hispanic/Latino; 2% Asian, non-Hispanic/Latino; 0.5% Native Hawaiian or other Pacific Islander, non-Hispanic/Latino. 29% 25 or older. Core. Calendar: semesters. Academic remediation for entering students, ESL program, services for LD students, advanced placement, independent study, distance learning, double major, summer session for credit, part-time degree program, adult/continuing education programs, co-op programs. Off campus study.

Entrance Requirements: Open admission except for nursing, nuclear energy technology programs. Options: electronic application, early admission, deferred admission. Required: high school transcript, basic skills test or minimum SAT score of 530 in math and 540 in English; high school GPA of 3.0 or higher needed for Gateway courses. Required for some: essay. Entrance: noncompetitive. Application deadline: rolling. Notification: continuous. Transfer credits accepted: Yes.

Collegiate Environment: Orientation program. Choral group. Student services: personal-psychological counseling, women's center. Campus security: 24-hour emergency response devices and patrols, late night transport-escort service. Michael S. Cettei Memorial Library.

■ SETON HALL UNIVERSITY

400 S Orange Ave.
South Orange, NJ 07079-2697
Tel: (973)761-9000; Free: 800-THE HALL
Fax: (973)761-9452
E-mail: maryclare.cullum@shu.edu
Web Site: www.shu.edu

Description: Independent Roman Catholic, university, coed. Awards bachelor's, master's, and doctoral degrees and post-master's certificates. Founded 1856. Setting: 58-acre suburban campus with easy access to New York City. Total enrollment: 9,903. Faculty: 952 (459 full-time, 493 part-time). Student-undergrad faculty ratio is 14:1. 10,730 applied, 79% were admitted. 35% from top 10% of their high school class, 62% from top quarter, 88% from top half. Full-time: 5,380 students, 58% women, 42% men. Part-time: 459 students, 63% women, 37% men. Students come from 42 states and territories, 55 other countries, 23% from out-of-state. 0.3% American Indian or Alaska Native, non-Hispanic/Latino; 17% Hispanic/Latino; 13% Black or African American, non-Hispanic/Latino; 8% Asian, non-Hispanic/Latino; 0.2% Native Hawaiian or other Pacific Islander, non-Hispanic/Latino; 3% international. 9% 25 or older, 39% live on campus, 7% transferred in. Retention: 84% of full-time freshmen returned the following year. Academic areas with the most degrees conferred: health professions and related sciences; business/marketing; social sciences. Core. Calendar: semesters. Academic remediation for entering students, ESL program, services for LD students, advanced placement, accelerated degree program, honors program, independent study, distance learning, double major, summer session for credit, part-time degree program, co-op programs and internships, graduate courses open to undergrads. Study abroad program. ROTC: Army.

Entrance Requirements: Options: electronic application, early action, deferred admission, international baccalaureate accepted. Required: essay, high school transcript, counselor report, SAT or ACT. Recommended: minimum 3 high school GPA, interview. Required for some: minimum 3 high school GPA, interview. Entrance: moderately difficult. Application deadlines: rolling, 11/15 for early action. Notification: continuous until 12/1, 12/30 for early action. SAT Reasoning Test deadline: 6/1. Transfer credits accepted: Yes. Applicants placed on waiting list: 2,203. Wait-listed applicants offered admission: 649.

Costs Per Year: Application fee: $55. Comprehensive fee: $57,954 includes full-time tuition ($39,900), mandatory fees ($2270), and college room and board ($15,784). College room only: $9846. Full-time tuition and fees vary according to course load. Room and board charges vary according to board plan and housing facility. Part-time tuition: $1220 per credit hour.

Collegiate Environment: Orientation program. Drama-theater group, choral group, student-run newspaper, radio station. Social organizations: 116 open to all; national fraternities, national sororities, local fraternities, local sororities. Most popular organizations: Martin Luther King Jr. Scholars Association, Adelante/Caribe, Black Student Union, National Council of Negro Women. Major annual events: University Day, Deck The Hall, Career Day. Student services: health clinic, personal-psychological counseling, women's center. Campus security: 24-hour emergency response devices and patrols, late night transport-escort service, controlled dormitory access. Walsh Library plus 1 other. 300 computers available on campus for general student use. Computer purchase/lease plans available. A computer is required for all students. A campuswide network can be accessed from student residence rooms and from off campus. Students can access the following: online class registration. Staffed computer lab on campus provides training in use of computers, software, and the Internet.

Community Environment: A upper middle class suburb, South Orange enjoys the cultural and recreational advantages of New York City and Newark. Mass transportation is available. Community facilities include a public library, two hospitals in nearby Livingston and Summit, and Catholic, Methodist, Episcopal and Presbyterian churches.

■ STEVENS INSTITUTE OF TECHNOLOGY

Castle Point on Hudson
Hoboken, NJ 07030
Tel: (201)216-5000; Free: 800-458-5323
Fax: (201)216-8348
E-mail: jackie.williams@stevens.edu
Web Site: www.stevens.edu

Description: Independent, university, coed. Awards bachelor's, master's, and doctoral degrees. Founded 1870. Setting: 55-acre urban campus with easy access to New York City. Total enrollment: 6,929. Faculty: 392 (264 full-time, 128 part-time). Student-undergrad faculty ratio is 10:1. 9,265 applied, 41% were admitted. 72% from top 10% of their high school class, 96% from top quarter, 100% from top half. 11 valedictorians. Full-time: 3,420 students, 29% women, 71% men. Part-time: 11 students, 45% women, 55% men. Students come from 40 states and territories, 47 other countries, 39% from out-of-state. 0.1% American Indian or Alaska Native, non-Hispanic/Latino; 11% Hispanic/Latino; 2% Black or African American, non-Hispanic/Latino; 15% Asian, non-Hispanic/Latino; 4% international. 64% live on campus, 1% transferred in. Retention: 95% of full-time freshmen returned the following year. Academic areas with the most degrees conferred: engineering; computer and information sciences; business/marketing. Core. Calendar: semesters. Services for LD students, advanced placement, accelerated degree program, honors program, independent study, distance learning, double major, summer session for credit, co-op programs and internships. Off campus study. Study abroad program. ROTC: Army (c), Air Force (c).

Entrance Requirements: Options: electronic application, early admission, early decision, deferred admission, international baccalaureate accepted. Required: essay, high school transcript, 2 recommendations. Recommended: interview. Required for some: digital portfolio for music and technology or visual arts and technology programs, SAT or ACT, SAT and SAT Subject Tests or ACT, Applicants to Music and Technology or Visual Arts and Technology may submit a digital portfolio in place of standardized test scores. International applicants may submit 2 SAT II scores, 2 AP scores, or 2 IB scores in place of standardized test scores. Entrance: very difficult. Application deadlines: 1/15, 11/15 for early decision plan 1, 1/15 for early decision plan 2. Notification: 4/1, 12/15 for early decision plan 1, 2/15 for early decision plan 2. SAT Reasoning Test deadline: 1/15. SAT Subject Test deadline: 1/15. Transfer credits accepted: Yes. Applicants placed on waiting list: 1,503. Wait-listed applicants offered admission: 0. Early decision applicants: 655. Early decision applicants admitted: 384.

Costs Per Year: Application fee: $70. Comprehensive fee: $69,784 includes full-time tuition ($52,134), mandatory fees ($1880), and college room and board ($15,770). College room only: $8910. Part-time tuition: $1738 per credit.

Collegiate Environment: Orientation program. Drama-theater group, choral group, student-run newspaper, radio station. Social organizations: 120 open to all; national fraternities, national sororities; 31% of eligible men and 49% of eligible women are members. Most popular organizations: Alpha Phi Omega, Computer & Gaming Society (C2GS), Society of Women Engineers, American Society of Mechanical Engineers (ASME), Ethnic Student Council.

Major annual events: Founders Day Ball, Techfest, Unity. Student services: health clinic, personal-psychological counseling, women's center. Campus security: 24-hour emergency response devices and patrols, late night transport-escort service, controlled dormitory access. 2,014 college housing spaces available; 1,838 were occupied in 2018-19. Freshmen guaranteed college housing. Options: coed, women-only housing available. Samuel C. Williams Library. Books: 66,492 (physical), 210,243 (digital/electronic); Serial titles: 898 (physical), 35,353 (digital/electronic); Databases: 71. Students can reserve study rooms. Operations spending for the previous fiscal year: $2.3 million. 11 computers available on campus for general student use. A computer is required for all students. A campuswide network can be accessed. Students can access the following: online class registration, online account information, debit dining program, laundry status. Staffed computer lab on campus (open 24 hours a day) provides training in use of computers, software, and the Internet.

Community Environment: Hoboken, a quaint, park-like community, is just one mile square and easily accessible to Manhattan. Recently it has become a residential center for young professionals. Many new shops, restaurants, and clubs have opened in the past ten years. The recreational and cultural advantages of New York are convenient for Hoboken, as well as many job opportunities. Stevens takes advantage of its location and has a popular cooperative education program, in addition to providing internships and research opportunities with leading companies.

■ **STOCKTON UNIVERSITY**
101 Vera King Farris Dr.
Galloway, NJ 08205-9441
Tel: (609)652-1776
Fax: (609)748-5541
Web Site: www.stockton.edu
Description: State-supported, comprehensive, coed. Part of New Jersey State College System. Awards bachelor's, master's, and doctoral degrees. Founded 1969. Setting: 2,000-acre suburban campus with easy access to Philadelphia. Endowment: $30.8 million. Research spending for the previous fiscal year: $1.9 million. Educational spending for the previous fiscal year: $6169 per student. Total enrollment: 9,621. Faculty: 771 (344 full-time, 427 part-time). Student-undergrad faculty ratio is 17:1. 6,084 applied, 84% were admitted. 18% from top 10% of their high school class, 44% from top quarter, 77% from top half. Full-time: 8,135 students, 58% women, 42% men. Part-time: 468 students, 58% women, 42% men. 2% from out-of-state. 0.2% American Indian or Alaska Native, non-Hispanic/Latino; 14% Hispanic/Latino; 8% Black or African American, non-Hispanic/Latino; 6% Asian, non-Hispanic/Latino; 0.2% Native Hawaiian or other Pacific Islander, non-Hispanic/Latino; 0.5% international. 37% live on campus, 12% transferred in. Retention: 85% of full-time freshmen returned the following year. Academic areas with the most degrees conferred: business/marketing; health professions and related sciences; social sciences. Core. Calendar: semesters. Academic remediation for entering students, ESL program, services for LD students, advanced placement, accelerated degree program, self-designed majors, honors program, independent study, distance learning, double major, summer session for credit, part-time degree program, adult/continuing education programs, internships, graduate courses open to undergrads. Off campus study at Washington Center for Internships and Academic Seminars. Study abroad program.
Entrance Requirements: Options: electronic application, early admission, international baccalaureate accepted. Required: high school transcript, minimum 2 high school GPA. Recommended: essay, minimum 3 high school GPA, 3 recommendations. Required for some: SAT or ACT. Entrance: very difficult. Notification: 5/15. SAT Reasoning Test deadline: 5/1. Applicants placed on waiting list: 351. Wait-listed applicants offered admission: 193.
Costs Per Year: Application fee: $50. State resident tuition: $8,862 full-time, $340.83 per credit part-time. Nonresident tuition: $15,989 full-time, $614.98 per credit part-time. Mandatory fees: $4,877 full-time, $187.56 per credit part-time, $120 per term part-time. Part-time tuition and fees vary according to course load. College room and board: $12,282. College room only: $8232. Room and board charges vary according to board plan and housing facility.
Collegiate Environment: Orientation program. Drama-theater group, choral group, student-run newspaper, radio station. Social organizations: 140 open to all; national fraternities, national sororities; 10% of eligible men and 10% of eligible women are members. Most popular organizations: Occupational Therapy Club, Sign Language Club, Animal Friendly Organization, Commuters on the Go, Archery Recreational Club of Stockton. Major annual events: Meet the Greeks, University Weekend, Lolla-No-Booza. Student services: health clinic, personal-psychological counseling, women's center. Campus

security: 24-hour emergency response devices and patrols, late night transport-escort service, controlled dormitory access. Freshmen guaranteed college housing. Option: coed housing available. Richard E. Bjork Library. Books: 215,712 (physical), 165,452 (digital/electronic); Serial titles: 85 (physical), 133,008 (digital/electronic); Databases: 184. Weekly public service hours: 91. Operations spending for the previous fiscal year: $4.2 million. 1,224 computers available on campus for general student use. A campuswide network can be accessed from student residence rooms and from off campus. Students can access the following: online class registration. Staffed computer lab on campus (open 24 hours a day) provides training in use of computers, software, and the Internet.

Community Environment: Pomona is located about 12 miles northwest of Atlantic City in an undeveloped forest area.

■ **STRAYER UNIVERSITY-CHERRY HILL CAMPUS**
2370 State Rte. 70 W
Ste. 335
Cherry Hill, NJ 08002
Tel: (856)482-4200; Free: 888-311-0355
Web Site: www.strayer.edu
Description: Proprietary, comprehensive, coed. Awards bachelor's and master's degrees.

■ **STRAYER UNIVERSITY-PISCATAWAY CAMPUS**
242 Old New Brunswick Rd.
Ste. 220
Piscataway, NJ 08854
Tel: (732)743-3800; Free: 888-311-0355
Web Site: www.strayer.edu
Description: Proprietary, comprehensive, coed. Awards bachelor's and master's degrees.

■ **STRAYER UNIVERSITY-WILLINGBORO CAMPUS**
300 Willingboro Pky.
Willingboro Town Ctr., Ste. 125
Willingboro, NJ 08046
Tel: (609)835-6000; Free: 888-311-0355
Web Site: www.strayer.edu
Description: Proprietary, comprehensive, coed. Awards bachelor's and master's degrees.

■ **SUSSEX COUNTY COMMUNITY COLLEGE**
1 College Hill
Newton, NJ 07860
Tel: (973)300-2100
E-mail: tpoltersdorf@sussex.edu
Web Site: www.sussex.edu
Description: State and locally supported, 2-year, coed. Part of New Jersey Commission on Higher Education. Awards certificates, transfer associate, and terminal associate degrees. Founded 1981. Setting: 160-acre small town campus with easy access to New York City. Total enrollment: 2,589. Full-time: 1,412 students, 47% women, 53% men. Part-time: 1,127 students, 58% women, 42% men. Students come from 3 states and territories. 0.4% American Indian or Alaska Native, non-Hispanic/Latino; 4% Hispanic/Latino; 2% Black or African American, non-Hispanic/Latino; 1% Asian, non-Hispanic/Latino; 0.1% Native Hawaiian or other Pacific Islander, non-Hispanic/Latino. 23% 25 or older. Core. Calendar: semesters. Academic remediation for entering students, ESL program, services for LD students, advanced placement, distance learning, double major, summer session for credit, part-time degree program, internships.
Entrance Requirements: Open admission. Option: electronic application. Entrance: noncompetitive. Application deadline: rolling. Notification: continuous. Transfer credits accepted: Yes.
Collegiate Environment: Orientation program. Drama-theater group, choral group, student-run newspaper. Student services: personal-psychological counseling. Campus security: late night transport-escort service, trained security personnel. Sussex County Community College Library. Students can reserve study rooms. 302 computers available on campus for general student use. A campuswide network can be accessed. Students can access the following: online class registration. Staffed computer lab on campus.

■ **TALMUDICAL ACADEMY OF NEW JERSEY**
868 Rte. 524
Adelphia, NJ 07710

Tel: (732)431-1600

Description: Independent Jewish, comprehensive, men only. Awards bachelor's and master's degrees. Founded 1967. Setting: small town campus. Total enrollment: 48. 15 applied, 100% were admitted. 8% 25 or older. Calendar: semesters.

■ **THOMAS EDISON STATE UNIVERSITY**

111 W State St.
Trenton, NJ 08608
Tel: (609)984-1100; Free: 888-442-8372
Fax: (609)292-9000
E-mail: admissions@tesu.edu
Web Site: www.tesu.edu

Description: State-supported, comprehensive, coed. Awards associate, bachelor's, master's, and doctoral degrees (offers only distance learning degree programs). Founded 1972. Setting: 2-acre urban campus with easy access to Philadelphia. Total enrollment: 16,233. Full-time: 49 students, 80% women, 20% men. Part-time: 15,189 students, 43% women, 57% men. 0.5% American Indian or Alaska Native, non-Hispanic/Latino; 10% Hispanic/Latino; 15% Black or African American, non-Hispanic/Latino; 4% Asian, non-Hispanic/Latino; 0.6% Native Hawaiian or other Pacific Islander, non-Hispanic/Latino; 1% international. Academic areas with the most degrees conferred: interdisciplinary studies; liberal arts/general studies; health professions and related sciences; business/marketing. Core. Calendar: continuous. Services for LD students, advanced placement, accelerated degree program, self-designed majors, independent study, distance learning, double major, summer session for credit, part-time degree program, external degree program, adult/continuing education programs, graduate courses open to undergrads.

Entrance Requirements: Open admission. Option: electronic application. Required: must be 21 or older and a high school graduate. Entrance: noncompetitive. Application deadline: rolling. Transfer credits accepted: Yes.

Costs Per Year: Application fee: $75. State resident tuition: $7519 full-time, $396 per credit hour part-time. Nonresident tuition: $9967 full-time, $499 per credit hour part-time.

Collegiate Environment: Campus security: 24-hour emergency response devices and patrols, late night transport-escort service, security officer from 7 am to 11 pm, local police patrol.

■ **UNION COUNTY COLLEGE**

1033 Springfield Ave.
Cranford, NJ 07016
Tel: (908)709-7000
Fax: (908)709-0527
E-mail: rodriguez@ucc.edu
Web Site: www.ucc.edu

Description: State and locally supported, 2-year, coed. Awards certificates, transfer associate, and terminal associate degrees. Founded 1933. Setting: 47-acre urban campus with easy access to New York City. Total enrollment: 9,412. 4,836 applied, 100% were admitted. Full-time: 4,223 students, 55% women, 45% men. Part-time: 5,189 students, 68% women, 32% men. 0.3% American Indian or Alaska Native, non-Hispanic/Latino; 39% Hispanic/Latino; 28% Black or African American, non-Hispanic/Latino; 4% Asian, non-Hispanic/Latino; 0.4% Native Hawaiian or other Pacific Islander, non-Hispanic/Latino; 1% international. 41% 25 or older, 8% transferred in. Core. Calendar: semesters. Academic remediation for entering students, ESL program, services for LD students, advanced placement, honors program, independent study, distance learning, summer session for credit, part-time degree program, adult/continuing education programs, internships. Off campus study. ROTC: Air Force (c).

Entrance Requirements: Open admission Admission to certain health science programs may require additional criteria for selection. Option: electronic application. Required: high school transcript, Immunization records. Required for some: essay, interview. Application deadline: rolling. Notification: continuous.

Costs Per Year: Application fee: $0. Area resident tuition: $5281 full-time, $214 part-time. State resident tuition: $10,562 full-time, $428 part-time. Nonresident tuition: $10,562 full-time, $428 part-time.

Collegiate Environment: Orientation program. Drama-theater group, student-run newspaper, radio station. Social organizations: 32 open to all. Student services: personal-psychological counseling. Campus security: 24-hour emergency response devices and patrols. College housing not available. MacKay Library plus 2 others. Books: 88,960 (physical), 239,464 (digital/electronic); Serial titles: 222 (physical), 363,355 (digital/electronic);

Databases: 96. 1,893 computers available on campus for general student use. A campuswide network can be accessed from off-campus. Students can access the following: online class registration. Staffed computer lab on campus provides training in use of computers, software, and the Internet.

Community Environment: A suburban area, 10 miles southwest of Newark, Cranford enjoys all the cultural and recreational advantages of nearby New York. Major forms of commercial transportation are available.

■ **WARREN COUNTY COMMUNITY COLLEGE**

475 Rte. 57 W
Washington, NJ 07882-4343
Tel: (908)835-9222
E-mail: shorwath@warren.edu
Web Site: www.warren.edu

Description: State and locally supported, 2-year, coed. Part of New Jersey Commission on Higher Education. Awards certificates, transfer associate, and terminal associate degrees. Founded 1981. Setting: 77-acre rural campus. Total enrollment: 2,180. Student-undergrad faculty ratio is 22:1. 26% 25 or older. Retention: 62% of full-time freshmen returned the following year. Core. Calendar: semesters. Academic remediation for entering students, ESL program, services for LD students, advanced placement, independent study, distance learning, double major, summer session for credit, part-time degree program, co-op programs and internships. Off campus study at Raritan Valley Community College, Union County College, Northampton County Area Community College.

Entrance Requirements: Open admission. Options: early admission, deferred admission. Entrance: noncompetitive. Application deadline: rolling.

Collegiate Environment: Drama-theater group, student-run newspaper. Social organizations: national fraternities. Campus security: evening and weekend security.

■ **WILLIAM PATERSON UNIVERSITY OF NEW JERSEY**

300 Pompton Rd.
Wayne, NJ 07470-8420
Tel: (973)720-2000; Free: 877-WPU-EXCEL
Fax: (973)720-2910
E-mail: leckeya@wpunj.edu
Web Site: www.wpunj.edu

Description: State-supported, comprehensive, coed. Awards bachelor's, master's, and doctoral degrees and post-master's certificates. Founded 1855. Setting: 370-acre suburban campus with easy access to New York City. Research spending for the previous fiscal year: $7.4 million. Educational spending for the previous fiscal year: $7779 per student. Total enrollment: 10,252. Faculty: 1,042 (410 full-time, 632 part-time). Student-undergrad faculty ratio is 14:1. 7,933 applied, 92% were admitted. Full-time: 7,282 students, 54% women, 46% men. Part-time: 1,550 students, 56% women, 44% men. Students come from 24 states and territories, 37 other countries, 2% from out-of-state. 0.1% American Indian or Alaska Native, non-Hispanic/Latino; 32% Hispanic/Latino; 17% Black or African American, non-Hispanic/Latino; 7% Asian, non-Hispanic/Latino; 0.5% international. 18% 25 or older, 24% live on campus, 11% transferred in. Retention: 77% of full-time freshmen returned the following year. Academic areas with the most degrees conferred: business/marketing; psychology; communication/journalism. Core. Calendar: semesters. Academic remediation for entering students, ESL program, services for LD students, advanced placement, accelerated degree program, freshman honors college, honors program, independent study, distance learning, double major, summer session for credit, part-time degree program, adult/continuing education programs, internships, graduate courses open to undergrads. Off campus study at members of the National Student Exchange, Mercer County Community College. Study abroad program. ROTC: Air Force (c).

Entrance Requirements: Options: electronic application, international baccalaureate accepted. Required: high school transcript, minimum 2 high school GPA, SAT or ACT. Required for some: essay, 1 recommendation, interview, portfolio for art, audition for music. Entrance: moderately difficult. Application deadline: 6/1. Notification: continuous. SAT Reasoning Test deadline: 6/1. Transfer credits accepted: Yes.

Costs Per Year: Application fee: $50. State resident tuition: $12,936 full-time, $414 per credit part-time. Nonresident tuition: $21,136 full-time, $685 per credit part-time. Mandatory fees: $124 full-time, $4 per credit part-time. Full-time tuition and fees vary according to course load and location. Part-time tuition and fees vary according to course load and location. College room and board: $11,445. College room only: $7135. Room and board charges vary according to board plan and housing facility.

Collegiate Environment: Orientation program. Drama-theater group, choral group, student-run newspaper, radio station. Social organizations: 90 open to all; national fraternities, national sororities, local fraternities; 1% of eligible men and 2% of eligible women are members. Most popular organizations: Student Activities Programming Board (SAPB), Students for Awareness Black Leadership and Equality (SABLE), Student Government Association (SGA), The B.A.B.Y. Dolls (Community Service org.), Pioneer Players (drama). Major annual events: Welcome Week, Music Fest, Greek Welcome Back BBQ. Student services: legal services, health clinic, personal-psychological counseling, women's center. Campus security: 24-hour emergency response devices and patrols, student patrols, late night transport-escort service, controlled dormitory access. David and Lorraine Cheng Library. Books: 369,216 (physical), 116,597 (digital/electronic); Serial titles: 3,772 (physical), 164,249 (digital/electronic); Databases: 126. Weekly public service hours: 102; students can reserve study rooms. 1,271 computers available on campus for general student use. Computer purchase/lease plans available. A campuswide network can be accessed from student residence rooms and from off campus. Students can access the following: online class registration. Staffed computer lab on campus provides training in use of computers, software, and the Internet.

Community Environment: Population 54,000, Wayne is a suburban community located in the center of Passaic County's Wayne Township. The University lies twenty miles west of New York City and is easily accessed by all major New Jersey arteries and nearby Newark Airport. Community facilities include excellent shopping, hospitals, churches of all denominations and numerous clubs and organizations. The University is located within an hour of New York City, the Jersey shore, the Delaware Water Gap and the Meadowlands all of which offer facilities for recreation.

■ YESHIVA BAIS AHARON

905 Park Ave.
Lakewood, NJ 08701

Description: Independent religious, 4-year, men only.

■ YESHIVA GEDOLAH SHAAREI SHMUEL

511 Ocean Ave.
Lakewood, NJ 08701
Web Site: www.yeshivagedolahshaareishmuel.com
Description: Independent Jewish, 4-year, coed.

■ YESHIVA GEDOLAH ZICHRON LEYMA

1000 Orchard Ter.
Linden, NJ 07036
Tel: (908)587-0502
Description: Independent Jewish, 4-year, coed. Awards bachelor's degrees.

■ YESHIVA TORAS CHAIM

999 Ridge Ave.
Lakewood, NJ 08701
Tel: (732)942-3090
Description: Independent Jewish, 4-year, coed. Awards bachelor's degrees.

■ YESHIVA YESODEI HATORAH

2 Yesodei Ct.
Lakewood, NJ 08701
Description: Independent religious, 4-year, men only.

■ YESHIVAS BE'ER YITZCHOK

1391 N Ave.
Elizabeth, NJ 07208
Tel: (908)354-6057
Web Site: www.elizabethkollel.org
Description: Independent Jewish, 4-year, coed. Awards bachelor's degrees.

■ BROOKLINE COLLEGE

4201 Central Ave. NW
Ste. J
Albuquerque, NM 87105-1649
Tel: (505)880-2877; Free: 888-660-2428
Fax: (505)833-2087
E-mail: awebb@brooklinecollege.edu
Web Site: brooklinecollege.edu
Description: Proprietary, 4-year, coed. Awards associate and bachelor's degrees. Setting: urban campus with easy access to Albuquerque. Total enrollment: 357. Faculty: 28 (13 full-time, 15 part-time). Student-undergrad faculty ratio is 19:1. 52% 25 or older. Core. Calendar: continuous. Accelerated degree program, part-time degree program.
Entrance Requirements: Open admission. Option: electronic application. Required: interview. Entrance: noncompetitive. Application deadline: rolling. Notification: continuous. Transfer credits accepted: Yes.
Collegiate Environment: Orientation program. Campus security: 24-hour emergency response devices. Learning Resource Center. 20 computers available on campus for general student use. A campuswide network can be accessed from off-campus. Staffed computer lab on campus provides training in use of computers, software, and the Internet.

■ CARRINGTON COLLEGE-ALBUQUERQUE

1001 Menaul Blvd. NE
Albuquerque, NM 87107
Tel: (505)254-7777
Web Site: www.carrington.edu
Description: Proprietary, 2-year, coed. Part of Carrington Colleges Group, Inc. Awards certificates and terminal associate degrees. Total enrollment: 434. Faculty: 24 (10 full-time, 14 part-time). Student-undergrad faculty ratio is 28:1. Full-time: 400 students, 84% women, 16% men. Part-time: 34 students, 79% women, 21% men. 2% from out-of-state. 31% American Indian or Alaska Native, non-Hispanic/Latino; 48% Hispanic/Latino; 2% Black or African American, non-Hispanic/Latino; 1% Asian, non-Hispanic/Latino. 52% 25 or older, 25% transferred in. Core.
Entrance Requirements: Required: essay, high school transcript, interview, institutional entrance exam. Notification: continuous.

■ CENTRAL NEW MEXICO COMMUNITY COLLEGE

525 Buena Vista Dr. SE
Albuquerque, NM 87106
Tel: (505)224-3000
Fax: (505)224-4740
E-mail: gdamiani@cnm.edu
Web Site: www.cnm.edu
Description: State-supported, 2-year, coed. Awards certificates, transfer associate, and terminal associate degrees. Founded 1965. Setting: 304-acre urban campus. Endowment: $1.9 million. Educational spending for the previous fiscal year: $4621 per student. Total enrollment: 23,717. Faculty: 959 (330 full-time, 629 part-time). Student-undergrad faculty ratio is 23:1. 4,758 applied, 100% were admitted. Full-time: 6,538 students, 55% women, 45% men. Part-time: 17,179 students, 60% women, 40% men. Students come from 18 other countries, 1% from out-of-state. 6% American Indian or Alaska Native, non-Hispanic/Latino; 52% Hispanic/Latino; 3% Black or African American, non-Hispanic/Latino; 2% Asian, non-Hispanic/Latino; 0.2% Native

Hawaiian or other Pacific Islander, non-Hispanic/Latino; 0.2% international. 39% 25 or older, 4% transferred in. Core. Calendar: trimesters. Academic remediation for entering students, ESL program, services for LD students, advanced placement, accelerated degree program, honors program, independent study, distance learning, summer session for credit, part-time degree program, adult/continuing education programs, co-op programs and internships. Off campus study. ROTC: Army (c), Naval (c), Air Force (c).
Entrance Requirements: Open admission. Option: electronic application. Entrance: noncompetitive. Application deadlines: rolling, rolling for nonresidents. Notification: continuous, continuous for nonresidents. Transfer credits accepted: Yes.
Costs Per Year: Application fee: $0. State resident tuition: $1320 full-time, $55 per credit hour part-time. Nonresident tuition: $7032 full-time, $293 per credit hour part-time. Mandatory fees: $306 full-time, $9 per credit hour part-time, $45 per term part-time.
Collegiate Environment: Orientation program. Student-run newspaper. Social organizations: 23 open to all. Campus security: 24-hour emergency response devices and patrols, late night transport-escort service. College housing not available. Main Campus Library plus 5 others. Books: 37,327 (physical), 246,604 (digital/electronic); Serial titles: 173 (physical), 1,511 (digital/electronic); Databases: 83. Operations spending for the previous fiscal year: $293,974.

■ CLOVIS COMMUNITY COLLEGE

417 Schepps Blvd.
Clovis, NM 88101-8381
Tel: (575)769-2811; Free: 800-769-1409
E-mail: admissions@clovis.edu
Web Site: www.clovis.edu
Description: State-supported, 2-year, coed. Awards certificates, transfer associate, and terminal associate degrees. Founded 1990. Setting: 25-acre small town campus. Endowment: $740,423. Educational spending for the previous fiscal year: $2260 per student. Total enrollment: 4,175. Faculty: 182 (52 full-time, 130 part-time). Student-undergrad faculty ratio is 21:1. 513 applied, 100% were admitted. Full-time: 995 students, 66% women, 34% men. Part-time: 3,180 students, 64% women, 36% men. 14% from out-of-state. 56% 25 or older, 8% transferred in. Retention: 43% of full-time freshmen returned the following year. Core. Calendar: semesters. Academic remediation for entering students, ESL program, services for LD students, advanced placement, independent study, distance learning, double major, summer session for credit, part-time degree program, adult/continuing education programs, co-op programs and internships.
Entrance Requirements: Open admission except for nursing, radiological technician, cosmetology, construction programs. Required: high school transcript. Required for some: interview. Entrance: noncompetitive. Application deadline: rolling. Notification: continuous. Transfer credits accepted: Yes.
Collegiate Environment: Orientation program. Drama-theater group, choral group. Social organizations: 10 open to all. Most popular organizations: Student Senate, Student Nursing Association, Black Advisory Council, Hispanic Advisory Council, student ambassadors. Major annual events: Graduation, Transfer Day, Concert Series. Student services: personal-psychological counseling. Campus security: student patrols, late night transport-escort service. Clovis Community College Library and Learning Resources Center. Operations spending for the previous fiscal year: $274,400. 305 computers available on campus for general student use. A

campuswide network can be accessed. Students can access the following: online class registration. Staffed computer lab on campus provides training in use of computers, software, and the Internet.

■ DOÑA ANA COMMUNITY COLLEGE

MSC-3DA, Box 30001
3400 S Espina St.
Las Cruces, NM 88003-8001
Tel: (505)527-7500; Free: 800-903-7503
Fax: (505)527-7515
Web Site: dacc.nmsu.edu

Description: State and locally supported, 2-year, coed. Part of New Mexico State University System. Awards certificates, transfer associate, and terminal associate degrees. Founded 1973. Setting: 15-acre urban campus with easy access to El Paso. Endowment: $18,682. Total enrollment: 8,891. Faculty: 344. Student-undergrad faculty ratio is 21:1. 556 applied. Full-time: 4,037 students, 56% women, 44% men. Part-time: 4,854 students, 57% women, 43% men. Students come from 14 states and territories, 1 other country, 12% from out-of-state. 2% American Indian or Alaska Native, non-Hispanic/Latino; 65% Hispanic/Latino; 3% Black or African American, non-Hispanic/Latino; 1% Asian, non-Hispanic/Latino; 2% international. 38% 25 or older, 2% transferred in. Retention: 85% of full-time freshmen returned the following year. Core. Calendar: semesters. Academic remediation for entering students, ESL program, services for LD students, advanced placement, freshman honors college, honors program, distance learning, summer session for credit, part-time degree program, adult/continuing education programs, co-op programs and internships. ROTC: Army (c), Air Force (c).

Entrance Requirements: Open admission except for radiological technology, nursing, respiratory care, paramedic, electrical apprenticeship, area vocational school programs. Options: electronic application, deferred admission. Required: high school transcript. Recommended: ACT, ACT ASSET, or ACT Compass. Entrance: noncompetitive. Application deadline: rolling.

Collegiate Environment: Orientation program. Drama-theater group, choral group, marching band, student-run newspaper, radio station. Social organizations: 21 open to all; national fraternities, national sororities, local fraternities, local sororities. Major annual events: Homecoming, Spring Fling, Return to Campus. Student services: legal services, health clinic, personal-psychological counseling, women's center. Campus security: 24-hour emergency response devices and patrols, late night transport-escort service, controlled dormitory access. Library/Media Center. Operations spending for the previous fiscal year: $570,144. 210 computers available on campus for general student use. Computer purchase/lease plans available. A campuswide network can be accessed from off-campus. Students can access the following: online class registration. Staffed computer lab on campus provides training in use of computers, software, and the Internet.

■ EASTERN NEW MEXICO UNIVERSITY

1500 S Ave. K
Portales, NM 88130
Tel: (575)562-1011; Free: 800-367-3668
Fax: (575)562-2118
Web Site: www.enmu.edu

Description: State-supported, comprehensive, coed. Administratively affiliated with Eastern New Mexico University-Ruidoso; Eastern New Mexico University-Roswell. Awards associate, bachelor's, and master's degrees. Founded 1934. Setting: 344-acre rural campus. Endowment: $9.8 million. Research spending for the previous fiscal year: $598,596. Educational spending for the previous fiscal year: $6199 per student. Total enrollment: 6,027. Faculty: 330 (156 full-time, 174 part-time). Student-undergrad faculty ratio is 19:1. 2,635 applied, 60% were admitted. 11% from top 10% of their high school class, 33% from top quarter, 68% from top half. Full-time: 2,590 students, 58% women, 42% men. Part-time: 2,009 students, 53% women, 47% men. Students come from 48 states and territories, 22 other countries, 22% from out-of-state. 2% American Indian or Alaska Native, non-Hispanic/Latino; 42% Hispanic/Latino; 6% Black or African American, non-Hispanic/Latino; 0.9% Asian, non-Hispanic/Latino; 0.7% Native Hawaiian or other Pacific Islander, non-Hispanic/Latino; 2% international. 32% 25 or older, 16% live on campus, 10% transferred in. Retention: 59% of full-time freshmen returned the following year. Academic areas with the most degrees conferred: business/marketing; health professions and related sciences; liberal arts/general studies. Core. Calendar: semesters. Academic remediation for entering students, ESL program, services for LD students, advanced placement, accelerated degree program, self-designed majors, independent study, distance learning, double major, summer session for

credit, part-time degree program, adult/continuing education programs, co-op programs and internships, graduate courses open to undergrads.

Entrance Requirements: Options: electronic application, international baccalaureate accepted. Required: official transcripts from any post-secondary institution attended, good standing with all previous institutions. Required for some: high school transcript, minimum 2.5 high school GPA, SAT, ACT. Entrance: noncompetitive. Application deadlines: 8/24, rolling for nonresidents. Notification: continuous until 8/1, continuous until 8/1 for nonresidents. SAT Reasoning Test deadline: 8/1. SAT Subject Test deadline: 8/1. Transfer credits accepted: Yes.

Costs Per Year: Application fee: $0. One-time mandatory fee: $95. State resident tuition: $3842 full-time, $259 per credit hour part-time. Nonresident tuition: $5764 full-time, $339 per credit hour part-time. Mandatory fees: $2364 full-time, $98.52 per credit hour part-time. College room and board: $7162. College room only: $3496.

Collegiate Environment: Orientation program. Drama-theater group, choral group, marching band, student-run newspaper, radio station. Social organizations: 55 open to all; national fraternities, national sororities. Most popular organizations: Student Government, Student Activities Board, Residence Hall Association, IFC (Inter-Fraternity Council)£anhellenic Council. Major annual events: Homecoming Weekend, Wagon Wheel Football Game (ENMU v. WTAMU), Dawg Days/Freshmen Move-In. Student services: health clinic, personal-psychological counseling. Campus security: 24-hour emergency response devices and patrols, late night transport-escort service, controlled dormitory access, University Emergency Notification System, security cameras, security lights. Golden Library plus 2 others. Operations spending for the previous fiscal year: $1.4 million. 453 computers available on campus for general student use. A campuswide network can be accessed. Students can access the following: online class registration. Staffed computer lab on campus provides training in use of computers, software, and the Internet.

■ EASTERN NEW MEXICO UNIVERSITY-ROSWELL

PO Box 6000
Roswell, NM 88202-6000
Tel: (575)624-7000; Free: 800-624-7000
Fax: (575)624-7119
Web Site: www.roswell.enmu.edu

Description: State-supported, 2-year, coed. Part of Eastern New Mexico University System. Awards certificates, transfer associate, and terminal associate degrees. Founded 1958. Setting: 241-acre small town campus. Total enrollment: 4,347. Student-undergrad faculty ratio is 20:1. 10% from out-of-state. 54% 25 or older. Core. Calendar: semesters. Academic remediation for entering students, ESL program, services for LD students, advanced placement, independent study, distance learning, summer session for credit, part-time degree program, adult/continuing education programs, co-op programs and internships. Off campus study at other units of the Eastern New Mexico University System. ROTC: Army (c), Naval (c), Air Force (c).

Entrance Requirements: Open admission except for nursing, occupational therapy programs. Option: early admission. Required: high school transcript. Recommended: ACT. Entrance: noncompetitive. Application deadline: rolling.

Collegiate Environment: Orientation program. Drama-theater group, choral group, student-run newspaper. Campus security: 24-hour emergency response devices, student patrols, late night transport-escort service. Learning Resource Center.

■ EC-COUNCIL UNIVERSITY

101 C Sun Ave. NE
Albuquerque, NM 87109
Tel: (505)922-2886
Web Site: www.eccu.edu

Description: Proprietary, upper-level, coed. Awards bachelor's and master's degrees. Founded 2003. Student-undergrad faculty ratio is 5:1. Core. Academic remediation for entering students, services for LD students, distance learning, part-time degree program, internships.

Collegiate Environment: Orientation program.

■ INSTITUTE OF AMERICAN INDIAN ARTS

83 Avan Nu Po Rd.
Santa Fe, NM 87508
Tel: (505)424-2300
Fax: (505)424-0505
E-mail: mary.silentwalker@iaia.edu

Web Site: www.iaia.edu

Description: Federally supported, comprehensive, coed. Awards associate, bachelor's, and master's degrees. Founded 1962. Setting: 140-acre suburban campus with easy access to Albuquerque. Total enrollment: 657. Student-undergrad faculty ratio is 7:1. Full-time: 299 students, 55% women, 45% men. Part-time: 308 students, 56% women, 44% men. 68% American Indian or Alaska Native, non-Hispanic/Latino; 14% Hispanic/Latino; 0.3% Black or African American, non-Hispanic/Latino; 1% Asian, non-Hispanic/Latino; 0.5% international. Core. Calendar: semesters. Academic remediation for entering students, services for LD students, advanced placement, independent study, distance learning, double major, summer session for credit, part-time degree program, internships. Off campus study. Study abroad program.

Entrance Requirements: Options: electronic application, deferred admission, international baccalaureate accepted. Required: high school transcript. Recommended: interview. Required for some: essay, interview. Application deadline: 8/4. Notification: continuous. Transfer credits accepted: Yes.

Costs Per Year: State resident tuition: $4700 full-time, $196 per semester hour part-time. Nonresident tuition: $4700 full-time, $196 per semester hour part-time. Mandatory fees: $280 full-time, $140 per term part-time. College room and board: $9604. College room only: $4144. Room and board charges vary according to board plan and housing facility.

Collegiate Environment: Orientation program. Drama-theater group, student-run newspaper. Major annual events: Spring Powwow, Art in the Raw Exhibition. Student services: personal-psychological counseling. Campus security: 24-hour patrols, late night transport-escort service, controlled dormitory access. IAIA Library plus 1 other. Students can reserve study rooms. 100 computers available on campus for general student use. A campuswide network can be accessed from student residence rooms. Students can access the following: online class registration. Staffed computer lab on campus provides training in use of computers, software, and the Internet.

■ **INTELLITEC COLLEGE**
5001 Montgomery Blvd. NE
Ste. A24
Albuquerque, NM 87109
Tel: (505)508-5225
Web Site: www.intelliteccollege.edu
Description: Proprietary, 2-year, coed. Awards certificates, transfer associate, and terminal associate degrees.

■ **LUNA COMMUNITY COLLEGE**
PO Box 1510
Las Vegas, NM 87701
Tel: (505)454-2500; Free: 800-588-7232
E-mail: hgriego@luna.cc.nm.us
Web Site: www.luna.edu
Description: State-supported, 2-year, coed. Awards certificates, diplomas, transfer associate, and terminal associate degrees. Setting: 25-acre small town campus. Total enrollment: 1,789. Full-time: 544 students, 56% women, 44% men. Part-time: 1,245 students, 56% women, 44% men. Students come from 6 states and territories, 1% from out-of-state. 25% 25 or older, 1% transferred in. Retention: 38% of full-time freshmen returned the following year. Core. Calendar: semesters. Academic remediation for entering students, honors program, independent study, distance learning, part-time degree program, co-op programs.

Entrance Requirements: Open admission. Option: electronic application. Required: high school transcript. Entrance: noncompetitive.

Collegiate Environment: Orientation program. Samuel F. Vigil Learning Resource Center plus 1 other.

■ **MESALANDS COMMUNITY COLLEGE**
911 S Tenth St.
Tucumcari, NM 88401
Tel: (575)461-4413
Fax: (505)461-1901
Web Site: www.mesalands.edu
Description: State-supported, 2-year, coed. Awards certificates, transfer associate, and terminal associate degrees. Founded 1979. Setting: small town campus. Total enrollment: 1,005. Faculty: 50 (15 full-time, 35 part-time). Student-undergrad faculty ratio is 18:1. 64% 25 or older. Calendar: semesters.

Entrance Requirements: Required: high school transcript. Entrance: minimally difficult. Application deadline: rolling.

Collegiate Environment: Campus security: 24-hour emergency response devices.

■ **NATIONAL AMERICAN UNIVERSITY (ALBUQUERQUE)**
4775 Indian School Rd. NE
Ste. 200
Albuquerque, NM 87110
Tel: (505)348-3700; Free: 800-895-9904
Fax: (505)265-7542
Web Site: www.national.edu
Description: Proprietary, 4-year, coed. Awards associate and bachelor's degrees. Founded 1941. Setting: 5-acre suburban campus. Total enrollment: 336. 90% 25 or older. Core. Calendar: quarters. Accelerated degree program, independent study, distance learning, double major, summer session for credit, part-time degree program, external degree program, adult/continuing education programs, co-op programs and internships. Off campus study.

Entrance Requirements: Open admission. Required: high school transcript. Entrance: noncompetitive. Application deadline: rolling.

Collegiate Environment: Orientation program. Campus security: 24-hour patrols, late night transport-escort service.

■ **NATIONAL AMERICAN UNIVERSITY (ALBUQUERQUE)**
10131 Coors Blvd. NW
Ste. I-01
Albuquerque, NM 87114
Tel: (505)348-3750; Free: 800-895-9904
Web Site: www.national.edu
Description: Proprietary, 4-year, coed. Awards associate degrees. Total enrollment: 231.
Entrance Requirements: Entrance: noncompetitive.

■ **NATIONAL COLLEGE OF MIDWIFERY**
1041 Reed St., Ste. C
Taos, NM 87571
Tel: (575)758-8914
Fax: (505)758-0302
Web Site: www.midwiferycollege.org
Description: Independent, comprehensive, women only. Awards associate, bachelor's, and master's degrees. Founded 1989. Calendar: trimesters.

■ **NAVAJO TECHNICAL UNIVERSITY**
PO Box 849
Crownpoint, NM 87313
Tel: (505)786-4100
Fax: (505)786-5644
Web Site: www.navajotech.edu
Description: Independent, comprehensive, coed. Awards associate, bachelor's, and master's degrees. Founded 1979. Total enrollment: 751. Student-undergrad faculty ratio is 18:1. 49% from out-of-state. 37% 25 or older. Calendar: semesters.
Entrance Requirements: Open admission.

■ **NEW MEXICO HIGHLANDS UNIVERSITY**
PO Box 9000
Las Vegas, NM 87701
Tel: (505)454-3000; Free: 800-338-6648
Fax: (505)454-3311
E-mail: admissions@nmhu.edu
Web Site: www.nmhu.edu
Description: State-supported, comprehensive, coed. Awards bachelor's and master's degrees and post-master's certificates. Founded 1893. Setting: small town campus. Total enrollment: 3,471. Faculty: 249 (138 full-time, 111 part-time). Student-undergrad faculty ratio is 15:1. 1,158 applied, 100% were admitted. 4% from top 10% of their high school class, 17% from top quarter, 58% from top half. Full-time: 1,442 students, 56% women, 44% men. Part-time: 739 students, 76% women, 24% men. 15% from out-of-state. 8% American Indian or Alaska Native, non-Hispanic/Latino; 58% Hispanic/Latino; 5% Black or African American, non-Hispanic/Latino; 0.6% Asian, non-Hispanic/Latino; 0.6% Native Hawaiian or other Pacific Islander, non-Hispanic/Latino; 5% international. 44% 25 or older, 22% live on campus, 18% transferred in. Retention: 53% of full-time freshmen returned the follow-

ing year. Academic areas with the most degrees conferred: health professions and related sciences; education; business/marketing. Core. Calendar: semesters. Academic remediation for entering students, services for LD students, advanced placement, accelerated degree program, honors program, independent study, distance learning, double major, summer session for credit, part-time degree program, adult/continuing education programs, co-op programs and internships, graduate courses open to undergrads. Off campus study at San Juan Community College, Santa Fe Community College, NMHU Center at Roswell; NMHU Center at Rio Rancho.

Entrance Requirements: Open admission. Options: electronic application, early admission, deferred admission, international baccalaureate accepted. Required: high school transcript, minimum 2 high school GPA. Required for some: 2 recommendations, interview. Entrance: minimally difficult. Transfer credits accepted: Yes.

Costs Per Year: One-time mandatory fee: $25. State resident tuition: $4320 full-time, $180 per credit hour part-time. Nonresident tuition: $8472 full-time, $353 per credit hour part-time. Mandatory fees: $1830 full-time, $70 per term part-time. College room and board: $7872. College room only: $3852. Room and board charges vary according to board plan and housing facility.

Collegiate Environment: Orientation program. Drama-theater group, choral group, marching band, student-run radio station. Social organizations: national fraternities, national sororities, local fraternities, local sororities. Most popular organizations: Vatos Rugby, Fire Escape Club, MeChA, NMHU Cheerleaders, NMHU Student Ambassadors. Major annual events: Homecoming Pageant, Welcome Back Week, Campus-Wide Thanksgiving Dinner. Student services: health clinic, personal-psychological counseling, women's center. Campus security: 24-hour emergency response devices and patrols, late night transport-escort service, controlled dormitory access. Thomas C. Donnelly Library.

Community Environment: Las Vegas has grown considerably since its days as a Mormon outpost on the Santa Fe Trail. The city is in the foothills of the Sangre de Cristo Mountains and produces lumber, dairy and wool products. The area has a stimulating, dry climate with winters that are bracing but sunny. Recreational facilities nearby include hunting, fishing and skiing. Some part-time employment is available for students.

■ NEW MEXICO INSTITUTE OF MINING AND TECHNOLOGY

801 Leroy Pl.
Socorro, NM 87801
Tel: (575)835-5434; Free: 800-428-TECH
Fax: (575)835-5989
E-mail: admission@nmt.edu
Web Site: www.nmt.edu

Description: State-supported, university, coed. Awards associate, bachelor's, master's, and doctoral degrees. Founded 1889. Setting: 320-acre small town campus with easy access to Albuquerque. Endowment: $45 million. Research spending for the previous fiscal year: $59.6 million. Educational spending for the previous fiscal year: $11,766 per student. Total enrollment: 2,009. Faculty: 188 (132 full-time, 56 part-time). Student-undergrad faculty ratio is 11:1. 1,513 applied, 22% were admitted. 35% from top 10% of their high school class, 68% from top quarter, 87% from top half. Full-time: 1,294 students, 27% women, 73% men. Part-time: 177 students, 52% women, 48% men. Students come from 30 states and territories, 7 other countries, 11% from out-of-state. 4% American Indian or Alaska Native, non-Hispanic/Latino; 30% Hispanic/Latino; 2% Black or African American, non-Hispanic/Latino; 4% Asian, non-Hispanic/Latino; 0.1% Native Hawaiian or other Pacific Islander, non-Hispanic/Latino; 2% international. 12% 25 or older, 50% live on campus, 5% transferred in. Retention: 74% of full-time freshmen returned the following year. Academic areas with the most degrees conferred: engineering; physical sciences; biological/life sciences. Core. Calendar: semesters. Services for LD students, advanced placement, accelerated degree program, self-designed majors, independent study, distance learning, double major, summer session for credit, co-op programs and internships, graduate courses open to undergrads.

Entrance Requirements: Options: electronic application, deferred admission. Required: high school transcript, minimum 2.5 high school GPA, SAT or ACT. Recommended: interview, ACT. Required for some: 2 recommendations. Entrance: moderately difficult. Application deadline: 8/1. Notification: continuous. SAT Reasoning Test deadline: 8/1. Transfer credits accepted: Yes.

Costs Per Year: Application fee: $15. State resident tuition: $6,440 full-time, $268.32 per credit hour part-time. Nonresident tuition: $20,938 full-time, $872.42 per credit hour part-time. Mandatory fees: $1494 full-time, $18 per

credit hour part-time, $443.93 per term part-time. Full-time tuition and fees vary according to reciprocity agreements. Part-time tuition and fees vary according to course load. College room and board: $8202. Room and board charges vary according to board plan and housing facility.

Collegiate Environment: Orientation program. Drama-theater group, choral group, student-run newspaper, radio station. Major annual events: 49'ers, Spring Fling, International Fair. Student services: health clinic, personal-psychological counseling. Campus security: 24-hour emergency response devices and patrols, late night transport-escort service. The Skeen Library. Students can reserve study rooms. Operations spending for the previous fiscal year: $1.6 million. 225 computers available on campus for general student use. A campuswide network can be accessed from student residence rooms and from off campus. Students can access the following: online class registration. Staffed computer lab on campus.

Community Environment: Located 75 miles south of Albuquerque, Socorro (Spanish meaning"help") is in the valley of the Rio Grande. Socorro is the county seat of Socorro County and relies primarily on a service economy and serves a trade territory encompassing both Socorro and Catron Counties. The town draws trade and population from those who work at Stallion Site on the northern end of the White Sands Missile Range, and at the Very Large Array (VLA), the largest radio telescope complex in the world, located on the San Augustin Plains, about 50 miles west of Socorro. The Tech campus provides facilities for golf, tennis, and swimming. The surrounding area provides mountain biking, hiking, and fishing. The town also supports an improving public school system, a general hospital, and 14 churches. Opportunities for part-time employment on the Tech campus are excellent.

■ NEW MEXICO JUNIOR COLLEGE

5317 Lovington Hwy.
Hobbs, NM 88240-9123
Tel: (575)392-4510; Free: 800-657-6260
Fax: (505)392-2527
Web Site: www.nmjc.edu

Description: State and locally supported, 2-year, coed. Part of New Mexico Commission on Higher Education. Awards certificates, transfer associate, and terminal associate degrees. Founded 1965. Setting: 185-acre small town campus. Research spending for the previous fiscal year: $21,370. Total enrollment: 3,222. Faculty: 120 (65 full-time, 55 part-time). Student-undergrad faculty ratio is 19:1. 9% from top 10% of their high school class, 24% from top quarter, 72% from top half. 5 valedictorians. Students come from 17 states and territories, 7 other countries, 10% from out-of-state. 52% 25 or older, 15% live on campus. Core. Calendar: semesters. Academic remediation for entering students, services for LD students, advanced placement, distance learning, summer session for credit, part-time degree program, co-op programs and internships.

Entrance Requirements: Open admission. Options: electronic application, early admission, deferred admission. Entrance: noncompetitive. Application deadlines: rolling, rolling for nonresidents, rolling for early decision plan 1, rolling for early decision plan 2, rolling for early action. Notification: continuous, continuous for nonresidents, rolling for early decision plan 1, rolling for early decision plan 2, rolling for early action. Transfer credits accepted: Yes.

Costs Per Year: Application fee: $0. Area resident tuition: $912 full-time, $38 per credit hour part-time. State resident tuition: $1368 full-time, $57 per credit hour part-time. Nonresident tuition: $1656 full-time, $69 per credit hour part-time. Mandatory fees: $432 full-time, $18 per credit hour part-time. Full-time tuition and fees vary according to course load. Part-time tuition and fees vary according to course load.

Collegiate Environment: Choral group. Most popular organizations: Student Nurses Association, Phi Theta Kappa, Fellowship of Christian Athletes. Major annual events: Cowboy Roundup Days, Southwest Poets' Conference, New Mexico Junior College Rodeo. Student services: health clinic, personal-psychological counseling. Campus security: 24-hour emergency response devices and patrols, late night transport-escort service, controlled dormitory access. Pannell Library. 275 computers available on campus for general student use. A campuswide network can be accessed from student residence rooms and from off campus. Students can access the following: online class registration. Staffed computer lab on campus provides training in use of computers, software, and the Internet.

Community Environment: A tent city sprang up in this once little-known ranchland corner of New Mexico when oil was discovered in 1927. The settlement soon became the terminal point for oil companies, producing 90% of the state's petroleum. Farmlands in the surrounding area are irrigated by artesian wells and produce alfalfa, cotton and grain sorghums. The city has an airport and bus service for transportation. Community facilities include churches representing major denominations, a library, a hospital, and various civic and fraternal organizations. Recreational areas within reasonable distance provide hunting, fishing, golf, boating and other water sports. Part-time employment is available for students.

■ NEW MEXICO MILITARY INSTITUTE

101 W College Blvd.
Roswell, NM 88201-5173
Tel: (575)622-6250; Free: 800-421-5376
Fax: (505)624-8067
E-mail: admissions@nmmi.edu
Web Site: www.nmmi.edu
Description: State-supported, 2-year, coed. Part of New Mexico Commission on Higher Education. Awards transfer associate degrees. Founded 1891. Setting: 42-acre small town campus. Endowment: $370.9 million. Total enrollment: 480. Faculty: 65 (all full-time). Student-undergrad faculty ratio is 17:1. 601 applied, 62% were admitted. Students come from 43 states and territories, 9 other countries, 59% from out-of-state. 100% live on campus. Retention: 93% of full-time freshmen returned the following year. Core. Calendar: semesters. Academic remediation for entering students, ESL program, summer session for credit. ROTC: Army.
Entrance Requirements: Options: early admission, deferred admission. Required: high school transcript, minimum 2.0 high school GPA, SAT or ACT. Entrance: moderately difficult. Application deadline: 8/1. Notification: continuous. Preference given to state residents.
Collegiate Environment: Orientation program. Drama-theater group, choral group, marching band, student-run newspaper. Social organizations: 30 open to all. Most popular organizations: band, chorus, drill teams, Officer's Club. Major annual events: Parents' Weekend, Homecoming, Open House. Student services: health clinic, personal-psychological counseling. Campus security: 24-hour emergency response devices and patrols, controlled dormitory access. Paul Horgan Library plus 2 others. Operations spending for the previous fiscal year: $165,220. 700 computers available on campus for general student use. Computer purchase/lease plans available. A campuswide network can be accessed from student residence rooms and from off campus. Staffed computer lab on campus.
Community Environment: With a population of approximately 45,000, Roswell, a Pecos Valley City, noted for its fine climate, is the distributing and supply point for a great agricultural, stockraising and oil producing territory. The summer mean temperature is 77.5 degrees, and the winter mean temperature is 41.2 degrees. The area is reached by bus, rail and air lines. Community services include several churches, a public library, a community museum and art center, a community concert association and 2 hospitals. A local park offers a swimming pool, tennis courts and golf courses.

■ NEW MEXICO STATE UNIVERSITY

PO Box 30001
Las Cruces, NM 88003-8001
Tel: (575)646-0111; Free: 800-662-6678
E-mail: admssions@nmsu.edu
Web Site: www.nmsu.edu
Description: State-supported, university, coed. Part of New Mexico State University System. Awards associate, bachelor's, master's, and doctoral degrees and post-master's certificates. Founded 1888. Setting: 900-acre suburban campus with easy access to El Paso, TX. Endowment: $167.5 million. Research spending for the previous fiscal year: $107.1 million. Educational spending for the previous fiscal year: $14,261 per student. Total enrollment: 14,432. Faculty: 976 (639 full-time, 337 part-time). Student-undergrad faculty ratio is 16:1. 8,192 applied, 64% were admitted. 21% from top 10% of their high school class, 51% from top quarter, 83% from top half. Full-time: 9,703 students, 55% women, 45% men. Part-time: 2,010 students, 54% women, 46% men. Students come from 54 states and territories, 50 other countries, 26% from out-of-state. 2% American Indian or Alaska Native, non-Hispanic/Latino; 59% Hispanic/Latino; 3% Black or African American, non-Hispanic/Latino; 1% Asian, non-Hispanic/Latino; 0.1% Native Hawaiian or other Pacific Islander, non-Hispanic/Latino; 4% international. 20% 25 or older, 20% live on campus, 5% transferred in. Retention: 74% of full-time freshmen returned the following year. Academic areas with the most degrees conferred: business/marketing; engineering; health professions and related sciences. Core. Calendar: semesters. Academic remediation for entering students, ESL program, services for LD students, advanced placement, accelerated degree program, self-designed majors, freshman honors college, honors program, independent study, distance learning, double major, summer session for credit, part-time degree program, co-op programs

and internships, graduate courses open to undergrads. Off campus study at Members of the National Student Exchange, other units of the New Mexico State University System. Study abroad program. ROTC: Army, Air Force.
Entrance Requirements: Options: electronic application, international baccalaureate accepted. Required: high school transcript, high school course requirements: 4 units of English, 4 of math, 2 of science beyond general science, and 1 foreign language/fine art; must have 2.75 HS GPA, rank in the top 20% of graduating class, or ACT composite score of 21 (SAT of 1060 new format), SAT or ACT. Required for some: 3 recommendations. Entrance: moderately difficult. Application deadline: rolling. Notification: continuous. SAT Reasoning Test deadline: 8/14. Transfer credits accepted: Yes.
Costs Per Year: Application fee: $20. One-time mandatory fee: $165. State resident tuition: $5,515 full-time, $229.80 per credit hour part-time. Nonresident tuition: $20,599 full-time, $858.30 per credit hour part-time. Mandatory fees: $1,171 full-time, $48.80 per credit hour part-time. Full-time tuition and fees vary according to course load and reciprocity agreements. Part-time tuition and fees vary according to course load and reciprocity agreements. College room and board: $9252. College room only: $5350. Room and board charges vary according to board plan and housing facility.
Collegiate Environment: Orientation program. Drama-theater group, choral group, marching band, student-run newspaper, radio station. Social organizations: 270 open to all; national fraternities, national sororities, local fraternities, academic fraternities; 5% of eligible men and 4% of eligible women are members. Major annual events: Keep State Great, The Big Event, Latino Week. Student services: legal services, health clinic, personal-psychological counseling. Campus security: 24-hour emergency response devices and patrols, late night transport-escort service, controlled dormitory access. New Mexico State University Library - Zuhl plus 1 other. Books: 1.2 million (physical), 160,068 (digital/electronic); Serial titles: 23,730 (physical), 135,113 (digital/electronic); Databases: 410. Weekly public service hours: 112; students can reserve study rooms. Operations spending for the previous fiscal year: $7.8 million. 708 computers available on campus for general student use. Computer purchase/lease plans available. A campuswide network can be accessed from student residence rooms and from off campus. Students can access the following: online class registration, antivirus software; student portal online with file share/storage space, student employee clock-in, payments system, hardware rentals, short-term tablet checkout, software discounts. Staffed computer lab on campus provides training in use of computers, software, and the Internet.

■ NEW MEXICO STATE UNIVERSITY-ALAMOGORDO

2400 N Scenic Dr.
Alamogordo, NM 88311-0477
Tel: (505)439-3600
E-mail: advisor@nmsu.edu
Web Site: nmsua.edu
Description: State-supported, 2-year, coed. Part of New Mexico State University System. Awards certificates, transfer associate, and terminal associate degrees. Founded 1958. Setting: 540-acre small town campus. Endowment: $147,086. Educational spending for the previous fiscal year: $6044 per student. Total enrollment: 1,710. Faculty: 89 (34 full-time, 55 part-time). Student-undergrad faculty ratio is 16:1. Full-time: 425 students, 56% women, 44% men. Part-time: 1,285 students, 64% women, 36% men. Students come from 9 states and territories, 3 other countries. 4% American Indian or Alaska Native, non-Hispanic/Latino; 45% Hispanic/Latino; 4% Black or African American, non-Hispanic/Latino; 1% Asian, non-Hispanic/Latino; 0.4% Native Hawaiian or other Pacific Islander, non-Hispanic/Latino; 2% international. 4% transferred in. Retention: 46% of full-time freshmen returned the following year. Core. Calendar: semesters. Academic remediation for entering students, services for LD students, advanced placement, independent study, distance learning, double major, summer session for credit, part-time degree program, adult/continuing education programs, internships. Off campus study at other branches of New Mexico State University. Study abroad program.
Entrance Requirements: Open admission. Options: electronic application, early admission, deferred admission. Required: high school transcript, minimum 2 high school GPA. Entrance: noncompetitive. Application deadlines: rolling, rolling for nonresidents. Notification: continuous, continuous for nonresidents. Transfer credits accepted: Yes.
Costs Per Year: Application fee: $20. Area resident tuition: $1872 full-time, $78 per credit hour part-time. State resident tuition: $2232 full-time, $93 per credit hour part-time. Nonresident tuition: $5184 full-time, $216 per credit hour part-time. Mandatory fees: $192 full-time, $8 per credit hour part-time.

Full-time tuition and fees vary according to course load and reciprocity agreements. Part-time tuition and fees vary according to reciprocity agreements.

Collegiate Environment: Orientation program. Social organizations: national fraternities. Major annual events: Health and Wellness Fair, Take Back the Night, Diversity Fair. Campus security: late night transport-escort service. David H. Townsend Library. Operations spending for the previous fiscal year: $510,543. 70 computers available on campus for general student use. A campuswide network can be accessed. Students can access the following: online class registration. Staffed computer lab on campus provides training in use of computers, software, and the Internet.

■ NEW MEXICO STATE UNIVERSITY-CARLSBAD

1500 University Dr.
Carlsbad, NM 88220-3509
Tel: (575)234-9200
E-mail: eshannon@nmsu.edu
Web Site: www.cavern.nmsu.edu

Description: State-supported, 2-year, coed. Part of New Mexico State University System. Awards certificates, diplomas, transfer associate, and terminal associate degrees. Founded 1950. Setting: 40-acre small town campus. Educational spending for the previous fiscal year: $2380 per student. Total enrollment: 1,998. Faculty: 91 (41 full-time, 50 part-time). 306 applied, 100% were admitted. Full-time: 583 students, 65% women, 35% men. Part-time: 1,415 students, 63% women, 37% men. Students come from 20 states and territories, 1% from out-of-state. 28% 25 or older, 5% transferred in. Retention: 41% of full-time freshmen returned the following year. Core. Calendar: semesters. Academic remediation for entering students, ESL program, services for LD students, advanced placement, self-designed majors, honors program, independent study, distance learning, double major, summer session for credit, part-time degree program, adult/continuing education programs, co-op programs and internships.

Entrance Requirements: Open admission except for nursing program. Options: electronic application, early admission. Required for some: high school transcript. Entrance: noncompetitive. Application deadline: rolling. Notification: continuous. Transfer credits accepted: Yes.

Collegiate Environment: Orientation program. Social organizations: 4 open to all. Most popular organizations: Student Nurses Association, Alpha Sigma Phi Criminal Justice Association, Phi Theta Kappa International Honors Society, Associated Students Student Government Association. Major annual events: Career Expo, Halloween Carnival, Welcome Week. Student services: health clinic, personal-psychological counseling. Campus security: 24-hour emergency response devices, late night transport-escort service. Library/Media Center. Operations spending for the previous fiscal year: $222,072. 300 computers available on campus for general student use. A campuswide network can be accessed. Students can access the following: online class registration. Staffed computer lab on campus provides training in use of computers, software, and the Internet.

■ NEW MEXICO STATE UNIVERSITY-GRANTS

1500 3rd St.
Grants, NM 87020-2025
Tel: (505)287-7981
Web Site: grants.nmsu.edu

Description: State-supported, 2-year, coed. Part of New Mexico State University System. Awards certificates, transfer associate, and terminal associate degrees. Founded 1968. Setting: small town campus. Total enrollment: 798. 49% 25 or older. Core. Calendar: semesters. Summer session for credit, part-time degree program.

Entrance Requirements: Open admission. Option: early admission. Required: high school transcript, CPT. Entrance: noncompetitive. Application deadline: 7/30.

Collegiate Environment: 150 computers available on campus for general student use. A campuswide network can be accessed. Staffed computer lab on campus.

■ NORTHERN NEW MEXICO COLLEGE

921 Paseo de Onate
Espanola, NM 87532
Tel: (505)747-2100
E-mail: dms@nnmc.edu
Web Site: www.nnmc.edu

Description: State-supported, 4-year, coed. Awards associate and bachelor's degrees. Founded 1909. Setting: 35-acre rural campus. Endow-

ment: $829,791. Total enrollment: 2,272. Faculty: 253 (45 full-time, 208 part-time). 320 applied, 100% were admitted. 5% from top 10% of their high school class, 23% from top quarter, 52% from top half. Students come from 5 states and territories, 1% from out-of-state. 60% 25 or older, 1% live on campus. Core. Calendar: semesters. Academic remediation for entering students, services for LD students, advanced placement, distance learning, summer session for credit, part-time degree program.

Entrance Requirements: Open admission. Options: early admission, deferred admission. Required: high school transcript. Entrance: noncompetitive. Application deadline: rolling.

Collegiate Environment: Social organizations: 9 open to all. Most popular organizations: nursing organization, radiography organization, AISES, Aikido Club, Phi Theta Kappa. Campus security: 24-hour emergency response devices and patrols. Northern New Mexico Community College Library. Operations spending for the previous fiscal year: $112,638. 12 computers available on campus for general student use. A campuswide network can be accessed from off-campus. Staffed computer lab on campus.

■ PIMA MEDICAL INSTITUTE

4400 Cutler Ave. NE
Albuquerque, NM 87110
Tel: (505)881-1234; Free: 800-477-PIMA
Fax: (505)884-8371
Web Site: www.pmi.edu

Description: Proprietary, primarily 2-year, coed. Part of Vocational Training Institutes, Inc. Awards certificates, terminal associate, and bachelor's degrees. Founded 1985. Setting: urban campus. Total enrollment: 716. 47% 25 or older. Calendar: modular. Academic remediation for entering students, services for LD students, distance learning, co-op programs and internships.

Entrance Requirements: Option: early admission. Required: interview, Wonderlic Scholastic Level Exam (SLE). Required for some: high school transcript. Entrance: minimally difficult.

Collegiate Environment: Orientation program. E-Global.

■ ST. JOHN'S COLLEGE

1160 Camino Cruz Blanca
Santa Fe, NM 87505
Tel: (505)984-6000; Free: 800-331-5232
E-mail: santafe.admissions@sjc.edu
Web Site: www.sjc.edu

Description: Independent, comprehensive, coed. Administratively affiliated with St. John's College - Annapolis. Awards bachelor's and master's degrees. Founded 1964. Setting: 250-acre small town campus with easy access to Albuquerque, NM. Endowment: $63 million. Educational spending for the previous fiscal year: $18,677 per student. Total enrollment: 371. Faculty: 48 (40 full-time, 8 part-time). Student-undergrad faculty ratio is 8:1. 358 applied, 67% were admitted. 27% from top 10% of their high school class, 50% from top quarter, 73% from top half. Full-time: 306 students, 45% women, 55% men. Part-time: 14 students, 21% women, 79% men. Students come from 42 states and territories, 27 other countries, 87% from out-of-state. 13% Hispanic/Latino; 0.3% Black or African American, non-Hispanic/Latino; 3% Asian, non-Hispanic/Latino; 23% international. 9% 25 or older, 87% live on campus, 3% transferred in. Retention: 76% of full-time freshmen returned the following year. Academic area with the most degrees conferred: liberal arts/general studies. Core. Calendar: semesters. ESL program, services for LD students, summer session for credit, internships, graduate courses open to undergrads. Off campus study at St. John's College in Annapolis, Maryland. Study abroad program.

Entrance Requirements: Options: electronic application, early admission, early action, deferred admission, international baccalaureate accepted. Required: essay, high school transcript, 2 recommendations. Recommended: interview. Required for some: outline of curriculum for home-schooled applicants, SAT or ACT, SAT/ACT, TOEFL/IELTS or interview for international applicants; SAT/ACT/CLT for homeschooled students and applicants who have not and will not graduate high school. Entrance: very difficult. Application deadlines: rolling, 11/15 for early action. Notification: continuous, 12/15 for early action. Transfer credits accepted: No. Applicants placed on waiting list: 16. Wait-listed applicants offered admission: 16. Early action applicants: 124. Early action applicants admitted: 99.

Costs Per Year: Application fee: $0. One-time mandatory fee: $100. Comprehensive fee: $49,270 includes full-time tuition ($35,000), mandatory fees ($1410), and college room and board ($12,860). College room only: $7152. Full-time tuition and fees vary according to location. Room and board charges vary according to board plan, housing facility, and location.

Collegiate Environment: Orientation program. Drama-theater group, choral group, student-run newspaper. Social organizations: 50 open to all. Most popular organizations: Student Government (Polity), Iron Bookworm Workout, Intramural sports, PiYo, International Student Association. Major annual events: Dean's Opening Lecture, All-College Seminar, Reality. Student services: health clinic, personal-psychological counseling. Campus security: 24-hour emergency response devices and patrols, late night transport-escort service, controlled dormitory access. 357 college housing spaces available; 280 were occupied in 2018-19. Freshmen guaranteed college housing. On-campus residence required through senior year. Options: coed, men-only, women-only housing available. Meem Library. Books: 69,127 (physical); Serial titles: 68 (physical); Databases: 9. Weekly public service hours: 82; study areas open 24 hours, 5-7 days a week. Operations spending for the previous fiscal year: $351,440. 16 computers available on campus for general student use. A campuswide network can be accessed from student residence rooms and from off campus. Students can access the following: free wi-fi access throughout the campus; support for 'bring your own'; mobile devices. Staffed computer lab on campus (open 24 hours a day) provides training in use of computers, software, and the Internet.

■ **SAN JUAN COLLEGE**
4601 College Blvd.
Farmington, NM 87402-4699
Tel: (505)326-3311
Fax: (505)599-3385
E-mail: calcotea@sanjuancollege.edu
Web Site: www.sanjuancollege.edu
Description: State-supported, 2-year, coed. Part of New Mexico Higher Education Department. Awards certificates, diplomas, transfer associate, and terminal associate degrees. Founded 1958. Setting: 698-acre small town campus. Endowment: $15.7 million. Educational spending for the previous fiscal year: $6790 per student. Total enrollment: 6,679. Faculty: 311 (144 full-time, 167 part-time). Student-undergrad faculty ratio is 20:1. Full-time: 2,212 students, 60% women, 40% men. Part-time: 2,578 students, 76% women, 24% men. Students come from 52 states and territories, 22 other countries, 30% from out-of-state. 34% American Indian or Alaska Native, non-Hispanic/Latino; 16% Hispanic/Latino; 1% Black or African American, non-Hispanic/Latino; 0.8% Asian, non-Hispanic/Latino; 0.2% Native Hawaiian or other Pacific Islander, non-Hispanic/Latino; 1% international. 45% 25 or older, 10% transferred in. Core. Calendar: semesters. Academic remediation for entering students, ESL program, services for LD students, advanced placement, freshman honors college, honors program, independent study, distance learning, double major, summer session for credit, part-time degree program, adult/continuing education programs, co-op programs and internships.
Entrance Requirements: Open admission. Options: electronic application, early admission, deferred admission. Required: high school transcript. Entrance: noncompetitive. Application deadline: rolling. Notification: continuous. Transfer credits accepted: Yes.
Costs Per Year: Application fee: $10. State resident tuition: $1470 full-time, $49 per credit hour part-time. Nonresident tuition: $4650 full-time, $155 per credit hour part-time. Mandatory fees: $415 full-time, $77.50 per term part-time. Full-time tuition and fees vary according to reciprocity agreements. Part-time tuition and fees vary according to course load and reciprocity agreements.
Collegiate Environment: Orientation program. Drama-theater group, choral group. Social organizations: 19 open to all; national fraternities, national sororities, PSI BETA, NSLS. Most popular organizations: National Society of Leadership and Success (NSLS), Student American Dental Hygienists' Association, Student Nurses Association, Society for Advancement of Chicanos and Native Americans in Science, All Nations Leadership Association. Major annual events: Student Rush/Welcome Back Week, Luminarias, Halloween Carnival. Student services: personal-psychological counseling. Campus security: 24-hour emergency response devices and patrols, late night transport-escort service. College housing not available. San Juan College Library. Books: 78,682 (physical), 208,891 (digital/electronic); Serial titles: 247 (physical), 30,188 (digital/electronic); Databases: 100. Weekly public service hours: 69. Operations spending for the previous fiscal year: $818,614. 1,401 computers available on campus for general student use. A campuswide network can be accessed from off-campus. Students can access the following: online class registration. Staffed computer lab on campus provides training in use of computers, software, and the Internet.
Community Environment: At the junction of the San Juan, Las Animas and La Plata Rivers, Farmington is a producer of gas and oil. This is the starting

point for two large natural gas pipelines, one leading to Los Angeles, San Diego and San Francisco, the other to the Pacific Northwest. Irrigated lands surrounding the general locale produce farm crops and grazing for livestock. The region is also noted for apple and peach raising. Some part-time employment is available for students.

■ **SANTA FE COMMUNITY COLLEGE**
6401 Richards Ave.
Santa Fe, NM 87508
Tel: (505)428-1000
Fax: (505)428-1237
E-mail: marcos.maez@sfcc.edu
Web Site: www.sfcc.edu
Description: State and locally supported, 2-year, coed. Awards certificates, transfer associate, and terminal associate degrees. Founded 1983. Setting: 366-acre rural campus with easy access to Albuquerque. Educational spending for the previous fiscal year: $3044 per student. Total enrollment: 6,101. Faculty: 490 (84 full-time, 406 part-time). Student-undergrad faculty ratio is 13:1. 353 applied, 100% were admitted. Full-time: 2,243 students, 62% women, 38% men. Part-time: 7,376 students, 63% women, 37% men. Students come from 42 states and territories. 5% American Indian or Alaska Native, non-Hispanic/Latino; 44% Hispanic/Latino; 2% Black or African American, non-Hispanic/Latino; 2% Asian, non-Hispanic/Latino; 0.1% Native Hawaiian or other Pacific Islander, non-Hispanic/Latino; 0.1% international. Retention: 51% of full-time freshmen returned the following year. Core. Calendar: semesters. Academic remediation for entering students, ESL program, services for LD students, advanced placement, honors program, independent study, distance learning, double major, summer session for credit, part-time degree program, external degree program, adult/continuing education programs, co-op programs and internships.
Entrance Requirements: Open admission except for nursing and respiratory programs. Options: electronic application, early admission, deferred admission, international baccalaureate accepted. Recommended: high school transcript. Entrance: noncompetitive. Application deadline: rolling. Notification: continuous. Transfer credits accepted: Yes.
Collegiate Environment: Orientation program. Social organizations: 9 open to all. Most popular organizations: Student Ambassadors, Student Government Association, The Clay Club, Phi Theta Kappa. Student services: personal-psychological counseling. Campus security: 24-hour emergency response devices and patrols, late night transport-escort service. Learning Resource Center. Operations spending for the previous fiscal year: $135,000.

■ **SOUTHWESTERN INDIAN POLYTECHNIC INSTITUTE**
9169 Coors, NW, Box 10146
Albuquerque, NM 87184-0146
Tel: (505)346-2347; Free: 800-586-7474
Fax: (505)346-2343
E-mail: tawna.harrison@bie.edu
Web Site: www.sipi.edu
Description: Federally supported, 2-year, coed. Awards certificates, transfer associate, and terminal associate degrees. Founded 1971. Setting: 144-acre suburban campus with easy access to Albuquerque. Research spending for the previous fiscal year: $72,958. Total enrollment: 402. Faculty: 41 (23 full-time, 18 part-time). Student-undergrad faculty ratio is 16:1. 183 applied, 86% were admitted. 3% from top 10% of their high school class, 11% from top quarter, 32% from top half. Full-time: 346 students, 53% women, 47% men. Part-time: 56 students, 73% women, 27% men. Students come from 18 states and territories. 39% 25 or older, 60% live on campus. Core. Calendar: trimesters. Academic remediation for entering students, services for LD students, advanced placement, distance learning, double major, summer session for credit, part-time degree program, co-op programs and internships.
Entrance Requirements: Required: high school transcript, Certificate of Indian Blood, physical, immunization records. Entrance: noncompetitive. Application deadline: 7/30. Notification: continuous. Preference given to Native Americans who are enrolled members of federally recognized tribes. Transfer credits accepted: Yes.
Costs Per Year: Application fee: $0. Comprehensive fee: $1770 includes full-time tuition ($0), mandatory fees ($1095), and college room and board ($675). Part-time mandatory fees: $290 per term. The Bureau of Indian Education (BIE) provides tuition, room board, and books to students at minimal charge.
Collegiate Environment: Social organizations: Phi Theta Kappa; 20% of

eligible men and 24% of eligible women are members. Most popular organizations: Dance Club, Student Senate, Culinary Arts, Natural Resources, Pow-Wow Club. Major annual events: Campus Blessing, Arts & Crafts fair. Student services: personal-psychological counseling. Campus security: 24-hour emergency response devices and patrols, late night transport-escort service. Southwestern Indian Polytechnic Institute Library. 350 computers available on campus for general student use. A campuswide network can be accessed. Staffed computer lab on campus provides training in use of computers and the Internet.

■ UNIVERSITY OF NEW MEXICO

Albuquerque, NM 87131-2039
Tel: (505)277-0111; Free: 800-CALL-UNM
Fax: (505)277-6686
E-mail: apply@unm.edu
Web Site: www.unm.edu

Description: State-supported, university, coed. Awards bachelor's, master's, and doctoral degrees and post-master's certificates. Founded 1889. Setting: 769-acre urban campus. Endowment: $400.8 million. Research spending for the previous fiscal year: $166.9 million. Total enrollment: 24,393. Faculty: 1,389 (1,069 full-time, 320 part-time). Student-undergrad faculty ratio is 16:1. 10,912 applied, 52% were admitted. Full-time: 13,591 students, 56% women, 44% men. Part-time: 4,268 students, 57% women, 43% men. 10% from out-of-state. 6% American Indian or Alaska Native, non-Hispanic/Latino; 49% Hispanic/Latino; 2% Black or African American, non-Hispanic/Latino; 4% Asian, non-Hispanic/Latino; 0.2% Native Hawaiian or other Pacific Islander, non-Hispanic/Latino; 2% international. 22% 25 or older, 9% live on campus, 9% transferred in. Retention: 74% of full-time freshmen returned the following year. Academic areas with the most degrees conferred: business/marketing; health professions and related sciences; psychology. Core. Calendar: semesters. Academic remediation for entering students, ESL program, services for LD students, advanced placement, accelerated degree program, self-designed majors, freshman honors college, honors program, independent study, distance learning, double major, summer session for credit, part-time degree program, adult/continuing education programs, co-op programs and internships, graduate courses open to undergrads. Off campus study at National Student Exchange, Western Undergraduate Exchange, Western Interstate Commission for Higher Education, International Student Exchange. Study abroad program. ROTC: Army, Naval, Air Force.

Entrance Requirements: Options: electronic application, early admission, deferred admission, international baccalaureate accepted. Required: high school transcript, minimum 2.5 high school GPA, SAT or ACT. Required for some: essay, interview. Entrance: moderately difficult. Application deadline: rolling. Notification: continuous. SAT Reasoning Test deadline: 6/15. SAT Subject Test deadline: 6/15. Transfer credits accepted: Yes.

Costs Per Year: Application fee: $25. State resident tuition: $5418 full-time, $255 per credit hour part-time. Nonresident tuition: $21,062 full-time, $878 per credit hour part-time. Mandatory fees: $1904 full-time, $63 per credit hour part-time. Full-time tuition and fees vary according to course level and program. Part-time tuition and fees vary according to course level, course load, and program. College room and board: $9864. Room and board charges vary according to board plan and housing facility.

Collegiate Environment: Orientation program. Drama-theater group, choral group, marching band, student-run newspaper, radio station. Social organizations: 425 open to all; national fraternities, national sororities, local sororities; 5% of eligible men and 6% of eligible women are members. Most popular organizations: Associated Students of UNM, Graduate and Professional Students Association, Golden Key National Honor Society. Major annual events: Spring Fiestas, Welcome Back Days, Homecoming. Student services: health clinic, personal-psychological counseling, women's center. Campus security: 24-hour emergency response devices and patrols, student patrols, late night transport-escort service, controlled dormitory access. 2,085 college housing spaces available. Freshmen guaranteed college housing. Option: coed housing available. College of University Libraries and Learning Sciences plus 7 others. Students can reserve study rooms. Operations spending for the previous fiscal year: $25 million. 990 computers available on campus for general student use. Computer purchase/lease plans available. A campuswide network can be accessed from student residence rooms and from off campus. Students can access the following: online class registration. Staffed computer lab on campus provides training in use of computers, software, and the Internet.

■ UNIVERSITY OF NEW MEXICO-GALLUP

705 Gurley Ave.
Gallup, NM 87301
Tel: (505)863-7500
Fax: (505)863-7532
Web Site: www.gallup.unm.edu

Description: State-supported, 2-year, coed. Part of New Mexico Commission on Higher Education. Awards certificates, diplomas, transfer associate, and terminal associate degrees. Founded 1968. Setting: 80-acre small town campus. Total enrollment: 2,473. Student-undergrad faculty ratio is 20:1. Full-time: 1,163 students, 62% women, 38% men. Part-time: 1,310 students, 62% women, 38% men. 11% from out-of-state. 76% American Indian or Alaska Native, non-Hispanic/Latino; 13% Hispanic/Latino; 0.5% Black or African American, non-Hispanic/Latino; 0.9% Asian, non-Hispanic/Latino; 0.4% international. 41% 25 or older, 4% transferred in. Retention: 56% of full-time freshmen returned the following year. Core. Calendar: semesters. Academic remediation for entering students, services for LD students, advanced placement, honors program, independent study, distance learning, double major, summer session for credit, part-time degree program, adult/continuing education programs, co-op programs and internships. Off campus study.

Entrance Requirements: Open admission. Option: electronic application. Required for some: high school transcript. Entrance: noncompetitive. Application deadline: rolling. Notification: continuous.

Collegiate Environment: Orientation program. Student-run newspaper. Campus security: late night transport-escort service. Zollinger Library plus 1 other. Study areas open 24 hours, 5-7 days a week.

■ UNIVERSITY OF NEW MEXICO-LOS ALAMOS BRANCH

4000 University Dr.
Los Alamos, NM 87544-2233
Tel: (505)662-5919
E-mail: l65130@unm.edu
Web Site: losalamos.unm.edu

Description: State-supported, 2-year, coed. Part of New Mexico Commission on Higher Education. Awards certificates, transfer associate, and terminal associate degrees. Founded 1980. Setting: 5-acre small town campus. Research spending for the previous fiscal year: $224,434. Educational spending for the previous fiscal year: $13,797 per student. Total enrollment: 744. Faculty: 88 (4 full-time, 84 part-time). Student-undergrad faculty ratio is 9:1. Full-time: 191 students, 49% women, 51% men. Part-time: 553 students, 59% women, 41% men. 1% from out-of-state. 5% American Indian or Alaska Native, non-Hispanic/Latino; 43% Hispanic/Latino; 1% Black or African American, non-Hispanic/Latino; 3% Asian, non-Hispanic/Latino; 0.4% Native Hawaiian or other Pacific Islander, non-Hispanic/Latino. 48% 25 or older, 3% transferred in. Retention: 57% of full-time freshmen returned the following year. Core. Calendar: semesters. Academic remediation for entering students, ESL program, services for LD students, advanced placement, distance learning, double major, summer session for credit, part-time degree program, adult/continuing education programs, co-op programs and internships. Off campus study at University of New Mexico, Northern New Mexico Community College, Santa Fe Community College.

Entrance Requirements: Required: high school transcript. Recommended: SAT or ACT.

Collegiate Environment: Orientation program. University of New Mexico - Los Alamos Library. Operations spending for the previous fiscal year: $127,566. 141 computers available on campus for general student use. A campuswide network can be accessed from off-campus. Students can access the following: online class registration. Staffed computer lab on campus provides training in use of computers, software, and the Internet.

■ UNIVERSITY OF NEW MEXICO-TAOS

115 Civic Plz. Dr.
Taos, NM 87571
Tel: (575)737-6200
Web Site: taos.unm.edu

Description: State-supported, 2-year, coed. Awards terminal associate degrees. Founded 1923. Total enrollment: 1,429. Student-undergrad faculty ratio is 19:1. 1% from out-of-state. 52% 25 or older. Calendar: semesters.
Entrance Requirements: Required: high school transcript.

■ UNIVERSITY OF NEW MEXICO-VALENCIA CAMPUS

280 La Entrada
Los Lunas, NM 87031-7633

Tel: (505)925-8580
Fax: (505)925-8563
Web Site: valencia.unm.edu

Description: State-supported, 2-year, coed. Part of New Mexico Commission on Higher Education. Awards certificates, transfer associate, and terminal associate degrees. Founded 1981. Setting: small town campus with easy access to Albuquerque. Total enrollment: 2,170. Student-undergrad faculty ratio is 25:1. 36% 25 or older. Core. Calendar: semesters. Academic remediation for entering students, ESL program, services for LD students, honors program, summer session for credit, part-time degree program, adult/continuing education programs.

Entrance Requirements: Open admission. Options: early admission, deferred admission. Recommended: high school transcript. Required for some: minimum 2.0 high school GPA. Entrance: noncompetitive. Application deadline: rolling. Notification: continuous until 8/25.

Collegiate Environment: Student services: personal-psychological counseling. Campus security: 24-hour emergency response devices and patrols, late night transport-escort service. 65 computers available on campus for general student use. A campuswide network can be accessed from off-campus. Staffed computer lab on campus.

■ UNIVERSITY OF THE SOUTHWEST

6610 Lovington Hwy.
Hobbs, NM 88240-9129
Tel: (575)392-6561; Free: 800-530-4400
E-mail: lterrazas@usw.edu
Web Site: www.usw.edu

Description: Independent Christian, comprehensive, coed. Awards bachelor's and master's degrees. Founded 1962. Setting: 162-acre small town campus. Endowment: $5.6 million. Educational spending for the previous fiscal year: $4936 per student. Total enrollment: 1,059. Faculty: 78 (35 full-time, 43 part-time). Student-undergrad faculty ratio is 17:1. 263 applied, 66% were admitted. 14% from top 10% of their high school class, 0.1% from top quarter, 44% from top half. Full-time: 301 students, 42% women, 58% men. Part-time: 149 students, 51% women, 49% men. Students come from 10 other countries, 48% from out-of-state. 0.4% American Indian or Alaska Native, non-Hispanic/Latino; 47% Hispanic/Latino; 14% Black or African American, non-Hispanic/Latino; 0.2% Asian, non-Hispanic/Latino; 0.4% Native Hawaiian or other Pacific Islander, non-Hispanic/Latino. 33% 25 or older, 55% live on campus, 20% transferred in. Retention: 56% of full-time freshmen returned the following year. Core. Calendar: semesters. Academic remediation for entering students, services for LD students, advanced placement, honors program, distance learning, double major, summer session for credit, part-time degree program, internships, graduate courses open to undergrads.

Entrance Requirements: Options: electronic application, early admission. Required: high school transcript, minimum 2 high school GPA, minimum ACT score of 18 or SAT of 940, top 50% of graduating class. Required for some: essay. Entrance: moderately difficult. Application deadline: rolling. Notification: continuous. Transfer credits accepted: Yes.

Collegiate Environment: Orientation program. Social organizations: 7 open to all. Most popular organizations: Student Government Association (SGA), Students in Free Enterprise (SIFE), Southwest Association of Future Educa-

tors, Fellowship of Christian Athletes, BEST. Major annual events: Homecoming, Mustang Stampede, Annual Distinguished Lecture Series. Student services: personal-psychological counseling. Campus security: student patrols, controlled dormitory access, night security. Scarborough Memorial Library. Operations spending for the previous fiscal year: $169,521. 65 computers available on campus for general student use. A campuswide network can be accessed from student residence rooms. Students can access the following: online class registration. Staffed computer lab on campus provides training in use of computers, software, and the Internet.

Community Environment: See New Mexico Junior College.

■ WESTERN NEW MEXICO UNIVERSITY

PO Box 680
Silver City, NM 88062-0680
Tel: (575)538-6011; Free: 800-872-WNMU
Fax: (505)538-6155
E-mail: tresslerd@wnmu.edu
Web Site: www.wnmu.edu

Description: State-supported, comprehensive, coed. Awards associate, bachelor's, and master's degrees. Founded 1893. Setting: 83-acre rural campus. Endowment: $5 million. Research spending for the previous fiscal year: $38,500. Total enrollment: 2,697. Faculty: 259 (128 full-time, 131 part-time). Student-undergrad faculty ratio is 17:1. 788 applied, 100% were admitted. 8% from top 10% of their high school class, 21% from top quarter, 40% from top half. Full-time: 1,363 students, 62% women, 38% men. Part-time: 856 students, 64% women, 36% men. Students come from 33 states and territories, 14 other countries. 46% 25 or older. Retention: 48% of full-time freshmen returned the following year. Academic areas with the most degrees conferred: business/marketing; education; liberal arts/general studies. Core. Calendar: semesters. Academic remediation for entering students, services for LD students, advanced placement, accelerated degree program, self-designed majors, summer session for credit, part-time degree program, adult/continuing education programs, co-op programs and internships, graduate courses open to undergrads.

Entrance Requirements: Open admission. Options: electronic application, early admission, deferred admission, international baccalaureate accepted. Required: high school transcript. Recommended: ACT. Entrance: noncompetitive. Application deadline: 8/1. Notification: continuous.

Collegiate Environment: Orientation program. Drama-theater group, choral group, student-run newspaper. Student services: personal-psychological counseling, women's center. Campus security: 24-hour emergency response devices and patrols, student patrols, late night transport-escort service. Miller Library plus 2 others. Operations spending for the previous fiscal year: $707,000. 85 computers available on campus for general student use. A campuswide network can be accessed from student residence rooms. Students can access the following: online class registration, online classes in Spanish. Staffed computer lab on campus.

Community Environment: Once an Apache Indian campsite and later a booming gold, silver, and zinc mining town, Silver City is a trading center for the cattle ranching and copper-mining area today. The city, located in the foothills of the mountains, has various active civic, fraternal, and veteran's organizations, and is served by commuter airline. Recreational activities include football, hunting, fishing, camping, and picnicking.

■ ADELPHI UNIVERSITY

One S Ave.
Garden City, NY 11530-0701
Tel: (516)877-3000; Free: 800-ADELPHI
Fax: (516)877-3039
E-mail: admissions@adelphi.edu
Web Site: www.adelphi.edu

Description: Independent, university, coed. Awards associate, bachelor's, master's, and doctoral degrees and post-master's certificates. Founded 1896. Setting: 75-acre suburban campus with easy access to New York City. Endowment: $188.6 million. Research spending for the previous fiscal year: $701,466. Educational spending for the previous fiscal year: $13,492 per student. Total enrollment: 8,149. Faculty: 1,060 (340 full-time, 720 part-time). Student-undergrad faculty ratio is 12:1. 13,006 applied, 74% were admitted. 26% from top 10% of their high school class, 59% from top quarter, 89% from top half. Full-time: 5,056 students, 69% women, 31% men. Part-time: 335 students, 63% women, 37% men. Students come from 38 states and territories, 48 other countries, 7% from out-of-state. 0.2% American Indian or Alaska Native, non-Hispanic/Latino; 17% Hispanic/Latino; 9% Black or African American, non-Hispanic/Latino; 11% Asian, non-Hispanic/Latino; 4% international. 9% 25 or older, 22% live on campus, 9% transferred in. Retention: 81% of full-time freshmen returned the following year. Academic areas with the most degrees conferred: health professions and related sciences; business/marketing; biological/life sciences. Core. Calendar: semesters. ROTC: Army (c), Air Force (c).

Entrance Requirements: Options: electronic application, early action, deferred admission, international baccalaureate accepted. Required: essay, high school transcript. Required for some: interview, auditions/portfolios for performing and fine arts, SAT or ACT. Entrance: moderately difficult. Application deadline: rolling. Notification: continuous. Transfer credits accepted: Yes. Early action applicants: 4,944. Early action applicants admitted: 4,078.

Costs Per Year: Application fee: $40. Comprehensive fee: $54,690 includes full-time tuition ($36,920), mandatory fees ($1740), and college room and board ($16,030). Full-time tuition and fees vary according to course level, course load, location, program, and student level. Room and board charges vary according to board plan and housing facility. Part-time tuition: $1125 per credit hour. Part-time mandatory fees: $448 per term. Part-time tuition and fees vary according to course level, course load, location, program, and student level.

Collegiate Environment: Drama-theater group, choral group, student-run newspaper, radio station. Social organizations: 80 open to all; national fraternities, national sororities, social fellowship; 9% of eligible men and 10% of eligible women are members. Most popular organizations: Student Activities Board, C. A. L. I. B. E. R. (Cause to Achieve Leadership, Intelligence, Brotherhood, Excellence, and Respect), Commuter Student Organization, Christian Fellowship, Circle K International. Major annual events: Family Weekend/Midnight Madness, Spring-In Festival/Spike It Volleyball Tournament, Spring Concert. Student services: health clinic, personal-psychological counseling. Campus security: 24-hour emergency response devices and patrols, late night transport-escort service, controlled dormitory access. 1,282 college housing spaces available; 1,159 were occupied in 2018-19. Freshmen given priority for college housing. Option: coed housing available. Swirbul Library. Books: 537,868 (physical), 240,988 (digital/electronic); Serial titles: 430 (physical), 87,949 (digital/electronic); Databases: 249. Students can reserve study rooms. Operations spending for the previous fiscal year: $6.6 million. 667 computers available on campus for general student use. Computer purchase/lease plans available. A campuswide network can be accessed from student residence rooms and from off campus. Students can access the following: online class registration, payment, drop/add classes, check application status. Staffed computer lab on campus provides training in use of computers, software, and the Internet.

Community Environment: Garden City, Long Island, was one of the first planned residential communities in the country. The settlement was established around the Cathedral of the Incarnation. The climate is temperate. Located near New York City, the area has good transportation connections with the adjoining metropolis. A library, churches of major denominations, and hospitals nearby all serve the city. There is some part-time employment in the immediate area. The locale has good shopping facilities and active civic, fraternal, and veteran's organizations.

■ ADIRONDACK COMMUNITY COLLEGE

640 Bay Rd.
Queensbury, NY 12804
Tel: (518)743-2200; Free: 888-SUNY-ADK
Fax: (518)745-1433
Web Site: www.sunyacc.edu

Description: State and locally supported, 2-year, coed. Part of State University of New York System. Awards certificates, transfer associate, and terminal associate degrees. Founded 1960. Setting: 141-acre small town campus. Endowment: $3.9 million. Total enrollment: 3,973. Faculty: 256 (90 full-time, 166 part-time). Student-undergrad faculty ratio is 17:1. 2,006 applied, 97% were admitted. Full-time: 2,189 students, 54% women, 46% men. Part-time: 1,784 students, 59% women, 41% men. Students come from 10 states and territories, 19 other countries, 1% from out-of-state. 0.5% American Indian or Alaska Native, non-Hispanic/Latino; 3% Hispanic/Latino; 3% Black or African American, non-Hispanic/Latino; 0.9% Asian, non-Hispanic/Latino; 0.2% international. 25% 25 or older, 5% transferred in. Retention: 63% of full-time freshmen returned the following year. Calendar: semesters. Academic remediation for entering students, ESL program, services for LD students, advanced placement, accelerated degree program, independent study, distance learning, double major, summer session for credit, part-time degree program, adult/continuing education programs, co-op programs and internships. Study abroad program.

Entrance Requirements: Open admission The Nursing AAS degree program has a separate admissions policy. Option: electronic application. Entrance: minimally difficult. Transfer credits accepted: Yes.

Costs Per Year: Application fee: $35. One-time mandatory fee: $35. State resident tuition: $4560 full-time, $190 per credit hour part-time. Nonresident tuition: $9120 full-time, $380 per credit hour part-time. Mandatory fees: $810 full-time, $20 per term part-time. Full-time tuition and fees vary according to course load and program. Part-time tuition and fees vary according to course load and program. College room and board: $11,600. College room only: $7860. Room and board charges vary according to board plan.

Collegiate Environment: Orientation program. Drama-theater group, choral group, student-run radio station. Student services: personal-psychological counseling. Campus security: late night transport-escort service, patrols by trained security personnel 8 am to 10 pm. SUNY Adirondack Library. 376 computers available on campus for general student use. A campuswide network can be accessed. Students can access the following: online class registration. Staffed computer lab on campus.

■ ALBANY COLLEGE OF PHARMACY AND HEALTH SCIENCES

106 New Scotland Ave.
Albany, NY 12208
Tel: (518)445-7200; Free: 888-203-8010
Fax: (518)445-7202
E-mail: admissions@acphs.edu
Web Site: www.acphs.edu

Description: Independent, comprehensive, coed. Awards bachelor's, master's, and doctoral degrees. Founded 1881. Setting: 35-acre urban campus. Total enrollment: 1,559. Faculty: 132 (101 full-time, 31 part-time). Student-undergrad faculty ratio is 14:1. 1,583 applied, 67% were admitted. 40% from top 10% of their high school class, 79% from top quarter, 99% from top half. Full-time: 1,055 students, 60% women, 40% men. Part-time: 23 students, 65% women, 35% men. Students come from 30 states and territories, 35 other countries, 23% from out-of-state. 0.4% American Indian or Alaska Native, non-Hispanic/Latino; 5% Hispanic/Latino; 3% Black or African American, non-Hispanic/Latino; 14% Asian, non-Hispanic/Latino; 0.1% Native Hawaiian or other Pacific Islander, non-Hispanic/Latino; 7% international. 10% 25 or older, 58% live on campus, 6% transferred in. Retention: 80% of full-time freshmen returned the following year. Academic area with the most degrees conferred: health professions and related sciences. Core. Calendar: semesters. Services for LD students, advanced placement, double major, summer session for credit, graduate courses open to undergrads. Off campus study at Hudson-Mohawk Association of Colleges and Universities.

Entrance Requirements: Options: electronic application, early admission, early decision. Required: essay, high school transcript, 2 recommendations, SAT or ACT. Recommended: minimum 3 high school GPA. Required for some: interview. Entrance: moderately difficult. Application deadlines: 2/1, 11/15 for early decision. Notification: 2/1, 12/1 for early decision. SAT Reasoning Test deadline: 2/1. SAT Subject Test deadline: 2/1. Transfer credits accepted: Yes. Early decision applicants: 99. Early decision applicants admitted: 86.

Collegiate Environment: Orientation program. Choral group. Social organizations: 35 open to all; national fraternities; 3% of eligible men and 1% of eligible women are members. Most popular organizations: American Pharmacists Association Academy of Students Pharmacists (APhA-ASP), Outdoors Club, Ski Club, Colleges Against Cancer, Dance Club. Major annual events: Health and Wellness Expo, Parents' Weekend, Springfest. Student services: health clinic, personal-psychological counseling. Campus security: 24-hour emergency response devices and patrols, controlled dormitory access. George and Leona Lewis Library.

■ ALFRED UNIVERSITY

One Saxon Dr.
Alfred, NY 14802-1205
Tel: (607)871-2111; Free: 800-541-9229
Fax: (607)871-2198
E-mail: admissions@alfred.edu
Web Site: www.alfred.edu

Description: Independent, university, coed. Awards bachelor's, master's, and doctoral degrees and post-master's certificates. Founded 1836. Setting: 232-acre rural campus with easy access to Rochester. Endowment: $129.3 million. Research spending for the previous fiscal year: $3.2 million. Educational spending for the previous fiscal year: $11,343 per student. Total enrollment: 2,302. Faculty: 194 (155 full-time, 39 part-time). Student-undergrad faculty ratio is 11:1. 4,296 applied, 63% were admitted. 13% from top 10% of their high school class, 34% from top quarter, 67% from top half. 3 valedictorians. Full-time: 1,572 students, 49% women, 51% men. Part-time: 99 students, 69% women, 31% men. Students come from 43 states and territories, 16 other countries, 18% from out-of-state. 0.4% American Indian or Alaska Native, non-Hispanic/Latino; 10% Hispanic/Latino; 11% Black or African American, non-Hispanic/Latino; 1% Asian, non-Hispanic/Latino; 3% international. 3% 25 or older, 69% live on campus, 6% transferred in. Retention: 73% of full-time freshmen returned the following year. Academic areas with the most degrees conferred: engineering; visual and performing arts; business/marketing. Calendar: semesters. Services for LD students, advanced placement, self-designed majors, honors program, independent study, double major, summer session for credit, part-time degree program, co-op programs and internships, graduate courses open to undergrads. Off campus study. Study abroad program. ROTC: Army (c).

Entrance Requirements: Options: electronic application, early admission, early decision, deferred admission, international baccalaureate accepted. Required: essay, high school transcript, 1 recommendation, SAT or ACT. Recommended: interview, SAT. Required for some: portfolio for applicants to the School of Art and Design. Entrance: moderately difficult. Application deadlines: rolling for nonresidents, 12/1 for early decision. Notification: continuous, continuous for nonresidents. SAT Reasoning Test deadline: 8/1. SAT Subject Test deadline: 8/1. Transfer credits accepted: Yes. Early decision applicants: 32. Early decision applicants admitted: 27.

Costs Per Year: Application fee: $50. Comprehensive fee: $47,488 includes full-time tuition ($33,760), mandatory fees ($1010), and college room and board ($12,718). College room only: $6418. Part-time tuition: $1036 per credit hour.

Collegiate Environment: Orientation program. Drama-theater group, choral group, student-run newspaper, radio station. Social organizations: 85 open to all. Most popular organizations: Carribean Student Association, Student Activities Board, Art Force 5, Student Senate. Major annual events: Hot Dog Day, Homecoming, Family Weekend. Student services: health clinic, personal-psychological counseling, women's center. Campus security: 24-hour emergency response devices, student patrols, late night transport-escort service, controlled dormitory access. 1,486 college housing spaces available; 1,100 were occupied in 2018-19. Freshmen guaranteed college housing. On-campus residence required through junior year. Options: coed, men-only, women-only housing available. Herrick Memorial Library plus 1 other. Books: 177,734 (physical), 865,873 (digital/electronic); Serial titles: 249 (physical), 108,773 (digital/electronic); Databases: 330. Study areas open 24 hours, 5-7 days a week; students can reserve study rooms. Operations spending for the previous fiscal year: $1.6 million. 1,231 computers available on campus for general student use. Computer purchase/lease plans available. A campuswide network can be accessed from student residence rooms and from off campus. Students can access the following: online class registration, online bill pay. Staffed computer lab on campus provides training in use of computers, software, and the Internet.

Community Environment: Alfred is a small residential community situated among the foothills of the Allegheny Mountains near the Finger Lakes Region of New York. It is served by air service in nearby cities (Rochester/Elmira), and also bus service. It is the home of the Davis Memorial Carillon, which contains the oldest carillon bells in the western hemisphere. Outdoor activities including hiking, white water rafting, downhill and cross-country skiing, and horseback riding are located a short distance from campus. Numerous groups sponsor appearances by visiting professors, speakers, and artists. Student groups sponsor a number of popular entertainers and rock and folk concerts. Both a current movie series and a classics series provide weekly films. The Fosdick Nelson Gallery shows exhibits of sculpture, glass, ceramics, paintings, lithographs and photographs. Additionally, student theatre and dance productions, as well as performances by musical ensembles, are scheduled throughout the year.

■ AMERICAN ACADEMY OF DRAMATIC ARTS-NEW YORK

120 Madison Ave.
New York, NY 10016-7004
Tel: (212)686-9244; Free: 800-463-8990
E-mail: kreilly@aada.edu
Web Site: www.aada.edu

Description: Independent, 2-year, coed. Administratively affiliated with American Academy of Dramatic Arts-Los Angeles. Awards certificates and terminal associate degrees. Founded 1884. Setting: urban campus. Total enrollment: 310. Faculty: 39 (8 full-time, 31 part-time). Student-undergrad faculty ratio is 8:1. 524 applied, 80% were admitted. Full-time: 310 students, 68% women, 32% men. Students come from 28 states and territories, 25 other countries, 84% from out-of-state. 0.3% American Indian or Alaska Native, non-Hispanic/Latino; 5% Hispanic/Latino; 8% Black or African American, non-Hispanic/Latino; 0.6% Asian, non-Hispanic/Latino; 28% international. 20% 25 or older, 53% live on campus. Retention: 75% of full-time freshmen returned the following year. Core. Calendar: semesters. Academic remediation for entering students, honors program.

Entrance Requirements: Options: electronic application, deferred admission. Required: essay, high school transcript, minimum 2 high school GPA, 2 recommendations, interview, audition. Entrance: moderately difficult. Application deadline: rolling. Notification: continuous. Transfer credits accepted: No.

Costs Per Year: Application fee: $50. Comprehensive fee: $53,155 includes full-time tuition ($34,410), mandatory fees ($750), and college room and board ($17,995). Room and board charges vary according to housing facility.

Collegiate Environment: Orientation program. Social organizations: 1 open to all. Major annual events: Academy Theatre Company Christmas Party, Graduation, Guest Lecturers. Student services: personal-psychological counseling. Campus security: 24-hour emergency response devices and patrols, controlled dormitory access, trained security guard during hours of operation and for campus housing. Academy/CBS Library. 5 computers available on campus for general student use. A campuswide network can be accessed.

■ AMERICAN ACADEMY MCALLISTER INSTITUTE OF FUNERAL SERVICE

619 W 54th St.
New York, NY 10019-3602
Tel: (212)757-1190; Free: 866-932-2264
Fax: (212)765-5923
Web Site: www.funeraleducation.org
Description: Independent, 2-year, coed. Awards diplomas and terminal associate degrees. Founded 1926. Setting: urban campus. Total enrollment: 317. Student-undergrad faculty ratio is 18:1. 30% from out-of-state. 68% 25 or older. Core. Calendar: semesters.
Entrance Requirements: Open admission. Options: early admission, deferred admission. Required: high school transcript, 2 recommendations. Recommended: interview. Entrance: noncompetitive. Application deadline: rolling. Notification: continuous until 8/15.
Collegiate Environment: American Academy MacAllister Institute Library.

■ ASA COLLEGE

81 Willoughby St.
Brooklyn, NY 11201
Tel: (718)522-9073; Free: 877-679-8772
Fax: (718)834-0835
Web Site: www.asa.edu
Description: Proprietary, 2-year, coed. Awards certificates and terminal associate degrees. Founded 1985. Setting: urban campus with easy access to New York City. Total enrollment: 6,475. 3,368 applied. Calendar: semesters. Academic remediation for entering students, ESL program, advanced placement, accelerated degree program, distance learning, part-time degree program, co-op programs and internships.
Entrance Requirements: Option: electronic application. Required: high school transcript, interview. Transfer credits accepted: Yes.
Collegiate Environment: Orientation program.

■ BARD COLLEGE

PO Box 5000
Annandale on Hudson, NY 12504
Tel: (845)758-6822
E-mail: admission@bard.edu
Web Site: www.bard.edu
Description: Independent, comprehensive, coed. Awards bachelor's, master's, and doctoral degrees. Founded 1860. Setting: 1,000-acre rural campus. Total enrollment: 2,284. Faculty: 297 (155 full-time, 142 part-time). Student-undergrad faculty ratio is 9:1. 4,922 applied, 58% were admitted. 41% from top 10% of their high school class, 66% from top quarter, 96% from top half. Full-time: 1,855 students, 59% women, 41% men. Part-time: 75 students, 53% women, 47% men. Students come from 46 states and territories, 55 other countries, 66% from out-of-state. 0.1% American Indian or Alaska Native, non-Hispanic/Latino; 6% Hispanic/Latino; 7% Black or African American, non-Hispanic/Latino; 4% Asian, non-Hispanic/Latino; 11% international. 1% 25 or older, 75% live on campus, 3% transferred in. Retention: 82% of full-time freshmen returned the following year. Core. Calendar: semesters. Services for LD students, advanced placement, self-designed majors, independent study, double major, part-time degree program, adult/continuing education programs, internships, graduate courses open to undergrads. Off campus study at Vassar College, State University of New York at New Paltz. Study abroad program.
Entrance Requirements: Options: electronic application, early admission, early decision, early action, deferred admission, international baccalaureate accepted. Required: essay, high school transcript, minimum 3 high school GPA, 3 recommendations. Entrance: moderately difficult. Application deadlines: 1/1, 11/1 for early decision, 11/1 for early action. Notification: 4/1, 1/1 for early action. Transfer credits accepted: Yes. Applicants placed on waiting list: 473. Wait-listed applicants offered admission: 33. Early decision applicants: 36. Early decision applicants admitted: 24.
Collegiate Environment: Orientation program. Drama-theater group, choral group, student-run newspaper, radio station. Social organizations: 150 open to all. Student services: legal services, health clinic, personal-psychological counseling. Campus security: 24-hour emergency response devices and patrols, student patrols, late night transport-escort service, controlled dormi-

tory access. Stevenson Library plus 3 others. Weekly public service hours: 75; students can reserve study rooms.
Community Environment: The town is situated on the Hudson River in eastern New York. The area is accessible via Metro North and Amtrak Railroad nearby, the Taconic State Parkway, or the New York Thruway, using Exit 19 and the Kingston-Rhinecliff Bridge.

■ BARNARD COLLEGE

3009 Broadway
New York, NY 10027-6598
Tel: (212)854-5262
Fax: (212)854-6220
E-mail: admissions@barnard.edu
Web Site: www.barnard.edu
Description: Independent, 4-year, women only. Administratively affiliated with Columbia University. Awards bachelor's degrees. Founded 1889. Setting: 4-acre urban campus. Endowment: $327.2 million. Total enrollment: 2,604. Faculty: 363 (226 full-time, 137 part-time). Student-undergrad faculty ratio is 10:1. 7,716 applied, 15% were admitted. 84% from top 10% of their high school class, 93% from top quarter, 100% from top half. Full-time: 2,574 students. Part-time: 30 students. Students come from 50 states and territories, 66 other countries, 73% from out-of-state. 0.2% American Indian or Alaska Native, non-Hispanic/Latino; 12% Hispanic/Latino; 6% Black or African American, non-Hispanic/Latino; 15% Asian, non-Hispanic/Latino; 0.1% Native Hawaiian or other Pacific Islander, non-Hispanic/Latino; 9% international. 91% live on campus, 3% transferred in. Retention: 95% of full-time freshmen returned the following year. Academic areas with the most degrees conferred: social sciences; psychology; biological/life sciences; visual and performing arts. Core. Calendar: semesters. Services for LD students, advanced placement, accelerated degree program, self-designed majors, independent study, double major, internships. Off campus study at Joint degree programs with Columbia University (3-2 Engineering, Master of International Affairs, and Master of Public Administration). Study at Teachers College, Manhattan School of Music, Juilliard School, and Jewish Theological Seminary. Spelman College exchange program. Study abroad program. ROTC: Army (c), Naval (c), Air Force (c).
Entrance Requirements: Options: electronic application, early admission, early decision, deferred admission, international baccalaureate accepted. Required: essay, high school transcript, 3 recommendations, Common Application with Barnard Supplement, SAT or ACT. Recommended: interview. Entrance: most difficult. Application deadlines: 1/1, 11/1 for early decision. Notification: 4/1, 12/15 for early decision. SAT Reasoning Test deadline: 1/1. SAT Subject Test deadline: 1/1. Transfer credits accepted: Yes. Applicants placed on waiting list: 1,703. Wait-listed applicants offered admission: 51. Early decision applicants: 934. Early decision applicants admitted: 289.
Costs Per Year: Application fee: $75. Comprehensive fee: $72,257 includes full-time tuition ($53,252), mandatory fees ($1780), and college room and board ($17,225). College room only: $10,435. Room and board charges vary according to board plan and housing facility. Part-time tuition: $1775 per credit hour.
Collegiate Environment: Orientation program. Drama-theater group, choral group, marching band, student-run newspaper, radio station. Social organizations: 100 open to all; national sororities. Most popular organizations: Community Impact (community service), Student Government Association, Take Back the Night, Student Activities Council, Musical Theater Society. Major annual events: Midnight Breakfast, Founder's Day, Take Back the Night. Student services: health clinic, personal-psychological counseling, women's center. Campus security: 24-hour emergency response devices and patrols, late night transport-escort service, controlled dormitory access, gated campus with permanent security posts. Lefrak Center plus 20 others. Study areas open 24 hours, 5-7 days a week. 165 computers available on campus for general student use. Computer purchase/lease plans available. A campuswide network can be accessed from student residence rooms and from off campus. Students can access the following: online class registration. Staffed computer lab on campus provides training in use of computers, software, and the Internet.
Community Environment: See Columbia University.

■ BARUCH COLLEGE OF THE CITY UNIVERSITY OF NEW YORK

1 Bernard Baruch Way
New York, NY 10010-5585
Tel: (646)312-1000
Web Site: www.baruch.cuny.edu
Description: State and locally supported, comprehensive, coed. Part of City

University of New York System. Awards bachelor's and master's degrees and post-master's certificates. Founded 1919. Setting: 4-acre urban campus. Total enrollment: 18,029. Faculty: 1,100 (493 full-time, 607 part-time). Student-undergrad faculty ratio is 18:1. 21,469 applied, 39% were admitted. 50% from top 10% of their high school class, 77% from top quarter, 95% from top half. Full-time: 11,495 students, 48% women, 52% men. Part-time: 3,529 students, 46% women, 54% men. Students come from 26 states and territories, 3% from out-of-state. 0.1% American Indian or Alaska Native, non-Hispanic/Latino; 26% Hispanic/Latino; 9% Black or African American, non-Hispanic/Latino; 32% Asian, non-Hispanic/Latino; 0.1% Native Hawaiian or other Pacific Islander, non-Hispanic/Latino; 11% international. 23% 25 or older, 2% live on campus, 10% transferred in. Retention: 89% of full-time freshmen returned the following year. Academic areas with the most degrees conferred: business/marketing; computer and information sciences; psychology. Core. Calendar: semesters. ESL program, services for LD students, advanced placement, accelerated degree program, self-designed majors, freshman honors college, honors program, independent study, distance learning, double major, summer session for credit, part-time degree program, adult/continuing education programs, internships, graduate courses open to undergrads. Study abroad program. ROTC: Army (c).

Entrance Requirements: Options: electronic application, early admission, early decision, deferred admission, international baccalaureate accepted. Required: high school transcript, minimum 2.5 high school GPA, 16 academic units, SAT or ACT. Required for some: interview. Entrance: very difficult. Application deadline: 2/1. Notification: 5/15. SAT Reasoning Test deadline: 4/1. Transfer credits accepted: Yes.

Costs Per Year: Application fee: $65. State resident tuition: $6530 full-time, $285 per credit hour part-time. Nonresident tuition: $17,400 full-time, $580 per credit hour part-time. Mandatory fees: $585 full-time, $162.95 per term part-time. Full-time tuition and fees vary according to course load. Part-time tuition and fees vary according to course load.

Collegiate Environment: Orientation program. Drama-theater group, choral group, student-run newspaper, radio station. Social organizations: national fraternities, national sororities, local fraternities, local sororities. Most popular organizations: Accounting Society, Caribbean Students Association, Association of Latino Professionals in Finance and Accounting, Golden Key International Honor Society, Helpline. Major annual events: Street Fair, Club Fair, Caribbean Cultural Festival. Student services: legal services, health clinic, personal-psychological counseling. Campus security: 24-hour emergency response devices and patrols, late night transport-escort service. 291 college housing spaces available; all were occupied in 2018-19. No special consideration for freshman housing applicants. Option: coed housing available. The William and Anita Newman Library. Books: 330,647 (physical), 515,356 (digital/electronic); Serial titles: 117,795 (physical), 117,795 (digital/electronic). Students can reserve study rooms. 1,300 computers available on campus for general student use. A campuswide network can be accessed. Students can access the following: online class registration. Staffed computer lab on campus provides training in use of computers, software, and the Internet.

■ **BE'ER YAAKOV TALMUDIC SEMINARY**
12 Jefferson Ave.
Spring Valley, NY 10977
Tel: (845)406-9699
Description: Independent Jewish, 4-year, coed. Awards bachelor's degrees.

■ **BEIS MEDRASH HEICHAL DOVID**
257 Beach 17th St.
Far Rockaway, NY 11691
Tel: (718)868-2300
Fax: (718)868-0517
Description: Proprietary, comprehensive, men only. Awards bachelor's and master's degrees. Total enrollment: 111. 37 applied.
Entrance Requirements: Recommended: high school transcript.

■ **THE BELANGER SCHOOL OF NURSING**
650 McClellan St.
Schenectady, NY 12304
Tel: (518)243-4471
E-mail: lansingc@ellismedicine.org
Web Site: www.ellismedicine.org/school-of-nursing
Description: Independent, 2-year, coed. Awards transfer associate and terminal associate degrees. Founded 1906. Setting: urban campus. Total enrollment: 114. Student-undergrad faculty ratio is 4:1. 5 applied. Full-time:

37 students, 89% women, 11% men. Part-time: 77 students, 78% women, 22% men. 0.9% American Indian or Alaska Native, non-Hispanic/Latino; 5% Hispanic/Latino; 8% Black or African American, non-Hispanic/Latino; 15% Asian, non-Hispanic/Latino. 61% 25 or older. Core. Honors program, summer session for credit, part-time degree program.

Entrance Requirements: Options: electronic application, international baccalaureate accepted. Required: essay, high school transcript, minimum 3 high school GPA, 2 recommendations, Kaplan Admission Test. Application deadline: 1/15. Notification: 3/15. Transfer credits accepted: Yes.

Collegiate Environment: Orientation program. Social organizations: 1 open to all; Honor Society; 25% of men are members. Most popular organization: Student Government. Campus security: on-campus security department 24/7. Ellis Medicine's Health Services Library. Books: 2,000 (physical). Weekly public service hours: 40. 24 computers available on campus for general student use. A campuswide network can be accessed.

■ **BERKELEY COLLEGE-NEW YORK CITY CAMPUS**
3 E 43rd St.
New York, NY 10017
Tel: (212)986-4343; Free: 800-446-5400
Fax: (212)697-3371
E-mail: info@berkeleycollege.edu
Web Site: www.berkeleycollege.edu
Description: Proprietary, 4-year, coed. Administratively affiliated with Berkeley College - Woodland Park Campus (NJ). Awards associate and bachelor's degrees. Founded 1936. Setting: urban campus with easy access to New York City. Educational spending for the previous fiscal year: $6838 per student. Total enrollment: 3,293. Student-undergrad faculty ratio is 23:1. 1,074 applied, 100% were admitted. Full-time: 2,475 students, 63% women, 37% men. Part-time: 818 students, 69% women, 31% men. Students come from 29 states and territories, 52 other countries, 11% from out-of-state. 0.3% American Indian or Alaska Native, non-Hispanic/Latino; 22% Hispanic/Latino; 23% Black or African American, non-Hispanic/Latino; 3% Asian, non-Hispanic/Latino; 9% international. 55% 25 or older, 12% transferred in. Retention: 66% of full-time freshmen returned the following year. Academic areas with the most degrees conferred: business/marketing; homeland security, law enforcement, firefighting, and protective services; health professions and related sciences. Core. Calendar: semesters. Academic remediation for entering students, ESL program, advanced placement, accelerated degree program, honors program, independent study, distance learning, part-time degree program, adult/continuing education programs, co-op programs and internships. Off campus study at Berkeley College NJ. Study abroad program.

Entrance Requirements: Options: electronic application, deferred admission. Required: essay, high school transcript. Recommended: interview. Entrance: minimally difficult. Application deadlines: rolling, rolling for nonresidents. Notification: continuous, continuous for nonresidents. Transfer credits accepted: Yes.

Collegiate Environment: Orientation program. Student-run newspaper. Most popular organizations: International Student, Latino/Hispanic Club, Student Veterans of America, Sista Circle, Business Club. Major annual events: Chat'n'Chew with the President, Community Service Week, Graduate Salute. Student services: personal-psychological counseling. Campus security: 24-hour emergency response devices. College housing not available. Books: 31,426 (physical), 168,797 (digital/electronic); Serial titles: 134 (physical), 72,544 (digital/electronic); Databases: 84. Operations spending for the previous fiscal year: $1.4 million. 500 computers available on campus for general student use. A campuswide network can be accessed from off-campus. Students can access the following: online class registration. Staffed computer lab on campus provides training in use of computers, software, and the Internet.

■ **BERKELEY COLLEGE-WHITE PLAINS CAMPUS**
99 Church St.
White Plains, NY 10601
Tel: (914)694-1122; Free: 800-446-5400
Fax: (914)694-5832
E-mail: info@berkeleycollege.edu
Web Site: www.berkeleycollege.edu
Description: Proprietary, 4-year, coed. Administratively affiliated with Berkeley College-New York City. Awards associate and bachelor's degrees. Founded 1945. Setting: suburban campus with easy access to New York City. Educational spending for the previous fiscal year: $6838 per student. Total enrollment: 403. Student-undergrad faculty ratio is 23:1. 258 applied,

98% were admitted. Full-time: 359 students, 61% women, 39% men. Part-time: 44 students, 80% women, 20% men. Students come from 17 states and territories, 8 other countries, 24% from out-of-state. 26% Hispanic/Latino; 21% Black or African American, non-Hispanic/Latino; 3% Asian, non-Hispanic/Latino; 9% international. 23% 25 or older, 20% live on campus, 7% transferred in. Retention: 62% of full-time freshmen returned the following year. Academic areas with the most degrees conferred: business/marketing; homeland security, law enforcement, firefighting, and protective services; health professions and related sciences. Core. Calendar: semesters. Academic remediation for entering students, advanced placement, accelerated degree program, honors program, independent study, distance learning, summer session for credit, part-time degree program, adult/continuing education programs, co-op programs and internships. Off campus study at Berkeley College NJ. Study abroad program.

Entrance Requirements: Options: electronic application, deferred admission. Required: essay, high school transcript. Recommended: interview. Entrance: minimally difficult. Application deadlines: rolling, rolling for nonresidents. Notification: continuous, continuous for nonresidents. Transfer credits accepted: Yes.

Collegiate Environment: Orientation program. Student-run newspaper. Student services: personal-psychological counseling. Campus security: 24-hour emergency response devices, controlled dormitory access. 100 college housing spaces available; 90 were occupied in 2018-19. No special consideration for freshman housing applicants. Option: coed housing available. Books: 168,797 (digital/electronic); Serial titles: 72,544 (digital/electronic); Databases: 84. 158 computers available on campus for general student use. A campuswide network can be accessed from student residence rooms and from off campus. Students can access the following: online class registration. Staffed computer lab on campus provides training in use of computers, software, and the Internet.

■ BET MEDRASH GADOL ATERET TORAH
1750 E Fourth St.
Brooklyn, NY 11223
Web Site: www.betmedrashgadolaterettorah.com
Description: Independent Jewish, 4-year, coed.

■ BETH HAMEDRASH SHAAREI YOSHER INSTITUTE
4102-10 Sixteenth Ave.
Brooklyn, NY 11204
Tel: (718)854-2290
Web Site: www.bethhamedrashshaareiyosher.com
Description: Independent Jewish, comprehensive, men only. Awards bachelor's and master's degrees. Founded 1962. Total enrollment: 82. 17 applied, 100% were admitted. Calendar: semesters.

■ BETH HATALMUD RABBINICAL COLLEGE
2127 Eighty-second St.
Brooklyn, NY 11214
Tel: (718)259-2525
Description: Independent Jewish, comprehensive, men only. Awards bachelor's and master's degrees. Founded 1950. Total enrollment: 75. 28 applied, 100% were admitted. Calendar: semesters.

■ BETH MEDRASH MEOR YITZCHOK
85 Dykstras Way E
Monsey, NY 10952
Web Site: www.bethmedrashmeoryitzchok.com
Description: Independent Jewish, 4-year, coed.

■ BILL AND SANDRA POMEROY COLLEGE OF NURSING AT CROUSE HOSPITAL
765 Irving Ave.
Syracuse, NY 13210
Tel: (315)470-7481
E-mail: amygraham@crouse.org
Web Site: www.crouse.org/nursing
Description: Independent, 2-year, coed. Awards transfer associate and terminal associate degrees. Founded 1913. Setting: urban campus. Total enrollment: 285. 253 applied. Students come from 2 states and territories, 1% from out-of-state. 52% 25 or older. Core. Calendar: semesters. Academic remediation for entering students, services for LD students, advanced placement, part-time degree program.
Entrance Requirements: Option: deferred admission. Required: high

school transcript, minimum 2.5 high school GPA, 2 recommendations. Recommended: SAT or ACT. Required for some: SAT or ACT. Entrance: moderately difficult. Application deadline: 2/1. Transfer credits accepted: Yes.
Collegiate Environment: Orientation program. Social organizations: 1 open to all. Most popular organization: NSNA. Student services: health clinic, personal-psychological counseling. Campus security: 24-hour emergency response devices and patrols, late night transport-escort service, controlled dormitory access. Crouse Hospital Library. 20 computers available on campus for general student use. A campuswide network can be accessed. Students can access the following: online class registration. Staffed computer lab on campus provides training in use of computers, software, and the Internet.

■ BINGHAMTON UNIVERSITY, STATE UNIVERSITY OF NEW YORK
4400 Vestal Pky. E
Binghamton, NY 13902-6000
Tel: (607)777-2000
E-mail: admit@binghamton.edu
Web Site: www.binghamton.edu
Description: State-supported, university, coed. Part of State University of New York System. Awards bachelor's, master's, and doctoral degrees and post-master's certificates. Founded 1946. Setting: 930-acre suburban campus. Endowment: $109.3 million. Research spending for the previous fiscal year: $31.3 million. Educational spending for the previous fiscal year: $13,423 per student. Total enrollment: 17,322. Faculty: 1,047 (754 full-time, 293 part-time). Student-undergrad faculty ratio is 19:1. 33,467 applied, 40% were admitted. Full-time: 13,337 students, 49% women, 51% men. Part-time: 371 students, 46% women, 54% men. Students come from 48 states and territories, 97 other countries, 6% from out-of-state. 0.1% American Indian or Alaska Native, non-Hispanic/Latino; 11% Hispanic/Latino; 5% Black or African American, non-Hispanic/Latino; 14% Asian, non-Hispanic/Latino; 0.1% Native Hawaiian or other Pacific Islander, non-Hispanic/Latino; 8% international. 3% 25 or older, 52% live on campus, 8% transferred in. Retention: 91% of full-time freshmen returned the following year. Academic areas with the most degrees conferred: social sciences; business/marketing; biological/life sciences. Core. Calendar: semesters. ESL program, services for LD students, advanced placement, accelerated degree program, self-designed majors, honors program, independent study, distance learning, double major, summer session for credit, part-time degree program, adult/continuing education programs, internships, graduate courses open to undergrads. Off campus study at National Student Exchange, New York State Visiting Student Program. Study abroad program. ROTC: Army (c), Air Force (c).
Entrance Requirements: Options: electronic application, early admission, early action, deferred admission, international baccalaureate accepted. Required: essay, high school transcript, 1 recommendation, SAT or ACT. Required for some: portfolio, audition. Entrance: very difficult. Application deadlines: rolling, 11/1 for early action. Notification: 4/1, 1/15 for early action. Transfer credits accepted: Yes. Applicants placed on waiting list: 1,543. Wait-listed applicants offered admission: 374. Early action applicants: 11,526. Early action applicants admitted: 5,366.
Costs Per Year: Application fee: $50. State resident tuition: $6870 full-time, $286 per credit hour part-time. Nonresident tuition: $23,710 full-time, $988 per credit hour part-time. Mandatory fees: $2938 full-time, $117.75 per credit hour part-time, $24.25 per term part-time. Full-time tuition and fees vary according to program. Part-time tuition and fees vary according to course load and program. College room and board: $15,058. College room only: $9882. Room and board charges vary according to board plan and housing facility.
Collegiate Environment: Orientation program. Drama-theater group, choral group, student-run newspaper, radio station. Social organizations: 373 open to all; national fraternities, national sororities, local fraternities, local sororities; 14% of eligible men and 11% of eligible women are members. Most popular organizations: Finance Society, Student Volunteer Center, Habitat for Humanity, Pre-Medical Association, Sno-Cats Ski and Snowboard Club. Major annual events: Spring Fling, Frost Fest, Rec Fest. Student services: legal services, health clinic, personal-psychological counseling, women's center. Campus security: 24-hour emergency response devices and patrols, student patrols, late night transport-escort service, controlled dormitory access, only main gate open to traffic 12-5 am, emergency text system, self-defense workshops. Glenn G. Bartle Library plus 4 others. Books: 2.3 million (physical), 1.1 million (digital/electronic); Serial titles: 683 (physical), 125,064 (digital/electronic); Databases: 358. Weekly public service hours: 136; study areas open 24 hours, 5-7 days a week; students can reserve study rooms. Operations spending for the previous fiscal year: $15.2 million. 1,184

computers available on campus for general student use. A campuswide network can be accessed from student residence rooms and from off campus. Students can access the following: online class registration, course management system, personal Web space, wiki, virtual desktop. Staffed computer lab on campus (open 24 hours a day) provides training in use of computers, software, and the Internet.

■ BORICUA COLLEGE

3755 Broadway
New York, NY 10032-1560
Tel: (212)694-1000
E-mail: mpfeffer@boricuacollege.edu
Web Site: www.boricuacollege.edu

Description: Independent, comprehensive, coed. Awards associate, bachelor's, and master's degrees. Founded 1974. Setting: urban campus. Endowment: $626,808. Educational spending for the previous fiscal year: $2599 per student. Total enrollment: 1,058. Faculty: 133 (57 full-time, 76 part-time). Student-undergrad faculty ratio is 20:1. 924 applied, 40% were admitted. Full-time: 1,004 students, 79% women, 21% men. Students come from 2 states and territories. 89% 25 or older. Retention: 53% of full-time freshmen returned the following year. Core. Calendar: 15-15-8. Accelerated degree program, honors program, summer session for credit, adult/continuing education programs, internships. Study abroad program.

Entrance Requirements: Option: deferred admission. Required: essay, high school transcript, 2 recommendations, interview, Boricua College Exam. Entrance: moderately difficult. Application deadline: rolling.

Collegiate Environment: Choral group. Campus security: 24-hour emergency response devices. Boricua College Library plus 1 other. Operations spending for the previous fiscal year: $192,471. 120 computers available on campus for general student use. Staffed computer lab on campus provides training in use of computers, software, and the Internet.

■ BOROUGH OF MANHATTAN COMMUNITY COLLEGE OF THE CITY UNIVERSITY OF NEW YORK

199 Chambers St.
New York, NY 10007-1097
Tel: (212)220-8000; Free: 866-583-5729
Fax: (212)346-8816
E-mail: admissions@bmcc.cuny.edu
Web Site: www.bmcc.cuny.edu

Description: State and locally supported, 2-year, coed. Part of City University of New York System. Awards certificates, transfer associate, and terminal associate degrees. Founded 1963. Setting: 5-acre urban campus. Total enrollment: 26,506. Faculty: 1,714 (519 full-time, 1,195 part-time). Student-undergrad faculty ratio is 24:1. 25,455 applied, 98% were admitted. Full-time: 18,076 students, 57% women, 43% men. Part-time: 8,430 students, 60% women, 40% men. 4% from out-of-state. 0.4% American Indian or Alaska Native, non-Hispanic/Latino; 45% Hispanic/Latino; 27% Black or African American, non-Hispanic/Latino; 11% Asian, non-Hispanic/Latino; 0.2% Native Hawaiian or other Pacific Islander, non-Hispanic/Latino; 6% international. 26% 25 or older, 7% transferred in. Core. Calendar: semesters. Academic remediation for entering students, ESL program, services for LD students, advanced placement, accelerated degree program, honors program, independent study, distance learning, summer session for credit, part-time degree program, adult/continuing education programs, co-op programs and internships. Off campus study at other units of the City University of New York System. Study abroad program.

Entrance Requirements: Open admission. Options: electronic application, deferred admission. Required: high school transcript. Recommended: SAT or ACT. Entrance: noncompetitive. Application deadline: rolling. Notification: continuous. Preference given to New York City residents. Transfer credits accepted: Yes.

Costs Per Year: Application fee: $65. Area resident tuition: $4800 full-time, $210 per credit part-time. State resident tuition: $4800 full-time, $210 per credit part-time. Nonresident tuition: $7680 full-time, $320 per credit part-time. Mandatory fees: $369 full-time, $100.

Collegiate Environment: Orientation program. Drama-theater group, choral group, student-run newspaper. Social organizations: 75 open to all. Most popular organizations: Bangladeshi Student Association, Health Information Technology, Muslim Students Association, Resurgence in Christ, Urban Mentors and Leaders Association. Major annual events: Career Fiesta, FAFSAcon, Volunteer Fair. Student services: health clinic, personal-psychological counseling, women's center. Campus security: 24-hour patrols. A. Philip Randolph Library plus 1 other. Books: 113,472 (physical),

580,303 (digital/electronic); Serial titles: 1,061 (physical), 114,687 (digital/electronic); Databases: 169. Weekly public service hours: 80; students can reserve study rooms.

■ BRONX COMMUNITY COLLEGE OF THE CITY UNIVERSITY OF NEW YORK

2155 University Ave.
Bronx, NY 10453
Tel: (718)289-5100
E-mail: admission@bcc.cuny.edu
Web Site: www.bcc.cuny.edu

Description: State and locally supported, 2-year, coed. Part of City University of New York System. Awards certificates, transfer associate, and terminal associate degrees. Founded 1959. Setting: 50-acre urban campus with easy access to New York City. Endowment: $469,572. Educational spending for the previous fiscal year: $4597 per student. Total enrollment: 11,368. Faculty: 406 (303 full-time, 103 part-time). Student-undergrad faculty ratio is 26:1. Full-time: 6,598 students, 55% women, 45% men. Part-time: 4,770 students, 60% women, 40% men. Students come from 119 other countries, 8% from out-of-state. 35% 25 or older, 9% transferred in. Retention: 65% of full-time freshmen returned the following year. Core. Calendar: semesters. Academic remediation for entering students, ESL program, services for LD students, advanced placement, accelerated degree program, honors program, independent study, distance learning, double major, summer session for credit, part-time degree program, adult/continuing education programs, co-op programs and internships. Off campus study. Study abroad program.

Entrance Requirements: Open admission. Option: early admission. Required: high school transcript. Recommended: SAT or ACT. Entrance: noncompetitive. Application deadline: 7/1. Notification: 8/15. Transfer credits accepted: Yes.

Collegiate Environment: Orientation program. Drama-theater group, choral group, student-run newspaper. Social organizations: 31 open to all. Most popular organizations: Muslim Students Association, Top Models Club, Anime/Manga Gaming Club, Business Club, Media Technology and Film Society. Major annual events: Freshman Convocation, Commencement and Related Programs, New Student Orientation. Student services: health clinic, personal-psychological counseling. Campus security: 24-hour emergency response devices and patrols, late night transport-escort service, free shuttle bus service provides transportation from campus to subway and bus lines between 5 pm-11 pm. Library & Gerald S. Lieblich Learning Resources Center. Operations spending for the previous fiscal year: $1.5 million. 1,425 computers available on campus for general student use. A campuswide network can be accessed from off-campus. Students can access the following: online class registration. Staffed computer lab on campus provides training in use of computers, software, and the Internet.

■ BROOKLYN COLLEGE OF THE CITY UNIVERSITY OF NEW YORK

2900 Bedford Ave.
Brooklyn, NY 11210-2889
Tel: (718)951-5000
E-mail: adminqry@brooklyn.cuny.edu
Web Site: www.brooklyn.cuny.edu

Description: State and locally supported, comprehensive, coed. Part of City University of New York System. Awards bachelor's and master's degrees and post-master's certificates. Founded 1930. Setting: 35-acre urban campus with easy access to Manhattan. Total enrollment: 17,580. Faculty: 1,286 (544 full-time, 742 part-time). Student-undergrad faculty ratio is 17:1. 20,608 applied, 37% were admitted. 17% from top 10% of their high school class, 49% from top quarter, 79% from top half. Full-time: 10,198 students, 58% women, 42% men. Part-time: 4,208 students, 60% women, 40% men. Students come from 30 states and territories, 143 other countries, 2% from out-of-state. 0.2% American Indian or Alaska Native, non-Hispanic/Latino; 23% Hispanic/Latino; 21% Black or African American, non-Hispanic/Latino; 19% Asian, non-Hispanic/Latino; 0.2% Native Hawaiian or other Pacific Islander, non-Hispanic/Latino; 3% international. 26% 25 or older, 15% transferred in. Retention: 82% of full-time freshmen returned the following year. Academic areas with the most degrees conferred: business/marketing; psychology; education. Core. Calendar: semesters. ESL program, services for LD students, advanced placement, freshman honors college, honors program, independent study, distance learning, double major, summer session for credit, part-time degree program, adult/continuing education programs, internships, graduate courses open to undergrads. Off campus study at other units of the City University of New York System. Study abroad program.

Entrance Requirements: Option: international baccalaureate accepted. Required: high school transcript, minimum 3.1 high school GPA, combined SAT or ACT scores of 1000, SAT or ACT. Entrance: moderately difficult. Application deadline: 2/1. Notification: continuous. Transfer credits accepted: Yes.

Costs Per Year: Application fee: $65. State resident tuition: $6730 full-time, $295 per credit part-time. Nonresident tuition: $18,000 full-time, $600 per credit part-time. Mandatory fees: $510 full-time, $192.37 per term part-time. Full-time tuition and fees vary according to course load. Part-time tuition and fees vary according to course load.

Collegiate Environment: Orientation program. Drama-theater group, choral group, student-run newspaper, radio station. Social organizations: 150 open to all; national fraternities, national sororities, local fraternities, local sororities; 3% of eligible men and 3% of eligible women are members. Most popular organizations: Academic Club Association, Kingsman and Excelsior Newspaper, NY Public Interest Group (NYPIRG), Student Government CIAS, SGS, and GSO, Student Forensics. Major annual events: Presidential Convocation, Graduation Ceremony, student government elections. Student services: health clinic, personal-psychological counseling, women's center. Campus security: 24-hour emergency response devices and patrols, late night transport-escort service. Brooklyn College Library plus 1 other. Students can reserve study rooms. Operations spending for the previous fiscal year: $4.6 million. 1,000 computers available on campus for general student use. A campuswide network can be accessed from off-campus. Students can access the following: online class registration. Staffed computer lab on campus provides training in use of computers, software, and the Internet.

■ BRYANT & STRATTON COLLEGE-ALBANY CAMPUS

1259 Central Ave.
Albany, NY 12205
Tel: (518)437-1802
Fax: (518)437-1048
Web Site: www.bryantstratton.edu

Description: Proprietary, 2-year, coed. Part of Bryant and Stratton College, Inc. Awards terminal associate degrees. Founded 1857. Setting: suburban campus. Total enrollment: 470. Faculty: 45 (12 full-time, 33 part-time). Full-time: 354 students, 79% women, 21% men. Part-time: 116 students, 74% women, 26% men. 51% 25 or older. Retention: 45% of full-time freshmen returned the following year. Core. Calendar: semesters. Academic remediation for entering students, services for LD students, independent study, distance learning, double major, summer session for credit, part-time degree program, internships.

Entrance Requirements: Option: deferred admission. Required: high school transcript, interview, entrance and placement evaluations, CPAt, ACCUPLACER. Recommended: SAT or ACT. Entrance: minimally difficult. Application deadline: rolling.

Collegiate Environment: Orientation program. Student-run newspaper. Campus security: 24-hour emergency response devices. Library. 110 computers available on campus for general student use. A campuswide network can be accessed. Staffed computer lab on campus.

■ BRYANT & STRATTON COLLEGE-AMHERST CAMPUS

3650 Millersport Hwy.
Getzville, NY 14068
Tel: (716)625-6300
E-mail: bkdioguardi@bryantstratton.edu
Web Site: www.bryantstratton.edu

Description: Proprietary, primarily 2-year, coed. Awards terminal associate and bachelor's degrees. Founded 1977. Setting: 5-acre suburban campus with easy access to Buffalo. Total enrollment: 474. Faculty: 67 (9 full-time, 58 part-time). Full-time: 277 students, 73% women, 27% men. Part-time: 197 students, 78% women, 22% men. 56% 25 or older, 9% transferred in. Core. Calendar: trimesters. Academic remediation for entering students, services for LD students, advanced placement, distance learning, summer session for credit, part-time degree program, adult/continuing education programs, internships.

Entrance Requirements: Options: electronic application, early admission. Required: high school transcript, interview, entrance and placement evaluations, TABE, CPAt or ACCUPLACER. Recommended: SAT or ACT. Required for some: essay. Application deadline: rolling.

Collegiate Environment: Orientation program. Most popular organizations: Phi Beta Lambda, Student Government Association, Information Technology Club, Ambassadors Club, National Technical Honor Society. Major annual

events: Career Fair, Bring a Friend Day, Health Fair. Library Resource Center. 100 computers available on campus for general student use. A campuswide network can be accessed from student residence rooms and from off campus. Staffed computer lab on campus provides training in use of computers, software, and the Internet.

■ BRYANT & STRATTON COLLEGE-BUFFALO CAMPUS

465 Main St.
Ste. 400
Buffalo, NY 14203
Tel: (716)884-9120
E-mail: pjstruebel@bryantstratton.edu
Web Site: www.bryantstratton.edu

Description: Proprietary, primarily 2-year, coed. Awards terminal associate and bachelor's degrees. Founded 1854. Setting: urban campus. Total enrollment: 693. Faculty: 53 (11 full-time, 42 part-time). 305 applied, 75% were admitted. Full-time: 473 students, 73% women, 27% men. Part-time: 220 students, 82% women, 18% men. 46% 25 or older, 7% transferred in. Core. Calendar: trimesters. Academic remediation for entering students, services for LD students, advanced placement, distance learning, summer session for credit, part-time degree program, adult/continuing education programs, internships.

Entrance Requirements: Options: electronic application, early admission. Required: high school transcript, interview, entrance and placement evaluation, TABE, CPAt or ACCUPLACER. Recommended: SAT or ACT. Required for some: essay. Application deadline: rolling.

Collegiate Environment: Orientation program. Most popular organizations: Medical Assisting Club, Criminal Justice Club, SHRM, National Technical Honor Society, Phi Beta Lambda. Major annual events: Bring A Friend Day, Career Fair, Health Fair. Library Resource Center plus 2 others. 150 computers available on campus for general student use.

Community Environment: See Canisius College.

■ BRYANT & STRATTON COLLEGE-GREECE CAMPUS

854 Long Pond Rd.
Rochester, NY 14612
Tel: (585)720-0660
Fax: (585)720-9226
Web Site: www.bryantstratton.edu

Description: Proprietary, 2-year, coed. Part of Bryant and Stratton College, Inc. Awards terminal associate degrees. Founded 1973. Setting: suburban campus. Educational spending for the previous fiscal year: $2734 per student. Total enrollment: 279. Faculty: 49 (8 full-time, 41 part-time). Student-undergrad faculty ratio is 10:1. Full-time: 192 students, 81% women, 19% men. Part-time: 87 students, 87% women, 13% men. 73% 25 or older, 4% transferred in. Core. Calendar: semesters. Academic remediation for entering students, services for LD students, advanced placement, independent study, distance learning, summer session for credit, part-time degree program, adult/continuing education programs, internships.

Entrance Requirements: Options: electronic application, deferred admission. Required: high school transcript, interview, entrance and placement evaluations, CPAt. Recommended: SAT or ACT. Entrance: minimally difficult. Application deadline: rolling.

Collegiate Environment: Orientation program. Social organizations: 3 open to all; 10% of eligible men and 90% of eligible women are members. Most popular organizations: Bryant and Stratton Student Association (BASSA), Student Ambassadors, Criminal Justice Club. Major annual events: Holiday Party, Backyard Bar-B-Cue, Spring Fling. Campus security: 24-hour emergency response devices, late night transport-escort service. Greece Campus Library. Operations spending for the previous fiscal year: $19,925. 88 computers available on campus for general student use. A campuswide network can be accessed.

■ BRYANT & STRATTON COLLEGE-HENRIETTA CAMPUS

1225 Jefferson Rd.
Rochester, NY 14623
Tel: (585)292-5627
Fax: (585)292-6015
Web Site: www.bryantstratton.edu

Description: Proprietary, 2-year, coed. Part of Bryant and Stratton College, Inc. Awards terminal associate degrees. Founded 1985. Setting: 1-acre urban campus. Educational spending for the previous fiscal year: $3525 per student. Total enrollment: 407. Faculty: 64 (17 full-time, 47 part-time). Student-undergrad faculty ratio is 10:1. 181 applied, 78% were admitted.

Full-time: 288 students, 77% women, 23% men. Part-time: 119 students, 82% women, 18% men. 47% 25 or older, 7% transferred in. Core. Calendar: semesters. Academic remediation for entering students, services for LD students, advanced placement, independent study, distance learning, summer session for credit, part-time degree program, adult/continuing education programs, internships.

Entrance Requirements: Options: electronic application, deferred admission. Required: high school transcript, interview, entrance and placement evaluations, CPAt. Recommended: minimum 2 high school GPA, SAT or ACT. Entrance: minimally difficult. Application deadline: rolling.

Collegiate Environment: Orientation program. Social organizations: 4 open to all; Bryant and Stratton Student Association (BASSA); 15% of eligible men and 85% of eligible women are members. Most popular organizations: BASSA, Student Ambassadors, Paralegal Club, Graphic Design Club. Major annual events: Student Christmas Parties, Spring Fling, Picnic in the Park. Campus security: late night transport-escort service. Henrietta Campus Library. Operations spending for the previous fiscal year: $44,201. 160 computers available on campus for general student use. A campuswide network can be accessed.

■ **BRYANT & STRATTON COLLEGE-ORCHARD PARK CAMPUS**
200 Redtail Rd.
Orchard Park, NY 14127
Tel: (716)677-9500
Web Site: www.bryantstratton.edu

Description: Proprietary, primarily 2-year, coed. Awards terminal associate and bachelor's degrees. Founded 1989. Setting: suburban campus with easy access to Buffalo. Total enrollment: 1,206. Faculty: 75 (23 full-time, 52 part-time). Full-time: 663 students, 80% women, 20% men. Part-time: 543 students, 79% women, 21% men. Students come from 27 states and territories, 1 other country, 60% from out-of-state. 49% 25 or older, 11% transferred in. Core. Calendar: trimesters. Academic remediation for entering students, services for LD students, advanced placement, distance learning, summer session for credit, part-time degree program, adult/continuing education programs, internships.

Entrance Requirements: Options: electronic application, early admission. Required: high school transcript, interview, entrance and placement evaluations, TABE, CPAt or ACCUPLACER. Recommended: SAT or ACT. Required for some: essay. Application deadline: rolling.

Collegiate Environment: Orientation program. Most popular organizations: Accounting/Business Club, Administrative Professionals Club, Phi Beta Lambda, National Technical Honor Society, student newsletter. Major annual events: Career Fair, Health Fair, Fall Festival. Library Resource Center. 125 computers available on campus for general student use.

■ **BRYANT & STRATTON COLLEGE-SYRACUSE CAMPUS**
953 James St.
Syracuse, NY 13203-2502
Tel: (315)472-6603
Fax: (315)474-4383
Web Site: www.bryantstratton.edu

Description: Proprietary, 2-year, coed. Part of Bryant and Stratton Business Institute, Inc. Awards terminal associate degrees. Founded 1854. Setting: 1-acre urban campus. Total enrollment: 715. Faculty: 55 (21 full-time, 34 part-time). Student-undergrad faculty ratio is 13:1. 254 applied, 94% were admitted. Full-time: 494 students, 74% women, 26% men. Part-time: 221 students, 77% women, 23% men. Students come from 2 states and territories, 2 other countries, 1% from out-of-state. 48% 25 or older, 12% live on campus, 6% transferred in. Retention: 38% of full-time freshmen returned the following year. Core. Calendar: semesters. Academic remediation for entering students, services for LD students, distance learning, double major, summer session for credit, part-time degree program, co-op programs and internships.

Entrance Requirements: Required: high school transcript, interview, CPAt. Recommended: SAT or ACT. Entrance: noncompetitive. Application deadline: rolling.

Collegiate Environment: Orientation program. Student-run newspaper. Social organizations: 10 open to all. Most popular organizations: Management Club, Travel Club, Medical Club, Computer Club, Veterans Club. Major annual events: Summer Picnic, Fall Pep Rally, Career Day. Campus security: 24-hour emergency response devices and patrols, controlled dormitory access. Bryant and Stratton, Syracuse Campus Library. 190 computers available on campus for general student use. Staffed computer lab on campus provides training in use of computers, software, and the Internet.

■ **BRYANT & STRATTON COLLEGE-SYRACUSE NORTH CAMPUS**
8687 Carling Rd.
Liverpool, NY 13090
Tel: (315)652-6500
Web Site: www.bryantstratton.edu

Description: Proprietary, 2-year, coed. Part of Bryant and Stratton Business Institute, Inc. Awards diplomas and terminal associate degrees. Founded 1983. Setting: 1-acre suburban campus with easy access to Syracuse. Total enrollment: 497. Faculty: 57 (16 full-time, 41 part-time). Student-undergrad faculty ratio is 9:1. Full-time: 333 students, 70% women, 30% men. Part-time: 164 students, 80% women, 20% men. 52% 25 or older. Core. Calendar: semesters. Academic remediation for entering students, services for LD students, advanced placement, independent study, distance learning, double major, summer session for credit, part-time degree program, adult/continuing education programs, co-op programs and internships.

Entrance Requirements: Open admission. Option: deferred admission. Required: high school transcript, interview, entrance and placement evaluations, TABE, CPAt. Recommended: minimum 2 high school GPA. Entrance: minimally difficult. Application deadline: rolling. Notification: continuous.

Collegiate Environment: Orientation program. Social organizations: 7 open to all; national fraternities. Student services: personal-psychological counseling. Campus security: 24-hour emergency response devices. Resource Center plus 1 other.

■ **BUFFALO STATE COLLEGE, STATE UNIVERSITY OF NEW YORK**
1300 Elmwood Ave.
Buffalo, NY 14222-1095
Tel: (716)878-4000
Fax: (716)878-6100
E-mail: admissions@buffalostate.edu
Web Site: www.buffalostate.edu

Description: State-supported, comprehensive, coed. Part of State University of New York System. Awards bachelor's and master's degrees and post-master's certificates. Founded 1867. Setting: 115-acre urban campus. Endowment: $42.9 million. Research spending for the previous fiscal year: $3.3 million. Educational spending for the previous fiscal year: $26,994 per student. Total enrollment: 9,516. Faculty: 816 (374 full-time, 442 part-time). Student-undergrad faculty ratio is 16:1. 14,663 applied, 60% were admitted. 4% from top 10% of their high school class, 54% from top quarter, 77% from top half. Full-time: 7,665 students, 57% women, 43% men. Part-time: 862 students, 45% women, 55% men. Students come from 27 states and territories, 35 other countries, 1% from out-of-state. 0.5% American Indian or Alaska Native, non-Hispanic/Latino; 13% Hispanic/Latino; 33% Black or African American, non-Hispanic/Latino; 3% Asian, non-Hispanic/Latino; 0.1% Native Hawaiian or other Pacific Islander, non-Hispanic/Latino; 1% international. 14% 25 or older, 29% live on campus, 10% transferred in. Retention: 66% of full-time freshmen returned the following year. Academic areas with the most degrees conferred: business/marketing; homeland security, law enforcement, firefighting, and protective services; education. Core. Calendar: semesters. Academic remediation for entering students, ESL program, services for LD students, advanced placement, freshman honors college, honors program, independent study, distance learning, double major, summer session for credit, part-time degree program, adult/continuing education programs, co-op programs and internships, graduate courses open to undergrads. Off campus study at Western New York Consortium, National Student Exchange. Study abroad program. ROTC: Army (c).

Entrance Requirements: Options: electronic application, early admission, deferred admission, international baccalaureate accepted. Required: high school transcript, minimum 3 high school GPA, SAT and SAT Subject Tests or ACT. Recommended: SAT. Required for some: essay, interview. Entrance: moderately difficult. Application deadline: rolling. Notification: continuous.

Costs Per Year: Application fee: $50. State resident tuition: $6870 full-time, $286 per semester hour part-time. Nonresident tuition: $16,650 full-time, $694 per semester hour part-time. Mandatory fees: $1340 full-time, $55.90 per semester hour part-time. Part-time tuition and fees vary according to course load. College room and board: $14,050. College room only: $8176. Room and board charges vary according to board plan, housing facility, and student level.

Collegiate Environment: Orientation program. Drama-theater group, choral group, student-run newspaper, radio station. Social organizations: 98 open to all; national fraternities, national sororities, local fraternities, local sororities; 1% of eligible men and 1% of eligible women are members. Most popular organizations: United Student Government, African-American

Student Organization, Caribbean Student Organization, The Record, WBNY radio. Major annual events: Homecoming, Commuter Daze. Student services: legal services, health clinic, personal-psychological counseling, women's center. Campus security: 24-hour emergency response devices and patrols, student patrols, late night transport-escort service, controlled dormitory access. E. H. Butler Library plus 1 other. Operations spending for the previous fiscal year: $3.5 million. 1,700 computers available on campus for general student use. A campuswide network can be accessed from student residence rooms and from off campus. Students can access the following: online class registration. Staffed computer lab on campus.

■ CANISIUS COLLEGE

2001 Main St.
Buffalo, NY 14208-1098
Tel: (716)883-7000; Free: 800-843-1517
Fax: (716)888-2377
E-mail: admissions@canisius.edu
Web Site: www.canisius.edu

Description: Independent Roman Catholic (Jesuit), comprehensive, coed. Awards associate, bachelor's, and master's degrees and post-master's certificates. Founded 1870. Setting: 72-acre urban campus with easy access to Buffalo-Niagara Falls. Endowment: $133.9 million. Research spending for the previous fiscal year: $1.1 million. Educational spending for the previous fiscal year: $8708 per student. Total enrollment: 3,464. Faculty: 368 (148 full-time, 220 part-time). Student-undergrad faculty ratio is 11:1. 3,549 applied, 79% were admitted. 20% from top 10% of their high school class, 45% from top quarter, 73% from top half. 7 valedictorians. Full-time: 2,166 students, 49% women, 51% men. Part-time: 90 students, 36% women, 64% men. Students come from 36 states and territories, 18 other countries, 11% from out-of-state. 0.3% American Indian or Alaska Native, non-Hispanic/Latino; 6% Hispanic/Latino; 9% Black or African American, non-Hispanic/Latino; 3% Asian, non-Hispanic/Latino; 0.2% Native Hawaiian or other Pacific Islander, non-Hispanic/Latino; 4% international. 3% 25 or older, 42% live on campus, 4% transferred in. Retention: 85% of full-time freshmen returned the following year. Academic areas with the most degrees conferred: business/marketing; biological/life sciences; social sciences. Core. Calendar: semesters. Academic remediation for entering students, ESL program, services for LD students, advanced placement, honors program, independent study, distance learning, double major, summer session for credit, part-time degree program, adult/continuing education programs, co-op programs and internships, graduate courses open to undergrads. Off campus study at Members of the Western New York Consortium. Study abroad program. ROTC: Army.
Entrance Requirements: Options: electronic application, early admission, early action, deferred admission, international baccalaureate accepted. Required: high school transcript, minimum 2 high school GPA, SAT or ACT. Recommended: essay, 1 recommendation, interview. Entrance: moderately difficult. Notification: continuous. Transfer credits accepted: Yes. Early action applicants: 904. Early action applicants admitted: 833.
Costs Per Year: Application fee: $0. Comprehensive fee: $40,844 includes full-time tuition ($27,940), mandatory fees ($1488), and college room and board ($11,416). College room only: $5880. Part-time tuition: $900 per credit hour. Part-time mandatory fees: $25 per credit hour, $85 per term.
Collegiate Environment: Orientation program. Drama-theater group, choral group, student-run newspaper, radio station. Social organizations: 124 open to all; national fraternities, national sororities; 1% of eligible men and 2% of eligible women are members. Most popular organizations: Residence Hall Association, UNITY, Afro-American Society, Project Conservation, FUSION Gaming Society. Major annual events: Griff Fest, Welcome Week, Relay for Life. Student services: health clinic, personal-psychological counseling. Campus security: 24-hour emergency response devices and patrols, late night transport-escort service, controlled dormitory access. 1,169 college housing spaces available; 1,055 were occupied in 2018-19. Freshmen given priority for college housing. On-campus residence required through sophomore year. Option: coed housing available. Andrew L. Bouwhuis Library plus 1 other. Books: 222,252 (physical), 1.7 million (digital/electronic); Serial titles: 1,143 (physical), 303,210 (digital/electronic); Databases: 108. Weekly public service hours: 110; students can reserve study rooms. Operations spending for the previous fiscal year: $1.7 million. 700 computers available on campus for general student use. Computer purchase/lease plans available. A campuswide network can be accessed from student residence rooms and from off campus. Students can access the following: online class registration, online accounts. Staffed computer lab on campus provides training in use of computers, software, and the Internet.

Community Environment: The Buffalo metropolitan area of over 1.2 million people offers varied cultural, athletic, and entertainment facilities. Among them are the world-famous Albright-Knox Art Gallery, renowned for its modern and contemporary collection; the Buffalo Philharmonic Orchestra, among the top ranked orchestras in North America, which makes its home in the acoustically excellent Kleinhans Music Hall; the Studio Arena, which offers legitimate theater; and the Buffalo Zoo, one of the leading zoos in the United States. For sports fans, there are the Buffalo Bills football team, the Buffalo Sabres hockey team, and the Buffalo Bisons baseball team. Niagara Falls, the ski areas of western New York, and many attractions in Canada are within easy driving distance of the College. The central location of the College also provides many opportunities for students interested in community service, internships, and employment.

■ CAYUGA COUNTY COMMUNITY COLLEGE

197 Franklin St.
Auburn, NY 13021-3099
Tel: (315)255-1743; Free: 866-598-8883
Web Site: www.cayuga-cc.edu

Description: State and locally supported, 2-year, coed. Part of State University of New York System. Awards certificates, transfer associate, and terminal associate degrees. Founded 1953. Setting: 50-acre small town campus with easy access to Rochester, Syracuse. Endowment: $14.1 million. Educational spending for the previous fiscal year: $4815 per student. Total enrollment: 4,921. Faculty: 222 (44 full-time, 178 part-time). Student-undergrad faculty ratio is 26:1. 670 applied. Full-time: 1,585 students, 59% women, 41% men. Part-time: 3,336 students, 61% women, 39% men. Students come from 11 states and territories, 10 other countries, 1% from out-of-state. 0.5% American Indian or Alaska Native, non-Hispanic/Latino; 4% Hispanic/Latino; 6% Black or African American, non-Hispanic/Latino; 1% Asian, non-Hispanic/Latino; 0.5% international. 40% 25 or older, 4% transferred in. Retention: 55% of full-time freshmen returned the following year. Core. Calendar: semesters. Academic remediation for entering students, services for LD students, advanced placement, honors program, distance learning, summer session for credit, part-time degree program, co-op programs and internships. Off campus study. Study abroad program.
Entrance Requirements: Open admission. Options: electronic application, international baccalaureate accepted. Required: high school transcript. Required for some: specific additional requirements for nursing and occupational therapy programs. Entrance: noncompetitive. Application deadline: rolling. Notification: continuous. Transfer credits accepted: Yes.
Costs Per Year: Application fee: $0. State resident tuition: $4658 full-time, $194 per credit hour part-time. Nonresident tuition: $9316 full-time, $388 per credit hour part-time. Mandatory fees: $528 full-time, $22 per credit hour part-time. Full-time tuition and fees vary according to course load, location, and program. Part-time tuition and fees vary according to course load, location, and program.
Collegiate Environment: Orientation program. Drama-theater group, choral group, student-run newspaper, radio station. Social organizations: 26 open to all; 30% of eligible men and 30% of eligible women are members. Most popular organizations: Student Activity Board, Student Government, Criminal Justice Club, Tutor Club, Early Childhood Club. Major annual events: Graduation, Orientation, National Society of Leadership and Success. Student services: health clinic, personal-psychological counseling. College housing not available. Norman F. Bourke Memorial Library plus 2 others. Books: 71,419 (physical), 151,020 (digital/electronic); Serial titles: 287 (physical), 61,585 (digital/electronic); Databases: 118. Weekly public service hours: 61; students can reserve study rooms. Operations spending for the previous fiscal year: $1.1 million. 510 computers available on campus for general student use. A campuswide network can be accessed. Students can access the following: online class registration. Staffed computer lab on campus provides training in use of computers, software, and the Internet.

■ CAZENOVIA COLLEGE

22 Sullivan St.
Cazenovia, NY 13035-1084
Tel: (315)655-7000; Free: 800-654-3210
Fax: (315)655-2190
E-mail: admission@cazenovia.edu
Web Site: www.cazenovia.edu

Description: Independent, 4-year, coed. Awards associate and bachelor's degrees. Founded 1824. Setting: 40-acre small town campus with easy access to Syracuse. Total enrollment: 893. Faculty: 118 (56 full-time, 62 part-time). Student-undergrad faculty ratio is 10:1. 1,802 applied, 92% were admitted. 5% from top 10% of their high school class, 23% from top quarter, 64% from top half. Full-time: 713 students, 71% women, 29% men. Part-time: 180 students, 74% women, 26% men. Students come from 3 other countries, 12% from out-of-state. 1% American Indian or Alaska Native, non-Hispanic/Latino; 5% Hispanic/Latino; 9% Black or African American, non-Hispanic/Latino; 1% Asian, non-Hispanic/Latino; 0.1% Native Hawaiian or other Pacific Islander, non-Hispanic/Latino; 0.6% international. 12% 25 or older, 81% live on campus, 4% transferred in. Retention: 68% of full-time freshmen returned the following year. Academic areas with the most degrees conferred: business/marketing; visual and performing arts; public administration and social services. Core. Calendar: semesters. Academic remediation for entering students, services for LD students, advanced placement, accelerated degree program, freshman honors college, honors program, independent study, distance learning, double major, summer session for credit, part-time degree program, adult/continuing education programs, internships. Off campus study. Study abroad program. ROTC: Army (c), Air Force (c).

Entrance Requirements: Options: electronic application, deferred admission, international baccalaureate accepted. Required: high school transcript, 1 recommendation. Recommended: essay, minimum 2 high school GPA, interview, portfolio for art and design students, SAT or ACT. Entrance: minimally difficult. Application deadline: rolling. SAT Reasoning Test deadline: 8/15. SAT Subject Test deadline: 8/15. Transfer credits accepted: Yes.

Costs Per Year: Application fee: $0. Comprehensive fee: $48,594 includes full-time tuition ($34,024), mandatory fees ($606), and college room and board ($13,964). College room only: $7810. Full-time tuition and fees vary according to class time, course load, and program. Room and board charges vary according to board plan and housing facility. Part-time tuition: $720 per credit hour. Part-time tuition varies according to class time and course load.

Collegiate Environment: Orientation program. Drama-theater group, choral group, student-run newspaper, radio station. Social organizations: 68 open to all. Most popular organizations: Activities Board, Multicultural Student Group, performing arts, student radio station, yearbook. Major annual events: Quad Day, Homecoming Weekend, Battle of the Air Bands. Student services: health clinic, personal-psychological counseling. Campus security: 24-hour emergency response devices and patrols, late night transport-escort service, controlled dormitory access. Witheral Library. Students can reserve study rooms.

Community Environment: The village of Cazenovia is a rural community near Syracuse with a population of 2,700. The climate is temperate with 4 definite seasons. Cazenovia has a local library, churches of many denominations, motels, inns, and restaurants, and various civic, fraternal, and veteran's organizations. Recreational activities include water sports, summer and winter mountain sports including hiking and skiing, as well as local and regional sports teams and cultural events.

■ **CENTRAL YESHIVA BETH JOSEPH**
1502 Ave. N
Brooklyn, NY 11230
Web Site: www.centralyeshivabethjoseph.com
Description: Independent Jewish, 4-year, coed.

■ **CENTRAL YESHIVA TOMCHEI TMIMIM-LUBAVITCH**
841-853 Ocean Pky.
Brooklyn, NY 11230
Tel: (718)434-0784
Description: Independent Jewish, comprehensive, men only. Awards bachelor's and master's degrees. Founded 1941. Total enrollment: 664. 260 applied, 100% were admitted. 2% 25 or older. Calendar: semesters.

■ **CITY COLLEGE OF THE CITY UNIVERSITY OF NEW YORK**
160 Convent Ave.
New York, NY 10031-9198
Tel: (212)650-7000
Fax: (212)650-6417
Web Site: www.ccny.cuny.edu
Description: State and locally supported, comprehensive, coed. Part of City University of New York System. Awards bachelor's, master's, and doctoral degrees and post-master's certificates. Founded 1847. Setting: 35-acre urban campus with easy access to New York City. Research spending for the previous fiscal year: $57.9 million. Total enrollment: 16,112. Faculty: 1,461 (504 full-time, 957 part-time). Student-undergrad faculty ratio is 15:1. 25,378 applied, 41% were admitted. Students come from 155 other countries, 4%

from out-of-state. 0.1% American Indian or Alaska Native, non-Hispanic/Latino; 38% Hispanic/Latino; 15% Black or African American, non-Hispanic/Latino; 24% Asian, non-Hispanic/Latino; 6% international. 24% 25 or older, 1% live on campus. Retention: 92% of full-time freshmen returned the following year. Academic areas with the most degrees conferred: engineering; psychology; biological/life sciences; social sciences; education. Core. Calendar: semesters. ESL program, services for LD students, advanced placement, accelerated degree program, self-designed majors, freshman honors college, honors program, independent study, summer session for credit, part-time degree program, adult/continuing education programs, internships, graduate courses open to undergrads. Off campus study at other units of the City University of New York System. Study abroad program. ROTC: Army.

Entrance Requirements: Options: early admission, deferred admission, international baccalaureate accepted. Required: high school transcript, SAT or ACT. Required for some: essay, recommendations, creative challenge for architecture, supplemental application for engineering. Entrance: moderately difficult. Application deadline: 2/1. Notification: continuous until 2/1. Transfer credits accepted: Yes.

Costs Per Year: Application fee: $65. State resident tuition: $6730 full-time, $295 per credit part-time. Nonresident tuition: $18,000 full-time, $600 per credit part-time. Mandatory fees: $127 full-time, $40 per term part-time.

Collegiate Environment: Orientation program. Drama-theater group, choral group, student-run newspaper, radio station. Social organizations: 140 open to all; national fraternities, local fraternities, local sororities. Most popular organizations: Latin American Engineering Student Assoc./Society of Hispanic Professional Engineers, National Society of Black Engineers, Bangladesh Student Association, Salsa-Mambo, InterVarsity Christian Fellowship. Major annual events: Fashion Show-FIC, Harlemween-USG. Student services: health clinic, personal-psychological counseling. Campus security: 24-hour patrols, late night transport-escort service, controlled dormitory access. Morris Raphael Cohen Library plus 8 others. Books: 950,000 (physical), 980,000 (digital/electronic); Serial titles: 118,000 (digital/electronic); Databases: 308. Weekly public service hours: 99; students can reserve study rooms. 3,000 computers available on campus for general student use. Computer purchase/lease plans available. A campuswide network can be accessed from off-campus. Students can access the following: online class registration. Staffed computer lab on campus provides training in use of software and the Internet.

■ **CLARKSON UNIVERSITY**
8 Clarkson Ave.
Potsdam, NY 13699
Tel: (315)268-6400; Free: 800-527-6577
Fax: (315)268-7647
E-mail: admissions@clarkson.edu
Web Site: www.clarkson.edu
Description: Independent, university, coed. Awards bachelor's, master's, and doctoral degrees. Founded 1896. Setting: 640-acre small town campus. Endowment: $198.3 million. Research spending for the previous fiscal year: $12 million. Educational spending for the previous fiscal year: $15,095 per student. Total enrollment: 4,274. Faculty: 357 (252 full-time, 105 part-time). Student-undergrad faculty ratio is 13:1. 6,885 applied, 71% were admitted. 35% from top 10% of their high school class, 69% from top quarter, 95% from top half. 15 valedictorians. Full-time: 3,016 students, 31% women, 69% men. Part-time: 75 students, 31% women, 69% men. Students come from 41 states and territories, 35 other countries, 29% from out-of-state. 0.3% American Indian or Alaska Native, non-Hispanic/Latino; 5% Hispanic/Latino; 2% Black or African American, non-Hispanic/Latino; 4% Asian, non-Hispanic/Latino; 2% international. 1% 25 or older, 80% live on campus, 3% transferred in. Retention: 89% of full-time freshmen returned the following year. Academic areas with the most degrees conferred: engineering; business/marketing; engineering technologies. Core. Calendar: semesters. ESL program, services for LD students, advanced placement, accelerated degree program, self-designed majors, honors program, independent study, distance learning, double major, summer session for credit, part-time degree program, co-op programs and internships, graduate courses open to undergrads. Off campus study at Associated Colleges of the St. Lawrence Valley; Semester at Sea; American University Washington Semester Program. Study abroad program. ROTC: Army, Air Force.

Entrance Requirements: Options: electronic application, early admission, early decision, deferred admission, international baccalaureate accepted. Required: essay, high school transcript, 2 recommendations, SAT or ACT. Recommended: interview, SAT Subject Tests. Entrance: very difficult. Application deadlines: 1/15, 12/1 for early decision. Notification: 2/1, 1/1 for early decision. SAT Reasoning Test deadline: 1/15. SAT Subject Test deadline: 1/15. Transfer credits accepted: Yes. Applicants placed on waiting list: 55. Wait-listed applicants offered admission: 0. Early decision applicants: 159. Early decision applicants admitted: 124.

Costs Per Year: Application fee: $50. Comprehensive fee: $66,468 includes full-time tuition ($49,858), mandatory fees ($1270), and college room and board ($15,340). College room only: $8240. Part-time tuition: $1662 per credit hour.

Collegiate Environment: Orientation program. Drama-theater group, choral group, student-run newspaper, radio station. Social organizations: 221 open to all; national fraternities, national sororities, local fraternities; 15% of eligible men and 13% of eligible women are members. Most popular organizations: Ski & Snowboard Club, Outing Club, Student Association for Engineering Management, Institute for Electrical and Electronics Engineers, Pep Band. Major annual events: SpringFest, First Saturday/FallFest, Cold Out Gold Out Winter Festival. Student services: legal services, health clinic, personal-psychological counseling. Campus security: 24-hour emergency response devices and patrols, controlled dormitory access. 2,509 college housing spaces available; 2,291 were occupied in 2018-19. Freshmen guaranteed college housing. On-campus residence required through senior year. Options: coed, men-only, women-only housing available. Harriet Call Burnap Memorial Library plus 1 other. Books: 116,048 (physical), 208,608 (digital/electronic); Serial titles: 9,525 (physical), 50,689 (digital/electronic); Databases: 134. Weekly public service hours: 97; students can reserve study rooms. Operations spending for the previous fiscal year: $1.9 million. 350 computers available on campus for general student use. A campuswide network can be accessed from student residence rooms and from off campus. Students can access the following: online class registration.

Community Environment: This is a college community with a population of 9,700. Bus and air lines serve the area. Local community services include a library, a museum, a hospital, churches of major denominations, and several civic, fraternal, and veterans' organizations. There are part-time jobs available at the campus and with businesses in the area. Recreational activities include bowling, canoeing, fishing, hiking, golfing, mountain biking, swimming, skiing, and theater.

■ CLINTON COMMUNITY COLLEGE
136 Clinton Point Dr.
Plattsburgh, NY 12901-9573
Tel: (518)562-4200; Free: 800-552-1160
Fax: (518)562-8621
Web Site: www.clinton.edu

Description: State and locally supported, 2-year, coed. Part of State University of New York System. Awards certificates, transfer associate, and terminal associate degrees. Founded 1969. Setting: 100-acre small town campus. Educational spending for the previous fiscal year: $4997 per student. Total enrollment: 1,913. Faculty: 111 (61 full-time, 50 part-time). Student-undergrad faculty ratio is 11:1. 1,206 applied, 30% were admitted. Full-time: 960 students, 58% women, 42% men. Part-time: 953 students, 58% women, 42% men. Students come from 12 states and territories, 22 other countries, 3% from out-of-state. 0.5% American Indian or Alaska Native, non-Hispanic/Latino; 2% Hispanic/Latino; 5% Black or African American, non-Hispanic/Latino; 2% Asian, non-Hispanic/Latino; 0.3% Native Hawaiian or other Pacific Islander, non-Hispanic/Latino; 2% international. 26% 25 or older, 10% live on campus, 17% transferred in. Retention: 58% of full-time freshmen returned the following year. Core. Calendar: semesters. Academic remediation for entering students, ESL program, services for LD students, advanced placement, self-designed majors, honors program, independent study, distance learning, summer session for credit, part-time degree program, external degree program, adult/continuing education programs, co-op programs and internships. Off campus study at State University of New York College at Plattsburgh.

Entrance Requirements: Open admission except for nursing, electronics technology and wind engine and turbine technology. Options: electronic application, deferred admission. Required: high school transcript. Required for some: essay, 3 recommendations, interview. Entrance: noncompetitive. Application deadline: 8/26. Notification: continuous, continuous for nonresidents. Preference given to Clinton County residents. Transfer credits accepted: Yes.

Costs Per Year: Application fee: $0. State resident tuition: $5062 full-time, $211 per credit hour part-time. Nonresident tuition: $10,464 full-time, $400 per credit hour part-time. Mandatory fees: $960 full-time, $40 per credit hour part-time. Full-time tuition and fees vary according to course load. Part-time tuition and fees vary according to course load.

Collegiate Environment: Orientation program. Drama-theater group, choral group, student-run newspaper. Social organizations: 30 open to all. Most popular organizations: Athletics, Future Human Services Professionals, PTK (honor society), Drama Club, Criminal Justice Club. Major annual events: Fall Carnival, Spring Club Fair, Drama Club Performances. Student services: health clinic, personal-psychological counseling. Campus security: 24-hour emergency response devices and patrols, late night transport-escort service, controlled dormitory access. Clinton Community College Learning Resource Center plus 1 other. Books: 10,000 (physical); Databases: 100. Study areas open 24 hours, 5-7 days a week; students can reserve study rooms. Operations spending for the previous fiscal year: $370,410. 300 computers available on campus for general student use. A campuswide network can be accessed from student residence rooms and from off campus. Students can access the following: online class registration. Staffed computer lab on campus provides training in use of computers and the Internet.

■ COCHRAN SCHOOL OF NURSING
967 N Broadway
Yonkers, NY 10701
Tel: (914)964-4606
E-mail: bhaughton@riversidehealth.org
Web Site: www.cochranschoolofnursing.us

Description: Independent, 2-year, coed. Administratively affiliated with Mercy College. Awards terminal associate degrees. Founded 1894. Setting: urban campus with easy access to New York City. Total enrollment: 120. Faculty: 9 (8 full-time, 1 part-time). Student-undergrad faculty ratio is 13:1. Full-time: 27 students, 89% women, 11% men. Part-time: 93 students, 86% women, 14% men. 6% from out-of-state. 38% Hispanic/Latino; 11% Black or African American, non-Hispanic/Latino; 2% Asian, non-Hispanic/Latino; 0.8% international. 88% 25 or older, 32% transferred in. Core. Calendar: semesters. Advanced placement, part-time degree program.

Entrance Requirements: Option: deferred admission. Required: high school transcript. Entrance: moderately difficult. Application deadline: 5/15. Notification: 5/15. Transfer credits accepted: Yes.

Costs Per Year: Application fee: $50. Tuition: $9517 full-time, $563 per credit part-time. Mandatory fees: $1731 full-time, $912 per term part-time. Full-time tuition and fees vary according to course load and student level. Part-time tuition and fees vary according to course load and student level.

Collegiate Environment: Major annual event: Spring Fling Dance. Student services: health clinic, personal-psychological counseling. Campus security: 24-hour emergency response devices and patrols, late night transport-escort service. Cochran School of Nursing Library. Books: 2,340 (physical), 559 (digital/electronic); Serial titles: 29 (physical), 7 (digital/electronic); Databases: 13. Weekly public service hours: 24; study areas open 24 hours, 5-7 days a week. 44 computers available on campus for general student use. A campuswide network can be accessed from off-campus. Students can access the following: online class registration, Moodle - learning management system. Staffed computer lab on campus provides training in use of computers, software, and the Internet.

■ COLGATE UNIVERSITY
13 Oak Dr.
Hamilton, NY 13346-1386
Tel: (315)228-1000
Fax: (315)228-7798
E-mail: admission@colgate.edu
Web Site: www.colgate.edu

Description: Independent, comprehensive, coed. Awards bachelor's and master's degrees. Founded 1819. Setting: 575-acre small town campus with easy access to Syracuse, Utica. Total enrollment: 2,969. Faculty: 355 (332 full-time, 23 part-time). Student-undergrad faculty ratio is 9:1. 9,716 applied, 25% were admitted. 77% from top 10% of their high school class, 94% from top quarter, 100% from top half. Full-time: 2,936 students, 55% women, 45% men. Part-time: 22 students, 45% women, 55% men. Students come from 50 states and territories, 51 other countries, 76% from out-of-state. 0.1% American Indian or Alaska Native, non-Hispanic/Latino; 9% Hispanic/Latino; 5% Black or African American, non-Hispanic/Latino; 5% Asian, non-Hispanic/Latino; 0.1% Native Hawaiian or other Pacific Islander, non-Hispanic/Latino; 9% international. 92% live on campus, 1% transferred in. Retention: 94% of full-time freshmen returned the following year. Academic areas with the most degrees conferred: social sciences; biological/life sciences; psychology. Core. Calendar: semesters. Services for LD students, advanced placement, self-designed majors, independent study, double major, internships, graduate courses open to undergrads. Off campus study at New York Six: Liberal

Arts Consortium Colgate University, Hamilton College, Hobart and William Smith Colleges, Skidmore College, St. Lawrence University, and Union College. Study abroad program. ROTC: Army (c).

Entrance Requirements: Options: electronic application, early decision, deferred admission, international baccalaureate accepted. Required: essay, high school transcript, 3 recommendations, Colgate supplement, SAT or ACT. Entrance: most difficult. Application deadlines: 1/15, 11/15 for early decision. Notification: 4/1, 12/15 for early decision plan 1, rolling for early decision plan 2. SAT Reasoning Test deadline: 1/15. Transfer credits accepted: Yes. Applicants placed on waiting list: 1,788. Wait-listed applicants offered admission: 0. Early decision applicants: 962. Early decision applicants admitted: 392.

Costs Per Year: Application fee: $60. One-time mandatory fee: $50. Comprehensive fee: $72,585 includes full-time tuition ($57,695), mandatory fees ($350), and college room and board ($14,540). College room only: $7020.

Collegiate Environment: Orientation program. Drama-theater group, choral group, student-run newspaper, radio station. Social organizations: 200 open to all; national fraternities, national sororities. Most popular organizations: COVE (35+ community service groups), Student Government Association, Cultural/ethnic interest groups, Student communications/publications (including WCRU radio station), Club sports/Outdoor Education. Major annual events: Dancefest, Global Leaders Lecture Series, Colgate/Cornell Hockey Game. Student services: legal services, health clinic, personal-psychological counseling, women's center. Campus security: 24-hour emergency response devices and patrols, student patrols, late night transport-escort service, controlled dormitory access. 2,958 college housing spaces available. Freshmen guaranteed college housing. On-campus residence required through junior year. Option: coed housing available. Case Library and Geyer Center for Information Technology plus 1 other. Books: 749,143 (physical), 444,977 (digital/electronic); Serial titles: 4,085 (physical), 145,811 (digital/electronic); Databases: 305. Study areas open 24 hours, 5-7 days a week; students can reserve study rooms. 150 computers available on campus for general student use. Computer purchase/lease plans available. A campuswide network can be accessed from student residence rooms and from off campus. Students can access the following: online class registration, software applications. Staffed computer lab on campus provides training in use of computers, software, and the Internet.

Community Environment: Hamilton (population 3,550) lies 25 miles south of Utica and 38 miles southeast of Syracuse, New York. Bus and airline connections are to be found in the neighboring cities. The climate is moderate. Part-time employment is available for students. The village has a library, a small museum with library, a movie theater, coffee house, restaurants, hospital, and numerous civic, fraternal and veterans' organizations. Local recreational facilities include hunting, fishing, boating, skiing, and golf.

■ THE COLLEGE AT BROCKPORT, STATE UNIVERSITY OF NEW YORK

350 New Campus Dr.
Brockport, NY 14420-2997
Tel: (585)395-2211
Fax: (585)395-5452
Web Site: www.brockport.edu

Description: State-supported, comprehensive, coed. Part of State University of New York System. Awards bachelor's and master's degrees and post-master's certificates. Founded 1867. Setting: 464-acre small town campus with easy access to Rochester. Endowment: $13.8 million. Research spending for the previous fiscal year: $715,772. Educational spending for the previous fiscal year: $10,490 per student. Total enrollment: 8,287. Faculty: 626 (328 full-time, 298 part-time). Student-undergrad faculty ratio is 17:1. 10,535 applied, 53% were admitted. 8% from top 10% of their high school class, 33% from top quarter, 76% from top half. 1 valedictorian. Full-time: 6,343 students, 56% women, 44% men. Part-time: 714 students, 64% women, 36% men. Students come from 25 states and territories, 20 other countries, 2% from out-of-state. 0.3% American Indian or Alaska Native, non-Hispanic/Latino; 8% Hispanic/Latino; 11% Black or African American, non-Hispanic/Latino; 2% Asian, non-Hispanic/Latino; 1% international. 13% 25 or older, 37% live on campus, 13% transferred in. Retention: 88% of full-time freshmen returned the following year. Academic areas with the most degrees conferred: health professions and related sciences; business/marketing; parks and recreation. Core. Calendar: semesters. ESL program, services for LD students, advanced placement, accelerated degree program, self-designed majors, freshman honors college, honors program, independent study, distance learning, double major,

summer session for credit, part-time degree program, co-op programs and internships, graduate courses open to undergrads. Off campus study at Rochester Area Colleges, New York State Visiting Student Program, Washington Semester. Study abroad program. ROTC: Army, Naval (c), Air Force (c).

Entrance Requirements: Options: electronic application, deferred admission, international baccalaureate accepted. Required: high school transcript, minimum 2.5 high school GPA, 1 recommendation, SAT or ACT. Recommended: essay, minimum 3 high school GPA, SAT, ACT. Required for some: essay, interview. Entrance: moderately difficult. Application deadlines: 8/1, 8/1 for nonresidents. Notification: continuous, continuous for nonresidents. Preference given to applicants with exceptional talent in arts, dance, and athletics. SAT Reasoning Test deadline: 8/1. Transfer credits accepted: Yes.

Costs Per Year: Application fee: $50. State resident tuition: $6670 full-time, $278 per credit hour part-time. Nonresident tuition: $16,320 full-time, $680 per credit hour part-time. Mandatory fees: $1484 full-time, $61.16 per credit hour part-time, $1484 per year part-time. Part-time tuition and fees vary according to course load. College room and board: $12,904. College room only: $7974. Room and board charges vary according to board plan and housing facility.

Collegiate Environment: Orientation program. Drama-theater group, choral group, student-run newspaper, radio station. Social organizations: 139 open to all; national fraternities, national sororities; 1% of eligible men and 1% of eligible women are members. Most popular organizations: Habitat for Humanity, Brockport Pre-Professional Health Club, Brockport Psychology Club, Student Nursing Organization, Caribbean Student Association. Major annual events: Homecoming/Family Weekend, Scholars' Day, Diversity Conference. Student services: legal services, health clinic, personal-psychological counseling, women's center. Campus security: 24-hour emergency response devices and patrols, student patrols, late night transport-escort service, controlled dormitory access. 2,705 college housing spaces available; 2,530 were occupied in 2018-19. Freshmen guaranteed college housing. On-campus residence required through sophomore year. Option: coed housing available. Drake Memorial Library plus 1 other. Books: 500,461 (physical), 185,000 (digital/electronic); Serial titles: 4,747 (physical), 113,396 (digital/electronic); Databases: 270. Weekly public service hours: 93; students can reserve study rooms. Operations spending for the previous fiscal year: $468,235. 1,000 computers available on campus for general student use. A campuswide network can be accessed from student residence rooms and from off campus. Students can access the following: online class registration. Staffed computer lab on campus provides training in use of computers, software, and the Internet.

■ COLLEGE OF MOUNT SAINT VINCENT

6301 Riverdale Ave.
Riverdale, NY 10471-1093
Tel: (718)405-3200; Free: 800-665-CMSV
Fax: (718)549-7945
Web Site: www.mountsaintvincent.edu

Description: Independent, comprehensive, coed. Awards bachelor's and master's degrees and post-master's certificates. Founded 1911. Setting: 70-acre suburban campus with easy access to New York City. Total enrollment: 1,910. Faculty: 226 (81 full-time, 145 part-time). Student-undergrad faculty ratio is 13:1. 2,740 applied, 91% were admitted. 3% from top 10% of their high school class, 17% from top quarter, 43% from top half. Full-time: 1,585 students, 69% women, 31% men. Part-time: 110 students, 79% women, 21% men. 12% from out-of-state. 0.1% American Indian or Alaska Native, non-Hispanic/Latino; 42% Hispanic/Latino; 15% Black or African American, non-Hispanic/Latino; 9% Asian, non-Hispanic/Latino; 1% international. 3% 25 or older, 49% live on campus, 6% transferred in. Core. Calendar: semesters. Academic remediation for entering students, services for LD students, advanced placement, accelerated degree program, honors program, independent study, double major, summer session for credit, part-time degree program, adult/continuing education programs, internships, graduate courses open to undergrads. Study abroad program. ROTC: Army (c), Air Force (c).

Entrance Requirements: Options: electronic application, early admission, early action, deferred admission, international baccalaureate accepted. Required: essay, high school transcript, minimum 2 high school GPA, SAT or ACT. Recommended: 2 recommendations, interview. Required for some: interview. Entrance: moderately difficult. Application deadlines: 7/29, 11/15 for early action. Notification: 12/15 for early action. SAT Reasoning Test deadline: 8/1. Transfer credits accepted: Yes. Applicants placed on waiting list: 181. Wait-listed applicants offered admission: 25.

Costs Per Year: Comprehensive fee: $48,680 includes full-time tuition ($36,700), mandatory fees ($1480), and college room and board ($10,500). Full-time tuition and fees vary according to student level. Part-time tuition: $1060 per credit hour.

Collegiate Environment: Orientation program. Drama-theater group, choral group, student-run newspaper, radio station. Student services: health clinic, personal-psychological counseling. Campus security: 24-hour emergency response devices and patrols, late night transport-escort service, controlled dormitory access, emergency call boxes. Elizabeth Seton Library.

Community Environment: See Fordham University.

■ THE COLLEGE OF NEW ROCHELLE

29 Castle Pl.
New Rochelle, NY 10805-2308
Tel: (914)654-5000; Free: 800-933-5923
Fax: (914)654-5554
E-mail: bsondey@cnr.edu
Web Site: www.cnr.edu

Description: Independent, comprehensive, coed. Awards bachelor's and master's degrees and post-master's certificates (also offers a non-traditional adult program with significant enrollment not reflected in profile). Founded 1904. Setting: 20-acre suburban campus with easy access to New York City. Endowment: $2.3 million. Total enrollment: 2,023. Faculty: 291 (60 full-time, 231 part-time). Student-undergrad faculty ratio is 10:1. 1,675 applied, 68% were admitted. Full-time: 1,151 students, 83% women, 17% men. Part-time: 177 students, 86% women, 14% men. Students come from 24 states and territories, 2 other countries, 9% from out-of-state. 30% Hispanic/Latino; 40% Black or African American, non-Hispanic/Latino; 6% Asian, non-Hispanic/Latino; 0.3% Native Hawaiian or other Pacific Islander, non-Hispanic/Latino; 0.1% international. 22% 25 or older, 32% live on campus, 14% transferred in. Retention: 71% of full-time freshmen returned the following year. Academic areas with the most degrees conferred: health professions and related sciences; public administration and social services; biological/life sciences; visual and performing arts; psychology. Core. Calendar: semesters. Academic remediation for entering students, services for LD students, advanced placement, accelerated degree program, self-designed majors, honors program, independent study, double major, summer session for credit, part-time degree program, adult/continuing education programs, co-op programs and internships, graduate courses open to undergrads. Off campus study. Study abroad program.

Entrance Requirements: Options: electronic application, deferred admission, international baccalaureate accepted. Required: high school transcript, SAT or ACT. Recommended: essay, 1 recommendation, interview. Entrance: moderately difficult. Application deadline: rolling. Notification: continuous. Transfer credits accepted: Yes.

Costs Per Year: Application fee: $35. Comprehensive fee: $52,322 includes full-time tuition ($36,180), mandatory fees ($1580), and college room and board ($14,562). Full-time tuition and fees vary according to course load, degree level, and program. Room and board charges vary according to housing facility. Part-time tuition: $1206 per credit. Part-time tuition varies according to course load, degree level, and program.

Collegiate Environment: Orientation program. Choral group. Social organizations: 23 open to all. Most popular organizations: Music Ensembles, CNR Model United Nations, Student Nurses Association, Campus Ministry, Student Government. Major annual events: Strawberry Festival, Family Weekend, Spirit Competition. Student services: health clinic, personal-psychological counseling. Campus security: 24-hour emergency response devices and patrols, late night transport-escort service, controlled dormitory access, 24-hour monitored security cameras at residence hall entrances. Gill Library plus 1 other. Books: 93,999 (physical), 153,914 (digital/electronic); Serial titles: 886 (physical), 94,336 (digital/electronic); Databases: 133. Weekly public service hours: 86; students can reserve study rooms. Operations spending for the previous fiscal year: $1.8 million. 86 computers available on campus for general student use. A campuswide network can be accessed from student residence rooms and from off campus. Students can access the following: online class registration. Staffed computer lab on campus provides training in use of computers, software, and the Internet.

Community Environment: See Iona College.

■ THE COLLEGE OF SAINT ROSE

432 Western Ave.
Albany, NY 12203-1419
Tel: (518)454-5111; Free: 800-637-8556
Fax: (518)451-2013

E-mail: admit@strose.edu
Web Site: www.strose.edu

Description: Independent, comprehensive, coed. Awards bachelor's and master's degrees and post-master's certificates. Founded 1920. Setting: 49-acre urban campus. Endowment: $44.7 million. Educational spending for the previous fiscal year: $17,450 per student. Total enrollment: 3,992. Faculty: 325 (173 full-time, 152 part-time). Student-undergrad faculty ratio is 14:1. 6,408 applied, 87% were admitted. 12% from top 10% of their high school class, 38% from top quarter, 71% from top half. Full-time: 2,402 students, 67% women, 33% men. Part-time: 87 students, 62% women, 38% men. Students come from 34 states and territories, 47 other countries, 12% from out-of-state. 0.5% American Indian or Alaska Native, non-Hispanic/Latino; 7% Hispanic/Latino; 17% Black or African American, non-Hispanic/Latino; 3% Asian, non-Hispanic/Latino; 0.2% Native Hawaiian or other Pacific Islander, non-Hispanic/Latino; 3% international. 5% 25 or older, 49% live on campus, 7% transferred in. Retention: 75% of full-time freshmen returned the following year. Academic areas with the most degrees conferred: business/marketing; education; visual and performing arts. Core. Calendar: semesters. Academic remediation for entering students, ESL program, services for LD students, advanced placement, accelerated degree program, self-designed majors, independent study, double major, summer session for credit, part-time degree program, internships, graduate courses open to undergrads. Off campus study at Association of Colleges of Sisters of Saint Joseph (ACSSJ). Study abroad program. ROTC: Army (c), Air Force (c).

Entrance Requirements: Options: electronic application, early admission, early action, deferred admission, international baccalaureate accepted. Required: high school transcript, 1 recommendation. Recommended: essay, minimum 2.5 high school GPA. Required for some: interview, SAT or ACT. Entrance: moderately difficult. Application deadlines: 5/1, 12/1 for early action. Notification: continuous, 12/15 for early action. SAT Reasoning Test deadline: 5/1. Transfer credits accepted: Yes. Early action applicants: 3,118. Early action applicants admitted: 2,851.

Costs Per Year: Application fee: $0. One-time mandatory fee: $455. Comprehensive fee: $46,354 includes full-time tuition ($32,218), mandatory fees ($1168), and college room and board ($12,968). College room only: $6522. Part-time tuition: $1072 per credit hour. Part-time mandatory fees: $45 per credit hour, $143 per term.

Collegiate Environment: Orientation program. Drama-theater group, choral group, student-run newspaper, radio station. Social organizations: 40 open to all. Most popular organizations: Student Association, Student Events Board, Spectrum-ALANA Student Union, Colleges Against Cancer, Music and Entertainment Industry Student Association. Major annual events: Midnight Madness, Rose Rock, Harvest Fest. Student services: health clinic, personal-psychological counseling. Campus security: 24-hour emergency response devices and patrols, late night transport-escort service, controlled dormitory access. 1,316 college housing spaces available; 1,240 were occupied in 2018-19. Freshmen guaranteed college housing. On-campus residence required in freshman year. Options: coed, men-only, women-only housing available. Neil Hellman Library plus 2 others. Books: 241,000 (physical), 116,500 (digital/electronic); Serial titles: 1,201 (physical), 10 (digital/electronic); Databases: 104. Weekly public service hours: 73; students can reserve study rooms. Operations spending for the previous fiscal year: $1.5 million. 801 computers available on campus for general student use. A campuswide network can be accessed from student residence rooms and from off campus. Students can access the following: online class registration. Staffed computer lab on campus (open 24 hours a day) provides training in use of computers, software, and the Internet.

Community Environment: See State University of New York at Albany.

■ COLLEGE OF STATEN ISLAND OF THE CITY UNIVERSITY OF NEW YORK

2800 Victory Blvd.
Staten Island, NY 10314-6600
Tel: (718)982-2000
Fax: (718)982-2500
Web Site: www.csi.cuny.edu

Description: State and locally supported, comprehensive, coed. Part of City University of New York. Awards associate, bachelor's, master's, and doctoral degrees and post-master's certificates. Founded 1955. Setting: 204-acre urban campus with easy access to New York City. Endowment: $8.8 million. Research spending for the previous fiscal year: $3.2 million. Educational spending for the previous fiscal year: $6454 per student. Total enrollment: 13,247. Faculty: 1,152 (350 full-time, 802 part-time). Student-undergrad faculty ratio is 18:1. 14,443 applied, 100% were admitted. Full-time: 9,567 students, 53% women, 47% men. Part-time: 2,644 students, 57% women, 43% men. Students come from 13 states and territories, 102 other countries, 1% from out-of-state. 0.2% American Indian or Alaska Native, non-Hispanic/Latino; 27% Hispanic/Latino; 15% Black or African American, non-Hispanic/Latino; 11% Asian, non-Hispanic/Latino; 0.2% Native Hawaiian or other Pacific Islander, non-Hispanic/Latino; 3% international. 18% 25 or older, 4% live on campus, 5% transferred in. Retention: 77% of full-time freshmen returned the following year. Academic areas with the most degrees conferred: business/marketing; psychology; social sciences. Core. Calendar: semesters. Academic remediation for entering students, ESL program, services for LD students, self-designed majors, honors program, independent study, double major, summer session for credit, adult/continuing education programs, co-op programs and internships, graduate courses open to undergrads. Study abroad program.

Entrance Requirements: Open admission. Options: electronic application, deferred admission, international baccalaureate accepted. Required: high school transcript, SAT or ACT. Required for some: essay, 2 recommendations, interview. Entrance: noncompetitive. Application deadlines: rolling, rolling for nonresidents. Notification: continuous until 2/1, continuous until 2/1 for nonresidents. SAT Reasoning Test deadline: 5/1. Transfer credits accepted: Yes.

Costs Per Year: Application fee: $65. State resident tuition: $6730 full-time, $295 per credit hour part-time. Nonresident tuition: $18,000 full-time, $600 per credit hour part-time. Mandatory fees: $559 full-time, $181.10 per term part-time. College room only: $14,315. Room charges vary according to housing facility.

Collegiate Environment: Orientation program. Drama-theater group, choral group, student-run newspaper, radio station. Social organizations: 45 open to all. Most popular organizations: Pre-Med/Pre-PA Society, International Student Club, United African Students in the USA, The CSI Gamers Club. Major annual events: Welcome Back Carnival and Involvement Fair, CSI's Got Talent, Spring Carnival and Club Festival. Student services: health clinic, personal-psychological counseling, women's center. Campus security: 24-hour emergency response devices and patrols, student patrols, late night transport-escort service, controlled dormitory access. 440 college housing spaces available; 438 were occupied in 2018-19. No special consideration for freshman housing applicants. Option: coed housing available. College of Staten Island Library. Books: 205,415 (physical), 538,477 (digital/electronic); Serial titles: 1,842 (physical), 110,942 (digital/electronic); Databases: 161. Weekly public service hours: 98; students can reserve study rooms. Operations spending for the previous fiscal year: $2.8 million. 1,700 computers available on campus for general student use. A campuswide network can be accessed from off-campus. Students can access the following: online class registration, MyInfo app. Staffed computer lab on campus provides training in use of computers, software, and the Internet.

■ THE COLLEGE OF WESTCHESTER

325 Central Ave.
White Plains, NY 10606
Tel: (914)559-2398; Free: 855-403-7722
E-mail: admissions@cw.edu
Web Site: www.cw.edu

Description: Proprietary, primarily 2-year, coed. Awards certificates, transfer associate, terminal associate, and bachelor's degrees. Founded 1915. Setting: suburban campus with easy access to New York City. Total enrollment: 915. Faculty: 69 (32 full-time, 37 part-time). Student-undergrad faculty ratio is 20:1. 1,002 applied, 98% were admitted. Full-time: 721 students, 62% women, 38% men. Part-time: 194 students, 72% women, 28% men. Students come from 5 states and territories, 4% from out-of-state. 0.1% American Indian or Alaska Native, non-Hispanic/Latino; 47% Hispanic/Latino; 38% Black or African American, non-Hispanic/Latino; 2% Asian, non-Hispanic/Latino; 0.2% Native Hawaiian or other Pacific Islander, non-Hispanic/Latino. 44% 25 or older, 10% transferred in. Retention: 65% of full-time freshmen returned the following year. Academic areas with the most degrees conferred: business/marketing; health professions and related sciences. Core. Calendar: semesters. Academic remediation for entering students, accelerated degree program, honors program, distance learning, double major, summer session for credit, part-time degree program, adult/continuing education programs, co-op programs and internships.

Entrance Requirements: Options: electronic application, deferred admission, international baccalaureate accepted. Required: high school transcript, interview. Recommended: SAT. Required for some: essay. Entrance: minimally difficult. Application deadline: rolling. Transfer credits accepted: Yes.

Costs Per Year: Application fee: $40. Tuition: $20,115 full-time, $745 per credit part-time. Mandatory fees: $900 full-time, $100 per course part-time.

Collegiate Environment: Orientation program. Student-run newspaper. Student services: personal-psychological counseling. Dr. William R. Papallo Library. 271 computers available on campus for general student use. A campuswide network can be accessed. Staffed computer lab on campus.

■ COLUMBIA-GREENE COMMUNITY COLLEGE

4400 Rte. 23
Hudson, NY 12534-0327
Tel: (518)828-4181
Fax: (518)828-8543
E-mail: rachel.kappel@sunycgcc.edu
Web Site: www.sunycgcc.edu

Description: State and locally supported, 2-year, coed. Part of State University of New York System. Awards certificates, transfer associate, and terminal associate degrees. Founded 1966. Setting: 143-acre rural campus. Total enrollment: 1,584. Faculty: 79 (40 full-time, 39 part-time). Student-undergrad faculty ratio is 15:1. 363 applied, 99% were admitted. Full-time: 623 students, 58% women, 42% men. Part-time: 961 students, 66% women, 34% men. Students come from 4 states and territories, 1 other country, 0.04% from out-of-state. 0.5% American Indian or Alaska Native, non-Hispanic/Latino; 10% Hispanic/Latino; 9% Black or African American, non-Hispanic/Latino; 2% Asian, non-Hispanic/Latino; 0.1% international. 4% 25 or older, 6% transferred in. Retention: 61% of full-time freshmen returned the following year. Core. Calendar: semesters. Academic remediation for entering students, ESL program, services for LD students, advanced placement, honors program, independent study, distance learning, summer session for credit, part-time degree program, co-op programs and internships.

Entrance Requirements: Open admission. Options: electronic application, deferred admission. Required: high school transcript. Required for some: interview. Application deadlines: rolling, rolling for nonresidents. Transfer credits accepted: Yes.

Costs Per Year: Application fee: $0. State resident tuition: $4680 full-time, $195 per semester hour part-time. Nonresident tuition: $9360 full-time, $390 per semester hour part-time. Mandatory fees: $414 full-time, $18 per semester hour part-time. Full-time tuition and fees vary according to course load and program. Part-time tuition and fees vary according to course load and program.

Collegiate Environment: Student-run radio station. Social organizations: 12 open to all. Most popular organizations: Criminal Justice Club, Human Services Club, Psychology Club, Student Senate, Animal Advocates. Major annual events: Welcome Week, Spring BBQ, Coffee House. Student services: personal-psychological counseling. Campus security: 24-hour emergency response devices and patrols, student patrols, late night transport-escort service. College housing not available. Columbia-Greene Library plus 1 other. 60 computers available on campus for general student use. Computer purchase/lease plans available. A campuswide network can be accessed from off-campus. Staffed computer lab on campus provides training in use of computers, software, and the Internet.

■ COLUMBIA UNIVERSITY

116th St. and Broadway
New York, NY 10027
Tel: (212)854-1754
Web Site: www.columbia.edu

Description: Independent, university, coed. Awards bachelor's, master's, and doctoral degrees. Founded 1754. Setting: 36-acre urban campus with easy access to New York City. Endowment: $10.9 billion. Total enrollment: 6,270. Student-undergrad faculty ratio is 6:1. 40,203 applied, 6% were admitted. Full-time: 6,270 students, 49% women, 51% men. Students come from 52 states and territories, 104 other countries, 78% from out-of-state. 2% American Indian or Alaska Native, non-Hispanic/Latino; 13% Hispanic/Latino; 10% Black or African American, non-Hispanic/Latino; 22% Asian, non-Hispanic/Latino; 16% international. 92% live on campus, 2% transferred in. Retention: 99% of full-time freshmen returned the following year. Academic areas with the most degrees conferred: social sciences; engineering; computer and information sciences. Core. Calendar: semesters. ESL program, services for LD students, advanced placement, accelerated degree program, self-designed majors, independent study, double major, summer session for credit, internships, graduate courses open to undergrads. Off campus study. Study abroad program. ROTC: Army (c), Naval, Air Force (c).

Entrance Requirements: Options: electronic application, early admission, early decision, deferred admission, international baccalaureate accepted.

Required: essay, high school transcript, 3 recommendations, SAT or ACT. Entrance: most difficult. Application deadlines: 1/1, 11/1 for early decision. Notification: 4/1, 12/15 for early decision. SAT Reasoning Test deadline: 2/1. SAT Subject Test deadline: 2/1. Transfer credits accepted: Yes. Early decision applicants: 4,085. Early decision applicants admitted: 717.

Collegiate Environment: Orientation program. Drama-theater group, choral group, marching band, student-run newspaper, radio station. Social organizations: 500 open to all; national fraternities, national sororities; 19% of eligible men and 16% of eligible women are members. Most popular organizations: community service, cultural organizations, performing arts, athletics, publications. Major annual events: Bacchanal (spring fest), Tree Lighting/Yule Log Ceremony, Varsity Show. Student services: health clinic, personal-psychological counseling, women's center. Campus security: 24-hour emergency response devices and patrols, late night transport-escort service, controlled dormitory access. Freshmen guaranteed college housing. On-campus residence required in freshman year. Option: coed housing available. Butler plus 18 others. Books: 10.7 million (physical), 2.6 million (digital/electronic); Databases: 1,587. Weekly public service hours: 86; study areas open 24 hours, 5-7 days a week; students can reserve study rooms. 460 computers available on campus for general student use. A campuswide network can be accessed from student residence rooms and from off campus. Students can access the following: online class registration. Staffed computer lab on campus.

■ COLUMBIA UNIVERSITY SCHOOL OF GENERAL STUDIES

2970 Broadway
408 Lewisohn Hall, MC 4101
New York, NY 10027-6939
Tel: (212)854-2772; Free: 800-895-1169
E-mail: gsdegree@columbia.edu
Web Site: www.gs.columbia.edu

Description: Independent, 4-year, coed. Part of Columbia University. Awards bachelor's degrees. Founded 1754. Setting: 36-acre urban campus with easy access to New York City. System endowment: $9 billion. Total enrollment: 2,068. 696 applied, 35% were admitted. Full-time: 1,504 students, 39% women, 61% men. Part-time: 564 students, 46% women, 54% men. 57% from out-of-state. 0.3% American Indian or Alaska Native, non-Hispanic/Latino; 10% Hispanic/Latino; 5% Black or African American, non-Hispanic/Latino; 9% Asian, non-Hispanic/Latino; 0.2% Native Hawaiian or other Pacific Islander, non-Hispanic/Latino; 21% international. 51% 25 or older, 28% live on campus, 23% transferred in. Academic areas with the most degrees conferred: social sciences; engineering; biological/life sciences. Core. Calendar: semesters. Services for LD students, advanced placement, accelerated degree program, self-designed majors, independent study, double major, summer session for credit, part-time degree program, adult/continuing education programs, internships. Off campus study. Study abroad program. ROTC: Army (c), Naval, Air Force (c).

Entrance Requirements: Options: electronic application, early action, deferred admission. Required: essay, high school transcript, 2 recommendations, SAT or ACT. Required for some: interview. Entrance: most difficult. Application deadlines: 6/1, 3/1 for early action. Notification: continuous, 5/1 for early action. SAT Reasoning Test deadline: 6/1. SAT Subject Test deadline: 6/1. Transfer credits accepted: Yes.

Costs Per Year: Application fee: $80. One-time mandatory fee: $105. Comprehensive fee: $71,739 includes full-time tuition ($54,660), mandatory fees ($2889), and college room and board ($14,190). College room only: $8770. Full-time tuition and fees vary according to course load and program. Room and board charges vary according to board plan and housing facility. Part-time tuition: $1822 per credit hour. Part-time tuition varies according to course load and program.

Collegiate Environment: Orientation program. Drama-theater group, choral group, marching band, student-run newspaper, radio station. Social organizations: 500 open to all; national fraternities, national sororities, local fraternities. Most popular organization: General Studies Student Council. Major annual event: Commencement. Student services: health clinic, personal-psychological counseling, women's center. Campus security: 24-hour emergency response devices and patrols, late night transport-escort service. Butler Library plus 20 others.

■ CONCORDIA COLLEGE-NEW YORK

171 White Plains Rd.
Bronxville, NY 10708-1998
Tel: (914)337-9300; Free: 800-YES-COLLEGE
Fax: (914)395-4500

E-mail: toral.bhatt@concordia-ny.edu
Web Site: www.concordia-ny.edu

Description: Independent Lutheran, comprehensive, coed. Part of Concordia University System. Awards associate, bachelor's, and master's degrees. Founded 1881. Setting: 33-acre suburban campus with easy access to New York City. Endowment: $6.4 million. Educational spending for the previous fiscal year: $6410 per student. Total enrollment: 1,597. Faculty: 148 (52 full-time, 96 part-time). Student-undergrad faculty ratio is 11:1. 942 applied, 78% were admitted. Students come from 14 states and territories, 31 other countries. 0.2% American Indian or Alaska Native, non-Hispanic/Latino; 22% Hispanic/Latino; 16% Black or African American, non-Hispanic/Latino; 4% Asian, non-Hispanic/Latino; 0.2% Native Hawaiian or other Pacific Islander, non-Hispanic/Latino; 11% international. 60% live on campus. Retention: 78% of full-time freshmen returned the following year. Academic areas with the most degrees conferred: health professions and related sciences; business/marketing; social sciences. Core. Calendar: semesters. Academic remediation for entering students, ESL program, services for LD students, accelerated degree program, self-designed majors, honors program, independent study, double major, part-time degree program, adult/continuing education programs, co-op programs and internships, graduate courses open to undergrads. Off campus study at Concordia University System. Study abroad program.

Entrance Requirements: Options: electronic application, early admission, early action, deferred admission, international baccalaureate accepted. Required: essay, high school transcript, 2 recommendations. Recommended: minimum 2.5 high school GPA. Required for some: interview, SAT or ACT, TOEFL or IELTS for students for whom English is not their first language. Entrance: moderately difficult. Application deadlines: 3/15, 11/15 for early action. Notification: continuous, 12/15 for early action. Transfer credits accepted: Yes. Early action applicants: 144. Early action applicants admitted: 130.

Costs Per Year: Application fee: $60. Comprehensive fee: $45,590 includes full-time tuition ($31,500), mandatory fees ($1400), and college room and board ($12,690). Full-time tuition and fees vary according to class time, course load, location, and program. Room and board charges vary according to board plan. Part-time tuition: $880 per credit. Part-time tuition varies according to class time, course load, location, and program.

Collegiate Environment: Orientation program. Drama-theater group, choral group, student-run newspaper. Social organizations: 22 open to all; local fraternities, local sororities; 12% of eligible men and 15% of eligible women are members. Most popular organizations: Student Government Association, Choral Groups, Campus Christian Ministries, International and Afro/Latin American Club, Yearbook and newspaper. Major annual events: Homecoming Weekend, Accepted Student Day, Spring Weekend. Student services: health clinic, personal-psychological counseling. Campus security: 24-hour emergency response devices and patrols, controlled dormitory access. Scheele Memorial Library plus 1 other. Operations spending for the previous fiscal year: $276,825.

■ COOPER UNION FOR THE ADVANCEMENT OF SCIENCE AND ART

30 Cooper Sq.
New York, NY 10003-7120
Tel: (212)353-4100
Fax: (212)353-4343
E-mail: admissions@cooper.edu
Web Site: www.cooper.edu

Description: Independent, comprehensive, coed. Awards bachelor's and master's degrees (also offers master's program primarily made up of currently-enrolled students). Founded 1859. Setting: urban campus with easy access to New York City. Endowment: $798.9 million. Research spending for the previous fiscal year: $498,473. Educational spending for the previous fiscal year: $33,924 per student. Total enrollment: 941. Faculty: 206 (57 full-time, 149 part-time). Student-undergrad faculty ratio is 8:1. 2,574 applied, 13% were admitted. 51% from top 10% of their high school class, 85% from top quarter, 99% from top half. Full-time: 859 students, 34% women, 66% men. Part-time: 8 students, 50% women, 50% men. Students come from 30 states and territories, 18 other countries, 50% from out-of-state. 10% Hispanic/Latino; 3% Black or African American, non-Hispanic/Latino; 20% Asian, non-Hispanic/Latino; 20% international. 3% 25 or older, 20% live on campus, 2% transferred in. Retention: 95% of full-time freshmen returned the following year. Academic areas with the most degrees conferred: engineering; visual and performing arts; architecture. Core. Calendar: semesters. Services for LD students, advanced placement, accelerated degree program, self-designed majors, independent study, summer session for credit, internships, graduate courses open to undergrads. Off campus study at East Coast members of the National Association of Schools of Art and Design, New York University, Eugene Lang College (New School), Members of Association of Independent Colleges of Art and Design Mobility Program. Study abroad program.

Entrance Requirements: Options: electronic application, early admission, early decision, deferred admission. Required: essay, high school transcript, SAT or ACT, studio test for architecture, home test for art. Recommended: minimum 3 high school GPA, 2 recommendations. Required for some: minimum 3.5 high school GPA, 3 recommendations, interview, portfolio for art, studio test for architecture, SAT Subject Tests. Entrance: most difficult. Application deadlines: 1/8, 11/1 for early decision plan 1, 12/1 for early decision plan 2. Notification: 3/31, 12/31 for early decision plan 1, 2/28 for early decision plan 2. SAT Reasoning Test deadline: 2/28. SAT Subject Test deadline: 2/28. Transfer credits accepted: Yes. Applicants placed on waiting list: 136. Wait-listed applicants offered admission: 19. Early decision applicants: 173. Early decision applicants admitted: 41.

Costs Per Year: Application fee: $75. Tuition: $44,550 full-time, $1310 per credit hour part-time. Mandatory fees: $1800 full-time, $1075 per term part-time. Full-time tuition and fees vary according to degree level and reciprocity agreements. Part-time tuition and fees vary according to degree level and reciprocity agreements. College room only: $12,638. Room charges vary according to housing facility.

Collegiate Environment: Orientation program. Drama-theater group, choral group, student-run newspaper. Social organizations: 120 open to all; national fraternities, national sororities; 5% of eligible men and 5% of eligible women are members. Most popular organizations: South Asian Society, Pro Musica, Chinese Student Association, Drama Society, Outdoors Club; Intervarsity Christian Fellowship. Major annual events: Fall Festival, Pro Musica Jam, Cultural Show and Food Festival. Student services: personal-psychological counseling. Campus security: 24-hour emergency response devices and patrols, controlled dormitory access, security guards. Cooper Union Library. Books: 98,400 (physical), 213,578 (digital/electronic); Serial titles: 71 (physical), 40,306 (digital/electronic); Databases: 48. Weekly public service hours: 69. Operations spending for the previous fiscal year: $1.3 million. 100 computers available on campus for general student use. Computer purchase/lease plans available. A campuswide network can be accessed from student residence rooms and from off campus. Students can access the following: online class registration. Staffed computer lab on campus provides training in use of computers, software, and the Internet.

■ **CORNELL UNIVERSITY**
144 E Ave.
Ithaca, NY 14853
Tel: (607)255-2000
Fax: (607)255-0659
Web Site: www.cornell.edu

Description: Independent, university, coed. Part of State University of New York System. Awards bachelor's, master's, and doctoral degrees. Founded 1865. Setting: 745-acre small town campus with easy access to Syracuse. Endowment: $681.5 million. Research spending for the previous fiscal year: $364.6 million. Total enrollment: 23,600. Faculty: 2,193 (1,817 full-time, 376 part-time). Student-undergrad faculty ratio is 9:1. 51,324 applied, 11% were admitted. 83% from top 10% of their high school class, 97% from top quarter, 100% from top half. Full-time: 15,182 students, 53% women, 47% men. Students come from 85 other countries, 59% from out-of-state. 0.4% American Indian or Alaska Native, non-Hispanic/Latino; 13% Hispanic/Latino; 7% Black or African American, non-Hispanic/Latino; 19% Asian, non-Hispanic/Latino; 0.1% Native Hawaiian or other Pacific Islander, non-Hispanic/Latino; 11% international. 1% 25 or older, 52% live on campus, 4% transferred in. Retention: 97% of full-time freshmen returned the following year. Academic areas with the most degrees conferred: engineering; business/marketing; biological/life sciences. Calendar: semesters. Academic remediation for entering students, ESL program, services for LD students, advanced placement, accelerated degree program, self-designed majors, honors program, independent study, distance learning, double major, summer session for credit, co-op programs and internships, graduate courses open to undergrads. Off campus study. Study abroad program. ROTC: Army, Naval, Air Force.

Entrance Requirements: Options: electronic application, early decision, deferred admission, international baccalaureate accepted. Required: essay, high school transcript, 2 recommendations, SAT or ACT. Required for some: interview, SAT Subject Tests. Entrance: most difficult. Application deadlines:

1/2, 11/1 for early decision. Notification: 3/31, 12/15 for early decision. Transfer credits accepted: Yes. Applicants placed on waiting list: 6,683. Wait-listed applicants offered admission: 164. Early decision applicants: 6,325. Early decision applicants admitted: 1,549.

Costs Per Year: Application fee: $80. Comprehensive fee: $69,634 includes full-time tuition ($54,584), mandatory fees ($234), and college room and board ($14,816). College room only: $8842. Room and board charges vary according to board plan and housing facility.

Collegiate Environment: Orientation program. Drama-theater group, choral group, marching band, student-run newspaper, radio station. Social organizations: 1,041 open to all; national fraternities, national sororities, local fraternities, local sororities, co-ed local Greek organizations; 26% of eligible men and 24% of eligible women are members. Most popular organizations: Class Councils, Cornell Hillel, Interfraternity Council/Panhellenic Association, Outing Club, Student Assembly. Major annual events: Slope Day (spring concert and celebration), Homecoming, Welcome Weekend/Orientation. Student services: health clinic, personal-psychological counseling, women's center. Campus security: 24-hour emergency response devices and patrols, late night transport-escort service, controlled dormitory access. 8,384 college housing spaces available; 7,866 were occupied in 2018-19. Freshmen guaranteed college housing. Options: coed, women-only housing available. Main library plus 16 others. Books: 5.1 million (physical), 1.7 million (digital/electronic); Serial titles: 240,579 (physical), 148,820 (digital/electronic); Databases: 4,207. Weekly public service hours: 146; study areas open 24 hours, 5-7 days a week; students can reserve study rooms. Operations spending for the previous fiscal year: $35.3 million. 1,500 computers available on campus for general student use. Computer purchase/lease plans available. A campuswide network can be accessed from student residence rooms and from off campus. Students can access the following: online class registration. Staffed computer lab on campus (open 24 hours a day) provides training in use of computers, software, and the Internet.

Community Environment: Population 30,000. Located at the southern tip of Cayuga Lake, the city encompasses scenic, deep gorges through which flow Six Mile, Fall and Cascadilla Creeks. Ithaca is in the heart of central New York's Finger Lakes region. Good transportation is provided by bus and airlines, as well as state highways. Ithaca has various fraternal, civic and veteran's organizations, and over 30 churches representative of most major denominations. Part-time employment is available for students. Recreational facilities within the vicinity include YMCA, theatres, 3 state parks, indoor ice rink, fishing, boating, swimming, hunting, horseback riding, bowling, a pistol range, archery, museums, golf courses, and 14 public parks.

■ **CORNING COMMUNITY COLLEGE**
One Academic Dr.
Corning, NY 14830-3297
Tel: (607)962-9222
Fax: (607)962-9456
Web Site: www.corning-cc.edu

Description: State and locally supported, 2-year, coed. Part of State University of New York System. Awards certificates, transfer associate, and terminal associate degrees. Founded 1956. Setting: 500-acre rural campus. Endowment: $521,628. Educational spending for the previous fiscal year: $6684 per student. Total enrollment: 3,972. Faculty: 229 (89 full-time, 140 part-time). Student-undergrad faculty ratio is 18:1. 1,772 applied, 100% were admitted. Full-time: 1,929 students, 55% women, 45% men. Part-time: 2,043 students, 61% women, 39% men. Students come from 9 states and territories, 14 other countries, 7% from out-of-state. 0.5% American Indian or Alaska Native, non-Hispanic/Latino; 2% Hispanic/Latino; 4% Black or African American, non-Hispanic/Latino; 1% Asian, non-Hispanic/Latino; 0.1% Native Hawaiian or other Pacific Islander, non-Hispanic/Latino; 0.2% international. 21% 25 or older, 6% live on campus, 3% transferred in. Retention: 56% of full-time freshmen returned the following year. Core. Calendar: semesters. Academic remediation for entering students, ESL program, services for LD students, advanced placement, accelerated degree program, self-designed majors, honors program, independent study, distance learning, double major, summer session for credit, part-time degree program, adult/continuing education programs, co-op programs and internships. Off campus study at ACE (Accelerated College Education): concurrent enrollment in regional high schools. Study abroad program.

Entrance Requirements: Open admission. Options: electronic application, early admission. Required: high school transcript. Required for some: interview. Entrance: noncompetitive. Application deadline: rolling. Notification: continuous. Preference given to residents of sponsoring counties. Transfer credits accepted: Yes.

Collegiate Environment: Orientation program. Drama-theater group, choral group, student-run newspaper, radio station. Social organizations: 35 open to all. Most popular organizations: Student Association, EQUAL, Nursing Society, Muse of Fire (theatre group), WCEB radio station. Major annual events: WoW (Welcome on Wednesday: Student Services fair), SPRINGfest, CLUBfest (student clubs/organizations fair). Student services: health clinic, personal-psychological counseling. Campus security: 24-hour emergency response devices and patrols, late night transport-escort service, controlled dormitory access. Arthur A. Houghton, Jr. Library. Books: 28,518 (physical), 185,642 (digital/electronic); Serial titles: 571 (physical), 27,480 (digital/electronic); Databases: 190. Weekly public service hours: 63; students can reserve study rooms. Operations spending for the previous fiscal year: $497,015. 350 computers available on campus for general student use. Computer purchase/lease plans available. A campuswide network can be accessed from student residence rooms and from off campus. Students can access the following: online class registration. Staffed computer lab on campus provides training in use of computers, software, and the Internet.

■ **THE CULINARY INSTITUTE OF AMERICA**
1946 Campus Dr.
Hyde Park, NY 12538-1499
Tel: (845)452-9600; Free: 800-CULINARY
Fax: (845)452-8629
E-mail: admissions@culinary.edu
Web Site: www.ciachef.edu
Description: Independent, 4-year, coed. Awards associate and bachelor's degrees. Founded 1946. Setting: 170-acre suburban campus. Endowment: $128.6 million. Research spending for the previous fiscal year: $198,746. Educational spending for the previous fiscal year: $12,703 per student. Total enrollment: 3,131. Faculty: 183 (141 full-time, 42 part-time). Student-undergrad faculty ratio is 20:1. 1,170 applied, 97% were admitted. 9% from top 10% of their high school class, 26% from top quarter, 58% from top half. Full-time: 3,116 students, 50% women, 50% men. Students come from 53 states and territories, 46 other countries, 66% from out-of-state. 0.4% American Indian or Alaska Native, non-Hispanic/Latino; 16% Hispanic/Latino; 6% Black or African American, non-Hispanic/Latino; 7% Asian, non-Hispanic/Latino; 0.4% Native Hawaiian or other Pacific Islander, non-Hispanic/Latino; 15% international. 18% 25 or older, 8% transferred in. Academic areas with the most degrees conferred: business/marketing; personal and culinary services; interdisciplinary studies. Core. Calendar: semesters plus 18 or 21 week externship program. Academic remediation for entering students, services for LD students, double major, internships. Off campus study. Study abroad program.
Entrance Requirements: Options: electronic application, early action, deferred admission, international baccalaureate accepted. Required: essay, high school transcript, 1 recommendation. Recommended: minimum 2 high school GPA. Required for some: Affidavit of Support. Entrance: moderately difficult. Application deadline: rolling. Transfer credits accepted: Yes.
Costs Per Year: Application fee: $50. Comprehensive fee: $44,280 includes full-time tuition ($30,200), mandatory fees ($2520), and college room and board ($11,560). College room only: $7860. Full-time tuition and fees vary according to location. Room and board charges vary according to board plan, housing facility, and location.
Collegiate Environment: Orientation program. Student-run newspaper. Social organizations: 24 open to all; Eta Sigma Delta National Honor Society. Most popular organizations: Bacchus Wine Society, Tea Club, KACIA, Culinary Christian Fellowship, Black Culinarian Society. Major annual events: Stars & Stripes Block Party, Chili Cook-off, Chowder Cook-Off. Student services: health clinic, personal-psychological counseling. Campus security: 24-hour emergency response devices and patrols, late night transport-escort service, controlled dormitory access, CCTV & Nightly Visitor Screening. Conrad N. Hilton Library. Books: 57,977 (physical), 1,149 (digital/electronic); Serial titles: 449 (physical), 22,228 (digital/electronic); Databases: 75. Weekly public service hours: 92; students can reserve study rooms. Operations spending for the previous fiscal year: $556,547. 227 computers available on campus for general student use. A campuswide network can be accessed from student residence rooms and from off campus. Students can access the following: online class registration, online course guides. Staffed computer lab on campus provides training in use of computers, software, and the Internet.

■ **DAEMEN COLLEGE**
4380 Main St.
Amherst, NY 14226-3592

Tel: (716)839-3600; Free: 800-462-7652
Fax: (716)839-8516
E-mail: admissions@daemen.edu
Web Site: www.daemen.edu
Description: Independent, comprehensive, coed. Awards bachelor's, master's, and doctoral degrees and post-master's certificates. Founded 1947. Setting: 35-acre suburban campus with easy access to Buffalo. Endowment: $14.4 million. Educational spending for the previous fiscal year: $8860 per student. Total enrollment: 2,636. Faculty: 304 (147 full-time, 157 part-time). Student-undergrad faculty ratio is 12:1. 3,529 applied, 49% were admitted. 24% from top 10% of their high school class, 58% from top quarter, 88% from top half. Full-time: 1,559 students, 70% women, 30% men. Part-time: 243 students, 79% women, 21% men. Students come from 18 other countries. 0.2% American Indian or Alaska Native, non-Hispanic/Latino; 7% Hispanic/Latino; 11% Black or African American, non-Hispanic/Latino; 3% Asian, non-Hispanic/Latino; 0.1% Native Hawaiian or other Pacific Islander, non-Hispanic/Latino; 2% international. 20% 25 or older, 36% live on campus, 14% transferred in. Retention: 76% of full-time freshmen returned the following year. Academic areas with the most degrees conferred: health professions and related sciences; interdisciplinary studies; business/marketing. Core. Calendar: semesters. Academic remediation for entering students, services for LD students, advanced placement, accelerated degree program, self-designed majors, honors program, independent study, distance learning, double major, summer session for credit, part-time degree program, adult/continuing education programs, internships, graduate courses open to undergrads. Off campus study at Western New York Consortium. Study abroad program. ROTC: Army (c).
Entrance Requirements: Options: electronic application, early admission, deferred admission, international baccalaureate accepted. Required: essay, high school transcript, minimum X high school GPA, 1 recommendation. Recommended: interview, SAT or ACT. Required for some: SAT or ACT, SAT/ACT or high school course grades, show rigor of courses and teacher recommendations. Entrance: moderately difficult. Application deadline: rolling. Notification: continuous. Transfer credits accepted: Yes.
Costs Per Year: Application fee: $25. Comprehensive fee: $41,495 includes full-time tuition ($27,990), mandatory fees ($590), and college room and board ($12,915). Full-time tuition and fees vary according to location and reciprocity agreements. Room and board charges vary according to board plan and housing facility. Part-time tuition: $933 per credit hour. Part-time mandatory fees: $9 per credit hour, $80 per term. Part-time tuition and fees vary according to course load, location, and reciprocity agreements.
Collegiate Environment: Orientation program. Drama-theater group, choral group, student-run newspaper. Social organizations: 44 open to all; local fraternities, local sororities; 2% of eligible men and 5% of eligible women are members. Most popular organizations: Game Club, Anime Club, Best Buddies, CRU, Pride Club. Major annual events: Homecoming and Family Weekend, Midnight Madness, Springfest. Student services: personal-psychological counseling. Campus security: 24-hour emergency response devices and patrols, late night transport-escort service, controlled dormitory access, 24-hour security cameras. Research and Information Commons. Books: 85,205 (physical), 138,085 (digital/electronic); Serial titles: 488 (physical); Databases: 38. Weekly public service hours: 117; students can reserve study rooms. Operations spending for the previous fiscal year: $907,115. 163 computers available on campus for general student use. A campuswide network can be accessed from student residence rooms and from off campus. Students can access the following: online class registration. Staffed computer lab on campus provides training in use of computers and software.
Community Environment: The college is located in a quiet suburban environment accessible to the City of Buffalo and the international boundary with Canada. Transportation hubs-plane, train, and bus-are located a short distance from the campus.

■ **DAVIS COLLEGE**
400 Riverside Dr.
Johnson City, NY 13790
Tel: (607)729-1581; Free: 877-949-3248
Fax: (607)729-2962
E-mail: hhempstead@davisny.edu
Web Site: www.davisny.edu
Description: Independent nondenominational, 4-year, coed. Awards associate and bachelor's degrees. Founded 1900. Setting: 22-acre suburban campus with easy access to Syracuse. Total enrollment: 216. Faculty: 31 (14 full-time, 17 part-time). Student-undergrad faculty ratio is 14:1. 120 applied,

52% were admitted. 10% from top 10% of their high school class, 30% from top quarter, 70% from top half. Full-time: 165 students, 44% women, 56% men. Part-time: 51 students, 63% women, 37% men. Students come from 5 other countries, 60% from out-of-state. 30% 25 or older, 61% live on campus, 20% transferred in. Retention: 85% of full-time freshmen returned the following year. Academic area with the most degrees conferred: theology and religious vocations. Core. Calendar: semesters. Academic remediation for entering students, ESL program, services for LD students, advanced placement, independent study, summer session for credit, part-time degree program, adult/continuing education programs, co-op programs and internships.

Entrance Requirements: Options: electronic application, deferred admission, international baccalaureate accepted. Required: essay, high school transcript, 1 recommendation. Recommended: minimum 2 high school GPA, interview, SAT or ACT. Entrance: minimally difficult. Application deadline: rolling. Notification: continuous. Transfer credits accepted: Yes.

Costs Per Year: Application fee: $45. Comprehensive fee: $25,250 includes full-time tuition ($15,750), mandatory fees ($1400), and college room and board ($8100). Full-time tuition and fees vary according to course load and location. Room and board charges vary according to board plan and housing facility. Part-time tuition: $525 per credit hour. Part-time mandatory fees: $700 per term. Part-time tuition and fees vary according to course load and location.

Collegiate Environment: Orientation program. Drama-theater group, choral group, student-run newspaper. Social organizations: 4 open to all. Most popular organizations: Student Missionary Fellowship, Student Wives Fellowship, Student Life Committee, Married Couples Fellowship. Major annual events: Annual Missions Conference, Fall Bible Conference, Pastor's and Leaders Conference. Student services: health clinic, personal-psychological counseling. Campus security: 24-hour emergency response devices and patrols, student patrols, late night transport-escort service, controlled dormitory access. Alice E. Chatlos Library. Students can reserve study rooms. 12 computers available on campus for general student use. A campuswide network can be accessed from student residence rooms. Students can access the following: online class registration. Staffed computer lab on campus.

■ **DEVRY COLLEGE OF NEW YORK-MIDTOWN MANHATTAN CAMPUS**
180 Madison Ave., Ste. 900
New York, NY 10016
Tel: (212)312-4300; Free: 866-338-7934
Web Site: www.devry.edu
Description: Proprietary, comprehensive, coed. Part of DeVry University. Awards associate, bachelor's, and master's degrees. Founded 1998. Setting: urban campus. Total enrollment: 1,495. Faculty: 87 (17 full-time, 70 part-time). Student-undergrad faculty ratio is 26:1. Full-time: 629 students, 32% women, 68% men. Part-time: 286 students, 31% women, 69% men. 18% from out-of-state. 0.7% American Indian or Alaska Native, non-Hispanic/Latino; 31% Hispanic/Latino; 39% Black or African American, non-Hispanic/Latino; 7% Asian, non-Hispanic/Latino; 1% Native Hawaiian or other Pacific Islander, non-Hispanic/Latino; 3% international. 75% 25 or older, 21% transferred in. Calendar: semesters. Part-time degree program, adult/continuing education programs.
Entrance Requirements: Required: high school transcript, interview. Entrance: minimally difficult.
Collegiate Environment: Orientation program. Learning Resource Center.

■ **DOMINICAN COLLEGE**
470 Western Hwy.
Orangeburg, NY 10962-1210
Tel: (845)359-7800; Free: 866-432-4636
Fax: (845)359-2313
E-mail: rob.tyrrell@dc.edu
Web Site: www.dc.edu
Description: Independent, comprehensive, coed. Awards associate, bachelor's, master's, and doctoral degrees. Founded 1952. Setting: 70-acre suburban campus with easy access to New York City. Endowment: $4.5 million. Total enrollment: 1,954. Faculty: 237 (77 full-time, 160 part-time). Student-undergrad faculty ratio is 15:1. 1,751 applied, 75% were admitted. Full-time: 1,271 students, 65% women, 35% men. Part-time: 154 students, 79% women, 21% men. Students come from 28 states and territories, 16 other countries, 22% from out-of-state. 30% Hispanic/Latino; 15% Black or African American, non-Hispanic/Latino; 6% Asian, non-Hispanic/Latino; 0.9%

Native Hawaiian or other Pacific Islander, non-Hispanic/Latino; 1% international. 48% live on campus, 10% transferred in. Retention: 74% of full-time freshmen returned the following year. Academic areas with the most degrees conferred: health professions and related sciences; social sciences; business/marketing. Core. Calendar: semesters. Academic remediation for entering students, services for LD students, advanced placement, accelerated degree program, honors program, independent study, distance learning, double major, summer session for credit, part-time degree program, adult/continuing education programs, co-op programs and internships, graduate courses open to undergrads. Off campus study. Study abroad program.

Entrance Requirements: Options: electronic application, deferred admission, international baccalaureate accepted. Required: high school transcript. Recommended: interview. Required for some: essay, interview. Entrance: noncompetitive. Application deadline: rolling. Notification: continuous. SAT Reasoning Test deadline: 8/16. SAT Subject Test deadline: 8/16. Transfer credits accepted: Yes. Applicants placed on waiting list: 0. Wait-listed applicants offered admission: 0.

Costs Per Year: Application fee: $35. Comprehensive fee: $42,150 includes full-time tuition ($28,140), mandatory fees ($860), and college room and board ($13,150). Full-time tuition and fees vary according to course load and degree level. Room and board charges vary according to board plan and housing facility. Part-time tuition: $851 per credit hour. Part-time mandatory fees: $200 per term. Part-time tuition and fees vary according to course load, degree level, and program.

Collegiate Environment: Orientation program. Drama-theater group, choral group, student-run radio station. Social organizations: 32 open to all. Most popular organizations: Student Government Association, Business Club, Aquin Players Drama Society, Anime Magna and Videogame Club, Student Nursing Association. Major annual events: Family Day, Big Charger Weekends, Spirit Week. Student services: health clinic, personal-psychological counseling. Campus security: 24-hour emergency response devices and patrols, student patrols, late night transport-escort service, controlled dormitory access. Sullivan Library plus 1 other. Books: 74,226 (physical), 117,187 (digital/electronic); Serial titles: 610 (physical), 75,067 (digital/electronic); Databases: 85. Weekly public service hours: 89; students can reserve study rooms. Operations spending for the previous fiscal year: $822,320. 150 computers available on campus for general student use. A campuswide network can be accessed from student residence rooms and from off campus. Students can access the following: online class registration, Web portal, learning management system. Staffed computer lab on campus provides training in use of computers, software, and the Internet.

Community Environment: Orangeburg, population 3,400, is located in southeast New York, located 3 miles southwest of Nyack on the northern border of New Jersey. The area may be reached by the New York State Thruway, Exit 12, or Palisades Parkway, Exit 6E.

■ **DUTCHESS COMMUNITY COLLEGE**
53 Pendell Rd.
Poughkeepsie, NY 12601-1595
Tel: (845)431-8000
Web Site: www.sunydutchess.edu
Description: State and locally supported, 2-year, coed. Part of State University of New York System. Awards certificates, transfer associate, and terminal associate degrees. Founded 1957. Setting: 130-acre suburban campus with easy access to New York City. Total enrollment: 9,061. Faculty: 554 (128 full-time, 426 part-time). Student-undergrad faculty ratio is 19:1. 5,732 applied, 70% were admitted. 5% from top 10% of their high school class, 26% from top quarter, 61% from top half. Full-time: 3,839 students, 51% women, 49% men. Part-time: 5,222 students, 58% women, 42% men. 1% from out-of-state. 0.1% American Indian or Alaska Native, non-Hispanic/Latino; 19% Hispanic/Latino; 11% Black or African American, non-Hispanic/Latino; 3% Asian, non-Hispanic/Latino; 0.1% Native Hawaiian or other Pacific Islander, non-Hispanic/Latino; 0.9% international. 13% 25 or older, 5% live on campus, 3% transferred in. Calendar: semesters. Academic remediation for entering students, ESL program, services for LD students, advanced placement, freshman honors college, honors program, distance learning, summer session for credit, part-time degree program, adult/continuing education programs, internships. Off campus study at Marist College, Vassar College, State University of New York College at New Paltz, Culinary Institute of America, Bard College, Mercy College.
Entrance Requirements: Open admission for most programs. Options: electronic application, early admission, deferred admission. Required: high school transcript. Entrance: noncompetitive. Application deadline: rolling. Notification: continuous. Preference given to county residents.

Costs Per Year: State resident tuition: $3864 full-time, $161 per credit hour part-time. Nonresident tuition: $7728 full-time, $322 per credit hour part-time. Mandatory fees: $472 full-time, $18 per credit hour part-time, $20 per term part-time. College room and board: $11,118. College room only: $7518. Room and board charges vary according to board plan.

Collegiate Environment: Orientation program. Drama-theater group, choral group, student-run newspaper, radio station. Social organizations: 33 open to all. Most popular organizations: Rap, Poetry and Music, Outdoor Adventure, Student Government Association, Gamers Club, Masquer's Guild Theatre Club. Major annual events: FalconFest, Halloween Dance, Lyceum Series of Speakers. Student services: health clinic, personal-psychological counseling. Campus security: 24-hour emergency response devices and patrols, late night transport-escort service, controlled dormitory access, Mass Notification System. Dutchess Library plus 1 other. Books: 89,515 (physical), 159,235 (digital/electronic); Serial titles: 128 (physical), 336,174 (digital/electronic); Databases: 70. Weekly public service hours: 70. 1,606 computers available on campus for general student use. A campuswide network can be accessed from student residence rooms and from off campus. Students can access the following: online class registration, 6 laptops available in dormitory. Staffed computer lab on campus provides training in use of computers, software, and the Internet.

■ **D'YOUVILLE COLLEGE**
320 Porter Ave.
Buffalo, NY 14201-1084
Tel: (716)829-8000; Free: 800-777-3921
Fax: (716)829-7790
E-mail: harmonm@dyc.edu
Web Site: www.dyc.edu

Description: Independent, comprehensive, coed. Awards bachelor's, master's, and doctoral degrees and post-master's certificates. Founded 1908. Setting: 11-acre urban campus. Endowment: $43.3 million. Research spending for the previous fiscal year: $119,056. Educational spending for the previous fiscal year: $10,544 per student. Total enrollment: 3,021. Faculty: 295 (189 full-time, 106 part-time). Student-undergrad faculty ratio is 9:1. 1,541 applied, 97% were admitted. 17% from top 10% of their high school class, 50% from top quarter, 84% from top half. Full-time: 1,295 students, 73% women, 27% men. Part-time: 440 students, 78% women, 22% men. Students come from 29 states and territories, 31 other countries, 9% from out-of-state. 0.5% American Indian or Alaska Native, non-Hispanic/Latino; 4% Hispanic/Latino; 9% Black or African American, non-Hispanic/Latino; 6% Asian, non-Hispanic/Latino; 0.1% Native Hawaiian or other Pacific Islander, non-Hispanic/Latino; 1% international. 23% 25 or older, 18% live on campus, 12% transferred in. Retention: 79% of full-time freshmen returned the following year. Academic areas with the most degrees conferred: health professions and related sciences; interdisciplinary studies; business/marketing. Core. Calendar: semesters plus summer session. Academic remediation for entering students, services for LD students, advanced placement, accelerated degree program, independent study, distance learning, double major, summer session for credit, part-time degree program, adult/continuing education programs, internships, graduate courses open to undergrads. Off campus study at Western New York Consortium. Study abroad program. ROTC: Army (c).

Entrance Requirements: Options: electronic application, deferred admission, international baccalaureate accepted. Required: high school transcript, minimum 2 high school GPA, SAT or ACT. Required for some: essay, minimum 3 high school GPA, interview. Entrance: moderately difficult. Application deadline: rolling. Notification: continuous. Transfer credits accepted: Yes.

Costs Per Year: Comprehensive fee: $38,974 includes full-time tuition ($26,120), mandatory fees ($630), and college room and board ($12,224). Full-time tuition and fees vary according to course load, degree level, and program. Room and board charges vary according to board plan and housing facility. Part-time tuition: $816 per credit hour. Part-time mandatory fees: $3 per credit hour, $55 per term. Part-time tuition and fees vary according to course load, degree level, and program. Tuition guaranteed not to increase for student's term of enrollment.

Collegiate Environment: Orientation program. Drama-theater group, choral group, student-run newspaper. Social organizations: 36 open to all. Most popular organizations: Student Association, Occupational Therapy Student Association, Physical Therapy Student Association, Student Nurses Association, Black Student Union. Major annual events: Family and Friends Weekend, Honors Convocation, ACES Ceremony. Student services: health clinic, personal-psychological counseling. Campus security: 24-hour

emergency response devices and patrols, late night transport-escort service, controlled dormitory access. Montante Family Library. Books: 69,415 (physical), 75,525 (digital/electronic); Serial titles: 572 (physical), 41,529 (digital/electronic); Databases: 84. Weekly public service hours: 87; study areas open 24 hours, 5-7 days a week; students can reserve study rooms. Operations spending for the previous fiscal year: $883,777. 120 computers available on campus for general student use. A campuswide network can be accessed from student residence rooms and from off campus. Students can access the following: online class registration. Staffed computer lab on campus (open 24 hours a day) provides training in use of computers, software, and the Internet.

■ **ELIM BIBLE INSTITUTE AND COLLEGE**
7245 College St.
Lima, NY 14485
Web Site: www.elim.edu

Description: Independent Christian, 2-year, coed.

■ **ELMIRA BUSINESS INSTITUTE**
303 N Main St.
Elmira, NY 14901
Tel: (607)733-7177; Free: 800-843-1812
Fax: (607)733-7178
E-mail: info@ebi-college.com
Web Site: www.ebi.edu

Description: Proprietary, 2-year, coed. Awards certificates, transfer associate, and terminal associate degrees. Founded 1858. Setting: urban campus. Total enrollment: 78. Student-undergrad faculty ratio is 9:1. Calendar: semesters. Academic remediation for entering students, advanced placement, part-time degree program, internships.

Entrance Requirements: Open admission. Option: electronic application. Required: high school transcript, interview. Required for some: essay. Application deadline: rolling. Transfer credits accepted: Yes.

Collegiate Environment: Orientation program. Campus security: 24-hour emergency response devices. Elmira Business Institute Library plus 1 other. 90 computers available on campus for general student use. A campuswide network can be accessed.

■ **ELMIRA COLLEGE**
One Park Pl.
Elmira, NY 14901
Tel: (607)735-1800; Free: 800-935-6472
Fax: (607)735-1718
E-mail: admissions@elmira.edu
Web Site: www.elmira.edu

Description: Independent, comprehensive, coed. Awards associate, bachelor's, and master's degrees. Founded 1855. Setting: 55-acre small town campus. Endowment: $38 million. Educational spending for the previous fiscal year: $10,095 per student. Total enrollment: 1,187. Faculty: 160 (69 full-time, 91 part-time). Student-undergrad faculty ratio is 11:1. 2,096 applied, 82% were admitted. 20% from top 10% of their high school class, 45% from top quarter, 69% from top half. 3 valedictorians. Full-time: 974 students, 69% women, 31% men. Part-time: 127 students, 80% women, 20% men. Students come from 33 states and territories, 12 other countries, 38% from out-of-state. 0.3% American Indian or Alaska Native, non-Hispanic/Latino; 4% Hispanic/Latino; 5% Black or African American, non-Hispanic/Latino; 2% Asian, non-Hispanic/Latino; 5% international. 11% 25 or older, 88% live on campus, 4% transferred in. Retention: 76% of full-time freshmen returned the following year. Academic areas with the most degrees conferred: business/marketing; health professions and related sciences; education. Core. Calendar: 4-4-1. Services for LD students, advanced placement, accelerated degree program, self-designed majors, honors program, independent study, distance learning, double major, summer session for credit, part-time degree program, adult/continuing education programs, internships, graduate courses open to undergrads. Off campus study. Study abroad program. ROTC: Army, Air Force (c).

Entrance Requirements: Options: electronic application, early action, deferred admission, international baccalaureate accepted. Required: essay, high school transcript, minimum 2 high school GPA, 1 recommendation. Recommended: interview. Required for some: interview. Entrance: moderately difficult. Application deadlines: rolling, 10/15 for early action. Notification: continuous until 11/15, 10/31 for early action. SAT Reasoning Test deadline: 8/1. Transfer credits accepted: Yes. Applicants placed on waiting list: 0. Early action applicants: 0. Early action applicants admitted: 0.

Costs Per Year: Application fee: $0. Comprehensive fee: $53,900 includes full-time tuition ($41,900) and college room and board ($12,000). College room only: $6400. Room and board charges vary according to board plan and housing facility. Part-time tuition: $1200 per credit hour. Part-time tuition varies according to class time.

Collegiate Environment: Orientation program. Drama-theater group, choral group, student-run newspaper, radio station. Social organizations: 80 open to all. Most popular organizations: SAB (Student Activities Board), Enactus, Colleges Against Cancer (Relay for Life), Orchesis, Habitat for Humanity. Major annual events: Mountain Day, Holiday Banquet and Ball, May Days. Student services: health clinic, personal-psychological counseling. Campus security: 24-hour emergency response devices and patrols, student patrols, late night transport-escort service, controlled dormitory access, 24-hour locked residence hall entrances. Gannett-Tripp Library. Books: 122,814 (physical), 154,862 (digital/electronic); Serial titles: 646 (physical), 31,991 (digital/electronic); Databases: 94. Weekly public service hours: 110. Operations spending for the previous fiscal year: $793,275. 355 computers available on campus for general student use. Computer purchase/lease plans available. A campuswide network can be accessed from student residence rooms and from off campus. Students can access the following: online class registration. Staffed computer lab on campus provides training in use of computers, software, and the Internet.

Community Environment: Founded as a commercial and transportation center, Elmira, population 30,000, dominates south-central New York State and nearby Pennsylvania as the trade, industrial, financial, and transportation hub of the southern Finger Lakes region. Light industrial activity remains as the economic base for the county, though a large portion of Chemung County is still rural in activity and atmosphere. Transportation is available with the Elmira-Corning Airport, buses, and car via Routes 13, 14, and 17. There are two hospitals, approximately 60 churches, a public library, theatres, good shopping centers, and more than 200 fraternal, service, and social organizations. Recreational facilities include parks, playgrounds, golf, swimming, bowling, tennis, horseback riding, picnic areas, fishing, ice skating, and skiing nearby. Located within walking distance of the campus is the Samuel Clemens Performing Arts Center.

■ **ELYON COLLEGE**
1400 W 6th St.
Brooklyn, NY 11204
Description: Proprietary, 2-year, coed.

■ **ERIE COMMUNITY COLLEGE**
121 Ellicott St.
Buffalo, NY 14203-2698
Tel: (716)851-1001
Fax: (716)842-1972
E-mail: admissions@ecc.edu
Web Site: www.ecc.edu
Description: State and locally supported, 2-year, coed. Part of State University of New York System. Awards certificates, diplomas, transfer associate, and terminal associate degrees. Founded 1971. Setting: 1-acre urban campus. Total enrollment: 2,417. Student-undergrad faculty ratio is 19:1. 2,573 applied, 73% were admitted. Full-time: 1,828 students, 58% women, 42% men. Part-time: 589 students, 67% women, 33% men. Students come from 14 states and territories, 7 other countries, 1% from out-of-state. 0.6% American Indian or Alaska Native, non-Hispanic/Latino; 9% Hispanic/Latino; 34% Black or African American, non-Hispanic/Latino; 6% Asian, non-Hispanic/Latino; 0.1% Native Hawaiian or other Pacific Islander, non-Hispanic/Latino; 2% international. 40% 25 or older, 7% transferred in. Core. Calendar: semesters plus summer sessions, winter intersession. Academic remediation for entering students, ESL program, services for LD students, advanced placement, self-designed majors, honors program, independent study, distance learning, double major, summer session for credit, part-time degree program, adult/continuing education programs, co-op programs and internships. Study abroad program. ROTC: Army (c).

Entrance Requirements: Open admission except for nursing and radiologic technology programs. Option: electronic application. Required: high school transcript. Required for some: interview. Entrance: noncompetitive. Application deadline: rolling. Notification: continuous. Transfer credits accepted: Yes.

Costs Per Year: Application fee: $25. One-time mandatory fee: $75. State resident tuition: $4900 full-time, $205 per credit hour part-time. Nonresident tuition: $9800 full-time, $410 per credit hour part-time. Mandatory fees: $675 full-time, $19 per credit hour part-time, $75 per term part-time.

Collegiate Environment: Orientation program. Social organizations: 2 open to all. Most popular organizations: Building Trades, Art Club. Major annual events: National Ice Cream Cone Day, Taco Tuesday, National Fast Food Day. Student services: health clinic, personal-psychological counseling, women's center. Campus security: 24-hour emergency response devices and patrols, late night transport-escort service. Leon E. Butler Library. Books: 20,998 (physical), 2,579 (digital/electronic); Serial titles: 162 (physical), 23 (digital/electronic); Databases: 71. Weekly public service hours: 63; students can reserve study rooms. 645 computers available on campus for general student use. A campuswide network can be accessed from off-campus. Students can access the following: online class registration. Staffed computer lab on campus provides training in use of computers, software, and the Internet.

■ **ERIE COMMUNITY COLLEGE, NORTH CAMPUS**
6205 Main St.
Williamsville, NY 14221-7095
Tel: (716)851-1002
Fax: (716)634-3802
E-mail: admissions@ecc.edu
Web Site: www.ecc.edu
Description: State and locally supported, 2-year, coed. Part of State University of New York System. Awards certificates, diplomas, transfer associate, and terminal associate degrees. Founded 1946. Setting: 120-acre suburban campus with easy access to Buffalo. Total enrollment: 4,929. Student-undergrad faculty ratio is 19:1. 4,191 applied, 71% were admitted. Full-time: 3,309 students, 47% women, 53% men. Part-time: 1,620 students, 56% women, 44% men. Students come from 17 states and territories, 26 other countries, 1% from out-of-state. 0.4% American Indian or Alaska Native, non-Hispanic/Latino; 5% Hispanic/Latino; 13% Black or African American, non-Hispanic/Latino; 5% Asian, non-Hispanic/Latino; 3% international. 33% 25 or older, 11% transferred in. Core. Calendar: semesters plus summer sessions, winter intersession. Academic remediation for entering students, ESL program, services for LD students, advanced placement, self-designed majors, honors program, independent study, distance learning, double major, summer session for credit, part-time degree program, adult/continuing education programs, co-op programs and internships. Study abroad program. ROTC: Army (c).

Entrance Requirements: Open admission except for nursing, dental hygiene and respiratory care programs. Option: electronic application. Required: high school transcript. Required for some: interview. Entrance: noncompetitive. Application deadline: rolling. Notification: continuous. Transfer credits accepted: Yes.

Costs Per Year: Application fee: $25. One-time mandatory fee: $75. State resident tuition: $4900 full-time, $205 per credit hour part-time. Nonresident tuition: $9800 full-time, $410 per credit hour part-time. Mandatory fees: $675 full-time, $19 per credit hour part-time, $75 per term part-time.

Collegiate Environment: Orientation program. Social organizations: 5 open to all. Most popular organizations: Dental Hygiene, American Public Works Association, Anime & Gaming, International Student Organization, Ancient & Paranormal Mysteries Research Club. Major annual events: Back to School Bash, Thanksgiving Festivities, Soul Food Day. Student services: health clinic, personal-psychological counseling, women's center. Campus security: 24-hour emergency response devices and patrols, late night transport-escort service. Richard R. Dry Memorial Library. Books: 48,505 (physical), 2,579 (digital/electronic); Serial titles: 238 (physical), 23 (digital/electronic); Databases: 71. Weekly public service hours: 65. 850 computers available on campus for general student use. A campuswide network can be accessed from off-campus. Students can access the following: online class registration. Staffed computer lab on campus provides training in use of computers, software, and the Internet.

■ **ERIE COMMUNITY COLLEGE, SOUTH CAMPUS**
4041 Southwestern Blvd.
Orchard Park, NY 14127-2199
Tel: (716)851-1003
Fax: (716)648-9953
E-mail: admissions@ecc.edu
Web Site: www.ecc.edu
Description: State and locally supported, 2-year, coed. Part of State University of New York System. Awards certificates, diplomas, transfer associate, and terminal associate degrees. Founded 1974. Setting: 110-acre suburban campus with easy access to Buffalo. Total enrollment: 3,789. Student-undergrad faculty ratio is 19:1. 2,639 applied, 83% were admitted.

Full-time: 2,132 students, 40% women, 60% men. Part-time: 1,657 students, 54% women, 46% men. Students come from 19 states and territories, 5 other countries, 1% from out-of-state. 1% American Indian or Alaska Native, non-Hispanic/Latino; 6% Hispanic/Latino; 9% Black or African American, non-Hispanic/Latino; 2% Asian, non-Hispanic/Latino; 0.2% Native Hawaiian or other Pacific Islander, non-Hispanic/Latino; 0.7% international. 21% 25 or older, 6% transferred in. Core. Calendar: semesters plus summer sessions, winter intersession. Academic remediation for entering students, ESL program, services for LD students, advanced placement, self-designed majors, honors program, independent study, distance learning, double major, summer session for credit, part-time degree program, adult/continuing education programs, co-op programs and internships. Study abroad program. ROTC: Army (c).

Entrance Requirements: Open admission. Option: electronic application. Required: high school transcript. Required for some: interview. Entrance: noncompetitive. Application deadline: rolling. Notification: continuous. Transfer credits accepted: Yes.

Costs Per Year: Application fee: $25. One-time mandatory fee: $75. State resident tuition: $4900 full-time, $205 per credit hour part-time. Nonresident tuition: $9800 full-time, $410 per credit hour part-time. Mandatory fees: $675 full-time, $19 per credit hour part-time, $75 per term part-time.

Collegiate Environment: Orientation program. Social organizations: 1 open to all. Most popular organization: Criminal Justice Club. Major annual events: Back to School Bash, Thanksgiving Dinner, Oktoberfest. Student services: health clinic, personal-psychological counseling, women's center. Campus security: 24-hour emergency response devices and patrols, late night transport-escort service. Library Resource Center. Books: 34,131 (physical), 2,579 (digital/electronic); Serial titles: 218 (physical), 23 (digital/electronic); Databases: 71. Weekly public service hours: 63. 725 computers available on campus for general student use. A campuswide network can be accessed from off-campus. Students can access the following: online class registration. Staffed computer lab on campus provides training in use of computers, software, and the Internet.

■ **EUGENE LANG COLLEGE OF LIBERAL ARTS**
65 W 11th St.
New York, NY 10011-8601
Tel: (212)229-5600; Free: 800-292-3040
Fax: (212)229-5355
E-mail: macluskc@newschool.edu
Web Site: www.newschool.edu/lang
Description: Independent, 4-year, coed. Part of The New School. Awards bachelor's degrees. Founded 1975. Setting: urban campus with easy access to New York City. System endowment: $322.3 million. Research spending for the previous fiscal year: $15.7 million. Educational spending for the previous fiscal year: $14,455 per student. Total enrollment: 1,738. Faculty: 158 (71 full-time, 87 part-time). Student-undergrad faculty ratio is 17:1. 2,939 applied, 84% were admitted. 15% from top 10% of their high school class, 30% from top quarter, 79% from top half. Full-time: 1,668 students, 79% women, 21% men. Part-time: 70 students, 80% women, 20% men. Students come from 49 states and territories, 49 other countries, 74% from out-of-state. 17% Hispanic/Latino; 8% Black or African American, non-Hispanic/Latino; 6% Asian, non-Hispanic/Latino; 0.2% Native Hawaiian or other Pacific Islander, non-Hispanic/Latino; 9% international. 3% 25 or older, 32% live on campus, 7% transferred in. Retention: 70% of full-time freshmen returned the following year. Academic areas with the most degrees conferred: communication/journalism; visual and performing arts; English. Core. Calendar: semesters. Academic remediation for entering students, ESL program, services for LD students, advanced placement, accelerated degree program, self-designed majors, independent study, distance learning, double major, summer session for credit, part-time degree program, co-op programs and internships. Off campus study at Sarah Lawrence College, Spelman College. Study abroad program.
Entrance Requirements: Options: electronic application, early action, deferred admission, international baccalaureate accepted. Required: essay, high school transcript, 2 recommendations, online application, 2 supplemental essays, counselor evaluation or teacher evaluation, academic paper (grade preferred). Recommended: minimum 3 high school GPA. Required for some: TOEFL, IELTS and PTE for some applicants whose first language is not English. Entrance: minimally difficult. Application deadlines: 1/15, 11/1 for early action. Notification: continuous until 3/15, 3/15 for early action. Transfer credits accepted: Yes. Early action applicants: 683. Early action applicants admitted: 654.
Collegiate Environment: Orientation program. Drama-theater group, choral

group, student-run newspaper. Social organizations: 43 open to all. Major annual events: block party, Bell Hooks + Jill Soloway at The New School, Frank Stella at the Parsons table. Student services: health clinic, personal-psychological counseling. Campus security: 24-hour emergency response devices, controlled dormitory access, 24-hour desk attendants in residence halls. New School Libraries & Archives plus 3 others. Books: 215,937 (physical), 840,933 (digital/electronic); Serial titles: 2,265 (physical), 113,452 (digital/electronic); Databases: 376. Weekly public service hours: 155; study areas open 24 hours, 5-7 days a week; students can reserve study rooms. Operations spending for the previous fiscal year: $1.1 million. 717 computers available on campus for general student use. A computer is required for all students. A campuswide network can be accessed from student residence rooms and from off campus. Students can access the following: online class registration. Staffed computer lab on campus (open 24 hours a day) provides training in use of computers, software, and the Internet.

■ **EUGENIO MARÍA DE HOSTOS COMMUNITY COLLEGE OF THE CITY UNIVERSITY OF NEW YORK**
500 Grand Concourse
Bronx, NY 10451
Tel: (718)518-4444
Fax: (718)518-4256
E-mail: admissions@hostos.cuny.edu
Web Site: www.hostos.cuny.edu
Description: State and locally supported, 2-year, coed. Part of City University of New York System. Awards certificates, transfer associate, and terminal associate degrees. Founded 1968. Setting: 8-acre urban campus. Total enrollment: 6,187. Student-undergrad faculty ratio is 19:1. 38% 25 or older. Core. Calendar: semesters. Academic remediation for entering students, ESL program, services for LD students, distance learning, double major, summer session for credit, part-time degree program, adult/continuing education programs, internships. Study abroad program.
Entrance Requirements: Open admission. Required: high school transcript. Entrance: noncompetitive. Application deadline: rolling. Notification: continuous until 8/15.
Collegiate Environment: Orientation program. Student-run newspaper. Student services: legal services, health clinic, personal-psychological counseling, women's center. Campus security: 24-hour emergency response devices and patrols, late night transport-escort service. Hostos Community College Library.

■ **EXCELSIOR COLLEGE**
7 Columbia Cir.
Albany, NY 12203-5159
Tel: (518)464-8500; Free: 888-647-2388
Fax: (518)464-8777
Web Site: www.excelsior.edu
Description: Independent, comprehensive, coed. Awards associate, bachelor's, and master's degrees and post-master's certificates (offers only external degree programs). Founded 1970. Setting: suburban campus with easy access to Albany, NY. Total enrollment: 28,031. Faculty: 1,483 (all part-time). Student-undergrad faculty ratio is 10:1. Part-time: 25,423 students, 48% women, 52% men. Students come from 55 states and territories, 38 other countries, 87% from out-of-state. 0.6% American Indian or Alaska Native, non-Hispanic/Latino; 11% Hispanic/Latino; 18% Black or African American, non-Hispanic/Latino; 3% Asian, non-Hispanic/Latino; 0.6% Native Hawaiian or other Pacific Islander, non-Hispanic/Latino. 88% 25 or older, 7% transferred in. Academic areas with the most degrees conferred: liberal arts/general studies; business/marketing; health professions and related sciences. Core. Calendar: continuous. Services for LD students, self-designed majors, independent study, distance learning, part-time degree program, external degree program, adult/continuing education programs, graduate courses open to undergrads.
Entrance Requirements: Open admission. Options: electronic application, international baccalaureate accepted. Required for some: college transcripts. Application deadline: rolling. Notification: continuous. Transfer credits accepted: Yes.
Costs Per Year: Application fee: $50. Tuition: $510 per credit part-time. Part-time tuition varies according to reciprocity agreements.
Collegiate Environment: Social organizations: nursing and engineering honor societies. Major annual event: Commencement. College housing not available. Excelsior College Library.

■ **FARMINGDALE STATE COLLEGE**
2350 Broadhollow Rd.
Farmingdale, NY 11735

Tel: (631)420-2000
Fax: (631)420-2633
Web Site: www.farmingdale.edu

Description: State-supported, comprehensive, coed. Part of State University of New York System. Awards associate, bachelor's, and master's degrees. Founded 1912. Setting: 380-acre suburban campus with easy access to New York City. Endowment: $5.9 million. Research spending for the previous fiscal year: $396,774. Educational spending for the previous fiscal year: $8721 per student. Total enrollment: 9,969. Faculty: 748 (250 full-time, 498 part-time). Student-undergrad faculty ratio is 20:1. 7,500 applied, 46% were admitted. 9% from top 10% of their high school class, 31% from top quarter, 71% from top half. Full-time: 7,689 students, 41% women, 59% men. Part-time: 2,227 students, 51% women, 49% men. Students come from 14 states and territories, 77 other countries, 0.3% from out-of-state. 0.2% American Indian or Alaska Native, non-Hispanic/Latino; 22% Hispanic/Latino; 10% Black or African American, non-Hispanic/Latino; 9% Asian, non-Hispanic/Latino; 0.2% Native Hawaiian or other Pacific Islander, non-Hispanic/Latino; 2% international. 21% 25 or older, 6% live on campus, 12% transferred in. Retention: 84% of full-time freshmen returned the following year. Academic areas with the most degrees conferred: business/marketing; engineering technologies; interdisciplinary studies. Core. Calendar: semesters. Academic remediation for entering students, services for LD students, advanced placement, independent study, distance learning, double major, summer session for credit, part-time degree program, co-op programs and internships. Study abroad program. ROTC: Army (c), Air Force (c).

Entrance Requirements: Options: electronic application, early admission, deferred admission, international baccalaureate accepted. Required: high school transcript, minimum 3 high school GPA, SAT or ACT. Required for some: interview. Entrance: moderately difficult. Application deadlines: rolling, rolling for nonresidents. Notification: continuous, continuous for nonresidents. SAT Reasoning Test deadline: 7/1. Transfer credits accepted: Yes.

Costs Per Year: Application fee: $50. State resident tuition: $6870 full-time, $286 per credit part-time. Nonresident tuition: $16,650 full-time, $694 per credit part-time. Mandatory fees: $1436 full-time, $59.15 per credit part-time, $10 per term part-time. Full-time tuition and fees vary according to program. Part-time tuition and fees vary according to course load and program. College room and board: $13,238. College room only: $8088. Room and board charges vary according to board plan and housing facility.

Collegiate Environment: Orientation program. Drama-theater group, student-run radio station. Social organizations: 66 open to all; national fraternities, national sororities; 4% of eligible men and 5% of eligible women are members. Most popular organizations: Student Government Association, Ram Nation Radio, Greek Life, E-Sports, Backstage Theater Company. Major annual events: Spring Fling, Farewell to Farmingdale, Ramchella. Student services: health clinic, personal-psychological counseling. Campus security: 24-hour emergency response devices and patrols, controlled dormitory access. 650 college housing spaces available; 542 were occupied in 2018-19. No special consideration for freshman housing applicants. Option: coed housing available. Greenley Library. Books: 120,000 (physical), 165,000 (digital/electronic); Databases: 102. Weekly public service hours: 86. 367 computers available on campus for general student use. A campuswide network can be accessed from student residence rooms and from off campus. Students can access the following: online class registration. Staffed computer lab on campus provides training in use of computers, software, and the Internet.

■ FASHION INSTITUTE OF TECHNOLOGY

Seventh Ave. at 27th St.
New York, NY 10001-5992
Tel: (212)217-7999
Fax: (212)217-7481
E-mail: fitinfo@fitnyc.edu
Web Site: www.fitnyc.edu

Description: State and locally supported, comprehensive, coed. Part of State University of New York System. Awards associate, bachelor's, and master's degrees. Founded 1944. Setting: 5-acre urban campus with easy access to New York City. Total enrollment: 8,767. Faculty: 1,116 (232 full-time, 884 part-time). Student-undergrad faculty ratio is 15:1. 4,507 applied, 53% were admitted. Full-time: 7,246 students, 84% women, 16% men. Part-time: 1,309 students, 80% women, 20% men. 31% from out-of-state. 0.1% American Indian or Alaska Native, non-Hispanic/Latino; 20% Hispanic/Latino; 9% Black or African American, non-Hispanic/Latino; 12% Asian, non-Hispanic/Latino; 0.2% Native Hawaiian or other Pacific Islander, non-Hispanic/Latino; 11% international. 17% 25 or older, 21% live on campus,

9% transferred in. Retention: 89% of full-time freshmen returned the following year. Academic areas with the most degrees conferred: business/marketing; visual and performing arts; communication/journalism. Core. Calendar: semesters. Academic remediation for entering students, ESL program, services for LD students, advanced placement, honors program, independent study, distance learning, summer session for credit, part-time degree program, internships. Study abroad program.

Entrance Requirements: Options: electronic application, international baccalaureate accepted. Required: essay, high school transcript. Required for some: portfolio for art and design programs. Entrance: moderately difficult. Application deadline: 1/1. Notification: 4/1. Transfer credits accepted: Yes.

Costs Per Year: Application fee: $50. State resident tuition: $6870 full-time, $286 per credit hour part-time. Nonresident tuition: $20,792 full-time, $866 per credit hour part-time. Mandatory fees: $850 full-time, $24.21 per credit hour part-time, $65 per term part-time. Full-time tuition and fees vary according to degree level. Part-time tuition and fees vary according to degree level. College room and board: $18,468. Room and board charges vary according to board plan and housing facility.

Collegiate Environment: Orientation program. Drama-theater group, choral group, student-run newspaper, radio station. Social organizations: 70 open to all. Student services: health clinic, personal-psychological counseling. Campus security: 24-hour emergency response devices and patrols, late night transport-escort service, controlled dormitory access. 2,300 college housing spaces available; all were occupied in 2018-19. Freshmen given priority for college housing. Options: coed, women-only housing available. Gladys Marcus Library.

■ FINGER LAKES COMMUNITY COLLEGE

3325 Marvin Sands Dr.
Canandaigua, NY 14424-8395
Tel: (585)394-3500
Fax: (585)394-5005
E-mail: admissions@flcc.edu
Web Site: www.flcc.edu

Description: State and locally supported, 2-year, coed. Part of State University of New York System. Awards certificates, transfer associate, and terminal associate degrees. Founded 1965. Setting: 300-acre small town campus with easy access to Rochester. Total enrollment: 6,521. Faculty: 313 (117 full-time, 196 part-time). Student-undergrad faculty ratio is 22:1. 2,493 applied, 89% were admitted. Full-time: 2,587 students, 52% women, 48% men. Part-time: 3,934 students, 61% women, 39% men. Students come from 15 states and territories, 2 other countries, 0.3% from out-of-state. 0.3% American Indian or Alaska Native, non-Hispanic/Latino; 5% Hispanic/Latino; 5% Black or African American, non-Hispanic/Latino; 1% Asian, non-Hispanic/Latino. 31% 25 or older, 3% transferred in. Core. Calendar: semesters. Academic remediation for entering students, services for LD students, advanced placement, accelerated degree program, honors program, independent study, distance learning, double major, summer session for credit, part-time degree program, internships. Off campus study at the Rochester Area Colleges, other SUNY colleges and universities. Study abroad program. ROTC: Air Force (c).

Entrance Requirements: Open admission except for nursing, therapeutic massage, integrative health care programs. Options: electronic application, early admission, deferred admission, international baccalaureate accepted. Required: high school transcript. Entrance: noncompetitive. Application deadline: 8/25. Transfer credits accepted: Yes.

Collegiate Environment: Orientation program. Drama-theater group, choral group, student-run radio station. Social organizations: 45 open to all. Student services: legal services, health clinic, personal-psychological counseling. Campus security: 24-hour emergency response devices and patrols, late night transport-escort service. Charles Meder Library. Students can reserve study rooms. 425 computers available on campus for general student use. A campuswide network can be accessed from off-campus. Staffed computer lab on campus provides training in use of computers and the Internet.

■ FINGER LAKES HEALTH COLLEGE OF NURSING

196 N St.
Geneva, NY 14456
Tel: (315)787-4005

Web Site: www.flhcon.edu
Description: Independent, 2-year, coed. Awards transfer associate and terminal associate degrees. Founded 2008.

■ **FIORELLO H. LAGUARDIA COMMUNITY COLLEGE OF THE CITY UNIVERSITY OF NEW YORK**
31-10 Thomson Ave.
Long Island City, NY 11101-3071
Tel: (718)482-7200
Fax: (718)482-5599
E-mail: admissions@lagcc.cuny.edu
Web Site: www.lagcc.cuny.edu
Description: State and locally supported, 2-year, coed. Part of City University of New York System. Awards certificates, transfer associate, and terminal associate degrees. Founded 1970. Setting: 25-acre urban campus with easy access to New York City. Total enrollment: 19,356. Faculty: 1,088 (418 full-time, 670 part-time). Student-undergrad faculty ratio is 21:1. 20,331 applied, 100% were admitted. Full-time: 10,838 students, 57% women, 43% men. Part-time: 8,518 students, 59% women, 41% men. Students come from 17 states and territories, 148 other countries, 0.4% from out-of-state. 0.6% American Indian or Alaska Native, non-Hispanic/Latino; 48% Hispanic/Latino; 17% Black or African American, non-Hispanic/Latino; 20% Asian, non-Hispanic/Latino; 0.4% Native Hawaiian or other Pacific Islander, non-Hispanic/Latino; 4% international. 35% 25 or older, 9% transferred in. Retention: 37% of full-time freshmen returned the following year. Core. Calendar: enhanced semester. Academic remediation for entering students, ESL program, services for LD students, advanced placement, accelerated degree program, self-designed majors, honors program, independent study, distance learning, double major, summer session for credit, part-time degree program, adult/continuing education programs, co-op programs and internships. Off campus study at Vassar College (Summer program), other units of the City University of New York System. Study abroad program.
Entrance Requirements: Open admission. Options: electronic application, early admission, deferred admission. Required: high school transcript. Entrance: noncompetitive. Application deadline: rolling. Notification: continuous. Transfer credits accepted: Yes.
Costs Per Year: Application fee: $65. State resident tuition: $4800 full-time, $210 per credit hour part-time. Nonresident tuition: $7680 full-time, $320 per credit hour part-time. Mandatory fees: $417 full-time, $104.95 per term part-time. College room and board: $6328. College room only: $4878.
Collegiate Environment: Orientation program. Drama-theater group, student-run newspaper, radio station. Social organizations: 30 open to all. Most popular organizations: Bangladesh Student Association, Christian Club, Chinese Club, Web Radio, Black Student Union. Major annual events: Spring Night: Bangladesh Student Association, Black Expo: Black Student Union, Halloween Havoc. Student services: legal services, health clinic, personal-psychological counseling, women's center. Campus security: 24-hour emergency response devices and patrols, late night transport-escort service. Fiorello H. LaGuardia Community College Library Media Resources Center plus 1 other. Books: 89,478 (physical), 545,512 (digital/electronic); Serial titles: 491 (physical), 105,706 (digital/electronic); Databases: 211,328. Weekly public service hours: 82; students can reserve study rooms. 2,571 computers available on campus for general student use. Computer purchase/lease plans available. A campuswide network can be accessed. Students can access the following: online class registration. Staffed computer lab on campus provides training in use of computers, software, and the Internet.

■ **FIVE TOWNS COLLEGE**
305 N Service Rd.
Dix Hills, NY 11746-6055
Tel: (631)424-7000
Fax: (631)656-2172
E-mail: cynthia.catalano@ftc.edu
Web Site: www.ftc.edu
Description: Independent, comprehensive, coed. Awards associate, bachelor's, master's, and doctoral degrees. Founded 1972. Setting: 35-acre suburban campus with easy access to New York City. Educational spending for the previous fiscal year: $4005 per student. Total enrollment: 681. Faculty: 85 (22 full-time, 63 part-time). Student-undergrad faculty ratio is 15:1. 382 applied, 62% were admitted. Full-time: 611 students, 32% women, 68% men. Part-time: 43 students, 37% women, 63% men. Students come from 10 states and territories, 4 other countries, 7% from out-of-state. 1% American Indian or Alaska Native, non-Hispanic/Latino; 15% Hispanic/

Latino; 20% Black or African American, non-Hispanic/Latino; 4% Asian, non-Hispanic/Latino; 0.2% Native Hawaiian or other Pacific Islander, non-Hispanic/Latino. 11% 25 or older, 15% live on campus, 10% transferred in. Retention: 74% of full-time freshmen returned the following year. Academic areas with the most degrees conferred: business/marketing; visual and performing arts; education. Core. Calendar: semesters. Services for LD students, advanced placement, independent study, distance learning, summer session for credit, part-time degree program, adult/continuing education programs, internships, graduate courses open to undergrads. Off campus study at Nassau BOCES, Western Suffolk BOCES, Eastern Suffolk BOCES, Nassau Community College, Suffolk County Community College.
Entrance Requirements: Options: electronic application, early decision, deferred admission, international baccalaureate accepted. Required: essay, minimum 2.3 high school GPA, 1 recommendation, immunization records; audition for music or theatre. Recommended: SAT or ACT. Required for some: interview. Entrance: moderately difficult. Application deadlines: rolling, 12/1 for early decision. Notification: continuous, 12/15 for early decision. Transfer credits accepted: Yes.
Collegiate Environment: Orientation program. Drama-theater group, choral group, student-run newspaper, radio station. Social organizations: 16 open to all. Most popular organizations: Film Video Club, Audio Club, Music Business Club, Jazz Club, yearbook. Major annual events: Long Island Music Industry Conference, College Senior Picnic, L. I. Media Art Show. Student services: personal-psychological counseling. Campus security: 24-hour emergency response devices and patrols, late night transport-escort service, controlled dormitory access. Five Towns College Library plus 1 other. Operations spending for the previous fiscal year: $517,938. 110 computers available on campus for general student use. A campuswide network can be accessed from student residence rooms. Staffed computer lab on campus provides training in use of computers and the Internet.
Community Environment: See Adelphi University.

■ **FORDHAM UNIVERSITY (BRONX)**
441 E Fordham Rd.
OIS, Fordham Bldg. 540
Bronx, NY 10458
E-mail: peek@fordham.edu

■ **FORDHAM UNIVERSITY**
441 E Fordham Rd.
New York, NY 10458
Tel: (718)817-1000; Free: 800-FORDHAM
Fax: (718)367-9404
E-mail: peek@fordham.edu
Web Site: www.fordham.edu
Description: Independent Roman Catholic (Jesuit), university, coed. Awards bachelor's, master's, and doctoral degrees and post-master's certificates (branch locations at Rose Hill and Lincoln Center). Founded 1841. Setting: 93-acre urban campus with easy access to New York City. Endowment: $729.2 million. Research spending for the previous fiscal year: $15.5 million. Educational spending for the previous fiscal year: $14,575 per student. Total enrollment: 16,515. Faculty: 1,800 (742 full-time, 1,058 part-time). Student-undergrad faculty ratio is 15:1. 46,308 applied, 46% were admitted. 44% from top 10% of their high school class, 76% from top quarter, 97% from top half. 51 National Merit Scholars, 26 valedictorians. Full-time: 11,779 students, 57% women, 43% men. Part-time: 587 students, 59% women, 41% men. Students come from 47 states and territories, 77 other countries, 58% from out-of-state. 0.1% American Indian or Alaska Native, non-Hispanic/Latino; 15% Hispanic/Latino; 4% Black or African American, non-Hispanic/Latino; 11% Asian, non-Hispanic/Latino; 0.1% Native Hawaiian or other Pacific Islander, non-Hispanic/Latino; 9% international. 5% 25 or older, 50% live on campus, 3% transferred in. Retention: 90% of full-time freshmen returned the following year. Academic areas with the most degrees conferred: business/marketing; social sciences; communication/journalism. Core. Calendar: semesters. ESL program, services for LD students, advanced placement, accelerated degree program, self-designed majors, honors program, independent study, double major, summer session for credit, part-time degree program, adult/continuing education programs, internships, graduate courses open to undergrads. Off campus study at The Juilliard School Evening Division. Study abroad program. ROTC: Army, Naval (c), Air Force (c).
Entrance Requirements: Options: electronic application, early admission, early decision, early action, deferred admission, international baccalaureate accepted. Required: essay, high school transcript, 1 recommendation, Com-

mon Application, SAT or ACT. Recommended: 1 recommendation. Entrance: very difficult. Application deadlines: 11/1, 11/1 for early decision, 11/1 for early action. Notification: 4/1, 12/20 for early decision, 12/20 for early action. SAT Reasoning Test deadline: 1/15. SAT Subject Test deadline: 1/15. Transfer credits accepted: Yes. Applicants placed on waiting list: 9,215. Waitlisted applicants offered admission: 68. Early decision applicants: 294. Early decision applicants admitted: 157. Early action applicants: 20,649. Early action applicants admitted: 11,127.

Costs Per Year: Application fee: $70. Comprehensive fee: $70,656 includes full-time tuition ($51,285), mandatory fees ($1402), and college room and board ($17,969). Room and board charges vary according to board plan, housing facility, and location. Part-time tuition: $1710 per credit. Part-time tuition varies according to class time and course load.

Collegiate Environment: Orientation program. Drama-theater group, choral group, marching band, student-run newspaper, radio station. Social organizations: 208 open to all. Most popular organizations: United Student Government, Commuting Student Association, Residence Hall Association, Ambassador Program (Admission Department Student Tour Guides), Campus Activities Board. Major annual events: President's Ball, Homecoming Weekend, Spring Weekend. Student services: health clinic, personal-psychological counseling. Campus security: 24-hour emergency response devices and patrols, student patrols, late night transport-escort service, controlled dormitory access. College housing designed to accommodate 4,862 students; 4,951 undergraduates lived in college housing during 2018-19. No special consideration for freshman housing applicants. Option: coed housing available. Walsh Library plus 3 others. Books: 1.5 million (physical), 992,000 (digital/electronic); Serial titles: 16,353 (physical), 94,307 (digital/electronic); Databases: 444. Weekly public service hours: 105; study areas open 24 hours, 5-7 days a week. Operations spending for the previous fiscal year: $18.2 million. 2,600 computers available on campus for general student use. Computer purchase/lease plans available. A campuswide network can be accessed from student residence rooms and from off campus. Students can access the following: online class registration, Video Streaming; IP TV Channels; Mobile Apps for University Services; Maker Spaces; University Supplied Software, WebEX Video Conferencing. Staffed computer lab on campus provides training in use of computers, software, and the Internet.

■ **FULTON-MONTGOMERY COMMUNITY COLLEGE**
2805 State Hwy. 67
Johnstown, NY 12095-3790
Tel: (518)762-4651
Fax: (518)762-6518
Web Site: www.fmcc.suny.edu
Description: State and locally supported, 2-year, coed. Part of State University of New York System. Awards certificates, transfer associate, and terminal associate degrees. Founded 1964. Setting: 195-acre rural campus. Endowment: $1.7 million. Total enrollment: 2,833. Faculty: 145 (54 full-time, 91 part-time). Student-undergrad faculty ratio is 24:1. Full-time: 1,863 students, 54% women, 46% men. Part-time: 970 students, 65% women, 35% men. Students come from 6 states and territories, 18 other countries, 1% from out-of-state. 29% 25 or older, 4% transferred in. Retention: 56% of full-time freshmen returned the following year. Core. Calendar: semesters plus winter session. Academic remediation for entering students, ESL program, services for LD students, advanced placement, accelerated degree program, self-designed majors, honors program, independent study, distance learning, double major, summer session for credit, part-time degree program, external degree program, adult/continuing education programs, co-op programs and internships. Off campus study at State University of New York College of Technology at Canton, State University of New York College of Agriculture and Technology at Cobleskill. Study abroad program.
Entrance Requirements: Open admission except for nursing program, radiological technology. Options: electronic application, early admission, deferred admission. Required: high school transcript. Entrance: noncompetitive. Application deadline: 9/10. Notification: continuous.
Costs Per Year: Application fee: $0. State resident tuition: $4600 full-time, $192 per credit hour part-time. Nonresident tuition: $9200 full-time, $284 per credit hour part-time. Mandatory fees: $455 full-time, $18 per credit hour part-time, $108 per term part-time. College room and board: $11,870. College room only: $7650.
Collegiate Environment: Orientation program. Drama-theater group, choral group, student-run newspaper. Social organizations: 30 open to all. Major annual events: Spring Fling, Orientation. Student services: personal-psychological counseling. Campus security: weekend and night security.

Evans Library. Operations spending for the previous fiscal year: $406,724. 400 computers available on campus for general student use. A campuswide network can be accessed from off-campus. Staffed computer lab on campus.

■ **GENESEE COMMUNITY COLLEGE**
1 College Rd.
Batavia, NY 14020-9704
Tel: (585)343-0055; Free: 866-CALL GCC
Fax: (585)345-4541
E-mail: tmlanemartin@genesee.edu
Web Site: www.genesee.edu
Description: State and locally supported, 2-year, coed. Part of State University of New York System. Awards certificates, transfer associate, and terminal associate degrees. Founded 1966. Setting: 256-acre small town campus with easy access to Buffalo, Rochester. Endowment: $5 million. Educational spending for the previous fiscal year: $4133 per student. Total enrollment: 5,906. Faculty: 347 (89 full-time, 258 part-time). Student-undergrad faculty ratio is 15:1. 2,885 applied, 100% were admitted. Students come from 25 states and territories, 20 other countries, 2% from out-of-state. 0.7% American Indian or Alaska Native, non-Hispanic/Latino; 4% Hispanic/Latino; 6% Black or African American, non-Hispanic/Latino; 1% Asian, non-Hispanic/Latino; 3% international. 27% 25 or older. Core. Calendar: semesters. Academic remediation for entering students, ESL program, services for LD students, advanced placement, honors program, independent study, distance learning, double major, summer session for credit, part-time degree program, adult/continuing education programs, co-op programs and internships. Study abroad program. ROTC: Army (c).
Entrance Requirements: Open admission except for nursing, physical therapy assistant, paralegal, respiratory care, veterinary technology, engineering science, and polysomnographic technology programs. Option: electronic application. Required: high school transcript. Required for some: 1 recommendation. Entrance: noncompetitive. Application deadline: rolling. Notification: continuous. Transfer credits accepted: Yes.
Costs Per Year: Application fee: $0. State resident tuition: $4150 full-time, $170 per credit hour part-time. Nonresident tuition: $4750 full-time, $195 per credit hour part-time. Mandatory fees: $490 full-time, $20 per credit hour part-time. College room and board: $8720. College room only: $6400. Room and board charges vary according to board plan and housing facility.
Collegiate Environment: Orientation program. Drama-theater group, choral group, student-run newspaper, radio station. Social organizations: 55 open to all; local sororities, Alpha Epsilon Gamma Service Organization. Most popular organizations: DECA (Distributive Education Clubs of America), PTK Honor Society, Multi Cultural Communications Club, Education Club, FORUM Theater Group. Major annual events: Commencement, Fashion Show, GCC Annual Awards Banquet. Student services: health clinic, personal-psychological counseling. Campus security: 24-hour emergency response devices and patrols, student patrols, late night transport-escort service, controlled dormitory access. Alfred C. OConnell Library. Books: 79,535 (physical), 17,645 (digital/electronic); Serial titles: 164 (physical), 67,604 (digital/electronic); Databases: 89. Weekly public service hours: 76. Operations spending for the previous fiscal year: $912,474. 850 computers available on campus for general student use. A campuswide network can be accessed from off-campus. Students can access the following: online class registration, Applications and Software. Staffed computer lab on campus provides training in use of computers, software, and the Internet.

■ **HAMILTON COLLEGE**
198 College Hill Rd.
Clinton, NY 13323-1296
Tel: (315)859-4011; Free: 800-843-2655
Fax: (315)859-4124
E-mail: admission@hamilton.edu
Web Site: www.hamilton.edu
Description: Independent, 4-year, coed. Awards bachelor's degrees. Founded 1812. Setting: 1,300-acre small town campus. Endowment: $964.2 million. Research spending for the previous fiscal year: $1 million. Educational spending for the previous fiscal year: $31,646 per student. Total enrollment: 1,915. Faculty: 229 (190 full-time, 39 part-time). Student-undergrad faculty ratio is 9:1. 6,240 applied, 21% were admitted. 81% from top 10% of their high school class, 98% from top quarter, 100% from top half. Full-time: 1,907 students, 53% women, 47% men. Part-time: 8 students, 63% women, 37% men. Students come from 45 states and territories, 46 other countries, 71% from out-of-state. 0.1% American Indian or Alaska Native, non-Hispanic/Latino; 10% Hispanic/Latino; 4% Black or African

American, non-Hispanic/Latino; 7% Asian, non-Hispanic/Latino; 7% international. 100% live on campus, 1% transferred in. Retention: 94% of full-time freshmen returned the following year. Academic areas with the most degrees conferred: social sciences; biological/life sciences; foreign languages and literature. Calendar: semesters. ESL program, services for LD students, advanced placement, accelerated degree program, self-designed majors, independent study, double major, part-time degree program, adult/continuing education programs, internships. Off campus study at Colgate University, Utica College. Study abroad program. ROTC: Army (c), Air Force (c).

Entrance Requirements: Options: electronic application, early decision, deferred admission, international baccalaureate accepted. Required: essay, high school transcript, 1 recommendation. Recommended: interview. Entrance: very difficult. Application deadlines: 1/1, 11/15 for early decision plan 1, 1/1 for early decision plan 2. Notification: 4/1, 12/15 for early decision plan 1, 2/15 for early decision plan 2. SAT Reasoning Test deadline: 2/1. SAT Subject Test deadline: 2/1. Transfer credits accepted: Yes. Applicants placed on waiting list: 1,406. Wait-listed applicants offered admission: 28. Early decision applicants: 581. Early decision applicants admitted: 244.

Costs Per Year: Application fee: $60. Comprehensive fee: $70,890 includes full-time tuition ($55,970), mandatory fees ($560), and college room and board ($14,360). College room only: $7850. Part-time tuition: $6996 per course.

Collegiate Environment: Orientation program. Drama-theater group, choral group, student-run newspaper, radio station. Social organizations: 218 open to all; national fraternities, local sororities; 17% of eligible men and 8% of eligible women are members. Most popular organizations: WHCL (Hamilton College Radio), Slow Food, Powder Club, Black & Latin Student Union (BLSU), Hamilton College Climbing Club. Major annual events: FebFest, Class & Charter Concert, Great Names/Common Ground. Student services: health clinic, personal-psychological counseling. Campus security: 24-hour emergency response devices and patrols, late night transport-escort service, controlled dormitory access, student safety program. 1,911 college housing spaces available; 1,877 were occupied in 2018-19. Freshmen guaranteed college housing. On-campus residence required through senior year. Option: coed housing available. Burke Library plus 1 other. Books: 491,977 (physical), 630,432 (digital/electronic); Serial titles: 5,000 (physical), 150,000 (digital/electronic); Databases: 245. Weekly public service hours: 114; study areas open 24 hours, 5-7 days a week; students can reserve study rooms. Operations spending for the previous fiscal year: $3.9 million. 849 computers available on campus for general student use. Computer purchase/lease plans available. A campuswide network can be accessed from student residence rooms and from off campus. Students can access the following: online class registration. Staffed computer lab on campus provides training in use of computers, software, and the Internet.

Community Environment: Clinton, population 1,918, is a suburban community 10 miles southwest of Utica, population 59,336. The climate is temperate. Access via bus, rail, and air lines are through Utica. Nearby Kirkland has a library, five churches, an art center, a Chamber of Commerce, and civic, fraternal, and veteran's organizations. Hockey, skiing, camping, and ice skating are popular recreational activities in the area.

■ **HARTWICK COLLEGE**
One Hartwick Dr.
Oneonta, NY 13820-4020
Tel: (607)431-4200; Free: 888-HARTWICK
Fax: (607)431-4138
E-mail: admissions@hartwick.edu
Web Site: www.hartwick.edu

Description: Independent, 4-year, coed. Awards bachelor's degrees. Founded 1797. Setting: 425-acre small town campus with easy access to Capital District, NY. Endowment: $74.3 million. Research spending for the previous fiscal year: $246,340. Educational spending for the previous fiscal year: $12,260 per student. Total enrollment: 1,176. Faculty: 161 (98 full-time, 63 part-time). Student-undergrad faculty ratio is 11:1. 3,019 applied, 89% were admitted. 8% from top 10% of their high school class, 32% from top quarter, 69% from top half. Full-time: 1,156 students, 58% women, 42% men. Part-time: 20 students, 70% women, 30% men. Students come from 28 states and territories, 20 other countries, 21% from out-of-state. 2% American Indian or Alaska Native, non-Hispanic/Latino; 5% Hispanic/Latino; 10% Black or African American, non-Hispanic/Latino; 3% Asian, non-Hispanic/Latino; 0.2% Native Hawaiian or other Pacific Islander, non-Hispanic/Latino; 2% international. 1% 25 or older, 87% live on campus, 3% transferred in. Retention: 69% of full-time freshmen returned the following

year. Academic areas with the most degrees conferred: social sciences; business/marketing; health professions and related sciences. Core. Calendar: 4-1-4. Services for LD students, advanced placement, accelerated degree program, self-designed majors, honors program, independent study, distance learning, double major, summer session for credit, part-time degree program, internships. Off campus study at State University of New York College at Oneonta. Study abroad program.

Entrance Requirements: Options: electronic application, early admission, early decision, deferred admission, international baccalaureate accepted. Required: high school transcript. Recommended: minimum 2.5 high school GPA. Required for some: audition for music program, portfolio for art majors, SAT or ACT. Entrance: moderately difficult. Application deadlines: rolling, 11/1 for early decision. Notification: continuous, 12/1 for early decision plan 1, rolling for early decision plan 2. SAT Reasoning Test deadline: 5/1. Transfer credits accepted: Yes. Early decision applicants: 26. Early decision applicants admitted: 14.

Costs Per Year: Application fee: $0. One-time mandatory fee: $400. Comprehensive fee: $59,756 includes full-time tuition ($45,990), mandatory fees ($936), and college room and board ($12,830). College room only: $6650. Part-time tuition: $1478 per credit hour.

Collegiate Environment: Orientation program. Drama-theater group, choral group, student-run newspaper, radio station. Social organizations: 65 open to all; national fraternities, national sororities, local fraternities, local sororities; 4% of eligible men and 7% of eligible women are members. Most popular organizations: Student Union, student radio station, Student Senate, Wine to Water, Cardboard Alley Players (theater). Major annual events: Alumni Weekend, OH Fest (concert), Midnight Madness (staff serves food late-night day before finals start). Student services: health clinic, personal-psychological counseling. Campus security: 24-hour emergency response devices and patrols, late night transport-escort service, controlled dormitory access. 1,200 college housing spaces available; 1,025 were occupied in 2018-19. Freshmen guaranteed college housing. On-campus residence required through senior year. Option: coed housing available. Stevens-German Library. Books: 209,006 (physical), 4,560 (digital/electronic); Serial titles: 1,392 (physical), 38,934 (digital/electronic); Databases: 59. Weekly public service hours: 96; students can reserve study rooms. 80 computers available on campus for general student use. A campuswide network can be accessed from student residence rooms and from off campus. Students can access the following: online class registration.

Community Environment: Oneonta, population 13,200, is large enough to support industries and two colleges, and serves as a regional commerce center. Cooperstown is 20 miles away and attracts many people annually who discover Oneonta (home of the National Soccer Hall of Fame) and its restaurants, motels, bed and breakfasts, and who use its local parks and facilities for swimming, golf, fishing, skiing, and boating. Public transportation is available in town. Oneonta is on Interstate 88, a freeway that connects Albany, New York, and central-eastern Pennsylvania.

■ **HELENE FULD COLLEGE OF NURSING**
24 E 120th St.
New York, NY 10035
Tel: (212)616-7200
Web Site: www.helenefuld.edu

Description: Independent, primarily 2-year, coed. Awards transfer associate, terminal associate, and bachelor's degrees (program only open to licensed practical nurses). Founded 1945. Setting: urban campus. Total enrollment: 354. Faculty: 19 (16 full-time, 3 part-time). Student-undergrad faculty ratio is 11:1. Full-time: 91 students, 92% women, 8% men. Part-time: 263 students, 86% women, 14% men. Students come from 4 states and territories, 8% from out-of-state. 12% Hispanic/Latino; 74% Black or African American, non-Hispanic/Latino; 6% Asian, non-Hispanic/Latino. 90% 25 or older, 100% transferred in. Academic area with the most degrees conferred: health professions and related sciences. Core. Calendar: quarters semester for BS program. Accelerated degree program, summer session for credit, part-time degree program.

Entrance Requirements: Option: deferred admission. Required: essay, high school transcript, 2 recommendations, must be Licensed Practical Nurse, Nelson Denny Reading Test. Required for some: interview. Entrance: moderately difficult. Application deadline: rolling. Transfer credits accepted: Yes.

Collegiate Environment: Orientation program. Student services: personal-psychological counseling. Campus security: security guard during hours of operation. Peggy Wines Memorial Library plus 1 other.

■ **HERKIMER COUNTY COMMUNITY COLLEGE**
100 Reservoir Rd.
Herkimer, NY 13350
Tel: (315)866-0300
Fax: (315)866-7253
Web Site: www.herkimer.edu
Description: State and locally supported, 2-year, coed. Part of State University of New York System. Awards certificates, transfer associate, and terminal associate degrees. Founded 1966. Setting: 500-acre small town campus with easy access to Syracuse. Total enrollment: 3,019. Faculty: 160 (51 full-time, 109 part-time). Student-undergrad faculty ratio is 21:1. 3% from top 10% of their high school class, 15% from top quarter, 49% from top half. Full-time: 1,752 students, 55% women, 45% men. Part-time: 1,267 students, 64% women, 36% men. Students come from 34 states and territories, 17 other countries, 4% from out-of-state. 0.5% American Indian or Alaska Native, non-Hispanic/Latino; 5% Hispanic/Latino; 11% Black or African American, non-Hispanic/Latino; 1% Asian, non-Hispanic/Latino; 3% international. 27% 25 or older, 19% live on campus, 7% transferred in. Calendar: semesters. Academic remediation for entering students, ESL program, services for LD students, advanced placement, honors program, independent study, distance learning, summer session for credit, part-time degree program, adult/continuing education programs, internships. ROTC: Army (c).
Entrance Requirements: Required: high school transcript.
Costs Per Year: State resident tuition: $4670 full-time, $169 per credit hour part-time. Nonresident tuition: $7300 full-time, $290 per credit hour part-time. Mandatory fees: $650 full-time, $15 per credit hour part-time, $50 per term part-time. Full-time tuition and fees vary according to location and program. Part-time tuition and fees vary according to location and program. College room and board: $8113. College room only: $6098. Room and board charges vary according to board plan and housing facility.
Collegiate Environment: Orientation program. Drama-theater group, choral group. Social organizations: 29 open to all. Most popular organizations: Phi Theta Kappa, Campus Christian Fellowship, International Students Association, Physical Therapy Assistants Club, Criminal Justice. Major annual events: Club/Organization Fair, Midnight Breakfast, Psychic Fair. Student services: personal-psychological counseling. Campus security: 24-hour emergency response devices and patrols. Herkimer County Community College Library. Books: 73,618 (physical), 33,173 (digital/electronic); Serial titles: 218 (physical), 58,707 (digital/electronic); Databases: 96. Weekly public service hours: 65. 317 computers available on campus for general student use. A campuswide network can be accessed from student residence rooms and from off campus. Students can access the following: online class registration.

■ **HILBERT COLLEGE**
5200 S Park Ave.
Hamburg, NY 14075-1597
Tel: (716)649-7900; Free: 800-649-8003
Fax: (716)649-0702
E-mail: bfiljones@hilbert.edu
Web Site: www.hilbert.edu
Description: Independent Roman Catholic, comprehensive, coed. Awards associate, bachelor's, and master's degrees. Founded 1957. Setting: 40-acre suburban campus with easy access to Buffalo. Endowment: $7 million. Educational spending for the previous fiscal year: $6520 per student. Total enrollment: 792. Faculty: 104 (38 full-time, 66 part-time). Student-undergrad faculty ratio is 12:1. 968 applied, 81% were admitted. Full-time: 680 students, 54% women, 46% men. Part-time: 66 students, 65% women, 35% men. Students come from 22 states and territories, 2 other countries, 5% from out-of-state. 2% American Indian or Alaska Native, non-Hispanic/Latino; 3% Hispanic/Latino; 6% Black or African American, non-Hispanic/Latino; 0.4% Asian, non-Hispanic/Latino; 0.3% Native Hawaiian or other Pacific Islander, non-Hispanic/Latino; 0.5% international. 13% 25 or older, 31% live on campus, 655% transferred in. Retention: 71% of full-time freshmen returned the following year. Academic areas with the most degrees conferred: homeland security, law enforcement, firefighting, and protective services; business/marketing; public administration and social services. Core. Calendar: semesters. Academic remediation for entering students, services for LD students, advanced placement, accelerated degree program, honors program, independent study, distance learning, summer session for credit, adult/continuing education programs, co-op programs and internships. Study abroad program. ROTC: Army (c).
Entrance Requirements: Options: electronic application, deferred admis-

sion, international baccalaureate accepted. Required: high school transcript. Recommended: essay, interview, SAT or ACT. Required for some: interview. Entrance: minimally difficult. Application deadline: rolling. Notification: continuous. Transfer credits accepted: Yes.
Costs Per Year: Application fee: $25. One-time mandatory fee: $50. Comprehensive fee: $31,700 includes full-time tuition ($21,750), mandatory fees ($600), and college room and board ($9350). Room and board charges vary according to board plan and housing facility. Part-time tuition: $560 per credit hour. Part-time mandatory fees: $13 per credit hour, $55 per term.
Collegiate Environment: Orientation program. Drama-theater group, student-run newspaper, radio station. Social organizations: 20 open to all. Most popular organizations: Student Government Association, Student Business and Accounting Association, SADD, Students in Free Enterprise (SIFE), Criminal Justice Association. Major annual events: Quad Party, Fall Fest, Student Life Awards. Student services: health clinic, personal-psychological counseling. Campus security: 24-hour emergency response devices and patrols, student patrols, late night transport-escort service, controlled dormitory access. McGrath Library. Books: 36,902 (physical), 9,442 (digital/electronic); Serial titles: 172 (physical), 100,109 (digital/electronic); Databases: 49. Weekly public service hours: 77; students can reserve study rooms. Operations spending for the previous fiscal year: $390,631. 146 computers available on campus for general student use. A campuswide network can be accessed from student residence rooms. Students can access the following: online class registration. Staffed computer lab on campus provides training in use of software and the Internet.
Community Environment: Hamburg, population 9,600, is a suburban area adjacent to Buffalo. Within the immediate vicinity there are 18 churches, a theater, shopping center, and major civic, fraternal, and veteran's organizations. Some part-time employment is available for students in the immediate area. The Buffalo Raceway and annual Erie County Fair are here. Rich Stadium, home of the Buffalo Bills, is 5 minutes away and area ski resorts are nearby. All the cultural, community service, and recreational facilities of Buffalo are easily accessible.

■ **HOBART AND WILLIAM SMITH COLLEGES**
300 Pulteney St.
Geneva, NY 14456
Tel: (315)781-3000; Free: 800-852-2256
Fax: (315)781-5471
Web Site: www.hws.edu
Description: Independent, comprehensive, coed. Awards bachelor's and master's degrees. Founded 1822. Setting: 200-acre small town campus with easy access to Rochester, Syracuse. Endowment: $202 million. Research spending for the previous fiscal year: $1.6 million. Educational spending for the previous fiscal year: $15,414 per student. Total enrollment: 2,244. Faculty: 244 (221 full-time, 23 part-time). Student-undergrad faculty ratio is 10:1. 4,409 applied, 61% were admitted. 33% from top 10% of their high school class, 59% from top quarter, 83% from top half. 15 valedictorians. Full-time: 2,220 students, 51% women, 49% men. Part-time: 17 students, 35% women, 65% men. Students come from 40 states and territories, 27 other countries, 60% from out-of-state. 0.4% American Indian or Alaska Native, non-Hispanic/Latino; 5% Hispanic/Latino; 6% Black or African American, non-Hispanic/Latino; 3% Asian, non-Hispanic/Latino; 6% international. 90% live on campus, 1% transferred in. Retention: 86% of full-time freshmen returned the following year. Academic areas with the most degrees conferred: social sciences; communication/journalism; psychology; biological/life sciences. Core. Calendar: semesters. ESL program, services for LD students, advanced placement, accelerated degree program, self-designed majors, honors program, independent study, double major, adult/continuing education programs, internships. Off campus study at New York State Visiting Student Program. Study abroad program. ROTC: Army (c), Air Force (c).
Entrance Requirements: Options: electronic application, early admission, early decision, deferred admission, international baccalaureate accepted. Required: essay, high school transcript, 1 recommendation. Recommended: interview. Required for some: SAT or ACT. Entrance: very difficult. Application deadlines: 2/1, 11/15 for early decision plan 1, 1/1 for early decision plan 2. Notification: 4/1, 12/15 for early decision plan 1, 2/1 for early decision plan 2. SAT Reasoning Test deadline: 2/1. Transfer credits accepted: Yes. Applicants placed on waiting list: 504. Wait-listed applicants offered admission: 29. Early decision applicants: 360. Early decision applicants admitted: 320.
Costs Per Year: Comprehensive fee: $69,290 includes full-time tuition ($54,060), mandatory fees ($1195), and college room and board ($14,035). Room and board charges vary according to board plan.

Collegiate Environment: Orientation program. Drama-theater group, choral group, student-run newspaper, radio station. Social organizations: 80 open to all; national fraternities, national sororities; 15% of eligible men and 2% of eligible women are members. Most popular organizations: Student Life and Leadership, student government, campus publications, Service Network, sports clubs. Major annual events: Day of Service, President's Forum, Charter Day/Moving Up Day. Student services: health clinic, personal-psychological counseling, women's center. Campus security: 24-hour emergency response devices and patrols, late night transport-escort service, controlled dormitory access. Warren Hunting Smith Library plus 1 other. Books: 389,139 (physical), 285,340 (digital/electronic); Serial titles: 1,485 (physical), 57,835 (digital/electronic); Databases: 134. Weekly public service hours: 114; study areas open 24 hours, 5-7 days a week; students can reserve study rooms. Operations spending for the previous fiscal year: $2.6 million. 247 computers available on campus for general student use. Computer purchase/lease plans available. A campuswide network can be accessed from student residence rooms and from off campus. Students can access the following: online class registration. Staffed computer lab on campus provides training in use of computers, software, and the Internet.

Community Environment: Geneva, population 13,500, is on Seneca Lake, the largest of the Finger Lakes. It is the center of a rich agricultural and nursery region with a number of diversified industries adding to the city's economy. There are several churches of major denominations, a public library, historical museum, YMCA, and many service and fraternal organizations within the town. Seneca lake offers excellent facilities for fishing, boating, and other water sports. Some part-time employment is available.

■ HOFSTRA UNIVERSITY

100 Hofstra University
Hempstead, NY 11549
Tel: (516)463-6600; Free: 800-HOFSTRA
Fax: (516)560-7660
E-mail: admission@hofstra.edu
Web Site: www.hofstra.edu

Description: Independent, university, coed. Awards bachelor's, master's, and doctoral degrees and post-master's certificates. Founded 1935. Setting: 244-acre suburban campus with easy access to New York City. Endowment: $575.8 million. Research spending for the previous fiscal year: $2.1 million. Educational spending for the previous fiscal year: $16,879 per student. Total enrollment: 10,871. Faculty: 1,236 (483 full-time, 753 part-time). Student-undergrad faculty ratio is 13:1. 27,620 applied, 63% were admitted. 28% from top 10% of their high school class, 59% from top quarter, 90% from top half. 5 valedictorians. Full-time: 6,329 students, 56% women, 44% men. Part-time: 372 students, 46% women, 54% men. Students come from 47 states and territories, 81 other countries, 38% from out-of-state. 0.4% American Indian or Alaska Native, non-Hispanic/Latino; 12% Hispanic/Latino; 9% Black or African American, non-Hispanic/Latino; 11% Asian, non-Hispanic/Latino; 0.2% Native Hawaiian or other Pacific Islander, non-Hispanic/Latino; 6% international. 4% 25 or older, 45% live on campus, 4% transferred in. Retention: 82% of full-time freshmen returned the following year. Academic areas with the most degrees conferred: business/marketing; communication/journalism; health professions and related sciences. Core. Calendar: semesters. ESL program, services for LD students, advanced placement, accelerated degree program, self-designed majors, freshman honors college, honors program, independent study, distance learning, double major, summer session for credit, part-time degree program, external degree program, co-op programs and internships, graduate courses open to undergrads. Off campus study at Hofstra University, St. John's University, Adelphi University, for a Doctor of Audiology Program. Study abroad program. ROTC: Army.

Entrance Requirements: Options: electronic application, early admission, early action, deferred admission, international baccalaureate accepted. Required: essay, high school transcript, 2 recommendations, Proof of degree required for all; TOEFL required for international students. Required for some: interview, TOEFL for international students. Entrance: moderately difficult. Application deadlines: rolling, 12/15 for early action. Notification: 1/15 for early action. Transfer credits accepted: Yes. Applicants placed on waiting list: 143. Wait-listed applicants offered admission: 24. Early action applicants: 13,801. Early action applicants admitted: 9,712.

Costs Per Year: Application fee: $70. Comprehensive fee: $61,408 includes full-time tuition ($44,640), mandatory fees ($1060), and college room and board ($15,708). College room only: $10,640. Full-time tuition and fees vary according to course load. Room and board charges vary according to board plan and housing facility. Part-time tuition: $1500 per credit hour. Part-time

mandatory fees: $155 per term. Part-time tuition and fees vary according to course load. Tuition guaranteed not to increase for student's term of enrollment.

Collegiate Environment: Orientation program. Drama-theater group, choral group, student-run newspaper, radio station. Social organizations: 223 open to all; national fraternities, national sororities, local sororities, 223 registered clubs and organizations; 8% of eligible men and 10% of eligible women are members. Most popular organizations: Hofstra Rock Climbing, transcenDANCE, DanceWorks, E-Sports, Student Government Association. Major annual events: Fall Festival, Welcome Week Club Carnival, Relay for Life. Student services: health clinic, personal-psychological counseling. Campus security: 24-hour emergency response devices and patrols, student patrols, late night transport-escort service, controlled dormitory access. 3,500 college housing spaces available; 2,887 were occupied in 2018-19. Freshmen given priority for college housing. Option: coed housing available. Axinn Library plus 3 others. Books: 859,300 (physical), 214,032 (digital/electronic); Serial titles: 1,761 (physical), 17,415 (digital/electronic); Databases: 241. Weekly public service hours: 110; study areas open 24 hours, 5-7 days a week; students can reserve study rooms. Operations spending for the previous fiscal year: $12.1 million. 1,536 computers available on campus for general student use. Computer purchase/lease plans available. A campuswide network can be accessed from student residence rooms and from off campus. Students can access the following: online class registration, Emergency alert system, online course management system, online card services balance update, online e-portfolio, software tutoring, support for specific tech-enhanced assignments, repair and rebuilding-after-virus services, and printing services. Staffed computer lab on campus provides training in use of computers, software, and the Internet.

Community Environment: Population 52,800. A residential community and retail shopping center, Hempstead is particularly interesting for its 3 historic churches. A suburban area, it is situated 25 miles east of New York City. The immediate vicinity has a public library, the Nassau Coliseum, shopping mall, YMCA, YWCA, a hospital, churches and synagogues. There are theaters, water sports, and several civic, fraternal and veterans organizations in the city. Kennedy and La Guardia airports are within 30 minutes of the campus.

■ HOLY TRINITY ORTHODOX SEMINARY

PO Box 36
Jordanville, NY 13361
Tel: (315)858-0945
Fax: (315)858-0945
E-mail: ejwillmarth@hts.edu
Web Site: www.hts.edu

Description: Independent Russian Orthodox, 4-year, men only. Awards bachelor's degrees. Founded 1948. Setting: 900-acre rural campus. Total enrollment: 77. Faculty: 21 (8 full-time, 13 part-time). Student-undergrad faculty ratio is 2:1. Full-time: 19 students. Part-time: 58 students. Students come from 8 states and territories, 8 other countries. 5% Hispanic/Latino; 5% Black or African American, non-Hispanic/Latino; 11% Asian, non-Hispanic/Latino; 42% international. 8% 25 or older. Academic area with the most degrees conferred: theology and religious vocations. Core. Calendar: semesters. ESL program, accelerated degree program, independent study, external degree program.

Entrance Requirements: Options: electronic application, deferred admission. Required: essay, high school transcript, minimum 2 high school GPA, 1 recommendation, Orthodoxy/Orthodox baptism, entrance exam, recommendation from spiritual father or parish priest. Entrance: noncompetitive. Application deadline: 6/1. Transfer credits accepted: Yes.

Collegiate Environment: Orientation program. Choral group, student-run newspaper. Social organizations: 1 open to all. Most popular organization: Student Union. Major annual events: Holy Trinity Seminary Colloquium, Seminary Feast Day, Graduation. Student services: health clinic, personal-psychological counseling. Campus security: 24-hour emergency response devices. Holy Trinity Orthodox Seminary Library. Books: 40,000 (physical). Weekly public service hours: 40. 2 computers available on campus for general student use. A computer is required for all students. A campuswide network can be accessed.

■ HOUGHTON COLLEGE

One Willard Ave.
Houghton, NY 14744
Tel: (585)567-9200; Free: 800-777-2556
Fax: (585)567-9522
E-mail: admission@houghton.edu

Web Site: www.houghton.edu

Description: Independent Wesleyan, comprehensive, coed. Awards associate, bachelor's, and master's degrees. Founded 1883. Setting: 1,300-acre rural campus with easy access to Buffalo, Rochester. Endowment: $46.4 million. Research spending for the previous fiscal year: $6156. Educational spending for the previous fiscal year: $11,958 per student. Total enrollment: 1,059. Faculty: 124 (67 full-time, 57 part-time). Student-undergrad faculty ratio is 13:1. 1,074 applied, 75% were admitted. 27% from top 10% of their high school class, 51% from top quarter, 83% from top half. 6 valedictorians. Full-time: 998 students, 62% women, 38% men. Part-time: 45 students, 67% women, 33% men. Students come from 36 states and territories, 44 other countries, 34% from out-of-state. 0.1% American Indian or Alaska Native, non-Hispanic/Latino; 1% Hispanic/Latino; 3% Black or African American, non-Hispanic/Latino; 3% Asian, non-Hispanic/Latino; 0.2% Native Hawaiian or other Pacific Islander, non-Hispanic/Latino; 12% international. 5% 25 or older, 89% live on campus, 6% transferred in. Retention: 86% of full-time freshmen returned the following year. Academic areas with the most degrees conferred: business/marketing; education; biological/life sciences. Core. Calendar: semesters. ESL program, services for LD students, advanced placement, accelerated degree program, self-designed majors, freshman honors college, honors program, independent study, distance learning, double major, summer session for credit, adult/continuing education programs, co-op programs and internships, graduate courses open to undergrads. Off campus study at Member of the Western New York Higher Education Consortium, Rochester Area Colleges, Council for Christian Colleges and Universities (CCCU), Five College Committee, and the Christian College Consortium (CCC). Study abroad program. ROTC: Army (c).

Entrance Requirements: Options: electronic application, deferred admission, international baccalaureate accepted. Required: high school transcript, 1 recommendation. Recommended: essay, minimum 3 high school GPA, interview, SAT or ACT. Required for some: essay. Entrance: moderately difficult. Application deadlines: rolling, rolling for nonresidents. Notification: continuous, continuous for nonresidents. Transfer credits accepted: Yes.

Costs Per Year: Application fee: $40. Comprehensive fee: $41,776 includes full-time tuition ($31,972), mandatory fees ($516), and college room and board ($9288). College room only: $4984. Full-time tuition and fees vary according to course load and location. Room and board charges vary according to board plan and housing facility. Part-time tuition: $1344 per credit hour. Part-time tuition varies according to course load and location.

Collegiate Environment: Orientation program. Drama-theater group, choral group, student-run newspaper. Social organizations: 23 open to all. Most popular organizations: Global Christian Fellowship, Student Government Association, Mercy Seat, Allegany County Outreach, Kairos (formerly Intercultural Student Association). Major annual events: SPOT (variety show), Midnight Breakfast, Homecoming. Student services: health clinic, personal-psychological counseling. Campus security: 24-hour emergency response devices and patrols, late night transport-escort service, controlled dormitory access, Emergency phone number rings directly to cell phone carried by officer on duty 24/7, automatic fire alarms throughout campus. Willard J. Houghton Library plus 1 other. Books: 176,037 (physical), 284,490 (digital/electronic); Serial titles: 821 (physical), 58,547 (digital/electronic); Databases: 118. Weekly public service hours: 82; students can reserve study rooms. Operations spending for the previous fiscal year: $499,635. 30 computers available on campus for general student use. A campuswide network can be accessed from student residence rooms and from off campus. Students can access the following: online class registration. Staffed computer lab on campus provides training in use of computers, software, and the Internet.

Community Environment: Houghton is a small rural community in southwestern New York, just south of Letchworth State Park. Nearby state park makes available good fishing, hunting, and skiing in season. The college also has its own ski slopes with rope-tow, an initiatives rope course, an equestrian riding program and miles of cross-country ski trails.

■ **HUDSON VALLEY COMMUNITY COLLEGE**
80 Vandenburgh Ave.
Troy, NY 12180-6096
Tel: (518)629-4822; Free: 877-325-HVCC
Web Site: www.hvcc.edu

Description: State and locally supported, 2-year, coed. Part of State University of New York System. Awards certificates, transfer associate, and terminal associate degrees. Founded 1953. Setting: 135-acre suburban campus. Total enrollment: 13,320. Student-undergrad faculty ratio is 20:1. 2% from out-of-state. 27% 25 or older. Calendar: semesters. Academic

remediation for entering students, services for LD students, advanced placement, self-designed majors, summer session for credit, part-time degree program, external degree program, adult/continuing education programs, co-op programs and internships. Off campus study at 14 members of the Hudson-Mohawk Association of Colleges and Universities. ROTC: Army, Air Force (c).

Entrance Requirements: Open admission for individual studies program. Options: early admission, deferred admission. Required: high school transcript. Entrance: minimally difficult. Application deadline: rolling. Notification: continuous.

Collegiate Environment: Drama-theater group, student-run newspaper, radio station. Student services: legal services, health clinic, personal-psychological counseling, women's center. Campus security: 24-hour emergency response devices and patrols, late night transport-escort service. Marvin Library.

■ **HUNTER COLLEGE OF THE CITY UNIVERSITY OF NEW YORK**
695 Park Ave.
New York, NY 10065-5085
Tel: (212)772-4000
E-mail: lori.janowski@hunter.cuny.edu
Web Site: www.hunter.cuny.edu

Description: State and locally supported, comprehensive, coed. Part of City University of New York System. Awards bachelor's, master's, and doctoral degrees and post-master's certificates. Founded 1870. Setting: urban campus. Endowment: $120 million. Research spending for the previous fiscal year: $30.5 million. Total enrollment: 23,202. Faculty: 2,110 (675 full-time, 1,435 part-time). Student-undergrad faculty ratio is 14:1. 31,030 applied, 36% were admitted. Full-time: 13,111 students, 65% women, 35% men. Part-time: 4,101 students, 65% women, 35% men. Students come from 41 states and territories, 162 other countries, 3% from out-of-state. 0.1% American Indian or Alaska Native, non-Hispanic/Latino; 22% Hispanic/Latino; 12% Black or African American, non-Hispanic/Latino; 31% Asian, non-Hispanic/Latino; 5% international. 18% 25 or older, 1% live on campus, 11% transferred in. Retention: 85% of full-time freshmen returned the following year. Academic areas with the most degrees conferred: psychology; social sciences; English. Core. Calendar: semesters. ESL program, services for LD students, advanced placement, self-designed majors, freshman honors college, honors program, independent study, distance learning, double major, summer session for credit, part-time degree program, internships, graduate courses open to undergrads. Off campus study at Marymount Manhattan College, New School for Social Research, YIVD Institute, other units of the City University of New York System. Study abroad program.

Entrance Requirements: Options: early admission, international baccalaureate accepted. Required: high school transcript, SAT or ACT. Entrance: moderately difficult. Notification: continuous.

Costs Per Year: Application fee: $65. State resident tuition: $6730 full-time, $295 per credit hour part-time. Nonresident tuition: $18,000 full-time, $600 per credit hour part-time. Mandatory fees: $450 full-time, $132.55 per term part-time. Full-time tuition and fees vary according to course load, degree level, and program. Part-time tuition and fees vary according to course load, degree level, and program. College room only: $4857. Room charges vary according to housing facility and location.

Collegiate Environment: Orientation program. Drama-theater group, choral group, student-run newspaper, radio station. Social organizations: local fraternities, local sororities. Student services: personal-psychological counseling, women's center. Campus security: 24-hour emergency response devices and patrols. 764 college housing spaces available. Option: coed housing available. Hunter College Library plus 1 other. Books: 438,832 (physical), 602,800 (digital/electronic); Serial titles: 3,893 (physical), 105,674 (digital/electronic); Databases: 280. Operations spending for the previous fiscal year: $6.3 million. 600 computers available on campus for general student use. A campuswide network can be accessed. Students can access the following: online class registration. Staffed computer lab on campus provides training in use of computers, software, and the Internet.

■ **IONA COLLEGE**
715 N Ave.
New Rochelle, NY 10801-1890
Tel: (914)633-2000; Free: 800-231-IONA
Fax: (914)633-2096
E-mail: admissions@iona.edu
Web Site: www.iona.edu

Description: Independent, comprehensive, coed, affiliated with Roman Catholic Church. Awards bachelor's and master's degrees and post-master's certificates. Founded 1940. Setting: 35-acre suburban campus with easy access to New York City. Endowment: $130.8 million. Research spending for the previous fiscal year: $168,000. Educational spending for the previous fiscal year: $8865 per student. Total enrollment: 3,926. Faculty: 329 (174 full-time, 155 part-time). Student-undergrad faculty ratio is 15:1. 10,062 applied, 88% were admitted. 11% from top 10% of their high school class, 32% from top quarter, 61% from top half. Full-time: 2,961 students, 50% women, 50% men. Part-time: 326 students, 54% women, 46% men. Students come from 35 states and territories, 38 other countries, 23% from out-of-state. 0.5% American Indian or Alaska Native, non-Hispanic/Latino; 23% Hispanic/Latino; 10% Black or African American, non-Hispanic/Latino; 3% Asian, non-Hispanic/Latino; 0.1% Native Hawaiian or other Pacific Islander, non-Hispanic/Latino; 2% international. 2% 25 or older, 45% live on campus, 3% transferred in. Retention: 75% of full-time freshmen returned the following year. Academic areas with the most degrees conferred: business/marketing; communication/journalism; homeland security, law enforcement, firefighting, and protective services. Core. Calendar: semesters. ESL program, services for LD students, advanced placement, accelerated degree program, honors program, independent study, distance learning, double major, summer session for credit, part-time degree program, adult/continuing education programs, internships, graduate courses open to undergrads. Study abroad program. ROTC: Army (c), Air Force (c).
Entrance Requirements: Options: electronic application, early action, deferred admission, international baccalaureate accepted. Required: high school transcript, SAT or ACT. Recommended: essay, 2 recommendations. Required for some: interview. Entrance: moderately difficult. Application deadline: 2/15. Notification: continuous. SAT Reasoning Test deadline: 2/15. Transfer credits accepted: Yes. Early action applicants: 3,656. Early action applicants admitted: 3,511.
Costs Per Year: Application fee: $0. Tuition: $37,972 full-time. Mandatory fees: $540 per term part-time.
Collegiate Environment: Orientation program. Drama-theater group, choral group, student-run newspaper, radio station. Social organizations: 80 open to all; national fraternities, national sororities, local fraternities, local sororities; 11% of eligible men and 21% of eligible women are members. Most popular organizations: Student Government Association, Gaels Activities Board, Council for Greek Governance, Student Leader Alliance for Multiculturalism, The Ionian - Student Newspaper. Major annual events: Involvement Fair/Club Day Activities, Homecoming, Spring Weekend. Student services: health clinic, personal-psychological counseling. Campus security: 24-hour emergency response devices and patrols, controlled dormitory access. 1,575 college housing spaces available; 1,361 were occupied in 2018-19. Freshmen guaranteed college housing. Option: coed housing available. Ryan Library plus 1 other. Books: 268,290 (physical), 330,337 (digital/electronic); Serial titles: 112 (physical), 369 (digital/electronic); Databases: 160. Weekly public service hours: 101; students can reserve study rooms. Operations spending for the previous fiscal year: $1.4 million.
Community Environment: Population 73,000. An attractive residential suburb is 35 minutes from the center of Manhattan. Located on Long Island Sound, New Rochelle was settled by the Huguenots in 1688. Many houses date from the days of Dutch and English occupancy. Easy access to New York City is provided by rail and bus lines. There are many churches, a YMCA, hospital, public library, and various fraternal, civic, and veteran's organizations. Recreation in the area is provided by 8 miles of Long Island Sound frontage, inland lakes, and public parks as well as facilities for golf, tennis, canoeing, fishing, skating, and hockey. Part-time employment is available.

■ **ISLAND DRAFTING AND TECHNICAL INSTITUTE**
128 Broadway
Amityville, NY 11701
Tel: (631)691-8733
Fax: (631)691-8738
E-mail: info@idti.edu
Web Site: www.idti.edu
Description: Proprietary, 2-year, coed. Awards certificates, diplomas, transfer associate, and terminal associate degrees. Founded 1957. Setting: suburban campus with easy access to New York City. Total enrollment: 112. Faculty: 11 (5 full-time, 6 part-time). Student-undergrad faculty ratio is 15:1. 5% from top 10% of their high school class, 25% from top quarter, 80% from top half. Full-time: 112 students, 5% women, 95% men. 2% American Indian or Alaska Native, non-Hispanic/Latino; 24% Hispanic/Latino; 11% Black or

African American, non-Hispanic/Latino; 0.9% Native Hawaiian or other Pacific Islander, non-Hispanic/Latino. 32% 25 or older. Retention: 91% of full-time freshmen returned the following year. Core. Calendar: semesters. Accelerated degree program, summer session for credit, adult/continuing education programs.
Entrance Requirements: Open admission. Options: early admission, international baccalaureate accepted. Required: interview. Recommended: high school transcript. Entrance: noncompetitive. Notification: continuous.

■ **ITHACA COLLEGE**
953 Danby Rd.
Ithaca, NY 14850
Tel: (607)274-3011; Free: 800-429-4274
Fax: (607)274-1900
Web Site: www.ithaca.edu
Description: Independent, comprehensive, coed. Awards bachelor's, master's, and doctoral degrees. Founded 1892. Setting: 669-acre small town campus with easy access to Syracuse. Endowment: $300.7 million. Research spending for the previous fiscal year: $1.8 million. Educational spending for the previous fiscal year: $13,691 per student. Total enrollment: 6,517. Faculty: 765 (519 full-time, 246 part-time). Student-undergrad faculty ratio is 10:1. 15,278 applied, 69% were admitted. 24% from top 10% of their high school class, 56% from top quarter, 91% from top half. 6 valedictorians. Full-time: 5,991 students, 57% women, 43% men. Part-time: 110 students, 50% women, 50% men. Students come from 45 states and territories, 42 other countries, 55% from out-of-state. 0.1% American Indian or Alaska Native, non-Hispanic/Latino; 9% Hispanic/Latino; 6% Black or African American, non-Hispanic/Latino; 4% Asian, non-Hispanic/Latino; 2% international. 1% 25 or older, 71% live on campus, 1% transferred in. Retention: 85% of full-time freshmen returned the following year. Academic areas with the most degrees conferred: communication/journalism; visual and performing arts; health professions and related sciences. Core. Calendar: semesters. Services for LD students, advanced placement, accelerated degree program, self-designed majors, freshman honors college, honors program, independent study, distance learning, double major, summer session for credit, part-time degree program, adult/continuing education programs, internships, graduate courses open to undergrads. Off campus study at Cornell University, Wells College. Study abroad program. ROTC: Army (c), Air Force (c).
Entrance Requirements: Options: electronic application, early admission, early decision, early action, deferred admission, international baccalaureate accepted. Required: essay, high school transcript, 1 recommendation. Recommended: minimum 3 high school GPA. Required for some: audition for some programs. Entrance: moderately difficult. Application deadlines: 2/1, 11/1 for early decision, 12/1 for early action. Notification: 4/15, 12/15 for early decision, 2/1 for early action. SAT Reasoning Test deadline: 2/1. SAT Subject Test deadline: 2/1. Applicants placed on waiting list: 838. Wait-listed applicants offered admission: 96. Early decision applicants: 147. Early decision applicants admitted: 132.
Costs Per Year: Application fee: $60. Comprehensive fee: $61,130 includes full-time tuition ($45,274) and college room and board ($15,856). College room only: $8768. Part-time tuition: $1509 per credit hour.
Collegiate Environment: Orientation program. Drama-theater group, choral group, student-run newspaper, radio station. Social organizations: 212 open to all; national fraternities; 2% of eligible men and 1% of eligible women are members. Most popular organizations: Student Governance Council, Colleges Against Cancer, Brothers 4 Brothers, International Club, Asian American Alliance. Major annual events: Major Concerts/Speakers on Campus, Dr. Martin Luther King Week, Cortaca Jug (annual football game). Student services: health clinic, personal-psychological counseling. Campus security: 24-hour emergency response devices and patrols, student patrols, late night transport-escort service, controlled dormitory access. Freshmen guaranteed college housing. On-campus residence required through junior year. Option: coed housing available. Ithaca College Library. Books: 315,000 (physical), 165,000 (digital/electronic); Serial titles: 640 (physical), 68,858 (digital/electronic); Databases: 155. Weekly public service hours: 148; study areas open 24 hours, 5-7 days a week. Operations spending for the previous fiscal year: $4 million. 640 computers available on campus for general student use. A campuswide network can be accessed. Students can access the following: online class registration. Staffed computer lab on campus provides training in use of computers, software, and the Internet.
Community Environment: See Cornell University.

■ JAMESTOWN BUSINESS COLLEGE
7 Fairmount Ave., Box 429
Jamestown, NY 14702-0429
Tel: (716)664-5100
Fax: (716)664-3144
E-mail: brendasalemme@jbc.edu
Web Site: www.jbc.edu

Description: Proprietary, primarily 2-year, coed. Awards certificates, terminal associate, and bachelor's degrees. Founded 1886. Setting: 1-acre small town campus. Total enrollment: 311. Faculty: 25 (6 full-time, 19 part-time). Student-undergrad faculty ratio is 23:1. 159 applied, 82% were admitted. 1% from top 10% of their high school class, 11% from top quarter, 39% from top half. Full-time: 305 students, 74% women, 26% men. Part-time: 6 students, 67% women, 33% men. Students come from 2 states and territories, 10% from out-of-state. 5% American Indian or Alaska Native, non-Hispanic/Latino; 20% Hispanic/Latino; 2% Black or African American, non-Hispanic/Latino; 0.3% Asian, non-Hispanic/Latino. 34% 25 or older, 14% transferred in. Academic area with the most degrees conferred: business/marketing. Core. Calendar: quarters. Advanced placement, double major, summer session for credit, part-time degree program.

Entrance Requirements: Required: essay, high school transcript, interview. Entrance: minimally difficult. Application deadline: rolling. Transfer credits accepted: Yes.

Collegiate Environment: Orientation program. Major annual events: School Picnics, The Battle of the Programs. Campus security: 24-hour emergency response devices, student key card for building entrance. James Prendergast Library. Books: 173,745 (physical), 12,508 (digital/electronic); Serial titles: 103 (physical), 70 (digital/electronic); Databases: 55. Weekly public service hours: 55; study areas open 24 hours, 5-7 days a week. 100 computers available on campus for general student use. A campuswide network can be accessed. Staffed computer lab on campus provides training in use of computers, software, and the Internet.

■ JAMESTOWN COMMUNITY COLLEGE
525 Falconer St.
Jamestown, NY 14701-1999
Tel: (716)338-1000; Free: 800-388-8557
E-mail: admissions@mail.sunyjcc.edu
Web Site: www.sunyjcc.edu

Description: State and locally supported, 2-year, coed. Part of State University of New York System. Awards certificates, transfer associate, and terminal associate degrees. Founded 1950. Setting: 107-acre small town campus. Total enrollment: 4,463. Faculty: 306 (72 full-time, 234 part-time). Student-undergrad faculty ratio is 16:1. 1,719 applied, 99% were admitted. 7% from top 10% of their high school class, 25% from top quarter, 54% from top half. Full-time: 2,060 students, 56% women, 44% men. Part-time: 2,403 students, 60% women, 40% men. Students come from 10 states and territories, 18 other countries, 10% from out-of-state. 1% American Indian or Alaska Native, non-Hispanic/Latino; 6% Hispanic/Latino; 5% Black or African American, non-Hispanic/Latino; 0.8% Asian, non-Hispanic/Latino; 0.1% Native Hawaiian or other Pacific Islander, non-Hispanic/Latino; 0.9% international. 28% 25 or older, 11% live on campus, 5% transferred in. Core. Calendar: semesters. Academic remediation for entering students, services for LD students, advanced placement, honors program, independent study, distance learning, summer session for credit, part-time degree program, adult/continuing education programs, internships. Off campus study. Study abroad program.

Entrance Requirements: Open admission except for nursing and occupational therapy assistant programs. Options: electronic application, deferred admission. Required: high school transcript. Entrance: noncompetitive. Application deadline: rolling. Notification: continuous. Transfer credits accepted: Yes.

Costs Per Year: Application fee: $0. One-time mandatory fee: $85. State resident tuition: $4870 full-time, $203 per credit hour part-time. Nonresident tuition: $9740 full-time, $405 per credit hour part-time. Mandatory fees: $29.50 per credit hour part-time. Full-time tuition varies according to course load and program. Part-time tuition and fees vary according to course load and program. College room only: $6700.

Collegiate Environment: Orientation program. Drama-theater group, choral group. Social organizations: 17 open to all; Phi Theta Kappa. Most popular organizations: Nursing Club, SOTA (occupational therapy), Earth Awareness Club, JCC Pride, Impact (Interfaith Christian Club). Major annual events: Welcome Back Picnic and Involvement Fair, Fall Fest, End of the Year Picnic. Student services: health clinic, personal-psychological counseling.

Campus security: 24-hour emergency response devices, controlled dormitory access. Hultquist Library plus 1 other. Books: 90,813 (physical), 2,360 (digital/electronic); Serial titles: 687 (physical), 14 (digital/electronic); Databases: 89. Weekly public service hours: 63. 740 computers available on campus for general student use. A campuswide network can be accessed from student residence rooms and from off campus. Students can access the following: online class registration. Staffed computer lab on campus.

■ JEFFERSON COMMUNITY COLLEGE
1220 Coffeen St.
Watertown, NY 13601
Tel: (315)786-2200; Free: 888-435-6522
Fax: (315)786-0158
E-mail: admissions@sunyjefferson.edu
Web Site: www.sunyjefferson.edu

Description: State and locally supported, 2-year, coed. Part of State University of New York System. Awards certificates, transfer associate, and terminal associate degrees. Founded 1961. Setting: 90-acre small town campus with easy access to Syracuse. Total enrollment: 3,632. Faculty: 239 (74 full-time, 165 part-time). Full-time: 2,082 students, 55% women, 45% men. Part-time: 1,550 students, 58% women, 42% men. 0.6% American Indian or Alaska Native, non-Hispanic/Latino; 10% Hispanic/Latino; 7% Black or African American, non-Hispanic/Latino; 1% Asian, non-Hispanic/Latino; 0.2% Native Hawaiian or other Pacific Islander, non-Hispanic/Latino; 0.9% international. 6% transferred in. Calendar: semesters. Academic remediation for entering students, services for LD students, advanced placement, self-designed majors, honors program, independent study, distance learning, double major, summer session for credit, part-time degree program, co-op programs and internships.

Entrance Requirements: Options: electronic application, early admission, deferred admission. Required: high school transcript. Recommended: SAT or ACT. Required for some: interview. Entrance: minimally difficult. Application deadline: 9/6. Notification: continuous. Preference given to county residents.

Costs Per Year: Application fee: $0. State resident tuition: $4752 full-time. Nonresident tuition: $9504 full-time. Mandatory fees: $672 full-time. College room and board: $13,626. College room only: $9150. Room and board charges vary according to board plan.

Collegiate Environment: Orientation program. Student-run newspaper. Social organizations: 30 open to all. Major annual events: Fall Fest/Spring Fest, Stage/Theater Production. Student services: health clinic, personal-psychological counseling. Campus security: 24-hour emergency response devices and patrols, late night transport-escort service, controlled dormitory access. Melvil Dewey Library plus 1 other. Students can reserve study rooms.

■ THE JEWISH THEOLOGICAL SEMINARY
3080 Broadway
New York, NY 10027-4649
Tel: (212)678-8000
Fax: (212)678-8947
E-mail: lcadmissions@jtsa.edu
Web Site: www.jtsa.edu

Description: Independent Jewish, university, coed. Awards bachelor's, master's, and doctoral degrees (double bachelor's degree with Barnard College, Columbia University, joint bachelor's degree with Columbia University). Founded 1886. Setting: 1-acre urban campus. Endowment: $105.7 million. Educational spending for the previous fiscal year: $13,909 per student. Total enrollment: 566. Faculty: 130 (63 full-time, 67 part-time). Student-undergrad faculty ratio is 5:1. 124 applied, 60% were admitted. Full-time: 182 students, 55% women, 45% men. Part-time: 8 students, 88% women, 12% men. Students come from 24 states and territories, 3 other countries, 81% from out-of-state. 75% live on campus. Retention: 100% of full-time freshmen returned the following year. Core. Calendar: semesters. Academic remediation for entering students, services for LD students, advanced placement, self-designed majors, freshman honors college, honors program, distance learning, double major, summer session for credit, part-time degree program, adult/continuing education programs, internships, graduate courses open to undergrads. Off campus study at Barnard College, Columbia University. Study abroad program. ROTC: Army (c), Naval (c), Air Force (c).

Entrance Requirements: Options: early admission, early decision, deferred admission, international baccalaureate accepted. Required: essay, high school transcript, 2 recommendations, SAT or ACT. Recommended:

minimum 3.0 high school GPA, interview. Entrance: very difficult. Application deadlines: 2/15, 11/15 for early decision plan 1, 1/15 for early decision plan 2. Notification: 4/15, 12/15 for early decision plan 1, 2/15 for early decision plan 2.

Collegiate Environment: Orientation program. Drama-theater group, choral group, student-run newspaper, radio station. Student services: health clinic, personal-psychological counseling, women's center. Campus security: 24-hour emergency response devices and patrols, late night transport-escort service, controlled dormitory access. Library of the Jewish Theological Seminary. Operations spending for the previous fiscal year: $2.7 million. 50 computers available on campus for general student use. A campuswide network can be accessed from student residence rooms and from off campus. Students can access the following: online class registration. Staffed computer lab on campus provides training in use of computers, software, and the Internet.

Community Environment: See Columbia University.

■ **JOHN JAY COLLEGE OF CRIMINAL JUSTICE OF THE CITY UNIVERSITY OF NEW YORK**
524 W 59th St.
New York, NY 10019
Tel: (212)237-8000; Free: 877-JOHNJAY
E-mail: vpapandrea@jjay.cuny.edu
Web Site: www.jjay.cuny.edu
Description: State and locally supported, comprehensive, coed. Part of City University of New York. Awards bachelor's and master's degrees. Founded 1964. Setting: urban campus with easy access to New York City. Total enrollment: 14,834. 18,090 applied, 55% were admitted. Full-time: 10,276 students, 58% women, 42% men. Part-time: 2,640 students, 47% women, 53% men. Students come from 21 states and territories, 36 other countries, 3% from out-of-state. 0.4% American Indian or Alaska Native, non-Hispanic/Latino; 44% Hispanic/Latino; 20% Black or African American, non-Hispanic/Latino; 12% Asian, non-Hispanic/Latino; 3% international. 20% 25 or older, 1% live on campus, 15% transferred in. Retention: 77% of full-time freshmen returned the following year. Academic areas with the most degrees conferred: homeland security, law enforcement, firefighting, and protective services; psychology; social sciences. Core. Calendar: semesters. Academic remediation for entering students, ESL program, services for LD students, advanced placement, honors program, independent study, distance learning, double major, summer session for credit, part-time degree program, co-op programs and internships, graduate courses open to undergrads. Off campus study at Other units of the City University of New York. Study abroad program.
Entrance Requirements: Options: deferred admission, international baccalaureate accepted. Required: high school transcript, minimum 2 high school GPA, minimum SAT score of 1100, SAT or ACT. Entrance: moderately difficult. Application deadline: 5/31. Notification: continuous until 2/15. SAT Reasoning Test deadline: 5/31. SAT Subject Test deadline: 5/31. Transfer credits accepted: Yes.
Costs Per Year: Application fee: $65. State resident tuition: $6730 full-time, $295 per credit hour part-time. Nonresident tuition: $14,400 full-time, $600 per credit hour part-time. Mandatory fees: $540 full-time, $182.95 per term part-time.
Collegiate Environment: Orientation program. Drama-theater group, choral group, student-run newspaper, radio station. Social organizations: 40 open to all. Most popular organizations: Auxiliary University Program, Student Athlete Advisory Community Club, Environmental Club, Law Society, Artists United. Student services: legal services, health clinic, personal-psychological counseling, women's center. Campus security: 24-hour emergency response devices and patrols, controlled dormitory access. Lloyd George Sealy Library. Books: 182,059 (physical), 631,447 (digital/electronic); Serial titles: 7,124 (physical), 101,219 (digital/electronic); Databases: 178. Weekly public service hours: 77; study areas open 24 hours, 5-7 days a week; students can reserve study rooms. 1,980 computers available on campus for general student use. A campuswide network can be accessed from off-campus. Students can access the following: online class registration. Staffed computer lab on campus provides training in use of computers, software, and the Internet.

■ **THE JUILLIARD SCHOOL**
60 Lincoln Ctr. Plz.
New York, NY 10023-6588
Tel: (212)799-5000
Fax: (212)724-0263

E-mail: admissions@juilliard.edu
Web Site: www.juilliard.edu
Description: Independent, comprehensive, coed. Awards bachelor's, master's, and doctoral degrees and post-master's certificates. Founded 1905. Setting: urban campus with easy access to New York City. Total enrollment: 942. Faculty: 352 (128 full-time, 224 part-time). Student-undergrad faculty ratio is 4:1. 4,045 applied, 5% were admitted. Full-time: 487 students, 47% women, 53% men. Part-time: 98 students, 45% women, 55% men. 85% from out-of-state. 7% Hispanic/Latino; 7% Black or African American, non-Hispanic/Latino; 12% Asian, non-Hispanic/Latino; 0.2% Native Hawaiian or other Pacific Islander, non-Hispanic/Latino; 23% international. 1% 25 or older, 2% transferred in. Academic area with the most degrees conferred: visual and performing arts. Calendar: semesters. Adult/continuing education programs.
Entrance Requirements: Option: electronic application. Required: essay, high school transcript, audition. Required for some: SAT or ACT. Entrance: most difficult. Application deadlines: 12/1, 12/1 for nonresidents. Notification: 4/1, 4/1 for nonresidents. SAT Reasoning Test deadline: 2/1. SAT Subject Test deadline: 2/1. Applicants placed on waiting list: 80. Wait-listed applicants offered admission: 23.
Costs Per Year: Application fee: $110. Comprehensive fee: $65,440 includes full-time tuition ($47,370), mandatory fees ($100), and college room and board ($17,970).
Collegiate Environment: Orientation program. Drama-theater group, student-run newspaper. Student services: health clinic, personal-psychological counseling. Campus security: 24-hour emergency response devices and patrols, controlled dormitory access, electronically operated main building entrances. Freshmen guaranteed college housing. On-campus residence required in freshman year. Option: coed housing available. Lila Acheson Wallace Library.
Community Environment: See New York University.

■ **KEHILATH YAKOV RABBINICAL SEMINARY**
340 Illington Rd.
Ossining, NY 10562
Tel: (718)963-1212
Fax: (718)387-8586
Web Site: kehilathyakov.com
Description: Independent Jewish, comprehensive, men only. Awards bachelor's and master's degrees. Founded 1950. Total enrollment: 88. Calendar: semesters.

■ **KEUKA COLLEGE**
141 Central Ave.
Keuka Park, NY 14478
Tel: (315)279-5000; Free: 800-33-KEUKA
Fax: (315)279-5216
E-mail: admissions@keuka.edu
Web Site: www.keuka.edu
Description: Independent, comprehensive, coed, affiliated with American Baptist Churches in the U.S.A. Awards bachelor's and master's degrees. Founded 1890. Setting: 173-acre rural campus with easy access to Rochester. Endowment: $13.3 million. Total enrollment: 2,003. Faculty: 439 (87 full-time, 352 part-time). Student-undergrad faculty ratio is 11:1. 1,996 applied, 94% were admitted. 10% from top 10% of their high school class, 33% from top quarter, 74% from top half. Full-time: 1,351 students, 72% women, 28% men. Part-time: 379 students, 83% women, 17% men. Students come from 3 states and territories, 12 other countries, 0.1% from out-of-state. 0.5% American Indian or Alaska Native, non-Hispanic/Latino; 5% Hispanic/Latino; 9% Black or African American, non-Hispanic/Latino; 0.6% Asian, non-Hispanic/Latino; 0.1% Native Hawaiian or other Pacific Islander, non-Hispanic/Latino; 3% international. 0.3% 25 or older, 46% live on campus, 3% transferred in. Retention: 70% of full-time freshmen returned the following year. Academic areas with the most degrees conferred: business/marketing; health professions and related sciences; public administration and social services. Core. Calendar: 4-1-4. Academic remediation for entering students, ESL program, services for LD students, advanced placement, accelerated degree program, self-designed majors, independent study, distance learning, double major, summer session for credit, part-time degree program, adult/continuing education programs, co-op programs and internships, graduate courses open to undergrads. Off campus study at Formal articulation programs with the following schools: Onondaga Community College, Rochester Institute of Technology, SUNY

Geneseo, SUNY Oswego, Syracuse University, Tompkins-Cortland Community College. Study abroad program.

Entrance Requirements: Options: electronic application, early admission, deferred admission. Required: high school transcript. Recommended: minimum 2.75 high school GPA, 1 recommendation, interview. Required for some: interview. Entrance: moderately difficult. Application deadline: rolling. Transfer credits accepted: Yes.

Costs Per Year: Application fee: $0. Comprehensive fee: $43,899 includes full-time tuition ($30,823), mandatory fees ($1220), and college room and board ($11,856). Full-time tuition and fees vary according to course load, degree level, location, program, and reciprocity agreements. Room and board charges vary according to housing facility. Part-time tuition: $1029 per credit hour. Part-time tuition varies according to course load, degree level, location, program, and reciprocity agreements.

Collegiate Environment: Orientation program. Drama-theater group, choral group, student-run newspaper. Social organizations: 41 open to all. Most popular organizations: Sigma Alpha Pi Honor Society, SOTA, ASL Club, Art Club, KC Chemistry Club. Major annual events: May Day Weekend, Academic Convocation, Spring Weekend. Student services: health clinic, personal-psychological counseling, women's center. Campus security: 24-hour emergency response devices and patrols, late night transport-escort service. Lightner Library plus 1 other. Books: 79,009 (physical), 1,083 (digital/electronic); Serial titles: 687 (physical), 112 (digital/electronic); Databases: 89. Weekly public service hours: 96. Operations spending for the previous fiscal year: $769,290. 185 computers available on campus for general student use. Computer purchase/lease plans available. A campuswide network can be accessed from student residence rooms and from off campus. Students can access the following: online class registration, phone app for cancellations. Staffed computer lab on campus provides training in use of computers, software, and the Internet.

Community Environment: The college is located on the western shore of Keuka Lake near Penn Yan, population 5,170. This pleasant rural setting is accessible by major roadways. The area provides boating, fishing, water sports, hunting, and winter sports.

■ THE KING'S COLLEGE

56 Broadway
New York, NY 10004
Tel: (212)659-7200; Free: 888-969-7200
E-mail: nhunter@tkc.edu
Web Site: www.tkc.edu

Description: Independent nondenominational, 4-year, coed. Awards bachelor's degrees. Founded 1939. Setting: urban campus with easy access to New York City. Endowment: $488,024. Educational spending for the previous fiscal year: $12,136 per student. Total enrollment: 555. Faculty: 55 (30 full-time, 25 part-time). Student-undergrad faculty ratio is 14:1. 2,098 applied, 41% were admitted. Full-time: 542 students, 64% women, 36% men. Part-time: 13 students, 85% women, 15% men. Students come from 45 states and territories, 10 other countries, 93% from out-of-state. 0.4% American Indian or Alaska Native, non-Hispanic/Latino; 7% Hispanic/Latino; 6% Black or African American, non-Hispanic/Latino; 4% Asian, non-Hispanic/Latino; 0.4% Native Hawaiian or other Pacific Islander, non-Hispanic/Latino; 3% international. 2% 25 or older, 11% transferred in. Retention: 73% of full-time freshmen returned the following year. Academic areas with the most degrees conferred: liberal arts/general studies; business/marketing. Core. Calendar: semesters. Services for LD students, advanced placement, independent study, distance learning, double major, summer session for credit, internships. Study abroad program. ROTC: Army (c).

Entrance Requirements: Options: electronic application, early action, deferred admission, international baccalaureate accepted. Required: high school transcript, SAT, ACT or CLT. Recommended: minimum 3 high school GPA, interview. Entrance: moderately difficult. Application deadline: rolling. Notification: continuous. Transfer credits accepted: Yes.

Costs Per Year: Application fee: $30. Tuition: $36,000 full-time, $1460 per credit hour part-time. Mandatory fees: $450 full-time, $225 per term part-time. Part-time tuition and fees vary according to course load. College room only: $16,840. Room charges vary according to location.

Collegiate Environment: Orientation program. Drama-theater group, choral group, student-run newspaper. Social organizations: 16 open to all; house system; 100% of eligible men and 100% of eligible women are members. Most popular organizations: The King's Players, King's Debate Society, Refuge, Empire State Tribune, The Kings of Swing. Major annual events: Spring Formal, Homecoming, Interregnum. Student services: personal-psychological counseling. Campus security: 24-hour emergency response

devices, 24-hour security/doormen, fire sprinklers, fire/evacuation emergency plan. Battles Library. Operations spending for the previous fiscal year: $174,129.

■ KINGSBOROUGH COMMUNITY COLLEGE OF THE CITY UNIVERSITY OF NEW YORK

2001 Oriental Blvd., Manhattan Beach
Brooklyn, NY 11235
Tel: (718)368-5000
E-mail: info@kbcc.cuny.edu
Web Site: www.kbcc.cuny.edu

Description: State and locally supported, 2-year, coed. Part of City University of New York System. Awards certificates, transfer associate, and terminal associate degrees. Founded 1963. Setting: 72-acre urban campus with easy access to New York City. Total enrollment: 15,280. Faculty: (333 full-time, 700 part-time). Full-time: 8,298 students, 54% women, 46% men. Part-time: 6,982 students, 56% women, 44% men. Students come from 13 states and territories, 136 other countries, 1% from out-of-state. 0.2% American Indian or Alaska Native, non-Hispanic/Latino; 17% Hispanic/Latino; 29% Black or African American, non-Hispanic/Latino; 15% Asian, non-Hispanic/Latino; 3% international. 23% 25 or older, 4% transferred in. Retention: 71% of full-time freshmen returned the following year. Core. Calendar: semesters. Academic remediation for entering students, ESL program, services for LD students, advanced placement, accelerated degree program, honors program, independent study, distance learning, summer session for credit, part-time degree program, adult/continuing education programs, co-op programs and internships. Off campus study at other units of the City University of New York System.

Entrance Requirements: Open admission. Option: electronic application. Required: high school transcript. Entrance: noncompetitive. Application deadline: 8/15.

Costs Per Year: Application fee: $65. State resident tuition: $4800 full-time, $210 per credit hour part-time. Nonresident tuition: $7680 full-time, $320 per credit hour part-time. Mandatory fees: $453 full-time, $121.45 per term part-time.

Collegiate Environment: Orientation program. Drama-theater group, choral group, student-run newspaper, radio station. Social organizations: 80 open to all. Most popular organizations: Peer Advisors, Caribbean Club, DECA. Major annual events: Club Fair, Family Day. Student services: legal services, health clinic, personal-psychological counseling, women's center. Campus security: 24-hour emergency response devices and patrols. Robert J. Kibbee Library. Books: 224,727 (physical), 481,635 (digital/electronic); Serial titles: 230 (physical), 77,212 (digital/electronic); Databases: 140. Weekly public service hours: 79. 900 computers available on campus for general student use. Computer purchase/lease plans available. A campuswide network can be accessed. Staffed computer lab on campus.

■ LE MOYNE COLLEGE

1419 Salt Springs Rd.
Syracuse, NY 13214
Tel: (315)445-4100; Free: 800-333-4733
Fax: (315)445-4711
Web Site: www.lemoyne.edu

Description: Independent Roman Catholic (Jesuit), comprehensive, coed. Awards bachelor's and master's degrees and post-master's certificates. Founded 1946. Setting: 161-acre suburban campus. Endowment: $179.1 million. Research spending for the previous fiscal year: $87,714. Educational spending for the previous fiscal year: $11,034 per student. Total enrollment: 3,431. Faculty: 335 (166 full-time, 169 part-time). Student-undergrad faculty ratio is 13:1. 7,429 applied, 64% were admitted. 23% from top 10% of their high school class, 51% from top quarter, 88% from top half. 11 class presidents, 10 valedictorians, 65 student government officers. Full-time: 2,410 students, 57% women, 43% men. Part-time: 378 students, 76% women, 24% men. Students come from 23 states and territories, 46 other countries, 6% from out-of-state. 0.3% American Indian or Alaska Native, non-Hispanic/Latino; 5% Hispanic/Latino; 6% Black or African American, non-Hispanic/Latino; 3% Asian, non-Hispanic/Latino; 0.1% Native Hawaiian or other Pacific Islander, non-Hispanic/Latino; 1% international. 5% 25 or older, 58% live on campus, 4% transferred in. Retention: 84% of full-time freshmen returned the following year. Academic areas with the most degrees conferred: business/marketing; biological/life sciences; psychology. Core. Calendar: semesters. Academic remediation for entering students, services for LD students, advanced placement, accelerated degree program, honors program, independent study, distance learning, double major, summer session for credit, part-time degree program, adult/continuing education programs, internships, graduate courses open to undergrads. Off campus study at The Syracuse Consortium for Culture and Medicine. Study abroad program. ROTC: Army (c), Air Force (c).

Entrance Requirements: Options: electronic application, early admission, early action, deferred admission, international baccalaureate accepted. Required: essay, high school transcript, 3 recommendations. Recommended: interview. Required for some: SAT or ACT. Entrance: moderately difficult. Application deadlines: 2/1, 11/15 for early action. Notification: continuous until 1/1, 12/15 for early action. SAT Reasoning Test deadline: 2/1. Transfer credits accepted: Yes. Applicants placed on waiting list: 142. Early action applicants: 3,970. Early action applicants admitted: 2,874.

Costs Per Year: Comprehensive fee: $48,405 includes full-time tuition ($33,560), mandatory fees ($1065), and college room and board ($13,780). College room only: $8590. Room and board charges vary according to board plan and housing facility. Part-time tuition: $704 per credit hour. Part-time tuition varies according to class time and course load.

Collegiate Environment: Orientation program. Drama-theater group, choral group, student-run newspaper, radio station. Social organizations: 98 open to all. Most popular organizations: Student Programming Board, Outing Club, Performing Arts Groups, Cultural Groups, New Student Orientation Committee. Major annual events: Spring Formal, Fall Pep Rally, Halloween Dance. Student services: health clinic, personal-psychological counseling. Campus security: 24-hour emergency response devices and patrols, late night transport-escort service, controlled dormitory access, lighted pathways, closed-circuit security cameras, and emergency code blue phones. Noreen Reale Falcone Library. Books: 261,183 (physical), 206,330 (digital/electronic); Serial titles: 1,391 (physical), 508 (digital/electronic); Databases: 270. Weekly public service hours: 109; study areas open 24 hours, 5-7 days a week; students can reserve study rooms. Operations spending for the previous fiscal year: $875,799. 330 computers available on campus for general student use. A campuswide network can be accessed from student residence rooms and from off campus. Students can access the following: online class registration, ECHO (campus-wide portal), some virtual access from off campus. Staffed computer lab on campus provides training in use of computers, software, and the Internet.

Community Environment: See Syracuse University.

■ LEHMAN COLLEGE OF THE CITY UNIVERSITY OF NEW YORK
250 Bedford Park Blvd. W
Bronx, NY 10468-1589
Tel: (718)960-8000; Free: 877-LEHMAN1
Fax: (718)960-8712
E-mail: enroll@lehman.cuny.edu
Web Site: www.lehman.cuny.edu

Description: State and locally supported, comprehensive, coed. Part of City University of New York System. Awards bachelor's and master's degrees and post-master's certificates. Founded 1931. Setting: 37-acre urban campus with easy access to New York City. Endowment: $7.1 million. Research spending for the previous fiscal year: $214,000. Educational spending for the previous fiscal year: $11,595 per student. Total enrollment: 13,829. Faculty: 938 (373 full-time, 565 part-time). Student-undergrad faculty ratio is 17:1. 15,138 applied, 35% were admitted. Full-time: 7,048 students, 66% women, 34% men. Part-time: 4,623 students, 69% women, 31% men. Students come from 15 states and territories, 99 other countries, 1% from out-of-state. 54% Hispanic/Latino; 30% Black or African American, non-Hispanic/Latino; 7% Asian, non-Hispanic/Latino; 3% international. 49% 25 or older. Retention: 86% of full-time freshmen returned the following year. Academic areas with the most degrees conferred: biological/life sciences; English; visual and performing arts. Core. Calendar: semesters. ESL program, services for LD students, advanced placement, self-designed majors, freshman honors college, honors program, independent study, distance learning, double major, summer session for credit, part-time degree program, adult/continuing education programs, co-op programs and internships, graduate courses open to undergrads. Off campus study at other units of the City University of New York System. Study abroad program. ROTC: Army (c).

Entrance Requirements: Options: deferred admission, international baccalaureate accepted. Required: high school transcript, minimum 3 high school GPA, SAT or ACT. Required for some: essay, interview. Entrance: moderately difficult. Application deadline: rolling. Notification: continuous.

Costs Per Year: Application fee: $65. State resident tuition: $6730 full-time, $295 per credit hour part-time. Nonresident tuition: $14,400 full-time, $600 per credit hour part-time. Mandatory fees: $480 full-time, $130 per term part-

time. Full-time tuition and fees vary according to course load. Part-time tuition and fees vary according to course load.

Collegiate Environment: Orientation program. Drama-theater group, choral group, student-run newspaper, radio station. Social organizations: 33 open to all. Most popular organizations: Club Mac, African Students Association, Dominican Student Association, The Sociology Club, Club Live. Major annual events: Multicultural Festival, Student Life Fair, Student Organization Open House. Student services: health clinic, personal-psychological counseling, women's center. Campus security: 24-hour emergency response devices and patrols, student patrols, late night transport-escort service. Leonard Lief Library plus 1 other. Books: 362,674 (physical); Serial titles: 299,414 (physical). Weekly public service hours: 40; students can reserve study rooms. Operations spending for the previous fiscal year: $1.5 million. 800 computers available on campus for general student use. A campuswide network can be accessed from student residence rooms. Students can access the following: online class registration. Staffed computer lab on campus.

■ LIM COLLEGE
12 E 53rd St.
New York, NY 10022-5268
Tel: (212)752-1530; Free: 800-677-1323
Fax: (212)832-6708
E-mail: admissions@limcollege.edu
Web Site: www.limcollege.edu

Description: Proprietary, comprehensive, coed. Awards bachelor's and master's degrees. Founded 1939. Setting: urban campus with easy access to New York City. Total enrollment: 1,781. Faculty: 230 (31 full-time, 199 part-time). Student-undergrad faculty ratio is 8:1. 1,348 applied, 83% were admitted. Full-time: 1,391 students, 89% women, 11% men. Part-time: 112 students, 87% women, 13% men. Students come from 42 states and territories, 28 other countries, 61% from out-of-state. 1% American Indian or Alaska Native, non-Hispanic/Latino; 12% Hispanic/Latino; 19% Black or African American, non-Hispanic/Latino; 11% Asian, non-Hispanic/Latino; 0.7% Native Hawaiian or other Pacific Islander, non-Hispanic/Latino; 1% international. 5% 25 or older, 24% live on campus, 13% transferred in. Retention: 75% of full-time freshmen returned the following year. Academic areas with the most degrees conferred: business/marketing; visual and performing arts. Core. Calendar: semesters. Academic remediation for entering students, services for LD students, advanced placement, accelerated degree program, honors program, distance learning, summer session for credit, part-time degree program, co-op programs and internships. Off campus study. Study abroad program.

Entrance Requirements: Options: electronic application, early action. Required: essay, high school transcript, 1 recommendation. Recommended: minimum 2 high school GPA. Required for some: interview. Application deadlines: rolling, rolling for nonresidents, 11/15 for early action. Transfer credits accepted: Yes.

Costs Per Year: Application fee: $40. Comprehensive fee: $48,650 includes full-time tuition ($26,990), mandatory fees ($820), and college room and board ($20,840). College room only: $16,840. Part-time tuition: $896 per credit hour.

Collegiate Environment: Orientation program. Student-run newspaper. Social organizations: 18 open to all. Most popular organizations: Fashion Show Production Club, Lexington Line Magazine, Student Life Activities Board, Dance Team, Black Retail Action Group. Major annual event: Student-Run Fashion Show. Student services: personal-psychological counseling. Campus security: 24-hour patrols, controlled dormitory access. No special consideration for freshman housing applicants. Option: coed housing available. Adrian G. Marcuse Library. Books: 15,000 (physical), 700 (digital/electronic); Serial titles: 172 (physical); Databases: 55. Students can reserve study rooms. 352 computers available on campus for general student use. Computer purchase/lease plans available. A campuswide network can be accessed from student residence rooms and from off campus. Students can access the following: online class registration. Staffed computer lab on campus provides training in use of computers and software.

Community Environment: LIM's location right in the center of the greatest fashion city, New York, gives its students the best of all possible worlds. Within a block of the school are internationally known department stores, French and Italian designers' boutiques, retailing establishments of every kind, with goods imported from every continent of the world. Only a few blocks away is the heart of the garment district, Seventh Avenue. Merchandising creativity originates here and finds its way into the shopping centers of America, Europe, and the Far East.

■ LONG ISLAND BUSINESS INSTITUTE
136-18 39th Ave., 5th Fl.
Flushing, NY 11354
Tel: (718)939-5100
Fax: (718)939-9235
E-mail: krobertson@libi.edu
Web Site: www.libi.edu
Description: Proprietary, 2-year, coed. Awards certificates and transfer associate degrees (information provided for Commack and Flushing campuses). Founded 1968. Setting: urban campus with easy access to New York City. Total enrollment: 1,118. Faculty: 129 (17 full-time, 112 part-time). Student-undergrad faculty ratio is 19:1. 234 applied, 93% were admitted. Full-time: 985 students, 73% women, 27% men. Part-time: 133 students, 40% women, 60% men. Students come from 2 states and territories, 19 other countries. 0.1% American Indian or Alaska Native, non-Hispanic/Latino; 21% Hispanic/Latino; 12% Black or African American, non-Hispanic/Latino; 52% Asian, non-Hispanic/Latino; 7% international. 86% 25 or older. Calendar: semesters. Academic remediation for entering students, ESL program, advanced placement, honors program, independent study, summer session for credit, part-time degree program, adult/continuing education programs, co-op programs.
Entrance Requirements: Option: electronic application. Required: high school transcript, interview. Entrance: noncompetitive. Application deadline: rolling. Transfer credits accepted: Yes.
Collegiate Environment: Orientation program. Most popular organizations: Small Business Club, Web Design Club, Investment Club, Court Reporting Alumni Association. Major annual events: Sneaker Day, Holiday Fundraiser, International Food Day. Campus security: 24-hour emergency response devices. Flushing Main Campus Library plus 2 others. Books: 2,000 (physical), 250 (digital/electronic); Serial titles: 10 (physical), 3 (digital/electronic); Databases: 5. 308 computers available on campus for general student use. Staffed computer lab on campus provides training in use of computers, software, and the Internet.

■ LONG ISLAND UNIVERSITY-LIU BROOKLYN
1 University Plz.
Brooklyn, NY 11201-8423
Tel: (718)488-1000; Free: 800-LIU-PLAN
E-mail: bkln-admissions@liu.edu
Web Site: www.liu.edu
Description: Independent, university, coed. Awards associate, bachelor's, master's, and doctoral degrees and post-master's certificates. Founded 1926. Setting: 11-acre urban campus with easy access to New York City. Endowment: $92.4 million. Research spending for the previous fiscal year: $2.5 million. Educational spending for the previous fiscal year: $15,182 per student. Total enrollment: 6,982. Faculty: 729 (281 full-time, 448 part-time). Student-undergrad faculty ratio is 13:1. 6,830 applied, 84% were admitted. 23% from top 10% of their high school class, 43% from top quarter, 69% from top half. Full-time: 3,396 students, 70% women, 30% men. Part-time: 549 students, 72% women, 28% men. Students come from 37 states and territories, 40 other countries, 13% from out-of-state. 0.4% American Indian or Alaska Native, non-Hispanic/Latino; 15% Hispanic/Latino; 22% Black or African American, non-Hispanic/Latino; 17% Asian, non-Hispanic/Latino; 0.2% Native Hawaiian or other Pacific Islander, non-Hispanic/Latino; 3% international. 23% 25 or older, 15% live on campus, 12% transferred in. Retention: 66% of full-time freshmen returned the following year. Academic areas with the most degrees conferred: health professions and related sciences; business/marketing; biological/life sciences. Core. Calendar: semesters. Academic remediation for entering students, ESL program, services for LD students, advanced placement, accelerated degree program, self-designed majors, freshman honors college, honors program, independent study, distance learning, double major, summer session for credit, part-time degree program, co-op programs and internships, graduate courses open to undergrads. Study abroad program. ROTC: Army (c).
Entrance Requirements: Options: electronic application, early action, deferred admission, international baccalaureate accepted. Required: essay, high school transcript, recommendations, SAT or ACT. Required for some: interview. Application deadlines: rolling, 12/1 for early action. Notification: continuous, 12/31 for early action. Transfer credits accepted: Yes.
Costs Per Year: Application fee: $50. Comprehensive fee: $51,783 includes full-time tuition ($35,737), mandatory fees ($2026), and college room and board ($14,020). Room and board charges vary according to board plan and housing facility. Part-time tuition: $1115 per credit. Part-time mandatory fees: $469 per term.

Collegiate Environment: Orientation program. Drama-theater group, choral group, student-run newspaper, radio station. Social organizations: 65 open to all; national fraternities, national sororities; 11% of eligible men and 5% of eligible women are members. Most popular organizations: The Student Government Association, The American Pharmacists Association, Hillel Jewish Students Organization, Student Activities Board, Indo American Pharmaceutical Association. Major annual events: Four Weeks of Welcome, Relay for Life, Blackbird Madness (Pep Rally). Student services: health clinic, personal-psychological counseling. Campus security: 24-hour emergency response devices and patrols, late night transport-escort service, controlled dormitory access, lighted pathways/sidewalks. Salena Library. Books: 257,706 (physical), 406,939 (digital/electronic); Serial titles: 27 (physical), 466,233 (digital/electronic); Databases: 495. Operations spending for the previous fiscal year: $4.4 million. 600 computers available on campus for general student use. A campuswide network can be accessed from student residence rooms and from off campus. Students can access the following: online class registration. Staffed computer lab on campus provides training in use of computers, software, and the Internet.
Community Environment: The campus in downtown Brooklyn, at Flatbush and DeKalb Avenues, within easy distance of the Brooklyn Academy of Music, Prospect Park, the Brooklyn Museum, and midtown Manhattan.

■ LONG ISLAND UNIVERSITY-LIU POST
720 Northern Blvd.
Brookville, NY 11548-1300
Tel: (516)299-2000; Free: 800-LIU-PLAN
E-mail: post-enroll@liu.edu
Web Site: www.liu.edu
Description: Independent, university, coed. Awards associate, bachelor's, master's, and doctoral degrees and post-master's certificates. Founded 1954. Setting: 322-acre suburban campus with easy access to New York City. Endowment: $100.1 million. Research spending for the previous fiscal year: $690,554. Educational spending for the previous fiscal year: $11,835 per student. Total enrollment: 8,499. Faculty: 650 (260 full-time, 390 part-time). Student-undergrad faculty ratio is 14:1. 6,951 applied, 83% were admitted. 10% from top 10% of their high school class, 33% from top quarter, 65% from top half. Full-time: 2,845 students, 60% women, 40% men. Part-time: 3,471 students, 59% women, 41% men. Students come from 38 states and territories, 28 other countries, 9% from out-of-state. 0.2% American Indian or Alaska Native, non-Hispanic/Latino; 15% Hispanic/Latino; 11% Black or African American, non-Hispanic/Latino; 4% Asian, non-Hispanic/Latino; 6% international. 14% 25 or older, 30% live on campus, 6% transferred in. Retention: 78% of full-time freshmen returned the following year. Academic areas with the most degrees conferred: health professions and related sciences; business/marketing; homeland security, law enforcement, firefighting, and protective services. Core. Calendar: semesters. Academic remediation for entering students, ESL program, services for LD students, advanced placement, accelerated degree program, self-designed majors, freshman honors college, honors program, independent study, distance learning, double major, summer session for credit, part-time degree program, co-op programs and internships, graduate courses open to undergrads. Study abroad program. ROTC: Army (c).
Entrance Requirements: Options: electronic application, early action, deferred admission, international baccalaureate accepted. Required: essay, high school transcript, 1 recommendation, SAT or ACT. Required for some: interview. Application deadlines: rolling, 12/1 for early action. Notification: continuous, 12/31 for early action. Transfer credits accepted: Yes.
Costs Per Year: Application fee: $50. Comprehensive fee: $51,783 includes full-time tuition ($35,737), mandatory fees ($2026), and college room and board ($14,020). Room and board charges vary according to board plan and housing facility. Part-time tuition: $1115 per credit. Part-time mandatory fees: $469 per term.
Collegiate Environment: Orientation program. Drama-theater group, choral group, marching band, student-run newspaper, radio station. Social organizations: 68 open to all; national fraternities, national sororities; 8% of eligible men and 11% of eligible women are members. Most popular organizations: Student Government Association, Student Activities Board, Resident Student Association, Commuter Student Association, Greek Programming Board. Major annual events: Homecoming & Spirit Week, Midnight Madness, Move-a-thon. Student services: health clinic, personal-psychological counseling. Campus security: 24-hour emergency response devices and patrols, student patrols, late night transport-escort service, controlled dormitory access, lighted pathways/sidewalks. B. Davis Schwartz Memorial Library. Books: 459,336 (physical), 203,430 (digital/electronic); Se-

rial titles: 482 (physical), 466,233 (digital/electronic); Databases: 478. Operations spending for the previous fiscal year: $5.5 million. 600 computers available on campus for general student use. A campuswide network can be accessed from student residence rooms and from off campus. Students can access the following: online class registration. Staffed computer lab on campus provides training in use of computers, software, and the Internet.

■ **MACHZIKEI HADATH RABBINICAL COLLEGE**
5407 Sixteenth Ave.
Brooklyn, NY 11204-1805
Tel: (718)854-8777
Description: Independent Jewish, comprehensive, men' only. Awards bachelor's and master's degrees. Founded 1956. Total enrollment: 112. 123 applied. 2% 25 or older. Core. Calendar: semesters. Academic remediation for entering students. Study abroad program.
Entrance Requirements: Required: interview. Entrance: moderately difficult. Application deadline: rolling. Notification: continuous.
Collegiate Environment: Abraham Koppel Library plus 1 other.

■ **MANDL SCHOOL**
254 W 54th St., 9th Fl.
New York, NY 10019
Tel: (212)247-3434
Web Site: www.mandl.edu
Description: Proprietary, 2-year, coed. Awards certificates, transfer associate, and terminal associate degrees.

■ **MANHATTAN COLLEGE**
4513 Manhattan College Pky.
Riverdale, NY 10471
Tel: (718)862-8000; Free: 800-622-9235
Fax: (718)862-8019
E-mail: admit@manhattan.edu
Web Site: www.manhattan.edu
Description: Independent, comprehensive, coed, affiliated with Roman Catholic Church. Awards bachelor's and master's degrees and post-master's certificates. Founded 1853. Setting: 31-acre urban campus with easy access to New York City. Endowment: $100.6 million. Research spending for the previous fiscal year: $1.3 million. Total enrollment: 4,132. Faculty: 466 (242 full-time, 224 part-time). Student-undergrad faculty ratio is 13:1. 7,882 applied, 75% were admitted. 23% from top 10% of their high school class, 54% from top quarter, 79% from top half. Full-time: 3,455 students, 46% women, 54% men. Part-time: 199 students, 30% women, 70% men. 0.2% American Indian or Alaska Native, non-Hispanic/Latino; 23% Hispanic/Latino; 6% Black or African American, non-Hispanic/Latino; 5% Asian, non-Hispanic/Latino; 3% international. 7% 25 or older, 67% live on campus, 5% transferred in. Retention: 82% of full-time freshmen returned the following year. Academic areas with the most degrees conferred: engineering; business/marketing; social sciences. Core. Calendar: semesters. ESL program, services for LD students, advanced placement, accelerated degree program, self-designed majors, honors program, independent study, distance learning, double major, summer session for credit, part-time degree program, adult/continuing education programs, co-op programs and internships, graduate courses open to undergrads. Off campus study. Study abroad program. ROTC: Army (c), Air Force.
Entrance Requirements: Options: electronic application, early admission, early decision, deferred admission, international baccalaureate accepted. Required: essay, high school transcript, minimum 2.5 high school GPA, 1 recommendation, SAT or ACT. Recommended: minimum 3 high school GPA, interview. Entrance: moderately difficult. Application deadline: 11/15 for early decision. Notification: continuous until 4/15, 12/1 for early decision. SAT Reasoning Test deadline: 3/1. Transfer credits accepted: Yes.
Collegiate Environment: Orientation program. Drama-theater group, choral group, student-run newspaper. Social organizations: 64 open to all; national fraternities, national sororities; 1% of eligible men and 1% of eligible women are members. Most popular organizations: Society of Hispanic Professional Engineers, Singers, Student Government, Social Life Commission, Manhattan College Players (Theater/Drama group). Major annual events: Spring Concert and Carnival, Manhattan Madness (basketball pep rally), Senior Formal. Student services: health clinic, personal-psychological counseling. Campus security: 24-hour emergency response devices and patrols, late night transport-escort service, controlled dormitory access. 2,095 college housing spaces available; 2,015 were occupied in 2018-19. Freshmen guaranteed college housing. Options: men-only, women-only housing avail-

able. Mary Alice and Tom OMalley Library. Books: 259,987 (physical), 191,706 (digital/electronic); Serial titles: 379 (physical), 186,500 (digital/electronic). Weekly public service hours: 168; study areas open 24 hours, 5-7 days a week. 450 computers available on campus for general student use. A campuswide network can be accessed from student residence rooms and from off campus. Students can access the following: online class registration, course management system, degree audit/planning tool, campus card access. Staffed computer lab on campus (open 24 hours a day) provides training in use of computers and the Internet.
Community Environment: See Fordham University.

■ **MANHATTAN SCHOOL OF MUSIC**
120 Claremont Ave.
New York, NY 10027-4698
Tel: (212)749-2802
Fax: (212)749-5471
E-mail: aanderson@msmnyc.edu
Web Site: www.msmnyc.edu
Description: Independent, comprehensive, coed. Awards bachelor's, master's, and doctoral degrees and post-master's certificates. Founded 1917. Setting: 1-acre urban campus. Endowment: $19.2 million. Educational spending for the previous fiscal year: $17,317 per student. Total enrollment: 957. Faculty: 251. Student-undergrad faculty ratio is 6:1. 897 applied, 45% were admitted. Full-time: 385 students, 55% women, 45% men. Part-time: 4 students, 75% women, 25% men. Students come from 32 states and territories, 20 other countries, 61% from out-of-state. 7% Hispanic/Latino; 2% Black or African American, non-Hispanic/Latino; 7% Asian, non-Hispanic/Latino; 43% international. 4% 25 or older, 67% live on campus, 5% transferred in. Retention: 81% of full-time freshmen returned the following year. Academic area with the most degrees conferred: visual and performing arts. Core. Calendar: semesters. Academic remediation for entering students, ESL program, services for LD students, advanced placement, graduate courses open to undergrads. Off campus study at Barnard College.
Entrance Requirements: Options: electronic application, deferred admission, international baccalaureate accepted. Required: essay, high school transcript, minimum 2.8 high school GPA, 2 recommendations, prescreening, audition. Recommended: minimum 3 high school GPA, SAT or ACT. Required for some: interview. Entrance: very difficult. Application deadline: 12/1. Notification: 4/1. Transfer credits accepted: Yes.
Collegiate Environment: Orientation program. Social organizations: 3 open to all. Most popular organizations: Student Council, Asian Student Association, Resident Community Council. Major annual events: Ice Cream Social with the President, Finals Week Study Breaks, Rite of Spring. Student services: health clinic, personal-psychological counseling. Campus security: 24-hour patrols, student patrols, controlled dormitory access. Peter J. Sharp Library plus 1 other. Operations spending for the previous fiscal year: $567,714. 20 computers available on campus for general student use. A campuswide network can be accessed from student residence rooms and from off campus. Students can access the following: online class registration. Staffed computer lab on campus.
Community Environment: See Columbia University.

■ **MANHATTANVILLE COLLEGE**
2900 Purchase St.
Purchase, NY 10577-2132
Tel: (914)694-2200; Free: 800-328-4553
Fax: (914)694-1732
E-mail: Jessica.Holt@mville.edu
Web Site: www.mville.edu
Description: Independent, comprehensive, coed. Awards bachelor's, master's, and doctoral degrees and post-master's certificates. Founded 1841. Setting: 100-acre suburban campus with easy access to New York City. Endowment: $30.8 million. Educational spending for the previous fiscal year: $9776 per student. Total enrollment: 2,492. Faculty: 375 (114 full-time, 261 part-time). Student-undergrad faculty ratio is 11:1. 3,577 applied, 90% were admitted. 14% from top 10% of their high school class, 34% from top quarter, 77% from top half. Full-time: 1,513 students, 60% women, 40% men. Part-time: 75 students, 63% women, 37% men. Students come from 32 states and territories, 44 other countries, 27% from out-of-state. 0.2% American Indian or Alaska Native, non-Hispanic/Latino; 27% Hispanic/Latino; 10% Black or African American, non-Hispanic/Latino; 2% Asian, non-Hispanic/Latino; 0.3% Native Hawaiian or other Pacific Islander, non-Hispanic/Latino; 7% international. 3% 25 or older, 60% live on campus, 3% transferred in. Retention: 70% of full-time freshmen returned the following

year. Academic areas with the most degrees conferred: business/marketing; communication/journalism; psychology. Core. Calendar: semesters. Services for LD students, advanced placement, accelerated degree program, self-designed majors, honors program, independent study, double major, summer session for credit, part-time degree program, adult/continuing education programs, internships, graduate courses open to undergrads. Off campus study at Norwalk Community College, Rockland Community College (SUNY), Westchester Community College (SUNY), New York Medical College, Landmark College. Study abroad program.

Entrance Requirements: Options: electronic application, early action, deferred admission, international baccalaureate accepted. Required: essay, high school transcript, minimum 2.5 high school GPA, 2 recommendations. Required for some: interview, If a student is applying for dance, theatre, musical theatre or studio art, please visit https://www.mville.edu/admissions/undergraduate-admissions/find-out-more/art-music-dance-theatre-applicants, SAT, ACT, SAT or ACT. Entrance: minimally difficult. Application deadline: rolling. Notification: continuous. Transfer credits accepted: Yes. Early action applicants: 1,149. Early action applicants admitted: 1,088.

Costs Per Year: Application fee: $50. Comprehensive fee: $54,090 includes full-time tuition ($38,120), mandatory fees ($1450), and college room and board ($14,520). College room only: $8680. Part-time tuition: $865 per credit. Part-time mandatory fees: $60 per term.

Collegiate Environment: Orientation program. Drama-theater group, choral group, student-run newspaper, radio station. Social organizations: 50 open to all. Most popular organizations: Students of Caribbean Affiliation (SOCA), Student Government Association (SGA), National Society for Leaderhsip and Success (NSLC), Asian American Student Association (AASA), Active Minds. Major annual events: Fall Fest'ville, Quad Jam, Thriller Nights Annual Halloween Costume Party. Student services: health clinic, personal-psychological counseling. Campus security: 24-hour emergency response devices and patrols, late night transport-escort service, controlled dormitory access, officer at the main campus gate 24/7, emergency notification system, seminars on campus safety and security practices. 1,147 college housing spaces available; 929 were occupied in 2018-19. Freshmen guaranteed college housing. Option: coed housing available. Manhattanville College Library. Books: 189,313 (physical), 177,686 (digital/electronic); Serial titles: 926 (physical), 60,205 (digital/electronic); Databases: 122. Weekly public service hours: 109; study areas open 24 hours, 5-7 days a week. Operations spending for the previous fiscal year: $1.4 million. 125 computers available on campus for general student use. A campuswide network can be accessed from student residence rooms and from off campus. Students can access the following: online class registration, Mobile Apps. Staffed computer lab on campus (open 24 hours a day).

Community Environment: Located approximately 25 miles from New York City, Purchase enjoys the cultural, civic, educational, and recreational facilities of its neighbor. There are railroad connections at nearby White Plains and Rye. Job opportunities are available within the immediate area.

■ MARIA COLLEGE

700 New Scotland Ave.
Albany, NY 12208-1798
Tel: (518)438-3111
E-mail: admissions@mariacollege.edu
Web Site: www.mariacollege.edu

Description: Independent, 4-year, coed. Awards associate and bachelor's degrees. Founded 1958. Setting: 9-acre urban campus. Total enrollment: 912. Faculty: 88 (32 full-time, 56 part-time). Student-undergrad faculty ratio is 10:1. 293 applied, 25% were admitted. Full-time: 243 students, 85% women, 15% men. Part-time: 669 students, 89% women, 11% men. Students come from 9 states and territories, 1 other country, 5% from out-of-state. 0.2% American Indian or Alaska Native, non-Hispanic/Latino; 6% Hispanic/Latino; 12% Black or African American, non-Hispanic/Latino; 6% Asian, non-Hispanic/Latino; 0.2% Native Hawaiian or other Pacific Islander, non-Hispanic/Latino. 56% 25 or older, 7% transferred in. Retention: 83% of full-time freshmen returned the following year. Academic areas with the most degrees conferred: health professions and related sciences; psychology. Calendar: semesters. ESL program, services for LD students, advanced placement, honors program, independent study, distance learning, summer session for credit, part-time degree program, adult/continuing education programs, co-op programs and internships. Off campus study.

Entrance Requirements: Options: electronic application, early admission, deferred admission. Required: high school transcript. Recommended: essay, minimum 2.5 high school GPA, 1 recommendation, interview, SAT or ACT. Required for some: TEAS for AAS in nursing and practical nursing certificate

programs. Entrance: minimally difficult. Notification: continuous. SAT Reasoning Test deadline: 8/23. Transfer credits accepted: Yes. Applicants placed on waiting list: 34. Wait-listed applicants offered admission: 34.

Costs Per Year: Application fee: $35. Tuition: $14,700 full-time, $630 per credit hour part-time. Mandatory fees: $440 full-time, $110 per term part-time. Full-time tuition and fees vary according to course load, program, and reciprocity agreements. Part-time tuition and fees vary according to course load, program, and reciprocity agreements.

Collegiate Environment: Orientation program. Student services: personal-psychological counseling. Campus security: late night transport-escort service, 8:30 am-10 pm security guard coverage in specified campus buildings. College housing not available. Maria College Library. Books: 19,779 (physical), 160,512 (digital/electronic); Serial titles: 55 (physical), 230,969 (digital/electronic); Databases: 27. Weekly public service hours: 131. 70 computers available on campus for general student use. A campuswide network can be accessed. Students can access the following: online class registration. Staffed computer lab on campus provides training in use of computers, software, and the Internet.

Community Environment: See State University of New York at Albany.

■ MARIST COLLEGE

3399 N Rd.
Poughkeepsie, NY 12601-1387
Tel: (845)575-3000; Free: 800-436-5483
Fax: (845)471-6213
E-mail: admission@marist.edu
Web Site: www.marist.edu

Description: Independent, comprehensive, coed. Awards bachelor's and master's degrees. Founded 1929. Setting: 210-acre suburban campus with easy access to Albany, New York City. Endowment: $71.2 million. Research spending for the previous fiscal year: $1.2 million. Educational spending for the previous fiscal year: $12,840 per student. Total enrollment: 6,624. Faculty: 595 (247 full-time, 348 part-time). Student-undergrad faculty ratio is 16:1. 11,207 applied, 46% were admitted. 22% from top 10% of their high school class, 51% from top quarter, 85% from top half. 4 valedictorians. Full-time: 5,139 students, 58% women, 42% men. Part-time: 531 students, 57% women, 43% men. Students come from 49 states and territories, 64 other countries, 53% from out-of-state. 0.1% American Indian or Alaska Native, non-Hispanic/Latino; 10% Hispanic/Latino; 4% Black or African American, non-Hispanic/Latino; 3% Asian, non-Hispanic/Latino; 0.1% Native Hawaiian or other Pacific Islander, non-Hispanic/Latino; 2% international. 4% 25 or older, 61% live on campus, 4% transferred in. Retention: 87% of full-time freshmen returned the following year. Academic areas with the most degrees conferred: business/marketing; communication/journalism; psychology. Core. Calendar: semesters. Academic remediation for entering students, ESL program, services for LD students, advanced placement, accelerated degree program, honors program, independent study, distance learning, double major, summer session for credit, part-time degree program, adult/continuing education programs, co-op programs and internships, graduate courses open to undergrads. Off campus study at Associated Colleges of the Mid-Hudson Area. Study abroad program. ROTC: Army.

Entrance Requirements: Options: electronic application, early admission, early decision, early action, deferred admission, international baccalaureate accepted. Required: essay, high school transcript, 2 recommendations. Entrance: very difficult. Application deadlines: 2/1, 11/15 for early decision plan 1, 2/1 for early decision plan 2, 11/15 for early action. Notification: continuous until 4/1, 12/15 for early decision plan 1, 2/15 for early decision plan 2, 1/15 for early action. SAT Reasoning Test deadline: 2/1. SAT Subject Test deadline: 2/1. Transfer credits accepted: Yes. Applicants placed on waiting list: 4,592. Wait-listed applicants offered admission: 106. Early decision applicants: 307. Early decision applicants admitted: 273. Early action applicants: 6,045. Early action applicants admitted: 3,141.

Costs Per Year: Application fee: $50. Comprehensive fee: $58,495 includes full-time tuition ($39,925), mandatory fees ($600), and college room and board ($17,970). College room only: $12,050.

Collegiate Environment: Orientation program. Drama-theater group, choral group, marching band, student-run newspaper, radio station. Social organizations: 81 open to all; national fraternities, national sororities, local fraternities, local sororities. Most popular organizations: Marist Singers, Dance Club, Student Government, Theater Club, Community Service and Campus Ministry. Major annual events: Giving Tree, Fox Fest/River Fest, Activities Fair. Student services: health clinic, personal-psychological counseling. Campus security: 24-hour emergency response devices and patrols, student patrols, late night transport-escort service, controlled dormitory access, night residence hall monitors. 3,485 college housing spaces available; 3,355 were occupied in 2018-19. Freshmen guaranteed college housing. Option: coed housing available. James A. Cannavino Library. Books: 108,161 (physical), 251,090 (digital/electronic); Serial titles: 1,085 (physical), 65,765 (digital/electronic); Databases: 119. Weekly public service hours: 113; students can reserve study rooms. Operations spending for the previous fiscal year: $2.7 million. 997 computers available on campus for general student use. Computer purchase/lease plans available. Students can access the following: online class registration, billing/payments, transcripts, degree audit, financial aid application and award review, student account summary, campus OneCard account, parking registration, cap and gown orders. Staffed computer lab on campus (open 24 hours a day) provides training in use of computers, software, and the Internet.

Community Environment: See Vassar College.

■ **MARYMOUNT MANHATTAN COLLEGE**
221 E 71st St.
New York, NY 10021-4597
Tel: (212)517-0400; Free: 800-627-9668
E-mail: gturner@mmm.edu
Web Site: www.mmm.edu

Description: Independent, 4-year, coed. Awards bachelor's degrees. Founded 1936. Setting: urban campus. Endowment: $20.9 million. Educational spending for the previous fiscal year: $11,025 per student. Total enrollment: 2,063. Faculty: 373 (92 full-time, 281 part-time). Student-undergrad faculty ratio is 11:1. 5,705 applied, 78% were admitted. Full-time: 1,861 students, 77% women, 23% men. Part-time: 202 students, 91% women, 9% men. Students come from 50 states and territories, 70 other countries, 63% from out-of-state. 0.2% American Indian or Alaska Native, non-Hispanic/Latino; 16% Hispanic/Latino; 9% Black or African American, non-Hispanic/Latino; 3% Asian, non-Hispanic/Latino; 0.1% Native Hawaiian or other Pacific Islander, non-Hispanic/Latino; 4% international. 9% 25 or older, 38% live on campus, 6% transferred in. Retention: 68% of full-time freshmen returned the following year. Academic areas with the most degrees conferred: visual and performing arts; communication/journalism; business/marketing. Core. Calendar: semesters plus summer and January mini-semesters. Academic remediation for entering students, services for LD students, advanced placement, accelerated degree program, self-designed majors, honors program, independent study, distance learning, double major, summer session for credit, part-time degree program, adult/continuing education programs, internships. Off campus study at Hunter College, Pace University Cooperative, International Center for Photography. Study abroad program.

Entrance Requirements: Options: electronic application, deferred admission, international baccalaureate accepted. Required: essay, high school transcript, 2 recommendations, SAT or ACT. Required for some: interview. Entrance: moderately difficult. Application deadline: rolling. Notification: continuous. SAT Reasoning Test deadline: 8/1. Transfer credits accepted: Yes.

Costs Per Year: Application fee: $60. Comprehensive fee: $53,827 includes full-time tuition ($33,980), mandatory fees ($1648), and college room and board ($18,199). College room only: $16,199. Part-time tuition: $1132 per credit hour. Part-time mandatory fees: $603 per term.

Collegiate Environment: Orientation program. Drama-theater group, choral group, student-run newspaper, radio station. Social organizations: 38 open to all. Most popular organizations: Student Government Association (SGA), Black and Latino Student Association (BLSA), The Monitor- Student Newspaper, Musical Theater Association (MTA), Christian Fellowship. Major annual events: Strawberry Festival/MMC Week, Apple Festival, Family, Friends and Alumni Weekend. Student services: health clinic, personal-psychological counseling. Campus security: 24-hour emergency response devices and patrols, student patrols, 24-hour security in residence halls. 773 college housing spaces available; 760 were occupied in 2018-19. Freshmen given priority for college housing. Options: coed, men-only, women-only housing available. Thomas J. Shanahan Library. Books: 39,888 (physical), 232,680 (digital/electronic); Serial titles: 98 (physical), 54,077 (digital/electronic); Databases: 70. Weekly public service hours: 80. Operations spending for the previous fiscal year: $983,503. 120 computers available on campus for general student use. A campuswide network can be accessed from student residence rooms and from off campus. Students can access the following: online class registration, online payments, direct deposits. Staffed computer lab on campus provides training in use of computers, software, and the Internet.

Community Environment: See New York University.

■ **MECHON L'HOYROA**
168 Maple Ave.
Monsey, NY 10952
Description: Independent religious, 4-year, men only.

■ **MEDAILLE COLLEGE**
18 Agassiz Cir.
Buffalo, NY 14214-2695
Tel: (716)880-2000; Free: 800-292-1582
Fax: (716)884-0291
E-mail: admissionsug@medaille.edu
Web Site: www.medaille.edu

Description: Independent, comprehensive, coed. Awards associate, bachelor's, master's, and doctoral degrees and post-master's certificates. Founded 1875. Setting: 13-acre urban campus with easy access to Buffal, Niagara. Endowment: $1.2 million. Total enrollment: 2,383. Faculty: 294 (87 full-time, 207 part-time). Student-undergrad faculty ratio is 14:1. 1,505 applied, 54% were admitted. Full-time: 1,637 students, 68% women, 32% men. Part-time: 166 students, 66% women, 34% men. Students come from 5 states and territories, 3 other countries, 1% from out-of-state. 0.7% American Indian or Alaska Native, non-Hispanic/Latino; 7% Hispanic/Latino; 21% Black or African American, non-Hispanic/Latino; 2% Asian, non-Hispanic/Latino; 0.2% Native Hawaiian or other Pacific Islander, non-Hispanic/Latino. 22% live on campus, 29% transferred in. Retention: 64% of full-time freshmen returned the following year. Academic areas with the most degrees conferred: business/marketing; education; health professions and related sciences; psychology. Core. Calendar: semesters (modular courses available for evening studies and weekend college program). Academic remediation for entering students, services for LD students, advanced placement, accelerated degree program, self-designed majors, honors program, independent study, distance learning, double major, summer session for credit, part-time degree program, adult/continuing education programs, internships, graduate courses open to undergrads. Off campus study at 16 members of the Western New York Consortium. Study abroad program. ROTC: Army (c).

Entrance Requirements: Options: electronic application, early admission, deferred admission. Required: high school transcript, interview, SAT or ACT. Recommended: essay, minimum 2 high school GPA, 1 recommendation, SAT. Required for some: essay, minimum 2.5 high school GPA for veterinary technology and elementary teacher education majors. Entrance: moderately difficult. Application deadline: 8/1. Notification: continuous.

Collegiate Environment: Orientation program. Drama-theater group, student-run newspaper, radio station. Social organizations: 27 open to all. Most popular organizations: Student Government, Club Green, Dance Team, WMCB The Lizard (college radio station), ice hockey club. Major annual events: Holiday Party, Reindeer Run, Annual Carnival. Student services: health clinic, personal-psychological counseling. Campus security: 24-hour emergency response devices and patrols, late night transport-escort service, controlled dormitory access. Medaille College Library. Operations spending for the previous fiscal year: $55,140. 120 computers available on campus for general student use. A campuswide network can be accessed from student residence rooms and from off campus. Students can access the following: online class registration. Staffed computer lab on campus provides training in use of computers, software, and the Internet.

Community Environment: See Canisius College.

■ **MEDGAR EVERS COLLEGE OF THE CITY UNIVERSITY OF NEW YORK**
1650 Bedford Ave.
Brooklyn, NY 11225-2298
Tel: (718)270-4900
E-mail: shannon@mec.cuny.edu
Web Site: www.mec.cuny.edu

Description: State and locally supported, 4-year, coed. Part of City University of New York System. Administratively affiliated with City University of New York System. Awards associate and bachelor's degrees. Founded 1969. Setting: 8-acre urban campus. Endowment: $515,142. Total enrollment: 6,652. Faculty: 534 (185 full-time, 349 part-time). Student-undergrad faculty ratio is 18:1. 10,834 applied, 100% were admitted. Full-time: 4,806 students, 71% women, 29% men. Part-time: 1,846 students, 75% women, 25% men. Students come from 7 states and territories, 77 other countries, 1% from out-of-state. 0.3% American Indian or Alaska Native, non-Hispanic/Latino; 14% Hispanic/Latino; 59% Black or African American, non-Hispanic/Latino; 2% Asian, non-Hispanic/Latino; 0.8% international. 39% 25 or older.

Academic areas with the most degrees conferred: biological/life sciences; business/marketing; psychology. Core. Calendar: semesters. Academic remediation for entering students, ESL program, services for LD students, advanced placement, honors program, independent study, double major, summer session for credit, part-time degree program, external degree program, adult/continuing education programs, co-op programs and internships. Off campus study at other units of the City University of New York System. Study abroad program.

Entrance Requirements: Open admission except for nursing program. Options: electronic application, deferred admission. Required: high school transcript. Recommended: SAT and SAT Subject Tests or ACT. Entrance: noncompetitive. Application deadline: rolling. Notification: continuous. Preference given to city residents.

Costs Per Year: Application fee: $65. State resident tuition: $6330 full-time, $275 per credit part-time. Nonresident tuition: $16,800 full-time, $560 per credit part-time. Mandatory fees: $320 full-time, $100.85 per term part-time. Full-time tuition and fees vary according to course load. Part-time tuition and fees vary according to course load.

Collegiate Environment: Drama-theater group, choral group, student-run newspaper, radio station. Social organizations: 32 open to all. Most popular organizations: American Marketing Association, Drama Students Association, Rising Stars, Medgar Evers College Society of Public Administrators, National Society of Black Accountants. Major annual events: Presidential Lecture Series, Black Solidarity Day, Club Fair. Student services: legal services, women's center. Campus security: 24-hour patrols. Charles Evans Inniss Memorial Library plus 1 other. 120 computers available on campus for general student use. Computer purchase/lease plans available. A campuswide network can be accessed from off-campus. Students can access the following: online class registration. Staffed computer lab on campus provides training in use of computers, software, and the Internet.

■ **MEMORIAL COLLEGE OF NURSING**
600 Northern Blvd.
Albany, NY 12204
Tel: (518)471-3260
Fax: (518)447-3559
Web Site: www.nehealth.com/son
Description: Independent, 2-year, coed. Awards terminal associate degrees. Total enrollment: 113. Calendar: semesters.
Entrance Requirements: Recommended: high school transcript.

■ **MERCY COLLEGE**
555 Broadway
Dobbs Ferry, NY 10522-1189
Tel: (914)693-4500; Free: 877-MERCY-GO
Fax: (914)674-7382
E-mail: admissions@mercy.edu
Web Site: www.mercy.edu
Description: Independent, comprehensive, coed, affiliated with Roman Catholic Church. Awards associate, bachelor's, master's, and doctoral degrees and post-master's certificates. Founded 1951. Setting: 66-acre suburban campus with easy access to New York City. Endowment: $245.5 million. Educational spending for the previous fiscal year: $6392 per student. Total enrollment: 9,031. Faculty: 839 (213 full-time, 626 part-time). Student-undergrad faculty ratio is 16:1. 6,851 applied, 79% were admitted. Full-time: 5,001 students, 65% women, 35% men. Part-time: 1,610 students, 68% women, 32% men. Students come from 36 states and territories, 33 other countries, 8% from out-of-state. 0.4% American Indian or Alaska Native, non-Hispanic/Latino; 41% Hispanic/Latino; 22% Black or African American, non-Hispanic/Latino; 4% Asian, non-Hispanic/Latino; 0.2% Native Hawaiian or other Pacific Islander, non-Hispanic/Latino; 1% international. 29% 25 or older, 12% live on campus, 10% transferred in. Retention: 74% of full-time freshmen returned the following year. Academic areas with the most degrees conferred: health professions and related sciences; business/marketing; social sciences. Core. Calendar: semesters. Services for LD students, advanced placement, accelerated degree program, freshman honors college, honors program, independent study, distance learning, double major, summer session for credit, part-time degree program, adult/continuing education programs, co-op programs and internships, graduate courses open to undergrads. Off campus study at Westchester Community College, Rockland Community College, Borough of Manhattan Community College, Nassau Community College, Suffolk Community College, Bergen Community College, Norwalk Community College, Orange Community College, LaGuardia Community College, Bergen Community College, Essex County

Community College, Queensborough Community College, Dutchess Community College, Maricopa Community College, Kingsborough Community College, Hostos Community College, Bronx Community College, Sullivan Community College. Study abroad program. ROTC: Army (c), Air Force (c).
Entrance Requirements: Options: electronic application, deferred admission, international baccalaureate accepted. Required: high school transcript, minimum 2 high school GPA. Recommended: 1 recommendation, interview. Required for some: essay, Portfolio required for art program; audition required for music program; R.N. required for nursing program; additional interview with program director required of nursing, occupational therapy, physical therapy, social work, veterinary technology, and computer arts program applicants. Entrance: moderately difficult. Application deadline: rolling. Notification: continuous. Transfer credits accepted: Yes.
Costs Per Year: Application fee: $40. Comprehensive fee: $33,442 includes full-time tuition ($18,400), mandatory fees ($642), and college room and board ($14,400). College room only: $9750. Full-time tuition and fees vary according to course load. Room and board charges vary according to board plan. Part-time tuition: $774 per credit. Part-time mandatory fees: $161 per term. Part-time tuition and fees vary according to course load.
Collegiate Environment: Orientation program. Choral group, student-run newspaper. Social organizations: 48 open to all. Most popular organizations: Model United Nations, Honors Club and 17 National Honor Societies, Mercy Gives Back, Maverick Society, ROTARACT Club for Community Volunteer Service. Major annual events: Founder's Day/Alumni Weekend, March Madness Tournament, Broadway Shows and Major League Baseball events. Student services: health clinic, personal-psychological counseling. Campus security: 24-hour emergency response devices and patrols, late night transport-escort service, controlled dormitory access. College housing designed to accommodate 744 students; 765 undergraduates lived in college housing during 2018-19. Freshmen given priority for college housing. Option: coed housing available. Mercy College Library plus 3 others. Books: 78,894 (physical), 72,328 (digital/electronic); Serial titles: 26 (physical), 61,974 (digital/electronic); Databases: 43. Students can reserve study rooms. Operations spending for the previous fiscal year: $2.5 million. 1,000 computers available on campus for general student use. Computer purchase/lease plans available. A campuswide network can be accessed from student residence rooms and from off campus. Students can access the following: online class registration. Staffed computer lab on campus (open 24 hours a day) provides training in use of computers, software, and the Internet.
Community Environment: Population 11,070. Primarily a residential community, Dobbs Ferry is located on the banks of the Hudson River and is 15 miles from New York City.

■ **MESIVTA OF EASTERN PARKWAY-YESHIVA ZICHRON MEILECH**
510 Dahill Rd.
Brooklyn, NY 11218-5559
Tel: (718)438-1002
Description: Independent Jewish, comprehensive, men only. Awards bachelor's and master's degrees. Founded 1947. Setting: 1-acre urban campus with easy access to New York City. Total enrollment: 25. 8 applied, 50% were admitted. Students come from 4 states and territories, 10% from out-of-state. Core. Calendar: semesters. Academic remediation for entering students, honors program, graduate courses open to undergrads.
Entrance Requirements: Required: high school transcript, 1 recommendation, interview, Orthodox Jewish commitment. Entrance: moderately difficult. Application deadline: rolling.

■ **MESIVTA TORAH VODAATH RABBINICAL SEMINARY**
425 E Ninth St.
Brooklyn, NY 11218-5299
Tel: (718)941-8000
Fax: (718)941-8032
Web Site: www.torahvodaath.org
Description: Independent Jewish, comprehensive, men only. Awards bachelor's and master's degrees. Founded 1918. Total enrollment: 354. 66 applied. 35% 25 or older. Core. Calendar: semesters. Summer session for credit, part-time degree program. Study abroad program.
Entrance Requirements: Options: early admission, deferred admission. Required: high school transcript, 2 recommendations. Entrance: moderately difficult. Application deadline: rolling. Notification: continuous. Preference given to Orthodox Jews.
Collegiate Environment: Student services: personal-psychological counseling.

■ **MESIVTHA TIFERETH JERUSALEM OF AMERICA**
145 E Broadway
New York, NY 10002-6301
Tel: (212)964-2830
Description: Independent Jewish, comprehensive, men only. Awards bachelor's and master's degrees. Founded 1907. Total enrollment: 72. 15 applied, 100% were admitted. Calendar: semesters.

■ **METROPOLITAN COLLEGE OF NEW YORK**
60 W St.
New York, NY 10006
Tel: (212)343-1234; Free: 800-33-THINK
Fax: (212)343-8470
Web Site: www.mcny.edu
Description: Independent, comprehensive, coed. Awards associate, bachelor's, and master's degrees. Founded 1964. Setting: urban campus. Total enrollment: 1,113. Faculty: 224 (23 full-time, 201 part-time). Student-undergrad faculty ratio is 11:1. 126 applied, 91% were admitted. Full-time: 681 students, 71% women, 29% men. Part-time: 96 students, 60% women, 40% men. Students come from 11 states and territories, 4% from out-of-state. 0.6% American Indian or Alaska Native, non-Hispanic/Latino; 29% Hispanic/Latino; 55% Black or African American, non-Hispanic/Latino; 3% Asian, non-Hispanic/Latino; 0.3% Native Hawaiian or other Pacific Islander, non-Hispanic/Latino; 1% international. 79% 25 or older, 29% transferred in. Retention: 47% of full-time freshmen returned the following year. Academic areas with the most degrees conferred: health professions and related sciences; social sciences; business/marketing. Core. Calendar: 3 15-week semesters. Academic remediation for entering students, ESL program, services for LD students, accelerated degree program, honors program, independent study, distance learning, summer session for credit, part-time degree program, adult/continuing education programs, co-op programs and internships. Study abroad program.
Entrance Requirements: Options: electronic application, deferred admission, international baccalaureate accepted. Required: high school transcript, 2 recommendations, interview. Recommended: essay, minimum 3 high school GPA, SAT or ACT. Required for some: ACCUPLACER. Entrance: moderately difficult. Application deadline: 9/9. Notification: continuous. Transfer credits accepted: Yes.
Collegiate Environment: Orientation program. Student-run newspaper. Social organizations: 10 open to all. Most popular organizations: Student Government, Student Newsletter, Networking Club, Yearbook Committee. Major annual events: Graduation Ceremony, New Student Orientation. Student services: personal-psychological counseling. Campus security: 24-hour patrols. Main Library plus 1 other. Books: 26,191 (physical), 156,497 (digital/electronic); Serial titles: 29,206 (digital/electronic); Databases: 91. Weekly public service hours: 72. 120 computers available on campus for general student use. A campuswide network can be accessed from off-campus. Students can access the following: online class registration. Staffed computer lab on campus (open 24 hours a day) provides training in use of computers and software.

■ **MILDRED ELLEY-NEW YORK CITY**
25 Broadway, 16th Fl.
New York, NY 10004-1010
Tel: (212)380-9004
Web Site: www.mildred-elley.edu
Description: Proprietary, 2-year, coed. Awards certificates and transfer associate degrees.

■ **MILDRED ELLEY SCHOOL**
855 Central Ave.
Albany, NY 12206
Tel: (518)786-0855; Free: 800-622-6327
Fax: (518)786-0898
Web Site: www.mildred-elley.edu
Description: Proprietary, 2-year, coed. Awards certificates, diplomas, transfer associate, and terminal associate degrees. Founded 1917. Setting: suburban campus. Total enrollment: 396. 130 applied. 65% 25 or older.
Entrance Requirements: Required: CPAt.
Collegiate Environment: Student services: legal services.

■ **MIRRER YESHIVA CENTRAL INSTITUTE**
1791 Ocean Pky.
Brooklyn, NY 11223-2010

Tel: (718)645-0536
Description: Independent Jewish, comprehensive, men only. Awards bachelor's and master's degrees. Founded 1926. Total enrollment: 307. 66 applied, 100% were admitted. 4% 25 or older. Calendar: semesters.

■ **MOHAWK VALLEY COMMUNITY COLLEGE**
1101 Sherman Dr.
Utica, NY 13501-5394
Tel: (315)792-5400
Fax: (315)792-5527
E-mail: kedwards@mvcc.edu
Web Site: www.mvcc.edu
Description: State and locally supported, 2-year, coed. Part of State University of New York System. Awards certificates, transfer associate, and terminal associate degrees. Founded 1946. Setting: 80-acre suburban campus. Endowment: $4.9 million. Educational spending for the previous fiscal year: $4978 per student. Total enrollment: 6,506. Faculty: 448 (133 full-time, 315 part-time). Student-undergrad faculty ratio is 18:1. 2,726 applied, 99% were admitted. 3% from top 10% of their high school class, 11% from top quarter, 44% from top half. Full-time: 3,324 students, 51% women, 49% men. Part-time: 3,182 students, 56% women, 44% men. Students come from 16 states and territories, 22 other countries, 41% from out-of-state. 0.3% American Indian or Alaska Native, non-Hispanic/Latino; 8% Hispanic/Latino; 11% Black or African American, non-Hispanic/Latino; 6% Asian, non-Hispanic/Latino; 0.2% Native Hawaiian or other Pacific Islander, non-Hispanic/Latino; 1% international. 28% 25 or older, 7% live on campus, 3% transferred in. Academic areas with the most degrees conferred: English; mechanic and repair technologies; health professions and related sciences. Core. Calendar: semesters. Academic remediation for entering students, ESL program, services for LD students, advanced placement, accelerated degree program, self-designed majors, honors program, independent study, distance learning, double major, summer session for credit, part-time degree program, internships. Off campus study at Mohawk Valley College Consortium.
Entrance Requirements: Open admission. Options: electronic application, deferred admission, international baccalaureate accepted. Recommended: interview. Required for some: high school transcript. Entrance: noncompetitive. Application deadline: rolling. Notification: continuous. Transfer credits accepted: Yes.
Costs Per Year: Application fee: $0. State resident tuition: $4370 full-time, $182 per credit hour part-time. Nonresident tuition: $8740 full-time, $364 per credit hour part-time. Mandatory fees: $896 full-time, $50 per credit hour part-time, $38 per term part-time.
Collegiate Environment: Orientation program. Drama-theater group, student-run newspaper. Social organizations: 50 open to all. Most popular organizations: Program Board, Student Congress, Gender Sexuality Alliance, Black Student Union, Drama Club. Student services: health clinic, personal-psychological counseling. Campus security: 24-hour emergency response devices and patrols, late night transport-escort service, controlled dormitory access. Mohawk Valley Community College Library plus 1 other. Books: 98,450 (physical), 278,863 (digital/electronic); Serial titles: 461 (physical), 105,147 (digital/electronic); Databases: 103. Weekly public service hours: 126. Operations spending for the previous fiscal year: $973,604. 145 computers available on campus for general student use. A campuswide network can be accessed from student residence rooms and from off campus. Students can access the following: online class registration, online file storage. Staffed computer lab on campus provides training in use of computers, software, and the Internet.

■ **MOLLOY COLLEGE**
1000 Hempstead Ave.
Rockville Centre, NY 11571-5002
Tel: (516)323-3000; Free: 888-4MOLLOY
E-mail: admissions@molloy.edu
Web Site: www.molloy.edu
Description: Independent, comprehensive, coed. Awards associate, bachelor's, master's, and doctoral degrees and post-master's certificates. Founded 1955. Setting: 30-acre suburban campus with easy access to New York City. Endowment: $38.2 million. Educational spending for the previous fiscal year: $16,294 per student. Total enrollment: 4,929. Faculty: 721 (191 full-time, 530 part-time). Student-undergrad faculty ratio is 10:1. 4,427 applied, 81% were admitted. 17% from top 10% of their high school class, 56% from top quarter, 84% from top half. Full-time: 2,762 students, 70% women, 30% men. Part-time: 677 students, 83% women, 17% men. Students come

from 33 states and territories, 12 other countries, 4% from out-of-state. 0.3% American Indian or Alaska Native, non-Hispanic/Latino; 17% Hispanic/Latino; 10% Black or African American, non-Hispanic/Latino; 8% Asian, non-Hispanic/Latino; 0.2% Native Hawaiian or other Pacific Islander, non-Hispanic/Latino; 0.4% international. 20% 25 or older, 8% live on campus, 9% transferred in. Retention: 89% of full-time freshmen returned the following year. Academic areas with the most degrees conferred: health professions and related sciences; business/marketing; education. Core. Calendar: 4-1-4. Academic remediation for entering students, ESL program, services for LD students, advanced placement, accelerated degree program, self-designed majors, honors program, independent study, distance learning, double major, summer session for credit, part-time degree program, adult/continuing education programs, internships. Study abroad program. ROTC: Army (c), Naval (c).

Entrance Requirements: Options: electronic application, early action, deferred admission, international baccalaureate accepted. Required: SAT or ACT. Recommended: interview. Required for some: essay, high school transcript, 1 recommendation. Entrance: moderately difficult. Application deadline: rolling. Notification: continuous. SAT Reasoning Test deadline: 8/30. Transfer credits accepted: Yes. Early action applicants: 598. Early action applicants admitted: 511.

Costs Per Year: Application fee: $40. Comprehensive fee: $46,522 includes full-time tuition ($30,270), mandatory fees ($1220), and college room and board ($15,032). Full-time tuition and fees vary according to degree level. Room and board charges vary according to board plan. Part-time tuition: $1005 per credit hour. Part-time tuition varies according to degree level.

Collegiate Environment: Orientation program. Drama-theater group, choral group, student-run newspaper. Social organizations: 64 open to all. Most popular organizations: Molloy Student Government, Molloy Nursing Student Association, Molloy Performing Arts Club, Men's Rugby, MolloyLife Media. Major annual events: Maroon Madness, Halloween Party, Welcome Back/End of Year BBQs. Student services: health clinic, personal-psychological counseling, women's center. Campus security: 24-hour emergency response devices and patrols, late night transport-escort service, controlled dormitory access. 286 college housing spaces available; all were occupied in 2018-19. Freshmen given priority for college housing. Option: coed housing available. James Edward Tobin Library plus 1 other. Books: 33,809 (physical), 295,138 (digital/electronic); Serial titles: 48 (physical), 62,642 (digital/electronic); Databases: 198. Operations spending for the previous fiscal year: $3.2 million. 750 computers available on campus for general student use. A campuswide network can be accessed from student residence rooms and from off campus. Students can access the following: online class registration. Staffed computer lab on campus.

Community Environment: Rockville Centre, population 24,200, is a suburb of New York City on Long Island. Good transportation facilities make all the cultural, recreational, civic services, and employment opportunities of New York easily accessible. Within the immediate area there are a public library, churches of major denominations, and a hospital. Some part-time work is available in the local area.

■ **MONROE COLLEGE**
2501 Jerome Ave.
Bronx, NY 10468
Tel: (718)933-6700; Free: 800-55MONROE
Web Site: www.monroecollege.edu
Description: Proprietary, comprehensive, coed. Awards associate, bachelor's, and master's degrees. Founded 1933. Setting: urban campus. Educational spending for the previous fiscal year: $6379 per student. Total enrollment: 6,862. Faculty: 471 (219 full-time, 252 part-time). Student-undergrad faculty ratio is 18:1. 4,146 applied, 45% were admitted. Full-time: 4,524 students, 60% women, 40% men. Part-time: 1,613 students, 72% women, 28% men. Students come from 19 states and territories, 14 other countries, 20% from out-of-state. 40% Hispanic/Latino; 44% Black or African American, non-Hispanic/Latino; 1% Asian, non-Hispanic/Latino; 0.4% Native Hawaiian or other Pacific Islander, non-Hispanic/Latino; 10% international. 36% 25 or older, 13% live on campus, 38% transferred in. Retention: 78% of full-time freshmen returned the following year. Academic areas with the most degrees conferred: business/marketing; health professions and related sciences; homeland security, law enforcement, firefighting, and protective services. Core. Calendar: semesters. Academic remediation for entering students, ESL program, services for LD students, advanced placement, accelerated degree program, freshman honors college, honors program, independent study, distance learning, summer session for credit, part-time degree program, adult/continuing education programs, co-op programs and internships. Study abroad program. ROTC: Army (c).

Entrance Requirements: Options: electronic application, early admission, early decision, early action, deferred admission, international baccalaureate accepted. Required: essay, high school transcript, interview. Required for some: 2 recommendations, SAT or ACT. Entrance: moderately difficult. Application deadline: 8/26. Notification: continuous until 9/3. Transfer credits accepted: Yes.

Costs Per Year: Application fee: $35. Comprehensive fee: $26,278 includes full-time tuition ($14,328), mandatory fees ($1100), and college room and board ($10,850). Full-time tuition and fees vary according to program. Room and board charges vary according to board plan and housing facility. Part-time tuition: $597 per credit. Part-time mandatory fees: $275 per term.

Collegiate Environment: Orientation program. Drama-theater group, marching band. Social organizations: 18 open to all. Most popular organizations: Students in Free Enterprise (SIFE), Creative Campus Club, Multicultural Student Association, Criminal Justice Club, Poetry is Truth. Major annual events: Homecoming, Athletics Playoffs, Spirit Day. Student services: health clinic, personal-psychological counseling. Campus security: 24-hour patrols, late night transport-escort service. Main library plus 1 other. Books: 44,109 (physical), 2,466 (digital/electronic); Serial titles: 739 (physical), 8 (digital/electronic); Databases: 73. Operations spending for the previous fiscal year: $657,979. 800 computers available on campus for general student use. A campuswide network can be accessed from student residence rooms and from off campus. Students can access the following: online class registration. Staffed computer lab on campus (open 24 hours a day) provides training in use of computers, software, and the Internet.

■ **MONROE COMMUNITY COLLEGE**
1000 E Henrietta Rd.
Rochester, NY 14623-5780
Tel: (585)292-2000
Fax: (585)427-2749
E-mail: admissions@monroecc.edu
Web Site: www.monroecc.edu
Description: State and locally supported, 2-year, coed. Part of State University of New York System. Awards certificates, transfer associate, and terminal associate degrees. Founded 1961. Setting: 314-acre suburban campus with easy access to Buffalo. Total enrollment: 12,907. Faculty: 740 (295 full-time, 445 part-time). Student-undergrad faculty ratio is 22:1. 16,328 applied, 73% were admitted. Full-time: 7,866 students, 52% women, 48% men. Part-time: 5,041 students, 53% women, 47% men. Students come from 40 states and territories, 46 other countries, 1% from out-of-state. 0.5% American Indian or Alaska Native, non-Hispanic/Latino; 10% Hispanic/Latino; 20% Black or African American, non-Hispanic/Latino; 5% Asian, non-Hispanic/Latino; 0.1% Native Hawaiian or other Pacific Islander, non-Hispanic/Latino; 1% international. 39% 25 or older. Retention: 51% of full-time freshmen returned the following year. Calendar: semesters. Academic remediation for entering students, ESL program, services for LD students, advanced placement, accelerated degree program, honors program, summer session for credit, part-time degree program, adult/continuing education programs, co-op programs and internships. Off campus study at Rochester Area Colleges. ROTC: Army (c), Naval (c), Air Force (c).

Entrance Requirements: Open admission except for allied health, business, computer science, engineering science programs. Options: electronic application, early admission. Required: high school transcript. Entrance: noncompetitive. Application deadline: rolling. Notification: continuous. Preference given to county residents. Transfer credits accepted: Yes.

Costs Per Year: State resident tuition: $4380 full-time, $183 per credit hour part-time. Nonresident tuition: $8760 full-time, $365 per credit hour part-time. Mandatory fees: $722 full-time. Full-time tuition and fees vary according to program. Part-time tuition varies according to course load and program. College room only: $7780. Room charges vary according to housing facility.

Collegiate Environment: Orientation program. Drama-theater group, choral group, student-run newspaper, radio station. Social organizations: 52 open to all. Most popular organizations: Student Newspaper, Phi Theta Kappa, Student Government. Student services: health clinic, personal-psychological counseling. Campus security: 24-hour emergency response devices and patrols, late night transport-escort service, controlled dormitory access. LeRoy V. Good Library. Weekly public service hours: 58; students can reserve study rooms.

■ **MONTEFIORE SCHOOL OF NURSING**
53 Valentine St.
Mount Vernon, NY 10550
Tel: (914)361-6221

Fax: (914)665-7047

Web Site: www.montefiorehealthsystem.org/landing.cfm?id=19

Description: Independent, 2-year, coed. Awards terminal associate degrees. Total enrollment: 134. Student-undergrad faculty ratio is 5:1. 10 applied, 10% were admitted. 87% 25 or older.

Entrance Requirements: Required: high school transcript, TEAS.

■ MOUNT SAINT MARY COLLEGE

330 Powell Ave.

Newburgh, NY 12550-3494

Tel: (845)561-0800; Free: 888-937-6762

Fax: (845)562-6762

E-mail: eileen.bardney@msmc.edu

Web Site: www.msmc.edu

Description: Independent, comprehensive, coed. Awards bachelor's and master's degrees and post-master's certificates. Founded 1960. Setting: 86-acre suburban campus with easy access to New York City. Endowment: $80.3 million. Educational spending for the previous fiscal year: $8651 per student. Total enrollment: 2,352. Faculty: 249 (79 full-time, 170 part-time). Student-undergrad faculty ratio is 13:1. 3,588 applied, 94% were admitted. 9% from top 10% of their high school class, 34% from top quarter, 66% from top half. Full-time: 1,675 students, 69% women, 31% men. Part-time: 330 students, 80% women, 20% men. Students come from 17 states and territories, 13% from out-of-state. 0.7% American Indian or Alaska Native, non-Hispanic/Latino; 17% Hispanic/Latino; 7% Black or African American, non-Hispanic/Latino; 2% Asian, non-Hispanic/Latino; 0.2% Native Hawaiian or other Pacific Islander, non-Hispanic/Latino; 0.7% international. 17% 25 or older, 48% live on campus, 8% transferred in. Retention: 85% of full-time freshmen returned the following year. Academic areas with the most degrees conferred: health professions and related sciences; business/marketing; psychology. Core. Calendar: semesters. Academic remediation for entering students, services for LD students, advanced placement, accelerated degree program, self-designed majors, freshman honors college, honors program, independent study, distance learning, double major, summer session for credit, part-time degree program, adult/continuing education programs, co-op programs and internships, graduate courses open to undergrads. Off campus study at Associated Colleges of the Mid-Hudson Area. Study abroad program. ROTC: Army (c).

Entrance Requirements: Options: electronic application, early admission, deferred admission. Required: essay, high school transcript, SAT or ACT. Recommended: minimum 3 high school GPA, 2 recommendations. Required for some: 2 recommendations, interview. Entrance: moderately difficult. Notification: continuous. SAT Reasoning Test deadline: 8/1. SAT Subject Test deadline: 8/1. Transfer credits accepted: Yes.

Costs Per Year: Application fee: $45. Comprehensive fee: $46,226 includes full-time tuition ($30,046), mandatory fees ($1072), and college room and board ($15,108). College room only: $8752. Full-time tuition and fees vary according to class time, course load, location, and program. Room and board charges vary according to board plan and housing facility. Part-time tuition: $1002 per credit. Part-time mandatory fees: $86 per year. Part-time tuition and fees vary according to class time, course load, location, and program.

Collegiate Environment: Orientation program. Drama-theater group, choral group, student-run newspaper, radio station. Social organizations: 28 open to all. Most popular organizations: Nursing Student Union, Alpha Knights Step Team, Dance Team, Improvology, Habitat for Humanity. Major annual events: Siblings' Week, Parents' Weekend, Spring Weekend. Student services: health clinic, personal-psychological counseling. Campus security: 24-hour emergency response devices and patrols, student patrols, late night transport-escort service, controlled dormitory access, monitored surveillance cameras in all residence halls. 1,095 college housing spaces available; 965 were occupied in 2018-19. Freshmen guaranteed college housing. On-campus residence required through junior year. Options: coed, men-only, women-only housing available. Kaplan Family Library and Learning Center. Books: 84,909 (physical), 11,569 (digital/electronic); Serial titles: 195 (physical), 59,481 (digital/electronic); Databases: 93. Students can reserve study rooms. Operations spending for the previous fiscal year: $1.1 million. 470 computers available on campus for general student use. Computer purchase/lease plans available. A campuswide network can be accessed from student residence rooms and from off campus. Students can access the following: online class registration. Staffed computer lab on campus provides training in use of computers, software, and the Internet.

Community Environment: Mount Saint Mary College is located in the historic Hudson Valley Region, at the foothills of the Catskill Mountains, 60 miles north of New York City. Cultural, historical, and outdoor activities abound.

■ NASSAU COMMUNITY COLLEGE

1 Education Dr.

Garden City, NY 11530-6793

Tel: (516)572-7500

Web Site: www.ncc.edu

Description: State and locally supported, 2-year, coed. Part of State University of New York System. Awards certificates, transfer associate, and terminal associate degrees. Founded 1959. Setting: 225-acre suburban campus with easy access to New York City. Total enrollment: 17,278. Faculty: 1,528 (418 full-time, 910 part-time). Student-undergrad faculty ratio is 21:1. Full-time: 9,844 students, 47% women, 53% men. Part-time: 7,434 students, 57% women, 43% men. Students come from 19 states and territories. 0.2% American Indian or Alaska Native, non-Hispanic/Latino; 29% Hispanic/Latino; 21% Black or African American, non-Hispanic/Latino; 7% Asian, non-Hispanic/Latino; 0.3% Native Hawaiian or other Pacific Islander, non-Hispanic/Latino; 0.8% international. Calendar: semesters. Academic remediation for entering students, ESL program, services for LD students, advanced placement, honors program, distance learning, summer session for credit, part-time degree program, adult/continuing education programs, co-op programs and internships. Off campus study at members of the Long Island Regional Advisory Council for Higher Education.

Entrance Requirements: Open admission for liberal arts students and some non-competitive programs. Options: electronic application, deferred admission, international baccalaureate accepted. Required: high school transcript. Recommended: minimum 2 high school GPA. Required for some: minimum 3 high school GPA, interview. Entrance: noncompetitive. Notification: continuous.

Costs Per Year: Application fee: $40. State resident tuition: $5350 full-time, $223 per credit part-time. Nonresident tuition: $10,700 full-time, $446 per credit part-time. Mandatory fees: $310 full-time, $50 per term part-time. Full-time tuition and fees vary according to program. Part-time tuition and fees vary according to program.

Collegiate Environment: Orientation program. Drama-theater group, choral group, student-run newspaper, radio station. Social organizations: 110 open to all. Most popular organizations: Muslim Student Association, Make a Difference Club, Interact Club, Political Science Club, Investment Club. Major annual events: Spring Festival, Multicultural Fair, Student Government Association Pep Rally. Student services: personal-psychological counseling, women's center. Campus security: 24-hour emergency response devices and patrols, late night transport-escort service. College housing not available. A. Holly Patterson Library. 1,250 computers available on campus for general student use. A campuswide network can be accessed from off-campus. Students can access the following: online class registration. Staffed computer lab on campus provides training in use of computers, software, and the Internet.

■ NAZARETH COLLEGE OF ROCHESTER

4245 E Ave.

Rochester, NY 14618

Tel: (585)389-2525; Free: 800-462-3944

Fax: (585)389-2826

Web Site: www.naz.edu

Description: Independent, comprehensive, coed. Awards bachelor's, master's, and doctoral degrees and post-master's certificates. Founded 1924. Setting: 150-acre suburban campus. Total enrollment: 2,987. Faculty: 483 (184 full-time, 299 part-time). Student-undergrad faculty ratio is 9:1. 4,273 applied, 64% were admitted. 25% from top 10% of their high school class, 58% from top quarter, 88% from top half. Full-time: 2,176 students, 74% women, 26% men. Part-time: 93 students, 77% women, 23% men. 11% from out-of-state. 0.2% American Indian or Alaska Native, non-Hispanic/Latino; 6% Hispanic/Latino; 5% Black or African American, non-Hispanic/Latino; 3% Asian, non-Hispanic/Latino; 1% international. 5% 25 or older. Core. Calendar: semesters. Academic remediation for entering students, ESL program, services for LD students, advanced placement, honors program, independent study, double major, summer session for credit, part-time degree program, adult/continuing education programs, co-op programs and internships. Off campus study. Study abroad program. ROTC: Army (c), Air Force (c).

Entrance Requirements: Options: electronic application, early admission, early decision, deferred admission, international baccalaureate accepted.

Required: essay, high school transcript, 1 recommendation. Recommended: interview. Required for some: audition/portfolio review, SAT, SAT or ACT, Student can submit they ACT or SAT. Application deadlines: 2/1, 11/15 for early decision plan 1, 1/10 for early decision plan 2. Notification: continuous until 3/1, 12/15 for early decision plan 1, 2/1 for early decision plan 2. SAT Reasoning Test deadline: 2/1. SAT Subject Test deadline: 2/1. Transfer credits accepted: Yes. Applicants placed on waiting list: 486. Early decision applicants: 308. Early decision applicants admitted: 357.

Costs Per Year: Application fee: $45. Comprehensive fee: $48,010 includes full-time tuition ($32,850), mandatory fees ($1430), and college room and board ($13,730).

Collegiate Environment: Orientation program. Drama-theater group, choral group, student-run newspaper, radio station. Social organizations: 55 open to all. Most popular organizations: Campus Activities Board, Center for Spirituality, Physical Therapy Club, Diversity Council, Intramurals. Major annual events: Spring Fest, Siblings' Weekend, Battle of the Beaks. Student services: health clinic, personal-psychological counseling, women's center. Campus security: 24-hour emergency response devices and patrols, late night transport-escort service, controlled dormitory access, security beeper, lighted pathways, alert system. Freshmen guaranteed college housing. On-campus residence required through sophomore year. Option: coed housing available. Lorette Wilmot Library. Students can reserve study rooms.

Community Environment: See University of Rochester.

■ **THE NEW SCHOOL COLLEGE OF PERFORMING ARTS**
66 W 12th St.
New York, NY 10011
Tel: (212)229-5600; Free: 800-292-3040
E-mail: hoskinga@newschool.edu
Web Site: www.newschool.edu/performing-arts

Description: Independent, comprehensive, coed. Part of The New School. Awards bachelor's and master's degrees. Setting: urban campus with easy access to New York City. System endowment: $322.3 million. Research spending for the previous fiscal year: $15.7 million. Educational spending for the previous fiscal year: $14,455 per student. Total enrollment: 895. Faculty: 454 (16 full-time, 438 part-time). Student-undergrad faculty ratio is 5:1. 1,259 applied, 51% were admitted. 14% from top 10% of their high school class, 37% from top quarter, 68% from top half. Full-time: 580 students, 45% women, 55% men. Part-time: 14 students, 21% women, 79% men. Students come from 38 states and territories, 47 other countries, 79% from out-of-state. 0.2% American Indian or Alaska Native, non-Hispanic/Latino; 9% Hispanic/Latino; 9% Black or African American, non-Hispanic/Latino; 4% Asian, non-Hispanic/Latino; 0.2% Native Hawaiian or other Pacific Islander, non-Hispanic/Latino; 30% international. 9% 25 or older, 30% live on campus, 8% transferred in. Retention: 81% of full-time freshmen returned the following year. Academic area with the most degrees conferred: visual and performing arts. Core. Calendar: semesters. Academic remediation for entering students, ESL program, services for LD students, accelerated degree program, self-designed majors, independent study, distance learning, double major, summer session for credit, part-time degree program, internships, graduate courses open to undergrads. Off campus study. Study abroad program.

Entrance Requirements: Options: electronic application, early action, deferred admission, international baccalaureate accepted. Required: essay, high school transcript, 1 recommendation. Recommended: minimum 3 high school GPA. Required for some: interview, prescreening, live audition/interview. Entrance: moderately difficult. Application deadlines: 1/15, 11/1 for early action. Notification: continuous until 3/15, 12/20 for early action. Transfer credits accepted: Yes. Early action applicants: 27. Early action applicants admitted: 24.

Collegiate Environment: Orientation program. Drama-theater group, choral group, student-run newspaper. Social organizations: 43 open to all. Major annual events: block party, Bell Hooks + Jill Soloway at the New School, Frank Stella at the Parsons Table. Student services: health clinic, personal-psychological counseling. Campus security: 24-hour emergency response devices, controlled dormitory access, 24-hour desk attendants in residence halls. New School Libraries & Archives plus 3 others. Books: 215,937 (physical), 840,933 (digital/electronic); Serial titles: 2,265 (physical), 113,452 (digital/electronic); Databases: 376. Weekly public service hours: 155; study areas open 24 hours, 5-7 days a week; students can reserve study rooms. Operations spending for the previous fiscal year: $1.1 million. 717 computers available on campus for general student use. A computer is required for all students. A campuswide network can be accessed from student residence rooms and from off campus. Students can access the following: online class

registration. Staffed computer lab on campus (open 24 hours a day) provides training in use of computers, software, and the Internet.

■ **THE NEW SCHOOL FOR PUBLIC ENGAGEMENT**
66 W 12th St.
New York, NY 10011
Tel: (212)229-5600; Free: 800-292-3040
Fax: (212)645-0661
E-mail: puleioe@newschool.edu
Web Site: www.newschool.edu/public-engagement

Description: Independent, comprehensive, coed. Part of The New School. Awards bachelor's, master's, and doctoral degrees and post-master's certificates. Founded 1919. Setting: urban campus with easy access to New York City. System endowment: $322.3 million. Research spending for the previous fiscal year: $15.7 million. Educational spending for the previous fiscal year: $14,455 per student. Total enrollment: 1,448. Faculty: 356 (82 full-time, 274 part-time). Student-undergrad faculty ratio is 5:1. 33 applied, 88% were admitted. Full-time: 231 students, 65% women, 35% men. Part-time: 240 students, 66% women, 34% men. Students come from 38 states and territories, 33 other countries, 48% from out-of-state. 16% Hispanic/Latino; 9% Black or African American, non-Hispanic/Latino; 3% Asian, non-Hispanic/Latino; 0.2% Native Hawaiian or other Pacific Islander, non-Hispanic/Latino; 11% international. 56% 25 or older, 25% live on campus, 26% transferred in. Academic areas with the most degrees conferred: liberal arts/general studies; visual and performing arts; family and consumer sciences. Core. Calendar: semesters. ESL program, services for LD students, advanced placement, accelerated degree program, self-designed majors, independent study, distance learning, double major, summer session for credit, part-time degree program, adult/continuing education programs, internships, graduate courses open to undergrads. Off campus study at Lebanese American University, Institute for Culinary Education. Study abroad program.

Entrance Requirements: Options: electronic application, early action, deferred admission, international baccalaureate accepted. Required: essay, high school transcript. Recommended: 1 recommendation. Entrance: noncompetitive. Application deadlines: 1/15, 11/1 for early action. Notification: continuous until 3/15, 3/15 for early action. Transfer credits accepted: Yes. Early action applicants: 0. Early action applicants admitted: 0.

Collegiate Environment: Orientation program. Drama-theater group, choral group, student-run newspaper. Social organizations: 43 open to all. Major annual events: block party, Bell Hooks + Jill Soloway at The New School, Frank Stella at the Parsons Table. Student services: health clinic, personal-psychological counseling. Campus security: 24-hour emergency response devices, controlled dormitory access, trained security personnel in central buildings and 24-hour desk attendants in residence halls. New School Libraries & Archives plus 3 others. Books: 215,937 (physical), 840,933 (digital/electronic); Serial titles: 2,265 (physical), 113,452 (digital/electronic); Databases: 376. Weekly public service hours: 155; study areas open 24 hours, 5-7 days a week; students can reserve study rooms. Operations spending for the previous fiscal year: $1.1 million. 717 computers available on campus for general student use. A computer is required for all students. A campuswide network can be accessed from student residence rooms and from off campus. Students can access the following: online class registration. Staffed computer lab on campus (open 24 hours a day) provides training in use of computers, software, and the Internet.

■ **NEW YORK CITY COLLEGE OF TECHNOLOGY OF THE CITY UNIVERSITY OF NEW YORK**
300 Jay St.
Brooklyn, NY 11201-2983
Tel: (718)260-5000
Fax: (718)260-5198
E-mail: achaconis@citytech.cuny.edu
Web Site: www.citytech.cuny.edu

Description: State and locally supported, 4-year, coed. Part of City University of New York System. Awards associate and bachelor's degrees. Founded 1946. Setting: urban campus with easy access to New York City. Endowment: $17.1 million. Research spending for the previous fiscal year: $729,424. Educational spending for the previous fiscal year: $11,163 per student. Total enrollment: 17,282. Faculty: 1,427 (445 full-time, 982 part-time). Student-undergrad faculty ratio is 17:1. 16,846 applied, 75% were admitted. Full-time: 10,912 students, 40% women, 60% men. Part-time: 6,370 students, 53% women, 47% men. Students come from 10 states and territories, 101 other countries, 5% from out-of-state. 0.4% American Indian or Alaska Native, non-Hispanic/Latino; 33% Hispanic/Latino; 30% Black or

African American, non-Hispanic/Latino; 20% Asian, non-Hispanic/Latino; 0.5% Native Hawaiian or other Pacific Islander, non-Hispanic/Latino; 5% international. 28% 25 or older, 9% transferred in. Retention: 77% of full-time freshmen returned the following year. Academic areas with the most degrees conferred: health professions and related sciences; visual and performing arts; engineering technologies; computer and information sciences. Core. Calendar: semesters. Academic remediation for entering students, ESL program, services for LD students, advanced placement, accelerated degree program, self-designed majors, freshman honors college, honors program, independent study, distance learning, summer session for credit, part-time degree program, adult/continuing education programs, internships. Off campus study. Study abroad program.

Entrance Requirements: Open admission except for upper-level bachelor's degree programs. Options: electronic application, deferred admission, international baccalaureate accepted. Required: high school transcript. Required for some: SAT or ACT. Entrance: noncompetitive. Application deadline: 2/1. Notification: continuous until 2/1. SAT Reasoning Test deadline: 8/1. Transfer credits accepted: Yes.

Collegiate Environment: Orientation program. Drama-theater group, student-run newspaper. Social organizations: 72 open to all. Most popular organizations: Art and Design Club, BMI Club, International Business Organization, SADHA (Dental Hygienists Club), National Society of Collegiate Scholars Club. Major annual events: Welcome Back Bash, Club Involvement Fair, SGA Forums. Student services: health clinic, personal-psychological counseling, women's center. Campus security: 24-hour emergency response devices and patrols. Ursula C. Schwerin Library. Books: 116,667 (physical), 487,902 (digital/electronic); Serial titles: 1,650 (physical), 95,329 (digital/electronic); Databases: 146. Weekly public service hours: 75; students can reserve study rooms. Operations spending for the previous fiscal year: $1.8 million.

■ NEW YORK COLLEGE OF HEALTH PROFESSIONS

6801 Jericho Tpke.
Syosset, NY 11791-4413
Tel: (516)364-0808; Free: 800-922-7337
Fax: (516)364-0989
Web Site: www.nycollege.edu

Description: Independent, comprehensive, coed. Awards associate, incidental bachelor's, and master's degrees. Founded 1981. Setting: suburban campus with easy access to New York City. Total enrollment: 879. Faculty: 93 (17 full-time, 76 part-time). Student-undergrad faculty ratio is 19:1. Full-time: 332 students, 77% women, 23% men. Part-time: 469 students, 75% women, 25% men. Academic area with the most degrees conferred: health professions and related sciences. Core. Calendar: trimesters. Academic remediation for entering students, services for LD students, advanced placement, accelerated degree program, double major, summer session for credit, part-time degree program, adult/continuing education programs, co-op programs and internships, graduate courses open to undergrads.

Entrance Requirements: Options: electronic application, deferred admission. Required: essay, high school transcript, minimum 2.0 high school GPA, interview. Entrance: moderately difficult. Application deadline: rolling. Notification: continuous.

Collegiate Environment: Orientation program. Student services: health clinic. Campus security: 24-hour emergency response devices and patrols, security guard evening and weekend hours. James and Lenore Jacobson Library at the Syosset Campus. 3 computers available on campus for general student use. Staffed computer lab on campus.

■ NEW YORK INSTITUTE OF TECHNOLOGY

PO Box 8000
Old Westbury, NY 11568-8000
Tel: (516)686-7516; Free: 800-345-NYIT
Fax: (516)686-7613
E-mail: admissions@nyit.edu
Web Site: www.nyit.edu

Description: Independent, comprehensive, coed. Awards associate, bachelor's, master's, and doctoral degrees and post-master's certificates. Founded 1955. Setting: 215-acre suburban campus with easy access to New York City. Endowment: $110.5 million. Research spending for the previous fiscal year: $11.7 million. Total enrollment: 7,422. Faculty: 900 (316 full-time, 584 part-time). Student-undergrad faculty ratio is 13:1. 9,945 applied, 77% were admitted. Full-time: 3,239 students, 37% women, 63% men. Part-time: 449 students, 33% women, 67% men. Students come from 40 states

and territories, 64 other countries, 15% from out-of-state. 0.3% American Indian or Alaska Native, non-Hispanic/Latino; 16% Hispanic/Latino; 9% Black or African American, non-Hispanic/Latino; 18% Asian, non-Hispanic/Latino; 0.4% Native Hawaiian or other Pacific Islander, non-Hispanic/Latino; 16% international. 11% 25 or older, 14% live on campus, 7% transferred in. Retention: 77% of full-time freshmen returned the following year. Academic areas with the most degrees conferred: engineering; business/marketing; health professions and related sciences. Core. Calendar: semesters. Academic remediation for entering students, ESL program, services for LD students, advanced placement, accelerated degree program, honors program, distance learning, double major, summer session for credit, part-time degree program, adult/continuing education programs, co-op programs and internships, graduate courses open to undergrads. Off campus study. Study abroad program. ROTC: Army (c), Air Force (c).

Entrance Requirements: Options: electronic application, deferred admission, international baccalaureate accepted. Required: essay, high school transcript, 2 recommendations, SAT or ACT. Recommended: minimum 2.7 high school GPA. Required for some: interview. Entrance: moderately difficult. Application deadline: rolling. Notification: continuous. SAT Reasoning Test deadline: 9/1. Transfer credits accepted: Yes.

Costs Per Year: Application fee: $50. Comprehensive fee: $51,180 includes full-time tuition ($35,585), mandatory fees ($1305), and college room and board ($14,290). College room only: $9320. Full-time tuition and fees vary according to program. Room and board charges vary according to housing facility and location. Part-time tuition: $1205 per credit. Part-time mandatory fees: $540 per term. Part-time tuition and fees vary according to course load and program.

Collegiate Environment: Orientation program. Student-run newspaper. Social organizations: 50 open to all; national fraternities, national sororities, local fraternities, local sororities; 3% of eligible men and 4% of eligible women are members. Major annual events: Greek Week, Welcome Week, May Fest. Student services: health clinic, personal-psychological counseling. Campus security: 24-hour emergency response devices and patrols, late night transport-escort service, controlled dormitory access. George and Gertrude Wisser Memorial Library plus 3 others. Books: 89,426 (physical), 70,248 (digital/electronic); Serial titles: 2,279 (physical), 23,926 (digital/electronic). Weekly public service hours: 78; students can reserve study rooms. Operations spending for the previous fiscal year: $4.9 million. 1,250 computers available on campus for general student use. A campuswide network can be accessed from student residence rooms and from off campus. Students can access the following: online class registration. Staffed computer lab on campus provides training in use of computers, software, and the Internet.

■ NEW YORK SCHOOL OF INTERIOR DESIGN

170 E 70th St.
New York, NY 10021-5110
Tel: (212)472-1500; Free: 800-336-9743
Fax: (212)472-1867
E-mail: admissions@nysid.edu
Web Site: www.nysid.edu

Description: Independent, comprehensive, coed. Awards associate, bachelor's, and master's degrees. Founded 1916. Setting: 1-acre urban campus. Endowment: $3.1 million. Total enrollment: 538. Faculty: 120 (5 full-time, 115 part-time). Student-undergrad faculty ratio is 8:1. 155 applied, 42% were admitted. Full-time: 128 students, 88% women, 12% men. Part-time: 253 students, 91% women, 9% men. 8% Hispanic/Latino; 3% Black or African American, non-Hispanic/Latino; 3% Asian, non-Hispanic/Latino; 12% international. 12% live on campus. Retention: 80% of full-time freshmen returned the following year. Core. Calendar: semesters. ESL program, services for LD students, advanced placement, independent study, summer session for credit, part-time degree program, external degree program, adult/continuing education programs, internships.

Entrance Requirements: Options: electronic application, deferred admission, international baccalaureate accepted. Required: essay, high school transcript, minimum 2.8 high school GPA, 2 recommendations, portfolio. Required for some: SAT or ACT. Entrance: moderately difficult. Application deadline: 2/1. Notification: 4/1. Transfer credits accepted: Yes.

Costs Per Year: Application fee: $60. Tuition: $33,000 full-time, $1000 per credit part-time. Mandatory fees: $834 full-time, $417 per term part-time. Full-time tuition and fees vary according to course load. Part-time tuition and fees vary according to course load.

Collegiate Environment: Orientation program. Social organizations: 3 open to all. Most popular organizations: American Society of Interior Designers,

Contract Club, Student Council. Major annual events: Lecture Series, ASID Student Auction, Gallery Exhibition Openings. Campus security: security during school hours. Operations spending for the previous fiscal year: $311,543. 135 computers available on campus for general student use. A campuswide network can be accessed from student residence rooms and from off campus. Students can access the following: online class registration. Staffed computer lab on campus provides training in use of computers and software.

■ NEW YORK UNIVERSITY
70 Washington Sq. S
New York, NY 10012-1019
Tel: (212)998-1212
Fax: (212)995-4902
E-mail: admissions@nyu.edu
Web Site: www.nyu.edu

Description: Independent, university, coed. Awards associate, bachelor's, master's, and doctoral degrees and post-master's certificates. Founded 1831. Setting: 230-acre urban campus with easy access to New York City. Endowment: $4.2 billion. Research spending for the previous fiscal year: $1.2 billion. Educational spending for the previous fiscal year: $32,226 per student. Total enrollment: 51,847. Faculty: 6,542 (2,974 full-time, 3,568 part-time). Student-undergrad faculty ratio is 10:1. 71,834 applied, 20% were admitted. Full-time: 25,725 students, 58% women, 42% men. Part-time: 1,008 students, 55% women, 45% men. Students come from 52 states and territories, 157 other countries, 66% from out-of-state. 0.2% American Indian or Alaska Native, non-Hispanic/Latino; 14% Hispanic/Latino; 6% Black or African American, non-Hispanic/Latino; 19% Asian, non-Hispanic/Latino; 0.2% Native Hawaiian or other Pacific Islander, non-Hispanic/Latino; 20% international. 4% 25 or older, 42% live on campus, 3% transferred in. Retention: 94% of full-time freshmen returned the following year. Academic areas with the most degrees conferred: visual and performing arts; social sciences; business/marketing. Core. Calendar: semesters. ESL program, services for LD students, advanced placement, accelerated degree program, self-designed majors, honors program, independent study, distance learning, double major, summer session for credit, part-time degree program, adult/continuing education programs, co-op programs and internships, graduate courses open to undergrads. Off campus study at Spelman College, Morehouse College, Xavier University of New Orleans, University of Puerto Rico (Rio Piedras), and University of Sacred Heart in Puerto Rico. Study abroad program. ROTC: Army (c), Air Force (c).

Entrance Requirements: Options: electronic application, early admission, early decision, deferred admission, international baccalaureate accepted. Required: essay, high school transcript, 1 recommendation. Required for some: audition or a portfolio for some specific programs, SAT and SAT Subject Tests or ACT. Entrance: very difficult. Application deadlines: 1/1, 11/1 for early decision plan 1, 1/1 for early decision plan 2. Notification: 4/1, 12/15 for early decision plan 1, 2/15 for early decision plan 2. SAT Reasoning Test deadline: 1/31. SAT Subject Test deadline: 1/31. Transfer credits accepted: Yes. Early decision applicants: 10,469. Early decision applicants admitted: 3,628.

Costs Per Year: Application fee: $80. Comprehensive fee: $69,984 includes full-time tuition ($49,256), mandatory fees ($2572), and college room and board ($18,156). College room only: $13,166. Full-time tuition and fees vary according to course load, program, and reciprocity agreements. Room and board charges vary according to board plan and housing facility. Part-time tuition: $1451 per credit hour. Part-time mandatory fees: $489 per term. Part-time tuition and fees vary according to program.

Collegiate Environment: Orientation program. Drama-theater group, choral group, student-run newspaper, radio station. Social organizations: 857 open to all; national fraternities, national sororities, local fraternities, local sororities; 5% of eligible men and 7% of eligible women are members. Major annual events: Fall Clubfest, Asian Heritage Month, StrawberryFest. Student services: health clinic, personal-psychological counseling, women's center. Campus security: 24-hour emergency response devices and patrols, student patrols, late night transport-escort service, controlled dormitory access. 11,582 college housing spaces available; 11,262 were occupied in 2018-19. Freshmen guaranteed college housing. Option: coed housing available. Elmer H. Bobst Library plus 10 others. Books: 3.4 million (physical), 1.6 million (digital/electronic); Serial titles: 51,377 (physical), 197,567 (digital/electronic); Databases: 1,152. Study areas open 24 hours, 5-7 days a week; students can reserve study rooms. Operations spending for the previous fiscal year: $54.9 million.

Community Environment: New York City, the largest city in the nation, is also its business, entertainment, and artistic capital. This teeming city is considered the greatest center of higher education in the country, and claims the largest library outside the Library of Congress. Its intellectual and cultural opportunities are limitless and virtually impossible to duplicate elsewhere. Broadway, one of the great theatre districts of the world, Lincoln Center for the Performing Arts, more than 60 museums, and many historic sites dating from the pre-Revolutionary period are among New York's cultural attractions. More than one-sixth of the city is park land, offering facilities for many sports and activities in beautifully planned areas such as Central Park and Riverside Park. The financial district, with famous Wall Street, houses the complex mechanism of banking and security markets. A vast system of subways, roadways and buses span the areas of New York's 5 boroughs, connecting richly diverse communities and people from virtually all walks of life. Points of interest on Manhattan island include: the United Nations complex, Rockefeller Center, the"tremendous city within a city," and skyscrapers like the renowned Empire State Building. New York City, with a population of over 8 million and limitless activity, provides a unique campus.

■ NIAGARA COUNTY COMMUNITY COLLEGE
3111 Saunders Settlement Rd.
Sanborn, NY 14132-9460
Tel: (716)614-6222
Fax: (716)731-4053
E-mail: admissions@niagaracc.suny.edu
Web Site: www.niagaracc.suny.edu

Description: State and locally supported, 2-year, coed. Part of State University of New York System. Awards certificates, transfer associate, and terminal associate degrees. Founded 1962. Setting: 287-acre rural campus with easy access to Buffalo. Endowment: $10 million. Educational spending for the previous fiscal year: $7663 per student. Total enrollment: 5,466. Faculty: 316 (102 full-time, 214 part-time). Student-undergrad faculty ratio is 17:1. 2,859 applied, 77% were admitted. 6% from top 10% of their high school class, 26% from top quarter, 63% from top half. Full-time: 3,228 students, 54% women, 46% men. Part-time: 2,238 students, 61% women, 39% men. Students come from 17 states and territories, 3 other countries, 1% from out-of-state. 1% American Indian or Alaska Native, non-Hispanic/Latino; 4% Hispanic/Latino; 11% Black or African American, non-Hispanic/Latino; 2% Asian, non-Hispanic/Latino. 21% 25 or older, 4% live on campus, 8% transferred in. Calendar: semesters. Academic remediation for entering students, services for LD students, advanced placement, self-designed majors, honors program, independent study, distance learning, double major, summer session for credit, part-time degree program, adult/continuing education programs, co-op programs and internships. Off campus study at 17 members of the Western New York Consortium. Study abroad program. ROTC: Army (c).

Entrance Requirements: Open admission. Options: electronic application, early admission. Required: high school transcript. Required for some: minimum 2 high school GPA. Entrance: noncompetitive. Notification: continuous until 8/31.

Collegiate Environment: Orientation program. Drama-theater group, choral group, student-run newspaper, radio station. Social organizations: 40 open to all. Most popular organizations: Student Radio Station, Student Nurses Association, Phi Theta Kappa, Alpha Beta Gamma, Physical Education Club. Major annual events: All College Picnics, Orientation, Theatrical/Musical Events. Student services: health clinic, personal-psychological counseling. Campus security: 24-hour emergency response devices and patrols, student patrols, late night transport-escort service. Henrietta G. Lewis Library. Books: 77,511 (physical); Serial titles: 290 (physical); Databases: 95. Weekly public service hours: 64; students can reserve study rooms. Operations spending for the previous fiscal year: $1.1 million. 414 computers available on campus for general student use. A campuswide network can be accessed. Students can access the following: online class registration. Staffed computer lab on campus provides training in use of computers, software, and the Internet.

■ NIAGARA UNIVERSITY
Niagara University, NY 14109
Tel: (716)285-1212; Free: 800-462-2111
Fax: (716)286-8355
E-mail: admissions@niagara.edu
Web Site: www.niagara.edu

Description: Independent, comprehensive, coed, affiliated with Roman Catholic Church. Awards associate, bachelor's, master's, and doctoral degrees and post-master's certificates. Founded 1856. Setting: 160-acre suburban campus with easy access to Buffalo, NY and Toronto, Ontario

(Canada). Endowment: $98 million. Educational spending for the previous fiscal year: $7750 per student. Total enrollment: 3,949. Faculty: 442 (166 full-time, 276 part-time). Student-undergrad faculty ratio is 11:1. 3,101 applied, 84% were admitted. 16% from top 10% of their high school class, 47% from top quarter, 76% from top half. Full-time: 2,827 students, 62% women, 38% men. Part-time: 167 students, 62% women, 38% men. Students come from 35 states and territories, 42 other countries, 8% from out-of-state. 0.6% American Indian or Alaska Native, non-Hispanic/Latino; 4% Hispanic/Latino; 5% Black or African American, non-Hispanic/Latino; 2% Asian, non-Hispanic/Latino; 13% international. 12% 25 or older, 40% live on campus, 4% transferred in. Retention: 83% of full-time freshmen returned the following year. Academic areas with the most degrees conferred: business/marketing; education; health professions and related sciences. Core. Calendar: semesters. Academic remediation for entering students, ESL program, services for LD students, advanced placement, accelerated degree program, self-designed majors, independent study, distance learning, double major, summer session for credit, part-time degree program, co-op programs and internships, graduate courses open to undergrads. Off campus study at Members of the New York State Visiting Student Program, the Western New York Consortium of Higher Education. Study abroad program. ROTC: Army.

Entrance Requirements: Options: electronic application, early admission, early action, deferred admission, international baccalaureate accepted. Required: high school transcript. Recommended: minimum 3 high school GPA, 3 recommendations, interview. Entrance: moderately difficult. Application deadline: 8/1. Notification: continuous. SAT Reasoning Test deadline: 8/1. Transfer credits accepted: Yes.

Costs Per Year: One-time mandatory fee: $200. Comprehensive fee: $46,380 includes full-time tuition ($31,700), mandatory fees ($1480), and college room and board ($13,200). Full-time tuition and fees vary according to program. Room and board charges vary according to housing facility. Part-time tuition: $1060 per credit hour. Part-time tuition varies according to program.

Collegiate Environment: Orientation program. Drama-theater group, choral group, student-run newspaper, radio station. Social organizations: 77 open to all; national fraternities, national sororities; 1% of eligible men and 3% of eligible women are members. Most popular organizations: Student Nursing Association, Future Teachers Association, NY Players (theatre), Beta Alpha Psi, Hospitality & Tourism Association. Major annual events: FirstFest (Welcome Back Week), Talent Night, RidgeFest (spring fest). Student services: health clinic, personal-psychological counseling. Campus security: 24-hour emergency response devices and patrols, late night transport-escort service, controlled dormitory access, 24-hour escort service, Emergency Notification System. Our Lady of Angels Library. Books: 122,720 (physical), 348,406 (digital/electronic); Serial titles: 32,000 (digital/electronic); Databases: 111. Weekly public service hours: 107; study areas open 24 hours, 5-7 days a week; students can reserve study rooms. Operations spending for the previous fiscal year: $1.3 million. 81 computers available on campus for general student use. A campuswide network can be accessed from student residence rooms. Students can access the following: online class registration. Staffed computer lab on campus (open 24 hours a day) provides training in use of computers, software, and the Internet.

■ NORTH COUNTRY COMMUNITY COLLEGE

23 Santanoni Ave.
Saranac Lake, NY 12983-0089
Tel: (518)891-2915; Free: 888-TRY-NCCC
Fax: (518)891-2915
E-mail: info@nccc.edu
Web Site: www.nccc.edu

Description: State and locally supported, 2-year, coed. Part of State University of New York System. Awards certificates, transfer associate, and terminal associate degrees. Founded 1967. Setting: 100-acre rural campus. Total enrollment: 1,751. Faculty: 151 (46 full-time, 105 part-time). Student-undergrad faculty ratio is 15:1. 8% from top 10% of their high school class, 25% from top quarter, 64% from top half. Full-time: 956 students, 64% women, 36% men. Part-time: 795 students, 59% women, 41% men. 31% 25 or older, 7% live on campus. Core. Calendar: semesters. Academic remediation for entering students, services for LD students, advanced placement, self-designed majors, distance learning, double major, summer session for credit, part-time degree program, internships.

Entrance Requirements: Open admission except for radiologic technology, nursing, massage therapy programs. Options: electronic application, early admission, early decision, deferred admission. Required: high school transcript. Recommended: essay, interview, SAT or ACT. Entrance: minimally

difficult. Application deadline: rolling. Notification: continuous. Preference given to residents of sponsoring counties.

Collegiate Environment: Drama-theater group, student-run newspaper. Most popular organizations: Student Government Association, Wilderness Recreation Club, Nursing Club, Radiology Club, Criminal Justice Club. Major annual events: Winter Carnival, Winter Fest, May Fest. Student services: personal-psychological counseling. Campus security: controlled dormitory access. North Country Community College Library plus 1 other. 140 computers available on campus for general student use. A campuswide network can be accessed. Students can access the following: online class registration. Staffed computer lab on campus (open 24 hours a day).

■ NYACK COLLEGE

1 S Blvd.
Nyack, NY 10960
Tel: (845)358-1710; Free: 800-33-NYACK
Fax: (845)358-3047
E-mail: admissions@nyack.edu
Web Site: www.nyack.edu

Description: Independent, comprehensive, coed, affiliated with The Christian and Missionary Alliance. Awards associate, bachelor's, master's, and doctoral degrees. Founded 1882. Setting: 125-acre suburban campus with easy access to New York City. Total enrollment: 2,455. Faculty: 262 (82 full-time, 180 part-time). Student-undergrad faculty ratio is 12:1. 435 applied, 98% were admitted. 5% from top 10% of their high school class, 16% from top quarter, 38% from top half. Full-time: 1,131 students, 58% women, 42% men. Part-time: 267 students, 57% women, 43% men. 35% from out-of-state. 0.7% American Indian or Alaska Native, non-Hispanic/Latino; 29% Hispanic/Latino; 30% Black or African American, non-Hispanic/Latino; 8% Asian, non-Hispanic/Latino; 0.6% Native Hawaiian or other Pacific Islander, non-Hispanic/Latino; 6% international. 27% 25 or older, 69% live on campus, 12% transferred in. Retention: 59% of full-time freshmen returned the following year. Academic areas with the most degrees conferred: business/marketing; theology and religious vocations; interdisciplinary studies. Core. Calendar: semesters. Academic remediation for entering students, services for LD students, advanced placement, self-designed majors, honors program, independent study, distance learning, double major, summer session for credit, part-time degree program, adult/continuing education programs, internships. Off campus study at Council for Christian Colleges and Universities. Study abroad program.

Entrance Requirements: Options: electronic application, early action, deferred admission, international baccalaureate accepted. Required: essay, high school transcript, minimum 2 high school GPA, 1 recommendation, signed statement of faith and community life form. Required for some: interview, SAT and SAT Subject Tests or ACT. Entrance: minimally difficult. Application deadline: rolling. Notification: continuous. SAT Reasoning Test deadline: 8/30. SAT Subject Test deadline: 8/30. Transfer credits accepted: Yes.

Costs Per Year: Application fee: $25. Comprehensive fee: $34,800 includes full-time tuition ($25,000), mandatory fees ($350), and college room and board ($9450). Room and board charges vary according to board plan and housing facility. Part-time tuition: $1040 per credit hour. Part-time tuition varies according to course load.

Collegiate Environment: Orientation program. Drama-theater group, choral group, student-run newspaper, radio station. Social organizations: 50 open to all. Most popular organizations: Student leadership, Choral groups, Lost & Found, Small group ministries, Intramurals. Major annual events: Deeper Life Series, Midnight Breakfasts, Fall Homecoming. Student services: health clinic, personal-psychological counseling. Campus security: 24-hour emergency response devices and patrols. Bailey Library plus 3 others.

Community Environment: Suburban village setting about 20 miles from New York City, Nyack is on the west bank of the Hudson River where it widens out to lake proportions. Early Dutch settlers called it the Tappan Zee. It has a local hospital, library, YMCA, and churches of all major denominations. The area has motels, hotels and shopping centers. Recreational facilities include bowling alleys, swimming pools, tennis, field sports, boating, lakes, ice skating, hunting, and fishing. There is ample part-time employment available for students.

■ OHR HAMEIR THEOLOGICAL SEMINARY

141 Furnace Woods Rd.
Cortlandt Manor, NY 10567
Tel: (914)736-1500
Web Site: www.ohrhameir.com

Description: Independent Jewish, comprehensive, men only. Awards bachelor's and master's degrees. Founded 1962. Total enrollment: 86. 4 applied, 100% were admitted. Calendar: semesters.

■ **OHR SOMAYACH/JOSEPH TANENBAUM EDUCATIONAL CENTER**
PO Box 334, 244 Rte. 306
Monsey, NY 10952-0334
Tel: (845)425-1370
Web Site: ohr.edu
Description: Independent Jewish, comprehensive, men only. Awards master's and doctoral degrees. Founded 1979. Setting: 7-acre small town campus with easy access to New York City. Research spending for the previous fiscal year: $23,000. Total enrollment: 50. Faculty: 12 (6 full-time, 6 part-time). 100 applied, 60% were admitted. Full-time: 40 students. Students come from 10 states and territories, 4 other countries, 60% from out-of-state. 75% 25 or older, 8% transferred in. Core. Calendar: semesters. Academic remediation for entering students, services for LD students, honors program, summer session for credit, part-time degree program, adult/continuing education programs, internships.
Entrance Requirements: Option: early admission. Required: interview. Recommended: high school transcript. Required for some: essay. Entrance: moderately difficult. Application deadline: rolling.
Collegiate Environment: Student services: personal-psychological counseling. Campus security: 24-hour emergency response devices and patrols, controlled dormitory access. Finer Library.

■ **ONONDAGA COMMUNITY COLLEGE**
4585 W Seneca Tpke.
Syracuse, NY 13215
Tel: (315)498-2622
Fax: (315)469-2107
E-mail: admissions@sunyocc.edu
Web Site: www.sunyocc.edu
Description: State and locally supported, 2-year, coed. Part of State University of New York System. Awards certificates, diplomas, transfer associate, and terminal associate degrees. Founded 1962. Setting: 280-acre suburban campus. Endowment: $10.5 million. Educational spending for the previous fiscal year: $5346 per student. Total enrollment: 11,886. Faculty: 645 (177 full-time, 468 part-time). Student-undergrad faculty ratio is 24:1. 1,331 applied, 66% were admitted. Full-time: 5,895 students, 49% women, 51% men. Part-time: 5,991 students, 54% women, 46% men. Students come from 25 states and territories, 19 other countries, 1% from out-of-state. 1% American Indian or Alaska Native, non-Hispanic/Latino; 5% Hispanic/Latino; 13% Black or African American, non-Hispanic/Latino; 3% Asian, non-Hispanic/Latino; 0.1% Native Hawaiian or other Pacific Islander, non-Hispanic/Latino; 0.4% international. 21% 25 or older, 6% live on campus, 49% transferred in. Calendar: semesters. Academic remediation for entering students, ESL program, services for LD students, advanced placement, accelerated degree program, honors program, distance learning, double major, summer session for credit, part-time degree program, external degree program, adult/continuing education programs, co-op programs and internships. Study abroad program. ROTC: Air Force (c).
Entrance Requirements: Open admission except for allied health, engineering, computer science, technology, art, music programs. Option: electronic application. Required: high school transcript. Required for some: minimum 2 high school GPA, interview. Entrance: noncompetitive. Notification: continuous. Preference given to county residents, members of the Armed Forces. Transfer credits accepted: Yes.
Costs Per Year: Application fee: $0. State resident tuition: $4900 full-time, $204 per credit hour part-time. Nonresident tuition: $9800 full-time, $408 per credit hour part-time. Mandatory fees: $584 full-time, $12.50 per credit hour part-time, $75 per term part-time. Full-time tuition and fees vary according to program. Part-time tuition and fees vary according to course load and program. College room and board: $9140. College room only: $6270. Room and board charges vary according to board plan.
Collegiate Environment: Orientation program. Drama-theater group, choral group, student-run newspaper, radio station. Social organizations: 27 open to all. Major annual events: Welcome Onondaga/Connect@OCC, Party on the Quad. Student services: personal-psychological counseling. Campus security: 24-hour emergency response devices and patrols, controlled dormitory access. Sidney B. Coulter Library plus 1 other. Books: 84,742 (physical), 542 (digital/electronic); Serial titles: 194 (physical), 10 (digital/electronic); Databases: 92. Weekly public service hours: 67; students can reserve study rooms. Operations spending for the previous fiscal year: $1.6 million. 2,000

computers available on campus for general student use. A campuswide network can be accessed from student residence rooms and from off campus. Students can access the following: online class registration. Staffed computer lab on campus provides training in use of computers, software, and the Internet.

■ **ORANGE COUNTY COMMUNITY COLLEGE**
115 S St.
Middletown, NY 10940-6437
Tel: (845)344-6222
Fax: (845)343-1228
E-mail: apply@sunyorange.edu
Web Site: www.sunyorange.edu
Description: State and locally supported, 2-year, coed. Part of State University of New York System. Awards certificates, transfer associate, and terminal associate degrees. Founded 1950. Setting: 37-acre suburban campus with easy access to New York City. Total enrollment: 6,876. Student-undergrad faculty ratio is 17:1. 1% from out-of-state. 24% 25 or older. Core. Calendar: semesters. Academic remediation for entering students, ESL program, services for LD students, accelerated degree program, honors program, summer session for credit, part-time degree program, external degree program, adult/continuing education programs, internships.
Entrance Requirements: Open admission except for dental hygiene, engineering, occupational therapy, physical therapy, computer science programs. Options: early admission, deferred admission. Required: high school transcript. Entrance: noncompetitive. Application deadline: 8/1. Notification: continuous. Preference given to county residents.
Collegiate Environment: Orientation program. Drama-theater group, choral group, student-run newspaper, radio station. Social organizations: local sororities. Student services: health clinic, personal-psychological counseling. Campus security: 24-hour emergency response devices, late night transport-escort service. Learning Resource Center.

■ **PACE UNIVERSITY**
One Pace Plz.
New York, NY 10038
Tel: (212)346-1200; Free: 800-874-7223
Fax: (212)346-1040
E-mail: acordon@pace.edu
Web Site: www.pace.edu/nyc
Description: Independent, university, coed. Awards associate, bachelor's, master's, and doctoral degrees and post-master's certificates. Founded 1906. Setting: urban campus with easy access to New York City. Endowment: $169.9 million. Research spending for the previous fiscal year: $4.8 million. Educational spending for the previous fiscal year: $12,044 per student. Total enrollment: 13,609. Faculty: 1,369 (519 full-time, 850 part-time). Student-undergrad faculty ratio is 16:1. 21,520 applied, 76% were admitted. 15% from top 10% of their high school class, 41% from top quarter, 77% from top half. Full-time: 7,943 students, 62% women, 38% men. Part-time: 1,017 students, 57% women, 43% men. 46% from out-of-state. 0.3% American Indian or Alaska Native, non-Hispanic/Latino; 12% Hispanic/Latino; 11% Black or African American, non-Hispanic/Latino; 8% Asian, non-Hispanic/Latino; 0.1% Native Hawaiian or other Pacific Islander, non-Hispanic/Latino; 10% international. 9% 25 or older, 42% live on campus, 6% transferred in. Retention: 79% of full-time freshmen returned the following year. Academic areas with the most degrees conferred: business/marketing; visual and performing arts; health professions and related sciences. Core. Calendar: semesters. ESL program, services for LD students, advanced placement, accelerated degree program, freshman honors college, honors program, independent study, distance learning, double major, summer session for credit, part-time degree program, adult/continuing education programs, co-op programs and internships, graduate courses open to undergrads. Study abroad program. ROTC: Army (c).
Entrance Requirements: Options: electronic application, early decision, early action, deferred admission, international baccalaureate accepted. Required: essay, high school transcript, 2 recommendations. Recommended: interview. Required for some: SAT or ACT. Entrance: moderately difficult. Application deadline: 2/15. Notification: continuous. Transfer credits accepted: Yes. Early decision applicants: 93. Early decision applicants admitted: 60.
Costs Per Year: Application fee: $50. Comprehensive fee: $63,809 includes full-time tuition ($43,624), mandatory fees ($1656), and college room and board ($18,529). Part-time tuition: $1251 per credit hour.
Collegiate Environment: Orientation program. Drama-theater group, choral

group, student-run newspaper, radio station. Social organizations: 98 open to all; national fraternities, national sororities, local fraternities, local sororities; 5% of eligible men and 13% of eligible women are members. Most popular organizations: Kappa Delta, Sigma Delta Tau, Beta Alpha Psi, Profashionals, Programming and Campus Entertainment Board. Major annual events: P.A.C.E Setter Jam, Amateur Jam, Culture Fest. Student services: health clinic, personal-psychological counseling. Campus security: 24-hour emergency response devices and patrols, late night transport-escort service, controlled dormitory access. Freshmen guaranteed college housing. Option: coed housing available. Henry Birnbaum Library. Books: 382,858 (physical), 224,418 (digital/electronic); Serial titles: 73 (physical), 576,860 (digital/electronic); Databases: 172. Weekly public service hours: 93; students can reserve study rooms. Operations spending for the previous fiscal year: $7.3 million. 209 computers available on campus for general student use. A campuswide network can be accessed. Students can access the following: online class registration, administrative functions (tuition, student records, financial aid, health insurance waiver). Staffed computer lab on campus.

Community Environment: The New York City campus is just a short walk from Wall Street and the South Street Seaport. Lincoln Center, the theater district, the Metropolitan Museum, and other world-famous centers of the arts are just a few minutes away by subway or cab. The Pleasantville/ Briarcliff campus is in a suburban setting in Westchester County, with access to twenty-three international corporate headquarters and excellent shopping nearby. The campus offers an environmental center, riding stables, and a variety of recreational facilities. The White Plains campus is adjacent to the train station.

■ PACE UNIVERSITY, PLEASANTVILLE CAMPUS

861 Bedford Rd.
Pleasantville, NY 10570
Tel: (914)773-3200; Free: 800-874-PACE
Fax: (914)773-3851
E-mail: acordon@pace.edu
Web Site: www.pace.edu/westchester

Description: Independent, university, coed. Awards associate, bachelor's, master's, and doctoral degrees and post-master's certificates. Founded 1906. Setting: suburban campus with easy access to New York City. Endowment: $169.9 million. Research spending for the previous fiscal year: $4.8 million. Educational spending for the previous fiscal year: $12,044 per student. Total enrollment: 3,517. Faculty: 467 (156 full-time, 311 part-time). Student-undergrad faculty ratio is 11:1. 4,758 applied, 76% were admitted. 14% from top 10% of their high school class, 41% from top quarter, 74% from top half. Full-time: 2,424 students, 62% women, 38% men. Part-time: 206 students, 34% women, 66% men. 27% from out-of-state. 0.3% American Indian or Alaska Native, non-Hispanic/Latino; 15% Hispanic/ Latino; 13% Black or African American, non-Hispanic/Latino; 5% Asian, non-Hispanic/Latino; 2% international. 11% 25 or older, 56% live on campus, 6% transferred in. Retention: 85% of full-time freshmen returned the following year. Academic areas with the most degrees conferred: business/marketing; health professions and related sciences; communication/journalism. Core. Calendar: semesters. ESL program, services for LD students, advanced placement, accelerated degree program, freshman honors college, honors program, independent study, distance learning, double major, summer session for credit, part-time degree program, adult/continuing education programs, co-op programs and internships, graduate courses open to undergrads. Study abroad program. ROTC: Army (c), Air Force (c).

Entrance Requirements: Options: electronic application, early decision, early action, deferred admission, international baccalaureate accepted. Required: essay, high school transcript, 2 recommendations. Recommended: interview. Required for some: SAT or ACT. Entrance: moderately difficult. Application deadline: 2/15. Notification: continuous. Transfer credits accepted: Yes. Early decision applicants: 34. Early decision applicants admitted: 23.

Costs Per Year: Application fee: $50. Comprehensive fee: $61,880 includes full-time tuition ($43,624), mandatory fees ($1656), and college room and board ($16,600). Full-time tuition and fees vary according to location. Room and board charges vary according to board plan, housing facility, location, and student level. Part-time tuition: $1251 per credit hour. Part-time tuition varies according to course load and location.

Collegiate Environment: Orientation program. Drama-theater group, choral group, student-run newspaper, radio station. Social organizations: 51 open to all; national fraternities, national sororities, local fraternities, local sororities; 7% of eligible men and 11% of eligible women are members. Most

popular organizations: Lubin Business Association, National Student Nurses Association, Future Leaders in Healthcare, Black Student Union, Accounting Society. Major annual events: Homecoming and Family Weekend, P4Kids Dance Marathon, Relay for Life. Student services: health clinic, personal-psychological counseling. Campus security: 24-hour emergency response devices and patrols, late night transport-escort service, controlled dormitory access. Freshmen guaranteed college housing. Option: coed housing available. Edward and Doris Mortola Library. Books: 167,456 (physical), 224,418 (digital/electronic); Serial titles: 34 (physical), 576,860 (digital/electronic); Databases: 172. Weekly public service hours: 113; students can reserve study rooms. Operations spending for the previous fiscal year: $7.3 million. 132 computers available on campus for general student use. A campuswide network can be accessed. Students can access the following: online class registration, administrative functions (tuition, student records, financial aid, health insurance waiver). Staffed computer lab on campus.

■ PARSONS SCHOOL OF DESIGN

66 Fifth Ave.
New York, NY 10011
Tel: (212)229-8900; Free: 800-292-3040
Fax: (212)229-8975
E-mail: stinee@newschool.edu
Web Site: www.newschool.edu/parsons

Description: Independent, comprehensive, coed. Part of The New School. Awards associate, bachelor's, and master's degrees. Founded 1896. Setting: urban campus with easy access to New York City. System endowment: $322.3 million. Research spending for the previous fiscal year: $15.7 million. Educational spending for the previous fiscal year: $14,455 per student. Total enrollment: 5,278. Faculty: 993 (159 full-time, 834 part-time). Student-undergrad faculty ratio is 11:1. 4,825 applied, 51% were admitted. 17% from top 10% of their high school class, 31% from top quarter, 82% from top half. Full-time: 3,859 students, 78% women, 22% men. Part-time: 432 students, 81% women, 19% men. Students come from 51 states and territories, 102 other countries, 75% from out-of-state. 0.1% American Indian or Alaska Native, non-Hispanic/Latino; 10% Hispanic/Latino; 4% Black or African American, non-Hispanic/Latino; 13% Asian, non-Hispanic/Latino; 0.1% Native Hawaiian or other Pacific Islander, non-Hispanic/Latino; 44% international. 16% 25 or older, 25% live on campus, 7% transferred in. Retention: 88% of full-time freshmen returned the following year. Academic areas with the most degrees conferred: visual and performing arts; computer and information sciences; architecture. Core. Calendar: semesters. Academic remediation for entering students, ESL program, services for LD students, advanced placement, accelerated degree program, self-designed majors, independent study, distance learning, double major, summer session for credit, part-time degree program, co-op programs and internships, graduate courses open to undergrads. Off campus study at Association of Independent Colleges of Art and Design. Study abroad program.

Entrance Requirements: Options: electronic application, early action, deferred admission, international baccalaureate accepted. Required: essay, high school transcript, 2 recommendations, online application, Parsons Challenge portfolio, artist statement. Recommended: minimum 3 high school GPA. Required for some: TOEFL/IELTS /PTE for students whose native language is not English. Entrance: moderately difficult. Application deadlines: 1/15, 11/1 for early action. Notification: continuous until 3/15, 3/15 for early action. Transfer credits accepted: Yes. Early action applicants: 688. Early action applicants admitted: 557.

Collegiate Environment: Orientation program. Drama-theater group, choral group, student-run newspaper. Social organizations: 43 open to all. Major annual events: block party, Bell Hooks + Jill Soloway at the New School, Frank Stella at the Parsons Table. Student services: health clinic, personal-psychological counseling. Campus security: 24-hour emergency response devices, controlled dormitory access, 24-hour security desk personnel. New School Libraries & Archives plus 3 others. Books: 215,937 (physical), 840,933 (digital/electronic); Serial titles: 2,265 (physical), 113,452 (digital/ electronic); Databases: 376. Weekly public service hours: 155; study areas open 24 hours, 5-7 days a week; students can reserve study rooms. Operations spending for the previous fiscal year: $1.1 million. 717 computers available on campus for general student use. A computer is required for all students. A campuswide network can be accessed from student residence rooms and from off campus. Students can access the following: online class registration. Staffed computer lab on campus (open 24 hours a day) provides training in use of computers, software, and the Internet.

■ PAUL SMITH'S COLLEGE
PO Box 265
Paul Smiths, NY 12970-0265
Tel: (518)327-6000; Free: 800-421-2605
Fax: (518)327-6060
E-mail: admissions@paulsmiths.edu
Web Site: www.paulsmiths.edu
Description: Independent, 4-year, coed. Awards associate and bachelor's degrees. Founded 1937. Setting: 14,200-acre rural campus. Endowment: $18.7 million. Research spending for the previous fiscal year: $80,900. Educational spending for the previous fiscal year: $6400 per student. Total enrollment: 875. Faculty: 83 (57 full-time, 26 part-time). Student-undergrad faculty ratio is 14:1. 1,103 applied, 73% were admitted. 5% from top 10% of their high school class, 17% from top quarter, 44% from top half. Full-time: 302 students, 38% women, 62% men. Part-time: 4 students, 50% women, 50% men. 85% live on campus, 17% transferred in. Core. Calendar: semesters. Academic remediation for entering students, services for LD students, advanced placement, honors program, double major, summer session for credit, adult/continuing education programs, co-op programs and internships. Study abroad program.
Entrance Requirements: Options: electronic application, deferred admission. Required: high school transcript. Recommended: essay, 2 recommendations, interview. Required for some: interview. Entrance: minimally difficult. Application deadline: rolling.
Costs Per Year: Application fee: $30. Comprehensive fee: $42,292 includes full-time tuition ($28,420), mandatory fees ($32), and college room and board ($13,840). College room only: $8240. Full-time tuition and fees vary according to reciprocity agreements. Room and board charges vary according to board plan and housing facility.
Collegiate Environment: Orientation program. Student-run newspaper, radio station. Social organizations: 30 open to all. Most popular organizations: Forestry Club, Junior American Culinary, Wildlife Society, Fish and Game Club, Koinonia. Major annual events: Parents' Weekend, Winter Carnival, Winter Weekend. Student services: health clinic, personal-psychological counseling. Campus security: 24-hour emergency response devices and patrols, controlled dormitory access. Joan Weill Adirondack Library. Operations spending for the previous fiscal year: $1 million. 300 computers available on campus for general student use. A campuswide network can be accessed from student residence rooms and from off campus. Students can access the following: online class registration.

■ PHILLIPS BETH ISRAEL SCHOOL OF NURSING
776 6th Ave.
Ste. 4
New York, NY 10001
Tel: (212)614-6110
Fax: (212)614-6109
E-mail: bstern@chpnet.org
Web Site: www.mountsinai.org/locations/beth-israel/pson
Description: Independent, primarily 2-year, coed. Awards transfer associate, terminal associate, and bachelor's degrees. Founded 1904. Setting: urban campus. Endowment: $750,000. Educational spending for the previous fiscal year: $6000 per student. Total enrollment: 254. Faculty: 30 (10 full-time, 20 part-time). Student-undergrad faculty ratio is 8:1. 67 applied, 3% were admitted. 20% from top 10% of their high school class, 80% from top quarter, 100% from top half. Full-time: 34 students, 74% women, 26% men. Part-time: 220 students, 80% women, 20% men. Students come from 7 states and territories, 5 other countries, 15% from out-of-state. 14% Hispanic/Latino; 30% Black or African American, non-Hispanic/Latino; 15% Asian, non-Hispanic/Latino; 7% Native Hawaiian or other Pacific Islander, non-Hispanic/Latino; 0.4% international. 65% 25 or older, 35% transferred in. Retention: 84% of full-time freshmen returned the following year. Core. Calendar: semesters. Academic remediation for entering students, services for LD students, advanced placement, accelerated degree program, honors program, distance learning, summer session for credit, part-time degree program. Off campus study at Pace University. Study abroad program.
Entrance Requirements: Options: deferred admission, international baccalaureate accepted. Required: essay, high school transcript, minimum 2.5 high school GPA, 2 recommendations, interview. Recommended: SAT. Entrance: moderately difficult. Application deadline: 4/1. Notification: continuous. Transfer credits accepted: Yes.
Collegiate Environment: Orientation program. Choral group, student-run newspaper. Social organizations: 2 open to all. Most popular organizations: Student Government Organization, National Student Nurses Association.

Major annual events: Holiday Party, Senior Luncheon, Senior Gala. Student services: health clinic, personal-psychological counseling. Campus security: 24-hour emergency response devices. Phillips Health Science Library. Books: 400 (physical), 25 (digital/electronic); Databases: 10. Operations spending for the previous fiscal year: $150,000. 40 computers available on campus for general student use. A computer is required for all students. Students can access the following: online class registration. Staffed computer lab on campus provides training in use of computers, software, and the Internet.

■ PLAZA COLLEGE
118-33 Queens Blvd.
Forest Hills, NY 11375
Tel: (718)779-1430
Fax: (718)779-1456
E-mail: info@plazacollege.edu
Web Site: www.plazacollege.edu
Description: Proprietary, primarily 2-year, coed. Awards certificates, transfer associate, terminal associate, and bachelor's degrees. Founded 1916. Setting: urban campus with easy access to New York City. Total enrollment: 726. Core. Calendar: semesters. Academic remediation for entering students, ESL program, services for LD students, summer session for credit, internships.
Entrance Requirements: Required: essay, interview, ACT Compass. Required for some: 2 recommendations. Entrance: moderately difficult. Application deadline: rolling. Transfer credits accepted: Yes.
Collegiate Environment: Orientation program. Drama-theater group. Most popular organizations: Ambassadors Club, VDAY, Performing Arts Society, Plaza College Psychology Society, Plaza College Social Media Society. Campus security: 24-hour emergency response devices.

■ PRATT INSTITUTE
200 Willoughby Ave.
Brooklyn, NY 11205-3899
Tel: (718)636-3600; Free: 800-331-0834
Fax: (718)636-3670
E-mail: visit@pratt.edu
Web Site: www.pratt.edu
Description: Independent, comprehensive, coed. Awards associate, bachelor's, and master's degrees and post-master's certificates. Founded 1887. Setting: 25-acre urban campus. Total enrollment: 4,829. Faculty: 1,148 (157 full-time, 991 part-time). Student-undergrad faculty ratio is 10:1. 6,044 applied, 50% were admitted. Full-time: 3,331 students, 70% women, 30% men. Part-time: 108 students, 67% women, 33% men. 72% from out-of-state. 10% Hispanic/Latino; 4% Black or African American, non-Hispanic/Latino; 13% Asian, non-Hispanic/Latino; 0.1% Native Hawaiian or other Pacific Islander, non-Hispanic/Latino; 30% international. 5% 25 or older, 53% live on campus, 4% transferred in. Retention: 88% of full-time freshmen returned the following year. Academic areas with the most degrees conferred: visual and performing arts; architecture; liberal arts/general studies. Calendar: semesters plus optional May term and summer session. Part-time degree program. ROTC: Army (c).
Entrance Requirements: Options: electronic application, early action, deferred admission, international baccalaureate accepted. Required: essay, high school transcript, 1 recommendation, SAT or ACT. Recommended: minimum 3 high school GPA. Required for some: portfolio, SAT Subject Tests. Entrance: very difficult. SAT Reasoning Test deadline: 2/1. SAT Subject Test deadline: 2/1. Applicants placed on waiting list: 2,038. Wait-listed applicants offered admission: 93.
Costs Per Year: Application fee: $50. Comprehensive fee: $64,492 includes full-time tuition ($49,810), mandatory fees ($2060), and college room and board ($12,622). College room only: $8862. Room and board charges vary according to board plan and housing facility. Part-time tuition: $1607 per credit hour.
Collegiate Environment: Orientation program. Campus security: 24-hour emergency response devices and patrols, late night transport-escort service. Pratt Institute Library.

■ PURCHASE COLLEGE, STATE UNIVERSITY OF NEW YORK
735 Anderson Hill Rd.
Purchase, NY 10577-1400
Tel: (914)251-6000
E-mail: admission@purchase.edu
Web Site: www.purchase.edu

Description: State-supported, comprehensive, coed. Part of State University of New York System. Awards bachelor's and master's degrees and post-master's certificates. Founded 1967. Setting: 500-acre small town campus with easy access to New York City. Total enrollment: 4,263. Faculty: 466 (183 full-time, 283 part-time). Student-undergrad faculty ratio is 14:1. 3,421 applied, 42% were admitted. Full-time: 3,833 students, 59% women, 41% men. Part-time: 330 students, 57% women, 43% men. Students come from 42 states and territories, 30 other countries, 13% from out-of-state. 0.3% American Indian or Alaska Native, non-Hispanic/Latino; 19% Hispanic/Latino; 11% Black or African American, non-Hispanic/Latino; 4% Asian, non-Hispanic/Latino; 0.2% Native Hawaiian or other Pacific Islander, non-Hispanic/Latino; 2% international. 8% 25 or older, 68% live on campus, 9% transferred in. Retention: 81% of full-time freshmen returned the following year. Academic areas with the most degrees conferred: visual and performing arts; liberal arts/general studies; social sciences. Core. Calendar: semesters. Academic remediation for entering students, ESL program, services for LD students, advanced placement, self-designed majors, independent study, double major, summer session for credit, part-time degree program, adult/continuing education programs, internships. Off campus study at Manhattanville College and every other SUNY institution. Study abroad program.

Entrance Requirements: Options: electronic application, early admission, early action, deferred admission. Required: high school transcript, minimum 3 high school GPA. Required for some: essay, 1 recommendation, interview, audition, portfolio. Entrance: moderately difficult. Application deadlines: 5/15, 5/15 for nonresidents, 11/15 for early action. Notification: continuous until 5/1, continuous for nonresidents, rolling for early action. SAT Reasoning Test deadline: 7/1. Transfer credits accepted: Yes.

Costs Per Year: Application fee: $50. One-time mandatory fee: $210. State resident tuition: $6870 full-time, $286 per credit hour part-time. Nonresident tuition: $16,650 full-time, $694 per credit hour part-time. Mandatory fees: $1828 full-time, $74.72 per credit hour part-time. Part-time tuition and fees vary according to course load. College room and board: $13,764. College room only: $8924. Room and board charges vary according to board plan and housing facility.

Collegiate Environment: Orientation program. Drama-theater group, choral group, student-run newspaper, radio station. Social organizations: 40 open to all. Most popular organizations: Student Union, WPUR radio station, Latinos Unidos, Gay/Lesbian/Bisexual/Transgender Union, Organization of African People in America. Major annual events: Culture Shock, Fall Ball, Pancake Madness. Student services: health clinic, personal-psychological counseling, women's center. Campus security: 24-hour emergency response devices and patrols, late night transport-escort service, controlled dormitory access, 24-hour patrols by police officers. 2,736 college housing spaces available. Freshmen given priority for college housing. Option: coed housing available. Purchase College Library plus 1 other. Books: 237,710 (physical), 11,422 (digital/electronic); Serial titles: 107 (physical), 65,714 (digital/electronic); Databases: 176. 600 computers available on campus for general student use. A campuswide network can be accessed from student residence rooms and from off campus. Students can access the following: online class registration, CNC-routers; 3D printers; Laser cutters; Vinyl Printers; a Virtual Reality Lab; a fabrication lab; Non-liner edit labs for film; Music Digital Audio Workstations, 24 and 48.

■ **QUEENS COLLEGE OF THE CITY UNIVERSITY OF NEW YORK**
65-30 Kissena Blvd.
Queens, NY 11367-1597
Tel: (718)997-5000
Fax: (718)997-5617
Web Site: www.qc.cuny.edu

Description: State and locally supported, comprehensive, coed. Part of City University of New York. Awards bachelor's and master's degrees and post-master's certificates. Founded 1937. Setting: 80-acre urban campus with easy access to New York City. Endowment: $55.5 million. Research spending for the previous fiscal year: $19.9 million. Educational spending for the previous fiscal year: $10,041 per student. Total enrollment: 19,746. Faculty: 1,629 (589 full-time, 1,040 part-time). Student-undergrad faculty ratio is 15:1. 18,862 applied, 48% were admitted. Full-time: 12,201 students, 54% women, 46% men. Part-time: 4,419 students, 55% women, 45% men. Students come from 23 states and territories, 145 other countries, 1% from out-of-state. 0.4% American Indian or Alaska Native, non-Hispanic/Latino; 29% Hispanic/Latino; 8% Black or African American, non-Hispanic/Latino; 29% Asian, non-Hispanic/Latino; 0.4% Native Hawaiian or other Pacific Islander, non-Hispanic/Latino; 6% international. 25% 25 or older, 2% live on

campus, 13% transferred in. Retention: 84% of full-time freshmen returned the following year. Academic areas with the most degrees conferred: social sciences; psychology; business/marketing. Core. Calendar: semesters. ESL program, services for LD students, advanced placement, accelerated degree program, honors program, independent study, double major, summer session for credit, part-time degree program, adult/continuing education programs, co-op programs and internships, graduate courses open to undergrads. Off campus study at other units of the City University of New York System. Study abroad program. ROTC: Army (c).

Entrance Requirements: Options: electronic application, deferred admission. Required: high school transcript, minimum 3 high school GPA, SAT or ACT. Required for some: essay, SAT Subject Tests. Entrance: very difficult. Application deadline: 2/1. Notification: 2/1. SAT Reasoning Test deadline: 2/1. Transfer credits accepted: Yes.

Costs Per Year: Application fee: $65. State resident tuition: $6730 full-time, $295 per credit part-time. Nonresident tuition: $18,000 full-time, $600 per credit part-time. Mandatory fees: $608 full-time, $208.85 per term part-time. Full-time tuition and fees vary according to course load. Part-time tuition and fees vary according to course load.

Collegiate Environment: Orientation program. Drama-theater group, choral group, student-run newspaper, radio station. Social organizations: 124 open to all; national fraternities, national sororities, local fraternities; 1% of eligible men and 1% of eligible women are members. Most popular organizations: Science Fiction and Animation, Chabad of QC, La Tertulia, PRISM: The Sexuality and Gender Alliance of QC, Muslim Students Association. Major annual events: Welcome Day, Orientation, Career Fair. Student services: health clinic, personal-psychological counseling. Campus security: 24-hour emergency response devices and patrols, controlled dormitory access. 498 college housing spaces available; 343 were occupied in 2018-19. No special consideration for freshman housing applicants. Option: coed housing available. The Benjamin S. Rosenthal Library plus 1 other. Books: 842,531 (physical), 405,360 (digital/electronic); Serial titles: 198 (physical), 226,727 (digital/electronic); Databases: 291. Weekly public service hours: 94; students can reserve study rooms. Operations spending for the previous fiscal year: $54,489. 2,477 computers available on campus for general student use. A campuswide network can be accessed from student residence rooms and from off campus. Students can access the following: online class registration. Staffed computer lab on campus.

■ **QUEENSBOROUGH COMMUNITY COLLEGE OF THE CITY UNIVERSITY OF NEW YORK**
222-05 56th Ave.
Bayside, NY 11364
Tel: (718)631-6262
Fax: (718)281-5189
E-mail: admissions@qcc.cuny.edu
Web Site: www.qcc.cuny.edu

Description: State and locally supported, 2-year, coed. Part of City University of New York. Awards certificates, transfer associate, and terminal associate degrees. Founded 1958. Setting: 37-acre urban campus with easy access to New York City. Total enrollment: 15,411. Faculty: 888 (438 full-time, 467 part-time). Student-undergrad faculty ratio is 20:1. 12,076 applied, 98% were admitted. Full-time: 9,232 students, 50% women, 50% men. Part-time: 6,179 students, 57% women, 43% men. Students come from 7 states and territories, 127 other countries, 2% from out-of-state. 1% American Indian or Alaska Native, non-Hispanic/Latino; 33% Hispanic/Latino; 24% Black or African American, non-Hispanic/Latino; 22% Asian, non-Hispanic/Latino; 0.7% Native Hawaiian or other Pacific Islander, non-Hispanic/Latino; 6% international. 24% 25 or older, 6% transferred in. Retention: 64% of full-time freshmen returned the following year. Core. Calendar: semesters. Academic remediation for entering students, ESL program, services for LD students, advanced placement, accelerated degree program, self-designed majors, honors program, independent study, distance learning, double major, summer session for credit, part-time degree program, co-op programs and internships. Off campus study at Any other institution within the City University of New York. Study abroad program. ROTC: Army (c).

Entrance Requirements: Open admission Different policies exist for home-schooled and out-of-state applicants. Contact our Admissions Office for more information. Options: electronic application, deferred admission, international baccalaureate accepted. Required: high school transcript. Required for some: A New York State High School Equivalency Diploma (GED/TASC) is required in lieu of high school diploma. Entrance: noncompetitive. Application deadline: 2/1. Notification: continuous. Transfer credits accepted: Yes.

Costs Per Year: Application fee: $65. State resident tuition: $4800 full-time, $210 per credit part-time. Nonresident tuition: $9600 full-time, $320 per credit part-time. Mandatory fees: $409 full-time, $106 per term part-time. Full-time tuition and fees vary according to course load. Part-time tuition and fees vary according to course load.

Collegiate Environment: Orientation program. Drama-theater group, choral group, student-run newspaper. Social organizations: 53 open to all. Most popular organizations: Phi Theta kappa, Student Organization for Disability Awareness (SODA), ASAP Club, CSTEP Club, Chemistry Club. Major annual events: Welcome Back/Club Fair Event, Transfer Day, Job Fair. Student services: legal services, health clinic, personal-psychological counseling. Campus security: 24-hour emergency response devices and patrols. College housing not available. The Kurt R. Schmeller Library. Books: 109,962 (physical), 581,791 (digital/electronic); Serial titles: 1,195 (physical), 103,782 (digital/electronic); Databases: 145. Weekly public service hours: 78. 72 computers available on campus for general student use. A campuswide network can be accessed. Students can access the following: online class registration. Staffed computer lab on campus.

■ **RABBINICAL ACADEMY MESIVTA RABBI CHAIM BERLIN**
1605 Coney Island Ave.
Brooklyn, NY 11230-4715
Tel: (718)377-0777
Description: Independent Jewish, comprehensive, men only. Awards bachelor's and master's degrees. Founded 1939. Total enrollment: 243. 20 applied, 100% were admitted. 10% 25 or older. Core. Calendar: semesters. Academic remediation for entering students, services for LD students.
Entrance Requirements: Entrance: moderately difficult.
Collegiate Environment: Student services: personal-psychological counseling.

■ **RABBINICAL COLLEGE BETH SHRAGA**
28 Saddle River Rd.
Monsey, NY 10952-3035
Tel: (914)356-1980
Description: Independent Jewish, comprehensive, men only. Awards bachelor's and master's degrees. Founded 1965. Setting: small town campus. Total enrollment: 42. 10 applied, 100% were admitted. Calendar: semesters.

■ **RABBINICAL COLLEGE BOBOVER YESHIVA B'NEI ZION**
1577 Forty-eighth St.
Brooklyn, NY 11219
Tel: (718)438-2018
Description: Independent Jewish, comprehensive, men only. Awards bachelor's and master's degrees. Founded 1947. Total enrollment: 235. Core. Calendar: semesters.
Entrance Requirements: Entrance: moderately difficult.

■ **RABBINICAL COLLEGE OF LONG ISLAND**
205 W Beech St.
Long Beach, NY 11561-3305
Tel: (516)431-7414
Description: Independent Jewish, comprehensive, men only. Awards bachelor's and master's degrees. Founded 1965. Setting: small town campus. Total enrollment: 145. 40 applied, 100% were admitted. Calendar: semesters.

■ **RABBINICAL COLLEGE OF OHR SHIMON YISROEL**
215-217 Hewes St.
Brooklyn, NY 11211
Tel: (718)855-4092
Description: Independent Jewish, 4-year, men only. Awards bachelor's degrees. Total enrollment: 186. 175 applied. 6% 25 or older.

■ **RABBINICAL COLLEGE OHR YISROEL**
8800 Seaview Ave.
Brooklyn, NY 11236
Web Site: www.rabbinicalcollegeohryisroel.com
Description: Independent Jewish, 4-year, coed.

■ **RABBINICAL SEMINARY OF AMERICA**
76-01 147th St.
Flushing, NY 11367

Tel: (718)268-4700
Description: Independent Jewish, comprehensive, men only. Awards bachelor's, master's, and doctoral degrees. Founded 1933. Setting: urban campus with easy access to New York City. Total enrollment: 516. 105 applied. 3% 25 or older, 90% live on campus. Core. Calendar: semesters. Academic remediation for entering students, honors program, adult/continuing education programs. Study abroad program.
Entrance Requirements: Option: early admission. Required: high school transcript, interview. Entrance: very difficult. Application deadline: 12/1. Notification: continuous.
Collegiate Environment: Student services: personal-psychological counseling. Rabbinical Seminary of America Otzar HaSeforim Library plus 3 others.
Community Environment: See Queens College of the City University of New York.

■ **RENSSELAER POLYTECHNIC INSTITUTE**
110 8th St.
Troy, NY 12180-3590
Tel: (518)276-6000
Fax: (518)276-4072
E-mail: admissions@rpi.edu
Web Site: www.rpi.edu
Description: Independent, university, coed. Awards bachelor's, master's, and doctoral degrees. Founded 1824. Setting: 284-acre suburban campus with easy access to Albany, NY. Endowment: $673.7 million. Research spending for the previous fiscal year: $111.9 million. Educational spending for the previous fiscal year: $20,149 per student. Total enrollment: 7,633. Faculty: 517 (467 full-time, 50 part-time). Student-undergrad faculty ratio is 13:1. 19,505 applied, 43% were admitted. 63% from top 10% of their high school class, 91% from top quarter, 98% from top half. 32 National Merit Scholars, 43 valedictorians. Full-time: 6,340 students, 32% women, 68% men. Part-time: 26 students, 38% women, 62% men. Students come from 50 states and territories, 39 other countries, 67% from out-of-state. 0.1% American Indian or Alaska Native, non-Hispanic/Latino; 9% Hispanic/Latino; 4% Black or African American, non-Hispanic/Latino; 12% Asian, non-Hispanic/Latino; 14% international. 1% 25 or older, 57% live on campus, 2% transferred in. Retention: 93% of full-time freshmen returned the following year. Academic areas with the most degrees conferred: engineering; computer and information sciences; business/marketing; engineering technologies; mathematics and statistics. Core. Calendar: semesters. ESL program, services for LD students, advanced placement, accelerated degree program, self-designed majors, honors program, independent study, double major, summer session for credit, part-time degree program, adult/continuing education programs, co-op programs and internships, graduate courses open to undergrads. Off campus study at Williams College, Harvey Mudd College. Study abroad program. ROTC: Army, Naval, Air Force.
Entrance Requirements: Options: electronic application, early admission, early decision, deferred admission, international baccalaureate accepted. Required: SAT or ACT. Recommended: minimum 3 high school GPA, 1 recommendation. Required for some: essay, high school transcript, interview, portfolio for electronic arts, SAT and SAT Subject Tests or ACT. Entrance: very difficult. Application deadlines: 1/15, 11/1 for early decision plan 1, 12/15 for early decision plan 2. Notification: 3/12, 12/10 for early decision plan 1, 1/14 for early decision plan 2. SAT Reasoning Test deadline: 12/31. Applicants placed on waiting list: 4,803. Wait-listed applicants offered admission: 22. Early decision applicants: 903. Early decision applicants admitted: 516.
Costs Per Year: Application fee: $70. Comprehensive fee: $69,140 includes full-time tuition ($52,550), mandatory fees ($1330), and college room and board ($15,260). College room only: $8650. Room and board charges vary according to board plan and location. Part-time tuition: $1640 per credit hour.
Collegiate Environment: Orientation program. Drama-theater group, choral group, student-run newspaper, radio station. Social organizations: 229 open to all; national fraternities, national sororities, local fraternities, local sororities; 21% of eligible men and 16% of eligible women are members. Most popular organizations: Red Army Spirit Club, Outing Club, Indian Student Association, Chinese American Student Association, pep band. Major annual events: Grand Marshal Week, Big Red Freakout, Fall Fest Weekend. Student services: legal services, health clinic, personal-psychological counseling, women's center. Campus security: 24-hour emergency response devices and patrols, late night transport-escort service, controlled dormitory access, campus foot patrols at night. Folsom Library plus 2 others. Students can reserve study rooms. Operations spending for the previous fiscal year: $3.7 million.

Community Environment: Troy, a city of 55,000, located at the head of navigation on the Hudson River, is an important industrial city and the eastern terminus of the New York State Barge Canal. The city, within 15 miles of Albany and Schenectady, is served by air, bus, and rail lines, houses of worship, 3 hospitals, and various civic, fraternal, and veteran's organizations. There are numerous opportunities for part-time student employment.

■ ROBERTS WESLEYAN COLLEGE

2301 Westside Dr.
Rochester, NY 14624-1997
Tel: (585)594-6000; Free: 800-777-4RWC
Fax: (585)594-6371
E-mail: admissions@roberts.edu
Web Site: www.roberts.edu

Description: Independent, comprehensive, coed, affiliated with Free Methodist Church of North America. Awards bachelor's, master's, and doctoral degrees. Founded 1866. Setting: 188-acre suburban campus with easy access to Rochester. Endowment: $24.2 million. Educational spending for the previous fiscal year: $10,388 per student. Total enrollment: 1,740. Faculty: 249 (90 full-time, 159 part-time). Student-undergrad faculty ratio is 12:1. 1,330 applied, 69% were admitted. 20% from top 10% of their high school class, 48% from top quarter, 83% from top half. Full-time: 1,248 students, 69% women, 31% men. Part-time: 73 students, 68% women, 32% men. Students come from 27 states and territories, 28 other countries, 8% from out-of-state. 0.2% American Indian or Alaska Native, non-Hispanic/Latino; 6% Hispanic/Latino; 9% Black or African American, non-Hispanic/Latino; 2% Asian, non-Hispanic/Latino; 0.2% Native Hawaiian or other Pacific Islander, non-Hispanic/Latino; 4% international. 27% 25 or older, 61% live on campus, 6% transferred in. Retention: 82% of full-time freshmen returned the following year. Academic areas with the most degrees conferred: health professions and related sciences; business/marketing; education. Core. Calendar: semesters. Academic remediation for entering students, ESL program, services for LD students, advanced placement, accelerated degree program, self-designed majors, honors program, independent study, distance learning, double major, summer session for credit, adult/continuing education programs, internships, graduate courses open to undergrads. Off campus study at Rochester Area Colleges, Council of Christian Colleges and Universities. Study abroad program. ROTC: Army (c), Air Force (c).

Entrance Requirements: Options: electronic application, early admission, early action, deferred admission. Required: essay, high school transcript, SAT or ACT. Recommended: minimum 2.7 high school GPA, interview. Entrance: moderately difficult. Application deadlines: 8/20, 11/15 for early action. Notification: continuous until 9/1, 12/6 for early action. Transfer credits accepted: Yes. Early action applicants: 0. Early action applicants admitted: 0.

Costs Per Year: Application fee: $0. One-time mandatory fee: $250. Comprehensive fee: $42,188 includes full-time tuition ($30,458), mandatory fees ($1110), and college room and board ($10,620). College room only: $6630. Room and board charges vary according to board plan and housing facility.

Collegiate Environment: Orientation program. Drama-theater group, choral group, student-run newspaper. Social organizations: 43 open to all. Most popular organizations: Intramurals, Foot of the Cross, Fellowship of Christian Athletes, Nursing Club, Drama Club. Major annual events: Spring Formal, LIVE (student variety show), Homecoming/Parents and Friends Weekend. Student services: health clinic, personal-psychological counseling. Campus security: 24-hour emergency response devices and patrols, student patrols, late night transport-escort service, controlled dormitory access, 24-hour Resident Life staff on-call. B. Thomas Golisano Library. Books: 128,708 (physical), 6,200 (digital/electronic); Databases: 105. Study areas open 24 hours, 5-7 days a week; students can reserve study rooms. Operations spending for the previous fiscal year: $953,578. 140 computers available on campus for general student use. A campuswide network can be accessed from student residence rooms and from off campus. Students can access the following: online class registration. Staffed computer lab on campus (open 24 hours a day) provides training in use of computers, software, and the Internet.

Community Environment: North Chili is a suburb of Rochester, New York. A municipal airport and bus service and railroad provide transportation to Rochester which has all major transportation facilities, as well as community services, public library, museums, art gallery, and hospitals. Part-time employment is available for students. Local recreational facilities include skiing, skating, tennis, swimming and golf.

■ ROCHESTER INSTITUTE OF TECHNOLOGY

One Lomb Memorial Dr.
Rochester, NY 14623-5603
Tel: (585)475-2411
Fax: (585)475-7424
E-mail: admissions@rit.edu
Web Site: www.rit.edu

Description: Independent, university, coed. Awards associate, bachelor's, master's, and doctoral degrees. Founded 1829. Setting: 1,300-acre suburban campus with easy access to Rochester. Endowment: $938.2 million. Educational spending for the previous fiscal year: $12,059 per student. Total enrollment: 16,463. Faculty: 1,425 (1,045 full-time, 380 part-time). Student-undergrad faculty ratio is 13:1. 19,335 applied, 66% were admitted. 37% from top 10% of their high school class, 73% from top quarter, 95% from top half. Full-time: 12,486 students, 33% women, 67% men. Part-time: 1,027 students, 28% women, 72% men. Students come from 52 states and territories, 67 other countries, 46% from out-of-state. 0.1% American Indian or Alaska Native, non-Hispanic/Latino; 7% Hispanic/Latino; 4% Black or African American, non-Hispanic/Latino; 9% Asian, non-Hispanic/Latino; 6% international. 5% 25 or older, 52% live on campus, 4% transferred in. Retention: 89% of full-time freshmen returned the following year. Academic areas with the most degrees conferred: engineering; computer and information sciences; visual and performing arts. Core. Calendar: semesters. ESL program, services for LD students, advanced placement, accelerated degree program, self-designed majors, honors program, independent study, distance learning, double major, summer session for credit, part-time degree program, adult/continuing education programs, co-op programs and internships, graduate courses open to undergrads. Off campus study at Rochester Area Colleges. Study abroad program. ROTC: Army, Naval (c), Air Force.

Entrance Requirements: Options: electronic application, early admission, early decision, deferred admission, international baccalaureate accepted. Required: essay, high school transcript, SAT or ACT. Recommended: minimum 3.4 high school GPA, 1 recommendation, interview. Required for some: portfolio of original artwork for School of Art, Design and Crafts; interview for BS/MS physician assistant program. Entrance: moderately difficult. Application deadlines: 1/15, 11/15 for early decision plan 1, 1/1 for early decision plan 2. Notification: continuous until 2/15, 12/15 for early decision. SAT Reasoning Test deadline: 6/1. Transfer credits accepted: Yes. Early decision applicants: 1,180. Early decision applicants admitted: 943.

Costs Per Year: Application fee: $65. Comprehensive fee: $57,176 includes full-time tuition ($43,546), mandatory fees ($584), and college room and board ($13,046). College room only: $7598. Full-time tuition and fees vary according to course load and student level. Room and board charges vary according to board plan and housing facility. Part-time mandatory fees: $72 per term. Part-time fees vary according to class time and course load.

Collegiate Environment: Orientation program. Drama-theater group, choral group, student-run newspaper, radio station. Social organizations: 305 open to all; national fraternities, national sororities, local fraternities, local sororities; 5% of eligible men and 6% of eligible women are members. Major annual events: Brick City Festival (fall/parents' weekend), Freezefest (Winter Weekend), Creativity and Innovation Festival/Spring Weekend. Student services: legal services, health clinic, personal-psychological counseling, women's center. Campus security: 24-hour emergency response devices and patrols, student patrols, late night transport-escort service, controlled dormitory access. 7,144 college housing spaces available. Freshmen guaranteed college housing. On-campus residence required in freshman year. Options: coed, men-only, women-only housing available. Wallace Memorial Library. Books: 429,176 (physical), 240,712 (digital/electronic); Serial titles: 58,293 (digital/electronic); Databases: 113. Weekly public service hours: 147; study areas open 24 hours, 5-7 days a week; students can reserve study rooms. 3,500 computers available on campus for general student use. Computer purchase/lease plans available. A campuswide network can be accessed from student residence rooms and from off campus. Students can access the following: online class registration, student account information. Staffed computer lab on campus provides training in use of computers, software, and the Internet.

Community Environment: The Greater Rochester area - the city and its immediate suburbs - has a population of about 1,100,000. Per capital income is among the highest for metropolitan areas in the nation. The area's many internationally known industries employ a high proportion of scientists, technologists and skilled workers. Rochester is the world center of photography, the largest producer of optical goods in the United States, and among the leaders in graphic arts and reproduction and in production of electronic equipment and precision instruments. Rochester's industries have always been closely associated with RIT's programs and progress to the mutual benefit of all.

■ **ROCKLAND COMMUNITY COLLEGE**
145 College Rd.
Suffern, NY 10901-3699
Tel: (845)574-4000; Free: 800-722-7666
Web Site: www.sunyrockland.edu
Description: State and locally supported, 2-year, coed. Part of State University of New York System. Awards certificates, transfer associate, and terminal associate degrees. Founded 1959. Setting: 150-acre suburban campus with easy access to New York City. Total enrollment: 7,434. Faculty: 490 (113 full-time, 377 part-time). Student-undergrad faculty ratio is 22:1. 1,471 applied, 100% were admitted. Full-time: 4,189 students, 47% women, 53% men. Part-time: 3,245 students, 61% women, 39% men. Students come from 5 states and territories, 78 other countries, 1% from out-of-state. 0.2% American Indian or Alaska Native, non-Hispanic/Latino; 19% Hispanic/Latino; 18% Black or African American, non-Hispanic/Latino; 5% Asian, non-Hispanic/Latino; 0.3% Native Hawaiian or other Pacific Islander, non-Hispanic/Latino; 0.9% international. 35% 25 or older, 6% transferred in. Retention: 70% of full-time freshmen returned the following year. Calendar: semesters. Academic remediation for entering students, ESL program, services for LD students, advanced placement, accelerated degree program, freshman honors college, honors program, independent study, distance learning, double major, summer session for credit, part-time degree program, external degree program, adult/continuing education programs, co-op programs and internships. Off campus study. Study abroad program.
Entrance Requirements: Open admission. Options: early admission, deferred admission. Required: high school transcript. Entrance: noncompetitive. Application deadline: rolling. Transfer credits accepted: Yes.
Costs Per Year: Application fee: $30. State resident tuition: $4746 full-time, $199 per credit hour part-time. Nonresident tuition: $9492 full-time, $398 per credit hour part-time. Mandatory fees: $434 full-time, $16.50 per credit hour part-time. Full-time tuition and fees vary according to course load and program. Part-time tuition and fees vary according to course load and program.
Collegiate Environment: Orientation program. Drama-theater group, student-run newspaper. Student services: personal-psychological counseling. Campus security: 24-hour emergency response devices and patrols, student patrols, late night transport-escort service. Rockland Community College Library.

■ **THE SAGE COLLEGES**
65 1st St.
Troy, NY 12180
Tel: (518)244-2000
E-mail: barres2@sage.edu
Web Site: www.sage.edu
Description: Independent, comprehensive, coed. Awards bachelor's, master's, and doctoral degrees and post-master's certificates. Founded 1916. Setting: 23-acre urban campus. System endowment: $36.6 million. Research spending for the previous fiscal year: $65,401. Educational spending for the previous fiscal year: $8433 per student. Total enrollment: 2,633. Faculty: 320 (122 full-time, 198 part-time). Student-undergrad faculty ratio is 13:1. 2,389 applied, 93% were admitted. 11% from top 10% of their high school class, 39% from top quarter, 72% from top half. Full-time: 1,360 students, 79% women, 21% men. Part-time: 117 students, 70% women, 30% men. 9% from out-of-state. 0.3% American Indian or Alaska Native, non-Hispanic/Latino; 10% Hispanic/Latino; 11% Black or African American, non-Hispanic/Latino; 4% Asian, non-Hispanic/Latino; 0.3% Native Hawaiian or other Pacific Islander, non-Hispanic/Latino; 1% international. 15% 25 or older, 48% live on campus, 15% transferred in. Retention: 78% of full-time freshmen returned the following year. Academic areas with the most degrees conferred: health professions and related sciences; business/marketing; visual and performing arts. Core. Calendar: semesters. Services for LD students, advanced placement, accelerated degree program, self-designed majors, honors program, independent study, distance learning, double major, summer session for credit, part-time degree program, adult/continuing education programs, co-op programs and internships, graduate courses open to undergrads. Off campus study at Hudson - Mohawk Association of Colleges & Universities. Study abroad program. ROTC: Army (c), Air Force (c).
Entrance Requirements: Options: electronic application, early admission,

early action, deferred admission. Required: essay, high school transcript, minimum 2.5 high school GPA, 2 recommendations. Recommended: interview. Required for some: portfolio for art and design programs, SAT or ACT. Entrance: moderately difficult. Application deadline: rolling. Notification: continuous. Transfer credits accepted: Yes. Early action applicants: 442. Early action applicants admitted: 434.
Costs Per Year: Application fee: $30. Tuition: $30,383 full-time, $1013 per credit hour part-time. Mandatory fees: $1500 full-time.
Collegiate Environment: Orientation program. Drama-theater group, choral group, student-run newspaper. Social organizations: 20 open to all. Most popular organizations: Dance Ensemble, SALANA (African American, Latino, Asian, Native American), BLSA (Black Latino), ASIC (Interior Design), AIGA (Graphic Design). Student services: health clinic, personal-psychological counseling, women's center. Campus security: 24-hour emergency response devices and patrols, late night transport-escort service, controlled dormitory access. 975 college housing spaces available; 643 were occupied in 2018-19. Freshmen guaranteed college housing. Options: coed, women-only housing available. James Wheelock Clark Library plus 1 other. Serial titles: 217 (physical), 68,930 (digital/electronic); Databases: 99. Weekly public service hours: 45; students can reserve study rooms. Operations spending for the previous fiscal year: $1.2 million. 416 computers available on campus for general student use. A campuswide network can be accessed from student residence rooms and from off campus. Students can access the following: online class registration. Staffed computer lab on campus provides training in use of computers, software, and the Internet.

■ **ST. BONAVENTURE UNIVERSITY**
3261 W State Rd.
Saint Bonaventure, NY 14778-2284
Tel: (716)375-2000; Free: 800-462-5050
Fax: (716)375-2005
E-mail: dbrady@sbu.edu
Web Site: www.sbu.edu
Description: Independent, comprehensive, coed, affiliated with Roman Catholic Church. Awards associate, bachelor's, and master's degrees and post-master's certificates. Founded 1858. Setting: 500-acre small town campus. Endowment: $65.2 million. Research spending for the previous fiscal year: $1.1 million. Educational spending for the previous fiscal year: $8957 per student. Total enrollment: 2,089. Faculty: 239 (127 full-time, 112 part-time). Student-undergrad faculty ratio is 11:1. 2,986 applied, 71% were admitted. 21% from top 10% of their high school class, 47% from top quarter, 76% from top half. 2 valedictorians. Full-time: 1,591 students, 48% women, 52% men. Part-time: 36 students, 50% women, 50% men. Students come from 33 states and territories, 17 other countries, 32% from out-of-state. 0.4% American Indian or Alaska Native, non-Hispanic/Latino; 8% Hispanic/Latino; 6% Black or African American, non-Hispanic/Latino; 4% Asian, non-Hispanic/Latino; 0.1% Native Hawaiian or other Pacific Islander, non-Hispanic/Latino; 3% international. 2% 25 or older, 80% live on campus, 4% transferred in. Retention: 84% of full-time freshmen returned the following year. Academic areas with the most degrees conferred: business/marketing; communication/journalism; biological/life sciences; social sciences. Core. Calendar: semesters. Services for LD students, advanced placement, accelerated degree program, self-designed majors, honors program, independent study, distance learning, double major, summer session for credit, part-time degree program, internships, graduate courses open to undergrads. Off campus study at American University. Study abroad program. ROTC: Army.
Entrance Requirements: Options: electronic application, deferred admission, international baccalaureate accepted. Required: high school transcript, 1 recommendation, SAT or ACT. Recommended: essay, minimum 3 high school GPA, 3 recommendations, interview. Required for some: essay, SAT and SAT Subject Tests or ACT. Entrance: moderately difficult. Application deadline: 7/1. Notification: continuous until 10/15. SAT Reasoning Test deadline: 8/15. SAT Subject Test deadline: 12/15. Transfer credits accepted: Yes.
Costs Per Year: Application fee: $0. Comprehensive fee: $47,351 includes full-time tuition ($33,336), mandatory fees ($965), and college room and board ($13,050). College room only: $6852. Room and board charges vary according to board plan and housing facility. Part-time tuition: $991 per credit hour. Part-time tuition varies according to course load.
Collegiate Environment: Orientation program. Drama-theater group, choral group, student-run newspaper, radio station. Social organizations: 65 open to all. Most popular organizations: Student Government Association, Bona Responds, BV newspaper, Students for the Mountain, Student Ambas-

sadors. Major annual events: Family Weekend, Spring Weekend, Junior Prom. Student services: health clinic, personal-psychological counseling. Campus security: 24-hour emergency response devices and patrols, late night transport-escort service, controlled dormitory access. Friedsam Memorial Library. Books: 371,691 (physical), 1.6 million (digital/electronic); Serial titles: 253 (physical), 269,989 (digital/electronic); Databases: 64. Weekly public service hours: 109; students can reserve study rooms. Operations spending for the previous fiscal year: $834,370. 320 computers available on campus for general student use. A campuswide network can be accessed from student residence rooms and from off campus. Students can access the following: online class registration. Staffed computer lab on campus provides training in use of computers, software, and the Internet.

Community Environment: Allegany (population 1,831) is a rural community located in southwest New York a short distance from Allegany State Park. The area is accessible by bus and the Southern Tier Expressway. Climate is temperate with 4 definite seasons. Allegany has 1 library, several churches of different denominations. Various civic and fraternal organizations are active here. Part-time work for students is available. Olean (population 14,799) is a manufacturing and regional commercial center where part-time employment is available for students. Transportation is provided by bus or airlines. Nearby"Enchanted Mountains" resort area provides hunting, fishing, skiing, and other sports. The city has a hospital, numerous restaurants, movie theaters, shopping areas, and most of the major service clubs found in larger cities.

■ ST. ELIZABETH COLLEGE OF NURSING
2215 Genesee St.
Utica, NY 13501
Tel: (315)798-8144
E-mail: dernst@secon.edu
Web Site: www.secon.edu

Description: Independent, 2-year, coed. Administratively affiliated with St. Elizabeth Medical Center. Awards terminal associate degrees. Founded 1904. Setting: 1-acre small town campus with easy access to Syracuse. Total enrollment: 159. Faculty: 18 (13 full-time, 5 part-time). Student-undergrad faculty ratio is 7:1. 19 applied, 32% were admitted. Full-time: 72 students, 82% women, 18% men. Part-time: 87 students, 90% women, 10% men. 2% Hispanic/Latino; 2% Black or African American, non-Hispanic/Latino; 1% Asian, non-Hispanic/Latino; 1% international. 47% 25 or older, 51% transferred in. Retention: 75% of full-time freshmen returned the following year. Core. Calendar: semesters. Academic remediation for entering students, services for LD students, advanced placement, part-time degree program. Off campus study at SUNY IT - Utica; Herkimer County Community College - Herkimer.

Entrance Requirements: Option: electronic application. Required: high school transcript, 2 recommendations, SAT or ACT. Recommended: minimum 3 high school GPA. Application deadline: rolling. Notification: continuous. SAT Reasoning Test deadline: 4/30. SAT Subject Test deadline: 4/30. Transfer credits accepted: Yes. Applicants placed on waiting list: 5. Wait-listed applicants offered admission: 4.

Collegiate Environment: Orientation program. Major annual events: Freshmen Pinning Ceremony, Moving Up Day Ceremony, Graduation Mass, Breakfast, and Ceremony. Student services: health clinic, personal-psychological counseling. Campus security: 24-hour emergency response devices and patrols. 30 computers available on campus for general student use. A campuswide network can be accessed from off-campus. Staffed computer lab on campus provides training in use of computers, software, and the Internet.

■ ST. FRANCIS COLLEGE
180 Remsen St.
Brooklyn Heights, NY 11201-4398
Tel: (718)522-2300
Fax: (718)522-1274
E-mail: lrandazzo@sfc.edu
Web Site: www.sfc.edu

Description: Independent Roman Catholic, comprehensive, coed. Awards associate, bachelor's, and master's degrees. Founded 1884. Setting: 1-acre urban campus with easy access to New York City. Endowment: $74.7 million. Total enrollment: 2,672. Faculty: 300 (82 full-time, 218 part-time). Student-undergrad faculty ratio is 17:1. Full-time: 2,393 students, 58% women, 42% men. Part-time: 205 students, 58% women, 42% men. Students come from 21 states and territories, 68 other countries, 2% from out-of-state. 11% 25 or older, 7% live on campus, 6% transferred in. Retention: 76% of full-time

freshmen returned the following year. Academic areas with the most degrees conferred: business/marketing; health professions and related sciences; communication/journalism. Core. Calendar: semesters. Academic remediation for entering students, ESL program, advanced placement, accelerated degree program, self-designed majors, honors program, independent study, double major, summer session for credit, part-time degree program, co-op programs and internships. Study abroad program. ROTC: Army (c), Air Force (c).

Entrance Requirements: Required: essay, high school transcript, minimum 2 high school GPA, 1 recommendation, SAT. Recommended: interview.

Collegiate Environment: Orientation program. Drama-theater group, choral group, student-run newspaper, radio station. Social organizations: 50 open to all; national fraternities, national sororities, local fraternities, local sororities. Most popular organizations: Latin American Society, Fine Arts Society, Power Lifting Club, Games Club, Haitian American Students Alliance. Major annual events: International Night, Franciscan Spirit Week, Community Day. Student services: personal-psychological counseling. Campus security: ID checks, crime awareness workshops, pamphlets, posters, films, emergency notification system. McCardle Student Library. Operations spending for the previous fiscal year: $957,029. 412 computers available on campus for general student use. A campuswide network can be accessed from off-campus. Students can access the following: online class registration. Staffed computer lab on campus provides training in use of computers, software, and the Internet.

■ ST. JOHN FISHER COLLEGE
3690 E Ave.
Rochester, NY 14618-3597
Tel: (585)385-8000; Free: 800-444-4640
Fax: (585)385-8129
E-mail: admissions@sjfc.edu
Web Site: www.sjfc.edu

Description: Independent, comprehensive, coed, affiliated with Roman Catholic Church. Awards bachelor's, master's, and doctoral degrees and post-master's certificates. Founded 1948. Setting: 154-acre suburban campus. Endowment: $93.8 million. Educational spending for the previous fiscal year: $11,343 per student. Total enrollment: 3,719. Faculty: 449 (229 full-time, 215 part-time). Student-undergrad faculty ratio is 12:1. 4,594 applied, 64% were admitted. 24% from top 10% of their high school class, 56% from top quarter, 85% from top half. Full-time: 2,623 students, 58% women, 42% men. Part-time: 123 students, 70% women, 30% men. Students come from 19 states and territories, 3 other countries, 4% from out-of-state. 0.3% American Indian or Alaska Native, non-Hispanic/Latino; 5% Hispanic/Latino; 4% Black or African American, non-Hispanic/Latino; 3% Asian, non-Hispanic/Latino; 0.1% international. 8% 25 or older, 52% live on campus, 6% transferred in. Retention: 87% of full-time freshmen returned the following year. Academic areas with the most degrees conferred: business/marketing; health professions and related sciences; biological/life sciences. Core. Calendar: semesters. Services for LD students, advanced placement, accelerated degree program, self-designed majors, honors program, independent study, distance learning, double major, summer session for credit, part-time degree program, adult/continuing education programs, internships, graduate courses open to undergrads. Off campus study at members of the Rochester Area Colleges. Study abroad program. ROTC: Army (c), Naval (c), Air Force (c).

Entrance Requirements: Options: electronic application, early decision, deferred admission, international baccalaureate accepted. Required: essay, high school transcript, minimum 3 high school GPA, 1 recommendation, SAT or ACT. Recommended: interview. Entrance: moderately difficult. Application deadlines: rolling, 12/1 for early decision. Notification: continuous until 12/1, 12/15 for early decision. SAT Reasoning Test deadline: 4/1. Transfer credits accepted: Yes. Early decision applicants: 97. Early decision applicants admitted: 85.

Costs Per Year: Application fee: $0. Tuition: $34,340 full-time, $936 part-time. Mandatory fees: $810 full-time.

Collegiate Environment: Orientation program. Drama-theater group, choral group, student-run newspaper. Social organizations: 75 open to all. Most popular organizations: Student Government, Student Activities Board, Commuter Council, Resident Student Association, Teddi Dance for Love. Major annual events: Teddi Project Dance Marathon, Family Weekend, Spring Event. Student services: health clinic, personal-psychological counseling. Campus security: 24-hour emergency response devices and patrols, late night transport-escort service, controlled dormitory access. 1,400 college housing spaces available; 1,395 were occupied in 2018-19. Freshmen guaranteed college housing. Options: coed, women-only housing available. Charles J. Lavery Library plus 1 other. Books: 138,569 (physical), 297,511 (digital/electronic). Databases: 156. Students can reserve study rooms. Operations spending for the previous fiscal year: $2.1 million. 550 computers available on campus for general student use. A campuswide network can be accessed from student residence rooms and from off campus. Students can access the following: online class registration. Staffed computer lab on campus (open 24 hours a day) provides training in use of computers, software, and the Internet.

■ **ST. JOHN'S UNIVERSITY**
8000 Utopia Pky.
Queens, NY 11439
Tel: (718)990-6161; Free: 888-9STJOHNS
Web Site: www.stjohns.edu
Description: Independent, university, coed, affiliated with Roman Catholic Church. Awards bachelor's, master's, and doctoral degrees and post-master's certificates. Founded 1870. Setting: 102-acre urban campus with easy access to New York City. Endowment: $716.5 million. Research spending for the previous fiscal year: $6.2 million. Educational spending for the previous fiscal year: $11,030 per student. Total enrollment: 21,346. Faculty: 1,460 (638 full-time, 822 part-time). Student-undergrad faculty ratio is 17:1. 27,179 applied, 68% were admitted. 31% from top 10% of their high school class, 43% from top quarter, 77% from top half. Full-time: 11,531 students, 57% women, 43% men. Part-time: 5,235 students, 59% women, 41% men. Students come from 47 states and territories, 101 other countries, 25% from out-of-state. 0.5% American Indian or Alaska Native, non-Hispanic/Latino; 9% Hispanic/Latino; 13% Black or African American, non-Hispanic/Latino; 14% Asian, non-Hispanic/Latino; 0.3% Native Hawaiian or other Pacific Islander, non-Hispanic/Latino; 4% international. 3% 25 or older, 26% live on campus, 2% transferred in. Retention: 84% of full-time freshmen returned the following year. Academic areas with the most degrees conferred: business/marketing; communication/journalism; health professions and related sciences. Core. Calendar: semesters. ESL program, services for LD students, advanced placement, accelerated degree program, honors program, independent study, distance learning, double major, summer session for credit, part-time degree program, adult/continuing education programs, internships, graduate courses open to undergrads. Off campus study. Study abroad program. ROTC: Army.
Entrance Requirements: Options: electronic application, early admission, early decision, early action, deferred admission, international baccalaureate accepted. Required: high school transcript, minimum 3 high school GPA. Recommended: essay, 2 recommendations. Required for some: essay, 2 recommendations, interview, SAT or ACT. Entrance: moderately difficult. Application deadlines: rolling, 11/15 for early decision, 12/15 for early action. Notification: continuous, 12/15 for early decision, 1/15 for early action. Transfer credits accepted: Yes. Applicants placed on waiting list: 412. Wait-listed applicants offered admission: 311.
Costs Per Year: Application fee: $0. One-time mandatory fee: $250. Comprehensive fee: $58,790 includes full-time tuition ($40,680), mandatory fees ($830), and college room and board ($17,280). College room only: $10,830. Full-time tuition and fees vary according to course load, location, program, reciprocity agreements, and student level. Room and board charges vary according to board plan, housing facility, and location. Part-time tuition: $1356 per credit. Part-time mandatory fees: $312.50 per term. Part-time tuition and fees vary according to course load, location, program, and student level.
Collegiate Environment: Orientation program. Drama-theater group, choral group, student-run newspaper, radio station. Social organizations: 180 open to all; national fraternities, national sororities, local fraternities, local sororities; 10% of eligible men and 9% of eligible women are members. Most popular organizations: Student Government, Incorporated, Haraya (Pan-African Students Coalition), American Pharmaceutical Association, Muslim Students, Pare- Philippine- Americans Reaching Everyone. Major annual events: Spring Fling, Red Storm Tip Off, Fall Activities Fair. Student services: health clinic, personal-psychological counseling. Campus security: 24-hour emergency response devices and patrols, late night transport-escort service, controlled dormitory access, Emergency Notification System, CNS Boards, Public Address System. St. John's University Library plus 3 others. Books: 534,824 (physical), 608,270 (digital/electronic); Serial titles: 68,549 (physical), 88,058 (digital/electronic); Databases: 226. Weekly public service hours: 92; students can reserve study rooms. Operations spending for the previous fiscal year: $10.4 million. 12,702 computers available on campus for general student use. Computer purchase/lease plans available. A

campuswide network can be accessed from student residence rooms and from off campus. Students can access the following: online class registration. Staffed computer lab on campus provides training in use of computers, software, and the Internet.

■ **ST. JOSEPH'S COLLEGE, LONG ISLAND CAMPUS**
155 W Roe Blvd.
Patchogue, NY 11772-2399
Tel: (631)687-5100
Fax: (631)447-1734
E-mail: glamens@sjcny.edu
Web Site: www.sjcny.edu
Description: Independent, comprehensive, coed. Awards bachelor's and master's degrees. Founded 1916. Setting: 32-acre suburban campus with easy access to New York City. Endowment: $28.5 million. Total enrollment: 4,115. Faculty: 456 (103 full-time, 353 part-time). Student-undergrad faculty ratio is 14:1. 1,693 applied, 77% were admitted. Full-time: 2,661 students, 68% women, 32% men. Part-time: 487 students, 70% women, 30% men. Students come from 13 states and territories, 2 other countries, 1% from out-of-state. 0.2% American Indian or Alaska Native, non-Hispanic/Latino; 15% Hispanic/Latino; 5% Black or African American, non-Hispanic/Latino; 2% Asian, non-Hispanic/Latino; 0.1% Native Hawaiian or other Pacific Islander, non-Hispanic/Latino. 23% 25 or older, 15% transferred in. Retention: 80% of full-time freshmen returned the following year. Academic areas with the most degrees conferred: business/marketing; education; English. Core. Calendar: 4-1-4. Services for LD students, advanced placement, accelerated degree program, honors program, independent study, distance learning, double major, summer session for credit, part-time degree program, adult/continuing education programs, internships, graduate courses open to undergrads. Off campus study. Study abroad program. ROTC: Army (c), Air Force (c).
Entrance Requirements: Options: electronic application, deferred admission, international baccalaureate accepted. Required: essay, high school transcript, minimum 3 high school GPA, 2 recommendations, SAT or ACT. Recommended: interview. Required for some: RN for RN-BSN program. Entrance: moderately difficult. Application deadline: rolling. Notification: continuous until 11/1. Transfer credits accepted: Yes. Applicants placed on waiting list: 22. Wait-listed applicants offered admission: 3.
Costs Per Year: Application fee: $25. Tuition: $27,230 full-time, $882 per credit hour part-time. Mandatory fees: $614 full-time. Full-time tuition and fees vary according to course load, location, and program. Part-time tuition varies according to course load, location, and program.
Collegiate Environment: Orientation program. Drama-theater group, choral group, student-run newspaper, radio station. Social organizations: 53 open to all; national fraternities, national sororities. Most popular organizations: STARS (Students Taking an Active Role in Society), All Greek Life (Alpha Phi Delta and Delta Kappa Epsilon Fraternities), Drama Society, Project Sunshine, SJC Sharps. Major annual events: Welcome Back BBQ, Welcome Back Evening Social, Club Fair. Student services: personal-psychological counseling. Campus security: 24-hour emergency response devices and patrols, late night transport-escort service. College housing not available. Callahan Library plus 1 other. Books: 113,712 (physical), 161,062 (digital/electronic); Serial titles: 224 (physical), 59,853 (digital/electronic); Databases: 129. Weekly public service hours: 80; students can reserve study rooms. Operations spending for the previous fiscal year: $1.2 million. 267 computers available on campus for general student use. A campuswide network can be accessed from off-campus. Students can access the following: online class registration, library databases, learning management system, course evaluations, print management, virtual application labs, office 365, student suggestion box. Staffed computer lab on campus provides training in use of computers and the Internet.

■ **ST. JOSEPH'S COLLEGE, NEW YORK**
245 Clinton Ave.
Brooklyn, NY 11205-3688
Tel: (718)940-5300
Fax: (718)636-7242
E-mail: cmurphy@sjcny.edu
Web Site: www.sjcny.edu
Description: Independent, comprehensive, coed. Awards bachelor's and master's degrees. Founded 1916. Setting: 5-acre urban campus with easy access to Manhattan. Endowment: $8.5 million. Total enrollment: 1,179. Faculty: 186 (57 full-time, 129 part-time). Student-undergrad faculty ratio is 11:1. 2,140 applied, 70% were admitted. Full-time: 824 students, 68%

women, 32% men. Part-time: 119 students, 69% women, 31% men. Students come from 27 states and territories, 26 other countries, 7% from out-of-state. 0.4% American Indian or Alaska Native, non-Hispanic/Latino; 24% Hispanic/Latino; 23% Black or African American, non-Hispanic/Latino; 6% Asian, non-Hispanic/Latino; 0.4% Native Hawaiian or other Pacific Islander, non-Hispanic/Latino. 24% 25 or older, 9% live on campus, 9% transferred in. Retention: 79% of full-time freshmen returned the following year. Academic areas with the most degrees conferred: business/marketing; education; health professions and related sciences. Core. Calendar: semesters. ESL program, services for LD students, advanced placement, accelerated degree program, honors program, independent study, distance learning, double major, summer session for credit, part-time degree program, adult/continuing education programs, internships, graduate courses open to undergrads. Off campus study. Study abroad program. ROTC: Army (c), Air Force (c).

Entrance Requirements: Options: electronic application, early admission, deferred admission, international baccalaureate accepted. Required: essay, high school transcript, minimum 2.5 high school GPA, 1 recommendation, SAT or ACT. Recommended: interview. Required for some: RN license for the RN to BSN Program. Entrance: moderately difficult. Application deadlines: rolling, rolling for nonresidents. Notification: continuous until 11/1, continuous for nonresidents. SAT Reasoning Test deadline: 8/31. Transfer credits accepted: Yes.

Costs Per Year: Application fee: $25. Tuition: $27,230 full-time, $882 per credit hour part-time. Mandatory fees: $614 full-time. Full-time tuition and fees vary according to course load and program. Part-time tuition varies according to course load and program.

Collegiate Environment: Orientation program. Drama-theater group. Social organizations: 30 open to all; national fraternities, local sororities. Most popular organizations: Campus Activities Board (C.A.B.), Student Senate, Chapel Players Dramatic Club, Council of Multicultural Organizations, Dance Club. Major annual events: International Festival, Back to School BBQ, Club Fair. Student services: health clinic, personal-psychological counseling. Campus security: 24-hour emergency response devices and patrols, late night transport-escort service, controlled dormitory access. No special consideration for freshman housing applicants. Option: coed housing available. McEntegart Hall Library plus 1 other. Books: 91,695 (physical), 161,062 (digital/electronic); Serial titles: 36 (physical), 59,853 (digital/electronic); Databases: 129. Weekly public service hours: 83; students can reserve study rooms. Operations spending for the previous fiscal year: $709,000. 207 computers available on campus for general student use. A campuswide network can be accessed from off-campus. Students can access the following: online class registration, library databases, learning management system, course evaluations, print management, virtual application labs, office software, student suggestion box.

■ **ST. JOSEPH'S COLLEGE OF NURSING**
206 Prospect Ave.
Syracuse, NY 13203
Tel: (315)448-5040
Fax: (315)448-5745
E-mail: collegeofnursing@sjhsyr.org
Web Site: www.sjhcon.edu

Description: Independent Roman Catholic, 2-year, coed. Awards terminal associate degrees. Founded 1898. Setting: urban campus. Educational spending for the previous fiscal year: $10,000 per student. Total enrollment: 273. Faculty: 30 (17 full-time, 13 part-time). Student-undergrad faculty ratio is 9:1. 42 applied, 55% were admitted. 100% from top half of their high school class. Full-time: 166 students, 90% women, 10% men. Part-time: 107 students, 93% women, 7% men. Students come from 2 states and territories, 0.01% from out-of-state. 20% live on campus. Core. Calendar: semesters. Academic remediation for entering students, services for LD students, advanced placement, part-time degree program, adult/continuing education programs, co-op programs and internships.

Entrance Requirements: Options: electronic application, deferred admission. Required: essay, high school transcript, minimum 3 high school GPA, 2 recommendations, interview, high school or college algebra, biology and chemistry, SAT or ACT. Entrance: moderately difficult. Application deadline: rolling for nonresidents. Notification: continuous, continuous for nonresidents. Transfer credits accepted: Yes.

Costs Per Year: Application fee: $50. Tuition: $18,700 full-time, $550 per credit hour part-time. Mandatory fees: $1395 full-time. Full-time tuition and fees vary according to program. Part-time tuition varies according to program.

Collegiate Environment: Orientation program. Social organizations: 10 open to all. Most popular organizations: New York State Student Nurse's Association, Syracuse Area Black Nurses Association, Student Body Organization. Major annual events: Holiday Parties, WalkRun Charity Events, Commitment to Nursing Ceremony. Student services: health clinic, personal-psychological counseling. Campus security: 24-hour patrols. St. Joseph's Hospital Health Center School of Nursing Library. Operations spending for the previous fiscal year: $27,000. 30 computers available on campus for general student use. A campuswide network can be accessed from student residence rooms and from off campus. Staffed computer lab on campus (open 24 hours a day) provides training in use of computers, software, and the Internet.

■ **ST. LAWRENCE UNIVERSITY**
23 Romoda Dr.
Canton, NY 13617
Tel: (315)229-5011; Free: 800-285-1856
Fax: (315)229-5502
E-mail: jfreeman@stlawu.edu
Web Site: www.stlawu.edu

Description: Independent, 4-year, coed. Awards bachelor's and master's degrees and post-master's certificates. Founded 1856. Setting: 1,100-acre small town campus. Endowment: $282.1 million. Research spending for the previous fiscal year: $206,519. Educational spending for the previous fiscal year: $17,795 per student. Total enrollment: 2,493. Faculty: 217 (175 full-time, 42 part-time). Student-undergrad faculty ratio is 11:1. 5,866 applied, 48% were admitted. 46% from top 10% of their high school class, 79% from top quarter, 95% from top half. 15 valedictorians. Full-time: 2,372 students, 56% women, 44% men. Part-time: 42 students, 43% women, 57% men. Students come from 43 states and territories, 53 other countries, 54% from out-of-state. 0.2% American Indian or Alaska Native, non-Hispanic/Latino; 5% Hispanic/Latino; 3% Black or African American, non-Hispanic/Latino; 1% Asian, non-Hispanic/Latino; 9% international. 1% 25 or older, 98% live on campus, 1% transferred in. Retention: 92% of full-time freshmen returned the following year. Academic areas with the most degrees conferred: social sciences; business/marketing; biological/life sciences. Core. Calendar: semesters. ESL program, services for LD students, advanced placement, self-designed majors, independent study, double major, summer session for credit, part-time degree program, internships. Off campus study at Clarkson University, State University of New York College of Technology at Canton, State University of New York College at Potsdam, Fisk University, American University, The Washington Center. Study abroad program. ROTC: Army (c), Air Force (c).

Entrance Requirements: Options: electronic application, early admission, early decision, deferred admission, international baccalaureate accepted. Required: essay, high school transcript, 2 recommendations. Recommended: interview. Entrance: moderately difficult. Application deadlines: 2/1, 11/1 for early decision. Notification: 3/31, rolling for early decision. SAT Reasoning Test deadline: 2/1. SAT Subject Test deadline: 2/1. Transfer credits accepted: Yes. Applicants placed on waiting list: 85. Wait-listed applicants offered admission: 0. Early decision applicants: 299. Early decision applicants admitted: 270.

Costs Per Year: Application fee: $60. Comprehensive fee: $68,980 includes full-time tuition ($54,454), mandatory fees ($392), and college room and board ($14,134). College room only: $7614. Room and board charges vary according to board plan. Part-time tuition: $1891 per unit.

Collegiate Environment: Orientation program. Drama-theater group, choral group, student-run newspaper, radio station. Social organizations: 120 open to all; national fraternities, national sororities, local sororities; 12% of eligible men and 17% of eligible women are members. Most popular organizations: The Thelomathesian Society (student government), Outing Club, Environmental Action Organization, Association for Campus Entertainment, La Sociedad Hispana. Major annual events: Moving-Up Day, Candlelight Concert, Charter Day. Student services: health clinic, personal-psychological counseling. Campus security: 24-hour emergency response devices and patrols, student patrols, late night transport-escort service, controlled dormitory access. Owen D. Young Library plus 2 others. Books: 602,154 (physical), 303,918 (digital/electronic); Serial titles: 98,010 (physical), 123,193 (digital/electronic); Databases: 170. Students can reserve study rooms. Operations spending for the previous fiscal year: $1.1 million. 738 computers available on campus for general student use. A campuswide network can be accessed from student residence rooms and from off campus. Students can access the following: online class registration. Staffed computer lab on campus provides training in use of computers, software, and the Internet.

■ ST. PAUL'S SCHOOL OF NURSING (QUEENS)

97-77 Queens Blvd.
Queens, NY 11374
Tel: (718)357-0500
Fax: (718)357-4683
Web Site: www.stpaulsschoolofnursing.edu

Description: Independent, 2-year, coed. Awards terminal associate degrees. Founded 1969. Setting: 2-acre suburban campus. Total enrollment: 106. Faculty: 10 (8 full-time, 2 part-time). Student-undergrad faculty ratio is 10:1. 737 applied, 9% were admitted. 25% from top 10% of their high school class, 75% from top quarter. Students come from 2 states and territories. 50% 25 or older. Core. Calendar: semesters. Part-time degree program.

Entrance Requirements: Option: deferred admission. Required: essay, high school transcript, college transcript, nursing exam. Entrance: moderately difficult. Application deadline: 4/1. Notification: continuous.

Collegiate Environment: Orientation program. 6 computers available on campus for general student use.

■ ST. PAUL'S SCHOOL OF NURSING (STATEN ISLAND)

Corporate Commons Two
2 Teleport Dr., Ste. 203
Staten Island, NY 10311
Tel: (718)818-6470
Web Site: www.stpaulsschoolofnursing.edu

Description: Proprietary, 2-year, coed. Awards certificates, transfer associate, and terminal associate degrees.

■ ST. THOMAS AQUINAS COLLEGE

125 Rte. 340
Sparkill, NY 10976
Tel: (845)398-4000
E-mail: sbazile@stac.edu
Web Site: www.stac.edu

Description: Independent, comprehensive, coed. Awards associate, bachelor's, and master's degrees and post-master's certificates. Founded 1952. Setting: 46-acre suburban campus with easy access to New York City. Endowment: $30.6 million. Total enrollment: 1,915. Faculty: 157 (58 full-time, 99 part-time). Student-undergrad faculty ratio is 12:1. 1,953 applied, 79% were admitted. 7% from top 10% of their high school class, 23% from top quarter, 67% from top half. Full-time: 1,091 students, 54% women, 46% men. Part-time: 687 students, 54% women, 46% men. Students come from 18 states and territories, 16 other countries, 21% from out-of-state. 23% Hispanic/Latino; 12% Black or African American, non-Hispanic/Latino; 2% Asian, non-Hispanic/Latino; 0.1% Native Hawaiian or other Pacific Islander, non-Hispanic/Latino; 5% international. 6% 25 or older, 52% live on campus, 5% transferred in. Retention: 74% of full-time freshmen returned the following year. Academic areas with the most degrees conferred: business/marketing; psychology; homeland security, law enforcement, firefighting, and protective services. Core. Calendar: semesters. Academic remediation for entering students, services for LD students, advanced placement, accelerated degree program, freshman honors college, honors program, independent study, double major, summer session for credit, part-time degree program, adult/continuing education programs, internships, graduate courses open to undergrads. Off campus study at New York University. Study abroad program. ROTC: Air Force (c).

Entrance Requirements: Options: electronic application, deferred admission. Required: high school transcript, minimum 2 high school GPA, SAT or ACT. Recommended: essay, 2 recommendations, interview. Required for some: 3 recommendations. Entrance: moderately difficult. Application deadline: rolling. SAT Reasoning Test deadline: 8/1. SAT Subject Test deadline: 8/1.

Costs Per Year: Application fee: $30. Comprehensive fee: $45,200 includes full-time tuition ($31,150), mandatory fees ($800), and college room and board ($13,250). College room only: $7150. Room and board charges vary according to board plan and housing facility. Part-time tuition: $990 per credit hour. Part-time mandatory fees: $200 per term.

Collegiate Environment: Orientation program. Drama-theater group, choral group, student-run newspaper, radio station. Social organizations: 25 open to all; national fraternities, local fraternities, local sororities. Most popular organizations: Spartan Volunteers, Campus Activities Board, WSTK campus radio, Bowling Club, Laetare Players. Major annual events: Spring Fest, Oktoberfest, Holiday Semi-Formal. Student services: health clinic, personal-psychological counseling. Campus security: 24-hour emergency response devices and patrols, student patrols, late night transport-escort service,

controlled dormitory access. Lougheed Library plus 1 other. Books: 50,000 (physical); Serial titles: 110 (physical), 75,000 (digital/electronic); Databases: 68. Weekly public service hours: 83; students can reserve study rooms. Operations spending for the previous fiscal year: $889,000. 200 computers available on campus for general student use. Computer purchase/lease plans available. A campuswide network can be accessed from student residence rooms and from off campus. Students can access the following: online class registration. Staffed computer lab on campus provides training in use of computers, software, and the Internet.

■ SAMARITAN HOSPITAL SCHOOL OF NURSING

1300 Massachusetts Ave.
Troy, NY 12180
Tel: (518)268-5010
Fax: (518)268-5040
Web Site: www.nehealth.com

Description: Independent, 2-year, coed. Administratively affiliated with Samaritan Hospital (Troy, NY). Awards diplomas, transfer associate, and terminal associate degrees. Total enrollment: 119. Faculty: 9 (5 full-time, 4 part-time). Full-time: 36 students, 94% women, 6% men. Part-time: 83 students, 89% women, 11% men. 57% 25 or older.

Entrance Requirements: Required: essay, high school transcript, TEAS. Recommended: SAT or ACT. Application deadline: rolling. Notification: continuous.

Collegiate Environment: Orientation program. Student services: health clinic, personal-psychological counseling, women's center. 8 computers available on campus for general student use. Staffed computer lab on campus provides training in use of computers, software, and the Internet.

■ SARAH LAWRENCE COLLEGE

1 Mead Way
Bronxville, NY 10708-5999
Tel: (914)337-0700; Free: 800-888-2858
Fax: (914)395-2668
E-mail: slcadmit@sarahlawrence.edu
Web Site: www.sarahlawrence.edu

Description: Independent, comprehensive, coed. Awards bachelor's and master's degrees. Founded 1926. Setting: 44-acre suburban campus with easy access to New York City. Endowment: $113.8 million. Research spending for the previous fiscal year: $89,243. Educational spending for the previous fiscal year: $22,598 per student. Total enrollment: 1,709. Faculty: 311 (119 full-time, 192 part-time). Student-undergrad faculty ratio is 9:1. 3,325 applied, 56% were admitted. 33% from top 10% of their high school class, 63% from top quarter, 91% from top half. Full-time: 1,396 students, 73% women, 27% men. Part-time: 14 students, 79% women, 21% men. Students come from 49 states and territories, 38 other countries, 81% from out-of-state. 0.1% American Indian or Alaska Native, non-Hispanic/Latino; 9% Hispanic/Latino; 4% Black or African American, non-Hispanic/Latino; 5% Asian, non-Hispanic/Latino; 12% international. 87% live on campus, 2% transferred in. Retention: 80% of full-time freshmen returned the following year. Academic area with the most degrees conferred: liberal arts/general studies. Core. Calendar: semesters. Services for LD students, advanced placement, accelerated degree program, self-designed majors, independent study, double major, summer session for credit, internships, graduate courses open to undergrads. Off campus study at Pitzer College, Spelman College. Study abroad program. ROTC: Air Force (c).

Entrance Requirements: Options: electronic application, early admission, early decision, early action, deferred admission, international baccalaureate accepted. Required: essay, high school transcript, 2 recommendations, counselor recommendation, school report. Recommended: minimum 3 high school GPA, interview. Entrance: very difficult. Application deadlines: 1/15, 11/1 for early decision plan 1, 1/2 for early decision plan 2, 11/1 for early action. Notification: 3/15, 12/15 for early decision plan 1, 2/15 for early decision plan 2, 12/15 for early action. SAT Reasoning Test deadline: 2/1. SAT Subject Test deadline: 2/1. Transfer credits accepted: Yes. Applicants placed on waiting list: 1,242. Wait-listed applicants offered admission: 34. Early decision applicants: 179. Early decision applicants admitted: 121.

Costs Per Year: Application fee: $60. Comprehensive fee: $71,270 includes full-time tuition ($54,440), mandatory fees ($1460), and college room and board ($15,370). College room only: $10,130. Full-time tuition and fees vary according to course load. Room and board charges vary according to board plan. Part-time tuition: $1,814.66 per credit hour. Part-time mandatory fees: $586 per term. Part-time tuition and fees vary according to course load.

Collegiate Environment: Orientation program. Drama-theater group, choral

group, student-run newspaper, radio station. Social organizations: 90 open to all. Most popular organizations: VOX: Voices of Planned Parenthood, SLC Food & Justice Coalition, Rock Climbing Club, Musical Theatre Collective, Interfaith Union. Major annual events: Fall Formal, Spring Formal, Winter Carnival and Student Organization Fair. Student services: health clinic, personal-psychological counseling. Campus security: 24-hour emergency response devices and patrols, late night transport-escort service, controlled dormitory access. 1,145 college housing spaces available; 1,077 were occupied in 2018-19. Freshmen guaranteed college housing. On-campus residence required in freshman year. Options: coed, men-only, women-only housing available. Esther Rauschenbush Library plus 2 others. Books: 235,763 (physical), 407,165 (digital/electronic); Serial titles: 4,884 (physical), 43,582 (digital/electronic); Databases: 143. Weekly public service hours: 109; study areas open 24 hours, 5-7 days a week; students can reserve study rooms. Operations spending for the previous fiscal year: $2.1 million. 143 computers available on campus for general student use. Computer purchase/lease plans available. A campuswide network can be accessed from student residence rooms and from off campus. Staffed computer lab on campus provides training in use of computers, software, and the Internet.

Community Environment: Population 6,455, Bronxville is a residential suburb in Westchester County. Public transportation in the area and to New York City is very accessible. Grand Central Station is only a 30 minute trip on the Metro North train.

■ **SCHENECTADY COUNTY COMMUNITY COLLEGE**
78 Washington Ave.
Schenectady, NY 12305-2294
Tel: (518)381-1200
E-mail: sampsodg@gw.sunysccc.edu
Web Site: www.sunysccc.edu

Description: State and locally supported, 2-year, coed. Part of State University of New York System. Awards certificates, transfer associate, and terminal associate degrees. Founded 1969. Setting: 50-acre urban campus. Total enrollment: 6,634. Faculty: 133 (57 full-time, 76 part-time). Student-undergrad faculty ratio is 21:1. 5,769 applied, 69% were admitted. 6% from top 10% of their high school class, 56% from top quarter, 72% from top half. Full-time: 2,184 students, 52% women, 48% men. Part-time: 4,450 students, 56% women, 44% men. 0.8% American Indian or Alaska Native, non-Hispanic/Latino; 7% Hispanic/Latino; 14% Black or African American, non-Hispanic/Latino; 7% Asian, non-Hispanic/Latino; 0.4% Native Hawaiian or other Pacific Islander, non-Hispanic/Latino. 30% 25 or older, 5% transferred in. Core. Calendar: semesters. Academic remediation for entering students, ESL program, services for LD students, advanced placement, honors program, distance learning, double major, summer session for credit, part-time degree program, adult/continuing education programs, internships. Off campus study at 14 members of the Hudson-Mohawk Association of Colleges and Universities.

Entrance Requirements: Open admission. Options: electronic application, early admission, deferred admission. Required: high school transcript. Entrance: noncompetitive. Application deadline: rolling. Notification: continuous. Preference given to county residents. Transfer credits accepted: Yes.

Costs Per Year: Application fee: $0. State resident tuition: $4176 full-time, $174 per credit hour part-time. Nonresident tuition: $8352 full-time, $348 per credit hour part-time. Mandatory fees: $624 full-time, $44 per credit hour part-time. Full-time tuition and fees vary according to course load and program. Part-time tuition and fees vary according to course load and program.

Collegiate Environment: Orientation program. Drama-theater group, choral group. Social organizations: local fraternities, local sororities. Student services: personal-psychological counseling. Campus security: 24-hour emergency response devices and patrols, late night transport-escort service. Begley Library.

■ **SCHOOL OF VISUAL ARTS**
209 E 23rd St.
New York, NY 10010-3994
Tel: (212)592-2000; Free: 800-436-4204
Fax: (212)592-2116
E-mail: admissions@sva.edu
Web Site: www.sva.edu

Description: Proprietary, comprehensive, coed. Awards bachelor's and master's degrees. Founded 1947. Setting: 1-acre urban campus. Total enrollment: 4,395. Faculty: 1,179 (216 full-time, 963 part-time). Student-undergrad faculty ratio is 9:1. 3,648 applied, 74% were admitted. Full-time:

3,506 students, 69% women, 31% men. Part-time: 246 students, 67% women, 33% men. 53% from out-of-state. 0.1% American Indian or Alaska Native, non-Hispanic/Latino; 11% Hispanic/Latino; 4% Black or African American, non-Hispanic/Latino; 14% Asian, non-Hispanic/Latino; 43% international. 9% 25 or older, 31% live on campus, 8% transferred in. Retention: 87% of full-time freshmen returned the following year. Academic areas with the most degrees conferred: visual and performing arts; communication technologies; communication/journalism. Core. Calendar: semesters. Academic remediation for entering students, ESL program, services for LD students, advanced placement, freshman honors college, honors program, independent study, summer session for credit, adult/continuing education programs, internships. Study abroad program.

Entrance Requirements: Options: electronic application, deferred admission. Required: essay, high school transcript, minimum 2.5 high school GPA, portfolio, SAT or ACT. Recommended: interview. Entrance: moderately difficult. Application deadline: rolling. Notification: continuous.

Costs Per Year: Application fee: $50. Comprehensive fee: $60,300 includes full-time tuition ($39,900) and college room and board ($20,400). College room only: $17,500. Room and board charges vary according to housing facility. Part-time tuition: $1335 per credit hour.

Collegiate Environment: Orientation program. Student-run newspaper, radio station. Student services: health clinic, personal-psychological counseling. Campus security: 24-hour patrols. School of Visual Arts Library.

■ **SH'OR YOSHUV RABBINICAL COLLEGE**
1 Cedarlawn Ave.
Lawrence, NY 11559-1714
Tel: (718)327-2048

Description: Independent Jewish, comprehensive, men only. Awards bachelor's and master's degrees. Founded 1963. Total enrollment: 257. Faculty: (17 full-time). Student-undergrad faculty ratio is 15:1. 83 applied. Full-time: 217 students. Students come from 10 states and territories, 5 other countries, 30% from out-of-state. 13% 25 or older, 84% live on campus, 12% transferred in. Retention: 85% of full-time freshmen returned the following year. Core. Calendar: semesters. Academic remediation for entering students, self-designed majors, independent study, summer session for credit, part-time degree program, external degree program, adult/continuing education programs, co-op programs and internships.

Entrance Requirements: Options: electronic application, international baccalaureate accepted. Required: interview. Required for some: essay, high school transcript. Entrance: noncompetitive. Application deadline: 9/20. Notification: 9/22.

Collegiate Environment: Major annual events: Purim Festivities, High Holiday Prayer, Winter Retreat. Student services: legal services, personal-psychological counseling. Bais Medrash Sifriya. Operations spending for the previous fiscal year: $50,000. 10 computers available on campus for general student use. Staffed computer lab on campus.

■ **SIENA COLLEGE**
515 Loudon Rd.
Loudonville, NY 12211-1462
Tel: (518)783-2300; Free: 888-AT-SIENA
Fax: (518)783-4293
E-mail: admissions@siena.edu
Web Site: www.siena.edu

Description: Independent Roman Catholic, comprehensive, coed. Awards bachelor's and master's degrees. Founded 1937. Setting: 175-acre suburban campus with easy access to Albany, NY. Endowment: $129.3 million. Research spending for the previous fiscal year: $777,713. Educational spending for the previous fiscal year: $9569 per student. Total enrollment: 3,236. Faculty: 332 (204 full-time, 128 part-time). Student-undergrad faculty ratio is 12:1. 7,626 applied, 78% were admitted. 22% from top 10% of their high school class, 49% from top quarter, 85% from top half. Full-time: 3,039 students, 53% women, 47% men. Part-time: 135 students, 53% women, 47% men. Students come from 35 states and territories, 32 other countries, 20% from out-of-state. 0.1% American Indian or Alaska Native, non-Hispanic/Latino; 8% Hispanic/Latino; 3% Black or African American, non-Hispanic/Latino; 4% Asian, non-Hispanic/Latino; 2% international. 3% 25 or older, 78% live on campus, 5% transferred in. Retention: 88% of full-time freshmen returned the following year. Academic areas with the most degrees conferred: business/marketing; psychology; biological/life sciences. Core. Calendar: semesters. ESL program, services for LD students, advanced placement, self-designed majors, honors program, independent study, double major, summer session for credit, part-time degree program, co-op programs and internships, graduate courses open to undergrads. Off campus study at Member of the Hudson-Mohawk Association of Colleges and Universities. Study abroad program. ROTC: Army, Air Force (c).

Entrance Requirements: Options: electronic application, early admission, early decision, early action, deferred admission, international baccalaureate accepted. Required: essay, high school transcript, 1 recommendation. Recommended: interview. Required for some: interview, SAT or ACT. Entrance: moderately difficult. Application deadlines: 2/15, 12/1 for early decision, 12/1 for early action. Notification: 3/15, 1/1 for early decision, 1/7 for early action. SAT Reasoning Test deadline: 2/15. Transfer credits accepted: Yes. Applicants placed on waiting list: 423. Wait-listed applicants offered admission: 22. Early decision applicants: 283. Early decision applicants admitted: 49. Early action applicants: 6,134. Early action applicants admitted: 3,762.

Costs Per Year: Application fee: $50. One-time mandatory fee: $625. Comprehensive fee: $51,975 includes full-time tuition ($36,675), mandatory fees ($300), and college room and board ($15,000). College room only: $8895. Full-time tuition and fees vary according to course load. Room and board charges vary according to board plan and housing facility. Part-time tuition: $675 per credit hour. Part-time mandatory fees: $80 per term. Part-time tuition and fees vary according to course load.

Collegiate Environment: Orientation program. Drama-theater group, choral group, student-run newspaper, radio station. Social organizations: 85 open to all. Most popular organizations: Outing Club, Best Buddies, Make-a-Wish Wishmakers on Campus, Fitness Club, Psychology Club. Major annual events: Club Fair, SienaFest Carnival, Mr. Siena (fundraiser for Habitat for Humanity). Student services: health clinic, personal-psychological counseling, women's center. Campus security: 24-hour emergency response devices and patrols, late night transport-escort service, controlled dormitory access. J. Spencer and Patricia Standish Library. Books: 281,429 (physical), 301,497 (digital/electronic); Serial titles: 29,000 (digital/electronic); Databases: 172. Weekly public service hours: 102; students can reserve study rooms. Operations spending for the previous fiscal year: $2.2 million. 402 computers available on campus for general student use. Computer purchase/lease plans available. A campuswide network can be accessed from student residence rooms and from off campus. Students can access the following: online class registration. Staffed computer lab on campus (open 24 hours a day) provides training in use of computers, software, and the Internet.

Community Environment: Population 11,000, Loudonville is a suburban community of Albany easily reached by bus, railroad, all major airlines, and interstate highways. The community provides a local church, hospital, and shopping facilities. Part-time employment is available for students. The Saratoga Performing Arts Center and Lake George are nearby.

■ SKIDMORE COLLEGE
815 N Broadway
Saratoga Springs, NY 12866
Tel: (518)580-5000; Free: 800-867-6007
Fax: (518)581-7462
E-mail: admissions@skidmore.edu
Web Site: www.skidmore.edu

Description: Independent, 4-year, coed. Awards bachelor's degrees. Founded 1903. Setting: 890-acre small town campus with easy access to Albany, NY. Endowment: $376 million. Total enrollment: 2,613. Faculty: 389 (286 full-time, 103 part-time). Student-undergrad faculty ratio is 8:1. 10,796 applied, 27% were admitted. 38% from top 10% of their high school class, 78% from top quarter, 96% from top half. Full-time: 2,585 students, 61% women, 39% men. Part-time: 27 students, 59% women, 41% men. Students come from 42 states and territories, 62 other countries, 65% from out-of-state. 9% Hispanic/Latino; 5% Black or African American, non-Hispanic/Latino; 5% Asian, non-Hispanic/Latino; 12% international. 0.4% 25 or older, 90% live on campus, 1% transferred in. Retention: 91% of full-time freshmen returned the following year. Academic areas with the most degrees conferred: social sciences; business/marketing; visual and performing arts. Core. Calendar: semesters plus optional 6-week internship period. Services for LD students, advanced placement, accelerated degree program, self-designed majors, honors program, independent study, distance learning, double major, summer session for credit, internships. Off campus study at Member institutions of the Hudson-Mohawk Association of Colleges and Universities in the Capital Region of New York State, New York 6. Study abroad program. ROTC: Army (c), Air Force (c).

Entrance Requirements: Options: electronic application, early admission, early decision, deferred admission, international baccalaureate accepted.

Required: essay, high school transcript, 2 recommendations. Recommended: interview. Required for some: SAT or ACT. Entrance: very difficult. Application deadlines: 1/15, 11/15 for early decision plan 1, 1/15 for early decision plan 2. Notification: 4/1, 12/15 for early decision plan 1, 2/15 for early decision plan 2. SAT Reasoning Test deadline: 2/1. SAT Subject Test deadline: 2/1. Transfer credits accepted: Yes. Applicants placed on waiting list: 2,459. Wait-listed applicants offered admission: 137. Early decision applicants: 705. Early decision applicants admitted: 358.

Costs Per Year: Application fee: $65. One-time mandatory fee: $150. Comprehensive fee: $68,764 includes full-time tuition ($53,258), mandatory fees ($1012), and college room and board ($14,494). College room only: $8568. Full-time tuition and fees vary according to course load. Room and board charges vary according to board plan and housing facility. Part-time tuition: $1775 per credit hour. Part-time mandatory fees: $25 per term. Part-time tuition and fees vary according to course load.

Collegiate Environment: Orientation program. Drama-theater group, choral group, student-run newspaper, radio station. Social organizations: 114 open to all. Most popular organizations: Student Government Association, Student radio station (WSPN), Benefaction (Student Volunteer), Outing Club, UJIMA. Major annual events: Fun Day, National College Comedy Festival, Earth Day Festival. Student services: health clinic, personal-psychological counseling. Campus security: 24-hour emergency response devices and patrols, late night transport-escort service, controlled dormitory access. College housing designed to accommodate 2,126 students; 2,184 undergraduates lived in college housing during 2018-19. Freshmen guaranteed college housing. On-campus residence required through sophomore year. Options: coed, women-only housing available. Scribner Library. Books: 415,117 (physical), 85,791 (digital/electronic); Serial titles: 2,129 (physical); Databases: 404. Weekly public service hours: 109; students can reserve study rooms.

Community Environment: This resort is famous for the beauty of its setting, the reputed health-giving properties of its water and the gaiety of its summer life. It is also gaining popularity as a winter sport center with downhill and cross-country skiing available nearby. The area has rail, bus, and airline service. Activities to be found within the area include Saratoga Performing Arts Center (summer home of the New York Ballet, Philadelphia Orchestra, and the Acting Company), thoroughbred racing, night harness racing, Yaddo Artist's Colony, Congress Park, Newport Jazz Festival, Petrified Sea Gardens, State Tree Nursery, Grant's Cottage on Mount McGregor, and the Saratoga Historical Museum in the Canfield Casino. Saratoga has churches representing the major denominations. Part-time employment is available.

■ STATE UNIVERSITY OF NEW YORK BROOME COMMUNITY COLLEGE
907 Upper Front St.
Binghamton, NY 13905
Tel: (607)778-5000
E-mail: admissions@sunybroome.edu
Web Site: www.sunybroome.edu

Description: State and locally supported, 2-year, coed. Part of State University of New York System. Awards certificates, transfer associate, and terminal associate degrees. Founded 1946. Setting: 223-acre suburban campus. Endowment: $1.3 million. Educational spending for the previous fiscal year: $4349 per student. Total enrollment: 6,877. Faculty: 406 (141 full-time, 265 part-time). Full-time: 4,655 students, 52% women, 48% men. Part-time: 2,222 students, 61% women, 39% men. Students come from 26 states and territories, 43 other countries, 1% from out-of-state. 29% 25 or older, 6% transferred in. Core. Calendar: semesters. Academic remediation for entering students, ESL program, services for LD students, advanced placement, self-designed majors, honors program, independent study, distance learning, summer session for credit, part-time degree program, external degree program, adult/continuing education programs, internships. Off campus study at State University of New York at Binghamton. Study abroad program.

Entrance Requirements: Open admission except for allied health, engineering technology, computer science programs. Options: electronic application, early admission. Required: high school transcript. Required for some: interview. Entrance: noncompetitive. Application deadline: rolling. Notification: continuous. Preference given to county residents.

Collegiate Environment: Orientation program. Choral group, student-run newspaper. Social organizations: 44 open to all. Most popular organizations: Broome Early Childhood Organization, Differentially Disabled Student Association, Ecology Club, Phi Theta Kappa, Criminal Justice Club. Major annual events: Student Activities Day, Convocation, Festival of the Arts. Student services: health clinic, personal-psychological counseling. Campus security: 24-hour emergency response devices and patrols. Cecil C. Tyrrell Learning Resources Center. Operations spending for the previous fiscal year: $833,029. 550 computers available on campus for general student use. A campuswide network can be accessed from off-campus. Students can access the following: online class registration. Staffed computer lab on campus.

■ STATE UNIVERSITY OF NEW YORK COLLEGE OF AGRICULTURE AND TECHNOLOGY AT COBLESKILL
State Rte. 7
Cobleskill, NY 12043
Tel: (518)255-5011; Free: 800-295-8988
Fax: (518)255-5333
E-mail: admissions@cobleskill.edu
Web Site: www.cobleskill.edu
Description: State-supported, 4-year, coed. Part of State University of New York System. Awards associate and bachelor's degrees. Founded 1916. Setting: 950-acre small town campus with easy access to Albany, NY. Endowment: $2.5 million. Research spending for the previous fiscal year: $130,844. Educational spending for the previous fiscal year: $7524 per student. Total enrollment: 2,298. Faculty: 178 (105 full-time, 73 part-time). Student-undergrad faculty ratio is 16:1. 3,089 applied, 94% were admitted. Full-time: 2,193 students, 52% women, 48% men. Part-time: 105 students, 60% women, 40% men. Students come from 17 states and territories, 10 other countries, 8% from out-of-state. 0.7% American Indian or Alaska Native, non-Hispanic/Latino; 4% Hispanic/Latino; 13% Black or African American, non-Hispanic/Latino; 2% Asian, non-Hispanic/Latino; 0.9% international. 9% 25 or older, 58% live on campus, 10% transferred in. Retention: 72% of full-time freshmen returned the following year. Academic areas with the most degrees conferred: business/marketing; natural resources/environmental science; agriculture. Core. Calendar: semesters. Academic remediation for entering students, ESL program, services for LD students, advanced placement, honors program, summer session for credit, part-time degree program, adult/continuing education programs, co-op programs and internships. Off campus study at other units of the State University of New York System. Study abroad program.
Entrance Requirements: Options: electronic application, early admission. Required: high school transcript. Required for some: essay, 3 recommendations, interview, SAT or ACT. Entrance: minimally difficult. Application deadline: rolling. Notification: continuous. SAT Reasoning Test deadline: 8/1. SAT Subject Test deadline: 8/1. Transfer credits accepted: Yes. Applicants placed on waiting list: 10. Wait-listed applicants offered admission: 6.
Costs Per Year: Application fee: $50. State resident tuition: $6870 full-time, $286.25 per credit hour part-time. Nonresident tuition: $16,650 full-time, $693.75 per credit hour part-time. Mandatory fees: $1784 full-time, $71.23 per credit hour part-time. Full-time tuition and fees vary according to course level and degree level. Part-time tuition and fees vary according to course level and degree level. College room and board: $13,350. College room only: $7960. Room and board charges vary according to board plan and housing facility.
Collegiate Environment: Orientation program. Drama-theater group, choral group. Social organizations: 46 open to all. Most popular organizations: Dairy Cattle Club, Wildlife Society, Cobleskill Christian Fellowship, Woodsmen's Club, American Fisheries Society. Major annual events: Kick-Off Super Bowl Party, Fisheries & Wildlife Festival, Spring Fling. Student services: health clinic, personal-psychological counseling. Campus security: 24-hour emergency response devices and patrols, student patrols, late night transport-escort service, controlled dormitory access, bicycle patrols, horse-mounted patrols. Jared van Wagenen Library. Books: 53,260 (physical), 54,322 (digital/electronic); Serial titles: 200 (physical), 91,655 (digital/electronic); Databases: 60. Weekly public service hours: 76; study areas open 24 hours, 5-7 days a week; students can reserve study rooms. Operations spending for the previous fiscal year: $607,948. 504 computers available on campus for general student use. A campuswide network can be accessed. Students can access the following: online class registration, web-based printing services. Staffed computer lab on campus provides training in use of computers.

■ STATE UNIVERSITY OF NEW YORK COLLEGE OF AGRICULTURE & TECHNOLOGY AT MORRISVILLE
80 Eaton St.
Morrisville, NY 13408
Tel: (315)684-6000; Free: 800-258-0111
Fax: (315)684-6116

Web Site: www.morrisville.edu
Description: State-supported, 4-year, coed. Part of State University of New York System. Awards associate and bachelor's degrees. Founded 1908. Setting: 185-acre rural campus with easy access to Syracuse. Total enrollment: 3,003. Faculty: 253 (139 full-time, 114 part-time). Student-undergrad faculty ratio is 11:1. 4,031 applied, 77% were admitted. 3% from top 10% of their high school class, 13% from top quarter, 45% from top half. Full-time: 2,624 students, 49% women, 51% men. Part-time: 379 students, 57% women, 43% men. Students come from 22 states and territories, 11 other countries, 6% from out-of-state. 0.4% American Indian or Alaska Native, non-Hispanic/Latino; 8% Hispanic/Latino; 17% Black or African American, non-Hispanic/Latino; 1% Asian, non-Hispanic/Latino; 2% international. 3% 25 or older, 53% live on campus, 7% transferred in. Retention: 65% of full-time freshmen returned the following year. Academic areas with the most degrees conferred: agriculture; business/marketing; homeland security, law enforcement, firefighting, and protective services. Core. Calendar: semesters. Academic remediation for entering students, services for LD students, advanced placement, self-designed majors, independent study, distance learning, double major, summer session for credit, part-time degree program, co-op programs and internships. Off campus study at other units of the State University of New York System. Study abroad program. ROTC: Army (c), Air Force (c).
Entrance Requirements: Options: electronic application, deferred admission. Required: essay, high school transcript. Recommended: minimum 2 high school GPA, recommendations, interview, SAT or ACT. Required for some: minimum 2.5 high school GPA, recommendations, SAT or ACT. Entrance: moderately difficult. Application deadline: 8/15. Notification: continuous. SAT Reasoning Test deadline: 8/14. SAT Subject Test deadline: 8/14. Transfer credits accepted: Yes.
Costs Per Year: Application fee: $50. State resident tuition: $6870 full-time, $286 per credit hour part-time. Nonresident tuition: $16,320 full-time, $680 per credit hour part-time. Mandatory fees: $1611 full-time, $67.60 per credit hour part-time. Full-time tuition and fees vary according to course level, degree level, location, and program. Part-time tuition and fees vary according to class time, course level, course load, degree level, location, and program. College room and board: $13,550. College room only: $7800. Room and board charges vary according to board plan, housing facility, and location.
Collegiate Environment: Orientation program. Drama-theater group, student-run newspaper, radio station. Social organizations: 40 open to all; 15% of eligible men and 15% of eligible women are members. Most popular organizations: Campus Activities Board, Conservation Tri Society, CASU, CollegiateFFA, Automotive Club. Major annual events: Mustang Weekend, Winterfest, SpringJam. Student services: health clinic, personal-psychological counseling. Campus security: 24-hour emergency response devices and patrols, student patrols, late night transport-escort service, controlled dormitory access. Morrisville State Library (Butcher Library) plus 1 other. Students can reserve study rooms. 100 computers available on campus for general student use. Computer purchase/lease plans available. A campuswide network can be accessed from student residence rooms and from off campus. Students can access the following: online class registration. Staffed computer lab on campus provides training in use of computers, software, and the Internet.

■ STATE UNIVERSITY OF NEW YORK COLLEGE AT CORTLAND
PO Box 2000
Cortland, NY 13045
Tel: (607)753-2011
Fax: (607)753-5999
E-mail: admissions@cortland.edu
Web Site: www.cortland.edu
Description: State-supported, comprehensive, coed. Part of State University of New York System. Awards bachelor's and master's degrees and post-master's certificates. Founded 1868. Setting: 191-acre small town campus with easy access to Syracuse. Total enrollment: 6,913. Faculty: 619 (309 full-time, 310 part-time). Student-undergrad faculty ratio is 16:1. 11,909 applied, 48% were admitted. 11% from top 10% of their high school class, 42% from top quarter, 89% from top half. Full-time: 6,196 students, 56% women, 44% men. Part-time: 150 students, 57% women, 43% men. 4% from out-of-state. 0.2% American Indian or Alaska Native, non-Hispanic/Latino; 13% Hispanic/Latino; 6% Black or African American, non-Hispanic/Latino; 1% Asian, non-Hispanic/Latino; 0.1% Native Hawaiian or other Pacific Islander, non-Hispanic/Latino; 0.7% international. 3% 25 or older, 10% transferred in. Retention: 80% of full-time freshmen returned the follow-

ing year. Calendar: semesters. Adult/continuing education programs. Off campus study at other units of the State University of New York System. ROTC: Army (c), Air Force (c).

Entrance Requirements: Options: electronic application, early admission, early action, deferred admission, international baccalaureate accepted. Required: essay, high school transcript, minimum 2.3 high school GPA, 1 recommendation. Recommended: minimum 3 high school GPA, 3 recommendations, interview. Required for some: SAT or ACT. Entrance: moderately difficult.

Costs Per Year: Application fee: $50. State resident tuition: $6870 full-time, $286 per credit hour part-time. Nonresident tuition: $16,650 full-time, $694 per credit hour part-time. Mandatory fees: $1666 full-time. Full-time tuition and fees vary according to course load and degree level. Part-time tuition varies according to course load and degree level. College room and board: $12,486. College room only: $7976. Room and board charges vary according to board plan and housing facility.

Collegiate Environment: Orientation program. Drama-theater group, choral group, student-run newspaper, radio station. Major annual event: Cortaca (annual Cortland vs. Ithaca football game). Campus security: 24-hour emergency response devices and patrols, late night transport-escort service. Memorial Library.

■ **STATE UNIVERSITY OF NEW YORK COLLEGE OF ENVIRONMENTAL SCIENCE AND FORESTRY**
1 Forestry Dr.
Syracuse, NY 13210-2779
Tel: (315)470-6500
Fax: (315)470-6933
E-mail: esfinfo@esf.edu
Web Site: www.esf.edu

Description: State-supported, university, coed. Part of State University of New York System. Awards associate, bachelor's, master's, and doctoral degrees. Founded 1911. Setting: 17-acre urban campus with easy access to Syracuse. Endowment: $37.6 million. Research spending for the previous fiscal year: $18.7 million. Educational spending for the previous fiscal year: $18,131 per student. Total enrollment: 2,256. Faculty: 172 (118 full-time, 54 part-time). Student-undergrad faculty ratio is 13:1. 2,018 applied, 61% were admitted. 25% from top 10% of their high school class, 63% from top quarter, 95% from top half. Full-time: 1,777 students, 47% women, 53% men. Part-time: 84 students, 54% women, 46% men. 19% from out-of-state. 0.2% American Indian or Alaska Native, non-Hispanic/Latino; 6% Hispanic/Latino; 1% Black or African American, non-Hispanic/Latino; 4% Asian, non-Hispanic/Latino; 3% international. 6% 25 or older, 35% live on campus, 13% transferred in. Retention: 84% of full-time freshmen returned the following year. Academic areas with the most degrees conferred: biological/life sciences; natural resources/environmental science; engineering. Core. Calendar: semesters. ESL program, services for LD students, advanced placement, accelerated degree program, freshman honors college, honors program, independent study, distance learning, double major, summer session for credit, part-time degree program, co-op programs and internships, graduate courses open to undergrads. Off campus study at State University of New York (all 64 campuses) and Syracuse University. Study abroad program. ROTC: Army (c), Air Force (c).

Entrance Requirements: Options: electronic application, early admission, early decision, deferred admission, international baccalaureate accepted. Required: essay, high school transcript, minimum 2.5 high school GPA, SAT or ACT. Recommended: 1 recommendation, interview. Entrance: very difficult. Application deadlines: 2/1, rolling for nonresidents, 12/1 for early decision. Notification: continuous until 2/1, continuous for nonresidents. SAT Reasoning Test deadline: 3/1. SAT Subject Test deadline: 3/1. Transfer credits accepted: Yes. Applicants placed on waiting list: 252. Wait-listed applicants offered admission: 10. Early decision applicants: 163. Early decision applicants admitted: 131.

Costs Per Year: Application fee: $50. State resident tuition: $6870 full-time, $286 per credit hour part-time. Nonresident tuition: $16,650 full-time, $694 per credit hour part-time. Mandatory fees: $1934 full-time, $86.58 per credit hour part-time. Full-time tuition and fees vary according to location. Part-time tuition and fees vary according to course load and location. College room and board: $16,440. College room only: $8600. Room and board charges vary according to board plan, housing facility, and location.

Collegiate Environment: Orientation program. Drama-theater group, choral group, marching band, student-run newspaper. Social organizations: 350 open to all. Most popular organizations: Bob Marshall/Outing Club, Forestry Club, Student Environmental Action Coalition, Student Green Campus Initia-

tive, Alpha Phi Omega (Service). Major annual events: Earth Day, Family and Friends Fall Barbecue, Awards Banquet. Student services: legal services, health clinic, personal-psychological counseling, women's center. Campus security: 24-hour emergency response devices and patrols, late night transport-escort service, controlled dormitory access. 600 college housing spaces available; all were occupied in 2018-19. Freshmen guaranteed college housing. On-campus residence required in freshman year. Option: coed housing available. F. Franklin Moon Library plus 1 other. Books: 57,565 (physical), 444,963 (digital/electronic); Serial titles: 1,568 (physical), 163,166 (digital/electronic); Databases: 181. Weekly public service hours: 97. Operations spending for the previous fiscal year: $1.3 million. 350 computers available on campus for general student use. Computer purchase/lease plans available. A campuswide network can be accessed from student residence rooms and from off campus. Students can access the following: online class registration. Staffed computer lab on campus.

Community Environment: See Syracuse University.

■ **STATE UNIVERSITY OF NEW YORK COLLEGE AT GENESEO**
1 College Cir.
Geneseo, NY 14454-1401
Tel: (585)245-5000; Free: 866-245-5211
Fax: (585)245-5005
E-mail: admissions@geneseo.edu
Web Site: www.geneseo.edu

Description: State-supported, comprehensive, coed. Part of State University of New York. Awards bachelor's and master's degrees. Founded 1871. Setting: 220-acre small town campus with easy access to Rochester. Endowment: $36.5 million. Research spending for the previous fiscal year: $1.1 million. Educational spending for the previous fiscal year: $10,252 per student. Total enrollment: 5,541. Faculty: 379 (256 full-time, 123 part-time). Student-undergrad faculty ratio is 19:1. 10,548 applied, 65% were admitted. 26% from top 10% of their high school class, 60% from top quarter, 93% from top half. 23 valedictorians. Full-time: 5,304 students, 61% women, 39% men. Part-time: 143 students, 52% women, 48% men. Students come from 27 states and territories, 26 other countries, 2% from out-of-state. 0.1% American Indian or Alaska Native, non-Hispanic/Latino; 9% Hispanic/Latino; 3% Black or African American, non-Hispanic/Latino; 6% Asian, non-Hispanic/Latino; 0.1% Native Hawaiian or other Pacific Islander, non-Hispanic/Latino; 1% international. 2% 25 or older, 55% live on campus, 5% transferred in. Retention: 85% of full-time freshmen returned the following year. Academic areas with the most degrees conferred: social sciences; psychology; business/marketing. Core. Calendar: semesters. ESL program, services for LD students, advanced placement, honors program, independent study, distance learning, double major, summer session for credit, part-time degree program, internships, graduate courses open to undergrads. Off campus study at Rochester Area Colleges. Study abroad program. ROTC: Army (c), Air Force (c).

Entrance Requirements: Options: electronic application, early admission, early decision, deferred admission, international baccalaureate accepted. Required: high school transcript, SAT or ACT. Recommended: essay, 1 recommendation. Entrance: moderately difficult. Application deadlines: 1/1, 11/15 for early decision. Notification: 3/1, 12/15 for early decision. SAT Reasoning Test deadline: 1/1. Transfer credits accepted: Yes. Applicants placed on waiting list: 2,182. Wait-listed applicants offered admission: 669. Early decision applicants: 300. Early decision applicants admitted: 253.

Costs Per Year: Application fee: $50. State resident tuition: $6870 full-time, $286 per credit hour part-time. Nonresident tuition: $16,650 full-time, $694 per credit hour part-time. Mandatory fees: $1781 full-time, $74.05 per credit hour part-time. Part-time tuition and fees vary according to course load. College room and board: $13,610. College room only: $8126. Room and board charges vary according to board plan and housing facility.

Collegiate Environment: Orientation program. Drama-theater group, choral group, student-run newspaper, radio station. Social organizations: 180 open to all; national fraternities, national sororities, local fraternities, local sororities; 20% of eligible men and 21% of eligible women are members. Most popular organizations: Phi Alpha Delta, Orchesis, Newman Catholic Community, Golden Key, Alpha Phi Omega. Major annual events: Relay for Life, Student Organization Expo, Great Day. Student services: legal services, health clinic, personal-psychological counseling. Campus security: 24-hour emergency response devices and patrols, student patrols, late night transport-escort service, controlled dormitory access. 3,255 college housing spaces available; 3,010 were occupied in 2018-19. Freshmen guaranteed college housing. On-campus residence required through sophomore year. Option: coed housing available. Milne Library plus 1 other. Books: 330,177 (physical), 64,961 (digital/electronic); Serial titles: 20 (physical), 2,226 (digital/electronic); Databases: 167. Students can reserve study rooms. Operations spending for the previous fiscal year: $2.1 million. 338 computers available on campus for general student use. A computer is required for all students. A campuswide network can be accessed from student residence rooms and from off campus. Students can access the following: online class registration. Staffed computer lab on campus provides training in use of computers, software, and the Internet.

■ **STATE UNIVERSITY OF NEW YORK COLLEGE AT OLD WESTBURY**
PO Box 210
Old Westbury, NY 11568-0210
Tel: (516)876-3000
Fax: (516)876-3307
E-mail: enroll@oldwestbury.edu
Web Site: www.oldwestbury.edu
Description: State-supported, comprehensive, coed. Part of State University of New York System. Awards bachelor's and master's degrees and post-master's certificates. Founded 1965. Setting: 604-acre suburban campus with easy access to New York City. Total enrollment: 4,461. Faculty: 351 (166 full-time, 185 part-time). Student-undergrad faculty ratio is 16:1. 3,545 applied, 69% were admitted. Full-time: 3,632 students, 59% women, 41% men. Part-time: 610 students, 59% women, 41% men. Students come from 14 states and territories, 11 other countries, 1% from out-of-state. 0.3% American Indian or Alaska Native, non-Hispanic/Latino; 24% Hispanic/Latino; 27% Black or African American, non-Hispanic/Latino; 11% Asian, non-Hispanic/Latino; 0.3% Native Hawaiian or other Pacific Islander, non-Hispanic/Latino; 0.1% international. 24% 25 or older, 19% live on campus, 20% transferred in. Retention: 81% of full-time freshmen returned the following year. Academic areas with the most degrees conferred: business/marketing; social sciences; psychology. Core. Calendar: semesters. Academic remediation for entering students, services for LD students, advanced placement, freshman honors college, honors program, independent study, distance learning, double major, summer session for credit, part-time degree program, internships. Off campus study at other units of the State University of New York System, Long Island University, C.W. Post Campus, New York Institute of Technology. Study abroad program. ROTC: Army (c), Air Force (c).
Entrance Requirements: Options: electronic application, early admission, early decision, deferred admission, international baccalaureate accepted. Required: essay, high school transcript, 2 recommendations, SAT or ACT. Required for some: interview. Entrance: moderately difficult. Application deadlines: rolling, 11/1 for early decision. Notification: continuous, 12/15 for early decision. SAT Reasoning Test deadline: 6/1. SAT Subject Test deadline: 6/1.
Costs Per Year: Application fee: $50. State resident tuition: $6670 full-time, $278 per credit hour part-time. Nonresident tuition: $16,320 full-time, $680 per credit hour part-time. Mandatory fees: $1213 full-time, $24.35 per credit hour part-time, $163 per term part-time. Part-time tuition and fees vary according to course load. College room and board: $11,020. College room only: $7300. Room and board charges vary according to housing facility.
Collegiate Environment: Orientation program. Drama-theater group, choral group, student-run newspaper, radio station. Social organizations: 55 open to all; national fraternities, national sororities, local fraternities, local sororities. Most popular organizations: Student Government Association, Alianza Latina, PRIDE, Step Tunes, Anime Magna Games Club. Major annual events: Midnight Madness, Meet the Greeks, Step and Stroll Exhibition. Student services: health clinic, personal-psychological counseling, women's center. Campus security: 24-hour emergency response devices and patrols, student patrols, late night transport-escort service, controlled dormitory access. SUNY College at Old Westbury Library plus 1 other. Books: 156,872 (physical), 144,263 (digital/electronic); Databases: 138. Weekly public service hours: 99. 480 computers available on campus for general student use. A campuswide network can be accessed from student residence rooms and from off campus. Students can access the following: online class registration, financial aid, billing information. Staffed computer lab on campus provides training in use of computers, software, and the Internet.

■ **STATE UNIVERSITY OF NEW YORK COLLEGE AT ONEONTA**
Ravine Pky.
Oneonta, NY 13820-4015
Tel: (607)436-3500; Free: 800-SUNY-123
Fax: (607)436-3074

E-mail: admissions@oneonta.edu
Web Site: www.oneonta.edu
Description: State-supported, comprehensive, coed. Part of State University of New York System. Awards bachelor's degrees and post-master's certificates. Founded 1889. Setting: 250-acre small town campus. Endowment: $49.1 million. Research spending for the previous fiscal year: $364,761. Educational spending for the previous fiscal year: $11,127 per student. Total enrollment: 6,358. Faculty: 490 (286 full-time, 204 part-time). Student-undergrad faculty ratio is 17:1. 11,100 applied, 60% were admitted. 11% from top 10% of their high school class, 39% from top quarter, 83% from top half. Full-time: 5,828 students, 60% women, 40% men. Part-time: 112 students, 45% women, 55% men. Students come from 18 states and territories, 32 other countries, 1% from out-of-state. 0.3% American Indian or Alaska Native, non-Hispanic/Latino; 14% Hispanic/Latino; 4% Black or African American, non-Hispanic/Latino; 2% Asian, non-Hispanic/Latino; 0.1% Native Hawaiian or other Pacific Islander, non-Hispanic/Latino; 0.8% international. 2% 25 or older, 59% live on campus, 10% transferred in. Retention: 85% of full-time freshmen returned the following year. Academic areas with the most degrees conferred: communication/journalism; business/marketing; family and consumer sciences. Core. Calendar: semesters. Academic remediation for entering students, ESL program, services for LD students, advanced placement, honors program, independent study, distance learning, double major, summer session for credit, part-time degree program, adult/continuing education programs, internships, graduate courses open to undergrads. Off campus study at Hartwick College. Study abroad program.
Entrance Requirements: Options: electronic application, early admission, early action, deferred admission, international baccalaureate accepted. Required: essay, high school transcript, SAT or ACT. Recommended: minimum 3 high school GPA, 3 recommendations. Entrance: very difficult. Application deadlines: rolling, 11/15 for early action. Notification: continuous, 12/1 for early action. SAT Reasoning Test deadline: 2/15. Transfer credits accepted: Yes.
Costs Per Year: Application fee: $50. State resident tuition: $6670 full-time, $278 per credit hour part-time. Nonresident tuition: $16,320 full-time, $680 per credit hour part-time. Mandatory fees: $1466 full-time, $42.35 per credit hour part-time. Part-time tuition and fees vary according to course load. College room and board: $12,658. College room only: $8350. Room and board charges vary according to housing facility.
Collegiate Environment: Orientation program. Drama-theater group, choral group, student-run newspaper, radio station. Social organizations: 115 open to all; national fraternities, national sororities, local fraternities, local sororities; 6% of eligible men and 7% of eligible women are members. Most popular organizations: Center for Social Responsibility and Community, Music Industry Club, Terpsichorean Dance Company, Student Government, Zombie Defense Corps. Major annual events: Homecoming and Family Weekend, Club Expo, Spring Weekend. Student services: health clinic, personal-psychological counseling, women's center. Campus security: 24-hour emergency response devices and patrols, late night transport-escort service, controlled dormitory access, Oneonta Emergency Squad: an organization of student volunteers with first responder credential. Milne Library. Books: 394,015 (physical), 417,737 (digital/electronic); Serial titles: 60 (physical), 119,484 (digital/electronic); Databases: 251. Students can reserve study rooms. Operations spending for the previous fiscal year: $2.4 million. 700 computers available on campus for general student use. Computer purchase/lease plans available. A campuswide network can be accessed from student residence rooms and from off campus. Students can access the following: online class registration, digital video/audio editing suites, presentation rehearsal room using lecture capture software, large format printing, network file storage space. Staffed computer lab on campus (open 24 hours a day) provides training in use of computers, software, and the Internet.

■ **STATE UNIVERSITY OF NEW YORK COLLEGE AT POTSDAM**
44 Pierrepont Ave.
Potsdam, NY 13676
Tel: (315)267-2000; Free: 877-POTSDAM
Fax: (315)267-2163
E-mail: admissions@potsdam.edu
Web Site: www.potsdam.edu
Description: State-supported, comprehensive, coed. Part of State University of New York System. Awards bachelor's and master's degrees and post-master's certificates. Founded 1816. Setting: 240-acre small town campus. Endowment: $32.9 million. Research spending for the previous fis-

cal year: $135,284. Educational spending for the previous fiscal year: $13,844 per student. Total enrollment: 3,521. Faculty: 346 (254 full-time, 92 part-time). Student-undergrad faculty ratio is 11:1. 6,423 applied, 64% were admitted. 15% from top 10% of their high school class, 23% from top quarter, 85% from top half. Full-time: 3,221 students, 60% women, 40% men. Part-time: 77 students, 47% women, 53% men. Students come from 28 states and territories, 7 other countries, 4% from out-of-state. 2% American Indian or Alaska Native, non-Hispanic/Latino; 15% Hispanic/Latino; 13% Black or African American, non-Hispanic/Latino; 2% Asian, non-Hispanic/Latino; 0.1% Native Hawaiian or other Pacific Islander, non-Hispanic/Latino; 0.2% international. 5% 25 or older, 59% live on campus, 7% transferred in. Retention: 75% of full-time freshmen returned the following year. Academic areas with the most degrees conferred: education; visual and performing arts; social sciences. Core. Calendar: semesters. Services for LD students, advanced placement, self-designed majors, honors program, independent study, distance learning, double major, summer session for credit, part-time degree program, internships, graduate courses open to undergrads. Off campus study at Associated Colleges of the St. Lawrence Valley, National Student Exchange. Study abroad program. ROTC: Army (c), Air Force (c).

Entrance Requirements: Options: electronic application, early admission, deferred admission, international baccalaureate accepted. Required: high school transcript, minimum 2.5 high school GPA, 1 recommendation. Required for some: essay, minimum 2 high school GPA, DVD audition for music. Entrance: moderately difficult. Application deadline: rolling. Notification: continuous. Transfer credits accepted: Yes.

Costs Per Year: Application fee: $50. State resident tuition: $6870 full-time, $286 per credit hour part-time. Nonresident tuition: $16,650 full-time, $694 per credit hour part-time. Mandatory fees: $1592 full-time, $84.50 per credit hour part-time. Full-time tuition and fees vary according to course load. Part-time tuition and fees vary according to course load. College room and board: $13,390. College room only: $7760. Room and board charges vary according to board plan and housing facility.

Collegiate Environment: Orientation program. Drama-theater group, choral group, student-run newspaper, radio station. Social organizations: 90 open to all; national fraternities, national sororities, local fraternities, local sororities; 3% of eligible men and 7% of eligible women are members. Most popular organizations: Student Government Association, Crane Student Association, Black Student Alliance, SOCO LOCO, Musical Theatre Organization. Major annual events: First Saturday, Welcome Weekend Carnival, Loko Festival. Student services: legal services, health clinic, personal-psychological counseling, women's center. Campus security: 24-hour emergency response devices and patrols, late night transport-escort service, controlled dormitory access, RAVE Guardian, Video Surveillance System, security escort service, self-defense education. 2,715 college housing spaces available; 1,955 were occupied in 2018-19. Freshmen guaranteed college housing. On-campus residence required through sophomore year. Option: coed housing available. F. W. Crumb Memorial Library plus 1 other. Books: 249,807 (physical), 43,861 (digital/electronic); Serial titles: 3,227 (physical), 107,915 (digital/electronic); Databases: 151. Weekly public service hours: 119; study areas open 24 hours, 5-7 days a week; students can reserve study rooms. Operations spending for the previous fiscal year: $1.5 million. 608 computers available on campus for general student use. Computer purchase/lease plans available. A campuswide network can be accessed. Students can access the following: online class registration, online access to financial aid status, unofficial transcripts, billing, meal plan and housing sign-up. Staffed computer lab on campus.

■ STATE UNIVERSITY OF NEW YORK COLLEGE OF TECHNOLOGY AT ALFRED

10 Upper College Dr.
Alfred, NY 14802
Tel: (607)587-4111; Free: 800-4-ALFRED
Fax: (607)587-4299
E-mail: admissions@alfredstate.edu
Web Site: www.alfredstate.edu

Description: State-supported, primarily 2-year, coed. Part of State University of New York System. Awards certificates, transfer associate, terminal associate, and bachelor's degrees. Founded 1908. Setting: 1,084-acre rural campus with easy access to Rochester. Endowment: $5.6 million. Research spending for the previous fiscal year: $95,581. Educational spending for the previous fiscal year: $10,234 per student. Total enrollment: 3,737. Faculty: 262 (170 full-time, 92 part-time). Student-undergrad faculty ratio is 18:1. 7,065 applied, 63% were admitted. Full-time: 3,456 students, 35% women, 65% men. Part-time: 281 students, 68% women, 32% men.

Students come from 32 states and territories, 15 other countries, 4% from out-of-state. 0.3% American Indian or Alaska Native, non-Hispanic/Latino; 9% Hispanic/Latino; 12% Black or African American, non-Hispanic/Latino; 1% Asian, non-Hispanic/Latino; 0.1% Native Hawaiian or other Pacific Islander, non-Hispanic/Latino; 0.7% international. 12% 25 or older, 63% live on campus, 8% transferred in. Retention: 69% of full-time freshmen returned the following year. Academic areas with the most degrees conferred: business/marketing; engineering technologies; health professions and related sciences. Calendar: semesters. Academic remediation for entering students, ESL program, services for LD students, advanced placement, accelerated degree program, self-designed majors, honors program, independent study, distance learning, double major, summer session for credit, part-time degree program, adult/continuing education programs, co-op programs and internships. Off campus study at Alfred University, Rochester Area Colleges, Consortium of Western New York Colleges, St. Bonaventure University (ROTC), Dutchess Community College. Study abroad program. ROTC: Army (c).

Entrance Requirements: Options: electronic application, international baccalaureate accepted. Required: high school transcript, minimum 2 high school GPA, Common Application with essay on supplemental application. Recommended: essay, interview, SAT or ACT. Entrance: moderately difficult. Application deadline: rolling. Notification: continuous. Transfer credits accepted: Yes. Applicants placed on waiting list: 160. Wait-listed applicants offered admission: 64.

Costs Per Year: Application fee: $50. One-time mandatory fee: $110. Area resident tuition: $6870 full-time, $286 per credit hour part-time. State resident tuition: $6870 full-time, $286 per credit hour part-time. Nonresident tuition: $10,740 full-time, $448 per credit hour part-time. Mandatory fees: $1700 full-time, $66 per credit hour part-time, $10. College room and board: $12,570. College room only: $7650.

Collegiate Environment: Orientation program. Drama-theater group, choral group, student-run newspaper, radio station. Social organizations: 125 open to all; local fraternities, local sororities; 5% of eligible men and 9% of eligible women are members. Most popular organizations: Outdoor Recreation Club, Caribbean Student Association, Alfred Programming Board, Pioneer Woodsmen, Disaster Relief Team. Major annual events: Hot Dog Day, Homecoming, Freshman Carnival. Student services: health clinic, personal-psychological counseling. Campus security: 24-hour emergency response devices and patrols, late night transport-escort service, controlled dormitory access, residence hall entrance guards. 2,607 college housing spaces available; 2,352 were occupied in 2018-19. Freshmen guaranteed college housing. Options: coed, men-only, women-only housing available. Walter C. Hinkle Memorial Library plus 1 other. Books: 33,901 (physical), 1,901 (digital/electronic); Serial titles: 175 (physical); Databases: 214. Weekly public service hours: 88. Operations spending for the previous fiscal year: $520,085. 108 computers available on campus for general student use. Computer purchase/lease plans available. A campuswide network can be accessed from student residence rooms and from off campus. Students can access the following: online class registration. Staffed computer lab on campus provides training in use of computers, software, and the Internet.

■ STATE UNIVERSITY OF NEW YORK COLLEGE OF TECHNOLOGY AT CANTON

Cornell Dr.
Canton, NY 13617
Tel: (315)386-7011; Free: 800-388-7123
Fax: (315)386-7930
E-mail: admissions@canton.edu
Web Site: www.canton.edu

Description: State-supported, 4-year, coed. Part of State University of New York System. Awards associate and bachelor's degrees. Founded 1906. Setting: 555-acre small town campus. Endowment: $11.9 million. Research spending for the previous fiscal year: $42,394. Educational spending for the previous fiscal year: $9846 per student. Total enrollment: 3,180. Faculty: 238 (128 full-time, 110 part-time). Student-undergrad faculty ratio is 17:1. 3,672 applied, 79% were admitted. 5% from top 10% of their high school class, 20% from top quarter, 51% from top half. Full-time: 2,657 students, 55% women, 45% men. Part-time: 523 students, 75% women, 25% men. Students come from 33 states and territories, 17 other countries, 3% from out-of-state. 1% American Indian or Alaska Native, non-Hispanic/Latino; 11% Hispanic/Latino; 15% Black or African American, non-Hispanic/Latino; 1% Asian, non-Hispanic/Latino; 0.1% Native Hawaiian or other Pacific Islander, non-Hispanic/Latino; 2% international. 25% 25 or older, 45% live on campus, 10% transferred in. Retention: 77% of full-time freshmen returned the following year. Academic areas with the most degrees conferred: health professions and related sciences; homeland security, law enforcement, firefighting, and protective services; business/marketing. Core. Calendar: semesters. Academic remediation for entering students, services for LD students, advanced placement, honors program, independent study, distance learning, summer session for credit, co-op programs and internships. Off campus study at Associated Colleges of the St. Lawrence Valley. Study abroad program. ROTC: Army (c), Air Force (c).

Entrance Requirements: Options: electronic application, deferred admission, international baccalaureate accepted. Required: high school transcript. Recommended: minimum 2 high school GPA. Required for some: essay, interview, SAT or ACT. Entrance: minimally difficult. Application deadlines: 8/30, rolling for nonresidents. Notification: continuous, continuous for nonresidents. SAT Reasoning Test deadline: 8/20. Transfer credits accepted: Yes. Applicants placed on waiting list: 38. Wait-listed applicants offered admission: 15.

Costs Per Year: Application fee: $50. One-time mandatory fee: $120. State resident tuition: $6870 full-time, $286 per credit hour part-time. Nonresident tuition: $16,650 full-time, $694 per credit hour part-time. Mandatory fees: $1519 full-time, $61.44 per credit hour part-time, $5 per term part-time. Full-time tuition and fees vary according to degree level. Part-time tuition and fees vary according to degree level. College room and board: $12,900. College room only: $7700. Room and board charges vary according to board plan and housing facility.

Collegiate Environment: Orientation program. Drama-theater group, choral group. Social organizations: 53 open to all; local fraternities, local sororities; 1% of eligible men and 2% of eligible women are members. Most popular organizations: Student Government Alliance, College Activities Board, Greek Council, Brother to Brother, Sister to Sister. Major annual events: Family Weekend, Springfest, Winterfest. Student services: health clinic, personal-psychological counseling. Campus security: 24-hour emergency response devices and patrols, late night transport-escort service, controlled dormitory access, student EMS group. Southworth Library. Books: 23,958 (physical), 168,143 (digital/electronic); Serial titles: 14 (physical), 5,928 (digital/electronic); Databases: 84. Weekly public service hours: 125. 825 computers available on campus for general student use. A campuswide network can be accessed. Students can access the following: online class registration, online bill payment. Staffed computer lab on campus.

■ **STATE UNIVERSITY OF NEW YORK COLLEGE OF TECHNOLOGY AT DELHI**
454 Delhi Dr.
Delhi, NY 13753
Tel: (607)746-4000; Free: 800-96-DELHI
Fax: (607)746-4104
Web Site: www.delhi.edu

Description: State-supported, comprehensive, coed. Part of State University of New York System. Awards associate, bachelor's, and master's degrees. Founded 1913. Setting: 625-acre rural campus. Endowment: $7.4 million. Research spending for the previous fiscal year: $93,627. Educational spending for the previous fiscal year: $10,228 per student. Total enrollment: 3,240. Faculty: 240 (150 full-time, 90 part-time). Student-undergrad faculty ratio is 16:1. 5,935 applied, 64% were admitted. 4% from top 10% of their high school class, 16% from top quarter, 49% from top half. Full-time: 2,514 students, 49% women, 51% men. Part-time: 664 students, 75% women, 25% men. Students come from 19 states and territories, 4 other countries, 4% from out-of-state. 0.5% American Indian or Alaska Native, non-Hispanic/Latino; 14% Hispanic/Latino; 15% Black or African American, non-Hispanic/Latino; 1% Asian, non-Hispanic/Latino; 0.1% Native Hawaiian or other Pacific Islander, non-Hispanic/Latino; 3% international. 25% 25 or older, 52% live on campus, 11% transferred in. Retention: 79% of full-time freshmen returned the following year. Academic areas with the most degrees conferred: health professions and related sciences; business/marketing; homeland security, law enforcement, firefighting, and protective services. Core. Calendar: semesters. Academic remediation for entering students, ESL program, services for LD students, advanced placement, accelerated degree program, honors program, independent study, distance learning, double major, summer session for credit, part-time degree program, adult/continuing education programs, internships, graduate courses open to undergrads. Off campus study at SUNY Delhi offers multiple online programs, as well as numerous opportunities with other colleges, including Onondaga Community College, Schenectady County Community College, Tompkins Cortland Community College, Suffolk County Community College, and more. Please refer to our website or contact our Admissions Office for more details. Study abroad program.

Entrance Requirements: Options: electronic application, deferred admission, international baccalaureate accepted. Required: high school transcript. Recommended: interview. Required for some: minimum 2 high school GPA, 2 recommendations, associate degree for some bachelor programs, RN license for BSN program. Letters of recommendation required at the graduate level. Entrance: moderately difficult. Application deadlines: rolling, 12/1 for early action. Notification: continuous, 12/15 for early action. SAT Reasoning Test deadline: 8/1. SAT Subject Test deadline: 8/1. Transfer credits accepted: Yes. Applicants placed on waiting list: 921. Wait-listed applicants offered admission: 46.

Costs Per Year: Application fee: $50.

Collegiate Environment: Orientation program. Drama-theater group, choral group, student-run newspaper, radio station. Social organizations: 57 open to all; national fraternities, national sororities, local fraternities, local sororities; 10% of eligible men and 7% of eligible women are members. Most popular organizations: New York State Association for Veterinary Technicians, National Student Nursing Association, Black Student Union, Bronco's Finest, Equine Club. Major annual events: Annual Spring Concert, Winterfest, Legacy Event. Student services: health clinic, personal-psychological counseling. Campus security: 24-hour emergency response devices and patrols, late night transport-escort service, controlled dormitory access. College housing designed to accommodate 1,660 students; 1,688 undergraduates lived in college housing during 2018-19. Freshmen given priority for college housing. On-campus residence required through sophomore year. Option: coed housing available. Resnick Library. Books: 37,908 (physical), 152,584 (digital/electronic); Serial titles: 350,364 (physical), 350,364 (digital/electronic); Databases: 68. Weekly public service hours: 93; students can reserve study rooms. Operations spending for the previous fiscal year: $668,207. 102 computers available on campus for general student use. A campuswide network can be accessed from student residence rooms and from off campus. Students can access the following: online class registration. Staffed computer lab on campus provides training in use of computers, software, and the Internet.

■ **STATE UNIVERSITY OF NEW YORK DOWNSTATE MEDICAL CENTER**
450 Clarkson Ave.
Brooklyn, NY 11203-2098
Tel: (718)270-1000
Fax: (718)270-7592
E-mail: admissions@downstate.edu
Web Site: www.downstate.edu

Description: State-supported, upper-level, coed. Part of State University of New York System. Awards bachelor's, master's, and doctoral degrees and post-master's certificates. Founded 1858. Setting: urban campus. Total enrollment: 1,694. Faculty: 981 (838 full-time, 143 part-time). 1,005 applied, 14% were admitted. Full-time: 193 students, 78% women, 22% men. Part-time: 150 students, 90% women, 10% men. 1% from out-of-state. 6% Hispanic/Latino; 39% Black or African American, non-Hispanic/Latino; 14% Asian, non-Hispanic/Latino; 1% international. Academic area with the most degrees conferred: health professions and related sciences. Core. Calendar: semesters. Services for LD students, advanced placement, accelerated degree program, independent study, summer session for credit, part-time degree program, internships. Off campus study.

Collegiate Environment: Orientation program. Student services: health clinic, personal-psychological counseling. Campus security: late night transport-escort service. 183 computers available on campus for general student use. A campuswide network can be accessed from student residence rooms and from off campus. Staffed computer lab on campus.

■ **STATE UNIVERSITY OF NEW YORK EMPIRE STATE COLLEGE**
2 Union Ave.
Saratoga Springs, NY 12866-4391
Tel: (518)587-2100; Free: 800-847-3000
Fax: (518)587-2100
E-mail: admissions@esc.edu
Web Site: www.esc.edu

Description: State-supported, comprehensive, coed. Part of State University of New York System. Awards associate, bachelor's, and master's degrees (branch locations at 7 regional centers with 35 auxiliary units). Founded 1971. Setting: small town campus. Endowment: $19.8 million. Research spending for the previous fiscal year: $18,558. Educational spending for the previous fiscal year: $9178 per student. Total enrollment: 11,024. Faculty: 913 (177 full-time, 736 part-time). Student-undergrad faculty ratio is

15:1. 1,081 applied, 84% were admitted. Full-time: 3,773 students, 71% women, 29% men. Part-time: 6,066 students, 56% women, 44% men. 5% from out-of-state. 0.4% American Indian or Alaska Native, non-Hispanic/Latino; 13% Hispanic/Latino; 15% Black or African American, non-Hispanic/Latino; 3% Asian, non-Hispanic/Latino; 0.2% Native Hawaiian or other Pacific Islander, non-Hispanic/Latino; 0.5% international. 82% 25 or older, 12% transferred in. Academic areas with the most degrees conferred: business/marketing; public administration and social services; health professions and related sciences. Core. Calendar: 5 terms. Services for LD students, advanced placement, accelerated degree program, self-designed majors, independent study, distance learning, double major, summer session for credit, part-time degree program, external degree program, adult/continuing education programs, graduate courses open to undergrads. Off campus study.

Entrance Requirements: Open admission. Options: electronic application, deferred admission, international baccalaureate accepted. Required: essay, high school transcript. Entrance: noncompetitive. Transfer credits accepted: Yes.

Costs Per Year: Application fee: $50. State resident tuition: $6670 full-time, $278 per credit part-time. Nonresident tuition: $16,134 full-time, $680 per credit part-time. Mandatory fees: $535 full-time. Full-time tuition and fees vary according to program. Part-time tuition varies according to program.

Collegiate Environment: Orientation program. Books: 229,000 (digital/electronic); Databases: 94. Operations spending for the previous fiscal year: $671,511. 300 computers available on campus for general student use. A campuswide network can be accessed from off-campus. Students can access the following: online class registration. Staffed computer lab on campus.

■ STATE UNIVERSITY OF NEW YORK AT FREDONIA

280 Central Ave.
Fredonia, NY 14063-1136
Tel: (716)673-3111; Free: 800-252-1212
Fax: (716)673-3249
E-mail: admissions@fredonia.edu
Web Site: www.fredonia.edu

Description: State-supported, comprehensive, coed. Part of State University of New York System. Awards bachelor's and master's degrees and post-master's certificates. Founded 1826. Setting: 249-acre small town campus with easy access to Buffalo. Endowment: $39.6 million. Research spending for the previous fiscal year: $1.1 million. Educational spending for the previous fiscal year: $11,812 per student. Total enrollment: 4,656. Faculty: 425 (249 full-time, 176 part-time). Student-undergrad faculty ratio is 14:1. 6,183 applied, 76% were admitted. 17% from top 10% of their high school class, 43% from top quarter, 76% from top half. 13 valedictorians. Full-time: 3,814 students, 52% women, 48% men. Part-time: 119 students, 45% women, 55% men. Students come from 29 states and territories, 13 other countries, 4% from out-of-state. 0.5% American Indian or Alaska Native, non-Hispanic/Latino; 10% Hispanic/Latino; 9% Black or African American, non-Hispanic/Latino; 2% Asian, non-Hispanic/Latino; 2% international. 4% 25 or older, 55% live on campus, 8% transferred in. Retention: 73% of full-time freshmen returned the following year. Academic areas with the most degrees conferred: business/marketing; education; visual and performing arts. Core. Calendar: semesters. ESL program, services for LD students, advanced placement, accelerated degree program, self-designed majors, honors program, independent study, distance learning, double major, summer session for credit, part-time degree program, adult/continuing education programs, internships, graduate courses open to undergrads. Off campus study at Western New York Consortium. Study abroad program.

Entrance Requirements: Options: electronic application, early admission, deferred admission, international baccalaureate accepted. Required: essay, high school transcript, 1 recommendation, SAT or ACT. Required for some: interview, audition for music, dance and theater programs: portfolio for visual arts and technical theatre programs. Entrance: moderately difficult. Application deadline: rolling. Notification: continuous. Transfer credits accepted: Yes.

Costs Per Year: Application fee: $50. State resident tuition: $6870 full-time, $286 per credit hour part-time. Nonresident tuition: $16,650 full-time, $694 per credit hour part-time. Mandatory fees: $1618 full-time, $67.20 per credit hour part-time. College room and board: $12,350. College room only: $7500. Room and board charges vary according to board plan and housing facility.

Collegiate Environment: Orientation program. Drama-theater group, choral group, student-run newspaper, radio station. Social organizations: 180 open to all; national fraternities, national sororities, local fraternities, local sorori-

ties; 3% of eligible men and 5% of eligible women are members. Most popular organizations: Student Association, Fredonia Radio Systems, Colleges Against Cancer, Applied Communication Association, Spectrum Entertainment Board. Major annual events: Homecoming, Pink-the-Rink, Family Weekend. Student services: legal services, health clinic, personal-psychological counseling. Campus security: 24-hour emergency response devices and patrols, late night transport-escort service, controlled dormitory access. 2,900 college housing spaces available; 2,400 were occupied in 2018-19. Freshmen guaranteed college housing. On-campus residence required through sophomore year. Options: coed, men-only, women-only housing available. Daniel A. Reed Library. Books: 18 million (physical); Serial titles: 48,000 (physical). Weekly public service hours: 68; students can reserve study rooms. Operations spending for the previous fiscal year: $1.4 million. 500 computers available on campus for general student use. Computer purchase/lease plans available. A campuswide network can be accessed. Students can access the following: online class registration. Staffed computer lab on campus provides training in use of computers, software, and the Internet.

■ STATE UNIVERSITY OF NEW YORK MARITIME COLLEGE

6 Pennyfield Ave.
Throggs Neck, NY 10465-4198
Tel: (718)409-7200
Fax: (718)409-7392
E-mail: rhowell@sunymaritime.edu
Web Site: www.sunymaritime.edu

Description: State-supported, comprehensive, coed. Part of State University of New York System. Awards associate, bachelor's, and master's degrees. Founded 1874. Setting: 55-acre urban campus with easy access to New York City. Endowment: $7.7 million. Research spending for the previous fiscal year: $138,241. Educational spending for the previous fiscal year: $4774 per student. Total enrollment: 1,734. Faculty: 146 (92 full-time, 54 part-time). Student-undergrad faculty ratio is 15:1. 1,355 applied, 72% were admitted. 50% from top 10% of their high school class, 50% from top quarter, 100% from top half. Full-time: 1,542 students, 12% women, 88% men. Part-time: 44 students, 14% women, 86% men. Students come from 33 states and territories, 15 other countries, 23% from out-of-state. 0.1% American Indian or Alaska Native, non-Hispanic/Latino; 14% Hispanic/Latino; 5% Black or African American, non-Hispanic/Latino; 4% Asian, non-Hispanic/Latino; 2% international. 7% 25 or older, 89% live on campus, 6% transferred in. Retention: 86% of full-time freshmen returned the following year. Academic areas with the most degrees conferred: engineering; transportation and materials moving; business/marketing. Core. Calendar: semesters plus 2-month summer sea term. Academic remediation for entering students, services for LD students, advanced placement, independent study, distance learning, double major, summer session for credit, part-time degree program, internships, graduate courses open to undergrads. Off campus study. Study abroad program. ROTC: Army (c), Naval.

Entrance Requirements: Options: electronic application, early decision, deferred admission, international baccalaureate accepted. Required: essay, SAT or ACT. Recommended: high school transcript, interview. Entrance: very difficult. Application deadlines: 1/31, 11/1 for early decision. Notification: 3/1, 12/15 for early decision. SAT Reasoning Test deadline: 3/15. SAT Subject Test deadline: 3/15. Transfer credits accepted: Yes. Applicants placed on waiting list: 41. Wait-listed applicants offered admission: 30. Early decision applicants: 101. Early decision applicants admitted: 88.

Costs Per Year: Application fee: $50. State resident tuition: $6870 full-time, $286 per credit hour part-time. Nonresident tuition: $16,650 full-time, $694 per credit hour part-time. Mandatory fees: $1413 full-time, $58.68 per term part-time. Full-time tuition and fees vary according to course load. Part-time tuition and fees vary according to course load. College room and board: $12,522. College room only: $7792. Room and board charges vary according to board plan and housing facility.

Collegiate Environment: Orientation program. Choral group, marching band. Social organizations: 40 open to all. Most popular organizations: Student Government, Maritime Activities and Programs, The Cultural Club, Campus Crusade for Christ, The Maritime Divers Association. Major annual events: Orientation and Indoctrination, Training Ship Cruise (Cadet), Spring Fest. Student services: health clinic, personal-psychological counseling. Campus security: 24-hour emergency response devices and patrols, student patrols, late night transport-escort service, controlled dormitory access. 1,460 college housing spaces available; 1,352 were occupied in 2018-19. No special consideration for freshman housing applicants. On-campus residence required through senior year. Option: coed housing available.

Stephen B. Luce Library. Books: 41,000 (physical), 60,567 (digital/electronic); Serial titles: 125 (physical), 323,000 (digital/electronic); Databases: 68. Weekly public service hours: 111; students can reserve study rooms. Operations spending for the previous fiscal year: $576,575. 160 computers available on campus for general student use. A campuswide network can be accessed from student residence rooms and from off campus. Students can access the following: online class registration. Staffed computer lab on campus.

Community Environment: The College is located on the Throgs Neck Peninsula, a small waterfront community within New York City.

■ STATE UNIVERSITY OF NEW YORK AT NEW PALTZ

1 Hawk Dr.
New Paltz, NY 12561
Tel: (845)257-7869
Fax: (845)257-3209
E-mail: admissions@newpaltz.edu
Web Site: www.newpaltz.edu

Description: State-supported, comprehensive, coed. Part of State University of New York System. Awards bachelor's and master's degrees and post-master's certificates. Founded 1828. Setting: 216-acre small town campus. Endowment: $20.4 million. Research spending for the previous fiscal year: $808,042. Educational spending for the previous fiscal year: $11,411 per student. Total enrollment: 7,565. Faculty: 624 (351 full-time, 273 part-time). Student-undergrad faculty ratio is 16:1. 13,753 applied, 44% were admitted. 31% from top 10% of their high school class, 69% from top quarter, 94% from top half. Full-time: 6,235 students, 62% women, 38% men. Part-time: 498 students, 57% women, 43% men. Students come from 24 states and territories, 37 other countries, 3% from out-of-state. 19% Hispanic/Latino; 6% Black or African American, non-Hispanic/Latino; 5% Asian, non-Hispanic/Latino; 0.1% Native Hawaiian or other Pacific Islander, non-Hispanic/Latino; 2% international. 7% 25 or older, 46% live on campus, 13% transferred in. Retention: 87% of full-time freshmen returned the following year. Academic areas with the most degrees conferred: education; business/marketing; communication/journalism. Core. Calendar: semesters. Academic remediation for entering students, ESL program, services for LD students, advanced placement, self-designed majors, honors program, independent study, distance learning, double major, summer session for credit, part-time degree program, external degree program, co-op programs and internships, graduate courses open to undergrads. Off campus study. Study abroad program.

Entrance Requirements: Options: electronic application, early admission, early action, international baccalaureate accepted. Required: essay, high school transcript, 1 recommendation, SAT or ACT. Required for some: portfolio for art program, audition for music and theater programs. Entrance: very difficult. Application deadlines: 5/1, 11/15 for early action. Notification: continuous, rolling for early action. SAT Reasoning Test deadline: 1/31. Transfer credits accepted: Yes.

Costs Per Year: Application fee: $50. State resident tuition: $6870 full-time, $286 per credit hour part-time. Nonresident tuition: $16,650 full-time, $694 per credit hour part-time. Mandatory fees: $1384 full-time, $40.02 per credit hour part-time, $209.50 per term part-time. College room and board: $13,462. College room only: $8862. Room and board charges vary according to board plan.

Collegiate Environment: Orientation program. Drama-theater group, choral group, student-run newspaper, radio station. Social organizations: national fraternities, national sororities, local fraternities, local sororities. Most popular organizations: Student Association, Residence Hall Student Association, Outing Club, The Oracle Newspaper, United Greek Association. Major annual events: SA Spring Concert, Dance Evolution, Spirit Weekend. Student services: legal services, health clinic, personal-psychological counseling. Campus security: 24-hour emergency response devices and patrols, late night transport-escort service, controlled dormitory access, safety seminars, RAD Women's Self Defense. Sojourner Truth Library. Books: 455,728 (physical), 149,851 (digital/electronic); Serial titles: 234 (physical), 85,306 (digital/electronic); Databases: 98. Weekly public service hours: 103; students can reserve study rooms. Operations spending for the previous fiscal year: $689,760. 800 computers available on campus for general student use. A campuswide network can be accessed from student residence rooms and from off campus. Students can access the following: online class registration. Staffed computer lab on campus provides training in use of computers, software, and the Internet.

■ STATE UNIVERSITY OF NEW YORK AT OSWEGO

7060 Rte. 104
Oswego, NY 13126
Tel: (315)312-2500
Fax: (315)312-5799
E-mail: admiss@oswego.edu
Web Site: www.oswego.edu

Description: State-supported, comprehensive, coed. Part of State University of New York System. Awards bachelor's and master's degrees and post-master's certificates. Founded 1861. Setting: 696-acre small town campus with easy access to Syracuse. Endowment: $28.8 million. Research spending for the previous fiscal year: $1.9 million. Educational spending for the previous fiscal year: $11,418 per student. Total enrollment: 8,026. Faculty: 578 (375 full-time, 203 part-time). Student-undergrad faculty ratio is 17:1. 10,715 applied, 54% were admitted. 13% from top 10% of their high school class, 50% from top quarter, 85% from top half. Full-time: 6,836 students, 49% women, 51% men. Part-time: 289 students, 48% women, 52% men. Students come from 28 states and territories, 35 other countries, 3% from out-of-state. 0.2% American Indian or Alaska Native, non-Hispanic/Latino; 12% Hispanic/Latino; 9% Black or African American, non-Hispanic/Latino; 3% Asian, non-Hispanic/Latino; 3% international. 6% 25 or older, 62% live on campus, 11% transferred in. Retention: 78% of full-time freshmen returned the following year. Academic areas with the most degrees conferred: business/marketing; communication/journalism; psychology. Core. Calendar: semesters. ESL program, services for LD students, advanced placement, accelerated degree program, freshman honors college, honors program, independent study, distance learning, double major, summer session for credit, part-time degree program, adult/continuing education programs, co-op programs and internships, graduate courses open to undergrads. Off campus study at Bryant and Stratton North Campus, Finger Lakes Community College, Jefferson-Lewis Board of Cooperative Educational Services, Onondage-Cortland-Madison Board of Cooperative Educational Services. Study abroad program. ROTC: Army (c), Air Force (c).

Entrance Requirements: Options: electronic application, early admission, early action, deferred admission, international baccalaureate accepted. Required: essay, high school transcript, 1 recommendation, SAT or ACT. Recommended: minimum 2.7 high school GPA, interview. Entrance: moderately difficult. Application deadlines: rolling, 11/5 for early action. Notification: 1/15, 12/15 for early action. SAT Reasoning Test deadline: 5/1. Transfer credits accepted: Yes.

Costs Per Year: Application fee: $50. State resident tuition: $6870 full-time, $286 per credit hour part-time. Nonresident tuition: $16,650 full-time, $694 per credit hour part-time. Mandatory fees: $1570 full-time, $49.46 per credit hour part-time. Part-time tuition and fees vary according to course load. College room and board: $14,140. College room only: $8790. Room and board charges vary according to board plan and housing facility.

Collegiate Environment: Orientation program. Drama-theater group, choral group, student-run newspaper, radio station. Social organizations: 228 open to all; national fraternities, national sororities, local fraternities, local sororities; 3% of eligible men and 3% of eligible women are members. Most popular organizations: club/intramural sports, student radio/television stations (WNYO and WTOP), Outdoor Club, Dance Organization (Del Sarte), Accounting Society. Major annual events: Quest, May Day/Spring Fling, Family and Friends Weekend. Student services: legal services, health clinic, personal-psychological counseling, women's center. Campus security: 24-hour emergency response devices and patrols, controlled dormitory access, Oswego Guardian. Penfield Library. Books: 331,049 (physical), 154,207 (digital/electronic); Serial titles: 1,932 (physical), 55,500 (digital/electronic); Databases: 139. Weekly public service hours: 96; study areas open 24 hours, 5-7 days a week; students can reserve study rooms. Operations spending for the previous fiscal year: $2.7 million. 1,250 computers available on campus for general student use. Computer purchase/lease plans available. A campuswide network can be accessed from student residence rooms and from off campus. Students can access the following: online class registration. Staffed computer lab on campus (open 24 hours a day) provides training in use of computers, software, and the Internet.

■ STATE UNIVERSITY OF NEW YORK AT PLATTSBURGH

101 Broad St.
Plattsburgh, NY 12901-2681
Tel: (518)564-2000; Free: 888-673-0012
Fax: (518)564-2045
E-mail: hamm1417@plattsburgh.edu
Web Site: www.plattsburgh.edu

Description: State-supported, comprehensive, coed. Part of State University of New York System. Awards bachelor's and master's degrees and post-master's certificates. Founded 1889. Setting: 265-acre small town campus with easy access to Montreal. Endowment: $21.1 million. Research spending for the previous fiscal year: $967,531. Educational spending for the previous fiscal year: $10,871 per student. Total enrollment: 5,704. Faculty: 436 (271 full-time, 165 part-time). Student-undergrad faculty ratio is 16:1. 9,201 applied, 54% were admitted. 18% from top 10% of their high school class, 43% from top quarter, 84% from top half. Full-time: 4,853 students, 57% women, 43% men. Part-time: 444 students, 61% women, 39% men. Students come from 30 states and territories, 66 other countries, 3% from out-of-state. 0.5% American Indian or Alaska Native, non-Hispanic/Latino; 10% Hispanic/Latino; 8% Black or African American, non-Hispanic/Latino; 2% Asian, non-Hispanic/Latino; 0.1% Native Hawaiian or other Pacific Islander, non-Hispanic/Latino; 6% international. 10% 25 or older, 55% live on campus, 9% transferred in. Retention: 78% of full-time freshmen returned the following year. Academic areas with the most degrees conferred: business/marketing; health professions and related sciences; communication/journalism. Core. Calendar: semesters plus 2 5-week summer sessions and 1 winter session. Academic remediation for entering students, ESL program, services for LD students, advanced placement, self-designed majors, honors program, independent study, distance learning, double major, summer session for credit, part-time degree program, co-op programs and internships, graduate courses open to undergrads. Off campus study. Study abroad program.

Entrance Requirements: Options: electronic application, early admission, deferred admission, international baccalaureate accepted. Required: essay, high school transcript, minimum 2.5 high school GPA, 1 recommendation, SAT or ACT. Recommended: minimum 3 high school GPA, interview. Required for some: minimum 3.4 high school GPA. Entrance: moderately difficult. Application deadline: rolling. Notification: continuous. SAT Reasoning Test deadline: 12/1. SAT Subject Test deadline: 12/1. Transfer credits accepted: Yes.

Costs Per Year: Application fee: $50. State resident tuition: $6870 full-time, $286 per credit hour part-time. Nonresident tuition: $16,650 full-time, $694 per credit hour part-time. Mandatory fees: $1609 full-time, $66.28 per credit hour part-time. College room and board: $13,080. College room only: $8340.

Collegiate Environment: Orientation program. Drama-theater group, choral group, student-run newspaper, radio station. Social organizations: 120 open to all; national fraternities, national sororities, local fraternities, local sororities; 15% of eligible men and 15% of eligible women are members. Most popular organizations: Student Association, Honor Societies, Student Media Organizations, service/leadership organizations, intramural and recreational sports. Major annual events: President's Gala, Volunteer Opportunities, Plattsburgh's Got Talent/Best Dance Crew Competitions. Student services: legal services, health clinic, personal-psychological counseling, women's center. Campus security: 24-hour emergency response devices and patrols, late night transport-escort service, controlled dormitory access. 2,474 college housing spaces available; 2,409 were occupied in 2018-19. Freshmen guaranteed college housing. On-campus residence required through sophomore year. Option: coed housing available. Feinberg Library. Books: 249,820 (physical), 54,170 (digital/electronic); Serial titles: 95 (physical), 463 (digital/electronic); Databases: 119. Weekly public service hours: 100; students can reserve study rooms. 450 computers available on campus for general student use. Computer purchase/lease plans available. A campuswide network can be accessed from student residence rooms and from off campus. Students can access the following: online class registration. Staffed computer lab on campus provides training in use of computers, software, and the Internet.

■ **STATE UNIVERSITY OF NEW YORK POLYTECHNIC INSTITUTE**
100 Seymour Rd.
Utica, NY 13502
Tel: (315)792-7100; Free: 866-278-6948
Fax: (315)792-7837
E-mail: admissions@sunyit.edu
Web Site: www.sunypoly.edu

Description: State-supported, comprehensive, coed. Part of State University of New York System. Awards bachelor's, master's, and doctoral degrees and post-master's certificates. Founded 1966. Setting: 850-acre suburban campus. System endowment: $5.5 million. Research spending for the previous fiscal year: $255.9 million. Educational spending for the previous fiscal year: $16,850 per student. Total enrollment: 2,933. Faculty: 274 (138 full-time, 136 part-time). Student-undergrad faculty ratio is 13:1. 2,984

applied, 62% were admitted. 45% from top 10% of their high school class, 66% from top quarter, 95% from top half. Full-time: 1,860 students, 28% women, 72% men. Part-time: 324 students, 70% women, 30% men. Students come from 15 states and territories, 16 other countries, 2% from out-of-state. 0.2% American Indian or Alaska Native, non-Hispanic/Latino; 9% Hispanic/Latino; 6% Black or African American, non-Hispanic/Latino; 6% Asian, non-Hispanic/Latino; 0.2% Native Hawaiian or other Pacific Islander, non-Hispanic/Latino; 1% international. 17% 25 or older, 44% live on campus, 14% transferred in. Retention: 80% of full-time freshmen returned the following year. Academic areas with the most degrees conferred: business/marketing; engineering technologies; computer and information sciences. Core. Calendar: semesters. Services for LD students, advanced placement, accelerated degree program, independent study, distance learning, double major, summer session for credit, part-time degree program, co-op programs and internships, graduate courses open to undergrads. Off campus study at Mohawk Valley Consortium, SUNY Cross Registration Agreement. Study abroad program. ROTC: Army (c), Air Force (c).

Entrance Requirements: Options: electronic application, early admission, early action, deferred admission, international baccalaureate accepted. Required: essay, high school transcript, minimum 3 high school GPA, 2 recommendations, SAT or ACT. Recommended: interview. Entrance: moderately difficult. Application deadlines: 6/1, 11/15 for early action. Notification: continuous until 1/15, 12/15 for early action. SAT Reasoning Test deadline: 7/15. SAT Subject Test deadline: 7/15. Transfer credits accepted: Yes. Early action applicants: 528. Early action applicants admitted: 462.

Costs Per Year: Application fee: $50. State resident tuition: $6870 full-time, $286 per credit hour part-time. Nonresident tuition: $16,650 full-time, $694 per credit hour part-time. Mandatory fees: $1578 full-time, $65.62 per credit hour part-time. Full-time tuition and fees vary according to course load, degree level, and location. Part-time tuition and fees vary according to course load, degree level, and location. College room and board: $12,722. Room and board charges vary according to board plan and location.

Collegiate Environment: Orientation program. Student-run newspaper, radio station. Social organizations: 40 open to all. Most popular organizations: International Student Association, SUNY Tech Gamers Club, Black and Latino American Student Union, Colleges Against Cancer, BAJA SAE (Society of Automotive Engineers). Major annual events: Wildcat Weekend (homecoming, alumni, parent weekend), Apocalypse Week, Carnival Day. Student services: legal services, health clinic, personal-psychological counseling. Campus security: 24-hour emergency response devices and patrols, student patrols, late night transport-escort service, controlled dormitory access, closed-circuit TV monitors, 24-hour police department. Peter J. Cayan Library. Books: 139,500 (physical), 108,500 (digital/electronic); Serial titles: 2,175 (physical), 49,045 (digital/electronic); Databases: 50. Weekly public service hours: 87; students can reserve study rooms. Operations spending for the previous fiscal year: $433,289. 380 computers available on campus for general student use. A campuswide network can be accessed from student residence rooms and from off campus. Students can access the following: online class registration.

■ **STATE UNIVERSITY OF NEW YORK UPSTATE MEDICAL UNIVERSITY**
750 E Adams St.
Syracuse, NY 13210
Tel: (315)464-5540; Free: 800-736-2171
Fax: (315)464-8823
E-mail: admiss@upstate.edu
Web Site: www.upstate.edu

Description: State-supported, upper-level, coed. Part of State University of New York System. Awards bachelor's, master's, and doctoral degrees and post-master's certificates. Founded 1950. Setting: 25-acre urban campus. Endowment: $60.1 million. Research spending for the previous fiscal year: $29.5 million. Educational spending for the previous fiscal year: $60,121 per student. Total enrollment: 1,787. Faculty: 54 (47 full-time, 7 part-time). 477 applied, 34% were admitted. Full-time: 213 students, 66% women, 34% men. Part-time: 83 students, 82% women, 18% men. Students come from 8 states and territories, 7% from out-of-state. 0.3% American Indian or Alaska Native, non-Hispanic/Latino; 5% Hispanic/Latino; 4% Black or African American, non-Hispanic/Latino; 3% Asian, non-Hispanic/Latino; 0.3% Native Hawaiian or other Pacific Islander, non-Hispanic/Latino; 3% international. 43% 25 or older, 50% live on campus, 43% transferred in. Academic area with the most degrees conferred: health professions and related sciences. Core. Calendar: semesters. Services for LD students, distance learning, summer session for credit, part-time degree program, internships, graduate courses open to undergrads. Off campus study. ROTC: Army (c).

Entrance Requirements: Transfer credits accepted: Yes.

Collegiate Environment: Orientation program. Choral group. Social organizations: 60 open to all. Most popular organizations: Upstate Student Government, Campus Activities Governing Board, Emergency Medicine Interest Group, Family Medicine Student Organization, Student National Medical Association. Major annual events: Elizabeth Blackwell Day, Black History Month, Welcome Week and Spring Weekend. Student services: health clinic, personal-psychological counseling. Campus security: 24-hour emergency response devices and patrols, late night transport-escort service, controlled dormitory access. Health Sciences Library. Operations spending for the previous fiscal year: $2.6 million. 150 computers available on campus for general student use. A campuswide network can be accessed from student residence rooms and from off campus. Students can access the following: online class registration. Staffed computer lab on campus provides training in use of computers, software, and the Internet.

Community Environment: See Syracuse University.

■ **STELLA AND CHARLES GUTTMAN COMMUNITY COLLEGE**
50 W 40th St.
New York, NY 10018
Tel: (646)313-8000
Web Site: guttman.cuny.edu
Description: State and locally supported, 2-year, coed. Awards transfer associate and terminal associate degrees.

■ **STONY BROOK UNIVERSITY, STATE UNIVERSITY OF NEW YORK**
Nicolls Rd.
Stony Brook, NY 11794
Tel: (631)632-6000
E-mail: enroll@stonybrook.edu
Web Site: www.stonybrook.edu
Description: State-supported, university, coed. Part of State University of New York System. Awards bachelor's, master's, and doctoral degrees and post-master's certificates. Founded 1957. Setting: 1,450-acre suburban campus with easy access to New York City. Endowment: $234 million. Research spending for the previous fiscal year: $169.9 million. Educational spending for the previous fiscal year: $22,730 per student. Total enrollment: 25,989. Faculty: 1,566 (1,075 full-time, 491 part-time). Student-undergrad faculty ratio is 18:1. 35,313 applied, 42% were admitted. 48% from top 10% of their high school class, 81% from top quarter, 95% from top half. 17 National Merit Scholars, 53 valedictorians. Full-time: 16,212 students, 47% women, 53% men. Part-time: 1,152 students, 45% women, 55% men. Students come from 44 states and territories, 130 other countries, 6% from out-of-state. 0.2% American Indian or Alaska Native, non-Hispanic/Latino; 12% Hispanic/Latino; 7% Black or African American, non-Hispanic/Latino; 24% Asian, non-Hispanic/Latino; 0.1% Native Hawaiian or other Pacific Islander, non-Hispanic/Latino; 14% international. 7% 25 or older, 53% live on campus, 9% transferred in. Retention: 90% of full-time freshmen returned the following year. Academic areas with the most degrees conferred: health professions and related sciences; biological/life sciences; psychology; engineering. Core. Calendar: semesters. Academic remediation for entering students, ESL program, services for LD students, advanced placement, accelerated degree program, self-designed majors, freshman honors college, honors program, independent study, distance learning, double major, summer session for credit, part-time degree program, adult/continuing education programs, co-op programs and internships, graduate courses open to undergrads. Off campus study at 17 members of the Long Island Regional Advisory Council for Higher Education, The National Student Exchange. Study abroad program. ROTC: Army, Naval (c), Air Force (c).

Entrance Requirements: Options: electronic application, deferred admission, international baccalaureate accepted. Required: essay, high school transcript, 1 recommendation, SAT or ACT. Recommended: minimum 3.5 high school GPA. Required for some: interview, audition. Entrance: very difficult. Application deadline: 1/15. Notification: 4/1. SAT Reasoning Test deadline: 2/1. SAT Subject Test deadline: 2/1. Transfer credits accepted: Yes. Applicants placed on waiting list: 3,778. Wait-listed applicants offered admission: 68.

Costs Per Year: Application fee: $50. State resident tuition: $6870 full-time, $286 per credit hour part-time. Nonresident tuition: $24,540 full-time, $1023 per credit hour part-time. Mandatory fees: $2,754 full-time, $136.67 per credit hour part-time. Full-time tuition and fees vary according to course load and program. Part-time tuition and fees vary according to course load and

program. College room and board: $13,698. College room only: $8654. Room and board charges vary according to board plan, housing facility, and location.

Collegiate Environment: Orientation program. Drama-theater group, choral group, marching band, student-run newspaper, radio station. Social organizations: 353 open to all; national fraternities, national sororities, local fraternities, local sororities; 6% of eligible men and 6% of eligible women are members. Most popular organizations: Community Service Organization, Residence Hall Association, Commuter Student Association, Asian Students Alliance, Chinese Association at Stony Brook. Major annual events: Roth Pond Regatta, Opening of School/First Night Out, Diversity Day/Strawberry Festival. Student services: legal services, health clinic, personal-psychological counseling, women's center. Campus security: 24-hour emergency response devices and patrols, late night transport-escort service, controlled dormitory access. Frank Melville, Jr. Memorial Library plus 7 others. Books: 1.9 million (physical), 348,868 (digital/electronic); Serial titles: 1,225 (physical), 190,674 (digital/electronic); Databases: 679. Weekly public service hours: 131; study areas open 24 hours, 5-7 days a week; students can reserve study rooms. Operations spending for the previous fiscal year: $17.6 million. 1,590 computers available on campus for general student use. Computer purchase/lease plans available. A campuswide network can be accessed from student residence rooms and from off campus. Students can access the following: online class registration. Staffed computer lab on campus provides training in use of computers, software, and the Internet.

■ **SUFFOLK COUNTY COMMUNITY COLLEGE**
533 College Rd.
Selden, NY 11784-2899
Tel: (631)451-4110
Web Site: www.sunysuffolk.edu
Description: State and locally supported, 2-year, coed. Part of State University of New York System. Awards certificates, diplomas, transfer associate, and terminal associate degrees. Founded 1959. Setting: 500-acre small town campus with easy access to New York City. Total enrollment: 28,294. Student-undergrad faculty ratio is 18:1. 2% from top 10% of their high school class, 19% from top quarter, 43% from top half. Students come from 14 states and territories, 1% from out-of-state. 33% 25 or older. Core. Calendar: semesters. Academic remediation for entering students, ESL program, services for LD students, advanced placement, freshman honors college, honors program, independent study, distance learning, summer session for credit, part-time degree program, adult/continuing education programs, co-op programs and internships. Off campus study at members of the Long Island Regional Advisory Council for Higher Education. Study abroad program. ROTC: Army (c).

Entrance Requirements: Open admission except for some programs. Options: electronic application, deferred admission, international baccalaureate accepted. Required: high school transcript. Required for some: interview. Entrance: noncompetitive. Application deadline: rolling. Notification: continuous. Preference given to county residents. Transfer credits accepted: Yes.

Costs Per Year: Application fee: $35. State resident tuition: $5220 full-time, $218 per credit hour part-time. Nonresident tuition: $10,440 full-time, $436 per credit hour part-time. Mandatory fees: $516 full-time, $9 per credit hour part-time, $75 per term part-time. Full-time tuition and fees vary according to course load, program, and reciprocity agreements. Part-time tuition and fees vary according to course load, program, and reciprocity agreements.

Collegiate Environment: Orientation program. Drama-theater group, choral group, student-run newspaper. Student services: personal-psychological counseling. Campus security: 24-hour emergency response devices and patrols.

■ **SULLIVAN COUNTY COMMUNITY COLLEGE**
112 College Rd.
Loch Sheldrake, NY 12759
Tel: (845)434-5750; Free: 800-577-5243
Fax: (845)434-4806
E-mail: salhona@sunysullivan.edu
Web Site: www.sullivan.suny.edu
Description: State and locally supported, 2-year, coed. Part of State University of New York System. Awards certificates, transfer associate, and terminal associate degrees. Founded 1962. Setting: 405-acre rural campus. Endowment: $921,102. Educational spending for the previous fiscal year: $6784 per student. Total enrollment: 1,538. Faculty: 93 (38 full-time, 55 part-time). Student-undergrad faculty ratio is 21:1. 1,300 applied, 99% were admitted. Full-time: 782 students, 51% women, 49% men. Part-time: 756

students, 59% women, 41% men. Students come from 2 states and territories, 9 other countries, 1% from out-of-state. 0.4% American Indian or Alaska Native, non-Hispanic/Latino; 24% Hispanic/Latino; 16% Black or African American, non-Hispanic/Latino; 2% Asian, non-Hispanic/Latino; 0.1% Native Hawaiian or other Pacific Islander, non-Hispanic/Latino; 1% international. 18% 25 or older, 16% live on campus, 6% transferred in. Core. Calendar: semesters. Academic remediation for entering students, services for LD students, advanced placement, honors program, independent study, distance learning, double major, summer session for credit, part-time degree program, adult/continuing education programs, co-op programs and internships. Off campus study at Hudson Valley Educational Consortium (HVEC).

Entrance Requirements: Open admission. Options: electronic application, early admission, deferred admission. Required: high school transcript. Entrance: noncompetitive. Application deadline: rolling. Notification: continuous. Transfer credits accepted: Yes.

Costs Per Year: State resident tuition: $4814 full-time, $199 per credit hour part-time. Nonresident tuition: $9628 full-time, $322 per credit hour part-time. Mandatory fees: $876 full-time, $37 per credit hour part-time. College room and board: $9828. College room only: $6228.

Collegiate Environment: Orientation program. Drama-theater group. Social organizations: 12 open to all. Most popular organizations: Science Alliance, Black Student Union, Gay-Straight Alliance, Dance Club, Honor Society. Major annual events: Talent Show, Convocation, Completion Day. Student services: legal services, health clinic, personal-psychological counseling. Campus security: 24-hour emergency response devices and patrols, student patrols, controlled dormitory access. 375 college housing spaces available; 249 were occupied in 2018-19. Freshmen given priority for college housing. Option: coed housing available. Hermann Memorial Library plus 1 other. Books: 59,923 (physical), 169,353 (digital/electronic); Serial titles: 128 (physical), 3 (digital/electronic); Databases: 94. Weekly public service hours: 62. Operations spending for the previous fiscal year: $319,908. 205 computers available on campus for general student use. A campuswide network can be accessed. Students can access the following: online class registration. Staffed computer lab on campus provides training in use of computers, software, and the Internet.

■ **SWEDISH INSTITUTE, COLLEGE OF HEALTH SCIENCES**
226 W 26th St.
New York, NY 10001-6700
Tel: (212)924-5900
Fax: (212)924-7600
E-mail: admissions@swedishinstitute.edu
Web Site: www.swedishinstitute.edu

Description: Proprietary, comprehensive, coed. Awards associate, bachelor's, master's, and doctoral degrees. Founded 1916. Setting: urban campus. Total enrollment: 480. Faculty: 50 (17 full-time, 33 part-time). Student-undergrad faculty ratio is 11:1. 202 applied, 95% were admitted. Students come from 6 states and territories, 4 other countries, 4% from out-of-state. 72% 25 or older. Calendar: trimesters. Services for LD students, advanced placement, part-time degree program, adult/continuing education programs, co-op programs.

Entrance Requirements: Required: essay, 2 recommendations, interview, Nelson-Denny. Required for some: high school transcript. Entrance: moderately difficult. Application deadline: 11/9.

Collegiate Environment: Campus security: 24-hour emergency response devices and patrols. The Lillian F. Phillips Library.

■ **SYRACUSE UNIVERSITY**
900 S Crouse Ave.
Syracuse, NY 13244
Tel: (315)443-1870
Web Site: www.syracuse.edu

Description: Independent, university, coed. Awards bachelor's, master's, and doctoral degrees and post-master's certificates. Founded 1870. Setting: 721-acre urban campus with easy access to Syracuse, NY. Endowment: $1.3 billion. Total enrollment: 22,803. Faculty: 1,724 (1,121 full-time, 603 part-time). Student-undergrad faculty ratio is 15:1. 34,981 applied, 50% were admitted. 39% from top 10% of their high school class, 71% from top quarter, 94% from top half. Full-time: 14,655 students, 54% women, 46% men. Part-time: 571 students, 51% women, 49% men. Students come from 50 states and territories, 92 other countries, 61% from out-of-state. 0.5% American Indian or Alaska Native, non-Hispanic/Latino; 9% Hispanic/Latino; 7% Black or African American, non-Hispanic/Latino; 7% Asian, non-Hispanic/Latino; 0.1% Native Hawaiian or other Pacific Islander, non-Hispanic/Latino; 14%

international. 3% 25 or older, 53% live on campus, 2% transferred in. Retention: 90% of full-time freshmen returned the following year. Academic areas with the most degrees conferred: communication/journalism; social sciences; business/marketing. Calendar: semesters. ESL program, services for LD students, advanced placement, accelerated degree program, self-designed majors, freshman honors college, honors program, independent study, distance learning, double major, summer session for credit, part-time degree program, adult/continuing education programs, co-op programs and internships, graduate courses open to undergrads. Off campus study. Study abroad program. ROTC: Army, Air Force.

Entrance Requirements: Options: electronic application, early admission, early decision, deferred admission, international baccalaureate accepted. Required: essay, high school transcript, 2 recommendations, Please visit the Apply to Syracuse web page at http://admissions.syr.edu for information on requirements for First-Year, Transfer, and International applicants., SAT or ACT. Recommended: interview. Entrance: very difficult. Application deadlines: 1/1, 11/15 for early decision. Notification: 3/15, 12/15 for early decision. SAT Reasoning Test deadline: 1/1. Transfer credits accepted: Yes. Applicants placed on waiting list: 6,523. Wait-listed applicants offered admission: 609. Early decision applicants: 2,004. Early decision applicants admitted: 1,167.

Costs Per Year: Application fee: $75. Comprehensive fee: $67,403 includes full-time tuition ($50,230), mandatory fees ($1623), and college room and board ($15,550). College room only: $8260. Full-time tuition and fees vary according to course load. Room and board charges vary according to board plan and housing facility. Part-time tuition: $2043 per credit hour. Part-time tuition varies according to course load.

Collegiate Environment: Orientation program. Drama-theater group, choral group, marching band, student-run newspaper, radio station. Social organizations: 313 open to all; national fraternities, national sororities; 26% of eligible men and 41% of eligible women are members. Most popular organizations: Student Association, University Union, Otto. Major annual events: Orange Central, Mayfest/Block Party, Juice Jam. Student services: legal services, health clinic, personal-psychological counseling, women's center. Campus security: 24-hour emergency response devices and patrols, student patrols, late night transport-escort service, controlled dormitory access. 8,092 college housing spaces available; 8,026 were occupied in 2018-19. Freshmen guaranteed college housing. On-campus residence required through sophomore year. Option: coed housing available. E. S. Bird Library plus 4 others. Books: 2.6 million (physical), 545,994 (digital/electronic); Serial titles: 33,881 (physical), 125,294 (digital/electronic); Databases: 586. Weekly public service hours: 146; study areas open 24 hours, 5-7 days a week; students can reserve study rooms. 3,500 computers available on campus for general student use. Computer purchase/lease plans available. A campuswide network can be accessed from student residence rooms and from off campus. Students can access the following: online class registration, Library; web conferencing; learning management system (Blackboard); blogging service; personal websites; 'View My Advising Report,' digital asset management system (Collage);Microsoft Office 365;Lynda.com online video training. Staffed computer lab on campus (open 24 hours a day) provides training in use of computers, software, and the Internet.

Community Environment: The city of Syracuse (metropolitan area population of 732,000) is the business, educational, and cultural hub of central New York. The city offers professional theater, symphony, opera, and visiting artists and performers. Highlights of the downtown area are the Everson Museum of Art, designed by I.M. Pei, the impressive Civic Center, and the popular Carousel Center shopping Mall. Central New York offers lakes, parks, mountains, and outstanding recreational opportunities. Syracuse is serviced by most major airlines, Amtrak, and Greyhound. Hancock International Airport is only a few miles from downtown and the University, and is served by taxis. The famous Finger Lakes region, offering excellent summer and winter activities, is easily accessible. Diversified industry includes medicine, education, manufacturing, banking, insurance, communications, engineering, and retailing. Part-time employment opportunities are available for students. A transportation network includes bus lines, airlines, and excellent highways and thruways. Parking is excellent in the downtown shopping and theatrical districts. Syracuse is home to 40 museums and galleries, 40 golf courses (more than any other area in the northeast), and has more than 50 parks and several nature centers in the Syracuse area.

■ **TALMUDICAL INSTITUTE OF UPSTATE NEW YORK**
769 Park Ave.
Rochester, NY 14607-3046
Tel: (716)473-2810

Fax: (716)442-0417

Web Site: www.tiuny.org

Description: Independent Jewish, 5-year, men only. Awards bachelor's degrees (also offers some graduate courses). Founded 1974. Setting: 1-acre urban campus. Total enrollment: 26. 13 applied, 100% were admitted. Calendar: semesters. Self-designed majors.

Entrance Requirements: Option: early admission. Required: high school transcript. Required for some: interview. Entrance: noncompetitive. Application deadline: rolling. Notification: continuous.

Collegiate Environment: Campus security: student patrols. Talmudical Library.

■ **TALMUDICAL SEMINARY OF BOBOV**

5120 New Utrecht Ave.

Brooklyn, NY 11219

Tel: (718)436-2122

Description: Independent Jewish, 4-year, coed. Awards bachelor's degrees.

■ **TALMUDICAL SEMINARY OHOLEI TORAH**

667 Eastern Pky.

Brooklyn, NY 11213-3310

Tel: (718)774-5050

Description: Independent Jewish, 4-year, men only. Awards bachelor's degrees. Founded 1956. Setting: urban campus. Total enrollment: 337. 65 applied, 100% were admitted. Core. Calendar: semesters. Honors program.

Entrance Requirements: Option: deferred admission. Required: high school transcript, interview, Talmudic examination. Application deadline: 9/1. Notification: continuous.

Collegiate Environment: Student services: personal-psychological counseling. Campus security: late night transport-escort service.

■ **TOMPKINS CORTLAND COMMUNITY COLLEGE**

170 N St.

Dryden, NY 13053-0139

Tel: (607)844-8211; Free: 888-567-8211

Fax: (607)844-6538

Web Site: www.TC3.edu

Description: State and locally supported, 2-year, coed. Part of State University of New York System. Awards certificates, transfer associate, and terminal associate degrees. Founded 1968. Setting: 300-acre rural campus. Total enrollment: 2,632. Faculty: 250 (62 full-time, 188 part-time). Student-undergrad faculty ratio is 18:1. Full-time: 1,830 students, 53% women, 47% men. Part-time: 802 students, 63% women, 37% men. Students come from 17 states and territories, 23 other countries, 3% from out-of-state. 0.2% American Indian or Alaska Native, non-Hispanic/Latino; 10% Hispanic/Latino; 14% Black or African American, non-Hispanic/Latino; 2% Asian, non-Hispanic/Latino; 3% international. 30% 25 or older, 8% transferred in. Core. Calendar: semesters. Academic remediation for entering students, ESL program, services for LD students, advanced placement, freshman honors college, honors program, independent study, distance learning, double major, summer session for credit, part-time degree program, adult/continuing education programs, co-op programs and internships. Off campus study at State University of New York College at Cortland. Study abroad program.

Entrance Requirements: Open admission except for nursing program. Options: electronic application, early admission, deferred admission. Required: high school transcript. Required for some: essay, interview. Entrance: noncompetitive. Application deadline: rolling. Notification: continuous. Transfer credits accepted: Yes.

Costs Per Year: State resident tuition: $4950 full-time, $181 per credit hour part-time. Nonresident tuition: $10,200 full-time, $372 per credit hour part-time. Mandatory fees: $1096 full-time, $39.30 per credit hour part-time, $18 per term part-time. Part-time tuition and fees vary according to course load. College room and board: $11,220. College room only: $8400. Room and board charges vary according to board plan and housing facility.

Collegiate Environment: Orientation program. Drama-theater group. Social organizations: 18 open to all. Most popular organizations: Sport Management Club, Nursing Club, Student Government Association, Writer's Guild. Major annual events: College Entertainment Board Programs, Registration Day, Voter Registration Drives. Student services: health clinic, personal-psychological counseling. Campus security: 24-hour patrols, late night transport-escort service, controlled dormitory access, armed peace officers. Gerald A. Barry Memorial Library plus 1 other. 300 computers available on campus for general student use. A campuswide network can be accessed. Students can access the following: online class registration. Staffed computer lab on campus.

■ **TORAH TEMIMAH TALMUDICAL SEMINARY**

507 Ocean Pky.

Brooklyn, NY 11218-5913

Tel: (718)853-8500

Description: Independent Jewish, 4-year, men only. Awards bachelor's degrees. Founded 1978. Total enrollment: 170. 55 applied, 100% were admitted. Calendar: semesters.

■ **TOURO COLLEGE**

27-33 W 23rd St.

New York, NY 10010

Tel: (212)463-0400

Fax: (212)779-2344

E-mail: david.luk@touro.edu

Web Site: www.touro.edu

Description: Independent, comprehensive, coed. Awards associate, bachelor's, master's, and doctoral degrees and post-master's certificates. Founded 1971. Setting: urban campus. Total enrollment: 12,021. Faculty: 1,335 (484 full-time, 851 part-time). 2,201 applied, 34% were admitted. Full-time: 5,055 students, 69% women, 31% men. Part-time: 1,857 students, 72% women, 28% men. 0.2% American Indian or Alaska Native, non-Hispanic/Latino; 8% Hispanic/Latino; 15% Black or African American, non-Hispanic/Latino; 4% Asian, non-Hispanic/Latino; 0.1% Native Hawaiian or other Pacific Islander, non-Hispanic/Latino; 4% international. 45% 25 or older, 13% transferred in. Retention: 66% of full-time freshmen returned the following year. Core. Calendar: semesters. Academic remediation for entering students, ESL program, services for LD students, advanced placement, accelerated degree program, self-designed majors, freshman honors college, honors program, independent study, distance learning, double major, summer session for credit, part-time degree program, external degree program, internships, graduate courses open to undergrads. Study abroad program.

Entrance Requirements: Options: early admission, deferred admission. Required: high school transcript. Recommended: essay, 1 recommendation, SAT or ACT. Required for some: minimum 3 high school GPA, 2 recommendations, interview. Entrance: moderately difficult. Application deadline: rolling. Notification: continuous. SAT Reasoning Test deadline: 7/5. SAT Subject Test deadline: 9/1. Transfer credits accepted: Yes.

Collegiate Environment: Orientation program. Student-run newspaper. Student services: personal-psychological counseling. Campus security: 24-hour emergency response devices and patrols. Touro College Library plus 14 others.

Community Environment: See New York University.

■ **TROCAIRE COLLEGE**

360 Choate Ave.

Buffalo, NY 14220-2094

Tel: (716)826-1200

Fax: (716)826-4704

Web Site: www.trocaire.edu

Description: Independent, primarily 2-year, coed. Awards certificates, terminal associate, and bachelor's degrees. Founded 1958. Setting: 1-acre urban campus. Endowment: $7.3 million. Educational spending for the previous fiscal year: $8390 per student. Total enrollment: 1,369. Faculty: 172 (41 full-time, 131 part-time). Student-undergrad faculty ratio is 11:1. 759 applied, 50% were admitted. Full-time: 621 students, 88% women, 12% men. Part-time: 748 students, 87% women, 13% men. Students come from 4 states and territories, 1 other country, 0.2% from out-of-state. 1% American Indian or Alaska Native, non-Hispanic/Latino; 5% Hispanic/Latino; 13% Black or African American, non-Hispanic/Latino; 1% Asian, non-Hispanic/Latino; 0.1% Native Hawaiian or other Pacific Islander, non-Hispanic/Latino; 0.1% international. 48% 25 or older, 16% transferred in. Core. Calendar: semesters. Academic remediation for entering students, services for LD students, advanced placement, independent study, distance learning, double major, summer session for credit, part-time degree program, external degree program, adult/continuing education programs, co-op programs and internships. Off campus study at members of the Western New York Consortium. Study abroad program.

Entrance Requirements: Options: electronic application, deferred admission. Required: high school transcript, ACCUPLACER. Recommended: minimum 1.87 high school GPA, interview. Required for some: essay, 1 recommendation. Entrance: minimally difficult. Application deadline: rolling. Transfer credits accepted: Yes.

Costs Per Year: Application fee: $0. Tuition: $17,290 full-time, $715 per credit hour part-time. Mandatory fees: $360 full-time, $30 per credit hour part-time. Full-time tuition and fees vary according to course load and program. Part-time tuition and fees vary according to course load and program.

Collegiate Environment: Orientation program. Student-run newspaper. Most popular organizations: Student Governance Association, TroGreen, Diversity Club. Major annual events: Welcome Back Picnic, Holiday Luncheon, T.G.I.O. (Thank God It's Over). Student services: personal-psychological counseling. Campus security: 24-hour emergency response devices and patrols, late night transport-escort service. The Rachel R. Savarino Library plus 1 other. Books: 10,822 (physical), 1,308 (digital/electronic); Databases: 90. Operations spending for the previous fiscal year: $332,688. 122 computers available on campus for general student use. A campuswide network can be accessed. Students can access the following: online class registration. Staffed computer lab on campus provides training in use of computers, software, and the Internet.

Community Environment: Trocaire is located in a residential area of South Buffalo, adjacent to Mercy Hospital and Cazenovia Park, a quiet corner of the city. Three bus lines serve the city and within a short distance is the New York State Thruway and the Buffalo Skyway.

■ **ULSTER COUNTY COMMUNITY COLLEGE**
491 Cottekill Rd.
Stone Ridge, NY 12484
Tel: (845)687-5000; Free: 800-724-0833
E-mail: admissionsoffice@sunyulster.edu
Web Site: www.sunyulster.edu
Description: State and locally supported, 2-year, coed. Part of State University of New York System. Awards certificates, diplomas, transfer associate, and terminal associate degrees. Founded 1961. Setting: 165-acre rural campus. Endowment: $8 million. Educational spending for the previous fiscal year: $7739 per student. Total enrollment: 3,416. Faculty: 151 (64 full-time, 87 part-time). Student-undergrad faculty ratio is 20:1. 459 applied, 100% were admitted. 3% from top 10% of their high school class, 8% from top quarter, 28% from top half. Full-time: 1,380 students, 54% women, 46% men. Part-time: 2,036 students, 53% women, 47% men. Students come from 8 states and territories, 2 other countries, 0.2% from out-of-state. 0.2% American Indian or Alaska Native, non-Hispanic/Latino; 12% Hispanic/Latino; 7% Black or African American, non-Hispanic/Latino; 1% Asian, non-Hispanic/Latino; 0.2% Native Hawaiian or other Pacific Islander, non-Hispanic/Latino; 0.5% international. 30% 25 or older, 5% transferred in. Core. Calendar: semesters. Academic remediation for entering students, ESL program, services for LD students, advanced placement, self-designed majors, honors program, independent study, distance learning, double major, summer session for credit, part-time degree program, adult/continuing education programs, co-op programs and internships. Off campus study at SUNY New Paltz; Study abroad opportunities with State University of New York Colleges; Hudson Valley Educational Consortium which includes: Ulster County Community College; Orange County Community College - Public Health; Sullivan County Community College - Green Building; Rockland County Community College -Fire Protection Tech; Jointly Registered program with Marist College for Individual Studies/Paralegal Degree/Certificate program. Study abroad program.
Entrance Requirements: Open admission except for nursing program. Options: electronic application, early admission, deferred admission, international baccalaureate accepted. Required: high school transcript: Entrance: noncompetitive. Application deadline: rolling. Notification: continuous. Transfer credits accepted: Yes.
Collegiate Environment: Orientation program. Drama-theater group, choral group. Social organizations: 10 open to all. Most popular organizations: Vet Tech, Biology Club, Nursing Club, Business Club, Visual Arts Club. Major annual events: Earth Day BBQ, Veterans Day Luncheon, Welcome Back BBQ. Student services: personal-psychological counseling. Campus security: 24-hour emergency response devices. McDonald Dewitt Library. Books: 77,078 (physical), 164,597 (digital/electronic); Serial titles: 139 (physical), 135,595 (digital/electronic); Databases: 77. Weekly public service hours: 44. Operations spending for the previous fiscal year: $715,812. 85 computers available on campus for general student use. A campuswide network can be accessed. Students can access the following: online class registration. Staffed computer lab on campus provides training in use of computers, software, and the Internet.

■ **UNION COLLEGE**
807 Union St.
Schenectady, NY 12308-2311

Tel: (518)388-6000; Free: 888-843-6688
Fax: (518)388-6986
Web Site: www.union.edu
Description: Independent, 4-year, coed. Awards bachelor's degrees. Founded 1795. Setting: 100-acre urban campus. Endowment: $427.6 million. Research spending for the previous fiscal year: $557,148. Educational spending for the previous fiscal year: $22,971 per student. Total enrollment: 2,206. Faculty: 241 (211 full-time, 30 part-time). Student-undergrad faculty ratio is 10:1. 6,716 applied, 39% were admitted. 61% from top 10% of their high school class, 80% from top quarter, 94% from top half. 8 National Merit Scholars, 1 class president, 6 valedictorians, 68 student government officers. Full-time: 2,195 students, 46% women, 54% men. Part-time: 11 students, 45% women, 55% men. 60% from out-of-state. 0.1% American Indian or Alaska Native, non-Hispanic/Latino; 8% Hispanic/Latino; 4% Black or African American, non-Hispanic/Latino; 5% Asian, non-Hispanic/Latino; 9% international. 88% live on campus. Retention: 95% of full-time freshmen returned the following year. Academic areas with the most degrees conferred: social sciences; biological/life sciences; engineering. Core. Calendar: trimesters. Advanced placement, accelerated degree program, self-designed majors, honors program, independent study, double major, summer session for credit, internships. Off campus study at Hudson-Mohawk Association of Colleges and Universities. Study abroad program. ROTC: Army (c), Naval (c), Air Force (c).
Entrance Requirements: Options: electronic application, early admission, early decision, deferred admission, international baccalaureate accepted. Required: essay, high school transcript, 2 recommendations. Recommended: interview. Required for some: SAT, SAT and SAT Subject Tests or ACT, SAT I and two SAT II tests or ACT for leadership in medicine program, SAT or ACT for law and public policy program. Entrance: very difficult. Application deadlines: 1/15, 11/15 for early decision. Notification: 4/1, 12/15 for early decision. SAT Reasoning Test deadline: 2/15. SAT Subject Test deadline: 2/15. Transfer credits accepted: Yes. Applicants placed on waiting list: 1,045. Wait-listed applicants offered admission: 13. Early decision applicants: 404. Early decision applicants admitted: 227.
Costs Per Year: Application fee: $0. Comprehensive fee: $68,853 includes full-time tuition ($54,819), mandatory fees ($471), and college room and board ($13,563). College room only: $7437.
Collegiate Environment: Orientation program. Drama-theater group, choral group, student-run newspaper, radio station. Social organizations: 125 open to all; national fraternities, national sororities, local fraternities, local sororities. Most popular organizations: U-Program (Programming Board), speaker's forum, student newspaper, Concert Committee, ski club. Major annual events: Spring Fest, large scale lectures, large concerts. Student services: health clinic, personal-psychological counseling, women's center. Campus security: 24-hour emergency response devices and patrols, late night transport-escort service, controlled dormitory access, awareness programs, bicycle patrol, shuttle service. Freshmen guaranteed college housing. On-campus residence required through junior year. Option: coed housing available. Schaffer Library. Study areas open 24 hours, 5-7 days a week; students can reserve study rooms. 554 computers available on campus for general student use. Computer purchase/lease plans available. A campuswide network can be accessed from student residence rooms and from off campus. Students can access the following: online class registration, Digital Studio and Learning Commons. Staffed computer lab on campus (open 24 hours a day) provides training in use of computers, software, and the Internet.

■ **UNITED STATES MERCHANT MARINE ACADEMY**
300 Steamboat Rd.
Kings Point, NY 11024-1699
Tel: (516)773-5000; Free: 866-546-4778
Fax: (516)773-5390
E-mail: admissions@usmma.edu
Web Site: www.usmma.edu
Description: Federally supported, comprehensive, coed. Awards bachelor's and master's degrees. Founded 1943. Setting: 82-acre suburban campus with easy access to New York City. Total enrollment: 975. Faculty: 132 (113 full-time, 19 part-time). Student-undergrad faculty ratio is 8:1. 1,855 applied, 22% were admitted. 33% from top 10% of their high school class, 57% from top quarter, 92% from top half. 12 National Merit Scholars, 7 valedictorians, 114 student government officers. Full-time: 954 students, 17% women, 83% men. Students come from 47 states and territories, 4 other countries, 93% from out-of-state. 1% American Indian or Alaska Native, non-Hispanic/Latino; 10% Hispanic/Latino; 3% Black or African American, non-Hispanic/Latino;

8% Asian, non-Hispanic/Latino; 0.2% Native Hawaiian or other Pacific Islander, non-Hispanic/Latino; 0.9% international. 2% 25 or older, 100% live on campus, 1% transferred in. Retention: 94% of full-time freshmen returned the following year. Core. Calendar: trimesters. Academic remediation for entering students, advanced placement, honors program, independent study, distance learning, internships. Off campus study at Sea Year Experience.

Entrance Requirements: Option: electronic application. Required: essay, high school transcript, 3 recommendations, SAT or ACT. Recommended: interview. Entrance: very difficult. Application deadline: 3/1. Notification: continuous until 4/1. SAT Reasoning Test deadline: 3/1. Transfer credits accepted: Yes. Applicants placed on waiting list: 204. Wait-listed applicants offered admission: 132.

Costs Per Year: Application fee: $0. Comprehensive fee: $1080 includes full-time tuition ($0), mandatory fees ($1080), and college room and board ($0). Midshipmen at the United States Merchant Marine Academy receive from the Federal Government their education, room and board, uniforms, and books. However, midshipmen are responsible for the payment of fees for mandatory educational supplies not provided by the government.

Collegiate Environment: Orientation program. Drama-theater group, choral group, marching band, student-run newspaper. Most popular organizations: Regimental Band, CFC, Neuman Club, Honor Guard. Major annual events: Homecoming, Parent's/Acceptance Weekend, Graduation/Commencement. Student services: health clinic, personal-psychological counseling. Campus security: 24-hour emergency response devices and patrols, controlled dormitory access. Schuyler Otis Bland Memorial Library. Books: 176,485 (physical), 2,791 (digital/electronic); Serial titles: 1,511 (physical), 505 (digital/electronic); Databases: 17. Weekly public service hours: 84.

■ **UNITED STATES MILITARY ACADEMY**
600 Thayer Rd.
West Point, NY 10996
Tel: (845)938-4011
Fax: (845)938-3021
E-mail: admissions@usma.edu
Web Site: www.usma.edu
Description: Federally supported, 4-year, coed. Awards bachelor's degrees. Founded 1802. Setting: 16,080-acre small town campus with easy access to New York City. Endowment: $348.2 million. Research spending for the previous fiscal year: $3.9 million. Educational spending for the previous fiscal year: $4536 per student. Total enrollment: 4,491. Faculty: 611 (all full-time). Student-undergrad faculty ratio is 7:1. 12,973 applied, 10% were admitted. 46% from top 10% of their high school class, 74% from top quarter, 94% from top half. 115 National Merit Scholars, 153 class presidents, 110 valedictorians, 319 student government officers. Full-time: 4,491 students, 22% women, 78% men. Students come from 30 other countries, 94% from out-of-state. 1% American Indian or Alaska Native, non-Hispanic/Latino; 10% Hispanic/Latino; 12% Black or African American, non-Hispanic/Latino; 8% Asian, non-Hispanic/Latino; 0.3% Native Hawaiian or other Pacific Islander, non-Hispanic/Latino; 1% international. 1% 25 or older, 100% live on campus. Retention: 96% of full-time freshmen returned the following year. Academic areas with the most degrees conferred: engineering; social sciences; business/marketing. Core. Calendar: semesters. Academic remediation for entering students, advanced placement, self-designed majors, honors program, independent study, double major. Off campus study at United States Naval Academy, United States Air Force Academy, United States Coast Guard Academy. Study abroad program.
Entrance Requirements: Options: electronic application, international baccalaureate accepted. Required: essay, high school transcript, 4 recommendations, Candidates will be notified if they can compete for admission into West Point after the Service Academies Pre-candidate Questionnaire is submitted to West PointÆs Admission office, SAT or ACT. Recommended: interview. Application deadline: 2/28. Notification: 2/28. SAT Reasoning Test deadline: 2/28.
Costs Per Year: Application fee: $0. Comprehensive fee: $0. Cadets receive a full scholarship and an annual salary. There is no tuition charge, but there is a requirement for an initial deposit. Room, board, and medical and dental care are provided by the US Government. A portion of the cadet pay is deposited to a 'Cadet Account' to help pay for uniforms, books, a laptop computer, and incidentals. The only cost is a one-time deposit upon admission to defray the initial issue of uniforms, books, supplies, and equipment. If needed, loans of $100 to $2,000 are available for the deposit. Upon graduation, cadets incur a 5-year Active Duty service obligation and 3 years of reserve duty in the US Army.

Collegiate Environment: Orientation program. Drama-theater group, choral group, student-run radio station. Social organizations: 86 open to all; 92% of eligible men and 93% of eligible women are members. Most popular organizations: Spirit Clubs, Big Brother/Big Sister, Cadet Fine Arts Forum, Film Forum, Philosophy Forum. Major annual events: Graduation Week, Homecoming/Ring Weekend, Army-Navy Football Week. Student services: legal services, health clinic, personal-psychological counseling. Campus security: 24-hour emergency response devices and patrols, late night transport-escort service, controlled dormitory access. United States Military Academy Library at West Point. Books: 422,671 (physical), 931,618 (digital/electronic); Serial titles: 110 (physical), 113,741 (digital/electronic); Databases: 270. Weekly public service hours: 100. Operations spending for the previous fiscal year: $5 million.

■ **UNITED TALMUDICAL SEMINARY**
191 Rodney St.
Brooklyn, NY 11211
Tel: (718)963-9260
Description: Independent Jewish, comprehensive, men only. Awards bachelor's and master's degrees. Founded 1949. Total enrollment: 1,500. 4% 25 or older. Calendar: semesters.
Entrance Requirements: Open admission.

■ **UNIVERSITY AT ALBANY, STATE UNIVERSITY OF NEW YORK**
1400 Washington Ave.
Albany, NY 12222-0001
Tel: (518)442-3300
E-mail: ugadmissions@albany.edu
Web Site: www.albany.edu
Description: State-supported, university, coed. Part of State University of New York System. Awards bachelor's, master's, and doctoral degrees and post-master's certificates. Founded 1844. Setting: 560-acre suburban campus. Endowment: $59.8 million. Research spending for the previous fiscal year: $89 million. Educational spending for the previous fiscal year: $1583 per student. Total enrollment: 17,743. Faculty: 1,185 (676 full-time, 509 part-time). Student-undergrad faculty ratio is 19:1. 24,887 applied, 54% were admitted. 16% from top 10% of their high school class, 48% from top quarter, 82% from top half. Full-time: 12,740 students, 51% women, 49% men. Part-time: 768 students, 47% women, 53% men. Students come from 36 states and territories, 25 other countries, 5% from out-of-state. 0.2% American Indian or Alaska Native, non-Hispanic/Latino; 17% Hispanic/Latino; 19% Black or African American, non-Hispanic/Latino; 8% Asian, non-Hispanic/Latino; 0.1% Native Hawaiian or other Pacific Islander, non-Hispanic/Latino; 5% international. 6% 25 or older, 56% live on campus, 11% transferred in. Retention: 83% of full-time freshmen returned the following year. Academic areas with the most degrees conferred: social sciences; business/marketing; biological/life sciences. Core. Calendar: semesters. ESL program, services for LD students, advanced placement, accelerated degree program, self-designed majors, freshman honors college, honors program, independent study, distance learning, double major, summer session for credit, part-time degree program, internships, graduate courses open to undergrads. Off campus study at New York State Visiting Student Program, Hudson-Mohawk Association of Colleges and Universities. Study abroad program. ROTC: Army, Air Force (c).
Entrance Requirements: Options: electronic application, early admission, early action, deferred admission, international baccalaureate accepted. Required: essay, high school transcript, 1 recommendation, SAT or ACT. Required for some: portfolio, audition. Entrance: very difficult. Application deadlines: 3/16, 11/1 for early action. Notification: continuous, 1/15 for early action. SAT Reasoning Test deadline: 3/16. SAT Subject Test deadline: 3/16. Transfer credits accepted: Yes. Applicants placed on waiting list: 1,105. Wait-listed applicants offered admission: 282. Early action applicants: 5,141. Early action applicants admitted: 4,128.
Costs Per Year: Application fee: $50. State resident tuition: $6870 full-time, $278 per credit hour part-time. Nonresident tuition: $23,710 full-time, $898 per credit hour part-time. Mandatory fees: $2946 full-time, $75.51 per credit hour part-time. Part-time tuition and fees vary according to course load. College room and board: $12,942. College room only: $8782. Room and board charges vary according to board plan and housing facility.
Collegiate Environment: Orientation program. Drama-theater group, choral group, student-run newspaper, radio station. Social organizations: 200 open to all; national fraternities, national sororities, local fraternities, local sororities; 2% of eligible men and 2% of eligible women are members. Most popular organizations: intramural athletics, cultural organizations, political

organizations, community service, honor societies. Major annual events: Purple Growl, Relay for Life. Student services: legal services, health clinic, personal-psychological counseling. Campus security: 24-hour emergency response devices and patrols, late night transport-escort service, controlled dormitory access, Five Quad Ambulance Service, on-campus car battery assistance. University Library plus 2 others. Books: 2.3 million (physical), 342,263 (digital/electronic); Serial titles: 97,614 (digital/electronic). Weekly public service hours: 113; students can reserve study rooms. Operations spending for the previous fiscal year: $12.9 million. 500 computers available on campus for general student use. Computer purchase/lease plans available. A campuswide network can be accessed from student residence rooms and from off campus. Students can access the following: online class registration. Staffed computer lab on campus provides training in use of computers, software, and the Internet.

■ **UNIVERSITY AT BUFFALO, THE STATE UNIVERSITY OF NEW YORK**

Capen Hall
Buffalo, NY 14260
Tel: (716)645-2000; Free: 888-UB-ADMIT
Fax: (716)645-6411
E-mail: ub-admissions@buffalo.edu
Web Site: www.buffalo.edu

Description: State-supported, university, coed. Part of State University of New York System. Awards bachelor's, master's, and doctoral degrees and post-master's certificates. Founded 1846. Setting: 1,350-acre suburban campus. Endowment: $659.2 million. Research spending for the previous fiscal year: $401.6 million. Educational spending for the previous fiscal year: $23,852 per student. Total enrollment: 31,503. Faculty: 1,813 (1,302 full-time, 511 part-time). Student-undergrad faculty ratio is 13:1. 31,196 applied, 56% were admitted. 35% from top 10% of their high school class, 70% from top quarter, 97% from top half. Full-time: 19,941 students, 43% women, 57% men. Part-time: 1,666 students, 53% women, 47% men. 2% from out-of-state. 0.3% American Indian or Alaska Native, non-Hispanic/Latino; 7% Hispanic/Latino; 8% Black or African American, non-Hispanic/Latino; 15% Asian, non-Hispanic/Latino; 0.1% Native Hawaiian or other Pacific Islander, non-Hispanic/Latino; 15% international. 6% 25 or older, 35% live on campus, 9% transferred in. Retention: 87% of full-time freshmen returned the following year. Academic areas with the most degrees conferred: business/marketing; engineering; social sciences. Core. Calendar: semesters. Academic remediation for entering students, ESL program, services for LD students, advanced placement, accelerated degree program, self-designed majors, freshman honors college, honors program, independent study, distance learning, double major, summer session for credit, part-time degree program, co-op programs and internships, graduate courses open to undergrads. Off campus study at WNY Consortium. Study abroad program. ROTC: Army (c).

Entrance Requirements: Options: electronic application, early admission, early action, international baccalaureate accepted. Required: essay, high school transcript, recommendations, SAT or ACT. Required for some: portfolio for architecture; audition for dance, music theatre, theatre and music. Entrance: moderately difficult. Application deadline: 11/15 for early action. Notification: continuous, continuous for nonresidents, 1/15 for early action. Transfer credits accepted: Yes. Applicants placed on waiting list: 2,841. Wait-listed applicants offered admission: 168.

Costs Per Year: Application fee: $50. State resident tuition: $6870 full-time, $286 per credit hour part-time. Nonresident tuition: $24,540 full-time, $1023 per credit hour part-time. Mandatory fees: $3,228 full-time, $139.10 per credit hour part-time. Part-time tuition and fees vary according to course load. College room and board: $14,213. College room only: $8273. Room and board charges vary according to board plan and housing facility.

Collegiate Environment: Orientation program. Drama-theater group, choral group, marching band, student-run newspaper, radio station. Social organizations: 400 open to all; national fraternities, national sororities, local fraternities, local sororities; 2% of eligible men and 2% of eligible women are members. Major annual events: Opening Weekend, Fallfest/Springfest, Homecoming/Parents' Weekend. Student services: legal services, health clinic, personal-psychological counseling, women's center. Campus security: 24-hour emergency response devices and patrols, student patrols, late night transport-escort service, controlled dormitory access. Freshmen guaranteed college housing. Option: coed housing available. Lockwood Memorial Library plus 11 others. Books: 3.4 million (physical), 826,650 (digital/electronic); Serial titles: 2,352 (physical), 175,278 (digital/electronic); Databases: 383. Weekly public service hours: 168; study areas open 24 hours, 5-7 days a

week; students can reserve study rooms. Operations spending for the previous fiscal year: $22 million. 3,061 computers available on campus for general student use. A campuswide network can be accessed from student residence rooms and from off campus. Students can access the following: online class registration. Staffed computer lab on campus (open 24 hours a day) provides training in use of computers, software, and the Internet.

■ **UNIVERSITY OF ROCHESTER**

Wilson Blvd.
Rochester, NY 14627
Tel: (585)275-2121; Free: 888-822-2256
Fax: (585)273-1118
E-mail: admit@admissions.rochester.edu
Web Site: www.rochester.edu

Description: Independent, university, coed. Awards bachelor's, master's, and doctoral degrees and post-master's certificates. Founded 1850. Setting: 655-acre suburban campus. Endowment: $2.1 billion. Total enrollment: 7,121. Faculty: (368 full-time). Student-undergrad faculty ratio is 10:1. 18,066 applied, 31% were admitted. 22 National Merit Scholars. Full-time: 5,570 students, 48% women, 52% men. Part-time: 226 students, 65% women, 35% men. Students come from 52 states and territories, 101 other countries, 59% from out-of-state. 0.1% American Indian or Alaska Native, non-Hispanic/Latino; 7% Hispanic/Latino; 5% Black or African American, non-Hispanic/Latino; 11% Asian, non-Hispanic/Latino; 26% international. 2% 25 or older, 90% live on campus, 2% transferred in. Retention: 96% of full-time freshmen returned the following year. Calendar: semesters plus optional summer term. ESL program, services for LD students, advanced placement, accelerated degree program, self-designed majors, honors program, independent study, double major, summer session for credit, part-time degree program, co-op programs and internships, graduate courses open to undergrads. Off campus study at Rochester area colleges. Study abroad program. ROTC: Army (c), Naval, Air Force (c).

Entrance Requirements: Options: electronic application, early decision, deferred admission, international baccalaureate accepted. Required: essay, high school transcript. Recommended: 2 recommendations, interview, SAT or ACT, SAT Subject Tests. Required for some: audition for Eastman School of Music, SAT and SAT Subject Tests or ACT. Entrance: very difficult. Application deadlines: 1/5, 11/1 for early decision. Notification: 4/1, 12/15 for early decision. SAT Reasoning Test deadline: 1/5. SAT Subject Test deadline: 1/5. Transfer credits accepted: Yes. Applicants placed on waiting list: 3,203. Wait-listed applicants offered admission: 6. Early decision applicants: 797. Early decision applicants admitted: 405.

Costs Per Year: Application fee: $50. Comprehensive fee: $69,685 includes full-time tuition ($52,867), mandatory fees ($958), and college room and board ($15,860). Room and board charges vary according to board plan and housing facility. Part-time tuition: $1652 per credit hour. Part-time tuition varies according to course load.

Collegiate Environment: Orientation program. Drama-theater group, choral group, marching band, student-run newspaper, radio station. Social organizations: 275 open to all; national fraternities, national sororities, local fraternities; 6% of eligible men and 8% of eligible women are members. Most popular organizations: Campus Activities Board, Black Students'; Union, Grassroots (environmental group), Women's Caucus, American Sign Language Club. Major annual events: Boar's Head Dinner, Mela, Meliora Weekend. Student services: legal services, health clinic, personal-psychological counseling, women's center. Campus security: 24-hour emergency response devices and patrols, student patrols, late night transport-escort service, controlled dormitory access. Rush Rhees Library plus 7 others. Study areas open 24 hours, 5-7 days a week; students can reserve study rooms. 700 computers available on campus for general student use. Computer purchase/lease plans available. A campuswide network can be accessed. Students can access the following: online class registration. Staffed computer lab on campus (open 24 hours a day) provides training in use of computers, software, and the Internet.

Community Environment: With Lake Ontario on its northern border and the scenic Finger Lakes on the south, the Rochester community of about one million people is located in an attractive setting. It offers a wide range of cultural and recreational opportunities-from concerts by the Rochester Philharmonic Orchestra and Eastman School ensembles, performances by resident professional theater companies, and an unusual concentration of first-class museums (including the University's own Memorial Art Gallery), to professional baseball and ice hockey and nearby opportunities for recreational canoeing, sculling, ice-skating, and skiing.

■ U.T.A. MESIVTA OF KIRYAS JOEL

48 Bakertown Rd.
Ste. 501
Monroe, NY 10950
Tel: (845)783-9901
Fax: (845)782-3620

Description: Independent Jewish, 4-year, men only. Awards bachelor's degrees. Total enrollment: 989. 1% 25 or older.

Entrance Requirements: Open admission.

■ UTICA COLLEGE

1600 Burrstone Rd.
Utica, NY 13502-4892
Tel: (315)792-3111; Free: 800-782-8884
Fax: (315)792-3003
Web Site: www.utica.edu

Description: Independent, comprehensive, coed. Awards bachelor's, master's, and doctoral degrees. Founded 1946. Setting: 128-acre suburban campus. Endowment: $25.9 million. Total enrollment: 5,196. Faculty: 469 (149 full-time, 320 part-time). Student-undergrad faculty ratio is 13:1. 4,224 applied, 84% were admitted. 13% from top 10% of their high school class, 35% from top quarter, 66% from top half. Full-time: 2,909 students, 57% women, 43% men. Part-time: 813 students, 69% women, 31% men. Students come from 48 states and territories, 28 other countries, 12% from out-of-state. 0.5% American Indian or Alaska Native, non-Hispanic/Latino; 9% Hispanic/Latino; 10% Black or African American, non-Hispanic/Latino; 4% Asian, non-Hispanic/Latino; 0.1% Native Hawaiian or other Pacific Islander, non-Hispanic/Latino; 0.8% international; 0.8% 25 or older, 34% live on campus, 4% transferred in. Retention: 70% of full-time freshmen returned the following year. Academic areas with the most degrees conferred: health professions and related sciences; homeland security, law enforcement, firefighting, and protective services; business/marketing. Core. Calendar: semesters. Academic remediation for entering students, ESL program, services for LD students, advanced placement, accelerated degree program, honors program, independent study, distance learning, double major, summer session for credit, part-time degree program, adult/continuing education programs, co-op programs and internships, graduate courses open to undergrads. Off campus study at members of the New York State Visiting Student Program. Study abroad program. ROTC: Army, Air Force (c).

Entrance Requirements: Options: electronic application, early decision, early action, deferred admission, international baccalaureate accepted. Required: essay, high school transcript, minimum 2 high school GPA, 1 recommendation. Recommended: interview. Required for some: minimum 3 high school GPA, SAT or ACT. Entrance: moderately difficult. Application deadline: rolling. Notification: 9/1. Early decision applicants: 34. Early decision applicants admitted: 26. Early action applicants: 814. Early action applicants admitted: 770.

Costs Per Year: Application fee: $40. Comprehensive fee: $32,630 includes full-time tuition ($20,832), mandatory fees ($550), and college room and board ($11,248). Full-time tuition and fees vary according to course load, degree level, and location. Room and board charges vary according to board plan. Part-time tuition: $694 per credit hour. Part-time mandatory fees: $50 per term. Part-time tuition and fees vary according to course load, degree level, and location.

Collegiate Environment: Orientation program. Drama-theater group, choral group, student-run newspaper, radio station. Social organizations: 81 open to all; national fraternities, national sororities, local fraternities, local sororities; 2% of eligible men and 2% of eligible women are members. Most popular organizations: Physical Therapy Society, Student Nurses Association, Kappa Delta Pi, Student Senate, Utica College Honor Association. Major annual events: Homecoming Weekend, Annual Faculty-Served Dinner, Midnight Breakfast. Student services: health clinic, personal-psychological counseling, women's center. Campus security: 24-hour emergency response devices and patrols, late night transport-escort service, controlled dormitory access. 1,034 college housing spaces available; all were occupied in 2018-19. Freshmen guaranteed college housing. On-campus residence required through sophomore year. Option: coed housing available. Frank E. Gannett Memorial Library. Books: 307,523 (physical); Serial titles: 267,023 (physical). Students can reserve study rooms. 430 computers available on campus for general student use. A campuswide network can be accessed from student residence rooms. Students can access the following: online class registration. Staffed computer lab on campus provides training in use of computers, software, and the Internet.

Community Environment: Utica is an area rich in the history of the Iroquois Confederacy, the French and Indian Wars, the American Revolution, the great migration to the Midwest and the western expansion of American commerce via the Erie Canal. Historic treasures in the area include the Oriskany Battlefield, Revolutionary Fort Stanwix (restored as a national monument) in Rome, and the homes of Revolutionary War heroes General Nicholas Herkimer and Major General Friedrich Wilhelm Baron von Steuben. Within an hour's drive of Utica are Johnson Hall, home of Sir William Johnson, colonial superintendent of Indian Affairs, in Johnstown; the Mansion House of the Oneida Community in Oneida; and Cooperstown, birthplace of James Fenimore Cooper, site of the Baseball Museum and Hall of Fame, the Farmer's Museum, and the headquarters of the New York State Historical Association. Utica's cultural assets include Munson-Williams-Proctor Institute and School of Art, one of the finest small art institutions in the country; the Oneida Historical Society; the Utica Civic Symphony; the Broadway Theatre League; the Players Theater Company; the Great Artists Concert series; the Utica Public Library and the Oneida County Junior Museum. These are greatly enhanced by the libraries, art galleries and cultural programs of the colleges in the area. The Utica area abounds in outdoor recreational resources. The city's park system includes the Val Bialas municipal ski slopes and ice skating rink just a mile from campus, an outstanding small zoo, 3 large public swimming pools, an 18-hole public golf course, public tennis courts, picnic grounds, and an abundance of public athletic fields. Excellent golfing, swimming, boating, fishing, hiking, and camping facilities surround the city. Nearby lakes include Otsego at Cooperstown, Oneida at Verona, Delta north of Rome, and the famous Fulton Chain of Lakes in the Adirondacks at Old Forge. Fine ski facilities near Utica include Snow Ridge at Turin, and Woods Valley near Rome.

■ VASSAR COLLEGE

124 Raymond Ave.
Poughkeepsie, NY 12604
Tel: (845)437-7000; Free: 800-827-7270
Fax: (845)437-7063
E-mail: admissions@vassar.edu
Web Site: www.vassar.edu

Description: Independent, 4-year, coed. Awards bachelor's and master's degrees. Founded 1861. Setting: 1,000-acre suburban campus with easy access to New York City. Endowment: $1.1 billion. Research spending for the previous fiscal year: $1.9 million. Educational spending for the previous fiscal year: $33,281 per student. Total enrollment: 2,456. Faculty: 342 (283 full-time, 59 part-time). Student-undergrad faculty ratio is 8:1. 8,312 applied, 25% were admitted. 61% from top 10% of their high school class, 91% from top quarter, 98% from top half. Full-time: 2,449 students, 59% women, 41% men. Part-time: 14 students, 64% women, 36% men. Students come from 52 states and territories, 40 other countries, 72% from out-of-state. 11% Hispanic/Latino; 4% Black or African American, non-Hispanic/Latino; 12% Asian, non-Hispanic/Latino; 9% international. 3% 25 or older, 97% live on campus, 1% transferred in. Academic areas with the most degrees conferred: social sciences; visual and performing arts; biological/life sciences. Calendar: semesters. Services for LD students, advanced placement, self-designed majors, independent study, double major, part-time degree program, co-op programs and internships. Off campus study at Howard University, Fisk University, Hampton University, Spelman College, Morehouse College, members of the Twelve College Exchange Program, Bard College. Study abroad program.

Entrance Requirements: Options: electronic application, early decision, deferred admission, international baccalaureate accepted. Required: essay, high school transcript, 2 recommendations, SAT or ACT. Entrance: very difficult. Application deadlines: 1/1, 11/15 for early decision plan 1, 1/1 for early decision plan 2. Notification: 4/1, 12/15 for early decision plan 1. SAT Reasoning Test deadline: 2/15. SAT Subject Test deadline: 2/15. Transfer credits accepted: Yes. Applicants placed on waiting list: 1,138. Wait-listed applicants offered admission: 48. Early decision applicants: 679. Early decision applicants admitted: 297.

Costs Per Year: Application fee: $65. One-time mandatory fee: $80. Comprehensive fee: $70,510 includes full-time tuition ($56,130), mandatory fees ($830), and college room and board ($13,550). Room and board charges vary according to housing facility. Part-time tuition: $6690 per unit.

Collegiate Environment: Orientation program. Drama-theater group, choral group, student-run newspaper, radio station. Social organizations: 170 open to all. Most popular organizations: Student Association, WVKR radio station, VICE (programming social events), Vassar Greens, Ultimate Frisbee. Major annual events: VICE Spring Concert, Founder' Day, All Campus Halloween Party. Student services: health clinic, personal-psychological counseling, women's center. Campus security: 24-hour emergency response devices and patrols, student patrols, late night transport-escort service, controlled dormitory access. Freshmen guaranteed college housing. On-campus residence required through senior year. Options: coed, women-only housing available. Vassar College Library plus 2 others. Books: 1.2 million (physical), 543,272 (digital/electronic); Serial titles: 15,914 (physical), 98,004 (digital/electronic); Databases: 847. Weekly public service hours: 145; study areas open 24 hours, 5-7 days a week; students can reserve study rooms. Operations spending for the previous fiscal year: $3.5 million. 135 computers available on campus for general student use. Computer purchase/lease plans available. A campuswide network can be accessed from student residence rooms and from off campus. Students can access the following: online class registration, Ethernet. Staffed computer lab on campus provides training in use of computers, software, and the Internet.

Community Environment: Poughkeepsie, population 30,355, originally settled by the Dutch, was the capital of New York from 1778 to 1783. Situated on a plateau above the Hudson River, Poughkeepsie is about 75 miles north of New York City and is easily accessible by car, train, bus, and air. Community services include a library, YMCA, YWCA, churches, art galleries, the Mid-Hudson Civic Center (with an ice-skating rink), the Bardavon Opera House (1869), and a Jewish Community Center. The area offers facilities for recreation and places of historic interest such as the Franklin D. Roosevelt National Historic Site in Hyde Park, and the Vanderbilt Mansion. Industries within the area include IBM and the Fairchild Corporation.

■ VAUGHN COLLEGE OF AERONAUTICS AND TECHNOLOGY

86-01 23rd Ave.
Flushing, NY 11369
Tel: (718)429-6600; Free: 866-6VAUGHN
Fax: (718)429-0256
E-mail: celso.alvarez@vaughn.edu
Web Site: www.vaughn.edu

Description: Independent, comprehensive, coed. Awards associate, bachelor's, and master's degrees. Founded 1932. Setting: 6-acre urban campus with easy access to New York City. Endowment: $24.4 million. Educational spending for the previous fiscal year: $10,752 per student. Total enrollment: 1,545. Faculty: 184 (40 full-time, 144 part-time). Student-undergrad faculty ratio is 15:1. 674 applied, 82% were admitted. Full-time: 1,294 students, 12% women, 88% men. Part-time: 244 students, 11% women, 89% men. Students come from 17 states and territories, 22 other countries, 12% from out-of-state. 0.3% American Indian or Alaska Native, non-Hispanic/Latino; 34% Hispanic/Latino; 18% Black or African American, non-Hispanic/Latino; 11% Asian, non-Hispanic/Latino; 1% Native Hawaiian or other Pacific Islander, non-Hispanic/Latino; 6% international. 35% 25 or older, 12% live on campus, 12% transferred in. Retention: 78% of full-time freshmen returned the following year. Academic areas with the most degrees conferred: engineering technologies; transportation and materials moving. Core. Calendar: semesters. Academic remediation for entering students, ESL program, services for LD students, advanced placement, distance learning, double major, summer session for credit, part-time degree program, internships. ROTC: Army (c), Air Force (c).

Entrance Requirements: Open admission for applicants to associate of applied sciences programs and the Aviation Training Institute. Options: electronic application, international baccalaureate accepted. Required: high school transcript, SAT or ACT. Recommended: essay, 2 recommendations, interview, SAT and SAT Subject Tests or ACT. Entrance: moderately difficult. Application deadline: rolling. Notification: continuous. SAT Reasoning Test deadline: 6/1. SAT Subject Test deadline: 6/1. Transfer credits accepted: Yes.

Costs Per Year: Application fee: $40. One-time mandatory fee: $160. Comprehensive fee: $41,364 includes full-time tuition ($25,680), mandatory fees ($960), and college room and board ($14,724). College room only: $11,425. Part-time tuition: $855 per credit.

Collegiate Environment: Orientation program. Social organizations: 19 open to all; academic fraternal organizations; 11% of men are members. Most popular organizations: Robotics Club (2106 Vex World Champions), Society of Women Engineers, Engineers Without Borders, The Unmanned Aerial Vehicle (UAV) Club, SHPE (Society of Hispanic Professional Engineers). Major annual events: Six Flags Fright Fest Trip, Clubs and Activities Fair, Holiday Tree Decorating. Student services: personal-psychological counseling. Campus security: 24-hour emergency response devices and patrols, controlled dormitory access. 200 college housing spaces available; 184 were occupied in 2018-19. Freshmen given priority for college housing. Option: coed housing available. Library and Learning Com-

mons. Weekly public service hours: 60. Operations spending for the previous fiscal year: $494,003. 220 computers available on campus for general student use. A campuswide network can be accessed. Students can access the following: online class registration, Vaughn Student Portal. Staffed computer lab on campus provides training in use of computers, software, and the Internet.

Community Environment: See Queens College of the City University of New York.

■ VILLA MARIA COLLEGE

240 Pine Ridge Rd.
Buffalo, NY 14225
Tel: (716)896-0700
Fax: (716)896-0705
E-mail: admissions@villa.edu
Web Site: www.villa.edu

Description: Independent, 4-year, coed, affiliated with Roman Catholic Church. Awards associate and bachelor's degrees. Founded 1960. Setting: 9-acre suburban campus with easy access to Buffalo-Niagara. Endowment: $1.9 million. Educational spending for the previous fiscal year: $18,528 per student. Total enrollment: 596. Faculty: 103 (34 full-time, 69 part-time). Student-undergrad faculty ratio is 9:1. 460 applied, 81% were admitted. Full-time: 490 students, 61% women, 39% men. Part-time: 106 students, 67% women, 33% men. Students come from 9 states and territories, 2 other countries, 3% from out-of-state. 0.5% American Indian or Alaska Native, non-Hispanic/Latino; 6% Hispanic/Latino; 33% Black or African American, non-Hispanic/Latino; 2% Asian, non-Hispanic/Latino; 0.3% international. 21% 25 or older, 13% transferred in. Retention: 61% of full-time freshmen returned the following year. Academic areas with the most degrees conferred: visual and performing arts; communication technologies; English. Core. Calendar: semesters. Services for LD students, advanced placement, honors program, independent study, distance learning, part-time degree program, co-op programs and internships. Off campus study. Study abroad program.

Entrance Requirements: Options: electronic application, international baccalaureate accepted. Required: high school transcript, application, financial aid forms if applying for assistance, health forms, essay, portfolio and interview for Art programs, audition for music programs. Recommended: essay. Required for some: interview. Entrance: moderately difficult. Application deadlines: rolling, rolling for nonresidents. Notification: continuous, continuous for nonresidents. Transfer credits accepted: Yes.

Costs Per Year: Tuition: $21,860 full-time, $730 per credit hour part-time. Mandatory fees: $1150 full-time. Full-time tuition and fees vary according to degree level, program, and reciprocity agreements. Part-time tuition varies according to course load, degree level, program, and reciprocity agreements.

Collegiate Environment: Orientation program. Choral group. Social organizations: 20 open to all. Major annual events: Spring Arts Festival, Music Series, Fall/Spring Fest. Student services: health clinic, personal-psychological counseling. Campus security: 24-hour emergency response devices, late night transport-escort service, security guard during hours of operation. Villa Maria College Library. Books: 17,213 (physical), 153,087 (digital/electronic); Serial titles: 82 (physical); Databases: 45. Operations spending for the previous fiscal year: $158,694. 275 computers available on campus for general student use. Computer purchase/lease plans available. A campuswide network can be accessed. Students can access the following: online class registration. Staffed computer lab on campus provides training in use of computers, software, and the Internet.

Community Environment: See Canisius College.

■ WAGNER COLLEGE

1 Campus Rd.
Staten Island, NY 10301-4495
Tel: (718)390-3100; Free: 800-221-1010
Fax: (718)390-3105
E-mail: jgibbons@wagner.edu
Web Site: www.wagner.edu

Description: Independent, comprehensive, coed. Awards bachelor's, master's, and doctoral degrees and post-master's certificates. Founded 1883. Setting: 105-acre urban campus with easy access to New York City. Endowment: $88.5 million. Educational spending for the previous fiscal year: $10,968 per student. Total enrollment: 2,289. Faculty: 265 (110 full-time, 155 part-time). Student-undergrad faculty ratio is 13:1. 2,834 applied, 70% were admitted. 25% from top 10% of their high school class, 50% from top quarter,

88% from top half. Full-time: 1,745 students, 63% women, 37% men. Part-time: 67 students, 67% women, 33% men. Students come from 41 states and territories, 43 other countries, 54% from out-of-state. 0.1% American Indian or Alaska Native, non-Hispanic/Latino; 12% Hispanic/Latino; 8% Black or African American, non-Hispanic/Latino; 4% Asian, non-Hispanic/Latino; 0.2% Native Hawaiian or other Pacific Islander, non-Hispanic/Latino; 4% international. 8% 25 or older, 71% live on campus, 7% transferred in. Retention: 85% of full-time freshmen returned the following year. Academic areas with the most degrees conferred: health professions and related sciences; business/marketing; visual and performing arts. Core. Calendar: semesters. Services for LD students, advanced placement, accelerated degree program, self-designed majors, honors program, independent study, double major, summer session for credit, part-time degree program, adult/continuing education programs, co-op programs and internships, graduate courses open to undergrads. Off campus study at Belmont University, California Lutheran University. Study abroad program. ROTC: Army (c).

Entrance Requirements: Options: electronic application, deferred admission, international baccalaureate accepted. Required: essay, high school transcript, minimum 2.5 high school GPA, 2 recommendations. Recommended: minimum 3 high school GPA, interview. Required for some: interview, SAT or ACT. Application deadlines: 2/15, 12/1 for early action. Notification: 2/15, 1/5 for early action. SAT Reasoning Test deadline: 2/15. SAT Subject Test deadline: 2/15. Transfer credits accepted: Yes.

Collegiate Environment: Orientation program. Drama-theater group, choral group, marching band, student-run newspaper, radio station. Social organizations: 66 open to all; national fraternities, national sororities, local fraternities, local sororities; 10% of eligible men and 7% of eligible women are members. Most popular organizations: Student Government Association, Student Activities Board, Wagner College Theatre, Wagner College Choir, student newspaper. Major annual events: Homecoming, Songfest, Spring Fling. Student services: health clinic, personal-psychological counseling. Campus security: 24-hour emergency response devices and patrols, late night transport-escort service, controlled dormitory access. August Horrmann Library. Books: 70,465 (physical), 180,000 (digital/electronic); Serial titles: 79,532 (physical); Databases: 61. Weekly public service hours: 120; students can reserve study rooms. Operations spending for the previous fiscal year: $822,961. 230 computers available on campus for general student use. A campuswide network can be accessed from student residence rooms and from off campus. Students can access the following: online class registration. Staffed computer lab on campus provides training in use of computers, software, and the Internet.

■ **WEBB INSTITUTE**
298 Crescent Beach Rd.
Glen Cove, NY 11542-1398
Tel: (516)671-2213
Fax: (516)674-9838
E-mail: admissions@webb.edu
Web Site: www.webb.edu

Description: Independent, 4-year, coed. Awards bachelor's degrees. Founded 1889. Setting: 26-acre suburban campus with easy access to New York City. Endowment: $66.3 million. Total enrollment: 98. Faculty: 14 (10 full-time, 4 part-time). Student-undergrad faculty ratio is 9:1. 106 applied, 35% were admitted. 88% from top 10% of their high school class, 12% from top quarter, 100% from top half. Full-time: 98 students, 20% women, 80% men. Students come from 27 states and territories, 2 other countries, 72% from out-of-state. 1% Hispanic/Latino; 11% Asian, non-Hispanic/Latino. 100% live on campus, 2% transferred in. Retention: 93% of full-time freshmen returned the following year. Academic area with the most degrees conferred: engineering. Core. Calendar: semesters. Services for LD students, independent study, double major, internships. Study abroad program.

Entrance Requirements: Options: electronic application, early decision, deferred admission, international baccalaureate accepted. Required: essay, high school transcript, minimum 3.5 high school GPA, 2 recommendations, interview, proof of U.S. citizenship or permanent residency status, SAT or ACT, SAT Subject Tests. Entrance: most difficult. Application deadlines: 2/1, 10/15 for early decision. Notification: 3/15, 12/15 for early decision. SAT Reasoning Test deadline: 2/1. SAT Subject Test deadline: 2/1. Transfer credits accepted: No. Applicants placed on waiting list: 8. Wait-listed applicants offered admission: 4. Early decision applicants: 41. Early decision applicants admitted: 8.

Costs Per Year: Application fee: $60. One-time mandatory fee: $3000. Comprehensive fee: $65,225 includes full-time tuition ($49,750), mandatory

fees ($425), and college room and board ($15,050). Webb provides scholarships that will fully cover the tuition expenses of U.S. citizens and permanent residents. One-time required fee is for a laptop charged in the first year only.

Collegiate Environment: Orientation program. Choral group. Social organizations: The Webb Women; 100% of women are members. Most popular organizations: Student Organization, Society of Naval Architects and Marine Engineers, American Society of Naval Engineers, Society of Women Engineers, Marine Technology Society. Major annual events: Family Weekend, Webbstock, Founder's Day. Student services: personal-psychological counseling. Campus security: 24-hour emergency response devices and patrols, controlled dormitory access. Livingston Library. Books: 44,800 (physical), 4,190 (digital/electronic); Serial titles: 817 (physical), 43,658 (digital/electronic); Databases: 62. Weekly public service hours: 35; study areas open 24 hours, 5-7 days a week. 25 computers available on campus for general student use. Computer purchase/lease plans available. A computer is required for all students. A campuswide network can be accessed from student residence rooms and from off campus. Staffed computer lab on campus provides training in use of computers, software, and the Internet.

Community Environment: Population 26,600, Glen Cove lies 22 miles from New York City on Long Island's historic North Shore. The Long Island Railroad furnishes commuter service to New York City. The area has excellent boating, swimming, horseback riding, and fishing facilities. Part-time employment is available.

■ **WELLS COLLEGE**
170 Main St.
Aurora, NY 13026
Tel: (315)364-3266; Free: 800-952-9355
Fax: (315)364-3227
Web Site: www.wells.edu

Description: Independent, 4-year, coed. Awards bachelor's degrees. Founded 1868. Setting: 365-acre rural campus with easy access to Syracuse. Endowment: $23.5 million. Research spending for the previous fiscal year: $35,000. Total enrollment: 488. Faculty: 58 (40 full-time, 18 part-time). Student-undergrad faculty ratio is 10:1. 1,693 applied, 80% were admitted. 14% from top 10% of their high school class, 45% from top quarter, 76% from top half. Full-time: 481 students, 64% women, 36% men. Part-time: 7 students, 43% women, 57% men. 23% from out-of-state. 1% American Indian or Alaska Native, non-Hispanic/Latino; 14% Hispanic/Latino; 13% Black or African American, non-Hispanic/Latino; 2% Asian, non-Hispanic/Latino. 3% 25 or older, 95% live on campus, 3% transferred in. Retention: 70% of full-time freshmen returned the following year. Academic areas with the most degrees conferred: psychology; social sciences; biological/life sciences. Core. Calendar: semesters. ESL program, services for LD students, advanced placement, self-designed majors, independent study, double major, part-time degree program, adult/continuing education programs, internships. Off campus study at members of the Association of Colleges and Universities of the State of New York, Cornell University, Ithaca College. Study abroad program.

Entrance Requirements: Options: electronic application, early admission, early decision, early action, deferred admission, international baccalaureate accepted. Required: essay, high school transcript, 2 recommendations. Recommended: minimum 3 high school GPA, interview. Entrance: moderately difficult. Application deadlines: 3/1, 12/15 for early decision, 12/15 for early action. Notification: continuous until 4/1, 1/15 for early decision, 2/1 for early action. SAT Reasoning Test deadline: 3/1. Transfer credits accepted: Yes.

Costs Per Year: Application fee: $0. Comprehensive fee: $54,800 includes full-time tuition ($39,200), mandatory fees ($1500), and college room and board ($14,100). College room only: $7050. Room and board charges vary according to housing facility. Part-time tuition: $800 per credit hour. Part-time mandatory fees: $200 per term. Part-time tuition and fees vary according to course load.

Collegiate Environment: Orientation program. Drama-theater group, choral group. Social organizations: 50 open to all; Odd/Even line; 100% of eligible men and 100% of eligible women are members. Most popular organizations: Umoja, Prodigy, Red Cross Club, Campus Greens, Programming Board. Major annual events: Spring Weekend, Fall Semi-Formal, Odd-Even Game/Weekend. Student services: health clinic, personal-psychological counseling, women's center. Campus security: 24-hour emergency response devices and patrols, late night transport-escort service, controlled dormitory access. Louis Jefferson Long Library. Students can reserve study rooms. Operations spending for the previous fiscal year: $440,000. 96 computers

available on campus for general student use. A campuswide network can be accessed from student residence rooms and from off campus. Students can access the following: online class registration. Staffed computer lab on campus provides training in use of computers, software, and the Internet.
Community Environment: The college has always shared a close relationship with the small, picturesque village of Aurora, New York; which is noted on the National Historic Registry. Aurora is also home to the highly acclaimed Aurora Inn and the nationally known company Mackenzie-Childs.

■ **WESTCHESTER COMMUNITY COLLEGE**
75 Grasslands Rd.
Valhalla, NY 10595
Tel: (914)606-6600
E-mail: admissions@sunywcc.edu
Web Site: www.sunywcc.edu
Description: State and locally supported, 2-year, coed. Part of State University of New York System. Awards certificates, transfer associate, and terminal associate degrees. Founded 1946. Setting: 218-acre suburban campus with easy access to New York City. Total enrollment: 11,535. Faculty: 801 (162 full-time, 639 part-time). 4,378 applied, 100% were admitted. Full-time: 6,156 students, 48% women, 52% men. Part-time: 5,379 students, 58% women, 42% men. 1% American Indian or Alaska Native, non-Hispanic/Latino; 37% Hispanic/Latino; 23% Black or African American, non-Hispanic/Latino; 4% Asian, non-Hispanic/Latino; 0.3% Native Hawaiian or other Pacific Islander, non-Hispanic/Latino; 1% international. 28% 25 or older, 7% transferred in. Calendar: semesters. Academic remediation for entering students, ESL program, services for LD students, advanced placement, honors program, independent study, distance learning, double major, summer session for credit, part-time degree program, adult/continuing education programs, co-op programs and internships. Off campus study. Study abroad program.
Entrance Requirements: Open admission. Options: electronic application, early action. Required: high school transcript. Required for some: interview. Entrance: noncompetitive. Application deadline: rolling. Transfer credits accepted: Yes.
Costs Per Year: Application fee: $35. Area resident tuition: $4380 full-time, $183 per credit hour part-time. State resident tuition: $4380 full-time, $183 per credit hour part-time. Nonresident tuition: $11,770 full-time, $493 per credit hour part-time. Mandatory fees: $456 full-time.
Collegiate Environment: Orientation program. Choral group, student-run newspaper, radio station. Most popular organizations: Deca Fashion Retail, Future Educators, Respiratory Club, Black Student Union, Diversity Action. Major annual events: Solidarity Day, Club Day, Talent Day. Student services: health clinic, personal-psychological counseling, women's center. Campus security: 24-hour emergency response devices and patrols, late night transport-escort service. College housing not available. Harold L. Drimmer Library.

■ **YESHIVA DERECH CHAIM**
1573 39th St.
Brooklyn, NY 11218
Tel: (718)438-3070
Description: Independent Jewish, comprehensive, men only. Awards bachelor's and master's degrees. Founded 1975. Total enrollment: 162. 31 applied, 100% were admitted. 3% 25 or older. Calendar: semesters.

■ **YESHIVA D'MONSEY RABBINICAL COLLEGE**
2 Roman Blvd.
Monsey, NY 10952
Tel: (914)352-5852
Fax: (914)362-3453
Description: Independent Jewish, 4-year, men only. Awards bachelor's degrees. Total enrollment: 72. 26 applied, 100% were admitted.

■ **YESHIVA OF FAR ROCKAWAY DERECH AYSON RABBINICAL SEMINARY**
802 Hicksville Rd.
Far Rockaway, NY 11691
Tel: (718)327-7600
Web Site: www.yofr.org
Description: Independent Jewish, 4-year, men only. Awards bachelor's degrees.

■ **YESHIVA GEDOLA OHR YISRAEL**
2899 Nostrand Ave.
Brooklyn, NY 11229
Web Site: www.ohryisroel.org
Description: Independent Jewish, 4-year, coed.

■ **YESHIVA GEDOLAH IMREI YOSEF D'SPINKA**
1466 56th St.
Brooklyn, NY 11219
Tel: (718)851-8721
Description: Independent Jewish, 4-year, men only. Awards bachelor's degrees. Total enrollment: 153. 5% 25 or older.
Entrance Requirements: Open admission.

■ **YESHIVA GEDOLAH KESSER TORAH**
28 Cedar Ln.
Monsey, NY 10952
Description: Independent religious, 4-year, men only.

■ **YESHIVA KARLIN STOLIN**
1818 54th St.
Brooklyn, NY 11204
Tel: (718)232-7800
Fax: (718)331-4833
Description: Independent Jewish, comprehensive, men only. Awards bachelor's and master's degrees. Founded 1948. Setting: urban campus. Total enrollment: 69. 30 applied, 100% were admitted. 7% 25 or older. Core. Calendar: semesters. Independent study, co-op programs. Study abroad program.
Entrance Requirements: Required: high school transcript, interview. Entrance: very difficult. Application deadline: rolling. Preference given to students from Mesivta Karlin Stolin.
Collegiate Environment: Student services: personal-psychological counseling. Campus security: 24-hour emergency response devices.

■ **YESHIVA AND KOLEL BAIS MEDRASH ELYON**
73 Main St.
Monsey, NY 10952
Tel: (845)356-7064
Description: Independent Jewish, 4-year, men only. Awards bachelor's degrees. Total enrollment: 24. 13 applied, 100% were admitted.

■ **YESHIVA AND KOLLEL HARBOTZAS TORAH**
1049 E 15th St.
Brooklyn, NY 11230
Tel: (718)692-0208
Description: Independent Jewish, 4-year, men only. Awards bachelor's degrees. Total enrollment: 31.

■ **YESHIVA KOLLEL TIFERETH ELIZER**
1227 47th St.
Brooklyn, NY 11219
Description: Independent religious, 4-year, men only.

■ **YESHIVA OF MACHZIKAI HADAS**
1321 43rd St.
Brooklyn, NY 11219
Tel: (718)853-2442
Description: Independent Jewish, 4-year, coed. Awards bachelor's degrees.

■ **YESHIVA OF NITRA RABBINICAL COLLEGE**
Croton Lake Rd.
Mount Kisco, NY 10549
Tel: (718)384-5460
Description: Independent Jewish, comprehensive, men only. Awards bachelor's and master's degrees. Founded 1946. Setting: small town campus with easy access to New York City. Total enrollment: 214. 252 applied. Calendar: semesters.

■ **YESHIVA OHR NAFTOLI**
701 Blooming Grove Tpke.
New Windsor, NY 12553
Description: Independent religious, 4-year, coed.

■ **YESHIVA SHAAR EPHRAIM**
178 Maple Ave.
Monsey, NY 10952
Description: Independent religious, 4-year, men only.

■ **YESHIVA SHAAR HATORAH TALMUDIC RESEARCH INSTITUTE**
117-06 84th Ave.
Kew Gardens, NY 11418-1469
Tel: (718)846-1940
Description: Independent Jewish, comprehensive, men only. Awards bachelor's and master's degrees. Founded 1976. Total enrollment: 141. 43 applied. Calendar: semesters.

■ **YESHIVA SHAAREI TORAH OF ROCKLAND**
91 W Carlton Rd.
Suffern, NY 10901
Tel: (845)352-3431
Description: Independent Jewish, 4-year, men only. Awards bachelor's degrees. Total enrollment: 46. 42 applied.

■ **YESHIVA SHOLOM SHACHNA**
401 Elmwood Ave.
Brooklyn, NY 11230
Description: Independent religious, 2-year, men only.

■ **YESHIVA OF THE TELSHE ALUMNI**
4904 Independence Ave.
Riverdale, NY 10471
Tel: (718)601-3523
Description: Independent Jewish, 4-year, men only. Awards bachelor's degrees. Total enrollment: 112. 26 applied, 100% were admitted.
Entrance Requirements: Recommended: high school transcript.

■ **YESHIVA UNIVERSITY**
500 W 185th St.
New York, NY 10033-3201
Tel: (212)960-5400
Fax: (212)960-0086
Web Site: www.yu.edu
Description: Independent, university, coed. Awards bachelor's, master's, and doctoral degrees and post-master's certificates (Yeshiva College and Stern College for Women are coordinate undergraduate colleges of arts and sciences for men and women, respectively. Sy Syms School of Business offers programs at both campuses). Founded 1886. Setting: urban campus. Endowment: $894.5 million. Research spending for the previous fiscal year: $235.2 million. Educational spending for the previous fiscal year: $17,926 per student. Total enrollment: 6,203. Faculty: 1,028 (720 full-time, 308 part-time). Student-undergrad faculty ratio is 7:1. 1,558 applied, 80% were admitted. Full-time: 2,691 students, 46% women, 54% men. Part-time: 53 students, 28% women, 72% men. Students come from 33 states and territories, 21 other countries, 66% from out-of-state. 0.2% Hispanic/Latino; 5% international. 1% 25 or older, 88% live on campus, 1% transferred in. Retention: 88% of full-time freshmen returned the following year. Academic areas with the most degrees conferred: business/marketing; biological/life sciences; psychology. Calendar: semesters. Advanced placement, self-designed majors, honors program, independent study, distance learning, double major, summer session for credit, co-op programs and internships, graduate courses open to undergrads. Off campus study at Fashion Institute of Technology. Study abroad program.
Entrance Requirements: Options: electronic application, early admission, early decision, deferred admission. Required: essay, high school transcript, 2 recommendations, interview, SAT or ACT. Entrance: moderately difficult. Application deadline: 2/1. Notification: 4/1. Transfer credits accepted: Yes.
Collegiate Environment: Orientation program. Drama-theater group, choral group, student-run newspaper, radio station. Student services: health clinic, personal-psychological counseling. Campus security: 24-hour emergency response devices and patrols, late night transport-escort service. Mendel Gottesman Library. Books: 1.1 million (physical), 24,407 (digital/electronic); Serial titles: 9,933 (physical); Databases: 401.
Community Environment: See New York University.

■ **YESHIVA ZICHRON ARYEH**
1213 Bay 25th St.
Far Rockaway, NY 11691

Web Site: www.yeshivazichronaryeh.com
Description: Independent Jewish, 4-year, coed.

■ **YESHIVAS MAHARIT D'SATMAR**
475 County Rte. 105
Monroe, NY 10950
Web Site: www.yeshivasmaharit.com
Description: Independent Jewish, 4-year, coed.

■ **YESHIVAS NOVOMINSK**
1569 47th St.
Brooklyn, NY 11219
Tel: (718)438-2727
Description: Independent Jewish, 4-year, men only. Awards bachelor's degrees. Total enrollment: 100. 25 applied, 100% were admitted.

■ **YESHIVAT MIKDASH MELECH**
1326 Ocean Pky.
Brooklyn, NY 11230-5601
Tel: (718)339-1090
Description: Independent Jewish, 4-year, men only. Awards bachelor's degrees. Founded 1972. Total enrollment: 78. 50 applied, 100% were admitted. 17% 25 or older. Calendar: continuous.
Entrance Requirements: Recommended: high school transcript. Application deadline: rolling. Notification: continuous.

■ **YESHIVATH VIZNITZ**
15 Elyon Rd.
Monsey, NY 10952
Tel: (845)731-3700
Description: Independent Jewish, comprehensive, men only. Awards bachelor's and master's degrees. Founded 1946. Setting: small town campus with easy access to New York City. Total enrollment: 420. 70 applied, 100% were admitted. Calendar: semesters.

■ **YESHIVATH ZICHRON MOSHE**
Laurel Park Rd.
South Fallsburg, NY 12779
Tel: (914)434-5240
Description: Independent Jewish, comprehensive, men only. Awards bachelor's and master's degrees. Founded 1969. Setting: 70-acre small town campus. Total enrollment: 222. 74 applied, 100% were admitted. Core. Calendar: semesters.
Collegiate Environment: Student services: personal-psychological counseling.

■ **YORK COLLEGE OF THE CITY UNIVERSITY OF NEW YORK**
94-20 Guy R. Brewer Blvd.
Jamaica, NY 11451
Tel: (718)262-2000
E-mail: lyates@york.cuny.edu
Web Site: www.york.cuny.edu
Description: State and locally supported, comprehensive, coed. Part of City University of New York System. Awards bachelor's and master's degrees. Founded 1967. Setting: 50-acre urban campus with easy access to New York City. Endowment: $890,940. Research spending for the previous fiscal year: $1.2 million. Educational spending for the previous fiscal year: $8837 per student. Total enrollment: 8,360. Student-undergrad faculty ratio is 23:1. 13,726 applied, 61% were admitted. Full-time: 5,066 students, 67% women, 33% men. Part-time: 3,192 students, 63% women, 37% men. Students come from 4 states and territories, 131 other countries, 1% from out-of-state. 0.9% American Indian or Alaska Native, non-Hispanic/Latino; 22% Hispanic/Latino; 40% Black or African American, non-Hispanic/Latino; 26% Asian, non-Hispanic/Latino; 4% international. 33% 25 or older, 10% transferred in. Retention: 73% of full-time freshmen returned the following year. Academic areas with the most degrees conferred: health professions and related sciences; psychology; business/marketing. Core. Calendar: semesters. ESL program, services for LD students, advanced placement, honors program, independent study, double major, summer session for credit, part-time degree program, adult/continuing education programs, co-op programs and internships. Off campus study at other units of the City University of New York System. Study abroad program. ROTC: Army.
Entrance Requirements: Options: electronic application, early admission, deferred admission, international baccalaureate accepted. Required: high

school transcript, minimum 2.8 high school GPA, SAT or ACT. Recommended: minimum 3 high school GPA. Required for some: minimum 2.5 high school GPA. Entrance: moderately difficult. Application deadline: rolling. Notification: continuous. SAT Reasoning Test deadline: 6/1. SAT Subject Test deadline: 6/1. Transfer credits accepted: Yes.

Costs Per Year: Application fee: $65. State resident tuition: $6730 full-time, $295 per credit part-time. Nonresident tuition: $18,000 full-time, $600 per credit part-time. Mandatory fees: $427 full-time, $131.10 per term part-time.

Collegiate Environment: Orientation program. Drama-theater group, choral group, student-run newspaper. Social organizations: 48 open to all. Most popular organizations: Haitian Students Association, Caribbean Students As-

sociation, Haitian Cultural Association, Latin Caucus, Muslim Student Association. Major annual events: Club Fairs, Talent Shows, Ethnic Fairs. Student services: health clinic, personal-psychological counseling, women's center. Campus security: 24-hour emergency response devices and patrols, late night transport-escort service. Main library plus 1 other. Books: 150,914 (physical), 473,723 (digital/electronic). Operations spending for the previous fiscal year: $2.7 million. 650 computers available on campus for general student use. A campuswide network can be accessed from off-campus. Students can access the following: online class registration. Staffed computer lab on campus provides training in use of computers, software, and the Internet.

■ ALAMANCE COMMUNITY COLLEGE

1247 Jimmie Kerr Rd.
Graham, NC 27253-8000
Tel: (336)578-2002
Fax: (336)578-1987
E-mail: brehlere@alamancecc.edu
Web Site: www.alamancecc.edu

Description: State-supported, 2-year, coed. Part of North Carolina Community College System. Awards certificates, diplomas, transfer associate, and terminal associate degrees. Founded 1958. Setting: 48-acre small town campus. Endowment: $2.9 million. Total enrollment: 4,243. Faculty: 435 (115 full-time, 320 part-time). Student-undergrad faculty ratio is 20:1. Full-time: 2,565 students, 63% women, 37% men. Part-time: 1,668 students, 56% women, 44% men. Students come from 7 states and territories, 6 other countries, 1% from out-of-state. 0.4% American Indian or Alaska Native, non-Hispanic/Latino; 9% Hispanic/Latino; 21% Black or African American, non-Hispanic/Latino; 2% Asian, non-Hispanic/Latino; 0.2% Native Hawaiian or other Pacific Islander, non-Hispanic/Latino; 0.6% international. 48% 25 or older, 28% transferred in. Calendar: semesters. Academic remediation for entering students, ESL program, services for LD students, independent study, distance learning, double major, summer session for credit, part-time degree program, adult/continuing education programs, co-op programs. Off campus study.

Entrance Requirements: Open admission. Option: electronic application. Required: high school transcript. Entrance: noncompetitive. Application deadline: rolling. Notification: continuous. Transfer credits accepted: Yes.

Costs Per Year: Application fee: $0. State resident tuition: $2432 full-time, $76 per credit hour part-time. Nonresident tuition: $8576 full-time, $268 per credit hour part-time. Mandatory fees: $30 full-time, $5 per credit hour part-time. Full-time tuition and fees vary according to course load. Part-time tuition and fees vary according to course load.

Collegiate Environment: Orientation program. Student services: personal-psychological counseling. Campus security: 24-hour emergency response devices and patrols, student patrols, late night transport-escort service. College housing not available. Learning Resources Center. Weekly public service hours: 64; students can reserve study rooms. 60 computers available on campus for general student use. A campuswide network can be accessed. Students can access the following: online class registration. Staffed computer lab on campus provides training in use of computers, software, and the Internet.

Community Environment: The industrialized economy of Alamance County depends primarily upon textiles, hosiery, electronics, metal cutting and fabricating, packaging and plastics. The bulk of the industries are located here. Planes and buses serve the area. A library, museum, YMCA, hospitals and various civic and service organizations are a part of the community. Some part-time employment is available for students. Recreational facilities include a supervised city recreational program, and many lakes are available for winter sports and outdoor living.

■ APEX SCHOOL OF THEOLOGY

1701 T.W. Alexander Dr.
Durham, NC 27703
Tel: (919)572-1625
Fax: (919)572-1762
E-mail: registrar@apexsot.edu
Web Site: www.apexsot.edu

Description: Independent interdenominational, comprehensive, coed. Awards associate, bachelor's, master's, and doctoral degrees. Founded 1995. Setting: suburban campus. Total enrollment: 721. Faculty: 41 (14 full-time, 27 part-time). Student-undergrad faculty ratio is 17:1. 362 applied, 83% were admitted. 2% Hispanic/Latino; 95% Black or African American, non-Hispanic/Latino. 100% 25 or older. Retention: 92% of full-time freshmen returned the following year. Core. Calendar: semesters. Independent study, distance learning, double major, internships.

Entrance Requirements: Option: electronic application. Required: essay, high school transcript, 1 recommendation. Entrance: moderately difficult. Transfer credits accepted: Yes.

Collegiate Environment: Choral group, student-run newspaper. ASOT Library.

■ APPALACHIAN STATE UNIVERSITY

287 Rivers St.
Boone, NC 28608
Tel: (828)262-2000
Fax: (828)262-3296
E-mail: admissions@appstate.edu
Web Site: www.appstate.edu

Description: State-supported, comprehensive, coed. Part of University of North Carolina System. Awards bachelor's, master's, and doctoral degrees and post-master's certificates. Founded 1899. Setting: 489-acre small town campus. Endowment: $122.4 million. Research spending for the previous fiscal year: $2.9 million. Educational spending for the previous fiscal year: $8230 per student. Total enrollment: 19,108. Faculty: 1,392 (1,004 full-time, 388 part-time). Student-undergrad faculty ratio is 16:1. 16,154 applied, 69% were admitted. 19% from top 10% of their high school class, 59% from top quarter, 93% from top half. Full-time: 16,421 students, 56% women, 44% men. Part-time: 960 students, 61% women, 39% men. Students come from 46 states and territories, 61 other countries, 8% from out-of-state. 0.3% American Indian or Alaska Native, non-Hispanic/Latino; 6% Hispanic/Latino; 3% Black or African American, non-Hispanic/Latino; 2% Asian, non-Hispanic/Latino; 0.1% Native Hawaiian or other Pacific Islander, non-Hispanic/Latino; 0.8% international. 7% 25 or older, 33% live on campus, 9% transferred in. Retention: 87% of full-time freshmen returned the following year. Academic areas with the most degrees conferred: business/marketing; health professions and related sciences; education. Core. Calendar: semesters. Academic remediation for entering students, ESL program, services for LD students, advanced placement, self-designed majors, honors program, independent study, distance learning, double major, summer session for credit, part-time degree program, adult/continuing education programs, internships, graduate courses open to undergrads. Off campus study at Appalachian Learning Alliance. Study abroad program. ROTC: Army.

Entrance Requirements: Options: electronic application, early action, deferred admission, international baccalaureate accepted. Required: high school transcript, SAT or ACT. Recommended: essay. Entrance: moderately difficult. Application deadlines: 3/1, 3/1 for nonresidents, 11/1 for early action. Notification: continuous until 1/25, continuous until 1/25 for nonresidents, 1/25 for early action. SAT Reasoning Test deadline: 3/15. Transfer credits accepted: Yes. Applicants placed on waiting list: 1,528. Wait-listed applicants offered admission: 226. Early action applicants: 13,484. Early action applicants admitted: 5,316.

Costs Per Year: Application fee: $65. State resident tuition: $4242 full-time, $143 per credit hour part-time. Nonresident tuition: $19,049 full-time,

$643.50 per credit hour part-time. Mandatory fees: $3122 full-time, $104 per credit hour part-time. Part-time tuition and fees vary according to course load. College room and board: $8304. College room only: $4470. Room and board charges vary according to board plan and housing facility. Tuition guaranteed not to increase for student's term of enrollment.

Collegiate Environment: Orientation program. Drama-theater group, choral group, marching band, student-run newspaper, radio station. Social organizations: 394 open to all; national fraternities, national sororities; 8% of eligible men and 12% of eligible women are members. Most popular organizations: Appalachian Educators, Exercise Science Club, App Sits Meditation Club, The Hiking Club, Gaming Club. Major annual events: Club Expo, Panhellenic Council Cod of Ethics Event, Homecoming Blood Drive. Student services: legal services, health clinic, personal-psychological counseling, women's center. Campus security: 24-hour emergency response devices and patrols, late night transport-escort service, controlled dormitory access. College housing designed to accommodate 5,674 students; 5,740 undergraduates lived in college housing during 2018-19. Freshmen guaranteed college housing. On-campus residence required in freshman year. Options: coed, women-only housing available. Carol Grotnes Belk Library plus 1 other. Books: 666,451 (physical), 831,648 (digital/electronic); Serial titles: 12,785 (physical), 161,860 (digital/electronic); Databases: 447. Weekly public service hours: 137; students can reserve study rooms. Operations spending for the previous fiscal year: $9.5 million. 2,280 computers available on campus for general student use. Computer purchase/lease plans available. A campuswide network can be accessed from student residence rooms and from off campus. Students can access the following: online class registration. Staffed computer lab on campus provides training in use of computers, software, and the Internet.

Community Environment: Located in Boone, North Carolina, Appalachian State University is in the middle of one of the most popular year-round recreation areas in the East. The campus is only a few miles from several major ski resorts, and Pisgah National Forest and the Appalachian Trail are easily accessible from Boone. Grandfather Mountain and"Tweetsie" railroad are famous tourist attractions."Horn in the West" is a historical drama portraying with music and dance the story of Daniel Boone and the struggle to establish freedom in the southern Appalachian Highlands. This is performed in an outdoor amphitheater in a lovely mountain setting during July and August. The climate in the area is temperate. The average summer temperature rarely climbs above 80 degrees, and when it does a brief, refreshing shower usually cools things off. Fall brings clear, brisk and color-splashed days and cool evenings. Winter means picturesque snowfalls and fireside nights. Besides skiing, the area offers ample opportunities for other outdoor recreation, including river canoeing, hiking and camping. Three highways, U.S. 421, reaching from the Great Lakes to the North Carolina coast, and U.S. 321 and 221, all come through Boone, providing easy travel in all directions. The scenic Blue Ridge Parkway is only six miles from campus. The area, both urban and rural, is rich in contrasts between a growing university town and traditional southern Appalachian folkways. The university offers a wide variety of cultural events throughout the academic year, ranging from symphony orchestras to bluegrass concerts and from student talent shows to Broadway plays.

■ ASHEVILLE-BUNCOMBE TECHNICAL COMMUNITY COLLEGE

340 Victoria Rd.
Asheville, NC 28801-4897
Tel: (828)254-1921
Fax: (828)251-6355
Web Site: www.abtech.edu

Description: State-supported, 2-year, coed. Part of North Carolina Community College System. Awards certificates, diplomas, transfer associate, and terminal associate degrees. Founded 1959. Setting: 126-acre urban campus. Total enrollment: 7,542. Student-undergrad faculty ratio is 15:1. 1% from out-of-state. 43% 25 or older. Core. Calendar: semesters. Academic remediation for entering students, services for LD students, advanced placement, independent study, distance learning, double major, summer session for credit, part-time degree program, adult/continuing education programs, co-op programs and internships.

Entrance Requirements: Open admission except for allied health programs. Option: deferred admission. Required: high school transcript. Required for some: interview. Entrance: noncompetitive. Application deadline: rolling. Notification: continuous.

Collegiate Environment: Orientation program. Drama-theater group, choral group, student-run newspaper. Student services: health clinic, personal-

psychological counseling. Campus security: 24-hour emergency response devices and patrols. Locke Learning Resources Center. Students can reserve study rooms.

Community Environment: The main campus is located on Victoria Road in Asheville, NC, a city repeatedly named as one of the most livable in America. Nestled between the Blue Ride and Great Smoky mountains, Asheville offers beautiful mountain scenery and an excellent quality of life. Recognized as an entrepreneurial hotspot, Asheville also enjoys a thriving business climate.

■ BARTON COLLEGE

PO Box 5000
Wilson, NC 27893-7000
Tel: (252)399-6300; Free: 800-345-4973
Fax: (252)237-4957
Web Site: www.barton.edu

Description: Independent, comprehensive, coed, affiliated with Christian Church (Disciples of Christ). Awards bachelor's and master's degrees. Founded 1902. Setting: 76-acre small town campus with easy access to Raleigh-Durham. Endowment: $29.1 million. Educational spending for the previous fiscal year: $9648 per student. Total enrollment: 1,059. Faculty: 128 (72 full-time, 56 part-time). Student-undergrad faculty ratio is 10:1. 3,486 applied, 40% were admitted. 12% from top 10% of their high school class, 34% from top quarter, 69% from top half. Full-time: 932 students, 62% women, 38% men. Part-time: 44 students, 86% women, 14% men. Students come from 34 states and territories, 25 other countries, 24% from out-of-state. 0.8% American Indian or Alaska Native, non-Hispanic/Latino; 9% Hispanic/Latino; 20% Black or African American, non-Hispanic/Latino; 1% Asian, non-Hispanic/Latino; 5% international. 14% 25 or older, 51% live on campus, 6% transferred in. Retention: 72% of full-time freshmen returned the following year. Academic areas with the most degrees conferred: health professions and related sciences; business/marketing; public administration and social services. Core. Calendar: semesters. Academic remediation for entering students, services for LD students, advanced placement, accelerated degree program, self-designed majors, honors program, independent study, distance learning, double major, summer session for credit, part-time degree program, adult/continuing education programs, internships. Study abroad program.

Entrance Requirements: Options: electronic application, international baccalaureate accepted. Required: SAT or ACT. Required for some: high school transcript. Entrance: minimally difficult. Application deadline: rolling. Notification: continuous. SAT Reasoning Test deadline: 8/1. Transfer credits accepted: Yes.

Costs Per Year: Application fee: $0. Comprehensive fee: $42,150 includes full-time tuition ($31,730) and college room and board ($10,420). College room only: $4500.

Collegiate Environment: Orientation program. Drama-theater group, choral group, student-run newspaper, radio station. Social organizations: 45 open to all; national fraternities, national sororities; 13% of eligible men and 13% of eligible women are members. Most popular organizations: Student Ambassador Program, Barton College Association of Nursing, Barton College Orientation Team, Barton College Catholic Campus Ministries, Minority Student Association. Major annual events: Day of Service, Welcome Back Barton Day, Greek Show. Student services: health clinic, personal-psychological counseling, women's center. Campus security: 24-hour emergency response devices and patrols, late night transport-escort service, controlled dormitory access. 613 college housing spaces available; 484 were occupied in 2018-19. Freshmen guaranteed college housing. On-campus residence required through sophomore year. Option: coed housing available. Willis N. Hackney Library. Books: 121,046 (physical), 421,508 (digital/electronic); Serial titles: 88,792 (digital/electronic); Databases: 160. Weekly public service hours: 96; students can reserve study rooms. Operations spending for the previous fiscal year: $429,002.

Community Environment: Bus and train transportation are available. Community facilities include churches of all denominations, a hospital, library, shopping centers, numerous civic and service organizations, and a drama theater. Recreational parks with swimming pools, golf courses, and a large stadium are located here. Part-time jobs are available.

■ BEAUFORT COUNTY COMMUNITY COLLEGE

PO Box 1069
Washington, NC 27889-1069
Tel: (252)946-6194
Fax: (252)946-0271
E-mail: garyb@beaufortccc.edu

Web Site: www.beaufortccc.edu

Description: State-supported, 2-year, coed. Part of North Carolina Community College System. Awards certificates, diplomas, transfer associate, and terminal associate degrees. Founded 1967. Setting: 67-acre rural campus. Total enrollment: 1,933. 856 applied, 100% were admitted. 0.6% American Indian or Alaska Native, non-Hispanic/Latino; 2% Hispanic/Latino; 32% Black or African American, non-Hispanic/Latino; 0.2% Asian, non-Hispanic/Latino. Calendar: semesters. Academic remediation for entering students, ESL program, services for LD students, advanced placement, distance learning, summer session for credit, part-time degree program, co-op programs.

Entrance Requirements: Open admission except for allied health programs (ADN, PN, MLT) and Basic Law Enforcement Training (BLET). Option: electronic application. Required: ACCUPLACER, ACT Compass, ACT AS-SET. Recommended: SAT or ACT. Required for some: high school transcript. Entrance: noncompetitive. Application deadline: rolling. Transfer credits accepted: Yes.

Collegiate Environment: Orientation program. Most popular organizations: Student Government Association, Gamma Beta Phi, BECANS-Nursing. Major annual events: Christmas, Thanksgiving, Fall and Spring Fling. Student services: personal-psychological counseling. Campus security: 24-hour emergency response devices and patrols, late night transport-escort service. Beaufort Community College Library. 60 computers available on campus for general student use. A campuswide network can be accessed from off-campus. Staffed computer lab on campus provides training in use of computers, software, and the Internet.

Community Environment: Washington, NC is located on the Pamlico River, which affords excellent fishing, boating, and water skiing. North Carolina's finest beach areas are only a short distance away. Year-round golf courses and tennis courts are also easily accessible. Other points of interest include the NC Estuarium, the Beaufort County Arts Council (located in the old Atlantic Coastal Railroad Depot), and the newly renovated Turnage Theater.

■ BELMONT ABBEY COLLEGE

100 Belmont-Mt. Holly Rd.
Belmont, NC 28012-1802
Tel: (704)825-6700; Free: 888-BAC-0110
Fax: (704)825-6670
E-mail: nicolefocareto@bac.edu
Web Site: www.belmontabbeycollege.edu

Description: Independent Roman Catholic, 4-year, coed. Awards bachelor's degrees. Founded 1876. Setting: 650-acre small town campus with easy access to Charlotte. Total enrollment: 1,524. Core. Calendar: semesters. Services for LD students, advanced placement, accelerated degree program, freshman honors college, honors program, independent study, double major, summer session for credit, part-time degree program, external degree program, adult/continuing education programs, co-op programs and internships. Off campus study at Charlotte Area Educational Consortium. Study abroad program.

Entrance Requirements: Options: electronic application, deferred admission, international baccalaureate accepted. Required: high school transcript, minimum 2.25 high school GPA. Recommended: interview. Required for some: essay. Entrance: moderately difficult. Application deadline: 8/1. Notification: continuous. Transfer credits accepted: Yes.

Costs Per Year: Comprehensive fee: $28,594 includes full-time tuition ($18,500) and college room and board ($10,094). College room only: $5828. Full-time tuition varies according to course load and reciprocity agreements. Room and board charges vary according to board plan and housing facility. Part-time tuition: $617 per credit hour. Part-time tuition varies according to course load and reciprocity agreements. Tuition guaranteed not to increase for student's term of enrollment.

Collegiate Environment: Orientation program. Drama-theater group, choral group, student-run newspaper. Social organizations: national fraternities, national sororities, local fraternities. Most popular organizations: Crusaders for Life, Improv Troupe, Abbey Volunteers, International Club, Green Team. Major annual events: Spring Formal, President's Ball, Crawfish Boil. Student services: health clinic, personal-psychological counseling. Campus security: 24-hour emergency response devices and patrols. Abbot Vincent Taylor Library plus 1 other.

Community Environment: In the southern Piedmont section of the state, Belmont is a growing textile center. Commercial transportation is available. The community facilities include churches of all denominations, hospitals and health services, a library, YMCA, and shopping centers. Numerous civic and service organizations are active. Hunting and fishing are popular sports

in the area as well as all water sports, enjoyed at Lake Wylie. The Belmont Abbey, located here, was the first Cathedral Abbey in the United States, and is listed in the National Register of Historical Places.

■ BENNETT COLLEGE

900 E Washington St.
Greensboro, NC 27401
Tel: (336)273-4431; Free: 800-413-5323
E-mail: jcrawford@bennett.edu
Web Site: www.bennett.edu

Description: Independent United Methodist, 4-year, women only. Awards bachelor's degrees. Founded 1873. Setting: 60-acre urban campus. Endowment: $12.6 million. Educational spending for the previous fiscal year: $10,692 per student. Total enrollment: 534. Faculty: 61 (36 full-time, 25 part-time). Student-undergrad faculty ratio is 10:1. 3,938 applied, 96% were admitted. Full-time: 463 students. Part-time: 71 students. Students come from 28 states and territories, 5 other countries, 50% from out-of-state. 2% Hispanic/Latino; 85% Black or African American, non-Hispanic/Latino; 0.2% Asian, non-Hispanic/Latino; 0.9% international. 2% 25 or older, 69% live on campus, 1% transferred in. Retention: 53% of full-time freshmen returned the following year. Academic areas with the most degrees conferred: business/marketing; psychology; communication/journalism. Core. Calendar: semesters. Academic remediation for entering students, ESL program, services for LD students, advanced placement, self-designed majors, honors program, independent study, distance learning, double major, summer session for credit, part-time degree program, co-op programs and internships. Off campus study at Greater Greensboro Consortium, Cooperative Program in Engineering with North Carolina Agricultural and Technical State Universit. Study abroad program. ROTC: Army (c), Air Force (c).

Entrance Requirements: Options: electronic application, deferred admission, international baccalaureate accepted. Required: high school transcript, minimum 2.5 high school GPA, 2 recommendations, SAT or ACT. Recommended: essay. Entrance: minimally difficult. Application deadline: rolling. SAT Reasoning Test deadline: 8/30. SAT Subject Test deadline: 8/30. Transfer credits accepted: Yes.

Costs Per Year: Application fee: $35. One-time mandatory fee: $225. Comprehensive fee: $26,627 includes full-time tuition ($15,964), mandatory fees ($2549), and college room and board ($8114). College room only: $4040. Full-time tuition and fees vary according to course load. Room and board charges vary according to board plan. Part-time tuition: $665 per credit hour. Part-time mandatory fees: $1067 per term. Part-time tuition and fees vary according to course load.

Collegiate Environment: Orientation program. Drama-theater group, choral group. Social organizations: 26 open to all; national sororities; 5% of eligible undergrads are members. Major annual events: Convocatum Est, Founder's Day, Charter Day. Student services: health clinic, personal-psychological counseling. Campus security: 24-hour emergency response devices and patrols, late night transport-escort service, controlled dormitory access, alerts and educational programs are offered. 484 college housing spaces available; 366 were occupied in 2018-19. Freshmen guaranteed college housing. On-campus residence required through sophomore year. Option: women-only housing available. Holgate Library. Books: 79,536 (physical), 203,358 (digital/electronic); Serial titles: 22 (physical), 22,014 (digital/electronic); Databases: 143. Weekly public service hours: 83. Operations spending for the previous fiscal year: $197,097. 225 computers available on campus for general student use. A campuswide network can be accessed. Students can access the following: online class registration, wireless capability is in all buildings except Steele and Shell halls. Staffed computer lab on campus provides training in use of computers, software, and the Internet.

Community Environment: See Greensboro College.

■ BLADEN COMMUNITY COLLEGE

PO Box 266
Dublin, NC 28332-0266
Tel: (910)879-5500
Fax: (910)879-5508
E-mail: acarterfisher@bladencc.edu
Web Site: www.bladencc.edu

Description: State and locally supported, 2-year, coed. Part of North Carolina Community College System. Awards certificates, diplomas, transfer associate, and terminal associate degrees. Founded 1967. Setting: 45-acre rural campus. Endowment: $72,151. Educational spending for the previous fiscal year: $2997 per student. Total enrollment: 1,736. Faculty: 85 (35 full-time, 50 part-time). 10% from top 10% of their high school class, 20% from top quarter, 78% from top half. 2 class presidents, 6 student government officers. Students come from 3 states and territories. 62% 25 or older. Retention: 35% of full-time freshmen returned the following year. Core. Calendar: semesters. Academic remediation for entering students, services for LD students, advanced placement, independent study, distance learning, double major, summer session for credit, part-time degree program, adult/continuing education programs.

Entrance Requirements: Open admission. Options: electronic application, deferred admission. Required: high school transcript, ACT Compass. Recommended: SAT or ACT. Entrance: noncompetitive. Application deadline: 8/1. Notification: continuous until 8/15.

Collegiate Environment: Orientation program. Most popular organizations: Student Government Association, National Honors English Society, History Club, Criminal Justice Club, Bladen Community College Gospel Choir. Major annual events: Spring Field Day, Christmas Dinner, Fall Convocation. Student services: personal-psychological counseling. Campus security: 14-hour patrols. Learning Resource Center. Operations spending for the previous fiscal year: $160,321. 150 computers available on campus for general student use. A campuswide network can be accessed from off-campus. Staffed computer lab on campus.

Community Environment: Dublin is located 30 miles south of Fayetteville. The principal business is agriculture. Community facilities include 15 churches of various denominations and a public library. Bladen Arts Council frequently sponsors cultural activities in the campus's 1,000-seat auditorium. A golf course, parks, state forest and several lakes provide facilities for excellent fishing and water sports.

■ BLUE RIDGE COMMUNITY COLLEGE
180 W Campus Dr.
Flat Rock, NC 28731
Tel: (828)694-1700
Fax: (828)694-1690
Web Site: www.blueridge.edu

Description: State and locally supported, 2-year, coed. Part of North Carolina Community College System. Awards certificates, diplomas, and transfer associate degrees. Founded 1969. Setting: 109-acre small town campus. Total enrollment: 2,488. Full-time: 766 students, 51% women, 49% men. Part-time: 1,722 students, 60% women, 40% men. Students come from 6 states and territories, 1% from out-of-state. 38% 25 or older. Core. Calendar: semesters. Academic remediation for entering students, ESL program, services for LD students, advanced placement, distance learning, double major, summer session for credit, part-time degree program, adult/continuing education programs, co-op programs and internships.

Entrance Requirements: Open admission except for nursing, surgical technology, pharmacy technology programs. Option: early admission. Required: high school transcript. Entrance: noncompetitive. Application deadline: rolling. Notification: continuous.

Collegiate Environment: Orientation program. Drama-theater group, student-run newspaper. Student services: personal-psychological counseling. Campus security: sheriff's deputy during class hours. Blue Ridge Community College Library plus 1 other.

■ BREVARD COLLEGE
1 Brevard College Dr.
Brevard, NC 28712-3306
Tel: (828)883-8292; Free: 800-527-9090
Fax: (828)884-3790
E-mail: admissions@brevard.edu
Web Site: www.brevard.edu

Description: Independent United Methodist, 4-year, coed. Awards bachelor's degrees. Founded 1853. Setting: 120-acre small town campus. Endowment: $24.2 million. Educational spending for the previous fiscal year: $7560 per student. Total enrollment: 705. Faculty: 95 (51 full-time, 44 part-time). Student-undergrad faculty ratio is 11:1. 2,858 applied, 43% were admitted. 6% from top 10% of their high school class, 24% from top quarter, 62% from top half. Full-time: 697 students, 42% women, 58% men. Part-time: 8 students, 38% women, 62% men. Students come from 35 states and territories, 29 other countries, 42% from out-of-state. 0.6% American Indian or Alaska Native, non-Hispanic/Latino; 2% Hispanic/Latino; 10% Black or African American, non-Hispanic/Latino; 0.9% Asian, non-Hispanic/Latino; 0.3% Native Hawaiian or other Pacific Islander, non-Hispanic/Latino; 6% international. 5% 25 or older, 76% live on campus, 9% transferred in. Retention: 59% of full-time freshmen returned the following year. Academic areas

with the most degrees conferred: parks and recreation; business/marketing; psychology; visual and performing arts. Core. Calendar: semesters. Academic remediation for entering students, services for LD students, advanced placement, self-designed majors, honors program, independent study, double major, part-time degree program, internships. Study abroad program.

Entrance Requirements: Options: electronic application, deferred admission, international baccalaureate accepted. Required: essay, high school transcript, minimum 2 high school GPA. Required for some: interview, audition, music test for music program; portfolio for art program, SAT or ACT. Entrance: minimally difficult. Application deadline: rolling. Notification: continuous. SAT Reasoning Test deadline: 8/1. Transfer credits accepted: Yes.

Collegiate Environment: Orientation program. Drama-theater group, choral group, student-run newspaper. Social organizations: 27 open to all. Most popular organizations: Fine Arts organizations, Omicron Delta Kappa, Fellowship of Christian Athletes, BC Greens, Business Club. Major annual events: Earth Week Service and Celebration/EarthFest, Move-a-Mountain Day, Martin Luther King, Jr. Community Celebration. Student services: health clinic, personal-psychological counseling, women's center. Campus security: 24-hour emergency response devices and patrols, controlled dormitory access. Jones Library. Operations spending for the previous fiscal year: $283,810. 100 computers available on campus for general student use. A campuswide network can be accessed from student residence rooms.

Community Environment: Brevard, known as the "Land of Waterfalls" is 33 miles southwest of Asheville, NC. The area is the location of the Carl Sandburg home, the Thomas Wolfe Home, and the Brevard Music Center. This popular summer resort is at the entrance of Pisgah National Forest. Community facilities include churches of most major denominations, hospital and many civic and service organizations. Part-time employment is available on and off campus. Recreational activities include camping, biking, backpacking, canoeing, snowskiing, kayaking, and mountain climbing.

■ BRUNSWICK COMMUNITY COLLEGE
50 College Rd.
Supply, NC 28462-0030
Tel: (910)755-7300; Free: 800-754-1050
Fax: (910)754-9609
E-mail: admissions@brunswickcc.edu
Web Site: www.brunswickcc.edu

Description: State-supported, 2-year, coed. Part of North Carolina Community College System. Awards certificates, diplomas, transfer associate, and terminal associate degrees. Founded 1979. Setting: 266-acre rural campus. Total enrollment: 1,558. Student-undergrad faculty ratio is 12:1. 4% from out-of-state. 37% 25 or older. Core. Calendar: semesters. Academic remediation for entering students, ESL program, services for LD students, advanced placement, independent study, distance learning, summer session for credit, part-time degree program, co-op programs and internships.

Entrance Requirements: Open admission except for allied health programs. Option: electronic application. Required: high school transcript. Required for some: interview. Entrance: noncompetitive. Application deadline: rolling. Notification: continuous.

Collegiate Environment: Student services: personal-psychological counseling. Campus security: late night transport-escort service, campus police. Brunswick Community College Library plus 1 other.

■ CABARRUS COLLEGE OF HEALTH SCIENCES
401 Medical Park Dr.
Concord, NC 28025
Tel: (704)403-1555
Fax: (704)403-2077
E-mail: mckenzie.allen@cabarruscollege.edu
Web Site: www.cabarruscollege.edu

Description: Independent, comprehensive, coed. Awards associate, bachelor's, and master's degrees. Founded 1942. Setting: 5-acre suburban campus with easy access to Charlotte. Endowment: $2 million. Total enrollment: 470. 28 applied, 100% were admitted. Full-time: 142 students, 87% women, 13% men. Part-time: 301 students, 89% women, 11% men. Students come from 5 states and territories, 3% from out-of-state. 0.2% American Indian or Alaska Native, non-Hispanic/Latino; 4% Hispanic/Latino; 11% Black or African American, non-Hispanic/Latino; 1% Asian, non-Hispanic/Latino; 0.5% Native Hawaiian or other Pacific Islander, non-Hispanic/Latino. 47% 25 or older, 30% transferred in. Academic areas with the most degrees conferred: health professions and related sciences;

interdisciplinary studies. Core. Calendar: semesters. Academic remediation for entering students, services for LD students, advanced placement, accelerated degree program, independent study, distance learning, part-time degree program, co-op programs.

Entrance Requirements: Option: electronic application. Required: essay, high school transcript, minimum 2 high school GPA, 2 recommendations, SAT or ACT. Recommended: minimum 3 high school GPA. Required for some: interview. Entrance: moderately difficult. Application deadline: 2/1. Notification: 3/15. SAT Reasoning Test deadline: 2/1. SAT Subject Test deadline: 2/1. Transfer credits accepted: Yes.

Costs Per Year: Application fee: $50. Tuition: $12,674 full-time, $406 per credit hour part-time. Mandatory fees: $370 full-time, $75 per term part-time. Full-time tuition and fees vary according to course load. Part-time tuition and fees vary according to course load.

Collegiate Environment: Orientation program. Most popular organizations: Rotaract Service Club, Cabarrus College Association of Nursing Students, Student Government Association, Honor Society, Christian Student Union. Major annual events: Welcome Convocation, Spring Picnic, Fall Festival. Student services: health clinic, personal-psychological counseling. Campus security: 24-hour emergency response devices and patrols. Cabarrus College Information Resource Center plus 1 other. Study areas open 24 hours, 5-7 days a week. 17 computers available on campus for general student use. A campuswide network can be accessed from off-campus. Students can access the following: online class registration, degree audits. Staffed computer lab on campus.

■ **CALDWELL COMMUNITY COLLEGE AND TECHNICAL INSTITUTE**
2855 Hickory Blvd.
Hudson, NC 28638-2397
Tel: (828)726-2200
Fax: (828)726-2490
E-mail: pbrinkley@cccti.edu
Web Site: www.cccti.edu

Description: State-supported, 2-year, coed. Part of North Carolina Community College System. Awards certificates, diplomas, transfer associate, and terminal associate degrees. Founded 1964. Setting: 50-acre small town campus. Total enrollment: 3,514. Faculty: 420 (130 full-time, 290 part-time). Student-undergrad faculty ratio is 18:1. 1,439 applied, 100% were admitted. Full-time: 1,240 students, 53% women, 47% men. Part-time: 2,274 students, 59% women, 41% men. 62% 25 or older. Core. Calendar: semesters. Academic remediation for entering students, services for LD students, advanced placement, independent study, distance learning, double major, summer session for credit, part-time degree program, adult/continuing education programs, co-op programs.

Entrance Requirements: Open admission except for allied health programs. Option: early admission. Required: high school transcript. Entrance: noncompetitive. Application deadline: rolling. Notification: continuous. Transfer credits accepted: Yes.

Costs Per Year: Application fee: $0. State resident tuition: $1872 full-time. Nonresident tuition: $6864 full-time. Mandatory fees: $38 full-time. Full-time tuition and fees vary according to course load and program.

Collegiate Environment: Orientation program. Drama-theater group, choral group. Student services: personal-psychological counseling. Campus security: trained security personnel during hours of operation. Broyhill Center for Learning Resources. Students can reserve study rooms. 850 computers available on campus for general student use. Computer purchase/lease plans available. A campuswide network can be accessed from off-campus. Students can access the following: online class registration. Staffed computer lab on campus provides training in use of computers, software, and the Internet.

Community Environment: Since more wood furniture is manufactured here than any other place in the South, Lenoir is known as "furniture land." Numerous parks and two recreation centers provide the facilities for relaxation. A number of churches are represented in the community.

■ **CAMPBELL UNIVERSITY**
450 Leslie Campbell Ave.
Buies Creek, NC 27506
Tel: (910)893-1200; Free: 800-334-4111
Fax: (910)893-1288
E-mail: adm@mailcenter.campbell.edu
Web Site: www.campbell.edu

Description: Independent, university, coed, affiliated with North Carolina Baptist State Convention. Awards associate, bachelor's, master's, and doctoral degrees. Founded 1887. Setting: 850-acre rural campus with easy access to Raleigh. Endowment: $104.7 million. Educational spending for the previous fiscal year: $11,437 per student. Total enrollment: 4,743. Faculty: 305 (196 full-time, 109 part-time). Student-undergrad faculty ratio is 14:1. 3,348 applied, 60% were admitted. 38% from top 10% of their high school class, 80% from top quarter, 92% from top half. 5 National Merit Scholars, 5 class presidents, 34 valedictorians, 94 student government officers. Full-time: 2,731 students, 53% women, 47% men. Part-time: 203 students, 36% women, 64% men. Students come from 50 states and territories, 42 other countries, 22% from out-of-state. 12% 25 or older, 62% live on campus, 16% transferred in. Retention: 71% of full-time freshmen returned the following year. Academic areas with the most degrees conferred: business/marketing; liberal arts/general studies; psychology. Core. Calendar: semesters. Advanced placement, accelerated degree program, freshman honors college, honors program, independent study, distance learning, double major, summer session for credit, part-time degree program, adult/continuing education programs, co-op programs and internships, graduate courses open to undergrads. Study abroad program. ROTC: Army.

Entrance Requirements: Options: electronic application, early admission, deferred admission, international baccalaureate accepted. Required: high school transcript, SAT or ACT. Recommended: essay, interview. Required for some: 3 recommendations. Entrance: moderately difficult. Application deadline: rolling. Notification: continuous.

Costs Per Year: Application fee: $35. Comprehensive fee: $43,710 includes full-time tuition ($31,150), mandatory fees ($1350), and college room and board ($11,210). College room only: $5390. Full-time tuition and fees vary according to class time, course load, location, and program. Room and board charges vary according to board plan and housing facility. Part-time tuition: $620 per credit hour. Part-time mandatory fees: $75 per credit hour. Part-time tuition and fees vary according to class time, course load, location, and program.

Collegiate Environment: Orientation program. Drama-theater group, choral group, student-run newspaper. Social organizations: 44 open to all. Most popular organizations: Student Government Association, Baptist Student Union, Campbell Catholic Community, Presidential Scholars Club, Pre-Pharmacy Club. Major annual events: Homecoming, Spring Fling, Parents' Day. Student services: health clinic, personal-psychological counseling. Campus security: 24-hour emergency response devices and patrols, late night transport-escort service, controlled dormitory access. Carrie Rich Memorial Library plus 2 others. Operations spending for the previous fiscal year: $3.4 million. 256 computers available on campus for general student use. A campuswide network can be accessed from student residence rooms and from off campus. Students can access the following: online class registration. Staffed computer lab on campus provides training in use of computers, software, and the Internet.

Community Environment: Located 30 miles south of Raleigh where the climate is mild, and 30 miles north of Fayetteville, the community is served by Baptist and United Methodist churches, a community civic club and a full-time campus infirmary. There is a hospital seven miles away. Part-time employment for students is available.

■ **CAPE FEAR COMMUNITY COLLEGE**
411 N Front St.
Wilmington, NC 28401-3993
Tel: (910)362-7000; Free: 877-799-2322
E-mail: admissions@cfcc.edu
Web Site: www.cfcc.edu

Description: State-supported, 2-year, coed. Part of North Carolina Community College System. Awards certificates, diplomas, transfer associate, and terminal associate degrees. Founded 1959. Setting: 150-acre urban campus. Endowment: $8.8 million. Educational spending for the previous fiscal year: $4362 per student. Total enrollment: 8,691. Faculty: 773 (301 full-time, 472 part-time). Student-undergrad faculty ratio is 12:1. 4,629 applied, 66% were admitted. Full-time: 3,898 students, 51% women, 49% men. Part-time: 5,169 students, 61% women, 39% men. Students come from 48 states and territories, 52 other countries, 6% from out-of-state. 0.7% American Indian or Alaska Native, non-Hispanic/Latino; 8% Hispanic/Latino; 12% Black or African American, non-Hispanic/Latino; 1% Asian, non-Hispanic/Latino; 0.2% Native Hawaiian or other Pacific Islander, non-Hispanic/Latino; 0.1% international. 43% 25 or older, 8% transferred in. Core. Calendar: semesters. Academic remediation for entering students, ESL program, services for LD students, advanced placement, independent study, distance learning, double major, summer session for credit, part-time degree program, adult/continuing education programs, co-op programs. Off campus study.

Entrance Requirements: Open admission except for health science programs. Options: electronic application, early admission. Required for some: high school transcript, interview. Entrance: noncompetitive. Application deadline: 8/18. Notification: continuous. Transfer credits accepted: Yes.

Costs Per Year: Application fee: $0. State resident tuition: $2432 full-time, $76 per credit hour part-time. Nonresident tuition: $8576 full-time, $268 per credit hour part-time. Mandatory fees: $316 full-time, $3 per credit hour part-time, $98 per term part-time. Full-time tuition and fees vary according to course load. Part-time tuition and fees vary according to course load.

Collegiate Environment: Orientation program. Choral group, student-run newspaper. Social organizations: 35 open to all. Most popular organizations: Nursing Club, Dental Hygiene Club, Pineapple Guild, Phi Theta Kappa, Occupational Therapy. Major annual events: Spring Fling, Fall Fest, Harvest Health and Wellness Fair. Student services: personal-psychological counseling. Campus security: 24-hour emergency response devices and patrols, late night transport-escort service, armed police officers. Cape Fear Community College Library. Operations spending for the previous fiscal year: $1.2 million. 2,088 computers available on campus for general student use. A campuswide network can be accessed from off-campus. Students can access the following: online class registration. Staffed computer lab on campus provides training in use of computers, software, and the Internet.

Community Environment: See University of North Carolina - Wilmington.

■ **CAROLINA CHRISTIAN COLLEGE**
4209 Indiana Ave.
Winston Salem, NC 27105
Tel: (336)744-0900
Fax: (336)744-0901
Web Site: www.carolina.edu

Description: Independent nondenominational, comprehensive, coed. Awards associate, bachelor's, and master's degrees. Founded 1945. Setting: 2-acre small town campus. Endowment: $250,000. Educational spending for the previous fiscal year: $417 per student. Total enrollment: 53. Faculty: 12 (2 full-time, 10 part-time). Student-undergrad faculty ratio is 11:1. 12 applied, 75% were admitted. 30% from top half of their high school class. Full-time: 47 students, 45% women, 55% men. Students come from 5 states and territories, 10% from out-of-state. 2% Hispanic/Latino; 87% Black or African American, non-Hispanic/Latino. 88% 25 or older, 9% transferred in. Retention: 83% of full-time freshmen returned the following year. Core. Calendar: semesters. Accelerated degree program, part-time degree program, external degree program, adult/continuing education programs, graduate courses open to undergrads.

Entrance Requirements: Open admission. Option: electronic application. Required: essay, high school transcript, 2 recommendations, interview. Entrance: noncompetitive. Application deadline: rolling. Notification: continuous. Transfer credits accepted: Yes.

Costs Per Year: Application fee: $50. One-time mandatory fee: $75. Tuition: $12,500 full-time, $2750 per term part-time. Mandatory fees: $1450 full-time, $600 per term part-time.

Collegiate Environment: Orientation program. Student services: personal-psychological counseling. Campus security: 24-hour emergency response devices. Aubrey Payne. Books: 14,200 (physical), 3,900 (digital/electronic); Serial titles: 1,006 (digital/electronic); Databases: 4. Weekly public service hours: 2. Operations spending for the previous fiscal year: $7645. 8 computers available on campus for general student use. A campuswide network can be accessed. Students can access the following: online class registration. Staffed computer lab on campus provides training in use of computers, software, and the Internet.

■ **CAROLINA COLLEGE OF BIBLICAL STUDIES**
817 S McPherson Church Rd.
Fayetteville, NC 28303
Tel: (910)323-5614
Web Site: carolinabiblecollege.org

Description: Independent Christian, 4-year, coed. Awards associate and bachelor's degrees. Founded 1973. Calendar: quarters.

■ **CAROLINAS COLLEGE OF HEALTH SCIENCES**
PO Box 32861, 1200 Blythe Blvd.
Charlotte, NC 28232-2861
Tel: (704)355-5043
Fax: (704)355-5967
E-mail: merritt.newman@carolinascollege.edu
Web Site: www.carolinascollege.edu

Description: Public, 2-year, coed. Awards certificates, diplomas, and terminal associate degrees. Founded 1990. Setting: 3-acre urban campus with easy access to Charlotte. Endowment: $2.4 million. Educational spending for the previous fiscal year: $6787 per student. Total enrollment: 433. Faculty: 51 (25 full-time, 26 part-time). Student-undergrad faculty ratio is 9:1. Full-time: 49 students, 88% women, 12% men. Part-time: 384 students, 91% women, 9% men. Students come from 12 states and territories, 10% from out-of-state. 0.2% American Indian or Alaska Native, non-Hispanic/Latino; 6% Hispanic/Latino; 10% Black or African American, non-Hispanic/Latino; 3% Asian, non-Hispanic/Latino; 0.5% Native Hawaiian or other Pacific Islander, non-Hispanic/Latino. 51% 25 or older. Core. Calendar: semesters. Services for LD students, advanced placement, independent study, distance learning, summer session for credit, part-time degree program. Off campus study. Study abroad program.

Entrance Requirements: Options: electronic application, international baccalaureate accepted. Required: minimum 2.5 high school GPA. Required for some: high school transcript, 3 recommendations, interview, SAT or ACT. Entrance: moderately difficult. Preference given to county residents. Transfer credits accepted: Yes.

Collegiate Environment: Orientation program. Student services: health clinic, personal-psychological counseling. Campus security: 24-hour emergency response devices and patrols, late night transport-escort service. AHEC Library. Study areas open 24 hours, 5-7 days a week; students can reserve study rooms. Operations spending for the previous fiscal year: $87,000. 40 computers available on campus for general student use. A campuswide network can be accessed from off-campus. Students can access the following: online class registration, online billing. Staffed computer lab on campus provides training in use of computers, software, and the Internet.

■ **CARTERET COMMUNITY COLLEGE**
3505 Arendell St.
Morehead City, NC 28557-2989
Tel: (252)222-6000
Fax: (252)222-6274
Web Site: www.carteret.edu

Description: State-supported, 2-year, coed. Part of North Carolina Community College System. Awards certificates, diplomas, transfer associate, and terminal associate degrees. Founded 1963. Setting: 41-acre small town campus. Endowment: $4.8 million. Total enrollment: 1,363. Faculty: 158 (57 full-time, 101 part-time). Student-undergrad faculty ratio is 10:1. 1,593 applied, 96% were admitted. Full-time: 571 students, 67% women, 33% men. Part-time: 792 students, 71% women, 29% men. Students come from 8 states and territories, 1% from out-of-state. 0.7% American Indian or Alaska Native, non-Hispanic/Latino; 4% Hispanic/Latino; 9% Black or African American, non-Hispanic/Latino; 1% Asian, non-Hispanic/Latino; 0.2% Native Hawaiian or other Pacific Islander, non-Hispanic/Latino. 45% 25 or older, 11% transferred in. Core. Calendar: semesters. Academic remediation for entering students, services for LD students, distance learning, double major, summer session for credit, part-time degree program, adult/continuing education programs, co-op programs and internships.

Entrance Requirements: Open admission except for health sciences, cosmetic arts, basic law enforcement training, and lateral entry. Options: electronic application, international baccalaureate accepted. Required for some: high school transcript. Entrance: noncompetitive. Application deadline: rolling. Notification: continuous. Transfer credits accepted: Yes.

Costs Per Year: Application fee: $0. State resident tuition: $1900 full-time, $76 per credit hour part-time. Nonresident tuition: $6522 full-time, $268 per credit hour part-time. Mandatory fees: $90 full-time, $24.20 per term part-time. Full-time tuition and fees vary according to course load and program. Part-time tuition and fees vary according to course load and program.

Collegiate Environment: Orientation program. Social organizations: 25 open to all; local fraternities, national honor societies; 15% of eligible men and 35% of eligible women are members. Most popular organizations: Student Government Association, Medical Assisting Club, Respiratory Therapy Club, Radiography Club, National Society of Leadership and Success. Major annual events: Springfest, Fall Fling. Campus security: late night transport-escort service, security service from 7 am until 11:30 pm. Michael J. Smith Learning Resource Center. Books: 18,182 (physical), 173,614 (digital/electronic); Databases: 74. Weekly public service hours: 63. Operations spending for the previous fiscal year: $298,280. 610 computers available on campus for general student use. A campuswide network can be accessed from off-campus. Students can access the following: online class registration. Staffed computer lab on campus provides training in use of computers, software, and the Internet.

Community Environment: Morehead City is one of the most popular coastal resorts in the state. The $4 million Port Terminal with its 2,600-foot pier affords excellent facilities for oceangoing vessels. Fishing, particularly for menhaden, is an important industry. The Atlantic Beach across Bogue Sound is an excellent 24-mile beach. Recreational facilities are numerous for all kinds of ocean fishing, and for hunting wild ducks and geese.

■ **CATAWBA COLLEGE**
2300 W Innes St.
Salisbury, NC 28144-2488
Tel: (704)637-4111; Free: 800-CATAWBA
Web Site: www.catawba.edu

Description: Independent, comprehensive, coed, affiliated with United Church of Christ. Awards bachelor's and master's degrees. Founded 1851. Setting: 276-acre small town campus with easy access to Charlotte, NC. Endowment: $61.9 million. Research spending for the previous fiscal year: $16,343. Educational spending for the previous fiscal year: $8213 per student. Total enrollment: 1,331. Faculty: 159 (86 full-time, 73 part-time). Student-undergrad faculty ratio is 12:1. 3,125 applied, 42% were admitted. 13% from top 10% of their high school class, 44% from top quarter, 77% from top half. Full-time: 1,267 students, 52% women, 48% men. Part-time: 58 students, 76% women, 24% men. Students come from 37 states and territories, 19 other countries, 19% from out-of-state. 0.3% American Indian or Alaska Native, non-Hispanic/Latino; 7% Hispanic/Latino; 19% Black or African American, non-Hispanic/Latino; 0.8% Asian, non-Hispanic/Latino; 0.1% Native Hawaiian or other Pacific Islander, non-Hispanic/Latino; 4% international. 13% 25 or older, 57% live on campus, 5% transferred in. Retention: 73% of full-time freshmen returned the following year. Academic areas with the most degrees conferred: business/marketing; visual and performing arts; education. Core. Calendar: semesters. Services for LD students, advanced placement, self-designed majors, honors program, independent study, double major, summer session for credit, part-time degree program, internships. Study abroad program. ROTC: Army (c), Air Force (c).

Entrance Requirements: Options: electronic application, early admission, deferred admission, international baccalaureate accepted. Required: essay, high school transcript, minimum 2 high school GPA, 2 recommendations. Recommended: interview. Entrance: moderately difficult. Application deadline: rolling. Notification: continuous. Transfer credits accepted: Yes.

Costs Per Year: Application fee: $0. Comprehensive fee: $41,008 includes full-time tuition ($30,520) and college room and board ($10,488). College room only: $6188. Full-time tuition varies according to class time, course load, and degree level. Part-time tuition: $816 per credit hour. Part-time tuition varies according to class time, course load, and degree level.

Collegiate Environment: Orientation program. Drama-theater group, choral group, marching band, student-run newspaper, radio station. Social organizations: 49 open to all. Most popular organizations: Volunteer Catawba, Catawba Ambassadors (admissions guides), Blue Masque (drama), Fellowship of Christian Athletes, Wigwam Productions (student activities board). Major annual events: Homecoming, Family Weekend, Catawbapalooza. Student services: health clinic, personal-psychological counseling. Campus security: 24-hour emergency response devices and patrols, late night transport-escort service, controlled dormitory access. Corriher-Linn-Black Memorial Library plus 1 other. Books: 149,877 (physical), 228,252 (digital/electronic); Serial titles: 12,505 (physical), 112,726 (digital/electronic); Databases: 100. Weekly public service hours: 83; students can reserve study rooms. Operations spending for the previous fiscal year: $541,721. 175 computers available on campus for general student use. A campuswide network can be accessed from student residence rooms and from off campus. Students can access the following: online class registration. Staffed computer lab on campus provides training in use of computers, software, and the Internet.

Community Environment: Salisbury was founded in 1753 and during the year 1781 the city served, at different times, as headquarters for both Cornwallis and Greene, British and patriot generals. Community facilities include numerous churches, a public library, hospitals, and various civic and service organizations. Recreational activities include golf, swimming, fishing, and other sports. Part-time employment is available.

■ **CATAWBA VALLEY COMMUNITY COLLEGE**
2550 Hwy. 70 SE
Hickory, NC 28602-9699
Tel: (828)327-7000
Fax: (828)327-7000

Web Site: www.cvcc.edu

Description: State-supported, 2-year, coed. Part of North Carolina Community College System. Awards certificates, diplomas, transfer associate, and terminal associate degrees. Founded 1960. Setting: 50-acre small town campus with easy access to Charlotte. Endowment: $3.2 million. Total enrollment: 4,571. Faculty: 429 (136 full-time, 293 part-time). Student-undergrad faculty ratio is 12:1. 3,714 applied, 89% were admitted. Full-time: 1,870 students, 53% women, 47% men. Part-time: 2,701 students, 61% women, 39% men. Students come from 3 states and territories. 0.8% American Indian or Alaska Native, non-Hispanic/Latino; 10% Hispanic/Latino; 9% Black or African American, non-Hispanic/Latino; 9% Asian, non-Hispanic/Latino; 0.2% Native Hawaiian or other Pacific Islander, non-Hispanic/Latino. 29% 25 or older, 21% transferred in. Core. Calendar: semesters. Academic remediation for entering students, ESL program, services for LD students, advanced placement, self-designed majors, independent study, distance learning, double major, summer session for credit, part-time degree program, adult/continuing education programs, co-op programs.

Entrance Requirements: Open admission except for allied health programs. Option: electronic application. Required: high school transcript, TABE for Basic Law Enforcement Training (BLET); PSB for nursing, dental hygiene, EMS, electroneurodiagnostic technology, health occupations, radiography, surgical technology; TEAS for surgical technology programs. Required for some: 1 recommendation. Entrance: noncompetitive. Application deadline: rolling. Notification: continuous. Transfer credits accepted: Yes.

Costs Per Year: Application fee: $0. State resident tuition: $2128 full-time, $76 per credit hour part-time. Nonresident tuition: $7504 full-time, $268 per credit hour part-time. Mandatory fees: $218 full-time, $109.25 per term part-time. Part-time tuition and fees vary according to course load.

Collegiate Environment: Orientation program. Drama-theater group, choral group. Social organizations: 12 open to all; 5% of eligible men and 5% of eligible women are members. Most popular organizations: SkillsUSA, Campus Crusade for Christ, Emerging Entrepreneurs, Circle K, Phi Theta Kappa. Major annual events: Fall Fling, Have a 'Dog' with the 'Big Dawg', Black History Celebration. Campus security: 24-hour emergency response devices, late night transport-escort service. CVCC Library. Books: 31,890 (physical), 61 (digital/electronic); Serial titles: 26 (physical), 11 (digital/electronic); Databases: 12. Weekly public service hours: 59; students can reserve study rooms. Operations spending for the previous fiscal year: $356,173. 1,400 computers available on campus for general student use. A campuswide network can be accessed from off-campus. Students can access the following: online class registration. Staffed computer lab on campus provides training in use of computers, software, and the Internet.

Community Environment: See Lenoir-Rhyne College.

■ **CENTRAL CAROLINA COMMUNITY COLLEGE**
1105 Kelly Dr.
Sanford, NC 27330-9000
Tel: (919)775-5401; Free: 800-682-8353
Fax: (919)775-1221
Web Site: www.cccc.edu

Description: State and locally supported, 2-year, coed. Part of North Carolina Community College System. Awards certificates, diplomas, transfer associate, and terminal associate degrees. Founded 1962. Setting: 41-acre small town campus with easy access to Raleigh, Fayetteville, NC. Endowment: $3 million. Educational spending for the previous fiscal year: $3589 per student. Total enrollment: 4,900. Faculty: 1,050 (370 full-time, 680 part-time). Full-time: 2,138 students, 64% women, 36% men. Part-time: 2,762 students, 68% women, 32% men. 6% from out-of-state. 53% 25 or older. Core. Calendar: semesters. Academic remediation for entering students, ESL program, services for LD students, advanced placement, independent study, distance learning, double major, summer session for credit, part-time degree program, adult/continuing education programs, internships.

Entrance Requirements: Open admission except for BLET, dental, medical assisting, motorcycle mechanics, nursing, physical therapist assistant, and veterinary medical technology programs. Options: electronic application, early admission, deferred admission. Required: high school transcript. Recommended: SAT or ACT. Required for some: SAT, ACT, ACT Compass, ACT ASSET, or ACCUPLACER. Entrance: noncompetitive. Application deadline: rolling. Notification: continuous. Transfer credits accepted: Yes.

Collegiate Environment: Orientation program. Student-run radio station. Major annual event: Activity Day. Student services: personal-psychological counseling. Campus security: 24-hour emergency response devices and patrols, student patrols, patrols by trained security personnel during hours of operation. Library/Learning Resources Center plus 2 others. Operations spending for the previous fiscal year: $886,647. 100 computers available on campus for general student use. A campuswide network can be accessed from off-campus. Students can access the following: online class registration. Staffed computer lab on campus provides training in use of computers, software, and the Internet.

Community Environment: Sanford, known as the brick capital of the nation, is nearly the exact center of North Carolina with all forms of commercial transportation available. Over 50 manufacturing and processing firms are located here. Modern shopping facilities and the privately owned hospital serve the community. Recreational opportunities are unparalleled at nearby Cape Fear and the resort areas of Pinehurst and Southern Pines.

■ CENTRAL PIEDMONT COMMUNITY COLLEGE
PO Box 35009
Charlotte, NC 28235-5009
Tel: (704)330-2722
Web Site: www.cpcc.edu
Description: State and locally supported, 2-year, coed. Part of North Carolina Community College System. Awards certificates, diplomas, transfer associate, and terminal associate degrees. Founded 1963. Setting: 37-acre urban campus. Endowment: $16.7 million. Educational spending for the previous fiscal year: $2896 per student. Total enrollment: 19,364. Faculty: 1,741 (337 full-time, 1,404 part-time). 2,243 applied, 100% were admitted. Full-time: 7,630 students, 54% women, 46% men. Part-time: 11,734 students, 57% women, 43% men. Students come from 13 states and territories, 117 other countries, 3% from out-of-state. 47% 25 or older, 11% transferred in. Core. Calendar: semesters. Academic remediation for entering students, ESL program, services for LD students, advanced placement, accelerated degree program, self-designed majors, honors program, distance learning, summer session for credit, part-time degree program, co-op programs. Off campus study at members of the Charlotte Area Educational Consortium.
Entrance Requirements: Open admission. Required: high school transcript. Entrance: noncompetitive. Application deadline: rolling. Notification: continuous.
Collegiate Environment: Orientation program. Drama-theater group, choral group, student-run newspaper. Social organizations: 22 open to all; local fraternities. Most popular organizations: Phi Theta Kappa, Black Students Organization, Students for Environmental Sanity, Sierra Club, Nursing Club. Major annual events: Fall Fest, Spring Fling, World Games. Student services: personal-psychological counseling, women's center. Campus security: 24-hour emergency response devices and patrols. Hagemeyer Learning Center plus 5 others. Operations spending for the previous fiscal year: $1.5 million.
Community Environment: See Queens College.

■ CHAMBERLAIN COLLEGE OF NURSING
2015 Ayrsley Town Blvd.
Charlotte, NC 28273
Web Site: www.chamberlain.edu
Description: Proprietary, 4-year, coed.

■ CHARLOTTE CHRISTIAN COLLEGE AND THEOLOGICAL SEMINARY
3117 Whiting Ave.
Charlotte, NC 28205
Tel: (704)334-6882
Fax: (704)334-6885
E-mail: gshears@charlottechristian.edu
Web Site: www.charlottechristian.edu
Description: Independent Christian, comprehensive, coed. Awards associate, bachelor's, master's, and doctoral degrees. Founded 1996. Setting: 3-acre urban campus with easy access to Charlotte, NC. Total enrollment: 97. Faculty: 24 (7 full-time, 17 part-time). Student-undergrad faculty ratio is 5:1. Full-time: 24 students, 63% women, 37% men. Part-time: 41 students, 68% women, 32% men. Students come from 9 states and territories, 8 other countries, 10% from out-of-state. 83% Black or African American, non-Hispanic/Latino; 3% Asian, non-Hispanic/Latino; 4% international. 94% 25 or older, 20% transferred in. Retention: 67% of full-time freshmen returned the following year. Academic area with the most degrees conferred: theology and religious vocations. Core. Calendar: quarters. Services for LD students, independent study, distance learning, double major, summer session for credit, part-time degree program, adult/continuing education programs, co-op programs. Off campus study.

Entrance Requirements: Open admission. Options: electronic application, international baccalaureate accepted. Required: essay, high school transcript, recommendations, certification of Church membership and involvement. Application deadline: rolling. Notification: continuous. Transfer credits accepted: Yes.
Costs Per Year: Application fee: $50. Tuition: $10,048 full-time, $454 per credit hour part-time. Mandatory fees: $420 full-time, $420 per year part-time. Full-time tuition and fees vary according to course load and program. Part-time tuition and fees vary according to course load and program. Tuition guaranteed not to increase for student's term of enrollment.
Collegiate Environment: Orientation program. Major annual events: Fundraising Banquet, Awards Banquet. Campus security: 24-hour emergency response devices. CCCTS Library. Books: 26,489 (physical), 1,100 (digital/electronic); Serial titles: 30 (physical); Databases: 1. Weekly public service hours: 50.

■ CHOWAN UNIVERSITY
One University Pl.
Murfreesboro, NC 27855
Tel: (252)398-6500; Free: 888-4-CHOWAN
Fax: (252)398-1190
E-mail: parkes@chowan.edu
Web Site: www.chowan.edu
Description: Independent Baptist, comprehensive, coed. Awards associate, bachelor's, and master's degrees. Founded 1848. Setting: 300-acre small town campus with easy access to Norfolk. Endowment: $26.1 million. Educational spending for the previous fiscal year: $5424 per student. Total enrollment: 1,503. Faculty: 132 (67 full-time, 65 part-time). Student-undergrad faculty ratio is 16:1. 4,379 applied, 60% were admitted. 5% from top 10% of their high school class, 25% from top quarter, 62% from top half. Full-time: 1,440 students, 53% women, 47% men. Part-time: 58 students, 72% women, 28% men. Students come from 31 states and territories, 22 other countries, 41% from out-of-state. 0.7% American Indian or Alaska Native, non-Hispanic/Latino; 4% Hispanic/Latino; 70% Black or African American, non-Hispanic/Latino; 0.3% Asian, non-Hispanic/Latino; 0.3% Native Hawaiian or other Pacific Islander, non-Hispanic/Latino; 3% international. 6% 25 or older, 89% live on campus, 4% transferred in. Retention: 48% of full-time freshmen returned the following year. Academic areas with the most degrees conferred: interdisciplinary studies; homeland security, law enforcement, firefighting, and protective services; psychology; parks and recreation. Core. Calendar: semesters. Academic remediation for entering students, services for LD students, advanced placement, self-designed majors, freshman honors college, honors program, independent study, double major, summer session for credit, part-time degree program, co-op programs and internships. Study abroad program.
Entrance Requirements: Options: electronic application, international baccalaureate accepted. Required: high school transcript, SAT or ACT. Recommended: minimum 2 high school GPA, 2 recommendations. Required for some: essay, interview. Entrance: minimally difficult. Application deadline: rolling. Notification: continuous. SAT Reasoning Test deadline: 8/23. SAT Subject Test deadline: 8/23. Transfer credits accepted: Yes.
Costs Per Year: Application fee: $20. Comprehensive fee: $34,380 includes full-time tuition ($24,980) and college room and board ($9400). Full-time tuition varies according to degree level. Room and board charges vary according to board plan. Part-time tuition: $400 per credit hour. Part-time tuition varies according to degree level.
Collegiate Environment: Orientation program. Drama-theater group, choral group, student-run newspaper. Social organizations: 35 open to all; national fraternities, national sororities, local fraternities, local sororities; 25% of eligible men and 25% of eligible women are members. Most popular organizations: Honors Societies, Rotaract, Campus Ministry, Psychology Club, Science Club. Major annual events: Relay For Life, Homecoming, Health Fair. Student services: health clinic, personal-psychological counseling. Campus security: 24-hour emergency response devices and patrols, late night transport-escort service, controlled dormitory access. Whitaker Library plus 1 other. Books: 163,497 (physical), 405,678 (digital/electronic); Serial titles: 1,310 (physical), 69,556 (digital/electronic); Databases: 135. Weekly public service hours: 84; students can reserve study rooms. Operations spending for the previous fiscal year: $395,255. 251 computers available on campus for general student use. Computer purchase/lease plans available. A campuswide network can be accessed from student residence rooms. Students can access the following: online class registration. Staffed computer lab on campus provides training in use of computers, software, and the Internet.

Community Environment: In the northeastern section of North Carolina, Murfreesboro is the location of several historical sites. Community facilities include several churches, museums and a library. A hospital and commercial transportation are available in nearby towns. Hunting, fishing, boating, jet skiing, and water skiing are some of the recreational activities.

■ **CLEVELAND COMMUNITY COLLEGE**
137 S Post Rd.
Shelby, NC 28152
Tel: (704)669-6000
Web Site: www.clevelandcc.edu
Description: State-supported, 2-year, coed. Part of North Carolina Community College System. Awards certificates, diplomas, transfer associate, and terminal associate degrees. Founded 1965. Setting: 43-acre small town campus with easy access to Charlotte. Total enrollment: 2,700. Student-undergrad faculty ratio is 11:1. Full-time: 990 students, 61% women, 39% men. Part-time: 1,710 students, 65% women, 35% men. 0.5% American Indian or Alaska Native, non-Hispanic/Latino; 4% Hispanic/Latino; 18% Black or African American, non-Hispanic/Latino; 0.9% Asian, non-Hispanic/Latino; 0.1% Native Hawaiian or other Pacific Islander, non-Hispanic/Latino; 0.7% international. Core. Calendar: semesters. Academic remediation for entering students, ESL program, advanced placement, independent study, distance learning, double major, summer session for credit, part-time degree program, adult/continuing education programs, co-op programs. Off campus study at Foothills Nursing Consortium.
Entrance Requirements: Open admission except for allied health programs. Options: electronic application, deferred admission. Required: high school transcript. Entrance: noncompetitive. Application deadline: rolling. Notification: continuous. Transfer credits accepted: Yes.
Costs Per Year: Application fee: $0. State resident tuition: $2432 full-time, $76 per credit hour part-time. Nonresident tuition: $8576 full-time, $268 per credit hour part-time. Mandatory fees: $120 full-time, $45 per term part-time. Full-time tuition and fees vary according to course load. Part-time tuition and fees vary according to course load.
Collegiate Environment: Orientation program. Drama-theater group. Student services: personal-psychological counseling. Campus security: security personnel during hours of operation. Jim & Patsy Rose Library.
Community Environment: Shelby is the county seat for Cleveland County and is a diversified manufacturing area. The principal businesses are mercantile, textiles, and machine parts. A city park and a large lake provide the area with recreation facilities.

■ **COASTAL CAROLINA COMMUNITY COLLEGE**
444 Western Blvd.
Jacksonville, NC 28546-6899
Tel: (910)455-1221
Fax: (910)455-2767
E-mail: calihanh@coastal.cc.nc.us
Web Site: www.coastalcarolina.edu
Description: State and locally supported, 2-year, coed. Part of North Carolina Community College System. Awards certificates, diplomas, transfer associate, and terminal associate degrees. Founded 1964. Setting: 98-acre small town campus. Endowment: $2.2 million. Educational spending for the previous fiscal year: $2880 per student. Total enrollment: 4,349. Faculty: 469 (140 full-time, 329 part-time). Student-undergrad faculty ratio is 17:1. 4,513 applied, 62% were admitted. Full-time: 1,476 students, 67% women, 33% men. Part-time: 2,873 students, 64% women, 36% men. Students come from 16 states and territories, 3% from out-of-state. 45% 25 or older, 9% transferred in. Retention: 61% of full-time freshmen returned the following year. Core. Calendar: semesters. Academic remediation for entering students, ESL program, services for LD students, advanced placement, independent study, distance learning, double major, summer session for credit, part-time degree program, adult/continuing education programs, internships.
Entrance Requirements: Open admission. Options: deferred admission, international baccalaureate accepted. Required: high school transcript. Required for some: 2 recommendations, interview. Entrance: noncompetitive. Application deadline: rolling. Notification: continuous.
Collegiate Environment: Orientation program. Drama-theater group. Social organizations: 7 open to all. Most popular organizations: Phi Theta Kappa, SPYS (social sciences group), Student Government, Star of Life, Association of Nursing Students. Major annual events: Spring Fling, Winter Meltdown, Fall Festival. Student services: personal-psychological counseling. Campus security: 24-hour emergency response devices and patrols, late night

transport-escort service. C. Louis Shields Learning Resources Center. Operations spending for the previous fiscal year: $418,421. 936 computers available on campus for general student use. A campuswide network can be accessed from off-campus. Staffed computer lab on campus.
Community Environment: The principal business of Jacksonville are marine-related industries, military support services, and wood products. Railroads serve the area. Thirty churches of various faiths, one library and numerous historical sites are within the community. Hunting and fishing are excellent, and there are also parks are in the area for other recreational activities.

■ **COLLEGE OF THE ALBEMARLE**
PO Box 2327
Elizabeth City, NC 27906-2327
Tel: (252)335-0821
Fax: (252)335-2011
Web Site: www.albemarle.edu
Description: State-supported, 2-year, coed. Part of North Carolina Community College System. Awards certificates, diplomas, transfer associate, and terminal associate degrees. Founded 1960. Setting: 40-acre small town campus. Total enrollment: 2,557. Full-time: 999 students, 64% women, 36% men. Part-time: 1,558 students, 65% women, 35% men. Students come from 5 states and territories. 0.4% American Indian or Alaska Native, non-Hispanic/Latino; 5% Hispanic/Latino; 16% Black or African American, non-Hispanic/Latino; 1% Asian, non-Hispanic/Latino; 0.3% Native Hawaiian or other Pacific Islander, non-Hispanic/Latino; 5% international. 24% 25 or older. Calendar: semesters. Academic remediation for entering students, ESL program, services for LD students, advanced placement, summer session for credit, part-time degree program, adult/continuing education programs, co-op programs.
Entrance Requirements: Open admission. Options: electronic application, early admission, deferred admission. Required: high school transcript. Entrance: noncompetitive. Application deadline: rolling. Notification: continuous. Transfer credits accepted: Yes.
Costs Per Year: Application fee: $0. State resident tuition: $2098 full-time. Nonresident tuition: $7601 full-time. Mandatory fees: $147 full-time.
Collegiate Environment: Drama-theater group, choral group. Social organizations: 18 open to all. Most popular organizations: Phi Beta Lambda, Phi Theta Kappa. Major annual events: Welcome Back Day, Spring Fling, Career Day. Student services: personal-psychological counseling. Campus security: 24-hour patrols. College housing not available. Learning Resources Center. 85 computers available on campus for general student use. Staffed computer lab on campus.
Community Environment: Elizabeth City is the home of a variety of manufacturing firms and serves as a shipping center for a large agricultural area producing corn, soybeans, potatoes, small grains, cabbage and other vegetables. All forms of commercial transportation are available. The Pasquotant River and nearby waterways provide for water sports, and deep sea and surf fishing on the Atlantic Ocean 40 miles away. The Dismal Swamp is a paradise for hunters, fishermen and naturalists. Big and small game include black bears, deer, foxes and many small mammals. Some of the historic points of interest are the Shiloh Baptist Church, the Old Brick House, Hall Creek Church, Winslow and Bayfield Home, the site of Culpepper's Rebellion in 1677-the first open rebellion against the king. Kitty Hawk, site of the Wright brothers' first powered flight, and Manteo, location of the first attempted English Colony, are nearby.

■ **CRAVEN COMMUNITY COLLEGE**
800 College Ct.
New Bern, NC 28562
Tel: (252)638-7200
Web Site: www.cravencc.edu
Description: State-supported, 2-year, coed. Part of North Carolina Community College System. Awards certificates, diplomas, transfer associate, and terminal associate degrees. Founded 1965. Setting: 100-acre suburban campus. Total enrollment: 3,021. Student-undergrad faculty ratio is 19:1. Full-time: 1,126 students, 54% women, 46% men. Part-time: 1,895 students, 60% women, 40% men. 0.7% American Indian or Alaska Native, non-Hispanic/Latino; 8% Hispanic/Latino; 16% Black or African American, non-Hispanic/Latino; 3% Asian, non-Hispanic/Latino; 0.5% Native Hawaiian or other Pacific Islander, non-Hispanic/Latino; 1% international. 13% transferred in. Core. Calendar: semesters. Academic remediation for entering students, ESL program, services for LD students, advanced placement, honors program, independent study, distance learning, double major, sum-

mer session for credit, part-time degree program, adult/continuing education programs, co-op programs and internships. Study abroad program.

Entrance Requirements: Open admission except for esthetics technology, associate degree in nursing, practical nursing, health information technology, medical assisting, pharmacy technology, and physical therapist assistant programs. Options: electronic application, international baccalaureate accepted. Required: high school transcript. Entrance: noncompetitive. Application deadline: rolling. Transfer credits accepted: Yes.

Costs Per Year: State resident tuition: $1824 full-time, $76 per credit hour part-time. Nonresident tuition: $6432 full-time, $268 per credit hour part-time. Mandatory fees: $229 full-time, $114.40 per term part-time. Full-time tuition and fees vary according to course load. Part-time tuition and fees vary according to course load.

Collegiate Environment: Orientation program. Choral group. Social organizations: 18 open to all. Student services: legal services, personal-psychological counseling. Campus security: 24-hour emergency response devices and patrols. R. C. Godwin Memorial Library. Books: 17,065 (physical), 240,000 (digital/electronic); Serial titles: 27 (physical), 18,759 (digital/electronic); Databases: 86. Students can reserve study rooms. 25 computers available on campus for general student use. A campuswide network can be accessed. Students can access the following: online class registration. Staffed computer lab on campus provides training in use of computers, software, and the Internet.

Community Environment: New Bern, one of the oldest towns in the state, is interesting for its old buildings and many historical sites and markers. The first Provincial Congresses met here in 1774 and 1775. Some points of interest are the Christ Church, Federal Building, First Presbyterian Church and the Tryon Palace Restoration.

■ DAVIDSON COLLEGE

405 N Main St.
Davidson, NC 28035
Tel: (704)894-2000; Free: 800-768-0380
Fax: (704)894-2016
E-mail: admission@davidson.edu
Web Site: www.davidson.edu

Description: Independent Presbyterian, 4-year, coed. Awards bachelor's degrees. Founded 1837. Setting: 665-acre small town campus with easy access to Charlotte. Endowment: $821.8 million. Research spending for the previous fiscal year: $1.3 million. Educational spending for the previous fiscal year: $20,597 per student. Total enrollment: 1,843. Faculty: 211 (201 full-time, 10 part-time). Student-undergrad faculty ratio is 10:1. 5,618 applied, 20% were admitted. 73% from top 10% of their high school class, 97% from top quarter, 100% from top half. Full-time: 1,843 students, 48% women, 52% men. Students come from 48 states and territories, 47 other countries, 78% from out-of-state. 0.5% American Indian or Alaska Native, non-Hispanic/Latino; 8% Hispanic/Latino; 7% Black or African American, non-Hispanic/Latino; 5% Asian, non-Hispanic/Latino; 0.2% Native Hawaiian or other Pacific Islander, non-Hispanic/Latino; 7% international. 95% live on campus, 1% transferred in. Retention: 95% of full-time freshmen returned the following year. Academic areas with the most degrees conferred: social sciences; biological/life sciences; English. Core. Calendar: semesters. Services for LD students, advanced placement, self-designed majors, independent study, double major, internships. Off campus study. Study abroad program. ROTC: Army.

Entrance Requirements: Options: electronic application, early admission, early decision, deferred admission, international baccalaureate accepted. Required: essay, high school transcript, 3 recommendations, SAT or ACT. Recommended: interview, SAT and SAT Subject Tests or ACT. Entrance: very difficult. Application deadlines: 1/2, 11/15 for early decision plan 1, 1/2 for early decision plan 2. Notification: 4/1, 12/15 for early decision plan 1, 2/1 for early decision plan 2. SAT Reasoning Test deadline: 1/2. SAT Subject Test deadline: 1/2. Transfer credits accepted: Yes. Early decision applicants: 691. Early decision applicants admitted: 297.

Costs Per Year: Application fee: $50. Comprehensive fee: $67,852 includes full-time tuition ($52,524), mandatory fees ($525), and college room and board ($14,803). College room only: $7534.

Collegiate Environment: Orientation program. Drama-theater group, choral group, student-run newspaper, radio station. Social organizations: 200 open to all; national fraternities, national sororities; 30% of eligible men and 49% of eligible women are members. Student services: health clinic, personal-psychological counseling, women's center. Campus security: 24-hour emergency response devices and patrols, late night transport-escort service, controlled dormitory access. 1,752 college housing spaces available; 1,734

were occupied in 2018-19. Freshmen guaranteed college housing. On-campus residence required through senior year. Option: coed housing available. E. H. Little Library plus 1 other. Books: 484,947 (physical), 1.2 million (digital/electronic); Serial titles: 8,359 (physical), 150,122 (digital/electronic); Databases: 763. Study areas open 24 hours, 5-7 days a week; students can reserve study rooms. Operations spending for the previous fiscal year: $3.5 million.

Community Environment: The town of Davidson has grown around Davidson College. The cultural, social and religious life of the community revolves around the college. Davidson is twenty minutes north of Charlotte, NC, and offers students the advantages of that city's services, amenities, and recreational opportunities.

■ DAVIDSON COUNTY COMMUNITY COLLEGE

PO Box 1287
Lexington, NC 27293-1287
Tel: (336)249-8186
Fax: (336)249-0379
E-mail: admissions@davidsonccc.edu
Web Site: www.davidsonccc.edu

Description: State and locally supported, 2-year, coed. Part of North Carolina Community College System. Awards certificates, diplomas, transfer associate, and terminal associate degrees. Founded 1958. Setting: 83-acre rural campus. Total enrollment: 4,101. Student-undergrad faculty ratio is 20:1. 53% 25 or older. Core. Calendar: semesters. Academic remediation for entering students, services for LD students, advanced placement, double major, summer session for credit, part-time degree program, adult/continuing education programs, co-op programs and internships. Off campus study at Rowan-Cabarrus Community College, Forsyth Technical Community College, Guilford Technical Community College, Rockingham Community College.

Entrance Requirements: Open admission except for nursing, allied health programs. Options: early admission, deferred admission. Required: high school transcript. Required for some: interview. Entrance: noncompetitive. Application deadline: rolling. Notification: continuous.

Costs Per Year: Application fee: $0. State resident tuition: $1824 full-time, $76 per credit hour part-time. Nonresident tuition: $6432 full-time, $268 per credit hour part-time. Mandatory fees: $155 full-time, $6 per credit hour part-time. Full-time tuition and fees vary according to course load and program. Part-time tuition and fees vary according to course load and program.

Collegiate Environment: Orientation program. Drama-theater group. Campus security: 24-hour patrols, late night transport-escort service, security guards. Grady E. Love Learning Resource Center.

Community Environment: Lexington is a suburban community located approximately 25 miles south of Greensboro, N.C. Industry here includes furniture, textiles, apparel, electronics, and food processing. Bus and train transportation are available. A YMCA, churches of all major denominations, a library, hospital, and numerous civic and service organizations serve the community. For recreation, High Rock Lake, about 12 miles south of Lexington, offers boating, fishing, swimming and picnicking. There are job opportunities for students.

■ DEVRY UNIVERSITY-CHARLOTTE CAMPUS

2015 Ayrsley Town Blvd., Ste. 109
Charlotte, NC 28273
Tel: (704)697-1020; Free: 866-338-7934
Web Site: www.devry.edu

Description: Proprietary, comprehensive, coed. Part of DeVry University. Awards associate, bachelor's, and master's degrees. Calendar: semesters.

Entrance Requirements: Application deadline: rolling. Notification: continuous.

■ DEVRY UNIVERSITY-MORRISVILLE CAMPUS

1600 Perimeter Park Dr., Ste. 100
Morrisville, NC 27560
Tel: (919)463-1380; Free: 866-338-7934
Fax: (919)468-5688
Web Site: www.devry.edu

Description: Proprietary, comprehensive, coed.

■ DUKE UNIVERSITY

Durham, NC 27708
Tel: (919)684-8111
Fax: (919)681-8941

E-mail: askduke@admiss.duke.edu

Web Site: www.duke.edu

Description: Independent, university, coed, affiliated with United Methodist Church. Awards bachelor's, master's, and doctoral degrees and post-master's certificates. Founded 1838. Setting: 8,500-acre suburban campus. Total enrollment: 16,294. Faculty: 1,542 (1,461 full-time, 81 part-time). Student-undergrad faculty ratio is 6:1. 33,077 applied, 10% were admitted. 90% from top 10% of their high school class, 75% from top quarter, 99% from top half. Full-time: 6,665 students, 50% women, 50% men. Part-time: 27 students, 33% women, 67% men. 85% from out-of-state. 0.7% American Indian or Alaska Native, non-Hispanic/Latino; 9% Hispanic/Latino; 10% Black or African American, non-Hispanic/Latino; 21% Asian, non-Hispanic/Latino; 0.2% Native Hawaiian or other Pacific Islander, non-Hispanic/Latino; 10% international. 1% 25 or older, 81% live on campus, 1% transferred in. Academic areas with the most degrees conferred: social sciences; engineering; biological/life sciences. Core. Calendar: semesters. Services for LD students, advanced placement, self-designed majors, independent study, double major, summer session for credit, part-time degree program, adult/continuing education programs, internships, graduate courses open to undergrads. Off campus study at University of North Carolina at Chapel Hill, North Carolina Central University, North Carolina State University, Howard University. Study abroad program. ROTC: Army, Naval, Air Force.

Entrance Requirements: Options: electronic application, early decision, international baccalaureate accepted. Required: essay, high school transcript, SAT and SAT Subject Tests or ACT. Recommended: interview. Required for some: audition tape for dance, drama, or music; slides of work for art. Entrance: most difficult. Application deadlines: 1/3, 11/1 for early decision. Notification: 4/1, 12/15 for early decision. Preference given to children of alumni, minorities, state residents. SAT Reasoning Test deadline: 1/3. SAT Subject Test deadline: 1/3. Transfer credits accepted: Yes. Early decision applicants: 3,451. Early decision applicants admitted: 852.

Collegiate Environment: Orientation program. Drama-theater group, choral group, marching band, student-run newspaper, radio station. Social organizations: national fraternities, national sororities. Student services: legal services, health clinic, personal-psychological counseling, women's center. Campus security: 24-hour emergency response devices and patrols, late night transport-escort service, controlled dormitory access. Perkins Library.

Community Environment: Durham, North Carolina, a city of about 200,000 people, is approximately 250 miles south of Washington, D.C. Durham and nearby Raleigh and Chapel Hill constitute the three points of what is known as the Research Triangle, one of the nation's foremost centers for research-oriented industries and government, research, and regulatory agencies. The combined population of the Raleigh, Durham, and Chapel Hill area is one million. Two major interstates and the Raleigh-Durham International Airport (a 20-minute drive from campus) make Durham easily accessible from almost anywhere in the United States. Nationally known hospitals and clinics, including the Duke University Medical Center, make Durham a center for medicine. Other community facilities include numerous churches, museums, parks, shopping areas, an arts center, and major civic and service organizations. Both beaches and mountains are within a three-hour drive.

■ **DURHAM TECHNICAL COMMUNITY COLLEGE**

1637 Lawson St.

Durham, NC 27703-5023

Tel: (919)686-3300

Web Site: www.durhamtech.edu

Description: State-supported, 2-year, coed. Part of North Carolina Community College System. Awards certificates, diplomas, transfer associate, and terminal associate degrees. Founded 1961. Setting: urban campus. Total enrollment: 5,170. 61% 25 or older. Core. Calendar: semesters. Academic remediation for entering students, ESL program, services for LD students, advanced placement, accelerated degree program, self-designed majors, distance learning, summer session for credit, part-time degree program, adult/continuing education programs, co-op programs and internships. Off campus study at University of North Carolina at Chapel Hill, University of North Carolina at Greensboro, Wake Technical Community College, Asheville-Buncombe Community College, Central Piedmont Community College, Guilford Technical Community College, Piedmont Community College.

Entrance Requirements: Open admission. Option: deferred admission. Required: high school transcript. Recommended: interview. Entrance: noncompetitive. Application deadline: rolling. Notification: continuous.

Collegiate Environment: Orientation program. Drama-theater group.

Student services: personal-psychological counseling. Campus security: 24-hour patrols, late night transport-escort service. Educational Resource Center.

Community Environment: See Duke University.

■ **EAST CAROLINA UNIVERSITY**

E 5th St.

Greenville, NC 27858-4353

Tel: (252)328-6131

Fax: (252)328-6495

Web Site: www.ecu.edu

Description: State-supported, university, coed. Part of University of North Carolina System. Awards bachelor's, master's, and doctoral degrees and post-master's certificates. Founded 1907. Setting: 1,600-acre urban campus. Endowment: $219.4 million. Research spending for the previous fiscal year: $29.4 million. Educational spending for the previous fiscal year: $11,305 per student. Total enrollment: 28,718. Faculty: 1,510 (1,215 full-time, 295 part-time). Student-undergrad faculty ratio is 19:1. 17,551 applied, 82% were admitted. 13% from top 10% of their high school class, 38% from top quarter, 76% from top half. Full-time: 19,562 students, 57% women, 43% men. Part-time: 3,509 students, 60% women, 40% men. Students come from 43 states and territories, 58 other countries, 10% from out-of-state. 0.6% American Indian or Alaska Native, non-Hispanic/Latino; 7% Hispanic/Latino; 16% Black or African American, non-Hispanic/Latino; 2% Asian, non-Hispanic/Latino; 0.1% Native Hawaiian or other Pacific Islander, non-Hispanic/Latino; 0.6% international. 13% 25 or older, 24% live on campus, 8% transferred in. Retention: 81% of full-time freshmen returned the following year. Academic areas with the most degrees conferred: business/marketing; health professions and related sciences; education. Core. Calendar: semesters. Academic remediation for entering students, ESL program, services for LD students, advanced placement, accelerated degree program, self-designed majors, freshman honors college, honors program, independent study, distance learning, double major, summer session for credit, part-time degree program, adult/continuing education programs, co-op programs and internships, graduate courses open to undergrads. Off campus study at any other University of North Carolina system institution (UNC Online). Study abroad program. ROTC: Army, Air Force.

Entrance Requirements: Options: electronic application, deferred admission, international baccalaureate accepted. Required: high school transcript, minimum 2.5 high school GPA, SAT or ACT. Entrance: moderately difficult. Notification: continuous. Preference given to North Carolina residents. SAT Reasoning Test deadline: 3/1. Transfer credits accepted: Yes.

Costs Per Year: Application fee: $75. State resident tuition: $4452 full-time, $247 per credit hour part-time. Nonresident tuition: $20,729 full-time, $1151 per credit hour part-time. Mandatory fees: $2736 full-time. Full-time tuition and fees vary according to location and program. Part-time tuition varies according to course load, location, and program. College room and board: $10,354. College room only: $5722. Room and board charges vary according to board plan and housing facility. Tuition guaranteed not to increase for student's term of enrollment.

Collegiate Environment: Orientation program. Drama-theater group, choral group, marching band, student-run newspaper, radio station. Social organizations: 485 open to all; national fraternities, national sororities; 5% of eligible men and 8% of eligible women are members. Most popular organizations: Student Government Association, Student Activities Board, Residence Hall Association, Student Pirate Club, Black Student Union. Major annual events: Halloween Havoc., Pirate Palooza, Barefoot on the Mall. Student services: legal services, health clinic, personal-psychological counseling, women's center. Campus security: 24-hour emergency response devices and patrols, student patrols, late night transport-escort service, controlled dormitory access. 5,408 college housing spaces available; 5,346 were occupied in 2018-19. Freshmen guaranteed college housing. On-campus residence required in freshman year. Options: coed, women-only housing available. Joyner Library plus 2 others. Books: 1 million (physical), 873,203 (digital/electronic); Serial titles: 8,238 (physical), 109,576 (digital/electronic); Databases: 456. Weekly public service hours: 142; study areas open 24 hours, 5-7 days a week; students can reserve study rooms. Operations spending for the previous fiscal year: $17 million. 2,760 computers available on campus for general student use. Computer purchase/lease plans available. A campuswide network can be accessed from student residence rooms and from off campus. Students can access the following: online class registration. Staffed computer lab on campus (open 24 hours a day) provides training in use of computers, software, and the Internet.

Community Environment: Greenville (population 69,500) is the largest medical, cultural and retailing center on eastern North Carolina. The climate is mild, the mean annual temperature being 61 degrees. There are churches of all major denominations, a major hospital, a community art center, one library, and various civic and service organizations in the community. Employment opportunities are good.

■ EDGECOMBE COMMUNITY COLLEGE

2009 W Wilson St.
Tarboro, NC 27886-9399
Tel: (252)823-5166
Fax: (252)823-6817
Web Site: www.edgecombe.edu

Description: State and locally supported, 2-year, coed. Part of North Carolina Community College System. Awards certificates, diplomas, transfer associate, and terminal associate degrees. Founded 1968. Setting: 90-acre small town campus. Total enrollment: 1,687. 57% 25 or older. Calendar: semesters. Academic remediation for entering students, ESL program, services for LD students, advanced placement, independent study, distance learning, double major, summer session for credit, part-time degree program, adult/continuing education programs, co-op programs. Off campus study.

Entrance Requirements: Open admission except for radiological technology, nursing, respiratory therapy, surgical technology, networking technology programs. Option: electronic application. Required: high school transcript, minimum 2.0 high school GPA. Entrance: noncompetitive. Application deadline: rolling. Notification: continuous.

Collegiate Environment: Orientation program.

Community Environment: See North Carolina Wesleyan College.

■ ELIZABETH CITY STATE UNIVERSITY

1704 Weeksville Rd.
Elizabeth City, NC 27909-7806
Tel: (252)335-3400; Free: 800-347-3278
Fax: (252)335-3731
E-mail: ddeure@ecsu.edu
Web Site: www.ecsu.edu

Description: State-supported, comprehensive, coed. Part of University of North Carolina System. Awards bachelor's and master's degrees. Founded 1891. Setting: 200-acre small town campus with easy access to Norfolk. Endowment: $6 million. Research spending for the previous fiscal year: $1.3 million. Educational spending for the previous fiscal year: $10,541 per student. Total enrollment: 1,677. Faculty: 135 (116 full-time, 19 part-time). Student-undergrad faculty ratio is 14:1. 2,461 applied, 59% were admitted. 2% from top 10% of their high school class, 4% from top quarter, 31% from top half. Full-time: 1,425 students, 56% women, 44% men. Part-time: 211 students, 64% women, 36% men. Students come from 25 states and territories, 5 other countries, 15% from out-of-state. 0.5% American Indian or Alaska Native, non-Hispanic/Latino; 4% Hispanic/Latino; 70% Black or African American, non-Hispanic/Latino; 0.6% Asian, non-Hispanic/Latino; 0.1% Native Hawaiian or other Pacific Islander, non-Hispanic/Latino; 0.3% international. 19% 25 or older, 51% live on campus, 7% transferred in. Retention: 72% of full-time freshmen returned the following year. Academic areas with the most degrees conferred: homeland security, law enforcement, firefighting, and protective services; business/marketing; education. Core. Calendar: semesters. Academic remediation for entering students, services for LD students, advanced placement, honors program, independent study, distance learning, double major, summer session for credit, part-time degree program, adult/continuing education programs, co-op programs and internships, graduate courses open to undergrads. Off campus study at North Carolina Model Teacher Education Consortium. Study abroad program. ROTC: Army.

Entrance Requirements: Options: electronic application, deferred admission. Required: high school transcript, minimum 2.3 high school GPA, SAT or ACT. Entrance: moderately difficult. Preference given to state residents. SAT Reasoning Test deadline: 8/1. Transfer credits accepted: Yes.

Costs Per Year: Application fee: $30. Area resident tuition: $500 full-time. State resident tuition: $500 full-time. Nonresident tuition: $2500 full-time. Mandatory fees: $3110 full-time. College room and board: $9991. Tuition guaranteed not to increase for student's term of enrollment.

Collegiate Environment: Orientation program. Drama-theater group, choral group, marching band, student-run newspaper. Social organizations: national fraternities, national sororities, local fraternities, local sororities. Most popular organizations: Vans (Vikings Assisting New Students), Student Activities Committee, Vike Nu' Fashion Troupe, Pep Squad, Essence of

Praise. Major annual events: Homecoming, Viking Fest, Student and Body Meetings. Student services: health clinic, personal-psychological counseling. Campus security: 24-hour emergency response devices and patrols, controlled dormitory access. Freshmen guaranteed college housing. Options: coed, men-only, women-only housing available. G. R. Little Library plus 1 other. Books: 231,406 (physical), 184,579 (digital/electronic); Serial titles: 1,923 (physical), 22,828 (digital/electronic); Databases: 101. Weekly public service hours: 82. Operations spending for the previous fiscal year: $1.2 million.

Community Environment: See College of the Albemarle.

■ ELON UNIVERSITY

2700 Campus Box
Elon, NC 27244-2010
Tel: (336)278-2000; Free: 800-334-8448
Fax: (336)538-3986
E-mail: admissions@elon.edu
Web Site: www.elon.edu

Description: Independent, comprehensive, coed, affiliated with United Church of Christ. Awards bachelor's, master's, and doctoral degrees. Founded 1889. Setting: 656-acre suburban campus with easy access to Raleigh. Endowment: $230.4 million. Total enrollment: 6,791. Faculty: 599 (433 full-time, 166 part-time). Student-undergrad faculty ratio is 12:1. 9,623 applied, 67% were admitted. 21% from top 10% of their high school class, 54% from top quarter, 89% from top half. Full-time: 5,885 students, 60% women, 40% men. Part-time: 160 students, 56% women, 44% men. Students come from 52 states and territories, 58 other countries, 82% from out-of-state. 0.1% American Indian or Alaska Native, non-Hispanic/Latino; 6% Hispanic/Latino; 5% Black or African American, non-Hispanic/Latino; 2% Asian, non-Hispanic/Latino; 2% international. 1% 25 or older, 64% live on campus, 1% transferred in. Retention: 89% of full-time freshmen returned the following year. Academic areas with the most degrees conferred: business/marketing; communication/journalism; social sciences. Core. Calendar: semesters 3-week winter term. ESL program, services for LD students, advanced placement, accelerated degree program, self-designed majors, honors program, independent study, distance learning, double major, summer session for credit, part-time degree program, internships. Off campus study. Study abroad program. ROTC: Army, Air Force (c).

Entrance Requirements: Options: electronic application, early admission, early decision, early action, deferred admission, international baccalaureate accepted. Required: essay, high school transcript, counselor evaluation form, SAT or ACT. Required for some: interview. Entrance: moderately difficult. Application deadlines: 1/10, 11/1 for early decision, 11/10 for early action. Notification: 3/20, 12/1 for early decision, 12/20 for early action. SAT Reasoning Test deadline: December. Transfer credits accepted: Yes. Applicants placed on waiting list: 2,117. Wait-listed applicants offered admission: 153. Early decision applicants: 378. Early decision applicants admitted: 373. Early action applicants: 6,196. Early action applicants admitted: 3,878.

Costs Per Year: Application fee: $50. Comprehensive fee: $47,549 includes full-time tuition ($34,850), mandatory fees ($469), and college room and board ($12,230). College room only: $6020. Room and board charges vary according to board plan and housing facility. Part-time tuition: $1110 per credit hour. Part-time mandatory fees: $166.50 per term. Part-time tuition and fees vary according to course load.

Collegiate Environment: Orientation program. Drama-theater group, choral group, marching band, student-run newspaper, radio station. Social organizations: 249 open to all; national fraternities, national sororities; 20% of eligible men and 39% of eligible women are members. Most popular organizations: Elon Volunteers, Student Media, Intramural Athletics, Religious Life, Habitat for Humanity. Major annual events: Homecoming, Family Weekend, Fall Convocation. Student services: health clinic, personal-psychological counseling, women's center. Campus security: 24-hour emergency response devices and patrols, late night transport-escort service, controlled dormitory access, Student Transport Service (Safe Rides). Carol Grotnes Belk. Books: 401,760 (physical), 1.3 million (digital/electronic); Serial titles: 217 (physical), 64,848 (digital/electronic); Databases: 179. Weekly public service hours: 143; study areas open 24 hours, 5-7 days a week; students can reserve study rooms. Operations spending for the previous fiscal year: $5 million. 1,200 computers available on campus for general student use. Computer purchase/lease plans available. A campuswide network can be accessed from student residence rooms and from off campus. Students can access the following: online class registration. Staffed computer lab on campus (open 24 hours a day) provides training in use of computers, software, and the Internet.

Community Environment: See Alamance Community College.

■ FAYETTEVILLE STATE UNIVERSITY

1200 Murchison Rd.
Fayetteville, NC 28301-4298
Tel: (910)672-1111; Free: 800-222-2594
Fax: (910)672-1769
Web Site: www.uncfsu.edu

Description: State-supported, comprehensive, coed. Part of University of North Carolina System. Awards bachelor's, master's, and doctoral degrees. Founded 1867. Setting: 156-acre urban campus with easy access to Raleigh. Research spending for the previous fiscal year: $1.1 million. Total enrollment: 6,318. Faculty: 333 (267 full-time, 79 part-time). Student-undergrad faculty ratio is 15:1. 4,130 applied, 68% were admitted. 7% from top 10% of their high school class, 26% from top quarter, 64% from top half. Full-time: 4,058 students, 68% women, 32% men. Part-time: 1,415 students, 68% women, 32% men. Students come from 40 states and territories, 20 other countries, 7% from out-of-state. 2% American Indian or Alaska Native, non-Hispanic/Latino; 8% Hispanic/Latino; 63% Black or African American, non-Hispanic/Latino; 2% Asian, non-Hispanic/Latino; 0.3% Native Hawaiian or other Pacific Islander, non-Hispanic/Latino; 0.6% international. 40% 25 or older, 22% live on campus, 17% transferred in. Retention: 78% of full-time freshmen returned the following year. Academic areas with the most degrees conferred: health professions and related sciences; homeland security, law enforcement, firefighting, and protective services; business/marketing; psychology. Core. Calendar: semesters. Academic remediation for entering students, services for LD students, advanced placement, accelerated degree program, honors program, independent study, distance learning, double major, summer session for credit, part-time degree program, adult/continuing education programs, co-op programs and internships, graduate courses open to undergrads. Study abroad program. ROTC: Army (c), Air Force.

Entrance Requirements: Options: electronic application, early admission, early decision, early action, deferred admission. Required: high school transcript, minimum 2.5 high school GPA, SAT or ACT. Recommended: essay. Entrance: minimally difficult. Notification: continuous. SAT Reasoning Test deadline: 7/1.

Costs Per Year: Application fee: $40. State resident tuition: $2982 full-time. Nonresident tuition: $14,590 full-time. Mandatory fees: $1933 full-time. Full-time tuition and fees vary according to course level, course load, degree level, location, and program. College room and board: $8236. College room only: $4298. Room and board charges vary according to board plan and housing facility.

Collegiate Environment: Orientation program. Drama-theater group, choral group, marching band, student-run newspaper, radio station. Social organizations: 30 open to all; national fraternities, national sororities, local fraternities, local sororities; 1% of eligible men and 1% of eligible women are members. Most popular organizations: Student Government Association, Student Activities Council, Pan-Hellenic Council, Residence Hall Association, Illusions and Black Millennium Modeling Clubs. Major annual events: Homecoming Week Activities, Rodeo Week Activities, National Pan Hellenic Council Campus Presentation. Student services: health clinic, personal-psychological counseling. Campus security: 24-hour emergency response devices and patrols, late night transport-escort service, controlled dormitory access. 1,400 college housing spaces available; 1,300 were occupied in 2018-19. Freshmen given priority for college housing. Options: coed, men-only, women-only housing available. Charles W. Chestnut Library. Books: 223,687 (physical), 224,581 (digital/electronic); Serial titles: 314 (physical), 30,747 (digital/electronic); Databases: 442. Weekly public service hours: 97; students can reserve study rooms. Operations spending for the previous fiscal year: $2.8 million. 600 computers available on campus for general student use. Computer purchase/lease plans available. A campuswide network can be accessed from student residence rooms and from off campus. Students can access the following: online class registration. Staffed computer lab on campus provides training in use of computers, software, and the Internet.

Community Environment: The"All-America City" of Fayetteville is located in Cumberland County with a metropolitan population of 299,060. It is near three of the most heavily traveled North-South Highways: US 301, US 401 and I-95. Fayetteville is the home of Pope Air Force Base and Fort Bragg, one of America's largest and most important military installations. It is the fourth largest urban population center in the state and one of the ten fastest growing counties in the southern states. Agriculture has contributed significantly to the area's economic growth and development.

■ FAYETTEVILLE TECHNICAL COMMUNITY COLLEGE

2201 Hull Rd.
Fayetteville, NC 28303-0236
Tel: (910)678-8400
Fax: (910)678-8407
E-mail: castleml@faytechcc.edu
Web Site: www.faytechcc.edu

Description: State-supported, 2-year, coed. Part of North Carolina Community College System. Awards certificates, diplomas, transfer associate, and terminal associate degrees. Founded 1961. Setting: 204-acre suburban campus with easy access to Raleigh. Endowment: $39,050. Educational spending for the previous fiscal year: $5869 per student. Total enrollment: 11,534. Faculty: 553 (279 full-time, 274 part-time). Student-undergrad faculty ratio is 19:1. 4,711 applied, 100% were admitted. 15% from top 10% of their high school class, 31% from top quarter, 68% from top half. Full-time: 4,509 students, 60% women, 40% men. Part-time: 7,025 students, 58% women, 42% men. Students come from 43 states and territories, 12 other countries, 25% from out-of-state. 2% American Indian or Alaska Native, non-Hispanic/Latino; 12% Hispanic/Latino; 37% Black or African American, non-Hispanic/Latino; 2% Asian, non-Hispanic/Latino; 0.4% Native Hawaiian or other Pacific Islander, non-Hispanic/Latino; 0.5% international. 54% 25 or older, 6% transferred in. Core. Calendar: semesters. Academic remediation for entering students, ESL program, services for LD students, advanced placement, accelerated degree program, freshman honors college, honors program, independent study, distance learning, double major, summer session for credit, part-time degree program, adult/continuing education programs, co-op programs and internships. Off campus study at University of North Carolina University System, Methodist University, Campbell University, High Point University, Mars Hill University, Meredith College, Montreat College, University of Mount Olive, North Carolina Wesleyan College, Shaw University, Southeastern Baptist Theological College, St. Andrews University, Wingate University, Fayetteville State University, Franklin University, Purdue University Global. ROTC: Air Force (c).

Entrance Requirements: Open admission except for allied health programs. Options: electronic application, deferred admission, international baccalaureate accepted. Required: high school transcript. Required for some: essay, interview. Entrance: noncompetitive. Application deadline: rolling. Notification: continuous. Transfer credits accepted: Yes.

Costs Per Year: Application fee: $0. One-time mandatory fee: $30. State resident tuition: $2432 full-time, $76 per credit hour part-time. Nonresident tuition: $8576 full-time, $268 per credit hour part-time. Mandatory fees: $112 full-time, $56 per term part-time. Full-time tuition and fees vary according to course load. Part-time tuition and fees vary according to course load.

Collegiate Environment: Choral group. Social organizations: 40 open to all. Most popular organizations: Parents for Higher Education, Phi Theta Kappa, Phi Beta Lambda, Sigma Kappa Delta, Student Veterans of America. Major annual events: Fall Fling, Spring Fling, On-Campus Job Fairs. Student services: personal-psychological counseling. Campus security: 24-hour emergency response devices and patrols, late night transport-escort service, campus-wide emergency notification system. College housing not available. Paul H. Thompson Library plus 1 other. Books: 35,540 (physical), 275,000 (digital/electronic); Serial titles: 53 (physical), 5 (digital/electronic); Databases: 200. Operations spending for the previous fiscal year: $1.6 million. 236 computers available on campus for general student use. Computer purchase/lease plans available. A campuswide network can be accessed from off-campus. Students can access the following: online class registration, admissions status, documents and notices, test scores, program evaluation, financial aid status, tuition payments. Staffed computer lab on campus provides training in use of computers, software, and the Internet.

Community Environment: See Fayetteville State University.

■ FORSYTH TECHNICAL COMMUNITY COLLEGE

2100 Silas Creek Pky.
Winston Salem, NC 27103-5197
Tel: (336)723-0371
Fax: (336)761-2098
E-mail: admissions@forsythtech.edu
Web Site: www.forsythtech.edu

Description: State-supported, 2-year, coed. Part of North Carolina Community College System. Awards certificates, diplomas, transfer associate, and terminal associate degrees. Founded 1964. Setting: 38-acre suburban campus. Total enrollment: 9,148. Student-undergrad faculty ratio is 13:1. Full-time: 3,726 students, 54% women, 46% men. Part-time: 5,422 students, 65% women, 35% men. 1% from out-of-state. 0.5% American Indian or

Alaska Native, non-Hispanic/Latino; 8% Hispanic/Latino; 29% Black or African American, non-Hispanic/Latino; 2% Asian, non-Hispanic/Latino; 0.1% Native Hawaiian or other Pacific Islander, non-Hispanic/Latino; 0.7% international. 45% 25 or older, 26% transferred in. Calendar: semesters. Academic remediation for entering students, ESL program, services for LD students, advanced placement, independent study, distance learning, double major, summer session for credit, part-time degree program, adult/continuing education programs, co-op programs and internships. Off campus study at Dual Enrollment with Winston-Salem State University.
Entrance Requirements: Required: high school transcript, ACT Compass.
Collegiate Environment: Orientation program. Student-run newspaper. Major annual events: Fall Festival, Spring Fling. Student services: personal-psychological counseling, women's center. Campus security: 24-hour emergency response devices and patrols, late night transport-escort service. Forsyth Technical Community College Library plus 1 other.
Community Environment: See Wake Forest University.

■ **GARDNER-WEBB UNIVERSITY**
110 S Main St.
Boiling Springs, NC 28017
Tel: (704)406-2361; Free: 800-253-6472
Fax: (704)434-4488
E-mail: admissions@gardner-webb.edu
Web Site: www.gardner-webb.edu
Description: Independent Baptist, university, coed. Awards associate, bachelor's, master's, and doctoral degrees. Founded 1905. Setting: 250-acre small town campus with easy access to Charlotte. Endowment: $51.1 million. Educational spending for the previous fiscal year: $5707 per student. Total enrollment: 3,884. Faculty: 300 (165 full-time, 135 part-time). Student-undergrad faculty ratio is 13:1. 4,310 applied, 10% were admitted. 13% from top 10% of their high school class, 34% from top quarter, 60% from top half. Full-time: 1,912 students, 61% women, 39% men. Part-time: 431 students, 77% women, 23% men. Students come from 42 states and territories, 9 other countries, 3% from out-of-state. 0.7% American Indian or Alaska Native, non-Hispanic/Latino; 3% Hispanic/Latino; 15% Black or African American, non-Hispanic/Latino; 1% Asian, non-Hispanic/Latino; 0.9% international. 51% live on campus. Retention: 66% of full-time freshmen returned the following year. Academic areas with the most degrees conferred: health professions and related sciences; business/marketing; psychology. Core. Calendar: semesters. Academic remediation for entering students, ESL program, services for LD students, advanced placement, accelerated degree program, honors program, independent study, distance learning, double major, summer session for credit, part-time degree program, adult/continuing education programs, co-op programs and internships, graduate courses open to undergrads. Off campus study. Study abroad program. ROTC: Army, Air Force (c).
Entrance Requirements: Options: electronic application, international baccalaureate accepted. Required: high school transcript, minimum 2.5 high school GPA, SAT or ACT. Recommended: essay, 2 recommendations. Required for some: 2 recommendations, interview. Entrance: moderately difficult. Application deadline: rolling. Notification: continuous. SAT Reasoning Test deadline: 8/15. Transfer credits accepted: Yes.
Costs Per Year: Application fee: $40. Comprehensive fee: $42,030 includes full-time tuition ($31,220), mandatory fees ($420), and college room and board ($10,390). College room only: $5260. Room and board charges vary according to board plan and housing facility. Part-time tuition: $496 per hour.
Collegiate Environment: Orientation program. Drama-theater group, choral group, marching band, student-run newspaper, radio station. Social organizations: 65 open to all. Most popular organizations: Campus Ministries United, Student Government Association, Dawg Pound, Honors Student Association, International Club. Major annual events: Homecoming, Parents' Weekend, Welcome Back Events. Student services: personal-psychological counseling. Campus security: 24-hour emergency response devices and patrols, student patrols, late night transport-escort service, controlled dormitory access. Dover Memorial Library plus 1 other. Operations spending for the previous fiscal year: $985,442. 121 computers available on campus for general student use. Computer purchase/lease plans available. A campuswide network can be accessed from student residence rooms and from off campus. Students can access the following: online class registration. Staffed computer lab on campus provides training in use of computers and the Internet.
Community Environment: Boiling Springs is located within the noted thermal belt; bus transportation is within five miles; three major railroad lines are within 10 miles; nearest airport is Charlotte, N.C., 50 miles. The com-

munity has access to the indoor swimming pool at the college, observatory, theatre, football stadium, gymnasium and the many cultural arts and entertainment programs at the college. Shopping facilities are good, other community facilities include United Methodist and Baptist churches, and in nearby Shelby, churches of most major denominations, plus numerous civic and service organizations. Part-time employment opportunities are good.

■ **GASTON COLLEGE**
201 Hwy. 321 S
Dallas, NC 28034-1499
Tel: (704)922-6200
Web Site: www.gaston.edu
Description: State and locally supported, 2-year, coed. Part of North Carolina Community College System. Awards certificates, diplomas, transfer associate, and terminal associate degrees. Founded 1963. Setting: 166-acre small town campus with easy access to Charlotte. Total enrollment: 6,507. Student-undergrad faculty ratio is 15:1. 50% 25 or older. Core. Calendar: semesters. Academic remediation for entering students, ESL program, services for LD students, advanced placement, summer session for credit, part-time degree program, co-op programs. Off campus study at 10 members of the Charlotte Area Educational Consortium.
Entrance Requirements: Open admission except for nursing, allied health programs. Required: high school transcript, ACT Compass. Required for some: SAT and SAT Subject Tests or ACT. Entrance: noncompetitive. Application deadline: rolling. Notification: continuous.
Collegiate Environment: Orientation program. Student-run radio station. Campus security: 24-hour patrols, late night transport-escort service. Gaston College Library.
Community Environment: The 140 textile plants of Gaston County, 59 of which are in Gastonia, manufacture more than 80 percent of the fine combed cotton yarn made in the United States. Gastonia is an important industrial city of the South. Railroads serve the area with the Charlotte Airport 15 miles away. Community facilities include numerous churches, hospitals, a public library, and a number of civic and service organizations. Rankin Lake is the city's natural reservoir. Adjoining it is a public park that provides a museum and planetarium as well as facilities for golfing, swimming, boating, fishing, and tennis. The Atlantic Coast is within a five-hour drive.

■ **GRACE COLLEGE OF DIVINITY**
5117 Cliffdale Rd.
Fayetteville, NC 28314
Tel: (910)221-2224
Web Site: www.gcd.edu
Description: Independent Christian, comprehensive, coed. Awards associate, bachelor's, and master's degrees. Calendar: semesters.

■ **GREENSBORO COLLEGE**
815 W Market St.
Greensboro, NC 27401-1875
Tel: (336)272-7102; Free: 800-346-8226
Fax: (336)271-6634
Web Site: www.greensboro.edu
Description: Independent United Methodist, comprehensive, coed. Awards bachelor's and master's degrees. Founded 1838. Setting: 75-acre urban campus with easy access to Charlotte. Endowment: $20.5 million. Educational spending for the previous fiscal year: $6394 per student. Total enrollment: 1,001. Faculty: 84 (63 full-time, 21 part-time). Student-undergrad faculty ratio is 12:1. 2,192 applied, 41% were admitted. 6% from top 10% of their high school class, 22% from top quarter, 52% from top half. Students come from 17 states and territories, 11 other countries, 4% from out-of-state. 0.2% American Indian or Alaska Native, non-Hispanic/Latino; 2% Hispanic/Latino; 32% Black or African American, non-Hispanic/Latino; 0.9% Asian, non-Hispanic/Latino; 0.1% Native Hawaiian or other Pacific Islander, non-Hispanic/Latino. 73% live on campus. Retention: 55% of full-time freshmen returned the following year. Core. Calendar: semesters. Academic remediation for entering students, ESL program, services for LD students, advanced placement, accelerated degree program, self-designed majors, freshman honors college, honors program, independent study, double major, summer session for credit, part-time degree program, adult/continuing education programs, internships. Off campus study at 7 members of the Greater Greensboro Consortium. Study abroad program. ROTC: Army (c), Air Force (c).
Entrance Requirements: Options: electronic application, early admission,

deferred admission, international baccalaureate accepted. Required: high school transcript, SAT or ACT. Recommended: essay. Required for some: interview. Entrance: minimally difficult. Application deadline: rolling. Notification: continuous. Transfer credits accepted: Yes.

Costs Per Year: Application fee: $0. Comprehensive fee: $39,940 includes full-time tuition ($28,440), mandatory fees ($700), and college room and board ($10,800). Full-time tuition and fees vary according to degree level and program. Room and board charges vary according to housing facility. Part-time tuition: $750 per credit hour. Part-time mandatory fees: $700 per year. Part-time tuition and fees vary according to course load, degree level, and program.

Collegiate Environment: Orientation program. Drama-theater group, choral group, marching band, student-run newspaper. Social organizations: 52 open to all; national fraternities, national sororities, local fraternities, local sororities; 2% of eligible men and 2% of eligible women are members. Most popular organizations: Pheta VI, Alpha Z Delta, Student Athletic Advisor Counsel, Pride Productions, United African American Society. Major annual events: Club Carnival, Homecoming, Gate City Soup Bowl Football Game. Student services: health clinic, personal-psychological counseling. Campus security: 24-hour patrols, late night transport-escort service, controlled dormitory access. James Addison Jones Library. Books: 77,657 (physical), 194,596 (digital/electronic). Weekly public service hours: 60; students can reserve study rooms. Operations spending for the previous fiscal year: $92,916. 180 computers available on campus for general student use. A campuswide network can be accessed from student residence rooms and from off campus.

Community Environment: Greensboro was named for General Nathanael Greene, hero of the Battle of Guilford Courthouse. Textiles are the predominant industry along with the manufacture of cigarettes. The War Memorial Auditorium and Coliseum provides one of the state's finest facilities for conventions, exhibitions, sports events, and shows. Recreation facilities include golf courses, swimming pools, and tennis courts. Part-time employment is available. Points of interest are the Greensboro Historical Museum and on the site of O. Henry's birthplace.

■ **GUILFORD COLLEGE**
5800 W Friendly Ave.
Greensboro, NC 27410-4173
Tel: (336)316-2000; Free: 800-992-7759
Fax: (336)316-2954
E-mail: admission@guilford.edu
Web Site: www.guilford.edu

Description: Independent, comprehensive, coed, affiliated with Society of Friends. Awards bachelor's and master's degrees. Founded 1837. Setting: 351-acre suburban campus. Endowment: $74.5 million. Research spending for the previous fiscal year: $174,786. Educational spending for the previous fiscal year: $6893 per student. Total enrollment: 1,680. Faculty: 185 (101 full-time, 84 part-time). Student-undergrad faculty ratio is 12:1. 1,865 applied, 91% were admitted. 13% from top 10% of their high school class, 32% from top quarter, 66% from top half. Full-time: 1,429 students, 53% women, 47% men. Part-time: 245 students, 54% women, 46% men. Students come from 39 states and territories, 10 other countries, 29% from out-of-state. 0.5% American Indian or Alaska Native, non-Hispanic/Latino; 9% Hispanic/Latino; 25% Black or African American, non-Hispanic/Latino; 3% Asian, non-Hispanic/Latino; 0.1% Native Hawaiian or other Pacific Islander, non-Hispanic/Latino; 1% international. 23% 25 or older, 74% live on campus, 6% transferred in. Retention: 66% of full-time freshmen returned the following year. Academic areas with the most degrees conferred: business/marketing; psychology; biological/life sciences; parks and recreation. Core. Calendar: 4-1-4. Services for LD students, advanced placement, accelerated degree program, self-designed majors, honors program, independent study, distance learning, double major, summer session for credit, part-time degree program, adult/continuing education programs, co-op programs and internships, graduate courses open to undergrads. Off campus study at Greater Greensboro Consortium. Study abroad program. ROTC: Army (c), Air Force (c).

Entrance Requirements: Options: electronic application, early admission, early decision, early action, deferred admission, international baccalaureate accepted. Required: essay, minimum 2 high school GPA. Recommended: minimum 3 high school GPA, interview, SAT or ACT. Required for some: high school transcript, 1 recommendation. Entrance: moderately difficult. Application deadlines: rolling, 11/1 for early decision, 12/1 for early action. Notification: continuous, 11/15 for early decision, 12/15 for early action. Preference

given to Quakers. SAT Reasoning Test deadline: 3/1. Transfer credits accepted: Yes. Early decision applicants: 18. Early decision applicants admitted: 16.

Collegiate Environment: Orientation program. Drama-theater group, choral group, student-run newspaper, radio station. Social organizations: 54 open to all. Most popular organizations: Student Government, Student Radio Station, Student Newspaper. Major annual events: Family Weekend, Gender Bender, Serendipity. Student services: health clinic, personal-psychological counseling. Campus security: 24-hour emergency response devices and patrols, student patrols, late night transport-escort service, controlled dormitory access. Hege Library. Books: 164,946 (physical), 326,808 (digital/electronic); Serial titles: 4,301 (physical), 45,891 (digital/electronic); Databases: 169. Weekly public service hours: 93; students can reserve study rooms. Operations spending for the previous fiscal year: $431,762. 275 computers available on campus for general student use. A campuswide network can be accessed from student residence rooms and from off campus. Students can access the following: online class registration, network storage. Staffed computer lab on campus provides training in use of computers, software, and the Internet.

Community Environment: See Greensboro College.

■ **GUILFORD TECHNICAL COMMUNITY COLLEGE**
PO Box 309
Jamestown, NC 27282-0309
Tel: (336)334-4822
Web Site: www.gtcc.edu

Description: State and locally supported, 2-year, coed. Part of North Carolina Community College System. Awards certificates, diplomas, transfer associate, and terminal associate degrees. Founded 1958. Setting: 158-acre urban campus with easy access to Raleigh, Charlotte, Greensboro. Endowment: $3.4 million. Educational spending for the previous fiscal year: $5327 per student. Total enrollment: 12,430. Faculty: 393 (314 full-time, 79 part-time). Student-undergrad faculty ratio is 20:1. 6,620 applied, 100% were admitted. Full-time: 5,783 students, 54% women, 46% men. Part-time: 6,647 students, 60% women, 40% men. Students come from 19 states and territories, 0.5% from out-of-state. 0.8% American Indian or Alaska Native, non-Hispanic/Latino; 7% Hispanic/Latino; 42% Black or African American, non-Hispanic/Latino; 4% Asian, non-Hispanic/Latino; 0.1% Native Hawaiian or other Pacific Islander, non-Hispanic/Latino; 1% international. 46% 25 or older, 9% transferred in. Retention: 50% of full-time freshmen returned the following year. Core. Calendar: semesters. Academic remediation for entering students, ESL program, services for LD students, advanced placement, self-designed majors, independent study, distance learning, double major, summer session for credit, part-time degree program, external degree program, adult/continuing education programs, co-op programs and internships. Off campus study at members of the Greater Greensboro Consortium. ROTC: Army (c), Air Force (c).

Entrance Requirements: Open admission except for health-related, aviation maintenance programs, automotive systems, and CCPI. Options: electronic application, early admission, deferred admission, international baccalaureate accepted. Required for some: high school transcript, interview. Entrance: noncompetitive. Application deadline: rolling. Notification: continuous. Transfer credits accepted: Yes.

Collegiate Environment: Orientation program. Drama-theater group. Social organizations: 57 open to all; national sororities, local fraternities. Student services: personal-psychological counseling. Campus security: 24-hour emergency response devices and patrols, late night transport-escort service. M. W. Bell Library plus 2 others. Operations spending for the previous fiscal year: $727,964.

Community Environment: Jamestown neighbors High Point and Greensboro. Primary businesses in Guilford County are textiles, furniture, and numerous other manufacturing concerns. Commercial transportation, one railroad, seven airlines, and recreational facilities are convenient in High Point and Greensboro.

■ **HALIFAX COMMUNITY COLLEGE**
PO Drawer 809
Weldon, NC 27890-0809
Tel: (252)536-2551
Fax: (252)536-4144
E-mail: asquire374@halifaxcc.edu
Web Site: www.halifaxcc.edu

Description: State and locally supported, 2-year, coed. Part of North Carolina Community College System. Awards certificates, diplomas, transfer associate, and terminal associate degrees. Founded 1967. Setting: 109-acre rural campus. Endowment: $1365. Educational spending for the previous fiscal year: $5669 per student. Total enrollment: 1,083. Faculty: 84 (44 full-time, 40 part-time). Student-undergrad faculty ratio is 11:1. 673 applied, 68% were admitted. 8% from top 10% of their high school class, 24% from top quarter, 35% from top half. Full-time: 409 students, 60% women, 40% men. Part-time: 674 students, 65% women, 35% men. 29% 25 or older. Core. Calendar: semesters. Academic remediation for entering students, ESL program, services for LD students, independent study, distance learning, double major, summer session for credit, part-time degree program, co-op programs and internships.

Entrance Requirements: Open admission. Required: high school transcript. Application deadlines: rolling, rolling for nonresidents. Notification: continuous, continuous for nonresidents. Transfer credits accepted: Yes.

Costs Per Year: State resident tuition: $2296 full-time, $76 per credit hour part-time. Nonresident tuition: $7672 full-time, $268 per credit hour part-time. Mandatory fees: $176 full-time, $76 per credit hour part-time, $88 per term part-time.

Collegiate Environment: Orientation program. Most popular organizations: Phi Theta Kappa, PRIDE, Women of Excellence. Major annual events: Fall Festival/Spring Fling, PRIDE and Women of Excellence Annual Conferences, Student Awards Ceremony. Student services: health clinic. Campus security: 24-hour emergency response devices, 12-hour patrols by trained security personnel. College housing not available. Learning Resources Center. Books: 23,686 (physical), 202,576 (digital/electronic); Serial titles: 86 (physical), 1,382 (digital/electronic); Databases: 89. Weekly public service hours: 52. Operations spending for the previous fiscal year: $168,879. 200 computers available on campus for general student use. Computer purchase/lease plans available. A campuswide network can be accessed. Students can access the following: online class registration, Computer repair. Staffed computer lab on campus provides training in use of computers, software, and the Internet.

Community Environment: Located in the northeastern section of North Carolina, Weldon is in a good agricultural area where the main industries are in textiles and paper goods. Community facilities include churches, a library, historical sites, shopping centers, and medical facilities nearby. There are three convenient lakes, with miles of shoreline, known as the Rockfish Capital of the world.

■ **HAYWOOD COMMUNITY COLLEGE**
185 Freedlander Dr.
Clyde, NC 28721-9453
Tel: (828)627-2821
Fax: (828)627-4513
Web Site: www.haywood.edu

Description: State and locally supported, 2-year, coed. Part of North Carolina Community College System. Awards certificates, diplomas, transfer associate, and terminal associate degrees. Founded 1965. Setting: 85-acre rural campus. Endowment: $9.1 million. Educational spending for the previous fiscal year: $5129 per student. Total enrollment: 1,627. Faculty: 235 (59 full-time, 176 part-time). 7% from top 10% of their high school class, 34% from top quarter, 89% from top half. Full-time: 574 students, 50% women, 50% men. Part-time: 1,053 students, 67% women, 33% men. 1% from out-of-state. 2% American Indian or Alaska Native, non-Hispanic/Latino; 4% Hispanic/Latino; 5% Black or African American, non-Hispanic/Latino; 1% Asian, non-Hispanic/Latino; 0.1% Native Hawaiian or other Pacific Islander, non-Hispanic/Latino; 0.1% international. 36% 25 or older, 12% transferred in. Retention: 74% of full-time freshmen returned the following year. Core. Calendar: semesters. Academic remediation for entering students, ESL program, services for LD students, advanced placement, honors program, independent study, distance learning, double major, summer session for credit, part-time degree program, adult/continuing education programs, co-op programs and internships. Study abroad program.

Entrance Requirements: Open admission except for nursing, some technical programs. Option: electronic application. Required: high school transcript. Required for some: interview. Entrance: noncompetitive. Application deadline: rolling.

Costs Per Year: Application fee: $0. State resident tuition: $2434 full-time, $76 per credit hour part-time. Nonresident tuition: $8579 full-time, $268 per credit hour part-time. Mandatory fees: $145 full-time, $130.50 per year part-time.

Collegiate Environment: Orientation program. Social organizations: 16 open to all. Most popular organizations: Wildlife Society, Timbersport Forestry Club, Student Association of Medical Assistants (SAMA), HCC

Student Nurses Association, HCC Skills USA Club. Major annual events: Week of Welcome, Spring Fling, Halloween Costume Contest. Campus security: Emergency Phone and Patrols while campus is open. College housing not available. Freedlander Learning Resource Center. Books: 36,213 (physical), 382,812 (digital/electronic); Serial titles: 123 (physical), 23,465 (digital/electronic); Databases: 91. Weekly public service hours: 47; students can reserve study rooms. Operations spending for the previous fiscal year: $2.1 million. 448 computers available on campus for general student use. Computer purchase/lease plans available. A campuswide network can be accessed. Students can access the following: online class registration.

Community Environment: Haywood is a growing county of 47,000 people with an ever-expanding economy. Fine roads serve the county and new and expanding industry is experiencing a rapid increase. Agriculture is diversifying, and vegetable growing and truck farming share the market with cattle, corn, and tobacco. New and expanding tourist and recreational facilities are being developed. The county's proximity to the Great Smoky Mountains National Park and the world-famous Lake Junaluska Methodist Assembly Grounds make the area a natural tourist attraction. A large ski resort and the nearby lakes and forests have earned the area the distinction of being a winter and summer playground.

■ **HERITAGE BIBLE COLLEGE**
PO Box 1628
Dunn, NC 28335-1628
Tel: (910)892-3178; Free: 800-297-6351
Fax: (910)892-1809
E-mail: iprince@heritagebiblecollege.edu
Web Site: www.heritagebiblecollege.edu

Description: Independent Pentecostal Free Will Baptist, 4-year, coed. Awards associate and bachelor's degrees. Founded 1971. Setting: 82-acre small town campus with easy access to Raleigh-Durham. Endowment: $53,446. Educational spending for the previous fiscal year: $6240 per student. Total enrollment: 69. Faculty: 18 (4 full-time, 14 part-time). 10 applied, 100% were admitted. 30% from top quarter of their high school class, 70% from top half. Full-time: 34 students, 50% women, 50% men. Part-time: 35 students, 43% women, 57% men. Students come from 7 states and territories, 13% from out-of-state. 23% Black or African American, non-Hispanic/Latino; 1% Native Hawaiian or other Pacific Islander, non-Hispanic/Latino. 77% 25 or older, 13% live on campus, 13% transferred in. Retention: 52% of full-time freshmen returned the following year. Academic area with the most degrees conferred: theology and religious vocations. Core. Calendar: semesters. Academic remediation for entering students, distance learning, double major, summer session for credit, part-time degree program, external degree program, adult/continuing education programs, internships. Off campus study.

Entrance Requirements: Open admission. Options: electronic application, international baccalaureate accepted. Required: essay, high school transcript, medical history required for all, immunization record required for some. Required for some: interview. Entrance: minimally difficult. Application deadline: rolling. Transfer credits accepted: Yes.

Costs Per Year: Application fee: $35. Tuition: $7560 full-time, $315 per credit hour part-time. Mandatory fees: $768 full-time, $32 per credit hour part-time.

Collegiate Environment: Orientation program. Choral group. Social organizations: 3 open to all. Major annual event: Heritage Day. Alphin Ellis Learning Center plus 1 other. Students can reserve study rooms. Operations spending for the previous fiscal year: $36,825. 25 computers available on campus for general student use. A campuswide network can be accessed from student residence rooms and from off campus. Students can access the following: online class registration. Staffed computer lab on campus provides training in use of computers, software, and the Internet.

■ **HIGH POINT UNIVERSITY**
One University Pky.
High Point, NC 27268
Tel: (336)841-9000; Free: 800-345-6993
Fax: (336)841-5123
E-mail: kramsay@highpoint.edu
Web Site: www.highpoint.edu

Description: Independent United Methodist, university, coed. Awards bachelor's, master's, and doctoral degrees. Founded 1924. Setting: 380-acre suburban campus with easy access to Charlotte. Endowment: $60.8 million. Research spending for the previous fiscal year: $1.5 million.

Educational spending for the previous fiscal year: $9318 per student. Total enrollment: 5,137. Faculty: 478 (314 full-time, 164 part-time). Student-undergrad faculty ratio is 14:1. 10,098 applied, 77% were admitted. 15% from top 10% of their high school class, 43% from top quarter, 74% from top half. 12 National Merit Scholars, 19 class presidents, 10 valedictorians, 107 student government officers. Full-time: 4,504 students, 57% women, 43% men. Part-time: 41 students, 63% women, 37% men. Students come from 46 states and territories, 39 other countries, 76% from out-of-state. 0.4% American Indian or Alaska Native, non-Hispanic/Latino; 5% Hispanic/Latino; 5% Black or African American, non-Hispanic/Latino; 2% Asian, non-Hispanic/Latino; 3% international. 94% live on campus, 1% transferred in. Retention: 81% of full-time freshmen returned the following year. Academic areas with the most degrees conferred: business/marketing; communication/journalism; parks and recreation. Core. Calendar: semesters. ESL program, services for LD students, advanced placement, accelerated degree program, self-designed majors, honors program, independent study, double major, summer session for credit, co-op programs and internships. Study abroad program. ROTC: Army (c), Air Force (c).

Entrance Requirements: Options: electronic application, early decision, early action, deferred admission, international baccalaureate accepted. Required: essay, high school transcript, 1 recommendation. Recommended: interview. Entrance: moderately difficult. Application deadlines: 3/1, 11/1 for early decision plan 1, 2/1 for early decision plan 2, 11/15 for early action. Notification: continuous until 2/1, 11/27 for early decision plan 1, 2/1 for early decision plan 2, 12/15 for early action. SAT Reasoning Test deadline: 8/15. Transfer credits accepted: Yes. Applicants placed on waiting list: 567. Wait-listed applicants offered admission: 84. Early decision applicants: 657. Early decision applicants admitted: 536. Early action applicants: 6,841. Early action applicants admitted: 5,945.

Costs Per Year: Application fee: $50. Comprehensive fee: $49,248 includes full-time tuition ($30,748), mandatory fees ($4370), and college room and board ($14,130). Full-time tuition and fees vary according to course load and reciprocity agreements. Room and board charges vary according to board plan and housing facility. Part-time tuition: $993 per credit hour. Part-time mandatory fees: $2185 per term. Part-time tuition and fees vary according to course load and reciprocity agreements.

Collegiate Environment: Orientation program. Drama-theater group, choral group, student-run newspaper, radio station. Social organizations: 139 open to all; national fraternities, national sororities, local fraternities, local sororities; 9% of eligible men and 26% of eligible women are members. Most popular organizations: Big Brothers Big Sisters, Campus Activities Team, Purple Reign, Entrepreneurship Club, Volunteer Center. Major annual events: Derby Day, Family Weekend, Fall/Spring Concerts. Student services: health clinic, personal-psychological counseling. Campus security: 24-hour emergency response devices and patrols, student patrols, late night transport-escort service, controlled dormitory access. 4,684 college housing spaces available; 4,285 were occupied in 2018-19. Freshmen guaranteed college housing. On-campus residence required through junior year. Options: coed, men-only, women-only housing available. Smith Library plus 1 other. Books: 181,000 (physical), 447,000 (digital/electronic); Serial titles: 41,000 (physical), 32,000 (digital/electronic); Databases: 185. Weekly public service hours: 168; study areas open 24 hours, 5-7 days a week; students can reserve study rooms. Operations spending for the previous fiscal year: $1.3 million. 749 computers available on campus for general student use. Computer purchase/lease plans available. A campuswide network can be accessed from student residence rooms and from off campus. Students can access the following: online class registration. Staffed computer lab on campus (open 24 hours a day) provides training in use of computers, software, and the Internet.

Community Environment: The city's name arose from the fact that the community was the highest point, on the original survey, for the old North Carolina Railroad between Goldsboro and Charlotte. Numerous diversified industries, including many furniture manufacturing plants and hosiery mills, are in High Point, the wood furniture manufacturing and hosiery production capital of the world. Parks, golf courses, and a lake provide the facilities for recreation.

■ **ISOTHERMAL COMMUNITY COLLEGE**
PO Box 804
Spindale, NC 28160-0804
Tel: (828)286-3636
Fax: (828)286-8109
E-mail: vsearcy@isothermal.edu
Web Site: www.isothermal.edu

Description: State-supported, 2-year, coed. Part of North Carolina Community College System. Awards certificates, diplomas, transfer associate, and terminal associate degrees. Founded 1965. Setting: 120-acre rural campus. Total enrollment: 2,005. Faculty: 114 (60 full-time, 54 part-time). Student-undergrad faculty ratio is 17:1. Full-time: 988 students, 64% women, 36% men. Part-time: 1,017 students, 65% women, 35% men. Students come from 3 other countries. 49% 25 or older. Retention: 33% of full-time freshmen returned the following year. Core. Calendar: semesters. Academic remediation for entering students, ESL program, services for LD students, advanced placement, self-designed majors, honors program, summer session for credit, part-time degree program, external degree program, adult/continuing education programs, co-op programs.

Entrance Requirements: Open admission. Options: early admission, deferred admission. Required: high school transcript. Entrance: noncompetitive. Application deadline: rolling. Notification: continuous.

Collegiate Environment: Orientation program. Choral group, student-run newspaper, radio station. Student services: personal-psychological counseling.

Community Environment: Spindale is located 20 miles from Shelby, 28 miles from Hendersonville, and 35 miles from Asheville.

■ **JAMES SPRUNT COMMUNITY COLLEGE**
PO Box 398
Kenansville, NC 28349-0398
Tel: (910)296-2400
Fax: (910)296-1222
E-mail: wedwards@jamessprunt.edu
Web Site: www.jamessprunt.edu

Description: State-supported, 2-year, coed. Part of North Carolina Community College System. Awards certificates, diplomas, transfer associate, and terminal associate degrees. Founded 1964. Setting: 51-acre rural campus with easy access to Raleigh, Wilmington. Endowment: $1.3 million. Educational spending for the previous fiscal year: $4082 per student. Total enrollment: 1,219. Faculty: 72 (34 full-time, 38 part-time). Student-undergrad faculty ratio is 10:1. 1,043 applied, 100% were admitted. Full-time: 424 students, 71% women, 29% men. Part-time: 795 students, 65% women, 35% men. Students come from 3 states and territories, 1% from out-of-state. 0.4% American Indian or Alaska Native, non-Hispanic/Latino; 21% Hispanic/Latino; 28% Black or African American, non-Hispanic/Latino; 0.3% Asian, non-Hispanic/Latino; 0.1% Native Hawaiian or other Pacific Islander, non-Hispanic/Latino; 0.3% international. 22% 25 or older, 6% transferred in. Core. Calendar: semesters. Academic remediation for entering students, ESL program, services for LD students, advanced placement, accelerated degree program, independent study, distance learning, double major, summer session for credit, part-time degree program, co-op programs and internships.

Entrance Requirements: Open admission except for allied health programs. Option: electronic application. Required: high school transcript. Entrance: noncompetitive. Application deadline: rolling. Notification: continuous. Transfer credits accepted: Yes.

Costs Per Year: Application fee: $0. State resident tuition: $2570 full-time, $76 per semester hour part-time. Nonresident tuition: $8714 full-time, $268 per semester hour part-time. Mandatory fees: $76 full-time, $35 per term part-time. Full-time tuition and fees vary according to course load. Part-time tuition and fees vary according to course load.

Collegiate Environment: Orientation program. Student-run newspaper. Social organizations: 4 open to all; national sororities, local sororities; 1% of eligible men and 2% of eligible women are members. Most popular organizations: Student Government Association, Phi Theta Kappa, Scholarly Men of Success, Scholarly Women of Tomorrow. Major annual events: Fall Fest, Spring Fling, Veteran's Day Celebration. Student services: personal-psychological counseling. Campus security: day, evening, and Saturday trained security personnel. James Sprunt Community College Library. Books: 24,762 (physical), 197,656 (digital/electronic); Serial titles: 58 (physical), 24,281 (digital/electronic); Databases: 92. Weekly public service hours: 46. Operations spending for the previous fiscal year: $126,107. 300 computers available on campus for general student use. Computer purchase/lease plans available. A campuswide network can be accessed. Students can access the following: online class registration, online financial aid information. Staffed computer lab on campus provides training in use of computers, software, and the Internet.

Community Environment: Located 40 miles from the principal city of Goldsboro and 4 miles from Interstate 40, Kenansville is a rural community with three churches, a library, and good shopping areas for this size community. The primary businesses of the area are farming, textiles, poultry, and swine production. Good fishing and hunting are available in the area.

■ JOHNSON C. SMITH UNIVERSITY
100 Beatties Ford Rd.
Charlotte, NC 28216-5398
Tel: (704)378-1000; Free: 800-782-7303
E-mail: vbillups@jcsu.edu
Web Site: www.jcsu.edu

Description: Independent, comprehensive, coed. Awards bachelor's and master's degrees. Founded 1867. Setting: 100-acre urban campus with easy access to Atlanta. Endowment: $68.2 million. Research spending for the previous fiscal year: $849,085. Total enrollment: 1,565. Faculty: 164 (87 full-time, 77 part-time). Student-undergrad faculty ratio is 12:1. 6,369 applied, 46% were admitted. Full-time: 1,428 students, 61% women, 39% men. Part-time: 52 students, 48% women, 52% men. Students come from 32 states and territories, 8 other countries, 40% from out-of-state. 0.4% American Indian or Alaska Native, non-Hispanic/Latino; 3% Hispanic/Latino; 85% Black or African American, non-Hispanic/Latino; 0.2% Asian, non-Hispanic/Latino; 0.2% Native Hawaiian or other Pacific Islander, non-Hispanic/Latino; 1% international. 17% 25 or older, 50% live on campus, 4% transferred in. Retention: 69% of full-time freshmen returned the following year. Academic areas with the most degrees conferred: business/marketing; social sciences; public administration and social services. Core. Calendar: semesters. ESL program, services for LD students, advanced placement, accelerated degree program, self-designed majors, independent study, distance learning, double major, summer session for credit, part-time degree program, adult/continuing education programs, co-op programs and internships. Study abroad program.

Entrance Requirements: Options: electronic application, deferred admission, international baccalaureate accepted. Required: high school transcript, SAT or ACT. Recommended: essay, 1 recommendation. Entrance: moderately difficult. Notification: continuous. Transfer credits accepted: Yes.

Costs Per Year: Application fee: $25. Comprehensive fee: $25,336 includes full-time tuition ($18,236) and college room and board ($7100). Full-time tuition varies according to course load. Room and board charges vary according to board plan and housing facility. Part-time tuition: $418 per credit hour. Part-time tuition varies according to course load.

Collegiate Environment: Orientation program. Drama-theater group, choral group, marching band. Social organizations: national fraternities, national sororities. Major annual events: Homecoming, Bullfest, Career Fair. Student services: health clinic, personal-psychological counseling. Campus security: 24-hour emergency response devices and patrols, late night transport-escort service, controlled dormitory access. 1,091 college housing spaces available; 738 were occupied in 2018-19. Freshmen guaranteed college housing. Options: coed, men-only, women-only housing available. James B. Duke Library. Books: 105,422 (physical), 203,337 (digital/electronic); Serial titles: 107 (physical), 23,465 (digital/electronic); Databases: 99. Weekly public service hours: 79; study areas open 24 hours, 5-7 days a week; students can reserve study rooms. Operations spending for the previous fiscal year: $729,813. 125 computers available on campus for general student use. Computer purchase/lease plans available. A campuswide network can be accessed from student residence rooms and from off campus. Students can access the following: online class registration. Staffed computer lab on campus provides training in use of computers, software, and the Internet.

Community Environment: Charlotte, the largest city of the Carolinas, with a population of more than 610,000, is a commercial and cultural center of the South. The city has tall buildings, huge warehouses, and numerous factories, but the residential sections are extensively gardened and beautifully landscaped. The area is rich in historical landmarks. Charlotte offers all the cultural and recreational facilities of any large city, including sports events, excellent shopping and dining facilities, rock and classical music, concerts, theater, and art. The area is served by Southern Railway and five major airlines. Major highways provide easy access to nearby beaches and mountains.

■ JOHNSON & WALES UNIVERSITY
801 W Trade St.
Charlotte, NC 28202
Tel: (980)598-1000; Free: 866-598-2427
E-mail: clt@admissions.jwu.edu
Web Site: www.jwu.edu/charlotte

Description: Independent, 4-year, coed. Awards associate and bachelor's degrees. Founded 2004. Total enrollment: 2,255. Faculty: 120 (90 full-time,

30 part-time). Student-undergrad faculty ratio is 22:1. 4,685 applied, 69% were admitted. Full-time: 2,207 students, 65% women, 35% men. Part-time: 48 students, 54% women, 46% men. 64% from out-of-state. 0.2% American Indian or Alaska Native, non-Hispanic/Latino; 6% Hispanic/Latino; 34% Black or African American, non-Hispanic/Latino; 0.8% Asian, non-Hispanic/Latino; 0.8% international. 9% 25 or older, 56% live on campus, 8% transferred in. Retention: 74% of full-time freshmen returned the following year. Academic areas with the most degrees conferred: family and consumer sciences; business/marketing; parks and recreation. Core. Calendar: quarters. ESL program, services for LD students, advanced placement, accelerated degree program, honors program, independent study, part-time degree program, co-op programs and internships. Study abroad program. ROTC: Army.

Entrance Requirements: Options: electronic application, early admission, deferred admission. Required: high school transcript. Recommended: minimum 2 high school GPA. Required for some: interview, SAT or ACT. Entrance: moderately difficult.

Collegiate Environment: Orientation program. Student-run newspaper. Student services: health clinic, personal-psychological counseling. Campus security: 24-hour emergency response devices and patrols, late night transport-escort service, controlled dormitory access. Johnson & Wales University Library.

■ JOHNSTON COMMUNITY COLLEGE
PO Box 2350
Smithfield, NC 27577-2350
Tel: (919)934-3051
Fax: (919)934-2150
E-mail: mlshaner@johnstoncc.edu
Web Site: www.johnstoncc.edu

Description: State-supported, 2-year, coed. Part of North Carolina Community College System. Awards certificates, diplomas, transfer associate, and terminal associate degrees. Founded 1969. Setting: 100-acre rural campus. Endowment: $6.4 million. Educational spending for the previous fiscal year: $3929 per student. Total enrollment: 4,152. Faculty: 285 (113 full-time, 172 part-time). Full-time: 1,546 students, 60% women, 40% men. Part-time: 2,606 students, 67% women, 33% men. 0.6% American Indian or Alaska Native, non-Hispanic/Latino; 14% Hispanic/Latino; 13% Black or African American, non-Hispanic/Latino; 0.7% Asian, non-Hispanic/Latino; 0.1% Native Hawaiian or other Pacific Islander, non-Hispanic/Latino; 1% international. Calendar: semesters. Academic remediation for entering students, services for LD students, advanced placement, honors program, independent study, distance learning, double major, summer session for credit, part-time degree program, adult/continuing education programs, co-op programs.

Entrance Requirements: Open admission. Options: electronic application, international baccalaureate accepted. Required: high school transcript, interview, NC DAP. Recommended: SAT or ACT. Entrance: noncompetitive. Application deadline: rolling. Notification: continuous.

Costs Per Year: Application fee: $0. State resident tuition: $2432 full-time. Nonresident tuition: $8576 full-time.

Collegiate Environment: Major annual events: Fall Festival, Spring Fling. Student services: personal-psychological counseling. Campus security: 24-hour patrols. College housing not available. Johnston Community College Library plus 1 other. Books: 27,174 (physical), 202,576 (digital/electronic); Serial titles: 64 (physical), 23,465 (digital/electronic); Databases: 131. Weekly public service hours: 57; students can reserve study rooms. Operations spending for the previous fiscal year: $288,181. 98 computers available on campus for general student use. Students can access the following: online class registration. Staffed computer lab on campus provides training in use of computers.

■ LEES-MCRAE COLLEGE
PO Box 128
Banner Elk, NC 28604
Tel: (828)898-5241; Free: 800-280-4562
Fax: (828)898-8814
E-mail: admissions@lmc.edu
Web Site: www.lmc.edu

Description: Independent, 4-year, coed, affiliated with Presbyterian Church (U.S.A.). Awards bachelor's degrees. Founded 1900. Setting: 460-acre rural campus. Endowment: $16.4 million. Educational spending for the previous fiscal year: $5814 per student. Total enrollment: 966. Faculty: 121 (61 full-time, 60 part-time). Student-undergrad faculty ratio is 13:1. 1,462 applied,

57% were admitted. Full-time: 915 students, 64% women, 36% men. Part-time: 49 students, 90% women, 10% men. Students come from 31 states and territories, 16 other countries, 28% from out-of-state. 1% American Indian or Alaska Native, non-Hispanic/Latino; 7% Hispanic/Latino; 8% Black or African American, non-Hispanic/Latino; 0.6% Asian, non-Hispanic/Latino; 0.1% Native Hawaiian or other Pacific Islander, non-Hispanic/Latino; 3% international. 21% 25 or older, 62% live on campus, 18% transferred in. Retention: 66% of full-time freshmen returned the following year. Academic areas with the most degrees conferred: health professions and related sciences; biological/life sciences; law/legal studies. Core. Calendar: semesters. Academic remediation for entering students, services for LD students, advanced placement, accelerated degree program, honors program, independent study, double major, summer session for credit, part-time degree program, adult/continuing education programs, co-op programs and internships. Off campus study. Study abroad program.

Entrance Requirements: Options: electronic application, early action, international baccalaureate accepted. Required: high school transcript, minimum 2 high school GPA. Required for some: essay, interview, SAT or ACT, SAT or ACT scores for prospective intercollegiate athletes and honors program students. Entrance: minimally difficult. Application deadline: rolling. Notification: continuous. Transfer credits accepted: Yes.

Costs Per Year: Application fee: $35. Comprehensive fee: $38,391 includes full-time tuition ($25,625), mandatory fees ($1896), and college room and board ($10,870). College room only: $5320. Part-time tuition: $710 per credit hour. Tuition guaranteed not to increase for student's term of enrollment.

Collegiate Environment: Orientation program. Drama-theater group, choral group. Social organizations: 16 open to all; Service Fraternities and Sororities. Major annual events: Mountain Day, Appalachian Heritage Week, Mountain Day of Service. Student services: health clinic, personal-psychological counseling. Campus security: 24-hour emergency response devices and patrols, controlled dormitory access. 704 college housing spaces available; 593 were occupied in 2018-19. Freshmen guaranteed college housing. Options: coed, men-only, women-only housing available. Dotti M. Shelton Learning Commons. Books: 70,132 (physical), 200,746 (digital/electronic); Serial titles: 225 (physical), 146,361 (digital/electronic); Databases: 144. Students can reserve study rooms. Operations spending for the previous fiscal year: $65,451.

Community Environment: Banner Elk is in the Blue Ridge Mountains of Western North Carolina, 100 miles from Charlotte and 83 miles northeast of Asheville. Elk River is nearby for trout fishing, and during the winter there is sufficient snow for outdoor winter sports.

■ LENOIR COMMUNITY COLLEGE

231 Hwy. 58 S
Kinston, NC 28502-0188
Tel: (252)527-6223
E-mail: krhill01@lenoircc.edu
Web Site: www.lenoircc.edu

Description: State-supported, 2-year, coed. Part of North Carolina Community College System. Awards certificates, diplomas, transfer associate, and terminal associate degrees. Founded 1960. Setting: 86-acre small town campus. Total enrollment: 2,664. Faculty: 130 (83 full-time, 47 part-time). Student-undergrad faculty ratio is 15:1. 1,750 applied, 89% were admitted. Full-time: 1,013 students, 60% women, 40% men. Part-time: 1,651 students, 62% women, 38% men. Students come from 27 states and territories, 1 other country, 3% from out-of-state. 0.6% American Indian or Alaska Native, non-Hispanic/Latino; 8% Hispanic/Latino; 34% Black or African American, non-Hispanic/Latino; 0.6% Asian, non-Hispanic/Latino; 0.1% Native Hawaiian or other Pacific Islander, non-Hispanic/Latino; 0.1% international. 32% 25 or older, 7% transferred in. Core. Calendar: semesters. Academic remediation for entering students, ESL program, advanced placement, independent study, distance learning, double major, summer session for credit, part-time degree program, adult/continuing education programs, co-op programs.

Entrance Requirements: Open admission except for health sciences programs and Basic Law Enforcement Training Program. Options: electronic application, early admission. Required: high school transcript. Recommended: SAT or ACT. Entrance: noncompetitive. Application deadline: rolling. Notification: continuous. Transfer credits accepted: Yes.

Costs Per Year: State resident tuition: $2280 full-time, $76 per credit part-time. Nonresident tuition: $8040 full-time, $268 per credit part-time. Mandatory fees: $119 full-time. Full-time tuition and fees vary according to course load. Part-time tuition varies according to course load.

Collegiate Environment: Orientation program. Choral group. Social

organizations: 25 open to all. Most popular organizations: Student Government Association, Surgical Technology, Computer Engineering, Nightingals, Transitional and Career Studies. Major annual events: Fall Festival, Spring Joust, Fall Orientation. Student services: personal-psychological counseling. Campus security: 24-hour emergency response devices and patrols, student patrols. Learning Resources Center plus 1 other. Books: 26,338 (physical), 370,363 (digital/electronic); Serial titles: 22 (physical), 135,249 (digital/electronic); Databases: 139. Students can reserve study rooms. 116 computers available on campus for general student use. A campuswide network can be accessed. Students can access the following: online class registration. Staffed computer lab on campus provides training in use of computers, software, and the Internet.

Community Environment: Kinston is an important bright-leaf tobacco market as well as a grain and livestock producing region. Commercial transportation is convenient. The community facilities include a library with branches, churches representing 25 denominations, a museum, little theatre, arts council, hospitals, good shopping areas, and various civic and service organizations. Good part-time employment opportunities are available for students. Parks, swimming pools, and golf courses provide the recreational facilities for the community.

■ LENOIR-RHYNE UNIVERSITY

625 7th Ave. NE
Hickory, NC 28601
Tel: (828)328-1741; Free: 800-277-5721
Fax: (828)328-7338
Web Site: www.lr.edu

Description: Independent Lutheran, comprehensive, coed. Awards bachelor's, master's, and doctoral degrees. Founded 1891. Setting: 100-acre small town campus with easy access to Charlotte. Endowment: $106.3 million. Educational spending for the previous fiscal year: $12,318 per student. Total enrollment: 2,557. Faculty: 271 (130 full-time, 141 part-time). Student-undergrad faculty ratio is 13:1. 5,356 applied, 74% were admitted. Full-time: 1,441 students, 57% women, 43% men. Part-time: 258 students, 71% women, 29% men. Students come from 30 states and territories, 24 other countries, 19% from out-of-state. 0.4% American Indian or Alaska Native, non-Hispanic/Latino; 6% Hispanic/Latino; 12% Black or African American, non-Hispanic/Latino; 2% Asian, non-Hispanic/Latino; 3% international. 6% 25 or older, 51% live on campus, 6% transferred in. Retention: 73% of full-time freshmen returned the following year. Academic areas with the most degrees conferred: health professions and related sciences; parks and recreation; business/marketing. Core. Calendar: semesters. Academic remediation for entering students, services for LD students, advanced placement, accelerated degree program, freshman honors college, honors program, independent study, distance learning, double major, summer session for credit, part-time degree program, adult/continuing education programs, internships, graduate courses open to undergrads. Off campus study. Study abroad program.

Entrance Requirements: Options: electronic application, early admission, early action, deferred admission, international baccalaureate accepted. Required: high school transcript, minimum 2.5 high school GPA, SAT or ACT. Recommended: essay, recommendations. Entrance: moderately difficult. Application deadlines: rolling, 11/7 for early action. Notification: continuous, 11/21 for early action. SAT Reasoning Test deadline: 8/1. Transfer credits accepted: Yes.

Costs Per Year: Application fee: $35. Comprehensive fee: $48,910 includes full-time tuition ($36,400) and college room and board ($12,510). Room and board charges vary according to board plan. Part-time tuition: $1500 per credit.

Collegiate Environment: Orientation program. Drama-theater group, choral group, marching band, student-run newspaper, radio station. Social organizations: 58 open to all; national sororities, local fraternities; 9% of eligible men and 13% of eligible women are members. Most popular organizations: Circle K, CAB, Nu Generation, Greek Organizations, Sign Troupe. Major annual events: Homecoming, The Red Carpet Event, The Final Flip (exam pancake breakfasts). Student services: health clinic, personal-psychological counseling. Campus security: 24-hour emergency response devices and patrols, late night transport-escort service, controlled dormitory access. Carl Rudisill Library. Books: 121,005 (physical), 537,443 (digital/electronic); Serial titles: 49 (physical), 28,271 (digital/electronic); Databases: 135. Weekly public service hours: 89. Operations spending for the previous fiscal year: $1.1 million. 150 computers available on campus for general student use. Computer purchase/lease plans available. A campuswide network can be accessed from student residence rooms and from off campus. Students can access the following: online class registration.

Community Environment: Hickory, located in the western Piedmont section, is best known as one of North Carolina's major furniture manufacturing cities. All forms of commercial transportation are available. The community facilities include hospitals, numerous churches, a museum of art, a city library, and various civic and service organizations. Nearby, Lake Hickory offers many recreational opportunities such as boating, fishing, and swimming, golf, and minor league baseball. Hickory is located 50 miles NW of Charlotte and just 40 miles from the Blue Ridge Mountains.

■ **LIVING ARTS COLLEGE**
3000 Wakefield Crossing Dr.
Raleigh, NC 27614
Tel: (919)488-8500; Free: 800-288-7442
E-mail: jwenta@living-arts-college.edu
Web Site: www.living-arts-college.edu

Description: Proprietary, 4-year, coed. Awards associate and bachelor's degrees. Founded 1992. Setting: suburban campus with easy access to Raleigh. Total enrollment: 578. Faculty: 53 (37 full-time, 16 part-time). Student-undergrad faculty ratio is 10:1. 95 applied, 100% were admitted. Students come from 8 states and territories, 1 other country, 1% from out-of-state. 33% 25 or older, 35% live on campus. Retention: 69% of full-time freshmen returned the following year. Core. Calendar: quarters. Summer session for credit, co-op programs.

Entrance Requirements: Options: electronic application, early admission, early decision, early action, deferred admission. Required: essay, high school transcript, interview, Wonderlic aptitude test. Required for some: portfolio. Entrance: moderately difficult. Application deadlines: rolling, rolling for early action. Notification: continuous, rolling for early action. Transfer credits accepted: Yes.

Collegiate Environment: Orientation program. Social organizations: 4 open to all. Most popular organizations: MODIV (student council), Student Ambassadors, Firebreathers Animation Studio, NVTHS (National Vocational Technical Honor Society). Major annual events: Career Fair, Student Advising Day/Professional Development, Student Talent Show. Campus security: controlled dormitory access. 420 computers available on campus for general student use. A campuswide network can be accessed. Staffed computer lab on campus provides training in use of computers, software, and the Internet.

■ **LIVINGSTONE COLLEGE**
701 W Monroe St.
Salisbury, NC 28144-5298
Tel: (704)216-6000; Free: 800-835-3435
Fax: (704)216-6217
E-mail: admissions@livingstone.edu
Web Site: www.livingstone.edu

Description: Independent, 4-year, coed, affiliated with African Methodist Episcopal Zion Church. Awards bachelor's degrees. Founded 1879. Setting: 45-acre small town campus. Endowment: $1.8 million. Educational spending for the previous fiscal year: $5782 per student. Total enrollment: 1,175. Faculty: 73 (51 full-time, 22 part-time). Student-undergrad faculty ratio is 15:1. 3,110 applied, 72% were admitted. 0.3% from top 10% of their high school class, 3% from top quarter, 15% from top half. Full-time: 1,164 students, 44% women, 56% men. Part-time: 11 students, 45% women, 55% men. Students come from 30 states and territories, 2 other countries, 35% from out-of-state. 0.5% American Indian or Alaska Native, non-Hispanic/Latino; 0.9% Hispanic/Latino; 91% Black or African American, non-Hispanic/Latino; 0.1% Asian, non-Hispanic/Latino; 0.3% international. 8% 25 or older, 60% live on campus. Retention: 50% of full-time freshmen returned the following year. Core. Calendar: semesters. Academic remediation for entering students, advanced placement, honors program, double major, part-time degree program, adult/continuing education programs, co-op programs and internships. ROTC: Army (c).

Entrance Requirements: Options: deferred admission, international baccalaureate accepted. Required: high school transcript, minimum 2 high school GPA, SAT or ACT. Entrance: minimally difficult. Application deadline: rolling. Notification: continuous.

Collegiate Environment: Orientation program. Drama-theater group, choral group, marching band. Social organizations: 35 open to all; national fraternities, national sororities; 25% of eligible men and 30% of eligible women are members. Most popular organizations: Greek Organizations, Modeling Troups, choirs, band, Rotary and Optimist Clubs (Community). Major annual

events: Homecoming, Greek Week, Bear Fest (Spring Fling). Student services: health clinic, personal-psychological counseling. Campus security: 24-hour emergency response devices and patrols, late night transport-escort service, controlled dormitory access. Carnegie Library plus 2 others. Operations spending for the previous fiscal year: $176,537. 100 computers available on campus for general student use. A campuswide network can be accessed from student residence rooms. Staffed computer lab on campus provides training in use of computers, software, and the Internet.

Community Environment: See Catawba College.

■ **LOUISBURG COLLEGE**
501 N Main St.
Louisburg, NC 27549-2399
Tel: (919)496-2521; Free: 800-775-0208
Fax: (919)496-1788
E-mail: admissions@louisburg.edu
Web Site: www.louisburg.edu

Description: Independent United Methodist, 2-year, coed. Awards transfer associate and terminal associate degrees. Founded 1787. Setting: 75-acre small town campus with easy access to Raleigh. Endowment: $9.7 million. Research spending for the previous fiscal year: $20,300. Educational spending for the previous fiscal year: $4329 per student. Total enrollment: 730. Faculty: 83 (45 full-time, 38 part-time). Student-undergrad faculty ratio is 13:1. 1,099 applied, 62% were admitted. 2% from top 10% of their high school class, 5% from top quarter, 19% from top half. Full-time: 717 students, 38% women, 62% men. Part-time: 13 students, 38% women, 62% men. Students come from 22 states and territories, 4 other countries, 34% from out-of-state. 4% 25 or older, 90% live on campus, 7% transferred in. Retention: 76% of full-time freshmen returned the following year. Core. Calendar: semesters. Academic remediation for entering students, services for LD students, advanced placement, accelerated degree program, self-designed majors, freshman honors college, honors program, independent study, distance learning, double major, part-time degree program, adult/continuing education programs. Off campus study.

Entrance Requirements: Option: deferred admission. Required: high school transcript, SAT or ACT. Required for some: interview. Entrance: minimally difficult. Application deadline: rolling. Notification: continuous.

Collegiate Environment: Orientation program. Drama-theater group, choral group, student-run newspaper, radio station. Social organizations: 12 open to all. Most popular organizations: Student Government Association, Workers Actively Volunteering Energetic Services, Drama Club, Christian Life Council, Ecological Concerns Club. Major annual events: Homecoming, Mud-Volleyball, Spring Dance. Student services: health clinic, personal-psychological counseling. Campus security: 24-hour emergency response devices and patrols, late night transport-escort service, controlled dormitory access. Robbins Library. Operations spending for the previous fiscal year: $148,590. 30 computers available on campus for general student use. A campuswide network can be accessed from student residence rooms and from off campus. Staffed computer lab on campus.

Community Environment: Louisburg, a county seat, is 30 miles from Raleigh, the state capital, where all forms of transportation are available. A hospital, churches, good shopping facilities, and various civic and social organizations are found in the community. There are many part-time job opportunities.

■ **MARS HILL UNIVERSITY**
PO Box 370
Mars Hill, NC 28754
Tel: (828)689-1307; Free: 866-648-4968
Fax: (828)689-1474
E-mail: admissions@mhu.edu
Web Site: www.mhu.edu

Description: Independent Baptist, comprehensive, coed. Awards bachelor's and master's degrees. Founded 1856. Setting: 194-acre small town campus. Endowment: $42 million. Educational spending for the previous fiscal year: $6166 per student. Total enrollment: 1,410. Faculty: 147 (91 full-time, 56 part-time). Student-undergrad faculty ratio is 12:1. 3,010 applied, 61% were admitted. 5% from top 10% of their high school class, 19% from top quarter, 56% from top half. Full-time: 1,284 students, 49% women, 51% men. Part-time: 111 students, 68% women, 32% men. Students come from 30 states and territories, 19 other countries, 26% from out-of-state. 1% American Indian or Alaska Native, non-Hispanic/Latino; 3% Hispanic/Latino; 22% Black or African American, non-Hispanic/Latino; 0.9% Asian, non-Hispanic/Latino; 0.1% Native Hawaiian or other Pacific Islander, non-Hispanic/Latino.

14% 25 or older, 69% live on campus, 7% transferred in. Retention: 59% of full-time freshmen returned the following year. Academic areas with the most degrees conferred: business/marketing; education; biological/life sciences. Core. Calendar: semesters. Academic remediation for entering students, ESL program, services for LD students, advanced placement, accelerated degree program, self-designed majors, honors program, independent study, double major, summer session for credit, part-time degree program, adult/continuing education programs, co-op programs and internships. Study abroad program.

Entrance Requirements: Options: electronic application, early admission, deferred admission, international baccalaureate accepted. Required: high school transcript, minimum 2 high school GPA, SAT or ACT. Recommended: essay, minimum 3 high school GPA. Required for some: interview. Entrance: moderately difficult. Application deadline: rolling. Transfer credits accepted: Yes.

Costs Per Year: Application fee: $25. Comprehensive fee: $42,560 includes full-time tuition ($32,968) and college room and board ($9592). Room and board charges vary according to housing facility.

Collegiate Environment: Orientation program. Drama-theater group, choral group, marching band. Social organizations: 35 open to all; national fraternities, national sororities, local fraternities, local sororities; 7% of eligible men and 16% of eligible women are members. Most popular organizations: Student Government Association, Fellowship of Christian Athletes, Christian Student Movement, Fraternity/Sorority, Athletic Trainers Association. Major annual events: Homecoming, Fall Festival, Spring Fling. Student services: health clinic, personal-psychological counseling. Campus security: 24-hour emergency response devices and patrols, late night transport-escort service, controlled dormitory access. Renfro Library plus 1 other. Books: 88,868 (physical), 139,088 (digital/electronic); Databases: 133. Operations spending for the previous fiscal year: $363,455. 188 computers available on campus for general student use. A campuswide network can be accessed from student residence rooms and from off campus. Students can access the following: online class registration. Staffed computer lab on campus provides training in use of computers, software, and the Internet.

Community Environment: Mars Hill is located 17 miles north of Asheville and 10 miles from Marshall. Plane and bus transportation are available. Community facilities include a medical center and convenient shopping.

■ MARTIN COMMUNITY COLLEGE

1161 Kehukee Park Rd.
Williamston, NC 27892
Tel: (252)792-1521
Fax: (252)792-4425
Web Site: www.martincc.edu

Description: State-supported, 2-year, coed. Part of North Carolina Community College System. Awards certificates, diplomas, transfer associate, and terminal associate degrees. Founded 1968. Setting: 65-acre rural campus. Total enrollment: 890. Calendar: semesters. Academic remediation for entering students, services for LD students, advanced placement, independent study, distance learning, summer session for credit, part-time degree program, co-op programs and internships. Off campus study.

Entrance Requirements: Open admission except for physical therapy assistant and dental assistant programs. Option: electronic application. Required: high school transcript. Entrance: noncompetitive. Application deadline: rolling. Notification: continuous until 8/17. Transfer credits accepted: Yes.

Collegiate Environment: Orientation program. Most popular organizations: Phi Theta Kappa, Student Government Association, Alpha Beta Gamma, Physical Therapy Club, Equine Club. Major annual events: Stampede in the Park, Spring Fling, Fall Festival. Student services: personal-psychological counseling. Campus security: 24-hour emergency response devices, part-time patrols by trained security personnel. Martin Community College Learning Resources Center. 215 computers available on campus for general student use. A campuswide network can be accessed from off-campus. Staffed computer lab on campus.

Community Environment: The college is located in the center of a prosperous agricultural area. Recreational facilities include tennis courts, parks, and several ball fields. The area is ideal for hunting, fishing, and camping. The Senator Bob Martin Eastern Agricultural Center attracts horse shows, rodeos, bull riding, concerts, and many other events.

■ MAYLAND COMMUNITY COLLEGE

PO Box 547
Spruce Pine, NC 28777-0547
Tel: (828)765-7351; Free: 800-462-9526
Fax: (828)765-0728
Web Site: www.mayland.edu

Description: State and locally supported, 2-year, coed. Part of North Carolina Community College System. Awards certificates, diplomas, transfer associate, and terminal associate degrees. Founded 1971. Setting: 38-acre rural campus. Total enrollment: 1,472. 39% 25 or older. Calendar: semesters. Academic remediation for entering students, services for LD students, advanced placement, independent study, distance learning, double major, summer session for credit, part-time degree program, adult/continuing education programs, co-op programs and internships.

Entrance Requirements: Open admission. Options: electronic application, deferred admission. Required: high school transcript. Required for some: CPT for nursing program. Entrance: noncompetitive. Application deadline: rolling. Notification: continuous.

Collegiate Environment: Student services: personal-psychological counseling. Carolyn Munro Wilson Learning Resources Center plus 1 other.

Community Environment: Mayland Community College is located in the Blue Ridge Mountains of Western North Carolina. The Main Campus is located on Highway 19E, two miles east of Spruce Pine.

■ MCDOWELL TECHNICAL COMMUNITY COLLEGE

54 College Dr.
Marion, NC 28752-9724
Tel: (828)652-6021
Fax: (828)652-1014
E-mail: rickw@mcdowelltech.edu
Web Site: www.mcdowelltech.edu

Description: State-supported, 2-year, coed. Part of North Carolina Community College System. Awards certificates, diplomas, transfer associate, and terminal associate degrees. Founded 1964. Setting: 31-acre rural campus. Total enrollment: 1,134. Faculty: 58 (40 full-time, 18 part-time). 50% 25 or older. Core. Calendar: semesters. Academic remediation for entering students, ESL program, services for LD students, accelerated degree program, independent study, distance learning, summer session for credit, part-time degree program, adult/continuing education programs, co-op programs.

Entrance Requirements: Open admission except for registered nursing, licensed practical nursing programs. Options: early admission, deferred admission. Required for some: high school transcript. Entrance: noncompetitive. Application deadline: rolling. Notification: continuous.

Collegiate Environment: Student services: personal-psychological counseling. Campus security: 24-hour emergency response devices.

Community Environment: Located in the foothills of the Blue Ridge Mountains, Marion enjoys a temperate climate. Trains, buses, and airlines provide the commercial transportation. To serve the people of this community, there are 96 churches and medical facilities. 26 major industries are located here, furnishing part-time job opportunities for students. Outdoor recreational facilities include the Blue Ridge Parkway, Mt Mitchell State Park, Lake James and Lake Tahoma.

■ MEREDITH COLLEGE

3800 Hillsborough St.
Raleigh, NC 27607-5298
Tel: (919)760-8600; Free: 800-MEREDITH
Fax: (919)829-2348
E-mail: admissions@meredith.edu
Web Site: www.meredith.edu

Description: Independent, comprehensive. Awards bachelor's and master's degrees. Founded 1891. Setting: 225-acre urban campus. Total enrollment: 1,981. Faculty: 222 (131 full-time, 91 part-time). Student-undergrad faculty ratio is 12:1. 1,737 applied, 69% were admitted. 17% from top 10% of their high school class, 45% from top quarter, 85% from top half. Full-time: 1,600 students, 100% women. Part-time: 82 students, 98% women, 2% men. Students come from 31 states and territories, 33 other countries, 12% from out-of-state. 0.8% American Indian or Alaska Native, non-Hispanic/Latino; 8% Hispanic/Latino; 8% Black or African American, non-Hispanic/Latino; 3% Asian, non-Hispanic/Latino; 0.1% Native Hawaiian or other Pacific Islander, non-Hispanic/Latino; 2% international. 6% 25 or older, 54% live on campus, 5% transferred in. Retention: 80% of full-time freshmen returned the following year. Academic areas with the most degrees conferred: business/marketing; biological/life sciences; visual and performing arts; psychology. Core. Calendar: semesters. Academic remediation for entering students, services for LD students, advanced placement, accelerated degree program, self-designed majors, honors program, independent study, double major, summer session for credit, part-time degree program, co-op programs and internships, graduate courses open to undergrads. Off campus study at Cooperating Raleigh Colleges. Study abroad program. ROTC: Army (c), Air Force (c).

Entrance Requirements: Options: electronic application, early admission, early decision, deferred admission, international baccalaureate accepted. Required: high school transcript, minimum 2 high school GPA, 2 recommendations, SAT or ACT. Recommended: essay. Required for some: essay, interview. Entrance: moderately difficult. Application deadlines: 2/15, 10/15 for early decision. Notification: continuous, 11/1 for early decision. SAT Reasoning Test deadline: 6/30. Transfer credits accepted: Yes.

Costs Per Year: Application fee: $40. Comprehensive fee: $48,106 includes full-time tuition ($37,076), mandatory fees ($100), and college room and board ($10,930). Full-time tuition and fees vary according to course load. Room and board charges vary according to board plan and housing facility. Part-time tuition: $920 per credit hour. Part-time mandatory fees: $50 per term. Part-time tuition and fees vary according to course load.

Collegiate Environment: Orientation program. Drama-theater group, choral group, student-run newspaper. Social organizations: 100 open to all. Most popular organizations: Student Government Association, Entertainment Association, Recreation Association, Class Organizations, choral groups. Major annual events: Cornhuskin', Day of Celebration, Spring Formal. Student services: health clinic, personal-psychological counseling. Campus security: 24-hour emergency response devices and patrols, late night transport-escort service, controlled dormitory access. Carlyle Campbell Library.

Community Environment: Meredith is located at the western edge of Raleigh, NC, the state capital and home of five other colleges and universities. The area is served by air, bus and rail. The campus is easily accessible from I-40, bordered by US 1 and Wade Avenue, with the front entrance facing Hillsborough Street. Raleigh is a part of the Research Triangle Area, which includes Durham and Chapel Hill, NC. It is a cultural center with the N.C. Museums of Art, History and Natural Science, the North Carolina Symphony and numerous theaters. Meredith itself is a center for many cultural events including the Fletcher School of the Performing Arts and the National Opera Company.

■ METHODIST UNIVERSITY

5400 Ramsey St.
Fayetteville, NC 28311-1498
Tel: (910)630-7000; Free: 800-488-7110
Fax: (910)630-7317
E-mail: admissions@methodist.edu
Web Site: www.methodist.edu

Description: Independent United Methodist, comprehensive, coed. Awards associate, bachelor's, and master's degrees. Founded 1956. Setting: 600-acre suburban campus with easy access to Raleigh-Durham. Endowment: $13.9 million. Educational spending for the previous fiscal year: $18,078 per student. Total enrollment: 2,416. Faculty: 213 (127 full-time, 86 part-time). Student-undergrad faculty ratio is 12:1. 2,904 applied, 63% were admitted. 10% from top 10% of their high school class, 33% from top quarter, 77% from top half. 28 class presidents, 3 valedictorians, 200 student government officers. Full-time: 1,930 students, 45% women, 55% men. Part-time: 287 students, 54% women, 46% men. Students come from 41 states and territories, 53 other countries, 47% from out-of-state. 1% American Indian or Alaska Native, non-Hispanic/Latino; 4% Hispanic/Latino; 22% Black or African American, non-Hispanic/Latino; 1% Asian, non-Hispanic/Latino; 0.4% Native Hawaiian or other Pacific Islander, non-Hispanic/Latino; 5% international. 24% 25 or older, 57% live on campus, 12% transferred in. Retention: 67% of full-time freshmen returned the following year. Academic areas with the most degrees conferred: business/marketing; social sciences; parks and recreation. Core. Calendar: semesters. Academic remediation for entering students, ESL program, services for LD students, advanced placement, accelerated degree program, honors program, independent study, distance learning, double major, summer session for credit, part-time degree program, adult/continuing education programs, co-op programs and internships. Study abroad program. ROTC: Army, Air Force (c).

Entrance Requirements: Options: deferred admission, international baccalaureate accepted. Required: high school transcript, SAT or ACT. Recommended: interview. Required for some: essay, interview. Entrance: moderately difficult. Application deadlines: rolling, rolling for nonresidents. Notification: 8/15.

Costs Per Year: Application fee: $25. Comprehensive fee: $46,511 includes full-time tuition ($33,480), mandatory fees ($366), and college room and board ($12,665). College room only: $6365. Full-time tuition and fees vary according to class time. Room and board charges vary according to housing facility.

Collegiate Environment: Orientation program. Drama-theater group, choral group, marching band, student-run newspaper. Social organizations: 76 open to all; national fraternities, national sororities, local fraternities, local sororities; 2% of eligible men and 3% of eligible women are members. Most popular organizations: Student Activities Committee, Student Government Association, Student Education Association, Fellowship of Christian Athletes, Residence Hall Association. Major annual events: Homecoming, Spring Fling, Show You Care Day. Student services: health clinic, personal-psychological counseling. Campus security: 24-hour emergency response devices and patrols, student patrols, late night transport-escort service, controlled dormitory access, regular patrol by county sheriff department. Davis Memorial Library plus 1 other. Operations spending for the previous fiscal year: $252,675. 200 computers available on campus for general student use. Computer purchase/lease plans available. A campuswide network can be accessed from student residence rooms and from off campus. Students can access the following: online class registration. Staffed computer lab on campus provides training in use of computers, software, and the Internet.

Community Environment: Fayetteville, a community of 105,000, is part of the Carolina Sandhills region in the heart of golf country and two hours from the coast. It is accessible by air, rail, and highway. Its economy is based on agriculture, manufacturing and processing, distribution, and the government. The community has 4 hospitals, a public library with 8 branches, an art guild, theater, art museum, symphony, and brass band. There are 53 public and private golf courses within an hour's drive of the city. Popular sports include golf, tennis, archery, boating, and skating.

■ MID-ATLANTIC CHRISTIAN UNIVERSITY

715 N Poindexter St.
Elizabeth City, NC 27909-4054
Tel: (252)334-2070; Free: 866-996-MACU
Fax: (252)334-2071
Web Site: www.macuniversity.edu

Description: Independent Christian, 4-year, coed. Awards associate and bachelor's degrees. Founded 1948. Setting: 19-acre small town campus with easy access to Norfolk. Endowment: $3.1 million. Educational spending for the previous fiscal year: $28,900 per student. Total enrollment: 192. Faculty: 33 (12 full-time, 21 part-time). Student-undergrad faculty ratio is 11:1. 189 applied, 53% were admitted. 11% from top 10% of their high school class, 23% from top quarter, 63% from top half. Full-time: 166 students, 56% women, 44% men. Part-time: 26 students, 50% women, 50% men. Students come from 17 states and territories, 3 other countries, 34% from out-of-state. 0.5% American Indian or Alaska Native, non-Hispanic/Latino; 6% Hispanic/Latino; 19% Black or African American, non-Hispanic/Latino; 0.5% Asian, non-Hispanic/Latino; 2% international. 17% 25 or older, 64% live on campus, 5% transferred in. Retention: 63% of full-time freshmen returned the following year. Academic areas with the most degrees conferred: theology and religious vocations; business/marketing; psychology; education. Core. Calendar: semesters. Academic remediation for entering students, advanced placement, distance learning, double major, summer session for credit, part-time degree program, adult/continuing education programs, internships. ROTC: Army (c).

Entrance Requirements: Options: electronic application, early admission, deferred admission, international baccalaureate accepted. Required: essay, high school transcript, minimum 2 high school GPA, 1 recommendation, reference from church or character reference. Required for some: interview, SAT or ACT. Entrance: minimally difficult. Application deadline: 8/1. Notification: continuous. Transfer credits accepted: Yes.

Costs Per Year: Application fee: $50. Comprehensive fee: $23,450 includes full-time tuition ($14,400), mandatory fees ($450), and college room and board ($8600). Full-time tuition and fees vary according to program. Room and board charges vary according to housing facility. Part-time tuition: $450 per credit hour. Part-time mandatory fees: $55 per credit hour. Part-time tuition and fees vary according to program.

Collegiate Environment: Orientation program. Social organizations: national sororities. Major annual event: Alumni Rally and Homecoming. Student services: personal-psychological counseling. Campus security: 24-hour emergency response devices, controlled dormitory access. Watson-Griffith Library. Books: 33,941 (physical), 1,572 (digital/electronic). Students can reserve study rooms. Operations spending for the previous fiscal year:

$139,038. 24 computers available on campus for general student use. A campuswide network can be accessed. Students can access the following: online class registration.

■ MILLER-MOTTE COLLEGE (CARY)
2205 Walnut St.
Cary, NC 27518
Tel: (919)532-7171; Free: 800-705-9182
Web Site: www.miller-motte.edu
Description: Proprietary, 2-year, coed. Awards certificates, transfer associate, and terminal associate degrees.

■ MILLER-MOTTE COLLEGE (FAYETTEVILLE)
3725 Ramsey St.
Fayetteville, NC 28311
Tel: (910)354-1900; Free: 800-705-9182
Web Site: www.miller-motte.edu
Description: Proprietary, 2-year, coed. Awards certificates, transfer associate, and terminal associate degrees.

■ MILLER-MOTTE COLLEGE (JACKSONVILLE)
1291 Hargett St.
Jacksonville, NC 28540
Tel: (910)478-4300; Free: 800-705-9182
Web Site: www.miller-motte.edu
Description: Proprietary, 2-year, coed. Awards certificates, transfer associate, and terminal associate degrees.

■ MILLER-MOTTE COLLEGE (RALEIGH)
3901 Capital Blvd.
Ste. 151
Raleigh, NC 27604
Tel: (919)723-2820; Free: 800-705-9182
Web Site: www.miller-motte.edu
Description: Proprietary, 2-year, coed. Awards certificates, transfer associate, and terminal associate degrees.

■ MILLER-MOTTE COLLEGE (WILMINGTON)
5000 Market St.
Wilmington, NC 28405
Tel: (910)392-4660; Free: 800-705-9182
Fax: (910)799-6224
Web Site: www.miller-motte.edu
Description: Proprietary, 2-year, coed. Awards terminal associate degrees. Founded 1989. Total enrollment: 707. 240 applied, 50% were admitted. Calendar: quarters.
Entrance Requirements: Required: high school transcript.

■ MITCHELL COMMUNITY COLLEGE
500 W Broad St.
Statesville, NC 28677
Tel: (704)878-3200
Fax: (704)878-0872
Web Site: www.mitchellcc.edu
Description: State-supported, 2-year, coed. Part of North Carolina Community College System. Awards certificates, diplomas, transfer associate, and terminal associate degrees. Founded 1852. Setting: 14-acre small town campus with easy access to Charlotte. Endowment: $18.4 million. Educational spending for the previous fiscal year: $3486 per student. Total enrollment: 3,164. Faculty: 170 (86 full-time, 84 part-time). Student-undergrad faculty ratio is 18:1. 1,679 applied, 100% were admitted. Full-time: 974 students, 56% women, 44% men. Part-time: 2,190 students, 62% women, 38% men. 0.4% American Indian or Alaska Native, non-Hispanic/Latino; 11% Hispanic/Latino; 11% Black or African American, non-Hispanic/Latino; 2% Asian, non-Hispanic/Latino; 0.1% Native Hawaiian or other Pacific Islander, non-Hispanic/Latino; 0.9% international. 33% 25 or older, 6% transferred in. Retention: 51% of full-time freshmen returned the following year. Core. Calendar: semesters. Academic remediation for entering students, ESL program, services for LD students, advanced placement, distance learning, summer session for credit, part-time degree program, adult/continuing education programs, co-op programs.
Entrance Requirements: Open admission All except for the nursing program are open admissions. Option: electronic application. Required: high

school transcript. Entrance: noncompetitive. Application deadline: rolling. Notification: continuous. Transfer credits accepted: Yes.
Costs Per Year: Application fee: $0. State resident tuition: $2432 full-time, $76 per credit hour part-time. Nonresident tuition: $8576 full-time, $268 per credit hour part-time. Mandatory fees: $218 full-time, $5.50 per credit hour part-time, $36.25 per term part-time.
Collegiate Environment: Orientation program. Choral group. Social organizations: 18 open to all. Most popular organizations: Cosmetology Club, Early Childhood Association, Student Nurses Association, Phi Theta Kappa, Student Government Association. Major annual events: New Student Orientation, Welcome Week, Fall and Spring Week. Student services: personal-psychological counseling. Campus security: late night transport-escort service, day and evening security guards. College housing not available. Huskins Library. Books: 14,669 (physical), 203,337 (digital/electronic); Serial titles: 2 (physical), 23,468 (digital/electronic); Databases: 93. Students can reserve study rooms. Operations spending for the previous fiscal year: $222,554. 50 computers available on campus for general student use. A campuswide network can be accessed. Students can access the following: online class registration. Staffed computer lab on campus provides training in use of computers, software, and the Internet.
Community Environment: On a plateau, surrounded by the foothills of the Blue Ridge Mountains, Statesville is in the heart of the Piedmont area. Industrial products and textiles, metal, and furniture are produced there. This is also a large milk-producing area. All forms of commercial transportation are available. There are churches of all denominations along with the various civic and service organizations. Excellent part-time job opportunities are available.

■ MONTGOMERY COMMUNITY COLLEGE
1011 Page St.
Troy, NC 27371
Tel: (910)898-9600; Free: 877-572-6222
Fax: (910)576-2176
Web Site: www.montgomery.edu
Description: State-supported, 2-year, coed. Part of North Carolina Community College System. Awards certificates, diplomas, transfer associate, and terminal associate degrees. Founded 1967. Setting: 159-acre rural campus. Total enrollment: 925. Faculty: 186 (33 full-time, 153 part-time). Student-undergrad faculty ratio is 8:1. Students come from 11 states and territories, 1% from out-of-state. 1% American Indian or Alaska Native, non-Hispanic/Latino; 17% Hispanic/Latino; 18% Black or African American, non-Hispanic/Latino; 2% Asian, non-Hispanic/Latino; 0.1% Native Hawaiian or other Pacific Islander, non-Hispanic/Latino; 0.3% international. 29% 25 or older. Retention: 70% of full-time freshmen returned the following year. Core. Calendar: semesters. Academic remediation for entering students, ESL program, services for LD students, advanced placement, distance learning, summer session for credit, part-time degree program.
Entrance Requirements: Open admission. Options: electronic application, early admission, deferred admission. Required: high school transcript. Entrance: noncompetitive. Application deadline: rolling. Notification: continuous. Transfer credits accepted: Yes.
Collegiate Environment: Orientation program. Social organizations: 10 open to all. Most popular organizations: Student Government Association, Nursing Club, Gunsmithing Society, Medical Assisting Club, Forestry Club. Major annual events: Spring Fling, Polar Volleyball, Holiday Feast. Student services: personal-psychological counseling. Campus security: 24-hour emergency response devices. Montgomery Community College Learning Resource Center. Books: 17,572 (physical), 197,546 (digital/electronic); Serial titles: 55 (physical), 24,280 (digital/electronic); Databases: 104. Weekly public service hours: 55; students can reserve study rooms. Operations spending for the previous fiscal year: $150,936. 46 computers available on campus for general student use. A campuswide network can be accessed. Students can access the following: online class registration. Staffed computer lab on campus provides training in use of computers, software, and the Internet.
Community Environment: Troy is located 50 miles from Greensboro where the main industries are lumber and textiles. Train transportation is available with air travel convenient to Greensboro and Charlotte. The Pee Dee River is 12 miles away providing facilities for water skiing, fishing, and boating.

■ MONTREAT COLLEGE
PO Box 1267
Montreat, NC 28757-1267
Tel: (828)669-8012; Free: 800-622-6968

Fax: (828)669-0120

E-mail: admissions@montreat.edu

Web Site: www.montreat.edu

Description: Independent, comprehensive, coed, affiliated with Presbyterian Church (U.S.A.). Awards associate, bachelor's, and master's degrees. Founded 1916. Setting: 112-acre small town campus. Total enrollment: 1,008. Faculty: 150 (31 full-time, 119 part-time). Student-undergrad faculty ratio is 12:1. 819 applied, 54% were admitted. 9% from top 10% of their high school class, 26% from top quarter, 60% from top half. Full-time: 506 students, 47% women, 53% men. Part-time: 302 students, 65% women, 35% men. 58% from out-of-state. 1% American Indian or Alaska Native, non-Hispanic/Latino; 3% Hispanic/Latino; 16% Black or African American, non-Hispanic/Latino; 2% Asian, non-Hispanic/Latino; 0.3% Native Hawaiian or other Pacific Islander, non-Hispanic/Latino; 5% international. 4% 25 or older, 80% live on campus, 8% transferred in. Retention: 59% of full-time freshmen returned the following year. Academic areas with the most degrees conferred: business/marketing; psychology; biological/life sciences. Core. Calendar: semesters. Services for LD students, advanced placement, accelerated degree program, self-designed majors, honors program, independent study, distance learning, double major, summer session for credit, part-time degree program, adult/continuing education programs, co-op programs and internships. Off campus study. Study abroad program.

Entrance Requirements: Options: early admission, deferred admission, international baccalaureate accepted. Required: essay, high school transcript, minimum 2.75 high school GPA, SAT or ACT. Required for some: 1 recommendation, interview. Entrance: moderately difficult. SAT Reasoning Test deadline: 8/1. SAT Subject Test deadline: 8/1.

Costs Per Year: Application fee: $0. Comprehensive fee: $39,750 includes full-time tuition ($28,600), mandatory fees ($1450), and college room and board ($9700). Full-time tuition and fees vary according to course load and degree level. Room and board charges vary according to board plan and housing facility.

Collegiate Environment: Orientation program. Drama-theater group, choral group, student-run newspaper. Major annual events: King of Hearts Men's Pageant, Winter Ball, Downhill Derby. Student services: health clinic, personal-psychological counseling. Campus security: 24-hour emergency response devices and patrols, controlled dormitory access. L. Nelson Bell Library.

Community Environment: Montreat is situated in the beautiful Blue Ridge Mountains, 17 miles from Asheville, and adjacent to the historic town of Black Mountain with picturesque avenues, stores, and restaurants. The climate is recognized as one of the world's finest and the region has long been a major vacation area. Montreat's recreational activities include golf, tennis, skiing, baseball, and basketball, as well as access to the Pisgah National Forest.

■ NASH COMMUNITY COLLEGE

522 N Old Carriage Rd.

Rocky Mount, NC 27804

Tel: (252)443-4011

Fax: (252)443-0828

E-mail: dgardner@nashcc.edu

Web Site: www.nashcc.edu

Description: State-supported, 2-year, coed. Part of North Carolina Community College System. Awards certificates, diplomas, transfer associate, and terminal associate degrees. Founded 1967. Setting: 69-acre rural campus. Total enrollment: 2,916. 41% 25 or older. Calendar: semesters. Academic remediation for entering students, ESL program, services for LD students, advanced placement, independent study, distance learning, double major, summer session for credit, part-time degree program, adult/continuing education programs.

Entrance Requirements: Open admission except for nursing, physical therapy assistant, cosmetology, phlebotomy programs. Option: deferred admission. Required: high school transcript. Recommended: interview. Required for some: SAT and SAT Subject Tests or ACT, ACT ASSET or ACT Compass. Entrance: noncompetitive. Application deadline: rolling. Notification: continuous.

Collegiate Environment: Orientation program. Student-run newspaper. Campus security: 24-hour emergency response devices, late night transport-escort service. Nash Community College Library plus 1 other.

Community Environment: See North Carolina Wesleyan College.

■ NORTH CAROLINA AGRICULTURAL AND TECHNICAL STATE UNIVERSITY

1601 E Market St.

Greensboro, NC 27411

Tel: (336)334-7500

Fax: (336)334-7082

E-mail: uadmit@ncat.edu

Web Site: www.ncat.edu

Description: State-supported, university, coed. Part of University of North Carolina System. Awards bachelor's, master's, and doctoral degrees and post-master's certificates. Founded 1891. Setting: 200-acre suburban campus with easy access to Charlotte. Total enrollment: 11,877. Faculty: 744 (513 full-time, 231 part-time). Student-undergrad faculty ratio is 18:1. 10,745 applied, 62% were admitted. 10% from top 10% of their high school class, 33% from top quarter, 73% from top half. Full-time: 9,304 students, 57% women, 43% men. Part-time: 1,037 students, 55% women, 45% men. 22% from out-of-state. 0.3% American Indian or Alaska Native, non-Hispanic/Latino; 4% Hispanic/Latino; 82% Black or African American, non-Hispanic/Latino; 0.8% Asian, non-Hispanic/Latino; 1% international. 15% 25 or older, 42% live on campus, 9% transferred in. Retention: 79% of full-time freshmen returned the following year. Academic areas with the most degrees conferred: engineering; business/marketing; communication/journalism. Core. Calendar: semesters. Academic remediation for entering students, advanced placement, accelerated degree program, honors program, distance learning, double major, summer session for credit, part-time degree program, adult/continuing education programs, co-op programs and internships, graduate courses open to undergrads. Off campus study at Bennett College; Elon University; Greensboro College; GTCC; Guilford College; High Point University; UNC-G. Study abroad program. ROTC: Army, Air Force.

Entrance Requirements: Options: early admission, deferred admission, international baccalaureate accepted. Required: high school transcript, minimum 2 high school GPA, SAT or ACT. Entrance: moderately difficult. Application deadline: rolling. Notification: continuous. SAT Reasoning Test deadline: 6/30. SAT Subject Test deadline: 6/30. Transfer credits accepted: Yes.

Costs Per Year: Application fee: $55. State resident tuition: $3540 full-time. Nonresident tuition: $16,750 full-time. Mandatory fees: $3,072 full-time. Full-time tuition and fees vary according to course load, degree level, and program. College room and board: $7644. College room only: $4009. Room and board charges vary according to board plan and housing facility.

Collegiate Environment: Orientation program. Drama-theater group, choral group, marching band, student-run newspaper, radio station. Social organizations: national fraternities, national sororities, local fraternities, local sororities. Most popular organization: Student Government. Major annual events: Homecoming, Martin Luther King, Jr. Celebration. Student services: health clinic, personal-psychological counseling. Campus security: 24-hour emergency response devices and patrols, late night transport-escort service, controlled dormitory access. F. D. Bluford Library.

Community Environment: See Greensboro College.

■ NORTH CAROLINA CENTRAL UNIVERSITY

1801 Fayetteville St.

Durham, NC 27707-3129

Tel: (919)560-6100; Free: 877-667-7533

Web Site: www.nccu.edu

Description: State-supported, comprehensive, coed. Part of University of North Carolina System. Awards bachelor's, master's, and doctoral degrees. Founded 1910. Setting: 115-acre urban campus with easy access to Raleigh. Endowment: $22.9 million. Research spending for the previous fiscal year: $7.2 million. Total enrollment: 8,097. Faculty: 564 (385 full-time, 179 part-time). Student-undergrad faculty ratio is 16:1. 6,671 applied, 83% were admitted. 8% from top 10% of their high school class, 18% from top quarter, 46% from top half. Full-time: 5,363 students, 66% women, 34% men. Part-time: 992 students, 71% women, 29% men. Students come from 39 states and territories, 47 other countries, 10% from out-of-state. 0.4% American Indian or Alaska Native, non-Hispanic/Latino; 6% Hispanic/Latino; 79% Black or African American, non-Hispanic/Latino; 1% Asian, non-Hispanic/Latino; 0.2% international. 19% 25 or older, 40% live on campus, 8% transferred in. Retention: 77% of full-time freshmen returned the following year. Academic areas with the most degrees conferred: business/marketing; health professions and related sciences; homeland security, law enforcement, firefighting, and protective services. Core. Calendar: semesters. Academic remediation for entering students, ESL program, services for LD students, advanced placement, accelerated degree program, honors program, independent study, distance learning, double major, summer session for credit, part-time degree program, external degree program, adult/continuing education programs, co-op programs and internships, graduate courses open to undergrads. Off campus study. Study abroad program. ROTC: Army, Air Force.

Entrance Requirements: Options: electronic application, deferred admission, international baccalaureate accepted. Required: high school transcript, minimum 2.5 high school GPA, University of North Carolina System minimum course requirements, SAT or ACT. Entrance: minimally difficult. Application deadline: 8/1. Notification: continuous until 10/15. Preference given to qualified state residents. SAT Reasoning Test deadline: 8/1. SAT Subject Test deadline: 8/1. Transfer credits accepted: Yes.

Costs Per Year: Application fee: $40. State resident tuition: $3728 full-time, $466 per credit hour part-time. Nonresident tuition: $16,435 full-time, $2054 per credit hour part-time. Mandatory fees: $2838 full-time, $599.67 per credit hour part-time. Part-time tuition and fees vary according to course load. College room and board: $8446. Room and board charges vary according to board plan, housing facility, and location. Tuition guaranteed not to increase for student's term of enrollment.

Collegiate Environment: Orientation program. Drama-theater group, choral group, marching band, student-run newspaper. Social organizations: national fraternities, national sororities, local fraternities, local sororities. Student services: health clinic, personal-psychological counseling, women's center. Campus security: 24-hour emergency response devices and patrols, student patrols, late night transport-escort service, controlled dormitory access. Shepherd Library plus 2 others. Study areas open 24 hours, 5-7 days a week; students can reserve study rooms. 1,262 computers available on campus for general student use. Computer purchase/lease plans available. A campuswide network can be accessed from student residence rooms and from off campus. Students can access the following: online class registration. Staffed computer lab on campus provides training in use of computers, software, and the Internet.

Community Environment: See Duke University.

■ **NORTH CAROLINA STATE UNIVERSITY**
Raleigh, NC 27695
Tel: (919)515-2011
Fax: (919)515-5039
E-mail: undergrad-admissions@ncsu.edu
Web Site: www.ncsu.edu

Description: State-supported, university, coed. Part of University of North Carolina System. Awards associate, bachelor's, master's, and doctoral degrees. Founded 1887. Setting: 2,137-acre urban campus with easy access to Raleigh-Durham. Endowment: $1.3 billion. Research spending for the previous fiscal year: $379.4 million. Educational spending for the previous fiscal year: $16,245 per student. Total enrollment: 35,479. Faculty: 2,616 (2,262 full-time, 354 part-time). Student-undergrad faculty ratio is 13:1. 30,193 applied, 47% were admitted. 48% from top 10% of their high school class, 85% from top quarter, 99% from top half. Full-time: 22,317 students, 47% women, 53% men. Part-time: 2,882 students, 42% women, 58% men. Students come from 53 states and territories, 105 other countries, 9% from out-of-state. 0.4% American Indian or Alaska Native, non-Hispanic/Latino; 6% Hispanic/Latino; 6% Black or African American, non-Hispanic/Latino; 7% Asian, non-Hispanic/Latino; 0.1% Native Hawaiian or other Pacific Islander, non-Hispanic/Latino; 4% international. 5% 25 or older, 38% live on campus, 5% transferred in. Retention: 94% of full-time freshmen returned the following year. Academic areas with the most degrees conferred: engineering; business/marketing; biological/life sciences. Core. Calendar: semesters. Academic remediation for entering students, ESL program, services for LD students, advanced placement, accelerated degree program, self-designed majors, honors program, independent study, distance learning, double major, summer session for credit, part-time degree program, adult/continuing education programs, co-op programs and internships, graduate courses open to undergrads. Off campus study at World Language Exchange, Great Plains IDEA, Cooperating Raleigh Colleges, UNC Interinstitutional Program. Study abroad program. ROTC: Army, Naval, Air Force.

Entrance Requirements: Options: electronic application, early action, deferred admission, international baccalaureate accepted. Required: SAT, ACT, SAT or ACT. Recommended: essay. Required for some: high school transcript, interview. Students applying for studio-based majors must provide a portfolio. Students applying for Professional Golf Management Students must provide a copy of their GHIN/Handicap scores from their local golf facility and a letter of recommendation from their golf coach or a PGA Professional. Entrance: very difficult. Application deadlines: 1/15, 11/1 for early ac-

tion. Notification: 3/30, 1/30 for early action. Preference given to Cap on out-of-state freshman enrollment set at 18%. SAT Reasoning Test deadline: 2/1. Transfer credits accepted: Yes. Applicants placed on waiting list: 4,133. Wait-listed applicants offered admission: 20. Early action applicants: 16,572. Early action applicants admitted: 10,051.

Costs Per Year: Application fee: $85. State resident tuition: $6535 full-time. Nonresident tuition: $25,878 full-time. Mandatory fees: $2566 full-time. College room and board: $11,078. College room only: $6714. Tuition guaranteed not to increase for student's term of enrollment.

Collegiate Environment: Orientation program. Drama-theater group, choral group, marching band, student-run newspaper, radio station. Social organizations: 630 open to all; national fraternities, national sororities; 13% of eligible men and 17% of eligible women are members. Most popular organizations: Inter-Residence Council, Student Alumni Association, Student Wolfpack Club, College of Education Graduate Advisory Board, American Society of Mechanical Engineers Student Section. Major annual events: Welcome Week, Homecoming, Campus Connections: Student Organization Fair. Student services: legal services, health clinic, personal-psychological counseling, women's center. Campus security: 24-hour emergency response devices and patrols, late night transport-escort service, controlled dormitory access. 9,247 college housing spaces available; 8,885 were occupied in 2018-19. Freshmen guaranteed college housing. On-campus residence required in freshman year. Options: coed, men-only, women-only housing available. D. H. Hill Jr. Library plus 5 others. Books: 2.6 million (physical), 1.2 million (digital/electronic); Serial titles: 47,189 (physical), 55,481 (digital/electronic); Databases: 635. Weekly public service hours: 146; study areas open 24 hours, 5-7 days a week; students can reserve study rooms. Operations spending for the previous fiscal year: $37.1 million. 3,050 computers available on campus for general student use. Computer purchase/lease plans available. A campuswide network can be accessed from student residence rooms and from off campus. Students can access the following: online class registration, online course materials, homework submission, testing/quizzes, financial aid/cashier's office account balances, blogging service, Web space, unlimited cloud storage, on site hardware and virus removal support. Staffed computer lab on campus (open 24 hours a day) provides training in use of computers, software, and the Internet.

■ **NORTH CAROLINA WESLEYAN COLLEGE**
3400 N Wesleyan Blvd.
Rocky Mount, NC 27804-8677
Tel: (252)985-5100; Free: 800-488-6292
Fax: (252)985-5325
E-mail: blilley@ncwc.edu
Web Site: www.ncwc.edu

Description: Independent, 4-year, coed, affiliated with United Methodist Church. Awards bachelor's degrees (also offers adult part-time degree program with significant enrollment not reflected in profile). Founded 1956. Setting: 200-acre suburban campus. Endowment: $10.6 million. Educational spending for the previous fiscal year: $5468 per student. Total enrollment: 2,093. Faculty: 313. Student-undergrad faculty ratio is 16:1. 1,666 applied, 98% were admitted. 8% from top 10% of their high school class, 23% from top quarter, 52% from top half. 2 valedictorians. Full-time: 1,754 students, 57% women, 43% men. Part-time: 339 students, 68% women, 32% men. Students come from 23 states and territories, 31 other countries, 13% from out-of-state. 1% American Indian or Alaska Native, non-Hispanic/Latino; 3% Hispanic/Latino; 42% Black or African American, non-Hispanic/Latino; 0.7% Asian, non-Hispanic/Latino; 5% international. 45% 25 or older, 72% live on campus, 7% transferred in. Retention: 60% of full-time freshmen returned the following year. Academic areas with the most degrees conferred: business/marketing; homeland security, law enforcement, firefighting, and protective services; psychology. Core. Calendar: semesters. Academic remediation for entering students, services for LD students, advanced placement, accelerated degree program, honors program, independent study, distance learning, double major, summer session for credit, part-time degree program, adult/continuing education programs, co-op programs and internships. ROTC: Army (c).

Entrance Requirements: Options: electronic application, international baccalaureate accepted. Required: high school transcript, SAT or ACT. Recommended: minimum 2 high school GPA, 2 recommendations, interview. Required for some: essay, interview. Entrance: moderately difficult. Application deadline: rolling. Notification: continuous. Transfer credits accepted: Yes.

Costs Per Year: Application fee: $0. Comprehensive fee: $40,200 includes full-time tuition ($29,750), mandatory fees ($400), and college room and

board ($10,050). College room only: $4650. Full-time tuition and fees vary according to location. Room and board charges vary according to housing facility. Part-time tuition: $500 per semester hour. Part-time tuition varies according to course load and location.

Collegiate Environment: Orientation program. Drama-theater group, choral group, marching band, student-run newspaper. Social organizations: 20 open to all; national fraternities, national sororities, local fraternities; 1% of eligible men and 1% of eligible women are members. Most popular organizations: Refuge Campus Ministry, NCWC Cheerleaders, Voices of Triumph, Campus Crusade for Christ, Visions of Beauty. Major annual events: Homecoming Week, Spring Fling, Wesleyan Symposium. Student services: health clinic, personal-psychological counseling. Campus security: 24-hour emergency response devices and patrols, late night transport-escort service, controlled dormitory access. Elizabeth Braswell Pearsall Library. Books: 78,800 (physical), 44,751 (digital/electronic); Serial titles: 4,326 (physical), 4,329 (digital/electronic); Databases: 86. Students can reserve study rooms. Operations spending for the previous fiscal year: $441,739. 223 computers available on campus for general student use. A campuswide network can be accessed from student residence rooms and from off campus. Staffed computer lab on campus provides training in use of computers, software, and the Internet.

Community Environment: Rocky Mount, population 56,600, is located three miles from Interstate 95 in the coastal plain region of the state. It is a progressive industrial and agricultural community, but still maintains its historic heritage. Nash General and Community Hospital are only 10 minutes from campus. Many recreational facilities are easily accessible.

■ PAMLICO COMMUNITY COLLEGE

PO Box 185
Grantsboro, NC 28529-0185
Tel: (252)249-1851
Fax: (252)249-2377
Web Site: www.pamlicocc.edu

Description: State-supported, 2-year, coed. Part of North Carolina Community College System. Awards certificates, diplomas, transfer associate, and terminal associate degrees. Founded 1963. Setting: 44-acre rural campus. Total enrollment: 300. Faculty: 10 (6 full-time, 4 part-time). 58% 25 or older. Core. Calendar: semesters. Academic remediation for entering students, services for LD students, summer session for credit, part-time degree program, adult/continuing education programs, co-op programs.

Entrance Requirements: Open admission. Options: early admission, deferred admission. Required: high school transcript. Entrance: noncompetitive. Application deadline: rolling. Notification: continuous.

Collegiate Environment: Student-run newspaper. Student services: personal-psychological counseling. Campus security: evening security guard. Pamlico Community College Library plus 1 other. 68 computers available on campus for general student use.

■ PFEIFFER UNIVERSITY

PO Box 960
Misenheimer, NC 28109-0960
Tel: (704)463-1360; Free: 800-338-2060
Fax: (704)463-1363
E-mail: emily.carella@pfeiffer.edu
Web Site: www.pfeiffer.edu

Description: Independent United Methodist, comprehensive, coed. Awards bachelor's and master's degrees and post-master's certificates. Founded 1885. Setting: 300-acre rural campus with easy access to Charlotte. Endowment: $15.3 million. Educational spending for the previous fiscal year: $8468 per student. Total enrollment: 1,306. Faculty: 126 (81 full-time, 45 part-time). Student-undergrad faculty ratio is 12:1. 1,860 applied, 66% were admitted. 10% from top 10% of their high school class, 28% from top quarter, 63% from top half. Full-time: 732 students, 51% women, 49% men. Part-time: 81 students, 60% women, 40% men. 19% from out-of-state. 0.5% American Indian or Alaska Native, non-Hispanic/Latino; 7% Hispanic/Latino; 23% Black or African American, non-Hispanic/Latino; 1% Asian, non-Hispanic/Latino; 0.2% Native Hawaiian or other Pacific Islander, non-Hispanic/Latino; 2% international. 17% 25 or older, 59% live on campus, 7% transferred in. Retention: 61% of full-time freshmen returned the following year. Academic areas with the most degrees conferred: business/marketing; health professions and related sciences; parks and recreation. Core. Calendar: semesters. Academic remediation for entering students, ESL program, services for LD students, advanced placement, accelerated degree program,

honors program, independent study, double major, summer session for credit, part-time degree program, co-op programs and internships. Study abroad program. ROTC: Army (c).

Entrance Requirements: Options: electronic application, early admission, deferred admission. Required: high school transcript. Recommended: minimum 2 high school GPA, interview. Required for some: 2 recommendations. Entrance: moderately difficult. Application deadline: rolling. Notification: continuous. Transfer credits accepted: Yes.

Costs Per Year: Comprehensive fee: $41,460 includes full-time tuition ($29,200), mandatory fees ($1034), and college room and board ($11,226). College room only: $5,924. Full-time tuition and fees vary according to course load. Room and board charges vary according to board plan and housing facility. Part-time tuition: $460 per semester hour. Part-time mandatory fees: $215 per term. Part-time tuition and fees vary according to course load.

Collegiate Environment: Orientation program. Drama-theater group, choral group, student-run newspaper. Social organizations: 49 open to all; 2% of eligible men and 6% of eligible women are members. Most popular organizations: Student Government Association, Religious Life Council, Commuter Student Association, Programming Activities Council, Residence Hall Association. Major annual events: Homecoming, Winterfest, Aprilfest. Student services: health clinic, personal-psychological counseling, women's center. Campus security: 24-hour emergency response devices and patrols, late night transport-escort service, controlled dormitory access. 671 college housing spaces available; 552 were occupied in 2018-19. Freshmen guaranteed college housing. On-campus residence required through senior year. Options: coed, women-only housing available. Gustavus A. Pfeiffer Library. Books: 125,000 (physical). Operations spending for the previous fiscal year: $173,688.

Community Environment: The setting for Misenheimer is a rural area with moderate mild climate. Commercial transportation is available at nearby Salisbury, and airlines at Charlotte. Recreational activities include swimming, boating, hunting and camping.

■ PIEDMONT COMMUNITY COLLEGE

PO Box 1197
Roxboro, NC 27573-1197
Tel: (336)599-1181
Fax: (336)597-3817
Web Site: www.piedmontcc.edu

Description: State-supported, 2-year, coed. Part of North Carolina Community College System. Awards certificates, diplomas, transfer associate, and terminal associate degrees. Founded 1970. Setting: 178-acre small town campus. Total enrollment: 1,311. Student-undergrad faculty ratio is 12:1. Core. Calendar: semesters. Academic remediation for entering students, ESL program, advanced placement, distance learning, double major, summer session for credit, part-time degree program, adult/continuing education programs, co-op programs. Off campus study at other technical institutes and community colleges in North Carolina.

Entrance Requirements: Open admission open admission for all programs except nursing and medical assisting programs. Options: electronic application, early admission, deferred admission. Required for some: high school transcript. Entrance: noncompetitive. Application deadline: rolling. Notification: continuous. Transfer credits accepted: Yes.

Costs Per Year: State resident tuition: $2432 full-time, $76 per credit hour part-time. Nonresident tuition: $8576 full-time, $268 per credit hour part-time. Mandatory fees: $114 full-time, $57.25 per term part-time. Full-time tuition and fees vary according to course load. Part-time tuition and fees vary according to course load.

Collegiate Environment: Drama-theater group. Campus security: routine patrols by the local sheriff department. Learning Resource Center.

■ PIEDMONT INTERNATIONAL UNIVERSITY

420 S Broad St.
Winston Salem, NC 27101-5197
Tel: (336)725-8344; Free: 800-937-5097
Fax: (336)725-5522
E-mail: stevensons@piedmontu.edu
Web Site: www.piedmontu.edu

Description: Independent Baptist, university, coed. Awards associate, bachelor's, master's, and doctoral degrees. Founded 1947. Setting: 12-acre urban campus. Total enrollment: 384. Student-undergrad faculty ratio is 10:1. 85 applied, 49% were admitted. Full-time: 149 students, 42% women, 58% men. Part-time: 48 students, 42% women, 58% men. Students come from

17 states and territories, 2 other countries, 30% from out-of-state. 2% Hispanic/Latino; 11% Black or African American, non-Hispanic/Latino; 0.5% Native Hawaiian or other Pacific Islander, non-Hispanic/Latino; 1% international. 30% 25 or older, 12% live on campus, 10% transferred in. Retention: 58% of full-time freshmen returned the following year. Academic area with the most degrees conferred: education. Core. Calendar: semesters. Academic remediation for entering students, advanced placement, distance learning, double major, summer session for credit, part-time degree program, adult/continuing education programs, internships, graduate courses open to undergrads. Study abroad program.

Entrance Requirements: Open admission. Options: electronic application, international baccalaureate accepted. Required: essay, high school transcript, 2 recommendations, medical history, proof of immunization, SAT or ACT. Recommended: minimum 2 high school GPA, interview. Entrance: noncompetitive. Application deadline: rolling. SAT Reasoning Test deadline: 7/1. SAT Subject Test deadline: 7/1. Transfer credits accepted: Yes.

Collegiate Environment: Orientation program. Drama-theater group, choral group. Social organizations: fellowship organizations based on major; 30% of eligible men and 30% of eligible women are members. Major annual events: Community Service Work Day, Artist Series, Christmas Concert. Campus security: 24-hour emergency response devices, student patrols, late night transport-escort service, controlled dormitory access, security guards on duty from dusk until dawn. George Manuel Memorial Library. 20 computers available on campus for general student use. A campuswide network can be accessed from student residence rooms and from off campus. Students can access the following: online class registration. Staffed computer lab on campus provides training in use of computers, software, and the Internet.

Community Environment: See Wake Forest University.

■ **PITT COMMUNITY COLLEGE**
1986 Pitt Tech Rd.
Winterville, NC 28590
Tel: (252)321-4200
Fax: (252)321-4401
E-mail: pittadm@pcc.pitt.cc.nc.us
Web Site: www.pittcc.edu

Description: State and locally supported, 2-year, coed. Part of North Carolina Community College System. Awards certificates, diplomas, transfer associate, and terminal associate degrees. Founded 1961. Setting: 294-acre small town campus. Total enrollment: 8,902. Faculty: 391 (187 full-time, 204 part-time). Full-time: 4,670 students, 58% women, 42% men. Part-time: 4,232 students, 63% women, 37% men. 0.3% American Indian or Alaska Native, non-Hispanic/Latino; 2% Hispanic/Latino; 28% Black or African American, non-Hispanic/Latino; 0.5% Asian, non-Hispanic/Latino; 0.1% Native Hawaiian or other Pacific Islander, non-Hispanic/Latino; 0.7% international. Retention: 68% of full-time freshmen returned the following year. Core. Calendar: semesters. Academic remediation for entering students, ESL program, services for LD students, advanced placement, independent study, distance learning, double major, summer session for credit, part-time degree program, external degree program, adult/continuing education programs, co-op programs and internships. ROTC: Army.

Entrance Requirements: Open admission except for health science programs. Options: electronic application, deferred admission. Required: high school transcript. Entrance: noncompetitive. Application deadline: rolling.

Costs Per Year: Application fee: $0. State resident tuition: $2432 full-time, $76 per credit hour part-time. Nonresident tuition: $8576 full-time, $268 per credit hour part-time. Mandatory fees: $116 full-time, $116.40 per year part-time. Full-time tuition and fees vary according to course load. Part-time tuition and fees vary according to course load.

Collegiate Environment: Orientation program. Drama-theater group, choral group. Student services: personal-psychological counseling. Campus security: 24-hour patrols, student patrols, late night transport-escort service. Pitt Community College Library.

Community Environment: See East Carolina University.

■ **QUEENS UNIVERSITY OF CHARLOTTE**
1900 Selwyn Ave.
Charlotte, NC 28274-0002
Tel: (704)337-2200; Free: 800-849-0202
Fax: (704)337-2403
E-mail: admissions@queens.edu
Web Site: www.queens.edu

Description: Independent Presbyterian, comprehensive, coed. Awards bachelor's and master's degrees. Founded 1857. Setting: 95-acre urban campus with easy access to Charlotte, NC. Endowment: $91.2 million. Educational spending for the previous fiscal year: $10,066 per student. Total enrollment: 2,536. Faculty: 300 (132 full-time, 168 part-time). Student-undergrad faculty ratio is 9:1. 2,419 applied, 79% were admitted. 15% from top 10% of their high school class, 46% from top quarter, 80% from top half. Full-time: 1,552 students, 66% women, 34% men. Part-time: 214 students, 74% women, 26% men. 43% from out-of-state. 0.7% American Indian or Alaska Native, non-Hispanic/Latino; 10% Hispanic/Latino; 16% Black or African American, non-Hispanic/Latino; 2% Asian, non-Hispanic/Latino; 0.2% Native Hawaiian or other Pacific Islander, non-Hispanic/Latino; 9% international. 1% 25 or older, 68% live on campus, 12% transferred in. Retention: 82% of full-time freshmen returned the following year. Academic areas with the most degrees conferred: health professions and related sciences; business/marketing; biological/life sciences. Core. Calendar: semesters. Advanced placement, honors program, independent study, distance learning, double major, summer session for credit, part-time degree program, adult/continuing education programs, internships, graduate courses open to undergrads. Off campus study at member of the Charlotte Area Educational Consortium. Study abroad program.

Entrance Requirements: Options: electronic application, early action, deferred admission, international baccalaureate accepted. Required: essay, high school transcript, 1 recommendation, SAT or ACT. Required for some: interview. Entrance: moderately difficult. Application deadline: rolling. Notification: continuous. SAT Reasoning Test deadline: 9/6. SAT Subject Test deadline: 9/6. Transfer credits accepted: Yes.

Costs Per Year: Application fee: $0. Tuition: $33,434 full-time. Full-time tuition varies according to course load, program, and student level.

Collegiate Environment: Orientation program. Drama-theater group, choral group, student-run newspaper, radio station. Social organizations: 45 open to all; national fraternities, national sororities; 13% of eligible men and 18% of eligible women are members. Most popular organizations: Senate, College Union Board, Royal Ambassadors, Students for Black Awareness, International Club. Major annual events: Casino Night, Boar's Head/Yule Log, Homecoming. Student services: health clinic, personal-psychological counseling. Campus security: 24-hour emergency response devices and patrols, late night transport-escort service, controlled dormitory access, Emergency Alert System. Freshmen guaranteed college housing. On-campus residence required through junior year. Option: coed housing available. Everett Library. Books: 41,620 (physical), 228,153 (digital/electronic); Serial titles: 106 (physical), 19,724 (digital/electronic); Databases: 81. Weekly public service hours: 93; students can reserve study rooms. Operations spending for the previous fiscal year: $546,707. 220 computers available on campus for general student use. A campuswide network can be accessed from student residence rooms. Students can access the following: online class registration. Staffed computer lab on campus provides training in use of computers, software, and the Internet.

■ **RANDOLPH COMMUNITY COLLEGE**
629 Industrial Park Ave.
Asheboro, NC 27205
Tel: (336)633-0200
Fax: (336)629-4695
E-mail: hdpritchard@randolph.edu
Web Site: www.randolph.edu

Description: State-supported, 2-year, coed. Part of North Carolina Community College System. Awards certificates, diplomas, transfer associate, and terminal associate degrees. Founded 1962. Setting: 44-acre small town campus with easy access to Greensboro, Winston-Salem, High Point. Endowment: $11.6 million. Total enrollment: 2,647. Faculty: 286 (82 full-time, 204 part-time). Student-undergrad faculty ratio is 10:1. 1,283 applied, 100% were admitted. Full-time: 914 students, 62% women, 38% men. Part-time: 1,733 students, 61% women, 39% men. Students come from 2 states and territories. 0.5% American Indian or Alaska Native, non-Hispanic/Latino; 10% Hispanic/Latino; 5% Black or African American, non-Hispanic/Latino; 0.8% Asian, non-Hispanic/Latino; 0.1% Native Hawaiian or other Pacific Islander, non-Hispanic/Latino; 0.4% international. 22% 25 or older, 2% transferred in. Core. Calendar: semesters. Academic remediation for entering students, ESL program, services for LD students, advanced placement, independent study, distance learning, double major, summer session for credit, part-time degree program, adult/continuing education programs, co-op programs and internships. Off campus study at other members of the North Carolina Community College System. ROTC: Air Force (c).

Entrance Requirements: Open admission. Options: electronic application, deferred admission, international baccalaureate accepted. Entrance: noncompetitive. Application deadline: rolling. Notification: continuous. Transfer credits accepted: Yes.

Costs Per Year: Application fee: $0. State resident tuition: $2432 full-time, $76 per credit hour part-time. Nonresident tuition: $8576 full-time, $268 per credit hour part-time. Mandatory fees: $108 full-time, $2.75 per credit hour part-time, $10 per term part-time.

Collegiate Environment: Social organizations: 19 open to all. Most popular organizations: Student Government Association, Phi Theta Kappa, Student Nurse Association, Phi Beta Lambda, Veterans Club. Major annual events: Fall Fling, Spring Fling, Holiday Party. Campus security: 24-hour emergency response devices, security officer during hours of operation. R. Alton Cox Learning Resources Center. Books: 25,000 (physical). 885 computers available on campus for general student use. A campuswide network can be accessed. Students can access the following: online class registration. Staffed computer lab on campus provides training in use of computers, software, and the Internet.

Community Environment: Asheboro is the county seat of Randolph County and is located near the geographical center of the state. The town has grown steadily with the surrounding area, which is mainly agricultural. Community facilities include numerous churches, a library, convenient shopping centers, and the North Carolina State Zoo. Several lakes nearby provide facilities for hunting, fishing, boating, and water skiing.

■ RICHMOND COMMUNITY COLLEGE
1042 W Hamlet Ave.
Hamlet, NC 28345
Tel: (910)410-1700
Fax: (910)410-7102
E-mail: ccholmes@richmondcc.edu
Web Site: www.richmondcc.edu

Description: State-supported, 2-year, coed. Part of North Carolina Community College System. Awards certificates, diplomas, transfer associate, and terminal associate degrees. Founded 1964. Setting: 163-acre rural campus. Total enrollment: 2,555. Student-undergrad faculty ratio is 15:1. Full-time: 1,056 students, 65% women, 35% men. Part-time: 1,499 students, 64% women, 36% men. 1% from out-of-state. 8% American Indian or Alaska Native, non-Hispanic/Latino; 5% Hispanic/Latino; 22% Black or African American, non-Hispanic/Latino; 1% Asian, non-Hispanic/Latino; 0.1% Native Hawaiian or other Pacific Islander, non-Hispanic/Latino; 0.4% international. 32% 25 or older. Calendar: semesters. Academic remediation for entering students, ESL program, advanced placement, self-designed majors, independent study, distance learning, double major, summer session for credit, part-time degree program, adult/continuing education programs, co-op programs and internships.

Entrance Requirements: Open admission. Options: electronic application, deferred admission. Required: high school transcript. Entrance: noncompetitive. Application deadline: rolling. Notification: continuous. Transfer credits accepted: Yes.

Costs Per Year: Application fee: $0. State resident tuition: $2432 full-time, $76 per credit hour part-time. Nonresident tuition: $8576 full-time, $268 per credit hour part-time. Mandatory fees: $84 full-time, $35 per term part-time. Full-time tuition and fees vary according to course load. Part-time tuition and fees vary according to course load.

Collegiate Environment: Orientation program. Choral group. Student services: personal-psychological counseling. Campus security: 24-hour emergency response devices. College housing not available. Richmond Community College Library.

Community Environment: Located 75 miles southeast of Charlotte, Hamlet is a town with a friendly atmosphere. Its primary businesses are manufacturing and textiles. Train and bus transportation is available. Community facilities include churches of various faiths, a library, shopping areas and good medical facilities. Recreational activities include swimming, boating, tennis, and fishing.

■ ROANOKE-CHOWAN COMMUNITY COLLEGE
109 Community College Rd.
Ahoskie, NC 27910
Tel: (252)862-1200
Fax: (252)862-1353
Web Site: www.roanokechowan.edu

Description: State-supported, 2-year, coed. Part of North Carolina Community College System. Awards certificates, diplomas, transfer associate,

and terminal associate degrees. Founded 1967. Setting: 39-acre rural campus. Total enrollment: 384. 50% 25 or older. Core. Calendar: semesters. Academic remediation for entering students, distance learning, summer session for credit, part-time degree program, adult/continuing education programs, co-op programs.

Entrance Requirements: Open admission except for nursing program. Option: early admission. Required for some: interview. Entrance: noncompetitive. Application deadline: rolling. Notification: continuous.

Collegiate Environment: Orientation program.

Community Environment: See Chowan College.

■ ROBESON COMMUNITY COLLEGE
5160 Fayetteville Rd.
Lumberton, NC 28359-1420
Tel: (910)272-3700
Fax: (910)272-3328
E-mail: plocklear@robeson.edu
Web Site: www.robeson.edu

Description: State-supported, 2-year, coed. Part of North Carolina Community College System. Awards transfer associate and terminal associate degrees. Founded 1965. Setting: 78-acre small town campus. Total enrollment: 2,869. Faculty: 114 (44 full-time, 70 part-time). Calendar: semesters. Academic remediation for entering students, services for LD students, distance learning, co-op programs.

Entrance Requirements: Open admission. Options: electronic application, early admission. Required: high school transcript. Entrance: noncompetitive. Application deadline: rolling. Notification: continuous. Transfer credits accepted: Yes.

Collegiate Environment: Orientation program. Student services: personal-psychological counseling. 100 computers available on campus for general student use. A campuswide network can be accessed from off-campus. Staffed computer lab on campus.

Community Environment: Located in a rural setting in Robeson County, this community is a short distance from Lumberton, the county seat, and has access to all the advantages of that city. Commercial transportation is available. Lumberton is also one of the major tobacco markets; other industries are here along with a number of churches and a library.

■ ROCKINGHAM COMMUNITY COLLEGE
PO Box 38
Wentworth, NC 27375-0038
Tel: (336)342-4261
E-mail: admissions@rockinghamcc.edu
Web Site: www.rockinghamcc.edu

Description: State-supported, 2-year, coed. Part of North Carolina Community College System. Awards certificates, diplomas, transfer associate, and terminal associate degrees. Founded 1964. Setting: 257-acre rural campus. Total enrollment: 1,779. Faculty: 131 (63 full-time, 68 part-time). Student-undergrad faculty ratio is 18:1. Full-time: 668 students, 55% women, 45% men. Part-time: 1,111 students, 62% women, 38% men. Students come from 2 states and territories. Calendar: semesters. Academic remediation for entering students, advanced placement, self-designed majors, summer session for credit, part-time degree program, adult/continuing education programs, co-op programs.

Entrance Requirements: Open admission except for allied health programs. Options: electronic application, early admission, deferred admission. Entrance: noncompetitive. Application deadline: rolling. Notification: continuous.

Collegiate Environment: Major annual events: Fall Kickoff, Spring Fling, Blood Drive. Student services: personal-psychological counseling. Campus security: 24-hour emergency response devices and patrols. Gerald B. James Library. 1,400 computers available on campus for general student use. A campuswide network can be accessed. Students can access the following: online class registration. Staffed computer lab on campus provides training in use of computers, software, and the Internet.

Community Environment: Located near Reidsville and Eden in Rockingham County.

■ ROWAN-CABARRUS COMMUNITY COLLEGE
1333 Jake Alexander Blvd. S
Salisbury, NC 28146
Tel: (704)216-7222
Web Site: www.rccc.edu

Description: State-supported, 2-year, coed. Part of North Carolina Community College System. Awards certificates, diplomas, transfer associate, and terminal associate degrees. Founded 1963. Setting: 100-acre small town campus with easy access to Charlotte. Total enrollment: 7,579. Faculty: 430 (150 full-time, 280 part-time). Student-undergrad faculty ratio is 15:1. Students come from 11 states and territories, 1% from out-of-state. 0.5% American Indian or Alaska Native, non-Hispanic/Latino; 10% Hispanic/Latino; 19% Black or African American, non-Hispanic/Latino; 2% Asian, non-Hispanic/Latino; 0.1% Native Hawaiian or other Pacific Islander, non-Hispanic/Latino; 1% international. 30% 25 or older. Calendar: semesters. Academic remediation for entering students, ESL program, services for LD students, advanced placement, distance learning, summer session for credit, part-time degree program, adult/continuing education programs, co-op programs and internships.

Entrance Requirements: Open admission. Required: high school transcript. Entrance: noncompetitive. Application deadline: rolling. Transfer credits accepted: Yes.

Costs Per Year: Application fee: $0. State resident tuition: $2432 full-time, $76 per credit hour part-time. Nonresident tuition: $8576 full-time, $268 per credit hour part-time. Mandatory fees: $194 full-time, $79 per term part-time. Full-time tuition and fees vary according to course load. Part-time tuition and fees vary according to course load.

Collegiate Environment: Orientation program. Student services: personal-psychological counseling. Campus security: on-campus security during hours of operation. Learning Resource Center. Students can reserve study rooms.

■ **ST. ANDREWS UNIVERSITY**
1700 Dogwood Mile
Laurinburg, NC 28352-5598
Tel: (910)277-5000; Free: 800-763-0198
Fax: (910)277-5087
E-mail: admission@sapc.edu
Web Site: www.sa.edu

Description: Independent Presbyterian, comprehensive, coed. Administratively affiliated with Webber International University. Awards bachelor's and master's degrees. Founded 1958. Setting: 600-acre small town campus. Total enrollment: 655. Faculty: 73 (30 full-time, 43 part-time). Student-undergrad faculty ratio is 14:1. 1,104 applied, 41% were admitted. 2% from top 10% of their high school class, 12% from top quarter, 35% from top half. Full-time: 593 students, 44% women, 56% men. Part-time: 34 students, 82% women, 18% men. Students come from 31 states and territories, 30 other countries, 40% from out-of-state. 1% American Indian or Alaska Native, non-Hispanic/Latino; 4% Hispanic/Latino; 24% Black or African American, non-Hispanic/Latino; 0.5% Asian, non-Hispanic/Latino; 13% international. 15% 25 or older, 85% live on campus, 9% transferred in. Retention: 42% of full-time freshmen returned the following year. Academic areas with the most degrees conferred: business/marketing; education; biological/life sciences; psychology. Core. Calendar: semesters. ESL program, services for LD students, advanced placement, self-designed majors, honors program, independent study, distance learning, double major, summer session for credit, part-time degree program, adult/continuing education programs, internships, graduate courses open to undergrads. Study abroad program.

Entrance Requirements: Options: electronic application, deferred admission, international baccalaureate accepted. Required: high school transcript. Recommended: minimum 2 high school GPA, SAT and SAT Subject Tests or ACT. Required for some: essay, interview. Entrance: moderately difficult. Transfer credits accepted: Yes.

Costs Per Year: Application fee: $35. Tuition: $25,618 full-time, $288 per credit part-time. Full-time tuition varies according to course load and location. Part-time tuition varies according to location.

Collegiate Environment: Orientation program. Drama-theater group, choral group. Campus security: 24-hour emergency response devices and patrols, late night transport-escort service. DeTamble Library. Books: 83,851 (physical), 345,661 (digital/electronic); Serial titles: 1,165 (physical), 31,450 (digital/electronic); Databases: 90. 100 computers available on campus for general student use. A campuswide network can be accessed from student residence rooms and from off campus. Staffed computer lab on campus provides training in use of software and the Internet.

■ **SAINT AUGUSTINE'S UNIVERSITY**
1315 Oakwood Ave.
Raleigh, NC 27610-2298
Tel: (919)516-4000; Free: 800-948-1126
Fax: (919)516-4415

E-mail: jesousa@st-aug.edu
Web Site: www.st-aug.edu

Description: Independent Episcopal, 4-year, coed. Awards bachelor's degrees. Founded 1867. Setting: 122-acre urban campus. Total enrollment: 944. Faculty: 96 (59 full-time, 37 part-time). Student-undergrad faculty ratio is 13:1. 4,040 applied, 71% were admitted. Full-time: 920 students, 46% women, 54% men. Part-time: 24 students, 38% women, 62% men. Students come from 13 states and territories, 3 other countries, 99.9% from out-of-state. 0.6% American Indian or Alaska Native, non-Hispanic/Latino; 1% Hispanic/Latino; 89% Black or African American, non-Hispanic/Latino; 0.1% Asian, non-Hispanic/Latino; 1% international. 907% 25 or older, 76% live on campus, 8% transferred in. Retention: 55% of full-time freshmen returned the following year. Core. Calendar: semesters. Services for LD students, advanced placement, accelerated degree program, freshman honors college, honors program, independent study, double major, summer session for credit, part-time degree program, adult/continuing education programs, co-op programs and internships. Off campus study at Consortium - cooperating Raleigh Colleges (Shaw University, Peace College, Meredith College, North Carolina State University). Study abroad program. ROTC: Army, Air Force (c).

Entrance Requirements: Options: electronic application, deferred admission, international baccalaureate accepted. Required: high school transcript, minimum 2 high school GPA, 2 recommendations, medical history, background check, SAT or ACT. Recommended: minimum 2.5 high school GPA. Required for some: essay, interview. Entrance: moderately difficult. Application deadline: rolling. Notification: continuous. SAT Reasoning Test deadline: 8/5. SAT Subject Test deadline: 8/5. Transfer credits accepted: Yes.

Costs Per Year: Application fee: $50. Comprehensive fee: $25,582 includes full-time tuition ($12,890), mandatory fees ($5000), and college room and board ($7692). College room only: $3182. Full-time tuition and fees vary according to course load. Room and board charges vary according to housing facility. Part-time tuition: $537 per credit hour. Part-time mandatory fees: $208 per credit hour. Part-time tuition and fees vary according to course load.

Collegiate Environment: Orientation program. Drama-theater group, choral group, marching band, student-run newspaper, radio station. Social organizations: 44 open to all; national fraternities, national sororities, local fraternities; 17% of eligible men and 15% of eligible women are members. Most popular organizations: Campus Activity Board, Christian Fellowship Organization, Collegiate 100 Black Men of America, Student Government Association/Student Leaders, Falcon Fanatic Pep Squad. Major annual events: Fall and Spring Fling, Homecoming, Community Day. Student services: health clinic, personal-psychological counseling, women's center. Campus security: 24-hour emergency response devices and patrols, RAVE: Emergency Notification System. Prezell R. Robinson Library. Students can reserve study rooms. 183 computers available on campus for general student use. A campuswide network can be accessed from student residence rooms and from off campus. Students can access the following: online class registration. Staffed computer lab on campus provides training in use of computers, software, and the Internet.

■ **SALEM COLLEGE**
601 S Church St.
Winston Salem, NC 27101
Tel: (336)721-2600; Free: 800-327-2536
Fax: (336)724-7102
E-mail: admissions@salem.edu
Web Site: www.salem.edu

Description: Independent Moravian, comprehensive, coed. Awards bachelor's and master's degrees (only students age 23 or over are eligible to enroll part-time). Founded 1772. Setting: 69-acre urban campus with easy access to Charlotte. Total enrollment: 1,087. Faculty: 142 (63 full-time, 79 part-time). Student-undergrad faculty ratio is 10:1. 929 applied, 60% were admitted. 37% from top 10% of their high school class, 73% from top quarter, 98% from top half. Full-time: 768 students, 97% women, 3% men. Part-time: 170 students, 88% women, 12% men. Students come from 31 states and territories, 8 other countries, 26% from out-of-state. 0.2% American Indian or Alaska Native, non-Hispanic/Latino; 12% Hispanic/Latino; 22% Black or African American, non-Hispanic/Latino; 3% Asian, non-Hispanic/Latino; 0.5% international. 29% 25 or older, 86% live on campus, 8% transferred in. Retention: 75% of full-time freshmen returned the following year. Core. Calendar: 4-1-4. Advanced placement, self-designed majors, freshman honors college, honors program, independent study, distance learning, double major, summer session for credit, part-time degree program, adult/continuing education programs, internships. Off campus study at Wake Forest University, American University, Brethren Colleges Abroad (BCA). Study abroad program. ROTC: Army (c), Air Force (c).

Entrance Requirements: Options: electronic application, early admission, deferred admission, international baccalaureate accepted. Required: essay, high school transcript, SAT or ACT. Recommended: interview. Entrance: moderately difficult. Application deadline: rolling. Notification: continuous.

Costs Per Year: Application fee: $30. Comprehensive fee: $41,266 includes full-time tuition ($28,950), mandatory fees ($466), and college room and board ($11,850). Room and board charges vary according to housing facility. Part-time tuition: $405 per semester hour.

Collegiate Environment: Orientation program. Drama-theater group, choral group, marching band, student-run newspaper. Social organizations: 41 open to all. Student services: health clinic, personal-psychological counseling. Campus security: 24-hour emergency response devices and patrols, late night transport-escort service, controlled dormitory access. Dale H. Gramley Library plus 2 others. Books: 119,591 (physical), 110,764 (digital/electronic); Databases: 123. 54 computers available on campus for general student use. Computer purchase/lease plans available. A campuswide network can be accessed from student residence rooms and from off campus. Students can access the following: online class registration. Staffed computer lab on campus provides training in use of computers.

Community Environment: See Wake Forest University.

■ **SAMPSON COMMUNITY COLLEGE**
1801 Sunset Ave.
Hwy. 24 W
Clinton, NC 28329-0318
Tel: (910)592-8081
Fax: (910)592-8048
Web Site: www.sampsoncc.edu

Description: State and locally supported, 2-year, coed. Part of North Carolina Community College System. Awards certificates, diplomas, transfer associate, and terminal associate degrees. Founded 1965. Setting: 55-acre rural campus. Total enrollment: 1,579. Faculty: 95 (45 full-time, 50 part-time). Student-undergrad faculty ratio is 20:1. 712 applied, 100% were admitted. Full-time: 679 students, 73% women, 27% men. Part-time: 900 students, 73% women, 27% men. Students come from 4 states and territories, 1% from out-of-state. 52% 25 or older, 1% transferred in. Core. Calendar: semesters. Academic remediation for entering students, services for LD students, advanced placement, independent study, summer session for credit, part-time degree program, adult/continuing education programs, co-op programs and internships.

Entrance Requirements: Open admission except for nursing program. Option: deferred admission. Required: high school transcript, interview. Recommended: minimum 2.0 high school GPA. Entrance: noncompetitive. Application deadline: rolling. Notification: continuous.

Collegiate Environment: Orientation program. Social organizations: 7 open to all. Most popular organizations: Student Government Association, Criminal Justice Club, Nursing Student Association, Cosmetology Alliance Club, Phi Beta Lambda. Major annual event: Field Day. Student services: personal-psychological counseling. Campus security: local police patrol. Sampson Community College Library. 78 computers available on campus for general student use. A campuswide network can be accessed. Staffed computer lab on campus.

Community Environment: The county seat of Sampson County, Clinton is in the coastal plain section of the state. Community facilities have grown as Clinton has grown in population. A complete shopping center is located here, along with churches representing most denominations. A county hospital and numerous civic and service organizations serve the community. 28 industrial firms are based here. Job opportunities are available. Recreational activities include golf, hunting, fishing, and swimming.

■ **SANDHILLS COMMUNITY COLLEGE**
3395 Airport Rd.
Pinehurst, NC 28374-8299
Tel: (910)692-6185; Free: 800-338-3944
Fax: (910)695-1823
E-mail: robledoi@sandhills.edu
Web Site: www.sandhills.edu

Description: State-supported, 2-year, coed. Part of North Carolina Community College System. Awards certificates, diplomas, transfer associate, and terminal associate degrees. Founded 1963. Setting: 240-acre small

town campus. Endowment: $10.7 million. Educational spending for the previous fiscal year: $3508 per student. Total enrollment: 4,571. Faculty: 409 (145 full-time, 264 part-time). Student-undergrad faculty ratio is 13:1. Core. Calendar: semesters. Academic remediation for entering students, ESL program, services for LD students, advanced placement, independent study, distance learning, double major, summer session for credit, part-time degree program, co-op programs and internships. Off campus study.

Entrance Requirements: Open admission. Options: electronic application, deferred admission. Required: high school transcript. Application deadline: rolling. Notification: continuous. Transfer credits accepted: Yes.

Collegiate Environment: Orientation program. Drama-theater group, choral group, marching band, student-run newspaper. Social organizations: 21 open to all. Most popular organizations: Rotaract (Service Club - College Affiliate of Rotary International), Student Government Association, Outdoors Club, New Beginning Gospel Choir, Revolutionary Gamers Club. Major annual events: Spring Fling, College Days, Health Career Day. Student services: personal-psychological counseling. Campus security: 24-hour emergency response devices, security on duty until 12 am. Boyd Library. Operations spending for the previous fiscal year: $672,583. 300 computers available on campus for general student use. A campuswide network can be accessed from off-campus. Staffed computer lab on campus.

Community Environment: Pinehurst, established originally as a health resort, has a small town environment. The area of Southern Pines is famous for its dry and mild climate, its golf and tourism as well as for major horse stables. Community facilities include three libraries, a twenty-five acre garden, churches of all denominations, and various civic and service organizations. Recreational activities include golf, tennis, horseback riding, hunting, and fishing.

■ **SHAW UNIVERSITY**
118 E S St.
Raleigh, NC 27601-2399
Tel: (919)546-8200; Free: 800-214-6683
Fax: (919)546-8271
Web Site: www.shawu.edu

Description: Independent Baptist, comprehensive, coed. Awards bachelor's and master's degrees. Founded 1865. Setting: 30-acre urban campus. Total enrollment: 1,660. Faculty: 139 (76 full-time, 63 part-time). Student-undergrad faculty ratio is 17:1. 12,060 applied, 53% were admitted. 2% from top 10% of their high school class, 5% from top quarter, 30% from top half. Full-time: 1,466 students, 58% women, 42% men. Part-time: 80 students, 64% women, 36% men. Students come from 38 states and territories, 19 other countries, 37% from out-of-state. 0.3% American Indian or Alaska Native, non-Hispanic/Latino; 0.1% Hispanic/Latino; 74% Black or African American, non-Hispanic/Latino; 1% Asian, non-Hispanic/Latino; 1% Native Hawaiian or other Pacific Islander, non-Hispanic/Latino; 4% international. 13% 25 or older, 58% live on campus, 6% transferred in. Retention: 43% of full-time freshmen returned the following year. Academic areas with the most degrees conferred: business/marketing; public administration and social services; parks and recreation. Core. Calendar: semesters. Academic remediation for entering students, services for LD students, advanced placement, accelerated degree program, self-designed majors, honors program, independent study, distance learning, double major, summer session for credit, part-time degree program, adult/continuing education programs, internships. Off campus study at Cooperating Raleigh Colleges. Study abroad program. ROTC: Army (c), Air Force (c).

Entrance Requirements: Options: electronic application, early admission, deferred admission, international baccalaureate accepted. Required: high school transcript, minimum 2 high school GPA, SAT or ACT. Entrance: minimally difficult. Application deadline: 7/30. Notification: continuous. Transfer credits accepted: Yes.

Costs Per Year: Application fee: $25. Comprehensive fee: $24,638 includes full-time tuition ($11,808), mandatory fees ($4672), and college room and board ($8158). College room only: $3842. Part-time tuition: $492 per credit hour. Part-time mandatory fees: $93 per credit hour, $290 per term.

Collegiate Environment: Orientation program. Drama-theater group, choral group, marching band, student-run newspaper, radio station. Social organizations: national fraternities, national sororities; 4% of eligible men and 5% of eligible women are members. Most popular organizations: Student Government Association, choir, University band, academic clubs, International Student Organization. Major annual events: University Convocation, Homecoming, Honors Convocation. Student services: health clinic, personal-psychological counseling. Campus security: 24-hour emergency response devices and patrols, late night transport-escort service, 24-hour electronic surveillance cameras. James E. Cheek Learning Resources Center.

Community Environment: See Meredith College.

■ SOUTH PIEDMONT COMMUNITY COLLEGE

PO Box 126
Polkton, NC 28135-0126
Tel: (704)272-7635; Free: 800-766-0319
E-mail: asecrest@spcc.edu
Web Site: www.spcc.edu

Description: State-supported, 2-year, coed. Part of North Carolina Community College System. Awards certificates, diplomas, transfer associate, and terminal associate degrees. Founded 1962. Setting: 56-acre rural campus with easy access to Charlotte. Endowment: $27,818. Educational spending for the previous fiscal year: $2802 per student. Total enrollment: 2,658. Faculty: 106. Student-undergrad faculty ratio is 17:1. 740 applied, 84% were admitted. 2% from top 10% of their high school class, 5% from top quarter, 10% from top half. Full-time: 732 students, 66% women, 34% men. Part-time: 1,926 students, 70% women, 30% men. Students come from 5 states and territories, 1% from out-of-state. 0.3% American Indian or Alaska Native, non-Hispanic/Latino; 11% Hispanic/Latino; 19% Black or African American, non-Hispanic/Latino; 2% Asian, non-Hispanic/Latino; 0.2% Native Hawaiian or other Pacific Islander, non-Hispanic/Latino; 2% international. 33% 25 or older, 5% transferred in. Retention: 58% of full-time freshmen returned the following year. Core. Calendar: semesters. Academic remediation for entering students, ESL program, services for LD students, accelerated degree program, independent study, distance learning, summer session for credit, part-time degree program, adult/continuing education programs, co-op programs and internships. Off campus study.

Entrance Requirements: Open admission. Options: electronic application, early admission, deferred admission. Required: high school transcript. Entrance: noncompetitive. Application deadline: rolling. Notification: continuous.

Costs Per Year: Application fee: $0. State resident tuition: $2432 full-time, $76 per semester hour part-time. Nonresident tuition: $8576 full-time, $268 per semester hour part-time. Mandatory fees: $167 full-time, $2 per semester hour part-time, $33.90 per term part-time. Full-time tuition and fees vary according to course load. Part-time tuition and fees vary according to course load.

Collegiate Environment: Orientation program. Choral group. Social organizations: 5 open to all. Most popular organizations: Student Association, Phi Beta Lambda, Phi Theta Kappa, Social Services Club, Criminal Justice Club. Major annual events: Spring Fling, Career Day, Christmas Party. Student services: personal-psychological counseling, women's center. Campus security: 24-hour emergency response devices and patrols, evening security. Martin Learning Resource Center. Operations spending for the previous fiscal year: $167,634. 150 computers available on campus for general student use. A campuswide network can be accessed from off-campus. Staffed computer lab on campus.

Community Environment: The college is located in the geographic center of the Carolinas and Southeast. Its location is equidistant from the Appalachian and Blue Ridge Mountains and the Grand Strand area of the Atlantic; and is situated halfway between Washington, D.C. and Atlanta, Georgia. The average annual temperature is 61 degrees; the coldest month is January (42.5 degrees), the warmest month is July (78.9 degrees). Annual rainfall is 49 inches.

■ SOUTHEASTERN BAPTIST THEOLOGICAL SEMINARY

120 S Wingate St.
Wake Forest, NC 27587
Tel: (919)761-2100; Free: 800-284-6317
Web Site: www.sebts.edu

Description: Independent Southern Baptist, comprehensive, coed. Awards associate, bachelor's, master's, and doctoral degrees. Founded 1950. Setting: 300-acre suburban campus with easy access to Raleigh. Total enrollment: 3,136. Faculty: 124 (55 full-time, 69 part-time). Student-undergrad faculty ratio is 15:1. 109 applied, 86% were admitted. Full-time: 308 students, 32% women, 68% men. Part-time: 208 students, 22% women, 78% men. Students come from 52 states and territories, 30 other countries, 66% from out-of-state. 1% American Indian or Alaska Native, non-Hispanic/Latino; 7% Hispanic/Latino; 11% Black or African American, non-Hispanic/Latino; 3% Asian, non-Hispanic/Latino; 0.6% international. 27% 25 or older, 8% transferred in. Retention: 69% of full-time freshmen returned the follow-

ing year. Core. Calendar: semesters. Academic remediation for entering students, independent study, distance learning, double major, summer session for credit, part-time degree program, adult/continuing education programs, internships, graduate courses open to undergrads. Off campus study.

Entrance Requirements: Open admission. Options: electronic application, international baccalaureate accepted. Required: essay, high school transcript, minimum 2 high school GPA, 3 recommendations, SAT or ACT. Entrance: noncompetitive. Notification: continuous until 8/20. SAT Reasoning Test deadline: 9/20. SAT Subject Test deadline: 9/20. Transfer credits accepted: Yes.

Collegiate Environment: Orientation program. Drama-theater group, choral group. Major annual events: Campus-Wide Spring Cook Out, Campus-Wide Fall Cook Out. Student services: health clinic, personal-psychological counseling, women's center. Campus security: 24-hour emergency response devices and patrols, late night transport-escort service. Freshmen given priority for college housing. On-campus residence required in freshman year. Options: men-only, women-only housing available. The Library at Southeastern plus 1 other. Books: 195,926 (physical), 420,952 (digital/electronic); Serial titles: 2,286 (physical), 31,776 (digital/electronic); Databases: 29. Weekly public service hours: 71; students can reserve study rooms. 55 computers available on campus for general student use. A campuswide network can be accessed from student residence rooms and from off campus. Students can access the following: online class registration. Staffed computer lab on campus.

Community Environment: Wake Forest is located 15 miles north of Raleigh and 22 miles east of Durham on US 1 and NC 98. The seminary is only 25 miles from the Raleigh-Durham Airport. 12 churches, a hospital, a public library, and numerous civic and service organizations are found within the community. A full-time recreational program, supervised by a recreational director, swimming pools, lighted athletic fields, tennis courts, racquetball courts, weight rooms, and two golf courses provide the recreational facilities.

■ SOUTHEASTERN COMMUNITY COLLEGE

PO Box 151
Whiteville, NC 28472-0151
Tel: (910)642-7141
Web Site: www.sccnc.edu

Description: State-supported, 2-year, coed. Part of North Carolina Community College System. Awards certificates, diplomas, transfer associate, and terminal associate degrees. Founded 1964. Setting: 106-acre rural campus. Educational spending for the previous fiscal year: $1328 per student. Total enrollment: 1,402. Faculty: 91 (75 full-time, 16 part-time). Student-undergrad faculty ratio is 20:1. 890 applied, 100% were admitted. 10% from top 10% of their high school class, 25% from top quarter, 50% from top half. Full-time: 766 students, 63% women, 37% men. Part-time: 636 students, 70% women, 30% men. 1% from out-of-state. 7% American Indian or Alaska Native, non-Hispanic/Latino; 3% Hispanic/Latino; 24% Black or African American, non-Hispanic/Latino; 0.4% Asian, non-Hispanic/Latino. 62% 25 or older. Retention: 48% of full-time freshmen returned the following year. Core. Calendar: semesters. Academic remediation for entering students, ESL program, services for LD students, advanced placement, honors program, independent study, distance learning, double major, summer session for credit, part-time degree program, adult/continuing education programs, co-op programs and internships.

Entrance Requirements: Open admission except for nursing, phlebotomy, medical laboratory technology programs. Options: electronic application, early admission, deferred admission. Required: high school transcript. Entrance: noncompetitive. Application deadline: rolling.

Collegiate Environment: Orientation program. Drama-theater group, choral group. Social organizations: 6 open to all. Most popular organizations: Student Government Association, Nursing Club, Environmental Club. Major annual events: High School Senior Day, 8th-Grader Day. Student services: personal-psychological counseling. Campus security: 24-hour emergency response devices. Southeastern Community College Library.

Community Environment: A rural community with a mean annual temperature of 64 degrees. Bus transportation is convenient, and there is plane service at Wilmington and Fayetteville. Shopping facilities, 14 churches representing a number of denominations, and a hospital are part of the community. A nearby lake, beaches, a golf course, swimming pools, and tennis courts provide recreational opportunities. Part-time employment is limited.

■ **SOUTHWESTERN COMMUNITY COLLEGE**
447 College Dr.
Sylva, NC 28779
Tel: (828)339-4000; Free: 800-447-7091
Fax: (828)586-4093
E-mail: m_ellison@southwesterncc.edu
Web Site: www.southwesterncc.edu
Description: State-supported, 2-year, coed. Part of North Carolina Community College System. Awards certificates, diplomas, and transfer associate degrees. Founded 1964. Setting: 77-acre small town campus. Total enrollment: 2,353. Student-undergrad faculty ratio is 16:1. Full-time: 816 students, 64% women, 36% men. Part-time: 1,537 students, 57% women, 43% men. 8% American Indian or Alaska Native, non-Hispanic/Latino; 9% Hispanic/Latino; 2% Black or African American, non-Hispanic/Latino; 1% Asian, non-Hispanic/Latino; 0.8% international. Core. Calendar: semesters. Academic remediation for entering students, ESL program, services for LD students, advanced placement, honors program, independent study, distance learning, double major, summer session for credit, part-time degree program, adult/continuing education programs, co-op programs. Off campus study at Western Carolina University.
Entrance Requirements: Required: high school transcript. Required for some: minimum 2.5 high school GPA, interview.
Costs Per Year: State resident tuition: $2212 full-time, $76 per credit hour part-time. Nonresident tuition: $7588 full-time, $268 per credit hour part-time. Mandatory fees: $85 full-time, $3 per credit hour part-time, $1 per year part-time. Full-time tuition and fees vary according to course load and program. Part-time tuition and fees vary according to course load and program.
Collegiate Environment: Orientation program. Social organizations: 24 open to all. Major annual events: Spring Fling, Fall Welcome Back, Fall Fest. Student services: personal-psychological counseling. Campus security: security during hours of operation. College housing not available. Holt Library.

■ **STANLY COMMUNITY COLLEGE**
141 College Dr.
Albemarle, NC 28001-7458
Tel: (704)982-0121
Fax: (704)982-0819
E-mail: dross7926@stanly.edu
Web Site: www.stanly.edu
Description: State-supported, 2-year, coed. Part of North Carolina Community College System. Awards certificates, diplomas, transfer associate, and terminal associate degrees. Founded 1971. Setting: 150-acre small town campus with easy access to Charlotte. Total enrollment: 3,200. Faculty: 106 (53 full-time, 53 part-time). Student-undergrad faculty ratio is 9:1. 642 applied, 100% were admitted. Students come from 13 states and territories, 3 other countries, 3% from out-of-state. 48% 25 or older. Calendar: semesters. Academic remediation for entering students, ESL program, services for LD students, advanced placement, independent study, distance learning, double major, summer session for credit, part-time degree program, adult/continuing education programs, co-op programs and internships. Study abroad program.
Entrance Requirements: Open admission except for health sciences programs. Options: electronic application, early admission, deferred admission. Required: high school transcript. Entrance: noncompetitive. Application deadline: rolling. Notification: continuous. Transfer credits accepted: Yes.
Collegiate Environment: Orientation program. Student-run newspaper. Student services: personal-psychological counseling. Campus security: 24-hour emergency response devices and patrols, late night transport-escort service. 100 computers available on campus for general student use. A campuswide network can be accessed from off-campus. Students can access the following: online class registration. Staffed computer lab on campus provides training in use of computers, software, and the Internet.

■ **STRAYER UNIVERSITY-GREENSBORO CAMPUS**
4900 Koger Blvd.
Ste. 400
Greensboro, NC 27407
Tel: (336)315-7800; Free: 888-311-0355
Web Site: www.strayer.edu
Description: Proprietary, comprehensive, coed. Awards associate, bachelor's, and master's degrees.

■ **STRAYER UNIVERSITY-HUNTERSVILLE CAMPUS**
13620 Reese Blvd.
Ste. 130
Huntersville, NC 28078
Tel: (704)379-6800; Free: 888-311-0355
Web Site: www.strayer.edu
Description: Proprietary, comprehensive, coed. Awards associate, bachelor's, and master's degrees.

■ **STRAYER UNIVERSITY-NORTH CHARLOTTE CAMPUS**
7870 Commons Park Cir. NW
Concord, NC 28027
Tel: (704)886-6500; Free: 888-311-0355
Web Site: www.strayer.edu
Description: Proprietary, comprehensive, coed. Awards associate, bachelor's, and master's degrees.

■ **STRAYER UNIVERSITY-NORTH RALEIGH CAMPUS**
8701 Wadford Dr.
Raleigh, NC 27616
Tel: (919)301-6500; Free: 888-311-0355
Web Site: www.strayer.edu
Description: Proprietary, comprehensive, coed. Awards associate, bachelor's, and master's degrees.

■ **STRAYER UNIVERSITY-RESEARCH TRIANGLE PARK CAMPUS**
4 Copley Pky.
Morrisville, NC 27560
Tel: (919)466-4400; Free: 888-311-0355
Web Site: www.strayer.edu
Description: Proprietary, comprehensive, coed. Awards associate, bachelor's, and master's degrees.

■ **STRAYER UNIVERSITY-SOUTH CHARLOTTE CAMPUS**
9101 Kings Parade Blvd.
Ste. 200
Charlotte, NC 28273
Tel: (704)499-9200; Free: 888-311-0355
Web Site: www.strayer.edu
Description: Proprietary, comprehensive, coed. Awards associate, bachelor's, and master's degrees.

■ **STRAYER UNIVERSITY-SOUTH RALEIGH CAMPUS**
3421 Olympia Dr.
Raleigh, NC 27603
Tel: (919)890-7500; Free: 888-311-0355
Web Site: www.strayer.edu
Description: Proprietary, comprehensive, coed. Awards associate, bachelor's, and master's degrees.

■ **SURRY COMMUNITY COLLEGE**
630 S Main St.
Dobson, NC 27017
Tel: (336)386-8121
Fax: (336)386-8951
E-mail: hazelwoodr@surry.edu
Web Site: www.surry.edu
Description: State-supported, 2-year, coed. Part of North Carolina Community College System. Awards certificates, diplomas, transfer associate, and terminal associate degrees. Founded 1965. Setting: 100-acre rural campus. Total enrollment: 3,600. Faculty: 450 (150 full-time, 300 part-time). Student-undergrad faculty ratio is 27:1. Students come from 3 states and territories, 4% from out-of-state. 42% 25 or older. Core. Calendar: semesters. Academic remediation for entering students, ESL program, services for LD students, advanced placement, independent study, distance learning, double major, summer session for credit, part-time degree program, adult/continuing education programs, co-op programs and internships. Off campus study at Forsyth Technical Community College, Guilford Technical Community College, Rockingham Community College.
Entrance Requirements: Open admission except for nursing program. Options: electronic application, early admission, deferred admission. Required: high school transcript, CPT. Entrance: noncompetitive.
Collegiate Environment: Orientation program. Drama-theater group, choral group, student-run radio station. Social organizations: 7 open to all. Most popular organizations: Student Government Association, Phi Beta Lambda, Phi Theta Kappa, BSU. Major annual events: Student Appreciation Day, New Student Orientation. Campus security: late night transport-escort service,

security guard during day and evening hours. Resource Center. 200 computers available on campus for general student use. A campuswide network can be accessed. Staffed computer lab on campus.

Community Environment: A rural community with temperate climate, Dobson is the county seat. Community facilities include a library, United Methodist and Baptist churches, a hospital within 11 miles, some shopping, and several civic and service organizations. There are job opportunities in textile factories and with a poultry processing plant.

■ TRI-COUNTY COMMUNITY COLLEGE

21 Campus Cir.
Murphy, NC 28906-7919
Tel: (828)837-6810
Fax: (828)837-3266
E-mail: sjones@tricountycc.edu
Web Site: www.tricountycc.edu

Description: State-supported, 2-year, coed. Part of North Carolina Community College System. Awards certificates, diplomas, transfer associate, and terminal associate degrees. Founded 1964. Setting: 40-acre rural campus. Total enrollment: 1,160. Faculty: 80 (46 full-time, 34 part-time). Student-undergrad faculty ratio is 21:1. 65% 25 or older. Calendar: semesters. Academic remediation for entering students, distance learning, double major, summer session for credit, part-time degree program, adult/continuing education programs, internships. Study abroad program.

Entrance Requirements: Open admission except for nursing, medical assistant programs. Option: electronic application. Required: high school transcript. Recommended: SAT and SAT Subject Tests or ACT. Entrance: noncompetitive. Application deadline: rolling. Notification: continuous. Preference given to state residents. Transfer credits accepted: Yes.

Collegiate Environment: Orientation program. Student services: personal-psychological counseling. 43 computers available on campus for general student use. A campuswide network can be accessed. Students can access the following: online class registration. Staffed computer lab on campus provides training in use of computers, software, and the Internet.

Community Environment: Located in a valley in the central part of Cherokee County, Murphy has available bus and train transportation; Andrews Airport is 11 miles away. Community facilities include seven church denominations, two hospitals, and a fully equipped clinic. Mountains, streams, lakes, and forests make Murphy a sports lover's paradise. Parks, playgrounds, and other recreational facilities are available, including a complex that offers swimming pools, an 18-hole golf course, and horseback riding.

■ UNIVERSITY OF MOUNT OLIVE

634 Henderson St.
Mount Olive, NC 28365
Tel: (919)658-2502; Free: 800-653-0854
Fax: (919)658-8934
Web Site: www.umo.edu

Description: Independent Free Will Baptist, comprehensive, coed. Awards associate, bachelor's, and master's degrees. Founded 1951. Setting: 123-acre small town campus with easy access to Raleigh. Total enrollment: 3,855. Faculty: 183 (81 full-time, 102 part-time). Student-undergrad faculty ratio is 26:1. 1,838 applied, 50% were admitted. 10% from top 10% of their high school class, 47% from top quarter, 74% from top half. Full-time: 2,955 students, 69% women, 31% men. Part-time: 900 students, 64% women, 36% men. Students come from 11 other countries, 5% from out-of-state. 67% 25 or older, 11% live on campus. Retention: 60% of full-time freshmen returned the following year. Academic areas with the most degrees conferred: business/marketing; health professions and related sciences; education. Core. Calendar: semester or continuous accelerated programs. Advanced placement, accelerated degree program, freshman honors college, honors program, independent study, double major, summer session for credit, part-time degree program, external degree program, adult/continuing education programs, co-op programs and internships. Off campus study at North Carolina Community College System, East Carolina University, North Carolina State University. ROTC: Air Force (c).

Entrance Requirements: Open admission for those 21 or older or who have 27 hours of transferable credit. Options: electronic application, deferred admission, international baccalaureate accepted. Required: high school transcript. Recommended: 2 recommendations, interview. Required for some: SAT or ACT for those under 21. Entrance: minimally difficult. Application deadline: 8/18. Notification: continuous. SAT Reasoning Test deadline: 5/15. SAT Subject Test deadline: 5/15. Transfer credits accepted: Yes.

Costs Per Year: Application fee: $20. Comprehensive fee: $29,150 includes full-time tuition ($20,600) and college room and board ($8550). Full-time tuition varies according to degree level. Room and board charges vary according to board plan. Part-time tuition: $440 per credit hour. Part-time tuition varies according to degree level.

Collegiate Environment: Orientation program. Choral group. Most popular organizations: Student Government Association, Phi Beta Lambda, commuters organization, Christian Student Fellowship, English Society. Major annual events: Pickle Classic Basketball Tournament, Mr. and Miss Mount Olive College, MOOS Day. Student services: health clinic, personal-psychological counseling. Campus security: overnight security patrols; weekend patrols. Moye Library.

Community Environment: Mount Olive is about 15 miles from the county seat, Goldsboro. Buses provide commercial transportation. Numerous civic and service organizations, hospitals in separate towns 15 miles away, churches, and a library contribute to the community. The coast is a one-hour drive for swimming and fresh water fishing; other activities are tennis, softball, and golf.

■ UNIVERSITY OF NORTH CAROLINA AT ASHEVILLE

One University Heights
Asheville, NC 28804-3299
Tel: (828)251-6600; Free: 800-531-9842
Fax: (828)251-6385
E-mail: admissions@unca.edu
Web Site: www.unca.edu

Description: State-supported, comprehensive, coed. Part of University of North Carolina System. Awards bachelor's and master's degrees. Founded 1927. Setting: 365-acre urban campus. Endowment: $44.2 million. Research spending for the previous fiscal year: $2.1 million. Educational spending for the previous fiscal year: $9312 per student. Total enrollment: 3,762. Faculty: 320 (221 full-time, 99 part-time). Student-undergrad faculty ratio is 13:1. 3,163 applied, 82% were admitted. 17% from top 10% of their high school class, 42% from top quarter, 80% from top half. Full-time: 3,232 students, 58% women, 42% men. Part-time: 511 students, 50% women, 50% men. Students come from 44 states and territories, 26 other countries, 12% from out-of-state. 0.6% American Indian or Alaska Native, non-Hispanic/Latino; 6% Hispanic/Latino; 5% Black or African American, non-Hispanic/Latino; 2% Asian, non-Hispanic/Latino; 0.1% Native Hawaiian or other Pacific Islander, non-Hispanic/Latino; 1% international. 12% 25 or older, 38% live on campus, 9% transferred in. Retention: 73% of full-time freshmen returned the following year. Academic areas with the most degrees conferred: visual and performing arts; business/marketing; psychology. Core. Calendar: semesters. Services for LD students, advanced placement, self-designed majors, honors program, independent study, distance learning, double major, summer session for credit, part-time degree program, adult/continuing education programs, co-op programs and internships, graduate courses open to undergrads. Off campus study at UNC Online, an online course exchange with other UNC institutions. Study abroad program.

Entrance Requirements: Options: electronic application, deferred admission, international baccalaureate accepted. Required: essay, high school transcript, 1 recommendation, minimum course requirement, SAT or ACT. Entrance: moderately difficult. Application deadline: 8/1. Notification: continuous until 9/18. SAT Reasoning Test deadline: 2/15. SAT Subject Test deadline: 2/15. Transfer credits accepted: Yes.

Costs Per Year: Application fee: $75. One-time mandatory fee: $150. State resident tuition: $4914 full-time, $139.26 per credit hour part-time. Nonresident tuition: $21,236 full-time, $704.22 per credit hour part-time. Mandatory fees: $3023 full-time, $16.55 per credit hour part-time. Full-time tuition and fees vary according to course load and degree level. Part-time tuition and fees vary according to course load and degree level. College room and board: $9380. College room only: $5288. Room and board charges vary according to board plan and housing facility.

Collegiate Environment: Orientation program. Drama-theater group, choral group, student-run newspaper, radio station. Social organizations: 85 open to all; national fraternities, national sororities; 3% of eligible men and 3% of eligible women are members. Most popular organizations: Student Government Association, Alliance, Black Student Association, Gaming Club, Underdog Productions. Major annual events: Undergraduate Research Symposium, Arts Festival, Rockypalooza. Student services: health clinic, personal-psychological counseling. Campus security: 24-hour emergency response devices and patrols, late night transport-escort service, controlled dormitory access. 1,366 college housing spaces available; 1,350 were occupied in 2018-19. Freshmen guaranteed college housing. On-campus residence required in freshman year. Option: coed housing available. Ramsey Library. Books: 306,273 (physical), 487,660 (digital/electronic); Serial titles: 113 (physical), 82,954 (digital/electronic); Databases: 138. Weekly public service hours: 99; students can reserve study rooms. Operations spending for the previous fiscal year: $2.1 million. 500 computers available on campus for general student use. Computer purchase/lease plans available. A campuswide network can be accessed. Students can access the following: online class registration. Staffed computer lab on campus provides training in use of computers, software, and the Internet.

■ **THE UNIVERSITY OF NORTH CAROLINA AT CHAPEL HILL**
Chapel Hill, NC 27599
Tel: (919)962-2211
Web Site: www.unc.edu
Description: State-supported, university, coed. Part of University of North Carolina System. Awards bachelor's, master's, and doctoral degrees and post-master's certificates. Founded 1789. Setting: 729-acre suburban campus with easy access to Raleigh-Durham. Endowment: $3.3 billion. Research spending for the previous fiscal year: $601.9 million. Educational spending for the previous fiscal year: $26,933 per student. Total enrollment: 30,011. Faculty: 2,310 (1,653 full-time, 657 part-time). Student-undergrad faculty ratio is 13:1. 43,473 applied, 22% were admitted. 78% from top 10% of their high school class, 96% from top quarter, 99% from top half. 255 valedictorians. Full-time: 18,526 students, 60% women, 40% men. Part-time: 591 students, 49% women, 51% men. Students come from 52 states and territories, 101 other countries, 15% from out-of-state. 0.5% American Indian or Alaska Native, non-Hispanic/Latino; 8% Hispanic/Latino; 8% Black or African American, non-Hispanic/Latino; 11% Asian, non-Hispanic/Latino; 0.1% Native Hawaiian or other Pacific Islander, non-Hispanic/Latino; 3% international. 3% 25 or older, 51% live on campus, 4% transferred in. Retention: 97% of full-time freshmen returned the following year. Academic areas with the most degrees conferred: social sciences; communication/journalism; biological/life sciences. Core. Calendar: semesters. Services for LD students, advanced placement, self-designed majors, honors program, independent study, distance learning, double major, summer session for credit, part-time degree program, internships, graduate courses open to undergrads. Off campus study at North Carolina Central University, Duke University, North Carolina State University, University of North Carolina at Greensboro, University of North Carolina at Charlotte. Study abroad program. ROTC: Army, Naval, Air Force.
Entrance Requirements: Options: electronic application, early action, deferred admission, international baccalaureate accepted. Required: essay, high school transcript, 1 recommendation, counselor's statement, SAT or ACT. Entrance: very difficult. Application deadlines: 1/15, 10/15 for early action. Notification: 3/31, 1/31 for early action. Preference given to state residents. SAT Reasoning Test deadline: 1/31. SAT Subject Test deadline: 1/31. Transfer credits accepted: Yes. Applicants placed on waiting list: 4,977. Wait-listed applicants offered admission: 22. Early action applicants: 25,870. Early action applicants admitted: 8,038.
Costs Per Year: Application fee: $85. State resident tuition: $7019 full-time. Nonresident tuition: $34,198 full-time. Mandatory fees: $2027 full-time. College room and board: $11,526. College room only: $6810.
Collegiate Environment: Orientation program. Drama-theater group, choral group, marching band, student-run newspaper, radio station. Social organizations: 822 open to all; national fraternities, national sororities, 1 co-ed fraternity; 20% of eligible men and 20% of eligible women are members. Most popular organizations: Residence Hall Association, Carolina Fever, Campus Y, UNC-CH Habitat for Humanity, Carolina for the Kids Foundation (Dance Marathon). Major annual events: Fall Fest, Late Night with Roy, Homecoming. Student services: legal services, health clinic, personal-psychological counseling, women's center. Campus security: 24-hour emergency response devices and patrols, late night transport-escort service, controlled dormitory access, crime prevention initiatives, campuswide emergency alert system, cell phone/GPS security options. 9,702 college housing spaces available; 9,298 were occupied in 2018-19. Freshmen guaranteed college housing. On-campus residence required in freshman year. Options: coed, men-only, women-only housing available. Davis Library plus 12 others. Books: 7.5 million (physical), 1.3 million (digital/electronic); Serial titles: 191,333 (digital/electronic); Databases: 1,249. Weekly public service hours: 140; study areas open 24 hours, 5-7 days a week; students can reserve study rooms. Operations spending for the previous fiscal year: $45.5 million. 867 computers available on campus for general student use. Computer purchase/lease plans available. A computer is required for all students. A campuswide network can be accessed from student residence rooms and from off campus. Students can access the following: online class

registration. Staffed computer lab on campus (open 24 hours a day) provides training in use of computers, software, and the Internet.

■ **THE UNIVERSITY OF NORTH CAROLINA AT CHARLOTTE**
9201 University City Blvd.
Charlotte, NC 28223-0001
Tel: (704)687-8622
Fax: (704)510-6483
E-mail: admissions@uncc.edu
Web Site: www.uncc.edu
Description: State-supported, university, coed. Part of University of North Carolina System. Awards bachelor's, master's, and doctoral degrees and post-master's certificates. Founded 1946. Setting: 1,000-acre suburban campus with easy access to Charlotte. Endowment: $83.2 million. Research spending for the previous fiscal year: $23 million. Educational spending for the previous fiscal year: $8825 per student. Total enrollment: 29,710. Faculty: 1,692 (1,169 full-time, 523 part-time). Student-undergrad faculty ratio is 19:1. 17,119 applied, 67% were admitted. 17% from top 10% of their high school class, 47% from top quarter, 86% from top half. Full-time: 21,025 students, 46% women, 54% men. Part-time: 3,362 students, 50% women, 50% men. Students come from 45 states and territories, 92 other countries, 5% from out-of-state. 0.3% American Indian or Alaska Native, non-Hispanic/Latino; 10% Hispanic/Latino; 16% Black or African American, non-Hispanic/Latino; 7% Asian, non-Hispanic/Latino; 0.1% Native Hawaiian or other Pacific Islander, non-Hispanic/Latino; 3% international. 14% 25 or older, 20% live on campus, 12% transferred in. Retention: 82% of full-time freshmen returned the following year. Academic areas with the most degrees conferred: business/marketing; engineering; psychology. Core. Calendar: semesters. ESL program, services for LD students, advanced placement, accelerated degree program, freshman honors college, honors program, independent study, distance learning, double major, summer session for credit, part-time degree program, adult/continuing education programs, co-op programs and internships, graduate courses open to undergrads. Off campus study at Greater Charlotte Consortium. Study abroad program. ROTC: Army, Air Force.
Entrance Requirements: Options: electronic application, early action, international baccalaureate accepted. Required: high school transcript, minimum 2 high school GPA, SAT or ACT. Entrance: moderately difficult. Application deadlines: 6/1, 6/1 for nonresidents, 11/1 for early action. Notification: continuous until 11/1, continuous until 11/1 for nonresidents, 1/30 for early action. Preference given to state residents. SAT Reasoning Test deadline: 6/1. Transfer credits accepted: Yes. Early action applicants: 8,330. Early action applicants admitted: 6,630.
Costs Per Year: Application fee: $60. State resident tuition: $3812 full-time. Nonresident tuition: $17,246 full-time. Mandatory fees: $3232 full-time. Full-time tuition and fees vary according to course load and program. College room and board: $11,100. College room only: $6370. Room and board charges vary according to board plan and housing facility.
Collegiate Environment: Orientation program. Drama-theater group, choral group, marching band, student-run newspaper, radio station. Social organizations: 363 open to all; national fraternities, national sororities, local fraternities, local sororities; 6% of eligible men and 10% of eligible women are members. Most popular organizations: Triveni (Indian Students Association), National Society of Leadership and Success, Kinesiology Student Organization, Habitat for Humanity, 49th Security Division. Major annual events: Week of Welcome (WOW), International Festival (IFEST), Student Organizations Showcase. Student services: health clinic, personal-psychological counseling. Campus security: 24-hour emergency response devices and patrols, late night transport-escort service, controlled dormitory access. 6,039 college housing spaces available; 5,953 were occupied in 2018-19. No special consideration for freshman housing applicants. Option: coed housing available. J. Murrey Atkins Library plus 1 other. Books: 812,959 (physical), 980,416 (digital/electronic); Serial titles: 4,578 (physical), 92,904 (digital/electronic); Databases: 675. Study areas open 24 hours, 5-7 days a week; students can reserve study rooms. Operations spending for the previous fiscal year: $12.5 million. 1,600 computers available on campus for general student use. A campuswide network can be accessed from student residence rooms and from off campus. Students can access the following: online class registration. Staffed computer lab on campus (open 24 hours a day) provides training in use of computers, software, and the Internet.

■ **THE UNIVERSITY OF NORTH CAROLINA AT GREENSBORO**
1400 Spring Garden St.
Greensboro, NC 27412-5001

Tel: (336)334-5000

Fax: (336)334-4180

Web Site: www.uncg.edu

Description: State-supported, university, coed. Part of University of North Carolina System. Awards bachelor's, master's, and doctoral degrees and post-master's certificates. Founded 1891. Setting: 250-acre urban campus. Endowment: $292 million. Research spending for the previous fiscal year: $17.9 million. Educational spending for the previous fiscal year: $9691 per student. Total enrollment: 20,106. Faculty: 1,126 (842 full-time, 284 part-time). Student-undergrad faculty ratio is 18:1. 8,170 applied, 84% were admitted. 14% from top 10% of their high school class, 38% from top quarter, 76% from top half. Full-time: 8,165 students, 41% women, 59% men. Part-time: 2,376 students, 69% women, 31% men. Students come from 46 states and territories, 55 other countries, 5% from out-of-state. 0.4% American Indian or Alaska Native, non-Hispanic/Latino; 10% Hispanic/Latino; 29% Black or African American, non-Hispanic/Latino; 5% Asian, non-Hispanic/Latino; 0.1% Native Hawaiian or other Pacific Islander, non-Hispanic/Latino; 2% international. 18% 25 or older, 34% live on campus, 18% transferred in. Retention: 76% of full-time freshmen returned the following year. Academic areas with the most degrees conferred: business/marketing; health professions and related sciences; computer and information sciences. Core. Calendar: semesters. Academic remediation for entering students, ESL program, services for LD students, advanced placement, accelerated degree program, self-designed majors, freshman honors college, honors program, independent study, distance learning, double major, summer session for credit, part-time degree program, adult/continuing education programs, internships, graduate courses open to undergrads. Off campus study at Greater Greensboro Consortium, North Carolina Inter-Institutional Agreement, UNC Online Inter-institutional Agreement. Study abroad program. ROTC: Army (c), Air Force (c).

Entrance Requirements: Options: electronic application, international baccalaureate accepted. Required: high school transcript, minimum 2.3 high school GPA, SAT or ACT. Entrance: moderately difficult. Application deadline: 8/1. Notification: continuous until 8/15. SAT Reasoning Test deadline: 3/1. Transfer credits accepted: Yes.

Costs Per Year: Application fee: $65. State resident tuition: $4422 full-time, $552.75 per credit hour part-time. Nonresident tuition: $19,581 full-time, $2,447.63 per credit hour part-time. Mandatory fees: $2897 full-time, $108.13 per credit hour part-time. Part-time tuition and fees vary according to course load. College room and board: $9038. College room only: $5382. Room and board charges vary according to board plan and housing facility.

Collegiate Environment: Orientation program. Drama-theater group, choral group, student-run newspaper, radio station. Social organizations: 323 open to all; national fraternities, national sororities; 2% of eligible men and 3% of eligible women are members. Most popular organizations: Alpha Lamda Delta, Beta Gamma Sigma, Sigma Theta Tau, Gamma Zeta, Golden Key, UNCG Leadership Challenge - Bronze. Major annual events: Homecoming, Fall Kick Off, Spring Fling. Student services: health clinic, personal-psychological counseling, women's center. Campus security: 24-hour emergency response devices and patrols, student patrols, late night transport-escort service, controlled dormitory access. 5,732 college housing spaces available; 5,627 were occupied in 2018-19. No special consideration for freshman housing applicants. Option: coed housing available. Walter Clinton Jackson Library plus 4 others. Books: 1.2 million (physical), 1.2 million (digital/electronic); Serial titles: 18,527 (physical), 109,122 (digital/electronic); Databases: 765. Weekly public service hours: 138; study areas open 24 hours, 5-7 days a week; students can reserve study rooms. Operations spending for the previous fiscal year: $13 million. 474 computers available on campus for general student use. Computer purchase/lease plans available. A campuswide network can be accessed from student residence rooms and from off campus. Students can access the following: online class registration, wireless printing services, cloud storage services. Staffed computer lab on campus provides training in use of computers, software, and the Internet.

■ THE UNIVERSITY OF NORTH CAROLINA AT PEMBROKE

One University Dr.

Pembroke, NC 28372-1510

Tel: (910)521-6000; Free: 800-949-UNCP

Web Site: www.uncp.edu

Description: State-supported, comprehensive, coed. Part of University of North Carolina System. Awards bachelor's and master's degrees and post-master's certificates. Founded 1887. Setting: 264-acre rural campus. Endowment: $20.4 million. Research spending for the previous fiscal year:

$410,273. Educational spending for the previous fiscal year: $7013 per student. Total enrollment: 7,137. Faculty: 402 (303 full-time, 99 part-time). Student-undergrad faculty ratio is 16:1. 4,316 applied, 81% were admitted. 1% from top 10% of their high school class, 6% from top quarter, 29% from top half. Full-time: 4,945 students, 60% women, 40% men. Part-time: 1,124 students, 66% women, 34% men. Students come from 33 states and territories, 12 other countries, 4% from out-of-state. 15% American Indian or Alaska Native, non-Hispanic/Latino; 6% Hispanic/Latino; 33% Black or African American, non-Hispanic/Latino; 2% Asian, non-Hispanic/Latino; 0.1% Native Hawaiian or other Pacific Islander, non-Hispanic/Latino; 0.9% international. 24% 25 or older, 34% live on campus, 14% transferred in. Retention: 74% of full-time freshmen returned the following year. Academic areas with the most degrees conferred: homeland security, law enforcement, firefighting, and protective services; biological/life sciences; business/marketing. Core. Calendar: semesters. Academic remediation for entering students, ESL program, services for LD students, advanced placement, accelerated degree program, honors program, distance learning, double major, summer session for credit, part-time degree program, adult/continuing education programs, co-op programs and internships, graduate courses open to undergrads. Off campus study at Richmond Community College, Fayetteville State University, Sandhills Community College, Southeastern Community College, Fayetteville Technical College. Study abroad program. ROTC: Army, Air Force.

Entrance Requirements: Options: electronic application, deferred admission. Required: high school transcript, SAT or ACT. Recommended: essay, minimum 2 high school GPA. Required for some: 1 recommendation, interview, TOEFL. Entrance: moderately difficult. Application deadline: 6/30. Notification: continuous. SAT Reasoning Test deadline: 6/30. SAT Subject Test deadline: 6/30. Transfer credits accepted: Yes.

Costs Per Year: Application fee: $45. State resident tuition: $1000 full-time. Nonresident tuition: $5000 full-time. Mandatory fees: $241 full-time.

Collegiate Environment: Orientation program. Drama-theater group, choral group, marching band, student-run newspaper, radio station. Social organizations: 100 open to all; national fraternities, national sororities, local fraternities, local sororities; 7% of eligible men and 4% of eligible women are members. Most popular organizations: Health Careers Club, Spectrum, Graduate Student Organization, Phi Alpha, National Association for the Advancement of Colored People. Major annual events: Pembroke Day, Family Day, Homecoming. Student services: health clinic, personal-psychological counseling. Campus security: 24-hour emergency response devices and patrols, late night transport-escort service, controlled dormitory access. 2,150 college housing spaces available; 2,074 were occupied in 2018-19. Freshmen given priority for college housing. On-campus residence required in freshman year. Options: coed, men-only, women-only housing available. Livermore Library. Books: 398,000 (physical), 165,000 (digital/electronic); Serial titles: 406 (physical), 54,000 (digital/electronic); Databases: 185. Weekly public service hours: 92; students can reserve study rooms. Operations spending for the previous fiscal year: $2.7 million. 501 computers available on campus for general student use. A campuswide network can be accessed from student residence rooms and from off campus. Students can access the following: online class registration, commuter/off campus connection to network, discounted computer software/hardware. Staffed computer lab on campus provides training in use of computers, software, and the Internet.

■ UNIVERSITY OF NORTH CAROLINA SCHOOL OF THE ARTS

1533 S Main St.

Winston Salem, NC 27127-2738

Tel: (336)770-3399

Fax: (336)770-3370

Web Site: www.uncsa.edu

Description: State-supported, comprehensive, coed. Part of University of North Carolina system. Awards bachelor's and master's degrees and post-master's certificates. Founded 1963. Setting: 74-acre urban campus. Endowment: $67.7 million. Educational spending for the previous fiscal year: $21,165 per student. Total enrollment: 1,042. Faculty: 189 (144 full-time, 45 part-time). Student-undergrad faculty ratio is 6:1. 1,185 applied, 38% were admitted. 11% from top 10% of their high school class, 39% from top quarter, 81% from top half. Full-time: 884 students, 53% women, 47% men. Part-time: 6 students, 50% women, 50% men. Students come from 46 states and territories, 14 other countries, 49% from out-of-state. 1% American Indian or Alaska Native, non-Hispanic/Latino; 8% Hispanic/Latino; 9% Black or African American, non-Hispanic/Latino; 2% Asian, non-Hispanic/Latino; 3% international. 4% 25 or older, 59% live on campus, 4% transferred in. Retention: 88% of full-time freshmen returned the following year. Academic area with the most degrees conferred: visual and performing arts. Core. Calendar: semesters. ESL program, services for LD students, advanced placement, independent study, summer session for credit, internships.

Entrance Requirements: Options: deferred admission, international baccalaureate accepted. Required: essay, high school transcript, minimum 2.5 high school GPA, 2 recommendations, interview, audition, SAT or ACT. Notification: continuous until 4/1. SAT Reasoning Test deadline: 4/15. Transfer credits accepted: Yes. Applicants placed on waiting list: 166. Wait-listed applicants offered admission: 1.

Costs Per Year: Application fee: $95. State resident tuition: $6497 full-time, $265.50 per credit hour part-time. Nonresident tuition: $23,040 full-time, $943.50 per credit hour part-time. Mandatory fees: $2861 full-time, $115 per credit hour part-time. College room and board: $9156. College room only: $4654. Tuition guaranteed not to increase for student's term of enrollment.

Collegiate Environment: Orientation program. Drama-theater group, choral group, student-run newspaper. Most popular organizations: A.R.T.S. Club (awareness on social issues through artistic expression), The Artist Underground, Art & Soul, UNCSA Artists of Color. Major annual events: Welcome Back Weekend, FrozeArts, Beaux Arts (end of the year celebration). Student services: health clinic, personal-psychological counseling. Campus security: 24-hour emergency response devices and patrols, late night transport-escort service, controlled dormitory access. 530 college housing spaces available; 520 were occupied in 2018-19. Freshmen guaranteed college housing. On-campus residence required through sophomore year. Option: coed housing available. UNCSA Library. Books: 101,097 (physical), 37,147 (digital/electronic); Serial titles: 1,171 (physical), 73,113 (digital/electronic); Databases: 121. Weekly public service hours: 90; students can reserve study rooms. Operations spending for the previous fiscal year: $1.2 million. 117 computers available on campus for general student use. Computer purchase/lease plans available. A campuswide network can be accessed from student residence rooms and from off campus. Students can access the following: online class registration. Staffed computer lab on campus provides training in use of computers and the Internet.

Community Environment: See Wake Forest University.

■ **THE UNIVERSITY OF NORTH CAROLINA WILMINGTON**
601 S College Rd.
Wilmington, NC 28403-3297
Tel: (910)962-3000
Fax: (910)962-3038
E-mail: admissions@uncw.edu
Web Site: www.uncw.edu

Description: State-supported, comprehensive, coed. Part of University of North Carolina System. Awards bachelor's, master's, and doctoral degrees and post-master's certificates. Founded 1947. Setting: 661-acre urban campus. Endowment: $83.4 million. Research spending for the previous fiscal year: $12.4 million. Educational spending for the previous fiscal year: $8813 per student. Total enrollment: 16,487. Faculty: 1,067 (647 full-time, 420 part-time). Student-undergrad faculty ratio is 18:1. 11,677 applied, 67% were admitted. 25% from top 10% of their high school class, 62% from top quarter, 93% from top half. Full-time: 12,346 students, 60% women, 40% men. Part-time: 2,156 students, 75% women, 25% men. Students come from 51 states and territories, 53 other countries, 12% from out-of-state. 0.5% American Indian or Alaska Native, non-Hispanic/Latino; 7% Hispanic/Latino; 4% Black or African American, non-Hispanic/Latino; 2% Asian, non-Hispanic/Latino; 0.1% Native Hawaiian or other Pacific Islander, non-Hispanic/Latino; 2% international. 19% 25 or older, 22% live on campus, 13% transferred in. Retention: 87% of full-time freshmen returned the following year. Academic areas with the most degrees conferred: business/marketing; health professions and related sciences; biological/life sciences. Core. Calendar: semesters. Academic remediation for entering students, ESL program, services for LD students, advanced placement, accelerated degree program, honors program, independent study, distance learning, double major, summer session for credit, co-op programs and internships, graduate courses open to undergrads. Off campus study. Study abroad program.

Entrance Requirements: Options: electronic application, early admission, early action, deferred admission, international baccalaureate accepted. Required: essay, high school transcript, 1 recommendation, SAT or ACT. Entrance: moderately difficult. Application deadlines: 2/1, 11/1 for early action. Notification: 4/1, 1/20 for early action. SAT Reasoning Test deadline: 2/1. Transfer credits accepted: Yes. Applicants placed on waiting list: 1,065.

Wait-listed applicants offered admission: 166. Early action applicants: 7,678. Early action applicants admitted: 5,463.

Costs Per Year: Application fee: $80. State resident tuition: $4443 full-time, $163.35 per credit hour part-time. Nonresident tuition: $18,508 full-time, $680.44 per credit hour part-time. Mandatory fees: $2557 full-time, $78.11 per credit hour part-time. Full-time tuition and fees vary according to course load and location. Part-time tuition and fees vary according to course load and location. College room and board: $10,686. College room only: $6660. Room and board charges vary according to board plan and housing facility.

Collegiate Environment: Orientation program. Drama-theater group, choral group, student-run newspaper, radio station. Social organizations: 270 open to all; national fraternities, national sororities; 10% of eligible men and 10% of eligible women are members. Most popular organizations: Student Government Association, Association of Campus Entertainment, Residence Hall Association, Sports Club Council, Graduate Student Association. Major annual events: Involvement Carnival, Festapalooza, Beach Blast. Student services: health clinic, personal-psychological counseling, women's center. Campus security: 24-hour emergency response devices and patrols, late night transport-escort service, controlled dormitory access. William Madison Randall Library. Books: 573,457 (physical), 272,920 (digital/electronic); Serial titles: 4,761 (physical), 71,907 (digital/electronic); Databases: 305. Weekly public service hours: 110; study areas open 24 hours, 5-7 days a week; students can reserve study rooms. Operations spending for the previous fiscal year: $6.7 million. 1,423 computers available on campus for general student use. Computer purchase/lease plans available. A campuswide network can be accessed from student residence rooms and from off campus. Students can access the following: online class registration. Staffed computer lab on campus provides training in use of computers, software, and the Internet.

■ **VANCE-GRANVILLE COMMUNITY COLLEGE**
PO Box 917
Henderson, NC 27536-0917
Tel: (252)492-2061
Fax: (252)430-0460
Web Site: www.vgcc.edu

Description: State-supported, 2-year, coed. Part of North Carolina Community College System. Awards certificates, diplomas, transfer associate, and terminal associate degrees. Founded 1969. Setting: 83-acre rural campus with easy access to Raleigh. Endowment: $3 million. Total enrollment: 4,057. Faculty: 353 (141 full-time, 212 part-time). Student-undergrad faculty ratio is 9:1. 1,765 applied, 100% were admitted. 12% from top 10% of their high school class, 22% from top quarter, 40% from top half. 35 student government officers. Full-time: 1,718 students, 65% women, 35% men. Part-time: 2,339 students, 68% women, 32% men. Students come from 10 states and territories, 15 other countries, 2% from out-of-state. 53% 25 or older, 2% transferred in. Core. Calendar: semesters. Academic remediation for entering students, ESL program, services for LD students, advanced placement, accelerated degree program, distance learning, double major, summer session for credit, part-time degree program, adult/continuing education programs, co-op programs and internships.

Entrance Requirements: Open admission except for nursing, radiology programs, electronics engineering. Options: early admission, deferred admission. Required: high school transcript. Entrance: noncompetitive. Application deadline: rolling. Notification: continuous. Preference given to district, then state residents.

Collegiate Environment: Orientation program. Drama-theater group. Most popular organizations: Vocational Club, Phi Theta Kappa, Computer Club, Criminal Justice Club, Business Club. Major annual events: Spring Sports Day, College-Wide Olympic Games, Career Day. Student services: personal-psychological counseling. Campus security: 24-hour emergency response devices and patrols. Vance-Granville Community College Learning Resource Center plus 1 other. 184 computers available on campus for general student use. A campuswide network can be accessed from off-campus. Staffed computer lab on campus.

■ **WAKE FOREST UNIVERSITY**
1834 Wake Forest Rd.
Winston Salem, NC 27109
Tel: (336)758-5000
Fax: (336)758-6074
Web Site: www.wfu.edu

Description: Independent, university, coed. Awards bachelor's, master's, and doctoral degrees. Founded 1834. Setting: 340-acre suburban campus.

Total enrollment: 8,116. Faculty: (579 full-time, 292 part-time). Student-undergrad faculty ratio is 11:1. 13,071 applied, 28% were admitted. 77% from top 10% of their high school class, 93% from top quarter, 98% from top half. Full-time: 5,046 students, 54% women, 46% men. Part-time: 56 students, 64% women, 36% men. 78% from out-of-state. 0.1% American Indian or Alaska Native, non-Hispanic/Latino; 7% Hispanic/Latino; 7% Black or African American, non-Hispanic/Latino; 4% Asian, non-Hispanic/Latino; 10% international. 0.2% 25 or older, 75% live on campus, 1% transferred in. Retention: 94% of full-time freshmen returned the following year. Academic areas with the most degrees conferred: social sciences; business/marketing; communication/journalism. Calendar: semesters. Services for LD students, advanced placement, honors program, independent study, distance learning, double major, summer session for credit, part-time degree program, internships. Study abroad program. ROTC: Army.

Entrance Requirements: Options: electronic application, early admission, early decision, international baccalaureate accepted. Required: essay, high school transcript, 1 recommendation. Recommended: interview. Entrance: very difficult. Application deadlines: 1/1, 11/15 for early decision. Notification: continuous, rolling for early decision. Early decision applicants: 1,842. Early decision applicants admitted: 815.

Costs Per Year: Application fee: $65. Comprehensive fee: $69,354 includes full-time tuition ($52,348), mandatory fees ($974), and college room and board ($16,032). College room only: $9282. Part-time tuition: $2170 per credit hour.

Collegiate Environment: Drama-theater group, choral group, marching band, student-run newspaper, radio station. Social organizations: national fraternities, national sororities. Student services: health clinic, personal-psychological counseling. Campus security: 24-hour emergency response devices and patrols, late night transport-escort service, controlled dormitory access. Z. Smith Reynolds Library.

Community Environment: Wake Forest is located in Piedmont North Carolina, an hour from the Blue Ridge mountains, in the northwestern suburb of Winston-Salem, a city of 150,000 dating from the 1700s. Wake Forest shares a close working relationship with Salem College, Winston-Salem State University, and the North Carolina School of the Arts. Winston-Salem is a city of colleges, business, recreation, and the arts. The numerous points of interest include Reynolda House and Gardens, Old Salem, Wachovia Museum, Southeastern Center of Contemporary Art, Museum of Early Southern Decorative Arts, Nature Science Museum, Tanglewood Estates Park, two annual craft fairs and numerous craft and art galleries.

■ **WAKE TECHNICAL COMMUNITY COLLEGE**
9101 Fayetteville Rd.
Raleigh, NC 27603-5696
Tel: (919)662-3400
Fax: (919)662-3529
Web Site: www.waketech.edu
Description: State and locally supported, 2-year, coed. Part of North Carolina Community College System. Awards certificates, diplomas, transfer associate, and terminal associate degrees. Founded 1958. Setting: 79-acre suburban campus. Total enrollment: 14,747. Student-undergrad faculty ratio is 11:1. 2% from out-of-state. 43% 25 or older. Retention: 71% of full-time freshmen returned the following year. Calendar: semesters. Academic remediation for entering students, advanced placement, distance learning, summer session for credit, part-time degree program, adult/continuing education programs.
Entrance Requirements: Open admission except for nursing program. Options: electronic application, early admission. Required: high school transcript. Entrance: noncompetitive. Application deadline: rolling.
Collegiate Environment: Campus security: 24-hour patrols. Bruce M. Howell Library.
Community Environment: See Meredith College.

■ **WARREN WILSON COLLEGE**
PO Box 9000
Asheville, NC 28815-9000
Tel: (828)298-3325; Free: 800-934-3536
Fax: (828)298-1440
E-mail: admit@warren-wilson.edu
Web Site: www.warren-wilson.edu
Description: Independent, comprehensive, coed, affiliated with Presbyterian Church (U.S.A.). Awards bachelor's and master's degrees. Founded 1894. Setting: 1,135-acre suburban campus. Total enrollment: 812. Faculty: 103 (63 full-time, 40 part-time). Student-undergrad faculty ratio is 10:1. 809 ap-

plied, 84% were admitted. 17% from top 10% of their high school class, 18% from top quarter, 77% from top half. Full-time: 741 students, 60% women, 40% men. Part-time: 12 students, 67% women, 33% men. 74% from out-of-state. 0.8% American Indian or Alaska Native, non-Hispanic/Latino; 9% Hispanic/Latino; 4% Black or African American, non-Hispanic/Latino; 1% Asian, non-Hispanic/Latino; 2% international. 4% 25 or older, 88% live on campus, 7% transferred in. Retention: 63% of full-time freshmen returned the following year. Academic areas with the most degrees conferred: natural resources/environmental science; English; social sciences. Core. Calendar: semesters. ESL program, services for LD students, advanced placement, self-designed majors, honors program, independent study, double major, summer session for credit, part-time degree program, co-op programs and internships. Off campus study at Asheville Area Educational Consortium: University of North Carolina at Asheville, and Mars Hill College. Study abroad program.

Entrance Requirements: Options: electronic application, early admission, early decision, early action, deferred admission, international baccalaureate accepted. Required: essay, high school transcript, Common Application, Common Application School Report Form. Recommended: minimum 2.5 high school GPA, 2 recommendations, interview. Entrance: moderately difficult. Transfer credits accepted: Yes. Early decision applicants: 58. Early decision applicants admitted: 56.

Costs Per Year: Application fee: $0. Comprehensive fee: $47,260 includes full-time tuition ($35,536), mandatory fees ($744), and college room and board ($10,980). Full-time tuition and fees vary according to course load. Room and board charges vary according to board plan. Part-time tuition: $1481 per credit hour. Part-time mandatory fees: $100 per term. Part-time tuition and fees vary according to course load.

Collegiate Environment: Orientation program. Drama-theater group, choral group, student-run newspaper. Social organizations: 20 open to all. Most popular organizations: Food Not Bombs, Club Sports: Paddling, Cycling, Cyclocross, Timbersports, Multicultural Student Organizations: Engage, WHOLA, Peace, Social and Environmental Justice Groups, Student Religious Groups: Christian, Jewish, Buddhist, Quaker, Pagan, and Unitarian Universalist. Major annual events: Circus, Work Day, Martin Luther King, Jr. Day. Student services: health clinic, personal-psychological counseling. Campus security: 24-hour emergency response devices and patrols, student patrols, late night transport-escort service, controlled dormitory access. Pew Learning Center and Ellison Library.

Community Environment: Situated in the Swannanoa Valley among the Blue Ridge Mountains of western North Carolina, the campus is ten miles east of Asheville. Inhabitants enjoy all the conveniences of the smaller local community, and all the advantages of the nearby city.

■ **WAYNE COMMUNITY COLLEGE**
PO Box 8002
Goldsboro, NC 27533-8002
Tel: (919)735-5151
Fax: (919)736-3204
E-mail: rlmatthews@waynecc.edu
Web Site: www.waynecc.edu
Description: State and locally supported, 2-year, coed. Part of North Carolina Community College System. Awards certificates, diplomas, transfer associate, and terminal associate degrees. Founded 1957. Setting: 175-acre small town campus with easy access to Raleigh. Endowment: $92,408. Educational spending for the previous fiscal year: $4605 per student. Total enrollment: 3,837. Faculty: 333 (140 full-time, 193 part-time). Student-undergrad faculty ratio is 20:1. 2,328 applied, 57% were admitted. Full-time: 1,813 students, 57% women, 43% men. Part-time: 2,024 students, 63% women, 37% men. 4% from out-of-state. 0.6% American Indian or Alaska Native, non-Hispanic/Latino; 8% Hispanic/Latino; 27% Black or African American, non-Hispanic/Latino; 2% Asian, non-Hispanic/Latino; 0.3% Native Hawaiian or other Pacific Islander, non-Hispanic/Latino; 0.3% international. 45% 25 or older, 26% transferred in. Calendar: semesters. Academic remediation for entering students, ESL program, services for LD students, advanced placement, honors program, distance learning, double major, summer session for credit, part-time degree program, external degree program, adult/continuing education programs, co-op programs.
Entrance Requirements: Open admission except for health occupations, Basic Law Enforcement Training programs. Options: electronic application, international baccalaureate accepted. Required: high school transcript, interview. Required for some: SAT or ACT. Entrance: noncompetitive. Application deadline: rolling. Notification: continuous. SAT Reasoning Test deadline: 8/17. Transfer credits accepted: Yes. Applicants placed on waiting list: 60. Wait-listed applicants offered admission: 17.

Costs Per Year: Application fee: $0. State resident tuition: $2432 full-time, $76 per credit hour part-time. Nonresident tuition: $8576 full-time, $268 per credit hour part-time. Mandatory fees: $92 full-time, $46 per term part-time.

Collegiate Environment: Orientation program. Choral group. Social organizations: 23 open to all. Most popular organizations: Student Government Association, Phi Beta Lambda, Phi Theta Kappa, Criminal Justice Club, International Club. Major annual events: Spring Spectacular, Welcome Bash, Fall Fest. Student services: personal-psychological counseling. Campus security: 24-hour emergency response devices and patrols. Dr. Clyde A. Erwin, Jr. Library. Operations spending for the previous fiscal year: $419,200. 75 computers available on campus for general student use. A campuswide network can be accessed. Students can access the following: online class registration. Staffed computer lab on campus provides training in use of computers, software, and the Internet.

Community Environment: 50% of the state's bright-leaf tobacco is produced within a radius of 60 miles of Goldsboro. The soil and climate also make livestock production and farming important. All forms of commercial transportation are available. Churches of all denominations, a hospital, and medical clinic are a part of the city's facilities. Job opportunities are plentiful. Recreational facilities are good for all outdoor sports.

■ WESTERN CAROLINA UNIVERSITY

Cullowhee, NC 28723
Tel: (828)227-7211; Free: 877-WCU4YOU
E-mail: admiss@email.wcu.edu
Web Site: www.wcu.edu

Description: State-supported, university, coed. Part of University of North Carolina System. Awards bachelor's, master's, and doctoral degrees and post-master's certificates. Founded 1889. Setting: 682-acre rural campus. Total enrollment: 10,805. Faculty: 688 (511 full-time, 177 part-time). Student-undergrad faculty ratio is 17:1. 18,297 applied, 41% were admitted. 14% from top 10% of their high school class, 38% from top quarter, 76% from top half. Full-time: 7,871 students, 54% women, 46% men. Part-time: 1,300 students, 59% women, 41% men. Students come from 39 states and territories, 40 other countries, 6% from out-of-state. 0.7% American Indian or Alaska Native, non-Hispanic/Latino; 6% Hispanic/Latino; 7% Black or African American, non-Hispanic/Latino; 1% Asian, non-Hispanic/Latino; 0.1% Native Hawaiian or other Pacific Islander, non-Hispanic/Latino; 1% international. 18% 25 or older, 9% transferred in. Retention: 80% of full-time freshmen returned the following year. Academic areas with the most degrees conferred: business/marketing; health professions and related sciences; education. Core. Calendar: semesters. ESL program, services for LD students, advanced placement, self-designed majors, honors program, independent study, distance learning, double major, summer session for credit, part-time degree program, co-op programs and internships, graduate courses open to undergrads. Study abroad program.

Entrance Requirements: Options: electronic application, early admission, early action, international baccalaureate accepted. Required: high school transcript, SAT or ACT. Recommended: ACT. Entrance: moderately difficult. SAT Reasoning Test deadline: 7/1. Transfer credits accepted: Yes.

Costs Per Year: Application fee: $65. State resident tuition: $1000 full-time. Nonresident tuition: $5000 full-time. Mandatory fees: $3220 full-time. Full-time tuition and fees vary according to degree level. College room and board: $9682. College room only: $4974. Room and board charges vary according to board plan and housing facility. Tuition guaranteed not to increase for student's term of enrollment.

Collegiate Environment: Orientation program. Drama-theater group, choral group, marching band, student-run newspaper, radio station. Social organizations: 163 open to all; national fraternities, national sororities. Major annual events: Mountain Heritage Day, Valley Ballyhoo, Homecoming. Student services: health clinic, personal-psychological counseling, women's center. Campus security: 24-hour emergency response devices and patrols, late night transport-escort service, controlled dormitory access. Hunter Library. Weekly public service hours: 96; study areas open 24 hours, 5-7 days a week; students can reserve study rooms.

Community Environment: Cullowhee is in an area containing several of the most scenic drives in western North Carolina. It is a rural area with bus transportation available. Asheville is nearby and provides an airport for air transportation. Student employment is available in clerical and cafeteria positions. Recreational activities include boating, fishing, water sports, mountain climbing and nature trails. Main shopping facilities are in Asheville.

■ WESTERN PIEDMONT COMMUNITY COLLEGE

1001 Burkemont Ave.
Morganton, NC 28655-4511

Tel: (828)438-6000
Fax: (828)438-6015
E-mail: swilliams@wpcc.edu
Web Site: www.wpcc.edu

Description: State-supported, 2-year, coed. Part of North Carolina Community College System. Awards certificates, diplomas, transfer associate, and terminal associate degrees. Founded 1964. Setting: 130-acre small town campus. Total enrollment: 2,933. 0.3% American Indian or Alaska Native, non-Hispanic/Latino; 5% Hispanic/Latino; 7% Black or African American, non-Hispanic/Latino; 7% Asian, non-Hispanic/Latino; 0.2% Native Hawaiian or other Pacific Islander, non-Hispanic/Latino. Core. Calendar: semesters. Academic remediation for entering students, ESL program, services for LD students, advanced placement, distance learning, double major, summer session for credit, part-time degree program, adult/continuing education programs, co-op programs.

Entrance Requirements: Open admission. Option: electronic application. Required: high school transcript. Entrance: noncompetitive. Application deadline: rolling. Notification: continuous.

Costs Per Year: State resident tuition: $2432 full-time, $76 per credit hour part-time. Nonresident tuition: $8576 full-time, $268 per credit hour part-time. Mandatory fees: $144 full-time, $5 per credit hour part-time, $6.20 per term part-time.

Collegiate Environment: Orientation program. Drama-theater group. Student services: personal-psychological counseling.

Community Environment: Western Piedmont Community College, in Morganton (population 17,000), is situated in the Appalachian foothills of western North Carolina near the Catawba River. Burke County (population 90,000) was established in 1777 and named in honor of the third governor of North Carolina, Thomas Burke. Manufacturing is diversified and includes furniture, textiles, electronics, and assembly plants. The major employer is the State of North Carolina with services at Broughton Hospital, Western Carolina Center, Western Correctional Center, and the North Carolina School for the Deaf. Burke County is located in the fastest growing region of the state but as yet maintains its rural values.

■ WILKES COMMUNITY COLLEGE

1328 Collegiate Dr.
Wilkesboro, NC 28697
Tel: (336)838-6100
Fax: (336)838-6277
E-mail: mac.warren@wilkescc.edu
Web Site: www.wilkescc.edu

Description: State-supported, 2-year, coed. Part of North Carolina Community College System. Awards certificates, diplomas, transfer associate, and terminal associate degrees. Founded 1965. Setting: 140-acre small town campus. Endowment: $2.7 million. Educational spending for the previous fiscal year: $2929 per student. Total enrollment: 2,558. Faculty: 362 (73 full-time, 289 part-time). Student-undergrad faculty ratio is 10:1. 1,215 applied, 100% were admitted. Students come from 13 states and territories, 15 other countries, 1% from out-of-state. 44% 25 or older. Core. Calendar: semesters. Academic remediation for entering students, ESL program, services for LD students, advanced placement, accelerated degree program, independent study, distance learning, double major, summer session for credit, part-time degree program, adult/continuing education programs, co-op programs and internships.

Entrance Requirements: Open admission. Options: electronic application, deferred admission. Required: high school transcript. Entrance: noncompetitive. Application deadline: rolling. Notification: continuous.

Collegiate Environment: Drama-theater group, choral group, student-run newspaper, radio station. Social organizations: 21 open to all. Most popular organizations: Student Government Association, Phi Theta Kappa, Phi Beta Lambda, Rotaract, Baptist Student Union. Major annual events: Alcohol Awareness Week Activities, Welcome Back Week Activities, Fall Festival. Student services: personal-psychological counseling. Campus security: 24-hour emergency response devices, student patrols, late night transport-escort service. Learning Resources Center. Operations spending for the previous fiscal year: $273,143. 255 computers available on campus for general student use. A campuswide network can be accessed. Students can access the following: campus e-mail system. Staffed computer lab on campus.

Community Environment: Located 50 miles from Winston-Salem, Wilkesboro is the county seat of Wilkes County. The community offers churches of various faiths, shopping areas, and adequate medical facilities. The Kerr Scott Dam and Reservoir provides boating, fishing, water skiing, and swimming. The Blue Ridge Mountains around the Boone area provides winter time sports such as skiing and ice skating.

■ WILLIAM PEACE UNIVERSITY

15 E Peace St.
Raleigh, NC 27604-1194
Tel: (919)508-2000
Fax: (919)508-2328
E-mail: admission@peace.edu
Web Site: www.peace.edu

Description: Independent, 4-year, coed, affiliated with Presbyterian Church (U.S.A.). Awards bachelor's degrees. Founded 1857. Setting: 21-acre urban campus with easy access to Raleigh-Cary. Endowment: $35.6 million. Educational spending for the previous fiscal year: $4140 per student. Total enrollment: 930. Faculty: 121 (34 full-time, 87 part-time). Student-undergrad faculty ratio is 14:1. 1,569 applied, 59% were admitted. Full-time: 814 students, 50% women, 50% men. Part-time: 116 students, 65% women, 35% men. Students come from 12 states and territories, 2 other countries, 8% from out-of-state. 1% American Indian or Alaska Native, non-Hispanic/Latino; 9% Hispanic/Latino; 28% Black or African American, non-Hispanic/Latino; 2% Asian, non-Hispanic/Latino; 0.2% Native Hawaiian or other Pacific Islander, non-Hispanic/Latino; 0.3% international. 20% 25 or older, 50% live on campus, 11% transferred in. Retention: 61% of full-time freshmen returned the following year. Academic areas with the most degrees conferred: business/marketing; psychology; communication/journalism. Core. Calendar: semesters. Academic remediation for entering students, services for LD students, advanced placement, accelerated degree program, honors program, independent study, distance learning, double major, summer session for credit, part-time degree program, adult/continuing education programs, co-op programs and internships. Off campus study at Cooperating Raleigh Colleges (CRC): Shaw University, North Carolina State University, Meredith College, St. Augustine's University, Wake Technical Community College. Study abroad program. ROTC: Army (c), Air Force (c).

Entrance Requirements: Options: electronic application, early admission, deferred admission, international baccalaureate accepted. Required: high school transcript, minimum 2.5 high school GPA, SAT or ACT. Recommended: essay, recommendations, interview. Required for some: essay. Entrance: moderately difficult. Application deadline: rolling. Notification: continuous. SAT Reasoning Test deadline: 7/1. SAT Subject Test deadline: 7/1. Transfer credits accepted: Yes.

Costs Per Year: Application fee: $35. Comprehensive fee: $41,600 includes full-time tuition ($30,000), mandatory fees ($500), and college room and board ($11,100). Full-time tuition and fees vary according to class time and course load. Room and board charges vary according to board plan. Part-time tuition: $1000 per credit hour. Part-time tuition varies according to class time and course load.

Collegiate Environment: Orientation program. Drama-theater group, choral group, student-run newspaper. Social organizations: 38 open to all; Gamma Sigma Sigma National Service Sorority; 2% of women are members. Most popular organizations: Campus Activities Board, Phi Beta Lambda, Gamma Sigma Sigma, Ambassadors for Christ, Class Councils. Major annual events: Late Night Breakfast, Red Rose Ball, Athletic Events. Student services: health clinic, personal-psychological counseling. Campus security: 24-hour emergency response devices and patrols, late night transport-escort service, controlled dormitory access. Lucy Cooper Finch Library. Books: 48,196 (physical), 250,000 (digital/electronic); Serial titles: 13 (physical), 25,000 (digital/electronic); Databases: 94. Weekly public service hours: 90; students can reserve study rooms. Operations spending for the previous fiscal year: $265,850. 101 computers available on campus for general student use. A campuswide network can be accessed from student residence rooms and from off campus. Students can access the following: online class registration. Staffed computer lab on campus (open 24 hours a day) provides training in use of computers, software, and the Internet.

Community Environment: Peace College is located in downtown Raleigh, NC, the state's political, education, and cultural center. The State Capitol, Legislative Building, State Library, and museums lie within a few blocks of campus. Shopping centers, restaurants, coffee shops and clubs are within a 10-block radius. Six other colleges and universities are located in the Raleigh area. The University of North Carolina at Chapel Hill and Duke University are within 25 miles of Peace. Numerous classical and popular concerts, dramatic presentations, and other cultural activities are available on campus, in the community, and in the surrounding Research Triangle Park area.

■ WILSON COMMUNITY COLLEGE

902 Herring Ave.
Wilson, NC 27893-3310
Tel: (252)291-1195
Fax: (252)243-7148
E-mail: mwilliams@wilsoncc.edu
Web Site: www.wilsoncc.edu

Description: State-supported, 2-year, coed. Part of North Carolina Community College System. Awards certificates, diplomas, transfer associate, and terminal associate degrees. Founded 1958. Setting: 35-acre small town campus with easy access to Raleigh. Total enrollment: 1,837. Faculty: 210 (52 full-time, 158 part-time). Student-undergrad faculty ratio is 12:1. Full-time: 897 students, 68% women, 32% men. Part-time: 940 students, 68% women, 32% men. Students come from 3 states and territories. 0.9% American Indian or Alaska Native, non-Hispanic/Latino; 5% Hispanic/Latino; 45% Black or African American, non-Hispanic/Latino; 0.7% Asian, non-Hispanic/Latino; 0.1% Native Hawaiian or other Pacific Islander, non-Hispanic/Latino. 49% 25 or older, 27% transferred in. Core. Calendar: semesters. Academic remediation for entering students, ESL program, services for LD students, advanced placement, independent study, distance learning, double major, summer session for credit, part-time degree program, co-op programs and internships.

Entrance Requirements: Open admission except for health occupations programs. Options: electronic application, deferred admission. Required: high school transcript. Entrance: noncompetitive. Application deadline: rolling. Notification: continuous.

Collegiate Environment: Orientation program. Campus security: 11-hour patrols by trained security personnel. 33 computers available on campus for general student use. A campuswide network can be accessed. Students can access the following: online class registration. Staffed computer lab on campus.

Community Environment: The campus is located in Wilson, NC, a community of 37,000. Raleigh, the capital, is 45 miles west of Wilson.

■ WINGATE UNIVERSITY

220 N Camden St.
Wingate, NC 28174
Tel: (704)233-8000; Free: 800-755-5550
E-mail: admit@wingate.edu
Web Site: www.wingate.edu

Description: Independent Baptist, comprehensive, coed. Awards bachelor's, master's, and doctoral degrees and post-master's certificates. Founded 1896. Setting: 400-acre small town campus with easy access to Charlotte. Total enrollment: 3,193. Faculty: 307 (181 full-time, 126 part-time). Student-undergrad faculty ratio is 14:1. 7,581 applied, 70% were admitted. 24% from top 10% of their high school class, 53% from top quarter, 85% from top half. Full-time: 2,044 students, 60% women, 40% men. Part-time: 40 students, 55% women, 45% men. Students come from 36 states and territories, 45 other countries, 24% from out-of-state. 0.5% American Indian or Alaska Native, non-Hispanic/Latino; 4% Hispanic/Latino; 15% Black or African American, non-Hispanic/Latino; 2% Asian, non-Hispanic/Latino; 4% international. 3% 25 or older, 75% live on campus, 4% transferred in. Retention: 77% of full-time freshmen returned the following year. Academic areas with the most degrees conferred: biological/life sciences; education; business/marketing; public administration and social services. Core. Calendar: semesters. Services for LD students, advanced placement, honors program, independent study, double major, summer session for credit, part-time degree program, adult/continuing education programs, internships, graduate courses open to undergrads. Off campus study at Member of the Greater Charlotte Area Consortium. Signatory Institution of Independent Comprehensive Articulation Agreement with North Carolina Independent Colleges and University and the North Carolina Community College System. Study abroad program. ROTC: Army (c), Air Force (c).

Entrance Requirements: Options: electronic application, deferred admission, international baccalaureate accepted. Required: high school transcript, minimum 2.7 high school GPA, SAT or ACT. Recommended: interview. Required for some: essay. Entrance: moderately difficult. Application deadline: rolling. Notification: continuous. SAT Reasoning Test deadline: 3/1. Transfer credits accepted: Yes.

Costs Per Year: Application fee: $0. Comprehensive fee: $43,946 includes full-time tuition ($33,166) and college room and board ($10,780). Part-time tuition: $1100 per credit hour. Part-time tuition varies according to course load.

Collegiate Environment: Orientation program. Drama-theater group, choral

group, student-run newspaper. Social organizations: 50 open to all; national fraternities, national sororities, local fraternities; 6% of eligible men and 19% of eligible women are members. Most popular organizations: University and Community Assistance Network (UCAN), Bulldog Activities Resource Committee, Fellowship of Christian Athletes, Student Bulldog Club, Student Government Association. Major annual events: International Festival, Homecoming, Spring Fling. Student services: health clinic, personal-psychological counseling. Campus security: 24-hour emergency response devices and patrols, late night transport-escort service, controlled dormitory access. Ethel K. Smith Library. Books: 96,673 (physical); Databases: 110. Students can reserve study rooms. 80 computers available on campus for general student use. A campuswide network can be accessed from student residence rooms and from off campus. Students can access the following: online class registration. Staffed computer lab on campus provides training in use of computers, software, and the Internet.

■ **WINSTON-SALEM STATE UNIVERSITY**
601 Martin Luther King Jr Dr.
Winston Salem, NC 27110-0003
Tel: (336)750-2000; Free: 800-257-4052
Fax: (336)750-2079
E-mail: legrandet@wssu.edu
Web Site: www.wssu.edu
Description: State-supported, comprehensive, coed. Part of University of North Carolina System. Awards bachelor's and master's degrees. Founded 1892. Setting: 94-acre urban campus. Endowment: $19.5 million. Research spending for the previous fiscal year: $1.2 million. Total enrollment: 6,427. Faculty: 336 (334 full-time, 2 part-time). Student-undergrad faculty ratio is 19:1. 4,068 applied, 54% were admitted. 6% from top 10% of their high school class, 24% from top quarter, 65% from top half. Full-time: 5,327 students, 69% women, 31% men. Part-time: 633 students, 79% women, 21% men. Students come from 35 states and territories, 8 other countries, 11% from out-of-state. 31% 25 or older, 36% live on campus, 11%

transferred in. Retention: 78% of full-time freshmen returned the following year. Academic areas with the most degrees conferred: health professions and related sciences; business/marketing; social sciences. Core. Calendar: semesters. Academic remediation for entering students, services for LD students, advanced placement, accelerated degree program, freshman honors college, honors program, independent study, distance learning, double major, summer session for credit, part-time degree program, co-op programs and internships. ROTC: Army, Air Force.

Entrance Requirements: Option: deferred admission. Required: high school transcript, SAT or ACT. Recommended: 1 recommendation. Entrance: minimally difficult. Application deadline: 2/15. Notification: 4/1.

Costs Per Year: Application fee: $40. State resident tuition: $3401 full-time, $425.13 per term part-time. Nonresident tuition: $13,648 full-time, $1706 per term part-time. Mandatory fees: $5089 full-time, $341.05 per term part-time. Full-time tuition and fees vary according to degree level and location. Part-time tuition and fees vary according to course load, degree level, and location. College room and board: $9586. College room only: $5912. Room and board charges vary according to board plan and housing facility.

Collegiate Environment: Orientation program. Drama-theater group, choral group, marching band, student-run newspaper, radio station. Social organizations: national fraternities, national sororities, local fraternities, local sororities; 5% of eligible men and 5% of eligible women are members. Major annual events: Homecoming, Lyceum Series, International Week. Student services: health clinic, personal-psychological counseling, women's center. Campus security: 24-hour emergency response devices and patrols. O'Kelly Library. Operations spending for the previous fiscal year: $4.1 million. 600 computers available on campus for general student use. A campuswide network can be accessed from student residence rooms and from off campus. Students can access the following: online class registration. Staffed computer lab on campus provides training in use of computers, software, and the Internet.

Community Environment: See Wake Forest University.

BISMARCK STATE COLLEGE

1500 Edwards Ave.
Bismarck, ND 58506-5587
Tel: (701)224-5400; Free: 800-445-5073
Fax: (701)224-5643
E-mail: karen.erickson@bismarckstate.edu
Web Site: www.bismarckstate.edu

Description: State-supported, primarily 2-year, coed. Part of North Dakota University System. Awards certificates, diplomas, transfer associate, terminal associate, and bachelor's degrees. Founded 1939. Setting: 120-acre urban campus. Endowment: $16.3 million. Educational spending for the previous fiscal year: $8745 per student. Total enrollment: 3,976. Faculty: 348 (121 full-time, 227 part-time). Student-undergrad faculty ratio is 14:1. 1,068 applied, 100% were admitted. 4% from top 10% of their high school class, 15% from top quarter, 43% from top half. Full-time: 2,241 students, 40% women, 60% men. Part-time: 1,735 students, 47% women, 53% men. Students come from 49 states and territories, 8 other countries, 22% from out-of-state. 2% American Indian or Alaska Native, non-Hispanic/Latino; 3% Hispanic/Latino; 3% Black or African American, non-Hispanic/Latino; 0.6% Asian, non-Hispanic/Latino; 0.2% Native Hawaiian or other Pacific Islander, non-Hispanic/Latino; 0.3% international. 34% 25 or older, 14% live on campus, 7% transferred in. Retention: 74% of full-time freshmen returned the following year. Academic area with the most degrees conferred: business/marketing. Core. Calendar: semesters. Academic remediation for entering students, services for LD students, advanced placement, independent study, distance learning, double major, summer session for credit, part-time degree program, adult/continuing education programs, co-op programs and internships. Study abroad program.

Entrance Requirements: Open admission except for some technical programs with limited enrollment space. Options: electronic application, early admission, deferred admission. Required: high school transcript. Recommended: ACT. Required for some: interview. Entrance: noncompetitive. Application deadline: rolling. Notification: continuous. SAT Reasoning Test deadline: 8/21. SAT Subject Test deadline: 8/21. Transfer credits accepted: Yes.

Collegiate Environment: Orientation program. Drama-theater group, choral group, student-run newspaper, radio station. Social organizations: 10 open to all. Most popular organizations: Intramural Sports, Campus Crusade, Student Government Association, Concert/Chamber Choir, Drama Club. Student services: personal-psychological counseling. Campus security: late night transport-escort service, controlled dormitory access. Bismarck State College Library. Books: 61,059 (physical), 16,804 (digital/electronic); Serial titles: 121 (physical), 114 (digital/electronic); Databases: 88. Weekly public service hours: 67; students can reserve study rooms. Operations spending for the previous fiscal year: $207,485. 745 computers available on campus for general student use. A campuswide network can be accessed from student residence rooms and from off campus. Students can access the following: online class registration, office software, writing software. Staffed computer lab on campus.

Community Environment: Bismarck, North Dakota's capital city, is the second largest city with a population of 57,000. Because of its central location, modern shopping centers and Civic Center, the city hosts many state and national conventions. Bismarck is considered the cultural, business and educational center of western and central North Dakota. It is also the medical center for the region with two modern medical centers and clinics. Bismarck has a large city library, a State Historical Library, and numerous libraries related to state and federal offices; a city orchestra, civic chorus, and amateur drama club; and many churches representing various denominations. The city has many parks and recreation areas, a city zoo, three golf courses, and clubs for a variety of recreational activities. The Missouri River and nearby Lake Sakakawea offer boating, fishing and other water sports. Bismarck has transportation service from several major air carriers, commuter airlines, and bus lines. Interstate 94 and U.S. Highway 83 meet in Bismarck. The city has a pleasant summer climate and moderate to severe winters.

CANKDESKA CIKANA COMMUNITY COLLEGE

PO Box 269
Fort Totten, ND 58335-0269
Tel: (701)766-4415; Free: 888-783-1463
Fax: (701)766-4077
Web Site: www.littlehoop.edu

Description: Federally supported, 2-year, coed. Awards certificates, transfer associate, and terminal associate degrees. Founded 1974. Setting: 1-acre small town campus. Total enrollment: 250. Student-undergrad faculty ratio is 9:1. 42% 25 or older. Core. Calendar: semesters. Academic remediation for entering students, services for LD students, self-designed majors, summer session for credit, part-time degree program, adult/continuing education programs, co-op programs. Off campus study at members of the American Indian Higher Education Consortium.

Entrance Requirements: Open admission. Options: early admission, deferred admission. Entrance: noncompetitive. Application deadline: 8/22. Notification: continuous.

Collegiate Environment: Drama-theater group. Student services: personal-psychological counseling. Campus security: late night transport-escort service.

DAKOTA COLLEGE AT BOTTINEAU

105 Simrall Blvd.
Bottineau, ND 58318-1198
Tel: (701)228-2277; Free: 800-542-6866
Fax: (701)228-5499
E-mail: heidi.hauf@dakotacollege.edu
Web Site: www.dakotacollege.edu

Description: State-supported, 2-year, coed. Part of North Dakota University System. Administratively affiliated with Minot State University. Awards certificates, diplomas, transfer associate, and terminal associate degrees. Founded 1906. Setting: 35-acre rural campus. Total enrollment: 996. Student-undergrad faculty ratio is 8:1. 4% American Indian or Alaska Native, non-Hispanic/Latino; 5% Hispanic/Latino; 9% Black or African American, non-Hispanic/Latino; 0.3% Asian, non-Hispanic/Latino; 0.1% Native Hawaiian or other Pacific Islander, non-Hispanic/Latino. Core. Calendar: semesters. Academic remediation for entering students, services for LD students, advanced placement, distance learning, double major, summer session for credit, part-time degree program, co-op programs. Off campus study at Minot State University (some 2-year programs), Valley City State University (Nursing, AA/AS), Paramedic (EMT) Technology program via distance delivery to sites but based in Minot and Williston.

Entrance Requirements: Open admission. Options: electronic application, early admission, deferred admission. Required: high school transcript, immunization records, previous college official transcripts. Entrance: noncompetitive. Application deadline: rolling. Transfer credits accepted: Yes.

Costs Per Year: Application fee: $35. State resident tuition: $4,568 full-time, $190.34 per credit hour part-time. Nonresident tuition: $6,444 full-time, $268.50 per credit hour part-time. Full-time tuition varies according to location, program, and reciprocity agreements. Part-time tuition varies according to location, program, and reciprocity agreements. College room and board: $6710. Room and board charges vary according to board plan and housing facility.

Collegiate Environment: Orientation program. Drama-theater group. Most popular organizations: Intramurals, LeaderJacks, Student Senate, LumberActs, Phi Theta Kappa. Major annual events: Homecoming Week, Advising Week. Student services: health clinic, personal-psychological counseling. Campus security: controlled dormitory access, security cameras, night security personnel. 263 college housing spaces available; 200 were occupied in 2018-19. Freshmen guaranteed college housing. On-campus residence required through sophomore year. Options: men-only, women-only housing available. Dakota College at Bottineau Library plus 1 other. 58 computers available on campus for general student use. Computer purchase/lease plans available. A campuswide network can be accessed from student residence rooms and from off campus. Students can access the following: online class registration. Staffed computer lab on campus provides training in use of computers, software, and the Internet.

■ DICKINSON STATE UNIVERSITY

291 Campus Dr.
Dickinson, ND 58601-4896
Tel: (701)483-2507; Free: 800-279-4295
Fax: (701)483-2006
E-mail: heidi.kippenhan@dickinsonstate.edu
Web Site: www.dickinsonstate.edu

Description: State-supported, comprehensive, coed. Part of North Dakota University System. Awards associate, bachelor's, and master's degrees. Founded 1918. Setting: 132-acre small town campus. Research spending for the previous fiscal year: $27,005. Educational spending for the previous fiscal year: $11,346 per student. Total enrollment: 1,425. Faculty: 169 (96 full-time, 73 part-time). Student-undergrad faculty ratio is 9:1. 388 applied, 99% were admitted. Full-time: 922 students, 56% women, 44% men. Part-time: 503 students, 69% women, 31% men. Students come from 36 states and territories, 30 other countries, 29% from out-of-state. 0.9% American Indian or Alaska Native, non-Hispanic/Latino; 5% Hispanic/Latino; 4% Black or African American, non-Hispanic/Latino; 0.8% Asian, non-Hispanic/Latino; 0.4% Native Hawaiian or other Pacific Islander, non-Hispanic/Latino; 5% international. 29% 25 or older, 21% live on campus, 12% transferred in. Retention: 64% of full-time freshmen returned the following year. Academic areas with the most degrees conferred: business/marketing; interdisciplinary studies; agriculture. Core. Calendar: semesters. Academic remediation for entering students, ESL program, services for LD students, advanced placement, honors program, independent study, distance learning, double major, summer session for credit, part-time degree program, external degree program, adult/continuing education programs, co-op programs and internships, graduate courses open to undergrads. Off campus study. Study abroad program.

Entrance Requirements: Open admission. Options: electronic application, early admission, early action, deferred admission, international baccalaureate accepted. Required: high school transcript, minimum 2 high school GPA, SAT or ACT. Required for some: essay, medical history, proof of measles-rubella shot. Entrance: minimally difficult. Application deadline: 8/15. Notification: continuous, rolling for early decision. SAT Reasoning Test deadline: 8/15. SAT Subject Test deadline: 8/15. Transfer credits accepted: Yes.

Costs Per Year: Application fee: $35. One-time mandatory fee: $100. State resident tuition: $5558 full-time, $231.57 per credit hour part-time. Nonresident tuition: $8336 full-time, $347.35 per credit hour part-time. Mandatory fees: $1210 full-time, $50.40 per credit hour part-time, $302.40 per term part-time. Full-time tuition and fees vary according to course load, location, and reciprocity agreements. Part-time tuition and fees vary according to course load, location, and reciprocity agreements. College room and board: $6898. College room only: $2900. Room and board charges vary according to board plan, housing facility, and location.

Collegiate Environment: Orientation program. Drama-theater group, choral group. Social organizations: 52 open to all; national fraternities; 9% of men are members. Most popular organizations: Rodeo Club, Blue Hawk Brigade, chorale, Business Club, Navigators. Major annual events: Homecoming Week, Sure Beats Winter Week, Back to School Week. Student services: health clinic, personal-psychological counseling. Campus security: 24-hour

emergency response devices and patrols, late night transport-escort service, controlled dormitory access, Crisis Manager App. for Phones, Automated Mass Notification System. Stoxen Library plus 1 other. Books: 73,571 (physical), 23,355 (digital/electronic); Serial titles: 119 (physical), 107,800 (digital/electronic); Databases: 71. Weekly public service hours: 56. Operations spending for the previous fiscal year: $547,374. 250 computers available on campus for general student use. A campuswide network can be accessed from student residence rooms and from off campus. Students can access the following: online class registration. Staffed computer lab on campus provides training in use of computers, software, and the Internet.

Community Environment: Dickinson, population 15,600, is approximately 95 miles from the state capital of Bismarck and is a shipping point for lignite coal, oil, grain, dairy products, meat products, and livestock. Nearby Patterson Lake and Recreational Area and Theodore Roosevelt National Park provide ample opportunities for outdoor sports and activities.

■ LAKE REGION STATE COLLEGE

1801 College Dr. N
Devils Lake, ND 58301-1598
Tel: (701)662-1600; Free: 800-443-1313
Fax: (701)662-1570
E-mail: merissa.halvorson@lrsc.edu
Web Site: www.lrsc.edu

Description: State-supported, 2-year, coed. Part of North Dakota University System. Awards certificates, diplomas, transfer associate, and terminal associate degrees. Founded 1941. Setting: 120-acre small town campus. Total enrollment: 2,072. Faculty: 101 (45 full-time, 56 part-time). Full-time: 538 students, 53% women, 47% men. Part-time: 1,534 students, 58% women, 42% men. Students come from 41 states and territories, 16 other countries, 15% from out-of-state. 3% American Indian or Alaska Native, non-Hispanic/Latino; 6% Hispanic/Latino; 4% Black or African American, non-Hispanic/Latino; 0.6% Asian, non-Hispanic/Latino; 0.4% Native Hawaiian or other Pacific Islander, non-Hispanic/Latino; 5% international. 20% 25 or older, 12% live on campus, 4% transferred in. Retention: 61% of full-time freshmen returned the following year. Core. Calendar: semesters. Academic remediation for entering students, ESL program, services for LD students, honors program, distance learning, double major, summer session for credit, part-time degree program, co-op programs and internships. Off campus study at Launch program located at the University of North Dakota.

Entrance Requirements: Open admission. Option: electronic application. Required for some: high school transcript, immunization records, college transcripts. Entrance: noncompetitive. Application deadline: rolling. Notification: continuous. Transfer credits accepted: Yes.

Costs Per Year: Application fee: $35. State resident tuition: $3,598 full-time, $149.90 per credit part-time. Nonresident tuition: $3,598 full-time, $149.90 per credit part-time. Mandatory fees: $877 full-time, $28.79 per credit part-time. Full-time tuition and fees vary according to program. Part-time tuition and fees vary according to program. College room and board: $6660. Room and board charges vary according to board plan and housing facility.

Collegiate Environment: Orientation program. Drama-theater group. Social organizations: 12 open to all. Most popular organizations: Student Senate, Phi Theta Kappa, Delta Epsilon Chi, Phi Theta Lambda, Student Nurse Organization. Major annual events: Orientation, Title IX Training, Movie nights/entertainers. Student services: personal-psychological counseling. Campus security: 24-hour emergency response devices, controlled dormitory access. 220 college housing spaces available; 200 were occupied in 2018-19. No special consideration for freshman housing applicants. Options: coed, men-only, women-only housing available. Paul Hoghaug Library. Books: 11,536 (physical), 75,983 (digital/electronic); Databases: 67. Students can reserve study rooms. 220 computers available on campus for general student use. Computer purchase/lease plans available. A campuswide network can be accessed from student residence rooms. Students can access the following: online class registration.

Community Environment: A center of scenic, historical and recreational attractions, Devils Lake (population 6,816) was named for the largest natural body of water in the state. There are scenic drives, a golf course, a skiway, and camping and recreation facilities at nearby Shelvers Grove, Roosevelt Park, and Lakewood Park. The area is noted for its abundance of ducks and geese. The city has churches of various denominations, hospitals and clinics, a library, six motels, and various civic, fraternal and veteran's organizations. Local recreational facilities include a theatre, baseball, golf, football, bowling alley, swimming pools, hockey, skating, curling, skiing, parks, and playgrounds. Part-time employment is available.

■ MAYVILLE STATE UNIVERSITY

330 3rd St., NE
Mayville, ND 58257-1299
Tel: (701)786-2301; Free: 800-437-4104
Fax: (701)786-4748
E-mail: james.morowski@mayvillestate.edu
Web Site: www.mayvillestate.edu

Description: State-supported, 4-year, coed. Part of North Dakota University System. Awards associate and bachelor's degrees. Founded 1889. Setting: 60-acre rural campus. Research spending for the previous fiscal year: $147,212. Educational spending for the previous fiscal year: $8050 per student. Total enrollment: 1,081. Faculty: 81 (46 full-time, 35 part-time). Student-undergrad faculty ratio is 13:1. 413 applied, 57% were admitted. Full-time: 635 students, 49% women, 51% men. Part-time: 421 students, 67% women, 33% men. Students come from 38 states and territories, 6 other countries, 41% from out-of-state. 2% American Indian or Alaska Native, non-Hispanic/Latino; 5% Hispanic/Latino; 7% Black or African American, non-Hispanic/Latino; 0.2% Asian, non-Hispanic/Latino; 0.5% Native Hawaiian or other Pacific Islander, non-Hispanic/Latino; 3% international. 22% 25 or older, 41% live on campus, 10% transferred in. Retention: 54% of full-time freshmen returned the following year. Academic areas with the most degrees conferred: education; business/marketing; liberal arts/general studies. Core. Calendar: semesters. Academic remediation for entering students, services for LD students, advanced placement, accelerated degree program, self-designed majors, distance learning, double major, summer session for credit, part-time degree program, adult/continuing education programs, co-op programs and internships. Off campus study at Lake Region State College, Williston State College, North Dakota State College of Science, Northland Community College, Bismarck State College, Minnesota Technical Colleges. ROTC: Army (c), Air Force (c).

Entrance Requirements: Open admission for freshmen who have completed college preparatory curriculum in high school. Options: electronic application, deferred admission, international baccalaureate accepted. Required: high school transcript, minimum 2 high school GPA, SAT or ACT. Entrance: noncompetitive. Application deadline: rolling. Notification: continuous until 1/1. SAT Reasoning Test deadline: 10/1. SAT Subject Test deadline: 10/1. Transfer credits accepted: Yes.

Costs Per Year: Application fee: $35. State resident tuition: $6,667 full-time, $277.79 per credit hour part-time. Nonresident tuition: $9,400 full-time, $391.66 per credit hour part-time. Full-time tuition varies according to course load, location, and reciprocity agreements. Part-time tuition varies according to course load, location, and reciprocity agreements. College room and board: $7240. College room only: $2840. Room and board charges vary according to board plan and housing facility.

Collegiate Environment: Orientation program. Drama-theater group, choral group, student-run newspaper, radio station. Social organizations: 23 open to all. Most popular organizations: Student Activities Council, Student Education Association, Health and Physical Education Club, Campus Crusade, Student Ambassadors. Major annual events: Homecoming, Spring Fling. Student services: health clinic, personal-psychological counseling. Campus security: controlled dormitory access. Byrnes-Quanbeck Library plus 1 other.

Community Environment: Mayville and its twin community, Portland, have a combined population of 2,500 in this rural farming area between Grand Forks and Fargo, North Dakota. The local community offers a city library, many churches, a modern hospital, medical clinic, and dental and optometry offices. A modern business district is also present with air transportation available at airports in Grand Forks and Fargo. A small airport is also located in the community. Housing off campus is abundant, with many choices of apartments, duplexes, and single-family dwellings. Recreational facilities are available for camping, hiking, fishing, golf, skiing, swimming, and horseshoes; a theatre and parks are also available.

■ MINOT STATE UNIVERSITY

500 University Ave., W
Minot, ND 58707-0002
Tel: (701)858-3000; Free: 800-777-0750
Fax: (701)839-6933
E-mail: askmsu@minotstateu.edu
Web Site: www.minotstateu.edu

Description: State-supported, comprehensive, coed. Part of North Dakota University System. Awards associate, bachelor's, and master's degrees. Founded 1913. Setting: 103-acre small town campus. Total enrollment: 3,216. Faculty: 291 (157 full-time, 134 part-time). Student-undergrad faculty ratio is 12:1. 709 applied, 69% were admitted. Full-time: 1,952 students, 60% women, 40% men. Part-time: 1,004 students, 59% women, 41% men. 19% from out-of-state. 2% American Indian or Alaska Native, non-Hispanic/Latino; 7% Hispanic/Latino; 5% Black or African American, non-Hispanic/Latino; 2% Asian, non-Hispanic/Latino; 0.3% Native Hawaiian or other Pacific Islander, non-Hispanic/Latino; 9% international. 13% 25 or older, 15% live on campus, 11% transferred in. Retention: 69% of full-time freshmen returned the following year. Academic areas with the most degrees conferred: business/marketing; education; health professions and related sciences. Core. Calendar: semesters. Academic remediation for entering students, ESL program, services for LD students, advanced placement, accelerated degree program, self-designed majors, honors program, independent study, distance learning, double major, summer session for credit, part-time degree program, co-op programs and internships, graduate courses open to undergrads. Study abroad program.

Entrance Requirements: Options: electronic application, deferred admission. Required: high school transcript, SAT or ACT. Required for some: minimum 2.5 high school GPA. Entrance: moderately difficult. SAT Reasoning Test deadline: 4/1. SAT Subject Test deadline: 4/1. Transfer credits accepted: Yes.

Costs Per Year: Application fee: $35. State resident tuition: $5616 full-time, $234 per credit hour part-time. Nonresident tuition: $5616 full-time, $234 per credit hour part-time. Mandatory fees: $1,448 full-time, $60.32 per credit hour part-time. Full-time tuition and fees vary according to class time, course load, degree level, location, program, and reciprocity agreements. Part-time tuition and fees vary according to class time, course load, degree level, location, program, and reciprocity agreements. College room and board: $6663. College room only: $2663. Room and board charges vary according to board plan and housing facility.

Collegiate Environment: Orientation program. Drama-theater group, choral group, marching band, student-run newspaper, radio station. Social organizations: local fraternities. Most popular organizations: Residence Hall Association, Student Government Association, Beavers on Business, Student Social Work Organization, National Student Speech and Hearing Association. Major annual events: Homecoming Week, Welcome Week, Winter Week. Student services: health clinic, personal-psychological counseling, women's center. Campus security: controlled dormitory access, patrols by trained security personnel. Gordon B. Olson Library.

Community Environment: Minot, population 35,000, began as a tent town of the Great Northern Railroad and now contains the electronic freight classification Gavin Yard. It grew so rapidly that it was called the"Magic City." Today it is a trade center for an area including part of Canada and Montana, as well as northern North Dakota. The town lies within the eastern boundaries of oil-rich Williston Basin and is surrounded by a number of lignite strip mines. The area has good highways, rail, bus, and air lines. Minot has many churches and active civic and fraternal organizations. Part-time job opportunities are available for students.

■ NORTH DAKOTA STATE COLLEGE OF SCIENCE

800 N Sixth St.
Wahpeton, ND 58076
Tel: (701)671-2401; Free: 800-342-4325
Fax: (701)671-2332
E-mail: justin.grams@ndscs.edu
Web Site: www.ndscs.edu

Description: State-supported, 2-year, coed. Part of North Dakota University System. Awards certificates, diplomas, transfer associate, and terminal associate degrees. Founded 1903. Setting: 128-acre rural campus. Endowment: $18.4 million. Educational spending for the previous fiscal year: $8690 per student. Total enrollment: 2,985. Faculty: 283 (104 full-time, 179 part-time). Student-undergrad faculty ratio is 13:1. 1,216 applied, 70% were admitted. Full-time: 1,707 students, 35% women, 65% men. Part-time: 1,278 students, 55% women, 45% men. Students come from 35 states and territories, 7 other countries, 42% from out-of-state. 0.8% American Indian or Alaska Native, non-Hispanic/Latino; 2% Hispanic/Latino; 7% Black or African American, non-Hispanic/Latino; 1% Asian, non-Hispanic/Latino; 1% international. 14% 25 or older, 58% live on campus, 7% transferred in. Core. Calendar: semesters. Academic remediation for entering students, ESL program, services for LD students, self-designed majors, independent study, distance learning, double major, summer session for credit, part-time degree program, co-op programs and internships.

Entrance Requirements: Open admission. Options: electronic application, early admission. Required: high school transcript. Entrance: noncompetitive. Application deadline: rolling. Notification: continuous. Transfer credits accepted: Yes.

Costs Per Year: Application fee: $35. State resident tuition: $130.82 per credit part-time. Nonresident tuition: $349.89 per credit part-time.

Collegiate Environment: Orientation program. Drama-theater group, choral group, marching band. Social organizations: 36 open to all; Phi Theta Kappa. Most popular organizations: SkillsUSA, Welding Club, Dental Club, Diesel Club, HVAC. Major annual events: Homecoming, Agawasie Day, Athletic Events. Student services: health clinic, personal-psychological counseling. Campus security: 24-hour patrols, late night transport-escort service, controlled dormitory access. Mildred Johnson Library. Books: 57,489 (physical), 15,859 (digital/electronic); Serial titles: 204 (physical), 23,940 (digital/electronic); Databases: 80. Operations spending for the previous fiscal year: $292,006. 115 computers available on campus for general student use. Computer purchase/lease plans available. A campuswide network can be accessed. Students can access the following: online class registration. Staffed computer lab on campus provides training in use of computers, software, and the Internet.

Community Environment: Wahpeton (population 8,220) is located at the origin of the Red River in southeastern North Dakota. The city is served by a bus line, and U.S. Highway 75, Interstates 29 and 94 and State Highways 13 & 81.

■ **NORTH DAKOTA STATE UNIVERSITY**

1340 Administration Ave.

Fargo, ND 58102

Tel: (701)231-8011; Free: 800-488-6378

Fax: (701)231-8802

E-mail: ndsu.admission@ndsu.edu

Web Site: www.ndsu.edu

Description: State-supported, university, coed. Part of North Dakota University System. Awards bachelor's, master's, and doctoral degrees and post-master's certificates. Founded 1890. Setting: 2,100-acre urban campus. Endowment: $512,215. Research spending for the previous fiscal year: $91.6 million. Educational spending for the previous fiscal year: $7601 per student. Total enrollment: 14,358. Faculty: 776 (676 full-time, 100 part-time). Student-undergrad faculty ratio is 18:1. 6,424 applied, 92% were admitted. 16% from top 10% of their high school class, 25% from top quarter. 11 National Merit Scholars. Full-time: 10,782 students, 45% women, 55% men. Part-time: 1,202 students, 58% women, 42% men. Students come from 39 states and territories, 52 other countries, 58% from out-of-state. 0.6% American Indian or Alaska Native, non-Hispanic/Latino; 2% Hispanic/Latino; 3% Black or African American, non-Hispanic/Latino; 1% Asian, non-Hispanic/Latino; 0.1% Native Hawaiian or other Pacific Islander, non-Hispanic/Latino; 2% international. 7% 25 or older, 39% live on campus, 6% transferred in. Retention: 79% of full-time freshmen returned the following year. Academic areas with the most degrees conferred: engineering; business/marketing; health professions and related sciences. Core. Calendar: semesters. Services for LD students, advanced placement, accelerated degree program, self-designed majors, honors program, independent study, distance learning, double major, summer session for credit, part-time degree program, co-op programs and internships, graduate courses open to undergrads. Off campus study at members of the Tri-College University-Concordia College (Moorhead, MN), Minnesota State University-Moorhead, Minnesota State Community and Technical College (Moorhead, MN), North Dakota State College of Science. Study abroad program. ROTC: Army, Air Force.

Entrance Requirements: Options: electronic application, international baccalaureate accepted. Required: high school transcript, minimum 2.75 high school GPA, SAT or ACT. Entrance: moderately difficult. Application deadline: 8/1. Notification: continuous. SAT Reasoning Test deadline: 8/1. SAT Subject Test deadline: 8/1. Transfer credits accepted: Yes.

Costs Per Year: Application fee: $35. One-time mandatory fee: $120. State resident tuition: $7957 full-time, $324.46 per credit hour part-time. Nonresident tuition: $11,936 full-time, $491.19 per credit hour part-time. Mandatory fees: $1337 full-time, $55.70 per credit hour part-time. Full-time tuition and fees vary according to course load, program, and reciprocity agreements. Part-time tuition and fees vary according to course load, program, and reciprocity agreements. College room and board: $8565. College room only: $3926. Room and board charges vary according to board plan and housing facility.

Collegiate Environment: Orientation program. Drama-theater group, choral group, marching band, student-run newspaper, radio station. Social organizations: 308 open to all; national fraternities, national sororities, local fraternities; 8% of eligible men and 8% of eligible women are members. Most popular organizations: Saddle and Sirloin, Students Today, Leaders Forever,

Chi Alpha Christian Organization, fraternities/sororities, CRU. Major annual events: Spring Concert, Little International, Blue Key Homecoming Show. Student services: health clinic, personal-psychological counseling. Campus security: 24-hour emergency response devices and patrols, late night transport-escort service, controlled dormitory access, Pathlight app. North Dakota State University Library plus 6 others. Books: 662,884 (physical), 162,977 (digital/electronic); Serial titles: 171,924 (physical), 99,565 (digital/electronic); Databases: 232. Weekly public service hours: 93; students can reserve study rooms. Operations spending for the previous fiscal year: $6.4 million. 601 computers available on campus for general student use. Computer purchase/lease plans available. A campuswide network can be accessed from student residence rooms. Students can access the following: online class registration, online course content (e.g., learning management system, lecture capture video recordings). Staffed computer lab on campus (open 24 hours a day) provides training in use of computers, software, and the Internet.

Community Environment: North Dakota's largest city at 90,599, Fargo is the largest distribution point between Minneapolis and Spokane. Fargo-Moorhead as seen designated as one of the top ten All-American cities for 2000. The metropolitan area has over a hundred manufacturing plants producing agricultural machinery, feed, fertilizers, foodstuffs, and dairy products. In addition, the community contains the largest medical complex between Minneapolis and the West Coast. Recreation facilities in the city's 765-acre park system include three golf courses, a winter sports building, and four swimming pools. There are part-time employment opportunities for students.

■ **NUETA HIDATSA SAHNISH COLLEGE**

220 8th Ave. N

New Town, ND 58763-0490

Tel: (701)627-4738

Fax: (701)627-3609

Web Site: www.nhsc.edu

Description: Independent, 2-year, coed. Awards certificates, transfer associate, and terminal associate degrees. Founded 1973. Setting: small town campus. Total enrollment: 323. Student-undergrad faculty ratio is 12:1. 61% 25 or older. Core. Calendar: semesters. Academic remediation for entering students, summer session for credit, part-time degree program, co-op programs and internships. Off campus study at University of North Dakota, Minot State University.

Entrance Requirements: Open admission except for nursing program. Option: deferred admission. Entrance: noncompetitive. Application deadline: rolling.

Collegiate Environment: Drama-theater group, student-run newspaper. Student services: legal services, health clinic, personal-psychological counseling.

■ **RASMUSSEN COLLEGE FARGO**

4012 19th Ave. S

Fargo, ND 58103

Tel: (701)277-3889; Free: 888-549-6755

Fax: (701)277-5604

E-mail: dwayne.bertotto@rasmussen.edu

Web Site: www.rasmussen.edu

Description: Proprietary, 4-year, coed. Part of Rasmussen College System. Awards associate and bachelor's degrees. Founded 1902. Setting: suburban campus. Total enrollment: 391. Faculty: 8 (4 full-time, 4 part-time). Student-undergrad faculty ratio is 22:1. 22 applied, 86% were admitted. Full-time: 280 students, 70% women, 30% men. Part-time: 111 students, 84% women, 16% men. 70% 25 or older. Core. Calendar: quarters. Academic remediation for entering students, accelerated degree program, distance learning, double major, summer session for credit, part-time degree program, adult/continuing education programs, internships.

Entrance Requirements: Options: electronic application, early admission, deferred admission. Required: high school transcript, minimum 2 high school GPA, institutional exam. Required for some: interview. Entrance: minimally difficult. Application deadline: rolling. Transfer credits accepted: Yes.

Collegiate Environment: Orientation program. Rasmussen College Library - Fargo. 87 computers available on campus for general student use. A campuswide network can be accessed from off-campus.

■ **SITTING BULL COLLEGE**

1341 92nd St.

Fort Yates, ND 58538-9701

Tel: (701)854-8000

Fax: (701)854-3403

Web Site: www.sittingbull.edu

Description: Independent, comprehensive, coed. Awards associate, bachelor's, and master's degrees. Founded 1973. Setting: rural campus. Endowment: $541,000. Educational spending for the previous fiscal year: $2001 per student. Total enrollment: 214. Faculty: 32 (16 full-time, 16 part-time). Student-undergrad faculty ratio is 6:1. 63 applied, 100% were admitted. 20% from top 10% of their high school class, 30% from top quarter, 50% from top half. 2 class presidents, 2 valedictorians, 10 student government officers. Students come from 2 states and territories. 35% 25 or older. Core. Calendar: semesters. Academic remediation for entering students, part-time degree program, adult/continuing education programs. Off campus study at members of the American Indian Higher Education Consortium.

Entrance Requirements: Open admission. Option: early admission. Required: high school transcript, medical questionnaire. Entrance: noncompetitive. Application deadline: 9/6. Notification: continuous.

Collegiate Environment: Student-run newspaper. Most popular organizations: Student Government, Future Teachers, Ikce Oyate Culture Club, Phi Beta Lambda, Ski Club. Major annual events: Homecoming, Thanksgiving Dinner, Student Awards Night. Student services: personal-psychological counseling. Sitting Bull College Library. 16 computers available on campus for general student use. Staffed computer lab on campus.

■ TRINITY BIBLE COLLEGE AND GRADUATE SCHOOL

50 Sixth Ave. S

Ellendale, ND 58436

Tel: (701)349-3621; Free: 800-523-1603

Fax: (701)349-5443

E-mail: admissions@trinitybiblecollege.edu

Web Site: www.trinitybiblecollege.edu

Description: Independent Assemblies of God, comprehensive, coed. Awards associate, bachelor's, and master's degrees. Founded 1948. Setting: 28-acre rural campus. Total enrollment: 230. 14% 25 or older. Core. Calendar: semesters. Academic remediation for entering students, advanced placement, accelerated degree program, distance learning, double major, summer session for credit, part-time degree program, internships. Off campus study at Valley City University.

Entrance Requirements: Options: electronic application, deferred admission, international baccalaureate accepted. Required: essay, high school transcript, minimum 2 high school GPA, 2 recommendations, health form, evidence of Christian conversion, background check, SAT or ACT. Required for some: interview. Entrance: noncompetitive. Application deadline: rolling. Notification: continuous. Transfer credits accepted: Yes.

Costs Per Year: Application fee: $25. Comprehensive fee: $20,720 includes full-time tuition ($14,270), mandatory fees ($2050), and college room and board ($4400). College room only: $2000. Full-time tuition and fees vary according to course load. Room and board charges vary according to board plan, housing facility, and student level. Part-time tuition: $493 per credit hour. Part-time mandatory fees: $528 per term. Part-time tuition and fees vary according to course load.

Collegiate Environment: Orientation program. Drama-theater group, choral group, student-run radio station. Student services: personal-psychological counseling. Campus security: 24-hour emergency response devices, student patrols, late night transport-escort service. Graham Library.

Community Environment: Ellendale is a rural community (population 1,500) just north of the South Dakota border and 62 miles south of Jamestown on U.S. Highway 281.

■ TURTLE MOUNTAIN COMMUNITY COLLEGE

Box 340

Belcourt, ND 58316-0340

Tel: (701)477-7862

Fax: (701)477-7892

Web Site: www.tm.edu

Description: Independent, 2-year, coed. Awards certificates, transfer associate, and terminal associate degrees. Founded 1972. Setting: 10-acre rural campus. Total enrollment: 1,058. Student-undergrad faculty ratio is 19:1. 41% 25 or older. Retention: 57% of full-time freshmen returned the following year. Core. Calendar: semesters. Academic remediation for entering students, part-time degree program, adult/continuing education programs.

Entrance Requirements: Open admission. Options: early admission,

deferred admission. Required: high school transcript, ACT. Entrance: noncompetitive. Application deadline: rolling.

Collegiate Environment: Student services: personal-psychological counseling. Turtle Mountain Community College Library.

■ UNITED TRIBES TECHNICAL COLLEGE

3315 University Dr.

Bismarck, ND 58504-7596

Tel: (701)255-3285

E-mail: vgillette@uttc.edu

Web Site: www.uttc.edu

Description: Federally supported, 2-year, coed. Awards certificates, transfer associate, and terminal associate degrees. Founded 1969. Setting: 105-acre small town campus. Total enrollment: 604. Faculty: 63 (49 full-time, 14 part-time). Student-undergrad faculty ratio is 8:1. 184 applied, 84% were admitted. Full-time: 552 students, 56% women, 44% men. Part-time: 52 students, 63% women, 37% men. Students come from 19 states and territories, 6% from out-of-state. 54% 25 or older, 16% transferred in. Retention: 30% of full-time freshmen returned the following year. Calendar: semesters. Academic remediation for entering students, honors program, independent study, summer session for credit, part-time degree program, co-op programs.

Entrance Requirements: Open admission. Required: high school transcript. Entrance: noncompetitive. Application deadline: rolling.

Collegiate Environment: Student-run newspaper. Major annual events: Basketball Games, Parent Breakfast. Student services: personal-psychological counseling. Campus security: 24-hour emergency response devices and patrols. United Tribes Technical College Library plus 1 other. 210 computers available on campus for general student use. Staffed computer lab on campus.

■ UNIVERSITY OF JAMESTOWN

6000 College Ln.

Jamestown, ND 58405

Tel: (701)252-3467; Free: 800-336-2554

Fax: (701)253-4318

E-mail: admissions@uj.edu

Web Site: www.uj.edu

Description: Independent Presbyterian, comprehensive, coed. Awards bachelor's, master's, and doctoral degrees. Founded 1883. Setting: 110-acre small town campus. Endowment: $35.6 million. Total enrollment: 1,136. Faculty: 111 (72 full-time, 39 part-time). Student-undergrad faculty ratio is 12:1. 1,154 applied, 65% were admitted. 15% from top 10% of their high school class, 37% from top quarter, 73% from top half. Full-time: 869 students, 50% women, 50% men. Part-time: 46 students, 57% women, 43% men. Students come from 36 states and territories, 20 other countries, 49% from out-of-state. 0.5% American Indian or Alaska Native, non-Hispanic/Latino; 7% Hispanic/Latino; 4% Black or African American, non-Hispanic/Latino; 0.7% Asian, non-Hispanic/Latino; 1% Native Hawaiian or other Pacific Islander, non-Hispanic/Latino; 10% international. 5% 25 or older, 74% live on campus, 5% transferred in. Retention: 72% of full-time freshmen returned the following year. Academic areas with the most degrees conferred: health professions and related sciences; business/marketing; parks and recreation. Core. Calendar: semesters. Services for LD students, advanced placement, self-designed majors, honors program, independent study, double major, summer session for credit, part-time degree program, co-op programs and internships, graduate courses open to undergrads. Study abroad program.

Entrance Requirements: Options: electronic application, deferred admission, international baccalaureate accepted. Required: high school transcript, minimum 2.5 high school GPA, SAT or ACT. Required for some: interview. Entrance: minimally difficult. Application deadline: rolling. SAT Reasoning Test deadline: 8/15. SAT Subject Test deadline: 8/15. Transfer credits accepted: Yes.

Costs Per Year: Application fee: $0. Comprehensive fee: $29,546 includes full-time tuition ($21,196), mandatory fees ($780), and college room and board ($7570). College room only: $3570. Full-time tuition and fees vary according to course load, degree level, and program. Room and board charges vary according to housing facility. Part-time tuition: $435 per credit hour. Part-time tuition varies according to course load, degree level, and program.

Collegiate Environment: Orientation program. Drama-theater group, choral group, student-run newspaper. Social organizations: 34 open to all; Jimmie Janes, Knight Society; 2% of eligible men and 5% of eligible women are members. Most popular organizations: Cru-Ignite, Student Senate, Relay for

Life, Habitat for Humanity, Fellowship of Athletes in Christ. Major annual events: Hypnotist, Relay for Life, Fall Musical. Student services: personal-psychological counseling. Campus security: 24-hour emergency response devices, late night transport-escort service, controlled dormitory access, campus security cameras. Raugust Library. Books: 94,318 (physical), 15,565 (digital/electronic); Serial titles: 822 (physical), 343 (digital/electronic); Databases: 87. Weekly public service hours: 89; students can reserve study rooms. Operations spending for the previous fiscal year: $543,312. 200 computers available on campus for general student use. A campuswide network can be accessed from student residence rooms and from off campus. Students can access the following: online class registration.

Community Environment: In the valley of the James River, Jamestown (population 14,800) was originally the site of Fort Seward, which was established in 1872. Jamestown is located in southeastern North Dakota and is provided transportation by bus lines, air, and major highways. The community has churches, one hospital, a library, two radio stations, and two shopping centers. Parks in the general area provide outdoor recreation facilities. There are several active civic, fraternal, and veteran's organizations in Jamestown.

■ UNIVERSITY OF MARY

7500 University Dr.
Bismarck, ND 58504-9652
Tel: (701)255-7500; Free: 800-288-6279
Fax: (701)255-7687
E-mail: mcheitkamp@umary.edu
Web Site: www.umary.edu

Description: Independent Roman Catholic, comprehensive, coed. Awards bachelor's, master's, and doctoral degrees. Founded 1959. Setting: 107-acre rural campus. Endowment: $44.2 million. Educational spending for the previous fiscal year: $6224 per student. Total enrollment: 2,872. Faculty: 272 (124 full-time, 148 part-time). Student-undergrad faculty ratio is 13:1. 900 applied, 96% were admitted. 2% from top 10% of their high school class, 6% from top quarter, 22% from top half. 24 valedictorians. Full-time: 1,706 students, 66% women, 34% men. Part-time: 343 students, 58% women, 42% men. Students come from 31 states and territories, 8 other countries, 42% from out-of-state. 2% American Indian or Alaska Native, non-Hispanic/Latino; 4% Hispanic/Latino; 2% Black or African American, non-Hispanic/Latino; 0.7% Asian, non-Hispanic/Latino; 0.1% Native Hawaiian or other Pacific Islander, non-Hispanic/Latino; 1% international. 13% 25 or older, 35% live on campus, 9% transferred in. Retention: 75% of full-time freshmen returned the following year. Core. Calendar: semesters. Academic remediation for entering students, services for LD students, advanced placement, accelerated degree program, self-designed majors, honors program, independent study, distance learning, double major, summer session for credit, part-time degree program, external degree program, adult/continuing education programs, co-op programs and internships, graduate courses open to undergrads. Off campus study. Study abroad program.

Entrance Requirements: Options: electronic application, early admission, deferred admission, international baccalaureate accepted. Required: high school transcript, minimum 2.0 GPA in College Prep curriculum, SAT or ACT. Recommended: minimum 2.5 high school GPA, 2 recommendations. Required for some: essay, interview. Entrance: minimally difficult. Application deadline: rolling. Transfer credits accepted: Yes.

Costs Per Year: Application fee: $25. Tuition: $16,800 full-time, $560 per credit hour part-time. Mandatory fees: $910 full-time, $22 per credit hour part-time, $125 per term part-time. Full-time tuition and fees vary according to course load, degree level, program, and student level. Part-time tuition and fees vary according to course load, degree level, program, and student level.

Collegiate Environment: Orientation program. Drama-theater group, choral group, student-run newspaper. Social organizations: 28 open to all. Most popular organizations: Collegians for Life, Nursing Students Association, Student Occupational Therapy, UMPHERD, Pre-PT Club. Major annual events: Homecoming Activities, Jazz Festival, Convocation Series. Student services: health clinic, personal-psychological counseling. Campus security: 24-hour emergency response devices and patrols, late night transport-escort service, controlled dormitory access. University of Mary Library. Operations spending for the previous fiscal year: $562,534. 130 computers available on campus for general student use. A campuswide network can be accessed from student residence rooms and from off campus. Students can access the following: online class registration.

Community Environment: Bismarck, North Dakota's capital city, is the second largest city with a population of 57,000. Because of its central location, modern shopping centers and Civic Center, the city hosts many state and national conventions. Bismarck is considered the cultural, business and educational center of western and central North Dakota. It is also the medical center for the region with two modern medical centers and clinics. Bismarck has a large city library, a State Historical Library, and numerous libraries related to state and federal offices; a city orchestra, civic chorus, and amateur drama club; and many churches representing various denominations. The city has many parks and recreation areas, a city zoo, three golf courses, and clubs for a variety of recreational activities. The Missouri River and nearby Lake Sakakawea offer boating, fishing and other water sports. Bismarck has transportation service from several major air carriers, commuter airlines, and bus lines. Interstate 94 and U.S. Highway 83 meet in Bismarck. The city has a pleasant summer climate and moderate to severe winters.

■ UNIVERSITY OF NORTH DAKOTA

264 Centennial Dr.
Grand Forks, ND 58202
Tel: (701)777-2011; Free: 800-CALL-UND
Fax: (701)777-3650
E-mail: und.admissions@und.edu
Web Site: www.und.edu

Description: State-supported, university, coed. Part of North Dakota University System. Awards bachelor's, master's, and doctoral degrees and post-master's certificates. Founded 1883. Setting: 521-acre urban campus. Endowment: $10.7 million. Research spending for the previous fiscal year: $69.1 million. Educational spending for the previous fiscal year: $15,474 per student. Total enrollment: 13,846. Faculty: 760 (712 full-time, 48 part-time). Student-undergrad faculty ratio is 21:1. 5,021 applied, 82% were admitted. 18% from top 10% of their high school class, 43% from top quarter, 74% from top half. Full-time: 8,184 students, 47% women, 53% men. Part-time: 2,334 students, 34% women, 66% men. Students come from 63 states and territories, 78 other countries, 61% from out-of-state. 1% American Indian or Alaska Native, non-Hispanic/Latino; 4% Hispanic/Latino; 2% Black or African American, non-Hispanic/Latino; 2% Asian, non-Hispanic/Latino; 0.1% Native Hawaiian or other Pacific Islander, non-Hispanic/Latino; 5% international. 17% 25 or older, 27% live on campus, 9% transferred in. Retention: 80% of full-time freshmen returned the following year. Academic areas with the most degrees conferred: business/marketing; engineering; health professions and related sciences. Core. Calendar: semesters. ESL program, services for LD students, advanced placement, accelerated degree program, self-designed majors, honors program, independent study, distance learning, double major, summer session for credit, part-time degree program, external degree program, adult/continuing education programs, co-op programs and internships, graduate courses open to undergrads. Off campus study at other NDUS institutions. Study abroad program. ROTC: Army, Air Force.

Entrance Requirements: Options: electronic application, deferred admission. Required: high school transcript. Recommended: minimum 2.5 high school GPA. Required for some: SAT and SAT Subject Tests or ACT. Entrance: minimally difficult. Transfer credits accepted: Yes.

Costs Per Year: Application fee: $35. State resident tuition: $7224 full-time, $301 per credit hour part-time. Nonresident tuition: $19,288 full-time, $803 per credit hour part-time. Mandatory fees: $1471 full-time. Full-time tuition and fees vary according to degree level, program, and reciprocity agreements. Part-time tuition varies according to course load, degree level, program, and reciprocity agreements. College room and board: $8974. Room and board charges vary according to board plan and housing facility.

Collegiate Environment: Orientation program. Drama-theater group, choral group, marching band, student-run newspaper, radio station. Social organizations: 215 open to all; national fraternities, national sororities; 12% of eligible men and 13% of eligible women are members. Most popular organizations: Mortar Board, Cru, Greek Liffe, Alpha Kappa Psi, African Student Union. Major annual events: Big Event, Welcome Weekend, Press Pause. Student services: legal services, health clinic, personal-psychological counseling, women's center. Campus security: 24-hour emergency response devices and patrols, late night transport-escort service, controlled dormitory access. 3,415 college housing spaces available; 2,472 were occupied in 2018-19. No special consideration for freshman housing applicants. Options: coed, men-only, women-only housing available. Chester Fritz Library plus 2 others. Books: 712,457 (physical), 194,647 (digital/electronic); Serial titles: 542,772 (physical), 59,846 (digital/electronic); Databases: 252. Weekly public service hours: 99. Operations spending for the previous fiscal year: $9 million. 500 computers available on campus for general student use.

Computer purchase/lease plans available. A campuswide network can be accessed. Students can access the following: online class registration. Staffed computer lab on campus provides training in use of computers, software, and the Internet.

■ VALLEY CITY STATE UNIVERSITY

101 College St., SW
Valley City, ND 58072
Tel: (701)845-7990; Free: 800-532-8641
Fax: (701)845-7245
E-mail: c.stenson@vcsu.edu
Web Site: www.vcsu.edu

Description: State-supported, comprehensive, coed. Part of North Dakota University System. Awards bachelor's and master's degrees. Founded 1890. Setting: 55-acre small town campus. Endowment: $6.8 million. Research spending for the previous fiscal year: $215,221. Educational spending for the previous fiscal year: $12,725 per student. Total enrollment: 1,547. Faculty: 110 (67 full-time, 43 part-time). Student-undergrad faculty ratio is 11:1. 460 applied, 74% were admitted. Full-time: 862 students, 54% women, 46% men. Part-time: 542 students, 65% women, 35% men. 35% from out-of-state. 1% American Indian or Alaska Native, non-Hispanic/Latino; 6% Hispanic/Latino; 2% Black or African American, non-Hispanic/Latino; 0.4% Asian, non-Hispanic/Latino; 0.3% Native Hawaiian or other Pacific Islander, non-Hispanic/Latino; 2% international. 25% 25 or older, 29% live on campus, 12% transferred in. Retention: 68% of full-time freshmen returned the following year. Academic areas with the most degrees conferred: education; business/marketing; parks and recreation. Core. Calendar: semesters. Academic remediation for entering students, services for LD students, self-designed majors, distance learning, double major, summer session for credit, part-time degree program, co-op programs and internships. Off campus study at North Dakota State University. Study abroad program.
Entrance Requirements: Option: electronic application. Required: high school transcript, SAT or ACT. Entrance: noncompetitive. Application deadlines: rolling, rolling for nonresidents. Notification: continuous, continuous for nonresidents. SAT Reasoning Test deadline: 8/30. SAT Subject Test deadline: 8/30. Transfer credits accepted: Yes.
Costs Per Year: Application fee: $35. State resident tuition: $5713 full-time, $190.42 per semester hour part-time. Nonresident tuition: $15,253 full-time, $508.43 per semester hour part-time. Mandatory fees: $1913 full-time, $79.70 per semester hour part-time. Full-time tuition and fees vary according to course load, degree level, location, program, and reciprocity agreements. Part-time tuition and fees vary according to course load, degree level, location, program, and reciprocity agreements. College room and board: $6446. College room only: $2378. Room and board charges vary according to board plan and housing facility.
Collegiate Environment: Orientation program. Choral group. Social organizations: 33 open to all; local fraternities, local sororities; 1% of eligible men and 1% of eligible women are members. Most popular organizations: departmental clubs, Fellowship of Christian Athletes, VCAB, Viking Ambassadors, local fraternities/sorotries. Major annual events: Music Productions, VCAB Activities and Events, Athletic Events. Student services: health clinic, personal-psychological counseling. Campus security: controlled dormitory access. Freshmen guaranteed college housing. On-campus residence required in freshman year. Options: coed, men-only, women-only housing available. Allen Memorial Library. Books: 77,906 (physical), 140,050 (digital/electronic); Serial titles: 1,301 (physical), 29,378 (digital/electronic); Databases: 86. Weekly public service hours: 61; students can reserve study rooms. Operations spending for the previous fiscal year: $440,821. 1,200 computers available on campus for general student use. Computer purchase/lease plans available. A computer is required for all students. A campuswide network can be accessed from student residence rooms and from off campus. Students can access the following: online class registration. Staffed computer lab on campus provides training in use of computers, software, and the Internet.
Community Environment: Valley City, in the Sheyenne River Valley, is the home of the North Dakota Winter Show, a statewide agricultural fair held in the first week in March. The area is served by buses, railroad, and Interstate Highways 94, 10, and 52.

■ WILLISTON STATE COLLEGE

1410 University Ave.
Williston, ND 58801
Tel: (701)774-4200; Free: 888-863-9455
Fax: (701)774-4211
E-mail: wsc.admission@willistonstate.edu
Web Site: www.willistonstate.edu

Description: State-supported, 2-year, coed. Part of North Dakota University System. Awards certificates, transfer associate, and terminal associate degrees. Founded 1957. Setting: 80-acre small town campus. Endowment: $52,232. Educational spending for the previous fiscal year: $3653 per student. Total enrollment: 1,098. Faculty: 34 (32 full-time, 2 part-time). Student-undergrad faculty ratio is 30:1. 564 applied, 82% were admitted. Full-time: 615 students, 58% women, 42% men. Part-time: 483 students, 62% women, 38% men. Students come from 29 states and territories, 7 other countries, 18% from out-of-state. 2% American Indian or Alaska Native, non-Hispanic/Latino; 7% Hispanic/Latino; 4% Black or African American, non-Hispanic/Latino; 0.7% Asian, non-Hispanic/Latino; 0.1% Native Hawaiian or other Pacific Islander, non-Hispanic/Latino; 3% international. 21% 25 or older, 15% transferred in. Retention: 57% of full-time freshmen returned the following year. Core. Calendar: semesters. Academic remediation for entering students, ESL program, services for LD students, advanced placement, self-designed majors, independent study, distance learning, double major, summer session for credit, part-time degree program, co-op programs. Study abroad program.
Entrance Requirements: Open admission except for practical nursing, welding, transportation technician, SLPP programs. Options: electronic application, deferred admission. Required: high school transcript. Entrance: noncompetitive. Application deadline: rolling. Notification: continuous. Transfer credits accepted: Yes.
Costs Per Year: Application fee: $35. One-time mandatory fee: $35. State resident tuition: $3,676 full-time, $122.54 per credit hour part-time. Nonresident tuition: $3,676 full-time, $122.54 per credit hour part-time. Mandatory fees: $1,691 full-time, $56.36 per credit hour part-time. Full-time tuition and fees vary according to course load, location, program, and reciprocity agreements. Part-time tuition and fees vary according to course load, location, program, and reciprocity agreements. College room and board: $7670. College room only: $4000. Room and board charges vary according to board plan and housing facility.
Collegiate Environment: Orientation program. Choral group, student-run newspaper. Social organizations: 13 open to all; 3% of eligible men and 3% of eligible women are members. Most popular organizations: Phi Theta Kappa, Student Senate, Teton Activity Board, Biz-Tech, Student Nurses Organization. Major annual events: Week of Welcome, Bowling Nights, Hypnotist. Student services: personal-psychological counseling. Campus security: controlled dormitory access. Williston State College Learning Commons. Books: 8,865 (physical), 6,889 (digital/electronic); Databases: 45. Students can reserve study rooms. Operations spending for the previous fiscal year: $32,110. 200 computers available on campus for general student use. A campuswide network can be accessed. Students can access the following: online class registration.
Community Environment: Midway between two dams, Fort Peck in Montana and Garrison in North Dakota, Williston has been a railroad and distributing center since its earliest days. In the farming and stock-raising region of the oil-rich Williston Basin, the city has more than 1,000 producing wells within its trade territory. This is a rural community with temperate climate. The area is served by bus, rail, and air lines. Good U.S. Highways intersect the city. Community services include 24 churches representing 18 denominations, a public library, museum, community concert association, modern hospital, and clinics. There are also various civic, fraternal, and veteran's organizations here. Local recreation includes theaters, a drive-in, golf clubs, bowling alley, tennis courts, baseball stadium, several softball complexes, and excellent fishing in Garrison Reservoir and the Missouri River.

■ AIC COLLEGE OF DESIGN

1171 E Kemper Rd.
Cincinnati, OH 45246
Tel: (513)751-1206
Fax: (513)751-1209
Web Site: www.aic-arts.edu

Description: Independent, primarily 2-year, coed. Awards terminal associate and bachelor's degrees. Founded 1976. Setting: 3-acre urban campus with easy access to Cincinnati. Educational spending for the previous fiscal year: $11,281 per student. Total enrollment: 34. Faculty: 11 (4 full-time, 7 part-time). Student-undergrad faculty ratio is 5:1. 36 applied, 67% were admitted. 1% from top 10% of their high school class, 57% from top quarter, 33% from top half. Full-time: 30 students, 67% women, 33% men. Part-time: 4 students, 50% women, 50% men. Students come from 3 states and territories, 27% from out-of-state. 18% Black or African American, non-Hispanic/Latino. 22% 25 or older. Retention: 90% of full-time freshmen returned the following year. Core. Academic remediation for entering students, services for LD students, advanced placement, accelerated degree program, part-time degree program, adult/continuing education programs, co-op programs.

Entrance Requirements: Options: early admission, early decision, deferred admission, international baccalaureate accepted. Required: essay, high school transcript, interview. Recommended: minimum 2 high school GPA, recommendations, SAT or ACT. Entrance: noncompetitive. Application deadline: rolling. Notification: continuous. Transfer credits accepted: Yes. Applicants placed on waiting list: 0. Wait-listed applicants offered admission: 0. Early decision applicants: 3. Early decision applicants admitted: 3.

Collegiate Environment: Orientation program. Social organizations: 1 open to all; 70% of eligible men and 80% of eligible women are members. Most popular organization: AIGA Student Chapter. Major annual events: Senior Show, Open House Art Showing, Annual Picnic. Student services: personal-psychological counseling. Campus security: 24-hour emergency response devices, SMS. AIC College of Design Library plus 1 other. Operations spending for the previous fiscal year: $17,500. 20 computers available on campus for general student use. Computer purchase/lease plans available. A computer is required for all students. A campuswide network can be accessed. Students can access the following: online class registration. Staffed computer lab on campus provides training in use of computers, software, and the Internet.

■ ALLEGHENY WESLEYAN COLLEGE

2161 Woodsdale Rd.
Salem, OH 44460
Tel: (330)337-6403; Free: 800-292-3153
Fax: (330)337-6255
Web Site: www.awc.edu

Description: Independent Wesleyan, 4-year, coed. Awards bachelor's degrees. Total enrollment: 54. 17% 25 or older. Calendar: semesters.
Entrance Requirements: Open admission.

■ AMERICAN INSTITUTE OF ALTERNATIVE MEDICINE

6685 Doubletree Ave.
Columbus, OH 43229
Tel: (614)825-6278
Web Site: www.aiam.edu

Description: Proprietary, 2-year, coed. Awards certificates, transfer associate, and terminal associate degrees.

■ AMERICAN NATIONAL UNIVERSITY (KETTERING)

1837 Woodman Ctr. Dr.
Kettering, OH 45420
Tel: (937)299-9450
Web Site: www.an.edu

Description: Proprietary, 2-year, coed. Awards diplomas and terminal associate degrees.

■ AMERICAN NATIONAL UNIVERSITY (YOUNGSTOWN)

3487 Belmont Ave.
Youngstown, OH 44505
Tel: (330)759-0205
Web Site: www.an.edu

Description: Proprietary, 2-year, coed. Awards diplomas and transfer associate degrees. Founded 2007.

■ ANTIOCH COLLEGE

1 Morgan Pl.
Yellow Springs, OH 45387
Tel: (937)767-1286
E-mail: screepingbear@antiochcollege.edu
Web Site: www.antiochcollege.edu

Description: Independent, 4-year, coed. Awards bachelor's degrees. Founded 2011. Setting: 1,100-acre rural campus with easy access to Columbus. Endowment: $9.2 million. Educational spending for the previous fiscal year: $18,709 per student. Total enrollment: 102. Faculty: 27 (24 full-time, 3 part-time). Student-undergrad faculty ratio is 4:1. 134 applied, 84% were admitted. Full-time: 102 students, 62% women, 38% men. Students come from 25 states and territories, 3 other countries, 28% from out-of-state. 1% American Indian or Alaska Native, non-Hispanic/Latino; 16% Hispanic/Latino; 17% Black or African American, non-Hispanic/Latino; 2% Asian, non-Hispanic/Latino. 6% 25 or older, 66% live on campus, 12% transferred in. Retention: 47% of full-time freshmen returned the following year. Academic areas with the most degrees conferred: liberal arts/general studies; visual and performing arts; social sciences. Core. Calendar: quarters. Academic remediation for entering students, services for LD students, advanced placement, self-designed majors, independent study, summer session for credit, co-op programs. Off campus study at Through Southwestern Ohio Council for Higher Education (SOCHE), students enrolled at any SOCHE member institution (including Antioch College) have the opportunity to register and receive credit for courses offered by other participating SOCHE institutions. Study abroad program.

Entrance Requirements: Options: electronic application, early admission, early decision, deferred admission. Required: essay, high school transcript, 2 recommendations. Required for some: interview. Entrance: moderately difficult. Application deadlines: 11/15 for early decision plan 1, 1/2 for early decision plan 2. Notification: continuous, continuous for nonresidents, 12/15 for early decision plan 1, 2/1 for early decision plan 2. Transfer credits accepted: Yes.

Costs Per Year: Application fee: $0. One-time mandatory fee: $150. Comprehensive fee: $44,633 includes full-time tuition ($35,949), mandatory fees ($1044), and college room and board ($7640). College room only:

$4622. Part-time tuition: $500 per credit hour. Tuition guaranteed not to increase for student's term of enrollment.

Collegiate Environment: Orientation program. Drama-theater group, student-run newspaper, radio station. Social organizations: 7 open to all. Most popular organizations: People of Color Group, Queer Center, Outdoors Club, Antioch Creative Collective, ei@A (Entrepreneurs & Innovation @ Antioch). Major annual events: Community Days, Div Dances, Co-op Swap. Student services: health clinic, personal-psychological counseling. Campus security: 24-hour emergency response devices and patrols, late night transport-escort service, controlled dormitory access. 223 college housing spaces available; 67 were occupied in 2018-19. No special consideration for freshman housing applicants. On-campus residence required through senior year. Option: coed housing available. Olive Kettering Library. Books: 158,578 (physical), 125,344 (digital/electronic); Serial titles: 1,402 (physical), 33,099 (digital/electronic); Databases: 199. Weekly public service hours: 72. Operations spending for the previous fiscal year: $330,467. 69 computers available on campus for general student use. A campuswide network can be accessed from student residence rooms. Students can access the following: online class registration. Staffed computer lab on campus.

■ ANTIOCH UNIVERSITY MIDWEST
900 Dayton St.
Yellow Springs, OH 45387-1609
Tel: (937)769-1800
Fax: (937)769-1805
Web Site: www.antioch.edu/midwest

Description: Independent, upper-level, coed. Part of Antioch University. Awards bachelor's and master's degrees and post-master's certificates. Founded 1988. Setting: 100-acre small town campus with easy access to Dayton. Total enrollment: 135. Full-time: 20 students, 85% women, 15% men. Part-time: 21 students, 62% women, 38% men. Students come from 13 states and territories, 1% from out-of-state. 8% Hispanic/Latino; 13% Black or African American, non-Hispanic/Latino. 1% 25 or older. Core. Calendar: semesters. Services for LD students, advanced placement, accelerated degree program, self-designed majors, independent study, distance learning, double major, summer session for credit, part-time degree program, adult/continuing education programs, co-op programs and internships, graduate courses open to undergrads. Off campus study at Southwestern Ohio Consortium of Higher Education (SOCHE) and all Antioch University campuses.

Costs Per Year: Application fee: $45. Tuition: $18,972 full-time, $527 per credit hour part-time. Mandatory fees: $400 full-time.

Collegiate Environment: Student services: personal-psychological counseling. Campus security: 24-hour emergency response devices. Midwest Library. 10 computers available on campus for general student use. A computer is required for all students. A campuswide network can be accessed. Students can access the following: online class registration, online bill pay and view/acceptance of financial aid award letter, narrative evaluations. Staffed computer lab on campus provides training in use of computers, software, and the Internet.

■ ANTONELLI COLLEGE
124 E Seventh St.
Cincinnati, OH 45202
Tel: (513)241-4338; Free: 877-500-4304
Fax: (513)241-9396
Web Site: www.antonellicollege.edu

Description: Proprietary, 2-year, coed. Awards diplomas and terminal associate degrees. Founded 1947. Setting: urban campus. Total enrollment: 377. 55% 25 or older. Core. Calendar: quarters. Honors program, summer session for credit, part-time degree program, internships.

Entrance Requirements: Open admission. Options: early admission, deferred admission. Required: high school transcript, interview. Required for some: art portfolio. Entrance: noncompetitive. Application deadline: rolling.

Collegiate Environment: Student services: personal-psychological counseling. Campus security: 24-hour emergency response devices, security personnel while classes are in session. Main library plus 1 other.

■ ART ACADEMY OF CINCINNATI
1212 Jackson St.
Cincinnati, OH 45202
Tel: (513)562-6262; Free: 800-323-5692
Fax: (513)562-8778
E-mail: admissions@artacademy.edu

Web Site: www.artacademy.edu

Description: Independent, comprehensive, coed. Awards associate, bachelor's, and master's degrees. Founded 1887. Setting: 184-acre urban campus. Endowment: $7 million. Total enrollment: 165. Faculty: 44 (14 full-time, 30 part-time). Student-undergrad faculty ratio is 10:1. 541 applied, 21% were admitted. Full-time: 153 students, 63% women, 37% men. Part-time: 11 students, 55% women, 45% men. Students come from 12 states and territories, 2 other countries, 24% from out-of-state. 8% 25 or older, 18% live on campus, 15% transferred in. Retention: 81% of full-time freshmen returned the following year. Academic area with the most degrees conferred: visual and performing arts. Core. Calendar: semesters. Services for LD students, advanced placement, self-designed majors, honors program, independent study, double major, summer session for credit, part-time degree program, adult/continuing education programs, co-op programs and internships, graduate courses open to undergrads. Off campus study at members of the Greater Cincinnati Consortium of Colleges and Universities, Association of Independent Colleges of Art and Design. Study abroad program.

Entrance Requirements: Options: electronic application, deferred admission. Required: essay, high school transcript, minimum 2.0 high school GPA, 1 recommendation, portfolio, SAT or ACT. Recommended: interview. Entrance: moderately difficult. Application deadline: 6/30. Notification: continuous.

Collegiate Environment: Orientation program. Major annual events: Annual Field Trips to Art Centers (Chicago and New York), Visiting Artists Lecture Series, Student Exhibitions. Student services: personal-psychological counseling. Campus security: 24-hour emergency response devices and patrols. 40 computers available on campus for general student use. A campuswide network can be accessed. Staffed computer lab on campus provides training in use of computers, software, and the Internet.

Community Environment: The Art Academy is located in Eden Park, a metropolitan park of 184 acres that also contains the Cincinnati Historical Society. Mirror Lake, the Krohm Conservatory, two dramatic theaters, one outdoor theater and the Ohio River overlook the area.

■ ASHLAND UNIVERSITY
401 College Ave.
Ashland, OH 44805-3702
Tel: (419)289-4142; Free: 800-882-1548
Fax: (419)289-5999
E-mail: enrollme@ashland.edu
Web Site: www.ashland.edu

Description: Independent, comprehensive, coed, affiliated with Brethren Church. Awards associate, bachelor's, master's, and doctoral degrees and post-master's certificates. Founded 1878. Setting: 135-acre small town campus with easy access to Cleveland, Akron. Endowment: $36.8 million. Educational spending for the previous fiscal year: $9088 per student. Total enrollment: 6,579. Faculty: 392 (174 full-time, 218 part-time). Student-undergrad faculty ratio is 12:1. 3,121 applied, 76% were admitted. Full-time: 3,414 students, 50% women, 50% men. Part-time: 1,122 students, 37% women, 63% men. Students come from 31 states and territories, 19 other countries, 7% from out-of-state. 0.5% American Indian or Alaska Native, non-Hispanic/Latino; 3% Hispanic/Latino; 13% Black or African American, non-Hispanic/Latino; 0.6% Asian, non-Hispanic/Latino; 0.1% Native Hawaiian or other Pacific Islander, non-Hispanic/Latino; 2% international. 12% 25 or older, 4% transferred in. Retention: 80% of full-time freshmen returned the following year. Academic areas with the most degrees conferred: education; business/marketing; health professions and related sciences. Core. Calendar: semesters. Academic remediation for entering students, ESL program, services for LD students, advanced placement, accelerated degree program, self-designed majors, honors program, independent study, distance learning, double major, summer session for credit, part-time degree program, external degree program, adult/continuing education programs, co-op programs and internships. Off campus study. Study abroad program.

Entrance Requirements: Options: electronic application, deferred admission, international baccalaureate accepted. Required: high school transcript, minimum 2.5 high school GPA, minimum 18 ACT or 860 SAT, SAT or ACT. Entrance: moderately difficult. Application deadline: rolling. Notification: continuous. SAT Reasoning Test deadline: 8/15. SAT Subject Test deadline: 8/15. Transfer credits accepted: Yes.

Costs Per Year: Application fee: $0. Comprehensive fee: $31,284 includes full-time tuition ($20,332), mandatory fees ($1010), and college room and board ($9942). College room only: $5356. Full-time tuition and fees vary according to class time, course level, course load, degree level, location, program, reciprocity agreements, and student level. Room and board charges vary according to board plan, housing facility, and location. Part-time tuition: $940 per credit hour. Part-time mandatory fees: $24 per credit hour. Part-time tuition and fees vary according to class time, course level, course load, degree level, location, program, reciprocity agreements, and student level.

Collegiate Environment: Orientation program. Drama-theater group, choral group, marching band, student-run newspaper, radio station. Social organizations: 90 open to all; national fraternities, national sororities, local fraternities, local sororities; 11% of eligible men and 23% of eligible women are members. Most popular organizations: Campus Activity Board, Fellowship of Christian Athletes, The Well Campus Ministry, intramurals, Sororities. Major annual events: Homecoming, Parents' Weekend, Banana Splittin'. Student services: health clinic, personal-psychological counseling. Campus security: 24-hour emergency response devices and patrols, student patrols, late night transport-escort service, controlled dormitory access. Ashland University Library plus 2 others. Books: 223,607 (physical), 255,789 (digital/electronic); Serial titles: 1,070 (physical), 114,001 (digital/electronic); Databases: 200. Weekly public service hours: 102; students can reserve study rooms. Operations spending for the previous fiscal year: $1.2 million. 760 computers available on campus for general student use. Computer purchase/lease plans available. A campuswide network can be accessed from student residence rooms and from off campus. Students can access the following: online class registration. Staffed computer lab on campus (open 24 hours a day) provides training in use of computers, software, and the Internet.

Community Environment: Five rubber manufacturers in Ashland produce most of the world's toy balloons. Other industries produce spray equipment, hydraulic cylinders, and clothing. Bus transportation is available while Mansfield Airport and Cleveland Airport furnish air transportation. Recreational facilities within the city are good and nearby Mohican State Park provides additional opportunities for fishing and camping.

■ AULTMAN COLLEGE OF NURSING AND HEALTH SCIENCES

2600 6th St., SW
Canton, OH 44710
Tel: (330)363-6347
E-mail: admissions@aultmancollege.edu
Web Site: www.aultmancollege.edu

Description: Independent, 4-year, coed. Awards associate and bachelor's degrees. Founded 2004. Setting: 5-acre urban campus with easy access to Cleveland. System endowment: $1.4 million. Research spending for the previous fiscal year: $375,290. Educational spending for the previous fiscal year: $9116 per student. Total enrollment: 394. Faculty: 66 (12 full-time, 54 part-time). Student-undergrad faculty ratio is 7:1. 51 applied, 88% were admitted. Full-time: 108 students, 86% women, 14% men. Part-time: 286 students, 91% women, 9% men. 1% American Indian or Alaska Native, non-Hispanic/Latino; 2% Hispanic/Latino; 4% Black or African American, non-Hispanic/Latino; 0.5% Asian, non-Hispanic/Latino; 0.3% Native Hawaiian or other Pacific Islander, non-Hispanic/Latino. 53% 25 or older, 25% transferred in. Academic area with the most degrees conferred: health professions and related sciences. Core. Calendar: semesters. Academic remediation for entering students, services for LD students, advanced placement, distance learning, part-time degree program, co-op programs and internships.

Entrance Requirements: Option: electronic application. Required: high school transcript. Recommended: SAT or ACT. Required for some: minimum 3 high school GPA, interview, SAT or ACT. Entrance: moderately difficult. Application deadline: 6/1. Notification: continuous until 10/1. SAT Reasoning Test deadline: 6/1. SAT Subject Test deadline: 6/1. Transfer credits accepted: Yes.

Costs Per Year: Application fee: $45. One-time mandatory fee: $200. Tuition: $17,510 full-time, $725 per credit hour part-time. Mandatory fees: $1000 full-time, $500 per term part-time. Full-time tuition and fees vary according to course load, degree level, and program. Part-time tuition and fees vary according to course load, degree level, and program.

Collegiate Environment: Orientation program. Social organizations: 10 open to all; 5% of eligible men and 10% of eligible women are members. Most popular organizations: Aultman College Student Nurse Association, Radiography Club, Aultman College Campus Ministry, Aultman College Veterans Association, Men in Nursing Association. Major annual events: Welcome Week, Title IX Awareness Week. Student services: health clinic. Campus security: 24-hour emergency response devices and patrols, late night transport-escort service. Aultman Health Sciences Library plus 1 other. Books: 2,448 (physical), 81,000 (digital/electronic); Serial titles: 129 (physical), 10,007 (digital/electronic); Databases: 145. Study areas open 24 hours,

5-7 days a week. Operations spending for the previous fiscal year: $198,656. 198 computers available on campus for general student use. A computer is required for all students. A campuswide network can be accessed. Students can access the following: online class registration. Staffed computer lab on campus provides training in use of computers, software, and the Internet.

■ BALDWIN WALLACE UNIVERSITY

275 Eastland Rd.
Berea, OH 44017-2088
Tel: (440)826-2900; Free: 877-BW-APPLY
Fax: (440)826-3830
E-mail: admission@bw.edu
Web Site: www.bw.edu

Description: Independent Methodist, comprehensive, coed. Awards bachelor's and master's degrees and post-master's certificates. Founded 1845. Setting: 100-acre suburban campus with easy access to Cleveland. Endowment: $174.8 million. Research spending for the previous fiscal year: $191,548. Educational spending for the previous fiscal year: $13,565 per student. Total enrollment: 3,741. Faculty: 460 (221 full-time, 239 part-time). Student-undergrad faculty ratio is 11:1. 3,926 applied, 74% were admitted. 18% from top 10% of their high school class, 46% from top quarter, 78% from top half. 7 National Merit Scholars, 9 class presidents, 8 valedictorians, 23 student government officers. Full-time: 2,923 students, 54% women, 46% men. Part-time: 213 students, 56% women, 44% men. Students come from 42 states and territories, 20 other countries, 24% from out-of-state. 0.1% American Indian or Alaska Native, non-Hispanic/Latino; 6% Hispanic/Latino; 9% Black or African American, non-Hispanic/Latino; 1% Asian, non-Hispanic/Latino; 0.7% international. 1% 25 or older, 57% live on campus, 5% transferred in. Retention: 82% of full-time freshmen returned the following year. Academic areas with the most degrees conferred: business/marketing; visual and performing arts; health professions and related sciences. Core. Calendar: semesters. Academic remediation for entering students, ESL program, services for LD students, advanced placement, accelerated degree program, self-designed majors, honors program, independent study, distance learning, double major, summer session for credit, part-time degree program, adult/continuing education programs, internships, graduate courses open to undergrads. Off campus study at Case Western Reserve University. Study abroad program. ROTC: Army (c), Air Force (c).

Entrance Requirements: Options: electronic application, deferred admission, international baccalaureate accepted. Required: essay, high school transcript. Recommended: minimum 3 high school GPA, 1 recommendation, interview. Required for some: minimum 3.0 cum GPA and recently graded paper in lieu of ACT or SAT scores for Test Optional applicants, SAT or ACT. Entrance: moderately difficult. Application deadline: 5/1. Notification: continuous. SAT Reasoning Test deadline: 8/1. Transfer credits accepted: Yes.

Costs Per Year: Application fee: $25. Comprehensive fee: $43,640 includes full-time tuition ($33,530) and college room and board ($10,110). College room only: $5678. Part-time tuition: $1042 per credit hour.

Collegiate Environment: Orientation program. Drama-theater group, choral group, marching band, student-run newspaper, radio station. Social organizations: 127 open to all; national fraternities, national sororities; 15% of eligible men and 19% of eligible women are members. Most popular organizations: Arts Management Association (AMA), Ohio Collegiate Music Educators Association (OCMEA), Rotaract, Sport Management Club (SMC), Voices of Praise Gospel Choir (VOP). Major annual events: April Reign, Bold & Gold Festival (Homecoming & Community Day), Saturday of Service. Student services: health clinic, personal-psychological counseling. Campus security: 24-hour emergency response devices and patrols, student patrols, late night transport-escort service, controlled dormitory access. 1,837 college housing spaces available; 1,541 were occupied in 2018-19. Freshmen given priority for college housing. On-campus residence required through sophomore year. Option: coed housing available. Ritter Library plus 2 others. Books: 106,091 (physical), 451,472 (digital/electronic); Serial titles: 148 (physical), 86,238 (digital/electronic); Databases: 265. Weekly public service hours: 90; study areas open 24 hours, 5-7 days a week; students can reserve study rooms. Operations spending for the previous fiscal year: $192,921. 457 computers available on campus for general student use. A computer is required for all students. A campuswide network can be accessed from student residence rooms. Students can access the following: online class registration. Staffed computer lab on campus (open 24 hours a day).

Community Environment: Berea, with its tree-lined streets and picturesque homes, is an ideal college town, yet it is only 20 minutes from the heart of Cleveland, home to many fortune 500 companies and recreational and cultural opportunities.

■ BECKFIELD COLLEGE

225 Pictoria Dr.
Ste. 200
Cincinnati, OH 45246
Tel: (513)671-1920
Web Site: www.beckfield.edu

Description: Proprietary, 2-year, coed. Awards diplomas and transfer associate degrees. Founded 1984. Setting: suburban campus. Calendar: quarters.

■ BELMONT COLLEGE

120 Fox Shannon Pl.
Saint Clairsville, OH 43950-9735
Tel: (740)695-9500; Free: 800-423-1188
Fax: (740)695-2247
Web Site: www.belmontcollege.edu

Description: State-supported, 2-year, coed. Part of Ohio Board of Regents. Awards diplomas and terminal associate degrees. Founded 1971. Setting: 55-acre rural campus. Total enrollment: 1,742. 46% 25 or older. Core. Calendar: quarters. Academic remediation for entering students, independent study, distance learning, summer session for credit, part-time degree program.

Entrance Requirements: Open admission except for nursing, emergency medical technology programs. Option: early admission. Entrance: noncompetitive. Application deadline: rolling.

Costs Per Year: State resident tuition: $3,232 full-time, $107.75 per credit hour part-time. Nonresident tuition: $6330 full-time, $211 per credit hour part-time. Mandatory fees: $1740 full-time, $58 per credit hour part-time. Full-time tuition and fees vary according to course load and reciprocity agreements. Part-time tuition and fees vary according to course load and reciprocity agreements.

Collegiate Environment: Orientation program. Student services: personal-psychological counseling.

Community Environment: Belmont Technical College is located in a rural area of Belmont County, Ohio, just 10 miles west of Wheeling, WV. The college is active in the community and exposes students to a variety of activities, including the fine arts.

■ BLUFFTON UNIVERSITY

1 University Dr.
Bluffton, OH 45817
Tel: (419)358-3000; Free: 800-488-3257
Fax: (419)358-3232
E-mail: admissions@bluffton.edu
Web Site: www.bluffton.edu

Description: Independent Mennonite, comprehensive, coed. Awards bachelor's and master's degrees. Founded 1899. Setting: 65-acre small town campus with easy access to Dayton. Endowment: $24.2 million. Educational spending for the previous fiscal year: $9900 per student. Total enrollment: 824. Faculty: 99 (50 full-time, 49 part-time). Student-undergrad faculty ratio is 11:1. 1,767 applied, 49% were admitted. 11% from top 10% of their high school class, 34% from top quarter, 64% from top half. 6 valedictorians, 24 student government officers. Full-time: 669 students, 49% women, 51% men. Part-time: 79 students, 51% women, 49% men. Students come from 15 states and territories, 8 other countries, 12% from out-of-state. 0.3% American Indian or Alaska Native, non-Hispanic/Latino; 4% Hispanic/Latino; 9% Black or African American, non-Hispanic/Latino; 0.5% Asian, non-Hispanic/Latino; 1% international. 7% 25 or older, 80% live on campus, 2% transferred in. Retention: 67% of full-time freshmen returned the following year. Academic areas with the most degrees conferred: business/marketing; education; parks and recreation. Core. Calendar: semesters. Academic remediation for entering students, ESL program, services for LD students, advanced placement, accelerated degree program, self-designed majors, honors program, independent study, distance learning, double major, summer session for credit, part-time degree program, adult/continuing education programs, internships. Off campus study at Washington Community Scholars Center with Eastern Mennonite University; Brethren Colleges Abroad; Council for International Education Exchange; Council for Christian Colleges and Universities. Study abroad program.

Entrance Requirements: Options: electronic application, deferred admission, international baccalaureate accepted. Required: high school transcript, minimum 2.3 high school GPA, 1 recommendation, rank in upper 50% of high school class or minimum ACT score of 19, SAT or ACT. Recommended: interview. Required for some: essay. Entrance: moderately difficult. Application deadline: rolling. Notification: continuous. SAT Reasoning Test deadline: 8/24. SAT Subject Test deadline: 8/24. Transfer credits accepted: Yes.

Costs Per Year: Application fee: $0. Comprehensive fee: $43,566 includes full-time tuition ($32,316), mandatory fees ($450), and college room and board ($10,800). College room only: $5316. Full-time tuition and fees vary according to course load, degree level, and program. Room and board charges vary according to board plan and housing facility. Part-time tuition: $1347 per credit hour. Part-time mandatory fees: $113 per term. Part-time tuition and fees vary according to course load, degree level, and program.

Collegiate Environment: Orientation program. Drama-theater group, choral group, student-run newspaper, radio station. Social organizations: 50 open to all. Most popular organizations: Marbeck Center Board, Multicultural Student Organization, Bluffton Education Association, Fellowship of Christian Athletes, Bluffton University Business Leaders. Major annual events: Dam Jam, Cabaret for a Cause, Riley Creek Festival. Student services: health clinic, personal-psychological counseling. Campus security: 24-hour emergency response devices, controlled dormitory access, night security guards. Musselman Library plus 1 other. Books: 73,648 (physical), 283,031 (digital/electronic); Serial titles: 1,001 (physical), 46,672 (digital/electronic); Databases: 258. Weekly public service hours: 74; students can reserve study rooms. Operations spending for the previous fiscal year: $509,527. 175 computers available on campus for general student use. A campuswide network can be accessed from student residence rooms and from off campus. Students can access the following: online class registration. Staffed computer lab on campus provides training in use of computers, software, and the Internet.

■ BOWLING GREEN STATE UNIVERSITY

Bowling Green, OH 43403
Tel: (419)372-2531
Web Site: www.bgsu.edu

Description: State-supported, university, coed. Awards bachelor's, master's, and doctoral degrees and post-master's certificates. Founded 1910. Setting: 1,338-acre small town campus with easy access to Toledo. Endowment: $162.3 million. Research spending for the previous fiscal year: $9.7 million. Educational spending for the previous fiscal year: $7665 per student. Total enrollment: 17,540. Faculty: 1,144 (744 full-time, 400 part-time). Student-undergrad faculty ratio is 18:1. 17,028 applied, 72% were admitted. 15% from top 10% of their high school class, 38% from top quarter, 70% from top half. 45 valedictorians. Full-time: 12,987 students, 56% women, 44% men. Part-time: 1,871 students, 50% women, 50% men. Students come from 51 states and territories, 57 other countries, 12% from out-of-state. 0.2% American Indian or Alaska Native, non-Hispanic/Latino; 4% Hispanic/Latino; 8% Black or African American, non-Hispanic/Latino; 1% Asian, non-Hispanic/Latino; 3% international. 6% 25 or older, 42% live on campus, 4% transferred in. Retention: 77% of full-time freshmen returned the following year. Academic areas with the most degrees conferred: education; business/marketing; health professions and related sciences. Core. Calendar: semesters. Academic remediation for entering students, ESL program, services for LD students, advanced placement, accelerated degree program, self-designed majors, freshman honors college, honors program, independent study, distance learning, double major, summer session for credit, part-time degree program, adult/continuing education programs, co-op programs and internships, graduate courses open to undergrads. Off campus study at University of Toledo, Lorain County Community College. Study abroad program. ROTC: Army, Air Force.

Entrance Requirements: Options: electronic application, deferred admission, international baccalaureate accepted. Required: high school transcript, SAT or ACT. Required for some: interview. Entrance: moderately difficult. Application deadlines: 7/15, 7/15 for nonresidents. Notification: continuous until 8/1, continuous until 8/1 for nonresidents. SAT Reasoning Test deadline: 8/1. Transfer credits accepted: Yes.

Costs Per Year: Application fee: $45. State resident tuition: $9096 full-time, $379 per credit hour part-time. Nonresident tuition: $17,084 full-time, $712 per credit hour part-time. Mandatory fees: $2,008 full-time, $83 per credit hour part-time. Full-time tuition and fees vary according to course load and location. Part-time tuition and fees vary according to course load and location. College room and board: $9168. Room and board charges vary according to board plan and housing facility.

Collegiate Environment: Orientation program. Drama-theater group, choral

group, marching band, student-run newspaper, radio station. Social organizations: 369 open to all; national fraternities, national sororities; 11% of eligible men and 10% of eligible women are members. Most popular organizations: Dance Marathon, Undergraduate Student Government, University Activities Organization, Alpha Phi Omega, Athletic Training Student Organization. Major annual events: CampusFest, Homecoming, Move-in Weekend and Week of Welcome. Student services: legal services, health clinic, personal-psychological counseling, women's center. Campus security: 24-hour emergency response devices and patrols, student patrols, late night transport-escort service, controlled dormitory access. 6,005 college housing spaces available; 5,709 were occupied in 2018-19. Freshmen guaranteed college housing. On-campus residence required through sophomore year. Options: coed, men-only, women-only housing available. William T. Jerome Library. Books: 1.6 million (physical), 230,668 (digital/electronic); Serial titles: 651 (physical), 12,290 (digital/electronic); Databases: 303. Weekly public service hours: 110; students can reserve study rooms. Operations spending for the previous fiscal year: $9.8 million. 1,500 computers available on campus for general student use. Computer purchase/lease plans available. A campuswide network can be accessed from student residence rooms and from off campus. Students can access the following: online class registration, wireless networking, OneDrive, Bursar billing information and payment, online mid-term grade reporting, view and change personal information, order official and unofficial transcripts, check meal plan balance, apply for graduation, etc. Staffed computer lab on campus provides training in use of computers, software, and the Internet.

Community Environment: Bowling Green, the county seat of Wood County, is located 23 miles south of Toledo. Community facilities in this metropolitan area include libraries, many churches, a hospital, shopping areas, and major civic and service organizations. Lake Erie and the Maumee River provide facilities for recreation.

■ **BOWLING GREEN STATE UNIVERSITY-FIRELANDS COLLEGE**
One University Dr.
Huron, OH 44839-9791
Tel: (419)433-5560
E-mail: mzahler@bgsu.edu
Web Site: www.firelands.bgsu.edu
Description: State-supported, primarily 2-year, coed. Part of Bowling Green State University System. Awards certificates, transfer associate, terminal associate, and bachelor's degrees (also offers some upper-level and graduate courses). Founded 1968. Setting: 216-acre rural campus with easy access to Cleveland, Toledo. Total enrollment: 1,970. Faculty: 102 (44 full-time, 58 part-time). Student-undergrad faculty ratio is 20:1. 5% from top 10% of their high school class, 27% from top quarter, 60% from top half. Full-time: 936 students, 62% women, 38% men. Part-time: 1,034 students, 65% women, 35% men. Students come from 6 states and territories, 1 other country, 1% from out-of-state. 0.2% American Indian or Alaska Native, non-Hispanic/Latino; 5% Hispanic/Latino; 6% Black or African American, non-Hispanic/Latino; 0.8% Asian, non-Hispanic/Latino; 0.1% international. 28% 25 or older. Retention: 53% of full-time freshmen returned the following year. Core. Calendar: semesters. Academic remediation for entering students, services for LD students, advanced placement, self-designed majors, honors program, independent study, distance learning, double major, summer session for credit, part-time degree program, adult/continuing education programs, co-op programs and internships. Study abroad program. ROTC: Army (c), Air Force (c).
Entrance Requirements: Open admission. Options: electronic application, early admission, deferred admission. Required: high school transcript. Entrance: noncompetitive. Application deadline: 8/6. Notification: continuous. Transfer credits accepted: Yes.
Costs Per Year: Application fee: $45. State resident tuition: $4,706 full-time, $196.10 per credit hour part-time. Nonresident tuition: $12,014 full-time, $510.10 per credit hour part-time. Mandatory fees: $240 full-time, $9.35 per credit hour part-time, $120.20 per term part-time. Full-time tuition and fees vary according to location and reciprocity agreements. Part-time tuition and fees vary according to location and reciprocity agreements.
Collegiate Environment: Orientation program. Drama-theater group, choral group. Social organizations: 20 open to all. Most popular organizations: Society of Fandom and Gaming, Student Government, Student Theater Guild, Safe Space, Society of Leadership and Success. Major annual events: Fall Banquet, Welcome Back Cookout, Homecoming Cookout. Campus security: 24-hour emergency response devices, late night transport-escort service, patrols by trained security personnel. BGSU Firelands Col-

lege Library. 300 computers available on campus for general student use. Computer purchase/lease plans available. A campuswide network can be accessed. Students can access the following: online class registration. Staffed computer lab on campus provides training in use of computers, software, and the Internet.

■ **BRADFORD SCHOOL**
2469 Stelzer Rd.
Columbus, OH 43219
Tel: (614)416-6200; Free: 800-678-7981
Web Site: www.bradfordschoolcolumbus.edu
Description: Proprietary, 2-year, coed. Awards diplomas and terminal associate degrees. Founded 1911. Setting: suburban campus. Total enrollment: 443. Calendar: semesters. Accelerated degree program, internships.

■ **BRYANT & STRATTON COLLEGE-AKRON CAMPUS**
190 Montrose W Ave.
Akron, OH 44321
Tel: (330)598-2500
Web Site: www.bryantstratton.edu
Description: Proprietary, 4-year, coed. Awards associate and bachelor's degrees.

■ **BRYANT & STRATTON COLLEGE-CLEVELAND CAMPUS**
3121 Euclid Ave.
Cleveland, OH 44115
Tel: (216)771-1700
Fax: (216)771-1700
Web Site: www.bryantstratton.edu
Description: Proprietary, 4-year, coed. Part of Bryant and Stratton College, Inc. Awards associate and bachelor's degrees. Founded 1929. Setting: urban campus. Educational spending for the previous fiscal year: $1500 per student. Total enrollment: 524. Faculty: 37 (13 full-time, 24 part-time). Student-undergrad faculty ratio is 10:1. Students come from 2 states and territories. 59% 25 or older, 10% live on campus. Academic area with the most degrees conferred: business/marketing. Core. Calendar: semesters. Academic remediation for entering students, services for LD students, independent study, distance learning, double major, summer session for credit, part-time degree program, adult/continuing education programs, co-op programs and internships.
Entrance Requirements: Option: deferred admission. Required: high school transcript, interview, entrance evaluation and placement evaluation, TABE. Recommended: SAT or ACT. Entrance: minimally difficult. Application deadline: rolling.
Collegiate Environment: Orientation program. Student-run newspaper. Most popular organization: student/staff softball. Major annual events: Summer Carnival, Team Spirit Day (hot dog sale). Campus security: controlled dormitory access. 66 computers available on campus for general student use. Students can access the following: e-mail. Staffed computer lab on campus.

■ **BRYANT & STRATTON COLLEGE-EASTLAKE CAMPUS**
35350 Curtis Blvd.
Eastlake, OH 44095
Tel: (440)510-1112
Web Site: www.bryantstratton.edu
Description: Proprietary, primarily 2-year, coed. Part of Bryant and Stratton College, Inc. Awards transfer associate, terminal associate, and bachelor's degrees. Founded 1987. Setting: suburban campus with easy access to Cleveland. Total enrollment: 762. Faculty: 63 (24 full-time, 39 part-time). Student-undergrad faculty ratio is 12:1. 312 applied. Full-time: 490 students, 89% women, 11% men. Part-time: 272 students, 86% women, 14% men. 63% 25 or older, 1% transferred in. Retention: 28% of full-time freshmen returned the following year. Core. Calendar: semesters. Academic remediation for entering students, advanced placement, independent study, distance learning, summer session for credit, part-time degree program, internships.
Entrance Requirements: Option: deferred admission. Required: high school transcript, interview, entrance and placement evaluations, CPAt. Recommended: minimum 2 high school GPA, SAT or ACT. Required for some: essay. Entrance: minimally difficult. Application deadline: rolling.
Collegiate Environment: Orientation program. Student-run newspaper. Social organizations: 6 open to all; 2% of eligible men and 10% of eligible women are members. Most popular organizations: Criminal Justice Club,

Rotaract, Medical Assisting Club, International Association of Administrative Professionals (IAAP), Student Senate. Major annual events: Portfolio Development Day, Academic Awards Ceremony. Campus security: 24-hour emergency response devices, late night transport-escort service. Main library plus 1 other. Operations spending for the previous fiscal year: $22,554. 300 computers available on campus for general student use. Staffed computer lab on campus provides training in use of computers, software, and the Internet.

■ BRYANT & STRATTON COLLEGE-PARMA CAMPUS

12955 Snow Rd.
Parma, OH 44130-1005
Tel: (216)265-3151
Fax: (216)265-0325
Web Site: www.bryantstratton.edu

Description: Proprietary, primarily 2-year, coed. Part of Bryant and Stratton College, Inc. Awards transfer associate, terminal associate, and bachelor's degrees. Founded 1981. Setting: 4-acre suburban campus with easy access to Cleveland. Research spending for the previous fiscal year: $4000. Educational spending for the previous fiscal year: $1335 per student. Total enrollment: 528. Faculty: 57 (16 full-time, 41 part-time). Student-undergrad faculty ratio is 12:1. 2% from top 10% of their high school class, 4% from top quarter, 46% from top half. Full-time: 288 students, 81% women, 19% men. Part-time: 240 students, 82% women, 18% men. 34% 25 or older. Retention: 60% of full-time freshmen returned the following year. Core. Calendar: semesters. Academic remediation for entering students, independent study, distance learning, double major, summer session for credit, part-time degree program, co-op programs and internships.

Entrance Requirements: Option: deferred admission. Required: high school transcript, interview, entrance and placement evaluations, CPAt. Recommended: SAT or ACT. Entrance: minimally difficult. Application deadline: rolling.

Collegiate Environment: Orientation program. Social organizations: 4 open to all. Most popular organizations: SHRM, Student Services Club, Sigma Psi Phi - Lambda Alpha Epsilon, Student Nursing Club, Medical Administrative Assistant Club. Major annual events: Summer Carnival, International Potluck, Halloween Party. Campus security: 24-hour emergency response devices. Main library plus 1 other. Operations spending for the previous fiscal year: $52,000. 96 computers available on campus for general student use.

■ CAPITAL UNIVERSITY

1 College and Main
Columbus, OH 43209-2394
Tel: (614)236-6011; Free: 866-544-6175
Fax: (614)236-6820
E-mail: ghudson@capital.edu
Web Site: www.capital.edu

Description: Independent, comprehensive, coed, affiliated with Evangelical Lutheran Church in America. Awards bachelor's, master's, and doctoral degrees. Founded 1830. Setting: 48-acre suburban campus with easy access to Columbus. Endowment: $78 million. Educational spending for the previous fiscal year: $9211 per student. Total enrollment: 3,384. Faculty: 409 (163 full-time, 246 part-time). Student-undergrad faculty ratio is 11:1. 4,208 applied, 69% were admitted. 18% from top 10% of their high school class, 48% from top quarter, 80% from top half. Full-time: 2,493 students, 60% women, 40% men. Part-time: 206 students, 70% women, 30% men. Students come from 34 states and territories, 22 other countries, 9% from out-of-state. 0.2% American Indian or Alaska Native, non-Hispanic/Latino; 4% Hispanic/Latino; 10% Black or African American, non-Hispanic/Latino; 1% Asian, non-Hispanic/Latino; 0.2% Native Hawaiian or other Pacific Islander, non-Hispanic/Latino; 2% international. 10% 25 or older, 59% live on campus, 3% transferred in. Retention: 78% of full-time freshmen returned the following year. Academic areas with the most degrees conferred: health professions and related sciences; business/marketing; education. Core. Calendar: semesters. ESL program, services for LD students, advanced placement, accelerated degree program, self-designed majors, freshman honors college, honors program, independent study, double major, summer session for credit, part-time degree program, external degree program, adult/continuing education programs, co-op programs and internships. Off campus study at members of the Higher Education Council of Columbus. Study abroad program. ROTC: Army, Air Force (c).

Entrance Requirements: Options: electronic application, deferred admission, international baccalaureate accepted. Required: high school transcript,

minimum 2.6 high school GPA, SAT or ACT. Recommended: interview. Required for some: 1 recommendation, audition for Conservatory of Music. Entrance: moderately difficult. Application deadline: 5/1. Notification: 9/30. SAT Reasoning Test deadline: 5/1. Transfer credits accepted: Yes.

Costs Per Year: Application fee: $25. Comprehensive fee: $46,050 includes full-time tuition ($35,146), mandatory fees ($320), and college room and board ($10,584). Full-time tuition and fees vary according to course load. Room and board charges vary according to board plan and housing facility. Part-time tuition: $1172 per credit hour. Part-time tuition varies according to course load.

Collegiate Environment: Orientation program. Drama-theater group, choral group, student-run newspaper, radio station. Social organizations: 60 open to all; national fraternities, national sororities, local fraternities; 2% of eligible men and 3% of eligible women are members. Most popular organizations: Campus Crusade for Christ, student government, University Programming, College Republicans, American Marketing Association. Major annual events: Homecoming, MLK Day of Learning, Up 'til Dawn. Student services: health clinic, personal-psychological counseling. Campus security: 24-hour emergency response devices and patrols, late night transport-escort service, controlled dormitory access. Blackmore Library. Operations spending for the previous fiscal year: $2.1 million. 457 computers available on campus for general student use. A campuswide network can be accessed from student residence rooms and from off campus. Students can access the following: online class registration. Staffed computer lab on campus provides training in use of computers, software, and the Internet.

Community Environment: See Ohio State University - Columbus Campus.

■ CASE WESTERN RESERVE UNIVERSITY

10900 Euclid Ave.
Cleveland, OH 44106
Tel: (216)368-2000
Fax: (216)368-5111
E-mail: admission@case.edu
Web Site: www.case.edu

Description: Independent, university, coed. Awards bachelor's, master's, and doctoral degrees and post-master's certificates. Founded 1826. Setting: 267-acre urban campus. Endowment: $1.8 billion. Research spending for the previous fiscal year: $374.7 million. Total enrollment: 11,824. Faculty: 1,007 (789 full-time, 218 part-time). Student-undergrad faculty ratio is 11:1. 25,380 applied, 33% were admitted. 70% from top 10% of their high school class, 95% from top quarter, 100% from top half. 68 National Merit Scholars, 46 valedictorians. Full-time: 4,978 students, 44% women, 56% men. Part-time: 172 students, 53% women, 47% men. Students come from 47 states and territories, 46 other countries, 72% from out-of-state. 0.1% American Indian or Alaska Native, non-Hispanic/Latino; 7% Hispanic/Latino; 4% Black or African American, non-Hispanic/Latino; 21% Asian, non-Hispanic/Latino; 0.1% Native Hawaiian or other Pacific Islander, non-Hispanic/Latino; 13% international. 1% 25 or older, 80% live on campus, 1% transferred in. Retention: 93% of full-time freshmen returned the following year. Academic areas with the most degrees conferred: engineering; business/marketing; biological/life sciences. Core. Calendar: semesters. ESL program, services for LD students, advanced placement, accelerated degree program, self-designed majors, honors program, independent study, double major, summer session for credit, part-time degree program, adult/continuing education programs, co-op programs and internships, graduate courses open to undergrads. Off campus study at Cleveland Institute of Art, Cleveland State University, Cuyahoga Community College, and John Carroll University. Study abroad program. ROTC: Army, Air Force (c).

Entrance Requirements: Options: electronic application, early admission, early decision, early action, deferred admission, international baccalaureate accepted. Required: essay, high school transcript, 2 recommendations, school report, including a counselor recommendation, SAT or ACT. Recommended: interview. Entrance: very difficult. Application deadlines: 1/15, 11/1 for early decision plan 1, 1/15 for early decision plan 2, 11/1 for early action. Notification: 3/20, 12/17 for early decision plan 1, 2/1 for early decision plan 2, 12/15 for early action. SAT Reasoning Test deadline: 1/15. SAT Subject Test deadline: 1/15. Transfer credits accepted: Yes. Applicants placed on waiting list: 7,178. Wait-listed applicants offered admission: 586. Early decision applicants: 485. Early decision applicants admitted: 182. Early action applicants: 11,419. Early action applicants admitted: 4,979.

Costs Per Year: Application fee: $70. One-time mandatory fee: $555. Comprehensive fee: $64,232 includes full-time tuition ($48,604), mandatory fees ($438), and college room and board ($15,190). College room only: $8830. Room and board charges vary according to board plan, housing facility, and student level. Part-time tuition: $2026 per credit hour. Part-time tuition varies according to course load.

Collegiate Environment: Orientation program. Drama-theater group, choral group, marching band, student-run newspaper, radio station. Social organizations: 249 open to all; national fraternities, national sororities, local sororities; 27% of eligible men and 26% of eligible women are members. Most popular organizations: SpartaTHON, Quidditch Team, Spartans for Special Olympics, Undergraduate Indian Student Association, Footlighters. Major annual events: Thwing Study Over, Springfest, Annual Snowball Dance. Student services: legal services, health clinic, personal-psychological counseling, women's center. Campus security: 24-hour emergency response devices and patrols, student patrols, late night transport-escort service, controlled dormitory access, crime prevention programs. Kelvin Smith Library plus 6 others. Books: 3.4 million (physical); Serial titles: 196,361 (physical); Databases: 470. Students can reserve study rooms. Operations spending for the previous fiscal year: $22.5 million. 357 computers available on campus for general student use. Computer purchase/lease plans available. A campuswide network can be accessed from student residence rooms and from off campus. Students can access the following: online class registration, software library, online reference databases, electronic books and journals, research computing, training. Staffed computer lab on campus provides training in use of computers, software, and the Internet.

Community Environment: The university is located on the eastern edge of Cleveland in University Circle, a 500-acre area of parks, gardens, museums, schools, hospitals, churches and human service institutions. The Cleveland Museum of Art and the Cleveland Orchestra are within walking distance, and downtown Cleveland, offering restaurants, music, theatre, and professional sports, is only ten minutes away by RTA rapid transit. Students also have easy access to many facilities provided by the city of Cleveland and the outlying areas. Among these are Cleveland's well-known "Emerald Necklace" of parks, and Blossom Music Center, the summer home of the Cleveland Orchestra. CWRU also owns a 400-acre farm in Hunting Valley, about 10 miles east of the campus, that is open to students. Recreational facilities include a picnic area, fishing ponds, hiking and ski trails, and buildings for social events.

■ **CEDARVILLE UNIVERSITY**
251 N Main St.
Cedarville, OH 45314
Tel: (937)766-7700; Free: 800-233-2784
Fax: (937)766-7575
E-mail: admissions@cedarville.edu
Web Site: www.cedarville.edu
Description: Independent Baptist, comprehensive, coed. Awards bachelor's, master's, and doctoral degrees and post-master's certificates. Founded 1887. Setting: 441-acre small town campus with easy access to Columbus, Dayton. Endowment: $30.8 million. Educational spending for the previous fiscal year: $9590 per student. Total enrollment: 4,160. Faculty: 346 (185 full-time, 161 part-time). Student-undergrad faculty ratio is 14:1. 3,741 applied, 79% were admitted. 29% from top 10% of their high school class, 60% from top quarter, 88% from top half. 30 valedictorians. Full-time: 3,278 students, 53% women, 47% men. Part-time: 481 students, 55% women, 45% men. Students come from 48 states and territories, 38 other countries, 57% from out-of-state. 0.3% American Indian or Alaska Native, non-Hispanic/Latino; 2% Hispanic/Latino; 1% Black or African American, non-Hispanic/Latino; 2% Asian, non-Hispanic/Latino; 0.1% Native Hawaiian or other Pacific Islander, non-Hispanic/Latino; 2% international. 2% 25 or older, 73% live on campus, 4% transferred in. Retention: 87% of full-time freshmen returned the following year. Academic areas with the most degrees conferred: health professions and related sciences; business/marketing; education. Core. Calendar: semesters. Academic remediation for entering students, services for LD students, advanced placement, self-designed majors, honors program, independent study, distance learning, double major, summer session for credit, part-time degree program, adult/continuing education programs, co-op programs and internships, graduate courses open to undergrads. Off campus study at Au Sable Institute of Environmental Studies, Focus Leadership Institute. Study abroad program. ROTC: Army (c), Air Force (c).
Entrance Requirements: Options: electronic application, early admission, deferred admission, international baccalaureate accepted. Required: essay, high school transcript, minimum 3 high school GPA, 1 recommendation, clear testimony of faith in Jesus Christ and evidence of a consistent Christian lifestyle, minimum ACT score of 22 or SAT score of 1020, minimum 3.0 unweighted, cumulative GPA in college prep course work, SAT or ACT, SAT

or ACT or CLT. Required for some: interview. Entrance: moderately difficult. Application deadlines: rolling, rolling for nonresidents. Notification: continuous, continuous for nonresidents. SAT Reasoning Test deadline: 8/1. Transfer credits accepted: Yes.
Costs Per Year: Application fee: $30. Comprehensive fee: $38,940 includes full-time tuition ($31,122), mandatory fees ($200), and college room and board ($7618). College room only: $4318. Part-time tuition: $1178 per credit. Part-time mandatory fees: $50 per term.
Collegiate Environment: Orientation program. Drama-theater group, choral group, student-run newspaper, radio station. Social organizations: 85 open to all; 50% of eligible men and 50% of eligible women are members. Most popular organizations: Student Nurses Association, Tau Delta Kappa, Mu Kappa, AYO, MISO (Multicultural International Student Org). Major annual events: Homecoming, Junior/Senior Banquet, ELLIV (talent/award show). Student services: health clinic, personal-psychological counseling. Campus security: 24-hour emergency response devices and patrols, late night transport-escort service, controlled dormitory access. College housing designed to accommodate 2,731 students; 2,747 undergraduates lived in college housing during 2018-19. Freshmen guaranteed college housing. On-campus residence required through senior year. Options: men-only, women-only housing available. Centennial Library. Books: 182,596 (physical), 132,747 (digital/electronic); Serial titles: 737 (physical), 27,560 (digital/electronic); Databases: 200. Weekly public service hours: 91; students can reserve study rooms. 1,500 computers available on campus for general student use. A campuswide network can be accessed from student residence rooms and from off campus. Students can access the following: online class registration, over 70 software packages. Staffed computer lab on campus provides training in use of computers, software, and the Internet.

■ **CENTRAL OHIO TECHNICAL COLLEGE**
1179 University Dr.
Newark, OH 43055-1767
Tel: (740)366-1351; Free: 800-9NEWARK
Fax: (740)366-5047
E-mail: garrabrant.34@mail.cotc.edu
Web Site: www.cotc.edu
Description: State-supported, 2-year, coed. Part of Ohio Department of Higher Education. Awards certificates and terminal associate degrees. Founded 1971. Setting: 177-acre small town campus with easy access to Columbus. Endowment: $3.2 million. Educational spending for the previous fiscal year: $4476 per student. Total enrollment: 3,442. Faculty: 207 (62 full-time, 145 part-time). Student-undergrad faculty ratio is 11:1. 374 applied, 100% were admitted. Full-time: 735 students, 62% women, 38% men. Part-time: 2,707 students, 68% women, 32% men. Students come from 44 states and territories, 2% from out-of-state. 0.2% American Indian or Alaska Native, non-Hispanic/Latino; 2% Hispanic/Latino; 9% Black or African American, non-Hispanic/Latino; 2% Asian, non-Hispanic/Latino; 0.1% Native Hawaiian or other Pacific Islander, non-Hispanic/Latino; 0.1% international. 28% 25 or older, 7% transferred in. Retention: 49% of full-time freshmen returned the following year. Core. Calendar: semesters. Academic remediation for entering students, services for LD students, advanced placement, accelerated degree program, self-designed majors, distance learning, double major, summer session for credit, part-time degree program, adult/continuing education programs, co-op programs and internships. Off campus study at Ohio State University-Newark Campus, Higher Education Council of Columbus.
Entrance Requirements: Open admission. Options: electronic application, early admission, deferred admission. Required for some: high school transcript. Entrance: noncompetitive. Application deadline: rolling. Transfer credits accepted: Yes.
Costs Per Year: Application fee: $0. One-time mandatory fee: $80. State resident tuition: $4536 full-time, $189 per credit hour part-time. Nonresident tuition: $7296 full-time, $304 per credit hour part-time. Full-time tuition varies according to course load. Part-time tuition varies according to course load.
Collegiate Environment: Orientation program. Drama-theater group, choral group. Social organizations: 30 open to all. Most popular organizations: Radiologic Technology Student Organization, Phi Theta Kappa, Society of Engineering Technology, The Human Services Committee, Digital Media Design Coshocton. Major annual events: Family and Friends Day, Annual Blood Battle Blood Drive, Fall Festival. Student services: personal-psychological counseling. Campus security: 24-hour emergency response devices and patrols, student patrols, late night transport-escort service. College housing not available. Newark Campus Library. Books: 45,000 (physical); Serial titles: 170 (physical). Students can reserve study rooms. Opera-

tions spending for the previous fiscal year: $221,724. 110 computers available on campus for general student use. Computer purchase/lease plans available. A campuswide network can be accessed. Students can access the following: online class registration. Staffed computer lab on campus provides training in use of computers, software, and the Internet.

■ CENTRAL STATE UNIVERSITY

1400 Brush Row Rd.
Wilberforce, OH 45384
Tel: (937)376-6011; Free: 800-388-2781
Fax: (937)376-6648
E-mail: admissions@centralstate.edu
Web Site: www.centralstate.edu

Description: State-supported, 4-year, coed. Part of Ohio Board of Regents. Awards bachelor's degrees. Founded 1887. Setting: 60-acre rural campus with easy access to Dayton. Endowment: $3.9 million. Research spending for the previous fiscal year: $2.8 million. Educational spending for the previous fiscal year: $5793 per student. Total enrollment: 2,099. Faculty: 201 (103 full-time, 98 part-time). Student-undergrad faculty ratio is 13:1. 12,353 applied, 57% were admitted. 7% from top 10% of their high school class, 23% from top quarter, 59% from top half. Full-time: 2,029 students, 60% women, 40% men. Part-time: 70 students, 57% women, 43% men. Students come from 29 states and territories, 11 other countries, 49% from out-of-state. 0.1% American Indian or Alaska Native, non-Hispanic/Latino; 0.5% Hispanic/Latino; 88% Black or African American, non-Hispanic/Latino; 0.1% Asian, non-Hispanic/Latino; 4% international. 6% 25 or older, 75% live on campus, 5% transferred in. Retention: 54% of full-time freshmen returned the following year. Academic areas with the most degrees conferred: business/marketing; homeland security, law enforcement, firefighting, and protective services; psychology. Core. Calendar: semesters. Services for LD students, honors program, independent study, double major, summer session for credit, part-time degree program, adult/continuing education programs, co-op programs and internships. Off campus study at members of the Southwestern Ohio Council for Higher Education. Study abroad program. ROTC: Army.

Entrance Requirements: Open admission. Option: electronic application. Required: essay, high school transcript. Required for some: minimum 2.2 high school GPA, 2 recommendations. Entrance: minimally difficult. Application deadline: rolling. Notification: continuous. Transfer credits accepted: Yes.

Costs Per Year: Application fee: $35. State resident tuition: $3926 full-time, $275 per credit hour part-time. Nonresident tuition: $5926 full-time, $625 per credit hour part-time. Mandatory fees: $2420 full-time. Full-time tuition and fees vary according to course load and reciprocity agreements. Part-time tuition varies according to course load and reciprocity agreements. College room and board: $10,232. College room only: $5500. Room and board charges vary according to board plan and housing facility.

Collegiate Environment: Orientation program. Drama-theater group, choral group, marching band, student-run newspaper, radio station. Social organizations: 40 open to all; national fraternities, national sororities, local fraternities, local sororities; 1% of eligible men and 1% of eligible women are members. Most popular organizations: Student Ambassadors, student government, Campus Tour Guides, Brotherhood of Strong Success, Family Community and Leadership in Action. Major annual events: Homecoming, Spring Week, Welcome Week activities. Student services: health clinic, personal-psychological counseling. Campus security: 24-hour emergency response devices and patrols, controlled dormitory access. 1,560 college housing spaces available; 1,503 were occupied in 2018-19. Freshmen guaranteed college housing. On-campus residence required through sophomore year. Options: coed, men-only, women-only housing available. Hallie Q. Brown Memorial Library plus 1 other. Books: 362,854 (physical), 187,392 (digital/electronic); Serial titles: 69 (physical); Databases: 277. Weekly public service hours: 77. Operations spending for the previous fiscal year: $628,820. 880 computers available on campus for general student use. A campuswide network can be accessed from student residence rooms and from off campus. Students can access the following: online class registration. Staffed computer lab on campus provides training in use of computers, software, and the Internet.

Community Environment: A college community, Wilberforce was named after William Wilberforce, the English philanthropist who fought for the abolition of slave trade. The community is known as a noted African-American cultural center. Part-time employment opportunities are available for students.

■ CHAMBERLAIN COLLEGE OF NURSING (CLEVELAND)

6700 Euclid Ave.
Cleveland, OH 44103
Tel: (216)361-6005; Free: 877-751-5783
Fax: (216)361-6257
Web Site: www.chamberlain.edu

Description: Proprietary, 4-year, coed. Awards bachelor's degrees. Total enrollment: 218. Faculty: 58 (8 full-time, 50 part-time). Student-undergrad faculty ratio is 6:1. Full-time: 127 students, 88% women, 12% men. Part-time: 91 students, 82% women, 18% men. 2% from out-of-state. 6% Hispanic/Latino; 22% Black or African American, non-Hispanic/Latino; 3% Asian, non-Hispanic/Latino; 0.5% international. 62% 25 or older, 25% transferred in. Academic area with the most degrees conferred: health professions and related sciences. Accelerated degree program, distance learning.

Entrance Requirements: Option: deferred admission. Required: SAT or ACT. Application deadline: rolling. Notification: continuous.

■ CHAMBERLAIN COLLEGE OF NURSING (COLUMBUS)

1350 Alum Creek Dr.
Columbus, OH 43209
Tel: (614)252-8890; Free: 877-751-5783
Fax: (614)251-6971
Web Site: www.chamberlain.edu

Description: Proprietary, 4-year, coed. Awards bachelor's degrees. Total enrollment: 500. Faculty: 62 (17 full-time, 45 part-time). Student-undergrad faculty ratio is 10:1. Full-time: 221 students, 87% women, 13% men. Part-time: 279 students, 92% women, 8% men. 1% from out-of-state. 4% Hispanic/Latino; 14% Black or African American, non-Hispanic/Latino; 5% Asian, non-Hispanic/Latino; 0.2% Native Hawaiian or other Pacific Islander, non-Hispanic/Latino. 56% 25 or older, 25% transferred in. Calendar: semesters. Accelerated degree program, distance learning.

Entrance Requirements: Option: deferred admission. Required: SAT or ACT. Application deadline: rolling. Notification: continuous.

■ CHATFIELD COLLEGE

20918 State Rte. 251
Saint Martin, OH 45118-9705
Tel: (513)875-3344
Fax: (513)875-3912
Web Site: www.chatfield.edu

Description: Independent, 2-year, coed, affiliated with Roman Catholic Church. Awards transfer associate and terminal associate degrees. Founded 1970. Setting: 200-acre rural campus with easy access to Cincinnati, Dayton. Endowment: $2.9 million. Educational spending for the previous fiscal year: $3002 per student. Total enrollment: 396. Faculty: 86 (5 full-time, 81 part-time). Student-undergrad faculty ratio is 8:1. 204 applied, 94% were admitted. Full-time: 197 students, 73% women, 27% men. Part-time: 199 students, 78% women, 22% men. 0.4% Hispanic/Latino; 62% Black or African American, non-Hispanic/Latino; 0.4% Asian, non-Hispanic/Latino; 0.4% international. 54% 25 or older, 1% transferred in. Core. Calendar: semesters. Academic remediation for entering students, advanced placement, summer session for credit, part-time degree program, adult/continuing education programs, internships. Off campus study at 14 members of the Greater Cincinnati Consortium of Colleges and Universities.

Entrance Requirements: Open admission. Options: early admission, deferred admission. Entrance: noncompetitive. Application deadline: rolling. Notification: continuous. Transfer credits accepted: Yes.

Collegiate Environment: Orientation program. Drama-theater group, choral group, student-run newspaper. Social organizations: 1 open to all. Most popular organization: Student Leadership. Student services: personal-psychological counseling. Campus security: 12-hour night patrols by security. Chatfield College Library. Books: 20,284 (physical), 89,098 (digital/electronic); Serial titles: 8 (physical); Databases: 47. Students can reserve study rooms. Operations spending for the previous fiscal year: $46,984. 58 computers available on campus for general student use. A campuswide network can be accessed from off-campus. Staffed computer lab on campus.

■ THE CHRIST COLLEGE OF NURSING AND HEALTH SCIENCES

2139 Auburn Ave.
Cincinnati, OH 45219
Tel: (513)585-2401
Fax: (513)585-3540
E-mail: bradley.jackson@thechristcollege.edu

Web Site: www.thechristcollege.edu

Description: Independent, 2-year, coed. Awards terminal associate degrees. Setting: urban campus with easy access to Cincinnati. Total enrollment: 346. Faculty: 41 (25 full-time, 16 part-time). Student-undergrad faculty ratio is 7:1. 70 applied, 64% were admitted. Full-time: 202 students, 92% women, 8% men. Part-time: 144 students, 92% women, 8% men. 1% Hispanic/Latino; 10% Black or African American, non-Hispanic/Latino; 0.9% Asian, non-Hispanic/Latino. 38% 25 or older, 22% transferred in. Core. Academic remediation for entering students, services for LD students, advanced placement, summer session for credit.

Entrance Requirements: Required: high school transcript, minimum 2.75 high school GPA, SAT or ACT. Transfer credits accepted: Yes.

Collegiate Environment: Orientation program. Student services: personal-psychological counseling. Campus security: 24-hour emergency response devices and patrols, late night transport-escort service. James N. Gamble Library. 60 computers available on campus for general student use. A campuswide network can be accessed from off-campus. Students can access the following: online class registration. Staffed computer lab on campus provides training in use of computers, software, and the Internet.

■ CINCINNATI CHRISTIAN UNIVERSITY

2700 Glenway Ave.
Cincinnati, OH 45204-3200
Tel: (513)244-8100; Free: 800-949-4CCU
Fax: (513)244-8140
Web Site: www.ccuniversity.edu

Description: Independent, comprehensive, coed, affiliated with Church of Christ. Awards associate, bachelor's, and master's degrees. Founded 1924. Setting: 40-acre urban campus with easy access to Cincinnati. Total enrollment: 838. Faculty: 82 (34 full-time, 48 part-time). Student-undergrad faculty ratio is 15:1. 241 applied, 59% were admitted. 8% from top 10% of their high school class, 17% from top quarter, 54% from top half. Full-time: 534 students, 48% women, 52% men. Part-time: 86 students, 51% women, 49% men. Students come from 12 states and territories, 36% from out-of-state. 0.4% American Indian or Alaska Native, non-Hispanic/Latino; 1% Hispanic/Latino; 18% Black or African American, non-Hispanic/Latino; 0.6% Asian, non-Hispanic/Latino; 0.4% Native Hawaiian or other Pacific Islander, non-Hispanic/Latino; 2% international. 24% 25 or older, 45% live on campus, 4% transferred in. Academic areas with the most degrees conferred: theology and religious vocations; business/marketing; psychology. Core. Calendar: semesters. Academic remediation for entering students, services for LD students, advanced placement, accelerated degree program, honors program, independent study, distance learning, double major, summer session for credit, part-time degree program, adult/continuing education programs, co-op programs and internships, graduate courses open to undergrads. Off campus study at College of Mount St. Joseph, Cincinnati State Technical & Community College, Greater Cincinnati Consortium of Colleges and Universities. Study abroad program.

Entrance Requirements: Options: electronic application, deferred admission. Required: high school transcript, 2 recommendations, SAT or ACT. Recommended: minimum 2 high school GPA, interview. Required for some: essay. Entrance: minimally difficult. Application deadline: 7/1. Notification: continuous. SAT Reasoning Test deadline: 7/1. SAT Subject Test deadline: 7/1. Transfer credits accepted: Yes.

Costs Per Year: Application fee: $40. Comprehensive fee: $25,588 includes full-time tuition ($16,530), mandatory fees ($698), and college room and board ($8360). Full-time tuition and fees vary according to course load and student level. Room and board charges vary according to board plan, housing facility, and student level. Part-time tuition: $650 per semester hour. Part-time mandatory fees: $175 per term. Part-time tuition and fees vary according to course load and student level.

Collegiate Environment: Orientation program. Drama-theater group, choral group, student-run newspaper. Major annual events: Fall College Picnic, Dorm Decorating Contest, Community Service Day. Student services: health clinic, personal-psychological counseling. Campus security: 24-hour emergency response devices and patrols, student patrols, late night transport-escort service, controlled dormitory access. George Mark Elliot Memorial Library. 45 computers available on campus for general student use. A campuswide network can be accessed from student residence rooms and from off campus. Students can access the following: online class registration. Staffed computer lab on campus provides training in use of computers, software, and the Internet.

■ CINCINNATI COLLEGE OF MORTUARY SCIENCE

645 W N Bend Rd.
Cincinnati, OH 45224-1462
Tel: (513)761-2020; Free: 888-377-8433
Fax: (513)761-3333
Web Site: www.ccms.edu

Description: Independent, 4-year, coed. Awards associate and bachelor's degrees. Founded 1882. Setting: 10-acre urban campus with easy access to Cincinnati. Endowment: $80,000. Research spending for the previous fiscal year: $3 million. Educational spending for the previous fiscal year: $8000 per student. Total enrollment: 100. Faculty: 10 (4 full-time, 6 part-time). Student-undergrad faculty ratio is 15:1. Full-time: 100 students, 65% women, 35% men. Students come from 9 states and territories, 9% from out-of-state. 86% American Indian or Alaska Native, non-Hispanic/Latino; 2% Hispanic/Latino; 10% Black or African American, non-Hispanic/Latino. 51% 25 or older, 45% transferred in. Core. Calendar: semesters. Academic remediation for entering students, services for LD students, advanced placement, adult/continuing education programs.

Entrance Requirements: Open admission. Options: electronic application, deferred admission, international baccalaureate accepted. Transfer credits accepted: Yes.

Costs Per Year: Application fee: $50. Tuition: $18,565 full-time. Mandatory fees: $2100 full-time. Tuition guaranteed not to increase for student's term of enrollment.

Collegiate Environment: Orientation program. Social organizations: national fraternities, national sororities; 10% of women are members. Campus security: 24-hour emergency response devices. The Cincinnati College of Mortuary Science Library. Books: 2,000 (physical); Serial titles: 2,000 (physical). Weekly public service hours: 8. Operations spending for the previous fiscal year: $52,000. 10 computers available on campus for general student use. A campuswide network can be accessed from off-campus. Students can access the following: online class registration. Staffed computer lab on campus (open 24 hours a day) provides training in use of computers, software, and the Internet.

Community Environment: See University of Cincinnati.

■ CINCINNATI STATE TECHNICAL AND COMMUNITY COLLEGE

3520 Central Pky.
Cincinnati, OH 45223-2690
Tel: (513)569-1500; Free: 877-569-0115
Fax: (513)569-1562
E-mail: adm@cincinnatistate.edu
Web Site: www.cincinnatistate.edu

Description: State-supported, 2-year, coed. Part of Ohio Board of Regents. Awards certificates, transfer associate, and terminal associate degrees. Founded 1966. Setting: 46-acre urban campus. Total enrollment: 9,630. Faculty: 963 (196 full-time, 767 part-time). Student-undergrad faculty ratio is 11:1. Full-time: 2,873 students, 49% women, 51% men. Part-time: 6,757 students, 57% women, 43% men. 9% from out-of-state. 0.4% American Indian or Alaska Native, non-Hispanic/Latino; 2% Hispanic/Latino; 26% Black or African American, non-Hispanic/Latino; 2% Asian, non-Hispanic/Latino; 0.1% Native Hawaiian or other Pacific Islander, non-Hispanic/Latino; 2% international. 46% 25 or older. Retention: 49% of full-time freshmen returned the following year. Core. Calendar: 5 10-week terms. Academic remediation for entering students, ESL program, services for LD students, advanced placement, self-designed majors, honors program, independent study, distance learning, double major, summer session for credit, part-time degree program, co-op programs and internships. Off campus study at 12 members of the Greater Cincinnati Consortium of Colleges and Universities. ROTC: Army (c).

Entrance Requirements: Open admission except for health technology programs. Options: electronic application, deferred admission. Required: high school transcript. Entrance: noncompetitive. Transfer credits accepted: Yes.

Costs Per Year: Application fee: $0. State resident tuition: $3,807 full-time, $158.64 per credit hour part-time. Nonresident tuition: $7,615 full-time, $317.28 per credit hour part-time. Mandatory fees: $258 full-time, $9 per credit hour part-time, $46.50 per term part-time.

Collegiate Environment: Orientation program. Social organizations: 25 open to all. Most popular organizations: Student government, Nursing Student Association, Phi Theta Kappa, American Society of Civil Engineers, Respiratory Care Club. Major annual events: Homecoming, Student Government Picnic, Spirit Week. Student services: personal-psychological counseling. Campus security: 24-hour emergency response devices and patrols, late night transport-escort service. Johnnie Mae Berry Library.

Community Environment: See University of Cincinnati.

■ **CLARK STATE COMMUNITY COLLEGE**
570 E Leffel Ln.
Springfield, OH 45501-0570
Tel: (937)325-0691
E-mail: admissions@clarkstate.edu
Web Site: www.clarkstate.edu

Description: State-supported, 2-year, coed. Part of Ohio Board of Regents. Awards certificates, transfer associate, and terminal associate degrees. Founded 1962. Setting: 60-acre suburban campus with easy access to Columbus, Dayton. Endowment: $9.2 million. Educational spending for the previous fiscal year: $1602 per student. Total enrollment: 5,653. Faculty: 472 (78 full-time, 394 part-time). Student-undergrad faculty ratio is 14:1. 3,638 applied, 100% were admitted. Full-time: 1,693 students, 61% women, 39% men. Part-time: 3,960 students, 66% women, 34% men. Students come from 8 states and territories, 11 other countries, 1% from out-of-state. 0.5% American Indian or Alaska Native, non-Hispanic/Latino; 1% Hispanic/Latino; 19% Black or African American, non-Hispanic/Latino; 0.9% Asian, non-Hispanic/Latino; 0.2% Native Hawaiian or other Pacific Islander, non-Hispanic/Latino; 0.7% international. 57% 25 or older, 15% transferred in. Retention: 39% of full-time freshmen returned the following year. Core. Calendar: quarters. Academic remediation for entering students, services for LD students, advanced placement, honors program, independent study, distance learning, double major, summer session for credit, part-time degree program, adult/continuing education programs, co-op programs and internships. Off campus study at 22 members of the Southwestern Ohio Council for Higher Education (SOCHE). ROTC: Army (c).

Entrance Requirements: Open admission. Option: electronic application. Required: high school transcript. Entrance: noncompetitive. Application deadline: rolling. Notification: continuous. Transfer credits accepted: Yes.

Costs Per Year: Application fee: $15. State resident tuition: $3,152 full-time, $131.33 per credit hour part-time. Nonresident tuition: $7,880 full-time, $262.66 per credit hour part-time. Mandatory fees: $576 full-time, $24 per credit hour part-time.

Collegiate Environment: Orientation program. Drama-theater group, choral group. Social organizations: 8 open to all. Most popular organizations: Student Senate, Gay Straight Alliance, Student Theatre Guild, Chi Alpha, Creative Writers Club. Major annual events: WoW (Week of Welcome), Welcome Back, Spring Fling. Student services: health clinic, personal-psychological counseling. Campus security: late night transport-escort service. Clark State Community College Library. Operations spending for the previous fiscal year: $331,306. 533 computers available on campus for general student use. A campuswide network can be accessed from off-campus. Students can access the following: online class registration. Staffed computer lab on campus provides training in use of computers, software, and the Internet.

Community Environment: See Wittenberg University.

■ **CLEVELAND INSTITUTE OF ART**
11610 Euclid Ave.
Cleveland, OH 44106
Tel: (216)421-7000; Free: 800-223-4700
Fax: (216)421-7438
Web Site: www.cia.edu

Description: Independent, 4-year, coed. Awards bachelor's degrees. Founded 1882. Setting: 2-acre urban campus with easy access to Cleveland. Endowment: $27.5 million. Total enrollment: 670. Faculty: 123 (53 full-time, 70 part-time). Student-undergrad faculty ratio is 7:1. 1,025 applied, 73% were admitted. 9% from top 10% of their high school class, 32% from top quarter, 64% from top half. Full-time: 649 students, 67% women, 33% men. Part-time: 21 students, 67% women, 33% men. Students come from 31 states and territories, 7 other countries, 32% from out-of-state. 0.2% American Indian or Alaska Native, non-Hispanic/Latino; 8% Hispanic/Latino; 11% Black or African American, non-Hispanic/Latino; 3% Asian, non-Hispanic/Latino; 0.2% Native Hawaiian or other Pacific Islander, non-Hispanic/Latino; 6% international. 7% 25 or older, 48% live on campus, 5% transferred in. Retention: 86% of full-time freshmen returned the following year. Academic areas with the most degrees conferred: visual and performing arts; communication technologies; health professions and related sciences. Core. Calendar: semesters. Services for LD students, advanced placement, independent study, distance learning, double major, part-time

degree program, internships. Off campus study at Case Western Reserve University, Cross Registration Articulations, Association of Independent Colleges of Art and Design. Study abroad program. ROTC: Army (c), Air Force (c).

Entrance Requirements: Options: electronic application, early admission, early action, deferred admission. Required: essay, high school transcript, minimum 2 high school GPA, 1 recommendation, portfolio. Recommended: interview. Entrance: moderately difficult. Notification: continuous. SAT Reasoning Test deadline: 7/1. Transfer credits accepted: Yes. Applicants placed on waiting list: 27. Wait-listed applicants offered admission: 6. Early action applicants: 659. Early action applicants admitted: 531.

Costs Per Year: Application fee: $40. Comprehensive fee: $54,640 includes full-time tuition ($40,480), mandatory fees ($2830), and college room and board ($11,330). College room only: $8680. Part-time tuition: $1690 per credit hour. Part-time mandatory fees: $75 per credit hour.

Collegiate Environment: Orientation program. Drama-theater group, choral group, marching band. Social organizations: 16 open to all; national fraternities, national sororities, local fraternities; 1% of eligible men and 1% of eligible women are members. Most popular organizations: Campus Activities Board, Student Independent Exhibition, International Interior Design Association, Student Leadership Council, Community Outreach Team. Major annual events: Halloween Party, Student Independent Exhibition, Pink Pig year-end picnic. Student services: health clinic, personal-psychological counseling, women's center. Campus security: 24-hour emergency response devices and patrols, controlled dormitory access. 401 college housing spaces available; 311 were occupied in 2018-19. Freshmen given priority for college housing. On-campus residence required through sophomore year. Option: coed housing available. Jessica R Gund Library. Books: 48,478 (physical), 288,857 (digital/electronic); Serial titles: 420 (physical), 11 (digital/electronic); Databases: 200. Weekly public service hours: 74; students can reserve study rooms. Operations spending for the previous fiscal year: $333,004. 250 computers available on campus for general student use. Computer purchase/lease plans available. A computer is required for all students. A campuswide network can be accessed. Students can access the following: online class registration, wireless Internet access available throughout campus. Staffed computer lab on campus provides training in use of computers, software, and the Internet.

Community Environment: See Case Western Reserve University.

■ **CLEVELAND INSTITUTE OF MUSIC**
11021 E Blvd.
Cleveland, OH 44106-1776
Tel: (216)791-5000
Fax: (216)791-1530
E-mail: william.fay@case.edu
Web Site: www.cim.edu

Description: Independent, comprehensive, coed. Awards bachelor's and master's degrees. Founded 1920. Setting: 488-acre urban campus. Total enrollment: 437. Student-undergrad faculty ratio is 7:1. 437 applied, 44% were admitted. 74% from out-of-state. Retention: 90% of full-time freshmen returned the following year. Academic area with the most degrees conferred: visual and performing arts. Calendar: semesters. Academic remediation for entering students, ESL program, advanced placement, accelerated degree program, independent study, distance learning, double major, summer session for credit, internships, graduate courses open to undergrads. Off campus study at Case Western Reserve University. Study abroad program. ROTC: Army (c), Air Force (c).

Entrance Requirements: Options: early admission, deferred admission, international baccalaureate accepted. Required: essay, high school transcript, 2 recommendations, audition. Recommended: interview. Required for some: SAT or ACT. Entrance: very difficult. Application deadline: 12/1. Notification: 4/1.

Collegiate Environment: Orientation program. Choral group. Student services: health clinic, personal-psychological counseling. Campus security: 24-hour emergency response devices and patrols, late night transport-escort service, controlled dormitory access. Cleveland Institute of Music Library.

Community Environment: See Case Western Reserve University.

■ **CLEVELAND STATE UNIVERSITY**
2121 Euclid Ave.
Cleveland, OH 44115
Tel: (216)687-2000; Free: 888-CSU-OHIO
Fax: (216)687-9366
E-mail: admissions@csuohio.edu

Web Site: www.csuohio.edu

Description: State-supported, university, coed. Part of University System of Ohio. Awards bachelor's, master's, and doctoral degrees and post-master's certificates. Founded 1964. Setting: 85-acre urban campus with easy access to Cleveland, OH. Endowment: $66.2 million. Research spending for the previous fiscal year: $66.6 million. Educational spending for the previous fiscal year: $7981 per student. Total enrollment: 16,607. Faculty: 1,178 (546 full-time, 632 part-time). Student-undergrad faculty ratio is 17:1. 8,351 applied, 88% were admitted. 15% from top 10% of their high school class, 39% from top quarter, 71% from top half. Full-time: 9,268 students, 53% women, 47% men. Part-time: 3,038 students, 56% women, 44% men. Students come from 33 states and territories, 96 other countries, 4% from out-of-state. 0.2% American Indian or Alaska Native, non-Hispanic/Latino; 6% Hispanic/Latino; 16% Black or African American, non-Hispanic/Latino; 3% Asian, non-Hispanic/Latino; 0.1% Native Hawaiian or other Pacific Islander, non-Hispanic/Latino; 5% international. 24% 25 or older, 6% live on campus, 11% transferred in. Retention: 70% of full-time freshmen returned the following year. Academic areas with the most degrees conferred: health professions and related sciences; business/marketing; social sciences. Core. Calendar: semesters. Academic remediation for entering students, ESL program, services for LD students, advanced placement, accelerated degree program, freshman honors college, honors program, independent study, distance learning, double major, summer session for credit, part-time degree program, adult/continuing education programs, co-op programs and internships, graduate courses open to undergrads. Off campus study at University System of Ohio institutions. Study abroad program. ROTC: Army (c), Air Force (c).

Entrance Requirements: Options: electronic application, early action, deferred admission. Required: high school transcript, minimum 2.3 high school GPA, SAT or ACT. Entrance: moderately difficult. Application deadlines: 5/15, 5/1 for early action. Notification: continuous. SAT Reasoning Test deadline: 8/10. Transfer credits accepted: Yes.

Collegiate Environment: Orientation program. Drama-theater group, choral group, student-run newspaper, radio station. Social organizations: 274 open to all; national fraternities, national sororities, local fraternities, local sororities; 1% of eligible men and 1% of eligible women are members. Most popular organizations: Black Student Union, Chinese Students and Scholars Association, Through the Cross Campus Ministries, Student Nurses Association, Joint Engineering Council. Major annual events: Weeks of Welcome, Springfest, Glow in the Dark Party. Student services: health clinic, personal-psychological counseling, women's center. Campus security: 24-hour emergency response devices and patrols, late night transport-escort service, controlled dormitory access, Campus Watch, CSU Alert Notification System, Community Emergency and Response Team (CERT). Michael Schwartz Library plus 1 other. Books: 524,556 (physical), 228,146 (digital/electronic); Serial titles: 6,155 (physical), 194 (digital/electronic); Databases: 733. Students can reserve study rooms. Operations spending for the previous fiscal year: $7.5 million. 736 computers available on campus for general student use. Computer purchase/lease plans available. A campuswide network can be accessed from student residence rooms and from off campus. Students can access the following: online class registration, each general purpose computer lab has a scanner and printer, students are allowed free black and white printing up to 2,000 pages per semester. Staffed computer lab on campus provides training in use of computers, software, and the Internet.

■ THE COLLEGE OF WOOSTER

1189 Beall Ave.

Wooster, OH 44691-2363

Tel: (330)263-2000; Free: 800-877-9905

Fax: (330)263-2621

E-mail: admissions@wooster.edu

Web Site: www.wooster.edu

Description: Independent, 4-year, coed, affiliated with Presbyterian Church (U.S.A.). Awards bachelor's degrees. Founded 1866. Setting: 240-acre small town campus with easy access to Cleveland. Endowment: $280.5 million. Research spending for the previous fiscal year: $1.4 million. Educational spending for the previous fiscal year: $15,258 per student. Total enrollment: 1,980. Faculty: 212 (165 full-time, 47 part-time). Student-undergrad faculty ratio is 11:1. 5,615 applied, 56% were admitted. 45% from top 10% of their high school class, 75% from top quarter, 92% from top half. Full-time: 1,962 students, 54% women, 46% men. Part-time: 18 students, 72% women, 28% men. Students come from 43 states and territories, 37 other countries, 63% from out-of-state. 1% American Indian or Alaska Native, non-Hispanic/Latino;

5% Hispanic/Latino; 9% Black or African American, non-Hispanic/Latino; 5% Asian, non-Hispanic/Latino; 13% international. 99% live on campus, 1% transferred in. Retention: 86% of full-time freshmen returned the following year. Academic areas with the most degrees conferred: social sciences; biological/life sciences; physical sciences. Core. Calendar: semesters. Services for LD students, advanced placement, self-designed majors, independent study, double major, internships. Off campus study. Study abroad program.

Entrance Requirements: Options: electronic application, early admission, early decision, early action, deferred admission, international baccalaureate accepted. Required: essay, high school transcript, SAT or ACT. Recommended: minimum X high school GPA, recommendations, interview. Entrance: moderately difficult. Application deadlines: 2/15, 11/1 for early decision plan 1, 1/15 for early decision plan 2, 11/15 for early action. Notification: 4/1, 11/15 for early decision plan 1, 2/1 for early decision plan 2, 12/31 for early action. SAT Reasoning Test deadline: 3/15. Transfer credits accepted: Yes. Applicants placed on waiting list: 727. Wait-listed applicants offered admission: 12. Early decision applicants: 151. Early decision applicants admitted: 116. Early action applicants: 2,968. Early action applicants admitted: 2,066.

Costs Per Year: Application fee: $0. Comprehensive fee: $62,100 includes full-time tuition ($49,810), mandatory fees ($440), and college room and board ($11,850). College room only: $5750. Full-time tuition and fees vary according to course load. Room and board charges vary according to board plan and housing facility. Part-time tuition: $1545 per credit hour. Part-time tuition varies according to course load.

Collegiate Environment: Orientation program. Drama-theater group, choral group, marching band, student-run newspaper, radio station. Social organizations: 125 open to all; local fraternities, local sororities, coed fraternity; 14% of eligible men and 17% of eligible women are members. Most popular organizations: Volunteer Network, International Student Association, Inter-Greek Council, Wooster Activities Crew, Women's Athletic and Recreation Association. Major annual events: Winter Gala, Spring Fest, Scot Spirit Day. Student services: health clinic, personal-psychological counseling, women's center. Campus security: 24-hour emergency response devices and patrols, student patrols, late night transport-escort service, controlled dormitory access. The College of Wooster Libraries plus 3 others. Books: 453,145 (physical), 719,794 (digital/electronic); Serial titles: 2,693 (physical), 102,227 (digital/electronic); Databases: 568. Weekly public service hours: 112; students can reserve study rooms. 450 computers available on campus for general student use. Computer purchase/lease plans available. A computer is required for all students. A campuswide network can be accessed from student residence rooms and from off campus. Students can access the following: online class registration, learning management system, campus blogging site, campus wiki site. Staffed computer lab on campus provides training in use of computers, software, and the Internet.

Community Environment: City of Wooster population of 25,700, county seat of Wayne County, and leading agricultural region in the United States. In Ohio, Wayne County ranks first in cash receipts from dairy products, cattle and calves, and first in production of hay and oats. The Ohio Agricultural Research and Development Center is second largest in the United States. Companies in the city include Newell Rubbermaid Incorporated, Wooster Brush Company, the Gerstenslager Company, Bell and Howell, Frito-Lay, and others. Other educational institutions include Ohio State University's Agricultural Technical Institute and the Wayne General and Technical College. Wooster has been designated"Tree City, U.S.A." Students have access to Cleveland, Columbus, Pittsburgh, Cincinnati, and Akron.

■ COLUMBUS COLLEGE OF ART & DESIGN

60 Cleveland Ave.

Columbus, OH 43215-1758

Tel: (614)224-9101; Free: 877-997-2223

E-mail: admissions@ccad.edu

Web Site: www.ccad.edu

Description: Independent, comprehensive, coed. Awards bachelor's and master's degrees. Founded 1879. Setting: 17-acre urban campus. Endowment: $11.7 million. Educational spending for the previous fiscal year: $9331 per student. Total enrollment: 1,095. Faculty: 190 (66 full-time, 124 part-time). Student-undergrad faculty ratio is 10:1. 612 applied, 79% were admitted. Full-time: 999 students, 69% women, 31% men. Part-time: 61 students, 57% women, 43% men. Students come from 38 states and territories, 23 other countries, 26% from out-of-state. 0.2% American Indian or Alaska Native, non-Hispanic/Latino; 6% Hispanic/Latino; 10% Black or African American, non-Hispanic/Latino; 4% Asian, non-Hispanic/Latino; 0.1% Native

Hawaiian or other Pacific Islander, non-Hispanic/Latino; 7% international. 8% 25 or older, 35% live on campus, 1% transferred in. Retention: 79% of full-time freshmen returned the following year. Academic area with the most degrees conferred: visual and performing arts. Core. Calendar: semesters. Academic remediation for entering students, ESL program, services for LD students, advanced placement, honors program, independent study, distance learning, double major, summer session for credit, internships. Off campus study at members of the Higher Education Council of Columbus. Study abroad program.

Entrance Requirements: Options: electronic application, deferred admission, international baccalaureate accepted. Required: essay, high school transcript, minimum 3 high school GPA, 2 recommendations, portfolio. Recommended: SAT or ACT. Required for some: interview. Entrance: moderately difficult. Application deadline: rolling. Notification: continuous. Transfer credits accepted: Yes. Applicants placed on waiting list: 5. Waitlisted applicants offered admission: 0.

Costs Per Year: Application fee: $50. Comprehensive fee: $44,990 includes full-time tuition ($34,920), mandatory fees ($500), and college room and board ($9570). Full-time tuition and fees vary according to course load. Room and board charges vary according to board plan, housing facility, location, and student level. Part-time tuition: $1455 per credit hour. Part-time tuition varies according to course load.

Collegiate Environment: Orientation program. Social organizations: 19 open to all. Most popular organizations: Student Government Association, Student Collective, Student Programming Board, CCAD Battle Alliance. Major annual events: Annual Student Art Exhibition, Big Boo Halloween Party, Family Weekend. Student services: personal-psychological counseling. Campus security: 24-hour emergency response devices and patrols, late night transport-escort service, controlled dormitory access. Packard Library. Books: 40,836 (physical), 28,701 (digital/electronic); Serial titles: 434 (physical), 253,828 (digital/electronic). Operations spending for the previous fiscal year: $787,077. 485 computers available on campus for general student use. A computer is required for all students. A campuswide network can be accessed. Students can access the following: online class registration. Staffed computer lab on campus provides training in use of computers, software, and the Internet.

Community Environment: See Ohio State University - Columbus Campus.

■ **COLUMBUS CULINARY INSTITUTE AT BRADFORD SCHOOL**
2435 Stelzer Rd.
Columbus, OH 43219
Free: 877-506-5006
Web Site: www.columbusculinary.com
Description: Private, 2-year, coed. Awards terminal associate degrees. Founded 2006. Setting: suburban campus. Total enrollment: 150. 560 applied, 58% were admitted. Calendar: semesters.

■ **COLUMBUS STATE COMMUNITY COLLEGE**
550 E Spring St.
Columbus, OH 43215
Tel: (614)287-2400; Free: 800-621-6407
Fax: (614)287-5117
Web Site: www.cscc.edu
Description: State-supported, 2-year, coed. Part of Ohio Department of Higher Education. Awards certificates, transfer associate, and terminal associate degrees. Founded 1963. Setting: 188-acre urban campus with easy access to Columbus. Educational spending for the previous fiscal year: $2445 per student. Total enrollment: 27,109. Student-undergrad faculty ratio is 19:1. 18,486 applied, 95% were admitted. Full-time: 7,025 students, 50% women, 50% men. Part-time: 20,084 students, 54% women, 46% men. Students come from 49 states and territories, 81 other countries, 2% from out-of-state. 0.4% American Indian or Alaska Native, non-Hispanic/Latino; 5% Hispanic/Latino; 18% Black or African American, non-Hispanic/Latino; 3% Asian, non-Hispanic/Latino; 0.1% Native Hawaiian or other Pacific Islander, non-Hispanic/Latino; 1% international. 43% 25 or older, 14% transferred in. Retention: 61% of full-time freshmen returned the following year. Core. Calendar: semesters. Academic remediation for entering students, ESL program, services for LD students, advanced placement, self-designed majors, honors program, independent study, distance learning, double major, summer session for credit, part-time degree program, adult/continuing education programs, co-op programs and internships. Off campus study at Member of the Higher Education Council of Columbus. Study abroad program. ROTC: Army (c).

Entrance Requirements: Open admission. Options: electronic application,

early admission, deferred admission, international baccalaureate accepted. Recommended: high school transcript. Required for some: essay, high school transcript, minimum 3 high school GPA, 1 recommendation, interview. Entrance: noncompetitive. Application deadlines: 8/21, 8/21 for nonresidents. Notification: continuous, continuous for nonresidents. Transfer credits accepted: Yes.

Collegiate Environment: Orientation program. Choral group. Social organizations: 30 open to all; Phi Theta Kappa Honor Society. Most popular organizations: Phi Theta Kappa, Student Nurses Association, Student American Dental Hygiene Association, Landscaping Association. Major annual events: Week of Welcome, Martin Luther King Celebration, Women's 'Herstory' Month Celebration. Student services: personal-psychological counseling. Campus security: 24-hour emergency response devices and patrols, late night transport-escort service, Vehicle Assistance with lockouts and jump starts. Columbus State Library plus 1 other. Books: 32,991 (physical), 52,921 (digital/electronic); Databases: 185. Weekly public service hours: 76. Operations spending for the previous fiscal year: $1.6 million.

Community Environment: See Ohio State University - Columbus Campus.

■ **CUYAHOGA COMMUNITY COLLEGE**
700 Carnegie Ave.
Cleveland, OH 44115-2878
Tel: (216)987-6000; Free: 800-954-8742
Fax: (216)987-5050
Web Site: www.tri-c.edu
Description: State and locally supported, 2-year, coed. Awards certificates, transfer associate, and terminal associate degrees. Founded 1963. Setting: urban campus. Endowment: $22.5 million. Total enrollment: 30,065. Faculty: 1,673 (359 full-time, 1,314 part-time). Student-undergrad faculty ratio is 18:1. 9,492 applied, 100% were admitted. Full-time: 10,590 students, 55% women, 45% men. Part-time: 19,475 students, 65% women, 35% men. Students come from 27 other countries, 1% from out-of-state. 0.9% American Indian or Alaska Native, non-Hispanic/Latino; 5% Hispanic/Latino; 28% Black or African American, non-Hispanic/Latino; 2% Asian, non-Hispanic/Latino; 1% international. 54% 25 or older, 5% transferred in. Retention: 48% of full-time freshmen returned the following year. Calendar: semesters. ESL program, services for LD students, advanced placement, independent study, distance learning, summer session for credit, part-time degree program, external degree program, adult/continuing education programs, co-op programs.

Entrance Requirements: Open admission. Options: early admission, deferred admission, international baccalaureate accepted. Required for some: high school transcript. Entrance: noncompetitive. Application deadline: rolling. Notification: continuous. Transfer credits accepted: Yes.

Costs Per Year: Application fee: $0. Area resident tuition: $3,436 full-time, $114.54 per credit hour part-time. State resident tuition: $4,332 full-time, $144.08 per credit hour part-time. Nonresident tuition: $8,136 full-time, $271.19 per credit hour part-time. Mandatory fees: $210 full-time.

Collegiate Environment: Orientation program. Drama-theater group, choral group, student-run newspaper. Social organizations: 47 open to all. Most popular organizations: Student Senate, Student Nursing Organization, Business Focus, Phi Theta Kappa. Major annual events: Welcome Back, Diversity Day. Student services: health clinic, personal-psychological counseling. Campus security: 24-hour emergency response devices and patrols, late night transport-escort service. Metro Library plus 3 others. 1,500 computers available on campus for general student use. A campuswide network can be accessed from off-campus. Staffed computer lab on campus.

■ **DAVIS COLLEGE**
4747 Monroe St.
Toledo, OH 43623-4307
Tel: (419)473-2700; Free: 800-477-7021
E-mail: tbrunner@daviscollege.edu
Web Site: www.daviscollege.edu
Description: Proprietary, 2-year, coed. Awards certificates, diplomas, and terminal associate degrees. Founded 1858. Setting: 1-acre urban campus with easy access to Detroit. Total enrollment: 159. Faculty: 25 (3 full-time, 22 part-time). Student-undergrad faculty ratio is 7:1. Full-time: 34 students, 88% women, 12% men. Part-time: 125 students, 78% women, 22% men. Students come from 2 states and territories, 2% from out-of-state. 0.6% American Indian or Alaska Native, non-Hispanic/Latino; 2% Hispanic/Latino; 40% Black or African American, non-Hispanic/Latino. 67% 25 or older. Core. Calendar: quarters. Academic remediation for entering students, advanced

placement, distance learning, summer session for credit, part-time degree program, adult/continuing education programs, internships.

Entrance Requirements: Options: electronic application, early admission, deferred admission. Required: high school transcript, interview. Entrance: minimally difficult. Application deadline: rolling. Notification: continuous. Transfer credits accepted: Yes.

Collegiate Environment: Orientation program. Student services: personal-psychological counseling. Campus security: interior and exterior security cameras. Davis College Resource Center. Books: 2,108 (physical); Serial titles: 109 (physical). 72 computers available on campus for general student use. A campuswide network can be accessed from off-campus. Staffed computer lab on campus provides training in use of computers, software, and the Internet.

■ **DAYMAR COLLEGE**
2745 Winchester Pke.
Columbus, OH 43232
Tel: (614)643-6680; Free: 877-258-7796
E-mail: hhankinson@daymarcollege.edu
Web Site: www.daymarcollege.edu
Description: Proprietary, 2-year, coed. Awards terminal associate degrees. Founded 1984. Total enrollment: 67. Student-undergrad faculty ratio is 11:1. 73% 25 or older. Calendar: quarters.
Entrance Requirements: Entrance: noncompetitive.

■ **DEFIANCE COLLEGE**
701 N Clinton St.
Defiance, OH 43512-1610
Tel: (419)784-4010; Free: 800-520-4632
Fax: (419)783-2468
E-mail: baveresch@defiance.edu
Web Site: www.defiance.edu
Description: Independent, comprehensive, coed, affiliated with United Church of Christ. Awards associate, bachelor's, and master's degrees. Founded 1850. Setting: 150-acre small town campus with easy access to Toledo. Endowment: $15.2 million. Educational spending for the previous fiscal year: $8579 per student. Total enrollment: 630. Faculty: 77 (36 full-time, 41 part-time). Student-undergrad faculty ratio is 11:1. 1,257 applied, 56% were admitted. 6% from top 10% of their high school class, 27% from top quarter, 64% from top half. Full-time: 525 students, 43% women, 57% men. Part-time: 74 students, 66% women, 34% men. Students come from 23 states and territories, 4 other countries, 30% from out-of-state. 0.3% American Indian or Alaska Native, non-Hispanic/Latino; 7% Hispanic/Latino; 12% Black or African American, non-Hispanic/Latino; 0.8% Asian, non-Hispanic/Latino; 2% international. 20% 25 or older, 50% live on campus, 6% transferred in. Retention: 60% of full-time freshmen returned the following year. Academic areas with the most degrees conferred: business/marketing; parks and recreation; education. Core. Calendar: semesters. Academic remediation for entering students, services for LD students, advanced placement, self-designed majors, honors program, independent study, double major, summer session for credit, adult/continuing education programs, internships, graduate courses open to undergrads. Off campus study at Northwest State Community College. Study abroad program.
Entrance Requirements: Options: electronic application, deferred admission, international baccalaureate accepted. Required: high school transcript, minimum 2.25 high school GPA, SAT or ACT. Required for some: essay, 1 recommendation, interview. Entrance: moderately difficult. Application deadline: 8/15. Notification: continuous, continuous for nonresidents. SAT Reasoning Test deadline: 8/15. Transfer credits accepted: Yes.
Costs Per Year: Application fee: $25. Comprehensive fee: $42,950 includes full-time tuition ($31,990), mandatory fees ($740), and college room and board ($10,220). College room only: $5500. Full-time tuition and fees vary according to course load. Room and board charges vary according to board plan and housing facility. Part-time tuition: $495 per credit hour. Part-time mandatory fees: $100 per term. Part-time tuition and fees vary according to course load.
Collegiate Environment: Orientation program. Drama-theater group, choral group, marching band, student-run newspaper. Social organizations: 30 open to all; national fraternities, national sororities, service fraternity; 6% of eligible men and 6% of eligible women are members. Most popular organizations: Campus Activities Board, Criminal Justice Society, Student Senate, Black Action Student Association, Tau Kappa Epsilon. Major annual events: Homecoming, Family Weekend, Dance Marathon. Student services: personal-psychological counseling. Campus security: late night transport-

escort service, controlled dormitory access. Pilgrim Library plus 1 other. Books: 62,576 (physical), 271,510 (digital/electronic); Serial titles: 308 (physical), 79,914 (digital/electronic); Databases: 162. Weekly public service hours: 90; students can reserve study rooms. Operations spending for the previous fiscal year: $676,692. 200 computers available on campus for general student use. Computer purchase/lease plans available. A campuswide network can be accessed from student residence rooms and from off campus. Students can access the following: online class registration. Staffed computer lab on campus (open 24 hours a day).

Community Environment: Defiance College is located in Defiance Ohio, site of Fort Defiance, and birthplace of the Indian Chief Pontiac. Today, Defiance is a community of over 18,000 residents and one of the fastest growing areas in Northwest Ohio. Highly diversified industry and some of the richest farmland in the nation contribute to the areas prosperity. A major shopping mall is 2 blocks north of the campus.

■ **DENISON UNIVERSITY**
100 W College St.
Granville, OH 43023
Tel: (740)587-0810; Free: 800-DENISON
Fax: (740)587-6306
E-mail: hills@denison.edu
Web Site: www.denison.edu
Description: Independent, 4-year, coed. Awards bachelor's degrees. Founded 1831. Setting: 931-acre suburban campus with easy access to Columbus. Total enrollment: 2,341. Faculty: 254 (218 full-time, 36 part-time). Student-undergrad faculty ratio is 9:1. 8,042 applied, 34% were admitted. 65% from top 10% of their high school class, 87% from top quarter, 100% from top half. Full-time: 2,319 students, 55% women, 45% men. Part-time: 22 students, 45% women, 55% men. 74% from out-of-state. 9% Hispanic/Latino; 7% Black or African American, non-Hispanic/Latino; 4% Asian, non-Hispanic/Latino; 0.1% Native Hawaiian or other Pacific Islander, non-Hispanic/Latino; 10% international. 99% live on campus, 1% transferred in. Retention: 91% of full-time freshmen returned the following year. Academic areas with the most degrees conferred: social sciences; communication/journalism; biological/life sciences. Calendar: semesters plus optional May term. Services for LD students, advanced placement, self-designed majors, honors program, independent study, double major, part-time degree program, internships. Off campus study at American University, Great Lakes Colleges Association, Marine Science Consortium. Study abroad program. ROTC: Army (c).
Entrance Requirements: Options: early admission, early decision, deferred admission. Required: essay, high school transcript, 2 recommendations. Recommended: interview. Entrance: very difficult. Application deadlines: 1/15, 11/15 for early decision plan 1, 1/15 for early decision plan 2. Notification: 4/1, 12/15 for early decision plan 1, 2/15 for early decision plan 2. SAT Reasoning Test deadline: 3/1. Transfer credits accepted: Yes. Applicants placed on waiting list: 1,502. Wait-listed applicants offered admission: 55. Early decision applicants: 377. Early decision applicants admitted: 245.
Costs Per Year: Application fee: $0. Comprehensive fee: $64,670 includes full-time tuition ($50,790), mandatory fees ($1170), and college room and board ($12,710). College room only: $7000. Room and board charges vary according to board plan and housing facility. Part-time tuition: $1590 per credit hour. Part-time tuition varies according to course load.
Collegiate Environment: Orientation program. Drama-theater group, choral group, student-run newspaper, radio station. Social organizations: national fraternities, national sororities. Student services: health clinic, personal-psychological counseling, women's center. Campus security: 24-hour emergency response devices and patrols, student patrols, late night transport-escort service, controlled dormitory access, security lighting, escort. William Howard Doane Library. Books: 1.4 million (physical), 912,952 (digital/electronic); Serial titles: 540 (physical), 653 (digital/electronic); Databases: 464. Weekly public service hours: 104; students can reserve study rooms. 650 computers available on campus for general student use. Computer purchase/lease plans available. A campuswide network can be accessed from student residence rooms and from off campus. Students can access the following: online class registration, eClassrooms; eSpaces; special purpose rooms and computer labs with specialized software; computers, digital video, audio and other media equipment may be checked out; software downloads. Staffed computer lab on campus (open 24 hours a day) provides training in use of computers, software, and the Internet.
Community Environment: Of interest are the many beautiful homes in Granville. The town was founded by settlers from the Massachusetts town of the same name in 1805. Granville is a delightful bit of New England tucked in the rolling hills of Central Ohio.

■ **DEVRY UNIVERSITY-CINCINNATI CAMPUS**

8800 Governors Hill Dr., Ste. 100
Cincinnati, OH 45249
Tel: (513)583-5000; Free: 866-338-7934
Fax: (513)583-5035
Web Site: www.devry.edu
Description: Proprietary, comprehensive, coed.

■ **DEVRY UNIVERSITY-COLUMBUS CAMPUS**

1350 Alum Creek Dr.
Columbus, OH 43209
Tel: (614)253-7291; Free: 866-338-7934
Web Site: www.devry.edu
Description: Proprietary, comprehensive, coed. Awards associate, bachelor's, and master's degrees. Founded 1952. Setting: urban campus. Total enrollment: 1,140. Faculty: 40 (8 full-time, 32 part-time). Student-undergrad faculty ratio is 35:1. 3% from out-of-state. 0.2% American Indian or Alaska Native, non-Hispanic/Latino; 3% Hispanic/Latino; 18% Black or African American, non-Hispanic/Latino; 2% Asian, non-Hispanic/Latino; 0.3% international. 70% 25 or older. Calendar: semesters.
Entrance Requirements: Entrance: minimally difficult. Application deadline: rolling. Notification: continuous.

■ **DEVRY UNIVERSITY-SEVEN HILLS CAMPUS**

4141 Rockside Rd., Ste. 110
Seven Hills, OH 44131
Tel: (216)328-8754; Free: 866-338-7934
Fax: (216)328-8764
Web Site: www.devry.edu
Description: Proprietary, comprehensive, coed. Awards associate, bachelor's, and master's degrees. Calendar: semesters.

■ **EASTERN GATEWAY COMMUNITY COLLEGE**

4000 Sunset Blvd.
Steubenville, OH 43952-3598
Tel: (740)264-5591; Free: 800-68-COLLEGE
Fax: (740)266-2706
E-mail: mbarker@egcc.edu
Web Site: www.egcc.edu
Description: State and locally supported, 2-year, coed. Part of Ohio Board of Regents. Awards certificates, transfer associate, and terminal associate degrees. Founded 1966. Setting: 83-acre small town campus with easy access to Pittsburgh. Endowment: $448,293. Educational spending for the previous fiscal year: $9481 per student. Total enrollment: 8,546. Faculty: 237 (42 full-time, 195 part-time). Student-undergrad faculty ratio is 23:1. Full-time: 1,770 students, 61% women, 39% men. Part-time: 6,776 students, 67% women, 33% men. Students come from 50 states and territories, 1 other country, 53% from out-of-state. 0.5% American Indian or Alaska Native, non-Hispanic/Latino; 9% Hispanic/Latino; 19% Black or African American, non-Hispanic/Latino; 1% Asian, non-Hispanic/Latino; 0.5% Native Hawaiian or other Pacific Islander, non-Hispanic/Latino. 35% 25 or older, 1% transferred in. Core. Calendar: semesters. Academic remediation for entering students, services for LD students, accelerated degree program, distance learning, double major, summer session for credit, part-time degree program, adult/continuing education programs, co-op programs. Off campus study at members of the Southeastern Ohio Technical Education Consortium.
Entrance Requirements: Open admission. Options: electronic application, early admission, deferred admission. Required for some: high school transcript, SAT or ACT. Entrance: noncompetitive. Notification: continuous. Transfer credits accepted: Yes.
Costs Per Year: Application fee: $20. Area resident tuition: $3630 full-time, $121 per credit hour part-time. State resident tuition: $3810 full-time, $127 per credit hour part-time. Nonresident tuition: $7050 full-time, $235 per credit hour part-time.
Collegiate Environment: Orientation program. Most popular organizations: Student Senate, Phi Theta Kappa. Campus security: 24-hour emergency response devices, day and evening security. Eastern Gateway Community College Library. Books: 15,948 (physical); Serial titles: 6 (physical), 29,684 (digital/electronic); Databases: 142. Operations spending for the previous fiscal year: $344,155.

■ **EDISON STATE COMMUNITY COLLEGE**

1973 Edison Dr.
Piqua, OH 45356-9253

Tel: (937)778-8600
Fax: (937)778-1920
E-mail: lcollins@edisonohio.edu
Web Site: www.edisonohio.edu
Description: State-supported, 2-year, coed. Part of Ohio Board of Regents. Awards certificates, transfer associate, and terminal associate degrees. Founded 1973. Setting: 131-acre small town campus with easy access to Dayton, Columbus, Cincinnati. Educational spending for the previous fiscal year: $4562 per student. Total enrollment: 3,248. Faculty: 178 (49 full-time, 129 part-time). Student-undergrad faculty ratio is 17:1. 1% from top 10% of their high school class, 17% from top quarter, 42% from top half. Full-time: 753 students, 55% women, 45% men. Part-time: 2,495 students, 61% women, 39% men. Students come from 8 states and territories, 12% from out-of-state. 0.2% American Indian or Alaska Native, non-Hispanic/Latino; 2% Hispanic/Latino; 5% Black or African American, non-Hispanic/Latino; 0.9% Asian, non-Hispanic/Latino; 0.3% Native Hawaiian or other Pacific Islander, non-Hispanic/Latino. 43% 25 or older, 1% transferred in. Retention: 83% of full-time freshmen returned the following year. Core. Calendar: semesters. Academic remediation for entering students, ESL program, services for LD students, advanced placement, accelerated degree program, self-designed majors, honors program, independent study, distance learning, double major, summer session for credit, part-time degree program, adult/continuing education programs, internships. Off campus study at Southwestern Ohio Council for Higher Education.
Entrance Requirements: Open admission except for nursing, medical technology, medical assisting, phlebotomy, physical therapy assisting, social service and early childhood education programs. Option: electronic application. Required: high school transcript. Entrance: noncompetitive. Application deadline: rolling. Transfer credits accepted: Yes.
Costs Per Year: Application fee: $0. State resident tuition: $4,699 full-time, $156.62 per credit hour part-time. Nonresident tuition: $8,608 full-time, $286.94 per credit hour part-time.
Collegiate Environment: Orientation program. Drama-theater group, student-run newspaper. Student services: health clinic. Campus security: late night transport-escort service, 18-hour patrols by trained security personnel. Edison Community College Library. Books: 18,825 (physical), 112,623 (digital/electronic); Serial titles: 61 (physical), 11,044 (digital/electronic); Databases: 149. Weekly public service hours: 50; students can reserve study rooms. Operations spending for the previous fiscal year: $280,073. 1,000 computers available on campus for general student use. Computer purchase/lease plans available. A campuswide network can be accessed from off-campus. Students can access the following: online class registration. Staffed computer lab on campus provides training in use of computers, software, and the Internet.
Community Environment: Located in Piqua, Ohio, Edison State Community College serves Darke, Miami, Shelby, and neighboring counties in west-central Ohio. The region, made up of small-sized and medium-sized towns, has an excellent balance among agricultural, industrial and residential areas.

■ **ETI TECHNICAL COLLEGE OF NILES**

2076 Youngstown-Warren Rd.
Niles, OH 44446-4398
Tel: (330)652-9919
Fax: (330)652-4399
E-mail: dianemarsteller@eticollege.edu
Web Site: eticollege.edu
Description: Proprietary, 2-year, coed. Awards diplomas and terminal associate degrees. Founded 1989. Setting: 1-acre small town campus with easy access to Cleveland, Pittsburgh. Total enrollment: 124. Faculty: 23 (8 full-time, 15 part-time). Student-undergrad faculty ratio is 5:1. 2 applied, 100% were admitted. Full-time: 62 students, 85% women, 15% men. Part-time: 62 students, 11% women, 89% men. Students come from 2 states and territories, 1% from out-of-state. 0.8% Hispanic/Latino; 23% Black or African American, non-Hispanic/Latino; 0.8% Asian, non-Hispanic/Latino. 45% 25 or older, 2% transferred in. Core. Calendar: semesters. Academic remediation for entering students, services for LD students, double major, part-time degree program, adult/continuing education programs, internships.
Entrance Requirements: Options: early admission, deferred admission. Required: high school transcript, interview. Entrance: moderately difficult. Application deadline: rolling. Notification: continuous. Transfer credits accepted: Yes.
Collegiate Environment: Orientation program. Social organizations: 1 open to all. Most popular organization: Student Government. Major annual events:

Christmas Party, Red Cross Blood Bank, Constitution Day. Campus security: 24-hour emergency response devices. Main Library plus 1 other. 100 computers available on campus for general student use. Staffed computer lab on campus provides training in use of computers, software, and the Internet.

■ **FORTIS COLLEGE (CENTERVILLE)**
555 E Alex Bell Rd.
Centerville, OH 45459
Tel: (937)433-3410; Free: 855-4-FORTIS
Fax: (937)435-6516
Web Site: www.fortis.edu
Description: Proprietary, 2-year, coed. Awards certificates, diplomas, transfer associate, and terminal associate degrees. Founded 1953. Setting: 4-acre suburban campus with easy access to Dayton. Endowment: $893. Educational spending for the previous fiscal year: $5000 per student. Total enrollment: 533. Faculty: 122 (41 full-time, 81 part-time). Student-undergrad faculty ratio is 18:1. Full-time: 533 students, 73% women, 27% men. Students come from 2 states and territories, 1% from out-of-state. 47% 25 or older, 1% transferred in. Core. Calendar: semesters. Advanced placement, summer session for credit, internships.
Entrance Requirements: Options: early admission, deferred admission. Required: high school transcript, interview. Entrance: noncompetitive. Application deadline: rolling.
Collegiate Environment: Orientation program. Campus security: 24-hour emergency response devices. RETS Library. Operations spending for the previous fiscal year: $11,900. 220 computers available on campus for general student use. A campuswide network can be accessed. Staffed computer lab on campus provides training in use of computers, software, and the Internet.

■ **FORTIS COLLEGE (CINCINNATI)**
11499 Chester Rd.
Ste. 200
Cincinnati, OH 45246
Tel: (513)771-2795; Free: 855-4-FORTIS
Web Site: www.fortis.edu
Description: Proprietary, 2-year, coed. Awards certificates, diplomas, transfer associate, and terminal associate degrees.

■ **FORTIS COLLEGE (CUYAHOGA FALLS)**
2545 Bailey Rd.
Cuyahoga Falls, OH 44221
Tel: (330)923-9959; Free: 855-4-FORTIS
Fax: (330)923-0886
Web Site: www.fortis.edu
Description: Proprietary, 2-year, coed. Awards certificates, diplomas, transfer associate, and terminal associate degrees. Total enrollment: 741. Student-undergrad faculty ratio is 13:1. 57% 25 or older.
Entrance Requirements: Entrance: noncompetitive.

■ **FORTIS COLLEGE (RAVENNA)**
653 Enterprise Pky.
Ravenna, OH 44266
Tel: (330)297-7319; Free: 855-4-FORTIS
Fax: (330)297-7315
Web Site: www.fortis.edu
Description: Proprietary, 2-year, coed. Awards certificates, diplomas, transfer associate, and terminal associate degrees. Total enrollment: 482. 168 applied. 57% 25 or older.

■ **FORTIS COLLEGE (WESTERVILLE)**
4151 Executive Pky.
Ste. 120
Westerville, OH 43081
Tel: (614)882-2551; Free: 855-4-FORTIS
Web Site: www.fortis.edu
Description: Proprietary, 2-year, coed. Awards certificates, diplomas, transfer associate, and terminal associate degrees.

■ **FRANCISCAN UNIVERSITY OF STEUBENVILLE**
1235 University Blvd.
Steubenville, OH 43952-1763
Tel: (740)283-3771; Free: 800-783-6220
Fax: (740)283-6472
E-mail: admissions@franciscan.edu
Web Site: www.franciscan.edu
Description: Independent Roman Catholic, comprehensive, coed. Awards associate, bachelor's, and master's degrees. Founded 1946. Setting: 235-acre suburban campus with easy access to Pittsburg, PA. Endowment: $54.5 million. Educational spending for the previous fiscal year: $8194 per student. Total enrollment: 2,759. Faculty: 240 (127 full-time, 113 part-time). Student-undergrad faculty ratio is 14:1. 1,760 applied, 79% were admitted. 25% from top 10% of their high school class, 50% from top quarter, 81% from top half. Full-time: 1,995 students, 61% women, 39% men. Part-time: 95 students, 44% women, 56% men. Students come from 50 states and territories, 10 other countries, 80% from out-of-state. 0.2% American Indian or Alaska Native, non-Hispanic/Latino; 11% Hispanic/Latino; 0.7% Black or African American, non-Hispanic/Latino; 2% Asian, non-Hispanic/Latino; 0.6% international. 4% 25 or older, 80% live on campus, 6% transferred in. Retention: 84% of full-time freshmen returned the following year. Academic areas with the most degrees conferred: theology and religious vocations; business/marketing; health professions and related sciences. Core. Calendar: semesters. Services for LD students, advanced placement, accelerated degree program, honors program, independent study, distance learning, double major, summer session for credit, part-time degree program, co-op programs and internships, graduate courses open to undergrads. Study abroad program. ROTC: Army, Air Force (c).
Entrance Requirements: Options: electronic application, deferred admission, international baccalaureate accepted. Required: high school transcript, minimum 2.4 high school GPA, SAT or ACT. Recommended: interview. Required for some: essay, 3 recommendations. Entrance: moderately difficult. Application deadline: rolling. Notification: continuous. SAT Reasoning Test deadline: 5/1. Transfer credits accepted: Yes. Applicants placed on waiting list: 0. Wait-listed applicants offered admission: 0.
Costs Per Year: Application fee: $20. Comprehensive fee: $36,130 includes full-time tuition ($27,170), mandatory fees ($460), and college room and board ($8500). College room only: $4900. Room and board charges vary according to board plan.
Collegiate Environment: Orientation program. Drama-theater group, choral group, student-run newspaper, radio station. Social organizations: 35 open to all. Major annual events: St. Francis/Medieval Festival, Encounter Conference, March for Life. Student services: health clinic, personal-psychological counseling. Campus security: 24-hour emergency response devices and patrols, student patrols, late night transport-escort service, controlled dormitory access. St. John Paul II Library. Books: 143,662 (physical), 254,496 (digital/electronic); Serial titles: 590 (physical), 51,894 (digital/electronic); Databases: 131. Weekly public service hours: 93. Operations spending for the previous fiscal year: $710,292. 126 computers available on campus for general student use. Computer purchase/lease plans available. A campuswide network can be accessed from student residence rooms. Students can access the following: online class registration. Staffed computer lab on campus provides training in use of computers, software, and the Internet.
Community Environment: The county seat of Jefferson County, Steubenville is a city in eastern Ohio situated on the Ohio River. An unlimited supply of both deep-mine and strip coal is available in the Steubenville district. Because of the coal and the Ohio River, more steam electricity is generated within a 40-mile radius of the city than in any other area in the world. Steel, iron, and paper are some of the products of industries here.

■ **FRANKLIN UNIVERSITY**
201 S Grant Ave.
Columbus, OH 43215-5399
Tel: (614)797-4700; Free: 877-341-6300
Fax: (614)224-8027
E-mail: hull@franklin.edu
Web Site: www.franklin.edu
Description: Independent, comprehensive, coed. Awards associate, bachelor's, and master's degrees. Founded 1902. Setting: 14-acre urban campus with easy access to Columbus. Endowment: $85.8 million. Educational spending for the previous fiscal year: $2896 per student. Total enrollment: 5,734. Faculty: 814 (61 full-time, 753 part-time). Student-undergrad faculty ratio is 11:1. Full-time: 1,571 students, 57% women, 43% men. Part-time: 3,105 students, 57% women, 43% men. Students come from 45 states and territories, 72 other countries, 21% from out-of-state. 0.2% American Indian or Alaska Native, non-Hispanic/Latino; 3% Hispanic/Latino; 21% Black or African American, non-Hispanic/Latino; 3% Asian, non-

Hispanic/Latino; 0.1% Native Hawaiian or other Pacific Islander, non-Hispanic/Latino; 1% international. 81% 25 or older, 20% transferred in. Academic areas with the most degrees conferred: business/marketing; health professions and related sciences; computer and information sciences. Core. Calendar: trimesters. Academic remediation for entering students, ESL program, services for LD students, advanced placement, accelerated degree program, self-designed majors, independent study, distance learning, double major, summer session for credit, part-time degree program, adult/continuing education programs, co-op programs and internships, graduate courses open to undergrads. Off campus study at Franklin University has (2 + 2) and (3 + 1) articulation agreements with over 250 community colleges across the United States. Study abroad program. ROTC: Army (c), Air Force (c).

Entrance Requirements: Open admission except for certain programs such as Healthcare Information Management and Nursing. Options: electronic application, deferred admission, international baccalaureate accepted. Required for some: high school transcript. Entrance: noncompetitive. Application deadline: rolling. Notification: continuous. Transfer credits accepted: Yes.

Costs Per Year: Application fee: $0. Tuition: $15,780 full-time, $526 per credit hour part-time. Full-time tuition varies according to program. Part-time tuition varies according to program.

Collegiate Environment: Orientation program. Social organizations: honor societies, major/industry groups. Campus security: 24-hour emergency response devices, late night transport-escort service, video monitoring capabilities of all public/customer facing locations. The Franklin University Nationwide Library. Operations spending for the previous fiscal year: $1 million. 500 computers available on campus for general student use. A campuswide network can be accessed from off-campus. Students can access the following: online class registration. Staffed computer lab on campus provides training in use of computers, software, and the Internet.

Community Environment: See Ohio State University - Columbus Campus.

■ **GALEN COLLEGE OF NURSING**
100 E Business Way
Ste. 200
Cincinnati, OH 45241
Tel: (513)475-3600; Free: 877-223-7040
Web Site: www.galencollege.edu
Description: Proprietary, 4-year, coed. Awards associate and bachelor's degrees.

■ **GOD'S BIBLE SCHOOL AND COLLEGE**
1810 Young St.
Cincinnati, OH 45202-6838
Tel: (513)721-7944; Free: 800-486-4637
Fax: (513)721-3971
E-mail: hcouch@gbs.edu
Web Site: www.gbs.edu
Description: Independent interdenominational, 4-year, coed. Awards associate and bachelor's degrees. Founded 1900. Setting: 14-acre urban campus. Total enrollment: 292. Student-undergrad faculty ratio is 12:1. 93 applied, 90% were admitted. 64% from out-of-state. 27% 25 or older. Retention: 69% of full-time freshmen returned the following year. Core. Calendar: semesters. Academic remediation for entering students, advanced placement, independent study, summer session for credit, part-time degree program, internships.
Entrance Requirements: Required: high school transcript, 3 recommendations, interview, SAT or ACT. Recommended: SAT. Application deadline: 8/18.
Collegiate Environment: Orientation program. Choral group, student-run newspaper. Student services: health clinic. Campus security: 24-hour patrols. R. G. Flexon Memorial Library.

■ **GOOD SAMARITAN COLLEGE OF NURSING AND HEALTH SCIENCE**
375 Dixmyth Ave.
Cincinnati, OH 45220
Tel: (513)862-2743
Fax: (513)862-3572
Web Site: www.gscollege.edu
Description: Proprietary, primarily 2-year, coed. Administratively affiliated with Good Samaritan College is a hospital-based program within Good Samaritan Hospital. Awards terminal associate and bachelor's degrees. Setting: urban campus with easy access to Cincinnati. Total enrollment: 353.

Faculty: 41 (30 full-time, 11 part-time). Student-undergrad faculty ratio is 7:1. 52 applied, 79% were admitted. 20% from top quarter of their high school class, 40% from top half. Full-time: 128 students, 87% women, 13% men. Part-time: 225 students, 93% women, 7% men. 14% from out-of-state. 3% Hispanic/Latino; 11% Black or African American, non-Hispanic/Latino; 2% Asian, non-Hispanic/Latino. 45% 25 or older, 22% transferred in. Academic area with the most degrees conferred: health professions and related sciences. Core. Calendar: semesters. Academic remediation for entering students, services for LD students, advanced placement, honors program, summer session for credit, part-time degree program, co-op programs.
Entrance Requirements: Option: electronic application. Required: high school transcript, minimum 2.5 high school GPA, average GPA of 2.25 in high school English, algebra, chemistry, and social studies, SAT or ACT. Entrance: minimally difficult. Transfer credits accepted: Yes.
Collegiate Environment: Orientation program. Campus security: 24-hour emergency response devices and patrols, late night transport-escort service.

■ **HEIDELBERG UNIVERSITY**
310 E Market St.
Tiffin, OH 44883-2462
Tel: (419)448-2000; Free: 800-434-3352
Fax: (419)448-2334
E-mail: mbrown@heidelberg.edu
Web Site: www.heidelberg.edu
Description: Independent, comprehensive, coed, affiliated with United Church of Christ. Awards bachelor's and master's degrees. Founded 1850. Setting: 115-acre small town campus with easy access to Toledo, Cleveland, Columbus. Endowment: $48.9 million. Research spending for the previous fiscal year: $1.5 million. Educational spending for the previous fiscal year: $9022 per student. Total enrollment: 1,209. Faculty: 124 (58 full-time, 66 part-time). Student-undergrad faculty ratio is 13:1. 1,721 applied, 76% were admitted. Full-time: 1,041 students, 46% women, 54% men. Part-time: 18 students, 39% women, 61% men. Students come from 26 states and territories, 2 other countries, 19% from out-of-state. 0.1% American Indian or Alaska Native, non-Hispanic/Latino; 3% Hispanic/Latino; 10% Black or African American, non-Hispanic/Latino; 0.9% Asian, non-Hispanic/Latino; 0.1% Native Hawaiian or other Pacific Islander, non-Hispanic/Latino. 2% 25 or older, 79% live on campus, 2% transferred in. Retention: 67% of full-time freshmen returned the following year. Academic areas with the most degrees conferred: business/marketing; health professions and related sciences; homeland security, law enforcement, firefighting, and protective services; psychology. Core. Calendar: semesters. Academic remediation for entering students, ESL program, services for LD students, advanced placement, self-designed majors, honors program, independent study, double major, summer session for credit, part-time degree program, internships, graduate courses open to undergrads. Off campus study at members of the East Central College Consortium. Study abroad program. ROTC: Army (c), Air Force (c).
Entrance Requirements: Options: electronic application, deferred admission, international baccalaureate accepted. Required: high school transcript, SAT or ACT. Recommended: essay, minimum 2.5 high school GPA, 1 recommendation. Required for some: essay, 2 recommendations. Entrance: moderately difficult. Application deadline: rolling. Notification: continuous. SAT Reasoning Test deadline: 6/1. SAT Subject Test deadline: 6/1. Transfer credits accepted: Yes.
Costs Per Year: Application fee: $0. Comprehensive fee: $41,400 includes full-time tuition ($30,400), mandatory fees ($600), and college room and board ($10,400). College room only: $5300. Room and board charges vary according to board plan and housing facility. Part-time tuition: $900 per contact hour.
Collegiate Environment: Orientation program. Drama-theater group, choral group, student-run newspaper, radio station. Social organizations: 75 open to all; local fraternities, local sororities; 12% of eligible men and 22% of eligible women are members. Most popular organizations: Alpha Phi Omega, BERG Events Council, Student Senate, Campus Fellowship, Black Student Union/World Student Union. Major annual events: Battle of the Bands, Greek Sing, Student Research Conference. Student services: health clinic, personal-psychological counseling. Campus security: 24-hour emergency response devices and patrols, student patrols, late night transport-escort service, controlled dormitory access. Beeghly Library plus 1 other. Books: 86,891 (physical), 279,499 (digital/electronic); Serial titles: 1,293 (physical), 61,058 (digital/electronic); Databases: 198. Weekly public service hours: 83. Operations spending for the previous fiscal year: $314,097. 125 computers available on campus for general student use. A campuswide network can be

accessed from student residence rooms and from off campus. Students can access the following: online class registration. Staffed computer lab on campus provides training in use of computers, software, and the Internet.

Community Environment: The 110-acre campus is located in Tiffin, Ohio, at the intersection of U.S. route 224 and Ohio Route 53, 50 miles southeast of Toledo and 92 miles west of Cleveland. Amtrack stops in Sandusky, Toledo, Lima and Crestline. Churches, civic, service and social service agencies, and private enterprises offer many opportunities for volunteer and class-related experiences. Places of worship are available on campus and in the immediate community for Protestants and Catholics, and within 23 miles for Jewish students.

■ HERZING UNIVERSITY (AKRON)

1600 S Arlington St.
Ste. 100
Akron, OH 44306
Tel: (330)724-1600; Free: 800-596-0724
Fax: (330)724-9688
Web Site: www.herzing.edu/akron
Description: Independent, primarily 2-year, coed. Awards diplomas, terminal associate, and bachelor's degrees. Founded 1970.

■ HERZING UNIVERSITY (TOLEDO)

5212 Hill Ave.
Toledo, OH 43615
Tel: (419)776-0300; Free: 800-596-0724
Fax: (419)776-0315
Web Site: www.herzing.edu/toledo
Description: Independent, primarily 2-year, coed. Awards diplomas, terminal associate, and bachelor's degrees.

■ HIRAM COLLEGE

11715 Garfield Rd.
Hiram, OH 44234
Tel: (330)569-3211; Free: 800-362-5280
Fax: (330)569-5944
E-mail: admission@hiram.edu
Web Site: www.hiram.edu
Description: Independent, comprehensive, coed, affiliated with Christian Church (Disciples of Christ). Awards bachelor's and master's degrees. Founded 1850. Setting: 110-acre rural campus with easy access to Cleveland. Endowment: $73.4 million. Educational spending for the previous fiscal year: $11,342 per student. Total enrollment: 1,255. Faculty: 111 (59 full-time, 52 part-time). Student-undergrad faculty ratio is 10:1. 2,687 applied, 58% were admitted. 2% from top 10% of their high school class, 8% from top quarter, 29% from top half. Full-time: 824 students, 54% women, 46% men. Part-time: 420 students, 63% women, 37% men. Students come from 31 states and territories, 8 other countries, 20% from out-of-state. 0.2% American Indian or Alaska Native, non-Hispanic/Latino; 6% Hispanic/Latino; 17% Black or African American, non-Hispanic/Latino; 2% Asian, non-Hispanic/Latino; 0.2% Native Hawaiian or other Pacific Islander, non-Hispanic/Latino; 1% international. 14% 25 or older, 82% live on campus, 3% transferred in. Retention: 76% of full-time freshmen returned the following year. Academic areas with the most degrees conferred: business/marketing; social sciences; biological/life sciences. Core. Calendar: semesters. ESL program, services for LD students, advanced placement, accelerated degree program, self-designed majors, honors program, independent study, distance learning, double major, summer session for credit, part-time degree program, adult/continuing education programs, co-op programs and internships. Off campus study at John Cabot University in Italy; Kansai Gadai in Japan; Kanda University in Japan; Bogazici University in Turkey; Istanbul Aydin University in Turkey; IDC - Herzilya in Israel. Study abroad program. ROTC: Army (c), Air Force (c).
Entrance Requirements: Options: electronic application, deferred admission, international baccalaureate accepted. Required: essay, high school transcript. Recommended: minimum 2.8 high school GPA, interview. Required for some: SAT or ACT, SAT or ACT for applicants with cumulative GPA below 2.8, nursing or education applicants, or Trustee and/or President's Scholarships applicants. Entrance: moderately difficult. Application deadline: rolling. Notification: continuous. SAT Reasoning Test deadline: 8/1. SAT Subject Test deadline: 8/1. Transfer credits accepted: Yes.
Costs Per Year: Application fee: $25. Comprehensive fee: $46,648 includes full-time tuition ($34,008), mandatory fees ($2350), and college room and board ($10,290). College room only: $5150. Part-time tuition: $1,134 per credit hour. Tuition guaranteed not to increase for student's term of enrollment.
Collegiate Environment: Orientation program. Drama-theater group, choral group. Social organizations: 45 open to all; local fraternities, local sororities; 2% of eligible men and 2% of eligible women are members. Most popular organizations: Black Students United, Intercultural Forum, Terrier Activities Board, Student-Athlete Advisory Committee, Theater Guild. Major annual events: Homecoming, Springfest, Sugar Day. Student services: health clinic, personal-psychological counseling. Campus security: 24-hour emergency response devices and patrols, student patrols, late night transport-escort service, controlled dormitory access. 727 college housing spaces available; 623 were occupied in 2018-19. Freshmen guaranteed college housing. On-campus residence required through senior year. Options: coed, men-only, women-only housing available. Hiram College Library. Books: 177,742 (physical), 168,829 (digital/electronic); Serial titles: 85 (physical), 7,340 (digital/electronic); Databases: 279. Weekly public service hours: 90. Operations spending for the previous fiscal year: $535,000. 72 computers available on campus for general student use. Computer purchase/lease plans available. A computer is required for all students. A campuswide network can be accessed from student residence rooms and from off campus. Students can access the following: online class registration.
Community Environment: Located in a dairy and orchard growing area, Hiram is a rural community with numerous buildings in the Western Reserve style. This area has long been famous for the production of maple syrup. Air, bus and train transportation is available. Nearby lakes provide the facilities for boating, swimming, and fishing. Job opportunities are available mainly at the college.

■ HOCKING COLLEGE

3301 Hocking Pky.
Nelsonville, OH 45764-9588
Tel: (740)753-3591
Fax: (740)753-7065
Web Site: www.hocking.edu
Description: State-supported, 2-year, coed. Part of Ohio Board of Regents. Awards certificates, diplomas, transfer associate, and terminal associate degrees. Founded 1968. Setting: 1,600-acre rural campus with easy access to Columbus. Endowment: $4.8 million. Educational spending for the previous fiscal year: $5994 per student. Total enrollment: 4,094. Faculty: 281 (173 full-time, 108 part-time). Student-undergrad faculty ratio is 16:1. 2,270 applied, 100% were admitted. Students come from 25 states and territories, 17 other countries, 3% from out-of-state. 0.5% American Indian or Alaska Native, non-Hispanic/Latino; 2% Hispanic/Latino; 4% Black or African American, non-Hispanic/Latino; 0.5% Asian, non-Hispanic/Latino; 2% international. 28% 25 or older, 18% live on campus. Retention: 44% of full-time freshmen returned the following year. Core. Calendar: semesters. Academic remediation for entering students, ESL program, services for LD students, advanced placement, accelerated degree program, self-designed majors, distance learning, double major, summer session for credit, part-time degree program, adult/continuing education programs, co-op programs and internships. Off campus study at Franklin University, Ohio University, University of Rio Grande. ROTC: Army (c).
Entrance Requirements: Open admission except for nursing program. Option: electronic application. Required: high school transcript. Entrance: noncompetitive. Application deadline: rolling. Notification: continuous. Transfer credits accepted: Yes.
Collegiate Environment: Orientation program. Drama-theater group, choral group. Social organizations: 40 open to all. Most popular organizations: Phi Theta Kappa, Recycling Club, Kappa Beta Delta (Business Honor Society), Alpha Beta Gamma, Native American Club. Student services: personal-psychological counseling. Campus security: 24-hour emergency response devices and patrols, student patrols, late night transport-escort service, controlled dormitory access. Hocking College Learning Resources Center. Operations spending for the previous fiscal year: $257,890. 280 computers available on campus for general student use. A campuswide network can be accessed from student residence rooms and from off campus. Students can access the following: online class registration.
Community Environment: Nelsonville is a small community on the Hocking River. It is easily accessible from all points north and south in Ohio via US route 33. It is 65 miles from Columbus and is serviced by Greyhound bus lines.

■ **HONDROS COLLEGE**
4140 Executive Pky.
Westerville, OH 43081-3855
Tel: (614)508-7277; Free: 888-HONDROS
Fax: (614)508-7279
Web Site: www.hondros.edu
Description: Proprietary, 2-year, coed. Awards certificates, transfer associate, and terminal associate degrees. Founded 1981. Total enrollment: 255. 123 applied. 63% 25 or older. Calendar: quarters.
Entrance Requirements: Open admission. Entrance: noncompetitive.
Collegiate Environment: Campus security: 24-hour emergency response devices.

■ **INTERNATIONAL COLLEGE OF BROADCASTING**
6 S Smithville Rd.
Dayton, OH 45431-1833
Tel: (937)258-8251; Free: 800-517-7284
Web Site: www.icb.edu
Description: Proprietary, 2-year, coed. Awards diplomas, transfer associate, and terminal associate degrees. Founded 1968. Setting: urban campus with easy access to Dayton. Core. Calendar: semesters. Academic remediation for entering students, services for LD students, internships.
Entrance Requirements: Open admission. Option: early admission. Required: high school transcript, interview. Transfer credits accepted: Yes.
Collegiate Environment: Orientation program. Student-run radio station.

■ **JAMES A. RHODES STATE COLLEGE**
4240 Campus Dr.
Lima, OH 45804-3597
Tel: (419)995-8000
Fax: (419)995-8098
E-mail: cox.t@rhodesstate.edu
Web Site: www.rhodesstate.edu
Description: State-supported, 2-year, coed. Awards certificates, transfer associate, and terminal associate degrees. Founded 1971. Setting: 565-acre small town campus. Endowment: $1.7 million. Educational spending for the previous fiscal year: $4756 per student. Total enrollment: 3,883. Faculty: 248 (104 full-time, 144 part-time). Student-undergrad faculty ratio is 15:1. 1,691 applied, 100% were admitted. Full-time: 1,548 students, 66% women, 34% men. Part-time: 2,335 students, 70% women, 30% men. Students come from 4 states and territories, 1% from out-of-state. 0.4% American Indian or Alaska Native, non-Hispanic/Latino; 2% Hispanic/Latino; 8% Black or African American, non-Hispanic/Latino; 0.6% Asian, non-Hispanic/Latino; 0.1% Native Hawaiian or other Pacific Islander, non-Hispanic/Latino. 45% 25 or older, 7% transferred in. Retention: 55% of full-time freshmen returned the following year. Core. Calendar: quarters. Academic remediation for entering students, services for LD students, advanced placement, self-designed majors, independent study, distance learning, summer session for credit, part-time degree program, adult/continuing education programs, co-op programs and internships. Off campus study.
Entrance Requirements: Open admission except for allied health programs. Options: electronic application, early admission, deferred admission. Required: high school transcript. Entrance: noncompetitive. Application deadline: rolling. Notification: continuous until 8/15.
Collegiate Environment: Orientation program. Drama-theater group, choral group, student-run newspaper. Student services: personal-psychological counseling. Campus security: 24-hour emergency response devices and patrols, student patrols, late night transport-escort service. Rhodes State/Ohio State Library.
Community Environment: Lima, population 38,608, is an industrial city and the county seat of Allen County. It is 68 miles SSW of Toledo. Its major industries include motor vehicles, steel castings, aircraft parts, machine tools, and building machinery. It is also the center of a diversified agricultural region.

■ **JOHN CARROLL UNIVERSITY**
1 John Carroll Blvd.
University Heights, OH 44118
Tel: (216)397-1886; Free: 888-335-6800
Fax: (216)397-3098
E-mail: svitatoe@jcu.edu
Web Site: www.jcu.edu
Description: Independent Roman Catholic (Jesuit), comprehensive, coed. Awards bachelor's and master's degrees and post-master's certificates.

Founded 1886. Setting: 60-acre suburban campus with easy access to Cleveland. Endowment: $211 million. Research spending for the previous fiscal year: $4.8 million. Educational spending for the previous fiscal year: $10,023 per student. Total enrollment: 3,523. Faculty: 442 (176 full-time, 266 part-time). Student-undergrad faculty ratio is 12:1. 3,840 applied, 85% were admitted. 29% from top 10% of their high school class, 57% from top quarter, 93% from top half. 11 valedictorians. Full-time: 2,935 students, 49% women, 51% men. Part-time: 91 students, 49% women, 51% men. Students come from 36 states and territories, 30 other countries, 31% from out-of-state. 0.1% American Indian or Alaska Native, non-Hispanic/Latino; 4% Hispanic/Latino; 5% Black or African American, non-Hispanic/Latino; 2% Asian, non-Hispanic/Latino; 2% international. 2% 25 or older, 53% live on campus, 2% transferred in. Retention: 84% of full-time freshmen returned the following year. Academic areas with the most degrees conferred: business/marketing; psychology; communication/journalism. Core. Calendar: semesters. Services for LD students, advanced placement, self-designed majors, honors program, independent study, distance learning, double major, summer session for credit, part-time degree program, internships, graduate courses open to undergrads. Off campus study at Cross-registration (limit: 1 course per semester) available with Baldwin Wallace University, Case Western Reserve University, Cleveland Institute of Art, Cleveland Institute of Music, Cuyahoga Community College, Hiram College, Cleveland State Univ., Lakeland Community College, Notre Dame College, and Ursuline College. Study abroad program. ROTC: Army.
Entrance Requirements: Options: electronic application, early admission, early action, deferred admission, international baccalaureate accepted. Required: essay, high school transcript, 1 recommendation, SAT or ACT. Required for some: 2 recommendations, interview. Entrance: moderately difficult. Application deadlines: rolling, 12/1 for early action. Notification: continuous until 12/1, 12/15 for early action. SAT Reasoning Test deadline: 3/1. SAT Subject Test deadline: 8/1. Transfer credits accepted: Yes. Early action applicants: 2,053. Early action applicants admitted: 1,930.
Costs Per Year: Application fee: $0. One-time mandatory fee: $325. Comprehensive fee: $53,214 includes full-time tuition ($39,840), mandatory fees ($1500), and college room and board ($11,874). Full-time tuition and fees vary according to degree level. Room and board charges vary according to board plan and housing facility. Part-time tuition: $1320 per credit hour. Part-time tuition varies according to course load and degree level.
Collegiate Environment: Orientation program. Drama-theater group, choral group, student-run newspaper, radio station. Social organizations: 98 open to all; national fraternities, national sororities; 9% of eligible men and 21% of eligible women are members. Most popular organizations: Community Outreach/Volunteer Service Organization, Student Union, Club Sports, Fraternities and Sororities, Carroll News. Major annual events: Homecoming, Streak Week, Christmas Carroll Eve. Student services: health clinic, personal-psychological counseling, women's center. Campus security: 24-hour emergency response devices and patrols, late night transport-escort service, controlled dormitory access, student-led EMS program. Grasselli Library. Books: 456,260 (physical), 91,554 (digital/electronic); Serial titles: 459,633 (physical), 115,548 (digital/electronic); Databases: 279. Weekly public service hours: 111; students can reserve study rooms. Operations spending for the previous fiscal year: $3.4 million. 396 computers available on campus for general student use. Computer purchase/lease plans available. A campuswide network can be accessed from student residence rooms and from off campus. Students can access the following: online class registration, campus student online registration, billing, advising system, JCU mobile app, course management site (BlackBoard), online financial aid and billing; online course sites; online housing selection. Staffed computer lab on campus (open 24 hours a day) provides training in use of computers, software, and the Internet.

■ **KENT STATE UNIVERSITY**
PO Box 5190
Kent, OH 44242-0001
Tel: (330)672-3000; Free: 800-988-KENT
Fax: (330)672-2499
E-mail: cbuttens@kent.edu
Web Site: www.kent.edu
Description: State-supported, university, coed. Part of Kent State University System. Awards bachelor's, master's, and doctoral degrees and post-master's certificates. Founded 1910. Setting: 866-acre suburban campus with easy access to Cleveland, Akron, Canton. System endowment: $129.1 million. Research spending for the previous fiscal year: $15.8 million. Educational spending for the previous fiscal year: $7685 per student. Total

enrollment: 28,972. Faculty: 1,846 (1,010 full-time, 836 part-time). Student-undergrad faculty ratio is 20:1. 15,538 applied, 88% were admitted. 15% from top 10% of their high school class, 39% from top quarter, 78% from top half. Full-time: 20,509 students, 61% women, 39% men. Part-time: 2,669 students, 59% women, 41% men. Students come from 51 states and territories, 96 other countries, 16% from out-of-state. 0.2% American Indian or Alaska Native, non-Hispanic/Latino; 4% Hispanic/Latino; 9% Black or African American, non-Hispanic/Latino; 2% Asian, non-Hispanic/Latino; 0.1% Native Hawaiian or other Pacific Islander, non-Hispanic/Latino; 5% international. 11% 25 or older, 5% transferred in. Retention: 80% of full-time freshmen returned the following year. Academic areas with the most degrees conferred: business/marketing; health professions and related sciences; communication/journalism. Core. Calendar: semesters. Academic remediation for entering students, ESL program, services for LD students, advanced placement, accelerated degree program, self-designed majors, freshman honors college, honors program, independent study, distance learning, double major, summer session for credit, part-time degree program, adult/continuing education programs, co-op programs and internships, graduate courses open to undergrads. Off campus study at National Student Exchange. Study abroad program. ROTC: Army, Air Force.

Entrance Requirements: Options: electronic application, deferred admission, international baccalaureate accepted. Required: high school transcript, SAT or ACT. Entrance: moderately difficult. Application deadline: 5/1. Notification: continuous. SAT Reasoning Test deadline: 5/1. Transfer credits accepted: Yes.

Costs Per Year: Application fee: $50. One-time mandatory fee: $150. State resident tuition: $10,012 full-time, $456 per credit hour part-time. Nonresident tuition: $18,714 full-time, $825 per credit hour part-time. Full-time tuition varies according to course load. Part-time tuition varies according to course load. College room and board: $11,362. College room only: $7080. Room and board charges vary according to board plan and housing facility. Tuition guaranteed not to increase for student's term of enrollment.

Collegiate Environment: Orientation program. Drama-theater group, choral group, marching band, student-run newspaper, radio station. Social organizations: 400 open to all; national fraternities, national sororities; 9% of eligible men and 12% of eligible women are members. Most popular organizations: Black United Students, Running Club, National Society of Leadership and Success, Kent Inter-hall Council, Kent Indian Association. Major annual events: Blast Off, Homecoming, FlashFest. Student services: legal services, health clinic, personal-psychological counseling, women's center. Campus security: 24-hour emergency response devices and patrols, student patrols, late night transport-escort service, controlled dormitory access, campus police and fire department, electronic locks on computer labs, studios and laboratory research areas. Kent State University Main Library plus 4 others. Books: 3 million (physical), 1.2 million (digital/electronic); Serial titles: 35,857 (physical), 14,996 (digital/electronic); Databases: 355. Weekly public service hours: 146; study areas open 24 hours, 5-7 days a week; students can reserve study rooms. Operations spending for the previous fiscal year: $15.4 million.

Community Environment: Kent, a city of some 30,000, on the banks of the Cuyahoga River, in Portage County, is situated 11 miles east of Akron, 33 miles south of Cleveland, 40 miles west of Youngstown and 28 miles north of Canton. The community provides students with many places to shop and entertain themselves and places of worship for most major denominations. Recreational activities include fishing, boating, skiing, swimming, and golf. The university is located near two major jetports, Cleveland Hopkins International and Akron-Canton.

■ **KENT STATE UNIVERSITY AT ASHTABULA**
3300 Lake Rd. W
Ashtabula, OH 44004-2299
Tel: (440)964-3322
Fax: (440)964-4269
E-mail: ashtabula_admissions@kent.edu
Web Site: www.ashtabula.kent.edu
Description: State-supported, primarily 2-year, coed. Part of Kent State University System. Awards certificates, transfer associate, terminal associate, and bachelor's degrees (also offers some upper-level and graduate courses). Founded 1958. Setting: 83-acre small town campus with easy access to Cleveland. Total enrollment: 1,974. Faculty: 99 (50 full-time, 49 part-time). Student-undergrad faculty ratio is 20:1. 375 applied, 99% were admitted. 4% from top 10% of their high school class, 17% from top quarter, 50% from top half. Full-time: 1,027 students, 60% women, 40% men. Part-time: 944 students, 69% women, 31% men. Students come from 25 states and

territories, 3 other countries, 5% from out-of-state. 0.2% American Indian or Alaska Native, non-Hispanic/Latino; 5% Hispanic/Latino; 5% Black or African American, non-Hispanic/Latino; 1% Asian, non-Hispanic/Latino; 0.2% Native Hawaiian or other Pacific Islander, non-Hispanic/Latino; 0.4% international. 42% 25 or older, 4% transferred in. Retention: 51% of full-time freshmen returned the following year. Academic area with the most degrees conferred: liberal arts/general studies. Core. Calendar: semesters. Academic remediation for entering students, services for LD students, advanced placement, self-designed majors, independent study, distance learning, double major, summer session for credit, part-time degree program, internships. Study abroad program. ROTC: Army (c), Air Force (c).

Entrance Requirements: Open admission. Options: electronic application, deferred admission, international baccalaureate accepted. Required: high school transcript. Recommended: SAT or ACT. Required for some: SAT or ACT. Entrance: noncompetitive. Application deadline: 8/1. Notification: continuous. SAT Reasoning Test deadline: 8/1. Transfer credits accepted: Yes.

Costs Per Year: Application fee: $40. One-time mandatory fee: $150. State resident tuition: $5664 full-time, $258 per credit hour part-time. Nonresident tuition: $14,196 full-time, $627 per credit hour part-time. Full-time tuition varies according to course level and course load. Part-time tuition varies according to course level and course load. Tuition guaranteed not to increase for student's term of enrollment.

Collegiate Environment: Orientation program. Social organizations: 19 open to all. Most popular organizations: Student Government, Student Veterans Association, Student Nurses Association, Student Occupational Therapy Association, Media Club. Campus security: 24-hour emergency response devices. Kent State at Ashtabula Library. Weekly public service hours: 56.

Community Environment: This growing industrial city is on Lake Erie at the mouth of the Ashtabula River. Two municipal parks on Lake Erie have excellent facilities for swimming, boating, and fishing.

■ **KENT STATE UNIVERSITY AT EAST LIVERPOOL**
400 E 4th St.
East Liverpool, OH 43920-3497
Tel: (330)385-3805
Fax: (330)385-6348
Web Site: www.eliv.kent.edu
Description: State-supported, primarily 2-year, coed. Part of Kent State University System. Awards certificates, transfer associate, terminal associate, and bachelor's degrees. Founded 1967. Setting: 3-acre small town campus with easy access to Pittsburgh, Youngstown. Total enrollment: 1,174. Faculty: 55 (21 full-time, 34 part-time). Student-undergrad faculty ratio is 25:1. 83 applied, 99% were admitted. 11% from top 10% of their high school class, 22% from top quarter, 52% from top half. Full-time: 635 students, 64% women, 36% men. Part-time: 539 students, 73% women, 27% men. Students come from 13 states and territories, 10 other countries, 6% from out-of-state. 0.2% American Indian or Alaska Native, non-Hispanic/Latino; 2% Hispanic/Latino; 5% Black or African American, non-Hispanic/Latino; 0.6% Asian, non-Hispanic/Latino; 0.6% international. 38% 25 or older, 4% transferred in. Retention: 65% of full-time freshmen returned the following year. Academic area with the most degrees conferred: liberal arts/general studies. Core. Calendar: semesters. Academic remediation for entering students, services for LD students, advanced placement, accelerated degree program, self-designed majors, freshman honors college, honors program, independent study, distance learning, double major, summer session for credit, part-time degree program, adult/continuing education programs, internships. Study abroad program. ROTC: Army (c), Air Force (c).

Entrance Requirements: Open admission. Options: electronic application, deferred admission, international baccalaureate accepted. Required: high school transcript. Recommended: SAT or ACT. Required for some: SAT or ACT. Entrance: noncompetitive. Application deadline: 8/1. Notification: continuous. SAT Reasoning Test deadline: 8/1. Transfer credits accepted: Yes.

Costs Per Year: Application fee: $40. One-time mandatory fee: $150. State resident tuition: $5664 full-time, $258 per credit hour part-time. Nonresident tuition: $14,196 full-time, $627 per credit hour part-time. Full-time tuition varies according to course level and course load. Part-time tuition varies according to course level and course load. Tuition guaranteed not to increase for student's term of enrollment.

Collegiate Environment: Orientation program. Social organizations: 7 open to all. Most popular organizations: Undergraduate Student Government,

Student Nurses Association, Environmental Club, Student Occupational Therapist Assistants, Physical Therapist Assistant Club. Major annual events: Christmas on Campus, Ohio River Arts Festival, Welcome Back Fest. Student services: personal-psychological counseling. Campus security: 24-hour emergency response devices, student patrols, late night transport-escort service. Paul Blair Memorial Library. Weekly public service hours: 46.

Community Environment: East Liverpool is in one of the most scenic sections of the upper Ohio Valley and is a leading pottery center producing semivitreous porcelain ware. Train and bus transportation is available and a local airport is available for private planes. Community facilities include numerous churches, representing 18 denominations, and a library. Thompson park provides facilities for all outdoor sports including winter sports; Beaver Creek provides facilities for camping, fishing, and picnicking.

■ **KENT STATE UNIVERSITY AT GEAUGA**
14111 Claridon-Troy Rd.
Burton, OH 44021-9500
Tel: (440)834-4187
Fax: (440)834-0919
E-mail: geaugaadmissions@kent.edu
Web Site: www.geauga.kent.edu
Description: State-supported, comprehensive, coed. Part of Kent State University System. Awards associate, bachelor's, and master's degrees. Founded 1964. Setting: 87-acre rural campus with easy access to Cleveland, Akron, Youngstown. Total enrollment: 2,248. Faculty: 132 (38 full-time, 94 part-time). Student-undergrad faculty ratio is 23:1. 782 applied, 98% were admitted. 3% from top 10% of their high school class, 9% from top quarter, 34% from top half. Full-time: 1,308 students, 57% women, 43% men. Part-time: 939 students, 68% women, 32% men. Students come from 5 states and territories, 4 other countries, 3% from out-of-state. 0.3% American Indian or Alaska Native, non-Hispanic/Latino; 3% Hispanic/Latino; 11% Black or African American, non-Hispanic/Latino; 2% Asian, non-Hispanic/Latino; 0.1% Native Hawaiian or other Pacific Islander, non-Hispanic/Latino; 0.5% international. 29% 25 or older, 6% transferred in. Retention: 58% of full-time freshmen returned the following year. Academic area with the most degrees conferred: liberal arts/general studies. Core. Calendar: semesters. Academic remediation for entering students, services for LD students, advanced placement, self-designed majors, distance learning, summer session for credit, part-time degree program, internships.
Entrance Requirements: Open admission. Options: electronic application, deferred admission, international baccalaureate accepted. Required: high school transcript. Recommended: SAT or ACT. Entrance: noncompetitive. Application deadline: 8/15. Notification: continuous. SAT Reasoning Test deadline: 8/1. Transfer credits accepted: Yes.
Costs Per Year: Application fee: $40. State resident tuition: $258 per credit hour part-time. Nonresident tuition: $627 per credit hour part-time. Part-time tuition varies according to course level and course load. Tuition guaranteed not to increase for student's term of enrollment.
Collegiate Environment: Orientation program. Social organizations: 7 open to all. Most popular organizations: National Student Nurse Association Twinsburg, Geauga Student Nurses Association, Alpha Delta Nu-Gamma Sigma Chapter, Kent State University Geauga College Republicans, Undergraduate Student Government. Major annual events: Beginning of Year Kickoff, Finals Week Activities. Campus security: 24-hour emergency response devices. Kent State University at Geauga Library. Books: 12,083 (physical); Serial titles: 43 (physical). Weekly public service hours: 53.
Community Environment: Burton located 30 miles from Cleveland, is primarily a residential area with a few small businesses. Planes and trains are within 18 miles. Community facilities include shopping facilities, churches, and civic and service organizations. Ski resort is nearby for all winter sports.

■ **KENT STATE UNIVERSITY AT SALEM**
2491 State Rte. 45 S
Salem, OH 44460-9412
Tel: (330)332-0361
Fax: (330)332-9256
Web Site: www.salem.kent.edu
Description: State-supported, primarily 2-year, coed. Part of Kent State University System. Awards certificates, transfer associate, and bachelor's degrees (also offers some upper-level and graduate courses). Founded 1966. Setting: 100-acre rural campus with easy access to Youngstown. Total enrollment: 1,694. Faculty: 115 (41 full-time, 74 part-time). Student-

undergrad faculty ratio is 19:1. 264 applied, 100% were admitted. 5% from top 10% of their high school class, 19% from top quarter, 47% from top half. Full-time: 1,062 students, 71% women, 29% men. Part-time: 632 students, 68% women, 32% men. Students come from 7 states and territories, 2% from out-of-state. 0.1% American Indian or Alaska Native, non-Hispanic/Latino; 2% Hispanic/Latino; 4% Black or African American, non-Hispanic/Latino; 0.9% Asian, non-Hispanic/Latino; 0.1% international. 32% 25 or older, 6% transferred in. Retention: 53% of full-time freshmen returned the following year. Academic areas with the most degrees conferred: health professions and related sciences; business/marketing; liberal arts/general studies. Core. Calendar: semesters. Academic remediation for entering students, services for LD students, advanced placement, accelerated degree program, self-designed majors, freshman honors college, honors program, independent study, distance learning, double major, summer session for credit, part-time degree program, adult/continuing education programs, co-op programs. Study abroad program. ROTC: Army (c), Air Force (c).
Entrance Requirements: Open admission. Options: electronic application, deferred admission, international baccalaureate accepted. Required: high school transcript. Recommended: SAT or ACT. Required for some: essay, SAT or ACT. Entrance: noncompetitive. Application deadline: 12/15. Notification: continuous. SAT Reasoning Test deadline: 8/1. Transfer credits accepted: Yes.
Costs Per Year: Application fee: $40. One-time mandatory fee: $150. State resident tuition: $5664 full-time, $258 per credit hour part-time. Nonresident tuition: $14,366 full-time, $627 per credit hour part-time. Full-time tuition varies according to course level and course load. Part-time tuition varies according to course level and course load. Tuition guaranteed not to increase for student's term of enrollment.
Collegiate Environment: Orientation program. Social organizations: 7 open to all. Student services: personal-psychological counseling. Campus security: 24-hour emergency response devices, late night transport-escort service. Kent State Salem Library. Books: 23,500 (physical); Serial titles: 4,500 (physical). 85 computers available on campus for general student use. A campuswide network can be accessed from off-campus. Students can access the following: online class registration.
Community Environment: Known as the"Quaker City" because of its founders, Salem is one of the most productive dairy and fruit growing sections of Ohio. Salem is an area of thriving manufacturing and commercial establishments were full- and part-time employment is available. Centennial Park offers varied recreational facilities.

■ **KENT STATE UNIVERSITY AT STARK**
6000 Frank Ave., NW
Canton, OH 44720-7599
Tel: (330)499-9600
Fax: (330)494-6121
E-mail: starkadmissions@kent.edu
Web Site: www.stark.kent.edu
Description: State-supported, comprehensive, coed. Part of Kent State University System. Awards associate, bachelor's, and master's degrees. Founded 1946. Setting: 200-acre suburban campus with easy access to Cleveland, Akron, Canton. Total enrollment: 5,030. Faculty: 276 (109 full-time, 167 part-time). Student-undergrad faculty ratio is 23:1. 1,127 applied, 100% were admitted. 7% from top 10% of their high school class, 20% from top quarter, 49% from top half. Full-time: 3,157 students, 59% women, 41% men. Part-time: 1,838 students, 63% women, 37% men. Students come from 11 states and territories, 4 other countries, 2% from out-of-state. 0.4% American Indian or Alaska Native, non-Hispanic/Latino; 2% Hispanic/Latino; 6% Black or African American, non-Hispanic/Latino; 1% Asian, non-Hispanic/Latino; 0.4% international. 23% 25 or older, 6% transferred in. Retention: 66% of full-time freshmen returned the following year. Academic areas with the most degrees conferred: liberal arts/general studies; visual and performing arts. Core. Calendar: semesters. Academic remediation for entering students, services for LD students, advanced placement, self-designed majors, honors program, independent study, distance learning, double major, summer session for credit, part-time degree program, adult/continuing education programs, internships. Off campus study. Study abroad program. ROTC: Army (c), Air Force (c).
Entrance Requirements: Open admission. Options: electronic application, deferred admission, international baccalaureate accepted. Required: high school transcript. Recommended: SAT or ACT. Entrance: noncompetitive. Application deadline: 8/15. SAT Reasoning Test deadline: 8/1. Transfer credits accepted: Yes.
Costs Per Year: Application fee: $40. State resident tuition: $258 per credit

hour part-time. Nonresident tuition: $627 per credit hour part-time. Part-time tuition varies according to course level and course load. Tuition guaranteed not to increase for student's term of enrollment.

Collegiate Environment: Orientation program. Drama-theater group, choral group. Social organizations: 17 open to all. Most popular organizations: Music Technology Club, Biology Club, SCRUBS (Nursing Organization), HDFS (Human Development Family Studies), Revive (Faith Based). Major annual events: Featured Speaker Series, Kentiki (end of spring semester celebration), Spirit Fest. Student services: personal-psychological counseling. Campus security: 24-hour emergency response devices, student patrols, late night transport-escort service. Kent State Stark Library. Serial titles: 600 (physical). Weekly public service hours: 72; students can reserve study rooms. 605 computers available on campus for general student use. A campuswide network can be accessed from off-campus. Students can access the following: online class registration. Staffed computer lab on campus provides training in use of computers, software, and the Internet.

Community Environment: The Kent State University Stark Campus is a commuter campus located Jackson Township in suburban Canton, Ohio.

■ **KENT STATE UNIVERSITY AT TRUMBULL**
4314 Mahoning Ave., NW
Warren, OH 44483-1998
Tel: (330)847-0571
E-mail: trumbullinfo@kent.edu
Web Site: www.trumbull.kent.edu

Description: State-supported, primarily 2-year, coed. Part of Kent State University System. Awards transfer associate and bachelor's degrees (also offers some upper-level and graduate courses). Founded 1954. Setting: 438-acre suburban campus with easy access to Akron, Youngstown. Total enrollment: 2,280. Faculty: 106 (51 full-time, 55 part-time). Student-undergrad faculty ratio is 25:1. 388 applied, 100% were admitted. 3% from top 10% of their high school class, 13% from top quarter, 46% from top half. Students come from 6 states and territories, 3% from out-of-state. 0.2% American Indian or Alaska Native, non-Hispanic/Latino; 3% Hispanic/Latino; 8% Black or African American, non-Hispanic/Latino; 0.9% Asian, non-Hispanic/Latino; 0.1% Native Hawaiian or other Pacific Islander, non-Hispanic/Latino; 0.4% international. 35% 25 or older. Retention: 60% of full-time freshmen returned the following year. Academic area with the most degrees conferred: liberal arts/general studies. Core. Calendar: semesters. Academic remediation for entering students, services for LD students, advanced placement, self-designed majors, freshman honors college, honors program, independent study, distance learning, double major, summer session for credit, part-time degree program, adult/continuing education programs, internships. ROTC: Army (c), Air Force (c).

Entrance Requirements: Open admission. Options: electronic application, deferred admission, international baccalaureate accepted. Required: high school transcript. Recommended: SAT or ACT. Entrance: noncompetitive. Application deadline: 8/15. SAT Reasoning Test deadline: 8/1. Transfer credits accepted: Yes.

Costs Per Year: Application fee: $40. One-time mandatory fee: $150. State resident tuition: $5664 full-time, $258 per credit hour part-time. Nonresident tuition: $14,366 full-time, $627 per credit hour part-time. Full-time tuition varies according to course level and course load. Part-time tuition varies according to course level and course load. Tuition guaranteed not to increase for student's term of enrollment.

Collegiate Environment: Orientation program. Drama-theater group. Social organizations: 10 open to all. Most popular organizations: The National Society for Leadership and Success, Sigma Alpha Pi, Jurisprudence Organization, Student Nurses Association, Pride Alliance, S.E.E.D.S. Major annual events: Flash Bash (fall), Finals Week Massage Therapy, Ugly Sweater Contest. Student services: personal-psychological counseling. Campus security: 24-hour emergency response devices, late night transport-escort service, patrols by trained security personnel during hours of operation. Gelbke Library at Kent State Trumbull. Books: 40,000 (physical), 100,000 (digital/electronic); Serial titles: 40 (physical); Databases: 459. Weekly public service hours: 56. 300 computers available on campus for general student use. A campuswide network can be accessed from off-campus. Students can access the following: online class registration. Staffed computer lab on campus provides training in use of computers, software, and the Internet.

Community Environment: Located in the northeastern part of Ohio, the New England influences brought here by early settlers are still strongly felt. Warren, an industrial city, is in the great Mahoning Valley steel district and also has an active electrical and automotive parts industry. Shopping facili-

ties here are good. Mosquito State Park, located 10 miles north, provides facilities for fishing, boating, swimming and camping. Points of interest are the John Stark Edwards House and the Nelson and Kennedy Ledges State Park.

■ **KENT STATE UNIVERSITY AT TUSCARAWAS**
330 University Dr., NE
New Philadelphia, OH 44663-9403
Tel: (330)339-3391
Fax: (330)339-3321
E-mail: infotusc@kent.edu
Web Site: www.tusc.kent.edu

Description: State-supported, primarily 2-year, coed. Part of Kent State University System. Awards certificates, diplomas, transfer associate, and bachelor's degrees (also offers some upper-level and graduate courses). Founded 1962. Setting: 180-acre small town campus with easy access to Akron, Canton. Total enrollment: 2,134. Faculty: 122 (47 full-time, 75 part-time). Student-undergrad faculty ratio is 22:1. 415 applied, 99% were admitted. 6% from top 10% of their high school class, 23% from top quarter, 52% from top half. Full-time: 1,299 students, 52% women, 48% men. Part-time: 832 students, 65% women, 35% men. Students come from 8 states and territories, 3 other countries, 2% from out-of-state. 0.4% American Indian or Alaska Native, non-Hispanic/Latino; 2% Hispanic/Latino; 4% Black or African American, non-Hispanic/Latino; 0.7% Asian, non-Hispanic/Latino; 0.5% international. 27% 25 or older, 6% transferred in. Retention: 62% of full-time freshmen returned the following year. Academic areas with the most degrees conferred: engineering technologies; liberal arts/general studies. Core. Calendar: semesters. Academic remediation for entering students, services for LD students, advanced placement, accelerated degree program, self-designed majors, freshman honors college, honors program, independent study, distance learning, double major, summer session for credit, part-time degree program, adult/continuing education programs, internships. Study abroad program. ROTC: Army (c), Air Force (c).

Entrance Requirements: Open admission. Options: electronic application, deferred admission, international baccalaureate accepted. Required: high school transcript. Recommended: SAT or ACT. Entrance: noncompetitive. Application deadline: 8/15. Notification: continuous. Transfer credits accepted: Yes.

Costs Per Year: Application fee: $40. One-time mandatory fee: $150. State resident tuition: $5664 full-time, $258 per credit hour part-time. Nonresident tuition: $14,366 full-time, $627 per credit hour part-time. Full-time tuition varies according to course level and course load. Part-time tuition varies according to course level and course load. Tuition guaranteed not to increase for student's term of enrollment.

Collegiate Environment: Orientation program. Choral group. Social organizations: 18 open to all. Most popular organizations: Student Nurses Association, Technology Club, Vet Tech Student Chapter, Realms of Roleplay, Vision. Major annual events: Parking Lot Pandemonium, Spring Fest, Chili Cook-off. Campus security: 24-hour emergency response devices. Kent State Tuscarawas Library. Books: 52,500 (physical), 12 (digital/electronic); Serial titles: 540 (physical). 194 computers available on campus for general student use. A campuswide network can be accessed from off-campus. Students can access the following: online class registration. Staffed computer lab on campus provides training in use of computers, software, and the Internet.

■ **KENYON COLLEGE**
106 College Park Dr.
Gambier, OH 43022
Tel: (740)427-5000; Free: 800-848-2468
Fax: (740)427-2634
E-mail: admissions@kenyon.edu
Web Site: www.kenyon.edu

Description: Independent, 4-year, coed. Awards bachelor's degrees. Founded 1824. Setting: 1,000-acre rural campus with easy access to Columbus. Endowment: $208.9 million. Research spending for the previous fiscal year: $463,428. Educational spending for the previous fiscal year: $24,747 per student. Total enrollment: 1,677. Faculty: 214 (167 full-time, 47 part-time). Student-undergrad faculty ratio is 9:1. 5,603 applied, 34% were admitted. 63% from top 10% of their high school class, 86% from top quarter, 100% from top half. 12 National Merit Scholars, 13 valedictorians. Full-time: 1,661 students, 56% women, 44% men. Part-time: 16 students, 56% women, 44% men. Students come from 47 states and territories, 46 other countries, 85% from out-of-state. 6% Hispanic/Latino; 3% Black or African

American, non-Hispanic/Latino; 3% Asian, non-Hispanic/Latino; 6% international. 100% live on campus, 1% transferred in. Retention: 93% of full-time freshmen returned the following year. Academic areas with the most degrees conferred: social sciences; English; visual and performing arts. Core. Calendar: semesters. Services for LD students, advanced placement, accelerated degree program, self-designed majors, honors program, independent study, double major, internships. Off campus study. Study abroad program.

Entrance Requirements: Options: electronic application, early admission, early decision, deferred admission, international baccalaureate accepted. Required: essay, high school transcript, counselor recommendation, SAT or ACT. Recommended: 2 recommendations, interview. Entrance: most difficult. Application deadlines: 1/15, 11/15 for early decision plan 1, 1/15 for early decision plan 2. Notification: 4/1, 12/15 for early decision plan 1, 2/1 for early decision plan 2. SAT Reasoning Test deadline: 2/15. SAT Subject Test deadline: 2/15. Transfer credits accepted: Yes. Applicants placed on waiting list: 1,656. Wait-listed applicants offered admission: 38. Early decision applicants: 345. Early decision applicants admitted: 229.

Costs Per Year: Application fee: $0. Comprehensive fee: $68,440 includes full-time tuition ($53,830), mandatory fees ($2100), and college room and board ($12,510). College room only: $5470. Full-time tuition and fees vary according to reciprocity agreements. Room and board charges vary according to housing facility and student level.

Collegiate Environment: Orientation program. Drama-theater group, choral group, student-run newspaper, radio station. Social organizations: 164 open to all; national fraternities, national sororities, local fraternities, local sororities; 27% of eligible men and 32% of eligible women are members. Most popular organizations: student advisory groups, student radio station, musical groups, intramural sports and clubs, outdoors club. Major annual events: Summer Send-off, Activities Fair, Founder's Day. Student services: health clinic, personal-psychological counseling, women's center. Campus security: 24-hour emergency response devices and patrols, student patrols, late night transport-escort service, controlled dormitory access. Olin Library plus 1 other. Books: 495,501 (physical), 42,965 (digital/electronic); Serial titles: 1,670 (physical), 43,534 (digital/electronic); Databases: 332. Weekly public service hours: 131; students can reserve study rooms. Operations spending for the previous fiscal year: $3.2 million. 715 computers available on campus for general student use. A campuswide network can be accessed from student residence rooms and from off campus. Students can access the following: online class registration, commercial databases. Staffed computer lab on campus provides training in use of computers, software, and the Internet.

Community Environment: Gambier, a hamlet in central Ohio, is 47 miles northeast of Columbus, and just east of Mount Vernon. It is a village dating from pre-Civil War days and many buildings of that era still remain.

■ **KETTERING COLLEGE**
3737 Southern Blvd.
Kettering, OH 45429-1299
Tel: (937)395-8601; Free: 800-433-5262
Fax: (937)395-8333
Web Site: www.kc.edu
Description: Independent Seventh-day Adventist, comprehensive, coed. Administratively affiliated with Kettering Health Network. Awards associate, bachelor's, and master's degrees. Founded 1967. Setting: 35-acre suburban campus. Total enrollment: 808. Faculty: 70 (55 full-time, 15 part-time). Student-undergrad faculty ratio is 10:1. 204 applied, 50% were admitted. 22% from top 10% of their high school class, 53% from top quarter, 81% from top half. Full-time: 394 students, 81% women, 19% men. Part-time: 347 students, 80% women, 20% men. Students come from 24 states and territories, 3 other countries, 7% from out-of-state. 48% 25 or older, 15% live on campus, 16% transferred in. Retention: 78% of full-time freshmen returned the following year. Academic area with the most degrees conferred: health professions and related sciences. Core. Calendar: semesters. Advanced placement, honors program, independent study, distance learning, summer session for credit, part-time degree program. Off campus study at members of the Southwestern Ohio Council for Higher Education. Study abroad program.

Entrance Requirements: Option: early admission. Required: essay, high school transcript, minimum 2.0 high school GPA, ACT. Recommended: minimum 3.0 high school GPA, interview, SAT. Entrance: moderately difficult. Application deadline: rolling. Notification: continuous.

Costs Per Year: Application fee: $25. Tuition: $16,200 full-time, $540 per credit hour part-time. Full-time tuition varies according to course load,

degree level, and program. Part-time tuition varies according to course load, degree level, and program. College room only: $4100.

Collegiate Environment: Drama-theater group, choral group. Social organizations: 3 open to all. Most popular organizations: Student Association/student life, Campus Ministries. Major annual events: Weeks of Spiritual Emphasis, Nursing Dedication Ceremony, Christmas Party. Student services: health clinic, personal-psychological counseling. Campus security: 24-hour emergency response devices and patrols, late night transport-escort service. Learning Resources Center plus 1 other. 30 computers available on campus for general student use. A campuswide network can be accessed from student residence rooms and from off campus. Students can access the following: online class registration. Staffed computer lab on campus.

Community Environment: The city is surrounded by rolling, wooded hills and is a suburb of Dayton. The recreational, educational, and cultural advantages of Dayton are enjoyed by the citizens of Kettering also. Kettering is the home of the world's largest supply of electronic components. Community facilities include 37 churches of many denominations and many shopping centers and plazas. Nine golf courses are in the area.

■ **LAKE ERIE COLLEGE**
391 W Washington St.
Painesville, OH 44077-3389
Tel: (440)296-1856; Free: 800-916-0904
Fax: (440)352-3533
E-mail: admissions@lec.edu
Web Site: www.lec.edu
Description: Independent, comprehensive, coed. Awards bachelor's and master's degrees. Founded 1856. Setting: 46-acre suburban campus with easy access to Cleveland. Endowment: $32.7 million. Educational spending for the previous fiscal year: $5948 per student. Total enrollment: 1,201. Faculty: 103 (42 full-time, 61 part-time). Student-undergrad faculty ratio is 14:1. 1,485 applied, 63% were admitted. Full-time: 745 students, 48% women, 52% men. Part-time: 210 students, 67% women, 33% men. Students come from 27 states and territories, 14 other countries, 26% from out-of-state. 0.7% American Indian or Alaska Native, non-Hispanic/Latino; 2% Hispanic/Latino; 14% Black or African American, non-Hispanic/Latino; 0.8% Asian, non-Hispanic/Latino; 4% international. 4% 25 or older, 66% live on campus, 4% transferred in. Retention: 70% of full-time freshmen returned the following year. Academic areas with the most degrees conferred: business/marketing; biological/life sciences; agriculture. Core. Calendar: semesters. Services for LD students, advanced placement, accelerated degree program, self-designed majors, honors program, independent study, double major, summer session for credit, part-time degree program, internships, graduate courses open to undergrads. Off campus study at Northeast Ohio Commission on Higher Education. Study abroad program.

Entrance Requirements: Options: electronic application, early action, deferred admission, international baccalaureate accepted. Required: high school transcript, minimum 2.5 high school GPA. Recommended: essay, interview, AP, CLEP, institutional exam. Required for some: essay, recommendations, SAT and SAT Subject Tests or ACT. Entrance: moderately difficult. Application deadlines: 8/1, 12/1 for early action. Notification: continuous, 12/14 for early action. SAT Reasoning Test deadline: 8/1. SAT Subject Test deadline: 8/1. Transfer credits accepted: Yes. Early action applicants: 208. Early action applicants admitted: 204.

Costs Per Year: Application fee: $30. Comprehensive fee: $41,330 includes full-time tuition ($29,986), mandatory fees ($1436), and college room and board ($9908). College room only: $4508. Full-time tuition and fees vary according to course load, degree level, and program. Room and board charges vary according to board plan and housing facility. Part-time tuition: $795 per credit hour. Part-time mandatory fees: $51 per credit hour. Part-time tuition and fees vary according to course load, degree level, and program.

Collegiate Environment: Orientation program. Drama-theater group, choral group. Social organizations: 37 open to all; national fraternities, national sororities. Most popular organizations: Student Athlete Advisory Committee, Intercollegiate Horse Show Association, Gamma Phi Beta Sorority, Spanish Club, Student Government Association. Major annual events: Spring Formal, Homecoming, Field Day. Campus security: 24-hour emergency response devices and patrols, late night transport-escort service. Lincoln Library. Books: 38,463 (physical), 299,340 (digital/electronic); Serial titles: 18,188 (digital/electronic); Databases: 107. Weekly public service hours: 56; students can reserve study rooms. 78 computers available on campus for general student use. A campuswide network can be accessed from student residence rooms and from off campus. Students can access the following: online class registration. Staffed computer lab on campus provides training in use of computers, software, and the Internet.

Community Environment: Painesville is a city of 30,000 residents located 25 miles east of Cleveland and 3 miles from Lake Erie. The surrounding area boasts numerous fine commercial nurseries, the home of President Garfield, maple sugar industries, and the Holden Arboretum. Lake Erie College sponsors an ongoing series of cultural activities at the B. K. Smith Fine Arts Gallery and the C. K. Rickel Theater on the Lake Erie campus. Other community facilities include a variety of churches, the YMCA, and Morley Library, as well as various civic and service organizations.

■ **LAKELAND COMMUNITY COLLEGE**
7700 Clocktower Dr.
Kirtland, OH 44094-5198
Tel: (440)525-7000; Free: 800-589-8520
Fax: (440)525-4330
Web Site: www.lakelandcc.edu
Description: State and locally supported, 2-year, coed. Part of Ohio Department of Higher Education. Awards certificates, transfer associate, and terminal associate degrees. Founded 1967. Setting: 380-acre suburban campus with easy access to Cleveland. Endowment: $35,367. Research spending for the previous fiscal year: $329,211. Educational spending for the previous fiscal year: $5509 per student. Total enrollment: 7,581. Faculty: 405 (103 full-time, 302 part-time). Student-undergrad faculty ratio is 17:1. Full-time: 2,198 students, 51% women, 49% men. Part-time: 5,383 students, 61% women, 39% men. Students come from 5 states and territories, 1 other country. 0.3% American Indian or Alaska Native, non-Hispanic/Latino; 3% Hispanic/Latino; 13% Black or African American, non-Hispanic/Latino; 1% Asian, non-Hispanic/Latino; 0.2% Native Hawaiian or other Pacific Islander, non-Hispanic/Latino; 0.1% international. 5% transferred in. Core. Calendar: semesters. Academic remediation for entering students, ESL program, services for LD students, advanced placement, independent study, distance learning, summer session for credit, part-time degree program, external degree program, adult/continuing education programs, co-op programs and internships. Off campus study. Study abroad program.
Entrance Requirements: Open admission except for allied health programs and Compass testing is required. Options: electronic application, early admission, deferred admission. Required: high school transcript, ACT Compass. Entrance: noncompetitive. Application deadline: 9/1. Notification: continuous until 9/1. Transfer credits accepted: Yes.
Costs Per Year: Application fee: $15. Area resident tuition: $3834 full-time, $127.80 per credit hour part-time. State resident tuition: $4683 full-time, $156.10 per credit hour part-time. Nonresident tuition: $10,023 full-time, $334.10 per credit hour part-time. Mandatory fees: $28 full-time, $14.25 per term part-time. Full-time tuition and fees vary according to course load. Part-time tuition and fees vary according to course load.
Collegiate Environment: Orientation program. Drama-theater group, choral group, student-run newspaper, radio station. Social organizations: 27 open to all; Phi Theta Kappa. Most popular organizations: Campus Activities Board, Lakeland Student Government, Lakeland Signers, Gamer's Guild. Major annual events: Halloween Party, Spring Fling Week, Student Leader Awards Banquet and Casino Night. Student services: health clinic, personal-psychological counseling, women's center. Campus security: 24-hour emergency response devices and patrols, student patrols, late night transport-escort service. Lakeland Community College Library. Operations spending for the previous fiscal year: $1.1 million. 185 computers available on campus for general student use. A campuswide network can be accessed. Students can access the following: online class registration. Staffed computer lab on campus provides training in use of computers, software, and the Internet.
Community Environment: Mentor is located in attractive Lake County, in the northeastern portion of the state along Lake Erie, 20 miles east of Cleveland. The land area amounts to 231 square miles with a total population of 232,800. The county itself consists of two distinctly different areas: a densely populated western end with approximately 68% of the population and a sparsely populated eastern end. The community offers exceptional opportunity for personal and professional growth.

■ **LORAIN COUNTY COMMUNITY COLLEGE**
1005 Abbe Rd., N
Elyria, OH 44035
Tel: (440)365-5222; Free: 800-995-5222
Fax: (440)365-6519
Web Site: www.lorainccc.edu
Description: State and locally supported, 2-year, coed. Part of University System of Ohio. Awards certificates, transfer associate, and terminal associ-

ate degrees. Founded 1963. Setting: 280-acre suburban campus with easy access to Cleveland. Total enrollment: 11,042. Faculty: 316 (62 full-time, 254 part-time). Full-time: 2,956 students, 57% women, 43% men. Part-time: 8,086 students, 63% women, 37% men. Students come from 28 states and territories, 29 other countries, 1% from out-of-state. 0.4% American Indian or Alaska Native, non-Hispanic/Latino; 10% Hispanic/Latino; 9% Black or African American, non-Hispanic/Latino; 1% Asian, non-Hispanic/Latino; 0.1% Native Hawaiian or other Pacific Islander, non-Hispanic/Latino; 0.6% international. 31% 25 or older, 5% transferred in. Retention: 63% of full-time freshmen returned the following year. Core. Calendar: semesters. Academic remediation for entering students, ESL program, services for LD students, advanced placement, self-designed majors, independent study, distance learning, double major, summer session for credit, part-time degree program, adult/continuing education programs, internships. Off campus study. Study abroad program.
Entrance Requirements: Open admission Certain Allied Health programs have selective admission processes. Please visit www.lorainccc.edu for more details. Option: electronic application. Required for some: high school transcript. Entrance: noncompetitive. Application deadline: rolling. Notification: continuous. Transfer credits accepted: Yes.
Costs Per Year: Application fee: $0. Area resident tuition: $3,041 full-time, $116.98 per credit hour part-time. State resident tuition: $3,696 full-time, $142.16 per credit hour part-time. Nonresident tuition: $7,637 full-time, $293.73 per credit hour part-time. Mandatory fees: $444 full-time, $17.06 per credit hour part-time.
Collegiate Environment: Orientation program. Drama-theater group, choral group, student-run newspaper, radio station. Most popular organizations: Phi Theta Kappa, Black Progressives, Los Unidos, Student Nurses Association, Student Dental Hygienist Club. Major annual events: Fall Picnic, Spring Picnic, Family Fest. Student services: legal services, health clinic, personal-psychological counseling, women's center. Campus security: 24-hour emergency response devices and patrols, late night transport-escort service. Barbara and Mike Bass Library & Community Resource Center plus 1 other. Books: 88,354 (physical), 192,532 (digital/electronic); Serial titles: 919 (physical), 132,353 (digital/electronic); Databases: 178. Weekly public service hours: 54; students can reserve study rooms. 400 computers available on campus for general student use. Computer purchase/lease plans available. A campuswide network can be accessed from off-campus. Students can access the following: online class registration. Staffed computer lab on campus provides training in use of computers, software, and the Internet.
Community Environment: Situated in the far northeast corner of the city of Elyria and 26 miles west of Cleveland, the campus is just four miles from downtown Elyria, a city of over 57,500 and the county seat; eight miles to the north lies Lorain, an industrial community on Lake Erie at the mouth of the Black River; its harbor is one of the best on the Great Lakes. One of Ford Motor Co.'s largest assembly plants is located here with Lake Shore Development. Community facilities include churches representing all denominations, YMCA, YWCA, six hospitals, and all leading civic and service organizations. Boating, fishing, swimming, golf, and tennis are some of the outdoor sports. Job opportunities are excellent. Lakeview Park is noted for its extensive rose garden and colorfully lighted fountain. Cascade Park is a favorite recreation area and is located in the city of Elyria. A rapidly expanding network of major state and interstate highways, including the nearby Ohio Turnpike, makes the college easily reached by automobile.

■ **LOURDES UNIVERSITY**
6832 Convent Blvd.
Sylvania, OH 43560-2898
Tel: (419)885-3211; Free: 800-878-3210
Fax: (419)882-3987
Web Site: www.lourdes.edu
Description: Independent Roman Catholic, comprehensive, coed. Awards associate, bachelor's, and master's degrees. Founded 1958. Setting: 113-acre suburban campus with easy access to Toledo. Endowment: $11 million. Educational spending for the previous fiscal year: $10,552 per student. Total enrollment: 1,426. Faculty: 185 (59 full-time, 126 part-time). Student-undergrad faculty ratio is 12:1. 919 applied, 89% were admitted. 10% from top 10% of their high school class, 29% from top quarter, 65% from top half. Full-time: 842 students, 62% women, 38% men. Part-time: 283 students, 73% women, 27% men. Students come from 32 states and territories, 7 other countries, 25% from out-of-state. 0.4% American Indian or Alaska Native, non-Hispanic/Latino; 9% Hispanic/Latino; 9% Black or African American, non-Hispanic/Latino; 0.4% Asian, non-Hispanic/Latino; 0.1% Na-

tive Hawaiian or other Pacific Islander, non-Hispanic/Latino; 0.9% international. 22% 25 or older, 35% live on campus, 10% transferred in. Retention: 72% of full-time freshmen returned the following year. Academic areas with the most degrees conferred: health professions and related sciences; business/marketing; interdisciplinary studies. Core. Calendar: semesters. Academic remediation for entering students, services for LD students, advanced placement, self-designed majors, freshman honors college, honors program, independent study, distance learning, double major, summer session for credit, part-time degree program, adult/continuing education programs, internships. Study abroad program. ROTC: Army (c), Air Force (c).

Entrance Requirements: Options: electronic application, early admission, deferred admission. Required: high school transcript, minimum 2.5 high school GPA, SAT or ACT. Entrance: moderately difficult. Application deadline: rolling. Notification: continuous. Transfer credits accepted: Yes.

Costs Per Year: Application fee: $25. One-time mandatory fee: $270. Comprehensive fee: $32,580 includes full-time tuition ($21,700), mandatory fees ($780), and college room and board ($10,100). College room only: $5400. Full-time tuition and fees vary according to course load. Room and board charges vary according to board plan and housing facility. Part-time tuition: $725 per credit hour. Part-time mandatory fees: $230 per term. Part-time tuition and fees vary according to course load.

Collegiate Environment: Orientation program. Drama-theater group, choral group. Social organizations: 20 open to all. Most popular organizations: Student Government Association, Student Nurses Association, Orbis Ars, Future Doctors of America, Active Minds. Major annual events: Farewell Fest, Wing and Sings, Build a Wolf. Student services: health clinic, personal-psychological counseling. Campus security: 24-hour emergency response devices and patrols, late night transport-escort service, controlled dormitory access. Duns Scotus Library plus 1 other. Books: 54,138 (physical), 325,641 (digital/electronic); Serial titles: 486 (physical), 2,057 (digital/electronic). Study areas open 24 hours, 5-7 days a week. Operations spending for the previous fiscal year: $393,170. 264 computers available on campus for general student use. Computer purchase/lease plans available. A campuswide network can be accessed from student residence rooms and from off campus. Students can access the following: online class registration, online course content, portfolio access, RRS news feeds, online polls, webcasting, business technologies. Staffed computer lab on campus provides training in use of computers, software, and the Internet.

Community Environment: Sylvania is a suburban area with a temperate climate; plane and bus transportation is available. Job opportunities are good for students. Community facilities include a public library, adequate hospital services, churches, numerous major civic and service organizations, and shopping facilities.

■ **MALONE UNIVERSITY**
2600 Cleveland Ave., NW
Canton, OH 44709
Tel: (330)471-8100; Free: 800-521-1146
Fax: (330)454-6977
E-mail: admissions@malone.edu
Web Site: www.malone.edu

Description: Independent, comprehensive, coed, affiliated with Evangelical Friends Church-Eastern Region. Awards bachelor's and master's degrees. Founded 1892. Setting: 96-acre suburban campus with easy access to Cleveland. Endowment: $19.4 million. Research spending for the previous fiscal year: $456,703. Educational spending for the previous fiscal year: $7464 per student. Total enrollment: 1,729. Faculty: 175 (81 full-time, 94 part-time). Student-undergrad faculty ratio is 12:1. 1,864 applied, 66% were admitted. 15% from top 10% of their high school class, 33% from top quarter, 67% from top half. 6 valedictorians. Full-time: 1,099 students, 57% women, 43% men. Part-time: 234 students, 66% women, 34% men. Students come from 25 states and territories, 11 other countries, 14% from out-of-state. 0.1% American Indian or Alaska Native, non-Hispanic/Latino; 3% Hispanic/Latino; 11% Black or African American, non-Hispanic/Latino; 0.5% Asian, non-Hispanic/Latino; 1% international. 14% 25 or older, 63% live on campus, 3% transferred in. Retention: 70% of full-time freshmen returned the following year. Academic areas with the most degrees conferred: business/marketing; health professions and related sciences; education. Core. Calendar: semesters. Academic remediation for entering students, services for LD students, advanced placement, accelerated degree program, self-designed majors, honors program, independent study, distance learning, double major, summer session for credit, part-time degree program, adult/continuing education programs, internships, graduate courses open to

undergrads. Off campus study at members of the Christian College Consortium, members of the Council for Christian Colleges and Universities. Study abroad program.

Entrance Requirements: Options: electronic application, early admission, deferred admission, international baccalaureate accepted. Required: high school transcript, minimum 2 high school GPA, SAT or ACT. Recommended: interview. Required for some: essay. Entrance: moderately difficult. Application deadline: rolling. Notification: continuous. SAT Reasoning Test deadline: 8/1. Transfer credits accepted: Yes.

Costs Per Year: Application fee: $20. Comprehensive fee: $40,360 includes full-time tuition ($29,900), mandatory fees ($960), and college room and board ($9500). College room only: $4700. Room and board charges vary according to board plan. Part-time tuition: $500 per credit hour. Part-time mandatory fees: $240 per term. Part-time tuition and fees vary according to course load.

Collegiate Environment: Orientation program. Drama-theater group, choral group, marching band, student-run newspaper. Social organizations: 45 open to all; 10 honor societies. Most popular organizations: Celebration Worship Services (and other Spiritual Formation activities), Student Activities Council, Student Senate, FCA (Fellowship of Christian Athletes), intramural athletics. Major annual events: Homecoming, Christmas Celebration, Air Band and Davenport Derby (residence hall programs). Student services: health clinic, personal-psychological counseling. Campus security: 24-hour emergency response devices and patrols, late night transport-escort service, controlled dormitory access. Everett L. Cattell Library plus 1 other. Books: 169,479 (physical), 312,753 (digital/electronic); Serial titles: 2,035 (physical), 39,854 (digital/electronic); Databases: 176. Weekly public service hours: 88. Operations spending for the previous fiscal year: $508,406. 254 computers available on campus for general student use. Computer purchase/lease plans available. A campuswide network can be accessed from student residence rooms and from off campus. Students can access the following: online class registration, online advising, online financial aid information, and online credit card payments. Staffed computer lab on campus provides training in use of computers, software, and the Internet.

Community Environment: Canton is an industrial, residential, and cultural city of 80,000. The city is the home of the Pro Football Hall of Fame, and birthplace of former president William McKinley. A beautiful Cultural Center for the Arts and an extensive park system enhances the city's beauty and provides many cultural and educational opportunities for the students.

■ **MARIETTA COLLEGE**
215 Fifth St.
Marietta, OH 45750-4000
Tel: (740)376-4000; Free: 800-331-7896
Fax: (740)376-4896
E-mail: admit@marietta.edu
Web Site: www.marietta.edu

Description: Independent, comprehensive, coed. Awards associate, bachelor's, and master's degrees. Founded 1835. Setting: 90-acre small town campus. Endowment: $70.3 million. Educational spending for the previous fiscal year: $13,787 per student. Total enrollment: 1,145. Faculty: 171 (98 full-time, 73 part-time). Student-undergrad faculty ratio is 9:1. 1,308 applied, 93% were admitted. 19% from top 10% of their high school class, 41% from top quarter, 74% from top half. Full-time: 954 students, 38% women, 62% men. Part-time: 111 students, 50% women, 50% men. Students come from 31 states and territories, 8 other countries, 33% from out-of-state. 0.2% American Indian or Alaska Native, non-Hispanic/Latino; 2% Hispanic/Latino; 5% Black or African American, non-Hispanic/Latino; 0.8% Asian, non-Hispanic/Latino; 17% international. 6% 25 or older, 70% live on campus, 3% transferred in. Retention: 67% of full-time freshmen returned the following year. Academic areas with the most degrees conferred: engineering; business/marketing; education. Core. Calendar: semesters. Academic remediation for entering students, ESL program, services for LD students, advanced placement, self-designed majors, honors program, independent study, double major, summer session for credit, part-time degree program, adult/continuing education programs, internships. Off campus study at American University, Central College, International Education of Students, The Education Abroad Network, International Studies Abroad, Athena Abroad, Academic Programs International, The Washington Center, Marist in Manhattan. Study abroad program.

Entrance Requirements: Options: electronic application, early admission, deferred admission, international baccalaureate accepted. Required: essay, high school transcript, minimum 2.5 high school GPA, SAT or ACT. Recommended: minimum 3.4 high school GPA, recommendations, interview, SAT

Subject Tests. Entrance: moderately difficult. Application deadline: 7/1. Notification: continuous until 7/1. SAT Reasoning Test deadline: 7/1. SAT Subject Test deadline: 7/1. Transfer credits accepted: Yes.

Costs Per Year: Application fee: $0. Comprehensive fee: $47,370 includes full-time tuition ($35,030), mandatory fees ($1010), and college room and board ($11,330). Full-time tuition and fees vary according to course load. Room and board charges vary according to board plan and housing facility. Part-time tuition: $1170 per credit hour. Part-time tuition varies according to course load.

Collegiate Environment: Orientation program. Drama-theater group, choral group, student-run newspaper, radio station. Social organizations: 80 open to all; national fraternities, national sororities, local fraternities; 14% of eligible men and 22% of eligible women are members. Most popular organizations: Pioneer Activities Council, student government, Panhellenic Council, Inter-Varsity Christian Fellowship, Inter Fraternity Council. Major annual events: Homecoming Weekend, Spirit Week, Family Weekend. Student services: health clinic, personal-psychological counseling. Campus security: 24-hour emergency response devices and patrols, student patrols, late night transport-escort service, controlled dormitory access. Legacy Library. Books: 183,103 (physical), 137,587 (digital/electronic); Serial titles: 230 (physical), 15,786 (digital/electronic); Databases: 186. Weekly public service hours: 95; students can reserve study rooms. Operations spending for the previous fiscal year: $849,847. 475 computers available on campus for general student use. A campuswide network can be accessed from student residence rooms and from off campus. Students can access the following: online class registration. Staffed computer lab on campus provides training in use of computers, software, and the Internet.

Community Environment: Founded in 1788, Marietta, has the distinction of being the first permanent settlement of America's Northwest Territory. The city is rich in history, with stately homes, brick paved streets, sternwheeler festivals, and an antique row of stores. Students have easy access to the town which is located 1 block from the campus. Large urban cities as Pittsburgh, PA and Columbus, OH are within a two-hour drive. Parkersburg, WV, with a population of 32,000, is 20 minutes away. Transportation is readily available. Part-time employment opportunities are available.

■ **MARION TECHNICAL COLLEGE**
1467 Mount Vernon Ave.
Marion, OH 43302-5694
Tel: (740)389-4636
Fax: (740)389-6136
E-mail: enroll@mtc.edu
Web Site: www.mtc.edu

Description: State-supported, 2-year, coed. Part of University System of Ohio. Awards certificates, transfer associate, and terminal associate degrees. Founded 1971. Setting: 180-acre small town campus with easy access to Columbus. Total enrollment: 2,765. Faculty: 185 (35 full-time, 150 part-time). Student-undergrad faculty ratio is 18:1. 0.2% American Indian or Alaska Native, non-Hispanic/Latino; 1% Hispanic/Latino; 5% Black or African American, non-Hispanic/Latino; 0.5% Asian, non-Hispanic/Latino. 49% 25 or older. Retention: 57% of full-time freshmen returned the following year. Calendar: quarters. Academic remediation for entering students, services for LD students, advanced placement, accelerated degree program, self-designed majors, independent study, distance learning, double major, summer session for credit, part-time degree program, adult/continuing education programs, co-op programs and internships. Off campus study at Rhodes State College for Respiratory Care and Occupational Therapist Assistant.

Entrance Requirements: Open admission except for health technologies, allied health, human and social services and criminal justice police academy. Options: electronic application, early admission, deferred admission. Required: high school transcript, ACT Compass or ACT. Recommended: interview. Required for some: minimum 2.5 high school GPA, ACT. Entrance: noncompetitive. Application deadline: rolling. Notification: continuous. Transfer credits accepted: Yes.

Collegiate Environment: Orientation program. Drama-theater group, choral group. Social organizations: 30 open to all. Most popular organizations: outdoor pursuits, Young Republicans, Economics and Business Club, Psychology Club. Major annual events: Welcome Week, Beat Michigan week. Student services: personal-psychological counseling. Marion Campus Library. 280 computers available on campus for general student use. A campuswide network can be accessed from off-campus. Students can access the following: online class registration. Staffed computer lab on campus provides training in use of computers, software, and the Internet.

■ **MERCY COLLEGE OF OHIO**
2221 Madison Ave.
Toledo, OH 43604
Tel: (419)251-1313; Free: 888-80-MERCY
Fax: (419)251-4116
E-mail: kristen.porter@mercycollege.edu
Web Site: www.mercycollege.edu

Description: Independent, comprehensive, coed, affiliated with Roman Catholic Church. Administratively affiliated with Mercy Health. Awards associate, bachelor's, and master's degrees. Founded 1993. Setting: urban campus with easy access to Toledo, OH. Total enrollment: 1,511. Faculty: 219 (51 full-time, 168 part-time). Student-undergrad faculty ratio is 7:1. 232 applied, 56% were admitted. Full-time: 434 students, 84% women, 16% men. Part-time: 1,029 students, 87% women, 13% men. Students come from 30 states and territories, 31% from out-of-state. 0.5% American Indian or Alaska Native, non-Hispanic/Latino; 4% Hispanic/Latino; 11% Black or African American, non-Hispanic/Latino; 2% Asian, non-Hispanic/Latino. 53% 25 or older, 28% transferred in. Retention: 81% of full-time freshmen returned the following year. Academic areas with the most degrees conferred: health professions and related sciences; biological/life sciences. Core. Calendar: semesters. Academic remediation for entering students, services for LD students, advanced placement, accelerated degree program, independent study, distance learning, double major, summer session for credit, part-time degree program, internships.

Entrance Requirements: Options: electronic application, deferred admission, international baccalaureate accepted. Required: high school transcript, minimum 2 high school GPA. Required for some: SAT or ACT. Entrance: moderately difficult. Application deadline: rolling. Notification: continuous. SAT Reasoning Test deadline: 8/15. SAT Subject Test deadline: 8/15. Transfer credits accepted: Yes.

Costs Per Year: Application fee: $0. One-time mandatory fee: $250. Tuition: $12,840 full-time, $472 per credit hour part-time. Mandatory fees: $2400 full-time, $60 per credit hour part-time, $300 per term part-time. Full-time tuition and fees vary according to course load and program. Part-time tuition and fees vary according to course load and program.

Collegiate Environment: Orientation program. Social organizations: 7 open to all. Most popular organizations: American Assembly of Men in Nursing, National Student Nurses Association, Student Government Association. Major annual events: Week of Welcome, Wellness Week. Student services: personal-psychological counseling. Campus security: 24-hour emergency response devices and patrols, late night transport-escort service. Mercy College of Ohio Library. Books: 7,081 (physical), 98,167 (digital/electronic); Serial titles: 334 (physical), 82,313 (digital/electronic); Databases: 15. Weekly public service hours: 57; students can reserve study rooms. 121 computers available on campus for general student use. A campuswide network can be accessed. Students can access the following: online class registration. Staffed computer lab on campus.

■ **MIAMI UNIVERSITY**
Oxford, OH 45056
Tel: (513)529-1809
Fax: (513)529-1550
Web Site: miamioh.edu

Description: State-related, university, coed. Part of Miami University System. Awards associate, bachelor's, master's, and doctoral degrees and post-master's certificates. Founded 1809. Setting: 2,100-acre small town campus with easy access to Cincinnati. System endowment: $534.7 million. Research spending for the previous fiscal year: $14.2 million. Educational spending for the previous fiscal year: $7972 per student. Total enrollment: 19,934. Faculty: 1,312 (994 full-time, 318 part-time). Student-undergrad faculty ratio is 17:1. 30,126 applied, 75% were admitted. 34% from top 10% of their high school class, 66% from top quarter, 92% from top half. 11 National Merit Scholars, 71 valedictorians. Full-time: 16,714 students, 50% women, 50% men. Part-time: 613 students, 49% women, 51% men. Students come from 52 states and territories, 102 other countries, 35% from out-of-state. 0.2% American Indian or Alaska Native, non-Hispanic/Latino; 5% Hispanic/Latino; 3% Black or African American, non-Hispanic/Latino; 2% Asian, non-Hispanic/Latino; 0.1% Native Hawaiian or other Pacific Islander, non-Hispanic/Latino; 15% international. 2% 25 or older, 45% live on campus, 1% transferred in. Retention: 92% of full-time freshmen returned the following year. Academic areas with the most degrees conferred: business/marketing; social sciences; communication/journalism. Core. Calendar: semesters. ESL program, services for LD students, advanced placement, self-designed majors, honors program, independent study, distance learning, double major, summer session for credit, co-op programs and internships, graduate courses open to undergrads. Off campus study at Greater Cincinnati Consortium of Colleges and Universities. Study abroad program. ROTC: Army (c), Naval, Air Force.

Entrance Requirements: Options: electronic application, early decision, early action, deferred admission, international baccalaureate accepted. Required: essay, high school transcript, 1 recommendation, SAT or ACT. Entrance: moderately difficult. Application deadlines: 2/1, 11/1 for early decision, 11/1 for early action. Notification: 3/15, 12/1 for early decision, 12/15 for early action. SAT Reasoning Test deadline: 2/1. Transfer credits accepted: Yes. Applicants placed on waiting list: 1,527. Wait-listed applicants offered admission: 72. Early decision applicants: 852. Early decision applicants admitted: 691. Early action applicants: 19,127. Early action applicants admitted: 16,238.

Costs Per Year: Application fee: $50. State resident tuition: $13,966 full-time. Nonresident tuition: $32,718 full-time. Mandatory fees: $859 full-time. Full-time tuition and fees vary according to location, program, and student level. College room and board: $13,031. College room only: $8063. Room and board charges vary according to board plan, housing facility, and student level. Tuition guaranteed not to increase for student's term of enrollment.

Collegiate Environment: Orientation program. Drama-theater group, choral group, marching band, student-run newspaper, radio station. Social organizations: 549 open to all; national fraternities, national sororities; 19% of eligible men and 29% of eligible women are members. Most popular organizations: CRU (formerly Campus Crusade for Christ), Alpha Phi Omega, College Republicans, 4 Paws for Ability, Best Buddies. Major annual events: Parents' Weekend, Kids' Fest Weekend, Homecoming. Student services: health clinic, personal-psychological counseling, women's center. Campus security: 24-hour emergency response devices and patrols, student patrols, late night transport-escort service, controlled dormitory access. 8,179 college housing spaces available; 7,869 were occupied in 2018-19. Freshmen guaranteed college housing. On-campus residence required through sophomore year. Options: coed, men-only, women-only housing available. King Library plus 3 others. Books: 1.3 million (physical), 773,916 (digital/electronic); Serial titles: 41,080 (physical), 287,002 (digital/electronic); Databases: 778. Weekly public service hours: 168; study areas open 24 hours, 5-7 days a week; students can reserve study rooms. Operations spending for the previous fiscal year: $11.9 million. 652 computers available on campus for general student use. Computer purchase/lease plans available. A campuswide network can be accessed from student residence rooms and from off campus. Students can access the following: online class registration. Staffed computer lab on campus (open 24 hours a day) provides training in use of computers, software, and the Internet.

Community Environment: A college town with many beautiful old homes, Oxford, the location of Miami University, is where Professor McGuffey compiled the first of his readers. Recreational facilities provide for tennis, bowling, golf, swimming. The Hueston Woods State Park also provides for swimming , boating, and picnicking.

■ **MIAMI UNIVERSITY HAMILTON**
1601 Peck Blvd.
Hamilton, OH 45011-3399
Tel: (513)785-3000
E-mail: nelsona3@muohio.edu
Web Site: regionals.miamioh.edu

Description: State-supported, comprehensive, coed. Part of Miami University System. Awards associate, bachelor's, and master's degrees (degrees awarded by Miami University main campus). Founded 1968. Setting: 78-acre suburban campus with easy access to Cincinnati. Total enrollment: 4,194. Faculty: 224 (84 full-time, 140 part-time). Student-undergrad faculty ratio is 21:1. Full-time: 3,280 students, 53% women, 47% men. Part-time: 902 students, 62% women, 38% men. 24% 25 or older, 5% transferred in. Core. Calendar: semesters plus summer sessions. Academic remediation for entering students, ESL program, services for LD students, advanced placement, self-designed majors, honors program, distance learning, double major, summer session for credit, part-time degree program, adult/continuing education programs, co-op programs and internships. Study abroad program. ROTC: Naval (c), Air Force (c).

Entrance Requirements: Open admission except for nursing program, transfer students. Option: electronic application. Required: high school transcript. Entrance: noncompetitive. Application deadline: rolling. Notification: continuous.

Collegiate Environment: Orientation program. Drama-theater group. Social

organizations: 16 open to all. Most popular organizations: Student Government, Campus Activities Committee, Ski Club, Student Nursing Association, OWLS (organization for wiser and world-wide learners). Major annual events: New Student Orientation, Spring Fest, Fall Picnic. Student services: personal-psychological counseling. Campus security: 24-hour emergency response devices and patrols, late night transport-escort service. Rentschler Library. 300 computers available on campus for general student use. Computer purchase/lease plans available. A campuswide network can be accessed from off-campus. Students can access the following: online class registration. Staffed computer lab on campus provides training in use of computers, software, and the Internet.

Community Environment: The town of Hamilton is easily accessible from most of northern and western Hamilton County via several state and interstate routes. Employment opportunities are good in this area.

■ **MIAMI UNIVERSITY MIDDLETOWN**
4200 E University Blvd.
Middletown, OH 45042-3497
Tel: (513)727-3200; Free: 866-426-4643
Fax: (513)727-3223
E-mail: cantondm@muohio.edu
Web Site: regionals.miamioh.edu

Description: State-supported, 4-year, coed. Part of Miami University System. Awards associate and bachelor's degrees (also offers up to 2 years of most bachelor's degree programs offered at Miami University main campus). Founded 1966. Setting: 141-acre small town campus with easy access to Cincinnati, Dayton. Total enrollment: 2,660. Faculty: 209 (79 full-time, 130 part-time). Student-undergrad faculty ratio is 13:1. 28% 25 or older. Retention: 71% of full-time freshmen returned the following year. Calendar: semesters. Academic remediation for entering students, services for LD students, advanced placement, self-designed majors, independent study, distance learning, double major, summer session for credit, part-time degree program, adult/continuing education programs, co-op programs and internships. Off campus study at members of the Greater Cincinnati Consortium of Colleges and Universities. Study abroad program. ROTC: Air Force (c).

Entrance Requirements: Open admission except for nursing program. Options: electronic application, early admission, deferred admission. Required: high school transcript. Entrance: noncompetitive. Application deadline: rolling. Notification: continuous.

Collegiate Environment: Orientation program. Social organizations: 28 open to all. Most popular organizations: student radio station, SEAL (Save Every Animal by Learning), Student Advisory Council, Model United Nations, Program Board. Major annual events: Haunted Trails, End of Year Picnic, MUMOXMUH. Student services: personal-psychological counseling, women's center. Campus security: 24-hour patrols, late night transport-escort service. Gardner-Harvey Library. 180 computers available on campus for general student use. A campuswide network can be accessed from off-campus. Students can access the following: online class registration. Staffed computer lab on campus.

Community Environment: Middletown, population 51,472, is an industrial city in Butler County, SW Ohio. Its industries include aircraft parts, steel, and paper products.

■ **THE MODERN COLLEGE OF DESIGN**
1725 E David Rd.
Kettering, OH 45440
Tel: (937)294-0592; Free: 877-300-9866
Fax: (937)294-5869
E-mail: mariesa@saa.edu
Web Site: www.saa.edu

Description: Proprietary, 2-year, coed. Awards terminal associate degrees. Founded 1983. Setting: 5-acre suburban campus with easy access to Columbus. Educational spending for the previous fiscal year: $4246 per student. Total enrollment: 194. Faculty: 21 (12 full-time, 9 part-time). Student-undergrad faculty ratio is 14:1. 547 applied, 49% were admitted. Full-time: 191 students, 70% women, 30% men. Part-time: 3 students, 33% women, 67% men. Students come from 3 states and territories, 9% from out-of-state. 1% American Indian or Alaska Native, non-Hispanic/Latino; 4% Hispanic/Latino; 6% Black or African American, non-Hispanic/Latino; 2% Asian, non-Hispanic/Latino. 1% 25 or older, 5% transferred in. Retention: 79% of full-time freshmen returned the following year. Core. Calendar: semesters.

Entrance Requirements: Option: electronic application. Required: high school transcript, minimum 2 high school GPA, interview. Required for some: essay, 2 recommendations. Entrance: minimally difficult. Transfer credits accepted: Yes.

Costs Per Year: Application fee: $0. Tuition: $27,778 full-time. Mandatory fees: $1070 full-time.

Collegiate Environment: Orientation program. Social organizations: 3 open to all. Most popular organizations: Fine Art Club, Photography Club, Student Senate. Major annual events: Halloween Party, Bowling Party, Fall Picnic. Student services: personal-psychological counseling. SAA Library. Books: 881 (physical), 45,000 (digital/electronic); Serial titles: 32 (physical); Databases: 2. Weekly public service hours: 60. Operations spending for the previous fiscal year: $28,335.

■ MOUNT CARMEL COLLEGE OF NURSING

127 S Davis Ave.
Columbus, OH 43222
Tel: (614)234-5800; Free: 800-556-6942
E-mail: kcampbell@mccn.edu
Web Site: www.mccn.edu

Description: Independent, comprehensive, coed. Administratively affiliated with Mount Carmel Health System. Awards bachelor's, master's, and doctoral degrees and post-master's certificates. Founded 1903. Setting: urban campus with easy access to Columbus. System endowment: $1.9 million. Total enrollment: 1,090. Faculty: 120 (57 full-time, 63 part-time). Student-undergrad faculty ratio is 11:1. 208 applied, 63% were admitted. 15% from top 10% of their high school class, 46% from top quarter, 87% from top half. Full-time: 606 students, 90% women, 10% men. Part-time: 267 students, 89% women, 11% men. 7% from out-of-state. 0.3% American Indian or Alaska Native, non-Hispanic/Latino; 2% Hispanic/Latino; 11% Black or African American, non-Hispanic/Latino; 2% Asian, non-Hispanic/Latino; 0.1% Native Hawaiian or other Pacific Islander, non-Hispanic/Latino. 32% 25 or older, 1% live on campus, 15% transferred in. Retention: 64% of full-time freshmen returned the following year. Academic area with the most degrees conferred: health professions and related sciences. Core. Calendar: semesters. Advanced placement, accelerated degree program, honors program, distance learning, summer session for credit, adult/continuing education programs. Off campus study at Columbus State Community College, Ohio University Lancaster, The Ohio State University. ROTC: Army (c), Air Force (c).

Entrance Requirements: Option: electronic application. Required: essay, high school transcript, activities/interests resume. Recommended: minimum 3 high school GPA. Required for some: interview, ACT. Entrance: moderately difficult. Notification: continuous. Transfer credits accepted: Yes.

Costs Per Year: Application fee: $30. Tuition: $20,461 full-time. Mandatory fees: $884 full-time. College room only: $5000.

Collegiate Environment: Orientation program. Social organizations: 5 open to all. Most popular organizations: Campus Ministry, Student Nurses Association of Mount Carmel (SNAM), Mount Carmel Rho Omicron Chapter of Sigma Theta Tau International Honor Society, Student Government Association (SGA), Student Ambassador Program. Major annual events: Convocation, Graduation. Student services: health clinic, personal-psychological counseling. Campus security: 24-hour emergency response devices and patrols, late night transport-escort service, controlled dormitory access. Freshmen given priority for college housing. On-campus residence required through sophomore year. Option: coed housing available. The Mount Carmel Health Sciences Library plus 1 other. Books: 8,163 (physical), 297,441 (digital/electronic); Serial titles: 683 (physical), 48,768 (digital/electronic); Databases: 178. Weekly public service hours: 61; study areas open 24 hours, 5-7 days a week; students can reserve study rooms. 25 computers available on campus for general student use. A campuswide network can be accessed from student residence rooms. Students can access the following: online class registration.

■ MOUNT ST. JOSEPH UNIVERSITY

5701 Delhi Rd.
Cincinnati, OH 45233-1670
Tel: (513)244-4200; Free: 800-654-9314
Fax: (513)244-4629
E-mail: admissions@msj.edu
Web Site: www.msj.edu

Description: Independent Roman Catholic, comprehensive, coed. Awards associate, bachelor's, master's, and doctoral degrees. Founded 1920. Setting: 92-acre suburban campus with easy access to Cincinnati, Ohio. Endowment: $39.7 million. Educational spending for the previous fiscal year: $8252 per student. Total enrollment: 2,168. Faculty: 220 (99 full-time, 121 part-time). Student-undergrad faculty ratio is 11:1. 1,832 applied, 60% were admitted. 11% from top 10% of their high school class, 33% from top quarter, 72% from top half. Full-time: 1,006 students, 53% women, 47% men. Part-time: 442 students, 73% women, 27% men. Students come from 16 states and territories, 18% from out-of-state. 0.2% American Indian or Alaska Native, non-Hispanic/Latino; 2% Hispanic/Latino; 10% Black or African American, non-Hispanic/Latino; 0.4% Asian, non-Hispanic/Latino; 0.1% Native Hawaiian or other Pacific Islander, non-Hispanic/Latino; 0.2% international. 12% 25 or older, 27% live on campus, 3% transferred in. Retention: 73% of full-time freshmen returned the following year. Academic areas with the most degrees conferred: health professions and related sciences; business/marketing; education. Core. Calendar: semesters. Academic remediation for entering students, services for LD students, advanced placement, accelerated degree program, honors program, independent study, distance learning, double major, summer session for credit, part-time degree program, co-op programs and internships, graduate courses open to undergrads. Off campus study at Art Academy of Cincinnati, The Athenaeum, Chatfield College, Cincinnati Christian University (formerly Cincinnati Bible College and Seminary), Cincinnati State Technical and Community College, Gateway Community and Technical College, God's Bible School and College; Good Samaritan College of Nursing and Health Sciences, Hebrew Union College-Jewish Institute of Religion, Miami University, Mount St. Joseph University, Northern Kentucky University, Thomas More College, Union Institute and University, University of Cincinnati, W. Study abroad program. ROTC: Army (c), Air Force (c).

Entrance Requirements: Options: electronic application, deferred admission, international baccalaureate accepted. Required: high school transcript, SAT or ACT. Recommended: minimum 3 high school GPA. Entrance: minimally difficult. Notification: continuous. SAT Reasoning Test deadline: 6/1. SAT Subject Test deadline: 6/1. Transfer credits accepted: Yes.

Costs Per Year: Application fee: $25. Comprehensive fee: $39,542 includes full-time tuition ($29,100), mandatory fees ($1000), and college room and board ($9442). Full-time tuition and fees vary according to course load, location, and reciprocity agreements. Room and board charges vary according to board plan, housing facility, and location. Part-time tuition: $540 per credit hour. Part-time tuition varies according to course load, location, and reciprocity agreements.

Collegiate Environment: Orientation program. Drama-theater group, choral group, marching band, student-run newspaper. Social organizations: 44 open to all; national fraternities. Most popular organizations: Black Student Union, Campus Activities Board, Student Government Association, Group Fitness, Residence Hall Council. Major annual events: Bingo, Homecoming Tailgate, Mount Madness. Student services: health clinic, personal-psychological counseling. Campus security: 24-hour emergency response devices and patrols, late night transport-escort service. 493 college housing spaces available; 385 were occupied in 2018-19. Freshmen given priority for college housing. On-campus residence required through sophomore year. Option: coed housing available. Archbishop Alter Library. Books: 49,354 (physical), 132,008 (digital/electronic); Serial titles: 76 (physical), 30,812 (digital/electronic); Databases: 143. Weekly public service hours: 82. Operations spending for the previous fiscal year: $473,965. 172 computers available on campus for general student use. A campuswide network can be accessed from student residence rooms and from off campus. Students can access the following: online class registration, wireless printing, storage space. Staffed computer lab on campus (open 24 hours a day) provides training in use of computers, software, and the Internet.

Community Environment: See University of Cincinnati.

■ MOUNT VERNON NAZARENE UNIVERSITY

800 Martinsburg Rd.
Mount Vernon, OH 43050-9500
Tel: (740)392-6868; Free: 866-462-6868
E-mail: admissions@mvnu.edu
Web Site: www.mvnu.edu

Description: Independent Nazarene, comprehensive, coed. Awards associate, bachelor's, and master's degrees. Founded 1968. Setting: 332-acre small town campus with easy access to Columbus. Endowment: $19.7 million. Educational spending for the previous fiscal year: $6559 per student. Total enrollment: 2,222. Faculty: 251 (75 full-time, 176 part-time). Student-undergrad faculty ratio is 14:1. 1,187 applied, 77% were admitted. 22% from top 10% of their high school class, 43% from top quarter, 79% from top half. Full-time: 1,439 students, 62% women, 38% men. Part-time: 389 students, 67% women, 33% men. Students come from 31 states and territories, 13 other countries, 8% from out-of-state. 0.1% American Indian or Alaska Native, non-Hispanic/Latino; 2% Hispanic/Latino; 3% Black or African American, non-Hispanic/Latino; 0.6% Asian, non-Hispanic/Latino; 0.1% Native Hawaiian or other Pacific Islander, non-Hispanic/Latino; 0.3% international. 22% 25 or older, 71% live on campus, 1% transferred in. Retention: 79% of full-time freshmen returned the following year. Academic areas with the most degrees conferred: business/marketing; public administration and social services; health professions and related sciences. Core. Calendar: semesters. Academic remediation for entering students, services for LD students, advanced placement, honors program, independent study, distance learning, double major, summer session for credit, part-time degree program, adult/continuing education programs, internships. Off campus study at Kenyon College, and Coalition for Christian Colleges and Universities. Study abroad program.

Entrance Requirements: Options: electronic application, deferred admission, international baccalaureate accepted. Required: essay, high school transcript, minimum 2.5 high school GPA, 2 recommendations, SAT or ACT. Entrance: moderately difficult. Application deadline: 7/15. Notification: 9/1. SAT Reasoning Test deadline: 7/1. SAT Subject Test deadline: 7/1. Transfer credits accepted: Yes.

Costs Per Year: Application fee: $25. Comprehensive fee: $37,364 includes full-time tuition ($28,944), mandatory fees ($250), and college room and board ($8170). College room only: $4564. Full-time tuition and fees vary according to program. Part-time tuition: $803 per credit hour. Part-time tuition varies according to course load and program.

Collegiate Environment: Orientation program. Drama-theater group, choral group, student-run newspaper, radio station. Social organizations: 25 open to all. Most popular organizations: Campus Ministry Groups, Student Government Association, Student Education Association, Drama Club, Music Department Ensembles. Major annual events: Welcome Week, Athletic Events and Concerts, Friday Night Live. Student services: health clinic, personal-psychological counseling. Campus security: 24-hour emergency response devices and patrols, late night transport-escort service, controlled dormitory access. Thorne Library/Learning Resource Center. Books: 100,952 (physical), 790 (digital/electronic); Serial titles: 900 (physical), 29,195 (digital/electronic); Databases: 242. Weekly public service hours: 93; study areas open 24 hours, 5-7 days a week; students can reserve study rooms. Operations spending for the previous fiscal year: $333,011. 250 computers available on campus for general student use. A campuswide network can be accessed from student residence rooms and from off campus. Students can access the following: online class registration. Staffed computer lab on campus provides training in use of computers, software, and the Internet.

■ MUSKINGUM UNIVERSITY

163 Stormont St.
New Concord, OH 43762
Tel: (740)826-8211; Free: 800-752-6082
Fax: (740)826-8404
E-mail: adminfo@muskingum.edu
Web Site: www.muskingum.edu

Description: Independent, comprehensive, coed, affiliated with Presbyterian Church (U.S.A.). Awards bachelor's and master's degrees. Founded 1837. Setting: 245-acre small town campus with easy access to Columbus. Endowment: $74.3 million. Educational spending for the previous fiscal year: $9664 per student. Total enrollment: 2,410. Faculty: 148 (98 full-time, 50 part-time). Student-undergrad faculty ratio is 12:1. 2,175 applied, 72% were admitted. 12% from top 10% of their high school class, 35% from top quarter, 71% from top half. 8 valedictorians, 30 student government officers. Full-time: 1,353 students, 52% women, 48% men. Part-time: 263 students, 74% women, 26% men. Students come from 22 states and territories, 4 other countries, 9% from out-of-state. 0.2% American Indian or Alaska Native, non-Hispanic/Latino; 2% Hispanic/Latino; 5% Black or African American, non-Hispanic/Latino; 0.7% Asian, non-Hispanic/Latino; 4% international. 14% 25 or older, 64% live on campus, 4% transferred in. Retention: 76% of full-time freshmen returned the following year. Academic areas with the most degrees conferred: health professions and related sciences; business/marketing; biological/life sciences; psychology; education. Core. Calendar: semesters. ESL program, services for LD students, advanced placement, accelerated degree program, self-designed majors, independent study, distance learning, double major, summer session for credit, part-time degree program, external degree program, adult/continuing education programs, internships, graduate courses open to undergrads. Off campus study. Study abroad program.

Entrance Requirements: Options: electronic application, early admission, deferred admission, international baccalaureate accepted. Required: high school transcript, minimum 2 high school GPA, SAT or ACT. Recommended: essay, minimum 3 high school GPA, 1 recommendation, interview. Entrance: moderately difficult. Notification: continuous. SAT Reasoning Test deadline: 7/1. Transfer credits accepted: Yes.

Costs Per Year: Application fee: $0. One-time mandatory fee: $250. Comprehensive fee: $40,640 includes full-time tuition ($28,100), mandatory fees ($778), and college room and board ($11,762). College room only: $5860. Part-time tuition: $625 per credit hour.

Collegiate Environment: Orientation program. Drama-theater group, choral group, marching band, student-run newspaper, radio station. Social organizations: 85 open to all; national fraternities, national sororities, local fraternities, local sororities; 26% of eligible men and 37% of eligible women are members. Most popular organizations: Campus Crusade for Christ (CRU), Greek Life, Muskingum Programming Board, Game Club, Multicultural Association:Black Student Union. Major annual events: Involvement Fair, Muskiepalooza, Varsity Revue/Homecoming. Student services: health clinic, personal-psychological counseling, women's center. Campus security: 24-hour emergency response devices and patrols, late night transport-escort service, controlled dormitory access. 1,096 college housing spaces available; 855 were occupied in 2018-19. Freshmen guaranteed college housing. On-campus residence required through junior year. Options: coed, men-only, women-only housing available. Roberta A. Smith Library. Books: 100,648 (physical), 368,006 (digital/electronic); Serial titles: 1,085 (physical), 77,990 (digital/electronic); Databases: 282. Weekly public service hours: 89; students can reserve study rooms. Operations spending for the previous fiscal year: $741,517. 266 computers available on campus for general student use. A campuswide network can be accessed from student residence rooms and from off campus. Students can access the following: online class registration. Staffed computer lab on campus provides training in use of computers, software, and the Internet.

Community Environment: New Concord is the boyhood home of John H. Glenn, Jr., the first American astronaut to orbit the earth. Also of interest is the log cabin birthplace of William Rainey Harper, first president of the University of Chicago and an alumnus of Muskingum College. Recreational activities in the area include golf, boating, fishing, hunting, and skating.

■ NORTH CENTRAL STATE COLLEGE

2441 Kenwood Cir.
Mansfield, OH 44901-0698
Tel: (419)755-4800; Free: 888-755-4899
Fax: (419)755-4750
E-mail: nfletcher@ncstatecollege.edu
Web Site: www.ncstatecollege.edu

Description: State-supported, 2-year, coed. Part of Ohio Board of Regents. Awards certificates and terminal associate degrees. Founded 1961. Setting: 600-acre suburban campus with easy access to Cleveland, Columbus. Total enrollment: 3,148. 43% 25 or older. Calendar: quarters. Academic remediation for entering students, services for LD students, advanced placement, self-designed majors, independent study, distance learning, summer session for credit, part-time degree program, adult/continuing education programs, internships.

Entrance Requirements: Open admission. Options: early admission, deferred admission. Required for some: high school transcript. Entrance: noncompetitive. Application deadline: rolling. Notification: continuous.

Collegiate Environment: Orientation program. Choral group, student-run radio station. Student services: personal-psychological counseling. Campus security: 24-hour emergency response devices and patrols, late night transport-escort service. Bromfield Library plus 1 other.

Community Environment: See Ohio State University - Mansfield Campus.

■ THE NORTH COAST COLLEGE

11724 Detroit Ave.
Lakewood, OH 44107
Tel: (216)221-8584
E-mail: rreihard@vmcad.edu
Web Site: www.thencc.edu

Description: Proprietary, 4-year, coed. Awards associate and bachelor's degrees. Founded 1966. Setting: urban campus with easy access to Cleveland. Total enrollment: 108. Student-undergrad faculty ratio is 12:1. 88 applied. 26% 25 or older. Retention: 62% of full-time freshmen returned the following year. Core. Calendar: quarters. Academic remediation for entering students, services for LD students, independent study, distance learning, summer session for credit, part-time degree program, adult/continuing education programs, internships.

Entrance Requirements: Options: electronic application, early admission, deferred admission. Required: essay, high school transcript, minimum 2 high school GPA, SAT or ACT. Recommended: 1 recommendation, interview. Required for some: entrance evaluation test, Wonderlic aptitude test. Entrance: moderately difficult. Application deadlines: rolling, rolling for nonresidents. Transfer credits accepted: Yes.

Collegiate Environment: Orientation program. Student services: personal-psychological counseling. Campus security: 24-hour emergency response devices. VMCAD Library.

■ **NORTHWEST STATE COMMUNITY COLLEGE**
22-600 State Rte. 34
Archbold, OH 43502-9542
Tel: (419)267-5511; Free: 855-267-5511
Fax: (419)267-3688
E-mail: apotts@northweststate.edu
Web Site: www.northweststate.edu

Description: State-supported, 2-year, coed. Part of Ohio Board of Regents. Awards certificates, transfer associate, and terminal associate degrees. Founded 1968. Setting: 80-acre rural campus with easy access to Toledo. Educational spending for the previous fiscal year: $5364 per student. Total enrollment: 3,614. Faculty: 142 (42 full-time, 100 part-time). Student-undergrad faculty ratio is 27:1. 1,360 applied, 100% were admitted. 11% from top quarter of their high school class, 48% from top half. Full-time: 713 students, 59% women, 41% men. Part-time: 2,901 students, 43% women, 57% men. Students come from 6 states and territories, 2 other countries, 4% from out-of-state. 0.1% American Indian or Alaska Native, non-Hispanic/Latino; 6% Hispanic/Latino; 3% Black or African American, non-Hispanic/Latino; 0.7% Asian, non-Hispanic/Latino. 53% 25 or older, 3% transferred in. Core. Calendar: semesters. Academic remediation for entering students, services for LD students, advanced placement, self-designed majors, independent study, distance learning, double major, summer session for credit, part-time degree program, external degree program, adult/continuing education programs, co-op programs and internships. Off campus study.

Entrance Requirements: Open admission. Options: electronic application, early admission, deferred admission. Required: high school transcript. Required for some: minimum 2.5 high school GPA, interview, NLN PAX with a relative score greater than or equal to 50 in each of the 3 sections for nursing. Entrance: noncompetitive. Application deadline: rolling. Notification: continuous. Transfer credits accepted: Yes.

Costs Per Year: Application fee: $0. One-time mandatory fee: $75. State resident tuition: $4,016 full-time, $167.33 per credit hour part-time. Nonresident tuition: $7,888 full-time, $328.66 per credit hour part-time. Mandatory fees: $82 full-time, $41 per term part-time. Full-time tuition and fees vary according to reciprocity agreements. Part-time tuition and fees vary according to reciprocity agreements.

Collegiate Environment: Orientation program. Social organizations: 5 open to all. Most popular organizations: Student Body Organziation (SBO), Students for Community Outreach and Awareness (SCOA), Phi Theta Kappa (PTK), Kappa Beta Delta (KBD), ev/Motorsports. Major annual events: Chili Cook-Off, Christmas for Kids, Spring Fling. Student services: personal-psychological counseling. Campus security: 24-hour emergency response devices, security patrols. Northwest State Community College Library plus 1 other. Operations spending for the previous fiscal year: $300,464. 570 computers available on campus for general student use. A campuswide network can be accessed. Students can access the following: online class registration. Staffed computer lab on campus provides training in use of computers, software, and the Internet.

Community Environment: The campus is in rural setting with a small town six miles to the north. The major metropolitan area of Toledo is 50 miles northeast, within easy access by major highways.

■ **NOTRE DAME COLLEGE**
4545 College Rd.
South Euclid, OH 44121-4293
Tel: (216)381-1680; Free: 877-NDC-OHIO
Fax: (216)381-3802
E-mail: admissinos@ndc.edu
Web Site: www.notredamecollege.edu

Description: Independent Roman Catholic, comprehensive, coed. Awards associate, bachelor's, and master's degrees. Founded 1922. Setting: 53-acre suburban campus with easy access to Cleveland. Endowment: $7.7 million. Educational spending for the previous fiscal year: $4807 per student. Total enrollment: 1,393. Faculty: 118 (34 full-time, 84 part-time). Student-undergrad faculty ratio is 13:1. 1,255 applied, 52% were admitted. 6% from top 10% of their high school class, 20% from top quarter, 57% from top half. Full-time: 793 students, 61% women, 39% men. Part-time: 447 students, 75% women, 25% men. Students come from 17 states and territories, 19 other countries, 11% from out-of-state. 22% 25 or older, 44% live on campus, 4% transferred in. Retention: 65% of full-time freshmen returned the following year. Core. Calendar: semesters. Academic remediation for entering students, services for LD students, advanced placement, accelerated degree program, self-designed majors, independent study, distance learning, double major, summer session for credit, part-time degree program, adult/continuing education programs, co-op programs and internships. Off campus study at members of the Northeast Ohio Commission on Higher Education. Study abroad program.

Entrance Requirements: Options: electronic application, deferred admission. Required: essay, high school transcript, minimum 2.0 high school GPA, interview, SAT or ACT. Recommended: minimum 2.5 high school GPA. Entrance: moderately difficult. Application deadline: rolling. Notification: continuous.

Collegiate Environment: Orientation program. Drama-theater group, choral group, student-run newspaper. Social organizations: 32 open to all. Most popular organizations: Undergraduate Student Senate, Resident Association Board, International Students/Multicultural Club, IHOP (I Help Other People), Bowling Club. Major annual events: Christmas Happening, Finals Week Stress Free Zone, All-Campus Picnic. Student services: personal-psychological counseling. Campus security: 24-hour emergency response devices and patrols, late night transport-escort service, controlled dormitory access. Clara Fritzsche Library. Operations spending for the previous fiscal year: $238,762. 65 computers available on campus for general student use. A campuswide network can be accessed. Staffed computer lab on campus.

■ **OBERLIN COLLEGE**
173 W Lorain St.
Oberlin, OH 44074
Tel: (440)775-8121; Free: 800-622-OBIE
Fax: (440)775-8886
E-mail: college.admissions@oberlin.edu
Web Site: www.oberlin.edu

Description: Independent, comprehensive, coed. Awards bachelor's and master's degrees. Founded 1833. Setting: 440-acre small town campus with easy access to Cleveland. Endowment: $820.3 million. Total enrollment: 2,853. Faculty: 381. Student-undergrad faculty ratio is 10:1. 7,762 applied, 34% were admitted. 58% from top 10% of their high school class, 79% from top quarter, 97% from top half. Full-time: 2,793 students, 58% women, 42% men. Part-time: 34 students, 50% women, 50% men. Students come from 52 states and territories, 46 other countries, 94% from out-of-state. 8% Hispanic/Latino; 5% Black or African American, non-Hispanic/Latino; 4% Asian, non-Hispanic/Latino; 0.1% Native Hawaiian or other Pacific Islander, non-Hispanic/Latino; 10% international. 93% live on campus, 1% transferred in. Retention: 91% of full-time freshmen returned the following year. Academic areas with the most degrees conferred: visual and performing arts; social sciences; biological/life sciences. Core. Calendar: 4-1-4. ESL program, services for LD students, advanced placement, self-designed majors, honors program, independent study, double major, part-time degree program, internships. Off campus study at Great Lakes Colleges Association (consortium). Study abroad program.

Entrance Requirements: Options: electronic application, early admission, early decision, deferred admission, international baccalaureate accepted. Required: essay, high school transcript, 2 recommendations, SAT or ACT. Recommended: interview. Required for some: interview, audition for the Conservatory of Music, detailed portfolio for homeschooled students, SAT and SAT Subject Tests or ACT. Entrance: very difficult. Application deadlines: 1/15, 11/15 for early decision plan 1, 1/2 for early decision plan 2. Notification: 4/1, 12/15 for early decision plan 1, 2/1 for early decision plan 2. SAT Reasoning Test deadline: 2/1. SAT Subject Test deadline: 2/1. Transfer credits accepted: Yes. Applicants placed on waiting list: 1,125. Wait-listed applicants offered admission: 124. Early decision applicants: 505. Early decision applicants admitted: 246.

Costs Per Year: Application fee: $0. Comprehensive fee: $71,390 includes full-time tuition ($54,346), mandatory fees ($706), and college room and board ($16,338). College room only: $8108. Room and board charges vary according to board plan and housing facility. Part-time tuition: $2266 per credit. Part-time tuition varies according to course load.

Collegiate Environment: Orientation program. Drama-theater group, choral group, student-run newspaper, radio station. Social organizations: 175 open to all. Most popular organizations: Experimental College, Community Outreach, Student Government, Student Cooperative Association, student radio station. Major annual events: Artist Recital Series, Convocation, The Big Parade. Student services: health clinic, personal-psychological counseling, women's center. Campus security: 24-hour emergency response devices and patrols, student patrols, late night transport-escort service, controlled dormitory access, crime prevention programs. Mudd Center Library plus 3 others. Books: 1.4 million (physical), 676,883 (digital/electronic); Serial titles: 188,472 (physical). Students can reserve study rooms. 250 computers available on campus for general student use. Computer purchase/lease plans available. A campuswide network can be accessed from student residence rooms and from off campus. Students can access the following: online class registration. Staffed computer lab on campus provides training in use of computers, software, and the Internet.
Community Environment: Oberlin College is located 35 miles southwest of Cleveland in a small town.

■ **OHIO BUSINESS COLLEGE (SANDUSKY)**
5202 Timber Commons Dr.
Sandusky, OH 44870
Tel: (419)627-8345; Free: 888-627-8345
Fax: (419)627-1958
Web Site: www.ohiobusinesscollege.edu
Description: Proprietary, 2-year, coed. Awards diplomas and transfer associate degrees. Founded 1982. Setting: 1-acre small town campus with easy access to Cleveland, Toledo. Total enrollment: 265. Faculty: 32 (6 full-time, 26 part-time). Student-undergrad faculty ratio is 8:1. Full-time: 170 students, 71% women, 29% men. Part-time: 95 students, 80% women, 20% men. 0.4% American Indian or Alaska Native, non-Hispanic/Latino; 5% Hispanic/Latino; 22% Black or African American, non-Hispanic/Latino; 0.4% Asian, non-Hispanic/Latino. 71% 25 or older. Calendar: quarters. Academic remediation for entering students, independent study, summer session for credit, part-time degree program, internships.
Entrance Requirements: Required: high school transcript.
Collegiate Environment: Orientation program. Main library plus 1 other. 58 computers available on campus for general student use. A campuswide network can be accessed.

■ **OHIO BUSINESS COLLEGE (SHEFFIELD VILLAGE)**
5095 Waterford Dr.
Sheffield Village, OH 44035
Tel: (440)934-3101; Free: 888-514-3126
Web Site: www.ohiobusinesscollege.edu
Description: Proprietary, 2-year, coed. Part of Tri State Educational Systems. Awards diplomas and terminal associate degrees. Founded 1903. Setting: suburban campus with easy access to Cleveland. Total enrollment: 350. Core. Calendar: quarters. Academic remediation for entering students, advanced placement, accelerated degree program, independent study, double major, summer session for credit, part-time degree program, external degree program, adult/continuing education programs, internships.
Entrance Requirements: Open admission. Option: electronic application. Required: high school transcript, interview. Entrance: noncompetitive. Application deadline: rolling. Transfer credits accepted: Yes.
Collegiate Environment: Orientation program. Ohio Business College Library. 125 computers available on campus for general student use. Computer purchase/lease plans available. A campuswide network can be accessed. Staffed computer lab on campus (open 24 hours a day) provides training in use of computers, software, and the Internet.

■ **OHIO CHRISTIAN UNIVERSITY**
1476 Lancaster Pke.
Circleville, OH 43113
Tel: (740)474-8896; Free: 877-762-8669
Fax: (740)477-7755
Web Site: www.ohiochristian.edu
Description: Independent, comprehensive, coed, affiliated with Churches of Christ in Christian Union. Awards associate, bachelor's, and master's degrees. Founded 1948. Setting: 40-acre small town campus with easy access to Columbus. Endowment: $4.1 million. Educational spending for the previous fiscal year: $4111 per student. Total enrollment: 4,661. Faculty: 368 (149 full-time, 219 part-time). Student-undergrad faculty ratio is 12:1. Full-time: 2,481 students, 65% women, 35% men. Part-time: 1,732 students,

63% women, 37% men. 0.3% American Indian or Alaska Native, non-Hispanic/Latino; 2% Hispanic/Latino; 27% Black or African American, non-Hispanic/Latino; 0.5% Asian, non-Hispanic/Latino; 0.3% international. 8% live on campus, 7% transferred in. Academic areas with the most degrees conferred: theology and religious vocations; psychology; business/marketing. Core. Calendar: semesters. Academic remediation for entering students, services for LD students, advanced placement, self-designed majors, honors program, independent study, double major, summer session for credit, part-time degree program, adult/continuing education programs, internships. Off campus study at Columbus State Community College, Ohio State University. ROTC: Air Force (c).
Entrance Requirements: Options: electronic application, early admission. Required: essay, high school transcript, 4 recommendations, medical form. Recommended: SAT. Required for some: interview, ACT. Entrance: minimally difficult. Application deadline: rolling. Notification: continuous. Transfer credits accepted: Yes.
Costs Per Year: Application fee: $25. Comprehensive fee: $28,782 includes full-time tuition ($19,456), mandatory fees ($1250), and college room and board ($8076). Full-time tuition and fees vary according to class time, course load, degree level, location, and program. Room and board charges vary according to board plan. Part-time tuition: $886 per credit hour. Part-time mandatory fees: $400 per term. Part-time tuition and fees vary according to class time, location, and program.
Collegiate Environment: Orientation program. Drama-theater group, choral group. Major annual events: Community Action Day, Church Action Day, Revival week. Student services: legal services, personal-psychological counseling. Campus security: controlled dormitory access, security checks after midnight. Melvin Maxwell Memorial Library. Books: 59,755 (physical), 96,276 (digital/electronic); Serial titles: 143 (physical), 6,473 (digital/electronic). Weekly public service hours: 88; students can reserve study rooms. Operations spending for the previous fiscal year: $228,967. 68 computers available on campus for general student use. A campuswide network can be accessed from student residence rooms. Students can access the following: online class registration. Staffed computer lab on campus provides training in use of computers, software, and the Internet.
Community Environment: Circleville is situated in the central part of the state, 23 miles south of Columbus. A shopping center and a number of civic and service organizations serve the community. The annual Circleville Pumpkin Show features a 350-pound pumpkin pie, five feet in diameter, attracting over 500,000 visitors from throughout the world.

■ **OHIO DOMINICAN UNIVERSITY**
1216 Sunbury Rd.
Columbus, OH 43219-2099
Tel: (614)253-2741; Free: 800-955-6446
Fax: (614)252-0776
E-mail: admissions@ohiodominican.edu
Web Site: www.ohiodominican.edu
Description: Independent Roman Catholic, comprehensive, coed. Awards associate, bachelor's, and master's degrees. Founded 1911. Setting: 92-acre urban campus with easy access to Columbus, OH. Endowment: $22.6 million. Educational spending for the previous fiscal year: $5952 per student. Total enrollment: 1,716. Faculty: 163 (61 full-time, 102 part-time). Student-undergrad faculty ratio is 14:1. 1,550 applied, 75% were admitted. 12% from top 10% of their high school class, 33% from top quarter, 71% from top half. Full-time: 952 students, 51% women, 49% men. Part-time: 236 students, 66% women, 34% men. Students come from 18 states and territories, 11 other countries, 6% from out-of-state. 0.7% American Indian or Alaska Native, non-Hispanic/Latino; 4% Hispanic/Latino; 26% Black or African American, non-Hispanic/Latino; 1% Asian, non-Hispanic/Latino; 0.1% Native Hawaiian or other Pacific Islander, non-Hispanic/Latino; 2% international. 20% 25 or older, 43% live on campus, 7% transferred in. Retention: 65% of full-time freshmen returned the following year. Academic areas with the most degrees conferred: business/marketing; education; social sciences. Core. Calendar: semesters. Academic remediation for entering students, services for LD students, advanced placement, accelerated degree program, self-designed majors, honors program, independent study, distance learning, double major, summer session for credit, part-time degree program, adult/continuing education programs, internships, graduate courses open to undergrads. Off campus study at Members of the Higher Education Council of Columbus. Study abroad program. ROTC: Army (c), Air Force (c).
Entrance Requirements: Options: electronic application, deferred admission, international baccalaureate accepted. Required: high school transcript, minimum 2.3 high school GPA. Recommended: interview. Required for

some: essay, SAT or ACT. Entrance: moderately difficult. Application deadline: rolling. Notification: continuous. SAT Reasoning Test deadline: 8/10. SAT Subject Test deadline: 8/10. Transfer credits accepted: Yes.

Costs Per Year: Application fee: $0. Comprehensive fee: $42,900 includes full-time tuition ($31,100), mandatory fees ($580), and college room and board ($11,220). Part-time tuition: $735 per credit hour. Part-time mandatory fees: $175 per term.

Collegiate Environment: Orientation program. Drama-theater group, choral group, marching band, student-run radio station. Social organizations: 36 open to all. Most popular organizations: Panther Activities Council, Student Athletic Advisory Committee, Black Student Union, World Student Club, Panther Players. Major annual events: Welcome Week, Homecoming Weekend, ODU Day. Student services: health clinic, personal-psychological counseling. Campus security: 24-hour emergency response devices and patrols, late night transport-escort service, controlled dormitory access. 603 college housing spaces available; 469 were occupied in 2018-19. Freshmen guaranteed college housing. On-campus residence required through sophomore year. Option: coed housing available. Ohio Dominican Library. Books: 76,976 (physical), 149,521 (digital/electronic); Serial titles: 5,327 (physical), 29,439 (digital/electronic); Databases: 216. Students can reserve study rooms. Operations spending for the previous fiscal year: $640,465. 350 computers available on campus for general student use. A campuswide network can be accessed from student residence rooms and from off campus. Students can access the following: online class registration. Staffed computer lab on campus provides training in use of computers, software, and the Internet.

Community Environment: See Ohio State University Columbus Campus.

■ OHIO NORTHERN UNIVERSITY

525 S Main
Ada, OH 45810-1599
Tel: (419)772-2000; Free: 888-408-4ONU
Fax: (419)772-2313
E-mail: admissions-ug@onu.edu
Web Site: www.onu.edu

Description: Independent, comprehensive, coed, affiliated with United Methodist Church. Awards bachelor's, master's, and doctoral degrees. Founded 1871. Setting: 342-acre small town campus. Endowment: $162 million. Total enrollment: 3,088. Faculty: 286 (224 full-time, 62 part-time). Student-undergrad faculty ratio is 11:1. 4,159 applied, 66% were admitted. 25% from top 10% of their high school class, 55% from top quarter, 89% from top half. Full-time: 2,092 students, 44% women, 56% men. Part-time: 220 students, 45% women, 55% men. Students come from 38 states and territories, 23 other countries, 17% from out-of-state. 0.1% American Indian or Alaska Native, non-Hispanic/Latino; 1% Hispanic/Latino; 4% Black or African American, non-Hispanic/Latino; 2% Asian, non-Hispanic/Latino; 0.1% Native Hawaiian or other Pacific Islander, non-Hispanic/Latino; 3% international. 2% 25 or older, 75% live on campus, 3% transferred in. Retention: 82% of full-time freshmen returned the following year. Academic areas with the most degrees conferred: engineering; business/marketing; health professions and related sciences. Core. Calendar: semesters. Academic remediation for entering students, ESL program, services for LD students, advanced placement, honors program, independent study, distance learning, double major, summer session for credit, part-time degree program, co-op programs and internships. Off campus study. Study abroad program. ROTC: Army (c), Air Force (c).

Entrance Requirements: Options: electronic application, deferred admission, international baccalaureate accepted. Required: high school transcript, SAT or ACT. Recommended: essay. Required for some: essay, 1 recommendation, interview. Entrance: moderately difficult. Application deadline: 8/15. Notification: continuous. SAT Reasoning Test deadline: 8/15. Transfer credits accepted: Yes.

Costs Per Year: Application fee: $0. Comprehensive fee: $43,910 includes full-time tuition ($31,350), mandatory fees ($910), and college room and board ($11,650). Full-time tuition and fees vary according to course load, degree level, and program. Room and board charges vary according to board plan, housing facility, and student level. Part-time tuition: $1310 per credit hour. Part-time tuition varies according to course load, degree level, and program.

Collegiate Environment: Orientation program. Drama-theater group, choral group, marching band, student-run newspaper, radio station. Social organizations: 200 open to all; national fraternities, national sororities. Most popular organizations: Habitat for Humanity, Student Planning Committee, Student Senate, Northern Christian Fellowship, Marching Band. Major an-

nual events: Homecoming, Hypnotist, Mud Volleyball. Student services: legal services, health clinic, personal-psychological counseling. Campus security: 24-hour emergency response devices and patrols, controlled dormitory access. Heterick Memorial Library plus 1 other. Students can reserve study rooms.

Community Environment: Ada, a community of nearly 5,000 people, is located 15 miles east of Lima, 22 miles south of Findlay, and only 8 miles from I-75. Health services are provided by the university. Some of the usual civic and service organizations are active.

■ THE OHIO STATE UNIVERSITY

281 W Ln. Ave.
Student Academic Services Bldg.
Columbus, OH 43210
Tel: (614)292-6446
Fax: (614)292-4818
Web Site: www.osu.edu

Description: State-supported, university, coed. Part of The Ohio State University. Awards associate, bachelor's, master's, and doctoral degrees and post-master's certificates. Founded 1870. Setting: 1,665-acre urban campus with easy access to Columbus. Endowment: $4.2 billion. Research spending for the previous fiscal year: $863.8 million. Educational spending for the previous fiscal year: $15,924 per student. Total enrollment: 61,170. Faculty: 5,682 (4,110 full-time, 1,572 part-time). Student-undergrad faculty ratio is 19:1. 47,782 applied, 48% were admitted. 63% from top 10% of their high school class, 94% from top quarter, 99% from top half. 331 valedictorians. Full-time: 42,831 students, 49% women, 51% men. Part-time: 3,989 students, 48% women, 52% men. Students come from 54 states and territories, 71 other countries, 19% from out-of-state. 0.1% American Indian or Alaska Native, non-Hispanic/Latino; 4% Hispanic/Latino; 6% Black or African American, non-Hispanic/Latino; 7% Asian, non-Hispanic/Latino; 0.1% Native Hawaiian or other Pacific Islander, non-Hispanic/Latino; 9% international. 7% 25 or older, 32% live on campus, 5% transferred in. Retention: 95% of full-time freshmen returned the following year. Academic areas with the most degrees conferred: business/marketing; engineering; social sciences; health professions and related sciences; biological/life sciences. Core. Calendar: semesters. Academic remediation for entering students, ESL program, services for LD students, advanced placement, accelerated degree program, self-designed majors, freshman honors college, honors program, independent study, distance learning, double major, summer session for credit, part-time degree program, adult/continuing education programs, co-op programs and internships, graduate courses open to undergrads. Off campus study at Higher Education Council of Columbus. Study abroad program. ROTC: Army, Naval, Air Force.

Entrance Requirements: Options: electronic application, early action, deferred admission, international baccalaureate accepted. Required: essay, high school transcript, SAT or ACT. Entrance: very difficult. Application deadlines: 2/1, 2/1 for nonresidents, 11/1 for early action. Notification: 3/31, 3/31 for nonresidents, 1/31 for early action. SAT Reasoning Test deadline: 2/1. Transfer credits accepted: Yes. Applicants placed on waiting list: 5,051. Wait-listed applicants offered admission: 852. Early action applicants: 27,209. Early action applicants admitted: 16,980.

Costs Per Year: Application fee: $60. State resident tuition: $10,726 full-time, $485.70 per credit hour part-time. Nonresident tuition: $30,742 full-time, $1,320 per credit hour part-time. Full-time tuition varies according to course load, degree level, location, program, reciprocity agreements, and student level. Part-time tuition varies according to course load, degree level, location, program, reciprocity agreements, and student level. College room and board: $12,434. Room and board charges vary according to board plan, housing facility, and location. Tuition guaranteed not to increase for student's term of enrollment.

Collegiate Environment: Orientation program. Drama-theater group, choral group, marching band, student-run newspaper, radio station. Social organizations: 1,430 open to all; national fraternities, national sororities, local sororities; 7% of eligible men and 11% of eligible women are members. Most popular organizations: Burritos Club, Vinyl Club, Guitar Club, Artificial Intelligence Club, H20 Students. Major annual events: OUAB Fall Concert, Autumn Student Involvement Fair, Homecoming Parade. Student services: legal services, health clinic, personal-psychological counseling. Campus security: 24-hour emergency response devices and patrols, student patrols, late night transport-escort service, controlled dormitory access. 14,313 college housing spaces available; 14,138 were occupied in 2018-19. Freshmen guaranteed college housing. On-campus residence required through sophomore year. Options: coed, women-only housing available. William

Oxley Thompson Library plus 10 others. Books: 5 million (physical), 1.3 million (digital/electronic); Serial titles: 664,616 (physical), 55,339 (digital/electronic); Databases: 2,046. Study areas open 24 hours, 5-7 days a week; students can reserve study rooms. Operations spending for the previous fiscal year: $39.5 million.

■ **THE OHIO STATE UNIVERSITY AGRICULTURAL TECHNICAL INSTITUTE**
1328 Dover Rd.
Wooster, OH 44691
Tel: (330)287-1331; Free: 800-647-8283
E-mail: morris.878@osu.edu
Web Site: www.ati.osu.edu
Description: State-supported, 2-year, coed. Part of The Ohio State University. Awards certificates, diplomas, transfer associate, and terminal associate degrees. Founded 1971. Setting: 1,942-acre small town campus with easy access to Cleveland, Columbus, Akron, Canton. Total enrollment: 757. Faculty: 70 (33 full-time, 37 part-time). Student-undergrad faculty ratio is 21:1. 630 applied, 93% were admitted. 7% from top 10% of their high school class, 27% from top quarter, 52% from top half. Full-time: 707 students, 51% women, 49% men. Part-time: 50 students, 44% women, 56% men. Students come from 9 states and territories, 2% from out-of-state. 8% 25 or older, 4% transferred in. Retention: 67% of full-time freshmen returned the following year. Core. Calendar: semesters. Academic remediation for entering students, services for LD students, advanced placement, accelerated degree program, self-designed majors, independent study, distance learning, double major, part-time degree program, adult/continuing education programs, co-op programs and internships. Off campus study. Study abroad program. ROTC: Army (c), Naval (c), Air Force (c).
Entrance Requirements: Open admission for Ohio residents. Option: electronic application. Required: high school transcript. Required for some: SAT or ACT. Entrance: noncompetitive. Application deadline: 6/1. Notification: continuous. Transfer credits accepted: Yes.
Costs Per Year: Application fee: $60. State resident tuition: $7608 full-time, $319 per credit hour part-time. Nonresident tuition: $27,624 full-time, $1153 per credit hour part-time. Full-time tuition varies according to course load, location, and program. Part-time tuition varies according to course load, location, and program. College room and board: $8696. College room only: $7024. Room and board charges vary according to board plan and location.
Collegiate Environment: Orientation program. Social organizations: 19 open to all. Most popular organizations: Hoof-n-Hide Club, Collegiate FFA, Campus Crusade for Christ, Phi Theta Kappa, Community Council. Major annual events: Welcome Days, Ag Olympics, Mud Volleyball Tournament. Student services: personal-psychological counseling. Campus security: 24-hour emergency response devices and patrols, controlled dormitory access. Agricultural Technical Institute Library plus 1 other. 85 computers available on campus for general student use. Computer purchase/lease plans available. A campuswide network can be accessed from student residence rooms and from off campus. Students can access the following: online class registration. Staffed computer lab on campus.
Community Environment: Wooster, population 25,600, is the county seat of Wayne County and is in a major agricultural area accessible from any area of the state. It is also home to the College of Wooster, and the corporate headquarters of Rubbermaid and other companies including Frito-Lay, Wooster Brush Company, Regal Ware, the Gerstenslager Company, and Bell and Howell. Students also have access to Cleveland, Columbus, Pittsburgh, Cincinnati, and Akron.

■ **THE OHIO STATE UNIVERSITY AT LIMA**
4240 Campus Dr.
Lima, OH 45804
Tel: (419)995-8600
Fax: (419)995-8483
Web Site: lima.osu.edu
Description: State-supported, comprehensive, coed. Part of The Ohio State University. Awards associate, bachelor's, and master's degrees. Founded 1960. Setting: 562-acre suburban campus. Endowment: $5.3 million. Research spending for the previous fiscal year: $78,259. Educational spending for the previous fiscal year: $6976 per student. Total enrollment: 1,010. Faculty: 79 (31 full-time, 48 part-time). Student-undergrad faculty ratio is 19:1. 1,704 applied, 99% were admitted. 9% from top 10% of their high school class, 31% from top quarter, 70% from top half. 5 valedictorians. Full-time: 851 students, 54% women, 46% men. Part-time: 159 students, 57% women, 43% men. Students come from 4 states and territories, 1 other

country, 0.3% from out-of-state. 0.3% American Indian or Alaska Native, non-Hispanic/Latino; 5% Hispanic/Latino; 4% Black or African American, non-Hispanic/Latino; 2% Asian, non-Hispanic/Latino; 0.2% international. 12% 25 or older, 5% transferred in. Retention: 69% of full-time freshmen returned the following year. Core. Calendar: semesters. Academic remediation for entering students, ESL program, services for LD students, advanced placement, accelerated degree program, self-designed majors, freshman honors college, honors program, independent study, distance learning, double major, summer session for credit, part-time degree program, adult/continuing education programs, co-op programs and internships, graduate courses open to undergrads. Off campus study at Higher Education Council of Columbus. Study abroad program.
Entrance Requirements: Open admission. Options: electronic application, international baccalaureate accepted. Required: high school transcript. Required for some: SAT or ACT. Entrance: noncompetitive. Application deadlines: 6/1, 6/1 for nonresidents. Notification: continuous, continuous for nonresidents. SAT Reasoning Test deadline: 6/1. Transfer credits accepted: Yes.
Costs Per Year: Application fee: $60. State resident tuition: $7644 full-time, $318.50 per credit hour part-time. Nonresident tuition: $27,660 full-time, $1,153 per credit hour part-time. Full-time tuition varies according to course load, location, program, reciprocity agreements, and student level. Part-time tuition varies according to course load, location, program, reciprocity agreements, and student level. Tuition guaranteed not to increase for student's term of enrollment.
Collegiate Environment: Orientation program. Drama-theater group, choral group. Social organizations: 23 open to all. Most popular organizations: United Way Club, Campus Activities Board, Nert Club, Student Senate, Psych Club. Major annual events: Welcome Back Picnic, Spring Fest. Student services: personal-psychological counseling. Campus security: 24-hour emergency response devices and patrols, late night transport-escort service. College housing not available. Lima Campus Library. Books: 74,972 (physical), 1.4 million (digital/electronic); Serial titles: 34 (physical), 54,576 (digital/electronic); Databases: 2,056. Weekly public service hours: 57; students can reserve study rooms. Operations spending for the previous fiscal year: $287,414.

■ **THE OHIO STATE UNIVERSITY AT MANSFIELD**
1680 University Dr.
Mansfield, OH 44906-1599
Tel: (419)755-4011
Web Site: www.mansfield.osu.edu
Description: State-supported, comprehensive, coed. Part of The Ohio State University. Awards associate and bachelor's degrees. Founded 1958. Setting: 620-acre small town campus with easy access to Columbus, Cleveland. Endowment: $2.3 million. Research spending for the previous fiscal year: $70,051. Educational spending for the previous fiscal year: $6709 per student. Total enrollment: 1,099. Faculty: 84 (33 full-time, 51 part-time). Student-undergrad faculty ratio is 19:1. 2,695 applied, 99% were admitted. 8% from top 10% of their high school class, 31% from top quarter, 66% from top half. 6 valedictorians. Full-time: 883 students, 53% women, 47% men. Part-time: 213 students, 51% women, 49% men. Students come from 6 states and territories, 2 other countries, 1% from out-of-state. 0.2% American Indian or Alaska Native, non-Hispanic/Latino; 3% Hispanic/Latino; 10% Black or African American, non-Hispanic/Latino; 3% Asian, non-Hispanic/Latino. 11% 25 or older, 20% live on campus, 5% transferred in. Retention: 70% of full-time freshmen returned the following year. Core. Calendar: semesters. Academic remediation for entering students, ESL program, services for LD students, advanced placement, self-designed majors, freshman honors college, honors program, independent study, distance learning, double major, summer session for credit, part-time degree program, adult/continuing education programs, co-op programs and internships. Off campus study. Study abroad program.
Entrance Requirements: Open admission. Options: electronic application, international baccalaureate accepted. Required: high school transcript. Required for some: SAT or ACT. Entrance: noncompetitive. Application deadlines: 6/1, 6/1 for nonresidents. Notification: continuous, continuous for nonresidents. SAT Reasoning Test deadline: 6/1. Transfer credits accepted: Yes.
Costs Per Year: Application fee: $60. State resident tuition: $7644 full-time, $318.50 per credit hour part-time. Nonresident tuition: $27,660 full-time, $1,153 per credit hour part-time. Full-time tuition varies according to course load, location, program, reciprocity agreements, and student level. Part-time tuition varies according to course load, location, program, reciprocity agree-

ments, and student level. College room and board: $8094. College room only: $6422. Room and board charges vary according to board plan, housing facility, and location. Tuition guaranteed not to increase for student's term of enrollment.

Collegiate Environment: Orientation program. Drama-theater group, choral group. Social organizations: 25 open to all. Most popular organizations: Campus Activities Board, Best Buddies, Awakening, College Democrats, College Republicans. Major annual events: Involvement and Community Fair, Welcome Week Cookout and Bonfire, April Craze Finale Event. Student services: personal-psychological counseling. Campus security: 24-hour emergency response devices and patrols. 191 college housing spaces available; 186 were occupied in 2018-19. Freshmen given priority for college housing. Option: coed housing available. Bromfield Library & Information Commons. Books: 43,903 (physical), 1.4 million (digital/electronic); Serial titles: 126 (physical), 54,781 (digital/electronic); Databases: 2,075. Weekly public service hours: 63; students can reserve study rooms. Operations spending for the previous fiscal year: $206,113.

■ **THE OHIO STATE UNIVERSITY AT MARION**
1465 Mount Vernon Ave.
Marion, OH 43302-5695
Tel: (740)389-6786
Web Site: osumarion.osu.edu
Description: State-supported, comprehensive, coed. Part of The Ohio State University. Awards associate and bachelor's degrees. Founded 1958. Setting: 188-acre small town campus with easy access to Columbus. Endowment: $5.6 million. Research spending for the previous fiscal year: $47,260. Educational spending for the previous fiscal year: $5939 per student. Total enrollment: 1,252. Faculty: 103 (38 full-time, 65 part-time). Student-undergrad faculty ratio is 19:1. 1,329 applied, 99% were admitted. 10% from top 10% of their high school class, 32% from top quarter, 70% from top half. 4 valedictorians. Full-time: 1,029 students, 48% women, 52% men. Part-time: 222 students, 50% women, 50% men. Students come from 8 states and territories, 1 other country, 1% from out-of-state. 0.3% American Indian or Alaska Native, non-Hispanic/Latino; 4% Hispanic/Latino; 4% Black or African American, non-Hispanic/Latino; 6% Asian, non-Hispanic/Latino; 0.1% international. 12% 25 or older, 3% transferred in. Retention: 74% of full-time freshmen returned the following year. Core. Calendar: semesters. Academic remediation for entering students, ESL program, services for LD students, advanced placement, self-designed majors, freshman honors college, honors program, independent study, distance learning, double major, summer session for credit, part-time degree program, adult/continuing education programs, co-op programs and internships. Off campus study at Higher Education Council of Columbus. Study abroad program.
Entrance Requirements: Open admission. Options: electronic application, international baccalaureate accepted. Required: high school transcript. Required for some: SAT or ACT. Entrance: noncompetitive. Application deadlines: 6/1, 6/1 for nonresidents. Notification: continuous, continuous for nonresidents. SAT Reasoning Test deadline: 6/1. Transfer credits accepted: Yes.
Costs Per Year: Application fee: $60. State resident tuition: $7644 full-time, $318.50 per credit hour part-time. Nonresident tuition: $27,660 full-time, $1,153 per credit hour part-time. Full-time tuition varies according to course load, location, program, reciprocity agreements, and student level. Part-time tuition varies according to course load, location, program, reciprocity agreements, and student level. Tuition guaranteed not to increase for student's term of enrollment.
Collegiate Environment: Orientation program. Drama-theater group, choral group. Social organizations: 31 open to all. Student services: personal-psychological counseling. Campus security: 24-hour emergency response devices. College housing not available. Marion Campus Library. Books: 46,290 (physical), 1.4 million (digital/electronic); Serial titles: 54,781 (digital/electronic); Databases: 2,056. Weekly public service hours: 57; students can reserve study rooms. Operations spending for the previous fiscal year: $281,133.

■ **THE OHIO STATE UNIVERSITY AT NEWARK**
1179 University Dr.
Newark, OH 43055-1797
Tel: (740)366-3321
E-mail: kanney.24@osu.edu
Web Site: www.newark.osu.edu
Description: State-supported, comprehensive, coed. Part of The Ohio State University. Awards associate, bachelor's, and master's degrees. Founded

1957. Setting: 111-acre small town campus with easy access to Columbus. Endowment: $4 million. Research spending for the previous fiscal year: $139,353. Educational spending for the previous fiscal year: $4392 per student. Total enrollment: 2,882. Faculty: 161 (46 full-time, 115 part-time). Student-undergrad faculty ratio is 28:1. 5,381 applied, 99% were admitted. 6% from top 10% of their high school class, 23% from top quarter, 58% from top half. 7 valedictorians. Full-time: 2,461 students, 50% women, 50% men. Part-time: 409 students, 54% women, 46% men. Students come from 10 states and territories, 1 other country, 0.4% from out-of-state. 0.1% American Indian or Alaska Native, non-Hispanic/Latino; 4% Hispanic/Latino; 15% Black or African American, non-Hispanic/Latino; 5% Asian, non-Hispanic/Latino. 6% 25 or older, 11% live on campus, 5% transferred in. Retention: 70% of full-time freshmen returned the following year. Core. Calendar: semesters. Academic remediation for entering students, ESL program, services for LD students, advanced placement, self-designed majors, freshman honors college, honors program, independent study, distance learning, double major, summer session for credit, part-time degree program, adult/continuing education programs, co-op programs and internships, graduate courses open to undergrads. Off campus study. Study abroad program. ROTC: Army.
Entrance Requirements: Open admission. Options: electronic application, international baccalaureate accepted. Required: high school transcript. Required for some: SAT or ACT. Entrance: noncompetitive. Application deadlines: 6/1, 6/1 for nonresidents. Notification: continuous, continuous for nonresidents. SAT Reasoning Test deadline: 6/1. Transfer credits accepted: Yes.
Costs Per Year: Application fee: $60. State resident tuition: $7644 full-time, $318.50 per credit hour part-time. Nonresident tuition: $27,660 full-time, $1,153 per credit hour part-time. Full-time tuition varies according to course load, location, program, reciprocity agreements, and student level. Part-time tuition varies according to course load, location, program, reciprocity agreements, and student level. College room and board: $9268. College room only: $7596. Room and board charges vary according to board plan, housing facility, and location. Tuition guaranteed not to increase for student's term of enrollment.
Collegiate Environment: Orientation program. Drama-theater group, choral group. Social organizations: 30 open to all. Most popular organizations: Campus Activities Board, Ebonye Horizons, Journay Campus Ministry, Collegiate 4 - H, American Sign Language. Major annual events: Convocation, Ice Skating Nights, Family and Friends Day. Student services: legal services, personal-psychological counseling. Campus security: 24-hour emergency response devices and patrols, late night transport-escort service. 308 college housing spaces available; 292 were occupied in 2018-19. Freshmen given priority for college housing. Option: coed housing available. John L. and Christine Warner Library. Books: 52,380 (physical), 1.4 million (digital/electronic); Serial titles: 491 (physical), 54,576 (digital/electronic); Databases: 2,056. Weekly public service hours: 69; students can reserve study rooms. Operations spending for the previous fiscal year: $271,619.

■ **OHIO TECHNICAL COLLEGE**
1374 E 51st St.
Cleveland, OH 44103
Tel: (216)881-1700; Free: 800-322-7000
Fax: (216)881-9145
Web Site: www.ohiotech.edu
Description: Proprietary, 2-year, coed. Awards certificates, diplomas, and terminal associate degrees. Founded 1969. Setting: 18-acre urban campus. Total enrollment: 905. Faculty: 63 (49 full-time, 14 part-time). Student-undergrad faculty ratio is 16:1. 226 applied, 100% were admitted. Full-time: 905 students, 7% women, 93% men. Students come from 14 states and territories, 2 other countries, 57% from out-of-state. 0.4% American Indian or Alaska Native, non-Hispanic/Latino; 6% Hispanic/Latino; 21% Black or African American, non-Hispanic/Latino; 0.2% Asian, non-Hispanic/Latino; 0.1% Native Hawaiian or other Pacific Islander, non-Hispanic/Latino. 18% 25 or older, 2% transferred in. Retention: 80% of full-time freshmen returned the following year. Core.
Entrance Requirements: Open admission. Option: electronic application. Required: high school transcript, interview. Application deadlines: rolling, rolling for nonresidents. Transfer credits accepted: Yes.
Costs Per Year: Tuition: $28,500 full-time. Tuition guaranteed not to increase for student's term of enrollment.
Collegiate Environment: Orientation program. Student services: personal-psychological counseling. Campus security: late night transport-escort service. No special consideration for freshman housing applicants. Ohio

Technical College Library Resource Center. Books: 3,859 (physical), 21 (digital/electronic); Databases: 6. Weekly public service hours: 40. 9 computers available on campus for general student use. A campuswide network can be accessed. Staffed computer lab on campus provides training in use of computers, software, and the Internet.

■ OHIO UNIVERSITY

Athens, OH 45701-2979
Tel: (740)593-1000
Fax: (740)593-4229
Web Site: www.ohio.edu

Description: State-supported, university, coed. Part of Ohio Board of Regents. Awards associate, bachelor's, master's, and doctoral degrees. Founded 1804. Setting: 1,800-acre small town campus. Endowment: $568.9 million. Research spending for the previous fiscal year: $47.3 million. Educational spending for the previous fiscal year: $11,681 per student. Total enrollment: 28,446. Faculty: 1,251 (988 full-time, 263 part-time). Student-undergrad faculty ratio is 17:1. 23,385 applied, 78% were admitted. 17% from top 10% of their high school class, 44% from top quarter, 82% from top half. 2 National Merit Scholars, 83 valedictorians. Full-time: 17,041 students, 54% women, 46% men. Part-time: 5,234 students, 80% women, 20% men. Students come from 47 states and territories, 62 other countries, 12% from out-of-state. 0.2% American Indian or Alaska Native, non-Hispanic/Latino; 3% Hispanic/Latino; 6% Black or African American, non-Hispanic/Latino; 1% Asian, non-Hispanic/Latino; 0.1% Native Hawaiian or other Pacific Islander, non-Hispanic/Latino; 2% international. 4% 25 or older, 43% live on campus, 2% transferred in. Retention: 82% of full-time freshmen returned the following year. Academic areas with the most degrees conferred: health professions and related sciences; business/marketing; communication/journalism. Core. Calendar: semesters. Academic remediation for entering students, ESL program, services for LD students, advanced placement, accelerated degree program, self-designed majors, freshman honors college, honors program, independent study, distance learning, double major, summer session for credit, part-time degree program, external degree program, adult/continuing education programs, co-op programs and internships, graduate courses open to undergrads. Off campus study. Study abroad program. ROTC: Army, Air Force.

Entrance Requirements: Options: electronic application, early admission, early action, deferred admission, international baccalaureate accepted. Required: SAT or ACT. Recommended: 2 recommendations. Required for some: essay, high school transcript, 2 recommendations, Audition required for dance and music programs. Interview required of selected Honors Tutorial College candidates. Portfolio required of visual communication applicants. Entrance: moderately difficult. Application deadlines: 2/1, 12/1 for early action. Notification: continuous, rolling for early action. SAT Reasoning Test deadline: 2/1. SAT Subject Test deadline: 2/1. Transfer credits accepted: Yes. Applicants placed on waiting list: 0. Wait-listed applicants offered admission: 0. Early action applicants: 15,170. Early action applicants admitted: 11,931.

Costs Per Year: Application fee: $50. State resident tuition: $12,192 full-time, $576 per semester hour part-time. Nonresident tuition: $21,656 full-time, $1042 per semester hour part-time. Full-time tuition varies according to degree level, location, program, and reciprocity agreements. Part-time tuition varies according to course load, degree level, location, program, and reciprocity agreements. College room and board: $11,830. College room only: $7060. Room and board charges vary according to board plan. Tuition guaranteed not to increase for student's term of enrollment.

Collegiate Environment: Orientation program. Drama-theater group, choral group, marching band, student-run newspaper, radio station. Social organizations: 530 open to all; national fraternities, national sororities; 6% of eligible men and 8% of eligible women are members. Most popular organizations: Student Senate, Student Alumni Board, International Student Union, University Program Council, Black Student Cultural Programming Board. Major annual events: Homecoming, Opening Weekend, Family Weekends. Student services: legal services, health clinic, personal-psychological counseling, women's center. Campus security: 24-hour emergency response devices and patrols, student patrols, late night transport-escort service, controlled dormitory access. 7,720 college housing spaces available; 7,100 were occupied in 2018-19. Freshmen guaranteed college housing. On-campus residence required through sophomore year. Options: coed, women-only housing available. Alden Library plus 3 others. Books: 3.2 million (physical), 1.1 million (digital/electronic); Serial titles: 155,515 (physical), 88,338 (digital/electronic); Databases: 558. Weekly public service hours: 146; study areas open 24 hours, 5-7 days a week; students can reserve

study rooms. Operations spending for the previous fiscal year: $14.2 million. 1,000 computers available on campus for general student use. Computer purchase/lease plans available. A campuswide network can be accessed from student residence rooms and from off campus. Students can access the following: online class registration. Staffed computer lab on campus (open 24 hours a day) provides training in use of computers, software, and the Internet.

Community Environment: Athens is a traditional college town with a nonstudent population of approximately 21,000. The city is located about 75 miles southeast of Columbus, the state capital, in the foothills of the Appalachian mountains and on the banks of the Hocking River. Several state parks and thousands of acres of national forests are within easy driving distance and provide ample facilities for swimming, hiking, camping, fishing, and picnicking.

■ OHIO UNIVERSITY-CHILLICOTHE

101 University Dr.
Chillicothe, OH 45601
Tel: (740)774-7200; Free: 877-462-6824
Fax: (740)774-7295
E-mail: evelandt@ohio.edu
Web Site: www.chillicothe.ohiou.edu

Description: State-supported, comprehensive, coed. Part of Ohio University. Awards associate, bachelor's, and master's degrees (offers first 2 years of most bachelor's degree programs available at the main campus in Athens; also offers several bachelor's degree programs that can be completed at this campus and several programs exclusive to this campus; also offers some graduate programs). Founded 1946. Setting: 124-acre small town campus with easy access to Columbus. Total enrollment: 2,200. Students come from 10 states and territories. Retention: 54% of full-time freshmen returned the following year. Core. Calendar: semesters. Academic remediation for entering students, services for LD students, advanced placement, distance learning, summer session for credit, part-time degree program, external degree program, adult/continuing education programs, co-op programs and internships. Study abroad program.

Entrance Requirements: Open admission for state residents. Options: electronic application, early admission, deferred admission. Required: high school transcript, ACCUPLACER. Entrance: noncompetitive. Application deadline: 8/25. Notification: continuous. Transfer credits accepted: Yes.

Collegiate Environment: Orientation program. Drama-theater group. Student services: personal-psychological counseling. Campus security: 24-hour emergency response devices, patrols by city police. Quinn Library.

■ OHIO UNIVERSITY-EASTERN

45425 National Rd.
Saint Clairsville, OH 43950-9724
Tel: (740)695-1720; Free: 800-648-3331
E-mail: jeffriee@ohio.edu
Web Site: www.eastern.ohiou.edu

Description: State-supported, comprehensive, coed. Part of Ohio Board of Regents. Awards associate, bachelor's, and master's degrees (also offers some graduate courses). Founded 1957. Setting: 300-acre rural campus. Total enrollment: 751. 26% 25 or older. Core. Calendar: semesters. Academic remediation for entering students, advanced placement, accelerated degree program, self-designed majors, distance learning, double major, summer session for credit, part-time degree program, external degree program, adult/continuing education programs.

Entrance Requirements: Open admission. Options: electronic application, early admission, deferred admission. Required: high school transcript. Entrance: noncompetitive. Application deadline: rolling. Transfer credits accepted: Yes.

Collegiate Environment: Orientation program. Drama-theater group. Student services: personal-psychological counseling. Campus security: late night transport-escort service. The Library and Learning Commons. Weekly public service hours: 75; students can reserve study rooms. 15 computers available on campus for general student use. A campuswide network can be accessed from off-campus. Students can access the following: online class registration. Staffed computer lab on campus provides training in use of computers, software, and the Internet.

■ OHIO UNIVERSITY-LANCASTER

1570 Granville Pke.
Lancaster, OH 43130-1097
Tel: (740)654-6711; Free: 888-446-4468

Fax: (740)687-9497
Web Site: www.ohiou.edu/lancaster
Description: State-supported, comprehensive, coed. Part of Ohio Board of Regents. Awards associate, bachelor's, and master's degrees. Founded 1968. Setting: 360-acre small town campus with easy access to Columbus. Total enrollment: 1,728. 31% 25 or older. Core. Calendar: quarters. Academic remediation for entering students, advanced placement, accelerated degree program, self-designed majors, independent study, distance learning, double major, summer session for credit, part-time degree program, external degree program, adult/continuing education programs, internships. ROTC: Army (c), Air Force (c).
Entrance Requirements: Open admission. Options: electronic application, early admission, deferred admission. Required: high school transcript. Recommended: interview. Entrance: noncompetitive. Application deadline: rolling. Notification: continuous.
Collegiate Environment: Orientation program. Drama-theater group. Hannah V. McCauley Library.

■ OHIO UNIVERSITY-SOUTHERN CAMPUS
1804 Liberty Ave.
Ironton, OH 45638-2214
Tel: (740)533-4600; Free: 800-626-0513
Fax: (740)533-4632
Web Site: www.ohiou.edu
Description: State-supported, comprehensive, coed. Part of Ohio Board of Regents. Awards associate, bachelor's, and master's degrees. Founded 1956. Setting: 9-acre small town campus. Total enrollment: 1,836. 350 applied, 100% were admitted. Students come from 3 states and territories, 50% from out-of-state. 51% 25 or older. Core. Calendar: quarters. Academic remediation for entering students, self-designed majors, summer session for credit, part-time degree program, adult/continuing education programs.
Entrance Requirements: Open admission. Options: electronic application, early admission, deferred admission. Required for some: high school transcript, ACT. Entrance: noncompetitive. Application deadline: rolling.
Collegiate Environment: Orientation program. Choral group. Student services: legal services. Ohio University-Southern Campus Library. 185 computers available on campus for general student use. Computer purchase/lease plans available. A campuswide network can be accessed. Students can access the following: online class registration. Staffed computer lab on campus provides training in use of computers, software, and the Internet.

■ OHIO UNIVERSITY-ZANESVILLE
1425 Newark Rd.
Zanesville, OH 43701-2695
Tel: (740)588-1439
E-mail: ouzservices@ohio.edu
Web Site: www.ohio.edu/zanesville
Description: State-supported, 4-year, coed. Administratively affiliated with Ohio University. Awards associate and bachelor's degrees (offers first 2 years of most bachelor's degree programs available at the main campus in Athens; also offers several bachelor's degree programs that can be completed at this campus; also offers some graduate courses). Founded 1946. Setting: 179-acre rural campus with easy access to Columbus. Total enrollment: 1,878. Faculty: 130 (31 full-time, 99 part-time). Student-undergrad faculty ratio is 18:1. 468 applied, 90% were admitted. Full-time: 1,388 students, 70% women, 30% men. Part-time: 490 students, 72% women, 28% men. 1% from out-of-state. 0.3% American Indian or Alaska Native, non-Hispanic/Latino; 1% Hispanic/Latino; 3% Black or African American, non-Hispanic/Latino; 0.6% Asian, non-Hispanic/Latino; 0.6% international. Core. Calendar: semesters. Academic remediation for entering students, services for LD students, advanced placement, accelerated degree program, self-designed majors, independent study, distance learning, double major, summer session for credit, part-time degree program, external degree program, adult/continuing education programs. Off campus study at Zane State College. Study abroad program.
Entrance Requirements: Open admission. Option: electronic application. Required: high school transcript. Required for some: SAT or ACT. Entrance: noncompetitive. Application deadline: rolling. Transfer credits accepted: Yes.
Costs Per Year: Application fee: $20. State resident tuition: $5280 full-time, $238 per semester hour part-time. Nonresident tuition: $8272 full-time, $374 per semester hour part-time. Mandatory fees: $210 full-time, $9 per semester hour part-time. Tuition guaranteed not to increase for student's term of enrollment.

Collegiate Environment: Orientation program. Student-run radio station. Most popular organizations: Student Senate, Student Nurses Association, Good Intentions Group, Green Bobcats, Habitat for Humanity Club. Major annual events: Spring Fest, Fall Fest. Student services: legal services, personal-psychological counseling. Campus security: student patrols, late night transport-escort service, night security. Zanesville Campus Library plus 1 other. Students can reserve study rooms. Operations spending for the previous fiscal year: $247,287. 200 computers available on campus for general student use. A campuswide network can be accessed from off-campus. Students can access the following: online class registration. Staffed computer lab on campus provides training in use of computers, software, and the Internet.

■ OHIO VALLEY COLLEGE OF TECHNOLOGY
15258 State Rte. 170
East Liverpool, OH 43920
Tel: (330)385-1070
Web Site: www.ovct.edu
Description: Proprietary, 2-year, coed. Awards terminal associate degrees. Founded 1886. Setting: small town campus with easy access to Pittsburgh. Total enrollment: 147. Faculty: 12 (4 full-time, 8 part-time). Student-undergrad faculty ratio is 18:1. Full-time: 132 students, 87% women, 13% men. Part-time: 15 students, 73% women, 27% men. 7% from out-of-state. 50% 25 or older. Core. Calendar: semesters. Summer session for credit, part-time degree program, internships.
Entrance Requirements: Required: high school transcript, interview, ACT Compass. Entrance: minimally difficult. Application deadline: rolling.
Collegiate Environment: Student services: personal-psychological counseling. 72 computers available on campus for general student use. A campuswide network can be accessed. Staffed computer lab on campus provides training in use of computers, software, and the Internet.

■ OHIO WESLEYAN UNIVERSITY
61 S Sandusky St.
Delaware, OH 43015
Tel: (740)368-2000; Free: 800-922-8953
Fax: (740)368-3314
E-mail: amcouch@owu.edu
Web Site: www.owu.edu
Description: Independent United Methodist, 4-year, coed. Awards bachelor's degrees. Founded 1842. Setting: 200-acre small town campus with easy access to Columbus. Total enrollment: 1,565. Faculty: 208 (137 full-time, 71 part-time). Student-undergrad faculty ratio is 9:1. 4,160 applied, 71% were admitted. 22% from top 10% of their high school class, 47% from top quarter, 78% from top half. Full-time: 1,550 students, 53% women, 47% men. Part-time: 15 students, 53% women, 47% men. 54% from out-of-state. 0.1% American Indian or Alaska Native, non-Hispanic/Latino; 6% Hispanic/Latino; 10% Black or African American, non-Hispanic/Latino; 3% Asian, non-Hispanic/Latino; 0.1% Native Hawaiian or other Pacific Islander, non-Hispanic/Latino; 5% international. 13% 25 or older, 86% live on campus, 2% transferred in. Retention: 78% of full-time freshmen returned the following year. Academic areas with the most degrees conferred: biological/life sciences; business/marketing; psychology. Core. Calendar: semesters. Services for LD students, self-designed majors, honors program, double major, summer session for credit, internships. Off campus study. Study abroad program. ROTC: Army (c), Air Force (c).
Entrance Requirements: Options: electronic application, early admission, early decision, early action, deferred admission, international baccalaureate accepted. Required: essay, high school transcript, minimum 2.5 high school GPA, 1 recommendation. Recommended: 2 recommendations, interview. Required for some: SAT or ACT. Entrance: very difficult. Application deadline: 11/15 for early decision. Notification: continuous, continuous for nonresidents, 12/1 for early decision, 1/15 for early action. Transfer credits accepted: Yes. Early decision applicants: 38. Early decision applicants admitted: 32.
Costs Per Year: Application fee: $0. Comprehensive fee: $58,190 includes full-time tuition ($45,500), mandatory fees ($260), and college room and board ($12,430). College room only: $6800. Full-time tuition and fees vary according to course load. Room and board charges vary according to board plan and housing facility. Part-time tuition: $4940 per course. Part-time tuition varies according to course load.
Collegiate Environment: Orientation program. Drama-theater group, choral group, student-run newspaper, radio station. Social organizations: national fraternities, national sororities. Student services: health clinic, personal-

psychological counseling, women's center. Campus security: 24-hour emergency response devices and patrols, late night transport-escort service, controlled dormitory access. Freshmen guaranteed college housing. On-campus residence required through senior year. Options: coed, women-only housing available. L. A. Beeghly Library.

Community Environment: Delaware, a city of 23,000 and county seat of Delaware County, is a 25-minute drive from Columbus, with convenient access by air, highway or bus. The Delaware State Parks provide facilities for fishing, boating, camping, and swimming. An annual event is the Little Brown Jug, which is the largest pacing event in the United States. About half the faculty live within a ten minute walk of student halls and houses, in the architecturally historic northwest section of the city. Ohio Wesleyan is a national school; 50% of the students are from Ohio, while the other 50% represent 40 U.S. states and 54 countries.

■ **OTTERBEIN UNIVERSITY**
1 S Grove St.
Westerville, OH 43081
Tel: (614)890-3000; Free: 800-488-8144
Fax: (614)823-1200
E-mail: uotterb@otterbein.edu
Web Site: www.otterbein.edu

Description: Independent United Methodist, comprehensive, coed. Awards bachelor's, master's, and doctoral degrees and post-master's certificates. Founded 1847. Setting: 142-acre suburban campus with easy access to Columbus. Endowment: $91.5 million. Educational spending for the previous fiscal year: $11,216 per student. Total enrollment: 2,936. Faculty: 328 (175 full-time, 153 part-time). Student-undergrad faculty ratio is 12:1. 3,119 applied, 76% were admitted. 2% from top 10% of their high school class, 28% from top quarter, 84% from top half. Full-time: 2,294 students, 62% women, 38% men. Part-time: 186 students, 66% women, 34% men. Students come from 38 states and territories, 8 other countries, 13% from out-of-state. 0.3% American Indian or Alaska Native, non-Hispanic/Latino; 3% Hispanic/Latino; 6% Black or African American, non-Hispanic/Latino; 2% Asian, non-Hispanic/Latino; 2% international. 6% 25 or older, 60% live on campus, 3% transferred in. Retention: 81% of full-time freshmen returned the following year. Academic areas with the most degrees conferred: business/marketing; health professions and related sciences; visual and performing arts. Core. Calendar: semesters. Academic remediation for entering students, ESL program, services for LD students, advanced placement, self-designed majors, honors program, distance learning, double major, summer session for credit, part-time degree program, adult/continuing education programs, co-op programs and internships, graduate courses open to undergrads. Off campus study at American University, University of Pittsburgh (Semester at Sea), members of the Higher Education Council of Columbus. Study abroad program. ROTC: Army (c), Air Force (c).

Entrance Requirements: Options: electronic application, deferred admission, international baccalaureate accepted. Required: high school transcript, SAT or ACT. Recommended: minimum 2.5 high school GPA, interview. Required for some: essay, 1 recommendation. Entrance: moderately difficult. Application deadline: 3/1. Notification: continuous. SAT Reasoning Test deadline: 4/15. SAT Subject Test deadline: 11/15. Transfer credits accepted: Yes.

Costs Per Year: Application fee: $35. Tuition: $31,424 full-time, $564 per credit hour part-time. Mandatory fees: $450 full-time, $250 per year part-time.

Collegiate Environment: Orientation program. Drama-theater group, choral group, marching band, student-run newspaper, radio station. Social organizations: 100 open to all; national fraternities, local fraternities, local sororities; 28% of eligible men and 28% of eligible women are members. Most popular organizations: Musical groups, Honoraries, Academic interest clubs, Governance. Major annual events: Homecoming, Otterbein Christian Fellowship, Martin Luther King, Jr. Convocation. Student services: health clinic, personal-psychological counseling. Campus security: 24-hour emergency response devices and patrols, student patrols, late night transport-escort service, controlled dormitory access, 24-hour locked residence hall entrances. Courtright Memorial Library. Books: 281,721 (physical), 243,407 (digital/electronic); Serial titles: 15,441 (physical), 7,204 (digital/electronic). Weekly public service hours: 102; students can reserve study rooms. Operations spending for the previous fiscal year: $1.4 million. 198 computers available on campus for general student use. A campuswide network can be accessed from student residence rooms and from off campus. Students can access the following: online class registration. Staffed computer lab on campus provides training in use of computers, software, and the Internet.

Community Environment: Westerville was settled in 1813 by Connecticut, New York, and Virginia families, and Quakers from Pennsylvania. The community, seven miles north of Columbus, has excellent city and college libraries, many churches, a modern medical center, and various civic and service organizations. A site of interest is the Hanby House. Hoover Reservoir is located about four miles east, and offers facilities for picnicking, fishing, and boating. Part-time employment is available.

■ **OWENS COMMUNITY COLLEGE**
PO Box 10000
Toledo, OH 43699-1947
Tel: (419)661-7000; Free: 800-GO-OWENS
E-mail: meghan_schmidbauer@owens.edu
Web Site: www.owens.edu

Description: State-supported, 2-year, coed. Awards certificates, transfer associate, and terminal associate degrees. Founded 1966. Setting: 420-acre suburban campus with easy access to Detroit. Endowment: $1.7 million. Educational spending for the previous fiscal year: $4499 per student. Total enrollment: 12,572. Faculty: 1,259 (189 full-time, 1,070 part-time). Student-undergrad faculty ratio is 16:1. 8,090 applied, 100% were admitted. 2% from top 10% of their high school class, 11% from top quarter, 38% from top half. Full-time: 4,257 students, 56% women, 44% men. Part-time: 8,315 students, 49% women, 51% men. Students come from 25 states and territories, 6 other countries, 3% from out-of-state. 0.4% American Indian or Alaska Native, non-Hispanic/Latino; 7% Hispanic/Latino; 15% Black or African American, non-Hispanic/Latino; 1% Asian, non-Hispanic/Latino; 1% international. 32% 25 or older, 1% transferred in. Core. Calendar: semesters. Academic remediation for entering students, ESL program, services for LD students, advanced placement, accelerated degree program, honors program, independent study, distance learning, double major, summer session for credit, part-time degree program, adult/continuing education programs, co-op programs and internships. Study abroad program.

Entrance Requirements: Open admission except for health technologies, Peace Officer Academy, early childhood education programs. Options: electronic application, early admission, deferred admission. Required for some: minimum 2 high school GPA, interview. Entrance: noncompetitive. Application deadline: rolling. Notification: continuous. Transfer credits accepted: Yes.

Collegiate Environment: Orientation program. Drama-theater group, choral group, student-run newspaper. Social organizations: 14 open to all. Major annual events: Fall Fest, Spring Fling. Student services: personal-psychological counseling. Campus security: 24-hour emergency response devices and patrols, student patrols, classroom doors lock from inside, campus alert system. Owens Community College Library plus 1 other. Operations spending for the previous fiscal year: $1.1 million. 264 computers available on campus for general student use. Computer purchase/lease plans available. A campuswide network can be accessed from off-campus. Students can access the following: online class registration, online catalog, advising 'chat', ONet personal network storage, learning management system, password reset, Toledo Blade Newspaper, Express Card, Office 365 software suite, education applications. Staffed computer lab on campus provides training in use of computers, software, and the Internet.

Community Environment: See University of Toledo.

■ **PONTIFICAL COLLEGE JOSEPHINUM**
7625 N High St.
Columbus, OH 43235
Tel: (614)885-5585; Free: 888-252-5812
E-mail: acrawford@pcj.edu
Web Site: www.pcj.edu

Description: Independent Roman Catholic, comprehensive, men only. Awards bachelor's, master's, and doctoral degrees. Founded 1888. Setting: 100-acre suburban campus. Endowment: $41.8 million. Educational spending for the previous fiscal year: $14,542 per student. Total enrollment: 119. Faculty: 22 (13 full-time, 9 part-time). Student-undergrad faculty ratio is 7:1. 8 applied, 75% were admitted. Full-time: 78 students. Students come from 13 states and territories, 3 other countries, 55% from out-of-state. 30% 25 or older, 100% live on campus, 17% transferred in. Retention: 30% of full-time freshmen returned the following year. Academic areas with the most degrees conferred: history; English; area and ethnic studies. Core. Calendar: semesters. Academic remediation for entering students, ESL program, services for LD students, advanced placement, honors program, double major, internships, graduate courses open to undergrads. Off campus study at 2 members of the Theological Cluster.

Entrance Requirements: Required: essay, high school transcript, 3 recommendations, interview, SAT or ACT. Entrance: minimally difficult. Application deadline: 7/31. Preference given to candidates for the priesthood.
Collegiate Environment: Orientation program. Drama-theater group, choral group. Student services: health clinic, personal-psychological counseling. Campus security: 24-hour emergency response devices, controlled dormitory access. Wehrle Memorial Library. Operations spending for the previous fiscal year: $303,425. 10 computers available on campus for general student use. A campuswide network can be accessed from student residence rooms. Staffed computer lab on campus.
Community Environment: See Ohio State University - Columbus Campus.

■ **PROFESSIONAL SKILLS INSTITUTE**
1505 Holland Rd.
Maumee, OH 43537
Tel: (419)531-9610
Fax: (419)531-4732
Web Site: www.proskills.edu
Description: Proprietary, 2-year, coed. Awards certificates, diplomas, and terminal associate degrees. Founded 1984. Setting: 2-acre urban campus with easy access to Detroit. Total enrollment: 292. 43 applied. 75% 25 or older. Core. Calendar: quarters. Services for LD students, part-time degree program, internships. Off campus study at Lourdes College.
Entrance Requirements: Required: high school transcript, minimum 2.0 high school GPA, interview, Wonderlic aptitude test. Entrance: moderately difficult. Notification: 9/15.
Collegiate Environment: Student services: health clinic. Campus security: 24-hour emergency response devices, security cameras. Professional Skills Institute Library plus 1 other.

■ **RABBINICAL COLLEGE OF TELSHE**
28400 Euclid Ave.
Wickliffe, OH 44092-2523
Tel: (216)943-5300
Description: Independent Jewish, comprehensive, men only. Awards bachelor's and master's degrees. Total enrollment: 57. Student-undergrad faculty ratio is 7:1. 25% from out-of-state. 14% 25 or older. Retention: 25% of full-time freshmen returned the following year.
Entrance Requirements: Open admission.

■ **REMINGTON COLLEGE-CLEVELAND CAMPUS**
14445 Broadway Ave.
Cleveland, OH 44125
Tel: (216)475-7520; Free: 800-323-8122
Fax: (216)475-6055
Web Site: www.remingtoncollege.edu
Description: Independent, 2-year, coed. Awards terminal associate degrees. Setting: 2-acre urban campus. Calendar: continuous. Co-op programs.
Collegiate Environment: Main library plus 2 others.

■ **ROSEDALE BIBLE COLLEGE**
2270 Rosedale Rd.
Irwin, OH 43029-9501
Tel: (740)857-1311
Fax: (877)857-1312
Web Site: www.rosedale.edu
Description: Independent Mennonite, 2-year, coed. Awards terminal associate degrees. Founded 1952. Setting: rural campus with easy access to Columbus. Total enrollment: 89. Faculty: (2 full-time, 4 part-time). Student-undergrad faculty ratio is 14:1. 86 applied, 81% were admitted. Core. Calendar: 4-1-4. Services for LD students, independent study, part-time degree program, adult/continuing education programs, co-op programs and internships. Off campus study at Akwachink Leadership Training School. Study abroad program. ROTC: Army (c), Naval (c), Air Force (c).
Entrance Requirements: Open admission. Options: electronic application, early admission. Required: essay, high school transcript, 2 recommendations. Entrance: noncompetitive. Application deadline: rolling. Transfer credits accepted: Yes.
Costs Per Year: Application fee: $50. Comprehensive fee: $14,381 includes full-time tuition ($8400), mandatory fees ($331), and college room and board ($5650). Full-time tuition and fees vary according to course load. Room and board charges vary according to housing facility. Part-time tuition: $280 per credit hour. Part-time mandatory fees: $70 per term.

Collegiate Environment: Orientation program. Drama-theater group, choral group. Student services: personal-psychological counseling. 7 computers available on campus for general student use. A campuswide network can be accessed from student residence rooms.

■ **ROSS COLLEGE (CANTON)**
4300 Munson St. NW
Canton, OH 44718
Tel: (330)494-1214; Free: 866-815-5578
Web Site: www.rosseducation.edu
Description: Proprietary, primarily 2-year, coed. Part of Education Management Corporation. Awards diplomas, terminal associate, and bachelor's degrees. Founded 1929. Setting: suburban campus. Calendar: quarters.

■ **ROSS COLLEGE (SYLVANIA)**
5834 Monroe St.
Ste. F-J
Sylvania, OH 43560
Tel: (419)882-3203; Free: 866-815-5578
Web Site: www.rosseducation.edu
Description: Proprietary, 2-year, coed.

■ **SHAWNEE STATE UNIVERSITY**
940 Second St.
Portsmouth, OH 45662
Tel: (740)347-1732; Free: 800-959-2778
Fax: (740)355-2470
E-mail: ameans@shawnee.edu
Web Site: www.shawnee.edu
Description: State-supported, comprehensive, coed. Part of Ohio Higher Educational System. Awards associate, bachelor's, and master's degrees. Founded 1986. Setting: 62-acre small town campus with easy access to Charleston-Huntington-Ashland Area. Endowment: $19.3 million. Total enrollment: 3,582. Faculty: 314 (151 full-time, 163 part-time). Student-undergrad faculty ratio is 13:1. 2,860 applied, 70% were admitted. 2% from top 10% of their high school class, 22% from top quarter, 25% from top half. Full-time: 2,832 students, 52% women, 48% men. Part-time: 574 students, 65% women, 35% men. Students come from 27 states and territories, 18 other countries, 12% from out-of-state. 0.6% American Indian or Alaska Native, non-Hispanic/Latino; 0.6% Hispanic/Latino; 5% Black or African American, non-Hispanic/Latino; 0.7% Asian, non-Hispanic/Latino; 0.1% Native Hawaiian or other Pacific Islander, non-Hispanic/Latino; 1% international. 15% 25 or older, 28% live on campus, 5% transferred in. Retention: 68% of full-time freshmen returned the following year. Academic areas with the most degrees conferred: business/marketing; social sciences; health professions and related sciences. Core. Calendar: semesters. Academic remediation for entering students, ESL program, services for LD students, advanced placement, accelerated degree program, self-designed majors, honors program, independent study, distance learning, double major, summer session for credit, part-time degree program, adult/continuing education programs, internships. Off campus study. Study abroad program.
Entrance Requirements: Open admission except for allied heath sciences, rehabilitation sports professions programs. Option: electronic application. Required: high school transcript. Required for some: essay, minimum 2.66 high school GPA, 1 recommendation, interview, ACT/SAT scores if student is under 21. Entrance: noncompetitive. Application deadline: rolling. Notification: continuous. Transfer credits accepted: Yes.
Costs Per Year: Application fee: $0. State resident tuition: $8556 full-time, $348.14 per credit hour part-time. Nonresident tuition: $14,714 full-time, $604.67 per credit hour part-time. Full-time tuition varies according to course load, program, and reciprocity agreements. Part-time tuition varies according to course load, program, and reciprocity agreements. College room and board: $10,864. College room only: $6896. Room and board charges vary according to board plan and housing facility. Tuition guaranteed not to increase for student's term of enrollment.
Collegiate Environment: Orientation program. Drama-theater group, choral group, student-run newspaper. Social organizations: 49 open to all; national fraternities, national sororities, local sororities; 1% of eligible men and 1% of eligible women are members. Most popular organizations: campus ministry, Health Executives and Administrators Learning Society, Student Programming Board, Student Government Association. Major annual events: Homecoming, Springfest, Scare Week. Student services: health clinic, personal-psychological counseling, women's center. Campus security: 24-hour emergency response devices and patrols. Clark Memorial Library.

Books: 122,670 (physical), 103,584 (digital/electronic); Serial titles: 140 (physical), 672 (digital/electronic); Databases: 543. Weekly public service hours: 91; study areas open 24 hours, 5-7 days a week; students can reserve study rooms. 620 computers available on campus for general student use. Computer purchase/lease plans available. A campuswide network can be accessed from student residence rooms and from off campus. Students can access the following: online class registration, financial aid, student billing, courses, student service portal. Staffed computer lab on campus provides training in use of computers, software, and the Internet.

Community Environment: A quaint city of 23,000 residents, Portsmouth is Scioto County's largest retail center and a popular tourist area as well. Its Bonneyfiddle area, with its old-world charm, is a treasure trove for antique buffs, and the winding Ohio River offers opportunities for boating, waterskiing, and fishing. Shawnee State Park provides nature trails, as well as boating, fishing and golf.

■ **SINCLAIR COMMUNITY COLLEGE**
444 W Third St.
Dayton, OH 45402-1460
Tel: (937)512-2500; Free: 800-315-3000
E-mail: ssmith@sinclair.edu
Web Site: www.sinclair.edu

Description: State and locally supported, 2-year, coed. Part of Ohio Board of Regents. Awards certificates, transfer associate, and terminal associate degrees. Founded 1887. Setting: 50-acre urban campus with easy access to Cincinnati. Total enrollment: 21,561. 50% 25 or older. Core. Calendar: quarters. Academic remediation for entering students, ESL program, services for LD students, self-designed majors, honors program, independent study, distance learning, summer session for credit, part-time degree program, external degree program, adult/continuing education programs, co-op programs and internships. Off campus study at 17 members of the Southwestern Ohio Council for Higher Education. ROTC: Army (c), Air Force (c).

Entrance Requirements: Open admission except for allied health programs. Options: electronic application, early admission, deferred admission. Required for some: high school transcript, interview. Entrance: noncompetitive. Application deadline: rolling. Notification: continuous.

Collegiate Environment: Orientation program. Drama-theater group, choral group, student-run newspaper. Social organizations: 55 open to all. Most popular organizations: African-American Men of the Future, Ohio Fellows, Phi Theta Kappa, Student Government, student newspaper. Major annual events: Welcome Week, Spring Fling, Student Health Fair. Student services: personal-psychological counseling. Campus security: 24-hour emergency response devices and patrols, student patrols, late night transport-escort service. Learning Resources Center.

■ **SOUTHERN STATE COMMUNITY COLLEGE**
100 Hobart Dr.
Hillsboro, OH 45133-9487
Tel: (937)393-3431
Fax: (937)393-9370
E-mail: wjohnson@sscc.edu
Web Site: www.sscc.edu

Description: State-supported, 2-year, coed. Awards certificates, transfer associate, and terminal associate degrees. Founded 1975. Setting: 60-acre rural campus. Endowment: $1.9 million. Total enrollment: 2,431. Faculty: 179 (58 full-time, 121 part-time). Student-undergrad faculty ratio is 16:1. 405 applied, 100% were admitted. Full-time: 1,175 students, 62% women, 38% men. Part-time: 1,256 students, 71% women, 29% men. Students come from 2 states and territories. 0.3% American Indian or Alaska Native, non-Hispanic/Latino; 0.7% Hispanic/Latino; 2% Black or African American, non-Hispanic/Latino; 0.5% Asian, non-Hispanic/Latino; 0.1% Native Hawaiian or other Pacific Islander, non-Hispanic/Latino. Core. Calendar: quarters. Academic remediation for entering students, services for LD students, advanced placement, self-designed majors, independent study, distance learning, double major, summer session for credit, part-time degree program, co-op programs and internships. Off campus study at 15 members of the Southwestern Ohio Council for Higher Education.

Entrance Requirements: Open admission. Options: electronic application, early admission, deferred admission. Recommended: high school transcript. Entrance: noncompetitive. Application deadline: rolling. Notification: continuous. Transfer credits accepted: Yes.

Collegiate Environment: Orientation program. Drama-theater group, choral group. Social organizations: 3 open to all. Most popular organizations: Student Government Association, Drama Club. Student services: personal-psychological counseling. Library plus 4 others. Operations spending for the previous fiscal year: $637,144. 550 computers available on campus for general student use. A campuswide network can be accessed from off-campus. Students can access the following: online class registration. Staffed computer lab on campus provides training in use of computers, software, and the Internet.

Community Environment: Hillsboro, approximately 40 miles east of Cincinnati, is in a primarily rural setting with small towns and villages.

■ **STARK STATE COLLEGE**
6200 Frank Ave., NW
North Canton, OH 44720-7299
Tel: (330)494-6170; Free: 800-797-8275
Fax: (330)497-6313
E-mail: info@starkstate.edu
Web Site: www.starkstate.edu

Description: State-related, 2-year, coed. Part of University System of Ohio. Awards certificates, transfer associate, and terminal associate degrees. Founded 1960. Setting: 100-acre suburban campus with easy access to Cleveland. Endowment: $6.2 million. Educational spending for the previous fiscal year: $4646 per student. Total enrollment: 11,028. Faculty: 480 (185 full-time, 295 part-time). Student-undergrad faculty ratio is 21:1. Full-time: 3,090 students, 52% women, 48% men. Part-time: 7,938 students, 61% women, 39% men. Students come from 10 states and territories, 1 other country, 1% from out-of-state. 0.4% American Indian or Alaska Native, non-Hispanic/Latino; 2% Hispanic/Latino; 13% Black or African American, non-Hispanic/Latino; 2% Asian, non-Hispanic/Latino; 0.1% Native Hawaiian or other Pacific Islander, non-Hispanic/Latino; 0.1% international. 46% 25 or older, 8% transferred in. Core. Calendar: semesters. Academic remediation for entering students, services for LD students, self-designed majors, independent study, distance learning, double major, summer session for credit, part-time degree program, external degree program, adult/continuing education programs, co-op programs and internships. Off campus study at Malone College, University of Akron, Walsh College, Kent State University, Stark Campus.

Entrance Requirements: Open admission. Option: electronic application. Required: high school transcript. Entrance: noncompetitive. Application deadlines: rolling, rolling for nonresidents. Notification: continuous, continuous for nonresidents.

Costs Per Year: One-time mandatory fee: $95. State resident tuition: $2796 full-time, $116.50 per credit hour part-time. Nonresident tuition: $4980 full-time, $245.50 per credit hour part-time. Mandatory fees: $1,274 full-time, $53.10 per credit hour part-time. Full-time tuition and fees vary according to course load and program. Part-time tuition and fees vary according to program.

Collegiate Environment: Orientation program. Student-run newspaper. Social organizations: 52 open to all. Most popular organizations: Phi Theta Kappa, Business Student Club, Institute of Management Accountants, Stark State College Association of Medical Assistants, Student Health Information Management Association. Major annual events: Halloween Costume Contest, Make A Difference Day, Spring Festival. Student services: personal-psychological counseling. Campus security: 24-hour emergency response devices and patrols, student patrols, late night transport-escort service, patrols by trained security personnel during hours of operation. Learning Resource Center plus 1 other. Operations spending for the previous fiscal year: $425,783. 1,860 computers available on campus for general student use. A campuswide network can be accessed from off-campus. Students can access the following: online class registration. Staffed computer lab on campus provides training in use of computers, software, and the Internet.

Community Environment: Set in small city environment - commuter campus only.

■ **STAUTZENBERGER COLLEGE (BRECKSVILLE)**
8001 Katherine Blvd.
Brecksville, OH 44141
Tel: (440)838-1999; Free: 800-437-2997
Web Site: www.sctoday.edu

Description: Proprietary, 2-year, coed. Awards certificates, diplomas, and transfer associate degrees.

■ **STAUTZENBERGER COLLEGE (MAUMEE)**
1796 Indian Wood Cir.
Maumee, OH 43537

Tel: (419)866-0261; Free: 800-552-5099
Fax: (419)867-9821
Web Site: www.sctoday.edu/maumee
Description: Proprietary, 2-year, coed. Awards certificates, diplomas, and terminal associate degrees. Setting: urban campus. Total enrollment: 867. Student-undergrad faculty ratio is 26:1. 5% from out-of-state. 62% 25 or older. Retention: 62% of full-time freshmen returned the following year. Calendar: quarters.
Entrance Requirements: Open admission.

■ TERRA STATE COMMUNITY COLLEGE
2830 Napoleon Rd.
Fremont, OH 43420-9670
Tel: (419)334-8400; Free: 866-AT-TERRA
Fax: (419)334-9035
Web Site: www.terra.edu
Description: State-supported, 2-year, coed. Part of Ohio Board of Regents. Awards certificates, diplomas, transfer associate, and terminal associate degrees. Founded 1968. Setting: 100-acre small town campus with easy access to Toledo. Total enrollment: 2,603. Faculty: 191 (40 full-time, 151 part-time). Student-undergrad faculty ratio is 15:1. 371 applied, 100% were admitted. Full-time: 822 students, 60% women, 40% men. Part-time: 1,781 students, 54% women, 46% men. 0.5% American Indian or Alaska Native, non-Hispanic/Latino; 9% Hispanic/Latino; 4% Black or African American, non-Hispanic/Latino; 0.4% Asian, non-Hispanic/Latino; 0.4% international. Core. Calendar: semesters. Academic remediation for entering students, services for LD students, advanced placement, self-designed majors, independent study, distance learning, double major, summer session for credit, part-time degree program, adult/continuing education programs, co-op programs and internships. Off campus study.
Entrance Requirements: Open admission. Options: electronic application, early admission, deferred admission. Required: high school transcript. Entrance: noncompetitive. Application deadline: rolling. Transfer credits accepted: Yes.
Collegiate Environment: Orientation program. Choral group. Social organizations: 5 open to all. Most popular organizations: Phi Theta Kappa, Student Activities Club, Society of Plastic Engineers, Koinonia, Student Senate. Major annual events: Student Orientation, Commencement, Open House. Student services: legal services, personal-psychological counseling. Campus security: 24-hour emergency response devices. Learning Resource Center.

■ TIFFIN UNIVERSITY
155 Miami St.
Tiffin, OH 44883-2161
Tel: (419)447-6442; Free: 800-968-6446
Fax: (419)447-9605
E-mail: depughst@tiffin.edu
Web Site: www.tiffin.edu
Description: Independent, comprehensive, coed. Awards associate, bachelor's, and master's degrees and post-master's certificates. Founded 1888. Setting: 135-acre small town campus with easy access to Toledo. Endowment: $10.9 million. Educational spending for the previous fiscal year: $4370 per student. Total enrollment: 3,096. Faculty: 306 (77 full-time, 229 part-time). Student-undergrad faculty ratio is 14:1. 3,977 applied, 69% were admitted. Full-time: 1,724 students, 46% women, 54% men. Part-time: 579 students, 64% women, 36% men. Students come from 26 states and territories, 18 other countries, 22% from out-of-state. 0.2% American Indian or Alaska Native, non-Hispanic/Latino; 3% Hispanic/Latino; 9% Black or African American, non-Hispanic/Latino; 0.2% Asian, non-Hispanic/Latino; 11% international. 22% 25 or older, 50% live on campus, 6% transferred in. Retention: 67% of full-time freshmen returned the following year. Academic areas with the most degrees conferred: business/marketing; homeland security, law enforcement, firefighting, and protective services; psychology. Core. Calendar: semesters. Academic remediation for entering students, ESL program, services for LD students, advanced placement, accelerated degree program, freshman honors college, independent study, distance learning, double major, summer session for credit, adult/continuing education programs, internships. Off campus study. Study abroad program. ROTC: Army (c), Air Force (c).
Entrance Requirements: Options: electronic application, international baccalaureate accepted. Required: high school transcript. Recommended: minimum 3 high school GPA. Required for some: essay, interview, SAT or

ACT. Entrance: moderately difficult. Application deadline: rolling. Notification: continuous. Transfer credits accepted: Yes.
Costs Per Year: Application fee: $20. Comprehensive fee: $37,650 includes full-time tuition ($25,710), mandatory fees ($400), and college room and board ($11,540). College room only: $6180. Part-time tuition: $857.
Collegiate Environment: Orientation program. Drama-theater group, choral group, marching band, student-run newspaper. Social organizations: 40 open to all; national fraternities, national sororities, local fraternities, local sororities; 1% of eligible men and 1% of eligible women are members. Most popular organizations: Student Government Association, H2O, International Student Association, Global Affairs Organization, Circle K. Major annual events: Late Night Breakfast, Homecoming, Faculty vs. Student Basketball Game. Student services: health clinic, personal-psychological counseling, women's center. Campus security: 24-hour emergency response devices, student patrols, late night transport-escort service, controlled dormitory access. 1,050 college housing spaces available; 1,035 were occupied in 2018-19. Freshmen guaranteed college housing. On-campus residence required through sophomore year. Options: coed, men-only, women-only housing available. Pfeiffer Library plus 1 other. Books: 43,505 (physical), 317,775 (digital/electronic); Serial titles: 331 (physical), 97,873 (digital/electronic); Databases: 216. Weekly public service hours: 73. Operations spending for the previous fiscal year: $371,194. 280 computers available on campus for general student use. Computer purchase/lease plans available. A campuswide network can be accessed from student residence rooms and from off campus. Students can access the following: online class registration. Staffed computer lab on campus provides training in use of computers, software, and the Internet.
Community Environment: See Heidelberg College.

■ TRI-STATE BIBLE COLLEGE
506 Margaret St.
South Point, OH 45680-8402
Tel: (740)377-2520
Fax: (740)377-0001
Web Site: www.tsbc.edu
Description: Independent nondenominational, comprehensive, coed. Awards associate, bachelor's, and master's degrees. Founded 1970. Setting: 4-acre suburban campus. Total enrollment: 65. 86% 25 or older. Calendar: semesters.
Entrance Requirements: Open admission.

■ UNION INSTITUTE & UNIVERSITY
440 E McMillan St.
Cincinnati, OH 45206-1925
Tel: (513)861-6400; Free: 800-486-3116
Fax: (513)861-0779
Web Site: www.myunion.edu
Description: Independent, university, coed. Awards bachelor's, master's, and doctoral degrees and post-master's certificates. Founded 1964. Setting: 5-acre urban campus with easy access to Cincinnati. Endowment: $793,428. Research spending for the previous fiscal year: $160,937. Educational spending for the previous fiscal year: $6062 per student. Total enrollment: 1,133. Faculty: 336 (35 full-time, 301 part-time). Student-undergrad faculty ratio is 8:1. Full-time: 399 students, 53% women, 47% men. Part-time: 438 students, 47% women, 53% men. Students come from 40 states and territories, 13% from out-of-state. 0.2% American Indian or Alaska Native, non-Hispanic/Latino; 25% Hispanic/Latino; 18% Black or African American, non-Hispanic/Latino; 0.8% Asian, non-Hispanic/Latino; 0.7% Native Hawaiian or other Pacific Islander, non-Hispanic/Latino. 94% 25 or older, 29% transferred in. Retention: 92% of full-time freshmen returned the following year. Core. Calendar: trimesters some programs offer split (8-week) sessions; some programs have two 6-month semesters. Academic remediation for entering students, services for LD students, advanced placement, accelerated degree program, independent study, distance learning, double major, summer session for credit, part-time degree program, external degree program, adult/continuing education programs, internships, graduate courses open to undergrads. Off campus study.
Entrance Requirements: Open admission except for undergraduate social work program. Options: electronic application, deferred admission. Required: essay, recommendation from program faculty. Recommended: interview. Required for some: high school transcript, 1 recommendation. Entrance: noncompetitive. Application deadline: rolling. Notification: continuous. Transfer credits accepted: Yes.
Collegiate Environment: Orientation program. Campus security: 24-hour

emergency response devices, late night transport-escort service, security personnel on site during business and class hours. Union Institute & University Library. Books: 3 million (digital/electronic); Serial titles: 77,317 (digital/electronic); Databases: 171. Weekly public service hours: 50. Operations spending for the previous fiscal year: $621,154. 65 computers available on campus for general student use. Computer purchase/lease plans available. A campuswide network can be accessed from off-campus. Students can access the following: online class registration, CampusWeb: access to basic information. Staffed computer lab on campus provides training in use of computers, software, and the Internet.

■ THE UNIVERSITY OF AKRON

302 Buchtel Common
Akron, OH 44325
Tel: (330)972-7111; Free: 800-655-4884
Fax: (330)972-7676
E-mail: gentile@uakron.edu
Web Site: www.uakron.edu

Description: State-supported, university, coed. Awards associate, bachelor's, master's, and doctoral degrees and post-master's certificates. Founded 1870. Setting: 223-acre urban campus with easy access to Cleveland. Endowment: $191.4 million. Research spending for the previous fiscal year: $26.7 million. Educational spending for the previous fiscal year: $8959 per student. Total enrollment: 20,169. Faculty: 1,452 (702 full-time, 750 part-time). Student-undergrad faculty ratio is 18:1. 15,109 applied, 93% were admitted. 24% from top 10% of their high school class, 50% from top quarter, 77% from top half. 8 National Merit Scholars, 48 valedictorians. Full-time: 13,562 students, 46% women, 54% men. Part-time: 3,309 students, 51% women, 49% men. Students come from 38 states and territories, 67 other countries, 6% from out-of-state. 0.1% American Indian or Alaska Native, non-Hispanic/Latino; 3% Hispanic/Latino; 12% Black or African American, non-Hispanic/Latino; 3% Asian, non-Hispanic/Latino; 2% international. 11% 25 or older, 17% live on campus, 3% transferred in. Retention: 73% of full-time freshmen returned the following year. Academic areas with the most degrees conferred: business/marketing; health professions and related sciences; engineering. Core. Calendar: semesters. Academic remediation for entering students, ESL program, services for LD students, advanced placement, accelerated degree program, self-designed majors, freshman honors college, honors program, independent study, distance learning, double major, summer session for credit, part-time degree program, external degree program, adult/continuing education programs, co-op programs and internships, graduate courses open to undergrads. Study abroad program. ROTC: Army, Air Force (c).

Entrance Requirements: Options: electronic application, early action, deferred admission, international baccalaureate accepted. Required: high school transcript, SAT or ACT. Required for some: essay, 3 recommendations, interview. Entrance: moderately difficult. Application deadlines: 8/11, 11/1 for early action. Notification: 9/15. SAT Reasoning Test deadline: 7/1. SAT Subject Test deadline: 7/1. Transfer credits accepted: Yes. Early action applicants: 6,486. Early action applicants admitted: 5,448.

Costs Per Year: Application fee: $45. State resident tuition: $8618 full-time, $359 per credit hour part-time. Nonresident tuition: $17,149 full-time, $715 per credit hour part-time. Mandatory fees: $1652 full-time. Full-time tuition and fees vary according to course load, degree level, location, and program. Part-time tuition varies according to course load, degree level, location, and program. College room and board: $12,296. College room only: $8026. Room and board charges vary according to board plan and housing facility.

Collegiate Environment: Orientation program. Drama-theater group, choral group, marching band, student-run newspaper, radio station. Social organizations: 300 open to all; national fraternities, national sororities, local fraternities; 4% of eligible men and 4% of eligible women are members. Most popular organizations: AK-Rowdies, Akron Animation Association, National Society of Leadership and Success, Golden Key International Honor Society, Alpha Phi Omega. Major annual events: Homecoming, Student Appreciation Day, Greek Week. Student services: legal services, health clinic, personal-psychological counseling, women's center. Campus security: 24-hour emergency response devices and patrols, student patrols, late night transport-escort service, controlled dormitory access. Bierce Library plus 2 others. Books: 1.1 million (physical); Serial titles: 25,089 (physical). Study areas open 24 hours, 5-7 days a week; students can reserve study rooms. Operations spending for the previous fiscal year: $9.9 million. 3,150 computers available on campus for general student use. Computer purchase/lease plans available. A campuswide network can be accessed from student residence rooms and from off campus. Students can access the following:

online class registration, library laptops for student checkout. Staffed computer lab on campus provides training in use of computers, software, and the Internet.

Community Environment: The city is a merchandising center and a vital distribution gateway between the industrial East and the Midwest. The Portage Lakes district south of the city provides facilities for boating, swimming, fishing and ice skating. A number of parks provide additional facilities for skiing and other outdoor activities. A short distance to the north, are the New Gateway Complex, Jacobs Field, home of the Cleveland Indians, Gund Arena, of the Cleveland Cavaliers, and the Rock'n Roll Hall of Fame. To the South is The Pro Football Hall of Fame. Local points of interest are the Akron Art Museum, Blossom Music Center, Canal Park Baseball Stadium, Goodyear Aircraft Hanger, Inventure Place, Perkins Mansion, and the Stan Hywet Hall. Special events are the World Series of Golf, held at the Firestone Country Club, and the All-American Soap Box Derby.

■ THE UNIVERSITY OF AKRON WAYNE COLLEGE

1901 Smucker Rd.
Orrville, OH 44667-9192
Tel: (330)683-2010; Free: 800-221-8308
Fax: (330)684-8989
E-mail: wayneadmissions@uakron.edu
Web Site: www.wayne.uakron.edu

Description: State-supported, primarily 2-year, coed. Part of The University of Akron. Awards certificates, transfer associate, terminal associate, and bachelor's degrees. Founded 1972. Setting: 157-acre rural campus. Research spending for the previous fiscal year: $600. Educational spending for the previous fiscal year: $7537 per student. Total enrollment: 2,353. Faculty: 186 (24 full-time, 162 part-time). Student-undergrad faculty ratio is 20:1. 1,053 applied, 77% were admitted. 4% from top 10% of their high school class, 20% from top quarter, 51% from top half. Full-time: 1,109 students, 57% women, 43% men. Part-time: 1,244 students, 62% women, 38% men. Students come from 2 states and territories, 2 other countries. 0.3% American Indian or Alaska Native, non-Hispanic/Latino; 1% Hispanic/Latino; 3% Black or African American, non-Hispanic/Latino; 0.6% Asian, non-Hispanic/Latino; 0.1% Native Hawaiian or other Pacific Islander, non-Hispanic/Latino. 33% 25 or older, 2% transferred in. Retention: 55% of full-time freshmen returned the following year. Core. Calendar: semesters. Academic remediation for entering students, services for LD students, advanced placement, honors program, independent study, distance learning, double major, summer session for credit, part-time degree program, adult/continuing education programs, co-op programs and internships. Off campus study at Walsh University (Walsh at Wayne). ROTC: Army (c), Air Force (c).

Entrance Requirements: Open admission. Options: electronic application, early admission, deferred admission. Recommended: SAT or ACT, ACT Compass. Required for some: high school transcript, SAT or ACT, ACT Compass. Entrance: noncompetitive. Application deadline: 8/13. Notification: continuous. Transfer credits accepted: Yes.

Collegiate Environment: Orientation program. Most popular organizations: Associated Student Government (ASG), Campus Crusade for Christ (CRU), Waynessence, Nursing Club, Adult Learner Student Organization (ALSO). Student services: personal-psychological counseling. Campus security: 24-hour emergency response devices, late night transport-escort service. Wayne College Library. Operations spending for the previous fiscal year: $297,096. 276 computers available on campus for general student use. Computer purchase/lease plans available. A campuswide network can be accessed from off-campus. Students can access the following: online class registration. Staffed computer lab on campus provides training in use of computers, software, and the Internet.

Community Environment: Orrville is a thriving community with a diversified business and industry base, best known for being the home of The J. M. Smucker Company. Located 30 miles southwest of Akron and The University of Akron campus, and 50 miles south of Cleveland, the city of Orrville has a population of 8,485. Residents of this area have relatively easy access to metropolitan amenities while enjoying a more relaxed rural-suburban atmosphere. The community park provides many recreational facilities and the Rehm Performing Arts Pavilion is the setting for many musical and cultural events. There are also 26 churches of various denominations, a community library, and a 38 bed hospital in Orrville.

■ UNIVERSITY OF CINCINNATI

PO Box 210063
Cincinnati, OH 45221
Tel: (513)556-6000

E-mail: admissions@uc.edu

Web Site: www.uc.edu

Description: State-supported, university, coed. Awards associate, bachelor's, master's, and doctoral degrees and post-master's certificates. Founded 1819. Setting: 137-acre urban campus with easy access to Cincinnati. Endowment: $1.3 billion. Research spending for the previous fiscal year: $187.9 million. Total enrollment: 37,204. Faculty: 3,511 (2,212 full-time, 1,299 part-time). Student-undergrad faculty ratio is 17:1. 21,161 applied, 78% were admitted. 22% from top 10% of their high school class, 48% from top quarter, 81% from top half. 70 National Merit Scholars, 55 valedictorians. Full-time: 22,671 students, 47% women, 53% men. Part-time: 3,937 students, 63% women, 37% men. Students come from 51 states and territories, 138 other countries, 15% from out-of-state. 0.1% American Indian or Alaska Native, non-Hispanic/Latino; 3% Hispanic/Latino; 7% Black or African American, non-Hispanic/Latino; 4% Asian, non-Hispanic/Latino; 0.1% Native Hawaiian or other Pacific Islander, non-Hispanic/Latino; 4% international. 12% 25 or older, 26% live on campus, 7% transferred in. Retention: 86% of full-time freshmen returned the following year. Academic areas with the most degrees conferred: business/marketing; health professions and related sciences; engineering. Core. Calendar: semesters. Academic remediation for entering students, ESL program, services for LD students, advanced placement, accelerated degree program, honors program, independent study, distance learning, double major, summer session for credit, adult/continuing education programs, co-op programs and internships, graduate courses open to undergrads. Off campus study at Greater Cincinnati Consortium of Colleges and Universities. Study abroad program. ROTC: Army, Air Force.

Entrance Requirements: Options: electronic application, early action, deferred admission, international baccalaureate accepted. Required: essay, high school transcript, SAT or ACT. Required for some: 1 recommendation, audition for performing arts majors. Entrance: moderately difficult. Application deadlines: 3/1, 12/1 for early action. Notification: continuous until 5/1, rolling for early action. SAT Reasoning Test deadline: 5/1. Transfer credits accepted: Yes.

Costs Per Year: Application fee: $50. State resident tuition: $9322 full-time, $389 per credit hour part-time. Nonresident tuition: $24,656 full-time, $1028 per credit hour part-time. Mandatory fees: $1678 full-time, $70 per credit hour part-time. Full-time tuition and fees vary according to course load, location, program, and reciprocity agreements. Part-time tuition and fees vary according to course load, location, program, and reciprocity agreements. College room and board: $11,340. College room only: $6756. Room and board charges vary according to board plan and housing facility.

Collegiate Environment: Orientation program. Drama-theater group, choral group, marching band, student-run newspaper, radio station. Social organizations: 542 open to all; national fraternities, national sororities, local fraternities, local sororities; 6% of eligible men and 6% of eligible women are members. Most popular organizations: Serve Beyond Cincinnati, University of Cincinnati Mountaineering Club, Rally Cats, Engineers Without Borders, UC League of Legends. Major annual events: Welcome Weekend, Homecoming, Annual Spring Concert. Student services: health clinic, personal-psychological counseling, women's center. Campus security: 24-hour emergency response devices and patrols, student patrols, late night transport-escort service, controlled dormitory access. Walter C. Langsam Library plus 13 others. Books: 2.7 million (physical), 1.6 million (digital/electronic); Serial titles: 98,491 (physical), 2.1 million (digital/electronic); Databases: 1,270. Study areas open 24 hours, 5-7 days a week; students can reserve study rooms. Operations spending for the previous fiscal year: $2.3 million. 499 computers available on campus for general student use. A campuswide network can be accessed from student residence rooms and from off campus. Students can access the following: online class registration. Staffed computer lab on campus (open 24 hours a day) provides training in use of computers, software, and the Internet.

Community Environment: Called by Longfellow,"The Queen City of the West," Cincinnati was founded in 1788 and was named Losantiville. The following year the name was changed to Cincinnati, after the Society of Cincinnati. The city is the third largest in Ohio and is situated on a series of plateaus above the Ohio River surrounded by hills. The altitude varies from 435 to 938 feet. Some of the industries located here are Proctor & Gamble Co., General Electric Co., Ford Motor Co., and the Kroger Co. The Cincinnati Convention-Exposition Center provides facilities for meetings as well as 95,000 square feet of exhibition space. Cultural facilities include the Cincinnati Symphony Orchestra, Art Academy of Cincinnati, and the University of Cincinnati College Conservatory of Music; Cincinnati is famous as a center of music and art. Recreational facilities are numerous. Among the points of interest are the Carew Tower Observatory, Cincinnati Art Museum, Cincinnati

Museum of Natural History, King's Island which is a recreational facility, Hebrew Union College Museum, Mount Airy Forest, St. Peter in Chains Cathedral, Stowe House, and Taft Museum.

■ UNIVERSITY OF CINCINNATI BLUE ASH COLLEGE

9555 Plainfield Rd.

Cincinnati, OH 45236-1007

Tel: (513)745-5600

Fax: (513)745-5780

Web Site: www.ucblueash.edu

Description: State-supported, primarily 2-year, coed. Part of Ohio Department of Higher Education. Administratively affiliated with University of Cincinnati. Awards certificates, transfer associate, terminal associate, and bachelor's degrees. Founded 1967. Setting: 120-acre suburban campus with easy access to Cincinnati. Endowment: $457,000. Research spending for the previous fiscal year: $21,377. Educational spending for the previous fiscal year: $6380 per student. Total enrollment: 5,065. Faculty: 339 (168 full-time, 171 part-time). Student-undergrad faculty ratio is 16:1. Full-time: 3,241 students, 55% women, 45% men. Part-time: 1,824 students, 63% women, 37% men. Students come from 9 states and territories, 12 other countries, 3% from out-of-state. 0.3% American Indian or Alaska Native, non-Hispanic/Latino; 3% Hispanic/Latino; 21% Black or African American, non-Hispanic/Latino; 3% Asian, non-Hispanic/Latino; 0.1% Native Hawaiian or other Pacific Islander, non-Hispanic/Latino; 2% international. 22% 25 or older, 11% transferred in. Retention: 64% of full-time freshmen returned the following year. Calendar: semesters. Academic remediation for entering students, services for LD students, advanced placement, distance learning, double major, summer session for credit, part-time degree program, adult/continuing education programs. Off campus study at 12 members of the Greater Cincinnati Consortium of Colleges and Universities. Study abroad program. ROTC: Army (c), Air Force (c).

Entrance Requirements: Open admission except for allied health and nursing programs. Options: electronic application, deferred admission, international baccalaureate accepted. Required: high school transcript. Entrance: noncompetitive. Application deadline: rolling. Notification: continuous. Transfer credits accepted: Yes.

Costs Per Year: Application fee: $50. State resident tuition: $6010 full-time, $251 per credit hour part-time. Nonresident tuition: $14,808 full-time, $617 per credit hour part-time. Mandatory fees: $736 full-time. Full-time tuition and fees vary according to course load, degree level, location, program, and reciprocity agreements. Part-time tuition varies according to course load, degree level, location, and reciprocity agreements.

Collegiate Environment: Orientation program. Student services: personal-psychological counseling. Campus security: 24-hour emergency response devices and patrols, student patrols, late night transport-escort service. UC Blue Ash College Library. Books: 19,690 (physical). Weekly public service hours: 50; students can reserve study rooms. 150 computers available on campus for general student use. A campuswide network can be accessed from off-campus. Students can access the following: online class registration. Staffed computer lab on campus.

Community Environment: See University of Cincinnati.

■ UNIVERSITY OF CINCINNATI CLERMONT COLLEGE

4200 Clermont College Dr.

Batavia, OH 45103-1785

Tel: (513)732-5200; Free: 866-446-2822

E-mail: jamie.adkins@uc.edu

Web Site: www.ucclermont.edu

Description: State-supported, primarily 2-year, coed. Part of University of Cincinnati System. Awards certificates, transfer associate, terminal associate, and bachelor's degrees. Founded 1972. Setting: 91-acre rural campus with easy access to Cincinnati. Total enrollment: 2,883. Faculty: 293 (93 full-time, 200 part-time). Student-undergrad faculty ratio is 13:1. 1,255 applied, 48% were admitted. 15% from top quarter of their high school class, 48% from top half. Full-time: 1,595 students, 53% women, 47% men. Part-time: 1,288 students, 61% women, 39% men. 4% from out-of-state. 0.2% American Indian or Alaska Native, non-Hispanic/Latino; 3% Hispanic/Latino; 2% Black or African American, non-Hispanic/Latino; 1% Asian, non-Hispanic/Latino; 0.1% Native Hawaiian or other Pacific Islander, non-Hispanic/Latino; 0.3% international. 26% 25 or older. Retention: 61% of full-time freshmen returned the following year. Calendar: semesters. Academic remediation for entering students, services for LD students, advanced placement, self-designed majors, independent study, distance learning, double major, summer session for credit, part-time degree program, adult/continuing education programs, co-op programs and internships. Off campus study at 11 members of the Greater Cincinnati Consortium of Colleges and Universities. Study abroad program. ROTC: Army (c).

Entrance Requirements: Open admission. Options: electronic application, deferred admission. Required: high school transcript. Entrance: noncompetitive. Application deadline: 7/11. Notification: continuous. Transfer credits accepted: Yes.

Costs Per Year: Application fee: $50. State resident tuition: $5316 full-time, $222 per credit hour part-time. Nonresident tuition: $12,548 full-time, $523 per credit hour part-time. Full-time tuition varies according to course level, degree level, program, and reciprocity agreements. Part-time tuition varies according to course level, degree level, program, and reciprocity agreements.

Collegiate Environment: Orientation program. Student-run newspaper. Social organizations: 14 open to all. Most popular organizations: Active Minds, PACE (Professionalism Academics Character Experiences), Phi Theta Kappa, Association of Paralegal Students, Cheerleading. Major annual events: Fall Fest, Spring Fling. Student services: personal-psychological counseling. Campus security: 24-hour emergency response devices and patrols. UC Clermont College Library. Students can reserve study rooms.

Community Environment: Batavia, the Clermont County seat, is central to the entire county. Clermont County is recognized as the fastest growing county in Ohio. The completion of the Interstate Highway System and belt-freeway have made the Cincinnati metropolitan and Northern Kentucky areas easily accessible.

■ UNIVERSITY OF DAYTON

300 College Park
Dayton, OH 45469
Tel: (937)229-1000; Free: 800-837-7433
Fax: (937)229-4545
E-mail: admission@udayton.edu
Web Site: www.udayton.edu

Description: Independent Roman Catholic, university, coed. Awards bachelor's, master's, and doctoral degrees and post-master's certificates. Founded 1850. Setting: 388-acre suburban campus with easy access to Cincinnati. Total enrollment: 11,241. Faculty: 959 (609 full-time, 350 part-time). Student-undergrad faculty ratio is 15:1. 16,693 applied, 72% were admitted. 26% from top 10% of their high school class, 58% from top quarter, 85% from top half. Full-time: 8,162 students, 48% women, 52% men. Part-time: 476 students, 42% women, 58% men. Students come from 50 states and territories, 39 other countries, 51% from out-of-state. 0.1% American Indian or Alaska Native, non-Hispanic/Latino; 6% Hispanic/Latino; 3% Black or African American, non-Hispanic/Latino; 1% Asian, non-Hispanic/Latino; 5% international. 3% 25 or older, 75% live on campus, 2% transferred in. Retention: 90% of full-time freshmen returned the following year. Academic areas with the most degrees conferred: business/marketing; engineering; communication/journalism. Core. Calendar: semesters plus 2 6-week summer terms. Academic remediation for entering students, ESL program, services for LD students, advanced placement, accelerated degree program, self-designed majors, honors program, independent study, distance learning, double major, summer session for credit, part-time degree program, adult/continuing education programs, co-op programs and internships, graduate courses open to undergrads. Off campus study at Southwestern Ohio Council for Higher Education, Chaminade University of Honolulu, St. Mary's University. Study abroad program. ROTC: Army, Air Force (c).

Entrance Requirements: Options: electronic application, early action, deferred admission, international baccalaureate accepted. Required: essay, high school transcript, 1 recommendation, SAT or ACT. Required for some: audition for music, music therapy, music education programs. Entrance: moderately difficult. Application deadline: 11/1 for early action. Notification: 12/1 for early action. SAT Reasoning Test deadline: 3/1. Transfer credits accepted: Yes. Early action applicants: 9,055. Early action applicants admitted: 8,657.

Costs Per Year: Application fee: $0. Comprehensive fee: $58,150 includes full-time tuition ($44,100) and college room and board ($14,050). College room only: $8420. Tuition guaranteed not to increase for student's term of enrollment.

Collegiate Environment: Orientation program. Drama-theater group, choral group, marching band, student-run newspaper, radio station. Social organizations: 230 open to all; national fraternities, national sororities, local fraternities; 12% of eligible men and 21% of eligible women are members. Most popular organizations: Student Government Association, Marching Band, Red Scare (basketball student cheering section), Campus Connec-

tion, Habitat for Humanity. Major annual events: Christmas on Campus, Family Weekend, Up the Organizations Day. Student services: health clinic, personal-psychological counseling, women's center. Campus security: 24-hour emergency response devices and patrols, student patrols, late night transport-escort service, controlled dormitory access, approximately 1000 recording video cameras, automated external defibrillators in high density residential facilities and other areas. Freshmen guaranteed college housing. On-campus residence required through sophomore year. Options: coed, men-only, women-only housing available. Roesch Library plus 3 others. Books: 881,689 (physical), 972,137 (digital/electronic); Serial titles: 2,325 (physical), 96,661 (digital/electronic); Databases: 316. Weekly public service hours: 134; students can reserve study rooms. 7,675 computers available on campus for general student use. A computer is required for all students. A campuswide network can be accessed from student residence rooms and from off campus. Students can access the following: online class registration, applications, admission/enrollment status, virtual orientation, online digital resources, online courses, assistive technology, learning management system, multimedia labs, payment, cyber cafes, centrally-licensed, downloadable software and training. Staffed computer lab on campus provides training in use of computers, software, and the Internet.

Community Environment: See Wright State University.

■ THE UNIVERSITY OF FINDLAY

1000 N Main St.
Findlay, OH 45840-3653
Tel: (419)422-8313; Free: 800-548-0932
Fax: (419)424-4822
E-mail: jordan@findlay.edu
Web Site: www.findlay.edu

Description: Independent, comprehensive, coed, affiliated with Church of God. Awards associate, bachelor's, master's, and doctoral degrees. Founded 1882. Setting: 390-acre small town campus. Endowment: $35.3 million. Educational spending for the previous fiscal year: $9320 per student. Total enrollment: 4,870. Faculty: 335 (242 full-time, 93 part-time). Student-undergrad faculty ratio is 16:1. 3,462 applied, 74% were admitted. Full-time: 2,434 students, 67% women, 33% men. Part-time: 1,180 students, 68% women, 32% men. Students come from 45 states and territories, 28 other countries, 19% from out-of-state. 0.2% American Indian or Alaska Native, non-Hispanic/Latino; 3% Hispanic/Latino; 3% Black or African American, non-Hispanic/Latino; 2% Asian, non-Hispanic/Latino; 0.1% Native Hawaiian or other Pacific Islander, non-Hispanic/Latino; 5% international. 18% 25 or older, 45% live on campus, 2% transferred in. Retention: 80% of full-time freshmen returned the following year. Academic areas with the most degrees conferred: health professions and related sciences; business/marketing; agriculture; biological/life sciences. Core. Calendar: semesters. Academic remediation for entering students, ESL program, services for LD students, advanced placement, accelerated degree program, self-designed majors, honors program, independent study, distance learning, double major, summer session for credit, part-time degree program, adult/continuing education programs, co-op programs and internships, graduate courses open to undergrads. Off campus study. Study abroad program. ROTC: Army (c), Air Force (c).

Entrance Requirements: Options: electronic application, deferred admission, international baccalaureate accepted. Required: high school transcript, minimum 2.5 high school GPA, SAT or ACT. Recommended: interview. Required for some: essay, 1 recommendation. Entrance: moderately difficult. Application deadline: rolling. Notification: continuous. SAT Reasoning Test deadline: 8/1. Transfer credits accepted: Yes.

Costs Per Year: Application fee: $0. Comprehensive fee: $45,610 includes full-time tuition ($34,200), mandatory fees ($1210), and college room and board ($10,200). College room only: $5090. Part-time tuition: $755 per semester hour. Part-time mandatory fees: $45 per semester hour.

Collegiate Environment: Orientation program. Drama-theater group, choral group, marching band, student-run newspaper, radio station. Social organizations: 90 open to all; national fraternities, national sororities; 1% of eligible men and 2% of eligible women are members. Most popular organizations: Habitat for Humanity, Pre-Vet Club, Horse Club, Stride, Black Student Union. Major annual events: Annual Black Tie Affair, International Night, Act, Speak, Build Week. Student services: health clinic, personal-psychological counseling, women's center. Campus security: 24-hour emergency response devices and patrols, student patrols, late night transport-escort service, controlled dormitory access, parking lot and building cameras (over 500), campus police. 1,350 college housing spaces available; 1,200 were occupied in 2018-19. Freshmen guaranteed college housing. On-campus residence required through sophomore year. Options: coed, women-only housing available. Shafer Library plus 4 others. Books: 98,272 (physical), 325,566 (digital/electronic); Serial titles: 361 (physical), 78,798 (digital/ electronic); Databases: 173. Weekly public service hours: 94; study areas open 24 hours, 5-7 days a week. Operations spending for the previous fiscal year: $932,373. 151 computers available on campus for general student use. Computer purchase/lease plans available. A campuswide network can be accessed from student residence rooms and from off campus. Students can access the following: online class registration. Staffed computer lab on campus provides training in use of computers, software, and the Internet.

Community Environment: Findlay is located in the northwestern part of Ohio, which is both a rich agricultural and manufacturing region. Excellent internship and employment opportunities are available. Recreational activities include swimming, golf, boating, and fishing.

■ **UNIVERSITY OF MOUNT UNION**

1972 Clark Ave.
Alliance, OH 44601-3993
Tel: (330)821-5320; Free: 800-334-6682
Fax: (330)821-0425
E-mail: admission@mountunion.edu
Web Site: www.mountunion.edu

Description: Independent United Methodist, comprehensive, coed. Awards bachelor's, master's, and doctoral degrees. Founded 1846. Setting: 123-acre suburban campus with easy access to Cleveland. Endowment: $141.9 million. Educational spending for the previous fiscal year: $9469 per student. Total enrollment: 2,309. Faculty: 253 (144 full-time, 109 part-time). Student-undergrad faculty ratio is 13:1. 2,396 applied, 96% were admitted. 20% from top 10% of their high school class, 45% from top quarter, 78% from top half. Full-time: 2,074 students, 47% women, 53% men. Part-time: 42 students, 62% women, 38% men. Students come from 27 states and territories, 9 other countries, 19% from out-of-state. 0.5% American Indian or Alaska Native, non-Hispanic/Latino; 4% Hispanic/Latino; 8% Black or African American, non-Hispanic/Latino; 0.7% Asian, non-Hispanic/Latino; 2% international. 2% transferred in. Retention: 77% of full-time freshmen returned the following year. Academic areas with the most degrees conferred: business/marketing; parks and recreation; education. Core. Calendar: semesters. ESL program, services for LD students, advanced placement, accelerated degree program, self-designed majors, honors program, independent study, distance learning, double major, summer session for credit, part-time degree program, adult/continuing education programs, co-op programs and internships. Off campus study. Study abroad program. ROTC: Army (c).

Entrance Requirements: Options: electronic application, early admission, deferred admission. Required: essay, high school transcript, minimum 2 high school GPA, 1 recommendation, SAT or ACT. Recommended: interview. Entrance: moderately difficult. Application deadline: rolling. Notification: continuous. Transfer credits accepted: Yes.

Costs Per Year: Application fee: $0. Comprehensive fee: $42,200 includes full-time tuition ($31,300), mandatory fees ($400), and college room and board ($10,500). College room only: $5200. Part-time tuition: $1330 per credit hour.

Collegiate Environment: Orientation program. Drama-theater group, choral group, marching band, student-run newspaper, radio station. Social organizations: 74 open to all; national fraternities, national sororities, local sororities; 50% of eligible men and 50% of eligible women are members. Most popular organizations: Alpha Phi Omega, Student Senate, FCA Fellowship of Christian Athletes, Black Student Union, Raider Programming Board. Major annual events: Homecoming, Scholar Day, Schooler Lecture. Student services: health clinic, personal-psychological counseling. Campus security: 24-hour emergency response devices and patrols, late night transport-escort service, controlled dormitory access. Freshmen guaranteed college housing. On-campus residence required through sophomore year. Options: coed, men-only, women-only housing available. University of Mount Union Library plus 1 other. Books: 224,248 (physical), 458,288 (digital/electronic); Serial titles: 2,492 (physical), 67,046 (digital/electronic); Databases: 230. Study areas open 24 hours, 5-7 days a week; students can reserve study rooms. Operations spending for the previous fiscal year: $1.2 million.

Community Environment: Alliance, population 22,801, is an industrial city located within a circle of large cities, Cleveland, Akron, and Pittsburgh. Heavy steel equipment and forgings are among the products of its industry. Commercial transportation is available. Recreational activities include swimming, golfing, fishing, boating and tennis. The Carnation Festival is an annual event. Part-time employment is available.

■ **UNIVERSITY OF NORTHWESTERN OHIO**

1441 N Cable Rd.
Lima, OH 45805-1498
Tel: (419)227-3141
Fax: (419)229-6926
E-mail: dmlowden@unoh.edu
Web Site: www.unoh.edu

Description: Independent, comprehensive, coed. Awards associate, bachelor's, and master's degrees. Founded 1920. Setting: 200-acre small town campus with easy access to Dayton, Toledo. Total enrollment: 3,848. Faculty: 127 (93 full-time, 34 part-time). Student-undergrad faculty ratio is 20:1. 4,900 applied. 2% from top 10% of their high school class, 9% from top quarter, 34% from top half. Students come from 42 states and territories, 30 other countries, 51% from out-of-state. 16% 25 or older, 33% live on campus. Academic areas with the most degrees conferred: business/marketing; mechanic and repair technologies; health professions and related sciences. Core. Calendar: quarters. Academic remediation for entering students, services for LD students, advanced placement, accelerated degree program, distance learning, double major, summer session for credit, part-time degree program, adult/continuing education programs, co-op programs and internships. ROTC: Army.

Entrance Requirements: Open admission. Options: electronic application, early admission, deferred admission. Required: high school transcript. Entrance: noncompetitive. Application deadline: rolling. Transfer credits accepted: Yes.

Collegiate Environment: Orientation program. Social organizations: 10 open to all. Most popular organizations: Business Professionals of America, ROTORAC, American Marketing Association, Optimist Club, Drag Club. Major annual events: Mud Volleyball, Car Show, Intramural Sports. Student services: personal-psychological counseling. Campus security: 24-hour emergency response devices and patrols, late night transport-escort service. Dr. Cheryl Mueller Library. Students can reserve study rooms. Operations spending for the previous fiscal year: $36,715. 200 computers available on campus for general student use. A campuswide network can be accessed from off-campus. Students can access the following: online class registration. Staffed computer lab on campus provides training in use of computers, software, and the Internet.

■ **UNIVERSITY OF RIO GRANDE**

218 N College Ave.
Rio Grande, OH 45674
Tel: (740)245-5353; Free: 800-282-7201
Fax: (740)245-9220
E-mail: admissions@rio.edu
Web Site: www.rio.edu

Description: Independent, comprehensive, coed. Awards associate, bachelor's, and master's degrees. Founded 1876. Setting: 170-acre rural campus. Endowment: $23.6 million. Educational spending for the previous fiscal year: $6239 per student. Total enrollment: 2,161. Faculty: 175 (86 full-time, 89 part-time). Student-undergrad faculty ratio is 19:1. 1,754 applied, 73% were admitted. 5% from top 10% of their high school class, 20% from top quarter, 49% from top half. Full-time: 1,719 students, 61% women, 39% men. Part-time: 387 students, 74% women, 26% men. Students come from 19 states and territories, 6 other countries, 4% from out-of-state. 0.2% American Indian or Alaska Native, non-Hispanic/Latino; 0.8% Hispanic/Latino; 5% Black or African American, non-Hispanic/Latino; 0.3% Asian, non-Hispanic/Latino; 0.1% Native Hawaiian or other Pacific Islander, non-Hispanic/Latino; 0.8% international. 35% 25 or older, 17% live on campus, 9% transferred in. Retention: 56% of full-time freshmen returned the following year. Academic areas with the most degrees conferred: education; business/marketing; health professions and related sciences. Core. Calendar: semesters. Academic remediation for entering students, services for LD students, advanced placement, accelerated degree program, self-designed majors, honors program, independent study, distance learning, double major, summer session for credit, part-time degree program, adult/continuing education programs, co-op programs and internships. Study abroad program.

Entrance Requirements: Open admission except for nursing, radiologic technology, education, social work programs. Option: electronic application. Required: high school transcript, medical history. Recommended: ACT. Entrance: noncompetitive. Application deadline: rolling. Notification: continuous. Transfer credits accepted: Yes.

Collegiate Environment: Orientation program. Drama-theater group, choral group, student-run newspaper, radio station. Social organizations: 41 open to all; national fraternities, national sororities, local fraternities, local sororities; 2% of eligible men and 1% of eligible women are members. Most popular organizations: Student Government, Honoraries, Bible studies, ENACTA. Major annual events: Community Service Day, Homecoming, Founders' Day. Student services: health clinic, personal-psychological counseling. Campus security: 24-hour emergency response devices and patrols, late night transport-escort service. Jeanette Albiez Davis Library. Operations spending for the previous fiscal year: $386,550. 300 computers available on campus for general student use. A campuswide network can be accessed from student residence rooms and from off campus. Students can access the following: online class registration. Staffed computer lab on campus provides training in use of computers, software, and the Internet.

Community Environment: Less than one mile from campus, the Bob Evans Farm offers canoe and horse rentals, trail rides, hiking, and fishing. A radio-controlled aircraft club meets monthly in good weather. The second weekend of October marks the annual Bob Evans Farm Festival, which brings visitors from surrounding states. Rio Grande students participate heavily in the Farm Festival as part of "Community Service Day" when most college classes are canceled. Annual campus-hosted events include World-Fest, Native American Pow Wow, and Celtic/Welsh festivals. Other recreational facilities within a reasonable driving distance include golf, boating, skiing, rock climbing, white-water rafting, camping, and fishing. A rural community, Rio Grande is located 90 miles southeast of Columbus, 130 miles east of Cincinnati, and 60 miles north of Charleston, WV. Local shopping is found in Jackson and Gallipolis, both within 20 miles. Lare malls are found in Charleston and Huntington, WV, both about 60 miles away. Gallipolis is a picturesque river town, settled on the banks of the Ohio River, one of the annual stops for the historic Delta Queen steamboat. The surrounding area includes active civic and service organizations, church groups, shopping facilities, the Holzer Medical Center, and Holzer Clinic. The Ohio Valley Symphony, the Valley Artist Series, and the French Art Colony provide music, theater, and fine arts cultural events and exhibits. Performances are held either on campus at the Merlyn Ross Fine Arts Center or in Gallipolis at the refurbished Victorian playhouse, the Ariel Theater. Students get special reduced rates to performances. Opportunities for part-time employment are good, primarily in retailing.

■ **THE UNIVERSITY OF TOLEDO**
2801 W Bancroft
Toledo, OH 43606-3390
Tel: (419)530-4636; Free: 800-5TOLEDO
Fax: (419)530-4940
E-mail: william.pierce@utoledo.edu
Web Site: www.utoledo.edu

Description: State-supported, university, coed. Awards bachelor's, master's, and doctoral degrees and post-master's certificates. Founded 1872. Setting: 858-acre urban campus with easy access to Detroit. Endowment: $306.9 million. Research spending for the previous fiscal year: $37.7 million. Educational spending for the previous fiscal year: $11,147 per student. Total enrollment: 20,304. Faculty: 1,119 (769 full-time, 350 part-time). Student-undergrad faculty ratio is 21:1. 10,792 applied, 94% were admitted. 20% from top 10% of their high school class, 43% from top quarter, 75% from top half. Full-time: 12,941 students, 49% women, 51% men. Part-time: 3,124 students, 50% women, 50% men. Students come from 49 states and territories, 66 other countries, 21% from out-of-state. 0.2% American Indian or Alaska Native, non-Hispanic/Latino; 5% Hispanic/Latino; 11% Black or African American, non-Hispanic/Latino; 2% Asian, non-Hispanic/Latino; 0.1% Native Hawaiian or other Pacific Islander, non-Hispanic/Latino; 6% international. 13% 25 or older, 23% live on campus, 7% transferred in. Retention: 76% of full-time freshmen returned the following year. Academic areas with the most degrees conferred: business/marketing; health professions and related sciences; engineering. Core. Calendar: semesters. Academic remediation for entering students, ESL program, services for LD students, advanced placement, accelerated degree program, self-designed majors, freshman honors college, honors program, independent study, distance learning, double major, summer session for credit, part-time degree program, adult/continuing education programs, co-op programs and internships, graduate courses open to undergrads. Off campus study at Bowling Green State University, Wright State Universitie. Study abroad program. ROTC: Army, Air Force (c).

Entrance Requirements: Open admission for in-state students. Options: electronic application, deferred admission, international baccalaureate accepted. Required: high school transcript, SAT or ACT. Required for some:

minimum 2 high school GPA, core high school curriculum. Entrance: noncompetitive. Application deadline: rolling. Notification: continuous. Transfer credits accepted: Yes.

Costs Per Year: Application fee: $40. State resident tuition: $8534 full-time, $355.85 per credit hour part-time. Nonresident tuition: $17,894 full-time, $745.85 per credit hour part-time. Mandatory fees: $1261 full-time, $53.60 per credit hour part-time. Full-time tuition and fees vary according to course load, program, reciprocity agreements, and student level. Part-time tuition and fees vary according to course load, program, reciprocity agreements, and student level. College room and board: $11,434. Room and board charges vary according to board plan and housing facility.

Collegiate Environment: Orientation program. Drama-theater group, choral group, marching band, student-run newspaper, radio station. Social organizations: 328 open to all; national fraternities, national sororities, local fraternities, local sororities; 7% of eligible men and 7% of eligible women are members. Most popular organizations: Student Government, University YMCA, Newman Club, International Student Association, Campus Activities and Programming. Major annual events: Homecoming, Songfest, Musicfest. Student services: legal services, health clinic, personal-psychological counseling, women's center. Campus security: 24-hour emergency response devices and patrols, student patrols, late night transport-escort service, controlled dormitory access, bicycle patrols by security staff, crime prevention officer. College housing designed to accommodate 3,550 students; 3,594 undergraduates lived in college housing during 2018-19. Freshmen guaranteed college housing. On-campus residence required through sophomore year. Option: coed housing available. Carlson Library plus 3 others. Books: 563,687 (physical), 339,697 (digital/electronic); Serial titles: 5,602 (physical), 74,382 (digital/electronic); Databases: 340. Weekly public service hours: 107; students can reserve study rooms. Operations spending for the previous fiscal year: $10.5 million. 5,000 computers available on campus for general student use. Computer purchase/lease plans available. A campuswide network can be accessed from student residence rooms and from off campus. Students can access the following: online class registration, online transcripts, student account. Staffed computer lab on campus (open 24 hours a day) provides training in use of computers, software, and the Internet.

Community Environment: Toledo's importance as a port stems from its location at the mouth of the Maumee River. It is the busiest freshwater port in the world. It ranks second on the Great Lakes, and ninth in the nation in tonnage handled.

■ **URBANA UNIVERSITY-A BRANCH CAMPUS OF FRANKLIN UNIVERSITY**
579 College Way
Urbana, OH 43078-2091
Tel: (937)484-1400; Free: 800-7-URBANA
Fax: (937)484-1389
E-mail: admiss@urbana.edu
Web Site: www.urbana.edu

Description: Independent, comprehensive, coed, affiliated with Church of the New Jerusalem. Administratively affiliated with We are a subsidiary of Franklin University, a non-profit university in Columbus, Ohio. Awards associate, bachelor's, and master's degrees. Founded 1850. Setting: 128-acre small town campus with easy access to Columbus, Dayton. Endowment: $415,000. Educational spending for the previous fiscal year: $14,220 per student. Total enrollment: 1,551. Faculty: 120 (55 full-time, 65 part-time). Student-undergrad faculty ratio is 16:1. 495 applied, 65% were admitted. Full-time: 904 students, 46% women, 54% men. Part-time: 557 students, 64% women, 36% men. 4% from out-of-state. 6% transferred in. Retention: 70% of full-time freshmen returned the following year. Academic areas with the most degrees conferred: education; homeland security, law enforcement, firefighting, and protective services; health professions and related sciences. Core. Calendar: semesters. Academic remediation for entering students, services for LD students, advanced placement, accelerated degree program, self-designed majors, freshman honors college, honors program, independent study, double major, summer session for credit, part-time degree program, adult/continuing education programs, co-op programs and internships. Off campus study at members of the Southwestern Ohio Council for Higher Education.

Entrance Requirements: Options: electronic application, deferred admission. Required: essay, high school transcript, minimum 2 high school GPA, SAT or ACT. Recommended: interview. Required for some: 2 recommendations. Entrance: moderately difficult. Application deadline: rolling. Notification: continuous.

Collegiate Environment: Orientation program. Drama-theater group, choral group, marching band, student-run newspaper, radio station. Social organizations: 20 open to all. Most popular organizations: Student Government Association, Business Club, Education Club, Drama Club, Student Activities Planning Committee. Major annual events: Homecoming, Spring Fling Week, Founders' Day. Student services: health clinic, personal-psychological counseling. Campus security: 24-hour emergency response devices and patrols, late night transport-escort service. Swedenborg Memorial Library. 75 computers available on campus for general student use. A campuswide network can be accessed from student residence rooms. Staffed computer lab on campus.

Community Environment: Urbana is the county seat of Champaign county and has a population in excess of 12,000 residents. The community has become well known regionally for the restoration of the historic downtown business district. The community provides a modern small-town environment with easy access to major metropolitan areas, being located just 15 minutes from downtown Springfield and 45 minutes from Dayton and Columbus.

■ **URSULINE COLLEGE**
2550 Lander Rd.
Pepper Pike, OH 44124-4398
Tel: (440)449-4200; Free: 888-URSULINE
Fax: (440)449-2235
E-mail: esmith2@ursuline.edu
Web Site: www.ursuline.edu

Description: Independent Roman Catholic, comprehensive, coed. Awards bachelor's, master's, and doctoral degrees and post-master's certificates (applications from men are also accepted). Founded 1871. Setting: 62-acre suburban campus with easy access to Cleveland. Endowment: $43.5 million. Educational spending for the previous fiscal year: $17,917 per student. Total enrollment: 1,123. Faculty: 170 (59 full-time, 111 part-time). Student-undergrad faculty ratio is 8:1. 525 applied, 93% were admitted. 17% from top 10% of their high school class, 50% from top quarter, 76% from top half. Full-time: 455 students, 94% women, 6% men. Part-time: 166 students, 89% women, 11% men. Students come from 17 states and territories, 11 other countries, 8% from out-of-state. 2% Hispanic/Latino; 21% Black or African American, non-Hispanic/Latino; 2% Asian, non-Hispanic/Latino; 2% international. 33% 25 or older, 25% live on campus, 12% transferred in. Retention: 71% of full-time freshmen returned the following year. Academic areas with the most degrees conferred: health professions and related sciences; business/marketing; psychology. Core. Calendar: semesters. Academic remediation for entering students, services for LD students, advanced placement, accelerated degree program, self-designed majors, independent study, distance learning, double major, summer session for credit, part-time degree program, adult/continuing education programs, internships, graduate courses open to undergrads. Off campus study at Fashion Institute of Technology. ROTC: Army (c).

Entrance Requirements: Options: electronic application, deferred admission. Required: essay, high school transcript, 1 recommendation, SAT or ACT. Recommended: minimum 2.5 high school GPA, interview. Entrance: minimally difficult. Application deadline: 2/1. Notification: continuous, continuous for nonresidents. SAT Reasoning Test deadline: 8/1. SAT Subject Test deadline: 8/1. Transfer credits accepted: Yes.

Costs Per Year: Application fee: $0. Comprehensive fee: $43,166 includes full-time tuition ($32,070), mandatory fees ($320), and college room and board ($10,776). Full-time tuition and fees vary according to class time, course load, degree level, location, and program. Room and board charges vary according to housing facility. Part-time tuition: $1069 per credit hour. Part-time mandatory fees: $120 per term. Part-time tuition and fees vary according to class time, course load, degree level, location, and program.

Collegiate Environment: Orientation program. Drama-theater group. Social organizations: 23 open to all; City Chapters of the National Pan-Hellenic Council; 1% of women are members. Most popular organizations: Programming Board, Student Nurses of Ursuline College, U-Earth, Women's Circle, Anime Club. Major annual events: Student Activity Fair, Family Fun Festival, Welcome Week Activities. Student services: personal-psychological counseling. Campus security: 24-hour emergency response devices and patrols, late night transport-escort service, controlled dormitory access. Ralph M. Besse Library. Books: 132,089 (physical), 137,533 (digital/electronic); Serial titles: 902 (physical), 14,413 (digital/electronic); Databases: 162. Weekly public service hours: 91; students can reserve study rooms. Operations spending for the previous fiscal year: $573,934. 72 computers available on campus for general student use. A campuswide network can be accessed from student residence rooms. Students can access the following: online class registration. Staffed computer lab on campus.

Community Environment: See Case Western Reserve University.

■ **VALOR CHRISTIAN COLLEGE**
4595 Gender Rd.
Canal Winchester, OH 43110
Web Site: www.valorcollege.edu
Description: Independent Christian, 2-year, coed.

■ **VET TECH INSTITUTE AT BRADFORD SCHOOL**
2469 Stelzer Rd.
Columbus, OH 43219
Tel: (614)416-6200; Free: 800-678-7981
Fax: (614)416-5197
Web Site: columbus.vettechinstitute.edu
Description: Private, 2-year, coed. Awards terminal associate degrees. Founded 2005. Setting: suburban campus. Total enrollment: 163. 524 applied, 33% were admitted. Calendar: semesters. Accelerated degree program, internships.

■ **WALSH UNIVERSITY**
2020 E Maple St., NW
North Canton, OH 44720-3396
Tel: (330)490-7090; Free: 800-362-8846
Fax: (330)490-7165
E-mail: admissions@walsh.edu
Web Site: www.walsh.edu

Description: Independent Roman Catholic, comprehensive, coed. Awards associate, bachelor's, master's, and doctoral degrees. Founded 1958. Setting: 134-acre small town campus with easy access to Cleveland. Endowment: $22.6 million. Research spending for the previous fiscal year: $23,374. Educational spending for the previous fiscal year: $7170 per student. Total enrollment: 2,759. Faculty: 242 (131 full-time, 111 part-time). Student-undergrad faculty ratio is 14:1. 1,693 applied, 78% were admitted. Full-time: 1,744 students, 58% women, 42% men. Part-time: 265 students, 68% women, 32% men. Students come from 34 states and territories, 24 other countries, 9% from out-of-state. 0.2% American Indian or Alaska Native, non-Hispanic/Latino; 4% Hispanic/Latino; 7% Black or African American, non-Hispanic/Latino; 0.6% Asian, non-Hispanic/Latino; 4% international. 17% 25 or older, 48% live on campus, 4% transferred in. Retention: 74% of full-time freshmen returned the following year. Academic areas with the most degrees conferred: business/marketing; biological/life sciences; education. Core. Calendar: semesters. Academic remediation for entering students, ESL program, services for LD students, advanced placement, accelerated degree program, honors program, independent study, distance learning, double major, summer session for credit, part-time degree program, external degree program, adult/continuing education programs, internships, graduate courses open to undergrads. Off campus study at Stark State College, Academic Alliance Cooperative Engineering Program—Youngstown State University. Study abroad program.

Entrance Requirements: Options: electronic application, early admission, deferred admission, international baccalaureate accepted. Required: high school transcript, minimum 2.4 high school GPA. Recommended: interview. Required for some: essay, minimum 3 high school GPA, 2 recommendations, SAT or ACT. Entrance: moderately difficult. Application deadline: rolling. Notification: continuous. SAT Reasoning Test deadline: 8/15. Transfer credits accepted: Yes.

Costs Per Year: Application fee: $25. Comprehensive fee: $40,660 includes full-time tuition ($28,480), mandatory fees ($1500), and college room and board ($10,680). College room only: $5570. Full-time tuition and fees vary according to location. Room and board charges vary according to board plan and housing facility. Part-time tuition: $950 per credit hour. Part-time mandatory fees: $65 per credit hour. Part-time tuition and fees vary according to location.

Collegiate Environment: Orientation program. Drama-theater group, choral group, marching band, student-run newspaper, radio station. Social organizations: 50 open to all. Most popular organizations: Student Government, University Programming Board, Business and Communication Club, Behavioral Science Club, Education Club. Major annual events: Homecoming, Walshfest, Finals Week Late Night Breakfast. Student services: health clinic, personal-psychological counseling. Campus security: 24-hour emergency response devices and patrols, late night transport-escort service, controlled dormitory access. Brother Edmond Drouin Library. Books: 97,575 (physical), 254,114 (digital/electronic); Serial titles: 995 (physical), 82,413 (digital/electronic); Databases: 167. Weekly public service hours: 79. Operations spending for the previous fiscal year: $776,753. 336 computers available on campus for general student use. A campuswide network can be accessed from student residence rooms and from off campus. Students can access the following: online class registration. Staffed computer lab on campus provides training in use of computers, software, and the Internet.

Community Environment: Walsh University is conveniently located and easily accessible, near Ohio Interstate 77 in North Canton, a residential suburban area. The Walsh campus, near Canton, which city of about 84,000 with a wide array of cultural, recreational, and athletic activities. Home of the Professional Football Hall of Fame and the President McKinley National Memorial, the city boasts a symphony orchestra, art institute, civic opera, theater guild, and ballet. A number of major employers are headquartered in Stark County, including the Hoover Company, the Timken Company, and Diebold, Inc. 20 miles north of campus is Akron, and within an hour's drive is Cleveland. The Akron-Canton Regional Airport, is north of campus and serves the Canton-Stark County area, as do Amtrak trains and Greyhound buses.

■ **WASHINGTON STATE COMMUNITY COLLEGE**

710 Colegate Dr.
Marietta, OH 45750-9225
Tel: (740)374-8716
Fax: (740)376-0257
E-mail: rperoni@wscc.edu
Web Site: www.wscc.edu

Description: State-supported, 2-year, coed. Part of Ohio Board of Regents. Awards certificates, transfer associate, and terminal associate degrees. Founded 1971. Setting: small town campus. Total enrollment: 2,184. Student-undergrad faculty ratio is 18:1. 15% from out-of-state. 44% 25 or older. Core. Calendar: quarters. Academic remediation for entering students, services for LD students, self-designed majors, independent study, double major, summer session for credit, part-time degree program, adult/continuing education programs, internships.

Entrance Requirements: Open admission except for medical laboratory technology, nursing programs. Options: early admission, deferred admission. Recommended: high school transcript. Required for some: high school transcript. Entrance: noncompetitive. Application deadline: rolling. Notification: continuous.

Collegiate Environment: Choral group. Student services: personal-psychological counseling.

■ **WILBERFORCE UNIVERSITY**

1055 N Bickett Rd.
Wilberforce, OH 45384
Tel: (937)376-2911; Free: 800-367-8568
Fax: (937)376-4751
E-mail: ddriscoll@wilberforce.edu
Web Site: www.wilberforce.edu

Description: Independent, comprehensive, coed, affiliated with African Methodist Episcopal Church. Awards bachelor's and master's degrees. Founded 1856. Setting: 125-acre rural campus with easy access to Dayton, Columbus. Total enrollment: 330. Faculty: 48 (19 full-time, 29 part-time). Student-undergrad faculty ratio is 8:1. 1,284 applied, 38% were admitted. Students come from 8 states and territories, 40% from out-of-state. 0.9% American Indian or Alaska Native, non-Hispanic/Latino; 92% Black or African American, non-Hispanic/Latino; 2% international. 19% 25 or older. Retention: 74% of full-time freshmen returned the following year. Core. Calendar: semesters. Academic remediation for entering students, advanced placement, freshman honors college, honors program, independent study, distance learning, double major, external degree program, adult/continuing education programs, co-op programs and internships. Off campus study at 18 members of the Southwestern Ohio Council for Higher Education. Study abroad program. ROTC: Army (c), Air Force (c).

Entrance Requirements: Options: electronic application, early admission, early decision, deferred admission. Required: essay, high school transcript, minimum 2.5 high school GPA, 2 recommendations, SAT or ACT. Entrance: minimally difficult. Application deadline: 7/1. Notification: continuous until 8/1. Transfer credits accepted: Yes.

Collegiate Environment: Orientation program. Drama-theater group, choral group, student-run newspaper, radio station. Social organizations: national fraternities, national sororities, local fraternities, local sororities. Student services: health clinic, personal-psychological counseling. Campus security: 24-hour emergency response devices and patrols, controlled dormitory access. Rembert E. Stokes Library.

Community Environment: Located in rural village of Wilberforce with a history of significant activity in the underground railroad of pre-Civil War days. The city of Xenia, Ohio is nearby with a population of 23,600 and is a good shopping center. It provides a resource for field study, cultural and recreational activities plus the close urban centers of Dayton, Springfield, Columbus and Cincinnati.

■ **WILMINGTON COLLEGE**

1870 Quaker Way
Wilmington, OH 45177
Tel: (937)382-6661; Free: 800-341-9318
Fax: (937)382-7077
E-mail: admissions@wilmington.edu
Web Site: www.wilmington.edu

Description: Independent Friends, comprehensive, coed. Awards bachelor's and master's degrees. Founded 1870. Setting: small town campus. Total enrollment: 1,458. Faculty: 119 (66 full-time, 53 part-time). Student-undergrad faculty ratio is 14:1. 1,651 applied. 11% from top 10% of their high school class, 36% from top quarter, 70% from top half. Full-time: 1,179 students, 52% women, 48% men. Part-time: 253 students, 60% women, 40% men. 6% from out-of-state. 15% 25 or older, 80% live on campus, 5% transferred in. Retention: 67% of full-time freshmen returned the following year. Academic areas with the most degrees conferred: business/marketing; education; agriculture. Core. Calendar: semesters. Part-time degree program, adult/continuing education programs. ROTC: Army (c).

Entrance Requirements: Option: deferred admission. Required: high school transcript. Recommended: minimum 2.5 high school GPA, 1 recommendation, interview, SAT or ACT. Entrance: moderately difficult. Application deadline: 8/1. Notification: continuous.

Collegiate Environment: Orientation program. Campus security: 24-hour emergency response devices and patrols, late night transport-escort service, controlled dormitory access. Watson Library.

■ **WITTENBERG UNIVERSITY**

PO Box 720
Springfield, OH 45501-0720
Tel: (937)327-6231; Free: 800-677-7558
Fax: (937)327-6379
E-mail: admission@wittenberg.edu
Web Site: www.wittenberg.edu

Description: Independent, comprehensive, coed, affiliated with Evangelical Lutheran Church. Awards bachelor's and master's degrees. Founded 1845. Setting: 114-acre suburban campus with easy access to Columbus, Dayton. Total enrollment: 1,884. Faculty: 185 (115 full-time, 70 part-time). Student-undergrad faculty ratio is 13:1. 7,249 applied, 72% were admitted. 14% from top 10% of their high school class, 39% from top quarter, 72% from top half. Full-time: 1,775 students, 53% women, 47% men. Part-time: 82 students, 65% women, 35% men. Students come from 38 states and territories, 11 other countries, 25% from out-of-state. 0.2% American Indian or Alaska Native, non-Hispanic/Latino; 4% Hispanic/Latino; 10% Black or African American, non-Hispanic/Latino; 1% Asian, non-Hispanic/Latino; 0.1% Native Hawaiian or other Pacific Islander, non-Hispanic/Latino; 1% international. 3% 25 or older, 85% live on campus, 2% transferred in. Retention: 72% of full-time freshmen returned the following year. Academic areas with the most degrees conferred: business/marketing; social sciences; biological/life sciences. Core. Calendar: semesters. Academic remediation for entering students, advanced placement, self-designed majors, freshman honors college, honors program, independent study, double major, summer session for credit, part-time degree program, adult/continuing education programs, co-op programs and internships. Off campus study at Member of the Southwestern Ohio Council for Higher Education. Study abroad program. ROTC: Army (c), Air Force (c).

Entrance Requirements: Options: electronic application, early admission, early decision, early action, deferred admission, international baccalaureate accepted. Required: high school transcript, interview. Recommended: essay, Test score optional. Entrance: moderately difficult. Application deadlines: 11/15 for early decision, 12/1 for early action. Notification: continuous, 12/15 for early decision, 1/1 for early action. Preference given to Lutherans, children of alumni, county residents, minorities. Transfer credits accepted: Yes. Early decision applicants: 773. Early decision applicants admitted: 470. Early action applicants: 3,462. Early action applicants admitted: 2,817.

Costs Per Year: Application fee: $40. Comprehensive fee: $49,856 includes full-time tuition ($38,680), mandatory fees ($820), and college room and board ($10,356). College room only: $5288. Room and board charges vary according to board plan and housing facility. Part-time tuition: $1289 per credit hour. Part-time tuition varies according to course load.

Collegiate Environment: Orientation program. Drama-theater group, choral group, student-run newspaper, radio station. Social organizations: 124 open to all; national fraternities, national sororities; 29% of eligible men and 32% of eligible women are members. Most popular organizations: Student Senate, Union Board, Choirs, Weaver Chapel Association. Major annual events: New Student Days, Wittfest, Activity Fair. Student services: health clinic, personal-psychological counseling, women's center. Campus security: 24-hour emergency response devices and patrols, student patrols, late night transport-escort service, controlled dormitory access, crime prevention programs. Thomas Library plus 1 other. Books: 135,595 (digital/electronic); Serial titles: 163,369 (digital/electronic); Databases: 209. Weekly public service hours: 93. 900 computers available on campus for general student use. A campuswide network can be accessed from student residence rooms and from off campus. Students can access the following: online class registration. Staffed computer lab on campus.

Community Environment: Springfield is located 25 miles northeast of Dayton with all forms of commercial transportation available. Community facilities include houses of worship of all denominations, two hospitals, libraries, art and historical museums, Springfield Performing Arts Center, a symphony orchestra, and two theatre groups. Recreational activities include tennis and golf. Job opportunities are available.

■ WRIGHT STATE UNIVERSITY

3640 Colonel Glenn Hwy.
Dayton, OH 45435
Tel: (937)775-3333; Free: 800-247-1770
Fax: (937)775-5795
E-mail: admissions@wright.edu
Web Site: www.wright.edu

Description: State-supported, university, coed. Part of University System of Ohio. Awards bachelor's, master's, and doctoral degrees and post-master's certificates. Founded 1964. Setting: 557-acre suburban campus with easy access to Dayton, Columbus, Cincinnati. Total enrollment: 15,957. 5,826 applied, 97% were admitted. 18% from top 10% of their high school class, 40% from top quarter, 68% from top half. Full-time: 9,423 students, 52% women, 48% men. Part-time: 2,692 students, 52% women, 48% men. 5% from out-of-state. 0.1% American Indian or Alaska Native, non-Hispanic/Latino; 4% Hispanic/Latino; 11% Black or African American, non-Hispanic/Latino; 3% Asian, non-Hispanic/Latino; 0.1% Native Hawaiian or other Pacific Islander, non-Hispanic/Latino; 3% international. 18% 25 or older, 19% live on campus, 8% transferred in. Retention: 63% of full-time freshmen returned the following year. Academic areas with the most degrees conferred: business/marketing; engineering; health professions and related sciences. Core. Calendar: semesters. Academic remediation for entering students, ESL program, services for LD students, advanced placement, self-designed majors, freshman honors college, honors program, independent study, distance learning, double major, summer session for credit, part-time degree program, adult/continuing education programs, co-op programs and internships, graduate courses open to undergrads. Off campus study at member of the Southwestern Ohio Council for Higher Education; Dayton Area Graduate Studies (DAGSI) - Masters in Engineering - University of Dayton and Air Force Institute of Technology; Dayton Area Graduate Studies - PhD in Engineering - University of Dayton and Air Force Institute of Technology; Doctor of Nurse Practitioner - University of Toledo. Study abroad program. ROTC: Army, Air Force.

Entrance Requirements: Options: electronic application, early admission, deferred admission, international baccalaureate accepted. Required: high school transcript, SAT or ACT. Recommended: minimum 2 high school GPA. Entrance: minimally difficult. Application deadline: 8/20. Notification: 9/1. SAT Reasoning Test deadline: 8/20. Transfer credits accepted: Yes.

Costs Per Year: Application fee: $30. State resident tuition: $9254 full-time, $417 per credit hour part-time. Nonresident tuition: $18,398 full-time, $838 per credit hour part-time. Full-time tuition varies according to course load, location, reciprocity agreements, and student level. Part-time tuition varies according to course load, location, reciprocity agreements, and student level. College room and board: $11,518. College room only: $6522. Room and board charges vary according to board plan, housing facility, location, and student level. Tuition guaranteed not to increase for student's term of enrollment.

Collegiate Environment: Orientation program. Drama-theater group, choral group, student-run newspaper, radio station. Social organizations: national fraternities, national sororities, local fraternities, local sororities. Student

services: legal services, health clinic, personal-psychological counseling, women's center. Campus security: 24-hour emergency response devices and patrols, student patrols, late night transport-escort service, controlled dormitory access. Paul Laurence Dunbar Library plus 1 other. Students can reserve study rooms.

Community Environment: Located in the Miami Valley at the junction of the Miami, Stillwater, and Mad Rivers in southwestern Ohio, Dayton is the state's fourth largest metropolitan area. Within a twenty-five mile radius, there is a population of over one million. The city lies fifty-four miles north of Cincinnati and seventy-two miles west of Columbus. Dayton International Airport, serviced by most major airlines, offers convenient access to almost any place in the Continental United States and abroad. The river corridor provides twenty-six scenic miles for walking, jogging, or cycling. Dayton also supports the arts, including a philharmonic orchestra, a ballet company, several art galleries and museums, and theater events for adults and children. The Opera Association presents fine productions with top stars on the bill each year.

■ WRIGHT STATE UNIVERSITY-LAKE CAMPUS

7600 Lake Campus Dr.
Celina, OH 45822-2921
Tel: (419)586-0300; Free: 800-237-1477
Fax: (419)586-0358
E-mail: jill.puthoff@wright.edu
Web Site: www.wright.edu/lake

Description: State-supported, comprehensive, coed. Administratively affiliated with Wright State University, Dayton. Awards associate, bachelor's, and master's degrees. Founded 1969. Setting: 211-acre small town campus. Total enrollment: 1,063. 357 applied, 99% were admitted. 7% from top 10% of their high school class, 20% from top quarter, 51% from top half. Full-time: 715 students, 57% women, 43% men. Part-time: 348 students, 57% women, 43% men. 3% Hispanic/Latino; 2% Black or African American, non-Hispanic/Latino; 0.5% Asian, non-Hispanic/Latino; 0.1% international. 11% 25 or older, 8% live on campus, 3% transferred in. Retention: 63% of full-time freshmen returned the following year. Academic areas with the most degrees conferred: business/marketing; education; engineering. Core. Calendar: semesters. Academic remediation for entering students, services for LD students, advanced placement, accelerated degree program, self-designed majors, honors program, independent study, distance learning, double major, summer session for credit, part-time degree program, adult/continuing education programs, co-op programs and internships, graduate courses open to undergrads. Off campus study at member of the Southwestern Ohio Council for Higher Education. Study abroad program. ROTC: Army (c), Air Force (c).

Entrance Requirements: Options: electronic application, deferred admission, international baccalaureate accepted. Required: high school transcript, SAT or ACT. Recommended: minimum 2 high school GPA. Entrance: minimally difficult. Application deadline: rolling. Notification: continuous. SAT Subject Test deadline: 8/20. Transfer credits accepted: Yes.

Costs Per Year: Application fee: $30. State resident tuition: $6194 full-time, $281 per credit hour part-time. Nonresident tuition: $15,338 full-time, $702 per credit hour part-time. Full-time tuition varies according to course load, location, reciprocity agreements, and student level. Part-time tuition varies according to course load, location, reciprocity agreements, and student level. College room and board: $10,842. College room only: $5846. Room and board charges vary according to board plan, housing facility, location, and student level. Tuition guaranteed not to increase for student's term of enrollment.

Collegiate Environment: Orientation program. Student services: health clinic, personal-psychological counseling. Campus security: 24-hour emergency response devices, WSU-Police Department presence, 40 hours per week. No special consideration for freshman housing applicants. Lake Campus Library & Technology Center plus 1 other. Operations spending for the previous fiscal year: $9.4 million.

■ XAVIER UNIVERSITY

3800 Victory Pky.
Cincinnati, OH 45207
Tel: (513)745-3000; Free: 877-XUADMIT
Fax: (513)745-4319
E-mail: xuadmit@xavier.edu
Web Site: www.xavier.edu

Description: Independent Roman Catholic, university, coed. Awards associate, bachelor's, master's, and doctoral degrees and post-master's certificates. Founded 1831. Setting: 189-acre urban campus with easy access to Cincinnati. Endowment: $153.5 million. Educational spending for the previous fiscal year: $9678 per student. Total enrollment: 6,538. Faculty: 699 (352 full-time, 347 part-time). Student-undergrad faculty ratio is 12:1. 11,605 applied, 73% were admitted. 20% from top 10% of their high school class, 48% from top quarter, 84% from top half. Full-time: 4,270 students, 54% women, 46% men. Part-time: 363 students, 50% women, 50% men. Students come from 49 states and territories, 47 other countries, 49% from out-of-state. 0.2% American Indian or Alaska Native, non-Hispanic/Latino; 5% Hispanic/Latino; 10% Black or African American, non-Hispanic/Latino; 2% Asian, non-Hispanic/Latino; 0.2% Native Hawaiian or other Pacific Islander, non-Hispanic/Latino; 2% international. 6% 25 or older, 52% live on campus, 2% transferred in. Retention: 85% of full-time freshmen returned the following year. Academic areas with the most degrees conferred: business/marketing; liberal arts/general studies; health professions and related sciences. Core. Calendar: semesters. Academic remediation for entering students, ESL program, services for LD students, advanced placement, honors program, independent study, distance learning, double major, summer session for credit, part-time degree program, adult/continuing education programs, co-op programs and internships, graduate courses open to undergrads. Off campus study at 13 members of the Greater Cincinnati Consortium of Colleges and Universities. Study abroad program. ROTC: Army, Air Force (c).

Entrance Requirements: Options: electronic application, deferred admission, international baccalaureate accepted. Required: essay, high school transcript, 1 recommendation, SAT or ACT. Required for some: minimum 3 high school GPA, interview. Entrance: moderately difficult. Application deadline: 2/1. Notification: continuous until 10/15. SAT Reasoning Test deadline: 2/1. Transfer credits accepted: Yes. Applicants placed on waiting list: 103. Wait-listed applicants offered admission: 9.

Costs Per Year: Application fee: $35. Comprehensive fee: $51,310 includes full-time tuition ($38,300), mandatory fees ($230), and college room and board ($12,780). College room only: $7020. Full-time tuition and fees vary according to course load, location, and program. Room and board charges vary according to board plan and housing facility. Part-time tuition: $715 per credit hour. Part-time mandatory fees: $9 per credit hour. Part-time tuition and fees vary according to course load, location, and program.

Collegiate Environment: Orientation program. Drama-theater group, choral group, student-run newspaper. Social organizations: 166 open to all. Most popular organizations: Student Government Association, Black Student Association, X-treme Fans, Alternative Spring Break, Club Sports. Major annual events: Club Day on the Mall, Orientation Leaders (Manresa), Spirit Celebration. Student services: health clinic, personal-psychological counseling, women's center. Campus security: 24-hour emergency response devices and patrols, late night transport-escort service, controlled dormitory access, campus-wide shuttle service. Xavier University Library plus 1 other. Operations spending for the previous fiscal year: $2.6 million. 450 computers available on campus for general student use. Computer purchase/lease plans available. A campuswide network can be accessed from student residence rooms and from off campus. Students can access the following: online class registration. Staffed computer lab on campus (open 24 hours a day) provides training in use of computers, software, and the Internet.

Community Environment: See University of Cincinnati.

■ **YOUNGSTOWN STATE UNIVERSITY**
One University Plz.
Youngstown, OH 44555-0001
Tel: (330)941-3000; Free: 877-468-6978
Fax: (330)941-1998
E-mail: enroll@ysu.edu
Web Site: www.ysu.edu
Description: State-supported, comprehensive, coed. Awards associate, bachelor's, master's, and doctoral degrees and post-master's certificates. Founded 1908. Setting: 160-acre urban campus with easy access to Cleveland, Pittsburgh. Endowment: $259.3 million. Research spending for the previous fiscal year: $4.7 million. Educational spending for the previous fiscal year: $2118 per student. Total enrollment: 12,689. Faculty: 1,049 (409 full-time, 640 part-time). Student-undergrad faculty ratio is 17:1. 10,541 applied, 68% were admitted. 13% from top 10% of their high school class, 36% from top quarter, 69% from top half. Full-time: 9,070 students, 51% women, 49% men. Part-time: 2,404 students, 59% women, 41% men. Students come from 39 states and territories, 77 other countries, 13% from out-of-state. 4% Hispanic/Latino; 9% Black or African American, non-Hispanic/Latino; 1% Asian, non-Hispanic/Latino; 3% international. 14% 25 or older,

21% live on campus, 4% transferred in. Retention: 75% of full-time freshmen returned the following year. Academic areas with the most degrees conferred: health professions and related sciences; business/marketing; engineering. Core. Calendar: semesters. Academic remediation for entering students, ESL program, services for LD students, advanced placement, accelerated degree program, self-designed majors, freshman honors college, honors program, independent study, distance learning, double major, summer session for credit, part-time degree program, adult/continuing education programs, co-op programs and internships, graduate courses open to undergrads. Off campus study at Consortium of Eastern Ohio Master of Public Health; Master of Health and Human Services University Partnership; Northeast Ohio Universities Master of fine Arts in Creative Writing. Study abroad program. ROTC: Army, Air Force (c).

Entrance Requirements: Options: electronic application, early admission, deferred admission, international baccalaureate accepted. Required: high school transcript, minimum 2 high school GPA, minimum ACT composite score of 17 or combined SAT score of 910 from evidence-based writing and reading test and math test, SAT or ACT. Entrance: minimally difficult. Application deadlines: 8/1, 8/1 for nonresidents. Notification: continuous, continuous for nonresidents. SAT Reasoning Test deadline: 8/1. SAT Subject Test deadline: 8/1. Transfer credits accepted: Yes.

Costs Per Year: Application fee: $45. State resident tuition: $8899 full-time, $371 per credit hour part-time. Nonresident tuition: $14,899 full-time, $621 per credit hour part-time. Mandatory fees: $240 full-time, $34 per term part-time. Full-time tuition and fees vary according to course load. Part-time tuition and fees vary according to course load. College room and board: $9400. Room and board charges vary according to board plan and housing facility. Tuition guaranteed not to increase for student's term of enrollment.

Collegiate Environment: Orientation program. Drama-theater group, choral group, marching band, student-run newspaper, radio station. Social organizations: 207 open to all; national fraternities, national sororities; 2% of eligible men and 3% of eligible women are members. Most popular organizations: National Society of Collegiate Scholars, Fraternities/Sororities (IFC, NPHC, Panhellenic), American Society of Mechanical Engineers, MCAT Club, American Medical Student Association. Major annual events: Homecoming, Welcome Week, Penguin Productions Concerts/Federal Frenzy/Fall Fire Fest. Student services: health clinic, personal-psychological counseling. Campus security: 24-hour emergency response devices and patrols, student patrols, late night transport-escort service, controlled dormitory access. 1,400 college housing spaces available; all were occupied in 2018-19. Freshmen given priority for college housing. Options: coed, women-only housing available. William F. Maag, Jr. Library plus 1 other. Books: 608,667 (physical), 103,922 (digital/electronic); Serial titles: 7,126 (physical), 46,162 (digital/electronic); Databases: 262. Weekly public service hours: 84; students can reserve study rooms. Operations spending for the previous fiscal year: $3.8 million. 500 computers available on campus for general student use. A campuswide network can be accessed from student residence rooms and from off campus. Students can access the following: online class registration. Staffed computer lab on campus provides training in use of computers, software, and the Internet.

Community Environment: The Youngstown area is a vibrant community, rich in heritage, natural and manmade resources, industry and business, and skilled responsible citizens. It is successfully undergoing a change from basic steelmaking to many diversified industries and businesses. Youngstown is located in bustling Northeast Ohio, five miles from the Pennsylvania line, equidistant between New York and Chicago, and 65 miles from both Pittsburgh and the Ohio River and the ports and beaches of Lake Erie. A network of interstate highways and Youngstown Airport have made it a major transportation center. Residents enjoy the areas lakes, fields, and forests, plus unusual 2,400-acre Mill Creek Park near the heart of the city. There are many churches, numerous fine teaching hospitals, a community playhouse, symphony orchestra, an outstanding public library system, excellent schools and many other cultural attractions, including the internationally famous Butler Institute of American Arts.

■ **ZANE STATE COLLEGE**
1555 Newark Rd.
Zanesville, OH 43701-2626
Tel: (740)454-2501; Free: 800-686-8324
Web Site: www.zanestate.edu
Description: State and locally supported, 2-year, coed. Awards certificates, transfer associate, and terminal associate degrees. Founded 1969. Setting: 170-acre small town campus with easy access to Columbus. Total enrollment: 2,592. Student-undergrad faculty ratio is 19:1. 1% from out-of-state.

49% 25 or older. Retention: 62% of full-time freshmen returned the following year. Core. Calendar: quarters. Academic remediation for entering students, services for LD students, self-designed majors, honors program, summer session for credit, part-time degree program, adult/continuing education programs, co-op programs and internships. Off campus study at Ohio University-Zanesville.

Entrance Requirements: Open admission except for health technology programs. Option: early admission. Required: high school transcript. Recommended: SAT or ACT. Required for some: interview. Entrance: noncompetitive. Application deadline: rolling. Notification: continuous.

Collegiate Environment: Student-run newspaper. Student services: personal-psychological counseling.

■ BACONE COLLEGE
2299 Old Bacone Rd.
Muskogee, OK 74403-1597
Tel: (918)683-4581; Free: 888-682-5514
Fax: (918)682-5514
Web Site: www.bacone.edu
Description: Independent, 4-year, coed, affiliated with American Baptist Churches in the U.S.A. Awards associate and bachelor's degrees. Founded 1880. Setting: 220-acre small town campus with easy access to Tulsa. Total enrollment: 884. 782 applied. 34% 25 or older. Core. Calendar: semesters. Academic remediation for entering students, services for LD students, advanced placement, accelerated degree program, self-designed majors, summer session for credit, part-time degree program, adult/continuing education programs, co-op programs and internships.
Entrance Requirements: Options: electronic application, early admission, deferred admission, international baccalaureate accepted. Required: high school transcript, minimum 2.0 high school GPA, SAT or ACT. Recommended: ACT. Required for some: essay, interview. Entrance: minimally difficult. Application deadline: rolling. Notification: continuous.
Collegiate Environment: Orientation program. Drama-theater group, choral group, student-run newspaper. Student services: health clinic, personal-psychological counseling. Campus security: 24-hour emergency response devices, controlled dormitory access, 8-hour patrols by trained security personnel. Bacone College Library.
Community Environment: Bacone is a suburban community, one mile from Muskogee, a town of 60,000. All the cultural, recreational, and community services are located in Muskogee.

■ CAMERON UNIVERSITY
2800 W Gore Blvd.
Lawton, OK 73505-6377
Tel: (580)581-2200; Free: 888-454-7600
Fax: (580)581-5514
E-mail: brendad@cameron.edu
Web Site: www.cameron.edu
Description: State-supported, comprehensive, coed. Part of Oklahoma State Regents for Higher Education. Awards associate, bachelor's, and master's degrees. Founded 1908. Setting: 360-acre small town campus. Endowment: $18.7 million. Research spending for the previous fiscal year: $55,561. Educational spending for the previous fiscal year: $8296 per student. Total enrollment: 4,290. Faculty: 252 (135 full-time, 117 part-time). Student-undergrad faculty ratio is 20:1. 1,120 applied, 100% were admitted. 3% from top 10% of their high school class, 14% from top quarter, 39% from top half. Full-time: 2,713 students, 60% women, 40% men. Part-time: 1,231 students, 64% women, 36% men. Students come from 32 states and territories, 32 other countries, 12% from out-of-state. 6% American Indian or Alaska Native, non-Hispanic/Latino; 15% Hispanic/Latino; 12% Black or African American, non-Hispanic/Latino; 2% Asian, non-Hispanic/Latino; 0.5% Native Hawaiian or other Pacific Islander, non-Hispanic/Latino; 3% international. 37% 25 or older, 9% live on campus, 8% transferred in. Retention: 60% of full-time freshmen returned the following year. Academic areas with the most degrees conferred: business/marketing; computer and information sciences; education. Core. Calendar: semesters. Academic remediation for entering students, services for LD students, advanced placement, accelerated degree program, self-designed majors, honors program, independent study, distance learning, double major, summer session for

credit, part-time degree program, adult/continuing education programs, internships, graduate courses open to undergrads. Off campus study at University of Oklahoma, Western Oklahoma State College, Rogers State University. ROTC: Army.
Entrance Requirements: Open admission. Options: electronic application, deferred admission, international baccalaureate accepted. Required for some: high school transcript, SAT or ACT. Entrance: noncompetitive. Application deadlines: rolling, rolling for nonresidents. Notification: continuous, continuous for nonresidents. Transfer credits accepted: Yes.
Costs Per Year: Application fee: $20. State resident tuition: $4740 full-time, $158 per credit hour part-time. Nonresident tuition: $14,160 full-time, $472 per credit hour part-time. Mandatory fees: $1710 full-time, $57 per credit hour part-time. Full-time tuition and fees vary according to course level, course load, location, program, and student level. Part-time tuition and fees vary according to course level, course load, location, program, and student level. College room and board: $5452. College room only: $2222. Room and board charges vary according to board plan and housing facility.
Collegiate Environment: Orientation program. Drama-theater group, choral group, student-run newspaper. Social organizations: 58 open to all; national fraternities, national sororities, local fraternities, local sororities; 2% of eligible men and 2% of eligible women are members. Most popular organizations: Student Government Association, Pre-Nursing Club, Phi Kappa Phi, Health Professions Society, Sigma Tau Delta. Major annual events: Welcome Week, Homecoming, The Goat Roast. Student services: health clinic, personal-psychological counseling. Campus security: 24-hour emergency response devices and patrols, late night transport-escort service, controlled dormitory access. 678 college housing spaces available; 302 were occupied in 2018-19. No special consideration for freshman housing applicants. Options: men-only, women-only housing available. Cameron University Library. Books: 82,620 (physical), 167,401 (digital/electronic); Serial titles: 2,000 (physical), 46,664 (digital/electronic); Databases: 70. Weekly public service hours: 34; students can reserve study rooms. Operations spending for the previous fiscal year: $1.1 million. 493 computers available on campus for general student use. A campuswide network can be accessed from student residence rooms and from off campus. Students can access the following: online class registration, online courses. Staffed computer lab on campus provides training in use of computers, software, and the Internet.
Community Environment: Lawton is a metropolitan area that enjoys a dry, temperate climate. The city is served by two airlines, two railroads for freight, bus service, and a turnpike. Community services include a public library, museum, churches of most denominations, two general and one public health hospital, major civic and fraternal organizations, and good shopping facilities. Part-time employment is available for students. Local recreational facilities include camping, water sports, theaters, and bowling.

■ CARL ALBERT STATE COLLEGE
1507 S McKenna
Poteau, OK 74953-5208
Tel: (918)647-1200
Fax: (918)647-1306
Web Site: www.carlalbert.edu
Description: State-supported, 2-year, coed. Part of Oklahoma State Regents for Higher Education. Awards certificates, transfer associate, and terminal associate degrees. Founded 1934. Setting: 78-acre small town campus. Total enrollment: 2,194. Student-undergrad faculty ratio is 16:1. Full-time: 1,320 students, 60% women, 40% men. Part-time: 874 students,

67% women, 33% men. Students come from 9 states and territories. 25% American Indian or Alaska Native, non-Hispanic/Latino; 7% Hispanic/Latino; 3% Black or African American, non-Hispanic/Latino; 0.3% Asian, non-Hispanic/Latino; 1% international. 36% 25 or older, 12% live on campus. Core. Calendar: semesters. Academic remediation for entering students, part-time degree program, adult/continuing education programs, co-op programs.

Entrance Requirements: Open admission. Required: high school transcript. Recommended: SAT or ACT. Entrance: noncompetitive. Notification: continuous.

Costs Per Year: Application fee: $0. State resident tuition: $2,555 full-time, $91.25 per credit hour part-time. Nonresident tuition: $6405 full-time, $228.75 per credit hour part-time. Mandatory fees: $1008 full-time, $36 per credit hour part-time. Full-time tuition and fees vary according to course load. Part-time tuition and fees vary according to course load. College room and board: $4000. Room and board charges vary according to board plan.

Collegiate Environment: Orientation program. Drama-theater group, choral group, student-run newspaper, radio station. Social organizations: 25 open to all. Most popular organizations: Student Government Association, Phi Theta Kappa, Baptist Student Union, BACCHUS, Student Physical Therapist Assistant Association. Major annual events: Welcome Week, Homecoming, Graduation. Student services: health clinic, personal-psychological counseling. Campus security: security guards. Joe E. White Library. 75 computers available on campus for general student use. A campuswide network can be accessed. Students can access the following: online class registration. Staffed computer lab on campus.

Community Environment: Poteau is located in central eastern Oklahoma in the Cavanal Mountain area. This is the county seat and may be reached by bus lines. Nearby Ouachita National Forest offers excellent recreational facilities.

■ **CLARY SAGE COLLEGE**
3131 S Sheridan
Tulsa, OK 74145
Tel: (918)298-8200
Fax: (918)298-0099
E-mail: rmahlberg@clarysagecollege.com
Web Site: www.clarysagecollege.com

Description: Proprietary, 2-year, coed. Awards diplomas and transfer associate degrees. Founded 2006. Setting: 6-acre urban campus with easy access to Tulsa. Educational spending for the previous fiscal year: $4168 per student. Total enrollment: 406. Faculty: 28 (all full-time). Student-undergrad faculty ratio is 15:1. Full-time: 406 students, 89% women, 11% men. Students come from 9 states and territories, 3% from out-of-state. 17% American Indian or Alaska Native, non-Hispanic/Latino; 5% Hispanic/Latino; 20% Black or African American, non-Hispanic/Latino; 3% Asian, non-Hispanic/Latino; 0.5% Native Hawaiian or other Pacific Islander, non-Hispanic/Latino. 51% 25 or older, 58% transferred in. Core. Calendar: continuous. Distance learning, adult/continuing education programs, internships.

Entrance Requirements: Open admission. Option: electronic application. Required: essay, high school transcript, interview. Entrance: noncompetitive. Application deadline: rolling. Notification: continuous. Transfer credits accepted: Yes.

Collegiate Environment: Orientation program. Social organizations: 1 open to all. Most popular organization: Student Ambassadors. Major annual events: Food Bank Drive, Clothing Drive, Blood Drive. Campus security: security guard during hours of operation. Operations spending for the previous fiscal year: $15,841. 30 computers available on campus for general student use. Computer purchase/lease plans available. A campuswide network can be accessed. Staffed computer lab on campus provides training in use of computers, software, and the Internet.

■ **COLLEGE OF THE MUSCOGEE NATION**
2170 Raven Cir.
Okmulgee, OK 74447-0917
Web Site: www.cmn.edu

Description: Public, 2-year, coed. Awards certificates, transfer associate, and terminal associate degrees.

■ **COMMUNITY CARE COLLEGE**
4242 S Sheridan Rd.
Tulsa, OK 74145
Tel: (918)610-0027

Fax: (918)610-0029
E-mail: kkirk@communitycarecollege.edu
Web Site: www.communitycarecollege.edu

Description: Independent, 2-year, coed. Awards diplomas and terminal associate degrees. Founded 1995. Setting: 6-acre urban campus with easy access to Tulsa. Educational spending for the previous fiscal year: $2331 per student. Total enrollment: 623. Faculty: 26 (24 full-time, 2 part-time). Student-undergrad faculty ratio is 25:1. Full-time: 623 students, 92% women, 8% men. Students come from 18 states and territories, 4% from out-of-state. 19% American Indian or Alaska Native, non-Hispanic/Latino; 7% Hispanic/Latino; 17% Black or African American, non-Hispanic/Latino; 2% Asian, non-Hispanic/Latino; 0.2% Native Hawaiian or other Pacific Islander, non-Hispanic/Latino. 62% 25 or older. Core. Calendar: continuous. Services for LD students, independent study, distance learning, adult/continuing education programs, internships.

Entrance Requirements: Open admission. Option: electronic application. Required: essay, high school transcript, interview. Required for some: 1 recommendation. Entrance: noncompetitive. Application deadline: rolling. Notification: continuous. Transfer credits accepted: Yes.

Collegiate Environment: Orientation program. Most popular organization: Student Ambassadors. Major annual events: Food Bank Drive, Clothing Drive, Blood Drive. Campus security: campus security personnel during school hours. Operations spending for the previous fiscal year: $22,667. 65 computers available on campus for general student use. A campuswide network can be accessed. Staffed computer lab on campus provides training in use of computers, software, and the Internet.

■ **CONNORS STATE COLLEGE**
Rte. 1 Box 1000
Warner, OK 74469-9700
Tel: (918)463-2931
Web Site: www.connorsstate.edu

Description: State-supported, 2-year, coed. Part of Oklahoma State Regents for Higher Education. Awards certificates, diplomas, transfer associate, and terminal associate degrees. Founded 1908. Setting: 1,658-acre rural campus. Total enrollment: 2,250. 38% 25 or older. Core. Calendar: semesters. Academic remediation for entering students, advanced placement, accelerated degree program, summer session for credit, part-time degree program, adult/continuing education programs, internships.

Entrance Requirements: Open admission. Options: early admission, deferred admission. Required for some: high school transcript. Entrance: noncompetitive. Application deadline: rolling.

Collegiate Environment: Drama-theater group, student-run newspaper. Student services: health clinic. Campus security: late night transport-escort service, trained security personnel. Carl Westbrook Library.

Community Environment: Warner is a rural community with mild winters and warm to hot summers. The area is provided transportation by bus lines, and U.S. Highways 64 and 266. There are several churches of various denominations, and civic and service clubs within the city. Recreational facilities within the area include theatres, restaurants, and nearby lakes. Within driving distance, there is the Five Civilized Tribes Museum.

■ **EAST CENTRAL UNIVERSITY**
1100 E 14th St.
Ada, OK 74820
Tel: (580)332-8000
Fax: (580)436-5495
E-mail: kstephens@ecok.edu
Web Site: www.ecok.edu

Description: State-supported, comprehensive, coed. Part of Oklahoma State Regents for Higher Education. Awards bachelor's and master's degrees and post-master's certificates. Founded 1909. Setting: 144-acre small town campus with easy access to Oklahoma City. Endowment: $31.3 million. Research spending for the previous fiscal year: $237,392. Total enrollment: 3,639. Faculty: 223 (151 full-time, 72 part-time). Student-undergrad faculty ratio is 18:1. 1,847 applied, 48% were admitted. Full-time: 2,372 students, 58% women, 42% men. Part-time: 657 students, 65% women, 35% men. Students come from 22 states and territories, 32 other countries, 7% from out-of-state. 15% American Indian or Alaska Native, non-Hispanic/Latino; 6% Hispanic/Latino; 4% Black or African American, non-Hispanic/Latino; 0.3% Asian, non-Hispanic/Latino; 0.3% Native Hawaiian or other Pacific Islander, non-Hispanic/Latino; 7% international. 19% 25 or older, 31% live on campus, 9% transferred in. Retention: 34% of full-time freshmen returned the following year. Academic areas with the most degrees conferred: health professions and related sciences; business/marketing; public administration and social services. Core. Calendar: semesters. Academic remediation for entering students, ESL program, services for LD students, advanced placement, self-designed majors, honors program, independent study, double major, summer session for credit, part-time degree program, adult/continuing education programs, internships, graduate courses open to undergrads. Off campus study. Study abroad program.

Entrance Requirements: Options: electronic application, early admission. Required: high school transcript, ACT. Recommended: SAT or ACT. Required for some: minimum 2.7 high school GPA, rank in upper 50% of high school class. Entrance: minimally difficult. Application deadline: rolling. Notification: continuous. SAT Reasoning Test deadline: 8/1. Transfer credits accepted: Yes.

Costs Per Year: Application fee: $20. State resident tuition: $5406 full-time, $180.20 per semester hour part-time. Nonresident tuition: $14,616 full-time, $487.20 per semester hour part-time. Mandatory fees: $1404 full-time, $46.80 per semester hour part-time. College room and board: $6848. College room only: $3538. Room and board charges vary according to board plan and housing facility. Tuition guaranteed not to increase for student's term of enrollment.

Collegiate Environment: Orientation program. Drama-theater group, choral group, marching band. Social organizations: 70 open to all; national fraternities, national sororities. Most popular organizations: Campus Connection, F.A.T.E, GSA, ECU Wesley, Tigers for Tigers. Major annual events: Homecoming Week, Orange Crush Week, Tiger Streak. Student services: health clinic, personal-psychological counseling. Campus security: 24-hour emergency response devices and patrols, student patrols, late night transport-escort service, controlled dormitory access, agreements with all local, state, federal, and tribal police departments for added crime and violation prevention. Linscheid Library. Books: 159,582 (physical), 25,548 (digital/electronic); Serial titles: 24,879 (physical), 825 (digital/electronic); Databases: 73. Weekly public service hours: 71; students can reserve study rooms. Operations spending for the previous fiscal year: $1.2 million. 800 computers available on campus for general student use. A campuswide network can be accessed from student residence rooms. Students can access the following: online class registration. Staffed computer lab on campus provides training in use of computers and software.

Community Environment: Ada is the commercial, industrial, service, and medical center for this area. An EPA world-class groundwater research laboratory (Robert S. Kerr Environmental Research Laboratory) and the seat of government of the Chickasaw Indian Nation are located in Ada. Ada's primary commercial employers include a cement plant, a plastics molding operation, and petroleum and cattle industries. The climate is temperate with mild winters. The average temperature is 64 degrees. Ada is approximately 90 miles southeast of Oklahoma City. Community services include a major regional medical center, thirty churches, and many active civic and fraternal organizations. Local recreational facilities include parks, swimming pools, picnic areas, hiking, golf, fishing, hunting, waterskiing, and tennis.

■ **EASTERN OKLAHOMA STATE COLLEGE**
1301 W Main
Wilburton, OK 74578-4999
Tel: (918)465-2361; Free: 855-534-3672
Fax: (918)465-2431
E-mail: lmiller@eosc.edu
Web Site: www.eosc.edu

Description: State-supported, 2-year, coed. Part of Oklahoma State Regents for Higher Education. Awards certificates, transfer associate, and terminal associate degrees. Founded 1908. Setting: 4,000-acre rural campus. Total enrollment: 1,772. 26% 25 or older. Core. Calendar: semesters. Academic remediation for entering students, advanced placement, honors program, double major, summer session for credit, part-time degree program, adult/continuing education programs, co-op programs and internships. Off campus study at E. T. Dunlap Higher Education Center, McAlester Higher Education Center.

Entrance Requirements: Open admission for state residents. Options: early admission, deferred admission. Required: high school transcript. Entrance: noncompetitive. Application deadline: rolling.

Collegiate Environment: Orientation program. Drama-theater group, choral group, student-run newspaper. Student services: personal-psychological counseling. Bill H. Hill Library.

Community Environment: Wilburton is a small community located in the San Bois Mountains. The area is served by commercial bus lines, U.S. Route 270 and State Highway 2. A small municipal airport is located here,

but commercial airlines are approximately 30 miles distant. Good recreational facilities for outdoor sports include nearby Robber's Cave State Park, and Kiamichi National Forest. The nearest large cities are Muskogee and Fort Smith, Arkansas.

■ **FAMILY OF FAITH CHRISTIAN UNIVERSITY**
30 Kinville
Shawnee, OK 74802
Tel: (405)273-5331
Web Site: www.familyoffaith.edu

Description: Independent Christian, 4-year, coed. Awards bachelor's degrees. Founded 1992. Calendar: semesters.

■ **LANGSTON UNIVERSITY**
PO Box 907
Langston, OK 73050
Tel: (405)466-2231
Fax: (405)466-3381
E-mail: jlane@langston.edu
Web Site: www.langston.edu

Description: State-supported, comprehensive, coed. Part of Oklahoma A&M System. Awards associate, bachelor's, master's, and doctoral degrees. Founded 1897. Setting: 40-acre rural campus with easy access to Oklahoma City. System endowment: $1.6 million. Research spending for the previous fiscal year: $10 million. Educational spending for the previous fiscal year: $5393 per student. Total enrollment: 2,222. Faculty: 221 (141 full-time, 80 part-time). Student-undergrad faculty ratio is 22:1. 9,244 applied, 61% were admitted. 4% from top 10% of their high school class, 14% from top quarter, 38% from top half. 3 valedictorians. Full-time: 1,664 students, 63% women, 37% men. Part-time: 349 students, 63% women, 37% men. Students come from 37 states and territories, 12 other countries, 38% from out-of-state. 2% American Indian or Alaska Native, non-Hispanic/Latino; 2% Hispanic/Latino; 79% Black or African American, non-Hispanic/Latino; 0.7% Native Hawaiian or other Pacific Islander, non-Hispanic/Latino; 0.7% international. 19% 25 or older, 67% live on campus, 9% transferred in. Retention: 47% of full-time freshmen returned the following year. Academic areas with the most degrees conferred: health professions and related sciences; business/marketing; psychology. Core. Calendar: semesters. Academic remediation for entering students, ESL program, services for LD students, advanced placement, accelerated degree program, honors program, independent study, distance learning, double major, summer session for credit, part-time degree program, external degree program, adult/continuing education programs, co-op programs and internships, graduate courses open to undergrads. Study abroad program. ROTC: Army (c).

Entrance Requirements: Options: electronic application, deferred admission. Required: high school transcript, minimum 2.7 high school GPA, SAT or ACT. Entrance: moderately difficult. Application deadline: rolling. Transfer credits accepted: Yes.

Collegiate Environment: Orientation program. Drama-theater group, choral group, marching band, student-run newspaper, radio station. Social organizations: 30 open to all; national fraternities, national sororities; 16% of eligible men and 19% of eligible women are members. Most popular organizations: Student Government Association, Student Senate, Sorority and Fraternity (Greek Letter), NAACP, Pre- Alumni Council. Major annual events: Homecoming, Spring Festival, Intramural Sports. Student services: health clinic, personal-psychological counseling, women's center. Campus security: 24-hour emergency response devices and patrols, student patrols, late night transport-escort service, controlled dormitory access. G. Lamar Harrison Library plus 2 others. Books: 44,337 (physical), 189,180 (digital/electronic); Serial titles: 111 (physical), 20,763 (digital/electronic); Databases: 61. Students can reserve study rooms. Operations spending for the previous fiscal year: $854,735. 300 computers available on campus for general student use. A campuswide network can be accessed from student residence rooms and from off campus. Students can access the following: online class registration. Staffed computer lab on campus provides training in use of computers and the Internet.

Community Environment: Langston is a small rural community located 40 miles northeast of Oklahoma City and 90 miles west of Tulsa, OK.

■ **MID-AMERICA CHRISTIAN UNIVERSITY**
3500 SW 119th St.
Oklahoma City, OK 73170-4504
Tel: (405)691-3800; Free: 888-436-3035
Fax: (405)692-5165

Web Site: www.macu.edu

Description: Independent, comprehensive, coed, affiliated with Church of God. Awards associate, bachelor's, and master's degrees and post-master's certificates. Founded 1953. Setting: 145-acre suburban campus with easy access to Oklahoma City, Oklahoma. System endowment: $2.6 million. Educational spending for the previous fiscal year: $16,738 per student. Total enrollment: 869. Student-undergrad faculty ratio is 11:1. 53% 25 or older. Core. Calendar: semesters. Academic remediation for entering students, services for LD students, advanced placement, accelerated degree program, distance learning, double major, summer session for credit, part-time degree program, adult/continuing education programs, internships.

Entrance Requirements: Open admission. Option: early admission. Required: high school transcript. Recommended: SAT or ACT. Required for some: 2 recommendations, interview. Entrance: noncompetitive. Application deadline: rolling.

Collegiate Environment: Orientation program. Choral group, student-run newspaper. Student services: personal-psychological counseling. Campus security: 24-hour patrols, student patrols. Charles Ewing Brown Library. Weekly public service hours: 70; study areas open 24 hours, 5-7 days a week; students can reserve study rooms. Operations spending for the previous fiscal year: $276,009. 24 computers available on campus for general student use. A campuswide network can be accessed. Students can access the following: online class registration. Staffed computer lab on campus (open 24 hours a day) provides training in use of computers, software, and the Internet.

Community Environment: See Oklahoma City University.

■ MURRAY STATE COLLEGE

One Murray Campus
Tishomingo, OK 73460
Tel: (580)387-7000
Fax: (580)371-9844
Web Site: www.mscok.edu

Description: State-supported, 2-year, coed. Part of Oklahoma State Regents for Higher Education. Awards transfer associate and terminal associate degrees. Founded 1908. Setting: 120-acre rural campus. Total enrollment: 2,674. Faculty: 152 (57 full-time, 95 part-time). Student-undergrad faculty ratio is 20:1. Students come from 19 states and territories, 9 other countries, 4% from out-of-state. 13% American Indian or Alaska Native, non-Hispanic/Latino; 6% Hispanic/Latino; 5% Black or African American, non-Hispanic/Latino; 0.3% Asian, non-Hispanic/Latino; 0.1% Native Hawaiian or other Pacific Islander, non-Hispanic/Latino; 0.1% international. 11% live on campus. Retention: 49% of full-time freshmen returned the following year. Core. Calendar: semesters. Academic remediation for entering students, services for LD students, advanced placement, honors program, distance learning, summer session for credit, part-time degree program, internships.

Entrance Requirements: Open admission. Options: electronic application, early admission. Required: high school transcript, SAT or ACT. Entrance: noncompetitive. Application deadline: rolling. Notification: continuous.

Collegiate Environment: Orientation program. Drama-theater group, choral group. Social organizations: 11 open to all. Student services: personal-psychological counseling. Campus security: 24-hour patrols. Murray State College Library plus 1 other. 50 computers available on campus for general student use. A campuswide network can be accessed. Students can access the following: online class registration. Staffed computer lab on campus provides training in use of computers, software, and the Internet.

Community Environment: Historically noted as the original capital of the Chickasaw Nation, Tishomingo is situated on the banks of Lake Texoma within a wildlife refuge. This is a rural area with a temperate climate. The city is served by five highways. Tishomingo has six churches, a hospital, and major civic, fraternal and veteran's organizations. Local recreational facilities include water sports, hunting, fishing, and hiking.

■ NATIONAL AMERICAN UNIVERSITY

8040 S Sheridan Rd.
Tulsa, OK 74133
Tel: (918)879-8400; Free: 800-209-0338
Web Site: www.national.edu

Description: Proprietary, 4-year, coed. Awards associate and bachelor's degrees. Calendar: quarters.

■ NORTHEASTERN OKLAHOMA AGRICULTURAL AND MECHANICAL COLLEGE

200 I St., NE
Miami, OK 74354-6434

Tel: (918)542-8441; Free: 800-464-6636
Fax: (918)542-9759
E-mail: neoadmission@neo.edu
Web Site: www.neo.edu

Description: State-supported, 2-year, coed. Part of Oklahoma State Regents for Higher Education. Awards certificates, transfer associate, and terminal associate degrees. Founded 1919. Setting: 340-acre small town campus. Total enrollment: 1,899. Faculty: 110 (77 full-time, 33 part-time). Student-undergrad faculty ratio is 17:1. Full-time: 1,396 students, 52% women, 48% men. Part-time: 503 students, 71% women, 29% men. 24% 25 or older. Retention: 58% of full-time freshmen returned the following year. Core. Calendar: semesters. Academic remediation for entering students, services for LD students, advanced placement, distance learning, double major, summer session for credit, part-time degree program, external degree program, adult/continuing education programs, internships.

Entrance Requirements: Open admission. Option: electronic application. Required: high school transcript. Entrance: noncompetitive. Application deadline: rolling. Notification: continuous.

Collegiate Environment: Drama-theater group, choral group, marching band, student-run newspaper. Social organizations: 50 open to all. Student services: health clinic, personal-psychological counseling. Campus security: 24-hour patrols. Learning Resource Center. 65 computers available on campus for general student use. Students can access the following: online class registration. Staffed computer lab on campus provides training in use of computers, software, and the Internet.

Community Environment: Miami is headquarters for the Grand Lake recreation area. Items produced by the city's manufacturers include automotive parts, tires and tubes, clothing, food products and boats and accessories. Part-time employment is available. The climate is temperate. There are dormitories and housing units on campus. Good health services are available.

■ NORTHEASTERN STATE UNIVERSITY

600 N Grand
Tahlequah, OK 74464-2399
Tel: (918)456-5511; Free: 800-722-9614
Fax: (918)458-2342
E-mail: cunningham@nsuok.edu
Web Site: www.nsuok.edu

Description: State-supported, comprehensive, coed. Part of Regional University System of Oklahoma. Awards bachelor's, master's, and doctoral degrees and post-master's certificates. Founded 1846. Setting: 200-acre small town campus with easy access to Tulsa. Endowment: $5.4 million. Research spending for the previous fiscal year: $802,466. Educational spending for the previous fiscal year: $6826 per student. Total enrollment: 7,899. Faculty: 427 (283 full-time, 144 part-time). Student-undergrad faculty ratio is 18:1. 1,474 applied, 97% were admitted. 24% from top 10% of their high school class, 48% from top quarter, 82% from top half. Full-time: 4,687 students, 59% women, 41% men. Part-time: 2,054 students, 67% women, 33% men. Students come from 26 states and territories, 54 other countries, 5% from out-of-state. 18% American Indian or Alaska Native, non-Hispanic/Latino; 6% Hispanic/Latino; 4% Black or African American, non-Hispanic/Latino; 2% Asian, non-Hispanic/Latino; 2% international. 36% 25 or older, 17% live on campus, 13% transferred in. Retention: 64% of full-time freshmen returned the following year. Academic areas with the most degrees conferred: business/marketing; education; psychology. Core. Calendar: semesters. Academic remediation for entering students, services for LD students, advanced placement, self-designed majors, honors program, independent study, distance learning, double major, summer session for credit, part-time degree program, adult/continuing education programs, co-op programs and internships, graduate courses open to undergrads. ROTC: Army.

Entrance Requirements: Options: electronic application, deferred admission. Required: high school transcript, minimum 2.7 high school GPA, upper 50% of class or minimum ACT composite of 20, ACT. Required for some: essay, recommendations, interview. Entrance: moderately difficult. Notification: continuous. SAT Reasoning Test deadline: 8/15.

Costs Per Year: Application fee: $25. State resident tuition: $5,528 full-time, $184.25 per credit hour part-time. Nonresident tuition: $13,598 full-time, $453.25 per credit hour part-time. Mandatory fees: $1122 full-time, $37.40 per credit hour part-time. Full-time tuition and fees vary according to course load and program. Part-time tuition and fees vary according to course load and program. College room and board: $7638. College room only: $3952. Room and board charges vary according to board plan and housing facility. Tuition guaranteed not to increase for student's term of enrollment.

Collegiate Environment: Orientation program. Drama-theater group, choral group, marching band, student-run newspaper. Social organizations: 123 open to all; national fraternities, national sororities, local fraternities, local sororities. Student services: health clinic, personal-psychological counseling. Campus security: 24-hour emergency response devices and patrols, late night transport-escort service, controlled dormitory access. 1,480 college housing spaces available; 1,178 were occupied in 2018-19. Freshmen given priority for college housing. On-campus residence required in freshman year. Options: coed, women-only housing available. John Vaughn Library. Books: 415,253 (physical), 64,575 (digital/electronic); Serial titles: 30,893 (physical), 92,125 (digital/electronic); Databases: 143. Weekly public service hours: 114. Operations spending for the previous fiscal year: $2.8 million. 1,160 computers available on campus for general student use. Computer purchase/lease plans available. A campuswide network can be accessed from student residence rooms and from off campus. Students can access the following: online class registration. Staffed computer lab on campus (open 24 hours a day) provides training in use of computers, software, and the Internet.

Community Environment: In a region of lakes within the foothills of the Ozark Mountains, Tahlequah is the former capital city of the Cherokee Indian Nation. There are many historic sites and artifacts in the area. The city is accessible by five highways. Community services includes several churches of various denominations, two hospitals, two libraries, and a museum. Apartments provide student housing. There are various civic and fraternal organizations within the city. Limited part-time employment is available for students. Local recreational facilities include boating, fishing, hunting, water skiing, and swimming.

■ NORTHERN OKLAHOMA COLLEGE

1220 E Grand Ave.
Tonkawa, OK 74653-0310
Tel: (580)628-6200
Fax: (580)628-6371
Web Site: www.noc.edu

Description: State-supported, 2-year, coed. Part of Oklahoma State Regents for Higher Education. Awards transfer associate and terminal associate degrees. Founded 1901. Setting: 10-acre rural campus. Total enrollment: 3,050. Faculty: 80 (45 full-time, 35 part-time). Student-undergrad faculty ratio is 35:1. Students come from 4 other countries. 40% 25 or older, 20% live on campus. Calendar: semesters. Academic remediation for entering students, services for LD students, advanced placement, summer session for credit, part-time degree program, adult/continuing education programs.

Entrance Requirements: Open admission except for nursing program. Option: early admission. Required: high school transcript. Entrance: noncompetitive. Application deadline: rolling.

Collegiate Environment: Drama-theater group, choral group, student-run newspaper, radio station. Social organizations: 15 open to all. Most popular organizations: Phi Theta Kappa, Law Enforcement Club, Fellowship of Christian Athletes, Student Nurses Association, Young Republicans. Major annual events: Homecoming, Drug Awareness Week. Student services: health clinic, personal-psychological counseling. Campus security: 24-hour emergency response devices and patrols. Vineyard Library. 150 computers available on campus for general student use. Staffed computer lab on campus.

Community Environment: Tonkawa is located 14 miles west of Ponca City and enjoys a mild climate. The city has a public library, churches representing 10 denominations, a nearby hospital, a Chamber of Commerce and other civic, fraternal and veteran's organizations. Housing for students is provided by dormitories and one hotel. There are limited job opportunities for students. Fishing in nearby rivers is considered excellent sport.

■ NORTHWESTERN OKLAHOMA STATE UNIVERSITY

709 Oklahoma Blvd.
Alva, OK 73717-2799
Tel: (580)327-1700
Fax: (580)327-1881
E-mail: recruit@nwosu.edu
Web Site: www.nwosu.edu

Description: State-supported, comprehensive, coed. Part of Oklahoma State Regents for Higher Education. Awards bachelor's, master's, and doctoral degrees. Founded 1897. Setting: 70-acre rural campus. Endowment: $35.7 million. Research spending for the previous fiscal year: $69,370. Educational spending for the previous fiscal year: $3090 per student. Total

enrollment: 1,992. Faculty: 159 (91 full-time, 68 part-time). Student-undergrad faculty ratio is 15:1. 1,170 applied, 62% were admitted. 11% from top 10% of their high school class, 30% from top quarter, 64% from top half. Full-time: 1,430 students, 57% women, 43% men. Part-time: 343 students, 66% women, 34% men. Students come from 47 states and territories, 18 other countries, 24% from out-of-state. 8% American Indian or Alaska Native, non-Hispanic/Latino; 10% Hispanic/Latino; 8% Black or African American, non-Hispanic/Latino; 0.5% Asian, non-Hispanic/Latino; 0.1% Native Hawaiian or other Pacific Islander, non-Hispanic/Latino; 2% international. 20% 25 or older, 30% live on campus, 11% transferred in. Retention: 60% of full-time freshmen returned the following year. Academic areas with the most degrees conferred: health professions and related sciences; business/marketing; agriculture; psychology; education. Core. Calendar: semesters. Academic remediation for entering students, services for LD students, advanced placement, honors program, independent study, distance learning, summer session for credit, part-time degree program, adult/continuing education programs, co-op programs and internships, graduate courses open to undergrads. Off campus study. Study abroad program.

Entrance Requirements: Options: electronic application, early admission, international baccalaureate accepted. Required: high school transcript, SAT or ACT. Required for some: essay, minimum 2.7 high school GPA, 3 recommendations. Entrance: moderately difficult. Application deadlines: rolling, rolling for nonresidents. Notification: continuous, continuous for nonresidents. Transfer credits accepted: Yes.

Costs Per Year: Application fee: $15. State resident tuition: $6382 full-time. Nonresident tuition: $13,822 full-time. Mandatory fees: $652 full-time. Full-time tuition and fees vary according to course load, degree level, location, and program. College room and board: $4480. College room only: $1780. Room and board charges vary according to board plan. Tuition guaranteed not to increase for student's term of enrollment.

Collegiate Environment: Orientation program. Drama-theater group, choral group, marching band, student-run newspaper, radio station. Social organizations: 60 open to all; local fraternities, local sororities. Most popular organizations: Student Government Association, Aggie Club, Delta Mu Delta, Baptist Student Union, SOEA. Major annual events: Bahama Breakaway, Homecoming, Family Day. Student services: personal-psychological counseling. Campus security: 24-hour emergency response devices and patrols, late night transport-escort service. 886 college housing spaces available; 600 were occupied in 2018-19. Freshmen guaranteed college housing. On-campus residence required in freshman year. Options: men-only, women-only housing available. J. W. Martin Library. Books: 91,123 (physical), 213,917 (digital/electronic); Serial titles: 23,390 (physical), 6 (digital/electronic); Databases: 45. Weekly public service hours: 84; students can reserve study rooms. Operations spending for the previous fiscal year: $466,913. 260 computers available on campus for general student use. A campuswide network can be accessed. Students can access the following: online class registration. Staffed computer lab on campus.

Community Environment: Alva is located in northwestern Oklahoma. The average mean temperature is 59.1 degrees. Rainfall averages 16 inches annually. Local public services include a hospital, many churches, five motels, and active civic and fraternal groups. A movie theatre, golf course, municipal swimming pool, park, picnic areas, lighted baseball fields, playgrounds, tennis courts, fishing, and hunting provide recreation and are all easily accessible. Little Sahara State Park and Alabaster Caverns are located approximately 25 miles distant.

■ OKLAHOMA BAPTIST UNIVERSITY

500 W University
Shawnee, OK 74804
Tel: (405)275-2850; Free: 800-654-3285
Fax: (405)878-2046
Web Site: www.okbu.edu

Description: Independent Southern Baptist, comprehensive, coed. Awards associate, bachelor's, and master's degrees. Founded 1910. Setting: 125-acre small town campus with easy access to Oklahoma City. Endowment: $116.2 million. Educational spending for the previous fiscal year: $8331 per student. Total enrollment: 2,085. Faculty: 187 (108 full-time, 79 part-time). Student-undergrad faculty ratio is 11:1. 4,434 applied, 64% were admitted. 22% from top 10% of their high school class, 49% from top quarter, 80% from top half. Full-time: 1,785 students, 60% women, 40% men. Part-time: 85 students, 66% women, 34% men. Students come from 45 states and territories, 41 other countries, 36% from out-of-state. 5% American Indian or Alaska Native, non-Hispanic/Latino; 2% Hispanic/Latino; 5% Black or African American, non-Hispanic/Latino; 1% Asian, non-Hispanic/Latino; 0.3% Native

Hawaiian or other Pacific Islander, non-Hispanic/Latino; 4% international. 9% 25 or older, 67% live on campus, 4% transferred in. Retention: 78% of full-time freshmen returned the following year. Academic areas with the most degrees conferred: health professions and related sciences; business/marketing; education. Core. Calendar: 4-1-4. Academic remediation for entering students, services for LD students, advanced placement, self-designed majors, honors program, independent study, double major, summer session for credit, part-time degree program, co-op programs and internships. Off campus study. Study abroad program. ROTC: Air Force (c).

Entrance Requirements: Options: electronic application, early admission, deferred admission, international baccalaureate accepted. Required: high school transcript, minimum 3 high school GPA, SAT or ACT. Required for some: essay, interview. Entrance: moderately difficult. Application deadline: rolling. Notification: continuous. Transfer credits accepted: Yes.

Costs Per Year: Comprehensive fee: $37,354 includes full-time tuition ($26,584), mandatory fees ($3280), and college room and board ($7490). College room only: $3390. Part-time tuition: $864 per credit hour. Part-time mandatory fees: $3280 per term.

Collegiate Environment: Orientation program. Drama-theater group, choral group, marching band, student-run newspaper. Social organizations: 42 open to all; local fraternities, local sororities; 6% of eligible men and 17% of eligible women are members. Most popular organizations: Campus Activities Board, University Concert Series, Student Foundation, Blitz Week Activities, Canterbury. Major annual events: Biggie, Freshmen Follies, Spring Affair. Student services: health clinic, personal-psychological counseling. Campus security: 24-hour emergency response devices and patrols, late night transport-escort service, controlled dormitory access. 1,634 college housing spaces available; 1,247 were occupied in 2018-19. Freshmen guaranteed college housing. On-campus residence required through junior year. Options: men-only, women-only housing available. Mabee Learning Center. Books: 162,334 (physical), 188,606 (digital/electronic); Serial titles: 1,140 (physical); Databases: 60. Weekly public service hours: 91; students can reserve study rooms. Operations spending for the previous fiscal year: $294,989. 175 computers available on campus for general student use. A campuswide network can be accessed from student residence rooms. Students can access the following: online class registration, campus portal, online course work. Staffed computer lab on campus provides training in use of software and the Internet.

Community Environment: On the North Canadian River, Shawnee is in a rich agricultural and oil-producing area. The altitude of the city is 1,080 feet above sea level and the average temperature is 62.3 degrees. It is located near the geographical center of the state approximately 40 miles by interstate highway from Oklahoma City. The area is accessible via bus lines and a municipal airport. There are churches of most denominations and a YMCA in town. Local recreational facilities provide for golf, fishing, tennis, boating, hunting, bowling, and roller skating as well as picnic grounds, three swimming pools, parks, theatres, museums, and one drive-in. Events include horse shows and rodeo. There are various civic, fraternal and veterans' organizations here.

■ **OKLAHOMA CHRISTIAN UNIVERSITY**
PO Box 11000
Oklahoma City, OK 73136-1100
Tel: (405)425-5000; Free: 800-877-5010
Fax: (405)425-5208
E-mail: admissions@oc.edu
Web Site: www.oc.edu

Description: Independent, comprehensive, coed, affiliated with Church of Christ. Awards bachelor's and master's degrees. Founded 1950. Setting: 200-acre suburban campus with easy access to Oklahoma City. Educational spending for the previous fiscal year: $6917 per student. Total enrollment: 2,248. Faculty: 219 (101 full-time, 118 part-time). Student-undergrad faculty ratio is 14:1. 2,452 applied, 65% were admitted. 21% from top 10% of their high school class, 52% from top quarter, 83% from top half. 4 National Merit Scholars. Full-time: 1,767 students, 51% women, 49% men. Part-time: 138 students, 44% women, 56% men. Students come from 42 states and territories, 36 other countries, 54% from out-of-state. 2% American Indian or Alaska Native, non-Hispanic/Latino; 7% Hispanic/Latino; 5% Black or African American, non-Hispanic/Latino; 0.8% Asian, non-Hispanic/Latino; 0.1% Native Hawaiian or other Pacific Islander, non-Hispanic/Latino; 5% international. 4% 25 or older, 77% live on campus, 4% transferred in. Retention: 75% of full-time freshmen returned the following year. Academic areas with the most degrees conferred: business/marketing; engineering; health professions and related sciences. Core. Calendar: semesters. Academic remediation for

entering students, ESL program, services for LD students, advanced placement, accelerated degree program, self-designed majors, honors program, independent study, distance learning, double major, summer session for credit, co-op programs and internships, graduate courses open to undergrads. Off campus study at University of Central Oklahoma. Study abroad program. ROTC: Army (c), Air Force (c).

Entrance Requirements: Options: electronic application, early admission, deferred admission, international baccalaureate accepted. Required: high school transcript, SAT or ACT. Required for some: interview. Entrance: moderately difficult. Application deadline: rolling. Notification: continuous. SAT Reasoning Test deadline: 8/25. Transfer credits accepted: Yes.

Costs Per Year: Application fee: $25. Comprehensive fee: $32,300 includes full-time tuition ($23,450), mandatory fees ($300), and college room and board ($8550). College room only: $4550.

Collegiate Environment: Orientation program. Drama-theater group, choral group, student-run newspaper, radio station. Social organizations: 56 open to all; local fraternities, local sororities; 30% of eligible men and 37% of eligible women are members. Most popular organizations: Ethos, Social Service Clubs, Student Government Association, Freshman Class club, Outreach mission organization. Major annual events: Spring Sing, Lighting of the Commons, Homecoming. Student services: health clinic, personal-psychological counseling. Campus security: 24-hour emergency response devices and patrols, late night transport-escort service, controlled dormitory access. 1,730 college housing spaces available; 1,430 were occupied in 2018-19. Freshmen guaranteed college housing. On-campus residence required through senior year. Options: men-only, women-only housing available. Tom and Ada Beam Library. Books: 108,575 (physical), 66,843 (digital/electronic); Serial titles: 1,241 (physical), 42,377 (digital/electronic); Databases: 76. Weekly public service hours: 82; students can reserve study rooms. Operations spending for the previous fiscal year: $599,673. 101 computers available on campus for general student use. A computer is required for all students. A campuswide network can be accessed from student residence rooms and from off campus. Students can access the following: online class registration. Staffed computer lab on campus provides training in use of computers and software.

Community Environment: Oklahoma City has a metropolitan population of 1,083,000. Closer to the University is the smaller suburban community of Edmond, population 74,800. Air transportation is available at Will Rogers World Airport. Many cultural, entertainment, and job opportunities are readily available.

■ **OKLAHOMA CITY COMMUNITY COLLEGE**
7777 S May Ave.
Oklahoma City, OK 73159-4419
Tel: (405)682-1611
E-mail: jhibblen@occc.edu
Web Site: www.occc.edu

Description: State-supported, 2-year, coed. Part of Oklahoma State Regents for Higher Education. Awards certificates, transfer associate, and terminal associate degrees. Founded 1969. Setting: 143-acre urban campus with easy access to Oklahoma City. Endowment: $310,298. Educational spending for the previous fiscal year: $3403 per student. Total enrollment: 12,314. Faculty: 554 (132 full-time, 422 part-time). Student-undergrad faculty ratio is 23:1. 3,983 applied, 73% were admitted. Full-time: 4,359 students, 54% women, 46% men. Part-time: 7,955 students, 62% women, 38% men. Students come from 22 states and territories, 94 other countries, 5% from out-of-state. 5% American Indian or Alaska Native, non-Hispanic/Latino; 17% Hispanic/Latino; 10% Black or African American, non-Hispanic/Latino; 5% Asian, non-Hispanic/Latino; 0.2% Native Hawaiian or other Pacific Islander, non-Hispanic/Latino; 3% international. 35% 25 or older, 29% transferred in. Core. Calendar: semesters. Academic remediation for entering students, services for LD students, advanced placement, accelerated degree program, self-designed majors, honors program, independent study, distance learning, double major, summer session for credit, part-time degree program, co-op programs and internships.

Entrance Requirements: Open admission except for applicants whose high school class has not graduated or nursing, emergency medical services, occupational therapy, physical therapy, speech language pathology programs, and anesthesia technology. Option: electronic application. Required for some: high school transcript, college and university transcripts. Entrance: noncompetitive. Application deadline: rolling. Notification: continuous. Transfer credits accepted: Yes.

Costs Per Year: Application fee: $30. One-time mandatory fee: $30. State resident tuition: $3,025 full-time, $100.84 per credit hour part-time.

Nonresident tuition: $8,776 full-time, $292.54 per credit hour part-time. Mandatory fees: $1,034 full-time, $34.45 per credit hour part-time. Full-time tuition and fees vary according to course level. Part-time tuition and fees vary according to course level.

Collegiate Environment: Orientation program. Drama-theater group, choral group, student-run newspaper. Social organizations: 28 open to all. Most popular organizations: Phi Theta Kappa, Hispanic Organization to Promote Education, Baptist Collegiate Ministry, Engineering Club, Black Student Association. Major annual events: Student Awards Ceremony, Volunteer Fair / Club & Organization Fair, Excel Series. Student services: personal-psychological counseling. Campus security: 24-hour emergency response devices and patrols, late night transport-escort service. Keith Leftwich Memorial Library. Books: 85,305 (physical), 19,895 (digital/electronic); Serial titles: 101 (physical), 11,707 (digital/electronic); Databases: 44. Weekly public service hours: 70. Operations spending for the previous fiscal year: $987,052. 675 computers available on campus for general student use. A campuswide network can be accessed from off-campus. Students can access the following: online class registration. Staffed computer lab on campus provides training in use of computers, software, and the Internet.

Community Environment: Oklahoma City was born on April 22, 1889, when the population jumped from zero to 10,000 as a result of a unique land run. The city is one of the largest municipalities in the nation, covering a total of 621 square miles. The more than 530,000 residents enjoy temperatures ranging from the mid-80s in July to the mid-30s in January. The community is served by all major forms of transportation. Entertainment, cultural and sports related activities are numerous.

■ OKLAHOMA CITY UNIVERSITY

2501 N Blackwelder
Oklahoma City, OK 73106-1402
Tel: (405)208-5000; Free: 800-633-7242
E-mail: michelle.cook@okcu.edu
Web Site: www.okcu.edu

Description: Independent United Methodist, comprehensive, coed. Awards bachelor's, master's, and doctoral degrees. Founded 1904. Setting: 104-acre urban campus with easy access to Oklahoma City. Endowment: $104.5 million. Educational spending for the previous fiscal year: $16,197 per student. Total enrollment: 2,821. Faculty: 268 (194 full-time, 74 part-time). Student-undergrad faculty ratio is 11:1. 1,820 applied, 72% were admitted. 31% from top 10% of their high school class, 61% from top quarter, 82% from top half. 3 National Merit Scholars. Full-time: 1,542 students, 69% women, 31% men. Part-time: 150 students, 59% women, 41% men. Students come from 47 states and territories, 51 other countries, 50% from out-of-state. 2% American Indian or Alaska Native, non-Hispanic/Latino; 9% Hispanic/Latino; 5% Black or African American, non-Hispanic/Latino; 2% Asian, non-Hispanic/Latino; 11% international. 17% 25 or older, 53% live on campus, 13% transferred in. Retention: 82% of full-time freshmen returned the following year. Academic areas with the most degrees conferred: health professions and related sciences; visual and performing arts; liberal arts/general studies. Core. Calendar: semesters. ESL program, services for LD students, advanced placement, accelerated degree program, honors program, independent study, distance learning, double major, summer session for credit, part-time degree program, adult/continuing education programs, co-op programs and internships, graduate courses open to undergrads. Off campus study at American University. Study abroad program. ROTC: Army (c), Air Force (c).

Entrance Requirements: Options: electronic application, deferred admission, international baccalaureate accepted. Required: essay, high school transcript, SAT or ACT. Required for some: interview. Application deadline: rolling. Notification: continuous. Transfer credits accepted: Yes.

Costs Per Year: Application fee: $55. One-time mandatory fee: $360. Comprehensive fee: $39,922 includes full-time tuition ($27,276), mandatory fees ($3750), and college room and board ($8896). College room only: $4100. Full-time tuition and fees vary according to course load. Room and board charges vary according to board plan, housing facility, and student level. Part-time tuition: $925 per credit hour. Part-time mandatory fees: $125 per credit hour.

Collegiate Environment: Orientation program. Drama-theater group, choral group, student-run newspaper. Social organizations: 65 open to all; national fraternities, national sororities, local fraternities, local sororities; 23% of eligible men and 11% of eligible women are members. Most popular organizations: Tri-Beta, Multicultural Student Association, Student Nursing Associate, Fellowship of Christian Athletes. Major annual events: Oozefest, Free Movie Night, Midnight Breakfast. Student services: health clinic,

personal-psychological counseling. Campus security: 24-hour emergency response devices and patrols, late night transport-escort service, controlled dormitory access. Dulaney Browne Library plus 1 other. Books: 279,046 (physical), 372,318 (digital/electronic); Serial titles: 5,543 (physical), 621,360 (digital/electronic); Databases: 114. Weekly public service hours: 99; students can reserve study rooms. Operations spending for the previous fiscal year: $1 million. 368 computers available on campus for general student use. Computer purchase/lease plans available. A campuswide network can be accessed from student residence rooms and from off campus. Students can access the following: online class registration. Staffed computer lab on campus provides training in use of computers, software, and the Internet.

Community Environment: Oklahoma City, the capital City of Oklahoma, offers a wide variety of cultural, civic, religious, entertainment and sports events in the unique setting of modern facilities and old-fashioned Western hospitality. With more than 1,000,000 people in the metropolitan area, Oklahoma City is a dynamic, growing location with a wide range of opportunities to offer its students. From the State Capitol and the center of Oklahoma's political and governmental activity, to the cultural offerings the Oklahoma City Philharmonic, Lyric Theater, Ballet Oklahoma, Oklahoma Zoo, Omniplex, and more. Oklahoma City stands as a vibrant, growing metropolitan center offerings the Southwest. Out-of-state students are able to make use of the excellent transportation facilities available to the City. Oklahoma City is linked by interstate highways to other major cities in the region, and the City's Will Rogers International Airport, one offerings the busiest in the region, provides jet service coast-to-coast and international flights to Europe, Asia, and South America.

■ OKLAHOMA PANHANDLE STATE UNIVERSITY

PO Box 430
Goodwell, OK 73939-0430
Tel: (580)349-2611; Free: 800-664-6778
Fax: (580)349-2302
E-mail: opsu@opsu.edu
Web Site: www.opsu.edu

Description: State-supported, 4-year, coed. Part of Oklahoma State Regents for Higher Education. Awards associate and bachelor's degrees. Founded 1909. Setting: 40-acre rural campus. Total enrollment: 1,387. Faculty: 91 (65 full-time, 26 part-time). Student-undergrad faculty ratio is 16:1. 316 applied, 100% were admitted. Full-time: 1,116 students, 45% women, 55% men. Part-time: 271 students, 70% women, 30% men. Students come from 25 states and territories, 15 other countries, 50% from out-of-state. 4% American Indian or Alaska Native, non-Hispanic/Latino; 18% Hispanic/Latino; 6% Black or African American, non-Hispanic/Latino; 0.2% Asian, non-Hispanic/Latino; 3% international. 24% 25 or older, 12% transferred in. Retention: 53% of full-time freshmen returned the following year. Academic areas with the most degrees conferred: agriculture; business/marketing; health professions and related sciences; biological/life sciences. Core. Calendar: semesters. Academic remediation for entering students, ESL program, services for LD students, advanced placement, distance learning, double major, summer session for credit.

Entrance Requirements: Options: electronic application, international baccalaureate accepted. Required: high school transcript. Recommended: SAT or ACT. Entrance: noncompetitive. Application deadline: rolling.

Collegiate Environment: Orientation program. Drama-theater group, choral group, marching band, student-run newspaper, radio station. Social organizations: local fraternities. Major annual events: Fall Homecoming, Annual Rodeo, talent show. Student services: health clinic, personal-psychological counseling. Campus security: safety bars over door latches. McKee Library.

Community Environment: Goodwell is located in the center of the Oklahoma Panhandle in Texas County. The climate is cool and arid. The area is served by railroad, and Highway 54. Goodwell has three churches, and various civic, fraternal and veteran's organizations.

■ OKLAHOMA STATE UNIVERSITY

Stillwater, OK 74078
Tel: (405)744-5000; Free: 800-233-5019
Fax: (405)744-5285
Web Site: www.okstate.edu

Description: State-supported, university, coed. Part of Oklahoma State University. Awards bachelor's, master's, and doctoral degrees and post-master's certificates. Founded 1890. Setting: 840-acre small town campus with easy access to Oklahoma City, Tulsa. System endowment: $875.5 million. Research spending for the previous fiscal year: $120 million.

Educational spending for the previous fiscal year: $8123 per student. Total enrollment: 24,649. Faculty: 1,320 (1,052 full-time, 268 part-time). Student-undergrad faculty ratio is 20:1. 14,405 applied, 74% were admitted. 27% from top 10% of their high school class, 55% from top quarter, 84% from top half. 22 National Merit Scholars, 321 valedictorians. Full-time: 17,684 students, 49% women, 51% men. Part-time: 2,890 students, 48% women, 52% men. Students come from 57 states and territories, 66 other countries, 27% from out-of-state. 4% American Indian or Alaska Native, non-Hispanic/Latino; 8% Hispanic/Latino; 4% Black or African American, non-Hispanic/Latino; 2% Asian, non-Hispanic/Latino; 0.1% Native Hawaiian or other Pacific Islander, non-Hispanic/Latino; 4% international. 9% 25 or older, 43% live on campus, 7% transferred in. Retention: 82% of full-time freshmen returned the following year. Academic areas with the most degrees conferred: business/marketing; engineering; agriculture. Core. Calendar: semesters. ESL program, services for LD students, advanced placement, accelerated degree program, self-designed majors, freshman honors college, honors program, independent study, distance learning, double major, summer session for credit, part-time degree program, internships. Off campus study at National Student Exchange. Study abroad program. ROTC: Army, Air Force.

Entrance Requirements: Options: electronic application, deferred admission, international baccalaureate accepted. Required: SAT or ACT. Required for some: essay. Entrance: moderately difficult. Application deadlines: rolling, rolling for nonresidents. Notification: continuous, continuous for nonresidents. Transfer credits accepted: Yes.

Costs Per Year: Application fee: $40. One-time mandatory fee: $95. State resident tuition: $5,356 full-time, $178.55 per credit hour part-time. Nonresident tuition: $20,877 full-time, $695.90 per credit hour part-time. Mandatory fees: $3,662 full-time, $122.05 per credit hour part-time. Full-time tuition and fees vary according to program. Part-time tuition and fees vary according to course load and program. College room and board: $8996. College room only: $5096. Room and board charges vary according to board plan and housing facility. Tuition guaranteed not to increase for student's term of enrollment.

Collegiate Environment: Orientation program. Drama-theater group, choral group, marching band, student-run newspaper, radio station. Social organizations: 500 open to all; national fraternities, national sororities. Major annual events: OSU Homecoming, Welcome Week, Remember the Ten Run. Student services: legal services, health clinic, personal-psychological counseling. Campus security: 24-hour emergency response devices and patrols, student patrols, late night transport-escort service, controlled dormitory access. 5,916 college housing spaces available; 5,642 were occupied in 2018-19. Freshmen given priority for college housing. On-campus residence required in freshman year. Options: coed, men-only, women-only housing available. Edmon Low Library plus 3 others. Weekly public service hours: 146; study areas open 24 hours, 5-7 days a week; students can reserve study rooms. Operations spending for the previous fiscal year: $18.1 million.

Community Environment: Stillwater is located in north central Oklahoma. The climate is mild with an average annual temperature of 59.8 degrees and average rainfall of 33.3 inches. The city is accessible by Highways 51 and 177, and nearby U.S. Highways 64 and Interstate 35. There are bus lines to the city. Stillwater has several churches of major denominations, a hospital, two clinics, and a health center. Local recreational facilities include 15 parks, three golf courses, fishing, camping, picnicking, hiking, hunting, boating, water-skiing, theatres, and a drive-in. Rooming houses, apartments and private homes provide housing for students. There is part-time employment available.

■ **OKLAHOMA STATE UNIVERSITY INSTITUTE OF TECHNOLOGY**
1801 E Fourth St.
Okmulgee, OK 74447-3901
Tel: (918)293-4678; Free: 800-722-4471
E-mail: kyleg@okstate.edu
Web Site: www.osuit.edu

Description: State-supported, primarily 2-year, coed. Part of Oklahoma State University. Awards transfer associate, terminal associate, and bachelor's degrees. Founded 1946. Setting: 160-acre small town campus with easy access to Tulsa. Endowment: $7.6 million. Educational spending for the previous fiscal year: $7723 per student. Total enrollment: 2,502. Faculty: 155 (117 full-time, 38 part-time). Student-undergrad faculty ratio is 15:1. 2,925 applied, 29% were admitted. 6% from top 10% of their high school class, 22% from top quarter, 54% from top half. Full-time: 1,744 students, 29% women, 71% men. Part-time: 758 students, 52% women, 48% men. Students come from 23 states and territories, 10 other countries,

7% from out-of-state. 12% American Indian or Alaska Native, non-Hispanic/Latino; 6% Hispanic/Latino; 5% Black or African American, non-Hispanic/Latino; 1% Asian, non-Hispanic/Latino; 0.6% international. 25% 25 or older, 25% live on campus, 9% transferred in. Retention: 64% of full-time freshmen returned the following year. Academic areas with the most degrees conferred: computer and information sciences; engineering technologies. Core. Calendar: trimesters. Academic remediation for entering students, services for LD students, advanced placement, independent study, distance learning, double major, summer session for credit, part-time degree program, adult/continuing education programs, internships.

Entrance Requirements: Open admission for associate degree programs. Option: deferred admission. Required: high school transcript. Recommended: ACT. Required for some: SAT or ACT. Entrance: noncompetitive. Application deadline: rolling. Transfer credits accepted: Yes.

Costs Per Year: State resident tuition: $4350 full-time, $145 per credit hour part-time. Nonresident tuition: $9960 full-time, $332 per credit hour part-time. Mandatory fees: $1200 full-time, $40 per credit hour part-time. Full-time tuition and fees vary according to course level, course load, degree level, location, program, and student level. Part-time tuition and fees vary according to course level, course load, degree level, location, program, and student level. College room and board: $6988. Room and board charges vary according to board plan and housing facility.

Collegiate Environment: Orientation program. Social organizations: 20 open to all. Most popular organizations: Phi Theta Kappa, Visual Communications Collective, Air Conditioning and Refrigeration Club, Future Chefs Association, Association of Information Technology Professionals. Major annual events: Carnifall, Fall Move-In Day, Welcome Back Lunches. Student services: health clinic, personal-psychological counseling. Campus security: 24-hour emergency response devices and patrols, late night transport-escort service, controlled dormitory access. Oklahoma State University Institute of Technology Library. Books: 9,520 (physical), 147,054 (digital/electronic); Serial titles: 149 (physical), 70,987 (digital/electronic); Databases: 106. Weekly public service hours: 73; students can reserve study rooms. Operations spending for the previous fiscal year: $429,236. 50 computers available on campus for general student use. Computer purchase/lease plans available. A campuswide network can be accessed from student residence rooms and from off campus. Students can access the following: online class registration. Staffed computer lab on campus.

■ **OKLAHOMA STATE UNIVERSITY-OKLAHOMA CITY**
900 N Portland Ave.
Oklahoma City, OK 73107-6120
Tel: (405)947-4421; Free: 800-560-4099
Fax: (405)945-3277
E-mail: wilkylw@osuokc.edu
Web Site: www.osuokc.edu

Description: State-supported, primarily 2-year, coed. Part of Oklahoma State University. Awards certificates, transfer associate, terminal associate, and bachelor's degrees. Founded 1961. Setting: 110-acre urban campus with easy access to Oklahoma City. Total enrollment: 5,839. Faculty: 355 (85 full-time, 270 part-time). Student-undergrad faculty ratio is 16:1. 3,765 applied, 34% were admitted. Full-time: 1,728 students, 54% women, 46% men. Part-time: 4,111 students, 65% women, 35% men. Students come from 28 states and territories, 12 other countries, 4% from out-of-state. 4% American Indian or Alaska Native, non-Hispanic/Latino; 16% Hispanic/Latino; 11% Black or African American, non-Hispanic/Latino; 3% Asian, non-Hispanic/Latino; 0.2% Native Hawaiian or other Pacific Islander, non-Hispanic/Latino; 2% international. 47% 25 or older, 13% transferred in. Retention: 51% of full-time freshmen returned the following year. Academic area with the most degrees conferred: homeland security, law enforcement, firefighting, and protective services. Core. Calendar: semesters. Academic remediation for entering students, services for LD students, advanced placement, honors program, independent study, distance learning, double major, summer session for credit, part-time degree program, internships. Study abroad program.

Entrance Requirements: Open admission Selective admission programs: Nursing, Radiologic Technology, Cardiovascular Sonography, Nutritional Sciences, Veterinary Tech, and Emergency Responder Administration. Option: electronic application. Required for some: high school transcript. Entrance: noncompetitive. Application deadline: rolling. Notification: continuous. Transfer credits accepted: Yes.

Costs Per Year: Application fee: $0. State resident tuition: $3697 full-time, $146.75 per credit hour part-time. Nonresident tuition: $10,778 full-time,

$382.75 per credit hour part-time. Mandatory fees: $781 full-time. Full-time tuition and fees vary according to program. Part-time tuition varies according to program.

Collegiate Environment: Orientation program. Social organizations: 19 open to all; 33% of eligible men and 67% of eligible women are members. Most popular organizations: OSU-OKC Chapter of the OK Student Nurse Association, Veterinary Technician Association, Hispanic Student Association, Phi Theta Kappa, Student Government Association. Major annual events: Howdy Week, Whdunit Dimer Theater, Movie Nights. Campus security: 24-hour patrols, late night transport-escort service. Oklahoma State University, Oklahoma City Library. Books: 34,772 (physical), 198,662 (digital/electronic); Serial titles: 229 (physical); Databases: 72. Weekly public service hours: 75. 715 computers available on campus for general student use. A campuswide network can be accessed from off-campus. Students can access the following: online class registration.

Community Environment: See Oklahoma City University.

■ OKLAHOMA TECHNICAL COLLEGE

4444 S Sheridan
Tulsa, OK 74145
Tel: (918)895-7500
E-mail: jcooper@oklahomatechnicalcollege.com
Web Site: www.oklahomatechnicalcollege.com

Description: Independent, 2-year, coed. Awards diplomas and transfer associate degrees. Founded 2009. Setting: 9-acre urban campus with easy access to Tulsa. Educational spending for the previous fiscal year: $3921 per student. Total enrollment: 186. Faculty: 19 (all full-time). Student-undergrad faculty ratio is 10:1. Full-time: 186 students, 4% women, 96% men. Students come from 6 states and territories, 5% from out-of-state. 18% American Indian or Alaska Native, non-Hispanic/Latino; 8% Hispanic/Latino; 11% Black or African American, non-Hispanic/Latino; 1% Asian, non-Hispanic/Latino; 0.5% Native Hawaiian or other Pacific Islander, non-Hispanic/Latino. 56% 25 or older. Core. Calendar: continuous. Services for LD students, adult/continuing education programs, internships.

Entrance Requirements: Open admission. Option: electronic application. Required: essay, high school transcript, interview. Entrance: noncompetitive. Application deadline: rolling. Notification: continuous. Transfer credits accepted: Yes.

Collegiate Environment: Orientation program. Social organizations: 1 open to all. Most popular organization: Student Ambassadors. Major annual events: Food Bank, Clothing Drive, Blood Drive. Student services: personal-psychological counseling. Campus security: campus security during school hours. Operations spending for the previous fiscal year: $5887. 12 computers available on campus for general student use. Computer purchase/lease plans available. A campuswide network can be accessed. Staffed computer lab on campus provides training in use of computers, software, and the Internet.

■ OKLAHOMA WESLEYAN UNIVERSITY

2201 Silver Lake Rd.
Bartlesville, OK 74006-6299
Tel: (918)335-6200; Free: 866-222-8226
Fax: (918)335-6229
E-mail: admissions@okwu.edu
Web Site: www.okwu.edu

Description: Independent, comprehensive, coed, affiliated with Wesleyan Church. Awards associate, bachelor's, and master's degrees. Founded 1909. Setting: 127-acre small town campus with easy access to Tulsa. Endowment: $3.5 million. Educational spending for the previous fiscal year: $5093 per student. Total enrollment: 1,527. Faculty: 111 (35 full-time, 76 part-time). Student-undergrad faculty ratio is 15:1. 235 applied, 85% were admitted. Full-time: 593 students, 52% women, 48% men. Part-time: 636 students, 76% women, 24% men. Students come from 41 states and territories, 24 other countries, 44% from out-of-state. 51% 25 or older, 10% transferred in. Retention: 53% of full-time freshmen returned the following year. Core. Calendar: semesters. Academic remediation for entering students, services for LD students, advanced placement, accelerated degree program, self-designed majors, independent study, distance learning, double major, summer session for credit, part-time degree program, external degree program, adult/continuing education programs, co-op programs and internships. Off campus study at Tri-County Technical College, Coalition for Christian Colleges and Universities. Study abroad program.

Entrance Requirements: Open admission. Option: electronic application. Required: high school transcript, minimum ACT score of 18, SAT or ACT.

Recommended: minimum 2 high school GPA. Required for some: interview. Entrance: minimally difficult. Application deadline: rolling. SAT Reasoning Test deadline: 8/15. Transfer credits accepted: Yes.

Costs Per Year: Application fee: $25. Comprehensive fee: $35,300 includes full-time tuition ($25,576), mandatory fees ($1380), and college room and board ($8344). College room only: $4280. Full-time tuition and fees vary according to class time, course load, degree level, location, and program. Room and board charges vary according to board plan and housing facility.

Collegiate Environment: Orientation program. Drama-theater group, choral group, student-run newspaper. Social organizations: 10 open to all. Most popular organizations: Operation Saturation (Community Service Opportunities), Fellowship of Christian Athletes, Missions Support Groups, intramurals, Student Government Groups. Major annual events: Homecoming Activities, Spiritual Emphasis Week, Seasonal Banquets. Student services: health clinic, personal-psychological counseling. Campus security: student patrols. Janice and Charles Drake Library. Operations spending for the previous fiscal year: $264,260. 33 computers available on campus for general student use. A campuswide network can be accessed from student residence rooms and from off campus. Students can access the following: online class registration.

■ ORAL ROBERTS UNIVERSITY

7777 S Lewis Ave.
Tulsa, OK 74171
Tel: (918)495-6161; Free: 800-678-8876
Fax: (918)495-6222
E-mail: admissions@oru.edu
Web Site: www.oru.edu

Description: Independent interdenominational, comprehensive, coed. Awards bachelor's, master's, and doctoral degrees. Founded 1963. Setting: 263-acre urban campus. Total enrollment: 3,919. Faculty: 296 (156 full-time, 140 part-time). Student-undergrad faculty ratio is 14:1. 2,433 applied, 93% were admitted. 22% from top 10% of their high school class, 46% from top quarter, 80% from top half. Full-time: 2,866 students, 60% women, 40% men. Part-time: 515 students, 56% women, 44% men. 56% from out-of-state. 3% American Indian or Alaska Native, non-Hispanic/Latino; 13% Hispanic/Latino; 13% Black or African American, non-Hispanic/Latino; 2% Asian, non-Hispanic/Latino; 10% international. 14% 25 or older, 61% live on campus, 6% transferred in. Retention: 84% of full-time freshmen returned the following year. Academic areas with the most degrees conferred: business/marketing; theology and religious vocations; health professions and related sciences. Calendar: semesters. Part-time degree program, adult/continuing education programs. ROTC: Air Force (c).

Entrance Requirements: Option: deferred admission. Required: essay, high school transcript, minimum 2 high school GPA, 1 recommendation, proof of immunization, SAT or ACT. Recommended: interview. Required for some: interview. Entrance: moderately difficult. Notification: continuous until 8/15. SAT Reasoning Test deadline: 6/15. SAT Subject Test deadline: 6/15.

Costs Per Year: Application fee: $35. Comprehensive fee: $37,178 includes full-time tuition ($26,700), mandatory fees ($1028), and college room and board ($9450). College room only: $4390. Full-time tuition and fees vary according to course load, degree level, and location. Room and board charges vary according to board plan and housing facility. Part-time tuition: $1115 per contact hour. Part-time tuition varies according to course load, degree level, and location.

Collegiate Environment: Orientation program. Campus security: 24-hour emergency response devices and patrols, late night transport-escort service. John D. Messick Resources Center.

Community Environment: Tulsa is located in northeast Oklahoma. The area has four distinct seasons, and is served by major airlines, bus lines, and U.S. highways. Tulsa is located on the fringe of the southwest's greatest inland vacation and recreation areas. Nearby lakes provide fishing, golf, boating, hunting, and other outdoor sports. Community services include many churches, an Opera Association, Philbrook and Gilcrease Museums, major health facilities, and civic organizations.

■ PLATT COLLEGE (MOORE)

201 N Eastern Ave.
Moore, OK 73160
Tel: (405)912-3260; Free: 877-392-6616
Fax: (405)912-4360
Web Site: www.plattcolleges.edu

Description: Proprietary, 2-year, coed. Awards terminal associate degrees. Total enrollment: 71. 178 applied, 100% were admitted.

■ **PLATT COLLEGE (OKLAHOMA CITY)**

2727 W Memorial Rd.
Oklahoma City, OK 73134
Tel: (405)749-2433; Free: 877-392-6616
Web Site: www.plattcolleges.edu
Description: Proprietary, 2-year, coed. Awards certificates, transfer associate, and terminal associate degrees. Founded 2003.

■ **PLATT COLLEGE (TULSA)**

3801 S Sheridan Rd.
Tulsa, OK 74145
Tel: (918)663-9000; Free: 877-392-6616
Fax: (918)622-1240
Web Site: www.plattcolleges.edu
Description: Proprietary, 2-year, coed. Awards terminal associate degrees. Founded 1979. Total enrollment: 415. Calendar: continuous.
Entrance Requirements: Entrance: noncompetitive.

■ **RANDALL UNIVERSITY**

3701 S I-35 Service Rd.
Moore, OK 73160-1208
Tel: (405)912-9000
Fax: (405)912-9050
E-mail: recruitment@hc.edu
Web Site: www.ru.edu
Description: Independent Free Will Baptist, comprehensive, coed. Awards associate, bachelor's, and master's degrees. Founded 1959. Setting: 41-acre suburban campus with easy access to Oklahoma City. Total enrollment: 233. Faculty: 47 (13 full-time, 34 part-time). Full-time: 186 students, 37% women, 63% men. Part-time: 39 students, 41% women, 59% men. 11% American Indian or Alaska Native, non-Hispanic/Latino; 16% Hispanic/Latino; 10% Black or African American, non-Hispanic/Latino; 0.4% Asian, non-Hispanic/Latino; 7% international. Retention: 60% of full-time freshmen returned the following year. Academic areas with the most degrees conferred: liberal arts/general studies; psychology; theology and religious vocations; business/marketing. Core. Calendar: semesters. Academic remediation for entering students, ESL program, advanced placement, accelerated degree program, independent study, summer session for credit, part-time degree program, adult/continuing education programs, internships.
Entrance Requirements: Options: electronic application, early admission, deferred admission. Required: high school transcript, 2 recommendations, SAT or ACT. Recommended: minimum 2 high school GPA. Required for some: interview. Entrance: noncompetitive. Transfer credits accepted: Yes.
Costs Per Year: Application fee: $20. Comprehensive fee: $22,268 includes full-time tuition ($10,700), mandatory fees ($4408), and college room and board ($7160). College room only: $3040. Full-time tuition and fees vary according to course load. Room and board charges vary according to board plan and housing facility. Part-time tuition: $450 per credit hour. Part-time mandatory fees: $50 per credit hour, $280 per term. Part-time tuition and fees vary according to course load.
Collegiate Environment: Drama-theater group, choral group. Social organizations: local fraternities, local sororities. Student services: personal-psychological counseling. Campus security: 24-hour emergency response devices, controlled dormitory access. Geri Ann Hull Learning Resource Center. 22 computers available on campus for general student use. A campuswide network can be accessed. Staffed computer lab on campus.
Community Environment: Community transportation is provided by bus and rail. Will Rogers International Airport is 10 minutes away. The city has many churches, a library, and health facilities. Nearby Lake Draper offers water skiing and fishing. There are many businesses in town, and part-time employment is available for students.

■ **REDLANDS COMMUNITY COLLEGE**

1300 S Country Club Rd.
El Reno, OK 73036-5304
Tel: (405)262-2552; Free: 866-415-6367
Web Site: www.redlandscc.edu
Description: State-supported, 2-year, coed. Part of Oklahoma State Regents for Higher Education. Awards certificates, transfer associate, and terminal associate degrees. Founded 1938. Setting: 55-acre suburban campus with easy access to Oklahoma City. Total enrollment: 2,560. Faculty: 113 (35 full-time, 78 part-time). Student-undergrad faculty ratio is 24:1. 513 applied, 99% were admitted. Full-time: 915 students, 61% women, 39% men. Part-time: 1,645 students, 67% women, 33% men. 97% from out-of-state. 14% American Indian or Alaska Native, non-Hispanic/Latino; 5% Hispanic/Latino; 6% Black or African American, non-Hispanic/Latino; 1% Asian, non-Hispanic/Latino; 0.1% Native Hawaiian or other Pacific Islander, non-Hispanic/Latino. 29% 25 or older, 10% live on campus, 9% transferred in. Retention: 41% of full-time freshmen returned the following year. Core. Calendar: semesters. Academic remediation for entering students, services for LD students, advanced placement, accelerated degree program, honors program, distance learning, double major, summer session for credit, part-time degree program, external degree program, adult/continuing education programs, co-op programs and internships.
Entrance Requirements: Open admission except for nursing, medical laboratory technology programs. Options: electronic application, early admission, deferred admission. Required: high school transcript. Recommended: SAT or ACT. Entrance: noncompetitive. Application deadline: rolling. Notification: continuous. SAT Reasoning Test deadline: 8/15.
Costs Per Year: Application fee: $25. State resident tuition: $4,645 full-time, $154.84 per credit hour part-time. Nonresident tuition: $7,210 full-time, $240.35 per credit hour part-time. Mandatory fees: $650 full-time, $21 per credit hour part-time, $25 per term part-time. Full-time tuition and fees vary according to reciprocity agreements. Part-time tuition and fees vary according to reciprocity agreements. College room and board: $7468. College room only: $5868. Room and board charges vary according to board plan and housing facility.
Collegiate Environment: Orientation program. Drama-theater group, choral group. Social organizations: 11 open to all. Most popular organizations: Nursing Club, Aggie Club, Baptist Student Union, Phi Theta Kappa, Outdoors Club. Major annual events: Back to School Bash, End of Year Party, Career Fair. Campus security: 24-hour patrols. Learning Resource Center.
Community Environment: El Reno is located on the south bank of the North Canadian River. The average annual temperature is 60 degrees. The city is served by bus lines, railroad, and an airport. Nearby lakes offer waterskiing, fishing, and boating. El Reno has many community service facilities including a hospital, hotel and many motels, a library, and various civic, service, and fraternal organizations. Part-time job opportunities are good. Local recreational facilities include two movie theatres, drive-ins, parks, tennis, golf, and a municipal swimming pool.

■ **ROGERS STATE UNIVERSITY**

1701 W Will Rogers Blvd.
Claremore, OK 74017-3252
Tel: (918)343-7777; Free: 800-256-7511
Fax: (918)343-7898
E-mail: admissions@rsu.edu
Web Site: www.rsu.edu
Description: State-supported, comprehensive, coed. Part of Oklahoma State Regents for Higher Education. Awards associate, bachelor's, and master's degrees. Founded 1909. Setting: 40-acre small town campus with easy access to Tulsa. Endowment: $13.1 million. Research spending for the previous fiscal year: $112,670. Educational spending for the previous fiscal year: $4594 per student. Total enrollment: 3,723. Faculty: 236 (102 full-time, 134 part-time). Student-undergrad faculty ratio is 11:1. 7,241 applied, 14% were admitted. 13% from top 10% of their high school class, 19% from top quarter, 63% from top half. Full-time: 2,180 students, 57% women, 43% men. Part-time: 1,514 students, 64% women, 36% men. Students come from 26 states and territories, 9 other countries, 5% from out-of-state. 8% American Indian or Alaska Native, non-Hispanic/Latino; 6% Hispanic/Latino; 4% Black or African American, non-Hispanic/Latino; 2% Asian, non-Hispanic/Latino; 0.2% Native Hawaiian or other Pacific Islander, non-Hispanic/Latino. 27% 25 or older, 20% live on campus, 9% transferred in. Retention: 46% of full-time freshmen returned the following year. Academic areas with the most degrees conferred: business/marketing; biological/life sciences; social sciences; health professions and related sciences. Core. Calendar: semesters. Academic remediation for entering students, services for LD students, advanced placement, honors program, independent study, distance learning, double major, summer session for credit, part-time degree program, adult/continuing education programs, co-op programs and internships. Off campus study at Northeast Technology Centers-Afton, Claremore, Kansas, and Pryor, OK; Tri-County Technology Center-Bartlesville, OK; Central Technology Center-Drumright, OK; Tulsa Technology Center-Tulsa, OK. Study abroad program.
Entrance Requirements: Open admission for associate degree programs. Option: electronic application. Required: high school transcript, SAT or ACT. Recommended: ACT. Required for some: minimum 2.7 high school GPA,

minimum ACT composite of 20 or 2.70, GPA and top 50% rank for baccalaureate programs. Entrance: noncompetitive. Application deadline: rolling. SAT Reasoning Test deadline: 8/17. Transfer credits accepted: Yes.
Costs Per Year: Application fee: $20. State resident tuition: $4380 full-time.
Nonresident tuition: $12,720 full-time. Mandatory fees: $2820 full-time. Full-
time tuition and fees vary according to course level, course load, location,
program, and student level. College room and board: $8050. College room
only: $4600. Room and board charges vary according to housing facility.
Collegiate Environment: Orientation program. Drama-theater group, choral
group, student-run radio station. Social organizations: 31 open to all;
national fraternities, national sororities; 1% of eligible men and 2% of eligible
women are members. Most popular organizations: Student Government Association, Student Nurses Association, President's Leadership Class, Pre-
Professional Health Club (Pre-SOMA), Student Athlete Advisory Committee.
Major annual events: Big Tent Day-Welcome Week, Mental Wealth Day,
Spring Fling. Student services: health clinic, personal-psychological counseling. Campus security: 24-hour patrols, student patrols, late night transport-
escort service, controlled dormitory access, state-certified law enforcement
officers, comprehensive camera surveillance system. Stratton Taylor Library.
Books: 80,238 (physical), 298,063 (digital/electronic); Serial titles: 491
(physical), 67,126 (digital/electronic); Databases: 81. Weekly public service
hours: 86; students can reserve study rooms. Operations spending for the
previous fiscal year: $882,489. 251 computers available on campus for
general student use. A campuswide network can be accessed from student
residence rooms. Students can access the following: online class registration, software to support courses.

■ **ROSE STATE COLLEGE**
6420 SE 15th St.
Midwest City, OK 73110-2799
Tel: (405)733-7673; Free: 866-621-0987
Fax: (405)733-7399
E-mail: maitson@ms.rose.cc.ok.us
Web Site: www.rose.edu
Description: State and locally supported, 2-year, coed. Part of Oklahoma
State Regents for Higher Education. Awards transfer associate and terminal
associate degrees. Founded 1968. Setting: 110-acre suburban campus with
easy access to Oklahoma City. Total enrollment: 7,000. Faculty: 412 (143
full-time, 269 part-time). Students come from 18 states and territories, 33
other countries. 60% 25 or older. Core. Calendar: semesters. Academic
remediation for entering students, services for LD students, advanced placement, accelerated degree program, honors program, independent study,
distance learning, summer session for credit, part-time degree program,
adult/continuing education programs, internships. Off campus study. ROTC:
Army (c), Air Force (c).
Entrance Requirements: Open admission except for health occupations
programs. Options: electronic application, early admission, deferred admission. Required: high school transcript. Entrance: noncompetitive. Application
deadline: rolling. Notification: continuous.
Collegiate Environment: Drama-theater group, choral group, student-run
newspaper. Student services: health clinic, personal-psychological counseling, women's center. Campus security: 24-hour patrols. Rose State College
Learning Resources Center. Operations spending for the previous fiscal
year: $1.3 million. 390 computers available on campus for general student
use. A campuswide network can be accessed from off-campus. Staffed
computer lab on campus.
Community Environment: See Oklahoma City University.

■ **SEMINOLE STATE COLLEGE**
2701 Boren Blvd.
Seminole, OK 74818-0351
Tel: (405)382-9950
Web Site: www.sscok.edu
Description: State-supported, 2-year, coed. Part of Oklahoma State
Regents for Higher Education. Awards certificates, diplomas, transfer associate, and terminal associate degrees. Founded 1931. Setting: 40-acre small
town campus with easy access to Oklahoma City. Endowment: $3.1 million.
Educational spending for the previous fiscal year: $3235 per student. Total
enrollment: 1,633. Faculty: 87 (40 full-time, 47 part-time). Student-undergrad
faculty ratio is 19:1. 404 applied, 100% were admitted. Full-time: 967
students, 62% women, 38% men. Part-time: 666 students, 68% women,
32% men. Students come from 9 states and territories, 9 other countries, 1%
from out-of-state. 26% American Indian or Alaska Native, non-Hispanic/
Latino; 2% Hispanic/Latino; 6% Black or African American, non-Hispanic/

Latino; 0.6% Asian, non-Hispanic/Latino; 0.2% Native Hawaiian or other
Pacific Islander, non-Hispanic/Latino; 1% international. 32% 25 or older, 10%
live on campus, 5% transferred in. Core. Calendar: semesters. Academic
remediation for entering students, ESL program, services for LD students,
advanced placement, independent study, distance learning, double major,
summer session for credit, part-time degree program, adult/continuing
education programs, co-op programs. Off campus study. Study abroad
program.
Entrance Requirements: Open admission. Options: early admission,
deferred admission. Recommended: high school transcript. Entrance:
noncompetitive. Application deadline: rolling. Notification: continuous.
Transfer credits accepted: Yes.
Costs Per Year: Application fee: $15. One-time mandatory fee: $25. State
resident tuition: $2880 full-time, $96 per credit hour part-time. Nonresident
tuition: $8820 full-time, $294 per credit hour part-time. Mandatory fees:
$1560 full-time, $52 per credit hour part-time. Full-time tuition and fees vary
according to course load, location, and program. Part-time tuition and fees
vary according to course load, location, and program. College room and
board: $7070.
Collegiate Environment: Social organizations: 8 open to all. Most popular
organizations: Student Government Association, Native American Student
Association, Psi Beta Honor Society, Student Nurses Association, Phi Theta
Kappa. Major annual events: Welcome Week, Freak Week for Halloween,
Finals Snack Week. Campus security: 24-hour emergency response devices
and patrols, student patrols, late night transport-escort service, controlled
dormitory access, police department staffed with state certified officers.
Boren Library plus 1 other. Books: 29,131 (physical); Serial titles: 35 (physical), 11 (digital/electronic); Databases: 8. Weekly public service hours: 48.
Operations spending for the previous fiscal year: $55,041. 100 computers
available on campus for general student use. A campuswide network can be
accessed from student residence rooms and from off campus. Staffed
computer lab on campus.
Community Environment: Seminole is an urban community enjoying
temperate climate. Local transportation services include railroad, bus, and
airlines. The city has a public library, 30 churches of various denominations,
a hospital, and three clinics. Some part-time employment is available for
students. Recreational facilities in Seminole include a theater, a drive-in,
bowling, and water sports. The major civic, fraternal and veteran's organizations are active within the immediate community. There are several historic
sites located nearby.

■ **SOUTHEASTERN OKLAHOMA STATE UNIVERSITY**
1405 N 4th Ave.
Durant, OK 74701-0609
Tel: (580)745-2000; Free: 800-435-1327
Fax: (580)745-7490
Web Site: www.se.edu
Description: State-supported, comprehensive, coed. Part of Oklahoma
State Regents for Higher Education. Awards bachelor's and master's
degrees and post-master's certificates. Founded 1909. Setting: 276-acre
small town campus. Endowment: $23.2 million. Research spending for the
previous fiscal year: $89,401. Educational spending for the previous fiscal
year: $5600 per student. Total enrollment: 3,724. Faculty: 251 (133 full-time,
118 part-time). Student-undergrad faculty ratio is 18:1. 1,174 applied, 72%
were admitted. 17% from top 10% of their high school class, 45% from top
quarter, 76% from top half. 17 valedictorians. Full-time: 2,411 students, 52%
women, 48% men. Part-time: 721 students, 62% women, 38% men.
Students come from 28 states and territories, 36 other countries, 25% from
out-of-state. 30% American Indian or Alaska Native, non-Hispanic/Latino; 6%
Hispanic/Latino; 6% Black or African American, non-Hispanic/Latino; 0.7%
Asian, non-Hispanic/Latino; 0.3% Native Hawaiian or other Pacific Islander,
non-Hispanic/Latino. 27% 25 or older, 18% live on campus, 11% transferred
in. Retention: 55% of full-time freshmen returned the following year.
Academic areas with the most degrees conferred: engineering technologies;
education; liberal arts/general studies. Core. Calendar: semesters.
Academic remediation for entering students, services for LD students,
advanced placement, accelerated degree program, honors program,
independent study, distance learning, double major, summer session for
credit, part-time degree program, adult/continuing education programs,
internships, graduate courses open to undergrads. Off campus study at
University Center of Southern Oklahoma-Ardmore, OK, E.T. Dunlap Higher
Education Center-Idabel, OK, Tinker Air Force Base, Grayson County College (Denison, TX and Van Alstyne, TX campuses).
Entrance Requirements: Open admission for adults over 21. Option:

electronic application. Required: high school transcript, SAT or ACT. Required for some: interview. Entrance: moderately difficult. Application deadline: rolling. Notification: continuous. SAT Reasoning Test deadline: 8/1.

Collegiate Environment: Orientation program. Drama-theater group, choral group, marching band, student-run newspaper, radio station. Social organizations: 68 open to all; national fraternities, national sororities; 2% of eligible men and 2% of eligible women are members. Most popular organizations: Baptist Collegiate Ministries, Greek Community, Student Government Association, Kappa Kappa Psi, Psychology Club. Major annual events: Welcome Week/Parent's Day, Homecoming, Martin Luther King Day of Service. Student services: health clinic, personal-psychological counseling. Campus security: 24-hour emergency response devices and patrols, late night transport-escort service, controlled dormitory access. Henry G. Bennett Memorial Library plus 1 other. Books: 192,351 (physical), 17,845 (digital/electronic); Serial titles: 83 (physical), 2,534 (digital/electronic); Databases: 108. Weekly public service hours: 79; students can reserve study rooms. Operations spending for the previous fiscal year: $992,477. 598 computers available on campus for general student use. A campuswide network can be accessed from student residence rooms. Students can access the following: online class registration, campus learning management system classes. Staffed computer lab on campus.

Community Environment: Durant is a rural community served by bus line and airport. The community has one hospital, Medical Center of Southeastern Oklahoma, and active civic, fraternal, and veteran's organizations. There are libraries, churches, and motels. Local recreational facilities include hunting, boating, fishing, golf and other sports.

■ SOUTHERN NAZARENE UNIVERSITY

6729 NW 39th Expy.
Bethany, OK 73008
Tel: (405)789-6400; Free: 800-648-9899
Fax: (405)491-6381
E-mail: admiss@snu.edu
Web Site: www.snu.edu

Description: Independent Nazarene, comprehensive, coed. Awards associate, bachelor's, and master's degrees. Founded 1899. Setting: 40-acre suburban campus with easy access to Oklahoma City. Endowment: $21.6 million. Educational spending for the previous fiscal year: $8446 per student. Total enrollment: 3,906. Faculty: (92 full-time). Student-undergrad faculty ratio is 12:1. 979 applied, 33% were admitted. 26% from top 10% of their high school class, 49% from top quarter, 78% from top half. Full-time: 1,598 students, 53% women, 47% men. Part-time: 49 students, 61% women, 39% men. Students come from 34 states and territories, 32 other countries, 25% from out-of-state. 5% American Indian or Alaska Native, non-Hispanic/Latino; 6% Hispanic/Latino; 13% Black or African American, non-Hispanic/Latino; 3% Asian, non-Hispanic/Latino; 0.5% Native Hawaiian or other Pacific Islander, non-Hispanic/Latino; 4% international. 39% 25 or older, 63% live on campus, 3% transferred in. Retention: 67% of full-time freshmen returned the following year. Core. Calendar: semesters. Academic remediation for entering students, ESL program, services for LD students, advanced placement, accelerated degree program, self-designed majors, honors program, independent study, distance learning, double major, summer session for credit, part-time degree program, external degree program, adult/continuing education programs, internships, graduate courses open to undergrads. Off campus study at Christian College Coalition Council for Christian Colleges and Universities. Study abroad program. ROTC: Army (c), Air Force (c).

Entrance Requirements: Open admission. Options: electronic application, deferred admission, international baccalaureate accepted. Required: high school transcript, minimum 2 high school GPA, 2 recommendations, interview, SAT or ACT. Recommended: ACT. Entrance: noncompetitive. Application deadline: 8/15. Notification: continuous. SAT Reasoning Test deadline: 8/15. SAT Subject Test deadline: 8/15. Transfer credits accepted: Yes.

Collegiate Environment: Orientation program. Drama-theater group, choral group, student-run newspaper. Social organizations: 30 open to all. Most popular organizations: Business Gaming Team, Campus Social Life Committee, intramural sports societies, Choral Society, Inter-Club. Major annual events: Lip Sync Contest, Homecoming, Pow-Wow Weekend. Student services: health clinic, personal-psychological counseling. Campus security: 24-hour emergency response devices, student patrols, late night transport-escort service, controlled dormitory access. R. T. Williams Learning Resources Center. Books: 108,231 (physical), 125,507 (digital/electronic); Serial titles: 4,512 (physical), 21,217 (digital/electronic); Databases: 72. Students can reserve study rooms. Operations spending for the previous fis-

cal year: $391,464. 120 computers available on campus for general student use. Computer purchase/lease plans available. A computer is required for all students. A campuswide network can be accessed from student residence rooms and from off campus. Staffed computer lab on campus.

Community Environment: Bethany is a metropolitan community in central Oklahoma with a mild climate. Located on U.S. Highway 66, eight miles from Will Rogers Airport, the city also has train service. The community includes active churches, a Chamber of Commerce, nearby health centers and hospitals, and numerous motels. Unusual job opportunities are available for students.

■ SOUTHWESTERN CHRISTIAN UNIVERSITY

PO Box 340
Bethany, OK 73008-0340
Tel: (405)789-7661
E-mail: admissions@swcu.edu
Web Site: www.swcu.edu

Description: Independent, comprehensive, coed, affiliated with Pentecostal Holiness Church. Awards associate, bachelor's, and master's degrees. Founded 1946. Setting: 7-acre suburban campus with easy access to Oklahoma City. Total enrollment: 450. Student-undergrad faculty ratio is 15:1. 2 valedictorians. Students come from 12 other countries. 30% 25 or older, 50% live on campus. Core. Calendar: semesters. Academic remediation for entering students, advanced placement, distance learning, double major, summer session for credit, part-time degree program, internships, graduate courses open to undergrads. Off campus study at Southern Nazarene University, Rhema Bible Training Center. ROTC: Army (c).

Entrance Requirements: Options: electronic application, early admission, deferred admission. Required: essay, high school transcript, minimum 2.5 high school GPA, minimum SAT score of 900 or ACT of 19, top 50% rank in class, SAT or ACT. Recommended: interview. Entrance: minimally difficult. Application deadline: rolling. Notification: continuous. SAT Reasoning Test deadline: 8/15. SAT Subject Test deadline: 8/15. Transfer credits accepted: Yes.

Costs Per Year: Application fee: $0. Comprehensive fee: $26,130 includes full-time tuition ($15,750), mandatory fees ($2880), and college room and board ($7500). Full-time tuition and fees vary according to course load, location, and program. Room and board charges vary according to housing facility. Part-time tuition: $525 per credit hour. Part-time mandatory fees: $1440 per term. Part-time tuition and fees vary according to course load, location, and program.

Collegiate Environment: Orientation program. Drama-theater group, choral group. Major annual events: Spring Banquet, Culture Dinner, Chrismon Service. Student services: personal-psychological counseling. Campus security: 24-hour emergency response devices and patrols, student patrols. Springer Learning Center. 12 computers available on campus for general student use. A campuswide network can be accessed from student residence rooms. Students can access the following: online class registration. Staffed computer lab on campus provides training in use of computers, software, and the Internet.

■ SOUTHWESTERN OKLAHOMA STATE UNIVERSITY

100 Campus Dr.
Weatherford, OK 73096-3098
Tel: (580)772-6611
Fax: (580)774-3795
E-mail: cassie.jones@swosu.edu
Web Site: www.swosu.edu

Description: State-supported, comprehensive, coed. Awards associate, bachelor's, master's, and doctoral degrees. Founded 1901. Setting: 73-acre small town campus with easy access to Oklahoma City. Endowment: $22.3 million. Research spending for the previous fiscal year: $506,866. Educational spending for the previous fiscal year: $7528 per student. Total enrollment: 5,320. Faculty: 280 (207 full-time, 73 part-time). Student-undergrad faculty ratio is 19:1. 3,131 applied, 91% were admitted. 24% from top 10% of their high school class, 48% from top quarter, 76% from top half. Full-time: 3,659 students, 56% women, 44% men. Part-time: 851 students, 69% women, 31% men. Students come from 40 states and territories, 24 other countries, 10% from out-of-state. 4% American Indian or Alaska Native, non-Hispanic/Latino; 9% Hispanic/Latino; 4% Black or African American, non-Hispanic/Latino; 2% Asian, non-Hispanic/Latino; 0.1% Native Hawaiian or other Pacific Islander, non-Hispanic/Latino; 5% international. 21% 25 or older, 22% live on campus, 10% transferred in. Retention: 69% of full-time freshmen returned the following year. Core. Calendar: semesters.

Academic remediation for entering students, advanced placement, accelerated degree program, freshman honors college, honors program, independent study, distance learning, double major, summer session for credit, part-time degree program, adult/continuing education programs, co-op programs and internships, graduate courses open to undergrads. Study abroad program.

Entrance Requirements: Open admission. Options: electronic application, deferred admission. Required: high school transcript, SAT or ACT. Recommended: ACT. Required for some: minimum 2.7 high school GPA, minimum ACT score of 20 (940 SAT) or rank in the upper 50% of high school graduating class or have a high school GPA of 2.7 in the 15-unit core curriculum. Entrance: minimally difficult. Application deadlines: rolling, rolling for nonresidents. Notification: continuous, continuous for nonresidents. Preference given to Oklahoma residents. SAT Reasoning Test deadline: 8/21. Transfer credits accepted: Yes.

Collegiate Environment: Orientation program. Drama-theater group, choral group, marching band, student-run newspaper. Social organizations: 104 open to all; national fraternities, national sororities, local fraternities, local sororities; 3% of eligible men and 4% of eligible women are members. Most popular organizations: Collegiate Activities Board, Southwestern International Student Association, Saudi Arabian Student Organization, SWOSU Computer Club, Kappa Epsilon and Sigma Sigma Chi. Major annual events: Fall Homecoming, Bulldog Blitz Talent Show, Organization Fair. Student services: legal services, health clinic, personal-psychological counseling. Campus security: late night transport-escort service, police available 24 hours a day. Al Harris Library plus 1 other. Books: 303,978 (physical), 364,203 (digital/electronic); Serial titles: 128 (physical), 47,086 (digital/electronic); Databases: 99. Weekly public service hours: 84; students can reserve study rooms. Operations spending for the previous fiscal year: $1.7 million. 250 computers available on campus for general student use. A campuswide network can be accessed from student residence rooms. Students can access the following: online class registration. Staffed computer lab on campus provides training in use of computers, software, and the Internet.

■ SPARTAN COLLEGE OF AERONAUTICS AND TECHNOLOGY
8820 E Pine St.
Tulsa, OK 74115
Tel: (918)836-6886; Free: 800-331-1204
Web Site: www.spartan.edu
Description: Proprietary, primarily 2-year, coed. Awards certificates, diplomas, terminal associate, and bachelor's degrees. Founded 1928. Setting: 26-acre urban campus. Total enrollment: 1,438. Student-undergrad faculty ratio is 14:1. 844 applied. Full-time: 1,438 students, 100% men. 76% from out-of-state. 30% 25 or older, 1% transferred in. Retention: 66% of full-time freshmen returned the following year. Calendar: calendar terms. Honors program, independent study, co-op programs.
Entrance Requirements: Required: high school transcript. Recommended: interview. Entrance: noncompetitive. Application deadline: rolling.

■ TULSA COMMUNITY COLLEGE
6111 E Skelly Dr.
Tulsa, OK 74135-6198
Tel: (918)595-7000
Fax: (918)595-7910
E-mail: traci.heck@tulsacc.edu
Web Site: www.tulsacc.edu
Description: State-supported, 2-year, coed. Part of Oklahoma State Regents for Higher Education. Awards certificates, transfer associate, and terminal associate degrees. Founded 1968. Setting: 160-acre urban campus. Total enrollment: 16,391. Faculty: 816 (279 full-time, 537 part-time). Student-undergrad faculty ratio is 19:1. 6,157 applied, 99% were admitted. Full-time: 4,820 students, 60% women, 40% men. Part-time: 11,571 students, 64% women, 36% men. 1% from out-of-state. 7% American Indian or Alaska Native, non-Hispanic/Latino; 11% Hispanic/Latino; 9% Black or African American, non-Hispanic/Latino; 4% Asian, non-Hispanic/Latino; 0.1% Native Hawaiian or other Pacific Islander, non-Hispanic/Latino; 3% international. 35% 25 or older, 3% transferred in. Core. Calendar: semesters. Academic remediation for entering students, ESL program, services for LD students, advanced placement, accelerated degree program, self-designed majors, freshman honors college, honors program, independent study, distance learning, summer session for credit, part-time degree program, adult/continuing education programs, co-op programs and internships. Off campus study. Study abroad program.

Entrance Requirements: Open admission. Options: electronic application, early admission. Required: high school transcript. Entrance: noncompetitive. Application deadline: rolling. Transfer credits accepted: Yes.
Costs Per Year: Application fee: $20. State resident tuition: $4187 full-time, $108.55 per credit hour part-time. Nonresident tuition: $10,727 full-time, $326.55 per credit hour part-time. Mandatory fees: $930 full-time, $29.45 per credit hour part-time, $5 per term part-time.
Collegiate Environment: Orientation program. Drama-theater group, choral group, student-run newspaper, radio station. Student services: health clinic, personal-psychological counseling, women's center. Campus security: 24-hour emergency response devices and patrols, student patrols, late night transport-escort service. College housing not available.

■ TULSA WELDING SCHOOL
2545 E 11th St.
Tulsa, OK 74104-3909
Tel: (918)587-6789; Free: 888-765-5555
Fax: (918)295-6821
E-mail: dburke@twsweld.com
Web Site: www.tulsaweldingschool.com
Description: Proprietary, 2-year, coed. Administratively affiliated with Tulsa Welding School, Jacksonville Branch. Awards diplomas, transfer associate, and terminal associate degrees. Founded 1949. Setting: 5-acre urban campus. Total enrollment: 604. Faculty: 17 (all full-time). Student-undergrad faculty ratio is 18:1. 37% 25 or older. Core. Calendar: continuous phased start every 3 weeks.
Entrance Requirements: Entrance: noncompetitive.
Collegiate Environment: Orientation program. Campus security: 24-hour emergency response devices. Technical Resource Center. 3 computers available on campus for general student use. A campuswide network can be accessed.

■ UNIVERSITY OF CENTRAL OKLAHOMA
100 N University Dr.
Edmond, OK 73034-5209
Tel: (405)974-2000
Fax: (405)974-4964
E-mail: onestop@uco.edu
Web Site: www.uco.edu
Description: State-supported, comprehensive, coed. Part of Oklahoma State Regents for Higher Education. Awards associate, bachelor's, and master's degrees. Founded 1890. Setting: 210-acre suburban campus with easy access to Oklahoma City. Endowment: $25.7 million. Research spending for the previous fiscal year: $887,915. Educational spending for the previous fiscal year: $3496 per student. Total enrollment: 15,973. Faculty: 1,030 (548 full-time, 482 part-time). Student-undergrad faculty ratio is 18:1. 4,722 applied, 81% were admitted. 14% from top 10% of their high school class, 37% from top quarter, 72% from top half. Full-time: 10,449 students, 59% women, 41% men. Part-time: 3,888 students, 59% women, 41% men. Students come from 43 states and territories, 88 other countries, 10% from out-of-state. 4% American Indian or Alaska Native, non-Hispanic/Latino; 10% Hispanic/Latino; 9% Black or African American, non-Hispanic/Latino; 4% Asian, non-Hispanic/Latino; 0.2% Native Hawaiian or other Pacific Islander, non-Hispanic/Latino; 6% international. 23% 25 or older, 11% live on campus, 10% transferred in. Retention: 64% of full-time freshmen returned the following year. Academic areas with the most degrees conferred: business/marketing; liberal arts/general studies; health professions and related sciences; homeland security, law enforcement, firefighting, and protective services. Core. Calendar: semesters. Academic remediation for entering students, ESL program, services for LD students, advanced placement, accelerated degree program, independent study, distance learning, double major, summer session for credit, part-time degree program, internships. Study abroad program. ROTC: Army.
Entrance Requirements: Options: electronic application, deferred admission, international baccalaureate accepted. Required: high school transcript, minimum 2.7 high school GPA, rank in upper 50% of high school class; composite ACT score of 20; 2.7 GPA in core curriculum classes, SAT or ACT. Recommended: SAT, ACT. Required for some: SAT and SAT Subject Tests or ACT. Entrance: minimally difficult. Application deadline: rolling. Notification: continuous. SAT Reasoning Test deadline: 8/18. Transfer credits accepted: Yes.
Costs Per Year: Application fee: $50. State resident tuition: $6,482 full-time, $216.05 per credit hour part-time. Nonresident tuition: $17,368 full-time, $578.95 per credit hour part-time. Mandatory fees: $1005 full-time, $33.50

per credit hour part-time. Full-time tuition and fees vary according to course level, course load, degree level, location, and program. Part-time tuition and fees vary according to course level, course load, degree level, location, and program. College room and board: $8050. College room only: $3900. Room and board charges vary according to board plan and housing facility. Tuition guaranteed not to increase for student's term of enrollment.

Collegiate Environment: Orientation program. Drama-theater group, choral group, marching band, student-run newspaper, radio station. Social organizations: 236 open to all; national fraternities, national sororities; 2% of eligible men and 4% of eligible women are members. Most popular organizations: Student Government Association, Student Programming Board, International Student Council, Panhellenic Council, Interfraternity Council. Major annual events: Stampede Week, Homecoming, Greek Week. Student services: health clinic, personal-psychological counseling, women's center. Campus security: 24-hour emergency response devices and patrols, late night transport-escort service. Max Chambers Library plus 1 other. Books: 555,825 (physical), 296,818 (digital/electronic); Serial titles: 23,218 (physical), 124,803 (digital/electronic); Databases: 239. Weekly public service hours: 107; students can reserve study rooms. Operations spending for the previous fiscal year: $4.6 million. 650 computers available on campus for general student use. A campuswide network can be accessed from student residence rooms and from off campus. Students can access the following: online class registration. Staffed computer lab on campus provides training in use of computers, software, and the Internet.

Community Environment: Edmond is a suburban city 12 miles north of Oklahoma City. All modes of transportation are available to the community. Edmond has churches of most denominations, a movie theatre, numerous parks, a swimming pool, and shopping centers. Part-time employment is plentiful.

■ UNIVERSITY OF OKLAHOMA

660 Parrington Oval
Norman, OK 73019-0390
Tel: (405)325-0311; Free: 800-234-6868
Fax: (405)325-7478
E-mail: admissions@ou.edu
Web Site: www.ou.edu

Description: State-supported, university, coed. Awards bachelor's, master's, and doctoral degrees. Founded 1890. Setting: 3,955-acre suburban campus with easy access to Oklahoma City. Endowment: $1.1 billion. Research spending for the previous fiscal year: $102.7 million. Educational spending for the previous fiscal year: $10,604 per student. Total enrollment: 28,527. Faculty: 1,454 (1,206 full-time, 248 part-time). Student-undergrad faculty ratio is 18:1. 16,777 applied, 69% were admitted. 36% from top 10% of their high school class, 65% from top quarter, 92% from top half. 314 National Merit Scholars, 258 valedictorians. Full-time: 19,054 students, 50% women, 50% men. Part-time: 2,978 students, 47% women, 53% men. Students come from 56 states and territories, 120 other countries, 36% from out-of-state. 4% American Indian or Alaska Native, non-Hispanic/Latino; 10% Hispanic/Latino; 5% Black or African American, non-Hispanic/Latino; 6% Asian, non-Hispanic/Latino; 0.1% Native Hawaiian or other Pacific Islander, non-Hispanic/Latino; 4% international. 10% 25 or older, 32% live on campus, 5% transferred in. Retention: 92% of full-time freshmen returned the following year. Academic areas with the most degrees conferred: business/marketing; engineering; communication/journalism. Core. Calendar: semesters. Academic remediation for entering students, ESL program, services for LD students, advanced placement, accelerated degree program, self-designed majors, freshman honors college, honors program, independent study, distance learning, double major, summer session for credit, part-time degree program, external degree program, adult/continuing education programs, co-op programs and internships, graduate courses open to undergrads. Off campus study. Study abroad program. ROTC: Army, Naval, Air Force.

Entrance Requirements: Options: electronic application, international baccalaureate accepted. Required: essay, high school transcript, 15 specified curricular units, SAT or ACT. Recommended: 1 recommendation. Entrance: moderately difficult. Application deadline: 2/1. Notification: continuous. SAT Reasoning Test deadline: 2/1. Transfer credits accepted: Yes. Applicants placed on waiting list: 1,929. Wait-listed applicants offered admission: 163.

Costs Per Year: Application fee: $40. State resident tuition: $4788 full-time, $159.60 per credit hour part-time. Nonresident tuition: $20,169 full-time, $672.30 per credit hour part-time. Mandatory fees: $4,274 full-time, $134.05 per credit hour part-time, $126.50 per term part-time. Full-time tuition and fees vary according to course load, degree level, location, and program. Part-time tuition and fees vary according to course load, degree level, location, and program. College room and board: $10,994. College room only: $6378. Room and board charges vary according to board plan and housing facility. Tuition guaranteed not to increase for student's term of enrollment.

Collegiate Environment: Orientation program. Drama-theater group, choral group, marching band, student-run newspaper, radio station. Social organizations: 552 open to all; national fraternities, national sororities, local fraternities, local sororities; 26% of eligible men and 33% of eligible women are members. Most popular organizations: Campus Activities Council Soonerthon, Campus Activities Council Homecoming, Engineers Club, Relay For Life, The Big Event. Major annual events: Campus Activities Council Homecoming, The Big Event, Campus Activities Council Soonerthon. Student services: legal services, health clinic, personal-psychological counseling, women's center. Campus security: 24-hour emergency response devices and patrols, late night transport-escort service, controlled dormitory access, crime prevention programs, police bicycle patrols, self-defense classes, emergency notification system, lighted pathways/sidewalks. Bizzell Memorial Library plus 5 others. Books: 4.4 million (physical), 1.4 million (digital/electronic); Serial titles: 71,289 (physical), 128,934 (digital/electronic); Databases: 311. Weekly public service hours: 114; students can reserve study rooms. Operations spending for the previous fiscal year: $21.3 million. 4,500 computers available on campus for general student use. Computer purchase/lease plans available. A campuswide network can be accessed from student residence rooms and from off campus. Students can access the following: online class registration. Staffed computer lab on campus provides training in use of computers, software, and the Internet.

Community Environment: Norman is a mid-sized city in central Oklahoma with award-winning public schools; cultural offerings, such as theaters and museums; community services including churches, hospitals, a public library; and recreational facilities, including parks, golf courses and nearby Lake Thunderbird. The community is served by major highways, bus lines, and Will Rogers World Airport, located 18 miles north in Oklahoma City. The university operates Max Westheimer Airpark, a general aviation, reliever category airport in Norman.

■ UNIVERSITY OF OKLAHOMA HEALTH SCIENCES CENTER

PO Box 26901
Oklahoma City, OK 73190
Tel: (405)271-4000
Fax: (405)271-2480
Web Site: www.ouhsc.edu

Description: State-supported, upper-level, coed. Part of University of Oklahoma. Awards bachelor's, master's, and doctoral degrees and post-master's certificates. Founded 1890. Setting: 300-acre urban campus with easy access to Oklahoma City. Endowment: $312.6 million. Research spending for the previous fiscal year: $115.5 million. Educational spending for the previous fiscal year: $43,700 per student. Total enrollment: 3,139. Faculty: 408 (298 full-time, 110 part-time). Student-undergrad faculty ratio is 10:1. Full-time: 737 students, 88% women, 12% men. Part-time: 49 students, 82% women, 18% men. Students come from 43 states and territories, 14 other countries, 17% from out-of-state. 4% American Indian or Alaska Native, non-Hispanic/Latino; 9% Hispanic/Latino; 3% Black or African American, non-Hispanic/Latino; 6% Asian, non-Hispanic/Latino; 0.1% Native Hawaiian or other Pacific Islander, non-Hispanic/Latino; 0.3% international. 31% 25 or older, 38% transferred in. Academic areas with the most degrees conferred: health professions and related sciences; interdisciplinary studies. Calendar: semesters. Advanced placement, honors program, distance learning, summer session for credit, part-time degree program, internships, graduate courses open to undergrads. ROTC: Army (c), Air Force (c).

Costs Per Year: State resident tuition: $4788 full-time, $159.60 per credit hour part-time. Nonresident tuition: $20,169 full-time, $672.30 per credit hour part-time. Mandatory fees: $2365 full-time, $62.15 per credit hour part-time, $250.25 per term part-time. Full-time tuition and fees vary according to course level, course load, degree level, location, program, and student level. Part-time tuition and fees vary according to course level, course load, degree level, location, program, and student level.

Collegiate Environment: Orientation program. Student-run radio station. Social organizations: 75 open to all. Most popular organizations: OU Health Sciences Center Student Association, OU College of Nursing Student Association, OU College of Medicine Student Association, OU College of Pharmacy Student Counsel, OU College of Allied Health Student Association. Major annual events: Campus Activities Board Events, DeStress Fest. Student services: health clinic, personal-psychological counseling, women's center. Campus security: 24-hour emergency response devices and patrols, late night transport-escort service. Robert M. Bird Health Sciences Library plus 1 other. Books: 286,469 (physical), 19,136 (digital/electronic); Serial titles: 158 (physical), 26,678 (digital/electronic); Databases: 157. Weekly public service hours: 111. Operations spending for the previous fiscal year: $4.8 million. 140 computers available on campus for general student use. Computer purchase/lease plans available. A campuswide network can be accessed from student residence rooms and from off campus. Students can access the following: online class registration, online bursar bill and payment. Staffed computer lab on campus provides training in use of computers, software, and the Internet.

Community Environment: See Oklahoma City University.

■ **UNIVERSITY OF SCIENCE AND ARTS OF OKLAHOMA**
1727 W Alabama
Chickasha, OK 73018
Tel: (405)224-3140; Free: 800-933-8726
Fax: (405)574-1220
E-mail: usao-admissions@usao.edu
Web Site: www.usao.edu

Description: State-supported, 4-year, coed. Part of Oklahoma State Regents for Higher Education. Awards bachelor's degrees. Founded 1908. Setting: 75-acre small town campus with easy access to Oklahoma City. Endowment: $13.1 million. Research spending for the previous fiscal year: $244,029. Total enrollment: 888. Faculty: 87 (54 full-time, 33 part-time). Student-undergrad faculty ratio is 12:1. 706 applied, 66% were admitted. 25% from top 10% of their high school class, 47% from top quarter, 78% from top half. Full-time: 787 students, 66% women, 34% men. Part-time: 101 students, 62% women, 38% men. Students come from 16 states and territories, 22 other countries, 14% from out-of-state. 14% American Indian or Alaska Native, non-Hispanic/Latino; 7% Hispanic/Latino; 5% Black or African American, non-Hispanic/Latino; 0.9% Asian, non-Hispanic/Latino; 8% international. 17% 25 or older, 44% live on campus, 9% transferred in. Retention: 77% of full-time freshmen returned the following year. Academic areas with the most degrees conferred: business/marketing; education; visual and performing arts. Core. Calendar: trimesters. Academic remediation for entering students, services for LD students, advanced placement, accelerated degree program, self-designed majors, independent study, double major, summer session for credit, part-time degree program, internships. Off campus study.

Entrance Requirements: Options: electronic application, deferred admission. Required: SAT or ACT. Recommended: minimum ACT score of 24 and 3.0 GPA/top 50% high school class, 3.0 GPA and top 25% high school class, or minimum ACT score of 22 and 3.0 GPA in 15-unit high school core. Required for some: high school transcript, minimum 3 high school GPA, minimum ACT score of 24 and 3.0 GPA/top 50% high school class, 3.0 GPA and top 25% high school class, or minimum ACT score of 22 and 3.0 GPA in 15-unit high school core. Entrance: moderately difficult. Application deadlines: 9/2, rolling for nonresidents. Notification: continuous until 1/2, continuous until 1/2 for nonresidents. SAT Reasoning Test deadline: 9/1. SAT Subject Test deadline: 9/1. Transfer credits accepted: Yes.

Costs Per Year: Application fee: $40. State resident tuition: $6030 full-time, $201 per credit hour part-time. Nonresident tuition: $16,380 full-time, $546 per credit hour part-time. Mandatory fees: $1650 full-time, $50 per credit hour part-time. College room and board: $6100. College room only: $3050. Room and board charges vary according to board plan and housing facility. Tuition guaranteed not to increase for student's term of enrollment.

Collegiate Environment: Orientation program. Drama-theater group, choral group, student-run newspaper. Social organizations: 24 open to all; national fraternities, local sororities; 1% of eligible men and 1% of eligible women are members. Most popular organizations: Student Activities Board, Volunteer Action Council, Psychology Club, Young Democrats, Young Conservatives. Major annual events: Montmartre Festival/Droverstock, Festival of Arts and Ideas, Drover Difference Day. Student services: health clinic, personal-psychological counseling. Campus security: 24-hour emergency response devices and patrols, controlled dormitory access. Nash Library plus 1 other. Books: 87,603 (physical), 4,798 (digital/electronic); Serial titles: 22 (physical), 10,500 (digital/electronic); Databases: 60. Weekly public service hours: 81. Operations spending for the previous fiscal year: $388,672. 185 computers available on campus for general student use. A campuswide network can be accessed from student residence rooms. Staffed computer lab on campus provides training in use of computers, software, and the Internet.

Community Environment: Chickasha is a suburban area southwest of Oklahoma City. Located in the fertile Washita River Valley, the city lies within one of the largest gas fields in the world. The community has rail, bus, and air service. The community includes Catholic and Protestant churches, a hospital, a public library, and major civic, fraternal, and veteran's organizations. Local recreational facilities include theatres and several good lakes within a few miles for boating, fishing and water sports. Some part-time employment is available for students.

■ **THE UNIVERSITY OF TULSA**
800 S Tucker Dr.
Tulsa, OK 74104-3189
Tel: (918)631-2000; Free: 800-331-3050
Fax: (918)631-2247

E-mail: admission@utulsa.edu
Web Site: www.utulsa.edu

Description: Independent, university, coed, affiliated with Presbyterian Church (U.S.A.). Awards bachelor's, master's, and doctoral degrees. Founded 1894. Setting: 209-acre urban campus with easy access to Tulsa. Total enrollment: 4,399. Faculty: 465 (356 full-time, 109 part-time). Student-undergrad faculty ratio is 11:1. 8,526 applied, 41% were admitted. 52% from top 10% of their high school class, 79% from top quarter, 95% from top half. Full-time: 3,162 students, 45% women, 55% men. Part-time: 133 students, 37% women, 63% men. Students come from 44 states and territories, 55 other countries, 42% from out-of-state. 3% American Indian or Alaska Native, non-Hispanic/Latino; 8% Hispanic/Latino; 6% Black or African American, non-Hispanic/Latino; 5% Asian, non-Hispanic/Latino; 15% international. 6% 25 or older, 40% live on campus, 4% transferred in. Retention: 88% of full-time freshmen returned the following year. Academic areas with the most degrees conferred: engineering; business/marketing; social sciences. Core. Calendar: semesters. ESL program, services for LD students, advanced placement, accelerated degree program, self-designed majors, honors program, independent study, double major, summer session for credit, part-time degree program, adult/continuing education programs, internships, graduate courses open to undergrads. Study abroad program. ROTC: Air Force (c).

Entrance Requirements: Options: electronic application, early admission, early action, deferred admission, international baccalaureate accepted. Required: essay, high school transcript, SAT or ACT. Recommended: interview. Entrance: very difficult. Application deadline: rolling. Notification: continuous. SAT Reasoning Test deadline: 8/1. Transfer credits accepted: Yes.

Costs Per Year: Application fee: $50. One-time mandatory fee: $485. Comprehensive fee: $53,688 includes full-time tuition ($41,698), mandatory fees ($540), and college room and board ($11,450). Part-time tuition: $1497 per credit hour.

Collegiate Environment: Orientation program. Drama-theater group, choral group, marching band, student-run newspaper, radio station. Social organizations: national fraternities, national sororities, local fraternities. Most popular organizations: Student Association, Residence Hall Association, Pre-Professional organizations, intramural sports, Greek life. Major annual events: Homecoming, Springfest, Parent's Weekend. Student services: legal services, health clinic, personal-psychological counseling. Campus security: 24-hour emergency response devices and patrols, late night transport-escort service, controlled dormitory access. 2,809 college housing spaces available; 2,316 were occupied in 2018-19. Freshmen guaranteed college housing. On-campus residence required through sophomore year. Options: coed, men-only, women-only housing available. McFarlin Library plus 1 other. Books: 1.2 million (physical), 460,240 (digital/electronic); Serial titles: 59,171 (digital/electronic); Databases: 289. Weekly public service hours: 94; study areas open 24 hours, 5-7 days a week; students can reserve study rooms. 710 computers available on campus for general student use. Computer purchase/lease plans available. A campuswide network can be accessed. Students can access the following: online class registration. Staffed computer lab on campus (open 24 hours a day) provides training in use of computers, software, and the Internet.

Community Environment: The climate is temperate. The average year-round high temperature is 71 degrees. The population is 382,400. The city features a professional opera company, a national ballet company, a symphony orchestra, museums, art galleries, community theatres, parks, minor league teams in hockey and baseball and recreation and shopping facilities. Public bus transportation is available.

■ **WESTERN OKLAHOMA STATE COLLEGE**
2801 N Main St.
Altus, OK 73521-1397
Tel: (580)477-2000
Fax: (580)477-7723
E-mail: chad.wiginton@wosc.edu
Web Site: www.wosc.edu

Description: State-supported, 2-year, coed. Part of Oklahoma State Regents for Higher Education. Awards certificates, transfer associate, and terminal associate degrees. Founded 1926. Setting: 142-acre rural campus. Endowment: $5.4 million. Educational spending for the previous fiscal year: $2195 per student. Total enrollment: 1,690. Faculty: 71 (37 full-time, 34 part-time). Student-undergrad faculty ratio is 19:1. 615 applied, 100% were admitted. 9% from top 10% of their high school class, 31% from top quarter, 60% from top half. Full-time: 675 students, 50% women, 50% men. Part-time: 1,015 students, 61% women, 39% men. Students come from 6 other countries, 12% from out-of-state. 2% American Indian or Alaska Native, non-Hispanic/Latino; 16% Hispanic/Latino; 10% Black or African American, non-Hispanic/Latino; 0.9% Asian, non-Hispanic/Latino; 0.2% Native Hawaiian or other Pacific Islander, non-Hispanic/Latino; 1% international. 35% 25 or older, 6% live on campus, 48% transferred in. Retention: 49% of full-time freshmen returned the following year. Core. Calendar: semesters. Academic remediation for entering students, ESL program, services for LD students, advanced placement, self-designed majors, honors program, independent study, distance learning, summer session for credit, part-time degree program, adult/continuing education programs. Off campus study at all state institutions in the Oklahoma Higher Education Televised Instructional System.

Entrance Requirements: Open admission. Options: electronic application, early admission. Required: high school transcript. Required for some: ACT. Entrance: noncompetitive. Application deadline: rolling. Notification: continuous. Transfer credits accepted: Yes.

Collegiate Environment: Orientation program. Drama-theater group, choral group. Most popular organizations: Baptist Student Union, Phi Theta Kappa,

Student Senate, Behavioral Science Club, Aggie Club. Major annual events: Homecoming, Organizational Competitions, Sporting Events. Student services: personal-psychological counseling. Campus security: 24-hour emergency response devices, trained security personnel 8am-10pm, Monday through Friday. Learning Resources Center. Operations spending for the previous fiscal year: $295,388. 130 computers available on campus for general student use. A campuswide network can be accessed from student residence rooms and from off campus. Students can access the following: online class registration. Staffed computer lab on campus provides training in use of computers, software, and the Internet.

Community Environment: Altus is an urban community served by bus, railroad, and major interstate highways. The climate is temperate. The community has one hospital, a public library, many churches, and recreational facilities.

■ **AMERICAN COLLEGE OF HEALTHCARE SCIENCES**

5005 SW Macadam Ave.

Portland, OR 97239-3719

Tel: (503)244-0726; Free: 800-487-8839

Fax: (503)244-0727

Web Site: www.achs.edu

Description: Independent, comprehensive, coed. Awards associate, bachelor's, and master's degrees. Setting: urban campus. 2 applied, 50% were admitted. Students come from 63 other countries. Academic remediation for entering students, services for LD students, accelerated degree program, self-designed majors, honors program, distance learning, double major, summer session for credit, part-time degree program, adult/continuing education programs, graduate courses open to undergrads. Off campus study. Study abroad program.

Entrance Requirements: Option: electronic application. Required: essay, high school transcript, recommendation from Admissions Committee. Recommended: minimum X high school GPA. Required for some: recommendations, interview. Transfer credits accepted: Yes.

Collegiate Environment: Orientation program. ACHS Virtual Library. Books: 2,971 (digital/electronic); Serial titles: 17,514 (digital/electronic); Databases: 70.

■ **BIRTHINGWAY COLLEGE OF MIDWIFERY**

12113 SE Foster Rd.

Portland, OR 97266

Tel: (503)760-3131

Web Site: www.birthingway.edu

Description: Independent, upper-level, coed. Awards bachelor's degrees. Founded 1993. Total enrollment: 79. Student-undergrad faculty ratio is 10:1. 75% 25 or older. Calendar: 3 semesters.

■ **BLUE MOUNTAIN COMMUNITY COLLEGE**

2411 NW Carden Ave.

Pendleton, OR 97801-1000

Tel: (541)276-1260

Fax: (541)278-5886

Web Site: www.bluecc.edu

Description: State and locally supported, 2-year, coed. Awards certificates, transfer associate, and terminal associate degrees. Founded 1962. Setting: 170-acre rural campus. Total enrollment: 1,782. 51% 25 or older. Core. Calendar: quarters. Academic remediation for entering students, ESL program, services for LD students, advanced placement, distance learning, summer session for credit, part-time degree program, adult/continuing education programs, co-op programs.

Entrance Requirements: Open admission. Option: electronic application. Required: high school transcript. Entrance: noncompetitive. Application deadline: rolling. Notification: continuous.

Costs Per Year: One-time mandatory fee: $35. State resident tuition: $4860 full-time, $108 per credit hour part-time. Nonresident tuition: $14,580 full-time, $324 per credit hour part-time. Mandatory fees: $1448 full-time, $29.50 per credit hour part-time. Full-time tuition and fees vary according to course load, program, and reciprocity agreements. Part-time tuition and fees vary according to course load, program, and reciprocity agreements. College room and board: $9158.

Collegiate Environment: Orientation program. Drama-theater group, choral group. Student services: personal-psychological counseling. Blue Mountain Community College Library.

Community Environment: Pendleton, pop. 16,636, is bordered by the Blue Mountains, the Columbia River, and rolling wheat fields with and agriculturally based economy. It is approximately 200 miles from Portland, OR, Spokane, WA, and Boise, ID. Community facilities include a public library, churches of major denominations, a hospital, shopping, and many services and civic organizations. Pendleton is known nationally for its annual event, The Pendleton Roundup. Other activities include a symphony, art shows, and many organized sports for children and adults. For the recreationist, the area offers a wide variety of seasonal sports, including skiing, fishing, hiking, and hunting.

■ **CENTRAL OREGON COMMUNITY COLLEGE**

2600 NW College Way

Bend, OR 97703

Tel: (541)383-7700

Fax: (541)383-7506

Web Site: www.cocc.edu

Description: District-supported, 2-year, coed. Part of Oregon Community College Association. Awards certificates, diplomas, transfer associate, and terminal associate degrees. Founded 1949. Setting: 193-acre small town campus. Endowment: $21.3 million. Total enrollment: 4,871. Faculty: 341 (130 full-time, 211 part-time). Student-undergrad faculty ratio is 19:1. 979 applied, 100% were admitted. Full-time: 2,303 students, 51% women, 49% men. Part-time: 2,568 students, 55% women, 45% men. 2% American Indian or Alaska Native, non-Hispanic/Latino; 12% Hispanic/Latino; 0.6% Black or African American, non-Hispanic/Latino; 1% Asian, non-Hispanic/Latino; 0.3% Native Hawaiian or other Pacific Islander, non-Hispanic/Latino. 9% transferred in. Retention: 61% of full-time freshmen returned the following year. Core. Calendar: quarters. Academic remediation for entering students, ESL program, services for LD students, self-designed majors, independent study, distance learning, double major, summer session for credit, part-time degree program, co-op programs and internships. Study abroad program. ROTC: Army (c).

Entrance Requirements: Open admission except for nursing, emergency medical services, r medical assistant, dental assistant, and massage therapy programs. Option: electronic application. Entrance: noncompetitive. Application deadline: rolling. Notification: continuous. Preference given to district residents for nursing program. Transfer credits accepted: Yes.

Costs Per Year: Application fee: $25. Area resident tuition: $3951 full-time, $99 per credit hour part-time. State resident tuition: $5373 full-time, $138.50 per credit hour part-time. Nonresident tuition: $10,575 full-time, $283 per credit hour part-time. Mandatory fees: $387 full-time, $10.75 per credit hour part-time. College room and board: $11,151. Room and board charges vary according to board plan.

Collegiate Environment: Orientation program. Drama-theater group, choral group, student-run newspaper. Most popular organizations: Club Sports, Student Newspaper, Criminal Justice Club, Aviation Club. Major annual events: Graduation Ceremonies, Native American Spring Festival, Jungle Run/Storm the Stairs. Student services: personal-psychological counseling. Campus security: 24-hour emergency response devices and patrols, late night transport-escort service, controlled dormitory access. 320 college housing spaces available; all were occupied in 2018-19. No special consideration for freshman housing applicants. Option: coed housing available. COCC Barber Library plus 1 other. Books: 58,892 (physical), 236,191 (digital/electronic); Serial titles: 5,544 (physical), 126,380 (digital/electronic); Databases: 135. Weekly public service hours: 79. 130 computers available on campus for general student use. A campuswide network can be accessed from student residence rooms and from off campus. Students can access the following: online class registration. Staffed computer lab on campus provides training in use of computers, software, and the Internet.

Community Environment: Bend is an extremely scenic town of some 60,000 people located at the foothills of the Oregon's Cascade Mountain range. The college serves a 10,000-square-mile district that includes part of Central Oregon's high desert country east of Bend. The area's primary industries are lumber and tourism. Bus lines connect Bend with other parts of the state. Two airlines serve the nearby town of Redmond, 14 miles distant, with jet air transport. Bend is 157 miles from Portland and 120 miles from Eugene, Oregon. Community facilities include a public library, churches of major denominations, three major shopping malls and many service and civic organizations. Bend is known nationally for its recreational environment. Bordering the 1.6 million-acre Deschutes National Forest, the town affords excellent hunting, fishing, hiking and camping opportunities. The full-facility Mt. Bachelor Ski Area, which is normally open from November through June, is 22 minutes from the college campus. Rain is rare in the area. Bend receives an average snowfall of three feet per year, although the mountainous areas receive considerably more.

■ **CHEMEKETA COMMUNITY COLLEGE**
4000 Lancaster Dr. NE
Salem, OR 97309
Tel: (503)399-5000
Fax: (503)399-3918
E-mail: admissions@chemeketa.edu
Web Site: www.chemeketa.edu

Description: State and locally supported, 2-year, coed. Awards certificates, diplomas, transfer associate, and terminal associate degrees. Founded 1955. Setting: 72-acre urban campus with easy access to Portland. Endowment: $3.7 million. Educational spending for the previous fiscal year: $3849 per student. Total enrollment: 12,371. Faculty: 740 (186 full-time, 554 part-time). Student-undergrad faculty ratio is 26:1. Full-time: 6,225 students, 55% women, 45% men. Part-time: 6,146 students, 59% women, 41% men. Students come from 21 states and territories, 20 other countries, 5% from out-of-state. 2% American Indian or Alaska Native, non-Hispanic/Latino; 18% Hispanic/Latino; 1% Black or African American, non-Hispanic/Latino; 2% Asian, non-Hispanic/Latino; 0.8% Native Hawaiian or other Pacific Islander, non-Hispanic/Latino; 0.6% international. 52% 25 or older, 1% transferred in. Retention: 61% of full-time freshmen returned the following year. Core. Calendar: quarters. Academic remediation for entering students, ESL program, services for LD students, advanced placement, independent study, distance learning, double major, summer session for credit, part-time degree program, adult/continuing education programs, co-op programs and internships. Study abroad program.

Entrance Requirements: Required for some: high school transcript, interview.

Collegiate Environment: Orientation program. Drama-theater group, choral group, student-run newspaper. Social organizations: 21 open to all. Most popular organizations: Student Center and Multicultural Center (the two largest), Phi Theta Kappa, Student Government, Juntos (promotes the Latin American culture, leadership development, community service, and higher education), Theater by Storm (all aspects of theater, including acting, technical theater, and management). Major annual events: Into the Streets (community service day), Indigenous Peoples' Day and Martin Luther King Day, Veterans' Day. Student services: personal-psychological counseling, women's center. Campus security: 24-hour emergency response devices and patrols, late night transport-escort service. Chemeketa Community College Library (CCRLS). Operations spending for the previous fiscal year: $3 million. 250 computers available on campus for general student use. A campuswide network can be accessed from off-campus. Students can access the following: online class registration. Staffed computer lab on campus provides training in use of computers, software, and the Internet.

Community Environment: See Willamette University.

■ **CLACKAMAS COMMUNITY COLLEGE**
19600 Molalla Ave.
Oregon City, OR 97045-7998
Tel: (503)657-6958
Fax: (503)650-6654

E-mail: pattyw@clackamas.edu
Web Site: www.clackamas.edu

Description: District-supported, 2-year, coed. Awards certificates, diplomas, transfer associate, and terminal associate degrees. Founded 1966. Setting: 175-acre suburban campus with easy access to Portland. Endowment: $9.7 million. Educational spending for the previous fiscal year: $3160 per student. Total enrollment: 8,144. Faculty: 577 (148 full-time, 429 part-time). Student-undergrad faculty ratio is 14:1. Full-time: 3,205 students, 52% women, 48% men. Part-time: 4,939 students, 54% women, 46% men. Students come from 21 states and territories, 16 other countries, 1% from out-of-state. 45% 25 or older, 41% transferred in. Retention: 91% of full-time freshmen returned the following year. Core. Calendar: quarters. Academic remediation for entering students, ESL program, services for LD students, advanced placement, accelerated degree program, honors program, independent study, distance learning, double major, summer session for credit, part-time degree program, adult/continuing education programs, co-op programs and internships. Study abroad program.

Entrance Requirements: Open admission except for nursing program, medical assistant, accelerated degree, PSU co-admit. Option: early admission. Entrance: noncompetitive. Application deadline: rolling.

Costs Per Year: Application fee: $0. State resident tuition: $4500 full-time, $100 per credit hour part-time. Nonresident tuition: $11,970 full-time, $266 per credit hour part-time. Mandatory fees: $444 full-time, $8 per credit hour part-time, $28 per term part-time.

Collegiate Environment: Orientation program. Drama-theater group, choral group, student-run newspaper. Social organizations: 21 open to all; national fraternities. Most popular organizations: Ski Club, Spanish Club, Phi Theta Kappa, Horticulture Club, Speech Club. Major annual events: Club Fair, Fall Craft Fair, Environmental Week. Student services: personal-psychological counseling, women's center. Campus security: 24-hour emergency response devices and patrols, student patrols, late night transport-escort service. Dye Learning Resource Center plus 1 other. Operations spending for the previous fiscal year: $408,101. 200 computers available on campus for general student use. A campuswide network can be accessed. Students can access the following: online class registration. Staffed computer lab on campus.

Community Environment: Oregon City was the capital of the Old Oregon Territory, founded in 1829. The city is on the bank of the Willamette River where there are 40-foot falls that provide waterpower for the production of paper, batteries, lumber and electric power. A municipal free elevator lifts pedestrians 90 feet up the steep face of a cliff to a residential business district. An observation deck at the top overlooks the downtown area and the falls. The Holly Knoll Museum is 7 miles southeast where antique furniture and harness and horsedrawn vehicles may be seen. The John McLoughlin House National Historic Site was built in 1846.

■ **CLATSOP COMMUNITY COLLEGE**
1651 Lexington Ave.
Astoria, OR 97103
Tel: (503)325-0910; Free: 855-252-8767
Fax: (503)325-5738
E-mail: admissions@clatsopcc.edu
Web Site: www.clatsopcc.edu

Description: County-supported, 2-year, coed. Awards certificates, transfer associate, and terminal associate degrees. Founded 1958. Setting: 20-acre small town campus. Educational spending for the previous fiscal year: $2839 per student. Total enrollment: 1,071. Faculty: 99 (27 full-time, 72 part-time). Student-undergrad faculty ratio is 13:1. 340 applied, 81% were admitted. 1 student government officer. Full-time: 455 students, 53% women, 47% men. Part-time: 616 students, 59% women, 41% men. Students come from 5 states and territories, 12% from out-of-state. 2% American Indian or Alaska Native, non-Hispanic/Latino; 12% Hispanic/Latino; 0.6% Black or African American, non-Hispanic/Latino; 1% Asian, non-Hispanic/Latino; 0.2% Native Hawaiian or other Pacific Islander, non-Hispanic/Latino. 44% 25 or older, 5% transferred in. Calendar: quarters. Academic remediation for entering students, ESL program, services for LD students, advanced placement, freshman honors college, honors program, independent study, distance learning, summer session for credit, part-time degree program, adult/continuing education programs, co-op programs and internships.

Entrance Requirements: Open admission. Option: electronic application. Recommended: high school transcript. Entrance: noncompetitive. Application deadline: rolling. Notification: continuous. Transfer credits accepted: Yes.

Costs Per Year: Application fee: $15. State resident tuition: $3672 full-time, $102 per credit hour part-time. Nonresident tuition: $7344 full-time, $204 per credit hour part-time. Mandatory fees: $420 full-time, $10 per credit hour part-time, $30 per term part-time. Full-time tuition and fees vary according to course load, program, and reciprocity agreements. Part-time tuition and fees vary according to course load, program, and reciprocity agreements.

Collegiate Environment: Orientation program. Student-run newspaper. Student services: personal-psychological counseling. Campus security: 24-hour emergency response devices, late night transport-escort service. Dora Badollet Library. Operations spending for the previous fiscal year: $313,925. 76 computers available on campus for general student use. A campuswide network can be accessed. Students can access the following: online class registration. Staffed computer lab on campus provides training in use of software and the Internet.

Community Environment: Located on the Columbia River, about 10 miles from its mouth, Astoria is known principally for its salmon and tuna industries. Astoria's history dates from the winter of 1805 when the Lewis and Clark expedition camped at Fort Clatsop. Many plants here are in the fish canning, curing, and freezing business. At the larger docks, ocean liners load for world ports. Commercial transportation is available. There are a number of churches, a city-owned library, museums, hospitals, and many of the major civic and service organizations in the community. The opportunities are good for part-time employment. Recreational facilities are numerous; lakes, streams, rivers, and the ocean for fishing, swimming, boating, picnicking and digging for clams. During the fishing season, August 1 to September 10, more than 15,000 large fish are taken from the Columbia River near Astoria. Some of the points of interest are the Astoria Column, 125 feet high, which illustrates incidents in the early history of the region, Clatsop County Historical Museum, the Columbia River Maritime Museum, and Fort Astoria. The Astoria Regatta is an annual event.

■ COLUMBIA GORGE COMMUNITY COLLEGE
400 E Scenic Dr.
The Dalles, OR 97058
Tel: (541)296-6182
Fax: (541)298-3104
Web Site: www.cgcc.edu
Description: State-supported, 2-year, coed. Awards certificates, diplomas, transfer associate, and terminal associate degrees. Founded 1977. Setting: 78-acre small town campus. Total enrollment: 1,245. Faculty: 125 (18 full-time, 107 part-time). Full-time: 542 students, 59% women, 41% men. Part-time: 703 students, 65% women, 35% men. Students come from 24 states and territories, 1% from out-of-state. 5% American Indian or Alaska Native, non-Hispanic/Latino; 7% Hispanic/Latino; 0.6% Black or African American, non-Hispanic/Latino; 0.8% Asian, non-Hispanic/Latino; 0.1% Native Hawaiian or other Pacific Islander, non-Hispanic/Latino. 48% 25 or older. Retention: 21% of full-time freshmen returned the following year. Calendar: quarters. Academic remediation for entering students, ESL program, services for LD students, honors program, independent study, distance learning, summer session for credit, part-time degree program, co-op programs.
Entrance Requirements: Open admission. Option: electronic application. Transfer credits accepted: Yes.
Collegiate Environment: Orientation program. Most popular organizations: Nursing Club, Delta Club, Japanese Culture Club, Environmental Club. Major annual events: Back to School Bash, Spring BBQ, Graduation. Campus security: 24-hour emergency response devices. Columbia Gorge Community College Library.

■ CONCORDE CAREER COLLEGE
1425 NE Irving St.
Portland, OR 97232
Tel: (503)281-4181
Fax: (503)281-6739
Web Site: www.concorde.edu
Description: Proprietary, 2-year, coed. Awards certificates and terminal associate degrees.

■ CONCORDIA UNIVERSITY
2811 NE Holman
Portland, OR 97211-6099
Tel: (503)288-9371; Free: 800-321-9371
Fax: (503)280-8531
E-mail: admissions@cu-portland.edu
Web Site: www.cu-portland.edu
Description: Independent, comprehensive, coed, affiliated with Lutheran Church-Missouri Synod. Part of Concordia University System. Awards associate, bachelor's, and master's degrees. Founded 1905. Setting: 13-acre urban campus. Endowment: $7.2 million. Educational spending for the previous fiscal year: $3784 per student. Total enrollment: 3,111. Faculty: 259 (65 full-time, 194 part-time). Student-undergrad faculty ratio is 19:1. 1,961 applied, 54% were admitted. 16% from top 10% of their high school class, 44% from top quarter, 79% from top half. Full-time: 1,147 students, 67% women, 33% men. Part-time: 222 students, 69% women, 31% men. Students come from 36 states and territories, 13 other countries, 42% from out-of-state. 0.9% American Indian or Alaska Native, non-Hispanic/Latino; 8% Hispanic/Latino; 7% Black or African American, non-Hispanic/Latino; 4% Asian, non-Hispanic/Latino; 2% Native Hawaiian or other Pacific Islander, non-Hispanic/Latino; 1% international. 28% 25 or older, 36% live on campus, 21% transferred in. Retention: 70% of full-time freshmen returned the following year. Academic areas with the most degrees conferred: business/marketing; health professions and related sciences; education. Core. Calendar: semesters. Academic remediation for entering students, ESL program, services for LD students, advanced placement, accelerated degree program, self-designed majors, honors program, independent study, distance learning, double major, summer session for credit, part-time degree program, adult/continuing education programs, internships. Off campus study at Oregon Independent Colleges Association, Concordia University System. Study abroad program. ROTC: Air Force (c).
Entrance Requirements: Options: electronic application, deferred admission. Required: essay, high school transcript, minimum 2.5 high school GPA, 1 recommendation, SAT or ACT. Recommended: interview. Required for some: interview. Entrance: moderately difficult. Application deadline: rolling. Notification: continuous. SAT Reasoning Test deadline: 7/1. Transfer credits accepted: Yes.
Collegiate Environment: Orientation program. Drama-theater group, choral group, student-run newspaper. Social organizations: 24 open to all. Most popular organizations: Hawaiian Club, The Navy - athletic boosters, Soccer Club, Ultimate Frisbee Club, Volunteer Corps (Teacher, Service, Athlete). Major annual events: Graduation, MLK Day of Service, Academy Awards (campus). Student services: health clinic, personal-psychological counseling. Campus security: 24-hour emergency response devices and patrols, late night transport-escort service, controlled dormitory access, extensive video camera security of main campus areas. Concordia University Library plus 2 others. Operations spending for the previous fiscal year: $851,000. 100 computers available on campus for general student use. A computer is required for all students. A campuswide network can be accessed from student residence rooms and from off campus. Students can access the following: online class registration. Staffed computer lab on campus provides training in use of computers, software, and the Internet.

■ CORBAN UNIVERSITY
5000 Deer Park Dr., SE
Salem, OR 97301-9392
Tel: (503)581-8600; Free: 800-845-3005
Fax: (503)585-4316
E-mail: admissions@corban.edu
Web Site: www.corban.edu
Description: Independent Christian, comprehensive, coed. Awards associate, bachelor's, master's, and doctoral degrees. Founded 1935. Setting: 145-acre suburban campus with easy access to Portland. Total enrollment: 1,187. Faculty: 134 (50 full-time, 84 part-time). Student-undergrad faculty ratio is 14:1. 1,943 applied, 33% were admitted. 25% from top 10% of their high school class, 60% from top quarter, 91% from top half. Full-time: 936 students, 61% women, 39% men. Part-time: 85 students, 64% women, 36% men. 46% from out-of-state. 1% American Indian or Alaska Native, non-Hispanic/Latino; 2% Hispanic/Latino; 1% Black or African American, non-Hispanic/Latino; 2% Asian, non-Hispanic/Latino; 0.6% Native Hawaiian or other Pacific Islander, non-Hispanic/Latino; 5% international. 2% 25 or older, 49% live on campus, 6% transferred in. Retention: 79% of full-time freshmen returned the following year. Academic areas with the most degrees conferred: education; business/marketing; psychology. Core. Calendar: semesters. ESL program, services for LD students, advanced placement, accelerated degree program, self-designed majors, honors program, independent study, distance learning, double major, summer session for credit, external degree program, adult/continuing education programs, co-op programs and internships, graduate courses open to undergrads. Off campus study at Oregon Alliance of Independent Colleges & Universities, Council of Christian Colleges and Universities Best Semester, AMBEX: American Bavarian Exchange Program. Study abroad program. ROTC: Army (c), Air Force (c).

Entrance Requirements: Options: electronic application, international baccalaureate accepted. Required: essay, high school transcript, minimum 2.7 high school GPA, 2 recommendations, SAT or ACT. Entrance: moderately difficult. Application deadline: 8/1. Notification: continuous. SAT Reasoning Test deadline: 8/1. SAT Subject Test deadline: 8/1. Transfer credits accepted: Yes.

Costs Per Year: Application fee: $40. One-time mandatory fee: $150. Comprehensive fee: $43,271 includes full-time tuition ($32,380), mandatory fees ($660), and college room and board ($10,231). College room only: $5852. Full-time tuition and fees vary according to course load, degree level, program, and reciprocity agreements. Room and board charges vary according to board plan. Part-time tuition: $1350 per credit hour. Part-time mandatory fees: $330 per term. Part-time tuition and fees vary according to course load, degree level, program, and reciprocity agreements.

Collegiate Environment: Orientation program. Drama-theater group, choral group, student-run newspaper. Social organizations: 21 open to all. Most popular organizations: Corban Recreation, Corban Community Garden, Stories of Glory, Dens and Leviathans, Corban Students for Life. Major annual events: Turkey Trot, Humans vs. Zombies, World Outreach Week. Student services: health clinic, personal-psychological counseling. Campus security: 24-hour emergency response devices and patrols, student patrols, late night transport-escort service, controlled dormitory access. Corban University Library. Books: 81,025 (physical), 126,255 (digital/electronic); Databases: 14. Students can reserve study rooms. 54 computers available on campus for general student use. Computer purchase/lease plans available. A campuswide network can be accessed from student residence rooms and from off campus. Students can access the following: online class registration. Staffed computer lab on campus provides training in use of computers, software, and the Internet.

Community Environment: See Willamette University.

■ EASTERN OREGON UNIVERSITY

1 University Blvd.
La Grande, OR 97850-2899
Tel: (541)962-3672; Free: 800-452-8639
Fax: (541)962-3418
Web Site: www.eou.edu

Description: State-supported, comprehensive, coed. Awards associate, bachelor's, and master's degrees. Founded 1929. Setting: 121-acre rural campus. Endowment: $11.3 million. Research spending for the previous fiscal year: $641,543. Educational spending for the previous fiscal year: $7013 per student. Total enrollment: 2,978. Faculty: 172 (111 full-time, 61 part-time). Student-undergrad faculty ratio is 17:1. 1,010 applied, 98% were admitted. 9% from top 10% of their high school class, 32% from top quarter, 77% from top half. Full-time: 1,689 students, 60% women, 40% men. Part-time: 1,055 students, 59% women, 41% men. 32% from out-of-state. 2% American Indian or Alaska Native, non-Hispanic/Latino; 11% Hispanic/Latino; 2% Black or African American, non-Hispanic/Latino; 2% Asian, non-Hispanic/Latino; 3% Native Hawaiian or other Pacific Islander, non-Hispanic/Latino; 1% international. 39% 25 or older, 15% live on campus, 15% transferred in. Retention: 68% of full-time freshmen returned the following year. Academic areas with the most degrees conferred: business/marketing; education; parks and recreation. Core. Calendar: quarters. Academic remediation for entering students, services for LD students, advanced placement, self-designed majors, honors program, independent study, distance learning, double major, summer session for credit, part-time degree program, external degree program, adult/continuing education programs, co-op programs and internships. Off campus study at National Student Exchange. Study abroad program. ROTC: Army.

Entrance Requirements: Options: electronic application, early admission, early action, deferred admission, international baccalaureate accepted. Required: high school transcript, minimum 2.75 high school GPA, SAT or ACT. Required for some: essay, 2 recommendations, SAT and SAT Subject Tests or ACT. Entrance: minimally difficult. Application deadlines: 9/1, 2/1 for early action. Notification: continuous, rolling for early action. SAT Subject Test deadline: 9/1. Transfer credits accepted: Yes.

Collegiate Environment: Orientation program. Drama-theater group, choral group, student-run newspaper, radio station. Most popular organizations: Outdoor Program, Pre-Professional Health Club, Student Government, International Student Association, Chemistry Club. Major annual events: Homecoming, Spring Symposium, Fall Honors Convocation. Student services: health clinic, personal-psychological counseling, women's center. Campus security: 24-hour emergency response devices, late night transport-escort service, controlled dormitory access. Freshmen given priority for college housing. On-campus residence required in freshman year. Option: coed housing available. Pierce Library. Books: 356,951 (physical), 66,379 (digital/electronic); Serial titles: 392 (physical), 145 (digital/electronic); Databases: 139. Weekly public service hours: 90; students can reserve study rooms. Operations spending for the previous fiscal year: $1.9 million.

■ GEORGE FOX UNIVERSITY

414 N Meridian
Newberg, OR 97132-2697
Tel: (503)538-8383; Free: 800-765-4369
Fax: (503)554-3830
E-mail: admissions@georgefox.edu
Web Site: www.georgefox.edu

Description: Independent Friends, university, coed. Awards bachelor's, master's, and doctoral degrees and post-master's certificates. Founded 1891. Setting: 108-acre small town campus with easy access to Portland. Total enrollment: 3,899. Faculty: 604 (195 full-time, 409 part-time). Student-undergrad faculty ratio is 14:1. 2,980 applied, 78% were admitted. 25% from top 10% of their high school class, 55% from top quarter, 83% from top half. Full-time: 2,348 students, 55% women, 45% men. Part-time: 221 students, 61% women, 39% men. 49% from out-of-state. 0.6% American Indian or Alaska Native, non-Hispanic/Latino; 11% Hispanic/Latino; 2% Black or African American, non-Hispanic/Latino; 4% Asian, non-Hispanic/Latino; 0.4% Native Hawaiian or other Pacific Islander, non-Hispanic/Latino; 4% international. 3% 25 or older, 55% live on campus, 1% transferred in. Retention: 80% of full-time freshmen returned the following year. Academic areas with the most degrees conferred: business/marketing; visual and performing arts; health professions and related sciences. Core. Calendar: semesters. Academic remediation for entering students, ESL program, services for LD students, advanced placement, accelerated degree program, self-designed majors, honors program, independent study, distance learning, double major, summer session for credit, part-time degree program, adult/continuing education programs, internships, graduate courses open to undergrads. Off campus study at Domestic: Oregon Extension, American Studies Program, Contemporary Music Center, Mission Year, National Theater Inst; International: Australia, Brazil, Chile, Costa Rica, Czech Republic, Ecuador, England (London), England (Oxford), France, France (Veritas), Germany, Italy (Ovietro), Italy (Rome), Kenya, Lithuania, Jordan, Oxford Summer Programme (England), Peru, Romania, Russia, Rwanda, Spain, Senegal, South African (Cornerstone), South Africa (Veritas), South Korea, Spain (Spanish majors), Spain (Veritas), Thailand, Uganda. Study abroad program. ROTC: Air Force (c).

Entrance Requirements: Options: electronic application, early action, deferred admission, international baccalaureate accepted. Required: essay, 1 recommendation, SAT or ACT. Recommended: high school transcript. Required for some: high school transcript. Entrance: moderately difficult. Application deadlines: rolling, 11/15 for early action. Notification: continuous until 10/1, 12/15 for early action. SAT Reasoning Test deadline: 8/31. Transfer credits accepted: Yes.

Costs Per Year: Application fee: $40. Comprehensive fee: $47,120 includes full-time tuition ($35,500), mandatory fees ($370), and college room and board ($11,250). Full-time tuition and fees vary according to reciprocity agreements. Room and board charges vary according to board plan.

Collegiate Environment: Orientation program. Drama-theater group, choral group, student-run newspaper, radio station. Social organizations: 35 open to all. Most popular organizations: Student Government, Christian Ministries, Orientation Committee, Outdoor Club and Bruin Ambassadors, Blue Zone. Major annual events: Serve Day, Juniors Abroad, Homecoming. Student services: health clinic, personal-psychological counseling. Campus security: 24-hour emergency response devices and patrols, student patrols, late night transport-escort service, controlled dormitory access, parking lot cameras, video surveillance of key buildings. Murdock Learning Resource Center plus 1 other. Books: 463,450 (physical); Serial titles: 101,027 (digital/electronic); Databases: 209. Weekly public service hours: 93; study areas open 24 hours, 5-7 days a week; students can reserve study rooms.

Community Environment: Located 24 miles southwest of Portland, Newberg has a number of churches, a community hospital, and various civic and service organizations. Commercial transportation is easily accessible. Part-time employment is available.

■ GUTENBERG COLLEGE

1883 University St.
Eugene, OR 97403
Tel: (541)683-5141

Fax: (541)683-6997

E-mail: egrasso@gutenberg.edu

Web Site: www.gutenberg.edu

Description: Independent Christian, 4-year, coed. Awards bachelor's degrees. Setting: urban campus. Total enrollment: 13. Faculty: 8 (4 full-time, 4 part-time). Student-undergrad faculty ratio is 2:1. Full-time: 13 students, 69% women, 31% men. 88% live on campus. Retention: 75% of full-time freshmen returned the following year. Academic area with the most degrees conferred: liberal arts/general studies. Core.

Entrance Requirements: Options: electronic application, early decision. Required: essay, high school transcript, 2 recommendations, interview, SAT or ACT, CLT. Entrance: moderately difficult. Application deadlines: 3/1, 1/1 for early decision.

Costs Per Year: Application fee: $40. Comprehensive fee: $18,500 includes full-time tuition ($13,000), mandatory fees ($500), and college room and board ($5000). Room and board charges vary according to housing facility.

Collegiate Environment: Orientation program. Major annual events: Junior Tea, President's Dinner, Student Art Show. Student services: legal services, personal-psychological counseling. 2 computers available on campus for general student use. A campuswide network can be accessed.

■ **KLAMATH COMMUNITY COLLEGE**

7390 S 6th St.

Klamath Falls, OR 97603

Tel: (541)882-3521

E-mail: garlock@klamathcc.edu

Web Site: www.klamathcc.edu

Description: State-supported, 2-year, coed. Awards certificates, transfer associate, and terminal associate degrees. Founded 1996. Setting: 58-acre small town campus. Endowment: $129,870. Educational spending for the previous fiscal year: $3310 per student. Total enrollment: 1,148. Faculty: 129 (28 full-time, 101 part-time). Student-undergrad faculty ratio is 14:1. Full-time: 385 students, 60% women, 40% men. Part-time: 763 students, 59% women, 41% men. Students come from 2 states and territories, 0.1% from out-of-state. 6% American Indian or Alaska Native, non-Hispanic/Latino; 13% Hispanic/Latino; 1% Black or African American, non-Hispanic/Latino; 0.6% Asian, non-Hispanic/Latino; 0.2% Native Hawaiian or other Pacific Islander, non-Hispanic/Latino. 52% 25 or older, 14% transferred in. Retention: 58% of full-time freshmen returned the following year. Core. Calendar: quarters. Academic remediation for entering students, ESL program, services for LD students, advanced placement, self-designed majors, independent study, distance learning, double major, summer session for credit, co-op programs and internships.

Entrance Requirements: Open admission. Option: electronic application. Required: high school transcript. Entrance: noncompetitive. Application deadline: rolling. Notification: continuous. Transfer credits accepted: Yes.

Collegiate Environment: Orientation program. Social organizations: 12 open to all; 10% of eligible men and 15% of eligible women are members. Most popular organizations: Phi Beta Lambda, Hispanic Club, Future Farmers of America, Veterans Club, Business Club. Major annual events: Welcome Back Barbecue, Luau, Halloween Bash. Student services: personal-psychological counseling. Campus security: 24-hour emergency response devices. Learning Resource Center. Operations spending for the previous fiscal year: $317,891.

■ **LANE COMMUNITY COLLEGE**

4000 E 30th Ave.

Eugene, OR 97405-0640

Tel: (541)747-4501

Fax: (541)744-3995

Web Site: www.lanecc.edu

Description: State and locally supported, 2-year, coed. Awards certificates, transfer associate, and terminal associate degrees. Founded 1964. Setting: 240-acre suburban campus. Total enrollment: 11,002. Full-time: 4,996 students, 47% women, 53% men. Part-time: 6,006 students, 54% women, 46% men. 2% American Indian or Alaska Native, non-Hispanic/Latino; 9% Hispanic/Latino; 2% Black or African American, non-Hispanic/Latino; 1% Asian, non-Hispanic/Latino; 0.6% Native Hawaiian or other Pacific Islander, non-Hispanic/Latino; 0.7% international. 46% 25 or older. Core. Calendar: quarters. Academic remediation for entering students, ESL program, services for LD students, advanced placement, summer session for credit, part-time degree program, adult/continuing education programs, internships.

Entrance Requirements: Open admission. Option: early admission.

Entrance: noncompetitive. Application deadline: rolling. Notification: continuous. Preference given to district residents.

Collegiate Environment: Orientation program. Drama-theater group, choral group, student-run newspaper, radio station. Student services: legal services, health clinic, personal-psychological counseling, women's center. Campus security: 24-hour emergency response devices and patrols, student patrols, late night transport-escort service. Lane Community College Library plus 1 other.

Community Environment: See University of Oregon.

■ **LEWIS & CLARK COLLEGE**

0615 SW Palatine Hill Rd.

Portland, OR 97219-7899

Tel: (503)768-7000; Free: 800-444-4111

Fax: (503)768-7055

Web Site: www.lclark.edu

Description: Independent, comprehensive, coed. Awards bachelor's, master's, and doctoral degrees and post-master's certificates. Founded 1867. Setting: 137-acre urban campus with easy access to Portland. Endowment: $236.6 million. Research spending for the previous fiscal year: $3.4 million. Educational spending for the previous fiscal year: $24,892 per student. Total enrollment: 3,396. Faculty: 480 (213 full-time, 267 part-time). Student-undergrad faculty ratio is 11:1. 6,139 applied, 74% were admitted. Full-time: 2,058 students, 61% women, 39% men. Part-time: 29 students, 48% women, 52% men. Students come from 50 states and territories, 55 other countries, 80% from out-of-state. 0.5% American Indian or Alaska Native, non-Hispanic/Latino; 12% Hispanic/Latino; 3% Black or African American, non-Hispanic/Latino; 5% Asian, non-Hispanic/Latino; 0.5% Native Hawaiian or other Pacific Islander, non-Hispanic/Latino; 8% international. 1% 25 or older, 69% live on campus, 2% transferred in. Retention: 82% of full-time freshmen returned the following year. Academic areas with the most degrees conferred: social sciences; biological/life sciences; psychology. Core. Calendar: semesters. ESL program, services for LD students, advanced placement, self-designed majors, honors program, independent study, double major, summer session for credit, internships, graduate courses open to undergrads. Off campus study at Oregon Alliance of Independent Colleges and Universities (OAICU). Study abroad program. ROTC: Army (c).

Entrance Requirements: Options: electronic application, early decision, early action, deferred admission, international baccalaureate accepted. Required: essay, high school transcript, 1 recommendation, SAT or ACT scores or Test-Optional Portfolio Path materials. Recommended: interview. Required for some: 2 recommendations, graded writing sample, math or science sample, 2 letters of recommendation for Test Optional Portfolio Path. Entrance: very difficult. Application deadlines: 1/15, 11/1 for early decision, 12/15 for early action. Notification: 4/1, 12/15 for early decision, 1/1 for early action. SAT Reasoning Test deadline: 1/15. Transfer credits accepted: Yes. Applicants placed on waiting list: 390. Wait-listed applicants offered admission: 7. Early decision applicants: 53. Early decision applicants admitted: 39. Early action applicants: 2,285. Early action applicants admitted: 1,931.

Costs Per Year: Application fee: $0. Comprehensive fee: $63,528 includes full-time tuition ($50,574), mandatory fees ($360), and college room and board ($12,594). College room only: $7064. Room and board charges vary according to board plan and housing facility. Part-time tuition: $2529 per credit hour. Part-time mandatory fees: $18 per credit hour. Part-time tuition and fees vary according to course load.

Collegiate Environment: Orientation program. Drama-theater group, choral group, student-run newspaper, radio station. Social organizations: 121 open to all. Most popular organizations: Bacchus MenÆs Ultimate Frisbee, Artemis WomenÆs Ultimate Frisbee, International Affairs Symposium, Hillel, Black Student Union. Major annual events: Pio Fair (student activities fair), Spring Carnival, Fall Ball. Student services: health clinic, personal-psychological counseling. Campus security: 24-hour emergency response devices and patrols, late night transport-escort service, controlled dormitory access. 1,417 college housing spaces available; 1,243 were occupied in 2018-19. Freshmen guaranteed college housing. On-campus residence required through sophomore year. Options: coed, women-only housing available. Aubrey Watzek Library plus 1 other. Books: 336,148 (physical), 313,729 (digital/electronic); Serial titles: 4,973 (physical), 56,436 (digital/electronic); Databases: 304. Weekly public service hours: 141; study areas open 24 hours, 5-7 days a week; students can reserve study rooms. Operations spending for the previous fiscal year: $5.5 million. 440 computers available on campus for general student use. A campuswide network can be accessed from student residence rooms and from off campus. Students can

access the following: online class registration. Staffed computer lab on campus provides training in use of computers, software, and the Internet.
Community Environment: See Portland State University.

■ LINFIELD COLLEGE

900 SE Baker St.
McMinnville, OR 97128-6894
Tel: (503)883-2200; Free: 800-640-2287
Fax: (503)883-2472
E-mail: admission@linfield.edu
Web Site: www.linfield.edu

Description: Independent American Baptist Churches in the USA, 4-year, coed. Part of Linfield College. Administratively affiliated with Linfield College-McMinnville Campus. Awards bachelor's degrees (Linfield College includes the Linfield College McMinnville Campus in McMinnville, Oregon; the Linfield-Good Samaritan School of Nursing in Portland, Oregon(Portland Campus) and the Linfield College Adult Degree Program online). Founded 1858. Setting: 189-acre small town campus with easy access to Portland. System endowment: $124.5 million. Total enrollment: 1,376. Faculty: 203 (123 full-time, 80 part-time). Student-undergrad faculty ratio is 10:1. 2,199 applied, 81% were admitted. Full-time: 1,334 students, 61% women, 39% men. Part-time: 42 students, 60% women, 40% men. Students come from 18 states and territories, 23 other countries, 42% from out-of-state. 0.9% American Indian or Alaska Native, non-Hispanic/Latino; 17% Hispanic/Latino; 2% Black or African American, non-Hispanic/Latino; 4% Asian, non-Hispanic/Latino; 1% Native Hawaiian or other Pacific Islander, non-Hispanic/Latino; 4% international. 2% 25 or older, 73% live on campus, 4% transferred in. Retention: 79% of full-time freshmen returned the following year. Academic areas with the most degrees conferred: business/marketing; social sciences; biological/life sciences. Core. Calendar: 4-1-4. ESL program, services for LD students, advanced placement, accelerated degree program, self-designed majors, independent study, distance learning, double major, summer session for credit, part-time degree program, external degree program, adult/continuing education programs, internships. Off campus study at American Baptist Colleges and Universities, Oregon Alliance of Independent Colleges & Universities. Study abroad program. ROTC: Air Force (c).

Entrance Requirements: Options: electronic application, early action, deferred admission, international baccalaureate accepted. Required: essay, high school transcript, 1 recommendation. Recommended: interview. Required for some: SAT or ACT. Entrance: moderately difficult. Application deadlines: 2/1, 11/1 for early action. Notification: continuous until 4/1, 1/15 for early action. SAT Reasoning Test deadline: 2/1. Transfer credits accepted: Yes. Early action applicants: 794. Early action applicants admitted: 780.

Costs Per Year: Application fee: $0. Comprehensive fee: $56,732 includes full-time tuition ($43,560), mandatory fees ($502), and college room and board ($12,670). College room only: $6970. Part-time tuition: $1360 per semester hour. Part-time mandatory fees: $280 per year.

Collegiate Environment: Orientation program. Drama-theater group, choral group, marching band, student-run newspaper, radio station. Social organizations: 40 open to all; national fraternities, national sororities, local fraternities, local sororities; 28% of eligible men and 27% of eligible women are members. Most popular organizations: Hawaiian Club, Linfield Ultimate Players Association, Residence Hall Associations, International Club, Outdoor Club. Major annual events: Luau, Wildstock, LipSync (Greek Week). Student services: health clinic, personal-psychological counseling. Campus security: 24-hour emergency response devices and patrols, late night transport-escort service, controlled dormitory access. 1,137 college housing spaces available; 1,004 were occupied in 2018-19. Freshmen guaranteed college housing. On-campus residence required through junior year. Options: coed, men-only, women-only housing available. Jereld R. Nicholson Library. Books: 192,329 (physical), 6,637 (digital/electronic); Serial titles: 1,785 (physical), 56,310 (digital/electronic); Databases: 192. Weekly public service hours: 95. 250 computers available on campus for general student use. Computer purchase/lease plans available. A campuswide network can be accessed from student residence rooms and from off campus. Students can access the following: online class registration. Staffed computer lab on campus provides training in use of computers, software, and the Internet.

Community Environment: Nestled in the heart of the Willamette Valley, McMinnville is a classic college town where students are quickly welcomed into the community. Downtown McMinnville boasts a charming historic shopping district, which includes art galleries, antique shops, coffeehouses, and nationally renowned restaurants like Nick's Italian Cafe, as well as a variety of job opportunities. Linfield students have many chances to get acquainted with their McMinnville neighbors while going to the Cinema 8 Multiplex or the Moonlight Theater and Pizzeria, attending community theatre productions or becoming members of one of the town's 28 churches.

■ LINN-BENTON COMMUNITY COLLEGE

6500 SW Pacific Blvd.
Albany, OR 97321
Tel: (541)917-4999
Fax: (541)917-4838
E-mail: admissions@linnbenton.edu
Web Site: www.linnbenton.edu

Description: State and locally supported, 2-year, coed. Awards certificates, transfer associate, and terminal associate degrees. Founded 1966. Setting: 104-acre small town campus. Research spending for the previous fiscal year: $188,901. Educational spending for the previous fiscal year: $4771 per student. Total enrollment: 5,617. 3,282 applied, 99% were admitted. Full-time: 2,604 students, 47% women, 53% men. Part-time: 3,013 students, 56% women, 44% men. 3% from out-of-state. 2% American Indian or Alaska Native, non-Hispanic/Latino; 8% Hispanic/Latino; 1% Black or African American, non-Hispanic/Latino; 2% Asian, non-Hispanic/Latino; 0.5% Native Hawaiian or other Pacific Islander, non-Hispanic/Latino; 2% international. 37% 25 or older, 10% transferred in. Retention: 55% of full-time freshmen returned the following year. Core. Calendar: quarters. Academic remediation for entering students, ESL program, services for LD students, advanced placement, self-designed majors, independent study, distance learning, summer session for credit, part-time degree program, co-op programs and internships. Study abroad program. ROTC: Army (c), Naval (c), Air Force (c).

Entrance Requirements: Open admission. Options: electronic application, deferred admission. Entrance: noncompetitive. Application deadline: rolling.

Collegiate Environment: Drama-theater group, choral group, student-run newspaper. Social organizations: 18 open to all. Most popular organizations: EBOP Club, Multicultural Club, Campus Family Co-op, Horticulture Club, Collegiate Secretary Club. Major annual events: Martin Luther King Celebration, Spring Daze, Children's Winter Festival. Student services: personal-psychological counseling. Campus security: 24-hour emergency response devices and patrols, student patrols, late night transport-escort service. Linn-Benton Community College Library. Operations spending for the previous fiscal year: $576,996. 500 computers available on campus for general student use. A campuswide network can be accessed from off-campus. Students can access the following: online class registration. Staffed computer lab on campus.

Community Environment: Noted for its rare metals industries, Albany is also in the fertile Willamette Valley, a rich timber area; the valley is one of the leading producers of rye grass seed and mint. The rare metals industries produce tantalum, tungsten, zirconium, hafnium, columbium, and molybdenum. Other manufactured products are plywood lumber, furniture, and mill machinery. The average rainfall is 39.7 inches. Community facilities include a number of churches, a YMCA, Boys Club, a hospital, and many clinics, excellent shopping areas, and a number of civic and service organizations. Part-time jobs are available. Recreational activities are swimming, tennis, and other sports. The World's Champion Timber Carnival in July draws loggers from all over to compete in log rolling, tree topping, axe throwing, and other events.

■ MOUNT ANGEL SEMINARY

Saint Benedict, OR 97373
Tel: (503)845-3951
Web Site: www.mountangelabbey.org/seminary

Description: Independent Roman Catholic, comprehensive. Awards bachelor's, master's, and doctoral degrees (only candidates for the priesthood are admitted). Founded 1887. Setting: 75-acre rural campus with easy access to Portland. Total enrollment: 181. 73 applied, 100% were admitted. 51% 25 or older. Core. Calendar: semesters. Academic remediation for entering students, ESL program, advanced placement, part-time degree program, adult/continuing education programs, graduate courses open to undergrads. Off campus study at Oregon Independent Colleges Association.

Entrance Requirements: Required: essay, high school transcript, minimum 2.0 high school GPA, 2 recommendations. Recommended: interview, SAT. Entrance: moderately difficult. Application deadline: 7/15. Notification: continuous. Preference given to Catholic seminarians.

Collegiate Environment: Orientation program. Choral group. Student services: health clinic, personal-psychological counseling. Campus security: 24-hour emergency response devices, patrols by police officers. Mount Angel Abbey Library.

■ MT. HOOD COMMUNITY COLLEGE
26000 SE Stark St.
Gresham, OR 97030-3300
Tel: (503)491-6422
Fax: (503)491-7388
Web Site: www.mhcc.edu

Description: State and locally supported, 2-year, coed. Awards certificates, diplomas, transfer associate, and terminal associate degrees. Founded 1966. Setting: 212-acre suburban campus with easy access to Portland. Research spending for the previous fiscal year: $75,611. Total enrollment: 8,771. Faculty: 638 (173 full-time, 465 part-time). Student-undergrad faculty ratio is 25:1. Full-time: 3,178 students, 53% women, 47% men. Part-time: 5,593 students, 57% women, 43% men. Students come from 16 states and territories, 6 other countries. 56% 25 or older. Core. Calendar: quarters. Academic remediation for entering students, ESL program, services for LD students, advanced placement, summer session for credit, part-time degree program, adult/continuing education programs, co-op programs and internships. Study abroad program.

Entrance Requirements: Open admission except for allied health, some professional-technical programs. Options: early admission, deferred admission. Required for some: high school transcript, minimum 2.0 high school GPA. Entrance: noncompetitive. Application deadline: rolling. Notification: continuous. Preference given to state residents.

Collegiate Environment: Drama-theater group, choral group, student-run newspaper, radio station. Student services: health clinic, personal-psychological counseling, women's center. Campus security: 24-hour emergency response devices and patrols, student patrols, late night transport-escort service. Library Resource Center. 100 computers available on campus for general student use. Staffed computer lab on campus.

■ MULTNOMAH UNIVERSITY
8435 NE Glisan St.
Portland, OR 97220-5898
Tel: (503)255-0332; Free: 877-251-6560
Fax: (503)254-1268
E-mail: admiss@multnomah.edu
Web Site: www.multnomah.edu

Description: Independent interdenominational, comprehensive, coed. Awards bachelor's, master's, and doctoral degrees. Founded 1936. Setting: 22-acre urban campus with easy access to Portland, OR. Endowment: $6.9 million. Educational spending for the previous fiscal year: $5789 per student. Total enrollment: 714. Faculty: 100 (26 full-time, 74 part-time). Student-undergrad faculty ratio is 12:1. 198 applied, 70% were admitted. 25% from top 10% of their high school class, 34% from top quarter, 57% from top half. Full-time: 364 students, 49% women, 51% men. Part-time: 53 students, 42% women, 58% men. Students come from 18 states and territories, 57% from out-of-state. 0.7% American Indian or Alaska Native, non-Hispanic/Latino; 8% Hispanic/Latino; 3% Black or African American, non-Hispanic/Latino; 1% Asian, non-Hispanic/Latino; 1% Native Hawaiian or other Pacific Islander, non-Hispanic/Latino. 25% 25 or older, 48% live on campus, 14% transferred in. Retention: 63% of full-time freshmen returned the following year. Academic areas with the most degrees conferred: theology and religious vocations; psychology; business/marketing. Core. Calendar: semesters. Academic remediation for entering students, services for LD students, advanced placement, distance learning, double major, summer session for credit, part-time degree program, adult/continuing education programs, internships.

Entrance Requirements: Options: electronic application, deferred admission, international baccalaureate accepted. Required: essay, high school transcript, minimum 2.5 high school GPA, 2 recommendations. Recommended: SAT or ACT. Entrance: moderately difficult. Notification: continuous. SAT Reasoning Test deadline: 8/1. Transfer credits accepted: Yes.

Costs Per Year: Application fee: $40. Comprehensive fee: $34,770 includes full-time tuition ($25,300), mandatory fees ($600), and college room and board ($8870). Full-time tuition and fees vary according to course load, degree level, location, and program. Room and board charges vary according to board plan and housing facility. Part-time tuition: $800 per quarter hour. Part-time mandatory fees: $155 per term. Part-time tuition and fees vary according to course load, degree level, location, and program.

Collegiate Environment: Orientation program. Choral group. Social

organizations: 10 open to all. Most popular organizations: Student Government, Commuter Life, Poetry Club, Brunch Chats, Res Life. Major annual events: Christian Life Conference, Global Missions Conference, New Wine/New Wineskins Retreat. Student services: personal-psychological counseling. Campus security: 24-hour emergency response devices and patrols, controlled dormitory access. John Mitchell Library. Books: 120,106 (physical), 152,698 (digital/electronic); Serial titles: 548 (physical), 20,000 (digital/electronic); Databases: 45. Weekly public service hours: 82; students can reserve study rooms. Operations spending for the previous fiscal year: $360,479. 36 computers available on campus for general student use. A campuswide network can be accessed from student residence rooms and from off campus. Students can access the following: online class registration. Staffed computer lab on campus provides training in use of computers and software.

Community Environment: See Portland State University.

■ NEW HOPE CHRISTIAN COLLEGE
2155 Bailey Hill Rd.
Eugene, OR 97405
Tel: (541)485-1780; Free: 800-322-2638
Fax: (541)343-5801
E-mail: sarahslater@newhope.edu
Web Site: www.newhope.edu

Description: Independent, 4-year, coed, affiliated with Open Bible Standard Churches. Awards bachelor's degrees. Founded 1925. Setting: 40-acre suburban campus. Total enrollment: 143. Faculty: 25 (9 full-time, 16 part-time). Student-undergrad faculty ratio is 11:1. 165 applied, 22% were admitted. Full-time: 134 students, 39% women, 61% men. Part-time: 9 students, 44% women, 56% men. 3% Hispanic/Latino; 3% Black or African American, non-Hispanic/Latino; 1% Asian, non-Hispanic/Latino; 0.7% Native Hawaiian or other Pacific Islander, non-Hispanic/Latino; 1% international. 24% 25 or older, 20% transferred in. Retention: 60% of full-time freshmen returned the following year. Calendar: semesters. Part-time degree program.

Entrance Requirements: Options: electronic application, deferred admission. Required: essay, high school transcript, minimum 2 high school GPA, 2 recommendations. Entrance: minimally difficult. Application deadline: 8/1. Notification: continuous.

Collegiate Environment: Orientation program. Campus security: 24-hour emergency response devices, student patrols, controlled dormitory access. Flint Memorial Library.

Community Environment: See University of Oregon.

■ NORTHWEST CHRISTIAN UNIVERSITY
828 E 11th Ave.
Eugene, OR 97401-3745
Tel: (541)343-1641; Free: 877-463-6622
Fax: (541)684-7317
E-mail: kgerdrum@nwcu.edu
Web Site: www.nwcu.edu

Description: Independent Christian, comprehensive, coed. Awards associate, bachelor's, and master's degrees. Founded 1895. Setting: 8-acre urban campus with easy access to Portland. Endowment: $14.3 million. Educational spending for the previous fiscal year: $4227 per student. Total enrollment: 800. Faculty: 76 (26 full-time, 50 part-time). Student-undergrad faculty ratio is 15:1. 479 applied, 62% were admitted. 13% from top 10% of their high school class, 42% from top quarter, 76% from top half. Full-time: 418 students, 61% women, 39% men. Part-time: 175 students, 61% women, 39% men. Students come from 17 states and territories, 7 other countries, 21% from out-of-state. 2% American Indian or Alaska Native, non-Hispanic/Latino; 6% Hispanic/Latino; 5% Black or African American, non-Hispanic/Latino; 2% Asian, non-Hispanic/Latino; 1% Native Hawaiian or other Pacific Islander, non-Hispanic/Latino; 1% international. 34% 25 or older, 78% live on campus, 6% transferred in. Retention: 71% of full-time freshmen returned the following year. Academic areas with the most degrees conferred: business/marketing; health professions and related sciences; education. Core. Calendar: quarters. Academic remediation for entering students, ESL program, services for LD students, advanced placement, accelerated degree program, independent study, distance learning, double major, summer session for credit, part-time degree program, adult/continuing education programs, co-op programs and internships, graduate courses open to undergrads. Study abroad program. ROTC: Army (c).

Entrance Requirements: Options: electronic application, deferred admission, international baccalaureate accepted. Required: essay, minimum 2.5 high school GPA, SAT or ACT. Recommended: interview. Required for some:

high school transcript. Entrance: minimally difficult. Application deadline: rolling. Notification: continuous. SAT Reasoning Test deadline: 7/1. SAT Subject Test deadline: 7/1. Transfer credits accepted: Yes.

Costs Per Year: Application fee: $0. Comprehensive fee: $41,110 includes full-time tuition ($31,200), mandatory fees ($210), and college room and board ($9700).

Collegiate Environment: Orientation program. Choral group, student-run newspaper. Social organizations: 8 open to all. Most popular organizations: Embrace the City (community service), FeMystique (Social justice club), Beacon Boards (game board club), History Club, Psychology Club. Major annual events: Embrace the City (community service), Beacon Madness (athletic prep rally), Beacon Nights (Friday night events). Student services: personal-psychological counseling. Campus security: 24-hour emergency response devices and patrols, late night transport-escort service, controlled dormitory access. 226 college housing spaces available; 216 were occupied in 2018-19. Freshmen guaranteed college housing. On-campus residence required through senior year. Options: men-only, women-only housing available. Edward P. Kellenberger Library. Books: 53,806 (physical), 222,316 (digital/electronic); Serial titles: 285,351 (digital/electronic); Databases: 108. Weekly public service hours: 70. Operations spending for the previous fiscal year: $358,543. 16 computers available on campus for general student use. A campuswide network can be accessed from student residence rooms and from off campus. Students can access the following: online class registration.

Community Environment: See University of Oregon.

■ OREGON COAST COMMUNITY COLLEGE
400 SE College Way
Newport, OR 97366
Tel: (541)265-2283
E-mail: webinfo@occc.cc.or.us
Web Site: www.oregoncoastcc.org

Description: Public, 2-year, coed. Awards certificates, transfer associate, and terminal associate degrees. Founded 1987. Setting: 24-acre small town campus. Educational spending for the previous fiscal year: $7201 per student. Total enrollment: 416. Faculty: 67 (10 full-time, 57 part-time). Student-undergrad faculty ratio is 17:1. 75 applied, 100% were admitted. Full-time: 227 students, 67% women, 33% men. Part-time: 259 students, 63% women, 37% men. Students come from 4 states and territories, 1% from out-of-state. 2% American Indian or Alaska Native, non-Hispanic/Latino; 13% Hispanic/Latino; 0.2% Black or African American, non-Hispanic/Latino; 1% Asian, non-Hispanic/Latino; 0.7% Native Hawaiian or other Pacific Islander, non-Hispanic/Latino. 38% 25 or older, 6% transferred in. Retention: 65% of full-time freshmen returned the following year. Core. Calendar: quarters. Academic remediation for entering students, ESL program, services for LD students, honors program, distance learning, summer session for credit, part-time degree program, co-op programs and internships.

Entrance Requirements: Open admission. Options: electronic application, international baccalaureate accepted. Required for some: essay, 2 recommendations, interview. Entrance: noncompetitive. Transfer credits accepted: Yes.

Costs Per Year: Application fee: $0. State resident tuition: $3780 full-time, $105 per credit part-time. Nonresident tuition: $7704 full-time, $214 per credit part-time. Mandatory fees: $576 full-time, $16 per credit part-time. Full-time tuition and fees vary according to course load and program. Part-time tuition and fees vary according to course load and program.

Collegiate Environment: Orientation program. Most popular organizations: Psych Club, Triangle Club, Writing Club, ASG. Major annual events: Fall Welcome, Oregon transfer day. Campus security: 24-hour emergency response devices. Oregon Coast Community College Library. Books: 13,033 (physical), 110,699 (digital/electronic); Serial titles: 2,771 (physical); Databases: 53. Students can reserve study rooms. Operations spending for the previous fiscal year: $182,316. 40 computers available on campus for general student use. A campuswide network can be accessed. Staffed computer lab on campus provides training in use of computers, software, and the Internet.

■ OREGON HEALTH & SCIENCE UNIVERSITY
3181 SW Sam Jackson Park Rd.
Portland, OR 97239-3098
Tel: (503)494-8311
Fax: (503)494-5738
Web Site: www.ohsu.edu

Description: State-related, upper-level, coed. Awards bachelor's, master's,

and doctoral degrees and post-master's certificates. Founded 1974. Setting: 120-acre urban campus. Total enrollment: 2,895. Faculty: 110 (94 full-time, 16 part-time). Full-time: 206 students, 86% women, 14% men. Part-time: 621 students, 84% women, 16% men. 0.2% American Indian or Alaska Native, non-Hispanic/Latino; 9% Hispanic/Latino; 0.5% Black or African American, non-Hispanic/Latino; 5% Asian, non-Hispanic/Latino; 0.8% international. Academic area with the most degrees conferred: health professions and related sciences. Core. Calendar: quarters. Advanced placement, accelerated degree program, distance learning, summer session for credit, part-time degree program, graduate courses open to undergrads. Off campus study at Oregon Consortium of Nursing Education.

Entrance Requirements: Transfer credits accepted: Yes.

Costs Per Year: Application fee: $120. State resident tuition: $13,932 full-time, $387 per credit hour part-time. Nonresident tuition: $25,524 full-time, $709 per credit hour part-time. Mandatory fees: $6,433 full-time, $1,896.41 per term part-time. Full-time tuition and fees vary according to course load, degree level, location, program, and reciprocity agreements. Part-time tuition and fees vary according to course load, degree level, location, program, and reciprocity agreements. Tuition guaranteed not to increase for student's term of enrollment.

Collegiate Environment: Orientation program. Choral group, student-run newspaper. Social organizations: 60 open to all; local fraternities. Student services: health clinic, personal-psychological counseling. Campus security: 24-hour emergency response devices and patrols, late night transport-escort service. OHSU Main Library.

■ OREGON INSTITUTE OF TECHNOLOGY
3201 Campus Dr.
Klamath Falls, OR 97601-8801
Tel: (541)885-1000; Free: 800-422-2017
Fax: (541)885-1115
Web Site: www.oit.edu

Description: State-supported, comprehensive, coed. Awards associate, bachelor's, and master's degrees. Founded 1947. Setting: 190-acre small town campus. Endowment: $7.9 million. Research spending for the previous fiscal year: $2 million. Educational spending for the previous fiscal year: $8706 per student. Total enrollment: 5,490. Faculty: 305 (169 full-time, 136 part-time). Student-undergrad faculty ratio is 16:1. 1,314 applied, 61% were admitted. 25% from top 10% of their high school class, 57% from top quarter, 86% from top half. Full-time: 2,284 students, 43% women, 57% men. Part-time: 3,100 students, 54% women, 46% men. Students come from 44 states and territories, 19 other countries, 25% from out-of-state. 1% American Indian or Alaska Native, non-Hispanic/Latino; 11% Hispanic/Latino; 2% Black or African American, non-Hispanic/Latino; 7% Asian, non-Hispanic/Latino; 0.7% Native Hawaiian or other Pacific Islander, non-Hispanic/Latino; 2% international. 43% 25 or older, 15% live on campus, 11% transferred in. Retention: 80% of full-time freshmen returned the following year. Academic areas with the most degrees conferred: health professions and related sciences; engineering; engineering technologies. Core. Calendar: quarters. Academic remediation for entering students, services for LD students, advanced placement, self-designed majors, honors program, distance learning, double major, summer session for credit, part-time degree program, external degree program, co-op programs and internships, graduate courses open to undergrads. Off campus study at Portland State University. Study abroad program. ROTC: Army (c).

Entrance Requirements: Options: electronic application, deferred admission. Required: high school transcript, minimum 3 high school GPA, SAT or ACT. Entrance: moderately difficult. Application deadline: 9/3. Notification: continuous. SAT Reasoning Test deadline: 9/3. SAT Subject Test deadline: 9/3. Transfer credits accepted: Yes.

Costs Per Year: Application fee: $50. State resident tuition: $8277 full-time, $184 per credit hour part-time. Nonresident tuition: $26,345 full-time, $585 per credit hour part-time. Mandatory fees: $1710 full-time, $208 per credit hour part-time, $558 per term part-time. Full-time tuition and fees vary according to course load, location, program, and reciprocity agreements. Part-time tuition and fees vary according to course load, location, program, and reciprocity agreements. College room and board: $9640. College room only: $5860. Room and board charges vary according to board plan and housing facility.

Collegiate Environment: Orientation program. Choral group, student-run newspaper, radio station. Social organizations: 68 open to all; national fraternities. Most popular organizations: Phi Delta Theta, Christian Fellowship, International Club, Society of Women Engineers, Association of Student Mechanical Engineers. Major annual events: Super Club Sign-Up,

Pink Out Athletic Games, Project Symposium. Student services: health clinic, personal-psychological counseling, women's center. Campus security: 24-hour emergency response devices and patrols, late night transport-escort service. Books: 140,000 (physical); Databases: 70. Students can reserve study rooms. Operations spending for the previous fiscal year: $1.9 million.

Community Environment: Klamath Falls is located nearly equidistant from Portland, OR, San Francisco, CA, and Reno, NV. Bus, train and air transportation is available. A local phenomenon is a stratum of hot water underlying certain sections of the city, which is used to heat homes and offices. Numerous lakes are in Klamath County, including Crater Lake National Park. Outdoor recreation of all sorts is readily available and enjoyed year-round.

■ OREGON STATE UNIVERSITY

Corvallis, OR 97331

Tel: (541)737-1000; Free: 800-291-4192

Fax: (541)737-6157

Web Site: www.oregonstate.edu

Description: State-supported, university, coed. Awards bachelor's, master's, and doctoral degrees and post-master's certificates. Founded 1868. Setting: 422-acre small town campus. Endowment: $624.5 million. Research spending for the previous fiscal year: $215.9 million. Educational spending for the previous fiscal year: $10,973 per student. Total enrollment: 30,896. Faculty: 1,697 (1,184 full-time, 513 part-time). Student-undergrad faculty ratio is 18:1. 14,595 applied, 77% were admitted. 26% from top 10% of their high school class, 58% from top quarter, 91% from top half. 16 National Merit Scholars. Full-time: 18,829 students, 46% women, 54% men. Part-time: 7,009 students, 47% women, 53% men. Students come from 58 states and territories, 81 other countries, 32% from out-of-state. 0.5% American Indian or Alaska Native, non-Hispanic/Latino; 10% Hispanic/Latino; 1% Black or African American, non-Hispanic/Latino; 8% Asian, non-Hispanic/Latino; 0.3% Native Hawaiian or other Pacific Islander, non-Hispanic/Latino; 7% international. 22% 25 or older, 17% live on campus, 8% transferred in. Retention: 85% of full-time freshmen returned the following year. Academic areas with the most degrees conferred: engineering; business/marketing; computer and information sciences. Core. Calendar: quarters. Academic remediation for entering students, ESL program, services for LD students, advanced placement, accelerated degree program, self-designed majors, freshman honors college, honors program, independent study, distance learning, double major, summer session for credit, part-time degree program, co-op programs and internships, graduate courses open to undergrads. Off campus study. Study abroad program. ROTC: Army, Naval, Air Force.

Entrance Requirements: Options: electronic application, early action, deferred admission, international baccalaureate accepted. Required: essay, high school transcript, minimum 3 high school GPA, SAT or ACT. Required for some: SAT Subject Tests. Entrance: moderately difficult. Application deadlines: 2/1, 11/1 for early action. Notification: continuous, 12/20 for early action. SAT Reasoning Test deadline: 9/1. Transfer credits accepted: Yes.

Costs Per Year: Application fee: $60. One-time mandatory fee: $350. State resident tuition: $9390 full-time, $202 per credit hour part-time. Nonresident tuition: $28,365 full-time, $608 per credit hour part-time. Mandatory fees: $1776 full-time, $514.97 per term part-time. Full-time tuition and fees vary according to course load, location, and program. Part-time tuition and fees vary according to course load, location, and program. College room and board: $12,855. College room only: $8895. Room and board charges vary according to board plan and housing facility.

Collegiate Environment: Orientation program. Drama-theater group, choral group, marching band, student-run newspaper, radio station. Social organizations: 400 open to all; national fraternities, national sororities; 10% of eligible men and 16% of eligible women are members. Most popular organizations: Ballroom Dance Club, Gaming Club, Organic Growers Club, Blood Drive Association, Residence Hall Association. Major annual events: Civil War Football Game, Homecoming, Parent's Weekends. Student services: legal services, health clinic, personal-psychological counseling, women's center. Campus security: 24-hour emergency response devices and patrols, student patrols, late night transport-escort service, controlled dormitory access, crime prevention office. Valley Library plus 2 others. Books: 1.7 million (physical), 481,665 (digital/electronic); Serial titles: 2,376 (physical), 74,203 (digital/electronic); Databases: 150. Weekly public service hours: 138; study areas open 24 hours, 5-7 days a week; students can reserve study rooms. Operations spending for the previous fiscal year: $15 million. 2,179 computers available on campus for general student use. Computer purchase/lease plans available. A campuswide network can be accessed from student residence rooms and from off campus. Students can access the following: online class registration. Staffed computer lab on campus (open 24 hours a day) provides training in use of computers, software, and the Internet.

Community Environment: Corvallis is situated in the Willamette Valley which is noted for crops and dairy goods. Air, rail and bus transportation is available. The community includes churches of major denominations, a hospital, library, shopping areas, and civic, fraternal, and veteran's organizations. The Willamette River is nearby for fishing and boating, and the Pacific Coast is a 50-mile drive. Part-time employment opportunities are fair.

■ OREGON STATE UNIVERSITY-CASCADES

2600 NW College Way

Bend, OR 97701

Tel: (541)322-3100

E-mail: cascadeadmit@osucascades.edu

Web Site: www.osucascades.edu

Description: State-supported, comprehensive, coed. Part of Oregon University System. Awards bachelor's and master's degrees. Founded 2001. Setting: 193-acre small town campus. Total enrollment: 611. Student-undergrad faculty ratio is 15:1. Students come from 15 states and territories, 1 other country, 5% from out-of-state. 44% 25 or older. Calendar: quarters. Services for LD students, advanced placement, double major, summer session for credit, internships. Study abroad program.

Entrance Requirements: Option: international baccalaureate accepted. Application deadline: rolling. Notification: continuous.

Collegiate Environment: Orientation program. Student-run newspaper. Student services: personal-psychological counseling, women's center.

■ PACIFIC BIBLE COLLEGE

28 S Fir St.

Medford, OR 97501

Description: Independent religious, 2-year, coed.

■ PACIFIC NORTHWEST COLLEGE OF ART

511 NW Broadway

Portland, OR 97209

Tel: (503)226-4391

Fax: (503)226-3587

Web Site: www.pnca.edu

Description: Independent, comprehensive, coed. Awards bachelor's and master's degrees. Founded 1909. Setting: 2-acre urban campus with easy access to Portland. Endowment: $12.9 million. Educational spending for the previous fiscal year: $17,682 per student. Total enrollment: 488. Faculty: 98 (26 full-time, 72 part-time). Student-undergrad faculty ratio is 9:1. 312 applied, 95% were admitted. Full-time: 363 students, 69% women, 31% men. Part-time: 42 students, 64% women, 36% men. Students come from 41 states and territories, 4 other countries, 54% from out-of-state. 1% American Indian or Alaska Native, non-Hispanic/Latino; 5% Hispanic/Latino; 2% Black or African American, non-Hispanic/Latino; 4% Asian, non-Hispanic/Latino; 0.5% Native Hawaiian or other Pacific Islander, non-Hispanic/Latino; 2% international. 22% 25 or older, 25% live on campus, 11% transferred in. Retention: 61% of full-time freshmen returned the following year. Academic area with the most degrees conferred: visual and performing arts. Core. Calendar: semesters. Services for LD students, advanced placement, self-designed majors, independent study, summer session for credit, part-time degree program, co-op programs and internships. Off campus study at Reed College, Oregon Independent Colleges Association, Association of Independent Colleges of Art and Design. Study abroad program.

Entrance Requirements: Options: electronic application, early admission, deferred admission. Required: essay, portfolio of artwork. Recommended: minimum 2.3 high school GPA. Required for some: high school transcript. Entrance: noncompetitive. Application deadline: rolling. Notification: continuous. Transfer credits accepted: Yes. Applicants placed on waiting list: 0. Wait-listed applicants offered admission: 0.

Costs Per Year: Application fee: $45. Tuition: $37,500 full-time, $1563 per credit hour part-time. Mandatory fees: $750 full-time, $75 per term part-time. Full-time tuition and fees vary according to degree level. Part-time tuition and fees vary according to course load and degree level. College room only: $9486.

Collegiate Environment: Orientation program. Social organizations: 15 open to all. Major annual events: Time-Based Arts Festival, Focus Week: Thesis Orals and Workshops, Commencement. Student services: personal-psychological counseling. Campus security: 24-hour emergency response devices, late night transport-escort service, controlled dormitory access, entrance security guards and patrols during hours of operation. Albert Solheim Library. Books: 34,806 (physical); Serial titles: 270 (physical); Databases: 52. Weekly public service hours: 87; students can reserve study rooms. Operations spending for the previous fiscal year: $313,364. 300 computers available on campus for general student use. A campuswide network can be accessed from student residence rooms and from off campus. Students can access the following: online class registration. Staffed computer lab on campus provides training in use of computers, software, and the Internet.

Community Environment: See Portland State University.

■ PACIFIC UNIVERSITY

2043 College Way
Forest Grove, OR 97116-1797
Tel: (503)357-6151; Free: 877-722-8648
Fax: (503)352-3191
E-mail: admissions@pacificu.edu
Web Site: www.pacificu.edu

Description: Independent, comprehensive, coed. Awards bachelor's, master's, and doctoral degrees and post-master's certificates. Founded 1849. Setting: 60-acre small town campus with easy access to Portland. Total enrollment: 3,810. 3,004 applied, 79% were admitted. Full-time: 1,881 students, 60% women, 40% men. Part-time: 43 students, 53% women, 47% men. 55% from out-of-state. 0.6% American Indian or Alaska Native, non-Hispanic/Latino; 13% Hispanic/Latino; 2% Black or African American, non-Hispanic/Latino; 12% Asian, non-Hispanic/Latino; 3% Native Hawaiian or other Pacific Islander, non-Hispanic/Latino; 2% international. 8% 25 or older, 59% live on campus, 6% transferred in. Retention: 77% of full-time freshmen returned the following year. Academic areas with the most degrees conferred: health professions and related sciences; psychology; education. Calendar: semesters. ROTC: Army (c), Air Force (c).

Entrance Requirements: Options: electronic application, deferred admission, international baccalaureate accepted. Required: essay, high school transcript, minimum 3 high school GPA, 1 recommendation, SAT or ACT. Recommended: interview. Entrance: moderately difficult.

Costs Per Year: Application fee: $40. Comprehensive fee: $56,826 includes full-time tuition ($43,288), mandatory fees ($1010), and college room and board ($12,528). College room only: $6910. Room and board charges vary according to board plan and housing facility. Part-time tuition: $1800 per credit hour. Part-time mandatory fees: $505 per term. Part-time tuition and fees vary according to course load.

Collegiate Environment: Orientation program. Campus security: 24-hour emergency response devices and patrols, late night transport-escort service, controlled dormitory access. Pacific University Library.

Community Environment: Located 30 miles west of Portland, Forest Grove (population 19,600) is the home of Pacific University, the first school to be chartered in the Oregon Territory. Part-time employment is available. Community facilities include 15 churches, 2 libraries, a hospital, and various civic and service organizations. Bus transportation is available. The Pacific Coast beaches are an hour's drive and skiing on Mt. Hood is 90 minutes away.

■ PIONEER PACIFIC COLLEGE

27501 SW Pky. Ave.
Wilsonville, OR 97070
Tel: (503)682-3903; Free: 866-PPC-INFO
Fax: (503)682-1514
E-mail: info@pioneerpacific.edu
Web Site: www.pioneerpacific.edu

Description: Proprietary, 4-year, coed. Awards associate and bachelor's degrees. Founded 1981. Setting: suburban campus with easy access to Portland. Core. Calendar: continuous. Accelerated degree program, honors program, internships.

Entrance Requirements: Open admission. Option: international baccalaureate accepted. Required: high school transcript, interview, ACT Compass. Required for some: essay. Entrance: noncompetitive. Application deadline: rolling.

Collegiate Environment: Orientation program. Social organizations: 1 open to all. Most popular organization: Phi Beta Lambda. Major annual event: Annual Picnic. Pioneer Pacific College Library. Operations spending for the previous fiscal year: $17,280. 300 computers available on campus for general student use. Computer purchase/lease plans available. A campuswide network can be accessed. Students can access the following: eglobal library.

■ PORTLAND COMMUNITY COLLEGE

PO Box 19000
Portland, OR 97280-0990
Tel: (971)722-6111; Free: 866-922-1010
Fax: (503)452-4988
Web Site: www.pcc.edu

Description: State and locally supported, 2-year, coed. Awards certificates, diplomas, transfer associate, and terminal associate degrees. Founded 1961. Setting: 400-acre urban campus. Total enrollment: 24,353. 52% 25 or older. Calendar: quarters. Academic remediation for entering students, ESL program, services for LD students, advanced placement, independent study, distance learning, double major, summer session for credit, part-time degree program, external degree program, adult/continuing education programs, co-op programs and internships. Off campus study at Governors State University, Marylhurst University, members of the Oregon University System. Study abroad program.

Entrance Requirements: Open admission. Options: electronic application, international baccalaureate accepted. Entrance: noncompetitive. Application deadline: rolling.

Collegiate Environment: Orientation program. Drama-theater group, choral group, student-run newspaper. Student services: personal-psychological counseling, women's center. Campus security: 24-hour emergency response devices and patrols, late night transport-escort service. Main library plus 4 others. 1,572 computers available on campus for general student use. Computer purchase/lease plans available. A campuswide network can be accessed from off-campus. Students can access the following: online class registration. Staffed computer lab on campus.

Community Environment: See Portland State University.

■ PORTLAND STATE UNIVERSITY

PO Box 751
Portland, OR 97207-0751
Tel: (503)725-3000; Free: 800-547-8887
Fax: (503)725-5525
Web Site: www.pdx.edu

Description: State-supported, university, coed. Awards bachelor's, master's, and doctoral degrees. Founded 1946. Setting: 49-acre urban campus with easy access to Portland. Endowment: $75.2 million. Research spending for the previous fiscal year: $44.1 million. Educational spending for the previous fiscal year: $9879 per student. Total enrollment: 26,379. Faculty: 1,528 (783 full-time, 745 part-time). Student-undergrad faculty ratio is 18:1. 6,743 applied, 90% were admitted. 16% from top 10% of their high school class, 47% from top quarter, 87% from top half. Full-time: 14,292 students, 55% women, 45% men. Part-time: 6,675 students, 52% women, 48% men. Students come from 50 states and territories, 70 other countries, 16% from out-of-state. 1% American Indian or Alaska Native, non-Hispanic/Latino; 15% Hispanic/Latino; 4% Black or African American, non-Hispanic/Latino; 9% Asian, non-Hispanic/Latino; 0.7% Native Hawaiian or other Pacific Islander, non-Hispanic/Latino; 6% international. 36% 25 or older, 9% live on campus, 13% transferred in. Retention: 74% of full-time freshmen returned the following year. Academic areas with the most degrees conferred: business/marketing; social sciences; health professions and related sciences. Core. Calendar: quarters. Academic remediation for entering students, ESL program, services for LD students, advanced placement, accelerated degree program, freshman honors college, honors program, independent study, distance learning, double major, summer session for credit, part-time degree program, adult/continuing education programs, co-op programs and internships, graduate courses open to undergrads. Off campus study at other members of the Oregon University System. Study abroad program. ROTC: Army (c), Naval (c), Air Force (c).

Entrance Requirements: Options: electronic application, early admission, deferred admission. Required: high school transcript, minimum 3 high school GPA. Required for some: SAT or ACT. Entrance: moderately difficult. Application deadline: rolling. Notification: continuous. Transfer credits accepted: Yes.

Costs Per Year: Application fee: $50. State resident tuition: $7695 full-time, $171 per credit hour part-time. Nonresident tuition: $25,650 full-time, $570 per credit hour part-time. Mandatory fees: $1410 full-time. College room and board: $13,482. College room only: $9204.

Collegiate Environment: Orientation program. Drama-theater group, choral group, student-run newspaper, radio station. Social organizations: 160 open to all; national fraternities, national sororities, local fraternities, local sororities; 1% of eligible men and 1% of eligible women are members. Student services: legal services, health clinic, personal-psychological counseling, women's center. Campus security: 24-hour emergency response devices and patrols, late night transport-escort service, controlled dormitory access. Freshmen guaranteed college housing. Option: coed housing available. Branford P. Millar Library plus 1 other. Students can reserve study rooms. Operations spending for the previous fiscal year: $10 million.

Community Environment: Portland lies along both sides of the Willamette River at its juncture with the Columbia River, where there is a splendid port deep enough for the largest ships to dock. Portland has a beautiful background of snowcapped mountain peaks to the north and east, and because of the Japanese Current, enjoys a mild and equable climate. The Columbia River Highway is a beautiful drive, particularly through the Columbia River Gorge with cliffs 2,000 feet high. The Columbia and Willamette Rivers nearby offer year-round water sports, the ocean beach is also nearby, and skiing is available at nearby Mount Hood. Part-time employment and commercial transportation are available. Some of the points of interest are the Hoyt Arboretum, Oregon Art Institute, Oregon Historical Center, Oregon Museum of Science and Industry, Crystal Spring Rhododendron Garden, Washington Park Zoo, Japanese Gardens, World Forestry Center, and the Washington Park Rose Test Gardens.

■ REED COLLEGE

3203 SE Woodstock Blvd.
Portland, OR 97202-8199
Tel: (503)771-1112; Free: 800-547-4750
Fax: (503)777-7553
E-mail: admission@reed.edu
Web Site: www.reed.edu

Description: Independent, comprehensive, coed. Awards bachelor's and master's degrees. Founded 1908. Setting: 116-acre urban campus with easy access to Portland. Total enrollment: 1,470. Faculty: 156 (145 full-time, 11 part-time). Student-undergrad faculty ratio is 10:1. 5,652 applied, 36% were admitted. 59% from top 10% of their high school class, 85% from top quarter, 98% from top half. Full-time: 1,408 students, 54% women, 46% men. Part-time: 39 students, 51% women, 49% men. 93% from out-of-state. 0.3% American Indian or Alaska Native, non-Hispanic/Latino; 10% Hispanic/Latino; 2% Black or African American, non-Hispanic/Latino; 6% Asian, non-Hispanic/Latino; 0.2% Native Hawaiian or other Pacific Islander, non-Hispanic/Latino; 11% international. 1% 25 or older, 65% live on campus, 1% transferred in. Retention: 88% of full-time freshmen returned the following year. Academic areas with the most degrees conferred: social sciences; biological/life sciences; visual and performing arts. Core. Calendar: semesters. Academic remediation for entering students, services for LD students, advanced placement, self-designed majors, independent study, double major, co-op programs and internships. Off campus study at Howard University, Sarah Lawrence College, Sea Education Association. Study abroad program.

Entrance Requirements: Options: electronic application, early admission, early decision, early action, deferred admission, international baccalaureate accepted. Required: essay, high school transcript, 2 recommendations, SAT or ACT. Recommended: interview. Entrance: very difficult. Application deadlines: 1/1, 11/15 for early decision plan 1, 12/20 for early decision plan 2, 11/15 for early action. Notification: 4/1, 12/15 for early decision plan 1, 2/1 for early decision plan 2, 1/31 for early action. SAT Reasoning Test deadline: 3/1. SAT Subject Test deadline: 3/1. Transfer credits accepted: Yes. Applicants placed on waiting list: 1,659. Wait-listed applicants offered admission: 0.

Costs Per Year: Application fee: $0. Comprehensive fee: $70,550 includes full-time tuition ($56,030), mandatory fees ($310), and college room and board ($14,210). College room only: $7440. Full-time tuition and fees vary according to degree level. Room and board charges vary according to board plan and housing facility. Part-time tuition: $9440 per course. Part-time tuition varies according to course load and degree level.

Collegiate Environment: Orientation program. Drama-theater group, choral group, student-run newspaper, radio station. Social organizations: 100 open to all. Major annual events: Paideia, Renn Fayre, Reed Arts Week. Student services: legal services, health clinic, personal-psychological counseling, women's center. Campus security: 24-hour emergency response devices and patrols, student patrols, late night transport-escort service, controlled dormitory access. Eric V. Hauser Memorial Library plus 1 other. Study areas open 24 hours, 5-7 days a week. 434 computers available on campus for general student use. Computer purchase/lease plans available. A campuswide network can be accessed from student residence rooms. Students can access the following: online class registration. Staffed computer lab on campus (open 24 hours a day) provides training in use of computers, software, and the Internet.

Community Environment: See Portland State University.

■ ROGUE COMMUNITY COLLEGE

3345 Redwood Hwy.
Grants Pass, OR 97527-9291
Tel: (541)956-7500
E-mail: jduarte@roguecc.edu
Web Site: www.roguecc.edu

Description: State and locally supported, 2-year, coed. Awards certificates, transfer associate, and terminal associate degrees. Founded 1970. Setting: 84-acre rural campus. Endowment: $9.3 million. Research spending for the previous fiscal year: $119,496. Educational spending for the previous fiscal year: $3572 per student. Total enrollment: 4,901. Faculty: 473 (71 full-time, 402 part-time). Student-undergrad faculty ratio is 18:1. 852 applied, 94% were admitted. Full-time: 1,896 students, 56% women, 44% men. Part-time: 3,005 students, 58% women, 42% men. Students come from 26 states and territories, 4 other countries, 3% from out-of-state. 1% American Indian or Alaska Native, non-Hispanic/Latino; 17% Hispanic/Latino; 0.9% Black or African American, non-Hispanic/Latino; 2% Asian, non-Hispanic/Latino; 0.5% Native Hawaiian or other Pacific Islander, non-Hispanic/Latino; 0.1% international. 45% 25 or older, 5% transferred in. Core. Calendar: quarters. Academic remediation for entering students, ESL program, services for LD students, advanced placement, independent study, distance learning, double major, summer session for credit, part-time degree program, adult/continuing education programs, co-op programs and internships. Study abroad program.

Entrance Requirements: Open admission except for nursing, human services, emergency medical technology, apprenticeship, dental assisting, massage therapy programs. Options: electronic application, early admission. Entrance: noncompetitive. Application deadlines: rolling, rolling for nonresidents. Preference given to local residents. Transfer credits accepted: Yes.

Costs Per Year: Application fee: $0. State resident tuition: $4173 full-time, $107 per credit hour part-time. Nonresident tuition: $5109 full-time, $131 per credit hour part-time. Mandatory fees: $693 full-time, $7 per credit hour part-time, $100 per term part-time. Full-time tuition and fees vary according to reciprocity agreements. Part-time tuition and fees vary according to reciprocity agreements. College room and board: $9450.

Collegiate Environment: Orientation program. Drama-theater group, choral group, student-run newspaper. Student services: personal-psychological counseling. Campus security: 24-hour emergency response devices and patrols, late night transport-escort service. Rogue Community College Library. Books: 26,630 (physical). Operations spending for the previous fiscal year: $914,550. 700 computers available on campus for general student use. A campuswide network can be accessed from off-campus. Students can access the following: online class registration. Staffed computer lab on campus provides training in use of computers, software, and the Internet.

Community Environment: See Southern Oregon State College.

■ SOUTHERN OREGON UNIVERSITY

1250 Siskiyou Blvd.
Ashland, OR 97520
Tel: (541)552-7672; Free: 855-470-3377
Fax: (541)552-6329
E-mail: admissions@sou.edu
Web Site: www.sou.edu

Description: State-supported, comprehensive, coed. Awards bachelor's and master's degrees. Founded 1926. Setting: 175-acre small town campus. Endowment: $24.6 million. Research spending for the previous fiscal year: $1.1 million. Educational spending for the previous fiscal year: $6996 per student. Total enrollment: 5,916. Faculty: 283 (167 full-time, 116 part-time). Student-undergrad faculty ratio is 21:1. 2,766 applied, 78% were admitted. Full-time: 3,598 students, 59% women, 41% men. Part-time: 1,716 students, 61% women, 39% men. Students come from 41 states and territories, 15 other countries, 40% from out-of-state. 1% American Indian or Alaska Native, non-Hispanic/Latino; 12% Hispanic/Latino; 2% Black or African American, non-Hispanic/Latino; 2% Asian, non-Hispanic/Latino; 0.7% Native Hawaiian or other Pacific Islander, non-Hispanic/Latino; 3% international. 28% 25 or older, 26% live on campus, 10% transferred in. Retention: 68% of full-time freshmen returned the following year. Academic areas with the most degrees conferred: business/marketing; visual and performing arts; education. Core. Calendar: quarters. Academic remediation for entering students, ESL program, services for LD students, advanced placement, accelerated degree program, self-designed majors, freshman honors college, honors program, independent study, distance learning, double major, summer session for credit, part-time degree program, adult/continuing education programs, co-op programs and internships. Off campus study at National Student Exchange, other members of the Oregon University System. Study abroad program. ROTC: Army.

Entrance Requirements: Options: electronic application, early admission, deferred admission, international baccalaureate accepted. Required: high school transcript, minimum 3 high school GPA, SAT or ACT. Required for some: essay, SAT and SAT Subject Tests or ACT. Entrance: moderately difficult. Application deadline: rolling. Notification: continuous. SAT Reasoning Test deadline: 9/1. SAT Subject Test deadline: 9/1. Transfer credits accepted: Yes.

Costs Per Year: Application fee: $60. State resident tuition: $7740 full-time, $172 per credit hour part-time. Nonresident tuition: $23,670 full-time, $526 per credit hour part-time. Mandatory fees: $1875 full-time. Full-time tuition and fees vary according to course load, program, and reciprocity agreements. Part-time tuition varies according to course load, program, and reciprocity agreements. College room and board: $12,255. Room and board charges vary according to board plan and housing facility.

Collegiate Environment: Orientation program. Drama-theater group, choral group, student-run newspaper, radio station. Social organizations: 65 open to all. Most popular organizations: Native American Student Union, International Student Association, Impact (religious club), Ho'opa'a Hawaii Club, Omicron Delta Kappa. Major annual events: Southern Oregon Arts and Research Symposium, International Week, One World (performing arts series). Student services: legal services, health clinic, personal-psychological counseling, women's center. Campus security: 24-hour emergency response devices and patrols, student patrols, late night transport-escort service, controlled dormitory access. Lenn and Dixie Hannon Library. Books: 340,015 (physical), 135,298 (digital/electronic); Databases: 80. Students can reserve study rooms. Operations spending for the previous fiscal year: $2.9 million. 750 computers available on campus for general student use. Computer purchase/lease plans available. A campuswide network can be accessed from student residence rooms and from off campus. Students can access the following: online class registration, online account information including bill payment, online employee records for student workers. Staffed computer lab on campus provides training in use of computers, software, and the Internet.

Community Environment: Ashland, a town of 20,000 people, is nestled at the base of the Sikiyou Mountains in the Rogue Valley of Oregon. Culturally the community has gained national recognition through the Oregon Shakespearean festival and associated legitimate theatres, annually drawing over 300,000 patrons. The town is surrounded by natural forests, mountain lakes and rivers, spectacular for outdoor sports and ecological studies. For the skier, it's only 30 minutes to the 7,000 foot Mt. Ashland Ski Resort.

■ **SOUTHWESTERN OREGON COMMUNITY COLLEGE**
1988 Newmark Ave.
Coos Bay, OR 97420-2912
Tel: (541)888-2525; Free: 800-962-2838
E-mail: lwells@socc.edu
Web Site: www.socc.edu
Description: State and locally supported, 2-year, coed. Awards certificates, diplomas, transfer associate, and terminal associate degrees. Founded 1961. Setting: 174-acre small town campus. Endowment: $851,280. Educational spending for the previous fiscal year: $4908 per student. Total enrollment: 2,338. Faculty: 182 (54 full-time, 128 part-time). Student-undergrad faculty ratio is 15:1. Full-time: 1,129 students, 50% women, 50% men. Part-time: 1,209 students, 58% women, 42% men. Students come from 24 states and territories, 6 other countries, 30% from out-of-state. 3% American Indian or Alaska Native, non-Hispanic/Latino; 9% Hispanic/Latino; 1% Black or African American, non-Hispanic/Latino; 1% Asian, non-Hispanic/Latino; 0.9% Native Hawaiian or other Pacific Islander, non-Hispanic/Latino; 0.9% international. 38% 25 or older, 17% live on campus. Core. Calendar: quarters. Academic remediation for entering students, ESL program, services for LD students, advanced placement, honors program, independent study, distance learning, double major, summer session for credit, part-time degree program, adult/continuing education programs, co-op programs and internships.
Entrance Requirements: Open admission except for culinary institute, nursing, emergency medical technology programs, surgical technician, pharmacy technician programs. Options: electronic application, early admission. Required for some: high school transcript. Entrance: noncompetitive. Application deadline: rolling. Notification: continuous. Transfer credits accepted: Yes.

Costs Per Year: Application fee: $40. State resident tuition: $4230 full-time, $94 per credit hour part-time. Nonresident tuition: $4230 full-time, $94 per credit hour part-time. Mandatory fees: $1810 full-time, $31 per credit hour part-time, $31. Full-time tuition and fees vary according to program. Part-time tuition and fees vary according to program. College room and board: $7767. Room and board charges vary according to board plan.

Collegiate Environment: Orientation program. Choral group. Major annual events: Orientation, Laker Week, Spring Fling. Campus security: 24-hour emergency response devices and patrols, late night transport-escort service, controlled dormitory access. Southwestern Oregon Community College Library. Books: 28,092 (physical), 857 (digital/electronic); Serial titles: 101 (physical); Databases: 58. Weekly public service hours: 43. Operations spending for the previous fiscal year: $266,711. 57 computers available on campus for general student use. A campuswide network can be accessed. Students can access the following: online class registration, myLakerLink portal for online self-service and elearning access. Staffed computer lab on campus provides training in use of computers, software, and the Internet.

Community Environment: Coos Bay is an important seaport and trading center as well as one of the world's largest lumber export points. Community facilities include a library, hospital, churches representing many major denominations, and civic and service organizations. Coos Bay and adjacent North Bend are the shopping centers for southwestern Oregon. The Golden and Silver Falls State Park is 24 miles away, offering facilities for picnicking, camping, and fishing, as do Millicoma-Myrtle Grove State Park and Shore Acres State Park. Opportunities for part-time employment are good.

■ **SUMNER COLLEGE**
15115 SW Sequoia Pky.
Ste. 200
Portland, OR 97224
Tel: (503)223-5100
Fax: (503)273-8093
Web Site: www.sumnercollege.edu
Description: Proprietary, 2-year, coed. Awards diplomas and terminal associate degrees. Founded 1974. Setting: urban campus with easy access to Portland. Educational spending for the previous fiscal year: $4912 per student. Total enrollment: 261. Faculty: 25 (12 full-time, 13 part-time). Student-undergrad faculty ratio is 15:1. Full-time: 261 students, 84% women, 16% men. 10% from out-of-state. 6% Hispanic/Latino; 15% Black or African American, non-Hispanic/Latino; 7% Asian, non-Hispanic/Latino. 65% 25 or older. Calendar: quarters. Academic remediation for entering students, distance learning.
Entrance Requirements: Required: high school transcript, interview. Required for some: essay, Entrance exam.
Costs Per Year: Comprehensive fee: $38,430 includes full-time tuition ($27,180), mandatory fees ($2340), and college room and board ($8910).
Collegiate Environment: Orientation program. Social organizations: 1 open to all. Most popular organization: Medical Club. College housing not available. Main library plus 1 other. Books: 800 (physical); Serial titles: 100 (digital/electronic); Databases: 2. Weekly public service hours: 50; students can reserve study rooms. Operations spending for the previous fiscal year: $3200. 45 computers available on campus for general student use. Staffed computer lab on campus provides training in use of computers.

■ **TILLAMOOK BAY COMMUNITY COLLEGE**
4301 Third St.
Tillamook, OR 97141
Tel: (503)842-8222
Fax: (503)842-2214
E-mail: rhodahanson@tillamookbaycc.edu
Web Site: www.tillamookbaycc.edu
Description: District-supported, 2-year, coed. Awards certificates, transfer associate, and terminal associate degrees. Founded 1984. Setting: 7-acre rural campus. Endowment: $475,359. Total enrollment: 261. Faculty: 53 (8 full-time, 45 part-time). Student-undergrad faculty ratio is 15:1. Full-time: 127 students, 59% women, 41% men. Part-time: 134 students, 52% women, 48% men. 2% American Indian or Alaska Native, non-Hispanic/Latino; 18% Hispanic/Latino; 2% Asian, non-Hispanic/Latino; 0.4% Native Hawaiian or other Pacific Islander, non-Hispanic/Latino; 4% international. 45% 25 or older, 3% transferred in. Retention: 14% of full-time freshmen returned the following year. Core. Calendar: quarters. Academic remediation for entering students, ESL program, services for LD students, advanced placement, independent study, distance learning, summer session for credit, part-time degree program.

Entrance Requirements: Open admission Open admission for Adult Basic Skills - ESOL, GED. Options: electronic application, international baccalaureate accepted. Recommended: high school transcript. Application deadline: rolling. Transfer credits accepted: Yes.

Costs Per Year: Application fee: $0. State resident tuition: $4320 full-time, $96 per credit hour part-time. Nonresident tuition: $5220 full-time, $116 per credit hour part-time. Mandatory fees: $270 full-time, $6 per credit hour part-time.

Collegiate Environment: Orientation program. Major annual events: Transfer Days, Employer Days. Campus security: alarmed exterior doors, classroom door locks. Tillamook Bay Community College Library. Books: 3,696 (physical), 172,327 (digital/electronic); Serial titles: 27 (physical), 44,286 (digital/electronic). Weekly public service hours: 48; students can reserve study rooms. Operations spending for the previous fiscal year: $148,407. 47 computers available on campus for general student use. A campuswide network can be accessed. Students can access the following: online class registration.

■ **TREASURE VALLEY COMMUNITY COLLEGE**
650 College Blvd.
Ontario, OR 97914-3423
Tel: (541)889-6493
Fax: (541)881-2721
E-mail: tmcfetri@tvcc.cc
Web Site: www.tvcc.cc

Description: State and locally supported, 2-year, coed. Awards certificates, transfer associate, and terminal associate degrees. Founded 1962. Setting: 90-acre rural campus with easy access to Boise. Endowment: $5.9 million. Total enrollment: 1,866. Faculty: 86 (47 full-time, 39 part-time). Student-undergrad faculty ratio is 21:1. 2,447 applied, 100% were admitted. Full-time: 807 students, 53% women, 47% men. Part-time: 1,059 students, 56% women, 44% men. Students come from 15 states and territories, 2 other countries, 67% from out-of-state. 1% American Indian or Alaska Native, non-Hispanic/Latino; 25% Hispanic/Latino; 2% Black or African American, non-Hispanic/Latino; 0.7% Asian, non-Hispanic/Latino; 0.3% Native Hawaiian or other Pacific Islander, non-Hispanic/Latino; 0.4% international. 46% 25 or older, 4% live on campus, 6% transferred in. Retention: 40% of full-time freshmen returned the following year. Core. Calendar: quarters. Academic remediation for entering students, ESL program, services for LD students, advanced placement, accelerated degree program, honors program, independent study, distance learning, summer session for credit, part-time degree program, adult/continuing education programs, co-op programs and internships. Off campus study at Eastern Oregon Collaborative Colleges Center (EOCCC)- Treasure Valley Community College, Eastern Oregon University, Blue Mountain Community College.

Entrance Requirements: Open admission. Options: electronic application, early admission, deferred admission. Entrance: noncompetitive. Application deadline: rolling. Notification: continuous. Transfer credits accepted: Yes.

Costs Per Year: Application fee: $0. State resident tuition: $4590 full-time, $102 per credit part-time. Nonresident tuition: $5040 full-time, $112 per credit part-time. Mandatory fees: $990 full-time, $22 per credit part-time. College room and board: $7373. College room only: $3926.

Collegiate Environment: Orientation program. Choral group. Social organizations: 11 open to all. Most popular organizations: Phi Theta Kappa, Natural Resources, International Business Club, Circle K International (service organization), Ag Ambassadors. Major annual events: Fall Festival, Artist and Lecture Series, Intramural and Recreation Events. Campus security: 24-hour emergency response devices, late night transport-escort service, controlled dormitory access. 142 college housing spaces available; 119 were occupied in 2018-19. Option: coed housing available. Treasure Valley Community College Library. Books: 26,100 (physical), 1.5 million (digital/electronic); Serial titles: 47 (physical), 3 (digital/electronic); Databases: 10. Weekly public service hours: 72; students can reserve study rooms. Operations spending for the previous fiscal year: $286,123. 85 computers available on campus for general student use. A campuswide network can be accessed from student residence rooms. Students can access the following: online class registration. Staffed computer lab on campus provides training in use of computers, software, and the Internet.

Community Environment: Ontario, one mile from the Oregon-Idaho state line, lies in an agricultural area that produces potatoes, onions, sugar beets, corn, and hay. All forms of commercial transportation are available. Community facilities include the Malheur County Library, a hospital, and several civic and service organizations. Mule, deer, and antelope hunting on the vast rangeland, and fishing on Owyhee Lake and the Malheur and Snake Rivers

attract the sportsman. Semiprecious stones may be found in Malheur County. Skiing may be enjoyed at nearby ski resorts. Job opportunities are available.

■ **UMPQUA COMMUNITY COLLEGE**
PO Box 967
Roseburg, OR 97470-0226
Tel: (541)440-4600
Fax: (541)440-4612
Web Site: www.umpqua.edu

Description: State and locally supported, 2-year, coed. Awards certificates, transfer associate, and terminal associate degrees. Founded 1964. Setting: 100-acre rural campus. Endowment: $7.3 million. Educational spending for the previous fiscal year: $3551 per student. Total enrollment: 2,046. Faculty: 149 (55 full-time, 94 part-time). Student-undergrad faculty ratio is 14:1. 176 applied, 100% were admitted. Full-time: 971 students, 59% women, 41% men. Part-time: 1,075 students, 60% women, 40% men. Students come from 15 states and territories. 42% 25 or older, 22% transferred in. Retention: 48% of full-time freshmen returned the following year. Core. Calendar: quarters. Academic remediation for entering students, ESL program, services for LD students, advanced placement, accelerated degree program, honors program, independent study, distance learning, summer session for credit, part-time degree program, adult/continuing education programs, co-op programs and internships. Study abroad program.

Entrance Requirements: Open admission except for registered nursing and emergency medical technology programs. Options: electronic application, early admission, deferred admission. Recommended: high school transcript. Entrance: noncompetitive. Application deadline: rolling.

Collegiate Environment: Orientation program. Drama-theater group, choral group, student-run newspaper. Social organizations: 11 open to all. Most popular organizations: Phi Theta Kappa, Computer Club, Phi Beta Lambda, Nursing Club, Umpqua Accounting Associates. Major annual events: Student Government Sponsored Quarterly BBQ, Transfer College Day, New Student Orientation. Student services: personal-psychological counseling. Campus security: 24-hour emergency response devices and patrols. Umpqua Community College Library. Operations spending for the previous fiscal year: $38,732. 428 computers available on campus for general student use. A campuswide network can be accessed from off-campus. Students can access the following: online class registration. Staffed computer lab on campus provides training in use of computers, software, and the Internet.

Community Environment: Roseburg is the county seat of Douglas County, one of the largest lumber centers in the country. Roseburg is also a noted sheep producing area. The town is the headquarters for the Umpqua National Forest, where good salmon and trout fishing may be enjoyed and in season, hunting of deer, elk, bear, and cougar is permitted.

■ **UNIVERSITY OF OREGON**
Eugene, OR 97403
Tel: (541)346-1000; Free: 800-232-3825
Fax: (541)346-5815
Web Site: www.uoregon.edu

Description: State-supported, university, coed. Awards bachelor's, master's, and doctoral degrees and post-master's certificates. Founded 1876. Setting: 295-acre suburban campus with easy access to Portland, Oregon. Endowment: $912.5 million. Research spending for the previous fiscal year: $119.4 million. Educational spending for the previous fiscal year: $12,174 per student. Total enrollment: 22,644. Faculty: 1,670 (1,163 full-time, 507 part-time). Student-undergrad faculty ratio is 17:1. 24,474 applied, 83% were admitted. 22% from top 10% of their high school class, 55% from top quarter, 87% from top half. 8 National Merit Scholars. Full-time: 17,550 students, 54% women, 46% men. Part-time: 1,551 students, 50% women, 50% men. Students come from 53 states and territories, 83 other countries, 42% from out-of-state. 0.6% American Indian or Alaska Native, non-Hispanic/Latino; 13% Hispanic/Latino; 2% Black or African American, non-Hispanic/Latino; 6% Asian, non-Hispanic/Latino; 0.4% Native Hawaiian or other Pacific Islander, non-Hispanic/Latino; 10% international. 7% 25 or older, 22% live on campus, 6% transferred in. Retention: 85% of full-time freshmen returned the following year. Academic areas with the most degrees conferred: social sciences; business/marketing; communication/journalism. Core. Calendar: quarters. ESL program, services for LD students, advanced placement, self-designed majors, honors program, independent study, distance learning, double major, summer session for credit, part-time degree program, co-op programs and internships, graduate courses open to undergrads. Off campus study at National Student Exchange. Study abroad program. ROTC: Army, Air Force (c).

Entrance Requirements: Options: electronic application, early action, deferred admission, international baccalaureate accepted. Required: essay, high school transcript, C+ or better in 15 college preparatory units, SAT or ACT. Required for some: SAT and SAT Subject Tests or ACT. Entrance: moderately difficult. Application deadlines: 1/15, 11/1 for early action. Notification: 4/1, 12/15 for early action. SAT Reasoning Test deadline: 2/15. SAT Subject Test deadline: 2/15. Transfer credits accepted: Yes. Applicants placed on waiting list: 264. Wait-listed applicants offered admission: 69.

Costs Per Year: Application fee: $65. One-time mandatory fee: $430. State resident tuition: $9765 full-time, $211 per credit hour part-time. Nonresident tuition: $33,345 full-time, $741 per credit hour part-time. Mandatory fees: $2133 full-time. Full-time tuition and fees vary according to course load. Part-time tuition varies according to course load. College room and board: $12,963. Room and board charges vary according to board plan and housing facility.

Collegiate Environment: Orientation program. Drama-theater group, choral group, marching band, student-run newspaper, radio station. Social organizations: 250 open to all; national fraternities, national sororities, local fraternities, local sororities; 16% of eligible men and 20% of eligible women are members. Most popular organizations: political and environmental action, cultural organizations, major-specific organizations, community service organizations, club sports. Major annual events: University Day, Homecoming, ASUO Fall and Spring Street Faires. Student services: legal services, health clinic, personal-psychological counseling, women's center. Campus security: 24-hour emergency response devices and patrols, late night transport-escort service, controlled dormitory access, Lighted pathways, emergency phones, self-defense classes. 4,538 college housing spaces available; 4,230 were occupied in 2018-19. Freshmen given priority for college housing. On-campus residence required in freshman year. Option: coed housing available. Knight Library plus 6 others. Books: 1.7 million (physical), 927,771 (digital/electronic); Serial titles: 74,186 (physical), 157,063 (digital/electronic); Databases: 514. Weekly public service hours: 124; students can reserve study rooms. Operations spending for the previous fiscal year: $18.6 million. 497 computers available on campus for general student use. A campuswide network can be accessed from student residence rooms and from off campus. Students can access the following: online class registration. Staffed computer lab on campus provides training in use of computers, software, and the Internet.

Community Environment: Eugene, the center of a vast recreational area, is an important high-technology and software center. Bicycles are a major form of student transportation. Airline, bus and train transportation are available. Eugene's facilities include more than 80 churches, a large public library, a YMCA, YWCA, three hospitals, and a number of motels. Eugene is 60 miles east of the Pacific Ocean and 60 miles west of the Cascade Mountains. The Willamette National Forest nearby provides fine hunting and fishing opportunities and skiing is enjoyed at the Hoodoo Ski Bowl and Willamette Pass Ski area.

■ UNIVERSITY OF PORTLAND

5000 N Willamette Blvd.
Portland, OR 97203-5798
Tel: (503)943-7911; Free: 888-627-5601
Fax: (503)943-7399
E-mail: admissions@up.edu
Web Site: www.up.edu

Description: Independent Roman Catholic, comprehensive, coed. Awards bachelor's, master's, and doctoral degrees and post-master's certificates. Founded 1901. Setting: 150-acre urban campus. Endowment: $147 million. Research spending for the previous fiscal year: $856,000. Educational spending for the previous fiscal year: $9722 per student. Total enrollment: 4,338. Faculty: 363 (223 full-time, 140 part-time). Student-undergrad faculty ratio is 14:1. 11,202 applied, 62% were admitted. 45% from top 10% of their high school class, 77% from top quarter, 96% from top half. Full-time: 3,698 students, 59% women, 41% men. Part-time: 72 students, 58% women, 42% men. Students come from 55 states and territories, 35 other countries, 70% from out-of-state. 0.2% American Indian or Alaska Native, non-Hispanic/Latino; 11% Hispanic/Latino; 1% Black or African American, non-Hispanic/Latino; 12% Asian, non-Hispanic/Latino; 2% Native Hawaiian or other Pacific Islander, non-Hispanic/Latino; 3% international. 2% 25 or older, 57% live on campus, 2% transferred in. Retention: 92% of full-time freshmen returned the following year. Academic areas with the most degrees conferred: health professions and related sciences; engineering; business/marketing. Core. Calendar: semesters. Services for LD students, advanced placement, honors program, independent study, double major, summer session for

credit, part-time degree program, adult/continuing education programs, internships, graduate courses open to undergrads. Off campus study. Study abroad program. ROTC: Army, Air Force.

Entrance Requirements: Options: electronic application, deferred admission, international baccalaureate accepted. Required: essay, high school transcript, 1 recommendation, SAT or ACT. Recommended: SAT, ACT. Entrance: moderately difficult. Application deadline: 6/1. Notification: continuous. SAT Reasoning Test deadline: 2/1. Transfer credits accepted: Yes. Applicants placed on waiting list: 2,862. Wait-listed applicants offered admission: 33.

Costs Per Year: Application fee: $50. Comprehensive fee: $59,354 includes full-time tuition ($45,564), mandatory fees ($340), and college room and board ($13,450). Full-time tuition and fees vary according to program. Room and board charges vary according to board plan and housing facility. Part-time tuition: $1427 per credit hour. Part-time tuition varies according to course load and program.

Collegiate Environment: Orientation program. Drama-theater group, choral group, student-run newspaper, radio station. Social organizations: 60 open to all. Most popular organizations: Hawaii Club, International Club, Student Nurses Association, Feminist Discussion Group, The Bluffoons (Improv Club). Major annual events: Riverboat, Rock the Bluff, Dance of the Decades. Student services: health clinic, personal-psychological counseling. Campus security: 24-hour emergency response devices and patrols, student patrols, late night transport-escort service, controlled dormitory access. Wilson M. Clark Library plus 1 other. Books: 191,219 (physical), 138,108 (digital/electronic); Serial titles: 1,080 (digital/electronic); Databases: 153. Weekly public service hours: 117; students can reserve study rooms. Operations spending for the previous fiscal year: $4.2 million. 157 computers available on campus for general student use. A campuswide network can be accessed from student residence rooms and from off campus. Students can access the following: online class registration. Staffed computer lab on campus (open 24 hours a day) provides training in use of computers, software, and the Internet.

Community Environment: See Portland State University.

■ WARNER PACIFIC UNIVERSITY

2219 SE 68th Ave.
Portland, OR 97215-4099
Tel: (503)517-1000; Free: 800-804-1510
Fax: (503)788-7425
E-mail: admiss@warnerpacific.edu
Web Site: www.warnerpacific.edu

Description: Independent, comprehensive, coed, affiliated with Church of God. Awards associate, bachelor's, and master's degrees and post-master's certificates. Founded 1937. Setting: 15-acre urban campus with easy access to Portland. Endowment: $10.2 million. Educational spending for the previous fiscal year: $8133 per student. Total enrollment: 409. Faculty: (33 full-time). Student-undergrad faculty ratio is 7:1. 476 applied, 63% were admitted. 11% from top 10% of their high school class, 34% from top quarter, 72% from top half. Full-time: 396 students, 60% women, 40% men. Part-time: 4 students, 25% women, 75% men. 1% American Indian or Alaska Native, non-Hispanic/Latino; 34% Hispanic/Latino; 10% Black or African American, non-Hispanic/Latino; 5% Asian, non-Hispanic/Latino; 2% Native Hawaiian or other Pacific Islander, non-Hispanic/Latino; 0.5% international. 9% 25 or older, 41% live on campus, 13% transferred in. Retention: 62% of full-time freshmen returned the following year. Core. Calendar: semesters. Academic remediation for entering students, services for LD students, advanced placement, accelerated degree program, self-designed majors, honors program, independent study, double major, summer session for credit, part-time degree program, adult/continuing education programs, co-op programs and internships, graduate courses open to undergrads. Off campus study at Mt. Hood Community College, Concordia College (OR), Oregon Independent Colleges Association, Council for Christian Colleges and Universities (CCCU). Study abroad program. ROTC: Air Force (c).

Entrance Requirements: Options: electronic application, international baccalaureate accepted. Required: essay, high school transcript, minimum 2.5 high school GPA, SAT or ACT. Recommended: minimum 3 high school GPA, interview. Required for some: 1 recommendation, interview. Entrance: moderately difficult. Application deadline: rolling. Notification: continuous. Transfer credits accepted: Yes.

Collegiate Environment: Orientation program. Drama-theater group, choral group, student-run newspaper. Social organizations: 9 open to all. Major annual events: Homecoming, Spring and Winter Banquets, Midnight Barbecue and Breakfast. Student services: personal-psychological counseling.

Campus security: 24-hour emergency response devices and patrols, student patrols, late night transport-escort service, controlled dormitory access. Otto F. Linn Library. Books: 65,397 (physical), 164,990 (digital/electronic); Serial titles: 257 (physical), 139,309 (digital/electronic); Databases: 478. Weekly public service hours: 7. Operations spending for the previous fiscal year: $428,921. 90 computers available on campus for general student use. A campuswide network can be accessed from student residence rooms and from off campus. Students can access the following: online class registration.

Community Environment: See Portland State University.

■ WESTERN OREGON UNIVERSITY

345 Monmouth Ave. N
Monmouth, OR 97361
Tel: (503)838-8000; Free: 877-877-1593
Fax: (503)838-8067
E-mail: wolfgram@wou.edu
Web Site: www.wou.edu

Description: State-supported, comprehensive, coed. Awards bachelor's and master's degrees. Founded 1856. Setting: 157-acre rural campus with easy access to Portland. Total enrollment: 5,285. Faculty: 378 (287 full-time, 91 part-time). Student-undergrad faculty ratio is 15:1. 2,942 applied, 81% were admitted. Full-time: 4,042 students, 62% women, 38% men. Part-time: 734 students, 62% women, 38% men. Students come from 33 states and territories, 22 other countries, 23% from out-of-state. 2% American Indian or Alaska Native, non-Hispanic/Latino; 16% Hispanic/Latino; 4% Black or African American, non-Hispanic/Latino; 5% Asian, non-Hispanic/Latino; 3% Native Hawaiian or other Pacific Islander, non-Hispanic/Latino; 6% international. 15% 25 or older, 24% live on campus, 13% transferred in. Retention: 72% of full-time freshmen returned the following year. Academic areas with the most degrees conferred: business/marketing; psychology; parks and recreation. Core. Calendar: quarters. Academic remediation for entering students, ESL program, services for LD students, advanced placement, self-designed majors, freshman honors college, honors program, independent study, distance learning, double major, summer session for credit, part-time degree program, internships, graduate courses open to undergrads. Off campus study. Study abroad program. ROTC: Army (c).

Entrance Requirements: Options: electronic application, international baccalaureate accepted. Required: high school transcript, minimum 2.75 high school GPA, general college preparatory program completion. Entrance: moderately difficult. Application deadline: rolling. Notification: continuous. Transfer credits accepted: Yes.

Costs Per Year: Application fee: $60. State resident tuition: $7740 full-time, $172 per credit hour part-time. Nonresident tuition: $24,615 full-time, $547 per credit hour part-time. Mandatory fees: $1800 full-time. Full-time tuition and fees vary according to course load. Part-time tuition varies according to course load. College room and board: $10,415. College room only: $8360. Room and board charges vary according to board plan and housing facility. Tuition guaranteed not to increase for student's term of enrollment.

Collegiate Environment: Orientation program. Drama-theater group, choral group, student-run newspaper, radio station. Social organizations: 30 open to all; national fraternities, national sororities. Most popular organizations: Model United Nations, Multicultural Student Union, Oregon Student Association, Alternative Spring Break (community service), M.E.Ch.A. Major annual events: Homecoming, Holiday Tree Lighting, Alcohol Awareness Week. Student services: health clinic, personal-psychological counseling, women's center. Campus security: 24-hour emergency response devices and patrols, late night transport-escort service, controlled dormitory access. Wayne and Lynn Hamersly Library. Books: 164,610 (physical), 193,700 (digital/electronic); Serial titles: 33,400 (physical), 223,223 (digital/electronic); Databases: 291. Study areas open 24 hours, 5-7 days a week; students can reserve study rooms. 411 computers available on campus for general student use. A campuswide network can be accessed from student residence rooms and from off campus. Students can access the following: online class registration. Staffed computer lab on campus provides training in use of computers and software.

Community Environment: Located in Monmouth, a town of 7,500, Western is 15 miles from Salem, the state capital, and is midway between the state's two largest cities, Portland and Eugene. Western is a short drive from the famed Oregon Coast to the west and the majestic Cascade Mountains to the east. Monmouth is located in the Willamette Valley. The University is the town's main employer and serves as the cultural and athletic center for the area.

■ WILLAMETTE UNIVERSITY

900 State St.
Salem, OR 97301-3931
Tel: (503)370-6300; Free: 877-542-2787
Fax: (503)375-5363
E-mail: bearcat@willamette.edu
Web Site: www.willamette.edu

Description: Independent United Methodist, comprehensive, coed. Awards bachelor's, master's, and doctoral degrees. Founded 1842. Setting: 72-acre urban campus with easy access to Portland. Endowment: $225.3 million. Research spending for the previous fiscal year: $2.9 million. Total enrollment: 2,472. Faculty: 263 (189 full-time, 74 part-time). Student-undergrad faculty ratio is 11:1. 4,206 applied, 84% were admitted. 46% from top 10% of their high school class, 73% from top quarter, 96% from top half. Full-time: 1,759 students, 58% women, 42% men. Part-time: 51 students, 47% women, 53% men. 74% from out-of-state. 0.7% American Indian or Alaska Native, non-Hispanic/Latino; 14% Hispanic/Latino; 2% Black or African American, non-Hispanic/Latino; 7% Asian, non-Hispanic/Latino; 0.3% Native Hawaiian or other Pacific Islander, non-Hispanic/Latino; 0.8% international. 1% 25 or older, 60% live on campus, 2% transferred in. Retention: 83% of full-time freshmen returned the following year. Academic areas with the most degrees conferred: social sciences; physical sciences; biological/life sciences; parks and recreation. Core. Calendar: semesters. Services for LD students, advanced placement, accelerated degree program, self-designed majors, independent study, double major, part-time degree program, internships, graduate courses open to undergrads. Off campus study at American University, Urban Life Center (Chicago, IL). Study abroad program. ROTC: Army (c), Air Force (c).

Entrance Requirements: Options: electronic application, early action, deferred admission, international baccalaureate accepted. Required: essay, high school transcript, minimum 2 high school GPA, 1 recommendation. Recommended: interview, SAT and SAT Subject Tests or ACT. Entrance: very difficult. Application deadlines: 1/15, 11/15 for early action. Notification: continuous until 5/1. SAT Reasoning Test deadline: 1/15. SAT Subject Test deadline: 1/15. Transfer credits accepted: Yes. Applicants placed on waiting list: 139. Wait-listed applicants offered admission: 23.

Costs Per Year: Comprehensive fee: $65,014 includes full-time tuition ($51,750), mandatory fees ($324), and college room and board ($12,940). Part-time tuition: $1617 per credit hour.

Collegiate Environment: Orientation program. Drama-theater group, choral group, student-run newspaper, radio station. Social organizations: 92 open to all; national fraternities, national sororities; 24% of eligible men and 18% of eligible women are members. Student services: health clinic, personal-psychological counseling, women's center. Campus security: 24-hour emergency response devices and patrols, student patrols, late night transport-escort service, controlled dormitory access. Freshmen guaranteed college housing. On-campus residence required through sophomore year. Option: coed housing available. Mark O. Hatfield Library plus 1 other. Study areas open 24 hours, 5-7 days a week; students can reserve study rooms.

Community Environment: Salem, the capital city, has a population of 148,750. All forms of commercial transportation are available. Recreational activities include tennis, fishing, swimming, boating, riding, and hiking. Ski area facilities and the Pacific Ocean are nearby. Part-time employment is available. Points of interest are Bush Park, a large city park planted with rare trees and shrubs, Salem Art Center, Mission Mill Museum and the Oregon State Capitol.

■ ALBRIGHT COLLEGE

13th and Bern Sts.
Reading, PA 19612-5234
Tel: (610)921-2381; Free: 800-252-1856
Fax: (610)921-7530
E-mail: admission@albright.edu
Web Site: www.albright.edu

Description: Independent, comprehensive, coed, affiliated with United Methodist Church. Awards bachelor's and master's degrees. Founded 1856. Setting: 118-acre suburban campus with easy access to Philadelphia. Endowment: $67.7 million. Educational spending for the previous fiscal year: $9544 per student. Total enrollment: 1,934. Faculty: 148 (97 full-time, 51 part-time). Student-undergrad faculty ratio is 14:1. 6,755 applied, 62% were admitted. 14% from top 10% of their high school class, 40% from top quarter, 76% from top half. Full-time: 1,887 students, 60% women, 40% men. Part-time: 25 students, 60% women, 40% men. Students come from 28 states and territories, 16 other countries, 42% from out-of-state. 1% American Indian or Alaska Native, non-Hispanic/Latino; 15% Hispanic/Latino; 23% Black or African American, non-Hispanic/Latino; 2% Asian, non-Hispanic/Latino; 2% international. 1% 25 or older, 80% live on campus, 2% transferred in. Retention: 69% of full-time freshmen returned the following year. Academic areas with the most degrees conferred: business/marketing; psychology; visual and performing arts. Core. Calendar: 4-1-4. Services for LD students, advanced placement, accelerated degree program, self-designed majors, honors program, independent study, distance learning, double major, summer session for credit, adult/continuing education programs, internships, graduate courses open to undergrads. Off campus study at The Washington Center, National Theatre Institute. Study abroad program.

Entrance Requirements: Options: electronic application, deferred admission, international baccalaureate accepted. Required: high school transcript, minimum 2.5 high school GPA. Required for some: essay, 1 recommendation, interview, secondary school report (guidance department), interview for students applying test-optional. Entrance: moderately difficult. Application deadline: rolling. Notification: continuous. SAT Reasoning Test deadline: 6/1. Transfer credits accepted: Yes.

Costs Per Year: Application fee: $35. Comprehensive fee: $38,122 includes full-time tuition ($24,500), mandatory fees ($1142), and college room and board ($12,480). College room only: $6864.

Collegiate Environment: Orientation program. Drama-theater group, choral group, student-run newspaper, radio station. Social organizations: 65 open to all; national fraternities, national sororities, local fraternities; 10% of eligible men and 13% of eligible women are members. Most popular organizations: Greek Organizations (combined), Alpha Phi Omega (service organization), Student Government Association, Albright College Activities Council, Albrightian (newspaper). Major annual events: Homecoming, Airbands, Block Party. Student services: health clinic, personal-psychological counseling, women's center. Campus security: 24-hour emergency response devices and patrols, student patrols, late night transport-escort service, controlled dormitory access. 1,303 undergraduates lived in college housing during 2018-19. Freshmen guaranteed college housing. On-campus residence required through senior year. Option: coed housing available. F. W. Gingrich Library plus 1 other. Databases: 60. Students can reserve study rooms. Operations spending for the previous fiscal year: $1 million.

Community Environment: The Reading and Berks County area has a temperate climate. The community is served by U.S. air and several bus companies. Reading is world famous for its outlet shopping. The city has many churches representing major denominations, a symphony orchestra, two major hospitals, four museums, several theaters, and beautiful park and recreational facilities. It is within easy driving distance from major metropolitan areas such as Philadelphia, New York City, Washington, D.C., and Baltimore, MD.

■ ALL-STATE CAREER SCHOOL-ESSINGTON CAMPUS

50 W Powhattan Ave.
Essington, PA 19029
Tel: (610)362-1124
Web Site: www.allstatecareer.edu

Description: Proprietary, 2-year, coed. Awards diplomas and terminal associate degrees.

■ ALLEGHENY COLLEGE

520 N Main St.
Meadville, PA 16335
Tel: (814)332-3100; Free: 800-521-5293
Fax: (814)337-0431
E-mail: admissions@allegheny.edu
Web Site: www.allegheny.edu

Description: Independent, 4-year, coed. Awards bachelor's degrees. Founded 1815. Setting: 566-acre suburban campus. Endowment: $220.8 million. Research spending for the previous fiscal year: $1.4 million. Educational spending for the previous fiscal year: $17,146 per student. Total enrollment: 1,771. Student-undergrad faculty ratio is 10:1. 5,479 applied, 64% were admitted. 28% from top 10% of their high school class, 66% from top quarter, 90% from top half. 5 National Merit Scholars, 3 class presidents, 13 valedictorians, 14 student government officers. Full-time: 1,724 students, 55% women, 45% men. Part-time: 47 students, 70% women, 30% men. Students come from 46 states and territories, 60 other countries, 48% from out-of-state. 0.3% American Indian or Alaska Native, non-Hispanic/Latino; 9% Hispanic/Latino; 9% Black or African American, non-Hispanic/Latino; 4% Asian, non-Hispanic/Latino; 0.1% Native Hawaiian or other Pacific Islander, non-Hispanic/Latino; 4% international. 1% 25 or older, 95% live on campus, 1% transferred in. Retention: 82% of full-time freshmen returned the following year. Academic areas with the most degrees conferred: biological/life sciences; social sciences; natural resources/environmental science. Core. Calendar: semesters. ESL program, services for LD students, advanced placement, self-designed majors, honors program, independent study, double major, internships. Off campus study at Washington Semester, American University, Washington DC; Duke University Marine Biological Laboratory, Beaufort NC and Bermuda; Ecosystems Center, Massachusetts; Oak Ridge National Laboratory, TN; New York Arts Program, NY; The Philadelphia Center Philadelphia PA; Newberry Seminar Research in the Humanities, Chicago IL. Study abroad program. ROTC: Army (c).

Entrance Requirements: Options: electronic application, early admission, early decision, early action, deferred admission, international baccalaureate accepted. Required: essay, high school transcript, 2 recommendations, college preparatory program. Recommended: interview. Entrance: very difficult. Application deadlines: 2/15, 11/15 for early decision plan 1, 2/1 for early decision plan 2, 12/1 for early action. Notification: 3/15, 11/30 for early decision plan 1, 2/15 for early decision plan 2, 1/1 for early action. SAT Reasoning Test deadline: 2/15. SAT Subject Test deadline: 2/15. Transfer credits accepted: Yes. Applicants placed on waiting list: 174. Wait-listed applicants offered admission: 13. Early decision applicants: 177. Early decision applicants admitted: 70. Early action applicants: 1,989. Early action applicants admitted: 1,627.

Costs Per Year: Comprehensive fee: $61,900 includes full-time tuition ($48,760), mandatory fees ($500), and college room and board ($12,640). College room only: $6670. Part-time tuition: $2032 per credit hour. Part-time mandatory fees: $250 per term.

Collegiate Environment: Orientation program. Drama-theater group, choral group, student-run newspaper, radio station. Social organizations: 89 open to all; national fraternities, national sororities; 22% of eligible men and 23% of eligible women are members. Most popular organizations: Student Government, Gators Activity Programming, Alpha Phi Omega (service fraternity), Outing Club, Greek life. Major annual events: Make A Difference Day, Orchesis Dance Performance, Springfest. Student services: health clinic, personal-psychological counseling. Campus security: 24-hour emergency response devices and patrols, student patrols, late night transport-escort service, controlled dormitory access. 1,776 college housing spaces available; 1,665 were occupied in 2018-19. Freshmen guaranteed college housing. On-campus residence required through senior year. Options: coed, men-only, women-only housing available. Lawrence Lee Pelletier Library. Books: 468,036 (physical), 456,202 (digital/electronic); Serial titles: 72 (physical), 52,931 (digital/electronic); Databases: 1. Weekly public service hours: 115; students can reserve study rooms. Operations spending for the previous fiscal year: $1.8 million. 207 computers available on campus for general student use. A campuswide network can be accessed from student residence rooms and from off campus. Students can access the following: online class registration, placement testing, course catalog, class lists, transcript review and ordering, billing, payroll time cards, internet kiosks, dataports for laptops, campus organizations, financial aid, room draw, registration, class schedules, grade reports.

Community Environment: Population 14,000, Meadville, the seat of Crawford County, is in a rich agricultural and active vacation area. The community lies on the western Appalachian slope. The area is served by plane, bus and interstate highways. There are many churches, a public library, active arts organizations, and a large medical center within the community. Most civic, fraternal, and veteran's organizations are represented here. Local recreational facilities include five movie screens, a professional theater, parks, lakes, and picnic groves. Activities include fishing, boating, hunting, swimming, golf, tennis, a major summer jazz festival, hot-air balloon festival, and folk-art festival. Part-time employment is available.

■ **ALVERNIA UNIVERSITY**
400 Saint Bernardine St.
Reading, PA 19607-1799
Tel: (610)796-8200
Fax: (610)796-8336
E-mail: admissions@alvernia.edu
Web Site: www.alvernia.edu

Description: Independent Roman Catholic, comprehensive, coed. Awards associate, bachelor's, master's, and doctoral degrees. Founded 1958. Setting: 121-acre suburban campus with easy access to Philadelphia. Endowment: $22.4 million. Educational spending for the previous fiscal year: $6910 per student. Total enrollment: 2,872. Faculty: 319 (108 full-time, 211 part-time). Student-undergrad faculty ratio is 12:1. 1,788 applied, 74% were admitted. 11% from top 10% of their high school class, 19% from top quarter, 72% from top half. Full-time: 1,719 students, 72% women, 28% men. Part-time: 604 students, 79% women, 21% men. Students come from 18 states and territories, 6 other countries, 20% from out-of-state. 0.3% American Indian or Alaska Native, non-Hispanic/Latino; 9% Hispanic/Latino; 10% Black or African American, non-Hispanic/Latino; 2% Asian, non-Hispanic/Latino; 0.1% Native Hawaiian or other Pacific Islander, non-Hispanic/Latino; 0.4% international. 7% 25 or older, 59% live on campus, 3% transferred in. Retention: 82% of full-time freshmen returned the following year. Academic areas with the most degrees conferred: health professions and related sciences; business/marketing; homeland security, law enforcement, firefighting, and protective services. Core. Calendar: semesters. Academic remediation for entering students, ESL program, services for LD students, advanced placement, accelerated degree program, self-designed majors, honors program, independent study, distance learning, double major, summer session for credit, part-time degree program, adult/continuing education programs, internships, graduate courses open to undergrads. Off campus study at Washington Center for Internships and Academic Seminars. Study abroad program. ROTC: Army (c).

Entrance Requirements: Options: electronic application, deferred admission, international baccalaureate accepted. Required: essay, high school transcript, SAT or ACT. Recommended: minimum 2 high school GPA, 1 recommendation. Required for some: 2 recommendations, interview. Entrance: moderately difficult. Application deadline: rolling. Notification: continuous. SAT Reasoning Test deadline: 8/1. Transfer credits accepted: Yes.

Collegiate Environment: Orientation program. Drama-theater group, choral group, student-run newspaper. Social organizations: 38 open to all. Most popular organizations: Student Government Association, Student Nurses Association of Alvernia (ASNA), Criminal Justice Association (CJA), Sport Management Association (SMA), Science Association. Major annual events: Spring Fling Weekend, Homecoming and Family Weekend, Winter Formal. Student services: health clinic, personal-psychological counseling. Campus security: 24-hour patrols, late night transport-escort service, controlled dormitory access. Dr. Frank A. Franco Library Learning Center. Books: 90,227 (physical), 7,907 (digital/electronic); Serial titles: 599 (physical), 45,037 (digital/electronic); Databases: 39. Weekly public service hours: 107; students can reserve study rooms. Operations spending for the previous fiscal year: $806,301. 424 computers available on campus for general student use. A campuswide network can be accessed from student residence rooms. Students can access the following: online class registration. Staffed computer lab on campus provides training in use of computers, software, and the Internet.

Community Environment: Alvernia College is located in a tree-lined neighborhood three miles south of the city of Reading. The 85-acre campus adjoins Angelica Lake. Public transportation provides service to within walking distance of the campus. Alvernia is noted for its accessibility to metropolitan and historical areas of interest. Near enough to New York, Philadelphia, and Baltimore to share their cultural and educational opportunities, the college is only a short distance from the Amish country in nearby Lancaster and York counties.

■ **ARCADIA UNIVERSITY**
450 S Easton Rd.
Glenside, PA 19038-3295
Tel: (215)572-2900; Free: 877-ARCADIA
Fax: (215)572-4049
E-mail: admiss@arcadia.edu
Web Site: www.arcadia.edu

Description: Independent, comprehensive, coed, affiliated with Presbyterian Church (U.S.A.). Awards bachelor's, master's, and doctoral degrees and post-master's certificates. Founded 1853. Setting: 76-acre suburban campus with easy access to Philadelphia. Total enrollment: 3,811. Faculty: 477 (179 full-time, 298 part-time). Student-undergrad faculty ratio is 11:1. 8,931 applied, 62% were admitted. 24% from top 10% of their high school class, 55% from top quarter, 89% from top half. Full-time: 2,177 students, 69% women, 31% men. Part-time: 213 students, 65% women, 35% men. Students come from 42 states and territories, 13 other countries, 38% from out-of-state. 0.2% American Indian or Alaska Native, non-Hispanic/Latino; 9% Hispanic/Latino; 10% Black or African American, non-Hispanic/Latino; 5% Asian, non-Hispanic/Latino; 0.2% Native Hawaiian or other Pacific Islander, non-Hispanic/Latino; 3% international. 5% 25 or older, 49% live on campus, 4% transferred in. Retention: 78% of full-time freshmen returned the following year. Academic areas with the most degrees conferred: business/marketing; biological/life sciences; social sciences. Core. Calendar: semesters. ESL program, services for LD students, advanced placement, accelerated degree program, self-designed majors, honors program, independent study, distance learning, double major, summer session for credit, part-time degree program, co-op programs and internships, graduate courses open to undergrads. Off campus study. Study abroad program.

Entrance Requirements: Options: electronic application, deferred admission, international baccalaureate accepted. Required: essay, high school transcript, 2 recommendations, SAT or ACT. Recommended: minimum 3 high school GPA. Required for some: portfolio, audition. Entrance: moderately difficult. Application deadline: 3/1. Notification: continuous until 9/1.

Costs Per Year: Application fee: $30. Comprehensive fee: $57,380 includes full-time tuition ($42,880), mandatory fees ($700), and college room and board ($13,800). College room only: $9000. Room and board charges vary according to board plan and housing facility. Part-time tuition: $715 per credit hour.

Collegiate Environment: Orientation program. Drama-theater group, choral group, student-run newspaper, radio station. Most popular organizations:

Student Program Board, Residence Hall Council, Student Government, Arcadia Christian Fellowship, Student Alumni Association. Major annual events: Mr. Beaver Contest, Woodstock, Spring Fling. Student services: health clinic, personal-psychological counseling. Campus security: 24-hour emergency response devices and patrols, student patrols, late night transport-escort service, controlled dormitory access. Bette E. Landman Library. Students can reserve study rooms.

Community Environment: Population 7,914. Glenside is a suburb of Philadelphia served by railroad, buses, and major highways. There are many churches in the immediate area as well as various civic and fraternal organizations. Local recreational facilities include golf courses, ice rinks, parks, and a swimming pool.

■ **THE ART INSTITUTE OF PITTSBURGH**
420 Blvd. of the Allies
Pittsburgh, PA 15219
Tel: (412)263-6600; Free: 800-275-2470
Fax: (412)263-6667
Web Site: www.artinstitutes.edu/pittsburgh
Description: Proprietary, 4-year, coed. Part of Education Management Corporation. Awards associate and bachelor's degrees. Founded 1921. Setting: urban campus. Calendar: quarters.

■ **BERKS TECHNICAL INSTITUTE**
2205 Ridgewood Rd.
Wyomissing, PA 19610-1168
Tel: (610)372-1722; Free: 866-591-8384
Fax: (610)376-4684
E-mail: abrussolo@berks.edu
Web Site: www.berks.edu
Description: Proprietary, 2-year, coed. Part of Delta Career Education Corporation. Awards diplomas, transfer associate, and terminal associate degrees. Founded 1977. Setting: 8-acre small town campus. Total enrollment: 609. Faculty: 54 (37 full-time, 17 part-time). Full-time: 490 students, 50% women, 50% men. Part-time: 119 students, 59% women, 41% men. 12% 25 or older. Core. Calendar: semesters. Part-time degree program, co-op programs.
Entrance Requirements: Option: early admission. Required: high school transcript, interview. Required for some: CPAt and ACT Compass. Entrance: noncompetitive.
Collegiate Environment: Orientation program. Campus security: 24-hour emergency response devices. Learning Resource Center. 8 computers available on campus for general student use. A campuswide network can be accessed. Students can access the following: online class registration. Staffed computer lab on campus.

■ **BIDWELL TRAINING CENTER**
1815 Metropolitan St.
Pittsburgh, PA 15233
Tel: (412)323-4000; Free: 800-516-1800
Fax: (412)321-2120
E-mail: admissions@mcg-btc.org
Web Site: www.bidwelltraining.edu
Description: Independent, 2-year, coed. Awards certificates and terminal associate degrees. Founded 1968. Total enrollment: 194. Student-undergrad faculty ratio is 12:1. 27 applied, 100% were admitted. 72% 25 or older.

■ **BLOOMSBURG UNIVERSITY OF PENNSYLVANIA**
400 E Second St.
Bloomsburg, PA 17815-1301
Tel: (570)389-4000
Web Site: www.bloomu.edu
Description: State-supported, comprehensive, coed. Part of Pennsylvania State System of Higher Education. Awards bachelor's, master's, and doctoral degrees. Founded 1839. Setting: 366-acre small town campus. Endowment: $45 million. Research spending for the previous fiscal year: $659,980. Educational spending for the previous fiscal year: $9921 per student. Total enrollment: 9,287. Faculty: 519 (419 full-time, 100 part-time). Student-undergrad faculty ratio is 19:1. 9,683 applied, 73% were admitted. 8% from top 10% of their high school class, 29% from top quarter, 63% from top half. Full-time: 7,863 students, 57% women, 43% men. Part-time: 743 students, 57% women, 43% men. Students come from 22 states and territories, 30 other countries, 9% from out-of-state. 0.2% American Indian or Alaska Native, non-Hispanic/Latino; 7% Hispanic/Latino; 9% Black or African

American, non-Hispanic/Latino; 1% Asian, non-Hispanic/Latino; 0.1% Native Hawaiian or other Pacific Islander, non-Hispanic/Latino; 0.5% international. 5% 25 or older, 41% live on campus, 5% transferred in. Retention: 74% of full-time freshmen returned the following year. Academic areas with the most degrees conferred: business/marketing; health professions and related sciences; communication/journalism. Core. Calendar: semesters. Academic remediation for entering students, ESL program, services for LD students, advanced placement, self-designed majors, honors program, independent study, distance learning, double major, summer session for credit, part-time degree program, co-op programs and internships, graduate courses open to undergrads. Off campus study at BAS Technical Leadership (degree completion programs) at Lehigh Carbon Community College, Reading Area Community College, Harrisburg Area Community College at Dixon Center, Northampton Community College, and State System @ Center City Philadelphia. Study abroad program. ROTC: Army, Air Force (c).
Entrance Requirements: Options: electronic application, early admission, early action, deferred admission, international baccalaureate accepted. Required: high school transcript, SAT or ACT. Entrance: minimally difficult. Application deadline: rolling. Notification: continuous until 9/18, 5/1 for early action. SAT Reasoning Test deadline: 12/30. Transfer credits accepted: Yes.
Costs Per Year: Application fee: $35. State resident tuition: $7716 full-time, $322 per credit part-time. Nonresident tuition: $19,290 full-time, $805 per credit part-time. Mandatory fees: $3242 full-time, $118.50 per credit part-time, $75 per term part-time. Full-time tuition and fees vary according to course load and location. Part-time tuition and fees vary according to course load and location. College room and board: $9686. College room only: $6308. Room and board charges vary according to board plan and housing facility.
Collegiate Environment: Orientation program. Drama-theater group, choral group, marching band, student-run newspaper, radio station. Social organizations: 250 open to all; national fraternities, national sororities, local fraternities, local sororities. Most popular organizations: Living and Learning Communities, Band and Music Groups, Greek Organizations, Residence Hall Councils, Club Sports. Major annual events: Homecoming, The Big Event (community service event), Parents/Family Weekend. Student services: legal services, health clinic, personal-psychological counseling, women's center. Campus security: 24-hour emergency response devices and patrols, late night transport-escort service, controlled dormitory access, monitored surveillance cameras. Andruss Library. Books: 374,393 (physical), 269,435 (digital/electronic); Serial titles: 5,838 (physical), 84,065 (digital/electronic); Databases: 165. Weekly public service hours: 98; students can reserve study rooms. Operations spending for the previous fiscal year: $3.8 million. 1,571 computers available on campus for general student use. Computer purchase/lease plans available. A campuswide network can be accessed. Students can access the following: online class registration. Staffed computer lab on campus.
Community Environment: Population 12,915. Bloomsburg is located 40 miles southeast of Williamsport. Average winter temperature is 31 degrees; with a summer mean temperature of 70 degrees. The area is served by railroad, bus, and airlines. The community has multiple lodging accommodations, several churches of various denominations, a public library, and a hospital. There are numerous civic, fraternal and veteran's organizations in the area. Part-time employment is available.

■ **BRYN ATHYN COLLEGE OF THE NEW CHURCH**
2965 College Dr.
Bryn Athyn, PA 19009-0717
Tel: (267)502-2400; Free: 800-767-9552
Fax: (267)502-2658
E-mail: admissions@brynathyn.edu
Web Site: www.brynathyn.edu
Description: Independent, comprehensive, coed, affiliated with Church of the New Jerusalem. Part of The Academy of the New Church. Awards associate, bachelor's, and master's degrees. Founded 1877. Setting: 130-acre suburban campus with easy access to Philadelphia. System endowment: $58.8 million. Research spending for the previous fiscal year: $263,787. Educational spending for the previous fiscal year: $12,415 per student. Total enrollment: 318. Faculty: 51 (42 full-time, 9 part-time). Student-undergrad faculty ratio is 6:1. 250 applied, 89% were admitted. Full-time: 282 students, 53% women, 47% men. Part-time: 27 students, 56% women, 44% men. 22% from out-of-state. 1% American Indian or Alaska Native, non-Hispanic/Latino; 8% Hispanic/Latino; 16% Black or African American, non-Hispanic/Latino; 2% Asian, non-Hispanic/Latino; 0.3% Native Hawaiian or other Pacific Islander, non-Hispanic/Latino; 5% international. 1% 25 or older, 44%

live on campus, 7% transferred in. Retention: 65% of full-time freshmen returned the following year. Academic areas with the most degrees conferred: business/marketing; psychology; biological/life sciences. Core. Calendar: trimesters. Academic remediation for entering students, ESL program, services for LD students, advanced placement, accelerated degree program, self-designed majors, independent study, part-time degree program, co-op programs and internships. Study abroad program. ROTC: Army (c), Air Force (c).

Entrance Requirements: Options: electronic application, deferred admission. Required: essay, high school transcript, minimum 2 high school GPA, 1 recommendation, SAT or ACT. Required for some: interview. Entrance: minimally difficult. Application deadline: rolling. Notification: continuous. Transfer credits accepted: Yes.

Costs Per Year: Application fee: $0. Comprehensive fee: $34,746 includes full-time tuition ($21,360), mandatory fees ($1500), and college room and board ($11,886). College room only: $5943. Part-time tuition: $880 per credit hour. Part-time mandatory fees: $58 per credit hour.

Collegiate Environment: Orientation program. Drama-theater group, choral group. Social organizations: 10 open to all. Most popular organizations: C.A.R.E. (Community Service), Social council, International Student Organization, Peer Advisory Council, Student Government. Major annual events: Charter Day, Service Day, Graduation. Student services: health clinic, personal-psychological counseling. Campus security: 24-hour emergency response devices, controlled dormitory access, 18-hour patrols by trained personnel. Freshmen given priority for college housing. Options: men-only, women-only housing available. Swedenborg Library plus 1 other. Books: 70,742 (physical), 252 (digital/electronic); Serial titles: 834 (physical), 74 (digital/electronic); Databases: 13. Operations spending for the previous fiscal year: $431,436. 18 computers available on campus for general student use. A computer is required for all students. A campuswide network can be accessed from student residence rooms and from off campus. Students can access the following: online class registration. Staffed computer lab on campus provides training in use of computers and software.

■ **BRYN MAWR COLLEGE**
101 N Merion Ave.
Bryn Mawr, PA 19010-2899
Tel: (610)526-5000; Free: 800-BMC-1885
Fax: (610)526-7471
E-mail: chorsey@brynmawr.edu
Web Site: www.brynmawr.edu

Description: Independent, comprehensive. Awards bachelor's, master's, and doctoral degrees. Founded 1885. Setting: 135-acre suburban campus with easy access to Philadelphia. Endowment: $852.7 million. Research spending for the previous fiscal year: $3.3 million. Educational spending for the previous fiscal year: $30,579 per student. Total enrollment: 1,640. Faculty: 201 (159 full-time, 42 part-time). Student-undergrad faculty ratio is 8:1. 2,936 applied, 38% were admitted. 68% from top 10% of their high school class, 91% from top quarter, 97% from top half. 6 valedictorians. Full-time: 1,325 students, 99% women, 1% men. Part-time: 9 students, 89% women, 11% men. Students come from 48 states and territories, 58 other countries, 82% from out-of-state. 9% Hispanic/Latino; 6% Black or African American, non-Hispanic/Latino; 12% Asian, non-Hispanic/Latino; 0.1% Native Hawaiian or other Pacific Islander, non-Hispanic/Latino; 23% international. 1% 25 or older, 91% live on campus, 1% transferred in. Retention: 92% of full-time freshmen returned the following year. Academic areas with the most degrees conferred: social sciences; mathematics and statistics; biological/life sciences; psychology; foreign languages and literature; interdisciplinary studies. Core. Calendar: semesters. Academic remediation for entering students, services for LD students, advanced placement, accelerated degree program, self-designed majors, independent study, double major, summer session for credit, internships, graduate courses open to undergrads. Off campus study at Haverford College, Swarthmore College, University of Pennsylvania, Spelman College, Villanova University, Temple University. Study abroad program. ROTC: Air Force (c).

Entrance Requirements: Options: electronic application, early admission, early decision, deferred admission, international baccalaureate accepted. Required: essay, high school transcript, 3 recommendations. Recommended: interview. Required for some: SAT and SAT Subject Tests or ACT. Entrance: most difficult. Application deadlines: 1/15, 11/15 for early decision plan 1, 1/1 for early decision plan 2. Notification: 4/1, 12/15 for early decision plan 1, 2/1 for early decision plan 2. SAT Reasoning Test deadline: 1/15. Transfer credits accepted: Yes. Applicants placed on waiting list: 734. Wait-listed applicants offered admission: 21. Early decision applicants: 276. Early decision applicants admitted: 145.

Costs Per Year: Application fee: $50. Comprehensive fee: $68,860 includes full-time tuition ($51,130), mandatory fees ($1230), and college room and board ($16,500). College room only: $9420. Part-time tuition: $6390 per course.

Collegiate Environment: Orientation program. Drama-theater group, choral group, student-run newspaper, radio station. Social organizations: 175 open to all. Most popular organization: Student Government Association. Major annual events: Fall Frolic, Lantern Night, May Day. Student services: health clinic, personal-psychological counseling, women's center. Campus security: 24-hour emergency response devices and patrols, late night transport-escort service, controlled dormitory access, shuttle bus service, awareness programs, bicycle registration, security Website. Canaday Library plus 2 others. Books: 740,887 (physical), 754,968 (digital/electronic); Serial titles: 9,146 (physical), 123,010 (digital/electronic); Databases: 170. Weekly public service hours: 105; study areas open 24 hours, 5-7 days a week. Operations spending for the previous fiscal year: $5.7 million. 125 computers available on campus for general student use. A campuswide network can be accessed from student residence rooms and from off campus. Students can access the following: online class registration. Staffed computer lab on campus provides training in use of computers, software, and the Internet.

Community Environment: Population 4,382, Bryn Mawr is a suburban area 11 miles from Philadelphia. The immediate area has two clinics and a hospital, a public library, and churches of major denominations. Nearby Philadelphia offers all the facilities of a large city. Part-time employment opportunities are limited.

■ **BUCKNELL UNIVERSITY**
One Dent Dr.
Lewisburg, PA 17837
Tel: (570)577-2000
Fax: (570)577-3760
E-mail: admissions@bucknell.edu
Web Site: www.bucknell.edu

Description: Independent, comprehensive, coed. Awards bachelor's and master's degrees. Founded 1846. Setting: 446-acre small town campus. Endowment: $851.3 million. Research spending for the previous fiscal year: $3.2 million. Educational spending for the previous fiscal year: $23,060 per student. Total enrollment: 3,668. Faculty: 422 (384 full-time, 38 part-time). Student-undergrad faculty ratio is 9:1. 10,144 applied, 33% were admitted. 58% from top 10% of their high school class, 85% from top quarter, 98% from top half. 5 National Merit Scholars, 19 valedictorians. Full-time: 3,581 students, 51% women, 49% men. Part-time: 16 students, 56% women, 44% men. Students come from 42 states and territories, 50 other countries, 79% from out-of-state. 0.1% American Indian or Alaska Native, non-Hispanic/Latino; 7% Hispanic/Latino; 4% Black or African American, non-Hispanic/Latino; 6% Asian, non-Hispanic/Latino; 7% international. 1% 25 or older, 92% live on campus, 1% transferred in. Retention: 92% of full-time freshmen returned the following year. Academic areas with the most degrees conferred: social sciences; engineering; business/marketing. Calendar: semesters. Services for LD students, advanced placement, self-designed majors, honors program, independent study, double major, summer session for credit, part-time degree program, internships, graduate courses open to undergrads. Off campus study at American University, Semester at Sea. Study abroad program. ROTC: Army.

Entrance Requirements: Options: electronic application, early decision, deferred admission, international baccalaureate accepted. Required: essay, high school transcript, 1 recommendation. Entrance: most difficult. Application deadlines: 1/15, 11/15 for early decision. Notification: 4/1, 12/15 for early decision. Preference given to children of alumni. SAT Reasoning Test deadline: 2/15. Transfer credits accepted: Yes. Applicants placed on waiting list: 2,726. Wait-listed applicants offered admission: 78. Early decision applicants: 719. Early decision applicants admitted: 400.

Costs Per Year: Application fee: $40. Comprehensive fee: $72,370 includes full-time tuition ($57,882), mandatory fees ($314), and college room and board ($14,174). College room only: $8644. Part-time tuition: $6352 per course.

Collegiate Environment: Orientation program. Drama-theater group, choral group, student-run newspaper, radio station. Social organizations: 176 open to all; national fraternities, national sororities; 48% of eligible men and 56% of eligible women are members. Most popular organizations: Black Student Union, Outing Club, Activities and Campus Events, French Club, Catholic Campus Ministries. Major annual events: Homecoming, Chrysalis Ball, Family Weekend. Student services: health clinic, personal-psychological counseling, women's center. Campus security: 24-hour emergency response devices and patrols, student patrols, late night transport-escort service, controlled dormitory access. 3,405 college housing spaces available; 3,353 were occupied in 2018-19. Freshmen guaranteed college housing. On-campus residence required through senior year. Options: coed, women-only housing available. Ellen Clarke Bertrand Library. Books: 673,158 (physical), 849,294 (digital/electronic); Serial titles: 264 (physical), 49,759 (digital/electronic); Databases: 237. Weekly public service hours: 125. Operations spending for the previous fiscal year: $4.3 million. 1,038 computers available on campus for general student use. A campuswide network can be accessed from student residence rooms and from off campus. Students can access the following: online class registration. Staffed computer lab on campus provides training in use of computers, software, and the Internet.

Community Environment: Lewisburg, population 5,500, is the county seat and the commercial center of a prosperous farming area. Some industries in the city produce textiles, furniture, business forms, and electronic materials. Some part-time employment is available.

■ **BUCKS COUNTY COMMUNITY COLLEGE**
275 Swamp Rd.
Newtown, PA 18940-1525
Tel: (215)968-8000
Fax: (215)968-8110
E-mail: marlene.barlow@bucks.edu
Web Site: www.bucks.edu

Description: County-supported, 2-year, coed. Awards certificates, transfer associate, and terminal associate degrees. Founded 1964. Setting: 200-acre suburban campus with easy access to Philadelphia. Endowment: $7.1 million. Total enrollment: 7,761. Faculty: 638 (146 full-time, 492 part-time). Student-undergrad faculty ratio is 15:1. 3,742 applied, 91% were admitted. Full-time: 2,852 students, 52% women, 48% men. Part-time: 4,909 students, 60% women, 40% men. Students come from 18 states and territories, 1% from out-of-state. 0.5% American Indian or Alaska Native, non-Hispanic/Latino; 8% Hispanic/Latino; 6% Black or African American, non-Hispanic/Latino; 4% Asian, non-Hispanic/Latino; 0.2% Native Hawaiian or other Pacific Islander, non-Hispanic/Latino; 0.4% international. 27% 25 or older, 72% transferred in. Retention: 69% of full-time freshmen returned the following year. Core. Calendar: semesters. Academic remediation for entering students, ESL program, services for LD students, advanced placement, self-designed majors, independent study, distance learning, summer session for credit, part-time degree program, external degree program, adult/continuing education programs, co-op programs and internships.

Entrance Requirements: Open admission. Options: electronic application, early admission. Required: high school transcript. Required for some: essay, interview. Entrance: noncompetitive. Transfer credits accepted: Yes.

Costs Per Year: Application fee: $0. Area resident tuition: $4500 full-time, $150 per credit hour part-time. State resident tuition: $9000 full-time, $300 per credit hour part-time. Nonresident tuition: $13,500 full-time, $450 per credit hour part-time. Mandatory fees: $1160 full-time, $62 per credit hour part-time, $247 per term part-time. Full-time tuition and fees vary according to program. Part-time tuition and fees vary according to program.

Collegiate Environment: Orientation program. Drama-theater group, choral group, student-run newspaper, radio station. Social organizations: 56 open to all; 1% of eligible men and 1% of eligible women are members. Most popular organizations: Bucks Lemon Club, Kinesiology & Sports Studies Club, NSLS, Bucks Business Association, Bucks County Anthropology Society. Major annual event: Spring Fling. Student services: personal-psychological counseling, women's center. Campus security: 24-hour emergency response devices and patrols, late night transport-escort service. College housing not available. Bucks County Community College Library. Books: 111,025 (physical), 8,473 (digital/electronic); Serial titles: 186 (physical), 66 (digital/electronic); Databases: 59. Weekly public service hours: 73; students can reserve study rooms. 1,406 computers available on campus for general student use. A campuswide network can be accessed from off-campus. Students can access the following: online class registration, e-mail, online course work, learning management system. Staffed computer lab on campus provides training in use of computers, software, and the Internet.

Community Environment: Population 2,256. Newtown is a suburb of Philadelphia located approximately 20 miles from the heart of the downtown area.

■ **BUTLER COUNTY COMMUNITY COLLEGE**
107 College Dr.
Butler, PA 16003-1203
Tel: (724)287-8711; Free: 888-826-2829

Fax: (724)285-6047
E-mail: robert.morris@bc3.edu
Web Site: www.bc3.edu

Description: County-supported, 2-year, coed. Awards certificates, transfer associate, and terminal associate degrees. Founded 1965. Setting: 300-acre rural campus with easy access to Pittsburgh. Total enrollment: 3,573. Faculty: 351. Student-undergrad faculty ratio is 18:1. 1% from out-of-state. 0.1% American Indian or Alaska Native, non-Hispanic/Latino; 2% Hispanic/Latino; 3% Black or African American, non-Hispanic/Latino; 0.3% Asian, non-Hispanic/Latino; 0.2% international. 29% 25 or older. Core. Calendar: semesters. Academic remediation for entering students, ESL program, services for LD students, advanced placement, distance learning, summer session for credit, part-time degree program, adult/continuing education programs, co-op programs and internships.

Entrance Requirements: Open admission except for nursing, metrology, physical therapist assistant, massage therapy, medical assistant programs. Option: electronic application. Required: high school transcript. Required for some: interview. Entrance: noncompetitive. Application deadline: 8/15. Notification: continuous until 8/15. Transfer credits accepted: Yes.

Costs Per Year: Application fee: $25. Area resident tuition: $3390 full-time, $113 per credit hour part-time. State resident tuition: $6390 full-time, $213 per credit hour part-time. Nonresident tuition: $9390 full-time, $313 per credit hour part-time. Mandatory fees: $1560 full-time, $52 per credit hour part-time.

Collegiate Environment: Orientation program. Student-run newspaper. Student services: personal-psychological counseling. Campus security: 24-hour emergency response devices, late night transport-escort service. John A. Beck, Jr. Library. Books: 60,000 (digital/electronic). 350 computers available on campus for general student use. Students can access the following: online class registration. Staffed computer lab on campus provides training in use of computers, software, and the Internet.

Community Environment: In a region rich in coal, oil, natural gas and limestone, Butler's industries produce steel, cement, oil, glass, and metal products. The climate is temperate, and the average annual temperature is 50.6 degrees. The community has access to rail and air, and services include hospitals, churches, a library, YMCA, and YWCA. Local recreation includes boating, swimming, skiing, golf, parks, and movie theaters. Part-time employment is available.

■ **CABRINI UNIVERSITY**
610 King of Prussia Rd.
Radnor, PA 19087
Tel: (610)902-8100; Free: 800-848-1003
Fax: (610)902-8309
E-mail: admit@cabrini.edu
Web Site: www.cabrini.edu

Description: Independent Roman Catholic, comprehensive, coed. Awards bachelor's, master's, and doctoral degrees. Founded 1957. Setting: 112-acre suburban campus with easy access to Philadelphia. Endowment: $43.7 million. Educational spending for the previous fiscal year: $7826 per student. Total enrollment: 2,436. Faculty: 231 (83 full-time, 148 part-time). Student-undergrad faculty ratio is 13:1. 3,186 applied, 71% were admitted. Full-time: 1,384 students, 62% women, 38% men. Part-time: 266 students, 56% women, 44% men. Students come from 24 states and territories, 1 other country, 29% from out-of-state. 0.1% American Indian or Alaska Native, non-Hispanic/Latino; 10% Hispanic/Latino; 20% Black or African American, non-Hispanic/Latino; 2% Asian, non-Hispanic/Latino; 0.2% Native Hawaiian or other Pacific Islander, non-Hispanic/Latino; 0.3% international. 6% 25 or older, 62% live on campus, 4% transferred in. Retention: 70% of full-time freshmen returned the following year. Academic areas with the most degrees conferred: business/marketing; education; communication/journalism. Core. Calendar: semesters. Academic remediation for entering students, services for LD students, advanced placement, self-designed majors, honors program, independent study, distance learning, double major, summer session for credit, part-time degree program, adult/continuing education programs, co-op programs and internships, graduate courses open to undergrads. Off campus study at Eastern University, Rosemont College, Valley Forge Military College, SouthEastern Pennsylvania Consortium for Higher Education (SEPCHE). Study abroad program. ROTC: Army (c), Naval (c), Air Force (c).

Entrance Requirements: Options: electronic application, deferred admission, international baccalaureate accepted. Required: essay, high school transcript, minimum 2 high school GPA. Recommended: minimum 2 high school GPA, 1 recommendation, interview, SAT or ACT. Entrance:

moderately difficult. Application deadline: rolling. SAT Reasoning Test deadline: 8/29. SAT Subject Test deadline: 8/29. Transfer credits accepted: Yes.

Costs Per Year: Application fee: $20. Comprehensive fee: $44,186 includes full-time tuition ($30,950), mandatory fees ($970), and college room and board ($12,266). Room and board charges vary according to board plan and housing facility. Part-time tuition: $550 per credit hour. Part-time mandatory fees: $45 per term. Part-time tuition and fees vary according to course load.

Collegiate Environment: Orientation program. Drama-theater group, choral group, student-run newspaper, radio station. Social organizations: 46 open to all; national fraternities, national sororities. Most popular organizations: Campus Activities and Programming (CAP) Board, Student Government Association (SGA), Black Student Union, Catholic Relief Services (CRS) Ambassadors, Cabrini Friends of Exceptional Children (CFEC). Major annual events: Cabrini Spirit Week, Cabrini Night at the Phillies, Arts, Research, and Scholarship Symposium. Student services: health clinic, personal-psychological counseling. Campus security: 24-hour emergency response devices and patrols, student patrols, late night transport-escort service, controlled dormitory access, Resident Assistants and Directors on nightly duty. Holy Spirit Library. Books: 143,980 (digital/electronic); Serial titles: 67 (physical), 68,500 (digital/electronic); Databases: 47. Weekly public service hours: 97. Operations spending for the previous fiscal year: $712,534. 575 computers available on campus for general student use. A campuswide network can be accessed from student residence rooms and from off campus. Students can access the following: online class registration, account balances. Staffed computer lab on campus (open 24 hours a day) provides training in use of computers, software, and the Internet.

Community Environment: See Villanova University.

■ **CAIRN UNIVERSITY**
200 Manor Ave.
Langhorne, PA 19047-2990
Tel: (215)752-5800; Free: 800-366-0049
Fax: (215)752-5812
E-mail: admissions@cairn.edu
Web Site: cairn.edu

Description: Independent nondenominational, comprehensive, coed. Awards bachelor's and master's degrees. Founded 1913. Setting: 115-acre suburban campus with easy access to Philadelphia. Endowment: $11 million. Educational spending for the previous fiscal year: $5995 per student. Total enrollment: 1,052. Faculty: 123 (45 full-time, 78 part-time). Student-undergrad faculty ratio is 12:1. 345 applied, 99% were admitted. 19% from top 10% of their high school class, 36% from top quarter, 58% from top half. Full-time: 726 students, 56% women, 44% men. Part-time: 36 students, 53% women, 47% men. Students come from 29 states and territories, 20 other countries, 46% from out-of-state. 0.3% American Indian or Alaska Native, non-Hispanic/Latino; 6% Hispanic/Latino; 13% Black or African American, non-Hispanic/Latino; 4% Asian, non-Hispanic/Latino; 3% international. 12% 25 or older, 62% live on campus, 9% transferred in. Retention: 74% of full-time freshmen returned the following year. Academic areas with the most degrees conferred: education; public administration and social services; psychology. Core. Calendar: semesters. Academic remediation for entering students, services for LD students, advanced placement, accelerated degree program, honors program, independent study, double major, summer session for credit, part-time degree program, adult/continuing education programs, internships, graduate courses open to undergrads. Off campus study. Study abroad program. ROTC: Air Force (c).

Entrance Requirements: Options: electronic application, early admission, deferred admission, international baccalaureate accepted. Required: essay, high school transcript, minimum 2 high school GPA, interview, SAT or ACT. Entrance: moderately difficult. Application deadline: rolling. Notification: continuous. Transfer credits accepted: Yes.

Costs Per Year: Application fee: $25. Comprehensive fee: $37,573 includes full-time tuition ($26,979), mandatory fees ($300), and college room and board ($10,294). College room only: $5389. Full-time tuition and fees vary according to course load. Room and board charges vary according to board plan and location. Part-time tuition: $800 per credit. Part-time tuition varies according to course load.

Collegiate Environment: Orientation program. Drama-theater group, choral group, student-run newspaper. Social organizations: 18 open to all. Most popular organizations: Ascend (outdoor adventure club), Chi Beta Sigma (Social Work Club), Enactus (Business), Mu Kappa (Missionary Kids Association), Student Visual Arts Society. Major annual events: Homecoming, Hoedown, Christmas Celebration. Student services: health clinic, personal-psychological counseling. Campus security: 24-hour emergency response devices and patrols, student patrols, late night transport-escort service, controlled dormitory access. Masland Learning Resource Center. Books: 104,860 (physical), 421,604 (digital/electronic); Serial titles: 945 (physical), 53,295 (digital/electronic); Databases: 177. Weekly public service hours: 86; students can reserve study rooms. Operations spending for the previous fiscal year: $982,922. 55 computers available on campus for general student use. Computer purchase/lease plans available. A campuswide network can be accessed from student residence rooms and from off campus. Students can access the following: online class registration. Staffed computer lab on campus provides training in use of computers, software, and the Internet.

■ **CALIFORNIA UNIVERSITY OF PENNSYLVANIA**
250 University Ave.
California, PA 15419-1394
Tel: (724)938-4000; Free: 888-412-0479
Fax: (724)938-4138
E-mail: sheetz@calu.edu
Web Site: www.calu.edu

Description: State-supported, comprehensive, coed. Part of Pennsylvania State System of Higher Education. Awards associate, bachelor's, master's, and doctoral degrees and post-master's certificates. Founded 1852. Setting: 188-acre rural campus with easy access to Pittsburgh. Endowment: $24.1 million. Research spending for the previous fiscal year: $124,671. Educational spending for the previous fiscal year: $8176 per student. Total enrollment: 7,312. Faculty: 416 (274 full-time, 142 part-time). Student-undergrad faculty ratio is 20:1. 2,909 applied, 97% were admitted. 5% from top 10% of their high school class, 22% from top quarter, 55% from top half. Full-time: 4,212 students, 53% women, 47% men. Part-time: 962 students, 60% women, 40% men. Students come from 49 states and territories, 36 other countries, 7% from out-of-state. 0.2% American Indian or Alaska Native, non-Hispanic/Latino; 3% Hispanic/Latino; 14% Black or African American, non-Hispanic/Latino; 0.9% Asian, non-Hispanic/Latino; 0.1% Native Hawaiian or other Pacific Islander, non-Hispanic/Latino; 0.9% international. 10% 25 or older, 48% live on campus, 14% transferred in. Retention: 71% of full-time freshmen returned the following year. Academic areas with the most degrees conferred: health professions and related sciences; business/marketing; parks and recreation. Core. Calendar: semesters. Academic remediation for entering students, ESL program, services for LD students, advanced placement, accelerated degree program, honors program, independent study, distance learning, double major, summer session for credit, part-time degree program, adult/continuing education programs, co-op programs and internships, graduate courses open to undergrads. Off campus study. Study abroad program. ROTC: Army.

Entrance Requirements: Options: electronic application, deferred admission. Required: high school transcript, SAT or ACT. Entrance: moderately difficult. Application deadline: rolling. Notification: continuous. Transfer credits accepted: Yes.

Costs Per Year: Application fee: $35.

Collegiate Environment: Orientation program. Drama-theater group, choral group, marching band, student-run newspaper, radio station. Social organizations: 179 open to all; national fraternities, national sororities; 5% of eligible men and 6% of eligible women are members. Most popular organizations: Commuter Council, STAND, Student Activities Board, University Band, Colleges Against Cancer. Major annual events: Homecoming, Sporting events, Concerts. Student services: legal services, health clinic, personal-psychological counseling, women's center. Campus security: 24-hour emergency response devices and patrols, student patrols, late night transport-escort service, controlled dormitory access. Freshmen guaranteed college housing. On-campus residence required in freshman year. Option: coed housing available. Manderino Library. Books: 220,974 (physical), 339,919 (digital/electronic); Serial titles: 22,122 (physical), 61,720 (digital/electronic); Databases: 96. Students can reserve study rooms. Operations spending for the previous fiscal year: $2.6 million. 1,300 computers available on campus for general student use. Students can access the following: online class registration. Staffed computer lab on campus.

Community Environment: Population 5,072. California is located 35 miles south of Pittsburgh on the Monogahela River. This is a coal mining region of the Appalachian Foothills. Some part-time employment is available.

■ **CARLOW UNIVERSITY**
3333 Fifth Ave.
Pittsburgh, PA 15213-3165
Tel: (412)578-6000; Free: 800-333-CARLOW

Fax: (412)578-6668
E-mail: admissions@carlow.edu
Web Site: www.carlow.edu
Description: Independent Roman Catholic, comprehensive, coed. Awards bachelor's, master's, and doctoral degrees and post-master's certificates. Founded 1929. Setting: 13-acre urban campus with easy access to Pittsburgh. Total enrollment: 2,140. Faculty: 260 (96 full-time, 164 part-time). Student-undergrad faculty ratio is 12:1. 877 applied, 91% were admitted. 16% from top 10% of their high school class, 41% from top quarter, 78% from top half. Full-time: 1,075 students, 84% women, 16% men. Part-time: 290 students, 86% women, 14% men. 5% from out-of-state. 0.2% American Indian or Alaska Native, non-Hispanic/Latino; 2% Hispanic/Latino; 18% Black or African American, non-Hispanic/Latino; 2% Asian, non-Hispanic/Latino; 0.1% Native Hawaiian or other Pacific Islander, non-Hispanic/Latino; 0.2% international. 27% 25 or older, 32% live on campus, 14% transferred in. Academic areas with the most degrees conferred: health professions and related sciences; business/marketing; psychology. Core. Calendar: semesters. Academic remediation for entering students, services for LD students, advanced placement, accelerated degree program, honors program, independent study, distance learning, double major, summer session for credit, part-time degree program, co-op programs and internships, graduate courses open to undergrads. Off campus study at 9 members of the Pittsburgh Council on Higher Education. Study abroad program. ROTC: Army (c), Naval (c), Air Force (c).
Entrance Requirements: Options: electronic application, deferred admission, international baccalaureate accepted. Required: high school transcript, SAT or ACT. Recommended: essay, minimum 2.5 high school GPA, interview, SAT and SAT Subject Tests or ACT. Entrance: minimally difficult. Application deadline: rolling. Notification: continuous. SAT Reasoning Test deadline: 8/15. Transfer credits accepted: Yes. Applicants placed on waiting list: 0.
Collegiate Environment: Orientation program. Drama-theater group, choral group, student-run newspaper. Social organizations: national fraternities, local sororities, Service sororities. Most popular organizations: Student Government Association, Campus Activities Board, SPiRiT (Student Ambassadors), SNAP (Student Nursing Association), PSEA (School Education Association). Major annual events: Spring Fair, Fashion for Kids' Sake, Campus Activities Fair. Student services: health clinic, personal-psychological counseling. Campus security: 24-hour emergency response devices and patrols, late night transport-escort service, controlled dormitory access. Grace Library.
Community Environment: The campus occupies 14 acres in the Oakland section of Pittsburgh, which is the educational heart of the city. Carlow is within walking distance of several other colleges and universities, and students enjoy all the educational and social opportunities this collection of institutions offers. The school is just 10 minutes from downtown Pittsburgh. The metropolitan center of Western Pennsylvania and one of the country's largest corporate headquarters, Pittsburgh is rich in educational, medical, entertainment, cultural, and business activities. Pittsburgh is also noted for its professional sports teams, ballet and theater companies, outdoor art festivals and river regattas, and multiple venues that attract a wide range of entertainment.

■ CARNEGIE MELLON UNIVERSITY
5000 Forbes Ave.
Pittsburgh, PA 15213-3891
Tel: (412)268-2000
Fax: (412)268-7838
E-mail: admission@andrew.cmu.edu
Web Site: www.cmu.edu
Description: Independent, university, coed. Awards bachelor's, master's, and doctoral degrees and post-master's certificates. Founded 1900. Setting: 153-acre urban campus with easy access to Pittsburgh. Endowment: $1.9 billion. Total enrollment: 14,625. Faculty: 1,098 (1,049 full-time, 49 part-time). Student-undergrad faculty ratio is 13:1. 24,351 applied, 17% were admitted. 87% from top 10% of their high school class, 97% from top quarter, 99% from top half. Full-time: 6,680 students, 50% women, 50% men. Part-time: 265 students, 45% women, 55% men. Students come from 50 states and territories, 54 other countries, 86% from out-of-state. 9% Hispanic/Latino; 4% Black or African American, non-Hispanic/Latino; 30% Asian, non-Hispanic/Latino; 22% international. 58% live on campus, 1% transferred in. Retention: 97% of full-time freshmen returned the following year. Academic areas with the most degrees conferred: engineering; computer and information sciences; business/marketing. Calendar: semesters. Services for LD

students, advanced placement, accelerated degree program, self-designed majors, independent study, distance learning, double major, summer session for credit, part-time degree program, co-op programs and internships, graduate courses open to undergrads. Off campus study at members of the Pittsburgh Council on Higher Education. Study abroad program. ROTC: Army (c), Naval, Air Force (c).
Entrance Requirements: Options: electronic application, early admission, early decision, deferred admission, international baccalaureate accepted. Required: essay, high school transcript, SAT or ACT. Recommended: SAT Subject Tests. Required for some: audition/portfolio for fine arts. Entrance: most difficult. Application deadlines: 1/1, 11/1 for early decision. Notification: 4/1, 12/15 for early decision. SAT Reasoning Test deadline: 12/1. SAT Subject Test deadline: 12/1. Applicants placed on waiting list: 3,677. Wait-listed applicants offered admission: 109. Early decision applicants: 1,641. Early decision applicants admitted: 346.
Costs Per Year: Application fee: $75. Comprehensive fee: $72,091 includes full-time tuition ($55,816), mandatory fees ($1303), and college room and board ($14,972). College room only: $8822. Part-time tuition: $776 per unit.
Collegiate Environment: Orientation program. Drama-theater group, choral group, marching band, student-run newspaper, radio station. Social organizations: national fraternities, national sororities. Major annual events: Spring Carnival, Homecoming, Drama Performances. Student services: legal services, health clinic, personal-psychological counseling. Campus security: 24-hour emergency response devices and patrols, late night transport-escort service, controlled dormitory access. 3,607 college housing spaces available; 3,581 were occupied in 2018-19. Freshmen guaranteed college housing. On-campus residence required in freshman year. Options: coed, men-only, women-only housing available. Hunt Library plus 2 others. Weekly public service hours: 168; study areas open 24 hours, 5-7 days a week; students can reserve study rooms. 462 computers available on campus for general student use. Computer purchase/lease plans available. A campuswide network can be accessed from student residence rooms and from off campus. Students can access the following: online class registration. Staffed computer lab on campus provides training in use of computers, software, and the Internet.
Community Environment: See University of Pittsburgh.

■ CEDAR CREST COLLEGE
100 College Dr.
Allentown, PA 18104-6196
Tel: (610)437-4471; Free: 800-360-1222
Fax: (610)606-4647
E-mail: admissions@cedarcrest.edu
Web Site: www.cedarcrest.edu
Description: Independent, comprehensive, coed, affiliated with United Church of Christ. Awards bachelor's and master's degrees and post-master's certificates. Founded 1867. Setting: 84-acre suburban campus with easy access to Philadelphia. Total enrollment: 1,664. Faculty: 221 (77 full-time, 144 part-time). Student-undergrad faculty ratio is 10:1. 1,208 applied, 63% were admitted. 20% from top 10% of their high school class, 44% from top quarter, 80% from top half. Full-time: 931 students, 88% women, 12% men. Part-time: 502 students, 88% women, 12% men. 15% from out-of-state. 0.1% American Indian or Alaska Native, non-Hispanic/Latino; 3% Hispanic/Latino; 9% Black or African American, non-Hispanic/Latino; 9% Asian, non-Hispanic/Latino; 1% Native Hawaiian or other Pacific Islander, non-Hispanic/Latino; 0.4% international. 36% 25 or older, 32% live on campus, 3% transferred in. Retention: 82% of full-time freshmen returned the following year. Academic areas with the most degrees conferred: health professions and related sciences; business/marketing; psychology. Core. Calendar: semesters. Academic remediation for entering students, services for LD students, advanced placement, self-designed majors, honors program, independent study, double major, summer session for credit, part-time degree program, internships, graduate courses open to undergrads. Off campus study at 6 members of the Lehigh Valley Association of Independent Colleges, OCICU Online Consortium of Independent Colleges and Universities.
Entrance Requirements: Options: electronic application, early admission, deferred admission, international baccalaureate accepted. Required: essay, high school transcript, SAT or ACT. Recommended: minimum 2 high school GPA, interview. Required for some: 2 recommendations. Entrance: moderately difficult. Application deadline: rolling. Notification: continuous. Transfer credits accepted: Yes.
Costs Per Year: Application fee: $0. Comprehensive fee: $50,760 includes full-time tuition ($38,616), mandatory fees ($600), and college room and

board ($11,544). College room only: $5420. Full-time tuition and fees vary according to class time, course load, and program. Room and board charges vary according to board plan and housing facility. Part-time tuition: $1287 per credit. Part-time mandatory fees: $150 per term. Part-time tuition and fees vary according to class time, course load, and program.

Collegiate Environment: Orientation program. Drama-theater group, choral group, student-run newspaper, radio station. Most popular organizations: Student Activities Board, Student Government Association, Commuter Awareness Board, Student Nurse Association, Forensic Student Science organization. Major annual events: Fall Festival, Midnight Breakfast, Spring Fling. Student services: health clinic, personal-psychological counseling. Campus security: 24-hour emergency response devices and patrols, late night transport-escort service, controlled dormitory access, crime prevention programs. Frank M. Cressman Library.

Community Environment: Population 107,000, Allentown is located on the Lehigh River within 55 miles of Philadelphia and 90 miles from New York City. It is Pennsylvania's third largest industrial market. Diversified manufacturing includes machinery and tools, trucks, electric appliances, electronic equipment, apparel, cement, and gas-generating equipment. The area has good transportation facilities including four railroad lines, air service, and bus lines. The community has many churches representing various denominations. Four hospitals, a dental hospital, a library system, a museum, and an Equity theatre company are located here. Local recreational facilities encompass volleyball, baseball, tennis, basketball, swimming, hiking, band concerts, opera, community theatre, five radio stations, and many movie theatres. Part-time employment is available for students.

■ **CENTRAL PENN COLLEGE**
College Hill & Valley Roads
Summerdale, PA 17093-0309
Tel: (717)732-0702; Free: 800-759-2727
Fax: (717)732-5254
Web Site: www.centralpenn.edu
Description: Proprietary, comprehensive, coed. Awards associate, bachelor's, and master's degrees. Founded 1881. Setting: 35-acre small town campus with easy access to Harrisburg. Total enrollment: 1,224. Faculty: 102 (44 full-time, 58 part-time). Student-undergrad faculty ratio is 10:1. 436 applied, 79% were admitted. Full-time: 316 students, 58% women, 42% men. Part-time: 880 students, 67% women, 33% men. Students come from 19 states and territories, 5% from out-of-state. 3% American Indian or Alaska Native, non-Hispanic/Latino; 4% Hispanic/Latino; 21% Black or African American, non-Hispanic/Latino; 3% Asian, non-Hispanic/Latino; 0.3% Native Hawaiian or other Pacific Islander, non-Hispanic/Latino; 0.7% international. 57% 25 or older, 23% live on campus, 14% transferred in. Retention: 47% of full-time freshmen returned the following year. Core. Calendar: quarters. Academic remediation for entering students, services for LD students, advanced placement, honors program, independent study, distance learning, summer session for credit, part-time degree program, adult/continuing education programs, internships.

Entrance Requirements: Option: electronic application. Required: high school transcript, minimum 2 high school GPA. Recommended: essay, 1 recommendation. Required for some: 1 recommendation, interview, SAT or ACT. Entrance: minimally difficult. Application deadline: rolling. Notification: continuous. Transfer credits accepted: Yes.

Costs Per Year: Application fee: $0. One-time mandatory fee: $100. Comprehensive fee: $26,130 includes full-time tuition ($17,784), mandatory fees ($930), and college room and board ($7416). College room only: $5346. Room and board charges vary according to board plan and housing facility. Part-time tuition: $494 per credit hour. Part-time mandatory fees: $310 per term.

Collegiate Environment: Orientation program. Drama-theater group, student-run newspaper. Social organizations: 26 open to all; honor and community service organizations. Most popular organizations: PTA Club, Student Government Association, Central Penn Players, Student Ambassadors, Colleges Against Cancer. Major annual events: Fall Harvest and Homecoming Weekend, Festival of Nations. Student services: personal-psychological counseling. Campus security: 24-hour emergency response devices and patrols, student patrols, late night transport-escort service, controlled dormitory access. Charles T Jones Leadership Library plus 1 other. Books: 24,566 (physical), 140,336 (digital/electronic); Serial titles: 67 (physical), 2 (digital/electronic); Databases: 34. Weekly public service hours: 74. 100 computers available on campus for general student use. A campuswide network can be accessed from student residence rooms and from off campus. Students can access the following: online class registration. Staffed computer lab on campus provides training in use of computers, software, and the Internet.

Community Environment: Located in the small town of Summerdale, Pennsylvania, Central Penn is just across the river from Harrisburg. As the state capital, Harrisburg is home to a variety of recreational, cultural, historic, and sporting attractions.

■ **CENTRAL PENNSYLVANIA INSTITUTE OF SCIENCE AND TECHNOLOGY**
540 N Harrison Rd.
Pleasant Gap, PA 16823
Tel: (814)359-2582
Description: District-supported, 2-year, coed. Founded 1958.

■ **CHATHAM UNIVERSITY**
Woodland Rd.
Pittsburgh, PA 15232-2826
Tel: (412)365-1100; Free: 800-837-1290
Fax: (412)365-1609
E-mail: admission@chatham.edu
Web Site: www.chatham.edu
Description: Independent, university, coed. Awards bachelor's, master's, and doctoral degrees and post-master's certificates. Founded 1869. Setting: 427-acre urban campus. Endowment: $77.7 million. Educational spending for the previous fiscal year: $29,623 per student. Total enrollment: 2,269. Faculty: 339 (120 full-time, 219 part-time). Student-undergrad faculty ratio is 10:1. 2,231 applied, 55% were admitted. 24% from top 10% of their high school class, 51% from top quarter, 79% from top half. Full-time: 951 students, 75% women, 25% men. Part-time: 257 students, 81% women, 19% men. Students come from 39 states and territories, 25 other countries, 21% from out-of-state. 0.4% American Indian or Alaska Native, non-Hispanic/Latino; 3% Hispanic/Latino; 5% Black or African American, non-Hispanic/Latino; 2% Asian, non-Hispanic/Latino; 0.2% Native Hawaiian or other Pacific Islander, non-Hispanic/Latino; 6% international. 13% 25 or older, 60% live on campus, 7% transferred in. Retention: 85% of full-time freshmen returned the following year. Academic areas with the most degrees conferred: health professions and related sciences; biological/life sciences; business/marketing. Calendar: 4-4-1. ESL program, services for LD students, advanced placement, accelerated degree program, self-designed majors, honors program, independent study, distance learning, double major, summer session for credit, part-time degree program, adult/continuing education programs, co-op programs and internships, graduate courses open to undergrads. Off campus study at members of the Pittsburgh Council on Higher Education. Study abroad program. ROTC: Army (c), Naval (c), Air Force (c).

Entrance Requirements: Options: electronic application, early admission, deferred admission, international baccalaureate accepted. Required: essay, high school transcript, minimum 2 high school GPA, 1 recommendation. Recommended: interview. Entrance: moderately difficult. Application deadline: 8/1. Notification: continuous. SAT Reasoning Test deadline: 8/1. Transfer credits accepted: Yes.

Costs Per Year: Application fee: $35. Comprehensive fee: $49,701 includes full-time tuition ($36,276), mandatory fees ($1335), and college room and board ($12,090). College room only: $6240. Room and board charges vary according to board plan and housing facility. Part-time tuition: $880 per credit hour. Part-time tuition varies according to course load.

Collegiate Environment: Orientation program. Drama-theater group, choral group, student-run newspaper. Social organizations: 60 open to all. Most popular organizations: Chatham Student Government, Residence Hall Council, Student Athletic Advisory Council (SAAC), Creative Writing Club and MFA Writing Council, Graduate Student Assembly. Major annual events: Spring Formal, Fall Talent Show, Thanksgiving Dinner. Student services: health clinic, personal-psychological counseling, women's center. Campus security: 24-hour emergency response devices and patrols, late night transport-escort service, controlled dormitory access, self-defense education, well-lighted pathways and sidewalks. Jennie King Mellon Library. Books: 88,368 (physical), 1,200 (digital/electronic); Serial titles: 92 (physical), 32,874 (digital/electronic); Databases: 65. Weekly public service hours: 99; study areas open 24 hours, 5-7 days a week; students can reserve study rooms. Operations spending for the previous fiscal year: $1.9 million. 202 computers available on campus for general student use. Computer purchase/lease plans available. A computer is required for all students. A campuswide network can be accessed from student residence rooms and from off campus. Students can access the following: online class registration. Staffed computer lab on campus provides training in use of computers, software, and the Internet.

Community Environment: See University of Pittsburgh.

■ CHESTNUT HILL COLLEGE
9601 Germantown Ave.
Philadelphia, PA 19118-2693
Tel: (215)248-7000; Free: 800-248-0052
Fax: (215)248-7056
E-mail: williamss@chc.edu
Web Site: www.chc.edu

Description: Independent Roman Catholic, comprehensive, coed. Awards associate, bachelor's, master's, and doctoral degrees and post-master's certificates (profile includes figures from both traditional and accelerated (part-time) programs). Founded 1924. Setting: 75-acre suburban campus with easy access to Philadelphia. Endowment: $9.4 million. Educational spending for the previous fiscal year: $5085 per student. Total enrollment: 1,846. Faculty: 297 (82 full-time, 215 part-time). Student-undergrad faculty ratio is 10:1. 1,286 applied, 96% were admitted. 6% from top 10% of their high school class, 21% from top quarter, 60% from top half. Full-time: 1,118 students, 60% women, 40% men. Part-time: 246 students, 77% women, 23% men. Students come from 27 states and territories, 39 other countries, 22% from out-of-state. 0.1% American Indian or Alaska Native, non-Hispanic/Latino; 9% Hispanic/Latino; 34% Black or African American, non-Hispanic/Latino; 2% Asian, non-Hispanic/Latino; 0.1% Native Hawaiian or other Pacific Islander, non-Hispanic/Latino; 2% international. 10% 25 or older, 52% live on campus, 5% transferred in. Retention: 79% of full-time freshmen returned the following year. Academic areas with the most degrees conferred: business/marketing; public administration and social services; psychology. Core. Calendar: semesters. Academic remediation for entering students, ESL program, services for LD students, advanced placement, accelerated degree program, self-designed majors, honors program, independent study, double major, summer session for credit, part-time degree program, adult/continuing education programs, co-op programs and internships, graduate courses open to undergrads. Off campus study at Sisters of St. Joseph Consortium (across the U.S.), Southeastern Penna Consortium (in the greater Philadelphia area). Study abroad program.

Entrance Requirements: Open admission only for students in the School of Continuing and Professional Studies. Options: electronic application, deferred admission, international baccalaureate accepted. Required: high school transcript, SAT or ACT. Recommended: essay, minimum X high school GPA. Required for some: interview. Entrance: moderately difficult. Application deadline: rolling. Notification: continuous. Transfer credits accepted: Yes.

Costs Per Year: Application fee: $35. One-time mandatory fee: $475. Comprehensive fee: $47,180 includes full-time tuition ($35,950), mandatory fees ($230), and college room and board ($11,000). Room and board charges vary according to housing facility. Part-time tuition: $745 per credit hour. Part-time mandatory fees: $230 per year. Part-time tuition and fees vary according to class time.

Collegiate Environment: Orientation program. Drama-theater group, choral group, student-run newspaper, radio station. Social organizations: 30 open to all. Most popular organizations: Student Government, Mask and Foil Drama Club, Association for Musical Performance, Campus Ministry Community Service Group, Business Club. Major annual events: Fall Fest/Homecoming, Christmas Decorating/Celebrations, Harry Potter Weekend. Student services: health clinic, personal-psychological counseling. Campus security: 24-hour emergency response devices and patrols, late night transport-escort service, controlled dormitory access. Logue Library. Books: 120,908 (physical), 226,691 (digital/electronic); Serial titles: 670 (physical), 271,184 (digital/electronic); Databases: 433. Weekly public service hours: 99; students can reserve study rooms. Operations spending for the previous fiscal year: $49,277. 70 computers available on campus for general student use. A campuswide network can be accessed. Students can access the following: online class registration. Staffed computer lab on campus provides training in use of computers, software, and the Internet.

Community Environment: Chestnut Hill College is located in a 45-acre suburban setting of Philadelphia. Historic homes, a regional art museum, a well-respected arboretum, stables, and quaint specialty shops are within two miles of the campus, which is 30 minutes from Center-city Philadelphia. Villanova University, Saint Joseph's University, the University of Pennsylvania, Drexel University, and LaSalle University are nearby.

■ CHEYNEY UNIVERSITY OF PENNSYLVANIA
1837 University Cir.
Cheyney, PA 19319
Tel: (610)399-2000; Free: 800-CHEYNEY
Fax: (610)399-2099
E-mail: spjeffery@cheyney.edu
Web Site: www.cheyney.edu

Description: State-supported, comprehensive, coed. Part of Pennsylvania State System of Higher Education. Awards bachelor's and master's degrees. Founded 1837. Setting: 275-acre suburban campus with easy access to Philadelphia. Total enrollment: 1,022. Faculty: 90 (45 full-time, 45 part-time). Student-undergrad faculty ratio is 16:1. 1,127 applied, 85% were admitted. 4% from top 10% of their high school class, 23% from top quarter, 54% from top half. Full-time: 936 students, 49% women, 51% men. Part-time: 61 students, 61% women, 39% men. Students come from 20 states and territories, 30% from out-of-state. 4% Hispanic/Latino; 86% Black or African American, non-Hispanic/Latino; 0.1% Native Hawaiian or other Pacific Islander, non-Hispanic/Latino; 0.2% international. 12% 25 or older, 80% live on campus, 13% transferred in. Retention: 55% of full-time freshmen returned the following year. Academic areas with the most degrees conferred: social sciences; psychology; visual and performing arts. Core. Calendar: semesters. Academic remediation for entering students, services for LD students, honors program, independent study, distance learning, double major, summer session for credit, part-time degree program, adult/continuing education programs, co-op programs and internships, graduate courses open to undergrads. Off campus study at West Chester University of Pennsylvania. Study abroad program. ROTC: Army (c).

Entrance Requirements: Options: electronic application, deferred admission. Required: essay, high school transcript, SAT and SAT Subject Tests or ACT. Recommended: interview. Required for some: 3 recommendations. Entrance: minimally difficult. Application deadline: 3/31. Notification: continuous. Preference given to state residents. SAT Reasoning Test deadline: 6/15. SAT Subject Test deadline: 6/15.

Costs Per Year: Application fee: $20. State resident tuition: $7716 full-time, $322 per credit hour part-time. Nonresident tuition: $12,732 full-time, $531 per credit hour part-time. Mandatory fees: $2817 full-time, $20 per credit hour part-time, $587 per term part-time. Full-time tuition and fees vary according to course load and location. Part-time tuition and fees vary according to course load and location. College room and board: $11,466. College room only: $7366. Room and board charges vary according to board plan and housing facility.

Collegiate Environment: Orientation program. Drama-theater group, choral group, marching band, student-run radio station. Social organizations: 42 open to all; national fraternities, national sororities, local fraternities, local sororities; 30% of eligible men and 30% of eligible women are members. Most popular organizations: National Council of Negro Women, Student Government Association, Alpha Kappa Alpha, Gospel Choir, Modern Men. Major annual events: Homecoming Concert, Sorority and Fraternity Step Shows, May Weekend. Student services: health clinic, personal-psychological counseling. Campus security: 24-hour emergency response devices and patrols. Leslie Pickney Hill. 162 computers available on campus for general student use. Computer purchase/lease plans available. A campuswide network can be accessed from student residence rooms and from off campus. Students can access the following: online class registration, online tutorials, various software packages, online payment/online Praxis study guide. Staffed computer lab on campus.

Community Environment: Cheyney's campus looks out on open fields and wooded hills in one of Pennsylvania's most scenic areas, yet the campus is less than an hour from Philadelphia. The summer temperatures range from 70 to 90 degrees, with winter ranges from 20 to 50 degrees. The area is served by bus and railroad. All major religious denominations are represented in town. There are very few shopping facilities in the immediate area. Part-time employment is available in neighboring community.

■ CLARION UNIVERSITY OF PENNSYLVANIA
840 Wood St.
Clarion, PA 16214
Tel: (814)393-2000; Free: 800-672-7171
Fax: (814)393-2030
E-mail: mdunlap@clarion.edu
Web Site: www.clarion.edu

Description: State-supported, comprehensive, coed. Part of Pennsylvania State System of Higher Education. Awards associate, bachelor's, master's, and doctoral degrees and post-master's certificates. Founded 1867. Setting: 201-acre rural campus. Endowment: $37 million. Research spending for the previous fiscal year: $92,658. Educational spending for the previous fiscal year: $3958 per student. Total enrollment: 4,869. Faculty: 278 (207 full-time,

71 part-time). Student-undergrad faculty ratio is 18:1. 2,373 applied, 94% were admitted. 10% from top 10% of their high school class, 32% from top quarter, 69% from top half. 8 valedictorians. Full-time: 3,132 students, 64% women, 36% men. Part-time: 810 students, 79% women, 21% men. Students come from 38 states and territories, 8 other countries, 7% from out-of-state. 0.2% American Indian or Alaska Native, non-Hispanic/Latino; 3% Hispanic/Latino; 7% Black or African American, non-Hispanic/Latino; 0.9% Asian, non-Hispanic/Latino; 0.1% Native Hawaiian or other Pacific Islander, non-Hispanic/Latino; 0.3% international. 20% 25 or older, 35% live on campus, 8% transferred in. Retention: 74% of full-time freshmen returned the following year. Academic areas with the most degrees conferred: health professions and related sciences; business/marketing; liberal arts/general studies. Core. Calendar: semesters. Academic remediation for entering students, ESL program, services for LD students, advanced placement, accelerated degree program, honors program, independent study, distance learning, double major, summer session for credit, part-time degree program, adult/continuing education programs, co-op programs and internships, graduate courses open to undergrads. Off campus study at California University of PA; Edinboro University of Pennsylvania. Study abroad program. ROTC: Army.

Entrance Requirements: Options: electronic application, early admission, deferred admission, international baccalaureate accepted. Required: high school transcript, minimum 2 high school GPA, SAT or ACT. Recommended: essay, 2 recommendations, interview. Required for some: essay, interview, NLN Test for ASN program, TOEFL, TSE or IELTS for international students. Entrance: minimally difficult. Application deadlines: rolling, rolling for nonresidents. Notification: continuous, continuous for nonresidents. Transfer credits accepted: Yes.

Costs Per Year: Application fee: $40. One-time mandatory fee: $50. State resident tuition: $7716 full-time, $322 per credit hour part-time. Nonresident tuition: $11,574 full-time, $482 per credit hour part-time. Mandatory fees: $3459 full-time. Full-time tuition and fees vary according to course load and location. Part-time tuition varies according to course load and location. College room and board: $12,670. Room and board charges vary according to board plan and housing facility.

Collegiate Environment: Orientation program. Drama-theater group, choral group, marching band, student-run newspaper, radio station. Social organizations: 159 open to all; national fraternities, national sororities, local fraternities, local sororities; 6% of eligible men and 12% of eligible women are members. Most popular organizations: The National Student Speech-Language Hearing Association, Phi Eta Sigma freshman honor society, Allies, Black Student Union, Cru. Major annual events: Activities Day, Homecoming/Autumn Leaf Parade, Campusfest Concert. Student services: health clinic, personal-psychological counseling, women's center. Campus security: 24-hour emergency response devices and patrols, student patrols, late night transport-escort service, controlled dormitory access. 1,745 college housing spaces available; 1,229 were occupied in 2018-19. Freshmen guaranteed college housing. On-campus residence required through sophomore year. Option: coed housing available. Carlson Library plus 1 other. Books: 444,818 (physical), 348,037 (digital/electronic); Serial titles: 179 (physical), 57,405 (digital/electronic); Databases: 102. Weekly public service hours: 94; students can reserve study rooms. Operations spending for the previous fiscal year: $2.5 million. 950 computers available on campus for general student use. A campuswide network can be accessed from student residence rooms and from off campus. Students can access the following: online class registration, Online Learning Management System, web-based personal disk space, other online student services (financial aid, billing etc.). Staffed computer lab on campus provides training in use of computers, software, and the Internet.

Community Environment: Clarion is in a rural area located near Cook Forest State Park and Allegheny National Forest. The area offers excellent hunting and fishing. The city has a public library, historical museum, nine churches, a hospital, and good shopping facilities. Two airports with commercial commuter and charter service are located within easy driving distance.

■ **CLARKS SUMMIT UNIVERSITY**
538 Venard Rd.
South Abington Township, PA 18411
Tel: (570)586-2400; Free: 800-451-7664
Fax: (570)585-9226
E-mail: pschwamb@clarkssummitu.edu
Web Site: www.clarkssummitu.edu
Description: Independent Baptist, comprehensive, coed. Awards associate,

bachelor's, master's, and doctoral degrees. Founded 1932. Setting: 124-acre suburban campus. Endowment: $2.1 million. Educational spending for the previous fiscal year: $5466 per student. Total enrollment: 1,001. Faculty: 47 (41 full-time, 6 part-time). Student-undergrad faculty ratio is 11:1. 424 applied, 38% were admitted. 35% from top 10% of their high school class, 50% from top quarter, 75% from top half. Full-time: 568 students, 52% women, 48% men. Part-time: 154 students, 43% women, 57% men. Students come from 34 states and territories, 86 other countries, 51% from out-of-state. 0.4% American Indian or Alaska Native, non-Hispanic/Latino; 2% Hispanic/Latino; 3% Black or African American, non-Hispanic/Latino; 0.6% Asian, non-Hispanic/Latino; 0.1% Native Hawaiian or other Pacific Islander, non-Hispanic/Latino; 0.1% international. 9% 25 or older, 91% live on campus, 7% transferred in. Retention: 47% of full-time freshmen returned the following year. Academic areas with the most degrees conferred: theology and religious vocations; education; psychology. Core. Calendar: semesters. Academic remediation for entering students, ESL program, advanced placement, self-designed majors, independent study, distance learning, double major, summer session for credit, part-time degree program, external degree program, adult/continuing education programs, internships, graduate courses open to undergrads. ROTC: Army (c), Naval (c), Air Force (c).

Entrance Requirements: Options: electronic application, early admission, deferred admission, international baccalaureate accepted. Required: essay, high school transcript, 2 recommendations, Christian testimony, SAT or ACT. Required for some: 1 recommendation, interview. Entrance: minimally difficult. Application deadline: 8/15. Notification: continuous. Transfer credits accepted: Yes.

Costs Per Year: Application fee: $40. Comprehensive fee: $30,210 includes full-time tuition ($23,890) and college room and board ($6320). College room only: $2380. Full-time tuition varies according to student level. Room and board charges vary according to board plan and student level. Part-time tuition: $710 per credit. Part-time tuition varies according to course load. Tuition guaranteed not to increase for student's term of enrollment.

Collegiate Environment: Orientation program. Drama-theater group, choral group. Major annual events: Homecoming Day, Spring and Fall Plays, Spring Banquet. Student services: health clinic, personal-psychological counseling. Campus security: 24-hour patrols, student patrols, controlled dormitory access. Murphy Memorial Library. Operations spending for the previous fiscal year: $232,867. 25 computers available on campus for general student use. A campuswide network can be accessed from student residence rooms. Students can access the following: online class registration. Staffed computer lab on campus.

Community Environment: Population of 5,000. Served by bus; major airport serves Scranton; train serves Harrisburg (100 miles). Public transportation serves campus. The community has a public library, nearby hospitals, recreational facilities, and many local parks. Part-time employment opportunities are excellent.

■ **COMMONWEALTH TECHNICAL INSTITUTE**
727 Goucher St.
Johnstown, PA 15905-3092
Tel: (814)255-8200; Free: 800-762-4211
E-mail: jgies@pa.gov
Web Site: www.dli.pa.gov/Individuals/Disability-Services/hgac/Pages/default.aspx
Description: State-supported, 2-year, coed. Awards diplomas and terminal associate degrees. Setting: 59-acre suburban campus. Total enrollment: 222. Faculty: 27 (all full-time). Student-undergrad faculty ratio is 15:1. Full-time: 222 students, 35% women, 65% men. Students come from 4 states and territories, 1% from out-of-state. 7% Black or African American, non-Hispanic/Latino; 1% Asian, non-Hispanic/Latino. 11% 25 or older. Retention: 74% of full-time freshmen returned the following year. Core. Calendar: trimesters. Academic remediation for entering students, services for LD students, advanced placement.

Entrance Requirements: Open admission. Option: international baccalaureate accepted. Recommended: high school transcript. Required for some: high school transcript. Entrance: noncompetitive. Application deadline: rolling. Notification: continuous. Preference given to applicants with disabilities.

Collegiate Environment: Orientation program. Drama-theater group, choral group. Student services: health clinic, personal-psychological counseling. Campus security: 24-hour patrols, controlled dormitory access. Commonwealth Technical Institute at the Hiram G.Andrews Center Library. 300 computers available on campus for general student use. A campuswide network can be accessed from student residence rooms. Staffed computer lab on campus provides training in use of computers and the Internet.

■ COMMUNITY COLLEGE OF ALLEGHENY COUNTY

800 Allegheny Ave.
Pittsburgh, PA 15233-1894
Tel: (412)323-2323
Web Site: www.ccac.edu

Description: County-supported, 2-year, coed. Awards certificates, diplomas, transfer associate, and terminal associate degrees. Founded 1966. Setting: 242-acre urban campus. Total enrollment: 16,086. Student-undergrad faculty ratio is 18:1. Full-time: 5,354 students, 52% women, 48% men. Part-time: 10,732 students, 56% women, 44% men. 0.5% American Indian or Alaska Native, non-Hispanic/Latino; 3% Hispanic/Latino; 17% Black or African American, non-Hispanic/Latino; 3% Asian, non-Hispanic/Latino; 0.1% Native Hawaiian or other Pacific Islander, non-Hispanic/Latino. Core. Calendar: semesters. Academic remediation for entering students, ESL program, services for LD students, accelerated degree program, honors program, distance learning, summer session for credit, part-time degree program. Off campus study. Study abroad program. ROTC: Army (c), Naval (c), Air Force (c).

Entrance Requirements: Recommended: high school transcript. Entrance: noncompetitive. Transfer credits accepted: Yes.

Costs Per Year: Area resident tuition: $3390 full-time, $113 per credit hour part-time. State resident tuition: $6780 full-time, $226 per credit hour part-time. Nonresident tuition: $10,170 full-time, $339 per credit hour part-time. Full-time tuition varies according to course load and program. Part-time tuition varies according to course load and program.

Collegiate Environment: Drama-theater group, choral group, student-run radio station. Social organizations: 90 open to all. Most popular organizations: Art Club, Veterans Club, Computer Science Club, Phi Theta Kappa, Women on a Mission. Major annual events: One College Reads Day, Job Fair, Commencement. Student services: health clinic, personal-psychological counseling. Campus security: 24-hour emergency response devices and patrols, late night transport-escort service. College housing not available. Community College of Allegheny County Libraries. Books: 121,707 (physical), 59,726 (digital/electronic); Serial titles: 509 (physical), 5 (digital/electronic); Databases: 114. Weekly public service hours: 12. 291 computers available on campus for general student use. A campuswide network can be accessed from off-campus. Students can access the following: online class registration, Free MS Office 365 license. Staffed computer lab on campus provides training in use of computers, software, and the Internet.

■ COMMUNITY COLLEGE OF BEAVER COUNTY

One Campus Dr.
Monaca, PA 15061-2588
Tel: (724)775-8561; Free: 800-335-0222
Fax: (724)728-7599
E-mail: admissions@ccbc.edu
Web Site: www.ccbc.edu

Description: State-supported, 2-year, coed. Awards certificates, diplomas, transfer associate, and terminal associate degrees. Founded 1966. Setting: 75-acre small town campus with easy access to Pittsburgh. Total enrollment: 2,779. Student-undergrad faculty ratio is 16:1. 2% from out-of-state. 33% 25 or older. Core. Calendar: semesters. Academic remediation for entering students, services for LD students, advanced placement, independent study, distance learning, double major, summer session for credit, part-time degree program, adult/continuing education programs, co-op programs and internships. Off campus study at Geneva College, Pennsylvania State University Beaver Campus of the Commonwealth College, La Roche College, Robert Morris College.

Entrance Requirements: Open admission except for nursing, medical laboratory technology programs. Option: early admission. Required: interview. Recommended: high school transcript. Entrance: noncompetitive. Application deadline: rolling. Notification: continuous.

Collegiate Environment: Social organizations: local fraternities, local sororities. Campus security: 24-hour emergency response devices and patrols, late night transport-escort service. Community College of Beaver County Library.

Community Environment: Beaver County covers 436 square miles of rolling hills and valleys in southwestern Pennsylvania. Professional sporting events, world-renowned museums, and numerous cultural events are within commuting distance in nearby Pittsburgh.

■ COMMUNITY COLLEGE OF PHILADELPHIA

1700 Spring Garden St.
Philadelphia, PA 19130-3991

Tel: (215)751-8000
Web Site: www.ccp.edu

Description: State and locally supported, 2-year, coed. Awards certificates, diplomas, transfer associate, and terminal associate degrees. Founded 1964. Setting: 14-acre urban campus with easy access to Philadelphia. Total enrollment: 30,194. Faculty: 1,038 (437 full-time, 601 part-time). Students come from 50 other countries. 54% 25 or older. Core. Calendar: semesters. Academic remediation for entering students, ESL program, services for LD students, advanced placement, accelerated degree program, self-designed majors, honors program, independent study, distance learning, summer session for credit, part-time degree program, external degree program, adult/continuing education programs, co-op programs and internships. Off campus study at Bucks, Delaware and Montgomery Community Colleges. Study abroad program. ROTC: Army (c).

Entrance Requirements: Open admission except for allied health, mental health/social service, engineering science programs. Options: electronic application, early admission, deferred admission. Required for some: high school transcript, specific entry requirements for allied health and nursing programs. Entrance: noncompetitive. Application deadline: rolling. Notification: continuous. Transfer credits accepted: Yes.

Costs Per Year: Application fee: $0. Area resident tuition: $5264 full-time, $159 per credit hour part-time. State resident tuition: $9320 full-time, $318 per credit hour part-time. Nonresident tuition: $13,376 full-time, $477 per credit hour part-time. Full-time tuition varies according to course load and program. Part-time tuition varies according to course load and program.

Collegiate Environment: Orientation program. Drama-theater group, choral group, student-run newspaper. Social organizations: 30 open to all; Phi Theta Kappa, Alpha Beta Gamma Honor Societies. Most popular organizations: Philadelphia L.E.A.D.S, Phi Theta Kappa, Student Government Association, Vanguard Student Newspaper, Fundraising Club. Major annual events: Spring Fling, International Festival, Fall Celebration. Student services: legal services, personal-psychological counseling, women's center. Campus security: 24-hour emergency response devices and patrols, late night transport-escort service, phone/alert systems in classrooms/buildings, electronic messages/alerts, ID required to enter buildings. Main Campus Library plus 2 others. Books: 84,000 (physical); Databases: 40. Weekly public service hours: 30; students can reserve study rooms. 350 computers available on campus for general student use. Computer purchase/lease plans available. Students can access the following: online class registration. Staffed computer lab on campus provides training in use of computers.

Community Environment: See Temple University.

■ CURTIS INSTITUTE OF MUSIC

1726 Locust St.
Philadelphia, PA 19103-6107
Tel: (215)893-5252
Fax: (215)893-7900
Web Site: www.curtis.edu

Description: Independent, comprehensive, coed. Awards bachelor's and master's degrees. Founded 1924. Setting: urban campus. Total enrollment: 164. 1% 25 or older. Core. Calendar: semesters. ESL program, advanced placement, accelerated degree program. Off campus study.

Entrance Requirements: Option: early admission. Required: essay, high school transcript, 2 recommendations, audition. Entrance: most difficult. Application deadline: 12/11. Notification: continuous.

Collegiate Environment: Orientation program. Student services: health clinic, personal-psychological counseling. Campus security: 24-hour patrols. The Rock Resource Center.

Community Environment: See Temple University.

■ DEAN INSTITUTE OF TECHNOLOGY

1501 W Liberty Ave.
Pittsburgh, PA 15226-1103
Tel: (412)531-4433
Fax: (412)531-4435
Web Site: www.deantech.edu

Description: Proprietary, 2-year, coed. Awards diplomas and terminal associate degrees. Founded 1947. Setting: 2-acre urban campus. Total enrollment: 132. 91% 25 or older. Core. Calendar: quarters. Part-time degree program.

Entrance Requirements: Open admission. Options: early admission, deferred admission. Entrance: noncompetitive. Application deadline: rolling.

Collegiate Environment: Campus security: 24-hour emergency response devices.

■ **DELAWARE COUNTY COMMUNITY COLLEGE**

901 S Media Line Rd.
Media, PA 19063-1094
Tel: (610)359-5000
E-mail: admiss@dccc.edu
Web Site: www.dccc.edu

Description: State and locally supported, 2-year, coed. Awards certificates, transfer associate, and terminal associate degrees. Founded 1967. Setting: 123-acre suburban campus with easy access to Philadelphia. Endowment: $3.8 million. Total enrollment: 13,248. Faculty: 802 (143 full-time, 659 part-time). Student-undergrad faculty ratio is 24:1. 4,818 applied, 100% were admitted. Students come from 9 states and territories, 53 other countries, 1% from out-of-state. 0.2% American Indian or Alaska Native, non-Hispanic/Latino; 2% Hispanic/Latino; 25% Black or African American, non-Hispanic/Latino; 4% Asian, non-Hispanic/Latino; 0.1% Native Hawaiian or other Pacific Islander, non-Hispanic/Latino. 56% 25 or older. Retention: 61% of full-time freshmen returned the following year. Calendar: semesters. Academic remediation for entering students, ESL program, services for LD students, advanced placement, self-designed majors, independent study, distance learning, double major, summer session for credit, part-time degree program, adult/continuing education programs, co-op programs and internships.

Entrance Requirements: Open admission except for international students, nursing, respiratory therapy, surgical technology, plumbing apprentice, municipal police training programs, paramedic, perioperative nursing. Option: early admission. Required: high school transcript. Entrance: noncompetitive. Application deadline: rolling. Notification: continuous. Preference given to residents of sponsoring school districts for nursing, respiratory therapy, surgical technology programs. Transfer credits accepted: Yes.

Collegiate Environment: Orientation program. Drama-theater group, student-run newspaper, radio station. Social organizations: 15 open to all. Most popular organizations: Business Society, Phi Theta Kappa, Student Government Association, Campus Bible Fellowship, Engineering Club. Student services: health clinic, personal-psychological counseling. Campus security: 24-hour emergency response devices and patrols, late night transport-escort service. Delaware County Community College Library.

Community Environment: Media, population 5,451, is in central Delaware County. The city is located 20 miles from Philadelphia with all its cultural, educational, and recreational opportunities.

■ **DELAWARE VALLEY UNIVERSITY**

700 E Butler Ave.
Doylestown, PA 18901-2697
Tel: (215)345-1500; Free: 800-2DELVAL
Fax: (215)345-5277
E-mail: dwayne.walker@delval.edu
Web Site: www.delval.edu

Description: Independent, comprehensive, coed. Awards bachelor's, master's, and doctoral degrees. Founded 1896. Setting: 571-acre suburban campus with easy access to Philadelphia. Endowment: $33.6 million. Research spending for the previous fiscal year: $182,392. Educational spending for the previous fiscal year: $8748 per student. Total enrollment: 2,428. Faculty: 274 (92 full-time, 182 part-time). Student-undergrad faculty ratio is 14:1. 2,423 applied, 66% were admitted. 10% from top 10% of their high school class, 33% from top quarter, 64% from top half. Full-time: 1,744 students, 59% women, 41% men. Part-time: 238 students, 60% women, 40% men. Students come from 25 states and territories, 8 other countries, 34% from out-of-state. 0.5% American Indian or Alaska Native, non-Hispanic/Latino; 7% Hispanic/Latino; 9% Black or African American, non-Hispanic/Latino; 1% Asian, non-Hispanic/Latino; 0.1% Native Hawaiian or other Pacific Islander, non-Hispanic/Latino; 0.6% international. 10% 25 or older, 49% live on campus, 7% transferred in. Retention: 72% of full-time freshmen returned the following year. Academic areas with the most degrees conferred: agriculture; biological/life sciences; business/marketing. Core. Calendar: semesters. Academic remediation for entering students, services for LD students, advanced placement, accelerated degree program, honors program, independent study, distance learning, double major, summer session for credit, part-time degree program, adult/continuing education programs, co-op programs and internships, graduate courses open to undergrads. Study abroad program.

Entrance Requirements: Options: electronic application, deferred admission. Required: essay, high school transcript, 1 recommendation, Test scores (SAT/ACT), additional short-answer questions for Zoo Science applicants, SAT or ACT. Required for some: interview, TOEFL. Entrance: minimally dif-

ficult. Application deadlines: rolling, rolling for nonresidents. Notification: continuous, continuous for nonresidents. SAT Reasoning Test deadline: 8/15. SAT Subject Test deadline: 8/15. Transfer credits accepted: Yes.

Costs Per Year: Application fee: $50. Comprehensive fee: $55,240 includes full-time tuition ($38,070), mandatory fees ($2550), and college room and board ($14,620). College room only: $6950. Part-time tuition: $1049 per credit hour. Part-time mandatory fees: $14 per course.

Collegiate Environment: Orientation program. Drama-theater group, choral group. Social organizations: 81 open to all; national fraternities, national sororities, local fraternities, local sororities; 1% of eligible men and 1% of eligible women are members. Most popular organizations: Animal Lifeline Club, Pre-Vet Club, Dairy Society, Sigma Alpha, A-Day. Major annual events: A-Day, Homecoming. Student services: health clinic, personal-psychological counseling. Campus security: 24-hour emergency response devices and patrols, late night transport-escort service, controlled dormitory access. 1,024 college housing spaces available; 980 were occupied in 2018-19. Freshmen guaranteed college housing. On-campus residence required in freshman year. Option: coed housing available. Joseph Krauskopf Memorial Library. Books: 45,500 (physical), 7,830 (digital/electronic); Serial titles: 74 (physical), 113,400 (digital/electronic); Databases: 44. Weekly public service hours: 92. Operations spending for the previous fiscal year: $622,202. 160 computers available on campus for general student use. A campuswide network can be accessed from student residence rooms. Students can access the following: online class registration. Staffed computer lab on campus provides training in use of computers, software, and the Internet.

Community Environment: Doylestown, population 19,000, and founded in 1745, is in Bucks County, one of the finest farming sections of the state. The city is located 30 miles north of Philadelphia, and can be reached by rail, bus, and good highways. There are several churches, a hospital, public library, historical society, and more than 50 civic, fraternal, and veteran's organizations in the community. Local recreational facilities include theaters, a swimming pool, bowling lanes, and a radio station. Part-time employment is available.

■ **DESALES UNIVERSITY**

2755 Station Ave.
Center Valley, PA 18034-9568
Tel: (610)282-1100
Fax: (610)282-2254
E-mail: derrick.wetzell@desales.edu
Web Site: www.desales.edu

Description: Independent Roman Catholic, comprehensive, coed. Awards bachelor's, master's, and doctoral degrees and post-master's certificates. Founded 1964. Setting: 480-acre suburban campus with easy access to Philadelphia, PA. Endowment: $80.1 million. Educational spending for the previous fiscal year: $9745 per student. Total enrollment: 3,315. Faculty: 346 (126 full-time, 220 part-time). Student-undergrad faculty ratio is 12:1. 3,033 applied, 74% were admitted. 34% from top 10% of their high school class, 52% from top quarter, 79% from top half. Full-time: 1,811 students, 59% women, 41% men. Part-time: 534 students, 70% women, 30% men. Students come from 29 states and territories, 3 other countries, 24% from out-of-state. 14% Hispanic/Latino; 5% Black or African American, non-Hispanic/Latino; 3% Asian, non-Hispanic/Latino; 0.1% international. 24% 25 or older, 46% live on campus, 3% transferred in. Retention: 81% of full-time freshmen returned the following year. Academic areas with the most degrees conferred: business/marketing; health professions and related sciences; visual and performing arts. Core. Calendar: semesters. Academic remediation for entering students, services for LD students, advanced placement, accelerated degree program, self-designed majors, honors program, independent study, distance learning, double major, summer session for credit, part-time degree program, external degree program, adult/continuing education programs, co-op programs and internships, graduate courses open to undergrads. Off campus study. Study abroad program. ROTC: Army (c).

Entrance Requirements: Open admission Part-time, returning adults. Options: electronic application, early admission, deferred admission. Required: essay, high school transcript, recommendations, SAT or ACT. Recommended: interview. Entrance: moderately difficult. Application deadline: 8/1. Notification: continuous until 10/6. SAT Reasoning Test deadline: 8/1. Transfer credits accepted: Yes.

Costs Per Year: Application fee: $0. One-time mandatory fee: $200. Comprehensive fee: $50,200 includes full-time tuition ($36,000), mandatory fees ($1400), and college room and board ($12,800). Full-time tuition and fees vary according to class time and course load. Room and board charges vary according to board plan and housing facility. Part-time tuition: $1500 per credit hour. Part-time tuition varies according to class time and course load.

Collegiate Environment: Orientation program. Drama-theater group, choral group, marching band, student-run newspaper, radio station. Social organizations: 60 open to all; Alpha Phi Omega. Most popular organizations: College Against Cancer, Outdoor Adventure Club, Student Nursing Association, Criminal Justice Association, Natural Science Club. Major annual events: Spring Fling/Relay for Life, Bulldog Blizzard, Opening Day BBQ. Student services: health clinic, personal-psychological counseling. Campus security: 24-hour emergency response devices and patrols, late night transport-escort service, controlled dormitory access. Trexler Library. Books: 155,243 (physical), 135,000 (digital/electronic); Serial titles: 260 (physical), 19,000 (digital/electronic); Databases: 87. Weekly public service hours: 102; students can reserve study rooms. Operations spending for the previous fiscal year: $848,008. 245 computers available on campus for general student use. A campuswide network can be accessed from student residence rooms and from off campus. Students can access the following: online class registration. Staffed computer lab on campus.

Community Environment: Center Valley is a suburban area that enjoys a temperate climate. Lehigh Valley is accessible by air, bus, and car (Route 309), and the nearby towns are Allentown (population 107,000) and Bethlehem (population 73,000).

■ DEVRY UNIVERSITY-FT. WASHINGTON CAMPUS

1140 Virginia Dr.
Fort Washington, PA 19034
Tel: (215)591-5700; Free: 866-338-7934
Web Site: www.devry.edu
Description: Proprietary, comprehensive, coed. Part of DeVry University. Awards associate, bachelor's, and master's degrees. Founded 2002. Total enrollment: 517. Faculty: 25 (13 full-time, 12 part-time). Student-undergrad faculty ratio is 17:1. Full-time: 164 students, 36% women, 64% men. Part-time: 272 students, 44% women, 56% men. 7% from out-of-state. 9% Hispanic/Latino; 26% Black or African American, non-Hispanic/Latino; 4% Asian, non-Hispanic/Latino; 0.7% international. 66% 25 or older, 24% transferred in. Calendar: semesters. Part-time degree program, adult/continuing education programs.
Entrance Requirements: Required: high school transcript, interview. Entrance: minimally difficult.
Collegiate Environment: Orientation program. Learning Resource Center.

■ DICKINSON COLLEGE

PO Box 1773
Carlisle, PA 17013-2896
Tel: (717)243-5121; Free: 800-644-1773
Fax: (717)245-1442
E-mail: admissions@dickinson.edu
Web Site: www.dickinson.edu
Description: Independent, 4-year, coed. Awards bachelor's degrees. Founded 1773. Setting: 144-acre suburban campus with easy access to Harrisburg. Endowment: $437.5 million. Research spending for the previous fiscal year: $3.4 million. Educational spending for the previous fiscal year: $20,121 per student. Total enrollment: 2,399. Faculty: 285 (223 full-time, 62 part-time). Student-undergrad faculty ratio is 9:1. 6,248 applied, 49% were admitted. 41% from top 10% of their high school class, 74% from top quarter, 96% from top half. Full-time: 2,361 students, 58% women, 42% men. Part-time: 38 students, 63% women, 37% men. Students come from 39 states and territories, 49 other countries, 77% from out-of-state. 0.2% American Indian or Alaska Native, non-Hispanic/Latino; 9% Hispanic/Latino; 5% Black or African American, non-Hispanic/Latino; 4% Asian, non-Hispanic/Latino; 14% international. 1% 25 or older, 100% live on campus, 1% transferred in. Retention: 91% of full-time freshmen returned the following year. Academic areas with the most degrees conferred: social sciences; business/marketing; biological/life sciences. Core. Calendar: semesters. ESL program, services for LD students, advanced placement, accelerated degree program, self-designed majors, independent study, double major, part-time degree program, adult/continuing education programs, internships. Off campus study at Baruch College's Zicklin School of Business, The Washington Center, Woods Hole Oceanographic Institution, College of the Atlantic, Consortium Exchange: Dickinson College, Franklin and Marshall College, Gettysburg College. Study abroad program. ROTC: Army.
Entrance Requirements: Options: electronic application, early decision, early action, deferred admission, international baccalaureate accepted. Required: essay, high school transcript, 2 recommendations. Recom-

mended: minimum 3 high school GPA, interview, SAT or ACT. Entrance: very difficult. Application deadlines: 1/15, 1/15 for nonresidents, 11/15 for early decision plan 1, 1/15 for early decision plan 2, 12/1 for early action. Notification: 3/23, 3/23 for nonresidents, 12/15 for early decision plan 1, 2/15 for early decision plan 2, 2/15 for early action. SAT Reasoning Test deadline: 1/15. SAT Subject Test deadline: 1/15. Transfer credits accepted: Yes. Applicants placed on waiting list: 644. Wait-listed applicants offered admission: 9. Early decision applicants: 392. Early decision applicants admitted: 266. Early action applicants: 3,166. Early action applicants admitted: 1,829.
Costs Per Year: Application fee: $65. One-time mandatory fee: $25. Comprehensive fee: $70,674 includes full-time tuition ($55,948), mandatory fees ($550), and college room and board ($14,176). College room only: $7310. Part-time tuition: $6995 per course. Part-time mandatory fees: $70 per course.
Collegiate Environment: Orientation program. Drama-theater group, choral group, student-run newspaper, radio station. Social organizations: 138 open to all; national fraternities, national sororities, local sororities; 4% of eligible men and 25% of eligible women are members. Most popular organizations: Multi-Organization Board, Outing Club, Student Senate, Admissions Volunteers, WDCV Radio Station. Major annual events: All College Formal, Spring Fest, Relay for Life. Student services: health clinic, personal-psychological counseling, women's center. Campus security: 24-hour emergency response devices and patrols, student patrols, late night transport-escort service, controlled dormitory access. 2,178 college housing spaces available; 2,096 were occupied in 2018-19. Freshmen guaranteed college housing. On-campus residence required through senior year. Option: coed housing available. Waidner-Spahr Library. Books: 516,871 (physical), 653,715 (digital/electronic); Serial titles: 3,559 (physical), 99,470 (digital/electronic); Databases: 506. Weekly public service hours: 114; students can reserve study rooms. Operations spending for the previous fiscal year: $3.3 million. 1,720 computers available on campus for general student use. Computer purchase/lease plans available. A campuswide network can be accessed from student residence rooms and from off campus. Students can access the following: online class registration. Staffed computer lab on campus (open 24 hours a day) provides training in use of computers, software, and the Internet.
Community Environment: Carlisle, population 18,000, is in the Cumberland Valley located at the western edge of Harrisburg, the state capital. It is 3 miles from I-76 and I-81, and within 2-3 hours of Baltimore, Washington and Philadelphia. Founded in 1751, it was the focus of the Scotch-Irish colonists who settled in Pennsylvania in the pre-revolutionary period. Several historic figures made their homes in Carlisle during the revolutionary period. Numerous buildings of Colonial and Federal architecture, many of native limestone, have been restored in the historic district of Carlisle. The eastern most ranges of the Appalachian Mountains are within a few miles of the downtown area, and the Appalachian Trail passes within five miles. Four state parks provide opportunities for hiking, fishing, hunting, and water and winter sports. The Carlisle Hospital, a variety of theatres, restaurants, and churches, three amusement parks, and public golf courses are within easy reach.

■ DOUGLAS EDUCATION CENTER

130 Seventh St.
Monessen, PA 15062
Tel: (724)684-3684; Free: 800-413-6013
Fax: (724)684-7463
Web Site: www.dec.edu
Description: Proprietary, 2-year, coed. Awards diplomas and terminal associate degrees. Founded 1904. Setting: small town campus with easy access to Pittsburgh. Educational spending for the previous fiscal year: $4633 per student. Total enrollment: 334. Faculty: 37 (13 full-time, 24 part-time). Student-undergrad faculty ratio is 16:1. Full-time: 334 students, 66% women, 34% men. Students come from 4 other countries, 32% from out-of-state. 0.6% American Indian or Alaska Native, non-Hispanic/Latino; 4% Hispanic/Latino; 4% Black or African American, non-Hispanic/Latino; 0.6% Asian, non-Hispanic/Latino; 0.6% Native Hawaiian or other Pacific Islander, non-Hispanic/Latino; 1% international. 61% 25 or older. Retention: 87% of full-time freshmen returned the following year. Core. Advanced placement.
Entrance Requirements: Open admission. Required: high school transcript, interview, Wonderlic aptitude test. Entrance: minimally difficult. Application deadline: rolling. Notification: continuous. Transfer credits accepted: Yes.
Collegiate Environment: Orientation program. Campus security: 24-hour emergency response devices. Douglas Education Center Library / Learning Resource Center plus 2 others. Operations spending for the previous fiscal

year: $135,000. 97 computers available on campus for general student use. Computer purchase/lease plans available. A computer is required for all students. A campuswide network can be accessed. Students can access the following: online Student Accounts/Financial Aid. Staffed computer lab on campus provides training in use of computers, software, and the Internet.

■ DREXEL UNIVERSITY
3141 Chestnut St.
Philadelphia, PA 19104-2875
Tel: (215)895-2000; Free: 800-2-DREXEL
Fax: (215)895-5939
E-mail: evelyn.k.thimba@drexel.edu
Web Site: www.drexel.edu
Description: Independent, university, coed. Awards bachelor's, master's, and doctoral degrees and post-master's certificates. Founded 1891. Setting: 96-acre urban campus with easy access to Philadelphia. Endowment: $650.3 million. Research spending for the previous fiscal year: $143.7 million. Educational spending for the previous fiscal year: $15,834 per student. Total enrollment: 24,190. Faculty: 2,017 (1,108 full-time, 909 part-time). Student-undergrad faculty ratio is 11:1. 28,454 applied, 79% were admitted. 36% from top 10% of their high school class, 65% from top quarter, 91% from top half. Full-time: 13,569 students, 45% women, 55% men. Part-time: 1,929 students, 69% women, 31% men. Students come from 48 states and territories, 117 other countries, 48% from out-of-state. 0.1% American Indian or Alaska Native, non-Hispanic/Latino; 6% Hispanic/Latino; 7% Black or African American, non-Hispanic/Latino; 16% Asian, non-Hispanic/Latino; 0.4% Native Hawaiian or other Pacific Islander, non-Hispanic/Latino; 12% international. 17% 25 or older, 22% live on campus, 5% transferred in. Retention: 89% of full-time freshmen returned the following year. Academic areas with the most degrees conferred: business/marketing; engineering; health professions and related sciences. Core. Calendar: quarters. Academic remediation for entering students, ESL program, services for LD students, advanced placement, accelerated degree program, self-designed majors, freshman honors college, honors program, independent study, distance learning, double major, summer session for credit, part-time degree program, adult/continuing education programs, co-op programs and internships, graduate courses open to undergrads. Study abroad program. ROTC: Army, Naval (c), Air Force (c).
Entrance Requirements: Options: electronic application, early admission, early decision, early action, deferred admission. Required: essay, high school transcript, minimum 2 high school GPA, SAT or ACT. Recommended: 2 recommendations, interview. Entrance: moderately difficult. Application deadlines: 1/15, 11/1 for early decision, 11/1 for early action. Notification: continuous until 4/1, 12/15 for early decision, 12/15 for early action. SAT Reasoning Test deadline: 1/15. Transfer credits accepted: Yes. Applicants placed on waiting list: 929. Wait-listed applicants offered admission: 2. Early decision applicants: 269. Early decision applicants admitted: 243. Early action applicants: 8,849. Early action applicants admitted: 8,440.
Costs Per Year: Application fee: $50. Comprehensive fee: $65,892 includes full-time tuition ($49,632), mandatory fees ($2370), and college room and board ($13,890). College room only: $8205. Full-time tuition and fees vary according to course load, location, program, and student level. Room and board charges vary according to board plan and housing facility. Part-time tuition: $1116 per credit hour. Part-time mandatory fees: $150 per term. Part-time tuition and fees vary according to course load and program.
Collegiate Environment: Orientation program. Drama-theater group, choral group, student-run newspaper, radio station. Social organizations: 459 open to all; national fraternities, national sororities, local fraternities, local sororities; 14% of eligible men and 13% of eligible women are members. Most popular organizations: Student Government, Black Student Union, Society of Hispanic Professional Engineers, Society of Minority Engineers and Scientists, Campus Activities Board. Major annual events: Spring Jam, Welcome Back, Homecoming. Student services: health clinic, personal-psychological counseling, women's center. Campus security: 24-hour emergency response devices and patrols, late night transport-escort service, controlled dormitory access. W. W. Hagerty Library plus 3 others. Books: 286,613 (physical), 215,379 (digital/electronic); Serial titles: 126 (physical), 51,775 (digital/electronic); Databases: 465. Weekly public service hours: 87; study areas open 24 hours, 5-7 days a week; students can reserve study rooms. Operations spending for the previous fiscal year: $11.5 million.
Community Environment: Philadelphia, a metropolitan city with historical significance, provides considerable cultural, social, and recreational resources, as well as excellent shopping and dining. Transportation includes public transit, major highways, Amtrak, and Philadelphia International Airport.

■ DUQUESNE UNIVERSITY
600 Forbes Ave.
Pittsburgh, PA 15282-0001
Tel: (412)396-6000; Free: 800-456-0590
Fax: (412)396-5779
E-mail: admissions@duq.edu
Web Site: www.duq.edu
Description: Independent Roman Catholic, university, coed. Awards bachelor's, master's, and doctoral degrees and post-master's certificates. Founded 1878. Setting: 50-acre urban campus with easy access to Pittsburgh. Endowment: $308.2 million. Research spending for the previous fiscal year: $15.5 million. Educational spending for the previous fiscal year: $12,641 per student. Total enrollment: 9,274. Faculty: 990 (505 full-time, 485 part-time). Student-undergrad faculty ratio is 14:1. 7,505 applied, 72% were admitted. 26% from top 10% of their high school class, 57% from top quarter, 87% from top half. 12 valedictorians. Full-time: 5,896 students, 64% women, 36% men. Part-time: 117 students, 55% women, 45% men. Students come from 44 states and territories, 44 other countries, 28% from out-of-state. 0.1% American Indian or Alaska Native, non-Hispanic/Latino; 4% Hispanic/Latino; 5% Black or African American, non-Hispanic/Latino; 3% Asian, non-Hispanic/Latino; 0.1% Native Hawaiian or other Pacific Islander, non-Hispanic/Latino; 3% international. 3% 25 or older, 60% live on campus, 3% transferred in. Retention: 84% of full-time freshmen returned the following year. Academic areas with the most degrees conferred: health professions and related sciences; business/marketing; education. Core. Calendar: semesters. Academic remediation for entering students, ESL program, services for LD students, advanced placement, accelerated degree program, self-designed majors, freshman honors college, honors program, independent study, distance learning, double major, summer session for credit, part-time degree program, external degree program, adult/continuing education programs, internships, graduate courses open to undergrads. Off campus study at Carlow University, Carnegie Mellon University, Chatham University, Community College of Allegheny County, LaRoche College, Pittsburgh Theological Seminary, Point Park University, Robert Morris University, University of Pittsburgh. Study abroad program. ROTC: Army, Naval (c), Air Force (c).
Entrance Requirements: Options: electronic application, early admission, early decision, early action, deferred admission, international baccalaureate accepted. Required: high school transcript. Recommended: minimum 3 high school GPA, interview. Required for some: essay, 1 recommendation, audition for School of Music; 40 hours of volunteer, paid, or shadowing experience for physical therapy, SAT or ACT. Entrance: moderately difficult. Application deadlines: 11/1 for early decision, 12/1 for early action. Notification: continuous until 10/1, continuous for nonresidents, 12/15 for early decision, 1/15 for early action. SAT Reasoning Test deadline: 7/1. Transfer credits accepted: Yes. Early action applicants: 1,687. Early action applicants admitted: 953.
Costs Per Year: Application fee: $50. Comprehensive fee: $53,080 includes full-time tuition ($39,992) and college room and board ($13,088). College room only: $7194. Part-time tuition: $1325.
Collegiate Environment: Orientation program. Drama-theater group, choral group, marching band, student-run newspaper, radio station. Social organizations: 250 open to all; national fraternities, national sororities, local fraternities; 17% of eligible men and 24% of eligible women are members. Most popular organizations: International Student's Org (ISO), Red and Blue Crew, Duquesne University Volunteers (DUV), Duquesne Program Council, Residence Hall Association. Major annual events: Autumn Fest, Night of Lights, ISO Night (international dinner). Student services: health clinic, personal-psychological counseling. Campus security: 24-hour emergency response devices and patrols, late night transport-escort service, controlled dormitory access, cameras monitor exterior 24-hours/day, card access for buildings, outside warning siren system. College housing designed to accommodate 3,728 students; 3,784 undergraduates lived in college housing during 2018-19. Freshmen guaranteed college housing. On-campus residence required through sophomore year. Options: coed, men-only, women-only housing available. Gumberg Library plus 1 other. Books: 562,314 (physical), 342,710 (digital/electronic); Serial titles: 123 (physical), 99,402 (digital/electronic); Databases: 227. Weekly public service hours: 112; students can reserve study rooms. Operations spending for the previous fiscal year: $6.7 million. 1,000 computers available on campus for general student use. Computer purchase/lease plans available. A campuswide network can be accessed from student residence rooms and from off campus. Students can access the following: online class registra-

tion. Staffed computer lab on campus (open 24 hours a day) provides training in use of computers, software, and the Internet.

Community Environment: Located adjacent to downtown Pittsburgh, Duquesne University's modern hilltop campus is readily accessible to the business, entertainment, and shopping centers of the city, while still offering students the privacy and peace of its own self-enclosed 43-acre site. Long noted as one of the world's great corporate centers, Pittsburgh combines the features of urban living with many of the charms and personal characteristics of a much smaller town. The world-renowned Pittsburgh Symphony Orchestra, Pittsburgh Opera, and Pittsburgh Ballet Theatre all perform regularly in the elegant Heinz Hall for the Performing Arts and the Benedum Center. The theatergoer can choose from productions of the Pittsburgh Public Theatre, local college drama departments and programs, and a wide variety of summer and after dinner club theatres. Duquesne students can visit such points of interest as The Pittsburgh Zoo, Carnegie Museum of Art and History, Scaife Gallery, the Conservatory Aviary, Carnegie Science Center and Buhl Planetarium, Pittsburgh History and Landmarks Museum, Duquesne Incline and Phipps Conservatory. Market Square, a redeveloped area in the heart of downtown Pittsburgh, and the Oakland-Shadyside area in the eastern end of the city are two of the major entertainment and nightlife centers. The success of the various professional and major college sports teams has won for Pittsburgh the title of"City of Champions.".

■ **EAST STROUDSBURG UNIVERSITY OF PENNSYLVANIA**
200 Prospect St.
East Stroudsburg, PA 18301-2999
Tel: (570)422-3211; Free: 877-230-5547
Fax: (570)422-3933
E-mail: admission@esu.edu
Web Site: www.esu.edu

Description: State-supported, comprehensive, coed. Part of Pennsylvania State System of Higher Education. Awards bachelor's, master's, and doctoral degrees and post-master's certificates. Founded 1893. Setting: 258-acre suburban campus. Endowment: $22.2 million. Research spending for the previous fiscal year: $823,892. Educational spending for the previous fiscal year: $6560 per student. Total enrollment: 6,425. Faculty: 352 (260 full-time, 92 part-time). Student-undergrad faculty ratio is 19:1. 9,713 applied, 72% were admitted. 8% from top 10% of their high school class, 24% from top quarter, 58% from top half. 1 valedictorian. Full-time: 5,243 students, 56% women, 44% men. Part-time: 470 students, 59% women, 41% men. Students come from 26 states and territories, 19 other countries, 21% from out-of-state. 0.3% American Indian or Alaska Native, non-Hispanic/Latino; 12% Hispanic/Latino; 20% Black or African American, non-Hispanic/Latino; 2% Asian, non-Hispanic/Latino; 0.2% Native Hawaiian or other Pacific Islander, non-Hispanic/Latino; 0.9% international. 10% 25 or older, 43% live on campus, 8% transferred in. Retention: 69% of full-time freshmen returned the following year. Academic areas with the most degrees conferred: health professions and related sciences; business/marketing; parks and recreation. Core. Calendar: semesters. Academic remediation for entering students, services for LD students, advanced placement, accelerated degree program, self-designed majors, honors program, independent study, distance learning, double major, summer session for credit, part-time degree program, adult/continuing education programs, internships, graduate courses open to undergrads. Off campus study at Member of Marine Science Consortium, Bloomsburg North Central PA Educational Consortium. Study abroad program. ROTC: Army, Air Force (c).

Entrance Requirements: Options: electronic application, deferred admission, international baccalaureate accepted. Required: high school transcript. Required for some: SAT or ACT. Entrance: moderately difficult. Application deadlines: 4/1, 4/1 for nonresidents, 11/15 for early action. Notification: 5/1, continuous for nonresidents, rolling for early action. Transfer credits accepted: Yes.

Costs Per Year: Application fee: $25. State resident tuition: $7716 full-time, $322 per credit hour part-time. Nonresident tuition: $19,290 full-time, $805 per credit hour part-time. Mandatory fees: $3002 full-time, $151 per credit hour part-time, $716 per term part-time. Full-time tuition and fees vary according to course load, location, and program. Part-time tuition and fees vary according to location and program. College room and board: $8700. College room only: $6120. Room and board charges vary according to board plan and housing facility. Tuition guaranteed not to increase for student's term of enrollment.

Collegiate Environment: Orientation program. Drama-theater group, choral group, marching band, student-run newspaper, radio station. Social organizations: 128 open to all; national fraternities, national sororities, local

sororities. Most popular organizations: Black Student Union, Council for Exceptional Children, National Student Speech Hearing Language Association, Student Governmnet, Stage II. Major annual events: Warrior Induction, Homecoming, Color Me Warrior. Student services: legal services, health clinic, personal-psychological counseling, women's center. Campus security: 24-hour emergency response devices and patrols, late night transport-escort service, controlled dormitory access, self-defense education, shuttle buses, lighted pathways/sidewalks, controlled building access. 2,970 college housing spaces available; 2,732 were occupied in 2018-19. Freshmen guaranteed college housing. On-campus residence required in freshman year. Option: coed housing available. Kemp Library. Books: 227,237 (physical), 411,580 (digital/electronic); Serial titles: 3,143 (physical), 76,680 (digital/electronic); Databases: 107. Weekly public service hours: 99. Operations spending for the previous fiscal year: $2.2 million. 500 computers available on campus for general student use. A campuswide network can be accessed. Students can access the following: online class registration, online classes. Staffed computer lab on campus provides training in use of computers, software, and the Internet.

Community Environment: Population 10,621. East Stroudsburg is an urban area with temperate climate. The community is served by bus lines and Routes 611, 80 and 191. The community has a public library, YMCA, a hospital, good shopping facilities, and churches of major denominations. Part-time employment opportunities are excellent. The area offers good recreational facilities with nearby resorts.

■ **EASTERN UNIVERSITY**
1300 Eagle Rd.
Saint Davids, PA 19087-3696
Tel: (610)341-5800; Free: 800-452-0996
Fax: (610)341-1723
E-mail: ugadm@eastern.edu
Web Site: www.eastern.edu

Description: Independent Christian, university, coed. Awards associate, bachelor's, master's, and doctoral degrees and post-master's certificates. Founded 1952. Setting: 114-acre suburban campus with easy access to Philadelphia. Endowment: $30.7 million. Total enrollment: 3,256. Faculty: 440 (116 full-time, 324 part-time). Student-undergrad faculty ratio is 10:1. 1,757 applied, 69% were admitted. Full-time: 1,463 students, 65% women, 35% men. Part-time: 422 students, 79% women, 21% men. Students come from 35 states and territories, 17 other countries, 41% from out-of-state. 0.2% American Indian or Alaska Native, non-Hispanic/Latino; 19% Hispanic/Latino; 20% Black or African American, non-Hispanic/Latino; 2% Asian, non-Hispanic/Latino; 0.1% Native Hawaiian or other Pacific Islander, non-Hispanic/Latino; 2% international. 3% 25 or older, 79% live on campus, 8% transferred in. Retention: 75% of full-time freshmen returned the following year. Academic areas with the most degrees conferred: business/marketing; education; health professions and related sciences. Core. Calendar: semesters. Academic remediation for entering students, ESL program, services for LD students, advanced placement, accelerated degree program, self-designed majors, honors program, independent study, distance learning, double major, summer session for credit, part-time degree program, external degree program, adult/continuing education programs, internships, graduate courses open to undergrads. Off campus study at Cabrini University, Rosemont College, Valley Forge Military Academy and College, Villanova University (Pre-Engineering only). Study abroad program. ROTC: Army (c), Air Force (c).

Entrance Requirements: Options: electronic application, early admission, deferred admission, international baccalaureate accepted. Required: essay, high school transcript, minimum 2 high school GPA, 1 recommendation. Recommended: 2 recommendations, interview. Entrance: moderately difficult. Application deadlines: rolling, rolling for nonresidents. Notification: continuous, continuous for nonresidents. Transfer credits accepted: Yes.

Costs Per Year: Application fee: $35. One-time mandatory fee: $70. Comprehensive fee: $45,390 includes full-time tuition ($33,304), mandatory fees ($550), and college room and board ($11,536). College room only: $6136. Part-time tuition: $730 per contact hour. Part-time mandatory fees: $275 per term.

Collegiate Environment: Orientation program. Drama-theater group, choral group, student-run newspaper. Social organizations: 63 open to all. Most popular organizations: Wednesday Night Worship, Ultimate Frisbee, Student Activities Board, MAAC, Student Chaplain Program. Major annual events: Welcome Back Bash, Homecoming Weekend, Midnight Breakfast. Student services: health clinic, personal-psychological counseling. Campus security: 24-hour emergency response devices and patrols, late night transport-escort service, controlled dormitory access. 986 college housing spaces available; 943 were occupied in 2018-19. Freshmen guaranteed college housing. On-campus residence required through senior year. Options: men-only, women-only housing available. Warner Memorial Library plus 1 other. Books: 170,630 (physical), 1.6 million (digital/electronic); Serial titles: 70 (physical), 61,842 (digital/electronic); Databases: 189. Weekly public service hours: 83; students can reserve study rooms. Operations spending for the previous fiscal year: $845,000.

■ EDINBORO UNIVERSITY OF PENNSYLVANIA
219 Meadville St.
Edinboro, PA 16444
Tel: (814)732-2000; Free: 888-846-2676
Fax: (814)732-2420
E-mail: eup_admissions@edinboro.edu
Web Site: www.edinboro.edu

Description: State-supported, comprehensive, coed. Part of Pennsylvania State System of Higher Education. Awards associate, bachelor's, master's, and doctoral degrees and post-master's certificates. Founded 1857. Setting: 585-acre small town campus. Endowment: $10.5 million. Research spending for the previous fiscal year: $23,720. Total enrollment: 6,837. Faculty: 371 (317 full-time, 54 part-time). Student-undergrad faculty ratio is 19:1. 3,143 applied, 99% were admitted. 7% from top 10% of their high school class, 24% from top quarter, 56% from top half. Full-time: 5,086 students, 58% women, 42% men. Part-time: 499 students, 54% women, 46% men. 12% from out-of-state. 0.2% American Indian or Alaska Native, non-Hispanic/Latino; 3% Hispanic/Latino; 9% Black or African American, non-Hispanic/Latino; 0.9% Asian, non-Hispanic/Latino; 0.1% Native Hawaiian or other Pacific Islander, non-Hispanic/Latino; 2% international. 13% 25 or older, 37% live on campus, 6% transferred in. Retention: 70% of full-time freshmen returned the following year. Academic areas with the most degrees conferred: visual and performing arts; health professions and related sciences; education. Core. Calendar: semesters. Academic remediation for entering students, services for LD students, advanced placement, self-designed majors, honors program, independent study, distance learning, double major, summer session for credit, part-time degree program, adult/continuing education programs, internships, graduate courses open to undergrads. Off campus study at Consortia: Clarion University, Pymatuning Lab of Ecology, Tom Ridge Environmental Ctr., Perseus House Charter School Prof Dev. Grant, Titusville Middle School Cohort, Roosevelt Middle School Prof. Dev. School, Schools to Watch Sponsor; Numerous Internships; Road Courses; Philadelphia Urban Experience; Harrisburg Internship; Medical Technology and Nuclear Medical Technology Clinical sites; LECOM; Temple; Study Abroad; Articulation Agreements. Study abroad program. ROTC: Army.

Entrance Requirements: Options: electronic application, deferred admission, international baccalaureate accepted. Required: high school transcript, SAT or ACT. Recommended: minimum 2.5 high school GPA. Required for some: essay, 1 recommendation, interview, music auditions. Entrance: moderately difficult. Notification: continuous. SAT Reasoning Test deadline: 8/15. Transfer credits accepted: Yes.

Costs Per Year: Application fee: $30. State resident tuition: $7716 full-time, $322 per credit hour part-time. Nonresident tuition: $11,574 full-time, $482 per credit hour part-time. Mandatory fees: $2826 full-time, $54.20 per credit hour part-time, $120 per term part-time. Full-time tuition and fees vary according to degree level, location, and program. Part-time tuition and fees vary according to course load, degree level, location, program, and reciprocity agreements. College room and board: $9634. College room only: $5956. Room and board charges vary according to board plan and housing facility.

Collegiate Environment: Orientation program. Drama-theater group, choral group, marching band, student-run newspaper, radio station. Social organizations: 131 open to all; national fraternities, national sororities; 0.3% of eligible men and 1% of eligible women are members. Most popular organizations: Student Government Association, University Programming Board, Greek Life, Recreational Sports, Student Leadership (Leadership Edinboro). Major annual events: Homecoming, Concerts/Performances, Welcome Week/Club Rush. Student services: legal services, health clinic, personal-psychological counseling, women's center. Campus security: 24-hour emergency response devices and patrols, late night transport-escort service, controlled dormitory access, self-defense education. Baron-Forness Library plus 1 other. Operations spending for the previous fiscal year: $1.1 million. 1,157 computers available on campus for general student use. Computer purchase/lease plans available. A campuswide network can be accessed from student residence rooms. Students can access the following:

online class registration, new students receive technology instruction during orientation, 24-hour computer lab, some software.

Community Environment: Population 6,737, Edinboro lies approximately 18 miles south of Erie, Pennsylvania. The community has several churches that represent various denominations. Bus and highway transportation is available. Local recreational facilities include hunting, boating, swimming, fishing, golf, and skiing. Edinboro Lake, which is one mile from the campus, has three beaches.

■ ELIZABETHTOWN COLLEGE
One Alpha Dr.
Elizabethtown, PA 17022-2298
Tel: (717)361-1000
E-mail: admissions@etown.edu
Web Site: www.etown.edu

Description: Independent, comprehensive, coed, affiliated with Church of the Brethren. Awards bachelor's and master's degrees. Founded 1899. Setting: 203-acre small town campus with easy access to Philadelphia, Baltimore, Harrisburg, Lancaster. System endowment: $79.1 million. Educational spending for the previous fiscal year: $14,171 per student. Total enrollment: 1,735. Faculty: 183 (128 full-time, 55 part-time). Student-undergrad faculty ratio is 11:1. 3,030 applied, 74% were admitted. 30% from top 10% of their high school class, 60% from top quarter, 88% from top half. 7 National Merit Scholars, 4 class presidents, 3 valedictorians, 47 student government officers. Full-time: 1,636 students, 62% women, 38% men. Part-time: 35 students, 46% women, 54% men. Students come from 28 states and territories, 23 other countries, 32% from out-of-state. 0.1% American Indian or Alaska Native, non-Hispanic/Latino; 4% Hispanic/Latino; 3% Black or African American, non-Hispanic/Latino; 3% Asian, non-Hispanic/Latino; 0.1% Native Hawaiian or other Pacific Islander, non-Hispanic/Latino; 2% international. 1% 25 or older, 84% live on campus, 1% transferred in. Retention: 87% of full-time freshmen returned the following year. Academic areas with the most degrees conferred: business/marketing; health professions and related sciences; social sciences. Core. Calendar: semesters. ESL program, services for LD students, advanced placement, honors program, independent study, distance learning, double major, summer session for credit, internships. Off campus study at Washington Center Program. Study abroad program.

Entrance Requirements: Options: electronic application, deferred admission, international baccalaureate accepted. Required: essay, high school transcript, minimum 2 high school GPA, 2 recommendations, SAT or ACT. Recommended: minimum 3 high school GPA, interview. Required for some: interview. Entrance: moderately difficult. Application deadline: 3/1. Notification: continuous. SAT Reasoning Test deadline: 3/1. Transfer credits accepted: Yes. Applicants placed on waiting list: 0. Wait-listed applicants offered admission: 0.

Costs Per Year: Application fee: $30. Comprehensive fee: $58,310 includes full-time tuition ($46,940) and college room and board ($11,370). College room only: $5630. Full-time tuition varies according to course load. Room and board charges vary according to board plan and housing facility. Part-time tuition: $1140 per credit hour. Part-time tuition varies according to course load.

Collegiate Environment: Orientation program. Drama-theater group, choral group, student-run newspaper, radio station. Social organizations: 88 open to all. Most popular organizations: Professional Organizations, Emotion Dance Club, Student Senate, A cappella groups, Religious groups. Major annual events: Into the Streets Service Weekend, Scholarship and Creative Arts Day, Homecoming and Alumni Weekend. Student services: health clinic, personal-psychological counseling. Campus security: 24-hour emergency response devices and patrols, student patrols, late night transport-escort service, controlled dormitory access, self-defense workshops, crime prevention program. High Library plus 1 other. Books: 253,054 (physical), 5,306 (digital/electronic); Serial titles: 1,628 (physical), 7,972 (digital/electronic); Databases: 73. Weekly public service hours: 102; students can reserve study rooms. Operations spending for the previous fiscal year: $747,139. 230 computers available on campus for general student use. Computer purchase/lease plans available. A campuswide network can be accessed from student residence rooms and from off campus. Students can access the following: online class registration, file space, personal Web page, financial aid, student billing, residence hall selection, personal and group blogs. Staffed computer lab on campus provides training in use of computers, software, and the Internet.

Community Environment: Population 18,900. Located in Lancaster County, Elizabethtown enjoys the advantages of the neighboring communities' facilities. This suburb has a library, several churches, and major fraternal and civic organizations within the immediate locale. Some part-time employment is available.

■ ELIZABETHTOWN COLLEGE SCHOOL OF CONTINUING AND PROFESSIONAL STUDIES
One Alpha Dr.
Elizabethtown, PA 17022
Tel: (717)361-3750
E-mail: randazzob@etown.edu
Web Site: www.etowndegrees.com
Description: Independent, comprehensive, coed, affiliated with Church of the Brethren. Part of Elizabethtown College. Awards associate, bachelor's, and master's degrees. Setting: 201 small town campus with easy access to Philadelphia, Baltimore, Harrisburg-Carlisle. System endowment: $67.7 million. Educational spending for the previous fiscal year: $12,161 per student. Total enrollment: 422. Faculty: 57 (all part-time). Student-undergrad faculty ratio is 7:1. Part-time: 346 students, 69% women, 31% men. Students come from 4 states and territories, 1 other country, 2% from out-of-state. 0.3% American Indian or Alaska Native, non-Hispanic/Latino; 5% Hispanic/Latino; 11% Black or African American, non-Hispanic/Latino; 0.9% Asian, non-Hispanic/Latino; 0.3% Native Hawaiian or other Pacific Islander, non-Hispanic/Latino; 0.3% international. 95% 25 or older, 12% transferred in. Academic areas with the most degrees conferred: business/marketing; public administration and social services; communication/journalism. Core. Calendar: semesters (3 sub-terms in each semester). Academic remediation for entering students, services for LD students, advanced placement, accelerated degree program, independent study, distance learning, double major, summer session for credit, part-time degree program, external degree program, adult/continuing education programs, internships. Off campus study.
Entrance Requirements: Options: electronic application, deferred admission, international baccalaureate accepted. Required: essay. Application deadline: rolling. Transfer credits accepted: Yes.
Costs Per Year: Application fee: $0. Tuition: $555 per credit hour part-time. Part-time tuition varies according to course load.
Collegiate Environment: Campus security: 24-hour emergency response devices and patrols, student patrols, controlled dormitory access, self-defense workshops, crime prevention program. High Library plus 1 other. Operations spending for the previous fiscal year: $1.2 million. 200 computers available on campus for general student use. Computer purchase/lease plans available. A campuswide network can be accessed from off-campus. Students can access the following: online class registration, file space, personal Web page, financial aid, student billing. Staffed computer lab on campus provides training in use of computers, software, and the Internet.

■ ERIE INSTITUTE OF TECHNOLOGY
940 Millcreek Mall
Erie, PA 16565
Tel: (814)868-9900; Free: 866-868-3743
Fax: (814)868-9977
Web Site: www.erieit.edu
Description: Independent, 2-year, coed. Awards certificates and terminal associate degrees. Founded 1991. Total enrollment: 279. Student-undergrad faculty ratio is 11:1. 7% from out-of-state. 58% 25 or older. Calendar: semesters.
Entrance Requirements: Open admission. Required: high school transcript, interview, Wonderlic Basic Skills Test. Entrance: noncompetitive.

■ FORTIS INSTITUTE (ERIE)
5757 W 26th St.
Erie, PA 16506
Tel: (814)838-7673; Free: 855-4-FORTIS
Fax: (814)838-8642
Web Site: www.fortis.edu
Description: Proprietary, 2-year, coed. Awards certificates, diplomas, transfer associate, and terminal associate degrees. Total enrollment: 1,603. Student-undergrad faculty ratio is 17:1. 40% from out-of-state. 58% 25 or older. Retention: 63% of full-time freshmen returned the following year.
Entrance Requirements: Required: interview.

■ FORTIS INSTITUTE (FORTY FORT)
166 Slocum St.
Forty Fort, PA 18704

Tel: (570)288-8400; Free: 855-4-FORTIS
Fax: (717)287-7936
Web Site: www.fortis.edu
Description: Proprietary, 2-year, coed. Awards certificates, diplomas, transfer associate, and terminal associate degrees. Founded 1984. Total enrollment: 402. 41 applied. 46% 25 or older.

■ FORTIS INSTITUTE (SCRANTON)
517 Ash St.
Scranton, PA 18509
Tel: (570)558-1818; Free: 855-4-FORTIS
Web Site: www.fortis.edu
Description: Proprietary, 2-year, coed. Awards certificates, diplomas, transfer associate, and terminal associate degrees.

■ FRANKLIN & MARSHALL COLLEGE
PO Box 3003
Lancaster, PA 17604-3003
Tel: (717)358-3911; Free: 877-678-9111
E-mail: julie.kerich@fandm.edu
Web Site: www.fandm.edu
Description: Independent, 4-year, coed. Awards bachelor's degrees. Founded 1787. Setting: 209-acre suburban campus with easy access to Philadelphia. Total enrollment: 2,283. Faculty: 273 (242 full-time, 31 part-time). Student-undergrad faculty ratio is 9:1. 6,720 applied, 34% were admitted. 68% from top 10% of their high school class, 90% from top quarter, 100% from top half. Full-time: 2,263 students, 54% women, 46% men. Part-time: 20 students, 60% women, 40% men. Students come from 47 states and territories, 47 other countries, 77% from out-of-state. 0.1% American Indian or Alaska Native, non-Hispanic/Latino; 10% Hispanic/Latino; 6% Black or African American, non-Hispanic/Latino; 5% Asian, non-Hispanic/Latino; 16% international. 99% live on campus, 1% transferred in. Retention: 92% of full-time freshmen returned the following year. Academic areas with the most degrees conferred: social sciences; biological/life sciences; business/marketing. Core. Calendar: semesters. Services for LD students, advanced placement, accelerated degree program, self-designed majors, independent study, double major, summer session for credit, internships. Off campus study at Central Pennsylvania Consortium. Study abroad program.
Entrance Requirements: Options: electronic application, early admission, early decision, deferred admission, international baccalaureate accepted. Required: essay, high school transcript, 2 recommendations, Common Application Supplement. Required for some: interview. Entrance: very difficult. Application deadlines: 1/15, 11/15 for early decision plan 1, 1/15 for early decision plan 2. Notification: 4/1, 12/15 for early decision plan 1, 2/15 for early decision plan 2. SAT Reasoning Test deadline: 1/15. SAT Subject Test deadline: 1/15. Transfer credits accepted: Yes. Applicants placed on waiting list: 2,335. Wait-listed applicants offered admission: 16. Early decision applicants: 559. Early decision applicants admitted: 346.
Costs Per Year: Application fee: $60. One-time mandatory fee: $200. Comprehensive fee: $70,600 includes full-time tuition ($56,450), mandatory fees ($100), and college room and board ($14,050). College room only: $8310. Room and board charges vary according to board plan and housing facility. Part-time tuition: $7056 per course. Part-time tuition varies according to course load.
Collegiate Environment: Orientation program. Drama-theater group, choral group, student-run newspaper, radio station. Social organizations: 140 open to all; national fraternities, national sororities, local fraternities; 20% of eligible men and 26% of eligible women are members. Most popular organizations: Intervarsity, Hillel, Mi Gente Latina, Cia Bella, F&M Players. Major annual events: Spring Arts, Flapjack Fest, Campus Activities Fair. Student services: health clinic, personal-psychological counseling, women's center. Campus security: 24-hour emergency response devices and patrols, late night transport-escort service, controlled dormitory access, residence hall security, campus security connected to city police and fire company. Shadek-Fackenthal Library plus 1 other. Books: 468,748 (physical), 135,071 (digital/electronic); Serial titles: 2,680 (physical), 167,874 (digital/electronic). Weekly public service hours: 110; students can reserve study rooms. 125 computers available on campus for general student use. A campuswide network can be accessed from student residence rooms and from off campus. Students can access the following: online class registration, online degree audit, unofficial transcripts, course material. Staffed computer lab on campus provides training in use of computers, software, and the Internet.
Community Environment: Metropolitan area of 300,000; vital, historic city.

■ **GANNON UNIVERSITY**
109 University Sq.
Erie, PA 16541-0001
Tel: (814)871-7000; Free: 800-GANNONU
Fax: (814)871-5803
E-mail: admissions@gannon.edu
Web Site: www.gannon.edu

Description: Independent Roman Catholic, university, coed. Awards associate, bachelor's, master's, and doctoral degrees and post-master's certificates. Founded 1925. Setting: 38-acre urban campus with easy access to Cleveland, Buffalo, Pittsburgh. Total enrollment: 4,149. Faculty: 403 (238 full-time, 165 part-time). Student-undergrad faculty ratio is 12:1. 4,642 applied, 80% were admitted. 22% from top 10% of their high school class, 53% from top quarter, 78% from top half. Full-time: 2,530 students, 56% women, 44% men. Part-time: 546 students, 58% women, 42% men. Students come from 31 states and territories, 39 other countries, 29% from out-of-state. 0.1% American Indian or Alaska Native, non-Hispanic/Latino; 3% Hispanic/Latino; 5% Black or African American, non-Hispanic/Latino; 1% Asian, non-Hispanic/Latino; 9% international. 0.1% 25 or older, 46% live on campus, 3% transferred in. Retention: 85% of full-time freshmen returned the following year. Academic areas with the most degrees conferred: health professions and related sciences; business/marketing; parks and recreation. Core. Calendar: semesters plus 2 summer sessions. Academic remediation for entering students, ESL program, services for LD students, advanced placement, accelerated degree program, honors program, independent study, distance learning, double major, summer session for credit, part-time degree program, adult/continuing education programs, co-op programs and internships, graduate courses open to undergrads. Off campus study. Study abroad program. ROTC: Army.
Entrance Requirements: Options: electronic application, deferred admission, international baccalaureate accepted. Required: high school transcript, minimum 2 high school GPA, counselor's recommendation, SAT or ACT. Recommended: essay. Required for some: minimum 3 high school GPA, 2 recommendations, interview. Entrance: moderately difficult. Application deadline: rolling. Notification: continuous. SAT Reasoning Test deadline: 9/1. Transfer credits accepted: Yes.
Collegiate Environment: Orientation program. Drama-theater group, choral group, student-run newspaper, radio station. Social organizations: 91 open to all; national fraternities, national sororities; 15% of eligible men and 12% of eligible women are members. Most popular organizations: GU Society of Physician Assistant, GU Habitat for Humanity, Activities Programming Board, Student Occupational Therapy Association, Organization of Women Leaders. Major annual events: GIVE Day (Gannon's Invitation to Volunteer Everywhere), Homecoming Weekend, Springtopia. Student services: health clinic, personal-psychological counseling. Campus security: 24-hour emergency response devices and patrols, late night transport-escort service, controlled dormitory access, security cameras in and outside of campus facilities, including streets and sidewalks. Nash Library. Books: 213,041 (physical), 252,244 (digital/electronic); Serial titles: 37 (physical), 52,805 (digital/electronic); Databases: 45. Weekly public service hours: 97; students can reserve study rooms. 386 computers available on campus for general student use. A campuswide network can be accessed from student residence rooms and from off campus. Students can access the following: online class registration. Staffed computer lab on campus provides training in use of computers and the Internet.
Community Environment: Pennsylvania's third largest city and its only port on the Great Lakes, Erie is a city of widely diversified industry and commerce. A public library was built on the waterfront and an observation tower to celebrate the city's bicentennial. The area is served by rail, air, and bus lines. The community has many churches representing the major denominations, numerous civic and fraternal organizations, and community health clinics and hospitals. Local facilities include theatres, restaurants, shops, golf courses, city parks, Presque Isle State Park, fishing, ice fishing, boating, beach volleyball, and skating. Part-time employment opportunities are excellent.

■ **GENEVA COLLEGE**
3200 College Ave.
Beaver Falls, PA 15010-3599
Tel: (724)846-5100; Free: 800-847-8255
Fax: (724)847-6687
E-mail: admissions@geneva.edu
Web Site: www.geneva.edu

Description: Independent, comprehensive, coed, affiliated with Reformed Presbyterian Church of North America. Awards associate, bachelor's, and master's degrees (also offers non-traditional programs in Philadelphia and western Pennsylvania with significant enrollment not reflected in profile). Founded 1848. Setting: 55-acre small town campus with easy access to Pittsburgh. Endowment: $42.1 million. Educational spending for the previous fiscal year: $7393 per student. Total enrollment: 1,543. Faculty: 207 (68 full-time, 139 part-time). Student-undergrad faculty ratio is 12:1. 1,941 applied, 63% were admitted. 12% from top 10% of their high school class, 27% from top quarter, 44% from top half. Full-time: 1,180 students, 46% women, 54% men. Part-time: 196 students, 58% women, 42% men. Students come from 33 states and territories, 8 other countries, 26% from out-of-state. 0.2% American Indian or Alaska Native, non-Hispanic/Latino; 2% Hispanic/Latino; 7% Black or African American, non-Hispanic/Latino; 1% Asian, non-Hispanic/Latino; 2% international. 11% 25 or older, 65% live on campus, 3% transferred in. Retention: 76% of full-time freshmen returned the following year. Academic areas with the most degrees conferred: business/marketing; engineering; education. Core. Calendar: semesters. Academic remediation for entering students, ESL program, services for LD students, advanced placement, accelerated degree program, self-designed majors, honors program, independent study, distance learning, double major, summer session for credit, part-time degree program, adult/continuing education programs, co-op programs and internships, graduate courses open to undergrads. Off campus study at Council for Christian Colleges and Universities, Community College of Beaver County, Roberts Wesleyan College, Arcadia University, Art Institute of Pittsburgh. Study abroad program. ROTC: Army (c).
Entrance Requirements: Options: electronic application, early admission, deferred admission, international baccalaureate accepted. Required: essay, high school transcript, minimum 2 high school GPA, SAT or ACT. Recommended: minimum 3 high school GPA, 2 recommendations, interview. Required for some: 1 unit of chemistry and physics and 4 units of college-prep mathematics (including trigonometry and pre-calculus) for engineering. Entrance: moderately difficult. Application deadline: rolling. Notification: continuous. SAT Reasoning Test deadline: 3/1. Transfer credits accepted: Yes.
Costs Per Year: Application fee: $40. Comprehensive fee: $38,720 includes full-time tuition ($27,670), mandatory fees ($520), and college room and board ($10,530). College room only: $5500. Part-time tuition: $930 per credit hour. Part-time mandatory fees: $260 per term.
Collegiate Environment: Orientation program. Drama-theater group, choral group, marching band, student-run newspaper. Social organizations: 50 open to all. Most popular organizations: marching band, Genevans Choir, Intramural sports, ministry groups, discipleship groups. Major annual events: Homecoming, My Generation Night, Film Fest. Student services: health clinic, personal-psychological counseling. Campus security: 24-hour emergency response devices and patrols, late night transport-escort service, controlled dormitory access. 942 college housing spaces available; 826 were occupied in 2018-19. Freshmen guaranteed college housing. Options: men-only, women-only housing available. McCartney Library plus 3 others. Books: 140,157 (physical), 12,739 (digital/electronic); Serial titles: 30,449 (physical); Databases: 54. Weekly public service hours: 84. 150 computers available on campus for general student use. A campuswide network can be accessed from student residence rooms and from off campus. Students can access the following: online class registration. Staffed computer lab on campus provides training in use of computers, software, and the Internet.
Community Environment: Rich in natural resources and historical heritage, Beaver County supports commercial and industrial growth as well as a thriving agribusiness enterprise. 18,000 acres of park lands, excellent health care facilities, and numerous churches of various denominations help to meet needs of residents. Public transportation is accessible and proximity to Pittsburgh makes cultural and professional sports events available year-round. Part-time employment is available.

■ **GETTYSBURG COLLEGE**
300 N Washington St.
Gettysburg, PA 17325-1483
Tel: (717)337-6000; Free: 800-431-0803
Fax: (717)337-6008
E-mail: admiss@gettysburg.edu
Web Site: www.gettysburg.edu

Description: Independent, 4-year, coed, affiliated with Evangelical Lutheran Church in America. Awards bachelor's degrees. Founded 1832. Setting: 200-acre suburban campus with easy access to Baltimore and Washington, D.C. Endowment: $313.8 million. Total enrollment: 2,409. Faculty: 305 (227 full-time, 78 part-time). Student-undergrad faculty ratio is 9:1. 6,384 applied, 46% were admitted. 65% from top 10% of their high school class, 84% from top quarter, 99% from top half. Full-time: 2,400 students, 53% women, 47% men. Part-time: 9 students, 78% women, 22% men. Students come from 38 states and territories, 38 other countries, 74% from out-of-state. 0.1% American Indian or Alaska Native, non-Hispanic/Latino; 8% Hispanic/Latino; 4% Black or African American, non-Hispanic/Latino; 2% Asian, non-Hispanic/Latino; 7% international. 1% 25 or older, 94% live on campus, 1% transferred in. Retention: 90% of full-time freshmen returned the following year. Academic areas with the most degrees conferred: social sciences; biological/life sciences; business/marketing. Core. Calendar: semesters. Advanced placement, self-designed majors, independent study, double major, adult/continuing education programs, internships. Off campus study at 2 members of the Central Pennsylvania Consortium. Study abroad program. ROTC: Army (c).

Entrance Requirements: Options: electronic application, early admission, early decision, deferred admission, international baccalaureate accepted. Required: essay, high school transcript, 2 recommendations. Recommended: minimum 3 high school GPA, interview, extracurricular activities. Required for some: SAT or ACT. Entrance: most difficult. Application deadlines: 1/15, 11/15 for early decision plan 1, 1/15 for early decision plan 2. Notification: 4/1, 12/15 for early decision plan 1, 2/15 for early decision plan 2. SAT Reasoning Test deadline: 1/15. Applicants placed on waiting list: 917. Early decision applicants: 415. Early decision applicants admitted: 286.

Costs Per Year: Application fee: $60. Comprehensive fee: $67,490 includes full-time tuition ($54,480) and college room and board ($13,010). College room only: $6980. Room and board charges vary according to board plan and housing facility.

Collegiate Environment: Orientation program. Drama-theater group, choral group, marching band, student-run newspaper, radio station. Social organizations: 120 open to all; national fraternities, national sororities, local fraternities; 32% of eligible men and 35% of eligible women are members. Most popular organizations: community service, music, athletics, student government. Major annual events: Family Weekend Programs, Thanksgiving Dinner, Snowball. Student services: health clinic, personal-psychological counseling, women's center. Campus security: 24-hour emergency response devices and patrols, student patrols, late night transport-escort service, controlled dormitory access. Musselman Library. Books: 370,500 (physical), 350,000 (digital/electronic); Databases: 299. Study areas open 24 hours, 5-7 days a week. 350 computers available on campus for general student use. A campuswide network can be accessed from student residence rooms and from off campus. Students can access the following: online class registration. Staffed computer lab on campus (open 24 hours a day) provides training in use of computers and software.

Community Environment: Historic area of 20,000 with easy access to Harrisburg, PA, Washington, DC, and Baltimore, MD. The college borders the town and the 3800-acre National Park. A wide variety of recreational opportunities are available.

■ **GREAT LAKES INSTITUTE OF TECHNOLOGY**
5100 Peach St.
Erie, PA 16509
Tel: (814)456-6217
Fax: (814)459-4712
Web Site: www.glit.edu
Description: Proprietary, 2-year, coed. Awards diplomas, transfer associate, and terminal associate degrees. Founded 1965.

■ **GROVE CITY COLLEGE**
100 Campus Dr.
Grove City, PA 16127-2104
Tel: (724)458-2000
Fax: (724)458-3395
E-mail: admissions@gcc.edu
Web Site: www.gcc.edu
Description: Independent Presbyterian, 4-year, coed. Awards bachelor's degrees. Founded 1876. Setting: 180-acre small town campus with easy access to Pittsburgh. Endowment: $128.2 million. Research spending for the previous fiscal year: $90,000. Educational spending for the previous fiscal year: $13,212 per student. Total enrollment: 2,338. Faculty: 221 (159 full-time, 61 part-time). Student-undergrad faculty ratio is 13:1. 1,544 applied, 93% were admitted. 33% from top 10% of their high school class, 81% from top quarter, 90% from top half. 11 National Merit Scholars, 11 class presidents, 27 valedictorians, 12 student government officers. Full-time:

2,280 students, 48% women, 52% men. Part-time: 58 students, 50% women, 50% men. Students come from 42 states and territories, 13 other countries, 45% from out-of-state. 0.1% American Indian or Alaska Native, non-Hispanic/Latino; 1% Hispanic/Latino; 0.7% Black or African American, non-Hispanic/Latino; 2% Asian, non-Hispanic/Latino; 0.9% international. 96% live on campus, 2% transferred in. Retention: 87% of full-time freshmen returned the following year. Academic areas with the most degrees conferred: business/marketing; engineering; education. Core. Calendar: semesters. Services for LD students, advanced placement, accelerated degree program, independent study, distance learning, double major, summer session for credit, internships. Off campus study. Study abroad program.

Entrance Requirements: Options: electronic application, early admission, early decision, deferred admission, international baccalaureate accepted. Required: essay, high school transcript, 2 recommendations, SAT or ACT, SAT, ACT, and/or CLT test scores. Recommended: interview. Entrance: moderately difficult. Application deadlines: 1/20, 11/1 for early decision. Notification: 2/20, 12/15 for early decision. Preference given to Legacy applicants. SAT Reasoning Test deadline: 2/1. Transfer credits accepted: Yes. Applicants placed on waiting list: 119. Wait-listed applicants offered admission: 24. Early decision applicants: 351. Early decision applicants admitted: 320.

Costs Per Year: Application fee: $50. Comprehensive fee: $28,530 includes full-time tuition ($18,470) and college room and board ($10,060). College room only: $6160. Part-time tuition: $595 per credit hour.

Collegiate Environment: Orientation program. Drama-theater group, choral group, marching band, student-run newspaper, radio station. Social organizations: 175 open to all; local fraternities, local sororities; 15% of eligible men and 19% of eligible women are members. Most popular organizations: Warriors for Christ, Orchesis, Orientation Board, Association for Women Students (AWS), Young Life. Major annual events: Homecoming, Family Weekend, President's Gala. Student services: health clinic, personal-psychological counseling. Campus security: 24-hour emergency response devices and patrols, student patrols, late night transport-escort service, controlled dormitory access. 2,248 college housing spaces available; 2,155 were occupied in 2018-19. Freshmen guaranteed college housing. On-campus residence required through senior year. Options: men-only, women-only housing available. Henry Buhl Library plus 1 other. Books: 168,520 (physical), 264,550 (digital/electronic); Serial titles: 25 (physical), 45,123 (digital/electronic); Databases: 107. Weekly public service hours: 103. Operations spending for the previous fiscal year: $1.6 million. 50 computers available on campus for general student use. Computer purchase/lease plans available. A computer is required for all students. A campuswide network can be accessed from student residence rooms and from off campus. Students can access the following: online class registration. Staffed computer lab on campus provides training in use of computers, software, and the Internet.

Community Environment: Grove City, population 7,800, is an urban community that produces compressors, gas and diesel engines, soldering equipment and linemen's supplies. The city has a hospital, several churches, a library, theatre, YMCA, and various civic and fraternal organizations. You can experience big-city shopping at the Grove City Factory Shops located just outside of town. Local recreation includes hunting, fishing, golf, football, baseball, swimming, tennis, basketball, bowling, boating, and ice and roller skating.

■ **GWYNEDD MERCY UNIVERSITY**
Sumneytown Pke.
Gwynedd Valley, PA 19437-0901
Tel: (215)646-7300; Free: 800-342-5462
Fax: (215)641-5556
E-mail: admissions@gmercyu.edu
Web Site: www.gmercyu.edu
Description: Independent Roman Catholic, comprehensive, coed. Awards bachelor's, master's, and doctoral degrees and post-master's certificates. Founded 1948. Setting: 170-acre suburban campus with easy access to Philadelphia. Endowment: $38.4 million. Educational spending for the previous fiscal year: $11,479 per student. Total enrollment: 2,839. Faculty: 332 (91 full-time, 241 part-time). Student-undergrad faculty ratio is 11:1. 1,213 applied, 92% were admitted. 6% from top 10% of their high school class, 21% from top quarter, 58% from top half. Full-time: 1,898 students, 76% women, 24% men. Part-time: 135 students, 73% women, 27% men. Students come from 22 states and territories, 35 other countries, 14% from out-of-state. 0.5% American Indian or Alaska Native, non-Hispanic/Latino; 5% Hispanic/Latino; 22% Black or African American, non-Hispanic/Latino;

6% Asian, non-Hispanic/Latino; 0.1% Native Hawaiian or other Pacific Islander, non-Hispanic/Latino. 34% 25 or older, 19% live on campus, 11% transferred in. Retention: 82% of full-time freshmen returned the following year. Academic areas with the most degrees conferred: health professions and related sciences; business/marketing; education. Core. Calendar: semesters. Academic remediation for entering students, services for LD students, advanced placement, accelerated degree program, honors program, independent study, distance learning, double major, summer session for credit, part-time degree program, external degree program, adult/continuing education programs, co-op programs and internships, graduate courses open to undergrads. Study abroad program.

Entrance Requirements: Options: electronic application, deferred admission. Required: SAT or ACT. Required for some: essay. Entrance: moderately difficult. Application deadline: rolling. Notification: continuous. SAT Reasoning Test deadline: 8/20. Transfer credits accepted: Yes. Applicants placed on waiting list: 12. Wait-listed applicants offered admission: 2.

Costs Per Year: Application fee: $0. One-time mandatory fee: $780. Comprehensive fee: $47,050 includes full-time tuition ($33,800), mandatory fees ($780), and college room and board ($12,470). College room only: $5520. Part-time tuition: $632 per credit hour. Part-time mandatory fees: $17 per credit hour.

Collegiate Environment: Orientation program. Choral group, student-run newspaper. Social organizations: 30 open to all. Most popular organizations: Voices of Gwynedd, Athletic Association, Student Government, Program Board, Peer Mentors. Major annual events: Fall Fest, Carol Night, International Night. Student services: health clinic, personal-psychological counseling. Campus security: 24-hour emergency response devices and patrols, late night transport-escort service, controlled dormitory access. 525 college housing spaces available; 428 were occupied in 2018-19. Freshmen given priority for college housing. Option: coed housing available. Keiss Library plus 1 other. Books: 85,778 (physical), 180,000 (digital/electronic); Serial titles: 21 (physical), 111,480 (digital/electronic); Databases: 46. Weekly public service hours: 76; students can reserve study rooms. Operations spending for the previous fiscal year: $785,964. 200 computers available on campus for general student use. A campuswide network can be accessed from student residence rooms and from off campus. Students can access the following: online class registration. Staffed computer lab on campus (open 24 hours a day) provides training in use of computers, software, and the Internet.

Community Environment: Gwynedd Valley is a suburban location with the community located 20 miles from Center City, Philadelphia, which has cultural, recreational, and community service opportunities. The immediate locale has churches, recreational facilities, shopping malls, movies and restaurants.

■ HARCUM COLLEGE

750 Montgomery Ave.
Bryn Mawr, PA 19010-3476
Tel: (610)525-4100
Fax: (610)526-6147
E-mail: enroll@harcum.edu
Web Site: www.harcum.edu

Description: Independent, 2-year, coed. Awards certificates, transfer associate, and terminal associate degrees. Founded 1915. Setting: 12-acre suburban campus with easy access to Philadelphia. Educational spending for the previous fiscal year: $5673 per student. Total enrollment: 1,154. Faculty: 190 (36 full-time, 154 part-time). Student-undergrad faculty ratio is 12:1. 485 applied, 65% were admitted. 20% live on campus. Retention: 64% of full-time freshmen returned the following year. Core. Calendar: semesters. Academic remediation for entering students, ESL program, services for LD students, advanced placement, accelerated degree program, honors program, independent study, distance learning, summer session for credit, part-time degree program, adult/continuing education programs, internships. Off campus study.

Entrance Requirements: Options: electronic application, deferred admission, international baccalaureate accepted. Required: high school transcript, minimum 2 high school GPA. Recommended: essay, SAT or ACT. Required for some: 1 recommendation, interview. Entrance: minimally difficult. Application deadline: rolling. Notification: continuous.

Collegiate Environment: Orientation program. Social organizations: 10 open to all. Most popular organizations: OATS (Organization for Animal Tech Students), Student Association of Dental Hygienist of America, Student Nurses Association, Dental Assisting Club, HAECY (Organization for Early

Childhood Development). Major annual events: College Transfer Fair, Semester Kick-off, Health and Wellness Fair. Student services: health clinic, personal-psychological counseling. Campus security: 24-hour emergency response devices and patrols, late night transport-escort service, controlled dormitory access. Harcum College Library. Operations spending for the previous fiscal year: $239,085. 86 computers available on campus for general student use. A campuswide network can be accessed from student residence rooms and from off campus. Students can access the following: online class registration. Staffed computer lab on campus provides training in use of computers, software, and the Internet.

Community Environment: Located in Bryn Mawr, Harcum College is neighbor to Villanova University, St. Joseph's University, Bryn Mawr College, Cabrini College, Eastern College, among others. Historical and residential, the local community offers many shops, banks, and activities for students. The city of Philadelphia is just 25 minutes away by car or train.

■ HARRISBURG AREA COMMUNITY COLLEGE

1 HACC Dr.
Harrisburg, PA 17110-2999
Tel: (717)780-2300; Free: 800-ABC-HACC
Fax: (717)231-7674
Web Site: www.hacc.edu

Description: State and locally supported, 2-year, coed. Awards certificates, diplomas, transfer associate, and terminal associate degrees. Founded 1964. Setting: 212-acre urban campus. Total enrollment: 18,081. Faculty: 1,076 (333 full-time, 743 part-time). Student-undergrad faculty ratio is 17:1. 12,698 applied, 100% were admitted. Full-time: 5,222 students, 56% women, 44% men. Part-time: 12,859 students, 68% women, 32% men. 3% from out-of-state. 0.2% American Indian or Alaska Native, non-Hispanic/Latino; 12% Hispanic/Latino; 10% Black or African American, non-Hispanic/Latino; 4% Asian, non-Hispanic/Latino; 0.1% Native Hawaiian or other Pacific Islander, non-Hispanic/Latino; 2% international. 42% 25 or older, 8% transferred in. Core. Calendar: semesters. Academic remediation for entering students, ESL program, services for LD students, advanced placement, honors program, independent study, distance learning, double major, summer session for credit, part-time degree program, adult/continuing education programs, internships. ROTC: Army.

Entrance Requirements: Open admission except for allied health and chef's apprenticeship programs. Options: electronic application, early admission, deferred admission. Required for some: high school transcript, 1 recommendation, interview. Entrance: noncompetitive. Transfer credits accepted: Yes.

Costs Per Year: Application fee: $0. Area resident tuition: $5408 full-time, $180 per credit hour part-time. State resident tuition: $6510 full-time, $217 per credit hour part-time. Nonresident tuition: $7860 full-time, $262 per credit hour part-time. Mandatory fees: $1245 full-time, $41.50 per credit hour part-time. Full-time tuition and fees vary according to location and program. Part-time tuition and fees vary according to location and program.

Collegiate Environment: Orientation program. Drama-theater group, student-run newspaper. Most popular organizations: Student Government Association, Phi Theta Kappa, African-American Student Association, Mosiaco Club, Fourth Estate. Campus security: 24-hour emergency response devices and patrols, late night transport-escort service. College housing not available. McCormick Library.

Community Environment: Population 47,472. On the Susquehanna River, Harrisburg lies between mountains which rise abruptly to the north and west and rolling hills which slope to the south and east. Extensive coal and iron mines in the vicinity furnish raw materials for the city's large steel plants. Part-time employment opportunities are good. Harrisburg is a metropolitan area served by airlines, railroad, and bus lines. The community has state and public libraries, a State Museum, several hospitals, and major civic, fraternal and veteran's organizations. Shopping facilities are excellent. Local recreational opportunities include theatres, summer theatres, parks, golf, professional hockey, and water sports.

■ HARRISBURG UNIVERSITY OF SCIENCE AND TECHNOLOGY

326 Market St.
Harrisburg, PA 17101
Tel: (717)901-5100; Free: 866-HBG-UNIV
Fax: (717)901-5150
Web Site: www.HarrisburgU.edu

Description: Independent, comprehensive, coed. Awards bachelor's, master's, and doctoral degrees. Founded 2005. Setting: urban campus. Educational spending for the previous fiscal year: $4951 per student. Total enrollment: 4,071. Student-undergrad faculty ratio is 34:1. Full-time: 441 students, 49% women, 51% men. Part-time: 70 students, 46% women, 54% men. Students come from 6 states and territories, 4 other countries, 28% from out-of-state. 0.6% American Indian or Alaska Native, non-Hispanic/Latino; 13% Hispanic/Latino; 38% Black or African American, non-Hispanic/Latino; 4% Asian, non-Hispanic/Latino; 1% international. 7% 25 or older, 6% transferred in. Retention: 54% of full-time freshmen returned the following year. Academic areas with the most degrees conferred: computer and information sciences; physical sciences; science technologies. Core. Calendar: semesters. Academic remediation for entering students, services for LD students, advanced placement, self-designed majors, independent study, double major, summer session for credit, part-time degree program, adult/continuing education programs, internships, graduate courses open to undergrads.

Entrance Requirements: Option: electronic application. Required: high school transcript. Recommended: essay, interview. Entrance: minimally difficult. Application deadline: rolling. Notification: continuous. Transfer credits accepted: Yes.

Costs Per Year: Application fee: $0. Tuition: $23,900 full-time, $1000 per semester hour part-time. Full-time tuition varies according to class time, course level, course load, degree level, location, program, reciprocity agreements, and student level. Part-time tuition varies according to class time, course level, course load, degree level, location, program, reciprocity agreements, and student level. College room only: $6800. Room charges vary according to housing facility.

Collegiate Environment: Orientation program. Student services: personal-psychological counseling. Campus security: 24-hour emergency response devices and patrols, trained security personnel during hours of operation. Information Commons. Books: 4,130 (physical), 26 (digital/electronic); Serial titles: 103 (physical), 126 (digital/electronic); Databases: 24. Study areas open 24 hours, 5-7 days a week. Operations spending for the previous fiscal year: $195,805. 10 computers available on campus for general student use. Computer purchase/lease plans available. A computer is required for all students. A campuswide network can be accessed from student residence rooms and from off campus. Staffed computer lab on campus.

■ **HAVERFORD COLLEGE**
370 Lancaster Ave.
Haverford, PA 19041-1392
Tel: (610)896-1000
Fax: (610)896-1338
E-mail: admission@haverford.edu
Web Site: www.haverford.edu

Description: Independent, 4-year, coed. Awards bachelor's degrees. Founded 1833. Setting: 216-acre suburban campus with easy access to Philadelphia. Endowment: $518.9 million. Research spending for the previous fiscal year: $3.4 million. Educational spending for the previous fiscal year: $26,776 per student. Total enrollment: 1,310. Faculty: 159 (135 full-time, 24 part-time). Student-undergrad faculty ratio is 9:1. 4,672 applied, 19% were admitted. 95% from top 10% of their high school class, 97% from top quarter, 100% from top half. Full-time: 1,308 students, 51% women, 49% men. Part-time: 2 students, 50% women, 50% men. Students come from 44 states and territories, 49 other countries, 86% from out-of-state. 0.2% American Indian or Alaska Native, non-Hispanic/Latino; 10% Hispanic/Latino; 7% Black or African American, non-Hispanic/Latino; 13% Asian, non-Hispanic/Latino; 11% international. 98% live on campus, 1% transferred in. Retention: 97% of full-time freshmen returned the following year. Academic areas with the most degrees conferred: social sciences; physical sciences; psychology. Core. Calendar: semesters. Services for LD students, advanced placement, self-designed majors, independent study, double major, internships. Off campus study at University of Pennsylvania, Swarthmore College, Bryn Mawr College. Study abroad program. ROTC: Air Force (c).

Entrance Requirements: Options: electronic application, early admission, early decision, deferred admission, international baccalaureate accepted. Required: essay, SAT or ACT. Recommended: interview. Required for some: high school transcript. Entrance: most difficult. Application deadlines: 1/15, 11/15 for early decision plan 1, 1/1 for early decision plan 2. Notification: 4/1, 12/15 for early decision plan 1, 2/15 for early decision plan 2. SAT Reasoning Test deadline: 2/1. SAT Subject Test deadline: 2/1. Transfer credits accepted: Yes. Applicants placed on waiting list: 1,349. Wait-listed applicants offered admission: 11. Early decision applicants: 444. Early decision applicants admitted: 196.

Costs Per Year: Application fee: $65. One-time mandatory fee: $246.

Comprehensive fee: $70,994 includes full-time tuition ($54,100), mandatory fees ($492), and college room and board ($16,402). College room only: $9428.

Collegiate Environment: Orientation program. Drama-theater group, choral group, student-run newspaper, radio station. Social organizations: 145 open to all. Most popular organizations: Volunteer Programs, Student government, Choral groups, Multicultural Groups, Orientation Team/Residential Life Leaders. Major annual events: Haverfest/May Day, Snowball, Athletic Events Against Swarthmore. Student services: health clinic, personal-psychological counseling, women's center. Campus security: 24-hour emergency response devices and patrols, late night transport-escort service, controlled dormitory access. 1,295 college housing spaces available; 1,277 were occupied in 2018-19. Freshmen guaranteed college housing. On-campus residence required in freshman year. Options: coed, men-only, women-only housing available. James P. Magill Library plus 3 others. Books: 475,604 (physical), 702,593 (digital/electronic); Serial titles: 18,525 (physical), 135,312 (digital/electronic); Databases: 91. Study areas open 24 hours, 5-7 days a week; students can reserve study rooms. 300 computers available on campus for general student use. A campuswide network can be accessed from student residence rooms and from off campus. Students can access the following: online class registration. Staffed computer lab on campus (open 24 hours a day) provides training in use of computers, software, and the Internet.

Community Environment: The school has cooperative arrangements with several colleges and universities (see Bryn Mawr College, Swarthmore College, University of Pennsylvania) and is located near many colleges and universities in metropolitan Philadelphia area.

■ **HOLY FAMILY UNIVERSITY**
9801 Frankford Ave.
Philadelphia, PA 19114
Tel: (215)637-7700
Fax: (215)281-1022
E-mail: admissions@holyfamily.edu
Web Site: www.holyfamily.edu

Description: Independent Roman Catholic, comprehensive, coed. Administratively affiliated with NA. Awards associate, bachelor's, master's, and doctoral degrees and post-master's certificates. Founded 1954. Setting: 47-acre suburban campus with easy access to Philadelphia. Endowment: $18.5 million. Educational spending for the previous fiscal year: $8237 per student. Total enrollment: 3,081. Faculty: 310 (77 full-time, 233 part-time). Student-undergrad faculty ratio is 15:1. 1,429 applied, 71% were admitted. 9% from top 10% of their high school class, 29% from top quarter, 58% from top half. Full-time: 1,621 students, 75% women, 25% men. Part-time: 472 students, 71% women, 29% men. Students come from 25 states and territories, 6 other countries, 14% from out-of-state. 0.2% American Indian or Alaska Native, non-Hispanic/Latino; 4% Hispanic/Latino; 12% Black or African American, non-Hispanic/Latino; 5% Asian, non-Hispanic/Latino; 0.4% Native Hawaiian or other Pacific Islander, non-Hispanic/Latino; 0.2% international. 15% 25 or older, 15% live on campus, 8% transferred in. Retention: 78% of full-time freshmen returned the following year. Academic areas with the most degrees conferred: health professions and related sciences; business/marketing; psychology. Core. Calendar: semesters. Academic remediation for entering students, services for LD students, advanced placement, accelerated degree program, honors program, independent study, distance learning, double major, summer session for credit, part-time degree program, adult/continuing education programs, co-op programs and internships, graduate courses open to undergrads. Off campus study at Southeastern Pennsylvania Consortium of Higher Education: Arcadia University, Cabrini College, Chestnut Hill College, Gwynedd Mercy University, Immaculata University, Neumann University, Rosemont College. Study abroad program. ROTC: Army (c).

Entrance Requirements: Options: electronic application, deferred admission, international baccalaureate accepted. Required: essay, high school transcript, minimum 2 high school GPA, 2 recommendations, SAT or ACT. Recommended: interview. Entrance: minimally difficult. Application deadline: rolling. Notification: continuous. SAT Reasoning Test deadline: 8/15. SAT Subject Test deadline: 8/15. Transfer credits accepted: Yes.

Costs Per Year: Application fee: $25. One-time mandatory fee: $504. Comprehensive fee: $43,922 includes full-time tuition ($29,338), mandatory fees ($1008), and college room and board ($13,576). College room only: $7140. Full-time tuition and fees vary according to class time, course level, course load, degree level, program, and reciprocity agreements. Room and board charges vary according to board plan and housing facility. Part-time tuition: $627 per credit hour. Part-time mandatory fees: $112 per term. Part-time tuition and fees vary according to class time, course level, course load, degree level, program, and reciprocity agreements.

Collegiate Environment: Orientation program. Drama-theater group, choral group, student-run newspaper. Social organizations: 24 open to all. Most popular organizations: Students at Your Service (S.A.Y.S.), Green Team, Campus Ministry Team, Habitat for Humanity, Student Nurses Association of Holy Family. Major annual events: Christmas Rose, Charter Day, Stress Reduction Week. Student services: health clinic, personal-psychological counseling. Campus security: 24-hour emergency response devices and patrols, late night transport-escort service, controlled dormitory access, video surveillance. Holy Family University Library plus 1 other. Books: 75,943 (physical), 27,681 (digital/electronic); Serial titles: 1,106 (physical), 22,214 (digital/electronic); Databases: 42. Weekly public service hours: 116; students can reserve study rooms. Operations spending for the previous fiscal year: $747,000. 300 computers available on campus for general student use. A campuswide network can be accessed from student residence rooms and from off campus. Students can access the following: online class registration, online course syllabi, online course evaluations. Staffed computer lab on campus provides training in use of computers, software, and the Internet.

Community Environment: The main campus of Holy Family College is located on 46 acres in the residential Torresdale section of northeast Philadelphia near the boundary with Bucks County, Pennsylvania. The main campus is easily reached by public transportation. The Newtown campus is located on 85 acres in the heart of suburban Bucks County, Pennsylvania. It is situated very close to the Newtown exit of Interstate-95.

■ **HUSSIAN COLLEGE, SCHOOL OF ART**
1500 Spring Garden St.
Ste. 101
Philadelphia, PA 19130
Tel: (215)981-0900
Fax: (215)864-9115
E-mail: mcernero@hussianart.edu
Web Site: www.hussiancollege.edu
Description: Proprietary, 4-year, coed. Awards bachelor's degrees. Founded 1946. Setting: 1-acre urban campus with easy access to Philadelphia. Total enrollment: 83. 126 applied, 25% were admitted. Full-time: 82 students, 52% women, 48% men. Part-time: 1 student, 100% men. 14% Hispanic/Latino; 20% Black or African American, non-Hispanic/Latino; 6% Asian, non-Hispanic/Latino. Core. Calendar: semesters. Independent study, internships.
Entrance Requirements: Options: electronic application, deferred admission. Required: high school transcript, interview, portfolio evaluation, creative assessment activity or portfolio development drawing workshop. Recommended: minimum 2.5 high school GPA. Entrance: minimally difficult. Application deadline: rolling. Notification: continuous. Transfer credits accepted: Yes.
Costs Per Year: Application fee: $0. Tuition: $21,990 full-time, $733 per credit hour part-time. Full-time tuition varies according to course load. Part-time tuition varies according to course load.
Collegiate Environment: Campus security: 24-hour patrols. Hussian Library. Books: 4,000 (physical); Serial titles: 15 (physical); Databases: 100.

■ **IMMACULATA UNIVERSITY**
1145 King Rd.
Immaculata, PA 19345
Tel: (610)647-4400; Free: 877-428-6329
Fax: (610)251-1668
E-mail: cesbensen@immaculata.edu
Web Site: www.immaculata.edu
Description: Independent Roman Catholic, university, coed. Awards associate, bachelor's, master's, and doctoral degrees and post-master's certificates. Founded 1920. Setting: 373-acre suburban campus with easy access to Philadelphia. Endowment: $19.7 million. Total enrollment: 2,477. Faculty: 318 (82 full-time, 236 part-time). Student-undergrad faculty ratio is 9:1. 1,639 applied, 81% were admitted. 9% from top 10% of their high school class, 28% from top quarter, 65% from top half. Full-time: 823 students, 70% women, 30% men. Part-time: 681 students, 77% women, 23% men. 25% from out-of-state. 0.1% American Indian or Alaska Native, non-Hispanic/Latino; 7% Hispanic/Latino; 16% Black or African American, non-Hispanic/Latino; 2% Asian, non-Hispanic/Latino; 0.1% Native Hawaiian or other Pacific Islander, non-Hispanic/Latino; 2% international. 37% 25 or older, 29% live on campus, 3% transferred in. Retention: 75% of full-time freshmen

returned the following year. Academic areas with the most degrees conferred: health professions and related sciences; business/marketing; parks and recreation. Core. Calendar: semesters. Academic remediation for entering students, services for LD students, advanced placement, accelerated degree program, honors program, independent study, distance learning, double major, summer session for credit, part-time degree program, adult/continuing education programs, internships, graduate courses open to undergrads. Off campus study. Study abroad program. ROTC: Army (c).
Entrance Requirements: Options: electronic application, deferred admission, international baccalaureate accepted. Required: essay, high school transcript, minimum 2 high school GPA, 1 recommendation. Recommended: minimum 3 high school GPA, interview. Required for some: minimum 3 high school GPA, 2 recommendations, audition for music students. Entrance: moderately difficult. Application deadline: rolling. Notification: continuous. SAT Reasoning Test deadline: 8/15. Transfer credits accepted: Yes.
Costs Per Year: Application fee: $35. Comprehensive fee: $39,970 includes full-time tuition ($26,500), mandatory fees ($850), and college room and board ($12,620). College room only: $6390. Part-time tuition: $540 per credit hour.
Collegiate Environment: Orientation program. Drama-theater group, choral group, student-run newspaper. Social organizations: 50 open to all; local fraternities, local sororities; 1% of eligible men and 3% of eligible women are members. Most popular organizations: National Society of Leadership and Success, Student Dietetic Association, Immaculata University Chorale, College of Undergraduate Studies Honor Society, Immaculata University Pre-Med. Major annual events: Late Night Breakfast, Cotillion, Block Party. Student services: health clinic, personal-psychological counseling. Campus security: 24-hour emergency response devices and patrols, late night transport-escort service, controlled dormitory access. 568 college housing spaces available; 380 were occupied in 2018-19. Freshmen guaranteed college housing. Options: coed, men-only, women-only housing available. Gabriele Library. Books: 117,336 (physical), 10,448 (digital/electronic); Databases: 53. Students can reserve study rooms. 600 computers available on campus for general student use. A campuswide network can be accessed from student residence rooms and from off campus. Students can access the following: online class registration. Staffed computer lab on campus provides training in use of computers, software, and the Internet.
Community Environment: Immaculata is a suburban area with a temperate climate. An airport, railroad, and bus lines serve the area. The school is located in Chester County, twenty miles west of Philadelphia, at the junction of routes 30 and 352. The community has a public library, churches of major denominations, two hospitals, and several large shopping centers. There are active civic and fraternal organizations within the area.

■ **INDIANA UNIVERSITY OF PENNSYLVANIA**
1011 S Dr.
Indiana, PA 15705
Tel: (724)357-2100; Free: 800-442-6830
Fax: (724)357-2685
Web Site: www.iup.edu
Description: State-supported, university, coed. Part of Pennsylvania State System of Higher Education. Awards associate, bachelor's, master's, and doctoral degrees and post-master's certificates. Founded 1875. Setting: 374-acre small town campus with easy access to Pittsburgh. Endowment: $67.5 million. Research spending for the previous fiscal year: $1.4 million. Educational spending for the previous fiscal year: $10,659 per student. Total enrollment: 11,325. Faculty: 654 (542 full-time, 112 part-time). Student-undergrad faculty ratio is 16:1. 9,522 applied, 93% were admitted. 8% from top 10% of their high school class, 23% from top quarter, 57% from top half. Full-time: 8,359 students, 59% women, 41% men. Part-time: 856 students, 47% women, 53% men. Students come from 29 states and territories, 35 other countries, 5% from out-of-state. 0.1% American Indian or Alaska Native, non-Hispanic/Latino; 5% Hispanic/Latino; 12% Black or African American, non-Hispanic/Latino; 1% Asian, non-Hispanic/Latino; 4% international. 6% 25 or older, 30% live on campus, 4% transferred in. Retention: 71% of full-time freshmen returned the following year. Academic areas with the most degrees conferred: business/marketing; social sciences; health professions and related sciences. Core. Calendar: semesters. Academic remediation for entering students, ESL program, services for LD students, advanced placement, accelerated degree program, self-designed majors, freshman honors college, honors program, independent study, distance learning, double major, summer session for credit, part-time degree program, external degree program, adult/continuing education programs, co-op programs and internships, graduate courses open to undergrads. Off

campus study at Bucks County Community College (CC), Butler County CC, Community College of Allegheny County, Community College of Beaver County, Community College of Philadelphia, Delaware County CC, Harrisburg Area CC, Lehigh-Carbon CC, Luzerne County CC, Montgomery County CC, Northampton CC, Penn Highlands CC, Reading Area CC, Westmoreland County CC, Pennsylvania State System of Higher Education (PASSHE). Study abroad program. ROTC: Army.

Entrance Requirements: Options: electronic application, early admission, deferred admission, international baccalaureate accepted. Required: high school transcript, SAT or ACT. Recommended: essay, 2 recommendations. Entrance: minimally difficult. Application deadlines: rolling, rolling for nonresidents. Notification: continuous, continuous for nonresidents. SAT Reasoning Test deadline: 5/1. Transfer credits accepted: Yes.

Costs Per Year: Application fee: $0. State resident tuition: $9570 full-time, $319 per credit hour part-time. Nonresident tuition: $13,890 full-time, $463 per credit hour part-time. Mandatory fees: $3,409 full-time, $121.20 per credit hour part-time, $50 per term part-time. Full-time tuition and fees vary according to course load. Part-time tuition and fees vary according to course load. College room and board: $12,592. College room only: $8950. Room and board charges vary according to board plan, housing facility, and location.

Collegiate Environment: Orientation program. Drama-theater group, choral group, marching band, student-run newspaper, radio station. Social organizations: 260 open to all; national fraternities, national sororities; 10% of eligible men and 9% of eligible women are members. Most popular organizations: Student Government Association, Panhellenic Association, Interfraternity Council, Student Association of Nutrition and Dietetics, Saudi Student Association. Major annual events: Homecoming, IUP Day, Winter Warm UP. Student services: legal services, health clinic, personal-psychological counseling. Campus security: 24-hour emergency response devices and patrols, late night transport-escort service, controlled dormitory access. 3,746 college housing spaces available; 2,770 were occupied in 2018-19. Freshmen guaranteed college housing. On-campus residence required in freshman year. Options: coed, women-only housing available. Stapleton Library plus 1 other. Books: 514,631 (physical), 100,229 (digital/electronic); Serial titles: 4,858 (physical). Weekly public service hours: 101; study areas open 24 hours, 5-7 days a week; students can reserve study rooms. Operations spending for the previous fiscal year: $4.5 million. 2,363 computers available on campus for general student use. Computer purchase/lease plans available. A campuswide network can be accessed from student residence rooms and from off campus. Students can access the following: online class registration. Staffed computer lab on campus provides training in use of computers, software, and the Internet.

Community Environment: Population 15,000. Indiana is known as the "Christmas Tree Capital of the World" and is the birthplace of actor Jimmy Stewart. The town is located 50 miles northeast of Pittsburgh in the foothills of the beautiful Allegheny Mountains. Indiana has churches of all denominations, a library, a recreation center, a hospital, and various civic, fraternal and veteran's organizations. Local recreational facilities include golf courses, theatres, swimming pool, ice skating rink, tennis, baseball fields, a grandstand and an outdoor stage. Some part-time employment is available.

■ **JNA INSTITUTE OF CULINARY ARTS**
1212 S Broad St.
Philadelphia, PA 19146
Tel: (215)468-8800
Fax: (215)468-8838
Web Site: www.culinaryarts.com

Description: Proprietary, 2-year, coed. Awards terminal associate degrees. Founded 1988. Setting: urban campus with easy access to Philadelphia. Educational spending for the previous fiscal year: $4322 per student. Total enrollment: 59. Full-time: 59 students, 51% women, 49% men. Students come from 7 states and territories, 10% from out-of-state. 11% Hispanic/Latino; 57% Black or African American, non-Hispanic/Latino; 3% Asian, non-Hispanic/Latino. 30% 25 or older. Retention: 60% of full-time freshmen returned the following year. Calendar: continuous.

Entrance Requirements: Entrance: noncompetitive.

Collegiate Environment: Operations spending for the previous fiscal year: $4636.

■ **JOHNSON COLLEGE**
3427 N Main Ave.
Scranton, PA 18508-1495
Tel: (570)342-6404; Free: 800-2WE-WORK
Fax: (570)348-2181
Web Site: www.johnson.edu

Description: Independent, 2-year, coed. Awards certificates and terminal associate degrees. Founded 1912. Setting: 65-acre urban campus. Total enrollment: 376. Faculty: 23 (21 full-time, 2 part-time). Student-undergrad faculty ratio is 17:1. Full-time: 363 students, 27% women, 73% men. Part-time: 13 students, 54% women, 46% men. 20% 25 or older. Retention: 69% of full-time freshmen returned the following year. Core. Calendar: semesters. Academic remediation for entering students, services for LD students, summer session for credit, part-time degree program, adult/continuing education programs, internships.

Entrance Requirements: Options: electronic application, deferred admission. Required: essay, high school transcript. Recommended: SAT. Required for some: interview, SAT. Entrance: minimally difficult. Application deadline: 5/1.

Collegiate Environment: Orientation program. Most popular organizations: Student Government, Social Force Club, trade/technical/clinical clubs. Major annual events: Career Fair, Spring Day, Welcome Back Week. Student services: personal-psychological counseling. Campus security: 24-hour emergency response devices. Johnson College Library. 75 computers available on campus for general student use. Staffed computer lab on campus.

■ **JUNIATA COLLEGE**
1700 Moore St.
Huntingdon, PA 16652-2119
Tel: (814)641-3000; Free: 877-JUNIATA
Fax: (814)641-3100
E-mail: bollmat@juniata.edu
Web Site: www.juniata.edu

Description: Independent, comprehensive, coed, affiliated with Church of the Brethren. Awards bachelor's and master's degrees. Founded 1876. Setting: 110-acre small town campus. Endowment: $122.3 million. Research spending for the previous fiscal year: $722,175. Educational spending for the previous fiscal year: $13,053 per student. Total enrollment: 1,433. Faculty: 168 (124 full-time, 44 part-time). Student-undergrad faculty ratio is 11:1. 2,437 applied, 70% were admitted. 31% from top 10% of their high school class, 67% from top quarter, 93% from top half. 2 National Merit Scholars, 6 valedictorians. Full-time: 1,339 students, 56% women, 44% men. Part-time: 84 students, 60% women, 40% men. Students come from 32 states and territories, 31 other countries, 30% from out-of-state. 0.2% American Indian or Alaska Native, non-Hispanic/Latino; 5% Hispanic/Latino; 3% Black or African American, non-Hispanic/Latino; 3% Asian, non-Hispanic/Latino; 7% international. 2% 25 or older, 87% live on campus, 1% transferred in. Retention: 84% of full-time freshmen returned the following year. Academic areas with the most degrees conferred: biological/life sciences; business/marketing; natural resources/environmental science. Core. Calendar: semesters. ESL program, services for LD students, advanced placement, self-designed majors, honors program, independent study, double major, summer session for credit, part-time degree program, internships. Off campus study at Philadelphia Urban Semester, Washington Center, University of Oregon, Great Lakes Colleges Associates, Philadelphia Center, Washington Internship Institute. Study abroad program.

Entrance Requirements: Options: electronic application, early admission, early decision, early action, deferred admission, international baccalaureate accepted. Required: essay, high school transcript, minimum 3 high school GPA, 1 recommendation. Recommended: interview, SAT, ACT, SAT or ACT. Entrance: moderately difficult. Application deadlines: 3/15, 11/15 for early decision, 1/5 for early action. Notification: 2/1, 12/23 for early decision plan 1, rolling for early decision plan 2, 2/15 for early action. SAT Reasoning Test deadline: 1/1. Transfer credits accepted: Yes. Wait-listed applicants offered admission: 0. Early decision applicants: 53. Early decision applicants admitted: 47. Early action applicants: 949. Early action applicants admitted: 770.

Costs Per Year: Application fee: $0. Comprehensive fee: $59,875 includes full-time tuition ($46,250), mandatory fees ($825), and college room and board ($12,800). College room only: $6814. Part-time tuition: $1765 per credit hour.

Collegiate Environment: Orientation program. Drama-theater group, choral group, student-run radio station. Social organizations: 97 open to all. Most popular organizations: Ministry of Games, Student Government Association, Health Professions Organization, Mud Junkies Ceramics Club, National Society of Leadership and Success. Major annual events: Lobsterfest, Mountain Day, Mr. Juniata. Student services: health clinic, personal-psychological counseling, women's center. Campus security: 24-hour emergency response devices and patrols, student patrols, late night transport-escort service, controlled dormitory access. 1,261 college housing spaces available; 1,150 were occupied in 2018-19. Freshmen guaranteed college housing. On-campus residence required through senior year. Options: coed, women-only housing available. Beeghly Library. Books: 139,415 (physical), 467,938 (digital/electronic); Serial titles: 379 (physical), 38,606 (digital/electronic); Databases: 53. Weekly public service hours: 107. Operations spending for the previous fiscal year: $1 million. 150 computers available on campus for general student use. A computer is required for all students. A campuswide network can be accessed from student residence rooms and from off campus. Students can access the following: online class registration, access to bills. Staffed computer lab on campus provides training in use of computers, software, and the Internet.

Community Environment: Huntingdon, population 6,800, on the Juniata River, is in one of the most scenic sections of the state. It was founded on the site of an Indian Village called Standing Stone. The city is the county seat and lies approximately 30 miles east of Altoona. The area is served by railroad. Penn State (32 miles away) offers cultural and social activities. Nearby state parks, forests, and the Raystown Lake recreation area provide excellent camping, fishing, canoeing, hunting, swimming, and boating opportunities. In winter ski slopes are less than 40 miles away.

■ KEYSTONE COLLEGE

One College Green
La Plume, PA 18440
Tel: (570)945-5141; Free: 877-4-COLLEGE
Web Site: www.keystone.edu
Description: Independent, comprehensive, coed. Awards associate, bachelor's, and master's degrees. Founded 1868. Setting: rural campus. Total enrollment: 1,423. Faculty: 188 (53 full-time, 135 part-time). Student-undergrad faculty ratio is 11:1. Full-time: 1,078 students, 58% women, 42% men. Part-time: 262 students, 79% women, 21% men. 16% from out-of-state. 0.3% American Indian or Alaska Native, non-Hispanic/Latino; 7% Hispanic/Latino; 9% Black or African American, non-Hispanic/Latino; 1% Asian, non-Hispanic/Latino; 0.1% Native Hawaiian or other Pacific Islander, non-Hispanic/Latino; 0.1% international. 25% 25 or older, 35% live on campus, 7% transferred in. Retention: 62% of full-time freshmen returned the following year. Academic areas with the most degrees conferred: business/marketing; psychology; homeland security, law enforcement, firefighting, and protective services. Core. Calendar: semesters. Academic remediation for entering students, ESL program, services for LD students, advanced placement, honors program, independent study, distance learning, double major, summer session for credit, part-time degree program, adult/continuing education programs, co-op programs and internships. Study abroad program.
Entrance Requirements: Options: electronic application, early admission, deferred admission, international baccalaureate accepted. Required: essay, high school transcript. Recommended: interview. Required for some: art portfolio for visual arts and art education. Notification: continuous. SAT Reasoning Test deadline: 6/1. SAT Subject Test deadline: 8/1. Transfer credits accepted: Yes.
Costs Per Year: Comprehensive fee: $38,620 includes full-time tuition ($24,920), mandatory fees ($1800), and college room and board ($11,900). College room only: $6000. Part-time tuition: $550 per credit hour.
Collegiate Environment: Orientation program. Drama-theater group, choral group, student-run newspaper, radio station. Student services: health clinic, personal-psychological counseling. Freshmen guaranteed college housing. On-campus residence required in freshman year. Option: coed housing available. Miller Library. 100 computers available on campus for general student use. A campuswide network can be accessed from student residence rooms and from off campus. Students can access the following: online class registration. Staffed computer lab on campus.
Community Environment: Population of Scranton is 73,120. The city is provided transportation by bus and air. Air facilities are located near Scranton. This is a semirural community with many churches and synagogues close at hand. There are service clubs active locally. Five modern hospitals are easily accessible. Local recreation includes movies, museum, art galleries, professional sports, lakes, streams, ski slopes, hunting, and fishing areas.

■ KING'S COLLEGE

133 N River St.
Wilkes Barre, PA 18711-0801
Tel: (570)208-5900; Free: 888-KINGSPA
Fax: (570)208-5971

E-mail: admissions@kings.edu
Web Site: www.kings.edu
Description: Independent Roman Catholic, comprehensive, coed. Awards bachelor's and master's degrees. Founded 1946. Setting: 48-acre urban campus. Endowment: $82.4 million. Research spending for the previous fiscal year: $42,885. Educational spending for the previous fiscal year: $10,614 per student. Total enrollment: 2,504. Faculty: 225 (135 full-time, 90 part-time). Student-undergrad faculty ratio is 13:1. 4,292 applied, 78% were admitted. 18% from top 10% of their high school class, 41% from top quarter, 68% from top half. Full-time: 2,066 students, 46% women, 54% men. Part-time: 203 students, 68% women, 32% men. Students come from 25 states and territories, 10 other countries, 28% from out-of-state. 0.1% American Indian or Alaska Native, non-Hispanic/Latino; 8% Hispanic/Latino; 4% Black or African American, non-Hispanic/Latino; 3% Asian, non-Hispanic/Latino; 9% international. 5% 25 or older, 48% live on campus, 4% transferred in. Retention: 74% of full-time freshmen returned the following year. Academic areas with the most degrees conferred: business/marketing; health professions and related sciences; biological/life sciences. Core. Calendar: semesters. ESL program, services for LD students, advanced placement, accelerated degree program, self-designed majors, honors program, independent study, distance learning, double major, summer session for credit, part-time degree program, adult/continuing education programs, internships. Off campus study at Misericordia University, Wilkes University. Study abroad program. ROTC: Army, Air Force (c).
Entrance Requirements: Options: electronic application, early decision, early action, deferred admission, international baccalaureate accepted. Required: essay, high school transcript. Recommended: interview, SAT or ACT. Entrance: moderately difficult. Application deadlines: rolling, rolling for nonresidents, 12/1 for early action. Notification: continuous, continuous for nonresidents. Transfer credits accepted: Yes. Early decision applicants: 0. Early action applicants admitted: 0. Early action applicants: 1,374. Early action applicants admitted: 1,207.
Costs Per Year: Application fee: $30. Comprehensive fee: $52,188 includes full-time tuition ($36,774), mandatory fees ($1950), and college room and board ($13,464). College room only: $7014. Part-time tuition: $600 per credit hour.
Collegiate Environment: Orientation program. Drama-theater group, choral group, student-run newspaper, radio station. Social organizations: 50 open to all. Most popular organizations: Association of Campus Events, Student Government Association, Accounting Association, International/Multicultural Club, Biology Club. Major annual events: Homecoming, Friends and Family Weekend, All College Ball. Student services: health clinic, personal-psychological counseling. Campus security: 24-hour emergency response devices and patrols, late night transport-escort service, controlled dormitory access. 1,075 college housing spaces available; 991 were occupied in 2018-19. Freshmen guaranteed college housing. On-campus residence required through sophomore year. Options: coed, men-only, women-only housing available. D. Leonard Corgan Library. Books: 176,086 (physical); Databases: 58. Weekly public service hours: 89; study areas open 24 hours, 5-7 days a week. Operations spending for the previous fiscal year: $1.3 million. 470 computers available on campus for general student use. Computer purchase/lease plans available. A campuswide network can be accessed from student residence rooms and from off campus. Students can access the following: online class registration. Staffed computer lab on campus provides training in use of computers, software, and the Internet.

■ KUTZTOWN UNIVERSITY OF PENNSYLVANIA

15200 Kutztown Rd.
Kutztown, PA 19530-0730
Tel: (610)683-4000; Free: 877-628-1915
Fax: (610)683-1375
Web Site: www.kutztown.edu
Description: State-supported, comprehensive, coed. Part of Pennsylvania State System of Higher Education. Awards bachelor's, master's, and doctoral degrees and post-master's certificates. Founded 1866. Setting: 289-acre rural campus with easy access to Philadelphia. Endowment: $22.2 million. Research spending for the previous fiscal year: $568,727. Educational spending for the previous fiscal year: $8231 per student. Total enrollment: 8,329. Faculty: 445 (388 full-time, 57 part-time). Student-undergrad faculty ratio is 18:1. 8,073 applied, 74% were admitted. 7% from top 10% of their high school class, 24% from top quarter, 55% from top half. Full-time: 7,053 students, 54% women, 46% men. Part-time: 436 students, 47% women, 53% men. Students come from 27 states and territories, 32 other countries, 12% from out-of-state. 0.2% American Indian or Alaska Native, non-

Hispanic/Latino; 9% Hispanic/Latino; 7% Black or African American, non-Hispanic/Latino; 1% Asian, non-Hispanic/Latino; 0.1% Native Hawaiian or other Pacific Islander, non-Hispanic/Latino; 0.9% international. 6% 25 or older, 45% live on campus, 8% transferred in. Retention: 74% of full-time freshmen returned the following year. Academic areas with the most degrees conferred: business/marketing; education; communication/journalism. Core. Calendar: semesters. Academic remediation for entering students, services for LD students, advanced placement, accelerated degree program, self-designed majors, honors program, independent study, distance learning, double major, summer session for credit, part-time degree program, adult/continuing education programs, internships. Off campus study at members of the Marine Science Consortium, Pennsylvania Consortium for International Education. Study abroad program. ROTC: Army (c).

Entrance Requirements: Options: electronic application, early admission, deferred admission, international baccalaureate accepted. Required: high school transcript, minimum 2 high school GPA, SAT or ACT. Required for some: audition for music, portfolio and/or art test for arts, SAT Subject Tests. Entrance: moderately difficult. Application deadline: rolling. Notification: continuous. Transfer credits accepted: Yes.

Costs Per Year: Application fee: $35. One-time mandatory fee: $108. State resident tuition: $7716 full-time, $322 per credit part-time. Nonresident tuition: $11,574 full-time, $805 per credit part-time. Mandatory fees: $3086 full-time. Full-time tuition and fees vary according to course load. Part-time tuition varies according to course load. College room and board: $10,334. College room only: $6484. Room and board charges vary according to board plan and housing facility.

Collegiate Environment: Orientation program. Drama-theater group, choral group, marching band, student-run newspaper, radio station. Social organizations: 180 open to all; national fraternities, national sororities; 5% of eligible men and 11% of eligible women are members. Most popular organizations: Marching Unit, Honors Club, American Marketing Association Kutztown Chapter, Humans versus Zombies: Kutztown Chapter, Paws for Love. Major annual events: Welcome Week, Bearfest, Homecoming. Student services: health clinic, personal-psychological counseling, women's center. Campus security: 24-hour emergency response devices and patrols, student patrols, late night transport-escort service, controlled dormitory access, secondary door electronic alarm system in residence halls, 24-hour student desk personnel at main entrance of residence halls. Rohrbach Library. Books: 317,044 (physical), 299,170 (digital/electronic); Serial titles: 88,613 (digital/electronic); Databases: 134. Weekly public service hours: 92; students can reserve study rooms. Operations spending for the previous fiscal year: $3.5 million. 1,075 computers available on campus for general student use. Computer purchase/lease plans available. A campuswide network can be accessed from student residence rooms. Students can access the following: online class registration.

Community Environment: Kutztown is a rural, small town located on U.S. Route 222, midway between Reading and Allentown, one and a half hours from Philadelphia, and three hours from New York City. Airports are located in Allentown and Reading, with bus transportation provided daily to Philadelphia and New York as well as to local destinations. The community has churches, civic organizations, and hospitals are located in nearby Reading and Allentown. Area recreation includes golf, bowling, tennis, hunting, fishing, swimming, basketball, football, theatre, nature study at Hawk Mountain Sanctuary, and the annual Kutztown Folk Festival.

■ LA ROCHE COLLEGE

9000 Babcock Blvd.
Pittsburgh, PA 15237-5898
Tel: (412)367-9300; Free: 800-838-4LRC
Fax: (412)536-1075
E-mail: admissions@laroche.edu
Web Site: www.laroche.edu

Description: Independent, comprehensive, coed, affiliated with Roman Catholic Church. Awards associate, bachelor's, master's, and doctoral degrees. Founded 1963. Setting: 43-acre suburban campus. Endowment: $5.7 million. Educational spending for the previous fiscal year: $6825 per student. Total enrollment: 1,535. Faculty: 210 (65 full-time, 145 part-time). Student-undergrad faculty ratio is 12:1. 1,197 applied, 97% were admitted. 8% from top 10% of their high school class, 30% from top quarter, 71% from top half. 1 valedictorian. Full-time: 1,163 students, 53% women, 47% men. Part-time: 215 students, 66% women, 34% men. Students come from 18 states and territories, 27 other countries, 10% from out-of-state. 0.4% American Indian or Alaska Native, non-Hispanic/Latino; 3% Hispanic/Latino; 10% Black or African American, non-Hispanic/Latino; 2% Asian, non-

Hispanic/Latino; 0.1% Native Hawaiian or other Pacific Islander, non-Hispanic/Latino; 15% international. 18% 25 or older, 37% live on campus, 12% transferred in. Retention: 68% of full-time freshmen returned the following year. Academic areas with the most degrees conferred: business/marketing; health professions and related sciences; computer and information sciences. Core. Calendar: semesters plus summer term. Academic remediation for entering students, ESL program, services for LD students, advanced placement, accelerated degree program, self-designed majors, freshman honors college, honors program, independent study, distance learning, double major, summer session for credit, part-time degree program, adult/continuing education programs, internships. Off campus study. Study abroad program. ROTC: Army (c), Air Force (c).

Entrance Requirements: Options: electronic application, early admission, deferred admission, international baccalaureate accepted. Required: high school transcript, minimum 2 high school GPA, 2 recommendations, SAT or ACT. Recommended: essay, minimum 3 high school GPA, interview. Entrance: minimally difficult. Application deadline: rolling. Notification: 9/15. Transfer credits accepted: Yes.

Costs Per Year: Application fee: $50. Comprehensive fee: $40,120 includes full-time tuition ($27,714), mandatory fees ($850), and college room and board ($11,556). College room only: $7316. Room and board charges vary according to board plan and housing facility. Part-time tuition: $700 per credit hour. Part-time mandatory fees: $40 per term.

Collegiate Environment: Orientation program. Student-run newspaper, radio station. Social organizations: 50 open to all. Most popular organizations: American Society of Interior Design, student government, Visions (environmental club). Major annual events: Gateway Clipper Cruise, Festival of Lights, Globe Fashion Show. Student services: health clinic, personal-psychological counseling. Campus security: 24-hour emergency response devices and patrols, student patrols, late night transport-escort service, controlled dormitory access. John J. Wright Library plus 1 other. Books: 75,803 (physical), 221,000 (digital/electronic); Databases: 1,248.

Community Environment: The college is located just ten miles north of the center of Pittsburgh. The campus has an ideal combination of rural and urban life: within a five-mile radius of its own natural beauty are the recreational facilities and wooded expanse of North Park and the shops, restaurants and theaters of the McKnight Road malls.

■ LA SALLE UNIVERSITY

1900 W Olney Ave.
Philadelphia, PA 19141-1199
Tel: (215)951-1000; Free: 800-328-1910
Fax: (215)951-1656
E-mail: admiss@lasalle.edu
Web Site: www.lasalle.edu

Description: Independent Roman Catholic, comprehensive, coed. Awards associate, bachelor's, master's, and doctoral degrees and post-master's certificates. Founded 1863. Setting: 133-acre urban campus with easy access to Philadelphia. Endowment: $84.3 million. Research spending for the previous fiscal year: $602,658. Educational spending for the previous fiscal year: $8283 per student. Total enrollment: 5,191. Faculty: 512 (219 full-time, 293 part-time). Student-undergrad faculty ratio is 11:1. 6,642 applied, 81% were admitted. 11% from top 10% of their high school class, 30% from top quarter, 67% from top half. Full-time: 3,363 students, 61% women, 39% men. Part-time: 541 students, 72% women, 28% men. Students come from 45 other countries, 31% from out-of-state. 0.1% American Indian or Alaska Native, non-Hispanic/Latino; 19% Hispanic/Latino; 20% Black or African American, non-Hispanic/Latino; 5% Asian, non-Hispanic/Latino; 0.2% Native Hawaiian or other Pacific Islander, non-Hispanic/Latino; 2% international. 12% 25 or older, 48% live on campus, 4% transferred in. Retention: 74% of full-time freshmen returned the following year. Academic areas with the most degrees conferred: business/marketing; health professions and related sciences; psychology. Core. Calendar: semesters. Academic remediation for entering students, ESL program, services for LD students, advanced placement, accelerated degree program, self-designed majors, freshman honors college, honors program, independent study, distance learning, double major, summer session for credit, part-time degree program, adult/continuing education programs, co-op programs and internships, graduate courses open to undergrads. Off campus study at Chestnut Hill College. Study abroad program. ROTC: Army (c), Air Force (c).

Entrance Requirements: Options: electronic application, early admission, early action, deferred admission, international baccalaureate accepted. Required: essay, high school transcript, 1 recommendation. Recommended: interview. Required for some: SAT or ACT. Entrance: moderately difficult. Application deadline: 11/15 for early action. Notification: continuous. Transfer credits accepted: Yes. Early action applicants: 3,013. Early action applicants admitted: 2,748.

Costs Per Year: One-time mandatory fee: $300. Comprehensive fee: $45,790 includes full-time tuition ($29,810), mandatory fees ($900), and college room and board ($15,080). College room only: $7990. Full-time tuition and fees vary according to course load and program. Room and board charges vary according to board plan and housing facility. Part-time tuition: $585 per credit hour. Part-time mandatory fees: $250 per term. Part-time tuition and fees vary according to course load and program.

Collegiate Environment: Orientation program. Drama-theater group, choral group, student-run newspaper, radio station. Social organizations: 121 open to all; national fraternities, national sororities, local fraternities, local sororities; 16% of eligible men and 17% of eligible women are members. Most popular organizations: Student Government Association, community service organization, La Salle Entertainment Organization, The Explorer (yearbook), The Masque (theater group). Major annual events: Branch Out Day, Homecoming, Spring Fling. Student services: health clinic, personal-psychological counseling, women's center. Campus security: 24-hour emergency response devices and patrols, student patrols, late night transport-escort service, controlled dormitory access. 1,868 college housing spaces available; 1,661 were occupied in 2018-19. Freshmen guaranteed college housing. On-campus residence required through sophomore year. Options: coed, men-only, women-only housing available. Connelly Library. Books: 314,203 (physical), 819,865 (digital/electronic); Serial titles: 2,982 (physical), 139,962 (digital/electronic); Databases: 88. Weekly public service hours: 96; students can reserve study rooms. Operations spending for the previous fiscal year: $1.9 million. 1,100 computers available on campus for general student use. A campuswide network can be accessed from student residence rooms and from off campus. Students can access the following: online class registration, course management system. Staffed computer lab on campus provides training in use of computers, software, and the Internet.

Community Environment: See Temple University.

■ **LACKAWANNA COLLEGE**
501 Vine St.
Scranton, PA 18509
Tel: (570)961-7810; Free: 877-346-3552
Fax: (570)961-7858
E-mail: perrye@lackawanna.edu
Web Site: www.lackawanna.edu

Description: Independent, primarily 2-year, coed. Awards certificates, diplomas, transfer associate, terminal associate, and bachelor's degrees. Founded 1894. Setting: 4-acre urban campus. Endowment: $5.7 million. Research spending for the previous fiscal year: $31,224. Educational spending for the previous fiscal year: $5453 per student. Total enrollment: 1,604. Faculty: 172 (29 full-time, 143 part-time). Student-undergrad faculty ratio is 16:1. Full-time: 1,169 students, 44% women, 56% men. Part-time: 435 students, 60% women, 40% men. Students come from 16 states and territories. 0.4% American Indian or Alaska Native, non-Hispanic/Latino; 11% Hispanic/Latino; 16% Black or African American, non-Hispanic/Latino; 1% Asian, non-Hispanic/Latino; 0.1% Native Hawaiian or other Pacific Islander, non-Hispanic/Latino; 0.4% international. 26% 25 or older, 10% transferred in. Retention: 55% of full-time freshmen returned the following year. Core. Calendar: semesters. Academic remediation for entering students, ESL program, services for LD students, double major, summer session for credit, part-time degree program, adult/continuing education programs, co-op programs and internships. ROTC: Army (c), Air Force (c).

Entrance Requirements: Open admission. Options: electronic application, early admission, deferred admission. Required: high school transcript, interview. Recommended: SAT or ACT. Entrance: noncompetitive. Application deadline: rolling. Transfer credits accepted: Yes.

Costs Per Year: Application fee: $35. Comprehensive fee: $25,960 includes full-time tuition ($14,850), mandatory fees ($810), and college room and board ($10,300). College room only: $6500. Full-time tuition and fees vary according to course load, location, and program. Room and board charges vary according to board plan. Part-time tuition: $520 per credit. Part-time mandatory fees: $405 per term. Part-time tuition and fees vary according to course load, location, and program.

Collegiate Environment: Orientation program. Social organizations: 17 open to all; Phi Theta Kappa, Phi Beta Lambda. Most popular organizations: Student Government Association, V.O.L.C. (Volunteers of Lackawanna College), Falcon Ambassador Board (FAB), COMMunity Club, Pineapple Club (Hospitality & Culinary Club). Major annual events: Homecoming Activities,

Spring Fling, College/Career Fair. Student services: personal-psychological counseling. Campus security: 24-hour emergency response devices and patrols, late night transport-escort service, controlled dormitory access, patrols by college liaison staff. Albright Memorial Library plus 1 other. Students can reserve study rooms. Operations spending for the previous fiscal year: $500. 186 computers available on campus for general student use. A campuswide network can be accessed. Students can access the following: online class registration. Staffed computer lab on campus provides training in use of computers and the Internet.

■ **LAFAYETTE COLLEGE**
730 High St.
Easton, PA 18042
Tel: (610)330-5000
Fax: (610)330-5127
E-mail: hydem@lafayette.edu
Web Site: www.lafayette.edu

Description: Independent, 4-year, coed, affiliated with Presbyterian Church (U.S.A.). Awards bachelor's degrees. Founded 1826. Setting: 340-acre suburban campus with easy access to New York City, Philadelphia. System endowment: $995.3 million. Research spending for the previous fiscal year: $2.2 million. Educational spending for the previous fiscal year: $22,819 per student. Total enrollment: 2,642. Faculty: 297 (239 full-time, 58 part-time). Student-undergrad faculty ratio is 10:1. 9,237 applied, 29% were admitted. 52% from top 10% of their high school class, 78% from top quarter, 96% from top half. 15 valedictorians. Full-time: 2,603 students, 52% women, 48% men. Part-time: 39 students, 36% women, 64% men. Students come from 46 states and territories, 53 other countries, 81% from out-of-state. 7% Hispanic/Latino; 5% Black or African American, non-Hispanic/Latino; 4% Asian, non-Hispanic/Latino; 9% international. 92% live on campus, 1% transferred in. Retention: 93% of full-time freshmen returned the following year. Academic areas with the most degrees conferred: social sciences; engineering; biological/life sciences. Core. Calendar: semesters plus interim January program. Academic remediation for entering students, services for LD students, advanced placement, accelerated degree program, self-designed majors, honors program, independent study, double major, summer session for credit, part-time degree program, internships. Off campus study at 5 members of the Lehigh Valley Association of Independent Colleges, American University. Study abroad program. ROTC: Army (c).

Entrance Requirements: Options: electronic application, early admission, early decision, deferred admission. Required: essay, high school transcript, 1 recommendation, SAT or ACT. Recommended: interview, SAT Subject Tests. Entrance: very difficult. Application deadlines: 1/15, 11/15 for early decision. Notification: 4/1. SAT Reasoning Test deadline: 1/25. SAT Subject Test deadline: 1/25. Transfer credits accepted: Yes. Applicants placed on waiting list: 2,332. Wait-listed applicants offered admission: 2. Early decision applicants: 772. Early decision applicants admitted: 398.

Costs Per Year: Application fee: $65. One-time mandatory fee: $750. Comprehensive fee: $71,256 includes full-time tuition ($54,512), mandatory fees ($490), and college room and board ($16,254). College room only: $10,057. Part-time tuition: $612.50 per credit hour.

Collegiate Environment: Orientation program. Drama-theater group, choral group, student-run newspaper, radio station. Social organizations: 250 open to all; national fraternities, national sororities; 24% of eligible men and 34% of eligible women are members. Most popular organizations: LAF (Lafayette Activities Forum), Student Government, Crew, International Students Association, Leopards Lair. Major annual events: Presidential Ball, Annual Spring Concert, Lafayette-Lehigh Football Weekend. Student services: health clinic, personal-psychological counseling, women's center. Campus security: 24-hour emergency response devices and patrols, student patrols, late night transport-escort service, controlled dormitory access. College housing designed to accommodate 2,309 students; 2,325 undergraduates lived in college housing during 2018-19. Freshmen guaranteed college housing. On-campus residence required through senior year. Options: coed, men-only, women-only housing available. Skillman Library plus 2 others. Books: 603,599 (physical), 344,469 (digital/electronic); Serial titles: 306 (physical), 68,298 (digital/electronic); Databases: 132. Weekly public service hours: 106. Operations spending for the previous fiscal year: $2.8 million. 690 computers available on campus for general student use. A campuswide network can be accessed from student residence rooms and from off campus. Students can access the following: online class registration. Staffed computer lab on campus (open 24 hours a day) provides training in use of computers, software, and the Internet.

Community Environment: Population 26,000, Easton is located at the confluence of the Lehigh and Delaware Rivers in the Lehigh Valley. The area is served by bus lines and a county airport. The valley has a YMCA, YWCA, nine hospitals, four public libraries, many churches and synagogues, a community concert association, and numerous civic and fraternal organizations. Recreational activities include baseball, softball, tennis, bowling, golf, boating, swimming, hunting, and fishing.

■ **LANCASTER BIBLE COLLEGE**
901 Eden Rd.
Lancaster, PA 17601
Tel: (717)569-7071; Free: 800-544-7335
Fax: (717)560-8213
E-mail: admissions@lbc.edu
Web Site: www.lbc.edu
Description: Independent nondenominational, comprehensive, coed. Awards associate, bachelor's, master's, and doctoral degrees. Founded 1933. Setting: 100-acre suburban campus with easy access to Philadelphia. Endowment: $14.3 million. Educational spending for the previous fiscal year: $7246 per student. Total enrollment: 2,122. Faculty: 86 (44 full-time, 42 part-time). Student-undergrad faculty ratio is 15:1. 192 applied, 57% were admitted. Full-time: 986 students, 52% women, 48% men. Part-time: 702 students, 52% women, 48% men. Students come from 17 states and territories, 3 other countries, 30% from out-of-state. 0.1% American Indian or Alaska Native, non-Hispanic/Latino; 5% Hispanic/Latino; 25% Black or African American, non-Hispanic/Latino; 1% Asian, non-Hispanic/Latino; 0.1% Native Hawaiian or other Pacific Islander, non-Hispanic/Latino; 0.1% international. 54% live on campus, 22% transferred in. Retention: 81% of full-time freshmen returned the following year. Academic areas with the most degrees conferred: theology and religious vocations; education; business/marketing. Core. Calendar: semesters. Academic remediation for entering students, services for LD students, advanced placement, independent study, double major, summer session for credit, part-time degree program, adult/continuing education programs, internships, graduate courses open to undergrads. Study abroad program.
Entrance Requirements: Options: early admission, deferred admission. Required: essay, high school transcript, minimum 2 high school GPA, 3 recommendations, SAT or ACT. Required for some: interview. Entrance: minimally difficult. Application deadline: rolling. Notification: continuous.
Costs Per Year: Application fee: $25. One-time mandatory fee: $300. Comprehensive fee: $33,720 includes full-time tuition ($24,290), mandatory fees ($680), and college room and board ($8750). Full-time tuition and fees vary according to degree level and student level. Room and board charges vary according to board plan. Part-time tuition: $810 per credit hour. Part-time mandatory fees: $35 per credit hour. Part-time tuition and fees vary according to course load and degree level.
Collegiate Environment: Orientation program. Drama-theater group, choral group, student-run newspaper. Social organizations: 19 open to all. Most popular organizations: Student Government Association, Student Missionary Fellowship, International Student Fellowship, Resident Affairs Council, Student Intramural Association. Major annual events: Homecoming, Missions Conference, Spiritual Life Week. Student services: health clinic, personal-psychological counseling. Campus security: student patrols, late night transport-escort service, controlled dormitory access. 405 college housing spaces available; all were occupied in 2018-19. Freshmen guaranteed college housing. On-campus residence required through senior year. Options: men-only, women-only housing available. Lancaster Bible College Library. Operations spending for the previous fiscal year: $294,383. 50 computers available on campus for general student use. A campuswide network can be accessed from student residence rooms. Staffed computer lab on campus.

■ **LANCASTER COUNTY CAREER AND TECHNOLOGY CENTER**
1730 Hans Herr Dr.
Willow Street, PA 17584
Tel: (717)464-7065
Fax: (717)464-9578
Web Site: www.lancasterctc.edu
Description: State and locally supported, 2-year, coed. Awards certificates, transfer associate, and terminal associate degrees.

■ **LANSDALE SCHOOL OF BUSINESS**
290 Wissahickon Ave.
North Wales, PA 19454
Tel: (215)699-5700; Free: 800-219-0486

Fax: (215)699-8770
Web Site: www.lsb.edu
Description: Proprietary, 2-year, coed. Awards certificates, diplomas, transfer associate, and terminal associate degrees. Founded 1918. Setting: suburban campus with easy access to Philadelphia. Total enrollment: 372. 73% 25 or older. Core. Calendar: semesters. Accelerated degree program, honors program, independent study, double major, summer session for credit, part-time degree program, adult/continuing education programs, internships. Off campus study.
Entrance Requirements: Required: high school transcript, interview. Entrance: minimally difficult. Application deadline: rolling.
Collegiate Environment: Orientation program. Student-run newspaper. Lansdale School of Business Library.

■ **LAUREL BUSINESS INSTITUTE**
11 E Penn St.
Uniontown, PA 15401
Tel: (724)439-4900
Fax: (724)439-3607
E-mail: ldolan@laurel.edu
Web Site: www.laurel.edu/locations/uniontown
Description: Proprietary, 2-year, coed. Awards certificates, diplomas, transfer associate, and terminal associate degrees. Founded 1985. Setting: 10-acre small town campus with easy access to Pittsburgh. Educational spending for the previous fiscal year: $3576 per student. Total enrollment: 305. Faculty: 25 (16 full-time, 9 part-time). Student-undergrad faculty ratio is 16:1. 415 applied, 59% were admitted. Full-time: 305 students, 77% women, 23% men. 50% 25 or older. Retention: 80% of full-time freshmen returned the following year. Core. Calendar: trimesters. Advanced placement, honors program, independent study, double major, part-time degree program, adult/continuing education programs, co-op programs and internships.
Entrance Requirements: Open admission. Options: electronic application, deferred admission. Required: essay, high school transcript, interview, Wonderlic aptitude test. Entrance: minimally difficult. Application deadline: rolling. Notification: continuous.
Collegiate Environment: Orientation program. Student Learning Center. 75 computers available on campus for general student use. A campuswide network can be accessed from off-campus. Staffed computer lab on campus.

■ **LAUREL TECHNICAL INSTITUTE**
200 Sterling Ave.
Sharon, PA 16146
Tel: (724)983-0700
Fax: (724)983-8355
E-mail: info@biop.edu
Web Site: www.laurel.edu/locations/sharon
Description: Proprietary, 2-year, coed. Awards certificates, diplomas, and terminal associate degrees. Founded 1926. Setting: 2-acre small town campus. Educational spending for the previous fiscal year: $4300 per student. Total enrollment: 106. Faculty: 9 (5 full-time, 4 part-time). Student-undergrad faculty ratio is 16:1. 49 applied, 80% were admitted. 14% from top 10% of their high school class, 27% from top quarter, 59% from top half. Full-time: 98 students, 93% women, 7% men. Part-time: 8 students, 100% women. 71% 25 or older, 2% transferred in. Calendar: quarters.
Entrance Requirements: Required: high school transcript, interview, ACT.
Collegiate Environment: Operations spending for the previous fiscal year: $1.4 million.

■ **LEBANON VALLEY COLLEGE**
101 N College Ave.
Annville, PA 17003-1400
Tel: (717)867-6100; Free: 866-LVC-4ADM
Fax: (717)867-6124
E-mail: admission@lvc.edu
Web Site: www.lvc.edu
Description: Independent United Methodist, comprehensive, coed. Awards bachelor's, master's, and doctoral degrees. Founded 1866. Setting: 357-acre small town campus. Endowment: $67.5 million. Educational spending for the previous fiscal year: $12,338 per student. Total enrollment: 1,916. Faculty: 255 (122 full-time, 133 part-time). Student-undergrad faculty ratio is 10:1. 2,731 applied, 78% were admitted. 22% from top 10% of their high school class, 48% from top quarter, 80% from top half. Full-time: 1,651 students, 53% women, 47% men. Part-time: 93 students, 56% women, 44% men. 20% from out-of-state. 0.1% American Indian or Alaska Native, non-

Hispanic/Latino; 5% Hispanic/Latino; 3% Black or African American, non-Hispanic/Latino; 2% Asian, non-Hispanic/Latino; 0.1% Native Hawaiian or other Pacific Islander, non-Hispanic/Latino; 1% international. 2% 25 or older, 77% live on campus, 3% transferred in. Retention: 82% of full-time freshmen returned the following year. Academic areas with the most degrees conferred: education; business/marketing; social sciences. Core. Calendar: semesters. Academic remediation for entering students, ESL program, services for LD students, advanced placement, accelerated degree program, self-designed majors, independent study, distance learning, double major, summer session for credit, part-time degree program, adult/continuing education programs, internships. Off campus study at The Philadelphia Center, The Washington Center of Internships and Academic Seminars. Study abroad program.

Entrance Requirements: Options: electronic application, early decision, international baccalaureate accepted. Required: high school transcript. Recommended: 2 recommendations, interview. Required for some: audition for music majors, specific requirements for physical therapy and athletic training programs. Entrance: moderately difficult. Application deadlines: rolling, 11/1 for early decision. Notification: continuous until 11/15. Transfer credits accepted: Yes. Early decision applicants: 74. Early decision applicants admitted: 69.

Costs Per Year: Application fee: $0. Comprehensive fee: $57,110 includes full-time tuition ($43,650), mandatory fees ($1260), and college room and board ($12,200). College room only: $5890.

Collegiate Environment: Orientation program. Drama-theater group, choral group, marching band, student-run newspaper. Social organizations: 93 open to all; national fraternities, national sororities, local fraternities, local sororities; 6% of eligible men and 9% of eligible women are members. Most popular organizations: Mini-THON, Student Government, Colleges Against Cancer, Wig and Buckle Theater Group, Valleyfest. Major annual events: Symposium on Inclusive Excellence, ValleyFest, Relay for Life. Student services: health clinic, personal-psychological counseling, women's center. Campus security: 24-hour emergency response devices and patrols, late night transport-escort service, controlled dormitory access. Freshmen guaranteed college housing. On-campus residence required through senior year. Option: coed housing available. Vernon and Doris Bishop Library. Books: 152,349 (physical), 204,880 (digital/electronic); Serial titles: 3,047 (physical), 59,331 (digital/electronic); Databases: 256. Weekly public service hours: 101; students can reserve study rooms. Operations spending for the previous fiscal year: $1.2 million. 202 computers available on campus for general student use. Computer purchase/lease plans available. A campuswide network can be accessed from student residence rooms and from off campus. Students can access the following: online class registration. Staffed computer lab on campus provides training in use of computers, software, and the Internet.

Community Environment: Population 4,500. Annville is located seven miles east of Hershey. The area has a temperate climate. The city has many churches that represent various denominations, a public library, three hospitals that are easily accessible, and major civic, fraternal, and veteran's organizations. Community recreational facilities include theaters and radio and TV stations. Community concerts are also available.

■ **LEHIGH CARBON COMMUNITY COLLEGE**
4525 Education Park Dr.
Schnecksville, PA 18078-2598
Tel: (610)799-2121
Fax: (610)799-1527
E-mail: admissions@lccc.edu
Web Site: www.lccc.edu

Description: State and locally supported, 2-year, coed. Awards certificates, diplomas, transfer associate, and terminal associate degrees. Founded 1966. Setting: 254-acre suburban campus with easy access to Philadelphia. System endowment: $5.7 million. Educational spending for the previous fiscal year: $3968 per student. Total enrollment: 6,953. Faculty: 460 (81 full-time, 379 part-time). Student-undergrad faculty ratio is 18:1. 4,125 applied, 100% were admitted. Full-time: 2,476 students, 54% women, 46% men. Part-time: 4,477 students, 65% women, 35% men. Students come from 11 states and territories, 18 other countries, 0.4% from out-of-state. 0.1% American Indian or Alaska Native, non-Hispanic/Latino; 22% Hispanic/Latino; 7% Black or African American, non-Hispanic/Latino; 2% Asian, non-Hispanic/Latino; 0.4% international. 36% 25 or older, 53% transferred in. Core. Calendar: semesters. Academic remediation for entering students, ESL program, services for LD students, advanced placement, honors program, independent study, distance learning, summer session for credit,

part-time degree program, external degree program, co-op programs and internships. Off campus study. ROTC: Army (c).

Entrance Requirements: Open admission except for allied health, aviation, veterinary technician programs. Option: electronic application. Required for some: essay, high school transcript, interview. Entrance: noncompetitive. Application deadline: rolling. Notification: continuous. Transfer credits accepted: Yes.

Costs Per Year: Area resident tuition: $3000 full-time, $100 per credit hour part-time. State resident tuition: $6270 full-time, $209 per credit hour part-time. Nonresident tuition: $9540 full-time, $318 per credit hour part-time. Mandatory fees: $1080 full-time, $40 per credit hour part-time. Full-time tuition and fees vary according to course load.

Collegiate Environment: Orientation program. Drama-theater group, choral group, student-run newspaper. Social organizations: 26 open to all. Most popular organizations: Phi Theta Kappa, Justice Society, PSI BETA (psychology club), Student Government Association, Teacher Education Student Association (TESA). Major annual events: Freshman Orientation, Spring Awards Program, Athletic Events. Student services: personal-psychological counseling. Campus security: 24-hour emergency response devices. Rothrock Library. Books: 48,142 (physical), 68,508 (digital/electronic); Serial titles: 220 (physical), 182 (digital/electronic); Databases: 46. Weekly public service hours: 71. Operations spending for the previous fiscal year: $1.2 million. 1,500 computers available on campus for general student use. Computer purchase/lease plans available. A campuswide network can be accessed. Students can access the following: online class registration. Staffed computer lab on campus.

Community Environment: See Muhlenberg College.

■ **LEHIGH UNIVERSITY**
27 Memorial Dr. W
Bethlehem, PA 18015
Tel: (610)758-3000
Fax: (610)758-4361
E-mail: admissions@lehigh.edu
Web Site: www.lehigh.edu

Description: Independent, university, coed. Awards bachelor's, master's, and doctoral degrees and post-master's certificates. Founded 1865. Setting: 2,355-acre suburban campus with easy access to Philadelphia. Endowment: $1.3 billion. Research spending for the previous fiscal year: $39.3 million. Educational spending for the previous fiscal year: $29,796 per student. Total enrollment: 7,017. Faculty: 699 (542 full-time, 157 part-time). Student-undergrad faculty ratio is 9:1. 13,871 applied, 25% were admitted. 63% from top 10% of their high school class, 89% from top quarter, 99% from top half. Full-time: 5,013 students, 45% women, 55% men. Part-time: 62 students, 40% women, 60% men. Students come from 52 states and territories, 62 other countries, 73% from out-of-state. 0.2% American Indian or Alaska Native, non-Hispanic/Latino; 9% Hispanic/Latino; 4% Black or African American, non-Hispanic/Latino; 8% Asian, non-Hispanic/Latino; 0.1% Native Hawaiian or other Pacific Islander, non-Hispanic/Latino; 9% international. 65% live on campus, 1% transferred in. Retention: 96% of full-time freshmen returned the following year. Academic areas with the most degrees conferred: business/marketing; engineering; social sciences. Calendar: semesters. ESL program, services for LD students, advanced placement, accelerated degree program, honors program, independent study, distance learning, double major, summer session for credit, external degree program, co-op programs and internships, graduate courses open to undergrads. Off campus study at Members of the Lehigh Valley Association of Independent Colleges, The Washington Semester at American University, The Philadelphia Urban Semester. Study abroad program. ROTC: Army.

Entrance Requirements: Options: electronic application, early admission, early decision, deferred admission. Required: essay, high school transcript, 2 recommendations, SAT or ACT. Recommended: SAT, ACT. Entrance: most difficult. Application deadlines: 1/1, 11/15 for early decision plan 1, 1/1 for early decision plan 2. Notification: 3/31, 12/15 for early decision plan 1, 2/15 for early decision plan 2. SAT Reasoning Test deadline: 1/31. SAT Subject Test deadline: 1/31. Transfer credits accepted: Yes. Applicants placed on waiting list: 6,516. Wait-listed applicants offered admission: 53. Early decision applicants: 1,116. Early decision applicants admitted: 669.

Costs Per Year: Application fee: $70. Comprehensive fee: $66,530 includes full-time tuition ($52,480), mandatory fees ($450), and college room and board ($13,600). College room only: $7930. Room and board charges vary according to board plan and housing facility. Part-time tuition: $2190 per credit hour.

Collegiate Environment: Orientation program. Drama-theater group, choral

group, marching band, student-run newspaper, radio station. Social organizations: 250 open to all; national fraternities, national sororities. Most popular organizations: Marching 97, Indian Student Association, Accounting Club, Student Senate, Phi Sigma Pi. Major annual events: Fall Club Expo, International Week, DanceFest. Student services: health clinic, personal-psychological counseling, women's center. Campus security: 24-hour emergency response devices and patrols, student patrols, late night transport-escort service, controlled dormitory access, self defense training. E. W. Fairchild-Martindale Library plus 1 other. Books: 798,207 (physical), 402,504 (digital/electronic); Serial titles: 2,050 (physical), 61,205 (digital/electronic); Databases: 191. Weekly public service hours: 83; students can reserve study rooms. 597 computers available on campus for general student use. Computer purchase/lease plans available. A campuswide network can be accessed from student residence rooms and from off campus. Students can access the following: online class registration. Staffed computer lab on campus provides training in use of computers, software, and the Internet.

Community Environment: Population: 72,900. Bethlehem is famous for the Moravian Community, the Bach Choir, the corporate headquarters of Bethlehem Steel and Lehigh University. The historic area of Bethlehem has many 18th century buildings still in use; others are being restored by active community groups. The town contains 6 colonial and Victorian museums. The Bach Festival is held annually in May in Packer Chapel on the Lehigh campus.

■ **LINCOLN TECHNICAL INSTITUTE (ALLENTOWN)**
5151 Tilghman St.
Allentown, PA 18104
Tel: (610)398-5300; Free: 844-215-1513
Web Site: www.lincolntech.edu
Description: Proprietary, 2-year, coed. Part of Lincoln Technical Institute, Inc. Awards diplomas and terminal associate degrees. Founded 1949. Setting: 10-acre suburban campus with easy access to Philadelphia. Total enrollment: 539. Core. Calendar: semesters. Summer session for credit.
Entrance Requirements: Open admission. Option: early admission. Required: high school transcript, interview. Entrance: noncompetitive. Application deadline: rolling.
Collegiate Environment: Orientation program.

■ **LINCOLN TECHNICAL INSTITUTE (PHILADELPHIA)**
9191 Torresdale Ave.
Philadelphia, PA 19136
Tel: (215)335-0800; Free: 844-215-1513
Fax: (215)335-1443
Web Site: www.lincolntech.edu
Description: Proprietary, 2-year, coed. Part of Lincoln Technical Institute, Inc. Awards terminal associate degrees. Founded 1946. Setting: 3-acre suburban campus. Total enrollment: 499. 31% 25 or older. Core. Calendar: modular. Part-time degree program, adult/continuing education programs, co-op programs.
Entrance Requirements: Open admission. Option: deferred admission. Required: high school transcript, minimum 2.0 high school GPA, interview. Entrance: noncompetitive. Application deadline: rolling.
Collegiate Environment: Student-run newspaper. Campus security: 16-hour patrols by trained security personnel.

■ **LINCOLN UNIVERSITY**
1570 Baltimore Pke.
Lincoln University, PA 19352
Tel: (484)365-8000; Free: 800-790-0191
E-mail: nfredericksen@lincoln.edu
Web Site: www.lincoln.edu
Description: State-related, comprehensive, coed. Awards bachelor's and master's degrees. Founded 1854. Setting: 422-acre rural campus with easy access to Philadelphia. Endowment: $38.6 million. Research spending for the previous fiscal year: $831,397. Educational spending for the previous fiscal year: $9509 per student. Total enrollment: 2,266. Faculty: 207 (97 full-time, 110 part-time). Student-undergrad faculty ratio is 15:1. 3,587 applied, 80% were admitted. 15% from top 10% of their high school class, 34% from top quarter, 60% from top half. 2 valedictorians. Full-time: 1,826 students, 66% women, 34% men. Part-time: 176 students, 68% women, 32% men. Students come from 30 states and territories, 13 other countries, 54% from out-of-state. 0.2% American Indian or Alaska Native, non-Hispanic/Latino; 3% Hispanic/Latino; 84% Black or African American, non-Hispanic/Latino;

0.1% Asian, non-Hispanic/Latino; 3% international. 10% 25 or older, 79% live on campus, 5% transferred in. Retention: 68% of full-time freshmen returned the following year. Academic areas with the most degrees conferred: health professions and related sciences; public administration and social services; business/marketing. Core. Calendar: semesters. Academic remediation for entering students, services for LD students, advanced placement, accelerated degree program, honors program, independent study, double major, summer session for credit, part-time degree program, external degree program, adult/continuing education programs, internships, graduate courses open to undergrads. Study abroad program. ROTC: Army (c).
Entrance Requirements: Options: electronic application, deferred admission, international baccalaureate accepted. Required: high school transcript, minimum 2 high school GPA, SAT or ACT. Recommended: essay, 2 recommendations, interview. Entrance: minimally difficult. Application deadline: 5/1. Notification: continuous. SAT Reasoning Test deadline: 5/1. Transfer credits accepted: Yes.
Costs Per Year: Application fee: $0. State resident tuition: $7868 full-time, $328 per credit hour part-time. Nonresident tuition: $13,004 full-time, $545 per credit hour part-time. Mandatory fees: $3798 full-time, $141 per credit hour part-time. Full-time tuition and fees vary according to course load, degree level, location, program, and student level. Part-time tuition and fees vary according to course load, degree level, program, and student level. College room and board: $9588. College room only: $5114. Room and board charges vary according to board plan and housing facility. Tuition guaranteed not to increase for student's term of enrollment.
Collegiate Environment: Orientation program. Drama-theater group, choral group, marching band, student-run newspaper, radio station. Social organizations: 60 open to all; national fraternities, national sororities, social fellowships. Most popular organizations: Student Government: Class sections, We R '1' Family, Residence Hall Association, International Students Association, Onyx Dance Troupe. Major annual events: Homecoming Step Show, Homecoming Concert, Campus-Wide Information Session. Student services: health clinic, personal-psychological counseling, women's center. Campus security: 24-hour emergency response devices and patrols, late night transport-escort service, controlled dormitory access, 24-hour command center, gated entrance/exit, medical transports. Langston Hughes Memorial Library. Weekly public service hours: 80; study areas open 24 hours, 5-7 days a week; students can reserve study rooms. Operations spending for the previous fiscal year: $570,829. 280 computers available on campus for general student use. A campuswide network can be accessed from student residence rooms and from off campus. Students can access the following: online class registration. Staffed computer lab on campus provides training in use of computers, software, and the Internet.

■ **LOCK HAVEN UNIVERSITY OF PENNSYLVANIA**
401 N Fairview St.
Lock Haven, PA 17745-2390
Tel: (570)893-2011; Free: 800-233-8978
Fax: (570)893-2201
Web Site: www.lockhaven.edu
Description: State-supported, comprehensive, coed. Part of Pennsylvania State System of Higher Education. Awards associate, bachelor's, and master's degrees. Founded 1870. Setting: 165-acre rural campus. Endowment: $11 million. Research spending for the previous fiscal year: $76,480. Educational spending for the previous fiscal year: $9221 per student. Total enrollment: 3,425. Faculty: 220 (195 full-time, 25 part-time). Student-undergrad faculty ratio is 17:1. 2,560 applied, 94% were admitted. 11% from top 10% of their high school class, 29% from top quarter, 63% from top half. Full-time: 2,798 students, 57% women, 43% men. Part-time: 269 students, 73% women, 27% men. Students come from 17 states and territories, 17 other countries, 4% from out-of-state. 0.6% American Indian or Alaska Native, non-Hispanic/Latino; 4% Hispanic/Latino; 8% Black or African American, non-Hispanic/Latino; 1% Asian, non-Hispanic/Latino; 0.8% international. 9% 25 or older, 31% live on campus, 5% transferred in. Retention: 65% of full-time freshmen returned the following year. Academic areas with the most degrees conferred: health professions and related sciences; parks and recreation; homeland security, law enforcement, firefighting, and protective services; business/marketing. Core. Calendar: semesters. Academic remediation for entering students, ESL program, services for LD students, advanced placement, self-designed majors, freshman honors college, honors program, independent study, distance learning, double major, summer session for credit, part-time degree program, adult/continuing education programs, co-op programs and internships, graduate courses open to undergrads. Off campus study at Pennsylvania Consortium for International Education. Study abroad program. ROTC: Army.

Entrance Requirements: Options: electronic application, deferred admission. Required: high school transcript, SAT or ACT. Recommended: interview. Required for some: essay. Entrance: moderately difficult. Application deadline: rolling. Notification: continuous.

Costs Per Year: Application fee: $25. State resident tuition: $7716 full-time, $322 per credit hour part-time. Nonresident tuition: $17,290 full-time, $720 per credit hour part-time. Mandatory fees: $3162 full-time, $167.55 per credit hour part-time. Full-time tuition and fees vary according to course load, location, and program. Part-time tuition and fees vary according to course load, location, and program. College room and board: $10,368. College room only: $6540. Room and board charges vary according to board plan and housing facility.

Collegiate Environment: Orientation program. Drama-theater group, choral group, marching band, student-run newspaper, radio station. Social organizations: 150 open to all; national fraternities, national sororities; 3% of eligible men and 4% of eligible women are members. Most popular organizations: Student Government, Residence Hall Association. Major annual events: Homecoming, Family Day, Celebration of Scholarship. Student services: health clinic, personal-psychological counseling, women's center. Campus security: 24-hour emergency response devices and patrols, late night transport-escort service, controlled dormitory access. 1,174 college housing spaces available; 938 were occupied in 2018-19. Freshmen given priority for college housing. On-campus residence required through sophomore year. Option: coed housing available. Stevenson Library plus 1 other. Books: 239,240 (physical), 216,376 (digital/electronic); Serial titles: 37,613 (physical), 61,655 (digital/electronic); Databases: 97. Weekly public service hours: 87; students can reserve study rooms. Operations spending for the previous fiscal year: $2.1 million. 290 computers available on campus for general student use. A campuswide network can be accessed from student residence rooms and from off campus. Students can access the following: online class registration. Staffed computer lab on campus (open 24 hours a day).

Community Environment: Population 8,700, Loch Haven was laid out at the site of old Fort Reed, which was erected to protect the frontier settlers from the Indians. The fort was evacuated in the great runaway of 1778. Today, lumbering is a major industry and paper products are produced here. The city lies in a central mountainous region with a moderate climate. Local recreation includes hunting, fishing, boating, hang gliding, and skiing. Private homes provide supplemental student housing.

■ **LUZERNE COUNTY COMMUNITY COLLEGE**
1333 S Prospect St.
Nanticoke, PA 18634-9804
Tel: (570)740-0300; Free: 800-377-5222
E-mail: admissions@luzerne.edu
Web Site: www.luzerne.edu

Description: County-supported, 2-year, coed. Awards certificates, diplomas, transfer associate, and terminal associate degrees. Founded 1966. Setting: 122-acre suburban campus. Total enrollment: 4,984. Faculty: 446 (105 full-time, 341 part-time). Student-undergrad faculty ratio is 15:1. 2,371 applied, 100% were admitted. Full-time: 2,064 students, 54% women, 46% men. Part-time: 2,920 students, 66% women, 34% men. 0.3% American Indian or Alaska Native, non-Hispanic/Latino; 15% Hispanic/Latino; 5% Black or African American, non-Hispanic/Latino; 2% Asian, non-Hispanic/Latino; 0.1% Native Hawaiian or other Pacific Islander, non-Hispanic/Latino. Retention: 56% of full-time freshmen returned the following year. Core. Calendar: semesters. Academic remediation for entering students, services for LD students, advanced placement, accelerated degree program, distance learning, summer session for credit, part-time degree program, external degree program, internships. ROTC: Army (c).

Entrance Requirements: Open admission except for health sciences programs. Option: electronic application. Recommended: high school transcript. Entrance: noncompetitive. Transfer credits accepted: Yes.

Collegiate Environment: Orientation program. Drama-theater group, choral group, student-run radio station. Most popular organizations: Student Government, Circle K, Nursing Forum, Science Club, SADAH. Major annual events: Alumni Career Fair, College Night, Craft Festival. Campus security: 24-hour patrols. College housing not available. Learning Resources Center plus 1 other. Students can reserve study rooms.

■ **LYCOMING COLLEGE**
700 College Pl.
Williamsport, PA 17701-5192
Tel: (570)321-4000; Free: 800-345-3920

Fax: (570)321-4337
E-mail: admissions@lycoming.edu
Web Site: www.lycoming.edu

Description: Independent United Methodist, 4-year, coed. Awards bachelor's degrees. Founded 1812. Setting: 35-acre small town campus. Endowment: $207.6 million. Educational spending for the previous fiscal year: $11,826 per student. Total enrollment: 1,142. Faculty: 116 (88 full-time, 28 part-time). Student-undergrad faculty ratio is 12:1. 2,430 applied, 66% were admitted. 21% from top 10% of their high school class, 46% from top quarter, 79% from top half. Full-time: 1,135 students, 53% women, 47% men. Part-time: 7 students, 57% women, 43% men. Students come from 28 states and territories, 18 other countries, 41% from out-of-state. 0.1% American Indian or Alaska Native, non-Hispanic/Latino; 12% Hispanic/Latino; 13% Black or African American, non-Hispanic/Latino; 1% Asian, non-Hispanic/Latino; 0.1% Native Hawaiian or other Pacific Islander, non-Hispanic/Latino; 6% international. 1% 25 or older, 87% live on campus, 2% transferred in. Retention: 75% of full-time freshmen returned the following year. Academic areas with the most degrees conferred: social sciences; business/marketing; psychology. Core. Calendar: semesters. Services for LD students, advanced placement, self-designed majors, honors program, independent study, double major, summer session for credit, part-time degree program, adult/continuing education programs, co-op programs and internships. Off campus study. Study abroad program. ROTC: Army (c).

Entrance Requirements: Options: electronic application, early decision, early action, deferred admission, international baccalaureate accepted. Required: essay, high school transcript, 2 recommendations. Recommended: minimum 2.3 high school GPA, interview, SAT or ACT. Entrance: moderately difficult. Application deadline: 11/15 for early decision. Notification: continuous until 12/15, 12/1 for early decision. SAT Reasoning Test deadline: 8/1. SAT Subject Test deadline: 8/1. Transfer credits accepted: Yes. Early decision applicants: 27. Early decision applicants admitted: 22.

Costs Per Year: One-time mandatory fee: $225. Comprehensive fee: $54,634 includes full-time tuition ($40,896), mandatory fees ($730), and college room and board ($13,008).

Collegiate Environment: Orientation program. Drama-theater group, choral group, student-run newspaper, radio station. Social organizations: 71 open to all; national fraternities, national sororities, local sororities; 11% of eligible men and 23% of eligible women are members. Most popular organizations: Campus Activities Board, Lycoming Pom and Dance Club, Society of Physics Students, Black Student Union, Creative Arts Society. Major annual events: Major Concert, Campus Carnival, Involvement Fair. Student services: health clinic, personal-psychological counseling. Campus security: 24-hour emergency response devices and patrols, student patrols, late night transport-escort service, controlled dormitory access. 1,124 college housing spaces available. Freshmen guaranteed college housing. On-campus residence required through senior year. Options: coed, women-only housing available. Snowden Library. Books: 135,456 (physical), 134,657 (digital/electronic); Serial titles: 1,045 (physical), 18,343 (digital/electronic); Databases: 89. Weekly public service hours: 107. Operations spending for the previous fiscal year: $1.3 million. 188 computers available on campus for general student use. A campuswide network can be accessed from student residence rooms and from off campus. Students can access the following: online class registration, online financial aid, free printing up to a limit, password management, free access to Office 365, streaming TV services, mobile phone plans for International students. Staffed computer lab on campus (open 24 hours a day) provides training in use of computers, software, and the Internet.

Community Environment: Population 30,000. This town, in a scenic mountainous region on the west branch of the Susquehanna River, was known as a great lumber center until the 1890s. As the forests were depleted, it became a manufacturing city and now has a diversified production including steel wire rope, computer components, batteries, flashbulbs, radio tubes, power piping, chemicals, lumber and its byproducts, aircraft engines, textiles, furniture, leather, and mobile homes. The area is provided transportation by bus and air lines. The community has many churches representing various faiths. There are two hospitals, numerous health agencies, a library, a community cultural center, a museum, and various civic, fraternal and veteran's organizations in the immediate area. Part-time employment is available. Local recreation includes boating, golf, hiking, picnic areas, fishing, hunting, skiing, and cycling.

■ **MANOR COLLEGE**
700 Fox Chase Rd.
Jenkintown, PA 19046

Tel: (215)885-2360
E-mail: swalker@manor.edu
Web Site: www.manor.edu
Description: Independent Byzantine Catholic, primarily 2-year, coed. Awards certificates, transfer associate, terminal associate, and bachelor's degrees. Founded 1947. Setting: 35-acre suburban campus with easy access to Philadelphia. Endowment: $2.8 million. Educational spending for the previous fiscal year: $7258 per student. Total enrollment: 669. Faculty: 68 (37 full-time, 31 part-time). Student-undergrad faculty ratio is 10:1. 857 applied, 94% were admitted. Full-time: 480 students, 66% women, 34% men. Part-time: 260 students, 70% women, 30% men. Students come from 6 states and territories, 2 other countries, 3% from out-of-state. 1% American Indian or Alaska Native, non-Hispanic/Latino; 14% Hispanic/Latino; 34% Black or African American, non-Hispanic/Latino; 3% Asian, non-Hispanic/Latino; 0.3% Native Hawaiian or other Pacific Islander, non-Hispanic/Latino; 0.3% international. 21% 25 or older, 11% live on campus, 10% transferred in. Retention: 58% of full-time freshmen returned the following year. Core. Calendar: semesters. Academic remediation for entering students, services for LD students, advanced placement, accelerated degree program, honors program, independent study, distance learning, double major, summer session for credit, part-time degree program, internships.
Entrance Requirements: Options: electronic application, deferred admission, international baccalaureate accepted. Required: high school transcript, minimum 2 high school GPA. Recommended: SAT or ACT. Required for some: essay, interview. Entrance: minimally difficult. Application deadline: rolling. Notification: continuous. SAT Reasoning Test deadline: 8/30. SAT Subject Test deadline: 8/30. Transfer credits accepted: Yes.
Costs Per Year: Application fee: $0. Comprehensive fee: $24,754 includes full-time tuition ($16,428), mandatory fees ($600), and college room and board ($7726). Part-time tuition: $669 per credit. Part-time mandatory fees: $100 per term.
Collegiate Environment: Orientation program. Choral group. Social organizations: 15 open to all. Most popular organizations: Rotoract (student service organization), Vet Tech Club, Campus Activities Board, Macrinian Yearbook, Phi Theta Kappa (honor society). Major annual events: Fall Semester BBQ, Founder' Day, Graduation Picnic. Student services: personal-psychological counseling. Campus security: 24-hour emergency response devices and patrols, late night transport-escort service. 88 college housing spaces available; 75 were occupied in 2018-19. No special consideration for freshman housing applicants. Option: coed housing available. Basileiad Library. Books: 27,188 (physical), 5,037 (digital/electronic); Serial titles: 3 (physical); Databases: 14. Weekly public service hours: 65. Operations spending for the previous fiscal year: $194,321. 140 computers available on campus for general student use. A campuswide network can be accessed from student residence rooms and from off campus. Students can access the following: online class registration. Staffed computer lab on campus provides training in use of computers and software.

■ **MANSFIELD UNIVERSITY OF PENNSYLVANIA**
Academy St.
Mansfield, PA 16933
Tel: (570)662-4000; Free: 800-577-6826
Fax: (570)662-4121
E-mail: admissions@mnsfld.edu
Web Site: www.mansfield.edu
Description: State-supported, comprehensive, coed. Part of Pennsylvania State System of Higher Education. Awards associate, bachelor's, and master's degrees. Founded 1857. Setting: 174-acre small town campus. Total enrollment: 1,637. Faculty: 137 (92 full-time, 45 part-time). Student-undergrad faculty ratio is 15:1. 1,595 applied, 92% were admitted. 8% from top 10% of their high school class, 28% from top quarter, 67% from top half. Full-time: 1,453 students, 60% women, 40% men. Part-time: 146 students, 67% women, 33% men. 17% from out-of-state. 0.1% American Indian or Alaska Native, non-Hispanic/Latino; 3% Hispanic/Latino; 10% Black or African American, non-Hispanic/Latino; 0.7% Asian, non-Hispanic/Latino; 0.1% Native Hawaiian or other Pacific Islander, non-Hispanic/Latino; 0.6% international. 12% 25 or older, 53% live on campus, 8% transferred in. Retention: 71% of full-time freshmen returned the following year. Academic areas with the most degrees conferred: visual and performing arts; health professions and related sciences; public administration and social services; psychology; biological/life sciences. Calendar: semesters. Part-time degree program, adult/continuing education programs. ROTC: Army (c).
Entrance Requirements: Options: electronic application, early admission, deferred admission, international baccalaureate accepted. Required: high

school transcript. Recommended: essay, minimum 2.5 high school GPA. Required for some: interview, SAT or ACT. Entrance: moderately difficult.
Costs Per Year: Application fee: $25. State resident tuition: $9450 full-time, $315 per credit hour part-time. Nonresident tuition: $18,900 full-time, $630 per credit hour part-time. Mandatory fees: $2880 full-time. College room and board: $11,998. College room only: $8468. Room and board charges vary according to board plan.
Collegiate Environment: Orientation program. Drama-theater group, choral group, marching band, student-run newspaper, radio station. Social organizations: national fraternities, national sororities, local fraternities, local sororities. Student services: health clinic, personal-psychological counseling, women's center. Campus security: 24-hour emergency response devices and patrols, student patrols, late night transport-escort service, controlled dormitory access. Freshmen guaranteed college housing. On-campus residence required through sophomore year. Option: coed housing available. North Hall Library.
Community Environment: Population 3,354, Mansfield is a rural town located on the north-central border of Pennsylvania at the intersection of U.S. Highways 6 and 15. It is mild in summer and often near freezing in winter. The community is served by bus lines. Ski slopes, camping areas, lakes, and hiking trails are all within an hours drive. Other recreational activities include river-rafting, cross-country skiing, fishing, and hunting.

■ **MARYWOOD UNIVERSITY**
2300 Adams Ave.
Scranton, PA 18509-1598
Tel: (570)348-6211; Free: 866-279-9663
Fax: (570)961-4763
E-mail: yourfuture@marywood.edu
Web Site: www.marywood.edu
Description: Independent Roman Catholic, comprehensive, coed. Awards bachelor's, master's, and doctoral degrees and post-master's certificates. Founded 1915. Setting: 123-acre suburban campus. Endowment: $38 million. Research spending for the previous fiscal year: $192,607. Educational spending for the previous fiscal year: $10,033 per student. Total enrollment: 2,869. Faculty: 402 (143 full-time, 259 part-time). Student-undergrad faculty ratio is 12:1. 2,137 applied, 75% were admitted. 17% from top 10% of their high school class, 45% from top quarter, 82% from top half. Full-time: 1,756 students, 67% women, 33% men. Part-time: 194 students, 74% women, 26% men. Students come from 20 states and territories, 11 other countries, 28% from out-of-state. 0.1% American Indian or Alaska Native, non-Hispanic/Latino; 8% Hispanic/Latino; 3% Black or African American, non-Hispanic/Latino; 2% Asian, non-Hispanic/Latino; 0.1% Native Hawaiian or other Pacific Islander, non-Hispanic/Latino; 2% international. 9% 25 or older, 35% live on campus, 5% transferred in. Retention: 86% of full-time freshmen returned the following year. Academic areas with the most degrees conferred: health professions and related sciences; business/marketing; architecture; education. Core. Calendar: semesters. ESL program, services for LD students, advanced placement, self-designed majors, honors program, independent study, double major, summer session for credit, part-time degree program, adult/continuing education programs, internships, graduate courses open to undergrads. Off campus study at University of Scranton, Online Consortium of Independent Colleges and Universities (OCICU). Study abroad program. ROTC: Army (c), Air Force (c).
Entrance Requirements: Options: electronic application, early admission, deferred admission, international baccalaureate accepted. Required: essay, high school transcript, minimum 2.5 high school GPA, 1 recommendation, SAT or ACT. Recommended: interview. Required for some: portfolio for art majors, audition for music majors. Entrance: moderately difficult. Application deadline: rolling. Notification: continuous. SAT Reasoning Test deadline: 9/1. Transfer credits accepted: Yes.
Costs Per Year: Application fee: $35. Comprehensive fee: $49,863 includes full-time tuition ($34,156), mandatory fees ($1750), and college room and board ($13,957). College room only: $7879. Part-time tuition: $650 per credit.
Collegiate Environment: Orientation program. Drama-theater group, choral group, student-run newspaper, radio station. Social organizations: 81 open to all; local sororities; 6% of eligible men and 6% of eligible women are members. Most popular organizations: Phi Beta Lambda (Business Club), Marywood Media Group, Volunteers in Action (VIA), Zeta Phi Delta, American Institute of Architects. Major annual events: Family Weekend, Marywood Madness, Spring Fling. Student services: health clinic, personal-psychological counseling. Campus security: 24-hour emergency response devices and patrols, late night transport-escort service, controlled dormitory

access, apartments with deadbolts, self-defense education, lighted pathways, seminars on safety. 913 college housing spaces available; 634 were occupied in 2018-19. Freshmen guaranteed college housing. On-campus residence required through sophomore year. Options: coed, women-only housing available. Learning Commons plus 2 others. Books: 185,509 (physical), 225,884 (digital/electronic); Serial titles: 62 (physical), 44,458 (digital/electronic); Databases: 62. Weekly public service hours: 99; students can reserve study rooms. Operations spending for the previous fiscal year: $2.2 million. 359 computers available on campus for general student use. A campuswide network can be accessed from student residence rooms and from off campus. Students can access the following: online class registration, degree audit, student account management, financial aid self-service, student planning. Staffed computer lab on campus (open 24 hours a day) provides training in use of computers, software, and the Internet.

Community Environment: The city of Scranton is a regional center for business, health care, social services, and recreation in northeastern Pennsylvania. It is 120 miles west of New York City and 115 miles north of Philadelphia. Sports, special events, music, theater, and parks are available. The nearby Pocono Mountains region offers six major ski areas, resorts, campgrounds, snowmobiling, canoeing, whitewater rafting, and various other activities. The Scranton area is home to seven other colleges and universities in addition to Marywood.

■ **MCCANN SCHOOL OF BUSINESS & TECHNOLOGY (AL-LENTOWN)**
2200 N Irving St.
Allentown, PA 18109
Web Site: www.mccann.edu
Description: Proprietary, 2-year, coed.

■ **MCCANN SCHOOL OF BUSINESS & TECHNOLOGY (LEWISBURG)**
7495 Westbranch Hwy.
Lewisburg, PA 17837
Tel: (570)497-8014; Free: 866-865-8065
Web Site: www.mccann.edu
Description: Proprietary, 2-year, coed. Awards certificates, transfer associate, and terminal associate degrees.

■ **MERCYHURST NORTH EAST**
16 W Division St.
North East, PA 16428
Tel: (717)725-6100; Free: 866-846-6042
Web Site: northeast.mercyhurst.edu
Description: Independent Roman Catholic, primarily 2-year, coed. Awards certificates, terminal associate, and bachelor's degrees. Founded 1991. Calendar: 4-3-3.
Costs Per Year: Comprehensive fee: $29,640 includes full-time tuition ($17,400), mandatory fees ($1720), and college room and board ($10,520). College room only: $5200. Full-time tuition and fees vary according to course load, location, and program. Room and board charges vary according to board plan, housing facility, and location.

■ **MERCYHURST UNIVERSITY**
501 E 38th St.
Erie, PA 16546
Tel: (814)824-2000; Free: 800-825-1926
Fax: (814)824-2071
Web Site: www.mercyhurst.edu
Description: Independent Roman Catholic, comprehensive, coed. Awards bachelor's and master's degrees. Founded 1926. Setting: 88-acre suburban campus with easy access to Buffalo. Endowment: $31.6 million. Total enrollment: 2,777. Faculty: (146 full-time). Student-undergrad faculty ratio is 15:1. 3,254 applied, 75% were admitted. 11% from top 10% of their high school class, 25% from top quarter, 70% from top half. 6 class presidents, 19 valedictorians, 28 student government officers. Full-time: 2,383 students, 57% women, 43% men. Part-time: 87 students, 71% women, 29% men. Students come from 42 states and territories, 31 other countries, 48% from out-of-state. 1% American Indian or Alaska Native, non-Hispanic/Latino; 4% Hispanic/Latino; 6% Black or African American, non-Hispanic/Latino; 2% Asian, non-Hispanic/Latino; 0.1% Native Hawaiian or other Pacific Islander, non-Hispanic/Latino; 9% international. 8% 25 or older, 68% live on campus, 2% transferred in. Retention: 80% of full-time freshmen returned the following year. Academic areas with the most degrees conferred: business/

marketing; health professions and related sciences; military science and military technologies. Core. Calendar: semesters. Academic remediation for entering students, services for LD students, advanced placement, accelerated degree program, self-designed majors, honors program, independent study, distance learning, double major, summer session for credit, part-time degree program, adult/continuing education programs, internships, graduate courses open to undergrads. Off campus study. Study abroad program. ROTC: Army, Air Force (c).
Entrance Requirements: Options: electronic application, deferred admission, international baccalaureate accepted. Required: essay, high school transcript. Recommended: interview. Required for some: 1 recommendation. Entrance: moderately difficult. Application deadline: rolling. Notification: continuous until 11/1. Transfer credits accepted: Yes.
Costs Per Year: Application fee: $0. Comprehensive fee: $50,950 includes full-time tuition ($35,400), mandatory fees ($2670), and college room and board ($12,880). Full-time tuition and fees vary according to class time, course load, degree level, location, and program. Room and board charges vary according to board plan, housing facility, and location. Part-time tuition: $1180 per credit. Part-time mandatory fees: $26 per credit, $710 per term. Part-time tuition and fees vary according to class time, course load, degree level, location, and program.
Collegiate Environment: Orientation program. Drama-theater group, choral group, marching band, student-run newspaper. Social organizations: 82 open to all. Most popular organizations: Student Government, chorus, Admission Ambassadors, Amnesty International, The Merciad (student newspaper). Major annual events: Christmas on Campus, Homecoming, Parent's Weekend. Student services: health clinic, personal-psychological counseling. Campus security: 24-hour emergency response devices and patrols, campus-wide camera system. Hammermill Library. Books: 108,088 (physical), 134,244 (digital/electronic); Serial titles: 500 (physical), 122,471 (digital/electronic); Databases: 66. Study areas open 24 hours, 5-7 days a week; students can reserve study rooms. 350 computers available on campus for general student use. A campuswide network can be accessed. Students can access the following: online class registration. Staffed computer lab on campus provides training in use of computers, software, and the Internet.
Community Environment: See Gannon University.

■ **MESSIAH COLLEGE**
One College Ave.
Mechanicsburg, PA 17055
Tel: (717)766-2511; Free: 800-233-4220
Fax: (717)796-5374
E-mail: admiss@messiah.edu
Web Site: www.messiah.edu
Description: Independent interdenominational, comprehensive, coed. Awards bachelor's, master's, and doctoral degrees and post-master's certificates. Founded 1909. Setting: 485-acre small town campus. Endowment: $138.2 million. Educational spending for the previous fiscal year: $12,254 per student. Total enrollment: 3,375. Faculty: 357 (195 full-time, 162 part-time). Student-undergrad faculty ratio is 12:1. 2,530 applied, 79% were admitted. 37% from top 10% of their high school class, 61% from top quarter, 90% from top half. 3 National Merit Scholars, 18 valedictorians. Full-time: 2,598 students, 61% women, 39% men. Part-time: 136 students, 68% women, 32% men. Students come from 38 states and territories, 30 other countries, 36% from out-of-state. 0.1% American Indian or Alaska Native, non-Hispanic/Latino; 5% Hispanic/Latino; 2% Black or African American, non-Hispanic/Latino; 2% Asian, non-Hispanic/Latino; 5% international. 2% 25 or older, 88% live on campus, 4% transferred in. Retention: 87% of full-time freshmen returned the following year. Academic areas with the most degrees conferred: health professions and related sciences; business/marketing; engineering. Core. Calendar: semesters. Academic remediation for entering students, ESL program, services for LD students, advanced placement, accelerated degree program, self-designed majors, freshman honors college, honors program, independent study, distance learning, double major, summer session for credit, part-time degree program, adult/continuing education programs, co-op programs and internships. Off campus study at Christian College Consortium, Council for Christian Colleges and Universities. Study abroad program.
Entrance Requirements: Options: electronic application, international baccalaureate accepted. Required: essay, high school transcript, SAT or ACT. Required for some: interview. Entrance: moderately difficult. Application deadline: rolling. Notification: continuous. Transfer credits accepted: Yes. Applicants placed on waiting list: 0. Wait-listed applicants offered admission: 0.

Costs Per Year: Application fee: $50. Comprehensive fee: $46,700 includes full-time tuition ($35,280), mandatory fees ($840), and college room and board ($10,580). College room only: $5630. Part-time tuition: $1470 per credit hour.

Collegiate Environment: Orientation program. Drama-theater group, choral group, student-run newspaper, radio station. Social organizations: 74 open to all. Most popular organizations: Outreach teams, student government, choral groups and ensembles, Small Group Program, Outdoors Club. Major annual events: Family Weekend, Homecoming, Christmas Tradition Banquet. Student services: health clinic, personal-psychological counseling. Campus security: 24-hour emergency response devices and patrols, student patrols, late night transport-escort service, controlled dormitory access. 2,383 college housing spaces available; 2,264 were occupied in 2018-19. Freshmen guaranteed college housing. On-campus residence required through senior year. Options: coed, men-only, women-only housing available. Murray Library. Books: 241,426 (physical), 576,178 (digital/electronic); Serial titles: 157 (physical), 104,750 (digital/electronic); Databases: 135. Weekly public service hours: 96; students can reserve study rooms. Operations spending for the previous fiscal year: $1.9 million. 571 computers available on campus for general student use. Computer purchase/lease plans available. A campuswide network can be accessed from student residence rooms and from off campus. Students can access the following: online class registration, access to software.

Community Environment: Population of Harrisburg 47,472. Grantham is a semirural community in south-central Pennsylvania located 12 miles southwest of the state capital, Harrisburg - providing easy access to urban centers such Harrisburg, Philadelphia, Baltimore, and Washington, D.C.

■ MILLERSVILLE UNIVERSITY OF PENNSYLVANIA

1 S George St.
Millersville, PA 17551-0302
Tel: (717)871-4636; Free: 800-MU-ADMIT
E-mail: admissions@millersville.edu
Web Site: www.millersville.edu

Description: State-supported, university, coed. Part of Pennsylvania State System of Higher Education. Awards associate, bachelor's, master's, and doctoral degrees and post-master's certificates. Founded 1855. Setting: 250-acre small town campus. Endowment: $11.3 million. Research spending for the previous fiscal year: $1 million. Educational spending for the previous fiscal year: $8274 per student. Total enrollment: 7,781. Faculty: 463 (287 full-time, 176 part-time). Student-undergrad faculty ratio is 18:1. 6,585 applied, 78% were admitted. 10% from top 10% of their high school class, 30% from top quarter, 68% from top half. Full-time: 5,537 students, 57% women, 43% men. Part-time: 1,222 students, 61% women, 39% men. Students come from 33 states and territories, 64 other countries, 7% from out-of-state. 0.4% American Indian or Alaska Native, non-Hispanic/Latino; 11% Hispanic/Latino; 9% Black or African American, non-Hispanic/Latino; 3% Asian, non-Hispanic/Latino; 0.1% Native Hawaiian or other Pacific Islander, non-Hispanic/Latino; 0.8% international. 13% 25 or older, 32% live on campus, 8% transferred in. Retention: 75% of full-time freshmen returned the following year. Academic areas with the most degrees conferred: business/marketing; education; social sciences. Core. Calendar: 4-1-4. Academic remediation for entering students, ESL program, services for LD students, advanced placement, accelerated degree program, self-designed majors, freshman honors college, honors program, independent study, distance learning, double major, summer session for credit, part-time degree program, adult/continuing education programs, co-op programs and internships, graduate courses open to undergrads. Off campus study at Franklin and Marshall College; Harrisburg Area Community College - Lancaster Campus; Reading Area Community College; Lancaster Theological Seminary; Chincoteague Bay Field Station at the Marine Science Consortium; Servicemembers Opportunity Colleges Consortium (SOCC); All PASSHE Schools: Bloomsburg, California University of PA, Cheyney, Clarion, East Stroudsburg, Edinboro, Indiana University of PA, Kutztown, Lock Haven, Mansfield, Shippensburg, Slippery Rock, West Chester. Study abroad program. ROTC: Army.

Entrance Requirements: Options: electronic application, early admission, deferred admission, international baccalaureate accepted. Required: essay, high school transcript, minimum 2 high school GPA, Health Examination required for all applicants. High school diploma or GED required for all applicants. SAT or ACT scores required for all applicants. Audition required for music applicants. Portfolio required for art applicants. Associate degree in Nursing or Diploma and RN license required for nur, SAT or ACT. Recommended: minimum 3 high school GPA, 2 recommendations. Required for

some: 1 recommendation, interview, Health Examination required for all applicants. High school diploma or GED required for all applicants. SAT or ACT scores required for all applicants. Audition required for music applicants. Portfolio required for art applicants. Associate degree in Nursing or Diploma and RN license required for nur. Entrance: moderately difficult. Application deadlines: rolling, rolling for nonresidents. Notification: continuous, continuous for nonresidents. Transfer credits accepted: Yes. Applicants placed on waiting list: 95. Wait-listed applicants offered admission: 2.

Costs Per Year: Application fee: $50. State resident tuition: $9570 full-time, $319 per credit part-time. Nonresident tuition: $19,290 full-time, $805 per credit part-time. Mandatory fees: $2656 full-time, $110.75 per credit part-time. Full-time tuition and fees vary according to course load and program. Part-time tuition and fees vary according to course load and program. College room and board: $13,658. Room and board charges vary according to board plan and housing facility.

Collegiate Environment: Orientation program. Drama-theater group, choral group, marching band, student-run newspaper, radio station. Social organizations: 176 open to all; national fraternities, national sororities; 4% of eligible men and 4% of eligible women are members. Most popular organizations: University Activities Board, Honors College Student Association, Mini-THON, Graduate Student Organization, Helping Paws. Major annual events: Organization Outbreak, Homecoming, Superfest. Student services: health clinic, personal-psychological counseling, women's center. Campus security: 24-hour emergency response devices and patrols, student patrols, late night transport-escort service, controlled dormitory access. 2,233 college housing spaces available; 2,165 were occupied in 2018-19. Freshmen guaranteed college housing. On-campus residence required through sophomore year. Option: coed housing available. The Francine G. McNairy Library and Learning Forum at Ganser Hall. Books: 316,579 (physical), 54,885 (digital/electronic); Serial titles: 4,191 (physical), 399,958 (digital/electronic); Databases: 179. Weekly public service hours: 94; students can reserve study rooms. Operations spending for the previous fiscal year: $3.2 million. 430 computers available on campus for general student use. A campuswide network can be accessed from student residence rooms and from off campus. Students can access the following: online class registration. Staffed computer lab on campus provides training in use of computers, software, and the Internet.

Community Environment: Population 7,583, Millersville is a suburban community adjacent to Lancaster. The climate is temperate. There is air and train service, bus lines, and major highways are easily accessible. The community has churches, theatres, hospitals, and shopping facilities located in Lancaster. Major civic, fraternal and veteran's organizations are represented here.

■ MISERICORDIA UNIVERSITY

301 Lake St.
Dallas, PA 18612-1098
Tel: (570)674-6400; Free: 866-262-6363
Fax: (570)675-2441
E-mail: admiss@misericordia.edu
Web Site: www.misericordia.edu

Description: Independent Roman Catholic, comprehensive, coed. Awards bachelor's, master's, and doctoral degrees and post-master's certificates. Founded 1924. Setting: 120-acre small town campus. Endowment: $49.2 million. Educational spending for the previous fiscal year: $9205 per student. Total enrollment: 2,764. Faculty: 304 (139 full-time, 165 part-time). Student-undergrad faculty ratio is 12:1. 1,823 applied, 74% were admitted. 21% from top 10% of their high school class, 51% from top quarter, 80% from top half. Full-time: 1,660 students, 64% women, 36% men. Part-time: 486 students, 77% women, 23% men. Students come from 28 states and territories, 1 other country, 27% from out-of-state. 0.3% American Indian or Alaska Native, non-Hispanic/Latino; 3% Hispanic/Latino; 3% Black or African American, non-Hispanic/Latino; 1% Asian, non-Hispanic/Latino; 0.1% Native Hawaiian or other Pacific Islander, non-Hispanic/Latino; 0.1% international. 19% 25 or older, 43% live on campus, 4% transferred in. Retention: 85% of full-time freshmen returned the following year. Academic areas with the most degrees conferred: health professions and related sciences; business/marketing; social sciences. Core. Calendar: semesters. Services for LD students, advanced placement, accelerated degree program, self-designed majors, honors program, independent study, distance learning, double major, summer session for credit, part-time degree program, adult/continuing education programs, co-op programs and internships, graduate courses open to undergrads. Off campus study at King's College (PA), Wilkes University. Study abroad program. ROTC: Army (c), Air Force (c).

Entrance Requirements: Options: electronic application, early admission, deferred admission, international baccalaureate accepted. Required: high school transcript, SAT or ACT. Recommended: interview. Required for some: essay, minimum 2.5 high school GPA, 2 recommendations. Entrance: moderately difficult. Application deadline: rolling. Notification: continuous. Transfer credits accepted: Yes. Applicants placed on waiting list: 70. Wait-listed applicants offered admission: 5.

Costs Per Year: Application fee: $35. Comprehensive fee: $47,200 includes full-time tuition ($31,530), mandatory fees ($1710), and college room and board ($13,960). College room only: $7600. Full-time tuition and fees vary according to degree level. Room and board charges vary according to board plan and housing facility. Part-time tuition: $610 per credit. Part-time tuition varies according to class time and location.

Collegiate Environment: Orientation program. Drama-theater group, choral group, student-run newspaper, radio station. Social organizations: 35 open to all. Most popular organizations: Physical Therapy club, MSOTA, Colleges against Cancer, Dance Ensemble, Medical Imaging club. Major annual events: Spring Fest Weekend, President's Christmas Dinner, Homecoming. Student services: health clinic, personal-psychological counseling, women's center. Campus security: 24-hour emergency response devices and patrols, late night transport-escort service, controlled dormitory access. Mary Kintz Bevevino Library. Books: 80,036 (physical), 13,154 (digital/electronic); Serial titles: 8,153 (physical), 28,230 (digital/electronic); Databases: 111. Students can reserve study rooms. Operations spending for the previous fiscal year: $1.2 million. 150 computers available on campus for general student use. Computer purchase/lease plans available. A campuswide network can be accessed from student residence rooms and from off campus. Students can access the following: online class registration. Staffed computer lab on campus provides training in use of computers, software, and the Internet.

Community Environment: The community of Dallas surrounding College Misericordia has a suburban atmosphere. It is located just nine miles from the city of Wilkes-Barre. The area provides shopping centers, a mall, cinemas, sporting events and a variety of cultural activities. Also nearby are Pennsylvania's largest natural lake, two state parks, the ski resorts of the Poconos, and five other colleges. New York and Philadelphia are within a two-hour drive. Public transportation is available to and from the campus.

■ MONTGOMERY COUNTY COMMUNITY COLLEGE

340 DeKalb Pke.
Blue Bell, PA 19422-0796
Tel: (215)641-6300
Fax: (215)653-0585
E-mail: admrec@admin.mc3.edu
Web Site: www.mc3.edu

Description: County-supported, 2-year, coed. Awards certificates, transfer associate, and terminal associate degrees. Founded 1964. Setting: 186-acre suburban campus with easy access to Philadelphia. Educational spending for the previous fiscal year: $3774 per student. Total enrollment: 10,392. Faculty: 766 (187 full-time, 579 part-time). Student-undergrad faculty ratio is 18:1. 7,608 applied, 100% were admitted. Full-time: 3,518 students, 48% women, 52% men. Part-time: 6,874 students, 61% women, 39% men. Students come from 7 states and territories, 96 other countries, 1% from out-of-state. 0.3% American Indian or Alaska Native, non-Hispanic/Latino; 8% Hispanic/Latino; 15% Black or African American, non-Hispanic/Latino; 6% Asian, non-Hispanic/Latino; 0.2% Native Hawaiian or other Pacific Islander, non-Hispanic/Latino; 2% international. 33% 25 or older. Retention: 60% of full-time freshmen returned the following year. Core. Calendar: semesters plus winter term. Academic remediation for entering students, ESL program, services for LD students, advanced placement, accelerated degree program, self-designed majors, honors program, independent study, distance learning, summer session for credit, part-time degree program, adult/continuing education programs, co-op programs and internships. Study abroad program.

Entrance Requirements: Open admission except for health sciences programs. Options: electronic application, early admission, deferred admission. Required: high school transcript. Required for some: interview. Entrance: noncompetitive. Notification: continuous. Preference given to county residents for some programs. Transfer credits accepted: Yes.

Costs Per Year: Area resident tuition: $4320 full-time, $144 per credit hour part-time. State resident tuition: $8640 full-time, $288 per credit hour part-time. Nonresident tuition: $12,960 full-time, $432 per credit hour part-time. Mandatory fees: $1410 full-time, $47 per credit hour part-time. Full-time tuition and fees vary according to program. Part-time tuition and fees vary according to program. College room and board: $6050. Room and board charges vary according to board plan.

Collegiate Environment: Orientation program. Drama-theater group, choral group, student-run newspaper, radio station. Social organizations: 41 open to all. Most popular organizations: West End Student Theater (drama club), Phi Theta Kappa, Writers Club, Japanese Culture Club, Student Government. Major annual events: Student Club and Involvement Fair, International Night, Drama Club Productions. Student services: health clinic, personal-psychological counseling. Campus security: 24-hour emergency response devices and patrols, late night transport-escort service, bicycle patrol. The Brendlinger Library. Books: 73,691 (physical), 98,911 (digital/electronic); Serial titles: 237 (physical), 19,750 (digital/electronic); Databases: 37. Weekly public service hours: 76; students can reserve study rooms. Operations spending for the previous fiscal year: $1.5 million. 1,336 computers available on campus for general student use. A campuswide network can be accessed from off-campus. Students can access the following: online class registration. Staffed computer lab on campus provides training in use of computers, software, and the Internet.

Community Environment: Rural community (under 2,500). Suburban campus environment. 5 miles from (north) Norristown. Some bus transportation. Approximately 45 minute commute to Philadelphia. Surrounding industries include pharmaceutical and chemical-product companies; some farming.

■ MOORE COLLEGE OF ART & DESIGN

20th and the Pky.
Philadelphia, PA 19103
Tel: (215)965-4000; Free: 800-523-2025
E-mail: enroll@moore.edu
Web Site: www.moore.edu

Description: Independent, comprehensive. Awards bachelor's and master's degrees. Founded 1848. Setting: 3-acre urban campus with easy access to Philadelphia. Endowment: $21.7 million. Total enrollment: 440. Faculty: 139 (24 full-time, 115 part-time). Student-undergrad faculty ratio is 7:1. 557 applied, 56% were admitted. Full-time: 392 students, 100% women. Part-time: 14 students, 100% women. Students come from 21 states and territories, 5 other countries, 40% from out-of-state. 0.5% American Indian or Alaska Native, non-Hispanic/Latino; 7% Hispanic/Latino; 21% Black or African American, non-Hispanic/Latino; 3% Asian, non-Hispanic/Latino; 1% international. 9% 25 or older, 38% live on campus, 8% transferred in. Retention: 73% of full-time freshmen returned the following year. Academic areas with the most degrees conferred: visual and performing arts; education; interdisciplinary studies. Core. Calendar: semesters. Academic remediation for entering students, services for LD students, advanced placement, independent study, double major, summer session for credit, part-time degree program, external degree program, co-op programs and internships. Off campus study. Study abroad program.

Entrance Requirements: Options: electronic application, deferred admission. Required: high school transcript, minimum 2.5 high school GPA, 1 recommendation, portfolio review. Recommended: essay, interview, SAT or ACT. Required for some: minimum 3 high school GPA. Entrance: moderately difficult. Application deadline: 8/15. Notification: continuous. Transfer credits accepted: Yes.

Collegiate Environment: Orientation program. Most popular organizations: Student Government Association, Student Orientation Staff, Student-run Gallery, Visionary Women Honors Program, Yearbook. Major annual events: Visionary Woman Awards, Fashion Show, Student and Senior Shows. Student services: health clinic, personal-psychological counseling. Campus security: 24-hour emergency response devices and patrols, late night transport-escort service, controlled dormitory access, RD and professional staff on call 24 /7. Connelly Library plus 1 other. Books: 50,000 (physical); Serial titles: 110 (physical), 1 (digital/electronic); Databases: 12. Operations spending for the previous fiscal year: $68,603.

Community Environment: See Temple University.

■ MORAVIAN COLLEGE

1200 Main St.
Bethlehem, PA 18018-6650
Tel: (610)861-1300; Free: 800-441-3191
Fax: (610)861-3956
E-mail: myersj02@moravian.edu
Web Site: www.moravian.edu

Description: Independent, comprehensive, coed, affiliated with Moravian Church. Awards bachelor's, master's, and doctoral degrees and post-master's certificates. Founded 1742. Setting: 85-acre suburban campus with easy access to Philadelphia. Endowment: $111.3 million. Research spending for the previous fiscal year: $162,072. Educational spending for the previous fiscal year: $12,394 per student. Total enrollment: 2,463. Faculty: 294 (141 full-time, 153 part-time). Student-undergrad faculty ratio is 11:1. 3,059 applied, 76% were admitted. 18% from top 10% of their high school class, 48% from top quarter, 85% from top half. 2 valedictorians. Full-time: 1,840 students, 59% women, 41% men. Part-time: 193 students, 65% women, 35% men. Students come from 22 states and territories, 16 other countries, 31% from out-of-state. 0.2% American Indian or Alaska Native, non-Hispanic/Latino; 10% Hispanic/Latino; 5% Black or African American, non-Hispanic/Latino; 2% Asian, non-Hispanic/Latino; 6% international. 4% 25 or older, 65% live on campus, 4% transferred in. Retention: 82% of full-time freshmen returned the following year. Academic areas with the most degrees conferred: health professions and related sciences; business/marketing; social sciences. Core. Calendar: semesters. Services for LD students, advanced placement, accelerated degree program, self-designed majors, honors program, independent study, distance learning, double major, summer session for credit, part-time degree program, adult/continuing education programs, co-op programs and internships, graduate courses open to undergrads. Off campus study at Five other members of the Lehigh Valley Association of Independent Colleges, Washington Semester. Study abroad program. ROTC: Army (c).

Entrance Requirements: Options: electronic application, deferred admission, international baccalaureate accepted. Required: essay, high school transcript, 1 recommendation, SAT or ACT. Required for some: portfolio for art majors; audition for music majors; 3.3 high school GPA, minimum SAT combined score of 1500 (with no section less than 500) or ACT score of 23 for nursing. Entrance: moderately difficult. Application deadline: 3/1. Notification: continuous until 11/15. SAT Reasoning Test deadline: 3/1. SAT Subject Test deadline: 3/1. Transfer credits accepted: Yes.

Costs Per Year: Application fee: $0. One-time mandatory fee: $500. Comprehensive fee: $57,014 includes full-time tuition ($41,905), mandatory fees ($1731), and college room and board ($13,378). College room only: $7538. Full-time tuition and fees vary according to class time and program. Room and board charges vary according to board plan and housing facility. Part-time tuition: $1164 per credit. Part-time tuition varies according to class time.

Collegiate Environment: Orientation program. Drama-theater group, choral group, marching band, student-run newspaper, radio station. Social organizations: 82 open to all; national fraternities, national sororities, local fraternities, local sororities; 11% of eligible men and 13% of eligible women are members. Most popular organizations: Moravian Activities Council, Black Student Union, Habitat for Humanity, Commuter Student Union, American Association of University Women. Major annual events: Homecoming, Christmas Vespers, Heritage Day. Student services: health clinic, personal-psychological counseling. Campus security: 24-hour emergency response devices and patrols, late night transport-escort service, controlled dormitory access. Reeves Library. Books: 198,012 (physical), 168,981 (digital/electronic); Serial titles: 2,490 (physical), 183 (digital/electronic); Databases: 67. Weekly public service hours: 86. Operations spending for the previous fiscal year: $1 million. 230 computers available on campus for general student use. Computer purchase/lease plans available. A computer is required for all students. A campuswide network can be accessed from student residence rooms and from off campus. Students can access the following: online class registration. Staffed computer lab on campus provides training in use of computers, software, and the Internet.

Community Environment: Town of about 75,000 residential neighborhood.

■ MOUNT ALOYSIUS COLLEGE

7373 Admiral Peary Hwy.
Cresson, PA 16630-1999
Tel: (814)886-4131; Free: 888-823-2220
Fax: (814)886-2978
E-mail: admissions@mtaloy.edu
Web Site: www.mtaloy.edu

Description: Independent Roman Catholic, comprehensive, coed. Awards associate, bachelor's, and master's degrees. Founded 1939. Setting: 193-acre small town campus. Total enrollment: 1,740. Faculty: 160 (71 full-time, 89 part-time). Student-undergrad faculty ratio is 11:1. 1,748 applied, 61% were admitted. Full-time: 999 students, 68% women, 32% men. Part-time: 689 students, 65% women, 35% men. 6% from out-of-state. 0.3% American Indian or Alaska Native, non-Hispanic/Latino; 1% Hispanic/Latino; 3% Black or African American, non-Hispanic/Latino; 0.7% Asian, non-Hispanic/Latino; 6% international. 23% 25 or older, 38% live on campus, 5% transferred in. Academic areas with the most degrees conferred: health professions and

related sciences; business/marketing; biological/life sciences. Core. Calendar: semesters. Academic remediation for entering students, advanced placement, accelerated degree program, self-designed majors, honors program, independent study, distance learning, double major, summer session for credit, part-time degree program, internships. Study abroad program.

Entrance Requirements: Options: electronic application, early admission, deferred admission, international baccalaureate accepted. Required: high school transcript, SAT or ACT. Recommended: interview, SAT, ACT. Required for some: essay, interview. Entrance: minimally difficult. Application deadline: rolling. Notification: continuous. Transfer credits accepted: Yes. Applicants placed on waiting list: 4. Wait-listed applicants offered admission: 4.

Costs Per Year: Application fee: $30. Comprehensive fee: $33,758 includes full-time tuition ($21,870), mandatory fees ($1240), and college room and board ($10,648). College room only: $5356. Part-time tuition: $825 per credit hour.

Collegiate Environment: Orientation program. Drama-theater group, choral group, student-run newspaper. Most popular organizations: Student Government, Campus Activity Board, Student Athletic Advisory Committee, Spirit Team, Dance Team. Major annual events: Club Fair, Mountie Madness, MAC's Got Talent. Student services: health clinic, personal-psychological counseling. Campus security: 24-hour emergency response devices and patrols, student patrols, late night transport-escort service, controlled dormitory access. Mount Aloysius College Library.

Community Environment: Population 4,200. Cresson is a rural community with a moderately humid climate and relatively high temperatures in summer. The area is served by bus, highway, and an airport at Martinsburg 45 minutes away. The city has two Catholic, a Methodist, Presbyterian, Christian, and Missionary Alliance Churches. There are several civic, fraternal, and veteran's organizations within the area. Theatres, concerts, sport events, and other recreational facilities are located in nearby Altoona and Johnstown. There are part-time employment opportunities for students on campus.

■ MUHLENBERG COLLEGE

2400 Chew St.
Allentown, PA 18104-5586
Tel: (484)664-3100
Fax: (484)664-3234
Web Site: www.muhlenberg.edu

Description: Independent, 4-year, coed, affiliated with Lutheran Church. Awards associate and bachelor's degrees. Founded 1848. Setting: 75-acre suburban campus with easy access to Philadelphia. Endowment: $246.9 million. Research spending for the previous fiscal year: $437,356. Educational spending for the previous fiscal year: $17,447 per student. Total enrollment: 2,408. Faculty: 297 (185 full-time, 112 part-time). Student-undergrad faculty ratio is 10:1. 4,636 applied, 48% were admitted. 36% from top 10% of their high school class, 71% from top quarter, 93% from top half. Full-time: 2,318 students, 60% women, 40% men. Part-time: 90 students, 62% women, 38% men. Students come from 35 states and territories, 13 other countries, 76% from out-of-state. 7% Hispanic/Latino; 3% Black or African American, non-Hispanic/Latino; 3% Asian, non-Hispanic/Latino; 3% international. 5% 25 or older, 92% live on campus, 1% transferred in. Retention: 90% of full-time freshmen returned the following year. Academic areas with the most degrees conferred: business/marketing; visual and performing arts; psychology. Core. Calendar: semesters. Services for LD students, advanced placement, accelerated degree program, self-designed majors, honors program, independent study, double major, summer session for credit, part-time degree program, adult/continuing education programs, internships. Off campus study at Lehigh Valley Association of Independent Colleges. Study abroad program. ROTC: Army (c).

Entrance Requirements: Options: electronic application, early admission, early decision, deferred admission, international baccalaureate accepted. Required: essay, high school transcript, 2 recommendations. Recommended: interview. Required for some: interview, graded paper, SAT or ACT. Entrance: very difficult. Application deadlines: 2/1, 11/15 for early decision plan 1, 2/1 for early decision plan 2. Notification: 3/20, 12/15 for early decision plan 1, 2/15 for early decision plan 2. SAT Reasoning Test deadline: 2/1. Transfer credits accepted: Yes. Applicants placed on waiting list: 1,530. Wait-listed applicants offered admission: 78. Early decision applicants: 341. Early decision applicants admitted: 289.

Costs Per Year: Application fee: $50. One-time mandatory fee: $120. Comprehensive fee: $64,360 includes full-time tuition ($51,860), mandatory fees ($735), and college room and board ($11,765). College room only:

$6395. Room and board charges vary according to board plan, housing facility, and location. Part-time tuition: $6100 per course. Part-time mandatory fees: $367.50 per term. Part-time tuition and fees vary according to program.
Collegiate Environment: Orientation program. Drama-theater group, choral group, student-run newspaper, radio station. Social organizations: 121 open to all; national fraternities, national sororities; 17% of eligible men and 21% of eligible women are members. Most popular organizations: Theater Association, Environmental Action Team, Jefferson School Partnership, Select Choir, Habitat for Humanity. Major annual events: Homecoming, Jefferson School Field Day, Family Weekend. Student services: health clinic, personal-psychological counseling. Campus security: 24-hour emergency response devices and patrols, late night transport-escort service, controlled dormitory access. Trexler Library. Books: 228,069 (physical), 515,579 (digital/electronic); Serial titles: 1,183 (physical), 40,276 (digital/electronic); Databases: 99. Weekly public service hours: 105; students can reserve study rooms. Operations spending for the previous fiscal year: $3.1 million. 450 computers available on campus for general student use. A campuswide network can be accessed from student residence rooms and from off campus. Students can access the following: online class registration. Staffed computer lab on campus provides training in use of computers, software, and the Internet.
Community Environment: Population 107,000. Allentown is located on the Lehigh River. It is Pennsylvania's third largest industrial market. Diversified manufacturing includes machinery and tools, trucks, electrical appliances, electronic equipment, apparel, cement, and gas-generating equipment. Other industries manufacture metal products, batteries, foodstuffs, textiles, and shoes. The area has good transportation facilities including four railroad lines, air service, and bus lines. The community has many churches representing various denominations. Four hospitals, a dental hospital, a library system, a museum and an Equity theater company are located here. Local recreational facilities encompass volleyball, baseball, tennis, basketball, pools, hiking, band concerts, opera, community theatre, five radio stations, and many motion picture and drive-in theatres. Part-time employment is available for students.

■ **NEUMANN UNIVERSITY**
One Neumann Dr.
Aston, PA 19014-1298
Tel: (610)459-0905; Free: 800-963-8626
E-mail: wrighte@neumann.edu
Web Site: www.neumann.edu
Description: Independent Roman Catholic, comprehensive, coed. Awards associate, bachelor's, master's, and doctoral degrees and post-master's certificates. Founded 1965. Setting: 68-acre suburban campus with easy access to Philadelphia. Endowment: $30.8 million. Educational spending for the previous fiscal year: $7118 per student. Total enrollment: 2,715. Faculty: 241 (96 full-time, 145 part-time). Student-undergrad faculty ratio is 15:1. 1,505 applied, 96% were admitted. Full-time: 1,462 students, 65% women, 35% men. Part-time: 623 students, 67% women, 33% men. Students come from 30 states and territories, 9 other countries, 31% from out-of-state. 0.1% American Indian or Alaska Native, non-Hispanic/Latino; 6% Hispanic/Latino; 24% Black or African American, non-Hispanic/Latino; 1% Asian, non-Hispanic/Latino; 0.1% Native Hawaiian or other Pacific Islander, non-Hispanic/Latino; 1% international. 23% 25 or older, 35% live on campus, 4% transferred in. Retention: 77% of full-time freshmen returned the following year. Academic areas with the most degrees conferred: health professions and related sciences; business/marketing; homeland security, law enforcement, firefighting, and protective services. Core. Calendar: semesters. Academic remediation for entering students, services for LD students, advanced placement, accelerated degree program, honors program, independent study, distance learning, double major, summer session for credit, part-time degree program, adult/continuing education programs, co-op programs and internships, graduate courses open to undergrads. Off campus study at Southeastern Pennsylvania Consortium for Higher Education (SEPCHE), Online Consortium of Independent Colleges and Universities (OCICU). Study abroad program. ROTC: Army (c), Air Force (c).
Entrance Requirements: Options: electronic application, deferred admission. Required: high school transcript, minimum 2.5 high school GPA, SAT or ACT. Recommended: essay, interview. Required for some: 1 recommendation. Entrance: minimally difficult. Application deadline: rolling. Notification: continuous. SAT Reasoning Test deadline: 8/15. Transfer credits accepted: Yes. Applicants placed on waiting list: 0. Wait-listed applicants offered admission: 0.
Costs Per Year: Application fee: $35. One-time mandatory fee: $100.

Comprehensive fee: $44,420 includes full-time tuition ($30,000), mandatory fees ($1400), and college room and board ($13,020). College room only: $7840. Full-time tuition and fees vary according to degree level. Room and board charges vary according to board plan and housing facility. Part-time tuition: $680 per credit hour. Part-time mandatory fees: $90 per term. Part-time tuition and fees vary according to degree level and program.
Collegiate Environment: Orientation program. Drama-theater group, choral group, student-run newspaper, radio station. Social organizations: 27 open to all. Most popular organizations: Student Nurses Association, Student Activities Board, Boogie Nights, Knights for Education, Neumann Media. Major annual events: Best Day Ever, Spring Formal, Homecoming and Family Weekend. Student services: health clinic, personal-psychological counseling. Campus security: 24-hour emergency response devices and patrols, late night transport-escort service, controlled dormitory access. Neumann University Library plus 1 other. Books: 51,000 (physical), 161,000 (digital/electronic); Serial titles: 20 (physical), 100,000 (digital/electronic); Databases: 45. Weekly public service hours: 80; students can reserve study rooms. Operations spending for the previous fiscal year: $615,000. 275 computers available on campus for general student use. Computer purchase/lease plans available. A campuswide network can be accessed from student residence rooms and from off campus. Students can access the following: online class registration. Staffed computer lab on campus provides training in use of computers, software, and the Internet.
Community Environment: Population of Philadelphia 1,463,281. Aston is a suburban township serving a commuter population from the Tri-state area of Philadelphia, Wilmington and South Jersey. The city enjoys temperate climate. Local historical sites include Valley Forge National Park, Brandywine Battlefield, and many others. Nearby Philadelphia offers all the cultural, recreational, and community service facilities normally found in a metropolis. The immediate area is served by railroad and bus lines with an airport located 10 miles away. There are three hospitals and numerous shopping centers in the area. Part-time employment opportunities are good.

■ **NEW CASTLE SCHOOL OF TRADES**
4117 Pulaski Rd.
New Castle, PA 16101
Tel: (724)964-8811; Free: 800-837-8299
Web Site: www.ncstrades.edu
Description: Independent, 2-year, coed. Awards diplomas and terminal associate degrees. Founded 1945. Setting: 20-acre rural campus with easy access to Pittsburgh. Educational spending for the previous fiscal year: $2500 per student. Total enrollment: 503. Faculty: 46 (31 full-time, 15 part-time). Student-undergrad faculty ratio is 10:1. Full-time: 503 students, 5% women, 95% men. Students come from 3 states and territories, 1 other country. 3% Hispanic/Latino; 14% Black or African American, non-Hispanic/Latino; 2% Asian, non-Hispanic/Latino; 0.2% international. Core. Calendar: quarters. Part-time degree program.
Entrance Requirements: Required: high school transcript, interview, Wonderlic aptitude test. Required for some: essay. Transfer credits accepted: Yes.
Collegiate Environment: Orientation program. Student services: personal-psychological counseling. Campus security: 24-hour emergency response devices. New Castle School of Trades plus 1 other. Books: 600 (physical). Weekly public service hours: 60. Operations spending for the previous fiscal year: $5000. 70 computers available on campus for general student use. A campuswide network can be accessed from off-campus. Staffed computer lab on campus (open 24 hours a day) provides training in use of computers and software.

■ **NORTHAMPTON COMMUNITY COLLEGE**
3835 Green Pond Rd.
Bethlehem, PA 18020-7599
Tel: (610)861-5300
E-mail: jrmccarthy@northampton.edu
Web Site: www.northampton.edu
Description: State and locally supported, 2-year, coed. Awards certificates, diplomas, transfer associate, and terminal associate degrees. Founded 1967. Setting: 165-acre suburban campus with easy access to Philadelphia. Total enrollment: 9,769. Faculty: 702 (121 full-time, 581 part-time). Student-undergrad faculty ratio is 19:1. 5,630 applied, 100% were admitted. 1% from top 10% of their high school class, 10% from top quarter, 35% from top half. Full-time: 4,255 students, 54% women, 46% men. Part-time: 5,514 students, 67% women, 33% men. 2% from out-of-state. 0.2% American Indian or Alaska Native, non-Hispanic/Latino; 23% Hispanic/Latino; 13% Black or

African American, non-Hispanic/Latino; 2% Asian, non-Hispanic/Latino; 0.2% Native Hawaiian or other Pacific Islander, non-Hispanic/Latino; 1% international. 34% 25 or older, 6% live on campus, 9% transferred in. Core. Calendar: semesters. Academic remediation for entering students, ESL program, services for LD students, advanced placement, self-designed majors, honors program, independent study, distance learning, summer session for credit, part-time degree program, adult/continuing education programs, internships. Off campus study. Study abroad program.

Entrance Requirements: Open admission Open admission policy for all students but selective admission to some programs. Options: electronic application, deferred admission. Required for some: high school transcript, minimum 2.5 high school GPA, interview, interview for radiography and veterinary programs. Entrance: noncompetitive. Application deadline: rolling. Notification: continuous. Transfer credits accepted: Yes.

Costs Per Year: Application fee: $25. Area resident tuition: $3120 full-time, $104 per credit hour part-time. State resident tuition: $6240 full-time, $208 per credit hour part-time. Nonresident tuition: $9360 full-time, $312 per credit hour part-time. Mandatory fees: $1260 full-time, $42 per credit hour part-time. Full-time tuition and fees vary according to course load. Part-time tuition and fees vary according to course load. College room and board: $9094. College room only: $5464. Room and board charges vary according to board plan and housing facility.

Collegiate Environment: Orientation program. Choral group, student-run newspaper, radio station. Most popular organizations: Phi Theta Kappa, Student Senate, Nursing Student Organization, American Dental Hygiene Association (ADHA), International Student Organization. Major annual events: Fall Quad Fest, Spartan Fest, Student Celebration. Student services: health clinic, personal-psychological counseling. Campus security: 24-hour emergency response devices and patrols, controlled dormitory access. No special consideration for freshman housing applicants. Option: coed housing available. Paul & Harriett Mack Library. Weekly public service hours: 83; students can reserve study rooms.

■ **PEIRCE COLLEGE**
1420 Pine St.
Philadelphia, PA 19102-4699
Tel: (215)545-6400; Free: 888-467-3472
Fax: (215)546-5996
E-mail: info@peirce.edu
Web Site: www.peirce.edu

Description: Independent, comprehensive, coed. Awards associate, bachelor's, and master's degrees. Founded 1865. Setting: 1-acre urban campus. Total enrollment: 1,478. Faculty: 99 (28 full-time, 71 part-time). Student-undergrad faculty ratio is 14:1. Full-time: 315 students, 59% women, 41% men. Part-time: 1,074 students, 75% women, 25% men. 9% from out-of-state. 0.1% American Indian or Alaska Native, non-Hispanic/Latino; 8% Hispanic/Latino; 65% Black or African American, non-Hispanic/Latino; 2% Asian, non-Hispanic/Latino; 0.1% Native Hawaiian or other Pacific Islander, non-Hispanic/Latino; 0.3% international. 79% 25 or older. Retention: 50% of full-time freshmen returned the following year. Academic areas with the most degrees conferred: business/marketing; computer and information sciences; law/legal studies. Core. Calendar: semesters. Services for LD students, advanced placement, accelerated degree program, distance learning, summer session for credit, part-time degree program, adult/continuing education programs, co-op programs and internships.

Entrance Requirements: Open admission selective admissions into the Professional Studies degree completion program. Option: electronic application. Required: high school transcript. Entrance: noncompetitive. Transfer credits accepted: Yes.

Collegiate Environment: Orientation program. Major annual events: Commencement, Academic Awards Ceremony, Student Appreciation Day. Campus security: 24-hour emergency response devices and patrols, late night transport-escort service, 24-hour security cameras. Peirce College Library.

■ **PENN COMMERCIAL BUSINESS AND TECHNICAL SCHOOL**
242 Oak Spring Rd.
Washington, PA 15301
Tel: (724)222-5330; Free: 888-309-7484
Fax: (724)222-4722
Web Site: www.penncommercial.edu

Description: Proprietary, 2-year, coed. Awards certificates, diplomas, transfer associate, and terminal associate degrees. Founded 1929. Setting: 1-acre small town campus with easy access to Pittsburgh. Total enrollment:

435. 165 applied. 67% 25 or older. Calendar: quarters. Academic remediation for entering students, summer session for credit, part-time degree program.

Entrance Requirements: Open admission. Options: early admission, deferred admission. Required: high school transcript. Entrance: noncompetitive. Application deadline: rolling. Notification: continuous.

Collegiate Environment: Student-run newspaper. Main library plus 1 other.

■ **PENN STATE ABINGTON**
1600 Woodland Rd.
Abington, PA 19001
Tel: (215)881-7300
E-mail: abingtonadmissions@psu.edu
Web Site: www.abington.psu.edu

Description: State-related, 4-year, coed. Part of Pennsylvania State University. Awards associate and bachelor's degrees (enrollment figures include students enrolled at The Graduate School at Penn State who are taking courses at this location). Founded 1950. Setting: small town campus. Total enrollment: 3,893. Faculty: 320 (146 full-time, 174 part-time). Student-undergrad faculty ratio is 17:1. 5,145 applied, 85% were admitted. 8% from top 10% of their high school class, 24% from top quarter, 64% from top half. Full-time: 3,312 students, 49% women, 51% men. Part-time: 576 students, 60% women, 40% men. 8% from out-of-state. 0.1% American Indian or Alaska Native, non-Hispanic/Latino; 11% Hispanic/Latino; 13% Black or African American, non-Hispanic/Latino; 16% Asian, non-Hispanic/Latino; 10% international. 12% 25 or older, 1% live on campus, 4% transferred in. Retention: 83% of full-time freshmen returned the following year. Academic areas with the most degrees conferred: health professions and related sciences; business/marketing; psychology. Calendar: semesters. Part-time degree program, external degree program, adult/continuing education programs. ROTC: Army (c), Air Force (c).

Entrance Requirements: Options: electronic application, early admission, deferred admission, international baccalaureate accepted. Required: high school transcript, SAT or ACT. Recommended: essay. Required for some: interview. Entrance: very difficult. Application deadline: rolling. Notification: continuous.

Collegiate Environment: Orientation program. Campus security: 24-hour emergency response devices and patrols. Penn State Abington Library.

■ **PENN STATE ALTOONA**
3000 Ivyside Park
Altoona, PA 16601
Tel: (814)949-5000; Free: 800-848-9843
Fax: (814)949-5011
E-mail: aaadmit@psu.edu
Web Site: www.altoona.psu.edu

Description: State-related, 4-year, coed. Part of Pennsylvania State University. Awards associate and bachelor's degrees (enrollment figures include students enrolled at The Graduate School at Penn State who are taking courses at this location). Founded 1939. Setting: suburban campus. Total enrollment: 3,482. Faculty: 288 (196 full-time, 92 part-time). Student-undergrad faculty ratio is 15:1. 5,430 applied, 92% were admitted. 7% from top 10% of their high school class, 27% from top quarter, 67% from top half. Full-time: 3,374 students, 45% women, 55% men. Part-time: 108 students, 45% women, 55% men. 16% from out-of-state. 0.1% American Indian or Alaska Native, non-Hispanic/Latino; 5% Hispanic/Latino; 6% Black or African American, non-Hispanic/Latino; 3% Asian, non-Hispanic/Latino; 8% international. 5% 25 or older, 27% live on campus, 2% transferred in. Retention: 82% of full-time freshmen returned the following year. Academic areas with the most degrees conferred: engineering; business/marketing; health professions and related sciences. Calendar: semesters. Independent study. ROTC: Army (c), Air Force (c).

Entrance Requirements: Options: electronic application, early admission, deferred admission, international baccalaureate accepted. Required: high school transcript, SAT or ACT. Recommended: essay. Required for some: interview. Entrance: very difficult. Application deadline: rolling. Notification: continuous.

Collegiate Environment: Orientation program. Campus security: 24-hour emergency response devices and patrols, late night transport-escort service. Robert E. Eiche Library.

■ **PENN STATE BEAVER**
100 University Dr.
Monaca, PA 15061

Tel: (724)773-3800
Fax: (724)773-3557
E-mail: br-admissions@psu.edu
Web Site: www.br.psu.edu
Description: State-related, 4-year, coed. Part of Pennsylvania State University. Awards bachelor's degrees. Founded 1964. Setting: small town campus. Total enrollment: 655. Faculty: 66 (34 full-time, 32 part-time). Student-undergrad faculty ratio is 14:1. 792 applied, 88% were admitted. 9% from top 10% of their high school class, 33% from top quarter, 68% from top half. Full-time: 563 students, 41% women, 59% men. Part-time: 92 students, 47% women, 53% men. 12% from out-of-state. 0.2% American Indian or Alaska Native, non-Hispanic/Latino; 5% Hispanic/Latino; 8% Black or African American, non-Hispanic/Latino; 4% Asian, non-Hispanic/Latino; 4% international. 8% 25 or older, 22% live on campus, 5% transferred in. Retention: 76% of full-time freshmen returned the following year. Academic areas with the most degrees conferred: business/marketing; homeland security, law enforcement, firefighting, and protective services; computer and information sciences. Calendar: semesters. Adult/continuing education programs.
Entrance Requirements: Options: electronic application, early admission, deferred admission. Required: high school transcript, SAT or ACT. Recommended: essay. Required for some: interview. Entrance: moderately difficult. Application deadline: rolling. Notification: continuous.
Collegiate Environment: Orientation program.

■ **PENN STATE BERKS**
Tulpehocken Rd.
Reading, PA 19610
Tel: (610)396-6000
E-mail: admissionsbk@psu.edu
Web Site: www.bk.psu.edu
Description: State-related, 4-year, coed. Part of Pennsylvania State University. Awards associate and bachelor's degrees (enrollment figures include students enrolled at The Graduate School at Penn State who are taking courses at this location). Founded 1924. Setting: suburban campus. Total enrollment: 2,719. Faculty: 227 (137 full-time, 90 part-time). Student-undergrad faculty ratio is 15:1. 2,447 applied, 86% were admitted. 8% from top 10% of their high school class, 28% from top quarter, 62% from top half. Full-time: 2,411 students, 41% women, 59% men. Part-time: 308 students, 45% women, 55% men. 7% from out-of-state. 0.1% American Indian or Alaska Native, non-Hispanic/Latino; 13% Hispanic/Latino; 8% Black or African American, non-Hispanic/Latino; 5% Asian, non-Hispanic/Latino; 0.1% Native Hawaiian or other Pacific Islander, non-Hispanic/Latino; 4% international. 10% 25 or older, 28% live on campus, 4% transferred in. Retention: 78% of full-time freshmen returned the following year. Academic areas with the most degrees conferred: business/marketing; computer and information sciences; biological/life sciences. Calendar: semesters. Part-time degree program, adult/continuing education programs. ROTC: Army (c).
Entrance Requirements: Options: electronic application, early admission, deferred admission, international baccalaureate accepted. Required: high school transcript, SAT or ACT. Recommended: essay. Required for some: interview. Entrance: very difficult. Application deadline: rolling. Notification: continuous.
Collegiate Environment: Orientation program. Campus security: 24-hour emergency response devices and patrols, late night transport-escort service, controlled dormitory access. Thun Library.

■ **PENN STATE BRANDYWINE**
25 Yearsley Mill Rd.
Media, PA 19063
Tel: (610)892-1200
E-mail: bwadmissions@psu.edu
Web Site: www.brandywine.psu.edu
Description: State-related, 4-year, coed. Part of Pennsylvania State University. Awards associate and bachelor's degrees. Founded 1966. Setting: small town campus. Total enrollment: 1,438. Faculty: 134 (65 full-time, 69 part-time). Student-undergrad faculty ratio is 15:1. 1,627 applied, 87% were admitted. 4% from top 10% of their high school class, 20% from top quarter, 57% from top half. Full-time: 1,245 students, 42% women, 58% men. Part-time: 193 students, 41% women, 59% men. 10% from out-of-state. 0.3% American Indian or Alaska Native, non-Hispanic/Latino; 6% Hispanic/Latino; 17% Black or African American, non-Hispanic/Latino; 13% Asian, non-Hispanic/Latino; 0.1% Native Hawaiian or other Pacific Islander, non-Hispanic/Latino; 2% international. 9% 25 or older, 15% live on campus, 3% transferred in. Retention: 74% of full-time freshmen returned the follow-

ing year. Academic areas with the most degrees conferred: business/marketing; psychology; family and consumer sciences. Calendar: semesters. Adult/continuing education programs. ROTC: Army (c), Air Force (c).
Entrance Requirements: Options: electronic application, early admission, deferred admission. Required: high school transcript, SAT or ACT. Entrance: moderately difficult. Application deadline: rolling. Notification: continuous.
Collegiate Environment: Orientation program. Campus security: late night transport-escort service, part-time trained security personnel.

■ **PENN STATE DUBOIS**
1 College Pl.
Dubois, PA 15801
Tel: (814)375-4700; Free: 800-346-7627
E-mail: duboisinfo@psi.edu
Web Site: www.ds.psu.edu
Description: State-related, primarily 2-year, coed. Part of Pennsylvania State University. Awards certificates, transfer associate, terminal associate, and bachelor's degrees. Founded 1935. Setting: small town campus. Total enrollment: 585. Faculty: 54 (38 full-time, 16 part-time). Student-undergrad faculty ratio is 12:1. 465 applied, 84% were admitted. 11% from top 10% of their high school class, 30% from top quarter, 62% from top half. Full-time: 464 students, 34% women, 66% men. Part-time: 121 students, 55% women, 45% men. 3% from out-of-state. 2% Hispanic/Latino; 2% Black or African American, non-Hispanic/Latino; 2% Asian, non-Hispanic/Latino; 1% international. 17% 25 or older, 4% transferred in. Retention: 80% of full-time freshmen returned the following year. Academic areas with the most degrees conferred: family and consumer sciences; business/marketing; engineering. Calendar: semesters. External degree program, adult/continuing education programs.
Entrance Requirements: Options: electronic application, early admission, deferred admission. Required: high school transcript, SAT or ACT. Recommended: essay. Required for some: interview. Entrance: moderately difficult. Application deadline: rolling. Notification: continuous.
Collegiate Environment: Orientation program.

■ **PENN STATE ERIE, THE BEHREND COLLEGE**
4701 College Dr.
Erie, PA 16563
Tel: (814)898-6000; Free: 866-374-3378
E-mail: behrend.admissions@psu.edu
Web Site: www.psbehrend.psu.edu
Description: State-related, comprehensive, coed. Part of Pennsylvania State University. Awards associate, bachelor's, and master's degrees. Founded 1948. Setting: 725-acre suburban campus. Total enrollment: 4,502. Faculty: 339 (271 full-time, 68 part-time). Student-undergrad faculty ratio is 15:1. 4,076 applied, 89% were admitted. 18% from top 10% of their high school class, 41% from top quarter, 76% from top half. Full-time: 4,138 students, 34% women, 66% men. Part-time: 207 students, 29% women, 71% men. 9% from out-of-state. 0.1% American Indian or Alaska Native, non-Hispanic/Latino; 3% Hispanic/Latino; 3% Black or African American, non-Hispanic/Latino; 3% Asian, non-Hispanic/Latino; 0.1% Native Hawaiian or other Pacific Islander, non-Hispanic/Latino; 9% international. 7% 25 or older, 37% live on campus, 2% transferred in. Retention: 84% of full-time freshmen returned the following year. Academic areas with the most degrees conferred: business/marketing; engineering; psychology. Calendar: semesters. Part-time degree program, adult/continuing education programs. ROTC: Army (c).
Entrance Requirements: Options: electronic application, early admission, deferred admission, international baccalaureate accepted. Required: high school transcript, SAT or ACT. Recommended: essay. Required for some: interview. Entrance: very difficult. Application deadline: rolling. Notification: continuous.
Collegiate Environment: Orientation program. Campus security: 24-hour emergency response devices and patrols, student patrols, late night transport-escort service, controlled dormitory access. John M. Lilley Library.

■ **PENN STATE FAYETTE, THE EBERLY CAMPUS**
2201 University Dr.
Lemont Furnace, PA 15456
Tel: (724)430-4100; Free: 877-568-4130
Fax: (724)430-4184
E-mail: feadm@psu.edu
Web Site: www.fe.psu.edu
Description: State-related, primarily 2-year, coed. Part of Pennsylvania

State University. Awards certificates, transfer associate, terminal associate, and bachelor's degrees. Founded 1934. Setting: small town campus. Total enrollment: 652. Faculty: 69 (39 full-time, 30 part-time). Student-undergrad faculty ratio is 12:1. 728 applied, 82% were admitted. 9% from top 10% of their high school class, 30% from top quarter, 68% from top half. Full-time: 589 students, 57% women, 43% men. Part-time: 63 students, 57% women, 43% men. 5% from out-of-state. 0.3% American Indian or Alaska Native, non-Hispanic/Latino; 3% Hispanic/Latino; 4% Black or African American, non-Hispanic/Latino; 0.8% Asian, non-Hispanic/Latino; 0.2% Native Hawaiian or other Pacific Islander, non-Hispanic/Latino; 1% international. 13% 25 or older, 5% transferred in. Retention: 78% of full-time freshmen returned the following year. Academic areas with the most degrees conferred: health professions and related sciences; business/marketing; family and consumer sciences. Calendar: semesters. External degree program, adult/continuing education programs.

Entrance Requirements: Options: electronic application, early admission, deferred admission. Required: high school transcript, SAT or ACT. Recommended: essay. Required for some: interview. Entrance: moderately difficult. Application deadline: rolling. Notification: continuous.

Collegiate Environment: Orientation program. Campus security: student patrols, 8-hour patrols by trained security personnel.

■ **PENN STATE GREATER ALLEGHENY**
4000 University Dr.
McKeesport, PA 15132
Tel: (412)675-9000
E-mail: psuga@psu.edu
Web Site: www.ga.psu.edu
Description: State-related, comprehensive, coed. Part of Pennsylvania State University. Awards associate and bachelor's degrees. Founded 1947. Setting: small town campus. Total enrollment: 497. Faculty: 65 (34 full-time, 31 part-time). Student-undergrad faculty ratio is 11:1. 579 applied, 82% were admitted. 9% from top 10% of their high school class, 33% from top quarter, 75% from top half. Full-time: 453 students, 36% women, 64% men. Part-time: 44 students, 39% women, 61% men. 7% from out-of-state. 4% Hispanic/Latino; 19% Black or African American, non-Hispanic/Latino; 6% Asian, non-Hispanic/Latino; 3% international. 12% 25 or older, 20% live on campus, 5% transferred in. Retention: 73% of full-time freshmen returned the following year. Academic areas with the most degrees conferred: business/marketing; psychology; communication/journalism. Calendar: semesters. Adult/continuing education programs.

Entrance Requirements: Options: electronic application, early admission, deferred admission. Required: high school transcript, SAT or ACT. Entrance: moderately difficult. Application deadline: rolling. Notification: continuous.

Collegiate Environment: Orientation program. Campus security: 24-hour patrols, controlled dormitory access.

■ **PENN STATE HARRISBURG**
777 W Harrisburg Pke.
Middletown, PA 17057
Tel: (717)948-6000; Free: 800-222-2056
E-mail: hbgadmit@psu.edu
Web Site: www.harrisburg.psu.edu
Description: State-related, comprehensive, coed. Part of Pennsylvania State University. Awards associate, bachelor's, master's, and doctoral degrees. Founded 1966. Setting: small town campus. Total enrollment: 5,077. Faculty: 372 (226 full-time, 146 part-time). Student-undergrad faculty ratio is 16:1. 5,574 applied, 84% were admitted. 11% from top 10% of their high school class, 35% from top quarter, 72% from top half. Full-time: 3,960 students, 39% women, 61% men. Part-time: 326 students, 39% women, 61% men. 17% from out-of-state. 0.1% American Indian or Alaska Native, non-Hispanic/Latino; 7% Hispanic/Latino; 9% Black or African American, non-Hispanic/Latino; 9% Asian, non-Hispanic/Latino; 0.1% Native Hawaiian or other Pacific Islander, non-Hispanic/Latino; 15% international. 12% 25 or older, 10% live on campus, 6% transferred in. Retention: 88% of full-time freshmen returned the following year. Academic areas with the most degrees conferred: engineering; business/marketing; computer and information sciences. Calendar: semesters. Part-time degree program, adult/continuing education programs. ROTC: Army (c).

Entrance Requirements: Options: electronic application, early admission, deferred admission, international baccalaureate accepted. Required: high school transcript, SAT or ACT. Recommended: essay. Required for some: interview. Entrance: very difficult. Application deadline: rolling. Notification: continuous.

Collegiate Environment: Orientation program. Campus security: 24-hour emergency response devices and patrols, student patrols, late night transport-escort service, controlled dormitory access. Penn State Harrisburg Library.

■ **PENN STATE HAZLETON**
76 University Dr.
Hazleton, PA 18202
Tel: (570)450-3000; Free: 800-279-8495
E-mail: admissions-hn@psu.edu
Web Site: www.hn.psu.edu
Description: State-related, 4-year, coed. Part of Pennsylvania State University. Awards associate and bachelor's degrees. Founded 1934. Setting: small town campus. Total enrollment: 755. Faculty: 62 (45 full-time, 17 part-time). Student-undergrad faculty ratio is 14:1. 602 applied, 94% were admitted. 13% from top 10% of their high school class, 39% from top quarter, 72% from top half. Full-time: 656 students, 50% women, 50% men. Part-time: 99 students, 42% women, 58% men. 14% from out-of-state. 0.1% American Indian or Alaska Native, non-Hispanic/Latino; 17% Hispanic/Latino; 9% Black or African American, non-Hispanic/Latino; 3% Asian, non-Hispanic/Latino; 0.3% Native Hawaiian or other Pacific Islander, non-Hispanic/Latino; 0.3% international. 9% 25 or older, 27% live on campus, 4% transferred in. Retention: 83% of full-time freshmen returned the following year. Academic areas with the most degrees conferred: business/marketing; health professions and related sciences; psychology. Calendar: semesters. Adult/continuing education programs. ROTC: Air Force (c).

Entrance Requirements: Options: electronic application, early admission, deferred admission. Required: high school transcript, SAT or ACT. Recommended: essay. Required for some: interview. Entrance: moderately difficult. Application deadline: rolling. Notification: continuous.

Collegiate Environment: Orientation program. Campus security: 24-hour patrols, late night transport-escort service, controlled dormitory access.

■ **PENN STATE LEHIGH VALLEY**
2809 Saucon Valley Rd.
Center Valley, PA 18034
Tel: (610)285-5000
E-mail: admissions-lv@psu.edu
Web Site: www.lv.psu.edu
Description: State-related, 4-year, coed. Part of Pennsylvania State University. Awards associate and bachelor's degrees (enrollment figures include students enrolled at The Graduate School at Penn State who are taking courses at this location). Founded 1912. Setting: rural campus. Total enrollment: 919. Faculty: 85 (42 full-time, 43 part-time). Student-undergrad faculty ratio is 14:1. 1,262 applied, 85% were admitted. 11% from top 10% of their high school class, 37% from top quarter, 74% from top half. Full-time: 739 students, 41% women, 59% men. Part-time: 161 students, 54% women, 46% men. 7% from out-of-state. 0.2% American Indian or Alaska Native, non-Hispanic/Latino; 15% Hispanic/Latino; 6% Black or African American, non-Hispanic/Latino; 9% Asian, non-Hispanic/Latino; 3% international. 14% 25 or older, 6% transferred in. Retention: 81% of full-time freshmen returned the following year. Academic areas with the most degrees conferred: business/marketing; psychology; health professions and related sciences. Calendar: semesters. Part-time degree program, external degree program, adult/continuing education programs. ROTC: Army (c).

Entrance Requirements: Options: electronic application, early admission, deferred admission. Required: high school transcript, SAT or ACT. Entrance: moderately difficult.

Collegiate Environment: Orientation program.

■ **PENN STATE MONT ALTO**
1 Campus Dr.
Mont Alto, PA 17237
Tel: (717)749-6000; Free: 800-392-6173
E-mail: psuma@psu.edu
Web Site: www.ma.psu.edu
Description: State-related, primarily 2-year, coed. Part of Pennsylvania State University. Awards certificates, transfer associate, terminal associate, and bachelor's degrees. Founded 1929. Setting: small town campus. Total enrollment: 917. Faculty: 95 (57 full-time, 38 part-time). Student-undergrad faculty ratio is 11:1. 711 applied, 78% were admitted. 11% from top 10% of their high school class, 39% from top quarter, 75% from top half. Full-time: 653 students, 52% women, 48% men. Part-time: 264 students, 59% women, 41% men. 15% from out-of-state. 8% Hispanic/Latino; 5% Black or African

American, non-Hispanic/Latino; 3% Asian, non-Hispanic/Latino; 0.5% international. 17% 25 or older, 24% live on campus, 3% transferred in. Retention: 83% of full-time freshmen returned the following year. Academic areas with the most degrees conferred: family and consumer sciences; business/marketing; computer and information sciences. Calendar: semesters. External degree program, adult/continuing education programs. ROTC: Army (c).

Entrance Requirements: Options: electronic application, early admission, deferred admission. Required: high school transcript, SAT or ACT. Recommended: essay. Required for some: interview. Entrance: moderately difficult. Application deadline: rolling. Notification: continuous.

Collegiate Environment: Orientation program. Campus security: 24-hour patrols, controlled dormitory access.

■ PENN STATE NEW KENSINGTON
3550 Seventh St. Rd.
New Kensington, PA 15068
Tel: (724)334-5466; Free: 888-968-7297
Fax: (724)334-6111
E-mail: nkadmissions@psu.edu
Web Site: www.nk.psu.edu

Description: State-related, 4-year, coed. Part of Pennsylvania State University. Awards associate and bachelor's degrees. Founded 1958. Setting: small town campus. Total enrollment: 595. Faculty: 68 (37 full-time, 31 part-time). Student-undergrad faculty ratio is 11:1. 555 applied, 77% were admitted. 9% from top 10% of their high school class, 31% from top quarter, 68% from top half. Full-time: 484 students, 35% women, 65% men. Part-time: 111 students, 63% women, 37% men. 3% from out-of-state. 3% Hispanic/Latino; 3% Black or African American, non-Hispanic/Latino; 1% Asian, non-Hispanic/Latino; 0.3% international. 15% 25 or older, 6% transferred in. Retention: 78% of full-time freshmen returned the following year. Academic areas with the most degrees conferred: health professions and related sciences; computer and information sciences; homeland security, law enforcement, firefighting, and protective services. Calendar: semesters. External degree program, adult/continuing education programs. ROTC: Air Force (c).

Entrance Requirements: Options: electronic application, early admission, deferred admission. Required: high school transcript, SAT or ACT. Recommended: essay. Required for some: interview. Entrance: moderately difficult. Application deadline: rolling. Notification: continuous.

Collegiate Environment: Orientation program. Campus security: part-time trained security personnel.

■ PENN STATE SCHUYLKILL
200 University Dr.
Schuylkill Haven, PA 17972
Tel: (570)385-6000
E-mail: sl-admissions@psu.edu
Web Site: www.sl.psu.edu

Description: State-related, 4-year, coed. Part of Pennsylvania State University. Awards associate and bachelor's degrees (bachelor's degree programs completed at the Harrisburg campus). Founded 1934. Setting: small town campus. Total enrollment: 732. Faculty: 60 (34 full-time, 26 part-time). Student-undergrad faculty ratio is 15:1. 642 applied, 76% were admitted. 7% from top 10% of their high school class, 26% from top quarter, 58% from top half. Full-time: 595 students, 54% women, 46% men. Part-time: 137 students, 75% women, 25% men. 12% from out-of-state. 0.1% American Indian or Alaska Native, non-Hispanic/Latino; 8% Hispanic/Latino; 14% Black or African American, non-Hispanic/Latino; 2% Asian, non-Hispanic/Latino; 0.1% Native Hawaiian or other Pacific Islander, non-Hispanic/Latino; 0.9% international. 14% 25 or older, 24% live on campus, 5% transferred in. Retention: 83% of full-time freshmen returned the following year. Academic areas with the most degrees conferred: health professions and related sciences; homeland security, law enforcement, firefighting, and protective services; psychology. Calendar: semesters. External degree program, adult/continuing education programs.

Entrance Requirements: Options: electronic application, early admission, deferred admission. Required: high school transcript, SAT or ACT. Entrance: moderately difficult. Application deadline: rolling. Notification: continuous.

Collegiate Environment: Orientation program. Campus security: 24-hour patrols, controlled dormitory access.

■ PENN STATE SHENANGO
147 Shenango Ave.
Sharon, PA 16146
Tel: (724)983-2803
Fax: (724)983-2820
E-mail: psushenango@psu.edu
Web Site: www.shenango.psu.edu

Description: State-related, 4-year, coed. Part of Pennsylvania State University. Awards associate and bachelor's degrees. Founded 1965. Setting: small town campus. Total enrollment: 490. Faculty: 47 (26 full-time, 21 part-time). Student-undergrad faculty ratio is 10:1. 276 applied, 74% were admitted. 4% from top 10% of their high school class, 26% from top quarter, 57% from top half. Full-time: 241 students, 66% women, 34% men. Part-time: 249 students, 78% women, 22% men. 21% from out-of-state. 3% Hispanic/Latino; 9% Black or African American, non-Hispanic/Latino; 0.9% Asian, non-Hispanic/Latino. 40% 25 or older, 7% transferred in. Retention: 55% of full-time freshmen returned the following year. Academic areas with the most degrees conferred: health professions and related sciences; family and consumer sciences; homeland security, law enforcement, firefighting, and protective services; business/marketing. Calendar: semesters. External degree program, adult/continuing education programs.

Entrance Requirements: Options: electronic application, early admission, deferred admission. Required: high school transcript, SAT or ACT. Entrance: moderately difficult. Application deadline: rolling. Notification: continuous.

Collegiate Environment: Orientation program.

■ PENN STATE UNIVERSITY PARK
201 Old Main
University Park, PA 16802
Tel: (814)865-4700
E-mail: admissions@psu.edu
Web Site: www.psu.edu

Description: State-related, university, coed. Part of The Pennsylvania State University. Awards associate, bachelor's, master's, and doctoral degrees. Founded 1855. Setting: 7,958-acre small town campus with easy access to Harrisburg. System endowment: $2.8 billion. Total enrollment: 47,119. Faculty: 3,066 (2,679 full-time, 387 part-time). Student-undergrad faculty ratio is 16:1. 56,114 applied, 50% were admitted. 35% from top 10% of their high school class, 73% from top quarter, 96% from top half. Full-time: 39,785 students, 47% women, 53% men. Part-time: 1,050 students, 39% women, 61% men. Students come from 55 states and territories, 133 other countries, 34% from out-of-state. 0.1% American Indian or Alaska Native, non-Hispanic/Latino; 7% Hispanic/Latino; 4% Black or African American, non-Hispanic/Latino; 6% Asian, non-Hispanic/Latino; 0.1% Native Hawaiian or other Pacific Islander, non-Hispanic/Latino; 12% international. 2% 25 or older, 35% live on campus, 1% transferred in. Retention: 93% of full-time freshmen returned the following year. Academic areas with the most degrees conferred: engineering; business/marketing; computer and information sciences. Core. Calendar: semesters. Academic remediation for entering students, ESL program, services for LD students, advanced placement, accelerated degree program, self-designed majors, freshman honors college, honors program, independent study, distance learning, double major, summer session for credit, part-time degree program, external degree program, adult/continuing education programs, co-op programs and internships, graduate courses open to undergrads. Off campus study at www.psu.edu/dept/enrmgmt/artic_agrmnts.html. Study abroad program. ROTC: Army, Naval, Air Force.

Entrance Requirements: Options: electronic application, early admission, deferred admission, international baccalaureate accepted. Required: high school transcript, SAT or ACT. Recommended: essay. Entrance: very difficult. Application deadline: rolling. Notification: continuous. Transfer credits accepted: Yes. Applicants placed on waiting list: 2,168. Wait-listed applicants offered admission: 0.

Collegiate Environment: Orientation program. Drama-theater group, choral group, marching band, student-run newspaper, radio station. Social organizations: 986 open to all; national fraternities, national sororities, local fraternities; 17% of eligible men and 20% of eligible women are members. Major annual events: Homecoming, Four Diamonds Dance Marathon, Parent's Weekend. Student services: legal services, health clinic, personal-psychological counseling, women's center. Campus security: 24-hour emergency response devices and patrols, student patrols, late night transport-escort service, controlled dormitory access. Pattee and Paterno Libraries plus 4 others. Books: 5 million (physical), 2.1 million (digital/electronic); Serial titles: 84,993 (physical), 160,000 (digital/electronic); Databases: 828. Weekly public service hours: 148; study areas open 24 hours, 5-7 days a week; students can reserve study rooms. 3,154 computers available on campus for general student use. A campuswide network can be accessed from student residence rooms and from off campus. Students can access the following: online class registration. Staffed computer lab on campus (open 24 hours a day) provides training in use of computers, software, and the Internet.

■ **PENN STATE WILKES-BARRE**
Old Rte. 115
Lehman, PA 18627
Tel: (570)675-2171
E-mail: wbadmissions@psu.edu
Web Site: www.wb.psu.edu
Description: State-related, 4-year, coed. Part of Pennsylvania State University. Awards associate and bachelor's degrees (enrollment figures include students enrolled at The Graduate School at Penn State who are taking courses at this location). Founded 1916. Setting: rural campus. Total enrollment: 467. Faculty: 51 (32 full-time, 19 part-time). Student-undergrad faculty ratio is 11:1. 433 applied, 82% were admitted. 11% from top 10% of their high school class, 32% from top quarter, 76% from top half. Full-time: 387 students, 27% women, 73% men. Part-time: 69 students, 58% women, 42% men. 7% from out-of-state. 0.2% American Indian or Alaska Native, non-Hispanic/Latino; 5% Hispanic/Latino; 6% Black or African American, non-Hispanic/Latino; 1% Asian, non-Hispanic/Latino; 0.2% Native Hawaiian or other Pacific Islander, non-Hispanic/Latino; 0.2% international. 9% 25 or older, 5% transferred in. Retention: 81% of full-time freshmen returned the following year. Academic areas with the most degrees conferred: homeland security, law enforcement, firefighting, and protective services; engineering; computer and information sciences. Calendar: semesters. External degree program, adult/continuing education programs. ROTC: Army (c), Air Force (c).
Entrance Requirements: Options: electronic application, early admission, deferred admission. Required: high school transcript, SAT or ACT. Entrance: moderately difficult. Application deadline: rolling. Notification: continuous.
Collegiate Environment: Orientation program.

■ **PENN STATE WORTHINGTON SCRANTON**
120 Ridge View Dr.
Dunmore, PA 18512
Tel: (570)963-2500
Fax: (570)963-2535
E-mail: wsadmissions@psu.edu
Web Site: www.sn.psu.edu
Description: State-related, 4-year, coed. Part of Pennsylvania State University. Awards associate and bachelor's degrees. Founded 1923. Setting: small town campus. Total enrollment: 1,029. Faculty: 85 (50 full-time, 35 part-time). Student-undergrad faculty ratio is 16:1. 883 applied, 78% were admitted. 5% from top 10% of their high school class, 30% from top quarter, 67% from top half. Full-time: 904 students, 47% women, 53% men. Part-time: 125 students, 61% women, 39% men. 5% from out-of-state. 7% Hispanic/Latino; 4% Black or African American, non-Hispanic/Latino; 7% Asian, non-Hispanic/Latino; 0.6% international. 15% 25 or older, 3% transferred in. Retention: 77% of full-time freshmen returned the following year. Academic areas with the most degrees conferred: business/marketing; health professions and related sciences; family and consumer sciences. Calendar: semesters. External degree program, adult/continuing education programs. ROTC: Army (c), Air Force (c).
Entrance Requirements: Options: electronic application, early admission, deferred admission. Required: high school transcript, SAT or ACT. Recommended: essay. Required for some: interview. Entrance: moderately difficult. Application deadline: rolling. Notification: continuous.
Collegiate Environment: Orientation program.

■ **PENN STATE YORK**
1031 Edgecomb Ave.
York, PA 17403
Tel: (717)771-4000; Free: 800-778-6227
Fax: (717)771-4062
E-mail: ykadmission@psu.edu
Web Site: www.york.psu.edu
Description: State-related, comprehensive, coed. Part of Pennsylvania State University. Awards associate, bachelor's, and master's degrees (also offers up to 2 years of most bachelor's degree programs offered at University Park campus). Founded 1926. Setting: suburban campus. Total enrollment: 983. Faculty: 87 (48 full-time, 39 part-time). Student-undergrad faculty ratio is 14:1. 1,474 applied, 82% were admitted. 11% from top 10% of their high

school class, 32% from top quarter, 74% from top half. Full-time: 793 students, 39% women, 61% men. Part-time: 174 students, 51% women, 49% men. 9% from out-of-state. 7% Hispanic/Latino; 6% Black or African American, non-Hispanic/Latino; 6% Asian, non-Hispanic/Latino; 0.1% Native Hawaiian or other Pacific Islander, non-Hispanic/Latino; 20% international. 14% 25 or older, 4% transferred in. Retention: 77% of full-time freshmen returned the following year. Academic areas with the most degrees conferred: business/marketing; family and consumer sciences; computer and information sciences. Calendar: semesters. Adult/continuing education programs.
Entrance Requirements: Options: electronic application, early admission, deferred admission. Required: high school transcript, SAT or ACT. Entrance: moderately difficult. Application deadline: rolling. Notification: continuous.
Collegiate Environment: Orientation program.

■ **PENNCO TECH**
3815 Otter St.
Bristol, PA 19007-3696
Tel: (215)824-3200; Free: 800-575-9399
Web Site: www.penncotech.edu
Description: Proprietary, 2-year, coed. Part of Pennco Institutes, Inc. Awards certificates, diplomas, and terminal associate degrees. Founded 1961. Setting: 7-acre suburban campus with easy access to Philadelphia. Educational spending for the previous fiscal year: $8200 per student. Total enrollment: 400. Faculty: 40 (30 full-time, 10 part-time). Student-undergrad faculty ratio is 18:1. 229 applied. Full-time: 245 students, 22% women, 78% men. Part-time: 155 students, 16% women, 84% men. Students come from 6 states and territories, 3% from out-of-state. 40% 25 or older, 3% live on campus, 1% transferred in. Retention: 78% of full-time freshmen returned the following year. Calendar: modular. Academic remediation for entering students, advanced placement, double major, adult/continuing education programs.
Entrance Requirements: Required: high school transcript, minimum 2 high school GPA, interview, interview and school visit, exam at campus. Required for some: essay. Entrance: minimally difficult. Application deadline: rolling. Transfer credits accepted: Yes.
Collegiate Environment: Orientation program. Major annual events: Toys for Tots, Food Drives, Coat Drives. Campus security: 24-hour emergency response devices, controlled dormitory access. Resource Center. Operations spending for the previous fiscal year: $5000. 14 computers available on campus for general student use. Staffed computer lab on campus provides training in use of computers, software, and the Internet.

■ **PENNSYLVANIA ACADEMY OF THE FINE ARTS**
128 N Broad St.
Philadelphia, PA 19102
Tel: (215)972-7600
E-mail: ptran@pafa.edu
Web Site: www.pafa.edu
Description: Independent, comprehensive, coed. Awards bachelor's and master's degrees. Founded 1805. Setting: urban campus. Total enrollment: 74. Faculty: 63 (18 full-time, 45 part-time). 173 applied, 90% were admitted. Calendar: semesters.
Entrance Requirements: Option: electronic application. Required: essay, minimum 3 high school GPA, 2 recommendations, portfolio of work. Required for some: TOEFL (suggested 600 paper based, 250 computer based, 100 iBT) or IELTS (suggested 6.0 paper based) for international students. Application deadlines: rolling for nonresidents, 12/1 for early decision, 12/1 for early action. Notification: continuous for nonresidents.
Costs Per Year: Application fee: $60. Tuition: $38,926 full-time, $1622 per credit part-time. Mandatory fees: $1450 full-time. College room only: $12,010.
Collegiate Environment: Campus security: 24-hour patrols. 60 college housing spaces available. Option: coed housing available. Arcadia Fine Arts Library. 75 computers available on campus for general student use.

■ **PENNSYLVANIA COLLEGE OF ART & DESIGN**
204 N Prince St.
Lancaster, PA 17608-0059
Tel: (717)396-7833; Free: 800-689-0379
Fax: (717)396-1339
Web Site: www.pcad.edu
Description: Independent, 4-year, coed. Awards bachelor's degrees. Founded 1982. Setting: urban campus with easy access to Philadelphia,

Baltimore. Total enrollment: 251. Faculty: 51 (10 full-time, 41 part-time). Student-undergrad faculty ratio is 13:1. 301 applied, 44% were admitted. Full-time: 243 students, 69% women, 31% men. Part-time: 8 students, 25% women, 75% men. 23% from out-of-state. 0.8% American Indian or Alaska Native, non-Hispanic/Latino; 4% Hispanic/Latino; 6% Black or African American, non-Hispanic/Latino; 5% Asian, non-Hispanic/Latino; 0.4% Native Hawaiian or other Pacific Islander, non-Hispanic/Latino. 4% 25 or older. Retention: 59% of full-time freshmen returned the following year. Academic area with the most degrees conferred: visual and performing arts. Core. Calendar: semesters. Advanced placement, internships.

Entrance Requirements: Options: electronic application, deferred admission. Required: essay, high school transcript, minimum 2.5 high school GPA, portfolio. Recommended: interview. Required for some: 2 recommendations. Entrance: moderately difficult. Application deadline: rolling. Notification: continuous. Transfer credits accepted: Yes.

Costs Per Year: Application fee: $40. Tuition: $25,000 full-time, $1042 per credit part-time. Mandatory fees: $1600 full-time.

Collegiate Environment: Orientation program. Social organizations: 2 open to all. Most popular organizations: Student Council, Anime Club, Student AIGA, Society of Illustrators - Student Group. Major annual events: Halloween Party, Thanksgiving Feast, Spring Picnic. Campus security: late night transport-escort service, trained evening/weekend security personnel. College housing not available. Pennsylvania College of Art & Design Library. 90 computers available on campus for general student use. A computer is required for all students. A campuswide network can be accessed. Students can access the following: online class registration. Staffed computer lab on campus provides training in use of computers and the Internet.

■ PENNSYLVANIA COLLEGE OF HEALTH SCIENCES
850 Greenfield Rd.
Lancaster, PA 17601
Tel: (717)544-4912; Free: 800-622-5443
Fax: (717)290-5970
Web Site: www.pacollege.edu

Description: Independent, comprehensive, coed. Awards associate, bachelor's, master's, and doctoral degrees. Founded 1903. Setting: 25-acre suburban campus with easy access to Harrisburg. Endowment: $5 million. Educational spending for the previous fiscal year: $28,661 per student. Total enrollment: 1,793. Faculty: 213 (74 full-time, 139 part-time). Student-undergrad faculty ratio is 12:1. 404 applied, 67% were admitted. Full-time: 527 students, 86% women, 14% men. Part-time: 1,159 students, 86% women, 14% men. Students come from 16 states and territories, 3% from out-of-state. 0.1% American Indian or Alaska Native, non-Hispanic/Latino; 8% Hispanic/Latino; 4% Black or African American, non-Hispanic/Latino; 3% Asian, non-Hispanic/Latino. 57% 25 or older, 20% transferred in. Retention: 64% of full-time freshmen returned the following year. Academic area with the most degrees conferred: health professions and related sciences. Core. Calendar: semesters. Services for LD students, advanced placement, accelerated degree program, distance learning, summer session for credit, part-time degree program, adult/continuing education programs.

Entrance Requirements: Options: electronic application, deferred admission. Required: minimum 3 high school GPA, 2 recommendations, transcripts of all institutions attended. Required for some: essay, SAT or ACT. Entrance: moderately difficult. Application deadline: 2/1. Notification: continuous. SAT Reasoning Test deadline: 2/1. SAT Subject Test deadline: 2/1. Transfer credits accepted: Yes.

Collegiate Environment: Orientation program. Student services: health clinic, personal-psychological counseling. Campus security: 24-hour emergency response devices and patrols, late night transport-escort service. Health Sciences Library. Books: 1,185 (physical), 598 (digital/electronic); Serial titles: 93 (physical), 13,436 (digital/electronic); Databases: 43. Students can reserve study rooms. Operations spending for the previous fiscal year: $694,923. 200 computers available on campus for general student use. A campuswide network can be accessed. Students can access the following: online class registration. Staffed computer lab on campus provides training in use of computers and software.

■ PENNSYLVANIA COLLEGE OF TECHNOLOGY
One College Ave.
Williamsport, PA 17701-5778
Tel: (570)326-3761; Free: 800-367-9222
Fax: (570)321-5551
E-mail: admissions@pct.edu
Web Site: www.pct.edu

Description: State-related, 4-year, coed. Administratively affiliated with The Pennsylvania State University. Awards associate and bachelor's degrees. Founded 1965. Setting: 994-acre suburban campus. Total enrollment: 5,382. Faculty: 448 (289 full-time, 159 part-time). Student-undergrad faculty ratio is 14:1. 6,115 applied, 79% were admitted. 4% from top 10% of their high school class, 16% from top quarter, 48% from top half. Full-time: 4,577 students, 31% women, 69% men. Part-time: 805 students, 61% women, 39% men. Students come from 27 states and territories, 12 other countries, 11% from out-of-state. 0.2% American Indian or Alaska Native, non-Hispanic/Latino; 4% Hispanic/Latino; 3% Black or African American, non-Hispanic/Latino; 1% Asian, non-Hispanic/Latino; 0.1% Native Hawaiian or other Pacific Islander, non-Hispanic/Latino; 0.6% international. 19% 25 or older, 31% live on campus, 8% transferred in. Retention: 75% of full-time freshmen returned the following year. Academic areas with the most degrees conferred: engineering technologies; health professions and related sciences; business/marketing. Core. Calendar: semesters. Academic remediation for entering students, ESL program, services for LD students, advanced placement, self-designed majors, independent study, distance learning, summer session for credit, part-time degree program, co-op programs and internships. Off campus study at Lycoming College, The Pennsylvania State University, Bucknell University (Army ROTC). Study abroad program. ROTC: Army.

Entrance Requirements: Open admission. Options: electronic application, early admission, deferred admission. Required for some: high school transcript, college transcripts for transfers, SAT. Entrance: noncompetitive. Application deadline: 7/1. Transfer credits accepted: Yes.

Costs Per Year: Application fee: $0. State resident tuition: $16,740 full-time, $475 per credit hour part-time. Nonresident tuition: $23,880 full-time, $713 per credit hour part-time. Mandatory fees: $2490 full-time, $83 per credit hour part-time. Full-time tuition and fees vary according to course load and program. Part-time tuition and fees vary according to course load and program. College room and board: $11,544. College room only: $6586. Room and board charges vary according to board plan and housing facility.

Collegiate Environment: Orientation program. Social organizations: 56 open to all; national fraternities. Most popular organizations: Student Government Association, Residence Hall Association, Wildcats Event Board, Association of Computing Machinery, Campus Ministry International. Major annual events: Career Expo/Career Fairs, Homecoming Events, Parent and Family Weekend. Student services: health clinic, personal-psychological counseling. Campus security: 24-hour emergency response devices and patrols, late night transport-escort service, controlled dormitory access. Penn College Madigan Library plus 1 other. Books: 89,117 (physical), 27,388 (digital/electronic); Serial titles: 9,342 (physical), 88,304 (digital/electronic); Databases: 169. Weekly public service hours: 86; students can reserve study rooms. 1,800 computers available on campus for general student use. A campuswide network can be accessed from student residence rooms and from off campus. Students can access the following: online class registration. Staffed computer lab on campus provides training in use of computers, software, and the Internet.

Community Environment: The main campus is in Williamsport, a city known internationally as the home of Little League Baseball. Williamsport (population 30,100) is the seat of Lycoming County (population 117,600); it offers the advantages of a city situated in a rural environment. The surrounding area is an outdoor-lovers' paradise, with hunting, fishing, hiking, camping, backpacking, and more, just minutes from downtown.

■ PENNSYLVANIA HIGHLANDS COMMUNITY COLLEGE
101 Community College Way
Johnstown, PA 15904
Tel: (814)262-6400; Free: 888-385-7325
E-mail: jmaul@pennhighlands.edu
Web Site: www.pennhighlands.edu

Description: State and locally supported, 2-year, coed. Awards certificates, diplomas, transfer associate, and terminal associate degrees. Founded 1994. Setting: small town campus. Total enrollment: 2,784. Faculty: 108 (27 full-time, 81 part-time). Student-undergrad faculty ratio is 18:1. 579 applied, 100% were admitted. Students come from 3 states and territories, 1% from out-of-state. 0.1% American Indian or Alaska Native, non-Hispanic/Latino; 2% Hispanic/Latino; 5% Black or African American, non-Hispanic/Latino; 0.7% Asian, non-Hispanic/Latino. 18% 25 or older. Retention: 48% of full-time freshmen returned the following year. Core. Calendar: semesters. Academic remediation for entering students, services for LD students, advanced placement, independent study, distance learning, summer session for credit, part-time degree program, adult/continuing education programs, co-op programs and internships.

Entrance Requirements: Open admission. Option: electronic application. Entrance: noncompetitive. Application deadline: rolling. Notification: continuous. Transfer credits accepted: Yes.

Costs Per Year: Area resident tuition: $3990 full-time, $133 per credit hour part-time. State resident tuition: $6300 full-time, $210 per credit hour part-time. Nonresident tuition: $9630 full-time, $321 per credit hour part-time. Mandatory fees: $1860 full-time, $62 per credit hour part-time. Full-time tuition and fees vary according to program. Part-time tuition and fees vary according to course load and program.

Collegiate Environment: Orientation program. Social organizations: 15 open to all. Most popular organizations: Student Senate Organization, Phi Theta Kappa Honor Society (PTK), National Society of Leadership and Success Organization (Sigma Alpha Pi), Black Bear Bowling Club, Anime Art Style Club. Major annual events: Campus Speaker Series, Homecoming, Haunted Week. Student services: personal-psychological counseling. Mangarella Library. Books: 1,274 (physical), 2,192 (digital/electronic); Databases: 35.

■ PENNSYLVANIA INSTITUTE OF HEALTH AND TECHNOLOGY
1015 Mount Braddock Rd.
Mount Braddock, PA 15465
Tel: (724)437-4600
Web Site: www.piht.edu
Description: Proprietary, 2-year, coed. Awards diplomas and terminal associate degrees.

■ PENNSYLVANIA INSTITUTE OF TECHNOLOGY
800 Manchester Ave.
Media, PA 19063
Tel: (610)892-1500; Free: 800-422-0025
Fax: (610)892-1510
E-mail: info@pit.edu
Web Site: www.pit.edu
Description: Independent, 2-year, coed. Awards certificates, transfer associate, and terminal associate degrees. Founded 1953. Setting: 12-acre small town campus with easy access to Philadelphia. Total enrollment: 447. Faculty: 62 (14 full-time, 48 part-time). Student-undergrad faculty ratio is 11:1. 60% 25 or older. Core. Calendar: 4 terms. Academic remediation for entering students, advanced placement, distance learning, summer session for credit, part-time degree program, adult/continuing education programs, co-op programs.
Entrance Requirements: Open admission. Options: electronic application, deferred admission. Required: high school transcript, interview. Recommended: essay. Entrance: noncompetitive. Application deadline: 10/8. Notification: continuous until 10/8. Transfer credits accepted: Yes.
Costs Per Year: Application fee: $25. Tuition: $10,260 full-time, $380 per credit hour part-time. Mandatory fees: $3105 full-time, $115 per credit hour part-time. Full-time tuition and fees vary according to course load and program. Part-time tuition and fees vary according to course load and program.
Collegiate Environment: Orientation program. Student services: personal-psychological counseling. Campus security: 24-hour emergency response devices. Pennsylvania Institute of Technology Library/Learning Resource Center plus 1 other. 400 computers available on campus for general student use. Staffed computer lab on campus.

■ PITTSBURGH CAREER INSTITUTE
421 Seventh Ave.
Pittsburgh, PA 15219-1907
Tel: (412)281-2600; Free: 800-333-6607
Fax: (412)281-0319
Web Site: www.pci.edu
Description: Proprietary, 2-year, coed. Awards terminal associate degrees. Founded 1980. Setting: urban campus. Total enrollment: 200. 44% 25 or older. Core. Calendar: continuous. Academic remediation for entering students, ESL program, services for LD students, advanced placement, accelerated degree program, adult/continuing education programs, co-op programs and internships.
Entrance Requirements: Options: electronic application, early admission, deferred admission. Required: high school transcript, interview. Recommended: SAT or ACT, SAT Subject Tests. Entrance: minimally difficult.
Collegiate Environment: Orientation program. Campus security: 24-hour emergency response devices, 14-hour security patrols Monday through Friday. Campus Library.

■ PITTSBURGH INSTITUTE OF AERONAUTICS
PO Box 10897
Pittsburgh, PA 15236-0897
Tel: (412)346-2100; Free: 800-444-1440
E-mail: admissions@pia.edu
Web Site: www.pia.edu
Description: Independent, 2-year, coed. Awards certificates, transfer associate, and terminal associate degrees. Founded 1929. Setting: suburban campus. Total enrollment: 368. Faculty: 32 (29 full-time, 3 part-time). Student-undergrad faculty ratio is 10:1. 64 applied, 100% were admitted. Full-time: 368 students, 6% women, 94% men. Students come from 19 states and territories, 26% from out-of-state. 0.8% American Indian or Alaska Native, non-Hispanic/Latino; 3% Hispanic/Latino; 6% Black or African American, non-Hispanic/Latino; 2% Asian, non-Hispanic/Latino; 0.5% Native Hawaiian or other Pacific Islander, non-Hispanic/Latino. 28% 25 or older, 8% transferred in. Core. Calendar: quarters. Academic remediation for entering students.
Entrance Requirements: Open admission. Options: electronic application, deferred admission. Required: high school transcript, PIA Math Skills Assessment. Recommended: interview. Entrance: noncompetitive. Application deadline: rolling. Notification: continuous.
Collegiate Environment: Student services: personal-psychological counseling. Technical Library. 30 computers available on campus for general student use. Staffed computer lab on campus provides training in use of computers.

■ PITTSBURGH INSTITUTE OF MORTUARY SCIENCE, INCORPORATED
5808 Baum Blvd.
Pittsburgh, PA 15206-3706
Tel: (412)362-8500
Fax: (412)362-1684
E-mail: pims5808@aol.com
Web Site: www.pims.edu
Description: Independent, 2-year, coed. Awards diplomas, transfer associate, and terminal associate degrees. Founded 1939. Setting: urban campus. Total enrollment: 193. Faculty: 24 (2 full-time, 22 part-time). Student-undergrad faculty ratio is 13:1. Full-time: 85 students, 51% women, 49% men. Part-time: 108 students, 37% women, 63% men. Students come from 12 states and territories, 1 other country, 37% from out-of-state. 53% 25 or older. Core. Calendar: trimesters. Academic remediation for entering students, services for LD students, distance learning, part-time degree program, adult/continuing education programs.
Entrance Requirements: Open admission. Options: electronic application, international baccalaureate accepted. Required: essay, high school transcript, minimum 2 high school GPA, 2 recommendations, interview, immunizations. Entrance: noncompetitive. Application deadline: rolling. Notification: continuous.
Costs Per Year: Application fee: $50. One-time mandatory fee: $500. Comprehensive fee: $30,625 includes full-time tuition ($12,000), mandatory fees ($2425), and college room and board ($16,200). Full-time tuition and fees vary according to program. Part-time tuition: $370 per credit hour. Part-time tuition varies according to program.
Collegiate Environment: Orientation program. Campus security: 24-hour emergency response devices. William J. Musmanno Memorial Library. Weekly public service hours: 12. 10 computers available on campus for general student use. A campuswide network can be accessed from off-campus. Staffed computer lab on campus provides training in use of computers, software, and the Internet.

■ PITTSBURGH TECHNICAL COLLEGE
1111 McKee Rd.
Oakdale, PA 15071
Tel: (412)809-5100; Free: 800-784-9675
Fax: (412)809-5388
E-mail: goodlin.nancy@ptcollege.edu
Web Site: www.ptcollege.edu
Description: Proprietary, primarily 2-year, coed. Awards certificates, terminal associate, and bachelor's degrees. Founded 1946. Setting: 180-acre suburban campus with easy access to Pittsburgh. Total enrollment: 1,835. Faculty: 153 (78 full-time, 75 part-time). Student-undergrad faculty ratio is 12:1. 1,608 applied, 87% were admitted. Full-time: 1,835 students, 42% women, 58% men. Students come from 17 states and territories, 2 other countries, 17% from out-of-state. 0.3% American Indian or Alaska Na-

tive, non-Hispanic/Latino; 0.4% Hispanic/Latino; 7% Black or African American, non-Hispanic/Latino; 0.7% Asian, non-Hispanic/Latino; 0.1% Native Hawaiian or other Pacific Islander, non-Hispanic/Latino. 24% 25 or older, 44% live on campus, 11% transferred in. Retention: 55% of full-time freshmen returned the following year. Core. Calendar: quarters. Academic remediation for entering students, services for LD students, advanced placement, distance learning, double major, adult/continuing education programs, co-op programs and internships.

Entrance Requirements: Open admission except for surgical technology, criminal justice, therapeutic massage, smart building technology, nursing and practical nursing, computer programming, and bachelor's degree programs. Options: electronic application, deferred admission, international baccalaureate accepted. Required: high school transcript, entrance exams for practical nursing certificate and nursing and surgical technology Associate degrees. Recommended: interview. Required for some: essay, minimum X high school GPA, criminal background check, minimum rank in top 80% of class, SAT or ACT. Application deadline: rolling. Notification: continuous. Transfer credits accepted: Yes. Applicants placed on waiting list: 191. Waitlisted applicants offered admission: 149.

Costs Per Year: Application fee: $0. Comprehensive fee: $26,847 includes full-time tuition ($16,920) and college room and board ($9927). College room only: $7344. Full-time tuition varies according to degree level and program. Room and board charges vary according to housing facility. Tuition guaranteed not to increase for student's term of enrollment.

Collegiate Environment: Orientation program. Drama-theater group. Social organizations: 13 open to all; professional organizations, student council. Most popular organizations: Software Development Club, Drama Club, DECA, Gay-Straight Alliance, Magic Club. Major annual events: Carnival, Halloween Bash, Luau. Student services: personal-psychological counseling. Campus security: 24-hour emergency response devices and patrols, student patrols, late night transport-escort service, controlled dormitory access. Library Resource Center. Books: 7,378 (physical), 46,000 (digital/electronic); Serial titles: 116 (physical), 6 (digital/electronic); Databases: 12. Weekly public service hours: 58. 316 computers available on campus for general student use. Computer purchase/lease plans available. A campuswide network can be accessed from off-campus. Staffed computer lab on campus provides training in use of computers, software, and the Internet.

■ POINT PARK UNIVERSITY

201 Wood St.
Pittsburgh, PA 15222-1984
Tel: (412)391-4100; Free: 800-321-0129
Fax: (412)391-1980
Web Site: www.pointpark.edu

Description: Independent, university, coed. Awards associate, bachelor's, master's, and doctoral degrees. Founded 1960. Setting: urban campus. Endowment: $33.5 million. Research spending for the previous fiscal year: $148,480. Educational spending for the previous fiscal year: $9761 per student. Total enrollment: 4,224. Faculty: 519 (149 full-time, 370 part-time). Student-undergrad faculty ratio is 13:1. 4,860 applied, 65% were admitted. 11% from top 10% of their high school class, 38% from top quarter, 71% from top half. Full-time: 2,758 students, 60% women, 40% men. Part-time: 523 students, 54% women, 46% men. Students come from 44 states and territories, 40 other countries, 24% from out-of-state. 0.2% American Indian or Alaska Native, non-Hispanic/Latino; 2% Hispanic/Latino; 15% Black or African American, non-Hispanic/Latino; 2% Asian, non-Hispanic/Latino; 0.3% Native Hawaiian or other Pacific Islander, non-Hispanic/Latino; 4% international. 22% 25 or older, 25% live on campus, 10% transferred in. Retention: 78% of full-time freshmen returned the following year. Academic areas with the most degrees conferred: visual and performing arts; business/marketing; communication/journalism. Core. Calendar: semesters. Academic remediation for entering students, ESL program, services for LD students, advanced placement, accelerated degree program, self-designed majors, honors program, independent study, distance learning, double major, summer session for credit, part-time degree program, adult/continuing education programs, co-op programs and internships, graduate courses open to undergrads. Off campus study at Fellow members of the Pittsburgh Council on Higher Education: Carlow University, Carnegie Mellon University, Chatham University, Community College of Allegheny County, Duquesne University, La Roche College, Pittsburgh Theological Seminary, Robert Morris University, and the University of Pittsburgh. Study abroad program. ROTC: Army (c), Air Force (c).

Entrance Requirements: Options: electronic application, deferred admis-

sion, international baccalaureate accepted. Required: high school transcript, SAT or ACT. Recommended: minimum 2.5 high school GPA. Required for some: essay, 2 recommendations, interview, audition. Entrance: moderately difficult. Application deadline: rolling. Notification: continuous. Transfer credits accepted: Yes.

Costs Per Year: Application fee: $40. Comprehensive fee: $43,650 includes full-time tuition ($29,980), mandatory fees ($1470), and college room and board ($12,200). College room only: $5320. Full-time tuition and fees vary according to program. Room and board charges vary according to board plan and housing facility. Part-time tuition: $844 per credit. Part-time mandatory fees: $165 per term. Part-time tuition and fees vary according to program.

Collegiate Environment: Orientation program. Drama-theater group, student-run newspaper, radio station. Social organizations: 50 open to all. Most popular organizations: WPPJ student radio station, The Body Christian Fellowship, Dance Club, Campus Activities Board, Action Sports Club. Major annual events: Pioneer Community (Service) Day, Spring Fling, Freshman Riverboat Cruise. Student services: health clinic, personal-psychological counseling. Campus security: 24-hour emergency response devices and patrols, late night transport-escort service, controlled dormitory access, campus patrolled by Accredited Law Enforcement Agency, 24-hour security desk, video security. Point Park University Library. Operations spending for the previous fiscal year: $822,045. 309 computers available on campus for general student use. Computer purchase/lease plans available. A campuswide network can be accessed. Students can access the following: online class registration. Staffed computer lab on campus.

Community Environment: The college is centrally located in the city of Pittsburgh, population 316,700. See also University of Pittsburgh, Pittsburgh Campus.

■ READING AREA COMMUNITY COLLEGE

PO Box 1706
Reading, PA 19603-1706
Tel: (610)372-4721
Fax: (610)375-8255
E-mail: dhettinger@racc.edu
Web Site: www.racc.edu

Description: County-supported, 2-year, coed. Awards certificates, diplomas, transfer associate, and terminal associate degrees. Founded 1971. Setting: 14-acre urban campus with easy access to Philadelphia. Endowment: $10.6 million. Total enrollment: 4,090. Faculty: 212 (58 full-time, 154 part-time). Student-undergrad faculty ratio is 18:1. 1,577 applied, 100% were admitted. Full-time: 936 students, 58% women, 42% men. Part-time: 3,154 students, 63% women, 37% men. 0.3% from out-of-state. 0.4% American Indian or Alaska Native, non-Hispanic/Latino; 32% Hispanic/Latino; 11% Black or African American, non-Hispanic/Latino; 2% Asian, non-Hispanic/Latino; 0.2% Native Hawaiian or other Pacific Islander, non-Hispanic/Latino. 34% 25 or older. Academic areas with the most degrees conferred: health professions and related sciences; liberal arts/general studies; business/marketing. Core. Calendar: semesters. Academic remediation for entering students, ESL program, services for LD students, advanced placement, honors program, distance learning, summer session for credit, part-time degree program, adult/continuing education programs, co-op programs.

Entrance Requirements: Open admission. Options: electronic application, early admission, international baccalaureate accepted. Recommended: high school transcript, SAT, ACT. Required for some: essay, high school transcript, 1 recommendation, interview, background/criminal check, physical exam, proof of insurance for selective admissions programs, TOEFL. Entrance: noncompetitive. Application deadline: rolling. Notification: continuous. Transfer credits accepted: Yes.

Collegiate Environment: Orientation program. Student-run newspaper. Social organizations: 6 open to all. Most popular organizations: Student Government Association, Environment Club, Legacy Organization, Multicultural/International Club, RACC Olympics. Major annual events: Spring Fling, International Festival, Welcome Week Picnics. Student services: personal-psychological counseling. Campus security: 24-hour emergency response devices, late night transport-escort service. Yocum Library. Operations spending for the previous fiscal year: $680,518. 776 computers available on campus for general student use. A campuswide network can be accessed from off-campus. Students can access the following: online class registration. Staffed computer lab on campus provides training in use of computers, software, and the Internet.

Community Environment: Reading is located about 60 miles north of Philadelphia and approximately 2 1/2 hours by bus or car to New York City.

■ THE RESTAURANT SCHOOL AT WALNUT HILL COLLEGE

4207 Walnut St.
Philadelphia, PA 19104-3518
Tel: (215)222-4200
Fax: (215)222-4219
E-mail: jenglish@walnuthillcollege.edu
Web Site: www.walnuthillcollege.edu

Description: Proprietary, primarily 2-year, coed. Awards terminal associate and bachelor's degrees. Founded 1974. Setting: 2-acre urban campus. Research spending for the previous fiscal year: $137,880. Educational spending for the previous fiscal year: $5570 per student. Total enrollment: 387. Faculty: 19 (18 full-time, 1 part-time). Student-undergrad faculty ratio is 22:1. 174 applied, 97% were admitted. 2 valedictorians. Full-time: 429 students, 49% women, 51% men. Students come from 2 other countries, 28% from out-of-state. 0.3% American Indian or Alaska Native, non-Hispanic/Latino; 6% Hispanic/Latino; 29% Black or African American, non-Hispanic/Latino; 2% Asian, non-Hispanic/Latino; 0.5% international. 12% 25 or older, 10% transferred in. Academic area with the most degrees conferred: personal and culinary services. Calendar: quarters. Part-time degree program, internships.

Entrance Requirements: Open admission. Options: electronic application, early admission, early decision, deferred admission. Required: essay, high school transcript, 2 recommendations, interview. Recommended: minimum 2 high school GPA, SAT or ACT. Application deadline: rolling. Transfer credits accepted: Yes. Early decision applicants: 56. Early decision applicants admitted: 55.

Costs Per Year: Application fee: $50. Tuition: $19,050 full-time. Mandatory fees: $3900 full-time.

Collegiate Environment: Orientation program. Social organizations: 30 open to all; 100% of eligible men and 100% of eligible women are members. Most popular organizations: Wine Club, Book Club, Coffee and Tea Club, Craft Club, Flair Bartending. Major annual events: Freshman Showcase, First Class, Club Fairs. Campus security: 24-hour emergency response devices and patrols, student patrols, controlled dormitory access. Alumni Resource Center plus 1 other. Weekly public service hours: 61. Operations spending for the previous fiscal year: $20,500. 60 computers available on campus for general student use. A campuswide network can be accessed from student residence rooms and from off campus. Students can access the following: all students receive a tablet computer. Staffed computer lab on campus provides training in use of computers and the Internet.

■ ROBERT MORRIS UNIVERSITY

6001 University Blvd.
Moon Township, PA 15108-1189
Tel: (412)397-3000; Free: 800-762-0097
Fax: (412)262-8619
E-mail: admissionsoffice@rmu.edu
Web Site: www.rmu.edu

Description: Independent, university, coed. Awards bachelor's, master's, and doctoral degrees. Founded 1921. Setting: 230-acre suburban campus with easy access to Pittsburgh. Endowment: $33.6 million. Educational spending for the previous fiscal year: $9829 per student. Total enrollment: 5,076. Faculty: 438 (202 full-time, 236 part-time). Student-undergrad faculty ratio is 15:1. 6,407 applied, 83% were admitted. 18% from top 10% of their high school class, 42% from top quarter, 76% from top half. Full-time: 3,840 students, 42% women, 58% men. Part-time: 403 students, 51% women, 49% men. Students come from 43 states and territories, 37 other countries, 13% from out-of-state. 0.1% American Indian or Alaska Native, non-Hispanic/Latino; 2% Hispanic/Latino; 6% Black or African American, non-Hispanic/Latino; 1% Asian, non-Hispanic/Latino; 0.1% Native Hawaiian or other Pacific Islander, non-Hispanic/Latino; 12% international. 15% 25 or older, 46% live on campus, 6% transferred in. Retention: 81% of full-time freshmen returned the following year. Academic areas with the most degrees conferred: business/marketing; health professions and related sciences; engineering. Core. Calendar: semesters. Academic remediation for entering students, services for LD students, accelerated degree program, honors program, independent study, distance learning, double major, summer session for credit, part-time degree program, adult/continuing education programs, co-op programs and internships, graduate courses open to undergrads. Off campus study at Pittsburgh Council on Higher Education. Study abroad program. ROTC: Army, Naval (c), Air Force (c).

Entrance Requirements: Options: electronic application, deferred admission, international baccalaureate accepted. Required: high school transcript, minimum 2 high school GPA, SAT or ACT. Recommended: essay, minimum

3 high school GPA, interview. Required for some: interview. Entrance: minimally difficult. Application deadline: rolling. Notification: continuous until 8/1. SAT Reasoning Test deadline: 8/15. SAT Subject Test deadline: 8/15. Transfer credits accepted: Yes. Applicants placed on waiting list: 191. Waitlisted applicants offered admission: 38.

Costs Per Year: Application fee: $30. Comprehensive fee: $41,700 includes full-time tuition ($29,060), mandatory fees ($1240), and college room and board ($11,400). College room only: $6340. Full-time tuition and fees vary according to course load and program. Room and board charges vary according to board plan and housing facility. Part-time tuition: $930 per credit hour. Part-time mandatory fees: $80 per credit hour. Part-time tuition and fees vary according to program.

Collegiate Environment: Orientation program. Drama-theater group, choral group, marching band, student-run newspaper, radio station. Social organizations: 174 open to all; national fraternities, national sororities, local fraternities; 10% of eligible men and 13% of eligible women are members. Most popular organizations: Student Government Association, Residence Hall Association, The Saudi Student Club, National Society of Collegiate Scholars, Top Secret Colonials. Major annual events: BobbyMania, Homecoming, Airband. Student services: health clinic, personal-psychological counseling. Campus security: 24-hour emergency response devices and patrols, late night transport-escort service, controlled dormitory access. Robert Morris University Library. Books: 97,693 (physical), 172,931 (digital/electronic); Serial titles: 244 (physical), 47,791 (digital/electronic); Databases: 104. Weekly public service hours: 101; study areas open 24 hours, 5-7 days a week; students can reserve study rooms. Operations spending for the previous fiscal year: $1.5 million. 375 computers available on campus for general student use. Computer purchase/lease plans available. A campuswide network can be accessed from student residence rooms and from off campus. Students can access the following: online class registration, online payment. Staffed computer lab on campus (open 24 hours a day) provides training in use of computers, software, and the Internet.

■ ROSEDALE TECHNICAL INSTITUTE

215 Beecham Dr.
Ste. 2
Pittsburgh, PA 15205-9791
Tel: (412)521-6200; Free: 800-521-6262
Fax: (412)521-9277
E-mail: admissions@rosedaletech.org
Web Site: www.rosedaletech.org

Description: Independent, 2-year, coed. Awards diplomas and terminal associate degrees. Founded 1949. Setting: 6-acre suburban campus. Total enrollment: 200. Faculty: 18 (14 full-time, 4 part-time). Student-undergrad faculty ratio is 13:1. 156 applied, 65% were admitted. Calendar: semesters.

■ ROSEMONT COLLEGE

1400 Montgomery Ave.
Rosemont, PA 19010-1699
Tel: (610)527-0200; Free: 888-2-ROSEMONT
Fax: (610)527-1041
E-mail: bettsy.thommen@rosemont.edu
Web Site: www.rosemont.edu

Description: Independent Roman Catholic, comprehensive, coed. Awards bachelor's and master's degrees. Founded 1921. Setting: 56-acre suburban campus with easy access to Philadelphia. Total enrollment: 1,008. Faculty: 164 (25 full-time, 139 part-time). Student-undergrad faculty ratio is 11:1. 1,315 applied, 70% were admitted. Full-time: 520 students, 64% women, 36% men. Part-time: 115 students, 58% women, 42% men. 25% from out-of-state. 0.5% American Indian or Alaska Native, non-Hispanic/Latino; 6% Hispanic/Latino; 40% Black or African American, non-Hispanic/Latino; 3% Asian, non-Hispanic/Latino; 0.3% Native Hawaiian or other Pacific Islander, non-Hispanic/Latino; 4% international. 5% 25 or older, 67% live on campus, 7% transferred in. Retention: 64% of full-time freshmen returned the following year. Academic areas with the most degrees conferred: business/marketing; social sciences; biological/life sciences. Core. Calendar: semesters. Services for LD students, advanced placement, accelerated degree program, self-designed majors, honors program, independent study, distance learning, double major, summer session for credit, part-time degree program, external degree program, adult/continuing education programs, internships, graduate courses open to undergrads. Off campus study. Study abroad program.

Entrance Requirements: Options: electronic application, deferred admis-

sion, international baccalaureate accepted. Required: high school transcript, minimum 2 high school GPA, SAT or ACT. Recommended: interview. Required for some: essay. Entrance: moderately difficult. Application deadline: rolling. Transfer credits accepted: Yes.

Costs Per Year: Application fee: $0. One-time mandatory fee: $285. Comprehensive fee: $32,338 includes full-time tuition ($18,900), mandatory fees ($1000), and college room and board ($12,438). Full-time tuition and fees vary according to course load and degree level. Room and board charges vary according to board plan and housing facility. Part-time tuition: $715 per credit. Part-time mandatory fees: $535 per year. Part-time tuition and fees vary according to course load and degree level.

Collegiate Environment: Orientation program. Drama-theater group, choral group, student-run newspaper. Major annual events: Founder's Day, Octoberfest/Family Weekend, Petaltones Annual Concert. Student services: health clinic, personal-psychological counseling. Campus security: 24-hour emergency response devices and patrols, late night transport-escort service, controlled dormitory access. Gertrude Kistler Memorial Library plus 1 other. Books: 143,162 (physical), 11,582 (digital/electronic); Serial titles: 20 (physical), 17,350 (digital/electronic); Databases: 40. Students can reserve study rooms.

Community Environment: See Villanova University.

■ SAINT CHARLES BORROMEO SEMINARY, OVERBROOK

100 E Wynnewood Rd.
Wynnewood, PA 19096
Tel: (610)667-3394
E-mail: jshenosky@scs.edu
Web Site: www.scs.edu

Description: Independent Roman Catholic, comprehensive, coed. Awards bachelor's and master's degrees (also offers coed part-time programs; students do not apply directly to the Seminary, but instead apply through their local Diocese). Founded 1832. Setting: 77-acre suburban campus with easy access to Philadelphia. Total enrollment: 212. Faculty: 33 (16 full-time, 17 part-time). Student-undergrad faculty ratio is 6:1. 8 applied, 100% were admitted. 72% from top 10% of their high school class, 33% from top quarter, 67% from top half. Full-time: 74 students, 100% men. Part-time: 24 students, 71% women, 29% men. Students come from 6 states and territories, 13% from out-of-state. 9% Hispanic/Latino; 2% Asian, non-Hispanic/Latino. 2% 25 or older, 100% live on campus, 5% transferred in. Retention: 78% of full-time freshmen returned the following year. Core. Calendar: semesters. Academic remediation for entering students, ESL program, advanced placement, accelerated degree program, independent study, summer session for credit, adult/continuing education programs, graduate courses open to undergrads.

Entrance Requirements: Options: deferred admission, international baccalaureate accepted. Required: essay, high school transcript, minimum 2 high school GPA, 3 recommendations, interview, sponsorship by diocese or religious community. Entrance: moderately difficult. Application deadline: 7/15. Notification: continuous. Transfer credits accepted: Yes.

Costs Per Year: Application fee: $0. Comprehensive fee: $34,975 includes full-time tuition ($20,000), mandatory fees ($1275), and college room and board ($13,700). College room only: $4500. Full-time tuition and fees vary according to degree level, program, and student level. Part-time tuition: $950 per course. Part-time mandatory fees: $100 per term. Part-time tuition and fees vary according to course level.

Collegiate Environment: Orientation program. Drama-theater group, choral group, student-run newspaper. Most popular organizations: Seminarians for Life, Student Council. Student services: health clinic, personal-psychological counseling. Campus security: 24-hour emergency response devices and patrols. Ryan Memorial Library. 60 computers available on campus for general student use. A campuswide network can be accessed.

■ SAINT FRANCIS UNIVERSITY

117 Evergreen Dr.
Loretto, PA 15940-0600
Tel: (814)472-3000; Free: 866-DIAL-SFU
Fax: (814)472-3044
E-mail: rbeener@francis.edu
Web Site: www.francis.edu

Description: Independent Roman Catholic, comprehensive, coed. Awards associate, bachelor's, master's, and doctoral degrees. Founded 1847. Setting: 600-acre rural campus. Endowment: $50.3 million. Research spending for the previous fiscal year: $764,829. Total enrollment: 2,619. Faculty: 185 (131 full-time, 54 part-time). Student-undergrad faculty ratio is 14:1. 1,706 applied, 75% were admitted. 31% from top 10% of their high school class,

60% from top quarter, 87% from top half. Full-time: 1,485 students, 64% women, 36% men. Part-time: 626 students, 69% women, 31% men. Students come from 36 states and territories, 23 other countries, 29% from out-of-state. 0.3% American Indian or Alaska Native, non-Hispanic/Latino; 2% Hispanic/Latino; 8% Black or African American, non-Hispanic/Latino; 2% Asian, non-Hispanic/Latino; 0.2% Native Hawaiian or other Pacific Islander, non-Hispanic/Latino; 1% international. 15% 25 or older, 83% live on campus, 4% transferred in. Retention: 87% of full-time freshmen returned the following year. Academic areas with the most degrees conferred: business/marketing; biological/life sciences; psychology. Core. Calendar: semesters. Academic remediation for entering students, ESL program, services for LD students, advanced placement, accelerated degree program, self-designed majors, freshman honors college, honors program, independent study, distance learning, double major, summer session for credit, part-time degree program, external degree program, adult/continuing education programs, co-op programs and internships, graduate courses open to undergrads. Off campus study at Washington Semester, CCSA. Study abroad program. ROTC: Army.

Entrance Requirements: Options: electronic application, deferred admission, international baccalaureate accepted. Required: essay, high school transcript, 1 recommendation, SAT or ACT. Recommended: interview. Entrance: moderately difficult. Application deadline: rolling. SAT Reasoning Test deadline: 8/15. SAT Subject Test deadline: 8/15. Transfer credits accepted: Yes. Applicants placed on waiting list: 113. Wait-listed applicants offered admission: 69.

Costs Per Year: Application fee: $30. One-time mandatory fee: $110. Comprehensive fee: $50,380 includes full-time tuition ($36,970), mandatory fees ($1300), and college room and board ($12,110). College room only: $6086. Part-time tuition: $1057 per credit.

Collegiate Environment: Orientation program. Drama-theater group, choral group, marching band, student-run newspaper, radio station. Social organizations: 80 open to all; national fraternities, national sororities, local sororities, national Greek-lettered service organizations; 7% of eligible men and 23% of eligible women are members. Most popular organizations: Student Activities Organization, Club Baseball, Student Government Association, Best Buddies, Cru. Major annual events: Parents' Weekend, Homecoming, Spring Fest. Student services: health clinic, personal-psychological counseling. Campus security: 24-hour emergency response devices and patrols, late night transport-escort service, controlled dormitory access. 1,500 college housing spaces available; 1,475 were occupied in 2018-19. Freshmen guaranteed college housing. On-campus residence required through junior year. Options: coed, men-only, women-only housing available. Saint Francis University Library. Books: 60,353 (physical), 1.3 million (digital/electronic); Databases: 74. Operations spending for the previous fiscal year: $2 million. 1,500 computers available on campus for general student use. Computer purchase/lease plans available. A computer is required for all students. A campuswide network can be accessed from student residence rooms and from off campus. Students can access the following: online class registration. Staffed computer lab on campus provides training in use of computers, software, and the Internet.

■ SAINT JOSEPH'S UNIVERSITY

5600 City Ave.
Philadelphia, PA 19131-1395
Tel: (610)660-1000; Free: 800-BE-A-HAWK
Web Site: www.sju.edu

Description: Independent Roman Catholic (Jesuit), comprehensive, coed. Awards associate, bachelor's, master's, and doctoral degrees and post-master's certificates. Founded 1851. Setting: 114-acre suburban campus with easy access to Philadelphia. Endowment: $280.3 million. Research spending for the previous fiscal year: $1.8 million. Educational spending for the previous fiscal year: $11,327 per student. Total enrollment: 7,589. Faculty: 681 (298 full-time, 383 part-time). Student-undergrad faculty ratio is 11:1. 8,843 applied, 76% were admitted. 19% from top 10% of their high school class, 50% from top quarter, 79% from top half. Full-time: 4,350 students, 54% women, 46% men. Part-time: 554 students, 60% women, 40% men. Students come from 36 states and territories, 36 other countries, 53% from out-of-state. 0.1% American Indian or Alaska Native, non-Hispanic/Latino; 7% Hispanic/Latino; 6% Black or African American, non-Hispanic/Latino; 3% Asian, non-Hispanic/Latino; 0.2% Native Hawaiian or other Pacific Islander, non-Hispanic/Latino; 2% international. 5% 25 or older, 48% live on campus, 2% transferred in. Retention: 89% of full-time freshmen returned the following year. Academic areas with the most degrees conferred: business/marketing; education; social sciences. Core. Calendar:

semesters. ESL program, services for LD students, advanced placement, accelerated degree program, self-designed majors, honors program, independent study, distance learning, double major, summer session for credit, part-time degree program, adult/continuing education programs, co-op programs and internships, graduate courses open to undergrads. Off campus study at members of the Jesuit Student Exchange. Study abroad program. ROTC: Army (c), Naval (c), Air Force.

Entrance Requirements: Options: electronic application, early decision, early action, deferred admission, international baccalaureate accepted. Required: essay, high school transcript, 1 recommendation. Entrance: moderately difficult. Application deadlines: 2/1, 11/1 for early decision plan 1, 1/15 for early decision plan 2, 11/1 for early action. Notification: 3/15, 12/20 for early decision plan 1, 2/15 for early decision plan 2, 12/20 for early action. SAT Reasoning Test deadline: 2/15. Transfer credits accepted: Yes. Early decision applicants: 144. Early decision applicants admitted: 106. Early action applicants: 4,693. Early action applicants admitted: 4,204.

Costs Per Year: Application fee: $50. Comprehensive fee: $61,410 includes full-time tuition ($46,370), mandatory fees ($200), and college room and board ($14,840). College room only: $9424. Part-time tuition: $584 per credit.

Collegiate Environment: Orientation program. Drama-theater group, choral group, student-run newspaper, radio station. Social organizations: 90 open to all; national fraternities, national sororities; 7% of eligible men and 24% of eligible women are members. Most popular organizations: Student Union Board, Hand-in-Hand, 54th Airborne / Booster Club, Appalachian Experience, Weekly Service. Major annual events: Activity Fair, Spring Concert, Hawk Fest. Student services: health clinic, personal-psychological counseling. Campus security: 24-hour emergency response devices and patrols, late night transport-escort service, controlled dormitory access. 2,568 college housing spaces available; 2,337 were occupied in 2018-19. Freshmen guaranteed college housing. On-campus residence required through sophomore year. Options: coed, men-only, women-only housing available. Post Learning Commons and Drexel Library. Books: 271,281 (physical), 467,643 (digital/electronic); Serial titles: 3,324 (physical), 76,020 (digital/electronic); Databases: 219. Weekly public service hours: 109; students can reserve study rooms. Operations spending for the previous fiscal year: $2.5 million. 901 computers available on campus for general student use. Computer purchase/lease plans available. A campuswide network can be accessed from student residence rooms and from off campus. Students can access the following: online class registration. Staffed computer lab on campus (open 24 hours a day) provides training in use of computers, software, and the Internet.

■ **SAINT VINCENT COLLEGE**
300 Fraser Purchase Rd.
Latrobe, PA 15650-2690
Tel: (724)532-6600; Free: 800-782-5549
Fax: (724)537-4554
E-mail: admission@stvincent.edu
Web Site: www.stvincent.edu

Description: Independent Roman Catholic, comprehensive, coed. Awards bachelor's, master's, and doctoral degrees. Founded 1846. Setting: 200-acre suburban campus with easy access to Pittsburgh. Endowment: $109.8 million. Research spending for the previous fiscal year: $142,801. Educational spending for the previous fiscal year: $9188 per student. Total enrollment: 1,867. Faculty: 233 (102 full-time, 131 part-time). Student-undergrad faculty ratio is 11:1. 2,354 applied, 68% were admitted. 22% from top 10% of their high school class, 38% from top quarter, 75% from top half. Full-time: 1,595 students, 45% women, 55% men. Part-time: 81 students, 43% women, 57% men. Students come from 30 states and territories, 8 other countries, 23% from out-of-state. 0.2% American Indian or Alaska Native, non-Hispanic/Latino; 3% Hispanic/Latino; 6% Black or African American, non-Hispanic/Latino; 1% Asian, non-Hispanic/Latino; 0.1% Native Hawaiian or other Pacific Islander, non-Hispanic/Latino; 0.7% international. 1% 25 or older, 72% live on campus, 3% transferred in. Retention: 82% of full-time freshmen returned the following year. Academic areas with the most degrees conferred: business/marketing; biological/life sciences; social sciences. Core. Calendar: semesters. Services for LD students, advanced placement, self-designed majors, honors program, independent study, distance learning, double major, summer session for credit, part-time degree program, external degree program, co-op programs and internships, graduate courses open to undergrads. Study abroad program. ROTC: Army (c), Air Force (c).

Entrance Requirements: Options: early admission, deferred admission,

international baccalaureate accepted. Required: essay, high school transcript, minimum 2.5 high school GPA, SAT or ACT. Recommended: minimum 3.2 high school GPA, 3 recommendations, interview. Entrance: moderately difficult. Application deadline: 5/1. Notification: continuous until 10/1. Transfer credits accepted: Yes. Applicants placed on waiting list: 0. Wait-listed applicants offered admission: 0.

Costs Per Year: Application fee: $25. Comprehensive fee: $47,344 includes full-time tuition ($34,520), mandatory fees ($1354), and college room and board ($11,470). Full-time tuition and fees vary according to course load and degree level. Room and board charges vary according to board plan and housing facility. Part-time tuition: $1080 per credit hour. Part-time tuition varies according to course load and degree level.

Collegiate Environment: Orientation program. Drama-theater group, choral group, marching band, student-run newspaper. Social organizations: 50 open to all. Most popular organizations: Activities Programming Board, Orientation Committee, Campus Ministry, Visionaries of Hope. Major annual events: MLK celebration, Homecoming, Honors Convocation. Student services: health clinic, personal-psychological counseling. Campus security: 24-hour emergency response devices and patrols, late night transport-escort service, controlled dormitory access. 1,166 undergraduates lived in college housing during 2018-19. Freshmen given priority for college housing. Option: coed housing available. Latimer Family Library plus 1 other. Books: 266,710 (physical); Serial titles: 224 (physical). Weekly public service hours: 84. Operations spending for the previous fiscal year: $219,310. 325 computers available on campus for general student use. A campuswide network can be accessed from student residence rooms and from off campus. Students can access the following: online class registration, program requirement evaluation.

Community Environment: Population 8,654. Located in the Laurel Highlands region of the Allegheny Mountains, Latrobe is 35 miles east of Pittsburgh. The area is accessible by air, railroad and major highways. There is a county airport adjacent to campus. The community has a public library, churches and a synagogue and multiple shopping malls.

■ **SETON HILL UNIVERSITY**
Seton Hill Dr.
Greensburg, PA 15601
Tel: (724)834-2200; Free: 800-826-6234
Fax: (724)830-4611
E-mail: admit@setonhill.edu
Web Site: www.setonhill.edu

Description: Independent Roman Catholic, comprehensive, coed. Awards bachelor's and master's degrees. Founded 1883. Setting: 200-acre small town campus with easy access to Pittsburgh. Total enrollment: 2,080. Faculty: 211 (100 full-time, 111 part-time). Student-undergrad faculty ratio is 14:1. 2,471 applied, 75% were admitted. 19% from top 10% of their high school class, 45% from top quarter, 77% from top half. Full-time: 1,592 students, 64% women, 36% men. Part-time: 118 students, 66% women, 34% men. Students come from 31 states and territories, 23 other countries, 23% from out-of-state. 0.3% American Indian or Alaska Native, non-Hispanic/Latino; 4% Hispanic/Latino; 9% Black or African American, non-Hispanic/Latino; 1% Asian, non-Hispanic/Latino; 0.3% Native Hawaiian or other Pacific Islander, non-Hispanic/Latino; 2% international. 4% 25 or older, 47% live on campus, 4% transferred in. Retention: 82% of full-time freshmen returned the following year. Academic areas with the most degrees conferred: business/marketing; visual and performing arts; health professions and related sciences. Core. Calendar: semesters. Academic remediation for entering students, ESL program, services for LD students, advanced placement, self-designed majors, honors program, independent study, distance learning, double major, summer session for credit, part-time degree program, adult/continuing education programs, internships, graduate courses open to undergrads. Off campus study. Study abroad program. ROTC: Army (c).

Entrance Requirements: Options: electronic application, deferred admission, international baccalaureate accepted. Required: essay, high school transcript, 1 recommendation. Recommended: interview, SAT or ACT. Required for some: portfolio for art, audition for music and theatre. Entrance: moderately difficult. Application deadline: 8/15. Notification: continuous. SAT Reasoning Test deadline: 8/15. Transfer credits accepted: Yes.

Costs Per Year: Application fee: $35. Comprehensive fee: $49,068 includes full-time tuition ($36,306), mandatory fees ($550), and college room and board ($12,212). College room only: $6700. Part-time tuition: $974.

Collegiate Environment: Orientation program. Drama-theater group, choral group, marching band, student-run newspaper. Social organizations: 58

open to all; academic honor societies; 25% of eligible men and 25% of eligible women are members. Most popular organizations: Student Body Activities Council, Future Greek leaders, Dietetics Club, Biology Club, intramurals. Major annual events: Homecoming Weekend, Christmas on the Hill, Midnight Breakfast. Student services: health clinic, personal-psychological counseling. Campus security: 24-hour emergency response devices and patrols, late night transport-escort service, controlled dormitory access. 774 college housing spaces available; 720 were occupied in 2018-19. Freshmen guaranteed college housing. On-campus residence required through junior year. Option: coed housing available. Reeves Memorial Library. Books: 72,274 (physical), 127,160 (digital/electronic); Serial titles: 2,919 (physical); Databases: 37. Students can reserve study rooms. 66 computers available on campus for general student use. Computer purchase/lease plans available. A campuswide network can be accessed from student residence rooms and from off campus. Students can access the following: online class registration. Staffed computer lab on campus provides training in use of computers, software, and the Internet.

■ SHIPPENSBURG UNIVERSITY OF PENNSYLVANIA

1871 Old Main Dr.
Shippensburg, PA 17257-2299
Tel: (717)477-7447
Fax: (717)477-1273
E-mail: admiss@ship.edu
Web Site: www.ship.edu

Description: State-supported, comprehensive, coed. Part of Pennsylvania State University System of Higher Education. Awards bachelor's, master's, and doctoral degrees and post-master's certificates. Founded 1871. Setting: 200-acre rural campus. Endowment: $38.9 million. Research spending for the previous fiscal year: $528,923. Educational spending for the previous fiscal year: $8049 per student. Total enrollment: 6,581. Faculty: 372 (299 full-time, 73 part-time). Student-undergrad faculty ratio is 19:1. 5,248 applied, 84% were admitted. 9% from top 10% of their high school class, 25% from top quarter, 59% from top half. Full-time: 5,160 students, 51% women, 49% men. Part-time: 425 students, 48% women, 52% men. Students come from 23 states and territories, 19 other countries, 7% from out-of-state. 0.2% American Indian or Alaska Native, non-Hispanic/Latino; 6% Hispanic/Latino; 10% Black or African American, non-Hispanic/Latino; 2% Asian, non-Hispanic/Latino; 0.7% international. 6% 25 or older, 30% live on campus, 5% transferred in. Retention: 71% of full-time freshmen returned the following year. Academic areas with the most degrees conferred: business/marketing; psychology; homeland security, law enforcement, firefighting, and protective services. Core. Calendar: semesters. Academic remediation for entering students, services for LD students, advanced placement, accelerated degree program, honors program, independent study, distance learning, double major, summer session for credit, part-time degree program, co-op programs and internships, graduate courses open to undergrads. Off campus study at Wilson College, Art Institutes International, Fashion Institute of Technology, Pennsylvania State System of Higher Education (PASSHE). Study abroad program. ROTC: Army.

Entrance Requirements: Options: electronic application, early admission, early action, deferred admission, international baccalaureate accepted. Required: high school transcript, SAT or ACT. Recommended: essay, class rank, letters of recommendation. Required for some: interview. Application deadline: rolling. Notification: continuous. SAT Reasoning Test deadline: 8/15. Transfer credits accepted: Yes.

Costs Per Year: Application fee: $45. State resident tuition: $9570 full-time, $319 per credit hour part-time. Nonresident tuition: $17,362 full-time, $725 per credit hour part-time. Mandatory fees: $3148 full-time, $131 per credit hour part-time. Full-time tuition and fees vary according to course load and location. Part-time tuition and fees vary according to course load and location. College room and board: $12,268. College room only: $8038. Room and board charges vary according to board plan and housing facility.

Collegiate Environment: Orientation program. Drama-theater group, choral group, marching band, student-run newspaper, radio station. Social organizations: 101 open to all; national fraternities, national sororities; 10% of eligible men and 10% of eligible women are members. Major annual events: Homecoming, Parents' Days, Spring Fest. Student services: health clinic, personal-psychological counseling, women's center. Campus security: 24-hour emergency response devices and patrols, late night transport-escort service, controlled dormitory access, surveillance cameras in certain parking lots and buildings; foot, vehicular and bicycle patrols by security officers. Ezra Lehman Memorial Library plus 1 other. Books: 359,138 (physical), 189,092 (digital/electronic); Serial titles: 50 (physical), 255 (digital/

electronic); Databases: 106. Weekly public service hours: 97. Operations spending for the previous fiscal year: $2.4 million. 1,100 computers available on campus for general student use. A campuswide network can be accessed from student residence rooms and from off campus. Students can access the following: online class registration, personal Web pages. Staffed computer lab on campus.

Community Environment: Located in south-central Pennsylvania, Shippensburg, population 5,600, is a semirural community. The area has 32 churches of various denominations, a library, and many civic and fraternal organizations. Recreational activities include fishing, hunting, swimming, football, baseball, and bowling. Limited part-time employment opportunities are available.

■ SLIPPERY ROCK UNIVERSITY OF PENNSYLVANIA

1 Morrow Way
Slippery Rock, PA 16057-1383
Tel: (724)738-9000; Free: 800-SRU-9111
Fax: (724)738-2098
Web Site: www.sru.edu

Description: State-supported, university, coed. Part of Pennsylvania State System of Higher Education. Awards bachelor's, master's, and doctoral degrees. Founded 1889. Setting: 660-acre small town campus with easy access to Pittsburgh. Endowment: $30.6 million. Research spending for the previous fiscal year: $167,847. Educational spending for the previous fiscal year: $6958 per student. Total enrollment: 8,895. Faculty: 419 (349 full-time, 70 part-time). Student-undergrad faculty ratio is 21:1. 5,836 applied, 71% were admitted. 13% from top 10% of their high school class, 36% from top quarter, 72% from top half. Full-time: 7,125 students, 56% women, 44% men. Part-time: 513 students, 68% women, 32% men. Students come from 47 states and territories, 33 other countries, 10% from out-of-state. 0.2% American Indian or Alaska Native, non-Hispanic/Latino; 2% Hispanic/Latino; 5% Black or African American, non-Hispanic/Latino; 0.9% Asian, non-Hispanic/Latino; 0.1% Native Hawaiian or other Pacific Islander, non-Hispanic/Latino; 1% international. 7% 25 or older, 36% live on campus, 7% transferred in. Retention: 81% of full-time freshmen returned the following year. Academic areas with the most degrees conferred: health professions and related sciences; business/marketing; education. Core. Calendar: semesters. Academic remediation for entering students, ESL program, services for LD students, advanced placement, self-designed majors, honors program, independent study, distance learning, double major, summer session for credit, part-time degree program, adult/continuing education programs, internships, graduate courses open to undergrads. Off campus study at Members of the Marine Science Consortium. Study abroad program. ROTC: Army.

Entrance Requirements: Options: electronic application, deferred admission, international baccalaureate accepted. Required: high school transcript, SAT or ACT. Recommended: minimum 3 high school GPA. Entrance: moderately difficult. Application deadline: rolling. Notification: continuous until 6/15. SAT Reasoning Test deadline: 5/1. Transfer credits accepted: Yes.

Costs Per Year: Application fee: $30. State resident tuition: $7716 full-time, $322 per credit hour part-time. Nonresident tuition: $15,432 full-time, $644 per credit hour part-time. Mandatory fees: $2790 full-time, $115 per credit hour part-time. Full-time tuition and fees vary according to course load. Part-time tuition and fees vary according to course load. College room and board: $10,446. College room only: $6876. Room and board charges vary according to board plan and housing facility.

Collegiate Environment: Orientation program. Drama-theater group, choral group, marching band, student-run newspaper, radio station. Social organizations: 204 open to all; national fraternities, national sororities, local fraternities; 6% of eligible men and 7% of eligible women are members. Most popular organizations: University Program Board, Interfraternity Council/Panhellenic Council, State Government Association, Black Action Society, Gamer's Guild. Major annual events: Homecoming, Family Day, Concerts. Student services: legal services, health clinic, personal-psychological counseling, women's center. Campus security: 24-hour emergency response devices and patrols, late night transport-escort service, controlled dormitory access. Bailey Library. Books: 282,009 (physical), 286,118 (digital/electronic); Serial titles: 248 (physical), 49,191 (digital/electronic); Databases: 134. Weekly public service hours: 98; students can reserve study rooms. Operations spending for the previous fiscal year: $3.2 million. 1,654 computers available on campus for general student use. Computer purchase/lease plans available. A campuswide network can be accessed from student residence rooms and from off campus. Students can access the following: online class registration. Staffed computer lab on campus provides training in use of computers, software, and the Internet.

Community Environment: Population 3,000, Slippery Rock is located approximately an hour's drive from Pittsburgh. The climate is pleasant both in winter and in summer. There are several Protestant and Catholic churches in the community. The area has good highways and bus service. Local recreation includes hunting, fishing, boating, swimming, golf, and theatres, all easily accessible. Rooms are available in private homes. Many special interest and veteran's clubs are active in the community.

■ SOUTH HILLS SCHOOL OF BUSINESS & TECHNOLOGY

480 Waupelani Dr.
State College, PA 16801
Tel: (814)234-7755; Free: 888-282-7427
Fax: (814)234-0926
E-mail: admissions@southhills.edu
Web Site: www.southhills.edu

Description: Proprietary, 2-year, coed. Awards certificates, diplomas, and terminal associate degrees (also includes Altoona campus). Founded 1970. Setting: 6-acre small town campus. Total enrollment: 630. Faculty: 65 (41 full-time, 24 part-time). Student-undergrad faculty ratio is 13:1. 439 applied, 92% were admitted. Full-time: 574 students, 66% women, 34% men. Part-time: 56 students, 71% women, 29% men. 0.3% American Indian or Alaska Native, non-Hispanic/Latino; 0.6% Hispanic/Latino; 2% Black or African American, non-Hispanic/Latino; 0.5% Asian, non-Hispanic/Latino; 0.2% international. 27% 25 or older, 15% transferred in. Retention: 70% of full-time freshmen returned the following year. Calendar: quarters. Advanced placement, part-time degree program, internships.

Entrance Requirements: Option: electronic application. Required: high school transcript, interview, Wonderlic aptitude test. Required for some: essay, 2 recommendations. Entrance: minimally difficult. Application deadline: rolling. Transfer credits accepted: Yes.

Collegiate Environment: Orientation program. Social organizations: 10 open to all. Most popular organizations: Phi Beta Lambda, South Hills Ambassadors, Club IT, C.O.P.S, Student Forum. Major annual events: Career Fair, Picnics, Trips. Campus security: 24-hour emergency response devices. Main library plus 1 other. 400 computers available on campus for general student use.

■ STRAYER UNIVERSITY-ALLENTOWN CAMPUS

520 Hamilton St.
Ste. 100
Allentown, PA 18101-1502
Tel: (484)809-7770; Free: 888-311-0355
Web Site: www.strayer.edu

Description: Proprietary, comprehensive, coed. Awards associate, bachelor's, and master's degrees.

■ STRAYER UNIVERSITY-CENTER CITY CAMPUS

1601 Cherry St.
Ste. 100
Philadelphia, PA 19102
Tel: (267)256-0200; Free: 888-311-0355
Web Site: www.strayer.edu

Description: Proprietary, comprehensive, coed. Awards associate, bachelor's, and master's degrees.

■ STRAYER UNIVERSITY-DELAWARE COUNTY CAMPUS

760 W Sproul Rd.
Ste. 200
Springfield, PA 19064
Tel: (610)604-7700; Free: 888-311-0355
Web Site: www.strayer.edu

Description: Proprietary, comprehensive, coed. Awards associate, bachelor's, and master's degrees.

■ STRAYER UNIVERSITY-LOWER BUCKS COUNTY CAMPUS

3800 Horizon Blvd.
Ste. 100
Trevose, PA 19053
Tel: (215)354-2700; Free: 888-311-0355
Web Site: www.strayer.edu

Description: Proprietary, comprehensive, coed. Awards associate, bachelor's, and master's degrees.

■ STRAYER UNIVERSITY-WARRENDALE CAMPUS

802 Warrendale Village Dr.
Warrendale, PA 15086
Tel: (724)799-2900; Free: 888-311-0355
Web Site: www.strayer.edu

Description: Proprietary, comprehensive, coed. Awards associate, bachelor's, and master's degrees.

■ SUSQUEHANNA UNIVERSITY

514 University Ave.
Selinsgrove, PA 17870
Tel: (570)374-0101; Free: 800-326-9672
Fax: (570)372-2722
E-mail: suadmiss@susqu.edu
Web Site: www.susqu.edu

Description: Independent, 4-year, coed, affiliated with Evangelical Lutheran Church in America. Awards bachelor's degrees (also offers evening associate degree program limited to local adult students). Founded 1858. Setting: 325-acre small town campus. Endowment: $143.2 million. Research spending for the previous fiscal year: $869,739. Educational spending for the previous fiscal year: $12,139 per student. Total enrollment: 2,266. Faculty: 260 (139 full-time, 121 part-time). Student-undergrad faculty ratio is 12:1. 4,896 applied, 85% were admitted. 26% from top 10% of their high school class, 57% from top quarter, 88% from top half. Full-time: 2,198 students, 56% women, 44% men. Part-time: 68 students, 63% women, 37% men. Students come from 38 states and territories, 21 other countries, 42% from out-of-state. 0.3% American Indian or Alaska Native, non-Hispanic/Latino; 7% Hispanic/Latino; 6% Black or African American, non-Hispanic/Latino; 2% Asian, non-Hispanic/Latino; 2% international. 2% 25 or older, 93% live on campus, 1% transferred in. Retention: 87% of full-time freshmen returned the following year. Academic areas with the most degrees conferred: business/marketing; communication/journalism; biological/life sciences. Core. Calendar: semesters. ESL program, services for LD students, advanced placement, accelerated degree program, self-designed majors, honors program, independent study, distance learning, double major, summer session for credit, part-time degree program, internships. Off campus study at Lutheran College Washington Consortium. Study abroad program. ROTC: Army (c).

Entrance Requirements: Options: electronic application, early admission, early decision, early action, deferred admission, international baccalaureate accepted. Required: essay, high school transcript, minimum 2.5 high school GPA, 1 recommendation. Recommended: minimum 3 high school GPA, interview. Required for some: writing portfolio, audition for music programs. Entrance: moderately difficult. Application deadlines: rolling, 11/15 for early decision, 11/1 for early action. Notification: continuous, 12/1 for early decision, 12/1 for early action. SAT Reasoning Test deadline: 4/1. Transfer credits accepted: Yes. Applicants placed on waiting list: 0. Wait-listed applicants offered admission: 0. Early decision applicants: 93. Early decision applicants admitted: 55. Early action applicants: 1,991. Early action applicants admitted: 1,677.

Costs Per Year: Application fee: $0. Comprehensive fee: $59,920 includes full-time tuition ($46,690), mandatory fees ($600), and college room and board ($12,630). College room only: $6630. Room and board charges vary according to board plan. Part-time tuition: $1485 per credit hour.

Collegiate Environment: Orientation program. Drama-theater group, choral group, student-run newspaper, radio station. Social organizations: 157 open to all; national fraternities, national sororities; 20% of eligible men and 19% of eligible women are members. Most popular organizations: Student Government Association, Alpha Phi Omega, Student Activities Committee, SU Dance Corps, Intramural Sports. Major annual events: Christmas Candlelight Service, Thanksgiving Dinner, Spring Weekend Carnival. Student services: health clinic, personal-psychological counseling, women's center. Campus security: 24-hour emergency response devices and patrols, late night transport-escort service, controlled dormitory access. Blough-Weis Library. Books: 161,900 (physical), 370,171 (digital/electronic); Serial titles: 612 (physical), 94,180 (digital/electronic); Databases: 137. Weekly public service hours: 106; students can reserve study rooms. Operations spending for the previous fiscal year: $1.3 million. 183 computers available on campus for general student use. A campuswide network can be accessed from student residence rooms and from off campus. Students can access the following: online class registration, online voting booth. Staffed computer lab on campus (open 24 hours a day) provides training in use of computers, software, and the Internet.

Community Environment: Population 5,400. The beautiful Susquehanna

River winds through this quiet town. Route 80 is one half hour north and the Pennsylvania Turnpike is one hour south of campus. Selinsgrove is 50 miles north of Harrisburg. Limited part-time employment is available.

■ SWARTHMORE COLLEGE
500 College Ave.
Swarthmore, PA 19081-1397
Tel: (610)328-8000; Free: 800-667-3110
Fax: (610)328-8673
Web Site: www.swarthmore.edu
Description: Independent, 4-year, coed. Awards bachelor's degrees. Founded 1864. Setting: 425-acre suburban campus with easy access to Philadelphia. Endowment: $1.7 million. Total enrollment: 1,641. Faculty: 225 (194 full-time, 31 part-time). Student-undergrad faculty ratio is 8:1. 9,382 applied, 11% were admitted. 91% from top 10% of their high school class, 99% from top quarter, 100% from top half. Full-time: 1,637 students, 51% women, 49% men. Part-time: 4 students, 25% women, 75% men. 87% from out-of-state. 0.2% American Indian or Alaska Native, non-Hispanic/Latino; 12% Hispanic/Latino; 7% Black or African American, non-Hispanic/Latino; 17% Asian, non-Hispanic/Latino; 0.1% Native Hawaiian or other Pacific Islander, non-Hispanic/Latino; 13% international. 0.1% 25 or older, 96% live on campus, 1% transferred in. Retention: 98% of full-time freshmen returned the following year. Academic areas with the most degrees conferred: social sciences; biological/life sciences; computer and information sciences. Core. Calendar: semesters. Services for LD students, accelerated degree program, self-designed majors, honors program, independent study, double major, internships. Study abroad program. ROTC: Air Force (c).
Entrance Requirements: Options: early admission, early decision, deferred admission. Required: essay, high school transcript, 3 recommendations, SAT or ACT. Application deadlines: 1/1, 11/15 for early decision plan 1, 1/1 for early decision plan 2. Notification: 4/1, 12/15 for early decision plan 1, 2/1 for early decision plan 2. Early decision applicants: 712. Early decision applicants admitted: 199.
Costs Per Year: Application fee: $60. Comprehensive fee: $68,062 includes full-time tuition ($52,190), mandatory fees ($398), and college room and board ($15,474). Room and board charges vary according to board plan.
Collegiate Environment: Orientation program. Drama-theater group, choral group, student-run newspaper, radio station. Social organizations: national fraternities, national sororities; 11% of eligible men and 5% of eligible women are members. Most popular organizations: Boy Meets Tractor (sketch comedy troupe), Rhythm N' Motion (performing dance styles of the African Diaspora), Multi (community for people who self-identify as multiracial, multiethnic, multicultural, and/or multireligious), Mixed Company (a cappella group). Student services: health clinic, personal-psychological counseling, women's center. Campus security: 24-hour emergency response devices and patrols, late night transport-escort service. McCabe Library plus 6 others.
Community Environment: Swarthmore, population 6,146, is in a suburban area 11 miles from Philadelphia. The climate is temperate. There is bus and rail service to Philadelphia, New York and Washington. Philadelphia International Airport is 15 minutes from campus by car, with a college shuttle before and after breaks and public rail service year-round. The immediate community has a library and churches of various denominations. There are hospitals nearby. For civic services, recreation and cultural facilities, see Philadelphia.

■ TALMUDICAL YESHIVA OF PHILADELPHIA
6063 Drexel Rd.
Philadelphia, PA 19131-1296
Tel: (215)473-1212
Fax: (215)477-5065
Description: Independent Jewish, 4-year, men only. Awards bachelor's degrees (also offers some graduate courses). Founded 1953. Setting: 3-acre urban campus. Total enrollment: 124. Full-time: 124 students. Students come from 13 states and territories, 3 other countries, 92% from out-of-state. 6% international. Core. Calendar: trimesters. Academic remediation for entering students, honors program, internships. Study abroad program.
Entrance Requirements: Options: early admission, deferred admission. Required: high school transcript, 1 recommendation, interview, oral examination. Entrance: moderately difficult. Application deadline: 7/15. Notification: 8/5.
Collegiate Environment: Student services: health clinic, personal-psychological counseling. Campus security: controlled dormitory access, night security patrol.

■ TEMPLE UNIVERSITY
1801 N Broad St.
Philadelphia, PA 19122-6096
Tel: (215)204-7000; Free: 888-340-2222
Fax: (215)204-5694
Web Site: www.temple.edu
Description: State-related, university, coed. Part of Commonwealth System of Higher Education. Awards associate, bachelor's, master's, and doctoral degrees and post-master's certificates. Founded 1884. Setting: 390-acre urban campus with easy access to Philadelphia. Endowment: $615.4 million. Research spending for the previous fiscal year: $204.9 million. Educational spending for the previous fiscal year: $14,101 per student. Total enrollment: 39,755. Faculty: 2,874 (1,578 full-time, 1,296 part-time). Student-undergrad faculty ratio is 14:1. 35,501 applied, 59% were admitted. 23% from top 10% of their high school class, 56% from top quarter, 91% from top half. Full-time: 26,784 students, 54% women, 46% men. Part-time: 2,700 students, 49% women, 51% men. Students come from 50 states and territories, 125 other countries, 21% from out-of-state. 0.1% American Indian or Alaska Native, non-Hispanic/Latino; 7% Hispanic/Latino; 13% Black or African American, non-Hispanic/Latino; 12% Asian, non-Hispanic/Latino; 0.1% Native Hawaiian or other Pacific Islander, non-Hispanic/Latino; 6% international. 9% 25 or older, 20% live on campus, 8% transferred in. Retention: 89% of full-time freshmen returned the following year. Academic areas with the most degrees conferred: business/marketing; communication/journalism; visual and performing arts. Core. Calendar: semesters. Academic remediation for entering students, ESL program, services for LD students, advanced placement, accelerated degree program, honors program, independent study, distance learning, double major, summer session for credit, part-time degree program, adult/continuing education programs, co-op programs and internships, graduate courses open to undergrads. Off campus study. Study abroad program. ROTC: Army, Naval (c), Air Force (c).
Entrance Requirements: Options: electronic application, early action, deferred admission, international baccalaureate accepted. Required: essay, high school transcript. Recommended: minimum 3 high school GPA, 1 recommendation. Entrance: moderately difficult. Notification: continuous. SAT Reasoning Test deadline: 3/1. Transfer credits accepted: Yes. Applicants placed on waiting list: 3,571. Wait-listed applicants offered admission: 1,283. Early action applicants: 13,161. Early action applicants admitted: 9,350.
Costs Per Year: Application fee: $55. State resident tuition: $16,080 full-time, $670 per credit hour part-time. Nonresident tuition: $28,176 full-time, $1174 per credit hour part-time. Mandatory fees: $890 full-time, $163 per term part-time. Full-time tuition and fees vary according to course load and program. Part-time tuition and fees vary according to course load and program. College room and board: $11,916. College room only: $8004. Room and board charges vary according to board plan, housing facility, and location.
Collegiate Environment: Orientation program. Drama-theater group, choral group, marching band, student-run newspaper, radio station. Social organizations: 338 open to all; national fraternities, national sororities; 2% of eligible men and 3% of eligible women are members. Most popular organizations: Queer Student Union, Habitat for Humanity, Temple University Community Service Association, Gamers Guild, Feminist Alliance. Major annual events: Welcome Week, Homecoming, Alumni Weekend. Student services: legal services, health clinic, personal-psychological counseling, women's center. Campus security: 24-hour emergency response devices and patrols, student patrols, late night transport-escort service, controlled dormitory access. 5,918 college housing spaces available; 5,779 were occupied in 2018-19. No special consideration for freshman housing applicants. Option: coed housing available. Paley Library plus 6 others. Books: 3.4 million (physical), 1.6 million (digital/electronic); Serial titles: 61,478 (physical), 189,776 (digital/electronic); Databases: 773. Students can reserve study rooms. Operations spending for the previous fiscal year: $23.7 million. 15,100 computers available on campus for general student use. Computer purchase/lease plans available. A campuswide network can be accessed from student residence rooms and from off campus. Students can access the following: online class registration, student accounts, Web hosting. Staffed computer lab on campus (open 24 hours a day) provides training in use of computers, software, and the Internet.
Community Environment: "Birthplace of the Nation", Philadelphia has retained much of the charm of its colonial origins even while developing into one of the great industrial cities of the world. Population of the greater metropolitan area is over 2,000,000. Distinctive colonial characteristics such as the Liberty Bell and Independence Hall blend with evidence of vast

manufacturing. Narrow cobblestone streets may be found within blocks of the business district. The city has museums, churches of all denominations, many libraries (including the first Free Library in the United States), Fairmon Park (the largest city park in the U.S.), a zoo, planetarium, major league and collegiate sports teams, numerous cultural and entertainment facilities, and all the fraternal, civic, and community service organizations of any large metropolis. Local recreation includes golf, tennis, horseback riding, hunting, boating, fishing, and swimming.

■ **THADDEUS STEVENS COLLEGE OF TECHNOLOGY**
750 E King St.
Lancaster, PA 17602-3198
Tel: (717)299-7730; Free: 800-842-3832
Fax: (717)391-6929
E-mail: kwiatkowski@stevenscollege.edu
Web Site: www.stevenscollege.edu
Description: State-supported, 2-year, coed. Awards certificates, transfer associate, and terminal associate degrees. Founded 1905. Setting: 33-acre urban campus with easy access to Philadelphia. Endowment: $696,058. Educational spending for the previous fiscal year: $549 per student. Total enrollment: 1,142. Faculty: 80 (58 full-time, 22 part-time). Student-undergrad faculty ratio is 12:1. 2,673 applied, 31% were admitted. Full-time: 1,135 students, 9% women, 91% men. Part-time: 7 students, 14% women, 86% men. 0.6% American Indian or Alaska Native, non-Hispanic/Latino; 14% Hispanic/Latino; 10% Black or African American, non-Hispanic/Latino; 1% Asian, non-Hispanic/Latino. 4% 25 or older, 45% live on campus, 7% transferred in. Retention: 69% of full-time freshmen returned the following year. Core. Calendar: semesters. Academic remediation for entering students, services for LD students, advanced placement, internships.
Entrance Requirements: Options: electronic application, deferred admission. Required: essay, high school transcript, minimum 2 high school GPA, ACT, SAT, or ACT Compass. Required for some: interview. Entrance: moderately difficult. Application deadline: 6/30. Notification: continuous until 7/15. Preference given to needy students, indigent orphans. SAT Reasoning Test deadline: 6/30. SAT Subject Test deadline: 6/30. Transfer credits accepted: Yes. Applicants placed on waiting list: 100. Wait-listed applicants offered admission: 15.
Costs Per Year: Application fee: $45. State resident tuition: $8000 full-time.
Collegiate Environment: Orientation program. Social organizations: 14 open to all; 90% of eligible men and 10% of eligible women are members. Most popular organizations: Phi Theta Kappa, Student Congress, Residence Hall Council, American Institute of Architectural Students (AIAS), Society of Manufacturing Engineers (SME). Major annual events: Student Orientation, Homecoming, Spring Picnic. Student services: personal-psychological counseling, women's center. Campus security: 24-hour emergency response devices and patrols, controlled dormitory access. K. W. Schuler Learning Resources Center plus 1 other. Books: 59,073 (physical), 1,187 (digital/electronic); Serial titles: 21 (physical), 2,823 (digital/electronic); Databases: 21. Weekly public service hours: 78; students can reserve study rooms. Operations spending for the previous fiscal year: $366,398. 95 computers available on campus for general student use. A campuswide network can be accessed from off-campus. Students can access the following: online class registration. Staffed computer lab on campus provides training in use of computers and the Internet.

■ **THIEL COLLEGE**
75 College Ave.
Greenville, PA 16125-2181
Tel: (724)589-2000; Free: 800-248-4435
Fax: (724)589-2013
E-mail: admissions@thiel.edu
Web Site: www.thiel.edu
Description: Independent, 4-year, coed, affiliated with Evangelical Lutheran Church in America. Awards associate and bachelor's degrees. Founded 1866. Setting: 135-acre rural campus with easy access to Cleveland, Pittsburgh. Endowment: $31.4 million. Educational spending for the previous fiscal year: $7994 per student. Total enrollment: 926. Faculty: 93 (59 full-time, 34 part-time). Student-undergrad faculty ratio is 13:1. 2,275 applied, 61% were admitted. 9% from top 10% of their high school class, 13% from top quarter, 90% from top half. Full-time: 903 students, 46% women, 54% men. Part-time: 23 students, 57% women, 43% men. Students come from 10 states and territories, 10 other countries, 30% from out-of-state. 0.1% American Indian or Alaska Native, non-Hispanic/Latino; 2% Hispanic/Latino; 9% Black or African American, non-Hispanic/Latino; 0.1% Native Hawaiian

or other Pacific Islander, non-Hispanic/Latino; 4% international. 1% 25 or older, 95% live on campus, 2% transferred in. Retention: 67% of full-time freshmen returned the following year. Academic areas with the most degrees conferred: business/marketing; psychology; biological/life sciences. Core. Calendar: semesters. Academic remediation for entering students, services for LD students, advanced placement, honors program, independent study, distance learning, double major, summer session for credit, part-time degree program, adult/continuing education programs, co-op programs and internships. Off campus study at American University, Art Institute of Pittsburgh, Bryant and Stratton Business Institute (Buffalo, NY), Community College of Allegheny County, Drew University, Harrisburg Area Community College, Union College (KY). Study abroad program.
Entrance Requirements: Options: electronic application, deferred admission, international baccalaureate accepted. Required: essay, high school transcript, minimum 2 high school GPA, 1 recommendation, SAT or ACT. Required for some: interview. Entrance: moderately difficult. Application deadline: rolling. Notification: continuous. SAT Reasoning Test deadline: 7/1. SAT Subject Test deadline: 8/1. Transfer credits accepted: Yes.
Costs Per Year: Application fee: $0. Comprehensive fee: $44,300 includes full-time tuition ($29,870), mandatory fees ($1830), and college room and board ($12,600). College room only: $6300. Full-time tuition and fees vary according to course load. Room and board charges vary according to housing facility. Part-time tuition: $960 per credit hour. Part-time mandatory fees: $70 per credit hour. Part-time tuition and fees vary according to course load.
Collegiate Environment: Orientation program. Drama-theater group, choral group, marching band, student-run newspaper, radio station. Social organizations: 30 open to all; national fraternities, national sororities, local fraternities; 24% of eligible men and 28% of eligible women are members. Most popular organizations: Thiel Players Theatre Group, student government, Thiel Choir, Ski Club, Thiel Christian Fellowship. Major annual events: Homecoming, Winter Weekend, Farewell Festival. Student services: health clinic, personal-psychological counseling. Campus security: 24-hour emergency response devices and patrols, late night transport-escort service, controlled dormitory access. Langenheim Memorial Library. Operations spending for the previous fiscal year: $473,649. 147 computers available on campus for general student use. Computer purchase/lease plans available. A computer is required for all students. A campuswide network can be accessed from student residence rooms and from off campus. Students can access the following: online class registration.
Community Environment: Local industry is devoted principally to the manufacture of steel, cars, tanks, structural steel and other steel and aluminum products. Greenville is a small town of 10,000 situated halfway between Erie and Pittsburgh. Cleveland and Youngstown are also with 1 to 1 1/2 hours driving. The community is served by railroad, bus lines, and airlines located at nearby Youngstown airport. Greenville has numerous churches, public library, hospital, and excellent shopping and restaurants. Part-time employment is available. Local recreational facilities include a symphony orchestra, theatre and a number of civic parks. Nearby lakes provide boating, swimming, fishing, water skiing, and golf courses. There are various civic, fraternal, and veteran's organizations active in the community.

■ **THOMAS JEFFERSON UNIVERSITY**
1020 Walnut St.
Philadelphia, PA 19107
Tel: (215)955-6000; Free: 877-533-3247
Fax: (215)503-7241
E-mail: chpadmissions@mail.tju.edu
Web Site: www.jefferson.edu/university.html
Description: Independent, university, coed. Awards associate, bachelor's, master's, and doctoral degrees. Founded 1824. Setting: 13-acre urban campus. Total enrollment: 3,326. Faculty: 215 (149 full-time, 66 part-time). Student-undergrad faculty ratio is 15:1. 61% 25 or older. Core. Calendar: semesters. Academic remediation for entering students, services for LD students, advanced placement, accelerated degree program, honors program, independent study, distance learning, double major, part-time degree program, adult/continuing education programs, co-op programs and internships, graduate courses open to undergrads. Off campus study. Study abroad program. ROTC: Air Force (c).
Entrance Requirements: Option: deferred admission. Required: essay, minimum 3 high school GPA, 2 recommendations, interview. Recommended: SAT or ACT. Required for some: high school transcript, NET. Entrance: moderately difficult. Application deadline: rolling. Notification: continuous.
Costs Per Year: Application fee: $50. Comprehensive fee: $53,966 includes full-time tuition ($39,495), mandatory fees ($1006), and college room and

board ($13,465). College room only: $6295. Full-time tuition and fees vary according to degree level and location. Room and board charges vary according to board plan, housing facility, and location. Part-time tuition: $605 per credit hour. Part-time mandatory fees: $30 per credit hour. Part-time tuition and fees vary according to class time and degree level.

Collegiate Environment: Orientation program. Choral group. Student services: health clinic, personal-psychological counseling. Campus security: 24-hour emergency response devices and patrols, late night transport-escort service, controlled dormitory access. Scott Memorial Library plus 1 other. Study areas open 24 hours, 5-7 days a week; students can reserve study rooms.

■ **THOMAS JEFFERSON UNIVERSITY-EAST FALLS CAMPUS**
4201 Henry Ave.
Philadelphia, PA 19144
Tel: (215)951-2700

■ **TRIANGLE TECH, BETHLEHEM**
3184 Airport Rd.
Bethlehem, PA 18017
Tel: (610)691-1300
Web Site: www.triangle-tech.edu
Description: Proprietary, 2-year, coed. Awards terminal associate degrees. Setting: urban campus. Total enrollment: 140. Faculty: 10 (8 full-time, 2 part-time). Student-undergrad faculty ratio is 15:1. 109 applied, 99% were admitted. Full-time: 140 students, 4% women, 96% men. Students come from 2 states and territories, 11% from out-of-state. 34% 25 or older, 4% transferred in. Core.
Entrance Requirements: Open admission. Required: high school transcript, interview. Entrance: noncompetitive. Transfer credits accepted: Yes.
Collegiate Environment: Orientation program. Main library plus 1 other. 27 computers available on campus for general student use.

■ **TRIANGLE TECH, DUBOIS**
225 Tannery Row Rd.
Falls Creek, PA 15840
Tel: (814)371-2090; Free: 800-874-8324
Fax: (814)371-9227
E-mail: tkucic@triangle-tech.com
Web Site: www.triangle-tech.edu
Description: Proprietary, 2-year, coed. Part of Triangle Tech Group, Inc. Awards diplomas and terminal associate degrees. Founded 1944. Setting: 5-acre small town campus. Total enrollment: 329. Faculty: 21 (all full-time). Student-undergrad faculty ratio is 15:1. 246 applied, 100% were admitted. Full-time: 329 students, 3% women, 97% men. Students come from 2 states and territories, 1 other country. 48% 25 or older. Core. Calendar: semesters. Academic remediation for entering students, advanced placement. Off campus study at all other campuses of Triangle Tech.
Entrance Requirements: Option: deferred admission. Required: high school transcript, minimum 2 high school GPA, interview. Entrance: minimally difficult. Application deadline: rolling. Transfer credits accepted: Yes.
Collegiate Environment: Orientation program. Social organizations: 1 open to all. Most popular organization: Student Council. Major annual events: Christmas Luncheon, Student Appreciation Luncheon. Library Resource Center. 54 computers available on campus for general student use. A campuswide network can be accessed. Staffed computer lab on campus provides training in use of computers, software, and the Internet.

■ **TRIANGLE TECH, ERIE**
2000 Liberty St.
Erie, PA 16502-2594
Tel: (814)453-6016; Free: 800-TRI-TECH
Fax: (814)454-2818
Web Site: www.triangle-tech.edu
Description: Proprietary, 2-year, coed. Part of Triangle Tech Group, Inc. Awards transfer associate and terminal associate degrees. Founded 1976. Setting: 1-acre urban campus. Total enrollment: 176. Faculty: 16 (14 full-time, 2 part-time). Student-undergrad faculty ratio is 12:1. 76 applied, 100% were admitted. Full-time: 176 students, 5% women, 95% men. Students come from 3 states and territories, 10% from out-of-state. 65% 25 or older. Core. Calendar: semesters. Academic remediation for entering students, services for LD students, advanced placement.

Entrance Requirements: Option: deferred admission. Required: high school transcript, interview. Entrance: minimally difficult. Application deadline: rolling.
Collegiate Environment: Orientation program. Social organizations: 1 open to all. Campus security: 24-hour emergency response devices. 50 computers available on campus for general student use. Staffed computer lab on campus provides training in use of computers, software, and the Internet.

■ **TRIANGLE TECH, GREENSBURG**
222 E Pittsburgh St.
Ste. A
Greensburg, PA 15601-3304
Tel: (724)832-1050; Free: 800-874-8324
Web Site: www.triangle-tech.edu
Description: Proprietary, 2-year, coed. Part of Triangle Tech Group, Inc. Awards diplomas and terminal associate degrees. Founded 1944. Setting: 1-acre small town campus with easy access to Pittsburgh. Total enrollment: 260. Faculty: 21 (all full-time). Student-undergrad faculty ratio is 12:1. 247 applied, 100% were admitted. Full-time: 260 students, 2% women, 98% men. 45% 25 or older. Core. Calendar: semesters. Academic remediation for entering students, advanced placement, summer session for credit, adult/continuing education programs.
Entrance Requirements: Option: deferred admission. Required: high school transcript, interview. Entrance: moderately difficult. Application deadline: rolling. Transfer credits accepted: Yes.
Collegiate Environment: Orientation program. Student services: personal-psychological counseling. Triangle Tech Library plus 1 other. 55 computers available on campus for general student use. A campuswide network can be accessed. Staffed computer lab on campus provides training in use of computers, software, and the Internet.

■ **TRIANGLE TECH, PITTSBURGH**
1940 Perrysville Ave.
Pittsburgh, PA 15214-3897
Tel: (412)359-1000; Free: 800-874-8324
Fax: (412)359-1012
E-mail: info@triangle-tech.edu
Web Site: www.triangle-tech.edu
Description: Proprietary, 2-year, coed. Part of Triangle Tech Group, Inc. Awards transfer associate and terminal associate degrees. Founded 1944. Setting: 5-acre urban campus. Total enrollment: 102. Student-undergrad faculty ratio is 12:1. Full-time: 103 students, 2% women, 98% men. Students come from 3 states and territories, 2% from out-of-state. 44% 25 or older, 1% transferred in. Retention: 78% of full-time freshmen returned the following year. Core. Calendar: semesters. Academic remediation for entering students.
Entrance Requirements: Required: high school transcript, minimum 2 high school GPA, interview. Entrance: moderately difficult. Application deadline: rolling.
Collegiate Environment: Campus security: 16-hour patrols by trained security personnel.

■ **TRIANGLE TECH, SUNBURY**
191 Performance Rd.
Sunbury, PA 17801
Tel: (570)988-0700
Web Site: www.triangle-tech.edu
Description: Proprietary, 2-year, coed. Awards terminal associate degrees. Setting: 4-acre rural campus. Total enrollment: 170. Faculty: 15 (14 full-time, 1 part-time). Student-undergrad faculty ratio is 12:1. 76 applied, 100% were admitted. Full-time: 170 students, 2% women, 98% men. Students come from 2 states and territories, 0.01% from out-of-state. 39% 25 or older. Retention: 75% of full-time freshmen returned the following year. Core. Calendar: semesters. Advanced placement, co-op programs.
Entrance Requirements: Required: high school transcript.
Collegiate Environment: Orientation program. Main library plus 1 other. 26 computers available on campus for general student use.

■ **THE UNIVERSITY OF THE ARTS**
320 S Broad St.
Philadelphia, PA 19102-4944
Tel: (215)717-6000; Free: 800-616-ARTS
Fax: (215)717-6045
E-mail: admissions@uarts.edu

Web Site: www.uarts.edu

Description: Independent, comprehensive, coed. Awards bachelor's and master's degrees. Founded 1876. Setting: 21-acre urban campus with easy access to Philadelphia. Total enrollment: 1,860. Faculty: 467 (106 full-time, 361 part-time). Student-undergrad faculty ratio is 8:1. 1,714 applied, 74% were admitted. Full-time: 1,653 students, 62% women, 38% men. Part-time: 28 students, 54% women, 46% men. Students come from 44 states and territories, 25 other countries, 58% from out-of-state. 0.4% American Indian or Alaska Native, non-Hispanic/Latino; 11% Hispanic/Latino; 17% Black or African American, non-Hispanic/Latino; 2% Asian, non-Hispanic/Latino; 0.1% Native Hawaiian or other Pacific Islander, non-Hispanic/Latino; 4% international. 5% 25 or older, 6% transferred in. Retention: 82% of full-time freshmen returned the following year. Academic area with the most degrees conferred: visual and performing arts. Core. Calendar: semesters. Academic remediation for entering students, ESL program, services for LD students, advanced placement, honors program, independent study, double major, summer session for credit, part-time degree program, internships, graduate courses open to undergrads. Off campus study at University of the Sciences in Philadelphia; Peirce College, Philadelphia. Study abroad program.

Entrance Requirements: Options: electronic application, early admission, deferred admission, international baccalaureate accepted. Required: high school transcript. Recommended: minimum 2 high school GPA. Required for some: interview, audition or portfolio required for performing arts programs; portfolio for design, visual arts, film programs. Entrance: moderately difficult. Application deadline: rolling. Notification: continuous. Transfer credits accepted: Yes.

Costs Per Year: Application fee: $60. Comprehensive fee: $61,102 includes full-time tuition ($44,780) and college room and board ($16,322). College room only: $10,540. Room and board charges vary according to board plan and housing facility. Part-time tuition: $1866 per credit hour. Part-time tuition varies according to course load.

Collegiate Environment: Orientation program. Drama-theater group, choral group. Social organizations: Alpha Psi Omega (National Theater Honor society). Student services: health clinic, personal-psychological counseling. Campus security: 24-hour emergency response devices and patrols, crime prevention workshops and seminars. Albert M. Greenfield Library plus 1 other.

Community Environment: The campus is located in the heart of Philadelphia's cultural community. The area has theaters, museums, galleries, music and dance facilities, restaurants of many ethnic varieties, and major department stores and shops. Philadelphia offers a broad mix of experiences of historical importance. The city is also known as a supporter of the arts. Urban and sophisticated, it is at the same time a series of small, close-knit neighborhoods. Fairmount Park, the largest municipal park in the world, provides facilities for boating, fishing, hiking, biking, picnicking, and relaxing.

■ **UNIVERSITY OF PENNSYLVANIA**

3451 Walnut St.
Philadelphia, PA 19104
Tel: (215)898-5000
Web Site: www.upenn.edu

Description: Independent, university, coed. Awards associate, bachelor's, master's, and doctoral degrees and post-master's certificates (also offers evening program with significant enrollment not reflected in profile). Founded 1740. Setting: 299-acre urban campus. Endowment: $12.2 billion. Research spending for the previous fiscal year: $757 million. Educational spending for the previous fiscal year: $366,105 per student. Total enrollment: 22,376. Faculty: 2,039 (1,570 full-time, 469 part-time). Student-undergrad faculty ratio is 6:1. 44,491 applied, 8% were admitted. 96% from top 10% of their high school class, 99% from top quarter, 100% from top half. Full-time: 9,931 students, 52% women, 48% men. Part-time: 252 students, 43% women, 57% men. 81% from out-of-state. 0.1% American Indian or Alaska Native, non-Hispanic/Latino; 10% Hispanic/Latino; 7% Black or African American, non-Hispanic/Latino; 21% Asian, non-Hispanic/Latino; 0.1% Native Hawaiian or other Pacific Islander, non-Hispanic/Latino; 13% international. 51% live on campus, 1% transferred in. Retention: 98% of full-time freshmen returned the following year. Academic areas with the most degrees conferred: business/marketing; social sciences; biological/life sciences. Core. Calendar: semesters plus 2 5-week summer sessions. Academic remediation for entering students, ESL program, services for LD students, advanced placement, accelerated degree program, self-designed majors, honors program, independent study, distance learning, double major, summer session for credit, part-time degree program, adult/continuing education

programs, co-op programs and internships, graduate courses open to undergrads. Off campus study at Bryn Mawr College, Haverford College, Swarthmore College. Study abroad program. ROTC: Army (c), Naval, Air Force (c).

Entrance Requirements: Options: electronic application, early admission, early decision, deferred admission, international baccalaureate accepted. Required: essay, high school transcript, 2 recommendations, SAT or ACT. Recommended: SAT Subject Tests. Entrance: most difficult. Application deadlines: 1/5, 11/1 for early decision. Notification: continuous until 4/1, 12/15 for early decision. SAT Reasoning Test deadline: 2/1. SAT Subject Test deadline: 2/1. Applicants placed on waiting list: 3,535. Wait-listed applicants offered admission: 9. Early decision applicants: 7,073. Early decision applicants admitted: 1,312.

Costs Per Year: Application fee: $75. Comprehensive fee: $73,960 includes full-time tuition ($51,156), mandatory fees ($6614), and college room and board ($16,190). College room only: $10,600.

Collegiate Environment: Orientation program. Drama-theater group, choral group, marching band, student-run newspaper, radio station. Social organizations: 350 open to all; national fraternities, national sororities; 30% of eligible men and 27% of eligible women are members. Most popular organizations: Kite and Key Society, Social Planning and Events Committee, Hillel at Penn, Sports Club Council, Interfraternity Council. Major annual events: Homecoming, Spring Fling, Hey Day. Student services: legal services, health clinic, personal-psychological counseling, women's center. Campus security: 24-hour emergency response devices and patrols, late night transport-escort service, controlled dormitory access. Freshmen guaranteed college housing. Option: coed housing available. Van Pelt Library plus 14 others. Books: 6.4 million (physical); Serial titles: 188,604 (physical). Study areas open 24 hours, 5-7 days a week; students can reserve study rooms. Operations spending for the previous fiscal year: $8.9 million.

Community Environment: Philadelphia is a large city with the feel of small villages; many with distinct characters. It is a center of history, culture and business, opera, symphony and ballet, museums, major sports teams and theater. The city is ideally located near both seashore and ski resorts.

■ **UNIVERSITY OF PITTSBURGH**

4200 Fifth Ave.
Pittsburgh, PA 15260
Tel: (412)624-4141
Fax: (412)648-8815
E-mail: oafa@pitt.edu
Web Site: www.pitt.edu

Description: State-related, university, coed. Part of Commonwealth System of Higher Education. Awards bachelor's, master's, and doctoral degrees and post-master's certificates. Founded 1787. Setting: 145-acre urban campus with easy access to Pittsburgh. Endowment: $4.2 billion. Total enrollment: 28,673. Faculty: 2,339 (1,791 full-time, 548 part-time). Student-undergrad faculty ratio is 14:1. 29,857 applied, 59% were admitted. 55% from top 10% of their high school class, 88% from top quarter, 99% from top half. Full-time: 18,421 students, 53% women, 47% men. Part-time: 909 students, 47% women, 53% men. Students come from 51 states and territories, 55 other countries, 27% from out-of-state. 0.1% American Indian or Alaska Native, non-Hispanic/Latino; 4% Hispanic/Latino; 5% Black or African American, non-Hispanic/Latino; 10% Asian, non-Hispanic/Latino; 5% international. 5% 25 or older, 43% live on campus, 4% transferred in. Retention: 93% of full-time freshmen returned the following year. Academic areas with the most degrees conferred: business/marketing; engineering; health professions and related sciences. Core. Calendar: semesters plus summer term. Academic remediation for entering students, ESL program, services for LD students, advanced placement, accelerated degree program, self-designed majors, freshman honors college, honors program, independent study, distance learning, double major, summer session for credit, part-time degree program, external degree program, adult/continuing education programs, co-op programs and internships, graduate courses open to undergrads. Off campus study at 10 other institutions in the surrounding area. Study abroad program. ROTC: Army, Naval (c), Air Force.

Entrance Requirements: Options: electronic application, international baccalaureate accepted. Required: high school transcript, SAT or ACT. Recommended: essay, interview. Entrance: very difficult. Application deadline: rolling. Notification: continuous. Transfer credits accepted: Yes. Applicants placed on waiting list: 1,664. Wait-listed applicants offered admission: 24.

Costs Per Year: Application fee: $45. State resident tuition: $18,130 full-time, $755 per credit hour part-time. Nonresident tuition: $31,102 full-time,

$1295 per credit hour part-time. Mandatory fees: $950 full-time, $279 per term part-time. Full-time tuition and fees vary according to location and program. Part-time tuition and fees vary according to location and program. College room and board: $11,050. College room only: $6400. Room and board charges vary according to board plan, housing facility, and location.

Collegiate Environment: Orientation program. Drama-theater group, choral group, marching band, student-run newspaper, radio station. Social organizations: 595 open to all; national fraternities, national sororities; 10% of eligible men and 12% of eligible women are members. Most popular organizations: Resident Student Association, Black Action Society, Pitt Program Council, Interfraternity Council, Panhellenic Association. Major annual events: Homecoming Laser and Fireworks Show, Fall Fest, Bigelow Bash. Student services: health clinic, personal-psychological counseling. Campus security: 24-hour emergency response devices and patrols, late night transport-escort service, controlled dormitory access. 7,831 college housing spaces available; all were occupied in 2018-19. Freshmen guaranteed college housing. Option: coed housing available. Hillman Library plus 16 others. Books: 4.3 million (physical), 1.7 million (digital/electronic); Serial titles: 108,985 (physical), 261,311 (digital/electronic); Databases: 571. Weekly public service hours: 145; study areas open 24 hours, 5-7 days a week; students can reserve study rooms. 1,156 computers available on campus for general student use. Computer purchase/lease plans available. A campuswide network can be accessed from student residence rooms and from off campus. Students can access the following: online class registration, online class listings, online tuition payment. Staffed computer lab on campus (open 24 hours a day) provides training in use of computers, software, and the Internet.

Community Environment: Pittsburgh is a city of hills, rivers, and bridges, and a mixture of traditional and contemporary lifestyles. Accessible by air, bus, and rail its attractions include concerts, folk festivals, the Pittsburgh Symphony, Phipps Conservatory, professional sports, museums, libraries, parks, and art galleries.

■ **UNIVERSITY OF PITTSBURGH AT BRADFORD**

300 Campus Dr.
Bradford, PA 16701-2812
Tel: (814)362-7500; Free: 800-872-1787
Fax: (814)362-7578
E-mail: monti@pitt.edu
Web Site: www.upb.pitt.edu

Description: State-related, 4-year, coed. Part of University of Pittsburgh System. Awards associate and bachelor's degrees. Founded 1963. Setting: 317-acre small town campus with easy access to Buffalo. Endowment: $26.7 million. Research spending for the previous fiscal year: $262,387. Educational spending for the previous fiscal year: $6801 per student. Total enrollment: 1,293. Faculty: 149 (75 full-time, 74 part-time). Student-undergrad faculty ratio is 16:1. 3,135 applied, 51% were admitted. 10% from top 10% of their high school class, 33% from top quarter, 70% from top half. 4 valedictorians. Full-time: 1,210 students, 55% women, 45% men. Part-time: 83 students, 63% women, 37% men. Students come from 30 states and territories, 13 other countries, 26% from out-of-state. 0.5% American Indian or Alaska Native, non-Hispanic/Latino; 6% Hispanic/Latino; 13% Black or African American, non-Hispanic/Latino; 3% Asian, non-Hispanic/Latino; 0.1% Native Hawaiian or other Pacific Islander, non-Hispanic/Latino; 2% international. 7% 25 or older, 72% live on campus, 8% transferred in. Retention: 68% of full-time freshmen returned the following year. Academic areas with the most degrees conferred: business/marketing; parks and recreation; homeland security, law enforcement, firefighting, and protective services. Core. Calendar: semesters. Academic remediation for entering students, services for LD students, advanced placement, accelerated degree program, self-designed majors, independent study, distance learning, double major, summer session for credit, part-time degree program, adult/continuing education programs, co-op programs and internships. Off campus study at University of Pittsburgh - Oakland, University of Pittsburgh - Greensburg, University of Pittsburgh - Johnstown, University of Pittsburgh - Titusville. Study abroad program. ROTC: Army (c).

Entrance Requirements: Options: electronic application, deferred admission, international baccalaureate accepted. Required: high school transcript, minimum 2 high school GPA, SAT or ACT. Recommended: essay, 2 recommendations, interview. Required for some: minimum 3 high school GPA. Entrance: minimally difficult. Application deadlines: rolling, rolling for nonresidents. Notification: continuous, continuous for nonresidents. SAT Reasoning Test deadline: 8/24. Transfer credits accepted: Yes. Applicants placed on waiting list: 0. Wait-listed applicants offered admission: 0.

Costs Per Year: One-time mandatory fee: $90. State resident tuition: $12,940 full-time, $539 per credit hour part-time. Nonresident tuition: $24,184 full-time, $1007 per credit hour part-time. Mandatory fees: $960 full-time, $165 per term part-time. Full-time tuition and fees vary according to course load and program. Part-time tuition and fees vary according to course load and program. College room and board: $10,222. College room only: $6272. Room and board charges vary according to board plan and housing facility.

Collegiate Environment: Orientation program. Drama-theater group, choral group, student-run radio station. Social organizations: 60 open to all; national fraternities, national sororities, local fraternities, local sororities; 2% of eligible men and 2% of eligible women are members. Most popular organizations: Student Government Association, Student Activities Board, The Source (student newspaper), Alpha Phi Omega, WDRQ (student radio station). Major annual events: Alumni Weekend, Winter Weekend, Spring Fling. Student services: health clinic, personal-psychological counseling. Campus security: 24-hour emergency response devices and patrols, late night transport-escort service, controlled dormitory access. 950 college housing spaces available; 903 were occupied in 2018-19. Freshmen guaranteed college housing. On-campus residence required in freshman year. Option: coed housing available. T. Edward and Tullah Hanley Library. Books: 107,555 (physical), 1.3 million (digital/electronic); Serial titles: 72 (physical), 261,311 (digital/electronic); Databases: 581. Weekly public service hours: 86; students can reserve study rooms. Operations spending for the previous fiscal year: $17,600. 133 computers available on campus for general student use. A campuswide network can be accessed from student residence rooms and from off campus. Students can access the following: online class registration, online bills. Staffed computer lab on campus provides training in use of computers, software, and the Internet.

■ **UNIVERSITY OF PITTSBURGH AT GREENSBURG**

150 Finoli Dr.
Greensburg, PA 15601-5860
Tel: (724)837-7040
Fax: (724)836-9901
E-mail: upgadmit@pitt.edu
Web Site: www.greensburg.pitt.edu

Description: State-related, 4-year, coed. Part of University of Pittsburgh System. Awards bachelor's degrees. Founded 1963. Setting: 219-acre small town campus with easy access to Pittsburgh. Total enrollment: 1,523. 2,518 applied, 73% were admitted. 9% from top 10% of their high school class, 31% from top quarter, 73% from top half. Full-time: 1,436 students, 54% women, 46% men. Part-time: 87 students, 54% women, 46% men. 4% from out-of-state. 0.1% American Indian or Alaska Native, non-Hispanic/Latino; 6% Hispanic/Latino; 6% Black or African American, non-Hispanic/Latino; 5% Asian, non-Hispanic/Latino; 0.1% Native Hawaiian or other Pacific Islander, non-Hispanic/Latino; 1% international. 8% 25 or older, 43% live on campus, 7% transferred in. Retention: 76% of full-time freshmen returned the following year. Academic areas with the most degrees conferred: business/marketing; psychology; biological/life sciences. Core. Calendar: semesters. Academic remediation for entering students, services for LD students, advanced placement, accelerated degree program, self-designed majors, independent study, distance learning, double major, summer session for credit, part-time degree program, adult/continuing education programs, internships. Off campus study at Seton Hill College, other units of the University of Pittsburgh, Westmoreland County Community College. Study abroad program. ROTC: Army, Air Force (c).

Entrance Requirements: Options: electronic application, early admission, deferred admission. Required: high school transcript, minimum 2.5 high school GPA, SAT or ACT. Recommended: essay, interview. Entrance: moderately difficult. Application deadline: rolling. Notification: continuous. Transfer credits accepted: Yes.

Costs Per Year: Application fee: $45. State resident tuition: $12,940 full-time, $539 per credit hour part-time. Nonresident tuition: $24,184 full-time, $1007 per credit hour part-time. Mandatory fees: $930 full-time, $174 per term part-time. Full-time tuition and fees vary according to program. Part-time tuition and fees vary according to program. College room and board: $10,520. College room only: $6450. Room and board charges vary according to board plan and housing facility.

Collegiate Environment: Orientation program. Drama-theater group, choral group, student-run newspaper. Social organizations: 40 open to all. Most popular organizations: Habitat for Humanity, Student Government Association, Student Activities Board, Outdoor Adventure and Community Service, Freshmen Honor Society - Phi Eta Sigma. Major annual events: Into the

Streets (community volunteer event), Big Bang (fall term kick-off), Up All Night (end of term event). Student services: health clinic, personal-psychological counseling. Campus security: 24-hour emergency response devices and patrols, late night transport-escort service, controlled dormitory access. Millstein Library.

■ UNIVERSITY OF PITTSBURGH AT JOHNSTOWN

450 Schoolhouse Rd.
Johnstown, PA 15904-2990
Tel: (814)269-7000; Free: 800-765-4875
Fax: (814)269-7044
E-mail: upjadmit@pitt.edu
Web Site: www.upj.pitt.edu

Description: State-related, 4-year, coed. Part of University of Pittsburgh System. Awards associate and bachelor's degrees. Founded 1927. Setting: 655-acre suburban campus with easy access to Pittsburgh. Total enrollment: 2,769. Faculty: 151 (137 full-time, 14 part-time). Student-undergrad faculty ratio is 20:1. 1,613 applied, 88% were admitted. 13% from top 10% of their high school class, 37% from top quarter, 72% from top half. 8 valedictorians. Full-time: 2,708 students, 44% women, 56% men. Part-time: 61 students, 51% women, 49% men. Students come from 14 states and territories, 12 other countries, 2% from out-of-state. 0.2% American Indian or Alaska Native, non-Hispanic/Latino; 2% Hispanic/Latino; 4% Black or African American, non-Hispanic/Latino; 2% Asian, non-Hispanic/Latino; 0.1% Native Hawaiian or other Pacific Islander, non-Hispanic/Latino; 2% international. 6% 25 or older, 59% live on campus, 4% transferred in. Retention: 79% of full-time freshmen returned the following year. Academic areas with the most degrees conferred: business/marketing; engineering technologies; biological/life sciences; psychology; English. Core. Calendar: semesters. Services for LD students, advanced placement, accelerated degree program, self-designed majors, independent study, distance learning, double major, summer session for credit, part-time degree program, adult/continuing education programs, co-op programs and internships. Off campus study at members of the Pittsburgh Council on Higher Education. Study abroad program.

Entrance Requirements: Options: electronic application, early admission, deferred admission, international baccalaureate accepted. Required: high school transcript, minimum 2 high school GPA, SAT or ACT. Recommended: essay, 3 recommendations, interview. Entrance: moderately difficult. Application deadline: rolling. Notification: continuous. SAT Reasoning Test deadline: 5/1. Transfer credits accepted: Yes.

Costs Per Year: State resident tuition: $12,940 full-time, $539 per credit part-time. Nonresident tuition: $24,184 full-time, $1007 per credit part-time. Mandatory fees: $936 full-time, $127 per term part-time. Full-time tuition and fees vary according to program. Part-time tuition and fees vary according to program. College room and board: $9950. College room only: $5810. Room and board charges vary according to board plan and housing facility.

Collegiate Environment: Orientation program. Drama-theater group, choral group, student-run newspaper, radio station. Social organizations: 95 open to all; national fraternities, national sororities; 8% of eligible men and 11% of eligible women are members. Most popular organizations: Dance Ensemble, Student Senate, Programming Board, academic clubs. Major annual events: Homecoming, Greek Week. Student services: health clinic, personal-psychological counseling. Campus security: 24-hour emergency response devices and patrols, late night transport-escort service, controlled dormitory access. Owen Library. Study areas open 24 hours, 5-7 days a week. 222 computers available on campus for general student use. Computer purchase/lease plans available. A campuswide network can be accessed from student residence rooms and from off campus. Students can access the following: online class registration. Staffed computer lab on campus provides training in use of computers, software, and the Internet.

■ UNIVERSITY OF PITTSBURGH AT TITUSVILLE

504 E Main St.
Titusville, PA 16354
Tel: (814)827-4400; Free: 888-878-0462
Fax: (814)827-4448
E-mail: motter@pitt.edu
Web Site: www.upt.pitt.edu

Description: State-related, 2-year, coed. Part of University of Pittsburgh System. Awards transfer associate and terminal associate degrees. Founded 1963. Setting: 10-acre small town campus. Endowment: $850,000. Total enrollment: 388. Faculty: 48 (25 full-time, 23 part-time). Student-undergrad faculty ratio is 15:1. 9% from top 10% of their high school class,

26% from top quarter, 68% from top half. 1 valedictorian. Full-time: 313 students, 63% women, 37% men. Part-time: 75 students, 76% women, 24% men. Students come from 15 states and territories, 8% from out-of-state. 4% Hispanic/Latino; 14% Black or African American, non-Hispanic/Latino; 2% Asian, non-Hispanic/Latino. 14% 25 or older, 57% live on campus, 4% transferred in. Core. Calendar: semesters. Academic remediation for entering students, advanced placement, distance learning, summer session for credit, part-time degree program, internships.

Entrance Requirements: Required: high school transcript, minimum 2 high school GPA, SAT or ACT. Recommended: interview. Required for some: essay.

Collegiate Environment: Orientation program. Social organizations: 20 open to all. Most popular organizations: Phi Theta Kappa, BSU, SAB, Dining Club, Diversity Club. Major annual events: Talent Show, Semi-formal Dance, Stress Relief Week. Student services: health clinic, personal-psychological counseling. Campus security: 24-hour emergency response devices and patrols, late night transport-escort service, controlled dormitory access. Haskell Memorial Library. 74 computers available on campus for general student use. A campuswide network can be accessed from student residence rooms and from off campus. Students can access the following: online class registration. Staffed computer lab on campus provides training in use of computers, software, and the Internet.

■ UNIVERSITY OF THE SCIENCES

600 S 43rd St.
Philadelphia, PA 19104-4495
Tel: (215)596-8800; Free: 888-996-8747
Fax: (215)895-1100
E-mail: admit@usciences.edu
Web Site: www.usciences.edu

Description: Independent, university, coed. Awards bachelor's, master's, and doctoral degrees. Founded 1821. Setting: 35-acre urban campus with easy access to Philadelphia. Endowment: $174.5 million. Research spending for the previous fiscal year: $41.6 million. Total enrollment: 2,664. Faculty: 419 (189 full-time, 230 part-time). Student-undergrad faculty ratio is 9:1. 3,738 applied, 58% were admitted. Full-time: 2,215 students, 61% women, 39% men. Part-time: 31 students, 71% women, 29% men. Students come from 33 states and territories, 56% from out-of-state. 0.5% American Indian or Alaska Native, non-Hispanic/Latino; 4% Hispanic/Latino; 6% Black or African American, non-Hispanic/Latino; 35% Asian, non-Hispanic/Latino; 0.1% Native Hawaiian or other Pacific Islander, non-Hispanic/Latino; 1% international. 2% transferred in. Retention: 90% of full-time freshmen returned the following year. Academic areas with the most degrees conferred: health professions and related sciences; biological/life sciences; parks and recreation. Core. Calendar: semesters. Academic remediation for entering students, services for LD students, advanced placement, accelerated degree program, honors program, distance learning, double major, summer session for credit, part-time degree program, adult/continuing education programs, co-op programs and internships, graduate courses open to undergrads. Off campus study at University of the Arts. Study abroad program. ROTC: Army (c), Air Force (c).

Entrance Requirements: Options: electronic application, deferred admission, international baccalaureate accepted. Required: essay, high school transcript, minimum 3 high school GPA, 1 recommendation, SAT or ACT. Required for some: interview, TOEFL or IELTS for non-English as first language applicants. Entrance: moderately difficult. Application deadline: 8/15. Notification: continuous, continuous for nonresidents. SAT Reasoning Test deadline: 8/15. SAT Subject Test deadline: 8/15. Transfer credits accepted: Yes.

Costs Per Year: Application fee: $45. Tuition: $25,000 full-time, $770 per credit hour part-time. Mandatory fees: $53 per credit hour part-time. Full-time tuition varies according to program. Part-time tuition and fees vary according to course load and program. Tuition guaranteed not to increase for student's term of enrollment.

Collegiate Environment: Orientation program. Drama-theater group, choral group, student-run newspaper. Social organizations: 65 open to all; national fraternities, national sororities, local fraternities, local sororities; 15% of eligible men and 15% of eligible women are members. Most popular organizations: Student Government Association, Hillel: Jewish Student Association, Pre-Medical Society, Society of Physics Students, American Chemical Society. Major annual events: Greek Week, Student Appreciation Day, Parent's Weekend. Student services: health clinic, personal-psychological counseling. Campus security: 24-hour emergency response devices and patrols, late night transport-escort service, controlled dormitory access. Joseph W. England Library. Operations spending for the previous fiscal year: $1.8 million.

■ THE UNIVERSITY OF SCRANTON

800 Linden St.
Scranton, PA 18510
Tel: (570)941-7400; Free: 888-SCRANTON
Fax: (570)941-5928
E-mail: admissions@scranton.edu
Web Site: www.scranton.edu

Description: Independent Roman Catholic (Jesuit), comprehensive, coed. Awards bachelor's, master's, and doctoral degrees and post-master's certificates. Founded 1888. Setting: 50-acre urban campus. Endowment: $187.2 million. Educational spending for the previous fiscal year: $38,817 per student. Total enrollment: 4,993. Faculty: 468 (281 full-time, 187 part-time). Student-undergrad faculty ratio is 12:1. 10,002 applied, 76% were admitted. 32% from top 10% of their high school class, 63% from top quarter, 89% from top half. Full-time: 3,630 students, 58% women, 42% men. Part-time: 180 students, 54% women, 46% men. Students come from 25 states and territories, 25 other countries, 61% from out-of-state. 0.2% American Indian or Alaska Native, non-Hispanic/Latino; 9% Hispanic/Latino; 2% Black or African American, non-Hispanic/Latino; 2% Asian, non-Hispanic/Latino; 0.2% Native Hawaiian or other Pacific Islander, non-Hispanic/Latino; 1% international. 2% 25 or older, 65% live on campus, 1% transferred in. Retention: 87% of full-time freshmen returned the following year. Academic areas with the most degrees conferred: business/marketing; health professions and related sciences; biological/life sciences. Core. Calendar: semesters. Academic remediation for entering students, services for LD students, advanced placement, accelerated degree program, self-designed majors, honors program, independent study, distance learning, double major, summer session for credit, part-time degree program, adult/continuing education programs, internships, graduate courses open to undergrads. Off campus study at Marywood University. Study abroad program. ROTC: Army, Air Force (c).

Entrance Requirements: Options: electronic application, early admission, early action, deferred admission, international baccalaureate accepted. Required: essay, high school transcript, 1 recommendation, SAT or ACT. Required for some: interview. Entrance: moderately difficult. Application deadlines: 3/1, 11/15 for early action. Notification: continuous until 1/5, 12/15 for early action. SAT Reasoning Test deadline: 3/1. Transfer credits accepted: Yes. Applicants placed on waiting list: 1,049. Wait-listed applicants offered admission: 88. Early action applicants: 5,468. Early action applicants admitted: 4,551.

Costs Per Year: Application fee: $0. Comprehensive fee: $59,714 includes full-time tuition ($44,132), mandatory fees ($400), and college room and board ($15,182). College room only: $8776. Room and board charges vary according to board plan and housing facility.

Collegiate Environment: Orientation program. Drama-theater group, choral group, student-run newspaper, radio station. Social organizations: 80 open to all. Most popular organizations: Service-oriented student clubs, United Colors, Retreat Programs, Biology/Pre-Medicine clubs, Pre-Law Society. Major annual events: Spring Fling, Senior Formal, President's Ball. Student services: health clinic, personal-psychological counseling, women's center. Campus security: 24-hour emergency response devices and patrols, student patrols, late night transport-escort service, controlled dormitory access, sprinkler systems in all University-owned housing. Harry and Jeanette Weinberg Memorial Library. Books: 331,804 (physical), 212,028 (digital/electronic); Serial titles: 2,677 (physical), 53,194 (digital/electronic); Databases: 120. Weekly public service hours: 95; study areas open 24 hours, 5-7 days a week; students can reserve study rooms. Operations spending for the previous fiscal year: $4.6 million. 988 computers available on campus for general student use. Computer purchase/lease plans available. A campuswide network can be accessed from student residence rooms and from off campus. Students can access the following: online class registration. Staffed computer lab on campus (open 24 hours a day) provides training in use of computers, software, and the Internet.

Community Environment: Settled in the late eighteenth century, Scranton is the commercial and industrial center of northeast Pennsylvania. Scranton's manufactured items include textiles, clothing, electronic equipment, furniture, plastic, canvas, and metal products. Lying in the Appalachian Mountains on the Lackawana River, Scranton is 10 minutes from the Montage Ski and Recreation Area. Also of interest are the Everhart Museum of Natural History, Science, and Art, Steamtown, and McDade State Park and Coal Mine Tour.

■ UNIVERSITY OF VALLEY FORGE

1401 Charlestown Rd.
Phoenixville, PA 19460
Tel: (610)935-0450; Free: 800-432-8322
E-mail: admissions@valleyforge.edu
Web Site: www.valleyforge.edu

Description: Independent Assemblies of God, comprehensive, coed. Awards associate, bachelor's, and master's degrees. Founded 1939. Setting: 150-acre small town campus with easy access to Philadelphia. Endowment: $2.6 million. Educational spending for the previous fiscal year: $5329 per student. Total enrollment: 764. Faculty: 117 (25 full-time, 92 part-time). Student-undergrad faculty ratio is 12:1. 498 applied, 53% were admitted. Full-time: 588 students, 51% women, 49% men. Part-time: 116 students, 59% women, 41% men. Students come from 37 states and territories, 13 other countries, 56% from out-of-state. 0.3% American Indian or Alaska Native, non-Hispanic/Latino; 17% Hispanic/Latino; 16% Black or African American, non-Hispanic/Latino; 2% Asian, non-Hispanic/Latino; 1% international. 18% 25 or older, 70% live on campus, 7% transferred in. Retention: 69% of full-time freshmen returned the following year. Academic areas with the most degrees conferred: theology and religious vocations; communication/journalism; education. Core. Calendar: semesters. Academic remediation for entering students, services for LD students, advanced placement, accelerated degree program, honors program, independent study, distance learning, double major, summer session for credit, part-time degree program, external degree program, adult/continuing education programs, internships, graduate courses open to undergrads. Study abroad program.

Entrance Requirements: Options: electronic application, deferred admission, international baccalaureate accepted. Required: essay, high school transcript. Recommended: minimum 2 high school GPA, SAT or ACT. Required for some: interview. Entrance: minimally difficult. Application deadline: 8/1. Notification: continuous. SAT Reasoning Test deadline: 8/1. SAT Subject Test deadline: 8/1. Transfer credits accepted: Yes.

Costs Per Year: Application fee: $25. Comprehensive fee: $31,324 includes full-time tuition ($20,266), mandatory fees ($1172), and college room and board ($9886). College room only: $5386. Full-time tuition and fees vary according to course load and location. Room and board charges vary according to board plan, housing facility, and location. Part-time tuition: $783 per credit hour. Part-time mandatory fees: $256 per term. Part-time tuition and fees vary according to course load and location.

Collegiate Environment: Orientation program. Drama-theater group, choral group. Social organizations: 16 open to all. Most popular organizations: Homeless Ministry, The Art Of, Noteworthy, Inspire India, Audience of One. Major annual events: Community Service Day, Sacred Assembly, Homecoming. Student services: health clinic, personal-psychological counseling. Campus security: 24-hour emergency response devices and patrols, student patrols, late night transport-escort service, controlled dormitory access. Storms Research Center. Books: 56,000 (physical), 175,000 (digital/electronic); Serial titles: 44 (physical); Databases: 48. Weekly public service hours: 81; students can reserve study rooms. Operations spending for the previous fiscal year: $375,838. 59 computers available on campus for general student use. Computer purchase/lease plans available. A campuswide network can be accessed from student residence rooms and from off campus. Students can access the following: online class registration. Staffed computer lab on campus provides training in use of computers, software, and the Internet.

Community Environment: Phoenixville is a quiet residential town on the boundary of Valley Forge State Park and is approximately 40 miles from Philadelphia. The climate is temperate. The immediate area provides an abundance of shopping areas and malls, as well as religious, medical and professional services. Recreational opportunities include picnicking, fishing, swimming, boating, camping, and tennis. There are considerable job opportunities available.

■ URSINUS COLLEGE

601 E Main St.
Collegeville, PA 19426
Tel: (610)409-3000
Fax: (610)489-0627
E-mail: admission@ursinus.edu
Web Site: www.ursinus.edu

Description: Independent, 4-year, coed. Awards bachelor's degrees. Founded 1869. Setting: 170-acre suburban campus with easy access to Philadelphia. Endowment: $144.9 million. Research spending for the previous fiscal year: $558,692. Educational spending for the previous fiscal year:

$14,118 per student. Total enrollment: 1,435. Faculty: 171 (122 full-time, 49 part-time). Student-undergrad faculty ratio is 11:1. 3,361 applied, 71% were admitted. 20% from top 10% of their high school class, 51% from top quarter, 78% from top half. Full-time: 1,408 students, 51% women, 49% men. Part-time: 27 students, 52% women, 48% men. Students come from 31 states and territories, 20 other countries, 39% from out-of-state. 0.1% American Indian or Alaska Native, non-Hispanic/Latino; 8% Hispanic/Latino; 8% Black or African American, non-Hispanic/Latino; 4% Asian, non-Hispanic/Latino; 0.1% Native Hawaiian or other Pacific Islander, non-Hispanic/Latino; 2% international. 93% live on campus, 1% transferred in. Retention: 89% of full-time freshmen returned the following year. Academic areas with the most degrees conferred: biological/life sciences; social sciences; psychology. Core. Calendar: semesters. ESL program, services for LD students, advanced placement, self-designed majors, honors program, independent study, double major, summer session for credit, co-op programs and internships. Off campus study at Philadelphia Experience allows students to study in Philadelphia for a semester; Direct Admission Partnership with Simon Business School at University of Rochester; Dual degree programs with Columbia's engineering school and Case Western's engineering program; Program benefits in MBA program at Saint Joseph's University; Intensive, liberal arts-focused internship experiences through Washington Internship Institute; Semester exchange program with Howard University. Study abroad program.

Entrance Requirements: Options: electronic application, early decision, early action, deferred admission, international baccalaureate accepted. Required: essay, high school transcript, 1 recommendation. Recommended: interview. Required for some: home schooled students must include detailed information about the depth of their curriculum, including reading lists and standardized tests, SAT or ACT. Entrance: moderately difficult. Application deadlines: 2/1, 12/1 for early decision, 11/1 for early action. Notification: continuous, 12/15 for early decision plan 1, rolling for early decision plan 2, 12/15 for early action. Transfer credits accepted: Yes. Applicants placed on waiting list: 125. Wait-listed applicants offered admission: 16. Early decision applicants: 78. Early decision applicants admitted: 68. Early action applicants: 1,456. Early action applicants admitted: 1,192.

Costs Per Year: Application fee: $0. Comprehensive fee: $66,730 includes full-time tuition ($53,610) and college room and board ($13,120). Part-time tuition: $1675 per credit hour.

Collegiate Environment: Orientation program. Drama-theater group, choral group, student-run newspaper, radio station. Social organizations: 100 open to all; national fraternities, national sororities, local fraternities, local sororities. Most popular organizations: Campus Activities Board, Ursinus College Student Government, Best Buddies, The Grizzly student newspaper, Gender Sexuality Alliance. Major annual events: Homecoming, Air Band Competition, Ball at the Bellevue. Student services: health clinic, personal-psychological counseling. Campus security: 24-hour emergency response devices and patrols, student patrols, late night transport-escort service, controlled dormitory access. 1,411 college housing spaces available. Freshmen guaranteed college housing. On-campus residence required through senior year. Options: coed, men-only, women-only housing available. Myrin Library. Books: 175,320 (physical), 396,143 (digital/electronic); Serial titles: 797 (physical), 52,952 (digital/electronic); Databases: 53. Weekly public service hours: 113. Operations spending for the previous fiscal year: $1.2 million.

Community Environment: Collegeville is 25 miles northwest of Philadelphia. Within a one-hour drive are museums, libraries, historical sights, educational institutions, recreational facilities, and theaters. Part-time employment is available.

■ **VALLEY FORGE MILITARY COLLEGE**
1001 Eagle Rd.
Wayne, PA 19087-3695
Tel: (610)989-1200; Free: 800-234-8362
Fax: (610)688-1545
E-mail: admissions@vfmac.edu
Web Site: www.vfmac.edu
Description: Independent, 2-year, coed. Awards transfer associate degrees. Founded 1928. Setting: 120-acre suburban campus with easy access to Philadelphia. Endowment: $7.2 million. Educational spending for the previous fiscal year: $6368 per student. Faculty: 26 (16 full-time, 10 part-time). Student-undergrad faculty ratio is 10:1. Students come from 6 other countries, 85% from out-of-state. 100% live on campus. Core. Calendar: 4-1-4. Academic remediation for entering students, ESL program, advanced placement. ROTC: Army, Air Force (c).

Entrance Requirements: Options: early admission, deferred admission. Required: high school transcript, guidance counselor/teacher evaluation form, SAT or ACT. Recommended: minimum 2.0 high school GPA, interview. Entrance: moderately difficult. Application deadline: 8/2. Notification: continuous.

Collegiate Environment: Orientation program. Drama-theater group, choral group, marching band, student-run newspaper. Social organizations: 12 open to all; national fraternities; 20% of men are members. Most popular organizations: Rotaract, Young Republicans, Phi Theta Kappa, Business Club, Criminal Justice Club. Major annual events: Class Trip, Winter Ball, Field Day. Student services: health clinic, personal-psychological counseling. Campus security: 24-hour patrols, student patrols. Baker Library. 44 computers available on campus for general student use. A campuswide network can be accessed from student residence rooms and from off campus. Staffed computer lab on campus.

■ **VET TECH INSTITUTE**
125 7th St.
Pittsburgh, PA 15222-3400
Tel: (412)391-7021; Free: 800-570-0693
Fax: (412)232-4348
Web Site: pittsburgh.vettechinstitute.edu
Description: Proprietary, 2-year, coed. Awards terminal associate degrees. Founded 1958. Setting: urban campus. Total enrollment: 372. 497 applied, 64% were admitted. Calendar: semesters. Accelerated degree program, internships.

■ **VILLANOVA UNIVERSITY**
800 Lancaster Ave.
Villanova, PA 19085-1699
Tel: (610)519-4500
Fax: (610)519-6450
Web Site: www.villanova.edu
Description: Independent Roman Catholic, university, coed. Awards bachelor's, master's, and doctoral degrees and post-master's certificates. Founded 1842. Setting: 254-acre suburban campus with easy access to Philadelphia. Endowment: $640 million. Total enrollment: 10,983. Faculty: 1,039 (618 full-time, 421 part-time). Student-undergrad faculty ratio is 12:1. 21,112 applied, 36% were admitted. 65% from top 10% of their high school class, 95% from top quarter, 98% from top half. Full-time: 6,525 students, 53% women, 47% men. Part-time: 441 students, 52% women, 48% men. Students come from 51 states and territories, 44 other countries, 79% from out-of-state. 0.1% American Indian or Alaska Native, non-Hispanic/Latino; 8% Hispanic/Latino; 5% Black or African American, non-Hispanic/Latino; 6% Asian, non-Hispanic/Latino; 2% international. 5% 25 or older, 66% live on campus, 2% transferred in. Retention: 95% of full-time freshmen returned the following year. Academic areas with the most degrees conferred: business/marketing; engineering; health professions and related sciences. Core. Calendar: semesters. ESL program, services for LD students, advanced placement, accelerated degree program, honors program, independent study, distance learning, double major, summer session for credit, part-time degree program, external degree program, adult/continuing education programs, co-op programs and internships, graduate courses open to undergrads. Off campus study. Study abroad program. ROTC: Army, Naval, Air Force (c).

Entrance Requirements: Options: electronic application, early admission, early decision, early action, deferred admission, international baccalaureate accepted. Required: essay, high school transcript, 1 recommendation, SAT or ACT. Entrance: very difficult. Application deadlines: 1/15, 11/1 for early decision, 11/1 for early action. Notification: 4/1, 12/20 for early decision, 1/15 for early action. SAT Reasoning Test deadline: 1/15. Transfer credits accepted: Yes. Applicants placed on waiting list: 6,276. Wait-listed applicants offered admission: 211.

Costs Per Year: Application fee: $80. One-time mandatory fee: $150. Comprehensive fee: $67,328 includes full-time tuition ($52,578), mandatory fees ($730), and college room and board ($14,020). College room only: $7470. Full-time tuition and fees vary according to degree level and location. Room and board charges vary according to board plan and housing facility. Part-time tuition: $2921 per credit hour. Part-time mandatory fees: $365 per term. Part-time tuition and fees vary according to course load, degree level, location, and program.

Collegiate Environment: Orientation program. Drama-theater group, choral group, marching band, student-run newspaper, radio station. Social organizations: 265 open to all; national fraternities, national sororities; 17%

of eligible men and 32% of eligible women are members. Most popular organizations: Blue Key Society, New Student Orientation Counselor Program, Special Olympics, Campus Activities Team, Student Government Association. Major annual events: St. Thomas of Villanova Day of Service, PA Special Olympics Fall Festival, Villanova Hoops Mania. Student services: health clinic, personal-psychological counseling. Campus security: 24-hour emergency response devices and patrols, late night transport-escort service, controlled dormitory access, Nova Alert: email, text messaging for emergency situations. Falvey Memorial Library plus 1 other. Study areas open 24 hours, 5-7 days a week; students can reserve study rooms. 700 computers available on campus for general student use. Computer purchase/lease plans available. A computer is required for all students. A campuswide network can be accessed. Students can access the following: online class registration, learning management system with anti-plagiarism software, testing software, online faculty hours, videoconferencing, electronic portfolios, data vaulting/backup service, software. Staffed computer lab on campus (open 24 hours a day) provides training in use of computers, software, and the Internet.

Community Environment: The"Main Line" is a suburban residential area located 12 miles due west of downtown Philadelphia, which includes the towns of Radnor, Rosemont, Villanova, St. Davids, Wayne, Haverford, and Merion Station. The mean temperature for the area is 54.3 degrees. The area is served by Amtrak and local commuter rail lines, regional bus lines, and the Schuylkill Expressway. The total locale has more than 200 civic, social, and church groups. There are art centers, theater groups, a symphony orchestra, several museums, many libraries, two hospitals, and good shopping facilities. Local recreation facilities include golf courses, swimming pools, skating rinks, parks, and playgrounds.

■ WASHINGTON & JEFFERSON COLLEGE
60 S Lincoln St.
Washington, PA 15301
Tel: (724)222-4400; Free: 888-WANDJAY
Fax: (724)223-5271
E-mail: admission@washjeff.edu
Web Site: www.washjeff.edu

Description: Independent, comprehensive, coed. Awards bachelor's and master's degrees. Founded 1781. Setting: 60-acre suburban campus with easy access to Pittsburgh. Endowment: $143.6 million. Research spending for the previous fiscal year: $261,437. Educational spending for the previous fiscal year: $14,768 per student. Total enrollment: 1,357. Faculty: 152 (114 full-time, 38 part-time). Student-undergrad faculty ratio is 11:1. 2,806 applied, 82% were admitted. 32% from top 10% of their high school class, 62% from top quarter, 89% from top half. 9 valedictorians, 73 student government officers. Full-time: 1,350 students, 49% women, 51% men. Part-time: 6 students, 50% women, 50% men. Students come from 36 states and territories, 37 other countries, 23% from out-of-state. 0.2% American Indian or Alaska Native, non-Hispanic/Latino; 5% Hispanic/Latino; 5% Black or African American, non-Hispanic/Latino; 2% Asian, non-Hispanic/Latino; 3% international. 0.3% 25 or older, 93% live on campus, 1% transferred in. Retention: 81% of full-time freshmen returned the following year. Academic areas with the most degrees conferred: business/marketing; social sciences; psychology. Core. Calendar: 4-1-4. Academic remediation for entering students, ESL program, services for LD students, advanced placement, accelerated degree program, self-designed majors, freshman honors college, honors program, independent study, double major, summer session for credit, part-time degree program, internships, graduate courses open to undergrads. Off campus study at Community College of Allegheny County (CCAC), Westmoreland County Community College (WCCC). Study abroad program. ROTC: Army, Air Force (c).

Entrance Requirements: Options: electronic application, early admission, early decision, early action, deferred admission, international baccalaureate accepted. Required: essay, high school transcript, recommendations. Recommended: interview. Entrance: very difficult. Application deadline: 12/1 for early decision. Notification: 4/1, 12/15 for early decision. SAT Reasoning Test deadline: 3/1. SAT Subject Test deadline: 3/1. Transfer credits accepted: Yes. Applicants placed on waiting list: 30. Wait-listed applicants offered admission: 2. Early decision applicants: 14. Early decision applicants admitted: 12. Early action applicants: 4,962. Early action applicants admitted: 2,106.

Costs Per Year: Application fee: $25. Comprehensive fee: $60,640 includes full-time tuition ($47,384), mandatory fees ($580), and college room and board ($12,676). College room only: $7438. Room and board charges vary according to board plan and housing facility. Part-time tuition: $1188 per credit hour.

Collegiate Environment: Orientation program. Drama-theater group, choral group, student-run newspaper, radio station. Social organizations: 93 open to all; national fraternities, national sororities; 38% of eligible men and 32% of eligible women are members. Most popular organizations: Student Government Association, Student Activities Board, Black Student Union, Mock Trial, Latino Culture Association. Major annual events: Welcome Week/Involvement Expo, Spring Concert, Street Fair. Student services: health clinic, personal-psychological counseling, women's center. Campus security: 24-hour emergency response devices and patrols, late night transport-escort service, controlled dormitory access. 1,422 college housing spaces available; 1,265 were occupied in 2018-19. Freshmen guaranteed college housing. On-campus residence required through senior year. Options: coed, men-only, women-only housing available. U. Grant Miller Library plus 4 others. Books: 91,909 (physical), 6,516 (digital/electronic); Serial titles: 654 (physical), 63,356 (digital/electronic); Databases: 78. Weekly public service hours: 107. Operations spending for the previous fiscal year: $1.1 million. 450 computers available on campus for general student use. Computer purchase/lease plans available. A campuswide network can be accessed from student residence rooms and from off campus. Students can access the following: online class registration. Staffed computer lab on campus (open 24 hours a day) provides training in use of computers, software, and the Internet.

■ WAYNESBURG UNIVERSITY
51 W College St.
Waynesburg, PA 15370-1222
Tel: (724)627-8191; Free: 800-225-7393
Fax: (724)627-8124
E-mail: admissions@waynesburg.edu
Web Site: www.waynesburg.edu

Description: Independent, comprehensive, coed, affiliated with Presbyterian Church (U.S.A.). Awards bachelor's, master's, and doctoral degrees. Founded 1849. Setting: 30-acre small town campus with easy access to Pittsburgh. Total enrollment: 1,674. Faculty: 201 (79 full-time, 122 part-time). Student-undergrad faculty ratio is 13:1. 1,590 applied, 91% were admitted. 11% from top 10% of their high school class, 37% from top quarter, 72% from top half. Full-time: 1,287 students, 57% women, 43% men. Part-time: 43 students, 84% women, 16% men. Students come from 35 states and territories, 2 other countries, 22% from out-of-state. 0.2% American Indian or Alaska Native, non-Hispanic/Latino; 2% Hispanic/Latino; 4% Black or African American, non-Hispanic/Latino; 0.9% Asian, non-Hispanic/Latino; 0.1% Native Hawaiian or other Pacific Islander, non-Hispanic/Latino; 0.2% international. 2% 25 or older, 80% live on campus, 3% transferred in. Retention: 78% of full-time freshmen returned the following year. Academic areas with the most degrees conferred: health professions and related sciences; business/marketing; homeland security, law enforcement, firefighting, and protective services. Core. Calendar: semesters. Services for LD students, advanced placement, accelerated degree program, honors program, independent study, distance learning, double major, summer session for credit, part-time degree program, adult/continuing education programs, internships, graduate courses open to undergrads. Study abroad program. ROTC: Army (c), Air Force (c).

Entrance Requirements: Options: electronic application, early admission. Required: high school transcript, minimum 2.75 high school GPA, SAT or ACT. Recommended: minimum 3 high school GPA, interview. Required for some: essay, 2 recommendations. Entrance: moderately difficult. Application deadline: rolling. Notification: continuous. SAT Reasoning Test deadline: 8/30. SAT Subject Test deadline: 8/30.

Costs Per Year: Application fee: $20. Comprehensive fee: $36,090 includes full-time tuition ($24,690), mandatory fees ($880), and college room and board ($10,520). College room only: $5320. Part-time tuition: $1020 per credit hour.

Collegiate Environment: Orientation program. Drama-theater group, choral group, student-run newspaper, radio station. Social organizations: 51 open to all. Most popular organizations: Student-Pennsylvania State Education Association, Lamplighter Choir, Student Nurses Association, Christian Fellowship. Major annual events: Homecoming, Spring Week, Charter Day. Student services: health clinic, personal-psychological counseling. Campus security: 24-hour emergency response devices and patrols, late night transport-escort service, controlled dormitory access. 1,171 college housing spaces available; 1,061 were occupied in 2018-19. Freshmen guaranteed college housing. On-campus residence required through junior year. Options: men-only, women-only housing available. Eberly Library. Books: 71,187 (physical), 162,938 (digital/electronic); Serial titles: 159 (physical),

111,249 (digital/electronic); Databases: 37. 160 computers available on campus for general student use. A campuswide network can be accessed from student residence rooms and from off campus. Students can access the following: online class registration. Staffed computer lab on campus.

Community Environment: Population 4,142, Waynesburg is located 50 miles from Pittsburgh in southwestern Pennsylvania. The climate is moderate. Community service facilities include a library, several churches, a hospital, hotels, motels, and rooming houses. There is bus service available. Local recreation includes theatres, hunting, boating, fishing, golf, and movies. Many civic, fraternal and veteran's organizations are active in the community.

■ **WEST CHESTER UNIVERSITY OF PENNSYLVANIA**
University Ave. and High St.
West Chester, PA 19383
Tel: (610)436-1000
Web Site: www.wcupa.edu
Description: State-supported, comprehensive, coed. Part of Pennsylvania State System of Higher Education. Awards bachelor's, master's, and doctoral degrees and post-master's certificates. Founded 1871. Setting: 409-acre suburban campus with easy access to Philadelphia. Endowment: $25.1 million. Research spending for the previous fiscal year: $2.1 million. Educational spending for the previous fiscal year: $8226 per student. Total enrollment: 17,527. Faculty: 981 (688 full-time, 293 part-time). Student-undergrad faculty ratio is 19:1. 12,002 applied, 74% were admitted. 9% from top 10% of their high school class, 32% from top quarter, 70% from top half. 12 valedictorians. Full-time: 13,060 students, 60% women, 40% men. Part-time: 1,507 students, 53% women, 47% men. Students come from 28 states and territories, 84 other countries, 13% from out-of-state. 0.1% American Indian or Alaska Native, non-Hispanic/Latino; 6% Hispanic/Latino; 11% Black or African American, non-Hispanic/Latino; 3% Asian, non-Hispanic/Latino; 0.1% Native Hawaiian or other Pacific Islander, non-Hispanic/Latino; 0.5% international. 11% 25 or older, 36% live on campus, 8% transferred in. Retention: 85% of full-time freshmen returned the following year. Academic areas with the most degrees conferred: business/marketing; health professions and related sciences; education. Core. Calendar: semesters. Academic remediation for entering students, ESL program, services for LD students, advanced placement, accelerated degree program, self-designed majors, freshman honors college, honors program, independent study, distance learning, double major, summer session for credit, part-time degree program, adult/continuing education programs, internships, graduate courses open to undergrads. Off campus study at member of the National Student Exchange. Study abroad program. ROTC: Army, Air Force (c).
Entrance Requirements: Options: electronic application, international baccalaureate accepted. Required: high school transcript, SAT or ACT. Recommended: minimum 3 high school GPA. Required for some: essay, interview. Entrance: moderately difficult. Application deadline: rolling. Notification: continuous. SAT Reasoning Test deadline: 2/1. Transfer credits accepted: Yes. Applicants placed on waiting list: 535. Wait-listed applicants offered admission: 92.
Costs Per Year: Application fee: $45. State resident tuition: $7716 full-time, $322 per credit part-time. Nonresident tuition: $19,290 full-time, $805 per credit part-time. Mandatory fees: $2,696 full-time, $112.41 per credit part-time. Full-time tuition and fees vary according to location. Part-time tuition and fees vary according to location. College room and board: $9216. College room only: $5516. Room and board charges vary according to board plan and housing facility.
Collegiate Environment: Orientation program. Drama-theater group, choral group, marching band, student-run newspaper, radio station. Social organizations: 285 open to all; national fraternities, national sororities; 12% of eligible men and 18% of eligible women are members. Most popular organizations: Student Government Association, Residence Hall Association, Fraternal Programming Board, Sports Club Council, CRU. Major annual events: Spring Weekend, Homecoming, Banana Day. Student services: legal services, health clinic, personal-psychological counseling, women's center. Campus security: 24-hour emergency response devices and patrols, late night transport-escort service, controlled dormitory access, camera systems in campus residence halls, recreational and classroom facilities and outdoor areas. 5,146 college housing spaces available; 5,140 were occupied in 2018-19. Freshmen given priority for college housing. Option: coed housing available. Francis Harvey Green Library plus 1 other. Books: 740,365 (physical), 1.1 million (digital/electronic); Serial titles: 1,921 (physical), 127,236 (digital/electronic); Databases: 275. Weekly public service hours: 107; study areas open 24 hours, 5-7 days a week. Operations spending for the previous

fiscal year: $6.7 million. 2,204 computers available on campus for general student use. Computer purchase/lease plans available. A campuswide network can be accessed from student residence rooms and from off campus. Students can access the following: online class registration, virtual software. Staffed computer lab on campus provides training in use of computers, software, and the Internet.
Community Environment: Population 18,000. Essentially a residential and college community, West Chester is the county seat of a region rich in colonial history. Local industries include pharmaceuticals, firefighting foam, electrical appliances, air compressors, tags and labels, and refrigerated cabinets. The average January temperature is 31.5 degrees, and the average July temperature is 75 degrees. The community is provided transportation by railroad, bus lines, and an airport nearby. There are several churches, a YMCA, hospital, and public library serving the community. Local recreation includes swimming, bowling, volleyball, tennis, hunting, fishing, and golf. Civic and fraternal organizations are active within the area.

■ **WESTMINSTER COLLEGE**
319 S Market St.
New Wilmington, PA 16172-0001
Tel: (724)946-8761; Free: 800-942-8033
Fax: (724)946-7171
E-mail: steinth@westminster.edu
Web Site: www.westminster.edu
Description: Independent, comprehensive, coed, affiliated with Presbyterian Church (U.S.A.). Awards bachelor's and master's degrees. Founded 1852. Setting: 350-acre small town campus with easy access to Pittsburgh. Endowment: $110.1 million. Educational spending for the previous fiscal year: $9949 per student. Total enrollment: 1,254. Faculty: 144 (90 full-time, 54 part-time). Student-undergrad faculty ratio is 11:1. 2,874 applied, 72% were admitted. 22% from top 10% of their high school class, 42% from top quarter, 75% from top half. Full-time: 1,171 students, 54% women, 46% men. Part-time: 21 students, 43% women, 57% men. Students come from 32 states and territories, 2 other countries, 34% from out-of-state. 0.3% American Indian or Alaska Native, non-Hispanic/Latino; 2% Hispanic/Latino; 5% Black or African American, non-Hispanic/Latino; 0.9% Asian, non-Hispanic/Latino; 0.1% Native Hawaiian or other Pacific Islander, non-Hispanic/Latino; 0.6% international. 1% 25 or older, 75% live on campus, 1% transferred in. Retention: 78% of full-time freshmen returned the following year. Academic areas with the most degrees conferred: business/marketing; education; biological/life sciences. Core. Calendar: semesters. Services for LD students, advanced placement, self-designed majors, honors program, independent study, distance learning, double major, summer session for credit, part-time degree program, adult/continuing education programs, internships, graduate courses open to undergrads. Off campus study at Midwestern State University British Studies Program, Yonsei University, Richmond American University in London. Study abroad program. ROTC: Army (c).
Entrance Requirements: Options: electronic application, deferred admission. Required: essay, high school transcript, minimum 2 high school GPA, 2 recommendations, SAT or ACT. Recommended: minimum 3 high school GPA, interview. Entrance: moderately difficult. Application deadline: 5/1. Notification: continuous. SAT Reasoning Test deadline: 5/1. SAT Subject Test deadline: 5/1. Transfer credits accepted: Yes.
Costs Per Year: Application fee: $35. Comprehensive fee: $47,936 includes full-time tuition ($35,360), mandatory fees ($1446), and college room and board ($11,130). College room only: $5940. Room and board charges vary according to board plan and housing facility. Part-time tuition: $1145 per credit hour.
Collegiate Environment: Orientation program. Drama-theater group, choral group, marching band, student-run newspaper, radio station. Social organizations: 85 open to all; national fraternities, national sororities; 33% of eligible men and 49% of eligible women are members. Most popular organizations: Student Government Association, Interfraternity Council/Panhellenic Council, Dance Theatre, Habitat for Humanity, Campus Programming Council. Major annual events: Homecoming, Christmas Vespers, Greek Week. Student services: health clinic, personal-psychological counseling. Campus security: 24-hour emergency response devices and patrols, late night transport-escort service, controlled dormitory access. McGill Memorial Library plus 1 other. Books: 160,296 (physical), 771,138 (digital/electronic); Serial titles: 89 (physical), 30,100 (digital/electronic); Databases: 70. Weekly public service hours: 104; students can reserve study rooms. Operations spending for the previous fiscal year: $846,370. 144 computers available on campus for general student use.

Computer purchase/lease plans available. A campuswide network can be accessed from student residence rooms and from off campus. Students can access the following: online class registration.

■ WESTMORELAND COUNTY COMMUNITY COLLEGE

145 Pavilion Ln.
Youngwood, PA 15697
Tel: (724)925-4000; Free: 800-262-2103
Fax: (724)925-1150
E-mail: littles@wccc.edu
Web Site: www.westmoreland.edu

Description: County-supported, 2-year, coed. Awards certificates, diplomas, transfer associate, and terminal associate degrees. Founded 1970. Setting: 85-acre rural campus with easy access to Pittsburgh. Endowment: $1.2 million. Educational spending for the previous fiscal year: $3173 per student. Total enrollment: 5,554. Faculty: 427 (82 full-time, 345 part-time). Student-undergrad faculty ratio is 17:1. 3,227 applied, 100% were admitted. Full-time: 2,340 students, 56% women, 44% men. Part-time: 3,214 students, 65% women, 35% men. Students come from 12 states and territories, 0.3% from out-of-state. 0.1% American Indian or Alaska Native, non-Hispanic/Latino; 2% Hispanic/Latino; 3% Black or African American, non-Hispanic/Latino; 0.6% Asian, non-Hispanic/Latino; 0.1% Native Hawaiian or other Pacific Islander, non-Hispanic/Latino. 34% 25 or older, 20% transferred in. Retention: 62% of full-time freshmen returned the following year. Core. Calendar: semesters. Academic remediation for entering students, ESL program, services for LD students, advanced placement, accelerated degree program, honors program, independent study, distance learning, double major, summer session for credit, part-time degree program, adult/continuing education programs, co-op programs and internships. Off campus study at Seton Hill College, University of Pittsburgh.

Entrance Requirements: Open admission except for allied health programs. Options: electronic application, early admission. Entrance: noncompetitive. Application deadline: rolling. Notification: continuous. Transfer credits accepted: Yes.

Costs Per Year: Application fee: $0. Area resident tuition: $3990 full-time, $133 per credit part-time. State resident tuition: $7980 full-time, $266 per credit part-time. Nonresident tuition: $11,970 full-time, $399 per credit part-time. Mandatory fees: $1710 full-time, $57 per credit part-time. Full-time tuition and fees vary according to course load. Part-time tuition and fees vary according to course load.

Collegiate Environment: Orientation program. Choral group. Social organizations: 22 open to all; Phi Theta Kappa, Sigma Alpha Pi. Most popular organizations: Phi Theta Kappa, Sigma Alpha Pi Leadership Society, Criminal Justice Fraternity, SNAP, SADAA/SADHA. Major annual events: Spring Carnival, Red Cross Blood Drive, Welcome Back. Student services: personal-psychological counseling. Campus security: 24-hour emergency response devices and patrols, late night transport-escort service, county police office on campus. Westmoreland County Community College Learning Resources Center. Books: 41,368 (physical), 168,542 (digital/electronic); Serial titles: 71 (physical); Databases: 24. Weekly public service hours: 60. Operations spending for the previous fiscal year: $289,992. 1,200 computers available on campus for general student use. A campuswide network can be accessed from off-campus. Students can access the following: online class registration. Staffed computer lab on campus provides training in use of computers, software, and the Internet.

■ WIDENER UNIVERSITY

One University Pl.
Chester, PA 19013-5792
Tel: (610)499-4000; Free: 888-WIDENER
Fax: (610)499-4676
Web Site: www.widener.edu

Description: Independent, comprehensive, coed. Awards associate, bachelor's, master's, and doctoral degrees and post-master's certificates. Founded 1821. Setting: 110-acre suburban campus with easy access to Philadelphia. Endowment: $91.8 million. Total enrollment: 6,601. Faculty: 641 (271 full-time, 370 part-time). Student-undergrad faculty ratio is 14:1. 6,422 applied, 70% were admitted. Full-time: 2,910 students, 55% women, 45% men. Part-time: 435 students, 69% women, 31% men. 40% from out-of-state. 0.1% American Indian or Alaska Native, non-Hispanic/Latino; 5% Hispanic/Latino; 13% Black or African American, non-Hispanic/Latino; 3% Asian, non-Hispanic/Latino; 2% international. 10% 25 or older, 47% live on campus, 3% transferred in. Retention: 80% of full-time freshmen returned the following year. Academic areas with the most degrees conferred: health

professions and related sciences; business/marketing; engineering. Core. Calendar: semesters. Academic remediation for entering students, ESL program, services for LD students, advanced placement, accelerated degree program, self-designed majors, honors program, independent study, distance learning, double major, summer session for credit, part-time degree program, adult/continuing education programs, co-op programs and internships, graduate courses open to undergrads. Off campus study. Study abroad program. ROTC: Army, Naval (c), Air Force (c).

Entrance Requirements: Options: electronic application, deferred admission, international baccalaureate accepted. Required: essay, high school transcript, SAT or ACT. Recommended: interview. Required for some: minimum 2.85 high school GPA. Entrance: moderately difficult. Application deadline: rolling. Notification: continuous. Transfer credits accepted: Yes. Applicants placed on waiting list: 81. Wait-listed applicants offered admission: 0.

Costs Per Year: Application fee: $0. Comprehensive fee: $108,442 includes full-time tuition ($46,378), mandatory fees ($47,328), and college room and board ($14,736). College room only: $7672. Part-time tuition: $1545 per credit hour.

Collegiate Environment: Orientation program. Drama-theater group, choral group, marching band. Social organizations: 85 open to all; national fraternities, national sororities; 10% of eligible men and 14% of eligible women are members. Major annual events: Spring Carnival, Greek Week, Homecoming. Student services: health clinic, personal-psychological counseling. Campus security: 24-hour emergency response devices and patrols, late night transport-escort service, controlled dormitory access. 1,772 college housing spaces available; 1,487 were occupied in 2018-19. Freshmen guaranteed college housing. On-campus residence required through junior year. Options: coed, men-only, women-only housing available. Wolfgram Memorial Library.

■ WILKES UNIVERSITY

84 W S St.
Wilkes Barre, PA 18766-0002
Tel: (570)408-5000; Free: 800-945-5378
Fax: (570)408-7820
E-mail: admissions@wilkes.edu
Web Site: www.wilkes.edu

Description: Independent, comprehensive, coed. Awards bachelor's, master's, and doctoral degrees. Founded 1933. Setting: 25-acre urban campus. Endowment: $51.6 million. Research spending for the previous fiscal year: $2.2 million. Educational spending for the previous fiscal year: $9615 per student. Total enrollment: 5,132. Faculty: 416 (180 full-time, 236 part-time). Student-undergrad faculty ratio is 14:1. 3,932 applied, 75% were admitted. 23% from top 10% of their high school class, 60% from top quarter, 84% from top half. Full-time: 2,212 students, 46% women, 54% men. Part-time: 243 students, 57% women, 43% men. Students come from 31 states and territories, 13 other countries, 21% from out-of-state. 0.3% American Indian or Alaska Native, non-Hispanic/Latino; 7% Hispanic/Latino; 5% Black or African American, non-Hispanic/Latino; 2% Asian, non-Hispanic/Latino; 0.1% Native Hawaiian or other Pacific Islander, non-Hispanic/Latino; 7% international. 8% 25 or older, 41% live on campus, 6% transferred in. Retention: 76% of full-time freshmen returned the following year. Academic areas with the most degrees conferred: business/marketing; health professions and related sciences; engineering. Core. Calendar: semesters. Academic remediation for entering students, ESL program, services for LD students, advanced placement, accelerated degree program, self-designed majors, honors program, independent study, distance learning, double major, summer session for credit, part-time degree program, adult/continuing education programs, co-op programs and internships, graduate courses open to undergrads. Off campus study. Study abroad program. ROTC: Army (c), Air Force.

Entrance Requirements: Options: electronic application, early admission, deferred admission, international baccalaureate accepted. Required: high school transcript, SAT or ACT. Recommended: interview. Entrance: moderately difficult. Application deadlines: rolling, rolling for nonresidents. Notification: continuous, continuous for nonresidents. Transfer credits accepted: Yes.

Costs Per Year: Application fee: $40. Comprehensive fee: $50,876 includes full-time tuition ($34,454), mandatory fees ($1740), and college room and board ($14,682). Room and board charges vary according to board plan and housing facility.

Collegiate Environment: Orientation program. Drama-theater group, choral group, marching band, student-run newspaper, radio station. Social

organizations: 70 open to all. Student services: health clinic, personal-psychological counseling. Campus security: 24-hour emergency response devices and patrols, late night transport-escort service, controlled dormitory access. 1,099 college housing spaces available; 1,002 were occupied in 2018-19. Freshmen guaranteed college housing. On-campus residence required through sophomore year. Options: coed, men-only, women-only housing available. Eugene S. Farley Library. Books: 184,565 (physical), 8,000 (digital/electronic); Serial titles: 60,000 (digital/electronic); Databases: 88. Students can reserve study rooms. Operations spending for the previous fiscal year: $1.4 million. 860 computers available on campus for general student use. Computer purchase/lease plans available. A campuswide network can be accessed from student residence rooms and from off campus. Students can access the following: online class registration. Staffed computer lab on campus (open 24 hours a day) provides training in use of computers, software, and the Internet.

■ WILLIAMSON COLLEGE OF THE TRADES
106 S New Middletown Rd.
Media, PA 19063
Tel: (610)566-1776
Fax: (610)566-6502
E-mail: jmerillat@williamson.edu
Web Site: www.williamson.edu
Description: Independent, 2-year, men only. Awards diplomas and terminal associate degrees. Founded 1888. Setting: 222-acre small town campus with easy access to Philadelphia. Total enrollment: 270. Faculty: (29 full-time). Student-undergrad faculty ratio is 12:1. 389 applied, 26% were admitted. 1% from top 10% of their high school class, 9% from top quarter, 29% from top half. Full-time: 270 students. Students come from 9 states and territories, 24% from out-of-state. 100% live on campus. Core. Calendar: semesters. Academic remediation for entering students, independent study. Off campus study at Delaware County Community College.
Entrance Requirements: Option: electronic application. Required: essay, high school transcript, minimum 2 high school GPA, interview, minimum average performance on the Armed Services Vocational Aptitude Battery (ASVAB), Armed Services Vocational Aptitude Battery (ASVAB). Entrance: moderately difficult. Application deadline: 2/22. Preference given to financially deserving young men. Applicants placed on waiting list: 40. Wait-listed applicants offered admission: 23.
Collegiate Environment: Orientation program. Choral group, student-run newspaper. Social organizations: 10 open to all; 40% of eligible undergrads are members. Most popular organizations: Ambassadors, SkillsUSA, Jazz Band, College Newspaper, Choir. Major annual events: Homecoming, Alumni Day, Founder's Day. Student services: health clinic, personal-psychological counseling. Campus security: evening patrols and gate security. Shrigley Library plus 3 others. 165 computers available on campus for general student use. A campuswide network can be accessed from student residence rooms and from off campus. Staffed computer lab on campus.

■ WILSON COLLEGE
1015 Philadelphia Ave.
Chambersburg, PA 17201-1285
Tel: (717)264-4141; Free: 800-421-8402
Fax: (717)264-1578
E-mail: admissions@wilson.edu
Web Site: www.wilson.edu
Description: Independent, comprehensive, coed, affiliated with Presbyterian Church (U.S.A.). Awards associate, bachelor's, and master's degrees. Founded 1869. Setting: 300-acre small town campus. Endowment: $51.3 million. Educational spending for the previous fiscal year: $7474 per student. Total enrollment: 662. Faculty: 94 (39 full-time, 55 part-time). Student-undergrad faculty ratio is 8:1. 450 applied, 53% were admitted. 20% from top 10% of their high school class, 53% from top quarter, 77% from top half. Full-time: 330 students, 94% women, 6% men. Part-time: 241 students, 80% women, 20% men. Students come from 19 states and territories, 12 other countries, 23% from out-of-state. 0.2% American Indian or Alaska Native, non-Hispanic/Latino; 3% Hispanic/Latino; 3% Black or African American, non-Hispanic/Latino; 0.4% Asian, non-Hispanic/Latino; 5% international. 35% 25 or older, 66% live on campus, 3% transferred in. Retention: 53% of full-time freshmen returned the following year. Academic areas with the most degrees conferred: health professions and related sciences; education; biological/life sciences. Core. Calendar: 4-1-4. Academic remediation for entering students, services for LD students, advanced placement, self-

designed majors, honors program, independent study, distance learning, double major, summer session for credit, part-time degree program, adult/continuing education programs, internships, graduate courses open to undergrads. Off campus study at Shippensburg University of Pennsylvania, Gettysburg College. Study abroad program. ROTC: Army (c).
Entrance Requirements: Options: electronic application, early admission, deferred admission, international baccalaureate accepted. Required: essay, high school transcript, 1 recommendation, college preparatory program that includes 4 units of English, 4 units of history/civics, 3 units of mathematics, 2 units of same foreign language, and 2 units of natural sciences with lab. Recommended: minimum 2.75 high school GPA, interview. Required for some: SAT or ACT, TOEFL/IELTS/STEP for international students. Entrance: moderately difficult. Application deadline: rolling. Notification: continuous. Transfer credits accepted: Yes.
Costs Per Year: Application fee: $0. Comprehensive fee: $36,189 includes full-time tuition ($23,745), mandatory fees ($850), and college room and board ($11,594). College room only: $5500. Full-time tuition and fees vary according to location and program. Room and board charges vary according to board plan and housing facility. Part-time tuition: $792 per semester hour. Part-time tuition varies according to course load, location, and program.
Collegiate Environment: Orientation program. Drama-theater group, choral group, student-run newspaper. Social organizations: 47 open to all. Most popular organizations: Muhibbah Club, Orchesis Club, student newspaper, Student Government, Campus Activity Board. Major annual events: White Dinner, Thanksgiving Dinner, Spring Fling/May Court. Student services: health clinic, personal-psychological counseling, women's center. Campus security: 24-hour emergency response devices and patrols, late night transport-escort service, controlled dormitory access. Stewart Library. Weekly public service hours: 88; students can reserve study rooms. 96 computers available on campus for general student use. A campuswide network can be accessed from student residence rooms. Students can access the following: online class registration, online databases. Staffed computer lab on campus provides training in use of computers, software, and the Internet.
Community Environment: Population 17,900, Chambersburg was occupied three times during the Civil War and burned in 1864 when it refused to pay an indemnity of $100,000. Today, this diversified manufacturing community is also considered the state's largest producer of apples and peaches. The city has 2 libraries, a hospital, and many churches and historic sites. Part-time employment is available for students both on and off campus.

■ THE WORKFORCE INSTITUTE'S CITY COLLEGE
1231 N Broad St.
Philadelphia, PA 19122
Tel: (215)568-9215
Fax: (215)568-3511
Web Site: www.wficitycollege.org
Description: Independent, 2-year, coed. Awards certificates and terminal associate degrees. Founded 1974. Setting: urban campus. Total enrollment: 31. Faculty: 12 (10 full-time, 2 part-time). Student-undergrad faculty ratio is 16:1. 6 applied, 100% were admitted. Full-time: 20 students, 45% women, 55% men. Part-time: 11 students, 45% women, 55% men. 85% 25 or older. Calendar: semesters.

■ YESHIVA BETH MOSHE
930 Hickory St.
Scranton, PA 18505-2124
Tel: (717)346-1747
Description: Independent Jewish, comprehensive, men only. Awards bachelor's, master's, and doctoral degrees. Founded 1965. Total enrollment: 54. Calendar: semesters.
Entrance Requirements: Open admission. Required: high school transcript, interview, oral examination.

■ YORK COLLEGE OF PENNSYLVANIA
441 Country Club Rd.
York, PA 17403-3651
Tel: (717)846-7788; Free: 800-455-8018
Web Site: www.ycp.edu
Description: Independent, comprehensive, coed. Awards associate, bachelor's, master's, and doctoral degrees and post-master's certificates. Founded 1787. Setting: 190-acre suburban campus with easy access to Baltimore. Total enrollment: 4,415. Faculty: 470 (179 full-time, 291 part-

time). Student-undergrad faculty ratio is 15:1. 5,209 applied, 70% were admitted. 8% from top 10% of their high school class, 34% from top quarter, 70% from top half. Full-time: 3,814 students, 54% women, 46% men. Part-time: 357 students, 50% women, 50% men. 40% from out-of-state. 0.1% American Indian or Alaska Native, non-Hispanic/Latino; 6% Hispanic/Latino; 5% Black or African American, non-Hispanic/Latino; 2% Asian, non-Hispanic/Latino; 0.1% Native Hawaiian or other Pacific Islander, non-Hispanic/Latino; 0.6% international. 6% 25 or older, 58% live on campus, 4% transferred in. Retention: 81% of full-time freshmen returned the following year. Academic areas with the most degrees conferred: business/marketing; health professions and related sciences; homeland security, law enforcement, firefighting, and protective services. Core. Calendar: semesters. Academic remediation for entering students, services for LD students, advanced placement, self-designed majors, honors program, independent study, double major, summer session for credit, part-time degree program, co-op programs and internships, graduate courses open to undergrads. Study abroad program.

Entrance Requirements: Options: electronic application, deferred admission, international baccalaureate accepted. Required: high school transcript, minimum 2 high school GPA, SAT or ACT. Recommended: essay, 1 recommendation. Required for some: interview. Entrance: moderately difficult. Notification: continuous. SAT Reasoning Test deadline: 8/15. SAT Subject Test deadline: 8/15. Transfer credits accepted: Yes.

Costs Per Year: Application fee: $0. Comprehensive fee: $31,300 includes full-time tuition ($18,180), mandatory fees ($1920), and college room and board ($11,200). College room only: $6330. Full-time tuition and fees vary according to program. Room and board charges vary according to board plan and housing facility. Part-time tuition: $555 per credit hour. Part-time mandatory fees: $410 per term.

Collegiate Environment: Orientation program. Drama-theater group, choral group, student-run newspaper, radio station. Social organizations: 90 open to all; national fraternities, national sororities; 9% of eligible men and 8% of eligible women are members. Most popular organizations: Pre-Med Society, Ski and Outdoor Club, Habitat for Humanity, Students in Free Enterprise (SIFE), WVYC Radio Station. Major annual events: Spartapalooza, Spring Weekend, Fall Fest. Student services: health clinic, personal-psychological counseling. Campus security: 24-hour emergency response devices and patrols, student patrols, late night transport-escort service, controlled dormitory access. Schmidt Library.

Community Environment: York College is located in the heart of one of

most naturally beautiful and historically rich sections of Pennsylvania. Traveling by car, York is just four hours from New York and Pittsburgh, less than two hours from Philadelphia and Washington, DC, and an hour from Baltimore. The area has much to offer, including great local food, interesting places to visit and shop, and parks, lakes, and miles of trails that afford opportunities for picnicking, hiking, and skiing. On the practical side, there is a shopping center, a bank, and York Hospital within walking distance of the campus. Culture is an important part of York's heritage as well. The York Symphony Orchestra, the York Little Theater, and the Strand-Capitol Performing Arts Center bring well-known performing artists to the area. Throughout the year, numerous galleries exhibit a wide variety of artwork.

■ **YTI CAREER INSTITUTE-ALTOONA**
2900 Fairway Dr.
Altoona, PA 16602
Tel: (814)944-5643
Web Site: www.yti.edu
Description: Proprietary, 2-year, coed. Awards diplomas and transfer associate degrees.

■ **YTI CAREER INSTITUTE-LANCASTER**
3050 Hempland Rd.
Lancaster, PA 17601
Description: Proprietary, 2-year, coed.

■ **YTI CAREER INSTITUTE-YORK**
1405 Williams Rd.
York, PA 17402-9017
Tel: (717)757-1100; Free: 800-557-6335
Fax: (717)757-4964
Web Site: www.yti.edu
Description: Proprietary, 2-year, coed. Part of York Technical Institute, LLC. Awards diplomas and terminal associate degrees. Founded 1967. Setting: suburban campus with easy access to Harrisburg. 0.1% American Indian or Alaska Native, non-Hispanic/Latino; 9% Hispanic/Latino; 9% Black or African American, non-Hispanic/Latino; 1% Asian, non-Hispanic/Latino; 0.3% Native Hawaiian or other Pacific Islander, non-Hispanic/Latino. Calendar: continuous.

■ BROWN UNIVERSITY

One Prospect St.
Providence, RI 02912
Tel: (401)863-1000
Fax: (401)863-9300
E-mail: admission_undergraduate@brown.edu
Web Site: www.brown.edu

Description: Independent, university, coed. Awards bachelor's, master's, and doctoral degrees. Founded 1764. Setting: 154-acre urban campus with easy access to Boston. Endowment: $3 billion. Research spending for the previous fiscal year: $116.4 million. Educational spending for the previous fiscal year: $34,086 per student. Total enrollment: 9,781. Faculty: 916 (793 full-time, 123 part-time). Student-undergrad faculty ratio is 7:1. 32,390 applied, 9% were admitted. 92% from top 10% of their high school class, 99% from top quarter, 100% from top half. Full-time: 6,565 students, 52% women, 48% men. Part-time: 361 students, 73% women, 27% men. Students come from 52 states and territories, 108 other countries, 95% from out-of-state. 0.5% American Indian or Alaska Native, non-Hispanic/Latino; 12% Hispanic/Latino; 7% Black or African American, non-Hispanic/Latino; 14% Asian, non-Hispanic/Latino; 0.2% Native Hawaiian or other Pacific Islander, non-Hispanic/Latino; 11% international. 1% 25 or older, 76% live on campus, 1% transferred in. Retention: 98% of full-time freshmen returned the following year. Academic areas with the most degrees conferred: social sciences; biological/life sciences; computer and information sciences. Calendar: semesters. Services for LD students, self-designed majors, honors program, independent study, double major, summer session for credit, adult/continuing education programs, internships, graduate courses open to undergrads. Off campus study at Cross-registration with Rhode Island School of Design, in addition to a 5-year dual degree program with Rhode Island School of Design (AB or ScB, plus BFA). Study abroad program. ROTC: Army (c), Naval (c), Air Force (c).

Entrance Requirements: Options: electronic application, early decision, deferred admission, international baccalaureate accepted. Required: essay, high school transcript, 2 recommendations, Common Application, Brown Supplemental Questions, Alumni Interview if convenient for the applicant, SAT or ACT. Recommended: interview, SAT Subject Tests. Entrance: most difficult. Application deadlines: 1/1, 11/1 for early decision. Notification: 3/31, 12/15 for early decision. SAT Reasoning Test deadline: 1/1. SAT Subject Test deadline: 1/1. Transfer credits accepted: Yes. Wait-listed applicants offered admission: 82. Early decision applicants: 3,030. Early decision applicants admitted: 669.

Costs Per Year: Application fee: $75. Comprehensive fee: $70,226 includes full-time tuition ($54,320), mandatory fees ($1236), and college room and board ($14,670). College room only: $9120. Room and board charges vary according to board plan. Part-time tuition: $6790 per course. Part-time tuition varies according to course load.

Collegiate Environment: Orientation program. Drama-theater group, choral group, marching band, student-run newspaper, radio station. Social organizations: 400 open to all; national fraternities, national sororities, local fraternities, local sororities; 11% of eligible men and 9% of eligible women are members. Major annual events: Spring Weekend Events, Campus Dance and Commencement Weekend, Ivy Film Festival. Student services: health clinic, personal-psychological counseling, women's center. Campus security: 24-hour emergency response devices and patrols, student patrols, late night transport-escort service, controlled dormitory access. John D. Rockefeller Library plus 7 others. Books: 2.6 million (physical), 1.8 million (digital/electronic); Serial titles: 1,667 (physical), 112,138 (digital/electronic); Databases: 415. Study areas open 24 hours, 5-7 days a week; students can reserve study rooms. Operations spending for the previous fiscal year: $24.8 million. 320 computers available on campus for general student use. Computer purchase/lease plans available. A campuswide network can be accessed from student residence rooms and from off campus. Students can access the following: online class registration. Staffed computer lab on campus (open 24 hours a day) provides training in use of computers, software, and the Internet.

Community Environment: In its early days, Providence was a shipping and shipbuilding town, running the Triangular Trade route with slaves, rum, and molasses between Africa, the West Indies and the colonies. Providence, the second largest city in New England, is the industrial and commercial center in addition to being the capital of Rhode Island. The city is one of the largest manufacturing centers in the world and excels in several branches of the metal and rubber industries. Textile manufacturing is of first importance. Historical sites and points of interest include Cathedral of St. John, Cathedral of St. Peter and St. Paul, John Brown House, the Arcade (oldest shopping center in the U.S.), Museum of the Rhode Island School of Design, Waterplace Park, the Athenaeum (oldest library in the U.S.), the Rhode Island Historical Society, Round Top Church, and the State House.

■ BRYANT UNIVERSITY

1150 Douglas Pke.
Smithfield, RI 02917
Tel: (401)232-6000; Free: 800-622-7001
Fax: (401)232-6741
E-mail: admission@bryant.edu
Web Site: www.bryant.edu

Description: Independent, comprehensive, coed. Awards bachelor's and master's degrees. Founded 1863. Setting: 435-acre suburban campus with easy access to Boston, Providence. Endowment: $183.8 million. Research spending for the previous fiscal year: $7 million. Educational spending for the previous fiscal year: $10,388 per student. Total enrollment: 3,788. Faculty: 309 (170 full-time, 139 part-time). Student-undergrad faculty ratio is 13:1. 7,235 applied, 76% were admitted. 26% from top 10% of their high school class, 55% from top quarter, 88% from top half. 8 class presidents, 4 valedictorians, 118 student government officers. Full-time: 3,453 students, 38% women, 62% men. Part-time: 46 students, 41% women, 59% men. Students come from 37 states and territories, 49 other countries, 87% from out-of-state. 0.3% American Indian or Alaska Native, non-Hispanic/Latino; 7% Hispanic/Latino; 3% Black or African American, non-Hispanic/Latino; 4% Asian, non-Hispanic/Latino; 0.1% Native Hawaiian or other Pacific Islander, non-Hispanic/Latino; 8% international. 1% 25 or older, 81% live on campus, 2% transferred in. Retention: 90% of full-time freshmen returned the following year. Academic areas with the most degrees conferred: business/marketing; communication/journalism; mathematics and statistics. Core. Calendar: semesters. ESL program, services for LD students, advanced placement, honors program, independent study, double major, summer session for credit, part-time degree program, adult/continuing education programs, internships, graduate courses open to undergrads. Off campus study at Washington Center Program. Study abroad program. ROTC: Army (c).

Entrance Requirements: Options: electronic application, early decision, early action, deferred admission, international baccalaureate accepted. Required: essay, high school transcript, 1 recommendation, senior year first-quarter grades, three short essay questions in place of test scores. Recommended: minimum 3.3 high school GPA, 2 recommendations, interview. Entrance: moderately difficult. Application deadlines: 2/1, 11/15 for early decision. Notification: 3/15, 12/15 for early decision, 1/15 for early action. SAT Reasoning Test deadline: 2/1. Transfer credits accepted: Yes. Applicants placed on waiting list: 212. Wait-listed applicants offered admission: 13. Early decision applicants: 136. Early decision applicants admitted: 126.

Costs Per Year: Application fee: $50. Comprehensive fee: $61,411 includes full-time tuition ($44,498), mandatory fees ($897), and college room and board ($16,016). College room only: $9401. Part-time tuition: $1102 per credit hour.

Collegiate Environment: Orientation program. Drama-theater group, choral group, student-run newspaper, radio station. Social organizations: 110 open to all; national fraternities, national sororities, local fraternities, local sororities; 4% of eligible men and 15% of eligible women are members. Most popular organizations: CALO Community Activism & Leadership Organization, Linked Through Leadership, Technology & Applied Analytics Club, Dawg Pound, Enactus. Major annual events: Reunion@Homecoming, REDay (Research & Engagement Day), Festival of Lights. Student services: health clinic, personal-psychological counseling, women's center. Campus security: 24-hour emergency response devices and patrols, late night transport-escort service, controlled dormitory access. Freshmen guaranteed college housing. Option: coed housing available. Douglas and Judith Krupp Library plus 1 other. Books: 121,623 (physical), 16,854 (digital/electronic); Serial titles: 3,183 (physical), 299 (digital/electronic); Databases: 80. Weekly public service hours: 110; students can reserve study rooms. Operations spending for the previous fiscal year: $1.6 million. 526 computers available on campus for general student use. Computer purchase/lease plans available. A computer is required for all students. A campuswide network can be accessed from student residence rooms and from off campus. Students can access the following: online class registration, e-mail, online library, student Web hosts. Staffed computer lab on campus provides training in use of computers, software, and the Internet.

Community Environment: The college is located in the midst of the social, cultural, and recreational center that is southern New England. Its 392-acre campus offers the best of two worlds: the security of its suburban location with easy access to the excitement of the city. The setting, the campus, and the ultramodern facilities have been designed to maximize the interaction between faculty, students and administrators. This integrative atmosphere contributes to an individualistic approach to education and fosters an intimate relationship among all segments of the college community.

■ **COMMUNITY COLLEGE OF RHODE ISLAND**
400 E Ave.
Warwick, RI 02886-1807
Tel: (401)825-1000
Fax: (401)825-2418
E-mail: webadmission@ccri.edu
Web Site: www.ccri.edu
Description: State-supported, 2-year, coed. Awards certificates, diplomas, and transfer associate degrees. Founded 1964. Setting: 205-acre urban campus with easy access to Boston. Total enrollment: 15,101. Faculty: 823 (327 full-time, 496 part-time). Student-undergrad faculty ratio is 18:1. 6,271 applied, 99% were admitted. Full-time: 4,441 students, 51% women, 49% men. Part-time: 10,660 students, 62% women, 38% men. Students come from 9 states and territories, 4% from out-of-state. 0.5% American Indian or Alaska Native, non-Hispanic/Latino; 20% Hispanic/Latino; 9% Black or African American, non-Hispanic/Latino; 3% Asian, non-Hispanic/Latino; 0.1% international. 38% 25 or older, 3% transferred in. Core. Calendar: semesters. Academic remediation for entering students, ESL program, services for LD students, advanced placement, honors program, independent study, distance learning, double major, summer session for credit, part-time degree program, external degree program, adult/continuing education programs, co-op programs and internships. Off campus study at Rhode Island College, University of Rhode Island. Study abroad program. ROTC: Army (c).
Entrance Requirements: Open admission except for nursing, dental, radiography, physical therapist assistant, computer programming, engineering, cardio-respiratory care, medical laboratory technician, occupational therapy assistant. Option: deferred admission. Entrance: noncompetitive. Application deadline: rolling. Notification: continuous. Preference given to state residents, New England Regional Student Program applicants.
Costs Per Year: Application fee: $20. State resident tuition: $4148 full-time, $189 per credit hour part-time. Nonresident tuition: $11,740 full-time, $561 per credit hour part-time. Mandatory fees: $416 full-time, $12 per credit hour

part-time, $30 per term part-time. Full-time tuition and fees vary according to program. Part-time tuition and fees vary according to course load and program.
Collegiate Environment: Orientation program. Drama-theater group, choral group, student-run newspaper. Social organizations: 75 open to all. Most popular organizations: Distributive Education Clubs of America, Players (theater group), SkillsUSA, Phi Theta Kappa, Student Government. Major annual events: Student Welcome/All Clubs Day, Thanksgiving Leadership Conference, Theatre Productions. Student services: health clinic, personal-psychological counseling. Campus security: 24-hour emergency response devices and patrols. Community College of Rhode Island Learning Resources Center plus 3 others. 1,200 computers available on campus for general student use. A campuswide network can be accessed from off-campus. Students can access the following: online class registration. Staffed computer lab on campus provides training in use of computers, software, and the Internet.

■ **IYRS SCHOOL OF TECHNOLOGY AND TRADES**
449 Thames St.
Newport, RI 02840
Tel: (401)848-5777

■ **JOHNSON & WALES UNIVERSITY**
8 Abbott Park Pl.
Providence, RI 02903-3703
Tel: (401)598-1000; Free: 800-342-5598
Fax: (401)598-1835
E-mail: pvd@admissions.jwu.edu
Web Site: www.jwu.edu/providence
Description: Independent, comprehensive, coed. Awards associate, bachelor's, master's, and doctoral degrees (branch locations in Charlotte, NC; Denver, CO; North Miami, FL). Founded 1914. Setting: 47-acre urban campus with easy access to Boston. Total enrollment: 9,454. Faculty: 617 (294 full-time, 323 part-time). Student-undergrad faculty ratio is 20:1. 11,971 applied, 82% were admitted. Full-time: 8,145 students, 60% women, 40% men. Part-time: 573 students, 62% women, 38% men. 81% from out-of-state. 0.1% American Indian or Alaska Native, non-Hispanic/Latino; 11% Hispanic/Latino; 11% Black or African American, non-Hispanic/Latino; 0.7% Asian, non-Hispanic/Latino; 9% international. 10% 25 or older, 44% live on campus, 5% transferred in. Retention: 78% of full-time freshmen returned the following year. Academic areas with the most degrees conferred: business/marketing; family and consumer sciences; parks and recreation. Core. Calendar: quarters. Academic remediation for entering students, ESL program, services for LD students, advanced placement, accelerated degree program, freshman honors college, honors program, independent study, summer session for credit, part-time degree program, adult/continuing education programs, co-op programs and internships, graduate courses open to undergrads. Study abroad program. ROTC: Army.
Entrance Requirements: Options: electronic application, early admission, deferred admission, international baccalaureate accepted. Required: high school transcript. Recommended: minimum 2 high school GPA. Required for some: essay, minimum 2.75 high school GPA, interview. Entrance: moderately difficult.
Collegiate Environment: Orientation program. Student-run newspaper. Social organizations: national fraternities, national sororities, local fraternities, local sororities. Student services: health clinic, personal-psychological counseling, women's center. Campus security: 24-hour emergency response devices and patrols, student patrols, late night transport-escort service. Johnson & Wales University Library.

■ **NEW ENGLAND INSTITUTE OF TECHNOLOGY**
One New England Tech Blvd.
East Greenwich, RI 02818
Tel: (401)467-7744; Free: 800-736-7744
E-mail: lmfawthrop@neit.edu
Web Site: www.neit.edu
Description: Independent, comprehensive, coed. Awards associate, bachelor's, master's, and doctoral degrees. Founded 1940. Setting: 225-acre suburban campus with easy access to Boston. Total enrollment: 2,705. Faculty: 329 (130 full-time, 199 part-time). Student-undergrad faculty ratio is 16:1. Full-time: 2,174 students, 31% women, 69% men. Part-time: 374 students, 46% women, 54% men. Students come from 10 states and territories, 22 other countries, 48% from out-of-state. 12% Hispanic/Latino; 2% Black or African American, non-Hispanic/Latino; 0.6% Asian, non-Hispanic/

Latino; 2% international. 49% 25 or older, 10% live on campus. Academic areas with the most degrees conferred: computer and information sciences; engineering technologies; health professions and related sciences. Core. Calendar: quarters. Academic remediation for entering students, ESL program, services for LD students, advanced placement, accelerated degree program, self-designed majors, distance learning, double major, summer session for credit, part-time degree program, adult/continuing education programs, co-op programs and internships, graduate courses open to undergrads.

Entrance Requirements: Open admission. Options: electronic application, early admission, deferred admission. Required: high school transcript, interview. Required for some: portfolio for advanced standing. Entrance: minimally difficult. Application deadlines: rolling, rolling for nonresidents. Notification: continuous, continuous for nonresidents. Transfer credits accepted: Yes.

Costs Per Year: Application fee: $25. Comprehensive fee: $45,180 includes full-time tuition ($29,100), mandatory fees ($1740), and college room and board ($14,340). Part-time tuition: $14,550 per year. Part-time mandatory fees: $1740 per year. Tuition guaranteed not to increase for student's term of enrollment.

Collegiate Environment: Orientation program. Student-run radio station. Social organizations: 22 open to all. Most popular organizations: Rotaract Club, Student Physical Therapist Assistant Club, Student Nurses Association, Video Club, Criminal Justice Club. Major annual events: Annual Cookouts, Intramural Sports, Spring Ice Cream Social. Student services: health clinic, personal-psychological counseling. Campus security: 24-hour emergency response devices and patrols, late night transport-escort service, controlled dormitory access. 400 college housing spaces available; 275 were occupied in 2018-19. Freshmen given priority for college housing. Option: coed housing available. New England Institute of Technology Library. Books: 46,006 (physical), 25,801 (digital/electronic); Serial titles: 316 (physical), 92,146 (digital/electronic); Databases: 64. Weekly public service hours: 66; students can reserve study rooms. 1,300 computers available on campus for general student use. A campuswide network can be accessed from off-campus. Students can access the following: online class registration. Staffed computer lab on campus provides training in use of computers, software, and the Internet.

■ **PROVIDENCE COLLEGE**
1 Cunningham Sq.
Providence, RI 02918
Tel: (401)865-1000; Free: 800-721-6444
Fax: (401)865-2826
Web Site: www.providence.edu
Description: Independent Roman Catholic, comprehensive, coed. Awards bachelor's and master's degrees. Founded 1917. Setting: 105-acre suburban campus with easy access to Boston. Endowment: $238.5 million. Research spending for the previous fiscal year: $907,875. Educational spending for the previous fiscal year: $14,105 per student. Total enrollment: 4,922. Faculty: 488 (302 full-time, 186 part-time). Student-undergrad faculty ratio is 12:1. 11,421 applied, 49% were admitted. 40% from top 10% of their high school class, 73% from top quarter, 93% from top half. 56 class presidents, 3 valedictorians, 246 student government officers. Full-time: 4,148 students, 55% women, 45% men. Part-time: 231 students, 58% women, 42% men. Students come from 40 states and territories, 24 other countries, 89% from out-of-state. 0.2% American Indian or Alaska Native, non-Hispanic/Latino; 10% Hispanic/Latino; 4% Black or African American, non-Hispanic/Latino; 1% Asian, non-Hispanic/Latino; 0.3% Native Hawaiian or other Pacific Islander, non-Hispanic/Latino; 2% international. 81% live on campus, 1% transferred in. Retention: 93% of full-time freshmen returned the following year. Academic areas with the most degrees conferred: business/marketing; social sciences; biological/life sciences. Core. Calendar: semesters. Services for LD students, advanced placement, self-designed majors, honors program, independent study, distance learning, double major, summer session for credit, part-time degree program, adult/continuing education programs, internships, graduate courses open to undergrads. Off campus study at American University Washington Semester Program. Study abroad program. ROTC: Army.
Entrance Requirements: Options: electronic application, early decision, early action, deferred admission, international baccalaureate accepted. Required: essay, high school transcript, 2 recommendations. Required for some: TOEFL or IELTS if English is not the applicant's first language. Entrance: moderately difficult. Application deadlines: 1/15, 11/15 for early decision plan 1, 1/15 for early decision plan 2, 11/1 for early action. Notifica-

tion: 4/1, 1/1 for early decision plan 1, 2/15 for early decision plan 2, 1/1 for early action. SAT Reasoning Test deadline: 2/15. SAT Subject Test deadline: 2/15. Transfer credits accepted: Yes. Applicants placed on waiting list: 3,154. Wait-listed applicants offered admission: 6. Early decision applicants: 453. Early decision applicants admitted: 365. Early action applicants: 6,392. Early action applicants admitted: 3,713.
Costs Per Year: Application fee: $65. Comprehensive fee: $67,578 includes full-time tuition ($51,490), mandatory fees ($948), and college room and board ($15,140). College room only: $8730. Part-time tuition: $2,145.42 per credit hour.
Collegiate Environment: Orientation program. Drama-theater group, choral group, student-run newspaper, radio station. Social organizations: 125 open to all. Most popular organizations: Student Congress, Board of Multicultural Student Affairs, Campus Ministry, Dance Club, Board of Programmers. Major annual events: Black and White Ball, Late Night Madness, Spring Concert. Student services: legal services, health clinic, personal-psychological counseling. Campus security: 24-hour emergency response devices and patrols, late night transport-escort service, controlled dormitory access. College housing designed to accommodate 3,019 students; 3,101 undergraduates lived in college housing during 2018-19. Freshmen guaranteed college housing. On-campus residence required through junior year. Options: coed, men-only, women-only housing available. Phillips Memorial Library. Books: 286,704 (physical), 1 million (digital/electronic); Serial titles: 241 (physical), 58,816 (digital/electronic); Databases: 397. Weekly public service hours: 116; students can reserve study rooms. Operations spending for the previous fiscal year: $4 million. 460 computers available on campus for general student use. Computer purchase/lease plans available. A campuswide network can be accessed from student residence rooms and from off campus. Students can access the following: online class registration. Staffed computer lab on campus provides training in use of computers, software, and the Internet.
Community Environment: See Brown University.

■ **RHODE ISLAND COLLEGE**
600 Mount Pleasant Ave.
Providence, RI 02908-1991
Tel: (401)456-8000; Free: 800-669-5760
Fax: (401)456-8379
E-mail: admissions@ric.edu
Web Site: www.ric.edu
Description: State-supported, comprehensive, coed. Awards bachelor's, master's, and doctoral degrees and post-master's certificates. Founded 1854. Setting: 180-acre suburban campus with easy access to Boston. Endowment: $18.2 million. Research spending for the previous fiscal year: $10.8 million. Total enrollment: 7,771. Faculty: 747 (334 full-time, 413 part-time). Student-undergrad faculty ratio is 14:1. 4,613 applied, 73% were admitted. 19% from top 10% of their high school class, 40% from top quarter, 74% from top half. Full-time: 5,108 students, 69% women, 31% men. Part-time: 1,580 students, 67% women, 33% men. 15% from out-of-state. 0.4% American Indian or Alaska Native, non-Hispanic/Latino; 21% Hispanic/Latino; 10% Black or African American, non-Hispanic/Latino; 3% Asian, non-Hispanic/Latino; 0.1% Native Hawaiian or other Pacific Islander, non-Hispanic/Latino; 0.2% international. 22% 25 or older, 14% live on campus, 10% transferred in. Retention: 73% of full-time freshmen returned the following year. Academic areas with the most degrees conferred: health professions and related sciences; business/marketing; education. Core. Calendar: semesters. Academic remediation for entering students, ESL program, services for LD students, advanced placement, self-designed majors, honors program, independent study, double major, summer session for credit, part-time degree program, adult/continuing education programs, internships, graduate courses open to undergrads. Off campus study at Community College of Rhode Island, Providence College, University of Rhode Island. Study abroad program. ROTC: Army (c).
Entrance Requirements: Options: electronic application, early admission. Required: essay, high school transcript, 1 recommendation, 1 letter from a guidance counselor, SAT or ACT. Recommended: minimum 3 high school GPA. Required for some: interview. Entrance: moderately difficult. Notification: continuous until 12/15, continuous for nonresidents. SAT Reasoning Test deadline: 3/15. SAT Subject Test deadline: 3/15. Transfer credits accepted: Yes.
Costs Per Year: Application fee: $50. State resident tuition: $7790 full-time, $306 per credit part-time. Nonresident tuition: $20,553 full-time, $755 per credit part-time. Mandatory fees: $1139 full-time, $39 per credit part-time. Part-time tuition and fees vary according to course load. College room and board: $12,978. Room and board charges vary according to housing facility.

Collegiate Environment: Orientation program. Drama-theater group, choral group, student-run newspaper, radio station. Social organizations: 73 open to all; national fraternities, national sororities. Most popular organizations: Theta Phi Alpha, Delta Phi Epsilon, Alpha Sigma Tau, Sojourn Collegiate Ministries, Student Community Government. Major annual events: Sex Toy BINGO, Spring RIC End, Campus Activities Day. Student services: legal services, health clinic, personal-psychological counseling, women's center. Campus security: 24-hour emergency response devices and patrols, late night transport-escort service, controlled dormitory access. Freshmen given priority for college housing. Option: coed housing available. Adams Library. Books: 306,080 (physical), 302,387 (digital/electronic); Serial titles: 3,081 (physical), 52,652 (digital/electronic); Databases: 123. Weekly public service hours: 80. Operations spending for the previous fiscal year: $3.2 million. 250 computers available on campus for general student use. Computer purchase/lease plans available. A campuswide network can be accessed. Students can access the following: online class registration. Staffed computer lab on campus provides training in use of computers, software, and the Internet.

■ **RHODE ISLAND SCHOOL OF DESIGN**
2 College St.
Providence, RI 02903-2784
Tel: (401)454-6100; Free: 800-364-7473
Fax: (401)454-6309
E-mail: admissions@risd.edu
Web Site: www.risd.edu
Description: Independent, comprehensive, coed. Awards bachelor's and master's degrees. Founded 1877. Setting: 19-acre urban campus with easy access to Boston, MA. Endowment: $351.4 million. Research spending for the previous fiscal year: $350,734. Educational spending for the previous fiscal year: $19,869 per student. Total enrollment: 2,468. Faculty: 440 (161 full-time, 279 part-time). Student-undergrad faculty ratio is 10:1. 3,913 applied, 24% were admitted. Full-time: 1,994 students, 68% women, 32% men. Students come from 48 states and territories, 46 other countries, 95% from out-of-state. 0.2% American Indian or Alaska Native, non-Hispanic/Latino; 9% Hispanic/Latino; 4% Black or African American, non-Hispanic/Latino; 18% Asian, non-Hispanic/Latino; 30% international. 2% 25 or older, 60% live on campus, 3% transferred in. Retention: 94% of full-time freshmen returned the following year. Academic areas with the most degrees conferred: visual and performing arts; architecture; precision production. Core. Calendar: 4-1-4. Services for LD students, advanced placement, honors program, independent study, double major, internships, graduate courses open to undergrads. Off campus study at Brown University, Association of Independent Colleges of Art and Design. Study abroad program. ROTC: Army (c).
Entrance Requirements: Options: electronic application, early decision, deferred admission. Required: essay, high school transcript, portfolio, drawing assignments, SAT or ACT. Recommended: 3 recommendations. Application deadlines: 2/1, 11/1 for early decision. SAT Reasoning Test deadline: 2/1. Early decision applicants: 285. Early decision applicants admitted: 138.
Costs Per Year: Application fee: $60. Comprehensive fee: $66,580 includes full-time tuition ($51,800), mandatory fees ($1060), and college room and board ($13,720).
Collegiate Environment: Orientation program. Drama-theater group, choral group, student-run newspaper, radio station. Social organizations: 73 open to all. Most popular organizations: athletic clubs, Religious clubs, South Asian Student Association, RISD Global Initiative, Community Service Club. Major annual events: Artists' Ball, Student and Alumni Art Sale, RISD Apparel Show. Student services: legal services, health clinic, personal-psychological counseling. Campus security: 24-hour emergency response devices and patrols, late night transport-escort service, controlled dormitory access. 1,467 college housing spaces available. Freshmen guaranteed college housing. On-campus residence required through sophomore year. Option: coed housing available. Fleet Library. Books: 131,412 (physical), 178,450 (digital/electronic); Serial titles: 1,662 (physical), 800 (digital/electronic); Databases: 48. Weekly public service hours: 89; students can reserve study rooms. Operations spending for the previous fiscal year: $108,198. 65 computers available on campus for general student use. Computer purchase/lease plans available. A campuswide network can be accessed from student residence rooms and from off campus. Students can access the following: online class registration.
Community Environment: See Brown University.

■ **ROGER WILLIAMS UNIVERSITY**
1 Old Ferry Rd.
Bristol, RI 02809
Tel: (401)253-1040; Free: 800-458-7144
Fax: (401)254-3557
Web Site: www.rwu.edu
Description: Independent, comprehensive, coed. Awards associate, bachelor's, master's, and doctoral degrees. Founded 1956. Setting: 140-acre small town campus with easy access to Boston. Endowment: $67.6 million. Research spending for the previous fiscal year: $2.6 million. Educational spending for the previous fiscal year: $19,034 per student. Total enrollment: 5,024. Faculty: 538 (217 full-time, 321 part-time). Student-undergrad faculty ratio is 14:1. 9,515 applied, 82% were admitted. 7 class presidents, 113 student government officers. Full-time: 4,042 students, 53% women, 47% men. Part-time: 661 students, 53% women, 47% men. Students come from 42 states and territories, 56 other countries, 79% from out-of-state. 0.1% American Indian or Alaska Native, non-Hispanic/Latino; 6% Hispanic/Latino; 2% Black or African American, non-Hispanic/Latino; 2% Asian, non-Hispanic/Latino; 0.1% Native Hawaiian or other Pacific Islander, non-Hispanic/Latino; 2% international. 10% 25 or older, 76% live on campus, 1% transferred in. Retention: 79% of full-time freshmen returned the following year. Academic areas with the most degrees conferred: business/marketing; homeland security, law enforcement, firefighting, and protective services; architecture. Core. Calendar: semesters. ESL program, services for LD students, advanced placement, accelerated degree program, self-designed majors, freshman honors college, honors program, independent study, distance learning, double major, summer session for credit, part-time degree program, adult/continuing education programs, co-op programs and internships, graduate courses open to undergrads. Study abroad program. ROTC: Army.
Entrance Requirements: Options: electronic application, early action, deferred admission, international baccalaureate accepted. Required: essay, 1 recommendation. Required for some: high school transcript, portfolio review, audition, specific preparatory courses for visual arts studies, graphic design communications, architecture, creative writing, dance and theater, SAT or ACT. Application deadlines: 2/1, 11/15 for early action. Notification: continuous, continuous for nonresidents. SAT Reasoning Test deadline: 2/1. Transfer credits accepted: Yes. Applicants placed on waiting list: 542. Wait-listed applicants offered admission: 60. Early action applicants: 5,195. Early action applicants admitted: 4,656.
Costs Per Year: Application fee: $50. Comprehensive fee: $48,074 includes full-time tuition ($30,326), mandatory fees ($2184), and college room and board ($15,564). College room only: $8310. Full-time tuition and fees vary according to class time, course load, degree level, and program. Room and board charges vary according to board plan and housing facility. Tuition guaranteed not to increase for student's term of enrollment.
Collegiate Environment: Orientation program. Drama-theater group, choral group, student-run newspaper, radio station. Social organizations: 75 open to all. Most popular organizations: Campus Entertainment Network, Dance Club, WQRI 88.3 Radio Station, Habitat for Humanity. Major annual events: Spring Week/Winter Weekend, Midnight Madness, Student Involvement Fair. Student services: health clinic, personal-psychological counseling, women's center. Campus security: 24-hour emergency response devices and patrols, late night transport-escort service, controlled dormitory access, Rave Guardian Emergency Communication App. Roger Williams University Library plus 1 other. Books: 219,429 (physical), 448,637 (digital/electronic); Serial titles: 493 (physical), 52,585 (digital/electronic); Databases: 189. Weekly public service hours: 111; students can reserve study rooms. Operations spending for the previous fiscal year: $3.5 million. 100 computers available on campus for general student use. A campuswide network can be accessed from student residence rooms and from off campus. Students can access the following: online class registration. Staffed computer lab on campus provides training in use of computers, software, and the Internet.

■ **SALVE REGINA UNIVERSITY**
100 Ochre Point Ave.
Newport, RI 02840-4192
Tel: (401)847-6650; Free: 888-GO SALVE
Fax: (401)848-2823
E-mail: emersonc@salve.edu
Web Site: www.salve.edu
Description: Independent Roman Catholic, comprehensive, coed. Awards associate, bachelor's, master's, and doctoral degrees and post-master's certificates. Founded 1934. Setting: 80-acre suburban campus with easy ac-

cess to Boston, Providence. Endowment: $62.7 million. Research spending for the previous fiscal year: $469,000. Educational spending for the previous fiscal year: $9236 per student. Total enrollment: 2,647. Faculty: 278 (128 full-time, 150 part-time). Student-undergrad faculty ratio is 14:1. 4,721 applied, 76% were admitted. 11% from top 10% of their high school class, 34% from top quarter, 73% from top half. Full-time: 1,957 students, 67% women, 33% men. Part-time: 64 students, 70% women, 30% men. Students come from 35 states and territories, 17 other countries, 82% from out-of-state. 0.2% American Indian or Alaska Native, non-Hispanic/Latino; 7% Hispanic/Latino; 2% Black or African American, non-Hispanic/Latino; 1% Asian, non-Hispanic/Latino; 2% international. 2% 25 or older, 60% live on campus, 2% transferred in. Retention: 83% of full-time freshmen returned the following year. Academic areas with the most degrees conferred: business/marketing; health professions and related sciences; education. Core. Calendar: semesters. ESL program, services for LD students, advanced placement, accelerated degree program, honors program, independent study, double major, summer session for credit, part-time degree program, adult/continuing education programs, internships, graduate courses open to undergrads. Off campus study. Study abroad program. ROTC: Army (c).

Entrance Requirements: Options: electronic application, early action, deferred admission, international baccalaureate accepted. Required: essay, high school transcript, 2 recommendations. Recommended: minimum 2.7 high school GPA. Application deadlines: 2/1, 11/1 for early action. Notification: 12/25. Transfer credits accepted: Yes. Applicants placed on waiting list: 0. Wait-listed applicants offered admission: 0. Early action applicants: 2,808. Early action applicants admitted: 2,186.

Costs Per Year: Application fee: $50. Comprehensive fee: $56,410 includes full-time tuition ($40,750), mandatory fees ($700), and college room and board ($14,960). Part-time tuition: $1358 per credit.

Collegiate Environment: Orientation program. Drama-theater group, choral group, student-run newspaper, radio station. Social organizations: 65 open to all. Most popular organizations: Orpheus Musical Society, Student Government Association, Student Outdoor Adventures, Student Nurse Organization, Stagefright Theatre Company. Major annual events: Family Weekend, Spring Weekend. Student services: health clinic, personal-psychological counseling. Campus security: 24-hour emergency response devices and patrols, late night transport-escort service, controlled dormitory access. 1,290 college housing spaces available; 1,174 were occupied in 2018-19. Freshmen guaranteed college housing. On-campus residence required through sophomore year. Options: coed, men-only, women-only housing available. McKillop Library. Books: 147,721 (physical), 347,549 (digital/electronic); Serial titles: 195 (physical), 75,064 (digital/electronic); Databases: 82. Weekly public service hours: 58; students can reserve study rooms. Operations spending for the previous fiscal year: $1.3 million. 215 computers available on campus for general student use. Computer purchase/lease plans available. A campuswide network can be accessed from student residence rooms and from off campus. Students can access the following: online class registration. Staffed computer lab on campus provides training in use of computers, software, and the Internet.

Community Environment: Newport, RI, an island community and home of Salve Regina, was founded in 1639 and thrived as a Colonial seaport. Today, yachting and sailing regattas still fill its harbor and the Museum of Yachting displays America's Cup memorabilia. The Newport Historical Society and Newport Preservation Society support the City-by-the-Sea's bountiful historic and architectural legacy, including colonial structures, Victorian cottages, and Gilded Age mansions. The Cliff Walk and Ocean Drive provide stirring ocean vistas. The Redwood Library is the oldest library building in the United States in continuous use. The Newport Art museum exhibitions focus on the art of Newport and New England. The Newport Casino, which contains the Tennis Hall of Fame, hosts international tennis matches on its grass courts. World-acclaimed musicians perform at the Newport Music Festival. Opportunities abound for students to participate in the rich historical and cultural aspects of the community through university-sponsored work-study, volunteer, and intern programs.

■ **UNIVERSITY OF RHODE ISLAND**
Kingston, RI 02881
Tel: (401)874-1000
Fax: (401)874-5523

E-mail: lynch@uri.edu
Web Site: www.uri.edu

Description: State-supported, university, coed. Awards bachelor's, master's, and doctoral degrees. Founded 1892. Setting: 1,200-acre small town campus. Endowment: $107.8 million. Research spending for the previous fiscal year: $78.9 million. Educational spending for the previous fiscal year: $7354 per student. Total enrollment: 18,098. Faculty: 1,146 (757 full-time, 389 part-time). Student-undergrad faculty ratio is 17:1. 22,667 applied, 69% were admitted. 17% from top 10% of their high school class, 48% from top quarter, 85% from top half. Full-time: 12,615 students, 56% women, 44% men. Part-time: 2,477 students, 61% women, 39% men. Students come from 43 states and territories, 38 other countries, 46% from out-of-state. 0.2% American Indian or Alaska Native, non-Hispanic/Latino; 10% Hispanic/Latino; 5% Black or African American, non-Hispanic/Latino; 3% Asian, non-Hispanic/Latino; 0.1% Native Hawaiian or other Pacific Islander, non-Hispanic/Latino; 2% international. 5% 25 or older, 41% live on campus, 4% transferred in. Retention: 85% of full-time freshmen returned the following year. Academic areas with the most degrees conferred: health professions and related sciences; business/marketing; engineering. Core. Calendar: semesters. Academic remediation for entering students, ESL program, services for LD students, advanced placement, accelerated degree program, honors program, independent study, distance learning, double major, summer session for credit, part-time degree program, adult/continuing education programs, co-op programs and internships, graduate courses open to undergrads. Off campus study at National Student Exchange, New England Land Grant University Exchange Program. Study abroad program. ROTC: Army.

Entrance Requirements: Options: electronic application, early admission, early action, deferred admission, international baccalaureate accepted. Required: essay, high school transcript, 1 recommendation, list of senior courses, SAT or ACT. Required for some: 2 recommendations. Entrance: moderately difficult. Application deadlines: 2/1, 12/1 for early action. Notification: 3/31, 1/31 for early action. SAT Reasoning Test deadline: 2/1. Transfer credits accepted: Yes. Applicants placed on waiting list: 1,134. Wait-listed applicants offered admission: 43. Early action applicants: 15,138. Early action applicants admitted: 1,460.

Costs Per Year: Application fee: $65. State resident tuition: $12,248 full-time, $510 per credit hour part-time. Nonresident tuition: $28,972 full-time, $1207 per credit hour part-time. Mandatory fees: $1890 full-time, $51 per credit hour part-time, $58 per term part-time. Full-time tuition and fees vary according to course load, location, and reciprocity agreements. Part-time tuition and fees vary according to course load, location, and reciprocity agreements. College room and board: $7850. College room only: $4500. Room and board charges vary according to board plan and housing facility.

Collegiate Environment: Orientation program. Drama-theater group, choral group, marching band, student-run newspaper, radio station. Social organizations: 100 open to all; national fraternities, national sororities, local fraternities. Most popular organizations: Student Entertainment Committee, student radio station, Intramural sport clubs, Student Alumni Association, student newspaper. Major annual events: First Night, Welcome Week, Winterfest. Student services: health clinic, personal-psychological counseling, women's center. Campus security: 24-hour emergency response devices and patrols, student patrols, late night transport-escort service, controlled dormitory access. Robert L. Carothers Library and Learning Commons plus 3 others. Study areas open 24 hours, 5-7 days a week; students can reserve study rooms. Operations spending for the previous fiscal year: $10.2 million. 2,500 computers available on campus for general student use. Computer purchase/lease plans available. A campuswide network can be accessed from student residence rooms and from off campus. Students can access the following: online class registration. Staffed computer lab on campus.

Community Environment: The quiet village of Kingston was founded about 1700. Some of the many interesting houses here date from pre-Revolutionary days. Community facilities include churches of all faiths, a museum, art center, hospitals, and numerous major civic, fraternal and veteran's organizations. Recreational activities include boating, fishing, golf, skiing, and summer theatre. International and deep-sea yacht races are special events. Many part-time jobs are available.

■ AIKEN TECHNICAL COLLEGE
2276 J. Davis Hwy.
Graniteville, SC 29829
Tel: (803)593-9231
E-mail: moonj@atc.edu
Web Site: www.atc.edu
Description: State and locally supported, 2-year, coed. Part of South Carolina State Board for Technical and Comprehensive Education. Awards certificates, diplomas, transfer associate, and terminal associate degrees. Founded 1972. Setting: 88-acre rural campus. Endowment: $4.7 million. Educational spending for the previous fiscal year: $1770 per student. Total enrollment: 2,357. Faculty: 200 (57 full-time, 143 part-time). 1,289 applied, 55% were admitted. Full-time: 694 students, 56% women, 44% men. Part-time: 1,663 students, 67% women, 33% men. 14% from out-of-state. 0.7% American Indian or Alaska Native, non-Hispanic/Latino; 5% Hispanic/Latino; 33% Black or African American, non-Hispanic/Latino; 1% Asian, non-Hispanic/Latino; 0.1% Native Hawaiian or other Pacific Islander, non-Hispanic/Latino. 41% 25 or older, 36% transferred in. Retention: 57% of full-time freshmen returned the following year. Core. Calendar: semesters. Academic remediation for entering students, services for LD students, advanced placement, accelerated degree program, independent study, distance learning, double major, summer session for credit, part-time degree program, co-op programs and internships. Off campus study at University of South Carolina-Aiken.
Entrance Requirements: Open admission except for health programs. Options: electronic application, deferred admission. Recommended: high school transcript. Entrance: noncompetitive. Application deadline: rolling. Notification: continuous. Transfer credits accepted: Yes.
Costs Per Year: Application fee: $0. Area resident tuition: $4296 full-time, $179 per credit hour part-time. State resident tuition: $4656 full-time, $194 per credit hour part-time. Nonresident tuition: $6408 full-time, $267 per credit hour part-time. Mandatory fees: $360 full-time, $180 per term part-time.
Collegiate Environment: Orientation program. Student services: personal-psychological counseling. Campus security: 24-hour emergency response devices and patrols, late night transport-escort service. Aiken Technical College Learning Resources Center. Books: 29,105 (physical), 133,000 (digital/electronic); Serial titles: 124 (physical), 391,523 (digital/electronic); Databases: 73. Weekly public service hours: 64; study areas open 24 hours, 5-7 days a week; students can reserve study rooms. Operations spending for the previous fiscal year: $210,205. 879 computers available on campus for general student use. A campuswide network can be accessed. Students can access the following: online class registration. Staffed computer lab on campus.

■ ALLEN UNIVERSITY
1530 Harden St.
Columbia, SC 29204
Tel: (803)254-4165; Free: 877-625-5368
Fax: (803)376-5731
E-mail: tparker@allenuniversity.edu
Web Site: www.allenuniversity.edu
Description: Independent African Methodist Episcopal, 4-year, coed. Awards bachelor's degrees. Founded 1870. Setting: suburban campus. Total enrollment: 827. Faculty: 41 (29 full-time, 12 part-time). 1,937 applied, 72% were admitted. Full-time: 804 students, 56% women, 44% men. Part-time: 23 students, 57% women, 43% men. 25% from out-of-state. 30% 25 or

older, 7% transferred in. Retention: 62% of full-time freshmen returned the following year. Academic areas with the most degrees conferred: business/marketing; social sciences; biological/life sciences. Core. Calendar: semesters. Academic remediation for entering students, honors program, independent study, summer session for credit, part-time degree program, adult/continuing education programs, co-op programs and internships. Study abroad program. ROTC: Army (c).
Entrance Requirements: Open admission. Option: electronic application. Required: essay, high school transcript, 2 recommendations. Recommended: SAT or ACT. Entrance: minimally difficult. Application deadline: 7/31. Transfer credits accepted: Yes.
Collegiate Environment: Orientation program. Choral group, student-run newspaper. Social organizations: 6 open to all; national fraternities, local fraternities, local sororities. Most popular organizations: International Students Club, Social Science Club, Gospel Choir, NAACP, Phi Beta Lambda and BASIC. Major annual events: Homecoming, Religious Emphasis Week, Black History Month observance. Student services: health clinic, personal-psychological counseling. Campus security: 24-hour emergency response devices and patrols, controlled dormitory access. J. S. Flipper Library.
Community Environment: See University of South Carolina.

■ ANDERSON UNIVERSITY
316 Blvd.
Anderson, SC 29621-4035
Tel: (864)231-2000; Free: 800-542-3594
Fax: (864)231-2004
E-mail: jqueen@andersonuniversity.edu
Web Site: www.andersonuniversity.edu
Description: Independent Baptist, comprehensive, coed. Awards bachelor's, master's, and doctoral degrees. Founded 1911. Setting: 271-acre urban campus with easy access to Greenville. System endowment: $44.7 million. Educational spending for the previous fiscal year: $5683 per student. Total enrollment: 3,497. Faculty: 341 (148 full-time, 193 part-time). Student-undergrad faculty ratio is 14:1. 2,322 applied, 79% were admitted. 37% from top 10% of their high school class, 58% from top quarter, 85% from top half. 15 valedictorians. Full-time: 2,550 students, 69% women, 31% men. Part-time: 433 students, 73% women, 27% men. Students come from 35 states and territories, 20 other countries, 19% from out-of-state. 0.1% American Indian or Alaska Native, non-Hispanic/Latino; 3% Hispanic/Latino; 6% Black or African American, non-Hispanic/Latino; 0.5% Asian, non-Hispanic/Latino; 1% international. 13% 25 or older, 46% live on campus, 5% transferred in. Retention: 75% of full-time freshmen returned the following year. Academic areas with the most degrees conferred: health professions and related sciences; business/marketing; education. Core. Calendar: semesters. Academic remediation for entering students, services for LD students, advanced placement, accelerated degree program, honors program, independent study, distance learning, double major, summer session for credit, part-time degree program, adult/continuing education programs, co-op programs and internships. Study abroad program. ROTC: Army (c), Air Force (c).
Entrance Requirements: Options: electronic application, deferred admission. Required: high school transcript, SAT or ACT. Recommended: minimum 2.9 high school GPA. Required for some: essay, 2 recommendations, interview. Entrance: minimally difficult. Application deadline: 8/1. Notification: continuous.

Costs Per Year: Application fee: $25. Comprehensive fee: $37,830 includes full-time tuition ($25,140), mandatory fees ($2860), and college room and board ($9830). College room only: $5030. Full-time tuition and fees vary according to course load and program. Room and board charges vary according to board plan and housing facility. Part-time tuition: $625 per credit hour. Part-time tuition varies according to course load and program.

Collegiate Environment: Orientation program. Drama-theater group, choral group, student-run newspaper. Social organizations: 29 open to all. Most popular organizations: Baptist Collegiate Ministries, Gamma Beta Phi, Anderson University Education Club, Ducks Unlimited, Council of Exceptional Children. Major annual events: Fall Fest, Homecoming Dance, Spring Fling Dance. Student services: health clinic, personal-psychological counseling. Campus security: 24-hour emergency response devices and patrols, late night transport-escort service, controlled dormitory access. Thrift Library. Books: 90,729 (physical), 99,204 (digital/electronic); Serial titles: 14,268 (physical), 174,052 (digital/electronic); Databases: 200. Weekly public service hours: 88; students can reserve study rooms. Operations spending for the previous fiscal year: $8.4 million. 192 computers available on campus for general student use. A campuswide network can be accessed from student residence rooms and from off campus. Students can access the following: online class registration. Staffed computer lab on campus (open 24 hours a day) provides training in use of computers, software, and the Internet.

Community Environment: Located in the Piedmont Plateau section, Anderson enjoys moderate climate and is a busy manufacturing town with 32 textile plants and many other factories. The area is accessed by major highways, air, bus, and limited rail service. The community has a county-wide library system, churches of many denominations, hotel and motels, hospitals, shopping malls, and various civic and fraternal organizations. Local recreation includes theatres, bowling, tennis, excellent golf facilities, two large lakes, swimming, boating, fishing, hunting, and other outdoor sports. Part-time employment is available.

■ **BENEDICT COLLEGE**
1600 Harden St.
Columbia, SC 29204
Tel: (803)256-4220; Free: 800-868-6598
Fax: (803)253-5167
Web Site: www.benedict.edu

Description: Independent Baptist, 4-year, coed. Awards bachelor's degrees. Founded 1870. Setting: 20-acre urban campus. Total enrollment: 2,641. 10% 25 or older. Calendar: semesters. Advanced placement, honors program, summer session for credit, part-time degree program, adult/continuing education programs, internships. ROTC: Army, Air Force (c).

Entrance Requirements: Open admission. Options: early admission, deferred admission. Required: high school transcript. Entrance: minimally difficult. Application deadline: rolling. Notification: continuous until 7/31.

Collegiate Environment: Orientation program. Campus security: 24-hour emergency response devices and patrols. Benjamin Payton Learning Resource Center.

Community Environment: See University of South Carolina.

■ **BOB JONES UNIVERSITY**
1700 Wade Hampton Blvd.
Greenville, SC 29614
Tel: (864)242-5100; Free: 800-252-6363
E-mail: admission@bju.edu
Web Site: www.bju.edu

Description: Independent Christian, university, coed. Awards associate, bachelor's, master's, and doctoral degrees and post-master's certificates. Founded 1927. Setting: 225-acre urban campus. Total enrollment: 2,936. Faculty: 217 (186 full-time, 31 part-time). Student-undergrad faculty ratio is 13:1. 1,062 applied, 86% were admitted. 13% from top 10% of their high school class, 35% from top quarter, 62% from top half. Full-time: 2,306 students, 55% women, 45% men. Part-time: 300 students, 56% women, 44% men. Students come from 55 states and territories, 40 other countries, 68% from out-of-state. 0.4% American Indian or Alaska Native, non-Hispanic/Latino; 6% Hispanic/Latino; 2% Black or African American, non-Hispanic/Latino; 2% Asian, non-Hispanic/Latino; 0.5% Native Hawaiian or other Pacific Islander, non-Hispanic/Latino; 6% international. 2% 25 or older, 69% live on campus, 3% transferred in. Retention: 82% of full-time freshmen returned the following year. Academic areas with the most degrees conferred: business/marketing; education; visual and performing arts. Core. Calendar: semesters. ESL program, services for LD students, advanced

placement, accelerated degree program, self-designed majors, distance learning, double major, summer session for credit, part-time degree program, adult/continuing education programs, internships. Off campus study.

Entrance Requirements: Options: electronic application, international baccalaureate accepted. Required: essay, high school transcript, 3 recommendations. Entrance: minimally difficult. Application deadline: 8/1. Notification: continuous. Transfer credits accepted: Yes.

Costs Per Year: Application fee: $0. Comprehensive fee: $25,126 includes full-time tuition ($17,250), mandatory fees ($900), and college room and board ($6976). Full-time tuition and fees vary according to course load and program. Part-time tuition: $860 per credit hour. Part-time tuition and fees vary according to course load and program.

Collegiate Environment: Orientation program. Drama-theater group, choral group, student-run newspaper, radio station. Social organizations: 38 open to all; Intra-societies. Most popular organizations: Community Service Council, Missions Advance, Societies, Mission Prayer Band, University Business Association. Major annual events: Bible conference, Artist series, Missions Emphasis Week. Student services: health clinic, personal-psychological counseling. Campus security: 24-hour patrols, student patrols, late night transport-escort service, controlled dormitory access, 24/7 emergency dispatcher. Mack Library plus 2 others. 450 computers available on campus for general student use. Computer purchase/lease plans available. A campuswide network can be accessed from student residence rooms and from off campus. Students can access the following: online class registration. Staffed computer lab on campus provides training in use of computers, software, and the Internet.

■ **CENTRAL CAROLINA TECHNICAL COLLEGE**
506 N Guignard Dr.
Sumter, SC 29150-2499
Tel: (803)778-1961; Free: 800-221-8711
Fax: (803)773-4859
E-mail: wrightb@cctech.edu
Web Site: www.cctech.edu

Description: State-supported, 2-year, coed. Part of South Carolina State Board for Technical and Comprehensive Education. Awards certificates, diplomas, transfer associate, and terminal associate degrees. Founded 1963. Setting: 70-acre small town campus with easy access to Columbia. Endowment: $1.4 million. Total enrollment: 4,522. Faculty: 258 (99 full-time, 159 part-time). Student-undergrad faculty ratio is 17:1. Full-time: 1,607 students, 63% women, 37% men. Part-time: 2,915 students, 74% women, 26% men. 1% from out-of-state. 0.1% American Indian or Alaska Native, non-Hispanic/Latino; 2% Hispanic/Latino; 48% Black or African American, non-Hispanic/Latino; 0.8% Asian, non-Hispanic/Latino. 49% 25 or older, 7% transferred in. Core. Calendar: semesters. Academic remediation for entering students, services for LD students, advanced placement, accelerated degree program, independent study, distance learning, summer session for credit, part-time degree program, external degree program, adult/continuing education programs, co-op programs and internships.

Entrance Requirements: Open admission except for selected health science programs. Option: electronic application. Required: ACT Compass/ACT ASSET. Required for some: high school transcript, SAT or ACT. Entrance: noncompetitive. Application deadline: rolling. Transfer credits accepted: Yes.

Collegiate Environment: Orientation program. Social organizations: 7 open to all. Most popular organizations: Creative Arts Society, Phi Theta Kappa, Computer Club, National Student Nurses Association (local chapter), Natural Resources Management Club. Major annual events: Spring Fling, Student Appreciation Day, Centralfest. Student services: personal-psychological counseling. Campus security: 24-hour emergency response devices, student patrols, security patrols parking lots and halls during working hours and off-duty police officers are deployed on main campus during peak hours. Central Carolina Technical College Library. Operations spending for the previous fiscal year: $241,681. 850 computers available on campus for general student use. A campuswide network can be accessed from off-campus. Students can access the following: online class registration, student account information. Staffed computer lab on campus.

Community Environment: See Morris College.

■ **CENTURA COLLEGE**
7500 Two Notch Rd.
Columbia, SC 29223
Tel: (803)754-7544
Web Site: www.centuracollege.edu

Description: Proprietary, 2-year, coed. Awards certificates and terminal associate degrees.

■ **CHARLESTON SOUTHERN UNIVERSITY**
PO Box 118087
Charleston, SC 29423-8087
Tel: (843)863-7000; Free: 800-947-7474
E-mail: enroll@csuniv.edu
Web Site: www.charlestonsouthern.edu
Description: Independent Baptist, comprehensive, coed. Awards bachelor's and master's degrees and post-master's certificates. Founded 1964. Setting: 500-acre suburban campus. Endowment: $18.2 million. Total enrollment: 3,493. Faculty: 315 (181 full-time, 134 part-time). Student-undergrad faculty ratio is 15:1. 4,125 applied, 56% were admitted. Full-time: 2,804 students, 62% women, 38% men. Part-time: 258 students, 61% women, 39% men. Students come from 41 states and territories, 17 other countries, 16% from out-of-state. 0.6% American Indian or Alaska Native, non-Hispanic/Latino; 4% Hispanic/Latino; 24% Black or African American, non-Hispanic/Latino; 2% Asian, non-Hispanic/Latino; 0.2% Native Hawaiian or other Pacific Islander, non-Hispanic/Latino; 0.7% international. 19% 25 or older, 42% live on campus, 9% transferred in. Retention: 66% of full-time freshmen returned the following year. Core. Calendar: 4-4-1. Academic remediation for entering students, services for LD students, advanced placement, accelerated degree program, honors program, double major, summer session for credit, part-time degree program, internships. Off campus study at Charleston Higher Education Consortium, University of North Carolina System, Clemson University. ROTC: Army, Air Force.
Entrance Requirements: Options: electronic application, international baccalaureate accepted. Required: high school transcript, minimum 2 high school GPA, SAT or ACT. Required for some: essay, 1 recommendation, interview. Entrance: moderately difficult. Application deadline: rolling. Notification: continuous. Transfer credits accepted: Yes.
Collegiate Environment: Orientation program. Drama-theater group, choral group, marching band, student-run newspaper. Social organizations: 20 open to all; national fraternities, national sororities, local fraternities, local sororities. Most popular organizations: Student Government, Baptist Student Union, Fellowship of Christian Athletes. Major annual events: Convocation, Homecoming. Student services: personal-psychological counseling. Campus security: 24-hour emergency response devices and patrols, late night transport-escort service, controlled dormitory access. L. Mendel Rivers Library plus 1 other. Books: 117,095 (physical), 303,641 (digital/electronic); Serial titles: 4,761 (physical), 53,688 (digital/electronic); Databases: 177. Weekly public service hours: 83; students can reserve study rooms. 250 computers available on campus for general student use. A campuswide network can be accessed from student residence rooms and from off campus. Students can access the following: online class registration, online course work. Staffed computer lab on campus provides training in use of computers.
Community Environment: See The Citadel.

■ **THE CITADEL, THE MILITARY COLLEGE OF SOUTH CAROLINA**
171 Moultrie St.
Charleston, SC 29409
Tel: (843)225-3294; Free: 800-868-1842
Fax: (843)953-7084
E-mail: john.powell@citadel.edu
Web Site: www.citadel.edu
Description: State-supported, comprehensive, coed. Awards bachelor's and master's degrees and post-master's certificates. Founded 1842. Setting: 300-acre suburban campus. Endowment: $254.3 million. Research spending for the previous fiscal year: $607,082. Educational spending for the previous fiscal year: $10,630 per student. Total enrollment: 3,717. Faculty: 317 (201 full-time, 116 part-time). Student-undergrad faculty ratio is 12:1. 2,642 applied, 81% were admitted. 9% from top 10% of their high school class, 30% from top quarter, 64% from top half. Full-time: 2,559 students, 9% women, 91% men. Part-time: 278 students, 21% women, 79% men. Students come from 42 states and territories, 8 other countries, 33% from out-of-state. 0.4% American Indian or Alaska Native, non-Hispanic/Latino; 7% Hispanic/Latino; 9% Black or African American, non-Hispanic/Latino; 2% Asian, non-Hispanic/Latino; 0.3% Native Hawaiian or other Pacific Islander, non-Hispanic/Latino; 0.8% international. 9% 25 or older, 100% live on campus, 5% transferred in. Retention: 85% of full-time freshmen returned the following year. Academic areas with the most degrees conferred: business/marketing; engineering; homeland security, law enforcement, firefighting, and protective services;

Core. Calendar: semesters. ESL program, services for LD students, advanced placement, honors program, independent study, distance learning, double major, summer session for credit, part-time degree program, adult/continuing education programs, co-op programs and internships. Off campus study at The Cooperative Center for Study Abroad is a consortium of U.S. colleges and universities, which jointly offers study abroad programs in English-speaking regions. A not-for-profit organization, CCSA is headquartered at Western Kentucky University in Bowling Green, Kentucky. Study abroad program. ROTC: Army, Naval, Air Force.
Entrance Requirements: Options: electronic application, international baccalaureate accepted. Required: high school transcript, SAT or ACT. Recommended: interview. Entrance: moderately difficult. Application deadline: rolling. Notification: continuous. Transfer credits accepted: Yes. Applicants placed on waiting list: 7. Wait-listed applicants offered admission: 3.
Costs Per Year: Application fee: $40. State resident tuition: $12,516 full-time, $485 per credit hour part-time. Nonresident tuition: $34,988 full-time, $902 per credit hour part-time. Mandatory fees: $2133 full-time. Full-time tuition and fees vary according to class time, degree level, program, and student level. Part-time tuition varies according to class time and program. College room and board: $6904.
Collegiate Environment: Orientation program. Choral group, marching band, student-run newspaper. Social organizations: 120 open to all. Most popular organizations: The Republican Society, Semper Fi Society, American Society of Civil Engineers, Campus Outreach, Criminal Justice Society. Major annual events: Parents' Weekend, Homecoming, Principled Leadership Symposium/Corps Day/Recognition Day. Student services: health clinic, personal-psychological counseling. Campus security: 24-hour patrols. Daniel Library. Books: 182,744 (physical), 225,852 (digital/electronic); Serial titles: 97 (physical); Databases: 250. Students can reserve study rooms. 350 computers available on campus for general student use. A campuswide network can be accessed from student residence rooms and from off campus. Students can access the following: online class registration. Staffed computer lab on campus provides training in use of computers, software, and the Internet.

■ **CLAFLIN UNIVERSITY**
400 Magnolia St.
Orangeburg, SC 29115
Tel: (803)535-5097; Free: 800-922-1276
Fax: (803)531-2860
Web Site: www.claflin.edu
Description: Independent United Methodist, comprehensive, coed. Awards bachelor's and master's degrees. Founded 1869. Setting: 46-acre small town campus with easy access to Columbia. Endowment: $21.7 million. Research spending for the previous fiscal year: $2.6 million. Educational spending for the previous fiscal year: $22,162 per student. Total enrollment: 1,886. Student-undergrad faculty ratio is 14:1. 4,073 applied, 60% were admitted. 12% from top 10% of their high school class, 32% from top quarter, 62% from top half. Full-time: 1,769 students, 64% women, 36% men. Part-time: 67 students, 63% women, 37% men. Students come from 27 states and territories, 18 other countries, 19% from out-of-state. 0.8% American Indian or Alaska Native, non-Hispanic/Latino; 2% Hispanic/Latino; 91% Black or African American, non-Hispanic/Latino; 0.4% Asian, non-Hispanic/Latino; 4% international. 15% 25 or older, 70% live on campus, 5% transferred in. Retention: 70% of full-time freshmen returned the following year. Academic areas with the most degrees conferred: business/marketing; social sciences; homeland security, law enforcement, firefighting, and protective services. Core. Calendar: semesters. Academic remediation for entering students, advanced placement, accelerated degree program, freshman honors college, honors program, independent study, distance learning, double major, summer session for credit, part-time degree program, adult/continuing education programs, co-op programs and internships. Off campus study at South Carolina State University, Medical University of South Carolina, Orangeburg-Calhoun Technical College, Clemson University. Study abroad program. ROTC: Army (c).
Entrance Requirements: Options: electronic application, deferred admission, international baccalaureate accepted. Required: essay, high school transcript, minimum 2 high school GPA, SAT or ACT. Entrance: minimally difficult. Application deadline: rolling. Notification: continuous. SAT Reasoning Test deadline: 8/1. Transfer credits accepted: Yes.
Costs Per Year: Application fee: $30. Comprehensive fee: $25,966 includes full-time tuition ($16,152), mandatory fees ($520), and college room and board ($9294). College room only: $3952. Full-time tuition and fees vary according to class time and course load. Room and board charges vary ac-

cording to housing facility. Part-time tuition: $673 per credit hour. Part-time mandatory fees: $260 per term. Part-time tuition and fees vary according to class time.

Collegiate Environment: Orientation program. Drama-theater group, choral group, student-run newspaper. Social organizations: 64 open to all; national fraternities, national sororities; 3% of eligible men and 6% of eligible women are members. Most popular organizations: Gospel Choir, NAACP, American Chemical Society, Sisters of Service, International Student Association. Major annual events: Homecoming, Spring Convocation, Honors and Awards Convocation. Student services: health clinic, personal-psychological counseling. Campus security: 24-hour emergency response devices and patrols, student patrols, controlled dormitory access. H. V. Manning Library plus 1 other. Operations spending for the previous fiscal year: $904,004. 530 computers available on campus for general student use. A campuswide network can be accessed from student residence rooms and from off campus. Students can access the following: online class registration. Staffed computer lab on campus.

■ **CLEMSON UNIVERSITY**
Clemson, SC 29634
Tel: (864)656-3311
Fax: (864)656-2464
Web Site: www.clemson.edu

Description: State-supported, university, coed. Awards bachelor's, master's, and doctoral degrees and post-master's certificates. Founded 1889. Setting: 1,400-acre small town campus. Endowment: $518.6 million. Research spending for the previous fiscal year: $130.8 million. Educational spending for the previous fiscal year: $10,188 per student. Total enrollment: 24,387. Faculty: 1,648 (1,248 full-time, 400 part-time). Student-undergrad faculty ratio is 16:1. 26,241 applied, 47% were admitted. 62% from top 10% of their high school class, 91% from top quarter, 99% from top half. Full-time: 18,642 students, 49% women, 51% men. Part-time: 760 students, 42% women, 58% men. Students come from 53 states and territories, 84 other countries, 29% from out-of-state. 0.2% American Indian or Alaska Native, non-Hispanic/Latino; 4% Hispanic/Latino; 7% Black or African American, non-Hispanic/Latino; 2% Asian, non-Hispanic/Latino; 0.9% international. 4% 25 or older, 37% live on campus, 8% transferred in. Retention: 93% of full-time freshmen returned the following year. Academic areas with the most degrees conferred: engineering; business/marketing; biological/life sciences. Core. Calendar: semesters. Academic remediation for entering students, ESL program, services for LD students, advanced placement, freshman honors college, honors program, independent study, distance learning, double major, summer session for credit, part-time degree program, co-op programs and internships, graduate courses open to undergrads. Off campus study. Study abroad program. ROTC: Army, Air Force.

Entrance Requirements: Options: electronic application, international baccalaureate accepted. Required: high school transcript, SAT or ACT. Recommended: essay. Entrance: very difficult. Application deadline: 5/1. Notification: continuous. Preference given to state residents, legacy. SAT Reasoning Test deadline: 4/30. SAT Subject Test deadline: 4/30. Transfer credits accepted: Yes. Applicants placed on waiting list: 2,649. Wait-listed applicants offered admission: 876.

Collegiate Environment: Orientation program. Drama-theater group, choral group, marching band, student-run newspaper, radio station. Social organizations: 350 open to all; national fraternities, national sororities; 22% of eligible men and 48% of eligible women are members. Most popular organizations: Student Government, Fellowship of Christian Athletes, Tiger Band. Major annual events: Homecoming/Tigerama, Welcome Back Festival, Campus Sweep. Student services: legal services, health clinic, personal-psychological counseling. Campus security: 24-hour emergency response devices and patrols, late night transport-escort service, controlled dormitory access. Robert Muldrow Cooper Library plus 1 other. Study areas open 24 hours, 5-7 days a week; students can reserve study rooms. Operations spending for the previous fiscal year: $13.5 million. 1,250 computers available on campus for general student use. Computer purchase/lease plans available. A computer is required for all students. A campuswide network can be accessed. Students can access the following: online class registration. Staffed computer lab on campus provides training in use of computers, software, and the Internet.

Community Environment: Clemson is located in the foothills of the Blue Ridge Mountains approximately 135 miles from Charlotte and Atlanta. The average temperature is 61 degrees. The area is served by U.S. Highways 76 and 123, and air service is available nearby. Clemson has several churches of different denominations, a library, YMCA, concert series, and Little

Theatre. Hotels, apartments, and rooming houses provide additional student housing. Local recreational facilities include fishing, hunting, golf, tennis, swimming, sailing, and skiing. Job opportunities are available.

■ **CLINTON COLLEGE**
1029 Crawford Rd.
Rock Hill, SC 29730
Tel: (803)327-7402; Free: 877-837-9645
Fax: (803)327-3261
Web Site: www.clintoncollege.edu

Description: Independent, 2-year, coed, affiliated with African Methodist Episcopal Zion Church. Awards terminal associate degrees. Founded 1894. Total enrollment: 148. Student-undergrad faculty ratio is 15:1. 45% from out-of-state. 17% 25 or older. Calendar: semesters.

Entrance Requirements: Entrance: noncompetitive.

■ **COASTAL CAROLINA UNIVERSITY**
PO Box 261954
Conway, SC 29528-6054
Tel: (843)347-3161; Free: 800-277-7000
Fax: (843)349-2127
Web Site: www.coastal.edu

Description: State-supported, comprehensive, coed. Awards bachelor's, master's, and doctoral degrees and post-master's certificates. Founded 1954. Setting: 621-acre suburban campus. Endowment: $44.7 million. Research spending for the previous fiscal year: $1.1 million. Educational spending for the previous fiscal year: $8612 per student. Total enrollment: 10,641. Faculty: 784 (490 full-time, 294 part-time). Student-undergrad faculty ratio is 17:1. 14,057 applied, 70% were admitted. 11% from top 10% of their high school class, 33% from top quarter, 69% from top half. Full-time: 8,941 students, 54% women, 46% men. Part-time: 976 students, 52% women, 48% men. Students come from 50 states and territories, 61 other countries, 51% from out-of-state. 0.3% American Indian or Alaska Native, non-Hispanic/Latino; 5% Hispanic/Latino; 19% Black or African American, non-Hispanic/Latino; 0.9% Asian, non-Hispanic/Latino; 0.1% Native Hawaiian or other Pacific Islander, non-Hispanic/Latino; 1% international. 6% 25 or older, 44% live on campus, 7% transferred in. Retention: 69% of full-time freshmen returned the following year. Academic areas with the most degrees conferred: business/marketing; biological/life sciences; parks and recreation. Core. Calendar: semesters. Services for LD students, advanced placement, accelerated degree program, self-designed majors, honors program, independent study, distance learning, double major, summer session for credit, part-time degree program, adult/continuing education programs, co-op programs and internships, graduate courses open to undergrads. Study abroad program. ROTC: Army.

Entrance Requirements: Options: electronic application, deferred admission, international baccalaureate accepted. Required: high school transcript, minimum 2 high school GPA, SAT or ACT. Recommended: essay, 1 recommendation, interview. Entrance: moderately difficult. Application deadline: rolling. Notification: continuous. Preference given to South Carolina residents. SAT Reasoning Test deadline: 5/1. Transfer credits accepted: Yes.

Costs Per Year: Application fee: $45. State resident tuition: $11,356 full-time, $483 per credit hour part-time. Nonresident tuition: $26,468 full-time, $1107 per credit hour part-time. Mandatory fees: $180 full-time, $5 per credit hour part-time. Full-time tuition and fees vary according to course load, degree level, and reciprocity agreements. Part-time tuition and fees vary according to course load, degree level, and reciprocity agreements. College room and board: $9190. College room only: $5440. Room and board charges vary according to board plan and housing facility.

Collegiate Environment: Orientation program. Drama-theater group, choral group, marching band, student-run newspaper, radio station. Social organizations: 194 open to all; national fraternities, national sororities; 3% of eligible men and 5% of eligible women are members. Most popular organizations: Club Rugby, Outdoor Adventure Club, Alpha Delta Pi, Salt Water Anglers, Aqua League (Scuba Club). Major annual events: Organization Kick Off, Cino Day, Relay for Life. Student services: health clinic, personal-psychological counseling, women's center. Campus security: 24-hour emergency response devices and patrols, late night transport-escort service. 4,636 college housing spaces available; 4,272 were occupied in 2018-19. Freshmen guaranteed college housing. On-campus residence required through sophomore year. Option: coed housing available. Kimbel Library. Books: 129,696 (physical), 433,254 (digital/electronic); Serial titles: 622 (physical), 79,146 (digital/electronic); Databases: 213. Weekly public service hours: 168; study areas open 24 hours, 5-7 days a week. Operations spending for the previous fiscal year: $3.3 million. 1,400 computers available on campus for general student use. Computer purchase/lease plans available. A campuswide network can be accessed from student residence rooms and from off campus. Students can access the following: online class registration. Staffed computer lab on campus (open 24 hours a day) provides training in use of computers, software, and the Internet.

Community Environment: Coastal Carolina University is located nine miles from the bustling resort area of Myrtle Beach, SC. Recreational and entertainment options provide many opportunities for internships for the Professional Golf Management and Resort Tourism programs, as well as part-time employment opportunities. Brookgreen Gardens, one of the world's finest outdoor sculpture gardens, provides a tranquil setting for relaxation, while Broadway on the Beach provides entertainment, shopping, and dining attractions.

■ COKER COLLEGE

300 E College Ave.
Hartsville, SC 29550
Tel: (843)383-8000; Free: 800-950-1908
Fax: (843)383-8056
E-mail: admissions@coker.edu
Web Site: www.coker.edu

Description: Independent, comprehensive, coed. Awards bachelor's and master's degrees (also offers evening program with significant enrollment not reflected in profile). Founded 1908. Setting: 37-acre small town campus with easy access to Charlotte. Endowment: $29.2 million. Research spending for the previous fiscal year: $113,781. Educational spending for the previous fiscal year: $6685 per student. Total enrollment: 1,093. Faculty: 95 (60 full-time, 35 part-time). Student-undergrad faculty ratio is 13:1. 1,389 applied, 62% were admitted. 9% from top 10% of their high school class, 22% from top quarter, 55% from top half. Full-time: 845 students, 60% women, 40% men. Part-time: 177 students, 60% women, 40% men. Students come from 33 states and territories, 15 other countries, 24% from out-of-state. 0.6% American Indian or Alaska Native, non-Hispanic/Latino; 3% Hispanic/Latino; 33% Black or African American, non-Hispanic/Latino; 0.5% Asian, non-Hispanic/Latino; 0.1% Native Hawaiian or other Pacific Islander, non-Hispanic/Latino; 3% international. 26% 25 or older, 56% live on campus, 10% transferred in. Retention: 61% of full-time freshmen returned the following year. Academic areas with the most degrees conferred: business/marketing; social sciences; parks and recreation. Core. Calendar: semesters. Services for LD students, advanced placement, self-designed majors, honors program, independent study, distance learning, double major, summer session for credit, part-time degree program, adult/continuing education programs, internships. Off campus study. Study abroad program.

Entrance Requirements: Options: electronic application, early action, deferred admission, international baccalaureate accepted. Required: high school transcript, SAT or ACT. Required for some: essay, interview, audition or portfolio for certain programs. Entrance: moderately difficult. Application deadlines: rolling, 12/1 for early action. Notification: continuous, 12/15 for early action. SAT Reasoning Test deadline: 6/30. Transfer credits accepted: Yes.

Costs Per Year: Application fee: $0. Comprehensive fee: $38,618 includes full-time tuition ($29,328), mandatory fees ($200), and college room and board ($9090). College room only: $4190. Full-time tuition and fees vary according to course load, degree level, location, and program. Room and board charges vary according to board plan and housing facility. Part-time tuition: $1222 per credit hour. Part-time tuition varies according to course load, degree level, location, and program.

Collegiate Environment: Orientation program. Drama-theater group, choral group. Social organizations: 34 open to all. Most popular organization: Student Government Association. Major annual events: Bandfest, Crew Race, COW Days (Coker Olympics of Winter). Student services: health clinic, personal-psychological counseling. Campus security: 24-hour patrols, late night transport-escort service, controlled dormitory access. The Charles W. and Joan S. Coker Library-Information Technology Center plus 1 other. Books: 81,626 (physical), 15,760 (digital/electronic). Weekly public service hours: 87; students can reserve study rooms. Operations spending for the previous fiscal year: $480,408. 116 computers available on campus for general student use. A campuswide network can be accessed from student residence rooms. Students can access the following: online class registration. Staffed computer lab on campus provides training in use of computers and the Internet.

Community Environment: Coker College is located in Hartsville, a community of approximately 20,000 people. It is located in the northeastern part

of the state, 20 miles off I-95, and approximately a two-hour drive from South Carolina's beautiful beaches and mountains. The climate is temperate and mild year-round. There is a township library and many churches of various denominations. Florence airport is 24 miles away. Part-time employment is available for students. Local recreational facilities include two theaters, Lake Robinson, Prestwood Lake, golf, tennis, two city parks, and racing. There are various civic and fraternal organizations that are active within the community. Health service facilities are available.

■ COLLEGE OF CHARLESTON

66 George St.
Charleston, SC 29424-0001
Tel: (843)953-5507
E-mail: admissions@cofc.edu
Web Site: www.cofc.edu

Description: State-supported, comprehensive, coed. Awards bachelor's and master's degrees and post-master's certificates (also offers graduate degree programs through University of Charleston, South Carolina). Founded 1770. Setting: 66-acre urban campus. Endowment: $92.3 million. Research spending for the previous fiscal year: $6.3 million. Educational spending for the previous fiscal year: $8923 per student. Total enrollment: 10,783. Faculty: 958 (558 full-time, 400 part-time). Student-undergrad faculty ratio is 15:1. 11,675 applied, 79% were admitted. 20% from top 10% of their high school class, 51% from top quarter, 87% from top half. 16 valedictorians. Full-time: 9,103 students, 65% women, 35% men. Part-time: 777 students, 53% women, 47% men. Students come from 48 states and territories, 62 other countries, 34% from out-of-state. 0.4% American Indian or Alaska Native, non-Hispanic/Latino; 6% Hispanic/Latino; 8% Black or African American, non-Hispanic/Latino; 2% Asian, non-Hispanic/Latino; 0.2% Native Hawaiian or other Pacific Islander, non-Hispanic/Latino; 1% international. 7% 25 or older, 31% live on campus, 5% transferred in. Retention: 79% of full-time freshmen returned the following year. Academic areas with the most degrees conferred: business/marketing; biological/life sciences; visual and performing arts. Core. Calendar: semesters. ESL program, services for LD students, advanced placement, accelerated degree program, honors program, independent study, distance learning, double major, summer session for credit, part-time degree program, adult/continuing education programs, co-op programs and internships, graduate courses open to undergrads. Off campus study at Medical University of South Carolina, The Citadel, Charleston Southern University. Study abroad program. ROTC: Air Force (c).

Entrance Requirements: Options: electronic application, early decision, early action, deferred admission, international baccalaureate accepted. Required: essay, high school transcript, SAT or ACT. Required for some: letters of recommendation for Honors College, International applicants not submitting an SAT/ACT score should submit an English language proficiency test score (TOEFL, IELTS, or iTEP). Entrance: moderately difficult. Application deadlines: 2/15, 11/1 for early decision, 12/1 for early action. Notification: 4/1, 12/1 for early decision, 1/1 for early action. SAT Reasoning Test deadline: 4/1. Transfer credits accepted: Yes. Applicants placed on waiting list: 0. Wait-listed applicants offered admission: 0. Early action applicants: 6,749. Early action applicants admitted: 5,723.

Costs Per Year: Application fee: $50. State resident tuition: $12,418 full-time, $517 per credit hour part-time. Nonresident tuition: $31,600 full-time, $1317 per credit hour part-time. Mandatory fees: $460 full-time, $16.25 per term part-time, $16.25 per term part-time. Full-time tuition and fees vary according to student level. Part-time tuition and fees vary according to course load and student level. College room and board: $12,166. College room only: $7866. Room and board charges vary according to board plan and housing facility.

Collegiate Environment: Orientation program. Drama-theater group, choral group, student-run newspaper, radio station. Social organizations: 220 open to all; national fraternities, national sororities; 10% of eligible men and 22% of eligible women are members. Most popular organizations: Student Government Association, Cougar Activities Board, Black Student Union, Charleston Miracle, Intramural Basketball. Major annual events: Maroon Mayhem, Cougar Night Lights, Pep Supper. Student services: health clinic, personal-psychological counseling, women's center. Campus security: 24-hour emergency response devices and patrols, student patrols, late night transport-escort service, controlled dormitory access. 3,419 college housing spaces available; 3,360 were occupied in 2018-19. Freshmen given priority for college housing. Options: coed, men-only, women-only housing available. Marlene and Nathan Addlestone Library plus 3 others. Books: 608,954 (physical), 635,379 (digital/electronic); Serial titles: 418 (physical), 89,449 (digital/electronic); Databases: 339. Weekly public service hours: 112;

students can reserve study rooms. Operations spending for the previous fiscal year: $6.6 million. 325 computers available on campus for general student use. Computer purchase/lease plans available. A campuswide network can be accessed. Students can access the following: online class registration. Staffed computer lab on campus provides training in use of computers, software, and the Internet.

Community Environment: See The Citadel.

■ COLUMBIA COLLEGE

1301 Columbia College Dr.
Columbia, SC 29203-5998
Tel: (803)786-3012; Free: 800-277-1301
Fax: (803)786-3674
E-mail: rlonge@columbiasc.edu
Web Site: www.columbiasc.edu

Description: Independent United Methodist, comprehensive, coed. Awards bachelor's and master's degrees. Founded 1854. Setting: 59-acre suburban campus. Endowment: $25.6 million. Educational spending for the previous fiscal year: $9539 per student. Total enrollment: 1,513. Faculty: 109 (55 full-time, 54 part-time). Student-undergrad faculty ratio is 15:1. 880 applied, 87% were admitted. 9% from top 10% of their high school class, 34% from top quarter, 72% from top half. Full-time: 802 students, 92% women, 8% men. Part-time: 577 students, 50% women, 50% men. Students come from 27 states and territories, 21 other countries, 11% from out-of-state. 0.8% American Indian or Alaska Native, non-Hispanic/Latino; 4% Hispanic/Latino; 33% Black or African American, non-Hispanic/Latino; 0.7% Asian, non-Hispanic/Latino; 0.1% Native Hawaiian or other Pacific Islander, non-Hispanic/Latino; 3% international. 49% 25 or older, 29% live on campus, 15% transferred in. Retention: 71% of full-time freshmen returned the following year. Academic areas with the most degrees conferred: homeland security, law enforcement, firefighting, and protective services; education; communication/journalism. Core. Calendar: semesters. Academic remediation for entering students, services for LD students, advanced placement, self-designed majors, honors program, independent study, distance learning, double major, summer session for credit, part-time degree program, adult/continuing education programs, internships. Off campus study. Study abroad program. ROTC: Army (c).

Entrance Requirements: Option: electronic application. Required: high school transcript. Recommended: essay. Required for some: interview. Entrance: moderately difficult. Application deadline: 8/1. SAT Reasoning Test deadline: 7/1. Transfer credits accepted: Yes.

Costs Per Year: Application fee: $0. One-time mandatory fee: $150. Comprehensive fee: $27,400 includes full-time tuition ($19,500) and college room and board ($7900). College room only: $3900. Full-time tuition varies according to class time and location. Room and board charges vary according to board plan and housing facility. Part-time tuition: $650 per semester hour. Part-time tuition varies according to class time and location.

Collegiate Environment: Orientation program. Drama-theater group, choral group, student-run newspaper. Social organizations: 50 open to all. Major annual events: Ludy Bowl, Follies, Mom's Day. Student services: health clinic, personal-psychological counseling, women's center. Campus security: 24-hour emergency response devices and patrols, late night transport-escort service, controlled dormitory access. J. Edens Drake Library. Books: 128,000 (physical), 92 (digital/electronic); Serial titles: 310 (physical); Databases: 84. Weekly public service hours: 70; students can reserve study rooms. Operations spending for the previous fiscal year: $152,760. 165 computers available on campus for general student use. Computer purchase/lease plans available. A campuswide network can be accessed. Students can access the following: online class registration. Staffed computer lab on campus (open 24 hours a day) provides training in use of computers, software, and the Internet.

■ COLUMBIA INTERNATIONAL UNIVERSITY

7435 Monticello Rd.
Columbia, SC 29203
Tel: (803)754-4100; Free: 800-777-2227
Fax: (803)786-4209
E-mail: yesciu@ciu.edu
Web Site: www.ciu.edu

Description: Independent nondenominational, university, coed. Awards associate, bachelor's, master's, and doctoral degrees and post-master's certificates. Founded 1923. Setting: 400-acre suburban campus with easy access to Columbia, SC. Endowment: $21.1 million. Research spending for the previous fiscal year: $18.7 million. Educational spending for the previous

fiscal year: $6023 per student. Total enrollment: 965. Faculty: 63 (38 full-time, 25 part-time). Student-undergrad faculty ratio is 16:1. 518 applied, 36% were admitted. 17% from top 10% of their high school class, 34% from top quarter, 63% from top half. Full-time: 454 students, 51% women, 49% men. Part-time: 43 students, 23% women, 77% men. Students come from 27 states and territories, 15 other countries, 48% from out-of-state. 4% Hispanic/Latino; 11% Black or African American, non-Hispanic/Latino; 2% Asian, non-Hispanic/Latino; 5% international. 5% 25 or older, 68% live on campus, 10% transferred in. Retention: 78% of full-time freshmen returned the following year. Academic areas with the most degrees conferred: theology and religious vocations; liberal arts/general studies; interdisciplinary studies. Core. Calendar: semesters. Academic remediation for entering students, services for LD students, advanced placement, accelerated degree program, honors program, independent study, distance learning, double major, summer session for credit, part-time degree program, co-op programs and internships, graduate courses open to undergrads. Off campus study. Study abroad program.

Entrance Requirements: Options: electronic application, deferred admission, international baccalaureate accepted. Required: essay, minimum 2 high school GPA, 1 recommendation, SAT or ACT. Recommended: high school transcript. Required for some: interview. Entrance: moderately difficult. Application deadline: 8/1. Notification: continuous, continuous for nonresidents. SAT Reasoning Test deadline: 8/1. Transfer credits accepted: Yes.

Costs Per Year: Application fee: $0. Comprehensive fee: $31,840 includes full-time tuition ($22,840), mandatory fees ($850), and college room and board ($8150). Full-time tuition and fees vary according to course load, program, and reciprocity agreements. Room and board charges vary according to board plan and housing facility. Part-time tuition: $950 per semester hour. Part-time mandatory fees: $10 per semester hour, $185 per term. Part-time tuition and fees vary according to course load, program, and reciprocity agreements.

Collegiate Environment: Orientation program. Drama-theater group, choral group, student-run newspaper. Social organizations: 14 open to all. Most popular organizations: Student Union, Mu Kappa, Student Missions Connection, GradLife, African American Fellowship Ministries. Major annual events: World Christian Week, Homecoming, Winter Formal Banquet. Student services: legal services, health clinic, personal-psychological counseling. Campus security: 24-hour emergency response devices and patrols, late night transport-escort service, controlled dormitory access. G. Allen Fleece Library. Books: 32,000 (physical), 100,000 (digital/electronic); Databases: 133. Weekly public service hours: 81; students can reserve study rooms. 106 computers available on campus for general student use. A campuswide network can be accessed from student residence rooms and from off campus. Students can access the following: online class registration. Staffed computer lab on campus provides training in use of computers, software, and the Internet.

Community Environment: See University of South Carolina.

■ CONVERSE COLLEGE

580 E Main St.
Spartanburg, SC 29302
Tel: (864)596-9000; Free: 800-766-1125
Fax: (864)596-9158
E-mail: admissions@converse.edu
Web Site: www.converse.edu

Description: Independent, comprehensive. Awards bachelor's and master's degrees and post-master's certificates. Founded 1889. Setting: 70-acre urban campus. Total enrollment: 1,319. Faculty: 84 (81 full-time, 3 part-time). Student-undergrad faculty ratio is 13:1. 1,359 applied, 60% were admitted. 18% from top 10% of their high school class, 50% from top quarter, 88% from top half. Full-time: 815 students, 100% women. Part-time: 55 students, 100% women. 24% from out-of-state. 4% Hispanic/Latino; 9% Black or African American, non-Hispanic/Latino; 0.6% Asian, non-Hispanic/Latino; 2% international. 11% 25 or older, 73% live on campus, 6% transferred in. Retention: 70% of full-time freshmen returned the following year. Academic areas with the most degrees conferred: psychology; visual and performing arts; business/marketing; education. Core. Calendar: 4-1-4. Advanced placement, self-designed majors, honors program, independent study, double major, summer session for credit, part-time degree program, adult/continuing education programs, co-op programs and internships, graduate courses open to undergrads. Off campus study at Wofford College. Study abroad program. ROTC: Army (c).

Entrance Requirements: Options: electronic application, deferred admis-

sion, international baccalaureate accepted. Required: high school transcript, SAT or ACT. Recommended: essay, minimum 3 high school GPA. Entrance: moderately difficult. Application deadlines: 8/1, rolling for nonresidents. Notification: continuous until 9/1, continuous for nonresidents. SAT Reasoning Test deadline: 7/1. Transfer credits accepted: Yes.

Costs Per Year: Application fee: $0. Comprehensive fee: $29,620 includes full-time tuition ($18,340), mandatory fees ($350), and college room and board ($10,930). Room and board charges vary according to board plan. Part-time tuition: $875 per credit. Part-time tuition varies according to course load.

Collegiate Environment: Orientation program. Drama-theater group, choral group, student-run newspaper. Social organizations: 55 open to all. Most popular organizations: Student Government, student volunteer services, Student Christian Organization, Student Activities Committee, Athletic Association. Major annual events: 1889 Day, Founders' Day, Spring Concert. Student services: health clinic, personal-psychological counseling, women's center. Campus security: 24-hour emergency response devices and patrols, late night transport-escort service, controlled dormitory access. Mickel Library. Books: 165,873 (physical), 252,047 (digital/electronic); Databases: 30. 140 computers available on campus for general student use. A campuswide network can be accessed from student residence rooms and from off campus. Students can access the following: online class registration. Staffed computer lab on campus provides training in use of computers, software, and the Internet.

Community Environment: One of the leading textile manufacturing cities in the South, Spartanburg is also one of the largest peach shipping centers in the world. The city was named after the Spartan Regiment, which represented this community in the Revolutionary War. The community is located in the Piedmont section of South Carolina and has an average temperature of 60 degrees. Airlines, railroads, and bus lines serve the area. There are many churches representing various denominations, 3 hospitals, libraries, a YMCA Family Center, and various civic and fraternal groups serving the city. Motels, hotels, and rooming houses are available for guests. Local recreation includes football, basketball, baseball, golf, stock car racing, swimming, tennis, picnicking, water skiing, theater, and series of concerts. Part-time employment is available.

■ DENMARK TECHNICAL COLLEGE
1126 Solomon Blatt Blvd.
Denmark, SC 29042-0327
Tel: (803)793-5100
Fax: (803)793-5942
E-mail: troyk@denmarktech.edu
Web Site: www.denmarktech.edu

Description: State-supported, 2-year, coed. Part of South Carolina State Board for Technical and Comprehensive Education. Awards certificates, diplomas, transfer associate, and terminal associate degrees. Founded 1948. Setting: 53-acre rural campus. Total enrollment: 1,043. Faculty: 63 (37 full-time, 26 part-time). Student-undergrad faculty ratio is 20:1. Full-time: 655 students, 59% women, 41% men. Part-time: 388 students, 60% women, 40% men. 4% from out-of-state. 0.2% American Indian or Alaska Native, non-Hispanic/Latino; 0.8% Hispanic/Latino; 92% Black or African American, non-Hispanic/Latino; 0.2% Asian, non-Hispanic/Latino. 60% 25 or older, 1% transferred in. Retention: 28% of full-time freshmen returned the following year. Calendar: semesters. Academic remediation for entering students, services for LD students, advanced placement, independent study, distance learning, summer session for credit, part-time degree program, adult/continuing education programs, co-op programs and internships. Off campus study at Voorhees College, South Carolina State University.

Entrance Requirements: Open admission. Options: electronic application, early admission, deferred admission. Required: high school transcript, ACT ASSET, ACCUPLACER, and TEAS (for nursing). Recommended: SAT or ACT. Required for some: essay, criminal background check, drug test, PPD test for LPN. Entrance: noncompetitive. Application deadline: rolling. Notification: continuous. Transfer credits accepted: Yes.

Collegiate Environment: Orientation program. Choral group. Social organizations: 25 open to all. Most popular organizations: Student Government Association, DTC Choir, Athletics, Phi Theta Kappa Internal Honor Society, Esquire Club (men and women). Major annual events: Homecoming, Commencement, Coronation. Student services: health clinic, personal-psychological counseling. Campus security: 24-hour emergency response devices and patrols, late night transport-escort service. Denmark Technical College Learning Resources Center. Books: 9,810 (physical); Databases: 2. Weekly public service hours: 40; study areas open 24 hours, 5-7 days a

week; students can reserve study rooms. 325 computers available on campus for general student use. A campuswide network can be accessed from student residence rooms. Staffed computer lab on campus provides training in use of computers, software, and the Internet.

■ ERSKINE COLLEGE
2 Washington St.
Due West, SC 29639
Tel: (864)379-2131; Free: 800-241-8721
Fax: (864)379-8759
Web Site: www.erskine.edu

Description: Independent, comprehensive, coed, affiliated with Associate Reformed Presbyterian Church. Administratively affiliated with Erskine Theological Seminary. Awards bachelor's, master's, and doctoral degrees. Founded 1839. Setting: 90-acre rural campus. Endowment: $39.8 million. Total enrollment: 761. Faculty: 82 (59 full-time, 23 part-time). Student-undergrad faculty ratio is 12:1. 991 applied, 64% were admitted. 35% from top 10% of their high school class, 69% from top quarter, 87% from top half. Full-time: 615 students, 46% women, 54% men. Part-time: 7 students, 43% women, 57% men. Students come from 19 states and territories, 11 other countries, 25% from out-of-state. 0.8% American Indian or Alaska Native, non-Hispanic/Latino; 4% Hispanic/Latino; 13% Black or African American, non-Hispanic/Latino; 1% Asian, non-Hispanic/Latino; 0.5% Native Hawaiian or other Pacific Islander, non-Hispanic/Latino. 1% 25 or older, 89% live on campus, 4% transferred in. Retention: 62% of full-time freshmen returned the following year. Academic areas with the most degrees conferred: business/marketing; biological/life sciences; physical sciences; parks and recreation. Core. Calendar: 4-1-4. Advanced placement, independent study, double major, summer session for credit, part-time degree program, internships, graduate courses open to undergrads. Off campus study at other colleges having a 4-1-4 calendar. Study abroad program.

Entrance Requirements: Options: electronic application, early admission, early action, deferred admission, international baccalaureate accepted. Required: essay, high school transcript, 1 recommendation, SAT or ACT. Recommended: interview. Entrance: moderately difficult. Application deadlines: rolling, 11/1 for early action. Notification: continuous, 11/15 for early action. Preference given to members of Associate Reformed Presbyterian Church. SAT Reasoning Test deadline: 8/15.

Collegiate Environment: Orientation program. Drama-theater group, choral group, student-run newspaper, radio station. Social organizations: 51 open to all. Most popular organizations: literary societies, religious organizations, Student Government Organization, publications, honor societies. Major annual events: Fall Fest, Spring Fling, Homecoming. Student services: health clinic, personal-psychological counseling. Campus security: 24-hour patrols, late night transport-escort service, controlled dormitory access. McCain Library. Students can reserve study rooms. Operations spending for the previous fiscal year: $502,600.

Community Environment: Due West is a town of approximately 1,300 residents. It enjoys a temperate climate. There is easy access to Interstate Routes 26 and 85, and the cities of Anderson, Greenwood, and Greenville are nearby. The major metropolitan areas of Atlanta and Charlotte are within a 2.5-hour drive. The college arranges transportation to meet students arriving at these points by train, bus or plane. Local recreational facilities include tennis courts, a swimming pool, movies and a physical education/athletic center.

■ FLORENCE-DARLINGTON TECHNICAL COLLEGE
2715 W Lucas St.
Florence, SC 29501-0548
Tel: (843)661-8324; Free: 800-228-5745
Fax: (843)661-8306
Web Site: www.fdtc.edu

Description: State-supported, 2-year, coed. Part of South Carolina State Board for Technical and Comprehensive Education. Awards certificates, diplomas, transfer associate, and terminal associate degrees. Founded 1963. Setting: 100-acre small town campus with easy access to Columbia. Total enrollment: 5,242. Student-undergrad faculty ratio is 26:1. 2% from out-of-state. 39% 25 or older. Core. Calendar: semesters. Academic remediation for entering students, ESL program, advanced placement, summer session for credit, part-time degree program, adult/continuing education programs, internships. Study abroad program. ROTC: Army (c).

Entrance Requirements: Open admission. Option: deferred admission. Entrance: noncompetitive. Application deadline: 8/1.

Collegiate Environment: Choral group, student-run newspaper. Student services: personal-psychological counseling. Campus security: 24-hour emergency response devices and patrols, late night transport-escort service. Florence-Darlington Technical College Library.

Community Environment: Agriculture and industry support the economy of Florence. There are several diversified manufacturing companies within the area. Florence can be called an urban and a suburban community. It is located approximately 50 miles from the Atlantic Ocean resort areas. The city enjoys a temperate climate. Community services include public library, hospitals, museums, many churches of various denominations, and major civic, fraternal, and veteran's organizations. Local entertainment and recreation encompasses the Little Theatre group, movie theatres, a YMCA, a Civic Center, swimming, hunting, golf, tennis, and ice hockey.

■ FORREST COLLEGE

601 E River St.
Anderson, SC 29624
Tel: (864)225-7653
Fax: (864)261-7471
E-mail: janieturmon@forrestcollege.edu
Web Site: www.forrestcollege.edu

Description: Proprietary, 2-year, coed. Awards certificates, diplomas, transfer associate, and terminal associate degrees. Founded 1946. Setting: 3-acre small town campus. Endowment: $60,000. Educational spending for the previous fiscal year: $5000 per student. Total enrollment: 99. Faculty: 28 (11 full-time, 17 part-time). Student-undergrad faculty ratio is 4:1. Full-time: 85 students, 89% women, 11% men. Part-time: 14 students, 93% women, 7% men. 2% Hispanic/Latino; 31% Black or African American, non-Hispanic/Latino. 60% 25 or older. Core. Calendar: quarters. Advanced placement, independent study, double major, summer session for credit, part-time degree program, co-op programs and internships.

Entrance Requirements: Required: essay, high school transcript, interview.

Collegiate Environment: Major annual event: Job Fair. Campus security: 24-hour emergency response devices, late night transport-escort service. Forrest College Library plus 1 other. Operations spending for the previous fiscal year: $12,000. 50 computers available on campus for general student use. Computer purchase/lease plans available. A campuswide network can be accessed from off-campus. Students can access the following: video chat with instructors and peers. Staffed computer lab on campus provides training in use of computers, software, and the Internet.

■ FORTIS COLLEGE

246 Stoneridge Dr.
Ste. 101
Columbia, SC 29210
Tel: (803)678-4800; Free: 855-4-FORTIS
Web Site: www.fortis.edu

Description: Proprietary, 2-year, coed. Awards certificates, diplomas, transfer associate, and terminal associate degrees.

■ FRANCIS MARION UNIVERSITY

PO Box 100547
Florence, SC 29502-0547
Tel: (843)661-1362; Free: 800-368-7551
Fax: (843)661-4635
E-mail: admissions@fmarion.edu
Web Site: www.fmarion.edu

Description: State-supported, comprehensive, coed. Awards bachelor's and master's degrees and post-master's certificates. Founded 1970. Setting: 400-acre rural campus. Endowment: $25.7 million. Research spending for the previous fiscal year: $165,466. Educational spending for the previous fiscal year: $8283 per student. Total enrollment: 3,786. Faculty: 258 (183 full-time, 75 part-time). Student-undergrad faculty ratio is 16:1. 3,787 applied, 60% were admitted. 14% from top 10% of their high school class, 44% from top quarter, 80% from top half. Full-time: 3,006 students, 68% women, 32% men. Part-time: 454 students, 69% women, 31% men. Students come from 21 states and territories, 21 other countries, 3% from out-of-state. 0.5% American Indian or Alaska Native, non-Hispanic/Latino; 2% Hispanic/Latino; 42% Black or African American, non-Hispanic/Latino; 1% Asian, non-Hispanic/Latino; 2% international. 10% 25 or older, 50% live on campus, 7% transferred in. Retention: 66% of full-time freshmen returned the following year. Academic areas with the most degrees conferred: health professions and related sciences; biological/life sciences; business/marketing. Core. Calendar: semesters. Services for LD students, advanced placement, accelerated degree program, honors program, independent study, distance

learning, double major, summer session for credit, part-time degree program, adult/continuing education programs, internships, graduate courses open to undergrads. Off campus study at University of South Carolina, Florence-Darlington Technical College, Clemson University. Study abroad program. ROTC: Army.

Entrance Requirements: Options: electronic application, early admission, deferred admission, international baccalaureate accepted. Required: minimum 2 high school GPA, SAT or ACT. Required for some: essay, high school transcript. Entrance: moderately difficult. Application deadline: 8/10. Notification: continuous until 9/1. SAT Reasoning Test deadline: 8/15. Transfer credits accepted: Yes.

Costs Per Year: Application fee: $41. State resident tuition: $10,384 full-time, $519.20 per credit hour part-time. Nonresident tuition: $20,768 full-time, $1,038 per credit hour part-time. Mandatory fees: $776 full-time, $15.60 per credit hour part-time, $126 per term part-time. Full-time tuition and fees vary according to degree level and program. Part-time tuition and fees vary according to course load, degree level, and program. College room and board: $7948. College room only: $4916. Room and board charges vary according to board plan and housing facility.

Collegiate Environment: Orientation program. Drama-theater group, choral group, student-run newspaper. Social organizations: 45 open to all; national fraternities, national sororities; 2% of eligible men and 6% of eligible women are members. Most popular organizations: Baptist Collegiate Ministries, University Programming Board, Psychology Club, Student Alumni Association, Young Gifted and Blessed Chorus. Major annual events: Homecoming, Arts International, University Programming Board Activities. Student services: health clinic, personal-psychological counseling. Campus security: 24-hour emergency response devices and patrols, late night transport-escort service, controlled dormitory access. James A. Rogers Library plus 1 other. Books: 343,000 (digital/electronic). Operations spending for the previous fiscal year: $1.9 million. 634 computers available on campus for general student use. A campuswide network can be accessed from student residence rooms. Students can access the following: online class registration, learning management system. Staffed computer lab on campus.

Community Environment: See Florence-Darlington Technical College.

■ FURMAN UNIVERSITY

3300 Poinsett Hwy.
Greenville, SC 29613
Tel: (864)294-2000
Fax: (864)294-3127
E-mail: admissions@furman.edu
Web Site: www.furman.edu

Description: Independent, comprehensive, coed. Awards bachelor's and master's degrees. Founded 1826. Setting: 800-acre suburban campus. Total enrollment: 2,947. Faculty: 327 (235 full-time, 92 part-time). Student-undergrad faculty ratio is 10:1. 5,469 applied, 61% were admitted. 41% from top 10% of their high school class, 71% from top quarter, 92% from top half. Full-time: 2,677 students, 60% women, 40% men. Part-time: 91 students, 55% women, 45% men. Students come from 46 states and territories, 34 other countries, 68% from out-of-state. 0.2% American Indian or Alaska Native, non-Hispanic/Latino; 6% Hispanic/Latino; 7% Black or African American, non-Hispanic/Latino; 2% Asian, non-Hispanic/Latino; 4% international. 3% 25 or older, 91% live on campus, 1% transferred in. Retention: 91% of full-time freshmen returned the following year. Academic areas with the most degrees conferred: social sciences; business/marketing; health professions and related sciences. Core. Calendar: semesters. Services for LD students, advanced placement, accelerated degree program, self-designed majors, independent study, double major, summer session for credit, part-time degree program, adult/continuing education programs, internships, graduate courses open to undergrads. Study abroad program. ROTC: Army.

Entrance Requirements: Options: electronic application, early decision, early action. Required: essay, high school transcript. Entrance: moderately difficult. Application deadlines: 1/15, 11/1 for early decision, 11/1 for early action. Notification: 3/1, 11/15 for early decision, 12/20 for early action. SAT Reasoning Test deadline: 1/15. Transfer credits accepted: Yes. Applicants placed on waiting list: 140. Wait-listed applicants offered admission: 24. Early decision applicants: 117. Early decision applicants admitted: 101. Early action applicants: 3,429. Early action applicants admitted: 2,400.

Costs Per Year: Application fee: $50. Comprehensive fee: $62,244 includes full-time tuition ($49,152), mandatory fees ($380), and college room and board ($12,712). College room only: $6954. Room and board charges vary according to board plan and housing facility. Part-time tuition: $1536 per credit. Part-time tuition varies according to course load.

Collegiate Environment: Orientation program. Drama-theater group, choral group, marching band, student-run newspaper, radio station. Social organizations: 150 open to all; national fraternities, national sororities; 32% of eligible men and 61% of eligible women are members. Major annual events: Homecoming, Fall Fest, Family Weekend. Student services: health clinic, personal-psychological counseling, women's center. Campus security: 24-hour emergency response devices and patrols, student patrols, late night transport-escort service, controlled dormitory access. College housing designed to accommodate 2,388 students; 2,423 undergraduates lived in college housing during 2018-19. Freshmen guaranteed college housing. On-campus residence required through senior year. Options: coed, men-only, women-only housing available. James Buchanan Duke Library plus 3 others. Books: 601,063 (physical), 921,761 (digital/electronic); Serial titles: 704,239 (physical). Study areas open 24 hours, 5-7 days a week. 500 computers available on campus for general student use. Computer purchase/lease plans available. A campuswide network can be accessed from student residence rooms and from off campus. Students can access the following: online class registration. Staffed computer lab on campus provides training in use of computers, software, and the Internet.

Community Environment: An industrial city, Greenville is in an important manufacturing region with very diverse industry. It is a metropolitan community that enjoys a temperate climate. Part-time employment is available. The city is served by air, rail and bus lines. Community facilities include a performing arts center, 16,000 seat arena, public library, art museum, YMCA, YWCA, 5 general and 1 children's hospital, and over 400 churches that represent major denominations. Local recreation includes several community theatre groups, lakes and rivers for water sports, mountains for hiking and camping, and most major sports, including golf and minor league baseball and hockey teams.

■ **GREENVILLE TECHNICAL COLLEGE**

PO Box 5616

Greenville, SC 29606-5616

Tel: (864)250-8000; Free: 800-723-0673

Fax: (864)250-8534

Web Site: www.gvltec.edu

Description: State-supported, 2-year, coed. Part of South Carolina State Board for Technical and Comprehensive Education. Awards certificates, diplomas, transfer associate, and terminal associate degrees. Founded 1962. Setting: 604-acre urban campus. Educational spending for the previous fiscal year: $6977 per student. Total enrollment: 11,745. Faculty: 742 (321 full-time, 421 part-time). Student-undergrad faculty ratio is 14:1. 4,922 applied, 99% were admitted. Full-time: 4,809 students, 56% women, 44% men. Part-time: 6,936 students, 62% women, 38% men. 1% from out-of-state. 0.3% American Indian or Alaska Native, non-Hispanic/Latino; 10% Hispanic/Latino; 22% Black or African American, non-Hispanic/Latino; 2% Asian, non-Hispanic/Latino; 0.1% Native Hawaiian or other Pacific Islander, non-Hispanic/Latino; 0.6% international. Core. Calendar: semesters. Academic remediation for entering students, ESL program, services for LD students, advanced placement, honors program, independent study, distance learning, double major, summer session for credit, part-time degree program, co-op programs and internships.

Entrance Requirements: Open admission Except for allied health, nursing programs. Options: electronic application, early admission, deferred admission, international baccalaureate accepted. Required: high school transcript. Entrance: noncompetitive. Application deadline: rolling. Notification: continuous until 8/18. Transfer credits accepted: Yes.

Costs Per Year: Application fee: $0. Area resident tuition: $4590 full-time, $179 per credit hour part-time. State resident tuition: $4998 full-time, $196 per credit hour part-time. Nonresident tuition: $9102 full-time, $367 per credit hour part-time. Mandatory fees: $294 full-time, $6 per credit hour part-time, $75 per term part-time. Full-time tuition and fees vary according to course load and program. Part-time tuition and fees vary according to course load and program.

Collegiate Environment: Orientation program. Social organizations: 26 open to all. Most popular organizations: Phi Theta Kappa, Kappa Omega Sigma - Cosmetology Club, Student Government Association (SGA). Major annual events: Back to School Bash, Spring Fling, Holiday Lunch. Campus security: 24-hour emergency response devices and patrols, late night transport-escort service. Option: coed housing available. J. Verne Smith Library plus 3 others. Books: 35,259 (physical), 450,552 (digital/electronic); Serial titles: 88 (physical), 28 (digital/electronic); Databases: 34. Weekly public service hours: 59. Operations spending for the previous fiscal year: $827,142. 2,026 computers available on campus for general student use. A campuswide network can be accessed from off-campus. Students can access the following: online class registration. Staffed computer lab on campus.

Community Environment: See Furman University.

■ **HORRY-GEORGETOWN TECHNICAL COLLEGE**

2050 Hwy. 501

Conway, SC 29528-6066

Tel: (843)347-3186

Fax: (843)347-4207

E-mail: cynthia.johnston@hgtc.edu

Web Site: www.hgtc.edu

Description: State and locally supported, 2-year, coed. Part of South Carolina State Board for Technical and Comprehensive Education. Awards certificates, diplomas, transfer associate, and terminal associate degrees. Founded 1966. Setting: 150-acre small town campus. Endowment: $2.7 million. Educational spending for the previous fiscal year: $4797 per student. Total enrollment: 7,018. Faculty: 352 (148 full-time, 204 part-time). Student-undergrad faculty ratio is 21:1. Full-time: 3,036 students, 57% women, 43% men. Part-time: 3,932 students, 68% women, 32% men. Students come from 26 states and territories, 38 other countries, 15% from out-of-state. 0.6% American Indian or Alaska Native, non-Hispanic/Latino; 4% Hispanic/Latino; 21% Black or African American, non-Hispanic/Latino; 1% Asian, non-Hispanic/Latino; 0.1% Native Hawaiian or other Pacific Islander, non-Hispanic/Latino; 0.1% international. 45% 25 or older, 7% transferred in. Retention: 57% of full-time freshmen returned the following year. Core. Calendar: semesters. Academic remediation for entering students, services for LD students, advanced placement, independent study, distance learning, double major, summer session for credit, part-time degree program, adult/continuing education programs, co-op programs and internships.

Entrance Requirements: Open admission. Option: early admission. Required for some: high school transcript. Application deadline: rolling. Notification: continuous.

Costs Per Year: Application fee: $25. Area resident tuition: $4980 full-time, $166 per credit hour part-time. State resident tuition: $6180 full-time, $206 per credit hour part-time. Nonresident tuition: $10,140 full-time, $338 per credit hour part-time. Mandatory fees: $268 full-time, $2 per credit hour part-time, $110 per term part-time.

Collegiate Environment: Orientation program. Student services: personal-psychological counseling. Campus security: 24-hour emergency response devices and patrols. Conway Campus Library plus 2 others. Operations spending for the previous fiscal year: $206,441.

Community Environment: The college is located at the center of the largest tourist recreational environment along the Eastern Seaboard. Over 75 miles of white sand beaches as well as golf courses, restaurants, and hotels abound in the area. Air and bus service is available and Highway 17, the "Kings Highway", is the major coastal route in the area. Major arts and entertainment centers, libraries, churches, as well as numerous fraternal and civic organizations serve the community. There are extensive part-time employment opportunities for students, especially from March through September, the height of the tourist season.

■ **LANDER UNIVERSITY**

320 Stanley Ave.

Greenwood, SC 29649-2099

Tel: (864)388-8000; Free: 888-452-6337

Fax: (864)388-8125

E-mail: admissions@lander.edu

Web Site: www.lander.edu

Description: State-supported, comprehensive, coed. Part of South Carolina Commission on Higher Education. Awards bachelor's and master's degrees. Founded 1872. Setting: 120-acre small town campus. Educational spending for the previous fiscal year: $4069 per student. Total enrollment: 3,049. Faculty: 249 (164 full-time, 85 part-time). Student-undergrad faculty ratio is 16:1. 3,342 applied, 42% were admitted. 13% from top 10% of their high school class, 45% from top quarter, 80% from top half. Full-time: 2,706 students, 69% women, 31% men. Part-time: 263 students, 71% women, 29% men. Students come from 23 states and territories, 28 other countries, 5% from out-of-state. 0.3% American Indian or Alaska Native, non-Hispanic/Latino; 1% Hispanic/Latino; 34% Black or African American, non-Hispanic/Latino; 0.4% Asian, non-Hispanic/Latino; 0.2% Native Hawaiian or other Pacific Islander, non-Hispanic/Latino; 3% international. 9% 25 or older, 45% live on campus, 7% transferred in. Retention: 61% of full-time freshmen returned the following year. Academic areas with the most degrees conferred: business/marketing; health professions and related sciences; education. Core. Calendar: semesters plus 3 summer sessions. Academic remediation for entering students, services for LD students, advanced placement, honors program, independent study, distance learning, double major, summer session for credit, part-time degree program, adult/continuing education programs, co-op programs and internships, graduate courses open to undergrads. Off campus study. Study abroad program. ROTC: Army.

Entrance Requirements: Options: electronic application, international baccalaureate accepted. Required: high school transcript, minimum 2 high school GPA, SAT or ACT. Recommended: interview. Entrance: moderately difficult. Application deadline: rolling. Notification: continuous.

Collegiate Environment: Orientation program. Drama-theater group, choral group, student-run newspaper, radio station. Social organizations: 65 open to all; national fraternities, national sororities, local fraternities, local sororities; 11% of eligible men and 12% of eligible women are members. Most popular organizations: Students Promoting Intelligent Choices and Experiences (S.P.I.C.E.), Lander Association of Biological Science, Minorities on the Move (MOM), Presidential Ambassadors, Lander Dance Company. Major annual events: Miss Lander Pageant, Homecoming, Graduation. Student services: health clinic, personal-psychological counseling. Campus security: 24-hour emergency response devices and patrols, late night transport-escort service, controlled dormitory access. Jackson Library. 300 computers available on campus for general student use. Computer purchase/lease plans available. A computer is required for all students. A campuswide network can be accessed from student residence rooms and from off campus. Students can access the following: online class registration. Staffed computer lab on campus provides training in use of computers, software, and the Internet.

Community Environment: Greenwood, an industrial city noted for its production of textiles, is located in west-central South Carolina. The climate is temperate and mild. Five rail lines, commercial air service, buses, and major highways serve the community. Public service facilities include one hospital and various health centers, an area mental health center, churches of all denominations, a library, and a YMCA. There are several motels, shopping, and various civic and fraternal organizations within the immediate area. Recreation includes several swimming pools, two recreation centers, 3 golf courses, baseball, football, tennis, basketball, and nearby Greenwood State Park, which provides water sports and picnic areas. Part-time employment is available.

■ **LIMESTONE COLLEGE**
1115 College Dr.
Gaffney, SC 29340-3799
Tel: (864)489-7151; Free: 800-795-7151
Fax: (864)487-8706
E-mail: lhobbs@limestone.edu
Web Site: www.limestone.edu

Description: Independent, comprehensive, coed. Awards associate, bachelor's, and master's degrees. Founded 1845. Setting: 123-acre suburban campus with easy access to Charlotte. Endowment: $20.5 million. Educational spending for the previous fiscal year: $6035 per student. Total enrollment: 2,346. Faculty: 285 (94 full-time, 191 part-time). Student-undergrad faculty ratio is 10:1. 3,057 applied, 44% were admitted. 4% from top 10% of their high school class, 15% from top quarter, 42% from top half. Full-time: 1,797 students, 54% women, 46% men. Part-time: 482 students, 65% women, 35% men. Students come from 30 states and territories, 31 other countries, 42% from out-of-state. 0.7% American Indian or Alaska Native, non-Hispanic/Latino; 4% Hispanic/Latino; 44% Black or African American, non-Hispanic/Latino; 0.6% Asian, non-Hispanic/Latino; 4% international. 36% 25 or older, 75% live on campus, 2% transferred in. Retention: 52% of full-time freshmen returned the following year. Academic areas with the most degrees conferred: business/marketing; public administration and social services; computer and information sciences. Core. Calendar: semesters. Academic remediation for entering students, services for LD students, advanced placement, accelerated degree program, self-designed majors, honors program, independent study, distance learning, double major, summer session for credit, part-time degree program, adult/continuing education programs, internships.

Entrance Requirements: Option: electronic application. Required: high school transcript, minimum 2 high school GPA, SAT or ACT. Recommended: 2 recommendations, interview. Required for some: minimum score of 500 on TOEFL or proof of successfully completed ESL program for students whose native language is not English. Entrance: minimally difficult. Application deadline: rolling. Notification: continuous. SAT Reasoning Test deadline: 9/1. Transfer credits accepted: Yes.

Costs Per Year: Application fee: $25. Comprehensive fee: $36,200 includes full-time tuition ($25,200), mandatory fees ($1100), and college room and board ($9900). Part-time tuition: $1038 per credit hour. Part-time mandatory fees: $1038 per credit hour.

Collegiate Environment: Orientation program. Drama-theater group, choral group, marching band. Social organizations: 35 open to all; national fraternities, national sororities; 1% of eligible men and 1% of eligible women are members. Most popular organizations: Fellowship of Christian Athletes, Student Government Association, Student Alumni Leadership Council, Campus Crusade (CRU), Limestone Activities Board (LAB). Major annual events: Christmas On Campus, Homecoming, Ms. Limestone Pageant. Student services: health clinic, personal-psychological counseling. Campus security: 24-hour emergency response devices and patrols, late night transport-escort service, controlled dormitory access. College housing designed to accommodate 696 students; 715 undergraduates lived in college housing during 2018-19. Freshmen given priority for college housing. On-campus residence required through junior year. Options: men-only, women-only housing available. A. J. Eastwood Library plus 1 other. Books: 67,000 (physical), 239,537 (digital/electronic); Serial titles: 111 (physical), 482,082 (digital/electronic); Databases: 156. Weekly public service hours: 70. Operations spending for the previous fiscal year: $113,724. 137 computers available on campus for general student use. A campuswide network can be accessed from student residence rooms and from off campus. Students can access the following: online class registration.

Community Environment: Once predominately a cotton-textile manufacturing city, Gaffney has many diversified industries today including the manufacture of frozen foods, roller bearings, clothes, gloves, rugs, clay and concrete products. The surrounding agricultural area is a major producer of peaches, and also grain and livestock. The city is located 2 miles from Interstate I-85. Approximately 45 miles north is the Charlotte International Airport, and 40 miles south is the Greenville-Spartanburg International Airport. The community has several churches representing many denominations, and many civic and service organizations.

■ **MEDICAL UNIVERSITY OF SOUTH CAROLINA**
179 Ashley Ave.
Charleston, SC 29425
Tel: (843)792-2300
Fax: (843)792-3764
E-mail: hudsonly@musc.edu
Web Site: www.musc.edu

Description: State-supported, upper-level, coed. Awards bachelor's, master's, and doctoral degrees and post-master's certificates. Founded 1824. Setting: 82-acre urban campus. System endowment: $230.3 million. Research spending for the previous fiscal year: $169.2 million. Educational spending for the previous fiscal year: $69,072 per student. Total enrollment: 2,775. Faculty: 223 (153 full-time, 70 part-time). Student-undergrad faculty ratio is 2:1. Full-time: 203 students, 77% women, 23% men. Part-time: 2 students, 100% men. Students come from 16 states and territories, 14% from out-of-state. 0.5% American Indian or Alaska Native, non-Hispanic/Latino; 2% Hispanic/Latino; 7% Black or African American, non-Hispanic/Latino; 3% Asian, non-Hispanic/Latino. 55% 25 or older. Academic area with the most degrees conferred: health professions and related sciences. Calendar: semesters. Services for LD students, distance learning, internships. Off campus study at University of South Carolina. ROTC: Air Force (c).

Collegiate Environment: Orientation program. Choral group. Social organizations: 77 open to all. Most popular organizations: MUSC Student Government Association, Multicultural Group Advisory Board, Public Health Interest Group, International Association, Crisis Ministries. Major annual events: Alhambra, Back to School Party, Halloween Horror Cruise. Student services: legal services, health clinic, personal-psychological counseling. Campus security: 24-hour emergency response devices and patrols, late night transport-escort service. Medical University of South Carolina Library plus 1 other. Operations spending for the previous fiscal year: $6.1 million. 200 computers available on campus for general student use. A campuswide network can be accessed from off-campus. Students can access the following: online class registration. Staffed computer lab on campus (open 24 hours a day) provides training in use of computers, software, and the Internet.

Community Environment: See The Citadel.

■ **MIDLANDS TECHNICAL COLLEGE**
PO Box 2408
Columbia, SC 29202-2408

Tel: (803)738-1400; Free: 800-922-8038

Fax: (803)738-7784

E-mail: admissions@midlandstech.edu

Web Site: www.midlandstech.edu

Description: State and locally supported, 2-year, coed. Part of South Carolina State Board for Technical and Comprehensive Education. Awards certificates, diplomas, transfer associate, and terminal associate degrees. Founded 1974. Setting: 156-acre suburban campus. Endowment: $6.9 million. Educational spending for the previous fiscal year: $4453 per student. Total enrollment: 10,946. Faculty: 658 (223 full-time, 435 part-time). Student-undergrad faculty ratio is 20:1. 5,753 applied, 65% were admitted. Full-time: 4,981 students, 53% women, 47% men. Part-time: 5,965 students, 65% women, 35% men. Students come from 30 states and territories, 65 other countries, 2% from out-of-state. 0.5% American Indian or Alaska Native, non-Hispanic/Latino; 4% Hispanic/Latino; 36% Black or African American, non-Hispanic/Latino; 2% Asian, non-Hispanic/Latino; 0.1% Native Hawaiian or other Pacific Islander, non-Hispanic/Latino. 37% 25 or older, 10% transferred in. Calendar: semesters. Academic remediation for entering students, ESL program, services for LD students, advanced placement, self-designed majors, distance learning, double major, summer session for credit, part-time degree program, adult/continuing education programs, co-op programs and internships. ROTC: Army (c), Naval (c), Air Force (c).

Entrance Requirements: Open admission except for health science/nursing program. Options: electronic application, early admission, deferred admission. Recommended: high school transcript, SAT or ACT. Required for some: ACT ASSET. Entrance: minimally difficult.

Costs Per Year: Application fee: $35. Area resident tuition: $4272 full-time, $178 per credit hour part-time. State resident tuition: $5352 full-time, $223 per credit hour part-time. Nonresident tuition: $12,816 full-time, $534 per credit hour part-time. Mandatory fees: $1966 full-time, $67 per credit hour part-time, $179 per term part-time. Full-time tuition and fees vary according to course load. Part-time tuition and fees vary according to course load.

Collegiate Environment: Orientation program. Drama-theater group, student-run newspaper. Social organizations: 20 open to all. Most popular organizations: Student Nurses Association, Human Services Association, Dental Hygiene Association, Health Information Management Student Association, Medical Laboratory Technology Club. Major annual events: Back-to-School Bash, African-American History Month Soul Fwd Test, Health and Wellness Week Activities. Campus security: 24-hour emergency response devices and patrols, late night transport-escort service. Midlands Technical College Library plus 5 others. Books: 50,329 (physical), 354,481 (digital/electronic); Serial titles: 295 (physical); Databases: 111. Weekly public service hours: 58; students can reserve study rooms. Operations spending for the previous fiscal year: $1.8 million. 272 computers available on campus for general student use. A campuswide network can be accessed from off-campus. Students can access the following: online class registration. Staffed computer lab on campus provides training in use of computers, software, and the Internet.

Community Environment: See University of South Carolina.

■ **MILLER-MOTTE TECHNICAL COLLEGE (CONWAY)**

2451 Hwy. 501 E

Conway, SC 29526

Tel: (843)591-1100; Free: 800-705-9182

Web Site: www.miller-motte.edu

Description: Proprietary, 2-year, coed. Awards certificates, transfer associate, and terminal associate degrees.

■ **MILLER-MOTTE TECHNICAL COLLEGE (NORTH CHARLESTON)**

8085 Rivers Ave.

North Charleston, SC 29406

Tel: (843)574-0101; Free: 800-705-9182

Fax: (843)266-3434

E-mail: juliasc@miller-mott.net

Web Site: www.miller-motte.edu

Description: Proprietary, 2-year, coed. Part of Delta Career Education Corporation. Awards certificates, diplomas, and terminal associate degrees. Founded 2000. Setting: urban campus. Total enrollment: 764. 352 applied. 57% 25 or older. Calendar: quarters. Distance learning, part-time degree program.

Entrance Requirements: Open admission. Required: high school transcript, interview, Wonderlic aptitude test.

Collegiate Environment: 150 computers available on campus for general student use.

■ **MORRIS COLLEGE**

100 W College St.

Sumter, SC 29150-3599

Tel: (803)934-3200; Free: 866-853-1345

Fax: (803)773-3687

E-mail: gscriven@morris.edu

Web Site: www.morris.edu

Description: Independent, 4-year, coed, affiliated with Baptist Educational and Missionary Convention of South Carolina. Awards bachelor's degrees. Founded 1908. Setting: 34-acre urban campus with easy access to Columbia, SC. Endowment: $10.9 million. Educational spending for the previous fiscal year: $8810 per student. Total enrollment: 746. Faculty: 56 (38 full-time, 18 part-time). Student-undergrad faculty ratio is 13:1. 2,616 applied, 79% were admitted. 0.01% from top 10% of their high school class, 0.1% from top quarter, 26% from top half. Full-time: 730 students, 56% women, 44% men. Part-time: 16 students, 44% women, 56% men. Students come from 21 states and territories, 17% from out-of-state. 0.1% American Indian or Alaska Native, non-Hispanic/Latino; 0.7% Hispanic/Latino; 98% Black or African American, non-Hispanic/Latino; 0.1% Asian, non-Hispanic/Latino. 11% 25 or older, 78% live on campus, 6% transferred in. Retention: 55% of full-time freshmen returned the following year. Academic areas with the most degrees conferred: homeland security, law enforcement, firefighting, and protective services; business/marketing; social sciences. Core. Calendar: semesters. Academic remediation for entering students, advanced placement, accelerated degree program, honors program, double major, summer session for credit, adult/continuing education programs, co-op programs and internships. Study abroad program. ROTC: Army.

Entrance Requirements: Open admission. Options: electronic application, deferred admission. Required: high school transcript. Required for some: interview. Entrance: noncompetitive. Application deadline: rolling. Notification: continuous. Transfer credits accepted: Yes.

Costs Per Year: Comprehensive fee: $19,915 includes full-time tuition ($12,521), mandatory fees ($1361), and college room and board ($6033). College room only: $2650. Part-time tuition: $522 per credit hour.

Collegiate Environment: Orientation program. Drama-theater group, choral group, student-run radio station. Social organizations: 58 open to all; local fraternities, local sororities; 4% of eligible men and 4% of eligible women are members. Most popular organizations: Student Government Association, New Emphasis on Nontraditional Students (NEONS), Block M Club, Pre Alumni Council, Baptist Student Union. Major annual events: Coronation of Miss Morris College, Religious Emphasis Week, Homecoming Week. Student services: health clinic, personal-psychological counseling. Campus security: 24-hour emergency response devices and patrols. Richardson-Johnson Learning Resources Center plus 1 other. Books: 95,133 (physical), 37,342 (digital/electronic); Serial titles: 427 (physical), 4 (digital/electronic); Databases: 74. Weekly public service hours: 76. Operations spending for the previous fiscal year: $1 million. 292 computers available on campus for general student use. A campuswide network can be accessed from student residence rooms. Students can access the following: online financial aid Information, learning management system. Staffed computer lab on campus provides training in use of computers, software, and the Internet.

Community Environment: Sumter was named for General Thomas Sumter, "The Gamecock of the Revolution." The community is served by two bus lines and is 50 miles from an airport and 35 miles from rail service. The mean summer temperature is 90 degrees, and the mean winter temperature is 40 degrees. The city has many churches of various faiths, as well as a public library. Sumter offers both large natural parks and many lakes, and is famed for its Swan Lake Iris Gardens. Sports and recreation go hand-in-hand with the compatible climate and natural resources found in the community, and includes four theatres, a skating rink, bowling, and night-lit tennis courts.

■ **NEWBERRY COLLEGE**

2100 College St.

Newberry, SC 29108-2197

Tel: (803)276-5010; Free: 800-845-4955

E-mail: admissions@newberry.edu

Web Site: www.newberry.edu

Description: Independent Evangelical Lutheran, 4-year, coed. Awards bachelor's degrees. Founded 1856. Setting: 90-acre small town campus with easy access to Columbia and Greenville, SC. Endowment: $18.8 million. Educational spending for the previous fiscal year: $5747 per student. Total enrollment: 1,181. Faculty: 133 (61 full-time, 72 part-time). Student-undergrad faculty ratio is 14:1. 1,573 applied, 82% were admitted. 8% from top 10% of their high school class, 30% from top quarter, 60% from top half. Full-time: 1,159 students, 44% women, 56% men. Part-time: 22 students, 41% women, 59% men. Students come from 30 states and territories, 25 other countries, 21% from out-of-state. 0.5% American Indian or Alaska Native, non-Hispanic/Latino; 4% Hispanic/Latino; 25% Black or African American, non-Hispanic/Latino; 0.4% Asian, non-Hispanic/Latino; 0.3% Native Hawaiian or other Pacific Islander, non-Hispanic/Latino; 5% international. 3% 25 or older, 82% live on campus, 7% transferred in. Retention: 65% of full-time freshmen returned the following year. Academic areas with the most degrees conferred: business/marketing; biological/life sciences; education. Core. Calendar: semesters. Academic remediation for entering students, services for LD students, advanced placement, self-designed majors, honors program, independent study, double major, summer session for credit, part-time degree program, adult/continuing education programs, internships. Study abroad program. ROTC: Army.

Entrance Requirements: Options: electronic application, deferred admission, international baccalaureate accepted. Required: high school transcript, minimum 2 high school GPA, SAT or ACT. Required for some: essay, interview. Entrance: moderately difficult. Application deadline: rolling. Notification: continuous. SAT Reasoning Test deadline: 8/15. Transfer credits accepted: Yes.

Costs Per Year: Comprehensive fee: $37,090 includes full-time tuition ($24,174), mandatory fees ($2250), and college room and board ($10,666). Full-time tuition and fees vary according to course load. Room and board charges vary according to board plan and housing facility. Part-time tuition: $820 per credit hour. Part-time mandatory fees: $70 per credit hour. Part-time tuition and fees vary according to course load.

Collegiate Environment: Orientation program. Drama-theater group, choral group, marching band, student-run radio station. Social organizations: 39 open to all; national fraternities, national sororities; 21% of eligible men and 27% of eligible women are members. Most popular organizations: National Society of Leadership and Success, Kappa Delta, Sigma Sigma Sigma, Alpha Xi Delta, Kappa Alpha Order. Major annual events: Homecoming, Jabali Afika. Student services: health clinic, personal-psychological counseling. Campus security: 24-hour emergency response devices and patrols, late night transport-escort service, controlled dormitory access. Wessels Library. Books: 36,525 (physical), 295,982 (digital/electronic); Serial titles: 33 (physical), 10,000 (digital/electronic); Databases: 108. Weekly public service hours: 91. Operations spending for the previous fiscal year: $139,596. 21 computers available on campus for general student use. A campuswide network can be accessed from student residence rooms and from off campus. Students can access the following: online class registration. Staffed computer lab on campus.

Community Environment: Newberry is located in the Piedmont region of South Carolina between Lakes Murray and Greenwood. The city enjoys mild weather. Community services include churches of many denominations, a hospital, a county library, and various civic and fraternal organizations. Local recreation and facilities include a swimming pool, barbecue facilities, parks, theaters, fishing, boating, swimming, and camping on nearby lakes. Part-time employment is available for college students.

■ **NORTH GREENVILLE UNIVERSITY**
PO Box 1892
Tigerville, SC 29688-1892
Tel: (864)977-7000; Free: 800-468-6642
Fax: (864)977-7177
Web Site: www.ngu.edu
Description: Independent Southern Baptist, comprehensive, coed. Awards bachelor's, master's, and doctoral degrees. Founded 1892. Setting: 380-acre rural campus with easy access to Greenville. Endowment: $258.4 million. Educational spending for the previous fiscal year: $5581 per student. Total enrollment: 2,567. Faculty: 218 (144 full-time, 74 part-time). Student-undergrad faculty ratio is 14:1. 1,701 applied, 60% were admitted. 20% from top 10% of their high school class, 38% from top quarter, 75% from top half. 2 National Merit Scholars, 35 class presidents, 28 valedictorians, 100 student government officers. Full-time: 2,083 students, 50% women, 50% men. Part-time: 280 students, 66% women, 34% men. Students come from 37 states and territories, 26 other countries, 20% from out-of-state. 0.5% American Indian or Alaska Native, non-Hispanic/Latino; 3% Hispanic/Latino; 8% Black or African American, non-Hispanic/Latino; 1% Asian, non-Hispanic/Latino; 0.1% Native Hawaiian or other Pacific Islander, non-Hispanic/Latino; 0.1% international. 8% 25 or older, 63% live on campus, 4% transferred in. Retention: 71% of full-time freshmen returned the following year. Academic areas with the most degrees conferred: business/marketing; liberal arts/

general studies; education. Core. Calendar: semesters. Academic remediation for entering students, ESL program, services for LD students, advanced placement, accelerated degree program, self-designed majors, freshman honors college, honors program, independent study, distance learning, double major, summer session for credit, part-time degree program, adult/continuing education programs, co-op programs and internships, graduate courses open to undergrads. Study abroad program. ROTC: Army (c).

Entrance Requirements: Options: electronic application, early admission, deferred admission, international baccalaureate accepted. Required: high school transcript, SAT or ACT. Recommended: minimum 2 high school GPA, CPT. Required for some: interview, CPT. Entrance: minimally difficult. Application deadline: 8/22. Notification: continuous. Preference given to Baptists. SAT Reasoning Test deadline: 8/26. SAT Subject Test deadline: 8/26. Transfer credits accepted: Yes.

Costs Per Year: Application fee: $30. Comprehensive fee: $29,990 includes full-time tuition ($19,750) and college room and board ($10,240). College room only: $4900. Full-time tuition varies according to course load. Room and board charges vary according to housing facility. Part-time tuition: $480 per credit hour.

Collegiate Environment: Orientation program. Drama-theater group, choral group, marching band, student-run radio station. Social organizations: 21 open to all. Most popular organizations: Baptist Student Union, Fellowship of Christians in Service, Fellowship of Christian Athletes, Black Student Fellowship, Education Club. Major annual events: Homecoming, Founder' Day, Miss NGU Pageant. Student services: personal-psychological counseling. Campus security: 24-hour emergency response devices and patrols, late night transport-escort service, controlled dormitory access. Hester Memorial Library. Books: 70,000 (physical), 250,000 (digital/electronic); Serial titles: 250 (physical), 150 (digital/electronic); Databases: 103. Weekly public service hours: 85. Operations spending for the previous fiscal year: $690,254. 95 computers available on campus for general student use. A campuswide network can be accessed from student residence rooms and from off campus. Staffed computer lab on campus provides training in use of computers.

Community Environment: Tigerville is a rural area adjacent to Greenville in the foothills of the Blue Ridge Mountains. The climate is temperate. There are several civic and fraternal organizations and a Baptist Church in the community. Part-time employment is available. Local recreation includes hunting, fishing, rafting, fine arts and the advantages of nearby Greenville.

■ **NORTHEASTERN TECHNICAL COLLEGE**
1201 Chesterfield Hwy.
Cheraw, SC 29520-1007
Tel: (843)921-6900; Free: 800-921-7399
Fax: (843)537-6148
E-mail: jhicks@netc.edu
Web Site: www.netc.edu
Description: State and locally supported, 2-year, coed. Part of South Carolina State Board for Technical and Comprehensive Education. Awards certificates, diplomas, transfer associate, and terminal associate degrees. Founded 1967. Setting: 59-acre rural campus. Endowment: $31,355. Educational spending for the previous fiscal year: $2999 per student. Total enrollment: 976. Student-undergrad faculty ratio is 25:1. 468 applied, 100% were admitted. Full-time: 446 students, 67% women, 33% men. Part-time: 530 students, 76% women, 24% men. Students come from 3 states and territories, 1% from out-of-state. 43% 25 or older, 3% transferred in. Core. Calendar: semesters. Academic remediation for entering students, advanced placement, independent study, distance learning, part-time degree program, adult/continuing education programs. Study abroad program.

Entrance Requirements: Open admission except for nursing program. Options: electronic application, early admission. Required: high school transcript, interview, ACT Compass. Required for some: SAT. Entrance: noncompetitive. Application deadline: 8/4. Notification: continuous.

Collegiate Environment: Orientation program. Social organizations: 2 open to all. Most popular organizations: Student Government Association, Alpha Beta Delta. Major annual events: Field Day, Christmas Refreshments. Student services: personal-psychological counseling. Campus security: 24-hour emergency response devices. Northeastern Technical College Library. Operations spending for the previous fiscal year: $158,573. 125 computers available on campus for general student use. A campuswide network can be accessed from off-campus. Staffed computer lab on campus.

Community Environment: Cheraw is a small community enjoying mild climate year-round. The city has a public library, a shopping center, churches of many denominations, and good medical facilities. There are several service and civic organizations active in the area.

■ ORANGEBURG-CALHOUN TECHNICAL COLLEGE

3250 St. Matthews Rd., NE
Orangeburg, SC 29118-8299
Tel: (803)536-0311; Free: 800-813-6519
Fax: (803)535-1388
Web Site: www.octech.edu

Description: State and locally supported, 2-year, coed. Part of State Board for Technical and Comprehensive Education, South Carolina. Awards certificates, diplomas, transfer associate, and terminal associate degrees. Founded 1968. Setting: 100-acre small town campus with easy access to Columbia. Total enrollment: 3,219. Faculty: 163 (75 full-time, 88 part-time). Student-undergrad faculty ratio is 20:1. Full-time: 1,538 students, 66% women, 34% men. Part-time: 1,681 students, 68% women, 32% men. Students come from 11 states and territories, 1 other country. 38% 25 or older. Calendar: semesters. Academic remediation for entering students, services for LD students, advanced placement, self-designed majors, independent study, distance learning, summer session for credit, part-time degree program, adult/continuing education programs, co-op programs and internships.

Entrance Requirements: Open admission. Required: high school transcript. Required for some: interview. Entrance: noncompetitive. Application deadline: rolling. Notification: continuous.

Collegiate Environment: Orientation program. Student services: personal-psychological counseling. Campus security: 24-hour emergency response devices and patrols. Gressette Learning Center plus 1 other. 361 computers available on campus for general student use. A campuswide network can be accessed from off-campus. Students can access the following: online class registration.

Community Environment: See South Carolina State University.

■ PIEDMONT TECHNICAL COLLEGE

620 N Emerald Rd.
Greenwood, SC 29648-1467
Tel: (864)941-8324; Free: 800-868-5528
Fax: (864)941-8555
Web Site: www.ptc.edu

Description: State-supported, 2-year, coed. Part of South Carolina State Board for Technical and Comprehensive Education. Awards certificates, diplomas, transfer associate, and terminal associate degrees. Founded 1966. Setting: 60-acre small town campus. Endowment: $1.1 million. Research spending for the previous fiscal year: $124,427. Educational spending for the previous fiscal year: $2515 per student. Total enrollment: 4,911. Faculty: 233 (103 full-time, 130 part-time). Student-undergrad faculty ratio is 18:1. 890 applied, 100% were admitted. Students come from 2 states and territories, 5 other countries, 1% from out-of-state. 38% 25 or older. Calendar: semesters. Academic remediation for entering students, services for LD students, advanced placement, independent study, distance learning, summer session for credit, part-time degree program, adult/continuing education programs, co-op programs and internships.

Entrance Requirements: Open admission except for nursing, health sciences programs. Options: electronic application, early admission, deferred admission. Required: high school transcript. Recommended: interview. Entrance: noncompetitive. Application deadline: rolling. Notification: continuous until 8/20.

Collegiate Environment: Orientation program. Choral group. Social organizations: 18 open to all. Most popular organizations: National Honor Society, Career Peers (student volunteers), Student Nurses Association, Psychology Club, Ebony Club. Major annual events: Spring Activities Day, Club Fairs, Fall Convocation/Back to School Bash. Student services: personal-psychological counseling, women's center. Campus security: 24-hour emergency response devices and patrols, late night transport-escort service. Piedmont Technical College Library. Operations spending for the previous fiscal year: $221,086. 320 computers available on campus for general student use. A campuswide network can be accessed from off-campus. Staffed computer lab on campus.

Community Environment: In additions to Greenwood county campus, Piedmont has 6 county center campuses serving students of the service area which includes Abbeville, Laurens, Edgefield, McCormick, Saluda, and Newberry.

■ PRESBYTERIAN COLLEGE

503 S Broad St.
Clinton, SC 29325
Tel: (864)833-2820; Free: 800-476-7272
Fax: (864)833-8481
E-mail: mfox@presby.edu
Web Site: www.presby.edu

Description: Independent, comprehensive, coed, affiliated with Presbyterian Church (U.S.A.). Awards bachelor's and doctoral degrees. Founded 1880. Setting: 240-acre small town campus with easy access to Greenville, Spartanburg. Endowment: $90.2 million. Total enrollment: 1,282. Faculty: 104 (74 full-time, 30 part-time). Student-undergrad faculty ratio is 13:1. 2,277 applied, 63% were admitted. 25% from top 10% of their high school class, 62% from top quarter, 88% from top half. Full-time: 976 students, 50% women, 50% men. Part-time: 40 students, 85% women, 15% men. Students come from 31 states and territories, 24 other countries, 27% from out-of-state. 0.4% American Indian or Alaska Native, non-Hispanic/Latino; 3% Hispanic/Latino; 12% Black or African American, non-Hispanic/Latino; 0.8% Asian, non-Hispanic/Latino; 5% international. 99% live on campus, 2% transferred in. Retention: 82% of full-time freshmen returned the following year. Academic areas with the most degrees conferred: business/marketing; psychology; English. Core. Calendar: semesters. ESL program, services for LD students, advanced placement, honors program, independent study, distance learning, double major, summer session for credit, internships, graduate courses open to undergrads. Off campus study at Gulf Coast Marine Laboratory, American University. Study abroad program. ROTC: Army.

Entrance Requirements: Options: electronic application, early decision, early action, deferred admission, international baccalaureate accepted. Required: essay, high school transcript, minimum 2 high school GPA, 1 recommendation. Recommended: interview. Required for some: SAT or ACT. Entrance: very difficult. Application deadlines: 6/30, 11/1 for early decision, 11/15 for early action. Notification: 3/15, 3/15 for nonresidents, 12/1 for early decision, 12/15 for early action. SAT Reasoning Test deadline: 6/30. SAT Subject Test deadline: 6/30. Transfer credits accepted: Yes. Applicants placed on waiting list: 0. Wait-listed applicants offered admission: 0. Early decision applicants: 166. Early decision applicants admitted: 74. Early action applicants: 943. Early action applicants admitted: 736.

Costs Per Year: Application fee: $0. Comprehensive fee: $49,140 includes full-time tuition ($35,800), mandatory fees ($2860), and college room and board ($10,480). College room only: $5100. Full-time tuition and fees vary according to course load and reciprocity agreements. Room and board charges vary according to board plan and housing facility. Part-time tuition: $1492 per credit hour. Part-time mandatory fees: $26 per credit hour, $25 per term. Part-time tuition and fees vary according to course load and program.

Collegiate Environment: Orientation program. Drama-theater group, choral group, student-run newspaper. Social organizations: 60 open to all; national fraternities, national sororities; 33% of eligible men and 50% of eligible women are members. Most popular organizations: Student Volunteer Services, Intramural sports, Student Union Board, Fellowship of Christian Athletes, Student Government Association. Major annual events: Homecoming, Special Olympics, Spring Fling. Student services: health clinic, personal-psychological counseling. Campus security: 24-hour emergency response devices and patrols, late night transport-escort service, controlled dormitory access. James H. Thomason Library. Books: 108,925 (physical), 227,396 (digital/electronic); Serial titles: 702 (physical), 16,342 (digital/electronic); Databases: 71. Study areas open 24 hours, 5-7 days a week; students can reserve study rooms. 100 computers available on campus for general student use. A campuswide network can be accessed from student residence rooms and from off campus. Students can access the following: online class registration. Staffed computer lab on campus provides training in use of computers, software, and the Internet.

Community Environment: Located in the Piedmont section of South Carolina, Clinton is approximately 64 miles northwest of Columbia. The annual mean January temperature is 43.6 degrees; July 79.9 degrees. The community has air and bus service and is adjacent to U.S. Highway 76, I-385; I-26. There are many churches of various denominations, a hospital, hotels and motels in town. Part-time employment is available. Local recreational facilities include tennis, golf, theatre and swimming; nearby Lake Greenwood provides boating, fishing and hunting. Various civic, fraternal and veteran's organizations are active in the community.

■ SOUTH CAROLINA STATE UNIVERSITY

300 College St. NE
Orangeburg, SC 29117-0001
Tel: (803)536-7000; Free: 800-260-5956

Fax: (803)536-8990

E-mail: admissions@scsu.edu

Web Site: www.scsu.edu

Description: State-supported, comprehensive, coed. Part of South Carolina Commission on Higher Education. Awards bachelor's, master's, and doctoral degrees. Founded 1896. Setting: 160-acre small town campus. Research spending for the previous fiscal year: $4.5 million. Educational spending for the previous fiscal year: $6172 per student. Total enrollment: 2,905. Faculty: 191 (137 full-time, 54 part-time). Student-undergrad faculty ratio is 17:1. 2,847 applied, 86% were admitted. 8% from top 10% of their high school class, 25% from top quarter, 36% from top half. Full-time: 2,282 students, 50% women, 50% men. Part-time: 247 students, 47% women, 53% men. Students come from 31 states and territories, 13 other countries, 15% from out-of-state. 0.2% American Indian or Alaska Native, non-Hispanic/Latino; 0.5% Hispanic/Latino; 96% Black or African American, non-Hispanic/Latino; 0.4% Asian, non-Hispanic/Latino; 0.2% international. 9% 25 or older, 68% live on campus, 5% transferred in. Retention: 70% of full-time freshmen returned the following year. Academic areas with the most degrees conferred: business/marketing; education; family and consumer sciences; biological/life sciences. Core. Calendar: semesters. Services for LD students, advanced placement, honors program, independent study, distance learning, double major, summer session for credit, part-time degree program, adult/continuing education programs, co-op programs and internships. Off campus study at National Student Exchange. Study abroad program. ROTC: Army.

Entrance Requirements: Options: electronic application, deferred admission. Required: high school transcript, minimum 2 high school GPA, SAT or ACT. Entrance: minimally difficult. Application deadline: 7/31. Notification: continuous. Transfer credits accepted: Yes.

Costs Per Year: Application fee: $25. State resident tuition: $9528 full-time, $461 per credit hour part-time. Nonresident tuition: $20,218 full-time, $906 per credit hour part-time. Mandatory fees: $1532 full-time. Full-time tuition and fees vary according to course load and reciprocity agreements. Part-time tuition varies according to course load and reciprocity agreements. College room and board: $9890. College room only: $6600. Room and board charges vary according to board plan and housing facility.

Collegiate Environment: Orientation program. Drama-theater group, choral group, marching band, student-run newspaper, radio station. Social organizations: 157 open to all; national fraternities, national sororities, local fraternities, local sororities; 15% of eligible men and 17% of eligible women are members. Most popular organizations: Student Government Association, Campus Activity Board, NAACP, United Voices of Christ, Student Media. Major annual events: Back to School Week, Homecoming Week, Bulldog Fest. Student services: health clinic, personal-psychological counseling. Campus security: 24-hour emergency response devices and patrols, late night transport-escort service, controlled dormitory access. Miller F. Whittaker Library. Books: 317,233 (physical), 195,578 (digital/electronic); Serial titles: 18,334 (digital/electronic); Databases: 114. Weekly public service hours: 74; students can reserve study rooms. Operations spending for the previous fiscal year: $1.5 million. 600 computers available on campus for general student use. A campuswide network can be accessed from student residence rooms. Students can access the following: online class registration. Staffed computer lab on campus provides training in use of computers, software, and the Internet.

Community Environment: Orangeburg is in an agricultural and dairying area. Its industries include textiles, wood products, meat packing, chemicals, and baking goods. This is a suburban community with a temperate climate. Airline service is available at nearby Columbia. Railroad and bus lines serve the immediate community. There is a public library, churches of major denominations, a hospital, and major civic and fraternal organizations. Some part-time employment is available. Local recreation includes four theatres, swimming, fishing and many sports.

■ **SOUTH UNIVERSITY**

9 Science Ct.

Columbia, SC 29203

Tel: (803)799-9082; Free: 866-629-3031

Fax: (803)799-9038

Web Site: www.southuniversity.edu/columbia

Description: Independent, comprehensive, coed. Part of Education Management Corporation. Awards associate, bachelor's, master's, and doctoral degrees. Founded 1935. Calendar: quarters.

■ **SOUTHERN WESLEYAN UNIVERSITY**

907 Wesleyan Dr.

Central, SC 29630-1020

Tel: (864)644-5000; Free: 800-CU-AT-SWU

Fax: (864)644-5900

E-mail: broe@swu.edu

Web Site: www.swu.edu

Description: Independent, comprehensive, coed, affiliated with Wesleyan Church. Awards associate, bachelor's, and master's degrees. Founded 1906. Setting: 350-acre small town campus. Endowment: $3.5 million. Educational spending for the previous fiscal year: $4075 per student. Total enrollment: 1,883. Faculty: 193 (57 full-time, 136 part-time). Student-undergrad faculty ratio is 18:1. 575 applied, 94% were admitted. 13% from top 10% of their high school class, 43% from top quarter, 75% from top half. Full-time: 1,440 students, 60% women, 40% men. Part-time: 16 students, 56% women, 44% men. Students come from 25 states and territories, 9 other countries, 16% from out-of-state. 0.6% American Indian or Alaska Native, non-Hispanic/Latino; 2% Hispanic/Latino; 27% Black or African American, non-Hispanic/Latino; 0.4% Asian, non-Hispanic/Latino; 0.8% international. 57% 25 or older, 55% live on campus, 6% transferred in. Retention: 70% of full-time freshmen returned the following year. Academic areas with the most degrees conferred: business/marketing; education; psychology. Core. Calendar: semesters. Academic remediation for entering students, ESL program, services for LD students, advanced placement, accelerated degree program, self-designed majors, honors program, independent study, distance learning, double major, summer session for credit, part-time degree program, adult/continuing education programs, internships. Off campus study at Clemson University, Clemson, SC; Tri-County Technical College, Pendleton, SC; Council for Christian Colleges and Universities, Los Angels, CA, Martha's Vineyard, MA, Washington, DC. Study abroad program. ROTC: Army (c), Air Force (c).

Entrance Requirements: Options: electronic application, deferred admission. Required: high school transcript, minimum 2.3 high school GPA, SAT or ACT. Required for some: interview. Entrance: minimally difficult. Application deadline: 8/1. Notification: continuous. SAT Reasoning Test deadline: 8/1. SAT Subject Test deadline: 8/1. Transfer credits accepted: Yes.

Collegiate Environment: Orientation program. Drama-theater group, choral group. Social organizations: 12 open to all. Most popular organizations: Student Government Association, Student Missions Focus, Ministry Teams, Music Club, Ignite student athlete fellowship group. Major annual events: Homecoming, Spiritual Emphasis Week, Christmas Banquet. Student services: health clinic, personal-psychological counseling. Campus security: 24-hour emergency response devices, late night security patrols until 2:00 am, restricted access to campus after midnight. Rickman Library. Operations spending for the previous fiscal year: $503,465. 95 computers available on campus for general student use. A campuswide network can be accessed from student residence rooms and from off campus. Students can access the following: online class registration. Staffed computer lab on campus provides training in use of computers, software, and the Internet.

Community Environment: Central is located in the Piedmont section of South Carolina, between Atlanta, Georgia, and Charlotte, North Carolina. The community is five miles North of Clemson and is located near the metropolitan area of Greenville.

■ **SPARTANBURG COMMUNITY COLLEGE**

107 Community College Dr.

Spartanburg, SC 29303

Tel: (864)592-4600; Free: 866-591-3700

E-mail: admissions@sccsc.edu

Web Site: www.sccsc.edu

Description: State-supported, 2-year, coed. Part of South Carolina State Board for Technical and Comprehensive Education. Awards certificates, diplomas, transfer associate, and terminal associate degrees. Founded 1961. Setting: 104-acre suburban campus with easy access to Charlotte. Educational spending for the previous fiscal year: $4633 per student. Total enrollment: 4,715. Faculty: 315 (109 full-time, 206 part-time). Student-undergrad faculty ratio is 15:1. Full-time: 2,179 students, 53% women, 47% men. Part-time: 2,536 students, 62% women, 38% men. Students come from 7 states and territories, 2 other countries, 2% from out-of-state. 0.4% American Indian or Alaska Native, non-Hispanic/Latino; 7% Hispanic/Latino; 21% Black or African American, non-Hispanic/Latino; 4% Asian, non-Hispanic/Latino; 0.1% Native Hawaiian or other Pacific Islander, non-Hispanic/Latino. 29% 25 or older, 8% transferred in. Retention: 63% of full-time freshmen returned the following year. Core. Calendar: semesters condensed semesters plus summer sessions. Academic remediation for entering students, ESL program, services for LD students, advanced placement, distance learning, summer session for credit, part-time degree program, adult/continuing education programs, co-op programs.

Entrance Requirements: Open admission. Options: electronic application, early admission, international baccalaureate accepted. Required: high school transcript. Recommended: interview. Required for some: SAT or ACT. Entrance: noncompetitive. Application deadline: rolling. Notification: continuous. Transfer credits accepted: Yes.

Costs Per Year: Application fee: $25. Area resident tuition: $4512 full-time, $188 per credit hour part-time. State resident tuition: $5592 full-time, $233 per credit hour part-time. Nonresident tuition: $9192 full-time, $383 per credit hour part-time. Mandatory fees: $150 full-time, $75 per term part-time. Full-time tuition and fees vary according to course load and location. Part-time tuition and fees vary according to location.

Collegiate Environment: Orientation program. Drama-theater group, student-run newspaper. Social organizations: 5 open to all. Student services: personal-psychological counseling, women's center. Campus security: 24-hour emergency response devices and patrols. Spartanburg Community College Library. Operations spending for the previous fiscal year: $754,842. 2,500 computers available on campus for general student use. A campuswide network can be accessed from off-campus. Students can access the following: online class registration. Staffed computer lab on campus provides training in use of computers, software, and the Internet.

Community Environment: See Converse College.

■ **SPARTANBURG METHODIST COLLEGE**
1000 Powell Mill Rd.
Spartanburg, SC 29301
Tel: (864)587-4000; Free: 800-772-7286
Fax: (864)587-4355
E-mail: admiss@smcsc.edu
Web Site: www.smcsc.edu

Description: Independent Methodist, 2-year, coed. Awards transfer associate and terminal associate degrees. Founded 1911. Setting: 110-acre suburban campus with easy access to Charlotte. Endowment: $22 million. Educational spending for the previous fiscal year: $3167 per student. Total enrollment: 790. Faculty: 65 (27 full-time, 38 part-time). Student-undergrad faculty ratio is 20:1. 1,748 applied, 61% were admitted. 2% from top 10% of their high school class, 12% from top quarter, 44% from top half. Full-time: 784 students, 49% women, 51% men. Part-time: 6 students, 50% women, 50% men. Students come from 16 states and territories, 3 other countries, 9% from out-of-state. 0.3% American Indian or Alaska Native, non-Hispanic/Latino; 8% Hispanic/Latino; 38% Black or African American, non-Hispanic/Latino; 0.9% Asian, non-Hispanic/Latino; 0.4% international. 0.6% 25 or older, 67% live on campus, 5% transferred in. Core. Calendar: semesters. Academic remediation for entering students, ESL program, services for LD students, advanced placement, honors program, independent study, summer session for credit, part-time degree program.

Entrance Requirements: Options: electronic application, deferred admission. Required: essay, high school transcript, minimum 2 high school GPA, SAT or ACT. Recommended: interview. Required for some: interview. Entrance: minimally difficult. Application deadline: rolling. Notification: continuous. Transfer credits accepted: Yes.

Costs Per Year: Application fee: $25. One-time mandatory fee: $200. Comprehensive fee: $26,410 includes full-time tuition ($15,750), mandatory fees ($1285), and college room and board ($9375). Full-time tuition and fees vary according to course load. Part-time tuition: $425 per credit hour. Part-time tuition varies according to course load.

Collegiate Environment: Orientation program. Drama-theater group, choral group, student-run newspaper. Social organizations: 14 open to all. Most popular organizations: College Christian Movement, Alpha Phi Omega, Campus Union, Fellowship of Christian Athletes, Kappa Sigma Alpha. Major annual events: College Wide Day of Service, Homecoming. Student services: health clinic, personal-psychological counseling. Campus security: 24-hour emergency response devices and patrols, student patrols, late night transport-escort service, controlled dormitory access. Marie Blair Burgess Library. Books: 46,541 (physical), 155,060 (digital/electronic); Databases: 80. Weekly public service hours: 72; students can reserve study rooms. Operations spending for the previous fiscal year: $263,140. 152 computers available on campus for general student use. A campuswide network can be accessed from student residence rooms and from off campus. Staffed computer lab on campus provides training in use of computers, software, and the Internet.

Community Environment: See Converse College.

■ **STRAYER UNIVERSITY-CHARLESTON CAMPUS**
5010 Wetland Crossing
North Charleston, SC 29418
Tel: (843)746-5100; Free: 888-311-0355
Web Site: www.strayer.edu

Description: Proprietary, comprehensive, coed. Awards associate, bachelor's, and master's degrees.

■ **STRAYER UNIVERSITY-COLUMBIA CAMPUS**
200 Ctr. Point Cir.
Ste. 300
Columbia, SC 29210
Tel: (803)750-2500; Free: 888-311-0355
Web Site: www.strayer.edu

Description: Proprietary, comprehensive, coed. Awards associate, bachelor's, and master's degrees.

■ **STRAYER UNIVERSITY-GREENVILLE CAMPUS**
777 Lowndes Hill Rd.
Bldg. 3, Ste. 300
Greenville, SC 29607
Tel: (864)250-7000; Free: 888-311-0355
Web Site: www.strayer.edu

Description: Proprietary, comprehensive, coed. Awards associate, bachelor's, and master's degrees.

■ **TECHNICAL COLLEGE OF THE LOWCOUNTRY**
921 Ribaut Rd.
Beaufort, SC 29901-1288
Tel: (843)525-8324
E-mail: rcole@tcl.edu
Web Site: www.tcl.edu

Description: State-supported, 2-year, coed. Part of South Carolina Technical and Comprehensive Education System. Awards certificates, diplomas, transfer associate, and terminal associate degrees. Founded 1972. Setting: 12-acre small town campus. Total enrollment: 2,332. Student-undergrad faculty ratio is 15:1. Full-time: 665 students, 62% women, 38% men. Part-time: 1,667 students, 71% women, 29% men. 6% from out-of-state. 0.5% American Indian or Alaska Native, non-Hispanic/Latino; 9% Hispanic/Latino; 35% Black or African American, non-Hispanic/Latino; 1% Asian, non-Hispanic/Latino. 12% transferred in. Calendar: semesters. Academic remediation for entering students, advanced placement, distance learning, summer session for credit, part-time degree program, adult/continuing education programs.

Entrance Requirements: Options: early admission, deferred admission. Required: ACT ASSET. Recommended: SAT and SAT Subject Tests or ACT. Entrance: noncompetitive. Application deadline: rolling.

Costs Per Year: Application fee: $25. Area resident tuition: $4392 full-time, $183 per credit hour part-time. State resident tuition: $4992 full-time, $208 per credit hour part-time. Nonresident tuition: $9744 full-time, $406 per credit hour part-time. Mandatory fees: $292 full-time, $8 per credit hour part-time, $50 per term part-time.

Collegiate Environment: Orientation program. Campus security: security during class hours.

■ **TRI-COUNTY TECHNICAL COLLEGE**
PO Box 587, 7900 Hwy. 76
Pendleton, SC 29670-0587
Tel: (864)646-8361
Web Site: www.tctc.edu

Description: State-supported, 2-year, coed. Part of South Carolina State Board for Technical and Comprehensive Education. Awards certificates, diplomas, transfer associate, and terminal associate degrees. Founded 1962. Setting: 100-acre rural campus. Endowment: $21.8 million. Educational spending for the previous fiscal year: $5033 per student. Total enrollment: 6,128. Student-undergrad faculty ratio is 21:1. Full-time: 3,451 students, 47% women, 53% men. Part-time: 2,677 students, 54% women, 46% men. Students come from 38 states and territories, 35 other countries, 2% from out-of-state. 0.2% American Indian or Alaska Native, non-Hispanic/Latino; 4% Hispanic/Latino; 10% Black or African American, non-Hispanic/Latino; 1% Asian, non-Hispanic/Latino; 0.1% Native Hawaiian or other Pacific Islander, non-Hispanic/Latino. 19% 25 or older, 6% transferred in.

Retention: 36% of full-time freshmen returned the following year. Calendar: semesters. Academic remediation for entering students, advanced placement, distance learning, summer session for credit, part-time degree program, adult/continuing education programs. Study abroad program. ROTC: Army (c), Air Force (c).

Entrance Requirements: Open admission except for allied health programs. Option: early admission. Entrance: noncompetitive. Application deadline: rolling. Notification: continuous.

Costs Per Year: Application fee: $30. Area resident tuition: $4,327 full-time, $180.28 per credit hour part-time. State resident tuition: $5,671 full-time, $236.28 per credit hour part-time. Nonresident tuition: $9,751 full-time, $406.28 per credit hour part-time.

Collegiate Environment: Campus security: 24-hour emergency response devices and patrols. Tri-County Technical College Library. Operations spending for the previous fiscal year: $509,488.

■ TRIDENT TECHNICAL COLLEGE

PO Box 118067
Charleston, SC 29423-8067
Tel: (843)574-6111
Fax: (843)574-6109
E-mail: clara.martin@tridenttech.edu
Web Site: www.tridenttech.edu

Description: State and locally supported, 2-year, coed. Part of South Carolina State Board for Technical and Comprehensive Education. Awards certificates, diplomas, transfer associate, and terminal associate degrees. Founded 1964. Setting: urban campus. Total enrollment: 13,271. Faculty: 627 (327 full-time, 300 part-time). Student-undergrad faculty ratio is 21:1. Full-time: 5,517 students, 58% women, 42% men. Part-time: 7,754 students, 61% women, 39% men. Students come from 85 other countries, 2% from out-of-state. 0.4% American Indian or Alaska Native, non-Hispanic/Latino; 6% Hispanic/Latino; 28% Black or African American, non-Hispanic/Latino; 2% Asian, non-Hispanic/Latino; 0.3% Native Hawaiian or other Pacific Islander, non-Hispanic/Latino. 27% 25 or older, 8% transferred in. Core. Calendar: semesters. Academic remediation for entering students, ESL program, services for LD students, advanced placement, distance learning, double major, summer session for credit, part-time degree program, co-op programs and internships. Off campus study at Dorchester County QuickJobs Training Center, St. Paul's Parish Site, Wando Partner, Mt. Pleasant. Study abroad program.

Entrance Requirements: Open admission except for nursing and allied health programs. Options: electronic application, early admission. Required for some: high school transcript. Entrance: noncompetitive. Application deadline: 8/6. Notification: continuous.

Costs Per Year: Application fee: $30. Area resident tuition: $4320 full-time, $180 per credit hour part-time. State resident tuition: $4800 full-time, $200 per credit hour part-time. Nonresident tuition: $8184 full-time, $341 per credit hour part-time. Mandatory fees: $34 full-time, $33.66 per year part-time.

Collegiate Environment: Orientation program. Drama-theater group, student-run newspaper, radio station. Social organizations: 52 open to all. Most popular organizations: Phi Theta Kappa, Lex Artis Paralegal Society, Hospitality and Culinary Student Association, Partnership for Change in Communities and Families. Student services: personal-psychological counseling. Campus security: 24-hour emergency response devices and patrols, late night transport-escort service. Learning Resource Center plus 2 others. Students can reserve study rooms. 1,700 computers available on campus for general student use. A campuswide network can be accessed from off-campus. Students can access the following: online class registration. Staffed computer lab on campus provides training in use of computers, software, and the Internet.

Community Environment: North Charleston is a suburb located just eight miles from downtown Charleston. The community enjoys all the cultural, recreational and civic advantages of the nearby larger community, yet retains an air of the small town. There are good shopping areas, churches, parks and theatres.

■ UNIVERSITY OF SOUTH CAROLINA

Columbia, SC 29208
Tel: (803)777-7000; Free: 800-868-5872
E-mail: wagnermt@mailbox.sc.edu
Web Site: www.sc.edu

Description: State-supported, university, coed. Part of University of South Carolina System. Awards associate, bachelor's, master's, and doctoral degrees and post-master's certificates. Founded 1801. Setting: 444-acre

urban campus. Total enrollment: 34,795. Faculty: 2,200 (1,527 full-time, 673 part-time). Student-undergrad faculty ratio is 17:1. 30,778 applied, 63% were admitted. 29% from top 10% of their high school class, 62% from top quarter, 91% from top half. Full-time: 25,633 students, 53% women, 47% men. Part-time: 1,100 students, 49% women, 51% men. 38% from out-of-state. 0.2% American Indian or Alaska Native, non-Hispanic/Latino; 5% Hispanic/Latino; 9% Black or African American, non-Hispanic/Latino; 3% Asian, non-Hispanic/Latino; 0.1% Native Hawaiian or other Pacific Islander, non-Hispanic/Latino; 3% international. 6% 25 or older, 27% live on campus, 7% transferred in. Retention: 88% of full-time freshmen returned the following year. Academic areas with the most degrees conferred: business/marketing; biological/life sciences; health professions and related sciences. Core. Calendar: semesters. ESL program, services for LD students, advanced placement, accelerated degree program, self-designed majors, freshman honors college, honors program, independent study, distance learning, double major, summer session for credit, part-time degree program, adult/continuing education programs, co-op programs and internships, graduate courses open to undergrads. Study abroad program. ROTC: Army, Naval, Air Force.

Entrance Requirements: Options: electronic application, early action, international baccalaureate accepted. Required: high school transcript, minimum 2 high school GPA, SAT or ACT. Entrance: moderately difficult. SAT Reasoning Test deadline: 2/1. Transfer credits accepted: Yes. Applicants placed on waiting list: 3,814. Wait-listed applicants offered admission: 125.

Costs Per Year: Application fee: $65. State resident tuition: $12,216 full-time, $509 per credit hour part-time. Nonresident tuition: $32,898 full-time, $1,370.75 per credit hour part-time. Mandatory fees: $400 full-time, $17 per credit hour part-time. Full-time tuition and fees vary according to program and reciprocity agreements. Part-time tuition and fees vary according to course load. College room and board: $10,388. College room only: $6530. Room and board charges vary according to board plan, housing facility, and location.

Collegiate Environment: Orientation program. Drama-theater group, choral group, marching band, student-run newspaper, radio station. Social organizations: 394 open to all; national fraternities, national sororities. Major annual events: Homecoming Week, Carolina-Clemson Blood Drive, Welcome Week. Student services: health clinic, personal-psychological counseling, women's center. Campus security: 24-hour emergency response devices and patrols, student patrols, late night transport-escort service, controlled dormitory access. Freshmen guaranteed college housing. On-campus residence required in freshman year. Options: coed, men-only, women-only housing available. Thomas Cooper Library plus 6 others. Books: 1.8 million (physical), 1.1 million (digital/electronic); Serial titles: 72,412 (physical), 18,860 (digital/electronic); Databases: 574.

Community Environment: Columbia is located in the Midlands, halfway between the coast and the mountains - an easy two-and-a-half hour drive to some of the nicest beaches on the East Coast and some of the Carolinas' best hiking trails. A few blocks east of the university lies bustling Five Points, a longtime favorite of students for it boutiques, bookstores, restaurants, and bars. West of the university lies the Congaree Vista, a more upscale shopping and eating district. As the state's capital city, Columbia is home to the state government, as well as several other colleges and universities. Culture and entertainment abound. The city has several theatre groups, an art museum, and an art center that brings in major musical, dance, and theatre entertainment. For relaxation on Columbia's balmy spring-like days, downtown's Finlay Park is close by, and nearby Lake Murray offers swimming, camping, and fishing.

■ UNIVERSITY OF SOUTH CAROLINA AIKEN

471 University Pky.
Aiken, SC 29801
Tel: (803)648-6851; Free: 888-WOW-USCA
Fax: (803)641-3727
E-mail: admit@usca.edu
Web Site: www.usca.edu

Description: State-supported, comprehensive, coed. Part of University of South Carolina System. Awards bachelor's and master's degrees. Founded 1961. Setting: 453-acre suburban campus with easy access to Columbia. Endowment: $26.6 million. Research spending for the previous fiscal year: $1.3 million. Educational spending for the previous fiscal year: $6332 per student. Total enrollment: 3,699. Faculty: 296 (153 full-time, 143 part-time). Student-undergrad faculty ratio is 15:1. 3,115 applied, 51% were admitted. 15% from top 10% of their high school class, 40% from top quarter, 75% from top half. Full-time: 2,670 students, 65% women, 35% men. Part-time:

674 students, 65% women, 35% men. Students come from 32 states and territories, 33 other countries, 12% from out-of-state. 0.4% American Indian or Alaska Native, non-Hispanic/Latino; 5% Hispanic/Latino; 26% Black or African American, non-Hispanic/Latino; 1% Asian, non-Hispanic/Latino; 0.1% Native Hawaiian or other Pacific Islander, non-Hispanic/Latino; 3% international. 18% 25 or older, 27% live on campus, 12% transferred in. Retention: 64% of full-time freshmen returned the following year. Academic areas with the most degrees conferred: business/marketing; health professions and related sciences; parks and recreation. Core. Calendar: semesters. ESL program, services for LD students, advanced placement, self-designed majors, honors program, independent study, distance learning, double major, summer session for credit, part-time degree program, adult/continuing education programs, co-op programs and internships. Off campus study at other units of the University of South Carolina System. Study abroad program.

Entrance Requirements: Options: electronic application, early admission, deferred admission, international baccalaureate accepted. Required: high school transcript, SAT or ACT. Entrance: moderately difficult. Application deadlines: 7/1, 7/1 for nonresidents. Notification: continuous, continuous for nonresidents. SAT Reasoning Test deadline: 8/1. Transfer credits accepted: Yes.

Costs Per Year: Application fee: $45. State resident tuition: $10,398 full-time, $433.25 per credit hour part-time. Nonresident tuition: $20,856 full-time, $869 per credit hour part-time. Mandatory fees: $362 full-time, $13 per credit hour part-time, $25 per term part-time. Full-time tuition and fees vary according to program and reciprocity agreements. Part-time tuition and fees vary according to course load, program, and reciprocity agreements. College room and board: $7766. College room only: $5066. Room and board charges vary according to board plan and housing facility.

Collegiate Environment: Orientation program. Drama-theater group, choral group, student-run newspaper. Social organizations: 101 open to all; national fraternities, national sororities; 9% of eligible men and 9% of eligible women are members. Most popular organizations: National Society of Leadership and Success, Pacer Fanatics, Alpha Omicron Pi, Zeta Tau Alpha, Phi Mu. Major annual events: Midnight Madness, Fall Fest, Homecoming Week. Student services: health clinic, personal-psychological counseling. Campus security: 24-hour emergency response devices and patrols, late night transport-escort service, controlled dormitory access. 974 college housing spaces available; 829 were occupied in 2018-19. Freshmen given priority for college housing. On-campus residence required in freshman year. Option: coed housing available. Gregg-Graniteville Library. Books: 133,161 (physical), 407,453 (digital/electronic); Serial titles: 16,034 (physical), 125,380 (digital/electronic); Databases: 217. Weekly public service hours: 78; students can reserve study rooms. Operations spending for the previous fiscal year: $1.4 million. 550 computers available on campus for general student use. A campuswide network can be accessed from student residence rooms and from off campus. Students can access the following: online class registration. Staffed computer lab on campus (open 24 hours a day) provides training in use of computers, software, and the Internet.

Community Environment: Aiken, population c. 27,490, is the seat of Aiken County and is about 17 miles from Augusta, Georgia.

■ UNIVERSITY OF SOUTH CAROLINA BEAUFORT

One University Blvd.
Bluffton, SC 29909
Tel: (843)208-8000
E-mail: monicaw@sc.edu
Web Site: www.uscb.edu

Description: State-supported, 4-year, coed. Part of University of South Carolina system. Awards associate and bachelor's degrees. Founded 1959. Setting: 200-acre suburban campus. Endowment: $4.2 million. Research spending for the previous fiscal year: $821,495. Educational spending for the previous fiscal year: $6616 per student. Total enrollment: 1,980. 1,968 applied, 63% were admitted. 7% from top 10% of their high school class, 27% from top quarter, 58% from top half. Full-time: 1,705 students, 65% women, 35% men. Part-time: 275 students, 62% women, 38% men. 16% from out-of-state. 0.4% American Indian or Alaska Native, non-Hispanic/Latino; 7% Hispanic/Latino; 22% Black or African American, non-Hispanic/Latino; 2% Asian, non-Hispanic/Latino; 0.1% Native Hawaiian or other Pacific Islander, non-Hispanic/Latino. 21% 25 or older, 37% live on campus, 9% transferred in. Retention: 58% of full-time freshmen returned the following year. Academic areas with the most degrees conferred: business/marketing; psychology; social sciences. Core. Calendar: semesters. Services for LD students, advanced placement, self-designed majors, independent study,

distance learning, double major, summer session for credit, part-time degree program, adult/continuing education programs, internships. Study abroad program.

Entrance Requirements: Options: electronic application, deferred admission, international baccalaureate accepted. Required: high school transcript, prerequisite high school courses, SAT or ACT. Recommended: minimum 2 high school GPA. Entrance: minimally difficult. Application deadline: rolling. Notification: continuous. Transfer credits accepted: Yes.

Costs Per Year: Application fee: $40. State resident tuition: $10,344 full-time, $431 per credit hour part-time. Nonresident tuition: $21,390 full-time, $891.25 per credit hour part-time. Mandatory fees: $436 full-time, $14 per credit hour part-time, $25 per term part-time. Full-time tuition and fees vary according to course load, program, and reciprocity agreements. Part-time tuition and fees vary according to course load, program, and reciprocity agreements. College room and board: $7120. College room only: $4320. Room and board charges vary according to board plan, housing facility, location, and student level.

Collegiate Environment: Orientation program. Drama-theater group, choral group. Social organizations: 8 open to all; national fraternities, national sororities. Most popular organizations: Student Government Association, Gamma Beta Phi, Black Student Organization, Business Club, Environmental Awareness Club. Major annual events: Welcome Week, Homecoming, Fall Fest/Fright Week. Student services: personal-psychological counseling. Campus security: 24-hour emergency response devices, controlled dormitory access, evening security service. University of South Carolina Beaufort Library plus 1 other. Books: 90,519 (physical), 505,463 (digital/electronic); Serial titles: 1,861 (physical), 7,031 (digital/electronic); Databases: 235. Students can reserve study rooms. Operations spending for the previous fiscal year: $644,827.

■ UNIVERSITY OF SOUTH CAROLINA LANCASTER

PO Box 889
Lancaster, SC 29721-0889
Tel: (803)313-7000
Fax: (803)313-7106
E-mail: jblackmo@mailbox.sc.edu
Web Site: usclancaster.sc.edu

Description: State-supported, 2-year, coed. Part of University of South Carolina System. Awards transfer associate and terminal associate degrees. Founded 1959. Setting: 17-acre small town campus with easy access to Charlotte. Educational spending for the previous fiscal year: $4680 per student. Total enrollment: 1,593. Faculty: 105 (63 full-time, 42 part-time). Student-undergrad faculty ratio is 14:1. 557 applied, 99% were admitted. 8% from top 10% of their high school class, 13% from top quarter, 50% from top half. 1 valedictorian. Students come from 10 states and territories, 2 other countries, 1% from out-of-state. 13% 25 or older. Calendar: semesters. Academic remediation for entering students, services for LD students, advanced placement, honors program, independent study, distance learning, part-time degree program, internships.

Entrance Requirements: Open admission. Options: electronic application, early admission. Required: high school transcript, SAT or ACT. Entrance: noncompetitive. Application deadline: rolling. Notification: continuous. Transfer credits accepted: Yes.

Costs Per Year: Application fee: $40. One-time mandatory fee: $50. State resident tuition: $7158 full-time, $298.25 per credit hour part-time. Nonresident tuition: $17,838 full-time, $743.25 per credit hour part-time. Mandatory fees: $530 full-time, $17 per credit hour part-time, $65 per term part-time.

Collegiate Environment: Orientation program. Drama-theater group, student-run newspaper. Student services: personal-psychological counseling. Medford Library. 40 computers available on campus for general student use. A campuswide network can be accessed. Students can access the following: online class registration. Staffed computer lab on campus.

■ UNIVERSITY OF SOUTH CAROLINA SALKEHATCHIE

PO Box 617
Allendale, SC 29810-0617
Tel: (803)584-3446; Free: 800-922-5500
E-mail: cdbrown@mailbox.sc.edu
Web Site: uscsalkehatchie.sc.edu

Description: State-supported, 2-year, coed. Part of University of South Carolina System. Awards transfer associate and terminal associate degrees. Founded 1965. Setting: 95-acre rural campus. Total enrollment: 1,076. Student-undergrad faculty ratio is 17:1. 654 applied, 59% were admitted. 5%

from out-of-state. 25% 25 or older. Retention: 45% of full-time freshmen returned the following year. Core. Calendar: semesters. Academic remediation for entering students, services for LD students, advanced placement, independent study, distance learning, summer session for credit, part-time degree program, adult/continuing education programs, co-op programs and internships. Study abroad program.

Entrance Requirements: Option: electronic application. Required: high school transcript, minimum 2 high school GPA, SAT or ACT. Entrance: noncompetitive. Application deadline: rolling. Transfer credits accepted: Yes.

Collegiate Environment: Orientation program. Campus security: 24-hour emergency response devices, late night transport-escort service. Salkehatchie Learning Resource Center.

■ UNIVERSITY OF SOUTH CAROLINA SUMTER

200 Miller Rd.
Sumter, SC 29150-2498
Tel: (803)775-8727
E-mail: kbritton@usc.sumter.edu
Web Site: www.uscsumter.edu

Description: State-supported, 2-year, coed. Part of University of South Carolina System. Awards transfer associate degrees. Founded 1966. Setting: 50-acre urban campus. Endowment: $1.8 million. Research spending for the previous fiscal year: $25,459. Educational spending for the previous fiscal year: $4064 per student. Total enrollment: 1,206. Faculty: 66 (41 full-time, 25 part-time). Student-undergrad faculty ratio is 19:1. 698 applied, 58% were admitted. 12% from top 10% of their high school class, 34% from top quarter, 67% from top half. 1 class president, 3 student government officers. 5% from out-of-state. 19% 25 or older. Retention: 57% of full-time freshmen returned the following year. Core. Calendar: semesters. Services for LD students, advanced placement, honors program, independent study, distance learning, summer session for credit, part-time degree program, adult/continuing education programs. ROTC: Army (c), Air Force (c).

Entrance Requirements: Options: electronic application, international baccalaureate accepted. Required: high school transcript, minimum 2.0 high school GPA, SAT or ACT. Entrance: moderately difficult. Application deadline: 8/8.

Costs Per Year: Application fee: $40. State resident tuition: $7158 full-time, $298.25 per credit hour part-time. Nonresident tuition: $17,838 full-time, $743.25 per credit hour part-time. Mandatory fees: $510 full-time, $17 per credit hour part-time. Part-time tuition and fees vary according to location.

Collegiate Environment: Orientation program. Drama-theater group, choral group. Social organizations: 16 open to all. Most popular organizations: Association of African-American Students, Baptist Student Union, Student Education Association, Gamecock Ambassadors, Environmental Club. Major annual events: Convocation, Alcohol Awareness Week Festival, Martin Luther King, Jr. Day festivities. Student services: personal-psychological counseling. Campus security: 24-hour patrols, late night transport-escort service. University of South Carolina at Sumter Library. Operations spending for the previous fiscal year: $302,089. 355 computers available on campus for general student use. A campuswide network can be accessed from off-campus. Students can access the following: online class registration, online course evaluation, online student surveys. Staffed computer lab on campus.

■ UNIVERSITY OF SOUTH CAROLINA UNION

PO Drawer 729
Union, SC 29379-0729
Tel: (864)427-3681
E-mail: greerm@mailbox.sc.edu
Web Site: uscunion.sc.edu

Description: State-supported, primarily 2-year, coed. Part of University of South Carolina System. Awards transfer associate and bachelor's degrees. Founded 1965. Setting: 7-acre small town campus with easy access to Charlotte, North Carolina. Endowment: $1.2 million. Research spending for the previous fiscal year: $20,903. Educational spending for the previous fiscal year: $3920 per student. Total enrollment: 905. Faculty: 42 (12 full-time, 30 part-time). Student-undergrad faculty ratio is 18:1. 1,378 applied, 67% were admitted. 5% from top 10% of their high school class, 15% from top quarter, 50% from top half. 5 student government officers. Students come from 3 states and territories, 1 other country, 2% from out-of-state. 3% Hispanic/Latino; 43% Black or African American, non-Hispanic/Latino. 7% 25 or older. Core. Calendar: semesters. Advanced placement, independent study, distance learning, double major, summer session for credit, part-time degree program, co-op programs and internships. Study abroad program.

Entrance Requirements: Option: electronic application. Required: high

school transcript, SAT or ACT. Entrance: minimally difficult. Application deadline: rolling. Notification: continuous. SAT Reasoning Test deadline: 8/1. SAT Subject Test deadline: 8/1. Transfer credits accepted: Yes.

Costs Per Year: Application fee: $40. State resident tuition: $285.41 per credit hour part-time. Nonresident tuition: $721.05 per credit hour part-time. Part-time tuition varies according to class time, location, program, and student level.

Collegiate Environment: Orientation program. Drama-theater group, choral group. Social organizations: 12 open to all. Student services: personal-psychological counseling. Campus security: 24-hour emergency response devices. College housing not available. Union Carnegie Library plus 1 other. Study areas open 24 hours, 5-7 days a week. Operations spending for the previous fiscal year: $96. 100 computers available on campus for general student use. A campuswide network can be accessed from off-campus. Students can access the following: online class registration. Staffed computer lab on campus provides training in use of computers.

■ UNIVERSITY OF SOUTH CAROLINA UPSTATE

800 University Way
Spartanburg, SC 29303-4999
Tel: (864)503-5000; Free: 800-277-8727
Fax: (864)503-5201
E-mail: dstewart@uscupstate.edu
Web Site: www.uscupstate.edu

Description: State-supported, comprehensive, coed. Part of University of South Carolina System. Awards bachelor's and master's degrees. Founded 1967. Setting: 330-acre urban campus with easy access to Charlotte. Endowment: $7.7 million. Research spending for the previous fiscal year: $197,743. Educational spending for the previous fiscal year: $5224 per student. Total enrollment: 5,821. Faculty: 451 (246 full-time, 205 part-time). Student-undergrad faculty ratio is 15:1. 3,633 applied, 56% were admitted. 10% from top 10% of their high school class, 37% from top quarter, 74% from top half. Students come from 35 states and territories, 20 other countries, 5% from out-of-state. 0.2% American Indian or Alaska Native, non-Hispanic/Latino; 5% Hispanic/Latino; 27% Black or African American, non-Hispanic/Latino; 2% Asian, non-Hispanic/Latino; 3% international. 19% 25 or older, 16% live on campus. Retention: 74% of full-time freshmen returned the following year. Academic areas with the most degrees conferred: health professions and related sciences; business/marketing; education. Core. Calendar: semesters. Academic remediation for entering students, ESL program, services for LD students, advanced placement, accelerated degree program, self-designed majors, honors program, independent study, distance learning, double major, summer session for credit, part-time degree program, adult/continuing education programs, co-op programs and internships. Off campus study at Wofford College, Greenville Higher Education Consortium. Study abroad program. ROTC: Army (c).

Entrance Requirements: Options: electronic application, deferred admission, international baccalaureate accepted. Required: high school transcript, minimum 2 high school GPA, college preparatory courses, SAT or ACT. Entrance: moderately difficult. Notification: continuous. SAT Reasoning Test deadline: 8/15. Transfer credits accepted: Yes.

Costs Per Year: Application fee: $40. One-time mandatory fee: $75. State resident tuition: $11,208 full-time, $467 per credit hour part-time. Nonresident tuition: $22,710 full-time, $946.25 per credit hour part-time. Mandatory fees: $480 full-time, $480 per year part-time. Full-time tuition and fees vary according to course load and program. Part-time tuition and fees vary according to course load and program. College room and board: $9480. Room and board charges vary according to board plan and housing facility.

Collegiate Environment: Orientation program. Drama-theater group, choral group, student-run newspaper. Social organizations: 97 open to all; national fraternities, national sororities. Most popular organizations: African-American Association, Campus Activity Board, Student Nurses Association, Student Government Association, Impact. Major annual events: Premier Fall Kick-Off, Technology Fair, Angel Tree Program. Student services: health clinic, personal-psychological counseling, women's center. Campus security: 24-hour emergency response devices and patrols, late night transport-escort service, campus security cameras. University of South Carolina Upstate Library. Operations spending for the previous fiscal year: $1.8 million. 450 computers available on campus for general student use. A campuswide network can be accessed from student residence rooms and from off campus. Students can access the following: online class registration. Staffed computer lab on campus provides training in use of computers, software, and the Internet.

Community Environment: Spartanburg, South Carolina, is one of the fastest-growing communities in the region, located on the thriving Interstate 85 corridor about three hours from Atlanta and an hour and a half from Charlotte, North Carolina. The Blue Ridge Mountains are less than an hour away; South Carolina's Grand Strand and historic Low Country are a four-hour drive in the other direction. The area has a growing international presence, and arts and cultural activities that would be the envy of many larger cities.

■ **VOORHEES COLLEGE**
213 Wiggins Dr.
Denmark, SC 29042
Tel: (803)780-1234; Free: 866-237-4570
Fax: (803)793-5773
E-mail: west@voorhees.edu
Web Site: www.voorhees.edu
Description: Independent Episcopal, 4-year, coed. Awards bachelor's degrees. Founded 1897. Setting: 350-acre rural campus. Endowment: $5.9 million. Total enrollment: 468. Faculty: 44 (39 full-time, 5 part-time). 2,776 applied, 50% were admitted. Full-time: 452 students, 54% women, 46% men. Part-time: 16 students, 44% women, 56% men. 9% 25 or older, 70% live on campus, 5% transferred in. Core. Calendar: semesters. Academic remediation for entering students, services for LD students, advanced placement, honors program, double major, summer session for credit, part-time degree program, adult/continuing education programs, co-op programs and internships. ROTC: Army (c).
Entrance Requirements: Options: electronic application, deferred admission. Required: high school transcript, minimum 2 high school GPA, secondary school GPA. Recommended: SAT or ACT. Required for some: interview. Entrance: moderately difficult. Application deadline: rolling.
Collegiate Environment: Orientation program. Drama-theater group, choral group, student-run newspaper, radio station. Social organizations: 30 open to all; national fraternities, national sororities, local fraternities; 20% of eligible men and 14% of eligible women are members. Major annual events: Founders' Day, Homecoming, Fall Convocation. Student services: health clinic, personal-psychological counseling. Campus security: 24-hour emergency response devices and patrols, student patrols, late night transport-escort service, controlled dormitory access. Wright-Potts Library. 300 computers available on campus for general student use. A campuswide network can be accessed from student residence rooms and from off campus. Students can access the following: online class registration. Staffed computer lab on campus provides training in use of computers, software, and the Internet.
Community Environment: Denmark is a rural community located in south central South Carolina. The climate is temperate. There is a public library, local hospitals and several churches representing various denominations. The Lions Club, Masonic Lodge, and Woodmen of the World are active within the community. Recreation includes golf, swimming, boating, fishing and a local theatre.

■ **WILLIAMSBURG TECHNICAL COLLEGE**
601 Martin Luther King, Jr Ave.
Kingstree, SC 29556-4197
Tel: (843)355-4110; Free: 800-768-2021
Fax: (843)355-4296
E-mail: dubosec@wiltech.edu
Web Site: www.wiltech.edu
Description: State-supported, 2-year, coed. Part of South Carolina State Board for Technical and Comprehensive Education. Awards certificates, diplomas, transfer associate, and terminal associate degrees. Founded 1969. Setting: 41-acre rural campus. Total enrollment: 732. Faculty: 49 (18 full-time, 31 part-time). Student-undergrad faculty ratio is 12:1. Full-time: 194 students, 64% women, 36% men. Part-time: 538 students, 59% women, 41% men. 0.1% American Indian or Alaska Native, non-Hispanic/Latino; 76% Black or African American, non-Hispanic/Latino; 0.3% Asian, non-Hispanic/Latino. 25% 25 or older, 4% transferred in. Retention: 45% of full-time freshmen returned the following year. Core. Calendar: semesters. Academic remediation for entering students, services for LD students, advanced placement, independent study, distance learning, double major, summer session for credit, part-time degree program.
Entrance Requirements: Open admission. Options: electronic application, early admission, deferred admission. Required: high school transcript. Entrance: noncompetitive. Application deadline: rolling. Notification: continuous. Transfer credits accepted: Yes.

Costs Per Year: Application fee: $0. Area resident tuition: $4176 full-time, $174 per credit hour part-time. State resident tuition: $4296 full-time, $179 per credit hour part-time. Nonresident tuition: $8088 full-time, $337 per credit hour part-time. Mandatory fees: $192 full-time, $8 per credit hour part-time.
Collegiate Environment: Orientation program. Social organizations: 2 open to all. Most popular organizations: Phi Theta Kappa, Student Government Association. Major annual events: Spring Fling, Fall Fling, SGA Christmas Party. Student services: personal-psychological counseling. Learning Resource Center. Books: 18,002 (physical), 391,203 (digital/electronic); Serial titles: 91 (physical); Databases: 44. Students can reserve study rooms.

■ **WINTHROP UNIVERSITY**
701 Oakland Ave.
Rock Hill, SC 29733
Tel: (803)323-2211; Free: 800-763-0230
Fax: (803)323-2137
E-mail: rollingsd@winthrop.edu
Web Site: www.winthrop.edu
Description: State-supported, comprehensive, coed. Part of South Carolina Commission on Higher Education. Awards bachelor's and master's degrees and post-master's certificates. Founded 1886. Setting: 456-acre suburban campus with easy access to Charlotte. Total enrollment: 5,813. Faculty: 546 (285 full-time, 261 part-time). Student-undergrad faculty ratio is 14:1. 5,175 applied, 67% were admitted. 13% from top 10% of their high school class, 42% from top quarter, 80% from top half. Full-time: 4,331 students, 70% women, 30% men. Part-time: 556 students, 68% women, 32% men. Students come from 41 states and territories, 66 other countries, 9% from out-of-state. 0.3% American Indian or Alaska Native, non-Hispanic/Latino; 5% Hispanic/Latino; 29% Black or African American, non-Hispanic/Latino; 1% Asian, non-Hispanic/Latino; 0.1% Native Hawaiian or other Pacific Islander, non-Hispanic/Latino; 1% international. 7% 25 or older, 48% live on campus, 6% transferred in. Retention: 75% of full-time freshmen returned the following year. Academic areas with the most degrees conferred: business/marketing; education; visual and performing arts. Core. Calendar: semesters. Services for LD students, advanced placement, self-designed majors, honors program, independent study, distance learning, double major, summer session for credit, part-time degree program, adult/continuing education programs, co-op programs and internships, graduate courses open to undergrads. Off campus study at National Student Exchange, 19 members of the Charlotte Area Educational Consortium. Study abroad program. ROTC: Army (c), Air Force (c).
Entrance Requirements: Options: electronic application, deferred admission, international baccalaureate accepted. Required: high school transcript, minimum 3 high school GPA, SAT or ACT. Required for some: essay. Entrance: moderately difficult. Notification: continuous. SAT Reasoning Test deadline: 5/1. Transfer credits accepted: Yes.
Costs Per Year: Application fee: $40. State resident tuition: $15,230 full-time, $635 per credit hour part-time. Nonresident tuition: $29,486 full-time, $1229 per credit hour part-time. Mandatory fees: $360 full-time. Full-time tuition and fees vary according to degree level, reciprocity agreements, and student level. Part-time tuition varies according to degree level and student level. College room and board: $8948. College room only: $5416. Room and board charges vary according to board plan and housing facility.
Collegiate Environment: Orientation program. Drama-theater group, choral group, student-run newspaper, radio station. Social organizations: 158 open to all; national fraternities, national sororities, local fraternities; 1% of eligible men and 2% of eligible women are members. Most popular organizations: Association of Ebonites, WU Crew, Greek Life, DiGiorgio Student Union, Campus Ministries. Major annual events: Homecoming, Greek Week, Convocation. Student services: health clinic, personal-psychological counseling. Campus security: 24-hour emergency response devices and patrols, late night transport-escort service, controlled dormitory access. 2,518 college housing spaces available; 2,221 were occupied in 2018-19. Freshmen guaranteed college housing. On-campus residence required through sophomore year. Options: coed, women-only housing available. Dacus Library plus 1 other. Books: 356,611 (physical), 281,972 (digital/electronic); Serial titles: 540 (physical), 36,003 (digital/electronic); Databases: 133. Weekly public service hours: 144; study areas open 24 hours, 5-7 days a week; students can reserve study rooms. 620 computers available on campus for general student use. Computer purchase/lease plans available. A campuswide network can be accessed from student residence rooms and from off campus. Students can access the following: online class registration, university services. Staffed computer lab on campus (open 24 hours a day) provides training in use of computers, software, and the Internet.

Community Environment: Rock Hill is a small progressive city of nearly 50,000 residents located 30 miles below Charlotte, North Carolina. The city is uniquely situated to offer the advantages of both small town living and big city amenities. Diversified industry fuels a growing local economy which produces textiles, wood, paper, concrete, plastic and chemical products. Rock Hill's facilities include the Museum of York County (featuring the world's largest collection of hooved African animals); Winthrop Galleries, host to local, national and international artists; Winthrop Coliseum, Glencairn Gardens, a six acre garden spot; and Cherry Park, a 68 acre recreation park featuring five major league baseball and softball diamonds, which attracts major tournaments from throughout the United States. Opportunities for recreation in the mild piedmont climate are plentiful. The city maintains a system of 28 parks that offer athletic fields and courts, play areas, fitness, walking and jogging trails, and amphitheaters. Lakes 20 minutes away are a convenient destination for water sports and sailing.

■ **WOFFORD COLLEGE**
429 N Church St.
Spartanburg, SC 29303-3663
Tel: (864)597-4000
Fax: (864)597-4149
E-mail: admission@wofford.edu
Web Site: www.wofford.edu
Description: Independent, 4-year, coed, affiliated with United Methodist Church. Awards bachelor's degrees. Founded 1854. Setting: 170-acre urban campus. Endowment: $194 million. Educational spending for the previous fiscal year: $13,821 per student. Total enrollment: 1,587. Faculty: 182 (148 full-time, 34 part-time). Student-undergrad faculty ratio is 10:1. 3,520 applied, 64% were admitted. 38% from top 10% of their high school class, 64% from top quarter, 91% from top half. 1 National Merit Scholar, 9 class presidents, 10 valedictorians, 42 student government officers. Full-time: 1,567 students, 53% women, 47% men. Part-time: 20 students, 75% women, 25% men. Students come from 42 states and territories, 24 other countries, 44% from out-of-state. 0.1% American Indian or Alaska Native, non-Hispanic/Latino; 4% Hispanic/Latino; 8% Black or African American, non-Hispanic/Latino; 2% Asian, non-Hispanic/Latino; 2% international. 97% live on campus, 1% transferred in. Retention: 88% of full-time freshmen returned the following year. Academic areas with the most degrees conferred: business/marketing; biological/life sciences; social sciences. Core. Calendar: 4-1-4. Advanced placement, accelerated degree program, self-designed majors, independent study, double major, summer session for credit, part-time degree program, internships. Off campus study. Study abroad program. ROTC: Army.
Entrance Requirements: Options: electronic application, early admission, early decision, early action, deferred admission, international baccalaureate accepted. Required: essay, high school transcript. Recommended: 2 recommendations, interview. Entrance: very difficult. Application deadlines: 1/15, 11/1 for early decision, 11/15 for early action. Notification: 3/1, 12/1 for early decision, 2/1 for early action. SAT Reasoning Test deadline: 2/1. Transfer credits accepted: Yes. Applicants placed on waiting list: 232. Wait-listed applicants offered admission: 8. Early decision applicants: 127. Early decision applicants admitted: 111.
Costs Per Year: Application fee: $35. Comprehensive fee: $58,935 includes full-time tuition ($44,135), mandatory fees ($1575), and college room and board ($13,225). College room only: $7315. Part-time tuition: $1825 per credit hour.
Collegiate Environment: Orientation program. Drama-theater group, choral group, student-run newspaper, radio station. Social organizations: 57 open to all; national fraternities, national sororities; 47% of eligible men and 55% of eligible women are members. Most popular organizations: W.A.R. - Wofford Athletics and Recreation, W.A.C. - Wofford Activities Council, Twin

Towers - Service Organization, Math Academy, Arcadia Volunteer Corp. Major annual events: Homecoming, Winter Lighting, Spring Weekend. Student services: health clinic, personal-psychological counseling. Campus security: 24-hour emergency response devices and patrols, late night transport-escort service, controlled dormitory access. 1,485 college housing spaces available; all were occupied in 2018-19. Freshmen given priority for college housing. On-campus residence required through senior year. Option: coed housing available. Sandor Teszler Library. Books: 114,660 (physical), 498,046 (digital/electronic); Serial titles: 372 (physical), 78,078 (digital/electronic); Databases: 201. 233 computers available on campus for general student use. A campuswide network can be accessed from student residence rooms and from off campus. Students can access the following: online class registration. Staffed computer lab on campus provides training in use of computers, software, and the Internet.
Community Environment: Spartanburg County (population 271,000) is a thriving, rapidly growing Sunbelt business center that is particularly well known for its international community. Wofford students live in a downtown setting near restaurants, churches of all denominations, shopping districts, a busy arts center, and four other college campuses. Memorial Auditorium, Wofford's next-door neighbor, features concerts, touring Broadway plays, and other special attractions. Several major airlines serve the convenient Greenville-Spartanburg Airport, which is only twenty miles from the campus. Interstate highways 26 and 85 intersect at Spartanburg. Charlotte, Atlanta, historic Charleston, and South Carolina's world-famous coastal resorts are all within a pleasant afternoon drive.

■ **YORK TECHNICAL COLLEGE**
452 S Anderson Rd.
Rock Hill, SC 29730-3395
Tel: (803)327-8000
Fax: (803)327-8059
E-mail: kaldridge@yorktech.com
Web Site: www.yorktech.edu
Description: State-supported, 2-year, coed. Part of South Carolina State Board for Technical and Comprehensive Education. Awards certificates, diplomas, transfer associate, and terminal associate degrees. Founded 1961. Setting: 110-acre small town campus with easy access to Charlotte. Total enrollment: 4,731. Faculty: 267 (128 full-time, 139 part-time). Student-undergrad faculty ratio is 16:1. Full-time: 2,279 students, 60% women, 40% men. Part-time: 2,452 students, 65% women, 35% men. 2% from out-of-state. 39% 25 or older. Core. Calendar: semesters. Academic remediation for entering students, ESL program, services for LD students, advanced placement, honors program, distance learning, summer session for credit, part-time degree program, adult/continuing education programs, co-op programs and internships. Off campus study at Charlotte Area Educational Consortium.
Entrance Requirements: Open admission except for health and human services program. Option: electronic application. Required for some: high school transcript, SAT, ACT, or ACT ASSET, ACT Compass. Entrance: noncompetitive. Application deadline: rolling. Notification: continuous.
Collegiate Environment: Orientation program. Social organizations: 16 open to all. Most popular organizations: Jacobin Society, Phi Theta Kappa, Student Government Association, Phi Beta Lambda, Student Activities Board. Major annual events: Welcome Back Blast, Health Fair. Campus security: 24-hour patrols, late night transport-escort service. Anne Springs Close Library. 250 computers available on campus for general student use. A campuswide network can be accessed from off-campus. Students can access the following: online class registration, course search, account detail, placement test scores. Staffed computer lab on campus provides training in use of computers.
Community Environment: See Winthrop University.

■ AUGUSTANA UNIVERSITY

2001 S Summit Ave.
Sioux Falls, SD 57197
Tel: (605)274-0770; Free: 800-727-2844
Fax: (605)274-5518
E-mail: admission@augie.edu
Web Site: www.augie.edu

Description: Independent, comprehensive, coed, affiliated with Evangelical Lutheran Church in America. Awards bachelor's and master's degrees. Founded 1860. Setting: 100-acre urban campus. Endowment: $81 million. Research spending for the previous fiscal year: $1.3 million. Educational spending for the previous fiscal year: $25,121 per student. Total enrollment: 2,080. Faculty: 176 (130 full-time, 46 part-time). Student-undergrad faculty ratio is 12:1. 1,975 applied, 68% were admitted. 35% from top 10% of their high school class, 64% from top quarter, 89% from top half. Full-time: 1,679 students, 62% women, 38% men. Part-time: 70 students, 60% women, 40% men. Students come from 33 states and territories, 32 other countries, 50% from out-of-state. 0.5% American Indian or Alaska Native, non-Hispanic/Latino; 3% Hispanic/Latino; 2% Black or African American, non-Hispanic/Latino; 1% Asian, non-Hispanic/Latino; 8% international. 4% 25 or older, 70% live on campus, 3% transferred in. Retention: 86% of full-time freshmen returned the following year. Academic areas with the most degrees conferred: business/marketing; education; biological/life sciences. Core. Calendar: 4-1-4. Academic remediation for entering students, services for LD students, advanced placement, accelerated degree program, self-designed majors, honors program, independent study, distance learning, double major, summer session for credit, part-time degree program, external degree program, internships. Off campus study at Higher Education Consortium for Urban Affairs (HECUA), Lutheran College, American University, Midwest Lutheran Colleges January/Interim term exchange. Study abroad program. ROTC: Army (c), Air Force (c).

Entrance Requirements: Options: electronic application, deferred admission, international baccalaureate accepted. Required: high school transcript, minimum 2.7 high school GPA, minimum ACT score of 20, SAT or ACT. Recommended: essay, 1 recommendation, interview. Entrance: moderately difficult. Application deadline: rolling. Notification: continuous until 10/1. SAT Reasoning Test deadline: 8/1. Transfer credits accepted: Yes.

Costs Per Year: Application fee: $0. Comprehensive fee: $41,266 includes full-time tuition ($32,488), mandatory fees ($530), and college room and board ($8248). College room only: $3778. Full-time tuition and fees vary according to course load and degree level. Room and board charges vary according to board plan and housing facility.

Collegiate Environment: Orientation program. Drama-theater group, choral group, student-run newspaper. Social organizations: 66 open to all; Academic Honor Greek Society. Most popular organizations: Augieholics (student athletics support organization), intramurals, Union Board of Governors (student union), Augie Green, Campus Ministries. Major annual events: Community Service Day, An Augustana Christmas (Vespers), Viking Days (homecoming). Student services: health clinic, personal-psychological counseling. Campus security: 24-hour, emergency response devices and patrols, late night transport-escort service, controlled dormitory access, special 'day lighting' night lights throughout the campus grounds. Mikkelsen Library. Students can reserve study rooms. Operations spending for the previous fiscal year: $1.1 million. 295 computers available on campus for general student use. Computer purchase/lease plans available. A campuswide network can be accessed from student residence rooms and from off campus. Students can access the following: online class registration. Staffed computer lab on campus (open 24 hours a day) provides training in use of computers, software, and the Internet.

Community Environment: See University of Sioux Falls.

■ BLACK HILLS STATE UNIVERSITY

1200 University St.
Spearfish, SD 57799
Tel: (605)642-6011; Free: 800-255-2478
E-mail: admissions@bhsu.edu
Web Site: www.bhsu.edu

Description: State-supported, comprehensive, coed. Part of South Dakota Board of Regents. Awards associate, bachelor's, and master's degrees and post-master's certificates. Founded 1883. Setting: 123-acre small town campus. Total enrollment: 4,178. Faculty: 128. 1,696 applied, 87% were admitted. Full-time: 2,195 students, 62% women, 38% men. Part-time: 1,752 students, 64% women, 36% men. Students come from 45 states and territories, 36 other countries, 31% from out-of-state. 4% American Indian or Alaska Native, non-Hispanic/Latino; 6% Hispanic/Latino; 2% Black or African American, non-Hispanic/Latino; 0.8% Asian, non-Hispanic/Latino; 1% international. 7% transferred in. Retention: 69% of full-time freshmen returned the following year. Core. Calendar: semesters. Academic remediation for entering students, ESL program, services for LD students, advanced placement, accelerated degree program, honors program, independent study, distance learning, double major, summer session for credit, part-time degree program, co-op programs and internships, graduate courses open to undergrads. Off campus study at South Dakota Board of Regents for Public Universities and Special Schools. Study abroad program. ROTC: Army.

Entrance Requirements: Required: high school transcript, minimum 2.0 high school GPA in core curriculum, SAT or ACT. SAT Reasoning Test deadline: 7/15. SAT Subject Test deadline: 7/15.

Costs Per Year: Application fee: $20. State resident tuition: $7626 full-time, $291.10 per credit hour part-time. Nonresident tuition: $10,671 full-time, $392.60 per credit hour part-time. Mandatory fees: $1107 full-time. Full-time tuition and fees vary according to course load, location, and reciprocity agreements. Part-time tuition varies according to course load, location, and reciprocity agreements. College room and board: $6978. College room only: $3530. Room and board charges vary according to board plan, housing facility, and location.

Collegiate Environment: Orientation program. Drama-theater group, choral group, student-run newspaper, radio station. Social organizations: 85 open to all; national fraternities, national sororities. Most popular organizations: Student Activities Committee, Student Government. Major annual events: Swarm Days, Geek Speak. Student services: health clinic, personal-psychological counseling. Campus security: 24-hour patrols, late night transport-escort service, controlled dormitory access. E. Y. Berry Library. Students can reserve study rooms.

Community Environment: Spearfish, population 9,355, is in a beautiful agricultural valley at the mouth of Spearfish Canyon. There are libraries, museums, churches, hospitals, and a number of civic and service organizations in the community and surrounding area. Recreational activities include hunting, fishing, hiking, skiing, golf, and boating. The Black Hills Passion Play is presented during the summer months in a specially constructed amphitheater. Part-time employment is available.

■ **DAKOTA STATE UNIVERSITY**

820 N Washington

Madison, SD 57042-1799

Tel: (605)256-5111; Free: 888-DSU-9988

Fax: (605)256-5316

E-mail: admissions@dsu.edu

Web Site: www.dsu.edu

Description: State-supported, comprehensive, coed. Part of South Dakota Board of Regents. Awards associate, bachelor's, master's, and doctoral degrees. Founded 1881. Setting: 62-acre rural campus with easy access to Sioux Falls. Endowment: $15.2 million. Research spending for the previous fiscal year: $3 million. Educational spending for the previous fiscal year: $7409 per student. Total enrollment: 3,382. Faculty: 153 (101 full-time, 52 part-time). 1,056 applied, 83% were admitted. 8% from top 10% of their high school class, 23% from top quarter, 54% from top half. Full-time: 1,448 students, 31% women, 69% men. Part-time: 1,545 students, 50% women, 50% men. Students come from 49 states and territories, 31 other countries, 39% from out-of-state. 0.6% American Indian or Alaska Native, non-Hispanic/Latino; 4% Hispanic/Latino; 3% Black or African American, non-Hispanic/Latino; 2% Asian, non-Hispanic/Latino; 0.1% Native Hawaiian or other Pacific Islander, non-Hispanic/Latino; 1% international. 29% 25 or older, 36% live on campus, 8% transferred in. Retention: 67% of full-time freshmen returned the following year. Academic areas with the most degrees conferred: computer and information sciences; education; business/marketing. Core. Calendar: semesters. Academic remediation for entering students, services for LD students, advanced placement, honors program, independent study, distance learning, double major, summer session for credit, part-time degree program, co-op programs and internships, graduate courses open to undergrads. Off campus study at South Dakota State University, University of South Dakota, Northern State University, Black Hills State University, South Dakota School of Mines and Technology, Southeast Technical Institute, Lake Area Technical Institute, Mitchell Tech, Western Dakota Tech, and Northwest Iowa Community College. Study abroad program. ROTC: Army (c), Air Force (c).

Entrance Requirements: Options: electronic application, deferred admission, international baccalaureate accepted. Required: high school transcript, minimum 2.6 high school GPA, SAT or ACT. Entrance: moderately difficult. Application deadlines: rolling, rolling for nonresidents. Notification: continuous, continuous for nonresidents. SAT Reasoning Test deadline: 9/1. Transfer credits accepted: Yes.

Costs Per Year: Application fee: $20. State resident tuition: $7299 full-time, $243.30 per credit hour part-time. Nonresident tuition: $10,272 full-time, $342.40 per credit hour part-time. Mandatory fees: $1977 full-time, $39.70 per credit hour part-time. Full-time tuition and fees vary according to location and reciprocity agreements. Part-time tuition and fees vary according to location and reciprocity agreements. College room and board: $6,873. College room only: $3,723. Room and board charges vary according to board plan and housing facility.

Collegiate Environment: Orientation program. Drama-theater group, choral group, student-run newspaper, radio station. Social organizations: 50 open to all. Most popular organizations: Gaming Club, Computer Club, Student Senate, Fellowship of Christian Athletes, Campus Crusade for Christ (Cru). Major annual events: Homecoming, Nanocon, Day of Service. Student services: health clinic, personal-psychological counseling. Campus security: late night transport-escort service, controlled dormitory access. 762 college housing spaces available. Freshmen guaranteed college housing. On-campus residence required through sophomore year. Options: coed, men-only housing available. Karl E. Mundt Library plus 1 other. Books: 49,261 (physical), 218,951 (digital/electronic); Serial titles: 200 (physical), 120 (digital/electronic); Databases: 140. Weekly public service hours: 85. Operations spending for the previous fiscal year: $761,276. 110 computers available on campus for general student use. A computer is required for all students. A campuswide network can be accessed from student residence rooms and from off campus. Students can access the following: online class registration.

Community Environment: Dakota State University is located in the heart of the Midwest, in Madison, South Dakota, just minutes from Interstates 29 and 90, which are major highways. Two nearby lakes provide the best in outdoor recreation. In the summer, this includes water sports, fishing and camping, followed in the fall and winter by hunting, snowmobiling, cross-country skiing and more. One of South Dakota's finest state parks provides excellent facilities for all of these activities. Cultural events are provided by a local arts association, a summer theater group and through college-sponsored events. Madison is also located just an hour away from the state's largest city, Sioux Falls.

■ **DAKOTA WESLEYAN UNIVERSITY**

1200 W University Ave.

Mitchell, SD 57301-4398

Tel: (605)995-2600; Free: 800-333-8506

Fax: (605)995-2699

E-mail: admissions@dwu.edu

Web Site: www.dwu.edu

Description: Independent United Methodist, comprehensive, coed. Awards associate, bachelor's, and master's degrees. Founded 1885. Setting: 50-acre small town campus. Endowment: $20.9 million. Research spending for the previous fiscal year: $138,654. Educational spending for the previous fiscal year: $5526 per student. Total enrollment: 836. Faculty: 70 (50 full-time, 20 part-time). Student-undergrad faculty ratio is 11:1. 659 applied, 73% were admitted. 9% from top 10% of their high school class, 36% from top quarter, 75% from top half. Full-time: 688 students, 53% women, 47% men. Part-time: 71 students, 63% women, 37% men. Students come from 29 states and territories, 2 other countries, 26% from out-of-state. 1% American Indian or Alaska Native, non-Hispanic/Latino; 2% Hispanic/Latino; 3% Black or African American, non-Hispanic/Latino; 1% Asian, non-Hispanic/Latino; 1% international. 14% 25 or older, 45% live on campus, 12% transferred in. Retention: 67% of full-time freshmen returned the following year. Academic areas with the most degrees conferred: health professions and related sciences; business/marketing; education. Core. Calendar: semesters. Academic remediation for entering students, services for LD students, advanced placement, self-designed majors, honors program, independent study, distance learning, double major, summer session for credit, part-time degree program, co-op programs and internships. Off campus study. Study abroad program. ROTC: Army.

Entrance Requirements: Option: electronic application. Required: high school transcript, SAT or ACT. Recommended: minimum 2 high school GPA. Entrance: moderately difficult. Application deadline: 8/27. Notification: continuous.

Costs Per Year: Application fee: $25. Comprehensive fee: $34,590 includes full-time tuition ($26,700), mandatory fees ($940), and college room and board ($6950). Full-time tuition and fees vary according to course load and location. Room and board charges vary according to board plan and housing facility.

Collegiate Environment: Orientation program. Drama-theater group, choral group, student-run newspaper. Social organizations: 27 open to all. Most popular organizations: Future Teachers Organization, Student Nurses Association, Multi-Culture Club, Human Services Club, Student Ministry Council. Major annual events: Blue and White Days (homecoming), Spring Week, Family Life Conference. Student services: health clinic, personal-psychological counseling. Campus security: 24-hour emergency response devices, student patrols, late night transport-escort service, controlled dormitory access, campus patrol from 2am to 6am by special request only. George and Eleanor McGovern Library plus 1 other. Operations spending for the previous fiscal year: $305,460. 100 computers available on campus for general student use. A campuswide network can be accessed from student residence rooms and from off campus. Students can access the following: online class registration, portal, course management system. Staffed computer lab on campus provides training in use of computers, software, and the Internet.

Community Environment: Located in the James River Valley, Mitchell (population 15,000) is one of the most fertile and diversified agricultural areas in the United States. Products are corn, sorghum, small grain, cattle and hogs. Mitchell is the trading center for the surrounding counties. Community facilities include shopping areas, churches, a library, YMCA, 2 hospitals and a number of the customary civic and service organizations. Recreational activities include boating, fishing, swimming and pheasant hunting.

■ **LAKE AREA TECHNICAL INSTITUTE**

1201 Arrow Ave.

Watertown, SD 57201

Tel: (605)882-5284; Free: 800-657-4344

E-mail: straitl@lakeareatech.edu

Web Site: www.lakeareatech.edu

Description: State-supported, 2-year, coed. Part of South Dakota Department of Education. Awards certificates, diplomas, and terminal associate degrees. Founded 1965. Setting: 40-acre small town campus. Endowment: $2.8 million. Educational spending for the previous fiscal year: $4305 per student. Total enrollment: 2,055. Faculty: 157 (109 full-time, 48 part-time). Student-undergrad faculty ratio is 17:1. Full-time: 1,517 students, 39% women, 61% men. Part-time: 538 students, 64% women, 36% men. Students come from 17 states and territories, 4 other countries, 19% from out-of-state. 2% American Indian or Alaska Native, non-Hispanic/Latino; 2% Hispanic/Latino; 0.7% Black or African American, non-Hispanic/Latino; 1% Asian, non-Hispanic/Latino; 0.3% Native Hawaiian or other Pacific Islander, non-Hispanic/Latino; 0.3% international. 12% 25 or older, 8% transferred in. Core. Calendar: semesters. Academic remediation for entering students, ESL program, services for LD students, advanced placement, independent study, distance learning, double major, summer session for credit, part-time degree program, co-op programs and internships. Off campus study.

Entrance Requirements: Open admission. Option: electronic application. Required: high school transcript. Recommended: ACT. Required for some: essay, interview, ACCUPLACER, TEAS. Entrance: minimally difficult. Application deadline: rolling. Notification: continuous. Transfer credits accepted: Yes. Applicants placed on waiting list: 59. Wait-listed applicants offered admission: 40.

Costs Per Year: Application fee: $25. State resident tuition: $3480 full-time, $116 per credit part-time. Nonresident tuition: $3480 full-time, $116 per credit part-time. Mandatory fees: $2884 full-time, $105 per credit part-time. Full-time tuition and fees vary according to course load and program. Part-time tuition and fees vary according to course load and program.

Collegiate Environment: Orientation program. Social organizations: 6 open to all. Most popular organizations: Campus Crusades, Campus Activities Board, Student Voice, Student Ambassador, SkillsUSA. Major annual events: Career Search Expo, Polar Plunge. Student services: personal-psychological counseling. Campus security: 24-hour emergency response devices, partnership with local police department. Leonard H. Timmerman Library plus 1 other. Books: 2,500 (physical), 250,000 (digital/electronic); Serial titles: 25 (physical); Databases: 40. Weekly public service hours: 58. Operations spending for the previous fiscal year: $135,865. 175 computers available on campus for general student use. Computer purchase/lease plans available. A campuswide network can be accessed from off-campus. Students can access the following: online class registration. Staffed computer lab on campus provides training in use of computers, software, and the Internet.

■ **MITCHELL TECHNICAL INSTITUTE**
1800 E Spruce St.
Mitchell, SD 57301
Tel: (605)995-3024; Free: 800-684-1969
Fax: (605)996-3299
E-mail: clayton.deuter@mitchelltech.edu
Web Site: www.mitchelltech.edu

Description: State-supported, 2-year, coed. Part of South Dakota Board of Technical Education. Awards certificates, diplomas, and terminal associate degrees. Founded 1968. Setting: 90-acre small town campus. Total enrollment: 1,198. Faculty: 77 (70 full-time, 7 part-time). Student-undergrad faculty ratio is 13:1. 926 applied, 60% were admitted. 11% from top 10% of their high school class, 32% from top quarter, 70% from top half. Full-time: 840 students, 30% women, 70% men. Part-time: 358 students, 38% women, 62% men. Students come from 19 states and territories, 10% from out-of-state. 3% American Indian or Alaska Native, non-Hispanic/Latino; 2% Hispanic/Latino; 0.8% Black or African American, non-Hispanic/Latino; 1% Asian, non-Hispanic/Latino; 0.1% Native Hawaiian or other Pacific Islander, non-Hispanic/Latino. 21% 25 or older, 10% transferred in. Retention: 81% of full-time freshmen returned the following year. Core. Calendar: semesters. Academic remediation for entering students, services for LD students, advanced placement, distance learning, double major, summer session for credit, part-time degree program, co-op programs and internships.

Entrance Requirements: Open admission. Option: electronic application. Required: high school transcript, ACCUPLACER. Recommended: minimum 2 high school GPA, ACT. Required for some: essay, interview. Entrance: minimally difficult. Application deadlines: rolling, rolling for nonresidents. Notification: continuous, continuous for nonresidents. SAT Reasoning Test deadline: 9/1. SAT Subject Test deadline: 9/1. Transfer credits accepted: Yes. Applicants placed on waiting list: 0. Wait-listed applicants offered admission: 0.

Costs Per Year: Application fee: $0. State resident tuition: $3712 full-time, $116 per credit hour part-time. Nonresident tuition: $3712 full-time, $116 per credit hour part-time. Mandatory fees: $2912 full-time, $94 per credit hour

part-time. Full-time tuition and fees vary according to course load and program. Part-time tuition and fees vary according to course load and program.

Collegiate Environment: Orientation program. Social organizations: 5 open to all. Most popular organizations: Student Representative Board, SkillsUSA, Student Veterans Organization, Rodeo Club, Diversity Club. Major annual events: Orientation Week, Christmas Party, Spring Picnic. Student services: personal-psychological counseling. Campus security: 24-hour emergency response devices. College housing not available. Center for Student Success. Books: 187 (physical), 929 (digital/electronic); Serial titles: 1 (physical); Databases: 17. Weekly public service hours: 45. 5 computers available on campus for general student use. Computer purchase/lease plans available. A computer is required for all students. A campuswide network can be accessed. Students can access the following: online class registration. Staffed computer lab on campus.

■ **MOUNT MARTY COLLEGE**
1105 W 8th St.
Yankton, SD 57078-3724
Tel: (605)668-1011; Free: 800-658-4552
Fax: (605)668-1607
E-mail: stephanie.moser@mtmc.edu
Web Site: www.mtmc.edu

Description: Independent Roman Catholic, comprehensive, coed. Awards associate, bachelor's, master's, and doctoral degrees and post-master's certificates. Founded 1936. Setting: 80-acre small town campus. Endowment: $26.6 million. Educational spending for the previous fiscal year: $6762 per student. Total enrollment: 1,044. Faculty: 49 (43 full-time, 6 part-time). Student-undergrad faculty ratio is 11:1. 523 applied, 69% were admitted. Full-time: 497 students, 60% women, 40% men. Part-time: 365 students, 52% women, 48% men. Students come from 28 states and territories, 11 other countries, 47% from out-of-state. 3% American Indian or Alaska Native, non-Hispanic/Latino; 8% Hispanic/Latino; 2% Black or African American, non-Hispanic/Latino; 1% Asian, non-Hispanic/Latino; 0.1% Native Hawaiian or other Pacific Islander, non-Hispanic/Latino; 2% international. 7% 25 or older, 75% live on campus, 8% transferred in. Retention: 71% of full-time freshmen returned the following year. Academic areas with the most degrees conferred: health professions and related sciences; business/marketing; education. Core. Calendar: semesters. Academic remediation for entering students, services for LD students, advanced placement, accelerated degree program, self-designed majors, honors program, independent study, distance learning, double major, summer session for credit, part-time degree program, adult/continuing education programs, co-op programs and internships. Off campus study. ROTC: Army (c).

Entrance Requirements: Options: electronic application, early admission, deferred admission. Required: high school transcript, minimum 2 high school GPA, SAT or ACT. Recommended: interview. Entrance: minimally difficult. Application deadline: rolling. Notification: continuous. SAT Reasoning Test deadline: 8/30. SAT Subject Test deadline: 8/30. Transfer credits accepted: Yes.

Costs Per Year: Application fee: $35. Comprehensive fee: $36,271 includes full-time tuition ($25,975), mandatory fees ($2150), and college room and board ($8146). Part-time tuition: $540 per credit hour. Part-time mandatory fees: $45 per credit hour.

Collegiate Environment: Orientation program. Drama-theater group, choral group. Social organizations: 40 open to all. Most popular organizations: Campus Ministry, Student Government Association, Nursing Club, Education Club, Theater Club. Major annual events: Homecoming, Blue and Gold Days, Mission Day. Student services: health clinic, personal-psychological counseling. Campus security: 24-hour emergency response devices and patrols, late night transport-escort service, controlled dormitory access. Freshmen guaranteed college housing. On-campus residence required through senior year. Options: coed, men-only, women-only housing available. Mount Marty College Library. Books: 80,395 (physical), 16,584 (digital/electronic); Serial titles: 171 (physical); Databases: 83. Weekly public service hours: 81; study areas open 24 hours, 5-7 days a week; students can reserve study rooms. Operations spending for the previous fiscal year: $238,038. 8 computers available on campus for general student use. A campuswide network can be accessed. Students can access the following: online class registration. Staffed computer lab on campus provides training in use of computers, software, and the Internet.

Community Environment: Yankton is situated on the Missouri River, 60 miles northwest of Sioux City, Iowa, and 80 miles southwest of Sioux Falls, S.D. The city is located four miles downstream from Gavins Point Dam, and

Lewis and Clark Lake, which provides some of the best fishing, swimming, boating, and picnicking areas in the Midwest. The All-American city served as the first capital of Dakota Territory and is known as the Mother City of the Dakotas. Its 14,000 friendly people take a deep interest in the activities of the college.

■ NATIONAL AMERICAN UNIVERSITY (ELLSWORTH AFB)

1000 Ellsworth St.
Rushmore Ctr., Ste. 2400B
Ellsworth AFB, SD 57706
Tel: (605)718-6550
Web Site: www.national.edu
Description: Proprietary, 4-year, coed. Awards associate degrees. Total enrollment: 209.
Entrance Requirements: Entrance: noncompetitive.

■ NATIONAL AMERICAN UNIVERSITY (RAPID CITY)

5301 Mt. Rushmore Rd.
Rapid City, SD 57701
Tel: (605)394-4800; Free: 800-209-0490
Fax: (605)394-4871
E-mail: abeck@national.edu
Web Site: www.national.edu
Description: Proprietary, 4-year, coed. Part of National College. Awards associate and bachelor's degrees. Founded 1941. Setting: 8-acre urban campus. Endowment: $30,000. Research spending for the previous fiscal year: $35,000. Educational spending for the previous fiscal year: $3320 per student. Total enrollment: 518. Faculty: 47 (13 full-time, 34 part-time). Student-undergrad faculty ratio is 26:1. Full-time: 350 students, 65% women, 35% men. Part-time: 131 students, 63% women, 37% men. Students come from 22 states and territories, 6 other countries, 15% from out-of-state. 55% 25 or older, 21% live on campus, 10% transferred in. Retention: 52% of full-time freshmen returned the following year. Academic areas with the most degrees conferred: business/marketing; health professions and related sciences; computer and information sciences. Core. Calendar: quarters. Academic remediation for entering students, ESL program, services for LD students, advanced placement, accelerated degree program, independent study, distance learning, summer session for credit, part-time degree program, external degree program, adult/continuing education programs, co-op programs and internships. ROTC: Army (c).
Entrance Requirements: Open admission. Options: electronic application, early admission, deferred admission. Recommended: interview, ACT. Required for some: high school transcript. Entrance: noncompetitive. Application deadline: rolling. Notification: continuous.
Collegiate Environment: Orientation program. Social organizations: local fraternities, local sororities; 6% of eligible men and 7% of eligible women are members. Most popular organizations: Student Senate, Phi Beta Lambda, Dormitory Council, Student Association of Legal Assistants, President's Advisory Council. Major annual events: Blood Drives, Community Clean-Up. Student services: personal-psychological counseling. Campus security: 24-hour emergency response devices, controlled dormitory access, part-time security personnel. Jefferson Library. 50 computers available on campus for general student use. A campuswide network can be accessed. Staffed computer lab on campus.
Community Environment: National College is located in a community of about 57,000 residents. Rapid City is a retail hub for several Midwestern states. Rapid City shops, entertainment facilities, and a wide array of dining establishments offer a"big city" feel. A strong Rapid City economy provides many part-time employment opportunities while students are in school. Only 20 minutes away lies one of the most popular tourist areas in the world—Mount Rushmore—which is nestled in the majestic Black Hills. From Rushmore Mall and the Dahl Fine Arts Center to wilderness mountain biking and downhill skiing, Rapid City offers the social and cultural diversity that students desire.

■ NATIONAL AMERICAN UNIVERSITY (SIOUX FALLS)

5801 S Corporate Pl.
Sioux Falls, SD 57108
Tel: (605)336-4600; Free: 800-388-5430
E-mail: lhoutsma@national.edu
Web Site: www.national.edu
Description: Proprietary, 4-year, coed. Part of National College. Awards associate and bachelor's degrees. Founded 1941. Setting: urban campus. Total enrollment: 375. Faculty: 35 (all part-time). 9 applied, 100% were

admitted. Students come from 6 states and territories. 76% 25 or older. Core. Calendar: quarters. Academic remediation for entering students, ESL program, advanced placement, accelerated degree program, distance learning, double major, summer session for credit, part-time degree program, adult/continuing education programs, co-op programs and internships.
Entrance Requirements: Open admission. Options: electronic application, deferred admission. Required: high school transcript, interview. Entrance: noncompetitive. Application deadline: rolling. Notification: continuous.
Collegiate Environment: Orientation program. Campus security: 24-hour emergency response devices. Main library plus 1 other. 60 computers available on campus for general student use. A campuswide network can be accessed. Staffed computer lab on campus.

■ NATIONAL AMERICAN UNIVERSITY (WATERTOWN)

925 29th St. SE
Watertown, SD 57201
Description: Proprietary, 4-year, coed.

■ NORTHERN STATE UNIVERSITY

1200 S Jay St.
Aberdeen, SD 57401-7198
Tel: (605)626-3011; Free: 800-678-5330
Fax: (605)626-3022
E-mail: admissions@northern.edu
Web Site: www.northern.edu
Description: State-supported, comprehensive, coed. Part of South Dakota Board of Regents. Awards associate, bachelor's, and master's degrees. Founded 1901. Setting: 72-acre small town campus. Endowment: $30.8 million. Research spending for the previous fiscal year: $207,696. Educational spending for the previous fiscal year: $8465 per student. Total enrollment: 3,493. Faculty: 102 (91 full-time, 11 part-time). Student-undergrad faculty ratio is 19:1. 1,066 applied, 88% were admitted. 9% from top 10% of their high school class, 29% from top quarter, 63% from top half. 12 valedictorians. Full-time: 1,333 students, 57% women, 43% men. Part-time: 1,718 students, 60% women, 40% men. Students come from 39 states and territories, 35 other countries, 30% from out-of-state. 3% American Indian or Alaska Native, non-Hispanic/Latino; 4% Hispanic/Latino; 2% Black or African American, non-Hispanic/Latino; 2% Asian, non-Hispanic/Latino; 0.2% Native Hawaiian or other Pacific Islander, non-Hispanic/Latino; 4% international. 13% 25 or older, 37% live on campus, 3% transferred in. Retention: 75% of full-time freshmen returned the following year. Academic areas with the most degrees conferred: business/marketing; education; biological/life sciences. Core. Calendar: semesters. Academic remediation for entering students, ESL program, services for LD students, advanced placement, accelerated degree program, self-designed majors, freshman honors college, honors program, independent study, distance learning, double major, summer session for credit, part-time degree program, adult/continuing education programs, co-op programs and internships, graduate courses open to undergrads. Off campus study at National Student Exchange. Study abroad program.
Entrance Requirements: Options: electronic application, early admission, deferred admission, international baccalaureate accepted. Required: high school transcript, minimum 2.6 high school GPA, SAT or ACT. Entrance: minimally difficult. Application deadlines: rolling, rolling for nonresidents. Notification: continuous, continuous for nonresidents. SAT Reasoning Test deadline: 9/1. SAT Subject Test deadline: 9/1. Transfer credits accepted: Yes.
Costs Per Year: Application fee: $20. State resident tuition: $7191 full-time, $240 per credit hour part-time. Nonresident tuition: $10,120 full-time, $337 per credit hour part-time. Mandatory fees: $1089 full-time, $36.30 per credit hour part-time. Full-time tuition and fees vary according to course load, program, and reciprocity agreements. Part-time tuition and fees vary according to course load, program, and reciprocity agreements. College room and board: $7844. College room only: $3640. Room and board charges vary according to board plan and housing facility.
Collegiate Environment: Orientation program. Drama-theater group, choral group, marching band, student-run newspaper. Social organizations: 45 open to all. Major annual events: Gypsy Days (homecoming), I Hate Winter, Commencement. Student services: legal services, health clinic, personal-psychological counseling. Campus security: 24-hour emergency response devices, controlled dormitory access. 853 college housing spaces available; 647 were occupied in 2018-19. Freshmen guaranteed college housing. On-campus residence required through sophomore year. Option: coed housing available. Beulah Williams Library. Books: 156,950 (physical), 15,000

(digital/electronic); Serial titles: 7,000 (physical), 250 (digital/electronic); Databases: 80. Weekly public service hours: 90; students can reserve study rooms. Operations spending for the previous fiscal year: $814,054. 130 computers available on campus for general student use. A computer is required for all students. A campuswide network can be accessed from student residence rooms and from off campus. Students can access the following: online class registration. Staffed computer lab on campus provides training in use of computers, software, and the Internet.

■ OGLALA LAKOTA COLLEGE

490 Piya Wiconi Rd.
Kyle, SD 57752-0490
Tel: (605)455-6000
Fax: (605)455-2787
Web Site: www.olc.edu

Description: State and locally supported, comprehensive, coed. Awards associate, bachelor's, and master's degrees. Founded 1970. Setting: rural campus. Total enrollment: 1,000. Students come from 2 states and territories. 70% 25 or older. Core. Calendar: semesters. Academic remediation for entering students, accelerated degree program, summer session for credit, part-time degree program, adult/continuing education programs, co-op programs and internships. Off campus study at American Indian Higher Education Consortium.

Entrance Requirements: Open admission. Option: early admission. Preference given to Native Americans.

Collegiate Environment: Social organizations: 10 open to all. Oglala Lakota College Learning Resource Center. 65 computers available on campus for general student use.

■ PRESENTATION COLLEGE

1500 N Main St.
Aberdeen, SD 57401-1299
Tel: (605)225-1634; Free: 800-437-6060
Fax: (605)229-8518
E-mail: admit@presentation.edu
Web Site: www.presentation.edu

Description: Independent Roman Catholic, 4-year, coed. Awards associate and bachelor's degrees. Founded 1951. Setting: 100-acre small town campus. Endowment: $7.6 million. Educational spending for the previous fiscal year: $5610 per student. Total enrollment: 748. Faculty: 73 (46 full-time, 27 part-time). Student-undergrad faculty ratio is 10:1. 340 applied, 74% were admitted. Full-time: 465 students, 66% women, 34% men. Part-time: 283 students, 80% women, 20% men. Students come from 23 states and territories, 3 other countries, 57% from out-of-state. 6% American Indian or Alaska Native, non-Hispanic/Latino; 4% Hispanic/Latino; 8% Black or African American, non-Hispanic/Latino; 1% Asian, non-Hispanic/Latino; 0.6% Native Hawaiian or other Pacific Islander, non-Hispanic/Latino; 0.5% international. 40% 25 or older, 21% live on campus, 19% transferred in. Retention: 49% of full-time freshmen returned the following year. Academic areas with the most degrees conferred: health professions and related sciences; business/marketing; public administration and social services. Core. Calendar: semesters. Academic remediation for entering students, advanced placement, accelerated degree program, distance learning, double major, summer session for credit, part-time degree program, external degree program, adult/continuing education programs, co-op programs and internships. Off campus study at Kilian Community College, Sioux Falls, SD.

Entrance Requirements: Option: electronic application. Required: high school transcript, SAT or ACT. Recommended: minimum 2 high school GPA. Required for some: 2 recommendations, college transcripts. Entrance: noncompetitive. Application deadline: rolling. Notification: continuous. SAT Reasoning Test deadline: 8/12. SAT Subject Test deadline: 8/12. Transfer credits accepted: Yes.

Collegiate Environment: Orientation program. Choral group. Social organizations: 17 open to all. Most popular organizations: Wellness/athletics, National Student Nursing Association, Social Work Organization, Rad Tech Organization, Student Ambassadors. Major annual events: Homecoming, Spring Fling. Student services: health clinic, personal-psychological counseling. Campus security: 24-hour emergency response devices, late night transport-escort service, controlled dormitory access. Presentation College Library plus 1 other. Operations spending for the previous fiscal year: $210,763. 35 computers available on campus for general student use. Computer purchase/lease plans available. A computer is required for all students. A campuswide network can be accessed from student residence

rooms. Students can access the following: online class registration. Staffed computer lab on campus provides training in use of computers, software, and the Internet.

Community Environment: Aberdeen is a regional retail and market center with a population of 25,000. It is served by two major U.S. highways, and daily airline service.

■ SINTE GLESKA UNIVERSITY

101 Antelope Lake Cir.
Mission, SD 57555
Tel: (605)856-8100
Fax: (605)747-2098
Web Site: www.sintegleska.edu

Description: Independent, comprehensive, coed. Awards associate, bachelor's, and master's degrees. Founded 1970. Setting: 52-acre rural campus. Total enrollment: 971. 70% 25 or older. Core. Calendar: semesters. Academic remediation for entering students, honors program, distance learning, double major, summer session for credit, part-time degree program, adult/continuing education programs, internships. Off campus study at American Indian Higher Education Consortium.

Entrance Requirements: Open admission. Required: high school transcript. Entrance: noncompetitive. Application deadline: 8/20. Notification: continuous until 8/30.

Collegiate Environment: Student services: personal-psychological counseling, women's center. Campus security: late night transport-escort service. Sinte Gleska University Library.

■ SISSETON-WAHPETON COLLEGE

Old Agency Box 689
Sisseton, SD 57262
Tel: (605)698-3966
Web Site: www.swc.tc

Description: Federally supported, 2-year, coed. Awards certificates, transfer associate, and terminal associate degrees. Founded 1979. Setting: 2-acre rural campus. Total enrollment: 175. Faculty: 30 (10 full-time, 20 part-time). Student-undergrad faculty ratio is 10:1. Full-time: 127 students, 60% women, 40% men. Part-time: 48 students, 63% women, 37% men. 14% from out-of-state. 85% American Indian or Alaska Native, non-Hispanic/Latino; 3% Hispanic/Latino; 5% Black or African American, non-Hispanic/Latino. 21% 25 or older, 2% transferred in. Core. Calendar: semesters. Academic remediation for entering students, double major, summer session for credit, part-time degree program, adult/continuing education programs, co-op programs and internships. Off campus study at members of the American Indian Higher Education Consortium.

Entrance Requirements: Open admission. Required: high school transcript, ACT Compass. Recommended: minimum 2 high school GPA, interview. Required for some: Certificate of Indian Blood for enrolled tribal members. Entrance: noncompetitive. Application deadlines: rolling, 7/8 for nonresidents. Transfer credits accepted: Yes.

Costs Per Year: Application fee: $0. One-time mandatory fee: $540. State resident tuition: $3250 full-time, $125 per credit hour part-time. Nonresident tuition: $3250 full-time, $125 per credit hour part-time. Mandatory fees: $590 full-time, $245 per term part-time. Full-time tuition and fees vary according to class time, course level, course load, degree level, location, program, and student level. Part-time tuition and fees vary according to class time, course level, course load, degree level, location, program, and student level. College room and board: $6500. College room only: $6500. Room and board charges vary according to board plan and student level. Tuition guaranteed not to increase for student's term of enrollment.

Collegiate Environment: Orientation program. Social organizations: 5 open to all. Most popular organizations: AIHEC, AISES, Student Senate, Student Nurses Association, AIBL. Major annual event: AIHEC. Student services: personal-psychological counseling. Campus security: 24-hour emergency response devices. Sisseton-Wahpeton Community College Library. 30 computers available on campus for general student use. Computer purchase/lease plans available. A campuswide network can be accessed. Staffed computer lab on campus (open 24 hours a day) provides training in use of computers, software, and the Internet.

■ SOUTH DAKOTA SCHOOL OF MINES AND TECHNOLOGY

501 E Saint Joseph St.
Rapid City, SD 57701-3995
Tel: (605)394-2511; Free: 800-544-8162
Fax: (605)394-2914

E-mail: admissions@sdsmt.edu

Web Site: www.sdsmt.edu

Description: State-supported, university, coed. Part of South Dakota Board of Regents. Awards associate, bachelor's, master's, and doctoral degrees. Founded 1885. Setting: 120-acre suburban campus. Endowment: $53.7 million. Research spending for the previous fiscal year: $12.5 million. Educational spending for the previous fiscal year: $4390 per student. Total enrollment: 2,859. Faculty: 177 (151 full-time, 26 part-time). Student-undergrad faculty ratio is 15:1. 1,368 applied, 85% were admitted. 24% from top 10% of their high school class, 56% from top quarter, 86% from top half. Full-time: 2,018 students, 20% women, 80% men. Part-time: 467 students, 30% women, 70% men. Students come from 42 states and territories, 27 other countries, 53% from out-of-state. 2% American Indian or Alaska Native, non-Hispanic/Latino; 5% Hispanic/Latino; 2% Black or African American, non-Hispanic/Latino; 1% Asian, non-Hispanic/Latino; 0.1% Native Hawaiian or other Pacific Islander, non-Hispanic/Latino; 3% international. 10% 25 or older, 60% live on campus, 4% transferred in. Retention: 78% of full-time freshmen returned the following year. Academic areas with the most degrees conferred: engineering; computer and information sciences; physical sciences. Core. Calendar: semesters. Academic remediation for entering students, ESL program, services for LD students, advanced placement, honors program, independent study, distance learning, double major, summer session for credit, part-time degree program, adult/continuing education programs, co-op programs and internships, graduate courses open to undergrads. Off campus study. Study abroad program. ROTC: Army.

Entrance Requirements: Options: electronic application, international baccalaureate accepted. Required: high school transcript, SAT or ACT. Recommended: minimum 2.75 high school GPA. Entrance: moderately difficult. Application deadline: rolling. Notification: continuous. SAT Reasoning Test deadline: 8/15. SAT Subject Test deadline: 8/15. Transfer credits accepted: Yes.

Costs Per Year: Application fee: $20. State resident tuition: $10,560 full-time, $249.70 per credit hour part-time. Nonresident tuition: $14,820 full-time, $291.10 per credit hour part-time. Full-time tuition varies according to course level, course load, program, and reciprocity agreements. Part-time tuition varies according to course level, course load, program, and reciprocity agreements. College room and board: $8440. Room and board charges vary according to board plan and housing facility.

Collegiate Environment: Orientation program. Drama-theater group, choral group, student-run newspaper, radio station. Social organizations: 105 open to all; national fraternities, national sororities; 12% of eligible men and 22% of eligible women are members. Most popular organizations: eSports 144, ASME (American Society of Mechanical Engineers), Skid Snowboard Club 115, AIChe 107, ASCE 105. Major annual events: Homecoming/M Week, Engineers' Week, Fall Career Fair. Student services: health clinic, personal-psychological counseling. Campus security: 24-hour emergency response devices and patrols, student patrols, late night transport-escort service, controlled dormitory access. Devereaux Library plus 1 other. Books: 130,971 (physical), 142,661 (digital/electronic); Serial titles: 1,663 (physical), 23,896 (digital/electronic); Databases: 200. Weekly public service hours: 32; students can reserve study rooms. Operations spending for the previous fiscal year: $924,184. 105 computers available on campus for general student use. Computer purchase/lease plans available. A computer is required for all students. A campuswide network can be accessed from student residence rooms and from off campus. Students can access the following: online class registration. Staffed computer lab on campus (open 24 hours a day) provides training in use of computers, software, and the Internet.

Community Environment: Rapid City, founded in 1876, two years after gold was discovered in the Black Hills, is now a trading center and tourist headquarters of the Black Hills area. All commercial transportation is available. Community facilities include many churches, museums, hospitals, a library, radio stations, three TV stations, and a number of the major civic and service organizations.

■ SOUTH DAKOTA STATE UNIVERSITY

Box 2201

Brookings, SD 57007

Tel: (605)688-4121; Free: 800-952-3541

Fax: (605)688-6384

E-mail: sdsu.admissions@sdstate.edu

Web Site: www.sdstate.edu

Description: State-supported, university, coed. Part of South Dakota Board of Regents. Awards associate, bachelor's, master's, and doctoral degrees and post-master's certificates. Founded 1881. Setting: 363-acre small town campus. Total enrollment: 12,613. Faculty: 696 (551 full-time, 145 part-time). Student-undergrad faculty ratio is 17:1. 5,173 applied, 91% were admitted. 14% from top 10% of their high school class, 37% from top quarter, 69% from top half. Full-time: 8,474 students, 50% women, 50% men. Part-time: 2,485 students, 60% women, 40% men. 0.9% American Indian or Alaska Native, non-Hispanic/Latino; 2% Hispanic/Latino; 2% Black or African American, non-Hispanic/Latino; 0.9% Asian, non-Hispanic/Latino; 0.1% Native Hawaiian or other Pacific Islander, non-Hispanic/Latino; 4% international. 6% transferred in. Retention: 79% of full-time freshmen returned the following year. Academic areas with the most degrees conferred: health professions and related sciences; agriculture; social sciences. Core. Calendar: semesters. Academic remediation for entering students, ESL program, services for LD students, advanced placement, accelerated degree program, freshman honors college, honors program, independent study, distance learning, double major, summer session for credit, part-time degree program, adult/continuing education programs, co-op programs and internships, graduate courses open to undergrads. Off campus study at National Student Exchange. Study abroad program. ROTC: Army, Air Force.

Entrance Requirements: Options: electronic application, international baccalaureate accepted. Required: high school transcript, minimum 2.6 high school GPA, SAT or ACT. Entrance: minimally difficult. Application deadline: rolling. Notification: continuous. SAT Reasoning Test deadline: 9/5. Transfer credits accepted: Yes.

Costs Per Year: Application fee: $20. State resident tuition: $7440 full-time, $248 per credit hour part-time. Nonresident tuition: $10,830 full-time, $361 per credit hour part-time. Mandatory fees: $1320 full-time, $44 per credit hour part-time. Full-time tuition and fees vary according to course level, course load, degree level, location, program, and reciprocity agreements. Part-time tuition and fees vary according to course level, course load, degree level, location, program, and reciprocity agreements. College room and board: $7076. College room only: $3832. Room and board charges vary according to board plan and housing facility.

Collegiate Environment: Orientation program. Drama-theater group, choral group, marching band, student-run newspaper, radio station. Social organizations: 200 open to all; national fraternities, national sororities. Major annual events: Hobo Day, Capers, Cavorts. Student services: legal services, health clinic, personal-psychological counseling. Campus security: 24-hour emergency response devices and patrols, student patrols, late night transport-escort service, controlled dormitory access. H. M. Briggs Library. Books: 778,376 (physical), 134,615 (digital/electronic); Serial titles: 19,899 (physical), 19,850 (digital/electronic); Databases: 108. Students can reserve study rooms. Operations spending for the previous fiscal year: $4.3 million. 120 computers available on campus for general student use. A campuswide network can be accessed from student residence rooms and from off campus. Students can access the following: online class registration.

Community Environment: Brookings is located in the eastern part of the state, an agriculturally rich area with diversified farming influenced by research done at South Dakota State University. Located 55 miles from Sioux Falls, the community facilities include a library, 23 churches, an hospital, and many civic and service clubs. Recreational activities include deer and pheasant hunting, golf, and water sports at the center lake region.

■ SOUTHEAST TECHNICAL INSTITUTE

2320 N Career Ave.

Sioux Falls, SD 57107-1301

Tel: (605)367-7624; Free: 800-247-0789

E-mail: scott.dorman@southeasttech.edu

Web Site: www.southeasttech.edu

Description: State-supported, 2-year, coed. Awards certificates, diplomas, and terminal associate degrees. Founded 1968. Setting: 138-acre urban campus. Educational spending for the previous fiscal year: $5351 per student. Total enrollment: 2,244. Faculty: 208 (102 full-time, 106 part-time). Student-undergrad faculty ratio is 15:1. 3,272 applied, 51% were admitted. Full-time: 1,426 students, 43% women, 57% men. Part-time: 818 students, 67% women, 33% men. Students come from 11 states and territories, 10% from out-of-state. 0.4% American Indian or Alaska Native, non-Hispanic/Latino; 4% Hispanic/Latino; 2% Black or African American, non-Hispanic/Latino; 3% Asian, non-Hispanic/Latino. 30% 25 or older, 2% live on campus, 17% transferred in. Retention: 72% of full-time freshmen returned the following year. Calendar: semesters. Academic remediation for entering students, ESL program, services for LD students, advanced placement, independent study, distance learning, double major, summer session for credit, part-time degree program, internships.

Entrance Requirements: Option: electronic application. Required: high school transcript, minimum 2 high school GPA. Recommended: ACT. Required for some: interview, background check, drug screening, ACT. Entrance: minimally difficult. Application deadline: rolling. Notification: continuous. Transfer credits accepted: Yes.

Collegiate Environment: Orientation program. Social organizations: 10 open to all. Most popular organizations: Student Government Association, SkillsUSA. Major annual events: Student Picnic, Movie/Pizza Night, Talent Show. Student services: personal-psychological counseling. Campus security: 24-hour patrols, late night transport-escort service, controlled dormitory access. Southeast Library.

■ **UNIVERSITY OF SIOUX FALLS**
1101 W 22nd St.
Sioux Falls, SD 57105-1699
Tel: (605)331-5000; Free: 800-888-1047
Fax: (605)331-6615
E-mail: admissions@usiouxfalls.edu
Web Site: www.usiouxfalls.edu

Description: Independent American Baptist Churches in the USA, comprehensive, coed. Awards associate, bachelor's, and master's degrees and post-master's certificates. Founded 1883. Setting: 140-acre suburban campus. Endowment: $30.4 million. Educational spending for the previous fiscal year: $6092 per student. Total enrollment: 1,615. Faculty: 122 (60 full-time, 62 part-time). Student-undergrad faculty ratio is 13:1. 2,000 applied, 91% were admitted. 13% from top 10% of their high school class, 37% from top quarter, 71% from top half. 1 National Merit Scholar, 6 valedictorians. Full-time: 1,137 students, 63% women, 37% men. Part-time: 182 students, 58% women, 42% men. Students come from 32 states and territories, 11 other countries, 42% from out-of-state. 0.2% American Indian or Alaska Native, non-Hispanic/Latino; 2% Hispanic/Latino; 6% Black or African American, non-Hispanic/Latino; 1% Asian, non-Hispanic/Latino; 0.2% Native Hawaiian or other Pacific Islander, non-Hispanic/Latino; 1% international. 14% 25 or older, 55% live on campus, 7% transferred in. Retention: 73% of full-time freshmen returned the following year. Academic areas with the most degrees conferred: business/marketing; health professions and related sciences; education. Core. Calendar: 4-1-4. Academic remediation for entering students, services for LD students, advanced placement, accelerated degree program, self-designed majors, honors program, independent study, distance learning, double major, summer session for credit, part-time degree program, adult/continuing education programs, internships, graduate courses open to undergrads. Off campus study at Augustana University (SD). Study abroad program. ROTC: Air Force (c).

Entrance Requirements: Options: electronic application, deferred admission, international baccalaureate accepted. Required: high school transcript, SAT or ACT. Recommended: minimum 2.8 high school GPA. Required for some: essay, 2 recommendations, interview. Entrance: moderately difficult. Application deadline: rolling. Notification: continuous. Transfer credits accepted: Yes.

Costs Per Year: Application fee: $25. Comprehensive fee: $26,460 includes full-time tuition ($18,610), mandatory fees ($300), and college room and board ($7550). College room only: $3970. Part-time tuition: $370 per semester hour.

Collegiate Environment: Orientation program. Drama-theater group, choral group, student-run newspaper, radio station. Social organizations: 50 open to all. Most popular organizations: Campus Ministries, Student Senate, Fellowship of Christian Athletes, Association for Supervision and Curriculum Development, Service Core. Major annual events: Homecoming, Service Day, Campus Olympics. Student services: personal-psychological counseling. Campus security: 24-hour emergency response devices and patrols, student patrols, late night transport-escort service, controlled dormitory access. 749 college housing spaces available; 581 were occupied in 2018-19. Freshmen guaranteed college housing. On-campus residence required through sophomore year. Options: coed, women-only housing available. Norman B. Mears Library. Books: 55,448 (physical), 158,760 (digital/electronic); Serial titles: 361 (physical), 30,000 (digital/electronic); Databases: 58. Weekly public service hours: 78. Operations spending for the previous fiscal year: $296,698. 190 computers available on campus for general student use. A campuswide network can be accessed from student residence rooms and from off campus. Students can access the following: online class registration. Staffed computer lab on campus provides training in use of computers, software, and the Internet.

Community Environment: Sioux Falls, population 139,500, is a commercial and industrial center. Credit card corporations, banking, retailing and meat packing are the leading industries of the community. Air and bus transporta-

tion are available. Community facilities include churches of many denominations, hospitals, an art center, and excellent shopping. Recreation includes all winter sports, water sports, hunting, and fishing. Part-time employment opportunities are excellent.

■ **UNIVERSITY OF SOUTH DAKOTA**
414 E Clark St.
Vermillion, SD 57069
Tel: (605)677-5011; Free: 877-269-6837
Fax: (605)677-6753
E-mail: Travis.Vlasman@usd.edu
Web Site: www.usd.edu

Description: State-supported, university, coed. Part of South Dakota Board of Regents. Awards bachelor's, master's, and doctoral degrees. Founded 1862. Setting: 274-acre small town campus. Endowment: $243.9 million. Research spending for the previous fiscal year: $16.6 million. Educational spending for the previous fiscal year: $9911 per student. Total enrollment: 10,066. Faculty: 682 (386 full-time, 296 part-time). Student-undergrad faculty ratio is 17:1. 4,119 applied, 86% were admitted. 13% from top 10% of their high school class, 37% from top quarter, 68% from top half. Full-time: 4,969 students, 62% women, 38% men. Part-time: 2,621 students, 65% women, 35% men. Students come from 47 states and territories, 51 other countries, 35% from out-of-state. 2% American Indian or Alaska Native, non-Hispanic/Latino; 4% Hispanic/Latino; 3% Black or African American, non-Hispanic/Latino; 1% Asian, non-Hispanic/Latino; 0.1% Native Hawaiian or other Pacific Islander, non-Hispanic/Latino; 2% international. 14% 25 or older, 34% live on campus, 7% transferred in. Retention: 77% of full-time freshmen returned the following year. Academic areas with the most degrees conferred: health professions and related sciences; education; business/marketing. Core. Calendar: semesters. Academic remediation for entering students, ESL program, services for LD students, advanced placement, accelerated degree program, self-designed majors, honors program, independent study, distance learning, double major, summer session for credit, part-time degree program, adult/continuing education programs, internships. Off campus study at National Student Exchange Study Abroad Alternative Week of Off-Campus Learning (AWOL). Study abroad program. ROTC: Army.

Entrance Requirements: Options: electronic application, early admission, international baccalaureate accepted. Required: high school transcript, SAT or ACT, College Prepatory program required for all degree seeking students. Entrance: moderately difficult. Application deadlines: rolling, rolling for nonresidents. Notification: continuous, continuous for nonresidents. SAT Reasoning Test deadline: 8/21. SAT Subject Test deadline: 8/21. Transfer credits accepted: Yes.

Costs Per Year: Application fee: $20. State resident tuition: $7,450 full-time, $248.35 per credit hour part-time. Nonresident tuition: $10,815 full-time, $360.50 per credit hour part-time. Mandatory fees: $1,610 full-time, $53.65 per credit hour part-time. Full-time tuition and fees vary according to location, program, and reciprocity agreements. Part-time tuition and fees vary according to location, program, and reciprocity agreements. College room and board: $8,216. College room only: $4,188. Room and board charges vary according to board plan and housing facility.

Collegiate Environment: Orientation program. Drama-theater group, choral group, marching band, student-run newspaper, radio station. Social organizations: 134 open to all; national fraternities, national sororities; 23% of eligible men and 13% of eligible women are members. Most popular organizations: Dakotathon, International Club, SERVE, Campus Activities Board. Major annual events: Dakota Days, Strollers, Rockfest. Student services: legal services, health clinic, personal-psychological counseling. Campus security: 24-hour emergency response devices and patrols, student patrols, late night transport-escort service, controlled dormitory access. College housing designed to accommodate 2,224 students; 2,230 undergraduates lived in college housing during 2018-19. Freshmen guaranteed college housing. On-campus residence required through sophomore year. Option: coed housing available. I. D. Weeks Library plus 2 others. Books: 528,075 (physical), 152,540 (digital/electronic); Serial titles: 4,739 (physical), 154,738 (digital/electronic); Databases: 230. Weekly public service hours: 103; students can reserve study rooms. Operations spending for the previous fiscal year: $3.6 million. 975 computers available on campus for general student use. A campuswide network can be accessed from student residence rooms and from off campus. Students can access the following: online class registration. Staffed computer lab on campus (open 24 hours a day) provides training in use of computers, software, and the Internet.

Community Environment: Vermillion is situated on a bluff overlooking the

Missouri and Vermillion Rivers and was named for the red clay on the riverbanks. There is a public library, museums, churches of a number of denominations, a hospital, and major civic and service organizations. Shopping facilities are excellent. Part-time employment opportunities are good. There are a number of recreational activities, and hunting and fishing opportunities are excellent.

■ WESTERN DAKOTA TECHNICAL INSTITUTE

800 Mickelson Dr.
Rapid City, SD 57703
Tel: (605)394-4034; Free: 800-544-8765
E-mail: jill.elder@wdt.edu
Web Site: www.wdt.edu

Description: State-supported, 2-year, coed. Awards certificates, diplomas, and terminal associate degrees. Founded 1968. Setting: 5-acre small town campus. Endowment: $187,302. Educational spending for the previous fiscal year: $6569 per student. Total enrollment: 1,049. Faculty: 86 (45 full-time, 41 part-time). Student-undergrad faculty ratio is 13:1. 634 applied, 52% were admitted. 16% from top 10% of their high school class, 36% from top quarter, 84% from top half. Full-time: 613 students, 42% women, 58% men. Part-time: 436 students, 66% women, 34% men. Students come from 13 states and territories, 5% from out-of-state. 13% American Indian or Alaska Native, non-Hispanic/Latino; 5% Hispanic/Latino; 2% Black or African American, non-Hispanic/Latino; 0.8% Asian, non-Hispanic/Latino; 0.2% Native Hawaiian or other Pacific Islander, non-Hispanic/Latino. 37% 25 or older, 11% transferred in. Academic areas with the most degrees conferred: health

professions and related sciences; precision production; mechanic and repair technologies. Core. Calendar: semesters. Academic remediation for entering students, services for LD students, advanced placement, independent study, distance learning, summer session for credit, part-time degree program, internships.

Entrance Requirements: Open admission. Option: electronic application. Required: high school transcript. Recommended: minimum 2 high school GPA, SAT or ACT. Required for some: essay, 3 recommendations, interview. Entrance: noncompetitive. Application deadline: 8/1. Notification: continuous until 8/15. Transfer credits accepted: Yes. Applicants placed on waiting list: 5. Wait-listed applicants offered admission: 3.

Costs Per Year: Application fee: $0. One-time mandatory fee: $170. State resident tuition: $3480 full-time, $116 per credit hour part-time. Nonresident tuition: $3480 full-time, $116 per credit hour part-time. Mandatory fees: $4230 full-time, $131 per credit hour part-time, $150 per term part-time. Full-time tuition and fees vary according to course load and program. Part-time tuition and fees vary according to course load and program.

Collegiate Environment: Orientation program. Campus security: 24-hour video surveillance. Western Dakota Technical Institute Library plus 1 other. Books: 3,500 (physical), 158,080 (digital/electronic); Databases: 12. Weekly public service hours: 48. Operations spending for the previous fiscal year: $89,941. 36 computers available on campus for general student use. A computer is required for all students. A campuswide network can be accessed. Students can access the following: online class registration. Staffed computer lab on campus provides training in use of computers, software, and the Internet.

■ AMERICAN BAPTIST COLLEGE

1800 Baptist World Ctr. Dr.
Nashville, TN 37207
Tel: (615)256-1463
Web Site: www.abcnash.edu

Description: Independent Baptist, 4-year, coed. Awards associate and bachelor's degrees. Founded 1924. Setting: 52-acre urban campus with easy access to Nashville. Endowment: $626,121. Educational spending for the previous fiscal year: $1765 per student. Total enrollment: 152. Faculty: 18 (4 full-time, 14 part-time). Student-undergrad faculty ratio is 12:1. 45 applied, 82% were admitted. Full-time: 114 students, 32% women, 68% men. Part-time: 38 students, 34% women, 66% men. Students come from 12 states and territories, 1 other country. 73% 25 or older, 30% live on campus, 8% transferred in. Retention: 6% of full-time freshmen returned the following year. Core. Calendar: semesters. Academic remediation for entering students, double major, summer session for credit, part-time degree program, adult/continuing education programs. Off campus study.

Entrance Requirements: Open admission. Options: electronic application, deferred admission, international baccalaureate accepted. Required: essay, high school transcript, minimum 2 high school GPA, 2 recommendations, official transcript(s). Required for some: interview. Entrance: noncompetitive. Application deadline: rolling. Notification: continuous. Transfer credits accepted: Yes.

Costs Per Year: Application fee: $30. Comprehensive fee: $13,737 includes full-time tuition ($8760), mandatory fees ($657), and college room and board ($4320). College room only: $2120. Full-time tuition and fees vary according to course load and program. Room and board charges vary according to board plan and housing facility. Part-time tuition: $380 per credit hour. Part-time tuition varies according to course load and program.

Collegiate Environment: Orientation program. Choral group. Social organizations: 6 open to all; national fraternities, local fraternities; 20% of men are members. Most popular organizations: Student Government Association, Vespers Service, Baptist Student Union, Choir, Greek Letter Fraternity and Hoi Adelphoi Fraternity. Major annual events: Garnett-Nabrit Lectures, ABC Days and Discovery Week, Presidential Scholarship Banquet. Student services: health clinic. Campus security: 24-hour emergency response devices and patrols, controlled dormitory access. T. L. Holcolm Library. Books: 14,290 (physical); Serial titles: 2 (physical); Databases: 2. Weekly public service hours: 2; students can reserve study rooms. Operations spending for the previous fiscal year: $63,646. 22 computers available on campus for general student use. A campuswide network can be accessed from student residence rooms and from off campus. Students can access the following: online class registration, IT support person on campus during regular campus hours. Staffed computer lab on campus provides training in use of computers, software, and the Internet.

■ AQUINAS COLLEGE

4210 Harding Pke.
Nashville, TN 37205-2005
Tel: (615)297-7545; Free: 800-649-9956
Fax: (615)297-7970
E-mail: hansomc@aquinascollege.edu
Web Site: www.aquinascollege.edu

Description: Independent Roman Catholic, comprehensive, coed. Administratively affiliated with The Dominican Sisters of the Saint Cecilia Congregation. Awards associate, bachelor's, and master's degrees and post-master's certificates. Founded 1961. Setting: 83-acre urban campus. Endowment: $16.5 million. Educational spending for the previous fiscal year: $10,754 per student. Total enrollment: 384. Faculty: 73 (28 full-time, 45 part-time). Student-undergrad faculty ratio is 8:1. 183 applied, 52% were admitted. 18% from top 10% of their high school class, 45% from top quarter, 73% from top half. Full-time: 196 students, 78% women, 22% men. Part-time: 141 students, 83% women, 17% men. Students come from 26 states and territories, 5 other countries, 23% from out-of-state. 0.3% American Indian or Alaska Native, non-Hispanic/Latino; 4% Hispanic/Latino; 6% Black or African American, non-Hispanic/Latino; 4% Asian, non-Hispanic/Latino; 2% Native Hawaiian or other Pacific Islander, non-Hispanic/Latino; 4% international. 41% 25 or older, 15% live on campus, 17% transferred in. Retention: 73% of full-time freshmen returned the following year. Academic areas with the most degrees conferred: education; health professions and related sciences; business/marketing. Core. Calendar: semesters. Academic remediation for entering students, advanced placement, accelerated degree program, independent study, double major, summer session for credit, part-time degree program, co-op programs and internships. Study abroad program.

Entrance Requirements: Options: electronic application, deferred admission, international baccalaureate accepted. Required: high school transcript, minimum 2.4 high school GPA, SAT or ACT. Required for some: essay. Entrance: minimally difficult. Application deadlines: rolling, rolling for nonresidents. Notification: continuous, continuous for nonresidents. SAT Reasoning Test deadline: 8/15. SAT Subject Test deadline: 8/15. Transfer credits accepted: Yes.

Costs Per Year: Application fee: $0. Tuition: $23,000 full-time, $830 per credit hour part-time. Full-time tuition varies according to course load and program. Part-time tuition varies according to course load and program.

Collegiate Environment: Orientation program. Choral group. Social organizations: 10 open to all; House Life; 33% of eligible men and 20% of eligible women are members. Most popular organizations: Campus Ministry, Student Activities Board, Association for Supervision and Curriculum Development, Association of Student Nurses, Socratic Club. Major annual events: Fall and Spring Festivals, St. Thomas Aquinas Feast Day, House Life Competitions. Student services: personal-psychological counseling. Campus security: 24-hour patrols, late night transport-escort service. Aquinas College Library. Books: 55,934 (physical), 71,042 (digital/electronic); Serial titles: 381 (physical), 17,998 (digital/electronic); Databases: 95. Weekly public service hours: 64. Operations spending for the previous fiscal year: $390,953. 59 computers available on campus for general student use. A campuswide network can be accessed. Students can access the following: online class registration. Staffed computer lab on campus provides training in use of computers, software, and the Internet.

Community Environment: See Vanderbilt University.

■ AUSTIN PEAY STATE UNIVERSITY

601 College St.
Clarksville, TN 37044
Tel: (931)221-7011; Free: 800-844-2778
Fax: (931)221-5994
E-mail: admissions@apsu.edu
Web Site: www.apsu.edu

Description: State-supported, comprehensive, coed. Awards associate, bachelor's, master's, and doctoral degrees and post-master's certificates. Founded 1927. Setting: 169-acre suburban campus with easy access to Nashville. Endowment: $9.9 million. Research spending for the previous fis-

cal year: $2.6 million. Educational spending for the previous fiscal year: $3063 per student. Total enrollment: 10,954. Faculty: 694 (371 full-time, 323 part-time). Student-undergrad faculty ratio is 18:1. 7,704 applied, 94% were admitted. 12% from top 10% of their high school class, 34% from top quarter, 72% from top half. Full-time: 6,993 students, 60% women, 40% men. Part-time: 2,878 students, 56% women, 44% men. Students come from 48 states and territories, 23 other countries, 11% from out-of-state. 0.3% American Indian or Alaska Native, non-Hispanic/Latino; 8% Hispanic/Latino; 22% Black or African American, non-Hispanic/Latino; 1% Asian, non-Hispanic/Latino; 0.3% Native Hawaiian or other Pacific Islander, non-Hispanic/Latino; 0.6% international. 26% 25 or older, 16% live on campus, 9% transferred in. Retention: 66% of full-time freshmen returned the following year. Academic areas with the most degrees conferred: health professions and related sciences; parks and recreation; business/marketing. Core. Calendar: semesters. Academic remediation for entering students, ESL program, services for LD students, advanced placement, accelerated degree program, honors program, independent study, distance learning, double major, summer session for credit, part-time degree program, adult/continuing education programs, co-op programs and internships, graduate courses open to undergrads. Study abroad program. ROTC: Army, Air Force (c).
Entrance Requirements: Options: electronic application, deferred admission, international baccalaureate accepted. Required: high school transcript. Required for some: minimum 2.75 high school GPA, SAT or ACT. Entrance: moderately difficult. Notification: continuous. SAT Reasoning Test deadline: 8/8. SAT Subject Test deadline: 8/8. Transfer credits accepted: Yes.
Costs Per Year: Application fee: $25. One-time mandatory fee: $75. State resident tuition: $6696 full-time, $266 per credit hour part-time. Nonresident tuition: $22,692 full-time, $901 per credit hour part-time. Mandatory fees: $1529 full-time. Full-time tuition and fees vary according to location and program. Part-time tuition varies according to location and program. College room and board: $9170. College room only: $5520. Room and board charges vary according to board plan and housing facility.
Collegiate Environment: Orientation program. Drama-theater group, choral group, marching band, student-run newspaper, radio station. Social organizations: 167 open to all; national fraternities, national sororities; 6% of eligible men and 7% of eligible women are members. Student services: health clinic, personal-psychological counseling. Campus security: 24-hour emergency response devices and patrols, student patrols, late night transport-escort service, controlled dormitory access. 1,803 college housing spaces available; 1,579 were occupied in 2018-19. On-campus residence required in freshman year. Options: coed, men-only, women-only housing available. Felix G. Woodward Library. Books: 196,384 (physical), 397,836 (digital/electronic); Serial titles: 53,295 (physical), 59,165 (digital/electronic); Databases: 299. Weekly public service hours: 109. Operations spending for the previous fiscal year: $3.2 million. 1,400 computers available on campus for general student use. Computer purchase/lease plans available. A campuswide network can be accessed from student residence rooms and from off campus. Students can access the following: online class registration. Staffed computer lab on campus provides training in use of computers.
Community Environment: Clarksville, an urban area, was founded in 1784 and was named for General George Rogers Clark. Bus transportation is available. Community facilities include a number of churches, a hospital, a public library, and major civic and service organizations. Water sports are enjoyed on the Cumberland River and nearby lakes. Some part-time employment is available.

■ **BAPTIST COLLEGE OF HEALTH SCIENCES**
1003 Monroe Ave.
Memphis, TN 38104
Tel: (901)227-4330; Free: 866-575-2247
Web Site: www.bchs.edu
Description: Independent Southern Baptist, comprehensive, coed. Administratively affiliated with Baptist Memorial Health Care. Awards bachelor's and doctoral degrees. Founded 1994. Setting: 17-acre urban campus with easy access to Memphis, TN. Endowment: $45.3 million. Educational spending for the previous fiscal year: $9133 per student. Total enrollment: 1,064. Faculty: (65 full-time). Student-undergrad faculty ratio is 11:1. 462 applied, 59% were admitted. Students come from 13 states and territories, 30% from out-of-state. 3% Hispanic/Latino; 43% Black or African American, non-Hispanic/Latino; 2% Asian, non-Hispanic/Latino. 10% live on campus. Retention: 74% of full-time freshmen returned the following year. Academic area with the most degrees conferred: health professions and related sciences. Core. Calendar: trimesters. Services for LD students,

advanced placement, accelerated degree program, honors program, distance learning, double major, summer session for credit, part-time degree program.
Entrance Requirements: Option: electronic application. Required: high school transcript, minimum 2.75 high school GPA, immunizations, health physical, SAT or ACT. Required for some: interview. Entrance: moderately difficult. SAT Reasoning Test deadline: 5/1. SAT Subject Test deadline: 5/1. Transfer credits accepted: Yes.
Costs Per Year: Application fee: $25. Tuition: $10,560 full-time, $440 per credit hour part-time. Mandatory fees: $1340 full-time. College room only: $2900.
Collegiate Environment: Orientation program. Most popular organizations: Student Government Association, Student Nursing Association, Allied Health Organization. Major annual events: Spiritual Renewal Week, Convocation, Graduation. Student services: health clinic, personal-psychological counseling. Campus security: 24-hour emergency response devices, late night transport-escort service, controlled dormitory access, trained security personnel. 140 college housing spaces available; 100 were occupied in 2018-19. No special consideration for freshman housing applicants. Option: coed housing available. Health Sciences Library. Books: 1,869 (physical), 4,542 (digital/electronic); Serial titles: 3 (physical), 134,650 (digital/electronic); Databases: 46. Students can reserve study rooms. Operations spending for the previous fiscal year: $444,287. 26 computers available on campus for general student use. A campuswide network can be accessed from student residence rooms and from off campus. Students can access the following: online class registration. Staffed computer lab on campus provides training in use of computers.

■ **BELHAVEN UNIVERSITY**
5100 Poplar Ave., Ste. 200
Memphis, TN 38137
Tel: (901)888-3343
Fax: (901)888-0771
Web Site: memphis.belhaven.edu
Description: Independent Presbyterian, comprehensive, coed. Awards associate, bachelor's, and master's degrees. Founded 1997. Calendar: semesters.
Entrance Requirements: Required: high school transcript. Required for some: essay, resume.

■ **BELMONT UNIVERSITY**
1900 Belmont Blvd.
Nashville, TN 37212
Tel: (615)460-6000
E-mail: david.mee@belmont.edu
Web Site: www.belmont.edu
Description: Independent Christian, university, coed. Awards bachelor's, master's, and doctoral degrees and post-master's certificates. Founded 1951. Setting: 77-acre urban campus. Endowment: $107.8 million. Educational spending for the previous fiscal year: $9385 per student. Total enrollment: 8,012. Faculty: 853 (361 full-time, 492 part-time). Student-undergrad faculty ratio is 14:1. 7,737 applied, 81% were admitted. 27% from top 10% of their high school class, 56% from top quarter, 85% from top half. Full-time: 6,161 students, 65% women, 35% men. Part-time: 336 students, 59% women, 41% men. Students come from 51 states and territories, 28 other countries, 70% from out-of-state. 0.3% American Indian or Alaska Native, non-Hispanic/Latino; 5% Hispanic/Latino; 5% Black or African American, non-Hispanic/Latino; 2% Asian, non-Hispanic/Latino; 0.1% Native Hawaiian or other Pacific Islander, non-Hispanic/Latino; 1% international. 6% 25 or older, 52% live on campus, 6% transferred in. Retention: 85% of full-time freshmen returned the following year. Academic areas with the most degrees conferred: visual and performing arts; business/marketing; health professions and related sciences. Core. Calendar: semesters. ESL program, services for LD students, advanced placement, accelerated degree program, self-designed majors, honors program, independent study, distance learning, double major, summer session for credit, part-time degree program, adult/continuing education programs, co-op programs and internships, graduate courses open to undergrads. Off campus study at Cool Springs Center. Study abroad program. ROTC: Army (c), Naval (c), Air Force (c).
Entrance Requirements: Options: electronic application, early admission, deferred admission, international baccalaureate accepted. Required: essay, high school transcript, SAT or ACT. Required for some: interview, resume of activities. Entrance: moderately difficult. Application deadline: 8/1. Notification: continuous. SAT Reasoning Test deadline: 8/1. Transfer credits accepted: Yes.

Costs Per Year: Application fee: $50. Comprehensive fee: $46,430 includes full-time tuition ($32,720), mandatory fees ($1590), and college room and board ($12,120). College room only: $6660. Full-time tuition and fees vary according to course load and location. Room and board charges vary according to board plan and housing facility. Part-time tuition: $1240 per credit hour. Part-time tuition varies according to course load and location.

Collegiate Environment: Orientation program. Drama-theater group, choral group, marching band, student-run newspaper, radio station. Social organizations: 80 open to all; national fraternities, national sororities. Most popular organizations: Service Corp, Alpha Sigma Tau, Phi Mu, Phi Kappa Tau, MOB. Major annual events: Fall Festival, Homecoming, Towering Traditions. Student services: health clinic, personal-psychological counseling, women's center. Campus security: 24-hour emergency response devices and patrols, late night transport-escort service, controlled dormitory access, bicycle patrol. Lila D. Bunch Library plus 1 other. Books: 184,352 (physical), 224,292 (digital/electronic); Serial titles: 1,033 (physical), 94,560 (digital/electronic); Databases: 288. Weekly public service hours: 127; students can reserve study rooms. Operations spending for the previous fiscal year: $2.4 million. 500 computers available on campus for general student use. Computer purchase/lease plans available. A campuswide network can be accessed from student residence rooms and from off campus. Students can access the following: online class registration, individual student information via course management system. Staffed computer lab on campus provides training in use of computers, software, and the Internet.

Community Environment: See Vanderbilt University.

■ **BETHEL UNIVERSITY**
325 Cherry Ave.
McKenzie, TN 38201
Tel: (731)352-4000
Fax: (731)352-4069
E-mail: hodgest@bethelu.edu
Web Site: www.bethelu.edu

Description: Independent Cumberland Presbyterian, comprehensive, coed. Awards associate, bachelor's, and master's degrees. Founded 1842. Setting: 100-acre small town campus. Endowment: $2.9 million. Educational spending for the previous fiscal year: $7327 per student. Total enrollment: 5,553. Faculty: 325 (184 full-time, 141 part-time). Student-undergrad faculty ratio is 14:1. 1,573 applied, 62% were admitted. 2 National Merit Scholars, 2 valedictorians, 8 student government officers. Full-time: 3,606 students, 54% women, 46% men. Part-time: 633 students, 63% women, 37% men. Students come from 25 states and territories, 19 other countries, 9% from out-of-state. 2% Hispanic/Latino; 50% Black or African American, non-Hispanic/Latino; 0.4% Asian, non-Hispanic/Latino; 0.2% Native Hawaiian or other Pacific Islander, non-Hispanic/Latino; 2% international. 55% 25 or older, 29% live on campus, 1% transferred in. Retention: 64% of full-time freshmen returned the following year. Academic areas with the most degrees conferred: business/marketing; homeland security, law enforcement, firefighting, and protective services; education. Core. Calendar: semesters. Academic remediation for entering students, services for LD students, advanced placement, accelerated degree program, self-designed majors, honors program, independent study, distance learning, double major, summer session for credit, part-time degree program, external degree program, adult/continuing education programs, co-op programs and internships, graduate courses open to undergrads. Off campus study.

Entrance Requirements: Open admission for non-traditional undergraduate program. Options: electronic application, early admission, deferred admission. Required: high school transcript, minimum 2 high school GPA. Recommended: SAT or ACT. Required for some: essay, interview. Entrance: minimally difficult. Application deadline: rolling. Notification: continuous. SAT Reasoning Test deadline: 8/1. SAT Subject Test deadline: 8/1. Transfer credits accepted: Yes.

Costs Per Year: Application fee: $30. Comprehensive fee: $25,750 includes full-time tuition ($15,292), mandatory fees ($1260), and college room and board ($9198). College room only: $5814. Full-time tuition and fees vary according to course load and program. Room and board charges vary according to board plan and housing facility. Part-time tuition: $462 per credit hour. Part-time mandatory fees: $53 per credit hour. Part-time tuition and fees vary according to course load and program.

Collegiate Environment: Orientation program. Drama-theater group, choral group, marching band. Social organizations: 17 open to all; local fraternities, local sororities; 20% of eligible men and 15% of eligible women are members. Most popular organizations: Campus Crusade for Christ, STEA (Education), Student Government Association, Students in Free Enterprise

(SIFE), Arete. Major annual events: Convocation, School-Wide Dances, Homecoming. Student services: personal-psychological counseling. Campus security: night patrols by trained security personnel. Burroughs Learning Center plus 1 other. Books: 24,618 (physical), 175,995 (digital/electronic); Serial titles: 26 (physical), 58,233 (digital/electronic); Databases: 92. Students can reserve study rooms. Operations spending for the previous fiscal year: $291,142. 12 computers available on campus for general student use. Computer purchase/lease plans available. A computer is required for all students. A campuswide network can be accessed from student residence rooms. Students can access the following: online class registration. Staffed computer lab on campus provides training in use of computers, software, and the Internet.

■ **BRYAN COLLEGE**
721 Bryan Dr.
Dayton, TN 37321
Tel: (423)775-2041; Free: 800-277-9522
Fax: (423)775-7330
E-mail: admissions@bryan.edu
Web Site: www.bryan.edu

Description: Independent interdenominational, comprehensive, coed. Awards associate, bachelor's, and master's degrees. Founded 1930. Setting: 130-acre small town campus. Total enrollment: 1,592. Faculty: 120 (40 full-time, 80 part-time). Student-undergrad faculty ratio is 15:1. 679 applied, 54% were admitted. 22% from top 10% of their high school class, 44% from top quarter, 89% from top half. Full-time: 802 students, 52% women, 48% men. Part-time: 599 students, 57% women, 43% men. 68% from out-of-state. 0.6% American Indian or Alaska Native, non-Hispanic/Latino; 5% Hispanic/Latino; 6% Black or African American, non-Hispanic/Latino; 0.8% Asian, non-Hispanic/Latino; 5% international. 1% 25 or older, 72% live on campus, 3% transferred in. Retention: 67% of full-time freshmen returned the following year. Academic areas with the most degrees conferred: business/marketing; psychology; education. Core. Calendar: semesters. Academic remediation for entering students, services for LD students, advanced placement, honors program, independent study, distance learning, double major, summer session for credit, part-time degree program, adult/continuing education programs, internships. Off campus study at CCCU Best Semesters: Nashville, Los Angeles, DC. Study abroad program.

Entrance Requirements: Options: electronic application, early action, deferred admission, international baccalaureate accepted. Required: essay, high school transcript, minimum 2 high school GPA, 3 recommendations, minimum ACT score of 18 or RSAT of 940, SAT or ACT. Required for some: interview. Entrance: moderately difficult. Application deadlines: rolling, 5/1 for early action. Notification: continuous, rolling for early action. SAT Reasoning Test deadline: 8/1. Transfer credits accepted: Yes.

Costs Per Year: Application fee: $35. Comprehensive fee: $34,300 includes full-time tuition ($26,800) and college room and board ($7500). Room and board charges vary according to housing facility. Part-time tuition: $1200 per credit hour.

Collegiate Environment: Orientation program. Drama-theater group, choral group, student-run newspaper. Most popular organizations: Practical Christian Involvement (PCI), International Students Association, Rugby club, Nutella Club, Navigators. Major annual events: All College Picnic, Midnight Cruise, Spring Banquet. Student services: health clinic, personal-psychological counseling. Campus security: controlled dormitory access, police patrols, night watch. Bryan College Library.

Community Environment: Dayton is located 38 miles from Chattanooga, enjoying a very desirable climate the year round. Air and bus transportation are convenient. Community facilities include some 20 churches representing Protestant and Roman Catholic faiths, a public library, a hospital, and motels. TVA lakes provide fishing and water sports. Part-time employment is available for students. The East Tennessee Strawberry Festival is held in May.

■ **CARSON-NEWMAN UNIVERSITY**
1646 Russell Ave.
Jefferson City, TN 37760
Tel: (865)471-2000; Free: 800-678-9061
Fax: (865)471-3502
E-mail: cnadmiss@cn.edu
Web Site: www.cn.edu

Description: Independent Southern Baptist, comprehensive, coed. Awards associate, bachelor's, master's, and doctoral degrees and post-master's certificates. Founded 1851. Setting: 90-acre small town campus with easy access to Knoxville. Endowment: $54.6 million. Educational spending for the previous fiscal year: $4909 per student. Total enrollment: 2,560. Faculty: 247 (121 full-time, 126 part-time). Student-undergrad faculty ratio is 13:1. 3,736 applied, 66% were admitted. Full-time: 1,661 students, 59% women, 41% men. Part-time: 113 students, 64% women, 36% men. 19% from out-of-state. 0.7% American Indian or Alaska Native, non-Hispanic/Latino; 3% Hispanic/Latino; 9% Black or African American, non-Hispanic/Latino; 0.7% Asian, non-Hispanic/Latino; 0.1% Native Hawaiian or other Pacific Islander, non-Hispanic/Latino; 3% international. 6% 25 or older, 49% live on campus, 6% transferred in. Retention: 63% of full-time freshmen returned the following year. Academic areas with the most degrees conferred: business/marketing; health professions and related sciences; education. Core. Calendar: semesters. Academic remediation for entering students, ESL program, services for LD students, advanced placement, accelerated degree program, self-designed majors, honors program, summer session for credit, part-time degree program, adult/continuing education programs, internships, graduate courses open to undergrads. Off campus study. Study abroad program. ROTC: Army.

Entrance Requirements: Options: electronic application, deferred admission, international baccalaureate accepted. Required: high school transcript, minimum 2.25 high school GPA, medical history, SAT or ACT. Recommended: interview. Required for some: essay. Entrance: moderately difficult. Notification: continuous.

Costs Per Year: Comprehensive fee: $36,710 includes full-time tuition ($26,700), mandatory fees ($1200), and college room and board ($8810). College room only: $3930. Part-time tuition: $1090 per credit hour.

Collegiate Environment: Orientation program. Drama-theater group, choral group, marching band, student-run newspaper. Social organizations: national fraternities, national sororities, local fraternities, local sororities. Most popular organizations: Baptist Student Union, Fellowship of Christian Athletes, Student Government Association, Student Ambassadors Association, Columbians. Major annual events: Welcome Week, Beach Fest, Homecoming. Student services: health clinic, personal-psychological counseling. Campus security: 24-hour emergency response devices and patrols, late night transport-escort service, controlled dormitory access. Freshmen guaranteed college housing. On-campus residence required through junior year. Options: men-only, women-only housing available. Stephens-Burnett Library plus 3 others. Study areas open 24 hours, 5-7 days a week; students can reserve study rooms. Operations spending for the previous fiscal year: $811,761. 200 computers available on campus for general student use. A campuswide network can be accessed from student residence rooms and from off campus. Students can access the following: online class registration. Staffed computer lab on campus provides training in use of computers and software.

Community Environment: Jefferson City is located 27 miles from Knoxville, a city of approximately 400,000. Plane and bus transportation are available. Recreational activities include fishing, water skiing, swimming, and boating at Cherokee and Douglas Lakes, a short drive away. Skiing is available in the Great Smoky Mountains National Park. Part-time employment opportunities are available.

■ **CHATTANOOGA COLLEGE-MEDICAL, DENTAL AND TECHNICAL CAREERS**
248 Northgate Mall Dr., Ste. 130
Chattanooga, TN 37415
Tel: (423)624-0078; Free: 877-313-2373
Web Site: www.chattanoogacollege.edu
Description: Proprietary, 2-year, coed. Awards transfer associate degrees. Setting: urban campus. Total enrollment: 330.
Entrance Requirements: Open admission.

■ **CHATTANOOGA STATE COMMUNITY COLLEGE**
4501 Amnicola Hwy.
Chattanooga, TN 37406-1097
Tel: (423)697-4400; Free: 866-547-3733
Fax: (423)697-4709
E-mail: brad.mccormick@chattanoogastate.edu
Web Site: www.chattanoogastate.edu
Description: State-supported, 2-year, coed. Part of Tennessee Board of Regents. Awards certificates, diplomas, transfer associate, and terminal associate degrees. Founded 1965. Setting: 100-acre urban campus. Endowment: $6.8 million. Educational spending for the previous fiscal year: $2224 per student. Total enrollment: 10,438. Faculty: 699 (224 full-time, 475 part-time). Student-undergrad faculty ratio is 19:1. 1,758 applied, 100% were

admitted. Full-time: 1,061 students, 56% women, 44% men. Part-time: 525 students, 59% women, 41% men. Students come from 23 states and territories, 9 other countries, 11% from out-of-state. 0.2% American Indian or Alaska Native, non-Hispanic/Latino; 2% Hispanic/Latino; 18% Black or African American, non-Hispanic/Latino; 1% Asian, non-Hispanic/Latino. 41% 25 or older, 210% transferred in. Core. Calendar: semesters. Academic remediation for entering students, services for LD students, advanced placement, accelerated degree program, honors program, independent study, distance learning, double major, summer session for credit, part-time degree program, external degree program, adult/continuing education programs, co-op programs and internships.

Entrance Requirements: Open admission. Options: electronic application, early admission, deferred admission. Recommended: high school transcript. Required for some: high school transcript, interview. Entrance: noncompetitive. Application deadline: rolling. Notification: continuous. Transfer credits accepted: Yes.

Costs Per Year: Application fee: $15. State resident tuition: $3936 full-time, $164 per credit hour part-time. Nonresident tuition: $19,251 full-time, $676 per credit hour part-time. Mandatory fees: $319 full-time, $19.40 per credit hour part-time. Full-time tuition and fees vary according to course load. Part-time tuition and fees vary according to course load.

Collegiate Environment: Orientation program. Drama-theater group, choral group, student-run newspaper. Social organizations: 35 open to all. Most popular organizations: Black Student Association, Adult Connections, Human Services Specialists, Student Government Association, Student Nurses Association. Major annual events: Fun in the Sun, Oktoberfest, Wellness Festival. Student services: personal-psychological counseling, women's center. Campus security: 24-hour emergency response devices and patrols, late night transport-escort service. Augusta R. Kolwyck Library. Operations spending for the previous fiscal year: $203,619. 500 computers available on campus for general student use. A campuswide network can be accessed from off-campus. Students can access the following: online class registration. Staffed computer lab on campus provides training in use of computers, software, and the Internet.

Community Environment: Located in southeastern Tennessee on the Tennessee River, Chattanooga is an important industrial center with over 500 manufacturing plants. All forms of commercial transportation are convenient. Part-time employment is available. Recreational facilities are plentiful, Chickamauga Lake, formed by the TVA dam, provides a wonderful place for water sports, and fishing; also there are other lakes, rivers and streams, and Harrison Bay State Park and Hamilton County State Park for other activities. Chattanooga has a number of city parks, and five golf courses for activities within the city. Some points of interest are Lookout Mountain, Lookout Mountain Incline Railway, Rock City Gardens, the Ruby Falls-Lookout Mountain Caves, and the Chattanooga Choo-Choo.

■ **CHRISTIAN BROTHERS UNIVERSITY**
650 E Pky. S
Memphis, TN 38104-5581
Tel: (901)321-3000; Free: 877-321-4CBU
Fax: (901)321-3202
E-mail: admissions@cbu.edu
Web Site: www.cbu.edu
Description: Independent Roman Catholic, comprehensive, coed. Awards associate, bachelor's, and master's degrees. Founded 1871. Setting: 75-acre urban campus with easy access to Memphis. Endowment: $38.6 million. Educational spending for the previous fiscal year: $6744 per student. Total enrollment: 1,888. Faculty: 194 (105 full-time, 89 part-time). Student-undergrad faculty ratio is 13:1. 2,810 applied, 56% were admitted. 28% from top 10% of their high school class, 61% from top quarter, 85% from top half. Full-time: 1,476 students, 50% women, 50% men. Part-time: 198 students, 58% women, 42% men. Students come from 28 states and territories, 30 other countries, 25% from out-of-state. 0.8% American Indian or Alaska Native, non-Hispanic/Latino; 8% Hispanic/Latino; 26% Black or African American, non-Hispanic/Latino; 5% Asian, non-Hispanic/Latino; 0.1% Native Hawaiian or other Pacific Islander, non-Hispanic/Latino; 4% international. 13% 25 or older, 40% live on campus, 4% transferred in. Retention: 79% of full-time freshmen returned the following year. Academic areas with the most degrees conferred: business/marketing; engineering; psychology. Core. Calendar: semesters. Services for LD students, advanced placement, accelerated degree program, self-designed majors, honors program, independent study, distance learning, double major, summer session for credit, part-time degree program, adult/continuing education programs, co-op programs and internships, graduate courses open to undergrads. Study abroad program. ROTC: Army (c), Naval (c), Air Force (c).

Entrance Requirements: Options: electronic application, deferred admission, international baccalaureate accepted. Required: essay, high school transcript, minimum 2 high school GPA, SAT or ACT. Recommended: interview. Required for some: 2 recommendations. Entrance: moderately difficult. Application deadline: rolling for nonresidents. Notification: 12/1, continuous for nonresidents. SAT Reasoning Test deadline: 5/1. Transfer credits accepted: Yes.

Costs Per Year: Application fee: $25. Comprehensive fee: $40,220 includes full-time tuition ($31,900), mandatory fees ($920), and college room and board ($7400). Full-time tuition and fees vary according to class time, course load, and program. Room and board charges vary according to housing facility. Part-time tuition: $1135 per credit hour. Part-time mandatory fees: $215 per term. Part-time tuition and fees vary according to class time, course load, and program.

Collegiate Environment: Orientation program. Choral group. Social organizations: 37 open to all; national fraternities, national sororities, local fraternities, local sororities; 25% of eligible men and 19% of eligible women are members. Most popular organizations: Black Student Association, Tri-Beta, Hola CBU, Delta Sigma Pi. Major annual events: Homecoming Weekend, Sofapalooza. Student services: health clinic, personal-psychological counseling. Campus security: 24-hour emergency response devices and patrols, late night transport-escort service, controlled dormitory access. 550 college housing spaces available; all were occupied in 2018-19. Freshmen guaranteed college housing. On-campus residence required through sophomore year. Options: coed, men-only, women-only housing available. Plough Memorial Library and Media Center. Books: 69,362 (physical), 180,750 (digital/electronic); Serial titles: 111 (physical), 39 (digital/electronic); Databases: 25. Weekly public service hours: 70; students can reserve study rooms. Operations spending for the previous fiscal year: $645,281. 310 computers available on campus for general student use. A campuswide network can be accessed from student residence rooms and from off campus. Students can access the following: online class registration. Staffed computer lab on campus provides training in use of computers, software, and the Internet.

Community Environment: See University of Memphis.

■ **CLEVELAND STATE COMMUNITY COLLEGE**
PO Box 3570
Cleveland, TN 37320-3570
Tel: (423)472-7141; Free: 800-604-2722
Fax: (423)478-6255
E-mail: sbayne@clevelandstatecc.edu
Web Site: www.clevelandstatecc.edu

Description: State-supported, 2-year, coed. Part of Tennessee Board of Regents. Awards certificates, transfer associate, and terminal associate degrees. Founded 1967. Setting: 83-acre suburban campus. Endowment: $8.8 million. Educational spending for the previous fiscal year: $4942 per student. Total enrollment: 3,264. Faculty: 212 (73 full-time, 141 part-time). Student-undergrad faculty ratio is 19:1. 1,830 applied. Full-time: 1,656 students, 54% women, 46% men. Part-time: 1,608 students, 61% women, 39% men. Students come from 6 states and territories, 1% from out-of-state. 0.2% American Indian or Alaska Native, non-Hispanic/Latino; 5% Hispanic/Latino; 6% Black or African American, non-Hispanic/Latino; 1% Asian, non-Hispanic/Latino; 0.2% Native Hawaiian or other Pacific Islander, non-Hispanic/Latino; 0.3% international. 24% 25 or older, 6% transferred in. Core. Calendar: semesters. Academic remediation for entering students, services for LD students, advanced placement, honors program, independent study, distance learning, double major, summer session for credit, part-time degree program, external degree program, adult/continuing education programs, co-op programs and internships. Off campus study.

Entrance Requirements: Open admission. Options: electronic application, early admission, deferred admission. Required: high school transcript. Entrance: noncompetitive. Application deadline: 8/15 for nonresidents. Notification: continuous. Transfer credits accepted: Yes.

Costs Per Year: Application fee: $0. State resident tuition: $4140 full-time, $164 per credit hour part-time. Nonresident tuition: $17,046 full-time, $676 per credit hour part-time. Mandatory fees: $299 full-time, $14.25 per credit hour part-time, $37 per term part-time. Full-time tuition and fees vary according to course load. Part-time tuition and fees vary according to course load.

Collegiate Environment: Orientation program. Choral group. Social organizations: 20 open to all. Most popular organizations: Human Services/Social Work, Computer-Aided Design, Phi Theta Kappa, Student Nursing Association, Early Childhood Education. Major annual events: Career Fair, Octoberfest, Multicultural Fair. Student services: personal-psychological

counseling. Campus security: 24-hour emergency response devices and patrols. College housing not available. Cleveland State Community College Library plus 1 other. Books: 50,426 (physical), 6,533 (digital/electronic); Serial titles: 426 (physical); Databases: 75. Operations spending for the previous fiscal year: $313,668. 1,011 computers available on campus for general student use. A campuswide network can be accessed from off-campus. Students can access the following: online class registration. Staffed computer lab on campus provides training in use of computers, software, and the Internet.

Community Environment: Cleveland was first settled in 1837 and served as headquarters for both General Grant and General Sherman during the Civil War. The city is in the heart of the great Tennessee Valley and is the gateway to the awe inspiring Cherokee National Forest. The climate is mild-temperate, long warm summers, and short mild winters. All forms of commercial transportation are available. The community facilities include a public library, many churches representing all denominations, YMCA, a hospital, community theatre, concert series, and a number of the usual civic and service organizations. Nearby, TVA lakes offer facilities for swimming, fishing, boating, and skiing; the city facilities provide for other activities such as tennis and golf. Part-time employment is available.

■ **COLUMBIA STATE COMMUNITY COLLEGE**
1665 Hampshire Pke.
Columbia, TN 38401
Tel: (931)540-2722
Fax: (931)540-2535
E-mail: scruggs@coscc.cc.tn.us
Web Site: www.columbiastate.edu

Description: State-supported, 2-year, coed. Awards certificates, transfer associate, and terminal associate degrees. Founded 1966. Setting: 179-acre small town campus with easy access to Nashville. Total enrollment: 4,633. 1,093 applied, 100% were admitted. 33% 25 or older. Core. Calendar: semesters. Academic remediation for entering students, services for LD students, advanced placement, honors program, double major, summer session for credit, part-time degree program, adult/continuing education programs.

Entrance Requirements: Option: early admission. Required: high school transcript. Entrance: noncompetitive. Application deadline: rolling.

Costs Per Year: Application fee: $10. State resident tuition: $3936 full-time, $164 per credit hour part-time. Nonresident tuition: $16,224 full-time, $676 per credit hour part-time. Mandatory fees: $333 full-time, $10 per credit hour part-time, $54 per term part-time. Full-time tuition and fees vary according to course load and program. Part-time tuition and fees vary according to program.

Collegiate Environment: Orientation program. Drama-theater group. Student services: health clinic, personal-psychological counseling. Campus security: 24-hour patrols. John W. Finney Memorial Learning Resources Center.

Community Environment: A metropolitan community with temperate climate, Columbia is the boyhood home of James K. Polk. In Bluegrass country, it is noted for its diversified industry and agriculture. Particularly notable are the phosphate industry, and the Saturn automobile plant. Numerous civic and service organizations and excellent shopping facilities are part of the community. Outstanding recreational facilities include city parks, tennis courts, swimming pools, golf courses, and many TVA lakes for swimming, boating, fishing, and skiing. The National Tennessee Walking Horse Spring Jubilee is held each May in Maury County Park, three miles west. The Maury County Fair is an annual event. There are good opportunities for part-time employment.

■ **CONCORDE CAREER COLLEGE**
5100 Poplar Ave.
Ste. 132
Memphis, TN 38137
Tel: (901)761-9494
Fax: (901)761-3293
E-mail: dvickers@concorde.edu
Web Site: www.concorde.edu

Description: Proprietary, 2-year, coed. Awards certificates and terminal associate degrees. Founded 1969. Total enrollment: 1,113. Student-undergrad faculty ratio is 24:1. 383 applied, 100% were admitted. 2% from out-of-state. 57% 25 or older.

Entrance Requirements: Required: high school transcript.

■ CUMBERLAND UNIVERSITY
1 Cumberland Sq.
Lebanon, TN 37087
Tel: (615)444-2562; Free: 800-467-0562
Fax: (615)444-2569
E-mail: admissions@cumberland.edu
Web Site: www.cumberland.edu
Description: Independent, comprehensive, coed. Awards associate, bachelor's, and master's degrees. Founded 1842. Setting: 44-acre small town campus with easy access to Nashville. Endowment: $11.5 million. Educational spending for the previous fiscal year: $5404 per student. Total enrollment: 1,481. Faculty: 159 (56 full-time, 103 part-time). Student-undergrad faculty ratio is 14:1. 713 applied, 46% were admitted. 20% from top 10% of their high school class, 34% from top quarter, 74% from top half. Full-time: 984 students, 55% women, 45% men. Part-time: 270 students, 69% women, 31% men. Students come from 31 states and territories, 19 other countries, 83% from out-of-state. 0.3% American Indian or Alaska Native, non-Hispanic/Latino; 3% Hispanic/Latino; 12% Black or African American, non-Hispanic/Latino; 0.9% Asian, non-Hispanic/Latino; 3% international. 27% 25 or older, 30% live on campus, 18% transferred in. Retention: 62% of full-time freshmen returned the following year. Academic areas with the most degrees conferred: health professions and related sciences; education; business/marketing. Core. Calendar: semesters. Academic remediation for entering students, services for LD students, advanced placement, accelerated degree program, freshman honors college, honors program, double major, summer session for credit, part-time degree program, adult/continuing education programs, co-op programs and internships, graduate courses open to undergrads. ROTC: Army.
Entrance Requirements: Options: electronic application, deferred admission, international baccalaureate accepted. Required: high school transcript, SAT or ACT. Recommended: essay, minimum 3 high school GPA, SAT. Required for some: 3 recommendations. Entrance: moderately difficult. Application deadline: rolling. Notification: continuous.
Costs Per Year: Application fee: $25. One-time mandatory fee: $100. Comprehensive fee: $31,491 includes full-time tuition ($21,841), mandatory fees ($1050), and college room and board ($8600). Full-time tuition and fees vary according to degree level. Room and board charges vary according to housing facility. Part-time tuition: $910 per credit hour. Part-time mandatory fees: $155 per term. Part-time tuition and fees vary according to course load and degree level.
Collegiate Environment: Orientation program. Drama-theater group, choral group, marching band, student-run newspaper, radio station. Social organizations: 15 open to all; national fraternities, national sororities; 6% of eligible men and 3% of eligible women are members. Most popular organizations: African-American Student Association, Baptist Collegiate Ministry, Law and Government Club, Student Government Association, Student Nurses' Association. Major annual events: Homecoming, Spring Fling Week, Coming Home. Student services: personal-psychological counseling. Campus security: 24-hour emergency response devices and patrols, late night transport-escort service. Doris and Harry Vise Library. Operations spending for the previous fiscal year: $362,273. 150 computers available on campus for general student use. A campuswide network can be accessed from student residence rooms and from off campus. Staffed computer lab on campus provides training in use of computers and software.
Community Environment: Named for the Biblical Lebanon because of the tall cedars found in the area. There are TVA Lakes on three sides of the town, and the Cedars of Lebanon State Park is on the fourth side. Bus transportation is available. Nashville Airport is 25 miles away. Community facilities include three libraries, many churches of major denominations, hospitals and clinic, four major shopping areas and a number of the civic and service organizations. Recreational facilities are excellent for fishing, boating, hunting, swimming, and water skiing.

■ DAYMAR COLLEGE (CLARKSVILLE)
2691 Trenton Rd.
Clarksville, TN 37040
Tel: (931)552-7600
Fax: (931)552-3624
Web Site: www.daymarcollege.edu
Description: Proprietary, primarily 2-year, coed. Awards certificates, diplomas, transfer associate, terminal associate, and bachelor's degrees. Founded 1987. Setting: small town campus. Total enrollment: 532. Faculty: 39 (20 full-time, 19 part-time). Student-undergrad faculty ratio is 7:1. Full-time: 381 students, 78% women, 22% men. Part-time: 151 students, 80%

women, 20% men. Students come from 12 states and territories, 2 other countries, 16% from out-of-state. 62% 25 or older. Core. Calendar: quarters. Services for LD students, honors program, independent study, distance learning, double major, part-time degree program, co-op programs and internships.
Entrance Requirements: Open admission. Required: high school transcript, interview. Entrance: noncompetitive. Application deadline: rolling. Notification: continuous. Transfer credits accepted: Yes.
Collegiate Environment: Orientation program. Social organizations: honor society. Major annual events: Spring Softball League, Annual Pic-Nic, Fall Festival.

■ DAYMAR COLLEGE (MURFREESBORO)
415 Golden Bear Ct.
Murfreesboro, TN 37128
Tel: (615)217-9347
Web Site: www.daymarcollege.edu
Description: Proprietary, primarily 2-year, coed. Awards certificates, transfer associate, and bachelor's degrees.

■ DAYMAR COLLEGE (NASHVILLE)
560 Royal Pky.
Nashville, TN 37214
Tel: (615)361-7555
Web Site: www.daymarcollege.edu
Description: Proprietary, 2-year, coed. Awards transfer associate and terminal associate degrees. Founded 1884. Setting: 5-acre suburban campus. Total enrollment: 286. 52% 25 or older. Core. Calendar: semesters. Academic remediation for entering students, summer session for credit, part-time degree program, internships.
Entrance Requirements: Open admission. Option: deferred admission. Required: high school transcript. Entrance: noncompetitive. Application deadline: rolling. Notification: continuous.
Collegiate Environment: Student-run newspaper. Student services: personal-psychological counseling. Campus security: 24-hour emergency response devices.

■ DEVRY UNIVERSITY-NASHVILLE CAMPUS
3343 Perimeter Hill Dr., Ste. 200
Nashville, TN 37211
Tel: (615)445-3456; Free: 866-338-7934
Web Site: www.devry.edu
Description: Proprietary, comprehensive, coed. Awards associate, bachelor's, and master's degrees.
Entrance Requirements: Application deadline: rolling. Notification: continuous.

■ DYERSBURG STATE COMMUNITY COLLEGE
1510 Lake Rd.
Dyersburg, TN 38024
Tel: (731)286-3200
Fax: (731)286-3325
E-mail: page@dscc.edu
Web Site: www.dscc.edu
Description: State-supported, 2-year, coed. Part of Tennessee Board of Regents. Awards certificates, transfer associate, and terminal associate degrees. Founded 1969. Setting: 115-acre small town campus with easy access to Memphis. Endowment: $4 million. Total enrollment: 2,816. Faculty: 130 (53 full-time, 77 part-time). Student-undergrad faculty ratio is 21:1. Full-time: 1,253 students, 64% women, 36% men. Part-time: 1,563 students, 67% women, 33% men. Students come from 4 states and territories, 1 other country, 0.01% from out-of-state. 0.4% American Indian or Alaska Native, non-Hispanic/Latino; 3% Hispanic/Latino; 19% Black or African American, non-Hispanic/Latino; 1% Asian, non-Hispanic/Latino; 0.2% international. 31% 25 or older, 5% transferred in. Retention: 50% of full-time freshmen returned the following year. Core. Calendar: semesters. Academic remediation for entering students, services for LD students, advanced placement, accelerated degree program, honors program, independent study, distance learning, double major, summer session for credit, part-time degree program, adult/continuing education programs, co-op programs and internships. Off campus study. Study abroad program.
Entrance Requirements: Open admission. Option: electronic application. Required: high school transcript, SAT or ACT. Required for some: ACT

Compass for students who are over 21. Application deadlines: rolling, rolling for nonresidents. Transfer credits accepted: Yes.

Costs Per Year: Application fee: $0. State resident tuition: $3936 full-time, $164 per credit hour part-time. Nonresident tuition: $16,224 full-time, $676 per credit hour part-time. Mandatory fees: $299 full-time, $149.50 per term part-time. Full-time tuition and fees vary according to course load. Part-time tuition and fees vary according to course load.

Collegiate Environment: Orientation program. Drama-theater group, choral group. Social organizations: 9 open to all. Most popular organizations: Psychology Club, Phi Theta Kappa, Student Government, Student Nurses Association, Criminal Justice Association. Major annual events: Spring Fling, Homecoming, FOCUS (open house). Student services: personal-psychological counseling. Campus security: 24-hour emergency response devices and patrols. Learning Resource Center plus 2 others. Books: 17,817 (physical), 225,400 (digital/electronic); Serial titles: 29 (digital/electronic); Databases: 121. Weekly public service hours: 66; students can reserve study rooms. Operations spending for the previous fiscal year: $326,673. 1,322 computers available on campus for general student use. A campus-wide network can be accessed from off-campus. Students can access the following: online class registration. Staffed computer lab on campus provides training in use of computers, software, and the Internet.

■ **EAST TENNESSEE STATE UNIVERSITY**
1276 Gilbreath Dr.
Johnson City, TN 37614
Tel: (423)439-1000; Free: 800-462-3878
Fax: (423)439-5770
E-mail: go2etsu@etsu.edu
Web Site: www.etsu.edu

Description: State-supported, university, coed. Part of State University and Community College System of Tennessee. Awards bachelor's, master's, and doctoral degrees and post-master's certificates. Founded 1911. Setting: 366-acre small town campus. Endowment: $113.3 million. Research spending for the previous fiscal year: $4.6 million. Educational spending for the previous fiscal year: $3497 per student. Total enrollment: 14,317. Faculty: 1,023 (601 full-time, 422 part-time). Student-undergrad faculty ratio is 15:1. 8,009 applied, 87% were admitted. 20% from top 10% of their high school class, 47% from top quarter, 75% from top half. Full-time: 9,533 students, 57% women, 43% men. Part-time: 1,735 students, 58% women, 42% men. Students come from 42 states and territories, 60 other countries, 20% from out-of-state. 0.2% American Indian or Alaska Native, non-Hispanic/Latino; 3% Hispanic/Latino; 6% Black or African American, non-Hispanic/Latino; 1% Asian, non-Hispanic/Latino; 0.1% Native Hawaiian or other Pacific Islander, non-Hispanic/Latino; 3% international. 17% 25 or older, 25% live on campus, 10% transferred in. Retention: 73% of full-time freshmen returned the following year. Academic areas with the most degrees conferred: health professions and related sciences; business/marketing; liberal arts/general studies; parks and recreation. Core. Calendar: semesters. ESL program, services for LD students, advanced placement, self-designed majors, freshman honors college, honors program, independent study, distance learning, double major, summer session for credit, part-time degree program, external degree program, adult/continuing education programs, co-op programs and internships, graduate courses open to undergrads. Off campus study at Milligan College, Emmanuel School of Religion. Study abroad program. ROTC: Army.

Entrance Requirements: Options: electronic application, early admission, international baccalaureate accepted. Required: high school transcript, minimum 2.3 high school GPA, minimum 2.3 high school GPA or ACT score of 19, SAT or ACT. Entrance: moderately difficult. Application deadline: rolling. Notification: continuous. SAT Reasoning Test deadline: 8/1. Transfer credits accepted: Yes.

Collegiate Environment: Orientation program. Drama-theater group, choral group, marching band, student-run newspaper, radio station. Social organizations: 200 open to all; national fraternities, national sororities; 5% of eligible men and 5% of eligible women are members. Most popular organizations: honor societies, Volunteer ETSU, religious groups, residence hall councils. Major annual events: Homecoming, Greek Week, Winter Cruise. Student services: health clinic, personal-psychological counseling, women's center. Campus security: 24-hour emergency response devices and patrols, student patrols, late night transport-escort service, controlled dormitory access. 3,069 college housing spaces available. No special consideration for freshman housing applicants. Options: coed, men-only, women-only housing available. Charles C. Sherrod Library plus 2 others. Books: 731,960 (physical), 98,312 (digital/electronic); Databases: 210. Study areas open 24 hours,

5-7 days a week; students can reserve study rooms. Operations spending for the previous fiscal year: $2.9 million. 1,400 computers available on campus for general student use. Computer purchase/lease plans available. A campuswide network can be accessed. Students can access the following: online class registration. Staffed computer lab on campus (open 24 hours a day) provides training in use of computers, software, and the Internet.

Community Environment: Johnson City, Kingsport and Bristol compose the Tri-Cities area, which is Tennessee's fifth largest metropolitan area, having one million people living within a 50-mile radius. Johnson City, a progressive city with a population of approximately 58,700, is located close to the state lines of Virginia, Kentucky, West Virginia, North Carolina and South Carolina. Recreational opportunities abound and include boating and water skiing on major TVA lakes, a variety of snow skiing resorts featuring downhill and cross-country, mountain hiking trails including easy access to the Appalachian Trail, and white water rafting. Interstate highways I-40, I-81 and I-26 provide access by automobile, with Tri-Cities Regional Airport providing access by commercial airlines. All major religious denominations are represented.

■ **L'ECOLE CULINAIRE-MEMPHIS**
1245 N Germantown Pky.
Cordova, TN 38016
Tel: (901)754-7115; Free: 888-238-2077
Web Site: www.lecole.edu/memphis
Description: Proprietary, 2-year, coed. Awards transfer associate degrees.

■ **FISK UNIVERSITY**
1000 17th Ave., N
Nashville, TN 37208-3051
Tel: (615)329-8500; Free: 888-702-0022
Fax: (615)329-8576
E-mail: lmcdonald@fisk.edu
Web Site: www.fisk.edu

Description: Independent, comprehensive, coed, affiliated with United Church of Christ. Awards bachelor's and master's degrees. Founded 1866. Setting: 40-acre urban campus. Endowment: $20.6 million. Research spending for the previous fiscal year: $4.1 million. Educational spending for the previous fiscal year: $10,264 per student. Total enrollment: 854. Faculty: 80 (46 full-time, 34 part-time). Student-undergrad faculty ratio is 13:1. 3,004 applied, 81% were admitted. 15% from top 10% of their high school class, 46% from top quarter, 74% from top half. Full-time: 738 students, 66% women, 34% men. Part-time: 67 students, 58% women, 42% men. Students come from 36 states and territories, 5 other countries, 74% from out-of-state. 3% Hispanic/Latino; 88% Black or African American, non-Hispanic/Latino; 0.7% Asian, non-Hispanic/Latino. 3% 25 or older, 82% live on campus, 4% transferred in. Retention: 82% of full-time freshmen returned the following year. Academic areas with the most degrees conferred: psychology; English; biological/life sciences. Core. Calendar: semesters. Academic remediation for entering students, services for LD students, advanced placement, self-designed majors, honors program, independent study, double major, summer session for credit, part-time degree program, external degree program, co-op programs and internships. Off campus study at Alabama A&M; Bloomsburg University; Case Western Reserve; Columbia University; Florida A&M University; Grambling State; Jackson Sate; Miami Data College; Oberlin College; Penn State University; Prescott College; Rochester Institute of Technology; Vanderbilt University; Belmont University; Howard University; Watkins College of Art, Design and Film; and Meharry Medical College. Study abroad program. ROTC: Army (c), Naval (c), Air Force (c).

Entrance Requirements: Options: electronic application, early admission, early decision, international baccalaureate accepted. Required: essay, high school transcript, 2 recommendations, SAT or ACT. Entrance: moderately difficult. Application deadline: 8/1. Notification: continuous, continuous for nonresidents. Transfer credits accepted: Yes.

Costs Per Year: Application fee: $25. Comprehensive fee: $32,270 includes full-time tuition ($19,624), mandatory fees ($1856), and college room and board ($10,790). College room only: $6162. Full-time tuition and fees vary according to course load and degree level. Room and board charges vary according to board plan. Part-time tuition: $817 per credit hour. Tuition guaranteed not to increase for student's term of enrollment.

Collegiate Environment: Orientation program. Drama-theater group, choral group, student-run newspaper. Social organizations: 56 open to all; national fraternities, national sororities. Most popular organizations: Student Government Association, State Clubs, Class organizations, Greek Fraternities and Sororities, University Choir. Major annual events: Homecoming, Spring Arts

Festival, Jubilee Day Convocation. Student services: health clinic, personal-psychological counseling. Campus security: 24-hour emergency response devices and patrols, late night transport-escort service, controlled dormitory access. John Hope and Aurelia E. Franklin Library. Books: 228,832 (physical); Databases: 97. 70 computers available on campus for general student use. Computer purchase/lease plans available. A campuswide network can be accessed from student residence rooms and from off campus. Students can access the following: online class registration. Staffed computer lab on campus provides training in use of computers, software, and the Internet.
Community Environment: See Vanderbilt University.

■ **FORTIS INSTITUTE (COOKEVILLE)**
1025 Hwy. 111
Cookeville, TN 38501
Tel: (931)526-3660; Free: 855-4-FORTIS
Fax: (931)372-2603
Web Site: www.fortis.edu
Description: Proprietary, 2-year, coed. Awards certificates, diplomas, transfer associate, and terminal associate degrees. Founded 1970. Setting: 4-acre small town campus. Total enrollment: 283. 237 applied. 60% 25 or older. Core. Calendar: quarters. Internships.
Entrance Requirements: Required: high school transcript, interview, Wonderlic aptitude test. Recommended: minimum 2.0 high school GPA, 2 recommendations. Entrance: noncompetitive. Application deadline: rolling. Notification: continuous.
Collegiate Environment: Orientation program.

■ **FORTIS INSTITUTE (NASHVILLE)**
3354 Perimeter Hill Dr.
Ste. 105
Nashville, TN 37211
Tel: (615)320-5917; Free: 855-4-FORTIS
Web Site: www.fortis.edu
Description: Proprietary, 2-year, coed. Awards certificates, diplomas, transfer associate, and terminal associate degrees.

■ **FREED-HARDEMAN UNIVERSITY**
158 E Main St.
Henderson, TN 38340-2399
Tel: (731)989-6000; Free: 800-FHU-FHU-1
Fax: (731)989-6047
Web Site: www.fhu.edu
Description: Independent, comprehensive, coed, affiliated with Church of Christ. Awards bachelor's, master's, and doctoral degrees and post-master's certificates. Founded 1869. Setting: 120-acre small town campus. Total enrollment: 1,906. Faculty: 157 (93 full-time, 64 part-time). Student-undergrad faculty ratio is 13:1. 791 applied, 96% were admitted. Full-time: 1,228 students, 56% women, 44% men. Part-time: 174 students, 67% women, 33% men. 41% from out-of-state. 0.1% American Indian or Alaska Native, non-Hispanic/Latino; 2% Hispanic/Latino; 4% Black or African American, non-Hispanic/Latino; 1% Asian, non-Hispanic/Latino; 0.1% Native Hawaiian or other Pacific Islander, non-Hispanic/Latino; 1% international. 5% 25 or older, 78% live on campus, 7% transferred in. Retention: 78% of full-time freshmen returned the following year. Academic areas with the most degrees conferred: business/marketing; education; theology and religious vocations. Core. Calendar: semesters. Academic remediation for entering students, services for LD students, advanced placement, accelerated degree program, self-designed majors, freshman honors college, honors program, independent study, distance learning, double major, summer session for credit, part-time degree program, co-op programs and internships, graduate courses open to undergrads. Off campus study at Union University. Study abroad program.
Entrance Requirements: Options: electronic application, deferred admission, international baccalaureate accepted. Required: high school transcript, minimum 2.25 high school GPA, SAT or ACT. Required for some: interview. Entrance: moderately difficult. Application deadline: rolling. Notification: continuous. SAT Reasoning Test deadline: 8/17. Transfer credits accepted: Yes.
Collegiate Environment: Orientation program. Drama-theater group, choral group, student-run newspaper, radio station. Social organizations: 5 co-ed social clubs on campus. Major annual events: Makin' Music, Homecoming, Bible Lectureship. Student services: health clinic, personal-psychological counseling. Campus security: 24-hour patrols, controlled dormitory access. Hope Barber Shull Academic Resource Center plus 1 other. Students can reserve study rooms.

Community Environment: Henderson is a rural town of 5,500 with an airport within 25 miles. A metropolitan area, Jackson, (population 62,000) is located within 15 miles and Memphis is only 80 miles away. The community facilities include churches, good shopping facilities, and some major civic and service organizations. The Tennessee River, Kentucky Lake, Chickasaw State Park, and Pickwick Dam provide a number of facilities for all kinds of water sports and other recreation. Some part-time employment is available.

■ **HIWASSEE COLLEGE**
225 Hiwassee College Dr.
Madisonville, TN 37354
Tel: (423)442-2001; Free: 800-356-2187
Fax: (423)442-3520
Web Site: www.hiwassee.edu
Description: Independent Methodist, 2-year, coed. Awards transfer associate and terminal associate degrees. Founded 1849. Setting: 410-acre rural campus. Endowment: $5.1 million. Educational spending for the previous fiscal year: $3021 per student. Total enrollment: 398. Faculty: 28 (21 full-time, 7 part-time). Student-undergrad faculty ratio is 15:1. 562 applied, 70% were admitted. 15% from top 10% of their high school class, 33% from top quarter, 67% from top half. 3 valedictorians. Full-time: 350 students, 55% women, 45% men. Part-time: 48 students, 75% women, 25% men. Students come from 11 states and territories, 8 other countries, 8% from out-of-state. 8% 25 or older, 40% live on campus, 6% transferred in. Core. Calendar: semesters. Academic remediation for entering students, ESL program, advanced placement, honors program, double major, summer session for credit, part-time degree program, adult/continuing education programs.
Entrance Requirements: Options: electronic application, early admission, deferred admission. Required: high school transcript, minimum 2.25 high school GPA, SAT or ACT. Required for some: 2 recommendations, interview. Entrance: minimally difficult. Application deadline: rolling.
Collegiate Environment: Orientation program. Drama-theater group, choral group, student-run newspaper. Social organizations: 20 open to all. Most popular organizations: Baptist Student Union, Christian Student Movement, Future Farmers of America, Theatre Hiwassee, Student Government Association. Major annual events: Homecoming Week, Welcome Week, Spring Formal. Student services: health clinic, personal-psychological counseling. Campus security: 24-hour emergency response devices, controlled dormitory access, late night security. Hardwick-Johnston Memorial Library. Operations spending for the previous fiscal year: $110,094. 61 computers available on campus for general student use. A campuswide network can be accessed from student residence rooms and from off campus. Staffed computer lab on campus.

■ **HUNTINGTON UNIVERSITY OF HEALTH SCIENCES**
117 Legacy View Way
Knoxville, TN 37918
Tel: (865)524-8079; Free: 800-290-4226
Fax: (865)524-8339
E-mail: admissions@huhs.edu
Web Site: www.huhs.edu
Description: Proprietary, comprehensive, coed. Awards associate, bachelor's, master's, and doctoral degrees (offers only external degree programs conducted through home study). Founded 1984. Setting: suburban campus. Educational spending for the previous fiscal year: $779 per student. Total enrollment: 134. Faculty: 19 (3 full-time, 16 part-time). Student-undergrad faculty ratio is 13:1. 5 applied, 100% were admitted. Full-time: 24 students, 75% women, 25% men. Part-time: 91 students, 85% women, 15% men. Students come from 33 states and territories, 72 other countries, 96% from out-of-state. 1% American Indian or Alaska Native, non-Hispanic/Latino; 11% Hispanic/Latino; 5% Black or African American, non-Hispanic/Latino; 1% Asian, non-Hispanic/Latino; 2% international. 88% 25 or older, 23% transferred in. Retention: 50% of full-time freshmen returned the following year. Academic area with the most degrees conferred: health professions and related sciences. Core. Calendar: continuous. Academic remediation for entering students, accelerated degree program, independent study, distance learning, summer session for credit, part-time degree program, external degree program, adult/continuing education programs.
Entrance Requirements: Open admission. Options: deferred admission, international baccalaureate accepted. Required: minimum 2 high school GPA. Required for some: high school transcript, interview. Entrance: noncompetitive. Application deadlines: rolling, rolling for nonresidents. Notification: continuous, continuous for nonresidents. Transfer credits accepted: Yes.

Costs Per Year: Application fee: $75. Tuition: $6360 full-time, $265 per credit hour part-time. Mandatory fees: $250 full-time.
Collegiate Environment: Orientation program. Social organizations: Delta Epsilon Tau - national honor society. College housing not available. HUHS Online Library. Books: 9,130 (digital/electronic); Serial titles: 484,490 (digital/ electronic); Databases: 13. Operations spending for the previous fiscal year: $5230.

■ **JACKSON STATE COMMUNITY COLLEGE**
2046 N Pky.
Jackson, TN 38301-3797
Tel: (731)424-3520; Free: 800-355-5722
Fax: (731)425-2647
E-mail: awinchester@jscc.edu
Web Site: www.jscc.edu
Description: State-supported, 2-year, coed. Part of Tennessee Board of Regents. Awards certificates, diplomas, transfer associate, and terminal associate degrees. Founded 1967. Setting: 100-acre suburban campus with easy access to Memphis. Total enrollment: 4,926. Faculty: 285 (88 full-time, 197 part-time). 1,219 applied, 76% were admitted. Core. Calendar: semesters. Academic remediation for entering students, services for LD students, advanced placement, accelerated degree program, honors program, independent study, distance learning, summer session for credit, part-time degree program, external degree program, adult/continuing education programs, co-op programs and internships. Off campus study. Study abroad program. ROTC: Army (c).
Entrance Requirements: Open admission except for allied health programs. Option: electronic application. Required: SAT or ACT, ACT Compass. Recommended: ACT. Required for some: high school transcript. Entrance: noncompetitive. Application deadline: 8/23. Notification: continuous. Preference given to state residents. Transfer credits accepted: Yes.
Costs Per Year: Application fee: $0. State resident tuition: $4140 full-time, $164 per credit hour part-time. Nonresident tuition: $12,906 full-time, $512 per credit hour part-time. Mandatory fees: $283 full-time, $9 per credit hour part-time, $29 per term part-time. Full-time tuition and fees vary according to course load and program. Part-time tuition and fees vary according to course load and program.
Collegiate Environment: Orientation program. Choral group. Social organizations: 16 open to all. Most popular organizations: Spanish Club, Gay/Straight Alliance, Art Club, H2O Wellness, Biology Club. Major annual events: Welcome Back Bash, Health and Career Fair, Alcohol Awareness. Student services: personal-psychological counseling. Campus security: 24-hour patrols, late night transport-escort service, field camera surveillance. Jackson State Community College Library. 1,000 computers available on campus for general student use. A campuswide network can be accessed from off-campus. Students can access the following: online class registration. Staffed computer lab on campus provides training in use of computers, software, and the Internet.
Community Environment: Jackson, at one time a small cotton port, is now a trading and shipping center. All forms of commercial transportation are available. Because of direct access to major thoroughfares, Jackson is one of the fastest growing cities in Tennessee and is the trade center for a large populated area. Its facilities include hospitals, clinics, many churches, an art association, and symphony orchestra. The city is known as the home and burial place of John Luther "Casey" Jones, who became a part of American folklore and a legend of early railroading. The Casey Jones Railroad Museum may be seen here.

■ **JOHN A. GUPTON COLLEGE**
1616 Church St.
Nashville, TN 37203-2920
Tel: (615)327-3927
Fax: (615)321-4518
Web Site: www.guptoncollege.edu
Description: Independent, 2-year, coed. Awards certificates, diplomas, transfer associate, and terminal associate degrees. Founded 1946. Setting: 1-acre urban campus with easy access to Nashville. Endowment: $60,000. Educational spending for the previous fiscal year: $2837 per student. Total enrollment: 120. Faculty: 13 (3 full-time, 10 part-time). Full-time: 70 students, 57% women, 43% men. Part-time: 50 students, 72% women, 28% men. Students come from 5 states and territories, 10% from out-of-state. 3% Hispanic/Latino; 23% Black or African American, non-Hispanic/Latino; 0.8% Asian, non-Hispanic/Latino. 51% 25 or older, 11% live on campus, 18% transferred in. Calendar: semesters. Part-time degree program.

Entrance Requirements: Options: electronic application, deferred admission. Required: essay, high school transcript, 2 recommendations, ACT. Entrance: minimally difficult. Application deadline: rolling. Transfer credits accepted: Yes.
Collegiate Environment: Orientation program. Campus security: controlled dormitory access, day patrols. Memorial Library plus 1 other. 12 computers available on campus for general student use. Staffed computer lab on campus provides training in use of computers and the Internet.

■ **JOHNSON UNIVERSITY**
7900 Johnson Dr.
Knoxville, TN 37998-1001
Tel: (865)573-4517; Free: 800-827-2122
Fax: (865)251-2337
E-mail: jschultz@johnsonu.edu
Web Site: www.johnsonu.edu
Description: Independent, comprehensive, coed, affiliated with Christian Churches and Churches of Christ. Awards associate, bachelor's, master's, and doctoral degrees and post-master's certificates. Founded 1893. Setting: 175-acre rural campus with easy access to Knoxville. Total enrollment: 1,158. Faculty: 165 (76 full-time, 89 part-time). Student-undergrad faculty ratio is 20:1. 247 applied, 98% were admitted. Full-time: 689 students, 49% women, 51% men. Part-time: 125 students, 38% women, 62% men. 65% from out-of-state. 0.2% American Indian or Alaska Native, non-Hispanic/ Latino; 2% Hispanic/Latino; 3% Black or African American, non-Hispanic/ Latino; 3% international. 16% 25 or older, 16% live on campus, 7% transferred in. Retention: 78% of full-time freshmen returned the following year. Academic areas with the most degrees conferred: health professions and related sciences; education; history. Core. Calendar: semesters. Academic remediation for entering students, ESL program, services for LD students, advanced placement, accelerated degree program, honors program, independent study, distance learning, double major, summer session for credit, part-time degree program, adult/continuing education programs, co-op programs and internships, graduate courses open to undergrads. Study abroad program.
Entrance Requirements: Options: electronic application, early admission, deferred admission. Required: essay, high school transcript, minimum 2.5 high school GPA, 3 recommendations, SAT or ACT. Required for some: interview. Entrance: moderately difficult. Application deadline: 7/1. Notification: continuous. Transfer credits accepted: Yes.
Costs Per Year: Application fee: $35. Comprehensive fee: $22,760 includes full-time tuition ($14,880), mandatory fees ($1180), and college room and board ($6700). College room only: $3000. Full-time tuition and fees vary according to class time, course load, degree level, location, and program. Room and board charges vary according to board plan, housing facility, and location. Part-time tuition: $470 per credit hour. Part-time tuition varies according to class time, course load, degree level, location, and program.
Collegiate Environment: Orientation program. Drama-theater group, choral group, student-run newspaper, radio station. Social organizations: 8 open to all. Most popular organizations: Student Government Association, International student Association, Harvesters (Missions), International Justice Mission, Students Promoting Social Unity. Major annual events: Homecoming, Founder' Day, Miller and Scott Christmas Banquet. Student services: health clinic, personal-psychological counseling. Campus security: 24-hour emergency response devices and patrols, student patrols, controlled dormitory access. Glass Memorial Library plus 1 other. Weekly public service hours: 80.
Community Environment: The college is located in the rural community of Kimberlin Heights within a 20-minute drive of Knoxville where shopping, jobs, recreation, hospitals, churches, and civic cultural, and service organizations are abundant.

■ **KING UNIVERSITY**
1350 King College Rd.
Bristol, TN 37620-2699
Tel: (423)968-1187; Free: 800-362-0014
Fax: (423)968-4456
E-mail: admissions@king.edu
Web Site: www.king.edu
Description: Independent, comprehensive, coed, affiliated with Presbyterian Church (U.S.A.). Awards associate, bachelor's, master's, and doctoral degrees and post-master's certificates. Founded 1867. Setting: 135-acre suburban campus. Endowment: $33.4 million. Educational spending for the previous fiscal year: $591 per student. Total enrollment: 1,948. Faculty: 255

(86 full-time, 169 part-time). Student-undergrad faculty ratio is 13:1. 1,152 applied, 59% were admitted. 12% from top 10% of their high school class, 26% from top quarter, 64% from top half. Full-time: 1,460 students, 62% women, 38% men. Part-time: 119 students, 64% women, 36% men. Students come from 41 states and territories, 24 other countries, 40% from out-of-state. 0.3% American Indian or Alaska Native, non-Hispanic/Latino; 3% Hispanic/Latino; 6% Black or African American, non-Hispanic/Latino; 0.9% Asian, non-Hispanic/Latino; 0.1% Native Hawaiian or other Pacific Islander, non-Hispanic/Latino; 3% international. 46% 25 or older, 21% live on campus, 3% transferred in. Retention: 69% of full-time freshmen returned the following year. Academic areas with the most degrees conferred: health professions and related sciences; business/marketing; computer and information sciences. Core. Calendar: semesters. Services for LD students, advanced placement, self-designed majors, honors program, independent study, distance learning, double major, summer session for credit, part-time degree program, adult/continuing education programs, internships. Off campus study at Los Angeles Film Studies Center, Oak Ridge Science Semester (TN), American Studies Program (Washington, DC), Contemporary Music Center in Nashville (CCCU), Oregon Extension. Study abroad program. ROTC: Army (c).

Entrance Requirements: Options: electronic application, deferred admission, international baccalaureate accepted. Required: high school transcript. Recommended: minimum 3 high school GPA. Required for some: essay. Entrance: moderately difficult. Application deadline: rolling. Notification: continuous. Transfer credits accepted: Yes.

Costs Per Year: Comprehensive fee: $49,640 includes full-time tuition ($38,948), mandatory fees ($1668), and college room and board ($9024). College room only: $4532.

Collegiate Environment: Orientation program. Drama-theater group, choral group, student-run newspaper. Social organizations: 21 open to all. Most popular organizations: Student Government Association, Women in STEM, King Security and Intelligence Studies Student Group, Enactus, STEA-KE. Major annual events: Dogwood Festival/Alumni Weekend, Family Weekend, Late Night Exam Breakfast. Student services: personal-psychological counseling. Campus security: 24-hour emergency response devices and patrols, late night transport-escort service, controlled dormitory access. 451 college housing spaces available; 298 were occupied in 2018-19. Freshmen guaranteed college housing. On-campus residence required through junior year. Options: men-only, women-only housing available. E. W. King Library plus 3 others. Books: 75,745 (physical), 191,050 (digital/electronic); Serial titles: 150 (physical); Databases: 99. Weekly public service hours: 85. 90 computers available on campus for general student use. A campuswide network can be accessed from student residence rooms and from off campus. Students can access the following: online class registration, Student Portal.

Community Environment: Located in the beautiful Southern Highlands, Bristol is a twin city on the Tennessee-Virginia state line. Four distinct seasons offer year-round recreation. With three access points to the Appalachian trail within an hour's drive from campus, students can quickly escape to a wilderness playground. Nearby Cherokee and Jefferson National Forests provide more than 250,000 acres of unspoiled woodlands for hiking and camping. More than 40 square miles of inland lakes and freshwater streams await water enthusiasts, including South Holston Lake, site of the world's third largest earthen dam. Several major ski resorts are located within an hour's drive. NASCAR fans enjoy the world's fastest half-mile track at the Bristol Motor Speedway, and Bristol's Viking Hall Civic Center serves as a stop for top-name concerts, sporting events and community-sponsored shows and bazaars.

■ **LANE COLLEGE**
545 Ln. Ave.
Jackson, TN 38301-4598
Tel: (731)426-7500; Free: 800-960-7533
Fax: (731)426-7559
E-mail: mclayborne@lanecollege.edu
Web Site: www.lanecollege.edu
Description: Independent, 4-year, coed, affiliated with Christian Methodist Episcopal Church. Awards bachelor's degrees. Founded 1882. Setting: 55-acre suburban campus with easy access to Memphis. Total enrollment: 1,427. Faculty: 75 (65 full-time, 10 part-time). Student-undergrad faculty ratio is 19:1. 5,311 applied, 50% were admitted. 5% from top 10% of their high school class, 17% from top quarter, 52% from top half. Full-time: 1,365 students, 48% women, 52% men. Part-time: 62 students, 39% women, 61% men. 40% from out-of-state. 0.1% American Indian or Alaska Native, non-

Hispanic/Latino; 0.2% Hispanic/Latino; 90% Black or African American, non-Hispanic/Latino; 0.2% Asian, non-Hispanic/Latino; 0.1% international. 8% 25 or older, 64% live on campus, 5% transferred in. Retention: 62% of full-time freshmen returned the following year. Academic areas with the most degrees conferred: social sciences; homeland security, law enforcement, firefighting, and protective services; biological/life sciences; business/marketing. Core. Calendar: semesters. Academic remediation for entering students, services for LD students, advanced placement, accelerated degree program, honors program, independent study, summer session for credit, part-time degree program, adult/continuing education programs, co-op programs and internships. Off campus study. Study abroad program. ROTC: Army.

Entrance Requirements: Options: electronic application, deferred admission. Required: high school transcript, 2 recommendations, SAT or ACT. Entrance: minimally difficult. Application deadlines: rolling, rolling for nonresidents. Notification: continuous.

Collegiate Environment: Orientation program. Drama-theater group, choral group, marching band. Social organizations: national fraternities, national sororities, local fraternities, local sororities. Most popular organizations: Student Government Association, Pre-Law Club, Student Christian Association, Drama Club, Sociology Club. Major annual events: Homecoming, Founder's Day, Convocation/Weekly Chapel. Student services: legal services, health clinic, personal-psychological counseling. Campus security: 24-hour emergency response devices and patrols, late night transport-escort service, surveillance cameras, lighted parking areas. Chambers-McClure Academic Center.

Community Environment: See Jackson State Community College.

■ **LEE UNIVERSITY**
PO Box 3450
Cleveland, TN 37320-3450
Tel: (423)614-8000; Free: 800-533-9930
Fax: (423)614-8533
E-mail: admissions@leeuniversity.edu
Web Site: www.leeuniversity.edu
Description: Independent, comprehensive, coed, affiliated with Church of God. Awards bachelor's, master's, and doctoral degrees and post-master's certificates. Founded 1918. Setting: 120-acre small town campus with easy access to Chattanooga, TN. Endowment: $21.9 million. Research spending for the previous fiscal year: $394,831. Educational spending for the previous fiscal year: $6901 per student. Total enrollment: 5,386. Faculty: 476 (189 full-time, 287 part-time). Student-undergrad faculty ratio is 16:1. 2,443 applied, 83% were admitted. 24% from top 10% of their high school class, 49% from top quarter, 78% from top half. Full-time: 3,780 students, 64% women, 36% men. Part-time: 1,103 students, 52% women, 48% men. Students come from 50 states and territories, 47 other countries, 54% from out-of-state. 0.4% American Indian or Alaska Native, non-Hispanic/Latino; 2% Hispanic/Latino; 5% Black or African American, non-Hispanic/Latino; 0.7% Asian, non-Hispanic/Latino; 0.2% Native Hawaiian or other Pacific Islander, non-Hispanic/Latino; 2% international. 15% 25 or older, 47% live on campus, 4% transferred in. Retention: 79% of full-time freshmen returned the following year. Academic areas with the most degrees conferred: theology and religious vocations; education; communication/journalism. Core. Calendar: semesters. Academic remediation for entering students, ESL program, services for LD students, advanced placement, self-designed majors, honors program, independent study, distance learning, double major, summer session for credit, part-time degree program, external degree program, adult/continuing education programs, co-op programs and internships. Off campus study. Study abroad program.

Entrance Requirements: Options: electronic application, early admission, deferred admission, international baccalaureate accepted. Required: high school transcript, minimum 2 high school GPA, MMR immunization record, SAT or ACT. Recommended: SAT, ACT. Required for some: 3 recommendations. Entrance: moderately difficult. Application deadlines: rolling, rolling for nonresidents. Notification: continuous, continuous for nonresidents. SAT Reasoning Test deadline: 8/1. SAT Subject Test deadline: 8/1. Transfer credits accepted: Yes.

Costs Per Year: Application fee: $25. Comprehensive fee: $27,095 includes full-time tuition ($18,120), mandatory fees ($650), and college room and board ($8325). College room only: $4575. Part-time tuition: $755 per credit hour. Part-time mandatory fees: $35 per term.

Collegiate Environment: Orientation program. Drama-theater group, choral group, student-run newspaper. Social organizations: 101 open to all; local fraternities, local sororities; 8% of eligible men and 8% of eligible women are members. Most popular organizations: Student Leadership Council, CRU,

Big Pal Little Pal, Delta Zeta Tau, Crossover. Major annual events: Homecoming, Dorm Wars, Convocation. Student services: health clinic, personal-psychological counseling. Campus security: 24-hour emergency response devices and patrols, late night transport-escort service, controlled dormitory access. 2,066 college housing spaces available; 2,004 were occupied in 2018-19. Freshmen guaranteed college housing. On-campus residence required through sophomore year. Options: men-only, women-only housing available. William G. Squires Library plus 2 others. Books: 158,156 (physical), 303,576 (digital/electronic); Serial titles: 244 (physical), 97,212 (digital/electronic); Databases: 137. Weekly public service hours: 93; students can reserve study rooms. Operations spending for the previous fiscal year: $1.4 million. 460 computers available on campus for general student use. A campuswide network can be accessed from student residence rooms and from off campus. Students can access the following: online class registration. Staffed computer lab on campus provides training in use of computers, software, and the Internet.

Community Environment: See Cleveland State Community College.

■ LEMOYNE-OWEN COLLEGE

807 Walker Ave.
Memphis, TN 38126-6595
Tel: (901)435-1000; Free: 800-737-7778
Fax: (901)942-6272
Web Site: www.loc.edu

Description: Independent, 4-year, coed, affiliated with United Church of Christ. Awards bachelor's degrees. Founded 1862. Setting: 15-acre urban campus. Endowment: $15.1 million. Educational spending for the previous fiscal year: $7184 per student. Total enrollment: 945. Faculty: 88 (55 full-time, 33 part-time). Student-undergrad faculty ratio is 14:1. 527 applied, 100% were admitted. Full-time: 836 students, 64% women, 36% men. Part-time: 109 students, 66% women, 34% men. Students come from 12 states and territories, 4 other countries, 12% from out-of-state. 0.4% Hispanic/Latino; 99% Black or African American, non-Hispanic/Latino; 1% international. 40% 25 or older, 31% live on campus, 14% transferred in. Retention: 43% of full-time freshmen returned the following year. Core. Calendar: semesters. Academic remediation for entering students, services for LD students, advanced placement, accelerated degree program, honors program, independent study, double major, summer session for credit, part-time degree program, co-op programs and internships. Off campus study at Greater Memphis Consortium. Study abroad program. ROTC: Army (c), Air Force (c).

Entrance Requirements: Open admission. Options: electronic application, international baccalaureate accepted. Required: high school transcript, minimum 2 high school GPA, SAT or ACT. Recommended: essay, 2 recommendations, interview. Entrance: minimally difficult. Application deadline: 4/1.

Collegiate Environment: Orientation program. Drama-theater group, choral group, student-run newspaper. Social organizations: 35 open to all; national fraternities, national sororities; 35% of eligible men and 65% of eligible women are members. Most popular organizations: Greek Fraternities and Sororities, Black Business Students Association, National Black Student Accountant Club, Gospel Choir, Pre-Alumni organization. Major annual events: Homecoming, Honors Week, Black History Month. Student services: health clinic, personal-psychological counseling. Campus security: 24-hour patrols, late night transport-escort service, controlled dormitory access. Hollis F. Price Library. 239 computers available on campus for general student use. Computer purchase/lease plans available. A campuswide network can be accessed from student residence rooms and from off campus. Students can access the following: online class registration. Staffed computer lab on campus.

Community Environment: See University of Memphis.

■ LINCOLN COLLEGE OF TECHNOLOGY

1524 Gallatin Ave.
Nashville, TN 37206
Tel: (615)226-3990; Free: 844-215-1513
Fax: (615)262-8488
E-mail: tlegg-smith@lincolntech.com
Web Site: www.lincolntech.edu

Description: Proprietary, 2-year, coed. Awards diplomas and terminal associate degrees. Founded 1919. Setting: 16-acre urban campus. Total enrollment: 1,375. Faculty: 63 (59 full-time, 4 part-time). Student-undergrad faculty ratio is 30:1. 2,924 applied, 89% were admitted. Full-time: 1,375 students, 1% women, 99% men. Students come from 50 states and ter-

ritories, 83% from out-of-state. 5% 25 or older, 21% live on campus. Calendar: continuous. Advanced placement, honors program, co-op programs.

Entrance Requirements: Options: electronic application, deferred admission. Required: high school transcript. Recommended: SAT or ACT. Required for some: interview. Entrance: minimally difficult. Application deadline: rolling.

Collegiate Environment: Orientation program. Campus security: 24-hour emergency response devices and patrols. Lincoln College of Technology Library. 40 computers available on campus for general student use. A campuswide network can be accessed. Staffed computer lab on campus (open 24 hours a day) provides training in use of computers.

■ LINCOLN MEMORIAL UNIVERSITY

6965 Cumberland Gap Pky.
Harrogate, TN 37752-1901
Tel: (423)869-3611; Free: 800-325-0900
Fax: (423)869-6250
Web Site: www.lmunet.edu

Description: Independent, university, coed. Awards associate, bachelor's, master's, and doctoral degrees and post-master's certificates. Founded 1897. Setting: 1,000-acre small town campus. Endowment: $40.8 million. Research spending for the previous fiscal year: $306,859. Educational spending for the previous fiscal year: $11,283 per student. Total enrollment: 4,770. Faculty: 343 (180 full-time, 163 part-time). Student-undergrad faculty ratio is 14:1. 1,676 applied, 61% were admitted. Full-time: 1,356 students, 66% women, 34% men. Part-time: 563 students, 81% women, 19% men. Students come from 49 states and territories, 24 other countries, 36% from out-of-state. 1% American Indian or Alaska Native, non-Hispanic/Latino; 0.3% Hispanic/Latino; 6% Black or African American, non-Hispanic/Latino; 1% Asian, non-Hispanic/Latino. 29% 25 or older, 37% live on campus, 13% transferred in. Retention: 73% of full-time freshmen returned the following year. Academic areas with the most degrees conferred: health professions and related sciences; business/marketing; parks and recreation. Core. Calendar: semesters. Academic remediation for entering students, ESL program, services for LD students, advanced placement, accelerated degree program, honors program, independent study, distance learning, double major, summer session for credit, part-time degree program, adult/continuing education programs, co-op programs and internships, graduate courses open to undergrads. Study abroad program. ROTC: Army (c).

Entrance Requirements: Options: electronic application, international baccalaureate accepted. Required: high school transcript, immunization records, financial aid application, SAT or ACT. Recommended: minimum 3 high school GPA. Entrance: moderately difficult. Application deadline: rolling. Notification: continuous. Transfer credits accepted: Yes.

Costs Per Year: Comprehensive fee: $29,250 includes full-time tuition ($21,480) and college room and board ($7770). College room only: $3450. Full-time tuition varies according to course load, degree level, location, and program. Room and board charges vary according to board plan and housing facility. Part-time tuition: $895 per credit hour. Part-time tuition varies according to course load, degree level, location, and program.

Collegiate Environment: Orientation program. Drama-theater group, choral group, student-run radio station. Social organizations: 57 open to all; national fraternities, national sororities; 5% of eligible men and 15% of eligible women are members. Most popular organizations: Enactus, Pre-Vet Club, Pre-Med Club, Fishing Club, Earth Club. Major annual events: Founder's Day, Convocation, SGA Fall and Spring Campus Clean UP. Student services: health clinic, personal-psychological counseling. Campus security: 24-hour emergency response devices and patrols, late night transport-escort service. Carnegie-Vincent Library. Books: 85,346 (physical), 355,314 (digital/electronic); Serial titles: 1,548 (physical), 32,592 (digital/electronic); Databases: 225. Weekly public service hours: 92; students can reserve study rooms. Operations spending for the previous fiscal year: $1.2 million. 121 computers available on campus for general student use. A campuswide network can be accessed from student residence rooms. Students can access the following: online class registration. Staffed computer lab on campus provides training in use of computers, software, and the Internet.

■ LIPSCOMB UNIVERSITY

One University Park Dr.
Nashville, TN 37204-3951
Tel: (615)966-1000; Free: 877-582-4766
Fax: (615)966-1804

E-mail: admissions@lipscomb.edu
Web Site: www.lipscomb.edu
Description: Independent, university, coed, affiliated with Church of Christ. Awards associate, bachelor's, master's, and doctoral degrees. Founded 1891. Setting: 89-acre suburban campus. Endowment: $79.1 million. Educational spending for the previous fiscal year: $11,368 per student. Total enrollment: 4,560. Faculty: 587 (231 full-time, 356 part-time). Student-undergrad faculty ratio is 14:1. 3,638 applied, 60% were admitted. 30% from top 10% of their high school class, 58% from top quarter, 87% from top half. 9 valedictorians. Full-time: 2,738 students, 61% women, 39% men. Part-time: 200 students, 64% women, 36% men. Students come from 47 states and territories, 44 other countries, 36% from out-of-state. 0.1% American Indian or Alaska Native, non-Hispanic/Latino; 8% Hispanic/Latino; 7% Black or African American, non-Hispanic/Latino; 3% Asian, non-Hispanic/Latino; 0.1% Native Hawaiian or other Pacific Islander, non-Hispanic/Latino; 3% international. 10% 25 or older, 47% live on campus, 6% transferred in. Retention: 81% of full-time freshmen returned the following year. Academic areas with the most degrees conferred: business/marketing; biological/life sciences; education. Core. Calendar: semesters. Academic remediation for entering students, ESL program, services for LD students, advanced placement, accelerated degree program, self-designed majors, honors program, independent study, distance learning, double major, summer session for credit, part-time degree program, adult/continuing education programs, internships, graduate courses open to undergrads. Study abroad program. ROTC: Army (c), Air Force (c).
Entrance Requirements: Options: electronic application, early admission, deferred admission, international baccalaureate accepted. Required: essay, high school transcript, minimum 2.5 high school GPA, 1 recommendation, SAT or ACT. Recommended: interview. Entrance: moderately difficult. Application deadline: rolling. Notification: continuous. SAT Reasoning Test deadline: 10/1. SAT Subject Test deadline: 10/1. Transfer credits accepted: Yes.
Costs Per Year: Application fee: $50. Comprehensive fee: $46,704 includes full-time tuition ($30,860), mandatory fees ($2564), and college room and board ($13,280). Part-time tuition: $1286 per credit hour.
Collegiate Environment: Orientation program. Drama-theater group, choral group, student-run newspaper, radio station. Social organizations: 50 open to all; local fraternities, local sororities; 23% of eligible men and 24% of eligible women are members. Most popular organizations: Sigma Pi Beta, business fraternities, Multicultural Association, Alpha Phi Chi men's service club, Pi Kappa Sigma women's service club. Major annual events: Singarama (annual spring student talent show), Annual Service Day (students, faculty, and staff), Paint the Herd. Student services: health clinic, personal-psychological counseling. Campus security: 24-hour emergency response devices and patrols, late night transport-escort service, controlled dormitory access. 1,620 college housing spaces available; 1,540 were occupied in 2018-19. Freshmen given priority for college housing. On-campus residence required through junior year. Options: men-only, women-only housing available. Beaman Library plus 1 other. Books: 157,824 (physical), 167,520 (digital/electronic); Serial titles: 253 (physical), 489 (digital/electronic); Databases: 100. Students can reserve study rooms. Operations spending for the previous fiscal year: $477,841. 150 computers available on campus for general student use. A campuswide network can be accessed from student residence rooms and from off campus. Students can access the following: online class registration. Staffed computer lab on campus provides training in use of computers, software, and the Internet.
Community Environment: Lipscomb University is a vital part of Nashville, the capital of Tennessee, and a regional and national center for education, business, and culture. Nashville is centrally located and easy to reach. Half the population of the United States is within 600 miles of its borders. There are 3 major interstates in addition to Nashville International Airport. Nashville abounds in history and culture. From antebellum mansions like the Hermitage, home of President Andrew Jackson, to Cheekwood Botanical Gardens, the Parthenon, and the Tennessee State Museum, Nashville offers abundant resources to strengthen and complement student education.

■ **MARTIN METHODIST COLLEGE**
433 W Madison St.
Pulaski, TN 38478-2716
Tel: (931)363-9868; Free: 800-467-1273
Fax: (931)363-9818
E-mail: admit@martinmethodist.edu
Web Site: www.martinmethodist.edu
Description: Independent United Methodist, 4-year, coed. Awards associate

and bachelor's degrees. Founded 1870. Setting: 6-acre small town campus with easy access to Nashville. Total enrollment: 924. 22% 25 or older. Core. Calendar: semesters. Academic remediation for entering students, ESL program, services for LD students, advanced placement, honors program, independent study, double major, summer session for credit, part-time degree program, adult/continuing education programs, internships.
Entrance Requirements: Options: electronic application, early admission, deferred admission. Required: high school transcript, minimum 2.0 high school GPA, SAT or ACT. Recommended: essay, interview. Entrance: minimally difficult. Application deadline: 8/26. Notification: continuous.
Collegiate Environment: Orientation program. Drama-theater group, choral group. Campus security: controlled dormitory access. Warden Memorial Library.
Community Environment: Located in south-central Tennessee where the climate is mild, Pulaski, between Nashville, Tennessee, and Huntsville, Alabama, is a small, friendly town with much civic pride.

■ **MARYVILLE COLLEGE**
502 E Lamar Alexander Pky.
Maryville, TN 37804-5907
Tel: (865)981-8000; Free: 800-597-2687
Fax: (865)983-0581
E-mail: admissions@maryvillecollege.edu
Web Site: www.maryvillecollege.edu
Description: Independent Presbyterian, 4-year, coed. Awards bachelor's degrees. Founded 1819. Setting: 263-acre suburban campus. Endowment: $69.2 million. Educational spending for the previous fiscal year: $7835 per student. Total enrollment: 1,181. Faculty: 117 (76 full-time, 41 part-time). Student-undergrad faculty ratio is 13:1. 2,778 applied, 49% were admitted. 21% from top 10% of their high school class, 43% from top quarter, 72% from top half. Full-time: 1,158 students, 54% women, 46% men. Part-time: 23 students, 57% women, 43% men. Students come from 35 states and territories, 23 other countries, 32% from out-of-state. 0.6% American Indian or Alaska Native, non-Hispanic/Latino; 4% Hispanic/Latino; 13% Black or African American, non-Hispanic/Latino; 0.9% Asian, non-Hispanic/Latino; 0.1% Native Hawaiian or other Pacific Islander, non-Hispanic/Latino; 3% international. 6% 25 or older, 74% live on campus, 6% transferred in. Retention: 72% of full-time freshmen returned the following year. Academic areas with the most degrees conferred: business/marketing; psychology; education. Core. Calendar: 4-1-4. Academic remediation for entering students, ESL program, services for LD students, advanced placement, self-designed majors, honors program, independent study, double major, summer session for credit, part-time degree program, adult/continuing education programs, internships. Off campus study. Study abroad program.
Entrance Requirements: Options: electronic application, early admission, deferred admission, international baccalaureate accepted. Required: high school transcript, minimum 2.5 high school GPA, recommendations, SAT or ACT. Required for some: essay, interview. Entrance: moderately difficult. Application deadline: 3/1. Notification: continuous until 4/1. SAT Reasoning Test deadline: 7/15. Transfer credits accepted: Yes.
Costs Per Year: Application fee: $0. Comprehensive fee: $46,304 includes full-time tuition ($34,070), mandatory fees ($810), and college room and board ($11,424). College room only: $5674. Room and board charges vary according to board plan and housing facility. Part-time tuition: $876 per credit hour. Part-time mandatory fees: $15 per credit hour, $195 per term. Part-time tuition and fees vary according to course load.
Collegiate Environment: Orientation program. Drama-theater group, choral group, student-run newspaper. Social organizations: 46 open to all. Most popular organizations: Voices of Praise, student government, Student Programming Board, Global Citizenship, Peer Mentors. Major annual events: Homecoming, Blister in the Sun, Spring Fling. Student services: health clinic, personal-psychological counseling. Campus security: 24-hour emergency response devices and patrols, late night transport-escort service, controlled dormitory access, campus-wide emergency alert system via cell phones, home phones, and email. Lamar Memorial Library plus 1 other. Books: 123,369 (physical), 272,064 (digital/electronic); Serial titles: 181 (physical), 37,204 (digital/electronic); Databases: 112. Weekly public service hours: 93; students can reserve study rooms. Operations spending for the previous fiscal year: $577,401. 290 computers available on campus for general student use. A campuswide network can be accessed. Students can access the following: online class registration. Staffed computer lab on campus provides training in use of computers, software, and the Internet.
Community Environment: Maryville was founded in 1819 and named for Mary Blount, wife of Governor William Blount. The town is located near the

entrance of the Great Smoky Mountains National Park. Bus and air transportation is available. Fishing, boating, water skiing, golfing, and hiking are favorite sports in the county. Maryville is a suburban community located 15 miles from Knoxville in a metropolitan area of half a million.

■ **MID-AMERICA BAPTIST THEOLOGICAL SEMINARY**
2095 Appling Rd.
Cordova, TN 38016
Tel: (901)751-8453; Free: 800-968-4508
Fax: (901)751-8454
Web Site: www.mabts.edu
Description: Independent Southern Baptist, comprehensive, men only. Awards associate, bachelor's, master's, and doctoral degrees. Founded 1972. Setting: suburban campus with easy access to Memphis. Endowment: $3.6 million. Total enrollment: 327. Faculty: 27 (all full-time). Student-undergrad faculty ratio is 11:1. 77 applied. Full-time: 29 students. Part-time: 22 students. Students come from 26 states and territories. Core. Calendar: semesters. Distance learning, summer session for credit, part-time degree program, internships, graduate courses open to undergrads.
Entrance Requirements: Open admission. Option: electronic application. Required: essay, 2 recommendations. Required for some: high school transcript. Entrance: noncompetitive. Application deadline: 7/1. SAT Reasoning Test deadline: 7/1. SAT Subject Test deadline: 7/1. Transfer credits accepted: Yes.
Costs Per Year: Application fee: $25. Tuition: $9450 full-time, $315 per credit hour part-time. Mandatory fees: $500 full-time, $250 per term part-time. Full-time tuition and fees vary according to course load, degree level, and location. Part-time tuition and fees vary according to course load and location.
Collegiate Environment: Orientation program. Campus security: 24-hour emergency response devices. Ora Byram Allison Memorial Library. Students can reserve study rooms. Operations spending for the previous fiscal year: $217,748. 10 computers available on campus for general student use. A campuswide network can be accessed.

■ **MID-SOUTH CHRISTIAN COLLEGE**
3097 Knight Rd.
Memphis, TN 38118-3151
E-mail: wendylambert@midsouthcc.org
Web Site: www.midsouthchristian.edu
Description: Independent, 4-year, coed. Awards associate and bachelor's degrees. Setting: 12-acre urban campus with easy access to Memphis, TN. Endowment: $138,731. Educational spending for the previous fiscal year: $9500 per student. Total enrollment: 22. Faculty: 13 (2 full-time, 11 part-time). Student-undergrad faculty ratio is 4:1. Full-time: 21 students, 38% women, 62% men. Part-time: 1 student, 100% women. Students come from 8 states and territories, 3 other countries, 53% from out-of-state. 14% Hispanic/Latino; 18% Black or African American, non-Hispanic/Latino; 32% international. 41% 25 or older, 95% live on campus, 14% transferred in. Retention: 67% of full-time freshmen returned the following year. Academic area with the most degrees conferred: theology and religious vocations. Core. Calendar: semesters. Academic remediation for entering students, services for LD students, advanced placement, honors program, independent study, distance learning, double major, part-time degree program, co-op programs and internships.
Entrance Requirements: Required: essay, high school transcript, minimum 2.25 high school GPA, 3 recommendations, ACT. Recommended: interview.
Costs Per Year: Comprehensive fee: $10,890 includes full-time tuition ($6400), mandatory fees ($1090), and college room and board ($3400). Full-time tuition and fees vary according to course load and program. Room and board charges vary according to board plan and housing facility. Part-time tuition: $200 per credit hour. Part-time tuition varies according to course load. Tuition guaranteed not to increase for student's term of enrollment.
Collegiate Environment: Orientation program. Major annual event: Real Life Youth Retreat. Campus security: controlled dormitory access. W. H. Griffin Memorial Resource Center. Books: 27,214 (physical). Weekly public service hours: 42; students can reserve study rooms. 4 computers available on campus for general student use. A computer is required for all students. A campuswide network can be accessed. Students can access the following: online class registration. Staffed computer lab on campus provides training in use of computers and the Internet.

■ **MIDDLE TENNESSEE STATE UNIVERSITY**
1301 E Main St.
Murfreesboro, TN 37132
Tel: (615)898-2300; Free: 800-331-MTSU
Web Site: www.mtsu.edu
Description: State-supported, university, coed. Administratively affiliated with Middle Tennessee State University. Awards bachelor's, master's, and doctoral degrees and post-master's certificates. Founded 1911. Setting: 500-acre urban campus with easy access to Nashville. Total enrollment: 21,630. Faculty: 1,256 (942 full-time, 314 part-time). Student-undergrad faculty ratio is 18:1. 8,055 applied, 94% were admitted. Full-time: 15,586 students, 54% women, 46% men. Part-time: 3,932 students, 56% women, 44% men. 0.2% American Indian or Alaska Native, non-Hispanic/Latino; 6% Hispanic/Latino; 19% Black or African American, non-Hispanic/Latino; 3% Asian, non-Hispanic/Latino; 0.1% Native Hawaiian or other Pacific Islander, non-Hispanic/Latino; 3% international. 14% 25 or older, 14% live on campus, 10% transferred in. Retention: 76% of full-time freshmen returned the following year. Academic areas with the most degrees conferred: business/marketing; liberal arts/general studies; visual and performing arts. Calendar: semesters. Part-time degree program, external degree program, adult/continuing education programs. ROTC: Army, Air Force (c).
Entrance Requirements: Option: international baccalaureate accepted. Required: high school transcript, minimum 3 high school GPA, SAT or ACT. Required for some: essay. Entrance: moderately difficult. SAT Reasoning Test deadline: 8/15. SAT Subject Test deadline: 8/15.
Costs Per Year: Application fee: $25. State resident tuition: $7380 full-time, $293 per credit hour part-time. Nonresident tuition: $26,538 full-time, $1053 per credit hour part-time. Mandatory fees: $1826 full-time, $76 per credit hour part-time. Full-time tuition and fees vary according to course load and program. Part-time tuition and fees vary according to course load and program. College room and board: $9436. College room only: $5436. Room and board charges vary according to board plan and housing facility.
Collegiate Environment: Orientation program. Drama-theater group, choral group, marching band, student-run newspaper, radio station. Social organizations: national fraternities, national sororities, local sororities. Student services: legal services, health clinic, personal-psychological counseling, women's center. Campus security: 24-hour emergency response devices and patrols, student patrols, late night transport-escort service, controlled dormitory access. No special consideration for freshman housing applicants. Options: coed, men-only, women-only housing available. James E. Walker Library.
Community Environment: Murfreesboro is a small city of about 60,000 that is 32 miles southeast of the state capital, Nashville. Capital of the state from 1819 to 1825, Murfreesboro is a city proud of its history, but one that is changing with the times. Community and area facilities include historical landmarks such as Stones River Battlefield and Old Fort Park. Facilities range from an amphitheater to tennis courts, growing industries, charming old homes, new apartment complexes, churches, numerous recreational areas including many for water sports, the Veteran's Hospital. Because of its geographic location in the center of the state, MTSU is easily accessible from any direction.

■ **MILLER-MOTTE TECHNICAL COLLEGE**
6397 Lee Hwy.
Ste. 100
Chattanooga, TN 37421
Tel: (423)414-3247; Free: 800-705-9182
Web Site: www.miller-motte.edu
Description: Proprietary, 2-year, coed. Awards certificates, transfer associate, and terminal associate degrees.

■ **MILLIGAN COLLEGE**
PO Box 500
Milligan College, TN 37682
Tel: (423)461-8700; Free: 800-262-8337
Fax: (423)461-8960
E-mail: admissions@milligan.edu
Web Site: www.milligan.edu
Description: Independent Christian, comprehensive, coed. Awards bachelor's, master's, and doctoral degrees. Founded 1866. Setting: 235-acre suburban campus. Endowment: $46 million. Educational spending for the previous fiscal year: $8618 per student. Total enrollment: 1,225. Faculty: 178 (96 full-time, 82 part-time). Student-undergrad faculty ratio is 9:1. 482 applied, 83% were admitted. Full-time: 734 students, 56% women, 44% men. Part-time: 95 students, 60% women, 40% men. Students come from 32 states and territories, 17 other countries, 36% from out-of-state. 5% Hispanic/Latino; 4% Black or African American, non-Hispanic/Latino; 2%

Asian, non-Hispanic/Latino; 0.4% Native Hawaiian or other Pacific Islander, non-Hispanic/Latino; 5% international. 14% 25 or older, 75% live on campus, 7% transferred in. Retention: 71% of full-time freshmen returned the following year. Academic areas with the most degrees conferred: business/marketing; psychology; communication/journalism. Core. Calendar: semesters. Academic remediation for entering students, advanced placement, self-designed majors, honors program, independent study, distance learning, double major, summer session for credit, part-time degree program, adult/continuing education programs, co-op programs and internships, graduate courses open to undergrads. Off campus study at East Tennessee State University. Study abroad program.

Entrance Requirements: Options: electronic application, deferred admission, international baccalaureate accepted. Required: essay, high school transcript, minimum 2 high school GPA, 2 recommendations, SAT or ACT. Recommended: minimum 3 high school GPA. Required for some: interview. Entrance: moderately difficult. Notification: continuous. SAT Reasoning Test deadline: 8/1. Transfer credits accepted: Yes.

Costs Per Year: Application fee: $30. Comprehensive fee: $41,950 includes full-time tuition ($33,450), mandatory fees ($1200), and college room and board ($7300). College room only: $3650. Part-time mandatory fees: $930 per semester hour, $375 per term. Tuition guaranteed not to increase for student's term of enrollment.

Collegiate Environment: Orientation program. Drama-theater group, choral group, student-run newspaper, radio station. Social organizations: 46 open to all. Most popular organizations: Student Government Association, Vespers-worship team, LINC-service organization, Campus Activities Board, Club Ultimate-frisbee. Major annual events: Wonderful Wednesday, Spirit Week, SUB7 Coffeehouse. Student services: health clinic, personal-psychological counseling. Campus security: 24-hour emergency response devices and patrols, late night transport-escort service, controlled dormitory access. 629 college housing spaces available; 573 were occupied in 2018-19. Freshmen guaranteed college housing. On-campus residence required through senior year. Options: men-only, women-only housing available. P. H. Welshimer Memorial Library plus 1 other. Books: 173,242 (physical), 281,617 (digital/electronic); Serial titles: 932 (physical), 44,498 (digital/electronic); Databases: 95. Weekly public service hours: 89; students can reserve study rooms. Operations spending for the previous fiscal year: $495,249. 102 computers available on campus for general student use. A campuswide network can be accessed from student residence rooms and from off campus. Students can access the following: online class registration. Staffed computer lab on campus provides training in use of computers, software, and the Internet.

■ **MOTLOW STATE COMMUNITY COLLEGE**
PO Box 8500
Lynchburg, TN 37352-8500
Tel: (931)393-1500; Free: 800-654-4877
Fax: (931)393-1681
Web Site: www.mscc.edu
Description: State-supported, 2-year, coed. Part of Tennessee Board of Regents. Awards certificates, transfer associate, and terminal associate degrees. Founded 1969. Setting: 187-acre rural campus with easy access to Nashville. Endowment: $7.1 million. Educational spending for the previous fiscal year: $3669 per student. Total enrollment: 6,886. Student-undergrad faculty ratio is 18:1. 4,013 applied, 100% were admitted. Full-time: 4,018 students, 65% women, 35% men. Part-time: 2,868 students, 75% women, 25% men. 1% from out-of-state. 0.3% American Indian or Alaska Native, non-Hispanic/Latino; 9% Hispanic/Latino; 12% Black or African American, non-Hispanic/Latino; 3% Asian, non-Hispanic/Latino; 0.1% Native Hawaiian or other Pacific Islander, non-Hispanic/Latino; 0.1% international. 21% 25 or older, 6% transferred in. Core. Calendar: semesters. Academic remediation for entering students, services for LD students, advanced placement, accelerated degree program, honors program, independent study, distance learning, double major, summer session for credit, part-time degree program, adult/continuing education programs, co-op programs. Study abroad program.

Entrance Requirements: Open admission. Options: electronic application, early admission, deferred admission. Required: high school transcript, SAT or ACT. Entrance: noncompetitive. Notification: continuous. Transfer credits accepted: Yes.

Costs Per Year: Application fee: $0. State resident tuition: $3936 full-time, $164 per credit hour part-time. Nonresident tuition: $12,288 full-time, $512 per credit hour part-time. Mandatory fees: $296 full-time, $9 per credit hour

part-time, $40 per term part-time. Full-time tuition and fees vary according to course load and program. Part-time tuition and fees vary according to program.

Collegiate Environment: Orientation program. Drama-theater group, choral group, student-run newspaper. Social organizations: 23 open to all. Most popular organizations: Phi Theta Kappa, Student Government Association, Baptist Collegiate Ministries, Art Club, Psi Beta. Major annual events: Spring Fling, Homecoming. Student services: personal-psychological counseling. Campus security: 24-hour patrols, late night transport-escort service. College housing not available. Clayton-Glass Library. Books: 63,642 (physical), 419,239 (digital/electronic); Serial titles: 94 (physical), 37,886 (digital/electronic); Databases: 58. Students can reserve study rooms. Operations spending for the previous fiscal year: $724,967.

Community Environment: Tullahoma is located in the southwest corner of Coffee County, not far from Shelbyville. See University of Tennessee - Space Institute.

■ **NASHVILLE STATE COMMUNITY COLLEGE**
120 White Bridge Rd.
Nashville, TN 37209-4515
Tel: (615)353-3333; Free: 800-272-7363
Fax: (615)353-3243
E-mail: recruiting@nscc.edu
Web Site: www.nscc.edu
Description: State-supported, 2-year, coed. Part of Tennessee Board of Regents. Awards certificates, transfer associate, and terminal associate degrees. Founded 1970. Setting: 85-acre urban campus. Total enrollment: 8,914. Student-undergrad faculty ratio is 19:1. Students come from 55 other countries, 2% from out-of-state. 0.3% American Indian or Alaska Native, non-Hispanic/Latino; 6% Hispanic/Latino; 27% Black or African American, non-Hispanic/Latino; 4% Asian, non-Hispanic/Latino; 0.2% Native Hawaiian or other Pacific Islander, non-Hispanic/Latino. 55% 25 or older. Core. Calendar: semesters. Academic remediation for entering students, ESL program, services for LD students, advanced placement, distance learning, double major, summer session for credit, part-time degree program, adult/continuing education programs, co-op programs. Off campus study. Study abroad program.

Entrance Requirements: Open admission except for occupational therapy, automotive services technology, surgical technology programs. Option: electronic application. Required: high school transcript, SAT or ACT. Entrance: noncompetitive. Application deadlines: rolling, rolling for nonresidents. Notification: continuous, continuous for nonresidents. Preference given to state residents.

Costs Per Year: Application fee: $20. State resident tuition: $3936 full-time, $164 per credit hour part-time. Nonresident tuition: $16,224 full-time, $676 per credit hour part-time. Mandatory fees: $255 full-time, $10 per credit hour part-time, $15 per term part-time. Full-time tuition and fees vary according to course load. Part-time tuition and fees vary according to course load.

Collegiate Environment: Orientation program. Drama-theater group, choral group, student-run newspaper. Social organizations: 38 open to all. Most popular organizations: National Society of Leadership and Success, Occupational Therapy Club, Phi Theta Kappa, Student Government Association, Black Student Association. Major annual events: Fall Festival, Spring Fling, Diversity Day. Student services: personal-psychological counseling. Campus security: 24-hour emergency response devices and patrols, late night transport-escort service. Jane G. Kisber Memorial Library. Students can reserve study rooms. 518 computers available on campus for general student use. Computer purchase/lease plans available. A campuswide network can be accessed from off-campus. Students can access the following: online class registration. Staffed computer lab on campus provides training in use of computers, software, and the Internet.

Community Environment: See Vanderbilt University.

■ **NATIONAL COLLEGE (BRISTOL)**
1328 Hwy. 11 W
Bristol, TN 37620
Tel: (423)878-4440; Free: 888-9-JOBREADY
Web Site: www.national-college.edu
Description: Proprietary, primarily 2-year, coed. Part of National College of Business and Technology. Awards diplomas, terminal associate, and bachelor's degrees. Founded 1992. Setting: small town campus. Core. Calendar: quarters. Services for LD students, advanced placement, honors program, double major, summer session for credit, part-time degree program, internships.

Entrance Requirements: Open admission. Option: electronic application. Required: high school transcript. Recommended: interview. Entrance: noncompetitive. Application deadline: rolling.

Collegiate Environment: Orientation program. National Business College-Bristol Campus Library.

■ NATIONAL COLLEGE (NASHVILLE)

1638 Bell Rd.
Nashville, TN 37211
Tel: (615)333-3344; Free: 888-9-JOBREADY
Web Site: www.national-college.edu

Description: Proprietary, 2-year, coed. Part of National College of Business and Technology. Awards diplomas and terminal associate degrees. Founded 1915. Setting: 1-acre urban campus. Core. Calendar: quarters. Services for LD students, honors program, double major, summer session for credit, part-time degree program.

Entrance Requirements: Open admission. Option: electronic application. Recommended: interview. Entrance: noncompetitive. Application deadline: rolling. Notification: continuous.

Collegiate Environment: Orientation program.

■ NORTH CENTRAL INSTITUTE

168 Jack Miller Blvd.
Clarksville, TN 37042
Tel: (931)431-9700; Free: 800-603-4116
Fax: (931)431-9771
E-mail: admissions@nci.edu
Web Site: www.nci.edu

Description: Proprietary, 2-year, coed. Awards terminal associate degrees. Founded 1988. Setting: 14-acre suburban campus. Total enrollment: 88. Faculty: (7 full-time). Student-undergrad faculty ratio is 10:1. 29% from out-of-state. 73% 25 or older. Core. Calendar: continuous. Advanced placement, independent study, summer session for credit, part-time degree program, external degree program.

Entrance Requirements: Open admission. Options: electronic application, early admission. Recommended: high school transcript. Entrance: noncompetitive. Application deadline: rolling. Notification: continuous. Transfer credits accepted: Yes.

Costs Per Year: Application fee: $35. Tuition: $292 per course part-time.

Collegiate Environment: Campus security: 24-hour emergency response devices. Media Resource Center.

■ NORTHEAST STATE COMMUNITY COLLEGE

PO Box 246
Blountville, TN 37617-0246
Tel: (423)323-3191; Free: 800-836-7822
Fax: (423)323-0215
E-mail: jgstarling@northeaststate.edu
Web Site: www.northeaststate.edu

Description: State-supported, 2-year, coed. Part of Tennessee Board of Regents. Awards certificates, transfer associate, and terminal associate degrees. Founded 1966. Setting: 95-acre small town campus. Endowment: $9.9 million. Educational spending for the previous fiscal year: $2484 per student. Total enrollment: 6,088. Faculty: 279 (124 full-time, 155 part-time). Student-undergrad faculty ratio is 24:1. 2,657 applied, 72% were admitted. 6% from top 10% of their high school class, 16% from top quarter, 33% from top half. Full-time: 3,421 students, 51% women, 49% men. Part-time: 2,667 students, 53% women, 47% men. Students come from 4 states and territories, 5 other countries, 2% from out-of-state. 0.3% American Indian or Alaska Native, non-Hispanic/Latino; 3% Hispanic/Latino; 2% Black or African American, non-Hispanic/Latino; 0.7% Asian, non-Hispanic/Latino; 0.1% Native Hawaiian or other Pacific Islander, non-Hispanic/Latino; 0.2% international. 25% 25 or older, 4% transferred in. Retention: 61% of full-time freshmen returned the following year. Core. Calendar: semesters. Academic remediation for entering students, services for LD students, advanced placement, honors program, distance learning, double major, summer session for credit, part-time degree program, co-op programs. Study abroad program.

Entrance Requirements: Open admission. Options: electronic application, international baccalaureate accepted. Required: high school transcript. Entrance: noncompetitive. Transfer credits accepted: Yes.

Costs Per Year: State resident tuition: $3936 full-time, $164 per credit hour part-time. Nonresident tuition: $16,224 full-time, $676 per credit hour part-time. Mandatory fees: $374 full-time, $13 per credit hour part-time, $31 per

term part-time. Full-time tuition and fees vary according to course load. Part-time tuition and fees vary according to course load.

Collegiate Environment: Orientation program. Drama-theater group. Social organizations: 33 open to all. Most popular organizations: Phi Theta Kappa, G.R.E.E.N.S, Argumentation and Debate Society, Skills, USA, Sci-Fi Fantasy Guild. Major annual events: The Big Event, Club Fair, Fall Carnival. Student services: personal-psychological counseling. Campus security: 24-hour emergency response devices and patrols, late night transport-escort service, Safe Northeast Program. Wayne G. Basler Library plus 1 other. Books: 63,647 (physical), 316,562 (digital/electronic); Serial titles: 132 (physical), 48,455 (digital/electronic); Databases: 93. Operations spending for the previous fiscal year: $886,178. 2,000 computers available on campus for general student use. A campuswide network can be accessed from off-campus. Students can access the following: online class registration, online transcripts. Staffed computer lab on campus.

Community Environment: Blountville is located in the center of the Tri-Cities triangle of Bristol-Kingsport-Johnson City, approximately 15 miles from each city. Chemical, defense, manufacturing, and banking industries are numerous. The medical industry is a growing part of the economy. The Northeast Tennessee area is bordered by Virginia and North Carolina and is less than a day's drive to both East Coast recreation areas and large metropolitan areas such as Atlanta, GA, and Washington, DC. A system of TVA lakes offer warm weather recreation and snow skiing is a short drive away in the winter. Part-time employment is available.

■ NOSSI COLLEGE OF ART

590 Creative Way
Madison, TN 37115
Tel: (615)514-2787; Free: 888-986-2787
Fax: (615)851-1087
E-mail: admissions@nossi.edu
Web Site: www.nossi.edu

Description: Proprietary, 4-year, coed. Awards associate and bachelor's degrees. Founded 1973. Setting: 10-acre urban campus with easy access to Nashville. Total enrollment: 254. Faculty: 38 (4 full-time, 34 part-time). Student-undergrad faculty ratio is 8:1. Full-time: 254 students, 62% women, 38% men. Students come from 9 states and territories, 37% from out-of-state. 0.8% American Indian or Alaska Native, non-Hispanic/Latino; 4% Hispanic/Latino; 20% Black or African American, non-Hispanic/Latino; 0.8% Asian, non-Hispanic/Latino; 0.4% Native Hawaiian or other Pacific Islander, non-Hispanic/Latino. 26% 25 or older, 11% transferred in. Retention: 88% of full-time freshmen returned the following year. Core. Calendar: semesters. Independent study, part-time degree program, internships. Off campus study at Pellissippi State.

Entrance Requirements: Options: electronic application, early admission. Required: essay, high school transcript, interview, portfolio of work. Required for some: ACT. Application deadline: rolling. Notification: continuous. Transfer credits accepted: Yes.

Costs Per Year: Application fee: $100. Tuition: $17,700 full-time. Mandatory fees: $100 full-time. Tuition guaranteed not to increase for student's term of enrollment.

Collegiate Environment: Orientation program. Social organizations: 2 open to all; national fraternities, national sororities, local fraternities; 6% of eligible men and 8% of eligible women are members. Most popular organizations: Kappa Pi, CMA.EDU, Fashion Alliance. Campus security: gated entrance, ID badges for building access, doors are locked at all times. Learning Resource Center. 22 computers available on campus for general student use. A computer is required for all students.

■ O'MORE SCHOOL OF DESIGN AT BELMONT UNIVERSITY

1900 Belmont Blvd.
Nashville, TN 37212
Tel: (615)794-4254; Free: 888-662-1970
Fax: (615)790-1662
E-mail: tbagsby@omorecollege.edu
Web Site: www.omorecollege.edu

Description: Independent, 4-year, coed. Awards bachelor's degrees. Founded 1970. Setting: 7-acre small town campus with easy access to Nashville. Total enrollment: 148. Faculty: 44 (12 full-time, 32 part-time). Student-undergrad faculty ratio is 7:1. 89 applied, 31% were admitted. 20% from top 10% of their high school class, 30% from top quarter, 50% from top half. 5 student government officers. Full-time: 131 students, 88% women, 12% men. Part-time: 17 students, 94% women, 6% men. Students come from 20 states and territories, 1 other country, 22% from out-of-state. 0.7%

American Indian or Alaska Native, non-Hispanic/Latino; 4% Hispanic/Latino; 6% Black or African American, non-Hispanic/Latino; 3% Asian, non-Hispanic/Latino; 0.7% Native Hawaiian or other Pacific Islander, non-Hispanic/Latino; 1% international. 21% 25 or older, 7% transferred in. Retention: 83% of full-time freshmen returned the following year. Academic area with the most degrees conferred: visual and performing arts. Core. Calendar: semesters. Services for LD students, advanced placement, independent study, summer session for credit, part-time degree program, co-op programs and internships.

Entrance Requirements: Options: electronic application, early admission, deferred admission, international baccalaureate accepted. Required: high school transcript, interview, minimum 3.0 GPA or ACT score of 20, SAT or ACT. Required for some: essay. Entrance: moderately difficult. Application deadline: 7/31. Notification: continuous, continuous for nonresidents. SAT Reasoning Test deadline: 7/31. SAT Subject Test deadline: 7/31. Transfer credits accepted: Yes.

Collegiate Environment: Orientation program. Social organizations: 6 open to all. Most popular organizations: Student Activities Council, Magnolia Social, O'More Fashion Association, LeP (Interior Design Association), Graphic Designers Guild. Major annual events: Lunch on the Lawn, Winter Welcome, Fall Ball. Campus security: on-campus security/contracted security until 10pm M-F, 24-hour studio key access. McAfee Library. Books: 2,242 (physical); Databases: 30. Weekly public service hours: 40. 19 computers available on campus for general student use. A computer is required for all students. A campuswide network can be accessed. Students can access the following: online class registration. Staffed computer lab on campus provides training in use of computers, software, and the Internet.

■ PELLISSIPPI STATE COMMUNITY COLLEGE
PO Box 22990
Knoxville, TN 37933-0990
Tel: (865)694-6400
Web Site: www.pstcc.edu

Description: State-supported, 2-year, coed. Part of Tennessee Board of Regents. Awards transfer associate and terminal associate degrees. Founded 1974. Setting: 144-acre suburban campus. Total enrollment: 10,297. Student-undergrad faculty ratio is 24:1. 3,834 applied, 100% were admitted. 1% from out-of-state. 33% 25 or older. Retention: 60% of full-time freshmen returned the following year. Core. Calendar: semesters. Academic remediation for entering students, ESL program, services for LD students, advanced placement, self-designed majors, freshman honors college, honors program, distance learning, double major, summer session for credit, part-time degree program, adult/continuing education programs, co-op programs and internships.

Entrance Requirements: Open admission. Options: electronic application, early admission, deferred admission. Required: high school transcript. Required for some: SAT or ACT. Entrance: noncompetitive. Application deadline: rolling. Notification: continuous.

Collegiate Environment: Orientation program. Drama-theater group, choral group, student-run newspaper. Student services: personal-psychological counseling. Campus security: 24-hour patrols. Educational Resources Center plus 1 other.

Community Environment: Located in Tennessee's third largest metropolitan area, Pellissippi State comprehensively serves the greater Knox and Blount County area and extends its engineering technology offerings to Anderson, Loudon, Roane, Cumberland, Campbell, Fentress, Scott, and Morgan Counties. The main campus is located west of Knoxville in Knox County. The city of Knoxville lies on the Tennessee River, about 40 miles from the Great Smoky Mountains National Park. Knoxville's population approaches 180,000, with approximately 655,000 in the metropolitan area. The city supports a wide variety of cultural and sports activities. The city is a business center in the East Tennessee Valley with markets in tobacco, livestock, marble, and zinc. It is home to the state's flagship higher education institution: the University of Tennessee. The headquarters of the Tennessee Valley Authority are also located in the city.

■ REMINGTON COLLEGE-MEMPHIS CAMPUS
2710 Nonconnah Blvd.
Memphis, TN 38132
Tel: (901)291-4200; Free: 800-323-8122
Fax: (901)396-8310
Web Site: www.remingtoncollege.edu

Description: Independent, primarily 2-year, coed. Awards transfer associate and bachelor's degrees. Calendar: quarters.

■ REMINGTON COLLEGE-NASHVILLE CAMPUS
441 Donelson Pke.
Ste. 150
Nashville, TN 37214
Tel: (615)889-5520; Free: 800-323-8122
Fax: (615)889-5528
Web Site: www.remingtoncollege.edu

Description: Independent, 2-year, coed. Awards terminal associate degrees. Founded 2003. Calendar: quarters.

■ RHODES COLLEGE
2000 N Pky.
Memphis, TN 38112-1690
Tel: (901)843-3000; Free: 800-844-5969
Fax: (901)843-3719
E-mail: adminfo@rhodes.edu
Web Site: www.rhodes.edu

Description: Independent, comprehensive, coed. Awards bachelor's and master's degrees (master's degree in accounting only). Founded 1848. Setting: 100-acre urban campus with easy access to Memphis. Endowment: $359.3 million. Research spending for the previous fiscal year: $1.1 million. Educational spending for the previous fiscal year: $16,957 per student. Total enrollment: 2,035. Faculty: 222 (180 full-time, 42 part-time). Student-undergrad faculty ratio is 10:1. 5,093 applied, 45% were admitted. 54% from top 10% of their high school class, 85% from top quarter, 99% from top half. Full-time: 1,992 students, 56% women, 44% men. Part-time: 16 students, 63% women, 37% men. Students come from 46 states and territories, 35 other countries, 71% from out-of-state. 0.2% American Indian or Alaska Native, non-Hispanic/Latino; 6% Hispanic/Latino; 9% Black or African American, non-Hispanic/Latino; 6% Asian, non-Hispanic/Latino; 0.1% Native Hawaiian or other Pacific Islander, non-Hispanic/Latino; 5% international. 69% live on campus, 1% transferred in. Retention: 90% of full-time freshmen returned the following year. Academic areas with the most degrees conferred: social sciences; biological/life sciences; business/marketing. Core. Calendar: semesters. Services for LD students, advanced placement, self-designed majors, honors program, independent study, double major, summer session for credit, part-time degree program, co-op programs and internships, graduate courses open to undergrads. Off campus study at University of Memphis, Christian Brothers University. Study abroad program. ROTC: Army (c), Naval (c), Air Force (c).

Entrance Requirements: Options: electronic application, early admission, early decision, early action, deferred admission, international baccalaureate accepted. Required: essay, high school transcript, SAT or ACT. Recommended: recommendations, interview. Entrance: very difficult. Application deadlines: 1/15, 11/1 for early decision plan 1, 11/1 for early decision plan 2, 11/15 for early action. Notification: 4/1, 12/1 for early decision plan 1, 2/1 for early decision plan 2, 1/15 for early action. SAT Reasoning Test deadline: 1/15. Transfer credits accepted: Yes. Applicants placed on waiting list: 1,253. Wait-listed applicants offered admission: 42. Early decision applicants: 155. Early decision applicants admitted: 97. Early action applicants: 2,753. Early action applicants admitted: 1,382.

Costs Per Year: Comprehensive fee: $59,293 includes full-time tuition ($47,580), mandatory fees ($310), and college room and board ($11,403). College room only: $5373. Part-time tuition: $1970 per credit hour.

Collegiate Environment: Orientation program. Drama-theater group, choral group, student-run newspaper, radio station. Social organizations: 147 open to all; national fraternities, national sororities; 34% of eligible men and 40% of eligible women are members. Most popular organizations: Rhodes Outdoors Club, South Asian Culture and Advocacy, Rhodes College Crew Team, Gender and Sexuality Alliance, Culture of Consent. Major annual events: Rites of Spring (concert), Crawfish Boil, Homecoming. Student services: health clinic, personal-psychological counseling, women's center. Campus security: 24-hour emergency response devices and patrols, student patrols, late night transport-escort service. 1,482 college housing spaces available; 1,399 were occupied in 2018-19. Freshmen guaranteed college housing. On-campus residence required through sophomore year. Options: coed, men-only, women-only housing available. Paul Barret, Jr. Library. Books: 246,054 (physical); Serial titles: 94,665 (digital/electronic); Databases: 151. Weekly public service hours: 113. Operations spending for the previous fiscal year: $3.2 million. 1,000 computers available on campus for general student use. A campuswide network can be accessed from student residence rooms and from off campus. Students can access the following: online class registration. Staffed computer lab on campus (open 24 hours a day) provides training in use of computers, software, and the Internet.

Community Environment: See University of Memphis.

■ ROANE STATE COMMUNITY COLLEGE

276 Patton Ln.
Harriman, TN 37748-5011
Tel: (865)354-3000; Free: 866-462-7722
Fax: (865)882-4562
E-mail: admissionsrecords@roanestate.edu
Web Site: www.roanestate.edu

Description: State-supported, 2-year, coed. Part of Tennessee Board of Regents. Awards certificates, transfer associate, and terminal associate degrees. Founded 1971. Setting: 104-acre small town campus with easy access to Knoxville. Endowment: $8.3 million. Total enrollment: 5,832. Faculty: 385 (121 full-time, 264 part-time). Student-undergrad faculty ratio is 17:1. 1,817 applied, 97% were admitted. Full-time: 2,358 students, 62% women, 38% men. Part-time: 3,474 students, 68% women, 32% men. Students come from 11 states and territories, 5 other countries, 1% from out-of-state. 0.3% American Indian or Alaska Native, non-Hispanic/Latino; 3% Hispanic/Latino; 3% Black or African American, non-Hispanic/Latino; 0.7% Asian, non-Hispanic/Latino; 0.1% Native Hawaiian or other Pacific Islander, non-Hispanic/Latino; 0.2% international. 34% 25 or older, 4% transferred in. Retention: 62% of full-time freshmen returned the following year. Core. Calendar: semesters. Academic remediation for entering students, services for LD students, advanced placement, accelerated degree program, honors program, independent study, distance learning, double major, summer session for credit, co-op programs and internships. Off campus study. Study abroad program. ROTC: Army (c), Air Force (c).

Entrance Requirements: Open admission except for allied health programs, nursing, and mechatronics. Options: electronic application, early admission, deferred admission. Required: high school transcript. Entrance: noncompetitive. Application deadline: rolling. Notification: continuous. Transfer credits accepted: Yes.

Costs Per Year: Application fee: $20. State resident tuition: $3936 full-time, $164 per credit hour part-time. Nonresident tuition: $16,224 full-time, $676 per credit hour part-time. Mandatory fees: $303 full-time, $16 per credit hour part-time, $27 per term part-time.

Collegiate Environment: Orientation program. Drama-theater group, choral group. Social organizations: 21 open to all. Most popular organizations: Baptist Student Union, American Chemical Society, Physical Therapy Student Association, Student Artists At Roane State (S.T.A.R.S.), Phi Theta Kappa. Major annual event: Spring Fling. Student services: personal-psychological counseling. Campus security: 24-hour patrols. Roane State Community College Library plus 3 others. 750 computers available on campus for general student use. A campuswide network can be accessed. Students can access the following: online class registration. Staffed computer lab on campus.

Community Environment: Harriman is located near the cities of Kingston and Rockwood and is easily accessible via U.S. highways.

■ SAE INSTITUTE NASHVILLE

7 Music Cir. N
Nashville, TN 37203
Tel: (615)244-5848
Web Site: www.sae.edu

Description: Proprietary, 2-year, coed. Awards diplomas, transfer associate, and terminal associate degrees.

■ SOUTH COLLEGE

720 N Fifth Ave.
Knoxville, TN 37917
Tel: (865)524-3043
Fax: (865)673-8019
Web Site: www.southcollegetn.edu

Description: Proprietary, comprehensive, coed. Awards associate, bachelor's, and master's degrees. Founded 1882. Setting: 2-acre urban campus. Total enrollment: 825. Student-undergrad faculty ratio is 16:1. 47 applied, 100% were admitted. 60% 25 or older. Retention: 35% of full-time freshmen returned the following year. Core. Calendar: quarters. Advanced placement, double major, summer session for credit, part-time degree program, adult/continuing education programs, internships.

Entrance Requirements: Options: early admission, deferred admission. Required: high school transcript, interview. Entrance: moderately difficult. Application deadline: 10/1.

Collegiate Environment: Orientation program. Campus security: evening and morning security patrols. Knoxville Business College Library.

■ SOUTHERN ADVENTIST UNIVERSITY

PO Box 370
Collegedale, TN 37315-0370
Tel: (423)236-2000; Free: 800-768-8437
Fax: (423)236-1000
E-mail: jlandivar@southern.edu
Web Site: www.southern.edu

Description: Independent Seventh-day Adventist, comprehensive, coed. Awards associate, bachelor's, master's, and doctoral degrees and post-master's certificates. Founded 1892. Setting: 1,000-acre small town campus with easy access to Chattanooga. Endowment: $38.1 million. Research spending for the previous fiscal year: $57,705. Total enrollment: 3,035. Faculty: 169 (166 full-time, 3 part-time). Student-undergrad faculty ratio is 14:1. 1,423 applied, 95% were admitted. Full-time: 2,160 students, 58% women, 42% men. Part-time: 404 students, 59% women, 41% men. Students come from 50 states and territories, 39 other countries. 0.1% American Indian or Alaska Native, non-Hispanic/Latino; 21% Hispanic/Latino; 10% Black or African American, non-Hispanic/Latino; 9% Asian, non-Hispanic/Latino; 0.5% Native Hawaiian or other Pacific Islander, non-Hispanic/Latino; 9% international. 18% 25 or older, 3% transferred in. Retention: 74% of full-time freshmen returned the following year. Academic areas with the most degrees conferred: health professions and related sciences; business/marketing; biological/life sciences. Core. Calendar: semesters. ESL program, services for LD students, advanced placement, self-designed majors, honors program, independent study, distance learning, double major, summer session for credit, internships, graduate courses open to undergrads. Off campus study. Study abroad program.

Entrance Requirements: Options: electronic application, deferred admission, international baccalaureate accepted. Required: high school transcript, minimum 2.5 high school GPA, SAT or ACT. Required for some: essay, minimum 2.25 high school GPA. Entrance: moderately difficult. Application deadline: rolling. Notification: continuous. SAT Reasoning Test deadline: 8/15. SAT Subject Test deadline: 8/15. Transfer credits accepted: Yes.

Costs Per Year: Application fee: $25. Comprehensive fee: $28,890 includes full-time tuition ($21,100), mandatory fees ($850), and college room and board ($6940). College room only: $4400. Full-time tuition and fees vary according to course load. Room and board charges vary according to board plan. Part-time tuition: $890 per credit hour. Part-time mandatory fees: $850 per term. Part-time tuition and fees vary according to course load.

Collegiate Environment: Orientation program. Drama-theater group, choral group, student-run newspaper, radio station. Social organizations: 46 open to all. Most popular organizations: Asian Club, Black Christian Union, Business Society, School of Nursing, Student Ministerial Association. Major annual events: Community Service Day, Christmas on the Promenade, Convocations. Student services: health clinic, personal-psychological counseling. Campus security: 24-hour emergency response devices and patrols, student patrols, late night transport-escort service, controlled dormitory access. McKee Library plus 7 others. Books: 173,284 (physical), 107,663 (digital/electronic); Serial titles: 510 (physical), 170 (digital/electronic); Databases: 160. Weekly public service hours: 82; students can reserve study rooms. Operations spending for the previous fiscal year: $1.5 million. 300 computers available on campus for general student use. A campuswide network can be accessed from student residence rooms and from off campus. Students can access the following: online class registration. Staffed computer lab on campus provides training in use of computers, software, and the Internet.

Community Environment: Collegedale is located 18 miles east of Chattanooga where the recreation areas of the TVA lake system are within 10 miles. There are residence halls for the students; part-time employment opportunities are available.

■ SOUTHWEST TENNESSEE COMMUNITY COLLEGE

PO Box 780
Memphis, TN 38101-0780
Tel: (901)333-5000; Free: 877-717-STCC
Fax: (901)333-4273
E-mail: vdowdy@southwest.tn.edu
Web Site: www.southwest.tn.edu

Description: State-supported, 2-year, coed. Part of Tennessee Board of Regents. Awards certificates, transfer associate, and terminal associate degrees. Founded 2000. Setting: 100-acre urban campus. Total enrollment:

10,167. 5,416 applied, 100% were admitted. Full-time: 4,183 students, 58% women, 42% men. Part-time: 5,984 students, 64% women, 36% men. Students come from 13 states and territories, 8 other countries, 2% from out-of-state. 37% 25 or older, 6% transferred in. Core. Calendar: semesters. Academic remediation for entering students, ESL program, services for LD students, advanced placement, accelerated degree program, self-designed majors, distance learning, double major, summer session for credit, part-time degree program, adult/continuing education programs, co-op programs and internships. ROTC: Army (c), Air Force (c).

Entrance Requirements: Open admission. Options: early admission, deferred admission, international baccalaureate accepted. Required: high school transcript. Entrance: noncompetitive. Notification: continuous.

Collegiate Environment: Orientation program. Drama-theater group, choral group, student-run newspaper. Social organizations: 18 open to all. Most popular organizations: Human Key Society, NAACP, Black Student Association, Honor Society, Collegiate Secretaries. Major annual events: College Transfer Day, International Night, Career Day. Student services: personal-psychological counseling. Campus security: 24-hour emergency response devices and patrols, late night transport-escort service. Infonet Library plus 4 others.

Community Environment: See University of Memphis.

■ STRAYER UNIVERSITY-KNOXVILLE CAMPUS

10118 Parkside Dr.
Ste. 200
Knoxville, TN 37922
Tel: (865)288-6000; Free: 888-311-0355
Web Site: www.strayer.edu

Description: Proprietary, comprehensive, coed. Awards associate, bachelor's, and master's degrees.

■ STRAYER UNIVERSITY-NASHVILLE CAMPUS

1809 Dabbs Ave.
Nashville, TN 37210
Tel: (615)871-2260; Free: 888-311-0355
Web Site: www.strayer.edu

Description: Proprietary, comprehensive, coed. Awards associate, bachelor's, and master's degrees.

■ STRAYER UNIVERSITY-SHELBY CAMPUS

7275 Appling Farms Pky.
Memphis, TN 38133
Tel: (901)251-7100; Free: 888-311-0355
Web Site: www.strayer.edu

Description: Proprietary, comprehensive, coed. Awards associate, bachelor's, and master's degrees.

■ STRAYER UNIVERSITY-THOUSAND OAKS CAMPUS

2620 Thousand Oaks Blvd.
Ste. 1100
Memphis, TN 38118
Tel: (901)370-5200; Free: 888-311-0355
Web Site: www.strayer.edu

Description: Proprietary, comprehensive, coed. Awards associate, bachelor's, and master's degrees.

■ TENNESSEE STATE UNIVERSITY

3500 John A Merritt Blvd.
Nashville, TN 37209-1561
Tel: (615)963-5000
Fax: (615)963-5108
E-mail: jcade@tnstate.edu
Web Site: www.tnstate.edu

Description: State-supported, comprehensive, coed. Part of Tennessee Board of Regents. Awards associate, bachelor's, master's, and doctoral degrees. Founded 1912. Setting: 450-acre urban campus with easy access to Nashville. Total enrollment: 8,753. Faculty: 658 (393 full-time, 265 part-time). Student-undergrad faculty ratio is 14:1. 8,857 applied, 53% were admitted. Full-time: 5,692 students, 58% women, 42% men. Part-time: 1,315 students, 65% women, 35% men. Students come from 46 states and territories, 21 other countries, 33% from out-of-state. 0.1% American Indian or Alaska Native, non-Hispanic/Latino; 1% Hispanic/Latino; 71% Black or African American, non-Hispanic/Latino; 0.8% Asian, non-Hispanic/Latino; 11% international. 25% 25 or older, 7% transferred in. Retention: 59% of

full-time freshmen returned the following year. Core. Calendar: semesters. Academic remediation for entering students, services for LD students, accelerated degree program, freshman honors college, honors program, independent study, summer session for credit, part-time degree program, external degree program, adult/continuing education programs, co-op programs and internships. Off campus study at Volunteer State Community College, Meharry Medical College. ROTC: Army (c), Naval (c), Air Force.

Entrance Requirements: Option: electronic application. Required: SAT or ACT. Entrance: minimally difficult. Application deadline: 8/1. Notification: continuous until 8/15. Preference given to state residents. Transfer credits accepted: Yes.

Costs Per Year: Application fee: $25. State resident tuition: $6576 full-time, $274 per hour part-time. Nonresident tuition: $19,296 full-time, $804 per hour part-time. Mandatory fees: $1108 full-time, $70 per hour part-time. College room and board: $7806. College room only: $3806.

Collegiate Environment: Orientation program. Drama-theater group, choral group, marching band, student-run newspaper, radio station. Social organizations: 103 open to all; national fraternities, national sororities, local fraternities, local sororities. Major annual events: Homecoming, Greek Weeks, Student Elections. Student services: health clinic, personal-psychological counseling, women's center. Campus security: 24-hour patrols, controlled dormitory access. Martha M. Brown/Lois H. Daniel Library plus 1 other. 1,025 computers available on campus for general student use. A campuswide network can be accessed from student residence rooms and from off campus. Students can access the following: online class registration. Staffed computer lab on campus provides training in use of computers, software, and the Internet.

Community Environment: See Vanderbilt University.

■ TENNESSEE TECHNOLOGICAL UNIVERSITY

N Dixie Ave.
Cookeville, TN 38505
Tel: (931)372-3101; Free: 800-255-8881
Fax: (931)372-6250
Web Site: www.tntech.edu

Description: State-supported, university, coed. Part of Tennessee Board of Regents. Awards bachelor's, master's, and doctoral degrees and post-master's certificates. Founded 1915. Setting: small town campus. Endowment: $65.9 million. Research spending for the previous fiscal year: $9.6 million. Educational spending for the previous fiscal year: $6916 per student. Total enrollment: 10,504. Faculty: 645 (425 full-time, 220 part-time). Student-undergrad faculty ratio is 18:1. 7,143 applied, 64% were admitted. 25% from top 10% of their high school class, 53% from top quarter, 83% from top half. 3 National Merit Scholars. Full-time: 8,259 students, 45% women, 55% men. Part-time: 1,106 students, 45% women, 55% men. Students come from 32 states and territories, 51 other countries, 3% from out-of-state. 0.1% American Indian or Alaska Native, non-Hispanic/Latino; 3% Hispanic/Latino; 4% Black or African American, non-Hispanic/Latino; 1% Asian, non-Hispanic/Latino; 4% international. 10% 25 or older, 30% live on campus, 8% transferred in. Retention: 79% of full-time freshmen returned the following year. Academic areas with the most degrees conferred: engineering; business/marketing; education. Core. Calendar: semesters. Academic remediation for entering students, ESL program, services for LD students, advanced placement, accelerated degree program, self-designed majors, honors program, independent study, distance learning, double major, summer session for credit, part-time degree program, external degree program, adult/continuing education programs, co-op programs and internships, graduate courses open to undergrads. Off campus study at Roane State Community College-Oak Ridge, TN; Pellissippi State Community College-Knoxville, TN; Motlow State Community College, McMinnville, TN; Chattanooga State Community College, Chattanooga, TN. Study abroad program. ROTC: Army, Air Force (c).

Entrance Requirements: Options: electronic application, early admission, deferred admission, international baccalaureate accepted. Required: high school transcript, minimum 2.5 high school GPA, SAT or ACT. Recommended: interview, ACT. Entrance: moderately difficult. Application deadline: 8/1. Notification: continuous. Transfer credits accepted: Yes.

Costs Per Year: Application fee: $25. State resident tuition: $8731 full-time, $390 per credit hour part-time. Nonresident tuition: $24,595 full-time, $1051 per credit hour part-time. Full-time tuition varies according to program. Part-time tuition varies according to program. College room and board: $9736. College room only: $5060. Room and board charges vary according to board plan and housing facility.

Collegiate Environment: Orientation program. Drama-theater group, choral

group, marching band, student-run newspaper. Social organizations: 241 open to all; national fraternities, national sororities; 20% of eligible men and 20% of eligible women are members. Most popular organizations: Baptist Collegiate Center, Fellowship of Christian Athletes, University Christian Student Center, Residence Hall Association. Major annual events: Homecoming, Greek Week, Career Day. Student services: health clinic, personal-psychological counseling, women's center. Campus security: 24-hour emergency response devices and patrols, late night transport-escort service, controlled dormitory access, student safety organization, lighted pathways. Angelo and Jennette Volpe Library and Media Center. Books: 235,249 (physical), 267,168 (digital/electronic); Serial titles: 120,118 (physical); Databases: 193. Operations spending for the previous fiscal year: $3 million. 227 computers available on campus for general student use. A campuswide network can be accessed. Students can access the following: online class registration, 590 additional computers are available for student use in individual departmental labs. Staffed computer lab on campus provides training in use of computers, software, and the Internet.

Community Environment: Cookeville, located in middle Tennessee, is predominantly an agricultural area. Bus transportation is available. Churches of most denominations, libraries, a hospital, and various civic and service organizations serve the community. Recreational activities include swimming, softball, baseball, tennis, and golf. Center Hill Dam and Reservoir are nearby for many other sports, such as boating, water sports, fishing, and camping.

■ **TENNESSEE WESLEYAN UNIVERSITY**
204 E College St.
Athens, TN 37303
Tel: (423)745-7504; Free: 800-PICK-TWU
Fax: (423)744-9968
E-mail: admissions@twcnet.edu
Web Site: www.tnwesleyan.edu

Description: Independent United Methodist, comprehensive, coed. Awards bachelor's and master's degrees (profile includes information for both the main and branch campuses). Founded 1857. Setting: 40-acre small town campus with easy access to Knoxville, Chattanooga. Endowment: $9.4 million. Educational spending for the previous fiscal year: $6021 per student. Total enrollment: 951. Faculty: 113 (63 full-time, 50 part-time). Student-undergrad faculty ratio is 12:1. 988 applied, 58% were admitted. 10% from top 10% of their high school class, 36% from top quarter, 74% from top half. Full-time: 863 students, 63% women, 37% men. Part-time: 72 students, 67% women, 33% men. Students come from 33 states and territories, 25 other countries, 14% from out-of-state. 0.1% American Indian or Alaska Native, non-Hispanic/Latino; 5% Hispanic/Latino; 9% Black or African American, non-Hispanic/Latino; 1% Asian, non-Hispanic/Latino; 4% international. 15% 25 or older, 30% live on campus, 13% transferred in. Retention: 68% of full-time freshmen returned the following year. Academic areas with the most degrees conferred: business/marketing; health professions and related sciences; parks and recreation. Core. Calendar: semesters. Academic remediation for entering students, services for LD students, advanced placement, accelerated degree program, self-designed majors, honors program, independent study, distance learning, double major, summer session for credit, part-time degree program, adult/continuing education programs, internships. Off campus study at Online Consortium of Independent Colleges (OCICU). Study abroad program.

Entrance Requirements: Options: electronic application, deferred admission, international baccalaureate accepted. Required: high school transcript, minimum 2.25 high school GPA, 1 recommendation, SAT or ACT. Recommended: essay. Required for some: essay, interview. Entrance: minimally difficult. Application deadline: rolling. Notification: continuous. SAT Subject Test deadline: 7/1. Transfer credits accepted: Yes.

Costs Per Year: Application fee: $0. Comprehensive fee: $32,180 includes full-time tuition ($23,300), mandatory fees ($1000), and college room and board ($7880). College room only: $2230. Full-time tuition and fees vary according to program. Room and board charges vary according to board plan and housing facility. Part-time tuition: $590 per credit hour. Part-time mandatory fees: $10 per credit hour. Part-time tuition and fees vary according to program.

Collegiate Environment: Orientation program. Drama-theater group, choral group, student-run newspaper. Social organizations: 48 open to all; national sororities, local fraternities, local sororities; 13% of eligible men and 6% of eligible women are members. Most popular organization: Student Government Association. Major annual events: Annual Day of Service, Opening Convocation, Honors Convocation. Student services: health clinic, personal-

psychological counseling. Campus security: 24-hour patrols, late night transport-escort service, controlled dormitory access, night patrols by trained security personnel. Merner-Pfeiffer Library plus 1 other. Books: 52,465 (physical), 356,697 (digital/electronic); Serial titles: 82 (physical); Databases: 76. Weekly public service hours: 69. Operations spending for the previous fiscal year: $119,860. 205 computers available on campus for general student use. A campuswide network can be accessed from student residence rooms. Students can access the following: online class registration. Staffed computer lab on campus (open 24 hours a day) provides training in use of computers, software, and the Internet.

Community Environment: Athens is the county seat of McMinn County, located between Chattanooga and Knoxville. The town is an industrial community providing jobs for approximately 13,000 people and serving as a shopping center for 50,000 rural residents. Recreational activities in the beautiful mountainous area include big game hunting, fresh water fishing, rafting, kayaking, hiking, and many other sports.

■ **TREVECCA NAZARENE UNIVERSITY**
333 Murfreesboro Rd.
Nashville, TN 37210-2877
Tel: (615)248-1200; Free: 888-210-4TNU
Fax: (615)248-7728
E-mail: admissions_und@trevecca.edu
Web Site: www.trevecca.edu

Description: Independent Nazarene, comprehensive, coed. Awards associate, bachelor's, master's, and doctoral degrees and post-master's certificates. Founded 1901. Setting: 80-acre urban campus. Endowment: $28.9 million. Educational spending for the previous fiscal year: $5378 per student. Total enrollment: 3,927. Faculty: 272 (99 full-time, 173 part-time). Student-undergrad faculty ratio is 18:1. 1,671 applied, 64% were admitted. 22% from top 10% of their high school class, 30% from top quarter, 17% from top half. Full-time: 1,886 students, 63% women, 37% men. Part-time: 425 students, 55% women, 45% men. 35% from out-of-state. 0.4% American Indian or Alaska Native, non-Hispanic/Latino; 9% Hispanic/Latino; 13% Black or African American, non-Hispanic/Latino; 1% Asian, non-Hispanic/Latino; 0.1% Native Hawaiian or other Pacific Islander, non-Hispanic/Latino; 6% international. 34% 25 or older, 39% live on campus, 4% transferred in. Academic areas with the most degrees conferred: business/marketing; health professions and related sciences; theology and religious vocations. Core. Calendar: semesters. Academic remediation for entering students, services for LD students, advanced placement, distance learning, double major, summer session for credit, adult/continuing education programs, internships. Study abroad program. ROTC: Army (c).

Entrance Requirements: Options: electronic application, early admission, deferred admission. Required: high school transcript, minimum 2.5 high school GPA, minimum ACT composite score of 18, SAT Evidence-Based Reading and Writing and Math score of 940, medical history and immunization records, SAT or ACT. Entrance: moderately difficult. Notification: continuous. SAT Reasoning Test deadline: 8/31. Transfer credits accepted: Yes.

Costs Per Year: Comprehensive fee: $34,998 includes full-time tuition ($25,198), mandatory fees ($900), and college room and board ($8900). College room only: $4450.

Collegiate Environment: Orientation program. Drama-theater group, choral group, marching band, student-run newspaper. Major annual events: Homecoming Week, Friday Night Live, Trojan Idol. Student services: health clinic, personal-psychological counseling. Campus security: 24-hour patrols, late night transport-escort service, weather alert warning system (phone, email, siren). On-campus residence required through senior year. Options: men-only, women-only housing available. Waggoner Library. Books: 85,560 (physical), 49,113 (digital/electronic); Serial titles: 299 (physical), 60,127 (digital/electronic); Databases: 44. Weekly public service hours: 91; students can reserve study rooms. Operations spending for the previous fiscal year: $1.2 million. 200 computers available on campus for general student use. A campuswide network can be accessed from student residence rooms and from off campus. Students can access the following: online class registration, Non-traditional and graduate students are registered through Academic Records. Staffed computer lab on campus.

Community Environment: See Vanderbilt University.

■ **TUSCULUM UNIVERSITY**
60 Shiloh Rd.
Greeneville, TN 37743-9997
Tel: (423)636-7300; Free: 800-729-0256
Fax: (423)638-7166

E-mail: admissions@tusculum.edu
Web Site: www.tusculum.edu
Description: Independent Presbyterian, comprehensive, coed. Awards associate, bachelor's, and master's degrees. Founded 1794. Setting: 140-acre small town campus. Endowment: $21.1 million. Total enrollment: 1,767. Faculty: 147 (72 full-time, 75 part-time). Student-undergrad faculty ratio is 17:1. 2,139 applied, 89% were admitted. Full-time: 1,376 students, 50% women, 50% men. Part-time: 112 students, 69% women, 31% men. 30% from out-of-state. 0.5% American Indian or Alaska Native, non-Hispanic/Latino; 4% Hispanic/Latino; 17% Black or African American, non-Hispanic/Latino; 0.3% Asian, non-Hispanic/Latino; 0.1% Native Hawaiian or other Pacific Islander, non-Hispanic/Latino; 5% international. 35% 25 or older, 5% transferred in. Retention: 65% of full-time freshmen returned the following year. Academic areas with the most degrees conferred: business/marketing; education; psychology. Core. Calendar: semesters. Academic remediation for entering students, services for LD students, advanced placement, self-designed majors, honors program, independent study, double major, summer session for credit, part-time degree program, adult/continuing education programs, internships. Study abroad program.
Entrance Requirements: Options: electronic application, early admission, early decision, deferred admission, international baccalaureate accepted. Required: SAT or ACT. Entrance: moderately difficult. Application deadline: rolling. Transfer credits accepted: Yes.
Costs Per Year: Comprehensive fee: $34,050 includes full-time tuition ($24,860) and college room and board ($9190). College room only: $5600. Part-time tuition: $768 per credit hour.
Collegiate Environment: Orientation program. Drama-theater group, choral group, marching band, student-run newspaper, radio station. Student services: health clinic, personal-psychological counseling, women's center. Campus security: 24-hour emergency response devices and patrols, student patrols, late night transport-escort service, controlled dormitory access, trained security personnel on duty. Thomas J. Garland Library plus 2 others. Students can reserve study rooms.
Community Environment: Greeneville, in Greene County, the birthplace of Davy Crockett, is accessible by bus and rail. The city has a full-time recreational director who supervises a year-round program in addition to the hunting, boating, fishing, golf, whitewater rafting, and cycling available in the area. Nearby is the Andrew Johnson Wildlife Management Area.

■ **UNION UNIVERSITY**

1050 Union University Dr.
Jackson, TN 38305-3697
Tel: (731)668-1818; Free: 800-33-UNION
Fax: (731)661-5187
E-mail: rgraves@uu.edu
Web Site: www.uu.edu
Description: Independent Southern Baptist, comprehensive, coed. Awards associate, bachelor's, master's, and doctoral degrees and post-master's certificates. Founded 1823. Setting: 360-acre suburban campus with easy access to Memphis. Endowment: $39.1 million. Research spending for the previous fiscal year: $273,824. Educational spending for the previous fiscal year: $11,658 per student. Total enrollment: 2,189. Faculty: 228 (223 full-time, 5 part-time). Student-undergrad faculty ratio is 9:1. 2,634 applied, 60% were admitted. 35% from top 10% of their high school class, 62% from top quarter, 89% from top half. Full-time: 1,487 students, 64% women, 36% men. Part-time: 94 students, 36% women, 64% men. Students come from 46 states and territories, 21 other countries, 25% from out-of-state. 1% American Indian or Alaska Native, non-Hispanic/Latino; 3% Hispanic/Latino; 9% Black or African American, non-Hispanic/Latino; 3% Asian, non-Hispanic/Latino; 0.1% Native Hawaiian or other Pacific Islander, non-Hispanic/Latino. 2% 25 or older, 3% transferred in. Retention: 83% of full-time freshmen returned the following year. Academic areas with the most degrees conferred: health professions and related sciences; business/marketing; education. Core. Calendar: 4-1-4. Academic remediation for entering students, ESL program, services for LD students, advanced placement, accelerated degree program, honors program, independent study, distance learning, double major, summer session for credit, part-time degree program, external degree program, adult/continuing education programs, co-op programs and internships, graduate courses open to undergrads. Off campus study at Freed-Hardeman University, Council for Christian Colleges and Universities. Study abroad program. ROTC: Army (c).
Entrance Requirements: Options: electronic application, early admission, deferred admission, international baccalaureate accepted. Required: high school transcript, minimum 2.5 high school GPA, SAT or ACT. Recom-

mended: essay, interview. Required for some: 3 recommendations. Entrance: moderately difficult. Application deadline: rolling. Notification: continuous.
Costs Per Year: Application fee: $35. Comprehensive fee: $43,090 includes full-time tuition ($31,550), mandatory fees ($1340), and college room and board ($10,200). College room only: $7900. Full-time tuition and fees vary according to class time, course load, degree level, location, and program. Room and board charges vary according to board plan and housing facility. Part-time tuition: $1015 per credit hour. Part-time mandatory fees: $45 per credit hour. Part-time tuition and fees vary according to class time, course load, degree level, location, and program.
Collegiate Environment: Orientation program. Drama-theater group, choral group, student-run newspaper. Social organizations: national fraternities, national sororities; 29% of eligible men and 30% of eligible women are members. Most popular organizations: Campus Ministries, Student Government Association, Student Activities Council, Students in Free Enterprise (SIFE). Major annual events: Campus Day, All-Sing Contest, Homecoming. Student services: health clinic, personal-psychological counseling. Campus security: 24-hour emergency response devices and patrols, student patrols, late night transport-escort service. The Logos Library plus 1 other. Books: 136,991 (physical), 265,352 (digital/electronic); Serial titles: 2,362 (physical), 33,609 (digital/electronic); Databases: 135. Weekly public service hours: 93; students can reserve study rooms. Operations spending for the previous fiscal year: $132,781. 202 computers available on campus for general student use. A campuswide network can be accessed from student residence rooms and from off campus. Students can access the following: online class registration. Staffed computer lab on campus provides training in use of computers, software, and the Internet.
Community Environment: Jackson is a city of 55,000 that is 75 miles from Memphis and 125 miles from Nashville. There are 3 other colleges located in the same town.

■ **UNIVERSITY OF MEMPHIS**

Memphis, TN 38152
Tel: (901)678-2000; Free: 800-669-2678
Fax: (901)678-3053
E-mail: dwelch@memphis.edu
Web Site: www.memphis.edu
Description: State-supported, university, coed. Awards bachelor's, master's, and doctoral degrees and post-master's certificates. Founded 1912. Setting: 1,160-acre urban campus with easy access to Memphis. Endowment: $216.2 million. Research spending for the previous fiscal year: $59.4 million. Educational spending for the previous fiscal year: $8790 per student. Total enrollment: 21,458. Faculty: 1,477 (908 full-time, 569 part-time). Student-undergrad faculty ratio is 16:1. 14,160 applied, 84% were admitted. 14% from top 10% of their high school class, 37% from top quarter, 69% from top half. 4 National Merit Scholars, 24 valedictorians. Full-time: 12,064 students, 58% women, 42% men. Part-time: 5,169 students, 61% women, 39% men. Students come from 47 states and territories, 49 other countries, 12% from out-of-state. 0.2% American Indian or Alaska Native, non-Hispanic/Latino; 6% Hispanic/Latino; 37% Black or African American, non-Hispanic/Latino; 4% Asian, non-Hispanic/Latino; 0.1% Native Hawaiian or other Pacific Islander, non-Hispanic/Latino; 2% international. 22% 25 or older, 14% live on campus, 8% transferred in. Retention: 76% of full-time freshmen returned the following year. Academic areas with the most degrees conferred: business/marketing; health professions and related sciences; interdisciplinary studies. Core. Calendar: semesters. ESL program, services for LD students, advanced placement, accelerated degree program, self-designed majors, honors program, independent study, distance learning, double major, summer session for credit, part-time degree program, external degree program, adult/continuing education programs, co-op programs and internships, graduate courses open to undergrads. Off campus study at University of Tennessee Health Science Center, Gulf Coast Research Laboratory. Study abroad program. ROTC: Army, Naval, Air Force.
Entrance Requirements: Options: electronic application, early admission, international baccalaureate accepted. Required: high school transcript, SAT or ACT. Required for some: essay, minimum 2 high school GPA, 2 recommendations, interview. Entrance: moderately difficult. Application deadlines: 7/1, 7/1 for nonresidents. Notification: continuous, continuous for nonresidents. Transfer credits accepted: Yes.
Costs Per Year: Application fee: $25. State resident tuition: $8064 full-time, $320 per credit hour part-time. Nonresident tuition: $19,776 full-time, $808 per credit hour part-time. Mandatory fees: $1637 full-time, $114 per credit hour part-time. Full-time tuition and fees vary according to course load,

degree level, program, and reciprocity agreements. Part-time tuition and fees vary according to course load, degree level, and program. College room and board: $9975. College room only: $5985. Room and board charges vary according to board plan, housing facility, and location.

Collegiate Environment: Orientation program. Drama-theater group, choral group, marching band, student-run newspaper, radio station. Social organizations: 277 open to all; national fraternities, national sororities; 6% of eligible men and 8% of eligible women are members. Most popular organizations: Student Activities Council, Fraternity and Sorority Life, Black Student Association, Student Government Association, Up 'til Dawn- St. Jude Philanthropy. Major annual events: Plug into the Blue (opening week events), Homecoming, Black History Month. Student services: health clinic, personal-psychological counseling, women's center. Campus security: 24-hour emergency response devices and patrols, student patrols, late night transport-escort service, controlled dormitory access. 2,565 college housing spaces available; 2,331 were occupied in 2018-19. No special consideration for freshman housing applicants. Options: coed, men-only, women-only housing available. McWherter Library plus 4 others. Books: 1.4 million (physical), 315,573 (digital/electronic); Serial titles: 17,630 (physical), 256,700 (digital/electronic); Databases: 400. Weekly public service hours: 91; students can reserve study rooms. Operations spending for the previous fiscal year: $9.7 million. 1,255 computers available on campus for general student use. A campuswide network can be accessed from student residence rooms and from off campus. Students can access the following: online class registration. Staffed computer lab on campus (open 24 hours a day) provides training in use of computers, software, and the Internet.

Community Environment: Memphis, with a metropolitan area population of over one million, is one of the South's largest and most attractive cities. As a primary medical, educational, communication, distribution, and transportation center, Memphis offers a rich and full range of research opportunities and cultural experiences. The city, known worldwide for its musical heritage, has many fine restaurants, museums, and theaters, as well as one of the nation's largest urban park systems. All forms of commercial transportation are available. Opportunities are numerous for part-time employment. Annual events include the St. Jude Liberty Bowl Football Classic, the Memphis in May International Festival, the Great River Carnival, and the Mid-South Fair. Some of the points of interest are the Brooks Memorial Art Gallery, Chuclissa Indian Villiage and Museum, Elvis Presley's Graceland, Mud Island, Libertyland, and the Great American Pyramid.

■ **THE UNIVERSITY OF THE SOUTH**

735 University Ave.
Sewanee, TN 37383-1000
Tel: (931)598-1000; Free: 800-522-2234
Fax: (931)598-1145
E-mail: admiss@sewanee.edu
Web Site: www.sewanee.edu

Description: Independent Episcopal, comprehensive, coed. Awards bachelor's, master's, and doctoral degrees and post-master's certificates. Founded 1857. Setting: 13,000-acre small town campus with easy access to Chattanooga. Endowment: $411 million. Research spending for the previous fiscal year: $239,315. Educational spending for the previous fiscal year: $19,312 per student. Total enrollment: 1,785. Faculty: 237 (168 full-time, 69 part-time). Student-undergrad faculty ratio is 10:1. 3,465 applied, 65% were admitted. 30% from top 10% of their high school class, 61% from top quarter, 92% from top half. Full-time: 1,678 students, 51% women, 49% men. Part-time: 20 students, 55% women, 45% men. Students come from 44 states and territories, 22 other countries, 78% from out-of-state. 0.1% American Indian or Alaska Native, non-Hispanic/Latino; 5% Hispanic/Latino; 5% Black or African American, non-Hispanic/Latino; 2% Asian, non-Hispanic/Latino; 3% international. 98% live on campus, 1% transferred in. Retention: 89% of full-time freshmen returned the following year. Academic areas with the most degrees conferred: social sciences; psychology; interdisciplinary studies. Core. Calendar: semesters. Services for LD students, advanced placement, self-designed majors, independent study, double major, summer session for credit, internships, graduate courses open to undergrads. Off campus study. Study abroad program.

Entrance Requirements: Options: electronic application, early admission, early decision, early action, deferred admission, international baccalaureate accepted. Required: essay, high school transcript, 2 recommendations. Recommended: interview, SAT or ACT. Required for some: TOEFL for international students. Entrance: very difficult. Application deadlines: 2/1, 11/15 for early decision plan 1, 1/15 for early decision plan 2, 12/1 for early action. Notification: 12/15 for early decision plan 1, 2/15 for early decision

plan 2. SAT Reasoning Test deadline: 3/1. SAT Subject Test deadline: 3/1. Transfer credits accepted: Yes. Applicants placed on waiting list: 513. Wait-listed applicants offered admission: 9. Early decision applicants: 166. Early decision applicants admitted: 143. Early action applicants: 1,871. Early action applicants admitted: 1,552.

Costs Per Year: Application fee: $0. Comprehensive fee: $59,740 includes full-time tuition ($46,200), mandatory fees ($272), and college room and board ($13,268). College room only: $6876. Part-time tuition: $1470 per credit hour.

Collegiate Environment: Orientation program. Drama-theater group, choral group, student-run newspaper, radio station. Social organizations: 90 open to all; national fraternities, national sororities, local fraternities, local sororities; 56% of eligible men and 64% of eligible women are members. Most popular organizations: Sewanee Outing Program, Sewanee Outreach, Organization for Cross Cultural Understanding, Alpha Phi Omega (APO) National Service Fraternity, African American Alliance. Major annual events: Perpetual Motion (student dance performance), Sewaneroo Music Festival, Sewanee Monologues. Student services: health clinic, personal-psychological counseling, women's center. Campus security: 24-hour emergency response devices and patrols, late night transport-escort service, controlled dormitory access. 1,800 college housing spaces available. Freshmen guaranteed college housing. On-campus residence required through senior year. Options: coed, men-only, women-only housing available. Jessie Ball duPont Library. Books: 512,993 (physical), 563,193 (digital/electronic); Serial titles: 4,034 (physical), 22,304 (digital/electronic); Databases: 382. Study areas open 24 hours, 5-7 days a week; students can reserve study rooms. 150 computers available on campus for general student use. A campuswide network can be accessed from student residence rooms and from off campus. Students can access the following: online class registration. Staffed computer lab on campus (open 24 hours a day) provides training in use of computers, software, and the Internet.

Community Environment: Sewanee is located on the Cuberland Plateau. It has an average temperature of 57 degrees and an average rainfall of 58 inches. Summer nights are cool and there is some snow in the winter. Churches, a hospital and clinic, and several civic and service organizations are a part of the community. Job opportunities are limited. Seventeen lakes in the surrounding area provide facilities for a number of sports, swimming, boating, fishing, and skating. Other activities are hunting, camping, mountain climbing, golf and tennis. There are many tourist attractions in this area.

■ **THE UNIVERSITY OF TENNESSEE**

Knoxville, TN 37996
Tel: (865)974-1000
E-mail: admissions@utk.edu
Web Site: www.utk.edu

Description: State-supported, university, coed. Part of University of Tennessee System. Awards bachelor's, master's, and doctoral degrees. Founded 1794. Setting: 600-acre urban campus. Endowment: $508.8 million. Research spending for the previous fiscal year: $285.7 million. Total enrollment: 28,894. Faculty: 1,799 (1,595 full-time, 204 part-time). Student-undergrad faculty ratio is 17:1. 18,872 applied, 77% were admitted. 36% from top 10% of their high school class, 66% from top quarter, 90% from top half. 20 National Merit Scholars. Full-time: 21,489 students, 51% women, 49% men. Part-time: 1,326 students, 46% women, 54% men. Students come from 46 states and territories, 43 other countries, 16% from out-of-state. 0.2% American Indian or Alaska Native, non-Hispanic/Latino; 4% Hispanic/Latino; 6% Black or African American, non-Hispanic/Latino; 4% Asian, non-Hispanic/Latino; 1% international. 6% 25 or older, 32% live on campus, 6% transferred in. Retention: 87% of full-time freshmen returned the following year. Academic areas with the most degrees conferred: business/marketing; engineering; parks and recreation. Core. Calendar: semesters. ESL program, services for LD students, advanced placement, accelerated degree program, self-designed majors, freshman honors college, honors program, independent study, distance learning, double major, summer session for credit, part-time degree program, external degree program, co-op programs and internships, graduate courses open to undergrads. Off campus study. Study abroad program. ROTC: Army, Air Force.

Entrance Requirements: Options: electronic application, early action, international baccalaureate accepted. Required: essay, high school transcript, minimum 2 high school GPA, SAT or ACT. Recommended: 1 recommendation. Entrance: moderately difficult. Application deadlines: rolling, rolling for nonresidents, 11/1 for early action. Notification: continuous until 9/15, continuous until 9/15 for nonresidents, 12/15 for early action. SAT Reasoning Test deadline: 7/10. Transfer credits accepted: Yes.

Costs Per Year: Application fee: $50. State resident tuition: $11,110 full-time, $371 per credit hour part-time. Nonresident tuition: $29,300 full-time, $1130 per credit hour part-time. Mandatory fees: $1896 full-time. Full-time tuition and fees vary according to course level, location, program, reciprocity agreements, and student level. Part-time tuition varies according to course level, location, program, reciprocity agreements, and student level. College room and board: $11,240. Room and board charges vary according to board plan and housing facility.

Collegiate Environment: Orientation program. Drama-theater group, choral group, marching band, student-run newspaper, radio station. Social organizations: 650 open to all; national fraternities, national sororities; 18% of eligible men and 31% of eligible women are members. Most popular organizations: Fraternities/Sororities, Religious organizations, Campus Events Board, Black Cultural Programming Committee, Student Government Association. Major annual events: Student Engagement Fair, Homecoming, Volapalooza. Student services: health clinic, personal-psychological counseling, women's center. Campus security: 24-hour emergency response devices and patrols, late night transport-escort service, controlled dormitory access. 7,587 college housing spaces available; 7,472 were occupied in 2018-19. Freshmen guaranteed college housing. On-campus residence required in freshman year. Options: coed, men-only, women-only housing available. John C. Hodges Library plus 4 others. Books: 1.5 million (physical), 824,325 (digital/electronic); Serial titles: 51,489 (physical), 158,361 (digital/electronic); Databases: 737. Weekly public service hours: 160; study areas open 24 hours, 5-7 days a week; students can reserve study rooms. Operations spending for the previous fiscal year: $28.9 million. 1,325 computers available on campus for general student use. Computer purchase/lease plans available. A campuswide network can be accessed from student residence rooms and from off campus. Students can access the following: online class registration, course management system. Staffed computer lab on campus (open 24 hours a day) provides training in use of computers, software, and the Internet.

■ **THE UNIVERSITY OF TENNESSEE AT CHATTANOOGA**
615 McCallie Ave.
Chattanooga, TN 37403-2598
Tel: (423)425-4111; Free: 800-882-6627
Fax: (423)425-4157
E-mail: admissions@utc.edu
Web Site: www.utc.edu
Description: State-supported, comprehensive, coed. Part of University of Tennessee System. Awards bachelor's, master's, and doctoral degrees and post-master's certificates. Founded 1886. Setting: 425-acre urban campus. Total enrollment: 11,587. Faculty: 717 (469 full-time, 248 part-time). Student-undergrad faculty ratio is 19:1. 7,235 applied, 83% were admitted. Full-time: 8,962 students, 57% women, 43% men. Part-time: 1,214 students, 50% women, 50% men. Students come from 36 states and territories, 28 other countries, 6% from out-of-state. 0.3% American Indian or Alaska Native, non-Hispanic/Latino; 4% Hispanic/Latino; 10% Black or African American, non-Hispanic/Latino; 2% Asian, non-Hispanic/Latino; 1% international. 12% 25 or older, 31% live on campus, 9% transferred in. Retention: 73% of full-time freshmen returned the following year. Academic areas with the most degrees conferred: business/marketing; education; parks and recreation. Core. Calendar: semesters. ESL program, services for LD students, advanced placement, accelerated degree program, self-designed majors, freshman honors college, honors program, independent study, distance learning, double major, summer session for credit, part-time degree program, co-op programs and internships, graduate courses open to undergrads. Off campus study. Study abroad program. ROTC: Army.
Entrance Requirements: Options: electronic application, early admission, deferred admission, international baccalaureate accepted. Required: high school transcript, 2.5 GPA with minimum ACT score of 21/SAT of 990 or minimum GPA of 2.85 with minimum ACT score of 18/SAT score of 870, SAT or ACT. Entrance: moderately difficult. Application deadline: 5/1. SAT Reasoning Test deadline: 5/1. SAT Subject Test deadline: 5/1. Transfer credits accepted: Yes.
Costs Per Year: Application fee: $30. State resident tuition: $6888 full-time, $287 per credit hour part-time. Nonresident tuition: $23,006 full-time, $959 per credit hour part-time. Mandatory fees: $1776 full-time, $59 per credit hour part-time, $205 per term part-time. Full-time tuition and fees vary according to degree level. Part-time tuition and fees vary according to degree level. College room and board: $9050. College room only: $5600. Room and board charges vary according to board plan, housing facility, and location.
Collegiate Environment: Orientation program. Drama-theater group, choral

group, marching band, student-run newspaper. Social organizations: national fraternities, national sororities, local fraternities, local sororities; 12% of eligible men and 18% of eligible women are members. Student services: health clinic, personal-psychological counseling, women's center. Campus security: 24-hour emergency response devices. UTC Library plus 1 other. Books: 743,490 (physical); Databases: 219. Study areas open 24 hours, 5-7 days a week; students can reserve study rooms. Operations spending for the previous fiscal year: $1.7 million.

■ **THE UNIVERSITY OF TENNESSEE AT MARTIN**
554 University St.
Martin, TN 38238
Tel: (731)881-7000; Free: 800-829-8861
Fax: (731)881-7029
E-mail: dtucker@utm.edu
Web Site: www.utm.edu
Description: State-supported, comprehensive, coed. Part of University of Tennessee System. Awards bachelor's and master's degrees. Founded 1900. Setting: 250-acre small town campus. Endowment: $35 million. Research spending for the previous fiscal year: $374,754. Educational spending for the previous fiscal year: $7396 per student. Total enrollment: 7,069. Faculty: 506 (285 full-time, 221 part-time). Student-undergrad faculty ratio is 15:1. 8,047 applied, 69% were admitted. 17% from top 10% of their high school class, 43% from top quarter, 78% from top half. 22 valedictorians. Full-time: 4,748 students, 58% women, 42% men. Part-time: 1,946 students, 64% women, 36% men. Students come from 44 states and territories, 20 other countries, 9% from out-of-state. 0.4% American Indian or Alaska Native, non-Hispanic/Latino; 3% Hispanic/Latino; 13% Black or African American, non-Hispanic/Latino; 0.8% Asian, non-Hispanic/Latino; 2% international. 18% 25 or older, 30% live on campus, 7% transferred in. Retention: 74% of full-time freshmen returned the following year. Academic areas with the most degrees conferred: business/marketing; agriculture; parks and recreation. Core. Calendar: semesters. ESL program, services for LD students, advanced placement, accelerated degree program, self-designed majors, honors program, independent study, distance learning, double major, summer session for credit, part-time degree program, adult/continuing education programs, co-op programs and internships, graduate courses open to undergrads. Off campus study at National Forensic Academy Collegiate Program and Gulf Coast Research Laboratory. Study abroad program. ROTC: Army.
Entrance Requirements: Options: electronic application, early admission, deferred admission, international baccalaureate accepted. Required: high school transcript, minimum 2.7 high school GPA, SAT or ACT. Entrance: moderately difficult. Application deadline: rolling. Notification: continuous until 8/1. Transfer credits accepted: Yes.
Costs Per Year: Application fee: $30. State resident tuition: $8052 full-time, $335 per credit hour part-time. Nonresident tuition: $14,092 full-time, $587 per credit hour part-time. Mandatory fees: $1460 full-time, $61 per credit hour part-time. Full-time tuition and fees vary according to student level. Part-time tuition and fees vary according to course level and course load. College room and board: $6164. College room only: $2820. Room and board charges vary according to board plan and housing facility.
Collegiate Environment: Orientation program. Drama-theater group, choral group, marching band, student-run newspaper, radio station. Social organizations: 170 open to all; national fraternities, national sororities, local sororities; 13% of eligible men and 14% of eligible women are members. Most popular organizations: Student Government Association, Black Student Association, National Society for Leadership and Success, Phi Eta Sigma, League of Striving Artists. Major annual events: Quad City, UTM Rodeo-n-Roundup Days, SAC-Lip Sync during Homecoming. Student services: health clinic, personal-psychological counseling, women's center. Campus security: 24-hour emergency response devices and patrols, student patrols, controlled dormitory access. 2,258 college housing spaces available; 1,662 were occupied in 2018-19. Freshmen given priority for college housing. On-campus residence required in freshman year. Options: men-only, women-only housing available. Paul Meek Library. Books: 302,341 (physical), 92,351 (digital/electronic); Serial titles: 47,314 (physical), 350,984 (digital/electronic); Databases: 231. Weekly public service hours: 92; study areas open 24 hours, 5-7 days a week. Operations spending for the previous fiscal year: $1.1 million. 1,214 computers available on campus for general student use. A campuswide network can be accessed from student residence rooms and from off campus. Students can access the following: online class registration, online fee payments, degree progress, financial aid data, housing applications, transcripts. Staffed computer lab on campus (open 24 hours a day) provides training in use of computers, software, and the Internet.

■ VANDERBILT UNIVERSITY

Nashville, TN 37240-1001
Tel: (615)322-7311; Free: 800-288-0432
Fax: (615)343-7765
E-mail: admissions@vanderbilt.edu
Web Site: www.vanderbilt.edu

Description: Independent, university, coed. Awards bachelor's, master's, and doctoral degrees. Founded 1873. Setting: 330-acre urban campus with easy access to Nashville, TN. Endowment: $3.8 billion. Research spending for the previous fiscal year: $175.3 million. Educational spending for the previous fiscal year: $50,501 per student. Total enrollment: 12,587. Faculty: 1,225 (956 full-time, 269 part-time). Student-undergrad faculty ratio is 8:1. 32,442 applied, 11% were admitted. 87% from top 10% of their high school class, 97% from top quarter, 99% from top half. 231 National Merit Scholars, 110 valedictorians, 544 student government officers. Full-time: 6,817 students, 51% women, 49% men. Part-time: 54 students, 41% women, 59% men. Students come from 53 states and territories, 47 other countries, 90% from out-of-state. 0.5% American Indian or Alaska Native, non-Hispanic/Latino; 9% Hispanic/Latino; 9% Black or African American, non-Hispanic/Latino; 12% Asian, non-Hispanic/Latino; 0.2% Native Hawaiian or other Pacific Islander, non-Hispanic/Latino; 7% international. 90% live on campus, 3% transferred in. Retention: 97% of full-time freshmen returned the following year. Academic areas with the most degrees conferred: social sciences; engineering; interdisciplinary studies. Core. Calendar: semesters. ESL program, services for LD students, advanced placement, accelerated degree program, self-designed majors, honors program, independent study, double major, summer session for credit, co-op programs and internships, graduate courses open to undergrads. Off campus study. Study abroad program. ROTC: Army, Naval, Air Force (c).

Entrance Requirements: Options: electronic application, early admission, early decision, deferred admission, international baccalaureate accepted. Required: essay, high school transcript, 3 recommendations, 3 letters of recommendation (2 from teachers in core subject areas and 1 from counselor), SAT or ACT. Entrance: most difficult. Application deadlines: 1/1, 11/1 for early decision plan 1, 1/1 for early decision plan 2. Notification: 4/1, 12/15 for early decision plan 1, 2/15 for early decision plan 2. SAT Reasoning Test deadline: 1/1. SAT Subject Test deadline: 1/1. Transfer credits accepted: Yes. Wait-listed applicants offered admission: 71. Early decision applicants: 3,702. Early decision applicants admitted: 885.

Costs Per Year: Application fee: $50. Comprehensive fee: $66,050 includes full-time tuition ($48,600), mandatory fees ($1216), and college room and board ($16,234). College room only: $10,620. Room and board charges vary according to board plan. Part-time tuition: $2025 per credit hour.

Collegiate Environment: Orientation program. Drama-theater group, choral group, marching band, student-run newspaper, radio station. Social organizations: 500 open to all; national fraternities, national sororities; 37% of eligible men and 51% of eligible women are members. Major annual events: Rites of Spring, Great Performances. Student services: health clinic, personal-psychological counseling, women's center. Campus security: 24-hour emergency response devices and patrols, student patrols, late night transport-escort service, controlled dormitory access. Jean and Alexander Heard Library plus 7 others. Books: 3.1 million (physical), 1.7 million (digital/electronic); Databases: 3,700. Operations spending for the previous fiscal year: $21.9 million.

Community Environment: Nashville, Tennessee's capital city, is one of the South's foremost centers for insurance, publishing, healthcare, and music. Ranking high among American cities in"quality of life" surveys, it offers four-star restaurants, sprawling shopping complexes, and entertainment to suit all tastes. The Tennessee Repertory Theatre, Community Concerts, Broadway touring companies, classical ensembles and the Nashville Symphony Orchestra, and the Circle Players perform regularly. The Tennessee Performing Arts Center continually hosts major orchestral and theatrical groups from throughout the nation. Among the attractions that bring visitors to Nashville each year are the Cheekwood Botanical Gardens and Fine Arts Center, the Cumberland Museum and Science Center, the Nashville Arena, and the Tennessee State Museum. Nashville is also home of an NFL team, the Tennessee Titans, and a NHS team, the Nashville Predators.

■ VISIBLE MUSIC COLLEGE

200 Madison Ave.
Memphis, TN 38103

Tel: (901)381-3939
Web Site: visible.edu
Description: Independent, 4-year, coed. Awards bachelor's degrees.

■ VOLUNTEER STATE COMMUNITY COLLEGE

1480 Nashville Pke.
Gallatin, TN 37066-3188
Tel: (615)452-8600; Free: 888-335-8722
Fax: (615)230-3577
E-mail: admissions@volstate.edu
Web Site: www.volstate.edu

Description: State-supported, 2-year, coed. Part of Tennessee Board of Regents. Awards certificates, transfer associate, and terminal associate degrees. Founded 1970. Setting: 110-acre suburban campus with easy access to Nashville. Endowment: $4.4 million. Educational spending for the previous fiscal year: $4849 per student. Total enrollment: 8,838. Faculty: 434 (180 full-time, 254 part-time). Student-undergrad faculty ratio is 23:1. 2,850 applied, 100% were admitted. Full-time: 4,974 students, 58% women, 42% men. Part-time: 3,864 students, 64% women, 36% men. Students come from 14 states and territories, 15 other countries, 1% from out-of-state. 0.4% American Indian or Alaska Native, non-Hispanic/Latino; 6% Hispanic/Latino; 10% Black or African American, non-Hispanic/Latino; 2% Asian, non-Hispanic/Latino; 0.1% Native Hawaiian or other Pacific Islander, non-Hispanic/Latino; 0.4% international. 24% 25 or older, 5% transferred in. Core. Calendar: semesters. Academic remediation for entering students, ESL program, services for LD students, advanced placement, accelerated degree program, honors program, independent study, distance learning, double major, summer session for credit, part-time degree program, adult/continuing education programs, co-op programs and internships. Study abroad program.

Entrance Requirements: Open admission. Options: electronic application, early admission, deferred admission. Required: high school transcript. Required for some: minimum 2 high school GPA, interview, SAT or ACT. Entrance: noncompetitive. Application deadline: 8/25. Notification: continuous. SAT Reasoning Test deadline: 8/25. SAT Subject Test deadline: 8/25. Transfer credits accepted: Yes.

Costs Per Year: State resident tuition: $4229 full-time, $164 per credit hour part-time. Nonresident tuition: $16,517 full-time, $676 per credit hour part-time. Mandatory fees: $293 full-time, $9 per credit hour part-time, $34 per term part-time. Full-time tuition and fees vary according to course load and program. Part-time tuition and fees vary according to course load and program.

Collegiate Environment: Orientation program. Drama-theater group, choral group, student-run newspaper, radio station. Social organizations: 18 open to all. Most popular organizations: Gamma Beta Phi, Returning Woman's Organization, Phi Theta Kappa, Student Government Association, The Settler. Major annual event: Homecoming. Student services: personal-psychological counseling. Campus security: 24-hour emergency response devices and patrols, late night transport-escort service. Thigpen Library. Operations spending for the previous fiscal year: $95,504. 700 computers available on campus for general student use. A campuswide network can be accessed from off-campus. Students can access the following: online class registration. Staffed computer lab on campus.

Community Environment: See Vanderbilt University.

■ WALTERS STATE COMMUNITY COLLEGE

500 S Davy Crockett Pky.
Morristown, TN 37813-6899
Tel: (423)585-2600; Free: 800-225-4770
E-mail: mike.campbell@ws.edu
Web Site: www.ws.edu

Description: State-supported, 2-year, coed. Part of Tennessee Board of Regents. Awards certificates, transfer associate, and terminal associate degrees. Founded 1970. Setting: 100-acre small town campus. Total enrollment: 6,075. Faculty: 358 (170 full-time, 188 part-time). Student-undergrad faculty ratio is 18:1. 3,987 applied, 99.9% were admitted. Full-time: 3,294 students, 57% women, 43% men. Part-time: 2,781 students, 67% women, 33% men. 1% from out-of-state. 0.3% American Indian or Alaska Native, non-Hispanic/Latino; 4% Hispanic/Latino; 3% Black or African American, non-Hispanic/Latino; 0.7% Asian, non-Hispanic/Latino; 0.1% Native Hawaiian or other Pacific Islander, non-Hispanic/Latino; 0.6% international. 16% 25 or older, 4% transferred in. Core. Calendar: semesters. Academic remediation for entering students, ESL program, services for LD students, advanced placement, accelerated degree program, self-designed majors, freshman honors college, honors program, independent study, distance learning, summer session for credit, part-time degree program, co-op programs and internships. Off campus study. Study abroad program. ROTC: Army (c).

Entrance Requirements: Open admission. Options: electronic application, early admission. Required: high school transcript. Entrance: noncompetitive. Application deadline: rolling. Notification: continuous. Transfer credits accepted: Yes.

Costs Per Year: Application fee: $0. State resident tuition: $3936 full-time, $164 per credit hour part-time. Nonresident tuition: $16,512 full-time, $712 per credit hour part-time. Mandatory fees: $288 full-time, $16 per credit hour part-time, $19.50 per term part-time. Full-time tuition and fees vary according to course load and program. Part-time tuition and fees vary according to course load and program.

Collegiate Environment: Orientation program. Drama-theater group, choral group. Most popular organizations: Baptist Collegiate Ministry, Phi Theta Kappa, Debate Club, Student Government Association, Service Learners Club. Major annual events: Student Appreciation Day, International Festival, International Education Events. Student services: health clinic, personal-psychological counseling. Campus security: 24-hour emergency response devices and patrols, late night transport-escort service, security cameras. Walters State Library.

Community Environment: Known as the City Between the Lakes, Morristown is centrally located in the college's 10-county service area. It has become a market center for the region with the establishment of a shopping mall as well as a growing industrial center. Farming remains an important part of the local economy with primary crops of light burley tobacco, corn, hay, and wheat. The lakes provide for fishing, swimming, hunting, and picnicking. Scenic drives lead to the nearby Great Smoky Mountains, Clinch Mountain, and the larger urban areas to both the north and south.

■ WATKINS COLLEGE OF ART, DESIGN, & FILM

2298 Rosa L. Parks Blvd.
Nashville, TN 37228
Tel: (615)383-4848
Fax: (615)383-4849
E-mail: admissions@watkins.edu
Web Site: www.watkins.edu

Description: Independent, comprehensive, coed. Awards bachelor's and master's degrees. Founded 1885. Setting: 13-acre urban campus. Endowment: $1.8 million. Educational spending for the previous fiscal year: $9513 per student. Total enrollment: 251. Faculty: 56 (20 full-time, 36 part-time). Student-undergrad faculty ratio is 13:1. 89 applied, 94% were admitted. Full-time: 194 students, 60% women, 40% men. Part-time: 52 students, 54% women, 46% men. Students come from 26 states and territories, 2 other countries, 27% from out-of-state. 0.4% American Indian or Alaska Native, non-Hispanic/Latino; 6% Hispanic/Latino; 14% Black or African American, non-Hispanic/Latino; 2% Asian, non-Hispanic/Latino; 0.4% Native Hawaiian or other Pacific Islander, non-Hispanic/Latino; 0.8% international. 19% 25 or older, 24% live on campus, 9% transferred in. Retention: 58% of full-time freshmen returned the following year. Academic area with the most degrees conferred: visual and performing arts. Core. Calendar: semesters. Services for LD students, advanced placement, independent study, summer session for credit, part-time degree program, co-op programs and internships.

Entrance Requirements: Options: electronic application, early admission, deferred admission, international baccalaureate accepted. Required: essay, high school transcript, minimum 2.6 high school GPA, 1 recommendation, SAT or ACT. Recommended: interview. Required for some: artistic exercises, optional portfolio. Entrance: moderately difficult. Application deadline: 7/15. Notification: 8/1. SAT Reasoning Test deadline: 7/15. SAT Subject Test deadline: 7/15. Transfer credits accepted: Yes.

Costs Per Year: Application fee: $50. Comprehensive fee: $34,950 includes full-time tuition ($22,500), mandatory fees ($1950), and college room and board ($10,500). College room only: $6750. Part-time tuition: $750 per credit hour. Part-time mandatory fees: $65 per credit hour.

Collegiate Environment: Orientation program. Social organizations: 7 open to all. Most popular organizations: Company Q (art society), Film club, sports club, Student Government. Major annual events: Welcome BBQ, YART Sale, Talent Show. Student services: health clinic, personal-psychological counseling. Campus security: 24-hour emergency response devices and patrols, late night transport-escort service, controlled dormitory access, monitored 24 hour camera security. The Watkins Library plus 1 other. Operations spending for the previous fiscal year: $86,198. 200 computers available on campus for general student use. A campuswide network can be accessed from student residence rooms and from off campus. Students can access the following: online class registration. Staffed computer lab on campus provides training in use of computers, software, and the Internet.

■ WELCH COLLEGE

1045 Bison Trl.
Gallatin, TN 37066
Tel: (615)844-5000; Free: 800-763-9222
Fax: (615)269-6028
E-mail: daniel.webster@welch.edu
Web Site: www.welch.edu

Description: Independent Free Will Baptist, comprehensive, coed. Awards associate, bachelor's, and master's degrees. Founded 1942. Setting: 120-acre suburban campus with easy access to Nashville. Endowment: $2.5 million. Educational spending for the previous fiscal year: $5796 per student. Total enrollment: 327. Faculty: 58 (16 full-time, 42 part-time). Student-undergrad faculty ratio is 8:1. 115 applied, 69% were admitted. 39% from top 10% of their high school class, 52% from top quarter, 70% from top half. Full-time: 220 students, 50% women, 50% men. Part-time: 107 students, 41% women, 59% men. Students come from 23 states and territories, 1 other country, 58% from out-of-state. 0.3% American Indian or Alaska Native, non-Hispanic/Latino; 3% Hispanic/Latino; 9% Black or African American, non-Hispanic/Latino; 1% Asian, non-Hispanic/Latino; 8% international. 21% 25 or older, 6% transferred in. Retention: 66% of full-time freshmen returned the following year. Core. Calendar: semesters. Academic remediation for entering students, advanced placement, self-designed majors, independent study, distance learning, double major, summer session for credit, part-time degree program, external degree program, adult/continuing education programs, internships. ROTC: Army (c), Air Force (c).

Entrance Requirements: Open admission. Options: electronic application, early admission, deferred admission, international baccalaureate accepted. Required: essay, high school transcript, 3 recommendations, medical history, SAT or ACT. Entrance: noncompetitive. Application deadline: rolling. Notification: continuous. Preference given to Free Will Baptists. SAT Reasoning Test deadline: 9/15. Transfer credits accepted: Yes.

Costs Per Year: Application fee: $35. Comprehensive fee: $26,716 includes full-time tuition ($19,012) and college room and board ($7704). College room only: $2926. Full-time tuition varies according to location. Room and board charges vary according to board plan. Part-time tuition: $648 per credit hour. Part-time tuition varies according to location.

Collegiate Environment: Orientation program. Drama-theater group, choral group. Social organizations: 17 open to all; local fraternities, local sororities; 75% of eligible men and 72% of eligible women are members. Most popular organizations: GMF-Global Missions Fellowship, Four Women's Societies, Four Men's Societies. Major annual events: Project Pumpkin, Semi-Annual Red Cross Blood Drive, Christmas on Richland (choral presentation). Student services: personal-psychological counseling. Campus security: 24-hour emergency response devices, student patrols, late night transport-escort service, controlled dormitory access. Welch Library. Books: 64,478 (physical), 48,741 (digital/electronic); Databases: 56. Operations spending for the previous fiscal year: $180,709. 15 computers available on campus for general student use. A campuswide network can be accessed from student residence rooms and from off campus. Staffed computer lab on campus.

Community Environment: See Vanderbilt University.

■ WEST TENNESSEE BUSINESS COLLEGE

1186 Hwy. 45 Byp.
Jackson, TN 38301
Tel: (731)668-7240
Web Site: www.wtbc.edu

Description: Proprietary, 2-year, coed. Awards certificates, transfer associate, and terminal associate degrees. Founded 1888.

■ WILLIAMSON COLLEGE

274 Mallory Station Rd.
Franklin, TN 37067
Tel: (615)771-7821
Fax: (615)771-7810
E-mail: laura@williamsoncc.edu
Web Site: www.williamsoncc.edu

Description: Independent interdenominational, comprehensive, coed. Awards associate, bachelor's, and master's degrees. Founded 1997. Setting: 1-acre suburban campus with easy access to Nashville. Research spending for the previous fiscal year: $1104. Educational spending for the previous fiscal year: $1453 per student. Total enrollment: 55. Faculty: 17 (5 full-time, 12 part-time). Student-undergrad faculty ratio is 7:1. 11 applied, 100% were admitted. Full-time: 39 students, 46% women, 54% men. Part-time: 2 students, 100% men. Students come from 3 states and territories, 4 other countries. 12% Hispanic/Latino; 7% Black or African American, non-Hispanic/Latino; 2% Asian, non-Hispanic/Latino. 35% 25 or older, 22% transferred in. Retention: 73% of full-time freshmen returned the following year. Academic areas with the most degrees conferred: business/marketing; theology and religious vocations. Core. Calendar: semesters. Advanced placement, accelerated degree program, independent study, distance learning, double major, part-time degree program, external degree program, adult/continuing education programs, internships.

Entrance Requirements: Options: early admission, deferred admission, international baccalaureate accepted. Required: essay, high school transcript, minimum 2 high school GPA, 1 recommendation. Required for some: interview, SAT or ACT. Entrance: noncompetitive. Application deadline: 9/1. Notification: continuous until 10/1. SAT Reasoning Test deadline: 8/1. SAT Subject Test deadline: 8/1. Transfer credits accepted: Yes.

Collegiate Environment: Orientation program. Social organizations: 1 open to all. Most popular organization: Student Government Association. Major annual event: Christmas Open House. Student services: health clinic, personal-psychological counseling. Campus security: 24-hour emergency response devices. John W. Neth, Jr. Library plus 1 other. Books: 4,836 (physical); Serial titles: 11,203 (digital/electronic); Databases: 70. Weekly public service hours: 40; students can reserve study rooms. Operations spending for the previous fiscal year: $2629. 3 computers available on campus for general student use. A computer is required for all students. A campuswide network can be accessed from off-campus.

■ ABILENE CHRISTIAN UNIVERSITY

1600 Campus Ct.
Abilene, TX 79699
Tel: (325)674-2000; Free: 800-460-6228
E-mail: info@admissions.acu.edu
Web Site: www.acu.edu

Description: Independent, university, coed, affiliated with Church of Christ. Awards associate, bachelor's, master's, and doctoral degrees and post-master's certificates. Founded 1906. Setting: 262-acre urban campus. Endowment: $384.6 million. Research spending for the previous fiscal year: $669,235. Educational spending for the previous fiscal year: $8993 per student. Total enrollment: 5,149. Faculty: 449 (266 full-time, 183 part-time). Student-undergrad faculty ratio is 13:1. 10,252 applied, 51% were admitted. 22% from top 10% of their high school class, 54% from top quarter, 84% from top half. 1 National Merit Scholar, 8 valedictorians. Full-time: 3,512 students, 59% women, 41% men. Part-time: 158 students, 57% women, 43% men. Students come from 50 states and territories, 42 other countries, 11% from out-of-state. 0.3% American Indian or Alaska Native, non-Hispanic/Latino; 17% Hispanic/Latino; 9% Black or African American, non-Hispanic/Latino; 1% Asian, non-Hispanic/Latino; 0.1% Native Hawaiian or other Pacific Islander, non-Hispanic/Latino; 4% international. 2% 25 or older, 47% live on campus, 3% transferred in. Retention: 77% of full-time freshmen returned the following year. Academic areas with the most degrees conferred: business/marketing; health professions and related sciences; visual and performing arts. Core. Calendar: semesters. ESL program, services for LD students, advanced placement, self-designed majors, honors program, independent study, distance learning, double major, summer session for credit, part-time degree program, internships, graduate courses open to undergrads. Off campus study at McMurry University, Hardin-Simmons University. Study abroad program.

Entrance Requirements: Options: electronic application, early admission, early action, international baccalaureate accepted. Required: high school transcript, SAT or ACT. Required for some: essay. Entrance: moderately difficult. Application deadline: 2/15. Notification: 3/15. SAT Reasoning Test deadline: 2/15. SAT Subject Test deadline: 2/15. Transfer credits accepted: Yes. Early action applicants: 5,599. Early action applicants admitted: 3,691.

Costs Per Year: Application fee: $50. Comprehensive fee: $45,200 includes full-time tuition ($34,800), mandatory fees ($50), and college room and board ($10,350). College room only: $5030. Full-time tuition and fees vary according to course load. Room and board charges vary according to board plan and housing facility. Part-time tuition: $1442 per credit hour. Part-time tuition varies according to course load.

Collegiate Environment: Orientation program. Drama-theater group, choral group, marching band, student-run newspaper, radio station. Social organizations: 114 open to all; local fraternities, local sororities; 28% of eligible men and 35% of eligible women are members. Most popular organizations: Student Association, Graduate Students Association, Spring Break Campaigns, International Students Association, LYNAY. Major annual events: Homecoming, Sing Song, Welcome Week. Student services: health clinic, personal-psychological counseling. Campus security: 24-hour emergency response devices and patrols, student patrols, late night transport-escort service, controlled dormitory access. Brown Library. Books: 406,890 (physical), 347,095 (digital/electronic); Serial titles: 20,683 (physical), 52,058 (digital/electronic); Databases: 109. Weekly public service hours: 97; students can reserve study rooms. Operations spending for the previous fiscal year: $2.4 million. 466 computers available on campus for general student use. Computer purchase/lease plans available. A campuswide network can be accessed from student residence rooms and from off campus. Students can access the following: online class registration. Staffed computer lab on campus provides training in use of computers, software, and the Internet.

Community Environment: Abilene, Texas, has the reputation of being a friendly and caring community. USA Today's annual "Make a Difference Day" issue has recognized Abilene's community efforts in each of the past three years. Abilene is located 150 miles west of the Dallas/Ft. Worth metroplex and has a population of about 115,000. Its climate is warm and sunny, with an occasional light snow some winters. Residents of Abilene are served by shopping malls, major restaurant chains, specialty shops, two hospitals, and a regional airport. Abilene is the home of Dyess Air Force Base. The city is second only to Houston in cultural events per capita in Texas, and has one of the lowest crime rates in the state. Part-time employment is available.

■ ALVIN COMMUNITY COLLEGE

3110 Mustang Rd.
Alvin, TX 77511-4898
Tel: (281)756-3500
Fax: (281)756-3854
Web Site: www.alvincollege.edu

Description: State and locally supported, 2-year, coed. Awards certificates, diplomas, transfer associate, and terminal associate degrees. Founded 1949. Setting: 114-acre suburban campus with easy access to Houston. Total enrollment: 5,785. Faculty: 361 (106 full-time, 255 part-time). Student-undergrad faculty ratio is 14:1. Full-time: 1,411 students, 55% women, 45% men. Part-time: 4,374 students, 57% women, 43% men. Students come from 2 other countries. 1% American Indian or Alaska Native, non-Hispanic/Latino; 40% Hispanic/Latino; 15% Black or African American, non-Hispanic/Latino; 5% Asian, non-Hispanic/Latino; 0.3% Native Hawaiian or other Pacific Islander, non-Hispanic/Latino; 1% international. 26% 25 or older. Retention: 62% of full-time freshmen returned the following year. Core. Calendar: semesters. Academic remediation for entering students, ESL program, services for LD students, advanced placement, accelerated degree program, self-designed majors, honors program, independent study, distance learning, double major, summer session for credit, part-time degree program, adult/continuing education programs, co-op programs and internships. Study abroad program.

Entrance Requirements: Open admission. Required for some: high school transcript. Transfer credits accepted: Yes.

Costs Per Year: Area resident tuition: $1104 full-time, $46 per credit hour part-time. State resident tuition: $2208 full-time, $92 per credit hour part-time. Nonresident tuition: $3360 full-time, $140 per credit hour part-time. Mandatory fees: $528 full-time, $7 per credit hour part-time, $204 per term part-time. Full-time tuition and fees vary according to course load and program. Part-time tuition and fees vary according to course load and program.

Collegiate Environment: Orientation program. Drama-theater group, choral group, student-run radio station. Social organizations: 18 open to all. Major annual events: Fall Festival, Constitution Day, Job Readiness Week. Student services: personal-psychological counseling. Campus security: 24-hour patrols, late night transport-escort service, Vehicle Assist, emergency messages. Alvin Community College Library. Books: 11,000 (physical), 30,000 (digital/electronic); Databases: 80. Weekly public service hours: 67; students can reserve study rooms.

Community Environment: Population 22,000, Alvin is a suburban community located 30 minutes from Houston, Galveston, and NASA. The city is served by a private airport, railroad, bus line, and State Routes 6 and 35. There are churches of major denominations, a public library, and hospital. Public recreation includes a theatre, bowling, fishing, and boating. Major civic, fraternal, and veteran's organizations are active in Alvin.

■ AMARILLO COLLEGE

PO Box 447
Amarillo, TX 79178-0001
Tel: (806)371-5000; Free: 800-227-8784
Fax: (806)371-5370
E-mail: askac@actx.edu
Web Site: www.actx.edu

Description: State and locally supported, 2-year, coed. Awards certificates, transfer associate, and terminal associate degrees. Founded 1929. Setting: 1,542-acre urban campus. Endowment: $40 million. Faculty: 775 (197 full-time, 578 part-time). 0.5% American Indian or Alaska Native, non-Hispanic/Latino; 39% Hispanic/Latino; 5% Black or African American, non-Hispanic/Latino; 3% Asian, non-Hispanic/Latino; 0.1% Native Hawaiian or other Pacific Islander, non-Hispanic/Latino. 36% 25 or older. Retention: 52% of full-time freshmen returned the following year. Core. Calendar: semesters. Academic remediation for entering students, ESL program, services for LD students, advanced placement, freshman honors college, honors program, distance learning, summer session for credit, part-time degree program, adult/continuing education programs, co-op programs.

Entrance Requirements: Open admission. Options: early admission, deferred admission. Required: high school transcript. Entrance: noncompetitive. Notification: continuous.

Costs Per Year: Application fee: $0. Area resident tuition: $2136 full-time, $89 per semester hour part-time. State resident tuition: $3168 full-time, $132 per semester hour part-time. Nonresident tuition: $4704 full-time, $196 per semester hour part-time. Full-time tuition varies according to course load. Part-time tuition varies according to course load.

Collegiate Environment: Orientation program. Drama-theater group, choral group, student-run newspaper, radio station. Major annual events: Fall Fest, Badgerama, Spring Fling. Student services: personal-psychological counseling. Campus security: 24-hour emergency response devices, late night transport-escort service, campus police patrol Monday through Saturday 7 am-11 pm. Lynn Library Learning Center plus 2 others. Operations spending for the previous fiscal year: $456,475. 2,000 computers available on campus for general student use. A campuswide network can be accessed. Students can access the following: online class registration. Staffed computer lab on campus provides training in use of computers, software, and the Internet.

Community Environment: Population 183,021. Situated on the high plains of the Texas Panhandle, Amarillo is the capital of the oil and as industry. Pipelines from adjacent fields extend as far as the east coast. The average temperature ranges from 37.4 degrees in winter to 76 degrees in summer. The community is provided transportation by bus, and airlines, as well as five interstate highways and one state highway. Amarillo has many churches representing various faiths, public libraries, museums, several hospitals, a YMCA, and various civic, fraternal, and veteran's organizations. Part-time employment is available. Off-campus housing is plentiful.

■ AMBERTON UNIVERSITY

1700 Eastgate Dr.
Garland, TX 75041-5595
Tel: (972)279-6511
Fax: (972)279-9773
E-mail: advisor@amberton.edu
Web Site: www.amberton.edu

Description: Independent nondenominational, upper-level, coed. Awards bachelor's and master's degrees. Founded 1971. Setting: 5-acre suburban campus with easy access to Dallas-Fort Worth. Endowment: $10 million. Educational spending for the previous fiscal year: $7400 per student. Total enrollment: 1,379. Faculty: 40 (15 full-time, 25 part-time). Student-undergrad faculty ratio is 25:1. Full-time: 33 students, 58% women, 42% men. Part-time: 198 students, 60% women, 40% men. 98% 25 or older. Academic areas with the most degrees conferred: business/marketing; interdisciplinary studies. Core. Calendar: 4 10-week terms. Self-designed majors, distance learning, summer session for credit, part-time degree program, external degree program, adult/continuing education programs, internships, graduate courses open to undergrads.

Entrance Requirements: Transfer credits accepted: Yes.

Costs Per Year: Application fee: $0. Tuition: $12,900 full-time, $265 per credit hour part-time. Mandatory fees: $120 full-time, $30 per term part-time.

Collegiate Environment: Campus security: 24-hour emergency response devices and patrols. Library Resource Center plus 1 other. Operations spending for the previous fiscal year: $100,000. 30 computers available on campus for general student use. Staffed computer lab on campus provides training in use of computers, software, and the Internet.

■ AMERICAN INTERCONTINENTAL UNIVERSITY HOUSTON

9999 Richmond Ave.
Houston, TX 77042
Tel: (832)201-3600; Free: 888-607-9888
Fax: (832)242-5775
Web Site: www.aiuniv.edu

Description: Proprietary, comprehensive, coed. Administratively affiliated with American InterContinental University. Awards associate, bachelor's, and master's degrees. Founded 2003. Total enrollment: 474. Faculty: 32. Full-time: 330 students, 53% women, 47% men. Part-time: 85 students, 56% women, 44% men. 53% 25 or older, 12% transferred in. Academic areas with the most degrees conferred: business/marketing; visual and performing arts; computer and information sciences. Core. Calendar: 5 10-week terms. Academic remediation for entering students, accelerated degree program, distance learning, part-time degree program, adult/continuing education programs, co-op programs.

Entrance Requirements: Options: electronic application, deferred admission, international baccalaureate accepted. Required: essay, high school transcript, interview. Application deadline: rolling. Notification: continuous.

Collegiate Environment: Orientation program. 149 computers available on campus for general student use. Computer purchase/lease plans available. A computer is required for all students. A campuswide network can be accessed. Students can access the following: online class registration, online campus bookstore. Staffed computer lab on campus.

■ ANGELINA COLLEGE

PO Box 1768
Lufkin, TX 75902-1768
Tel: (936)639-1301
Fax: (936)639-4299
Web Site: www.angelina.edu

Description: State and locally supported, 2-year, coed. Awards certificates, diplomas, transfer associate, and terminal associate degrees. Founded 1968. Setting: 140-acre small town campus. Total enrollment: 5,422. Student-undergrad faculty ratio is 8:1. 1% from out-of-state. 29% 25 or older. Core. Calendar: semesters. Academic remediation for entering students, services for LD students, advanced placement, self-designed majors, honors program, distance learning, double major, summer session for credit, part-time degree program, adult/continuing education programs, co-op programs and internships. Off campus study. ROTC: Army (c).

Entrance Requirements: Open admission. Options: electronic application, early admission, deferred admission. Required: high school transcript. Entrance: noncompetitive. Application deadline: rolling. Notification: continuous.

Collegiate Environment: Orientation program. Drama-theater group, choral group, student-run newspaper. Social organizations: local fraternities, local sororities. Student services: personal-psychological counseling. Campus security: 24-hour patrols. Angelina College Library.

Community Environment: Population 33,500. Lufkin derives most of its income from the lumber and paper-making industries, two iron foundries and one chromium corporation. This urban community is headquarters for four national forests. The climate is temperate and mild. Lufkin is served by three railroad lines, airlines, and U.S. Routes 59 and 69. The community has a public library, 20 churches, three hospitals, and many civic, fraternal, and veteran's organizations. Part-time employment opportunities are unlimited. Local recreation includes theatres, hunting, fishing, boating, nearby Rayburn Lake, baseball, and swimming pools.

■ ANGELO STATE UNIVERSITY

2601 W Ave. N
San Angelo, TX 76909
Tel: (325)942-2555; Free: 800-946-8627
Fax: (325)942-2038
E-mail: admissions@angelo.edu
Web Site: www.angelo.edu

Description: State-supported, comprehensive, coed. Part of Texas Tech

University System. Awards bachelor's, master's, and doctoral degrees. Founded 1928. Setting: 268-acre urban campus. Endowment: $189.3 million. Research spending for the previous fiscal year: $791,831. Educational spending for the previous fiscal year: $5467 per student. Total enrollment: 10,387. Faculty: 435 (307 full-time, 128 part-time). Student-undergrad faculty ratio is 20:1. 4,152 applied, 73% were admitted. 12% from top 10% of their high school class, 35% from top quarter, 72% from top half. Full-time: 5,499 students, 56% women, 44% men. Part-time: 3,253 students, 60% women, 40% men. Students come from 39 states and territories, 26 other countries, 3% from out-of-state. 0.4% American Indian or Alaska Native, non-Hispanic/Latino; 36% Hispanic/Latino; 6% Black or African American, non-Hispanic/Latino; 1% Asian, non-Hispanic/Latino; 0.2% Native Hawaiian or other Pacific Islander, non-Hispanic/Latino; 3% international. 11% 25 or older, 34% live on campus, 5% transferred in. Retention: 67% of full-time freshmen returned the following year. Academic areas with the most degrees conferred: business/marketing; interdisciplinary studies; health professions and related sciences. Core. Calendar: semesters. Academic remediation for entering students, ESL program, advanced placement, honors program, independent study, distance learning, double major, summer session for credit, part-time degree program, internships, graduate courses open to undergrads. Study abroad program. ROTC: Air Force.

Entrance Requirements: Options: electronic application, early admission, deferred admission, international baccalaureate accepted. Required: high school transcript, high school class rank, SAT or ACT. Entrance: moderately difficult. Application deadline: rolling. Notification: continuous. SAT Reasoning Test deadline: 8/24. Transfer credits accepted: Yes.

Costs Per Year: Application fee: $35. State resident tuition: $5415 full-time, $181 per credit hour part-time. Nonresident tuition: $18,075 full-time, $601 per credit hour part-time. Mandatory fees: $3306 full-time. College room and board: $9130. Tuition guaranteed not to increase for student's term of enrollment.

Collegiate Environment: Orientation program. Drama-theater group, choral group, marching band, student-run newspaper, radio station. Social organizations: 95 open to all; national fraternities, national sororities; 6% of eligible men and 4% of eligible women are members. Most popular organizations: Association of Mexican-American Students, Block and Bridle Club, Air Force ROTC, University Center Program Council, Baptist Student Union. Major annual events: Homecoming, Parents' Day, Rambunctious Weekend. Student services: health clinic, personal-psychological counseling. Campus security: 24-hour emergency response devices and patrols, student patrols, late night transport-escort service, controlled dormitory access. 2,213 college housing spaces available; 2,065 were occupied in 2018-19. On-campus residence required through sophomore year. Option: coed housing available. Porter Henderson Library. Books: 309,338 (physical), 100,539 (digital/electronic); Serial titles: 105 (physical), 54,329 (digital/electronic); Databases: 243. Weekly public service hours: 137; study areas open 24 hours, 5-7 days a week; students can reserve study rooms. Operations spending for the previous fiscal year: $2.9 million. 750 computers available on campus for general student use. Computer purchase/lease plans available. A campuswide network can be accessed from student residence rooms and from off campus. Students can access the following: online class registration, online courses, tuition payments, book purchase, parking permits, university calendar, discounted hardware and software. Staffed computer lab on campus (open 24 hours a day) provides training in use of computers, software, and the Internet.

Community Environment: Population approx 88,000. San Angelo is an attractive city located in the heart of West Texas ranch country. San Angelo and the surrounding area provide a readily accessible social and physical environment for cultural and recreational activities so essential to the university community. Three nearby lakes make water sports a popular attraction among students and those living in San Angelo.

■ **ARLINGTON BAPTIST UNIVERSITY**
3001 W Division
Arlington, TX 76012-3425
Tel: (817)461-8741
Fax: (817)274-1138
E-mail: mhayward@abu.edu
Web Site: www.abu.edu
Description: Independent Baptist, comprehensive, coed. Awards bachelor's and master's degrees. Founded 1939. Setting: 32-acre urban campus with easy access to Dallas-Fort Worth. Endowment: $17,000. Educational spending for the previous fiscal year: $4400 per student. Total enrollment: 179. Faculty: 32 (11 full-time, 21 part-time). Student-undergrad faculty ratio is 9:1.

126 applied, 59% were admitted. Students come from 5 states and territories, 1 other country, 6% from out-of-state. 1% American Indian or Alaska Native, non-Hispanic/Latino; 17% Hispanic/Latino; 24% Black or African American, non-Hispanic/Latino; 0.6% Asian, non-Hispanic/Latino; 0.6% Native Hawaiian or other Pacific Islander, non-Hispanic/Latino; 0.6% international. 20% 25 or older, 35% live on campus. Retention: 35% of full-time freshmen returned the following year. Academic areas with the most degrees conferred: education; theology and religious vocations. Core. Calendar: semesters. Academic remediation for entering students, independent study, distance learning, double major, summer session for credit, part-time degree program, internships.

Entrance Requirements: Options: electronic application, early admission, deferred admission, international baccalaureate accepted. Required: essay, 1 recommendation, pastoral recommendation, medical examination. Required for some: high school transcript, interview, SAT or ACT. Entrance: noncompetitive. Application deadline: rolling. Notification: continuous. Preference given to professing Christians. Transfer credits accepted: Yes.

Costs Per Year: Application fee: $25. One-time mandatory fee: $250. Comprehensive fee: $20,490 includes full-time tuition ($13,100), mandatory fees ($990), and college room and board ($6400). Full-time tuition and fees vary according to course load. Room and board charges vary according to board plan. Part-time tuition: $405 per credit hour. Part-time mandatory fees: $445 per term. Part-time tuition and fees vary according to course load.

Collegiate Environment: Orientation program. Choral group. Most popular organization: Collegians. Major annual events: RUSH, Homecoming Weekend, Hilltop Conference. Student services: personal-psychological counseling. Campus security: controlled dormitory access, night security guards. Earl K. Oldham Library. Databases: 5. Weekly public service hours: 73. Operations spending for the previous fiscal year: $90,666. 25 computers available on campus for general student use. A campuswide network can be accessed from student residence rooms. Students can access the following: online class registration. Staffed computer lab on campus provides training in use of computers, software, and the Internet.

Community Environment: See University of Texas at Arlington.

■ **THE ART INSTITUTE OF AUSTIN, A BRANCH OF THE ART INSTITUTE OF HOUSTON**
101 W Louis Henna Blvd.
Ste. 100
Austin, TX 78728
Tel: (512)691-1707; Free: 866-583-7952
Web Site: www.artinstitutes.edu/austin
Description: Proprietary, 4-year, coed. Part of Education Management Corporation. Awards associate and bachelor's degrees.

■ **THE ART INSTITUTE OF DALLAS, A BRANCH OF MIAMI INTERNATIONAL UNIVERSITY OF ART & DESIGN**
8080 Park Ln.
Ste. 100
Dallas, TX 75231-5993
Tel: (214)692-8080; Free: 800-275-4243
Fax: (214)750-9460
Web Site: www.artinstitutes.edu/dallas
Description: Proprietary, comprehensive, coed. Part of Education Management Corporation. Awards associate, bachelor's, and master's degrees. Founded 1978. Setting: 2-acre urban campus. Calendar: quarters.

■ **THE ART INSTITUTE OF HOUSTON**
4140 SW Fwy.
Houston, TX 77027
Tel: (713)623-2040; Free: 800-275-4244
Fax: (713)966-2797
Web Site: www.artinstitutes.edu/houston
Description: Proprietary, 4-year, coed. Part of Education Management Corporation. Awards associate and bachelor's degrees. Founded 1978. Setting: urban campus. Calendar: quarters.

■ **THE ART INSTITUTE OF SAN ANTONIO, A BRANCH OF THE ART INSTITUTE OF HOUSTON**
1000 IH-10 W, Ste. 200
San Antonio, TX 78230
Tel: (210)338-7320; Free: 888-222-0040
Fax: (210)338-7321
Web Site: www.artinstitutes.edu/san-antonio

Description: Proprietary, 4-year, coed. Awards associate and bachelor's degrees.

■ **AUGUSTE ESCOFFIER SCHOOL OF CULINARY ARTS**
6020-B Dillard
Austin, TX 78752
Tel: (512)451-5743
Web Site: www.escoffier.edu
Description: Proprietary, 2-year, coed. Awards certificates, transfer associate, and terminal associate degrees.

■ **AUSTIN COLLEGE**
900 N Grand Ave.
Sherman, TX 75090-4400
Tel: (903)813-2000; Free: 800-526-4276
Fax: (903)813-3198
E-mail: admission@austincollege.edu
Web Site: www.austincollege.edu
Description: Independent Presbyterian, comprehensive, coed. Awards bachelor's and master's degrees. Founded 1849. Setting: 60-acre small town campus with easy access to Dallas-Fort Worth. Total enrollment: 1,237. Faculty: 113 (99 full-time, 14 part-time). Student-undergrad faculty ratio is 11:1. 3,832 applied, 55% were admitted. 24% from top 10% of their high school class, 26% from top quarter, 79% from top half. Full-time: 1,284 students, 51% women, 49% men. Part-time: 4 students, 25% women, 75% men. Students come from 30 states and territories, 16 other countries, 7% from out-of-state. 0.5% American Indian or Alaska Native, non-Hispanic/Latino; 21% Hispanic/Latino; 10% Black or African American, non-Hispanic/Latino; 13% Asian, non-Hispanic/Latino; 0.2% Native Hawaiian or other Pacific Islander, non-Hispanic/Latino; 2% international. 86% live on campus, 1% transferred in. Retention: 82% of full-time freshmen returned the following year. Academic areas with the most degrees conferred: business/marketing; biological/life sciences; social sciences. Core. Calendar: 4-1-4. Services for LD students, advanced placement, self-designed majors, honors program, independent study, double major, summer session for credit, part-time degree program, internships, graduate courses open to undergrads. Off campus study. Study abroad program.
Entrance Requirements: Options: electronic application, early admission, early decision, early action, deferred admission, international baccalaureate accepted. Required: high school transcript. Recommended: minimum 3 high school GPA, 2 recommendations, interview. Required for some: essay, SAT or ACT. Entrance: moderately difficult. Application deadlines: 3/1, 11/1 for early decision, 12/1 for early action. Notification: 4/1, 12/4 for early decision, 1/15 for early action. SAT Reasoning Test deadline: 4/1. Transfer credits accepted: Yes. Early decision applicants: 19. Early decision applicants admitted: 19.
Costs Per Year: Application fee: $0. One-time mandatory fee: $25. Comprehensive fee: $53,932 includes full-time tuition ($40,970), mandatory fees ($210), and college room and board ($12,752). College room only: $5900.
Collegiate Environment: Orientation program. Drama-theater group, choral group, student-run newspaper. Social organizations: 50 open to all; local fraternities, local sororities, e-sports; 76% of eligible men and 77% of eligible women are members. Most popular organizations: Inter-Varsity Christian Fellowship (IVCF), Campus Activity Board (CAB), Indian Cultural Association, Students Today Alumni Tomorrow (STAT), ACtivators. Major annual events: Homecoming, Great Day of Service, Kangapalooza (spring concert). Student services: health clinic, personal-psychological counseling. Campus security: 24-hour emergency response devices and patrols, late night transport-escort service, controlled dormitory access. 994 college housing spaces available; 893 were occupied in 2018-19. Freshmen guaranteed college housing. On-campus residence required through junior year. Options: coed, men-only, women-only housing available. Abell Library. Books: 227,390 (physical). Study areas open 24 hours, 5-7 days a week; students can reserve study rooms. 160 computers available on campus for general student use. A campuswide network can be accessed from student residence rooms and from off campus. Students can access the following: online class registration. Staffed computer lab on campus.
Community Environment: Sherman, population 37,000, is a retail trade and industrial center located in north central Texas 60 miles north of Dallas. The climate is mild and temperate. The average annual temperature is 64 degrees. Two bus lines, and U.S. Highways 82 and 75 serve the area. The community has a library, two hospitals, a shopping mall, two theatres, and various civic and fraternal organizations. Local recreation includes golf,

bowling, skating, hunting, and on Lake Texoma with a 1,250 mile shoreline, fishing, swimming, water skiing, and boating. Part-time employment is available.

■ **AUSTIN COMMUNITY COLLEGE DISTRICT**
5930 Middle Fiskville Rd.
Austin, TX 78752-4390
Tel: (512)223-7000
Fax: (512)223-7665
E-mail: admission@austincc.edu
Web Site: www.austincc.edu
Description: State and locally supported, primarily 2-year, coed. Awards certificates, transfer associate, terminal associate, and bachelor's degrees. Founded 1972. Setting: urban campus with easy access to Austin. Endowment: $5.9 million. Total enrollment: 40,799. Faculty: 1,856 (579 full-time, 1,277 part-time). Student-undergrad faculty ratio is 20:1. Students come from 52 states and territories, 94 other countries, 2% from out-of-state. 0.7% American Indian or Alaska Native, non-Hispanic/Latino; 37% Hispanic/Latino; 7% Black or African American, non-Hispanic/Latino; 5% Asian, non-Hispanic/Latino; 0.2% Native Hawaiian or other Pacific Islander, non-Hispanic/Latino; 1% international. 38% 25 or older. Core. Calendar: semesters. Academic remediation for entering students, ESL program, services for LD students, advanced placement, accelerated degree program, honors program, independent study, distance learning, summer session for credit, part-time degree program, adult/continuing education programs, co-op programs and internships. ROTC: Army (c), Air Force (c).
Entrance Requirements: Open admission. Options: electronic application, international baccalaureate accepted. Required: high school transcript. Entrance: noncompetitive. Application deadline: rolling. Transfer credits accepted: Yes.
Costs Per Year: Application fee: $0. Area resident tuition: $2010 full-time, $67 per credit hour part-time. State resident tuition: $10,290 full-time, $343 per credit hour part-time. Nonresident tuition: $12,480 full-time, $416 per credit hour part-time. Mandatory fees: $540 full-time, $18 per credit hour part-time. Full-time tuition and fees vary according to course load. Part-time tuition and fees vary according to course load.
Collegiate Environment: Orientation program. Social organizations: 83 open to all. Most popular organizations: Intramurals, Students for Environmental Outreach, Phi Theta Kappa (PTK), National Society of Collegiate Scholars, Students for Community Involvement. Major annual events: Welcome Week, Riverbat Bash, Nite in the Life. Student services: personal-psychological counseling. Campus security: 24-hour emergency response devices, late night transport-escort service. College housing not available. Main library plus 11 others. Books: 158,142 (physical), 50,957 (digital/electronic); Serial titles: 394 (physical), 83,559 (digital/electronic); Databases: 110. Weekly public service hours: 83; students can reserve study rooms. Operations spending for the previous fiscal year: $7.4 million. 2,090 computers available on campus for general student use. A campuswide network can be accessed. Students can access the following: online class registration. Staffed computer lab on campus provides training in use of computers, software, and the Internet.
Community Environment: See University of Texas at Austin.

■ **AUSTIN GRADUATE SCHOOL OF THEOLOGY**
7640 Guadalupe St.
Austin, TX 78752
Tel: (512)476-2772; Free: 866-AUS-GRAD
Fax: (512)476-3919
E-mail: registrar@austingrad.edu
Web Site: www.austingrad.edu
Description: Independent, upper-level, coed, affiliated with Church of Christ. Awards bachelor's and master's degrees. Founded 1917. Setting: 2-acre urban campus with easy access to Austin. Endowment: $4.6 million. Research spending for the previous fiscal year: $8140. Total enrollment: 36. Faculty: 10 (4 full-time, 6 part-time). Student-undergrad faculty ratio is 4:1. Students come from 1 other country, 1% from out-of-state. 14% Hispanic/Latino; 41% Black or African American, non-Hispanic/Latino. 80% 25 or older. Core. Calendar: semesters. Summer session for credit, part-time degree program, adult/continuing education programs.
Entrance Requirements: Transfer credits accepted: Yes.
Collegiate Environment: Orientation program. Social organizations: 1 open to all. Most popular organization: Student Association (government). Major annual events: Christmas Party, Spring Picnic, Chili Cook-Off. David Worley Library. Operations spending for the previous fiscal year: $115,486. 6

computers available on campus for general student use. A campuswide network can be accessed. Staffed computer lab on campus.

■ BAPTIST HEALTH SYSTEM SCHOOL OF HEALTH PROFESSIONS
8400 Datapoint Dr.
San Antonio, TX 78229
Tel: (210)297-9636
Web Site: www.bshp.edu
Description: Proprietary, 4-year, coed. Awards associate and bachelor's degrees.

■ BAPTIST MISSIONARY ASSOCIATION THEOLOGICAL SEMINARY
1530 E Pine St.
Jacksonville, TX 75766-5407
Tel: (903)586-2501; Free: 800-259-5673
Web Site: www.bmats.edu
Description: Independent Baptist, comprehensive, coed. Awards associate, bachelor's, and master's degrees. Founded 1955. Setting: 17-acre small town campus. Endowment: $1.2 million. Total enrollment: 117. Faculty: 11 (5 full-time, 6 part-time). 9 applied. Full-time: 23 students, 13% women, 87% men. Part-time: 33 students, 18% women, 82% men. 82% 25 or older, 29% live on campus. Academic area with the most degrees conferred: theology and religious vocations. Core. Calendar: semesters. Independent study, distance learning, summer session for credit, part-time degree program, adult/continuing education programs, internships, graduate courses open to undergrads.
Entrance Requirements: Open admission. Required: 3 recommendations, interview, Church approval statement. Entrance: noncompetitive. Application deadline: 7/25. Notification: continuous. Transfer credits accepted: Yes.
Costs Per Year: Application fee: $35. Tuition: $6000 full-time, $220 per credit hour part-time. Mandatory fees: $150 full-time, $75 per term part-time. Full-time tuition and fees vary according to course load and location. Part-time tuition and fees vary according to course load and location.
Collegiate Environment: Major annual events: Bible Lectures, Thanksgiving Meal, Back-to-School Picnic. Student services: personal-psychological counseling. Kellar Library. 3 computers available on campus for general student use. A campuswide network can be accessed.

■ BAPTIST UNIVERSITY OF THE AMERICAS
7838 Barlite Blvd.
San Antonio, TX 78224
Tel: (210)924-4338; Free: 800-721-1396
Fax: (210)924-2701
E-mail: admissions@bua.edu
Web Site: www.bua.edu
Description: Independent Baptist, 4-year, coed. Awards associate and bachelor's degrees (associate degree in Cross-Cultural Studies). Founded 1947. Setting: 75-acre urban campus with easy access to San Antonio. Endowment: $2.1 million. Educational spending for the previous fiscal year: $2594 per student. Total enrollment: 195. Faculty: 36 (8 full-time, 28 part-time). Student-undergrad faculty ratio is 8:1. 10% from top half of their high school class. Full-time: 128 students, 44% women, 56% men. Part-time: 67 students, 57% women, 43% men. Students come from 3 states and territories, 14 other countries, 21% from out-of-state. 70% Hispanic/Latino; 2% Black or African American, non-Hispanic/Latino; 1% Asian, non-Hispanic/Latino; 21% international. 52% 25 or older, 40% live on campus, 9% transferred in. Retention: 87% of full-time freshmen returned the following year. Core. Calendar: semesters May term is a two week intensive course. Academic remediation for entering students, ESL program, services for LD students, advanced placement, independent study, distance learning, double major, part-time degree program, internships. Off campus study at DBU, online courses and courses taking at SA campus at BUA.
Entrance Requirements: Required: essay, high school transcript, minimum 2 high school GPA, 2 recommendations, meningitis vaccination for students under 22 years, SAT and SAT Subject Tests or ACT, ACCUPLACER, THEA (Texas Higher Education Assessment), CPT (Computer Proficiency Test) and TSI. Recommended: minimum 2 high school GPA, 2 recommendations, SAT or ACT. Required for some: minimum 2 high school GPA, 2 recommendations, interview.
Collegiate Environment: Orientation program. Choral group. Social organizations: 5 open to all; 15% of eligible men and 20% of eligible women are members. Most popular organizations: Called Club, Spanish Club, Missions Society, Business Society, BUA Band. Major annual events: Rollins Lectures, Student Orientation/Inauguration of Student Council, Commence-

ment Ceremony. Student services: personal-psychological counseling. Campus security: 24-hour emergency response devices, student patrols, late night transport-escort service, Gate code is required to enter the residence area. Baptist University of the Americas Learning Resource Center plus 1 other. Books: 21,947 (physical), 362 (digital/electronic); Serial titles: 252 (physical), 252 (digital/electronic); Databases: 8. Weekly public service hours: 72; students can reserve study rooms. Operations spending for the previous fiscal year: $196,942. 122 computers available on campus for general student use. A campuswide network can be accessed. Students can access the following: online class registration. Staffed computer lab on campus provides training in use of computers, software, and the Internet.

■ BAYLOR UNIVERSITY
Waco, TX 76798
Tel: (254)710-1011; Free: 800-BAYLORU
E-mail: admissions@baylor.edu
Web Site: www.baylor.edu
Description: Independent Baptist, university, coed. Awards bachelor's, master's, and doctoral degrees and post-master's certificates. Founded 1845. Setting: 1,000-acre urban campus with easy access to Dallas-Fort Worth. Endowment: $1.3 billion. Total enrollment: 17,217. Faculty: 1,392 (1,096 full-time, 296 part-time). Student-undergrad faculty ratio is 14:1. 34,681 applied, 52% were admitted. 40% from top 10% of their high school class, 73% from top quarter, 95% from top half. 72 National Merit Scholars. Full-time: 13,976 students, 60% women, 40% men. Part-time: 212 students, 54% women, 46% men. Students come from 51 states and territories, 72 other countries, 32% from out-of-state. 0.4% American Indian or Alaska Native, non-Hispanic/Latino; 16% Hispanic/Latino; 6% Black or African American, non-Hispanic/Latino; 7% Asian, non-Hispanic/Latino; 0.1% Native Hawaiian or other Pacific Islander, non-Hispanic/Latino; 3% international. 2% 25 or older, 36% live on campus, 2% transferred in. Retention: 89% of full-time freshmen returned the following year. Academic areas with the most degrees conferred: business/marketing; health professions and related sciences; biological/life sciences. Core. Calendar: semesters. Services for LD students, advanced placement, accelerated degree program, self-designed majors, honors program, double major, summer session for credit, part-time degree program, internships, graduate courses open to undergrads. Study abroad program. ROTC: Army, Air Force.
Entrance Requirements: Options: electronic application, early admission, early action, deferred admission, international baccalaureate accepted. Required: high school transcript, SAT or ACT. Required for some: essay, minimum 2.5 high school GPA, 2 recommendations. Entrance: moderately difficult. Application deadlines: 2/1, 11/1 for early action. Notification: 4/10, 1/15 for early action. SAT Reasoning Test deadline: 2/1. Applicants placed on waiting list: 5,644. Wait-listed applicants offered admission: 791.
Costs Per Year: Application fee: $0. Comprehensive fee: $60,356 includes full-time tuition ($42,842), mandatory fees ($4522), and college room and board ($12,992). College room only: $7150. Part-time tuition: $1785 per semester hour. Part-time mandatory fees: $188 per semester hour.
Collegiate Environment: Orientation program. Drama-theater group, choral group, marching band, student-run newspaper, radio station. Social organizations: 316 open to all; national fraternities, national sororities, local fraternities, local sororities; 20% of eligible men and 34% of eligible women are members. Major annual events: Diadeloso (Student Day of Fun), Homecoming, All-University Sing. Student services: legal services, health clinic, personal-psychological counseling. Campus security: 24-hour emergency response devices and patrols, late night transport-escort service, controlled dormitory access. 5,370 college housing spaces available; 4,891 were occupied in 2018-19. Freshmen guaranteed college housing. On-campus residence required in freshman year. Options: coed, men-only, women-only housing available. Moody Memorial Library plus 8 others.
Community Environment: The campus adjoins the historic Brazos River in Waco, a Central Texas city of 110,000 people. The climate is temperate with a mean annual temperature of 67.4 degrees, and an average rainfall of 35 inches. Waco is reached by interstate, airlines, railroad, and bus lines. There are almost 200 churches of various faiths, public hospitals and a veteran's hospital, excellent libraries, and convenient shopping facilities in the area. Nineteen civic clubs and many fraternal organizations are active in Waco. Local recreation includes boating, swimming, fishing, picnicking, bowling, biking, golfing, hiking, tennis, parks, a zoo, and Lake Waco. Part-time employment is available for students.

■ BLINN COLLEGE
902 College Ave.
Brenham, TX 77833-4049

Tel: (979)830-4000
E-mail: jennifer.bynum@blinn.edu
Web Site: www.blinn.edu

Description: State and locally supported, 2-year, coed. Awards certificates, diplomas, transfer associate, and terminal associate degrees. Founded 1883. Setting: 100-acre small town campus with easy access to Houston. Endowment: $10.3 million. Total enrollment: 18,747. Faculty: 1,094 (788 full-time, 306 part-time). Full-time: 10,473 students, 48% women, 52% men. Part-time: 8,274 students, 55% women, 45% men. Students come from 42 other countries, 1% from out-of-state. 0.4% American Indian or Alaska Native, non-Hispanic/Latino; 21% Hispanic/Latino; 10% Black or African American, non-Hispanic/Latino; 2% Asian, non-Hispanic/Latino; 0.1% Native Hawaiian or other Pacific Islander, non-Hispanic/Latino; 0.7% international. 9% live on campus, 10% transferred in. Core. Calendar: semesters. Academic remediation for entering students, ESL program, services for LD students, advanced placement, freshman honors college, distance learning, double major, summer session for credit, part-time degree program, adult/continuing education programs.

Entrance Requirements: Open admission. Options: electronic application, early admission, deferred admission. Required: high school transcript. Entrance: noncompetitive. Application deadline: rolling. Transfer credits accepted: Yes.

Costs Per Year: Application fee: $0. Area resident tuition: $1296 full-time, $54 per credit hour part-time. State resident tuition: $2664 full-time, $111 per credit hour part-time. Nonresident tuition: $6504 full-time, $271 per credit hour part-time. Mandatory fees: $1536 full-time, $64 per credit hour part-time. Full-time tuition and fees vary according to course load. Part-time tuition and fees vary according to course load. College room and board: $8103. College room only: $4315. Room and board charges vary according to board plan and housing facility.

Collegiate Environment: Orientation program. Drama-theater group, choral group, marching band, student-run newspaper. Social organizations: 42 open to all. Most popular organizations: Student Government Association, Phi Theta Kappa, Baptist student ministries, Blinn Ethnic Student Organization, Circle K. Major annual events: Homecoming, Blinnfest, Transfer Day. Student services: personal-psychological counseling. Campus security: 24-hour emergency response devices and patrols, controlled dormitory access. W. L. Moody, Jr. Library plus 1 other. Operations spending for the previous fiscal year: $1.6 million. 1,200 computers available on campus for general student use. A campuswide network can be accessed from student residence rooms and from off campus. Students can access the following: online class registration. Staffed computer lab on campus provides training in use of computers and the Internet.

Community Environment: Population 10,900. Brenham is a suburban community enjoying temperate climate. The city has libraries, and churches of various denominations. Railroad, bus lines, and major highways serve the area. Part-time employment is available for students. There are motels and apartment houses available for student housing. Brenham has hospitals, and civic and fraternal organizations are active within the area. Local recreation includes theaters, hunting, fishing, golf, and sports.

■ **BRAZOSPORT COLLEGE**
500 College Dr.
Lake Jackson, TX 77566-3199
Tel: (979)230-3000
Fax: (979)230-3443
Web Site: www.brazosport.edu

Description: State and locally supported, primarily 2-year, coed. Awards certificates, transfer associate, terminal associate, and bachelor's degrees. Founded 1968. Setting: 160-acre small town campus with easy access to Houston. Total enrollment: 3,893. Student-undergrad faculty ratio is 17:1. 32% 25 or older. Retention: 52% of full-time freshmen returned the following year. Calendar: semesters. Academic remediation for entering students, advanced placement, honors program, distance learning, summer session for credit, part-time degree program, adult/continuing education programs, co-op programs and internships.

Entrance Requirements: Open admission. Options: early admission, deferred admission. Required for some: high school transcript. Entrance: noncompetitive. Application deadline: 8/15.

Collegiate Environment: Orientation program. Drama-theater group, choral group, student-run newspaper. Campus security: 24-hour patrols. Brazosport College Library.

Community Environment: Population 27,000, Lake Jackson is located 50 miles south of Houston. Major cities in the district are Lake Jackson and Freeport (population 12,600), located on a stretch of beach on the Gulf Coast. The area is serviced by rail, four major highways, commuter planes, and good local bus service. Recreation in the area includes fishing, surfing, swimming, and other water sports in the Gulf of Mexico.

■ **BROOKHAVEN COLLEGE**
3939 Valley View Ln.
Farmers Branch, TX 75244-4997
Tel: (972)860-4700
Fax: (972)860-4897
E-mail: bhcadmissions@dcccd.edu
Web Site: www.brookhavencollege.edu

Description: County-supported, 2-year, coed. Part of Dallas County Community College District System. Awards certificates, transfer associate, and terminal associate degrees. Founded 1978. Setting: 200-acre suburban campus with easy access to Dallas-Fort Worth. Educational spending for the previous fiscal year: $6683 per student. Total enrollment: 13,284. Faculty: 588 (127 full-time, 461 part-time). Student-undergrad faculty ratio is 21:1. Full-time: 2,257 students, 49% women, 51% men. Part-time: 11,027 students, 60% women, 40% men. Students come from 35 states and territories, 88 other countries, 3% from out-of-state. 2% American Indian or Alaska Native, non-Hispanic/Latino; 31% Hispanic/Latino; 14% Black or African American, non-Hispanic/Latino; 12% Asian, non-Hispanic/Latino; 0.2% Native Hawaiian or other Pacific Islander, non-Hispanic/Latino; 2% international. 40% 25 or older, 9% transferred in. Core. Calendar: semesters. Academic remediation for entering students, ESL program, services for LD students, advanced placement, self-designed majors, honors program, independent study, distance learning, summer session for credit, part-time degree program, adult/continuing education programs, co-op programs and internships. Off campus study. Study abroad program.

Entrance Requirements: Open admission except for nursing program. Options: electronic application, early admission, deferred admission, international baccalaureate accepted. Required: high school transcript. Required for some: HESI score, minimum GPA in prerequisite courses, completion of support courses for nursing program. Entrance: noncompetitive. Application deadline: rolling. Transfer credits accepted: Yes.

Costs Per Year: Application fee: $0. Area resident tuition: $1770 full-time, $59 per credit hour part-time. State resident tuition: $3330 full-time, $111 per credit hour part-time. Nonresident tuition: $5220 full-time, $174 per credit hour part-time.

Collegiate Environment: Orientation program. Drama-theater group, choral group, student-run newspaper. Student services: health clinic, personal-psychological counseling. Campus security: 24-hour emergency response devices and patrols, late night transport-escort service. Brookhaven College Learning Resources Center plus 1 other. Books: 55,595 (physical); Serial titles: 80 (physical). 172 computers available on campus for general student use. A campuswide network can be accessed. Students can access the following: online class registration. Staffed computer lab on campus provides training in use of computers, software, and the Internet.

■ **CARRINGTON COLLEGE-MESQUITE**
3733 W Emporium Cir.
Mesquite, TX 75150-6509
Tel: (972)682-2800
Web Site: www.carrington.edu

Description: Proprietary, 2-year, coed.

■ **CEDAR VALLEY COLLEGE**
3030 N Dallas Ave.
Lancaster, TX 75134-3799
Tel: (972)860-8201
Web Site: www.cedarvalleycollege.edu

Description: State-supported, 2-year, coed. Part of Dallas County Community College District System. Awards certificates, transfer associate, and terminal associate degrees. Founded 1977. Setting: 353-acre suburban campus with easy access to Dallas-Fort Worth. Educational spending for the previous fiscal year: $3717 per student. Total enrollment: 7,249. Faculty: 296 (75 full-time, 221 part-time). Student-undergrad faculty ratio is 24:1. 1,138 applied, 100% were admitted. Students come from 49 states and territories, 6 other countries, 15% from out-of-state. 0.4% American Indian or Alaska Native, non-Hispanic/Latino; 29% Hispanic/Latino; 44% Black or African American, non-Hispanic/Latino; 3% Asian, non-Hispanic/Latino; 0.1% Native Hawaiian or other Pacific Islander, non-Hispanic/Latino; 0.2% international. 43% 25 or older. Retention: 17% of full-time freshmen returned the following year. Core. Calendar: semesters. Academic remediation for entering students, ESL program, services for LD students, advanced placement, distance learning, double major, summer session for credit, part-time degree program, co-op programs and internships. Off campus study.

Entrance Requirements: Open admission. Option: electronic application. Required: high school transcript, minimum 2 high school GPA, SAT or ACT, TSI. Required for some: SAT and SAT Subject Tests or ACT.

Collegiate Environment: Orientation program. Choral group. Social organizations: 30 open to all; 3% of eligible men and 5% of eligible women are members. Most popular organizations: Phi Theta Kappa (PTK), Brother 2 Brother, Sustainability, Commercial Music Association, Family Music Club. Major annual events: CVC Educational Art Gallery, CVC Athletics, Community & Organizational Development. Student services: health clinic, personal-psychological counseling. Campus security: 24-hour emergency response devices and patrols, late night transport-escort service. Cedar Valley College Library plus 1 other. Operations spending for the previous fiscal year: $310,778.

■ CENTER FOR ADVANCED LEGAL STUDIES

800 W Sam Houston Pky. S, Ste. 100
Houston, TX 77042
Tel: (713)529-2778; Free: 800-446-6931
Fax: (713)523-2715
E-mail: james.scheffer@paralegal.edu
Web Site: www.paralegal.edu

Description: Proprietary, 2-year, coed. Awards certificates and terminal associate degrees. Founded 1987. Total enrollment: 176. Faculty: 25 (2 full-time, 23 part-time). Student-undergrad faculty ratio is 17:1. Full-time: 176 students, 88% women, 12% men. 60% 25 or older.

Entrance Requirements: Required: essay. Required for some: high school transcript. Application deadline: rolling.

Collegiate Environment: Orientation program. 30 computers available on campus for general student use. A campuswide network can be accessed from off-campus.

■ CENTRAL TEXAS COLLEGE

PO Box 1800
Killeen, TX 76540-1800
Tel: (254)526-7161; Free: 800-792-3348
Web Site: www.ctcd.edu

Description: State and locally supported, 2-year, coed. Awards certificates, transfer associate, and terminal associate degrees. Founded 1967. Setting: 500-acre suburban campus with easy access to Austin. Endowment: $8.2 million. Educational spending for the previous fiscal year: $3940 per student. Total enrollment: 16,073. Faculty: 1,145 (206 full-time, 939 part-time). Student-undergrad faculty ratio is 17:1. Full-time: 4,355 students, 60% women, 40% men. Part-time: 11,718 students, 49% women, 51% men. Students come from 54 states and territories, 31% from out-of-state. 0.6% American Indian or Alaska Native, non-Hispanic/Latino; 25% Hispanic/Latino; 27% Black or African American, non-Hispanic/Latino; 3% Asian, non-Hispanic/Latino; 1% Native Hawaiian or other Pacific Islander, non-Hispanic/Latino; 0.4% international. 59% 25 or older, 1% live on campus, 7% transferred in. Retention: 52% of full-time freshmen returned the following year. Core. Calendar: semesters. Academic remediation for entering students, ESL program, services for LD students, advanced placement, accelerated degree program, self-designed majors, distance learning, summer session for credit, part-time degree program, external degree program, adult/continuing education programs, co-op programs and internships. ROTC: Army.

Entrance Requirements: Open admission. Options: electronic application, early admission, deferred admission. Required: high school transcript. Required for some: TSI Assessment required for those that are not TSI exempt or waived. Entrance: noncompetitive. Application deadline: rolling. Transfer credits accepted: Yes.

Costs Per Year: Application fee: $0. Area resident tuition: $2700 full-time, $90 per credit hour part-time. State resident tuition: $3390 full-time, $113 per credit hour part-time. Nonresident tuition: $7050 full-time, $235 per credit hour part-time. College room and board: $5794.

Collegiate Environment: Orientation program. Drama-theater group. Social organizations: 18 open to all. Most popular organizations: International Student Association, Phi Theta Kappa, Net Impact, Student Nurses Association, Student Veterans Organization. Major annual events: Graduation, Annual Job Fair, Wellness Fair. Campus security: 24-hour emergency response devices and patrols. 120 college housing spaces available; 75 were oc-

cupied in 2018-19. No special consideration for freshman housing applicants. Option: coed housing available. Oveta Culp Hobby Memorial Library. Books: 37,738 (physical), 279,575 (digital/electronic); Serial titles: 126 (physical); Databases: 82. Weekly public service hours: 85; students can reserve study rooms. Operations spending for the previous fiscal year: $795,552.

Community Environment: Population 100,200. Killeen is considered an outstanding recreation area with beautiful lakes and streams located nearby. The climate is temperate. All types of transportation are accessible. The community has shopping centers, medical facilities, and churches of many different faiths. Part-time employment is available.

■ CHAMBERLAIN COLLEGE OF NURSING (HOUSTON)

11025 Equity Dr.
Houston, TX 77041
Tel: (713)277-9800; Free: 877-751-5783
Fax: (713)277-9980
Web Site: www.chamberlain.edu

Description: Proprietary, 4-year, coed. Awards bachelor's degrees. Total enrollment: 439. Faculty: 104 (14 full-time, 90 part-time). Student-undergrad faculty ratio is 5:1. Full-time: 90 students, 83% women, 17% men. Part-time: 349 students, 85% women, 15% men. 2% from out-of-state. 20% Hispanic/Latino; 33% Black or African American, non-Hispanic/Latino; 16% Asian, non-Hispanic/Latino; 0.7% Native Hawaiian or other Pacific Islander, non-Hispanic/Latino; 0.9% international. 66% 25 or older, 27% transferred in. Academic area with the most degrees conferred: health professions and related sciences. Accelerated degree program, distance learning.

Entrance Requirements: Option: deferred admission. Required: SAT or ACT. Entrance: moderately difficult. Application deadline: rolling. Notification: continuous.

■ CHAMBERLAIN COLLEGE OF NURSING (IRVING)

4800 Regent Blvd.
Irving, TX 75063
Tel: (469)706-6705; Free: 866-593-8669
Web Site: www.chamberlain.edu

Description: Proprietary, 4-year, coed.

■ CHAMBERLAIN COLLEGE OF NURSING (PEARLAND)

12000 Shadow Creek Pky.
Pearland, TX 77584
Tel: (832)664-7000; Free: 877-751-5783
Fax: (832)664-7001
Web Site: www.chamberlain.edu

Description: Proprietary, 4-year, coed. Awards bachelor's degrees. Total enrollment: 260. Faculty: 33 (8 full-time, 25 part-time). Student-undergrad faculty ratio is 9:1. Full-time: 87 students, 80% women, 20% men. Part-time: 173 students, 85% women, 15% men. 1% from out-of-state. 20% Hispanic/Latino; 32% Black or African American, non-Hispanic/Latino; 17% Asian, non-Hispanic/Latino; 1% Native Hawaiian or other Pacific Islander, non-Hispanic/Latino. 55% 25 or older, 38% transferred in. Accelerated degree program, distance learning.

Entrance Requirements: Option: deferred admission. Required: SAT or ACT. Application deadline: rolling. Notification: continuous.

■ CISCO COLLEGE

101 College Heights
Cisco, TX 76437-9321
Tel: (254)442-5000
Fax: (254)442-5100
E-mail: oodom@cjc.edu
Web Site: www.cisco.edu

Description: State and locally supported, 2-year, coed. Awards certificates, transfer associate, and terminal associate degrees. Founded 1940. Setting: 40-acre rural campus. Total enrollment: 4,022. Faculty: 120. Student-undergrad faculty ratio is 18:1. 1,227 applied, 100% were admitted. Full-time: 1,601 students, 59% women, 41% men. Part-time: 2,421 students, 73% women, 27% men. 12% live on campus. Retention: 56% of full-time freshmen returned the following year. Core. Calendar: semesters. Academic remediation for entering students, advanced placement, summer session for credit, part-time degree program. ROTC: Army (c).

Entrance Requirements: Open admission. Option: early admission. Required: high school transcript. Recommended: SAT, ACT. Entrance: noncompetitive. Application deadline: rolling.

Collegiate Environment: Orientation program. Drama-theater group, marching band. Most popular organizations: Christian Athletes Association, Agricultural Club. Major annual events: Homecoming, Ranch Day. Campus security: late night transport-escort service. Maner Library. 300 computers available on campus for general student use. A campuswide network can be accessed from student residence rooms and from off campus. Students can access the following: online class registration. Staffed computer lab on campus (open 24 hours a day) provides training in use of computers and the Internet.

Community Environment: Population 3,833. Cisco is a rural community that enjoys a temperate climate. The community is served by railroad, bus lines, and highways 80, 380, 183, 206 and Interstate-20. Local service facilities include a hospital, Rotary Club, Lions Club, and Veterans of Foreign Wars and Veterans of World War I. Merchants in the community provide jobs for many students. Recreation includes nearby Lake Cisco for boating, fishing, and water sports.

■ CLARENDON COLLEGE
PO Box 968
Clarendon, TX 79226-0968
Tel: (806)874-3571; Free: 800-687-9737
E-mail: martha.smith@clarendoncollege.edu
Web Site: www.clarendoncollege.edu

Description: State and locally supported, 2-year, coed. Awards certificates, transfer associate, and terminal associate degrees. Founded 1898. Setting: 109-acre rural campus. Endowment: $2.1 million. Educational spending for the previous fiscal year: $2130 per student. Total enrollment: 1,214. Faculty: 94 (36 full-time, 58 part-time). Student-undergrad faculty ratio is 19:1. 498 applied, 100% were admitted. Full-time: 576 students, 55% women, 45% men. Part-time: 638 students, 61% women, 39% men. Students come from 14 states and territories, 2 other countries, 4% from out-of-state. 1% American Indian or Alaska Native, non-Hispanic/Latino; 21% Hispanic/Latino; 4% Black or African American, non-Hispanic/Latino; 0.3% Asian, non-Hispanic/Latino; 0.8% international. 29% 25 or older, 21% live on campus. Core. Calendar: semesters. Academic remediation for entering students, ESL program, services for LD students, advanced placement, independent study, distance learning, double major, summer session for credit, part-time degree program, adult/continuing education programs.

Entrance Requirements: Open admission. Options: electronic application, early admission, international baccalaureate accepted. Required: high school transcript. Required for some: interview. Entrance: noncompetitive. Application deadline: rolling. Notification: continuous. Transfer credits accepted: Yes.

Costs Per Year: Application fee: $0. State resident tuition: $1224 full-time, $51 per credit hour part-time. Nonresident tuition: $1968 full-time, $82 per credit hour part-time. Mandatory fees: $1320 full-time, $55 per credit hour part-time. College room and board: $2,088.

Collegiate Environment: Orientation program. Drama-theater group, choral group. Campus security: 8-hour patrols by trained security personnel, text-based emergency notification system. Vera Dial Dickey Library plus 1 other. Operations spending for the previous fiscal year: $127,571. 57 computers available on campus for general student use. A campuswide network can be accessed from student residence rooms and from off campus. Students can access the following: online class registration. Staffed computer lab on campus.

Community Environment: Population 2,021. A rural community, Clarendon is the center of a ranching and farming area 54 miles southwest of Amarillo. The climate is temperate with an average temperature of 61 degrees, and rainfall average of 23 inches. The area is served by railroad, bus lines, and Highways 70 and U.S. 287. The community has many churches, a hospital and clinic, museum, and adequate shopping facilities. Local recreation includes a city park, theatres, a Youth Center, golf course, hunting and fishing, all sports, and Greenbelt Lake with a 35-mile shoreline. Part-time employment is available.

■ COASTAL BEND COLLEGE
3800 Charco Rd.
Beeville, TX 78102-2197
Tel: (361)358-2838; Free: 866-262-2838
Fax: (361)354-2254
E-mail: tadams@coastalbend.edu
Web Site: www.coastalbend.edu

Description: County-supported, 2-year, coed. Awards certificates, transfer associate, and terminal associate degrees. Founded 1965. Setting: 100-acre rural campus. Endowment: $514,263. Educational spending for the previous fiscal year: $1632 per student. Total enrollment: 3,776. Faculty: 157 (73 full-time, 84 part-time). Student-undergrad faculty ratio is 13:1. 519 applied, 100% were admitted. Full-time: 1,353 students, 63% women, 37% men. Part-time: 2,423 students, 62% women, 38% men. Students come from 2 states and territories, 1 other country, 1% from out-of-state. 26% 25 or older, 5% live on campus, 5% transferred in. Core. Calendar: semesters. Academic remediation for entering students, services for LD students, advanced placement, distance learning, summer session for credit, part-time degree program, adult/continuing education programs, co-op programs and internships.

Entrance Requirements: Open admission. Options: electronic application, deferred admission. Required: high school transcript. Entrance: noncompetitive. Application deadline: rolling. Notification: continuous.

Collegiate Environment: Orientation program. Social organizations: 15 open to all. Most popular organizations: Student Government, Computer Science Club, Creative Writing Club, Drama Club, Art Club. Major annual events: Transfer Day, Job Fair, CBC Day. Student services: personal-psychological counseling. Campus security: 24-hour emergency response devices, night security. Grady C. Hogue Learning Resource Center. Operations spending for the previous fiscal year: $549,751. 970 computers available on campus for general student use. A campuswide network can be accessed from off-campus. Students can access the following: online class registration. Staffed computer lab on campus.

■ COLLEGE OF BIBLICAL STUDIES-HOUSTON
7000 Regency Sq. Blvd.
Houston, TX 77036
Tel: (713)785-5995; Free: 844-227-9673
Fax: (713)785-5998
E-mail: admissions@cbshouston.edu
Web Site: www.cbshouston.edu

Description: Independent nondenominational, 4-year, coed. Awards associate and bachelor's degrees. Founded 1976. Setting: 14-acre urban campus with easy access to Houston. Endowment: $656,713. Total enrollment: 428. Faculty: 48 (16 full-time, 32 part-time). Student-undergrad faculty ratio is 10:1. Full-time: 66 students, 36% women, 64% men. Part-time: 362 students, 47% women, 53% men. Students come from 2 states and territories. 28% Hispanic/Latino; 42% Black or African American, non-Hispanic/Latino; 1% Asian, non-Hispanic/Latino. 88% 25 or older, 71% transferred in. Retention: 50% of full-time freshmen returned the following year. Core. Calendar: semesters. Academic remediation for entering students, ESL program, services for LD students, accelerated degree program, independent study, distance learning, double major, summer session for credit, part-time degree program, adult/continuing education programs, co-op programs. Off campus study at Dallas Theological Seminary.

Entrance Requirements: Open admission. Option: electronic application. Required: essay, high school transcript. Required for some: interview. Entrance: noncompetitive. Application deadline: rolling. Transfer credits accepted: Yes.

Costs Per Year: Application fee: $40. Tuition: $6576 full-time, $274 per credit hour part-time. Mandatory fees: $370 full-time, $185 per term part-time.

Collegiate Environment: Orientation program. Choral group. Most popular organization: Student Ministries. Major annual events: Student Appreciation Week, Annual Alumni BBQ, Black History Month Speaker Series. Student services: personal-psychological counseling. Campus security: 24-hour emergency response devices, late night transport-escort service, hourly patrols by trained security guards and police. College of Biblical Studies Library. Books: 88,005 (physical), 161,601 (digital/electronic); Serial titles: 476 (physical), 5,325 (digital/electronic). Weekly public service hours: 53; students can reserve study rooms. Operations spending for the previous fiscal year: $265,484. 50 computers available on campus for general student use. A campuswide network can be accessed from off-campus. Students can access the following: online class registration. Staffed computer lab on campus provides training in use of computers, software, and the Internet.

■ THE COLLEGE OF HEALTH CARE PROFESSIONS (AUSTIN)
6505 Airport Blvd.
Austin, TX 78752
Tel: (512)892-2835
Web Site: www.chcp.edu

Description: Proprietary, 2-year, coed. Awards certificates, transfer associate, and terminal associate degrees. Calendar: continuous.

■ **THE COLLEGE OF HEALTH CARE PROFESSIONS (FORT WORTH)**
4248 N Fwy.
Fort Worth, TX 76137-5021
Tel: (817)632-5900
Web Site: www.chcp.edu
Description: Proprietary, 2-year, coed. Awards certificates, transfer associate, and terminal associate degrees.

■ **THE COLLEGE OF HEALTH CARE PROFESSIONS (HOUSTON)**
240 NW Mall Blvd.
Houston, TX 77092
Tel: (713)862-2633; Free: 800-487-6728
Fax: (713)746-5466
Web Site: www.chcp.edu
Description: Proprietary, 2-year, coed. Awards certificates and terminal associate degrees. Founded 1988. Total enrollment: 1,296. 48% 25 or older. Calendar: semesters.
Entrance Requirements: Required: high school transcript.

■ **THE COLLEGE OF HEALTH CARE PROFESSIONS (MCALLEN)**
1917 Nolana Ave.
Ste. 100
McAllen, TX 78504
Web Site: www.chcp.edu
Description: Proprietary, 2-year, coed.

■ **THE COLLEGE OF HEALTH CARE PROFESSIONS (SAN ANTONIO)**
4738 NW Loop 410
San Antonio, TX 78229
Tel: (210)298-3600
Web Site: www.chcp.edu
Description: Proprietary, 2-year, coed. Awards certificates, transfer associate, and terminal associate degrees.

■ **COLLEGE OF THE MAINLAND**
1200 Amburn Rd.
Texas City, TX 77591-2499
Tel: (409)938-1211; Free: 888-258-8859
Fax: (409)938-1306
E-mail: mperez@com.edu
Web Site: www.com.edu
Description: State and locally supported, 2-year, coed. Awards certificates, diplomas, transfer associate, and terminal associate degrees. Founded 1967. Setting: 128-acre suburban campus with easy access to Houston. Educational spending for the previous fiscal year: $5878 per student. Total enrollment: 4,188. Faculty: 270 (108 full-time, 162 part-time). Student-undergrad faculty ratio is 15:1. 1,781 applied, 47% were admitted. 1% from top 10% of their high school class, 11% from top quarter, 35% from top half. Full-time: 1,121 students, 54% women, 46% men. Part-time: 3,067 students, 60% women, 40% men. Students come from 3 states and territories. 0.4% American Indian or Alaska Native, non-Hispanic/Latino; 27% Hispanic/Latino; 16% Black or African American, non-Hispanic/Latino; 3% Asian, non-Hispanic/Latino; 0.2% Native Hawaiian or other Pacific Islander, non-Hispanic/Latino. 33% 25 or older, 5% transferred in. Retention: 54% of full-time freshmen returned the following year. Core. Calendar: semesters. Academic remediation for entering students, ESL program, services for LD students, honors program, distance learning, summer session for credit, part-time degree program, adult/continuing education programs, co-op programs and internships. ROTC: Air Force (c).
Entrance Requirements: Open admission. Options: electronic application, early admission, deferred admission. Recommended: SAT or ACT. Required for some: high school transcript. Entrance: noncompetitive. Application deadline: rolling. Notification: continuous. Transfer credits accepted: Yes.
Collegiate Environment: Orientation program. Social organizations: 28 open to all. Most popular organizations: Process Technology Club, Geology Club, Veterans' Club, Biology Club, Phi Theta Kappa. Major annual events: Picnic with the President, Sport and Spirit Day, Transfer Fair. Student services: personal-psychological counseling. Campus security: 24-hour emergency response devices and patrols, student patrols, late night transport-escort service, Vehicular assistance - lock outs, jump starts. COM Library plus 1 other. Operations spending for the previous fiscal year: $402,834. 50 computers available on campus for general student use. A campuswide network can be accessed from off-campus. Students can ac-

cess the following: online class registration. Staffed computer lab on campus provides training in use of computers, software, and the Internet.
Community Environment: Population 44,200 Texas City is a suburban community located approximately 40 miles from the center of Houston.

■ **COLLIN COUNTY COMMUNITY COLLEGE DISTRICT**
3452 Spur 399
McKinney, TX 75069
Tel: (972)548-6790
Fax: (972)758-5468
E-mail: tfields@collin.edu
Web Site: www.collin.edu
Description: State and locally supported, 2-year, coed. Awards certificates, transfer associate, and terminal associate degrees. Founded 1985. Setting: 277-acre suburban campus with easy access to Dallas-Fort Worth. Endowment: $9.5 million. Educational spending for the previous fiscal year: $3877 per student. Total enrollment: 31,619. Faculty: 1,195 (410 full-time, 785 part-time). Student-undergrad faculty ratio is 24:1. 5,763 applied, 100% were admitted. Full-time: 10,231 students, 51% women, 49% men. Part-time: 21,388 students, 57% women, 43% men. Students come from 51 states and territories, 99 other countries, 5% from out-of-state. 0.4% American Indian or Alaska Native, non-Hispanic/Latino; 20% Hispanic/Latino; 12% Black or African American, non-Hispanic/Latino; 10% Asian, non-Hispanic/Latino; 0.2% Native Hawaiian or other Pacific Islander, non-Hispanic/Latino; 3% international. 23% 25 or older, 6% transferred in. Retention: 66% of full-time freshmen returned the following year. Core. Calendar: semesters. Academic remediation for entering students, ESL program, services for LD students, advanced placement, honors program, distance learning, summer session for credit, part-time degree program, adult/continuing education programs, co-op programs and internships. ROTC: Air Force (c).
Entrance Requirements: Open admission. Options: electronic application, international baccalaureate accepted. Required for some: high school transcript. Entrance: noncompetitive. Application deadline: rolling. Notification: continuous. Transfer credits accepted: Yes.
Costs Per Year: Application fee: $0. Area resident tuition: $1440 full-time, $48 per credit hour part-time. State resident tuition: $2820 full-time, $94 per credit hour part-time. Nonresident tuition: $4800 full-time, $160 per credit hour part-time. Mandatory fees: $64 full-time, $2 per credit hour part-time, $2 per term part-time.
Collegiate Environment: Orientation program. Drama-theater group, choral group. Social organizations: 86 open to all; Local and national societies and groups. Most popular organizations: Phi Theta Kappa, National Society of Collegiate Scholars, Student Government Association, Fellowship of Christian University Students, Collin Organized Greek Society. Major annual events: Wild West at the Park, SpringFest, Rocking the Ridge. Student services: personal-psychological counseling. Campus security: 24-hour emergency response devices and patrols, late night transport-escort service. Collin College Library. Books: 229,978 (physical), 36,785 (digital/electronic); Serial titles: 841 (physical), 94 (digital/electronic); Databases: 120. Students can reserve study rooms. Operations spending for the previous fiscal year: $3.2 million. 4,053 computers available on campus for general student use. A campuswide network can be accessed. Students can access the following: online class registration. Staffed computer lab on campus provides training in use of computers, software, and the Internet.

■ **COMMONWEALTH INSTITUTE OF FUNERAL SERVICE**
415 Barren Springs Dr.
Houston, TX 77090
Tel: (281)873-0262; Free: 800-628-1580
Fax: (281)873-5232
E-mail: p.moreno@commonwealth.edu
Web Site: www.commonwealth.edu
Description: Independent, 2-year, coed. Awards certificates and terminal associate degrees. Founded 1988. Setting: urban campus with easy access to Houston. Total enrollment: 122. 55 applied, 100% were admitted. 52% 25 or older. Core. Calendar: quarters. External degree program, adult/continuing education programs.
Entrance Requirements: Required: high school transcript. Recommended: SAT or ACT. Required for some: Wonderlic aptitude test or THEA. Entrance: moderately difficult. Application deadline: rolling. Notification: continuous.
Collegiate Environment: Social organizations: local fraternities. Campus security: 24-hour emergency response devices, daytime trained security personnel. Commonwealth Institute Library and York Learning Resource

Center. 15 computers available on campus for general student use. Staffed computer lab on campus provides training in use of computers, software, and the Internet.

■ CONCORDE CAREER COLLEGE (DALLAS)

12606 Greenville Ave.
Ste. 130
Dallas, TX 75243
Tel: (469)221-3400
Web Site: www.concorde.edu
Description: Proprietary, 2-year, coed. Awards certificates and terminal associate degrees.

■ CONCORDE CAREER COLLEGE (GRAND PRAIRIE)

3015 W Interstate 20
Grand Prairie, TX 75052
Tel: (469)348-2500; Free: 800-693-7010
Web Site: www.concorde.edu
Description: Proprietary, 2-year, coed. Awards certificates and terminal associate degrees.

■ CONCORDE CAREER COLLEGE (SAN ANTONIO)

4803 NW Loop 410
Ste. 200
San Antonio, TX 78229
Tel: (210)428-2000
Web Site: www.concorde.edu
Description: Proprietary, 2-year, coed. Awards certificates and terminal associate degrees.

■ CONCORDIA UNIVERSITY TEXAS

11400 Concordia University Dr.
Austin, TX 78726
Tel: (512)313-3000; Free: 800-865-4282
Fax: (512)459-8517
E-mail: admissions@concordia.edu
Web Site: www.concordia.edu
Description: Independent, comprehensive, coed, affiliated with Lutheran Church-Missouri Synod. Part of Concordia University System. Awards associate, bachelor's, and master's degrees. Founded 1926. Setting: 385-acre urban campus with easy access to Austin. Total enrollment: 2,504. Faculty: 302 (71 full-time, 231 part-time). Student-undergrad faculty ratio is 11:1. 853 applied, 83% were admitted. 14% from top 10% of their high school class, 38% from top quarter, 73% from top half. Full-time: 1,192 students, 62% women, 38% men. Part-time: 375 students, 70% women, 30% men. Students come from 29 states and territories, 2 other countries, 6% from out-of-state. 0.6% American Indian or Alaska Native, non-Hispanic/Latino; 22% Hispanic/Latino; 12% Black or African American, non-Hispanic/Latino; 3% Asian, non-Hispanic/Latino; 0.5% international. 36% 25 or older, 13% live on campus, 5% transferred in. Retention: 61% of full-time freshmen returned the following year. Academic areas with the most degrees conferred: business/marketing; health professions and related sciences; education. Core. Calendar: semesters. Academic remediation for entering students, services for LD students, advanced placement, accelerated degree program, honors program, independent study, summer session for credit, part-time degree program, adult/continuing education programs, internships. Study abroad program. ROTC: Army (c), Air Force (c).
Entrance Requirements: Options: electronic application, early admission, deferred admission, international baccalaureate accepted. Required: high school transcript, minimum 2.5 high school GPA, SAT or ACT. Required for some: essay, interview. Entrance: moderately difficult. Application deadline: rolling. Notification: continuous. SAT Reasoning Test deadline: 8/1. Transfer credits accepted: Yes.
Collegiate Environment: Orientation program. Drama-theater group, choral group, student-run newspaper, radio station. Social organizations: non-Greek social and service organizations. Most popular organizations: Student Government, Business Club (The Executives), Education Club, Student Nursing Association, Student Athlete Advisory Committee. Major annual events: Tornado Tuesday, Coffee House, Spring Banquet. Student services: personal-psychological counseling. Campus security: student patrols, late night transport-escort service, controlled dormitory access. Concordia University Library. 25 computers available on campus for general student use. A campuswide network can be accessed from student residence rooms

and from off campus. Students can access the following: online class registration. Staffed computer lab on campus provides training in use of software and the Internet.

■ CRISWELL COLLEGE

4010 Gaston Ave.
Dallas, TX 75246-1537
Tel: (214)821-5433; Free: 800-899-0012
Fax: (214)818-1310
E-mail: shagos@criswell.edu
Web Site: www.criswell.edu
Description: Independent, comprehensive, coed, affiliated with Southern Baptist Convention. Awards associate, bachelor's, and master's degrees. Founded 1970. Setting: urban campus with easy access to Dallas-Fort Worth. Endowment: $15 million. Educational spending for the previous fiscal year: $11,467 per student. Total enrollment: 264. Faculty: 31 (16 full-time, 15 part-time). Student-undergrad faculty ratio is 8:1. 27 applied, 93% were admitted. 29% from top quarter of their high school class, 57% from top half. Full-time: 103 students, 32% women, 68% men. Part-time: 95 students, 35% women, 65% men. 2% from out-of-state. 14% Hispanic/Latino; 14% Black or African American, non-Hispanic/Latino; 1% Asian, non-Hispanic/Latino; 3% international. 51% 25 or older, 12% transferred in. Retention: 92% of full-time freshmen returned the following year. Academic areas with the most degrees conferred: theology and religious vocations; psychology. Core. Calendar: semesters. Academic remediation for entering students, services for LD students, advanced placement, independent study, distance learning, double major, summer session for credit, part-time degree program, graduate courses open to undergrads.
Entrance Requirements: Options: electronic application, international baccalaureate accepted. Required: essay, 1 recommendation. Required for some: high school transcript, SAT or ACT. Entrance: minimally difficult. Application deadline: rolling. Notification: continuous. Transfer credits accepted: Yes.
Costs Per Year: Application fee: $35. Tuition: $9960 full-time, $415 per credit hour part-time. Mandatory fees: $750 full-time, $750 per year part-time. Full-time tuition and fees vary according to course load. Part-time tuition and fees vary according to course load.
Collegiate Environment: Orientation program. Student services: personal-psychological counseling. Campus security: 24-hour emergency response devices, late night transport-escort service, electronically-operated building entrances. Wallace Library. Books: 45,906 (physical), 200,891 (digital/electronic); Serial titles: 8 (physical), 19,721 (digital/electronic); Databases: 71. Students can reserve study rooms. Operations spending for the previous fiscal year: $22,683. 21 computers available on campus for general student use. Staffed computer lab on campus provides training in use of computers, software, and the Internet.

■ CULINARY INSTITUTE LENOTRE

7070 Allensby
Houston, TX 77022-4322
Tel: (713)692-0077; Free: 888-LENOTRE
Fax: (713)692-7399
E-mail: ehogaboom@ciaml.com
Web Site: www.culinaryinstitute.edu
Description: Proprietary, 2-year, coed. Awards certificates, diplomas, and terminal associate degrees. Founded 1998. Setting: urban campus with easy access to Houston. Total enrollment: 320. Student-undergrad faculty ratio is 12:1. Students come from 6 other countries. Core. Academic remediation for entering students, part-time degree program, adult/continuing education programs, co-op programs and internships.
Entrance Requirements: Open admission. Option: electronic application. Required: high school transcript, interview, ACCUPLACER. Entrance: noncompetitive. Transfer credits accepted: Yes.
Collegiate Environment: Orientation program. Campus security: late night transport-escort service, security personnel patrol during class hours. Learning Resource Center. 40 computers available on campus for general student use. A campuswide network can be accessed. Staffed computer lab on campus provides training in use of computers, software, and the Internet.

■ DALLAS BAPTIST UNIVERSITY

3000 Mountain Creek Pky.
Dallas, TX 75211-9299
Tel: (214)333-7100; Free: 800-460-1328
Fax: (214)333-5447

E-mail: richardn@dbu.edu

Web Site: www.dbu.edu

Description: Independent, comprehensive, coed, affiliated with Baptist General Convention of Texas. Awards associate, bachelor's, master's, and doctoral degrees and post-master's certificates. Founded 1965. Setting: 368-acre suburban campus with easy access to Dallas-Fort Worth. Endowment: $51.4 million. Educational spending for the previous fiscal year: $9479 per student. Total enrollment: 4,766. Faculty: 636 (133 full-time, 503 part-time). Student-undergrad faculty ratio is 13:1. 2,757 applied, 88% were admitted. 18% from top 10% of their high school class, 46% from top quarter, 77% from top half. 3 valedictorians. Full-time: 2,364 students, 57% women, 43% men. Part-time: 650 students, 63% women, 37% men. Students come from 36 states and territories, 47 other countries, 8% from out-of-state. 0.7% American Indian or Alaska Native, non-Hispanic/Latino; 18% Hispanic/Latino; 10% Black or African American, non-Hispanic/Latino; 2% Asian, non-Hispanic/Latino; 0.3% Native Hawaiian or other Pacific Islander, non-Hispanic/Latino; 8% international. 18% 25 or older, 64% live on campus, 7% transferred in. Retention: 77% of full-time freshmen returned the following year. Academic areas with the most degrees conferred: business/marketing; theology and religious vocations; interdisciplinary studies. Core. Calendar: 4-1-4. Academic remediation for entering students, ESL program, services for LD students, advanced placement, accelerated degree program, honors program, independent study, distance learning, double major, summer session for credit, part-time degree program, adult/continuing education programs, internships, graduate courses open to undergrads. Off campus study at Institutions that are members of the Council for Christian Colleges and Universities. Also: American Studies Program in Washington, D.C.; Contemporary Music Center in Nashville, TN; Los Angeles Film Studies Center; Australia Studies Centre in Brisbane, Queensland; Latin American Studies Program based in San Jose, Costa Rica; Middle East Studies Program in Amman, Jordan; Northern Ireland Semester based in Belfast; Oxford Summer Programme and Scholars' Semester both in England at the University of Oxford; Uganda Studi. Study abroad program. ROTC: Army (c), Air Force (c).

Entrance Requirements: Options: electronic application, early admission, deferred admission, international baccalaureate accepted. Required: essay, high school transcript, minimum 2.5 high school GPA, rank in upper 50% of high school class, SAT or ACT. Recommended: interview. Entrance: moderately difficult. Application deadlines: rolling, rolling for nonresidents. Notification: continuous, continuous for nonresidents. SAT Reasoning Test deadline: 8/31. Transfer credits accepted: Yes.

Costs Per Year: Application fee: $25. Comprehensive fee: $38,546 includes full-time tuition ($29,220), mandatory fees ($1100), and college room and board ($8226). College room only: $4015. Part-time tuition: $974 per credit hour.

Collegiate Environment: Orientation program. Drama-theater group, choral group. Social organizations: 48 open to all; local fraternities, local sororities, International, Service, Spiritual, Sports; 17% of eligible men and 24% of eligible women are members. Most popular organizations: Ministry Fellowship, Baptist Student Ministry, Student Government Association, Student Education Association, International Student Organization. Major annual events: Homecoming, Student Welcome and Transition Week (SWAT), Welcome Back Week. Student services: health clinic, personal-psychological counseling. Campus security: 24-hour emergency response devices and patrols, late night transport-escort service, controlled dormitory access. 2,326 college housing spaces available; 1,990 were occupied in 2018-19. Freshmen given priority for college housing. Options: men-only, women-only housing available. Vance Memorial Library plus 3 others. Books: 247,606 (physical), 153,056 (digital/electronic); Serial titles: 561 (physical), 46,112 (digital/electronic); Databases: 203. Weekly public service hours: 108. Operations spending for the previous fiscal year: $1.4 million. 214 computers available on campus for general student use. A campuswide network can be accessed from student residence rooms and from off campus. Students can access the following: online class registration. Staffed computer lab on campus provides training in use of computers, software, and the Internet.

Community Environment: See University of Texas at Dallas.

■ **DALLAS CHRISTIAN COLLEGE**

2700 Christian Pky.

Dallas, TX 75234-7299

Tel: (972)241-3371; Free: 800-688-1029

Fax: (972)241-8021

E-mail: ahudspeth@dallas.edu

Web Site: www.dallas.edu

Description: Independent, 4-year, coed, affiliated with Christian Churches and Churches of Christ. Awards associate and bachelor's degrees. Founded 1950. Setting: 22-acre suburban campus with easy access to Dallas-Fort Worth. Endowment: $169,907. Total enrollment: 213. Faculty: 56 (8 full-time, 48 part-time). Student-undergrad faculty ratio is 16:1. 132 applied, 37% were admitted. 7% from top 10% of their high school class, 23% from top quarter, 42% from top half. Full-time: 167 students, 36% women, 64% men. Part-time: 45 students, 53% women, 47% men. Students come from 11 states and territories, 5 other countries, 16% from out-of-state. 15% Hispanic/Latino; 24% Black or African American, non-Hispanic/Latino; 1% Asian, non-Hispanic/Latino; 0.5% Native Hawaiian or other Pacific Islander, non-Hispanic/Latino; 3% international. 40% 25 or older, 46% live on campus, 13% transferred in. Retention: 50% of full-time freshmen returned the following year. Academic areas with the most degrees conferred: business/marketing; theology and religious vocations; psychology. Core. Calendar: semesters. Academic remediation for entering students, advanced placement, accelerated degree program, independent study, distance learning, double major, summer session for credit, part-time degree program, adult/continuing education programs, internships.

Entrance Requirements: Options: electronic application, deferred admission, international baccalaureate accepted. Required: SAT or ACT. Required for some: high school transcript. Entrance: moderately difficult. Application deadline: rolling. Preference given to Christians. Transfer credits accepted: Yes.

Costs Per Year: Application fee: $30. Comprehensive fee: $25,516 includes full-time tuition ($15,596), mandatory fees ($910), and college room and board ($9010). Full-time tuition and fees vary according to program. Part-time tuition: $557 per credit hour. Part-time mandatory fees: $285 per term. Part-time tuition and fees vary according to program.

Collegiate Environment: Orientation program. Drama-theater group, choral group. Major annual events: Day of Service, International Convention of Missions, Community Building Day. Student services: personal-psychological counseling. Campus security: controlled dormitory access. 136 college housing spaces available; 104 were occupied in 2018-19. On-campus residence required through sophomore year. Options: men-only, women-only housing available. The Crawford Library. Books: 35,000 (physical), 26,000 (digital/electronic); Serial titles: 100 (physical); Databases: 60. 16 computers available on campus for general student use. A campuswide network can be accessed from student residence rooms. Students can access the following: online class registration. Staffed computer lab on campus.

Community Environment: A manufacturing, financial and distributing center, Dallas is a center for scientifically oriented industry in the electronics and aerospace fields and ranks high in cotton, oil and consumer goods production. The city also houses a principal banking and insurance complex. Dallas is a transportation hub for rail, bus and airlines.

■ **DALLAS INSTITUTE OF FUNERAL SERVICE**

3909 S Buckner Blvd.

Dallas, TX 75227

Tel: (214)388-5466; Free: 800-235-5444

Fax: (214)388-0316

E-mail: oretana@dallasinstitute.edu

Web Site: www.dallasinstitute.edu

Description: Independent, 2-year, coed. Part of Pierce Mortuary Colleges, Inc. Awards certificates, transfer associate, and terminal associate degrees. Founded 1945. Setting: 4-acre urban campus with easy access to Dallas-Fort Worth. Educational spending for the previous fiscal year: $2010 per student. Total enrollment: 95. Faculty: 10. Student-undergrad faculty ratio is 15:1. Full-time: 95 students, 51% women, 49% men. Students come from 6 states and territories, 12% from out-of-state. 23% Hispanic/Latino; 35% Black or African American, non-Hispanic/Latino; 3% Asian, non-Hispanic/Latino. 59% 25 or older, 42% transferred in. Core. Calendar: quarters. Services for LD students, advanced placement, distance learning, co-op programs.

Entrance Requirements: Open admission. Option: electronic application. Required: high school transcript. Entrance: noncompetitive. Application deadline: rolling. Transfer credits accepted: Yes.

Collegiate Environment: Social organizations: 3 open to all. Most popular organizations: Lions Club International, Women in Black, Epsilon Chapter of Pi Sigma Eta National Mortician's Honors Fraternity. Major annual events: Meet and Greet Picnic, Job Fair. Campus security: 24-hour emergency response devices, electronically locked doors. J. Frank Pierce Library. Books: 2,223 (physical); Databases: 1. Operations spending for the previous fiscal year: $2236. 24 computers available on campus for general student use. A campuswide network can be accessed.

■ DALLAS INTERNATIONAL UNIVERSITY
7500 W Camp Wisdom Rd.
Dallas, TX 75236
Tel: (972)708-7340
Fax: (972)708-7433
Description: Independent, comprehensive, coed. Founded 1999. Calendar: two 20-week terms (bimester).

■ DALLAS NURSING INSTITUTE
12170 N Abrams Rd.
Ste. 200
Dallas, TX 75243
Tel: (214)351-0223
Web Site: www.dni.edu
Description: Proprietary, primarily 2-year, coed. Awards transfer associate, terminal associate, and bachelor's degrees.

■ DEL MAR COLLEGE
101 Baldwin Blvd.
Corpus Christi, TX 78404-3897
Tel: (361)698-1200; Free: 800-652-3357
Fax: (361)698-1559
Web Site: www.delmar.edu
Description: State and locally supported, 2-year, coed. Awards certificates, transfer associate, and terminal associate degrees. Founded 1935. Setting: 159-acre urban campus. Educational spending for the previous fiscal year: $3578 per student. Total enrollment: 11,833. Faculty: 560 (267 full-time, 293 part-time). Student-undergrad faculty ratio is 18:1. Full-time: 2,671 students, 48% women, 52% men. Part-time: 9,162 students, 60% women, 40% men. Students come from 41 states and territories, 30 other countries, 2% from out-of-state. 0.2% American Indian or Alaska Native, non-Hispanic/Latino; 67% Hispanic/Latino; 3% Black or African American, non-Hispanic/Latino; 2% Asian, non-Hispanic/Latino; 0.2% Native Hawaiian or other Pacific Islander, non-Hispanic/Latino; 0.2% international. 44% 25 or older, 6% transferred in. Retention: 56% of full-time freshmen returned the following year. Core. Calendar: semesters. Academic remediation for entering students, ESL program, services for LD students, advanced placement, accelerated degree program, freshman honors college, honors program, distance learning, double major, summer session for credit, part-time degree program, adult/continuing education programs, co-op programs and internships. Off campus study. ROTC: Army.
Entrance Requirements: Open admission except for allied health programs. Options: electronic application, early admission, deferred admission, international baccalaureate accepted. Required: high school transcript. Entrance: noncompetitive. Application deadline: rolling. Transfer credits accepted: Yes.
Collegiate Environment: Orientation program. Drama-theater group, choral group, student-run newspaper, radio station. Social organizations: 25 open to all. Most popular organizations: Phi Theta Kappa, Alpha Beta Gamma, Student Government Association. Student services: personal-psychological counseling. Campus security: 24-hour emergency response devices and patrols. White Library plus 1 other. Books: 145,107 (physical), 192,073 (digital/electronic); Serial titles: 1,635 (physical), 74,730 (digital/electronic); Databases: 172. Operations spending for the previous fiscal year: $2.6 million. 800 computers available on campus for general student use. A campuswide network can be accessed from off-campus. Students can access the following: online class registration. Staffed computer lab on campus provides training in use of computers, software, and the Internet.
Community Environment: See Texas A&M University Corpus Christi.

■ DEVRY UNIVERSITY-AUSTIN CAMPUS
Stratum Executive Ctr.
11044 Research Blvd., Ste. B-100
Austin, TX 78759
Tel: (512)231-2500; Free: 866-338-7934
Web Site: www.devry.edu
Description: Proprietary, comprehensive, coed.

■ DEVRY UNIVERSITY-IRVING CAMPUS
4800 Regent Blvd., Ste. 200
Irving, TX 75063
Tel: (972)929-6777; Free: 866-338-7934
Web Site: www.devry.edu
Description: Proprietary, comprehensive, coed. Part of DeVry University.

Awards associate, bachelor's, and master's degrees. Founded 1969. Setting: suburban campus. Total enrollment: 566. Faculty: 40 (4 full-time, 36 part-time). Student-undergrad faculty ratio is 20:1. Full-time: 167 students, 28% women, 72% men. Part-time: 236 students, 32% women, 68% men. 2% from out-of-state. 21% Hispanic/Latino; 27% Black or African American, non-Hispanic/Latino; 3% Asian, non-Hispanic/Latino; 0.5% Native Hawaiian or other Pacific Islander, non-Hispanic/Latino; 0.7% international. 84% 25 or older, 27% transferred in. Calendar: semesters. Part-time degree program, adult/continuing education programs.
Entrance Requirements: Option: deferred admission. Required: high school transcript, interview. Entrance: minimally difficult. Application deadline: rolling. Notification: continuous.
Collegiate Environment: Orientation program. Learning Resource Center.

■ DEVRY UNIVERSITY-SAN ANTONIO CAMPUS
618 NW Loop 410, Ste. 202
San Antonio, TX 78216
Tel: (210)524-5400; Free: 866-338-7934
Fax: (210)979-9960
Web Site: www.devry.edu
Description: Proprietary, comprehensive, coed.

■ EAST TEXAS BAPTIST UNIVERSITY
One Tiger Dr.
Marshall, TX 75670-1498
Tel: (903)935-7963; Free: 800-804-ETBU
Fax: (903)938-1705
E-mail: admissions@etbu.edu
Web Site: www.etbu.edu
Description: Independent Baptist, comprehensive, coed. Awards bachelor's and master's degrees. Founded 1912. Setting: 250-acre small town campus. Endowment: $71.5 million. Educational spending for the previous fiscal year: $6511 per student. Total enrollment: 1,613. Faculty: 149 (72 full-time, 77 part-time). Student-undergrad faculty ratio is 15:1. 1,849 applied, 54% were admitted. 13% from top 10% of their high school class, 36% from top quarter, 71% from top half. 4 valedictorians. Full-time: 1,296 students, 53% women, 47% men. Part-time: 189 students, 65% women, 35% men. Students come from 24 states and territories, 6 other countries, 11% from out-of-state. 0.2% American Indian or Alaska Native, non-Hispanic/Latino; 10% Hispanic/Latino; 16% Black or African American, non-Hispanic/Latino; 0.4% Asian, non-Hispanic/Latino; 0.1% Native Hawaiian or other Pacific Islander, non-Hispanic/Latino; 0.8% international. 6% 25 or older, 81% live on campus, 9% transferred in. Retention: 63% of full-time freshmen returned the following year. Academic areas with the most degrees conferred: education; business/marketing; interdisciplinary studies. Core. Calendar: semesters. ESL program, services for LD students, advanced placement, accelerated degree program, self-designed majors, honors program, independent study, distance learning, double major, summer session for credit, part-time degree program, adult/continuing education programs, internships, graduate courses open to undergrads. Off campus study. Study abroad program.
Entrance Requirements: Options: electronic application, international baccalaureate accepted. Required: high school transcript, SAT or ACT. Entrance: moderately difficult. Application deadlines: 8/27, 8/27 for nonresidents. Notification: continuous. SAT Reasoning Test deadline: 8/27. SAT Subject Test deadline: 8/27. Transfer credits accepted: Yes.
Costs Per Year: Application fee: $25. Comprehensive fee: $36,538 includes full-time tuition ($26,100), mandatory fees ($1110), and college room and board ($9328). College room only: $4576. Part-time tuition: $870 per credit hour. Part-time mandatory fees: $46 per credit hour.
Collegiate Environment: Orientation program. Drama-theater group, choral group, marching band. Social organizations: 20 open to all; local sororities. Most popular organizations: Fellowship of Christian Athletes (FCA), Student Foundation, Student Government Association (SGA), Enactus, Chem Club. Major annual events: Connexus, Bingo Night, Homecoming. Student services: personal-psychological counseling. Campus security: 24-hour emergency response devices and patrols, student patrols, late night transport-escort service, controlled dormitory access. 1,176 college housing spaces available; 1,118 were occupied in 2018-19. Freshmen given priority for college housing. On-campus residence required through senior year. Options: men-only, women-only housing available. Mamye Jarrett Library. Books: 89,001 (physical), 520,411 (digital/electronic); Serial titles: 1,119 (physical), 81,485 (digital/electronic); Databases: 184. Weekly public service hours: 88. Operations spending for the previous fiscal year: $704,330. 301 computers available on campus for general student use. A campuswide

network can be accessed from student residence rooms. Students can access the following: online class registration.
Community Environment: See Wiley College.

■ **EASTFIELD COLLEGE**
3737 Motley Dr.
Mesquite, TX 75150-2099
Tel: (972)860-7100
Fax: (972)860-8373
E-mail: efc@dcccd.edu
Web Site: www.eastfieldcollege.edu
Description: State and locally supported, 2-year, coed. Part of Dallas County Community College District System. Awards certificates, transfer associate, and terminal associate degrees. Founded 1970. Setting: 244-acre suburban campus with easy access to Dallas-Fort Worth. Educational spending for the previous fiscal year: $4091 per student. Total enrollment: 12,403. Faculty: 564 (121 full-time, 443 part-time). Student-undergrad faculty ratio is 24:1. 3,200 applied, 100% were admitted. Full-time: 3,026 students, 53% women, 47% men. Part-time: 9,377 students, 60% women, 40% men. Students come from 7 states and territories, 26 other countries, 1% from out-of-state. 37% 25 or older, 2% transferred in. Core. Calendar: semesters. Academic remediation for entering students, ESL program, services for LD students, advanced placement, honors program, distance learning, summer session for credit, part-time degree program, adult/continuing education programs, co-op programs.
Entrance Requirements: Open admission. Options: early admission, deferred admission. Recommended: high school transcript. Entrance: noncompetitive. Application deadline: rolling. Notification: continuous.
Collegiate Environment: Drama-theater group, choral group, student-run newspaper. Most popular organizations: LULAC, Rodeo Club, Phi Theta Kappa, Rising Star, Communications Club. Major annual events: Student Leadership Academy, Back to School Parties, performing artists and speakers series. Student services: health clinic, personal-psychological counseling, women's center. Campus security: 24-hour emergency response devices and patrols. Eastfield College Learning Resource Center. Operations spending for the previous fiscal year: $580,478. 50 computers available on campus for general student use. A campuswide network can be accessed from off-campus. Students can access the following: online class registration. Staffed computer lab on campus.
Community Environment: See University of Texas at Dallas.

■ **EL CENTRO COLLEGE**
801 Main St.
Dallas, TX 75202-3604
Tel: (214)860-2037
Fax: (214)860-2335
E-mail: rgarza@dcccd.edu
Web Site: www.elcentrocollege.edu
Description: County-supported, 2-year, coed. Part of Dallas County Community College District System. Awards certificates, transfer associate, and terminal associate degrees. Founded 1966. Setting: 2-acre urban campus. Total enrollment: 10,101. Faculty: 493 (135 full-time, 358 part-time). Student-undergrad faculty ratio is 19:1. Full-time: 2,314 students, 67% women, 33% men. Part-time: 7,787 students, 65% women, 35% men. Students come from 49 countries, 1% from out-of-state. 0.3% American Indian or Alaska Native, non-Hispanic/Latino; 38% Hispanic/Latino; 19% Black or African American, non-Hispanic/Latino; 3% Asian, non-Hispanic/Latino; 0.3% international. 46% 25 or older, 74% transferred in. Retention: 39% of full-time freshmen returned the following year. Core. Calendar: semesters. Academic remediation for entering students, ESL program, services for LD students, advanced placement, freshman honors college, honors program, double major, summer session for credit, part-time degree program, adult/continuing education programs, co-op programs and internships. ROTC: Army (c).
Entrance Requirements: Required for some: high school transcript, 1 recommendation.
Collegiate Environment: Orientation program. Choral group. Social organizations: 38 open to all. Most popular organizations: Phi Theta Kappa, student government, Paralegal Student Association, El Centro Computer Society, Conflict Resolution Society. Major annual events: Student Recognition, African American Read-In, Spring and Fall Semester Welcome Festivals. Student services: health clinic, personal-psychological counseling. Campus security: 24-hour emergency response devices and patrols, late night transport-escort service, e-mail and text message alerts. El Centro Col-

lege Library. 1,317 computers available on campus for general student use. A campuswide network can be accessed from off-campus. Students can access the following: online class registration. Staffed computer lab on campus.
Community Environment: See University of Texas at Dallas.

■ **EL PASO COMMUNITY COLLEGE**
PO Box 20500
El Paso, TX 79998-0500
Tel: (915)831-2000
Fax: (915)831-6145
E-mail: clachica@epcc.edu
Web Site: www.epcc.edu
Description: County-supported, 2-year, coed. Awards certificates, transfer associate, and terminal associate degrees. Founded 1969. Setting: urban campus. Endowment: $742,942. Research spending for the previous fiscal year: $77,753. Educational spending for the previous fiscal year: $4541 per student. Total enrollment: 28,750. Faculty: 1,231. Student-undergrad faculty ratio is 13:1. Full-time: 8,710 students, 55% women, 45% men. Part-time: 20,040 students, 58% women, 42% men. Students come from 49 states and territories, 34 other countries, 3% from out-of-state. 0.2% American Indian or Alaska Native, non-Hispanic/Latino; 85% Hispanic/Latino; 2% Black or African American, non-Hispanic/Latino; 0.7% Asian, non-Hispanic/Latino; 0.1% Native Hawaiian or other Pacific Islander, non-Hispanic/Latino; 2% international. 23% 25 or older, 4% transferred in. Core. Calendar: semesters. Academic remediation for entering students, ESL program, services for LD students, advanced placement, honors program, independent study, distance learning, summer session for credit, part-time degree program, external degree program, adult/continuing education programs, co-op programs and internships. Off campus study at University of Texas at El Paso. ROTC: Army (c).
Entrance Requirements: Open admission. Options: electronic application, early admission, deferred admission. Entrance: noncompetitive. Transfer credits accepted: Yes.
Costs Per Year: Application fee: $10. State resident tuition: $2520 full-time, $105 per credit hour part-time. Nonresident tuition: $4368 full-time, $215 per credit hour part-time. Mandatory fees: $480 full-time, $20 per credit hour part-time. Full-time tuition and fees vary according to course level, course load, program, and student level. Part-time tuition and fees vary according to course level, course load, program, and student level.
Collegiate Environment: Orientation program. Drama-theater group, choral group, student-run newspaper, radio station. Student services: health clinic, personal-psychological counseling. Campus security: 24-hour patrols, late night transport-escort service. El Paso Community College Learning Resource Center plus 4 others. Books: 140,571 (physical), 149,708 (digital/electronic); Serial titles: 231 (physical), 56 (digital/electronic); Databases: 90. Weekly public service hours: 80. Operations spending for the previous fiscal year: $2.6 million.
Community Environment: See University of Texas - El Paso.

■ **FLORIDA CAREER COLLEGE**
70-A Farm to Market Rd. 1960 W
Houston, TX 77090
Web Site: www.floridacareercollege.edu
Description: Proprietary, 2-year, coed.

■ **FORTIS COLLEGE (GRAND PRAIRIE)**
401 E Palace Pky.
Ste. 100
Grand Prairie, TX 75050
Tel: (972)375-0006; Free: 855-4-FORTIS
Web Site: www.fortis.edu
Description: Proprietary, 2-year, coed.

■ **FORTIS COLLEGE (HOUSTON)**
1201 W Oaks Mall
Houston, TX 77082
Tel: (713)266-6594; Free: 855-4-FORTIS
Web Site: www.fortis.edu
Description: Proprietary, 2-year, coed.

■ **FRANK PHILLIPS COLLEGE**
Box 5118
Borger, TX 79008-5118

Tel: (806)457-4200
Fax: (806)274-6835
E-mail: mstevens@fpctx.edu
Web Site: www.fpctx.edu

Description: State and locally supported, 2-year, coed. Awards certificates, transfer associate, and terminal associate degrees. Founded 1948. Setting: 60-acre small town campus. Endowment: $1.3 million. Total enrollment: 1,148. Faculty: 75 (35 full-time, 40 part-time). Student-undergrad faculty ratio is 16:1. Full-time: 501 students, 50% women, 50% men. Part-time: 647 students, 56% women, 44% men. Students come from 15 states and territories, 6 other countries, 10% from out-of-state. 3% American Indian or Alaska Native, non-Hispanic/Latino; 17% Hispanic/Latino; 5% Black or African American, non-Hispanic/Latino; 0.8% Asian, non-Hispanic/Latino; 0.2% Native Hawaiian or other Pacific Islander, non-Hispanic/Latino; 0.2% international. 20% 25 or older, 20% live on campus, 7% transferred in. Retention: 41% of full-time freshmen returned the following year. Core. Calendar: semesters. Academic remediation for entering students, services for LD students, advanced placement, accelerated degree program, honors program, distance learning, summer session for credit, part-time degree program, adult/continuing education programs, co-op programs and internships.

Entrance Requirements: Open admission. Options: electronic application, early admission, deferred admission. Required: high school transcript. Entrance: noncompetitive. Application deadline: 8/25. Notification: continuous until 8/25. Transfer credits accepted: Yes.

Collegiate Environment: Orientation program. Choral group. Student services: personal-psychological counseling. Campus security: 24-hour emergency response devices and patrols, controlled dormitory access. James W. Dillard Library. Operations spending for the previous fiscal year: $158,260.

Community Environment: Population 13,305, one of the youngest towns in Texas, Borger was born as an oil boomtown in 1926. Today it is the center of the Panhandle gas reservoir, which produces more natural gas and allied products than any other field in the world. The community enjoys temperate climate. Air, rail, and bus service is available. Community services include a public library, churches of major denominations, a hospital, major civic, fraternal, and veteran's organizations, and shopping facilities. Local recreation includes theaters, golf, and other sports. Lake Meredith also offers recreational opportunities. The Oil Show, Rodeo, and Art Show are held annually. Part-time employment is available.

■ **GALEN COLLEGE OF NURSING**
7411 John Smith Dr.
Ste. 1400
San Antonio, TX 78229
Tel: (210)733-3056; Free: 877-223-7040
Web Site: www.galencollege.edu

Description: Proprietary, 2-year, coed. Awards transfer associate degrees. Founded 1991.

■ **GALVESTON COLLEGE**
4015 Ave. Q
Galveston, TX 77550
Tel: (409)944-4242
Fax: (409)944-1500
Web Site: www.gc.edu

Description: State and locally supported, 2-year, coed. Awards certificates, transfer associate, and terminal associate degrees. Founded 1967. Setting: 11-acre urban campus with easy access to Houston. Total enrollment: 2,208. Faculty: 97 (53 full-time, 44 part-time). Student-undergrad faculty ratio is 16:1. Full-time: 584 students, 56% women, 44% men. Part-time: 1,624 students, 63% women, 37% men. 0.3% American Indian or Alaska Native, non-Hispanic/Latino; 38% Hispanic/Latino; 16% Black or African American, non-Hispanic/Latino; 3% Asian, non-Hispanic/Latino; 0.2% Native Hawaiian or other Pacific Islander, non-Hispanic/Latino; 1% international. 37% 25 or older, 12% transferred in. Retention: 53% of full-time freshmen returned the following year. Core. Calendar: semesters. Services for LD students, advanced placement, distance learning, summer session for credit, part-time degree program, adult/continuing education programs, co-op programs and internships. Off campus study at Brazosport College, College of the Mainland.

Entrance Requirements: Open admission except for allied health programs. Option: electronic application. Required: TSI or exemption test

scores and documentation. Required for some: high school transcript. Entrance: noncompetitive. Application deadline: rolling. Notification: continuous. Transfer credits accepted: Yes.

Collegiate Environment: Orientation program. Drama-theater group, choral group. Social organizations: 19 open to all; Phi Theta Kappa Honor Society (based on GPA). Most popular organizations: Student Government, Phi Theta Kappa, Student Nurses Association, ATTC, Hispanic Student Organization. Major annual events: College Night, Back to School Activity, Business Symposium. Student services: personal-psychological counseling. Campus security: 24-hour emergency response devices and patrols, late night transport-escort service. David Glenn Hunt Memorial Library. Books: 48,028 (physical), 91,209 (digital/electronic); Serial titles: 73 (physical); Databases: 68. Students can reserve study rooms. 173 computers available on campus for general student use. A campuswide network can be accessed. Students can access the following: online class registration. Staffed computer lab on campus (open 24 hours a day) provides training in use of computers, software, and the Internet.

Community Environment: Galveston is a port and recreational city. Major business activities include the tourist, maritime, and banking industries. Known as the "playground of the Southwest," Galveston has an average maximum temperature of 74.9 degrees, and an average minimum of 65.2 degrees. The climate is semitropical. The community is reached by rail, bus, and air. There are churches of various faiths, a library, YMCA, YWCA, medical facilities, a civic orchestra, Little Theatre, civic music association, an art league, and various fraternal, civic, and veteran's organizations in the community. Local recreation includes 32 miles of hard sand beaches, bathing, motoring, water sports, boating, deep-sea fishing, golf, and horseback riding. Part-time employment is abundant.

■ **GEMINI SCHOOL OF VISUAL ARTS & COMMUNICATION**
501 Prize Oaks Dr.
Cedar Park, TX 78613
Description: Proprietary, 4-year, coed.

■ **GRACE SCHOOL OF THEOLOGY**
3705 College Park Dr. Ste. 140
Conroe, TX 77384-4894
Web Site: www.gsot.edu
Description: Independent, comprehensive, coed. Awards associate, bachelor's, and master's degrees.

■ **GRAYSON COLLEGE**
6101 Grayson Dr.
Denison, TX 75020-8299
Tel: (903)465-6030
Fax: (903)463-5284
E-mail: lesliec@grayson.edu
Web Site: www.grayson.edu

Description: State and locally supported, 2-year, coed. Awards certificates, diplomas, transfer associate, and terminal associate degrees. Founded 1964. Setting: 500-acre rural campus with easy access to Dallas-Fort Worth. Endowment: $8.7 million. Educational spending for the previous fiscal year: $2487 per student. Total enrollment: 5,014. Faculty: 240 (105 full-time, 135 part-time). Student-undergrad faculty ratio is 26:1. 3% from top 10% of their high school class. Full-time: 2,101 students, 57% women, 43% men. Part-time: 2,913 students, 62% women, 38% men. Students come from 14 states and territories, 18 other countries, 5% from out-of-state. 2% American Indian or Alaska Native, non-Hispanic/Latino; 12% Hispanic/Latino; 7% Black or African American, non-Hispanic/Latino; 1% Asian, non-Hispanic/Latino; 0.2% Native Hawaiian or other Pacific Islander, non-Hispanic/Latino; 2% international. 39% 25 or older, 17% live on campus, 12% transferred in. Retention: 53% of full-time freshmen returned the following year. Core. Calendar: semesters. Academic remediation for entering students, ESL program, advanced placement, freshman honors college, honors program, distance learning, summer session for credit, part-time degree program, adult/continuing education programs.

Entrance Requirements: Open admission. Options: electronic application, early admission, deferred admission. Entrance: noncompetitive. Application deadline: 8/31. Notification: continuous. Transfer credits accepted: Yes.

Collegiate Environment: Orientation program. Drama-theater group, choral group, student-run newspaper. Social organizations: 31 open to all. Most popular organizations: Graduate Nursing Student Association, Vocational Nursing Student Association, Phi Theta Kappa, Dental Assisting Club, TIPS/ Culinary student club. Major annual events: Fall Welcome Picnic,

SpringFest, Hallowfest. Campus security: 24-hour emergency response devices and patrols, student patrols, late night transport-escort service, controlled dormitory access. Grayson College Library plus 1 other. Operations spending for the previous fiscal year: $442,948. 70 computers available on campus for general student use. A campuswide network can be accessed from student residence rooms and from off campus. Students can access the following: online class registration, online financial aid applications. Staffed computer lab on campus provides training in use of computers, software, and the Internet.

Community Environment: Population 23,648. Principal industries in this manufacturing city include railroad cars, furniture, fishing lures, wigs, pickup campers, mattresses, venetian blinds, food processing and pipes. This is a metropolitan community served by railway transite and bus lines. The community has a library, over 40 churches representing most denominations, four hospitals, and various civic, fraternal and veteran's organizations. Some part-time job opportunities are available. Local recreation includes nearby lakes featuring all water sports, and three downtown theater complexes.

■ HALLMARK UNIVERSITY

10401 IH 10 W
San Antonio, TX 78230
Tel: (210)690-9000; Free: 800-880-6600
Fax: (210)697-8225
E-mail: jsanchez@hallmarkuniversity.edu
Web Site: www.hallmarkuniversity.edu

Description: Independent, comprehensive, coed. Administratively affiliated with Hallmark University. Awards associate, bachelor's, and master's degrees. Founded 1969. Setting: 2-acre suburban campus with easy access to San Antonio. Educational spending for the previous fiscal year: $1051 per student. Total enrollment: 883. Faculty: 65 (33 full-time, 32 part-time). Student-undergrad faculty ratio is 20:1. Full-time: 872 students, 28% women, 72% men. Students come from 17 states and territories, 2% from out-of-state. 2% American Indian or Alaska Native, non-Hispanic/Latino; 45% Hispanic/Latino; 12% Black or African American, non-Hispanic/Latino; 2% Asian, non-Hispanic/Latino; 1% Native Hawaiian or other Pacific Islander, non-Hispanic/Latino. 74% 25 or older, 2% transferred in. Retention: 47% of full-time freshmen returned the following year. Academic areas with the most degrees conferred: computer and information sciences; business/marketing; transportation and materials moving. Core. Calendar: continuous. Academic remediation for entering students, advanced placement, accelerated degree program, distance learning, internships.

Entrance Requirements: Options: electronic application, early admission, international baccalaureate accepted. Required: high school transcript, interview, hybrid readiness test (main campus only), Wonderlic aptitude test for Main Campus, Aviation Assessment for Satellite Campus, SAT/ACT is used for some degree programs. Required for some: essay, recommendations. Entrance: moderately difficult. Application deadline: rolling. Notification: continuous. Transfer credits accepted: Yes.

Costs Per Year: One-time mandatory fee: $110. Tuition: $36,806 full-time. Mandatory fees: $900 full-time. Full-time tuition and fees vary according to degree level, location, and program.

Collegiate Environment: Orientation program. Social organizations: 2 open to all; Alpha Beta Kappa Honor Society; 4% of eligible men and 2% of eligible women are members. Most popular organizations: Alpha Beta Kappa Honor Society, Student Veteran's Organization. Major annual events: Student Appreciation Day, Veterans Day, Constitution Day. Campus security: 24-hour emergency response devices and patrols, security guard on duty during hours when students are on campus. Randall K. Williams Assessment Center/ Virtual Library plus 1 other. Books: 172,325 (digital/electronic); Serial titles: 26,880 (digital/electronic); Databases: 32. Weekly public service hours: 4. Operations spending for the previous fiscal year: $48,401. 250 computers available on campus for general student use. A campuswide network can be accessed from off-campus. Students can access the following: online class registration. Staffed computer lab on campus provides training in use of computers, software, and the Internet.

■ HARDIN-SIMMONS UNIVERSITY

2200 Hickory St.
Abilene, TX 79698-0001
Tel: (325)670-1000; Free: 877-464-7889
Fax: (325)677-8351
E-mail: grant.t.greenwood@hsutx.edu
Web Site: www.hsutx.edu

Description: Independent Baptist, comprehensive, coed. Awards bachelor's,

master's, and doctoral degrees and post-master's certificates. Founded 1891. Setting: 220-acre urban campus. System endowment: $176.2 million. Educational spending for the previous fiscal year: $11,292 per student. Total enrollment: 2,343. Student-undergrad faculty ratio is 12:1. 1,766 applied, 84% were admitted. 17% from top 10% of their high school class, 24% from top quarter, 70% from top half. 3 valedictorians. Full-time: 1,625 students, 53% women, 47% men. Part-time: 140 students, 56% women, 44% men. Students come from 18 states and territories, 26 other countries, 3% from out-of-state. 0.3% American Indian or Alaska Native, non-Hispanic/Latino; 19% Hispanic/Latino; 9% Black or African American, non-Hispanic/Latino; 2% Asian, non-Hispanic/Latino; 3% international. 7% 25 or older, 54% live on campus, 6% transferred in. Academic areas with the most degrees conferred: business/marketing; health professions and related sciences; psychology. Core. Calendar: semesters. Academic remediation for entering students, services for LD students, advanced placement, accelerated degree program, honors program, independent study, distance learning, double major, summer session for credit, part-time degree program, adult/continuing education programs, internships, graduate courses open to undergrads. Off campus study at Abilene Christian University, McMurry University, Patty Hanks School of Nursing. Study abroad program.

Entrance Requirements: Options: electronic application, deferred admission, international baccalaureate accepted. Required: high school transcript, minimum 2 high school GPA, SAT or ACT. Entrance: moderately difficult. Application deadline: rolling. Notification: continuous. SAT Reasoning Test deadline: 8/15. Transfer credits accepted: Yes.

Costs Per Year: Application fee: $0. Comprehensive fee: $39,990 includes full-time tuition ($28,390), mandatory fees ($1750), and college room and board ($9850). College room only: $4470. Part-time tuition: $850 per credit hour. Part-time mandatory fees: $400 per term.

Collegiate Environment: Orientation program. Drama-theater group, choral group, marching band, student-run newspaper. Social organizations: 56 open to all; local fraternities, local sororities; 11% of eligible men and 15% of eligible women are members. Most popular organizations: Baptist Student Ministries, Student Government, Alpha Phi Omega, Student Activities Board, Fellowship of Christian Athletes. Major annual events: Homecoming, All-School Sing, Western Heritage Day. Student services: personal-psychological counseling. Campus security: 24-hour emergency response devices and patrols, late night transport-escort service, controlled dormitory access. 910 college housing spaces available; 844 were occupied in 2018-19. Freshmen guaranteed college housing. On-campus residence required through sophomore year. Options: men-only, women-only housing available. Richardson Library plus 1 other. Books: 201,169 (physical), 41,773 (digital/electronic); Serial titles: 183 (physical), 67,899 (digital/electronic); Databases: 142. Weekly public service hours: 89. Operations spending for the previous fiscal year: $1.9 million. 115 computers available on campus for general student use. A campuswide network can be accessed from student residence rooms and from off campus. Students can access the following: online class registration. Staffed computer lab on campus provides training in use of computers, software, and the Internet.

Community Environment: See Abilene Christian University.

■ HILL COLLEGE

112 Lamar Dr.
Hillsboro, TX 76645
Tel: (254)582-2555
E-mail: enrollmentinfo@hillcollege.edu
Web Site: www.hillcollege.edu

Description: District-supported, 2-year, coed. Awards certificates, transfer associate, and terminal associate degrees. Founded 1923. Setting: 80-acre small town campus with easy access to Dallas-Fort Worth. Total enrollment: 4,075. Faculty: (209 full-time). Student-undergrad faculty ratio is 17:1. 0.6% American Indian or Alaska Native, non-Hispanic/Latino; 23% Hispanic/Latino; 5% Black or African American, non-Hispanic/Latino; 0.7% Asian, non-Hispanic/Latino; 0.3% Native Hawaiian or other Pacific Islander, non-Hispanic/Latino; 1% international. 26% 25 or older. Retention: 53% of full-time freshmen returned the following year. Core. Calendar: semesters. Academic remediation for entering students, services for LD students, advanced placement, distance learning, summer session for credit, co-op programs.

Entrance Requirements: Open admission. Options: electronic application, early admission. Required: high school transcript. Application deadline: rolling. Transfer credits accepted: Yes.

Collegiate Environment: Drama-theater group, choral group. Social organizations: 2 open to all. Most popular organizations: Student Government, Phi Theta Kappa. Campus security: 24-hour emergency response devices, late night transport-escort service, security officers. Hill College Library plus 1 other. Books: 55,000 (physical), 203 (digital/electronic); Serial titles: 75 (physical), 1 (digital/electronic); Databases: 105. Weekly public service hours: 65.

■ HOUSTON BAPTIST UNIVERSITY

7502 Fondren Rd.
Houston, TX 77074-3298
Tel: (281)649-3000; Free: 800-696-3210
Fax: (281)649-3209
Web Site: www.hbu.edu

Description: Independent Baptist, comprehensive, coed. Awards bachelor's, master's, and doctoral degrees. Founded 1960. Setting: 100-acre suburban campus with easy access to Houston. Endowment: $102.8 million. Educational spending for the previous fiscal year: $77,310 per student. Total enrollment: 3,325. Faculty: 279 (151 full-time, 128 part-time). Student-undergrad faculty ratio is 14:1. 6,461 applied, 69% were admitted. 22% from top 10% of their high school class, 51% from top quarter, 78% from top half. Full-time: 2,098 students, 63% women, 37% men. Part-time: 218 students, 77% women, 23% men. Students come from 24 states and territories, 30 other countries, 3% from out-of-state. 0.3% American Indian or Alaska Native, non-Hispanic/Latino; 35% Hispanic/Latino; 18% Black or African American, non-Hispanic/Latino; 9% Asian, non-Hispanic/Latino; 0.3% Native Hawaiian or other Pacific Islander, non-Hispanic/Latino; 3% international. 12% 25 or older, 36% live on campus, 8% transferred in. Retention: 72% of full-time freshmen returned the following year. Academic areas with the most degrees conferred: business/marketing; health professions and related sciences; biological/life sciences. Core. Calendar: semesters. Academic remediation for entering students, services for LD students, advanced placement, accelerated degree program, freshman honors college, honors program, independent study, distance learning, double major, summer session for credit, part-time degree program, adult/continuing education programs, internships, graduate courses open to undergrads. Off campus study. ROTC: Army (c), Naval (c), Air Force (c).
Entrance Requirements: Options: electronic application, deferred admission, international baccalaureate accepted. Required: high school transcript, SAT or ACT. Required for some: essay. Entrance: moderately difficult. Application deadline: rolling. Notification: continuous. SAT Reasoning Test deadline: 8/31. Transfer credits accepted: Yes.
Costs Per Year: Application fee: $0. Comprehensive fee: $41,344 includes full-time tuition ($30,480), mandatory fees ($2050), and college room and board ($8814). College room only: $4800. Room and board charges vary according to board plan and housing facility. Part-time tuition: $1270 per semester hour. Part-time mandatory fees: $1025 per term. Part-time tuition and fees vary according to course load.
Collegiate Environment: Orientation program. Drama-theater group, choral group, marching band, student-run newspaper. Social organizations: 55 open to all; national fraternities, national sororities; 5% of eligible men and 9% of eligible women are members. Most popular organizations: Filipino Student Association, Baptist Student Ministry, Nursing Student Association, Phi Mu, Alpha Epsilon Delta. Major annual events: Homecoming, Late Night Breakfast, Welcome Week. Student services: health clinic, personal-psychological counseling. Campus security: 24-hour emergency response devices and patrols, late night transport-escort service, controlled dormitory access. Moody Library. Books: 109,715 (physical); Serial titles: 252 (physical), 57,209 (digital/electronic); Databases: 111. Students can reserve study rooms. Operations spending for the previous fiscal year: $894,770. 100 computers available on campus for general student use. A campuswide network can be accessed from student residence rooms. Students can access the following: online class registration, office software for 5 devices for each student.
Community Environment: See University of Houston.

■ HOUSTON COMMUNITY COLLEGE

3100 Main St.
Houston, TX 77002
Tel: (713)718-2000; Free: 877-422-6111
Fax: (713)718-2111
E-mail: student.info@hccs.edu
Web Site: www.hccs.edu

Description: State and locally supported, 2-year, coed. Awards certificates, transfer associate, and terminal associate degrees. Founded 1971. Setting: urban campus with easy access to Houston. Total enrollment: 57,120.

Faculty: 2,375 (830 full-time, 1,545 part-time). Student-undergrad faculty ratio is 24:1. Full-time: 17,226 students, 55% women, 45% men. Part-time: 39,894 students, 60% women, 40% men. Students come from 30 states and territories, 145 other countries. 0.2% American Indian or Alaska Native, non-Hispanic/Latino; 34% Hispanic/Latino; 28% Black or African American, non-Hispanic/Latino; 10% Asian, non-Hispanic/Latino; 0.2% Native Hawaiian or other Pacific Islander, non-Hispanic/Latino; 12% international. 44% 25 or older, 7% transferred in. Core. Calendar: semesters. Academic remediation for entering students, ESL program, services for LD students, advanced placement, honors program, distance learning, summer session for credit, part-time degree program, co-op programs and internships. Study abroad program. ROTC: Army (c), Air Force (c).
Entrance Requirements: Open admission. Option: electronic application. Required for some: high school transcript, interview. Entrance: noncompetitive. Application deadline: rolling. Transfer credits accepted: Yes.
Costs Per Year: Area resident tuition: $1632 full-time, $411 per term part-time. State resident tuition: $3360 full-time, $843 per term part-time. Nonresident tuition: $3756 full-time, $942 per term part-time. Full-time tuition varies according to course load. Part-time tuition varies according to course load.
Collegiate Environment: Orientation program. Student-run newspaper. Campus security: 24-hour emergency response devices and patrols, late night transport-escort service, crime prevention services. Houston Community College Libraries. Students can reserve study rooms.

■ HOWARD COLLEGE

1001 Birdwell Ln.
Big Spring, TX 79720
Tel: (915)264-5000; Free: 866-HC-HAWKS
Fax: (915)264-5082
E-mail: trichardson@howardcollege.edu
Web Site: www.howardcollege.edu

Description: State and locally supported, 2-year, coed. Part of Howard County Junior College District System. Awards certificates, transfer associate, and terminal associate degrees. Founded 1945. Setting: 120-acre small town campus. Endowment: $1.2 million. Educational spending for the previous fiscal year: $1636 per student. Total enrollment: 4,103. Faculty: 243 (144 full-time, 99 part-time). Student-undergrad faculty ratio is 14:1. Full-time: 1,636 students, 60% women, 40% men. Part-time: 2,467 students, 62% women, 38% men. 29% 25 or older, 8% live on campus. Retention: 54% of full-time freshmen returned the following year. Core. Calendar: semesters. Academic remediation for entering students, ESL program, services for LD students, advanced placement, independent study, distance learning, summer session for credit, part-time degree program, adult/continuing education programs, co-op programs and internships.
Entrance Requirements: Open admission. Options: electronic application, early admission. Required: high school transcript. Entrance: noncompetitive. Application deadline: rolling. Notification: continuous until 8/31. Transfer credits accepted: Yes.
Collegiate Environment: Orientation program. Drama-theater group, choral group. Social organizations: 10 open to all. Most popular organizations: Phi Theta Kappa, Student Government Association, Mexican-American Student Association, Baptist Student Ministries. Major annual events: Talent Shows, Awards Convocation, Athletic Events/Games. Student services: personal-psychological counseling. Campus security: 24-hour emergency response devices and patrols. Howard College Library. Operations spending for the previous fiscal year: $351,428. 300 computers available on campus for general student use. A campuswide network can be accessed from student residence rooms and from off campus. Students can access the following: online class registration. Staffed computer lab on campus provides training in use of computers, software, and the Internet.
Community Environment: Big Spring, population 24,250, is an urban community noted for its varied industries, which include oil refining and production, petrochemical manufacturing, one carbon black plants, two bottling plants, and an ammonia plant. The climate is temperate and dry. The community is served by air, rail, and bus lines. There is a public library, YMCA, many churches of various faiths, three general and one Veteran's hospital, a crippled children's rehabilitation center, three theatres, good shopping facilities, and various civic, fraternal, and veteran's organizations in the area. Local recreation includes skating, bowling, and water sports on nearby lakes. Part-time employment opportunities are limited.

■ HOWARD PAYNE UNIVERSITY

1000 Fisk St.
Brownwood, TX 76801-2715

Tel: (325)646-2502; Free: 800-880-4478
Fax: (325)649-8905
E-mail: enroll@hputx.edu
Web Site: www.hputx.edu

Description: Independent, comprehensive, coed, affiliated with Baptist General Convention of Texas. Awards bachelor's and master's degrees. Founded 1889. Setting: 80-acre small town campus. Endowment: $56.5 million. Educational spending for the previous fiscal year: $8702 per student. Total enrollment: 1,081. Faculty: 141 (83 full-time, 58 part-time). Student-undergrad faculty ratio is 10:1. 1,305 applied, 59% were admitted. 9% from top 10% of their high school class, 26% from top quarter, 62% from top half. Full-time: 866 students, 47% women, 53% men. Part-time: 124 students, 49% women, 51% men. Students come from 10 states and territories, 2% from out-of-state. 1% American Indian or Alaska Native, non-Hispanic/Latino; 12% Hispanic/Latino; 5% Black or African American, non-Hispanic/Latino; 1% Asian, non-Hispanic/Latino; 0.7% Native Hawaiian or other Pacific Islander, non-Hispanic/Latino. 13% 25 or older, 59% live on campus, 9% transferred in. Retention: 48% of full-time freshmen returned the following year. Core. Calendar: semesters. Academic remediation for entering students, services for LD students, advanced placement, accelerated degree program, honors program, independent study, distance learning, double major, summer session for credit, part-time degree program, internships, graduate courses open to undergrads. Off campus study. Study abroad program.

Entrance Requirements: Options: electronic application, early admission, international baccalaureate accepted. Required: high school transcript, SAT or ACT. Recommended: essay, minimum 3 high school GPA. Required for some: 3 recommendations, interview, ACCUPLACER. Entrance: moderately difficult. Application deadline: rolling. Notification: continuous. SAT Reasoning Test deadline: 8/1. Transfer credits accepted: Yes.

Costs Per Year: Application fee: $0. Comprehensive fee: $36,476 includes full-time tuition ($25,290), mandatory fees ($2800), and college room and board ($8386). Full-time tuition and fees vary according to course load, location, and program. Room and board charges vary according to board plan and housing facility. Part-time tuition: $845 per credit hour. Part-time tuition varies according to location and program.

Collegiate Environment: Orientation program. Drama-theater group, choral group, marching band, student-run newspaper. Social organizations: 7 open to all; national fraternities, national sororities, local fraternities, local sororities; 10% of eligible men and 10% of eligible women are members. Most popular organizations: Baptist Student Ministry, Fellowship of Christian Athletes, Gaming Guild, Spanish Club, Social Work Club. Major annual events: Homecoming, HPU Fest, Pancake Supper. Student services: health clinic, personal-psychological counseling. Campus security: 24-hour emergency response devices and patrols, late night transport-escort service, controlled dormitory access. Walker Memorial Library. Books: 125,784 (physical), 144,053 (digital/electronic); Serial titles: 27,347 (physical). Weekly public service hours: 84. Operations spending for the previous fiscal year: $221,474. 260 computers available on campus for general student use. A campuswide network can be accessed from student residence rooms and from off campus. Staffed computer lab on campus provides training in use of computers, software, and the Internet.

Community Environment: Population 20,000. Brownwood is located 26 miles from the geographic center of the state, which designates the community "deep in the heart of Texas." The annual average temperature is 66.7 degrees, with an average annual rainfall of 27.4 inches. Railroad, airlines, and bus lines serve the area. The community has many churches of various faiths, a public library, two hospitals, and various civic, fraternal and veteran's organizations. Recreation includes Lake Brownwood with fishing, hunting, boating, water skiing, bathing, and picnicking; many city parks, golf course, municipal swimming pool, tennis courts, and five ball parks.

■ **HUSTON-TILLOTSON UNIVERSITY**
900 Chicon St.
Austin, TX 78702-2795
Tel: (512)505-3000
Fax: (512)505-3190
E-mail: slstinson@htu.edu
Web Site: www.htu.edu

Description: Independent interdenominational, comprehensive, coed. Awards associate, bachelor's, and master's degrees. Founded 1875. Setting: 23-acre urban campus. Total enrollment: 1,103. 4,167 applied, 30% were admitted. Full-time: 1,003 students, 61% women, 39% men. Part-time: 50 students, 54% women, 46% men. 0.2% American Indian or Alaska Native, non-Hispanic/Latino; 27% Hispanic/Latino; 62% Black or African American, non-Hispanic/Latino; 0.1% Asian, non-Hispanic/Latino; 3% international. Retention: 51% of full-time freshmen returned the following year. Academic areas with the most degrees conferred: business/marketing; homeland security, law enforcement, firefighting, and protective services; parks and recreation; psychology. Core. Calendar: semesters. Academic remediation for entering students, ESL program, services for LD students, advanced placement, honors program, independent study, distance learning, double major, summer session for credit, part-time degree program, co-op programs and internships. Study abroad program.

Entrance Requirements: Options: electronic application, deferred admission, international baccalaureate accepted. Required: high school transcript, minimum 2.5 high school GPA, SAT or ACT. Recommended: SAT, ACT, SAT and SAT Subject Tests or ACT. Required for some: interview. Entrance: moderately difficult. SAT Reasoning Test deadline: 5/1. SAT Subject Test deadline: 5/1. Transfer credits accepted: Yes.

Costs Per Year: Application fee: $25. Comprehensive fee: $21,914 includes full-time tuition ($12,262), mandatory fees ($2084), and college room and board ($7568). College room only: $3642. Full-time tuition and fees vary according to course load. Room and board charges vary according to housing facility. Part-time tuition: $410 per credit hour. Part-time tuition varies according to course load.

Collegiate Environment: Orientation program. Drama-theater group, choral group. Social organizations: national fraternities, national sororities, local fraternities, local sororities. Most popular organizations: Campus Ministries, Zeta Phi Beta Sorority, Inc, Alpha Phi Alpha Fraternity, Inc, The Gentlemen's Club, Pre-Alumni Council. Major annual events: Coronation, Charter Day, Graduation Day. Student services: health clinic, personal-psychological counseling. Campus security: 24-hour emergency response devices and patrols, late night transport-escort service, controlled dormitory access. Downs-Jones Library.

Community Environment: See University of Texas at Austin.

■ **INTERACTIVE COLLEGE OF TECHNOLOGY (HOUSTON)**
6200 Hillcroft Ave.
Ste. 200
Houston, TX 77081
Tel: (713)771-5336
Web Site: ict.edu

Description: Proprietary, 2-year, coed. Awards certificates, diplomas, and terminal associate degrees. Calendar: semesters. Academic remediation for entering students, ESL program, distance learning, co-op programs and internships.

■ **INTERACTIVE COLLEGE OF TECHNOLOGY (HOUSTON)**
4473 I-45 N Fwy.
Airline Plz.
Houston, TX 77022
Tel: (281)931-7717
Web Site: ict.edu

Description: Proprietary, 2-year, coed. Awards certificates, diplomas, and terminal associate degrees. Setting: urban campus. Core. Calendar: semesters. Academic remediation for entering students, ESL program, advanced placement, distance learning, co-op programs and internships.
Entrance Requirements: Required: high school transcript, interview.

■ **INTERACTIVE COLLEGE OF TECHNOLOGY (PASADENA)**
213 W Southmore St.
Ste. 101
Pasadena, TX 77502
Tel: (713)920-1120
Web Site: ict.edu

Description: Proprietary, 2-year, coed. Awards diplomas, transfer associate, and terminal associate degrees. Core. Calendar: semesters. Academic remediation for entering students, ESL program, advanced placement, distance learning, part-time degree program, internships.
Entrance Requirements: Required: high school transcript, interview.
Collegiate Environment: Orientation program.

■ **INTERNATIONAL BUSINESS COLLEGE (EL PASO)**
1155 N Zaragosa Rd.
El Paso, TX 79907
Tel: (915)859-0422
Fax: (915)859-4142

Web Site: www.ibcelpaso.edu
Description: Proprietary, 2-year, coed. Awards certificates, transfer associate, and terminal associate degrees.

■ **INTERNATIONAL BUSINESS COLLEGE (EL PASO)**
1156 Barranca Dr.
El Paso, TX 79935
Tel: (915)842-0422
Fax: (915)242-6937
Web Site: www.ibcelpaso.edu
Description: Proprietary, 2-year, coed. Awards certificates, transfer associate, and terminal associate degrees. Founded 1898.

■ **JACKSONVILLE COLLEGE**
105 B J Albritton Dr.
Jacksonville, TX 75766-4759
Tel: (903)586-2518; Free: 800-256-8522
E-mail: admissions@jacksonville-college.org
Web Site: www.jacksonville-college.edu
Description: Independent Baptist, 2-year, coed. Awards diplomas, transfer associate, and terminal associate degrees. Founded 1899. Setting: 20-acre small town campus. Total enrollment: 327. Student-undergrad faculty ratio is 15:1. 7% from out-of-state. 17% 25 or older. Core. Calendar: semesters. Academic remediation for entering students, advanced placement, summer session for credit, part-time degree program, adult/continuing education programs.
Entrance Requirements: Open admission. Options: electronic application, early admission. Required for some: SAT, ACT, THEA. Entrance: noncompetitive. Application deadline: 8/15. Notification: continuous until 7/1.
Collegiate Environment: Drama-theater group, choral group. Student services: health clinic, personal-psychological counseling. Campus security: 24-hour emergency response devices, evening security personnel. Weatherby Memorial Building.
Community Environment: Population 14,000, Jacksonville is a small community enjoying temperate climate. The average annual rainfall is approximately 45 inches. The community is reached by way of railroad, major airlines, bus lines and highways. Community service facilities include many churches, two hospitals, a public library, and a local radio station. There are parks and facilities for golf, hunting, fishing, rodeos, and swimming. Various civic and fraternal organizations are active in the area. Part-time employment is available.

■ **JARVIS CHRISTIAN COLLEGE**
PR 7631 @ U S Hwy. 80 E
Hawkins, TX 75765-1470
Tel: (903)769-5700
Fax: (903)769-4842
Web Site: www.jarvis.edu
Description: Independent, 4-year, coed, affiliated with Christian Church (Disciples of Christ). Awards bachelor's degrees. Founded 1912. Setting: 465-acre rural campus. Endowment: $11.5 million. Educational spending for the previous fiscal year: $9729 per student. Faculty: 37 (32 full-time, 5 part-time). Student-undergrad faculty ratio is 26:1. 983 applied, 54% were admitted. 1% from top 10% of their high school class, 16% from top quarter, 46% from top half. Students come from 29 states and territories, 1 other country, 17% from out-of-state. 16% 25 or older, 85% live on campus. Retention: 53% of full-time freshmen returned the following year. Academic areas with the most degrees conferred: education; business/marketing; homeland security, law enforcement, firefighting, and protective services. Core. Calendar: semesters. Academic remediation for entering students, ESL program, advanced placement, self-designed majors, honors program, double major, summer session for credit, part-time degree program, adult/continuing education programs, co-op programs and internships. Off campus study at University of Texas at Tyler, Texas College, Paul Quinn College, Huston-Tillotson University, Wiley College.
Entrance Requirements: Open admission. Option: electronic application. Required: high school transcript, SAT or ACT. Recommended: minimum 2 high school GPA. Entrance: minimally difficult. Application deadline: 8/1. Notification: 8/15, 8/15 for nonresidents. Transfer credits accepted: Yes.
Collegiate Environment: Orientation program. Drama-theater group, choral group. Social organizations: 26 open to all; national fraternities, national sororities; 53% of eligible men and 77% of eligible women are members. Most popular organizations: Student Government Association, Pre-Alumni Club, Student Ministers' Association, Women 2 Women, Panhellenic

Council. Major annual events: Homecoming/Founders' Week, Miss Jarvis Coronation, Annual Christmas Concert. Student services: health clinic. Campus security: 24-hour emergency response devices and patrols. Olin Library. Books: 85,971 (physical); Serial titles: 432 (physical); Databases: 63. Operations spending for the previous fiscal year: $100,653. 100 computers available on campus for general student use. A campuswide network can be accessed from student residence rooms. Students can access the following: online class registration. Staffed computer lab on campus provides training in use of computers, software, and the Internet.
Community Environment: Hawkins is located in southwestern Wood County, population 41,776. The area enjoys moderate, temperate climate. Serviced by U.S. Highway 80 and bus lines, there are churches of many denominations, a hospital and clinic, and various civic, fraternal, and veteran's organizations. Local recreation includes camping and hunting, with rivers, creeks, springs and lakes furnishing opportunities for fishing and boating.

■ **KD CONSERVATORY COLLEGE OF FILM AND DRAMATIC ARTS**
2600 Stemmons Fwy., No.117
Dallas, TX 75207
Tel: (214)638-0484; Free: 877-278-2283
Fax: (214)630-5140
E-mail: mschraeder@kdstudio.com
Web Site: www.kdstudio.com
Description: Proprietary, 2-year, coed. Awards transfer associate and terminal associate degrees. Founded 1979. Setting: urban campus. Educational spending for the previous fiscal year: $2405 per student. Total enrollment: 236. Faculty: 28 (all full-time). Student-undergrad faculty ratio is 12:1. 70 applied, 34% were admitted. Full-time: 236 students, 46% women, 54% men. Students come from 11 states and territories, 1 other country, 5% from out-of-state. 44% 25 or older. Retention: 69% of full-time freshmen returned the following year. Core. Calendar: semesters.
Entrance Requirements: Open admission. Options: electronic application, deferred admission. Required: essay, high school transcript, interview, audition and/or interview with Program Chair or Director of School. Entrance: noncompetitive. Application deadline: rolling. Transfer credits accepted: Yes.
Costs Per Year: Application fee: $0. Tuition: $15,300 full-time. Mandatory fees: $450 full-time. Full-time tuition and fees vary according to program. Tuition guaranteed not to increase for student's term of enrollment.
Collegiate Environment: Drama-theater group. Social organizations: 1 open to all. Most popular organization: Student Council. Major annual events: In-House Plays/Productions, Alumni Dance Shows, Halloween Costume Day. Campus security: 24-hour emergency response devices and patrols. KD Studio Library. Operations spending for the previous fiscal year: $28,693. 5 computers available on campus for general student use. Staffed computer lab on campus provides training in use of computers, software, and the Internet.

■ **KILGORE COLLEGE**
1100 Broadway Blvd.
Kilgore, TX 75662-3299
Tel: (903)984-8531
Fax: (903)983-8607
E-mail: register@kilgore.cc.tx.us
Web Site: www.kilgore.edu
Description: State and locally supported, 2-year, coed. Awards certificates, transfer associate, and terminal associate degrees. Founded 1935. Setting: 35-acre small town campus with easy access to Dallas-Fort Worth. Endowment: $10 million. Educational spending for the previous fiscal year: $5929 per student. Total enrollment: 5,666. Faculty: 308 (149 full-time, 159 part-time). Student-undergrad faculty ratio is 17:1. Full-time: 2,245 students, 53% women, 47% men. Part-time: 3,421 students, 61% women, 39% men. Students come from 25 states and territories, 18 other countries, 2% from out-of-state. 0.5% American Indian or Alaska Native, non-Hispanic/Latino; 18% Hispanic/Latino; 19% Black or African American, non-Hispanic/Latino; 1% Asian, non-Hispanic/Latino; 0.7% international. 28% 25 or older, 7% live on campus, 6% transferred in. Retention: 52% of full-time freshmen returned the following year. Core. Calendar: semesters. Academic remediation for entering students, services for LD students, advanced placement, honors program, distance learning, summer session for credit, part-time degree program, adult/continuing education programs, co-op programs and internships.
Entrance Requirements: Open admission except for associate degree allied health programs. Options: electronic application, early admission,

international baccalaureate accepted. Required: high school transcript. Required for some: interview. Entrance: noncompetitive. Application deadline: rolling. Transfer credits accepted: Yes.

Collegiate Environment: Orientation program. Drama-theater group, choral group, marching band, student-run newspaper. Student services: health clinic, personal-psychological counseling. Campus security: 24-hour emergency response devices and patrols. Randolph C. Watson Library plus 1 other. Books: 44,165 (physical), 34,163 (digital/electronic); Serial titles: 153 (physical), 50,534 (digital/electronic); Databases: 106. Weekly public service hours: 62. Operations spending for the previous fiscal year: $676,674. 500 computers available on campus for general student use. A campuswide network can be accessed from student residence rooms and from off campus. Students can access the following: online class registration. Staffed computer lab on campus provides training in use of the Internet.

Community Environment: Kilgore, population 11,800, is a suburban area enjoying temperate climate and four distinct seasons. The area is reached by bus, rail, air, and Interstate Highway 20, U.S. 259, and State 31. The community has over 40 churches representing various faiths, a library, medical facilities, and many civic, fraternal, and veteran's organizations. There are apartments available for student housing. Local recreation facilities include a swimming pool, tennis courts, picnic areas, bowling alleys, theatres, go-cart track, golf course, as well as water skiing, fishing, camping, and hunting. Part-time employment is available.

■ THE KING'S UNIVERSITY

2121 E Southlake Blvd.
Southlake, TX 76092
Tel: (817)552-3700; Free: 888-779-8040
E-mail: tyler.maxey@tku.edu
Web Site: www.tku.edu

Description: Independent, comprehensive, coed, affiliated with International Church of the Foursquare Gospel. Awards associate, bachelor's, and master's degrees. Setting: suburban campus with easy access to Dallas-Fort Worth. Total enrollment: 704. Calendar: semesters.

■ LAMAR INSTITUTE OF TECHNOLOGY

855 E Lavaca
Beaumont, TX 77705
Tel: (409)880-8321; Free: 800-950-6989
E-mail: jrpitts@lit.edu
Web Site: www.lit.edu

Description: State-supported, 2-year, coed. Awards certificates and terminal associate degrees. Founded 1995. Setting: 11-acre urban campus. Educational spending for the previous fiscal year: $5611 per student. Total enrollment: 3,265. Faculty: 171 (87 full-time, 84 part-time). Full-time: 1,365 students, 45% women, 55% men. Part-time: 2,200 students, 61% women, 39% men. Students come from 3 states and territories. 0.7% American Indian or Alaska Native, non-Hispanic/Latino; 19% Hispanic/Latino; 27% Black or African American, non-Hispanic/Latino; 3% Asian, non-Hispanic/Latino; 0.1% Native Hawaiian or other Pacific Islander, non-Hispanic/Latino. 23% 25 or older. Calendar: semesters.

Entrance Requirements: Entrance: noncompetitive.

Collegiate Environment: Most popular organizations: Operating Process Technology Club, Radiologic Technology Student Organization, Student Government Association, Phi Theta Kappa. Major annual events: Project Interview, Job Fair, Awareness month programming(Hispanic heritage month; black history month). Campus security: 24-hour emergency response devices and patrols, late night transport-escort service, controlled dormitory access. The Mary and John Gray Library. Books: 621,094 (physical), 71,446 (digital/electronic); Serial titles: 19,735 (physical), 46,546 (digital/electronic); Databases: 127. Weekly public service hours: 93. 63 computers available on campus for general student use. Students can access the following: online class registration.

■ LAMAR STATE COLLEGE-ORANGE

410 Front St.
Orange, TX 77630
Tel: (409)883-7750
Fax: (409)882-3374
Web Site: www.lsco.edu

Description: State-supported, 2-year, coed. Part of Texas State University System. Awards certificates, transfer associate, and terminal associate degrees. Founded 1969. Setting: 21-acre small town campus. Total enrollment: 2,426. Faculty: 96 (50 full-time, 46 part-time). Student-undergrad

faculty ratio is 19:1. Full-time: 992 students, 69% women, 31% men. Part-time: 1,434 students, 69% women, 31% men. 0.5% American Indian or Alaska Native, non-Hispanic/Latino; 6% Hispanic/Latino; 16% Black or African American, non-Hispanic/Latino; 2% Asian, non-Hispanic/Latino. 38% 25 or older. Retention: 47% of full-time freshmen returned the following year. Calendar: semesters. Academic remediation for entering students, distance learning, double major, summer session for credit, part-time degree program, internships.

Entrance Requirements: Open admission except for some programs. Required: high school transcript. Entrance: noncompetitive. Application deadline: rolling. Notification: continuous.

Collegiate Environment: Orientation program. Campus security: 24-hour emergency response devices, late night transport-escort service. Lamar State College-Orange Library plus 1 other. 70 computers available on campus for general student use. A campuswide network can be accessed from off-campus. Staffed computer lab on campus provides training in use of computers and the Internet.

■ LAMAR STATE COLLEGE-PORT ARTHUR

PO Box 310
Port Arthur, TX 77641-0310
Tel: (409)983-4921; Free: 800-477-5872
Fax: (409)984-6032
E-mail: nichoca@lamarpa.edu
Web Site: www.lamarpa.edu

Description: State-supported, 2-year, coed. Part of Texas State University System. Awards certificates, transfer associate, and terminal associate degrees. Founded 1909. Setting: 34-acre suburban campus with easy access to Houston. Total enrollment: 2,208. Student-undergrad faculty ratio is 18:1. 17% 25 or older. Core. Calendar: semesters. Academic remediation for entering students, ESL program, services for LD students, advanced placement, accelerated degree program, honors program, independent study, distance learning, double major, summer session for credit, part-time degree program, adult/continuing education programs, co-op programs and internships. Off campus study at Lamar University-Beaumont, Lamar University-Orange. ROTC: Army (c).

Entrance Requirements: Open admission. Options: early admission, deferred admission. Required: high school transcript. Required for some: interview. Entrance: noncompetitive. Application deadline: rolling. Notification: continuous.

Collegiate Environment: Orientation program. Drama-theater group, choral group. Social organizations: local fraternities, local sororities. Student services: personal-psychological counseling. Campus security: 24-hour emergency response devices, student patrols, late night transport-escort service. Gates Memorial Library.

■ LAMAR UNIVERSITY

4400 Martin Luther King Pky.
Beaumont, TX 77710
Tel: (409)880-7011
Fax: (409)880-8463
E-mail: admissions@lamar.edu
Web Site: www.lamar.edu

Description: State-supported, university, coed. Part of Texas State University System. Awards bachelor's, master's, and doctoral degrees and post-master's certificates. Founded 1923. Setting: 292-acre suburban campus with easy access to Houston. Endowment: $114.9 million. Research spending for the previous fiscal year: $2.8 million. Total enrollment: 14,783. Faculty: 614 (483 full-time, 131 part-time). Student-undergrad faculty ratio is 18:1. 5,652 applied, 86% were admitted. 15% from top 10% of their high school class, 39% from top quarter, 71% from top half. Full-time: 5,735 students, 56% women, 44% men. Part-time: 3,169 students, 62% women, 38% men. Students come from 37 states and territories, 46 other countries, 3% from out-of-state. 0.6% American Indian or Alaska Native, non-Hispanic/Latino; 19% Hispanic/Latino; 27% Black or African American, non-Hispanic/Latino; 5% Asian, non-Hispanic/Latino; 0.1% Native Hawaiian or other Pacific Islander, non-Hispanic/Latino; 1% international. 26% 25 or older, 26% live on campus, 8% transferred in. Retention: 64% of full-time freshmen returned the following year. Academic areas with the most degrees conferred: health professions and related sciences; interdisciplinary studies; engineering; business/marketing. Core. Calendar: semesters. Academic remediation for entering students, ESL program, services for LD students, advanced placement, accelerated degree program, self-designed majors, freshman honors college, honors program, independent study, distance learning, double major, summer session for credit, part-time degree program, co-op programs and internships, graduate courses open to undergrads. Off campus study. Study abroad program. ROTC: Air Force (c).

Entrance Requirements: Options: electronic application, early admission, international baccalaureate accepted. Required: high school transcript, SAT or ACT. Required for some: essay. Entrance: minimally difficult. Transfer credits accepted: Yes.

Costs Per Year: Application fee: $25. One-time mandatory fee: $10. State resident tuition: $7391 full-time, $246 per credit hour part-time. Nonresident tuition: $19,841 full-time, $661 per credit hour part-time. Mandatory fees: $2801 full-time, $382 per credit hour part-time. Full-time tuition and fees vary according to course load, location, and program. Part-time tuition and fees vary according to course load, location, and program. College room and board: $8920. College room only: $5670. Room and board charges vary according to board plan. Tuition guaranteed not to increase for student's term of enrollment.

Collegiate Environment: Orientation program. Drama-theater group, choral group, marching band, student-run newspaper. Social organizations: 277 open to all; national fraternities, national sororities, local fraternities. Major annual events: Homecoming, Week of Welcome, Open House. Student services: health clinic, personal-psychological counseling. Campus security: 24-hour emergency response devices and patrols, student patrols, late night transport-escort service, controlled dormitory access. 2,515 college housing spaces available; 2,264 were occupied in 2018-19. Freshmen guaranteed college housing. On-campus residence required in freshman year. Option: coed housing available. Mary and John Gray Library plus 1 other. Books: 496,121 (physical), 91,469 (digital/electronic); Serial titles: 42,694 (physical), 47,629 (digital/electronic); Databases: 142. Weekly public service hours: 87; students can reserve study rooms. 1,104 computers available on campus for general student use. A campuswide network can be accessed from student residence rooms and from off campus. Students can access the following: online class registration. Staffed computer lab on campus provides training in use of computers and software.

Community Environment: Beaumont and the surrounding area form one of the largest concentrations of petroleum refineries in the nation. Top manufactures of the area include deep sea and dry-land oil-drilling equipment and oil-processing apparatus. The city is located on the Neches River approximately 20 miles north of the Gulf of Mexico. The climate is mild the year round. Airlines, railroad, and bus lines serve the community. The community has many churches representing various faiths, three libraries, YMCA, and YWCA, several hospitals, and various civic and fraternal organizations. Part-time employment is available.

■ **LAREDO COLLEGE**
W End Washington St.
Laredo, TX 78040-4395
Tel: (956)722-0521
Fax: (956)721-5493
Web Site: www.laredo.edu

Description: State and locally supported, 2-year, coed. Awards certificates, transfer associate, and terminal associate degrees. Founded 1946. Setting: 186-acre urban campus. Endowment: $2 million. Total enrollment: 8,152. Faculty: 343 (203 full-time, 140 part-time). Student-undergrad faculty ratio is 18:1. 987 applied, 100% were admitted. Full-time: 3,044 students, 57% women, 43% men. Part-time: 5,108 students, 59% women, 41% men. Students come from 4 states and territories, 5 other countries, 8% from out-of-state. 34% 25 or older. Retention: 86% of full-time freshmen returned the following year. Core. Calendar: semesters. Academic remediation for entering students, ESL program, services for LD students, advanced placement, freshman honors college, honors program, independent study, distance learning, double major, summer session for credit, part-time degree program, adult/continuing education programs, internships.

Entrance Requirements: Open admission. Options: early admission, deferred admission. Required: high school transcript. Recommended: SAT, ACT. Entrance: noncompetitive. Application deadline: rolling.

Collegiate Environment: Drama-theater group, choral group, student-run newspaper. Student services: personal-psychological counseling, women's center. Campus security: 24-hour emergency response devices and patrols, student patrols. Yeary Library.

Community Environment: Population approximately 208,000. A chief port of entry into Mexico, Laredo is separated from Nuevo Laredo, Mexico, by the Rio Grande. This is a metropolitan community located in the center of a rich cattle, oil, gas and agricultural district. It is a major import-export center. The city is reached by airlines, railroad, and bus service. The climate is temper-

ate and dry. Laredo has a public library, churches of major denominations, two hospitals, and various civic and fraternal organizations. Shopping facilities are good. Part-time employment is available for students. Local recreation includes theaters, water sports, and most major sports.

■ **LEE COLLEGE**
PO Box 818
Baytown, TX 77522-0818
Tel: (281)427-5611
Fax: (281)425-6831
Web Site: www.lee.edu

Description: District-supported, 2-year, coed. Awards certificates, transfer associate, and terminal associate degrees. Founded 1934. Setting: 35-acre suburban campus with easy access to Houston. Endowment: $5.2 million. Total enrollment: 5,347. Faculty: 399 (185 full-time, 214 part-time). Student-undergrad faculty ratio is 14:1. Full-time: 1,795 students, 62% women, 38% men. Part-time: 3,552 students, 48% women, 52% men. Students come from 17 states and territories, 44 other countries, 5% from out-of-state. 50% 25 or older, 1% transferred in. Core. Calendar: semesters. Academic remediation for entering students, ESL program, advanced placement, honors program, independent study, distance learning, summer session for credit, part-time degree program, adult/continuing education programs, co-op programs and internships. ROTC: Army (c).

Entrance Requirements: Open admission except for nursing program. Options: early admission, deferred admission. Required for some: high school transcript. Entrance: noncompetitive. Application deadline: rolling. Notification: continuous.

Collegiate Environment: Orientation program. Drama-theater group, choral group, student-run newspaper. Social organizations: 27 open to all. Most popular organizations: Student Congress, Health Information Student Association, Lee College Awareness, Digital Information Society, ASHRAE (Air Conditioning Society of Heat and Refrigeration Engineers). Major annual events: Fall Fiesta, Spring Fling, Annual Blood Drive. Student services: personal-psychological counseling. Campus security: 24-hour patrols, late night transport-escort service, emergency telephones. Erma Wood Carlson Learning Resource Center. 800 computers available on campus for general student use. A campuswide network can be accessed. Staffed computer lab on campus.

Community Environment: Population 68,000. Baytown is located midway between Houston and the open sea on the Houston Ship Channel. The city is a consolidation of three towns: Baytown, Goose Creek, and Pelly. There are many churches in the immediate area, and four hospitals are easily accessible.

■ **LETOURNEAU UNIVERSITY**
PO Box 7001
Longview, TX 75607-7001
Tel: (903)233-3000; Free: 800-759-8811
Fax: (903)233-3411
Web Site: www.letu.edu

Description: Independent nondenominational, comprehensive, coed. Awards associate, bachelor's, and master's degrees. Founded 1946. Setting: 162-acre suburban campus. Total enrollment: 3,175. Faculty: 249 (87 full-time, 162 part-time). Student-undergrad faculty ratio is 15:1. 1,922 applied, 46% were admitted. 22% from top 10% of their high school class, 50% from top quarter, 85% from top half. Full-time: 1,317 students, 36% women, 64% men. Part-time: 1,484 students, 58% women, 42% men. 33% from out-of-state. 0.6% American Indian or Alaska Native, non-Hispanic/Latino; 9% Hispanic/Latino; 7% Black or African American, non-Hispanic/Latino; 2% Asian, non-Hispanic/Latino; 0.1% Native Hawaiian or other Pacific Islander, non-Hispanic/Latino; 2% international. 31% 25 or older, 69% live on campus, 6% transferred in. Retention: 79% of full-time freshmen returned the following year. Academic areas with the most degrees conferred: engineering; business/marketing; education. Core. Calendar: semesters. ESL program, services for LD students, advanced placement, accelerated degree program, freshman honors college, honors program, independent study, distance learning, double major, summer session for credit, part-time degree program, co-op programs and internships, graduate courses open to undergrads. Study abroad program.

Entrance Requirements: Options: electronic application, deferred admission, international baccalaureate accepted. Required for some: SAT or ACT. Entrance: moderately difficult. Application deadline: rolling. Notification: continuous. Transfer credits accepted: Yes.

Costs Per Year: Application fee: $0. Comprehensive fee: $41,240 includes full-time tuition ($30,520), mandatory fees ($750), and college room and board ($9970).

Collegiate Environment: Orientation program. Drama-theater group, choral group. Student services: personal-psychological counseling. Campus security: 24-hour emergency response devices and patrols, student patrols, late night transport-escort service, controlled dormitory access. Freshmen guaranteed college housing. On-campus residence required through junior year. Options: men-only, women-only housing available. Margaret Estes Library plus 1 other. Books: 36,096 (physical), 233,126 (digital/electronic); Serial titles: 29,406 (digital/electronic); Databases: 95. Weekly public service hours: 87.

Community Environment: Population 75,600. Oil is the major source of economy for this community. Longview has a city library, community center, two hospitals, and a number of medical clinics. Major civic and fraternal clubs are active in the area. Longview is reached by airlines, railroad, and bus lines. Residence halls and apartments furnish student housing. Local recreation includes theatres, symphony, parks, swimming, hunting, fishing, golf, and water skiing. Part-time employment is available.

■ **LINCOLN COLLEGE OF TECHNOLOGY**
2915 Alouette Dr.
Grand Prairie, TX 75052
Tel: (972)660-5701; Free: 844-215-1513
Web Site: www.lincolntech.edu
Description: Proprietary, 2-year, coed. Awards certificates, transfer associate, and terminal associate degrees.

■ **LONE STAR COLLEGE-CYFAIR**
9191 Barker Cypress Rd.
Cypress, TX 77433-1383
Tel: (281)290-3200
E-mail: cfc.info@lonestar.edu
Web Site: www.lonestar.edu/cyfair
Description: State and locally supported, 2-year, coed. Part of Lone Star College. Awards certificates, diplomas, transfer associate, and terminal associate degrees. Founded 2002. Setting: suburban campus with easy access to Houston. Total enrollment: 21,636. Faculty: 658 (142 full-time, 516 part-time). Student-undergrad faculty ratio is 37:1. 3,424 applied, 100% were admitted. Full-time: 6,757 students, 53% women, 47% men. Part-time: 14,879 students, 58% women, 42% men. Students come from 67 other countries. 0.2% American Indian or Alaska Native, non-Hispanic/Latino; 43% Hispanic/Latino; 13% Black or African American, non-Hispanic/Latino; 11% Asian, non-Hispanic/Latino. 25% 25 or older, 25% transferred in. Core. Calendar: semesters. Academic remediation for entering students, ESL program, services for LD students, advanced placement, accelerated degree program, honors program, independent study, distance learning, double major, summer session for credit, part-time degree program, adult/continuing education programs, co-op programs and internships. Study abroad program.
Entrance Requirements: Open admission. Options: electronic application, early admission. Recommended: high school transcript. Entrance: noncompetitive. Transfer credits accepted: Yes.
Costs Per Year: Application fee: $0. Area resident tuition: $1088 full-time, $44 per credit hour part-time. State resident tuition: $3368 full-time, $139 per credit hour part-time. Nonresident tuition: $4208 full-time, $174 per credit hour part-time. Mandatory fees: $544 full-time, $20 per credit hour part-time, $32 per term part-time. Full-time tuition and fees vary according to course load and program. Part-time tuition and fees vary according to course load and program. Tuition guaranteed not to increase for student's term of enrollment.
Collegiate Environment: Orientation program. Drama-theater group, choral group. Major annual events: Fall Festival, Spring Fling, Commencement. Student services: personal-psychological counseling. Campus security: 24-hour emergency response devices and patrols, late night transport-escort service. LSC-CyFair Library.

■ **LONE STAR COLLEGE-KINGWOOD**
20000 Kingwood Dr.
Kingwood, TX 77339-3801
Tel: (281)312-1600
Fax: (281)312-1477
E-mail: kingwoodadvising@lonestar.edu
Web Site: www.lonestar.edu/kingwood.htm

Description: State and locally supported, 2-year, coed. Part of Lone Star College. Awards certificates, transfer associate, and terminal associate degrees. Founded 1984. Setting: 264-acre suburban campus with easy access to Houston. Total enrollment: 12,287. Faculty: 684 (132 full-time, 552 part-time). Student-undergrad faculty ratio is 21:1. 1,590 applied, 100% were admitted. Full-time: 3,785 students, 57% women, 43% men. Part-time: 8,502 students, 64% women, 36% men. Students come from 48 other countries. 0.3% American Indian or Alaska Native, non-Hispanic/Latino; 35% Hispanic/Latino; 14% Black or African American, non-Hispanic/Latino; 4% Asian, non-Hispanic/Latino. 29% 25 or older, 28% transferred in. Core. Calendar: semesters. Academic remediation for entering students, ESL program, services for LD students, advanced placement, accelerated degree program, honors program, independent study, distance learning, double major, summer session for credit, part-time degree program, adult/continuing education programs, co-op programs and internships. Study abroad program.
Entrance Requirements: Open admission. Options: electronic application, early admission. Recommended: high school transcript. Entrance: noncompetitive. Application deadline: rolling. Transfer credits accepted: Yes.
Collegiate Environment: Orientation program. Drama-theater group, choral group. Major annual events: Fall Festival, Spring Fling, Commencement. Student services: personal-psychological counseling. Campus security: 24-hour emergency response devices and patrols, late night transport-escort service. LSC-Kingwood Library.

■ **LONE STAR COLLEGE-MONTGOMERY**
3200 College Park Dr.
Conroe, TX 77384
Tel: (936)273-7000
Fax: (936)273-7234
Web Site: www.lonestar.edu/montgomery
Description: State and locally supported, 2-year, coed. Part of Lone Star College. Awards certificates, transfer associate, and terminal associate degrees. Founded 1995. Setting: suburban campus with easy access to Houston. Total enrollment: 14,411. Faculty: 658 (142 full-time, 516 part-time). Student-undergrad faculty ratio is 25:1. 1,852 applied, 100% were admitted. Full-time: 4,466 students, 55% women, 45% men. Part-time: 9,945 students, 62% women, 38% men. Students come from 63 other countries. 0.3% American Indian or Alaska Native, non-Hispanic/Latino; 30% Hispanic/Latino; 10% Black or African American, non-Hispanic/Latino; 4% Asian, non-Hispanic/Latino. 29% 25 or older, 26% transferred in. Core. Calendar: semesters. Academic remediation for entering students, ESL program, services for LD students, advanced placement, honors program, independent study, distance learning, double major, summer session for credit, part-time degree program, adult/continuing education programs, co-op programs and internships. Study abroad program.
Entrance Requirements: Open admission. Options: electronic application, early admission. Recommended: high school transcript. Entrance: noncompetitive. Application deadline: rolling. Transfer credits accepted: Yes.
Costs Per Year: Area resident tuition: $1088 full-time, $44 per credit hour part-time. State resident tuition: $3368 full-time, $139 per credit hour part-time. Nonresident tuition: $4208 full-time, $174 per credit hour part-time. Mandatory fees: $544 full-time, $20 per credit hour part-time, $32 per term part-time. Full-time tuition and fees vary according to course load and program. Part-time tuition and fees vary according to course load and program. Tuition guaranteed not to increase for student's term of enrollment.
Collegiate Environment: Orientation program. Drama-theater group, choral group. Most popular organizations: Campus Crusade for Christ, Criminal Justice Club, Phi Theta Kappa, Latino-American Student Association, African-American Cultural Awareness. Major annual events: Career Day, College/University Transfer Day. Student services: personal-psychological counseling. Campus security: 24-hour emergency response devices and patrols, late night transport-escort service. LSC-Montgomery Library.

■ **LONE STAR COLLEGE-NORTH HARRIS**
2700 W W Thorne Dr.
Houston, TX 77073-3499
Tel: (281)618-5400
E-mail: nhcounselor@lonestar.edu
Web Site: www.lonestar.edu/northharris
Description: State and locally supported, 2-year, coed. Part of Lone Star College. Awards certificates, transfer associate, and terminal associate degrees. Founded 1972. Setting: suburban campus with easy access to Houston. Total enrollment: 16,290. Faculty: 897 (210 full-time, 687 part-time). Student-undergrad faculty ratio is 20:1. 2,228 applied, 100% were

admitted. Full-time: 4,797 students, 54% women, 46% men. Part-time: 11,493 students, 62% women, 38% men. Students come from 49 other countries. 0.2% American Indian or Alaska Native, non-Hispanic/Latino; 46% Hispanic/Latino; 26% Black or African American, non-Hispanic/Latino; 5% Asian, non-Hispanic/Latino. 37% 25 or older, 27% transferred in. Core. Calendar: semesters. Academic remediation for entering students, ESL program, services for LD students, advanced placement, honors program, independent study, distance learning, double major, summer session for credit, part-time degree program, adult/continuing education programs, co-op programs and internships. Study abroad program.

Entrance Requirements: Open admission except for nursing, respiratory therapy programs. Options: electronic application, early admission. Entrance: noncompetitive. Application deadline: rolling. Transfer credits accepted: Yes.

Costs Per Year: Application fee: $0. Area resident tuition: $1088 full-time, $44 per credit hour part-time. State resident tuition: $3368 full-time, $139 per credit hour part-time. Nonresident tuition: $4208 full-time, $174 per credit hour part-time. Mandatory fees: $544 full-time, $20 per credit hour part-time, $32 per term part-time. Full-time tuition and fees vary according to course load and program. Part-time tuition and fees vary according to course load and program. Tuition guaranteed not to increase for student's term of enrollment.

Collegiate Environment: Orientation program. Drama-theater group, choral group. Social organizations: 33 open to all. Most popular organizations: Student Government Association, Phi Theta Kappa, Ambassadors, Honors Student Organizations, Soccer Club. Major annual events: Fall Festival, Cajun Fest, Spring Fling/Health Fair. Student services: personal-psychological counseling, women's center. Campus security: 24-hour emergency response devices and patrols, late night transport-escort service. LSC-North Harris Library.

■ LONE STAR COLLEGE-TOMBALL

30555 Tomball Pky.
Tomball, TX 77375-4036
Tel: (281)351-3300
Fax: (281)351-3384
E-mail: tcinfo@lonestar.edu
Web Site: www.lonestar.edu/tomball

Description: State and locally supported, 2-year, coed. Part of Lone Star College. Awards certificates, transfer associate, and terminal associate degrees. Founded 1988. Setting: suburban campus with easy access to Houston. Total enrollment: 9,013. Faculty: 393 (102 full-time, 291 part-time). Student-undergrad faculty ratio is 24:1. 1,114 applied, 100% were admitted. Full-time: 2,705 students, 59% women, 41% men. Part-time: 6,308 students, 63% women, 37% men. Students come from 44 other countries. 0.3% American Indian or Alaska Native, non-Hispanic/Latino; 29% Hispanic/Latino; 13% Black or African American, non-Hispanic/Latino; 5% Asian, non-Hispanic/Latino. 35% 25 or older, 31% transferred in. Core. Calendar: semesters. Academic remediation for entering students, ESL program, services for LD students, advanced placement, honors program, independent study, distance learning, double major, summer session for credit, part-time degree program, adult/continuing education programs, co-op programs and internships. Study abroad program.

Entrance Requirements: Open admission. Options: electronic application, early admission. Recommended: high school transcript. Entrance: noncompetitive. Application deadline: rolling. Transfer credits accepted: Yes.

Costs Per Year: Application fee: $0. Area resident tuition: $1088 full-time, $44 per credit hour part-time. State resident tuition: $3368 full-time, $139 per credit hour part-time. Nonresident tuition: $4208 full-time, $174 per credit hour part-time. Mandatory fees: $544 full-time, $20 per credit hour part-time, $32 per term part-time. Full-time tuition and fees vary according to course load and program. Part-time tuition and fees vary according to course load and program. Tuition guaranteed not to increase for student's term of enrollment.

Collegiate Environment: Orientation program. Drama-theater group, choral group. Most popular organizations: Phi Theta Kappa, Occupational Therapy OTA, Veterinary Technicians Student Organization, STARS, Student Nurses Association. Major annual events: Spring Fling, Winter Wonderland, Fall Festival. Student services: personal-psychological counseling. Campus security: 24-hour emergency response devices and patrols, late night transport-escort service, trained security personnel during hours of operation. LSC-Tomball Community Library.

■ LONE STAR COLLEGE-UNIVERSITY PARK

20515 SH 249
Houston, TX 77070
Tel: (281)290-2600
Web Site: www.lonestar.edu/universitypark

Description: State and locally supported, 2-year, coed. Part of Lone Star College. Awards certificates, transfer associate, and terminal associate degrees. Founded 2010. Setting: suburban campus with easy access to Houston. Total enrollment: 12,024. Faculty: 511 (78 full-time, 433 part-time). Student-undergrad faculty ratio is 29:1. Full-time: 3,645 students, 53% women, 47% men. Part-time: 8,379 students, 59% women, 41% men. Students come from 57 other countries. 0.2% American Indian or Alaska Native, non-Hispanic/Latino; 38% Hispanic/Latino; 13% Black or African American, non-Hispanic/Latino; 12% Asian, non-Hispanic/Latino. 27% 25 or older, 25% transferred in. Core. Academic remediation for entering students, ESL program, services for LD students, advanced placement, honors program, independent study, distance learning, summer session for credit, part-time degree program, co-op programs and internships. Off campus study. Study abroad program.

Entrance Requirements: Recommended: high school transcript.

Costs Per Year: Area resident tuition: $1088 full-time, $44 per credit hour part-time. State resident tuition: $3368 full-time, $139 per credit hour part-time. Nonresident tuition: $4208 full-time, $174 per credit hour part-time. Mandatory fees: $544 full-time, $20 per credit hour part-time, $32 per term part-time. Full-time tuition and fees vary according to course load and program. Part-time tuition and fees vary according to course load and program. Tuition guaranteed not to increase for student's term of enrollment.

Collegiate Environment: Orientation program. Student services: personal-psychological counseling. Campus security: 24-hour emergency response devices and patrols, late night transport-escort service.

■ LUBBOCK CHRISTIAN UNIVERSITY

5601 19th St.
Lubbock, TX 79407-2099
Tel: (806)796-8800; Free: 800-933-7601
Fax: (806)796-8917
E-mail: admissions@lcu.edu
Web Site: www.lcu.edu

Description: Independent, comprehensive, coed, affiliated with Church of Christ. Awards bachelor's and master's degrees. Founded 1957. Setting: 120-acre suburban campus. Endowment: $19.7 million. Educational spending for the previous fiscal year: $8524 per student. Total enrollment: 1,805. Faculty: 190 (95 full-time, 95 part-time). Student-undergrad faculty ratio is 13:1. 696 applied, 90% were admitted. 22% from top 10% of their high school class, 47% from top quarter, 78% from top half. Full-time: 6,272 students, 92% women, 8% men. Part-time: 167 students, 65% women, 35% men. Students come from 34 states and territories, 19 other countries, 10% from out-of-state. 1% American Indian or Alaska Native, non-Hispanic/Latino; 24% Hispanic/Latino; 4% Black or African American, non-Hispanic/Latino; 0.7% Asian, non-Hispanic/Latino; 0.4% Native Hawaiian or other Pacific Islander, non-Hispanic/Latino; 2% international. 16% 25 or older, 37% live on campus, 2% transferred in. Retention: 69% of full-time freshmen returned the following year. Academic areas with the most degrees conferred: health professions and related sciences; business/marketing; education. Core. Calendar: semesters. Academic remediation for entering students, services for LD students, advanced placement, honors program, distance learning, double major, summer session for credit, part-time degree program, adult/continuing education programs, co-op programs and internships, graduate courses open to undergrads. Study abroad program. ROTC: Army (c), Air Force (c).

Entrance Requirements: Options: electronic application, early decision, early action, international baccalaureate accepted. Required: high school transcript, SAT or ACT. Entrance: moderately difficult. Application deadlines: 6/1, 6/1 for nonresidents, 10/31 for early decision plan 1, 1/1 for early decision plan 2, 6/15 for early action. Notification: continuous, continuous for nonresidents, 12/15 for early decision plan 1, 2/15 for early decision plan 2, 7/15 for early action. SAT Reasoning Test deadline: 8/15. Transfer credits accepted: Yes. Early decision applicants: 815. Early decision applicants admitted: 679.

Costs Per Year: Application fee: $25. Comprehensive fee: $31,270 includes full-time tuition ($23,330) and college room and board ($7940). Part-time tuition: $755 per credit hour. Part-time mandatory fees: $60 per term.

Collegiate Environment: Orientation program. Drama-theater group, choral group, student-run newspaper, radio station. Social organizations: 23 open to all; local fraternities, local sororities; 20% of eligible men and 18% of eligible women are members. Most popular organizations: Student Senate, Enactus, Ag Club, Behavioral Science Society, International Student Association. Major annual events: Masterfollies, Homecoming, Spiritual Development Week. Student services: health clinic, personal-psychological counseling. Campus security: 24-hour patrols, late night transport-escort service, controlled dormitory access. 802 college housing spaces available; 535 were occupied in 2018-19. Freshmen guaranteed college housing. On-campus residence required through sophomore year. Options: men-only, women-only housing available. University Library. Books: 124,676 (physical), 176,165 (digital/electronic); Serial titles: 5 (digital/electronic); Databases: 92. Weekly public service hours: 93. Operations spending for the previous fiscal year: $711,140. 169 computers available on campus for general student use. A campuswide network can be accessed from student residence rooms and from off campus. Students can access the following: online class registration. Staffed computer lab on campus provides training in use of computers, software, and the Internet.

Community Environment: Population 209,737. The industrial, agricultural and educational center of the South Plains of Texas, Lubbock is the third largest inland cotton market in the Nation. There are also many oil wells in the community. This metropolitan center is called"The Hub of the Plains." The climate is mild and arid. Community service facilities include over 200 churches, county libraries, hospitals, a planetarium, museum, and municipal auditorium. There are four TV stations, seven radio stations, four golf courses, movie theaters, drive-ins, hunting, water skiing, horseback riding, and many other forms of recreation available in the area. Part-time employment is available. The city is served by railroad, airlines, and a bus line.

■ MCLENNAN COMMUNITY COLLEGE

1400 College Dr.
Waco, TX 76708-1499
Tel: (254)299-8622
E-mail: astraten@mclennan.edu
Web Site: www.mclennan.edu

Description: County-supported, 2-year, coed. Awards certificates, transfer associate, and terminal associate degrees. Founded 1965. Setting: 200-acre urban campus. Endowment: $15.3 million. Total enrollment: 8,799. Faculty: 389. Student-undergrad faculty ratio is 17:1. 2,362 applied, 100% were admitted. Students come from 17 states and territories, 2% from out-of-state. 0.4% American Indian or Alaska Native, non-Hispanic/Latino; 30% Hispanic/Latino; 12% Black or African American, non-Hispanic/Latino; 1% Asian, non-Hispanic/Latino. 32% 25 or older. Core. Calendar: semesters. Academic remediation for entering students, services for LD students, advanced placement, honors program, distance learning, summer session for credit, part-time degree program, adult/continuing education programs, co-op programs and internships. Off campus study at Baylor University. Study abroad program. ROTC: Air Force (c).

Entrance Requirements: Open admission except for health careers programs. Options: electronic application, early admission. Required: high school transcript. Entrance: noncompetitive. Application deadline: rolling. Notification: continuous until 9/2. Transfer credits accepted: Yes.

Costs Per Year: Application fee: $0. Area resident tuition: $3180 full-time, $106 per semester hour part-time. State resident tuition: $3720 full-time, $124 per semester hour part-time. Nonresident tuition: $5430 full-time, $181 per semester hour part-time. Mandatory fees: $270 full-time, $9 per semester hour part-time.

Collegiate Environment: Orientation program. Drama-theater group, choral group, student-run newspaper. Major annual event: Highland Games. Student services: personal-psychological counseling. Campus security: 24-hour emergency response devices and patrols. McLennan Community College Library. Books: 69,255 (physical), 237,879 (digital/electronic); Serial titles: 290 (physical), 61 (digital/electronic); Databases: 134. Students can reserve study rooms. Operations spending for the previous fiscal year: $1.1 million. 425 computers available on campus for general student use. A campuswide network can be accessed from off-campus. Students can access the following: online class registration. Staffed computer lab on campus provides training in use of computers, software, and the Internet.

Community Environment: See Baylor University.

■ MCMURRY UNIVERSITY

1400 Sayles Blvd.
Abilene, TX 79697
Tel: (325)793-3800; Free: 800-460-2392
Fax: (325)691-6599

E-mail: admissions@mcm.edu
Web Site: www.mcm.edu

Description: Independent United Methodist, comprehensive, coed. Awards bachelor's and master's degrees. Founded 1923. Setting: 52-acre suburban campus. Endowment: $81.5 million. Educational spending for the previous fiscal year: $9368 per student. Total enrollment: 1,108. Faculty: 124 (78 full-time, 46 part-time). Student-undergrad faculty ratio is 11:1. 1,843 applied, 43% were admitted. 12% from top 10% of their high school class, 33% from top quarter, 73% from top half. Full-time: 956 students, 49% women, 51% men. Part-time: 149 students, 43% women, 57% men. Students come from 17 states and territories, 10 other countries, 5% from out-of-state. 0.8% American Indian or Alaska Native, non-Hispanic/Latino; 26% Hispanic/Latino; 15% Black or African American, non-Hispanic/Latino; 1% Asian, non-Hispanic/Latino; 0.1% Native Hawaiian or other Pacific Islander, non-Hispanic/Latino; 6% international. 17% 25 or older, 54% live on campus, 12% transferred in. Retention: 62% of full-time freshmen returned the following year. Academic areas with the most degrees conferred: education; business/marketing; interdisciplinary studies. Core. Calendar: semesters plus May term. Academic remediation for entering students, ESL program, services for LD students, advanced placement, accelerated degree program, self-designed majors, honors program, distance learning, double major, summer session for credit, part-time degree program, adult/continuing education programs, internships. Off campus study at Patty Hanks Shelton School of Nursing- Abilene, TX. Study abroad program.

Entrance Requirements: Options: electronic application, deferred admission, international baccalaureate accepted. Required: essay, high school transcript, minimum 2 high school GPA, SAT or ACT. Required for some: 3 recommendations, interview. Entrance: moderately difficult. Application deadline: 8/15. Notification: continuous. SAT Reasoning Test deadline: 8/15. Transfer credits accepted: Yes.

Costs Per Year: Application fee: $25. One-time mandatory fee: $175. Comprehensive fee: $35,846 includes full-time tuition ($27,154), mandatory fees ($90), and college room and board ($8602). College room only: $4186. Full-time tuition and fees vary according to course load. Room and board charges vary according to board plan and housing facility. Part-time tuition: $848 per credit hour. Part-time mandatory fees: $3 per credit hour. Part-time tuition and fees vary according to course load.

Collegiate Environment: Orientation program. Drama-theater group, choral group, marching band, student-run newspaper. Social organizations: 20 open to all; local fraternities, local sororities; 15% of eligible men and 18% of eligible women are members. Most popular organizations: Alpha Phi Omega, Religious Life Council, McMurry Student Government, Campus Activity Board, Servant Leadership. Major annual events: Homecoming, Spring Thing, Spring McMadness. Student services: health clinic, personal-psychological counseling. Campus security: 24-hour emergency response devices and patrols, late night transport-escort service, controlled dormitory access. Jay-Rollins Library. Books: 128,329 (physical), 193,689 (digital/electronic); Serial titles: 115 (physical), 377 (digital/electronic); Databases: 95. Weekly public service hours: 86. Operations spending for the previous fiscal year: $293,303. 50 computers available on campus for general student use. Computer purchase/lease plans available. A computer is required for all students. A campuswide network can be accessed from student residence rooms and from off campus. Students can access the following: online class registration, learning management system. Staffed computer lab on campus provides training in use of computers and software.

■ MEDIATECH INSTITUTE

13300 Branch View Ln.
Dallas, TX 75234
Tel: (972)869-1122; Free: 866-498-1122
Web Site: www.mediatech.edu

Description: Proprietary, 2-year, coed. Awards certificates, diplomas, and transfer associate degrees.

■ MESSENGER COLLEGE

400 S Industrial Blvd., Ste. 300
Euless, TX 76040
Tel: (817)554-5950; Free: 800-385-8940
E-mail: enrollment@messengercollege.edu
Web Site: www.messengercollege.edu

Description: Independent Pentecostal, 4-year, coed. Awards associate and bachelor's degrees. Founded 1987. Setting: 3-acre suburban campus with easy access to Dallas-Fort Worth. Endowment: $543,454. Educational spending for the previous fiscal year: $2602 per student. Total enrollment:

45. Faculty: 24 (2 full-time, 22 part-time). 44 applied, 27% were admitted. Full-time: 34 students, 59% women, 41% men. Part-time: 11 students, 27% women, 73% men. Students come from 12 states and territories, 73% from out-of-state. 20% Hispanic/Latino; 4% Black or African American, non-Hispanic/Latino. 29% 25 or older, 58% live on campus, 4% transferred in. Retention: 89% of full-time freshmen returned the following year. Academic area with the most degrees conferred: business/marketing. Core. Calendar: semesters. Academic remediation for entering students, advanced placement, honors program, independent study, distance learning, double major, part-time degree program, external degree program, co-op programs and internships.

Entrance Requirements: Options: electronic application, early admission. Required: essay, high school transcript, minimum 2 high school GPA, 3 recommendations, health form. Required for some: interview, SAT or ACT. Entrance: moderately difficult. Application deadlines: 8/14, 8/14 for nonresidents. Notification: continuous, continuous for nonresidents. Transfer credits accepted: Yes.

Costs Per Year: Application fee: $35. Comprehensive fee: $17,230 includes full-time tuition ($9750), mandatory fees ($1330), and college room and board ($6150). College room only: $3350. Part-time tuition: $325 per credit hour. Part-time mandatory fees: $660 per term.

Collegiate Environment: Orientation program. Campus security: 24-hour emergency response devices, student patrols, controlled dormitory access. 76 college housing spaces available; 26 were occupied in 2018-19. No special consideration for freshman housing applicants. Options: men-only, women-only housing available. McDole-McDonald Library. Books: 12,617 (physical), 10,290 (digital/electronic); Serial titles: 12,705 (physical), 14,979 (digital/electronic); Databases: 15. Students can reserve study rooms. Operations spending for the previous fiscal year: $20,118. 5 computers available on campus for general student use. A campuswide network can be accessed from student residence rooms. Students can access the following: online class registration. Staffed computer lab on campus provides training in use of computers, software, and the Internet.

■ **MIDLAND COLLEGE**
3600 N Garfield
Midland, TX 79705-6329
Tel: (432)685-4500
Fax: (432)685-4714
E-mail: amyw@midland.edu
Web Site: www.midland.edu

Description: State and locally supported, 4-year, coed. Awards associate and bachelor's degrees. Founded 1969. Setting: 163-acre suburban campus. Total enrollment: 5,564. Student-undergrad faculty ratio is 17:1. Full-time: 1,603 students, 62% women, 38% men. Part-time: 3,961 students, 54% women, 46% men. 0.5% American Indian or Alaska Native, non-Hispanic/Latino; 49% Hispanic/Latino; 6% Black or African American, non-Hispanic/Latino; 2% Asian, non-Hispanic/Latino; 0.2% Native Hawaiian or other Pacific Islander, non-Hispanic/Latino. 25% 25 or older, 7% transferred in. Academic area with the most degrees conferred: business/marketing. Core. Calendar: semesters. Academic remediation for entering students, ESL program, services for LD students, advanced placement, honors program, distance learning, summer session for credit, co-op programs. Off campus study.

Entrance Requirements: Open admission except for nursing, respiratory therapy, radiological technology programs. Options: electronic application, international baccalaureate accepted. Entrance: noncompetitive. Application deadline: rolling. Notification: continuous. Transfer credits accepted: Yes.

Collegiate Environment: Orientation program. Drama-theater group, choral group, student-run newspaper. Social organizations: 20 open to all; 20% of eligible men and 80% of eligible women are members. Most popular organizations: OIKOS, Midland College Latin American Student Society, Student Government Association, Student Nurses Association, Baptist Student Ministries. Major annual events: Homecoming Night, Chappapalooza, Club Fair. Student services: personal-psychological counseling. Campus security: 24-hour patrols, controlled dormitory access. Murray Fasken Learning Resource Center. Weekly public service hours: 84. 950 computers available on campus for general student use. A campuswide network can be accessed. Students can access the following: online class registration. Staffed computer lab on campus provides training in use of computers, software, and the Internet.

■ **MIDWESTERN STATE UNIVERSITY**
3410 Taft Blvd.
Wichita Falls, TX 76308

Tel: (940)397-4000; Free: 800-842-1922
Fax: (940)397-4302
E-mail: leah.vineyard@mwsu.edu
Web Site: www.mwsu.edu

Description: State-supported, comprehensive, coed. Awards associate, bachelor's, and master's degrees. Founded 1922. Setting: 255-acre urban campus. Endowment: $20.9 million. Research spending for the previous fiscal year: $615,996. Educational spending for the previous fiscal year: $8527 per student. Total enrollment: 6,043. Faculty: 345 (236 full-time, 109 part-time). Student-undergrad faculty ratio is 18:1. 2,854 applied, 76% were admitted. 14% from top 10% of their high school class, 39% from top quarter, 73% from top half. 8 valedictorians. Full-time: 4,055 students, 57% women, 43% men. Part-time: 1,232 students, 59% women, 41% men. Students come from 50 states and territories, 53 other countries, 8% from out-of-state. 0.6% American Indian or Alaska Native, non-Hispanic/Latino; 17% Hispanic/Latino; 14% Black or African American, non-Hispanic/Latino; 3% Asian, non-Hispanic/Latino; 0.2% Native Hawaiian or other Pacific Islander, non-Hispanic/Latino; 9% international. 27% 25 or older, 28% live on campus, 10% transferred in. Retention: 70% of full-time freshmen returned the following year. Academic areas with the most degrees conferred: health professions and related sciences; business/marketing; interdisciplinary studies. Core. Calendar: semesters. Academic remediation for entering students, ESL program, services for LD students, advanced placement, honors program, independent study, distance learning, double major, summer session for credit, part-time degree program, adult/continuing education programs, internships, graduate courses open to undergrads. Study abroad program. ROTC: Air Force (c).

Entrance Requirements: Option: electronic application. Required: high school transcript, SAT or ACT. Required for some: SAT and SAT Subject Tests or ACT. Entrance: moderately difficult. Application deadline: 8/1. Notification: continuous. SAT Reasoning Test deadline: 8/1. SAT Subject Test deadline: 8/1. Transfer credits accepted: Yes.

Collegiate Environment: Orientation program. Drama-theater group, choral group, marching band, student-run newspaper. Social organizations: 75 open to all; national fraternities, national sororities, local fraternities; 8% of eligible men and 9% of eligible women are members. Most popular organizations: Caribbean Students Organization, Baptist Student Ministry, Catholic Campus Ministry, African Students Organization, University Programming Board. Major annual events: Homecoming, Welcome Week, Family Day. Student services: legal services, health clinic, personal-psychological counseling. Campus security: 24-hour emergency response devices and patrols, controlled dormitory access. Moffett Library plus 1 other. Books: 331,562 (physical), 193,374 (digital/electronic); Databases: 123. Operations spending for the previous fiscal year: $1.4 million. 405 computers available on campus for general student use. A campuswide network can be accessed from student residence rooms and from off campus. Students can access the following: online class registration. Staffed computer lab on campus (open 24 hours a day) provides training in use of computers, software, and the Internet.

Community Environment: Population 100,000. A distributing point for both southern Oklahoma and northwestern Texas, Wichita Falls is one of the important trade centers of the Southwest. The community has a library, museum, two hospitals, 3 YMCA's and YWCA. Various civic, fraternal and veteran's organizations serve the city. Part-time employment is available. Local recreational facilities include theatres, nightclubs, bowling, skating, boating, fishing, municipal golf course, and two country club golf courses.

■ **MOUNTAIN VIEW COLLEGE**
4849 W Illinois Ave.
Dallas, TX 75211-6599
Tel: (214)860-8600
Fax: (214)860-8570
E-mail: ghall@dcccd.edu
Web Site: www.mountainviewcollege.edu

Description: State and locally supported, 2-year, coed. Part of Dallas County Community College District System. Awards certificates, transfer associate, and terminal associate degrees. Founded 1970. Setting: 200-acre urban campus. Total enrollment: 9,068. Faculty: 386 (86 full-time, 300 part-time). Student-undergrad faculty ratio is 28:1. 2,500 applied, 100% were admitted. Full-time: 2,066 students, 51% women, 49% men. Part-time: 7,002 students, 60% women, 40% men. Students come from 12 states and territories. 0.3% American Indian or Alaska Native, non-Hispanic/Latino; 53% Hispanic/Latino; 26% Black or African American, non-Hispanic/Latino; 4% Asian, non-Hispanic/Latino; 0.3% international. 37% 25 or older, 18%

transferred in. Retention: 57% of full-time freshmen returned the following year. Core. Calendar: semesters. Academic remediation for entering students, ESL program, services for LD students, advanced placement, freshman honors college, honors program, independent study, distance learning, double major, summer session for credit, part-time degree program, external degree program, adult/continuing education programs, co-op programs and internships.

Entrance Requirements: Open admission except for nursing programs. Options: electronic application, early admission, deferred admission. Required: high school transcript. Entrance: noncompetitive. Application deadline: rolling. Notification: continuous. Transfer credits accepted: Yes.

Collegiate Environment: Orientation program. Drama-theater group, choral group. Student services: health clinic, personal-psychological counseling. Campus security: 24-hour patrols, late night transport-escort service.

Community Environment: See University of Texas at Dallas.

■ NATIONAL AMERICAN UNIVERSITY (AUSTIN)
13801 Burnet Rd.
Ste. 300
Austin, TX 78727
Tel: (512)651-4100; Free: 888-628-8392
Web Site: www.national.edu
Description: Proprietary, 4-year, coed.

■ NATIONAL AMERICAN UNIVERSITY (GEORGETOWN)
1015 W University Ave.
Ste. 700
Georgetown, TX 78628
Tel: (512)942-6750; Free: 888-628-8392
Web Site: www.national.edu
Description: Proprietary, 4-year, coed.

■ NATIONAL AMERICAN UNIVERSITY (HOUSTON)
11511 Katy Fwy.
Ste. 200
Houston, TX 77079
Tel: (832)619-7300; Free: 855-455-8029
Web Site: www.national.edu
Description: Proprietary, 4-year, coed.

■ NATIONAL AMERICAN UNIVERSITY (LEWISVILLE)
475 State Hwy. 121 Byp.
Ste. 150
Lewisville, TX 75067
Tel: (972)829-2150; Free: 800-548-0605
Web Site: www.national.edu
Description: Proprietary, 4-year, coed.

■ NATIONAL AMERICAN UNIVERSITY (MESQUITE)
18600 LBJ Fwy.
Mesquite, TX 75150
Tel: (972)773-8800; Free: 800-548-0605
Web Site: www.national.edu
Description: Proprietary, 4-year, coed. Awards associate and bachelor's degrees.

■ NATIONAL AMERICAN UNIVERSITY (RICHARDSON)
300 N Coit Rd.
Ste. 225
Richardson, TX 75080
Tel: (972)773-8650; Free: 800-548-0605
Web Site: www.national.edu
Description: Proprietary, 4-year, coed.

■ NAVARRO COLLEGE
3200 W 7th Ave.
Corsicana, TX 75110-4899
Tel: (903)874-6501; Free: 800-628-2776
E-mail: tammy.adams@navarrocollege.edu
Web Site: www.navarrocollege.edu
Description: State and locally supported, 2-year, coed. Awards certificates, diplomas, transfer associate, and terminal associate degrees. Founded 1946. Setting: 275-acre small town campus with easy access to Dallas-Fort Worth. Total enrollment: 8,968. Faculty: 497 (136 full-time, 361 part-time).

Student-undergrad faculty ratio is 16:1. Full-time: 3,057 students, 57% women, 43% men. Part-time: 5,911 students, 60% women, 40% men. Students come from 39 other countries, 2% from out-of-state. 0.6% American Indian or Alaska Native, non-Hispanic/Latino; 22% Hispanic/Latino; 18% Black or African American, non-Hispanic/Latino; 1% Asian, non-Hispanic/Latino; 0.3% Native Hawaiian or other Pacific Islander, non-Hispanic/Latino; 1% international. 19% 25 or older, 25% live on campus. Core. Calendar: semesters. Academic remediation for entering students, services for LD students, advanced placement, self-designed majors, freshman honors college, honors program, distance learning, summer session for credit, part-time degree program, adult/continuing education programs, co-op programs.

Entrance Requirements: Open admission. Options: electronic application, early admission. Required: high school transcript. Entrance: noncompetitive. Transfer credits accepted: Yes.

Costs Per Year: Area resident tuition: $1260 full-time, $126 per credit hour part-time. State resident tuition: $1470 full-time, $147 per credit hour part-time. Nonresident tuition: $3120 full-time, $312 per credit hour part-time. Mandatory fees: $1170 full-time, $110 per credit hour part-time. Full-time tuition and fees vary according to course load. Part-time tuition and fees vary according to course load. College room and board: $6876. Room and board charges vary according to board plan.

Collegiate Environment: Orientation program. Drama-theater group, choral group, marching band. Social organizations: 35 open to all. Most popular organizations: Student Government Association, Phi Theta Kappa, Ebony Club, Que Pasa. Major annual events: Homecoming, Bulldog Bash, Mr. & Ms. NC contest. Student services: personal-psychological counseling. Campus security: 24-hour emergency response devices. Richard M. Sanchez Library. 80 computers available on campus for general student use. Computer purchase/lease plans available. Staffed computer lab on campus.

Community Environment: Navarro College is located in historic Corsicana, Texas. The economy is diversified and part-time jobs are available for students. The local climate is moderate to mild. The area is served by bus and major highways. There are several churches, a library, YMCA, and outstanding medical facilities. Residents can enjoy restaurants, shopping, and local fine arts events as well as excellent recreational facilities for boating, water skiing, fishing, golf, and hunting. Annual events include rodeo finals, bicycle races, and food festivals.

■ NORTH AMERICAN UNIVERSITY
11929 W Airport Blvd.
Stafford, TX 77477
Tel: (832)230-5555
Fax: (281)272-0124
E-mail: admissions@na.edu
Web Site: www.na.edu
Description: Independent, comprehensive, coed. Awards bachelor's and master's degrees. Founded 2010. Setting: 12-acre urban campus with easy access to Houston, TX. Research spending for the previous fiscal year: $223,351. Total enrollment: 568. Faculty: 42 (8 full-time, 34 part-time). Student-undergrad faculty ratio is 19:1. 215 applied, 57% were admitted. Full-time: 313 students, 41% women, 59% men. Part-time: 27 students, 33% women, 67% men. Students come from 21 states and territories, 52 other countries, 11% from out-of-state. 15% Hispanic/Latino; 11% Black or African American, non-Hispanic/Latino; 5% Asian, non-Hispanic/Latino; 58% international. 16% 25 or older, 6% transferred in. Retention: 46% of full-time freshmen returned the following year. Academic areas with the most degrees conferred: business/marketing; computer and information sciences; education. Core. Calendar: semesters. Academic remediation for entering students, ESL program, advanced placement, distance learning, summer session for credit, part-time degree program, internships.

Entrance Requirements: Open admission for undergraduate/baccalaureate programs. Options: electronic application, early admission, deferred admission, international baccalaureate accepted. Required: high school transcript, interview. Recommended: minimum 2.7 high school GPA, SAT or ACT. Required for some: essay, 1 recommendation. Entrance: minimally difficult. Application deadline: rolling. Notification: continuous. SAT Reasoning Test deadline: 8/1. SAT Subject Test deadline: 8/1. Transfer credits accepted: Yes.

Costs Per Year: Application fee: $0. One-time mandatory fee: $110. Comprehensive fee: $18,800 includes full-time tuition ($9450), mandatory fees ($450), and college room and board ($8900). College room only: $4500. Full-time tuition and fees vary according to course load, degree level, and program. Room and board charges vary according to board plan. Part-time tuition: $475 per credit hour. Part-time mandatory fees: $225 per term. Part-time tuition and fees vary according to course load, degree level, and program. Tuition guaranteed not to increase for student's term of enrollment. **Collegiate Environment:** Orientation program. Social organizations: 15 open to all. Most popular organizations: Computer Science, Women's Computer Science, NAU Care Services, Student Athlete Association, Harmony Stallions Association. Major annual events: International Culture Day, Homecoming, Halloween Dance. Student services: personal-psychological counseling. North American University Library. Books: 4,857 (physical), 168,629 (digital/electronic); Serial titles: 3 (physical), 2 (digital/electronic); Databases: 8. Weekly public service hours: 61; students can reserve study rooms. Operations spending for the previous fiscal year: $95,127. 150 computers available on campus for general student use. Computer purchase/lease plans available. A campuswide network can be accessed from student residence rooms and from off campus. Students can access the following: online class registration. Staffed computer lab on campus provides training in use of computers, software, and the Internet.

■ **NORTH CENTRAL TEXAS COLLEGE**
1525 W California St.
Gainesville, TX 76240-4699
Tel: (940)668-7731
Fax: (940)668-6049
E-mail: mcarroll@nctc.edu
Web Site: www.nctc.edu
Description: State and locally supported, 2-year, coed. Awards certificates, diplomas, transfer associate, and terminal associate degrees. Founded 1924. Setting: 132-acre suburban campus with easy access to Dallas-Fort Worth. Endowment: $4.3 million. Research spending for the previous fiscal year: $111,173. Educational spending for the previous fiscal year: $2051 per student. Total enrollment: 10,327. Faculty: 403 (152 full-time, 251 part-time). Student-undergrad faculty ratio is 16:1. Full-time: 2,693 students, 53% women, 47% men. Part-time: 7,634 students, 58% women, 42% men. Students come from 28 states and territories, 15 other countries, 1% from out-of-state. 0.7% American Indian or Alaska Native, non-Hispanic/Latino; 23% Hispanic/Latino; 9% Black or African American, non-Hispanic/Latino; 3% Asian, non-Hispanic/Latino; 0.1% Native Hawaiian or other Pacific Islander, non-Hispanic/Latino; 2% international. 23% 25 or older, 1% live on campus, 8% transferred in. Retention: 99% of full-time freshmen returned the following year. Core. Calendar: semesters. Academic remediation for entering students, services for LD students, advanced placement, distance learning, summer session for credit, part-time degree program, adult/continuing education programs, co-op programs and internships. ROTC: Army (c).
Entrance Requirements: Open admission except for allied health, legal assistant, equine technology, occupational therapy assistant programs. Options: electronic application, early admission, international baccalaureate accepted. Required: high school transcript. Entrance: noncompetitive. Application deadline: rolling. Transfer credits accepted: Yes.
Collegiate Environment: Orientation program. Drama-theater group, choral group. Social organizations: 15 open to all. Most popular organizations: Student Nursing Association, Residence Hall Association, Cosmetology Student Association, Student Government Association, Gainesville Program Council. Major annual events: Welcome Back Party, NCTC's Got Talent. Student services: personal-psychological counseling. Campus security: late night transport-escort service, controlled dormitory access, security cameras. North Central Texas College Library plus 1 other. Operations spending for the previous fiscal year: $608,794. 51 computers available on campus for general student use. A campuswide network can be accessed from off-campus. Students can access the following: online class registration. Staffed computer lab on campus.
Community Environment: Population 16,500. Gainesville is a rural community that enjoys a temperate climate. The area is reached by bus lines. There is a public library, churches of major denominations, a local hospital, and over 80 civic, fraternal and veteran's organizations in the city. Part-time employment is limited. Local recreation includes boating, tennis, fishing, and golf.

■ **NORTH LAKE COLLEGE**
5001 N MacArthur Blvd.
Irving, TX 75038-3899
Tel: (972)273-3000
Web Site: www.northlakecollege.edu
Description: County-supported, 2-year, coed. Part of Dallas County Com-

munity College District System. Awards certificates, transfer associate, and terminal associate degrees. Founded 1977. Setting: 250-acre suburban campus with easy access to Dallas-Fort Worth. Research spending for the previous fiscal year: $1465. Total enrollment: 10,174. Faculty: 504 (95 full-time, 409 part-time). Student-undergrad faculty ratio is 21:1. Full-time: 3,171 students, 47% women, 53% men. Part-time: 7,003 students, 57% women, 43% men. Students come from 18 states and territories, 23 other countries, 9% from out-of-state. 38% 25 or older, 8% transferred in. Retention: 55% of full-time freshmen returned the following year. Core. Calendar: semesters. Academic remediation for entering students, ESL program, services for LD students, advanced placement, accelerated degree program, independent study, distance learning, double major, summer session for credit, part-time degree program, external degree program, adult/continuing education programs, co-op programs and internships. Off campus study. Study abroad program.
Entrance Requirements: Open admission. Options: electronic application, early admission. Recommended: high school transcript. Entrance: noncompetitive. Application deadline: rolling. Notification: continuous. Transfer credits accepted: Yes.
Collegiate Environment: Orientation program. Drama-theater group, choral group, student-run newspaper. Major annual events: International Day, Career Day. Student services: health clinic, personal-psychological counseling. Campus security: 24-hour emergency response devices, student patrols, late night transport-escort service. North Lake College Library plus 3 others. Operations spending for the previous fiscal year: $501,000. 250 computers available on campus for general student use. A campuswide network can be accessed. Students can access the following: online class registration. Staffed computer lab on campus provides training in use of computers, software, and the Internet.

■ **NORTHEAST LAKEVIEW COLLEGE**
1201 Kitty Hawk Rd.
Universal City, TX 78148
Web Site: www.alamo.edu/nlc
Description: District-supported, 2-year, coed.

■ **NORTHEAST TEXAS COMMUNITY COLLEGE**
PO Box 1307
Mount Pleasant, TX 75456-1307
Tel: (903)572-1911; Free: 800-870-0142
Fax: (903)572-6712
E-mail: lbond@ntcc.edu
Web Site: www.ntcc.edu
Description: State and locally supported, 2-year, coed. Awards certificates, transfer associate, and terminal associate degrees. Founded 1985. Setting: 175-acre rural campus. Total enrollment: 3,282. Faculty: 178 (76 full-time, 102 part-time). Student-undergrad faculty ratio is 17:1. Full-time: 446 students, 55% women, 45% men. Part-time: 360 students, 41% women, 59% men. Students come from 19 states and territories, 4 other countries, 2% from out-of-state. 0.2% American Indian or Alaska Native, non-Hispanic/Latino; 24% Hispanic/Latino; 13% Black or African American, non-Hispanic/Latino; 0.4% Asian, non-Hispanic/Latino; 0.1% Native Hawaiian or other Pacific Islander, non-Hispanic/Latino; 1% international. 26% 25 or older. Retention: 50% of full-time freshmen returned the following year. Core. Calendar: semesters. Academic remediation for entering students, services for LD students, advanced placement, honors program, independent study, distance learning, summer session for credit, part-time degree program, adult/continuing education programs, co-op programs.
Entrance Requirements: Open admission. Options: electronic application, early admission. Required: high school transcript. Entrance: noncompetitive. Application deadline: rolling. Transfer credits accepted: Yes.
Collegiate Environment: Orientation program. Drama-theater group, choral group, student-run newspaper. Social organizations: 34 open to all. Most popular organizations: Phi Theta Kappa, Student Government Association. Major annual event: Scare Affair. Campus security: 24-hour patrols. Learning Resource Center. 52 computers available on campus for general student use. A campuswide network can be accessed from student residence rooms and from off campus. Students can access the following: online class registration. Staffed computer lab on campus.

■ **NORTHWEST VISTA COLLEGE**
3535 N Ellison Dr.
San Antonio, TX 78251
Tel: (210)486-4000

E-mail: rsandberg@alamo.edu

Web Site: www.alamo.edu/nvc

Description: District-supported, 2-year, coed. Part of Alamo Community College District System. Awards certificates, transfer associate, and terminal associate degrees. Founded 1995. Setting: 137-acre urban campus with easy access to San Antonio. Total enrollment: 13,115. Faculty: 564 (177 full-time, 387 part-time). Student-undergrad faculty ratio is 25:1. Full-time: 4,043 students, 53% women, 47% men. Part-time: 9,072 students, 54% women, 46% men. 0.2% American Indian or Alaska Native, non-Hispanic/Latino; 65% Hispanic/Latino; 6% Black or African American, non-Hispanic/Latino; 3% Asian, non-Hispanic/Latino; 0.2% Native Hawaiian or other Pacific Islander, non-Hispanic/Latino; 0.3% international. 27% 25 or older, 7% transferred in. Core. Calendar: semesters. Academic remediation for entering students, ESL program, services for LD students, advanced placement, independent study, distance learning, double major, summer session for credit, part-time degree program, co-op programs and internships. Off campus study. Study abroad program. ROTC: Army (c).

Entrance Requirements: Open admission. Options: electronic application, early admission. Required: high school transcript. Entrance: noncompetitive. Transfer credits accepted: Yes.

Costs Per Year: Application fee: $0. Area resident tuition: $2064 full-time, $86 per credit hour part-time. State resident tuition: $4848 full-time, $202 per credit hour part-time. Nonresident tuition: $10,872 full-time, $453 per credit hour part-time. Mandatory fees: $122 full-time, $3 per credit hour part-time, $25 per term part-time. Full-time tuition and fees vary according to course load. Part-time tuition and fees vary according to course load.

Collegiate Environment: Orientation program. Drama-theater group. Social organizations: 17 open to all; Natl Society Leadership & Success; Phi Theta K. Most popular organizations: Business Student Organization, Psychology Club, Neko Anime Club. Major annual events: Viva la Vista, End of Semester Bash, Halloween Bash. Student services: personal-psychological counseling. Campus security: 24-hour emergency response devices, student patrols, late night transport-escort service. Redbud Learning Center. Books: 19,338 (physical), 233,202 (digital/electronic); Serial titles: 48 (physical), 33,000 (digital/electronic); Databases: 133. Weekly public service hours: 67. 3,000 computers available on campus for general student use. A campuswide network can be accessed. Students can access the following: online class registration. Staffed computer lab on campus provides training in use of computers, software, and the Internet.

■ **ODESSA COLLEGE**

201 W University Ave.

Odessa, TX 79764-7127

Tel: (432)335-6400

Fax: (432)335-6860

E-mail: tavery@odessa.edu

Web Site: www.odessa.edu

Description: State and locally supported, 2-year, coed. Awards certificates, transfer associate, and terminal associate degrees. Founded 1946. Setting: 87-acre urban campus. Total enrollment: 6,308. Faculty: 190 (130 full-time, 60 part-time). Full-time: 2,243 students, 64% women, 36% men. Part-time: 4,065 students, 61% women, 39% men. Students come from 24 states and territories, 4 other countries, 6% from out-of-state. 0.5% American Indian or Alaska Native, non-Hispanic/Latino; 63% Hispanic/Latino; 5% Black or African American, non-Hispanic/Latino; 1% Asian, non-Hispanic/Latino; 0.1% Native Hawaiian or other Pacific Islander, non-Hispanic/Latino; 1% international. 23% 25 or older. Core. Calendar: semesters. Academic remediation for entering students, services for LD students, advanced placement, independent study, distance learning, summer session for credit, part-time degree program, adult/continuing education programs, co-op programs and internships.

Entrance Requirements: Open admission Allied health programs have selective admissions. Options: electronic application, early admission, deferred admission. Entrance: noncompetitive. Application deadline: rolling. Notification: continuous.

Collegiate Environment: Choral group. Social organizations: 13 open to all. Most popular organizations: Baptist Student Union, Student Government Association, Rodeo Club, Physical Therapy Assistant Club, American Chemical Society. Major annual events: Back-to-School Picnic, Homecoming, Spring Fest. Student services: personal-psychological counseling. Campus security: 24-hour emergency response devices and patrols, late night transport-escort service, controlled dormitory access. Murry H. Fly Learning Resources Center plus 1 other. 300 computers available on campus for general student use. A campuswide network can be accessed from student residence rooms and from off campus. Staffed computer lab on campus.

Community Environment: Population of Odessa 93,500; of Midland 99,200. Odessa is one of the largest domestic oilfield supply centers in Texas. The community enjoys a mild climate. The city is reached by airlines, two bus lines, and railroad. Churches representing all denominations, two hospitals, a library, and many civic and fraternal organizations serve the area. Part-time employment is available. Local recreation includes theatres, bowling alleys, hunting, ice skating, and sports.

■ **OUR LADY OF THE LAKE UNIVERSITY**

411 SW 24th St.

San Antonio, TX 78207-4689

Tel: (210)434-6711; Free: 800-436-6558

Fax: (210)436-0824

E-mail: sytijeria@lake.ollusa.edu

Web Site: www.ollusa.edu

Description: Independent Roman Catholic, comprehensive, coed. Awards bachelor's, master's, and doctoral degrees. Founded 1895. Setting: 75-acre urban campus with easy access to San Antonio, TX. Endowment: $27.7 million. Educational spending for the previous fiscal year: $10,707 per student. Total enrollment: 3,212. Faculty: 315 (102 full-time, 213 part-time). Student-undergrad faculty ratio is 14:1. 3,389 applied, 91% were admitted. 13% from top 10% of their high school class, 36% from top quarter, 75% from top half. Full-time: 1,221 students, 69% women, 31% men. Part-time: 121 students, 77% women, 23% men. 2% from out-of-state. 0.5% American Indian or Alaska Native, non-Hispanic/Latino; 76% Hispanic/Latino; 8% Black or African American, non-Hispanic/Latino; 0.5% Asian, non-Hispanic/Latino; 0.1% Native Hawaiian or other Pacific Islander, non-Hispanic/Latino; 2% international. 22% 25 or older, 39% live on campus, 12% transferred in. Retention: 61% of full-time freshmen returned the following year. Academic areas with the most degrees conferred: public administration and social services; business/marketing; health professions and related sciences; psychology. Core. Calendar: semesters plus summer sessions. Services for LD students, advanced placement, accelerated degree program, honors program, independent study, distance learning, double major, summer session for credit, part-time degree program, adult/continuing education programs, co-op programs and internships, graduate courses open to undergrads. Off campus study at United Colleges of San Antonio. Study abroad program. ROTC: Army (c).

Entrance Requirements: Option: early action. Required: high school transcript, minimum 2 high school GPA, SAT or ACT.

Costs Per Year: Application fee: $35. Comprehensive fee: $38,342 includes full-time tuition ($27,912), mandatory fees ($828), and college room and board ($9602). College room only: $5814. Full-time tuition and fees vary according to course load and location. Room and board charges vary according to board plan and housing facility. Part-time tuition: $895 per credit hour. Part-time mandatory fees: $414 per term. Part-time tuition and fees vary according to course load and location.

Collegiate Environment: Orientation program. Drama-theater group, choral group, student-run newspaper. Social organizations: 50 open to all; national sororities, local fraternities. Most popular organizations: First Year Connection, Kappa Delta Chi, Epsilon Sigma Alpha, Social Justice Organization, Higher Achievement Through Leadership Opportunities. Major annual events: Spirit Day, Right Foot Week, Spring Break Bash. Student services: health clinic, personal-psychological counseling, women's center. Campus security: 24-hour emergency response devices and patrols, late night transport-escort service, controlled dormitory access. The Sueltenfuss Library. Books: 82,924 (physical), 51,160 (digital/electronic); Serial titles: 16,651 (physical), 167,665 (digital/electronic); Databases: 96. Weekly public service hours: 95; study areas open 24 hours, 5-7 days a week. Operations spending for the previous fiscal year: $1.3 million. 236 computers available on campus for general student use. A campuswide network can be accessed from student residence rooms and from off campus. Students can access the following: online class registration. Staffed computer lab on campus (open 24 hours a day) provides training in use of computers and the Internet.

Community Environment: See San Antonio College.

■ **PALO ALTO COLLEGE**

1400 W Villaret

San Antonio, TX 78224-2499

Tel: (210)921-5000

E-mail: eaguilar-villarr@alamo.edu

Web Site: www.alamo.edu/pac

Description: District-supported, 2-year, coed. Part of Alamo Community College District System. Awards certificates, transfer associate, and terminal associate degrees. Founded 1987. Setting: urban campus. Total enrollment: 8,376. Faculty: 2,943 (1,423 full-time, 1,520 part-time). Student-undergrad faculty ratio is 24:1. 1,354 applied, 100% were admitted. Full-time: 1,533 students, 62% women, 38% men. Part-time: 6,843 students, 60% women, 40% men. Students come from 15 states and territories, 0.3% from out-of-state. 0.3% American Indian or Alaska Native, non-Hispanic/Latino; 69% Hispanic/Latino; 3% Black or African American, non-Hispanic/Latino; 1% Asian, non-Hispanic/Latino; 0.2% Native Hawaiian or other Pacific Islander, non-Hispanic/Latino; 0.1% international. 29% 25 or older, 34% transferred in. Core. Calendar: semesters. Academic remediation for entering students, ESL program, summer session for credit, part-time degree program, adult/continuing education programs, co-op programs.

Entrance Requirements: Open admission. Option: early admission. Required: high school transcript. Entrance: noncompetitive. Application deadline: rolling.

Collegiate Environment: Drama-theater group, student-run newspaper. Social organizations: 20 open to all. Most popular organizations: Catholic Campus Ministries, International Club, Veterinary Technician Association, Movimiento Estudiantil Chicano De Aztlan, Phi Theta Kappa. Major annual events: PACFest, PAChanga. Student services: health clinic, personal-psychological counseling. Campus security: 24-hour emergency response devices and patrols. Ozuna Learning and Resource Center. 300 computers available on campus for general student use. A campuswide network can be accessed from off-campus. Staffed computer lab on campus.

■ PANOLA COLLEGE

1109 W Panola St.
Carthage, TX 75633-2397
Tel: (903)693-2000
E-mail: bsimpson@panola.edu
Web Site: www.panola.edu

Description: State and locally supported, 2-year, coed. Awards certificates, transfer associate, and terminal associate degrees. Founded 1947. Setting: 35-acre small town campus. Total enrollment: 2,646. Faculty: 152 (70 full-time, 82 part-time). Student-undergrad faculty ratio is 18:1. Full-time: 1,334 students, 67% women, 33% men. Part-time: 1,312 students, 70% women, 30% men. Students come from 10 states and territories, 10 other countries, 8% from out-of-state. 0.4% American Indian or Alaska Native, non-Hispanic/Latino; 11% Hispanic/Latino; 23% Black or African American, non-Hispanic/Latino; 0.6% Asian, non-Hispanic/Latino; 2% international. 8% 25 or older, 11% transferred in. Core. Calendar: semesters. Academic remediation for entering students, ESL program, services for LD students, advanced placement, distance learning, summer session for credit, part-time degree program, co-op programs.

Entrance Requirements: Open admission. Option: electronic application. Recommended: high school transcript. Required for some: high school transcript. Transfer credits accepted: Yes.

Costs Per Year: Area resident tuition: $810 full-time, $60 per semester hour part-time. State resident tuition: $2550 full-time, $116 per semester hour part-time. Nonresident tuition: $3660 full-time, $293 per semester hour part-time. Mandatory fees: $1530 full-time, $51 per semester hour part-time. College room and board: $5016.

Collegiate Environment: Orientation program. Drama-theater group, choral group, student-run newspaper. Social organizations: 18 open to all; honor fraternity and academic area fraternities; 4% of eligible men and 7% of eligible women are members. Most popular organizations: History Club, SOTA (Student Occupational Therapy Assistant), NSLS (National Society of Leadership and Success, PTK (Phi Theta Kappa), BSM (Baptist Student Ministry). Major annual events: Fall Frolic, Spring Fling. Student services: personal-psychological counseling. Campus security: controlled dormitory access, 24-hour campus police department. M. P. Baker Library. Books: 27,616 (physical), 651,787 (digital/electronic); Serial titles: 42 (physical), 15 (digital/electronic); Databases: 72. Weekly public service hours: 64; students can reserve study rooms. 192 computers available on campus for general student use. A campuswide network can be accessed. Students can access the following: online class registration, Cloud-based course management system, email, and website. Staffed computer lab on campus provides training in use of computers, software, and the Internet.

Community Environment: Population 6,611, Carthage is in a rural area with a temperate climate. The community is served by rail, bus, and U.S. Routes 59 and 79. Facilities include a public library, hospital, churches of eight denominations, theatres, a 35-mile lake shoreline for all water sports, a swimming pool, bowling alley, golf courses. Several rodeos and livestock shows are held annually. Part-time employment is somewhat limited.

■ PARIS JUNIOR COLLEGE

2400 Clarksville St.
Paris, TX 75460-6298
Tel: (903)785-7661; Free: 800-232-5804
Web Site: www.parisjc.edu

Description: State and locally supported, 2-year, coed. Awards certificates, diplomas, transfer associate, and terminal associate degrees. Founded 1924. Setting: 54-acre rural campus with easy access to Dallas-Fort Worth. Endowment: $22 million. Educational spending for the previous fiscal year: $3978 per student. Total enrollment: 4,835. Faculty: 203 (81 full-time, 122 part-time). Full-time: 1,829 students, 58% women, 42% men. Part-time: 3,006 students, 60% women, 40% men. Students come from 21 states and territories, 5 other countries, 3% from out-of-state. 1% American Indian or Alaska Native, non-Hispanic/Latino; 17% Hispanic/Latino; 11% Black or African American, non-Hispanic/Latino; 1% Asian, non-Hispanic/Latino; 0.2% Native Hawaiian or other Pacific Islander, non-Hispanic/Latino; 0.2% international. 21% 25 or older, 6% live on campus, 3% transferred in. Core. Calendar: semesters. Academic remediation for entering students, services for LD students, advanced placement, distance learning, double major, summer session for credit, part-time degree program, adult/continuing education programs, co-op programs.

Entrance Requirements: Open admission except for allied health programs. Options: electronic application, early admission, international baccalaureate accepted. Required: high school transcript. Entrance: noncompetitive. Application deadlines: rolling, rolling for nonresidents. Notification: continuous, continuous for nonresidents. Transfer credits accepted: Yes.

Costs Per Year: Application fee: $0. Area resident tuition: $1650 full-time, $55 per credit hour part-time. State resident tuition: $3150 full-time, $105 per credit hour part-time. Nonresident tuition: $4650 full-time, $155 per credit hour part-time. Mandatory fees: $750 full-time. Full-time tuition and fees vary according to class time, course level, course load, degree level, location, program, and student level. Part-time tuition varies according to class time, course level, course load, degree level, location, program, and student level. College room and board: $5000. Room and board charges vary according to board plan and housing facility.

Collegiate Environment: Orientation program. Drama-theater group, choral group, student-run newspaper. Most popular organizations: Student Government Organization, Blends Club (for all ethic groups). Major annual events: Homecoming, Year-End Cookout, Weekly Activities. Campus security: 24-hour emergency response devices and patrols, late night transport-escort service, controlled dormitory access. Mike Rheudasil Learning Center. Operations spending for the previous fiscal year: $336,268. 82 computers available on campus for general student use. A campuswide network can be accessed. Students can access the following: online class registration. Staffed computer lab on campus provides training in use of computers, software, and the Internet.

Community Environment: Population 26,500, Paris, a farming and industrial center, has a modern attractiveness which is the result of planned reconstruction following a fire that swept the town in 1916. Today the local industries produce furniture, light bulb parts, clothing, and food items. Located in the heart of Red River Valley, the area has a mean annual temperature of 63.9 degrees. There are four rail lines, two bus lines, five main highways, and an airport approximately seven miles away to serve the community. A public library, theatres, two hospitals, and civic and fraternal organizations are active in the city. Local recreation includes the parks, bowling, golf, and nearby Pat Mayse Lake providing boating, swimming, and fishing.

■ PAUL QUINN COLLEGE

3837 Simpson-Stuart Rd.
Dallas, TX 75241-4331
Tel: (214)376-1000; Free: 877-346-1063
Fax: (214)302-3559
Web Site: www.pqc.edu

Description: Independent African Methodist Episcopal, 4-year, coed. Awards bachelor's degrees. Founded 1872. Setting: 132-acre suburban campus. Endowment: $5.3 million. Educational spending for the previous fiscal year: $12,400 per student. Total enrollment: 243. Faculty: 17 (10 full-time, 7 part-time). Student-undergrad faculty ratio is 11:1. 632 applied, 99% were admitted. 10% from top 10% of their high school class, 20% from top quarter, 39% from top half. 7 student government officers. Full-time: 216 students, 53% women, 47% men. Part-time: 27 students, 67% women, 33% men. Students come from 19 states and territories, 29% from out-of-state. 0.4% American Indian or Alaska Native, non-Hispanic/Latino; 11% Hispanic/

Latino; 87% Black or African American, non-Hispanic/Latino. 21% 25 or older, 39% live on campus, 17% transferred in. Retention: 57% of full-time freshmen returned the following year. Academic areas with the most degrees conferred: business/marketing; homeland security, law enforcement, firefighting, and protective services; education. Core. Calendar: semesters. Academic remediation for entering students, services for LD students, honors program, independent study, summer session for credit, part-time degree program, external degree program, adult/continuing education programs, co-op programs and internships. Off campus study.

Entrance Requirements: Option: electronic application. Required: essay, high school transcript, minimum 2.5 high school GPA, recommendations, interview, meningitis vaccination, SAT or ACT. Entrance: moderately difficult. Application deadline: 6/1. Notification: continuous, continuous for nonresidents. SAT Reasoning Test deadline: 6/1. SAT Subject Test deadline: 6/1. Transfer credits accepted: Yes.

Collegiate Environment: Orientation program. Drama-theater group, choral group, marching band. Social organizations: 5 open to all; national fraternities, national sororities, local fraternities, local sororities; 43% of eligible men and 48% of eligible women are members. Most popular organizations: Student Ambassadors, NAACP, Student Government Association, intramurals, Honda Campus All Star Challenge (academic quiz bowl). Major annual events: Homecoming, Spring Fest, intramural sports. Student services: health clinic, personal-psychological counseling. Campus security: 24-hour patrols. Zale Library plus 1 other. Operations spending for the previous fiscal year: $450,000. 50 computers available on campus for general student use. A campuswide network can be accessed from student residence rooms. Students can access the following: online class registration. Staffed computer lab on campus provides training in use of computers, software, and the Internet.

Community Environment: See University of Texas at Dallas.

■ PIMA MEDICAL INSTITUTE (EL PASO)

6926 Gateway Blvd. E
El Paso, TX 79915
Web Site: www.pmi.edu

Description: Proprietary, 2-year, coed.

■ PIMA MEDICAL INSTITUTE (HOUSTON)

10201 Katy Fwy.
Houston, TX 77024
Tel: (712)778-0778; Free: 800-477-PIMA
E-mail: cluebke@pmi.edu
Web Site: www.pmi.edu

Description: Proprietary, 2-year, coed. Awards certificates, transfer associate, and terminal associate degrees. Setting: urban campus. Core. Distance learning, co-op programs and internships.

Entrance Requirements: Required: high school transcript, interview, Wonderlic Scholastic Level Exam (SLE).

Collegiate Environment: Orientation program.

■ PRAIRIE VIEW A&M UNIVERSITY

700 University Dr.
Prairie View, TX 77446
Tel: (936)261-3311
E-mail: admissions@pvamu.edu
Web Site: www.pvamu.edu

Description: State-supported, university, coed. Part of Texas A&M University System. Awards bachelor's, master's, and doctoral degrees and post-master's certificates. Founded 1878. Setting: 1,502-acre small town campus with easy access to Houston. Endowment: $80.9 million. Research spending for the previous fiscal year: $16.8 million. Educational spending for the previous fiscal year: $5239 per student. Total enrollment: 9,516. Faculty: 506 (434 full-time, 72 part-time). Student-undergrad faculty ratio is 18:1. 7,158 applied, 74% were admitted. 6% from top 10% of their high school class, 25% from top quarter, 65% from top half. Full-time: 7,953 students, 64% women, 36% men. Part-time: 578 students, 57% women, 43% men. Students come from 40 states and territories, 26 other countries, 8% from out-of-state. 0.2% American Indian or Alaska Native, non-Hispanic/Latino; 9% Hispanic/Latino; 84% Black or African American, non-Hispanic/Latino; 2% Asian, non-Hispanic/Latino; 0.1% Native Hawaiian or other Pacific Islander, non-Hispanic/Latino; 1% international. 8% 25 or older, 45% live on campus, 6% transferred in. Retention: 74% of full-time freshmen returned the following year. Academic areas with the most degrees conferred: engineering; health professions and related sciences; business/marketing.

Core. Calendar: semesters. Academic remediation for entering students, services for LD students, advanced placement, accelerated degree program, honors program, independent study, distance learning, double major, summer session for credit, part-time degree program, co-op programs and internships, graduate courses open to undergrads. Off campus study. Study abroad program. ROTC: Army, Naval, Air Force (c).

Entrance Requirements: Options: electronic application, early admission, deferred admission, international baccalaureate accepted. Required: high school transcript, minimum 2.75 high school GPA, SAT or ACT. Entrance: moderately difficult. Notification: 8/15. SAT Reasoning Test deadline: 8/1. Transfer credits accepted: Yes.

Costs Per Year: Application fee: $40. One-time mandatory fee: $40. State resident tuition: $7043 full-time. Nonresident tuition: $21,912 full-time. Mandatory fees: $3743 full-time. College room and board: $8859. College room only: $5890. Tuition guaranteed not to increase for student's term of enrollment.

Collegiate Environment: Orientation program. Drama-theater group, choral group, marching band, student-run newspaper, radio station. Social organizations: 175 open to all; national fraternities, national sororities, local fraternities, local sororities; 8% of eligible men and 4% of eligible women are members. Most popular organizations: Student Government Association, Campus Activities Board, National Association for the Advancement of Colored People, National Society of Black Engineers, Peer Advisors to Leadership Students. Major annual events: Weeks of Welcome, Homecoming, Spring Fest. Student services: health clinic, personal-psychological counseling, women's center. Campus security: 24-hour emergency response devices and patrols, late night transport-escort service, controlled dormitory access. 4,270 college housing spaces available; 4,255 were occupied in 2018-19. Freshmen given priority for college housing. Options: men-only, women-only housing available. John B. Coleman Library plus 3 others. Books: 232,516 (physical), 344,581 (digital/electronic); Serial titles: 199 (physical); Databases: 23. Weekly public service hours: 97; students can reserve study rooms. Operations spending for the previous fiscal year: $2.7 million. 3,500 computers available on campus for general student use. A campuswide network can be accessed from student residence rooms and from off campus. Students can access the following: online class registration. Staffed computer lab on campus provides training in use of computers, software, and the Internet.

■ QUEST COLLEGE

5430 Fredericksburg Rd.
Ste. 310
San Antonio, TX 78229
Tel: (210)366-2701
Web Site: www.questcollege.edu

Description: Proprietary, 2-year, coed. Awards certificates, transfer associate, and terminal associate degrees.

■ RANGER COLLEGE

1100 College Cir.
Ranger, TX 76470
Tel: (254)647-3234
Web Site: www.rangercollege.edu

Description: State-related, 2-year, coed. Awards transfer associate and terminal associate degrees. Founded 1926. Setting: 100-acre rural campus with easy access to Dallas-Fort Worth. Total enrollment: 843. Faculty: 51 (28 full-time, 23 part-time). 15% from top 10% of their high school class, 75% from top half. Students come from 7 states and territories, 4 other countries. 45% live on campus. Core. Calendar: semesters. Academic remediation for entering students, advanced placement, self-designed majors, freshman honors college, honors program, summer session for credit, part-time degree program, adult/continuing education programs.

Entrance Requirements: Open admission. Option: early admission. Entrance: noncompetitive. Application deadline: rolling. Notification: continuous.

Collegiate Environment: Choral group, marching band. Student services: health clinic, personal-psychological counseling. Campus security: controlled dormitory access. Golemon Library. 42 computers available on campus for general student use. Staffed computer lab on campus.

Community Environment: Population 2,535. Ranger's name was derived from a camp of Texas Rangers, organized near here to protect settlers from marauding Indians. In 1917, oil was discovered and the community expanded. Today, there are several churches representing the major denominations. The community is reached by railroad and interstate highway. Local recreation includes fishing, swimming, boating, water skiing, a municipally owned swimming pool, hunting for deer, duck, dove, squirrel, and rabbit. Part-time employment is limited.

■ REMINGTON COLLEGE-DALLAS CAMPUS
1800 Eastgate Dr.
Garland, TX 75041
Tel: (972)686-7878; Free: 800-323-8122
Fax: (972)686-5116
Web Site: www.remingtoncollege.edu
Description: Independent, 2-year, coed. Awards terminal associate degrees. Founded 1987.

■ REMINGTON COLLEGE-FORT WORTH CAMPUS
300 E Loop 820
Fort Worth, TX 76112
Tel: (817)451-0017; Free: 800-323-8122
Fax: (817)496-1257
Web Site: www.remingtoncollege.edu
Description: Independent, 2-year, coed. Awards terminal associate degrees.

■ REMINGTON COLLEGE-HOUSTON SOUTHEAST CAMPUS
20985 Gulf Fwy.
Webster, TX 77598
Tel: (713)581-9000; Free: 800-323-8122
Web Site: www.remingtoncollege.edu
Description: Independent, 2-year, coed. Awards terminal associate degrees.

■ REMINGTON COLLEGE-NORTH HOUSTON CAMPUS
11310 Greens Crossing Blvd.
Ste. 300
Houston, TX 77067
Tel: (832)699-2221; Free: 800-323-8122
Web Site: www.remingtoncollege.edu
Description: Independent, 2-year, coed. Awards transfer associate and terminal associate degrees.

■ RICE UNIVERSITY
6100 Main St.
Houston, TX 77251-1892
Tel: (713)348-0000
Fax: (713)348-5323
Web Site: www.rice.edu
Description: Independent, university, coed. Awards bachelor's, master's, and doctoral degrees. Founded 1912. Setting: 300-acre urban campus with easy access to Houston. Endowment: $6.3 billion. Research spending for the previous fiscal year: $125 million. Educational spending for the previous fiscal year: $47,520 per student. Total enrollment: 7,124. Faculty: 879 (683 full-time, 196 part-time). Student-undergrad faculty ratio is 6:1. 20,923 applied, 11% were admitted. 87% from top 10% of their high school class, 96% from top quarter, 99% from top half. Full-time: 3,899 students, 48% women, 52% men. Part-time: 93 students, 38% women, 62% men. Students come from 53 states and territories, 55 other countries, 53% from out-of-state. 0.2% American Indian or Alaska Native, non-Hispanic/Latino; 15% Hispanic/Latino; 7% Black or African American, non-Hispanic/Latino; 26% Asian, non-Hispanic/Latino; 0.2% Native Hawaiian or other Pacific Islander, non-Hispanic/Latino; 12% international. 71% live on campus, 1% transferred in. Retention: 97% of full-time freshmen returned the following year. Academic areas with the most degrees conferred: engineering; social sciences; parks and recreation. Core. Calendar: semesters. ESL program, services for LD students, advanced placement, accelerated degree program, self-designed majors, honors program, independent study, double major, summer session for credit, internships, graduate courses open to undergrads. Off campus study. Study abroad program. ROTC: Army (c), Naval, Air Force (c).
Entrance Requirements: Options: electronic application, early decision, deferred admission, international baccalaureate accepted. Required: essay, high school transcript, 2 recommendations, SAT or ACT. Recommended: interview, SAT Subject Tests. Required for some: portfolio for architecture, audition for music. Entrance: most difficult. Application deadlines: 1/1, 11/1 for early decision. Notification: 4/1, 12/15 for early decision. SAT Reasoning Test deadline: 1/1. SAT Subject Test deadline: 1/1. Transfer credits ac-

cepted: Yes. Applicants placed on waiting list: 3,296. Wait-listed applicants offered admission: 31. Early decision applicants: 1,675. Early decision applicants admitted: 370.
Costs Per Year: Application fee: $75. Comprehensive fee: $63,252 includes full-time tuition ($48,330), mandatory fees ($782), and college room and board ($14,140). College room only: $9700. Part-time tuition: $2014 per credit hour.
Collegiate Environment: Orientation program. Drama-theater group, choral group, marching band, student-run newspaper, radio station. Social organizations: 284 open to all. Most popular organizations: Drama Club, Community service/volunteer program, intramural sports, College government, Marching Owl Band. Major annual events: Annual Bike Relay Race and Parade, Campus-Wide Formals, Homecoming. Student services: health clinic, personal-psychological counseling, women's center. Campus security: 24-hour emergency response devices and patrols, late night transport-escort service, controlled dormitory access. 2,857 college housing spaces available. Freshmen given priority for college housing. Option: coed housing available. Fondren Library. Books: 3 million (physical), 51,950 (digital/electronic); Serial titles: 172,172 (digital/electronic). Operations spending for the previous fiscal year: $29.2 million. 245 computers available on campus for general student use. A campuswide network can be accessed from student residence rooms and from off campus. Students can access the following: online class registration. Staffed computer lab on campus.

■ RICHLAND COLLEGE
12800 Abrams Rd.
Dallas, TX 75243
Tel: (972)238-6100
Fax: (972)238-6957
E-mail: rlcadmissions@dcccd.edu
Web Site: www.richlandcollege.edu
Description: State and locally supported, 2-year, coed. Part of Dallas County Community College District System. Awards certificates, transfer associate, and terminal associate degrees. Founded 1972. Setting: 250-acre suburban campus. Total enrollment: 19,736. Faculty: 665 (165 full-time, 500 part-time). Students come from 24 states and territories, 21 other countries. 34% Hispanic/Latino; 19% Black or African American, non-Hispanic/Latino; 16% Asian, non-Hispanic/Latino. 34% 25 or older. Core. Calendar: semesters. Academic remediation for entering students, ESL program, services for LD students, advanced placement, freshman honors college, honors program, distance learning, summer session for credit, part-time degree program, adult/continuing education programs, co-op programs. Off campus study. Study abroad program.
Entrance Requirements: Open admission. Options: electronic application, international baccalaureate accepted. Required for some: high school transcript. Entrance: noncompetitive. Application deadlines: rolling, rolling for nonresidents. Notification: continuous, continuous for nonresidents. Transfer credits accepted: Yes.
Collegiate Environment: Orientation program. Drama-theater group, choral group, student-run newspaper, radio station. Student services: health clinic, personal-psychological counseling, women's center. Campus security: 24-hour emergency response devices and patrols, late night transport-escort service, emergency call boxes. Richland College Library. 400 computers available on campus for general student use. A campuswide network can be accessed. Students can access the following: online class registration. Staffed computer lab on campus.

■ RIO GRANDE BIBLE INSTITUTE
4300 S US Hwy. 281
Edinburg, TX 78539
Tel: (956)380-8100
Fax: (956)380-8256
Web Site: www.riogrande.edu
Description: Independent Christian, 4-year, coed. Awards bachelor's degrees.
Entrance Requirements: Required: doctrinal statement.

■ ST. EDWARD'S UNIVERSITY
3001 S Congress Ave.
Austin, TX 78704
Tel: (512)448-8400; Free: 800-555-0164
Fax: (512)448-8492
E-mail: seu.admit@stedwards.edu
Web Site: www.stedwards.edu

Description: Independent Roman Catholic, comprehensive, coed. Awards bachelor's and master's degrees. Founded 1885. Setting: 160-acre urban campus with easy access to Austin. Endowment: $94.9 million. Educational spending for the previous fiscal year: $9471 per student. Total enrollment: 4,601. Faculty: 481 (196 full-time, 285 part-time). Student-undergrad faculty ratio is 14:1. 6,046 applied, 74% were admitted. 24% from top 10% of their high school class, 60% from top quarter, 88% from top half. Full-time: 3,610 students, 60% women, 40% men. Part-time: 446 students, 63% women, 37% men. Students come from 49 states and territories, 54 other countries, 14% from out-of-state. 0.4% American Indian or Alaska Native, non-Hispanic/Latino; 41% Hispanic/Latino; 4% Black or African American, non-Hispanic/Latino; 3% Asian, non-Hispanic/Latino; 0.1% Native Hawaiian or other Pacific Islander, non-Hispanic/Latino; 8% international. 7% 25 or older, 37% live on campus, 6% transferred in. Retention: 81% of full-time freshmen returned the following year. Academic areas with the most degrees conferred: business/marketing; communication/journalism; psychology. Core. Calendar: semesters. Academic remediation for entering students, services for LD students, advanced placement, honors program, independent study, double major, summer session for credit, part-time degree program, adult/continuing education programs, internships. Study abroad program. ROTC: Army (c), Air Force (c).

Entrance Requirements: Options: electronic application, deferred admission, international baccalaureate accepted. Required: essay, high school transcript, 1 recommendation, SAT or ACT. Recommended: interview. Entrance: moderately difficult. Application deadline: 5/1. Notification: continuous. SAT Reasoning Test deadline: 5/1. Transfer credits accepted: Yes. Applicants placed on waiting list: 985. Wait-listed applicants offered admission: 137.

Costs Per Year: Application fee: $50. One-time mandatory fee: $250. Tuition: $46,690 full-time, $1555 per credit hour part-time. Mandatory fees: $500 full-time. Full-time tuition and fees vary according to degree level. Part-time tuition varies according to course load and degree level.

Collegiate Environment: Orientation program. Drama-theater group, choral group, student-run newspaper, radio station. Social organizations: 136 open to all. Most popular organizations: American Medical Student Association, Students for Sustainability, Academy of Science, PRIDE, Asian Student Association. Major annual events: The Big Event, Hillfest, Student Homecoming Events. Student services: health clinic, personal-psychological counseling. Campus security: 24-hour emergency response devices and patrols, late night transport-escort service, controlled dormitory access, self-defense education, informal discussions, pamphlets, posters, alcohol awareness meetings, lighted pathways and sidewalks. Munday Library. Books: 71,983 (physical), 273,440 (digital/electronic); Serial titles: 202 (physical), 121,477 (digital/electronic); Databases: 230. Weekly public service hours: 103; students can reserve study rooms. Operations spending for the previous fiscal year: $2 million. 928 computers available on campus for general student use. A campuswide network can be accessed from student residence rooms and from off campus. Students can access the following: online class registration, access to address and biographical data, transcripts, statements of account, online progress reports and degree audit, campus job postings, student timesheets, financial aid information. Staffed computer lab on campus (open 24 hours a day) provides training in use of computers, software, and the Internet.

■ ST. MARY'S UNIVERSITY

1 Camino Santa Maria
San Antonio, TX 78228
Tel: (210)436-3011; Free: 800-367-7868
Fax: (210)431-6742
E-mail: uadm@stmarytx.edu
Web Site: www.stmarytx.edu

Description: Independent Roman Catholic, comprehensive, coed. Awards bachelor's, master's, and doctoral degrees and post-master's certificates. Founded 1852. Setting: 135-acre urban campus with easy access to San Antonio. System endowment: $183 million. Research spending for the previous fiscal year: $692,000. Educational spending for the previous fiscal year: $16,866 per student. Total enrollment: 3,648. Faculty: 404 (220 full-time, 184 part-time). Student-undergrad faculty ratio is 11:1. 5,350 applied, 75% were admitted. 34% from top 10% of their high school class, 58% from top quarter, 83% from top half. Full-time: 2,262 students, 56% women, 44% men. Part-time: 111 students, 40% women, 60% men. Students come from 32 states and territories, 34 other countries, 8% from out-of-state. 0.2% American Indian or Alaska Native, non-Hispanic/Latino; 67% Hispanic/Latino; 3% Black or African American, non-Hispanic/Latino; 2% Asian, non-Hispanic/

Latino; 8% international. 7% 25 or older, 56% live on campus, 4% transferred in. Retention: 75% of full-time freshmen returned the following year. Academic areas with the most degrees conferred: business/marketing; social sciences; biological/life sciences. Core. Calendar: semesters. Academic remediation for entering students, ESL program, services for LD students, advanced placement, honors program, independent study, distance learning, double major, summer session for credit, part-time degree program, adult/continuing education programs, co-op programs and internships, graduate courses open to undergrads. Off campus study at University of the Incarnate Word, Our Lady of the Lake University of San Antonio, Oblate School of Theology, University of Dayton, Chaminade University, University of Notre Dame. Study abroad program. ROTC: Army, Air Force (c).

Entrance Requirements: Options: electronic application, deferred admission, international baccalaureate accepted. Required: essay, high school transcript, minimum 2.5 high school GPA, 1 recommendation, SAT or ACT. Required for some: interview. Entrance: moderately difficult. Application deadline: rolling. Notification: continuous. Transfer credits accepted: Yes.

Costs Per Year: Application fee: $0. Comprehensive fee: $42,860 includes full-time tuition ($31,170), mandatory fees ($970), and college room and board ($10,720). College room only: $6860. Part-time tuition: $970 per credit hour. Part-time mandatory fees: $270 per term.

Collegiate Environment: Orientation program. Drama-theater group, choral group, student-run newspaper. Social organizations: 103 open to all; national fraternities, national sororities, local fraternities; 15% of eligible men and 13% of eligible women are members. Most popular organizations: Alpha Phi Omega (Professional Service Fraternity), Beta Beta Beta Biological Honor Society, Delta Sigma Pi (Professional Business Fraternity), Society of Hispanic Engineers, Pre-Medical Society. Major annual events: Continuing the Heritage, Battle of the Bands, Rattler Fest (concert series). Student services: health clinic, personal-psychological counseling. Campus security: 24-hour emergency response devices and patrols, late night transport-escort service, controlled dormitory access. 1,622 college housing spaces available; 1,312 were occupied in 2018-19. Freshmen given priority for college housing. On-campus residence required in freshman year. Option: coed housing available. Louis J. Blume Library plus 1 other. Books: 207,131 (physical), 479,714 (digital/electronic); Serial titles: 429 (physical), 99,503 (digital/electronic); Databases: 134. Weekly public service hours: 100. Operations spending for the previous fiscal year: $2.9 million. 200 computers available on campus for general student use. Computer purchase/lease plans available. A computer is required for all students. A campuswide network can be accessed from student residence rooms and from off campus. Students can access the following: online class registration. Staffed computer lab on campus provides training in use of computers, software, and the Internet.

■ ST. PHILIP'S COLLEGE

1801 Martin Luther King Dr.
San Antonio, TX 78203-2098
Tel: (210)486-2000
Fax: (210)531-4831
E-mail: amolina@alamo.edu
Web Site: www.alamo.edu/spc

Description: District-supported, 2-year, coed. Part of Alamo Community College District System. Awards certificates, diplomas, transfer associate, and terminal associate degrees. Founded 1898. Setting: 68-acre urban campus with easy access to San Antonio. Educational spending for the previous fiscal year: $5238 per student. Total enrollment: 12,050. Faculty: 398 (212 full-time, 186 part-time). Student-undergrad faculty ratio is 19:1. Full-time: 1,601 students, 55% women, 45% men. Part-time: 10,449 students, 57% women, 43% men. 1% from out-of-state. 0.4% American Indian or Alaska Native, non-Hispanic/Latino; 57% Hispanic/Latino; 9% Black or African American, non-Hispanic/Latino; 2% Asian, non-Hispanic/Latino; 0.1% Native Hawaiian or other Pacific Islander, non-Hispanic/Latino; 0.2% international. 35% 25 or older, 5% transferred in. Core. Calendar: semesters. Academic remediation for entering students, ESL program, services for LD students, advanced placement, honors program, independent study, distance learning, double major, summer session for credit, part-time degree program, adult/continuing education programs, co-op programs and internships. Off campus study. Study abroad program. ROTC: Army (c).

Entrance Requirements: Open admission special requirements for nursing and certain allied health programs. Options: electronic application, early admission. Required: high school transcript. Entrance: noncompetitive. Application deadline: rolling. Notification: continuous. Transfer credits accepted: Yes.

Costs Per Year: Application fee: $0. Area resident tuition: $2580 full-time, $86 per credit hour part-time. State resident tuition: $6060 full-time, $202 per credit hour part-time. Nonresident tuition: $13,590 full-time, $453 per credit hour part-time. Mandatory fees: $140 full-time, $3 per credit hour part-time, $25 per term part-time. Full-time tuition and fees vary according to course load and program. Part-time tuition and fees vary according to course load and program.

Collegiate Environment: Orientation program. Drama-theater group, choral group. Social organizations: 6 open to all. Most popular organizations: Student Government, Future United Latino Leaders of Change, Collegiate 100. Major annual events: Culture Fest, Hispanic Heritage Month, Black History Month. Student services: health clinic. Campus security: 24-hour emergency response devices and patrols, late night transport-escort service. St. Philip's College Library. Books: 63,136 (physical), 56,724 (digital/electronic); Serial titles: 53 (physical), 72,126 (digital/electronic); Databases: 118. Weekly public service hours: 68. 2,974 computers available on campus for general student use. A campuswide network can be accessed from off-campus. Students can access the following: online class registration. Staffed computer lab on campus provides training in use of computers, software, and the Internet.

■ **SAM HOUSTON STATE UNIVERSITY**
Huntsville, TX 77341
Tel: (936)294-1111; Free: 866-232-7528
E-mail: agb003@shsu.edu
Web Site: www.shsu.edu

Description: State-supported, university, coed. Part of Texas State University System. Awards bachelor's, master's, and doctoral degrees. Founded 1879. Setting: small town campus with easy access to Houston. Endowment: $96.5 million. Total enrollment: 20,938. Faculty: 955 (626 full-time, 329 part-time). Student-undergrad faculty ratio is 23:1. 12,365 applied, 75% were admitted. 19% from top 10% of their high school class, 46% from top quarter, 78% from top half. Full-time: 14,808 students, 62% women, 38% men. Part-time: 3,608 students, 60% women, 40% men. 1% from out-of-state. 0.6% American Indian or Alaska Native, non-Hispanic/Latino; 23% Hispanic/Latino; 18% Black or African American, non-Hispanic/Latino; 2% Asian, non-Hispanic/Latino; 0.2% Native Hawaiian or other Pacific Islander, non-Hispanic/Latino; 1% international. 18% 25 or older, 21% live on campus, 14% transferred in. Retention: 77% of full-time freshmen returned the following year. Academic areas with the most degrees conferred: business/marketing; homeland security, law enforcement, firefighting, and protective services; interdisciplinary studies. Core. Calendar: semesters. Academic remediation for entering students, ESL program, services for LD students, advanced placement, honors program, independent study, distance learning, double major, summer session for credit, part-time degree program, internships, graduate courses open to undergrads. Off campus study at American Institute for Foreign Study. Study abroad program. ROTC: Army.

Entrance Requirements: Options: electronic application, early admission, international baccalaureate accepted. Required: high school transcript, SAT or ACT. Entrance: moderately difficult. Application deadline: 8/1. SAT Reasoning Test deadline: 8/1. Transfer credits accepted: Yes.

Costs Per Year: Application fee: $45. State resident tuition: $7020 full-time, $234 per credit hour part-time. Nonresident tuition: $19,470 full-time, $649 per credit hour part-time. Mandatory fees: $3163 full-time. Full-time tuition and fees vary according to course load and location. Part-time tuition varies according to course load and location. College room and board: $9180. College room only: $5240. Room and board charges vary according to board plan and housing facility. Tuition guaranteed not to increase for student's term of enrollment.

Collegiate Environment: Orientation program. Drama-theater group, choral group, marching band, student-run newspaper, radio station. Social organizations: 180 open to all; national fraternities, national sororities, local fraternities. Student services: legal services, health clinic, personal-psychological counseling. Campus security: 24-hour emergency response devices and patrols, student patrols, late night transport-escort service, controlled dormitory access. Newton Gresham Library. Students can reserve study rooms. 1,600 computers available on campus for general student use. A campuswide network can be accessed from student residence rooms and from off campus. Students can access the following: online class registration. Staffed computer lab on campus (open 24 hours a day) provides training in use of computers, software, and the Internet.

Community Environment: Huntsville, population 36,699, is located in the pine belt 70 miles north of Houston. This was the home of General Sam Houston, and local museums commemorate his honor. The average

temperatures are 51.1 degrees in winter and 82.6 degrees in summer. The community has a hospital, various fraternal, civic, and veteran's organizations, and is served by bus and U.S. Highway I-45. A nearby state park offers fishing, boating, swimming, picnicking, and camping. Part-time employment is available.

■ **SAN ANTONIO COLLEGE**
1819 N Main Ave.
San Antonio, TX 78212-3941
Tel: (210)486-0000; Free: 844-202-5266
Fax: (210)733-2200
Web Site: www.alamo.edu/sac

Description: District-supported, 2-year, coed. Part of Alamo Community College District System. Awards certificates, transfer associate, and terminal associate degrees. Founded 1925. Setting: 45-acre urban campus. Total enrollment: 21,800. Faculty: 1,000 (407 full-time, 593 part-time). Student-undergrad faculty ratio is 22:1. Full-time: 8,375 students, 57% women, 43% men. Part-time: 13,425 students, 62% women, 38% men. Students come from 112 other countries, 3% from out-of-state. 36% 25 or older, 8% transferred in. Core. Calendar: semesters. Academic remediation for entering students, ESL program, services for LD students, advanced placement, honors program, independent study, distance learning, summer session for credit, part-time degree program, adult/continuing education programs, co-op programs and internships. ROTC: Army, Air Force (c).

Entrance Requirements: Open admission. Option: early admission. Required: ACT ASSET, THEA, ACCUPLACER. Recommended: high school transcript. Required for some: high school transcript. Entrance: noncompetitive. Application deadline: rolling.

Collegiate Environment: Orientation program. Drama-theater group, choral group, student-run newspaper, radio station. Student services: health clinic, personal-psychological counseling, women's center. Campus security: 24-hour emergency response devices and patrols, late night transport-escort service. San Antonio College Library and Media Services. 1,700 computers available on campus for general student use. A campuswide network can be accessed from off-campus. Students can access the following: online class registration. Staffed computer lab on campus.

Community Environment: Population 1,256,509. Called the cradle of Texas liberty because of its history, San Antonio is the birthplace of the rough riders and the home of the Alamo. San Antonio is a mixture of its early Spanish background and a modern metropolis. Skyscrapers exist alongside 18th-century adobe restorations. There are many historic sites to be seen in the area. The transportation to and within the city is excellent. There are local and transcontinental bus lines. More than 500 churches representing most denominations, many civic and fraternal organizations, hospitals and museums serve the community. San Antonio has a symphony orchestra and an art museum. The annual Fiesta San Jacinto, Everett Colborn World's Championship Rodeo, and Grand Opera Festival are held here. Local recreation includes 56 parks, sunken garden theater, golf courses, polo fields, baseball diamonds, tennis courts, bridle paths, picnic grounds, swimming pools, hunting, fishing, and boating. Part-time employment is available.

■ **SAN JACINTO COLLEGE DISTRICT**
4624 Fairmont Pky.
Pasadena, TX 77504-3323
Tel: (281)998-6150
Web Site: www.sanjac.edu

Description: State and locally supported, 2-year, coed. Awards certificates, diplomas, and transfer associate degrees. Founded 1961. Setting: 483-acre suburban campus with easy access to Houston. Endowment: $7 million. Educational spending for the previous fiscal year: $9378 per student. Total enrollment: 32,137. Faculty: 1,136 (467 full-time, 669 part-time). Student-undergrad faculty ratio is 21:1. 13,410 applied, 57% were admitted. 5% from top 10% of their high school class, 22% from top quarter, 56% from top half. Full-time: 7,348 students, 55% women, 45% men. Part-time: 24,789 students, 59% women, 41% men. Students come from 44 states and territories, 66 other countries, 1% from out-of-state. 0.2% American Indian or Alaska Native, non-Hispanic/Latino; 60% Hispanic/Latino; 9% Black or African American, non-Hispanic/Latino; 5% Asian, non-Hispanic/Latino; 0.1% Native Hawaiian or other Pacific Islander, non-Hispanic/Latino; 1% international. 29% 25 or older, 5% transferred in. Retention: 61% of full-time freshmen returned the following year. Calendar: semesters. Academic remediation for entering students, ESL program, services for LD students, advanced placement, accelerated degree program, self-designed majors, honors program, distance learning, double major, summer session for credit, part-time degree program, adult/continuing education programs, co-op programs. Study abroad program. ROTC: Army (c), Air Force (c).

Entrance Requirements: Open admission Special requirements for health science program. Psychological Services Bureau test and interview required of nursing applicants. SAT or ACT score used for nursing, medical laboratory technology, radiography, and respiratory programs. Options: electronic application, early admission. Required: high school transcript. Recommended: interview for nursing and EMT programs. Required for some: interview. Entrance: noncompetitive. Application deadlines: rolling, rolling for nonresidents. Notification: continuous, continuous for nonresidents. Transfer credits accepted: Yes.

Costs Per Year: Application fee: $0. Area resident tuition: $1548 full-time, $50 per credit hour part-time. State resident tuition: $2628 full-time, $95 per credit hour part-time. Nonresident tuition: $4188 full-time, $160 per credit hour part-time. Mandatory fees: $348 full-time. Full-time tuition and fees vary according to course load. Part-time tuition varies according to course load.

Collegiate Environment: Orientation program. Drama-theater group, choral group, student-run newspaper. Social organizations: 64 open to all; local fraternities, local sororities. Most popular organizations: Phi Theta Kappa honor society, Phi Beta Lambda, Student Government Association, Nurses Association, Men of Honor. Major annual events: Fall Welcome Mixer, Emerging Leaders Series, Discovery Lecture Series. Student services: personal-psychological counseling. Campus security: 24-hour emergency response devices and patrols, late night transport-escort service. College housing not available. Lee Davis Library(Central),Edwin E. Lehr(North-),Parker Williams(South). Books: 363,626 (physical), 15,541 (digital/electronic); Serial titles: 1,234 (physical), 1 (digital/electronic); Databases: 152. Weekly public service hours: 68; students can reserve study rooms. Operations spending for the previous fiscal year: $2.4 million. 655 computers available on campus for general student use. A campuswide network can be accessed from off-campus. Students can access the following: online class registration. Staffed computer lab on campus provides training in use of computers, software, and the Internet.

■ SCHOOL OF AUTOMOTIVE MACHINISTS & TECHNOLOGY
1911 Antoine Dr.
Houston, TX 77055
Tel: (713)683-3817
Fax: (713)683-7077
Web Site: www.samtech.edu
Description: Proprietary, 2-year, coed. Awards certificates, transfer associate, and terminal associate degrees. Founded 1985.

■ SCHREINER UNIVERSITY
2100 Memorial Blvd.
Kerrville, TX 78028-5697
Tel: (830)896-5411; Free: 800-343-4919
Fax: (830)792-7226
E-mail: carandall@schreiner.edu
Web Site: www.schreiner.edu
Description: Independent Presbyterian, comprehensive, coed. Awards associate, bachelor's, and master's degrees. Founded 1923. Setting: 211-acre small town campus with easy access to San Antonio, Austin. Endowment: $69.2 million. Educational spending for the previous fiscal year: $8355 per student. Total enrollment: 1,308. Faculty: 125 (63 full-time, 62 part-time). Student-undergrad faculty ratio is 13:1. 998 applied, 91% were admitted. 20% from top 10% of their high school class, 41% from top quarter, 77% from top half. Full-time: 1,075 students, 55% women, 45% men. Part-time: 162 students, 74% women, 26% men. Students come from 15 states and territories, 14 other countries, 3% from out-of-state. 0.3% American Indian or Alaska Native, non-Hispanic/Latino; 37% Hispanic/Latino; 3% Black or African American, non-Hispanic/Latino; 1% Asian, non-Hispanic/Latino; 0.8% international. 17% 25 or older, 61% live on campus, 5% transferred in. Retention: 69% of full-time freshmen returned the following year. Academic areas with the most degrees conferred: health professions and related sciences; parks and recreation; psychology; biological/life sciences. Core. Calendar: semesters. Academic remediation for entering students, services for LD students, advanced placement, accelerated degree program, self-designed majors, honors program, independent study, distance learning, double major, summer session for credit, part-time degree program, co-op programs and internships, graduate courses open to undergrads. Study abroad program.
Entrance Requirements: Options: electronic application, deferred admission, international baccalaureate accepted. Required: high school transcript,

SAT or ACT. Entrance: moderately difficult. Application deadline: 5/1. Notification: continuous. SAT Reasoning Test deadline: 8/1. SAT Subject Test deadline: 8/1. Transfer credits accepted: Yes.

Costs Per Year: Application fee: $25. Comprehensive fee: $38,468 includes full-time tuition ($25,990), mandatory fees ($1970), and college room and board ($10,508). College room only: $5156. Full-time tuition and fees vary according to course load, location, and program. Room and board charges vary according to board plan and housing facility. Part-time tuition: $1111 per credit hour. Part-time mandatory fees: $1290 per year, $645 per term. Part-time tuition and fees vary according to course load and program.

Collegiate Environment: Orientation program. Drama-theater group, choral group, student-run newspaper. Social organizations: 32 open to all; national fraternities, national sororities. Most popular organizations: Student Senate, Greek Life, Campus Ministry, honor societies, Hall Councils. Major annual events: BINGO Night, Fall Ball, Comedy Nights. Student services: health clinic, personal-psychological counseling. Campus security: 24-hour emergency response devices and patrols, student patrols, late night transport-escort service, controlled dormitory access. W. M. Logan Library. Books: 80,478 (physical); Serial titles: 404 (physical). Weekly public service hours: 30; students can reserve study rooms. 120 computers available on campus for general student use. Computer purchase/lease plans available. A campuswide network can be accessed from student residence rooms and from off campus. Students can access the following: online class registration. Staffed computer lab on campus provides training in use of computers, software, and the Internet.

Community Environment: Population 22,000. In the rugged hill region by the Guadalupe River, Kerrville is a popular summer and winter resort area. The hill country is famous for fishing and hunting. The city is located 65 miles northwest of San Antonio and enjoys moderate climate. The community has churches of major denominations, a hospital, and various civic, fraternal, and veteran's organizations. Local recreation includes theatres, boating, fishing, water skiing, and deer and turkey hunting. Job opportunities are available.

■ SOUTH PLAINS COLLEGE
1401 S College Ave.
Levelland, TX 79336-6595
Tel: (806)894-9611
Fax: (806)897-3167
E-mail: arangel@southplainscollege.edu
Web Site: www.southplainscollege.edu
Description: State and locally supported, 2-year, coed. Awards certificates, transfer associate, and terminal associate degrees. Founded 1958. Setting: 177-acre small town campus. Endowment: $3 million. Educational spending for the previous fiscal year: $1432 per student. Total enrollment: 9,053. Faculty: 454 (271 full-time, 183 part-time). Student-undergrad faculty ratio is 20:1. 1,577 applied, 100% were admitted. 10% from top 10% of their high school class, 32% from top quarter, 60% from top half. 8 valedictorians. Full-time: 4,605 students, 50% women, 50% men. Part-time: 4,448 students, 59% women, 41% men. Students come from 31 states and territories, 28 other countries, 2% from out-of-state. 0.4% American Indian or Alaska Native, non-Hispanic/Latino; 45% Hispanic/Latino; 6% Black or African American, non-Hispanic/Latino; 1% Asian, non-Hispanic/Latino; 0.1% Native Hawaiian or other Pacific Islander, non-Hispanic/Latino; 0.9% international. 24% 25 or older, 10% live on campus, 29% transferred in. Retention: 8% of full-time freshmen returned the following year. Core. Calendar: semesters. Academic remediation for entering students, services for LD students, advanced placement, accelerated degree program, distance learning, double major, summer session for credit, part-time degree program, adult/continuing education programs, internships. Off campus study. Study abroad program. ROTC: Army (c), Air Force (c).
Entrance Requirements: Open admission. Options: electronic application, early admission. Required: high school transcript, proof of meningitis vaccination. Recommended: SAT or ACT. Entrance: noncompetitive. Application deadline: rolling. Notification: continuous. Transfer credits accepted: Yes.
Collegiate Environment: Orientation program. Drama-theater group, choral group, student-run newspaper, radio station. Most popular organizations: Student Government, Phi Theta Kappa, Law Enforcement Association. Major annual events: Welcome Week, Homecoming, Miss Cap Rock Pageant. Student services: health clinic, personal-psychological counseling. Campus security: 24-hour emergency response devices and patrols, controlled dormitory access. South Plains College Library plus 1 other. Weekly public service hours: 57; students can reserve study rooms. 130 computers available on campus for general student use. A campuswide network can be accessed from student residence rooms and from off campus. Students can access

the following: online class registration. Staffed computer lab on campus provides training in use of computers, software, and the Internet.

Community Environment: Levelland, population 12,777, a rural community enjoying a temperate climate. The area is served by bus, an airport, and Routes 114 and 385. The city has a public library, hospital, churches of major denominations, theatres, and active civic, fraternal, and veteran's organizations. Local recreation includes outdoor sports and rodeo. Part-time employment is available.

■ **SOUTH TEXAS COLLEGE**
3201 W Pecan
McAllen, TX 78501
Tel: (956)618-8323; Free: 800-742-7822
Fax: (956)928-4445
E-mail: mshebbar@southtexascollege.edu
Web Site: www.southtexascollege.edu
Description: District-supported, primarily 2-year, coed. Awards certificates, transfer associate, terminal associate, and bachelor's degrees. Founded 1993. Setting: 20-acre suburban campus. Endowment: $222,114. Total enrollment: 19,827. Faculty: 629 (434 full-time, 195 part-time). Student-undergrad faculty ratio is 25:1. 25% from top quarter of their high school class, 34% from top half. Full-time: 7,027 students, 57% women, 43% men. Part-time: 12,800 students, 59% women, 41% men. 27% 25 or older. Retention: 57% of full-time freshmen returned the following year. Calendar: semesters. Academic remediation for entering students, services for LD students, accelerated degree program, summer session for credit, part-time degree program, adult/continuing education programs, co-op programs. Off campus study at University of Texas-Pan American. ROTC: Army (c).
Entrance Requirements: Open admission. Options: early admission, deferred admission. Required: high school transcript. Required for some: THEA. Entrance: noncompetitive. Application deadline: rolling.
Collegiate Environment: Orientation program. Most popular organizations: Beta Epsilon Mu Honor Society, Automotive Technology Club, Child Care and Development Association Club, Heating, Air Conditioning, and Ventilation Club, Writing in Literary Discussion Club. Major annual events: Career Day, Cinco de Mayo, Thanksgiving Food Drive. Student services: personal-psychological counseling. Campus security: 24-hour emergency response devices and patrols, late night transport-escort service. Learning Resources Center. Operations spending for the previous fiscal year: $144,832. 2,550 computers available on campus for general student use. A campuswide network can be accessed from off-campus. Students can access the following: online class registration. Staffed computer lab on campus provides training in use of computers, software, and the Internet.

■ **SOUTH UNIVERSITY**
1220 W Louis Henna Blvd.
Round Rock, TX 78681
Tel: (512)516-8800; Free: 877-659-5706
Fax: (512)516-8680
Web Site: www.southuniversity.edu/austin.aspx
Description: Independent, comprehensive, coed. Awards associate, bachelor's, and master's degrees.

■ **SOUTHERN METHODIST UNIVERSITY**
6425 Boaz Ln.
Dallas, TX 75275
Tel: (214)768-2000; Free: 800-323-0672
E-mail: ugadmission@smu.edu
Web Site: www.smu.edu
Description: Independent, university, coed, affiliated with United Methodist Church. Awards bachelor's, master's, and doctoral degrees and post-master's certificates. Founded 1911. Setting: 234-acre urban campus with easy access to Dallas-Fort Worth. Endowment: $1.5 billion. Total enrollment: 11,789. Faculty: 1,156 (758 full-time, 398 part-time). Student-undergrad faculty ratio is 11:1. 13,128 applied, 49% were admitted. 52% from top 10% of their high school class, 79% from top quarter, 95% from top half. Full-time: 6,240 students, 50% women, 50% men. Part-time: 212 students, 50% women, 50% men. Students come from 47 states and territories, 62 other countries, 55% from out-of-state. 0.3% American Indian or Alaska Native, non-Hispanic/Latino; 11% Hispanic/Latino; 5% Black or African American, non-Hispanic/Latino; 6% Asian, non-Hispanic/Latino; 0.1% Native Hawaiian or other Pacific Islander, non-Hispanic/Latino; 9% international. 3% 25 or older, 54% live on campus, 4% transferred in. Retention: 91% of full-time freshmen returned the following year. Academic areas with the most degrees

conferred: business/marketing; social sciences; communication/journalism. Core. Calendar: semesters. Academic remediation for entering students, ESL program, services for LD students, advanced placement, accelerated degree program, self-designed majors, honors program, independent study, distance learning, double major, summer session for credit, part-time degree program, adult/continuing education programs, co-op programs and internships, graduate courses open to undergrads. Study abroad program. ROTC: Army, Air Force (c).
Entrance Requirements: Options: electronic application, early decision, early action, deferred admission, international baccalaureate accepted. Required: high school transcript, minimum 2 high school GPA, 1 recommendation, statement of good standing from prior institution(s), SAT or ACT. Recommended: essay, minimum 2.7 high school GPA. Required for some: SAT Subject Tests. Entrance: moderately difficult. Application deadlines: 1/15, 11/1 for early decision plan 1, 1/15 for early decision plan 2, 11/1 for early action. Notification: continuous, 12/31 for early decision plan 1, 4/1 for early decision plan 2, 12/31 for early action. SAT Reasoning Test deadline: 3/15. Transfer credits accepted: Yes. Applicants placed on waiting list: 1,423. Wait-listed applicants offered admission: 69. Early decision applicants: 738. Early decision applicants admitted: 266.
Costs Per Year: Application fee: $60. Comprehensive fee: $71,338 includes full-time tuition ($48,365), mandatory fees ($6128), and college room and board ($16,845). Room and board charges vary according to board plan and housing facility. Part-time tuition: $2020 per credit hour. Part-time tuition varies according to course load.
Collegiate Environment: Orientation program. Drama-theater group, choral group, marching band, student-run newspaper, radio station. Social organizations: 180 open to all; national fraternities, national sororities; 28% of eligible men and 35% of eligible women are members. Most popular organizations: Program Council, Student Senate, Student Foundation, Residence Hall Association, SPARC (Students Promoting Awareness, Responsibility, and Citizenship). Major annual events: Homecoming, Sing Song, Mane Event (all-school block party). Student services: health clinic, personal-psychological counseling, women's center. Campus security: 24-hour emergency response devices and patrols, late night transport-escort service, controlled dormitory access. Fondren Library plus 7 others. Books: 3 million (physical), 1.2 million (digital/electronic); Serial titles: 16,580 (physical), 139,891 (digital/electronic); Databases: 667. Weekly public service hours: 150; study areas open 24 hours, 5-7 days a week; students can reserve study rooms. 758 computers available on campus for general student use. A campuswide network can be accessed from student residence rooms and from off campus. Students can access the following: online class registration, online billing/payment processing. Staffed computer lab on campus provides training in use of computers, software, and the Internet.
Community Environment: See University of Texas at Dallas.

■ **SOUTHWEST TEXAS JUNIOR COLLEGE**
2401 Garner Field Rd.
Uvalde, TX 78801-6297
Tel: (830)278-4401
Web Site: www.swtjc.edu
Description: State and locally supported, 2-year, coed. Awards certificates, transfer associate, and terminal associate degrees. Founded 1946. Setting: 97-acre small town campus with easy access to San Antonio. Educational spending for the previous fiscal year: $2722 per student. Students come from 8 states and territories, 3 other countries, 0.01% from out-of-state. 0.8% American Indian or Alaska Native, non-Hispanic/Latino; 85% Hispanic/Latino; 1% Black or African American, non-Hispanic/Latino; 0.2% Asian, non-Hispanic/Latino. 14% 25 or older, 9% live on campus. Core. Calendar: semesters. Academic remediation for entering students, ESL program, advanced placement, distance learning, summer session for credit, part-time degree program, external degree program, adult/continuing education programs.
Entrance Requirements: Open admission. Options: electronic application, early admission, deferred admission. Required: high school transcript. Entrance: noncompetitive. Application deadline: rolling. Notification: continuous. Preference given to local residents. Transfer credits accepted: Yes.
Costs Per Year: State resident tuition: $1830 full-time, $183 per semester hour part-time. Nonresident tuition: $6464 full-time, $606 per semester hour part-time. Mandatory fees: $1146 full-time. College room and board: $6000. College room only: $2960. Room and board charges vary according to board plan.
Collegiate Environment: Orientation program. Drama-theater group,

student-run newspaper. Social organizations: 25 open to all. Most popular organizations: Catholic Students Club, Business Administration Club. Major annual events: Spring Palms Festival, Grillin' with the President. Student services: health clinic, personal-psychological counseling. Campus security: 24-hour patrols, controlled dormitory access. Will C. Miller Memorial Library. 300 computers available on campus for general student use. A campuswide network can be accessed from student residence rooms and from off campus. Students can access the following: online class registration. Staffed computer lab on campus.

Community Environment: Population 16,400. Uvalde is located at the base of the Texas Hill Country 75 miles west of San Antonio and is known for its agriculture production; hunting for deer, wild turkey, quail and doves; and fishing. The climate is moderate. City services include a memorial hospital, public library, community theatre in the historic Grand Opera House, U.S. Vice-President John Nance Garner Memorial Museum, and churches of various denominations. Uvalde is reached by buslines, major highways and a private airport. Dormitories, apartments and rental houses provide student housing. Local recreation includes six screen theater complex, 18-hole golf course, parks, two rivers, private clubs, various community celebrations.

■ **SOUTHWEST UNIVERSITY AT EL PASO**

1414 Geronimo Dr.

El Paso, TX 79925

Tel: (915)778-4001

Web Site: southwestuniversity.edu

Description: Proprietary, 4-year, coed. Awards associate and bachelor's degrees.

■ **SOUTHWESTERN ADVENTIST UNIVERSITY**

100 Hillcrest Dr.

Keene, TX 76059

Tel: (817)645-3921; Free: 800-433-2240

Fax: (817)556-4744

E-mail: rahneeka@swau.edu

Web Site: www.swau.edu

Description: Independent Seventh-day Adventist, comprehensive, coed. Awards associate, bachelor's, and master's degrees. Founded 1894. Setting: 150-acre small town campus with easy access to Dallas-Fort Worth. Endowment: $11.4 million. Educational spending for the previous fiscal year: $824 per student. Total enrollment: 818. Faculty: 81 (49 full-time, 32 part-time). Student-undergrad faculty ratio is 12:1. 1,400 applied, 60% were admitted. 8 class presidents, 2 valedictorians, 25 student government officers. Full-time: 653 students, 58% women, 42% men. Part-time: 146 students, 55% women, 45% men. Students come from 35 states and territories, 18 other countries, 31% from out-of-state. 0.3% American Indian or Alaska Native, non-Hispanic/Latino; 44% Hispanic/Latino; 14% Black or African American, non-Hispanic/Latino; 4% Asian, non-Hispanic/Latino; 2% Native Hawaiian or other Pacific Islander, non-Hispanic/Latino; 8% international. 18% 25 or older, 47% live on campus, 7% transferred in. Retention: 81% of full-time freshmen returned the following year. Academic areas with the most degrees conferred: education; theology and religious vocations; psychology. Core. Calendar: semesters. Academic remediation for entering students, ESL program, services for LD students, advanced placement, accelerated degree program, self-designed majors, honors program, independent study, distance learning, double major, summer session for credit, part-time degree program, external degree program, adult/continuing education programs, internships, graduate courses open to undergrads. Off campus study at Tarleton State University, Andrews University. Study abroad program.

Entrance Requirements: Options: electronic application, early admission, deferred admission. Required: high school transcript, minimum 2.5 high school GPA, SAT or ACT. Required for some: essay, 1 recommendation, interview. Entrance: minimally difficult. Application deadline: 8/1. Notification: continuous. SAT Reasoning Test deadline: 10/1. Transfer credits accepted: Yes.

Costs Per Year: Application fee: $25. Comprehensive fee: $29,164 includes full-time tuition ($20,904), mandatory fees ($660), and college room and board ($7600). College room only: $3800. Full-time tuition and fees vary according to program. Room and board charges vary according to board plan. Part-time tuition: $871 per semester hour. Part-time mandatory fees: $660 per term. Part-time tuition and fees vary according to program.

Collegiate Environment: Orientation program. Drama-theater group, choral group, student-run newspaper, radio station. Social organizations: 10 open to all. Most popular organizations: Student Association, Enactus (to enable

progress through entrepreneurial action), Education/Psychology Club, Theology Club, Nursing Club. Major annual events: Mimosa Memories, Student Appreciation Week, Handshake. Student services: health clinic, personal-psychological counseling. Campus security: 24-hour emergency response devices, student patrols, controlled dormitory access. Chan Shun Centennial Library. Books: 90,431 (physical), 29,515 (digital/electronic); Serial titles: 5,000 (digital/electronic); Databases: 85. Weekly public service hours: 60; students can reserve study rooms. Operations spending for the previous fiscal year: $526,767. 275 computers available on campus for general student use. A campuswide network can be accessed from student residence rooms and from off campus. Students can access the following: online class registration. Staffed computer lab on campus provides training in use of computers, software, and the Internet.

Community Environment: Population 5,952. Keene is a small community in a rural area. The climate is temperate. The city is reached by bus lines and U.S. Route 67. There is a local Seventh Day Adventist Church. A shopping center is located seven miles distant. Part-time employment is available.

■ **SOUTHWESTERN ASSEMBLIES OF GOD UNIVERSITY**

1200 Sycamore St.

Waxahachie, TX 75165-5735

Tel: (972)937-4010; Free: 888-937-7248

E-mail: jmartin@sagu.edu

Web Site: www.sagu.edu

Description: Independent, comprehensive, coed, affiliated with Assemblies of God. Awards associate, bachelor's, and master's degrees. Founded 1927. Setting: 70-acre small town campus with easy access to Dallas-Fort Worth. Endowment: $10.3 million. Educational spending for the previous fiscal year: $7914 per student. Total enrollment: 2,162. Faculty: 148 (73 full-time, 75 part-time). Student-undergrad faculty ratio is 16:1. 515 applied, 97% were admitted. Full-time: 1,492 students, 51% women, 49% men. Part-time: 298 students, 57% women, 43% men. 3% American Indian or Alaska Native, non-Hispanic/Latino; 17% Hispanic/Latino; 13% Black or African American, non-Hispanic/Latino; 0.7% Asian, non-Hispanic/Latino; 0.6% Native Hawaiian or other Pacific Islander, non-Hispanic/Latino; 0.6% international. Retention: 72% of full-time freshmen returned the following year. Core. Calendar: semesters. Academic remediation for entering students, services for LD students, advanced placement, distance learning, double major, summer session for credit, part-time degree program, external degree program, adult/continuing education programs, internships, graduate courses open to undergrads.

Entrance Requirements: Options: electronic application, international baccalaureate accepted. Required: essay, high school transcript, minimum 2 high school GPA, 1 recommendation, SAT or ACT. Recommended: ACT. Entrance: noncompetitive. Application deadline: 8/1. Notification: continuous. SAT Reasoning Test deadline: 8/1. Transfer credits accepted: Yes.

Costs Per Year: Application fee: $35. Comprehensive fee: $28,452 includes full-time tuition ($19,992), mandatory fees ($960), and college room and board ($7500). Full-time tuition and fees vary according to course load, degree level, and location. Room and board charges vary according to board plan, housing facility, and location.

Collegiate Environment: Orientation program. Drama-theater group, choral group, student-run newspaper. Social organizations: 16 open to all. Most popular organizations: Student Congress, Southwestern Missions Association, Street Hope, Gold Jackets, Women in Ministry. Major annual events: All School Fellowship/Battle of the Dorms, Homecoming, Class Night. Student services: health clinic, personal-psychological counseling. Campus security: 24-hour patrols, late night transport-escort service, controlled dormitory access, camera surveillance, 24-hour dispatch monitored fire alarm systems (offsite). P. C. Nelson Memorial Library plus 1 other. Books: 100,582 (physical), 256 (digital/electronic); Serial titles: 414 (physical), 13,284 (digital/electronic); Databases: 70. Weekly public service hours: 90; students can reserve study rooms. Operations spending for the previous fiscal year: $272,930. 80 computers available on campus for general student use. A campuswide network can be accessed from student residence rooms and from off campus. Students can access the following: online class registration. Staffed computer lab on campus provides training in use of computers and the Internet.

Community Environment: Population 25,500, Waxahachie is the capital of Ellis County. It is located 28 miles south of Dallas and 40 miles southeast of Fort Worth. The area can be reached by rail, bus, and major highways. Community facilities include a medical center, a hospital and health clinic, many churches of various denominations, and several civic and fraternal organizations. Local recreation includes baseball, bowling, golf, hunting, boating, and fishing. Apartments and part-time employment are available.

■ SOUTHWESTERN CHRISTIAN COLLEGE

Box 10
200 Bowser St.
Terrell, TX 75160
Tel: (972)524-3341
Web Site: www.swcc.edu

Description: Independent, 4-year, coed, affiliated with Church of Christ. Awards associate and bachelor's degrees. Founded 1949. Setting: 25-acre small town campus with easy access to Dallas-Fort Worth. 80% live on campus. Core. Calendar: semesters. Academic remediation for entering students, part-time degree program.

Entrance Requirements: Open admission. Options: early admission, deferred admission. Required: high school transcript, 2 recommendations, immunization record. Entrance: noncompetitive. Application deadline: 8/1.

Collegiate Environment: Orientation program. Choral group, student-run newspaper. Social organizations: national fraternities, national sororities, local fraternities, local sororities. Campus security: 24-hour patrols. Hogan Stewart Learning Center.

Community Environment: Terrell is a suburban community enjoying dry, temperate climate. The city is reached by bus, railroad, and major highways. Community services include many churches representing most major denominations, hospitals, a public library, YMCA, and YWCA. There are theatres, parks, and nearby lakes for water sports. Part-time employment opportunities are limited. Various civic, fraternal and veteran's organizations are active in Terrell. Small city and all necessary items are within walking distance.

■ SOUTHWESTERN UNIVERSITY

1001 E University Ave.
Georgetown, TX 78626
Tel: (512)863-6511; Free: 800-252-3166
Fax: (512)863-6511
E-mail: admission@southwestern.edu
Web Site: www.southwestern.edu

Description: Independent Methodist, 4-year, coed. Awards bachelor's degrees. Founded 1840. Setting: 700-acre suburban campus with easy access to Austin. Endowment: $281.5 million. Research spending for the previous fiscal year: $227,114. Educational spending for the previous fiscal year: $12,509 per student. Total enrollment: 1,430. Faculty: 144 (110 full-time, 34 part-time). Student-undergrad faculty ratio is 11:1. 4,551 applied, 45% were admitted. 34% from top 10% of their high school class, 70% from top quarter, 94% from top half. 2 National Merit Scholars, 7 valedictorians. Full-time: 1,416 students, 55% women, 45% men. Part-time: 14 students, 57% women, 43% men. Students come from 34 states and territories, 12 other countries, 9% from out-of-state. 0.2% American Indian or Alaska Native, non-Hispanic/Latino; 24% Hispanic/Latino; 5% Black or African American, non-Hispanic/Latino; 3% Asian, non-Hispanic/Latino; 1% international. 3% 25 or older, 78% live on campus, 3% transferred in. Retention: 81% of full-time freshmen returned the following year. Academic areas with the most degrees conferred: business/marketing; social sciences; biological/life sciences. Core. Calendar: semesters. Services for LD students, advanced placement, self-designed majors, honors program, independent study, double major, summer session for credit, internships. Off campus study at GLCA Arts Program in New York; Southwestern University students also participate in the Washington D.C. semesters but grades are assigned by SU faculty rather than another institution. Study abroad program. ROTC: Air Force (c).

Entrance Requirements: Options: electronic application, early admission, early decision, early action, deferred admission, international baccalaureate accepted. Required: essay, high school transcript, 1 recommendation, counselor recommendation, SAT or ACT. Recommended: interview. Entrance: very difficult. Application deadlines: 2/1, 2/1 for nonresidents, 11/1 for early decision, 12/1 for early action. Notification: 4/1, 4/1 for nonresidents, 12/1 for early decision, 3/1 for early action. SAT Reasoning Test deadline: 6/1. Transfer credits accepted: Yes. Applicants placed on waiting list: 138. Wait-listed applicants offered admission: 3. Early decision applicants: 107. Early decision applicants admitted: 33. Early action applicants: 1,703. Early action applicants admitted: 1,081.

Costs Per Year: Application fee: $0. Comprehensive fee: $55,880 includes full-time tuition ($43,560) and college room and board ($12,320). College room only: $6670. Part-time tuition: $1815 per credit hour.

Collegiate Environment: Orientation program. Drama-theater group, choral group, student-run newspaper, radio station. Social organizations: 97 open to all; national fraternities, national sororities, local sororities, Sigma Phi Lamba/Kappa Delta Chi; 35% of eligible men and 31% of eligible women are members. Most popular organizations: Students for Environmental Activism and Knowledge (SEAK), Alpha Phi Omega, Women's Panhellenic, Men's IFC, Coalition for Diversity and Social Justice. Major annual events: Late Night Breakfast, Research and Creative Works Symposium, Shilling Lecture. Student services: health clinic, personal-psychological counseling, women's center. Campus security: 24-hour emergency response devices and patrols, late night transport-escort service, controlled dormitory access. 1,004 college housing spaces available; 1,001 were occupied in 2018-19. Freshmen guaranteed college housing. On-campus residence required through sophomore year. Options: coed, men-only, women-only housing available. A. Frank Smith, Jr. Library Center. Books: 267,609 (physical), 566,353 (digital/electronic); Serial titles: 245 (physical), 73,126 (digital/electronic); Databases: 156. Weekly public service hours: 90; study areas open 24 hours, 5-7 days a week. Operations spending for the previous fiscal year: $1.9 million. 410 computers available on campus for general student use. A campuswide network can be accessed from student residence rooms and from off campus. Students can access the following: online class registration, transcripts. Staffed computer lab on campus (open 24 hours a day) provides training in use of computers, software, and the Internet.

Community Environment: Population 39,000, Georgetown enjoys the advantage of being a small town yet is only 26 miles from the state capital, Austin. The climate is moderate, both in winter and summer. The community is served by rail, bus lines, Austin-Bergstrom International Airport, and Interstate Highway 35 and has a modern hospital and clinic. Located in the heart of the highland lakes region, recreational opportunities include fishing, boating, and water sports. Part-time employment is available.

■ STEPHEN F. AUSTIN STATE UNIVERSITY

1936 N St.
Nacogdoches, TX 75962
Tel: (936)468-2011; Free: 800-731-2902
Fax: (936)468-3849
E-mail: admissions@sfasu.edu
Web Site: www.sfasu.edu

Description: State-supported, comprehensive, coed. Awards bachelor's, master's, and doctoral degrees. Founded 1923. Setting: 419-acre small town campus. Endowment: $81.7 million. Research spending for the previous fiscal year: $3.7 million. Total enrollment: 12,614. Faculty: 718 (512 full-time, 206 part-time). Student-undergrad faculty ratio is 19:1. 11,081 applied, 65% were admitted. 13% from top 10% of their high school class, 43% from top quarter, 77% from top half. Full-time: 9,567 students, 63% women, 37% men. Part-time: 1,418 students, 60% women, 40% men. Students come from 37 states and territories, 40 other countries, 2% from out-of-state. 0.5% American Indian or Alaska Native, non-Hispanic/Latino; 19% Hispanic/Latino; 17% Black or African American, non-Hispanic/Latino; 1% Asian, non-Hispanic/Latino; 0.1% Native Hawaiian or other Pacific Islander, non-Hispanic/Latino; 0.6% international. 10% 25 or older, 44% live on campus, 8% transferred in. Retention: 72% of full-time freshmen returned the following year. Academic areas with the most degrees conferred: business/marketing; health professions and related sciences; interdisciplinary studies. Core. Calendar: semesters. Academic remediation for entering students, services for LD students, advanced placement, accelerated degree program, self-designed majors, freshman honors college, honors program, independent study, distance learning, double major, summer session for credit, part-time degree program, adult/continuing education programs, co-op programs and internships, graduate courses open to undergrads. Off campus study. Study abroad program. ROTC: Army.

Entrance Requirements: Options: electronic application, international baccalaureate accepted. Required: high school transcript, SAT or ACT. Entrance: moderately difficult. Application deadline: rolling. Notification: continuous. Transfer credits accepted: Yes.

Costs Per Year: Application fee: $45. State resident tuition: $7260 full-time, $242 per credit hour part-time. Nonresident tuition: $19,710 full-time, $657 per credit hour part-time. Mandatory fees: $182.50 per credit hour part-time. Full-time tuition varies according to course load, degree level, and location. Part-time tuition and fees vary according to course load, degree level, and location. College room and board: $8964. Room and board charges vary according to board plan and housing facility. Tuition guaranteed not to increase for student's term of enrollment.

Collegiate Environment: Orientation program. Drama-theater group, choral

group, marching band, student-run newspaper, radio station. Social organizations: 212 open to all; national fraternities, national sororities, local fraternities; 15% of eligible men and 10% of eligible women are members. Most popular organizations: Residence Hall Association, Baptist Student Ministries, Greek Life, Student Activities Association, Student Government Association. Major annual events: Homecoming, Spring Fest, Jacks Back Welcome Week. Student services: health clinic, personal-psychological counseling. Campus security: 24-hour emergency response devices and patrols, student patrols, late night transport-escort service, controlled dormitory access. Ralph W. Steen Library. Books: 685,436 (physical), 341,357 (digital/electronic); Serial titles: 5,582 (physical), 119,163 (digital/electronic); Databases: 265. Weekly public service hours: 99; students can reserve study rooms. Operations spending for the previous fiscal year: $4.7 million. 1,000 computers available on campus for general student use. A campuswide network can be accessed from student residence rooms and from off campus. Students can access the following: online class registration. Staffed computer lab on campus provides training in use of computers, software, and the Internet.

Community Environment: Population 30,800. Nacogdoches is one of the oldest settlements in Texas. This is a rural community enjoying temperate climate. There are more than 30 churches representing 15 different denominations, a library, museums, two hospitals, garden clubs, and major civic and fraternal organizations within the community. Nacogdoches is reached by railroad, bus lines, and Highways 59, 259, 7 and 21. Part-time employment is available. Local recreation includes movie theatres, several lakes for boating, swimming, and other water sports, and national forests for hiking, picnicking and hunting.

■ **STRAYER UNIVERSITY-CEDAR HILL CAMPUS**
610 Uptown Blvd.
Ste. 3500
Cedar Hill, TX 75104
Tel: (469)454-3400; Free: 888-311-0355
Web Site: www.strayer.edu
Description: Proprietary, comprehensive, coed. Awards associate, bachelor's, and master's degrees.

■ **STRAYER UNIVERSITY-NORTH AUSTIN CAMPUS**
8501 N Mopac Expy.
Ste. 100
Austin, TX 78759
Tel: (512)568-3300; Free: 888-311-0355
Web Site: www.strayer.edu
Description: Proprietary, comprehensive, coed. Awards associate, bachelor's, and master's degrees.

■ **STRAYER UNIVERSITY-NORTH DALLAS CAMPUS**
2711 LBJ Fwy.
Ste. 450
Farmers Branch, TX 75234-7315
Tel: (972)773-8300
Web Site: www.strayer.edu
Description: Proprietary, comprehensive, coed.

■ **STRAYER UNIVERSITY-NORTHWEST HOUSTON CAMPUS**
10343 Sam Houston Park Dr.
Ste. 110
Houston, TX 77064
Tel: (281)949-1800; Free: 888-311-0355
Web Site: www.strayer.edu
Description: Proprietary, comprehensive, coed. Awards associate, bachelor's, and master's degrees.

■ **STRAYER UNIVERSITY-SAN ANTONIO CAMPUS**
40 NE Loop 410
Ste. 500
San Antonio, TX 78216
Tel: (210)202-3700
Web Site: www.strayer.edu
Description: Proprietary, comprehensive, coed.

■ **STRAYER UNIVERSITY-STAFFORD CAMPUS**
12603 SW Fwy.
Ste. 400

Stafford, TX 77477
Tel: (281)201-3800
Web Site: www.strayer.edu
Description: Proprietary, comprehensive, coed.

■ **SUL ROSS STATE UNIVERSITY**
PO Box C - 114
Alpine, TX 79832
Tel: (432)837-8011; Free: 888-722-7778
Fax: (432)837-8334
Web Site: www.sulross.edu
Description: State-supported, comprehensive, coed. Part of Texas State University System. Awards bachelor's and master's degrees. Founded 1920. Setting: 640-acre rural campus. Total enrollment: 1,973. Faculty: 148 (93 fulltime, 55 part-time). Student-undergrad faculty ratio is 13:1. 1,143 applied, 80% were admitted. 3% from top 10% of their high school class, 20% from top quarter, 56% from top half. Full-time: 1,080 students, 46% women, 54% men. Part-time: 279 students, 53% women, 47% men. 2% from out-of-state. 0.4% American Indian or Alaska Native, non-Hispanic/Latino; 10% Hispanic/Latino; 52% Black or African American, non-Hispanic/Latino; 0.6% Asian, non-Hispanic/Latino; 0.1% Native Hawaiian or other Pacific Islander, non-Hispanic/Latino; 0.4% international. 85% 25 or older, 48% live on campus, 9% transferred in. Retention: 60% of full-time freshmen returned the following year. Academic areas with the most degrees conferred: biological/life sciences; parks and recreation; homeland security, law enforcement, firefighting, and protective services. Core. Calendar: semesters. Self-designed majors, honors program, independent study, distance learning, double major, summer session for credit, part-time degree program, internships, graduate courses open to undergrads. Study abroad program.
Entrance Requirements: Option: deferred admission. Required: high school transcript, SAT or ACT. Recommended: interview. Entrance: noncompetitive. Application deadline: rolling. Notification: continuous.
Costs Per Year: State resident tuition: $6,140 full-time, $204.67 per credit hour part-time. Nonresident tuition: $18,530 full-time, $617.67 per credit hour part-time. Mandatory fees: $2,169 full-time, $71.02 per credit hour part-time, $136 per term part-time. Full-time tuition and fees vary according to location. Part-time tuition and fees vary according to location. College room and board: $6000. College room only: $2750. Room and board charges vary according to board plan and housing facility.
Collegiate Environment: Orientation program. Drama-theater group, marching band, student-run newspaper. Major annual events: Sully Showcase, Micro Film Festival. Student services: health clinic, personal-psychological counseling. Campus security: 24-hour patrols, late night transport-escort service. Bryan Wildenthal Memorial Library.
Community Environment: Population 6,065, Alpine, located between El Paso on the west and Del Rio on the east, is known for its Highland Hereford breed of cattle. The city is also the gateway to travel to Big Bend National Park, Fort Davis National Historic Sites, Davis Mountains State Park, and McDonald Observatory. The climate in the area is mild. Railroad, commuter airline, and three bus lines serve the community. Local recreation includes baseball, hunting, golf, fishing, a theatre, and Summer Theatre during July and August. There is a hospital, library, and churches of various denominations within the city. Part-time employment is available.

■ **TARLETON STATE UNIVERSITY**
Box T-0001
Tarleton Station
Stephenville, TX 76402
Tel: (254)968-9000; Free: 800-687-8236
Fax: (254)968-9920
E-mail: uadm@tarleton.edu
Web Site: www.tarleton.edu
Description: State-supported, comprehensive, coed. Part of Texas A&M University System. Awards associate, bachelor's, master's, and doctoral degrees. Founded 1899. Setting: 175-acre small town campus with easy access to Fort Worth. Endowment: $29.8 million. Research spending for the previous fiscal year: $9.1 million. Educational spending for the previous fiscal year: $6125 per student. Total enrollment: 13,019. Faculty: 766 (393 fulltime, 373 part-time). Student-undergrad faculty ratio is 17:1. 7,158 applied, 74% were admitted. 10% from top 10% of their high school class, 29% from top quarter, 88% from top half. Full-time: 8,428 students, 61% women, 39% men. Part-time: 2,860 students, 60% women, 40% men. 2% from out-of-state. 0.5% American Indian or Alaska Native, non-Hispanic/Latino; 20% Hispanic/Latino; 8% Black or African American, non-Hispanic/Latino; 1%

Asian, non-Hispanic/Latino; 0.2% Native Hawaiian or other Pacific Islander, non-Hispanic/Latino; 0.3% international. 22% 25 or older, 25% live on campus, 13% transferred in. Retention: 67% of full-time freshmen returned the following year. Academic areas with the most degrees conferred: business/marketing; interdisciplinary studies; agriculture. Core. Calendar: semesters. Academic remediation for entering students, services for LD students, advanced placement, accelerated degree program, freshman honors college, honors program, independent study, distance learning, double major, summer session for credit, part-time degree program, adult/continuing education programs, co-op programs and internships, graduate courses open to undergrads. Off campus study. Study abroad program. ROTC: Army, Air Force (c).

Entrance Requirements: Options: electronic application, early action, international baccalaureate accepted. Required: high school transcript, SAT or ACT. Entrance: moderately difficult. Application deadlines: 8/20, 3/1 for early action. SAT Reasoning Test deadline: 8/20. Transfer credits accepted: Yes.

Costs Per Year: Application fee: $45. State resident tuition: $5025 full-time, $167 per credit hour part-time. Nonresident tuition: $17,475 full-time, $583 per credit hour part-time. Mandatory fees: $4066 full-time. Full-time tuition and fees vary according to course load, degree level, program, and student level. Part-time tuition varies according to course load, degree level, program, and student level. College room and board: $9872. College room only: $6220. Room and board charges vary according to board plan and housing facility. Tuition guaranteed not to increase for student's term of enrollment.

Collegiate Environment: Orientation program. Drama-theater group, choral group, marching band, student-run newspaper, radio station. Social organizations: 120 open to all; national fraternities, national sororities; 11% of eligible men and 18% of eligible women are members. Most popular organizations: Student Government Association, Student Programming Association, Kappa Delta Rho, Delta Zeta, Chi Alpha. Major annual events: Homecoming, Halloween Carnival, Vegas Night. Student services: legal services, health clinic, personal-psychological counseling. Campus security: 24-hour emergency response devices and patrols, student patrols, late night transport-escort service, controlled dormitory access. Dick Smith Library plus 1 other. Students can reserve study rooms. Operations spending for the previous fiscal year: $2.9 million. 1,200 computers available on campus for general student use. A campuswide network can be accessed from student residence rooms and from off campus. Students can access the following: online class registration. Staffed computer lab on campus.

Community Environment: Stephenville, Texas, with a population of 15,900 is located in west central Texas, approximately 60 miles from the Ft. Worth/Dallas metroplex. With a typically mild climate average rainfall of 32 inches yearly, the region is commonly known as the Cross Timbers area, a term that refers to the many varieties of oak trees, including a heavy concentration of the live oak tree. Community services include churches of all denominations, a full-service hospital, including a new emergency wing and 24 hour care flight service, libraries and dozens of restaurants and shopping options. Railroad, bus, and a local airport are available. In addition, the Dallas/Ft. Worth International Airport is within a one and one-half hour drive.

■ **TARRANT COUNTY COLLEGE DISTRICT**
1500 Houston St.
Fort Worth, TX 76102-6599
Tel: (817)515-5100
Fax: (817)515-5295
E-mail: nichole.mancone@tccd.edu
Web Site: www.tccd.edu

Description: County-supported, 2-year, coed. Awards certificates, transfer associate, and terminal associate degrees. Founded 1967. Setting: 667-acre urban campus with easy access to Dallas-Fort Worth. Endowment: $5.8 million. Educational spending for the previous fiscal year: $5294 per student. Total enrollment: 51,350. Faculty: 2,062 (702 full-time, 1,360 part-time). Student-undergrad faculty ratio is 25:1. 8,053 applied, 100% were admitted. Full-time: 14,922 students, 54% women, 46% men. Part-time: 36,428 students, 59% women, 41% men. Students come from 40 states and territories, 64 other countries. 0.4% American Indian or Alaska Native, non-Hispanic/Latino; 32% Hispanic/Latino; 17% Black or African American, non-Hispanic/Latino; 6% Asian, non-Hispanic/Latino; 0.2% Native Hawaiian or other Pacific Islander, non-Hispanic/Latino; 0.9% international. 32% 25 or older, 4% transferred in. Core. Calendar: semesters. Academic remediation for entering students, ESL program, services for LD students, advanced

placement, honors program, distance learning, summer session for credit, part-time degree program, adult/continuing education programs. ROTC: Army (c), Air Force (c).

Entrance Requirements: Open admission except for nursing, allied health programs. Option: electronic application. Entrance: noncompetitive. Application deadline: rolling. Transfer credits accepted: Yes.

Costs Per Year: Application fee: $0. Area resident tuition: $1661 full-time, $64 per credit hour part-time. State resident tuition: $3132 full-time, $126 per credit hour part-time. Nonresident tuition: $7560 full-time, $305 per credit hour part-time. Full-time tuition varies according to course load and program. Part-time tuition varies according to course load and program.

Collegiate Environment: Orientation program. Drama-theater group, choral group, student-run newspaper. Social organizations: 48 open to all. Student services: health clinic, personal-psychological counseling. Campus security: 24-hour emergency response devices and patrols, late night transport-escort service. Main library plus 5 others. Books: 200,377 (physical), 197,576 (digital/electronic); Serial titles: 496 (physical), 63,698 (digital/electronic); Databases: 155. Operations spending for the previous fiscal year: $5.5 million. 2,000 computers available on campus for general student use. Students can access the following: online class registration. Staffed computer lab on campus.

■ **TEMPLE COLLEGE**
2600 S First St.
Temple, TX 76504-7435
Tel: (254)298-8282
E-mail: carey.rose@templejc.edu
Web Site: www.templejc.edu

Description: District-supported, 2-year, coed. Awards certificates, transfer associate, and terminal associate degrees. Founded 1926. Setting: 106-acre suburban campus with easy access to Austin. Endowment: $638,964. Educational spending for the previous fiscal year: $3327 per student. Total enrollment: 5,344. Faculty: 289 (123 full-time, 166 part-time). Student-undergrad faculty ratio is 25:1. Students come from 24 states and territories, 6 other countries, 2% from out-of-state. 40% 25 or older. Core. Calendar: semesters. Academic remediation for entering students, ESL program, services for LD students, advanced placement, distance learning, summer session for credit, part-time degree program, adult/continuing education programs, co-op programs and internships. Off campus study at East Williamson County Higher Education Center, Taylor, TX; Cameron Education Center, Cameron, TX; McClennan Community College (Radiologic Technology), Texas BioScience Institute, Temple TX. Study abroad program.

Entrance Requirements: Open admission except for health programs with clinical requirements. Options: electronic application, early admission, international baccalaureate accepted. Required: high school transcript. Entrance: noncompetitive. Application deadline: rolling. Transfer credits accepted: Yes.

Costs Per Year: Application fee: $0. Area resident tuition: $2310 full-time, $77 per credit hour part-time. State resident tuition: $4500 full-time, $150 per credit hour part-time. Nonresident tuition: $6900 full-time, $312 per credit hour part-time. Mandatory fees: $660 full-time, $22 per credit hour part-time. Full-time tuition and fees vary according to course load, location, and program. Part-time tuition and fees vary according to course load, location, and program.

Collegiate Environment: Orientation program. Drama-theater group, choral group. Social organizations: 18 open to all; academic, service, and honor societies. Most popular organizations: Baptist Student Ministries, student government, Phi Theta Kappa, Delta Epsilon Chi, Nursing Student Organization. Major annual events: Fall Festival, Spring Fling. Student services: personal-psychological counseling. Campus security: 24-hour emergency response devices and patrols. Hubert Dawson Library. Operations spending for the previous fiscal year: $467,913. 102 computers available on campus for general student use. A campuswide network can be accessed from student residence rooms. Students can access the following: online class registration. Staffed computer lab on campus provides training in use of computers, software, and the Internet.

Community Environment: Population 55,447. Temple today is a medical center visited annually by thousands of patients. Located in central Texas, the city enjoys a temperate climate. The community has air, rail, and bus service available. Community service facilities include four excellent hospitals, many churches representing all major denominations, a library, and several hotels and motels. There are various civic, fraternal, and veteran's organizations active in the area. Local recreation includes hunting, fishing, boating, water skiing, and most water sports at nearby Lake Belton. Part-time employment is available.

■ TEXARKANA COLLEGE

2500 N Robison Rd.

Texarkana, TX 75599-0001

Tel: (903)838-4541

Fax: (903)832-5030

E-mail: lee.williams@texarkanacollege.edu

Web Site: www.texarkanacollege.edu

Description: State and locally supported, 2-year, coed. Awards certificates, transfer associate, and terminal associate degrees. Founded 1927. Setting: 105-acre urban campus. Educational spending for the previous fiscal year: $4962 per student. Total enrollment: 4,239. Faculty: 129 (92 full-time, 111 part-time). Student-undergrad faculty ratio is 22:1. Full-time: 397 students, 57% women, 43% men. Part-time: 131 students, 56% women, 44% men. 0.9% American Indian or Alaska Native, non-Hispanic/Latino; 8% Hispanic/Latino; 22% Black or African American, non-Hispanic/Latino; 1% Asian, non-Hispanic/Latino; 0.1% Native Hawaiian or other Pacific Islander, non-Hispanic/Latino; 0.9% international. 27% 25 or older, 1% live on campus, 20% transferred in. Core. Calendar: semesters. Academic remediation for entering students, services for LD students, advanced placement, freshman honors college, honors program, independent study, distance learning, summer session for credit, part-time degree program, adult/continuing education programs, co-op programs and internships. Study abroad program.

Entrance Requirements: Open admission. Options: electronic application, early admission, deferred admission, international baccalaureate accepted. Required: high school transcript. Recommended: interview for nursing program, meningitis vaccine. Entrance: noncompetitive. Application deadline: rolling. Transfer credits accepted: Yes.

Costs Per Year: Application fee: $0. Area resident tuition: $1296 full-time, $54 per credit hour part-time. State resident tuition: $2592 full-time, $108 per credit hour part-time. Nonresident tuition: $3816 full-time, $159 per credit hour part-time. Mandatory fees: $940 full-time, $35 per credit hour part-time, $50 per term part-time. Full-time tuition and fees vary according to program. Part-time tuition and fees vary according to program. College room and board: $6883.

Collegiate Environment: Orientation program. Drama-theater group, choral group, student-run newspaper. Social organizations: 16 open to all. Most popular organizations: Black Student Association, Earth Club, Culinary Arts Club, Cultural Awareness Student Association, Cosmetology Club. Major annual events: Fall Fest/Bulldog Bash, Spring Fling. Student services: personal-psychological counseling. Campus security: 24-hour patrols. 6 college housing spaces available; 4 were occupied in 2018-19. No special consideration for freshman housing applicants. Option: coed housing available. Palmer Memorial Library. Books: 46,602 (physical), 28,549 (digital/electronic); Serial titles: 143 (physical), 2 (digital/electronic); Databases: 101. Operations spending for the previous fiscal year: $585,602. 500 computers available on campus for general student use. A campuswide network can be accessed. Students can access the following: online class registration. Staffed computer lab on campus.

Community Environment: Texarkana is located on the Arkansas-Texas border which runs approximately through the center of town. A trading center, there are many railroad lines coming into the area. The community has two hospitals, motels and hotels, and various civic, fraternal and veteran's organizations. Local recreation includes golf, hunting, fishing, boating, and water skiing. Part-time employment is available.

■ TEXAS A&M INTERNATIONAL UNIVERSITY

5201 University Blvd.

Laredo, TX 78041

Tel: (956)326-2001; Free: 888-489-2648

Fax: (956)326-2348

E-mail: adms@tamiu.edu

Web Site: www.tamiu.edu

Description: State-supported, comprehensive, coed. Part of Texas A&M University System. Awards bachelor's, master's, and doctoral degrees. Founded 1969. Setting: 300-acre urban campus. Endowment: $52.1 million. Research spending for the previous fiscal year: $4.2 million. Educational spending for the previous fiscal year: $6559 per student. Total enrollment: 7,884. Faculty: 361 (208 full-time, 153 part-time). Student-undergrad faculty ratio is 21:1. 7,211 applied, 52% were admitted. 21% from top 10% of their high school class, 52% from top quarter, 85% from top half. Full-time: 5,235 students, 59% women, 41% men. Part-time: 1,757 students, 63% women, 37% men. Students come from 26 states and territories, 24 other countries, 1% from out-of-state. 95% Hispanic/Latino; 0.4% Black or African American, non-Hispanic/Latino; 0.4% Asian, non-Hispanic/Latino; 2% international.

13% 25 or older, 9% live on campus, 7% transferred in. Retention: 77% of full-time freshmen returned the following year. Academic areas with the most degrees conferred: business/marketing; homeland security, law enforcement, firefighting, and protective services; psychology. Core. Calendar: semesters. Academic remediation for entering students, ESL program, services for LD students, advanced placement, honors program, independent study, distance learning, double major, summer session for credit, part-time degree program, internships, graduate courses open to undergrads. Study abroad program. ROTC: Army.

Entrance Requirements: Options: electronic application, deferred admission, international baccalaureate accepted. Required: high school transcript, SAT or ACT. Entrance: moderately difficult. Notification: continuous. SAT Reasoning Test deadline: 8/15. SAT Subject Test deadline: 8/15. Transfer credits accepted: Yes.

Costs Per Year: Application fee: $0. State resident tuition: $4773 full-time, $159.10 per credit hour part-time. Nonresident tuition: $17,433 full-time, $581.10 per credit hour part-time. Mandatory fees: $4071 full-time, $268.62 per credit hour part-time, $132.65. College room and board: $8618. College room only: $5732. Tuition guaranteed not to increase for student's term of enrollment.

Collegiate Environment: Orientation program. Choral group, student-run newspaper. Social organizations: 87 open to all; national fraternities, national sororities, local fraternities; 1% of eligible men and 2% of eligible women are members. Most popular organizations: Student Government Association, Campus Activities Board, Greek Association, Criminal Justice Association, Ballet Folklorico. Major annual events: Halloweenfest, Pre-Exam Jam, Welcome Week. Student services: health clinic, personal-psychological counseling. Campus security: 24-hour emergency response devices and patrols, late night transport-escort service, controlled dormitory access, active shooter response training for faculty, staff, and new students; timely ongoing threat information dissemination. 711 college housing spaces available; 633 were occupied in 2018-19. No special consideration for freshman housing applicants. Option: coed housing available. Sue and Radcliff Killam Library. Books: 256,158 (physical), 620,245 (digital/electronic); Serial titles: 6,348 (physical), 80,261 (digital/electronic); Databases: 282. Weekly public service hours: 96; students can reserve study rooms. Operations spending for the previous fiscal year: $3 million. 970 computers available on campus for general student use. A campuswide network can be accessed. Students can access the following: online class registration. Staffed computer lab on campus provides training in use of computers, software, and the Internet.

■ TEXAS A&M UNIVERSITY

400 Bizzell St.

College Station, TX 77843

Tel: (979)845-3211

Web Site: www.tamu.edu

Description: State-supported, university, coed. Part of Texas A&M University System. Awards bachelor's, master's, and doctoral degrees and post-master's certificates. Founded 1876. Setting: suburban campus with easy access to Houston. System endowment: $11.6 billion. Educational spending for the previous fiscal year: $13,924 per student. Total enrollment: 67,580. Faculty: 3,585 (2,798 full-time, 787 part-time). Student-undergrad faculty ratio is 20:1. 37,191 applied, 70% were admitted, 60% from top 10% of their high school class, 88% from top quarter, 98% from top half. Full-time: 46,724 students, 48% women, 52% men. Part-time: 6,341 students, 45% women, 55% men. Students come from 53 states and territories, 96 other countries, 4% from out-of-state. 0.3% American Indian or Alaska Native, non-Hispanic/Latino; 23% Hispanic/Latino; 3% Black or African American, non-Hispanic/Latino; 7% Asian, non-Hispanic/Latino; 0.1% Native Hawaiian or other Pacific Islander, non-Hispanic/Latino; 1% international. 3% 25 or older, 23% live on campus, 5% transferred in. Retention: 92% of full-time freshmen returned the following year. Academic areas with the most degrees conferred: business/marketing; engineering; interdisciplinary studies. Core. Calendar: semesters. Academic remediation for entering students, ESL program, services for LD students, advanced placement, accelerated degree program, honors program, independent study, distance learning, double major, summer session for credit, part-time degree program, co-op programs and internships, graduate courses open to undergrads. Off campus study at Texas A&M University at Galveston. Study abroad program. ROTC: Army, Naval, Air Force.

Entrance Requirements: Options: electronic application, international baccalaureate accepted. Required: essay, high school transcript, SAT or ACT. Required for some: Apply Texas application, minimum SAT math score of 550 or ACT math score of 24 for the College of Engineering. Entrance:

moderately difficult. Application deadline: 12/1. Notification: continuous. Preference given to students graduating in the top 10% of Texas high schools. SAT Reasoning Test deadline: 12/8.

Costs Per Year: Application fee: $75. State resident tuition: $7,406 full-time, $246.88 per credit hour part-time. Nonresident tuition: $33,074 full-time, $1,102.48 per credit hour part-time. Mandatory fees: $3562 full-time. Full-time tuition and fees vary according to program. Part-time tuition varies according to program. College room and board: $10,436. Room and board charges vary according to board plan, housing facility, and location. Tuition guaranteed not to increase for student's term of enrollment.

Collegiate Environment: Orientation program. Drama-theater group, choral group, marching band, student-run newspaper, radio station. Social organizations: 1,066 open to all; national fraternities, national sororities, local fraternities, local sororities; 8% of eligible men and 13% of eligible women are members. Most popular organizations: Memorial Student Center, Corps of Cadets, Fish Camp, Student Government. Major annual events: Big Event, Parents' Weekend, Aggie Muster. Student services: legal services, health clinic, personal-psychological counseling, women's center. Campus security: 24-hour emergency response devices and patrols, late night transport-escort service, controlled dormitory access, student escorts. Sterling C. Evans Library plus 9 others. Books: 4.3 million (physical), 1.9 million (digital/electronic); Serial titles: 10,083 (physical), 199,378 (digital/electronic); Databases: 1,162. Weekly public service hours: 144; study areas open 24 hours, 5-7 days a week; students can reserve study rooms. Operations spending for the previous fiscal year: $47.4 million. 2,776 computers available on campus for general student use. A campuswide network can be accessed from student residence rooms and from off campus. Students can access the following: online class registration. Staffed computer lab on campus (open 24 hours a day) provides training in use of computers, software, and the Internet.

■ TEXAS A&M UNIVERSITY-CENTRAL TEXAS
1001 Leadership Pl.
Killeen, TX 76549
Tel: (254)519-5400
Web Site: www.tamuct.edu

Description: State-supported, upper-level, coed. Part of Texas A&M University System. Awards bachelor's and master's degrees and post-master's certificates. Founded 2009. Setting: 662-acre rural campus. Research spending for the previous fiscal year: $808,011. Educational spending for the previous fiscal year: $5728 per student. Total enrollment: 2,464. Faculty: 190 (62 full-time, 128 part-time). Student-undergrad faculty ratio is 20:1. Full-time: 684 students, 55% women, 45% men. Part-time: 1,229 students, 59% women, 41% men. Students come from 33 states and territories, 6 other countries, 5% from out-of-state. 0.5% American Indian or Alaska Native, non-Hispanic/Latino; 24% Hispanic/Latino; 27% Black or African American, non-Hispanic/Latino; 3% Asian, non-Hispanic/Latino; 0.6% Native Hawaiian or other Pacific Islander, non-Hispanic/Latino; 0.1% international. 73% 25 or older, 101% transferred in. Academic areas with the most degrees conferred: business/marketing; liberal arts/general studies; psychology. Core. Calendar: semesters. Services for LD students, advanced placement, accelerated degree program, independent study, distance learning, double major, summer session for credit, part-time degree program, co-op programs and internships. Off campus study at Central Texas College, Temple College. Study abroad program. ROTC: Army.

Entrance Requirements: Transfer credits accepted: Yes.

Costs Per Year: State resident tuition: $20,325 full-time, $184.94 part-time. Nonresident tuition: $30,284 full-time, $601 part-time. Mandatory fees: $2085 full-time, $210.63 part-time. Tuition guaranteed not to increase for student's term of enrollment.

Collegiate Environment: Orientation program. Student-run newspaper. Student services: personal-psychological counseling. Campus security: 24-hour emergency response devices and patrols. College housing not available. University Library. Books: 86,646 (physical), 387,198 (digital/electronic); Serial titles: 160 (physical), 173,928 (digital/electronic); Databases: 283. Weekly public service hours: 81; students can reserve study rooms. Operations spending for the previous fiscal year: $1.4 million. 48 computers available on campus for general student use. A campuswide network can be accessed. Students can access the following: online class registration. Staffed computer lab on campus provides training in use of software.

■ TEXAS A&M UNIVERSITY-COMMERCE
1700 Hwy. 24
Commerce, TX 75429

Tel: (903)886-5081; Free: 888-868-2682
Fax: (903)886-5888
E-mail: admissions@tamu-commerce.edu
Web Site: www.tamuc.edu

Description: State-supported, university, coed. Part of Texas A&M University System. Awards bachelor's, master's, and doctoral degrees. Founded 1889. Setting: 1,883-acre small town campus with easy access to Dallas-Fort Worth. Total enrollment: 12,490. Faculty: 674 (390 full-time, 284 part-time). Student-undergrad faculty ratio is 18:1. 9,730 applied, 34% were admitted. 15% from top 10% of their high school class, 43% from top quarter, 77% from top half. Full-time: 5,650 students, 59% women, 41% men. Part-time: 2,381 students, 61% women, 39% men. 3% from out-of-state. 0.6% American Indian or Alaska Native, non-Hispanic/Latino; 21% Hispanic/Latino; 22% Black or African American, non-Hispanic/Latino; 2% Asian, non-Hispanic/Latino; 0.2% Native Hawaiian or other Pacific Islander, non-Hispanic/Latino; 2% international. 25% 25 or older, 31% live on campus, 17% transferred in. Retention: 68% of full-time freshmen returned the following year. Academic areas with the most degrees conferred: interdisciplinary studies; business/marketing; psychology. Core. Calendar: semesters. Academic remediation for entering students, ESL program, services for LD students, advanced placement, accelerated degree program, self-designed majors, freshman honors college, honors program, independent study, distance learning, double major, summer session for credit, part-time degree program, adult/continuing education programs, co-op programs and internships, graduate courses open to undergrads. Off campus study at Federation of North Texas Area Universities; Navarro College; Collin College. Study abroad program. ROTC: Air Force (c).

Entrance Requirements: Options: electronic application, deferred admission, international baccalaureate accepted. Required: high school transcript, SAT or ACT. Required for some: interview for honors college. Entrance: moderately difficult. Application deadline: 8/1. SAT Reasoning Test deadline: 7/31. Transfer credits accepted: Yes.

Costs Per Year: Application fee: $0. State resident tuition: $4790 full-time, $160 per credit hour part-time. Nonresident tuition: $17,240 full-time, $575 per credit hour part-time. Mandatory fees: $3958 full-time. Full-time tuition and fees vary according to course load, degree level, location, program, and reciprocity agreements. Part-time tuition varies according to course load, degree level, location, program, and reciprocity agreements. College room and board: $8326. College room only: $4426. Room and board charges vary according to board plan and housing facility.

Collegiate Environment: Orientation program. Drama-theater group, choral group, marching band, student-run newspaper, radio station. Social organizations: national fraternities, national sororities. Most popular organizations: National Society for Leadership and Success, Residence Hall Association, Indian Students Association, The Pride Alliance, National Association of Colored Women's Club, Inc. Major annual events: Homecoming, Lions Roar, Lions Leap. Student services: legal services, health clinic, personal-psychological counseling. Campus security: 24-hour emergency response devices and patrols, controlled dormitory access. Gee Library.

■ TEXAS A&M UNIVERSITY-CORPUS CHRISTI
6300 Ocean Dr.
Corpus Christi, TX 78412
Tel: (361)825-5700; Free: 800-482-6822
Fax: (361)825-5810
E-mail: monica.martinez@tamucc.edu
Web Site: www.tamucc.edu

Description: State-supported, university, coed. Part of Texas A&M University System. Awards bachelor's, master's, and doctoral degrees. Founded 1947. Setting: 317-acre suburban campus. Endowment: $12.4 million. Research spending for the previous fiscal year: $24 million. Total enrollment: 12,236. Faculty: 723 (487 full-time, 236 part-time). Student-undergrad faculty ratio is 18:1. 9,002 applied, 86% were admitted. 7% from top 10% of their high school class, 27% from top quarter, 73% from top half. Full-time: 8,357 students, 58% women, 42% men. Part-time: 1,817 students, 61% women, 39% men. Students come from 43 states and territories, 41 other countries, 3% from out-of-state. 0.2% American Indian or Alaska Native, non-Hispanic/Latino; 50% Hispanic/Latino; 6% Black or African American, non-Hispanic/Latino; 3% Asian, non-Hispanic/Latino; 2% international. 13% 25 or older, 51% live on campus, 8% transferred in. Retention: 55% of full-time freshmen returned the following year. Academic areas with the most degrees conferred: health professions and related sciences; business/marketing; parks and recreation. Core. Calendar: semesters. Academic remediation for entering students, ESL program, services for LD students, advanced placement, honors program, independent study, distance learning, double major, summer session for credit, part-time degree program, co-op programs and internships, graduate courses open to undergrads. Off campus study. Study abroad program. ROTC: Army.

Entrance Requirements: Options: electronic application, international baccalaureate accepted. Required: high school transcript, minimum 2 high school GPA, SAT or ACT. Entrance: moderately difficult. Application deadline: 7/1. Notification: continuous, continuous for nonresidents. SAT Reasoning Test deadline: 7/1. SAT Subject Test deadline: 7/1. Transfer credits accepted: Yes.

Costs Per Year: Application fee: $50. State resident tuition: $4719 full-time, $175 per credit hour part-time. Nonresident tuition: $14,527 full-time, $586 per credit hour part-time. Mandatory fees: $4336 full-time, $429 per credit hour part-time. Full-time tuition and fees vary according to course load, degree level, location, program, and student level. Part-time tuition and fees vary according to course load, degree level, location, program, and student level. Tuition guaranteed not to increase for student's term of enrollment.

Collegiate Environment: Orientation program. Drama-theater group, choral group, student-run newspaper. Social organizations: 91 open to all; national fraternities, national sororities; 4% of eligible men and 4% of eligible women are members. Most popular organizations: Student Accounting Society: Alpha Epsilon Delta, Student Art Association: Golden Key, Islander Cultural Alliance: Kinesiology Club, Graduate Student Association: Sea Turtle Club, Student Nurses Association. Major annual events: Late Night Breakfast, Waves of Welcome Week, Homecoming. Student services: health clinic, personal-psychological counseling. Campus security: 24-hour emergency response devices and patrols, late night transport-escort service, controlled dormitory access. Mary and Jeff Bell Library. Books: 329,340 (physical), 145,756 (digital/electronic); Serial titles: 10,348 (physical), 80,843 (digital/electronic); Databases: 271. Weekly public service hours: 106; students can reserve study rooms. Operations spending for the previous fiscal year: $5.9 million. 1,236 computers available on campus for general student use. A campuswide network can be accessed from student residence rooms and from off campus. Students can access the following: online class registration. Staffed computer lab on campus provides training in use of computers, software, and the Internet.

■ TEXAS A&M UNIVERSITY-KINGSVILLE

700 University Blvd.
Kingsville, TX 78363
Tel: (361)593-2111; Free: 800-687-6000
E-mail: laura.knippers@tamuk.edu
Web Site: www.tamuk.edu

Description: State-supported, university, coed. Part of Texas A&M University System. Awards bachelor's, master's, and doctoral degrees and post-master's certificates. Founded 1925. Setting: 250-acre small town campus. Total enrollment: 8,674. 6,717 applied, 84% were admitted. Full-time: 5,020 students, 46% women, 54% men. Part-time: 1,755 students, 55% women, 45% men. 0.2% American Indian or Alaska Native, non-Hispanic/Latino; 71% Hispanic/Latino; 6% Black or African American, non-Hispanic/Latino; 0.8% Asian, non-Hispanic/Latino; 0.2% Native Hawaiian or other Pacific Islander, non-Hispanic/Latino; 4% international. 13% 25 or older, 27% live on campus, 7% transferred in. Core. Calendar: semesters. Academic remediation for entering students, ESL program, services for LD students, advanced placement, honors program, independent study, distance learning, double major, summer session for credit, part-time degree program, adult/continuing education programs, internships, graduate courses open to undergrads. Off campus study. Study abroad program. ROTC: Army.

Entrance Requirements: Options: electronic application, international baccalaureate accepted. Required: SAT or ACT. Required for some: essay, high school transcript, minimum 2 high school GPA, 2 recommendations, written statement and two letters of recommendation for alternate admissions process. Entrance: moderately difficult. Application deadline: rolling. SAT Reasoning Test deadline: 8/1. Transfer credits accepted: Yes.

Costs Per Year: Application fee: $25. State resident tuition: $8462 full-time, $120 per credit hour part-time. Nonresident tuition: $22,034 full-time, $465 per credit hour part-time. Mandatory fees: $4,131 full-time. Full-time tuition and fees vary according to course load and degree level. Part-time tuition varies according to course load and degree level. College room and board: $9096. Room and board charges vary according to board plan and housing facility. Tuition guaranteed not to increase for student's term of enrollment.

Collegiate Environment: Orientation program. Drama-theater group, choral group, marching band, student-run newspaper, radio station. Social

organizations: national fraternities, national sororities. Student services: health clinic, personal-psychological counseling. Campus security: controlled dormitory access. James C. Jernigan Library. Students can reserve study rooms.

■ TEXAS A&M UNIVERSITY-SAN ANTONIO

One University Way
San Antonio, TX 78224
Tel: (210)784-1000
E-mail: jennifer.zamarripa@tamusa.tamus.edu
Web Site: www.tamusa.edu

Description: State-supported, comprehensive, coed. Awards bachelor's and master's degrees.

Entrance Requirements: Required: high school transcript. Application deadline: 8/15.

■ TEXAS A&M UNIVERSITY-TEXARKANA

7101 University Ave.
Texarkana, TX 75503
Tel: (903)223-3000
Fax: (903)832-8890
E-mail: admissions@tamut.edu
Web Site: www.tamut.edu

Description: State-supported, comprehensive, coed. Part of Texas A&M University System. Awards bachelor's, master's, and doctoral degrees. Founded 1971. Setting: 1-acre small town campus. Endowment: $6.8 million. Research spending for the previous fiscal year: $75,441. Total enrollment: 2,066. Student-undergrad faculty ratio is 15:1. 3,766 applied, 65% were admitted. 15% from top 10% of their high school class, 44% from top quarter, 78% from top half. Full-time: 1,191 students, 59% women, 41% men. Part-time: 453 students, 67% women, 33% men. 20% from out-of-state. 0.8% American Indian or Alaska Native, non-Hispanic/Latino; 15% Hispanic/Latino; 14% Black or African American, non-Hispanic/Latino; 1% Asian, non-Hispanic/Latino; 0.2% Native Hawaiian or other Pacific Islander, non-Hispanic/Latino; 2% international. 38% 25 or older, 15% live on campus, 17% transferred in. Retention: 57% of full-time freshmen returned the following year. Academic areas with the most degrees conferred: interdisciplinary studies; business/marketing; psychology. Core. Calendar: semesters. Services for LD students, advanced placement, self-designed majors, independent study, distance learning, summer session for credit, part-time degree program, internships, graduate courses open to undergrads.

Entrance Requirements: Options: electronic application, international baccalaureate accepted. Required: high school transcript, SAT or ACT. Entrance: noncompetitive. Application deadline: rolling. Notification: continuous. Transfer credits accepted: Yes.

Costs Per Year: Application fee: $30. One-time mandatory fee: $30. State resident tuition: $5,978 full-time, $243.86 per credit hour part-time. Nonresident tuition: $21,014 full-time, $744.95 per credit hour part-time. Mandatory fees: $2,092 full-time, $110.65 per credit hour part-time, $150 per term part-time. College room and board: $8732. College room only: $4596. Room and board charges vary according to board plan and housing facility. Tuition guaranteed not to increase for student's term of enrollment.

Collegiate Environment: Orientation program. Student-run newspaper. Social organizations: 40 open to all; 5% of eligible men and 6% of eligible women are members. Most popular organizations: Campus Activities Board, Student Government Association, Alpha Sigma Alpha, Omega Delta Chi, Phi Lambda Chi. Major annual events: The Big Event, Homecoming, Best Week Ever. Student services: personal-psychological counseling. Campus security: 24-hour patrols, late night transport-escort service. John F. Moss Library plus 1 other. Books: 128,838 (physical), 583,387 (digital/electronic); Serial titles: 1,184 (physical), 72,678 (digital/electronic); Databases: 299. Weekly public service hours: 84; students can reserve study rooms.

■ TEXAS CHRISTIAN UNIVERSITY

2800 S University Dr.
Fort Worth, TX 76129-0002
Tel: (817)257-7000; Free: 800-828-3764
E-mail: frogmail@tcu.edu
Web Site: www.tcu.edu

Description: Independent, university, coed, affiliated with Christian Church (Disciples of Christ). Awards bachelor's, master's, and doctoral degrees and post-master's certificates. Founded 1873. Setting: 299-acre suburban campus with easy access to Dallas-Fort Worth. Endowment: $1.6 billion. Research spending for the previous fiscal year: $9.5 million. Educational spending for the previous fiscal year: $17,983 per student. Total enrollment: 10,918. Faculty: 1,041 (698 full-time, 343 part-time). Student-undergrad faculty ratio is 13:1. 20,156 applied, 41% were admitted. 50% from top 10% of their high school class, 78% from top quarter, 96% from top half. Full-time: 9,162 students, 59% women, 41% men. Part-time: 283 students, 53% women, 47% men. Students come from 53 states and territories, 77 other countries, 48% from out-of-state. 0.8% American Indian or Alaska Native, non-Hispanic/Latino; 14% Hispanic/Latino; 6% Black or African American, non-Hispanic/Latino; 3% Asian, non-Hispanic/Latino; 0.2% Native Hawaiian or other Pacific Islander, non-Hispanic/Latino; 5% international. 5% 25 or older, 51% live on campus, 5% transferred in. Retention: 92% of full-time freshmen returned the following year. Academic areas with the most degrees conferred: business/marketing; communication/journalism; health professions and related sciences. Core. Calendar: semesters. ESL program, services for LD students, advanced placement, accelerated degree program, self-designed majors, honors program, independent study, distance learning, double major, summer session for credit, part-time degree program, internships, graduate courses open to undergrads. Study abroad program. ROTC: Army, Air Force.

Entrance Requirements: Options: electronic application, early decision, early action, deferred admission, international baccalaureate accepted. Required: essay, high school transcript, 2 recommendations, SAT or ACT. Entrance: very difficult. Application deadlines: 2/1, 11/1 for early decision, 11/1 for early action. Notification: 4/1, 12/1 for early decision, 12/15 for early action. SAT Reasoning Test deadline: 3/1. Transfer credits accepted: Yes. Applicants placed on waiting list: 1,725. Wait-listed applicants offered admission: 55. Early decision applicants: 1,196. Early decision applicants admitted: 400. Early action applicants: 10,408. Early action applicants admitted: 6,055.

Costs Per Year: Application fee: $50. Comprehensive fee: $62,360 includes full-time tuition ($49,160) and college room and board ($13,200). College room only: $8060.

Collegiate Environment: Orientation program. Drama-theater group, choral group, marching band, student-run newspaper, radio station. Social organizations: 200 open to all; national fraternities, national sororities, local fraternities, local sororities, local coed music fraternities. Most popular organizations: Entrepreneurship Club, Foodies, National Society of Collegiate Scholars, College Republicans, Best Buddies. Major annual events: Student Government Associate Fall Concert, Christmas Tree lighting, Football Games. Student services: health clinic, personal-psychological counseling, women's center. Campus security: 24-hour emergency response devices and patrols, late night transport-escort service, controlled dormitory access. College housing designed to accommodate 3,341 students; 4,679 undergraduates lived in college housing during 2018-19. Freshmen guaranteed college housing. On-campus residence required through sophomore year. Options: coed, men-only, women-only housing available. Mary Couts Burnett Library. Books: 1.4 million (physical), 1.2 million (digital/electronic); Serial titles: 11,126 (physical), 143,171 (digital/electronic); Databases: 554. Weekly public service hours: 139; study areas open 24 hours, 5-7 days a week; students can reserve study rooms. Operations spending for the previous fiscal year: $9.7 million. 1,400 computers available on campus for general student use. A campuswide network can be accessed from student residence rooms and from off campus. Students can access the following: online class registration. Staffed computer lab on campus (open 24 hours a day) provides training in use of computers, software, and the Internet.

Community Environment: The University is easily accessible to a variety of recreational, educational, and professional opportunities in the Fort Worth/Dallas metroplex. Major museums, parks, theatres, churches, and restaurants are within a few miles from the campus.

■ TEXAS COLLEGE

2404 N Grand Ave.
Tyler, TX 75712-4500
Tel: (903)593-8311; Free: 800-306-6299
E-mail: rmcdowell@texascollege.edu
Web Site: www.texascollege.edu

Description: Independent, 4-year, coed, affiliated with Christian Methodist Episcopal Church. Awards associate and bachelor's degrees. Founded 1894. Setting: 25-acre urban campus. Endowment: $1.3 million. Educational spending for the previous fiscal year: $2225 per student. Total enrollment: 960. Faculty: 46 (38 full-time, 8 part-time). Student-undergrad faculty ratio is 20:1. 4,190 applied, 32% were admitted. Full-time: 932 students, 41% women, 59% men. Part-time: 28 students, 43% women, 57% men. Students

come from 26 states and territories, 6 other countries, 14% from out-of-state. 0.1% American Indian or Alaska Native, non-Hispanic/Latino; 7% Hispanic/Latino; 87% Black or African American, non-Hispanic/Latino; 0.1% Asian, non-Hispanic/Latino; 2% international. 18% 25 or older, 48% live on campus, 18% transferred in. Retention: 70% of full-time freshmen returned the following year. Core. Calendar: semesters. Academic remediation for entering students, services for LD students, advanced placement, distance learning, summer session for credit, adult/continuing education programs, internships.

Entrance Requirements: Open admission. Options: electronic application, early admission. Required: high school transcript, minimum 2 high school GPA. Application deadline: rolling. Notification: continuous. Transfer credits accepted: Yes.

Costs Per Year: Application fee: $20. Comprehensive fee: $18,008 includes full-time tuition ($8208), mandatory fees ($1800), and college room and board ($8000). College room only: $4200. Part-time tuition: $342 per credit hour.

Collegiate Environment: Orientation program. Choral group, marching band. Social organizations: national fraternities, national sororities, local fraternities, local sororities; 30% of eligible men and 15% of eligible women are members. Major annual events: Preview Day, Homecoming, Religious Emphasis Week. Student services: health clinic. Campus security: 24-hour emergency response devices and patrols. D. R. Glass Library. Books: 40,000 (physical), 155,000 (digital/electronic); Serial titles: 500 (physical); Databases: 73. Weekly public service hours: 69; students can reserve study rooms. Operations spending for the previous fiscal year: $58,715. 300 computers available on campus for general student use. A campuswide network can be accessed from student residence rooms. Staffed computer lab on campus (open 24 hours a day) provides training in use of computers, software, and the Internet.

■ TEXAS LUTHERAN UNIVERSITY

1000 W Ct. St.
Seguin, TX 78155-5999
Tel: (830)372-8000; Free: 800-771-8521
Fax: (830)372-8096
E-mail: almccain@tlu.edu
Web Site: www.tlu.edu

Description: Independent, comprehensive, coed, affiliated with Evangelical Lutheran Church. Awards bachelor's and master's degrees. Founded 1891. Setting: 196-acre suburban campus with easy access to San Antonio, Austin. Total enrollment: 1,443. Faculty: 134 (86 full-time, 48 part-time). Student-undergrad faculty ratio is 14:1. 2,198 applied, 54% were admitted. 11% from top 10% of their high school class, 42% from top quarter, 78% from top half. Full-time: 1,338 students, 50% women, 50% men. Part-time: 73 students, 58% women, 42% men. 2% from out-of-state. 0.2% American Indian or Alaska Native, non-Hispanic/Latino; 37% Hispanic/Latino; 9% Black or African American, non-Hispanic/Latino; 0.7% Asian, non-Hispanic/Latino; 0.1% Native Hawaiian or other Pacific Islander, non-Hispanic/Latino; 0.4% international. 5% 25 or older, 55% live on campus, 5% transferred in. Retention: 71% of full-time freshmen returned the following year. Academic areas with the most degrees conferred: business/marketing; health professions and related sciences; education. Core. Calendar: semesters. Services for LD students, advanced placement, honors program, independent study, double major, summer session for credit, part-time degree program, external degree program, internships. Study abroad program. ROTC: Army (c), Naval (c).

Entrance Requirements: Options: electronic application, early admission. Required: high school transcript, SAT or ACT. Required for some: recommendations. Entrance: moderately difficult. Application deadline: 11/15 for early action. Transfer credits accepted: Yes.

Costs Per Year: One-time mandatory fee: $300. Comprehensive fee: $40,110 includes full-time tuition ($29,650), mandatory fees ($310), and college room and board ($10,150). College room only: $5750. Full-time tuition and fees vary according to course load. Room and board charges vary according to board plan and housing facility. Part-time tuition: $980 per semester hour. Part-time mandatory fees: $155 per term.

Collegiate Environment: Orientation program. Drama-theater group, choral group, student-run newspaper. Social organizations: 71 open to all; local fraternities, local sororities; 7% of eligible men and 11% of eligible women are members. Most popular organizations: Alpha Lambda Delta, Pre Health Professions Club, Xi Tau, Sigma Phi Theta, Mexican American Student Association. Major annual events: KROST Symposium, Christmas Vespers, Spring Fling. Student services: health clinic, personal-psychological counseling, women's center. Campus security: 24-hour emergency response devices and patrols, late night transport-escort service, controlled dormitory access. 986 college housing spaces available; 751 were occupied in 2018-19. Freshmen guaranteed college housing. Option: coed housing available. Blumberg Memorial Library plus 1 other. Weekly public service hours: 86; students can reserve study rooms.

Community Environment: Population 24,230, Seguin is a suburban community enjoying temperate climate. The city is reached by Interstate 10. There is a library, a museum, churches representing 10 different denominations, and a hospital serving the community. Various job opportunities are available here. Various civic, fraternal and veteran's organizations are active in Seguin. Nearby Lake McQueeney offers water skiing.

■ **TEXAS SOUTHERN UNIVERSITY**
3100 Cleburne Ave.
Houston, TX 77004-4584
Tel: (713)313-7011
Fax: (713)527-7842
E-mail: eservices@em.tsu.edu
Web Site: www.tsu.edu

Description: State-supported, university, coed. Awards bachelor's, master's, and doctoral degrees. Founded 1947. Setting: 147-acre urban campus. Endowment: $43.5 million. Research spending for the previous fiscal year: $7 million. Educational spending for the previous fiscal year: $9114 per student. Total enrollment: 9,233. Faculty: 605 (347 full-time, 258 part-time). Student-undergrad faculty ratio is 18:1. 10,239 applied, 51% were admitted. 6% from top 10% of their high school class, 19% from top quarter, 54% from top half. Full-time: 5,842 students, 56% women, 44% men. Part-time: 1,073 students, 61% women, 39% men. Students come from 40 states and territories, 35 other countries, 10% from out-of-state. 0.5% American Indian or Alaska Native, non-Hispanic/Latino; 7% Hispanic/Latino; 82% Black or African American, non-Hispanic/Latino; 2% Asian, non-Hispanic/Latino; 0.1% Native Hawaiian or other Pacific Islander, non-Hispanic/Latino; 6% international. 29% 25 or older, 22% live on campus, 14% transferred in. Retention: 53% of full-time freshmen returned the following year. Academic areas with the most degrees conferred: business/marketing; health professions and related sciences; communication/journalism. Core. Calendar: semesters. Academic remediation for entering students, ESL program, services for LD students, advanced placement, accelerated degree program, honors program, independent study, distance learning, double major, summer session for credit, part-time degree program, external degree program, adult/continuing education programs, co-op programs and internships, graduate courses open to undergrads. Off campus study at Houston Community College Pinemont Center, North Harris College Career Center. Study abroad program. ROTC: Army, Naval (c), Air Force (c).

Entrance Requirements: Open admission. Options: electronic application, early admission, early decision. Required: high school transcript, minimum 2.5 high school GPA. Required for some: TSI (Texas Success Initiative) Assessment, minimum ACT score of 17/SAT 820, SAT or ACT. Entrance: noncompetitive. Application deadline: 8/15. Notification: 8/28. SAT Reasoning Test deadline: 8/15. SAT Subject Test deadline: 8/15. Transfer credits accepted: Yes.

Collegiate Environment: Orientation program. Drama-theater group, choral group, marching band, student-run newspaper, radio station. Social organizations: 58 open to all; national fraternities, national sororities, local fraternities, local sororities. Most popular organizations: Debate Team, University Program Council, Student Government Association, Band, Greek Letter Organizations. Major annual events: Homecoming Festival, Labor Day Classic Game, Spring Festival. Student services: legal services, health clinic, personal-psychological counseling, women's center. Campus security: 24-hour emergency response devices and patrols, student patrols, late night transport-escort service. Robert J. Terry Library plus 2 others.

Community Environment: See University of Houston.

■ **TEXAS SOUTHMOST COLLEGE**
80 Fort Brown
Brownsville, TX 78520-4991
Tel: (956)882-8200; Free: 877-882-8721
Web Site: www.utb.edu

Description: District-supported, 2-year, coed. Part of University of Texas System. Awards certificates, transfer associate, and terminal associate degrees. Founded 1926. Setting: 65-acre urban campus. Calendar: semesters. Summer session for credit, part-time degree program.

Entrance Requirements: Open admission. Entrance: noncompetitive. Application deadline: 8/1.

Collegiate Environment: Campus security: 24-hour emergency response devices and patrols. Arnulfo L. Oliveira Library.

■ **TEXAS STATE TECHNICAL COLLEGE**
3801 Campus Dr.
Waco, TX 76705-1695
Tel: (254)799-3611; Free: 800-792-8784
E-mail: mary.daniel@tstc.edu
Web Site: www.tstc.edu

Description: State-supported, 2-year, coed. Awards certificates, transfer associate, and terminal associate degrees. Founded 1965. Setting: 200-acre suburban campus. Total enrollment: 12,717. Faculty: 645 (530 full-time, 115 part-time). Student-undergrad faculty ratio is 13:1. Full-time: 4,931 students, 25% women, 75% men. Part-time: 7,786 students, 38% women, 62% men. Students come from 35 states and territories. 0.3% American Indian or Alaska Native, non-Hispanic/Latino; 55% Hispanic/Latino; 6% Black or African American, non-Hispanic/Latino; 0.6% Asian, non-Hispanic/Latino; 0.1% Native Hawaiian or other Pacific Islander, non-Hispanic/Latino. 29% 25 or older, 8% transferred in. Calendar: trimesters. Academic remediation for entering students, services for LD students, distance learning, summer session for credit, part-time degree program, adult/continuing education programs, co-op programs and internships.

Entrance Requirements: Open admission. Options: electronic application, early admission. Required: high school transcript, Texas Success Initiative assessment. Required for some: interview. Entrance: noncompetitive. Application deadline: rolling. Notification: continuous. Transfer credits accepted: Yes.

Costs Per Year: Application fee: $0. State resident tuition: $5123 full-time, $2561 per term part-time. Nonresident tuition: $10,080 full-time, $5040 per term part-time. Full-time tuition varies according to course load and program. Part-time tuition varies according to course load and program. College room and board: $6742. College room only: $4117. Room and board charges vary according to board plan and housing facility.

Collegiate Environment: Orientation program. Social organizations: 25 open to all. Most popular organizations: Student Ambassador Association, SkillsUSA, Student Leadership Council, Phi Theta Kappa, Hispanic Student Association. Major annual events: DIA Techsana, Christmas Parade, Halloween Festival. Student services: health clinic, personal-psychological counseling, women's center. Campus security: 24-hour emergency response devices and patrols, late night transport-escort service, controlled dormitory access. Texas State Technical College-Waco Campus Library. 1,300 computers available on campus for general student use. Computer purchase/lease plans available. A campuswide network can be accessed from student residence rooms and from off campus. Students can access the following: online class registration, software packages. Staffed computer lab on campus (open 24 hours a day) provides training in use of computers, software, and the Internet.

■ **TEXAS STATE UNIVERSITY**
601 University Dr.
San Marcos, TX 78666
Tel: (512)245-2111
Fax: (512)245-8044
E-mail: admissions@txstate.edu
Web Site: www.txstate.edu

Description: State-supported, university, coed. Part of Texas State University System. Awards bachelor's, master's, and doctoral degrees. Founded 1899. Setting: 491-acre suburban campus with easy access to San Antonio, Austin. Endowment: $186.7 million. Research spending for the previous fiscal year: $51.9 million. Educational spending for the previous fiscal year: $6017 per student. Total enrollment: 38,666. Faculty: 2,013 (1,419 full-time, 594 part-time). Student-undergrad faculty ratio is 21:1. 24,277 applied, 73% were admitted. 14% from top 10% of their high school class, 51% from top quarter, 94% from top half. 3 National Merit Scholars, 126 class presidents, 35 valedictorians, 357 student government officers. Full-time: 28,019 students, 58% women, 42% men. Part-time: 6,161 students, 54% women, 46% men. Students come from 50 states and territories, 49 other countries, 2% from out-of-state. 0.3% American Indian or Alaska Native, non-Hispanic/Latino; 37% Hispanic/Latino; 10% Black or African American, non-Hispanic/Latino; 2% Asian, non-Hispanic/Latino; 0.2% Native Hawaiian or other Pacific Islander, non-Hispanic/Latino; 0.5% international. 13% 25 or older, 20% live on campus, 11% transferred in. Retention: 78% of full-time freshmen returned the following year. Academic areas with the most degrees conferred: business/marketing; communication/journalism; interdisciplinary studies. Core. Calendar: semesters. Academic remediation for entering students, ESL program, services for LD students, advanced placement, accelerated degree program, freshman honors college, honors program, independent study, distance learning, double major, summer session for credit, part-time degree program, adult/continuing education programs, internships, graduate courses open to undergrads. Off campus study at The University of Texas at San Antonio. Study abroad program. ROTC: Army, Air Force.

Entrance Requirements: Options: electronic application, early admission, deferred admission. Required: essay, high school transcript, SAT or ACT. Recommended: SAT, ACT. Required for some: TOEFL for international students. Entrance: moderately difficult. Application deadline: 3/1. Notification: continuous. SAT Reasoning Test deadline: 3/1. Transfer credits accepted: Yes.

Costs Per Year: Application fee: $75. State resident tuition: $8,335 full-time, $277.82 per credit hour part-time. Nonresident tuition: $20,785 full-time, $692.82 per credit hour part-time. Mandatory fees: $2,600 full-time, $55.74 per credit hour part-time, $464 per term part-time. Full-time tuition and fees vary according to course load and degree level. Part-time tuition and fees vary according to course load and degree level. College room and board: $9374. College room only: $6580. Room and board charges vary according to board plan and housing facility. Tuition guaranteed not to increase for student's term of enrollment.

Collegiate Environment: Orientation program. Drama-theater group, choral group, marching band, student-run newspaper, radio station. Social organizations: 455 open to all; national fraternities, national sororities, local fraternities, local sororities. Most popular organizations: Veterans Alliance of Texas State, Texas State Strutters (Dance performance group), Student Foundation, Sport Clubs Alliance, Student Association for Campus Activities. Major annual events: Homecoming, Springfest, Bobcat Build. Student services: legal services, health clinic, personal-psychological counseling. Campus security: 24-hour emergency response devices and patrols, late night transport-escort service, controlled dormitory access, Emergency Notification System (electronic signs) within classrooms and offices. Alkek Library plus 1 other. Books: 1.5 million (physical), 664,569 (digital/electronic); Serial titles: 32,501 (physical), 129,479 (digital/electronic); Databases: 503. Weekly public service hours: 103; students can reserve study rooms. Operations spending for the previous fiscal year: $18.5 million. 3,233 computers available on campus for general student use. Computer purchase/lease plans available. A campuswide network can be accessed from student residence rooms and from off campus. Students can access the following: online class registration. Staffed computer lab on campus (open 24 hours a day) provides training in use of computers, software, and the Internet.

Community Environment: The university is located in San Marcos, a historic community of 37,000 on I-35 located between San Antonio, 45 miles to the south, and Austin, 30 miles to the north. Both cities are within commuting distance of San Marcos and have major airports. San Marcos has a municipal airport. The central Texas climate offers sunshine most of the year with moderate to cool winters and warm to hot summers. The area enjoys a healthy economy bolstered by clean, light industry, active tourism, and well-preserved historic districts. It is the home to churches of many denominations and various civic organizations. Local recreation includes golfing, fishing, hunting, swimming,"tubing," canoeing and other outdoor activities. Annual celebrations include Chilympiad, Sights and Sounds of Christmas, Summerfest, Cinco de Mayo, and weekly summer concerts in the park.

■ TEXAS TECH UNIVERSITY

2500 Broadway
Lubbock, TX 79409
Tel: (806)742-2011
Fax: (806)742-3055
Web Site: www.ttu.edu

Description: State-supported, university, coed. Part of Texas Tech University System. Awards bachelor's, master's, and doctoral degrees. Founded 1923. Setting: 1,839-acre urban campus. Endowment: $764.5 million. Research spending for the previous fiscal year: $180.1 million. Educational spending for the previous fiscal year: $5738 per student. Total enrollment: 38,209. Faculty: 1,802 (1,606 full-time, 196 part-time). Student-undergrad faculty ratio is 20:1. 24,452 applied, 71% were admitted. 19% from top 10% of their high school class, 51% from top quarter, 84% from top half. 23 National Merit Scholars, 104 valedictorians. Full-time: 27,648 students, 47% women, 53% men. Part-time: 4,309 students, 44% women, 56% men. Students come from 52 states and territories, 98 other countries,

6% from out-of-state. 0.4% American Indian or Alaska Native, non-Hispanic/Latino; 30% Hispanic/Latino; 7% Black or African American, non-Hispanic/Latino; 3% Asian, non-Hispanic/Latino; 0.1% Native Hawaiian or other Pacific Islander, non-Hispanic/Latino; 3% international. 9% 25 or older, 26% live on campus, 8% transferred in. Retention: 85% of full-time freshmen returned the following year. Academic areas with the most degrees conferred: business/marketing; engineering; interdisciplinary studies. Core. Calendar: semesters. Academic remediation for entering students, ESL program, services for LD students, advanced placement, accelerated degree program, self-designed majors, freshman honors college, honors program, independent study, distance learning, double major, summer session for credit, part-time degree program, external degree program, co-op programs and internships, graduate courses open to undergrads. Off campus study at South Plains College - Tech Transfer Acceleration Program (TTAP). Study abroad program. ROTC: Army, Air Force.

Entrance Requirements: Options: electronic application, international baccalaureate accepted. Required: high school transcript, SAT or ACT. Recommended: essay. Entrance: moderately difficult. Application deadline: 8/1. Notification: 9/1. SAT Reasoning Test deadline: 8/1. SAT Subject Test deadline: 8/1. Transfer credits accepted: Yes.

Costs Per Year: Application fee: $75. State resident tuition: $8220 full-time, $274 per credit hour part-time. Nonresident tuition: $20,670 full-time, $689 per credit hour part-time. Mandatory fees: $2825 full-time, $53.50 per credit hour part-time, $610 per term part-time. Full-time tuition and fees vary according to course load, location, program, and reciprocity agreements. Part-time tuition and fees vary according to course load, location, program, and reciprocity agreements. College room and board: $9772. College room only: $6236. Room and board charges vary according to board plan and housing facility.

Collegiate Environment: Orientation program. Drama-theater group, choral group, marching band, student-run newspaper, radio station. Social organizations: 550 open to all; national fraternities, national sororities, local fraternities; 15% of eligible men and 38% of eligible women are members. Most popular organizations: Society of Petroleum Engineers, Hispanic Student Society, Pre-Nursing Association, Alpha Lambda Delta and Phi Eta Sigma, Catholic Student Association. Major annual events: Homecoming, Carol of Lights, Arbor Day. Student services: legal services, health clinic, personal-psychological counseling. Campus security: 24-hour emergency response devices and patrols, late night transport-escort service, controlled dormitory access. 8,177 college housing spaces available; 7,953 were occupied in 2018-19. Freshmen guaranteed college housing. On-campus residence required in freshman year. Options: coed, men-only, women-only housing available. Texas Tech Library plus 3 others. Books: 2.9 million (physical), 159,373 (digital/electronic); Serial titles: 1,464 (physical), 200,332 (digital/electronic); Databases: 405. Weekly public service hours: 146; study areas open 24 hours, 5-7 days a week; students can reserve study rooms. Operations spending for the previous fiscal year: $24.3 million. 2,087 computers available on campus for general student use. Computer purchase/lease plans available. A campuswide network can be accessed from student residence rooms and from off campus. Students can access the following: online class registration, online degree plans, accounts, transcripts, financial aid, course and instructor evaluations, scholarship applications and submissions. Staffed computer lab on campus provides training in use of computers, software, and the Internet.

Community Environment: Lubbock, with a population of nearly 210,000, is located on top of the caprock on the South Plains of Texas. Its climate is excellent, with over 3,550 hours of sunshine every year. Summers are dry and not extremely hot, while winters are dry and moderate (average rainfall is only 18 inches). An average annual temperature of 60 degrees coupled with the average noon humidity of 46 percent combine to make Lubbock comfortable year-round. The city lies 320 miles west of Dallas, and an equal distance 320 miles south east of Albuquerque, New Mexico. Several airlines and an interstate bus line serve the city, as well as four U.S. highways, including an interstate highway.

■ TEXAS WESLEYAN UNIVERSITY

1201 Wesleyan St.
Fort Worth, TX 76105
Tel: (817)531-4444; Free: 800-580-8980
Fax: (817)531-7515
E-mail: admissions@txwes.edu
Web Site: www.txwes.edu

Description: Independent United Methodist, university, coed. Awards bachelor's, master's, and doctoral degrees. Founded 1890. Setting: 74-acre urban campus with easy access to Dallas-Fort Worth. Endowment: $59.7 million. Research spending for the previous fiscal year: $52,144. Educational spending for the previous fiscal year: $23,552 per student. Total enrollment: 2,619. Faculty: 234 (135 full-time, 99 part-time). Student-undergrad faculty ratio is 13:1. 2,959 applied, 41% were admitted. 12% from top 10% of their high school class, 38% from top quarter, 74% from top half. Full-time: 1,487 students, 50% women, 50% men. Part-time: 418 students, 55% women, 45% men. Students come from 28 states and territories, 48 other countries, 6% from out-of-state. 0.8% American Indian or Alaska Native, non-Hispanic/Latino; 29% Hispanic/Latino; 15% Black or African American, non-Hispanic/Latino; 1% Asian, non-Hispanic/Latino; 16% international. 29% 25 or older, 30% live on campus, 18% transferred in. Retention: 41% of full-time freshmen returned the following year. Academic areas with the most degrees conferred: business/marketing; psychology; interdisciplinary studies. Core. Calendar: semesters. Academic remediation for entering students, services for LD students, advanced placement, accelerated degree program, honors program, independent study, distance learning, double major, summer session for credit, part-time degree program, internships, graduate courses open to undergrads. Off campus study. Study abroad program. ROTC: Army (c), Air Force (c).

Entrance Requirements: Options: electronic application, deferred admission, international baccalaureate accepted. Required: minimum 2.5 high school GPA, minimum ACT score of 19 or SAT of 920, SAT or ACT. Required for some: essay, high school transcript. Entrance: moderately difficult. Application deadline: rolling. Notification: continuous. SAT Reasoning Test deadline: 8/1. SAT Subject Test deadline: 8/1. Transfer credits accepted: Yes.

Costs Per Year: Application fee: $0. Comprehensive fee: $40,859 includes full-time tuition ($26,328), mandatory fees ($3972), and college room and board ($10,559). College room only: $5986. Full-time tuition and fees vary according to course level, course load, degree level, and program. Room and board charges vary according to housing facility. Part-time tuition: $878 per credit hour. Part-time tuition varies according to course level, course load, degree level, and program.

Collegiate Environment: Orientation program. Drama-theater group, choral group, student-run newspaper, radio station. Social organizations: 37 open to all; national fraternities, national sororities, local fraternities, local sororities; 5% of eligible men and 4% of eligible women are members. Most popular organizations: Mortar Board, Delta Sigma Phi, Alpha Xi Delta, Bilingual Education Student Organization, Alpha Lambda Delta. Major annual events: President's Picnic, Homecoming, Club T-Dub (alcohol awareness). Student services: health clinic, personal-psychological counseling. Campus security: 24-hour emergency response devices and patrols, student patrols, late night transport-escort service, controlled dormitory access. Eunice and James L. West Library plus 1 other. Books: 185,461 (physical), 171,492 (digital/electronic); Serial titles: 1,500 (physical), 150,836 (digital/electronic); Databases: 104. Weekly public service hours: 101. Operations spending for the previous fiscal year: $1.3 million. 507 computers available on campus for general student use. A campuswide network can be accessed from student residence rooms and from off campus. Students can access the following: online class registration. Staffed computer lab on campus provides training in use of software and the Internet.

Community Environment: The campus is located in the Dallas/Fort Worth metropolitan area. Local public transportation is available in close proximity to the regional international airport, trains and buses. There are world-famous museums, cultural events, and professional football, basketball, baseball, and soccer teams in the area. The economy is widely diverse.

■ TEXAS WOMAN'S UNIVERSITY

304 Administration Dr.
Denton, TX 76204
Tel: (940)898-2000; Free: 866-809-6130
Fax: (940)898-3198
E-mail: admissions@twu.edu
Web Site: www.twu.edu

Description: State-supported, university, coed. Awards bachelor's, master's, and doctoral degrees and post-master's certificates. Founded 1901. Setting: 270-acre suburban campus with easy access to Dallas-Fort Worth. Endowment: $72.2 million. Research spending for the previous fiscal year: $4.9 million. Educational spending for the previous fiscal year: $6361 per student. Total enrollment: 15,520. Faculty: 939 (506 full-time, 433 part-time). Student-undergrad faculty ratio is 18:1. 5,727 applied, 87% were admitted. 18% from top 10% of their high school class, 49% from top quarter, 81% from top half. 5 valedictorians. Full-time: 6,880 students, 90% women, 10% men. Part-

time: 3,510 students, 83% women, 17% men. Students come from 32 states and territories, 23 other countries, 2% from out-of-state. 0.5% American Indian or Alaska Native, non-Hispanic/Latino; 30% Hispanic/Latino; 17% Black or African American, non-Hispanic/Latino; 9% Asian, non-Hispanic/Latino; 0.9% international. 22% 25 or older, 19% live on campus, 13% transferred in. Retention: 73% of full-time freshmen returned the following year. Academic areas with the most degrees conferred: health professions and related sciences; business/marketing; liberal arts/general studies. Core. Calendar: semesters. Academic remediation for entering students, services for LD students, advanced placement, accelerated degree program, honors program, independent study, distance learning, double major, summer session for credit, part-time degree program, adult/continuing education programs, co-op programs and internships, graduate courses open to undergrads. Off campus study at Federation of North Texas Area Universities. Study abroad program. ROTC: Army (c), Naval (c), Air Force (c).

Entrance Requirements: Open admission. Options: electronic application, early admission, deferred admission, international baccalaureate accepted. Required: minimum 2 high school GPA, Transcripts from prior colleges attended. Required for some: high school transcript, SAT or ACT. Entrance: moderately difficult. Application deadline: 8/25. Notification: continuous. Preference given to students graduating in the top 10% of class. SAT Reasoning Test deadline: 8/24. SAT Subject Test deadline: 8/24. Transfer credits accepted: Yes.

Costs Per Year: Application fee: $50. Area resident tuition: $6789 full-time, $226.30 per credit hour part-time. State resident tuition: $6789 full-time, $226.30 per credit hour part-time. Nonresident tuition: $19,449 full-time, $648.30 per credit hour part-time. Mandatory fees: $2959 full-time, $97.56 per credit hour part-time, $298 per term part-time. College room and board: $8950. College room only: $5250. Tuition guaranteed not to increase for student's term of enrollment.

Collegiate Environment: Orientation program. Drama-theater group, choral group, student-run newspaper. Social organizations: 172 open to all; national fraternities, national sororities, local fraternities, local sororities; 3% of eligible men and 4% of eligible women are members. Most popular organizations: Residence Hall Association, Helping Hands Service Ambassadors, Athenian Honor Society, Phi Kappa Phi Student Scholars, University Network Intercultural Team and Education. Major annual events: Spring Fling, Family Day, Athletic Events. Student services: legal services, health clinic, personal-psychological counseling, women's center. Campus security: 24-hour emergency response devices and patrols, late night transport-escort service, controlled dormitory access. 2,257 college housing spaces available; 2,021 were occupied in 2018-19. Freshmen guaranteed college housing. On-campus residence required through sophomore year. Options: coed, men-only, women-only housing available. Blagg-Huey Library. Books: 387,169 (physical), 504,151 (digital/electronic); Serial titles: 131,848 (physical), 209,764 (digital/electronic); Databases: 306. Weekly public service hours: 116; students can reserve study rooms. Operations spending for the previous fiscal year: $1.7 million. 296 computers available on campus for general student use. Computer purchase/lease plans available. A campuswide network can be accessed from student residence rooms and from off campus. Students can access the following: online class registration. Staffed computer lab on campus provides training in use of computers, software, and the Internet.

■ TRINITY UNIVERSITY

One Trinity Pl.
San Antonio, TX 78212-7200
Tel: (210)999-7011; Free: 800-TRINITY
Fax: (210)999-8164
E-mail: admissions@trinity.edu
Web Site: www.trinity.edu

Description: Independent, comprehensive, coed, affiliated with Presbyterian Church. Awards bachelor's and master's degrees. Founded 1869. Setting: 117-acre urban campus with easy access to San Antonio. Endowment: $1.2 billion. Educational spending for the previous fiscal year: $16,574 per student. Total enrollment: 2,604. Faculty: 322 (236 full-time, 86 part-time). Student-undergrad faculty ratio is 9:1. 7,663 applied, 38% were admitted. 45% from top 10% of their high school class, 76% from top quarter, 97% from top half. 9 National Merit Scholars. Full-time: 2,383 students, 54% women, 46% men. Part-time: 45 students, 42% women, 58% men. Students come from 48 states and territories, 62 other countries, 22% from out-of-state. 0.3% American Indian or Alaska Native, non-Hispanic/Latino; 21% Hispanic/Latino; 4% Black or African American, non-Hispanic/Latino; 7% Asian, non-Hispanic/Latino; 6% international. 80% live on campus, 1%

transferred in. Retention: 89% of full-time freshmen returned the following year. Academic areas with the most degrees conferred: business/marketing; social sciences; biological/life sciences. Core. Calendar: semesters. Services for LD students, advanced placement, accelerated degree program, self-designed majors, honors program, independent study, double major, summer session for credit, part-time degree program, internships. Off campus study at Special Studies Semesters in the US: American University Washington Semester and Marine Biological Laboratory's Semester in Environmental Science (SES) in Wood Hole, MA. Study abroad program. ROTC: Army (c), Air Force (c).

Entrance Requirements: Options: electronic application, early decision, early action, deferred admission, international baccalaureate accepted. Required: essay, high school transcript, 2 recommendations, SAT or ACT. Recommended: interview. Entrance: very difficult. Application deadlines: 2/1, 11/1 for early decision plan 1, 1/1 for early decision plan 2, 11/1 for early action. Notification: 4/1, 12/1 for early decision plan 1, 2/1 for early decision plan 2, 12/1 for early action. SAT Reasoning Test deadline: 2/1. Transfer credits accepted: Yes. Applicants placed on waiting list: 592. Wait-listed applicants offered admission: 43. Early decision applicants: 71. Early decision applicants admitted: 52. Early action applicants: 3,426. Early action applicants admitted: 2,356.

Costs Per Year: Application fee: $0. Comprehensive fee: $56,440 includes full-time tuition ($42,360), mandatory fees ($616), and college room and board ($13,464). College room only: $8690. Full-time tuition and fees vary according to course load. Room and board charges vary according to board plan. Part-time tuition: $1765 per credit hour. Part-time mandatory fees: $12.50 per credit hour. Part-time tuition and fees vary according to course load.

Collegiate Environment: Orientation program. Drama-theater group, choral group, student-run newspaper, radio station. Social organizations: 92 open to all; local fraternities, local sororities; 17% of eligible men and 32% of eligible women are members. Most popular organizations: Tiger Stand Band, Alpha Phi Omega, Association of Student Representatives, Acabellas/Trinitones, Multicultural Network. Major annual events: TigerFest Gala, Chocolate Festival, Trinity Spotlight. Student services: health clinic, personal-psychological counseling. Campus security: 24-hour emergency response devices and patrols, late night transport-escort service, controlled dormitory access. Elizabeth Huth Coates Library plus 1 other. Books: 716,500 (physical); Serial titles: 1,907 (physical), 95,000 (digital/electronic); Databases: 297. Weekly public service hours: 96; students can reserve study rooms. 500 computers available on campus for general student use. Computer purchase/lease plans available. A campuswide network can be accessed from student residence rooms and from off campus. Students can access the following: online class registration. Staffed computer lab on campus (open 24 hours a day) provides training in use of computers, software, and the Internet.

Community Environment: San Antonio, population of more than one million, is the 8th largest city in the United States and is rich in history. It has a healthy economy and supports many cultural, and recreational activities. An international airport provides wide access.

■ TRINITY VALLEY COMMUNITY COLLEGE
100 Cardinal Dr.
Athens, TX 75751-2765
Tel: (903)675-6200
Web Site: www.tvcc.edu
Description: State and locally supported, 2-year, coed. Awards certificates, diplomas, transfer associate, and terminal associate degrees. Founded 1946. Setting: 65-acre rural campus with easy access to Dallas-Fort Worth. Educational spending for the previous fiscal year: $4678 per student. Total enrollment: 4,449. Faculty: 247 (162 full-time, 85 part-time). Student-undergrad faculty ratio is 19:1. Students come from 28 states and territories, 15 other countries, 1% from out-of-state. 0.2% American Indian or Alaska Native, non-Hispanic/Latino; 2% Hispanic/Latino; 17% Black or African American, non-Hispanic/Latino; 0.5% Asian, non-Hispanic/Latino; 0.1% Native Hawaiian or other Pacific Islander, non-Hispanic/Latino. 44% 25 or older, 6% live on campus. Core. Calendar: semesters. Academic remediation for entering students, ESL program, services for LD students, advanced placement, honors program, independent study, distance learning, double major, summer session for credit, part-time degree program, adult/continuing education programs, co-op programs and internships.
Entrance Requirements: Open admission. Options: electronic application, early admission. Required: high school transcript. Entrance: noncompetitive. Application deadline: rolling. Notification: continuous. Transfer credits accepted: Yes.

Costs Per Year: Area resident tuition: $39 per credit hour part-time. State resident tuition: $39 per credit hour part-time. Nonresident tuition: $150 per credit hour part-time. Mandatory fees: $1470 full-time, $49 per credit hour part-time. College room and board: $5937.

Collegiate Environment: Orientation program. Drama-theater group, choral group, marching band, student-run newspaper. Social organizations: 3 open to all. Most popular organizations: Student Senate, Phi Theta Kappa, Delta Epsilon Chi. Major annual events: Homecoming, Cardette Spring Show. Student services: personal-psychological counseling. Campus security: 24-hour emergency response devices and patrols, controlled dormitory access. 500 college housing spaces available; 378 were occupied in 2018-19. No special consideration for freshman housing applicants. Options: coed, men-only, women-only housing available. Ginger Murchison Learning Resource Center plus 3 others. Books: 47,948 (physical), 49,908 (digital/electronic); Serial titles: 124 (physical), 3 (digital/electronic); Databases: 68. Operations spending for the previous fiscal year: $368,023. 944 computers available on campus for general student use. A campuswide network can be accessed from student residence rooms. Students can access the following: online class registration. Staffed computer lab on campus provides training in use of computers, software, and the Internet.

Community Environment: Population 12,559, Athens is a rural community located approximately 70 miles from Dallas. The climate is unusually mild and dry. The average high temperature is 95 degrees, and the low temperature range is 18 to 30 degrees, with an annual rainfall of 25 inches. Airport facilities, bus lines, and six major highways provide transportation for the city. There is a hospital, libraries, churches of various denominations, and various civic and fraternal organizations. Recreation includes theaters, drive-ins, hunting, fishing, golf, boating, tennis, parks, and swimming pools. Part-time employment is available.

■ TYLER JUNIOR COLLEGE
PO Box 9020
Tyler, TX 75711-9020
Tel: (903)510-2200; Free: 800-687-5680
Web Site: www.tjc.edu
Description: State and locally supported, primarily 2-year, coed. Awards certificates, diplomas, transfer associate, terminal associate, and bachelor's degrees. Founded 1926. Setting: 137-acre suburban campus. Endowment: $42.2 million. Total enrollment: 10,106. Faculty: 559 (313 full-time, 246 part-time). Student-undergrad faculty ratio is 20:1. 10,778 applied, 100% were admitted. Full-time: 6,026 students, 59% women, 41% men. Part-time: 4,080 students, 66% women, 34% men. Students come from 27 states and territories, 31 other countries, 3% from out-of-state. 0.9% American Indian or Alaska Native, non-Hispanic/Latino; 26% Hispanic/Latino; 21% Black or African American, non-Hispanic/Latino; 2% Asian, non-Hispanic/Latino; 0.1% Native Hawaiian or other Pacific Islander, non-Hispanic/Latino; 0.4% international. 24% 25 or older, 11% live on campus, 6% transferred in. Retention: 54% of full-time freshmen returned the following year. Core. Calendar: semesters. Academic remediation for entering students, services for LD students, advanced placement, accelerated degree program, freshman honors college, honors program, distance learning, summer session for credit, part-time degree program, adult/continuing education programs. Study abroad program.
Entrance Requirements: Open admission. Options: electronic application, early admission, international baccalaureate accepted. Required: high school transcript. Entrance: noncompetitive. Application deadline: rolling. Notification: continuous. Preference given to district residents. Transfer credits accepted: Yes.
Collegiate Environment: Orientation program. Drama-theater group, choral group, marching band, student-run newspaper. Social organizations: 48 open to all; national sororities, local fraternities, local sororities. Most popular organizations: Student Government, Religious Affiliation Clubs, Phi Theta Kappa. Major annual events: Homecoming, Annual Career Day, Fall Preview. Student services: health clinic, personal-psychological counseling. Campus security: 24-hour emergency response devices and patrols, controlled dormitory access. 1,206 college housing spaces available; all were occupied in 2018-19. No special consideration for freshman housing applicants. Options: coed, men-only, women-only housing available. Vaughn Library and Learning Resource Center. Books: 85,418 (physical), 135,816 (digital/electronic); Databases: 100. Weekly public service hours: 74. Operations spending for the previous fiscal year: $738,568.
Community Environment: Tyler, population 91,936, was incorporated in 1846 and named for President John Tyler who was responsible for bringing Texas into the Union. Industry is varied with production of fieldgrown rose

bushes for shipment throughout the United States, an economic mainstay. Located in the Pine region of East Texas, the community is reached by rail, bus, and air, as well as eight major highways. Community facilities include a symphony orchestra, a library system, hospitals, and medical facilities with Tyler being the medical center for East Texas. Local recreation includes golf courses, parks, and nearby Tyler State Park and Lake Tyler. Part-time employment is available.

■ **UNIVERSITY OF DALLAS**
1845 E Northgate Dr.
Irving, TX 75062-4736
Tel: (972)721-5000; Free: 800-628-6999
Fax: (972)721-5017
E-mail: crusader@udallas.edu
Web Site: www.udallas.edu

Description: Independent Roman Catholic, university, coed. Awards bachelor's, master's, and doctoral degrees and post-master's certificates. Founded 1955. Setting: 215-acre suburban campus with easy access to Dallas-Fort Worth. Endowment: $76 million. Research spending for the previous fiscal year: $101,835. Educational spending for the previous fiscal year: $9641 per student. Total enrollment: 2,542. Faculty: 194 (140 full-time, 54 part-time). Student-undergrad faculty ratio is 10:1. 4,188 applied, 61% were admitted. 41% from top 10% of their high school class, 66% from top quarter, 86% from top half. 7 National Merit Scholars, 7 valedictorians. Full-time: 1,447 students, 53% women, 47% men. Part-time: 24 students, 33% women, 67% men. Students come from 22 other countries, 47% from out-of-state. 0.4% American Indian or Alaska Native, non-Hispanic/Latino; 24% Hispanic/Latino; 2% Black or African American, non-Hispanic/Latino; 7% Asian, non-Hispanic/Latino; 0.1% Native Hawaiian or other Pacific Islander, non-Hispanic/Latino; 3% international. 2% 25 or older, 60% live on campus, 3% transferred in. Retention: 80% of full-time freshmen returned the following year. Academic areas with the most degrees conferred: business/marketing; social sciences; biological/life sciences. Core. Calendar: semesters. Services for LD students, advanced placement, self-designed majors, independent study, double major, summer session for credit, part-time degree program, internships, graduate courses open to undergrads. Off campus study at Dual degree program with University of Texas at Arlington in Electrical Engineering Dual degree program with Texas Woman's University in Nursing. Study abroad program. ROTC: Army (c), Air Force (c).

Entrance Requirements: Options: electronic application, early action, deferred admission, international baccalaureate accepted. Required: essay, high school transcript, 2 recommendations, SAT or ACT. Required for some: interview. Entrance: moderately difficult. Application deadlines: 8/1, 8/1 for nonresidents, 12/1 for early action. Notification: continuous, continuous for nonresidents, 1/15 for early action. SAT Reasoning Test deadline: 8/1. Transfer credits accepted: Yes.

Costs Per Year: Application fee: $50. Comprehensive fee: $56,412 includes full-time tuition ($40,652), mandatory fees ($3000), and college room and board ($12,760). College room only: $6900. Part-time tuition: $1653 per credit hour.

Collegiate Environment: Orientation program. Drama-theater group, choral group, student-run newspaper. Social organizations: 42 open to all. Most popular organizations: CAB (Campus Activities Board), Residence Hall Association, Student Government, Best Buddies, Alexander Hamilton Society. Major annual events: Charity Week, Groundhog, Spring Formal. Student services: health clinic, personal-psychological counseling. Campus security: 24-hour emergency response devices and patrols, late night transport-escort service, controlled dormitory access. 839 college housing spaces available; 726 were occupied in 2018-19. Freshmen guaranteed college housing. On-campus residence required through junior year. Options: coed, men-only, women-only housing available. William A. Blakley Library. Books: 235,868 (physical), 237,409 (digital/electronic); Serial titles: 294 (physical), 179 (digital/electronic); Databases: 215. Weekly public service hours: 99. Operations spending for the previous fiscal year: $1.6 million. 125 computers available on campus for general student use. Computer purchase/lease plans available. A campuswide network can be accessed from student residence rooms and from off campus. Students can access the following: online class registration. Staffed computer lab on campus (open 24 hours a day).

Community Environment: Population 193,600. Irving is a suburb of Dallas. The community enjoys a temperate climate. Transportation facilities in the community include a railroad, bus lines, excellent highways, and air lines at nearby Dallas and Fort Worth airports. The city has a public library, YMCA, many churches of various faiths, and hospital facilities. Some part-time employment is available. Local recreation includes four theaters, water sports on nearby lakes, and athletic facilities of neighboring communities. There are major civic, fraternal and veteran's organizations active in the area. The Dallas-Ft. Worth area has a population of nearly 3,000,000.

■ **UNIVERSITY OF HOUSTON**
4800 Calhoun Rd.
Houston, TX 77204
Tel: (713)743-1000
Fax: (713)743-9633
E-mail: mrmaxwe2@central.uh.edu
Web Site: www.uh.edu

Description: State-supported, university, coed. Part of University of Houston System. Awards bachelor's, master's, and doctoral degrees. Founded 1927. Setting: 594-acre urban campus with easy access to Houston. Endowment: $826.3 million. Research spending for the previous fiscal year: $151.8 million. Educational spending for the previous fiscal year: $6392 per student. Total enrollment: 46,324. Faculty: 2,450 (1,562 full-time, 888 part-time). Student-undergrad faculty ratio is 22:1. 22,461 applied, 62% were admitted. 32% from top 10% of their high school class, 66% from top quarter, 89% from top half. 17 National Merit Scholars, 36 valedictorians. Full-time: 28,029 students, 50% women, 50% men. Part-time: 10,319 students, 49% women, 51% men. Students come from 51 states and territories, 100 other countries, 2% from out-of-state. 0.1% American Indian or Alaska Native, non-Hispanic/Latino; 35% Hispanic/Latino; 10% Black or African American, non-Hispanic/Latino; 22% Asian, non-Hispanic/Latino; 0.1% Native Hawaiian or other Pacific Islander, non-Hispanic/Latino; 4% international. 16% 25 or older, 17% live on campus, 14% transferred in. Retention: 85% of full-time freshmen returned the following year. Academic areas with the most degrees conferred: business/marketing; engineering; psychology. Core. Calendar: semesters. Academic remediation for entering students, services for LD students, advanced placement, freshman honors college, honors program, independent study, distance learning, double major, summer session for credit, part-time degree program, adult/continuing education programs, co-op programs and internships, graduate courses open to undergrads. Off campus study at University of Texas Health Science Center, Baylor College of Medicine, Rice University, Texas Southern University. Study abroad program. ROTC: Army, Naval (c), Air Force.

Entrance Requirements: Options: electronic application, international baccalaureate accepted. Required: high school transcript, SAT or ACT. Entrance: moderately difficult. Application deadlines: 6/7, 6/7 for nonresidents. Notification: continuous, continuous for nonresidents. SAT Reasoning Test deadline: 6/15. Transfer credits accepted: Yes.

Costs Per Year: Application fee: $75. State resident tuition: $10,271 full-time, $342 per credit hour part-time. Nonresident tuition: $25,934 full-time, $864 per credit hour part-time. Mandatory fees: $1002 full-time. College room and board: $9368. Tuition guaranteed not to increase for student's term of enrollment.

Collegiate Environment: Orientation program. Drama-theater group, choral group, marching band, student-run newspaper, radio station. Social organizations: 430 open to all; national fraternities, national sororities; 4% of eligible men and 3% of eligible women are members. Most popular organizations: Graduate Indian Student Organization, Filipino Student Association, The National Society of Leadership and Success, Houston Panhellenic Council, Society of Women Engineers. Major annual events: Homecoming, Cat's Back, Frontier Fiesta. Student services: legal services, health clinic, personal-psychological counseling, women's center. Campus security: 24-hour emergency response devices and patrols, student patrols, late night transport-escort service, controlled dormitory access. 7,200 college housing spaces available; 6,368 were occupied in 2018-19. No special consideration for freshman housing applicants. Option: coed housing available. M. D. Anderson Library plus 4 others. Books: 1.5 million (physical), 724,075 (digital/electronic); Serial titles: 50,880 (physical), 108,834 (digital/electronic); Databases: 419. Weekly public service hours: 122; study areas open 24 hours, 5-7 days a week; students can reserve study rooms. Operations spending for the previous fiscal year: $21.7 million. 1,010 computers available on campus for general student use. Computer purchase/lease plans available. A campuswide network can be accessed from student residence rooms and from off campus. Students can access the following: online class registration, Bus loop schedule; Academic calendar; Student media; Alerts; Social Media Directory. Staffed computer lab on campus (open 24 hours a day) provides training in use of computers, software, and the Internet.

Community Environment: Population 2,016,582. Although Houston lies 50 miles inland, it is a major seaport due to the conversion of Buffalo Bayou into the Houston Ship Channel. The city was named in honor of Sam Houston, hero of the Battle of San Jacinto. The community has excellent air, bus, and railroad facilities. Many points of interest in the city include L. B. Johnson Manned Spacecraft Center, Texas Medical Center, Jones Hall, Wortham Theatre, Emron Baseball Field, Burke Barker Planetarium, Museum of Fine Arts, Contemporary Arts Museum, Zoological Gardens, and the San Jacinto Battleground and Monument, the Astrodome and Battleship U.S.S. Texas. There are over one thousand churches representing all the major denominations, excellent medical facilities, ample shopping centers, and good student housing in the area. Full- and part-time employment is available.

■ **UNIVERSITY OF HOUSTON-CLEAR LAKE**
2700 Bay Area Blvd.
Houston, TX 77058-1002
Tel: (281)283-7600
Fax: (281)283-2530
Web Site: www.uhcl.edu
Description: State-supported, comprehensive, coed. Part of University of Houston System. Awards bachelor's, master's, and doctoral degrees and post-master's certificates. Founded 1971. Setting: 524-acre suburban campus with easy access to Houston. Total enrollment: 8,961. Student-undergrad faculty ratio is 15:1. 1,830 applied, 45% were admitted. 14% from top 10% of their high school class, 41% from top quarter, 74% from top half. Full-time: 3,099 students, 60% women, 40% men. Part-time: 3,113 students, 65% women, 35% men. Students come from 19 other countries. 0.3% American Indian or Alaska Native, non-Hispanic/Latino; 41% Hispanic/Latino; 8% Black or African American, non-Hispanic/Latino; 6% Asian, non-Hispanic/Latino; 1% international. 50% 25 or older, 3% live on campus, 25% transferred in. Retention: 74% of full-time freshmen returned the following year. Academic areas with the most degrees conferred: business/marketing; interdisciplinary studies; psychology. Core. Calendar: semesters. Academic remediation for entering students, ESL program, services for LD students, advanced placement, independent study, distance learning, double major, summer session for credit, part-time degree program, internships, graduate courses open to undergrads. Off campus study. Study abroad program.
Entrance Requirements: Options: electronic application, early admission, deferred admission, international baccalaureate accepted. Required: high school transcript, State of Texas Uniform Admission Policy criteria, SAT or ACT. Required for some: essay, 2 recommendations. Entrance: minimally difficult. Application deadlines: 8/1, 8/1 for nonresidents. SAT Reasoning Test deadline: 8/1. Transfer credits accepted: Yes.
Costs Per Year: Application fee: $45. Area resident tuition: $6790 full-time. State resident tuition: $6790 full-time. Nonresident tuition: $22,980 full-time. Mandatory fees: $784 full-time. College room only: $4310.
Collegiate Environment: Orientation program. Drama-theater group, student-run newspaper. Social organizations: 106 open to all. Student services: health clinic, personal-psychological counseling, women's center. Campus security: 24-hour emergency response devices and patrols, student patrols, late night transport-escort service. 264 college housing spaces available; 259 were occupied in 2018-19. Freshmen given priority for college housing. Alfred R. Neuman Library. Books: 441,306 (physical), 503,332 (digital/electronic); Serial titles: 5,402 (physical), 93,891 (digital/electronic); Databases: 212. Weekly public service hours: 89; students can reserve study rooms. 723 computers available on campus for general student use. A campuswide network can be accessed from student residence rooms and from off campus. Students can access the following: online class registration. Staffed computer lab on campus provides training in use of computers, software, and the Internet.
Community Environment: A planned community 20 miles south of Houston, and 35 miles from Galveston, Texas. Mixture of education and space related employers. Many cultural activities available, both in the Clear Lake area, and within easy access of Houston. Abundance of outdoor recreational opportunities.

■ **UNIVERSITY OF HOUSTON-DOWNTOWN**
One Main St.
Houston, TX 77002
Tel: (713)221-8000
Fax: (713)221-8157
E-mail: uhdadmit@uhd.edu
Web Site: www.uhd.edu
Description: State-supported, comprehensive, coed. Part of University of Houston System. Awards bachelor's and master's degrees. Founded 1974. Setting: 24-acre urban campus. Total enrollment: 14,265. Faculty: 751 (371

full-time, 380 part-time). Student-undergrad faculty ratio is 19:1. 4,416 applied, 83% were admitted. 6% from top 10% of their high school class, 27% from top quarter, 68% from top half. Full-time: 6,201 students, 59% women, 41% men. Part-time: 6,479 students, 62% women, 38% men. 1% from out-of-state. 0.3% American Indian or Alaska Native, non-Hispanic/Latino; 50% Hispanic/Latino; 19% Black or African American, non-Hispanic/Latino; 9% Asian, non-Hispanic/Latino; 0.2% Native Hawaiian or other Pacific Islander, non-Hispanic/Latino; 6% international. 50% 25 or older, 17% transferred in. Retention: 71% of full-time freshmen returned the following year. Academic areas with the most degrees conferred: interdisciplinary studies; business/marketing; homeland security, law enforcement, firefighting, and protective services. Core. Calendar: semesters. Academic remediation for entering students, ESL program, services for LD students, advanced placement, honors program, independent study, distance learning, double major, summer session for credit, part-time degree program, internships, graduate courses open to undergrads. Off campus study. Study abroad program. ROTC: Army (c), Air Force (c).
Entrance Requirements: Options: electronic application, international baccalaureate accepted. Required: high school transcript, SAT or ACT. Entrance: noncompetitive. Application deadline: 6/1. SAT Reasoning Test deadline: 7/15. Transfer credits accepted: Yes.
Costs Per Year: Application fee: $50. State resident tuition: $6990 full-time, $233 per credit hour part-time. Nonresident tuition: $19,650 full-time, $655 per credit hour part-time. Mandatory fees: $1196 full-time.
Collegiate Environment: Orientation program. Drama-theater group, student-run newspaper, radio station. Social organizations: 90 open to all; national fraternities, national sororities, local sororities. Most popular organizations: Student Government Association, Campus Activities Board, Professional Accounting Society, American Marketing Association, Bilingual Education Student Organization. Major annual events: Bayou Bash, Welcome Week Activities, Homecoming Activities. Student services: legal services, health clinic, personal-psychological counseling. Campus security: 24-hour emergency response devices and patrols, late night transport-escort service. College housing not available. W. I. Dykes Library. Study areas open 24 hours, 5-7 days a week; students can reserve study rooms.

■ **UNIVERSITY OF HOUSTON-VICTORIA**
3007 N Ben Wilson St.
Victoria, TX 77901-4450
Tel: (361)570-4848; Free: 877-970-4848
Fax: (361)572-9377
E-mail: worthamt@uhv.edu
Web Site: www.uhv.edu
Description: State-supported, upper-level, coed. Part of University of Houston System. Awards bachelor's and master's degrees and post-master's certificates. Founded 1973. Setting: 20-acre small town campus. Endowment: $7.5 million. Research spending for the previous fiscal year: $264,909. Educational spending for the previous fiscal year: $3883 per student. Total enrollment: 4,407. Faculty: 239 (136 full-time, 103 part-time). Student-undergrad faculty ratio is 18:1. 3,950 applied, 56% were admitted. Full-time: 1,541 students, 64% women, 36% men. Part-time: 1,471 students, 68% women, 32% men. 0.2% American Indian or Alaska Native, non-Hispanic/Latino; 34% Hispanic/Latino; 16% Black or African American, non-Hispanic/Latino; 8% Asian, non-Hispanic/Latino; 0.2% Native Hawaiian or other Pacific Islander, non-Hispanic/Latino; 2% international. 56% 25 or older, 16% transferred in. Retention: 55% of full-time entering class returned the following year. Academic areas with the most degrees conferred: business/marketing; interdisciplinary studies; health professions and related sciences. Core. Calendar: semesters. Accelerated degree program, honors program, independent study, distance learning, double major, part-time degree program, adult/continuing education programs, internships, graduate courses open to undergrads. Study abroad program. ROTC: Air Force (c).
Entrance Requirements: Transfer credits accepted: Yes.
Costs Per Year: Application fee: $0. State resident tuition: $6,013 full-time, $200.42 per credit hour part-time. Nonresident tuition: $18,463 full-time, $615.42 per credit hour part-time. Mandatory fees: $1,717 full-time, $94.10 per credit hour part-time. Full-time tuition and fees vary according to course level and course load. Part-time tuition and fees vary according to course level and course load. College room and board: $7730. Room and board charges vary according to board plan and housing facility. Tuition guaranteed not to increase for student's term of enrollment.
Collegiate Environment: Orientation program. Student services: personal-psychological counseling. Campus security: 24-hour emergency response devices and patrols, controlled dormitory access. VC/UHV Library.

Community Environment: The campus is located in Victoria, a city of 58,000 inhabitants at the center of the South Texas Crossroads in the heart of the Golden Gulf Coast. This expanding city on the banks of the Guadalupe River is more than 150 years old, and is one of the first three towns chartered by The Republic of Texas. The city is near the Gulf of Mexico and is a popular coastal route between Houston and Mexico. The home of many petrochemical companies, such as DuPont, Alcoa, and Union Carbide, it is surrounded by vast expanses of ranchland.

■ UNIVERSITY OF THE INCARNATE WORD

4301 Broadway
San Antonio, TX 78209-6397
Tel: (210)829-6000; Free: 800-749-WORD
Fax: (210)829-3921
E-mail: jsdelaro@uiwtx.edu
Web Site: www.uiw.edu

Description: Independent Roman Catholic, comprehensive, coed. Awards associate, bachelor's, master's, and doctoral degrees. Founded 1881. Setting: 200-acre urban campus with easy access to San Antonio. Endowment: $142 million. Research spending for the previous fiscal year: $526,291. Educational spending for the previous fiscal year: $8961 per student. Total enrollment: 8,263. Faculty: 766 (347 full-time, 419 part-time). Student-undergrad faculty ratio is 15:1. 4,894 applied, 88% were admitted. 16% from top 10% of their high school class, 23% from top quarter, 72% from top half. Full-time: 4,103 students, 62% women, 38% men. Part-time: 1,455 students, 58% women, 42% men. Students come from 46 states and territories, 44 other countries, 6% from out-of-state. 0.3% American Indian or Alaska Native, non-Hispanic/Latino; 56% Hispanic/Latino; 7% Black or African American, non-Hispanic/Latino; 2% Asian, non-Hispanic/Latino; 0.3% Native Hawaiian or other Pacific Islander, non-Hispanic/Latino; 5% international. 37% 25 or older, 18% live on campus, 9% transferred in. Retention: 74% of full-time freshmen returned the following year. Academic areas with the most degrees conferred: business/marketing; health professions and related sciences; biological/life sciences. Core. Calendar: semesters. Academic remediation for entering students, ESL program, services for LD students, advanced placement, accelerated degree program, freshman honors college, honors program, independent study, distance learning, double major, summer session for credit, part-time degree program, adult/continuing education programs, co-op programs and internships, graduate courses open to undergrads. Off campus study at United Colleges of San Antonio Consortium for exchange of course offerings and of faculty members with Our Lady of the Lake University of San Antonio, St. Mary's University of San Antonio, and Oblate School of Theology. Study abroad program. ROTC: Army (c).

Entrance Requirements: Options: electronic application, deferred admission. Required: high school transcript, SAT or ACT. Recommended: minimum 2 high school GPA, interview. Required for some: essay. Entrance: minimally difficult. Application deadline: rolling. Notification: continuous. Transfer credits accepted: Yes.

Costs Per Year: Application fee: $20. Comprehensive fee: $45,400 includes full-time tuition ($29,900), mandatory fees ($2676), and college room and board ($12,824). Part-time tuition: $950 per credit hour.

Collegiate Environment: Orientation program. Drama-theater group, choral group, marching band, student-run newspaper, radio station. Social organizations: 104 open to all; national fraternities, national sororities, local fraternities, local sororities. Most popular organizations: Business Club, Biology Club, Student Government Association, International Students Association, Multicultural Greek Council. Major annual events: Light the Way, Asian New Year Celebration, Alamo Heights Night. Student services: health clinic, personal-psychological counseling. Campus security: 24-hour emergency response devices and patrols, late night transport-escort service, controlled dormitory access. 1,166 college housing spaces available; 1,014 were occupied in 2018-19. No special consideration for freshman housing applicants. Options: coed, men-only, women-only housing available. J. E. and M. E. Mabee Library plus 1 other. Books: 159,953 (physical), 60,292 (digital/electronic); Serial titles: 1,063 (physical), 86,652 (digital/electronic); Databases: 206. Weekly public service hours: 105. Operations spending for the previous fiscal year: $2.4 million. 406 computers available on campus for general student use. Computer purchase/lease plans available. A computer is required for all students. A campuswide network can be accessed from student residence rooms and from off campus. Students can access the following: online class registration. Staffed computer lab on campus provides training in use of computers, software, and the Internet.

Community Environment: See San Antonio College.

■ UNIVERSITY OF MARY HARDIN-BAYLOR

900 College St.
Belton, TX 76513
Tel: (254)295-8642; Free: 800-727-8642
Fax: (254)295-4535
E-mail: njones@umhb.edu
Web Site: www.umhb.edu

Description: Independent Southern Baptist, comprehensive, coed. Awards bachelor's, master's, and doctoral degrees and post-master's certificates. Founded 1845. Setting: 340-acre small town campus with easy access to Austin. Endowment: $88.2 million. Research spending for the previous fiscal year: $101,120. Educational spending for the previous fiscal year: $8626 per student. Total enrollment: 3,888. Faculty: 277 (167 full-time, 110 part-time). Student-undergrad faculty ratio is 18:1. 11,783 applied, 87% were admitted. 18% from top 10% of their high school class, 45% from top quarter, 76% from top half. Full-time: 3,181 students, 64% women, 36% men. Part-time: 216 students, 72% women, 28% men. Students come from 34 states and territories, 25 other countries, 3% from out-of-state. 0.8% American Indian or Alaska Native, non-Hispanic/Latino; 22% Hispanic/Latino; 14% Black or African American, non-Hispanic/Latino; 2% Asian, non-Hispanic/Latino; 0.1% Native Hawaiian or other Pacific Islander, non-Hispanic/Latino; 0.9% international. 13% 25 or older, 59% live on campus, 7% transferred in. Retention: 73% of full-time freshmen returned the following year. Academic areas with the most degrees conferred: health professions and related sciences; business/marketing; education. Core. Calendar: semesters. Academic remediation for entering students, ESL program, services for LD students, advanced placement, honors program, independent study, distance learning, double major, summer session for credit, part-time degree program, adult/continuing education programs, internships, graduate courses open to undergrads. Off campus study. Study abroad program. ROTC: Army, Air Force (c).

Entrance Requirements: Options: electronic application, early admission, deferred admission. Required: high school transcript, SAT or ACT. Required for some: essay, interview. Entrance: moderately difficult. Application deadline: rolling. Notification: continuous. Transfer credits accepted: Yes.

Costs Per Year: Application fee: $35. Comprehensive fee: $35,336 includes full-time tuition ($24,640), mandatory fees ($2250), and college room and board ($8446). Full-time tuition and fees vary according to course load and degree level. Room and board charges vary according to board plan and housing facility. Part-time tuition: $880 per credit hour. Part-time tuition varies according to course load and degree level.

Collegiate Environment: Orientation program. Drama-theater group, choral group, student-run newspaper. Social organizations: 58 open to all. Most popular organizations: Baptist Student Ministry, Student Government Association, Nursing Student Association, Campus Activities Board, Search Cru. Major annual events: Homecoming, Easter Pageant, Play Day. Student services: health clinic, personal-psychological counseling. Campus security: 24-hour emergency response devices and patrols, late night transport-escort service, controlled dormitory access. 2,112 college housing spaces available; 2,020 were occupied in 2018-19. Freshmen given priority for college housing. Options: men-only, women-only housing available. Townsend Memorial Library. Books: 183,933 (physical), 28,294 (digital/electronic); Serial titles: 340 (physical), 277,950 (digital/electronic); Databases: 146. Weekly public service hours: 99; students can reserve study rooms. Operations spending for the previous fiscal year: $903,026. 275 computers available on campus for general student use. Computer purchase/lease plans available. A campuswide network can be accessed from student residence rooms and from off campus. Students can access the following: online class registration. Staffed computer lab on campus.

Community Environment: Belton, population 15,530, located in central Texas, has a mild climate. The community is served by railroad lines, bus lines, U.S. Highway I-35 and Texas State 317. There is an airport 15 miles away. Local community services include a library, museum, several churches, a hospital, and various civic, fraternal and veteran's organizations. The city is a one-hour drive from Waco and Austin for out-of-town entertainment. Belton has nearby Lake Belton for fishing, water skiing, swimming, and speed boat races. Part-time employment is available.

■ UNIVERSITY OF NORTH TEXAS

1155 Union Cir. No.311425
Denton, TX 76203
Tel: (940)565-2000; Free: 800-868-8211
Fax: (940)565-2408
E-mail: randall.nunn@unt.edu

Web Site: www.unt.edu

Description: State-supported, university, coed. Part of University of North Texas System. Awards bachelor's, master's, and doctoral degrees. Founded 1890. Setting: 875-acre suburban campus with easy access to Dallas-Fort Worth. Endowment: $166.4 million. Research spending for the previous fiscal year: $27.7 million. Educational spending for the previous fiscal year: $6568 per student. Total enrollment: 38,081. Faculty: 1,683 (1,118 full-time, 565 part-time). Student-undergrad faculty ratio is 24:1. 16,826 applied, 72% were admitted. 20% from top 10% of their high school class, 50% from top quarter, 90% from top half. 26 National Merit Scholars. Full-time: 25,618 students, 53% women, 47% men. Part-time: 5,787 students, 48% women, 52% men. Students come from 54 states and territories, 139 other countries, 3% from out-of-state. 0.3% American Indian or Alaska Native, non-Hispanic/Latino; 25% Hispanic/Latino; 14% Black or African American, non-Hispanic/Latino; 6% Asian, non-Hispanic/Latino; 0.1% Native Hawaiian or other Pacific Islander, non-Hispanic/Latino; 3% international. 15% 25 or older, 19% live on campus, 13% transferred in. Retention: 78% of full-time freshmen returned the following year. Academic areas with the most degrees conferred: business/marketing; interdisciplinary studies; liberal arts/general studies. Core. Calendar: semesters. Academic remediation for entering students, ESL program, services for LD students, advanced placement, accelerated degree program, freshman honors college, honors program, independent study, distance learning, double major, summer session for credit, part-time degree program, co-op programs and internships, graduate courses open to undergrads. Off campus study. Study abroad program. ROTC: Army, Air Force.

Entrance Requirements: Options: electronic application, early admission, deferred admission, international baccalaureate accepted. Required: high school transcript, SAT or ACT. Required for some: essay. Entrance: moderately difficult. Application deadline: 8/1. Notification: continuous. SAT Reasoning Test deadline: 8/10. Transfer credits accepted: Yes.

Costs Per Year: Application fee: $75. State resident tuition: $8,403 full-time, $280.11 per semester hour part-time. Nonresident tuition: $20,853 full-time, $695.11 per semester hour part-time. Mandatory fees: $2,847 full-time, $94.90 per semester hour part-time. Full-time tuition and fees vary according to course load and program. Part-time tuition and fees vary according to course load and program. College room and board: $9727. Room and board charges vary according to board plan and housing facility. Tuition guaranteed not to increase for student's term of enrollment.

Collegiate Environment: Orientation program. Drama-theater group, choral group, marching band, student-run newspaper, radio station. Social organizations: 373 open to all; national fraternities, national sororities; 5% of eligible men and 6% of eligible women are members. Most popular organizations: Student Government Association, Residence Hall Association, Panhellenic Association, Interfraternity Council, Black Student Union. Major annual events: Homecoming, University Day, Mean Green Spring Fling. Student services: legal services, health clinic, personal-psychological counseling. Campus security: 24-hour emergency response devices and patrols, late night transport-escort service, controlled dormitory access. Willis Library plus 5 others. Books: 2.1 million (physical), 1 million (digital/electronic); Serial titles: 19,763 (physical), 166,076 (digital/electronic); Databases: 391. Weekly public service hours: 168; study areas open 24 hours, 5-7 days a week; students can reserve study rooms. Operations spending for the previous fiscal year: $18 million. 925 computers available on campus for general student use. A campuswide network can be accessed from student residence rooms and from off campus. Students can access the following: online class registration. Staffed computer lab on campus (open 24 hours a day) provides training in use of computers, software, and the Internet.

Community Environment: Denton is a community of approximately 73,050. Texas' largest and most modern airport, Dallas - Fort Worth International, is only a short drive from Denton.

■ **UNIVERSITY OF NORTH TEXAS AT DALLAS**
7300 University Hills Blvd.
Dallas, TX 75241
Tel: (972)780-3600
E-mail: admissions@untdallas.edu
Web Site: untdallas.edu

Description: State-supported, comprehensive, coed. Part of University of North Texas System. Awards bachelor's, master's, and doctoral degrees. Founded 2001. Setting: 264-acre urban campus with easy access to Dallas-Fort Worth. Endowment: $823,724. Research spending for the previous fiscal year: $4129. Educational spending for the previous fiscal year: $4792 per student. Total enrollment: 3,509. Faculty: 167 (94 full-time, 73 part-time). Student-undergrad faculty ratio is 15:1. 1,483 applied, 74% were admitted. 25% from top 10% of their high school class, 47% from top quarter, 80% from top half. Full-time: 1,705 students, 67% women, 33% men. Part-time: 1,022 students, 70% women, 30% men. Students come from 11 states and territories, 17 other countries, 1% from out-of-state. 0.1% American Indian or Alaska Native, non-Hispanic/Latino; 52% Hispanic/Latino; 31% Black or African American, non-Hispanic/Latino; 2% Asian, non-Hispanic/Latino; 0.1% Native Hawaiian or other Pacific Islander, non-Hispanic/Latino; 1% international. 47% 25 or older, 20% transferred in. Retention: 66% of full-time freshmen returned the following year. Academic areas with the most degrees conferred: interdisciplinary studies; business/marketing; homeland security, law enforcement, firefighting, and protective services. Core. Services for LD students, advanced placement, accelerated degree program, independent study, distance learning, summer session for credit, part-time degree program, co-op programs and internships, graduate courses open to undergrads. Off campus study.

Entrance Requirements: Option: electronic application. Required: high school transcript, SAT or ACT. Application deadline: 8/15. Transfer credits accepted: Yes.

Costs Per Year: Application fee: $50. State resident tuition: $7548 full-time, $251.63 per credit hour part-time. Nonresident tuition: $19,788 full-time, $659.63 per credit hour part-time. Mandatory fees: $300 full-time, $10 per credit hour part-time. Full-time tuition and fees vary according to degree level. Part-time tuition and fees vary according to degree level. College room and board: $8948. Room and board charges vary according to board plan and housing facility. Tuition guaranteed not to increase for student's term of enrollment.

Collegiate Environment: Orientation program. Social organizations: national fraternities, national sororities; 1% of eligible men and 1% of eligible women are members. Major annual events: Welcome Week, Jaguar Welcome Convocation, Spring Fling Week. Student services: personal-psychological counseling. Campus security: 24-hour emergency response devices, late night transport-escort service. UNTD Library. Books: 3,980 (physical), 44,401 (digital/electronic); Serial titles: 330 (physical), 10,899 (digital/electronic); Databases: 281. Operations spending for the previous fiscal year: $10,083.

■ **UNIVERSITY OF PHOENIX-DALLAS CAMPUS**
12400 Coit Rd.
Dallas, TX 75251
Tel: (972)385-1055; Free: 866-766-0766
Fax: (972)385-1700
Web Site: www.phoenix.edu

Description: Proprietary, comprehensive, coed. Awards bachelor's and master's degrees. Founded 2001. Setting: urban campus. Total enrollment: 1,371. Faculty: 181 (15 full-time, 166 part-time). Full-time: 1,075 students, 64% women, 36% men. 90% 25 or older. Academic areas with the most degrees conferred: business/marketing; public administration and social services. Core. Calendar: continuous. Services for LD students, advanced placement, accelerated degree program, independent study, distance learning, external degree program, adult/continuing education programs, graduate courses open to undergrads.

Entrance Requirements: Open admission. Options: electronic application, deferred admission. Required: 1 recommendation. Required for some: high school transcript. Entrance: noncompetitive. Application deadline: rolling.

Collegiate Environment: Campus security: late night transport-escort service. Operations spending for the previous fiscal year: $6.8 million.

■ **UNIVERSITY OF PHOENIX-HOUSTON CAMPUS**
11451 Katy Fwy.
Ste. 100
Houston, TX 77079-2004
Tel: (281)596-0363; Free: 866-766-0766
Fax: (281)596-0336
Web Site: www.phoenix.edu

Description: Proprietary, comprehensive, coed. Awards bachelor's and master's degrees. Founded 2001. Setting: urban campus. Total enrollment: 2,748. Faculty: 325 (16 full-time, 309 part-time). Full-time: 2,286 students, 68% women, 32% men. 89% 25 or older. Academic areas with the most degrees conferred: business/marketing; health professions and related sciences. Core. Calendar: continuous. Services for LD students, advanced placement, accelerated degree program, independent study, distance learning, external degree program, adult/continuing education programs, graduate courses open to undergrads.

Entrance Requirements: Open admission. Options: electronic application, deferred admission. Required: 1 recommendation. Required for some: high school transcript. Entrance: noncompetitive. Application deadline: rolling.

Collegiate Environment: Campus security: late night transport-escort service. University Library. Operations spending for the previous fiscal year: $6.8 million.

■ UNIVERSITY OF PHOENIX-SAN ANTONIO CAMPUS

8200 IH-10 W

San Antonio, TX 78230

Tel: (210)524-2100; Free: 866-766-0766

Web Site: www.phoenix.edu

Description: Proprietary, comprehensive, coed. Awards bachelor's, master's, and doctoral degrees.

■ UNIVERSITY OF ST. THOMAS

3800 Montrose Blvd.

Houston, TX 77006-4696

Tel: (713)522-7911; Free: 800-856-8565

Fax: (713)525-3558

E-mail: admissions@stthom.edu

Web Site: www.stthom.edu

Description: Independent Roman Catholic, comprehensive, coed. Awards bachelor's, master's, and doctoral degrees. Founded 1947. Setting: 23-acre urban campus with easy access to Houston, TX. Endowment: $102.4 million. Educational spending for the previous fiscal year: $12,838 per student. Total enrollment: 3,314. Faculty: 337 (154 full-time, 183 part-time). Student-undergrad faculty ratio is 10:1. 1,216 applied, 82% were admitted. 23% from top 10% of their high school class, 52% from top quarter, 81% from top half. Full-time: 1,573 students, 68% women, 32% men. Part-time: 474 students, 43% women, 57% men. Students come from 33 states and territories, 58 other countries, 2% from out-of-state. 0.2% American Indian or Alaska Native, non-Hispanic/Latino; 47% Hispanic/Latino; 7% Black or African American, non-Hispanic/Latino; 12% Asian, non-Hispanic/Latino; 0.2% Native Hawaiian or other Pacific Islander, non-Hispanic/Latino; 8% international. 27% 25 or older, 20% live on campus, 10% transferred in. Retention: 82% of full-time freshmen returned the following year. Academic areas with the most degrees conferred: business/marketing; biological/life sciences; liberal arts/general studies. Core. Calendar: semesters. Services for LD students, advanced placement, accelerated degree program, self-designed majors, honors program, independent study, distance learning, double major, summer session for credit, part-time degree program, adult/continuing education programs, internships, graduate courses open to undergrads. Off campus study at Glassell School of Art, Notre Dame, Texas Women University, The Catholic University of America. Study abroad program. ROTC: Army (c), Air Force (c).

Entrance Requirements: Options: electronic application, early action, deferred admission, international baccalaureate accepted. Required: minimum 2.8 high school GPA, SAT or ACT. Recommended: 3 recommendations. Entrance: moderately difficult. Notification: continuous until 11/1. SAT Reasoning Test deadline: 8/1. SAT Subject Test deadline: 8/1. Transfer credits accepted: Yes.

Costs Per Year: Application fee: $0. Comprehensive fee: $40,760 includes full-time tuition ($30,800), mandatory fees ($660), and college room and board ($9300). College room only: $5710. Part-time tuition: $1100 per credit hour.

Collegiate Environment: Orientation program. Drama-theater group, choral group. Social organizations: 80 open to all. Most popular organizations: Health Occupations Students of America (HOSA), Filipino Student Association (FSA), Tri-Beta, Psi Chi, Pre-Health Professional Society. Major annual events: Neewollah-Annual Halloween Party, Late Night Breakfast, Deck the Mall. Student services: personal-psychological counseling. Campus security: 24-hour emergency response devices and patrols, late night transport-escort service, controlled dormitory access. 400 college housing spaces available; 386 were occupied in 2018-19. Freshmen given priority for college housing. Options: coed, men-only, women-only housing available. Doherty Library. Books: 262,245 (physical), 2,496 (digital/electronic); Serial titles: 74,347 (physical), 74,347 (digital/electronic); Databases: 274. Weekly public service hours: 100. Operations spending for the previous fiscal year: $1.9 million. 490 computers available on campus for general student use. Computer purchase/lease plans available. A campuswide network can be accessed from student residence rooms. Students can access the following: online class registration. Staffed computer lab on campus.

■ THE UNIVERSITY OF TEXAS AT ARLINGTON

701 S Nedderman Dr.

Arlington, TX 76019

Tel: (817)272-2011

Fax: (817)272-5656

Web Site: www.uta.edu

Description: State-supported, university, coed. Part of University of Texas System. Awards bachelor's, master's, and doctoral degrees and post-master's certificates. Founded 1895. Setting: 420-acre urban campus with easy access to Dallas-Fort Worth. Endowment: $115.3 million. Research spending for the previous fiscal year: $58.5 million. Educational spending for the previous fiscal year: $2698 per student. Total enrollment: 39,740. 10,245 applied, 61% were admitted. 27% from top 10% of their high school class, 72% from top quarter, 96% from top half. Full-time: 15,957 students, 52% women, 48% men. Part-time: 13,926 students, 70% women, 30% men. Students come from 55 states and territories, 91 other countries, 11% from out-of-state. 0.3% American Indian or Alaska Native, non-Hispanic/Latino; 24% Hispanic/Latino; 15% Black or African American, non-Hispanic/Latino; 11% Asian, non-Hispanic/Latino; 0.3% Native Hawaiian or other Pacific Islander, non-Hispanic/Latino; 5% international. 46% 25 or older, 13% live on campus, 19% transferred in. Retention: 69% of full-time freshmen returned the following year. Academic areas with the most degrees conferred: health professions and related sciences; business/marketing; biological/life sciences; liberal arts/general studies; interdisciplinary studies; engineering. Core. Calendar: 4-1-4-1. Academic remediation for entering students, ESL program, services for LD students, advanced placement, self-designed majors, freshman honors college, honors program, independent study, distance learning, double major, summer session for credit, part-time degree program, adult/continuing education programs, co-op programs and internships, graduate courses open to undergrads. Off campus study. Study abroad program. ROTC: Army, Air Force (c).

Entrance Requirements: Options: electronic application, deferred admission, international baccalaureate accepted. Required: high school transcript, class rank, SAT or ACT. Entrance: moderately difficult. Application deadline: 6/1. Notification: continuous. SAT Reasoning Test deadline: 6/1. Transfer credits accepted: Yes.

Costs Per Year: Application fee: $60. State resident tuition: $10,250 full-time. Nonresident tuition: $25,134 full-time. Full-time tuition varies according to course load, degree level, location, program, and reciprocity agreements. College room and board: $10,302. Room and board charges vary according to board plan and housing facility.

Collegiate Environment: Orientation program. Drama-theater group, choral group, marching band, student-run newspaper, radio station. Social organizations: 300 open to all; national fraternities, national sororities, local fraternities, local sororities; 5% of eligible men and 3% of eligible women are members. Most popular organizations: Delta Delta Delta Sorority, EXCEL Campus Activities, Baptist Student Ministry, Honors College Council, Beta Alpha Psi - Accounting. Major annual events: Homecoming Activities, Activities Fair Day/Maverick Cook Out, MavsMeet Convocation and After Party. Student services: legal services, health clinic, personal-psychological counseling. Campus security: 24-hour emergency response devices and patrols, late night transport-escort service, controlled dormitory access, remote emergency telephones, bicycle patrols, crime prevention program, student shuttle service. Central Library plus 2 others. Operations spending for the previous fiscal year: $11.8 million. 500 computers available on campus for general student use. A campuswide network can be accessed from student residence rooms. Students can access the following: online class registration. Staffed computer lab on campus (open 24 hours a day).

■ THE UNIVERSITY OF TEXAS AT AUSTIN

Austin, TX 78712-1111

Tel: (512)471-3434

Fax: (512)475-7475

E-mail: admissions@austin.utexas.edu

Web Site: www.utexas.edu

Description: State-supported, university, coed. Part of University of Texas System. Awards bachelor's, master's, and doctoral degrees. Founded 1883. Setting: 431-acre urban campus with easy access to Austin. System endowment: $4 billion. Research spending for the previous fiscal year: $539.3 million. Educational spending for the previous fiscal year: $14,688 per student. Total enrollment: 51,832. Faculty: 2,994 (2,472 full-time, 522 part-time). Student-undergrad faculty ratio is 18:1. 50,575 applied, 39% were admitted. 85% from top 10% of their high school class, 95% from top quarter, 99% from top half. Full-time: 38,097 students, 54% women, 46% men. Part-time:

2,707 students, 48% women, 52% men. Students come from 52 states and territories, 102 other countries, 6% from out-of-state. 0.1% American Indian or Alaska Native, non-Hispanic/Latino; 24% Hispanic/Latino; 4% Black or African American, non-Hispanic/Latino; 22% Asian, non-Hispanic/Latino; 0.1% Native Hawaiian or other Pacific Islander, non-Hispanic/Latino; 5% international. 3% 25 or older, 18% live on campus, 4% transferred in. Retention: 95% of full-time freshmen returned the following year. Academic areas with the most degrees conferred: engineering; business/marketing; communication/journalism; social sciences. Core. Calendar: semesters. Academic remediation for entering students, ESL program, services for LD students, advanced placement, accelerated degree program, self-designed majors, honors program, independent study, distance learning, double major, summer session for credit, part-time degree program, co-op programs and internships, graduate courses open to undergrads. Off campus study at The University of Texas Health Science Center at Houston School of Public Health. Study abroad program. ROTC: Army, Naval, Air Force.

Entrance Requirements: Options: electronic application, international baccalaureate accepted. Required: essay, high school transcript, SAT or ACT. Entrance: moderately difficult. Application deadlines: 12/1, 12/1 for nonresidents. Notification: continuous. SAT Reasoning Test deadline: 12/31. Transfer credits accepted: Yes. Applicants placed on waiting list: 0. Waitlisted applicants offered admission: 0.

Costs Per Year: Application fee: $75. State resident tuition: $10,606 full-time. Nonresident tuition: $37,480 full-time. Full-time tuition varies according to course load and program. College room and board: $10,804. Room and board charges vary according to housing facility. Tuition guaranteed not to increase for student's term of enrollment.

Collegiate Environment: Orientation program. Drama-theater group, choral group, marching band, student-run newspaper, radio station. Social organizations: 1,184 open to all; national fraternities, national sororities, local fraternities, local sororities; 13% of eligible men and 20% of eligible women are members. Most popular organizations: Alpha Phi Omega, University Panhellenic Council, Asian Business Students Association, Longhorn Band Student Organization, Campus Events + Entertainment. Major annual events: Gone to Texas (freshman welcome), 40 Acres Fest, Commencement. Student services: legal services, health clinic, personal-psychological counseling, women's center. Campus security: 24-hour emergency response devices and patrols, late night transport-escort service, controlled dormitory access. 8,100 college housing spaces available; 7,412 were occupied in 2018-19. Freshmen given priority for college housing. Options: coed, men-only, women-only housing available. PCL (Perry Castaneda Library) plus 19 others. Books: 11.5 million (physical), 1.5 million (digital/electronic); Serial titles: 252,967 (physical), 471,535 (digital/electronic); Databases: 941. Weekly public service hours: 94; study areas open 24 hours, 5-7 days a week; students can reserve study rooms. Operations spending for the previous fiscal year: $35.3 million. 3,150 computers available on campus for general student use. A campuswide network can be accessed from student residence rooms and from off campus. Students can access the following: online class registration. Staffed computer lab on campus provides training in use of computers, software, and the Internet.

■ THE UNIVERSITY OF TEXAS AT DALLAS

800 W Campbell Rd.
Richardson, TX 75080
Tel: (972)883-2111; Free: 800-889-2443
Fax: (972)883-6803
E-mail: interest@utdallas.edu
Web Site: www.utdallas.edu

Description: State-supported, university, coed. Part of University of Texas System. Awards bachelor's, master's, and doctoral degrees. Founded 1969. Setting: 500-acre suburban campus with easy access to Dallas-Fort Worth. Endowment: $482.8 million. Research spending for the previous fiscal year: $113.2 million. Educational spending for the previous fiscal year: $16,424 per student. Total enrollment: 27,642. Faculty: 1,319 (895 full-time, 424 part-time). Student-undergrad faculty ratio is 23:1. 11,791 applied, 76% were admitted. 35% from top 10% of their high school class, 64% from top quarter, 89% from top half. 157 National Merit Scholars, 38 valedictorians. Full-time: 15,294 students, 43% women, 57% men. Part-time: 3,094 students, 43% women, 57% men. Students come from 48 states and territories, 78 other countries, 4% from out-of-state. 0.2% American Indian or Alaska Native, non-Hispanic/Latino; 18% Hispanic/Latino; 6% Black or African American, non-Hispanic/Latino; 31% Asian, non-Hispanic/Latino; 0.2% Native Hawaiian or other Pacific Islander, non-Hispanic/Latino; 4% international. 17% 25 or older, 26% live on campus, 11% transferred in. Retention: 87% of full-time

freshmen returned the following year. Academic areas with the most degrees conferred: business/marketing; biological/life sciences; engineering. Core. Calendar: semesters. Academic remediation for entering students, services for LD students, advanced placement, accelerated degree program, self-designed majors, freshman honors college, honors program, independent study, distance learning, double major, summer session for credit, part-time degree program, adult/continuing education programs, co-op programs and internships, graduate courses open to undergrads. Study abroad program. ROTC: Army (c), Air Force (c).

Entrance Requirements: Options: electronic application, deferred admission, international baccalaureate accepted. Required: essay, high school transcript, SAT or ACT. Recommended: 3 recommendations. Required for some: interview, THEA. Entrance: very difficult. Application deadline: 5/1. Notification: continuous. SAT Reasoning Test deadline: 8/1. SAT Subject Test deadline: 8/1. Transfer credits accepted: Yes.

Costs Per Year: Application fee: $50. State resident tuition: $13,034 full-time. Nonresident tuition: $36,876 full-time. Full-time tuition varies according to course load and degree level. College room and board: $11,532. Room and board charges vary according to board plan and housing facility. Tuition guaranteed not to increase for student's term of enrollment.

Collegiate Environment: Orientation program. Drama-theater group, choral group, student-run newspaper, radio station. Social organizations: 438 open to all; national fraternities, national sororities, local fraternities, local sororities; 6% of eligible men and 7% of eligible women are members. Most popular organizations: Student Government Association, Golden Key National Honor Society, Muslim Students Association, Indian Student Association, Friendship Association of Chinese Students and Scholars. Major annual events: Jazz Concert, Homecoming Dance, Holiday Sing. Student services: legal services, health clinic, personal-psychological counseling, women's center. Campus security: 24-hour emergency response devices and patrols, student patrols, late night transport-escort service, controlled dormitory access. Eugene McDermott Library plus 1 other. Books: 652,018 (physical), 1.5 million (digital/electronic); Serial titles: 135,287 (physical), 149,406 (digital/electronic); Databases: 530. Weekly public service hours: 152; study areas open 24 hours, 5-7 days a week; students can reserve study rooms. Operations spending for the previous fiscal year: $9.1 million. 170 computers available on campus for general student use. Computer purchase/lease plans available. A campuswide network can be accessed from student residence rooms and from off campus. Students can access the following: online class registration. Staffed computer lab on campus provides training in use of computers, software, and the Internet.

■ THE UNIVERSITY OF TEXAS AT EL PASO

500 W University Ave.
El Paso, TX 79968-0001
Tel: (915)747-5000; Free: 877-74MINER
Fax: (915)747-5122
E-mail: futureminer@utep.edu
Web Site: www.utep.edu

Description: State-supported, university, coed. Part of University of Texas System. Awards bachelor's, master's, and doctoral degrees. Founded 1913. Setting: 360-acre urban campus. Total enrollment: 25,151. Faculty: 1,315 (799 full-time, 516 part-time). Student-undergrad faculty ratio is 21:1. 9,382 applied, 100% were admitted. 18% from top 10% of their high school class, 39% from top quarter, 67% from top half. Full-time: 14,044 students, 52% women, 48% men. Part-time: 7,420 students, 55% women, 45% men. Students come from 53 states and territories, 80 other countries, 4% from out-of-state. 0.1% American Indian or Alaska Native, non-Hispanic/Latino; 83% Hispanic/Latino; 2% Black or African American, non-Hispanic/Latino; 0.9% Asian, non-Hispanic/Latino; 0.1% Native Hawaiian or other Pacific Islander, non-Hispanic/Latino; 6% international. 22% 25 or older, 9% transferred in. Retention: 73% of full-time freshmen returned the following year. Academic areas with the most degrees conferred: business/marketing; health professions and related sciences; engineering. Calendar: semesters. Honors program, independent study, distance learning, double major. Study abroad program. ROTC: Army.

Entrance Requirements: Option: deferred admission. Required: high school transcript, SAT or ACT. Entrance: minimally difficult. Transfer credits accepted: Yes.

Collegiate Environment: Drama-theater group, choral group, marching band, student-run newspaper, radio station. Social organizations: national fraternities, national sororities. Student services: legal services, health clinic, personal-psychological counseling, women's center. Campus security: 24-hour emergency response devices and patrols, late night transport-escort service. 988 college housing spaces available; 642 were occupied in 2018-19. No special consideration for freshman housing applicants. Option: coed housing available. University Library. Books: 914,412 (physical), 407,455 (digital/electronic); Serial titles: 15,278 (physical), 101,613 (digital/electronic); Databases: 395.

■ THE UNIVERSITY OF TEXAS HEALTH SCIENCE CENTER AT HOUSTON

PO Box 20036
Houston, TX 77225-0036
Tel: (713)500-3333
Fax: (713)500-3026
Web Site: www.uthouston.edu
Description: State-supported, upper-level, coed. Part of University of Texas System. Awards bachelor's, master's, and doctoral degrees and post-master's certificates. Founded 1972. Setting: urban campus with easy access to Houston. Endowment: $217.5 million. Research spending for the previous fiscal year: $182.2 million. Educational spending for the previous fiscal year: $122,583 per student. Total enrollment: 4,811. Faculty: 128 (84 full-time, 44 part-time). Student-undergrad faculty ratio is 9:1. Full-time: 534 students, 87% women, 13% men. Part-time: 143 students, 78% women, 22% men. Students come from 2 states and territories, 4 other countries, 1% from out-of-state. 1% American Indian or Alaska Native, non-Hispanic/Latino; 23% Hispanic/Latino; 11% Black or African American, non-Hispanic/Latino; 16% Asian, non-Hispanic/Latino; 0.9% Native Hawaiian or other Pacific Islander, non-Hispanic/Latino; 5% international. 50% 25 or older, 15% transferred in. Core. Calendar: semesters. Accelerated degree program, independent study, distance learning, summer session for credit, part-time degree program, internships, graduate courses open to undergrads. ROTC: Army (c).
Entrance Requirements: Transfer credits accepted: Yes.
Collegiate Environment: Orientation program. Student-run newspaper. Most popular organizations: Student Inter-council (SIC), School of Nursing Student Government Organization (School of Nursing), Student Council (Dental Branch), Student Senate (Medical School), SPH Student Association (School of Public Health). Major annual event: UT Medics Community Projects. Student services: health clinic, personal-psychological counseling. Campus security: 24-hour emergency response devices and patrols, late night transport-escort service, controlled access to all buildings. The Texas Medical Center Library plus 1 other. Operations spending for the previous fiscal year: $2.6 million.

■ THE UNIVERSITY OF TEXAS HEALTH SCIENCE CENTER AT SAN ANTONIO

7703 Floyd Curl Dr.
San Antonio, TX 78229-3900
Tel: (210)567-7000
Fax: (210)567-2685
Web Site: www.uthscsa.edu
Description: State-supported, upper-level, coed. Part of University of Texas System. Awards bachelor's, master's, and doctoral degrees. Founded 1976. Setting: 100-acre suburban campus. Total enrollment: 3,093. Student-undergrad faculty ratio is 3:1. 32 applied. 54% 25 or older. Core. Calendar: semesters. Distance learning, summer session for credit, part-time degree program, adult/continuing education programs. ROTC: Army (c), Air Force (c).
Collegiate Environment: Campus security: 24-hour emergency response devices and patrols, late night transport-escort service. Dolph Briso Library.

■ THE UNIVERSITY OF TEXAS MD ANDERSON CANCER CENTER

1515 Holcombe Blvd.
Houston, TX 77030
Tel: (713)792-2121
Web Site: www.mdanderson.org/education-and-research
Description: State-supported, upper-level, coed. Awards bachelor's and master's degrees.

■ THE UNIVERSITY OF TEXAS MEDICAL BRANCH

301 University Blvd.
Galveston, TX 77555
Tel: (409)772-1011
Fax: (409)772-5056
Web Site: www.utmb.edu
Description: State-supported, comprehensive, coed. Part of University of

Texas System. Awards bachelor's, master's, and doctoral degrees and post-master's certificates. Founded 1891. Setting: 85-acre small town campus with easy access to Houston. Endowment: $368.5 million. Research spending for the previous fiscal year: $145.2 million. Total enrollment: 2,430. Full-time: 315 students, 81% women, 19% men. Part-time: 177 students, 79% women, 21% men. Students come from 5 states and territories, 12 other countries, 1% from out-of-state. 65% 25 or older. Academic area with the most degrees conferred: health professions and related sciences. Core. Calendar: semesters (early semester). Services for LD students, advanced placement, accelerated degree program, independent study, distance learning, summer session for credit, part-time degree program, internships.
Entrance Requirements: Options: electronic application, international baccalaureate accepted. Entrance: very difficult. Preference given to state residents. Transfer credits accepted: Yes.
Collegiate Environment: Orientation program. Student-run newspaper. Social organizations: 40 open to all; national fraternities, local fraternities. Most popular organizations: Texas Medical Association, American Medical Student Association, American Medical Women's Association, Texas Association Latin American Medical Students, National Medical Student Association. Major annual events: Quest and Orientation, All Sports Day, Primary Care Day. Student services: legal services, health clinic, personal-psychological counseling. Campus security: 24-hour emergency response devices and patrols, late night transport-escort service. Moody Medical Library.

■ THE UNIVERSITY OF TEXAS OF THE PERMIAN BASIN

4901 E University Blvd.
Odessa, TX 79762-0001
Tel: (432)552-2020; Free: 866-552-UTPB
Fax: (432)552-2109
Web Site: www.utpb.edu
Description: State-supported, comprehensive, coed. Part of The University of Texas System. Awards bachelor's and master's degrees. Founded 1969. Setting: 600-acre urban campus. Endowment: $42.2 million. Research spending for the previous fiscal year: $1.2 million. Educational spending for the previous fiscal year: $4958 per student. Total enrollment: 7,022. Faculty: 290 (116 full-time, 174 part-time). Student-undergrad faculty ratio is 27:1. 940 applied, 82% were admitted. 23% from top 10% of their high school class, 56% from top quarter, 86% from top half. Full-time: 2,192 students, 53% women, 47% men. Part-time: 3,873 students, 59% women, 41% men. Students come from 42 states and territories, 36 other countries, 3% from out-of-state. 0.4% American Indian or Alaska Native, non-Hispanic/Latino; 47% Hispanic/Latino; 5% Black or African American, non-Hispanic/Latino; 3% Asian, non-Hispanic/Latino; 0.2% Native Hawaiian or other Pacific Islander, non-Hispanic/Latino; 2% international. 37% 25 or older, 19% live on campus, 7% transferred in. Retention: 66% of full-time freshmen returned the following year. Academic areas with the most degrees conferred: business/marketing; psychology; engineering. Core. Calendar: semesters. Academic remediation for entering students, ESL program, services for LD students, advanced placement, accelerated degree program, honors program, independent study, distance learning, double major, summer session for credit, part-time degree program, co-op programs and internships, graduate courses open to undergrads. Study abroad program.
Entrance Requirements: Options: electronic application, international baccalaureate accepted. Required: high school transcript, SAT or ACT. Entrance: moderately difficult. Notification: continuous. SAT Reasoning Test deadline: 7/15. Transfer credits accepted: Yes.
Costs Per Year: Application fee: $40. State resident tuition: $5662 full-time, $188.73 per credit hour part-time. Nonresident tuition: $6812 full-time. Mandatory fees: $1462 full-time, $69.56 per credit hour part-time. Full-time tuition and fees vary according to course load, degree level, and location. Part-time tuition and fees vary according to course load, degree level, and location. College room and board: $10,944. College room only: $7200. Room and board charges vary according to board plan and housing facility. Tuition guaranteed not to increase for student's term of enrollment.
Collegiate Environment: Orientation program. Drama-theater group, choral group, marching band, student-run newspaper. Social organizations: 50 open to all; national fraternities. Most popular organizations: The American Society for Mechanical Engineers, The Student Veteran Association, Marketing Experiences, The National Society for Leadership and Success, Students in Free Enterprise. Major annual events: Falcon Palooza, The Big Party, Homecoming. Student services: health clinic, personal-psychological counseling. Campus security: 24-hour emergency response devices and patrols, late night transport-escort service, controlled dormitory access.

1,173 college housing spaces available; 782 were occupied in 2018-19. No special consideration for freshman housing applicants. Option: coed housing available. J. Conrad Dunagan Library. Books: 294,556 (physical), 1 million (digital/electronic); Serial titles: 358 (physical), 86,390 (digital/electronic); Databases: 226. Weekly public service hours: 86; students can reserve study rooms. Operations spending for the previous fiscal year: $1.4 million. 511 computers available on campus for general student use. A campuswide network can be accessed from student residence rooms and from off campus. Students can access the following: online class registration. Staffed computer lab on campus provides training in use of computers, software, and the Internet.

Community Environment: Metropolitan area of Odessa-Midland, population 237,000. International Airport and Interstate Highway 20 access to campus.

■ **THE UNIVERSITY OF TEXAS RIO GRANDE VALLEY**
1201 W University Dr.
Edinburg, TX 78539
Tel: (956)381-2011
E-mail: debbie.gilchrist@utrgv.edu
Web Site: www.utrgv.edu
Description: State-supported, university, coed. Part of University of Texas System. Awards bachelor's, master's, and doctoral degrees and post-master's certificates. Founded 1927. Setting: 414-acre small town campus with easy access to McAllen, Edinburg, Mission. Total enrollment: 28,644. 10,710 applied, 81% were admitted. 22% from top 10% of their high school class, 51% from top quarter, 80% from top half. Full-time: 19,128 students, 57% women, 43% men. Part-time: 5,550 students, 55% women, 45% men. Students come from 33 states and territories, 50 other countries, 1% from out-of-state. 90% Hispanic/Latino; 0.4% Black or African American, non-Hispanic/Latino; 1% Asian, non-Hispanic/Latino; 2% international. 16% 25 or older, 4% live on campus, 7% transferred in. Retention: 71% of full-time freshmen returned the following year. Academic areas with the most degrees conferred: business/marketing; biological/life sciences; health professions and related sciences. Core. Calendar: semesters. Academic remediation for entering students, ESL program, services for LD students, advanced placement, accelerated degree program, honors program, independent study, distance learning, double major, summer session for credit, part-time degree program, adult/continuing education programs, co-op programs and internships, graduate courses open to undergrads. Off campus study. Study abroad program. ROTC: Army.
Entrance Requirements: Option: electronic application. Required: high school transcript, minimum 2 high school GPA, SAT or ACT. Required for some: interview. Entrance: noncompetitive. Application deadline: 7/1. Notification: continuous. SAT Reasoning Test deadline: 7/1. Transfer credits accepted: Yes.
Costs Per Year: Application fee: $0. State resident tuition: $6345 full-time, $376.20 per credit hour part-time. Nonresident tuition: $18,795 full-time, $791.20 per credit hour part-time. Mandatory fees: $1468 full-time, $184.93 per credit hour part-time. Full-time tuition and fees vary according to degree level and program. Part-time tuition and fees vary according to degree level and program. College room and board: $8124. College room only: $4976. Room and board charges vary according to board plan and housing facility. Tuition guaranteed not to increase for student's term of enrollment.
Collegiate Environment: Orientation program. Drama-theater group, choral group, student-run newspaper, radio station. Social organizations: national fraternities, national sororities, local sororities. Most popular organizations: Alpha Lambda Delta National Honor Society for First-Year Students, The National Society of Collegiate Scholars, Golden Key International Honor Society, Pre-Medical Bio-Medical Society, Environmental Awareness Club. Major annual events: Hispanic Engineering, Science, and Technology Week, Homecoming. Student services: health clinic, personal-psychological counseling. Campus security: 24-hour emergency response devices and patrols, late night transport-escort service. No special consideration for freshman housing applicants. Options: men-only, women-only housing available. University Library. Students can reserve study rooms.
Community Environment: Population 62,735. Edinburg is located in the subtropical lower Rio Grande Valley of Texas and enjoys a mild year-round climate. The average summer maximum temperature is about 90 degrees, with winter average of 70 degrees. The community is served by bus lines and U.S. Highway 281. Edinburg has a hospital and major civic, fraternal and veteran's organizations. Part-time employment is available. Local recreation includes hunting, fishing, golf, and swimming in the Gulf of Mexico approximately 70 miles away.

■ **THE UNIVERSITY OF TEXAS AT SAN ANTONIO**
One UTSA Cir.
San Antonio, TX 78249-0617
Tel: (210)458-4011; Free: 800-669-0919
E-mail: prospects@utsa.edu
Web Site: www.utsa.edu
Description: State-supported, university, coed. Part of University of Texas System. Awards bachelor's, master's, and doctoral degrees. Founded 1969. Setting: 725-acre suburban campus with easy access to San Antonio. Endowment: $134.5 million. Total enrollment: 30,768. Faculty: 1,276 (885 full-time, 391 part-time). Student-undergrad faculty ratio is 25:1. 15,973 applied, 79% were admitted. 17% from top 10% of their high school class, 58% from top quarter, 90% from top half. Full-time: 21,510 students, 51% women, 49% men. Part-time: 4,934 students, 46% women, 54% men. Students come from 51 states and territories, 75 other countries, 2% from out-of-state. 0.2% American Indian or Alaska Native, non-Hispanic/Latino; 55% Hispanic/Latino; 9% Black or African American, non-Hispanic/Latino; 6% Asian, non-Hispanic/Latino; 0.2% Native Hawaiian or other Pacific Islander, non-Hispanic/Latino; 2% international. 15% 25 or older, 12% live on campus, 10% transferred in. Retention: 74% of full-time freshmen returned the following year. Academic areas with the most degrees conferred: business/marketing; engineering; psychology. Core. Calendar: semesters. Academic remediation for entering students, ESL program, services for LD students, advanced placement, self-designed majors, honors program, independent study, distance learning, double major, summer session for credit, part-time degree program, adult/continuing education programs, co-op programs and internships, graduate courses open to undergrads. Off campus study at National Student Exchange. Study abroad program. ROTC: Army, Air Force.
Entrance Requirements: Options: electronic application, international baccalaureate accepted. Required: high school transcript, SAT or ACT. Recommended: essay, 1 recommendation. Required for some: transfer applicants with less than 30 hours must meet freshman requirements and have a 2.25 GPA on a 4.0 scale and submit all college transcripts; transfer applicants with 30 or more completed hours must have a 2.25 GPA on a 4.0 scale and submit all college transcripts. Entrance: moderately difficult. Application deadline: 6/1. Notification: continuous, continuous for nonresidents. SAT Reasoning Test deadline: 6/1. SAT Subject Test deadline: 6/1. Transfer credits accepted: Yes.
Collegiate Environment: Orientation program. Choral group, marching band, student-run newspaper, radio station. Social organizations: 350 open to all; national fraternities, national sororities; 3% of eligible men and 5% of eligible women are members. Most popular organizations: Student Government, VOICES, Chi Alpha Christian Fellowship, Hispanic Student Association, Panhellenic Council. Major annual events: Best Fest, Fiesta UTSA, Party on the Paseo. Student services: health clinic, personal-psychological counseling, women's center. Campus security: 24-hour emergency response devices and patrols, late night transport-escort service, controlled dormitory access, close to 1000 security cameras, Reverse 911 emergency telephone notification system, warning speaker arrays. John Peace Library plus 3 others. Students can reserve study rooms. 510 computers available on campus for general student use. Computer purchase/lease plans available. A campuswide network can be accessed from student residence rooms and from off campus. Students can access the following: online class registration. Staffed computer lab on campus (open 24 hours a day) provides training in use of computers, software, and the Internet.

■ **THE UNIVERSITY OF TEXAS AT TYLER**
3900 University Blvd.
Tyler, TX 75799-0001
Tel: (903)566-7000; Free: 800-UTTYLER
Fax: (903)566-7068
E-mail: admissions@uttyler.edu
Web Site: www.uttyler.edu
Description: State-supported, comprehensive, coed. Part of University of Texas System. Awards bachelor's, master's, and doctoral degrees and post-master's certificates. Founded 1971. Setting: 200-acre urban campus. Total enrollment: 8,785. 2,468 applied, 64% were admitted. 10% from top 10% of their high school class, 35% from top quarter, 64% from top half. Full-time: 4,569 students, 57% women, 43% men. Part-time: 1,749 students, 57% women, 43% men. 1% from out-of-state. 0.3% American Indian or Alaska Native, non-Hispanic/Latino; 16% Hispanic/Latino; 9% Black or African American, non-Hispanic/Latino; 3% Asian, non-Hispanic/Latino; 0.1% Native Hawaiian or other Pacific Islander, non-Hispanic/Latino; 2% international. 28% 25 or older, 19% live on campus, 16% transferred in. Retention: 62% of

full-time freshmen returned the following year. Academic areas with the most degrees conferred: business/marketing; health professions and related sciences; interdisciplinary studies. Core. Calendar: semesters. Services for LD students, advanced placement, honors program, independent study, distance learning, double major, part-time degree program, adult/continuing education programs, internships. Study abroad program.

Entrance Requirements: Options: electronic application, deferred admission, international baccalaureate accepted. Required: high school transcript, SAT or ACT. Entrance: moderately difficult. SAT Reasoning Test deadline: 8/24.

Collegiate Environment: Orientation program. Choral group, student-run newspaper. Social organizations: national fraternities, national sororities. Campus security: 24-hour emergency response devices and patrols, late night transport-escort service, controlled dormitory access. Robert Muntz Library.

■ VERNON COLLEGE

4400 College Dr.
Vernon, TX 76384-4092
Tel: (940)552-6291
Fax: (940)553-1753
Web Site: www.vernoncollege.edu

Description: State and locally supported, 2-year, coed. Awards certificates, transfer associate, and terminal associate degrees. Founded 1970. Setting: 100-acre small town campus. Total enrollment: 3,163. Student-undergrad faculty ratio is 17:1. 4% from out-of-state. 35% 25 or older. Core. Calendar: semesters. Academic remediation for entering students, services for LD students, advanced placement, distance learning, double major, summer session for credit, part-time degree program, adult/continuing education programs, co-op programs and internships.

Entrance Requirements: Open admission. Options: electronic application, early admission. Entrance: noncompetitive. Application deadline: rolling.

Collegiate Environment: Drama-theater group, choral group. Social organizations: 3 open to all. Most popular organizations: Student Government Association, Baptist Student Union. Major annual event: Sports Day. Student services: health clinic, personal-psychological counseling. Campus security: 24-hour patrols. Wright Library. 100 computers available on campus for general student use. A campuswide network can be accessed. Students can access the following: online class registration. Staffed computer lab on campus.

■ VET TECH INSTITUTE OF HOUSTON

4669 SW Fwy.
Ste. 100
Houston, TX 77027
Tel: (713)629-1500; Free: 800-275-2736
Fax: (713)629-0059
Web Site: houston.vettechinstitute.edu

Description: Proprietary, 2-year, coed. Awards terminal associate degrees. Founded 1958. Setting: suburban campus. Total enrollment: 216. 455 applied, 62% were admitted. Calendar: semesters. Accelerated degree program, internships.

■ VICTORIA COLLEGE

2200 E Red River
Victoria, TX 77901-4494
Tel: (361)573-3291; Free: 877-843-4369
Fax: (361)572-3850
E-mail: registrar@victoriacollege.edu
Web Site: www.victoriacollege.edu

Description: County-supported, 2-year, coed. Awards certificates, transfer associate, and terminal associate degrees. Founded 1925. Setting: 80-acre rural campus. Total enrollment: 4,000. Faculty: 211 (88 full-time, 123 part-time). Student-undergrad faculty ratio is 17:1. 866 applied, 100% were admitted. Full-time: 1,053 students, 55% women, 45% men. Part-time: 2,947 students, 69% women, 31% men. Students come from 5 states and territories, 0.1% from out-of-state. 0.2% American Indian or Alaska Native, non-Hispanic/Latino; 48% Hispanic/Latino; 6% Black or African American, non-Hispanic/Latino; 2% Asian, non-Hispanic/Latino; 0.1% Native Hawaiian or other Pacific Islander, non-Hispanic/Latino. 37% 25 or older, 6% transferred in. Core. Calendar: semesters. Academic remediation for entering students, ESL program, services for LD students, advanced placement, distance learning, summer session for credit, part-time degree program. Off campus study.

Entrance Requirements: Open admission Victoria College is a public, open-admission college. Additional admission requirements are necessary for designated selective admission programs. Please refer to the VC Catalog. Options: electronic application, early admission. Required: high school transcript. Entrance: noncompetitive. Application deadline: rolling. Transfer credits accepted: Yes.

Costs Per Year: Area resident tuition: $1440 full-time, $48 per credit hour part-time. State resident tuition: $2910 full-time, $97 per credit hour part-time. Nonresident tuition: $3690 full-time, $123 per credit hour part-time. Mandatory fees: $1350 full-time, $45 per credit hour part-time. Full-time tuition and fees vary according to program. Part-time tuition and fees vary according to program.

Collegiate Environment: Orientation program. Choral group. Social organizations: 27 open to all. Most popular organization: Student Government Association. Major annual event: Lyceum. Student services: personal-psychological counseling. Campus security: 24-hour emergency response devices. Victoria College/University of Houston-Victoria Library. Books: 118,781 (physical), 119,216 (digital/electronic); Serial titles: 133 (physical), 81,953 (digital/electronic); Databases: 137. Weekly public service hours: 76; students can reserve study rooms. Operations spending for the previous fiscal year: $514,325. 181 computers available on campus for general student use. A campuswide network can be accessed. Students can access the following: online class registration. Staffed computer lab on campus provides training in use of computers, software, and the Internet.

Community Environment: Population 61,790. After the battle of San Jacinto, the first military capital of the new republic was established here in Victoria. Today, the area is known for its cattle raising. The city is located 25 miles from the Gulf of Mexico. Local industries include chemicals, sand and gravel mining, and oil and gas production. Part-time employment is limited. The climate is mild. Victoria is reached by bus and airline connections. The community has several churches. Local recreation includes salt water fishing, boating, swimming and water skiing in the Gulf of Mexico, a municipal park and golf courses.

■ VISTA COLLEGE

6101 Montana Ave.
El Paso, TX 79925
Tel: (915)779-8031; Free: 866-442-4197
Web Site: www.vistacollege.edu

Description: Proprietary, 2-year, coed. Awards certificates, diplomas, transfer associate, and terminal associate degrees. Founded 1985. Setting: urban campus. Total enrollment: 4,349. 55% 25 or older. Calendar: 8 6-week terms.

Entrance Requirements: Open admission. Entrance: noncompetitive.

■ VISTA COLLEGE-ONLINE CAMPUS

300 N Coit Rd.
Ste. 300
Richardson, TX 75080
Web Site: www.vistacollege.edu

Description: Proprietary, 2-year, coed. Awards certificates, diplomas, transfer associate, and terminal associate degrees. Founded 1983.

■ WADE COLLEGE

Infomart, 1950 N Stemmons Fwy.
Ste. 4080, LB 562
Dallas, TX 75207
Tel: (214)637-3530; Free: 800-624-4850
Fax: (214)637-0827
Web Site: www.wadecollege.edu

Description: Proprietary, primarily 2-year, coed. Awards transfer associate, terminal associate, and bachelor's degrees. Founded 1965. Setting: 175-acre urban campus with easy access to Dallas Fort Worth. Total enrollment: 238. Faculty: 18 (9 full-time, 9 part-time). Student-undergrad faculty ratio is 12:1. Students come from 4 other countries, 10% from out-of-state. 60% 25 or older. Retention: 60% of full-time freshmen returned the following year. Core. Calendar: trimesters. Academic remediation for entering students, services for LD students, advanced placement, summer session for credit, part-time degree program, internships.

Entrance Requirements: Open admission. Option: electronic application. Required: high school transcript, interview. Entrance: minimally difficult. Application deadline: 9/26. Notification: continuous. Transfer credits accepted: Yes.

Costs Per Year: Tuition: $24,975 full-time, $1665 per course part-time.

Mandatory fees: $25 full-time. Full-time tuition and fees vary according to course load and degree level. Part-time tuition and fees vary according to course load and degree level. Tuition guaranteed not to increase for student's term of enrollment.

Collegiate Environment: Orientation program. Student-run newspaper. Social organizations: 1 open to all. Most popular organization: Wade College Student Association. Campus security: 24-hour emergency response devices and patrols, late night transport-escort service, controlled dormitory access. College Library. Books: 8,500 (physical), 45,000 (digital/electronic); Databases: 10. 75 computers available on campus for general student use. A campuswide network can be accessed from off-campus. Staffed computer lab on campus provides training in use of computers, software, and the Internet.

■ WAYLAND BAPTIST UNIVERSITY

1900 W Seventh St.
Plainview, TX 79072-6998
Tel: (806)291-1000; Free: 800-588-1928
Fax: (806)291-1960
E-mail: admityou@wbu.edu
Web Site: www.wbu.edu

Description: Independent Baptist, comprehensive, coed. Awards associate, bachelor's, master's, and doctoral degrees (branch locations in Anchorage, AK; Amarillo, TX; Luke Air Force Base, AZ; Glorieta, NM; Aiea, HI; Lubbock, TX; San Antonio, TX; Wichita Falls, TX). Founded 1908. Setting: 80-acre small town campus. Endowment: $82.8 million. Educational spending for the previous fiscal year: $11,113 per student. Total enrollment: 4,827. Faculty: 554 (141 full-time, 413 part-time). Student-undergrad faculty ratio is 8:1. 652 applied, 98% were admitted. 10% from top 10% of their high school class, 21% from top quarter, 57% from top half. Full-time: 978 students, 41% women, 59% men. Part-time: 2,565 students, 54% women, 46% men. Students come from 44 states and territories, 26 other countries, 30% from out-of-state. 0.8% American Indian or Alaska Native, non-Hispanic/Latino; 32% Hispanic/Latino; 18% Black or African American, non-Hispanic/Latino; 2% Asian, non-Hispanic/Latino; 0.9% Native Hawaiian or other Pacific Islander, non-Hispanic/Latino; 1% international. 57% 25 or older, 52% live on campus, 10% transferred in. Retention: 42% of full-time freshmen returned the following year. Academic areas with the most degrees conferred: business/marketing; liberal arts/general studies; homeland security, law enforcement, firefighting, and protective services. Core. Calendar: semesters. Academic remediation for entering students, services for LD students, advanced placement, accelerated degree program, honors program, distance learning, double major, summer session for credit, part-time degree program, external degree program, adult/continuing education programs, graduate courses open to undergrads. Study abroad program. ROTC: Army (c), Air Force (c).

Entrance Requirements: Option: electronic application. Required: high school transcript, SAT or ACT. Required for some: interview. Entrance: minimally difficult. Application deadline: 8/1. Notification: continuous. SAT Reasoning Test deadline: 8/1. Transfer credits accepted: Yes.

Costs Per Year: Application fee: $35. Comprehensive fee: $27,934 includes full-time tuition ($18,780), mandatory fees ($1290), and college room and board ($7864). College room only: $3196. Full-time tuition and fees vary according to course load and location. Room and board charges vary according to board plan and housing facility. Part-time tuition: $626 per credit hour. Part-time tuition varies according to course load and location.

Collegiate Environment: Orientation program. Drama-theater group, choral group, marching band, student-run newspaper, radio station. Social organizations: 35 open to all; national fraternities, national sororities, local fraternities, local sororities; 1% of eligible men and 2% of eligible women are members. Most popular organizations: Student Government, Wayland Singers, Baptist Student Ministries, International Choir, President's Ambassadors. Major annual events: Homecoming, Big Weekend, Pioneer Pride Week. Student services: health clinic, personal-psychological counseling. Campus security: 24-hour emergency response devices and patrols, security lighting, campus police department. J.E. and L.E. Mabee Learning Resource Center. Books: 130,903 (physical), 49,479 (digital/electronic); Serial titles: 555,663 (digital/electronic); Databases: 104. Operations spending for the previous fiscal year: $643,922. 840 computers available on campus for general student use. Computer purchase/lease plans available. A campuswide network can be accessed from student residence rooms and from off campus. Students can access the following: online class registration. Staffed computer lab on campus provides training in use of computers, software, and the Internet.

Community Environment: Population 21,900. Plainview is an agricultural and industrial community located on the High Plains of Northwest Texas. The area is served by railroad, bus, and U.S. Highway 70 and Interstate 27; State Highways 194 and FM400. The city has many churches, a municipal airport, a memorial library, YMCA, and one hospital as well as several clinics to serve the community. Local recreation includes five swimming pools, summer baseball programs, golf courses, theatres, miniature golf, bowling facilities, and boating facilities. There are a great many civic and fraternal groups active in the area. Part-time employment is available.

■ WEATHERFORD COLLEGE

225 College Park Dr.
Weatherford, TX 76086
Tel: (817)594-5471; Free: 800-287-5471
Fax: (817)598-6205
E-mail: rwillingham@wc.edu
Web Site: www.wc.edu

Description: State and locally supported, 2-year, coed. Awards certificates, diplomas, transfer associate, and terminal associate degrees. Founded 1869. Setting: 94-acre small town campus with easy access to Dallas-Fort Worth. Total enrollment: 5,637. Faculty: 220 (95 full-time, 125 part-time). Student-undergrad faculty ratio is 22:1. 23% 25 or older, 7% live on campus. Core. Calendar: semesters. Academic remediation for entering students, services for LD students, self-designed majors, freshman honors college, honors program, distance learning, summer session for credit, part-time degree program, adult/continuing education programs, co-op programs and internships. ROTC: Army (c), Air Force (c).

Entrance Requirements: Open admission. Options: electronic application, early admission. Recommended: high school transcript. Entrance: noncompetitive. Notification: continuous. Transfer credits accepted: Yes.

Costs Per Year: Application fee: $0. Area resident tuition: $2040 full-time, $85 per semester hour part-time. State resident tuition: $3168 full-time, $132 per semester hour part-time. Nonresident tuition: $4488 full-time, $187 per semester hour part-time. Full-time tuition varies according to course load and program. Part-time tuition varies according to course load and program. College room and board: $7673. Room and board charges vary according to board plan.

Collegiate Environment: Orientation program. Drama-theater group, choral group. Social organizations: 21 open to all. Most popular organizations: Black Awareness Student Organization, Criminal Justice Club, Phi Theta Kappa. Major annual events: Homecoming, Halloween Dance, Family Weekend. Student services: personal-psychological counseling. Campus security: 24-hour emergency response devices and patrols, late night transport-escort service. Weatherford College Library. Books: 50,220 (physical). Students can reserve study rooms. 85 computers available on campus for general student use. A campuswide network can be accessed from off-campus. Students can access the following: online class registration, online catalog. Staffed computer lab on campus provides training in use of computers and the Internet.

Community Environment: Weatherford, population 23,300, is the county seat of Parker County. In a diversified crop and livestock market, watermelons are their best known product. Cutting horse ranches are a major market. It can be reached by rail, bus, and air lines, and Interstate 20. The climate is mild with a mean average temperature of 64 degrees and an average rainfall of 31.6 inches. There is a city library, a local hospital, several churches representing the major denominations, and various civic and fraternal organizations. The Parker Plaza Shopping Center and College Park Shopping Center serve the surrounding area. Local recreation includes Weatherford Lake with boating, fishing, and swimming, a local picnic grounds, golf, and three public parks. Part-time employment opportunities are very limited.

■ WEST COAST UNIVERSITY

8435 N Stemmons Fwy.
Dallas, TX 75247
Tel: (214)453-4533; Free: 866-508-2684
Web Site: www.westcoastuniversity.edu

Description: Proprietary, 4-year, coed. Awards bachelor's degrees. Setting: urban campus with easy access to Dallas-Fort Worth.

■ WEST TEXAS A&M UNIVERSITY

2501 4th Ave.
Canyon, TX 79015
Tel: (806)651-2000; Free: 800-99-WTAMU

Fax: (806)651-2126

E-mail: tmiller@wtamu.edu

Web Site: www.wtamu.edu

Description: State-supported, comprehensive, coed. Part of Texas A&M University System. Awards bachelor's, master's, and doctoral degrees. Founded 1909. Setting: 128-acre small town campus. Endowment: $80.4 million. Research spending for the previous fiscal year: $4.4 million. Educational spending for the previous fiscal year: $5105 per student. Total enrollment: 10,060. Faculty: 444 (342 full-time, 102 part-time). Student-undergrad faculty ratio is 20:1. 6,116 applied, 61% were admitted. 15% from top 10% of their high school class, 43% from top quarter, 80% from top half. 27 valedictorians. Full-time: 5,615 students, 57% women, 43% men. Part-time: 1,779 students, 58% women, 42% men. Students come from 53 states and territories, 65 other countries, 14% from out-of-state. 0.4% American Indian or Alaska Native, non-Hispanic/Latino; 28% Hispanic/Latino; 5% Black or African American, non-Hispanic/Latino; 2% Asian, non-Hispanic/Latino; 0.1% Native Hawaiian or other Pacific Islander, non-Hispanic/Latino; 2% international. 22% 25 or older, 26% live on campus, 14% transferred in. Retention: 64% of full-time freshmen returned the following year. Academic areas with the most degrees conferred: business/marketing; health professions and related sciences; liberal arts/general studies. Core. Calendar: semesters. Academic remediation for entering students, ESL program, services for LD students, advanced placement, honors program, independent study, distance learning, double major, summer session for credit, part-time degree program, adult/continuing education programs, co-op programs and internships. Study abroad program.

Entrance Requirements: Options: electronic application, deferred admission. Required: high school transcript, class rank and Texas high school curriculum or equivalent, SAT or ACT. Entrance: moderately difficult. Application deadline: rolling. Notification: continuous. SAT Reasoning Test deadline: 8/15. SAT Subject Test deadline: 8/15. Transfer credits accepted: Yes.

Collegiate Environment: Orientation program. Drama-theater group, choral group, marching band, student-run newspaper, radio station. Social organizations: 130 open to all; national fraternities, national sororities; 6% of eligible men and 6% of eligible women are members. Most popular organizations: Residence Hall Association, Wesley, Student Government, SAGE, Baptist Student Ministries. Major annual events: Buffalo Branding, Workathon, Homecoming. Student services: health clinic, personal-psychological counseling. Campus security: 24-hour emergency response devices and patrols, late night transport-escort service, controlled dormitory access. Cornette Library plus 3 others. Books: 305,487 (physical), 516,531 (digital/electronic); Serial titles: 12,207 (physical), 12,592 (digital/electronic); Databases: 181. Weekly public service hours: 91; students can reserve study rooms. Operations spending for the previous fiscal year: $2.7 million. 1,200 computers available on campus for general student use. Computer purchase/lease plans available. A campuswide network can be accessed from student residence rooms and from off campus. Students can access the following: online class registration. Staffed computer lab on campus (open 24 hours a day) provides training in use of computers, software, and the Internet.

■ WESTERN TECHNICAL COLLEGE (EL PASO)

9451 Diana Dr.

El Paso, TX 79930-2610

Tel: (915)566-9621; Free: 800-201-9232

E-mail: lpena@westerntech.edu

Web Site: www.westerntech.edu

Description: Proprietary, 2-year, coed. Awards certificates and terminal associate degrees. Total enrollment: 545. Student-undergrad faculty ratio is 12:1. 177 applied. 8% from out-of-state. 49% 25 or older. Retention: 69% of full-time freshmen returned the following year.

Entrance Requirements: Entrance: noncompetitive.

■ WESTERN TECHNICAL COLLEGE (EL PASO)

9624 Plz. Cir.

El Paso, TX 79927

Tel: (915)532-3737

E-mail: bterrell@wtc-ep.edu

Web Site: www.westerntech.edu

Description: Proprietary, 2-year, coed. Awards certificates, transfer associate, and terminal associate degrees. Total enrollment: 825. Faculty: 130 (98 full-time, 32 part-time). Student-undergrad faculty ratio is 18:1. Calendar: continuous.

Entrance Requirements: Open admission. Options: early admission, deferred admission.

Collegiate Environment: 25 computers available on campus for general student use. Computer purchase/lease plans available. A campuswide network can be accessed from off-campus. Staffed computer lab on campus.

■ WESTERN TEXAS COLLEGE

6200 College Ave.

Snyder, TX 79549

Tel: (325)573-8511; Free: 888-GO-TO-WTC

E-mail: dmorris@wtc.edu

Web Site: www.wtc.edu

Description: State and locally supported, 2-year, coed. Awards certificates, transfer associate, and terminal associate degrees. Founded 1969. Setting: 165-acre small town campus. Educational spending for the previous fiscal year: $1079 per student. Total enrollment: 2,250. Faculty: 88 (34 full-time, 54 part-time). Student-undergrad faculty ratio is 22:1. 668 applied, 90% were admitted. Full-time: 579 students, 46% women, 54% men. Part-time: 1,671 students, 50% women, 50% men. Students come from 30 states and territories, 17 other countries, 4% from out-of-state. 0.8% American Indian or Alaska Native, non-Hispanic/Latino; 42% Hispanic/Latino; 9% Black or African American, non-Hispanic/Latino; 1% Asian, non-Hispanic/Latino; 0.1% Native Hawaiian or other Pacific Islander, non-Hispanic/Latino; 6% international. 11% 25 or older, 50% live on campus, 3% transferred in. Core. Calendar: semesters. Academic remediation for entering students, services for LD students, advanced placement, self-designed majors, honors program, independent study, distance learning, summer session for credit, part-time degree program, adult/continuing education programs, internships.

Entrance Requirements: Open admission. Options: electronic application, early admission, deferred admission, international baccalaureate accepted. Required: high school transcript. Entrance: noncompetitive. Application deadline: rolling. Notification: continuous. Transfer credits accepted: Yes.

Costs Per Year: Application fee: $0. Area resident tuition: $1740 full-time, $58 per credit hour part-time. State resident tuition: $2850 full-time, $95 per credit hour part-time. Nonresident tuition: $3960 full-time, $132 per credit hour part-time. Mandatory fees: $990 full-time, $33 per credit hour part-time. Full-time tuition and fees vary according to course load, location, and program. Part-time tuition and fees vary according to course load, location, and program. College room and board: $5275. Room and board charges vary according to housing facility.

Collegiate Environment: Orientation program. Drama-theater group, student-run radio station. Social organizations: 5 open to all; Phi Theta Kappa; 35% of eligible men and 35% of eligible women are members. Most popular organizations: Student Government Association, Phi Theta Kappa, Agriculture Club, Art Club, Fellowship of Christian Athletes. Major annual events: Move-In Day, Fall Festival, Veteran's Day Observance. Student services: health clinic, personal-psychological counseling. Campus security: 24-hour emergency response devices and patrols, late night transport-escort service. Western Texas College Resource Center. Books: 31,884 (physical), 29,077 (digital/electronic); Serial titles: 97 (physical); Databases: 25. Weekly public service hours: 56. Operations spending for the previous fiscal year: $131,436. 175 computers available on campus for general student use. A campuswide network can be accessed from student residence rooms and from off campus. Students can access the following: online class registration. Staffed computer lab on campus provides training in use of computers, software, and the Internet.

Community Environment: Snyder is a small rural city, population 10,580. Agriculture and oil are important industries.

■ WHARTON COUNTY JUNIOR COLLEGE

911 Boling Hwy.

Wharton, TX 77488-3298

Tel: (979)532-4560

E-mail: albertb@wcjc.edu

Web Site: www.wcjc.edu

Description: State and locally supported, 2-year, coed. Awards certificates, transfer associate, and terminal associate degrees. Founded 1946. Setting: 90-acre rural campus with easy access to Houston. Total enrollment: 6,115. Faculty: 257 (136 full-time, 121 part-time). Student-undergrad faculty ratio is 22:1. 5% from top 10% of their high school class, 50% from top half. Students come from 8 states and territories, 5 other countries. 30% 25 or older, 5% live on campus. Core. Calendar: semesters. Academic remediation for entering students, advanced placement, self-designed majors, summer session for credit, part-time degree program, adult/continuing education programs.

Entrance Requirements: Open admission. Required: high school transcript, minimum 2.0 high school GPA. Entrance: noncompetitive. Application deadline: 8/14.

Collegiate Environment: Drama-theater group. Student services: personal-psychological counseling. Campus security: 24-hour patrols. J. M. Hodges Library. 350 computers available on campus for general student use. Staffed computer lab on campus.

Community Environment: Population 9,374, Wharton is situated on the banks of the Colorado River, 45 miles from the Gulf of Mexico. The community is served by bus lines, a municipal airport, and U.S. Highway 59. Community facilities include a county library, hospital and clinic, several churches of various faiths, and many civic and fraternal organizations. It also has a museum, theatre, concert series, health club, municipal swimming pool, hunting, and fishing. An annual Wharton County Youth Rodeo is held here. Part-time employment is available.

■ **WILEY COLLEGE**
711 Wiley Ave.
Marshall, TX 75670-5199
Tel: (903)927-3300; Free: 800-658-6889
Fax: (903)938-8100
Web Site: www.wileyc.edu

Description: Independent, 4-year, coed, affiliated with United Methodist Church. Awards associate and bachelor's degrees. Founded 1873. Setting: 58-acre small town campus. Endowment: $3.9 million. Educational spending for the previous fiscal year: $15,881 per student. Total enrollment: 925. Faculty: 80 (51 full-time, 29 part-time). Student-undergrad faculty ratio is 15:1. 976 applied, 40% were admitted. 1% from top quarter of their high school class, 2% from top half. Full-time: 803 students, 59% women, 41% men. Part-time: 122 students, 61% women, 39% men. Students come from 25 states and territories, 7 other countries, 45% from out-of-state. 39% 25 or older, 51% live on campus, 11% transferred in. Retention: 100% of full-time freshmen returned the following year. Academic areas with the most degrees conferred: business/marketing; social sciences; education. Core. Calendar: semesters. Academic remediation for entering students, self-designed majors, summer session for credit, part-time degree program, adult/continuing education programs. Off campus study at Howard University. Study abroad program.

Entrance Requirements: Open admission. Options: electronic application, early admission, deferred admission, international baccalaureate accepted. Required: high school transcript, 1 recommendation. Recommended: SAT or ACT. Entrance: minimally difficult. Application deadline: 8/1. Notification: continuous until 8/10.

Collegiate Environment: Orientation program. Drama-theater group, student-run newspaper. Social organizations: national fraternities, national sororities. Student services: health clinic, personal-psychological counseling. Campus security: 24-hour patrols, controlled dormitory access. T. Winston Cole, Sr. Library. Operations spending for the previous fiscal year: $52,832. 198 computers available on campus for general student use. Computer purchase/lease plans available. A campuswide network can be accessed from student residence rooms and from off campus. Students can access the following: online class registration.

Community Environment: Population 24,000. Marshall is located at the junction of Highways U.S. 59 and 80 and Interstate 20, approximately 40 miles west of Shreveport, and 150 miles east of Dallas. The climate is temperate and mild. Natural gas fields surround the city. Railroad and bus lines serve the community, and Harrison County Memorial Airport located three miles east offers airline facilities. There are many churches of various faiths, hospitals, radio stations, and public library serving the area. Skilled and unskilled employment opportunities are available. Local recreation includes camping, fishing, and hunting.

■ **AMERITECH COLLEGE OF HEALTHCARE**

12257 S Business Park Dr.

Ste. 108

Draper, UT 84020-6545

Tel: (801)816-1444

Web Site: www.ameritech.edu

Description: Proprietary, primarily 2-year, coed. Awards transfer associate, terminal associate, and bachelor's degrees.

■ **BRIGHAM YOUNG UNIVERSITY**

Provo, UT 84602-1001

Tel: (801)422-1211

Fax: (801)422-5278

E-mail: admissions@byu.edu

Web Site: www.byu.edu

Description: Independent, university, coed, affiliated with The Church of Jesus Christ of Latter-day Saints. Part of Church Education System (CES) of The Church of Jesus Christ of Latter-day Saints. Awards bachelor's, master's, and doctoral degrees and post-master's certificates. Founded 1875. Setting: 557-acre suburban campus with easy access to Salt Lake City. Total enrollment: 34,334. Faculty: 1,840 (1,256 full-time, 584 part-time). Student-undergrad faculty ratio is 20:1. 12,858 applied, 52% were admitted. 54% from top 10% of their high school class, 85% from top quarter, 98% from top half. Full-time: 28,156 students, 49% women, 51% men. Part-time: 3,077 students, 47% women, 53% men. 64% from out-of-state. 0.3% American Indian or Alaska Native, non-Hispanic/Latino; 6% Hispanic/Latino; 0.5% Black or African American, non-Hispanic/Latino; 2% Asian, non-Hispanic/Latino; 0.7% Native Hawaiian or other Pacific Islander, non-Hispanic/Latino; 3% international. 13% 25 or older, 19% live on campus, 2% transferred in. Retention: 90% of full-time freshmen returned the following year. Academic areas with the most degrees conferred: business/marketing; biological/life sciences; education. Calendar: semesters. Part-time degree program, external degree program, adult/continuing education programs. Off campus study at BYU Salt Lake Center. ROTC: Army, Air Force.

Entrance Requirements: Options: electronic application, early admission, deferred admission. Required: essay, high school transcript, 1 recommendation, interview, SAT or ACT. Entrance: moderately difficult. Application deadline: 12/15. SAT Reasoning Test deadline: 12/15.

Costs Per Year: Application fee: $35. Comprehensive fee: $13,248 includes full-time tuition ($5620) and college room and board ($7628). Room and board charges vary according to board plan, housing facility, and location. Part-time tuition: $294 per credit hour. Part-time tuition varies according to course load.

Collegiate Environment: Orientation program. Campus security: 24-hour emergency response devices and patrols, late night transport-escort service, controlled dormitory access. Harold B. Lee Library plus 2 others.

Community Environment: Located 45 miles from Salt Lake City. Local industries also produce steel, computer software, pig iron, and foundry products. The community may be reached by air, railroad, bus lines, and Highways 6, 91, 89, 50, and Interstate 15. The community has hospitals, shopping centers, and national monuments nearby. Part-time employment is available. Local recreation includes hunting, fishing, picnicking, hiking, swimming, boating, water-skiing, horseback riding, golf, tennis, ice skating, bobsledding, and snow skiing.

■ **BROADVIEW UNIVERSITY-WEST JORDAN**

1902 W 7800 S

West Jordan, UT 84088

Tel: (801)542-7600; Free: 866-304-4224

Fax: (801)542-7601

Web Site: www.broadviewuniversity.edu

Description: Proprietary, comprehensive, coed. Part of Globe Education Network (GEN). Awards associate, bachelor's, and master's degrees. Setting: 4-acre urban campus. Total enrollment: 237. Faculty: 33 (13 full-time, 20 part-time). Full-time: 142 students, 71% women, 29% men. Part-time: 87 students, 79% women, 21% men. Students come from 10 states and territories, 11% from out-of-state. 56% 25 or older, 21% transferred in. Academic areas with the most degrees conferred: business/marketing; homeland security, law enforcement, firefighting, and protective services; law/legal studies. Core. Calendar: quarters. Academic remediation for entering students, services for LD students, advanced placement, accelerated degree program, independent study, distance learning, summer session for credit, part-time degree program, adult/continuing education programs, internships. Off campus study at Globe Education Network, including Broadview University, Duluth Business University, Globe University, Minnesota School of Business, Minnesota School of Cosmetology, and The Institute of Production and Recording.

Entrance Requirements: Open admission. Option: electronic application. Required: high school transcript, interview, ACCUPLACER is required of most applicants unless documentation of a minimum ACT composite score of 21 or documentation of a minimum composite score of 1485 on the SAT is presented. Required for some: essay. Application deadline: rolling. Notification: continuous. Transfer credits accepted: Yes.

Collegiate Environment: Orientation program. Campus security: 24-hour emergency response devices, late night transport-escort service. West Jordan Campus Library.

■ **CAREERS UNLIMITED**

1176 S 1480 W

Orem, UT 84058

Tel: (801)426-8234

Web Site: www.ucdh.edu

Description: Proprietary, 4-year, coed. Awards bachelor's degrees.

■ **DIXIE STATE UNIVERSITY**

225 S 700 E

Saint George, UT 84770-3876

Tel: (435)652-7500

Fax: (435)656-4005

Web Site: www.dixie.edu

Description: State-supported, 4-year, coed. Part of Utah System of Higher Education. Awards associate and bachelor's degrees. Founded 1911. Setting: 117-acre small town campus. Endowment: $14.4 million. Research spending for the previous fiscal year: $79,602. Educational spending for the previous fiscal year: $2386 per student. Total enrollment: 8,993. Faculty: 582 (211 full-time, 371 part-time). Student-undergrad faculty ratio is 20:1. 15,486 applied, 100% were admitted. 9% from top 10% of their high school class, 26% from top quarter, 59% from top half. Full-time: 5,673 students, 55% women, 45% men. Part-time: 3,320 students, 55% women, 45% men. Students come from 50 states and territories, 29 other countries, 22% from out-of-state. 1% American Indian or Alaska Native, non-Hispanic/Latino; 11% Hispanic/Latino; 2% Black or African American, non-Hispanic/Latino; 1% Asian, non-Hispanic/Latino; 1% Native Hawaiian or other Pacific Islander, non-Hispanic/Latino; 2% international. 23% 25 or older, 7% live on campus, 6% transferred in. Retention: 54% of full-time freshmen returned the following year. Academic areas with the most degrees conferred: business/marketing; communication/journalism; health professions and related sciences. Core. Calendar: semesters. Academic remediation for entering students, ESL program, services for LD students, advanced placement, accelerated degree program, self-designed majors, honors program, independent study, distance learning, double major, summer session for credit, part-time degree program, adult/continuing education programs, co-op programs and internships. Off campus study. Study abroad program. ROTC: Army.

Entrance Requirements: Open admission. Options: electronic application, early admission, deferred admission. Required: high school transcript. Entrance: noncompetitive. Application deadlines: 8/15, rolling for nonresidents. Notification: continuous, continuous for nonresidents. Transfer credits accepted: Yes.

Costs Per Year: Application fee: $0. State resident tuition: $5253 full-time, $186 per credit hour part-time. Nonresident tuition: $14,256 full-time, $594 per credit hour part-time. Mandatory fees: $795 full-time, $33 per credit hour part-time. Full-time tuition and fees vary according to course load. Part-time tuition and fees vary according to course load. College room and board: $5615. Room and board charges vary according to board plan, housing facility, and location.

Collegiate Environment: Orientation program. Drama-theater group, choral group, marching band, student-run newspaper, radio station. Social organizations: 83 open to all. Most popular organizations: Dixie Spirit, Outdoor Club, Association of Women Students, intramurals, Futbol Club. Major annual events: Homecoming, D-Week, Week of Welcome. Student services: health clinic, personal-psychological counseling, women's center. Campus security: 24-hour emergency response devices and patrols. Val A. Browning Library. Books: 92,371 (physical), 133,819 (digital/electronic); Serial titles: 265 (physical), 41,536 (digital/electronic); Databases: 126. Weekly public service hours: 96. Operations spending for the previous fiscal year: $250,498. 400 computers available on campus for general student use. Computer purchase/lease plans available. A campuswide network can be accessed from student residence rooms. Students can access the following: online class registration. Staffed computer lab on campus provides training in use of computers, software, and the Internet.

■ EAGLE GATE COLLEGE (LAYTON)
915 N 400 W
Layton, UT 84041
Tel: (801)546-7500; Free: 866-29-EAGLE
Web Site: eaglegatecollege.edu
Description: Proprietary, 4-year, coed. Part of Eagle Gate College Group. Awards associate and bachelor's degrees. Setting: suburban campus with easy access to Salt Lake City. Calendar: quarters.

■ EAGLE GATE COLLEGE (MURRAY)
5588 S Green St.
Murray, UT 84123
Tel: (801)333-8100; Free: 866-29-EAGLE
Web Site: eaglegatecollege.edu
Description: Proprietary, 4-year, coed. Part of Eagle Gate College Group. Awards associate and bachelor's degrees. Setting: suburban campus with easy access to Salt Lake City. Calendar: quarters.

■ FORTIS COLLEGE
3949 S 700 E
Ste. 150
Salt Lake City, UT 84107
Tel: (801)713-0915; Free: 855-4-FORTIS
Web Site: www.fortis.edu
Description: Proprietary, 2-year, coed. Awards certificates, diplomas, transfer associate, and terminal associate degrees.

■ INDEPENDENCE UNIVERSITY
4021 S 700 E
Ste. 400
Salt Lake City, UT 84107
Free: 800-917-6391

Fax: (801)263-0345
Web Site: www.independence.edu
Description: Proprietary, comprehensive, coed. Awards associate, bachelor's, and master's degrees (offers primarily external degree programs). Founded 1978. Setting: 2-acre urban campus with easy access to San Diego. Calendar: continuous. Distance learning, part-time degree program, external degree program.
Entrance Requirements: Open admission. Option: deferred admission. Required: high school transcript. Recommended: employment in a health science field. Required for some: employment in a health science field. Entrance: noncompetitive. Application deadline: rolling.

■ LDS BUSINESS COLLEGE
95 N 300 W
Salt Lake City, UT 84101
Tel: (801)524-8100; Free: 800-999-5767
Fax: (801)524-1900
E-mail: admissions@ldsbc.edu
Web Site: www.ldsbc.edu
Description: Independent, 2-year, coed, affiliated with The Church of Jesus Christ of Latter-day Saints. Part of The Church Educational System (CES) of The Church of Jesus Christ of Latter-day Saints. Awards certificates, transfer associate, and terminal associate degrees. Founded 1886. Setting: 2-acre urban campus with easy access to Salt Lake City. Student-undergrad faculty ratio is 25:1. 0.4% American Indian or Alaska Native, non-Hispanic/Latino; 14% Hispanic/Latino; 2% Black or African American, non-Hispanic/Latino; 1% Asian, non-Hispanic/Latino; 2% Native Hawaiian or other Pacific Islander, non-Hispanic/Latino; 22% international. Core. Calendar: semesters. Academic remediation for entering students, ESL program, services for LD students, advanced placement, distance learning, double major, summer session for credit, part-time degree program, adult/continuing education programs, internships. ROTC: Army (c), Air Force (c).
Entrance Requirements: Open admission. Options: electronic application, deferred admission. Recommended: SAT or ACT. Entrance: noncompetitive. Application deadline: rolling. Notification: continuous. Transfer credits accepted: Yes.
Costs Per Year: Application fee: $35. Tuition: $1670 full-time.
Collegiate Environment: Orientation program. Choral group. Social organizations: 15 open to all. Most popular organizations: DECA, Baseball Club, Soccer Club, Mentor, Service. Major annual events: Elevate Conference, Evening of Talents, Evening of Gratitude. Student services: personal-psychological counseling. Campus security: 24-hour emergency response devices and patrols. LDS Business College Library. Weekly public service hours: 74; students can reserve study rooms. 500 computers available on campus for general student use. A campuswide network can be accessed from off-campus. Students can access the following: online class registration.

■ MIDWIVES COLLEGE OF UTAH
1174 E 2700 S, Ste. 2
Salt Lake City, UT 84106
Tel: (801)764-9068; Free: 866-680-2756
Fax: (801)434-8704
E-mail: admission@midwifery.edu
Web Site: www.midwifery.edu
Description: Independent, comprehensive, women only. Awards bachelor's and master's degrees. Founded 1980. Setting: urban campus with easy access to Salt Lake City. Educational spending for the previous fiscal year: $170 per student. Total enrollment: 242. Faculty: 22. Full-time: 235 students. Students come from 12 other countries. 1% American Indian or Alaska Native, non-Hispanic/Latino; 9% Hispanic/Latino; 5% Black or African American, non-Hispanic/Latino. 11% transferred in. Academic area with the most degrees conferred: health professions and related sciences. Core. Calendar: semesters. Services for LD students, independent study, distance learning, part-time degree program, adult/continuing education programs, internships, graduate courses open to undergrads. Off campus study.
Entrance Requirements: Options: electronic application, deferred admission, international baccalaureate accepted. Required: essay, 2 recommendations. Required for some: high school transcript, interview, transcripts from previous college. Application deadline: 3/5. Notification: 4/16. Transfer credits accepted: Yes.
Costs Per Year: Application fee: $50. One-time mandatory fee: $235. Tuition: $4400 full-time, $2200 per year part-time. Mandatory fees: $345 full-time, $345 per year part-time.

Collegiate Environment: Orientation program. Student services: personal-psychological counseling. MCU Library. Books: 644 (physical); Serial titles: 5 (digital/electronic); Databases: 1. Weekly public service hours: 35.

■ NEUMONT COLLEGE OF COMPUTER SCIENCE
143 S Main St.
Salt Lake City, UT 84111
Tel: (801)302-2800; Free: 888-NEUMONT
Fax: (801)302-2880
Web Site: www.neumont.edu
Description: Proprietary, 4-year, coed. Awards bachelor's degrees. Founded 2002. Setting: urban campus with easy access to Salt Lake City. Total enrollment: 431. Faculty: 46 (16 full-time, 30 part-time). Student-undergrad faculty ratio is 29:1. 833 applied, 84% were admitted. Full-time: 431 students, 11% women, 89% men. 81% from out-of-state. 0.7% American Indian or Alaska Native, non-Hispanic/Latino; 13% Hispanic/Latino; 5% Black or African American, non-Hispanic/Latino; 3% Asian, non-Hispanic/Latino; 0.7% Native Hawaiian or other Pacific Islander, non-Hispanic/Latino. 5% 25 or older, 41% transferred in. Academic area with the most degrees conferred: computer and information sciences. Core. Calendar: quarters. Services for LD students, accelerated degree program, internships.
Entrance Requirements: Option: electronic application. Required: essay, high school transcript, SAT or ACT. Recommended: 2 recommendations, interview. Entrance: moderately difficult. Application deadline: rolling. SAT Reasoning Test deadline: 9/1. SAT Subject Test deadline: 9/1. Transfer credits accepted: Yes.
Costs Per Year: Application fee: $35. One-time mandatory fee: $2500. Tuition: $22,950 full-time, $6000 per term part-time. Mandatory fees: $1800 full-time. Full-time tuition and fees vary according to course load, degree level, program, and student level. Part-time tuition varies according to course load, degree level, program, and student level. College room only: $5970. Room charges vary according to housing facility.
Collegiate Environment: Orientation program. Social organizations: 13 open to all. Most popular organizations: Unified Student Government, Society of Women Engineers, Pathfinder- (RPG group), Game Gurus, Soccer Club. Major annual events: Week-One Done, Career Week, Project Showcase. Student services: health clinic, personal-psychological counseling. Campus security: 24-hour emergency response devices and patrols.

■ NEW CHARTER UNIVERSITY
50 W Broadway, Ste. 300
Salt Lake City, UT 84101
Tel: (801)883-8336; Free: 888-639-1388
E-mail: admissions@aju.edu
Web Site: www.new.edu
Description: Proprietary, comprehensive, coed. Awards associate, bachelor's, master's, and doctoral degrees (offers primarily external degree programs). Founded 1994. Setting: suburban campus with easy access to Birmingham. Total enrollment: 472. Faculty: 50 (all part-time). Student-undergrad faculty ratio is 11:1. 115 applied, 87% were admitted. Part-time: 230 students, 31% women, 69% men. 95% from out-of-state. 95% 25 or older. Academic areas with the most degrees conferred: business/marketing; social sciences; communication/journalism. Core. Advanced placement, accelerated degree program, independent study, distance learning, summer session for credit, part-time degree program, external degree program, adult/continuing education programs. Off campus study.
Entrance Requirements: Open admission. Option: electronic application. Required: interview. Required for some: essay, high school transcript. Entrance: noncompetitive. Transfer credits accepted: Yes.
Collegiate Environment: Orientation program.

■ NIGHTINGALE COLLEGE
4155 Harrison Blvd. No.100
Ogden, UT 84403
Tel: (801)689-2160
Web Site: www.nightingale.edu
Description: Proprietary, primarily 2-year, coed. Awards diplomas, transfer associate, and bachelor's degrees. Setting: suburban campus with easy access to Salt Lake City. 96 applied, 75% were admitted. Retention: 95% of full-time freshmen returned the following year. Academic area with the most degrees conferred: health professions and related sciences. Calendar: semesters. Part-time degree program.
Entrance Requirements: Open admission. Options: electronic application, early admission. Required: essay, high school transcript, interview, Nightingale Entrance Exam.

■ PROVO COLLEGE
1450 W 820 N
Provo, UT 84601
Tel: (801)818-8900; Free: 877-777-5886
Fax: (801)375-9728
Web Site: www.provocollege.edu
Description: Proprietary, 2-year, coed. Awards terminal associate degrees. Founded 1984. Total enrollment: 656.
Entrance Requirements: Entrance: noncompetitive.

■ SALT LAKE COMMUNITY COLLEGE
PO Box 30808
Salt Lake City, UT 84130-0808
Tel: (801)957-4111
Fax: (801)957-4958
Web Site: www.slcc.edu
Description: State-supported, 2-year, coed. Part of Utah System of Higher Education. Awards certificates, diplomas, transfer associate, and terminal associate degrees. Founded 1948. Setting: 114-acre urban campus with easy access to Salt Lake City. Endowment: $837,612. Total enrollment: 29,620. Faculty: 1,514 (328 full-time, 1,186 part-time). Student-undergrad faculty ratio is 17:1. 4,397 applied, 100% were admitted. Full-time: 7,811 students, 52% women, 48% men. Part-time: 21,809 students, 52% women, 48% men. 0.8% American Indian or Alaska Native, non-Hispanic/Latino; 18% Hispanic/Latino; 2% Black or African American, non-Hispanic/Latino; 4% Asian, non-Hispanic/Latino; 1% Native Hawaiian or other Pacific Islander, non-Hispanic/Latino; 1% international. 33% 25 or older, 7% transferred in. Core. Calendar: semesters. Academic remediation for entering students, ESL program, services for LD students, advanced placement, self-designed majors, distance learning, double major, summer session for credit, part-time degree program, co-op programs and internships. Study abroad program. ROTC: Army (c), Air Force (c).
Entrance Requirements: Open admission except for health science programs. Options: electronic application, early admission. Entrance: noncompetitive. Application deadline: rolling. Transfer credits accepted: Yes.
Costs Per Year: Application fee: $40. State resident tuition: $3369 full-time, $140 per credit hour part-time. Nonresident tuition: $11,732 full-time, $488 per credit hour part-time. Mandatory fees: $474 full-time.
Collegiate Environment: Orientation program. Drama-theater group, choral group, marching band, student-run newspaper, radio station. Social organizations: local fraternities, local sororities. Student services: health clinic, personal-psychological counseling. Campus security: 24-hour emergency response devices and patrols, late night transport-escort service. Markosian Library plus 2 others. Operations spending for the previous fiscal year: $1.7 million.
Community Environment: The capital of the state, Salt Lake City, is located at the foot of the beautiful Wasatch Mountains. The Great Salt Lake is northwest of the city was founded by Brigham Young and his followers, and many of the original buildings may still be seen. The city is a metropolis today enjoying excellent transportation facilities. There are five libraries, a law library, many churches of various denominations, hospitals, and clinics to serve the community. Some part-time employment is available. Local recreation facilities includes 23 parks, golf courses, fishing, hunting, bowling, skiing, several theatres, and outdoor sports. There are excellent shopping facilities located here. The Utah State Fair is held annually as well as the Music Festival.

■ SNOW COLLEGE
150 E College Ave.
Ephraim, UT 84627-1203
Tel: (435)283-7000
Fax: (435)283-6879
E-mail: rachel.wade@snow.edu
Web Site: www.snow.edu
Description: State-supported, 2-year, coed. Part of Utah System of Higher Education. Awards certificates, diplomas, transfer associate, and terminal associate degrees. Founded 1888. Setting: 50-acre rural campus. Endowment: $8.9 million. Research spending for the previous fiscal year: $50,815. Educational spending for the previous fiscal year: $13,252 per student. Total enrollment: 5,574. Faculty: 281 (155 full-time, 126 part-time). Student-undergrad faculty ratio is 21:1. 7,676 applied, 100% were admitted. Full-time: 3,227 students, 55% women, 45% men. Part-time: 2,347 students, 56% women, 44% men. Students come from 35 states and territories, 42 other countries, 5% from out-of-state. 1% American Indian or Alaska Native,

non-Hispanic/Latino; 7% Hispanic/Latino; 0.6% Black or African American, non-Hispanic/Latino; 0.4% Asian, non-Hispanic/Latino; 2% Native Hawaiian or other Pacific Islander, non-Hispanic/Latino; 3% international. 9% 25 or older, 20% live on campus, 1% transferred in. Retention: 46% of full-time freshmen returned the following year. Core. Calendar: semesters. Academic remediation for entering students, ESL program, services for LD students, advanced placement, honors program, independent study, distance learning, summer session for credit, part-time degree program, external degree program, adult/continuing education programs, co-op programs.
Entrance Requirements: Open admission. Options: electronic application, early admission. Required: high school transcript. Recommended: SAT or ACT. Notification: continuous.
Costs Per Year: Application fee: $30.
Collegiate Environment: Orientation program. Drama-theater group, choral group, student-run newspaper, radio station. Social organizations: 30 open to all. Most popular organizations: Phi Beta Lambda & DECA (Business Club), Latter Day Saints Student Association, International Student Society, Western Swing Club, Dead Cats Society (Life Science Club). Major annual events: Orientation, Homecoming, International Food Festival. Student services: personal-psychological counseling. Campus security: 24-hour emergency response devices and patrols, student patrols, late night transport-escort service, controlled dormitory access. 444 college housing spaces available; 400 were occupied in 2018-19. No special consideration for freshman housing applicants. Options: coed, men-only, women-only housing available. Karen Huntsman Library plus 1 other. Books: 57,726 (physical); Serial titles: 775 (physical); Databases: 85. Weekly public service hours: 66. Operations spending for the previous fiscal year: $68,370. 400 computers available on campus for general student use. A campuswide network can be accessed from student residence rooms and from off campus. Students can access the following: online class registration. Staffed computer lab on campus provides training in use of computers and software.
Community Environment: Ephraim is a small, rural, college town located in central Utah. The area has a moderate climate with four definite seasons. The community is reached by bus lines and Highway 89. The city has four churches in the immediate vicinity and others in the surrounding area, a hospital 13 miles distant, and a clinic in the town. Public restaurants, motels, and limited entertainment facilities are available. Student housing and part-time employments opportunities are available in the community. Local recreation includes boating, fishing, hunting, cross-country skiing, golf, and winter sports. The county fairs and local festivities highlight the heritages of local communities.

■ SOUTHERN UTAH UNIVERSITY
351 W University Blvd.
Cedar City, UT 84720-2498
Tel: (435)586-7700
Fax: (435)586-5475
Web Site: www.suu.edu
Description: State-supported, comprehensive, coed. Part of Utah System of Higher Education. Awards associate, bachelor's, and master's degrees. Founded 1897. Setting: 130-acre small town campus. Endowment: $273.2 million. Research spending for the previous fiscal year: $86,270. Educational spending for the previous fiscal year: $7030 per student. Total enrollment: 9,468. Faculty: 581 (303 full-time, 278 part-time). Student-undergrad faculty ratio is 19:1. 11,693 applied, 76% were admitted. 48% from top 10% of their high school class, 44% from top quarter, 73% from top half. Full-time: 6,279 students, 54% women, 46% men. Part-time: 2,271 students, 63% women, 37% men. Students come from 51 states and territories, 46 other countries, 17% from out-of-state. 1% American Indian or Alaska Native, non-Hispanic/Latino; 6% Hispanic/Latino; 2% Black or African American, non-Hispanic/Latino; 1% Asian, non-Hispanic/Latino; 1% Native Hawaiian or other Pacific Islander, non-Hispanic/Latino; 6% international. 16% 25 or older, 8% live on campus, 4% transferred in. Retention: 71% of full-time freshmen returned the following year. Academic areas with the most degrees conferred: business/marketing; education; family and consumer sciences. Core. Calendar: semesters. Academic remediation for entering students, ESL program, services for LD students, advanced placement, honors program, independent study, distance learning, double major, summer session for credit, part-time degree program, adult/continuing education programs, co-op programs and internships, graduate courses open to undergrads. Study abroad program. ROTC: Army.
Entrance Requirements: Options: electronic application, deferred admission, international baccalaureate accepted. Required: high school transcript, SAT or ACT. Entrance: moderately difficult. Application deadline: 5/1.

Notification: continuous, continuous for nonresidents. SAT Reasoning Test deadline: 5/1. Transfer credits accepted: Yes.
Costs Per Year: Application fee: $50. State resident tuition: $6006 full-time. Nonresident tuition: $19,822 full-time. Mandatory fees: $764 full-time. Full-time tuition and fees vary according to program. College room and board: $7250. College room only: $3350. Room and board charges vary according to board plan and housing facility.
Collegiate Environment: Orientation program. Drama-theater group, choral group, student-run newspaper, radio station. Social organizations: national fraternities, national sororities, local sororities. Student services: health clinic, personal-psychological counseling, women's center. Campus security: 24-hour emergency response devices, student patrols, late night transport-escort service, controlled dormitory access. Gerald R Sherratt Library. Books: 241,434 (physical), 441,219 (digital/electronic); Serial titles: 676 (physical), 22,603 (digital/electronic); Databases: 218. Students can reserve study rooms. Operations spending for the previous fiscal year: $2.4 million.
Community Environment: Cedar City is located within a few hours of the Grand Canyon, Lake Powell, Cedar Breaks National Monument, Bryce Canyon, Zion National Park and other scenic wonders. It is 2 1/2 hours from Las Vegas. Cedar City is accessible by airlines, railroad, bus lines, and major highways. The community has churches representing most denominations, a hospital, public library, and a museum. Student housing is available in the community. Various civic, fraternal, and veteran's organizations are active in the area. Local recreation includes indoor and outdoor theatres, hunting, fishing, skiing, golf, and boating. There is a shopping center in the area.

■ STEVENS-HENAGER COLLEGE (LOGAN)
755 S Main St.
Logan, UT 84321
Tel: (435)752-0903; Free: 800-622-2640
Web Site: www.stevenshenager.edu
Description: Independent, 4-year, coed. Awards associate and bachelor's degrees.

■ STEVENS-HENAGER COLLEGE (OREM)
1476 S Sandhill Rd.
Orem, UT 84058
Tel: (801)373-0285; Free: 800-622-2640
Web Site: www.stevenshenager.edu
Description: Independent, 4-year, coed. Awards associate and bachelor's degrees. Founded 1962.

■ STEVENS-HENAGER COLLEGE (SAINT GEORGE)
720 S River Rd.
Ste. C-130
Saint George, UT 84790
Tel: (435)628-9150; Free: 800-622-2640
Web Site: www.stevenshenager.edu
Description: Independent, 4-year, coed. Awards associate and bachelor's degrees.

■ STEVENS-HENAGER COLLEGE (SALT LAKE CITY)
383 W Vine St.
Salt Lake City, UT 84123
Tel: (801)531-1180; Free: 800-622-2640
Web Site: www.stevenshenager.edu
Description: Independent, comprehensive, coed. Awards associate, bachelor's, and master's degrees.

■ STEVENS-HENAGER COLLEGE (WEST HAVEN)
1890 S 1350 W
West Haven, UT 84401
Tel: (801)392-1471; Free: 800-622-2640
Web Site: www.stevenshenager.edu
Description: Independent, 4-year, coed. Awards associate and bachelor's degrees. Founded 1891. Setting: 1-acre urban campus with easy access to Salt Lake City. Total enrollment: 371. Student-undergrad faculty ratio is 18:1. 5% from out-of-state. 54% 25 or older. Retention: 78% of full-time freshmen returned the following year. Calendar: quarters. Part-time degree program, adult/continuing education programs.
Entrance Requirements: Open admission. Options: early admission, deferred admission. Required: high school transcript, Wonderlic aptitude

test. Recommended: SAT or ACT. Entrance: noncompetitive. Application deadline: rolling. Notification: continuous.

■ **UNIVERSITY OF UTAH**

201 Presidents Cir.
Salt Lake City, UT 84112-1107
Tel: (801)581-7200; Free: 800-685-8856
Fax: (801)585-3034
E-mail: mremsburg@sa.utah.edu
Web Site: www.utah.edu

Description: State-supported, university, coed. Part of Utah System of Higher Education. Awards bachelor's, master's, and doctoral degrees and post-master's certificates. Founded 1850. Setting: 1,535-acre urban campus with easy access to Salt Lake City. Endowment: $958 million. Research spending for the previous fiscal year: $316.3 million. Educational spending for the previous fiscal year: $16,278 per student. Total enrollment: 32,760. Faculty: 2,196 (1,508 full-time, 688 part-time). Student-undergrad faculty ratio is 16:1. 22,400 applied, 66% were admitted. Full-time: 18,066 students, 47% women, 53% men. Part-time: 6,569 students, 47% women, 53% men. Students come from 52 states and territories, 105 other countries, 20% from out-of-state. 0.4% American Indian or Alaska Native, non-Hispanic/Latino; 12% Hispanic/Latino; 1% Black or African American, non-Hispanic/Latino; 6% Asian, non-Hispanic/Latino; 0.5% Native Hawaiian or other Pacific Islander, non-Hispanic/Latino; 5% international. 21% 25 or older, 14% live on campus, 8% transferred in. Retention: 91% of full-time freshmen returned the following year. Academic areas with the most degrees conferred: business/marketing; social sciences; engineering. Core. Calendar: semesters. Academic remediation for entering students, ESL program, services for LD students, advanced placement, accelerated degree program, self-designed majors, freshman honors college, honors program, independent study, distance learning, double major, summer session for credit, part-time degree program, co-op programs and internships, graduate courses open to undergrads. Off campus study at members of the National Student Exchange. Study abroad program. ROTC: Army, Naval, Air Force.

Entrance Requirements: Options: electronic application, early admission, early action, deferred admission, international baccalaureate accepted. Required: high school transcript, SAT or ACT. Entrance: moderately difficult. Application deadlines: 4/1, 12/1 for early action. Notification: continuous, continuous for nonresidents. SAT Reasoning Test deadline: 3/15. SAT Subject Test deadline: 3/15. Transfer credits accepted: Yes.

Costs Per Year: Application fee: $55. State resident tuition: $7997 full-time, $224.65 per credit hour part-time. Nonresident tuition: $27,990 full-time, $772.37 per credit hour part-time. Mandatory fees: $1225 full-time. Full-time tuition and fees vary according to course level, course load, degree level, location, program, and student level. Part-time tuition varies according to course level, course load, degree level, location, program, and student level. College room and board: $10,262. College room only: $5323. Room and board charges vary according to board plan, housing facility, and location.

Collegiate Environment: Orientation program. Drama-theater group, choral group, marching band, student-run newspaper, radio station. Social organizations: 605 open to all; national fraternities, national sororities, local fraternities, local sororities; 6% of eligible men and 7% of eligible women are members. Most popular organizations: TEK Club, International Business Club, Golden Key International Honours Society, Tennis Club, Thai Student Association. Major annual events: Welcome Week, Redfest, Homecoming. Student services: health clinic, personal-psychological counseling, women's center. Campus security: 24-hour emergency response devices and patrols, student patrols, late night transport-escort service, controlled dormitory access. J. Willard Marriott Library plus 3 others. Books: 3.2 million (physical), 460,000 (digital/electronic); Serial titles: 500 (physical), 11,500 (digital/electronic); Databases: 325. Weekly public service hours: 111; students can reserve study rooms. Operations spending for the previous fiscal year: $24.2 million. 1,099 computers available on campus for general student use. A campuswide network can be accessed from student residence rooms and from off campus. Students can access the following: online class registration, online classes. Staffed computer lab on campus provides training in use of computers, software, and the Internet.

Community Environment: The capital of the state, Salt Lake City, is located at the foot of the beautiful Wasatch Mountains. The Great Salt Lake is northwest of the city, and the desert is only a few miles away to the west. The city was founded by Brigham Young and his followers, and many of the original buildings may still be seen. The city is a metropolis today enjoying excellent transportation facilities. There are five libraries, a law library, many churches of various denominations, hospitals, and clinics to serve the community. Salt Lake City is the headquarters of the Church of Jesus Christ of Latter Day Saints, and is noted for Temple Square and the Mormon Temple and Tabernacle. Part-time employment is available. Local recreation facilities includes parks, golf courses, fishing, hunting, bowling, skiing, theatres, and outdoor sports. There are excellent shopping facilities located here. The Utah State Fair is held annually.

■ **UTAH STATE UNIVERSITY**

Old Main Hill
Logan, UT 84322
Tel: (435)797-1000; Free: 800-488-8108
Fax: (435)797-3900
E-mail: admit@usu.edu
Web Site: www.usu.edu

Description: State-supported, university, coed. Part of Utah System of Higher Education. Awards associate, bachelor's, master's, and doctoral degrees. Founded 1888. Setting: 456-acre urban campus. Endowment: $377 million. Research spending for the previous fiscal year: $160.7 million. Educational spending for the previous fiscal year: $8332 per student. Total enrollment: 27,932. Faculty: 1,289 (1,007 full-time, 282 part-time). Student-undergrad faculty ratio is 20:1. 15,099 applied, 89% were admitted. 21% from top 10% of their high school class, 47% from top quarter, 77% from top half. Full-time: 17,394 students, 52% women, 48% men. Part-time: 7,486 students, 59% women, 41% men. Students come from 53 states and territories, 59 other countries, 27% from out-of-state. 2% American Indian or Alaska Native, non-Hispanic/Latino; 6% Hispanic/Latino; 0.9% Black or African American, non-Hispanic/Latino; 1% Asian, non-Hispanic/Latino; 0.3% Native Hawaiian or other Pacific Islander, non-Hispanic/Latino; 1% international. 20% 25 or older, 6% transferred in. Retention: 73% of full-time freshmen returned the following year. Academic areas with the most degrees conferred: business/marketing; education; social sciences. Core. Calendar: semesters. Academic remediation for entering students, ESL program, services for LD students, advanced placement, accelerated degree program, self-designed majors, freshman honors college, honors program, independent study, distance learning, double major, summer session for credit, part-time degree program, adult/continuing education programs, co-op programs and internships, graduate courses open to undergrads. Off campus study. Study abroad program. ROTC: Army, Air Force.

Entrance Requirements: Options: electronic application, deferred admission, international baccalaureate accepted. Required: high school transcript, SAT or ACT. Recommended: minimum 2.75 high school GPA. Entrance: moderately difficult. Application deadline: rolling. Notification: continuous. SAT Reasoning Test deadline: 8/26. SAT Subject Test deadline: 8/26. Transfer credits accepted: Yes.

Costs Per Year: Application fee: $50. State resident tuition: $6,342 full-time. Nonresident tuition: $20,423 full-time. Mandatory fees: $1082 full-time. Full-time tuition and fees vary according to course level, course load, program, and reciprocity agreements. College room and board: $6400. College room only: $2240. Room and board charges vary according to board plan and housing facility.

Collegiate Environment: Orientation program. Drama-theater group, choral group, marching band, student-run newspaper, radio station. Social organizations: 354 open to all; national fraternities, national sororities, local fraternities; 3% of eligible men and 3% of eligible women are members. Most popular organizations: Latter-Day Saints Student Association, multicultural clubs, volunteer groups, college councils. Major annual events: Homecoming, Halloween Howl, A-Day. Student services: legal services, health clinic, personal-psychological counseling, women's center. Campus security: 24-hour emergency response devices and patrols, student patrols, late night transport-escort service. 3,647 college housing spaces available. No special consideration for freshman housing applicants. Options: coed, men-only, women-only housing available. Merrill-Cazier Library plus 4 others. Books: 1.9 million (physical), 768,007 (digital/electronic); Serial titles: 44,565 (physical), 74,377 (digital/electronic); Databases: 4,418. Weekly public service hours: 101; students can reserve study rooms. Operations spending for the previous fiscal year: $12.5 million. 1,000 computers available on campus for general student use. Computer purchase/lease plans available. A campuswide network can be accessed from student residence rooms and from off campus. Students can access the following: online class registration. Staffed computer lab on campus provides training in use of computers, software, and the Internet.

Community Environment: Located in the fertile Cache Valley, Logan is the headquarters for the adjacent Cache National Forest. The Cache Valley was originally an ancient lakebed 500 feet deep, and shorelines of the lake are still visible along the foothills. Today, the community has excellent transportation with airlines, railroad, and bus connections. Major highways enter the city from four directions. Dairying is an important economic feature of the community, and the city has one of the largest Swiss cheese factories in the world. Some part-time employment is available. Local recreation includes hunting, fishing, skiing, and all the water sports.

■ UTAH VALLEY UNIVERSITY

800 W University Pky.
Orem, UT 84058-5999
Tel: (801)863-8000
Fax: (801)225-4677
E-mail: coleskr@uvu.edu
Web Site: www.uvu.edu

Description: State-supported, comprehensive, coed, affiliated with Advent Christian Church. Part of Utah System of Higher Education. Awards associate, bachelor's, and master's degrees. Founded 1941. Setting: 524-acre suburban campus with easy access to Salt Lake City. Total enrollment: 39,931. Faculty: 2,096 (724 full-time, 1,372 part-time). Student-undergrad faculty ratio is 25:1. 10,117 applied, 100% were admitted. 10% from top 10% of their high school class, 28% from top quarter, 59% from top half. Full-time: 19,261 students, 46% women, 54% men. Part-time: 20,136 students, 49% women, 51% men. Students come from 50 states and territories, 71 other countries, 12% from out-of-state. 0.6% American Indian or Alaska Native, non-Hispanic/Latino; 12% Hispanic/Latino; 1% Black or African American, non-Hispanic/Latino; 1% Asian, non-Hispanic/Latino; 0.8% Native Hawaiian or other Pacific Islander, non-Hispanic/Latino; 2% international. 13% 25 or older, 7% transferred in. Retention: 64% of full-time freshmen returned the following year. Academic areas with the most degrees conferred: business/marketing; psychology; education. Core. Calendar: semesters. Academic remediation for entering students, ESL program, services for LD students, advanced placement, self-designed majors, honors program, independent study, distance learning, double major, summer session for credit, part-time degree program, co-op programs and internships, graduate courses open to undergrads. Off campus study at Wasatch Campus, North Valley Campus, South Valley Campus, National Guard/West Campus. Study abroad program. ROTC: Army, Air Force (c).

Entrance Requirements: Open admission. Options: electronic application, deferred admission, international baccalaureate accepted. Required: high school transcript. Notification: continuous, continuous for nonresidents. Transfer credits accepted: Yes.

Costs Per Year: Application fee: $35. State resident tuition: $5036 full-time, $207 per credit part-time. Nonresident tuition: $15,606 full-time, $642 per credit part-time. Mandatory fees: $690 full-time, $345 per term part-time. Full-time tuition and fees vary according to course load and program. Part-time tuition and fees vary according to course load.

Collegiate Environment: Orientation program. Drama-theater group, choral group, student-run newspaper. Social organizations: national fraternities, national sororities. Major annual events: Homecoming, Club All-Nighter, Club Rush. Student services: legal services, health clinic, personal-psychological counseling, women's center. Campus security: 24-hour patrols. College housing not available. Utah Valley University Library plus 1 other. Students can reserve study rooms.

Community Environment: See Brigham Young University.

■ WEBER STATE UNIVERSITY

3848 Harrison Blvd.
Ogden, UT 84408-1001
Tel: (801)626-6000; Free: 800-848-7770
Fax: (801)626-6747
E-mail: andrewyoung@weber.edu
Web Site: www.weber.edu

Description: State-supported, comprehensive, coed. Part of Utah System of Higher Education. Awards associate, bachelor's, and master's degrees and post-master's certificates. Founded 1889. Setting: 504-acre urban campus with easy access to Salt Lake City. Endowment: $149 million. Research spending for the previous fiscal year: $1.1 million. Educational spending for the previous fiscal year: $5877 per student. Total enrollment: 28,247. Faculty: 1,404 (521 full-time, 883 part-time). Student-undergrad faculty ratio is 21:1. 7,251 applied, 100% were admitted. Full-time: 11,444 students, 54% women, 46% men. Part-time: 16,021 students, 56% women, 44% men. Students come from 54 states and territories, 61 other countries, 8% from out-of-state. 0.5% American Indian or Alaska Native, non-Hispanic/Latino; 11% Hispanic/Latino; 1% Black or African American, non-Hispanic/Latino;

2% Asian, non-Hispanic/Latino; 0.5% Native Hawaiian or other Pacific Islander, non-Hispanic/Latino; 1% international. 28% 25 or older, 4% live on campus, 5% transferred in. Retention: 65% of full-time freshmen returned the following year. Academic areas with the most degrees conferred: health professions and related sciences; business/marketing; computer and information sciences. Core. Calendar: semesters. Academic remediation for entering students, ESL program, services for LD students, advanced placement, accelerated degree program, self-designed majors, freshman honors college, honors program, independent study, distance learning, double major, summer session for credit, part-time degree program, external degree program, adult/continuing education programs, co-op programs and internships, graduate courses open to undergrads. Off campus study at Utah State University, Southern Utah University, Dixie College, Utah Valley University, Salt Lake Community College. Study abroad program. ROTC: Army, Naval (c), Air Force (c).

Entrance Requirements: Open admission WSU has a couple of programs with additional admission requirements, however students are free to choose other programs. Options: electronic application, early admission, deferred admission, international baccalaureate accepted. Required: high school transcript. Recommended: SAT or ACT. Required for some: ACCUPLACER. Entrance: noncompetitive. Notification: continuous, continuous for nonresidents. SAT Reasoning Test deadline: 7/1. SAT Subject Test deadline: 7/1. Transfer credits accepted: Yes.

Costs Per Year: Application fee: $30. State resident tuition: $4,892 full-time, $2,886.48 per year part-time. Nonresident tuition: $14,679 full-time, $8,661 per year part-time. Mandatory fees: $948 full-time, $593.34 per year part-time. Full-time tuition and fees vary according to course level, course load, degree level, program, and reciprocity agreements. Part-time tuition and fees vary according to course level, course load, degree level, program, and reciprocity agreements. College room and board: $8400. Room and board charges vary according to board plan and housing facility.

Collegiate Environment: Orientation program. Drama-theater group, choral group, marching band, student-run newspaper, radio station. Social organizations: 218 open to all; national fraternities, national sororities, local fraternities, local sororities; 12% of eligible men and 15% of eligible women are members. Most popular organizations: LDSSA (Latter-day Saint Student Association), SAA (Student Alumni Association), GSA (Gay-Straight Alliance), Chinese Club, Golden Key Honor Society. Major annual events: Homecoming, Graduation, Block Party. Student services: legal services, health clinic, personal-psychological counseling, women's center. Campus security: 24-hour emergency response devices and patrols, student patrols, late night transport-escort service, controlled dormitory access. 1,001 college housing spaces available; 737 were occupied in 2018-19. No special consideration for freshman housing applicants. Options: men-only, women-only housing available. Stewart Library. Books: 498,531 (physical); Serial titles: 425 (physical); Databases: 223,410. Operations spending for the previous fiscal year: $3.3 million. 650 computers available on campus for general student use. Computer purchase/lease plans available. A campuswide network can be accessed from student residence rooms and from off campus. Students can access the following: online class registration. Staffed computer lab on campus provides training in use of computers, software, and the Internet.

Community Environment: Located at the confluence of the Weber and Ogden Rivers, this community is an important railroad distribution center for products directed to west coast markets. Mormon pioneers settled the community. The climate is temperate with four distinct seasons. Ogden is reached by railroad, airlines, and highways. The community has many churches representing over 30 denominations. There are two hospitals, four health centers, a library and branch, 2 major shopping malls, and various civic and fraternal organizations serving the area. There are also five TV stations and a radio station. Part-time employment is available. Local recreation includes fishing, hunting, swimming, skiing, boating, picnicking, camping, golfing, and horseback riding.

■ WESTERN GOVERNORS UNIVERSITY

4001 S 700 E, Ste. 700
Salt Lake City, UT 84107
Tel: (801)274-3280; Free: 866-225-5948
Fax: (801)274-3305
Web Site: www.wgu.edu

Description: Independent, comprehensive, coed. Awards bachelor's and master's degrees. Founded 1998. Setting: urban campus. Total enrollment: 57,821. Faculty: 1,654 (1,093 full-time, 561 part-time). Student-undergrad faculty ratio is 41:1. Full-time: 44,499 students, 60% women, 40% men.

Students come from 58 states and territories. 0.6% American Indian or Alaska Native, non-Hispanic/Latino; 8% Hispanic/Latino; 9% Black or African American, non-Hispanic/Latino; 4% Asian, non-Hispanic/Latino; 0.5% Native Hawaiian or other Pacific Islander, non-Hispanic/Latino; 0.1% international. 92% 25 or older, 97% transferred in. Retention: 73% of full-time freshmen returned the following year. Academic areas with the most degrees conferred: health professions and related sciences; business/marketing; education. Core. Calendar: continuous. Services for LD students, accelerated degree program, independent study, distance learning, double major, part-time degree program, external degree program, adult/continuing education programs.

Entrance Requirements: Option: electronic application. Required for some: high school transcript. Entrance: minimally difficult.

Collegiate Environment: Orientation program. WGU Central Library (online).

■ **WESTMINSTER COLLEGE**
1840 S 1300, E
Salt Lake City, UT 84105-3697
Tel: (801)484-7651; Free: 800-748-4753
Fax: (801)484-3252
E-mail: admission@westminstercollege.edu
Web Site: www.westminstercollege.edu

Description: Independent, comprehensive, coed. Awards bachelor's and master's degrees. Founded 1875. Setting: 27-acre suburban campus. Endowment: $77.4 million. Educational spending for the previous fiscal year: $12,224 per student. Total enrollment: 2,570. Faculty: 382 (152 full-time, 230 part-time). Student-undergrad faculty ratio is 9:1. 1,702 applied, 93% were admitted. 28% from top 10% of their high school class, 53% from top quarter, 88% from top half. 17 valedictorians. Full-time: 1,906 students, 59% women, 41% men. Part-time: 124 students, 51% women, 49% men. 39% from out-of-state. 0.6% American Indian or Alaska Native, non-Hispanic/Latino; 11% Hispanic/Latino; 2% Black or African American, non-Hispanic/Latino; 3% Asian, non-Hispanic/Latino; 0.3% Native Hawaiian or other Pacific Islander, non-Hispanic/Latino; 5% international. 15% 25 or older, 30% live on campus, 7% transferred in. Retention: 80% of full-time freshmen returned the following year. Academic areas with the most degrees conferred: business/marketing; health professions and related sciences; biological/life sciences; social sciences. Core. Calendar: semesters. Academic remediation for entering students, ESL program, services for LD students, advanced placement, accelerated degree program, self-designed majors, freshman honors college, honors program, independent study, distance learning, double major, summer session for credit, part-time degree program, external degree program, adult/continuing education programs, co-op programs and internships. Off campus study. Study abroad program. ROTC: Army (c), Naval (c), Air Force (c).

Entrance Requirements: Options: electronic application, deferred admission, international baccalaureate accepted. Required: essay, high school transcript, minimum 2.5 high school GPA, 1 recommendation, SAT or ACT. Recommended: interview. Entrance: moderately difficult. Application deadline: rolling. Notification: continuous. SAT Reasoning Test deadline: 8/1. Transfer credits accepted: Yes.

Costs Per Year: Application fee: $50. One-time mandatory fee: $300. Comprehensive fee: $43,524 includes full-time tuition ($33,480), mandatory fees ($520), and college room and board ($9524). College room only: $5526. Full-time tuition and fees vary according to course load and program. Room and board charges vary according to board plan and housing facility. Part-time tuition: $1395 per credit hour. Part-time mandatory fees: $154 per credit hour. Part-time tuition and fees vary according to course load and program.

Collegiate Environment: Orientation program. Drama-theater group, choral group, student-run newspaper. Social organizations: 54 open to all. Most popular organizations: Westminster Ski and Snowboard Club (WSSC), Residence Hall Association (Residential Government), Feminist Club, Latin X, Theatre Society. Major annual events: Westminster Welcome Back Week, Vagina Monologues, Late Night Breakfast. Student services: health clinic, personal-psychological counseling. Campus security: 24-hour emergency response devices and patrols, student patrols, late night transport-escort service, controlled dormitory access. Giovale Library plus 1 other. Books: 95,039 (physical), 364,687 (digital/electronic); Databases: 56. Students can reserve study rooms. Operations spending for the previous fiscal year: $1.2 million. 200 computers available on campus for general student use. A computer is required for all students. A campuswide network can be accessed. Students can access the following: online class registration. Staffed computer lab on campus provides training in use of computers, software, and the Internet.

■ **BENNINGTON COLLEGE**
One College Dr.
Bennington, VT 05201
Tel: (802)442-5401; Free: 800-833-6845
Fax: (802)447-4269
E-mail: admissions@bennington.edu
Web Site: www.bennington.edu
Description: Independent, comprehensive, coed. Awards bachelor's and master's degrees. Founded 1932. Setting: 440-acre small town campus with easy access to Albany, NY. Endowment: $19.2 million. Educational spending for the previous fiscal year: $20,082 per student. Total enrollment: 851. Faculty: 125 (60 full-time, 65 part-time). Student-undergrad faculty ratio is 10:1. 1,465 applied, 57% were admitted. Full-time: 724 students, 67% women, 33% men. Part-time: 51 students, 33% women, 67% men. Students come from 45 states and territories, 56 other countries, 98% from out-of-state. 0.4% American Indian or Alaska Native, non-Hispanic/Latino; 10% Hispanic/Latino; 4% Black or African American, non-Hispanic/Latino; 2% Asian, non-Hispanic/Latino; 0.1% Native Hawaiian or other Pacific Islander, non-Hispanic/Latino; 17% international. 2% 25 or older, 98% live on campus, 1% transferred in. Retention: 78% of full-time freshmen returned the following year. Academic areas with the most degrees conferred: visual and performing arts; English; social sciences. Calendar: semesters plus winter work term in January and February. ESL program, services for LD students, advanced placement, self-designed majors, independent study, double major, internships. Off campus study at Association of Vermont Independent Colleges (AVIC). Study abroad program.
Entrance Requirements: Options: electronic application, early admission, early decision, early action, deferred admission, international baccalaureate accepted. Required: essay, high school transcript, 2 recommendations, graded analytic paper. Recommended: interview. Entrance: very difficult. Application deadlines: 1/15, 11/15 for early decision plan 1, 1/15 for early decision plan 2, 12/1 for early action. Notification: 3/22, 12/14 for early decision plan 1, 2/8 for early decision plan 2, 2/1 for early action. SAT Reasoning Test deadline: 1/3. SAT Subject Test deadline: 1/3. Transfer credits accepted: Yes. Early decision applicants: 90. Early decision applicants admitted: 48. Early action applicants: 408. Early action applicants admitted: 281.
Costs Per Year: Application fee: $0. One-time mandatory fee: $650. Comprehensive fee: $69,470 includes full-time tuition ($53,160), mandatory fees ($700), and college room and board ($15,610). College room only: $8460. Full-time tuition and fees vary according to degree level. Room and board charges vary according to board plan. Part-time tuition: $2215 per credit hour.
Collegiate Environment: Orientation program. Drama-theater group, choral group, student-run newspaper, radio station. Social organizations: 43 open to all. Most popular organizations: Program Activity Council, Bennington Free Press, Student Endowment for the Arts, SILO: Student Journal of Arts and Letters, The Purple Carrot Farm. Major annual events: Sunfest, Midnight Breakfast, Convocation. Student services: health clinic, personal-psychological counseling. Campus security: 24-hour emergency response devices and patrols, late night transport-escort service, controlled dormitory access, prevention/awareness program. Crossett Library plus 1 other. Books: 89,000 (physical), 162,000 (digital/electronic); Serial titles: 200 (physical), 48,000 (digital/electronic); Databases: 56. Weekly public service hours: 111; students can reserve study rooms. Operations spending for the previous fiscal year: $823,382. 40 computers available on campus for general student use. A campuswide network can be accessed from student

residence rooms and from off campus. Students can access the following: online class registration. Staffed computer lab on campus provides training in use of computers, software, and the Internet.
Community Environment: Situated on 550 acres in the foothills of Vermont's Green Mountains, Bennington College is a short drive from some of the region's top ski resorts. The College is four miles from the village of Bennington and one mile from North Bennington. Twenty miles to the south is Williamstown, MA, and the Berkshires, home to the nationally renowned museums The Clark Institute and MASSMoCA, while featuring such esteemed performing arts venues as the Williamstown Theatre Festival, Jacob's Pillow, and Tanglewood. Twenty miles north is Manchester, VT, and its fine restaurants and shopping, as well as a state-of-the-art ice skating rink. Approximately 40 miles to the west is Albany, NY, which provides numerous amenities as well as rail transportation to Boston, New York City, and elsewhere. Local historical sites include the Bennington Museum, Bennington Battle Monument, and Old First Church, where poet Robert Frost is buried.

■ **CASTLETON UNIVERSITY**
Castleton, VT 05735
Tel: (802)468-5611; Free: 800-639-8521
Fax: (802)468-1476
E-mail: info@castleton.edu
Web Site: www.castleton.edu
Description: State-supported, comprehensive, coed. Part of Vermont State Colleges System. Awards associate, bachelor's, and master's degrees and post-master's certificates. Founded 1787. Setting: 165-acre rural campus. Endowment: $7.5 million. Educational spending for the previous fiscal year: $7639 per student. Total enrollment: 2,184. Faculty: 228 (102 full-time, 126 part-time). Student-undergrad faculty ratio is 13:1. 2,397 applied, 78% were admitted. 6% from top 10% of their high school class, 29% from top quarter, 61% from top half. 3 valedictorians. Full-time: 1,720 students, 50% women, 50% men. Part-time: 265 students, 63% women, 37% men. Students come from 26 states and territories, 17 other countries, 30% from out-of-state. 0.5% American Indian or Alaska Native, non-Hispanic/Latino; 2% Hispanic/Latino; 2% Black or African American, non-Hispanic/Latino; 0.7% Asian, non-Hispanic/Latino; 2% international. 6% 25 or older, 54% live on campus, 9% transferred in. Retention: 70% of full-time freshmen returned the following year. Academic areas with the most degrees conferred: health professions and related sciences; business/marketing; communication/journalism. Core. Calendar: semesters. Academic remediation for entering students, services for LD students, advanced placement, self-designed majors, honors program, independent study, double major, summer session for credit, part-time degree program, co-op programs and internships. Off campus study at Vermont State Colleges (Johnson State, Lyndon State, Vermont Technical College, Community College of Vermont). Study abroad program. ROTC: Army.
Entrance Requirements: Options: electronic application, deferred admission. Required: essay, high school transcript, minimum 3 high school GPA, 2 recommendations, SAT or ACT. Entrance: moderately difficult. Application deadline: rolling. Notification: continuous. SAT Reasoning Test deadline: 5/1. Transfer credits accepted: Yes.
Collegiate Environment: Orientation program. Drama-theater group, choral group, marching band, student-run newspaper, radio station. Social organizations: 40 open to all. Most popular organizations: community service, clubs in the academic majors, Women's issues organization, Span-

ish and International, Skiing/Snowboarding. Major annual events: Sound-ings, Spring Weekend, Fall Festival. Student services: health clinic, personal-psychological counseling. Campus security: 24-hour emergency response devices and patrols, student patrols, late night transport-escort service, controlled dormitory access. Calvin Coolidge Library. Operations spending for the previous fiscal year: $416,498. 250 computers available on campus for general student use. Computer purchase/lease plans available. A campuswide network can be accessed from student residence rooms and from off campus. Students can access the following: online class registra-tion, Castleton app for smartphones/tablets. Staffed computer lab on campus provides training in use of computers, software, and the Internet.

Community Environment: Adjacent to outstanding ski and summer resorts, the area is rural and surrounded by Vermont's beautiful lakes and mountains.

■ **CHAMPLAIN COLLEGE**

PO Box 670

Burlington, VT 05402-0670

Tel: (802)860-2700; Free: 800-570-5858

Fax: (802)862-2772

E-mail: admission@champlain.edu

Web Site: www.champlain.edu

Description: Independent, comprehensive, coed. Awards associate, bachelor's, and master's degrees. Founded 1878. Setting: 27-acre suburban campus with easy access to Montreal. Endowment: $24.3 million. Educational spending for the previous fiscal year: $8011 per student. Total enrollment: 2,862. Faculty: 274 (114 full-time, 160 part-time). Student-undergrad faculty ratio is 14:1. 4,977 applied, 75% were admitted. 14% from top 10% of their high school class, 35% from top quarter, 70% from top half. Full-time: 2,158 students, 41% women, 59% men. Part-time: 82 students, 28% women, 72% men. Students come from 43 states and territories, 79% from out-of-state. 0.2% American Indian or Alaska Native, non-Hispanic/Latino; 7% Hispanic/Latino; 3% Black or African American, non-Hispanic/Latino; 3% Asian, non-Hispanic/Latino; 0.8% international. 3% 25 or older, 71% live on campus, 2% transferred in. Retention: 78% of full-time freshmen returned the following year. Academic areas with the most degrees conferred: computer and information sciences; business/marketing; visual and performing arts. Core. Calendar: semesters. Services for LD students, advanced placement, independent study, distance learning, double major, summer session for credit, part-time degree program, adult/continuing education programs, co-op programs and internships, graduate courses open to undergrads. Off campus study. Study abroad program. ROTC: Army (c).

Entrance Requirements: Options: electronic application, early admission, early decision, deferred admission, international baccalaureate accepted. Required: essay, high school transcript. Recommended: 2 recommenda-tions. Required for some: portfolio for creative media, filmmaking, game art and animation, game design, and graphic design and digital media majors. Entrance: moderately difficult. Application deadlines: 1/15, 11/15 for early decision. Notification: 3/15, 12/15 for early decision. SAT Reasoning Test deadline: 2/1. SAT Subject Test deadline: 2/1. Transfer credits accepted: Yes. Applicants placed on waiting list: 65. Wait-listed applicants offered admission: 28. Early decision applicants: 274. Early decision applicants admitted: 251.

Costs Per Year: Application fee: $0. Comprehensive fee: $57,594 includes full-time tuition ($41,728), mandatory fees ($100), and college room and board ($15,766). Part-time tuition: $1762 per credit hour.

Collegiate Environment: Orientation program. Drama-theater group, choral group, student-run newspaper, radio station. Social organizations: 50 open to all. Most popular organizations: Diversity Champlain, International Club, community service organization, Champlain Players (theater group), Outing Club/Skiing Snowboarding Club. Major annual events: Parents' Weekend, Halloween Masquerade Dance, Spring Meltdown. Student services: health clinic, personal-psychological counseling, women's center. Campus security: 24-hour emergency response devices and patrols, late night transport-escort service, controlled dormitory access. 1,463 college housing spaces avail-able; 1,428 were occupied in 2018-19. Freshmen guaranteed college hous-ing. Options: coed, women-only housing available. Miller Information Com-mons. Books: 50,200 (physical), 210,502 (digital/electronic); Serial titles: 150 (physical), 65,578 (digital/electronic); Databases: 151. Weekly public service hours: 105; students can reserve study rooms. Operations spending for the previous fiscal year: $1.5 million. 640 computers available on campus for general student use. A campuswide network can be accessed from student

residence rooms and from off campus. Students can access the following: online class registration. Staffed computer lab on campus provides training in use of software.

Community Environment: Burlington offers the best of both worlds: the excitement of life in the city and the tranquility and recreational splendor of the northern Vermont countryside. Three blocks from the Champlain campus, the Church Street Marketplace provides an exciting collection of more than 100 shops, services, and restaurants. Within one hour's drive are five major ski resorts: Stowe, Sugarbush, Bolton Valley, Mad River Glen, and Smugglers' Notch.

■ **COLLEGE OF ST. JOSEPH**

71 Clement Rd.

Rutland, VT 05701-3899

Tel: (802)773-5900; Free: 877-270-9998

E-mail: admissions@csj.edu

Web Site: www.csj.edu

Description: Independent Roman Catholic, comprehensive, coed. Awards associate, bachelor's, and master's degrees. Founded 1950. Setting: 117-acre small town campus. Endowment: $4.5 million. Educational spending for the previous fiscal year: $4345 per student. Total enrollment: 377. Faculty: 58 (12 full-time, 46 part-time). Student-undergrad faculty ratio is 10:1. 146 applied, 69% were admitted. 1% from top 10% of their high school class, 20% from top quarter, 50% from top half. 5 student government officers. Full-time: 164 students, 58% women, 42% men. Part-time: 73 students, 67% women, 33% men. Students come from 19 states and territories, 26% from out-of-state. 1% American Indian or Alaska Native, non-Hispanic/Latino; 1% Hispanic/Latino; 10% Black or African American, non-Hispanic/Latino. 38% 25 or older, 33% live on campus, 13% transferred in. Retention: 53% of full-time freshmen returned the following year. Academic areas with the most degrees conferred: psychology; business/marketing; English. Core. Calendar: semesters. Academic remediation for entering students, services for LD students, advanced placement, accelerated degree program, independent study, double major, summer session for credit, part-time degree program, adult/continuing education programs, internships, graduate courses open to undergrads.

Entrance Requirements: Options: electronic application, early admission, deferred admission, international baccalaureate accepted. Required: essay, high school transcript, minimum 2 high school GPA, 2 recommendations, SAT or ACT. Recommended: interview. Entrance: minimally difficult. Applica-tion deadline: rolling. Notification: continuous. Transfer credits accepted: Yes.

Collegiate Environment: Orientation program. Choral group. Social organizations: 14 open to all. Most popular organizations: Humans vs. Zombies Club, Business Club, Human Services Club, Student Government Association, Cooking Club. Major annual events: Bonfire/DJ, Beach Barbecue, Oktoberfest. Student services: personal-psychological counsel-ing. Campus security: 24-hour emergency response devices, trained security personnel from 8 pm to 6 am. Giorgetti Library. Operations spending for the previous fiscal year: $124,238. 33 computers available on campus for general student use. A campuswide network can be accessed. Students can access the following: online statements/ability to pay tuition online. Staffed computer lab on campus provides training in use of computers, software, and the Internet.

Community Environment: Rutland, though a small city of 30,000, is the third largest city in Vermont. All forms of commercial transportation are avail-able. The community includes churches, a hospital, library, museum, com-munity concert series, and a number of civic and service organizations. Recreational areas provide facilities for boating, swimming, fishing, camping, horseback riding, hunting, mountain climbing, and cross-country and alpine skiing at nearby Pico and Killington Ski areas. Rutland is the headquarters for the Green Mountain National Forest.

■ **COMMUNITY COLLEGE OF VERMONT**

660 Elm St.

Montpelier, VT 05602

Tel: (802)828-2800

Fax: (802)828-2805

Web Site: www.ccv.edu

Description: State-supported, 2-year, coed. Part of Vermont State Colleges System. Awards certificates, transfer associate, and terminal associate degrees. Founded 1973. Setting: rural campus. Total enrollment: 6,385. Faculty: 735 (all part-time). Student-undergrad faculty ratio is 13:1. 1,695 ap-plied, 59% were admitted. Students come from 25 states and territories, 4%

from out-of-state. 46% 25 or older. Retention: 57% of full-time freshmen returned the following year. Core. Calendar: semesters. Academic remediation for entering students, ESL program, services for LD students, advanced placement, accelerated degree program, self-designed majors, independent study, distance learning, double major, summer session for credit, part-time degree program, external degree program, adult/continuing education programs, co-op programs and internships. Study abroad program.

Entrance Requirements: Open admission. Option: electronic application. Recommended: SAT or ACT. Required for some: ACCUPLACER or SAT/ACT. Entrance: noncompetitive. Application deadlines: rolling, rolling for nonresidents. Notification: continuous, continuous for nonresidents. Transfer credits accepted: Yes.

Costs Per Year: Application fee: $0. State resident tuition: $8040 full-time, $268 per credit hour part-time. Nonresident tuition: $16,080 full-time, $536 per credit hour part-time. Mandatory fees: $150 full-time, $75 per term part-time. Full-time tuition and fees vary according to reciprocity agreements. Part-time tuition and fees vary according to reciprocity agreements.

Collegiate Environment: Orientation program. Hartness Library plus 1 other. 880 computers available on campus for general student use. A campuswide network can be accessed from off-campus. Students can access the following: online class registration. Staffed computer lab on campus provides training in use of computers, software, and the Internet.

■ **GODDARD COLLEGE**
123 Pitkin Rd.
Plainfield, VT 05667-9432
Tel: (802)454-8311; Free: 800-906-8312
Fax: (802)454-1029
E-mail: admissions@goddard.edu
Web Site: www.goddard.edu

Description: Independent, comprehensive, coed. Awards bachelor's and master's degrees. Founded 1938. Setting: 200-acre rural campus. Total enrollment: 505. Faculty: 89 (12 full-time, 77 part-time). 16 applied, 56% were admitted. Full-time: 182 students, 73% women, 27% men. Part-time: 12 students, 67% women, 33% men. Students come from 24 states and territories, 1 other country, 69% from out-of-state. 4% American Indian or Alaska Native, non-Hispanic/Latino; 2% Hispanic/Latino; 1% Black or African American, non-Hispanic/Latino; 3% Asian, non-Hispanic/Latino. 73% 25 or older, 40% transferred in. Retention: 66% of full-time freshmen returned the following year. Core. Calendar: semesters. Services for LD students, advanced placement, accelerated degree program, self-designed majors, independent study, distance learning, double major, part-time degree program, external degree program, adult/continuing education programs, internships. Off campus study. Study abroad program.

Entrance Requirements: Options: electronic application, deferred admission, international baccalaureate accepted. Required: essay, 2 recommendations, interview. Recommended: 4 years of English, mathematics, social studies, natural sciences; 3 years of lab science; 2 years of a foreign language; creative portfolio for arts. Required for some: high school transcript, 3 recommendations. Entrance: minimally difficult. Application deadline: rolling. Notification: continuous. Transfer credits accepted: Yes.

Collegiate Environment: Orientation program. Student-run radio station. Major annual events: Graduating Senior Project Presentations, Student Cabarets, Art Crawl. Student services: personal-psychological counseling. Campus security: 24-hour patrols, patrols by trained security personnel 9 pm to 6 am. Eliot Pratt Center. Books: 34,000 (physical), 151,000 (digital/electronic); Databases: 21. 55 computers available on campus for general student use. A computer is required for all students. A campuswide network can be accessed from student residence rooms and from off campus. Students can access the following: online class registration. Staffed computer lab on campus provides training in use of computers, software, and the Internet.

Community Environment: Located in the Upper Valley of Winooski River, this rural setting has the typical beauty of northern New England surrounded by the lower ranges of the Green Mountains. Winters are cold with heavy snow for good skiing. Opportunities are few for part-time employment.

■ **LANDMARK COLLEGE**
River Rd. S
Putney, VT 05346
Tel: (802)387-4767
Fax: (802)387-4779
E-mail: admissions@landmark.edu

Web Site: www.landmark.edu

Description: Independent, primarily 2-year, coed. Awards certificates, terminal associate, and bachelor's degrees. Founded 1983. Setting: 125-acre small town campus. Endowment: $19.1 million. Educational spending for the previous fiscal year: $13,565 per student. Total enrollment: 514. Faculty: 78 (all full-time). Student-undergrad faculty ratio is 6:1. 266 applied, 86% were admitted. Full-time: 494 students, 27% women, 73% men. Part-time: 20 students, 30% women, 70% men. Students come from 39 states and territories, 7 other countries, 93% from out-of-state. 0.2% American Indian or Alaska Native, non-Hispanic/Latino; 4% Hispanic/Latino; 4% Black or African American, non-Hispanic/Latino; 2% Asian, non-Hispanic/Latino; 0.2% Native Hawaiian or other Pacific Islander, non-Hispanic/Latino; 2% international. 6% 25 or older, 95% live on campus, 15% transferred in. Retention: 66% of full-time freshmen returned the following year. Core. Calendar: semesters. Academic remediation for entering students, services for LD students, advanced placement, distance learning, summer session for credit, internships. Study abroad program.

Entrance Requirements: Options: electronic application, early action, deferred admission, international baccalaureate accepted. Required: essay, high school transcript, diagnosis of LD and/or ADHD and cognitive testing, Wechsler Adult Intelligence Scale III, Nelson Denny Reading Test, or the equivalent. Recommended: 2 recommendations, interview. Entrance: moderately difficult. Application deadlines: rolling, 12/1 for early action. Notification: continuous, 1/5 for early action. Transfer credits accepted: Yes. Early action applicants: 0. Early action applicants admitted: 0.

Costs Per Year: Application fee: $75. Comprehensive fee: $68,640 includes full-time tuition ($56,800) and college room and board ($11,840). College room only: $6110. Room and board charges vary according to board plan and housing facility.

Collegiate Environment: Orientation program. Drama-theater group, choral group, student-run newspaper, radio station. Social organizations: 16 open to all. Most popular organizations: Student Government Association, Campus Activities Board, Phi Theta Kappa Honor Society, Equestrian Club, PBL Business Club. Major annual events: Charity Casino Night, Spring Fest, Spring Semiformal Dance. Student services: health clinic, personal-psychological counseling, women's center. Campus security: 24-hour emergency response devices and patrols, late night transport-escort service, controlled dormitory access. Landmark College Library. Operations spending for the previous fiscal year: $388,457. 120 computers available on campus for general student use. Computer purchase/lease plans available. A computer is required for all students. A campuswide network can be accessed from student residence rooms and from off campus. Students can access the following: online access to attendance and other course data, pay bills, view/print unofficial transcripts. Staffed computer lab on campus provides training in use of computers, software, and the Internet.

■ **MARLBORO COLLEGE**
PO Box A, S Rd.
Marlboro, VT 05344
Tel: (802)257-4333; Free: 800-343-0049
Web Site: www.marlboro.edu

Description: Independent, comprehensive, coed. Awards bachelor's and master's degrees. Founded 1946. Setting: 350-acre rural campus. Endowment: $37.3 million. Educational spending for the previous fiscal year: $24,897 per student. Total enrollment: 241. Faculty: 42 (32 full-time, 10 part-time). Student-undergrad faculty ratio is 5:1. 120 applied, 97% were admitted. Full-time: 177 students, 54% women, 46% men. Part-time: 6 students, 33% women, 67% men. Students come from 34 states and territories, 4 other countries, 93% from out-of-state. 0.5% American Indian or Alaska Native, non-Hispanic/Latino; 3% Hispanic/Latino; 4% Black or African American, non-Hispanic/Latino; 1% Asian, non-Hispanic/Latino; 2% international. 13% 25 or older, 78% live on campus, 13% transferred in. Retention: 85% of full-time freshmen returned the following year. Academic areas with the most degrees conferred: visual and performing arts; English; social sciences. Calendar: semesters. ESL program, services for LD students, advanced placement, accelerated degree program, self-designed majors, independent study, double major, internships, graduate courses open to undergrads. Off campus study at Brattleboro School of Music, The Six College Collaborative (The Community College of Vermont, Landmark College, Marlboro College, SIT Graduate Institute, Union Institute & University and Vermont Technical College). Study abroad program.

Entrance Requirements: Options: electronic application, early admission, early decision, early action, deferred admission, international baccalaureate accepted. Required: essay, high school transcript, 2 recommendations, analytical essay. Recommended: interview, SAT or ACT. Required for some: interview. Entrance: moderately difficult. Application deadlines: 3/1, 11/15 for early decision, 1/15 for early action. Notification: continuous until 3/15, 12/1 for early decision, 2/1 for early action. SAT Reasoning Test deadline: 3/1. Transfer credits accepted: Yes. Early decision applicants: 2. Early decision applicants admitted: 2.

Costs Per Year: Application fee: $50. Comprehensive fee: $53,225 includes full-time tuition ($39,870), mandatory fees ($970), and college room and board ($12,385). College room only: $7142. Full-time tuition and fees vary according to reciprocity agreements. Room and board charges vary according to board plan. Part-time tuition: $1329 per credit hour. Part-time mandatory fees: $105 per term. Part-time tuition and fees vary according to course load.

Collegiate Environment: Orientation program. Drama-theater group, choral group, student-run newspaper, radio station. Social organizations: 22 open to all. Most popular organizations: outdoor program, theater, farm program, Gay/Lesbian/Bisexual Alliance, madrigal and a cappella groups. Major annual events: Midnight Breakfast, Broomball Tournament, Work Day. Student services: health clinic, personal-psychological counseling, women's center. Campus security: 24-hour emergency response devices and patrols. Rice-Aron Library. Books: 88,500 (physical), 137,548 (digital/electronic); Serial titles: 5,400 (physical), 150 (digital/electronic); Databases: 75. Study areas open 24 hours, 5-7 days a week. Operations spending for the previous fiscal year: $284,121. 47 computers available on campus for general student use. Computer purchase/lease plans available. A campuswide network can be accessed. Students can access the following: online class registration. Staffed computer lab on campus (open 24 hours a day) provides training in use of computers, software, and the Internet.

Community Environment: Marlboro is located on the scenic Molly Stark Trail near Hogback Mountain which offers a panoramic view of the area. Recreational activities include canoeing, kayaking, cross country skiing, hiking, rock climbing, and biking. The Marlboro Summer Music Festival is an annual event.

■ MIDDLEBURY COLLEGE

Middlebury, VT 05753-6002
Tel: (802)443-5000
Fax: (802)443-2056
E-mail: admissions@middlebury.edu
Web Site: www.middlebury.edu

Description: Independent, comprehensive, coed. Awards bachelor's, master's, and doctoral degrees. Founded 1800. Setting: 350-acre small town campus. System endowment: $1.1 billion. Total enrollment: 2,626. Faculty: 357 (301 full-time, 56 part-time). Student-undergrad faculty ratio is 8:1. 9,227 applied, 17% were admitted. Full-time: 2,551 students, 53% women, 47% men. Part-time: 28 students, 75% women, 25% men. Students come from 52 states and territories, 68 other countries, 94% from out-of-state. 10% Hispanic/Latino; 4% Black or African American, non-Hispanic/Latino; 7% Asian, non-Hispanic/Latino; 11% international. 95% live on campus, 1% transferred in. Retention: 96% of full-time freshmen returned the following year. Academic areas with the most degrees conferred: social sciences; biological/life sciences; natural resources/environmental science; visual and performing arts. Core. Calendar: 4-1-4. Services for LD students, advanced placement, accelerated degree program, self-designed majors, honors program, independent study, double major, summer session for credit, internships. Off campus study at Spelman College, Swarthmore College, Association of Vermont Independent Colleges, Woods Hole Marine Biological Laboratory Dartmouth University, Columbia University. Study abroad program. ROTC: Army (c).

Entrance Requirements: Options: electronic application, early admission, early decision, deferred admission, international baccalaureate accepted. Required: essay, high school transcript, 2 recommendations, SAT and SAT Subject Tests or ACT. Recommended: interview. Entrance: most difficult. Application deadlines: 1/1, 11/1 for early decision. Notification: 3/31, 12/15 for early decision. SAT Reasoning Test deadline: 1/1. SAT Subject Test deadline: 1/1. Transfer credits accepted: Yes. Applicants placed on waiting list: 1,215. Wait-listed applicants offered admission: 24. Early decision applicants: 853. Early decision applicants admitted: 365.

Costs Per Year: Application fee: $65. Comprehensive fee: $72,248 includes full-time tuition ($55,790), mandatory fees ($426), and college room and board ($16,032).

Collegiate Environment: Orientation program. Drama-theater group, choral group, student-run newspaper, radio station. Social organizations: 150 open to all. Most popular organizations: Middlebury College Activities Board,

Middlebury Mountain Club, Student Government Association, International Students Organization, WRMC. Major annual events: Senior Activities, Winter Carnival, Student Concert Series. Student services: health clinic, personal-psychological counseling, women's center. Campus security: 24-hour emergency response devices and patrols, student patrols, late night transport-escort service, controlled dormitory access. 2,546 college housing spaces available; 2,417 were occupied in 2018-19. Freshmen guaranteed college housing. On-campus residence required through junior year. Option: coed housing available. Davis Family Library plus 2 others. Books: 764,667 (physical), 644,056 (digital/electronic); Databases: 695. Weekly public service hours: 112; students can reserve study rooms.

Community Environment: Middlebury, population 8,000, is located between Burlington and Rutland. Churches, libraries, and various civic and service organizations serve the community. The college's Bread Loaf Mountain is nearby and has facilities for skiing and other winter sports. The College owns and operates an 18-hole golf course, an alpine ski area, and 2 cross-country ski areas. Other sports facilities in the area provide for tennis and horseback riding. Lake Champlain and Green Mountain National Forest are nearby and provide numerous additional facilities.

■ NEW ENGLAND CULINARY INSTITUTE

7 School St.
Montpelier, VT 05602
Tel: (802)223-6324; Free: 877-223-6324
Fax: (802)223-0634
E-mail: admissions@neci.edu
Web Site: www.neci.edu

Description: Proprietary, primarily 2-year, coed. Awards certificates, transfer associate, and bachelor's degrees. Founded 1980. Setting: small town campus. Educational spending for the previous fiscal year: $7533 per student. Total enrollment: 300. Faculty: 27 (16 full-time, 11 part-time). Student-undergrad faculty ratio is 15:1. Full-time: 257 students, 46% women, 54% men. Part-time: 43 students, 42% women, 58% men. Students come from 39 states and territories, 6 other countries, 80% from out-of-state. 1% American Indian or Alaska Native, non-Hispanic/Latino; 5% Hispanic/Latino; 8% Black or African American, non-Hispanic/Latino; 4% Asian, non-Hispanic/Latino. 32% 25 or older, 6% transferred in. Retention: 86% of full-time freshmen returned the following year. Academic area with the most degrees conferred: personal and culinary services. Core. Calendar: quarters. Academic remediation for entering students, services for LD students, advanced placement, accelerated degree program, honors program, distance learning, co-op programs and internships.

Entrance Requirements: Options: electronic application, early admission, deferred admission. Required: essay, high school transcript, 1 recommendation, interview. Recommended: culinary experience, SAT or ACT. Entrance: moderately difficult. Application deadline: rolling. Transfer credits accepted: Yes.

Collegiate Environment: Orientation program. Most popular organizations: American Culinary Federation, Slow Food, Student Council, Special Guest Lecture Series, Student Ambassadors (leadership program). Major annual events: Graduation, New Student Orientation, Wedding Cake Presentations. Campus security: 24-hour emergency response devices, student patrols. New England Culinary Institute Library.

■ NORTHERN VERMONT UNIVERSITY-JOHNSON

337 College Hill
Johnson, VT 05656
Tel: (802)635-2356; Free: 800-635-2356
Fax: (802)635-1230
E-mail: admissions@jsc.edu
Web Site: www.northernvermont.edu

Description: State-supported, comprehensive, coed. Part of Vermont State Colleges System. Awards associate, bachelor's, and master's degrees and post-master's certificates. Founded 2018. Setting: 350-acre rural campus with easy access to Montreal. Endowment: $2.3 million. Educational spending for the previous fiscal year: $6102 per student. Total enrollment: 1,662. Faculty: 179 (44 full-time, 135 part-time). Student-undergrad faculty ratio is 14:1. 1,291 applied, 86% were admitted. 6% from top 10% of their high school class, 12% from top quarter, 31% from top half. Full-time: 979 students, 60% women, 40% men. Part-time: 479 students, 73% women, 27% men. Students come from 18 states and territories, 20 other countries, 19% from out-of-state. 35% 25 or older, 60% live on campus, 11% transferred in. Retention: 64% of full-time freshmen returned the following year. Academic areas with the most degrees conferred: liberal arts/general studies; business/marketing; psychology. Core. Calendar: semesters. ESL program, services for LD students, advanced placement, accelerated degree program, honors program, independent study, distance learning, double major, summer session for credit, part-time degree program, external degree program, co-op programs and internships, graduate courses open to undergrads. Off campus study at Vermont State Colleges System, National Student Exchange. Study abroad program. ROTC: Army (c).

Entrance Requirements: Options: electronic application, early admission, early action, deferred admission, international baccalaureate accepted. Required: essay, high school transcript, minimum 2 high school GPA, 1 recommendation. Recommended: minimum 3 high school GPA, interview, SAT or ACT. Entrance: moderately difficult. Application deadline: rolling. Notification: continuous.

Costs Per Year: Application fee: $40. State resident tuition: $10,944 full-time, $456 per credit hour part-time. Nonresident tuition: $24,264 full-time, $1011 per credit hour part-time. Mandatory fees: $2260 full-time, $1130 per term part-time. Full-time tuition and fees vary according to reciprocity agreements and student level. Part-time tuition and fees vary according to course load, reciprocity agreements, and student level. College room and board: $11,598. College room only: $6312. Room and board charges vary according to board plan.

Collegiate Environment: Orientation program. Drama-theater group, choral group, student-run newspaper, radio station. Social organizations: 35 open to all. Most popular organizations: SERVE (Break Away), A Global partnership: Students for Children's Right, Ski/Snowboarding Club, Dance Club, Christian Fellowship Club. Major annual events: Winterfest, Charity Casino Night, Dance Ensemble Performances. Student services: health clinic, personal-psychological counseling, women's center. Campus security: 24-hour emergency response devices and patrols, student patrols, late night transport-escort service, controlled dormitory access. Willey Library plus 1 other. Books: 111,100 (physical), 6,500 (digital/electronic). Study areas open 24 hours, 5-7 days a week. Operations spending for the previous fiscal year: $735,339. 160 computers available on campus for general student use. A campuswide network can be accessed from student residence rooms and from off campus. Students can access the following: online class registration. Staffed computer lab on campus provides training in use of computers, software, and the Internet.

Community Environment: The 350-acre hilltop campus of Johnson State is home for more than 1,500 students. Its location, in the heart of the Green Mountains, places it just minutes away from some of the East's finest skiing and snowboarding at Stowe and Smuggler's Notch. Students have access to our on-campus snowboard park. Its modern facilities include one of the finest performing arts centers in northern New England.

■ NORTHERN VERMONT UNIVERSITY-LYNDON

1001 College Rd.
Lyndonville, VT 05851
Tel: (802)626-6200; Free: 800-225-1998
Fax: (802)626-6335
E-mail: admissions@lyndonstate.edu
Web Site: www.northernvermont.edu

Description: State-supported, comprehensive, coed. Part of Vermont State Colleges System. Awards associate, bachelor's, and master's degrees and post-master's certificates. Founded 2018. Setting: 175-acre rural campus. Faculty: 257 (94 full-time, 163 part-time). Student-undergrad faculty ratio is 15:1. Students come from 19 states and territories, 11 other countries, 39% from out-of-state. 8% 25 or older. Retention: 59% of full-time freshmen returned the following year. Academic areas with the most degrees conferred: parks and recreation; business/marketing; visual and performing arts. Core. Calendar: semesters. Academic remediation for entering students, services for LD students, advanced placement, accelerated degree program, self-designed majors, honors program, independent study, distance learning, double major, summer session for credit, part-time degree program, external degree program, adult/continuing education programs, co-op programs and internships. Off campus study. Study abroad program. ROTC: Army (c), Air Force (c).

Entrance Requirements: Options: electronic application, early admission, deferred admission. Required: high school transcript, minimum 2 high school GPA, 1 recommendation. Recommended: minimum 3 high school GPA, interview. Required for some: essay, minimum 3 high school GPA. Entrance: moderately difficult. Application deadline: rolling. Notification: continuous. Transfer credits accepted: Yes.

Costs Per Year: Application fee: $36. State resident tuition: $10,944 full-time. Nonresident tuition: $24,264 full-time. Mandatory fees: $1490 full-time.

Full-time tuition and fees vary according to course load. College room and board: $11,598. College room only: $6312. Room and board charges vary according to board plan and housing facility.

Collegiate Environment: Orientation program. Drama-theater group, choral group, student-run newspaper, radio station. Social organizations: 70 open to all. Most popular organizations: American Meteorological Society, ASSIST and SERVE, Student Government, Campus Activities, Outing Club, Dance Club. Major annual events: Dance ensemble, Spring weekend, Gregg Fest. Student services: health clinic, personal-psychological counseling. Campus security: 24-hour emergency response devices, student patrols, late night transport-escort service, controlled dormitory access. Samuel Read Hall Library (NVU-Lyndon) and Willey Library (NVU-Johnson). Weekly public service hours: 38.

Community Environment: Lyndon is a rural community in the northeastern part of Vermont with community facilities that include churches of major denominations, civic and service organizations, a library, two hospitals, and good shopping areas. A ski resort at Burke Mountain and Jay Peak provide facilities for skiing and other winter sports.

■ NORWICH UNIVERSITY

158 Harmon Dr.
Northfield, VT 05663
Tel: (802)485-2000; Free: 800-468-6679
Fax: (802)485-2580
Web Site: www.norwich.edu

Description: Independent, comprehensive, coed. Awards bachelor's and master's degrees and post-master's certificates. Founded 1819. Setting: 1,125-acre small town campus with easy access to Burlington. Total enrollment: 3,672. Faculty: 332 (151 full-time, 181 part-time). Student-undergrad faculty ratio is 16:1. 3,138 applied, 66% were admitted. Full-time: 2,271 students, 24% women, 76% men. Part-time: 378 students, 16% women, 84% men. 86% from out-of-state. 0.5% American Indian or Alaska Native, non-Hispanic/Latino; 7% Hispanic/Latino; 4% Black or African American, non-Hispanic/Latino; 2% Asian, non-Hispanic/Latino; 0.4% Native Hawaiian or other Pacific Islander, non-Hispanic/Latino; 2% international. 18% 25 or older, 75% live on campus, 4% transferred in. Retention: 73% of full-time freshmen returned the following year. Academic areas with the most degrees conferred: homeland security, law enforcement, firefighting, and protective services; military science and military technologies; social sciences; engineering. Calendar: semesters. Academic remediation for entering students, ESL program, services for LD students, advanced placement, honors program, independent study, distance learning, double major, summer session for credit, part-time degree program, external degree program, adult/continuing education programs, co-op programs and internships, graduate courses open to undergrads. Study abroad program. ROTC: Army, Naval, Air Force.

Entrance Requirements: Option: electronic application. Required: essay, high school transcript. Recommended: minimum 2 high school GPA, 2 recommendations, interview. Required for some: portfolio, SAT or ACT. Entrance: moderately difficult.

Collegiate Environment: Orientation program. Drama-theater group, choral group, marching band, student-run newspaper, radio station. Most popular organizations: DREAM, NUEMS, IEEE, CJSA, Politeia/Model UN. Major annual events: Regimental Ball Weekend, Junior Weekend, Homecoming/Alumni Weekend. Student services: health clinic, personal-psychological counseling. Campus security: 24-hour emergency response devices and patrols, late night transport-escort service. Kreitzberg Library.

Community Environment: A rural community in the central section of Vermont, Northfield is 11 miles south of Montpelier, the state capital. Rail, bus and air transportation is available. Recreational activities include skiing, hiking, bicycling, fishing, and hunting.

■ SAINT MICHAEL'S COLLEGE

One Winooski Park
Colchester, VT 05439
Tel: (802)654-2000; Free: 800-762-8000
Fax: (802)654-2242
E-mail: admission@smcvt.edu
Web Site: www.smcvt.edu

Description: Independent Roman Catholic, comprehensive, coed. Awards bachelor's and master's degrees and post-master's certificates. Founded 1904. Setting: 440-acre suburban campus with easy access to Montreal. Endowment: $87.5 million. Research spending for the previous fiscal year: $1.4 million. Educational spending for the previous fiscal year: $11,458 per student. Total enrollment: 2,077. Faculty: 170 (138 full-time, 32 part-time). Student-undergrad faculty ratio is 13:1. 3,094 applied, 85% were admitted. 25% from top 10% of their high school class, 48% from top quarter, 76% from top half. Full-time: 1,766 students, 55% women, 45% men. Part-time: 26 students, 58% women, 42% men. Students come from 36 states and territories, 24 other countries, 85% from out-of-state. 0.1% American Indian or Alaska Native, non-Hispanic/Latino; 5% Hispanic/Latino; 2% Black or African American, non-Hispanic/Latino; 1% Asian, non-Hispanic/Latino; 0.1% Native Hawaiian or other Pacific Islander, non-Hispanic/Latino; 4% international. 1% 25 or older, 96% live on campus, 2% transferred in. Retention: 83% of full-time freshmen returned the following year. Academic areas with the most degrees conferred: business/marketing; social sciences; biological/life sciences; psychology. Core. Calendar: semesters. ESL program, services for LD students, advanced placement, accelerated degree program, self-designed majors, honors program, independent study, distance learning, double major, summer session for credit, part-time degree program, co-op programs and internships, graduate courses open to undergrads. Off campus study at Washington Semester Program (American University), Sea Education Association (SEA Semester) Woods Hole, MA., Semester exchange program with Vermont Private Colleges. Study abroad program. ROTC: Army (c), Air Force (c).

Entrance Requirements: Options: electronic application, early action, deferred admission, international baccalaureate accepted. Required: essay, high school transcript, 1 recommendation. Recommended: minimum 3 high school GPA, 3 recommendations, interview. Entrance: moderately difficult. Application deadlines: 2/1, 11/1 for early action. Notification: 4/1, 12/21 for early action. SAT Reasoning Test deadline: 2/1. Transfer credits accepted: Yes. Applicants placed on waiting list: 158. Wait-listed applicants offered admission: 6. Early action applicants: 2,105. Early action applicants admitted: 1,867.

Costs Per Year: Application fee: $50. Comprehensive fee: $57,595 includes full-time tuition ($45,050), mandatory fees ($325), and college room and board ($12,220). Full-time tuition and fees vary according to course load. Room and board charges vary according to board plan and housing facility. Part-time tuition: $1445 per credit hour. Part-time tuition varies according to course load.

Collegiate Environment: Orientation program. Drama-theater group, choral group, student-run newspaper, radio station. Social organizations: 50 open to all; 50% of eligible men and 50% of eligible women are members. Most popular organizations: Student Association (governing board), Mobilization of Volunteer Efforts (MOVE), Wilderness Program, Martin Luther King Society, ShredMC. Major annual events: Jib Fest (fall), Martin Luther King, Jr. Convocation (winter), Academic Symposium (spring). Student services: health clinic, personal-psychological counseling, women's center. Campus security: 24-hour emergency response devices and patrols, student patrols, late night transport-escort service, controlled dormitory access, bicycle patrols, fire and rescue squad with professionals and trained student volunteers. Durick Library. Books: 231,418 (physical), 231,171 (digital/electronic); Serial titles: 1,653 (physical), 128,515 (digital/electronic); Databases: 142. Weekly public service hours: 102. Operations spending for the previous fiscal year: $1.7 million. 97 computers available on campus for general student use. Computer purchase/lease plans available. A campuswide network can be accessed from student residence rooms and from off campus. Students can access the following: online class registration. Staffed computer lab on campus provides training in use of computers, software, and the Internet.

■ SOUTHERN VERMONT COLLEGE

982 Mansion Dr.
Bennington, VT 05201
Tel: (802)447-4000
Fax: (802)447-4695
E-mail: admissions@svc.edu
Web Site: www.svc.edu

Description: Independent, 4-year, coed. Awards associate and bachelor's degrees. Founded 1926. Setting: 371-acre small town campus with easy access to Albany, NY. Endowment: $3.5 million. Educational spending for the previous fiscal year: $22,611 per student. Total enrollment: 361. Faculty: 50 (22 full-time, 28 part-time). Student-undergrad faculty ratio is 14:1. 353 applied, 91% were admitted. 11% from top 10% of their high school class, 35% from top quarter, 65% from top half. Full-time: 339 students, 58% women, 42% men. Part-time: 22 students, 50% women, 50% men. Students come from 19 states and territories, 1 other country, 75% from out-of-state. 0.3% American Indian or Alaska Native, non-Hispanic/Latino; 8% Hispanic/Latino;

9% Black or African American, non-Hispanic/Latino; 1% Asian, non-Hispanic/Latino; 0.3% international. 10% 25 or older, 67% live on campus, 10% transferred in. Retention: 64% of full-time freshmen returned the following year. Academic areas with the most degrees conferred: health professions and related sciences; psychology; biological/life sciences. Core. Calendar: semesters. Academic remediation for entering students, services for LD students, advanced placement, self-designed majors, independent study, distance learning, double major, summer session for credit, part-time degree program, co-op programs and internships. Off campus study at Consortium of Vermont Colleges, Hudson Mohawk Association of Colleges and Universities, Bennington College. Study abroad program.

Entrance Requirements: Options: electronic application, early admission, deferred admission, international baccalaureate accepted. Required: high school transcript, SAT or ACT. Recommended: essay, minimum 2 high school GPA. Required for some: college transcripts for transfer students. Entrance: noncompetitive. Application deadline: rolling. Notification: continuous. Transfer credits accepted: Yes.

Costs Per Year: Application fee: $30. One-time mandatory fee: $100. Comprehensive fee: $36,511 includes full-time tuition ($25,236), mandatory fees ($275), and college room and board ($11,000). Room and board charges vary according to board plan and housing facility. Part-time tuition: $1052 per credit hour. Part-time tuition varies according to course load.

Collegiate Environment: Orientation program. Drama-theater group. Social organizations: 15 open to all. Most popular organizations: Student Government Association, Mountaineer Event Board, Japanese Culture and Anime Club, Big Brothers Big Sisters, Moosecorps. Major annual events: Homecoming Weekend, Moosapalooza, Fall Fest. Student services: health clinic, personal-psychological counseling. Campus security: 24-hour patrols, late night transport-escort service, controlled dormitory access. Southern Vermont College Library. Books: 10,025 (physical), 8,818 (digital/electronic); Serial titles: 792 (physical); Databases: 70. Students can reserve study rooms. Operations spending for the previous fiscal year: $207,270. 50 computers available on campus for general student use. A campuswide network can be accessed from student residence rooms and from off campus. Students can access the following: online class registration.

Community Environment: See Bennington College.

■ STERLING COLLEGE

PO Box 72
Craftsbury Common, VT 05827-0072
Tel: (802)586-7711; Free: 800-648-3591
E-mail: tpatterson@sterlingcollege.edu
Web Site: www.sterlingcollege.edu

Description: Independent, 4-year, coed. Awards bachelor's degrees. Founded 1958. Setting: 430-acre rural campus. Endowment: $1.3 million. Educational spending for the previous fiscal year: $14,981 per student. Total enrollment: 119. Faculty: 16 (14 full-time, 2 part-time). Student-undergrad faculty ratio is 7:1. 18% from top 10% of their high school class, 35% from top quarter, 71% from top half. 4 student government officers. Full-time: 119 students, 49% women, 51% men. Students come from 22 states and territories, 4 other countries, 82% from out-of-state. 2% Hispanic/Latino; 4% Black or African American, non-Hispanic/Latino; 0.8% Asian, non-Hispanic/Latino; 3% international. 14% 25 or older, 85% live on campus, 15% transferred in. Retention: 52% of full-time freshmen returned the following year. Academic areas with the most degrees conferred: agriculture; natural resources/environmental science; liberal arts/general studies. Core. Calendar: semesters. Academic remediation for entering students, services for LD students, advanced placement, self-designed majors, independent study, double major, summer session for credit, co-op programs and internships. Off campus study at Association of Vermont Independent Colleges (AVIC) Semester Exchange Program, Yestermorrow Natural Building and Design School, National Outdoor Leadership School (NOLS). Study abroad program.

Entrance Requirements: Required: essay, high school transcript, 2 recommendations, interview. Recommended: minimum 2 high school GPA.

Costs Per Year: Comprehensive fee: $48,000 includes full-time tuition ($34,000), mandatory fees ($4100), and college room and board ($9900). Full-time tuition and fees vary according to course load. Room and board charges vary according to board plan.

Collegiate Environment: Orientation program. Drama-theater group. Social organizations: 10 open to all; 90% of eligible men and 90% of eligible women are members. Most popular organizations: Nordic Ski Team, Trail Running Team, Shooting Club, Environmental and Social Justice Club, Outdoor Club. Major annual events: All College Work Day, Town Meeting, Wood and Art

Show. Student services: personal-psychological counseling, women's center. Campus security: 24-hour emergency response devices, 24-hour pager. Brown Library plus 1 other. Books: 11,773 (physical), 959 (digital/electronic); Serial titles: 28,324 (physical); Databases: 27. Weekly public service hours: 45; study areas open 24 hours, 5-7 days a week. Operations spending for the previous fiscal year: $107,893. 21 computers available on campus for general student use. Computer purchase/lease plans available. A campuswide network can be accessed from student residence rooms. Staffed computer lab on campus (open 24 hours a day) provides training in use of computers, software, and the Internet.

■ **UNIVERSITY OF VERMONT**
Burlington, VT 05405
Tel: (802)656-3131
E-mail: admissions@uvm.edu
Web Site: www.uvm.edu
Description: State-supported, university, coed. Awards bachelor's, master's, and doctoral degrees and post-master's certificates. Founded 1791. Setting: 459-acre suburban campus. Endowment: $490.8 million. Research spending for the previous fiscal year: $106.2 million. Educational spending for the previous fiscal year: $16,087 per student. Total enrollment: 13,395. Faculty: 814 (616 full-time, 198 part-time). Student-undergrad faculty ratio is 17:1. 21,263 applied, 68% were admitted. 37% from top 10% of their high school class, 73% from top quarter, 94% from top half. Full-time: 10,434 students, 59% women, 41% men. Part-time: 894 students, 60% women, 40% men. Students come from 50 states and territories, 51 other countries, 71% from out-of-state. 4% Hispanic/Latino; 1% Black or African American, non-Hispanic/Latino; 3% Asian, non-Hispanic/Latino; 5% international. 2% 25 or older, 51% live on campus, 4% transferred in. Retention: 87% of full-time freshmen returned the following year. Academic areas with the most degrees conferred: business/marketing; social sciences; natural resources/environmental science. Calendar: semesters. Services for LD students, advanced placement, self-designed majors, freshman honors college, honors program, independent study, distance learning, double major, summer session for credit, part-time degree program, adult/continuing education programs, co-op programs and internships, graduate courses open to undergrads. Off campus study at 2-2 B.S. in animal science, biological science, and engineering programs with Vermont Tech Coll. 2-2 B.A., B.S., and B.S.Ed. programs with Comm Coll of Vermont Associates. 3-2 B.S. in engineering program with Saint Michael's Coll. Study abroad program. ROTC: Army.
Entrance Requirements: Options: electronic application, early admission, early action, deferred admission, international baccalaureate accepted. Required: essay, high school transcript, 1 recommendation, SAT or ACT. Required for some: audition for music or music education. Entrance: moderately difficult. Application deadlines: 1/15, 1/15 for nonresidents, 11/1 for early action. Notification: 3/31, 3/31 for nonresidents, 12/15 for early action. Preference given to Vermont residents. SAT Reasoning Test deadline: 2/15. Transfer credits accepted: Yes. Applicants placed on waiting list: 3,855. Wait-listed applicants offered admission: 110. Early action applicants: 12,428. Early action applicants admitted: 9,619.
Costs Per Year: Application fee: $55. State resident tuition: $15,936 full-time, $664 per credit hour part-time. Nonresident tuition: $40,176 full-time, $1674 per credit hour part-time. Mandatory fees: $2340 full-time, $20 per credit hour part-time. Full-time tuition and fees vary according to reciprocity agreements. Part-time tuition and fees vary according to course load and reciprocity agreements. College room and board: $12,492. College room only: $8196. Room and board charges vary according to board plan and housing facility.
Collegiate Environment: Orientation program. Drama-theater group, choral group, student-run newspaper, radio station. Social organizations: 200 open to all; national fraternities, national sororities, local fraternities; 8% of eligible men and 7% of eligible women are members. Most popular organizations: Ski and Snowboard Club, Outing Club, Volunteer in Action, Climbing Team. Major annual events: Springfest, Convocation, Banff Mountain Film Festival. Student services: legal services, health clinic, personal-psychological counseling, women's center. Campus security: 24-hour emergency response devices and patrols, late night transport-escort service, controlled dormitory access. 5,828 college housing spaces available; 5,512 were occupied in 2018-19. Freshmen guaranteed college housing. On-campus residence required through sophomore year. Option: coed housing available. David W. Howe Memorial Library plus 3 others. Books: 1.2 million (physical), 334,751 (digital/electronic); Serial titles: 42,611 (physical), 90,435 (digital/electronic);

Databases: 395. Weekly public service hours: 102; study areas open 24 hours, 5-7 days a week; students can reserve study rooms. Operations spending for the previous fiscal year: $15.1 million. 530 computers available on campus for general student use. Computer purchase/lease plans available. A campuswide network can be accessed from student residence rooms and from off campus. Students can access the following: online class registration, Web pages, online course support, learning management system. Staffed computer lab on campus.
Community Environment: Burlington is Vermont's largest city and, while the University is a significant resource, the city has many cultural, recreational, and social offerings. Burlington is a tourist and business center with a rich history and significant business development.

■ **VERMONT TECHNICAL COLLEGE**
PO Box 500
Randolph Center, VT 05061-0500
Tel: (802)728-1000; Free: 800-442-VTC1
Fax: (802)728-1390
E-mail: admissions@vtc.edu
Web Site: www.vtc.edu
Description: State-supported, comprehensive, coed. Part of Vermont State Colleges System. Awards associate, bachelor's, and master's degrees. Founded 1866. Setting: 544-acre rural campus. Endowment: $5.5 million. Research spending for the previous fiscal year: $16,139. Educational spending for the previous fiscal year: $11,557 per student. Total enrollment: 1,616. Faculty: 165 (79 full-time, 86 part-time). Student-undergrad faculty ratio is 12:1. 1,039 applied, 69% were admitted. 7% from top 10% of their high school class, 26% from top quarter, 60% from top half. Full-time: 1,069 students, 43% women, 57% men. Part-time: 541 students, 56% women, 44% men. Students come from 23 states and territories, 6 other countries, 15% from out-of-state. 0.2% American Indian or Alaska Native, non-Hispanic/Latino; 2% Hispanic/Latino; 1% Black or African American, non-Hispanic/Latino; 0.9% Asian, non-Hispanic/Latino; 2% international. 37% 25 or older, 31% live on campus, 21% transferred in. Retention: 71% of full-time freshmen returned the following year. Academic areas with the most degrees conferred: engineering technologies; business/marketing; health professions and related sciences. Core. Calendar: semesters. Academic remediation for entering students, ESL program, services for LD students, advanced placement, accelerated degree program, honors program, independent study, distance learning, double major, summer session for credit, part-time degree program, co-op programs and internships. ROTC: Army (c).
Entrance Requirements: Option: electronic application. Required: high school transcript. Recommended: minimum 3 high school GPA, 2 recommendations, interview. Required for some: essay, 2 recommendations, SAT. Entrance: moderately difficult. Application deadline: rolling. Notification: continuous. Transfer credits accepted: Yes. Applicants placed on waiting list: 20. Wait-listed applicants offered admission: 6.
Costs Per Year: Application fee: $47. State resident tuition: $14,304 full-time, $596 per credit hour part-time. Nonresident tuition: $27,336 full-time, $1139 per credit hour part-time. Mandatory fees: $1667 full-time, $49 per credit hour part-time. College room and board: $10,920. College room only: $6504.
Collegiate Environment: Orientation program. Choral group, student-run radio station. Social organizations: 25 open to all. Most popular organizations: Student Council (student government), Adventurer's Guild (board and video gaming), WVTC (student radio station), Outing Club, Veterinary Technology Club. Major annual events: October Fiesta, Late-Night Breakfast (spring and fall). Student services: health clinic. Campus security: 24-hour emergency response devices and patrols, late night transport-escort service, controlled dormitory access. 600 college housing spaces available; 440 were occupied in 2018-19. No special consideration for freshman housing applicants. On-campus residence required through sophomore year. Option: coed housing available. Hartness Library. Books: 59,000 (physical). Operations spending for the previous fiscal year: $914,872. 480 computers available on campus for general student use. A campuswide network can be accessed from student residence rooms and from off campus. Students can access the following: online class registration, online (network) file storage. Staffed computer lab on campus (open 24 hours a day) provides training in use of computers, software, and the Internet.
Community Environment: Randolph Center is a rural area, four miles from Randolph. A library, hospital, churches, shopping facilities, and several civic and service organizations serve the town. Outdoor sports include golf, fishing, hunting, skiing, ice skating, and tennis.

■ **ADVANCED TECHNOLOGY INSTITUTE**
5700 Southern Blvd.
Virginia Beach, VA 23462
Tel: (757)490-1241; Free: 888-468-1093
Web Site: www.auto.edu
Description: Proprietary, 2-year, coed. Awards certificates and terminal associate degrees. Total enrollment: 827. Student-undergrad faculty ratio is 24:1. 431 applied, 75% were admitted. 26% from out-of-state. 45% 25 or older.

■ **AMERICAN NATIONAL UNIVERSITY (CHARLOTTESVILLE)**
3926 Seminole Trl.
Charlottesville, VA 22911
Tel: (434)220-7960; Free: 888-9-JOBREADY
Fax: (434)986-1344
Web Site: www.an.edu
Description: Proprietary, 2-year, coed. Part of National College of Business and Technology. Awards certificates, diplomas, and terminal associate degrees. Founded 1975. Setting: small town campus with easy access to Richmond. Core. Calendar: quarters. Services for LD students, advanced placement, honors program, double major, summer session for credit, part-time degree program, internships.
Entrance Requirements: Open admission. Option: electronic application. Recommended: interview. Required for some: high school transcript. Entrance: noncompetitive. Application deadline: rolling.
Collegiate Environment: Orientation program.

■ **AMERICAN NATIONAL UNIVERSITY (DANVILLE)**
336 Old Riverside Dr.
Danville, VA 24541
Tel: (434)793-6822; Free: 888-9-JOBREADY
Fax: (434)793-3634
Web Site: www.an.edu
Description: Proprietary, primarily 2-year, coed. Part of National College of Business and Technology. Awards diplomas, terminal associate, and bachelor's degrees. Founded 1975. Setting: small town campus. Calendar: quarters. Summer session for credit, part-time degree program.
Entrance Requirements: Open admission. Option: electronic application. Recommended: interview. Required for some: high school transcript. Entrance: noncompetitive. Application deadline: rolling.
Collegiate Environment: Orientation program.

■ **AMERICAN NATIONAL UNIVERSITY (HARRISONBURG)**
1515 Country Club Rd.
Harrisonburg, VA 22802
Tel: (540)432-0943; Free: 888-9-JOBREADY
Fax: (540)986-1344
Web Site: www.an.edu
Description: Proprietary, primarily 2-year, coed. Part of National College of Business and Technology. Awards diplomas, terminal associate, and bachelor's degrees. Founded 1988. Setting: small town campus. Core. Calendar: quarters. Services for LD students, advanced placement, honors program, double major, summer session for credit, part-time degree program, internships.
Entrance Requirements: Open admission. Option: electronic application.

Recommended: interview. Required for some: high school transcript. Entrance: noncompetitive. Application deadline: rolling. Notification: continuous.
Collegiate Environment: Orientation program.

■ **AMERICAN NATIONAL UNIVERSITY (LYNCHBURG)**
104 Candlewood Ct.
Lynchburg, VA 24502
Tel: (434)239-3500; Free: 888-9-JOBREADY
Fax: (434)986-1344
Web Site: www.an.edu
Description: Proprietary, primarily 2-year, coed. Part of National College of Business and Technology. Awards diplomas, terminal associate, and bachelor's degrees. Founded 1979. Setting: 2-acre small town campus. Core. Calendar: quarters. Services for LD students, advanced placement, honors program, double major, summer session for credit, part-time degree program, internships.
Entrance Requirements: Open admission. Option: electronic application. Recommended: interview. Required for some: high school transcript. Entrance: noncompetitive. Application deadline: rolling.
Collegiate Environment: Orientation program.

■ **AMERICAN NATIONAL UNIVERSITY (SALEM)**
1813 E Main St.
Salem, VA 24153
Tel: (540)986-1800; Free: 888-9-JOBREADY
Fax: (540)986-1344
Web Site: www.an.edu
Description: Proprietary, comprehensive, coed. Part of National College of Business and Technology. Awards associate, bachelor's, and master's degrees. Founded 1886. Setting: 3-acre urban campus. Calendar: quarters. Academic remediation for entering students, advanced placement, summer session for credit, part-time degree program.
Entrance Requirements: Open admission. Required: high school transcript. Recommended: interview. Entrance: noncompetitive. Application deadline: rolling. Notification: continuous.
Collegiate Environment: Orientation program.

■ **ARGOSY UNIVERSITY, NORTHERN VIRGINIA**
1550 Wilson Blvd., Ste. 600
Arlington, VA 22209
Tel: (703)526-5800; Free: 866-703-2777
Fax: (703)526-5850
Web Site: www.argosy.edu/locations/northern-virginia
Description: Proprietary, university, coed. Part of Argosy Education Group. Awards associate, bachelor's, master's, and doctoral degrees. Founded 1994. Setting: urban campus. Calendar: semesters.

■ **THE ART INSTITUTE OF VIRGINIA BEACH, A BRANCH OF THE ART INSTITUTE OF ATLANTA**
Two Columbus Ctr.
4500 Main St., Ste. 100
Virginia Beach, VA 23462
Tel: (757)493-6700; Free: 877-437-4428
Fax: (757)493-6800

Web Site: www.artinstitutes.edu/virginia-beach
Description: Proprietary, 4-year, coed. Awards associate and bachelor's degrees.

■ **AVERETT UNIVERSITY**
420 W Main St.
Danville, VA 24541-3692
Tel: (434)791-5600; Free: 800-AVERETT
Fax: (434)791-5637
E-mail: joel.nester@averett.edu
Web Site: www.averett.edu
Description: Independent, comprehensive, coed, affiliated with Baptist General Association of Virginia. Awards bachelor's degrees. Founded 1859. Setting: 185-acre small town campus with easy access to Greensboro, NC. Endowment: $29.1 million. Educational spending for the previous fiscal year: $12,515 per student. Total enrollment: 965. Faculty: 123 (52 full-time, 71 part-time). Student-undergrad faculty ratio is 12:1. 2,812 applied, 61% were admitted. 8% from top 10% of their high school class, 27% from top quarter, 56% from top half. Full-time: 934 students, 42% women, 58% men. Part-time: 31 students, 58% women, 42% men. Students come from 24 states and territories, 20 other countries, 44% from out-of-state. 0.4% American Indian or Alaska Native, non-Hispanic/Latino; 4% Hispanic/Latino; 29% Black or African American, non-Hispanic/Latino; 0.6% Asian, non-Hispanic/Latino; 0.4% Native Hawaiian or other Pacific Islander, non-Hispanic/Latino; 6% international. 5% 25 or older, 58% live on campus, 7% transferred in. Retention: 63% of full-time freshmen returned the following year. Academic areas with the most degrees conferred: health professions and related sciences; business/marketing; parks and recreation. Core. Calendar: semesters. Academic remediation for entering students, services for LD students, advanced placement, accelerated degree program, self-designed majors, honors program, independent study, distance learning, double major, summer session for credit, part-time degree program, external degree program, adult/continuing education programs, co-op programs and internships, graduate courses open to undergrads. Off campus study. Study abroad program.
Entrance Requirements: Options: electronic application, deferred admission, international baccalaureate accepted. Required: high school transcript, minimum 2.5 high school GPA, SAT or ACT, TOEFL for international students. Recommended: essay, 1 recommendation, interview. Entrance: moderately difficult. Notification: continuous. Transfer credits accepted: Yes.
Costs Per Year: Comprehensive fee: $44,496 includes full-time tuition ($34,400), mandatory fees ($120), and college room and board ($9976). College room only: $6370. Full-time tuition and fees vary according to class time, course load, degree level, location, and program. Room and board charges vary according to board plan and housing facility. Part-time tuition: $1075 per credit. Part-time mandatory fees: $30 per term. Part-time tuition and fees vary according to class time, course load, degree level, location, and program.
Collegiate Environment: Orientation program. Drama-theater group, choral group, student-run newspaper. Social organizations: 30 open to all; national fraternities, local fraternities, local sororities; 8% of eligible men and 6% of eligible women are members. Most popular organizations: Cougar Activities Board (CAB), Student Athletic Advisory Committee (SAAC), Student Government Association (SGA), FOCUS/Christian Student Fellowship, Rainbow Club. Major annual events: Homecoming, Spring Formal, Late Night Breakfast. Student services: health clinic, personal-psychological counseling. Campus security: 24-hour emergency response devices and patrols, late night transport-escort service, controlled dormitory access. 617 college housing spaces available; 548 were occupied in 2018-19. Freshmen guaranteed college housing. On-campus residence required through junior year. Options: coed, men-only, women-only housing available. Mary B. Blount Library. Books: 86,432 (physical), 313,632 (digital/electronic); Serial titles: 98 (physical), 35,069 (digital/electronic); Databases: 160. Weekly public service hours: 81; students can reserve study rooms. Operations spending for the previous fiscal year: $531,373. 150 computers available on campus for general student use. A campuswide network can be accessed from student residence rooms. Students can access the following: online class registration. Staffed computer lab on campus (open 24 hours a day).

■ **BETHEL COLLEGE**
1705 Todds Ln.
Hampton, VA 23666
Tel: (757)826-1426
Web Site: www.bcva.edu

Description: Independent, 4-year, coed, affiliated with Assembly of God Church. Awards associate and bachelor's degrees. Founded 1996. Setting: suburban campus. Part-time: 58 students, 55% women, 45% men. 20% live on campus. Core. Calendar: semesters. Academic remediation for entering students, independent study, distance learning, double major, summer session for credit, part-time degree program, adult/continuing education programs, co-op programs and internships. Off campus study.
Entrance Requirements: Option: early admission. Required: SAT or ACT. Entrance: minimally difficult.
Costs Per Year: Tuition: $260 per credit part-time. Mandatory fees: $50 per term part-time.
Collegiate Environment: Orientation program. Drama-theater group, choral group. Student services: personal-psychological counseling. Campus security: controlled dormitory access. 4 computers available on campus for general student use. A campuswide network can be accessed from student residence rooms. Staffed computer lab on campus (open 24 hours a day) provides training in use of computers, software, and the Internet.

■ **BLUE RIDGE COMMUNITY COLLEGE**
PO Box 80
Weyers Cave, VA 24486-0080
Tel: (540)234-9261; Free: 888-750-2722
Web Site: www.brcc.edu
Description: State-supported, 2-year, coed. Part of Virginia Community College System. Awards certificates, diplomas, transfer associate, and terminal associate degrees. Founded 1967. Setting: 65-acre rural campus. Total enrollment: 4,466. Student-undergrad faculty ratio is 22:1. 1% from out-of-state. 32% 25 or older. Retention: 57% of full-time freshmen returned the following year. Calendar: semesters. Academic remediation for entering students, ESL program, services for LD students, advanced placement, honors program, distance learning, double major, summer session for credit, part-time degree program, adult/continuing education programs, co-op programs and internships. Off campus study. Study abroad program.
Entrance Requirements: Open admission except for veterinary technology, nursing programs. Options: electronic application, early admission. Required: College Preparedness Test. Required for some: high school transcript, interview. Entrance: noncompetitive. Application deadline: rolling. Notification: continuous.
Collegiate Environment: Orientation program. Student services: personal-psychological counseling, women's center. Campus security: 24-hour emergency response devices and patrols, late night transport-escort service. Houff Library.
Community Environment: Weyers Cave is a rural community located near Staunton and Harrisonburg.

■ **BLUEFIELD COLLEGE**
3000 College Ave.
Bluefield, VA 24605-1799
Tel: (276)326-3682; Free: 800-872-0175
Fax: (276)326-4288
E-mail: mrh263676@bluefield.edu
Web Site: www.bluefield.edu
Description: Independent Southern Baptist, comprehensive, coed. Awards bachelor's and master's degrees. Founded 1922. Setting: 82-acre small town campus. Endowment: $6.7 million. Educational spending for the previous fiscal year: $22,898 per student. Total enrollment: 1,000. Faculty: 110 (43 full-time, 67 part-time). Student-undergrad faculty ratio is 14:1. 1,521 applied, 91% were admitted. 7% from top 10% of their high school class, 25% from top quarter, 59% from top half. Full-time: 833 students, 53% women, 47% men. Part-time: 118 students, 57% women, 43% men. Students come from 33 states and territories, 28 other countries, 26% from out-of-state. 5% Hispanic/Latino; 23% Black or African American, non-Hispanic/Latino; 0.2% Asian, non-Hispanic/Latino; 0.2% Native Hawaiian or other Pacific Islander, non-Hispanic/Latino; 4% international. 27% 25 or older, 61% live on campus, 13% transferred in. Retention: 53% of full-time freshmen returned the following year. Academic areas with the most degrees conferred: business/marketing; public administration and social services; health professions and related sciences. Core. Calendar: semesters. Academic remediation for entering students, services for LD students, advanced placement, honors program, independent study, distance learning, double major, summer session for credit, part-time degree program, adult/continuing education programs, co-op programs and internships, graduate courses open to undergrads. Off campus study at Appalachian College of Pharmacy, Virginia

Community College System, Kentucky Community & Technical College System, Edward Via Virginia College of Osteopathic Medicine. Study abroad program.

Entrance Requirements: Option: electronic application. Required: high school transcript, minimum 2 high school GPA, SAT or ACT. Required for some: essay. Application deadline: rolling. Notification: continuous. Transfer credits accepted: Yes.

Costs Per Year: Comprehensive fee: $34,314 includes full-time tuition ($24,520), mandatory fees ($770), and college room and board ($9024). College room only: $3770. Full-time tuition and fees vary according to course load and program. Room and board charges vary according to housing facility. Part-time tuition: $970 per credit hour. Part-time mandatory fees: $28 per credit hour. Part-time tuition and fees vary according to course load and program.

Collegiate Environment: Orientation program. Drama-theater group, choral group, student-run newspaper. Social organizations: 13 open to all; local fraternities, local sororities; 15% of eligible men and 20% of eligible women are members. Most popular organizations: Baptist Collegiate Ministries, Fellowship of Christian Athletes, Student Union Board, Student Government Association, Arts Club. Major annual events: Homecoming Dance, Spring Formal, Mud Pig Day. Student services: personal-psychological counseling. Campus security: controlled dormitory access, night security patrols. Easley Library. Books: 44,352 (physical), 165,829 (digital/electronic); Serial titles: 7,976 (physical), 334 (digital/electronic); Databases: 72. Students can reserve study rooms. Operations spending for the previous fiscal year: $210,247. 110 computers available on campus for general student use. A campuswide network can be accessed from student residence rooms. Students can access the following: online class registration.

Community Environment: A suburban area in the Virginia Highlands, Bluefield is a center of diversified industry. Products of its industries are fabric dyes, mattresses, hardwood flooring, textiles, and mining equipment. All commercial transportation is available. Public libraries, churches, hospitals, and a number of civic and service organizations are a part of the community. Nearby mountains provide opportunities for numerous recreational activities. Some part-time employment is available.

■ **BON SECOURS MEMORIAL COLLEGE OF NURSING**
8550 Magellan Pky.
Ste. 1100
Richmond, VA 23227-1149
Tel: (804)627-5300; Free: 866-238-7414
Web Site: www.bsmcon.edu
Description: Independent, 4-year, coed. Awards associate and bachelor's degrees.

■ **BRIDGEWATER COLLEGE**
402 E College St.
Bridgewater, VA 22812-1599
Tel: (540)828-8000; Free: 800-759-8328
Fax: (540)828-5481
E-mail: admissions@bridgewater.edu
Web Site: www.bridgewater.edu
Description: Independent, comprehensive, coed, affiliated with Church of the Brethren. Awards bachelor's and master's degrees. Founded 1880. Setting: 300-acre small town campus. Endowment: $98.1 million. Educational spending for the previous fiscal year: $6893 per student. Total enrollment: 1,857. Faculty: 169 (116 full-time, 53 part-time). Student-undergrad faculty ratio is 14:1. 6,360 applied, 66% were admitted. 14% from top 10% of their high school class, 38% from top quarter, 72% from top half. 3 valedictorians, 31 student government officers. Full-time: 1,832 students, 55% women, 45% men. Part-time: 7 students, 71% women, 29% men. Students come from 28 states and territories, 22 other countries, 25% from out-of-state. 0.3% American Indian or Alaska Native, non-Hispanic/Latino; 7% Hispanic/Latino; 16% Black or African American, non-Hispanic/Latino; 1% Asian, non-Hispanic/Latino; 0.2% Native Hawaiian or other Pacific Islander, non-Hispanic/Latino; 2% international. 1% 25 or older, 82% live on campus, 2% transferred in. Retention: 68% of full-time freshmen returned the following year. Academic areas with the most degrees conferred: business/marketing; social sciences; parks and recreation. Core. Calendar: semesters. Services for LD students, advanced placement, honors program, independent study, distance learning, double major, summer session for credit, part-time degree program, adult/continuing education programs, internships. Off campus study at George Mason University: Smithsonian-Mason Semester program. Study abroad program.

Entrance Requirements: Options: electronic application, deferred admission, international baccalaureate accepted. Required: high school transcript, SAT or ACT. Recommended: minimum 3 high school GPA. Entrance: moderately difficult. Notification: continuous. SAT Reasoning Test deadline: 4/15. Transfer credits accepted: Yes. Applicants placed on waiting list: 47. Wait-listed applicants offered admission: 1.

Costs Per Year: Application fee: $0. Comprehensive fee: $49,570 includes full-time tuition ($35,700), mandatory fees ($900), and college room and board ($12,970). Part-time tuition: $1230 per credit hour.

Collegiate Environment: Orientation program. Drama-theater group, choral group, student-run newspaper, radio station. Most popular organizations: Eagle Productions (program board), Physics Club, Active Minds, BC Allies. Major annual events: Homecoming, Welcome Week, SpringFest Concert. Student services: health clinic, personal-psychological counseling. Campus security: 24-hour emergency response devices and patrols, controlled dormitory access, emergency alert system. 1,542 college housing spaces available; 1,512 were occupied in 2018-19. No special consideration for freshman housing applicants. On-campus residence required through junior year. Options: coed, men-only, women-only housing available. Alexander Mack Memorial Library. Books: 105,776 (physical), 23,752 (digital/electronic); Serial titles: 264 (physical), 130 (digital/electronic); Databases: 110. Weekly public service hours: 92. Operations spending for the previous fiscal year: $987,837. 135 computers available on campus for general student use. A computer is required for all students. A campuswide network can be accessed from student residence rooms and from off campus. Students can access the following: online class registration, course management system, campus bulletin board system.

Community Environment: Bridgewater is located in the Shenandoah Valley, seven miles south of Harrisonburg. The community facilities include churches, banks, restaurants, parks, museums, and shops. The city, its suburbs and the surrounding area offer entertainment, fine dining experiences, a shopping mall, libraries, a hospital, historic towns, civil war battlefields, the George Washington National Forest, the Massanutten Four Seasons Resort, the Shenandoah Regional Airport, various civic organizations, and events at James Madison University Convocation Center. The College is conveniently located 10 minutes from Harrisonburg, 50 minutes from Charlottesville, an hour and 40 minutes from Roanoke and approximately 2 hours from Richmond or Washington, D.C.

■ **BRYANT & STRATTON COLLEGE-HAMPTON CAMPUS**
4410 E Claiborne Sq., Ste. 233
Hampton, VA 23666
Tel: (757)896-6001
Web Site: www.bryantstratton.edu
Description: Proprietary, 4-year, coed. Awards associate and bachelor's degrees.

■ **BRYANT & STRATTON COLLEGE-RICHMOND CAMPUS**
8141 Hull St. Rd.
Richmond, VA 23235
Tel: (804)745-2444
Fax: (804)499-7799
E-mail: tlawson@bryanstratton.edu
Web Site: www.bryantstratton.edu
Description: Proprietary, primarily 2-year, coed. Part of Bryant and Stratton Business Institute, Inc. Awards terminal associate and bachelor's degrees. Founded 1952. Setting: suburban campus. Total enrollment: 572. Faculty: 49 (14 full-time, 35 part-time). Student-undergrad faculty ratio is 10:1. Full-time: 280 students, 80% women, 20% men. Part-time: 292 students, 85% women, 15% men. 84% 25 or older, 7% transferred in. Academic area with the most degrees conferred: business/marketing. Core. Calendar: semesters. Academic remediation for entering students, advanced placement, independent study, distance learning, double major, summer session for credit, part-time degree program, adult/continuing education programs, internships.

Entrance Requirements: Option: deferred admission. Required: high school transcript, interview, entrance and placement evaluations, TABE, CPAt. Recommended: SAT or ACT. Entrance: minimally difficult. Application deadline: rolling.

Collegiate Environment: Orientation program. Social organizations: 7 open to all. Most popular organizations: Phi Beta Lambda, Alpha Beta Gamma, Student Council, Medical Assisting Club, Paralegal Club. Major annual events: Portfolio Development Day, Meet and Greet the Faculty and Staff, Spring Fling. Campus security: late night transport-escort service. Bryant and Stratton Library. 50 computers available on campus for general student use. A campuswide network can be accessed. Staffed computer lab on campus.

■ **BRYANT & STRATTON COLLEGE-VIRGINIA BEACH CAMPUS**
301 Centre Pointe Dr.
Virginia Beach, VA 23462
Tel: (757)499-7900
Fax: (757)499-7799
Web Site: www.bryantstratton.edu
Description: Proprietary, primarily 2-year, coed. Part of Bryant and Stratton Business Institute, Inc. Awards terminal associate and bachelor's degrees. Founded 1952. Setting: suburban campus. Total enrollment: 595. Faculty: 60 (20 full-time, 40 part-time). Student-undergrad faculty ratio is 12:1. 259 applied, 88% were admitted. Full-time: 267 students, 71% women, 29% men. Part-time: 328 students, 82% women, 18% men. Students come from 2 states and territories, 1% from out-of-state. 64% 25 or older, 10% transferred in. Academic area with the most degrees conferred: business/marketing. Core. Calendar: semesters. Academic remediation for entering students, services for LD students, advanced placement, independent study, double major, summer session for credit, part-time degree program, adult/continuing education programs, internships.
Entrance Requirements: Open admission. Option: electronic application. Required: essay, high school transcript, interview, CPAt. Entrance: minimally difficult. Application deadline: rolling.
Collegiate Environment: Orientation program. Student-run newspaper. Campus security: 24-hour emergency response devices, late night transport-escort service. Campus Library. 100 computers available on campus for general student use. A campuswide network can be accessed. Staffed computer lab on campus provides training in use of computers, software, and the Internet.

■ **CENTRA COLLEGE OF NURSING**
905 Lakeside Dr., Ste. A
Lynchburg, VA 24501
Tel: (434)947-3070
Web Site: www.centrahealth.com/facilities/centra-college-nursing
Description: Independent, 2-year, coed. Awards certificates, transfer associate, and terminal associate degrees.

■ **CENTRAL VIRGINIA COMMUNITY COLLEGE**
3506 Wards Rd.
Lynchburg, VA 24502-2498
Tel: (434)832-7600; Free: 800-562-3060
Fax: (434)832-7626
Web Site: www.centralvirginia.edu
Description: State-supported, 2-year, coed. Part of Virginia Community College System. Awards certificates, diplomas, transfer associate, and terminal associate degrees. Founded 1966. Setting: 104-acre suburban campus. Total enrollment: 4,128. Faculty: 333 (56 full-time, 277 part-time). Student-undergrad faculty ratio is 18:1. 705 applied, 99% were admitted. Students come from 12 states and territories, 1% from out-of-state. 0.4% American Indian or Alaska Native, non-Hispanic/Latino; 3% Hispanic/Latino; 18% Black or African American, non-Hispanic/Latino; 3% Asian, non-Hispanic/Latino; 0.1% Native Hawaiian or other Pacific Islander, non-Hispanic/Latino. 22% 25 or older. Core. Calendar: semesters. Academic remediation for entering students, services for LD students, advanced placement, independent study, distance learning, summer session for credit, part-time degree program, co-op programs and internships.
Entrance Requirements: Open admission. Options: electronic application, early admission, deferred admission. Entrance: noncompetitive. Application deadline: rolling. Notification: continuous. Transfer credits accepted: Yes.
Costs Per Year: Application fee: $0. State resident tuition: $4838 full-time, $161.25 per credit hour part-time. Nonresident tuition: $10,766 full-time, $358.85 per credit hour part-time.
Collegiate Environment: Orientation program. Major annual events: Fall Student Appreciation Picnic, Spring Student Appreciation Picnic. Campus security: 24-hour emergency response devices. Bedford Learning Resources Center.
Community Environment: See Lynchburg College.

■ **CENTURA COLLEGE (CHESAPEAKE)**
932 Ventures Way
Chesapeake, VA 23320

Tel: (757)549-2121; Free: 877-575-5627
Fax: (757)548-1196
Web Site: www.centuracollege.edu
Description: Proprietary, 2-year, coed. Awards terminal associate degrees. Founded 1982. Total enrollment: 212. Student-undergrad faculty ratio is 24:1. 2% from out-of-state. 60% 25 or older.

■ **CENTURA COLLEGE (NEWPORT NEWS)**
616 Denbigh Blvd.
Newport News, VA 23608
Tel: (757)874-2121; Free: 877-575-5627
Fax: (757)874-3857
Web Site: www.centuracollege.edu
Description: Proprietary, 2-year, coed. Awards diplomas and terminal associate degrees. Founded 1969. Total enrollment: 250. Student-undergrad faculty ratio is 8:1. 20% 25 or older.

■ **CENTURA COLLEGE (NORFOLK)**
7020 N Military Hwy.
Norfolk, VA 23518
Tel: (757)853-2121; Free: 877-575-5627
Fax: (757)852-9017
Web Site: www.centuracollege.edu
Description: Proprietary, 2-year, coed. Awards diplomas and terminal associate degrees. Total enrollment: 380. Student-undergrad faculty ratio is 17:1. 53% 25 or older.

■ **CENTURA COLLEGE (NORTH CHESTERFIELD)**
7914 Midlothian Tpke.
North Chesterfield, VA 23235-5230
Tel: (804)330-0111; Free: 877-575-5627
Fax: (804)330-3809
Web Site: www.centuracollege.edu
Description: Proprietary, 2-year, coed. Awards certificates and terminal associate degrees. Total enrollment: 290. Student-undergrad faculty ratio is 10:1. 58% 25 or older.
Entrance Requirements: Entrance: noncompetitive.

■ **CENTURA COLLEGE (VIRGINIA BEACH)**
2697 Dean Dr.
Ste. 100
Virginia Beach, VA 23452
Tel: (757)340-2121; Free: 877-575-5627
Fax: (757)340-9704
Web Site: www.centuracollege.edu
Description: Proprietary, primarily 2-year, coed. Awards terminal associate and bachelor's degrees. Founded 1969. Total enrollment: 1,639. Student-undergrad faculty ratio is 35:1. 86% from out-of-state. 72% 25 or older.
Entrance Requirements: Entrance: noncompetitive.

■ **CHAMBERLAIN COLLEGE OF NURSING**
2450 Crystal Dr.
Ste. 319
Arlington, VA 22202
Tel: (703)416-7300; Free: 877-751-5783
Fax: (703)416-7490
Web Site: www.chamberlain.edu
Description: Proprietary, 4-year, coed. Awards bachelor's degrees. Total enrollment: 544. Faculty: 57 (13 full-time, 44 part-time). Student-undergrad faculty ratio is 11:1. Full-time: 164 students, 83% women, 17% men. Part-time: 380 students, 87% women, 13% men. 48% from out-of-state. 30% American Indian or Alaska Native, non-Hispanic/Latino; 7% Hispanic/Latino; 30% Black or African American, non-Hispanic/Latino; 0.5% Asian, non-Hispanic/Latino; 15% Native Hawaiian or other Pacific Islander, non-Hispanic/Latino; 0.9% international. 74% 25 or older, 33% transferred in. Academic area with the most degrees conferred: health professions and related sciences. Calendar: semesters.
Entrance Requirements: Option: deferred admission. Required: SAT or ACT. Application deadline: rolling. Notification: continuous.

■ **CHESTER CAREER COLLEGE**
751 W Hundred Rd.
Chester, VA 23836
Tel: (804)751-9191

Web Site: www.chestercareercollege.edu
Description: Proprietary, 2-year, coed. Calendar: semesters.

■ **CHRISTENDOM COLLEGE**
134 Christendom Dr.
Front Royal, VA 22630-5103
Tel: (540)636-2900; Free: 800-877-5456
Fax: (540)636-1655
E-mail: sam.phillips@christendom.edu
Web Site: www.christendom.edu
Description: Independent Roman Catholic, comprehensive, coed. Awards associate, bachelor's, and master's degrees. Founded 1977. Setting: 200-acre rural campus with easy access to Washington, DC. Endowment: $15.8 million. Total enrollment: 573. Faculty: 50 (25 full-time, 25 part-time). Student-undergrad faculty ratio is 15:1. 322 applied, 89% were admitted. 1 National Merit Scholar. Full-time: 489 students, 57% women, 43% men. Part-time: 4 students, 50% women, 50% men. Students come from 45 states and territories, 4 other countries, 75% from out-of-state. 4% Hispanic/Latino; 0.2% Black or African American, non-Hispanic/Latino; 2% Asian, non-Hispanic/Latino; 3% international. 1% 25 or older, 90% live on campus, 3% transferred in. Retention: 85% of full-time freshmen returned the following year. Academic areas with the most degrees conferred: history; English; theology and religious vocations; social sciences. Core. Calendar: semesters. Academic remediation for entering students, services for LD students, advanced placement, accelerated degree program, independent study, double major, summer session for credit, co-op programs and internships, graduate courses open to undergrads. Study abroad program.
Entrance Requirements: Options: electronic application, early admission, early action. Required: essay, high school transcript, 1 recommendation, SAT or ACT. Recommended: minimum 2 high school GPA, interview. Required for some: 2 recommendations, two writing samples for those with SAT scores lower than 1000 or ACT scores lower than 21. Entrance: moderately difficult. Application deadlines: 3/1, 12/1 for early action. Notification: 4/1, 12/15 for early action. SAT Reasoning Test deadline: 8/1. Transfer credits accepted: Yes. Early action applicants: 199. Early action applicants admitted: 180.
Costs Per Year: Application fee: $0. Comprehensive fee: $36,640 includes full-time tuition ($25,460), mandatory fees ($900), and college room and board ($10,280).
Collegiate Environment: Orientation program. Drama-theater group, choral group, student-run newspaper. Social organizations: 30 open to all. Most popular organizations: drama, choir, Chester-Belloc Debate Society, Swing Dance Club, Shields of Rose Pro-life group. Major annual events: Christmas Dinner Dance, Dorm Wars Competition, St. Patrick's Day. Student services: health clinic, personal-psychological counseling. Campus security: 24-hour emergency response devices, late night transport-escort service, night patrols by trained security personnel. St. John the Evangelist Library. Books: 100,000 (physical), 1,000 (digital/electronic); Serial titles: 250 (physical), 1,000 (digital/electronic); Databases: 45. Weekly public service hours: 97. Operations spending for the previous fiscal year: $478,680.
Community Environment: Located in northwestern Virginia, the College community offers a wide variety of attractions. Visitors can choose from a wide variety of facilities and activities: fine restaurants, historic Bed & Breakfasts, Civil War battlefields, countless hiking trails, numerous golf courses, and tours of Skyline Drive and Skyline Caverns.

■ **CHRISTOPHER NEWPORT UNIVERSITY**
1 Ave. of the Arts
Newport News, VA 23606-3072
Tel: (757)594-7000; Free: 800-333-4268
Fax: (757)594-7333
E-mail: admit@cnu.edu
Web Site: www.cnu.edu
Description: State-supported, comprehensive, coed. Awards bachelor's and master's degrees. Founded 1960. Setting: 260-acre suburban campus with easy access to Virginia Beach. Endowment: $35.4 million. Research spending for the previous fiscal year: $1.6 million. Educational spending for the previous fiscal year: $7489 per student. Total enrollment: 4,957. Faculty: 465 (282 full-time, 183 part-time). Student-undergrad faculty ratio is 15:1. 7,430 applied, 68% were admitted. 17% from top 10% of their high school class, 51% from top quarter, 87% from top half. Full-time: 4,789 students, 56% women, 44% men. Part-time: 68 students, 54% women, 46% men. Students come from 34 states and territories, 34 other countries, 8% from out-of-state. 0.2% American Indian or Alaska Native, non-Hispanic/Latino; 6% Hispanic/

Latino; 6% Black or African American, non-Hispanic/Latino; 3% Asian, non-Hispanic/Latino; 0.1% Native Hawaiian or other Pacific Islander, non-Hispanic/Latino; 0.4% international. 1% 25 or older, 78% live on campus, 3% transferred in. Retention: 87% of full-time freshmen returned the following year. Academic areas with the most degrees conferred: business/marketing; social sciences; psychology. Core. Calendar: semesters. Advanced placement, self-designed majors, honors program, independent study, double major, summer session for credit, internships, graduate courses open to undergrads. Off campus study at Virginia Tidewater Consortium (VTC) arrangements, members include College of William and Mary, Eastern Shore Community College, Eastern Virginia Medical School, Hampton University, Joint Forces Staff College, Norfolk State University, Old Dominion University, Paul D. Camp Community College, Regent University, Thomas Nelson Community College, Tidewater Community College, and Virginia Wesleyan College. Study abroad program. ROTC: Army.
Entrance Requirements: Options: electronic application, early admission, early decision, early action, deferred admission, international baccalaureate accepted. Required: essay, high school transcript. Recommended: minimum 3.5 high school GPA, 2 recommendations. Required for some: interview, SAT or ACT. Entrance: moderately difficult. Application deadlines: 2/1, 2/1 for nonresidents, 11/15 for early decision, 12/1 for early action. Notification: 3/15, 3/15 for nonresidents, 12/15 for early decision, 1/15 for early action. SAT Reasoning Test deadline: 2/1. Transfer credits accepted: Yes. Applicants placed on waiting list: 1,221. Wait-listed applicants offered admission: 118. Early decision applicants: 437. Early decision applicants admitted: 353. Early action applicants: 3,994. Early action applicants admitted: 3,136.
Costs Per Year: Application fee: $65. State resident tuition: $9032 full-time, $376 per credit hour part-time. Nonresident tuition: $21,498 full-time, $895 per credit hour part-time. Mandatory fees: $5722 full-time, $238 per credit hour part-time. Full-time tuition and fees vary according to course load. Part-time tuition and fees vary according to course load. College room and board: $11,460. College room only: $7054. Room and board charges vary according to board plan and housing facility.
Collegiate Environment: Orientation program. Drama-theater group, choral group, marching band, student-run newspaper, radio station. Social organizations: 200 open to all; national fraternities, national sororities; 24% of eligible men and 34% of eligible women are members. Most popular organizations: Intervarsity Christian Fellowship, Alpha Delta Pi, Delta Gamma, Gamma Phi Beta, Alpha Phi. Major annual events: Homecoming, Spring Fest, Glow in the Dar Cappella. Student services: health clinic, personal-psychological counseling. Campus security: 24-hour emergency response devices and patrols, late night transport-escort service, controlled dormitory access. College housing designed to accommodate 3,805 students; 3,864 undergraduates lived in college housing during 2018-19. Freshmen guaranteed college housing. On-campus residence required through junior year. Option: coed housing available. Paul and Rosemary Trible Library. Books: 229,577 (physical), 578,114 (digital/electronic); Serial titles: 745 (physical), 65,202 (digital/electronic); Databases: 282. Weekly public service hours: 101; study areas open 24 hours, 5-7 days a week; students can reserve study rooms. Operations spending for the previous fiscal year: $2.5 million. 540 computers available on campus for general student use. A campuswide network can be accessed from student residence rooms and from off campus. Students can access the following: online class registration. Staffed computer lab on campus (open 24 hours a day) provides training in use of computers, software, and the Internet.
Community Environment: The 125-acre campus located in Newport News, VA, is easily accessible to residents of that city. The campus is centrally located between recreational centers at Colonial Williamsburg and the Norfolk/Virginia Beach resorts.

■ **THE COLLEGE OF WILLIAM AND MARY**
PO Box 8795
Williamsburg, VA 23187-8795
Tel: (757)221-4000
Fax: (757)221-1242
E-mail: admission@wm.edu
Web Site: www.wm.edu
Description: State-supported, university, coed. Awards bachelor's, master's, and doctoral degrees and post-master's certificates. Founded 1693. Setting: 1,200-acre small town campus with easy access to Richmond. Endowment: $935.5 million. Research spending for the previous fiscal year: $56.5 million. Educational spending for the previous fiscal year: $15,353 per student. Total enrollment: 8,817. 14,644 applied, 37% were admitted. 77% from top 10% of their high school class, 95% from top quarter, 99% from top half. Full-time:

6,300 students, 58% women, 42% men. Part-time: 77 students, 65% women, 35% men. Students come from 55 states and territories, 84 other countries, 31% from out-of-state. 0.2% American Indian or Alaska Native, non-Hispanic/Latino; 9% Hispanic/Latino; 7% Black or African American, non-Hispanic/Latino; 8% Asian, non-Hispanic/Latino; 0.1% Native Hawaiian or other Pacific Islander, non-Hispanic/Latino; 6% international. 1% 25 or older, 71% live on campus, 3% transferred in. Retention: 95% of full-time freshmen returned the following year. Academic areas with the most degrees conferred: social sciences; business/marketing; biological/life sciences. Core. Calendar: semesters. ESL program, services for LD students, advanced placement, accelerated degree program, self-designed majors, honors program, independent study, distance learning, double major, summer session for credit, part-time degree program, internships, graduate courses open to undergrads. Off campus study. Study abroad program. ROTC: Army.

Entrance Requirements: Options: electronic application, early admission, early decision, deferred admission, international baccalaureate accepted. Required: essay, high school transcript, 1 recommendation, SAT or ACT. Recommended: 2 recommendations. Entrance: most difficult. Application deadlines: 1/1, 11/1 for early decision. Notification: 4/1, 12/1 for early decision. Preference given to Virginia residents, children of alumni. SAT Reasoning Test deadline: 2/15. SAT Subject Test deadline: 2/15. Transfer credits accepted: Yes. Applicants placed on waiting list: 4,133. Wait-listed applicants offered admission: 94. Early decision applicants: 922. Early decision applicants admitted: 537.

Costs Per Year: Application fee: $75. State resident tuition: $17,434 full-time, $425 per credit hour part-time. Nonresident tuition: $38,735 full-time, $1235 per credit hour part-time. Mandatory fees: $5966 full-time. College room and board: $12,236. College room only: $7436. Room and board charges vary according to board plan and housing facility.

Collegiate Environment: Orientation program. Drama-theater group, choral group, student-run newspaper, radio station. Social organizations: 475 open to all; national fraternities, national sororities; 29% of eligible men and 32% of eligible women are members. Most popular organizations: Alma Mater Productions, Student Assembly, Residence Hall Association, Alpha Phi Omega, International Relations Club. Major annual events: Yule Log Ceremony, King and Queen Ball, Opening Convocation Exercises. Student services: legal services, health clinic, personal-psychological counseling. Campus security: 24-hour emergency response devices and patrols, late night transport-escort service, controlled dormitory access. 4,867 college housing spaces available; 4,531 were occupied in 2018-19. Freshmen guaranteed college housing. On-campus residence required in freshman year. Option: coed housing available. Earl Gregg Swem Library plus 7 others. Books: 1.1 million (physical), 2.2 million (digital/electronic); Serial titles: 40,428 (physical), 153,205 (digital/electronic); Databases: 540. Weekly public service hours: 110; study areas open 24 hours, 5-7 days a week; students can reserve study rooms. Operations spending for the previous fiscal year: $9.9 million. 400 computers available on campus for general student use. Computer purchase/lease plans available. A computer is required for all students. A campuswide network can be accessed from student residence rooms. Students can access the following: online class registration.

Community Environment: Williamsburg, the historic capital of Colonial Virginia, has been restored as nearly as possible to its 18th-century appearance. The Colonial Williamsburg project has been made possible by the generous provisions of the late John D. Rockefeller, Jr. The restored town offers excellent facilities, and the colonial shops on Merchant's Square provide historical interest. Williamsburg is a popular tourist center and has recreational activities such as fishing, boating, golf, and hunting. Major historic points of interest include William and Mary's Sir Christopher Wren Building (1695), the Bruton Parish Church, the Capitol, Governor's Palace, Peyton Randolph House, Raleigh Tavern, and the Wythe House.

■ **COLUMBIA COLLEGE**
8620 Westwood Ctr. Dr.
Vienna, VA 22182
Tel: (703)206-0508
Web Site: www.ccdc.edu
Description: Proprietary, 2-year, coed. Awards certificates, transfer associate, and terminal associate degrees.

■ **CULINARY INSTITUTE OF VIRGINIA**
2428 Almeda Ave., Ste. 316
Norfolk, VA 23513

Tel: (757)853-3508; Free: 866-619-CHEF
Fax: (757)857-4869
E-mail: hsadmissions@chefva.com
Web Site: www.chefva.com
Description: Proprietary, 4-year, coed. Administratively affiliated with ECPI College of Technology. Awards associate and bachelor's degrees. Setting: urban campus. Faculty: 19 (16 full-time, 3 part-time). Core. Academic remediation for entering students, advanced placement, internships.
Entrance Requirements: Option: electronic application. Required: interview. Entrance: minimally difficult. Application deadline: rolling. Notification: continuous. Transfer credits accepted: Yes.
Collegiate Environment: Orientation program. Campus security: trained evening security personnel. 96 computers available on campus for general student use. Staffed computer lab on campus provides training in use of software and the Internet.

■ **DABNEY S. LANCASTER COMMUNITY COLLEGE**
1000 Dabney Dr.
Clifton Forge, VA 24422
Tel: (540)863-2800; Free: 877-73-DSLCC
Fax: (540)863-2915
E-mail: sostling@dslcc.edu
Web Site: www.dslcc.edu
Description: State-supported, 2-year, coed. Part of Virginia Community College System. Awards certificates, transfer associate, and terminal associate degrees. Founded 1964. Setting: 117-acre rural campus. Endowment: $6.6 million. Educational spending for the previous fiscal year: $5714 per student. Total enrollment: 1,186. Faculty: 116 (18 full-time, 98 part-time). Student-undergrad faculty ratio is 10:1. 1,010 applied, 100% were admitted. Full-time: 428 students, 56% women, 44% men. Part-time: 758 students, 64% women, 36% men. Students come from 3 states and territories, 4% from out-of-state. 0.7% American Indian or Alaska Native, non-Hispanic/Latino; 2% Hispanic/Latino; 4% Black or African American, non-Hispanic/Latino; 0.6% Asian, non-Hispanic/Latino; 0.1% international. 23% 25 or older, 29% transferred in. Calendar: semesters. Academic remediation for entering students, services for LD students, advanced placement, independent study, distance learning, double major, summer session for credit, part-time degree program, adult/continuing education programs, co-op programs and internships. Off campus study.
Entrance Requirements: Open admission. Options: electronic application, international baccalaureate accepted. Recommended: high school transcript. Required for some: SAT and SAT Subject Tests or ACT. Entrance: noncompetitive. Notification: continuous, continuous for nonresidents, rolling for early decision plan 1, rolling for early decision plan 2, rolling for early action. SAT Reasoning Test deadline: 8/23. SAT Subject Test deadline: 8/23. Transfer credits accepted: Yes.
Costs Per Year: State resident tuition: $3696 full-time, $154 per credit hour part-time. Nonresident tuition: $9918 full-time, $330.60 per credit hour part-time. Mandatory fees: $84 full-time, $3.50 per credit hour part-time.
Collegiate Environment: Orientation program. Social organizations: 11 open to all; Phi Theta Kappa; 1% of eligible men and 4% of eligible women are members. Most popular organizations: Nursing Student Association, Phi Theta Kappa, National Student Leadership Society, LGBT+, Forestry Club. Major annual events: Spring Picnic, Fall Picnic, Annual Transfer College Fair. Student services: personal-psychological counseling. Campus security: 24-hour emergency response devices, Security Cameras at Rockbridge Regional Center. DSLCC Library. Books: 35,154 (physical), 74,281 (digital/electronic); Serial titles: 5 (physical), 95,157 (digital/electronic); Databases: 117. Weekly public service hours: 60; students can reserve study rooms. Operations spending for the previous fiscal year: $260,231.
Community Environment: A rural community, Clifton Forge is served by limited modes of transportation. Libraries, churches of major denominations, a hospital, and various civic and service organizations are part of the community. Some part-time job opportunities are available. A state park, lakes and streams provide facilities for fishing and outdoor sports; other activities include baseball, basketball, football, tennis, canoeing, backpacking and skiing.

■ **DANVILLE COMMUNITY COLLEGE**
1008 S Main St.
Danville, VA 24541-4088
Tel: (434)797-2222; Free: 800-560-4291
Fax: (434)797-8541
E-mail: cpulliam@dcc.vccs.edu

Web Site: www.dcc.vccs.edu

Description: State-supported, 2-year, coed. Part of Virginia Community College System. Awards certificates, diplomas, transfer associate, and terminal associate degrees. Founded 1967. Setting: 76-acre urban campus. Total enrollment: 4,387. Student-undergrad faculty ratio is 18:1. 1% from out-of-state. 36% 25 or older. Core. Calendar: semesters. Academic remediation for entering students, advanced placement, honors program, distance learning, summer session for credit, part-time degree program, adult/continuing education programs, co-op programs.

Entrance Requirements: Open admission. Options: early admission, deferred admission. Required: high school transcript. Entrance: noncompetitive. Application deadline: rolling. Notification: continuous. Preference given to district residents.

Collegiate Environment: Campus security: 24-hour patrols. Learning Resource Center.

Community Environment: See Averett College.

■ **DEVRY UNIVERSITY-ARLINGTON CAMPUS**
2450 Crystal Dr.
Arlington, VA 22202
Tel: (703)414-4000; Free: 866-338-7934
Fax: (703)414-4040
Web Site: www.devry.edu

Description: Proprietary, comprehensive, coed. Part of DeVry University. Awards associate, bachelor's, and master's degrees. Founded 2001. Total enrollment: 486. Faculty: 39 (3 full-time, 36 part-time). Student-undergrad faculty ratio is 17:1. Full-time: 124 students, 31% women, 69% men. Part-time: 128 students, 35% women, 65% men. 50% from out-of-state. 0.8% American Indian or Alaska Native, non-Hispanic/Latino; 18% Hispanic/Latino; 38% Black or African American, non-Hispanic/Latino; 3% Asian, non-Hispanic/Latino; 0.8% Native Hawaiian or other Pacific Islander, non-Hispanic/Latino; 2% international. 84% 25 or older, 29% transferred in. Calendar: semesters. Part-time degree program, adult/continuing education programs.

Entrance Requirements: Option: deferred admission. Required: high school transcript, interview. Entrance: minimally difficult. Application deadline: rolling. Notification: continuous.

Collegiate Environment: Learning Resource Center.

■ **DEVRY UNIVERSITY-CHESAPEAKE CAMPUS**
1317 Executive Blvd., Ste. 100
Chesapeake, VA 23320
Tel: (757)382-5680; Free: 866-338-7934
Web Site: www.devry.edu

Description: Proprietary, comprehensive, coed. Awards associate, bachelor's, and master's degrees.

Entrance Requirements: Application deadline: rolling. Notification: continuous.

■ **EASTERN MENNONITE UNIVERSITY**
1200 Park Rd.
Harrisonburg, VA 22802-2462
Tel: (540)432-4000; Free: 800-368-2665
Fax: (540)432-4444
E-mail: admiss@emu.edu
Web Site: www.emu.edu

Description: Independent Mennonite, comprehensive, coed. Awards associate, bachelor's, master's, and doctoral degrees. Founded 1917. Setting: 93-acre small town campus. Endowment: $27.5 million. Research spending for the previous fiscal year: $241,419. Educational spending for the previous fiscal year: $11,711 per student. Total enrollment: 1,444. Faculty: 184 (95 full-time, 89 part-time). Student-undergrad faculty ratio is 9:1. 1,245 applied, 59% were admitted. Full-time: 849 students, 60% women, 40% men. Part-time: 191 students, 82% women, 18% men. Students come from 30 states and territories, 33 other countries, 38% from out-of-state. 0.3% American Indian or Alaska Native, non-Hispanic/Latino; 7% Hispanic/Latino; 9% Black or African American, non-Hispanic/Latino; 3% Asian, non-Hispanic/Latino; 0.2% Native Hawaiian or other Pacific Islander, non-Hispanic/Latino; 4% international. 24% 25 or older, 44% live on campus, 4% transferred in. Retention: 70% of full-time freshmen returned the following year. Academic areas with the most degrees conferred: health professions and related sciences; business/marketing; liberal arts/general studies. Core. Calendar: semesters. ESL program, services for LD students, advanced placement, honors program, independent study, distance learning, double major, sum-

mer session for credit, part-time degree program, adult/continuing education programs, internships, graduate courses open to undergrads. Off campus study at Council for Christian Colleges and Universities, Brethren College Abroad. Study abroad program.

Entrance Requirements: Options: electronic application, deferred admission, international baccalaureate accepted. Required: high school transcript, minimum 2.2 high school GPA, Community Lifestyle Commitment, SAT or ACT. Recommended: interview. Required for some: 2 recommendations. Entrance: moderately difficult. Application deadline: rolling. Notification: continuous. SAT Reasoning Test deadline: 8/15. Transfer credits accepted: Yes.

Costs Per Year: Application fee: $25. Comprehensive fee: $48,260 includes full-time tuition ($36,760), mandatory fees ($340), and college room and board ($11,160). Room and board charges vary according to board plan and housing facility. Part-time tuition: $1400 per credit hour. Part-time tuition varies according to course load.

Collegiate Environment: Orientation program. Drama-theater group, choral group, student-run newspaper. Social organizations: 34 open to all. Most popular organizations: Young People's Christian Association, Student Government Association, Student Education Association, Creation Care Council, Black Student Union. Major annual events: Fall Festival, Multicultural Week, Spring Fling. Student services: health clinic, personal-psychological counseling. Campus security: 24-hour emergency response devices, controlled dormitory access. 660 college housing spaces available; 458 were occupied in 2018-19. Freshmen guaranteed college housing. On-campus residence required through junior year. Option: coed housing available. Sadie Hartzler Library. Books: 137,998 (physical), 236,023 (digital/electronic); Serial titles: 2,083 (physical), 79,742 (digital/electronic); Databases: 156. Weekly public service hours: 92. Operations spending for the previous fiscal year: $812,859. 154 computers available on campus for general student use. A campuswide network can be accessed from student residence rooms and from off campus. Students can access the following: online class registration.

Community Environment: The college is located in the heart of Virginia's beautiful Shenandoah Valley, near a national park.

■ **EASTERN SHORE COMMUNITY COLLEGE**
29300 Lankford Hwy.
Melfa, VA 23410-3000
Tel: (757)789-1789; Free: 877-871-8455
Fax: (757)789-1737
E-mail: cmills@es.vccs.edu
Web Site: www.es.vccs.edu

Description: State-supported, 2-year, coed. Part of Virginia Community College System. Awards certificates, transfer associate, and terminal associate degrees. Founded 1971. Setting: 117-acre rural campus with easy access to Hampton Roads/Virginia Beach, Norfolk. Total enrollment: 857. Faculty: 87 (17 full-time, 70 part-time). Student-undergrad faculty ratio is 13:1. 1% from out-of-state. 0.2% American Indian or Alaska Native, non-Hispanic/Latino; 6% Hispanic/Latino; 39% Black or African American, non-Hispanic/Latino; 1% Asian, non-Hispanic/Latino. Core. Calendar: semesters. Academic remediation for entering students, services for LD students, distance learning, summer session for credit, part-time degree program, adult/continuing education programs, internships. Off campus study at members of the Virginia Tidewater Consortium for Continuing Higher Education.

Entrance Requirements: Open admission except for practical nursing program. Option: electronic application. Required: high school transcript. Entrance: noncompetitive. Application deadline: rolling. Notification: continuous. Preference given to residents of Accomack or Northampton counties. Transfer credits accepted: Yes.

Collegiate Environment: Orientation program. Social organizations: 6 open to all. Most popular organizations: All Christians Together in Service (ACTS), Phi Theta Kappa, Phi Beta Lambda, The Electronics Club, Chess Club. Major annual events: Heritage Celebration, Science Fair, Phi Theta Kappa Lecture Series. Campus security: security guards, day and night during classes when the college is in session. Learning Resources Center plus 1 other. 75 computers available on campus for general student use. A campuswide network can be accessed from off-campus. Students can access the following: online class registration. Staffed computer lab on campus provides training in use of computers, software, and the Internet.

Community Environment: Located midway down the Delmarva Peninsula, which separates Chesapeake Bay from the Atlantic Ocean, Melfa has a population of 450. The area is known for vegetables, poultry, oysters, fish, sailing, and swimming.

■ **EASTERN VIRGINIA CAREER COLLEGE**
10304 Spotsylvania Ave.
Ste. 400
Fredericksburg, VA 22408
Tel: (540)373-2200
Web Site: www.evcc.edu
Description: Proprietary, 2-year, coed. Awards certificates, transfer associate, and terminal associate degrees.

■ **ECPI UNIVERSITY**
5555 Greenwich Rd.
Virginia Beach, VA 23462
Tel: (757)517-3903; Free: 844-611-0766
Fax: (757)671-8661
E-mail: csamuelson@ecpi.edu
Web Site: www.ecpi.edu
Description: Proprietary, comprehensive, coed. Awards associate, bachelor's, and master's degrees. Founded 1966. Setting: 8-acre suburban campus. Total enrollment: 11,739. Faculty: 1,109 (429 full-time, 680 part-time). Student-undergrad faculty ratio is 16:1. 4,176 applied, 84% were admitted. Full-time: 11,512 students, 56% women, 44% men. Students come from 52 states and territories, 4 other countries, 8% from out-of-state. 1% American Indian or Alaska Native, non-Hispanic/Latino; 9% Hispanic/Latino; 42% Black or African American, non-Hispanic/Latino; 3% Asian, non-Hispanic/Latino; 0.6% Native Hawaiian or other Pacific Islander, non-Hispanic/Latino. 69% 25 or older, 17% transferred in. Retention: 53% of full-time freshmen returned the following year. Academic areas with the most degrees conferred: computer and information sciences; business/marketing; engineering technologies. Core. Calendar: continuous. Academic remediation for entering students, services for LD students, advanced placement, accelerated degree program, independent study, distance learning, double major, summer session for credit, part-time degree program, adult/continuing education programs, co-op programs and internships, graduate courses open to undergrads. Off campus study. Study abroad program.
Entrance Requirements: Options: electronic application, deferred admission, international baccalaureate accepted. Required: high school transcript, interview, Entrance Exam. Required for some: minimum 2.5 high school GPA. Entrance: moderately difficult. Notification: continuous. Transfer credits accepted: Yes.
Costs Per Year: Application fee: $45. One-time mandatory fee: $100. Tuition: $15,984 full-time. Full-time tuition varies according to course load, degree level, location, program, and reciprocity agreements. Tuition guaranteed not to increase for student's term of enrollment.
Collegiate Environment: Orientation program. Social organizations: national fraternities, national sororities, local fraternities, local sororities; 25% of eligible men and 25% of eligible women are members. Most popular organizations: Student Electronic Technicians Association (SETA), Institute of Electrical and Electronic Engineers (IEEE), Phi Theta Kappa Honor Society, Information Technology Exchange (ITE), Medical Student Association. Major annual events: Picnic, Fall Fest. Student services: personal-psychological counseling. Campus security: building and parking lot security. ECPI-Virginia Beach Campus Library plus 14 others. Books: 25,945 (physical), 189,050 (digital/electronic); Serial titles: 118 (physical); Databases: 83. Weekly public service hours: 62; students can reserve study rooms. 6,500 computers available on campus for general student use. Computer purchase/lease plans available. A campuswide network can be accessed from off-campus. Students can access the following: online class registration. Staffed computer lab on campus provides training in use of computers, software, and the Internet.

■ **EMORY & HENRY COLLEGE**
PO Box 947
Emory, VA 24327-0947
Tel: (276)944-4121; Free: 800-848-5493
Fax: (276)944-6934
E-mail: mcrisman@ehc.edu
Web Site: www.ehc.edu
Description: Independent United Methodist, comprehensive, coed. Awards bachelor's, master's, and doctoral degrees. Founded 1836. Setting: 330-acre rural campus. Endowment: $81.8 million. Research spending for the previous fiscal year: $294,620. Educational spending for the previous fiscal year: $11,780 per student. Total enrollment: 1,226. Faculty: 147 (95 full-time, 52 part-time). Student-undergrad faculty ratio is 11:1. 1,426 applied, 72% were admitted. Full-time: 966 students, 51% women, 49% men. Part-time:

34 students, 41% women, 59% men. 58% from out-of-state. 0.4% American Indian or Alaska Native, non-Hispanic/Latino; 4% Hispanic/Latino; 8% Black or African American, non-Hispanic/Latino; 1% Asian, non-Hispanic/Latino; 0.2% Native Hawaiian or other Pacific Islander, non-Hispanic/Latino; 0.4% international. 2% 25 or older, 78% live on campus, 6% transferred in. Retention: 76% of full-time freshmen returned the following year. Academic areas with the most degrees conferred: education; social sciences; business/marketing. Core. Calendar: semesters. Academic remediation for entering students, services for LD students, advanced placement, self-designed majors, honors program, independent study, double major, summer session for credit, part-time degree program, co-op programs and internships, graduate courses open to undergrads. Study abroad program.
Entrance Requirements: Options: electronic application, early decision, international baccalaureate accepted. Required: high school transcript, SAT or ACT. Recommended: essay, interview. Application deadlines: rolling, 11/15 for early decision plan 1, 1/15 for early decision plan 2. Notification: continuous, 12/15 for early decision. SAT Reasoning Test deadline: 8/1. SAT Subject Test deadline: 8/1. Transfer credits accepted: Yes.
Costs Per Year: Application fee: $0. Comprehensive fee: $47,100 includes full-time tuition ($34,500), mandatory fees ($500), and college room and board ($12,100). College room only: $6300. Full-time tuition and fees vary according to degree level, location, and student level. Room and board charges vary according to board plan and housing facility. Tuition guaranteed not to increase for student's term of enrollment.
Collegiate Environment: Orientation program. Drama-theater group, choral group, marching band, student-run newspaper, radio station. Social organizations: 40 open to all; local fraternities, local sororities. Most popular organizations: E&H Outdoor Program, Alpha Psi Omega Honors Fraternity, Alpha Phi Omega Honors Fraternity, Blue Key/ Cardinal Key Honors Society, The Emory Activities Board. Major annual events: Martin Luther King Jr. Day Celebration, Service Plunge, Homecoming Pep Rally. Student services: health clinic, personal-psychological counseling. Campus security: 24-hour emergency response devices and patrols, late night transport-escort service, controlled dormitory access. Kelly Library plus 1 other. Books: 225,739 (physical), 126,654 (digital/electronic); Serial titles: 728 (physical), 113,345 (digital/electronic); Databases: 105. Weekly public service hours: 90; students can reserve study rooms. 200 computers available on campus for general student use. A campuswide network can be accessed. Students can access the following: online class registration. Staffed computer lab on campus provides training in use of computers, software, and the Internet.
Community Environment: Emory, in the Virginia Highlands, is approximately 20 miles north of Bristol, VA, just off exit 26 of I-81. The area is known for its scenic beauty, recreational opportunities, and abundance of talented craftspeople. In Abingdon, an historic town dating from the middle 1700's, the annual Virginia Highlands Festival brings together artists and craftspeople from throughout the eastern U.S. Just twenty minutes from the college campus is Mt. Rogers National Recreational Area, featuring numerous campgrounds, mountain streams, and miles of the Appalachian Trail.

■ **FERRUM COLLEGE**
PO Box 1000
Ferrum, VA 24088
Tel: (540)365-2121; Free: 800-868-9797
Fax: (540)365-4266
E-mail: admissions@ferrum.edu
Web Site: www.ferrum.edu
Description: Independent United Methodist, 4-year, coed. Awards bachelor's degrees. Founded 1913. Setting: 720-acre rural campus. Total enrollment: 1,451. Faculty: 116 (78 full-time, 38 part-time). Student-undergrad faculty ratio is 16:1. 3,286 applied, 73% were admitted. 1% from top 10% of their high school class, 12% from top quarter, 40% from top half. Full-time: 1,432 students, 47% women, 53% men. Part-time: 19 students, 68% women, 32% men. 19% from out-of-state. 0.4% American Indian or Alaska Native, non-Hispanic/Latino; 5% Hispanic/Latino; 30% Black or African American, non-Hispanic/Latino; 0.6% Asian, non-Hispanic/Latino; 0.2% Native Hawaiian or other Pacific Islander, non-Hispanic/Latino; 0.8% international. 2% 25 or older, 89% live on campus, 5% transferred in. Retention: 47% of full-time freshmen returned the following year. Academic areas with the most degrees conferred: homeland security, law enforcement, firefighting, and protective services; health professions and related sciences; business/marketing. Core. Calendar: semesters. Academic remediation for entering students, services for LD students, advanced placement, self-designed majors, honors program, independent study, double major, summer session for credit, adult/continuing education programs, internships. Study abroad program.

Entrance Requirements: Options: electronic application, early admission, deferred admission, international baccalaureate accepted. Required: high school transcript, SAT or ACT. Recommended: essay, minimum 2 high school GPA, interview. Required for some: interview. Entrance: minimally difficult.

Costs Per Year: Application fee: $25. Comprehensive fee: $45,745 includes full-time tuition ($34,060), mandatory fees ($115), and college room and board ($11,570). Part-time tuition: $685 per credit hour.

Collegiate Environment: Orientation program. Drama-theater group, choral group, student-run newspaper, radio station. Social organizations: national sororities, local fraternities, local sororities. Most popular organizations: Student Government Association, Agriculture Club, BACCHUS, Panther Productions, African American Student Association, Students in Free Enterprise (SIFE). Major annual events: Homecoming, Folklife Festival, Spring Fling. Student services: health clinic, personal-psychological counseling. Campus security: 24-hour emergency response devices and patrols, student patrols, late night transport-escort service, controlled dormitory access. Stanley Library.

Community Environment: Located in the Blue Ridge Mountains of Virginia, Ferrum has an ideal environment for study and cultural enrichment. The College's proximity to the mountains and lakes enables students to enjoy outdoor activities such as hiking, camping, fishing, boating, swimming and skiing. Ferrum is 35 miles south of Roanoke, Virginia, which has excellent shopping, living, cultural and recreational facilities. Bus service and air transportation are available in Roanoke.

■ FORTIS COLLEGE (NORFOLK)

6300 Ctr. Dr.
Ste. 100
Norfolk, VA 23502
Tel: (757)499-5447; Free: 855-4-FORTIS
Web Site: www.fortis.edu

Description: Proprietary, 2-year, coed. Awards certificates, diplomas, transfer associate, and terminal associate degrees.

■ FORTIS COLLEGE (RICHMOND)

2000 Westmoreland St.
Ste. A
Richmond, VA 23230
Tel: (804)323-1020; Free: 855-4-FORTIS
Web Site: www.fortis.edu

Description: Proprietary, 2-year, coed. Awards certificates, diplomas, transfer associate, and terminal associate degrees.

■ GEORGE MASON UNIVERSITY

4400 University Dr.
Fairfax, VA 22030
Tel: (703)993-1000; Free: 888-627-6612
E-mail: mbevacqu@gmu.edu
Web Site: www.gmu.edu

Description: State-supported, university, coed. Awards bachelor's, master's, and doctoral degrees and post-master's certificates. Founded 1972. Setting: 817-acre suburban campus with easy access to Washington, DC. Endowment: $84.9 million. Research spending for the previous fiscal year: $115.4 million. Educational spending for the previous fiscal year: $9894 per student. Total enrollment: 37,316. Faculty: 2,765 (1,334 full-time, 1,431 part-time). Student-undergrad faculty ratio is 17:1. 19,557 applied, 81% were admitted. 18% from top 10% of their high school class, 50% from top quarter, 87% from top half. Full-time: 21,213 students, 50% women, 50% men. Part-time: 4,979 students, 47% women, 53% men. Students come from 49 states and territories, 106 other countries, 10% from out-of-state. 0.1% American Indian or Alaska Native, non-Hispanic/Latino; 15% Hispanic/Latino; 11% Black or African American, non-Hispanic/Latino; 20% Asian, non-Hispanic/Latino; 0.3% Native Hawaiian or other Pacific Islander, non-Hispanic/Latino; 5% international. 19% 25 or older, 23% live on campus, 11% transferred in. Retention: 86% of full-time freshmen returned the following year. Academic areas with the most degrees conferred: business/marketing; social sciences; health professions and related sciences. Core. Calendar: semesters. ESL program, services for LD students, advanced placement, accelerated degree program, self-designed majors, freshman honors college, honors program, independent study, distance learning, double major, summer session for credit, part-time degree program, adult/continuing education programs, co-op programs and internships, graduate courses open to undergrads. Off

campus study at Members of the Consortium of Universities of the Washington Metropolitan Area. Study abroad program. ROTC: Army, Air Force (c).

Entrance Requirements: Options: electronic application, early admission, early action, deferred admission, international baccalaureate accepted. Required: high school transcript. Recommended: 3 recommendations. Required for some: essay, audition for dance and music, portfolio for art and visual technology and computer game design, interview and audition or portfolio for theater, SAT or ACT. Entrance: moderately difficult. Application deadlines: 1/15, 11/15 for early action. Notification: 12/15 for early action. SAT Reasoning Test deadline: 1/15. Transfer credits accepted: Yes. Applicants placed on waiting list: 1,889. Wait-listed applicants offered admission: 76. Early action applicants: 10,215. Early action applicants admitted: 8,654.

Costs Per Year: Application fee: $70. State resident tuition: $9060 full-time, $378 per credit hour part-time. Nonresident tuition: $32,520 full-time, $1355 per credit hour part-time. Mandatory fees: $3402 full-time, $141.75 per credit hour part-time. Full-time tuition and fees vary according to course load. Part-time tuition and fees vary according to course load. College room and board: $11,460. Room and board charges vary according to board plan and housing facility.

Collegiate Environment: Orientation program. Drama-theater group, choral group, student-run newspaper, radio station. Social organizations: 459 open to all; national fraternities, national sororities, local fraternities. Most popular organizations: Catholic Campus Ministry, Indian Student Association, Black Student Alliance, Muslim Student Association, CRU (Campus Crusade for Christ). Major annual events: Mason Day, Welcome2Mason, Homecoming. Student services: health clinic, personal-psychological counseling, women's center. Campus security: 24-hour emergency response devices and patrols, student patrols, late night transport-escort service, controlled dormitory access. 6,190 college housing spaces available; 5,772 were occupied in 2018-19. Freshmen guaranteed college housing. Option: coed housing available. Fenwick Library plus 3 others. Books: 1.1 million (physical), 1.4 million (digital/electronic); Serial titles: 1,049 (physical), 127,898 (digital/electronic); Databases: 772. Weekly public service hours: 100; study areas open 24 hours, 5-7 days a week; students can reserve study rooms. Operations spending for the previous fiscal year: $23.1 million. 622 computers available on campus for general student use. Computer purchase/lease plans available. A campuswide network can be accessed from student residence rooms and from off campus. Students can access the following: online class registration. Staffed computer lab on campus provides training in use of computers, software, and the Internet.

Community Environment: Fairfax is a rapidly growing residential area on the western fringes of Washington, DC. Shopping facilities, commercial transportation, recreation activities, part-time employment and moderate-to-expensive rental apartments are available nearby.

■ GERMANNA COMMUNITY COLLEGE

2130 Germanna Hwy.
Locust Grove, VA 22508-2102
Tel: (540)727-3000
Fax: (540)727-3207
Web Site: www.germanna.edu

Description: State-supported, 2-year, coed. Part of Virginia Community College System. Awards certificates, transfer associate, and terminal associate degrees. Founded 1970. Setting: 100-acre suburban campus with easy access to Washington, DC. Total enrollment: 7,035. Faculty: 372 (69 full-time, 303 part-time). Student-undergrad faculty ratio is 19:1. 1,338 applied, 100% were admitted. Full-time: 2,296 students, 57% women, 43% men. Part-time: 4,739 students, 65% women, 35% men. 28% 25 or older. Calendar: semesters. Academic remediation for entering students, ESL program, services for LD students, advanced placement, independent study, distance learning, double major, summer session for credit, part-time degree program. Off campus study at University of Mary Washington, other members of the Virginia Community College System. Study abroad program.

Entrance Requirements: Open admission except for nursing program. Options: electronic application, early admission. Required for some: high school transcript. Entrance: noncompetitive. Application deadline: rolling. Notification: continuous.

Collegiate Environment: Orientation program. Drama-theater group. Most popular organizations: Student Nurses Association, Student Government Association, Phi Theta Kappa. Student services: personal-psychological counseling. Campus security: 24-hour patrols. Locust Grove Campus Library plus 2 others. 55 computers available on campus for general student use.

Students can access the following: online class registration. Staffed computer lab on campus provides training in use of computers, software, and the Internet.

■ HAMPDEN-SYDNEY COLLEGE

PO Box 859
Hampden Sydney, VA 23943
Tel: (434)223-6000; Free: 800-755-0733
Fax: (434)223-6346
E-mail: hsapp@hsc.edu
Web Site: www.hsc.edu

Description: Independent, 4-year, men only, affiliated with Presbyterian Church (U.S.A.). Awards bachelor's degrees. Founded 1776. Setting: 1,343-acre rural campus with easy access to Richmond, Lynchburg, Charlottesville. Endowment: $170.7 million. Research spending for the previous fiscal year: $130,923. Educational spending for the previous fiscal year: $72,401 per student. Total enrollment: 1,072. Faculty: 111 (96 full-time, 15 part-time). Student-undergrad faculty ratio is 10:1. 3,240 applied, 59% were admitted. 11% from top 10% of their high school class, 22% from top quarter, 64% from top half. 36 student government officers. Full-time: 1,070 students. Part-time: 2 students. Students come from 31 states and territories, 5 other countries, 30% from out-of-state. 0.5% American Indian or Alaska Native, non-Hispanic/Latino; 4% Hispanic/Latino; 5% Black or African American, non-Hispanic/Latino; 0.7% Asian, non-Hispanic/Latino; 0.1% Native Hawaiian or other Pacific Islander, non-Hispanic/Latino; 0.4% international. 0.4% 25 or older, 98% live on campus, 1% transferred in. Retention: 81% of full-time freshmen returned the following year. Academic areas with the most degrees conferred: business/marketing; social sciences; biological/life sciences. Core. Calendar: semesters. Academic remediation for entering students, advanced placement, honors program, independent study, double major, summer session for credit, co-op programs and internships. Off campus study at Seven-College Exchange Program, Longwood College Cooperative Program. Study abroad program. ROTC: Army (c).

Entrance Requirements: Options: electronic application, early admission, early decision, early action, international baccalaureate accepted. Required: essay, high school transcript, 2 recommendations, SAT or ACT. Recommended: interview, SAT and SAT Subject Tests or ACT. Entrance: moderately difficult. Application deadline: 11/1 for early decision. Notification: 4/15, 12/1 for early decision, 12/1 for early action. SAT Reasoning Test deadline: 3/1. SAT Subject Test deadline: 3/1. Transfer credits accepted: Yes. Early decision applicants: 166. Early decision applicants admitted: 74. Early action applicants: 2,357. Early action applicants admitted: 1,521.

Costs Per Year: Application fee: $30. Comprehensive fee: $60,602 includes full-time tuition ($44,532), mandatory fees ($2358), and college room and board ($13,712). Part-time tuition: $1394 per credit hour.

Collegiate Environment: Orientation program. Drama-theater group, choral group, student-run newspaper, radio station. Social organizations: 89 open to all; national fraternities; 30% of eligible undergrads are members. Most popular organizations: Republican Society, Pre-Health Society, Outdoors Club, Tiger Athletic Club, Pre-Law Society. Major annual events: Homecoming, Greek Weekend, Macon Week/Midwinters. Student services: health clinic, personal-psychological counseling. Campus security: 24-hour emergency response devices and patrols. 1,122 college housing spaces available; 1,025 were occupied in 2018-19. Freshmen guaranteed college housing. On-campus residence required through senior year. Option: men-only housing available. Walter M. Bortz III Library. Books: 211,996 (physical), 184,419 (digital/electronic); Serial titles: 57 (physical), 103,133 (digital/electronic); Databases: 95. Weekly public service hours: 99; students can reserve study rooms. Operations spending for the previous fiscal year: $1 million. 200 computers available on campus for general student use. Computer purchase/lease plans available. A campuswide network can be accessed from student residence rooms and from off campus. Students can access the following: online class registration. Staffed computer lab on campus provides training in use of computers, software, and the Internet.

■ HAMPTON UNIVERSITY

100 Cemetery Rd.
Hampton, VA 23668
Tel: (757)727-5000; Free: 800-624-3328
Fax: (757)727-5084
E-mail: patra.johnson@hamptonu.edu
Web Site: www.hamptonu.edu

Description: Independent, comprehensive, coed. Awards associate, bachelor's, master's, and doctoral degrees and post-master's certificates. Founded 1868. Setting: 314-acre urban campus with easy access to Norfolk. Total enrollment: 4,619. Faculty: 367 (288 full-time, 79 part-time). Student-undergrad faculty ratio is 13:1. 12,130 applied, 36% were admitted. 12% from top 10% of their high school class, 22% from top quarter, 71% from top half. Full-time: 3,651 students, 67% women, 33% men. Part-time: 148 students, 61% women, 39% men. Students come from 44 states and territories, 22 other countries, 73% from out-of-state. 0.4% American Indian or Alaska Native, non-Hispanic/Latino; 1% Hispanic/Latino; 96% Black or African American, non-Hispanic/Latino; 0.3% Asian, non-Hispanic/Latino; 0.1% Native Hawaiian or other Pacific Islander, non-Hispanic/Latino; 0.7% international. 5% 25 or older, 64% live on campus, 2% transferred in. Retention: 77% of full-time freshmen returned the following year. Academic areas with the most degrees conferred: business/marketing; communication/journalism; psychology; biological/life sciences. Core. Calendar: semesters. Academic remediation for entering students, ESL program, services for LD students, advanced placement, accelerated degree program, honors program, independent study, distance learning, double major, summer session for credit, part-time degree program, adult/continuing education programs, co-op programs and internships, graduate courses open to undergrads. Off campus study at 11 members of the Virginia Tidewater Consortium for Higher Education. Study abroad program. ROTC: Army, Naval.

Entrance Requirements: Options: electronic application, early admission, early action, deferred admission, international baccalaureate accepted. Required: essay, high school transcript, minimum 2.5 high school GPA, 1 recommendation. Required for some: interview, audition for music, SAT or ACT. Entrance: moderately difficult. Application deadlines: 3/1, 11/1 for early action. Notification: 12/15 for early action. SAT Reasoning Test deadline: 6/15. Transfer credits accepted: Yes.

Collegiate Environment: Orientation program. Drama-theater group, choral group, marching band, student-run newspaper, radio station. Social organizations: 85 open to all; national fraternities, national sororities, local fraternities, local sororities; 5% of eligible men and 4% of eligible women are members. Most popular organizations: Student Government, student leaders, Student Union Board, student recruitment team, resident assistants. Major annual events: Homecoming, Founder' Day, Convocation. Student services: health clinic, personal-psychological counseling, women's center. Campus security: 24-hour emergency response devices and patrols. William R. and Norma B. Harvey Library plus 4 others. Books: 307,143 (physical), 91,991 (digital/electronic); Serial titles: 8,240 (physical); Databases: 115. Study areas open 24 hours, 5-7 days a week; students can reserve study rooms. 1,500 computers available on campus for general student use. Computer purchase/lease plans available. A campuswide network can be accessed from student residence rooms and from off campus. Students can access the following: online class registration, learning management system. Staffed computer lab on campus provides training in use of computers, software, and the Internet.

Community Environment: Hampton is the oldest English settlement still in existence in the nation; the city was settled in 1610. Hampton is the center of the fishing industry of Virginia. All modes of transportation are available. The Syms-Eaton Academy, first free school of America, and Hampton University, of which Booker T. Washington was an alumnus, are only two of the area's important sites. St. John's Church, which survived a partial burning during the Civil War, is another historic point of interest. Its most precious relic is communion silver made in 1618. The window dedicated to Pocahontas was donated by Indian students at Hampton Institute.

■ HOLLINS UNIVERSITY

7916 Williamson Rd.
Roanoke, VA 24020
Tel: (540)362-6000; Free: 800-456-9595
Fax: (540)362-6218
E-mail: huadm@hollins.edu
Web Site: www.hollins.edu

Description: Independent, comprehensive. Awards bachelor's and master's degrees and post-master's certificates. Founded 1842. Setting: 475-acre suburban campus. Endowment: $186.3 million. Research spending for the previous fiscal year: $5902. Educational spending for the previous fiscal year: $19,327 per student. Total enrollment: 804. Faculty: 98 (70 full-time, 28 part-time). Student-undergrad faculty ratio is 10:1. 2,842 applied, 48% were admitted. 23% from top 10% of their high school class, 55% from top quarter, 82% from top half. Full-time: 666 students, 99% women, 1% men. Part-time: 10 students, 90% women, 10% men. Students come from 44 states and territories, 16 other countries, 50% from out-of-state. 0.6% American Indian or

Alaska Native, non-Hispanic/Latino; 8% Hispanic/Latino; 10% Black or African American, non-Hispanic/Latino; 2% Asian, non-Hispanic/Latino; 0.3% Native Hawaiian or other Pacific Islander, non-Hispanic/Latino; 7% international. 5% 25 or older, 87% live on campus, 2% transferred in. Retention: 78% of full-time freshmen returned the following year. Academic areas with the most degrees conferred: visual and performing arts; social sciences; biological/life sciences; English. Core. Calendar: 4-1-4. Services for LD students, advanced placement, accelerated degree program, self-designed majors, honors program, independent study, double major, part-time degree program, adult/continuing education programs, co-op programs and internships, graduate courses open to undergrads. Off campus study at members of the Seven-College Exchange Program. Study abroad program.
Entrance Requirements: Options: electronic application, early admission, early decision, early action, deferred admission, international baccalaureate accepted. Required: essay, high school transcript, 1 recommendation, SAT or ACT. Recommended: interview. Entrance: moderately difficult. Application deadlines: rolling, 11/1 for early decision, 11/15 for early action. Notification: continuous. SAT Reasoning Test deadline: 5/1. Transfer credits accepted: Yes. Early decision applicants: 5. Early decision applicants admitted: 5. Early action applicants: 1,215. Early action applicants admitted: 706.
Costs Per Year: Application fee: $0. Comprehensive fee: $53,940 includes full-time tuition ($39,360), mandatory fees ($650), and college room and board ($13,930). Part-time tuition: $1233 per credit hour. Part-time mandatory fees: $325 per year.
Collegiate Environment: Orientation program. Drama-theater group, choral group. Social organizations: 20 open to all. Most popular organizations: Hollins Activity Board, Black Student Alliance, Hollins Repertory Dance Club, Arts Association, Voices for Unity. Major annual events: Fall Formal, Spring Cotillion, Spring Sing (A Capella event). Student services: health clinic, personal-psychological counseling, women's center. Campus security: 24-hour emergency response devices and patrols, late night transport-escort service, controlled dormitory access. 688 college housing spaces available; 463 were occupied in 2018-19. Freshmen guaranteed college housing. On-campus residence required through senior year. Option: women-only housing available. Wyndham Robertson Library plus 1 other. Books: 246,065 (physical), 122,121 (digital/electronic); Serial titles: 1,160 (physical), 51,262 (digital/electronic); Databases: 130. Weekly public service hours: 94. Operations spending for the previous fiscal year: $898,695. 102 computers available on campus for general student use. Computer purchase/lease plans available. A campuswide network can be accessed from student residence rooms. Students can access the following: online class registration. Staffed computer lab on campus (open 24 hours a day) provides training in use of computers, software, and the Internet.
Community Environment: In this suburban area, the city of Roanoke is the business, cultural, and commercial center of Southwest Virginia. Air and bus transportation are available in Roanoke. Other community facilities of Roanoke are accessible to the students. There is also a symphony, opera company, ballet company, theatre company, art and science museums, and a farmers' market.

■ **IGLOBAL UNIVERSITY**
8133 Leesburg Pke.
No.230
Vienna, VA 22182
Tel: (703)941-2020
Web Site: www.igu.edu
Description: Proprietary, comprehensive, coed. Awards bachelor's and master's degrees. Founded 2008.

■ **J. SARGEANT REYNOLDS COMMUNITY COLLEGE**
PO Box 85622
Richmond, VA 23285-5622
Tel: (804)371-3000
Fax: (804)371-3650
Web Site: www.reynolds.edu
Description: State-supported, 2-year, coed. Part of Virginia Community College System. Awards certificates, transfer associate, and terminal associate degrees. Founded 1972. Setting: 207-acre suburban campus with easy access to Richmond. Endowment: $10 million. Total enrollment: 9,334. Faculty: 585 (129 full-time, 456 part-time). Student-undergrad faculty ratio is 17:1. Full-time: 2,567 students, 54% women, 46% men. Part-time: 6,767 students, 61% women, 39% men. Students come from 21 states and territories, 16 other countries, 1% from out-of-state. 0.4% American Indian or Alaska Native, non-Hispanic/Latino; 3% Hispanic/Latino; 33% Black or African

American, non-Hispanic/Latino; 6% Asian, non-Hispanic/Latino; 0.2% Native Hawaiian or other Pacific Islander, non-Hispanic/Latino. 39% 25 or older, 5% transferred in. Retention: 51% of full-time freshmen returned the following year. Calendar: semesters. Academic remediation for entering students, ESL program, services for LD students, advanced placement, honors program, independent study, distance learning, double major, summer session for credit, part-time degree program, adult/continuing education programs, internships. Off campus study at Northern Virginia Community College.
Entrance Requirements: Open admission. Option: electronic application. Required: high school transcript. Required for some: interview, interview, criminal background check and/or drug screening, physical standard minimum. Entrance: noncompetitive. Application deadline: rolling. Notification: continuous. Transfer credits accepted: Yes.
Costs Per Year: Application fee: $0. State resident tuition: $4,846 full-time, $145.85 per credit hour part-time. Nonresident tuition: $10,814 full-time, $322.45 per credit hour part-time. Mandatory fees: $510 full-time, $17 per credit hour part-time. Full-time tuition and fees vary according to course load and program. Part-time tuition and fees vary according to course load and program.
Collegiate Environment: Orientation program. Social organizations: 27 open to all. Student services: personal-psychological counseling. Campus security: 24-hour emergency response devices and patrols, late night transport-escort service, security during hours of operation. J. Sargeant Reynolds Community College Library plus 2 others. Books: 85,000 (physical), 62,000 (digital/electronic); Serial titles: 225 (physical), 52,000 (digital/electronic); Databases: 145. Weekly public service hours: 66. 300 computers available on campus for general student use. A campuswide network can be accessed from off-campus. Students can access the following: online class registration. Staffed computer lab on campus provides training in use of computers, software, and the Internet.
Community Environment: See University of Richmond.

■ **JAMES MADISON UNIVERSITY**
800 S Main St.
Harrisonburg, VA 22807
Tel: (540)568-6211
Fax: (540)568-3332
Web Site: www.jmu.edu
Description: State-supported, comprehensive, coed. Awards bachelor's, master's, and doctoral degrees (also offers specialist in education degree). Founded 1908. Setting: 721-acre small town campus. Total enrollment: 21,836. Faculty: 1,541 (1,044 full-time, 497 part-time). Student-undergrad faculty ratio is 16:1. 21,099 applied, 75% were admitted. 16% from top 10% of their high school class, 51% from top quarter, 94% from top half. Full-time: 18,905 students, 59% women, 41% men. Part-time: 1,070 students, 51% women, 49% men. 23% from out-of-state. 0.1% American Indian or Alaska Native, non-Hispanic/Latino; 7% Hispanic/Latino; 5% Black or African American, non-Hispanic/Latino; 5% Asian, non-Hispanic/Latino; 0.1% Native Hawaiian or other Pacific Islander, non-Hispanic/Latino; 2% international. 4% 25 or older, 30% live on campus, 4% transferred in. Retention: 90% of full-time freshmen returned the following year. Academic areas with the most degrees conferred: health professions and related sciences; business/marketing; communication/journalism. Core. Calendar: semesters. ESL program, services for LD students, advanced placement, accelerated degree program, self-designed majors, freshman honors college, honors program, independent study, distance learning, double major, summer session for credit, part-time degree program, adult/continuing education programs, internships, graduate courses open to undergrads. Off campus study at Distance Learning for Virginia Educators (DLVE): A degree for teachers who work with hearing impaired students. Partners are: JMU, Hampton University, and Longwood University. Visual Impairment (VI): A program for teachers who work with visually impaired students. JMU and GMU partner on this program. Study abroad program. ROTC: Army, Air Force (c).
Entrance Requirements: Options: electronic application, early action, deferred admission, international baccalaureate accepted. Required: high school transcript. Recommended: minimum 3 high school GPA. Entrance: very difficult. Application deadline: 1/15. Notification: 4/1. Preference given to state residents. SAT Reasoning Test deadline: 1/15. Transfer credits accepted: Yes. Applicants placed on waiting list: 2,500. Wait-listed applicants offered admission: 225.
Costs Per Year: Application fee: $70. State resident tuition: $6620 full-time, $220 per credit hour part-time. Nonresident tuition: $23,334 full-time, $777 per credit hour part-time. Mandatory fees: $4766 full-time. College room and board: $10,092. College room only: $5220. Room and board charges vary according to board plan.

Collegiate Environment: Orientation program. Drama-theater group, choral group, marching band, student-run newspaper, radio station. Social organizations: 385 open to all; national fraternities, national sororities. Student services: health clinic, personal-psychological counseling, women's center. Campus security: 24-hour emergency response devices and patrols, student patrols, late night transport-escort service, controlled dormitory access, lighted pathways. Carrier Library plus 2 others. Students can reserve study rooms.

Community Environment: Located in the geographic center of Shenandoah Valley, Harrisonburg is an attractive city of 30,000 people. The Shenandoah National Park and the George Washington National Forest are here. All forms of commercial transportation are available. Community facilities include a number of churches, a library, hospital, and various civic and service organizations. Recreational facilities are available for camping, fishing, and picnicking. A snow skiing resort is also nearby.

■ **JEFFERSON COLLEGE OF HEALTH SCIENCES**

101 Elm Ave. SE
Roanoke, VA 24013
Tel: (540)985-8483; Free: 888-985-8483
Fax: (540)985-9773
Web Site: www.jchs.edu

Description: Independent, comprehensive, coed. Awards associate, bachelor's, master's, and doctoral degrees. Founded 1982. Setting: 1-acre urban campus. Endowment: $2.4 million. Educational spending for the previous fiscal year: $24,095 per student. Total enrollment: 1,062. 510 applied. Full-time: 666 students, 80% women, 20% men. Part-time: 134 students, 86% women, 14% men. Students come from 22 states and territories, 7% from out-of-state. 5% Hispanic/Latino; 10% Black or African American, non-Hispanic/Latino; 2% Asian, non-Hispanic/Latino; 0.3% international. 36% 25 or older, 16% live on campus, 22% transferred in. Retention: 66% of full-time freshmen returned the following year. Academic areas with the most degrees conferred: health professions and related sciences; parks and recreation; psychology. Core. Calendar: semesters. ESL program, services for LD students, advanced placement, accelerated degree program, independent study, distance learning, double major, summer session for credit, part-time degree program, adult/continuing education programs, co-op programs and internships. Off campus study.

Entrance Requirements: Options: electronic application, early action, deferred admission, international baccalaureate accepted. Required: high school transcript, minimum 2.5 high school GPA, SAT or ACT. Recommended: SAT. Required for some: interview. Entrance: moderately difficult. Application deadline: rolling. Notification: continuous. Transfer credits accepted: Yes.

Costs Per Year: Application fee: $35. Comprehensive fee: $36,380 includes full-time tuition ($26,416), mandatory fees ($450), and college room and board ($9514). Full-time tuition and fees vary according to course load. Room and board charges vary according to location. Part-time tuition: $765 per credit hour. Part-time mandatory fees: $150 per year. Part-time tuition and fees vary according to course load.

Collegiate Environment: Orientation program. Choral group, student-run newspaper. Social organizations: 5 open to all. Most popular organizations: Jefferson Activities Group (JAG), Student Ambassadors, Hands of Healing, American Medical Students Association (AMSA), Student Nurses Association. Major annual events: Organization and Wellness Day, Spirit Day, Halloween Party. Student services: personal-psychological counseling. Campus security: 24-hour emergency response devices and patrols, late night transport-escort service, controlled dormitory access. JCHS Library. Books: 4,971 (physical), 41,000 (digital/electronic); Serial titles: 99 (physical), 65 (digital/electronic); Databases: 29. 72 computers available on campus for general student use. A campuswide network can be accessed from student residence rooms. Students can access the following: online class registration. Staffed computer lab on campus provides training in use of computers, software, and the Internet.

■ **JOHN TYLER COMMUNITY COLLEGE**

13101 Jefferson Davis Hwy.
Chester, VA 23831-5316
Tel: (804)796-4000; Free: 800-552-3490
Fax: (804)796-4163
E-mail: lbaxter@jtcc.edu
Web Site: www.jtcc.edu

Description: State-supported, 2-year, coed. Part of Virginia Community College System. Awards certificates, transfer associate, and terminal associate

degrees. Founded 1967. Setting: 160-acre suburban campus with easy access to Richmond. Total enrollment: 10,144. Faculty: 420 (108 full-time, 312 part-time). Student-undergrad faculty ratio is 20:1. Full-time: 2,431 students, 55% women, 45% men. Part-time: 7,713 students, 57% women, 43% men. 3% from out-of-state. 0.4% American Indian or Alaska Native, non-Hispanic/Latino; 10% Hispanic/Latino; 22% Black or African American, non-Hispanic/Latino; 3% Asian, non-Hispanic/Latino; 0.2% Native Hawaiian or other Pacific Islander, non-Hispanic/Latino. 24% 25 or older. Core. Calendar: semesters. Academic remediation for entering students, services for LD students, advanced placement, honors program, distance learning, summer session for credit, part-time degree program, external degree program, adult/continuing education programs. Off campus study. Study abroad program. ROTC: Army (c).

Entrance Requirements: Open admission. Options: electronic application, early admission, deferred admission. Recommended: high school transcript. Entrance: noncompetitive. Application deadline: rolling. Notification: continuous. Preference given to residents of the political subdivisions supporting the College.

Costs Per Year: Application fee: $0. State resident tuition: $4650 full-time, $155 per credit hour part-time. Nonresident tuition: $9948 full-time, $331.60 per credit hour part-time. Mandatory fees: $150 full-time, $5 per credit hour part-time. Full-time tuition and fees vary according to course load. Part-time tuition and fees vary according to course load.

Collegiate Environment: Drama-theater group, choral group. Social organizations: 22 open to all. Most popular organizations: Phi Theta Kappa, Human Services Club, Future Teachers Club, Student Nurses'; Association, Student Veteran's Organization. Major annual events: Hello, JTCC, International Food Festival, Modern Makers. Campus security: 24-hour emergency response devices and patrols. College housing not available. John Tyler Community College Learning Resource and Technology Center. 2,115 computers available on campus for general student use. A campuswide network can be accessed from off-campus. Students can access the following: online class registration. Staffed computer lab on campus provides training in use of computers, software, and the Internet.

Community Environment: Located 10 miles from Richmond, the state capital, and Petersburg.

■ **LIBERTY UNIVERSITY**

1971 University Blvd.
Lynchburg, VA 24515
Tel: (434)582-2000; Free: 800-543-5317
Fax: (434)582-2304
E-mail: admissions@liberty.edu
Web Site: www.liberty.edu

Description: Independent nondenominational, comprehensive, coed. Awards associate, bachelor's, master's, and doctoral degrees and post-master's certificates (also offers external degree program with significant enrollment not reflected in profile). Founded 1971. Setting: 6,500-acre suburban campus. Total enrollment: 15,420. 12,429 applied, 53% were admitted. 25% from top 10% of their high school class, 54% from top quarter, 84% from top half. Full-time: 12,849 students, 55% women, 45% men. Part-time: 711 students, 45% women, 55% men. Students come from 52 states and territories, 84 other countries, 61% from out-of-state. 0.4% American Indian or Alaska Native, non-Hispanic/Latino; 5% Hispanic/Latino; 4% Black or African American, non-Hispanic/Latino; 2% Asian, non-Hispanic/Latino; 0.1% Native Hawaiian or other Pacific Islander, non-Hispanic/Latino; 4% international. 2% 25 or older, 58% live on campus, 11% transferred in. Retention: 85% of full-time freshmen returned the following year. Academic areas with the most degrees conferred: business/marketing; visual and performing arts; health professions and related sciences. Core. Calendar: semesters. Academic remediation for entering students, ESL program, services for LD students, advanced placement, accelerated degree program, self-designed majors, honors program, independent study, distance learning, double major, summer session for credit, part-time degree program, external degree program, co-op programs and internships, graduate courses open to undergrads. Off campus study. Study abroad program. ROTC: Army, Air Force (c).

Entrance Requirements: Options: electronic application, international baccalaureate accepted. Required: essay, high school transcript, minimum 2 high school GPA, SAT or ACT. Recommended: minimum 2 high school GPA. Entrance: minimally difficult. Application deadline: rolling. Notification: continuous. Transfer credits accepted: Yes.

Costs Per Year: Application fee: $50. Comprehensive fee: $35,446 includes

full-time tuition ($23,800), mandatory fees ($1106), and college room and board ($10,540). College room only: $6760. Part-time tuition: $815 per credit.

Collegiate Environment: Orientation program. Drama-theater group, choral group, marching band, student-run newspaper, radio station. Most popular organization: Campus Serve. Major annual events: Coffeehouse, Homecoming, Block Party. Student services: health clinic, personal-psychological counseling. Campus security: 24-hour patrols, late night transport-escort service, 24-hour emergency dispatch. 8,511 college housing spaces available; 7,434 were occupied in 2018-19. Freshmen guaranteed college housing. On-campus residence required through senior year. Options: men-only, women-only housing available. Jerry Falwell Library plus 1 other. Books: 313,657 (physical), 377,967 (digital/electronic); Serial titles: 4,323 (physical), 118,877 (digital/electronic); Databases: 512. Students can reserve study rooms. 1,640 computers available on campus for general student use. A campuswide network can be accessed from student residence rooms and from off campus. Students can access the following: online class registration. Staffed computer lab on campus provides training in use of computers, software, and the Internet.

Community Environment: Lynchburg, with a population of 67,000, is in the heart of Virginia on the south bank of the historic James River, with the scenic Blue Ridge Mountains nearby. The city is over 200 years old and is noted for its culture, beauty and educational advantages. It is at the crossroads of U.S. highways 29 and 460 and has adequate transportation facilities by bus, railway and air.

■ **LONGWOOD UNIVERSITY**
201 High St.
Farmville, VA 23909
Tel: (434)395-2000; Free: 800-281-4677
Fax: (434)395-2332
E-mail: faulkjc@longwood.edu
Web Site: www.longwood.edu

Description: State-supported, comprehensive, coed. Awards bachelor's and master's degrees and post-master's certificates. Founded 1839. Setting: 60-acre small town campus with easy access to Richmond. Endowment: $59.1 million. Research spending for the previous fiscal year: $59,010. Educational spending for the previous fiscal year: $8887 per student. Total enrollment: 4,883. Faculty: 340 (248 full-time, 92 part-time). Student-undergrad faculty ratio is 14:1. 4,873 applied, 92% were admitted. 9% from top 10% of their high school class, 29% from top quarter, 63% from top half. Full-time: 3,952 students, 67% women, 33% men. Part-time: 434 students, 62% women, 38% men. Students come from 31 states and territories, 26 other countries, 4% from out-of-state. 0.3% American Indian or Alaska Native, non-Hispanic/Latino; 5% Hispanic/Latino; 10% Black or African American, non-Hispanic/Latino; 1% Asian, non-Hispanic/Latino; 0.2% Native Hawaiian or other Pacific Islander, non-Hispanic/Latino; 2% international. 3% 25 or older, 66% live on campus, 5% transferred in. Retention: 80% of full-time freshmen returned the following year. Academic areas with the most degrees conferred: liberal arts/general studies; business/marketing; health professions and related sciences. Core. Calendar: semesters. ESL program, services for LD students, accelerated degree program, honors program, independent study, distance learning, double major, summer session for credit, internships, graduate courses open to undergrads. Off campus study at Hampden-Sydney College. Study abroad program. ROTC: Army.

Entrance Requirements: Options: electronic application, early admission, early action, deferred admission, international baccalaureate accepted. Required: essay, high school transcript, SAT or ACT. Recommended: 3 recommendations. Entrance: moderately difficult. Application deadlines: 3/1, 12/1 for early action. Notification: 6/1, 1/15 for early action. Transfer credits accepted: Yes. Applicants placed on waiting list: 18. Wait-listed applicants offered admission: 1. Early action applicants: 3,648. Early action applicants admitted: 1,945.

Costs Per Year: Application fee: $50. State resident tuition: $7940 full-time, $273 per credit hour part-time. Nonresident tuition: $23,300 full-time, $785 per credit hour part-time. Mandatory fees: $5400 full-time, $180 per credit hour part-time. Full-time tuition and fees vary according to course load and program. Part-time tuition and fees vary according to course load and program. College room and board: $11,026. College room only: $7336. Room and board charges vary according to board plan, housing facility, and location.

Collegiate Environment: Orientation program. Drama-theater group, choral group, student-run newspaper, radio station. Social organizations: 207 open to all; national fraternities, national sororities, local sororities; 14% of eligible

men and 14% of eligible women are members. Most popular organizations: Alpha Lambda Delta, Student Nursing Association, Longwood University, Bare Naked Ladies, Chi Alpha, Sigma Alpha Pi. Major annual events: Oktoberfest, Spring Weekend, Rock The Block. Student services: health clinic, personal-psychological counseling. Campus security: 24-hour emergency response devices and patrols, late night transport-escort service, controlled dormitory access. The Janet D. Greenwood Library. Books: 216,525 (physical), 333,909 (digital/electronic); Serial titles: 2,667 (physical), 403 (digital/electronic); Databases: 295. Weekly public service hours: 93. Operations spending for the previous fiscal year: $2.4 million. 291 computers available on campus for general student use. A computer is required for all students. A campuswide network can be accessed from student residence rooms.

Community Environment: Farmville is a small residential town. Bus transportation is available. Most major religious denominations are represented, and a community hospital is 5 blocks from campus. Nearby state parks provide swimming, boating, camping and hiking facilities.

■ **LORD FAIRFAX COMMUNITY COLLEGE**
173 Skirmisher Ln.
Middletown, VA 22645
Tel: (540)868-7000; Free: 800-906-LFCC
Fax: (540)868-7100
E-mail: kbucher@lfcc.edu
Web Site: www.lfcc.edu

Description: State-supported, 2-year, coed. Part of Virginia Community College System. Awards certificates, transfer associate, and terminal associate degrees. Founded 1969. Setting: 100-acre rural campus with easy access to Washington, DC. Total enrollment: 6,644. Student-undergrad faculty ratio is 22:1. 1% from out-of-state. 28% 25 or older. Retention: 60% of full-time freshmen returned the following year. Core. Calendar: semesters. Academic remediation for entering students, services for LD students, advanced placement, honors program, distance learning, summer session for credit, part-time degree program, adult/continuing education programs, co-op programs.

Entrance Requirements: Open admission. Option: early admission. Recommended: high school transcript. Entrance: noncompetitive. Application deadline: rolling. Notification: continuous.

Collegiate Environment: Drama-theater group. Student services: personal-psychological counseling, women's center. Campus security: late night transport-escort service. Learning Resources Center.

Community Environment: The area is rural and does not offer public transportation. There is medium industry and seasonal employment in the apple industry.

■ **MARY BALDWIN UNIVERSITY**
201 E Frederick St.
Staunton, VA 24401-3610
Tel: (540)887-7000; Free: 800-468-2262
Fax: (540)886-6634
E-mail: mmunsey@marybaldwin.edu
Web Site: www.marybaldwin.edu

Description: Independent, comprehensive, coed. Awards bachelor's, master's, and doctoral degrees. Founded 1842. Setting: 59-acre small town campus. Endowment: $35.1 million. Educational spending for the previous fiscal year: $8703 per student. Total enrollment: 1,654. Faculty: 235 (97 full-time, 138 part-time). Student-undergrad faculty ratio is 9:1. 1,397 applied, 95% were admitted. 18% from top 10% of their high school class, 55% from top quarter, 77% from top half. Full-time: 720 students, 95% women, 5% men. Part-time: 417 students, 88% women, 12% men. Students come from 39 states and territories, 13 other countries, 23% from out-of-state. 0.9% American Indian or Alaska Native, non-Hispanic/Latino; 7% Hispanic/Latino; 20% Black or African American, non-Hispanic/Latino; 2% Asian, non-Hispanic/Latino; 0.1% Native Hawaiian or other Pacific Islander, non-Hispanic/Latino; 2% international. 37% 25 or older, 85% live on campus, 11% transferred in. Retention: 65% of full-time freshmen returned the following year. Academic areas with the most degrees conferred: social sciences; business/marketing; health professions and related sciences. Core. Calendar: 4-1-4. Academic remediation for entering students, ESL program, services for LD students, advanced placement, accelerated degree program, self-designed majors, freshman honors college, honors program, independent study, distance learning, double major, summer session for credit, part-time degree program, external degree program, adult/continuing education programs, internships, graduate courses open to undergrads. Off campus study at Member of the Seven-College Exchange Consortium. Study abroad program. ROTC: Army (c), Naval (c), Air Force (c).

Entrance Requirements: Options: electronic application, early admission, deferred admission, international baccalaureate accepted. Required: high school transcript, SAT or ACT. Recommended: 1 recommendation. Required for some: essay, 1 recommendation, interview. Entrance: moderately difficult. Application deadline: rolling. Notification: continuous until 9/15. SAT Reasoning Test deadline: 8/25. Transfer credits accepted: Yes.

Costs Per Year: Application fee: $0. Comprehensive fee: $40,495 includes full-time tuition ($30,690), mandatory fees ($395), and college room and board ($9410). Room and board charges vary according to housing facility and student level. Part-time tuition: $460 per semester hour. Part-time mandatory fees: $60 per term. Part-time tuition and fees vary according to program.

Collegiate Environment: Orientation program. Drama-theater group, choral group, marching band. Social organizations: 49 open to all. Most popular organizations: Minority Clubs United, Greater Things Dance Ministry, MBU Cheer, Ladies of Elegance, Math Club. Major annual events: Apple Day, Signature Ball, Opening Convocation. Student services: health clinic, personal-psychological counseling. Campus security: 24-hour emergency response devices and patrols, late night transport-escort service, controlled dormitory access. Grafton Library. Books: 104,405 (physical), 367,524 (digital/electronic); Serial titles: 348 (physical), 31,879 (digital/electronic); Databases: 76. Weekly public service hours: 92; students can reserve study rooms. Operations spending for the previous fiscal year: $529,767. 247 computers available on campus for general student use. A campuswide network can be accessed from student residence rooms and from off campus. Students can access the following: online class registration. Staffed computer lab on campus provides training in use of computers, software, and the Internet.

Community Environment: Staunton, one of the oldest cities west of the Blue Ridge Mountains, originated the city manager form of government. Annual snowfall here is 16 inches. All modes of commercial transportation are available. Community facilities include a public library, YMCA, hospital, many churches, shopping areas, and civic and service organizations. Recreational activities include golf, tennis, skiing, horseback riding, bowling, swimming, fishing, and hunting. Some of the points of interest are the birthplace of Woodrow Wilson, the Old Trinity Church, and American Frontier Museum. Opportunities for part-time work are available.

■ MARYMOUNT UNIVERSITY

2807 N Glebe Rd.
Arlington, VA 22207-4299
Tel: (703)522-5600; Free: 800-548-7638
Fax: (703)522-0349
E-mail: admissions@marymount.edu
Web Site: www.marymount.edu

Description: Independent, comprehensive, coed, affiliated with Roman Catholic Church. Awards bachelor's, master's, and doctoral degrees and post-master's certificates. Founded 1950. Setting: 21-acre suburban campus with easy access to Washington, DC. Endowment: $46.3 million. Educational spending for the previous fiscal year: $12,880 per student. Total enrollment: 3,418. Faculty: 343 (166 full-time, 177 part-time). Student-undergrad faculty ratio is 13:1. 2,873 applied, 91% were admitted. 8% from top 10% of their high school class, 25% from top quarter, 61% from top half. Full-time: 2,070 students, 64% women, 36% men. Part-time: 217 students, 62% women, 38% men. Students come from 38 states and territories, 62 other countries, 40% from out-of-state. 0.3% American Indian or Alaska Native, non-Hispanic/Latino; 18% Hispanic/Latino; 14% Black or African American, non-Hispanic/Latino; 8% Asian, non-Hispanic/Latino; 0.3% Native Hawaiian or other Pacific Islander, non-Hispanic/Latino; 17% international. 19% 25 or older, 30% live on campus, 10% transferred in. Retention: 72% of full-time freshmen returned the following year. Academic areas with the most degrees conferred: health professions and related sciences; business/marketing; computer and information sciences. Core. Calendar: semesters plus 2 summer terms. Academic remediation for entering students, services for LD students, advanced placement, accelerated degree program, self-designed majors, honors program, independent study, distance learning, double major, summer session for credit, part-time degree program, internships, graduate courses open to undergrads. Off campus study at Consortium of Universities of the Washington Metropolitan Area. Study abroad program. ROTC: Army (c), Air Force (c).

Entrance Requirements: Options: electronic application, early action, deferred admission, international baccalaureate accepted. Required: high

school transcript, minimum 2.6 high school GPA, 1 recommendation. Recommended: essay. Required for some: interview, SAT or ACT. Entrance: moderately difficult. Application deadlines: rolling, 11/15 for early action. Notification: continuous, 12/14 for early action. SAT Reasoning Test deadline: 8/15. Transfer credits accepted: Yes.

Costs Per Year: Application fee: $40. One-time mandatory fee: $460. Comprehensive fee: $44,655 includes full-time tuition ($30,990), mandatory fees ($475), and college room and board ($13,190). Room and board charges vary according to board plan and housing facility. Part-time tuition: $1010 per credit hour. Part-time mandatory fees: $11 per credit hour.

Collegiate Environment: Orientation program. Drama-theater group, choral group, student-run newspaper. Social organizations: 40 open to all. Most popular organizations: Fashion Club, Student Nurses Association, International Club, Association for Campus Events, Blue Harmony (show choir). Major annual events: Portfolio in Motion Fashion Show, Snowball Winter Dance, International Week. Student services: health clinic, personal-psychological counseling. Campus security: 24-hour emergency response devices and patrols, student patrols, late night transport-escort service, controlled dormitory access. 900 college housing spaces available; 700 were occupied in 2018-19. Freshmen given priority for college housing. On-campus residence required through sophomore year. Options: coed, women-only housing available. Emerson C. Reinsch Library plus 1 other. Weekly public service hours: 104; students can reserve study rooms. Operations spending for the previous fiscal year: $3 million. 270 computers available on campus for general student use. A campuswide network can be accessed from student residence rooms and from off campus. Students can access the following: online class registration, Online drive space. Staffed computer lab on campus.

Community Environment: Located in Arlington, Virginia, just minutes from Washington, DC, Marymount provides students with an easy access to the resources of the nation's capital, including the Library of Congress, the National Archives, the Smithsonian Institution, the John F. Kennedy Center for the Performing Arts, and the Capitol. The University location offers both professional and scholarly opportunities for faculty; the opportunity to bring leaders from government, commerce, and the professions to the University campus; resources for instruction and research; internships placements for students; and employment opportunities for graduates.

■ MOUNTAIN EMPIRE COMMUNITY COLLEGE

3441 Mountain Empire Rd.
Big Stone Gap, VA 24219
Tel: (276)523-2400
Web Site: www.mecc.edu

Description: State-supported, 2-year, coed. Part of Virginia Community College System. Awards certificates, transfer associate, and terminal associate degrees. Founded 1972. Setting: rural campus. Total enrollment: 2,924. Faculty: 160 (44 full-time, 116 part-time). Students come from 9 states and territories, 4% from out-of-state. 0.3% American Indian or Alaska Native, non-Hispanic/Latino; 0.4% Hispanic/Latino; 2% Black or African American, non-Hispanic/Latino; 0.2% Asian, non-Hispanic/Latino. 28% 25 or older. Retention: 61% of full-time freshmen returned the following year. Calendar: semesters. Academic remediation for entering students, advanced placement, self-designed majors, independent study, distance learning, double major, summer session for credit, part-time degree program, external degree program, adult/continuing education programs, co-op programs and internships.

Entrance Requirements: Open admission except for nursing (RN), respiratory therapy, and health information management programs. Options: electronic application, early admission, deferred admission. Required: high school transcript. Required for some: minimum 2 high school GPA. Entrance: noncompetitive. Application deadline: rolling. Notification: continuous. Transfer credits accepted: Yes.

Collegiate Environment: Orientation program. Drama-theater group. Social organizations: 18 open to all. Most popular organizations: Phi Theta Kappa, Healing Hands, Rho Nu (SNAV), Students in Free Enterprise (SIFE), Merits. Major annual events: Spring Fling, Home Crafts Day, Pro-Art. Student services: personal-psychological counseling. Campus security: 24-hour emergency response devices and patrols. Wampler Library. 400 computers available on campus for general student use. A campuswide network can be accessed from off-campus. Students can access the following: online class registration. Staffed computer lab on campus provides training in use of computers and software.

Community Environment: Big Stone Gap is a rural community in the southwest corner of Virginia, situated in the Cumberland Mountains. It has a population of 5,854. Many state parks and recreational areas are within an easy drive of the campus. Kingsport, Tennessee is approximately 30 miles south of the campus.

■ **NEW RIVER COMMUNITY COLLEGE**
5251 College Dr.
Dublin, VA 24084
Tel: (540)674-3600; Free: 866-462-6722
Fax: (540)674-3644
E-mail: tsmith@nr.edu
Web Site: www.nr.edu
Description: State-supported, 2-year, coed. Part of Virginia Community College System. Awards certificates, diplomas, transfer associate, and terminal associate degrees. Founded 1969. Setting: 100-acre rural campus. Total enrollment: 4,400. Calendar: semesters. Academic remediation for entering students, services for LD students, advanced placement, independent study, distance learning, double major, summer session for credit, part-time degree program, adult/continuing education programs, co-op programs and internships.
Entrance Requirements: Open admission. Options: electronic application, early admission, international baccalaureate accepted. Recommended: high school transcript. Required for some: high school transcript. Entrance: noncompetitive. Application deadline: rolling. Notification: continuous. Transfer credits accepted: Yes.
Collegiate Environment: Orientation program. Most popular organizations: Phi Theta Kappa, Phi Beta Lambda, NRCC Computer Club. Campus security: 24-hour patrols. New River Community College Library plus 1 other.

■ **NORFOLK STATE UNIVERSITY**
700 Park Ave.
Norfolk, VA 23504
Tel: (757)823-8600; Free: 800-274-1821
Fax: (757)823-9435
E-mail: admissions@nsu.edu
Web Site: www.nsu.edu
Description: State-supported, comprehensive, coed. Part of State Council of Higher Education for Virginia. Awards associate, bachelor's, master's, and doctoral degrees. Founded 1935. Setting: 134-acre urban campus. Total enrollment: 6,027. 2,817 applied, 67% were admitted. Full-time: 4,416 students, 62% women, 38% men. Part-time: 940 students, 71% women, 29% men. 14% from out-of-state. 0.2% American Indian or Alaska Native, non-Hispanic/Latino; 3% Hispanic/Latino; 83% Black or African American, non-Hispanic/Latino; 0.5% Asian, non-Hispanic/Latino; 0.2% Native Hawaiian or other Pacific Islander, non-Hispanic/Latino; 0.4% international. 28% 25 or older, 38% live on campus, 8% transferred in. Academic areas with the most degrees conferred: construction trades; business/marketing; social sciences. Calendar: semesters. ROTC: Army, Naval.
Entrance Requirements: Options: electronic application, deferred admission. Required: high school transcript, minimum 2.3 high school GPA, SAT or ACT. Entrance: moderately difficult.
Costs Per Year: State resident tuition: $5752 full-time, $431 per credit hour part-time. Nonresident tuition: $16,920 full-time, $939 per credit hour part-time. Mandatory fees: $3738 full-time. Full-time tuition and fees vary according to course load. Part-time tuition varies according to course load. College room and board: $10,360. College room only: $6862. Room and board charges vary according to board plan and housing facility.
Collegiate Environment: Orientation program. Campus security: 24-hour emergency response devices and patrols, late night transport-escort service. Lymon Beecher Brooks Library.
Community Environment: See Old Dominion University.

■ **NORTHERN VIRGINIA COMMUNITY COLLEGE**
8333 Little River Tpke.
Annandale, VA 22003
Tel: (703)323-3000
Web Site: www.nvcc.edu
Description: State-supported, 2-year, coed. Part of Virginia Community College System. Awards certificates, transfer associate, and terminal associate degrees. Founded 1965. Setting: 435-acre suburban campus with easy access to Washington, DC. Total enrollment: 76,868. Faculty: 2,657 (719 full-time, 1,938 part-time). 3% from out-of-state. 42% 25 or older. Core. Calendar: semesters. Academic remediation for entering students, ESL program, services for LD students, advanced placement, honors program, distance learning, double major, summer session for credit, part-time degree

program, external degree program, adult/continuing education programs, co-op programs. Study abroad program.
Entrance Requirements: Open admission except for veterinary technology, dental hygiene, other health-related programs. Options: early admission, deferred admission. Required for some: high school transcript. Application deadline: rolling. Notification: continuous.
Collegiate Environment: Student-run newspaper. Campus security: 24-hour emergency response devices, campus police.
Community Environment: Northern Virginia Community College is a five campus college located in the suburban communities of Northern Virginia, just outside Washington, D.C. The Northern Virginia region is rapidly growing, provides excellent job opportunities and has high quality public schools and community services. Part-time job opportunities are excellent for students and graduates of the occupational and technical programs and career placements attractive. Students seeking transfer to a university to earn a Bachelor's degree can enroll in appropriate programs that parallel most university programs.

■ **OLD DOMINION UNIVERSITY**
5115 Hampton Blvd.
Norfolk, VA 23529
Tel: (757)683-3000; Free: 800-348-7926
Fax: (757)683-5357
E-mail: admissions@odu.edu
Web Site: www.odu.edu
Description: State-supported, university, coed. Awards bachelor's, master's, and doctoral degrees and post-master's certificates. Founded 1930. Setting: 251-acre urban campus with easy access to Virginia Beach. Endowment: $249.7 million. Research spending for the previous fiscal year: $50.9 million. Educational spending for the previous fiscal year: $8557 per student. Total enrollment: 24,176. Faculty: 1,559 (853 full-time, 706 part-time). Student-undergrad faculty ratio is 18:1. 13,335 applied, 87% were admitted. 9% from top 10% of their high school class, 30% from top quarter, 71% from top half. Full-time: 15,003 students, 55% women, 45% men. Part-time: 4,369 students, 57% women, 43% men. Students come from 50 states and territories, 88 other countries, 8% from out-of-state. 0.3% American Indian or Alaska Native, non-Hispanic/Latino; 9% Hispanic/Latino; 31% Black or African American, non-Hispanic/Latino; 5% Asian, non-Hispanic/Latino; 0.3% Native Hawaiian or other Pacific Islander, non-Hispanic/Latino; 1% international. 26% 25 or older, 25% live on campus, 10% transferred in. Retention: 79% of full-time freshmen returned the following year. Academic areas with the most degrees conferred: health professions and related sciences; business/marketing; social sciences. Core. Calendar: semesters. ROTC: Army, Naval.
Entrance Requirements: Options: electronic application, early admission, early action, deferred admission, international baccalaureate accepted. Required: high school transcript, minimum 2.7 high school GPA. Recommended: essay, 1 recommendation. Required for some: SAT or ACT. Entrance: moderately difficult. Application deadlines: 2/1, 12/1 for early action. Notification: continuous, 1/15 for early action. SAT Reasoning Test deadline: 5/1. SAT Subject Test deadline: 6/1. Transfer credits accepted: Yes. Applicants placed on waiting list: 1,079. Wait-listed applicants offered admission: 261. Early action applicants: 6,988. Early action applicants admitted: 5,806.
Costs Per Year: Application fee: $50. State resident tuition: $10,872 full-time, $352 per credit hour part-time. Nonresident tuition: $29,772 full-time, $982 per credit hour part-time. Mandatory fees: $312 full-time, $66 per term part-time. Full-time tuition and fees vary according to location. Part-time tuition and fees vary according to location. College room and board: $12,338. College room only: $7248. Room and board charges vary according to board plan, housing facility, location, and student level.
Collegiate Environment: Drama-theater group, choral group, marching band, student-run newspaper, radio station. Social organizations: 291 open to all; national fraternities, national sororities; 8% of eligible men and 5% of eligible women are members. Most popular organizations: Asian Pacific American Student Union, Student Government Association, Student Veterans Association, Colleges Against Cancer, Student Activities Council. Major annual events: Homecoming, Exam Jam, Relay for Life. Student services: health clinic, personal-psychological counseling, women's center. Campus security: 24-hour emergency response devices and patrols, student patrols, late night transport-escort service, controlled dormitory access. 4,830 college housing spaces available; 4,822 were occupied in 2018-19. Freshmen guaranteed college housing. Options: coed, women-only housing available. Patricia W. and Douglas Perry Library plus 3 others. Books: 1 mil-

lion (physical), 1.5 million (digital/electronic); Serial titles: 19,020 (physical), 110,572 (digital/electronic); Databases: 550. Weekly public service hours: 146; study areas open 24 hours, 5-7 days a week; students can reserve study rooms. Operations spending for the previous fiscal year: $9.5 million. 2,030 computers available on campus for general student use. A campus-wide network can be accessed from student residence rooms and from off campus. Students can access the following: online class registration, online courses. Staffed computer lab on campus (open 24 hours a day) provides training in use of computers, software, and the Internet.

Community Environment: See Virginia Wesleyan College.

■ **PATRICK HENRY COLLEGE**
Ten Patrick Henry Cir.
Purcellville, VA 20132
Tel: (540)338-1776; Free: 888-338-1776
Fax: (540)338-8707
E-mail: admissions@phc.edu
Web Site: www.phc.edu

Description: Independent nondenominational, 4-year, coed. Awards bachelor's degrees. Founded 2000. Setting: 119-acre small town campus with easy access to Washington, DC. Endowment: $1.2 million. Educational spending for the previous fiscal year: $15,230 per student. Total enrollment: 277. Faculty: 41 (19 full-time, 22 part-time). Student-undergrad faculty ratio is 10:1. 227 applied, 95% were admitted. Full-time: 245 students, 47% women, 53% men. Part-time: 32 students, 44% women, 56% men. Students come from 35 states and territories, 80% from out-of-state. 5% Hispanic/Latino; 0.4% Black or African American, non-Hispanic/Latino; 3% Asian, non-Hispanic/Latino; 0.4% Native Hawaiian or other Pacific Islander, non-Hispanic/Latino. 3% 25 or older, 83% live on campus, 3% transferred in. Retention: 83% of full-time freshmen returned the following year. Academic areas with the most degrees conferred: social sciences; liberal arts/general studies; communication/journalism. Core. Calendar: semesters. Advanced placement, independent study, distance learning, double major, summer session for credit, co-op programs and internships. Off campus study.

Entrance Requirements: Options: electronic application, early action, deferred admission. Required: essay, high school transcript, 2 recommendations, interview, official transcripts from all colleges attended, reading list, SAT or ACT. Entrance: moderately difficult. Application deadlines: 6/15, 11/1 for early action. Notification: continuous, rolling for early action. SAT Reasoning Test deadline: 6/15.

Collegiate Environment: Orientation program. Drama-theater group, choral group, student-run newspaper. Social organizations: 16 open to all. Most popular organizations: Drama Club, Eden Troupe, Student Government, Chorale, College Republicans, Debate/Moot Court. Major annual events: Homecoming, Harmonic Comedy, Eden Troupe productions. Student services: health clinic, personal-psychological counseling. Campus security: 24-hour emergency response devices and patrols, student patrols, late night transport-escort service, controlled dormitory access, after hours patrols by trained security personnel. Patrick Henry College Library. Books: 38,995 (physical), 387,798 (digital/electronic); Serial titles: 240 (physical), 42,361 (digital/electronic); Databases: 33. Weekly public service hours: 80; students can reserve study rooms. Operations spending for the previous fiscal year: $817,747. 10 computers available on campus for general student use. Computer purchase/lease plans available. A computer is required for all students. A campuswide network can be accessed from student residence rooms and from off campus. Students can access the following: online class registration.

■ **PATRICK HENRY COMMUNITY COLLEGE**
645 Patriot Ave.
Martinsville, VA 24112
Tel: (276)638-8777
Fax: (276)656-0247
Web Site: www.patrickhenry.edu

Description: State-supported, 2-year, coed. Part of Virginia Community College System. Awards certificates, transfer associate, and terminal associate degrees. Founded 1962. Setting: 137-acre rural campus with easy access to Greensboro. Endowment: $10.6 million. Total enrollment: 2,405. Faculty: 237 (55 full-time, 182 part-time). Student-undergrad faculty ratio is 20:1. Full-time: 1,214 students, 56% women, 44% men. Part-time: 1,191 students, 61% women, 39% men. Students come from 6 states and territories, 1% from out-of-state. 0.1% American Indian or Alaska Native, non-Hispanic/Latino; 7% Hispanic/Latino; 19% Black or African American, non-Hispanic/Latino; 0.8% Asian, non-Hispanic/Latino; 0.4% international. 26% 25 or

older. Retention: 65% of full-time freshmen returned the following year. Calendar: semesters. Academic remediation for entering students, services for LD students, advanced placement, independent study, distance learning, summer session for credit, part-time degree program, adult/continuing education programs, co-op programs and internships.

Entrance Requirements: Open admission except for nursing program. Options: electronic application, early admission. Required: high school transcript. Entrance: noncompetitive. Application deadline: rolling. Notification: continuous. Transfer credits accepted: Yes.

Collegiate Environment: Orientation program. Drama-theater group. Most popular organizations: Student Government Association, Student Support Services, Phi Theta Kappa, Multi Cutural, Cross Cultural Club. Major annual events: Fall Festival, Spring Play Day, Awards Banquet. Student services: personal-psychological counseling. Campus security: 24-hour emergency response devices and patrols, late night transport-escort service. Lester Library. Books: 25,464 (physical), 197,427 (digital/electronic); Serial titles: 174 (physical), 73,546 (digital/electronic); Databases: 190. Operations spending for the previous fiscal year: $134,855. 804 computers available on campus for general student use. Computer purchase/lease plans available. A campuswide network can be accessed from off-campus. Students can access the following: online class registration. Staffed computer lab on campus provides training in use of computers, software, and the Internet.

Community Environment: Martinsville is an important textile and furniture market as well as an industrial city with a wide range of products. It provides all forms of commercial transportation. Job opportunities are excellent and shopping is good. Philpott Reservoir, about 19 miles northwest of Martinsville, is a popular spot for fishing, boating, water skiing, and swimming. Other facilities within the city provide for swimming, baseball, and football.

■ **PAUL D. CAMP COMMUNITY COLLEGE**
PO Box 737, 100 N College Dr.
Franklin, VA 23851-0737
Tel: (757)569-6700
E-mail: tjones@pdc.edu
Web Site: www.pdc.edu

Description: State-supported, 2-year, coed. Part of Virginia Community College System. Awards certificates, transfer associate, and terminal associate degrees. Founded 1971. Setting: 99-acre small town campus. Endowment: $500,000. Total enrollment: 1,579. Faculty: 161 (18 full-time, 143 part-time). Student-undergrad faculty ratio is 16:1. 597 applied, 100% were admitted. 5% from top 10% of their high school class, 20% from top quarter, 45% from top half. Students come from 2 states and territories, 2 other countries, 1% from out-of-state. 38% Black or African American, non-Hispanic/Latino. 40% 25 or older. Retention: 66% of full-time freshmen returned the following year. Core. Calendar: semesters. Academic remediation for entering students, advanced placement, honors program, independent study, distance learning, summer session for credit, part-time degree program, adult/continuing education programs, co-op programs and internships. Off campus study at members of the Virginia Consortium for Continuing Higher Education.

Entrance Requirements: Open admission. Options: electronic application, deferred admission. Required: high school transcript. Entrance: noncompetitive. Application deadline: rolling. Notification: continuous. Preference given to state residents. Transfer credits accepted: Yes.

Collegiate Environment: Student-run newspaper. Most popular organizations: African-American History Club, Phi Beta Lambda, Phi Theta Kappa, Student Government Association, student newspaper. Campus security: late night transport-escort service. Paul D. Camp Community College Library. Operations spending for the previous fiscal year: $258,883. 298 computers available on campus for general student use. A campuswide network can be accessed. Students can access the following: online class registration. Staffed computer lab on campus provides training in use of computers, software, and the Internet.

Community Environment: Franklin is in a rural setting with a population of 8,594.

■ **PIEDMONT VIRGINIA COMMUNITY COLLEGE**
501 College Dr.
Charlottesville, VA 22902
Tel: (434)977-3900
Fax: (434)971-8232
E-mail: mwalsh@pvcc.edu
Web Site: www.pvcc.edu

Description: State-supported, 2-year, coed. Part of Virginia Community College System. Awards certificates, transfer associate, and terminal associate degrees. Founded 1972. Setting: 114-acre suburban campus with easy access to Richmond. Endowment: $6.8 million. Educational spending for the previous fiscal year: $4656 per student. Total enrollment: 5,608. 0.3% American Indian or Alaska Native, non-Hispanic/Latino; 7% Hispanic/Latino; 13% Black or African American, non-Hispanic/Latino; 5% Asian, non-Hispanic/Latino; 0.2% Native Hawaiian or other Pacific Islander, non-Hispanic/Latino. Core. Calendar: semesters. Academic remediation for entering students, ESL program, services for LD students, advanced placement, honors program, independent study, distance learning, summer session for credit, part-time degree program, adult/continuing education programs, co-op programs and internships. ROTC: Army (c), Air Force (c).

Entrance Requirements: Open admission except for certain health and life sciences programs. Options: electronic application, early admission, deferred admission. Required for some: high school transcript, prerequisite courses for nursing, practical nursing, radiography, sonography, surgical technology, emergency medical services, health information management, and patient admissions coordination. Entrance: noncompetitive. Application deadline: rolling. Notification: continuous. Transfer credits accepted: Yes.

Costs Per Year: Application fee: $0. State resident tuition: $4650 full-time, $155 per credit hour part-time. Nonresident tuition: $9948 full-time, $331.60 per credit hour part-time. Mandatory fees: $140 full-time. Full-time tuition and fees vary according to course load. Part-time tuition varies according to course load.

Collegiate Environment: Orientation program. Drama-theater group, choral group, student-run newspaper. Major annual events: plays and concerts, fall/spring picnics. Campus security: 24-hour emergency response devices and patrols, late night transport-escort service, establishment of Campus Police. Jessup Library.

Community Environment: Charlottesville is situated in the foothills of the Blue Ridge Mountains. The area has many old homes and estates. Albemarle County is renown for its horses, dogs and fruit orchards. Outdoor activities available include: golf, tennis, hunting, fishing and hiking. Points of interest are the Lewis and Clark Memorial, Monticello, and the University of Virginia. Commercial transportation and part-time employment are available.

■ RADFORD UNIVERSITY

801 E Main St.
Radford, VA 24142
Tel: (540)831-5000
Fax: (540)831-5138
E-mail: admissions@radford.edu
Web Site: www.radford.edu

Description: State-supported, university, coed. Awards bachelor's, master's, and doctoral degrees and post-master's certificates. Founded 1910. Setting: 204-acre small town campus. Endowment: $50.3 million. Research spending for the previous fiscal year: $706,863. Educational spending for the previous fiscal year: $9019 per student. Total enrollment: 9,335. Faculty: 737 (463 full-time, 274 part-time). Student-undergrad faculty ratio is 16:1. 14,161 applied, 75% were admitted. 5% from top 10% of their high school class, 16% from top quarter, 49% from top half. Full-time: 7,556 students, 58% women, 42% men. Part-time: 370 students, 47% women, 53% men. Students come from 41 states and territories, 62 other countries, 6% from out-of-state. 0.3% American Indian or Alaska Native, non-Hispanic/Latino; 7% Hispanic/Latino; 17% Black or African American, non-Hispanic/Latino; 2% Asian, non-Hispanic/Latino; 0.1% Native Hawaiian or other Pacific Islander, non-Hispanic/Latino; 1% international. 6% 25 or older, 41% live on campus, 7% transferred in. Retention: 71% of full-time freshmen returned the following year. Academic areas with the most degrees conferred: business/marketing; interdisciplinary studies; psychology. Core. Calendar: semesters. ESL program, services for LD students, advanced placement, accelerated degree program, self-designed majors, honors program, independent study, distance learning, double major, summer session for credit, part-time degree program, internships, graduate courses open to undergrads. Off campus study. Study abroad program. ROTC: Army.

Entrance Requirements: Options: electronic application, early admission, early action, deferred admission, international baccalaureate accepted. Required: high school transcript. Recommended: SAT or ACT. Entrance: minimally difficult. Application deadlines: 2/1, 12/1 for early action. Notification: 4/1, 1/15 for early action. SAT Reasoning Test deadline: 4/1. Transfer credits accepted: Yes. Applicants placed on waiting list: 542. Wait-listed applicants offered admission: 313. Early action applicants: 10,161. Early action applicants admitted: 8,122.

Costs Per Year: Application fee: $0. State resident tuition: $7922 full-time,

$329 per credit hour part-time. Nonresident tuition: $19,557 full-time, $814 per credit hour part-time. Mandatory fees: $3288 full-time, $138 per credit hour part-time. Full-time tuition and fees vary according to course load. Part-time tuition and fees vary according to course load. College room and board: $9406. College room only: $5177. Room and board charges vary according to board plan and housing facility.

Collegiate Environment: Orientation program. Drama-theater group, choral group, student-run newspaper, radio station. Social organizations: 250 open to all; national fraternities, national sororities; 11% of eligible men and 10% of eligible women are members. Most popular organizations: Radford Crafty, American Sign Language Club, Radford Student Programming and Campus Events (R-SPaCE), National Society for Collegiate Scholars, Scholar-Citizen Initiative Student Organization. Major annual events: Club Fair, Be S.E.E.N. (Be Successful Through Engagement and Education Now), Radford After Dark Programs. Student services: health clinic, personal-psychological counseling. Campus security: 24-hour emergency response devices and patrols, late night transport-escort service, controlled dormitory access. College housing designed to accommodate 3,156 students; 3,476 undergraduates lived in college housing during 2018-19. Freshmen guaranteed college housing. On-campus residence required through sophomore year. Option: coed housing available. McConnell Library. Books: 271,383 (physical), 332,165 (digital/electronic); Serial titles: 558 (physical), 28,298 (digital/electronic); Databases: 535. Students can reserve study rooms. Operations spending for the previous fiscal year: $4 million. 900 computers available on campus for general student use. Computer purchase/lease plans available. A campuswide network can be accessed from student residence rooms and from off campus. Students can access the following: online class registration, online financial aid status and student accounts payable. Staffed computer lab on campus (open 24 hours a day) provides training in use of computers, software, and the Internet.

Community Environment: Located on the banks of the scenic New River in the foothills of the beautiful Blue Ridge Mountains, the city of Radford, Virginia (population 14,500), is 45 miles southwest of Roanoke. First settled in 1756, the city features a number of churches, a public library, hospital, and many civic and service organizations. The city is clean and the weather is moderate. Outdoor sports enthusiasts can enjoy nearby Claytor Lake, the New River, the Appalachian Trail and many other streams, lakes and trails in close proximity.

■ RANDOLPH COLLEGE

2500 Rivermont Ave.
Lynchburg, VA 24503
Tel: (434)947-8000; Free: 800-745-7692
Fax: (434)947-8996
E-mail: admissions@randolphcollege.edu
Web Site: www.randolphcollege.edu

Description: Independent Methodist, comprehensive, coed. Awards bachelor's and master's degrees. Founded 1891. Setting: 100-acre suburban campus. Total enrollment: 626. Faculty: 69 (68 full-time, 1 part-time). Student-undergrad faculty ratio is 9:1. 1,576 applied, 87% were admitted. 12% from top 10% of their high school class, 33% from top quarter, 70% from top half. Full-time: 586 students, 63% women, 37% men. Part-time: 14 students, 57% women, 43% men. 23% from out-of-state. 7% Hispanic/Latino; 16% Black or African American, non-Hispanic/Latino; 3% Asian, non-Hispanic/Latino; 0.2% Native Hawaiian or other Pacific Islander, non-Hispanic/Latino; 3% international. 3% 25 or older, 77% live on campus, 6% transferred in. Retention: 65% of full-time freshmen returned the following year. Academic areas with the most degrees conferred: social sciences; biological/life sciences; visual and performing arts. Calendar: semesters. Part-time degree program, adult/continuing education programs.

Entrance Requirements: Options: electronic application, early admission, early action, deferred admission, international baccalaureate accepted. Required: essay, high school transcript, 2 recommendations, SAT or ACT. Recommended: interview. Entrance: moderately difficult. Transfer credits accepted: Yes.

Costs Per Year: Application fee: $0. Comprehensive fee: $54,711 includes full-time tuition ($40,521), mandatory fees ($610), and college room and board ($13,580). Part-time tuition: $1625 per credit hour.

Collegiate Environment: Orientation program. Campus security: 24-hour emergency response devices and patrols, late night transport-escort service. Freshmen guaranteed college housing. On-campus residence required through senior year. Option: coed housing available. Lipscomb Library.

■ RANDOLPH-MACON COLLEGE

PO Box 5005
Ashland, VA 23005-5505
Tel: (804)752-7200; Free: 800-888-1762
Fax: (804)752-4707
E-mail: admissions@rmc.edu
Web Site: www.rmc.edu

Description: Independent United Methodist, 4-year, coed. Awards bachelor's degrees. Founded 1830. Setting: 124-acre suburban campus with easy access to Richmond. Endowment: $166.2 million. Total enrollment: 1,488. Faculty: 172 (111 full-time, 61 part-time). Student-undergrad faculty ratio is 11:1. 2,907 applied, 67% were admitted. 15% from top 10% of their high school class, 40% from top quarter, 73% from top half. Full-time: 1,464 students, 53% women, 47% men. Part-time: 24 students, 46% women, 54% men. Students come from 30 states and territories, 28 other countries, 22% from out-of-state. 0.5% American Indian or Alaska Native, non-Hispanic/Latino; 4% Hispanic/Latino; 10% Black or African American, non-Hispanic/Latino; 1% Asian, non-Hispanic/Latino; 0.2% Native Hawaiian or other Pacific Islander, non-Hispanic/Latino; 2% international. 1% 25 or older, 83% live on campus, 3% transferred in. Retention: 86% of full-time freshmen returned the following year. Academic areas with the most degrees conferred: social sciences; business/marketing; biological/life sciences. Core. Calendar: 4-1-4. Academic remediation for entering students, services for LD students, advanced placement, accelerated degree program, honors program, independent study, double major, summer session for credit, part-time degree program, internships. Off campus study at member of the Seven-College Exchange Program. Study abroad program. ROTC: Army (c).

Entrance Requirements: Options: electronic application, early admission, early action, deferred admission, international baccalaureate accepted. Required: essay, high school transcript, minimum 2 high school GPA, 1 recommendation, SAT or ACT. Recommended: interview, SAT Subject Tests. Entrance: moderately difficult. Application deadlines: 3/1, 11/15 for early action. Notification: 4/1. SAT Reasoning Test deadline: 3/1. SAT Subject Test deadline: 6/1. Transfer credits accepted: Yes. Applicants placed on waiting list: 108. Wait-listed applicants offered admission: 11. Early action applicants: 1,304. Early action applicants admitted: 241.

Costs Per Year: Application fee: $0. One-time mandatory fee: $100. Comprehensive fee: $54,770 includes full-time tuition ($41,200), mandatory fees ($1350), and college room and board ($12,220). College room only: $6800. Part-time tuition: $4450 per course. Part-time mandatory fees: $110 per credit hour.

Collegiate Environment: Orientation program. Drama-theater group, choral group, marching band, student-run newspaper, radio station. Social organizations: 81 open to all; national fraternities, national sororities; 29% of eligible men and 25% of eligible women are members. Most popular organizations: Habitat for Humanity, Macon Outdoors, Relay for Life, College Panhellenic Council, R-MC Angler's Club. Major annual events: The EDGE Boot Camp, Macon a Difference Day, Camptown. Student services: health clinic, personal-psychological counseling, women's center. Campus security: 24-hour emergency response devices and patrols, late night transport-escort service, controlled dormitory access. 1,235 college housing spaces available; 1,232 were occupied in 2018-19. Freshmen guaranteed college housing. On-campus residence required through junior year. Options: coed, men-only, women-only housing available. McGraw-Page Library. Books: 129,311 (physical), 457,041 (digital/electronic); Serial titles: 430 (physical), 144,340 (digital/electronic); Databases: 148. Study areas open 24 hours, 5-7 days a week; students can reserve study rooms. Operations spending for the previous fiscal year: $1.1 million. 345 computers available on campus for general student use. Computer purchase/lease plans available. A campuswide network can be accessed from student residence rooms and from off campus. Students can access the following: online class registration. Staffed computer lab on campus (open 24 hours a day) provides training in use of computers, software, and the Internet.

Community Environment: Ashland is a suburban area 15 miles from Richmond, and 90 miles south of Washington DC. Community facilities include a public library, six churches, 2 medical centers, and a number of civic and service organizations.

■ RAPPAHANNOCK COMMUNITY COLLEGE

12745 College Dr.
Glenns, VA 23149-2616
Tel: (804)758-6700; Free: 800-836-9381
Fax: (804)758-3852
Web Site: www.rappahannock.edu

Description: State and locally supported, 2-year, coed. Part of Virginia Community College System. Awards certificates, transfer associate, and terminal associate degrees. Founded 1970. Setting: rural campus. Total enrollment: 3,463. Calendar: semesters. Academic remediation for entering students, services for LD students, honors program, distance learning, summer session for credit, part-time degree program, adult/continuing education programs, internships. Off campus study.

Entrance Requirements: Open admission except for ADN and practical nursing programs. Options: electronic application, early admission. Entrance: noncompetitive. Application deadline: rolling. Notification: continuous.

Costs Per Year: Application fee: $0. State resident tuition: $4620 full-time, $154 per credit hour part-time. Nonresident tuition: $9918 full-time, $330.60 per credit hour part-time. Mandatory fees: $200 full-time, $6.65 per credit hour part-time. Full-time tuition and fees vary according to course load. Part-time tuition and fees vary according to course load.

Collegiate Environment: Orientation program. Student services: personal-psychological counseling.

Community Environment: Glenns is centrally located in the Rappahannock River Tidewaters serving a 13-county region.

■ REGENT UNIVERSITY

1000 Regent University Dr.
Virginia Beach, VA 23464-9800
Tel: (757)352-4127; Free: 800-373-5504
E-mail: admissions@regent.edu
Web Site: www.regent.edu

Description: Independent Christian, comprehensive, coed. Awards associate, bachelor's, master's, and doctoral degrees and post-master's certificates. Founded 1977. Setting: 70-acre suburban campus. Endowment: $80.2 million. Research spending for the previous fiscal year: $246,765. Educational spending for the previous fiscal year: $1901 per student. Total enrollment: 11,271. Faculty: 907 (145 full-time, 762 part-time). Student-undergrad faculty ratio is 21:1. 2,854 applied, 84% were admitted. 11% from top 10% of their high school class, 40% from top quarter, 64% from top half. Full-time: 2,402 students, 61% women, 39% men. Part-time: 2,244 students, 64% women, 36% men. Students come from 50 states and territories, 19 other countries, 58% from out-of-state. 0.5% American Indian or Alaska Native, non-Hispanic/Latino; 9% Hispanic/Latino; 27% Black or African American, non-Hispanic/Latino; 1% Asian, non-Hispanic/Latino; 0.4% Native Hawaiian or other Pacific Islander, non-Hispanic/Latino; 0.6% international. 61% 25 or older, 15% live on campus, 20% transferred in. Retention: 77% of full-time freshmen returned the following year. Academic areas with the most degrees conferred: business/marketing; communication/journalism; psychology; theology and religious vocations. Core. Calendar: trimesters. Academic remediation for entering students, services for LD students, advanced placement, freshman honors college, honors program, distance learning, double major, summer session for credit, part-time degree program, external degree program, adult/continuing education programs, internships, graduate courses open to undergrads. Off campus study at Virginia Tidewater Consortium for Higher Education (VTC). Study abroad program. ROTC: Army (c), Naval (c).

Entrance Requirements: Options: electronic application, deferred admission, international baccalaureate accepted. Required: high school transcript. Required for some: essay, minimum 3 high school GPA, SAT or ACT. Entrance: minimally difficult. Application deadlines: rolling, rolling for nonresidents. Notification: continuous, continuous for nonresidents. SAT Reasoning Test deadline: 8/1. Transfer credits accepted: Yes.

Costs Per Year: Application fee: $50. Comprehensive fee: $26,360 includes full-time tuition ($17,880), mandatory fees ($1400), and college room and board ($7080). College room only: $4560. Part-time tuition: $596 per credit hour.

Collegiate Environment: Orientation program. Drama-theater group, choral group, student-run newspaper. Social organizations: 55 open to all; national fraternities, national sororities, local fraternities. Most popular organizations: College Student Leadership Board, Student Activities Board, Psychology Club, Student Alumni Ambassadors (SAA), Undergraduate Debate Association. Major annual events: Back to School BBQ, Harvest Festival, Christmas Ball. Student services: personal-psychological counseling. Campus security: 24-hour emergency response devices and patrols, student patrols, late night transport-escort service, controlled dormitory access. 611 undergraduates lived in college housing during 2018-19. Freshmen given priority for college housing. On-campus residence required in freshman year. Options: men-only, women-only housing available. Regent University Library plus 1 other.

Books: 314,660 (physical), 531,636 (digital/electronic); Serial titles: 97 (physical), 95,377 (digital/electronic); Databases: 159. Weekly public service hours: 99; students can reserve study rooms. Operations spending for the previous fiscal year: $1.2 million. 70 computers available on campus for general student use. A campuswide network can be accessed from student residence rooms and from off campus. Students can access the following: online class registration. Staffed computer lab on campus provides training in use of computers, software, and the Internet.

■ RICHARD BLAND COLLEGE OF THE COLLEGE OF WILLIAM AND MARY

8311 Halifax Rd.
Petersburg, VA 23805
Tel: (804)862-6100
Fax: (804)862-6189
E-mail: apply@rbc.edu
Web Site: www.rbc.edu

Description: State-supported, 2-year, coed. Administratively affiliated with College of William and Mary. Awards transfer associate degrees. Founded 1961. Setting: 712-acre rural campus with easy access to Richmond. Total enrollment: 1,634. Faculty: 71 (33 full-time, 38 part-time). Student-undergrad faculty ratio is 25:1. 897 applied, 89% were admitted. 6% from top 10% of their high school class, 20% from top quarter, 48% from top half. Full-time: 1,038 students, 62% women, 38% men. Part-time: 596 students, 67% women, 33% men. Students come from 5 states and territories, 2 other countries, 1% from out-of-state. 11% 25 or older, 6% transferred in. Retention: 59% of full-time freshmen returned the following year. Core. Calendar: semesters. Academic remediation for entering students, services for LD students, advanced placement, accelerated degree program, summer session for credit, part-time degree program. ROTC: Army (c).

Entrance Requirements: Option: electronic application. Required: essay, high school transcript, minimum 2 high school GPA, in-state residency form. Recommended: SAT or ACT. Required for some: interview. Entrance: minimally difficult. Application deadline: 8/15. Notification: continuous.

Collegiate Environment: Orientation program. Drama-theater group, choral group, student-run newspaper. Social organizations: 20 open to all. Most popular organizations: RBC Newspaper, Student Ambassadors, Student Government, Spanish Club, Biology Club. Major annual events: Fall Orientation, International Forum. Campus security: 24-hour emergency response devices and patrols, controlled dormitory access, full-time dedicated Campus Police Force. Richard Bland College Library. 130 computers available on campus for general student use. A campuswide network can be accessed from student residence rooms and from off campus. Students can access the following: online class registration. Staffed computer lab on campus provides training in use of computers, software, and the Internet.

■ RIVERSIDE COLLEGE OF HEALTH CAREERS

316 Main St.
Newport News, VA 23601
Tel: (757)240-2200
Web Site: www.riverside.edu

Description: Independent, 2-year, coed. Awards certificates, transfer associate, and terminal associate degrees.

■ ROANOKE COLLEGE

221 College Ln.
Salem, VA 24153-3794
Tel: (540)375-2500; Free: 800-388-2276
Fax: (540)375-2267
Web Site: www.roanoke.edu

Description: Independent, 4-year, coed, affiliated with Evangelical Lutheran Church in America. Awards bachelor's degrees. Founded 1842. Setting: 80-acre suburban campus. Endowment: $152.6 million. Research spending for the previous fiscal year: $310,073. Educational spending for the previous fiscal year: $10,464 per student. Total enrollment: 2,017. Faculty: 220 (168 full-time, 52 part-time). Student-undergrad faculty ratio is 11:1. 5,122 applied, 72% were admitted. 18% from top 10% of their high school class, 41% from top quarter, 80% from top half. 3 National Merit Scholars, 10 class presidents, 6 valedictorians, 52 student government officers. Full-time: 1,956 students, 58% women, 42% men. Part-time: 61 students, 64% women, 36% men. Students come from 39 states and territories, 32 other countries, 44% from out-of-state. 0.2% American Indian or Alaska Native, non-Hispanic/Latino; 5% Hispanic/Latino; 5% Black or African American, non-Hispanic/Latino; 1% Asian, non-Hispanic/Latino; 0.1% Native Hawaiian or other

Pacific Islander, non-Hispanic/Latino; 2% international. 2% 25 or older, 77% live on campus, 3% transferred in. Retention: 78% of full-time freshmen returned the following year. Academic areas with the most degrees conferred: business/marketing; social sciences; parks and recreation. Core. Calendar: semesters. ESL program, services for LD students, advanced placement, accelerated degree program, honors program, independent study, distance learning, double major, summer session for credit, part-time degree program, adult/continuing education programs, internships. Off campus study at Hollins University cross registration, Lutheran College Washington DC Semester. Study abroad program.

Entrance Requirements: Options: electronic application, early admission, early decision, deferred admission, international baccalaureate accepted. Required: high school transcript, SAT or ACT scores or must meet specific criteria to apply test-optional., SAT or ACT. Recommended: essay, 1 recommendation, interview. Entrance: moderately difficult. Application deadlines: 3/15, 3/15 for nonresidents, 11/15 for early decision. Notification: continuous until 4/1, continuous until 4/1 for nonresidents, 12/15 for early decision. SAT Reasoning Test deadline: 3/15. Transfer credits accepted: Yes. Applicants placed on waiting list: 203. Wait-listed applicants offered admission: 1. Early decision applicants: 93. Early decision applicants admitted: 76.

Costs Per Year: Application fee: $30. One-time mandatory fee: $125. Comprehensive fee: $59,568 includes full-time tuition ($43,818), mandatory fees ($1616), and college room and board ($14,134). College room only: $6562. Part-time tuition: $2096 per course. Part-time mandatory fees: $60 per term.

Collegiate Environment: Orientation program. Drama-theater group, choral group, student-run newspaper, radio station. Social organizations: 100 open to all; national fraternities, national sororities, co-educational service fraternity; 18% of eligible men and 19% of eligible women are members. Most popular organizations: Habitat for Humanity, Nerf Gun Wars, Student Firearms Association, Biology Club, Lambda Alliance. Major annual events: President's Ball, Alumni Weekend, Fowler Public Policy Lectures. Student services: health clinic, personal-psychological counseling. Campus security: 24-hour emergency response devices and patrols, late night transport-escort service, controlled dormitory access. 1,582 college housing spaces available; 1,541 were occupied in 2018-19. Freshmen guaranteed college housing. On-campus residence required through senior year. Options: coed, women-only housing available. Fintel Library. Books: 188,670 (physical), 227,793 (digital/electronic); Serial titles: 249 (physical), 89,398 (digital/electronic); Databases: 294. Weekly public service hours: 93; study areas open 24 hours, 5-7 days a week; students can reserve study rooms. Operations spending for the previous fiscal year: $1.3 million. 228 computers available on campus for general student use. Computer purchase/lease plans available. A campuswide network can be accessed from student residence rooms and from off campus. Students can access the following: online class registration, discounts on computer hardware and software purchases, free office software, free security software. Staffed computer lab on campus provides training in use of computers, software, and the Internet.

Community Environment: Salem is located in the heart of the Roanoke Valley between the Blue Ridge Mountains to the east, and the Allegheny Mountains to the west. Many national manufacturing companies contribute to the diversified industry of Salem. Plane and bus transportation are available. Part-time employment opportunities are excellent. The Dixie Caverns subterranean wonderland is seven miles away. State parks, the Blue Ridge Parkway & the Appalachian Trail provide outdoor activities, and facilities within the city provide for tennis, skating, and golf.

■ SAINT MICHAEL COLLEGE OF ALLIED HEALTH

8305 Richmond Hwy.
Alexandria, VA 22309
Web Site: www.stmichaelcollegeva.edu

Description: Proprietary, 2-year, coed.

■ SENTARA COLLEGE OF HEALTH SCIENCES

1441 Crossways Blvd.
Crossways I, Ste. 105
Chesapeake, VA 23320
Tel: (757)388-2900
Web Site: www.sentara.edu

Description: Independent, 4-year, coed. Administratively affiliated with Sentara Healthcare. Awards associate and bachelor's degrees. Founded 1892. Setting: urban campus with easy access to Virginia Beach. Total enrollment: 440. Faculty: 63 (28 full-time, 35 part-time). Students come from 4 states and territories. 0.2% American Indian or Alaska Native, non-

Hispanic/Latino; 4% Hispanic/Latino; 10% Black or African American, non-Hispanic/Latino; 8% Asian, non-Hispanic/Latino; 0.9% Native Hawaiian or other Pacific Islander, non-Hispanic/Latino. Academic area with the most degrees conferred: health professions and related sciences. Core. Calendar: semesters. Academic remediation for entering students, services for LD students, advanced placement, distance learning, summer session for credit, part-time degree program, adult/continuing education programs.

Entrance Requirements: Open admission RN/BSN rolling admissions. Options: electronic application, international baccalaureate accepted. Required: ATI Teas (BSN, CVT, ST). Required for some: high school transcript, minimum 3.5 high school GPA, For our BSN, early Admission option: earn courses, cumulative GPA of 3.3 on all college transcripts. Transfer credits accepted: Yes.

Costs Per Year: Application fee: $85. One-time mandatory fee: $85. Tuition: $10,472 full-time, $357 per credit hour part-time. Mandatory fees: $2447 full-time, $2447 per year part-time. Full-time tuition and fees vary according to course level, course load, degree level, and program. Part-time tuition and fees vary according to course level, course load, degree level, and program.

Collegiate Environment: Orientation program. Social organizations: 2 open to all. Most popular organizations: Sentara Nursing Student Association (SNSA), Alpha Eta National Honor Society for Allied Health Professionals, Sigma Theta Tau International Nursing Honor Society, Chi Kappa Chapter (STTI), Student Community Outreach Program of Excellence (SCOPE). Major annual event: Red Cross Blood Drive. Student services: personal-psychological counseling. Campus security: 24-hour emergency response devices. Sentara Healthcare Library. Books: 1,790 (physical); Serial titles: 65 (physical); Databases: 29. Operations spending for the previous fiscal year: $1 million. 13 computers available on campus for general student use. A computer is required for all students. A campuswide network can be accessed.

■ SHENANDOAH UNIVERSITY

1460 University Dr.
Winchester, VA 22601-5195
Tel: (540)665-4500; Free: 800-432-2266
Fax: (540)665-4627
E-mail: admit@su.edu
Web Site: www.su.edu

Description: Independent United Methodist, university, coed. Awards bachelor's, master's, and doctoral degrees and post-master's certificates. Founded 1875. Setting: 359-acre suburban campus with easy access to Washington, D.C. Endowment: $63.4 million. Research spending for the previous fiscal year: $99,523. Educational spending for the previous fiscal year: $13,269 per student. Total enrollment: 3,844. Faculty: 460 (251 full-time, 209 part-time). Student-undergrad faculty ratio is 10:1. 1,737 applied, 83% were admitted. Full-time: 1,991 students, 60% women, 40% men. Part-time: 72 students, 65% women, 35% men. Students come from 39 states and territories, 17 other countries, 40% from out-of-state. 0.7% American Indian or Alaska Native, non-Hispanic/Latino; 7% Hispanic/Latino; 11% Black or African American, non-Hispanic/Latino; 3% Asian, non-Hispanic/Latino; 0.2% Native Hawaiian or other Pacific Islander, non-Hispanic/Latino; 3% international. 13% 25 or older, 48% live on campus, 8% transferred in. Retention: 80% of full-time freshmen returned the following year. Academic areas with the most degrees conferred: health professions and related sciences; biological/life sciences; visual and performing arts. Core. Calendar: semesters. ESL program, services for LD students, advanced placement, accelerated degree program, self-designed majors, independent study, distance learning, double major, summer session for credit, part-time degree program, adult/continuing education programs, internships, graduate courses open to undergrads. Off campus study. Study abroad program.

Entrance Requirements: Options: electronic application, international baccalaureate accepted. Required: high school transcript, SAT or ACT. Required for some: essay, interview, audition for conservatory applicants, interview for some Conservatory programs and for Guaranteed Admission for Health Professions programs. Transfer credits accepted: Yes.

Costs Per Year: Application fee: $30. Comprehensive fee: $42,900 includes full-time tuition ($31,280), mandatory fees ($1250), and college room and board ($10,370). Full-time tuition and fees vary according to course load and program. Room and board charges vary according to board plan and housing facility. Part-time tuition: $910 per credit hour. Part-time mandatory fees: $90 per term. Part-time tuition and fees vary according to course load and program.

Collegiate Environment: Orientation program. Drama-theater group, choral group, student-run newspaper, radio station. Social organizations: 91 open to all; 91 clubs and organizations. Most popular organizations: Student Government Association, Graduate Student Assembly, Campus Activities Network, Athletic Training Club, Variety of Groups for Professional Fraternities. Major annual events: Homecoming, Movie Nights, Apple Blossom-Rock the Bloom Events. Student services: health clinic, personal-psychological counseling, women's center. Campus security: 24-hour emergency response devices and patrols, late night transport-escort service, controlled dormitory access, LiveSafe mobile app, anonymous reporting, side-door alarms, campus shuttle, Safe in Sixty Seconds Program, Safe Walk/Safe Ride Program. Alson H. Smith, Jr. Library plus 1 other. Books: 122,422 (physical), 217,000 (digital/electronic); Serial titles: 700 (physical), 86,500 (digital/electronic); Databases: 135. Weekly public service hours: 96; students can reserve study rooms. Operations spending for the previous fiscal year: $1.8 million. 32 computers available on campus for general student use. A campuswide network can be accessed from student residence rooms and from off campus. Students can access the following: online class registration, online student account information.

Community Environment: Winchester/Frederick County, a community of approximately 70,000 persons, is located 72 miles from Washington, D.C. near the northern end of the historic Shenandoah Valley. Winchester was founded in 1732 and played an important part in the French and Indian War and the Civil War. Bus transportation is available. Community facilities include a public library, museums, churches of major denominations, a medical center, excellent shopping areas, and a number of various civic and service organizations. Winchester is the host to the Shenandoah Apple Blossom Festival. George Washington began his career in Winchester in 1748 as surveyor to Lord Fairfax. Some of the historical points of interest are Abram's Delight (the Hollingsworth Home), Sheridan's Headquarters, "Stonewall" Jackson's Headquarters, Glen Burnie (home of James Wood), and Washington's Office.

■ SOUTH UNIVERSITY (GLEN ALLEN)

2151 Old Brick Rd.
Glen Allen, VA 23060
Tel: (804)727-6800; Free: 888-422-5076
Fax: (804)727-6790
Web Site: www.southuniversity.edu/richmond
Description: Independent, comprehensive, coed. Awards associate, bachelor's, and master's degrees and post-master's certificates.

■ SOUTH UNIVERSITY (VIRGINIA BEACH)

301 Bendix Rd., Ste. 100
Virginia Beach, VA 23452
Tel: (757)493-6900; Free: 877-206-1845
Fax: (757)493-6990
Web Site: www.southuniversity.edu/virginia-beach
Description: Independent, comprehensive, coed. Awards associate, bachelor's, and master's degrees.

■ SOUTHERN VIRGINIA UNIVERSITY

One College Hill Dr.
Buena Vista, VA 24416
Tel: (540)261-8400; Free: 800-229-8420
Fax: (540)261-8559
E-mail: admissions@southernvirginia.edu
Web Site: www.svu.edu

Description: Independent Latter-day Saints, 4-year, coed. Awards bachelor's degrees. Founded 1867. Setting: 155-acre small town campus. Endowment: $1 million. Educational spending for the previous fiscal year: $5102 per student. Total enrollment: 749. Faculty: 69 (34 full-time, 35 part-time). Student-undergrad faculty ratio is 16:1. 1,346 applied, 52% were admitted. 17% from top 10% of their high school class, 36% from top quarter, 72% from top half. Full-time: 714 students, 54% women, 46% men. Part-time: 35 students, 49% women, 51% men. Students come from 47 states and territories, 17 other countries, 74% from out-of-state. 4% 25 or older, 65% live on campus, 13% transferred in. Retention: 48% of full-time freshmen returned the following year. Academic areas with the most degrees conferred: parks and recreation; visual and performing arts; business/marketing. Core. Calendar: semesters. Summer session for credit, co-op programs. Study abroad program. ROTC: Army (c).

Entrance Requirements: Required: high school transcript, ecclesiastical endorsement, SAT or ACT. Recommended: minimum 2.0 high school GPA. Required for some: essay, interview. Entrance: moderately difficult. Application deadline: 7/31.

Collegiate Environment: Orientation program. Drama-theater group, choral group. Most popular organizations: Student Association, LDS Institute of Religion. Student services: health clinic, personal-psychological counseling. Campus security: 24-hour emergency response devices and patrols. Von Canon Library.

■ **SOUTHSIDE REGIONAL MEDICAL CENTER PROFESSIONAL SCHOOLS**
430 Clairmont Ct., Ste. 200
Colonial Heights, VA 23834
Tel: (804)765-5800
Web Site: www.srmconline.com/Southside-Regional-Medical-Center/nursingeducation.aspx
Description: Proprietary, 2-year, coed. Awards transfer associate and terminal associate degrees.

■ **SOUTHSIDE VIRGINIA COMMUNITY COLLEGE**
109 Campus Dr.
Alberta, VA 23821-9719
Tel: (434)949-1000
Fax: (434)949-7863
E-mail: rhina.jones@sv.vccs.edu
Web Site: www.southside.edu
Description: State-supported, 2-year, coed. Part of Virginia Community College System. Awards certificates, diplomas, transfer associate, and terminal associate degrees. Founded 1970. Setting: 207-acre rural campus. Endowment: $1.3 million. Educational spending for the previous fiscal year: $4120 per student. Total enrollment: 6,353. Faculty: 290 (73 full-time, 217 part-time). Student-undergrad faculty ratio is 17:1. 438 applied, 100% were admitted. Full-time: 1,924 students, 65% women, 35% men. Part-time: 4,429 students, 61% women, 39% men. Students come from 5 states and territories, 0.1% from out-of-state. 49% 25 or older. Core. Calendar: semesters. Academic remediation for entering students, services for LD students, advanced placement, honors program, distance learning, summer session for credit, part-time degree program. Off campus study at Hampden-Sydney College, Saint Paul's College, Longwood College. Study abroad program. ROTC: Army (c).
Entrance Requirements: Open admission except for nursing program. Options: electronic application, deferred admission. Required: high school transcript, interview. Entrance: noncompetitive. Application deadline: rolling. Notification: continuous. Preference given to district residents.
Collegiate Environment: Orientation program. Choral group. Most popular organizations: Student Forum, Phi Theta Kappa, Phi Beta Lambda, Alpha Delta Omega. Major annual events: Women's Festivals, Cultural Events, Kwanza Celebration. Julian M. Howell Library plus 1 other. Operations spending for the previous fiscal year: $300,000. 200 computers available on campus for general student use. A campuswide network can be accessed. Students can access the following: online class registration, e-mail. Staffed computer lab on campus.
Community Environment: See Hampden-Sydney College.

■ **SOUTHWEST VIRGINIA COMMUNITY COLLEGE**
PO Box SVCC
Richlands, VA 24641
Tel: (276)964-2555; Free: 800-822-7822
Fax: (276)964-9307
E-mail: dionne.cook@sw.edu
Web Site: www.sw.edu
Description: State-supported, 2-year, coed. Part of Virginia Community College System. Awards certificates, diplomas, transfer associate, and terminal associate degrees. Founded 1968. Setting: 100-acre rural campus. Endowment: $20 million. Educational spending for the previous fiscal year: $4983 per student. Total enrollment: 2,304. Faculty: 110 (40 full-time, 70 part-time). Student-undergrad faculty ratio is 24:1. 15% from top 10% of their high school class. Students come from 7 states and territories, 1 other country, 3% from out-of-state. 0.4% American Indian or Alaska Native, non-Hispanic/Latino; 0.7% Hispanic/Latino; 3% Black or African American, non-Hispanic/Latino; 0.4% Asian, non-Hispanic/Latino. 25% 25 or older. Retention: 55% of full-time freshmen returned the following year. Core. Calendar: semesters. Academic remediation for entering students, advanced placement, accelerated degree program, honors program, distance learning, double major, summer session for credit, part-time degree program, adult/continuing education programs, internships. Off campus study.
Entrance Requirements: Open admission except for allied health,

engineering programs. Options: electronic application, early admission, deferred admission. Required: high school transcript, interview, VCCS Math and English Assessments. Entrance: noncompetitive. Application deadline: rolling. Preference given to service region residents. Transfer credits accepted: Yes.
Costs Per Year: Application fee: $0. State resident tuition: $4620 full-time, $154 per credit hour part-time. Nonresident tuition: $9918 full-time, $330.60 per credit hour part-time. Mandatory fees: $82 full-time, $2.75 per credit hour part-time. Full-time tuition and fees vary according to reciprocity agreements. Part-time tuition and fees vary according to course load and reciprocity agreements.
Collegiate Environment: Choral group. Social organizations: 23 open to all. Most popular organizations: Phi Theta Kappa, Phi Beta Lambda, Intervoice, Helping Minds Club, Project ACHEIVE. Major annual events: Back to School Bash, End of the Year Bash, Annual Halloween Costume Contest. Student services: personal-psychological counseling. Campus security: 24-hour emergency response devices and patrols, student patrols, extensive security camera system. Southwest Virginia Community College Library. Books: 42,207 (physical), 62,566 (digital/electronic); Serial titles: 275 (physical), 118,007 (digital/electronic); Databases: 118. Students can reserve study rooms. 450 computers available on campus for general student use. A campuswide network can be accessed from off-campus. Students can access the following: online class registration. Staffed computer lab on campus provides training in use of computers and the Internet.
Community Environment: Richlands is a rural community in the Appalachian Mountain region. Bus and plane transportation are available. The main industries of the area are agriculture, mining, and manufacturing.

■ **SOVAH HEALTH SCHOOL OF HEALTH PROFESSIONS**
142 S Main St.
Danville, VA 24541
Description: Proprietary, 2-year, coed.

■ **STANDARD HEALTHCARE SERVICES, COLLEGE OF NURSING**
7704 Leesburg Pke.
Ste. 1000
Falls Church, VA 22043
Tel: (703)891-1787
Web Site: www.standardcollege.edu
Description: Proprietary, 2-year, coed. Awards certificates, transfer associate, and terminal associate degrees.

■ **STRATFORD UNIVERSITY (ALEXANDRIA)**
2900 Eisenhower Ave.
Alexandria, VA 22314
Tel: (571)699-3200; Free: 800-444-0804
E-mail: alexandriaadmissions@stratford.edu
Web Site: www.stratford.edu
Description: Proprietary, comprehensive, coed. Awards associate, bachelor's, and master's degrees. Founded 1976. Setting: urban campus with easy access to Washington DC. Total enrollment: 309. Faculty: 45 (9 full-time, 36 part-time). Full-time: 61 students, 59% women, 41% men. Part-time: 231 students, 68% women, 32% men. Students come from 3 states and territories, 60% from out-of-state. 5% American Indian or Alaska Native, non-Hispanic/Latino; 7% Hispanic/Latino; 63% Black or African American, non-Hispanic/Latino; 4% Asian, non-Hispanic/Latino; 0.3% Native Hawaiian or other Pacific Islander, non-Hispanic/Latino. 74% 25 or older, 64% transferred in. Core. Calendar: quarters. Academic remediation for entering students, services for LD students, accelerated degree program, distance learning, summer session for credit, part-time degree program, adult/continuing education programs, co-op programs and internships. Off campus study.
Entrance Requirements: Open admission. Option: electronic application. Required: high school transcript, interview. Recommended: essay. Application deadline: rolling. Notification: continuous. Transfer credits accepted: Yes.
Costs Per Year: Application fee: $50. One-time mandatory fee: $100. Tuition: $24,975 full-time, $1665 per course part-time. Full-time tuition varies according to course level, course load, degree level, and program. Part-time tuition varies according to course level, course load, degree level, and program.
Collegiate Environment: Orientation program. Learning Resource Center.

■ **STRATFORD UNIVERSITY (FALLS CHURCH)**
7777 Leesburg Pke.
Falls Church, VA 22043

Tel: (703)821-8570; Free: 800-444-0804
Fax: (703)556-9892
E-mail: fcadmissions@stratford.edu
Web Site: www.stratford.edu
Description: Proprietary, comprehensive, coed. Awards associate, bachelor's, master's, and doctoral degrees. Founded 1976. Setting: urban campus with easy access to Washington, DC. Total enrollment: 809. Faculty: 128 (26 full-time, 102 part-time). Full-time: 118 students, 63% women, 37% men. Part-time: 289 students, 82% women, 18% men. 0.6% American Indian or Alaska Native, non-Hispanic/Latino; 15% Hispanic/Latino; 57% Black or African American, non-Hispanic/Latino; 13% Asian, non-Hispanic/Latino; 0.3% Native Hawaiian or other Pacific Islander, non-Hispanic/Latino. Core. Calendar: quarters. Academic remediation for entering students, ESL program, services for LD students, accelerated degree program, independent study, distance learning, summer session for credit, part-time degree program, adult/continuing education programs, co-op programs and internships. Off campus study.
Entrance Requirements: Open admission. Option: electronic application. Required: high school transcript, interview. Recommended: essay. Entrance: noncompetitive. Application deadline: rolling. Notification: continuous. Transfer credits accepted: Yes.
Costs Per Year: Application fee: $50. One-time mandatory fee: $100. Tuition: $24,975 full-time, $1665 per course part-time. Full-time tuition varies according to course level, course load, degree level, and program. Part-time tuition varies according to course level, course load, degree level, and program.
Collegiate Environment: Orientation program. Learning Resource Center.

■ **STRATFORD UNIVERSITY (GLEN ALLEN)**
11104 W Broad St.
Glen Allen, VA 23060
Tel: (804)290-4231; Free: 877-373-5173
E-mail: gaadmissions@stratford.edu
Web Site: www.stratford.edu
Description: Proprietary, comprehensive, coed. Awards associate, bachelor's, and master's degrees. Founded 1976. Setting: suburban campus with easy access to Richmond, VA. Total enrollment: 249. Faculty: 57 (9 full-time, 48 part-time). Full-time: 23 students, 43% women, 57% men. Part-time: 153 students, 65% women, 35% men. 1% American Indian or Alaska Native, non-Hispanic/Latino; 5% Hispanic/Latino; 69% Black or African American, non-Hispanic/Latino; 0.6% Asian, non-Hispanic/Latino; 0.6% Native Hawaiian or other Pacific Islander, non-Hispanic/Latino. Core. Calendar: quarters. Academic remediation for entering students, services for LD students, accelerated degree program, independent study, distance learning, summer session for credit, part-time degree program, adult/continuing education programs, co-op programs and internships. Off campus study.
Entrance Requirements: Required: high school transcript, interview. Recommended: essay.
Costs Per Year: One-time mandatory fee: $100. Tuition: $24,975 full-time, $1665 per course part-time. Full-time tuition varies according to course level, course load, degree level, and program. Part-time tuition varies according to course level, course load, degree level, and program.
Collegiate Environment: Orientation program. Learning Resource Center.

■ **STRATFORD UNIVERSITY (NEWPORT NEWS)**
836 J. Clyde Morris Blvd.
Newport News, VA 23601
Tel: (757)873-4235; Free: 855-873-4235
E-mail: newportnewsadmissions@stratford.edu
Web Site: www.stratford.edu
Description: Proprietary, comprehensive, coed. Awards associate, bachelor's, and master's degrees. Founded 1976. Setting: urban campus with easy access to Richmond. Total enrollment: 309. Faculty: 62 (12 full-time, 50 part-time). Full-time: 70 students, 47% women, 53% men. Part-time: 195 students, 73% women, 27% men. Students come from 2 states and territories, 1% from out-of-state. 0.8% American Indian or Alaska Native, non-Hispanic/Latino; 4% Hispanic/Latino; 71% Black or African American, non-Hispanic/Latino; 2% Asian, non-Hispanic/Latino; 0.4% Native Hawaiian or other Pacific Islander, non-Hispanic/Latino. 81% 25 or older, 47% transferred in. Retention: 71% of full-time freshmen returned the following year. Core. Calendar: quarters. Academic remediation for entering students, services for LD students, accelerated degree program, independent study, distance learning, summer session for credit, part-time degree program, adult/continuing education programs, co-op programs and internships.

Entrance Requirements: Required: high school transcript, interview. Recommended: essay.
Costs Per Year: One-time mandatory fee: $100. Tuition: $24,975 full-time, $1665 per course part-time. Full-time tuition varies according to course level, course load, degree level, and program. Part-time tuition varies according to course level, course load, degree level, and program.
Collegiate Environment: Orientation program. Learning Resource Center.

■ **STRATFORD UNIVERSITY (VIRGINIA BEACH)**
555 S Independence Blvd.
Virginia Beach, VA 23452
Tel: (757)497-4466; Free: 866-528-8363
E-mail: virginiabeachadmissions@stratford.edu
Web Site: www.stratford.edu
Description: Proprietary, comprehensive, coed. Awards associate, bachelor's, and master's degrees. Founded 1976. Setting: urban campus. Total enrollment: 288. Faculty: 56 (11 full-time, 45 part-time). Full-time: 93 students, 43% women, 57% men. Part-time: 152 students, 74% women, 26% men. Students come from 3 states and territories, 2% from out-of-state. 3% American Indian or Alaska Native, non-Hispanic/Latino; 7% Hispanic/Latino; 54% Black or African American, non-Hispanic/Latino; 3% Asian, non-Hispanic/Latino; 0.8% Native Hawaiian or other Pacific Islander, non-Hispanic/Latino. 78% 25 or older, 10% transferred in. Core. Calendar: quarters. Academic remediation for entering students, accelerated degree program, distance learning, summer session for credit, part-time degree program, adult/continuing education programs, co-op programs and internships.
Entrance Requirements: Open admission. Option: electronic application. Required: high school transcript, interview. Recommended: essay. Application deadline: rolling. Notification: continuous. Transfer credits accepted: Yes.
Costs Per Year: Application fee: $50. One-time mandatory fee: $100. Tuition: $24,975 full-time, $1665 per course part-time. Full-time tuition varies according to course level, course load, degree level, and program. Part-time tuition varies according to course level, course load, degree level, and program.
Collegiate Environment: Orientation program. Learning Resource Center.

■ **STRATFORD UNIVERSITY (WOODBRIDGE)**
14349 Gideon Dr.
Woodbridge, VA 22192
Tel: (703)897-1982; Free: 888-546-1250
E-mail: woodbridgeadmissions@stratford.edu
Web Site: www.stratford.edu
Description: Proprietary, comprehensive, coed. Awards associate, bachelor's, and master's degrees. Founded 1976. Setting: suburban campus with easy access to Washington DC. Total enrollment: 395. Faculty: 77 (18 full-time, 59 part-time). Full-time: 97 students, 64% women, 36% men. Part-time: 264 students, 71% women, 29% men. Students come from 8 states and territories, 7% from out-of-state. 6% American Indian or Alaska Native, non-Hispanic/Latino; 12% Hispanic/Latino; 44% Black or African American, non-Hispanic/Latino; 6% Asian, non-Hispanic/Latino; 0.3% Native Hawaiian or other Pacific Islander, non-Hispanic/Latino. 74% 25 or older, 60% transferred in. Core. Calendar: quarters. Academic remediation for entering students, accelerated degree program, independent study, distance learning, summer session for credit, part-time degree program, adult/continuing education programs, co-op programs and internships.
Entrance Requirements: Open admission. Option: electronic application. Required: high school transcript, interview. Recommended: essay. Required for some: recommendations. Application deadline: rolling. Notification: continuous. Transfer credits accepted: Yes.
Costs Per Year: Application fee: $50. One-time mandatory fee: $100. Tuition: $24,975 full-time, $1665 per course part-time. Full-time tuition varies according to course level, course load, degree level, and program. Part-time tuition varies according to course level, course load, degree level, and program.
Collegiate Environment: Orientation program. Learning Resource Center.

■ **STRAYER UNIVERSITY-ALEXANDRIA CAMPUS**
2730 Eisenhower Ave.
Alexandria, VA 22314
Tel: (703)329-9100; Free: 888-311-0355
Web Site: www.strayer.edu

Description: Proprietary, comprehensive, coed. Awards associate, bachelor's, and master's degrees.

■ **STRAYER UNIVERSITY-ARLINGTON CAMPUS**
2121 15th St. N
Arlington, VA 22201
Tel: (703)892-5100; Free: 888-311-0355
Web Site: www.strayer.edu
Description: Proprietary, comprehensive, coed. Awards associate, bachelor's, and master's degrees.

■ **STRAYER UNIVERSITY-CHESAPEAKE CAMPUS**
676 Independence Pky.
Ste. 300
Chesapeake, VA 23320
Tel: (757)382-9900; Free: 888-311-0355
Web Site: www.strayer.edu
Description: Proprietary, comprehensive, coed. Awards associate, bachelor's, and master's degrees.

■ **STRAYER UNIVERSITY-CHESTERFIELD CAMPUS**
15521 Midlothian Tpke.
Ste. 401
Midlothian, VA 23113
Tel: (804)794-2033; Free: 888-311-0355
Web Site: www.strayer.edu
Description: Proprietary, comprehensive, coed. Awards associate, bachelor's, and master's degrees.

■ **STRAYER UNIVERSITY-FREDERICKSBURG CAMPUS**
150 Riverside Pky.
Ste. 100
Fredericksburg, VA 22406
Tel: (540)374-4300; Free: 888-311-0355
Web Site: www.strayer.edu
Description: Proprietary, comprehensive, coed. Awards associate, bachelor's, and master's degrees.

■ **STRAYER UNIVERSITY-HENRICO CAMPUS**
11501 Nuckols Rd.
Glen Allen, VA 23059
Tel: (804)527-1000; Free: 888-311-0355
Web Site: www.strayer.edu
Description: Proprietary, comprehensive, coed. Awards associate, bachelor's, and master's degrees. Founded 1892.

■ **STRAYER UNIVERSITY-LOUDOUN CAMPUS**
45150 Russell Branch Pky.
Ste. 200
Ashburn, VA 20147
Tel: (703)729-8800; Free: 888-311-0355
Web Site: www.strayer.edu
Description: Proprietary, comprehensive, coed. Awards associate, bachelor's, and master's degrees.

■ **STRAYER UNIVERSITY-MANASSAS CAMPUS**
9990 Battleview Pky.
Manassas, VA 20109
Tel: (703)330-8400; Free: 888-311-0355
Web Site: www.strayer.edu
Description: Proprietary, comprehensive, coed. Awards associate, bachelor's, and master's degrees.

■ **STRAYER UNIVERSITY-NEWPORT NEWS CAMPUS**
99 Old Oyster Point Rd.
Newport News, VA 23602
Tel: (757)881-5100; Free: 888-311-0355
Web Site: www.strayer.edu
Description: Proprietary, comprehensive, coed. Awards associate, bachelor's, and master's degrees.

■ **STRAYER UNIVERSITY-VIRGINIA BEACH CAMPUS**
249 Central Park Ave.
Ste. 350
Virginia Beach, VA 23462
Tel: (757)493-6000; Free: 888-311-0355
Web Site: www.strayer.edu
Description: Proprietary, comprehensive, coed. Awards associate, bachelor's, and master's degrees.

■ **STRAYER UNIVERSITY-WOODBRIDGE CAMPUS**
13385 Minnieville Rd.
Woodbridge, VA 22192
Tel: (703)878-2800; Free: 888-311-0355
Web Site: www.strayer.edu
Description: Proprietary, comprehensive, coed. Awards associate, bachelor's, and master's degrees.

■ **SWEET BRIAR COLLEGE**
Sweet Briar, VA 24595
Tel: (434)381-6100; Free: 800-381-6142
Fax: (434)381-6173
E-mail: admissions@sbc.edu
Web Site: www.sbc.edu
Description: Independent, comprehensive, women only. Awards bachelor's and master's degrees. Founded 1901. Setting: 3,250-acre rural campus. Endowment: $74.8 million. Research spending for the previous fiscal year: $158,684. Educational spending for the previous fiscal year: $34,810 per student. Total enrollment: 337. Faculty: 75 (60 full-time, 15 part-time). Student-undergrad faculty ratio is 5:1. 654 applied, 76% were admitted. Full-time: 331 students. Part-time: 5 students. Students come from 33 states and territories, 6 other countries, 48% from out-of-state. 8% Hispanic/Latino; 9% Black or African American, non-Hispanic/Latino; 2% Asian, non-Hispanic/Latino; 0.3% Native Hawaiian or other Pacific Islander, non-Hispanic/Latino; 3% international. 4% 25 or older, 93% live on campus, 4% transferred in. Retention: 72% of full-time freshmen returned the following year. Academic areas with the most degrees conferred: business/marketing; social sciences; psychology. Core. Calendar: semesters. Services for LD students, advanced placement, self-designed majors, honors program, independent study, double major, summer session for credit, part-time degree program, adult/continuing education programs, internships. Off campus study at Seven-College Exchange Program, Tri-College Exchange Program, American University. Study abroad program.
Entrance Requirements: Options: electronic application, deferred admission, international baccalaureate accepted. Required: essay, high school transcript. Recommended: 2 recommendations. Required for some: SAT or ACT. Entrance: minimally difficult. Application deadlines: rolling for nonresidents, 10/1 for early action. Notification: continuous, continuous for nonresidents, rolling for early action. SAT Reasoning Test deadline: 8/15. Transfer credits accepted: Yes.
Costs Per Year: Application fee: $0. Comprehensive fee: $0.
Collegiate Environment: Orientation program. Drama-theater group, choral group, student-run newspaper, radio station. Major annual events: Spring Fling, Founder' Day, Winter Mixer. Student services: health clinic, personal-psychological counseling, women's center. Campus security: 24-hour emergency response devices and patrols, student patrols, late night transport-escort service, controlled dormitory access, front gate security. 700 college housing spaces available. Freshmen guaranteed college housing. On-campus residence required through senior year. Option: women-only housing available. Mary Helen Cochran Library plus 1 other. Books: 245,124 (physical); Serial titles: 1,215 (physical), 31,479 (digital/electronic); Databases: 214. Study areas open 24 hours, 5-7 days a week. Operations spending for the previous fiscal year: $240,887.
Community Environment: Sweet Briar is located on U.S. 29, 165 miles southwest of Washington, D.C., 50 miles south of Charlottesville, VA., and 100 miles west of Richmond. The nearest shopping area is in the town of Amherst, two miles north of Sweet Briar. Lynchburg, home of three other colleges, is 12 miles south of Sweet Briar. The Blue Ridge Mountains, visible a few miles to the west, offer numerous recreational possibilities, including the ski slopes at Wintergreen.

■ **THOMAS NELSON COMMUNITY COLLEGE**
PO Box 9407
Hampton, VA 23670-0407
Tel: (757)825-2700

E-mail: admissions@tncc.edu
Web Site: www.tncc.edu
Description: State-supported, 2-year, coed. Part of Virginia Community College System. Awards certificates, diplomas, transfer associate, and terminal associate degrees. Founded 1968. Setting: 85-acre suburban campus with easy access to Virginia Beach. Total enrollment: 10,942. Student-undergrad faculty ratio is 22:1. Calendar: semesters. Academic remediation for entering students, ESL program, services for LD students, advanced placement, accelerated degree program, honors program, distance learning, summer session for credit, part-time degree program, adult/continuing education programs, co-op programs and internships. Off campus study.
Entrance Requirements: Open admission. Options: electronic application, early admission, deferred admission. Recommended: high school transcript. Required for some: interview. Entrance: noncompetitive. Application deadline: rolling. Notification: continuous. Transfer credits accepted: Yes.
Collegiate Environment: Orientation program. Drama-theater group, choral group. Most popular organizations: Phi Theta Kappa, Student Nurses Association, International Club, Student Government Association. Major annual events: Fall Festival, Spring Fest, Literature Circles. Student services: personal-psychological counseling. Campus security: 24-hour emergency response devices and patrols, late night transport-escort service. Thomas Nelson Community College Library. 111 computers available on campus for general student use. A campuswide network can be accessed. Students can access the following: online class registration. Staffed computer lab on campus provides training in use of computers, software, and the Internet.
Community Environment: See Hampton University.

■ **TIDEWATER COMMUNITY COLLEGE**
121 College Pl.
Norfolk, VA 23510
Tel: (757)822-1122
Fax: (757)822-1060
Web Site: www.tcc.edu
Description: State-supported, 2-year, coed. Part of Virginia Community College System. Awards certificates, transfer associate, and terminal associate degrees. Founded 1968. Setting: 520-acre suburban campus. Endowment: $7.1 million. Total enrollment: 20,941. Faculty: 1,141 (306 full-time, 835 part-time). Student-undergrad faculty ratio is 20:1. 17% from out-of-state. 0.4% American Indian or Alaska Native, non-Hispanic/Latino; 9% Hispanic/Latino; 30% Black or African American, non-Hispanic/Latino; 4% Asian, non-Hispanic/Latino; 0.5% Native Hawaiian or other Pacific Islander, non-Hispanic/Latino; 0.7% international. 45% 25 or older. Retention: 54% of full-time freshmen returned the following year. Core. Calendar: semesters. Academic remediation for entering students, ESL program, services for LD students, advanced placement, accelerated degree program, honors program, independent study, distance learning, summer session for credit, part-time degree program, adult/continuing education programs, co-op programs and internships. Off campus study at members of the Virginia Tidewater Consortium for Continuing Higher Education.
Entrance Requirements: Open admission. Options: electronic application, early admission, deferred admission. Entrance: noncompetitive. Application deadline: rolling. Notification: continuous.
Costs Per Year: Application fee: $0. State resident tuition: $4056 full-time, $156 per credit hour part-time. Nonresident tuition: $8,648 full-time, $332.60 per credit hour part-time. Mandatory fees: $763 full-time, $29.35 per credit hour part-time.
Collegiate Environment: Orientation program. Drama-theater group, student-run newspaper. Student services: personal-psychological counseling, women's center. Campus security: 24-hour patrols. College housing not available. Main library plus 5 others. Operations spending for the previous fiscal year: $604,201.
Community Environment: A metropolitan area, Tidewater is located on the Chesapeake Bay, and has been a strategic military location in this country's conflicts because of its shipbuilding and ship repair. All forms of commercial transportation are available. Recreational activities are numerous, all water sports are enjoyed on nearby beaches. There is excellent hunting and fishing in the area also. Part-time employment opportunities are limited.

■ **UNIVERSITY OF LYNCHBURG**
1501 Lakeside Dr.
Lynchburg, VA 24501-3199
Tel: (434)544-8100; Free: 800-426-8101
Fax: (434)544-8653
Web Site: www.lynchburg.edu

Description: Independent, comprehensive, coed, affiliated with Christian Church (Disciples of Christ). Awards bachelor's, master's, and doctoral degrees and post-master's certificates. Founded 1903. Setting: 264-acre suburban campus. Endowment: $109.7 million. Research spending for the previous fiscal year: $80,105. Educational spending for the previous fiscal year: $16,241 per student. Total enrollment: 3,081. Faculty: 270 (187 full-time, 83 part-time). Student-undergrad faculty ratio is 11:1. 3,830 applied, 100% were admitted. 13% from top 10% of their high school class, 22% from top quarter, 69% from top half. Full-time: 1,930 students, 60% women, 40% men. Part-time: 156 students, 74% women, 26% men. Students come from 33 states and territories, 11 other countries, 29% from out-of-state. 0.5% American Indian or Alaska Native, non-Hispanic/Latino; 5% Hispanic/Latino; 11% Black or African American, non-Hispanic/Latino; 1% Asian, non-Hispanic/Latino; 1% international. 0.1% 25 or older, 74% live on campus, 4% transferred in. Retention: 79% of full-time freshmen returned the following year. Academic areas with the most degrees conferred: health professions and related sciences; social sciences; biological/life sciences. Core. Calendar: semesters. ESL program, services for LD students, advanced placement, accelerated degree program, self-designed majors, honors program, independent study, distance learning, double major, summer session for credit, part-time degree program, adult/continuing education programs, internships, graduate courses open to undergrads. Off campus study at Tri-College Consortium: Lynchburg College, Randolph College, and Sweet Briar College. Study abroad program.
Entrance Requirements: Options: electronic application, early admission, early decision, deferred admission. Required: high school transcript, SAT or ACT. Recommended: essay, 2 recommendations, interview. Entrance: moderately difficult. Application deadlines: rolling, 11/15 for early decision. Notification: continuous, 12/15 for early decision. Transfer credits accepted: Yes.
Costs Per Year: Application fee: $30. Comprehensive fee: $50,330 includes full-time tuition ($38,560), mandatory fees ($970), and college room and board ($10,800). College room only: $5800. Room and board charges vary according to housing facility. Part-time tuition: $525 per credit hour. Part-time mandatory fees: $5.10 per credit hour. Part-time tuition and fees vary according to course load.
Collegiate Environment: Orientation program. Drama-theater group, choral group, student-run newspaper. Social organizations: 80 open to all; national fraternities, national sororities; 12% of eligible men and 12% of eligible women are members. Most popular organizations: Student Government Association, Student Activities Board, Enrollment Student Ambassadors, Emergency Services, Greek Life. Major annual events: Homecoming, Turkey Bowl, Red Letter Day. Student services: health clinic, personal-psychological counseling. Campus security: 24-hour emergency response devices and patrols, late night transport-escort service, controlled dormitory access. 1,800 college housing spaces available. Freshmen guaranteed college housing. On-campus residence required through junior year. Option: coed housing available. Knight-Capron Library. Books: 109,236 (physical), 323,591 (digital/electronic); Serial titles: 109 (physical), 58,732 (digital/electronic); Databases: 98. Study areas open 24 hours, 5-7 days a week; students can reserve study rooms. Operations spending for the previous fiscal year: $884,786. 300 computers available on campus for general student use. A campuswide network can be accessed from student residence rooms and from off campus. Students can access the following: online class registration. Staffed computer lab on campus provides training in use of computers and the Internet.
Community Environment: Founded in 1786, Lynchburg is rich in history. It is a modern community with diversified industry in a traditional, handsome setting. Although it has a metropolitan area population of 214,000, Lynchburg maintains intimate contact with the countryside since it is very near the Blue Ridge Mountains and is in the center of perhaps the most historic of states. Washington, D.C., is less than 4 hours away, Williamsburg approximately 3, and Richmond about 2 1/2. The area provides excellent climate, convenient shopping, and many cultural opportunities. There is an active Lynchburg Fine Arts Center, and professional musical and theatrical groups visit. Some of the 7 colleges in the area also present fine arts programs.

■ **UNIVERSITY OF MANAGEMENT AND TECHNOLOGY**
1901 Fort Myer Dr.
Arlington, VA 22209-1609
Tel: (703)516-0035; Free: 800-924-4883
Fax: (703)516-0985
Web Site: www.umtweb.edu

Description: Proprietary, comprehensive, coed. Awards associate, bachelor's, master's, and doctoral degrees and post-master's certificates. Founded 1998. Setting: urban campus with easy access to Washington, DC. Total enrollment: 1,293. Student-undergrad faculty ratio is 25:1. Calendar: continuous. Part-time degree program, adult/continuing education programs, graduate courses open to undergrads.

Entrance Requirements: Open admission. Transfer credits accepted: Yes.

Costs Per Year: Application fee: $30. Tuition: $9360 full-time. Mandatory fees: $90 full-time.

Collegiate Environment: Books: 9,149 (physical), 35 (digital/electronic).

■ **UNIVERSITY OF MARY WASHINGTON**
1301 College Ave.
Fredericksburg, VA 22401-5358
Tel: (540)654-1000; Free: 800-468-5614
Fax: (540)654-1073
E-mail: myak@umw.edu
Web Site: www.umw.edu

Description: State-supported, comprehensive, coed. Awards bachelor's and master's degrees. Founded 1908. Setting: 234-acre small town campus with easy access to Richmond; Washington, D.C. Endowment: $50 million. Research spending for the previous fiscal year: $301,494. Educational spending for the previous fiscal year: $6845 per student. Total enrollment: 4,808. Faculty: 402 (251 full-time, 151 part-time). Student-undergrad faculty ratio is 14:1. 5,977 applied, 73% were admitted. 16% from top 10% of their high school class, 46% from top quarter, 85% from top half. 6 valedictorians. Full-time: 3,905 students, 64% women, 36% men. Part-time: 493 students, 65% women, 35% men. Students come from 34 states and territories, 20 other countries, 8% from out-of-state. 0.3% American Indian or Alaska Native, non-Hispanic/Latino; 9% Hispanic/Latino; 8% Black or African American, non-Hispanic/Latino; 4% Asian, non-Hispanic/Latino; 0.1% Native Hawaiian or other Pacific Islander, non-Hispanic/Latino; 1% international. 10% 25 or older, 57% live on campus, 9% transferred in. Retention: 84% of full-time freshmen returned the following year. Academic areas with the most degrees conferred: business/marketing; social sciences; psychology; liberal arts/general studies. Core. Calendar: semesters. Services for LD students, advanced placement, accelerated degree program, self-designed majors, honors program, independent study, distance learning, double major, summer session for credit, part-time degree program, adult/continuing education programs, internships, graduate courses open to undergrads. Study abroad program. ROTC: Army (c).

Entrance Requirements: Options: electronic application, early admission, early decision, early action, deferred admission, international baccalaureate accepted. Required: essay, high school transcript. Required for some: SAT or ACT. Entrance: very difficult. Application deadlines: 2/1, 11/1 for early decision, 11/15 for early action. Notification: 4/1, 1/31 for early decision, 1/31 for early action. Preference given to state residents. SAT Reasoning Test deadline: 3/1. Transfer credits accepted: Yes. Applicants placed on waiting list: 536. Wait-listed applicants offered admission: 19. Early decision applicants: 127. Early decision applicants admitted: 108. Early action applicants: 2,593. Early action applicants admitted: 2,253.

Costs Per Year: Application fee: $50. State resident tuition: $5772 full-time. Nonresident tuition: $20,362 full-time. Mandatory fees: $5858 full-time. Full-time tuition and fees vary according to course load, degree level, and location. College room and board: $11,118. College room only: $7326. Room and board charges vary according to board plan and housing facility.

Collegiate Environment: Orientation program. Drama-theater group, choral group, student-run newspaper, radio station. Social organizations: 140 open to all. Most popular organizations: Class Council, Campus Programming Board, Community Outreach and Participation, Association of Residence Halls, Student Government Association. Major annual events: Multicultural Fair, Devil Goat Day, Lip Sync. Student services: health clinic, personal-psychological counseling. Campus security: 24-hour emergency response devices and patrols, student patrols, late night transport-escort service, controlled dormitory access, self-defense and safety classes. Guardian App. Simpson Library plus 2 others. Books: 373,290 (physical), 243,338 (digital/electronic); Serial titles: 3,164 (physical), 76,994 (digital/electronic); Databases: 210. Weekly public service hours: 90; students can reserve study rooms. Operations spending for the previous fiscal year: $2.6 million. 579 computers available on campus for general student use. Computer purchase/lease plans available. A campuswide network can be accessed. Students can access the following: online class registration, student Web hosting. Staffed computer lab on campus provides training in use of computers, software, and the Internet.

Community Environment: Fredericksburg is located an hour south of Washington, DC and an hour north of Richmond, in one of the fastest growing regions in the state. One of the most historic cities in the country, Fredericksburg was the childhood home of George Washington and was the site of several major battles of the Civil War. Today the surrounding metropolitan population reaches upwards of 150,000 people yet still maintains the charm of a small town. The 40-block Historic District is located within easy walking distance of the campus and includes fine shopping, restaurants, movie theaters as well as historic attractions. Located on I-95, Fredericksburg offers access to both Washington and Richmond by Amtrak, various bus lines, and transportation service to National Airport in Washington and Richmond International. Fredericksburg is on the regularly scheduled commuter rail to Washington.

■ **UNIVERSITY OF RICHMOND**
410 Westhampton Way
Richmond, VA 23173
Tel: (804)289-8000; Free: 800-700-1662
Fax: (804)287-6003
E-mail: admissions@richmond.edu
Web Site: www.richmond.edu

Description: Independent, comprehensive, coed. Awards bachelor's, master's, and doctoral degrees. Founded 1830. Setting: 350-acre suburban campus. Endowment: $2.5 billion. Research spending for the previous fiscal year: $5 million. Educational spending for the previous fiscal year: $23,665 per student. Total enrollment: 4,002. Faculty: 439 (344 full-time, 95 part-time). Student-undergrad faculty ratio is 8:1. 11,882 applied, 30% were admitted. 56% from top 10% of their high school class, 86% from top quarter, 96% from top half. 29 National Merit Scholars, 23 class presidents, 8 valedictorians. Full-time: 3,019 students, 52% women, 48% men. Part-time: 208 students, 57% women, 43% men. Students come from 48 states and territories, 63 other countries, 81% from out-of-state. 0.1% American Indian or Alaska Native, non-Hispanic/Latino; 9% Hispanic/Latino; 7% Black or African American, non-Hispanic/Latino; 8% Asian, non-Hispanic/Latino; 10% international. 91% live on campus, 2% transferred in. Retention: 94% of full-time freshmen returned the following year. Academic areas with the most degrees conferred: business/marketing; social sciences; biological/life sciences. Core. Calendar: semesters. ESL program, services for LD students, advanced placement, self-designed majors, honors program, independent study, double major, summer session for credit, part-time degree program, internships. Off campus study at American University Washington Semester Program, Duke University Marine Sciences Laboratory, Marine Biological Laboratory Semester in Environmental Science - Woods Hole. Study abroad program. ROTC: Army.

Entrance Requirements: Options: electronic application, early decision, early action, deferred admission, international baccalaureate accepted. Required: essay, high school transcript, 1 recommendation, SAT or ACT. Entrance: very difficult. Application deadlines: 1/15, 11/1 for early decision, 11/1 for early action. Notification: 4/1, 12/15 for early decision, 1/20 for early action. SAT Reasoning Test deadline: 2/15. SAT Subject Test deadline: 2/15. Transfer credits accepted: Yes. Applicants placed on waiting list: 3,653. Wait-listed applicants offered admission: 28. Early decision applicants: 662. Early decision applicants admitted: 319.

Costs Per Year: Application fee: $50. Comprehensive fee: $67,590 includes full-time tuition ($54,690) and college room and board ($12,900). College room only: $6000. Part-time tuition: $2231 per credit hour.

Collegiate Environment: Orientation program. Drama-theater group, choral group, student-run newspaper, radio station. Social organizations: 192 open to all; national fraternities, national sororities; 22% of eligible men and 30% of eligible women are members. Most popular organizations: Greek Life, Sport Clubs, SpiderBoard Concert, SpiderFest, Block Parties. Major annual events: Homecoming, Pig Roast, SpiderFest. Student services: health clinic, personal-psychological counseling, women's center. Campus security: 24-hour emergency response devices and patrols, late night transport-escort service, controlled dormitory access. 2,857 college housing spaces available; 2,766 were occupied in 2018-19. Freshmen guaranteed college housing. Options: coed, men-only, women-only housing available. Boatwright Memorial Library plus 2 others. Books: 541,127 (physical), 578,842 (digital/electronic); Serial titles: 427 (physical), 154,436 (digital/electronic); Databases: 460. Weekly public service hours: 100; study areas open 24 hours, 5-7 days a week; students can reserve study rooms. Operations spending for the previous fiscal year: $14.2 million. 971 computers available on campus for general student use. A campuswide network can be accessed from student residence rooms and from off campus. Students can access

the following: online class registration. Staffed computer lab on campus provides training in use of computers, software, and the Internet.

■ UNIVERSITY OF VALLEY FORGE VIRGINIA CAMPUS
13909 Smoketown Rd.
Woodbridge, VA 22192
Tel: (703)580-4810; Free: 800-432-8322
Fax: (703)580-4806
Web Site: www.valleyforge.edu

Description: Independent Assemblies of God, 4-year, coed. Administratively affiliated with Valley Forge Christian College. Awards associate and bachelor's degrees. Setting: suburban campus with easy access to Washington, DC. Total enrollment: 131. Faculty: 36 (4 full-time, 32 part-time). Student-undergrad faculty ratio is 6:1. 53 applied, 81% were admitted. Full-time: 59 students, 56% women, 44% men. Part-time: 72 students, 67% women, 33% men. 11% Hispanic/Latino; 32% Black or African American, non-Hispanic/Latino; 2% Native Hawaiian or other Pacific Islander, non-Hispanic/Latino; 3% international. Core. Academic remediation for entering students, services for LD students, advanced placement, independent study, distance learning, double major, summer session for credit, part-time degree program, adult/continuing education programs, co-op programs and internships. Off campus study.

Entrance Requirements: Option: electronic application. Required: essay, high school transcript, minimum 1.5 high school GPA, interview, pastoral recommendation. Entrance: minimally difficult. Application deadline: rolling. Notification: continuous. Transfer credits accepted: Yes.

Collegiate Environment: Orientation program. Campus security: 24-hour emergency response devices. Off Site Library. 40 computers available on campus for general student use. Students can access the following: online class registration. Staffed computer lab on campus provides training in use of computers, software, and the Internet.

■ UNIVERSITY OF VIRGINIA
Charlottesville, VA 22903
Tel: (434)924-0311
Fax: (434)924-3587
E-mail: undergrad-admission@virginia.edu
Web Site: www.virginia.edu

Description: State-supported, university, coed. Awards bachelor's, master's, and doctoral degrees and post-master's certificates. Founded 1819. Setting: 1,167-acre suburban campus with easy access to Richmond. System endowment: $6.3 billion. Research spending for the previous fiscal year: $411.6 million. Educational spending for the previous fiscal year: $20,835 per student. Total enrollment: 27,639. Faculty: 1,573 (1,493 full-time, 80 part-time). Student-undergrad faculty ratio is 15:1. 37,182 applied, 26% were admitted. 90% from top 10% of their high school class, 98% from top quarter, 100% from top half. Full-time: 16,007 students, 55% women, 45% men. Part-time: 780 students, 64% women, 36% men. Students come from 52 states and territories, 125 other countries, 28% from out-of-state. 0.1% American Indian or Alaska Native, non-Hispanic/Latino; 6% Hispanic/Latino; 7% Black or African American, non-Hispanic/Latino; 15% Asian, non-Hispanic/Latino; 0.1% Native Hawaiian or other Pacific Islander, non-Hispanic/Latino; 4% international. 3% 25 or older, 38% live on campus, 4% transferred in. Retention: 97% of full-time freshmen returned the following year. Academic areas with the most degrees conferred: liberal arts/general studies; social sciences; engineering. Core. Calendar: semesters. ESL program, services for LD students, advanced placement, accelerated degree program, self-designed majors, honors program, independent study, distance learning, double major, summer session for credit, part-time degree program, adult/continuing education programs, co-op programs and internships, graduate courses open to undergrads. Study abroad program. ROTC: Army, Naval, Air Force.

Entrance Requirements: Options: electronic application, early action, deferred admission, international baccalaureate accepted. Required: essay, high school transcript, 2 recommendations, SAT or ACT. Entrance: very difficult. Application deadlines: 1/1, 11/1 for early action. Notification: 4/1, 1/31 for early action. Preference given to state residents, children of alumni. SAT Reasoning Test deadline: 1/1. SAT Subject Test deadline: 1/1. Transfer credits accepted: Yes. Applicants placed on waiting list: 5,972. Wait-listed applicants offered admission: 13. Early action applicants: 21,535. Early action applicants admitted: 5,964.

Collegiate Environment: Orientation program. Drama-theater group, choral group, marching band, student-run newspaper, radio station. Social organizations: national fraternities, national sororities, local fraternities, local

sororities; 31% of eligible men and 31% of eligible women are members. Most popular organizations: Madison House, student government, university guides, University Union, The Cavalier Daily. Major annual events: Family Weekend, Homecoming, Finals Weekend. Student services: legal services, health clinic, personal-psychological counseling, women's center. Campus security: 24-hour emergency response devices and patrols, student patrols, late night transport-escort service, controlled dormitory access. 6,425 college housing spaces available; 6,215 were occupied in 2018-19. Freshmen guaranteed college housing. On-campus residence required in freshman year. Option: coed housing available. Alderman Library plus 14 others. Books: 5.1 million (physical), 785,258 (digital/electronic); Serial titles: 7,910 (physical), 207,644 (digital/electronic); Databases: 1,340. Weekly public service hours: 149; study areas open 24 hours, 5-7 days a week; students can reserve study rooms. Operations spending for the previous fiscal year: $36.1 million. 250 computers available on campus for general student use. Computer purchase/lease plans available. A campuswide network can be accessed from student residence rooms and from off campus. Students can access the following: online class registration, online course management tool. Staffed computer lab on campus (open 24 hours a day) provides training in use of computers, software, and the Internet.

Community Environment: Charlottesville, situated in the foothills of the Blue Ridge Mountains, was the home of Thomas Jefferson and James Monroe. Numerous old homes and estates in Charlottesville and the surrounding areas, reveal Jefferson's architectural influence. All forms of commercial transportation are available. Albemarle County is known for its horses, dogs, fox hunting, and for its peach and apple orchards. The many outdoor activities include golf, tennis, hunting, fishing, and hiking. Some part-time employment is available for students. Points of interest include the Lewis and Clark Memorial, Monticello, the home of Thomas Jefferson, Old Courthouse, and the University of Virginia-founded by Thomas Jefferson.

■ THE UNIVERSITY OF VIRGINIA'S COLLEGE AT WISE
1 College Ave.
Wise, VA 24293
Tel: (276)328-0100; Free: 888-282-9324
Fax: (276)328-0251
E-mail: admissions@uvawise.edu
Web Site: www.uvawise.edu

Description: State-supported, 4-year, coed. Part of University of Virginia. Awards bachelor's degrees. Founded 1954. Setting: 396-acre small town campus. Endowment: $6.5 billion. Research spending for the previous fiscal year: $8144. Educational spending for the previous fiscal year: $8335 per student. Total enrollment: 2,095. Faculty: 162 (102 full-time, 60 part-time). Student-undergrad faculty ratio is 12:1. 845 applied, 78% were admitted. 18% from top 10% of their high school class, 44% from top quarter, 74% from top half. 2 valedictorians. Full-time: 1,210 students, 52% women, 48% men. Part-time: 885 students, 72% women, 28% men. Students come from 18 states and territories, 11 other countries, 6% from out-of-state. 0.2% American Indian or Alaska Native, non-Hispanic/Latino; 1% Hispanic/Latino; 12% Black or African American, non-Hispanic/Latino; 1% Asian, non-Hispanic/Latino. 8% 25 or older, 23% live on campus, 5% transferred in. Retention: 68% of full-time freshmen returned the following year. Academic areas with the most degrees conferred: education; business/marketing; social sciences. Core. Calendar: semesters. Academic remediation for entering students, services for LD students, advanced placement, accelerated degree program, self-designed majors, honors program, independent study, distance learning, double major, summer session for credit, part-time degree program, adult/continuing education programs, co-op programs and internships. ROTC: Army.

Entrance Requirements: Options: early admission, early action, international baccalaureate accepted. Required: high school transcript, minimum 2.3 high school GPA, SAT or ACT. Recommended: 2 recommendations. Entrance: moderately difficult. Application deadlines: 8/1, 12/1 for early action. Notification: 8/20, 12/15 for early action. SAT Reasoning Test deadline: 5/1. Transfer credits accepted: Yes.

Collegiate Environment: Orientation program. Drama-theater group, choral group, marching band, student-run newspaper, radio station. Social organizations: 60 open to all; national fraternities, national sororities, local fraternities, local sororities. Most popular organizations: Student Government, Student Activities Board, Multicultural Association, Residence Hall Association, intramurals. Major annual events: Holly Ball, Homecoming. Student services: health clinic, personal-psychological counseling. Campus security: 24-hour emergency response devices and patrols, student patrols, late night transport-escort service, self-defense, informal discussions, pamphlets/posters/films, and crime prevention office. University of Virginia's College at Wise Library. Books: 148,612 (physical), 179,697 (digital/electronic); Serial titles: 719 (physical), 3,284 (digital/electronic); Databases: 124. Weekly public service hours: 78; study areas open 24 hours, 5-7 days a week; students can reserve study rooms. Operations spending for the previous fiscal year: $928,656. 330 computers available on campus for general student use. Computer purchase/lease plans available. A campuswide network can be accessed from student residence rooms and from off campus. Students can access the following: online class registration. Staffed computer lab on campus provides training in use of computers, software, and the Internet.

■ **VIRGINIA BAPTIST COLLEGE**
4111 Plank Rd.
Fredericksburg, VA 22407
Web Site: www.vbc.edu
Description: Independent, comprehensive, coed. Awards associate, bachelor's, and master's degrees.

■ **VIRGINIA COMMONWEALTH UNIVERSITY**
901 W Franklin St.
Richmond, VA 23284-9005
Tel: (804)828-0100; Free: 800-841-3638
Fax: (804)828-1899
Web Site: www.vcu.edu
Description: State-supported, university, coed. Awards bachelor's, master's, and doctoral degrees and post-master's certificates. Founded 1838. Setting: 174-acre urban campus. Endowment: $147.3 million. Research spending for the previous fiscal year: $182.7 million. Educational spending for the previous fiscal year: $13,349 per student. Total enrollment: 31,076. Faculty: 2,158 (1,284 full-time, 874 part-time). Student-undergrad faculty ratio is 18:1. 16,847 applied, 77% were admitted. 17% from top 10% of their high school class, 27% from top quarter, 44% from top half. Full-time: 20,508 students, 61% women, 39% men. Part-time: 3,550 students, 57% women, 43% men. Students come from 44 states and territories, 80 other countries, 7% from out-of-state. 0.2% American Indian or Alaska Native, non-Hispanic/Latino; 10% Hispanic/Latino; 19% Black or African American, non-Hispanic/Latino; 14% Asian, non-Hispanic/Latino; 0.1% Native Hawaiian or other Pacific Islander, non-Hispanic/Latino; 3% international. 10% 25 or older, 28% live on campus, 7% transferred in. Retention: 85% of full-time freshmen returned the following year. Academic areas with the most degrees conferred: business/marketing; visual and performing arts; psychology. Core. Calendar: semesters. Academic remediation for entering students, ESL program, services for LD students, advanced placement, accelerated degree program, self-designed majors, freshman honors college, honors program, independent study, distance learning, double major, summer session for credit, part-time degree program, adult/continuing education programs, co-op programs and internships, graduate courses open to undergrads. Off campus study. Study abroad program. ROTC: Army (c).
Entrance Requirements: Options: electronic application, early admission, deferred admission. Required: high school transcript. Required for some: SAT or ACT. Application deadline: 1/15. Notification: 11/1. SAT Reasoning Test deadline: 2/1. Transfer credits accepted: Yes. Applicants placed on waiting list: 386. Wait-listed applicants offered admission: 195.
Costs Per Year: Application fee: $65. State resident tuition: $12,094 full-time, $417 per credit hour part-time. Nonresident tuition: $32,742 full-time, $1129 per credit hour part-time. Mandatory fees: $2396 full-time, $9 per credit hour part-time. College room and board: $10,428. Room and board charges vary according to board plan and housing facility.
Collegiate Environment: Orientation program. Drama-theater group, choral group, student-run newspaper, radio station. Social organizations: 550 open to all; national fraternities, national sororities, local fraternities, local sororities. Major annual events: Welcome Week, Intercultural Festival, Homecoming. Student services: health clinic, personal-psychological counseling, women's center. Campus security: 24-hour emergency response devices and patrols, student patrols, late night transport-escort service, controlled dormitory access, security personnel in res. halls, RAD classes/special event coverage, more than 90 sworn officers and 200 security personnel. 6,585 college housing spaces available. Freshmen given priority for college housing. Option: coed housing available. Cabell Library and Thompkins McCaw Library plus 3 others. Databases: 500. Weekly public service hours: 146; study areas open 24 hours, 5-7 days a week; students can reserve study rooms. Operations spending for the previous fiscal year: $23.6 million. 2,500 computers available on campus for general student use. Computer

purchase/lease plans available. A computer is required for all students. A campuswide network can be accessed from student residence rooms and from off campus. Students can access the following: online class registration. Staffed computer lab on campus provides training in use of computers, software, and the Internet.
Community Environment: See University of Richmond.

■ **VIRGINIA HIGHLANDS COMMUNITY COLLEGE**
100 VHCC Dr. Abingdon
Abingdon, VA 24212
Tel: (276)739-2400; Free: 877-207-6115
Fax: (276)739-2590
E-mail: kcheers@vhcc.edu
Web Site: www.vhcc.edu
Description: State-supported, 2-year, coed. Part of Virginia Community College System. Awards certificates, diplomas, transfer associate, and terminal associate degrees. Founded 1967. Setting: 100-acre small town campus. Total enrollment: 2,580. Faculty: 97 (58 full-time, 39 part-time). 15% from top 10% of their high school class, 35% from top quarter, 65% from top half. Full-time: 1,001 students, 52% women, 48% men. Part-time: 1,579 students, 55% women, 45% men. Students come from 7 states and territories, 9% from out-of-state. 52% 25 or older, 7% transferred in. Retention: 47% of full-time freshmen returned the following year. Calendar: semesters. Academic remediation for entering students, services for LD students, advanced placement, summer session for credit, part-time degree program, adult/continuing education programs, co-op programs.
Entrance Requirements: Open admission except for nursing, radiology, physical therapy programs. Options: early admission, deferred admission. Required: high school transcript. Entrance: noncompetitive. Application deadline: rolling. Notification: continuous. Preference given to district, then state residents.
Collegiate Environment: Orientation program. Drama-theater group, choral group. Student services: personal-psychological counseling. 240 computers available on campus for general student use. A campuswide network can be accessed from off-campus. Staffed computer lab on campus.
Community Environment: Abingdon is known as a handicraft center as well as being the largest burley tobacco market and the largest livestock auction in Virginia. Commercial transportation is available. The Blue Ridge and Holston Mountains are nearby providing facilities for many outdoor activities.

■ **VIRGINIA INTERNATIONAL UNIVERSITY**
4401 Village Dr.
Fairfax, VA 22030
Tel: (703)591-7042; Free: 800-514-6848
Fax: (703)591-7048
E-mail: admissions@viu.edu
Web Site: www.viu.edu
Description: Proprietary, comprehensive, coed. Awards bachelor's and master's degrees.

■ **VIRGINIA MILITARY INSTITUTE**
319 Letcher Ave.
Lexington, VA 24450
Tel: (540)464-7230; Free: 800-767-4207
Fax: (540)464-7746
E-mail: admissions@vmi.edu
Web Site: www.vmi.edu
Description: State-supported, 4-year, coed. Awards bachelor's degrees. Founded 1839. Setting: 134-acre small town campus. Endowment: $381.9 million. Research spending for the previous fiscal year: $100,000. Educational spending for the previous fiscal year: $12,932 per student. Total enrollment: 1,722. Faculty: 207 (136 full-time, 71 part-time). Student-undergrad faculty ratio is 11:1. 1,718 applied, 53% were admitted. 15% from top 10% of their high school class, 45% from top quarter, 81% from top half. Full-time: 1,722 students, 12% women, 88% men. Students come from 46 states and territories, 6 other countries, 36% from out-of-state. 0.5% American Indian or Alaska Native, non-Hispanic/Latino; 7% Hispanic/Latino; 6% Black or African American, non-Hispanic/Latino; 4% Asian, non-Hispanic/Latino; 0.3% Native Hawaiian or other Pacific Islander, non-Hispanic/Latino; 2% international. 100% live on campus, 3% transferred in. Retention: 87% of full-time freshmen returned the following year. Academic areas with the most degrees conferred: social sciences; engineering; biological/life sciences. Core. Calendar: semesters. Services for LD students, advanced placement,

honors program, independent study, double major, summer session for credit, internships. Study abroad program. ROTC: Army, Naval, Air Force.

Entrance Requirements: Options: electronic application, early decision, international baccalaureate accepted. Required: high school transcript, SAT or ACT. Recommended: essay, 2 recommendations, interview, statement of good standing from prior institution. Entrance: moderately difficult. Application deadlines: 2/1, 11/15 for early decision. Notification: continuous, 12/15 for early decision. SAT Reasoning Test deadline: 5/1. Transfer credits accepted: Yes. Applicants placed on waiting list: 309. Wait-listed applicants offered admission: 4. Early decision applicants: 408. Early decision applicants admitted: 232.

Costs Per Year: Application fee: $40. State resident tuition: $9284 full-time, $340 per credit hour part-time. Nonresident tuition: $36,128 full-time, $1060 per credit hour part-time. Mandatory fees: $9578 full-time, $72 per term part-time. College room and board: $9482.

Collegiate Environment: Orientation program. Drama-theater group, choral group, marching band, student-run newspaper. Social organizations: 40 open to all. Most popular organizations: Newman Club, Officers Christian Fellowship, strength and fitness organizations, Promaji, Pre-Law Society. Major annual events: New Market Day, Parents' Weekend, Founder's Day. Student services: health clinic, personal-psychological counseling. Campus security: 24-hour emergency response devices and patrols, student patrols. Preston Library. Books: 280,000 (physical), 240,000 (digital/electronic); Databases: 150. Weekly public service hours: 113. Operations spending for the previous fiscal year: $2.7 million. 200 computers available on campus for general student use. A campuswide network can be accessed from student residence rooms and from off campus. Students can access the following: online class registration. Staffed computer lab on campus provides training in use of computers, software, and the Internet.

Community Environment: VMI offers a small town flavor, with a hallowed history and breathtaking scenery.

■ **VIRGINIA POLYTECHNIC INSTITUTE AND STATE UNIVERSITY**
Blacksburg, VA 24061
Tel: (540)231-6000
Fax: (540)231-3242
Web Site: www.vt.edu

Description: State-supported, university, coed. Awards bachelor's, master's, and doctoral degrees and post-master's certificates. Founded 1872. Setting: 2,600-acre small town campus. Endowment: $1.1 billion. Total enrollment: 34,850. Faculty: 2,256 (1,841 full-time, 415 part-time). Student-undergrad faculty ratio is 14:1. 31,936 applied, 65% were admitted. 38% from top 10% of their high school class, 77% from top quarter, 97% from top half. Full-time: 27,162 students, 43% women, 57% men. Part-time: 631 students, 37% women, 63% men. Students come from 48 states and territories, 86 other countries, 24% from out-of-state. 0.1% American Indian or Alaska Native, non-Hispanic/Latino; 6% Hispanic/Latino; 4% Black or African American, non-Hispanic/Latino; 10% Asian, non-Hispanic/Latino; 0.1% Native Hawaiian or other Pacific Islander, non-Hispanic/Latino; 7% international. 2% 25 or older, 33% live on campus, 4% transferred in. Academic areas with the most degrees conferred: engineering; business/marketing; family and consumer sciences. Core. Calendar: semesters. ESL program, services for LD students, advanced placement, accelerated degree program, honors program, independent study, distance learning, double major, summer session for credit, part-time degree program, adult/continuing education programs, co-op programs and internships, graduate courses open to undergrads. Study abroad program. ROTC: Army, Naval, Air Force.

Entrance Requirements: Options: electronic application, early admission, early decision, deferred admission, international baccalaureate accepted. Required: high school transcript, SAT or ACT. Recommended: essay. Entrance: moderately difficult. Application deadlines: 1/15, 11/1 for early decision plan 1, 12/15 for early decision plan 2, 12/1 for early action. Notification: 4/1, 2/22 for early action. Applicants placed on waiting list: 6,920. Wait-listed applicants offered admission: 545. Early decision applicants: 2,952. Early decision applicants admitted: 1,341.

Costs Per Year: Application fee: $60. State resident tuition: $11,420 full-time, $475.75 per hour part-time. Nonresident tuition: $29,104 full-time, $1,212.75 per hour part-time. Mandatory fees: $2200 full-time, $550 per term part-time. Full-time tuition and fees vary according to course load and program. Part-time tuition and fees vary according to course load and program. College room and board: $8934. Room and board charges vary according to board plan and housing facility.

Collegiate Environment: Orientation program. Drama-theater group, choral group, marching band, student-run newspaper, radio station. Social

organizations: 700 open to all; national fraternities, national sororities, local fraternities; 13% of eligible men and 19% of eligible women are members. Most popular organizations: Virginia Tech Union, Student Government Association, International student organizations. Major annual events: The Big Event, International Street Fair, Homecoming Week. Student services: legal services, health clinic, personal-psychological counseling, women's center. Campus security: 24-hour emergency response devices and patrols, student patrols, late night transport-escort service, controlled dormitory access. 9,300 college housing spaces available; 9,213 were occupied in 2018-19. Freshmen guaranteed college housing. On-campus residence required in freshman year. Options: coed, men-only, women-only housing available. Newman Library plus 2 others. Study areas open 24 hours, 5-7 days a week.

Community Environment: Blacksburg is a town with a population of 39,000 located on a plateau between the Blue Ridge and Allegheny Mountains, 38 miles southwest of Roanoke. Bus service is convenient and free to the university community. Civic and service organizations are active and welcome student participation. Outdoor recreation opportunities include hiking, horseback riding, fishing, swimming, boating, water skiing, and camping. Nearby are the Jefferson National Forest, the Appalachian Trail, the New River, and other parks and lakes.

■ **VIRGINIA STATE UNIVERSITY**
1 Hayden Dr.
Petersburg, VA 23806-0001
Tel: (804)524-5000; Free: 800-871-7611
Fax: (804)524-5055
E-mail: rhall@vsu.edu
Web Site: www.vsu.edu

Description: State-supported, comprehensive, coed. Part of State Council of Higher Education for Virginia. Awards bachelor's, master's, and doctoral degrees. Founded 1882. Setting: 236-acre suburban campus with easy access to Richmond. Endowment: $32.5 million. Research spending for the previous fiscal year: $6.5 million. Educational spending for the previous fiscal year: $8266 per student. Total enrollment: 4,584. Faculty: 480 (282 full-time, 198 part-time). Student-undergrad faculty ratio is 13:1. 5,722 applied, 94% were admitted. 5% from top 10% of their high school class, 17% from top quarter, 57% from top half. Full-time: 4,023 students, 57% women, 43% men. Part-time: 142 students, 60% women, 40% men. Students come from 39 states and territories, 25% from out-of-state. 0.3% American Indian or Alaska Native, non-Hispanic/Latino; 1% Hispanic/Latino; 61% Black or African American, non-Hispanic/Latino; 0.5% Asian, non-Hispanic/Latino; 0.2% international. 10% 25 or older, 6% transferred in. Retention: 74% of full-time freshmen returned the following year. Academic areas with the most degrees conferred: homeland security, law enforcement, firefighting, and protective services; education; business/marketing. Core. Calendar: semesters. Services for LD students, advanced placement, self-designed majors, honors program, independent study, double major, summer session for credit, part-time degree program, adult/continuing education programs, co-op programs and internships. Off campus study. Study abroad program. ROTC: Army.

Entrance Requirements: Options: electronic application, international baccalaureate accepted. Required: high school transcript, minimum 2.2 high school GPA, 2 recommendations, SAT or ACT. Recommended: essay. Entrance: minimally difficult. Application deadline: 5/1. Notification: continuous. SAT Reasoning Test deadline: 7/1. Transfer credits accepted: Yes.

Costs Per Year: Application fee: $25. State resident tuition: $5540 full-time, $396 per credit hour part-time. Nonresident tuition: $16,060 full-time, $876 per credit hour part-time. Mandatory fees: $3516 full-time, $10 per credit hour part-time. Full-time tuition and fees vary according to course load. Part-time tuition and fees vary according to course load. College room and board: $11,208. College room only: $6548. Room and board charges vary according to board plan and housing facility.

Collegiate Environment: Orientation program. Drama-theater group, choral group, marching band, student-run newspaper. Social organizations: 54 open to all; national fraternities, national sororities, local fraternities, local sororities. Most popular organizations: AbstraKt Entertainment, Golden Key Honor Society, The Betterment of Brothers and Sisters, Diversified Virtue Entertainment, Sankofa. Major annual events: Homecoming, Spring Fling, Welcome to the Land of Troy. Student services: health clinic, personal-psychological counseling. Campus security: 24-hour emergency response devices and patrols, late night transport-escort service, controlled dormitory access. Johnston Memorial Library. Books: 434,496 (physical); Serial titles: 5,805 (physical); Databases: 245. Weekly public service hours: 82. Operations spending for the previous fiscal year: $2.1 million. 1,400 computers available on campus for general student use. A campuswide network can be accessed from student residence rooms and from off campus. Students can access the following: online class registration. Staffed computer lab on campus (open 24 hours a day).

Community Environment: The immediate environs of the university offer an exciting atmosphere involving a variety of interesting sites and events for leisure-time activities. The Petersburg National Battlefield and Old Blandford Church are historical landmarks that are recognized in the National Historical Register. Other popular attractions include museums, art exhibits, parks, the Petersburg Symphony, and theatrical groups. The close proximity of Virginia's capital, Richmond, 25 minutes north, enhances the"VSU experience." Colonial Williamsburg and nearby Busch Gardens; Norfolk, home of one of America's busiest seaports; Virginia Beach, the top tourist attraction in the state; and the Blue Ridge Mountains are within easy driving distance.

■ VIRGINIA UNION UNIVERSITY

1500 N Lombardy St.
Richmond, VA 23220-1170
Tel: (804)257-5600; Free: 800-368-3227
E-mail: dvmorrison@vuu.edu
Web Site: www.vuu.edu

Description: Independent Baptist, comprehensive, coed. Awards bachelor's, master's, and doctoral degrees. Founded 1865. Setting: 100-acre urban campus. Total enrollment: 1,922. Faculty: 138 (75 full-time, 63 part-time). Student-undergrad faculty ratio is 15:1. 7,337 applied, 49% were admitted. 5% from top 10% of their high school class, 11% from top quarter, 34% from top half. Full-time: 1,419 students, 57% women, 43% men. Part-time: 90 students, 76% women, 24% men. Students come from 22 states and territories, 19 other countries, 46% from out-of-state. 0.7% American Indian or Alaska Native, non-Hispanic/Latino; 0.9% Hispanic/Latino; 92% Black or African American, non-Hispanic/Latino; 0.3% Asian, non-Hispanic/Latino; 0.4% international. 1% 25 or older, 72% live on campus, 6% transferred in. Retention: 60% of full-time freshmen returned the following year. Academic areas with the most degrees conferred: social sciences; business/marketing; biological/life sciences. Core. Calendar: semesters. Academic remediation for entering students, ESL program, advanced placement, honors program, double major, summer session for credit, adult/continuing education programs, co-op programs and internships. Off campus study at University of Richmond, Virginia Commonwealth University, Virginia State University. ROTC: Army (c).

Entrance Requirements: Options: electronic application, deferred admission. Required: high school transcript, SAT or ACT. Recommended: essay. Required for some: interview. Entrance: moderately difficult. Application deadline: rolling. Notification: continuous. SAT Reasoning Test deadline: 6/30. SAT Subject Test deadline: 6/30. Transfer credits accepted: Yes. Applicants placed on waiting list: 0. Wait-listed applicants offered admission: 0.

Costs Per Year: Application fee: $25. One-time mandatory fee: $350. Comprehensive fee: $26,046 includes full-time tuition ($15,530), mandatory fees ($1918), and college room and board ($8598). College room only: $3976. Full-time tuition and fees vary according to course level, course load, and reciprocity agreements. Room and board charges vary according to housing facility. Part-time tuition: $482 per credit hour. Part-time mandatory fees: $43 per credit hour. Part-time tuition and fees vary according to course level, course load, and reciprocity agreements.

Collegiate Environment: Orientation program. Drama-theater group, choral group, marching band, student-run newspaper. Social organizations: 51 open to all; national fraternities, national sororities; 10% of eligible men and 10% of eligible women are members. Most popular organizations: Student Government Association, Panther PALS (Peer Advisory Leadership Students), Men About Positive Purpose, NAACP, Student Athlete Advisory Committee. Major annual events: Homecoming, Founder's Day, Panther-Fest. Student services: health clinic, personal-psychological counseling. Campus security: 24-hour emergency response devices and patrols, controlled dormitory access. L. Douglas Wilder Learning Resource Center and Library plus 1 other. Books: 123,475 (physical), 66,271 (digital/electronic); Databases: 100. Weekly public service hours: 41; students can reserve study rooms. 237 computers available on campus for general student use. A campuswide network can be accessed from student residence rooms. Students can access the following: online class registration. Staffed computer lab on campus provides training in use of the Internet.

Community Environment: See University of Richmond.

■ VIRGINIA UNIVERSITY OF LYNCHBURG

2058 Garfield Ave.
Lynchburg, VA 24501-6417

Tel: (804)528-5276
Fax: (804)528-4257
E-mail: cglass@vul.edu
Web Site: www.vul.edu

Description: Independent Baptist, comprehensive, coed. Awards associate, bachelor's, master's, and doctoral degrees. Founded 1886. Setting: urban campus. Educational spending for the previous fiscal year: $5550 per student. Total enrollment: 327. Faculty: 66 (22 full-time, 44 part-time). Student-undergrad faculty ratio is 9:1. Full-time: 138 students, 57% women, 43% men. Part-time: 95 students, 47% women, 53% men. Students come from 3 states and territories, 1% from out-of-state. 61% 25 or older, 14% live on campus, 19% transferred in. Retention: 100% of full-time freshmen returned the following year. Academic areas with the most degrees conferred: business/marketing; social sciences. Core. Calendar: semesters. Academic remediation for entering students, services for LD students, advanced placement, independent study, distance learning, summer session for credit, part-time degree program, external degree program, adult/continuing education programs, graduate courses open to undergrads.

Entrance Requirements: Open admission. Option: international baccalaureate accepted. Required: high school transcript. Entrance: noncompetitive. Application deadline: rolling. Notification: continuous. Transfer credits accepted: Yes.

Collegiate Environment: Orientation program. Choral group. Social organizations: 3 open to all. Most popular organizations: choir, community service, intramural basketball. Major annual events: Founder's Day, Sacrificial Day, Multicultural Day. Student services: health clinic, personal-psychological counseling. Campus security: 24-hour emergency response devices, monitored camera security system with electronic backup saved. Mary Jane Cachelin Library. 10 computers available on campus for general student use. A campuswide network can be accessed from student residence rooms and from off campus. Staffed computer lab on campus provides training in use of computers, software, and the Internet.

■ VIRGINIA WESLEYAN UNIVERSITY

5817 Wesleyan Dr.
Virginia Beach, VA 23455
Tel: (757)455-3200; Free: 800-737-8684
Fax: (757)461-5238
E-mail: admissions@vwu.edu
Web Site: www.vwu.edu

Description: Independent United Methodist, comprehensive, coed. Awards bachelor's and master's degrees. Founded 1961. Setting: 284-acre urban campus with easy access to Hampton Roads. Endowment: $56.6 million. Educational spending for the previous fiscal year: $10,062 per student. Total enrollment: 1,470. Faculty: 128 (91 full-time, 37 part-time). Student-undergrad faculty ratio is 12:1. 2,200 applied, 71% were admitted. 15% from top 10% of their high school class, 33% from top quarter, 63% from top half. Full-time: 1,354 students, 60% women, 40% men. Part-time: 82 students, 60% women, 40% men. Students come from 34 states and territories, 11 other countries, 24% from out-of-state. 1% American Indian or Alaska Native, non-Hispanic/Latino; 8% Hispanic/Latino; 26% Black or African American, non-Hispanic/Latino; 1% Asian, non-Hispanic/Latino; 0.1% Native Hawaiian or other Pacific Islander, non-Hispanic/Latino; 3% international. 10% 25 or older, 64% live on campus, 7% transferred in. Retention: 63% of full-time freshmen returned the following year. Academic areas with the most degrees conferred: business/marketing; homeland security, law enforcement, firefighting, and protective services; psychology. Core. Calendar: 4-1-4. Academic remediation for entering students, services for LD students, advanced placement, self-designed majors, freshman honors college, honors program, independent study, double major, summer session for credit, part-time degree program, external degree program, adult/continuing education programs, internships. Off campus study at Old Dominion University, Norfolk State University, Virginia Tidewater Consortium for Higher Education. Study abroad program. ROTC: Army (c).

Entrance Requirements: Options: electronic application, international baccalaureate accepted. Required: high school transcript, SAT or ACT. Recommended: recommendations. Required for some: interview. Entrance: moderately difficult. Application deadline: rolling. Notification: continuous. SAT Reasoning Test deadline: 7/1. Transfer credits accepted: Yes.

Costs Per Year: One-time mandatory fee: $1520. Comprehensive fee: $45,916 includes full-time tuition ($36,010), mandatory fees ($650), and college room and board ($9256). Full-time tuition and fees vary according to course load. Room and board charges vary according to board plan and housing facility. Part-time tuition: $1500 per credit hour. Part-time tuition varies according to course load.

Collegiate Environment: Orientation program. Drama-theater group, choral group, student-run newspaper, radio station. Social organizations: 60 open to all; national fraternities, national sororities; 7% of eligible men and 15% of eligible women are members. Most popular organizations: Wesleyan Activities Council, community service, Student Government Association, student newspaper, Black Student Union. Major annual events: Homecoming, Lake Taylor Music Festival, Seafood Party in the Dell. Student services: health clinic, personal-psychological counseling, women's center. Campus security: 24-hour emergency response devices and patrols, late night transport-escort service, controlled dormitory access, well-lit pathways. H. C. Hofheimer II Library plus 1 other. Books: 118,216 (physical), 256,770 (digital/electronic); Serial titles: 111 (physical), 71,260 (digital/electronic); Databases: 73. Weekly public service hours: 93; study areas open 24 hours, 5-7 days a week; students can reserve study rooms. Operations spending for the previous fiscal year: $612,280. 137 computers available on campus for general student use. Computer purchase/lease plans available. A campuswide network can be accessed from student residence rooms. Students can access the following: online class registration. Staffed computer lab on campus provides training in use of computers, software, and the Internet.

Community Environment: Tidewater, Virginia, is the cultural center of the Commonwealth. Norfolk features the Chrysler Museum, MacArthur Memorial, Scope Arena, Chrysler Hall for professional theatre, an opera house, and is headquarters of the Virginia Orchestra Group, Feldman String Quartet, and the Tidewater Ballet Association. Virginia Beach, in addition to its world-famous beaches, is proud of Seashore State Park, the Little Theater, Edgar Cayce's Association for Research and Enlightenment, the Virginia Beach Pops and other groups. Within one hour's driving time are Colonial Williamsburg, Yorktown and Jamestown, several nationally known museums including the Mariners Museum, and Busch Gardens.

■ VIRGINIA WESTERN COMMUNITY COLLEGE

PO Box 14007
Roanoke, VA 24038
Tel: (540)857-7311
Fax: (540)857-7204
Web Site: www.virginiawestern.edu

Description: State-supported, 2-year, coed. Part of Virginia Community College System. Awards certificates, transfer associate, and terminal associate degrees. Founded 1966. Setting: 70-acre suburban campus. Total enrollment: 8,632. Student-undergrad faculty ratio is 34:1. 2,770 applied. Full-time: 2,527 students, 55% women, 45% men. Part-time: 6,105 students, 55% women, 45% men. Students come from 34 states and territories, 62 other countries, 2% from out-of-state. 0.3% American Indian or Alaska Native, non-Hispanic/Latino; 3% Hispanic/Latino; 15% Black or African American, non-Hispanic/Latino; 3% Asian, non-Hispanic/Latino; 0.1% Native Hawaiian or other Pacific Islander, non-Hispanic/Latino; 0.3% international. 32% 25 or older, 3% transferred in. Retention: 53% of full-time freshmen returned the following year. Core. Calendar: semesters. Academic remediation for entering students, ESL program, services for LD students, advanced placement, honors program, independent study, distance learning, double major, summer session for credit, part-time degree program, co-op programs and internships.

Entrance Requirements: Open admission except for health technology programs. Options: electronic application, early admission, deferred admission. Recommended: high school transcript. Required for some: high school transcript. Entrance: noncompetitive. Application deadline: rolling. Notification: continuous. Preference given to local residents.

Costs Per Year: Application fee: $0. State resident tuition: $4680 full-time, $156 per credit hour part-time. Nonresident tuition: $9978 full-time, $333 per credit hour part-time. Mandatory fees: $675 full-time, $22.49 per credit hour part-time.

Collegiate Environment: Drama-theater group, student-run newspaper. Major annual events: Spring Fling and Art Show, Warm Welcome. Student services: personal-psychological counseling. Campus security: 24-hour emergency response devices and patrols, late night transport-escort service. Brown Library.

Community Environment: Roanoke is a manufacturing, regional service and trading center, and a metropolitan area with all modes of transportation available. Community facilities include libraries, YMCA, YWCA, many churches, hospitals, and a number of the civic and service organizations. Part-time employment opportunities are available to certain students. Roanoke is headquarters for the Norfolk and Western Railway System and the Blue Ridge Parkway. Smith Mountain Lake is a favorite water recreation area. Carvin's Cove Lake nine and one-half miles north offers fishing, boat-

ing, and picnicking. Some of the points of interest are the Crystal Spring, Mill Mountain, and Transportation Museum.

■ WASHINGTON AND LEE UNIVERSITY

204 W Washington St.
Lexington, VA 24450
Tel: (540)458-8400
Fax: (540)463-8062
E-mail: admissions@wlu.edu
Web Site: www.wlu.edu

Description: Independent, comprehensive, coed. Awards bachelor's and doctoral degrees. Founded 1749. Setting: 415-acre small town campus. Endowment: $1.5 billion. Research spending for the previous fiscal year: $1.9 million. Educational spending for the previous fiscal year: $32,849 per student. Total enrollment: 2,220. Faculty: 234 (204 full-time, 30 part-time). Student-undergrad faculty ratio is 8:1. 5,455 applied, 22% were admitted. 81% from top 10% of their high school class, 96% from top quarter, 100% from top half. Full-time: 1,823 students, 48% women, 52% men. Part-time: 4 students, 25% women, 75% men. Students come from 50 states and territories, 33 other countries, 84% from out-of-state. 5% Hispanic/Latino; 2% Black or African American, non-Hispanic/Latino; 3% Asian, non-Hispanic/Latino; 4% international. 75% live on campus, 1% transferred in. Retention: 96% of full-time freshmen returned the following year. Academic areas with the most degrees conferred: business/marketing; social sciences; biological/life sciences; foreign languages and literature. Core. Calendar: 4-4-2. Services for LD students, advanced placement, self-designed majors, honors program, independent study, double major, internships, graduate courses open to undergrads. Off campus study at Hampden-Sydney College, Mary Baldwin College, Randolph-Macon College, Randolph College, Sweet Briar College, Hollins University, Bates College, Morehouse College, Spelman College, Virginia Military Institute. Study abroad program. ROTC: Army (c).

Entrance Requirements: Options: electronic application, early decision, deferred admission, international baccalaureate accepted. Required: high school transcript, 3 recommendations, SAT or ACT. Recommended: essay, interview. Entrance: most difficult. Application deadlines: 1/1, 11/1 for early decision. Notification: 4/1, 12/22 for early decision. SAT Reasoning Test deadline: 2/15. Transfer credits accepted: Yes. Applicants placed on waiting list: 1,634. Wait-listed applicants offered admission: 32. Early decision applicants: 579. Early decision applicants admitted: 268.

Costs Per Year: Application fee: $60. Comprehensive fee: $66,380 includes full-time tuition ($51,420), mandatory fees ($1035), and college room and board ($13,925). College room only: $7300. Full-time tuition and fees vary according to degree level. Room and board charges vary according to board plan. Part-time tuition: $1714 per credit hour. Part-time tuition varies according to degree level.

Collegiate Environment: Orientation program. Drama-theater group, choral group, student-run newspaper, radio station. Social organizations: 130 open to all; national fraternities, national sororities, local fraternities; 73% of eligible men and 77% of eligible women are members. Most popular organizations: Mock Convention, General Activities Board, Nabors Service League, Outing Club, Sports Clubs. Major annual events: Fancy Dress Ball, Homecoming, Alumni Weekend. Student services: health clinic, personal-psychological counseling. Campus security: 24-hour emergency response devices and patrols, late night transport-escort service, controlled dormitory access, Emergency Alert System. 1,494 college housing spaces available; 1,376 were occupied in 2018-19. Freshmen guaranteed college housing. On-campus residence required through junior year. Options: coed, men-only, women-only housing available. James G. Leyburn Library plus 2 others. Books: 1 million (physical), 321,493 (digital/electronic); Serial titles: 66,967 (digital/electronic); Databases: 441. Study areas open 24 hours, 5-7 days a week; students can reserve study rooms. Operations spending for the previous fiscal year: $5.3 million. 176 computers available on campus for general student use. A campuswide network can be accessed from student residence rooms and from off campus. Students can access the following: online class registration. Staffed computer lab on campus provides training in use of computers, software, and the Internet.

Community Environment: Lexington is located in the Shenandoah Valley of Virginia between the Blue Ridge and Allegheny Mountains. Two of the greatest Confederate heroes, Robert E. Lee and Thomas J. "Stonewall" Jackson, lived and are buried in Lexington, the "Shrine of the South." Bus transportation is available. Some of the points of interest are the Natural Bridge, Lee Chapel, Home of "Stonewall" Jackson, Virginia Military Institute, and Washington and Lee University. Cyrus McCormick, inventor of the reaper, lived nearby. Lexington is also the home of the Virginia Horse Center.

■ **WAVE LEADERSHIP COLLEGE**
1000 N Great Neck Rd.
Virginia Beach, VA 23454
Description: Independent religious, 2-year, coed.

■ **WYTHEVILLE COMMUNITY COLLEGE**
1000 E Main St.
Wytheville, VA 24382-3308
Tel: (276)223-4700; Free: 800-468-1195
Fax: (276)223-4778
Web Site: www.wcc.vccs.edu
Description: State-supported, 2-year, coed. Part of Virginia Community College System. Awards certificates, diplomas, transfer associate, and terminal associate degrees. Founded 1963. Setting: 141-acre rural campus. Educational spending for the previous fiscal year: $5621 per student. Total enrollment: 2,745. Faculty: 137 (40 full-time, 97 part-time). Student-undergrad faculty ratio is 23:1. Students come from 9 states and territories, 2% from out-of-state. 0.4% American Indian or Alaska Native, non-Hispanic/Latino; 2% Hispanic/Latino; 4% Black or African American, non-Hispanic/Latino; 0.8% Asian, non-Hispanic/Latino; 0.1% Native Hawaiian or other Pacific Islander, non-Hispanic/Latino. 26% 25 or older. Retention: 62% of full-time freshmen returned the following year. Core. Calendar: semesters. Academic remediation for entering students, services for LD students, advanced placement, independent study, distance learning, summer session for credit, part-time degree program, external degree program, adult/continuing education programs.

Entrance Requirements: Open admission. Options: electronic application, early admission. Required: high school transcript. Required for some: interview. Entrance: noncompetitive. Application deadline: rolling. Notification: continuous. Preference given to service region residents for allied health programs.
Costs Per Year: State resident tuition: $4620 full-time, $154 per credit hour part-time. Nonresident tuition: $9918 full-time, $330.60 per credit hour part-time. Mandatory fees: $105 full-time, $3.50 per credit hour part-time.
Collegiate Environment: Drama-theater group. Campus security: 24-hour emergency response devices and patrols. Wytheville Community College Library. Books: 33,041 (physical), 51,770 (digital/electronic); Serial titles: 3,319 (physical), 3,418 (digital/electronic); Databases: 101. Students can reserve study rooms. Operations spending for the previous fiscal year: $232,783. 537 computers available on campus for general student use. A campuswide network can be accessed. Students can access the following: online class registration. Staffed computer lab on campus provides training in use of computers, software, and the Internet.
Community Environment: Wytheville is located in a rich agricultural and cattle-raising area with most forms of commercial transportation available. A growing number of industries are located in the area, providing good part-time employment opportunities. Community facilities include a public library, churches, Jewish Synagogues in the neighboring towns of Bluefield and Bristol, a hospital, shopping areas, and a number of the civic and service organizations. Claytor Lake and the Jefferson National Forest provide opportunities for hunting, fishing, camping, and picnicking; other facilities within the city offer swimming and golf.

■ ANTIOCH UNIVERSITY SEATTLE

2400 3rd Ave.
Ste. 200
Seattle, WA 98121
Tel: (206)441-5352; Free: 888-268-4477
E-mail: admissions@antiochseattle.edu
Web Site: www.antioch.edu/seattle

Description: Independent, university, coed. Part of Antioch University. Awards bachelor's, master's, and doctoral degrees. Founded 1975. Setting: urban campus. Total enrollment: 486. Students come from 9 states and territories, 1 other country. 8% Hispanic/Latino; 3% Black or African American, non-Hispanic/Latino; 4% Asian, non-Hispanic/Latino. 5% 25 or older. Calendar: quarters. Summer session for credit.

Entrance Requirements: Options: electronic application, deferred admission. Entrance: noncompetitive.

Costs Per Year: Application fee: $75. Tuition: $21,600 full-time, $600 per credit hour part-time. Mandatory fees: $435 full-time, $105 per term part-time. Full-time tuition and fees vary according to course load, degree level, location, and program. Part-time tuition and fees vary according to course load, degree level, location, and program.

Collegiate Environment: Antioch Seattle Library. Books: 8,425 (physical), 264,631 (digital/electronic); Serial titles: 40,950 (digital/electronic); Databases: 222.

■ ARGOSY UNIVERSITY, SEATTLE

2601-A Elliott Ave.
Seattle, WA 98121
Tel: (206)283-4500; Free: 866-283-2777
Fax: (206)393-3592
Web Site: www.argosy.edu/locations/seattle

Description: Proprietary, university, coed. Part of Education Management Corporation. Awards associate, bachelor's, master's, and doctoral degrees and post-master's certificates. Founded 1995. Setting: urban campus. Calendar: semesters.

■ THE ART INSTITUTE OF SEATTLE

2323 Elliott Ave.
Seattle, WA 98121-1642
Tel: (206)448-6600; Free: 800-275-2471
Fax: (206)269-0275
Web Site: www.artinstitutes.edu/seattle

Description: Proprietary, 4-year, coed. Part of Education Management Corporation. Awards associate and bachelor's degrees. Founded 1982. Setting: urban campus. Calendar: quarters.

■ BASTYR UNIVERSITY

14500 Juanita Dr., NE
Kenmore, WA 98028-4966
Tel: (425)823-1300
Fax: (425)823-6222
E-mail: admissions@bastyr.edu
Web Site: www.bastyr.edu

Description: Independent, upper-level, coed. Awards bachelor's, master's, and doctoral degrees and post-master's certificates. Founded 1978. Setting: 51-acre suburban campus with easy access to Seattle. Total enrollment:

1,266. Faculty: 299 (43 full-time, 256 part-time). Full-time: 217 students, 86% women, 14% men. Part-time: 70 students, 91% women, 9% men. Students come from 27 states and territories, 9 other countries, 28% from out-of-state. 2% American Indian or Alaska Native, non-Hispanic/Latino; 5% Hispanic/Latino; 4% Black or African American, non-Hispanic/Latino; 8% Asian, non-Hispanic/Latino; 0.9% Native Hawaiian or other Pacific Islander, non-Hispanic/Latino; 3% international. 55% 25 or older, 10% live on campus. Academic areas with the most degrees conferred: health professions and related sciences; psychology. Calendar: quarters. Independent study, double major, summer session for credit, part-time degree program, co-op programs and internships, graduate courses open to undergrads.

Costs Per Year: Application fee: $60. Tuition: $26,091 full-time, $734 per credit part-time. Full-time tuition varies according to course load and program. Part-time tuition varies according to course load and program.

Collegiate Environment: Orientation program. Social organizations: 69 open to all. Most popular organizations: Naturopaths Without Borders, Nature Club, Multicultural Student Association of Natural Medicine, Environmental Action Team, Venture Grant. Major annual events: Community Day, Talent/No Talent Show, Graduation Party and Dance. Student services: health clinic, personal-psychological counseling. Campus security: student patrols, late night transport-escort service, controlled dormitory access. Bastyr University Library.

■ BATES TECHNICAL COLLEGE

1101 S Yakima Ave.
Tacoma, WA 98405-4895
Tel: (253)596-1500
Web Site: www.bates.ctc.edu

Description: State-supported, 2-year, coed. Part of Washington State Board for Community and Technical Colleges. Awards certificates, diplomas, and terminal associate degrees. Setting: urban campus with easy access to Seattle. Total enrollment: 5,463. 68% 25 or older. Calendar: quarters.

Entrance Requirements: Open admission. Application deadline: rolling. Notification: continuous.

Collegiate Environment: Student-run newspaper, radio station. Campus security: 24-hour emergency response devices, on-campus weekday security to 10 pm.

■ BELLEVUE COLLEGE

3000 Landerholm Cir., SE
Bellevue, WA 98007-6484
Tel: (425)564-1000
Fax: (425)564-2261
Web Site: www.bellevuecollege.edu

Description: State-supported, primarily 2-year, coed. Part of Washington State Board for Community and Technical Colleges. Awards certificates, transfer associate, terminal associate, and bachelor's degrees. Founded 1966. Setting: 96-acre suburban campus with easy access to Seattle. Total enrollment: 12,305. 37% 25 or older. Core. Calendar: quarters. Academic remediation for entering students, ESL program, services for LD students, advanced placement, honors program, independent study, distance learning, summer session for credit, part-time degree program, co-op programs and internships.

Entrance Requirements: Open admission. Option: electronic application. Entrance: noncompetitive. Application deadline: rolling.

Collegiate Environment: Orientation program. Drama-theater group, student-run newspaper, radio station. Student services: health clinic, personal-psychological counseling, women's center. Bellevue Community College Library.

Community Environment: Bellevue is a suburban community of Seattle and enjoys temperate climate with an average rainfall of 33.5 inches. The city has churches of most denominations, a hospital, good shopping facilities, and major civic and fraternal organizations serving the area.

■ BELLINGHAM TECHNICAL COLLEGE

3028 Lindbergh Ave.
Bellingham, WA 98225
Tel: (360)752-7000
Fax: (360)676-2798
Web Site: www.btc.edu

Description: State-supported, 2-year, coed. Part of Washington State Board for Community and Technical Colleges. Awards certificates, transfer associate, and terminal associate degrees. Founded 1957. Setting: 21-acre suburban campus with easy access to Vancouver, BC; Seattle, WA. Educational spending for the previous fiscal year: $4136 per student. Total enrollment: 2,864. Faculty: 189 (126 full-time, 63 part-time). Student-undergrad faculty ratio is 24:1. 2,562 applied, 100% were admitted. 61% 25 or older. Calendar: quarters. Academic remediation for entering students, ESL program, services for LD students, distance learning, summer session for credit, part-time degree program, internships.

Entrance Requirements: Open admission. Options: electronic application, early admission, deferred admission. Required: ACCUPLACER or waiver. Required for some: high school transcript, prerequisite courses. Entrance: noncompetitive. Application deadline: rolling. Transfer credits accepted: Yes.

Costs Per Year: Application fee: $0. State resident tuition: $3960 full-time, $108.26 per credit part-time. Nonresident tuition: $4500 full-time, $285.68 per credit part-time. Full-time tuition varies according to course load and degree level. Part-time tuition varies according to course load and degree level.

Collegiate Environment: Orientation program. Major annual event: Diversity celebrations. Student services: personal-psychological counseling. Bellingham Technical College Library. Books: 15,500 (physical), 120,000 (digital/electronic); Serial titles: 90 (physical); Databases: 13. Weekly public service hours: 70; students can reserve study rooms. Operations spending for the previous fiscal year: $417,305. 750 computers available on campus for general student use. A campuswide network can be accessed from off-campus. Students can access the following: online class registration. Staffed computer lab on campus provides training in use of computers, software, and the Internet.

■ BIG BEND COMMUNITY COLLEGE

7662 Chanute St., NE
Moses Lake, WA 98837-3299
Tel: (509)793-2222; Free: 877-745-1212
Fax: (509)762-6243
E-mail: admissions@bigbend.edu
Web Site: www.bigbend.edu

Description: State-supported, 2-year, coed. Awards certificates, transfer associate, and terminal associate degrees. Founded 1962. Setting: 159-acre small town campus. Total enrollment: 2,016. Student-undergrad faculty ratio is 22:1. Full-time: 1,458 students, 50% women, 50% men. Part-time: 558 students, 59% women, 41% men. 0.6% American Indian or Alaska Native, non-Hispanic/Latino; 35% Hispanic/Latino; 1% Black or African American, non-Hispanic/Latino; 2% Asian, non-Hispanic/Latino; 0.5% international. 28% 25 or older, 7% live on campus. Core. Calendar: quarters. Academic remediation for entering students, ESL program, services for LD students, advanced placement, distance learning, summer session for credit, part-time degree program, co-op programs.

Entrance Requirements: Open admission except for aviation and nursing programs. Options: electronic application, early admission, deferred admission. Required for some: high school transcript. Entrance: noncompetitive. Application deadline: rolling. Notification: continuous. Transfer credits accepted: Yes.

Collegiate Environment: Orientation program. Choral group. Student services: personal-psychological counseling. Campus security: 24-hour emergency response devices, late night transport-escort service, daytime security during the week, dorm security six evenings/week, Enhanced Campus Notification System, video surveillance on campus. William C. Bonaudi Library. Books: 37,906 (physical), 3,484 (digital/electronic); Serial

titles: 102 (physical); Databases: 29. Weekly public service hours: 68; students can reserve study rooms. 765 computers available on campus for general student use. A campuswide network can be accessed from student residence rooms and from off campus. Students can access the following: online class registration, new student orientation online. Staffed computer lab on campus.

Community Environment: Moses Lake is an important agricultural processing and shipping center for the Columbia Basin. This is a rural area with dry climate. The community has a library, many churches, a museum, a hospital and clinics, and modern shopping facilities. Local recreation includes lakes for fishing, swimming, boating, water skiing, and hydroplane boat races, as well as picnic areas and hunting areas for geese and pheasant. The community has major civic, fraternal and veteran's organizations. Grant County Fair, and a rodeo and parade are held here annually. Part-time employment is available.

■ CARRINGTON COLLEGE-SPOKANE

10102 E Knox Ave.
Ste. 200
Spokane, WA 99206
Tel: (509)462-3722
Web Site: www.carrington.edu

Description: Proprietary, 2-year, coed. Part of Carrington Colleges Group, Inc. Awards certificates and terminal associate degrees. Founded 1976. Total enrollment: 407. Faculty: 13 (11 full-time, 2 part-time). Student-undergrad faculty ratio is 35:1. Full-time: 407 students, 81% women, 19% men. 18% from out-of-state. 3% American Indian or Alaska Native, non-Hispanic/Latino; 12% Hispanic/Latino; 2% Black or African American, non-Hispanic/Latino; 2% Asian, non-Hispanic/Latino; 0.5% Native Hawaiian or other Pacific Islander, non-Hispanic/Latino. 51% 25 or older, 19% transferred in.

Entrance Requirements: Required: essay, high school transcript, interview, institutional entrance exam.

■ CASCADIA COLLEGE

18345 Campus Way, NE
Bothell, WA 98011
Tel: (425)352-8000
Fax: (425)398-5730
E-mail: admissions@cascadia.edu
Web Site: www.cascadia.edu

Description: State-supported, primarily 2-year, coed. Part of Washington State Board for Community and Technical Colleges. Awards certificates, diplomas, transfer associate, terminal associate, and bachelor's degrees. Founded 1999. Setting: 128-acre suburban campus. Total enrollment: 2,759. Faculty: 129 (31 full-time, 98 part-time). 2,939 applied. Students come from 12 states and territories. 0.8% American Indian or Alaska Native, non-Hispanic/Latino; 18% Hispanic/Latino; 3% Black or African American, non-Hispanic/Latino; 15% Asian, non-Hispanic/Latino; 0.4% Native Hawaiian or other Pacific Islander, non-Hispanic/Latino; 12% international. Core. Calendar: quarters. Academic remediation for entering students, ESL program, services for LD students, advanced placement, accelerated degree program, independent study, distance learning, double major, summer session for credit, part-time degree program, adult/continuing education programs, co-op programs and internships. Off campus study. Study abroad program.

Entrance Requirements: Open admission. Option: electronic application. Entrance: noncompetitive. Application deadline: rolling. Notification: continuous.

Collegiate Environment: Orientation program. Drama-theater group, student-run newspaper. Student services: personal-psychological counseling. Campus security: 24-hour emergency response devices, late night transport-escort service. Campus Library. Books: 90,000 (physical), 600,000 (digital/electronic); Serial titles: 600 (physical), 100,000 (digital/electronic); Databases: 600. Weekly public service hours: 86; students can reserve study rooms.

■ CENTRAL WASHINGTON UNIVERSITY

400 E University Way
Ellensburg, WA 98926
Tel: (509)963-1111
Fax: (509)963-3022
E-mail: admissions@cwu.edu
Web Site: www.cwu.edu

Description: State-supported, comprehensive, coed. Awards bachelor's and master's degrees and post-master's certificates. Founded 1891. Setting: 380-acre small town campus with easy access to Seattle. Endowment: $5.7 million. Research spending for the previous fiscal year: $2.8 million. Educational spending for the previous fiscal year: $7987 per student. Total enrollment: 14,972. Faculty: 678 (420 full-time, 258 part-time). Student-undergrad faculty ratio is 18:1. 12,320 applied, 64% were admitted. Full-time: 10,101 students, 51% women, 49% men. Part-time: 4,326 students, 56% women, 44% men. 8% from out-of-state. 0.5% American Indian or Alaska Native, non-Hispanic/Latino; 16% Hispanic/Latino; 4% Black or African American, non-Hispanic/Latino; 4% Asian, non-Hispanic/Latino; 0.9% Native Hawaiian or other Pacific Islander, non-Hispanic/Latino; 3% international. 20% 25 or older, 31% live on campus, 9% transferred in. Retention: 69% of full-time freshmen returned the following year. Academic areas with the most degrees conferred: education; business/marketing; computer and information sciences; social sciences. Core. Calendar: quarters. Academic remediation for entering students, ESL program, services for LD students, advanced placement, self-designed majors, freshman honors college, honors program, independent study, distance learning, double major, summer session for credit, part-time degree program, co-op programs and internships, graduate courses open to undergrads. Off campus study at all Washington State community colleges. Study abroad program. ROTC: Army, Air Force.

Entrance Requirements: Options: electronic application, international baccalaureate accepted. Required: high school transcript, minimum 2 high school GPA, SAT or ACT. Required for some: essay, interview. Entrance: moderately difficult. Application deadline: rolling for nonresidents. Notification: continuous, continuous for nonresidents. SAT Reasoning Test deadline: 9/1. Transfer credits accepted: Yes.

Costs Per Year: Application fee: $50. Area resident tuition: $6170 full-time. State resident tuition: $6170 full-time. Nonresident tuition: $21,151 full-time. Mandatory fees: $1191 full-time. College room and board: $13,066. College room only: $5783.

Collegiate Environment: Orientation program. Drama-theater group, choral group, marching band, student-run newspaper, radio station. Social organizations: 120 open to all; non-Greek clubs recognized by student government; 47% of eligible men and 53% of eligible women are members. Most popular organizations: SISTERS, Brother 2 Brother, Cosplay, Alpha Kappa Si, Society of Human Resource Management. Major annual events: Symposium of University Research and Creative Expression, Yakima River Clean Up, Waffle Night. Student services: health clinic, personal-psychological counseling. Campus security: 24-hour emergency response devices and patrols, late night transport-escort service, controlled dormitory access, alert update system: emergency notification across digital platforms, Rape Aggression Defense System: realistic self-defense for women. Freshmen guaranteed college housing. On-campus residence required in freshman year. Option: coed housing available. James E. Brooks Library plus 2 others. Books: 900,981 (physical), 251,073 (digital/electronic); Serial titles: 327 (physical), 72,453 (digital/electronic); Databases: 112. Weekly public service hours: 101; students can reserve study rooms. Operations spending for the previous fiscal year: $3.5 million. 791 computers available on campus for general student use. Computer purchase/lease plans available. A campuswide network can be accessed from student residence rooms and from off campus. Students can access the following: online class registration, online data storage, office software. Staffed computer lab on campus provides training in use of computers, software, and the Internet.

Community Environment: Ellensburg is a small university town in central Washington. The climate is mild and dry. The community has several churches, three libraries, a hospital and infirmary. Ellensburg may be reached by railroad, bus lines, and Interstate 90 and 82. Local recreation includes camping, hiking, river rafting, rodeo, snow sports, fishing, hunting, boating, skiing and golf. There are many job opportunities available at the university. Various civic and fraternal organizations are active in the community.

■ **CENTRALIA COLLEGE**
600 Centralia College Blvd.
Centralia, WA 98531-4099
Tel: (360)736-9391
E-mail: admissions@centralia.edu
Web Site: www.centralia.edu
Description: State-supported, 2-year, coed. Part of Washington State Board for Community and Technical Colleges. Awards certificates, transfer associate, and terminal associate degrees. Founded 1925. Setting: 31-acre small

town campus. Total enrollment: 3,574. Student-undergrad faculty ratio is 20:1. 54% 25 or older. Core. Calendar: quarters. Academic remediation for entering students, ESL program, services for LD students, advanced placement, freshman honors college, honors program, independent study, distance learning, summer session for credit, part-time degree program, external degree program, adult/continuing education programs, co-op programs. Study abroad program.

Entrance Requirements: Open admission except for nursing program. Options: electronic application, international baccalaureate accepted. Required: high school transcript. Entrance: noncompetitive. Application deadline: rolling. Notification: continuous until 9/15.

Collegiate Environment: Orientation program. Drama-theater group, choral group, marching band, student-run newspaper, radio station. Student services: personal-psychological counseling. Campus security: 24-hour patrols, student patrols, late night transport-escort service. Kirk Library.

■ **CHARTER COLLEGE**
17720 SE Mill Plain Blvd.
Ste. 170
Vancouver, WA 98683
Web Site: www.chartercollege.edu
Description: Proprietary, comprehensive, coed.

■ **CITY UNIVERSITY OF SEATTLE**
521 Wall St.
Ste. 100
Seattle, WA 98121
Tel: (206)239-4500; Free: 800-426-5596
E-mail: info@cityu.edu
Web Site: www.cityu.edu
Description: Independent, comprehensive, coed. Awards associate, bachelor's, master's, and doctoral degrees and post-master's certificates. Founded 1973. Setting: 1-acre urban campus with easy access to Seattle. Educational spending for the previous fiscal year: $5199 per student. Total enrollment: 2,065. Faculty: 332 (47 full-time, 285 part-time). Student-undergrad faculty ratio is 15:1. 86 applied, 100% were admitted. Full-time: 532 students, 55% women, 45% men. Part-time: 503 students, 55% women, 45% men. Students come from 45 states and territories, 24 other countries. 74% 25 or older, 13% transferred in. Core. Calendar: quarters. ESL program, services for LD students, advanced placement, accelerated degree program, self-designed majors, independent study, distance learning, double major, summer session for credit, part-time degree program, adult/continuing education programs, internships. Study abroad program.

Entrance Requirements: Open admission. Options: electronic application, deferred admission, international baccalaureate accepted. Recommended: high school transcript. Entrance: noncompetitive. Application deadline: rolling. Notification: continuous. Transfer credits accepted: Yes.

Collegiate Environment: Orientation program. Student services: personal-psychological counseling. Campus security: 24-hour emergency response devices. City University Library. Operations spending for the previous fiscal year: $1.2 million. 148 computers available on campus for general student use. A campuswide network can be accessed from off-campus. Students can access the following: online class registration. Staffed computer lab on campus.

■ **CLARK COLLEGE**
1933 Fort Vancouver Way
Vancouver, WA 98663-3598
Tel: (360)992-2000
E-mail: admissions@clark.edu
Web Site: www.clark.edu
Description: State-supported, primarily 2-year, coed. Part of Washington State Board for Community and Technical Colleges. Awards certificates, diplomas, transfer associate, terminal associate, and bachelor's degrees. Founded 1933. Setting: 101-acre urban campus with easy access to Portland. Endowment: $61 million. Total enrollment: 10,477. Student-undergrad faculty ratio is 24:1. 1,349 applied, 100% were admitted. Full-time: 5,035 students, 56% women, 44% men. Part-time: 5,442 students, 58% women, 42% men. 4% from out-of-state. 0.6% American Indian or Alaska Native, non-Hispanic/Latino; 9% Hispanic/Latino; 2% Black or African American, non-Hispanic/Latino; 4% Asian, non-Hispanic/Latino; 0.1% Native Hawaiian or other Pacific Islander, non-Hispanic/Latino; 1% international. 34% 25 or older, 3% transferred in. Core. Calendar: quarters. Academic remediation for entering students, ESL program, services for LD students,

honors program, distance learning, summer session for credit, part-time degree program, adult/continuing education programs, co-op programs and internships. ROTC: Army (c), Air Force (c).

Entrance Requirements: Options: electronic application, early admission, deferred admission, international baccalaureate accepted. Entrance: noncompetitive. Transfer credits accepted: Yes.

Costs Per Year: Application fee: $25. State resident tuition: $4,287 full-time, $113.32 per credit hour part-time. Nonresident tuition: $9,718 full-time, $290.74 per credit hour part-time. Full-time tuition varies according to course level, course load, degree level, program, and reciprocity agreements. Part-time tuition varies according to course level, course load, degree level, program, and reciprocity agreements.

Collegiate Environment: Orientation program. Drama-theater group, choral group, student-run newspaper. Student services: legal services, health clinic, personal-psychological counseling. Campus security: 24-hour patrols, late night transport-escort service, security staff during hours of operation. Lewis D. Cannell Library. Students can reserve study rooms. Operations spending for the previous fiscal year: $1.7 million.

Community Environment: The oldest city in the state, Vancouver is located at the head of the deep-water navigation of the Columbia River. This is an industrial city with job opportunities for students. The city is served by rail, bus and major highways. Local recreation includes fishing, hunting, boating, skiing, and nearby beaches.

■ CLOVER PARK TECHNICAL COLLEGE
4500 Steilacoom Blvd., SW
Lakewood, WA 98499
Tel: (253)589-5678
Web Site: www.cptc.edu

Description: State-supported, 2-year, coed. Part of Washington State Board for Community and Technical Colleges. Awards certificates and terminal associate degrees. Founded 1942. Total enrollment: 9,829. 85% 25 or older. Core. Academic remediation for entering students, ESL program, services for LD students, accelerated degree program, distance learning, part-time degree program, co-op programs and internships.

Entrance Requirements: Open admission. Options: electronic application, international baccalaureate accepted. Required for some: high school transcript, interview. Entrance: noncompetitive. Application deadline: 9/27. Notification: continuous until 9/27.

Collegiate Environment: Orientation program. Student-run newspaper. Most popular organizations: Accounting Numbers Club, Auto Tech Club, Computer Users Club, Social Services Club. Major annual events: Veteran's Day Celebration, Martin Luther King, Jr. Celebration, Car Show. Student services: personal-psychological counseling. Campus security: 24-hour patrols, late night transport-escort service. CPTC Library.

■ COLUMBIA BASIN COLLEGE
2600 N 20th Ave.
Pasco, WA 99301-3397
Tel: (509)547-0511
Fax: (509)546-0401
E-mail: admissions@columbiabasin.edu
Web Site: www.columbiabasin.edu

Description: State-supported, 2-year, coed. Part of Washington State Board for Community and Technical Colleges. Awards transfer associate and terminal associate degrees. Founded 1955. Setting: 156-acre small town campus. Total enrollment: 6,978. Student-undergrad faculty ratio is 22:1. 2% from out-of-state. 41% 25 or older. Retention: 58% of full-time freshmen returned the following year. Core. Calendar: quarters. Academic remediation for entering students, ESL program, services for LD students, advanced placement, accelerated degree program, distance learning, summer session for credit, part-time degree program, adult/continuing education programs, co-op programs and internships.

Entrance Requirements: Open admission except for nursing program. Options: electronic application, international baccalaureate accepted. Required: high school transcript. Entrance: noncompetitive. Application deadline: rolling. Notification: continuous.

Collegiate Environment: Orientation program. Drama-theater group, choral group, student-run newspaper. Student services: personal-psychological counseling, women's center. Campus security: 24-hour patrols. Columbia Basin College Library.

■ CORNISH COLLEGE OF THE ARTS
1000 Lenora St.
Seattle, WA 98121

Tel: (206)726-5151; Free: 800-726-ARTS
Fax: (206)720-1011
E-mail: admissions@cornish.edu
Web Site: www.cornish.edu

Description: Independent, 4-year, coed. Awards bachelor's degrees. Founded 1914. Setting: 4-acre urban campus with easy access to Seattle. Total enrollment: 654. Faculty: 203 (54 full-time, 149 part-time). Student-undergrad faculty ratio is 6:1. 1,023 applied, 63% were admitted. Full-time: 652 students, 66% women, 34% men. Part-time: 2 students, 100% women. Students come from 40 states and territories, 5 other countries, 51% from out-of-state. 0.8% American Indian or Alaska Native, non-Hispanic/Latino; 14% Hispanic/Latino; 3% Black or African American, non-Hispanic/Latino; 4% Asian, non-Hispanic/Latino; 0.6% Native Hawaiian or other Pacific Islander, non-Hispanic/Latino; 1% international. 8% 25 or older, 7% transferred in. Retention: 99.9% of full-time freshmen returned the following year. Academic area with the most degrees conferred: visual and performing arts. Core. Calendar: semesters. Services for LD students, advanced placement, accelerated degree program, independent study, summer session for credit, co-op programs and internships. Study abroad program.

Entrance Requirements: Options: electronic application, early action, deferred admission, international baccalaureate accepted. Required: essay, high school transcript, minimum 2.5 high school GPA, portfolio or audition. Recommended: 2 recommendations, interview, SAT or ACT. Required for some: 2 recommendations. Entrance: moderately difficult. Application deadlines: rolling, 12/1 for early action. Notification: continuous. Transfer credits accepted: Yes.

Costs Per Year: Application fee: $60. Comprehensive fee: $53,142 includes full-time tuition ($40,442), mandatory fees ($1200), and college room and board ($11,500). College room only: $8400. Full-time tuition and fees vary according to course load and program. Room and board charges vary according to board plan and housing facility. Part-time tuition: $1686 per credit hour. Part-time mandatory fees: $600 per term. Part-time tuition and fees vary according to course load.

Collegiate Environment: Orientation program. Drama-theater group, choral group. Most popular organizations: Student Leadership Council, Black Student Alliance, Sigma Alpha Phi, AIGA, Cheese Tasting. Major annual events: Spring Festival/Drag Show, Cabaret, BFA Art Show. Student services: personal-psychological counseling. Campus security: 24-hour emergency response devices and patrols, late night transport-escort service, controlled dormitory access. Cornish Library. Books: 30,000 (physical), 130,000 (digital/electronic).

Community Environment: Urban.

■ DIGIPEN INSTITUTE OF TECHNOLOGY
9931 Willows Rd. NE
Redmond, WA 98052
Tel: (425)558-0299; Free: 866-478-5236
Fax: (425)558-0299
E-mail: admissions@digipen.edu
Web Site: www.digipen.edu

Description: Proprietary, comprehensive, coed. Awards bachelor's and master's degrees. Founded 1988. Setting: 3-acre suburban campus with easy access to Seattle. Total enrollment: 1,166. Faculty: 172 (69 full-time, 103 part-time). Student-undergrad faculty ratio is 11:1. 669 applied, 57% were admitted. Full-time: 991 students, 23% women, 77% men. Part-time: 73 students, 33% women, 67% men. 50% from out-of-state. 0.3% American Indian or Alaska Native, non-Hispanic/Latino; 6% Hispanic/Latino; 0.9% Black or African American, non-Hispanic/Latino; 7% Asian, non-Hispanic/Latino; 0.3% Native Hawaiian or other Pacific Islander, non-Hispanic/Latino; 10% international. 9% transferred in. Retention: 70% of full-time freshmen returned the following year. Academic areas with the most degrees conferred: computer and information sciences; communication technologies; interdisciplinary studies. Calendar: semesters. Academic remediation for entering students, ESL program, services for LD students, advanced placement, accelerated degree program, independent study, summer session for credit, co-op programs and internships, graduate courses open to undergrads.

Entrance Requirements: Options: electronic application, deferred admission, international baccalaureate accepted. Required: essay, high school transcript, minimum 2.5 high school GPA. Recommended: 2 recommendations. Required for some: pre-calculus for Bachelor of Science, art portfolio for BFA in Digital Art and Animation, performance portfolio for BA in Music and Sound Design, design portfolio for Bachelor of Art in Game Design, SAT or ACT. Entrance: minimally difficult. Application deadline: rolling. Notification: continuous. Transfer credits accepted: Yes.

Costs Per Year: Application fee: $60. One-time mandatory fee: $150. Tuition: $32,400 full-time, $1045 per credit part-time. Mandatory fees: $200 full-time. College room only: $7500.

Collegiate Environment: Orientation program. Choral group. Social organizations: 39 open to all. Most popular organizations: PRISM Club, Cage of the Week Club, Halo Club, Outbreak Club, Wellness Club. Major annual events: Halloween Pageant, LAN Party, Midnight Breakfast (part of Wellness Week). Student services: personal-psychological counseling. Campus security: 24-hour patrols, late night transport-escort service, controlled dormitory access, on-site security during campus hours. 250 college housing spaces available. Freshmen given priority for college housing. Options: coed, men-only, women-only housing available. DigiPen Library. Books: 5,946 (physical), 196,396 (digital/electronic); Serial titles: 36 (physical), 6,756 (digital/electronic); Databases: 11. Weekly public service hours: 84. 1,040 computers available on campus for general student use. A campuswide network can be accessed from student residence rooms and from off campus. Students can access the following: online class registration. Staffed computer lab on campus provides training in use of computers, software, and the Internet.

■ **EASTERN WASHINGTON UNIVERSITY**
526 5th St.
Cheney, WA 99004-2431
Tel: (509)359-6200
Fax: (509)359-4330
E-mail: admissions@ewu.edu
Web Site: www.ewu.edu

Description: State-supported, comprehensive, coed. Awards bachelor's, master's, and doctoral degrees. Founded 1882. Setting: 335-acre suburban campus with easy access to Spokane. Total enrollment: 12,635. Faculty: 730 (475 full-time, 255 part-time). Student-undergrad faculty ratio is 21:1. 8,367 applied, 63% were admitted. Full-time: 9,912 students, 54% women, 46% men. Part-time: 1,498 students, 53% women, 47% men. 6% from out-of-state. 1% American Indian or Alaska Native, non-Hispanic/Latino; 17% Hispanic/Latino; 4% Black or African American, non-Hispanic/Latino; 3% Asian, non-Hispanic/Latino; 0.3% Native Hawaiian or other Pacific Islander, non-Hispanic/Latino; 4% international. 18% 25 or older, 17% live on campus, 10% transferred in. Retention: 74% of full-time freshmen returned the following year. Academic areas with the most degrees conferred: business/marketing; social sciences; biological/life sciences. Core. Calendar: quarters. Academic remediation for entering students, ESL program, services for LD students, advanced placement, accelerated degree program, self-designed majors, honors program, independent study, distance learning, double major, summer session for credit, part-time degree program, adult/continuing education programs, co-op programs and internships, graduate courses open to undergrads. Off campus study at Intercollegiate Center for Nursing. Study abroad program. ROTC: Army.

Entrance Requirements: Required: high school transcript, minimum 2 high school GPA, SAT or ACT. Recommended: minimum 3 high school GPA. Required for some: essay. SAT Reasoning Test deadline: 5/15.

Costs Per Year: Application fee: $60. Area resident tuition: $6522 full-time. State resident tuition: $6522 full-time, $217.76 per credit hour part-time. Nonresident tuition: $24,018 full-time, $801.33 per credit hour part-time. Mandatory fees: $939 full-time. College room and board: $12,708. College room only: $7260.

Collegiate Environment: Orientation program. Drama-theater group, choral group, marching band, student-run newspaper, radio station. Social organizations: national fraternities, national sororities. Student services: health clinic, personal-psychological counseling, women's center. Campus security: 24-hour emergency response devices and patrols, student patrols, late night transport-escort service, controlled dormitory access. 2,253 college housing spaces available. Freshmen guaranteed college housing. On-campus residence required in freshman year. Option: coed housing available. John F. Kennedy Library. Students can reserve study rooms.

Community Environment: Cheney is located 16 miles southwest of Spokane. The community is reached by major highways, rail, bus, and air lines with Spokane Airport approximately 11 miles away. The city has many churches and various civic, fraternal, and veteran's organizations. Local recreation includes hunting, fishing, skiing, and swimming on nearby lakes. Part-time employment is available.

■ **EDMONDS COMMUNITY COLLEGE**
20000 68th Ave. W
Lynnwood, WA 98036

Tel: (425)640-1500
Fax: (425)640-1159
E-mail: nanci.froemming@edcc.edu
Web Site: www.edcc.edu

Description: State and locally supported, 2-year, coed. Part of Washington State Board for Community and Technical Colleges. Awards certificates, transfer associate, and terminal associate degrees. Founded 1967. Setting: 115-acre suburban campus with easy access to Seattle. Endowment: $2.7 million. Educational spending for the previous fiscal year: $3600 per student. Total enrollment: 8,435. Faculty: 480 (145 full-time, 335 part-time). Student-undergrad faculty ratio is 21:1. 1,770 applied, 100% were admitted. Full-time: 3,656 students, 53% women, 47% men. Part-time: 4,779 students, 61% women, 39% men. Students come from 55 other countries, 2% from out-of-state. 11% 25 or older, 1% transferred in. Core. Calendar: quarters. Academic remediation for entering students, ESL program, services for LD students, advanced placement, self-designed majors, honors program, distance learning, summer session for credit, part-time degree program, adult/continuing education programs, co-op programs and internships. Off campus study at other community colleges in Washington. Study abroad program.

Entrance Requirements: Open admission. Options: electronic application, early admission, deferred admission. Entrance: noncompetitive. Application deadline: rolling. Notification: continuous.

Collegiate Environment: Orientation program. Drama-theater group, choral group, student-run newspaper. Social organizations: 40 open to all. Most popular organizations: Phi Theta Kappa, AITP, AAWCC, International Club, Pottery/Art Club. Major annual events: Commencement, Campus Barbecues, music performances. Student services: personal-psychological counseling, women's center. Campus security: 24-hour emergency response devices and patrols, student patrols, late night transport-escort service. Edmonds Community College Library. Operations spending for the previous fiscal year: $915,656. 735 computers available on campus for general student use. A campuswide network can be accessed from off-campus. Students can access the following: online class registration. Staffed computer lab on campus.

Community Environment: Lynnwood overlooks the Puget Sound and the Olympic Mountains, and is connected with the Olympic Peninsula by ferry. This is a large, rapidly growing suburban community. The city has a large public marina, good shopping facilities, and good recreation areas. There is a public library, churches, and theatres. Good skiing and winter sports may be found within an hour's drive.

■ **EVERETT COMMUNITY COLLEGE**
2000 Twr. St.
Everett, WA 98201-1327
Tel: (425)388-9100
Fax: (425)388-9173
E-mail: admissions@everettcc.edu
Web Site: www.everettcc.edu

Description: State-supported, 2-year, coed. Part of Washington State Board for Community and Technical Colleges. Awards certificates, diplomas, transfer associate, and terminal associate degrees. Founded 1941. Setting: 22-acre suburban campus with easy access to Seattle. Total enrollment: 7,562. Faculty: 369 (135 full-time, 234 part-time). Student-undergrad faculty ratio is 24:1. Full-time: 3,707 students, 57% women, 43% men. Part-time: 3,855 students, 57% women, 43% men. Students come from 24 other countries, 3% from out-of-state. 32% 25 or older, 3% transferred in. Retention: 46% of full-time freshmen returned the following year. Core. Calendar: quarters. Academic remediation for entering students, ESL program, services for LD students, advanced placement, independent study, distance learning, summer session for credit, part-time degree program, adult/continuing education programs, co-op programs and internships. Study abroad program.

Entrance Requirements: Open admission except for some programs such as cosmetology, aviation, criminal justice, fire science, nursing, and medical assisting. Options: electronic application, early admission, deferred admission. Required: ACT ASSET, ACT Compass. Recommended: high school transcript. Entrance: noncompetitive. Application deadline: rolling. Notification: continuous.

Collegiate Environment: Orientation program. Drama-theater group, choral group, student-run newspaper. Social organizations: 30 open to all. Most popular organizations: United Native American Council, Nippon Friendship Club, Student Nurses Association, International Students Club, Math, Engineering and Science Student Organization. Major annual events:

Student Activities Kick-Off, Campus Awareness Days, Artist and Lecture Series. Student services: personal-psychological counseling, women's center. Campus security: 24-hour emergency response devices and patrols, late night transport-escort service. John Terrey Library/Media Center. 900 computers available on campus for general student use. A campuswide network can be accessed from off-campus. Students can access the following: online class registration. Staffed computer lab on campus.

Community Environment: Located on a natural landlocked harbor at the mouth of the Snohomish River, Everett looks across the Sound at the snowy crags of the Olympic Range. The chief industries of the area are lumbering and the manufacture of airplanes. Railroad lines, bus lines, and Interstate 5 serve the community. More than 60 churches of major denominations, two hospitals, and a library are within the immediate community. Local recreation includes a civic auditorium and stadium, ballfields, tennis courts, roller rinks, bowling alleys, golf courses, outdoor theaters, hunting, fishing, and boating. Skiing areas are a few hours away. Part-time employment is available for students.

■ THE EVERGREEN STATE COLLEGE

2700 Evergreen Pky., NW
Olympia, WA 98505
Tel: (360)867-6000
Fax: (360)867-6577
Web Site: www.evergreen.edu

Description: State-supported, comprehensive, coed. Part of Washington State Public Baccalaureate Institution. Awards bachelor's and master's degrees. Founded 1967. Setting: 1,000-acre rural campus with easy access to Seattle. Endowment: $13.4 million. Research spending for the previous fiscal year: $78,968. Educational spending for the previous fiscal year: $7608 per student. Total enrollment: 3,327. Faculty: 190 (134 full-time, 56 part-time). Student-undergrad faculty ratio is 21:1. 1,194 applied, 95% were admitted. 19% from top 10% of their high school class, 24% from top quarter, 60% from top half. Full-time: 2,781 students, 58% women, 42% men. Part-time: 237 students, 59% women, 41% men. Students come from 42 states and territories, 11 other countries, 18% from out-of-state. 3% American Indian or Alaska Native, non-Hispanic/Latino; 12% Hispanic/Latino; 5% Black or African American, non-Hispanic/Latino; 3% Asian, non-Hispanic/Latino; 0.5% Native Hawaiian or other Pacific Islander, non-Hispanic/Latino; 0.2% international. 37% 25 or older, 23% live on campus, 14% transferred in. Retention: 66% of full-time freshmen returned the following year. Academic areas with the most degrees conferred: liberal arts/general studies; interdisciplinary studies. Calendar: quarters. Services for LD students, advanced placement, accelerated degree program, self-designed majors, independent study, double major, summer session for credit, part-time degree program, internships, graduate courses open to undergrads. Off campus study at Jackson School of International Studies at Univ. of Washington, Consortium for Innovative Environments in Learning (CIEL) (Bennington Coll., Fairhaven Coll. of Interdisciplinary Studies at Western Washington Univ., Hampshire College, Johnston Ctr. for Integrative Studies at Univ. of Redlands, Marlboro College, New College at the Univ. of Alabama, New College of Florida, Prescott College, School of Individualized Study at Rochester Inst. of Technology, School of Integrative Studies at George Mason Univ., Stockton University). Study abroad program.

Entrance Requirements: Options: electronic application, deferred admission, international baccalaureate accepted. Required: high school transcript, minimum 2 high school GPA, SAT or ACT. Required for some: essay. Entrance: moderately difficult. Application deadline: 2/1. Notification: continuous until 11/1. Preference given to eligible veterans or National Guard members. SAT Reasoning Test deadline: 2/1. Transfer credits accepted: Yes.

Costs Per Year: Application fee: $50. State resident tuition: $6825 full-time, $227.50 per credit hour part-time. Nonresident tuition: $25,335 full-time, $844.50 per credit hour part-time. Mandatory fees: $849 full-time, $9.25 per credit hour part-time, $15 per term part-time. Full-time tuition and fees vary according to course load, location, and program. Part-time tuition and fees vary according to course load, location, and program. College room and board: $11,346. College room only: $8046. Room and board charges vary according to board plan, housing facility, location, and student level.

Collegiate Environment: Orientation program. Drama-theater group, choral group, student-run newspaper, radio station. Social organizations: 55 open to all. Most popular organizations: Flaming Eggplant, Geoduck Student Union, Cooper Point Journal, Gaming Guild, Myco-Collective. Major annual events: Harvest Festival, Student Activities Fair, Arts and Crafts Fair. Student services: health clinic, personal-psychological counseling, women's center. Campus security: 24-hour emergency response devices and patrols, student

patrols, late night transport-escort service, controlled dormitory access, car lockouts, jump-starts. 991 college housing spaces available; 677 were occupied in 2018-19. Freshmen guaranteed college housing. Option: coed housing available. Daniel J. Evans Library. Books: 377,812 (physical), 216,358 (digital/electronic); Serial titles: 69 (physical), 73,705 (digital/electronic); Databases: 103. Weekly public service hours: 77; students can reserve study rooms. Operations spending for the previous fiscal year: $3.2 million. 556 computers available on campus for general student use. A campuswide network can be accessed from student residence rooms and from off campus. Students can access the following: online class registration, online payment, student accounts history, financial aid records, academic history, housing application, evaluations. Staffed computer lab on campus provides training in use of computers, software, and the Internet.

Community Environment: Olympia is a seaport community of 37,000, located at the southernmost tip of Puget Sound. The Pacific Ocean is about an hour's drive west of the campus. The rain forests of the Olympic Peninsula lie to the northwest, and the Cascade mountain range is a few hours east of the campus. Seattle, 60 miles from campus, offers all the cultural and recreational activities typically found in a large city.

■ FAITH INTERNATIONAL UNIVERSITY

3504 N Pearl St.
Tacoma, WA 98407
Tel: (253)752-2020; Free: 888-777-7675
Fax: (253)759-1790

Description: Independent Lutheran, comprehensive, coed. Founded 1969. Calendar: quarters.

■ GONZAGA UNIVERSITY

502 E Boone Ave.
Spokane, WA 99258
Tel: (509)328-4220; Free: 800-322-2584
Fax: (509)324-5780
E-mail: admissions@gonzaga.edu
Web Site: www.gonzaga.edu

Description: Independent Roman Catholic, university, coed. Awards bachelor's, master's, and doctoral degrees. Founded 1887. Setting: 152-acre urban campus. Endowment: $276 million. Research spending for the previous fiscal year: $1.1 million. Educational spending for the previous fiscal year: $11,893 per student. Total enrollment: 7,563. Faculty: 813 (455 full-time, 358 part-time). Student-undergrad faculty ratio is 12:1. 8,400 applied, 66% were admitted. 41% from top 10% of their high school class, 76% from top quarter, 97% from top half. 87 class presidents, 276 student government officers. Full-time: 5,244 students, 53% women, 47% men. Part-time: 73 students, 48% women, 52% men. Students come from 45 states and territories, 26 other countries, 52% from out-of-state. 0.6% American Indian or Alaska Native, non-Hispanic/Latino; 11% Hispanic/Latino; 1% Black or African American, non-Hispanic/Latino; 5% Asian, non-Hispanic/Latino; 0.3% Native Hawaiian or other Pacific Islander, non-Hispanic/Latino; 1% international. 2% 25 or older, 52% live on campus, 3% transferred in. Retention: 94% of full-time freshmen returned the following year. Academic areas with the most degrees conferred: business/marketing; social sciences; engineering. Core. Calendar: semesters. ESL program, services for LD students, advanced placement, accelerated degree program, honors program, independent study, distance learning, double major, summer session for credit, part-time degree program, adult/continuing education programs, internships. Off campus study at American University, Washington Semester Internship Program. Study abroad program. ROTC: Army.

Entrance Requirements: Options: electronic application, early action, deferred admission, international baccalaureate accepted. Required: essay, high school transcript, 1 recommendation, SAT or ACT. Recommended: interview. Entrance: moderately difficult. Application deadlines: 2/1, 11/15 for early action. Notification: 3/15, 1/15 for early action. SAT Reasoning Test deadline: 2/15. Transfer credits accepted: Yes. Applicants placed on waiting list: 774. Wait-listed applicants offered admission: 36. Early action applicants: 4,685. Early action applicants admitted: 3,328.

Costs Per Year: Application fee: $50. Comprehensive fee: $57,470 includes full-time tuition ($44,280), mandatory fees ($860), and college room and board ($12,330). College room only: $6240. Part-time tuition: $1210 per credit. Part-time mandatory fees: $105 per term.

Collegiate Environment: Orientation program. Drama-theater group, choral group, student-run newspaper, radio station. Social organizations: 140 open to all; 10% of eligible men and 10% of eligible women are members. Most popular organizations: Student Body Association, Kennel Club, Search,

Circle K, Encore. Major annual events: Orientation Events, Kennel Club activities, Aprilfest. Student services: health clinic, personal-psychological counseling. Campus security: 24-hour emergency response devices and patrols, late night transport-escort service, controlled dormitory access. 3,064 college housing spaces available; 2,720 were occupied in 2018-19. Freshmen guaranteed college housing. On-campus residence required through sophomore year. Options: coed, men-only, women-only housing available. Ralph E. and Helen Higgins Foley Center plus 1 other. Books: 291,713 (physical), 76,847 (digital/electronic); Serial titles: 11,876 (physical), 60,184 (digital/electronic); Databases: 254. Weekly public service hours: 112; study areas open 24 hours, 5-7 days a week; students can reserve study rooms. Operations spending for the previous fiscal year: $6.6 million. 500 computers available on campus for general student use. Computer purchase/lease plans available. A campuswide network can be accessed from student residence rooms and from off campus. Students can access the following: online class registration. Staffed computer lab on campus provides training in use of computers, software, and the Internet.

Community Environment: See Spokane Falls Community College.

■ **GRAYS HARBOR COLLEGE**
1620 Edward P Smith Dr.
Aberdeen, WA 98520-7599
Tel: (360)532-9020; Free: 800-562-4830
Fax: (360)538-4293
Web Site: www.ghc.edu

Description: State-supported, 2-year, coed. Part of Washington State Board for Community and Technical Colleges. Awards certificates, diplomas, transfer associate, and terminal associate degrees. Founded 1930. Setting: 125-acre small town campus. Endowment: $8.6 million. Research spending for the previous fiscal year: $915,120. Educational spending for the previous fiscal year: $5376 per student. Total enrollment: 1,966. Faculty: 134 (70 full-time, 64 part-time). Student-undergrad faculty ratio is 19:1. Full-time: 1,312 students, 50% women, 50% men. Part-time: 654 students, 48% women, 52% men. 3% American Indian or Alaska Native, non-Hispanic/Latino; 8% Hispanic/Latino; 4% Black or African American, non-Hispanic/Latino; 2% Asian, non-Hispanic/Latino; 0.5% Native Hawaiian or other Pacific Islander, non-Hispanic/Latino; 0.2% international. 54% 25 or older, 21% transferred in. Retention: 57% of full-time freshmen returned the following year. Core. Calendar: quarters. Academic remediation for entering students, ESL program, services for LD students, advanced placement, accelerated degree program, honors program, independent study, distance learning, double major, summer session for credit, part-time degree program, external degree program, adult/continuing education programs, co-op programs and internships. Study abroad program.

Entrance Requirements: Open admission. Options: electronic application, early admission. Recommended: high school transcript. Entrance: noncompetitive. Application deadline: rolling. Notification: continuous. Transfer credits accepted: Yes.

Collegiate Environment: Orientation program. Drama-theater group, choral group, student-run newspaper. Social organizations: 12 open to all. Most popular organizations: Phi Theta Kappa, TYEE, Student Nurses Association, Human Services Student Association, Student Council. Major annual events: Sporting Events, Bishop Center, Drama Events. Student services: personal-psychological counseling, women's center. Campus security: 24-hour emergency response devices, late night transport-escort service. Spellman Library. Operations spending for the previous fiscal year: $414,231. 400 computers available on campus for general student use. A campuswide network can be accessed. Students can access the following: online class registration. Staffed computer lab on campus.

Community Environment: Aberdeen is located in a heavily wooded area and is known chiefly for its lumbering and fishing. The area has good harbors where the fishing fleet anchors. The city has mild winters and cool summers, with up to 75 inches of rainfall per year. Aberdeen may be reached by bus and state highways. There is a public library, YMCA, two hospitals, churches of major denominations, theatres, public parks, and civic, fraternal, and veteran's organizations serving the community. Local recreation includes hunting, fishing, golf, swimming, tennis, and skiing three hours drive away. Part-time employment is available.

■ **GREEN RIVER COLLEGE**
12401 SE 320th St.
Auburn, WA 98092-3699
Tel: (253)833-9111
Fax: (253)288-3454

Web Site: www.greenriver.edu

Description: State-supported, 2-year, coed. Part of Washington State Board for Community and Technical Colleges. Awards certificates, diplomas, transfer associate, and terminal associate degrees. Founded 1965. Setting: 168-acre small town campus with easy access to Seattle. Total enrollment: 8,205. Faculty: 436 (134 full-time, 302 part-time). Student-undergrad faculty ratio is 23:1. Students come from 41 other countries. 29% 25 or older. Retention: 61% of full-time freshmen returned the following year. Core. Calendar: quarters. Academic remediation for entering students, ESL program, services for LD students, advanced placement, distance learning, summer session for credit, part-time degree program, adult/continuing education programs, co-op programs and internships. Off campus study. Study abroad program.

Entrance Requirements: Open admission except for nursing, physical therapy, and occupational therapy programs. Options: electronic application, early admission, deferred admission. Required for some: high school transcript. Entrance: noncompetitive. Application deadline: rolling. Notification: continuous. Transfer credits accepted: Yes.

Costs Per Year: Application fee: $0. State resident tuition: $1,527 full-time. Nonresident tuition: $1,672 full-time. Mandatory fees: $184 full-time. Full-time tuition and fees vary according to course load and degree level.

Collegiate Environment: Orientation program. Drama-theater group, choral group, student-run newspaper, radio station. Student services: health clinic, personal-psychological counseling, women's center. Campus security: 24-hour emergency response devices and patrols, student patrols, late night transport-escort service. Holman Library.

Community Environment: Auburn is a suburban community in the Seattle area. It is located approximately 30 miles from the heart of downtown Seattle. The climate is mild. Auburn may be reached by railroad, the Seattle airport, and major highways. One library, several churches, a museum, YMCA, general hospital, and clinics serve the community. Local recreation includes a city park, a golf club, community theater, a nearby beach and rivers, hunting for deer, bear, birds and elk, lake fishing, water sports, skiing and mountain climbing. Some part-time employment is available. Various civic and fraternal organizations are active in the community. There are good shopping facilities.

■ **HERITAGE UNIVERSITY**
3240 Fort Rd.
Toppenish, WA 98948-9599
Tel: (509)865-8500; Free: 888-272-6190
Fax: (509)865-4469
E-mail: admissions@heritage.edu
Web Site: www.heritage.edu

Description: Independent, comprehensive, coed. Awards associate, bachelor's, and master's degrees and post-master's certificates. Founded 1982. Setting: 48-acre rural campus with easy access to Tri-Cities, Washington. Total enrollment: 1,241. Faculty: 185 (74 full-time, 111 part-time). Student-undergrad faculty ratio is 8:1. Full-time: 724 students, 75% women, 25% men. Part-time: 137 students, 78% women, 22% men. 5% American Indian or Alaska Native, non-Hispanic/Latino; 62% Hispanic/Latino; 1% Black or African American, non-Hispanic/Latino; 0.7% Asian, non-Hispanic/Latino; 0.7% Native Hawaiian or other Pacific Islander, non-Hispanic/Latino; 1% international. Retention: 68% of full-time freshmen returned the following year. Core. Calendar: semesters. Academic remediation for entering students, ESL program, services for LD students, advanced placement, self-designed majors, honors program, independent study, distance learning, double major, summer session for credit, part-time degree program, adult/continuing education programs, co-op programs and internships, graduate courses open to undergrads.

Entrance Requirements: Required: high school transcript. Required for some: interview, SAT or ACT.

Costs Per Year: One-time mandatory fee: $140. Tuition: $17,824 full-time, $743 per semester hour part-time.

Collegiate Environment: Orientation program. Choral group. Social organizations: 17 open to all; national sororities. Most popular organizations: Student Government Association, ENACTUS (Business Club), MECHA (National Cultural Club), Nursing Club, Omega Delta Phi (Fraternity). Major annual events: Spring Faire, Convocation, Commencement. Student services: personal-psychological counseling. Campus security: 24-hour emergency response devices, late night transport-escort service, 24-hour camera monitoring. Donald N. Kay North Library. 350 computers available on campus for general student use. A campuswide network can be accessed from off-campus. Students can access the following: online class registration. Staffed computer lab on campus.

Community Environment: Toppenish is located twenty miles south of Yakima, in the fertile lower Yakima Valley which produces fruit and hops and supports agricultural related industries. The climate is mild and dry. Toppenish has churches representing most denominations, a hospital, symphony, civic theatre, community concert series, and arts events. Local recreation includes swimming, skiing, boating, fishing, hunting, and golf. Local events include the Toppenish Rodeo and Pow-Wow, the Cinco de Mayo celebrations, and Yakima Indian Nation Cultural Center events.

■ HIGHLINE COLLEGE

2400 S 240th St.
Des Moines, WA 98198-9800
Tel: (206)878-3710
Fax: (206)870-3782
Web Site: www.highline.edu

Description: State-supported, 2-year, coed. Part of Washington State Board for Community and Technical Colleges. Awards certificates, diplomas, transfer associate, and terminal associate degrees. Founded 1961. Setting: 81-acre suburban campus with easy access to Seattle. Endowment: $1.4 million. Educational spending for the previous fiscal year: $3719 per student. Total enrollment: 6,743. Faculty: 360 (144 full-time, 216 part-time). Student-undergrad faculty ratio is 19:1. 4,445 applied, 100% were admitted. Full-time: 3,932 students, 56% women, 44% men. Part-time: 2,811 students, 61% women, 39% men. Students come from 6 states and territories, 50 other countries, 1% from out-of-state. 0.7% American Indian or Alaska Native, non-Hispanic/Latino; 7% Hispanic/Latino; 11% Black or African American, non-Hispanic/Latino; 15% Asian, non-Hispanic/Latino; 1% Native Hawaiian or other Pacific Islander, non-Hispanic/Latino; 7% international. 51% 25 or older, 71% transferred in. Retention: 57% of full-time freshmen returned the following year. Core. Calendar: quarters. Academic remediation for entering students, ESL program, services for LD students, advanced placement, self-designed majors, freshman honors college, honors program, independent study, distance learning, summer session for credit, part-time degree program, co-op programs and internships. Off campus study. Study abroad program. ROTC: Army (c), Air Force (c).

Entrance Requirements: Open admission. Option: electronic application. Entrance: noncompetitive. Application deadline: rolling. Transfer credits accepted: Yes.

Collegiate Environment: Orientation program. Drama-theater group, choral group, student-run newspaper. Social organizations: 47 open to all. Most popular organizations: Black Student Union, Pacific Islander Club, Friends of Bosnia, United Latino Association, Muslim Student Association. Major annual event: Thunderweek (fall opening week). Student services: personal-psychological counseling, women's center. Campus security: 24-hour emergency response devices and patrols, late night transport-escort service. Highline Community College Library. Operations spending for the previous fiscal year: $1.7 million. 300 computers available on campus for general student use. A campuswide network can be accessed. Students can access the following: online class registration, online degree planning. Staffed computer lab on campus provides training in use of computers, software, and the Internet.

Community Environment: Overlooking the Puget Sound, Des Moines is a suburb of Seattle, approximately 15 miles from the heart of downtown. (See Seattle University.) The community has all the advantages of a small town, and yet is easily accessible to all the cultural, recreational, and civic opportunities of the neighboring community.

■ LAKE WASHINGTON INSTITUTE OF TECHNOLOGY

11605 132nd Ave. NE
Kirkland, WA 98034-8506
Tel: (425)739-8100
E-mail: info@lwtc.edu
Web Site: www.lwtech.edu

Description: State-supported, 2-year, coed. Part of Washington State Board for Community and Technical Colleges. Awards certificates, transfer associate, and terminal associate degrees. Founded 1949. Setting: 57-acre suburban campus with easy access to Seattle. Total enrollment: 3,996. Calendar: quarters. Academic remediation for entering students, ESL program, services for LD students, advanced placement, summer session for credit, co-op programs and internships.

Entrance Requirements: Open admission except for allied health programs. Option: early admission. Required for some: high school transcript. Entrance: noncompetitive. Application deadline: rolling. Notification: continuous.

Collegiate Environment: Student services: personal-psychological counseling, women's center. Campus security: 24-hour emergency response devices, late night transport-escort service, parking lot security, security cameras. Lake Washington Technical College Library/Media Center.

■ LOWER COLUMBIA COLLEGE

1600 Maple St.
Longview, WA 98632-0310
Tel: (360)442-2311; Free: 866-900-2311
Fax: (360)442-2109
E-mail: registration@lowercolumbia.edu
Web Site: www.lowercolumbia.edu

Description: State-supported, 2-year, coed. Part of Washington State Board for Community and Technical Colleges. Awards certificates, diplomas, transfer associate, and terminal associate degrees. Founded 1934. Setting: 39-acre rural campus with easy access to Portland. Endowment: $14.9 million. Educational spending for the previous fiscal year: $3875 per student. Total enrollment: 3,152. Faculty: 196 (67 full-time, 129 part-time). Student-undergrad faculty ratio is 15:1. Full-time: 1,633 students, 60% women, 40% men. Part-time: 1,519 students, 69% women, 31% men. Core. Calendar: quarters. Academic remediation for entering students, ESL program, services for LD students, advanced placement, self-designed majors, independent study, distance learning, summer session for credit, part-time degree program, external degree program, adult/continuing education programs, co-op programs and internships.

Entrance Requirements: Open admission. Option: electronic application. Recommended: high school transcript. Entrance: noncompetitive. Application deadline: rolling. Notification: continuous. Transfer credits accepted: Yes.

Collegiate Environment: Orientation program. Drama-theater group, choral group. Social organizations: 29 open to all. Most popular organizations: Phi Theta Kappa, Electric Vehicle Club, Multicultural Club, Global Medical Brigade, Sustainability Club. Major annual events: Welcome Back Week, Red Devil Days. Student services: personal-psychological counseling. Campus security: 24-hour emergency response devices and patrols. Alan Thompson Library plus 1 other. Operations spending for the previous fiscal year: $404,606.

Community Environment: Longview is a planned city located on the banks of the Columbia and Cowlitz Rivers. The city is 50 miles north of Portland, Oregon, and has a mild climate. There are several churches, a public library, YMCA and two hospitals accessible. Longview may be reached by five railroad lines, and an airport. Local recreation includes theatres, boating, fishing, golf, hunting, skiing, and other sports. Part-time employment is available for students. Hotels, motels, and apartments are available for student housing. The community has several large shopping centers.

■ NORTH SEATTLE COLLEGE

9600 College Way N
Seattle, WA 98103-3599
Tel: (206)527-3600
Fax: (206)527-3635
E-mail: arrc@seattlecolleges.edu
Web Site: www.northseattle.edu

Description: State-supported, 2-year, coed. Part of Seattle Community College District System. Awards certificates, diplomas, transfer associate, and terminal associate degrees. Founded 1970. Setting: 65-acre urban campus. Endowment: $4.4 million. Educational spending for the previous fiscal year: $4522 per student. Total enrollment: 6,303. Faculty: 305 (89 full-time, 216 part-time). Student-undergrad faculty ratio is 20:1. 5,726 applied, 100% were admitted. Full-time: 1,953 students, 52% women, 48% men. Part-time: 4,350 students, 63% women, 37% men. Students come from 39 other countries, 5% from out-of-state. 0.8% American Indian or Alaska Native, non-Hispanic/Latino; 7% Hispanic/Latino; 7% Black or African American, non-Hispanic/Latino; 12% Asian, non-Hispanic/Latino; 1% Native Hawaiian or other Pacific Islander, non-Hispanic/Latino. 65% 25 or older, 23% transferred in. Core. Calendar: quarters. Academic remediation for entering students, ESL program, services for LD students, advanced placement, independent study, distance learning, summer session for credit, part-time degree program, external degree program, adult/continuing education programs, co-op programs and internships. Study abroad program. ROTC: Army (c).

Entrance Requirements: Open admission. Options: electronic application, early admission, deferred admission. Required: high school transcript. Required for some: essay. Entrance: noncompetitive. Application deadline: rolling. Notification: continuous until 9/24.

Collegiate Environment: Orientation program. Drama-theater group, choral group. Social organizations: 25 open to all. Most popular organizations: Muslim Students Association, Indonesian Community Club, Literary Guild, Phi Theta Kappa, Vietnamese Student Association. Major annual events: Cinco de Mayo, Welcome Back BBQ and Success Fair, Spring Fest. Student services: personal-psychological counseling, women's center. Campus security: 24-hour emergency response devices, late night transport-escort service, patrols by security. North Seattle Community College Library. 1,600 computers available on campus for general student use. A campuswide network can be accessed from off-campus. Students can access the following: online class registration. Staffed computer lab on campus.
Community Environment: See Seattle University.

■ **NORTHWEST COLLEGE OF ART & DESIGN**
1126 Pacific Ave.
Ste. 101
Tacoma, WA 98402
Tel: (253)272-1126; Free: 800-769-ARTS
Fax: (253)572-9058
E-mail: amiller@ncad.edu
Web Site: www.ncad.edu
Description: Proprietary, 4-year, coed. Awards bachelor's degrees. Founded 1982. Setting: urban campus with easy access to Seattle. Total enrollment: 104. Faculty: 12 (all part-time). Student-undergrad faculty ratio is 5:1. 3% American Indian or Alaska Native, non-Hispanic/Latino; 7% Hispanic/Latino; 6% Black or African American, non-Hispanic/Latino; 11% Asian, non-Hispanic/Latino. 12% 25 or older. Retention: 58% of full-time freshmen returned the following year. Academic area with the most degrees conferred: visual and performing arts. Core. Calendar: semesters. Services for LD students, accelerated degree program, double major, summer session for credit, internships.
Entrance Requirements: Required: essay, high school transcript, interview, 5 piece portfolio.
Costs Per Year: Tuition: $18,000 full-time, $765 per credit hour part-time. Mandatory fees: $100 full-time, $100 per year part-time.
Collegiate Environment: Orientation program. Northwest College of Art & Design Library plus 1 other. Books: 1,686 (physical); Serial titles: 366 (physical). Weekly public service hours: 40. 86 computers available on campus for general student use. A campuswide network can be accessed from off-campus. Staffed computer lab on campus provides training in use of computers, software, and the Internet.

■ **NORTHWEST INDIAN COLLEGE**
2522 Kwina Rd.
Bellingham, WA 98226
Tel: (360)676-2772; Free: 866-676-2772
Fax: (360)738-0136
E-mail: admissions@nwic.edu
Web Site: www.nwic.edu
Description: Federally supported, primarily 2-year, coed. Awards certificates, transfer associate, terminal associate, and bachelor's degrees (also offers bachelor's degree in elementary education in conjunction with Washington State University). Founded 1978. Setting: 5-acre rural campus. Total enrollment: 609. Student-undergrad faculty ratio is 13:1. 17% from out-of-state. 54% 25 or older. Core. Calendar: quarters. Academic remediation for entering students, self-designed majors, summer session for credit, part-time degree program, external degree program, adult/continuing education programs, co-op programs and internships. Study abroad program.
Entrance Requirements: Open admission. Required: high school transcript. Entrance: noncompetitive. Notification: continuous. Preference given to Native Americans.
Collegiate Environment: Drama-theater group, choral group, student-run newspaper. Student services: personal-psychological counseling.

■ **NORTHWEST SCHOOL OF WOODEN BOATBUILDING**
42 N Water St.
Port Hadlock, WA 98339
Tel: (360)385-4948
Fax: (360)385-5089
Web Site: www.nwswb.edu
Description: Independent, 2-year, coed. Awards diplomas and terminal associate degrees. Founded 1980. Setting: 6-acre small town campus. Faculty: 8 (6 full-time, 2 part-time). Student-undergrad faculty ratio is 12:1. Students

come from 20 states and territories, 3 other countries, 59% from out-of-state. 85% 25 or older. Core. Calendar: quarters.
Entrance Requirements: Option: electronic application. Required: essay, high school transcript. Transfer credits accepted: Yes.
Collegiate Environment: Orientation program. Major annual events: Port Townsend Wooden Boat Festival, Annual NWSWB Sail-in, Potlucks, BBQ's and Movie Nights. School Library. 2 computers available on campus for general student use. A campuswide network can be accessed.

■ **NORTHWEST UNIVERSITY**
5520 108th Ave., NE
Kirkland, WA 98033
Tel: (425)822-8266; Free: 800-669-3781
Fax: (425)425-0148
E-mail: admissions@northwestu.edu
Web Site: www.northwestu.edu
Description: Independent, comprehensive, coed, affiliated with Assemblies of God. Awards associate, bachelor's, master's, and doctoral degrees. Founded 1934. Setting: 56-acre suburban campus with easy access to Seattle. Endowment: $6.8 million. Educational spending for the previous fiscal year: $13,488 per student. Total enrollment: 2,583. Faculty: 252 (82 full-time, 170 part-time). Student-undergrad faculty ratio is 14:1. 493 applied, 99% were admitted. Full-time: 1,377 students, 60% women, 40% men. Part-time: 494 students, 60% women, 40% men. Students come from 34 states and territories, 24 other countries, 26% from out-of-state. 2% American Indian or Alaska Native, non-Hispanic/Latino; 10% Hispanic/Latino; 6% Black or African American, non-Hispanic/Latino; 6% Asian, non-Hispanic/Latino; 2% Native Hawaiian or other Pacific Islander, non-Hispanic/Latino; 0.8% international. 33% 25 or older, 55% live on campus, 13% transferred in. Retention: 80% of full-time freshmen returned the following year. Academic areas with the most degrees conferred: business/marketing; health professions and related sciences; theology and religious vocations. Core. Calendar: semesters. Academic remediation for entering students, ESL program, advanced placement, accelerated degree program, independent study, double major, summer session for credit, part-time degree program, adult/continuing education programs, co-op programs and internships. Study abroad program. ROTC: Army (c), Air Force (c).
Entrance Requirements: Options: electronic application, early action, deferred admission, international baccalaureate accepted. Required: essay, high school transcript, minimum 2.3 high school GPA, 2 recommendations, SAT or ACT. Required for some: interview. Entrance: moderately difficult. Application deadlines: 8/1, 1/15 for early action. Notification: continuous, 2/15 for early action. SAT Reasoning Test deadline: 8/1. Transfer credits accepted: Yes.
Costs Per Year: Application fee: $30. Comprehensive fee: $40,170 includes full-time tuition ($31,100), mandatory fees ($440), and college room and board ($8630). College room only: $4315. Full-time tuition and fees vary according to class time, course load, location, program, and reciprocity agreements. Room and board charges vary according to housing facility and location. Part-time tuition: $1250 per credit hour. Part-time mandatory fees: $120 per term. Part-time tuition and fees vary according to class time, course load, and location.
Collegiate Environment: Orientation program. Drama-theater group, choral group, student-run newspaper. Social organizations: 19 open to all. Most popular organizations: Student Ministries, Pursuit (worship service), Northwest University Business Club, Environmental Stewardship Club. Major annual events: Christmas Party, Floor Olympics, The Evening Formal Event. Student services: health clinic, personal-psychological counseling. Campus security: 24-hour emergency response devices and patrols, late night transport-escort service, controlled dormitory access. Hurst Library. Books: 170,000 (physical); Serial titles: 7,000 (physical); Databases: 81. Weekly public service hours: 91; study areas open 24 hours, 5-7 days a week; students can reserve study rooms. Operations spending for the previous fiscal year: $533,000. 134 computers available on campus for general student use. A campuswide network can be accessed from student residence rooms and from off campus. Students can access the following: online class registration, online classes. Staffed computer lab on campus provides training in use of computers, software, and the Internet.

■ **OLYMPIC COLLEGE**
1600 Chester Ave.
Bremerton, WA 98337-1699
Tel: (360)792-6050; Free: 800-259-6718
Fax: (360)792-2135

E-mail: ndownard@olympic.edu

Web Site: www.olympic.edu

Description: State-supported, primarily 2-year, coed. Part of Washington State Board for Community and Technical Colleges. Awards certificates, diplomas, transfer associate, terminal associate, and bachelor's degrees. Founded 1946. Setting: 33-acre suburban campus with easy access to Seattle, Tacoma. Total enrollment: 7,253. Faculty: 473 (129 full-time, 344 part-time). 2% American Indian or Alaska Native, non-Hispanic/Latino; 8% Hispanic/Latino; 5% Black or African American, non-Hispanic/Latino; 10% Asian, non-Hispanic/Latino; 2% international. 48% 25 or older, 1% live on campus. Core. Calendar: quarters. Academic remediation for entering students, ESL program, services for LD students, advanced placement, independent study, distance learning, summer session for credit, part-time degree program, adult/continuing education programs, co-op programs and internships. Off campus study at Brandman University, Old Dominion University, Western Washington University, Washington State University, Western Governors University, and other community and technical colleges in Washington state. Study abroad program.

Entrance Requirements: Open admission except for nursing/medical office assistant, physical therapy assistant, Bachelor of Applied Science Information Systems program and Bachelor of Applied Science Organizational Leadership and Technical Management programs. Option: electronic application. Required for some: essay, high school transcript, 2 recommendations. Entrance: noncompetitive. Application deadline: rolling. Transfer credits accepted: Yes.

Collegiate Environment: Orientation program. Drama-theater group, choral group, student-run newspaper. Most popular organizations: International Club, Armed Forces Club, Gay/Straight Alliance, Engineering Club, Clay Club. Major annual events: Commencement, Student Appreciation Day, Student Awards Ceremony. Student services: personal-psychological counseling. Campus security: 24-hour emergency response devices and patrols, student patrols, late night transport-escort service. Haselwood Library plus 1 other. Students can reserve study rooms. 1,300 computers available on campus for general student use. A campuswide network can be accessed. Students can access the following: online class registration. Staffed computer lab on campus provides training in use of computers, software, and the Internet.

Community Environment: Bremerton is a metropolitan community enjoying mild summer and winter temperatures. The major local industry is shipbuilding. The community has a library, hospital, churches of most denominations, and active civic, fraternal, and veteran's organizations. Rooming and boarding houses and small apartments are available for student housing. Local recreation includes sports, cultural events, boating, skiing, and snow boarding, all within a 3 hr. drive. Job opportunities are available for students.

■ **PACIFIC LUTHERAN UNIVERSITY**

Tacoma, WA 98447

Tel: (253)531-6900; Free: 800-274-6758

Fax: (253)536-5136

E-mail: admission@plu.edu

Web Site: www.plu.edu

Description: Independent, comprehensive, coed, affiliated with Evangelical Lutheran Church in America. Awards bachelor's, master's, and doctoral degrees and post-master's certificates. Founded 1890. Setting: 156-acre suburban campus with easy access to Seattle. Endowment: $99.8 million. Research spending for the previous fiscal year: $13.2 million. Educational spending for the previous fiscal year: $10,860 per student. Total enrollment: 3,111. Faculty: 269 (198 full-time, 71 part-time). Student-undergrad faculty ratio is 15:1. 3,740 applied, 80% were admitted. Full-time: 2,712 students, 64% women, 36% men. Part-time: 57 students, 47% women, 53% men. Students come from 43 states and territories, 26 other countries, 22% from out-of-state. 0.6% American Indian or Alaska Native, non-Hispanic/Latino; 12% Hispanic/Latino; 4% Black or African American, non-Hispanic/Latino; 10% Asian, non-Hispanic/Latino; 1% Native Hawaiian or other Pacific Islander, non-Hispanic/Latino; 3% international. 9% 25 or older, 44% live on campus, 6% transferred in. Retention: 83% of full-time freshmen returned the following year. Academic areas with the most degrees conferred: business/marketing; health professions and related sciences; social sciences. Core. Calendar: 4-1-4. ESL program, services for LD students, advanced placement, self-designed majors, honors program, independent study, distance learning, double major, summer session for credit, part-time degree program, co-op programs and internships, graduate courses open to undergrads. Study abroad program. ROTC: Army.

Entrance Requirements: Options: electronic application, deferred admis-

sion, international baccalaureate accepted. Required: essay, high school transcript, 1 recommendation, SAT or ACT. Recommended: minimum 2.5 high school GPA. Required for some: interview. Entrance: moderately difficult. Application deadlines: rolling, rolling for nonresidents. Notification: continuous, continuous for nonresidents. SAT Reasoning Test deadline: 8/30. Transfer credits accepted: Yes.

Costs Per Year: Application fee: $40. Comprehensive fee: $54,550 includes full-time tuition ($43,264), mandatory fees ($410), and college room and board ($10,876). College room only: $4940. Part-time tuition: $1352 per credit hour.

Collegiate Environment: Orientation program. Drama-theater group, choral group, student-run newspaper, radio station. Social organizations: 68 open to all. Most popular organizations: Chemistry Club, Delta Iota Chi, Black Student Union, APISA, Na Hoaloha O Hawaii. Major annual events: Homecoming, Convocation, EXPLORE Retreat. Student services: health clinic, personal-psychological counseling, women's center. Campus security: 24-hour emergency response devices and patrols, student patrols, late night transport-escort service, controlled dormitory access. 1,625 college housing spaces available; 1,382 were occupied in 2018-19. Freshmen guaranteed college housing. On-campus residence required through sophomore year. Options: coed, women-only housing available. Robert A. L. Mortvedt Library. Books: 222,754 (physical), 40,703 (digital/electronic); Serial titles: 34,315 (physical); Databases: 118. Weekly public service hours: 80; students can reserve study rooms. Operations spending for the previous fiscal year: $4.7 million. 522 computers available on campus for general student use. A campuswide network can be accessed from student residence rooms and from off campus. Students can access the following: online class registration. Staffed computer lab on campus provides training in use of computers, software, and the Internet.

Community Environment: The third largest city in Washington, Tacoma is a shipping, industrial, and distribution center located in the Puget Sound region. The city has diversified industries including electrochemicals, food and beverage processing, clothing manufacturing, iron and steel works, and shipyards. The city has several parks, a public library system, museums, hospitals, and many civic and fraternal organizations serving the community. Transportation is provided by railroads, airlines, twelve bus lines, and major highways. Its residents enjoy easy access to ocean beaches, the many waterways of Puget Sound, and Mt. Rainier, Olympic, and North Cascades National Parks. Nearby lakes and streams offer excellent fishing and numerous water sports.

■ **PENINSULA COLLEGE**

1502 E Lauridsen Blvd.

Port Angeles, WA 98362-2779

Tel: (360)452-9277; Free: 877-452-9277

Fax: (360)457-8100

E-mail: admissions@pencol.edu

Web Site: www.pencol.edu

Description: State-supported, primarily 2-year, coed. Part of Washington State Board for Community and Technical Colleges. Awards certificates, transfer associate, terminal associate, and bachelor's degrees. Founded 1961. Setting: 75-acre small town campus. Total enrollment: 3,321. Faculty: 156 (57 full-time, 99 part-time). Student-undergrad faculty ratio is 21:1. Calendar: quarters. Academic remediation for entering students, ESL program, services for LD students, advanced placement, honors program, distance learning, summer session for credit, part-time degree program, adult/continuing education programs, internships.

Entrance Requirements: Open admission except for management, nursing, industrial electronics, business computer systems programs, massage therapy programs. Required for some: high school transcript. Entrance: noncompetitive. Application deadline: rolling. Notification: continuous.

Collegiate Environment: Orientation program. Student-run newspaper. Student services: women's center. Campus security: 8-hour patrols by trained security personnel. John D Glann Library.

Community Environment: Called the gateway to Olympic National Park, Port Angeles is a popular resort and tourist area located between the Olympic Mountains and Strait of Juan de Fuca. The area enjoys temperate climate with temperature ranges from 30 to 80 degrees. Average rainfall is 22.8 inches. The city may be reached by airlines and highways. There are libraries, churches representing many denominations, a YMCA, and a modern hospital. Local recreation includes theatres, parks, concerts, plays, swimming, golf, skiing, bowling, hiking, crabbing, fishing, sailing and other sports. The community has many civic organizations, a symphony orchestra, choral and theater groups.

■ PERRY TECHNICAL INSTITUTE

2011 W Washington Ave.
Yakima, WA 98903-1296
Tel: (509)453-0374
Fax: (509)453-0375
Description: Independent, 2-year, coed. Founded 1940.

■ PIERCE COLLEGE FORT STEILACOOM

9401 Farwest Dr. SW
Lakewood, WA 98498
Tel: (253)964-6500
E-mail: admiss1@pierce.ctc.edu
Web Site: www.pierce.ctc.edu
Description: State-supported, 2-year, coed. Awards certificates, diplomas, transfer associate, and terminal associate degrees. Total enrollment: 8,188. Student-undergrad faculty ratio is 22:1. 52% 25 or older. Calendar: quarters.
Entrance Requirements: Open admission.

■ PIERCE COLLEGE PUYALLUP

1601 39th Ave. SE
Puyallup, WA 98374
Tel: (253)840-8400
Fax: (253)840-8423
Web Site: www.pierce.ctc.edu
Description: State-supported, 2-year, coed. Part of Washington State Board for Community and Technical Colleges. Awards certificates, diplomas, transfer associate, and terminal associate degrees. Founded 1967. Setting: 140-acre suburban campus with easy access to Seattle. Total enrollment: 13,294. Faculty: 600. Students come from 12 other countries. 56% 25 or older. Core. Calendar: quarters. Academic remediation for entering students, ESL program, services for LD students, advanced placement, independent study, distance learning, summer session for credit, part-time degree program, adult/continuing education programs, co-op programs and internships. Off campus study. Study abroad program. ROTC: Army (c).
Entrance Requirements: Open admission except for international students, veterinary technology, dental hygiene and nursing programs. Options: electronic application, early admission. Entrance: noncompetitive. Application deadline: rolling. Notification: continuous. Transfer credits accepted: Yes.
Collegiate Environment: Orientation program. Drama-theater group, choral group, student-run newspaper. Social organizations: 20 open to all. Most popular organizations: Student Life, Phi Theta Kappa, Dental Hygiene Association, Veterinary Technology Association. Student services: women's center. Campus security: 24-hour emergency response devices and patrols, late night transport-escort service. 350 computers available on campus for general student use. Staffed computer lab on campus.

■ PIMA MEDICAL INSTITUTE (RENTON)

555 S Renton Village Pl.
Renton, WA 98057
Tel: (425)228-9600; Free: 800-477-PIMA
Web Site: www.pmi.edu
Description: Proprietary, 2-year, coed. Awards certificates, transfer associate, and terminal associate degrees. Setting: urban campus. Core. Distance learning, co-op programs and internships.
Entrance Requirements: Required: high school transcript, interview, Wonderlic Scholastic Level Exam (SLE).
Collegiate Environment: Orientation program.

■ PIMA MEDICAL INSTITUTE (SEATTLE)

9709 Third Ave. NE
Ste. 400
Seattle, WA 98115
Tel: (206)322-6100; Free: 800-477-PIMA
Fax: (206)324-1985
Web Site: www.pmi.edu
Description: Proprietary, primarily 2-year, coed. Part of Vocational Training Institutes, Inc. Awards certificates, terminal associate, and bachelor's degrees. Founded 1989. Setting: urban campus. Total enrollment: 357. 57% 25 or older. Calendar: modular. Distance learning.
Entrance Requirements: Required: interview, Wonderlic aptitude test. Required for some: high school transcript. Entrance: minimally difficult.
Collegiate Environment: E-Global.

■ RENTON TECHNICAL COLLEGE

3000 NE Fourth St.
Renton, WA 98056
Tel: (425)235-2352
Fax: (425)235-7832
Web Site: www.rtc.edu
Description: State-supported, primarily 2-year, coed. Part of Washington State Board for Community and Technical Colleges. Awards certificates, diplomas, transfer associate, terminal associate, and bachelor's degrees. Founded 1942. Setting: 30-acre suburban campus with easy access to Seattle. Endowment: $837,103. Research spending for the previous fiscal year: $177,092. Total enrollment: 3,546. Faculty: 242 (71 full-time, 171 part-time). Student-undergrad faculty ratio is 16:1. 0.5% American Indian or Alaska Native, non-Hispanic/Latino; 13% Hispanic/Latino; 16% Black or African American, non-Hispanic/Latino; 19% Asian, non-Hispanic/Latino; 1% Native Hawaiian or other Pacific Islander, non-Hispanic/Latino; 0.9% international. Academic area with the most degrees conferred: computer and information sciences. Core. Calendar: quarters. Academic remediation for entering students, ESL program, services for LD students, advanced placement, distance learning, summer session for credit, part-time degree program, adult/continuing education programs, co-op programs and internships. Off campus study.
Entrance Requirements: Options: electronic application, early admission, international baccalaureate accepted. Required for some: essay, high school transcript, interview, ACT ASSET, CLEP, ACCUPLACER, DSP. Entrance: noncompetitive. Application deadline: rolling. Notification: continuous. Preference given to veterans for selective programs. Transfer credits accepted: Yes.
Costs Per Year: Application fee: $30. State resident tuition: $4836 full-time, $124.59 per credit hour part-time. Nonresident tuition: $138.73 per credit hour part-time. Full-time tuition varies according to course load, degree level, and program. Part-time tuition varies according to course load, degree level, and program.
Collegiate Environment: Orientation program. Major annual events: Graduation, Orientation. Student services: personal-psychological counseling. Campus security: patrols by security, security system. College housing not available. Renton Technical College Library. Books: 24,464 (physical), 64,437 (digital/electronic); Serial titles: 354 (physical), 19,981 (digital/electronic); Databases: 22. Weekly public service hours: 62. Operations spending for the previous fiscal year: $587,005. 96 computers available on campus for general student use. A campuswide network can be accessed. Students can access the following: online class registration, We provide numerous computer labs and classroom (podium-like setup) for instructional purposes. Staffed computer lab on campus.

■ SAINT MARTIN'S UNIVERSITY

5000 Abbey Way SE
Lacey, WA 98503
Tel: (360)491-4700; Free: 800-368-8803
Fax: (360)459-4124
Web Site: www.stmartin.edu
Description: Independent Roman Catholic, comprehensive, coed. Awards bachelor's and master's degrees and post-master's certificates. Founded 1895. Setting: 300-acre suburban campus with easy access to Seattle. Endowment: $21.8 million. Research spending for the previous fiscal year: $150,156. Educational spending for the previous fiscal year: $8315 per student. Total enrollment: 1,609. Faculty: 197 (79 full-time, 118 part-time). Student-undergrad faculty ratio is 11:1. 1,125 applied, 96% were admitted. 27% from top 10% of their high school class, 57% from top quarter, 85% from top half. Full-time: 1,172 students, 49% women, 51% men. Part-time: 172 students, 42% women, 58% men. Students come from 34 states and territories, 6 other countries, 28% from out-of-state. 1% American Indian or Alaska Native, non-Hispanic/Latino; 13% Hispanic/Latino; 6% Black or African American, non-Hispanic/Latino; 9% Asian, non-Hispanic/Latino; 5% Native Hawaiian or other Pacific Islander, non-Hispanic/Latino; 6% international. 24% 25 or older, 39% live on campus, 11% transferred in. Retention: 78% of full-time freshmen returned the following year. Academic areas with the most degrees conferred: business/marketing; psychology; engineering. Core. Calendar: semesters. Academic remediation for entering students, ESL program, services for LD students, advanced placement, honors program, independent study, distance learning, double major, summer session for credit, part-time degree program, adult/continuing education programs, co-op programs and internships, graduate courses open to undergrads. Off campus study. Study abroad program. ROTC: Army (c), Air Force (c).

Entrance Requirements: Options: electronic application, deferred admission, international baccalaureate accepted. Required: essay, high school transcript, 1 recommendation, SAT or ACT. Entrance: moderately difficult. Notification: continuous, continuous for nonresidents. SAT Reasoning Test deadline: 7/31. Transfer credits accepted: Yes.

Costs Per Year: Application fee: $0. Comprehensive fee: $50,560 includes full-time tuition ($38,150), mandatory fees ($410), and college room and board ($12,000). College room only: $5750. Part-time tuition: $1275 per credit.

Collegiate Environment: Orientation program. Drama-theater group, choral group, student-run newspaper. Social organizations: 30 open to all. Student services: health clinic, personal-psychological counseling. Campus security: 24-hour emergency response devices and patrols, student patrols, late night transport-escort service, controlled dormitory access, close-circuit TV cameras throughout campus, emergency text messaging/notification. 630 college housing spaces available; 521 were occupied in 2018-19. Freshmen guaranteed college housing. On-campus residence required through sophomore year. Option: coed housing available. O'Grady Library. Books: 88,291 (physical), 233,172 (digital/electronic); Serial titles: 98 (physical), 54,407 (digital/electronic); Databases: 114. Weekly public service hours: 88; students can reserve study rooms. Operations spending for the previous fiscal year: $88,002. 80 computers available on campus for general student use. A campuswide network can be accessed from student residence rooms. Students can access the following: online class registration. Staffed computer lab on campus provides training in use of computers, software, and the Internet.

■ SEATTLE CENTRAL COLLEGE

1701 Broadway
Seattle, WA 98122-2400
Tel: (206)587-3800
Web Site: www.seattlecentral.edu

Description: State-supported, 2-year, coed. Part of Seattle Community College District System. Awards certificates, transfer associate, and terminal associate degrees. Founded 1966. Setting: 15-acre urban campus. Total enrollment: 7,774. 1% from out-of-state. 49% 25 or older. Core. Calendar: quarters. Academic remediation for entering students, ESL program, services for LD students, summer session for credit, part-time degree program, external degree program, adult/continuing education programs, co-op programs and internships. ROTC: Army (c), Naval (c), Air Force (c).

Entrance Requirements: Open admission except for nursing program. Entrance: noncompetitive. Application deadline: rolling.

Collegiate Environment: Orientation program. Drama-theater group, choral group, student-run newspaper. Social organizations: 30 open to all. Most popular organizations: Triangle Club, African Brothers of Unity, MECHA, Asian/Pacific Islander Student Union, Sea-King Club for the Deaf. Major annual events: Student Studies Institute, Student Leadership. Student services: personal-psychological counseling, women's center. Campus security: 24-hour emergency response devices. Main Library.

Community Environment: See Seattle University.

■ SEATTLE PACIFIC UNIVERSITY

3307 Third Ave. W
Seattle, WA 98119-1997
Tel: (206)281-2000; Free: 800-366-3344
E-mail: admissions@spu.edu
Web Site: www.spu.edu

Description: Independent Free Methodist, comprehensive, coed. Awards bachelor's, master's, and doctoral degrees and post-master's certificates. Founded 1891. Setting: 40-acre urban campus. Total enrollment: 3,813. Faculty: 395 (209 full-time, 186 part-time). Student-undergrad faculty ratio is 13:1. 3,692 applied, 91% were admitted. Full-time: 2,783 students, 67% women, 33% men. Part-time: 128 students, 60% women, 40% men. 37% from out-of-state. 0.3% American Indian or Alaska Native, non-Hispanic/Latino; 12% Hispanic/Latino; 4% Black or African American, non-Hispanic/Latino; 12% Asian, non-Hispanic/Latino; 0.9% Native Hawaiian or other Pacific Islander, non-Hispanic/Latino; 5% international. 6% 25 or older, 52% live on campus, 7% transferred in. Retention: 79% of full-time freshmen returned the following year. Academic areas with the most degrees conferred: business/marketing; social sciences; health professions and related sciences. Core. Calendar: quarters. Academic remediation for entering students, services for LD students, advanced placement, self-designed majors, honors program, independent study, distance learning, double major, summer session for credit, part-time degree program, external degree

program, adult/continuing education programs, internships, graduate courses open to undergrads. Off campus study. Study abroad program. ROTC: Army (c), Naval (c), Air Force (c).

Entrance Requirements: Options: electronic application, early admission, early action, international baccalaureate accepted. Required: essay, high school transcript, minimum 2.5 high school GPA, 2 recommendations, SAT or ACT. Recommended: interview. Required for some: SAT and SAT Subject Tests or ACT. Entrance: moderately difficult. Application deadlines: 2/1, 11/15 for early action. Notification: 3/1, 1/5 for early action. SAT Reasoning Test deadline: 2/1. SAT Subject Test deadline: 2/1. Transfer credits accepted: Yes. Applicants placed on waiting list: 270. Wait-listed applicants offered admission: 26.

Costs Per Year: Application fee: $50. Comprehensive fee: $54,735 includes full-time tuition ($42,480), mandatory fees ($459), and college room and board ($11,796). College room only: $6399. Room and board charges vary according to board plan and housing facility. Part-time tuition: $1180 per credit hour. Part-time tuition varies according to course load.

Collegiate Environment: Orientation program. Drama-theater group, choral group, student-run newspaper, radio station. Social organizations: 50 open to all. Most popular organizations: Centurions, Falconettes, forensics organization, Amnesty International, University Players. Major annual events: Homecoming, Spring Picnic, Ivy Cutting Event. Student services: health clinic, personal-psychological counseling. Campus security: 24-hour emergency response devices and patrols, student patrols, late night transport-escort service, closed-circuit TV monitors. University Library. 150 computers available on campus for general student use. A campuswide network can be accessed from student residence rooms and from off campus. Students can access the following: online class registration. Staffed computer lab on campus provides training in use of computers and software.

Community Environment: See Seattle University.

■ SEATTLE UNIVERSITY

902 12th Ave.
Seattle, WA 98122-1090
Tel: (206)296-6000; Free: 800-426-7123
Fax: (206)296-5656
Web Site: www.seattleu.edu

Description: Independent Roman Catholic, comprehensive, coed. Awards bachelor's, master's, and doctoral degrees and post-master's certificates. Founded 1891. Setting: 50-acre urban campus with easy access to Seattle. Educational spending for the previous fiscal year: $15,759 per student. Total enrollment: 7,291. Faculty: 729 (510 full-time, 219 part-time). Student-undergrad faculty ratio is 11:1. 8,640 applied, 76% were admitted. 27% from top 10% of their high school class, 64% from top quarter, 94% from top half. Full-time: 4,519 students, 61% women, 39% men. Part-time: 245 students, 53% women, 47% men. Students come from 50 states and territories, 101 other countries, 59% from out-of-state. 0.3% American Indian or Alaska Native, non-Hispanic/Latino; 12% Hispanic/Latino; 3% Black or African American, non-Hispanic/Latino; 16% Asian, non-Hispanic/Latino; 0.8% Native Hawaiian or other Pacific Islander, non-Hispanic/Latino; 11% international. 9% 25 or older, 50% live on campus, 9% transferred in. Retention: 85% of full-time freshmen returned the following year. Academic areas with the most degrees conferred: business/marketing; health professions and related sciences; engineering. Core. Calendar: quarters. ESL program, services for LD students, advanced placement, accelerated degree program, self-designed majors, freshman honors college, honors program, independent study, double major, summer session for credit, part-time degree program, adult/continuing education programs, internships, graduate courses open to undergrads. Off campus study at Photographic Center Northwest. Study abroad program. ROTC: Army, Naval (c), Air Force (c).

Entrance Requirements: Options: electronic application, early action, deferred admission, international baccalaureate accepted. Required: essay, high school transcript, minimum 2.5 high school GPA, 2 recommendations, SAT or ACT. Entrance: moderately difficult. Application deadlines: rolling, 11/15 for early action. Notification: continuous until 3/1. SAT Reasoning Test deadline: 7/1. SAT Subject Test deadline: 7/1. Transfer credits accepted: Yes.

Costs Per Year: Application fee: $55. Comprehensive fee: $59,121 includes full-time tuition ($45,765), mandatory fees ($825), and college room and board ($12,531). College room only: $8481. Part-time tuition: $1017 per credit.

Collegiate Environment: Orientation program. Drama-theater group, choral group, student-run newspaper, radio station. Social organizations: 105 open to all. Most popular organizations: Student Government of Seattle University

(SGSU), Student Events and Activities Council (SEAC), Redzone, Dance Marathon, Hui 'O Nani Hawaii Club. Major annual events: Quadstock, Christmas Tree Lighting, Luau. Student services: health clinic, personal-psychological counseling, women's center. Campus security: 24-hour emergency response devices and patrols, late night transport-escort service, controlled dormitory access. 2,085 college housing spaces available; 1,965 were occupied in 2018-19. Freshmen guaranteed college housing. On-campus residence required through sophomore year. Option: coed housing available. Lemieux Library & McGoldrick Learning Commons plus 1 other. Books: 472,572 (physical), 257,641 (digital/electronic); Serial titles: 118,353 (physical), 8,597 (digital/electronic); Databases: 235. Students can reserve study rooms. 467 computers available on campus for general student use. Computer purchase/lease plans available. A campuswide network can be accessed from student residence rooms and from off campus. Students can access the following: online class registration. Staffed computer lab on campus (open 24 hours a day) provides training in use of the Internet.

Community Environment: Built upon the hills between Lake Washington and Puget Sound, Seattle is the metropolis of the Pacific Northwest. A fine protected harbor makes the city one of the world's great seaports. The community has a prosperous fishing industry, and is important for shipping of fir, red cedar and salmon. Other industries in the area include software and computer-related industries, aerospace and related fields, foundries, electronics, marine science firms and the processing of food and forest products. The summer average temperature is 63 degrees, and the winter average is 42 degrees. Mountains surround the city and 193 miles of waterfront accommodate oceangoing vessels. The community has 45 parks, art galleries, museums, year-round theater, and opera. There are churches representing all major denominations, and civic, fraternal and veteran's organizations active in the area. Part-time employment is available. Professional sport teams include the Seahawks (football), Mariners (baseball), and Sonics (basketball).

■ **SHORELINE COMMUNITY COLLEGE**
16101 Greenwood Ave. N
Shoreline, WA 98133-5696
Tel: (206)546-4101
Fax: (206)546-4599
Web Site: www.shoreline.edu

Description: State-supported, 2-year, coed. Part of Washington State Board for Community and Technical Colleges. Awards certificates, diplomas, and transfer associate degrees. Founded 1964. Setting: 80-acre suburban campus. Total enrollment: 8,591. Faculty: 415 (155 full-time, 260 part-time). Student-undergrad faculty ratio is 21:1. 45% 25 or older. Core. Calendar: quarters. Academic remediation for entering students, ESL program, services for LD students, advanced placement, independent study, distance learning, summer session for credit, part-time degree program, adult/continuing education programs, co-op programs and internships. Study abroad program.

Entrance Requirements: Open admission. Option: electronic application. Required: high school transcript. Recommended: ACT ASSET or ACT Compass. Entrance: noncompetitive. Application deadline: rolling. Transfer credits accepted: Yes.

Collegiate Environment: Orientation program. Student services: personal-psychological counseling, women's center. Campus security: 24-hour emergency response devices and patrols. Ray W. Howard Library/Media Center. 385 computers available on campus for general student use. A campuswide network can be accessed. Students can access the following: online class registration. Staffed computer lab on campus provides training in use of computers and software.

Community Environment: See Seattle University.

■ **SKAGIT VALLEY COLLEGE**
2405 College Way
Mount Vernon, WA 98273-5899
Tel: (360)416-7600
Fax: (360)416-7890
E-mail: karenmarie.bade@skagit.edu
Web Site: www.skagit.edu

Description: State-supported, 2-year, coed. Part of Washington State Board for Community and Technical Colleges. Awards certificates, diplomas, transfer associate, and terminal associate degrees. Founded 1926. Setting: 85-acre small town campus with easy access to Seattle. Endowment: $3.2 million. Total enrollment: 6,858. Faculty: 301. Student-undergrad faculty ratio is 22:1. 3,321 applied, 60% were admitted. Students come from 4 states and

territories, 23 other countries, 3% from out-of-state. 68% 25 or older, 1% live on campus. Core. Calendar: quarters. Academic remediation for entering students, ESL program, services for LD students, advanced placement, accelerated degree program, self-designed majors, independent study, distance learning, summer session for credit, part-time degree program, external degree program, adult/continuing education programs, co-op programs and internships. Study abroad program.

Entrance Requirements: Open admission except for some programs. Options: electronic application, deferred admission. Required for some: high school transcript, interview. Entrance: noncompetitive. Application deadline: rolling.

Collegiate Environment: Orientation program. Drama-theater group, choral group, student-run newspaper, radio station. Social organizations: 42 open to all. Most popular organizations: Phi Theta Kappa, Calling All Colors, Business Management Training, Human Services, Paralegal Club. Major annual events: Cardinal Day, Honors Banquet, Commencement. Student services: personal-psychological counseling, women's center. Campus security: 24-hour patrols, late night transport-escort service, telephone/pager system. Norwood Cole Library. 200 computers available on campus for general student use. A campuswide network can be accessed from off-campus. Staffed computer lab on campus.

Community Environment: Agriculture, mixed industries and tourism are the principal industries in this city located on the Skagit River. The climate here is moderate with neither cold nor hot extremes. Mount Vernon is accessible by railroad, bus lines and major highways and is 90 minutes from the Seattle Pacific Airport by automobile. The community has several churches, two hospitals and YMCA serving the residents. Local recreation includes hunting, fishing, skiing, golfing, boating, swimming, salt water or fresh water sports and nearby mountains and forests recreation areas. Various fraternal and civic organizations are found within the community.

■ **SOUTH PUGET SOUND COMMUNITY COLLEGE**
2011 Mottman Rd., SW
Olympia, WA 98512-6292
Tel: (360)754-7711
Fax: (360)664-9407
E-mail: hdearborn@spcc.edu
Web Site: www.spscc.edu

Description: State-supported, 2-year, coed. Part of Washington State Board for Community and Technical Colleges. Awards certificates, diplomas, transfer associate, and terminal associate degrees. Founded 1970. Setting: 102-acre suburban campus with easy access to Seattle. Educational spending for the previous fiscal year: $4709 per student. Total enrollment: 4,955. Faculty: 263 (88 full-time, 175 part-time). Student-undergrad faculty ratio is 18:1. 525 applied, 100% were admitted. Full-time: 2,693 students, 53% women, 47% men. Part-time: 2,262 students, 64% women, 36% men. Students come from 16 states and territories, 27 other countries, 0.4% from out-of-state. 1% American Indian or Alaska Native, non-Hispanic/Latino; 8% Hispanic/Latino; 2% Black or African American, non-Hispanic/Latino; 5% Asian, non-Hispanic/Latino; 0.7% Native Hawaiian or other Pacific Islander, non-Hispanic/Latino; 1% international. 42% 25 or older, 33% transferred in. Retention: 59% of full-time freshmen returned the following year. Core. Calendar: quarters. Academic remediation for entering students, ESL program, services for LD students, advanced placement, distance learning, summer session for credit, part-time degree program, adult/continuing education programs, co-op programs and internships. Study abroad program. ROTC: Army (c).

Entrance Requirements: Open admission except for nursing, fire protection, dental assisting programs. Options: electronic application, early admission, deferred admission. Entrance: noncompetitive. Application deadline: rolling. Notification: continuous. Transfer credits accepted: Yes.

Collegiate Environment: Orientation program. Drama-theater group, student-run newspaper. Social organizations: 20 open to all. Most popular organizations: Building Revolution by Increasing Community Knowledge (BRICK), Christian Club, Welding Club, Automotive Club, Psychology/Sociology Club. Major annual events: Career Fair, International Celebration, Cinco de Mayo Celebration. Student services: personal-psychological counseling. Campus security: 24-hour emergency response devices and patrols, late night transport-escort service. Library/Media Center plus 1 other. 250 computers available on campus for general student use. A campuswide network can be accessed from off-campus. Students can access the following: online class registration. Staffed computer lab on campus provides training in use of computers, software, and the Internet.

■ SOUTH SEATTLE COLLEGE

6000 16th Ave., SW
Seattle, WA 98106-1499
Tel: (206)764-5300
Web Site: southseattle.edu
Description: State-supported, 2-year, coed. Part of Seattle Community College District System. Awards certificates, diplomas, transfer associate, and terminal associate degrees. Founded 1970. Setting: 65-acre urban campus. Total enrollment: 6,769. Faculty: 285 (75 full-time, 210 part-time). Students come from 24 other countries. 54% 25 or older. Calendar: quarters. Academic remediation for entering students, ESL program, services for LD students, advanced placement, summer session for credit, part-time degree program, adult/continuing education programs. Off campus study at 9 community colleges in the Seattle metropolitan area.
Entrance Requirements: Open admission except for international students. Option: early admission. Entrance: noncompetitive. Application deadline: rolling.
Collegiate Environment: Drama-theater group, choral group, student-run newspaper. Most popular organizations: Phi Theta Kappa, Vietnamese Club, Afro-American Club, Delta Epsilon Chi, International Student Clubs. Major annual events: Rainbow Festival, Holiday Dinner. Student services: personal-psychological counseling, women's center. Campus security: 24-hour emergency response devices and patrols. South Seattle Community College Instructional Resource Center. 300 computers available on campus for general student use. A campuswide network can be accessed. Staffed computer lab on campus.

■ SPOKANE COMMUNITY COLLEGE

1810 N Greene St.
Spokane, WA 99217-5399
Tel: (509)533-7000; Free: 800-248-5644
Fax: (509)533-8839
E-mail: mlee@ccs.spokane.edu
Web Site: www.scc.spokane.edu
Description: State-supported, 2-year, coed. Part of Washington State Board for Community and Technical Colleges. Awards certificates, diplomas, transfer associate, and terminal associate degrees. Founded 1963. Setting: 108-acre urban campus. Endowment: $33,508. Total enrollment: 6,982. Faculty: 509 (296 full-time, 213 part-time). Student-undergrad faculty ratio is 14:1. Full-time: 4,393 students, 57% women, 43% men. Part-time: 2,589 students, 49% women, 51% men. 3% from out-of-state. 32% 25 or older, 28% transferred in. Core. Calendar: quarters. Academic remediation for entering students, ESL program, services for LD students, advanced placement, self-designed majors, independent study, distance learning, summer session for credit, part-time degree program, adult/continuing education programs, co-op programs and internships. ROTC: Army (c).
Entrance Requirements: Open admission. Options: early admission, deferred admission. Recommended: high school transcript. Entrance: noncompetitive. Application deadline: rolling. Notification: continuous.
Collegiate Environment: Orientation program. Drama-theater group, student-run newspaper. Social organizations: 25 open to all. Most popular organizations: VICA (Vocational Industrial Clubs of America), Delta Epsilon Chi, Intercultural Student Organization, Rho Beta Psi, Student Awareness League. Major annual events: Spring Fling, Celebration of Cultures, Job Fair. Campus security: 24-hour emergency response devices and patrols, student patrols, late night transport-escort service. Learning Resources Center plus 1 other. Operations spending for the previous fiscal year: $786,010. 700 computers available on campus for general student use. A campuswide network can be accessed. Students can access the following: online class registration. Staffed computer lab on campus.
Community Environment: See Spokane Falls Community College.

■ SPOKANE FALLS COMMUNITY COLLEGE

3410 W Fort George Wright Dr.
Spokane, WA 99224-5288
Tel: (509)533-3500; Free: 888-509-7944
Fax: (509)533-3433
Web Site: www.spokanefalls.edu
Description: State-supported, 2-year, coed. Part of State Board for Washington Community and Technical Colleges. Awards certificates, diplomas, transfer associate, and terminal associate degrees. Founded 1967. Setting: 125-acre urban campus. Total enrollment: 5,658. Faculty: 545 (164 full-time, 381 part-time). Student-undergrad faculty ratio is 27:1. Full-time: 3,974 students, 55% women, 45% men. Part-time: 1,684 students,

62% women, 38% men. 19% 25 or older. Core. Calendar: quarters. Academic remediation for entering students, ESL program, services for LD students, advanced placement, self-designed majors, summer session for credit, part-time degree program, adult/continuing education programs, co-op programs and internships. ROTC: Army (c).
Entrance Requirements: Open admission. Options: early admission, deferred admission. Recommended: high school transcript. Entrance: noncompetitive. Application deadline: rolling. Notification: continuous.
Collegiate Environment: Drama-theater group, choral group, student-run newspaper, radio station. Social organizations: 30 open to all. Most popular organizations: DECA, Associated Men Students, Associated Women Students, chorale, Forensics Club. Major annual events: Spring Fling, Winter Fest, Club Orientation Week. Student services: personal-psychological counseling, women's center. Campus security: late night transport-escort service, 24-hour emergency dispatch. Learning Resources Center plus 1 other. 400 computers available on campus for general student use. A campuswide network can be accessed. Students can access the following: online class registration. Staffed computer lab on campus.
Community Environment: The second largest city in the state, Spokane has diversified natural resources including timber lands, tremendous waterpower, and mineral wealth. There are many industries in the area, and part-time work is available. The city is considered the economic and cultural capital of the region between the Rockies and the Cascades. The mean temperature is 47 degrees. Two airports, and several private fields, railroads, and bus lines serve the area. Over 200 churches of all denominations, a public library system, several hospitals, and many civic and fraternal organizations are active here. There are military establishments representing all the services within the area. The community has many fine cultural and recreational facilities as well as excellent shopping facilities.

■ TACOMA COMMUNITY COLLEGE

6501 S 19th St.
Tacoma, WA 98466
Tel: (253)566-5000
Fax: (253)566-5376
Web Site: www.tacomacc.edu
Description: State-supported, 2-year, coed. Part of Washington State Board for Community and Technical Colleges. Awards certificates, diplomas, transfer associate, and terminal associate degrees. Founded 1965. Setting: 150-acre urban campus with easy access to Seattle. Total enrollment: 6,318. Student-undergrad faculty ratio is 21:1. 2% from out-of-state. 44% 25 or older. Retention: 56% of full-time freshmen returned the following year. Calendar: quarters. Academic remediation for entering students, advanced placement, distance learning, summer session for credit, part-time degree program, adult/continuing education programs. Off campus study at members of the Concurrent Enrollment Program. Study abroad program. ROTC: Army (c).
Entrance Requirements: Open admission except for some vocational programs. Option: early admission. Entrance: noncompetitive. Application deadline: rolling.
Collegiate Environment: Orientation program. Campus security: Sonitrol electronic system. Pearl Wanamaker Library.
Community Environment: The third largest city in Washington, Tacoma is a shipping, industrial and distributing center located in the Puget Sound region. The city has diversified industries including electrochemicals, food and beverage processing, clothing manufacturing, iron, steel, and shipyards. The area is provided transportation by rail, air, bus, and major highways. The city has many parks, a public library system, museums, hospitals, and many civic and fraternal organizations to serve the community. Tacoma is near Mt. Rainier National park and its residents enjoy easy access to ocean beaches, the many waterways of Puget Sound, and Olympic and North Cascades National Parks. Nearby lakes and streams offer excellent fishing.

■ UNIVERSITY OF PUGET SOUND

1500 N Warner St.
Tacoma, WA 98416
Tel: (253)879-3100; Free: 800-396-7191
Fax: (253)879-3500
E-mail: admission@pugetsound.edu
Web Site: www.pugetsound.edu
Description: Independent, comprehensive, coed. Awards bachelor's, master's, and doctoral degrees. Founded 1888. Setting: 97-acre urban campus with easy access to Seattle. Endowment: $369 million. Research spending for the previous fiscal year: $1.4 million. Educational spending for

the previous fiscal year: $19,534 per student. Total enrollment: 2,666. Faculty: 288 (230 full-time, 58 part-time). Student-undergrad faculty ratio is 11:1. 5,730 applied, 88% were admitted. 28% from top 10% of their high school class, 58% from top quarter, 91% from top half. Full-time: 2,348 students, 60% women, 40% men. Part-time: 16 students, 69% women, 31% men. Students come from 44 states and territories, 6 other countries, 77% from out-of-state. 0.1% American Indian or Alaska Native, non-Hispanic/Latino; 9% Hispanic/Latino; 2% Black or African American, non-Hispanic/Latino; 6% Asian, non-Hispanic/Latino; 0.6% Native Hawaiian or other Pacific Islander, non-Hispanic/Latino; 0.4% international. 1% 25 or older, 66% live on campus, 2% transferred in. Retention: 81% of full-time freshmen returned the following year. Academic areas with the most degrees conferred: social sciences; business/marketing; biological/life sciences. Core. Calendar: semesters. Services for LD students, advanced placement, self-designed majors, honors program, independent study, double major, summer session for credit, part-time degree program, co-op programs and internships. Study abroad program. ROTC: Army (c).

Entrance Requirements: Options: electronic application, early admission, early decision, early action, deferred admission, international baccalaureate accepted. Required: essay, high school transcript, 2 recommendations. Recommended: minimum 3 high school GPA, interview. Entrance: moderately difficult. Transfer credits accepted: Yes. Applicants placed on waiting list: 30. Wait-listed applicants offered admission: 1. Early decision applicants: 110. Early decision applicants admitted: 98. Early action applicants: 2,840. Early action applicants admitted: 2,667.

Costs Per Year: Application fee: $60. Comprehensive fee: $64,740 includes full-time tuition ($51,470), mandatory fees ($270), and college room and board ($13,000). College room only: $7020. Part-time tuition: $6500 per unit.

Collegiate Environment: Orientation program. Drama-theater group, choral group, student-run newspaper, radio station. Social organizations: 105 open to all; national fraternities, national sororities; 26% of eligible men and 27% of eligible women are members. Most popular organizations: Puget Sound Outdoors, Repertory Dance Group, Ka Ohana me ke Aloha, Student Theatre Productions, Relay for Life. Major annual events: Log Jam (opening weekend of fall semester), Ka Ohana me ke Aloha Luau/Spring Family Weekend, Midnight Breakfast. Student services: health clinic, personal-psychological counseling. Campus security: 24-hour emergency response devices and patrols, student patrols, late night transport-escort service, controlled dormitory access. 1,725 college housing spaces available; 1,568 were occupied in 2018-19. Freshmen guaranteed college housing. On-campus residence required through sophomore year. Option: coed housing available. Collins Memorial Library. Operations spending for the previous fiscal year: $3.2 million. 329 computers available on campus for general student use. Computer purchase/lease plans available. A campuswide network can be accessed from student residence rooms and from off campus. Students can access the following: online class registration, financial aid, admission, student employment. Staffed computer lab on campus (open 24 hours a day) provides training in use of computers, software, and the Internet.

Community Environment: Founded in 1888, the campus is located in residential North Tacoma. Thirty miles south of Seattle and easily accessible from Interstate 5, Tacoma is a dynamic city of 187,200 people. The university occupies 38 buildings on a 97 acre park-like campus; architecture is Tudor Gothic with its distinctive red-brick pattern arches and porticoes. Located close to the shores of Puget Sound and a short distance from ski slopes and the Pacific Ocean, the University is also the center for much of Tacoma's cultural life. Tacoma also features Point Defiance Zoo and Aquarium, many parks, a public library system, museums and hospitals.

■ **UNIVERSITY OF WASHINGTON**
Seattle, WA 98195
Tel: (206)543-2100
Web Site: www.washington.edu
Description: State-supported, university, coed. Part of University of Washington. Awards bachelor's, master's, and doctoral degrees and post-master's certificates. Founded 1861. Setting: 634-acre urban campus with easy access to Seattle, WA. Endowment: $3.4 billion. Research spending for the previous fiscal year: $794.6 million. Educational spending for the previous fiscal year: $24,874 per student. Total enrollment: 47,361. Faculty: 2,675 (2,015 full-time, 660 part-time). Student-undergrad faculty ratio is 19:1. 45,907 applied, 49% were admitted. Full-time: 29,496 students, 54% women, 46% men. Part-time: 2,603 students, 50% women, 50% men. Students come from 51 states and territories, 86 other countries, 19% from out-of-state. 0.5% American Indian or Alaska Native, non-Hispanic/Latino; 8% Hispanic/Latino; 3% Black or African American, non-Hispanic/Latino;

25% Asian, non-Hispanic/Latino; 0.4% Native Hawaiian or other Pacific Islander, non-Hispanic/Latino; 16% international. 6% 25 or older, 29% live on campus, 22% transferred in. Retention: 94% of full-time freshmen returned the following year. Academic areas with the most degrees conferred: social sciences; biological/life sciences; business/marketing. Core. Calendar: quarters. ESL program, services for LD students, advanced placement, self-designed majors, honors program, independent study, distance learning, double major, summer session for credit, part-time degree program, external degree program, adult/continuing education programs, co-op programs and internships, graduate courses open to undergrads. Off campus study at University of Washington Bothell and University of Washington Tacoma, National Student Exchange. Study abroad program. ROTC: Army, Naval, Air Force.

Entrance Requirements: Options: electronic application, early admission, international baccalaureate accepted. Required: essay. Required for some: high school transcript. Entrance: very difficult. Notification: 3/15. SAT Reasoning Test deadline: 12/31. Transfer credits accepted: Yes.

Costs Per Year: Application fee: $80. State resident tuition: $10,127 full-time, $338 per credit part-time. Nonresident tuition: $35,508 full-time, $1184 per credit part-time. Mandatory fees: $1080 full-time, $28 per credit part-time, $84 per term part-time. Full-time tuition and fees vary according to course load and location. Part-time tuition and fees vary according to course load and location. College room and board: $12,798. Room and board charges vary according to board plan, housing facility, and location.

Collegiate Environment: Orientation program. Drama-theater group, choral group, marching band, student-run newspaper, radio station. Social organizations: 800 open to all; national fraternities, national sororities, local fraternities, local sororities, National PanHellenic Council, United Greek Council; 16% of eligible men and 15% of eligible women are members. Most popular organizations: Interfraternity Council/Pan-Hellenic Council, Taiwanese Student Association, Chinese Student Association, Yacht Club, Asian American Intervarsity Christian Fellowship/Muslim Students Association. Major annual events: Dawg Daze and Fall Fling, Spring Concert, Taiwanese Student Association Night Market. Student services: legal services, health clinic, personal-psychological counseling, women's center. Campus security: 24-hour emergency response devices and patrols, late night transport-escort service, controlled dormitory access. College housing designed to accommodate 8,754 students; 9,444 undergraduates lived in college housing during 2018-19. No special consideration for freshman housing applicants. Option: coed housing available. Odegaard Undergraduate Library plus 12 others. Books: 9 million (physical), 1.2 million (digital/electronic); Serial titles: 156,594 (physical), 183,555 (digital/electronic); Databases: 283. Weekly public service hours: 124; study areas open 24 hours, 5-7 days a week; students can reserve study rooms. Operations spending for the previous fiscal year: $47.4 million. 919 computers available on campus for general student use. A campuswide network can be accessed from student residence rooms and from off campus. Students can access the following: online class registration. Staffed computer lab on campus (open 24 hours a day) provides training in use of computers, software, and the Internet.

■ **UNIVERSITY OF WASHINGTON, BOTHELL**
18115 Campus Way NE
Bothell, WA 98011
Tel: (425)352-5000
Web Site: www.uwb.edu
Description: State-supported, comprehensive, coed. Part of University of Washington. Awards bachelor's and master's degrees. Founded 1990. Setting: 127-acre suburban campus with easy access to Seattle. Endowment: $4.1 million. Research spending for the previous fiscal year: $4.8 million. Educational spending for the previous fiscal year: $7965 per student. Total enrollment: 5,979. Faculty: 340 (201 full-time, 139 part-time). Student-undergrad faculty ratio is 20:1. 3,022 applied, 79% were admitted. Full-time: 4,623 students, 47% women, 53% men. Part-time: 778 students, 53% women, 47% men. Students come from 25 states and territories, 24 other countries, 2% from out-of-state. 0.5% American Indian or Alaska Native, non-Hispanic/Latino; 10% Hispanic/Latino; 7% Black or African American, non-Hispanic/Latino; 29% Asian, non-Hispanic/Latino; 0.5% Native Hawaiian or other Pacific Islander, non-Hispanic/Latino; 9% international. 20% 25 or older, 6% live on campus, 14% transferred in. Retention: 87% of full-time freshmen returned the following year. Academic areas with the most degrees conferred: business/marketing; health professions and related sciences; computer and information sciences. Core. Calendar: quarters. ESL program, services for LD students, advanced placement, self-designed majors, honors

program, independent study, distance learning, double major, summer session for credit, part-time degree program, adult/continuing education programs, co-op programs and internships, graduate courses open to undergrads. Off campus study at University of Washington Seattle and University of Washington Tacoma. Study abroad program. ROTC: Army (c), Naval (c), Air Force (c).

Entrance Requirements: Options: electronic application, international baccalaureate accepted. Required: essay, high school transcript, minimum 2 high school GPA, SAT or ACT. Required for some: 1 recommendation. Entrance: moderately difficult. Application deadline: 1/15. Notification: continuous. Transfer credits accepted: Yes.

Costs Per Year: Application fee: $60. State resident tuition: $10,127 full-time, $339 per credit part-time. Nonresident tuition: $35,508 full-time, $1184 per credit part-time. Mandatory fees: $1011 full-time, $34 per credit part-time. Full-time tuition and fees vary according to course load. Part-time tuition and fees vary according to course load. College room and board: $11,877. Room and board charges vary according to board plan, housing facility, and location.

Collegiate Environment: Orientation program. Student-run newspaper, radio station. Social organizations: 99 open to all. Most popular organizations: Campus Events Board, Social Justice Organizers, Associated Students of University of Washington Bothell (ASUWB), Recreation and Intramurals Program, Club Council. Major annual events: Welcome Week, SpringFest, Intercultural Night. Student services: personal-psychological counseling. Campus security: 24-hour emergency response devices and patrols, late night transport-escort service. Freshmen given priority for college housing. Option: coed housing available. Campus Library. Books: 119,564 (physical), 1.2 million (digital/electronic); Serial titles: 1,100 (physical), 183,555 (digital/electronic); Databases: 283. Weekly public service hours: 86; students can reserve study rooms. Operations spending for the previous fiscal year: $3.1 million. 538 computers available on campus for general student use. A campuswide network can be accessed from off-campus. Students can access the following: online class registration. Staffed computer lab on campus provides training in use of computers, software, and the Internet.

■ **UNIVERSITY OF WASHINGTON, TACOMA**
1900 Commerce St.
Tacoma, WA 98402-3100
Tel: (253)692-4000; Free: 800-736-7750
E-mail: uwtinfo@uw.edu
Web Site: www.tacoma.uw.edu

Description: State-supported, comprehensive, coed. Part of University of Washington. Awards bachelor's, master's, and doctoral degrees. Founded 1990. Setting: 31-acre urban campus with easy access to Seattle. Endowment: $40.5 million. Research spending for the previous fiscal year: $2.7 million. Educational spending for the previous fiscal year: $8877 per student. Total enrollment: 5,346. Faculty: 338 (261 full-time, 77 part-time). Student-undergrad faculty ratio is 16:1. 2,036 applied, 86% were admitted. Full-time: 3,995 students, 51% women, 49% men. Part-time: 549 students, 50% women, 50% men. Students come from 29 states and territories, 20 other countries, 1% from out-of-state. 0.8% American Indian or Alaska Native, non-Hispanic/Latino; 15% Hispanic/Latino; 9% Black or African American, non-Hispanic/Latino; 20% Asian, non-Hispanic/Latino; 1% Native Hawaiian or other Pacific Islander, non-Hispanic/Latino; 4% international. 26% 25 or older, 6% live on campus, 14% transferred in. Retention: 81% of full-time freshmen returned the following year. Academic areas with the most degrees conferred: computer and information sciences; business/marketing; health professions and related sciences; psychology. Core. Calendar: quarters. Academic remediation for entering students, services for LD students, advanced placement, self-designed majors, honors program, independent study, distance learning, double major, summer session for credit, part-time degree program, external degree program, internships, graduate courses open to undergrads. Off campus study at University of Washington Bothell and University of Washington Seattle. Study abroad program. ROTC: Army (c), Naval (c), Air Force (c).

Entrance Requirements: Options: electronic application, deferred admission, international baccalaureate accepted. Required: essay, SAT or ACT. Required for some: high school transcript, 3 recommendations. Entrance: moderately difficult. Notification: continuous. SAT Reasoning Test deadline: 6/1. SAT Subject Test deadline: 6/1. Transfer credits accepted: Yes.

Costs Per Year: Application fee: $60. State resident tuition: $10,127 full-time, $339 per credit part-time. Nonresident tuition: $35,508 full-time, $1184 per credit part-time. Mandatory fees: $1134 full-time, $38 per credit part-

time. Full-time tuition and fees vary according to course load. Part-time tuition and fees vary according to course load. College room and board: $11,028. Room and board charges vary according to housing facility and location.

Collegiate Environment: Orientation program. Drama-theater group, choral group, student-run newspaper. Social organizations: 111 open to all. Most popular organizations: Accounting Student Association, International Student Association, Partners in Action to Transform Healthcare (PATH), Asian Pacific Islander Student Union (APISU). Major annual events: Block Party, O.S.C.A.R.S, RSO Canned Food Drive. Student services: health clinic, personal-psychological counseling. Campus security: 24-hour emergency response devices and patrols, late night transport-escort service, key card access to buildings after hours. Freshmen given priority for college housing. University of Washington Tacoma Library. Books: 133,442 (physical), 1.2 million (digital/electronic); Serial titles: 924 (physical), 183,555 (digital/electronic); Databases: 283. Weekly public service hours: 84; students can reserve study rooms. Operations spending for the previous fiscal year: $1.6 million. 166 computers available on campus for general student use. A campuswide network can be accessed from student residence rooms and from off campus. Students can access the following: online class registration, learning management system, course management system. Staffed computer lab on campus provides training in use of computers, software, and the Internet.

■ **WALLA WALLA COMMUNITY COLLEGE**
500 Tausick Way
Walla Walla, WA 99362-9267
Tel: (509)522-2500; Free: 877-992-9922
Fax: (509)527-3361
Web Site: www.wwcc.edu

Description: State-supported, 2-year, coed. Part of Washington State Board for Community and Technical Colleges. Awards certificates, diplomas, transfer associate, and terminal associate degrees. Founded 1967. Setting: 125-acre small town campus. Total enrollment: 5,109. Faculty: 313 (123 full-time, 190 part-time). Student-undergrad faculty ratio is 20:1. Full-time: 2,969 students, 44% women, 56% men. Part-time: 2,140 students, 41% women, 59% men. Students come from 11 states and territories, 24% from out-of-state. 1% American Indian or Alaska Native, non-Hispanic/Latino; 17% Hispanic/Latino; 4% Black or African American, non-Hispanic/Latino; 1% Asian, non-Hispanic/Latino; 0.4% Native Hawaiian or other Pacific Islander, non-Hispanic/Latino; 0.1% international. 54% 25 or older, 15% transferred in. Retention: 67% of full-time freshmen returned the following year. Calendar: quarters. Academic remediation for entering students, advanced placement, distance learning, summer session for credit, part-time degree program, external degree program, adult/continuing education programs, co-op programs. Off campus study at other members of the Washington State Board for Community and Technical Colleges.

Entrance Requirements: Open admission. Option: electronic application. Recommended: high school transcript. Required for some: interview. Entrance: noncompetitive. Application deadline: rolling. Transfer credits accepted: Yes.

Collegiate Environment: Orientation program. Drama-theater group. Campus security: student patrols, late night transport-escort service. Walla Walla Community College Library plus 1 other. 400 computers available on campus for general student use. Computer purchase/lease plans available. A campuswide network can be accessed from off-campus. Students can access the following: online class registration. Staffed computer lab on campus provides training in use of computers, software, and the Internet.

Community Environment: Walla Walla is rich agricultural area in southern Washington near the Oregon State line. The chief crop is wheat. The area has excellent highways, a commuter airline and buslines serving the community. The climate is mild. Local recreation includes hunting, boating, fishing, camping and skiing in the nearby mountains. There are churches representing most denominations, health facilities and shopping centers in the area. All major lodges and service clubs are active here. Frontier days and a rodeo are held annually in September.

■ **WALLA WALLA UNIVERSITY**
204 S College Ave.
College Place, WA 99324
Tel: (509)527-2615; Free: 800-541-8900
Fax: (509)527-2397
Web Site: www.wallawalla.edu

Description: Independent Seventh-day Adventist, comprehensive, coed.

Awards associate, bachelor's, and master's degrees. Founded 1892. Setting: 77-acre small town campus. Total enrollment: 1,894. Faculty: 171 (100 full-time, 71 part-time). Student-undergrad faculty ratio is 15:1. Full-time: 1,585 students, 50% women, 50% men. Part-time: 115 students, 45% women, 55% men. 62% from out-of-state. 0.6% American Indian or Alaska Native, non-Hispanic/Latino; 15% Hispanic/Latino; 3% Black or African American, non-Hispanic/Latino; 6% Asian, non-Hispanic/Latino; 0.7% Native Hawaiian or other Pacific Islander, non-Hispanic/Latino; 3% international. 6% 25 or older, 72% live on campus, 7% transferred in. Academic areas with the most degrees conferred: health professions and related sciences; engineering; business/marketing. Core. Calendar: quarters. Academic remediation for entering students, services for LD students, advanced placement, freshman honors college, honors program, independent study, distance learning, double major, summer session for credit, part-time degree program, co-op programs and internships, graduate courses open to undergrads. Off campus study. Study abroad program.

Entrance Requirements: Option: electronic application. Required: high school transcript, minimum 2.5 high school GPA, SAT or ACT. Entrance: moderately difficult. Application deadline: rolling. Notification: continuous.

Costs Per Year: Application fee: $40. Comprehensive fee: $35,490 includes full-time tuition ($27,120), mandatory fees ($915), and college room and board ($7455). College room only: $4275. Part-time tuition: $755 per quarter hour.

Collegiate Environment: Orientation program. Drama-theater group, choral group, student-run newspaper. Most popular organizations: Associated Students of Walla Walla University, Campus Ministries, Village Club, OPS Club (Men's residence hall club), AGA Club (women's residence hall club). Major annual events: CommUnity, Service Day, Welcome Back Bash. Student services: health clinic, personal-psychological counseling. Campus security: 24-hour emergency response devices and patrols, student patrols, late night transport-escort service, controlled dormitory access. Peterson Memorial Library plus 3 others.

Community Environment: College Place is a residential community adjacent to Walla Walla. The climate is temperate. Three miles away, all major forms of transportation are available. The immediate community has four churches and two hospitals. Part-time employment opportunities are fair.

■ **WASHINGTON STATE UNIVERSITY**
Pullman, WA 99164
Tel: (509)335-3564; Free: 888-468-6978
E-mail: admissions@wsu.edu
Web Site: www.wsu.edu
Description: State-supported, university, coed. Awards bachelor's, master's, and doctoral degrees and post-master's certificates. Founded 1890. Setting: 620-acre small town campus with easy access to Spokane. Endowment: $1 billion. Research spending for the previous fiscal year: $220.4 million. Educational spending for the previous fiscal year: $10,452 per student. Total enrollment: 21,297. Faculty: 1,803 (1,334 full-time, 469 part-time). Student-undergrad faculty ratio is 15:1. 20,762 applied, 79% were admitted. Full-time: 17,653 students, 50% women, 50% men. Part-time: 979 students, 37% women, 63% men. Students come from 50 states and territories, 75 other countries, 16% from out-of-state. 0.6% American Indian or Alaska Native, non-Hispanic/Latino; 14% Hispanic/Latino; 4% Black or African American, non-Hispanic/Latino; 6% Asian, non-Hispanic/Latino; 0.5% Native Hawaiian or other Pacific Islander, non-Hispanic/Latino; 5% international. 5% 25 or older, 25% live on campus, 7% transferred in. Retention: 80% of full-time freshmen returned the following year. Academic areas with the most degrees conferred: business/marketing; engineering; social sciences; communication/journalism. Core. Calendar: semesters. Academic remediation for entering students, ESL program, services for LD students, advanced placement, accelerated degree program, self-designed majors, freshman honors college, honors program, independent study, distance learning, double major, summer session for credit, part-time degree program, external degree program, adult/continuing education programs, co-op programs and internships, graduate courses open to undergrads. Off campus study at University of Idaho, National Student Exchange, Eastern Washington University, Whitworth University. Study abroad program. ROTC: Army, Naval (c), Air Force.

Entrance Requirements: Options: electronic application, international baccalaureate accepted. Required: high school transcript, minimum 2 high school GPA, SAT or ACT. Recommended: essay. Entrance: moderately difficult. Application deadlines: 1/31, rolling for nonresidents. Notification:

continuous until 11/1, continuous for nonresidents. Transfer credits accepted: Yes. Applicants placed on waiting list: 0. Wait-listed applicants offered admission: 0.

Collegiate Environment: Orientation program. Drama-theater group, choral group, marching band, student-run newspaper, radio station. Social organizations: 400 open to all; national fraternities, national sororities; 17% of eligible men and 21% of eligible women are members. Most popular organizations: Panhellenic Association - Sororities, Interfraternity Council - Fraternities, Student Entertainment Board, International Students Council, ChiLaStAl (Chicana/o Latina/o Student Alliance). Major annual events: Up All Night, Springfest, Cougfest. Student services: legal services, health clinic, personal-psychological counseling, women's center. Campus security: 24-hour emergency response devices and patrols, student patrols, late night transport-escort service, controlled dormitory access. 7,752 college housing spaces available; 6,162 were occupied in 2018-19. Freshmen guaranteed college housing. On-campus residence required in freshman year. Options: coed, men-only, women-only housing available. Holland and Terrell Libraries plus 3 others. Books: 2.4 million (physical), 750,000 (digital/electronic); Serial titles: 93,000 (digital/electronic); Databases: 216. Weekly public service hours: 140; students can reserve study rooms. Operations spending for the previous fiscal year: $15.5 million. 2,500 computers available on campus for general student use. A campuswide network can be accessed from student residence rooms and from off campus. Students can access the following: online class registration. Staffed computer lab on campus provides training in use of computers, software, and the Internet.

Community Environment: Pullman is located 7 miles west of the Idaho border. The summer temperature averages in the 80s and the winter temperature averages around 30 degrees. The area is accessible by airlines and bus lines. There are 30 churches, a public library, and various civic, fraternal, and veteran's organizations serving the community. Local recreation includes four parks, baseball diamonds, swimming pools, theaters, bowling alleys, a golf course, tennis courts and nearby lakes and rivers offering swimming, boating and skating.

■ **WASHINGTON STATE UNIVERSITY-GLOBAL CAMPUS**
Washington State University
Pullman, WA 99164-5220
Free: 800-222-4978
E-mail: admissions@wsu.edu
Web Site: www.globalcampus.wsu.edu
Description: State-supported, comprehensive, coed. Awards bachelor's and master's degrees and post-master's certificates. Total enrollment: 3,007. 127 applied, 48% were admitted. Full-time: 876 students, 73% women, 27% men. Part-time: 1,129 students, 65% women, 35% men. Students come from 40 states and territories, 30 other countries, 17% from out-of-state. 1% American Indian or Alaska Native, non-Hispanic/Latino; 11% Hispanic/Latino; 3% Black or African American, non-Hispanic/Latino; 5% Asian, non-Hispanic/Latino; 0.5% Native Hawaiian or other Pacific Islander, non-Hispanic/Latino; 6% international. 67% 25 or older, 24% transferred in. Academic areas with the most degrees conferred: business/marketing; social sciences; psychology. Calendar: semesters. Distance learning, part-time degree program, adult/continuing education programs.

Entrance Requirements: Options: electronic application, international baccalaureate accepted. Required: high school transcript, minimum 2 high school GPA, SAT or ACT. Recommended: essay. Entrance: moderately difficult. Application deadline: 7/24. Transfer credits accepted: Yes.

■ **WASHINGTON STATE UNIVERSITY-SPOKANE**
412 E Spokane Falls Blvd.
Spokane, WA 99210-1495
Tel: (509)358-7500
Fax: (509)358-7505
Web Site: www.spokane.wsu.edu
Description: State-supported, upper-level, coed. Awards bachelor's, master's, and doctoral degrees. Founded 1989. Setting: 48-acre urban campus. Total enrollment: 1,677. 2 applied. Full-time: 534 students, 86% women, 14% men. Part-time: 40 students, 80% women, 20% men. Students come from 11 states and territories, 6 other countries, 9% from out-of-state. 0.9% American Indian or Alaska Native, non-Hispanic/Latino; 10% Hispanic/Latino; 4% Black or African American, non-Hispanic/Latino; 6% Asian, non-Hispanic/Latino; 0.2% Native Hawaiian or other Pacific Islander, non-Hispanic/Latino; 1% international. 24% 25 or older, 17% transferred in. Academic areas with the most degrees conferred: health professions and related sciences; biological/life sciences. Core. Calendar: semesters. ESL

program, services for LD students, advanced placement, accelerated degree program, self-designed majors, freshman honors college, honors program, independent study, distance learning, double major, summer session for credit, part-time degree program, external degree program, adult/continuing education programs, co-op programs and internships, graduate courses open to undergrads. Off campus study. Study abroad program.

Entrance Requirements: Transfer credits accepted: Yes. Applicants placed on waiting list: 0.

Collegiate Environment: Orientation program. Social organizations: 50 open to all. Most popular organizations: ASWSU Spokane, Simulation Club, Multicultural Club, IHI Open School (Interprofessional Club), Diversity Club. Major annual events: Fall/Spring Bingo Night, Fall/Spring BBQ, Week of Welcome. Student services: personal-psychological counseling. Campus security: 24-hour emergency response devices and patrols. College housing not available.

■ WASHINGTON STATE UNIVERSITY-TRI-CITIES

2710 Crimson Way
Richland, WA 99354
Tel: (509)372-7000
Fax: (509)372-7100
Web Site: www.tricities.wsu.edu

Description: State-supported, comprehensive, coed. Awards bachelor's, master's, and doctoral degrees. Founded 1989. Setting: 84-acre urban campus. Total enrollment: 1,841. 663 applied, 65% were admitted. Full-time: 1,262 students, 56% women, 44% men. Part-time: 363 students, 60% women, 40% men. Students come from 18 states and territories, 6 other countries, 3% from out-of-state. 0.4% American Indian or Alaska Native, non-Hispanic/Latino; 35% Hispanic/Latino; 1% Black or African American, non-Hispanic/Latino; 4% Asian, non-Hispanic/Latino; 0.2% Native Hawaiian or other Pacific Islander, non-Hispanic/Latino; 0.6% international. 27% 25 or older, 14% transferred in. Retention: 76% of full-time freshmen returned the following year. Academic areas with the most degrees conferred: health professions and related sciences; engineering; education; business/marketing. Core. Calendar: semesters. ESL program, services for LD students, advanced placement, accelerated degree program, independent study, distance learning, double major, summer session for credit, part-time degree program, external degree program, adult/continuing education programs, co-op programs and internships, graduate courses open to undergrads. Study abroad program.

Entrance Requirements: Options: electronic application, international baccalaureate accepted. Required: high school transcript, minimum 2 high school GPA, SAT or ACT. Recommended: essay. Entrance: moderately difficult. Application deadline: 1/31. Notification: continuous until 11/1, continuous for nonresidents. Transfer credits accepted: Yes.

Collegiate Environment: Orientation program. Social organizations: 19 open to all. Most popular organizations: American Society of Civil Engineers, Environmental Club, Gaming Club, Pre-Health Club, Robotics Club. Major annual events: Week of Welcome, Career Fair, Crimson Fest. Student services: personal-psychological counseling. Campus security: 24-hour emergency response devices. Option: coed housing available. Max E. Benitz Memorial Library plus 2 others.

■ WASHINGTON STATE UNIVERSITY-VANCOUVER

14204 NE Salmon Creek Ave.
Vancouver, WA 98686
Tel: (360)546-9788
Fax: (360)546-9041
E-mail: van.admissions@wsu.edu
Web Site: www.vancouver.wsu.edu

Description: State-supported, comprehensive, coed. Awards bachelor's, master's, and doctoral degrees. Founded 1989. Setting: 351-acre suburban campus with easy access to Portland, OR. Total enrollment: 3,577. 1,225 applied, 64% were admitted. Full-time: 2,517 students, 53% women, 47% men. Part-time: 664 students, 52% women, 48% men. Students come from 23 states and territories, 15 other countries, 5% from out-of-state. 0.4% American Indian or Alaska Native, non-Hispanic/Latino; 13% Hispanic/Latino; 2% Black or African American, non-Hispanic/Latino; 7% Asian, non-Hispanic/Latino; 0.7% Native Hawaiian or other Pacific Islander, non-Hispanic/Latino; 1% international. 32% 25 or older, 19% transferred in. Retention: 74% of full-time freshmen returned the following year. Academic areas with the most degrees conferred: business/marketing; engineering; social sciences. Core. Calendar: semesters. ESL program, services for LD students, advanced placement, accelerated degree program, self-designed

majors, honors program, independent study, distance learning, double major, summer session for credit, part-time degree program, external degree program, adult/continuing education programs, co-op programs and internships, graduate courses open to undergrads. Off campus study. Study abroad program. ROTC: Army (c), Air Force (c).

Entrance Requirements: Options: electronic application, international baccalaureate accepted. Required: high school transcript, minimum 2 high school GPA, SAT or ACT. Recommended: essay. Entrance: moderately difficult. Application deadline: 1/31. Notification: continuous until 11/1, continuous for nonresidents. Transfer credits accepted: Yes.

Collegiate Environment: Orientation program. Student-run newspaper, radio station. Social organizations: 56 open to all. Major annual events: Week of Welcome, Back To School BBQ and Field Day, Career and Internship Fair. Student services: personal-psychological counseling. Campus security: 24-hour emergency response devices and patrols, student patrols. College housing not available. WSU Vancouver Library plus 1 other. Students can reserve study rooms.

■ WENATCHEE VALLEY COLLEGE

1300 Fifth St.
Wenatchee, WA 98801-1799
Tel: (509)682-6800
Fax: (509)664-2511
Web Site: www.wvc.edu

Description: State and locally supported, 2-year, coed. Part of Washington State Board for Community and Technical Colleges. Awards certificates, diplomas, transfer associate, and terminal associate degrees. Founded 1939. Setting: 56-acre small town campus. Total enrollment: 3,218. Full-time: 2,334 students, 56% women, 44% men. Part-time: 884 students, 62% women, 38% men. 2% American Indian or Alaska Native, non-Hispanic/Latino; 36% Hispanic/Latino; 0.8% Black or African American, non-Hispanic/Latino; 1% Asian, non-Hispanic/Latino; 0.1% international. Core. Calendar: quarters. Academic remediation for entering students, ESL program, services for LD students, advanced placement, independent study, distance learning, summer session for credit, part-time degree program, external degree program, adult/continuing education programs, co-op programs and internships. Study abroad program.

Entrance Requirements: Open admission except for allied health programs. Options: electronic application, early admission, deferred admission. Required for some: high school transcript. Entrance: noncompetitive. Application deadline: rolling.

Collegiate Environment: Orientation program. Drama-theater group, choral group. Campus security: 24-hour patrols, controlled dormitory access. John Brown Library plus 1 other.

Community Environment: Situated at the confluence of the Wenatchee and Columbia Rivers, Wenatchee is known as the apple capital of the world. In the eastern foothills of the Cascade Mountains, the city has a temperate climate with four definite seasons. The average maximum temperature is 75 degrees, with an average minimum of 28 degrees, with an average rainfall of 9.58 inches. The community is accessible by bus, air, and major highways. There are almost 40 churches representing various denominations, a YMCA, YWCA, library, museum, theatres, medical facilities, motels, hotels, good shopping, and many civic and fraternal organizations. Local recreation includes hunting, boating, fishing, golf, and skiing. A state apple blossom festival is held annually. Part-time employment is available.

■ WESTERN WASHINGTON UNIVERSITY

516 High St.
Bellingham, WA 98225-5996
Tel: (360)650-3000
E-mail: admissions@wwu.edu
Web Site: www.wwu.edu

Description: State-supported, comprehensive, coed. Awards bachelor's and master's degrees and post-master's certificates. Founded 1893. Setting: 223-acre small town campus with easy access to Seattle, WA and Vancouver, BC Canada. Endowment: $85.2 million. Research spending for the previous fiscal year: $8.4 million. Educational spending for the previous fiscal year: $10,167 per student. Total enrollment: 16,121. Faculty: 949 (639 full-time, 310 part-time). Student-undergrad faculty ratio is 18:1. 11,124 applied, 88% were admitted. 24% from top 10% of their high school class, 56% from top quarter, 86% from top half. Full-time: 13,893 students, 58% women, 42% men. Part-time: 1,277 students, 49% women, 51% men. Students come from 48 states and territories, 42 other countries, 14% from out-of-state. 0.3% American Indian or Alaska Native, non-Hispanic/Latino; 9%

Hispanic/Latino; 2% Black or African American, non-Hispanic/Latino; 6% Asian, non-Hispanic/Latino; 0.2% Native Hawaiian or other Pacific Islander, non-Hispanic/Latino; 1% international. 8% 25 or older, 26% live on campus, 8% transferred in. Retention: 81% of full-time freshmen returned the following year. Academic areas with the most degrees conferred: business/marketing; social sciences; interdisciplinary studies. Core. Calendar: quarters. ESL program, services for LD students, advanced placement, accelerated degree program, self-designed majors, honors program, independent study, distance learning, double major, summer session for credit, part-time degree program, external degree program, co-op programs and internships, graduate courses open to undergrads. Off campus study at National Student Exchange. Study abroad program.

Entrance Requirements: Options: electronic application, early action, deferred admission, international baccalaureate accepted. Required: high school transcript, SAT or ACT. Recommended: essay. Entrance: moderately difficult. Application deadline: 1/31. Notification: continuous until 11/1. SAT Reasoning Test deadline: 1/31. Transfer credits accepted: Yes. Applicants placed on waiting list: 484. Wait-listed applicants offered admission: 64. Early action applicants: 4,043. Early action applicants admitted: 3,851.

Costs Per Year: Application fee: $60. State resident tuition: $7038 full-time, $235 per credit hour part-time. Nonresident tuition: $22,450 full-time, $748 per credit hour part-time. Mandatory fees: $1094 full-time. Full-time tuition and fees vary according to course load, location, and reciprocity agreements. Part-time tuition varies according to course load, location, and reciprocity agreements. College room and board: $11,466. Room and board charges vary according to board plan, housing facility, and location.

Collegiate Environment: Orientation program. Drama-theater group, choral group, student-run newspaper, radio station. Social organizations: 230 open to all. Most popular organizations: Intramurals, Residence Hall Association, Associated Students, Outdoor Center, Ethnic Student Center. Major annual events: Fall New Student Convocation, Information Faire, Earth Day. Student services: legal services, health clinic, personal-psychological counseling, women's center. Campus security: 24-hour emergency response devices and patrols, student patrols, late night transport-escort service, controlled dormitory access. 4,145 college housing spaces available; 4,056 were occupied in 2018-19. Freshmen guaranteed college housing. Option: coed housing available. Wilson Library plus 2 others. Books: 631,958 (physical), 363,547 (digital/electronic); Serial titles: 21,547 (physical), 101,542 (digital/electronic); Databases: 95. Weekly public service hours: 97; students can reserve study rooms. Operations spending for the previous fiscal year: $8.7 million. 2,268 computers available on campus for general student use. A campuswide network can be accessed from student residence rooms and from off campus. Students can access the following: online class registration. Staffed computer lab on campus provides training in use of computers, software, and the Internet.

Community Environment: Bellingham overlooks Puget Sound and the San Juan Islands. The city enjoys a temperate climate with a summer temperature seldom exceeding 73 degrees, and winter temperatures range from 28 to 55 degrees. There are frequently winters without snow, and the average rainfall is 34 inches. County industries include shipbuilding, food processing, oil refining, and manufacturing of aluminum, cement, plywood, and paper products. There is also a commercial fishing fleet. The community has hospitals, theatres, and major civic and fraternal organizations. Local recreation includes hiking, fishing, sailing, golf, baseball, softball, and bowling. Mt. Baker for skiing and climbing is 50 miles away. Part-time employment is available.

■ **WHATCOM COMMUNITY COLLEGE**
237 W Kellogg Rd.
Bellingham, WA 98226-8003
Tel: (360)383-3000
Fax: (360)676-2171
E-mail: admit@whatcom.ctc.edu
Web Site: www.whatcom.ctc.edu

Description: State-supported, 2-year, coed. Part of Washington State Board for Community and Technical Colleges. Awards certificates, diplomas, transfer associate, and terminal associate degrees. Founded 1970. Setting: 52-acre small town campus with easy access to Vancouver. Endowment: $2 million. Total enrollment: 6,233. Faculty: 225 (75 full-time, 150 part-time). Students come from 30 other countries, 5% from out-of-state. 34% 25 or older. Core. Calendar: quarters. Academic remediation for entering students, ESL program, services for LD students, advanced placement, accelerated degree program, self-designed majors, honors program, independent study, distance learning, summer session for credit, part-time degree program,

external degree program, adult/continuing education programs, co-op programs and internships. Study abroad program.

Entrance Requirements: Open admission. Option: electronic application. Entrance: noncompetitive. Application deadline: rolling. Notification: continuous. Transfer credits accepted: Yes.

Collegiate Environment: Orientation program. Drama-theater group, choral group, student-run newspaper. Social organizations: 15 open to all. Most popular organizations: Japanime, Ethnic Student Association, Queer/Straight Alliance, Phi Theta Kappa, International Friendship Club. Major annual events: Commencement, Spring BBQ, Fall Welcome. Student services: personal-psychological counseling. Campus security: 24-hour emergency response devices. Whatcom Community College Library. 100 computers available on campus for general student use. Students can access the following: online class registration. Staffed computer lab on campus.

■ **WHITMAN COLLEGE**
345 Boyer Ave.
Walla Walla, WA 99362-2083
Tel: (509)527-5111; Free: 877-462-9448
Fax: (509)527-4967
E-mail: admission@whitman.edu
Web Site: www.whitman.edu

Description: Independent, 4-year, coed. Awards bachelor's degrees. Founded 1859. Setting: 117-acre small town campus. Endowment: $518.3 million. Research spending for the previous fiscal year: $796,621. Educational spending for the previous fiscal year: $21,503 per student. Total enrollment: 1,510. Faculty: 222 (165 full-time, 57 part-time). Student-undergrad faculty ratio is 9:1. 4,081 applied, 52% were admitted. 59% from top 10% of their high school class, 88% from top quarter, 98% from top half. Full-time: 1,455 students, 57% women, 43% men. Part-time: 55 students, 44% women, 56% men. 66% from out-of-state. 0.5% American Indian or Alaska Native, non-Hispanic/Latino; 7% Hispanic/Latino; 2% Black or African American, non-Hispanic/Latino; 5% Asian, non-Hispanic/Latino; 0.5% Native Hawaiian or other Pacific Islander, non-Hispanic/Latino; 7% international. 1% 25 or older, 64% live on campus, 1% transferred in. Retention: 94% of full-time freshmen returned the following year. Academic areas with the most degrees conferred: social sciences; biological/life sciences; visual and performing arts. Core. Calendar: semesters. Services for LD students, advanced placement, self-designed majors, honors program, independent study, double major, co-op programs and internships. Off campus study at Special academic programs include study programs in Chicago, Philadelphia, and Washington; A 3-2 Environmental Management and Forestry program with Duke University; a 3-2 Engineering and Computer Science program with Washington University in St. Louis, California Institute of Technology, Columbia University, and the University of Washington; a 3-3 Law program with Columbia University; a 3-2 Oceanography program with University of Washington. Study abroad program.

Entrance Requirements: Options: electronic application, early decision, deferred admission, international baccalaureate accepted. Required: high school transcript. Recommended: essay, interview. Required for some: statement of good standing from prior institutions, SAT or ACT. Entrance: very difficult. Application deadlines: 1/15, 11/15 for early decision. Notification: 4/1, 12/20 for early decision. SAT Reasoning Test deadline: 1/15. SAT Subject Test deadline: 1/15. Transfer credits accepted: Yes. Applicants placed on waiting list: 998. Wait-listed applicants offered admission: 76. Early decision applicants: 179. Early decision applicants admitted: 127.

Costs Per Year: Application fee: $50. Comprehensive fee: $64,882 includes full-time tuition ($51,370), mandatory fees ($394), and college room and board ($13,118). College room only: $5844. Room and board charges vary according to board plan, housing facility, and location. Part-time tuition: $2140 per credit. Part-time tuition varies according to course load.

Collegiate Environment: Orientation program. Drama-theater group, choral group, student-run newspaper, radio station. Social organizations: 100 open to all; national fraternities, national sororities, local fraternities; 44% of eligible men and 44% of eligible women are members. Major annual events: Choral Contest, Power & Privilege Symposium, Student Activities Fair. Student services: health clinic, personal-psychological counseling, women's center. Campus security: 24-hour emergency response devices and patrols, student patrols, late night transport-escort service, controlled dormitory access. Penrose Library plus 1 other. Books: 406,675 (physical), 305,206 (digital/electronic); Serial titles: 5,082 (physical), 98,012 (digital/electronic); Databases: 206. Weekly public service hours: 84; study areas open 24 hours, 5-7 days a week; students can reserve study rooms. Operations spending for the previous fiscal year: $2.8 million. 397 computers available on campus for general student use. A campuswide network can be accessed from student residence rooms and from off campus. Students can access the following: online class registration. Staffed computer lab on campus (open 24 hours a day).

■ WHITWORTH UNIVERSITY

300 W Hawthorne Rd.
Spokane, WA 99251-0001
Tel: (509)777-1000; Free: 800-533-4668
Fax: (509)777-3773
E-mail: admission@whitworth.edu
Web Site: www.whitworth.edu

Description: Independent Presbyterian, comprehensive, coed. Awards bachelor's and master's degrees and post-master's certificates. Founded 1890. Setting: 200-acre suburban campus. Endowment: $151.2 million. Research spending for the previous fiscal year: $1.3 million. Educational spending for the previous fiscal year: $9485 per student. Total enrollment: 2,776. Faculty: 314 (192 full-time, 122 part-time). Student-undergrad faculty ratio is 11:1. 3,731 applied, 91% were admitted. 34% from top 10% of their high school class, 64% from top quarter, 91% from top half. Full-time: 2,304 students, 60% women, 40% men. Part-time: 51 students, 51% women, 49% men. Students come from 35 states and territories, 38 other countries, 26% from out-of-state. 0.7% American Indian or Alaska Native, non-Hispanic/Latino; 10% Hispanic/Latino; 2% Black or African American, non-Hispanic/Latino; 5% Asian, non-Hispanic/Latino; 0.8% Native Hawaiian or other Pacific Islander, non-Hispanic/Latino; 4% international. 3% 25 or older, 51% live on campus, 4% transferred in. Retention: 82% of full-time freshmen returned the following year. Academic areas with the most degrees conferred: business/marketing; interdisciplinary studies; social sciences. Core. Calendar: 4-1-4. Services for LD students, advanced placement, self-designed majors, honors program, independent study, double major, summer session for credit, part-time degree program, adult/continuing education programs, internships, graduate courses open to undergrads. Off campus study at Intercollegiate Center for Nursing through Washington State University, Spokane branch. Study abroad program. ROTC: Army (c).

Entrance Requirements: Options: electronic application, early admission, early action, deferred admission, international baccalaureate accepted. Required: essay, high school transcript, 1 recommendation. Required for some: minimum 3 high school GPA, 2 recommendations, interview, SAT or ACT. Entrance: moderately difficult. Application deadlines: rolling, rolling for nonresidents, 1/15 for early action. Notification: continuous, continuous for nonresidents, rolling for early action. Transfer credits accepted: Yes. Early action applicants: 3,302. Early action applicants admitted: 3,039.

Costs Per Year: Application fee: $0. Comprehensive fee: $56,740 includes full-time tuition ($43,800), mandatory fees ($1140), and college room and board ($11,800). College room only: $6450. Part-time tuition: $1825 per credit hour.

Collegiate Environment: Orientation program. Drama-theater group, choral group, student-run newspaper, radio station. Social organizations: 46 open to all. Most popular organizations: International Club, Whitworth Student Investment Group, En Christo, Hawaiian Club, Swing and Ballroom Dance Club. Major annual events: Homecoming, Community Building Day, Spring Fest. Student services: health clinic, personal-psychological counseling. Campus security: 24-hour emergency response devices and patrols, late night transport-escort service, controlled dormitory access. 1,368 college

housing spaces available; 1,181 were occupied in 2018-19. Freshmen guaranteed college housing. On-campus residence required through sophomore year. Options: coed, men-only, women-only housing available. Harriet Cheney Cowles Library. Books: 217,713 (physical), 447,336 (digital/electronic); Serial titles: 1,549 (physical), 41,985 (digital/electronic); Databases: 207. Weekly public service hours: 97; students can reserve study rooms. Operations spending for the previous fiscal year: $1.9 million. 280 computers available on campus for general student use. A campuswide network can be accessed from student residence rooms and from off campus. Students can access the following: online class registration, learning management system. Staffed computer lab on campus provides training in use of computers, software, and the Internet.

Community Environment: See Spokane Community College.

■ YAKIMA VALLEY COMMUNITY COLLEGE

PO Box 22520
Yakima, WA 98907-2520
Tel: (509)574-4600
Fax: (509)574-6860
E-mail: admis@yvcc.edu
Web Site: www.yvcc.edu

Description: State-supported, 2-year, coed. Part of Washington State Board for Community and Technical Colleges. Awards certificates, transfer associate, and terminal associate degrees. Founded 1928. Setting: 20-acre small town campus. Total enrollment: 4,479. Faculty: 319 (106 full-time, 213 part-time). Student-undergrad faculty ratio is 20:1. 496 applied, 100% were admitted. Full-time: 2,786 students, 62% women, 38% men. Part-time: 1,693 students, 69% women, 31% men. 36% 25 or older, 1% live on campus. Core. Calendar: quarters. Academic remediation for entering students, ESL program, services for LD students, advanced placement, distance learning, summer session for credit, part-time degree program, adult/continuing education programs, co-op programs and internships.

Entrance Requirements: Open admission except for nursing, dental hygiene, radiological technology, allied health programs. Required: ACT Compass. Recommended: high school transcript. Required for some: high school transcript, interview. Entrance: noncompetitive. Application deadline: 8/12. Notification: continuous until 9/12.

Collegiate Environment: Orientation program. Drama-theater group, choral group. Student services: personal-psychological counseling. Campus security: 24-hour emergency response devices, student patrols, late night transport-escort service, controlled dormitory access. Raymond Library. 375 computers available on campus for general student use. A campuswide network can be accessed. Students can access the following: online class registration, degree audit and financial aid information. Staffed computer lab on campus provides training in use of software and the Internet.

Community Environment: Located in the fertile Yakima Valley known as the"Fruit Bowl of the Nation," the area produces cherries, peaches, pears, apples, and other small fruit. The climate is mild and dry with an average of 302 days of sun per year. The community is served by railroad, air, and main arterial highways. Local recreation includes swimming, skiing, boating, fishing, hunting and golf. Part-time employment is available for students. There are churches representing most of the religious denominations, as well as many civic and fraternal organizations serving the community. Many "western" type celebrations are held in the area. Yakima was named an "All-American City" in 1994.

■ ALDERSON BROADDUS UNIVERSITY

101 College Hill Dr.
Philippi, WV 26416
Tel: (304)457-1700; Free: 800-263-1549
Fax: (304)457-6239
E-mail: thonel@ab.edu
Web Site: www.ab.edu

Description: Independent, comprehensive, coed, affiliated with American Baptist Churches in the U.S.A. Awards associate, bachelor's, and master's degrees. Founded 1871. Setting: 170-acre rural campus. Endowment: $17.6 million. Research spending for the previous fiscal year: $196,978. Educational spending for the previous fiscal year: $5430 per student. Total enrollment: 1,052. Faculty: 87 (56 full-time, 31 part-time). Student-undergrad faculty ratio is 17:1. 4,103 applied, 41% were admitted. 9% from top 10% of their high school class, 27% from top quarter, 59% from top half. Full-time: 934 students, 45% women, 55% men. Part-time: 47 students, 70% women, 30% men. Students come from 52 states and territories, 18 other countries, 63% from out-of-state. 0.7% American Indian or Alaska Native, non-Hispanic/Latino; 4% Hispanic/Latino; 18% Black or African American, non-Hispanic/Latino; 1% Asian, non-Hispanic/Latino; 0.4% Native Hawaiian or other Pacific Islander, non-Hispanic/Latino; 5% international. 6% 25 or older, 84% live on campus, 6% transferred in. Retention: 55% of full-time freshmen returned the following year. Academic areas with the most degrees conferred: health professions and related sciences; business/marketing; biological/life sciences. Core. Calendar: semesters. Services for LD students, advanced placement, honors program, independent study, double major, summer session for credit, part-time degree program, internships. Study abroad program.

Entrance Requirements: Options: electronic application, deferred admission. Required: high school transcript, minimum 2 high school GPA, SAT and SAT Subject Tests or ACT. Required for some: 3 recommendations, interview. Entrance: moderately difficult. Application deadline: rolling. Notification: 8/31. SAT Reasoning Test deadline: 8/1. SAT Subject Test deadline: 8/1. Transfer credits accepted: Yes.

Costs Per Year: Application fee: $0. Comprehensive fee: $36,870 includes full-time tuition ($27,700), mandatory fees ($210), and college room and board ($8960). Room and board charges vary according to housing facility. Part-time tuition: $924 per credit hour. Part-time mandatory fees: $52.50 per term.

Collegiate Environment: Orientation program. Drama-theater group, choral group, marching band, student-run newspaper, radio station. Social organizations: 42 open to all; local fraternities, local sororities; 5% of eligible men and 4% of eligible women are members. Most popular organizations: AAPA/Hu C. Myers Society, Alpha Beta Nu, Student Athletic Advisory Committee, Sigma Alpha Iota, Kappa Xi Omega. Major annual events: Homecoming, Greek Week, Gold Rush Games. Student services: health clinic, personal-psychological counseling. Campus security: 24-hour patrols, controlled dormitory access, emergency notification system, lighted pathways and sidewalks. Pickett Library. Books: 40,000 (physical), 160,000 (digital/electronic); Serial titles: 8 (physical), 11,000 (digital/electronic); Databases: 31. Weekly public service hours: 78; study areas open 24 hours, 5-7 days a week; students can reserve study rooms. Operations spending for the previous fiscal year: $241,032. 100 computers available on campus for general student use. A campuswide network can be accessed from student residence rooms and from off campus. Students can access the following: online class registration, course materials, student record information. Staffed computer lab on campus provides training in use of computers, software, and the Internet.

Community Environment: Philippi is a rural community enjoying a moderate climate ranging from balmy summers to snowy winters. There are churches of major denominations, a hospital, clinic, and more than 50 civic, fraternal, and veteran's organizations active in the community. Local recreation includes swimming, bowling, theater, and major outdoor sports. Skiing and whitewater rafting are within minutes of the campus. Some part-time employment is available.

■ AMERICAN PUBLIC UNIVERSITY SYSTEM

111 W Congress St.
Charles Town, WV 25414
Free: 877-755-2787
E-mail: info@apus.edu
Web Site: www.apus.edu

Description: Proprietary, comprehensive, coed. Awards associate, bachelor's, master's, and doctoral degrees (profile includes American Public University, American Military University and American Community College). Founded 1991. Setting: rural campus with easy access to Washington, DC. Total enrollment: 46,088. Student-undergrad faculty ratio is 20:1. Full-time: 2,324 students, 50% women, 50% men. Part-time: 35,422 students, 35% women, 65% men. 0.6% American Indian or Alaska Native, non-Hispanic/Latino; 13% Hispanic/Latino; 16% Black or African American, non-Hispanic/Latino; 2% Asian, non-Hispanic/Latino; 0.9% Native Hawaiian or other Pacific Islander, non-Hispanic/Latino; 0.7% international. 83% 25 or older, 14% transferred in. Retention: 98% of full-time freshmen returned the following year. Academic areas with the most degrees conferred: business/marketing; homeland security, law enforcement, firefighting, and protective services; computer and information sciences. Core. Calendar: courses start on the first Monday of each month. Services for LD students, advanced placement, independent study, distance learning, summer session for credit, part-time degree program, external degree program, internships.

Entrance Requirements: Open admission. Options: electronic application, deferred admission, international baccalaureate accepted. Required: high school transcript. Entrance: noncompetitive. Transfer credits accepted: Yes.

Costs Per Year: Application fee: $0. Tuition: $6480 full-time, $270 per credit hour part-time. Mandatory fees: $400 full-time.

Collegiate Environment: Orientation program. College housing not available. APUS Online Library.

■ APPALACHIAN BIBLE COLLEGE

161 College Dr.
Mount Hope, WV 25880
Tel: (304)877-6428; Free: 800-678-9ABC
E-mail: admissions@abc.edu
Web Site: www.abc.edu

Description: Independent nondenominational, comprehensive, coed. Awards associate, bachelor's, and master's degrees. Founded 1950. Setting: 110-acre small town campus. Endowment: $316,677. Total enrollment: 262. Faculty: 35 (23 full-time, 12 part-time). Student-undergrad faculty ratio is 8:1. 133 applied, 56% were admitted. Full-time: 148 students, 48% women, 52% men. Part-time: 111 students, 26% women, 74% men. Students come from 23 states and territories, 9 other countries, 61% from out-of-state. 0.7% Hispanic/Latino; 1% Black or African American, non-Hispanic/Latino; 1% Asian, non-Hispanic/Latino; 4% international. 95% live on campus, 7% transferred in. Retention: 74% of full-time freshmen returned the following year. Academic area with the most degrees conferred: theology and religious vocations. Core. Calendar: semesters. Academic remediation for entering students, advanced placement, self-designed majors, honors program, independent study, distance learning, double major, part-time degree program, adult/continuing education programs, internships, graduate courses open to undergrads.

Entrance Requirements: Open admission. Options: electronic application, early admission, deferred admission, international baccalaureate accepted. Required: essay, high school transcript, 2 recommendations, SAT or ACT. Recommended: minimum 2.25 high school GPA. Required for some: interview. Entrance: noncompetitive. Application deadline: rolling. SAT Reasoning Test deadline: 9/15. SAT Subject Test deadline: 9/15. Transfer credits accepted: Yes.

Costs Per Year: Application fee: $35. Comprehensive fee: $21,880 includes full-time tuition ($13,010), mandatory fees ($910), and college room and board ($7960). Full-time tuition and fees vary according to course load. Room and board charges vary according to housing facility. Part-time tuition: $395 per credit hour. Part-time mandatory fees: $42 per credit hour, $160 per term. Part-time tuition and fees vary according to course load.

Collegiate Environment: Orientation program. Drama-theater group, choral group. Major annual events: Spring Music Festival, Christmas Concert, Bible Conference. Student services: health clinic, personal-psychological counseling. Campus security: 24-hour emergency response devices, controlled dormitory access, patrols by trained security personnel. John Van Pufflen Library. 15 computers available on campus for general student use. A campuswide network can be accessed from student residence rooms and from off campus.

Community Environment: Bradley is a rural community enjoying temperate climate. There is a railroad line 15 miles distant, an airline 14 miles away, buses, and Highways I-77, I-64, 19, 21, and 16 to serve the community. The city has 5 churches and a Lions Club. Within walking distance is Crossroads Mall. The community provides numerous part-time employment opportunities, and enjoys all the cultural, recreational, and medical facilities of nearby Beckley.

■ **BETHANY COLLEGE**
31 E Campus Dr.
Bethany, WV 26032
Tel: (304)829-7000; Free: 800-922-7611
Fax: (304)829-7142
E-mail: enrollment@bethanywv.edu
Web Site: www.bethanywv.edu
Description: Independent, comprehensive, coed, affiliated with Christian Church (Disciples of Christ). Awards bachelor's and master's degrees. Founded 1840. Setting: 1,300-acre rural campus with easy access to Pittsburgh. Endowment: $49.8 million. Educational spending for the previous fiscal year: $34,665 per student. Total enrollment: 737. Faculty: 83 (51 full-time, 32 part-time). Student-undergrad faculty ratio is 12:1. 1,168 applied, 70% were admitted. 5% from top 10% of their high school class, 20% from top quarter, 53% from top half. Full-time: 703 students, 41% women, 59% men. Part-time: 7 students, 43% women, 57% men. 86% from out-of-state. 0.6% American Indian or Alaska Native, non-Hispanic/Latino; 5% Hispanic/Latino; 18% Black or African American, non-Hispanic/Latino; 0.3% Asian, non-Hispanic/Latino; 0.1% Native Hawaiian or other Pacific Islander, non-Hispanic/Latino; 2% international. 3% 25 or older, 98% live on campus, 3% transferred in. Retention: 63% of full-time freshmen returned the following year. Academic areas with the most degrees conferred: communication/journalism; psychology; education. Core. Calendar: semesters. Academic remediation for entering students, ESL program, services for LD students, advanced placement, accelerated degree program, self-designed majors, independent study, distance learning, double major, summer session for credit, part-time degree program, co-op programs and internships. Off campus study at Art Institute of Pittsburgh. Study abroad program.
Entrance Requirements: Options: electronic application, deferred admission, international baccalaureate accepted. Required: essay, high school transcript, SAT or ACT. Recommended: minimum 2.5 high school GPA, 2 recommendations, interview, documentation of student involvement in extracurricular activities. Required for some: TOEFL/IELTS. Entrance: moderately difficult. Application deadline: rolling. Notification: continuous. Preference given to applicants with a relationship to alumni. SAT Reasoning Test deadline: 8/1. Transfer credits accepted: Yes.

Costs Per Year: Application fee: $0. Comprehensive fee: $40,353 includes full-time tuition ($28,107), mandatory fees ($1666), and college room and board ($10,580). College room only: $5100. Full-time tuition and fees vary according to course load. Room and board charges vary according to board plan and housing facility. Part-time tuition: $1171 per credit hour. Part-time mandatory fees: $40.25 per credit hour, $100 per term. Part-time tuition and fees vary according to course load.

Collegiate Environment: Orientation program. Drama-theater group, choral group, marching band, student-run newspaper, radio station. Social organizations: 50 open to all; national fraternities, national sororities, local fraternities, local sororities; 33% of eligible men and 54% of eligible women are members. Most popular organizations: Student Government Association, Culture Clubs, Equestrian Club, Outdoors Club, Black Alliance. Major annual events: Homecoming, Family Weekend, Spring Weekend. Student services: health clinic, personal-psychological counseling. Campus security: 24-hour emergency response devices and patrols, late night transport-escort service, controlled dormitory access. T. W. Phillips Memorial Library. Books: 126,369 (physical), 135,500 (digital/electronic); Serial titles: 3,975 (physical); Databases: 50. Weekly public service hours: 88. Operations spending for the previous fiscal year: $360,778. 145 computers available on campus for general student use. A campuswide network can be accessed from student residence rooms and from off campus. Students can access the following: online class registration.

■ **BLUE RIDGE COMMUNITY AND TECHNICAL COLLEGE**
13650 Apple Harvest Dr.
Martinsburg, WV 25403
Tel: (304)260-4380
Fax: (304)260-4376
E-mail: bneal@blueridgectc.edu
Web Site: www.blueridgectc.edu
Description: State-supported, 2-year, coed. Part of Community and Technical College System of West Virginia. Awards certificates, transfer associate, and terminal associate degrees. Founded 1974. Setting: 46-acre small town campus. Total enrollment: 6,273. Faculty: 200 (84 full-time, 116 part-time). Student-undergrad faculty ratio is 22:1. Full-time: 1,113 students, 59% women, 41% men. Part-time: 5,160 students, 65% women, 35% men. 10% from out-of-state. 0.3% American Indian or Alaska Native, non-Hispanic/Latino; 2% Hispanic/Latino; 6% Black or African American, non-Hispanic/Latino; 2% Asian, non-Hispanic/Latino; 0.3% Native Hawaiian or other Pacific Islander, non-Hispanic/Latino. 73% 25 or older. Core. Calendar: semesters. Academic remediation for entering students, ESL program, services for LD students, advanced placement, accelerated degree program, independent study, double major, part-time degree program, adult/continuing education programs, internships.

Entrance Requirements: Open admission. Options: electronic application, deferred admission. Required: high school transcript. Recommended: SAT and SAT Subject Tests or ACT. Required for some: interview. Entrance: noncompetitive. Transfer credits accepted: Yes.

Costs Per Year: Application fee: $25. State resident tuition: $4128 full-time, $172 per credit hour part-time. Nonresident tuition: $7464 full-time, $311 per credit hour part-time. Full-time tuition varies according to class time and course load. Part-time tuition varies according to class time and course load.

Collegiate Environment: Orientation program. Drama-theater group. Social organizations: 16 open to all. Most popular organizations: Student Leadership Academy, Drama Club, Phi Theta Kappa, Phi Beta Lambda, Student Nurses Association. Major annual events: Family Night, Fall Festival, Friends and Family Night. Student services: personal-psychological counseling. Campus security: late night transport-escort service. College housing not available. 71 computers available on campus for general student use. A campuswide network can be accessed. Students can access the following: online class registration. Staffed computer lab on campus provides training in use of computers, software, and the Internet.

■ **BLUEFIELD STATE COLLEGE**
219 Rock St.
Bluefield, WV 24701-2198
Tel: (304)327-4000; Free: 800-654-7798
Fax: (304)327-7747
Web Site: www.bluefieldstate.edu
Description: State-supported, 4-year, coed. Part of West Virginia Higher Education Policy Commission. Awards associate and bachelor's degrees. Founded 1895. Setting: 45-acre small town campus. Total enrollment: 1,362. Faculty: 117 (75 full-time, 42 part-time). Student-undergrad faculty ratio is

13:1. 653 applied, 83% were admitted. 13% from top 10% of their high school class, 42% from top quarter, 74% from top half. Full-time: 1,117 students, 60% women, 40% men. Part-time: 245 students, 71% women, 29% men. 2% from out-of-state. 0.2% American Indian or Alaska Native, non-Hispanic/Latino; 1% Hispanic/Latino; 8% Black or African American, non-Hispanic/Latino; 0.8% Asian, non-Hispanic/Latino; 2% international. 34% 25 or older, 9% transferred in. Retention: 68% of full-time freshmen returned the following year. Academic areas with the most degrees conferred: health professions and related sciences; engineering technologies; liberal arts/general studies. Calendar: semesters. Part-time degree program, adult/continuing education programs.

Entrance Requirements: Options: early admission, deferred admission. Required: high school transcript, minimum 2 high school GPA, SAT or ACT. Entrance: noncompetitive.

Costs Per Year: Application fee: $0. State resident tuition: $7056 full-time, $294 per credit hour part-time. Nonresident tuition: $13,536 full-time, $564 per credit hour part-time.

Collegiate Environment: Orientation program. Drama-theater group, choral group, student-run newspaper, radio station. Social organizations: national fraternities, national sororities, local fraternities, local sororities. Student services: health clinic, personal-psychological counseling. Campus security: 24-hour emergency response devices and patrols, student patrols. Hardway Library.

Community Environment: At the foot of the East River Mountain, high in the Appalachian chain, Bluefield is situated at the southern tip of West Virginia, bordering on the Virginia state line. The city is the commercial and industrial center for the surrounding area. The climate is temperate with a mean annual temperature of 53.7 degrees and an average rainfall of 38.52 inches. Due to a high altitude and low humidity, the city known as "Nature's Air Conditioned City." Bluefield is accessible by airlines, bus lines, and major highways. There are many churches representing most denominations, community health facilities, and major civic, fraternal, and veteran's organizations to serve the community. Local recreation includes nearby Bluestone Reservoir and lakes for fishing, swimming, and boating; municipal swimming pools, golf, a football stadium, tennis courts, softball, and Little Theatre group.

■ **BRIDGEVALLEY COMMUNITY AND TECHNICAL COLLEGE (MONTGOMERY)**
619 2nd Ave.
Montgomery, WV 25136
Tel: (304)734-6600
Web Site: www.bridgevalley.edu
Description: County-supported, 2-year, coed. Awards certificates and terminal associate degrees. Total enrollment: 760. 30% 25 or older.
Entrance Requirements: Open admission.

■ **BRIDGEVALLEY COMMUNITY AND TECHNICAL COLLEGE (SOUTH CHARLESTON)**
2001 Union Carbide Dr.
South Charleston, WV 25303
Tel: (304)205-6600
E-mail: castosb@wvstateu.edu
Web Site: www.bridgevalley.edu
Description: County-supported, 2-year, coed. Part of West Council for Community and Technical College Education. Awards certificates, transfer associate, and terminal associate degrees. Setting: 5,219-acre suburban campus. Educational spending for the previous fiscal year: $2562 per student. Total enrollment: 1,717. Faculty: 87 (35 full-time, 52 part-time). 2,704 applied, 63% were admitted. Full-time: 1,064 students, 61% women, 39% men. Part-time: 653 students, 73% women, 27% men. 7% from out-of-state. 51% 25 or older, 6% transferred in. Retention: 61% of full-time freshmen returned the following year. Academic remediation for entering students, ESL program, services for LD students, advanced placement, self-designed majors, independent study, distance learning, double major, summer session for credit, external degree program, adult/continuing education programs, co-op programs and internships. Study abroad program.
Entrance Requirements: Required: high school transcript, ACT. Recommended: essay.
Costs Per Year: State resident tuition: $4370 full-time, $182 per credit hour part-time. Nonresident tuition: $10,406 full-time, $434 per credit hour part-time. Full-time tuition varies according to course level, course load, degree level, and program. Part-time tuition varies according to course level, course load, and degree level.

Collegiate Environment: Campus security: 24-hour emergency response devices and patrols, late night transport-escort service, controlled dormitory access. Drain Jordan Library plus 1 other.

■ **CONCORD UNIVERSITY**
Vermillion St.
Athens, WV 24712-1000
Tel: (304)384-3115; Free: 888-384-5249
Fax: (304)384-9044
E-mail: admissions@concord.edu
Web Site: www.concord.edu
Description: State-supported, comprehensive, coed. Part of State College System of West Virginia. Awards bachelor's and master's degrees and post-master's certificates. Founded 1872. Setting: 100-acre rural campus. Endowment: $24.5 million. Research spending for the previous fiscal year: $133,175. Educational spending for the previous fiscal year: $5092 per student. Total enrollment: 2,194. Faculty: 172 (116 full-time, 56 part-time). Student-undergrad faculty ratio is 15:1. 2,507 applied, 90% were admitted. 15% from top 10% of their high school class, 42% from top quarter, 73% from top half. Full-time: 1,696 students, 58% women, 42% men. Part-time: 157 students, 60% women, 40% men. Students come from 24 states and territories, 26 other countries, 14% from out-of-state. 0.3% American Indian or Alaska Native, non-Hispanic/Latino; 1% Hispanic/Latino; 6% Black or African American, non-Hispanic/Latino; 0.9% Asian, non-Hispanic/Latino; 0.2% Native Hawaiian or other Pacific Islander, non-Hispanic/Latino; 6% international. 12% 25 or older, 40% live on campus, 5% transferred in. Retention: 64% of full-time freshmen returned the following year. Academic areas with the most degrees conferred: liberal arts/general studies; business/marketing; education. Core. Calendar: semesters. Academic remediation for entering students, ESL program, services for LD students, advanced placement, accelerated degree program, self-designed majors, honors program, independent study, distance learning, double major, summer session for credit, part-time degree program, external degree program, adult/continuing education programs, co-op programs and internships, graduate courses open to undergrads. Off campus study. Study abroad program.
Entrance Requirements: Options: electronic application, early admission, international baccalaureate accepted. Required: high school transcript, minimum 2 high school GPA, SAT or ACT. Recommended: interview. Required for some: essay, interview. Entrance: minimally difficult. Application deadline: rolling. Notification: continuous. Transfer credits accepted: Yes.
Costs Per Year: Application fee: $0. State resident tuition: $7876 full-time. Nonresident tuition: $17,320 full-time. Mandatory fees: $150 full-time. Full-time tuition and fees vary according to course load and program. College room and board: $8988. College room only: $4502. Room and board charges vary according to board plan.
Collegiate Environment: Orientation program. Drama-theater group, choral group, marching band, student-run newspaper, radio station. Social organizations: 62 open to all; national fraternities, national sororities, local fraternities, local sororities; 20% of eligible men and 25% of eligible women are members. Most popular organizations: Service Groups, student government, student-run publications, intramurals, Student Activities Committee. Major annual events: Homecoming, CU Community Fair, Spring Fling. Student services: health clinic, personal-psychological counseling. Campus security: 24-hour emergency response devices and patrols, student patrols, late night transport-escort service, controlled dormitory access. J. Frank Marsh Library. Books: 162,020 (physical), 34,329 (digital/electronic); Serial titles: 68 (physical), 110 (digital/electronic); Databases: 14. Weekly public service hours: 77; study areas open 24 hours, 5-7 days a week; students can reserve study rooms. Operations spending for the previous fiscal year: $406,152. 350 computers available on campus for general student use. A campuswide network can be accessed. Students can access the following: online class registration. Staffed computer lab on campus (open 24 hours a day) provides training in use of computers, software, and the Internet.
Community Environment: Located in the mountains in a quiet rural area, this is an excellent atmosphere for students. The climate is moderate with cool summers. Local recreation includes good hunting and fishing. Pipestem State Park and Winterplace Ski Resort are located nearby.

■ **DAVIS & ELKINS COLLEGE**
100 Campus Dr.
Elkins, WV 26241-3996
Tel: (304)637-1900; Free: 800-624-3157
Fax: (304)637-1800

E-mail: admiss@davisandelkins.edu
Web Site: www.dewv.edu
Description: Independent Presbyterian, 4-year, coed. Awards associate and bachelor's degrees. Founded 1904. Setting: 170-acre small town campus. Endowment: $22.7 million. Educational spending for the previous fiscal year: $7510 per student. Total enrollment: 640. Faculty: 64 (44 full-time, 20 part-time). Student-undergrad faculty ratio is 10:1. 351 applied, 75% were admitted. 11% from top 10% of their high school class, 28% from top quarter, 50% from top half. Full-time: 568 students, 63% women, 37% men. Part-time: 72 students, 78% women, 22% men. Students come from 19 states and territories, 21 other countries, 34% from out-of-state. 24% 25 or older, 49% live on campus, 10% transferred in. Retention: 66% of full-time freshmen returned the following year. Academic areas with the most degrees conferred: business/marketing; education; parks and recreation. Core. Calendar: 4-1-4. ESL program, services for LD students, advanced placement, accelerated degree program, self-designed majors, honors program, independent study, double major, summer session for credit, part-time degree program, external degree program, adult/continuing education programs, co-op programs and internships. Study abroad program.
Entrance Requirements: Options: electronic application, early admission, deferred admission, international baccalaureate accepted. Required: high school transcript, minimum 2.0 high school GPA, SAT or ACT. Recommended: essay, interview. Required for some: essay, 2 recommendations, interview. Entrance: moderately difficult. Application deadline: rolling. Notification: continuous.
Costs Per Year: Application fee: $35. Comprehensive fee: $38,640 includes full-time tuition ($28,800), mandatory fees ($590), and college room and board ($9250). Full-time tuition and fees vary according to course load. Part-time tuition: $1200 per credit hour. Part-time tuition varies according to course load.
Collegiate Environment: Orientation program. Drama-theater group, choral group, student-run newspaper, radio station. Social organizations: 42 open to all; national fraternities, national sororities; 4% of eligible men and 8% of eligible women are members. Most popular organizations: Beta Alpha Beta, campus radio station, Student Nurses Association, Student Education Association, International Student Organization. Major annual events: Parents' Weekend, Alumni Homecoming Weekend, Deja vu Weekend. Student services: health clinic, personal-psychological counseling. Campus security: 24-hour emergency response devices, late night transport-escort service, controlled dormitory access, late night security personnel. Booth Library. Operations spending for the previous fiscal year: $266,454. 80 computers available on campus for general student use. Computer purchase/lease plans available. A campuswide network can be accessed from student residence rooms and from off campus. Staffed computer lab on campus provides training in use of computers, software, and the Internet.
Community Environment: Elkins is located in the foothills of the Alleghenies and is the headquarters for the nearby Monongahela National Forest. The community is accessible by auto and airline. The climate is temperate. Elkins has several churches of various denominations, a hospital, YMCA, and major civic and fraternal organizations. The nearby national forest offers excellent trout streams, hunting, camping, 4 modern ski resorts, and bathing beaches. An annual autumn State Forest Festival is held here. Part-time employment is limited.

■ **EASTERN WEST VIRGINIA COMMUNITY AND TECHNICAL COLLEGE**
HC 65 Box 402
Moorefield, WV 26836
Tel: (304)434-8000; Free: 877-982-2322
E-mail: askeast@eastern.wvnet.edu
Web Site: www.eastern.wvnet.edu
Description: State-supported, 2-year, coed. Awards certificates, transfer associate, and terminal associate degrees. Founded 1999. Setting: rural campus. Total enrollment: 639. Student-undergrad faculty ratio is 20:1. 44% 25 or older. Calendar: semesters. Academic remediation for entering students, services for LD students, advanced placement, self-designed majors, independent study, distance learning, double major, part-time degree program, external degree program, internships.

■ **FAIRMONT STATE UNIVERSITY**
1201 Locust Ave.
Fairmont, WV 26554
Tel: (304)367-4000; Free: 800-641-5678
Fax: (304)367-4789

E-mail: admit@fairmontstate.edu
Web Site: www.fairmontstate.edu
Description: State-supported, comprehensive, coed. Part of State College System of West Virginia. Awards associate, bachelor's, and master's degrees. Founded 1865. Setting: 120-acre small town campus. Endowment: $22.6 million. Research spending for the previous fiscal year: $165,568. Educational spending for the previous fiscal year: $4824 per student. Total enrollment: 4,041. Faculty: 325 (173 full-time, 152 part-time). Student-undergrad faculty ratio is 15:1. 2,943 applied, 66% were admitted. 10% from top 10% of their high school class, 33% from top quarter, 71% from top half. Full-time: 3,259 students, 54% women, 46% men. Part-time: 548 students, 66% women, 34% men. Students come from 31 states and territories, 35 other countries, 9% from out-of-state. 0.2% American Indian or Alaska Native, non-Hispanic/Latino; 2% Hispanic/Latino; 5% Black or African American, non-Hispanic/Latino; 0.5% Asian, non-Hispanic/Latino; 0.1% Native Hawaiian or other Pacific Islander, non-Hispanic/Latino; 3% international. 21% 25 or older, 21% live on campus, 9% transferred in. Retention: 64% of full-time freshmen returned the following year. Academic areas with the most degrees conferred: business/marketing; engineering technologies; homeland security, law enforcement, firefighting, and protective services. Core. Calendar: semesters. Academic remediation for entering students, ESL program, services for LD students, advanced placement, accelerated degree program, honors program, independent study, distance learning, double major, summer session for credit, part-time degree program, adult/continuing education programs, co-op programs and internships, graduate courses open to undergrads. Off campus study at Pierpont Community & Technical College. Study abroad program. ROTC: Army, Air Force (c).
Entrance Requirements: Option: electronic application. Required: high school transcript, SAT or ACT. Recommended: minimum 2 high school GPA. Entrance: minimally difficult. Application deadline: rolling. Notification: continuous. SAT Reasoning Test deadline: 8/15. SAT Subject Test deadline: 8/15. Transfer credits accepted: Yes.
Costs Per Year: Application fee: $0. State resident tuition: $7514 full-time, $305 per credit hour part-time. Nonresident tuition: $16,324 full-time, $672 per credit hour part-time. Full-time tuition varies according to location and reciprocity agreements. Part-time tuition varies according to course load, location, and reciprocity agreements. College room and board: $9004. Room and board charges vary according to board plan and housing facility.
Collegiate Environment: Orientation program. Drama-theater group, choral group, marching band, student-run newspaper. Social organizations: 80 open to all; national fraternities, national sororities, local fraternities; 2% of eligible men and 2% of eligible women are members. Most popular organizations: Alpha Phi Omega, Circle K, Society for Non-traditional Students, Criminal Justice Club, Honors Association. Major annual events: Homecoming, Student Leadership Conference, Alcohol Awareness Week. Student services: legal services, health clinic, personal-psychological counseling. Campus security: 24-hour emergency response devices and patrols, student patrols, controlled dormitory access. Musick Library. Study areas open 24 hours, 5-7 days a week. Operations spending for the previous fiscal year: $712,306. 1,350 computers available on campus for general student use. Computer purchase/lease plans available. A campuswide network can be accessed from student residence rooms and from off campus. Students can access the following: online class registration. Staffed computer lab on campus (open 24 hours a day) provides training in use of computers, software, and the Internet.
Community Environment: The College's 80-acre campus, with its twelve major buildings, is attractively located in Fairmont, West Virginia. Approximately ninety miles south of Pittsburgh on Interstate 79, Fairmont, with a population of about 19,000, is the county seat of Marion County.

■ **GLENVILLE STATE COLLEGE**
200 High St.
Glenville, WV 26351-1200
Tel: (304)462-7361; Free: 800-924-2010
Fax: (304)462-8619
E-mail: ashley.weir@glenville.edu
Web Site: www.glenville.edu
Description: State-supported, 4-year, coed. Part of West Virginia Higher Education Policy Commission. Awards associate and bachelor's degrees. Founded 1872. Setting: 331-acre rural campus. Endowment: $8.7 million. Educational spending for the previous fiscal year: $4680 per student. Total enrollment: 1,732. Faculty: 130 (63 full-time, 67 part-time). Student-undergrad faculty ratio is 15:1. 1,430 applied, 72% were admitted. 8% from top 10% of their high school class, 26% from top quarter, 56% from top half.

1 class president, 5 valedictorians, 3 student government officers. Full-time: 1,044 students, 43% women, 57% men. Part-time: 688 students, 47% women, 53% men. Students come from 30 states and territories, 2 other countries, 20% from out-of-state. 2% Hispanic/Latino; 19% Black or African American, non-Hispanic/Latino; 0.6% Asian, non-Hispanic/Latino; 0.4% international. 31% 25 or older, 33% live on campus, 6% transferred in. Retention: 62% of full-time freshmen returned the following year. Academic areas with the most degrees conferred: education; business/marketing; natural resources/environmental science. Core. Calendar: semesters. Academic remediation for entering students, services for LD students, advanced placement, accelerated degree program, self-designed majors, honors program, distance learning, double major, summer session for credit, part-time degree program, external degree program, adult/continuing education programs, co-op programs and internships. Off campus study. Study abroad program. ROTC: Army.

Entrance Requirements: Open admission. Options: electronic application, deferred admission. Required: high school transcript, minimum 3 high school GPA, college preparatory program, SAT or ACT. Required for some: interview. Entrance: noncompetitive. Application deadline: rolling. Notification: continuous. Preference given to Hidden Promise Consortium. SAT Reasoning Test deadline: 8/15. SAT Subject Test deadline: 8/15. Transfer credits accepted: Yes.

Costs Per Year: Application fee: $20. State resident tuition: $7308 full-time, $304.50 per credit hour part-time. Nonresident tuition: $16,518 full-time, $688.25 per credit hour part-time. Full-time tuition varies according to course load. College room and board: $9942. College room only: $5782. Room and board charges vary according to board plan and housing facility.

Collegiate Environment: Orientation program. Drama-theater group, choral group, marching band, student-run newspaper. Social organizations: 46 open to all; national fraternities, local fraternities, local sororities; 1% of eligible men and 1% of eligible women are members. Most popular organizations: Music Educators National Conference, Student Government Association, Student Support Services, Student Advisory Committee, Glenville Student Action. Major annual events: Homecoming, GSC Week, Convocation. Student services: health clinic, personal-psychological counseling. Campus security: 24-hour emergency response devices and patrols, student patrols, late night transport-escort service, controlled dormitory access. Robert F. Kidd Library plus 1 other. Books: 117,347 (physical), 64,412 (digital/electronic); Serial titles: 3,857 (physical), 10,004 (digital/electronic); Databases: 62. Weekly public service hours: 71. Operations spending for the previous fiscal year: $101,712. 183 computers available on campus for general student use. A campuswide network can be accessed from student residence rooms and from off campus. Students can access the following: online class registration, WebVista, Wimba Classroom. Staffed computer lab on campus provides training in use of computers, software, and the Internet.

Community Environment: Glenville is located in the approximate geographical center of the state. Interstate 79 passes within 15 miles of the campus. Glenville has 5 churches, a modern clinic, motel, and several civic and fraternal organizations. Within the area there are facilities for hunting, fishing, golf, baseball, softball. A state park is located 6 miles away. Job opportunities are available. An annual West Virginia Folk Festival is held each year in June.

■ **HUNTINGTON JUNIOR COLLEGE**
900 Fifth Ave.
Huntington, WV 25701-2004
Tel: (304)697-7550; Free: 800-344-4522
Fax: (304)697-7554
Web Site: www.huntingtonjuniorcollege.com
Description: Proprietary, 2-year, coed. Awards terminal associate degrees. Founded 1936. Setting: urban campus. Total enrollment: 745. 68% 25 or older. Core. Calendar: quarters. Academic remediation for entering students, services for LD students, summer session for credit, part-time degree program.
Entrance Requirements: Open admission. Required: high school transcript. Entrance: minimally difficult. Application deadline: rolling.
Collegiate Environment: Orientation program.

■ **MARSHALL UNIVERSITY**
One John Marshall Dr.
Huntington, WV 25755
Tel: (304)696-3170; Free: 800-642-3499
Fax: (304)696-3135
E-mail: admissions@marshall.edu

Web Site: www.marshall.edu
Description: State-supported, university, coed. Part of University System of West Virginia. Awards bachelor's, master's, and doctoral degrees and post-master's certificates. Founded 1837. Setting: 114-acre urban campus. Research spending for the previous fiscal year: $15.5 million. Educational spending for the previous fiscal year: $8155 per student. Total enrollment: 13,204. Faculty: 712 (484 full-time, 228 part-time). Student-undergrad faculty ratio is 19:1. 4,987 applied, 91% were admitted. Full-time: 7,460 students, 57% women, 43% men. Part-time: 2,133 students, 60% women, 40% men. 18% from out-of-state. 0.3% American Indian or Alaska Native, non-Hispanic/Latino; 2% Hispanic/Latino; 6% Black or African American, non-Hispanic/Latino; 0.9% Asian, non-Hispanic/Latino; 0.1% Native Hawaiian or other Pacific Islander, non-Hispanic/Latino; 2% international. 15% 25 or older, 5% transferred in. Retention: 72% of full-time freshmen returned the following year. Academic areas with the most degrees conferred: health professions and related sciences; business/marketing; liberal arts/general studies. Core. Calendar: semesters. Academic remediation for entering students, ESL program, services for LD students, advanced placement, accelerated degree program, honors program, independent study, distance learning, double major, summer session for credit, part-time degree program, adult/continuing education programs, co-op programs and internships, graduate courses open to undergrads. Off campus study at National Student Exchange. Study abroad program. ROTC: Army.
Entrance Requirements: Options: electronic application, deferred admission, international baccalaureate accepted. Required: SAT or ACT. Required for some: high school transcript. Entrance: moderately difficult. Application deadline: rolling. Notification: continuous.
Costs Per Year: Application fee: $40. State resident tuition: $7006 full-time, $292 per credit hour part-time. Nonresident tuition: $17,492 full-time, $729 per credit hour part-time. Mandatory fees: $1122 full-time, $47 per credit hour part-time. Full-time tuition and fees vary according to degree level, location, program, and reciprocity agreements. Part-time tuition and fees vary according to course load, degree level, location, program, and reciprocity agreements. College room and board: $10,450. College room only: $6454. Room and board charges vary according to board plan and housing facility.
Collegiate Environment: Orientation program. Drama-theater group, choral group, marching band, student-run newspaper, radio station. Social organizations: national fraternities, national sororities. Most popular organizations: Campus Crusade for Christ, Gamma Beta Phi, The International Students'; Organization, Newman Association, Phi Alpha Theta. Major annual events: Homecoming, Spring Fest, Independence Daze. Student services: legal services, health clinic, personal-psychological counseling, women's center. Campus security: 24-hour emergency response devices and patrols, student patrols, late night transport-escort service, controlled dormitory access. Freshmen guaranteed college housing. On-campus residence required through sophomore year. Options: coed, women-only housing available. John Deaver Drinko Library plus 1 other. Books: 398,144 (physical), 224,894 (digital/electronic); Serial titles: 2,030 (physical), 49,727 (digital/electronic); Databases: 256. Weekly public service hours: 133; study areas open 24 hours, 5-7 days a week; students can reserve study rooms. Operations spending for the previous fiscal year: $5 million. 1,200 computers available on campus for general student use. Computer purchase/lease plans available. A campuswide network can be accessed from student residence rooms and from off campus. Students can access the following: online class registration, virtual computer lab: remote and Web conferencing. Staffed computer lab on campus (open 24 hours a day) provides training in use of computers, software, and the Internet.
Community Environment: Huntington is a busy river terminal and serves as the shipping point for millions of tons of coal mined annually from the great bituminous fields to the south of the city. It is also the center of a large natural gas and oil-producing area. The annual mean temperature is 56.6 degrees with an annual rainfall of 41.8 inches. The community is accessed by bus, rail, and air. There are medical facilities, a public library, YMCA, YWCA, and over 140 churches of various denominations serving the area. Recreation includes municipal swimming pools, roller skating rinks, golf, tennis, bowling, boating, the Memorial Field House, theatres, and the Huntington Civic Center which attracts top entertainment. Part-time employment is available.

■ **MARTINSBURG COLLEGE**
341 Aikens Ctr.
Martinsburg, WV 25404
Web Site: www.martinsburgcollege.edu
Description: Proprietary, 2-year, coed.

■ MOUNTAIN STATE COLLEGE

1508 Spring St.
Parkersburg, WV 26101-3993
Tel: (304)485-5487; Free: 800-841-0201
Fax: (304)485-3524
E-mail: jsutton@msc.edu
Web Site: www.msc.edu
Description: Proprietary, 2-year, coed. Awards diplomas and terminal associate degrees. Founded 1888. Setting: small town campus. Total enrollment: 176. Faculty: 11 (7 full-time, 4 part-time). Student-undergrad faculty ratio is 17:1. Full-time: 174 students, 92% women, 8% men. Part-time: 2 students, 100% women. Students come from 2 states and territories. 55% 25 or older, 3% transferred in. Retention: 70% of full-time freshmen returned the following year. Core. Calendar: quarters. Services for LD students, independent study, distance learning, part-time degree program, internships.
Entrance Requirements: Required: interview, CPAt.
Collegiate Environment: Orientation program. Social organizations: Golden Honor Society. Student services: personal-psychological counseling. Mountain State College Library. 30 computers available on campus for general student use. Staffed computer lab on campus.

■ MOUNTWEST COMMUNITY & TECHNICAL COLLEGE

One Mountwest Way
Huntington, WV 25701
Free: 866-676-5533
E-mail: admissions@marshall.edu
Web Site: www.mctc.edu
Description: County-supported, 2-year, coed. Part of Community and Technical College System of West Virginia. Awards certificates and terminal associate degrees. Setting: 70-acre urban campus. Endowment: $27,466. Educational spending for the previous fiscal year: $3554 per student. Total enrollment: 2,534. Faculty: 156 (49 full-time, 107 part-time). Student-undergrad faculty ratio is 21:1. 601 applied, 100% were admitted. Full-time: 1,400 students, 50% women, 50% men. Part-time: 1,134 students, 39% women, 61% men. Students come from 26 states and territories, 5 other countries, 16% from out-of-state. 47% 25 or older, 9% transferred in. Retention: 43% of full-time freshmen returned the following year. Core. Calendar: semesters. Academic remediation for entering students, ESL program, services for LD students, accelerated degree program, independent study, distance learning, double major, summer session for credit, part-time degree program, co-op programs and internships. Off campus study. ROTC: Army.
Entrance Requirements: Open admission. Options: electronic application, deferred admission, international baccalaureate accepted. Required: high school transcript, minimum 2 high school GPA. Entrance: noncompetitive. Application deadline: rolling. Notification: continuous.
Collegiate Environment: Orientation program. Drama-theater group, choral group, marching band, student-run newspaper, radio station. Social organizations: national fraternities, national sororities. Student services: legal services, health clinic, personal-psychological counseling, women's center. Campus security: 24-hour emergency response devices and patrols, controlled dormitory access. John Deaver Drinko Library plus 2 others. 1,461 computers available on campus for general student use. A campuswide network can be accessed from student residence rooms and from off campus. Students can access the following: online class registration. Staffed computer lab on campus.

■ NEW RIVER COMMUNITY AND TECHNICAL COLLEGE

280 University Dr.
Beaver, WV 25813
Tel: (304)255-5821
Web Site: www.newriver.edu
Description: County-supported, 2-year, coed. Awards certificates, transfer associate, and terminal associate degrees. Founded 2003. Total enrollment: 2,232. 41% 25 or older.

■ OHIO VALLEY UNIVERSITY

One Campus View Dr.
Vienna, WV 26105-8000
Tel: (304)865-6000; Free: 877-446-8668
Fax: (304)865-6001
E-mail: admissions@ovu.edu
Web Site: www.ovu.edu
Description: Independent, comprehensive, coed, affiliated with Church of Christ. Awards associate, bachelor's, and master's degrees. Founded 1960.

Setting: 299-acre small town campus. Total enrollment: 433. Faculty: 79 (20 full-time, 59 part-time). Student-undergrad faculty ratio is 10:1. 845 applied, 64% were admitted. 14% from top 10% of their high school class, 29% from top quarter, 68% from top half. Full-time: 390 students, 48% women, 52% men. Part-time: 13 students, 62% women, 38% men. 68% from out-of-state. 0.2% American Indian or Alaska Native, non-Hispanic/Latino; 6% Hispanic/Latino; 11% Black or African American, non-Hispanic/Latino; 0.7% Asian, non-Hispanic/Latino; 12% international. 6% 25 or older, 51% live on campus, 10% transferred in. Retention: 45% of full-time freshmen returned the following year. Academic areas with the most degrees conferred: business/marketing; education; psychology. Core. Calendar: semesters. Academic remediation for entering students, ESL program, services for LD students, advanced placement, self-designed majors, honors program, independent study, distance learning, double major, summer session for credit, part-time degree program, adult/continuing education programs, internships, graduate courses open to undergrads. Off campus study at The Washington Center. Study abroad program.
Entrance Requirements: Option: electronic application. Required: high school transcript. Required for some: essay, interview, SAT or ACT. Entrance: minimally difficult. Transfer credits accepted: Yes.
Costs Per Year: Comprehensive fee: $29,730 includes full-time tuition ($21,750) and college room and board ($7980). Full-time tuition varies according to course load. Room and board charges vary according to board plan, housing facility, and location. Part-time tuition: $875 per credit hour. Part-time tuition varies according to course load.
Collegiate Environment: Orientation program. Drama-theater group, choral group, student-run newspaper. Social organizations: local fraternities, local sororities. Most popular organizations: Social Clubs, intramural sports, Theatre Production, A cappella Choir, Ambassadors. Major annual events: OVU Homecoming, OVU Expressions, Winter/Spring Banquets. Campus security: 24-hour emergency response devices and patrols, controlled dormitory access. Icy Belle Library.

■ PIERPONT COMMUNITY & TECHNICAL COLLEGE

1201 Locust Ave.
Fairmont, WV 26554
Tel: (304)367-4892; Free: 800-641-5678
Fax: (304)367-4692
Web Site: www.pierpont.edu
Description: State-supported, 2-year, coed. Administratively affiliated with Fairmont State College. Awards certificates, transfer associate, and terminal associate degrees. Founded 1974. Setting: 90-acre small town campus. Endowment: $9.9 million. Research spending for the previous fiscal year: $602,614. Educational spending for the previous fiscal year: $3500 per student. Total enrollment: 2,852. Faculty: 495 (232 full-time, 263 part-time). Student-undergrad faculty ratio is 18:1. 1,339 applied, 92% were admitted. 4% from top quarter of their high school class, 10% from top half. Full-time: 1,672 students, 61% women, 39% men. Part-time: 1,180 students, 58% women, 42% men. Students come from 14 states and territories, 6 other countries, 3% from out-of-state. 31% 25 or older, 12% live on campus, 5% transferred in. Retention: 60% of full-time freshmen returned the following year. Core. Calendar: semesters. Summer session for credit, part-time degree program, external degree program, adult/continuing education programs.
Entrance Requirements: Open admission except for health career programs. Options: electronic application, deferred admission, international baccalaureate accepted. Required: SAT or ACT. Recommended: high school transcript. Entrance: minimally difficult. Application deadline: rolling. Notification: continuous.
Collegiate Environment: Orientation program. Drama-theater group, choral group, marching band, student-run newspaper. Social organizations: 90 open to all; national fraternities, national sororities; 4% of eligible men and 3% of eligible women are members. Student services: health clinic, personal-psychological counseling. 1,150 computers available on campus for general student use. Computer purchase/lease plans available. A campuswide network can be accessed from student residence rooms and from off campus. Students can access the following: online class registration. Staffed computer lab on campus (open 24 hours a day) provides training in use of computers, software, and the Internet.

■ POTOMAC STATE COLLEGE OF WEST VIRGINIA UNIVERSITY

101 Fort Ave.
Keyser, WV 26726-2698
Tel: (304)788-6800; Free: 800-262-7332

Fax: (304)788-6939
E-mail: go2psc@mail.wvu.edu
Web Site: www.potomacstatecollege.edu
Description: State-supported, primarily 2-year, coed. Part of West Virginia Higher Education Policy Commission. Awards transfer associate, terminal associate, and bachelor's degrees. Founded 1901. Setting: 18-acre small town campus. Total enrollment: 1,340. Faculty: 80 (49 full-time, 31 part-time). Student-undergrad faculty ratio is 22:1. 2,284 applied, 76% were admitted. 12% from top 10% of their high school class, 32% from top quarter, 60% from top half. Full-time: 1,018 students, 54% women, 46% men. Part-time: 322 students, 66% women, 34% men. 20% from out-of-state. 0.2% American Indian or Alaska Native, non-Hispanic/Latino; 3% Hispanic/Latino; 8% Black or African American, non-Hispanic/Latino; 1% Asian, non-Hispanic/Latino; 0.1% Native Hawaiian or other Pacific Islander, non-Hispanic/Latino; 0.4% international. 8% 25 or older, 52% live on campus, 4% transferred in. Retention: 39% of full-time freshmen returned the following year. Academic area with the most degrees conferred: liberal arts/general studies. Core. Calendar: semesters. Academic remediation for entering students, services for LD students, advanced placement, honors program, independent study, distance learning, double major, summer session for credit, part-time degree program, adult/continuing education programs, co-op programs and internships. Study abroad program.
Entrance Requirements: Open admission for West Virginia residents. Options: electronic application, international baccalaureate accepted. Required: high school transcript. Entrance: noncompetitive. Application deadline: rolling. Transfer credits accepted: Yes.
Costs Per Year: Application fee: $0. State resident tuition: $4488 full-time, $187 per credit hour part-time. Nonresident tuition: $11,376 full-time, $474 per credit hour part-time. Full-time tuition varies according to degree level and program. Part-time tuition varies according to degree level. College room and board: $8524. Room and board charges vary according to board plan and housing facility.
Collegiate Environment: Orientation program. Drama-theater group, choral group, student-run newspaper. Social organizations: 33 open to all. Most popular organizations: Agriculture and Forestry Club, Black Student Alliance, Gamers and Geeks Club, Campus and Community Ministries. Major annual events: Fall Fest/Spring Bash, Humans vs. Zombies Week, Habitat for Humanity Spring Break Trip. Student services: health clinic, personal-psychological counseling. Campus security: 24-hour patrols, late night transport-escort service, controlled dormitory access. 720 college housing spaces available; 637 were occupied in 2018-19. Freshmen given priority for college housing. On-campus residence required through sophomore year. Option: coed housing available. Mary F. Shipper Library. Books: 7,011 (physical), 617,383 (digital/electronic); Serial titles: 19 (physical), 93,783 (digital/electronic); Databases: 687. Operations spending for the previous fiscal year: $17,425. 69 computers available on campus for general student use. Students can access the following: online class registration. Staffed computer lab on campus provides training in use of software.
Community Environment: During the Civil War, the country around Keyser was a frequent battleground. The community was a supply point for, alternately, the Union Army and the Confederate forces. It changed hands 14 times in 4 years of war. The climate is temperate. There are churches of many denominations, libraries, a hospital and various civic, fraternal, and veteran's organizations serving the area. The city has good shopping facilities and is accessible by railroad, buses, and U.S. Highways 48,50 and 220. Residence Halls provide student housing. Part-time employment is available. Local recreation includes hunting, boating, fishing, golf, swimming, skiing, and tennis.

■ **SALEM INTERNATIONAL UNIVERSITY**
223 W Main St.
Salem, WV 26426-0500
Tel: (304)782-5011; Free: 888-235-5024
E-mail: admissions@salemiu.edu
Web Site: www.salemu.edu
Description: Independent, comprehensive, coed. Awards associate, bachelor's, and master's degrees and post-master's certificates. Founded 1888. Setting: 300-acre rural campus. Total enrollment: 850. Faculty: 60 (26 full-time, 34 part-time). Student-undergrad faculty ratio is 18:1. Full-time: 631 students, 62% women, 38% men. Students come from 13 states and territories, 13 other countries, 59% from out-of-state. 0.6% American Indian or Alaska Native, non-Hispanic/Latino; 5% Hispanic/Latino; 23% Black or African American, non-Hispanic/Latino; 0.5% Asian, non-Hispanic/Latino; 0.2% Native Hawaiian or other Pacific Islander, non-Hispanic/Latino; 5%

international. 40% 25 or older, 32% live on campus. Retention: 43% of full-time freshmen returned the following year. Core. Calendar: modular. Academic remediation for entering students, ESL program, services for LD students, advanced placement, accelerated degree program, independent study, distance learning, double major, summer session for credit; part-time degree program, internships, graduate courses open to undergrads. Off campus study at West Virginia Association of Independent Colleges and Universities. Study abroad program.
Entrance Requirements: Required: high school transcript, minimum 2 high school GPA. Recommended: essay, interview. Required for some: interview, SAT or ACT.
Collegiate Environment: Orientation program. Social organizations: 25 open to all; national fraternities, national sororities, local fraternities, local sororities; 1% of eligible men and 1% of eligible women are members. Most popular organizations: Student Government, Alpha Phi Omega, Gamma Beta Phi. Major annual events: Homecoming, Spring Fling, Convocation. Student services: personal-psychological counseling. Campus security: 24-hour emergency response devices and patrols. Benedum Library. 104 computers available on campus for general student use. A campuswide network can be accessed from student residence rooms and from off campus. Students can access the following: online class registration. Staffed computer lab on campus provides training in use of computers, software, and the Internet.
Community Environment: Tucked into a quiet valley, Salem-Teikyo University is surrounded by the scenic mountains for which West Virginia is known. Nearby parks provide excellent hiking, biking, white water rafting, skiing and fishing locations. Although the atmosphere is rural, students are within minutes of shopping malls, cinemas, fine restaurants, and the Benedum Airport. There is easy access to metropolitan areas such as Pittsburgh, Washington, D.C., and New York.

■ **SHEPHERD UNIVERSITY**
PO Box 5000
Shepherdstown, WV 25443
Tel: (304)876-5000; Free: 800-344-5231
Fax: (304)876-5165
E-mail: admission@shepherd.edu
Web Site: www.shepherd.edu
Description: State-supported, comprehensive, coed. Part of West Virginia Higher Education Policy Commission. Awards bachelor's, master's, and doctoral degrees. Founded 1871. Setting: 325-acre small town campus with easy access to Washington, D.C. Endowment: $25.9 million. Research spending for the previous fiscal year: $227,853. Educational spending for the previous fiscal year: $5776 per student. Total enrollment: 3,736. Faculty: 347 (136 full-time, 211 part-time). Student-undergrad faculty ratio is 15:1. 1,573 applied, 89% were admitted. Full-time: 2,613 students, 58% women, 42% men. Part-time: 807 students, 51% women, 49% men. Students come from 50 states and territories, 11 other countries, 33% from out-of-state. 0.5% American Indian or Alaska Native, non-Hispanic/Latino; 4% Hispanic/Latino; 8% Black or African American, non-Hispanic/Latino; 2% Asian, non-Hispanic/Latino; 0.1% Native Hawaiian or other Pacific Islander, non-Hispanic/Latino; 0.7% international. 17% 25 or older, 34% live on campus, 10% transferred in. Retention: 65% of full-time freshmen returned the following year. Academic areas with the most degrees conferred: liberal arts/general studies; business/marketing; health professions and related sciences. Core. Calendar: semesters. Academic remediation for entering students, ESL program, services for LD students, advanced placement, honors program, independent study, distance learning, double major, summer session for credit, part-time degree program, adult/continuing education programs, co-op programs and internships, graduate courses open to undergrads. Study abroad program. ROTC: Air Force (c).
Entrance Requirements: Options: electronic application, early admission, early action, deferred admission, international baccalaureate accepted. Required: high school transcript, minimum 2 high school GPA, SAT or ACT. Recommended: essay, minimum 3 high school GPA, 2 recommendations. Entrance: moderately difficult. Application deadlines: rolling, 11/15 for early action. Notification: continuous until 8/15, 12/15 for early action. SAT Reasoning Test deadline: 8/15. Transfer credits accepted: Yes. Early action applicants: 388. Early action applicants admitted: 297.
Costs Per Year: Application fee: $45. State resident tuition: $7548 full-time, $315 per credit hour part-time. Nonresident tuition: $18,052 full-time, $752 per credit hour part-time. Full-time tuition varies according to program and reciprocity agreements. Part-time tuition varies according to program. College room and board: $10,500. Room and board charges vary according to board plan and housing facility.

Collegiate Environment: Orientation program. Drama-theater group, choral group, marching band, student-run newspaper, radio station. Social organizations: 87 open to all; national fraternities, national sororities; 3% of eligible men and 4% of eligible women are members. Most popular organizations: Relay for Life, Student Government Association, Ram Marching Band, Sigma Sigma Sigma, Alpha Phi Omega. Major annual events: Homecoming, Midnight Breakfast, Relay for Life. Student services: health clinic, personal-psychological counseling. Campus security: 24-hour emergency response devices and patrols, late night transport-escort service, controlled dormitory access, student security in academic buildings, RAVE emergency alert system. Scarborough Library. Books: 143,245 (physical), 6,727 (digital/electronic); Serial titles: 373 (physical), 69,441 (digital/electronic); Databases: 71. Weekly public service hours: 87; study areas open 24 hours, 5-7 days a week; students can reserve study rooms. Operations spending for the previous fiscal year: $1.2 million. 567 computers available on campus for general student use. A campuswide network can be accessed from student residence rooms. Students can access the following: online class registration, virtual labs. Staffed computer lab on campus provides training in use of computers, software, and the Internet.

Community Environment: Shepherdstown is a small town of about 5,000 located near Martinsburg, Charles Town and Harpers Ferry, West Virginia, and Hagerstown, Maryland. The town was established by English and German farmers who had crossed the river from Maryland before 1730. There are many historic sites in the area. The climate is temperate and the community is reached by State Route 45. There are 10 churches, 4 libraries, and 4 hospitals nearby. Some part-time employment is available in the surrounding area.

■ **SOUTHERN WEST VIRGINIA COMMUNITY AND TECHNICAL COLLEGE**

Dempsey Branch Rd.
Mount Gay, WV 25637-2900
Tel: (304)792-7160
Fax: (304)792-7028
E-mail: admissions@southern.wvnet.edu
Web Site: southernwv.edu

Description: State-supported, 2-year, coed. Part of State College System of West Virginia. Awards certificates, transfer associate, and terminal associate degrees. Founded 1971. Setting: 23-acre rural campus. Total enrollment: 1,900. Faculty: 171 (66 full-time, 105 part-time). Student-undergrad faculty ratio is 20:1. 603 applied, 100% were admitted. 5% from top 10% of their high school class, 12% from top quarter, 32% from top half. Full-time: 1,192 students, 71% women, 29% men. Part-time: 708 students, 77% women, 23% men. Students come from 3 states and territories, 9% from out-of-state. 24% 25 or older, 5% transferred in. Core. Calendar: semesters. Academic remediation for entering students, services for LD students, advanced placement, summer session for credit, part-time degree program, external degree program, adult/continuing education programs, co-op programs.

Entrance Requirements: Open admission except for nursing, medical laboratory technology, radiological technology programs. Options: early admission, deferred admission. Required: high school transcript. Entrance: noncompetitive. Application deadline: rolling. Notification: continuous.

Collegiate Environment: Drama-theater group. Student services: personal-psychological counseling. Harless Library plus 1 other. 92 computers available on campus for general student use. A campuswide network can be accessed from off-campus. Staffed computer lab on campus.

■ **STRAYER UNIVERSITY-TEAYS VALLEY CAMPUS**

135 Corporate Ctr. Dr.
Scott Depot, WV 25560
Tel: (304)760-1700; Free: 888-311-0355
Web Site: www.strayer.edu

Description: Proprietary, comprehensive, coed. Awards associate, bachelor's, and master's degrees.

■ **UNIVERSITY OF CHARLESTON**

2300 MacCorkle Ave., SE
Charleston, WV 25304-1099
Tel: (304)357-4800; Free: 800-995-GOUC
Fax: (304)357-4781
E-mail: admissions@ucwv.edu
Web Site: www.ucwv.edu

Description: Independent, comprehensive, coed. Awards associate, bachelor's, master's, and doctoral degrees. Founded 1888. Setting: 40-acre

small town campus. Total enrollment: 2,481. 2,737 applied, 64% were admitted. Full-time: 1,220 students, 57% women, 43% men. Part-time: 611 students, 21% women, 79% men. Students come from 49 states and territories, 42 other countries, 48% from out-of-state. 1% American Indian or Alaska Native, non-Hispanic/Latino; 2% Hispanic/Latino; 8% Black or African American, non-Hispanic/Latino; 1% Asian, non-Hispanic/Latino; 0.4% Native Hawaiian or other Pacific Islander, non-Hispanic/Latino; 7% international. 39% 25 or older, 10% transferred in. Retention: 61% of full-time freshmen returned the following year. Academic areas with the most degrees conferred: business/marketing; health professions and related sciences; biological/life sciences. Core. Calendar: semesters. Academic remediation for entering students, ESL program, services for LD students, advanced placement, accelerated degree program, self-designed majors, freshman honors college, honors program, independent study, distance learning, double major, summer session for credit, part-time degree program, adult/continuing education programs, co-op programs and internships, graduate courses open to undergrads. Off campus study. Study abroad program. ROTC: Army.

Entrance Requirements: Options: electronic application, early admission, deferred admission, international baccalaureate accepted. Required: high school transcript, minimum 2.25 high school GPA. Recommended: essay. Required for some: interview. Entrance: moderately difficult. Application deadline: rolling. Notification: continuous. Transfer credits accepted: Yes.

Costs Per Year: Application fee: $25. Comprehensive fee: $40,080 includes full-time tuition ($29,900), mandatory fees ($1000), and college room and board ($9180). College room only: $5000. Full-time tuition and fees vary according to location and program. Room and board charges vary according to board plan, housing facility, and location. Part-time tuition: $380 per credit hour. Part-time tuition varies according to course load, location, and program.

Collegiate Environment: Orientation program. Choral group, marching band, student-run newspaper. Social organizations: 29 open to all; national fraternities, national sororities. Most popular organizations: Student Activities Board, American Society of Interior Designers, Student Government Association, Capito Association of Nursing Students, International Student Organization. Major annual events: Governor's Cup Regatta, Homecoming, Family Weekend. Student services: health clinic, personal-psychological counseling. Campus security: 24-hour emergency response devices and patrols, student patrols, late night transport-escort service, controlled dormitory access, radio connection to city police and ambulance. Schoenbaum Library plus 1 other. Books: 189,000 (physical), 210,000 (digital/electronic); Databases: 56. Students can reserve study rooms. 200 computers available on campus for general student use. A campuswide network can be accessed. Students can access the following: online class registration. Staffed computer lab on campus provides training in use of software.

Community Environment: Charleston, with a metropolitan population of 307,700, is the state capital, as well as the cultural, social, political, and economic center of West Virginia. Located in the Kanawha Valley, near the foothills of the Appalachian Mountains, it offers scenic tranquility as well as the convenience and excitement of a modern city. Downtown Charleston, just a 5-minute drive from campus, offers social and cultural opportunities that can be found only in a large city.

■ **VALLEY COLLEGE**

287 Aikens Ctr.
Martinsburg, WV 25404
Tel: (304)263-0979
Fax: (304)263-2413
E-mail: gkennedy@vct.edu

Description: Proprietary, 2-year, coed. Awards certificates and terminal associate degrees. Founded 1983. Setting: suburban campus. Total enrollment: 47. Faculty: 6 (4 full-time, 2 part-time). Student-undergrad faculty ratio is 14:1. Full-time: 47 students, 94% women, 6% men. Calendar: continuous.

Entrance Requirements: Required: high school transcript, interview.

■ **WEST LIBERTY UNIVERSITY**

208 University Dr.
West Liberty, WV 26074
Tel: (304)336-5000; Free: 866-WESTLIB
Fax: (304)336-8285
E-mail: wladmsn1@westliberty.edu
Web Site: www.westliberty.edu

Description: State-supported, comprehensive, coed. Part of West Virginia Higher Education Policy Commission. Awards associate, bachelor's, and master's degrees. Founded 1837. Setting: rural campus. Total enrollment: 2,340. 1,692 applied, 72% were admitted. 15% from top 10% of their high school class, 43% from top quarter, 74% from top half. Full-time: 1,847 students, 60% women, 40% men. Part-time: 319 students, 59% women, 41% men. 32% from out-of-state. 0.7% Hispanic/Latino; 4% Black or African American, non-Hispanic/Latino; 0.7% Asian, non-Hispanic/Latino; 0.1% Native Hawaiian or other Pacific Islander, non-Hispanic/Latino; 2% international. 9% 25 or older, 44% live on campus, 7% transferred in. Retention: 70% of full-time freshmen returned the following year. Academic areas with the most degrees conferred: education; health professions and related sciences; business/marketing. Calendar: semesters. Academic remediation for entering students, services for LD students, advanced placement, accelerated degree program, self-designed majors, honors program, independent study, distance learning, double major, summer session for credit, part-time degree program, external degree program, adult/continuing education programs, co-op programs and internships. Off campus study. Study abroad program.

Entrance Requirements: Option: electronic application. Required: high school transcript, minimum 2 high school GPA, SAT or ACT. Recommended: interview. Entrance: minimally difficult. SAT Reasoning Test deadline: 8/1. SAT Subject Test deadline: 8/1. Transfer credits accepted: Yes.

Collegiate Environment: Orientation program. Campus security: 24-hour emergency response devices and patrols, controlled dormitory access. Paul N. Elbin Library.

Community Environment: West Liberty is located 10 miles from the city limits of Wheeling. There are 2 Protestant churches and a visiting priest for Catholic students. Famous Oglebay Park, 6 miles from the campus, is used for recreation. Job opportunities are good in the area. There are dormitories, campus health services, and an infirmary for students. Fraternities and sororities are prominent here.

■ WEST VIRGINIA JUNIOR COLLEGE-BRIDGEPORT
176 Thompson Dr.
Bridgeport, WV 26330
Tel: (304)842-4007; Free: 800-470-5627
E-mail: kkirk@wvjc.edu
Web Site: www.wvjc.edu

Description: Proprietary, 2-year, coed. Awards diplomas, transfer associate, and terminal associate degrees. Founded 1922. Setting: 3-acre small town campus. Total enrollment: 150. Faculty: 10 (5 full-time, 5 part-time). Student-undergrad faculty ratio is 15:1. Full-time: 150 students, 87% women, 13% men. Students come from 4 states and territories. 30% 25 or older, 7% transferred in. Retention: 80% of full-time freshmen returned the following year. Core. Calendar: quarters. Academic remediation for entering students, services for LD students, independent study, distance learning, summer session for credit, co-op programs and internships.

Entrance Requirements: Open admission. Option: electronic application. Required: minimum 2.5 high school GPA, interview, meeting with an Admissions Representative. Recommended: high school transcript. Required for some: essay, 1 recommendation. Entrance: minimally difficult. Application deadline: rolling. Notification: continuous. Transfer credits accepted: Yes.

Collegiate Environment: Orientation program. Social organizations: 50% of eligible men and 50% of eligible women are members. Most popular organizations: Medical Club, Business Club, Computer Club, Dental Assisting Club, Pharmacy Tech Club. Major annual events: Annual Alumni Picnic, Thanksgiving Covered Dish Dinner, Graduation. Campus security: 24-hour emergency response devices. WVJC Library plus 1 other. Books: 350 (physical), 15 (digital/electronic); Serial titles: 12 (physical); Databases: 5. Weekly public service hours: 50. Operations spending for the previous fiscal year: $10,000. 150 computers available on campus for general student use. A campuswide network can be accessed. Students can access the following: online class registration. Staffed computer lab on campus provides training in use of computers, software, and the Internet.

■ WEST VIRGINIA JUNIOR COLLEGE-CHARLESTON
1000 Virginia St. E
Charleston, WV 25301-2817
Tel: (304)345-2820; Free: 800-924-5208
Web Site: www.wvjc.edu

Description: Proprietary, 2-year, coed. Awards terminal associate degrees. Founded 1892. Setting: urban campus. Total enrollment: 201. Student-undergrad faculty ratio is 17:1. 52% 25 or older. Retention: 61% of full-time freshmen returned the following year. Calendar: quarters. Summer session for credit, part-time degree program, adult/continuing education programs.

Entrance Requirements: Open admission. Entrance: noncompetitive. Application deadline: rolling.

■ WEST VIRGINIA JUNIOR COLLEGE-MORGANTOWN
148 Willey St.
Morgantown, WV 26505-5521
Tel: (304)296-8282
Web Site: www.wvjcmorgantown.edu

Description: Proprietary, 2-year, coed. Awards terminal associate degrees (also offers non-degree programs with significant enrollment not reflected in profile). Founded 1922. Setting: small town campus with easy access to Pittsburgh. Total enrollment: 150. Student-undergrad faculty ratio is 32:1. 3% from out-of-state. 39% 25 or older. Retention: 64% of full-time freshmen returned the following year. Calendar: quarters. Adult/continuing education programs.

Entrance Requirements: Open admission. Required: high school transcript, interview. Entrance: noncompetitive. Application deadline: rolling. Notification: continuous.

■ WEST VIRGINIA NORTHERN COMMUNITY COLLEGE
1704 Market St.
Wheeling, WV 26003-3699
Tel: (304)233-5900
Fax: (304)233-5900
E-mail: jfike@northern.wvnet.edu
Web Site: www.wvncc.edu

Description: State-supported, 2-year, coed. Awards certificates, transfer associate, and terminal associate degrees. Founded 1972. Setting: small town campus with easy access to Pittsburgh. Endowment: $659,426. Educational spending for the previous fiscal year: $1552 per student. Total enrollment: 2,505. Faculty: 190 (58 full-time, 132 part-time). 350 applied, 100% were admitted. 5% from top 10% of their high school class, 10% from top quarter, 19% from top half. Full-time: 1,156 students, 67% women, 33% men. Part-time: 1,349 students, 69% women, 31% men. Students come from 14 states and territories, 24% from out-of-state. 0.3% American Indian or Alaska Native, non-Hispanic/Latino; 0.4% Hispanic/Latino; 5% Black or African American, non-Hispanic/Latino; 0.4% Asian, non-Hispanic/Latino. 50% 25 or older, 12% transferred in. Core. Calendar: semesters. Academic remediation for entering students, services for LD students, advanced placement, accelerated degree program, self-designed majors, honors program, distance learning, double major, summer session for credit, part-time degree program, adult/continuing education programs, co-op programs and internships.

Entrance Requirements: Open admission except for health science programs. Options: electronic application, early admission, deferred admission. Recommended: ACT Compass. Required for some: high school transcript, ACT Compass. Entrance: noncompetitive. Application deadline: rolling. Transfer credits accepted: Yes.

Collegiate Environment: Orientation program. Student-run newspaper. Social organizations: Phi Theta Kappa; 23% of eligible men and 77% of eligible women are members. Most popular organization: Community Outreach Opportunity Program (COOP). Campus security: police officer on staff during the day at Main Campus, security personnel during evening and during night classes. Wheeling B&O Campus Library plus 2 others. Operations spending for the previous fiscal year: $121,220. 300 computers available on campus for general student use. A campuswide network can be accessed. Students can access the following: online class registration, Student Portal.

Community Environment: Wheeling, one of the country's most liveable small cities, is a one-hour drive from Pittsburgh, PA, and a two-hour drive from Columbus, OH. It is in a central area of approximately 150,000 people. Many cultural and recreational facilities are available, including 1,500-acre Oglebay Park and 250-acre Wheeling Park. Excellent local recreation areas provide opportunities for camping, hiking, skiing, swimming, golf, and other such activities.

■ WEST VIRGINIA STATE UNIVERSITY
PO Box 1000
Institute, WV 25112-1000
Tel: (304)766-3000; Free: 800-987-2112
Fax: (304)766-4158
E-mail: jmeans9@wvstateu.edu
Web Site: www.wvstateu.edu

Description: State-supported, comprehensive, coed. Part of West Virginia four-year public higher education system. Awards bachelor's and master's degrees and post-master's certificates. Founded 1891. Setting: 98-acre small town campus. Endowment: $7.1 million. Research spending for the previous fiscal year: $8.1 million. Educational spending for the previous fiscal year: $3804 per student. Total enrollment: 3,692. Faculty: 193 (106 full-time, 87 part-time). Student-undergrad faculty ratio is 13:1. 3,182 applied, 98% were admitted. Full-time: 1,644 students, 56% women, 44% men. Part-time: 1,927 students, 62% women, 38% men. Students come from 25 states and territories, 13 other countries, 15% from out-of-state. 1% American Indian or Alaska Native, non-Hispanic/Latino; 2% Hispanic/Latino; 14% Black or African American, non-Hispanic/Latino; 0.6% Asian, non-Hispanic/Latino; 0.3% Native Hawaiian or other Pacific Islander, non-Hispanic/Latino; 2% international. 26% 25 or older, 21% live on campus, 6% transferred in. Retention: 59% of full-time freshmen returned the following year. Academic areas with the most degrees conferred: liberal arts/general studies; education; business/marketing. Core. Calendar: semesters. Academic remediation for entering students, services for LD students, advanced placement, accelerated degree program, honors program, double major, summer session for credit, part-time degree program, external degree program, adult/continuing education programs, co-op programs and internships, graduate courses open to undergrads. ROTC: Army.

Entrance Requirements: Option: electronic application. Required: high school transcript, minimum 2 high school GPA, minimum ACT composite score of 18 (870 SAT), SAT or ACT. Entrance: minimally difficult. Notification: continuous, continuous for nonresidents. SAT Reasoning Test deadline: 8/17. SAT Subject Test deadline: 8/17. Transfer credits accepted: Yes.

Costs Per Year: Application fee: $20. State resident tuition: $8050 full-time, $332 per credit hour part-time. Nonresident tuition: $17,166 full-time, $746 per credit hour part-time. Mandatory fees: $700 full-time. College room and board: $12,486. College room only: $7852.

Collegiate Environment: Orientation program. Choral group, marching band, student-run newspaper, radio station. Social organizations: 45 open to all; national fraternities, national sororities. Most popular organizations: Student Social Work Organization 20, WVSU College Chapter - NAACP 17, CHOICES Peer Educators 13, WVSU International Student Services 13, C.E. Jones Historical Society 12. Major annual events: Homecoming, State Stride, Cares Day. Student services: health clinic, personal-psychological counseling. Campus security: 24-hour emergency response devices and patrols, late night transport-escort service, controlled dormitory access. 381 college housing spaces available; 340 were occupied in 2018-19. On-campus residence required through sophomore year. Option: coed housing available. Drain-Jordan Library. Books: 135,848 (physical), 25,361 (digital/electronic); Serial titles: 1,454 (physical), 33,375 (digital/electronic); Databases: 28. Weekly public service hours: 82. 625 computers available on campus for general student use. A campuswide network can be accessed from student residence rooms and from off campus. Students can access the following: online class registration. Staffed computer lab on campus provides training in use of computers, software, and the Internet.

Community Environment: Institute is a suburb of Charleston and is reached by railroad, bus lines, feeder airlines, and a local transit system. There are churches of major denominations and community services in the easily accessible neighboring community. Part-time employment is available.

■ WEST VIRGINIA UNIVERSITY

University Ave.
Morgantown, WV 26506
Tel: (304)293-0111; Free: 800-344-9881
Fax: (304)293-3080
E-mail: marilyn.potts@mail.wvu.edu
Web Site: www.wvu.edu

Description: State-supported, university, coed. Part of West Virginia Higher Education Policy Commission. Awards bachelor's, master's, and doctoral degrees. Founded 1867. Setting: 1,892-acre small town campus with easy access to Pittsburgh. System endowment: $574.9 million. Research spending for the previous fiscal year: $133.4 million. Total enrollment: 28,410. Faculty: 1,486 (1,142 full-time, 344 part-time). Student-undergrad faculty ratio is 20:1. 20,594 applied, 72% were admitted. 18% from top 10% of their high school class, 44% from top quarter, 77% from top half. Full-time: 20,713 students, 47% women, 53% men. Part-time: 1,791 students, 54% women, 46% men. Students come from 52 states and territories, 84 other countries, 43% from out-of-state. 0.1% American Indian or Alaska Native, non-Hispanic/Latino; 4% Hispanic/Latino; 4% Black or African American, non-Hispanic/Latino; 2% Asian, non-Hispanic/Latino; 0.1% Native Hawaiian or other Pacific Islander, non-Hispanic/Latino; 7% international. 6% 25 or older, 15% live on campus, 4% transferred in. Retention: 80% of full-time freshmen returned the following year. Academic areas with the most degrees conferred: engineering; business/marketing; communication/journalism.

Core. Calendar: semesters. Academic remediation for entering students, ESL program, services for LD students, advanced placement, accelerated degree program, self-designed majors, honors program, independent study, distance learning, double major, summer session for credit, part-time degree program, external degree program, adult/continuing education programs, internships, graduate courses open to undergrads. Off campus study at Academic Common Market, Garrett County Community College. Study abroad program. ROTC: Army, Air Force.

Entrance Requirements: Options: electronic application, international baccalaureate accepted. Required: high school transcript, minimum 2 high school GPA, SAT or ACT. Required for some: essay, minimum 2.25 high school GPA. Entrance: moderately difficult. Application deadline: 8/1. Preference given to state residents. SAT Reasoning Test deadline: 8/1. Transfer credits accepted: Yes.

Costs Per Year: Application fee: $45. State resident tuition: $8856 full-time, $369 per credit hour part-time. Nonresident tuition: $24,950 full-time, $1040 per credit hour part-time. Full-time tuition varies according to location, program, and reciprocity agreements. Part-time tuition varies according to course load, location, program, and reciprocity agreements. College room and board: $10,918. Room and board charges vary according to board plan, housing facility, and location.

Collegiate Environment: Orientation program. Drama-theater group, choral group, marching band, student-run newspaper, radio station. Social organizations: 467 open to all; national fraternities, national sororities, local fraternities, local sororities; 7% of eligible men and 6% of eligible women are members. Most popular organizations: Residential Hall Association, Alpha Phi Omega, WVU Greek System, Mountaineer Maniacs, Campus Crusade for Christ. Major annual events: Mountaineer Week, Fall Fest, Parent's Weekend and Homecoming. Student services: legal services, health clinic, personal-psychological counseling, women's center. Campus security: 24-hour emergency response devices and patrols, student patrols, late night transport-escort service, controlled dormitory access, patrol officers just for housing. Downtown Library Complex plus 5 others. Books: 1.1 million (physical), 621,166 (digital/electronic); Serial titles: 56,340 (physical), 96,553 (digital/electronic); Databases: 975. Study areas open 24 hours, 5-7 days a week; students can reserve study rooms. Operations spending for the previous fiscal year: $17.4 million. 1,800 computers available on campus for general student use. Computer purchase/lease plans available. A campuswide network can be accessed from student residence rooms and from off campus. Students can access the following: online class registration. Staffed computer lab on campus provides training in use of computers, software, and the Internet.

Community Environment: West Virginia University's main campus is located in Morgantown, a small city of 30,000 in the Appalachian Mountains on West Virginia's northern border. Although the state is rural and the community quiet, Greater Morgantown is within easy traveling distance, on modern interstate highways, of the metropolitan areas of Pittsburgh, about 70 miles north, and Baltimore and Washington, D.C., about 200 miles to the east. The community has churches of various denominations, two hospitals, a city library, and various civic and fraternal organizations. Local recreation is available through the city's park system which includes several municipal pools and an ice skating rink. The area has golf courses, 1,800-acre Cheat Lake, whitewater rafting, and nearby Cooper's Rock State Forest. A half dozen snow skiing areas are within easy driving distance, as are some of the best remaining wilderness areas in the eastern United States.

■ WEST VIRGINIA UNIVERSITY INSTITUTE OF TECHNOLOGY

512 S Kanawha St.
Beckley, WV 25801
Tel: (304)442-3071; Free: 888-554-8324
Fax: (304)442-3097
E-mail: tech-admissions@mail.wvu.edu
Web Site: www.wvutech.edu

Description: State-supported, 4-year, coed. Administratively affiliated with West Virginia University. Awards bachelor's degrees. Founded 1895. Setting: 114-acre small town campus. System endowment: $532.6 million. Total enrollment: 1,755. Faculty: 124 (95 full-time, 29 part-time). Student-undergrad faculty ratio is 13:1. 1,517 applied, 61% were admitted. 21% from top 10% of their high school class, 51% from top quarter, 87% from top half. Full-time: 1,175 students, 42% women, 58% men. Part-time: 580 students, 55% women, 45% men. Students come from 31 states and territories, 29 other countries, 11% from out-of-state. 0.3% American Indian or Alaska Native, non-Hispanic/Latino; 3% Hispanic/Latino; 6% Black or African American, non-Hispanic/Latino; 0.8% Asian, non-Hispanic/Latino; 5%

international. 12% 25 or older, 23% live on campus, 6% transferred in. Retention: 56% of full-time freshmen returned the following year. Academic areas with the most degrees conferred: engineering; liberal arts/general studies; business/marketing. Core. Calendar: semesters. Academic remediation for entering students, services for LD students, advanced placement, self-designed majors, independent study, distance learning, double major, summer session for credit, part-time degree program, co-op programs and internships. Study abroad program. ROTC: Army.

Entrance Requirements: Options: electronic application, early admission. Required: high school transcript, minimum 2 high school GPA, minimum ACT composite score of 18 or 870 SAT math and verbal or minimum 3.0 high school GPA, SAT or ACT. Required for some: TOEFL or IELTS. Entrance: minimally difficult. Application deadlines: rolling, rolling for nonresidents. Notification: continuous until 8/15, continuous for nonresidents. SAT Reasoning Test deadline: 8/16. SAT Subject Test deadline: 8/16. Transfer credits accepted: Yes.

Costs Per Year: Application fee: $0. State resident tuition: $7464 full-time, $311 per credit hour part-time. Nonresident tuition: $18,648 full-time, $777 per credit hour part-time. Full-time tuition varies according to program. Part-time tuition varies according to course load and program. College room and board: $11,390. Room and board charges vary according to board plan and housing facility.

Collegiate Environment: Orientation program. Drama-theater group, student-run newspaper. Social organizations: 42 open to all; national fraternities, national sororities, local sororities. Most popular organizations: Christian Student Union, Student Activities Board, Alpha Phi Omega, Student Government Association, American Society of Mechanical Engineers. Major annual events: Homecoming, Light Up Old Main, Pre-Exam Jam. Student services: health clinic, personal-psychological counseling. Campus security: 24-hour emergency response devices and patrols. 446 college housing spaces available; 310 were occupied in 2018-19. Freshmen guaranteed college housing. On-campus residence required through sophomore year. Option: coed housing available. Vining Library plus 1 other. Books: 14,844 (physical), 586,819 (digital/electronic); Serial titles: 154 (physical), 95,919 (digital/electronic). Students can reserve study rooms. 200 computers available on campus for general student use. A campuswide network can be accessed from student residence rooms and from off campus. Students can access the following: online class registration, electronic course materials. Staffed computer lab on campus provides training in use of software.

Community Environment: The community has nearby plants that include the world's largest producer of ferro alloys for steel and a steam-produced electric power plant. Montgomery may be reached by bus lines and Amtrak.

■ WEST VIRGINIA UNIVERSITY AT PARKERSBURG

300 Campus Dr.
Parkersburg, WV 26104
Tel: (304)424-8000; Free: 800-WVA-WVUP
E-mail: christine.post@mail.wvu.edu
Web Site: www.wvup.edu

Description: State-supported, primarily 2-year, coed. Administratively affiliated with West Virginia University. Awards certificates, transfer associate, terminal associate, and bachelor's degrees. Founded 1961. Setting: 120-acre small town campus. Total enrollment: 4,223. Student-undergrad faculty ratio is 24:1. 1% from out-of-state. 44% 25 or older. Retention: 57% of full-time freshmen returned the following year. Core. Calendar: semesters. Academic remediation for entering students, ESL program, services for LD students, advanced placement, independent study, distance learning, summer session for credit, part-time degree program, co-op programs and internships. Study abroad program.

Entrance Requirements: Open admission except for nursing, bachelor of science degree programs, surgical technology, paramedic science. Options: electronic application, early admission, deferred admission. Required for some: high school transcript. Entrance: noncompetitive. Application deadline: rolling. Notification: continuous.

Collegiate Environment: Orientation program. Drama-theater group, student-run newspaper. Student services: health clinic, personal-psychological counseling. WVUP Library.

■ WEST VIRGINIA WESLEYAN COLLEGE

59 College Ave.
Buckhannon, WV 26201
Tel: (304)473-8000; Free: 800-722-9933
Fax: (304)472-2571

E-mail: admission@wvwc.edu
Web Site: www.wvwc.edu

Description: Independent, comprehensive, coed, affiliated with United Methodist Church. Awards bachelor's and master's degrees and post-master's certificates. Founded 1890. Setting: 180-acre small town campus. Endowment: $47.4 million. Educational spending for the previous fiscal year: $7483 per student. Total enrollment: 1,449. Faculty: 150 (83 full-time, 67 part-time). Student-undergrad faculty ratio is 13:1. 2,278 applied, 71% were admitted. 20% from top 10% of their high school class, 49% from top quarter, 83% from top half. Full-time: 1,289 students, 56% women, 44% men. Part-time: 31 students, 52% women, 48% men. Students come from 37 states and territories, 27 other countries, 38% from out-of-state. 0.4% American Indian or Alaska Native, non-Hispanic/Latino; 3% Hispanic/Latino; 9% Black or African American, non-Hispanic/Latino; 0.2% Asian, non-Hispanic/Latino; 0.1% Native Hawaiian or other Pacific Islander, non-Hispanic/Latino; 6% international. 2% 25 or older, 76% live on campus, 3% transferred in. Retention: 74% of full-time freshmen returned the following year. Academic areas with the most degrees conferred: physical sciences; business/marketing; education. Core. Calendar: semesters. Academic remediation for entering students, ESL program, services for LD students, advanced placement, self-designed majors, honors program, independent study, distance learning, double major, summer session for credit, part-time degree program, internships, graduate courses open to undergrads. Off campus study. Study abroad program.

Entrance Requirements: Options: electronic application, deferred admission. Required: high school transcript, SAT or ACT. Recommended: essay, interview. Required for some: recommendations, SAT Subject Tests. Entrance: moderately difficult. Notification: continuous. SAT Reasoning Test deadline: 8/15. SAT Subject Test deadline: 8/15. Transfer credits accepted: Yes.

Costs Per Year: Application fee: $35. Comprehensive fee: $40,496 includes full-time tuition ($30,462), mandatory fees ($1178), and college room and board ($8856). College room only: $4326. Full-time tuition and fees vary according to course load and student level. Room and board charges vary according to housing facility.

Collegiate Environment: Orientation program. Drama-theater group, choral group, marching band, student-run newspaper, radio station. Social organizations: 84 open to all; national fraternities, national sororities, local fraternities; 25% of eligible men and 25% of eligible women are members. Most popular organizations: Campus Activities Board, Green Club, WE LEAD, Wesleyan Ambassadors, Enactus. Major annual events: Founder's Day/Homecoming, Festival of Lessons and Carols, Spring Weekend. Student services: health clinic, personal-psychological counseling. Campus security: 24-hour emergency response devices and patrols, student patrols, late night transport-escort service, controlled dormitory access. Annie Merner Pfeifer Library plus 1 other. Books: 122,495 (physical), 271,641 (digital/electronic); Serial titles: 11,057 (physical), 112,139 (digital/electronic); Databases: 110. Students can reserve study rooms. Operations spending for the previous fiscal year: $755,202.

Community Environment: Buckhannon is a rural community supported by agriculture, coal, natural gas, and local industries. The climate is temperate with an average annual temperature of 53 degrees. Bus and airlines are accessible 25 miles distant at Clarksburg. The community has a public library, restaurants, hotels, churches of most denominations, 1 hospital, and a YWCA. Part-time employment is available. Buckhannon is the home of the West Virginia Strawberry Festival. Local recreation includes hunting, fishing, boating, skiing, white-water rafting, and most outdoor sports. Civic, fraternal, and veterans' organizations are active in the area.

■ WHEELING JESUIT UNIVERSITY

316 Washington Ave.
Wheeling, WV 26003-6295
Tel: (304)243-2000; Free: 800-624-6992
Fax: (304)243-2397
E-mail: crouhier@wju.edu
Web Site: www.wju.edu

Description: Independent Roman Catholic (Jesuit), comprehensive, coed. Awards bachelor's, master's, and doctoral degrees and post-master's certificates. Founded 1954. Setting: 65-acre suburban campus with easy access to Pittsburgh. Endowment: $12.5 million. Research spending for the previous fiscal year: $2 million. Educational spending for the previous fiscal year: $8887 per student. Total enrollment: 1,289. Faculty: 155 (77 full-time, 78 part-time). Student-undergrad faculty ratio is 10:1. 1,020 applied, 93% were admitted. 17% from top 10% of their high school class, 36% from top quarter, 69% from top half. Full-time: 790 students, 47% women, 53% men. Part-time: 155 students, 70% women, 30% men. Students come from 37 states and territories, 26 other countries, 66% from out-of-state. 0.5% American Indian or Alaska Native, non-Hispanic/Latino; 3% Hispanic/Latino; 8% Black or African American, non-Hispanic/Latino; 0.9% Asian, non-Hispanic/Latino; 0.9% Native Hawaiian or other Pacific Islander, non-Hispanic/Latino; 5% international. 16% 25 or older, 68% live on campus, 3% transferred in. Retention: 71% of full-time freshmen returned the following year. Academic areas with the most degrees conferred: health professions and related sciences; business/marketing; psychology. Core. Calendar: semesters. Academic remediation for entering students, ESL program, services for LD students, advanced placement, accelerated degree program, self-designed majors, honors program, independent study, distance learning, double major, summer session for credit, part-time degree program, adult/continuing education programs, internships, graduate courses open to undergrads. Off campus study at Belmont College, Community College of Allegheny, Eastern Gateway Community College, West Virginia Northern Community College. Study abroad program.

Entrance Requirements: Options: electronic application, deferred admission, international baccalaureate accepted. Required: high school transcript, SAT or ACT. Recommended: essay, minimum 3 high school GPA, 2 recommendations, interview. Required for some: interview. Entrance: moderately difficult. Application deadline: rolling. Notification: continuous. SAT Reasoning Test deadline: 7/31. SAT Subject Test deadline: 7/31. Transfer credits accepted: Yes.

Costs Per Year: Application fee: $25. Comprehensive fee: $39,190 includes full-time tuition ($29,090), mandatory fees ($200), and college room and board ($9900). Room and board charges vary according to board plan, housing facility, and student level. Part-time tuition: $735 per credit hour.

Collegiate Environment: Orientation program. Drama-theater group, choral group, student-run newspaper. Social organizations: 27 open to all. Most popular organizations: Campus Activity Board (CAB), Theater Guild, Student Senate, International Student Club, Campus Ministry. Major annual events: Culture Fest, Last Blast Carnival, Homecoming/Family Weekend. Student services: health clinic, personal-psychological counseling. Campus security: 24-hour patrols, late night transport-escort service, controlled dormitory access, cameras at residence hall entrances. Bishop Hodges Library. Books: 134,540 (physical), 165,927 (digital/electronic); Serial titles: 107 (physical), 42 (digital/electronic); Databases: 69. Weekly public service hours: 85; students can reserve study rooms. Operations spending for the previous fiscal year: $350,481. 215 computers available on campus for general student use. A campuswide network can be accessed from student residence rooms and from off campus. Students can access the following: online class registration.

Community Environment: Wheeling, one of the country's most liveable small cities, is a one-hour drive from Pittsburgh, PA and a two-hour drive from Columbus, OH. In a central area of approximately 150,000 people, many cultural and recreational facilities are available for golf, camping, hiking, skiing, and swimming, including 1,500-acre Oglebay Park and 250-acre Wheeling Park.

■ ALVERNO COLLEGE
3400 S 43rd St.
Milwaukee, WI 53234-3922
Tel: (414)382-6000; Free: 800-933-3401
Fax: (414)382-6354
E-mail: admissions@alverno.edu
Web Site: www.alverno.edu
Description: Independent Roman Catholic, comprehensive. Awards associate, bachelor's, master's, and doctoral degrees and post-master's certificates (also offers weekend program with significant enrollment not reflected in profile). Founded 1887. Setting: 46-acre urban campus. Endowment: $30 million. Research spending for the previous fiscal year: $219,019. Educational spending for the previous fiscal year: $7979 per student. Total enrollment: 1,851. Faculty: 231 (90 full-time, 141 part-time). Student-undergrad faculty ratio is 10:1. 747 applied, 67% were admitted. Full-time: 995 students, 100% women. Part-time: 224 students, 97% women, 3% men. Students come from 14 states and territories, 1 other country, 7% from out-of-state. 0.7% American Indian or Alaska Native, non-Hispanic/Latino; 30% Hispanic/Latino; 14% Black or African American, non-Hispanic/Latino; 5% Asian, non-Hispanic/Latino; 0.2% international. 28% 25 or older, 17% live on campus, 9% transferred in. Retention: 68% of full-time freshmen returned the following year. Academic areas with the most degrees conferred: health professions and related sciences; business/marketing; psychology. Core. Calendar: semesters. Academic remediation for entering students, services for LD students, advanced placement, accelerated degree program, self-designed majors, honors program, independent study, double major, summer session for credit, part-time degree program, adult/continuing education programs, internships. Study abroad program. ROTC: Army (c), Air Force (c).
Entrance Requirements: Options: electronic application, deferred admission, international baccalaureate accepted. Required: essay, high school transcript, minimum 2.0 college GPA, SAT or ACT. Recommended: minimum 2 high school GPA, interview. Entrance: moderately difficult. Application deadline: rolling. Notification: continuous. Transfer credits accepted: Yes.
Costs Per Year: Application fee: $0. Comprehensive fee: $36,848 includes full-time tuition ($27,552), mandatory fees ($750), and college room and board ($8546). Full-time tuition and fees vary according to program. Room and board charges vary according to board plan and housing facility. Part-time tuition: $1148 per credit hour. Part-time tuition varies according to program.
Collegiate Environment: Orientation program. Drama-theater group, choral group, student-run newspaper, radio station. Social organizations: 38 open to all; local sororities. Most popular organizations: Alverno Cru, CHICA, Love Your Melon Crew, Circle K, Gay-Straight Alliance. Major annual events: Convocation, Homecoming, Community Day. Student services: health clinic, personal-psychological counseling. Campus security: 24-hour emergency response devices and patrols, late night transport-escort service, controlled dormitory access, well-lit parking lots and pathways, emergency first-aid and CPR, crisis intervention team and plan in place. 269 college housing spaces available; 199 were occupied in 2018-19. Freshmen guaranteed college housing. Option: women-only housing available. Alverno College Library. Books: 65,917 (physical), 157,042 (digital/electronic); Serial titles: 478 (physical), 52,613 (digital/electronic); Databases: 57. Weekly public service hours: 84. Operations spending for the previous fiscal year: $751,006. 664 computers available on campus for general student use. A campuswide network can be accessed from student residence rooms and from off

campus. Students can access the following: online class registration. Staffed computer lab on campus provides training in use of computers, software, and the Internet.
Community Environment: See Milwaukee Area Technical College.

■ BELLIN COLLEGE
3201 Eaton Rd.
Green Bay, WI 54305
Tel: (920)433-3560; Free: 800-236-8707
Fax: (920)433-7416
E-mail: admissions@bellincollege.edu
Web Site: www.bellincollege.edu
Description: Independent, comprehensive, coed. Administratively affiliated with Belling Health System. Awards bachelor's and master's degrees. Founded 1909. Setting: 25-acre small town campus. Total enrollment: 405. Faculty: 47 (29 full-time, 18 part-time). Student-undergrad faculty ratio is 11:1. 92 applied. Full-time: 233 students, 89% women, 11% men. Part-time: 129 students, 93% women, 7% men. Students come from 6 states and territories, 7% from out-of-state. 0.5% American Indian or Alaska Native, non-Hispanic/Latino; 2% Hispanic/Latino; 1% Black or African American, non-Hispanic/Latino; 1% Asian, non-Hispanic/Latino. 25% 25 or older, 5% transferred in. Retention: 72% of full-time freshmen returned the following year. Academic area with the most degrees conferred: health professions and related sciences. Calendar: semesters. Academic remediation for entering students, services for LD students, advanced placement, honors program, independent study, distance learning, summer session for credit, adult/continuing education programs, internships. Off campus study at University of Wisconsin-Green Bay, St. Norbert College, UW Colleges. Study abroad program.
Entrance Requirements: Options: electronic application, international baccalaureate accepted. Required: essay, high school transcript, minimum 3.25 high school GPA, 3 recommendations, interview, SAT or ACT. Recommended: minimum 3.25 high school GPA. Entrance: moderately difficult. Application deadline: 5/1. Notification: continuous. Transfer credits accepted: Yes. Applicants placed on waiting list: 0. Wait-listed applicants offered admission: 0.
Collegiate Environment: Orientation program. Social organizations: 10 open to all. Most popular organizations: Bellin Student Nurses Association, Institute for Healthcare Improvement, American Assembly for Men in Nursing, Student Senate, Bellin College Love Your Melon Campus Crew. Major annual events: Scholarship Salute, Bellin Banquet, Commencement. Student services: legal services, health clinic, personal-psychological counseling. Campus security: 24-hour emergency response devices and patrols, late night transport-escort service, electronically operated building access after hours. Phil and Betsy Hendrickson Library. Weekly public service hours: 63; students can reserve study rooms. 41 computers available on campus for general student use. A campuswide network can be accessed from off-campus. Staffed computer lab on campus provides training in use of computers, software, and the Internet.

■ BELOIT COLLEGE
700 College St.
Beloit, WI 53511-5596
Tel: (608)363-2000; Free: 800-9-BELOIT
Fax: (608)363-2075

E-mail: virgok@beloit.edu

Web Site: www.beloit.edu

Description: Independent, 4-year, coed. Awards bachelor's degrees. Founded 1846. Setting: 84-acre small town campus with easy access to Chicago, Milwaukee. Endowment: $160.9 million. Research spending for the previous fiscal year: $69,871. Educational spending for the previous fiscal year: $14,894 per student. Total enrollment: 1,275. Faculty: 135 (117 full-time, 18 part-time). Student-undergrad faculty ratio is 11:1. 4,200 applied, 56% were admitted. 15% from top 10% of their high school class, 56% from top quarter, 87% from top half. Full-time: 1,228 students, 54% women, 46% men. Part-time: 47 students, 64% women, 36% men. Students come from 44 states and territories, 44 other countries, 84% from out-of-state. 0.2% American Indian or Alaska Native, non-Hispanic/Latino; 11% Hispanic/Latino; 7% Black or African American, non-Hispanic/Latino; 4% Asian, non-Hispanic/Latino; 0.2% Native Hawaiian or other Pacific Islander, non-Hispanic/Latino; 18% international. 1% 25 or older, 88% live on campus, 2% transferred in. Retention: 78% of full-time freshmen returned the following year. Academic areas with the most degrees conferred: social sciences; physical sciences; English. Core. Calendar: semesters. ESL program, services for LD students, advanced placement, self-designed majors, independent study, double major, summer session for credit, adult/continuing education programs, internships. Off campus study at University of Wisconsin-Madison, American University, Duke University, Associated Colleges of the Midwest. Study abroad program.

Entrance Requirements: Options: electronic application, early decision, early action. Required: essay, high school transcript, 1 recommendation. Recommended: interview. Required for some: SAT or ACT. Application deadlines: 1/15, 11/1 for early decision. Notification: continuous, 12/1 for early decision. Transfer credits accepted: Yes. Applicants placed on waiting list: 69. Wait-listed applicants offered admission: 15. Early decision applicants: 71. Early decision applicants admitted: 19.

Costs Per Year: Comprehensive fee: $58,870 includes full-time tuition ($49,564), mandatory fees ($476), and college room and board ($8830). College room only: $5030. Room and board charges vary according to board plan. Part-time tuition: $1549 per unit.

Collegiate Environment: Orientation program. Drama-theater group, choral group, student-run newspaper, radio station. Social organizations: 60 open to all; national fraternities, national sororities, local fraternities. Most popular organizations: BSFFA - Beloit Science Fiction and Fantasy Association, Ceramics Club, Anthropology Club, Yoga Club, Outdoor Environmental Club. Major annual events: Folk 'n' Blues Festival, Chelonia Dance Performance, Spring Day. Student services: health clinic, personal-psychological counseling, women's center. Campus security: 24-hour emergency response devices and patrols, late night transport-escort service, controlled dormitory access. 1,207 college housing spaces available; 1,187 were occupied in 2018-19. Freshmen guaranteed college housing. On-campus residence required through junior year. Options: coed, women-only housing available. Morse Library and Black Information Center. Books: 207,000 (physical), 210,000 (digital/electronic); Serial titles: 11,700 (physical), 76,000 (digital/electronic); Databases: 151. Weekly public service hours: 109; students can reserve study rooms. 300 computers available on campus for general student use. A campuswide network can be accessed from student residence rooms and from off campus. Students can access the following: online class registration.

Community Environment: Beloit College is located in Beloit, Wisconsin (population 36,000), 90 miles northwest of Chicago, 50 miles south of Madison, and 70 miles southwest of Milwaukee. Students take advantage of the varied resources offered by these three major metropolitan areas, as well as those offered by the city of Beloit itself. Beloit's hospital, clinics, manufacturers, and various civic and service organizations provide numerous internship, job shadowing, enrichment, and community outreach opportunities. Year-round sports and recreation areas are available in southern Wisconsin and northern Illinois. There is direct bus service from O'Hare International Airport, and the same bus continues on to the University of Wisconsin in Madison.

■ **BLACKHAWK TECHNICAL COLLEGE**

6004 S County Rd. G

Janesville, WI 53546-9458

Tel: (608)758-6900

Fax: (608)757-9407

Web Site: www.blackhawk.edu

Description: District-supported, 2-year, coed. Part of Wisconsin Technical College System. Awards certificates, diplomas, transfer associate, and terminal associate degrees. Founded 1968. Setting: 84-acre small town campus. Educational spending for the previous fiscal year: $13,063 per student. Total enrollment: 2,034. Faculty: 290 (89 full-time, 201 part-time). Student-undergrad faculty ratio is 8:1. Full-time: 822 students, 50% women, 50% men. Part-time: 1,212 students, 63% women, 37% men. Students come from 3 states and territories, 1% from out-of-state. 0.6% American Indian or Alaska Native, non-Hispanic/Latino; 10% Hispanic/Latino; 6% Black or African American, non-Hispanic/Latino; 1% Asian, non-Hispanic/Latino. 55% 25 or older. Retention: 54% of full-time freshmen returned the following year. Core. Calendar: semesters. Academic remediation for entering students, ESL program, services for LD students, advanced placement, accelerated degree program, self-designed majors, independent study, distance learning, summer session for credit, part-time degree program, adult/continuing education programs, co-op programs and internships.

Entrance Requirements: Open admission. Option: electronic application. Required: high school transcript. Entrance: noncompetitive. Application deadline: rolling. Notification: continuous. Preference given to district residents. Transfer credits accepted: Yes.

Collegiate Environment: Orientation program. Student-run newspaper. Social organizations: 15 open to all. Most popular organizations: Student Government Association, Public Safety Association, Epicurean Club, Veterans Club, Phi Theta Kappa Honor Society. Major annual events: Fall Carnival, Winter Social, Back Yard Bash. Campus security: student patrols. Blackhawk Technical College Library. Books: 12,369 (physical), 89,551 (digital/electronic); Serial titles: 109 (physical), 13 (digital/electronic); Databases: 68. Weekly public service hours: 57. Operations spending for the previous fiscal year: $227,664. 1,089 computers available on campus for general student use. A campuswide network can be accessed. Students can access the following: online class registration. Staffed computer lab on campus.

■ **BRYANT & STRATTON COLLEGE-BAYSHORE CAMPUS**

500 W Silver Spring Dr.

Bayshore Town Ctr., Ste. K340

Glendale, WI 53217

Tel: (414)961-9600

Web Site: www.bryantstratton.edu

Description: Proprietary, primarily 2-year, coed. Awards certificates, terminal associate, and bachelor's degrees.

■ **BRYANT & STRATTON COLLEGE-MILWAUKEE CAMPUS**

310 W Wisconsin Ave.

Ste. 500 E

Milwaukee, WI 53203

Tel: (414)276-5200

Web Site: www.bryantstratton.edu

Description: Proprietary, primarily 2-year, coed. Part of Bryant and Stratton College, Inc. Awards terminal associate and bachelor's degrees. Founded 1863. Setting: urban campus. Educational spending for the previous fiscal year: $1427 per student. Total enrollment: 828. Faculty: 102 (19 full-time, 83 part-time). Student-undergrad faculty ratio is 13:1. 433 applied, 89% were admitted. Full-time: 460 students, 84% women, 16% men. Part-time: 368 students, 84% women, 16% men. 33% transferred in. Retention: 70% of full-time freshmen returned the following year. Core. Calendar: semesters. Academic remediation for entering students, advanced placement, independent study, distance learning, double major, summer session for credit, part-time degree program, adult/continuing education programs, co-op programs and internships.

Entrance Requirements: Option: electronic application. Required: high school transcript, interview, entrance and placement evaluations, CPAt, ACCUPLACER. Recommended: SAT or ACT. Entrance: minimally difficult. Application deadline: rolling. Notification: continuous.

Collegiate Environment: Orientation program. Student-run newspaper. Most popular organizations: Phi Beta Lambda, Association of Information Technology Professionals, Allied Health Association, Institute of Management Accountants, Student Advisory Board. Major annual events: Portfolio Development Day, Career Fair, All-School Picnic. Campus security: 24-hour emergency response devices and patrols. Bryant and Stratton College Library plus 1 other. Operations spending for the previous fiscal year: $20,915. 130 computers available on campus for general student use. A campuswide network can be accessed from off-campus. Staffed computer lab on campus provides training in use of computers, software, and the Internet.

■ BRYANT & STRATTON COLLEGE-WAUWATOSA CAMPUS

10950 W Potter Rd.
Wauwatosa, WI 53226
Tel: (414)302-7000
Web Site: www.bryantstratton.edu

Description: Proprietary, 4-year, coed. Awards associate and bachelor's degrees. Setting: suburban campus with easy access to Milwaukee. Total enrollment: 1,264. Student-undergrad faculty ratio is 10:1. Students come from 2 states and territories. 48% 25 or older. Retention: 88% of full-time freshmen returned the following year. Calendar: semesters. Academic remediation for entering students, services for LD students, advanced placement, independent study, distance learning, double major, part-time degree program, adult/continuing education programs, co-op programs and internships.

Entrance Requirements: Option: electronic application. Required: high school transcript, interview, entrance and placement evaluation, TABE, CPAt. Recommended: SAT or ACT. Application deadline: rolling. Notification: continuous.

Collegiate Environment: Orientation program. Library and Learning Resource Center plus 2 others. 125 computers available on campus for general student use. A campuswide network can be accessed. Students can access the following: online class registration. Staffed computer lab on campus provides training in use of computers.

■ CARDINAL STRITCH UNIVERSITY

6801 N Yates Rd.
Milwaukee, WI 53217-3985
Tel: (414)410-4000; Free: 800-347-8822
Fax: (414)410-4239
E-mail: admissions@stritch.edu
Web Site: www.stritch.edu

Description: Independent Roman Catholic, university, coed. Awards associate, bachelor's, master's, and doctoral degrees and post-master's certificates. Founded 1937. Setting: 40-acre suburban campus with easy access to Milwaukee. Endowment: $19.4 million. Total enrollment: 2,355. Faculty: 311 (83 full-time, 228 part-time). Student-undergrad faculty ratio is 10:1. 642 applied, 78% were admitted. 21% from top 10% of their high school class, 52% from top quarter, 79% from top half. Full-time: 901 students, 67% women, 33% men. Part-time: 642 students, 69% women, 31% men. Students come from 27 states and territories, 39 other countries, 13% from out-of-state. 0.5% American Indian or Alaska Native, non-Hispanic/Latino; 16% Hispanic/Latino; 16% Black or African American, non-Hispanic/Latino; 2% Asian, non-Hispanic/Latino; 0.1% Native Hawaiian or other Pacific Islander, non-Hispanic/Latino; 11% international. 47% 25 or older, 10% live on campus, 12% transferred in. Retention: 77% of full-time freshmen returned the following year. Academic areas with the most degrees conferred: business/marketing; health professions and related sciences; education. Core. Calendar: semesters. Academic remediation for entering students, services for LD students, advanced placement, accelerated degree program, independent study, distance learning, double major, summer session for credit, part-time degree program, adult/continuing education programs, co-op programs and internships, graduate courses open to undergrads. Off campus study at Online Consortium of Independent Colleges and Universities. Study abroad program.

Entrance Requirements: Options: electronic application, deferred admission, international baccalaureate accepted. Required for some: high school transcript, minimum 2 high school GPA, SAT or ACT, TOEFL for international students. Entrance: moderately difficult. Application deadline: rolling. Notification: continuous. SAT Reasoning Test deadline: 9/1. SAT Subject Test deadline: 9/1. Transfer credits accepted: Yes.

Costs Per Year: Application fee: $0. Comprehensive fee: $38,622 includes full-time tuition ($29,998) and college room and board ($8624). Full-time tuition varies according to degree level, program, and reciprocity agreements. Room and board charges vary according to board plan and housing facility. Part-time tuition: $936 per credit hour. Part-time tuition varies according to course load, degree level, program, and reciprocity agreements.

Collegiate Environment: Orientation program. Drama-theater group, choral group. Social organizations: 29 open to all; national fraternities, local fraternities; 2% of men are members. Most popular organizations: Student Government, Student Programming Board, Hispanic Club, University Ministry, Circle K International. Major annual events: Late Night Breakfast, End of the Year Bash. Student services: health clinic, personal-psychological counseling. Campus security: 24-hour emergency response devices and patrols, controlled dormitory access. Cardinal Stritch University Library. Books:

122,184 (physical), 146,127 (digital/electronic); Serial titles: 66 (physical), 68 (digital/electronic); Databases: 71. Weekly public service hours: 90. Operations spending for the previous fiscal year: $764,467. 458 computers available on campus for general student use. Computer purchase/lease plans available. A campuswide network can be accessed from student residence rooms and from off campus. Students can access the following: online class registration. Staffed computer lab on campus provides training in use of computers, software, and the Internet.

Community Environment: See Milwaukee Area Technical College.

■ CARROLL UNIVERSITY

100 NE Ave.
Waukesha, WI 53186-5593
Tel: (262)547-1211; Free: 800-CARROLL
Fax: (262)524-7139
E-mail: info@carrollu.edu
Web Site: www.carrollu.edu

Description: Independent Presbyterian, comprehensive, coed. Awards bachelor's, master's, and doctoral degrees. Founded 1846. Setting: 136-acre suburban campus with easy access to Milwaukee. Endowment: $57.5 million. Educational spending for the previous fiscal year: $17,074 per student. Total enrollment: 3,451. Faculty: 401 (135 full-time, 266 part-time). Student-undergrad faculty ratio is 16:1. 3,688 applied, 71% were admitted. Full-time: 2,736 students, 65% women, 35% men. Part-time: 245 students, 58% women, 42% men. Students come from 30 states and territories, 38 other countries, 31% from out-of-state. 0.3% American Indian or Alaska Native, non-Hispanic/Latino; 8% Hispanic/Latino; 2% Black or African American, non-Hispanic/Latino; 4% Asian, non-Hispanic/Latino; 0.1% Native Hawaiian or other Pacific Islander, non-Hispanic/Latino; 3% international. 6% 25 or older, 59% live on campus, 3% transferred in. Retention: 79% of full-time freshmen returned the following year. Academic areas with the most degrees conferred: parks and recreation; health professions and related sciences; business/marketing. Core. Calendar: semesters. Academic remediation for entering students, ESL program, services for LD students, advanced placement, self-designed majors, honors program, independent study, distance learning, double major, summer session for credit, part-time degree program, adult/continuing education programs, internships, graduate courses open to undergrads. Study abroad program. ROTC: Army (c), Air Force (c).

Entrance Requirements: Options: electronic application, deferred admission, international baccalaureate accepted. Required: high school transcript, minimum 2 high school GPA, 1 recommendation, SAT or ACT. Recommended: interview, ACT. Required for some: essay. Entrance: moderately difficult. Application deadline: rolling. Notification: 8/20. SAT Reasoning Test deadline: 7/1. SAT Subject Test deadline: 7/1. Transfer credits accepted: Yes.

Costs Per Year: Application fee: $0. One-time mandatory fee: $270. Comprehensive fee: $41,814 includes full-time tuition ($31,162), mandatory fees ($756), and college room and board ($9896). College room only: $5180. Full-time tuition and fees vary according to program. Room and board charges vary according to board plan and housing facility. Part-time tuition: $400 per credit hour. Part-time tuition varies according to course load and program.

Collegiate Environment: Orientation program. Drama-theater group, choral group, student-run newspaper, radio station. Social organizations: 53 open to all; national sororities, local fraternities. Most popular organizations: College Activities Board, Student Senate, Black Student Union, Intervarsity Christian Fellowship, Latin American Student Organization. Major annual events: Homecoming, Parents' Weekend, Spring Fling. Student services: health clinic, personal-psychological counseling. Campus security: 24-hour emergency response devices and patrols, student patrols, late night transport-escort service, controlled dormitory access. Todd Wehr Memorial Library. Operations spending for the previous fiscal year: $1.5 million. 400 computers available on campus for general student use. Computer purchase/lease plans available. A campuswide network can be accessed from student residence rooms and from off campus. Students can access the following: online class registration. Staffed computer lab on campus provides training in use of computers, software, and the Internet.

■ CARTHAGE COLLEGE

2001 Alford Park Dr.
Kenosha, WI 53140
Tel: (262)551-8500; Free: 800-351-4058
Fax: (262)551-5762

E-mail: admissions@carthage.edu

Web Site: www.carthage.edu

Description: Independent, comprehensive, coed, affiliated with Evangelical Lutheran Church in America. Awards bachelor's and master's degrees. Founded 1847. Setting: 72-acre suburban campus with easy access to Chicago, Milwaukee. Total enrollment: 2,885. Faculty: 338 (178 full-time, 160 part-time). Student-undergrad faculty ratio is 12:1. 5,260 applied, 99.9% were admitted. 21% from top 10% of their high school class, 47% from top quarter, 81% from top half. Full-time: 2,649 students, 56% women, 44% men. Part-time: 127 students, 60% women, 40% men. Students come from 37 states and territories, 17 other countries, 64% from out-of-state. 0.5% American Indian or Alaska Native, non-Hispanic/Latino; 14% Hispanic/ Latino; 6% Black or African American, non-Hispanic/Latino; 2% Asian, non-Hispanic/Latino; 0.2% Native Hawaiian or other Pacific Islander, non-Hispanic/Latino; 1% international. 4% 25 or older, 66% live on campus, 3% transferred in. Retention: 77% of full-time freshmen returned the following year. Academic areas with the most degrees conferred: business/marketing; visual and performing arts; biological/life sciences; communication/ journalism; psychology. Core. Calendar: 4-1-4. Services for LD students, advanced placement, accelerated degree program, self-designed majors, honors program, double major, summer session for credit, part-time degree program, adult/continuing education programs, internships. Off campus study at University of Wisconsin-Parkside, Marquette University. Study abroad program. ROTC: Army (c), Air Force (c).

Entrance Requirements: Options: electronic application, deferred admission, international baccalaureate accepted. Required: high school transcript. Recommended: essay, interview, SAT and SAT Subject Tests or ACT. Required for some: minimum 2.25 high school GPA, 2 recommendations, statement of good standing from prior institution(s). Entrance: moderately difficult. Application deadline: rolling. Notification: continuous. Transfer credits accepted: Yes.

Costs Per Year: Application fee: $35. Comprehensive fee: $101,800 includes full-time tuition ($45,100), mandatory fees ($45,100), and college room and board ($11,600). Part-time tuition: $595 per credit. Part-time mandatory fees: $595 per credit.

Collegiate Environment: Orientation program. Drama-theater group, choral group, student-run newspaper, radio station. Social organizations: 115 open to all; national fraternities, national sororities, local fraternities, local sororities. Most popular organizations: Tau Sigma Chi, Alpha Phi Omega, Intervarsity Christian Fellowship, Alpha Lambda Delta, Beta Beta Beta. Major annual events: Kick Off Carnival, Monthly Bingo, Homecoming. Student services: health clinic, personal-psychological counseling. Campus security: 24-hour emergency response devices and patrols, student patrols, late night transport-escort service, controlled dormitory access. 1,740 college housing spaces available; 1,684 were occupied in 2018-19. Freshmen guaranteed college housing. On-campus residence required through junior year. Options: coed, men-only, women-only housing available. Hedberg Library. Books: 103,144 (physical), 328,850 (digital/electronic); Serial titles: 4,243 (physical), 555,934 (digital/electronic); Databases: 334. Students can reserve study rooms. 130 computers available on campus for general student use. Computer purchase/lease plans available. A campuswide network can be accessed from student residence rooms and from off campus. Students can access the following: online class registration. Staffed computer lab on campus provides training in use of computers, software, and the Internet.

Community Environment: See Gateway Technical College.

■ **CHIPPEWA VALLEY TECHNICAL COLLEGE**

620 W Clairemont Ave.

Eau Claire, WI 54701-6162

Tel: (715)833-6200; Free: 800-547-2882

Fax: (715)833-6470

E-mail: infocenter@cvtc.edu

Web Site: www.cvtc.edu

Description: District-supported, 2-year, coed. Part of Wisconsin Technical College System. Awards certificates, diplomas, transfer associate, and terminal associate degrees. Founded 1912. Setting: 255-acre suburban campus. Total enrollment: 7,134. Faculty: 411 (221 full-time, 190 part-time). Student-undergrad faculty ratio is 13:1. Full-time: 2,129 students, 45% women, 55% men. Part-time: 5,005 students, 55% women, 45% men. 0.7% American Indian or Alaska Native, non-Hispanic/Latino; 2% Hispanic/Latino; 1% Black or African American, non-Hispanic/Latino; 4% Asian, non-Hispanic/ Latino; 0.2% Native Hawaiian or other Pacific Islander, non-Hispanic/Latino. 5% transferred in. Retention: 60% of full-time freshmen returned the follow-

ing year. Calendar: semesters. Academic remediation for entering students, ESL program, services for LD students, advanced placement, accelerated degree program, self-designed majors, honors program, independent study, distance learning, double major, summer session for credit, part-time degree program, adult/continuing education programs, co-op programs and internships.

Entrance Requirements: Open admission. Options: electronic application, early admission, deferred admission. Entrance: noncompetitive. Application deadline: rolling. Notification: continuous. Transfer credits accepted: Yes.

Costs Per Year: Application fee: $30. State resident tuition: $4026 full-time, $134.20 per credit part-time. Nonresident tuition: $6039 full-time, $201.30 per credit part-time. Mandatory fees: $338 full-time. Full-time tuition and fees vary according to course load and reciprocity agreements. Part-time tuition varies according to course load and reciprocity agreements.

Collegiate Environment: Orientation program. Social organizations: 42 open to all; Phi Theta Kappa. Most popular organizations: Chippewa Valley Nurses, Radiography (IMAGERS), Criminal Justice, Physical Therapy, Structural Drafting. Major annual events: Club Fair, Career Fair, Family Events. Student services: health clinic, personal-psychological counseling. Campus security: 24-hour emergency response devices, late night transport-escort service, security cameras. The Learning Center. Books: 10,758 (physical), 158,463 (digital/electronic); Serial titles: 110 (physical), 3,589 (digital/electronic); Databases: 116. Weekly public service hours: 66; students can reserve study rooms. 1,534 computers available on campus for general student use. A campuswide network can be accessed from off-campus. Students can access the following: online class registration. Staffed computer lab on campus provides training in use of computers, software, and the Internet.

Community Environment: See University of Wisconsin Eau Claire.

■ **COLLEGE OF MENOMINEE NATION**

PO Box 1179

Keshena, WI 54135

Tel: (715)799-5600; Free: 800-567-2344

Fax: (715)799-1308

Web Site: www.menominee.edu

Description: Independent, 2-year, coed. Awards certificates, transfer associate, and terminal associate degrees. Founded 1993. Total enrollment: 634. Student-undergrad faculty ratio is 16:1. 58% 25 or older. Calendar: semesters.

Entrance Requirements: Open admission. Required: high school transcript, ACCUPLACER. Entrance: noncompetitive. Application deadline: 8/14.

■ **COLUMBIA COLLEGE OF NURSING**

4425 N Port Washington Rd.

Glendale, WI 53212

Tel: (414)326-2330

Web Site: www.ccon.edu

Description: Independent, upper-level, coed. Awards bachelor's and master's degrees (nursing degree is awarded in conjunction with Mount Mary College). Founded 1901. Setting: 1-acre urban campus with easy access to Milwaukee. Endowment: $700,000. Research spending for the previous fiscal year: $69,321. Educational spending for the previous fiscal year: $6858 per student. Total enrollment: 169. Faculty: 21 (18 full-time, 3 part-time). Student-undergrad faculty ratio is 9:1. Full-time: 154 students, 95% women, 5% men. Part-time: 15 students, 100% women. Students come from 3 states and territories, 4% from out-of-state. 0.6% American Indian or Alaska Native, non-Hispanic/Latino; 4% Hispanic/Latino; 8% Black or African American, non-Hispanic/Latino; 2% Asian, non-Hispanic/Latino. 44% 25 or older, 14% transferred in. Retention: 88% of full-time entering class returned the following year. Academic area with the most degrees conferred: health professions and related sciences. Core. Calendar: semesters. Academic remediation for entering students, advanced placement, honors program, independent study, double major, summer session for credit, part-time degree program, co-op programs. Off campus study at Mount Mary College, Milwaukee, WI. Study abroad program.

Entrance Requirements: Transfer credits accepted: Yes.

Costs Per Year: Application fee: $25. Tuition: $28,600 full-time, $1160 per credit part-time. Mandatory fees: $1150 full-time, $50 per credit part-time. Part-time tuition and fees vary according to program.

Collegiate Environment: Orientation program. Social organizations: 2 open to all; 1% of eligible men and 13% of eligible women are members. Most popular organizations: Student Senate, Student Nurses Association. Major annual events: Holiday Party, Spring Banquet, Student Luncheon. Student services: health clinic, personal-psychological counseling. Campus security: 24-hour emergency response devices and patrols, student patrols, late night transport-escort service, security card entrances to academic areas. Columbia St. Mary's Library. Operations spending for the previous fiscal year: $72,129. 46 computers available on campus for general student use. A campuswide network can be accessed from student residence rooms and from off campus. Students can access the following: online class registration. Staffed computer lab on campus provides training in use of computers, software, and the Internet.

■ CONCORDIA UNIVERSITY WISCONSIN

12800 N Lake Shore Dr.
Mequon, WI 53097-2402
Tel: (262)243-5700; Free: 888-628-9472
Fax: (262)243-4351
E-mail: admission@cuw.edu
Web Site: www.cuw.edu

Description: Independent, comprehensive, coed, affiliated with Lutheran Church-Missouri Synod. Part of Concordia University System. Awards associate, bachelor's, master's, and doctoral degrees and post-master's certificates. Founded 1881. Setting: 192-acre suburban campus with easy access to Milwaukee. Total enrollment: 7,288. Faculty: 508 (208 full-time, 300 part-time). Student-undergrad faculty ratio is 11:1. 3,612 applied, 63% were admitted. 19% from top 10% of their high school class, 51% from top quarter, 88% from top half. Full-time: 2,616 students, 63% women, 37% men. Part-time: 1,093 students, 74% women, 26% men. 25% from out-of-state. 0.9% American Indian or Alaska Native, non-Hispanic/Latino; 1% Hispanic/Latino; 12% Black or African American, non-Hispanic/Latino; 2% Asian, non-Hispanic/Latino; 0.1% Native Hawaiian or other Pacific Islander, non-Hispanic/Latino; 3% international. 29% 25 or older, 46% live on campus, 2% transferred in. Retention: 82% of full-time freshmen returned the following year. Academic areas with the most degrees conferred: health professions and related sciences; business/marketing; biological/life sciences. Core. Calendar: 4-1-4. Academic remediation for entering students, ESL program, services for LD students, advanced placement, accelerated degree program, self-designed majors, independent study, distance learning, double major, summer session for credit, part-time degree program, adult/continuing education programs, internships. Off campus study at Milwaukee Area Technical College, Milwaukee Institute of Art and Design, Cardinal Stritch University, Mount Mary College. Study abroad program.

Entrance Requirements: Option: international baccalaureate accepted. Required: high school transcript, minimum 2 high school GPA, SAT or ACT. Recommended: interview. Required for some: essay, minimum 3 high school GPA, 3 recommendations. Entrance: moderately difficult. Notification: continuous.

Costs Per Year: Comprehensive fee: $40,300 includes full-time tuition ($29,180), mandatory fees ($270), and college room and board ($10,850). Full-time tuition and fees vary according to program. Room and board charges vary according to board plan.

Collegiate Environment: Orientation program. Drama-theater group, choral group, student-run newspaper, radio station. Student services: health clinic, personal-psychological counseling. Campus security: 24-hour patrols, student patrols, late night transport-escort service, controlled dormitory access. Rinker Memorial Library.

Community Environment: See Milwaukee Area Technical College.

■ EDGEWOOD COLLEGE

1000 Edgewood College Dr.
Madison, WI 53711-1997
Tel: (608)663-4861; Free: 800-444-4861
Fax: (608)663-3291
E-mail: admissions@edgewood.edu
Web Site: www.edgewood.edu

Description: Independent Roman Catholic, comprehensive, coed. Awards bachelor's, master's, and doctoral degrees. Founded 1927. Setting: 55-acre urban campus. Endowment: $37.8 million. Educational spending for the previous fiscal year: $9360 per student. Total enrollment: 2,221. Faculty: 284 (152 full-time, 132 part-time). Student-undergrad faculty ratio is 9:1. 1,447 applied, 71% were admitted. 17% from top 10% of their high school class, 46% from top quarter, 81% from top half. 3 valedictorians. Full-time: 1,361 students, 73% women, 27% men. Part-time: 203 students, 70% women, 30% men. Students come from 19 states and territories, 20 other countries, 8% from out-of-state. 0.3% American Indian or Alaska Native, non-Hispanic/Latino; 6% Hispanic/Latino; 3% Black or African American, non-Hispanic/

Latino; 3% Asian, non-Hispanic/Latino; 0.2% Native Hawaiian or other Pacific Islander, non-Hispanic/Latino; 3% international. 15% 25 or older, 35% live on campus, 6% transferred in. Retention: 78% of full-time freshmen returned the following year. Academic areas with the most degrees conferred: health professions and related sciences; business/marketing; education. Core. Calendar: semesters. Academic remediation for entering students, services for LD students, advanced placement, accelerated degree program, self-designed majors, honors program, independent study, distance learning, double major, summer session for credit, part-time degree program, adult/continuing education programs, co-op programs and internships, graduate courses open to undergrads. Off campus study at University of Wisconsin-Madison, Online Consortium of Independent Colleges and Universities (OCICU), and Madison Area Technical College. Study abroad program. ROTC: Army (c), Naval (c), Air Force (c).

Entrance Requirements: Options: electronic application, deferred admission, international baccalaureate accepted. Required: high school transcript, minimum 2.5 high school GPA, two of the following: cumulative high school GPA of 2.5 on a 4.0 scale, a rank in the top 50% of their high school graduating class and/or a composite score of 18 on the ACT or an equivalent SAT score, SAT or ACT. Required for some: essay, 2 recommendations, interview. Entrance: moderately difficult. Application deadline: 8/1. Notification: continuous until 8/15. SAT Reasoning Test deadline: 8/1. Transfer credits accepted: Yes.

Costs Per Year: Application fee: $30. Comprehensive fee: $40,520 includes full-time tuition ($29,500) and college room and board ($11,020). Full-time tuition varies according to degree level. Room and board charges vary according to housing facility. Part-time tuition: $927 per credit. Part-time tuition varies according to course load and degree level.

Collegiate Environment: Orientation program. Drama-theater group, choral group, student-run newspaper. Social organizations: 48 open to all; 1% of eligible men and 1% of eligible women are members. Most popular organizations: Circle K, Student Education Association, Student Government Association, Rotaract, Ambassadors. Major annual events: Winterfrost, Fall Fest, Spring Fest. Student services: health clinic, personal-psychological counseling. Campus security: 24-hour emergency response devices and patrols, student patrols, late night transport-escort service, controlled dormitory access, lighted pathways/sidewalks, Eagle Alert System, Public Address System, Safe Ride Shuttle, extensive video surveillance system. Oscar Rennebohm Library. Books: 82,008 (physical), 140,319 (digital/electronic); Serial titles: 219 (physical), 38,116 (digital/electronic); Databases: 90. Weekly public service hours: 98; students can reserve study rooms. Operations spending for the previous fiscal year: $927,574. 180 computers available on campus for general student use. Computer purchase/lease plans available. A campuswide network can be accessed from student residence rooms and from off campus. Students can access the following: online class registration.

Community Environment: See University of Wisconsin - Madison.

■ FOX VALLEY TECHNICAL COLLEGE

1825 N Bluemound
Appleton, WI 54912-2277
Tel: (920)735-5600; Free: 800-735-3882
Fax: (920)735-2582
Web Site: www.fvtc.edu

Description: State and locally supported, 2-year, coed. Part of Wisconsin Technical College System. Awards certificates, diplomas, and terminal associate degrees. Founded 1967. Setting: 100-acre suburban campus. Endowment: $3.8 million. Educational spending for the previous fiscal year: $12,660 per student. Total enrollment: 11,658. Faculty: 813 (315 full-time, 498 part-time). Student-undergrad faculty ratio is 11:1. 2,358 applied, 69% were admitted. Full-time: 2,186 students, 40% women, 60% men. Part-time: 9,472 students, 45% women, 55% men. Students come from 13 states and territories, 5 other countries, 1% from out-of-state. 0.9% American Indian or Alaska Native, non-Hispanic/Latino; 4% Hispanic/Latino; 2% Black or African American, non-Hispanic/Latino; 4% Asian, non-Hispanic/Latino; 0.2% Native Hawaiian or other Pacific Islander, non-Hispanic/Latino; 0.6% international. 44% 25 or older. Core. Calendar: semesters. Academic remediation for entering students, ESL program, services for LD students, advanced placement, accelerated degree program, self-designed majors, independent study, distance learning, double major, summer session for credit, part-time degree program, co-op programs and internships. Off campus study. Study abroad program.

Entrance Requirements: Open admission. Option: electronic application.

Required for some: high school transcript, interview, ACT or ACCUPLACER, TEAS, Bennett Mechanical Comprehension Test. Application deadline: rolling. Transfer credits accepted: Yes.

Costs Per Year: Application fee: $30. State resident tuition: $4026 full-time, $134.20 per credit part-time. Nonresident tuition: $6039 full-time, $201.30 per credit part-time. Mandatory fees: $539 full-time, $17.95 per credit part-time.

Collegiate Environment: Orientation program. Student-run newspaper. Social organizations: 45 open to all. Most popular organizations: Student Government Association, Phi Theta Kappa, Culinary Arts Club, Machine Tool Club, Post Secondary Agribusiness Club. Major annual events: Lecture Series, Speaker Series, Family Events. Student services: health clinic, personal-psychological counseling. Campus security: 24-hour emergency response devices, late night transport-escort service, trained security personnel patrol during hours of operation. Student Success Center Library. Books: 9,016 (physical), 354,485 (digital/electronic); Serial titles: 35 (physical), 31,678 (digital/electronic); Databases: 111. Weekly public service hours: 65; students can reserve study rooms. Operations spending for the previous fiscal year: $426,043. 250 computers available on campus for general student use. A campuswide network can be accessed from off-campus. Students can access the following: online class registration, personal Web pages. Staffed computer lab on campus provides training in use of computers, software, and the Internet.

■ **GATEWAY TECHNICAL COLLEGE**
3520 30th Ave.
Kenosha, WI 53144-1690
Tel: (262)564-2200
Fax: (262)564-2201
E-mail: admissions@gtc.edu
Web Site: www.gtc.edu
Description: State and locally supported, 2-year, coed. Part of Wisconsin Technical College System. Awards certificates, diplomas, and terminal associate degrees. Founded 1911. Setting: 10-acre urban campus with easy access to Chicago, Milwaukee. Endowment: $5.7 million. Educational spending for the previous fiscal year: $10,553 per student. Total enrollment: 8,722. Faculty: 699 (242 full-time, 457 part-time). Student-undergrad faculty ratio is 10:1. 2,804 applied, 66% were admitted. Full-time: 1,379 students, 47% women, 53% men. Part-time: 7,343 students, 58% women, 42% men. Students come from 5 states and territories, 2% from out-of-state. 0.5% American Indian or Alaska Native, non-Hispanic/Latino; 15% Hispanic/Latino; 10% Black or African American, non-Hispanic/Latino; 1% Asian, non-Hispanic/Latino; 0.1% Native Hawaiian or other Pacific Islander, non-Hispanic/Latino. 48% 25 or older, 10% transferred in. Retention: 57% of full-time freshmen returned the following year. Core. Calendar: semesters. Academic remediation for entering students, ESL program, services for LD students, advanced placement, self-designed majors, independent study, distance learning, double major, summer session for credit, part-time degree program, co-op programs and internships. Off campus study at University of Wisconsin Parkside.
Entrance Requirements: Open admission. Options: electronic application, early admission, deferred admission. Required: high school transcript. Required for some: interview. Entrance: noncompetitive. Application deadline: rolling. Notification: continuous. Transfer credits accepted: Yes.
Costs Per Year: Application fee: $30. State resident tuition: $4242 full-time, $132.20 per credit part-time. Nonresident tuition: $5806 full-time, $198.30 per credit part-time. Mandatory fees: $480 full-time. Full-time tuition and fees vary according to course level, course load, program, and reciprocity agreements. Part-time tuition varies according to course level, course load, program, and reciprocity agreements.
Collegiate Environment: Orientation program. Student-run newspaper. Most popular organizations: International Club, United Student Government, Outdoor Adventure Club, Team EXCEED, Collegiate DECA. Major annual events: Gateway Days (fall and spring semesters), Summer Fun Fest, Hispanic Heritage Celebration. Student services: personal-psychological counseling. Campus security: 24-hour emergency response devices, late night transport-escort service, patrols by trained security when open, locked/alarmed when closed. Library/Learning Resources Center plus 2 others. Books: 23,575 (physical), 4,369 (digital/electronic); Serial titles: 131 (physical); Databases: 41. Weekly public service hours: 59; students can reserve study rooms. Operations spending for the previous fiscal year: $1.2 million. 250 computers available on campus for general student use. A campuswide network can be accessed from off-campus. Students can access the following: online class registration. Staffed computer lab on campus provides training in use of computers, software, and the Internet.

Community Environment: Located on the shore of Lake Michigan, Kenosha (population 95,240) has an excellent harbor with 83% of its shoreline providing recreation. It is surrounded by a prosperous agricultural area and is one of the chief industrial centers of the state. Both Chicago and Milwaukee are an hour away. Points of interest are the Hall of Fame, Art Museum, County Historical Society, and Petrifying Springs Park.

■ **HERZING UNIVERSITY (BROOKFIELD)**
555 S Executive Dr.
Brookfield, WI 53005
Tel: (262)649-1710; Free: 800-596-0724
Fax: (262)797-9090
Web Site: www.herzing.edu/brookfield
Description: Independent, 4-year, coed. Awards associate and bachelor's degrees.

■ **HERZING UNIVERSITY (KENOSHA)**
4006 Washington Rd.
Kenosha, WI 53144
Tel: (262)671-0675; Free: 800-596-0724
Fax: (262)653-1434
Web Site: www.herzing.edu/kenosha
Description: Independent, 4-year, coed. Awards associate and bachelor's degrees.

■ **HERZING UNIVERSITY (MADISON)**
5218 E Ter. Dr.
Madison, WI 53718
Tel: (608)249-6611; Free: 800-596-0724
Fax: (608)249-8593
Web Site: www.herzing.edu/madison
Description: Independent, comprehensive, coed. Awards associate, bachelor's, and master's degrees. Founded 1948. Setting: suburban campus with easy access to Madison, Milwaukee. Calendar: semesters. Summer session for credit.
Entrance Requirements: Transfer credits accepted: Yes.

■ **HERZING UNIVERSITY ONLINE**
W140N8917 Lilly Rd.
Menomonee Falls, WI 53051
Free: 866-508-0748
Web Site: www.herzingonline.edu
Description: Independent, comprehensive, coed. Awards bachelor's and master's degrees.

■ **LAC COURTE OREILLES OJIBWA COMMUNITY COLLEGE**
13466 W Trepania Rd.
Hayward, WI 54843-2181
Tel: (715)634-4790; Free: 888-526-6221
Web Site: www.lco.edu
Description: Federally supported, 2-year, coed. Awards certificates, transfer associate, and terminal associate degrees. Founded 1982. Setting: 2-acre rural campus. Endowment: $2.3 million. Total enrollment: 561. Faculty: 70 (15 full-time, 55 part-time). Student-undergrad faculty ratio is 15:1. 135 applied, 100% were admitted. Full-time: 341 students, 65% women, 35% men. Part-time: 220 students, 71% women, 29% men. 63% 25 or older, 6% transferred in. Core. Calendar: semesters. Academic remediation for entering students, services for LD students, honors program, independent study, distance learning, double major, part-time degree program, external degree program, adult/continuing education programs, internships.
Entrance Requirements: Open admission. Option: early admission. Required: high school transcript, ACT Compass. Entrance: noncompetitive. Application deadline: rolling. Transfer credits accepted: Yes.
Collegiate Environment: Orientation program. Drama-theater group. Social organizations: 4 open to all. Most popular organizations: Student Association, AISES, Drama Club, Student Ambassadors. Major annual events: Welcome Feast, Thanksgiving Feast, Graduation. Campus security: 24-hour emergency response devices. Lac Courte Oreilles Ojibwa Community College Library. 63 computers available on campus for general student use. A campuswide network can be accessed. Staffed computer lab on campus (open 24 hours a day) provides training in use of computers, software, and the Internet.

■ LAKELAND UNIVERSITY

W3718 S Dr.
Plymouth, WI 53073
Tel: (920)565-1000; Free: 800-569-2166
Fax: (920)565-1206
E-mail: admissions@lakeland.edu
Web Site: www.lakeland.edu
Description: Independent, comprehensive, coed, affiliated with United Church of Christ. Awards bachelor's and master's degrees. Founded 1862. Setting: 240-acre rural campus with easy access to Milwaukee. Endowment: $12.1 million. Educational spending for the previous fiscal year: $6767 per student. Total enrollment: 3,749. Faculty: 71 (57 full-time, 14 part-time). Student-undergrad faculty ratio is 15:1. 687 applied, 77% were admitted. 15% from top 10% of their high school class, 30% from top quarter, 70% from top half. 5 valedictorians. Full-time: 995 students, 48% women, 52% men. Part-time: 1,969 students, 61% women, 39% men. Students come from 30 states and territories, 16 other countries, 17% from out-of-state. 1% American Indian or Alaska Native, non-Hispanic/Latino; 5% Hispanic/Latino; 6% Black or African American, non-Hispanic/Latino; 2% Asian, non-Hispanic/Latino; 0.1% Native Hawaiian or other Pacific Islander, non-Hispanic/Latino; 3% international. 15% 25 or older, 67% live on campus, 6% transferred in. Retention: 81% of full-time freshmen returned the following year. Academic areas with the most degrees conferred: business/marketing; computer and information sciences; social sciences. Core. Calendar: 4-4-1. Academic remediation for entering students, ESL program, services for LD students, advanced placement, honors program, independent study, distance learning, double major, summer session for credit, part-time degree program, adult/continuing education programs, internships, graduate courses open to undergrads. Off campus study. Study abroad program.
Entrance Requirements: Options: electronic application, deferred admission, international baccalaureate accepted. Required: essay, high school transcript, minimum 2 high school GPA, SAT or ACT. Required for some: interview. Entrance: minimally difficult. Application deadline: rolling. Notification: continuous until 9/1. SAT Reasoning Test deadline: 8/15.
Collegiate Environment: Orientation program. Drama-theater group, choral group, student-run newspaper. Social organizations: 40 open to all; local fraternities, local sororities; 20% of eligible men and 15% of eligible women are members. Most popular organizations: Lakeland College Campus Activities Board, Student Association, Black Student Union, Mortar Board, Global Students Association. Major annual events: Homecoming, Family Weekend, Spring Fling. Student services: health clinic, personal-psychological counseling. Campus security: 24-hour emergency response devices, student patrols, late night transport-escort service, controlled dormitory access. Esch Memorial Library. Operations spending for the previous fiscal year: $287,841. 157 computers available on campus for general student use. Computer purchase/lease plans available. A campuswide network can be accessed from student residence rooms and from off campus. Students can access the following: online class registration. Staffed computer lab on campus provides training in use of computers and software.
Community Environment: The college is located 12 miles northwest of Sheboygan, Wisconsin, 60 miles north of Milwaukee and 60 miles south of Green Bay. Sheboygan has a population of 48,800 and offers students off-campus opportunities for work and recreation. Sheboygan's county airport, the bus depot, and Interstate 43 offer easy access to Lakeland.

■ LAKESHORE TECHNICAL COLLEGE

1290 N Ave.
Cleveland, WI 53015-1414
Tel: (920)693-1000; Free: 888-GO TO LTC
Fax: (920)693-1363
Web Site: www.gotoltc.edu
Description: State and locally supported, 2-year, coed. Part of Wisconsin Technical College System. Awards certificates, diplomas, transfer associate, and terminal associate degrees. Founded 1967. Setting: 160-acre rural campus with easy access to Milwaukee. Research spending for the previous fiscal year: $229,270. Educational spending for the previous fiscal year: $12,451 per student. Faculty: 229 (99 full-time, 130 part-time). Student-undergrad faculty ratio is 14:1. 1,982 applied, 51% were admitted. Students come from 5 states and territories, 1% from out-of-state. 54% 25 or older. Core. Calendar: semesters. Academic remediation for entering students, ESL program, services for LD students, advanced placement, accelerated degree program, self-designed majors, independent study, distance learning, double major, summer session for credit, part-time degree program, external degree program, adult/continuing education programs, co-op programs and internships.

Entrance Requirements: Open admission. Options: electronic application, early admission, deferred admission. Recommended: SAT or ACT, ACCUPLACER/ACT ASSET. Required for some: high school transcript, interview. Entrance: noncompetitive. Application deadline: rolling. Notification: continuous.
Collegiate Environment: Orientation program. Social organizations: 14 open to all. Most popular organizations: Student Government, Business Professionals of America, Police Science Club, Lakeshore Student Nurse Association, Dairy Herd Club. Major annual events: Hypnotist, Fun Flicks, Virtual Reality. Student services: health clinic, personal-psychological counseling. Campus security: 24-hour patrols, student patrols, late night transport-escort service. Operations spending for the previous fiscal year: $252,795. 900 computers available on campus for general student use. A campuswide network can be accessed. Students can access the following: online class registration. Staffed computer lab on campus provides training in use of computers, software, and the Internet.
Community Environment: See Lakeland College.

■ LAWRENCE UNIVERSITY

711 E Boldt Way
Appleton, WI 54911
Tel: (920)832-7000; Free: 800-227-0982
Fax: (920)832-6606
E-mail: marybeth.petrie@lawrence.edu
Web Site: www.lawrence.edu
Description: Independent, 4-year, coed. Awards bachelor's degrees. Founded 1847. Setting: 88-acre small town campus. Endowment: $339.8 million. Research spending for the previous fiscal year: $602,913. Educational spending for the previous fiscal year: $18,146 per student. Total enrollment: 1,472. Faculty: 204 (173 full-time, 31 part-time). Student-undergrad faculty ratio is 8:1. 3,502 applied, 62% were admitted. 35% from top 10% of their high school class, 69% from top quarter, 91% from top half. Full-time: 1,420 students, 54% women, 46% men. Part-time: 52 students, 52% women, 48% men. Students come from 47 states and territories, 37 other countries, 73% from out-of-state. 0.3% American Indian or Alaska Native, non-Hispanic/Latino; 10% Hispanic/Latino; 5% Black or African American, non-Hispanic/Latino; 5% Asian, non-Hispanic/Latino; 0.1% Native Hawaiian or other Pacific Islander, non-Hispanic/Latino; 13% international. 94% live on campus, 1% transferred in. Retention: 85% of full-time freshmen returned the following year. Academic areas with the most degrees conferred: visual and performing arts; social sciences; biological/life sciences. Core. Calendar: trimesters. Services for LD students, advanced placement, self-designed majors, independent study, double major, part-time degree program, internships. Off campus study at Associated Colleges of the Midwest, Great Lakes Colleges Association, American University, Woods Hole Oceanographic Institute, Coe College Wilderness Field Station. Study abroad program.
Entrance Requirements: Options: electronic application, early decision, early action, deferred admission, international baccalaureate accepted. Required: essay, high school transcript, 1 recommendation. Recommended: minimum 3 high school GPA, interview. Required for some: audition for music majors, English Language Proficiency Exam (SAT/TOEFL/IELTS/ACT). Entrance: very difficult. Application deadlines: 1/15, 10/31 for early decision plan 1, 11/1 for early decision plan 2, 12/1 for early action. Notification: continuous until 4/1, 12/1 for early decision plan 1, 12/15 for early decision plan 2, 1/25 for early action. Transfer credits accepted: Yes. Applicants placed on waiting list: 87. Wait-listed applicants offered admission: 3. Early decision applicants: 24. Early decision applicants admitted: 20. Early action applicants: 1,241. Early action applicants admitted: 1,060.
Costs Per Year: Application fee: $0. Comprehensive fee: $59,841 includes full-time tuition ($48,822), mandatory fees ($300), and college room and board ($10,719). College room only: $5448.
Collegiate Environment: Orientation program. Drama-theater group, choral group, student-run newspaper, radio station. Social organizations: 130 open to all; national fraternities, national sororities; 10% of eligible men and 14% of eligible women are members. Most popular organizations: Gaming, Dance, Lawrence International, Outdoor Recreation Club, Sustainable Lawrence University Gardens (SLUG). Major annual events: Activities Fair, Winter Carnival, LU-Aroo. Student services: health clinic, personal-psychological counseling. Campus security: 24-hour emergency response devices and patrols, student patrols, late night transport-escort service, controlled dormitory access, evening patrols by trained security personnel. 1,476 college housing spaces available; 1,302 were occupied in 2018-19. Freshmen guaranteed college housing. On-campus residence required

through senior year. Options: coed, men-only, women-only housing available. Seeley G. Mudd Library. Books: 553,969 (physical), 220,704 (digital/electronic); Serial titles: 544 (physical), 68,015 (digital/electronic); Databases: 160. Weekly public service hours: 110; students can reserve study rooms. Operations spending for the previous fiscal year: $199,369. 250 computers available on campus for general student use. Computer purchase/lease plans available. A campuswide network can be accessed from student residence rooms and from off campus. Students can access the following: online class registration, online transcripts, financial aid, financial account information. Staffed computer lab on campus provides training in use of computers, software, and the Internet.

Community Environment: Appleton is a thriving and dynamic small city (pop. 70,217), located in the papermaking center of the country and rated among the best communities in the United States for quality of life. The city is accessible by car, bus, and plane.

■ MADISON AREA TECHNICAL COLLEGE
1701 Wright St.
Madison, WI 53704
Tel: (608)246-6100; Free: 800-322-6282
Fax: (608)246-6880
E-mail: enrollmentservices@madisoncollege.edu
Web Site: madisoncollege.edu

Description: District-supported, 2-year, coed. Part of Wisconsin Technical College System. Awards certificates, diplomas, transfer associate, and terminal associate degrees. Founded 1911. Setting: 150-acre urban campus. Research spending for the previous fiscal year: $195,238. Total enrollment: 13,479. Faculty: 1,476 (471 full-time, 1,006 part-time). Student-undergrad faculty ratio is 13:1. Full-time: 5,037 students, 55% women, 45% men. Part-time: 11,500 students, 61% women, 39% men. Students come from 10 states and territories, 5 other countries, 3% from out-of-state. 0.5% American Indian or Alaska Native, non-Hispanic/Latino; 9% Hispanic/Latino; 6% Black or African American, non-Hispanic/Latino; 4% Asian, non-Hispanic/Latino; 0.1% Native Hawaiian or other Pacific Islander, non-Hispanic/Latino; 1% international. 50% 25 or older, 5% transferred in. Core. Calendar: semesters. Academic remediation for entering students, ESL program, services for LD students, accelerated degree program, distance learning, summer session for credit, part-time degree program, adult/continuing education programs, co-op programs and internships. Off campus study at University of Wisconsin-Baraboo/Sauk County.

Entrance Requirements: Open admission except for data processing, technology, health occupations, quota programs. Options: electronic application, early admission. Required for some: high school transcript. Entrance: noncompetitive. Application deadline: 7/1. Notification: continuous. Preference given to state residents. Transfer credits accepted: Yes.

Costs Per Year: Application fee: $25. State resident tuition: $4026 full-time, $134.20 per credit hour part-time. Nonresident tuition: $6039 full-time, $201.30 per credit hour part-time. Mandatory fees: $375 full-time, $12.50 per credit hour part-time. Full-time tuition and fees vary according to course load. Part-time tuition and fees vary according to course load.

Collegiate Environment: Drama-theater group, choral group, student-run newspaper. Social organizations: 45 open to all. Most popular organizations: Marketing Club, Minority Networking Groups, Data Processing Management Association, Student Nurses Association, Business Professionals of America. Major annual events: spring picnic, Celebrate Diversity Series, service-learning activities. Student services: health clinic, personal-psychological counseling, women's center. Campus security: 24-hour emergency response devices and patrols, late night transport-escort service. Truax-Information Resource Center. Operations spending for the previous fiscal year: $921,250. 1,500 computers available on campus for general student use. Staffed computer lab on campus.

Community Environment: Home of the state capital and the University of Wisconsin, Madison is a lovely city situated between two lakes. Four campuses are in smaller cities with growing industrial bases.

■ MADISON MEDIA INSTITUTE
2702 Agriculture Dr.
Madison, WI 53718
Tel: (608)663-2000; Free: 800-236-4997
Fax: (608)442-0141
Web Site: www.mediainstitute.edu

Description: Proprietary, 2-year, coed. Awards terminal associate degrees. Founded 1969. Setting: urban campus. Total enrollment: 133. Faculty: 22 (20 full-time, 2 part-time). Calendar: semesters.

Entrance Requirements: Entrance: noncompetitive. Application deadline: rolling. Notification: continuous.

■ MARANATHA BAPTIST UNIVERSITY
745 W Main St.
Watertown, WI 53094
Tel: (920)261-9300; Free: 800-622-2947
Fax: (920)261-9109
E-mail: admissions@mbu.edu
Web Site: www.mbu.edu

Description: Independent Baptist, comprehensive, coed. Awards associate, bachelor's, master's, and doctoral degrees. Founded 1968. Setting: 60-acre small town campus with easy access to Milwaukee. Total enrollment: 1,139. Faculty: 138 (43 full-time, 95 part-time). Student-undergrad faculty ratio is 11:1. 279 applied, 73% were admitted. 13% from top 10% of their high school class, 37% from top quarter, 70% from top half. Full-time: 591 students, 55% women, 45% men. Part-time: 335 students, 58% women, 42% men. 75% from out-of-state. 0.1% American Indian or Alaska Native, non-Hispanic/Latino; 3% Hispanic/Latino; 2% Black or African American, non-Hispanic/Latino; 1% Asian, non-Hispanic/Latino; 0.1% Native Hawaiian or other Pacific Islander, non-Hispanic/Latino; 0.6% international. 6% 25 or older, 72% live on campus, 4% transferred in. Retention: 67% of full-time freshmen returned the following year. Academic areas with the most degrees conferred: education; theology and religious vocations; business/marketing; interdisciplinary studies. Core. Calendar: semesters. Academic remediation for entering students, advanced placement, independent study, distance learning, double major, summer session for credit, part-time degree program, adult/continuing education programs, internships, graduate courses open to undergrads. Off campus study. Study abroad program. ROTC: Army, Air Force (c).

Entrance Requirements: Option: electronic application. Required: essay, high school transcript, 4 recommendations, SAT or ACT. Entrance: noncompetitive. Preference given to Christians. SAT Reasoning Test deadline: 7/31. SAT Subject Test deadline: 7/31. Transfer credits accepted: Yes.

Costs Per Year: Application fee: $50. Comprehensive fee: $22,510 includes full-time tuition ($14,250), mandatory fees ($1160), and college room and board ($7100). Full-time tuition and fees vary according to location and program. Part-time tuition: $594 per semester hour. Part-time mandatory fees: $48 per semester hour. Part-time tuition and fees vary according to course load.

Collegiate Environment: Orientation program. Drama-theater group, choral group. Major annual events: Christmas Festival of Music, Semi-Annual College Play, Commencement. Student services: health clinic, personal-psychological counseling. Campus security: student patrols, late night transport-escort service, controlled dormitory access. Cedarholm Library and Resource Center. Students can reserve study rooms.

■ MARIAN UNIVERSITY
45 S National Ave.
Fond du Lac, WI 54935-4699
Tel: (920)923-7600; Free: 800-2-MARIAN
Fax: (920)923-8755
E-mail: admission@marianuniversity.edu
Web Site: www.marianuniversity.edu

Description: Independent Roman Catholic, comprehensive, coed. Awards bachelor's, master's, and doctoral degrees and post-master's certificates. Founded 1936. Setting: 78-acre small town campus with easy access to Milwaukee. Endowment: $11.7 million. Educational spending for the previous fiscal year: $6915 per student. Total enrollment: 1,971. Faculty: 233 (96 full-time, 137 part-time). Student-undergrad faculty ratio is 9:1. 1,245 applied, 77% were admitted. Full-time: 1,250 students, 68% women, 32% men. Part-time: 212 students, 72% women, 28% men. Students come from 23 states and territories, 12 other countries, 16% from out-of-state. 1% American Indian or Alaska Native, non-Hispanic/Latino; 6% Hispanic/Latino; 6% Black or African American, non-Hispanic/Latino; 2% Asian, non-Hispanic/Latino; 0.3% Native Hawaiian or other Pacific Islander, non-Hispanic/Latino; 1% international. 13% 25 or older, 6% transferred in. Retention: 68% of full-time freshmen returned the following year. Academic areas with the most degrees conferred: health professions and related sciences; business/marketing; homeland security, law enforcement, firefighting, and protective services. Core. Calendar: semesters. Academic remediation for entering students, services for LD students, advanced placement, accelerated degree program, self-designed majors, honors program, independent study, distance learning, double major, summer session for credit, part-time degree program, co-op programs and internships. Study abroad program. ROTC: Army (c).

Entrance Requirements: Options: electronic application, deferred admission. Required: high school transcript, SAT or ACT. Recommended: interview, ACT. Required for some: interview. Entrance: moderately difficult. Application deadline: rolling. Notification: 8/15. Transfer credits accepted: Yes.

Costs Per Year: Application fee: $20. Comprehensive fee: $34,622 includes full-time tuition ($26,950), mandatory fees ($450), and college room and board ($7222). College room only: $4352. Full-time tuition and fees vary according to course load and program. Room and board charges vary according to board plan. Part-time tuition: $450 per credit hour. Part-time tuition varies according to course load and program.

Collegiate Environment: Orientation program. Choral group, student-run newspaper. Social organizations: 30 open to all; national sororities. Most popular organizations: Student Senate, Student Nurses Association, Student Education Association, Science and Math Association, Business Club. Major annual events: Big Band Event, Academic Symposium, Midnight Madness. Student services: health clinic, personal-psychological counseling. Campus security: 24-hour emergency response devices and patrols, student patrols, late night transport-escort service, controlled dormitory access. Cardinal Meyer Library plus 1 other. Books: 210,079 (physical), 147,236 (digital/electronic); Databases: 1,805. Operations spending for the previous fiscal year: $610,642. 500 computers available on campus for general student use. Computer purchase/lease plans available. A campuswide network can be accessed. Students can access the following: online class registration. Staffed computer lab on campus provides training in use of computers, software, and the Internet.

Community Environment: Marian College of Fond du Lac, Wisconsin (population 42,400) is located on the edge of the scenic Kettle Moraine region, the dominant glacial formation of Wisconsin. It is less than a mile from beautiful Lake Winnebago. The campus is easily reached by U.S. Highways 41, 45, and 151. There is efficient bus service from other cities and airports. Fond du Lac offers its own cultural attractions: a modern public library, churches, local community theaters, and the Civic Music Center. Students who wish to expand their cultural horizons may easily travel to the nearby cities of Green Bay, Madison, Milwaukee, or Oshkosh.

■ **MARQUETTE UNIVERSITY**
PO Box 1881
Milwaukee, WI 53201-1881
Tel: (414)288-7250; Free: 800-222-6544
E-mail: admissions@marquette.edu
Web Site: www.marquette.edu

Description: Independent Roman Catholic (Jesuit), university, coed. Awards bachelor's, master's, and doctoral degrees and post-master's certificates. Founded 1881. Setting: 107-acre urban campus with easy access to Milwaukee. Total enrollment: 11,605. Faculty: 1,194 (674 full-time, 520 part-time). Student-undergrad faculty ratio is 14:1. 15,574 applied, 82% were admitted. 36% from top 10% of their high school class, 69% from top quarter, 95% from top half. Full-time: 8,121 students, 54% women, 46% men. Part-time: 314 students, 45% women, 55% men. 69% from out-of-state. 0.2% American Indian or Alaska Native, non-Hispanic/Latino; 13% Hispanic/Latino; 4% Black or African American, non-Hispanic/Latino; 7% Asian, non-Hispanic/Latino; 0.1% Native Hawaiian or other Pacific Islander, non-Hispanic/Latino; 3% international. 1% 25 or older, 54% live on campus, 2% transferred in. Retention: 87% of full-time freshmen returned the following year. Academic areas with the most degrees conferred: business/marketing; biological/life sciences; engineering. Core. Calendar: semesters. ESL program, services for LD students, advanced placement, accelerated degree program, self-designed majors, honors program, independent study, distance learning, double major, summer session for credit, part-time degree program, adult/continuing education programs, co-op programs and internships, graduate courses open to undergrads. Off campus study at Milwaukee Institute of Art and Design, Les Aspin Center for Government, Washington, DC. Study abroad program. ROTC: Army, Naval, Air Force.

Entrance Requirements: Options: electronic application, deferred admission, international baccalaureate accepted. Required: essay, high school transcript, minimum 2.5 high school GPA, SAT or ACT. Recommended: minimum 3.4 high school GPA. Entrance: moderately difficult. Notification: 12/23. SAT Reasoning Test deadline: 12/1. Transfer credits accepted: Yes. Applicants placed on waiting list: 775. Wait-listed applicants offered admission: 198.

Costs Per Year: Application fee: $0.

Collegiate Environment: Orientation program. Drama-theater group, choral group, student-run newspaper, radio station. Social organizations: 300 open to all; national fraternities, national sororities, local fraternities. Most popular organizations: Student Government, club sports, community service organizations, band/jazz/orchestra, Residence Hall Association. Major annual events: Winter Flurry, Hunger Clean-Up, Midnight Madness Basketball Kick-Off. Student services: health clinic, personal-psychological counseling. Campus security: 24-hour emergency response devices and patrols, student patrols, late night transport-escort service. Freshmen guaranteed college housing. On-campus residence required through sophomore year. Options: coed, men-only, women-only housing available. Raynor Memorial Libraries plus 1 other. Study areas open 24 hours, 5-7 days a week; students can reserve study rooms.

Community Environment: Located in the heart of the city, students have access to a multitude of social, educational and cultural opportunities. Marquette's mission statement comes alive with the countless opportunities to volunteer. Whether it's tutoring elementary school students or building homes through Habitat for Humanity, Marquette students put the "community" in community service and have been nationally recognized for their efforts. The Milwaukee business district provides students with an excellent chance to network with professionals in their field, or to gain valuable experience through internships or part-time work. Theaters, concerts, and museums offer a fun and relaxing way to expand the college experience and the lakefront recreational area and downtown shopping provide students with a way to unwind after a week of classes.

■ **MID-STATE TECHNICAL COLLEGE**
500 32nd St. N
Wisconsin Rapids, WI 54494-5599
Tel: (715)422-5300
Fax: (715)422-5345
Web Site: www.mstc.edu

Description: State and locally supported, 2-year, coed. Part of Wisconsin Technical College System. Awards certificates, diplomas, transfer associate, and terminal associate degrees. Founded 1917. Setting: 155-acre small town campus. Endowment: $1.2 million. Educational spending for the previous fiscal year: $5646 per student. Total enrollment: 2,636. Faculty: 178 (81 full-time, 97 part-time). Student-undergrad faculty ratio is 12:1. 1,100 applied, 95% were admitted. Full-time: 950 students, 48% women, 52% men. Part-time: 1,686 students, 67% women, 33% men. 1% American Indian or Alaska Native, non-Hispanic/Latino; 1% Hispanic/Latino; 1% Black or African American, non-Hispanic/Latino; 3% Asian, non-Hispanic/Latino; 0.1% Native Hawaiian or other Pacific Islander, non-Hispanic/Latino. 33% 25 or older, 3% transferred in. Core. Calendar: semesters. Academic remediation for entering students, ESL program, services for LD students, independent study, distance learning, double major, summer session for credit, part-time degree program, adult/continuing education programs, co-op programs and internships.

Entrance Requirements: Open admission. Options: electronic application, early admission, deferred admission. Required: high school transcript. Entrance: noncompetitive. Application deadline: rolling. Notification: continuous.

Costs Per Year: Application fee: $30. State resident tuition: $4026 full-time. Nonresident tuition: $6039 full-time. Mandatory fees: $201 full-time.

Collegiate Environment: Student-run newspaper. Most popular organizations: Business Professionals of America, Civil Tech Club, Barber and Cosmetology Club, Society of Hosteurs, UICA. Major annual events: Tech Fest, Winter Fest. Student services: health clinic, personal-psychological counseling, women's center. Mid-State Technical College Library. Operations spending for the previous fiscal year: $274,887. 120 computers available on campus for general student use. A campuswide network can be accessed from off-campus. Staffed computer lab on campus.

Community Environment: The college serves the area which includes Marshfield (population 19,400), Stevens Point (population 24,298), and Wisconsin Rapids (population 17,621), the county seat of Wood, near the geographical center of the state of Wisconsin.

■ **MILWAUKEE AREA TECHNICAL COLLEGE**
700 W State St.
Milwaukee, WI 53233-1443
Tel: (414)297-6600
Fax: (414)297-7990
E-mail: adamss4@matc.edu
Web Site: www.matc.edu

Description: District-supported, 2-year, coed. Part of Wisconsin Technical College System. Awards certificates, diplomas, transfer associate, and terminal associate degrees. Founded 1912. Setting: urban campus. Total enrollment: 20,215. Faculty: 1,351 (580 full-time, 771 part-time). Student-undergrad faculty ratio is 14:1. 13,086 applied, 51% were admitted. Full-time: 7,048 students, 47% women, 53% men. Part-time: 13,167 students, 59% women, 41% men. Students come from 16 states and territories, 50 other countries, 1% from out-of-state. 55% 25 or older, 16% transferred in. Retention: 47% of full-time freshmen returned the following year. Core. Calendar: semesters. Academic remediation for entering students, ESL program, services for LD students, advanced placement, accelerated degree program, self-designed majors, freshman honors college, honors program, independent study, distance learning, double major, summer session for credit, part-time degree program, external degree program, adult/continuing education programs, co-op programs and internships. Off campus study. Study abroad program.

Entrance Requirements: Open admission for students satisfying minimum degree requirements (students not meeting these requirements are placed in pre-program curricula). Option: electronic application. Required: high school transcript, ACCUPLACER. Entrance: noncompetitive. Application deadline: rolling. Notification: continuous until 8/20. Transfer credits accepted: Yes. Applicants placed on waiting list: 1,148. Wait-listed applicants offered admission: 701.

Collegiate Environment: Orientation program. Choral group, student-run newspaper. Social organizations: 50 open to all. Most popular organizations: Student Senate, MATC Times, Ethnic Organizations (Latino Students, Black Student Union, Native American, and Asian student groups), Black Engineers Organization, Future Hospitality Managers of America. Major annual events: Honors Induction Ceremonies, Soul Food Dinner Grand Ball, Ethnic Festivals. Student services: legal services, personal-psychological counseling, women's center. Campus security: 24-hour emergency response devices and patrols, student patrols, late night transport-escort service. William F. Rasche Library plus 4 others. 3,500 computers available on campus for general student use. A campuswide network can be accessed from off-campus. Students can access the following: online class registration. Staffed computer lab on campus provides training in use of computers, software, and the Internet.

Community Environment: Located on the west shore of Lake Michigan, Milwaukee (population 640,000) is the largest city in Wisconsin with all major forms of commercial transportation available. Milwaukee is the nation's brewing center, also a major grain market and manufacturing center. Products of industry are metal, machinery, food, leather, chemicals, textiles, electrical machinery, and other items. The city is headquarters of the Lake States National Forest Region. The county has a park system and many of the units contain public golf courses, tennis courts, and other recreational facilities. Milwaukee's State Fair is held each year in August.

■ **MILWAUKEE CAREER COLLEGE**
3077 N Mayfair Rd.
Ste. 300
Milwaukee, WI 53222
Tel: (414)257-2939
Web Site: www.mkecc.edu
Description: Proprietary, 2-year, coed. Awards certificates and terminal associate degrees.

■ **MILWAUKEE INSTITUTE OF ART AND DESIGN**
273 E Erie St.
Milwaukee, WI 53202-6003
Tel: (414)276-7889; Free: 888-749-MIAD
Fax: (414)291-8077
E-mail: admissions@miad.edu
Web Site: www.miad.edu
Description: Independent, 4-year, coed. Awards bachelor's degrees. Founded 1974. Setting: urban campus with easy access to Milwaukee. Total enrollment: 630. Student-undergrad faculty ratio is 15:1. 921 applied, 53% were admitted. Full-time: 617 students, 55% women, 45% men. Part-time: 13 students, 62% women, 38% men. 33% from out-of-state. 0.5% American Indian or Alaska Native, non-Hispanic/Latino; 14% Hispanic/Latino; 7% Black or African American, non-Hispanic/Latino; 3% Asian, non-Hispanic/Latino; 0.2% Native Hawaiian or other Pacific Islander, non-Hispanic/Latino; 1% international. 8% 25 or older, 7% transferred in. Retention: 81% of full-time freshmen returned the following year. Academic area with the most degrees conferred: visual and performing arts. Core. Calendar: semesters.

Academic remediation for entering students, services for LD students, advanced placement, independent study, double major, summer session for credit, adult/continuing education programs, co-op programs and internships. Off campus study at Marquette University, Association of Independent Colleges of Art and Design. Study abroad program.

Entrance Requirements: Options: electronic application, deferred admission. Required: high school transcript, portfolio. Recommended: essay, minimum 2 high school GPA, interview. Entrance: moderately difficult. Application deadline: rolling. Transfer credits accepted: Yes.

Costs Per Year: Application fee: $0. Tuition: $35,950 full-time, $1200 per credit part-time. Mandatory fees: $1660 full-time. College room only: $7870.

Collegiate Environment: Orientation program. Drama-theater group. Student services: health clinic, personal-psychological counseling. Campus security: 24-hour emergency response devices, late night transport-escort service.

■ **MILWAUKEE SCHOOL OF ENGINEERING**
1025 N Broadway
Milwaukee, WI 53202-3109
Tel: (414)277-7300; Free: 800-332-6763
Fax: (414)277-7475
E-mail: mitchell@msoe.edu
Web Site: www.msoe.edu
Description: Independent, comprehensive, coed. Awards bachelor's and master's degrees. Founded 1903. Setting: 22-acre urban campus. Endowment: $65 million. Research spending for the previous fiscal year: $5.5 million. Educational spending for the previous fiscal year: $11,959 per student. Total enrollment: 2,823. Faculty: 252 (138 full-time, 114 part-time). Student-undergrad faculty ratio is 16:1. 2,893 applied, 63% were admitted. Full-time: 2,508 students, 27% women, 73% men. Part-time: 102 students, 14% women, 86% men. Students come from 42 states and territories, 26 other countries, 34% from out-of-state. 0.2% American Indian or Alaska Native, non-Hispanic/Latino; 6% Hispanic/Latino; 2% Black or African American, non-Hispanic/Latino; 4% Asian, non-Hispanic/Latino; 10% international. 12% 25 or older, 30% live on campus, 7% transferred in. Retention: 85% of full-time freshmen returned the following year. Academic areas with the most degrees conferred: engineering; health professions and related sciences; business/marketing. Core. Calendar: quarters. Academic remediation for entering students, ESL program, services for LD students, advanced placement, honors program, independent study, double major, summer session for credit, part-time degree program, adult/continuing education programs, internships, graduate courses open to undergrads. Study abroad program. ROTC: Army (c), Naval (c), Air Force (c).

Entrance Requirements: Options: electronic application, deferred admission. Required: high school transcript, minimum 3 high school GPA, SAT or ACT. Required for some: essay, interview. Entrance: moderately difficult. Application deadlines: 1/1, rolling for nonresidents. Notification: continuous until 10/1, continuous for nonresidents. SAT Reasoning Test deadline: 9/1. SAT Subject Test deadline: 9/1. Transfer credits accepted: Yes.

Costs Per Year: Application fee: $0. Comprehensive fee: $50,157 includes full-time tuition ($39,039), mandatory fees ($1710), and college room and board ($9408). College room only: $5889. Full-time tuition and fees vary according to course load. Room and board charges vary according to board plan and housing facility. Part-time tuition: $678 per credit hour. Part-time mandatory fees: $12.50 per credit hour. Part-time tuition and fees vary according to course load.

Collegiate Environment: Orientation program. Drama-theater group, choral group, student-run radio station. Social organizations: 82 open to all; national fraternities, national sororities, local fraternities, local sororities; 5% of eligible men and 12% of eligible women are members. Most popular organizations: Student Union Board, Greek Council, Student Government Association, Residence Hall Association, Intervarsity Christian Fellowship. Major annual events: Sub-Zero Days, Decompression Chamber, St. Pat's Week Activities. Student services: health clinic, personal-psychological counseling, women's center. Campus security: 24-hour emergency response devices and patrols, late night transport-escort service, controlled dormitory access. Walter Schroeder. Books: 51,408 (physical), 370,802 (digital/electronic); Serial titles: 345 (physical), 114,238 (digital/electronic); Databases: 124. Weekly public service hours: 96; students can reserve study rooms. Operations spending for the previous fiscal year: $717,209. 50 computers available on campus for general student use. Computer purchase/lease plans available. A computer is required for all students. A campuswide network can be accessed from student residence rooms and from off campus. Students can access the following: online class registration. Staffed computer lab on campus (open 24 hours a day) provides training in use of computers, software, and the Internet.

Community Environment: See Milwaukee Area Technical College.

■ MORAINE PARK TECHNICAL COLLEGE

235 N National Ave.
Fond du Lac, WI 54936-1940
Tel: (920)922-8611; Free: 800-472-4554
Fax: (920)924-2471
E-mail: kjarvis@morainepark.edu
Web Site: www.morainepark.edu

Description: District-supported, 2-year, coed. Part of Wisconsin Technical College System. Awards certificates, diplomas, transfer associate, and terminal associate degrees. Founded 1967. Setting: 40-acre small town campus with easy access to Milwaukee. Educational spending for the previous fiscal year: $8889 per student. Total enrollment: 6,613. Faculty: 270 (145 full-time, 125 part-time). 55% 25 or older. Core. Calendar: semesters. Academic remediation for entering students, ESL program, services for LD students, advanced placement, accelerated degree program, self-designed majors, independent study, distance learning, double major, summer session for credit, part-time degree program, external degree program, adult/continuing education programs, internships. Study abroad program.

Entrance Requirements: Required: high school transcript, interview, ACT, ACCUPLACER or ACT Compass. Required for some: interview, criminal background ground check.

Collegiate Environment: Orientation program. Social organizations: 31 open to all; 7% of eligible men and 7% of eligible women are members. Most popular organizations: Student Government, Student Nurses Association Club, Electrical Power Distribution Club, Electricity Club, Auto Technician Club. Major annual events: Welcome Back Week, Last Blast End of the Year Celebration, Student Awards Banquet. Student services: personal-psychological counseling. Campus security: late night transport-escort service, Campus Security Services between 5-10 pm M-Th during the academic year, night patrols. Moraine Park Technical College Library/Learning Resource Center. Operations spending for the previous fiscal year: $858,254. 1,599 computers available on campus for general student use. A campuswide network can be accessed from off-campus. Students can access the following: online class registration. Staffed computer lab on campus provides training in use of computers, software, and the Internet.

Community Environment: See Marian College of Fond du Lac.

■ MOUNT MARY UNIVERSITY

2900 N Menomonee River Pky.
Milwaukee, WI 53222-4597
Tel: (414)930-3000; Free: 800-321-6265
E-mail: mmu-admiss@mtmary.edu
Web Site: www.mtmary.edu

Description: Independent Roman Catholic, comprehensive. Awards bachelor's, master's, and doctoral degrees and post-master's certificates. Founded 1913. Setting: 80-acre urban campus with easy access to Milwaukee. Endowment: $17 million. Total enrollment: 1,358. Faculty: 194 (61 full-time, 133 part-time). Student-undergrad faculty ratio is 11:1. 709 applied, 56% were admitted. 19% from top 10% of their high school class, 44% from top quarter, 72% from top half. Full-time: 652 students, 100% women. Part-time: 83 students, 98% women, 2% men. Students come from 6 states and territories, 14 other countries, 2% from out-of-state. 0.1% American Indian or Alaska Native, non-Hispanic/Latino; 20% Hispanic/Latino; 17% Black or African American, non-Hispanic/Latino; 8% Asian, non-Hispanic/Latino; 0.3% Native Hawaiian or other Pacific Islander, non-Hispanic/Latino; 1% international. 21% 25 or older, 31% live on campus, 6% transferred in. Retention: 79% of full-time freshmen returned the following year. Academic areas with the most degrees conferred: visual and performing arts; health professions and related sciences; business/marketing. Core. Calendar: semesters. Academic remediation for entering students, services for LD students, advanced placement, accelerated degree program, self-designed majors, honors program, independent study, double major, summer session for credit, part-time degree program, internships, graduate courses open to undergrads. Study abroad program.

Entrance Requirements: Options: electronic application, deferred admission, international baccalaureate accepted. Required: high school transcript, SAT or ACT. Recommended: minimum 2.5 high school GPA. Required for some: essay, 1 recommendation. Entrance: moderately difficult. Application deadline: rolling. Notification: continuous. SAT Reasoning Test deadline: 8/15. SAT Subject Test deadline: 8/15. Transfer credits accepted: Yes.

Costs Per Year: Application fee: $0. Comprehensive fee: $38,700 includes full-time tuition ($29,510), mandatory fees ($590), and college room and board ($8600). Full-time tuition and fees vary according to degree level and program. Room and board charges vary according to board plan. Part-time tuition: $895 per credit hour. Part-time mandatory fees: $370 per year. Part-time tuition and fees vary according to course load, degree level, and program.

Collegiate Environment: Orientation program. Choral group, student-run newspaper. Social organizations: 41 open to all. Most popular organizations: Programming and Activities Council, Student Government Association, International Club, Caroline Hall Council, Department Affiliated Clubs. Major annual events: Weeks of Welcome, Christmas on the Mount, Spring Formal. Student services: personal-psychological counseling. Campus security: 24-hour emergency response devices and patrols, late night transport-escort service, controlled dormitory access. The Patrick and Beatrice Haggerty Library. Books: 77,098 (physical), 142,434 (digital/electronic); Serial titles: 5,268 (physical), 155,028 (digital/electronic); Databases: 92. Students can reserve study rooms. Operations spending for the previous fiscal year: $232,195. 177 computers available on campus for general student use. A campuswide network can be accessed from student residence rooms and from off campus. Students can access the following: online class registration. Staffed computer lab on campus provides training in use of computers, software, and the Internet.

Community Environment: Mount Mary is one of 5 private colleges in Milwaukee. The campus is located on the northwest side of the city, about 15 minutes from the downtown area. It is within walking distance of a shopping mall and restaurants. The city of Milwaukee boasts a major symphony, well-respected dance companies, a beautiful lakefront art museum, and a fine natural history museum. Three professional sports divide the Milwaukee seasons. It is also the ideal site in which to explore various career options.

■ NICOLET AREA TECHNICAL COLLEGE

Box 518
Rhinelander, WI 54501-0518
Tel: (715)365-4410; Free: 800-544-3039
Fax: (715)365-4445
E-mail: inquire@nicoletcollege.edu
Web Site: www.nicoletcollege.edu

Description: State and locally supported, 2-year, coed. Part of Wisconsin Technical College System. Awards certificates, diplomas, transfer associate, and terminal associate degrees. Founded 1968. Setting: 280-acre rural campus. Total enrollment: 1,600. Faculty: 100. Student-undergrad faculty ratio is 16:1. Students come from 8 states and territories, 4 other countries, 1% from out-of-state. 64% 25 or older. Core. Calendar: semesters. Academic remediation for entering students, ESL program, services for LD students, advanced placement, independent study, distance learning, double major, summer session for credit, part-time degree program, adult/continuing education programs, co-op programs and internships. Study abroad program.

Entrance Requirements: Open admission. Options: electronic application, early admission. Required: high school transcript, ACCUPLACER or ACT. Recommended: ACT. Entrance: noncompetitive. Application deadline: rolling. Notification: continuous. Preference given to district residents. Transfer credits accepted: Yes.

Collegiate Environment: Orientation program. Drama-theater group, student-run newspaper. Student services: personal-psychological counseling. Campus security: 24-hour emergency response devices, student patrols. Richard Brown Library. 100 computers available on campus for general student use. A campuswide network can be accessed from off-campus. Students can access the following: online class registration. Staffed computer lab on campus provides training in use of computers and software.

Community Environment: The county seat for Oneida County, Rhinelander (population 7,889) is a summer and winter resort, located in the most concentrated lake area of the Middle West. Rhinelander has one of the largest paper mills under one roof in America. All commercial transportation is available. Parks and many lakes and trout streams and rivers provide facilities for all water sports and fishing. The Logging Museum is a reproduction of a logging camp with living quarters. Also on display is a narrow gauge engine built in 1879.

■ NORTHCENTRAL TECHNICAL COLLEGE

1000 W Campus Dr.
Wausau, WI 54401-1899
Tel: (715)675-3331

Fax: (715)675-9776

Web Site: www.ntc.edu

Description: District-supported, 2-year, coed. Part of Wisconsin Technical College System. Awards certificates, diplomas, transfer associate, and terminal associate degrees. Founded 1912. Setting: 96-acre rural campus. Total enrollment: 5,167. Student-undergrad faculty ratio is 23:1. Full-time: 1,361 students, 48% women, 52% men. Part-time: 3,806 students, 62% women, 38% men. Students come from 24 states and territories. 0.8% American Indian or Alaska Native, non-Hispanic/Latino; 2% Hispanic/Latino; 0.9% Black or African American, non-Hispanic/Latino; 5% Asian, non-Hispanic/Latino; 0.1% Native Hawaiian or other Pacific Islander, non-Hispanic/Latino. 44% 25 or older. Calendar: semesters. Academic remediation for entering students, ESL program, services for LD students, advanced placement, accelerated degree program, self-designed majors, independent study, distance learning, double major, summer session for credit, part-time degree program, adult/continuing education programs, co-op programs and internships. Off campus study.

Entrance Requirements: Open admission except for associate degree nursing, dental hygiene, and radiography programs. Options: electronic application, early admission, deferred admission. Required for some: high school transcript, interview. Entrance: noncompetitive. Application deadline: rolling. Notification: continuous. Preference given to district residents. Transfer credits accepted: Yes.

Costs Per Year: Application fee: $30. State resident tuition: $3,553 full-time, $134.20 per credit hour part-time. Nonresident tuition: $5,164 full-time, $201.30 per credit hour part-time. Mandatory fees: $11.85 per credit hour part-time, $6 per term part-time. Full-time tuition varies according to course load and program. Part-time tuition and fees vary according to course load and program. College room and board: $6265. College room only: $4365. Room and board charges vary according to board plan and housing facility.

Collegiate Environment: Orientation program. Student services: personal-psychological counseling, women's center. Campus security: 24-hour emergency response devices, student patrols, late night transport-escort service. Northcentral Technical College, Wausau Campus Library. 1,700 computers available on campus for general student use. A campuswide network can be accessed from off-campus. Students can access the following: online class registration. Staffed computer lab on campus provides training in use of computers, software, and the Internet.

Community Environment: Wausau (population 37,292) is one of the major industrial centers in the state. Over 70 highly diversified industries are located here, producing over 40 different products. The area is one of the nation's leading producers of cheddar cheese, and it is a major center of dairy farming in both the state and nation and a leading exporter of ginseng. The community offers many cultural and recreational programs plus an excellent public school system. The school works closely with the branch campus of the University of Wisconsin to maximize use of facilities and programs and to eliminate duplication.

■ NORTHEAST WISCONSIN TECHNICAL COLLEGE

2740 W Mason St.

Green Bay, WI 54307-9042

Tel: (920)498-5400; Free: 888-385-6982

Web Site: www.nwtc.edu

Description: State and locally supported, 2-year, coed. Part of Wisconsin Technical College System. Awards certificates, diplomas, and terminal associate degrees. Founded 1913. Setting: 192-acre suburban campus. Total enrollment: 8,105. 47% 25 or older. Core. Calendar: semesters. Academic remediation for entering students, ESL program, services for LD students, advanced placement, accelerated degree program, self-designed majors, distance learning, summer session for credit, part-time degree program, adult/continuing education programs.

Entrance Requirements: Option: early admission. Required for some: high school transcript. Entrance: minimally difficult. Application deadline: rolling. Preference given to state residents.

Collegiate Environment: Student services: health clinic, personal-psychological counseling. Campus security: 24-hour emergency response devices, late night transport-escort service.

Community Environment: Green Bay, population 101,200 and the oldest permanent settlement in Wisconsin, is in an important harbor for the Great Lakes-St. Lawrence Seaway System. Industries in the area include shipping, cheese producing, paper, and jobbers wholesale and distribution. Points of interest are the Bay Beach Park, Heritage Hill Park, Neville Public Museum, Cotton House, Fort Howard Hospital Museum, Lambeau Stadium, National Railroad Museum, Tank Cottage, and the Green Bay Packer Hall of Fame.

■ NORTHLAND COLLEGE

1411 Ellis Ave.

Ashland, WI 54806-3925

Tel: (715)682-1699; Free: 800-753-1040

Fax: (715)682-1258

E-mail: admit@northland.edu

Web Site: www.northland.edu

Description: Independent, 4-year, coed, affiliated with United Church of Christ. Awards bachelor's degrees. Founded 1892. Setting: 130-acre small town campus. Endowment: $22.6 million. Research spending for the previous fiscal year: $840,446. Educational spending for the previous fiscal year: $11,244 per student. Total enrollment: 635. Faculty: 69 (50 full-time, 19 part-time). Student-undergrad faculty ratio is 11:1. 1,625 applied, 61% were admitted. 16% from top 10% of their high school class, 41% from top quarter, 75% from top half. Full-time: 594 students, 53% women, 47% men. Part-time: 41 students, 61% women, 39% men. Students come from 37 states and territories, 4 other countries, 50% from out-of-state. 2% American Indian or Alaska Native, non-Hispanic/Latino; 5% Hispanic/Latino; 3% Black or African American, non-Hispanic/Latino; 1% Asian, non-Hispanic/Latino; 4% international. 4% 25 or older, 74% live on campus, 6% transferred in. Retention: 73% of full-time freshmen returned the following year. Academic areas with the most degrees conferred: natural resources/environmental science; biological/life sciences; business/marketing; education. Core. Calendar: 4-4-1. Services for LD students, advanced placement, self-designed majors, honors program, independent study, double major, summer session for credit, part-time degree program, internships. Off campus study at Eco League (Alaska Pacific University, College of the Atlantic, Dickenson College, Green Mountain College, Northland College, Prescott College). Study abroad program.

Entrance Requirements: Options: electronic application, deferred admission, international baccalaureate accepted. Required: high school transcript. Required for some: SAT or ACT. Entrance: moderately difficult. Application deadline: rolling. Notification: continuous. SAT Reasoning Test deadline: 8/15. Transfer credits accepted: Yes.

Costs Per Year: Application fee: $0. Comprehensive fee: $45,359 includes full-time tuition ($34,666), mandatory fees ($1517), and college room and board ($9176). College room only: $4234. Full-time tuition and fees vary according to course load. Room and board charges vary according to board plan and housing facility. Part-time tuition: $670 per credit. Part-time tuition varies according to course load.

Collegiate Environment: Orientation program. Drama-theater group, choral group, student-run newspaper. Most popular organizations: Northland Volunteer Program, Northland College Student Association, Native American Student Association, Environmental Council, SAAC (Student Athlete Organization). Major annual events: Job and Internship Fair, Fall Convocation, Everybody Party. Student services: health clinic, personal-psychological counseling. Campus security: 24-hour emergency response devices and patrols, late night transport-escort service, controlled dormitory access. Dexter Library. Books: 74,451 (physical); Serial titles: 82 (physical), 50 (digital/electronic); Databases: 38. Weekly public service hours: 88; students can reserve study rooms. Operations spending for the previous fiscal year: $285,250. 125 computers available on campus for general student use. Computer purchase/lease plans available. A campuswide network can be accessed from student residence rooms and from off campus. Students can access the following: online class registration.

Community Environment: Ashland (population 8,306) is located on Lake Superior near the Chequamegon National Forest.

■ PURDUE UNIVERSITY GLOBAL

201 W Wisconsin Ave.

Milwaukee, WI 53203

Description: Independent, comprehensive, coed.

■ RASMUSSEN COLLEGE GREEN BAY

904 S Taylor St.

Ste. 100

Green Bay, WI 54303

Tel: (920)593-8400; Free: 888-549-6755

E-mail: susan.hammerstrom@rasmussen.edu

Web Site: www.rasmussen.edu

Description: Proprietary, 4-year, coed. Part of Rasmussen College System. Awards associate and bachelor's degrees. Setting: suburban campus. Total enrollment: 449. Faculty: 53 (12 full-time, 41 part-time). Student-undergrad faculty ratio is 22:1. 31 applied, 81% were admitted. Full-time: 238 students,

84% women, 16% men. Part-time: 211 students, 80% women, 20% men. 69% 25 or older. Core. Calendar: quarters. Academic remediation for entering students, accelerated degree program, distance learning, double major, summer session for credit, part-time degree program, adult/continuing education programs, internships.

Entrance Requirements: Options: electronic application, early admission, deferred admission. Required: high school transcript, minimum 2 high school GPA, institutional exam. Required for some: interview. Entrance: minimally difficult. Application deadline: rolling. Transfer credits accepted: Yes.

Collegiate Environment: Orientation program. Rasmussen College Library - Green Bay. 137 computers available on campus for general student use. A campuswide network can be accessed from off-campus.

■ RASMUSSEN COLLEGE WAUSAU

1101 Westwood Dr.
Wausau, WI 54401
Tel: (715)841-8000; Free: 888-549-6755
E-mail: susan.hammerstrom@rasmussen.edu
Web Site: www.rasmussen.edu

Description: Proprietary, 4-year, coed. Part of Rasmussen College System. Awards associate and bachelor's degrees. Setting: suburban campus. Total enrollment: 254. Faculty: 48 (8 full-time, 40 part-time). Student-undergrad faculty ratio is 22:1. 15 applied, 93% were admitted. Full-time: 158 students, 79% women, 21% men. Part-time: 96 students, 72% women, 28% men. 73% 25 or older. Core. Calendar: quarters. Academic remediation for entering students, accelerated degree program, distance learning, double major, summer session for credit, part-time degree program, adult/continuing education programs, internships.

Entrance Requirements: Options: electronic application, early admission, deferred admission. Required: high school transcript, minimum 2 high school GPA, institutional exam. Required for some: interview. Entrance: minimally difficult. Application deadline: rolling. Transfer credits accepted: Yes.

Collegiate Environment: Orientation program. Rasmussen College Library - Wausau. 74 computers available on campus for general student use. A campuswide network can be accessed from off-campus.

■ RIPON COLLEGE

300 Seward St.
Ripon, WI 54971
Tel: (920)748-8115; Free: 800-947-4766
Fax: (920)748-7243
E-mail: adminfo@ripon.edu
Web Site: www.ripon.edu

Description: Independent, 4-year, coed. Awards bachelor's degrees. Founded 1851. Setting: 250-acre small town campus with easy access to Milwaukee. Endowment: $84.5 million. Educational spending for the previous fiscal year: $13,857 per student. Total enrollment: 756. Faculty: 78 (62 full-time, 16 part-time). Student-undergrad faculty ratio is 12:1. 2,553 applied, 65% were admitted. 16% from top 10% of their high school class, 43% from top quarter, 79% from top half. Full-time: 739 students, 54% women, 46% men. Part-time: 17 students, 59% women, 41% men. Students come from 30 states and territories, 7 other countries, 30% from out-of-state. 0.3% American Indian or Alaska Native, non-Hispanic/Latino; 9% Hispanic/Latino; 4% Black or African American, non-Hispanic/Latino; 0.9% Asian, non-Hispanic/Latino; 4% international. 1% 25 or older, 93% live on campus, 2% transferred in. Retention: 71% of full-time freshmen returned the following year. Academic areas with the most degrees conferred: social sciences; psychology; biological/life sciences; business/marketing; parks and recreation. Core. Calendar: semesters. Services for LD students, advanced placement, accelerated degree program, self-designed majors, double major, part-time degree program, internships. Off campus study at American University, Newberry Library, Oak Ridge National Laboratory, University of Chicago, Associated Colleges of the Midwest Wilderness Field Station. Study abroad program. ROTC: Army.

Entrance Requirements: Options: electronic application, deferred admission, international baccalaureate accepted. Required: high school transcript, minimum 2 high school GPA, 1 recommendation. Recommended: essay, interview. Required for some: essay, interview. Entrance: moderately difficult. Application deadline: rolling. Notification: continuous. Transfer credits accepted: Yes.

Costs Per Year: Application fee: $30. Comprehensive fee: $52,208 includes full-time tuition ($43,508), mandatory fees ($300), and college room and board ($8400). Part-time tuition: $1500 per credit.

Collegiate Environment: Orientation program. Drama-theater group, choral

group, student-run newspaper, radio station. Social organizations: 60 open to all; national fraternities, national sororities, local fraternities, local sororities; 29% of eligible men and 23% of eligible women are members. Most popular organizations: Environmental Group, Student Senate, Community Service Coalition, SMAC (Student Media and Activities Committee). Major annual events: Springfest, Winterfest, Frisbee Golf Tournament. Student services: health clinic, personal-psychological counseling. Campus security: 24-hour emergency response devices and patrols, student patrols, late night transport-escort service, controlled dormitory access. Lane Library. Books: 160,664 (physical), 142,427 (digital/electronic); Serial titles: 86 (physical), 61,132 (digital/electronic); Databases: 26. Weekly public service hours: 52; students can reserve study rooms. Operations spending for the previous fiscal year: $486,208. 150 computers available on campus for general student use. A campuswide network can be accessed from student residence rooms and from off campus. Staffed computer lab on campus provides training in use of computers, software, and the Internet.

Community Environment: Students who select Ripon seek a small-town community and enjoy the recreational opportunities of Green Lake. In east central Wisconsin, the town is a one and one-half hour drive to Madison and Milwaukee, and 3 hours from Chicago. Various community groups encourage student participation in service-oriented activities.

■ ST. NORBERT COLLEGE

100 Grant St.
De Pere, WI 54115-2099
Tel: (920)337-3181; Free: 800-236-4878
Fax: (920)403-4088
E-mail: admit@snc.edu
Web Site: www.snc.edu

Description: Independent Roman Catholic, comprehensive, coed. Awards bachelor's and master's degrees. Founded 1898. Setting: 113-acre suburban campus. Endowment: $145.8 million. Research spending for the previous fiscal year: $421,205. Educational spending for the previous fiscal year: $11,301 per student. Total enrollment: 2,228. Faculty: 203 (139 full-time, 64 part-time). Student-undergrad faculty ratio is 13:1. 4,118 applied, 78% were admitted. 26% from top 10% of their high school class, 57% from top quarter, 85% from top half. Full-time: 2,083 students, 58% women, 42% men. Part-time: 49 students, 65% women, 35% men. Students come from 26 states and territories, 18 other countries, 21% from out-of-state. 0.9% American Indian or Alaska Native, non-Hispanic/Latino; 5% Hispanic/Latino; 2% Black or African American, non-Hispanic/Latino; 1% Asian, non-Hispanic/Latino; 2% international. 1% 25 or older, 82% live on campus, 1% transferred in. Retention: 83% of full-time freshmen returned the following year. Academic areas with the most degrees conferred: business/marketing; biological/life sciences; social sciences; education. Core. Calendar: semesters. Academic remediation for entering students, ESL program, services for LD students, advanced placement, self-designed majors, honors program, independent study, distance learning, double major, summer session for credit, part-time degree program, internships. Off campus study at Higher Education Consortium for Urban Affairs, American University. Study abroad program. ROTC: Army.

Entrance Requirements: Options: electronic application, deferred admission, international baccalaureate accepted. Required: high school transcript, SAT or ACT. Recommended: essay, interview. Entrance: moderately difficult. Application deadlines: rolling, rolling for nonresidents. Notification: continuous, continuous for nonresidents. Preference given to children of alumni, siblings of current or former students, dependents of employees. SAT Reasoning Test deadline: 7/15. SAT Subject Test deadline: 7/15. Transfer credits accepted: Yes.

Costs Per Year: Application fee: $0. Comprehensive fee: $49,964 includes full-time tuition ($38,714), mandatory fees ($815), and college room and board ($10,435). College room only: $5841. Part-time tuition: $1209 per credit.

Collegiate Environment: Orientation program. Drama-theater group, choral group, student-run newspaper, radio station. Social organizations: 106 open to all; national fraternities, national sororities; 10% of eligible men and 10% of eligible women are members. Most popular organizations: Pre-Health Science Club, Adventure Club, CC Hams, BUD, American Medical Student Association. Major annual events: Opening Campus Picnic/Convocation, E2K Homecoming, SNC Day. Student services: health clinic, personal-psychological counseling, women's center. Campus security: 24-hour emergency response devices and patrols, student patrols, late night transport-escort service, controlled dormitory access. 1,821 college housing spaces available; 1,756 were occupied in 2018-19. Freshmen guaranteed college housing. On-campus residence required through senior year. Options: coed, women-only housing available. Miriam B. and James J. Mulva Library plus 1 other. Books: 252,444 (physical), 207,312 (digital/electronic); Serial titles: 103,421 (physical), 103,236 (digital/electronic). Weekly public service hours: 116; students can reserve study rooms. Operations spending for the previous fiscal year: $1.1 million. 167 computers available on campus for general student use. Computer purchase/lease plans available. A computer is required for all students. A campuswide network can be accessed from student residence rooms and from off campus. Students can access the following: online class registration. Staffed computer lab on campus provides training in use of computers, software, and the Internet.

■ SILVER LAKE COLLEGE OF THE HOLY FAMILY

2406 S Alverno Rd.
Manitowoc, WI 54220-9319
Tel: (920)686-6175; Free: 800-236-4752
Fax: (920)686-6322
E-mail: dan.connolly@sl.edu
Web Site: www.sl.edu

Description: Independent Roman Catholic, comprehensive, coed. Awards bachelor's and master's degrees. Founded 1869. Setting: 30-acre rural campus with easy access to Milwaukee. Endowment: $7.2 million. Educational spending for the previous fiscal year: $7024 per student. Total enrollment: 475. Faculty: 73 (28 full-time, 45 part-time). Student-undergrad faculty ratio is 9:1. 877 applied, 52% were admitted. Full-time: 267 students, 66% women, 34% men. Part-time: 125 students, 64% women, 36% men. Students come from 10 states and territories, 9 other countries, 15% from out-of-state. 0.5% American Indian or Alaska Native, non-Hispanic/Latino; 7% Hispanic/Latino; 18% Black or African American, non-Hispanic/Latino; 5% Asian, non-Hispanic/Latino; 4% international. 10% 25 or older, 50% live on campus, 9% transferred in. Retention: 73% of full-time freshmen returned the following year. Academic areas with the most degrees conferred: business/marketing; education; psychology. Core. Calendar: semesters. Academic remediation for entering students, services for LD students, advanced placement, accelerated degree program, self-designed majors, independent study, distance learning, double major, summer session for credit, part-time degree program, adult/continuing education programs, internships, graduate courses open to undergrads. Off campus study.

Entrance Requirements: Options: electronic application, deferred admission, international baccalaureate accepted. Required: high school transcript, minimum 2 high school GPA, 1 recommendation. Recommended: SAT or ACT. Required for some: essay, interview. Entrance: minimally difficult. Application deadline: rolling. Notification: continuous until 9/1. SAT Reasoning Test deadline: 9/1. Transfer credits accepted: Yes.

Costs Per Year: Application fee: $50. One-time mandatory fee: $290. Comprehensive fee: $35,900 includes full-time tuition ($27,800), mandatory fees ($300), and college room and board ($7800). College room only: $3600. Full-time tuition and fees vary according to course load and degree level. Room and board charges vary according to board plan and housing facility. Part-time tuition: $560 per credit hour. Part-time tuition varies according to course load and degree level.

Collegiate Environment: Orientation program. Choral group. Social organizations: 8 open to all. Most popular organizations: Wellness Club, Card and Game Club, Student For Life, Campus Activity Board, Silver Lake Serves. Major annual events: Homecoming, Halloween Dance, Campus-Wide Easter Egg Hunt. Student services: health clinic, personal-psychological counseling. Campus security: 24-hour emergency response devices and patrols, student patrols, late night transport-escort service, controlled dormitory access. The Erma M. and Theodore M. Zigmunt Library. Books: 53,862 (physical), 93 (digital/electronic); Serial titles: 488 (physical), 1 (digital/electronic); Databases: 32. Weekly public service hours: 80; study areas open 24 hours, 5-7 days a week; students can reserve study rooms. Operations spending for the previous fiscal year: $173,000. 120 computers available on campus for general student use. Computer purchase/lease plans available. A campuswide network can be accessed from student residence rooms. Students can access the following: online class registration. Staffed computer lab on campus provides training in use of computers, software, and the Internet.

Community Environment: The communities of Manitowoc and Two Rivers were founded in 1838 and are located on the shore of Lake Michigan with convenient access to major Wisconsin cities. This industrial and tourism-based community has 37 churches, 3 modern hospitals, museums, and numerous parks and recreation areas.

■ SOUTHWEST WISCONSIN TECHNICAL COLLEGE

1800 Bronson Blvd.
Fennimore, WI 53809-9778
Tel: (608)822-3262; Free: 800-362-3322
Fax: (608)822-6019
Web Site: www.swtc.edu

Description: State and locally supported, 2-year, coed. Part of Wisconsin Technical College System. Awards certificates, diplomas, and terminal associate degrees. Founded 1967. Setting: 53-acre rural campus. Endowment: $2.7 million. Educational spending for the previous fiscal year: $12,137 per student. Total enrollment: 2,009. Faculty: 125 (77 full-time, 48 part-time). Student-undergrad faculty ratio is 18:1. 813 applied, 90% were admitted. Full-time: 730 students, 49% women, 51% men. Part-time: 1,279 students, 63% women, 37% men. Students come from 20 states and territories, 10% from out-of-state. 0.4% American Indian or Alaska Native, non-Hispanic/Latino; 2% Hispanic/Latino; 2% Black or African American, non-Hispanic/Latino; 0.6% Asian, non-Hispanic/Latino. 40% 25 or older, 7% live on campus, 23% transferred in. Core. Calendar: semesters. Academic remediation for entering students, ESL program, services for LD students, advanced placement, self-designed majors, independent study, distance learning, double major, summer session for credit, part-time degree program, internships. Off campus study at Lakeshore Technical College (pharmacy technician); Western Technical College (respiratory therapist), Nicolet College (university transfer liberal arts).

Entrance Requirements: Open admission. Options: electronic application, early admission. Required: high school transcript, interview. Required for some: TABE, HESI for nursing students. Entrance: noncompetitive. Application deadlines: rolling, rolling for nonresidents. Notification: continuous, continuous for nonresidents. Preference given to district residents. Transfer credits accepted: Yes.

Collegiate Environment: Orientation program. Social organizations: 3 open to all. Most popular organizations: Student Senate, Student Ambassadors, Phi Theta Kappa. Major annual events: Spring and Fall Campus Picnics, Variety Shows/Comedians/Open-Mic, Motivational Speakers. Student services: personal-psychological counseling. Campus security: 24-hour emergency response devices. 112 college housing spaces available; all were occupied in 2018-19. No special consideration for freshman housing applicants. Option: coed housing available. Knox Learning Center. Books: 8,867 (physical), 180,598 (digital/electronic); Serial titles: 109 (physical); Databases: 42. Weekly public service hours: 58. Operations spending for the previous fiscal year: $11,049. 107 computers available on campus for general student use. A campuswide network can be accessed from off-campus. Students can access the following: online class registration. Staffed computer lab on campus provides training in use of computers, software, and the Internet.

■ UNIVERSITY OF WISCONSIN-BARABOO/SAUK COUNTY

1006 Connie Rd.
Baraboo, WI 53913
Tel: (608)356-8351
Fax: (608)356-4074
Web Site: www.baraboo.uwc.edu

Description: State-supported, primarily 2-year, coed. Part of University of Wisconsin System. Awards certificates, transfer associate, terminal associate, and bachelor's degrees. Founded 1968. Setting: 68-acre small town campus with easy access to Madison. Total enrollment: 512. Student-undergrad faculty ratio is 16:1. Academic area with the most degrees conferred: liberal arts/general studies. Calendar: semesters. Academic remediation for entering students, services for LD students, advanced placement, self-designed majors, honors program, independent study, distance learning, summer session for credit, part-time degree program, external degree program, internships. Off campus study at other units of the University of Wisconsin Colleges, four-year campuses of the University of Wisconsin and University of Wisconsin Extension, also UW Colleges distance learning, University of Plymouth Colleges, England. Study abroad program.

Entrance Requirements: Option: electronic application. Required: high school transcript, ACT. Application deadlines: 8/30, rolling for nonresidents. SAT Reasoning Test deadline: 8/31. SAT Subject Test deadline: 8/31. Transfer credits accepted: Yes.

Collegiate Environment: Orientation program. Drama-theater group, choral group, student-run newspaper. Social organizations: 25 open to all. Student services: personal-psychological counseling. T. N. Savides Library plus 1 other.

■ UNIVERSITY OF WISCONSIN-BARRON COUNTY

1800 College Dr.
Rice Lake, WI 54868
Tel: (715)234-8176
Web Site: www.barron.uwc.edu

Description: State-supported, primarily 2-year, coed. Part of University of Wisconsin System. Awards transfer associate, terminal associate, and bachelor's degrees. Founded 1968. Setting: 110-acre small town campus. Total enrollment: 505. Student-undergrad faculty ratio is 12:1. Academic area with the most degrees conferred: liberal arts/general studies. Calendar: semesters. Academic remediation for entering students, services for LD students, advanced placement, independent study, distance learning, summer session for credit, part-time degree program, adult/continuing education programs, internships. Off campus study at other units of the University of Wisconsin Colleges, four-year campuses of the University of Wisconsin. Study abroad program.

Entrance Requirements: Options: electronic application, deferred admission. Required: high school transcript, ACT. Application deadline: 8/30. SAT Reasoning Test deadline: 8/31. SAT Subject Test deadline: 8/31. Transfer credits accepted: Yes.

Collegiate Environment: Orientation program. Social organizations: 26 open to all. UW Barron County Library plus 1 other.

■ UNIVERSITY OF WISCONSIN COLLEGES ONLINE

34 Schroeder Ct.
Ste. 200
Madison, WI 53711
Web Site: www.online.uwc.edu

Description: State-supported, 2-year, coed. Awards certificates, transfer associate, and terminal associate degrees. Founded 1998. Total enrollment: 2,370. Student-undergrad faculty ratio is 20:1. Calendar: semesters. Part-time degree program, external degree program.

Entrance Requirements: Application deadline: 8/30. SAT Reasoning Test deadline: 8/31. SAT Subject Test deadline: 8/31. Transfer credits accepted: Yes.

■ UNIVERSITY OF WISCONSIN-EAU CLAIRE

PO Box 4004
Eau Claire, WI 54702-4004
Tel: (715)836-2637
Fax: (715)836-2380
E-mail: admissions@uwec.edu
Web Site: www.uwec.edu

Description: State-supported, comprehensive, coed. Part of University of Wisconsin System. Awards associate, bachelor's, master's, and doctoral degrees and post-master's certificates. Founded 1916. Setting: 337-acre small town campus with easy access to Minneapolis-St. Paul. Endowment: $73.3 million. Research spending for the previous fiscal year: $1.2 million. Educational spending for the previous fiscal year: $6110 per student. Total enrollment: 10,811. Faculty: 559 (381 full-time, 178 part-time). Student-undergrad faculty ratio is 22:1. 5,855 applied, 86% were admitted. 17% from top 10% of their high school class, 48% from top quarter, 93% from top half. 54 valedictorians. Full-time: 9,448 students, 62% women, 38% men. Part-time: 665 students, 62% women, 38% men. Students come from 41 states and territories, 24 other countries, 30% from out-of-state. 0.2% American Indian or Alaska Native, non-Hispanic/Latino; 3% Hispanic/Latino; 1% Black or African American, non-Hispanic/Latino; 3% Asian, non-Hispanic/Latino; 2% international. 6% 25 or older, 35% live on campus, 5% transferred in. Retention: 82% of full-time freshmen returned the following year. Academic areas with the most degrees conferred: business/marketing; health professions and related sciences; education. Core. Calendar: semesters. Academic remediation for entering students, ESL program, services for LD students, advanced placement, accelerated degree program, self-designed majors, honors program, independent study, distance learning, double major, summer session for credit, part-time degree program, external degree program, co-op programs and internships, graduate courses open to undergrads. Off campus study at National Student Exchange. Study abroad program. ROTC: Army.

Entrance Requirements: Options: electronic application, early admission, international baccalaureate accepted. Required: essay, high school transcript, SAT or ACT. Entrance: moderately difficult. Application deadline: 8/20. Notification: continuous. SAT Reasoning Test deadline: 6/30. SAT Subject Test deadline: 6/30. Transfer credits accepted: Yes. Applicants placed on waiting list: 475. Wait-listed applicants offered admission: 100.

Costs Per Year: Application fee: $50. State resident tuition: $7361 full-time, $307 per credit part-time. Nonresident tuition: $15,637 full-time, $652 per credit part-time. Mandatory fees: $1459 full-time, $61 per credit part-time. Full-time tuition and fees vary according to program and reciprocity agreements. Part-time tuition and fees vary according to program and reciprocity agreements. College room and board: $7813. College room only: $4657. Room and board charges vary according to board plan and housing facility.

Collegiate Environment: Orientation program. Drama-theater group, choral group, marching band, student-run newspaper, radio station. Social organizations: 230 open to all; national fraternities, national sororities; 1% of eligible men and 1% of eligible women are members. Most popular organizations: Student Wisconsin Education Association, Pre- Professional Health Club, Kinesiology Club, RHA (Residence Hall Association), Blugold Beginnings. Major annual events: Blugold Organizations Bash (BOB), Homecoming, Davies Center Welcome Home Party. Student services: legal services, health clinic, personal-psychological counseling, women's center. Campus security: 24-hour emergency response devices and patrols, student patrols, late night transport-escort service, controlled dormitory access. 4,015 college housing spaces available; 3,700 were occupied in 2018-19. Freshmen guaranteed college housing. On-campus residence required through sophomore year. Option: coed housing available. William D. McIntyre Library. Books: 432,031 (physical), 203,469 (digital/electronic); Serial titles: 141 (physical), 216,577 (digital/electronic); Databases: 233. Weekly public service hours: 112; study areas open 24 hours, 5-7 days a week; students can reserve study rooms. Operations spending for the previous fiscal year: $3 million. 900 computers available on campus for general student use. A campuswide network can be accessed from student residence rooms and from off campus. Students can access the following: online class registration, course management system, online library databases and card catalog, other online library services (e.g. Interlibrary loan), library reference staff online chat, check open seats in computer labs, laptop check out, poster printing. Staffed computer lab on campus provides training in use of computers, software, and the Internet.

Community Environment: Eau Claire is a cultural, commercial, educational, and medical center in west-central Wisconsin. The city, which is located at the confluence of the Eau Claire and Chippewa Rivers, is served by air and bus lines. Community facilities and services include numerous hotels, motels, hospitals, churches, restaurants, shopping areas, a public library and YMCA, as well as numerous civic organizations and clubs. The city and the surrounding area abound in colorful, natural beauty and offers numerous year-round recreational activities. Local lakes and parks provide opportunities to enjoy aquatic sports, golf, skiing, skating, tennis, baseball, and many other sports.

■ UNIVERSITY OF WISCONSIN-FOND DU LAC

400 University Dr.
Fond du Lac, WI 54935
Tel: (920)929-1100
Web Site: www.fdl.uwc.edu

Description: State-supported, 2-year, coed. Part of University of Wisconsin System. Awards certificates, transfer associate, and terminal associate degrees. Founded 1972. Setting: 183-acre small town campus with easy access to Milwaukee. Total enrollment: 519. Student-undergrad faculty ratio is 15:1. 1% from out-of-state. Core. Calendar: semesters. Academic remediation for entering students, services for LD students, advanced placement, accelerated degree program, independent study, distance learning, summer session for credit, part-time degree program, external degree program, co-op programs. Off campus study at other units of the University of Wisconsin Colleges, four-year campuses of the University of Wisconsin. Study abroad program.

Entrance Requirements: Option: electronic application. Required: high school transcript, ACT. Application deadline: 8/30. SAT Reasoning Test deadline: 8/31. SAT Subject Test deadline: 8/31. Transfer credits accepted: Yes.

Collegiate Environment: Orientation program. Drama-theater group, choral group, student-run newspaper. Social organizations: 10 open to all. Student services: personal-psychological counseling. Campus security: 24-hour emergency response devices. UW-Fond du Lac Library plus 1 other. 65 computers available on campus for general student use. A campuswide network can be accessed. Students can access the following: online class registration, financial aid application. Staffed computer lab on campus provides training in use of computers.

■ UNIVERSITY OF WISCONSIN-FOX VALLEY

1478 Midway Rd.
Menasha, WI 54952
Tel: (920)832-2600
Fax: (920)832-2674
Web Site: www.uwfox.uwc.edu

Description: State-supported, 2-year, coed. Part of University of Wisconsin System. Awards certificates, transfer associate, and terminal associate degrees. Founded 1960. Setting: 45-acre small town campus. Total enrollment: 1,364. Student-undergrad faculty ratio is 17:1. Core. Calendar: semesters. Academic remediation for entering students, services for LD students, advanced placement, accelerated degree program, honors program, independent study, distance learning, summer session for credit, part-time degree program, external degree program, co-op programs and internships. Off campus study at other units of the University of Wisconsin Colleges and four-year campuses of the University of Wisconsin. Study abroad program.

Entrance Requirements: Option: electronic application. Required: high school transcript, ACT. Application deadline: 8/30. SAT Reasoning Test deadline: 8/31. SAT Subject Test deadline: 8/31. Transfer credits accepted: Yes.

Collegiate Environment: Orientation program. Drama-theater group, choral group, student-run newspaper, radio station. Social organizations: 36 open to all. Student services: personal-psychological counseling. Campus security: 24-hour emergency response devices, late night transport-escort service. UW-Fox Valley Library plus 1 other. Students can reserve study rooms. 150 computers available on campus for general student use. A campuswide network can be accessed from off-campus. Students can access the following: online class registration, financial aid application. Staffed computer lab on campus.

■ UNIVERSITY OF WISCONSIN-GREEN BAY

2420 Nicolet Dr.
Green Bay, WI 54311-7001
Tel: (920)465-2000
Fax: (920)465-2032
E-mail: uwgb@uwgb.edu
Web Site: www.uwgb.edu

Description: State-supported, comprehensive, coed. Part of University of Wisconsin System. Awards associate, bachelor's, and master's degrees. Founded 1968. Setting: 700-acre suburban campus with easy access to Milwaukee. Endowment: $28 million. Research spending for the previous fiscal year: $1.2 million. Educational spending for the previous fiscal year: $6125 per student. Total enrollment: 7,030. Faculty: 308 (185 full-time, 123 part-time). Student-undergrad faculty ratio is 22:1. 2,126 applied, 92% were admitted. Full-time: 4,009 students, 65% women, 35% men. Part-time: 2,749 students, 70% women, 30% men. Students come from 40 states and territories, 38 other countries, 8% from out-of-state. 1% American Indian or Alaska Native, non-Hispanic/Latino; 4% Hispanic/Latino; 2% Black or African American, non-Hispanic/Latino; 3% Asian, non-Hispanic/Latino; 0.1% Native Hawaiian or other Pacific Islander, non-Hispanic/Latino; 1% international. 30% 25 or older, 33% live on campus, 10% transferred in. Retention: 74% of full-time freshmen returned the following year. Academic areas with the most degrees conferred: business/marketing; interdisciplinary studies; liberal arts/general studies. Core. Calendar: semesters. Academic remediation for entering students, services for LD students, advanced placement, self-designed majors, independent study, distance learning, double major, summer session for credit, part-time degree program, external degree program, adult/continuing education programs, internships, graduate courses open to undergrads. Off campus study at National Student Exchange; Collaborative Nursing Program (BSN@Home); Northeast Wisconsin Engineering Program (Milwaukee). Study abroad program. ROTC: Army (c).

Entrance Requirements: Options: electronic application, deferred admission, international baccalaureate accepted. Required: essay, high school transcript, SAT or ACT. Required for some: interview. Entrance: moderately difficult. Application deadline: rolling. Notification: continuous. Transfer credits accepted: Yes. Applicants placed on waiting list: 0. Wait-listed applicants offered admission: 0.

Collegiate Environment: Orientation program. Drama-theater group, choral group, student-run newspaper, radio station. Social organizations: 80 open to all; local fraternities, local sororities; 1% of eligible men and 1% of eligible women are members. Most popular organizations: Good Times, Psychology and Human Development Club, Student Ambassadors, Residence Hall Apartment Association, Student Government Association. Major annual events: Welcome Week, Frost Fest, Senior Celebration. Student services: health clinic, personal-psychological counseling. Campus security: 24-hour emergency response devices and patrols, late night transport-escort service, controlled dormitory access. Cofrin Library. Books: 353,331 (physical); Serial titles: 7,592 (physical); Databases: 179. Weekly public service hours: 100; students can reserve study rooms. Operations spending for the previous fiscal year: $1.4 million. 550 computers available on campus for general student use. Computer purchase/lease plans available. A campuswide network can be accessed from student residence rooms and from off campus. Students can access the following: online class registration, online degree progress, online financial records and bill paying. Staffed computer lab on campus provides training in use of computers, software, and the Internet.

Community Environment: Green Bay, a trading and transportation center in Northeastern Wisconsin, is a city of approximately 100,000 inhabitants located in Wisconsin's third largest population area. The city has an outstanding regional museum, an excellent public library system and many parks. A community symphony orchestra, community chorus and several theater groups provide cultural enrichment and added opportunities for participation and performance by qualified students. Nearby resort areas provide a variety of recreational opportunities and summer jobs for students. The university is easy to reach by air, bus or interstate highway.

■ UNIVERSITY OF WISCONSIN-LA CROSSE

1725 State St.
La Crosse, WI 54601-3742
Tel: (608)785-8000
Fax: (608)785-6695
E-mail: admissions@uwlax.edu
Web Site: www.uwlax.edu

Description: State-supported, comprehensive, coed. Part of University of Wisconsin System. Awards associate, bachelor's, master's, and doctoral degrees and post-master's certificates. Founded 1909. Setting: 128-acre suburban campus. Endowment: $25.6 million. Research spending for the previous fiscal year: $3.3 million. Educational spending for the previous fiscal year: $6914 per student. Total enrollment: 10,542. Faculty: 625 (460 full-time, 165 part-time). Student-undergrad faculty ratio is 19:1. 6,048 applied, 78% were admitted. 21% from top 10% of their high school class, 57% from top quarter, 96% from top half. 54 valedictorians. Full-time: 9,130 students, 57% women, 43% men. Part-time: 546 students, 47% women, 53% men. Students come from 42 states and territories, 30 other countries, 17% from out-of-state. 0.1% American Indian or Alaska Native, non-Hispanic/Latino; 3% Hispanic/Latino; 0.8% Black or African American, non-Hispanic/Latino; 2% Asian, non-Hispanic/Latino; 1% international. 3% 25 or older, 35% live on campus, 4% transferred in. Retention: 86% of full-time freshmen returned the following year. Academic areas with the most degrees conferred: business/marketing; biological/life sciences; health professions and related sciences. Core. Calendar: semesters. Academic remediation for entering students, ESL program, services for LD students, advanced placement, honors program, independent study, distance learning, double major, summer session for credit, part-time degree program, internships, graduate courses open to undergrads. Off campus study at National Student Exchange, UW System Online Consortium. Study abroad program. ROTC: Army.

Entrance Requirements: Options: electronic application, international baccalaureate accepted. Required: essay, high school transcript, SAT or ACT. Entrance: moderately difficult. Application deadline: rolling. Notification: continuous. Transfer credits accepted: Yes. Applicants placed on waiting list: 0. Wait-listed applicants offered admission: 0.

Costs Per Year: Application fee: $50. State resident tuition: $7885 full-time. Nonresident tuition: $16,254 full-time. Mandatory fees: $1348 full-time. Full-time tuition and fees vary according to reciprocity agreements. College room and board: $6331. College room only: $3825. Room and board charges vary according to board plan and housing facility.

Collegiate Environment: Orientation program. Drama-theater group, choral group, marching band, student-run newspaper, radio station. Social organizations: 250 open to all; national fraternities, national sororities, Academic, social, religious, volunteer, diversity; 1% of eligible men and 1% of eligible women are members. Most popular organizations: Sports and Activities Club, Residential Hall Council, Religious/Spiritual Organizations, Human Diversity Organizations, Departmental/Professional. Major annual events: Sample the City, Involvement Fest, Campus Activities Board Events. Student services: legal services, health clinic, personal-psychological counseling. Campus security: 24-hour emergency response devices and patrols, late night transport-escort service, controlled dormitory access. College housing designed to accommodate 3,097 students; 3,401 undergraduates lived in college housing during 2018-19. Freshmen given priority for college housing. On-campus residence required in freshman year. Option: coed housing available. Murphy Library plus 1 other. Books: 422,070 (physical), 670,354 (digital/electronic); Serial titles: 7,822 (physical), 135,820 (digital/electronic); Databases: 230. Weekly public service hours: 107; students can reserve study rooms. Operations spending for the previous fiscal year: $3.4 million. 200 computers available on campus for general student use. A campuswide network can be accessed from student residence rooms and from off campus. Students can access the following: online class registration. Staffed computer lab on campus provides training in use of computers, software, and the Internet.

Community Environment: Founded in 1842 as an Indian trading post, La Crosse is situated on the east bank of the Mississippi River in southern Wisconsin. It is approximately midway between Minneapolis-St. Paul and Chicago. Noted for its exceptional natural beauty and outstanding recreational opportunities, the city is the industrial, commercial and medical center of Wisconsin's famous"Coulee Country." The population is approximately 50,000. All commercial transportation is convenient.

■ UNIVERSITY OF WISCONSIN-MADISON

500 Lincoln Dr.
Madison, WI 53706-1380
Tel: (608)262-1234
Fax: (608)262-1429
E-mail: onwisconsin@admissions.wisc.edu
Web Site: www.wisc.edu

Description: State-supported, university, coed. Part of University of Wisconsin System. Awards bachelor's, master's, and doctoral degrees. Founded 1848. Setting: 936-acre urban campus with easy access to Milwaukee. Endowment: $2.5 billion. Research spending for the previous fiscal year: $928 million. Total enrollment: 43,820. Faculty: 2,858 (2,392 full-time, 466 part-time). Student-undergrad faculty ratio is 18:1. 35,615 applied, 54% were admitted. 52% from top 10% of their high school class, 89% from top quarter, 99% from top half. Full-time: 29,016 students, 52% women, 48% men. Part-time: 3,180 students, 47% women, 53% men. Students come from 52 states and territories, 79 other countries, 34% from out-of-state. 0.2% American Indian or Alaska Native, non-Hispanic/Latino; 5% Hispanic/Latino; 2% Black or African American, non-Hispanic/Latino; 6% Asian, non-Hispanic/Latino; 0.1% Native Hawaiian or other Pacific Islander, non-Hispanic/Latino; 9% international. 2% 25 or older, 25% live on campus, 4% transferred in. Retention: 95% of full-time freshmen returned the following year. Academic areas with the most degrees conferred: business/marketing; biological/life sciences; engineering. Core. Calendar: semesters. ESL program, services for LD students, advanced placement, accelerated degree program, self-designed majors, honors program, independent study, distance learning, double major, summer session for credit, part-time degree program, adult/continuing education programs, co-op programs and internships, graduate courses open to undergrads. Study abroad program. ROTC: Army, Naval, Air Force.

Entrance Requirements: Options: electronic application, early action, deferred admission, international baccalaureate accepted. Required: essay, high school transcript, SAT or ACT. Recommended: 2 recommendations. Entrance: very difficult. Application deadlines: 2/1, 11/1 for early action. Notification: 3/31, 1/31 for early action. SAT Reasoning Test deadline: 2/6. Transfer credits accepted: Yes.

Costs Per Year: Application fee: $60. State resident tuition: $9,273 full-time, $386.39 per credit hour part-time. Nonresident tuition: $35,523 full-time, $1,480.13 per credit hour part-time. Mandatory fees: $1,282 full-time, $101.09 per credit hour part-time. Full-time tuition and fees vary according to program and reciprocity agreements. Part-time tuition and fees vary according to course load, program, and reciprocity agreements. College room and board: $11,114. Room and board charges vary according to board plan and housing facility.

Collegiate Environment: Orientation program. Drama-theater group, choral group, marching band, student-run newspaper, radio station. Social organizations: 995 open to all; national fraternities, national sororities, local fraternities, local sororities; 9% of eligible men and 8% of eligible women are members. Student services: health clinic, personal-psychological counseling, women's center. Campus security: 24-hour emergency response devices and patrols, late night transport-escort service, controlled dormitory access. Memorial Library plus 40 others. Study areas open 24 hours, 5-7 days a week; students can reserve study rooms. Operations spending for the previous fiscal year: $35.3 million. 1,000 computers available on campus for general student use. A campuswide network can be accessed from student residence rooms and from off campus. Students can access the following: online class registration. Staffed computer lab on campus provides training in use of computers, software, and the Internet.

Community Environment: Founded in 1836, the city was named for James Madison, the fourth President of the United States, and is the capital of Wisconsin. Madison is the center of one of the richest dairy regions in America and has over 200 industries. The city is also important as a medical center with its 12 hospitals and its manufacturing of precision surgical instruments. Recreational facilities include 10 golf courses, 3 of which are public, tennis courts, and a number of beaches for water sports. Fishing boats are for hire. Points of interest are the Henry Vilas Park Zoo, Nevin Fish Hatchery, U.S. Forest Products Laboratory, State Historical Society Museum, and the Wisconsin State Capitol which is one of the most impressive in the United States.

■ UNIVERSITY OF WISCONSIN-MANITOWOC

705 Viebahn St.
Manitowoc, WI 54220
Tel: (920)683-4700
Fax: (920)683-4776
Web Site: www.manitowoc.uwc.edu

Description: State-supported, 2-year, coed. Part of University of Wisconsin System. Awards certificates, transfer associate, and terminal associate degrees. Founded 1962. Setting: 40-acre small town campus with easy access to Milwaukee. Total enrollment: 354. Student-undergrad faculty ratio is 14:1. 458 applied, 100% were admitted. Core. Calendar: semesters. Academic remediation for entering students, services for LD students, advanced placement, self-designed majors, distance learning, part-time degree program, external degree program, co-op programs and internships. Off campus study at other units of the University of Wisconsin Colleges, four-year campuses of the University of Wisconsin. Study abroad program.

Entrance Requirements: Options: electronic application, early admission, deferred admission, international baccalaureate accepted. Required: high school transcript, SAT or ACT. Application deadline: 8/30. SAT Reasoning Test deadline: 8/31. SAT Subject Test deadline: 8/31.

Collegiate Environment: Orientation program. Drama-theater group, choral group, student-run newspaper. Social organizations: 21 open to all. Student services: personal-psychological counseling. UW-Manitowoc Library plus 1 other. 65 computers available on campus for general student use. A campuswide network can be accessed from off-campus. Students can access the following: online class registration, financial aid application. Staffed computer lab on campus.

■ UNIVERSITY OF WISCONSIN-MARATHON COUNTY

518 S 7th Ave.
Wausau, WI 54401
Tel: (715)261-6100; Free: 888-367-8962
Fax: (715)261-6333
Web Site: www.uwmc.uwc.edu

Description: State-supported, 2-year, coed. Part of University of Wisconsin System. Awards certificates, transfer associate, and terminal associate degrees. Founded 1997. Setting: 7-acre small town campus. Total enrollment: 838. Student-undergrad faculty ratio is 17:1. Core. Calendar: semesters. Academic remediation for entering students, advanced placement, self-designed majors, honors program, summer session for credit, part-time degree program, external degree program. Off campus study at other units of the University of Wisconsin Colleges, four-year campuses of the University of Wisconsin. Study abroad program. ROTC: Army (c).

Entrance Requirements: Options: electronic application, early admission, deferred admission. Required: high school transcript, ACT. Application deadline: 8/29. SAT Reasoning Test deadline: 8/31. SAT Subject Test deadline: 8/31. Transfer credits accepted: Yes.

Collegiate Environment: Orientation program. Social organizations: 12 open to all. Campus security: 24-hour emergency response devices, controlled dormitory access. UW-Marathon County Library plus 1 other.

■ UNIVERSITY OF WISCONSIN-MARINETTE

750 W Bay Shore
Marinette, WI 54143
Tel: (715)735-4300
Web Site: www.marinette.uwc.edu

Description: State-supported, 2-year, coed. Part of University of Wisconsin

System. Awards certificates, transfer associate, and terminal associate degrees. Founded 1972. Setting: 36-acre small town campus. Total enrollment: 286. Student-undergrad faculty ratio is 10:1. Core. Calendar: semesters. Academic remediation for entering students, ESL program, services for LD students, advanced placement, independent study, distance learning, summer session for credit, part-time degree program, external degree program, co-op programs and internships. Off campus study at other units of the University of Wisconsin Colleges, four-year campuses of the University of Wisconsin.

Entrance Requirements: Option: electronic application. Required: high school transcript, ACT. Application deadline: 8/30. SAT Reasoning Test deadline: 8/31. SAT Subject Test deadline: 8/31. Transfer credits accepted: Yes.

Collegiate Environment: Orientation program. Drama-theater group, choral group, student-run newspaper. Social organizations: 5 open to all. Most popular organizations: Student Senate, Writers Club/Literature Club, Phi Theta Kappa, Student Ambassadors. Major annual events: Spring Banquet, End of Year Party, Commencement. Student services: personal-psychological counseling. UW-Marinette Library plus 1 other.

■ **UNIVERSITY OF WISCONSIN-MARSHFIELD/WOOD COUNTY**
2000 W 5th St.
Marshfield, WI 54449
Tel: (715)389-6500
Web Site: marshfield.uwc.edu
Description: State-supported, primarily 2-year, coed. Part of University of Wisconsin System. Awards certificates, transfer associate, terminal associate, and bachelor's degrees. Founded 1963. Setting: 114-acre small town campus. Total enrollment: 535. Student-undergrad faculty ratio is 15:1. Academic area with the most degrees conferred: liberal arts/general studies. Core. Calendar: semesters. Academic remediation for entering students, services for LD students, advanced placement, accelerated degree program, independent study, distance learning, summer session for credit, part-time degree program, external degree program. Off campus study at other units of the University of Wisconsin Colleges, four-year campuses of the University of Wisconsin. Study abroad program. ROTC: Army (c).
Entrance Requirements: Options: electronic application, early admission, deferred admission. Required: high school transcript, ACT. Application deadline: 8/30. SAT Reasoning Test deadline: 8/31. SAT Subject Test deadline: 8/31. Transfer credits accepted: Yes.
Collegiate Environment: Orientation program. Drama-theater group, choral group, student-run newspaper. Social organizations: 12 open to all. Campus security: 24-hour patrols, patrols by city police. Hamilton Roddis Memorial Library plus 1 other.

■ **UNIVERSITY OF WISCONSIN-MILWAUKEE**
PO Box 413
Milwaukee, WI 53201-0413
Tel: (414)229-1122
Fax: (414)229-6940
E-mail: uwmlook@uwm.edu
Web Site: www.uwm.edu
Description: State-supported, university, coed. Part of University of Wisconsin System. Awards bachelor's, master's, and doctoral degrees and post-master's certificates. Founded 1956. Setting: 104-acre urban campus with easy access to Milwaukee. Endowment: $167.2 million. Research spending for the previous fiscal year: $51.8 million. Total enrollment: 24,933. Faculty: 1,546 (992 full-time, 554 part-time). Student-undergrad faculty ratio is 19:1. 10,046 applied, 72% were admitted. 10% from top 10% of their high school class, 21% from top quarter, 68% from top half. Full-time: 16,669 students, 53% women, 47% men. Part-time: 3,587 students, 54% women, 46% men. Students come from 52 states and territories, 91 other countries, 11% from out-of-state. 0.4% American Indian or Alaska Native, non-Hispanic/Latino; 11% Hispanic/Latino; 7% Black or African American, non-Hispanic/Latino; 7% Asian, non-Hispanic/Latino; 0.1% Native Hawaiian or other Pacific Islander, non-Hispanic/Latino; 4% international. 24% 25 or older, 20% live on campus, 7% transferred in. Retention: 74% of full-time freshmen returned the following year. Academic areas with the most degrees conferred: business/marketing; health professions and related sciences; engineering. Core. Calendar: semesters. Academic remediation for entering students, ESL program, services for LD students, advanced placement, accelerated degree program, self-designed majors, freshman honors college, honors program, independent study, distance learning, double major, summer session for credit, part-time degree program, external degree program,

adult/continuing education programs, co-op programs and internships, graduate courses open to undergrads. Off campus study. Study abroad program. ROTC: Army (c), Naval (c), Air Force (c).
Entrance Requirements: Options: electronic application, deferred admission, international baccalaureate accepted. Required: high school transcript. Recommended: essay. Required for some: SAT or ACT, TOEFL for students whose native language is not English and who were not educated in an entirely English-speaking country. Entrance: moderately difficult. Application deadline: rolling. Notification: continuous. SAT Reasoning Test deadline: 8/10. Transfer credits accepted: Yes.
Costs Per Year: Application fee: $50. Area resident tuition: $9588 full-time. State resident tuition: $9588 full-time. Nonresident tuition: $20,868 full-time. College room and board: $10,792.
Collegiate Environment: Orientation program. Drama-theater group, choral group, student-run newspaper. Social organizations: national fraternities, national sororities, local fraternities, local sororities. Major annual events: Fall Welcome, PantherFest. Student services: legal services, health clinic, personal-psychological counseling, women's center. Campus security: 24-hour emergency response devices and patrols, student patrols, late night transport-escort service, controlled dormitory access. 4,283 college housing spaces available; 3,797 were occupied in 2018-19. Freshmen given priority for college housing. On-campus residence required in freshman year. Option: coed housing available. Golda Meir Library. Books: 2.5 million (physical), 178,268 (digital/electronic); Serial titles: 112,752 (physical). Students can reserve study rooms. Operations spending for the previous fiscal year: $9.2 million. 500 computers available on campus for general student use. Computer purchase/lease plans available. A campuswide network can be accessed from student residence rooms and from off campus. Students can access the following: online class registration. Staffed computer lab on campus (open 24 hours a day) provides training in use of computers, software, and the Internet.
Community Environment: Located on the west shore of Lake Michigan, Milwaukee (population 578,800) is the largest city in Wisconsin. All major forms of commercial transportation are available. Milwaukee is the nation's brewing center, as well as a major grain market and manufacturing center. Products of industry are metal, machinery, food, leather, chemicals, textiles, electrical machinery, and other items. The city is the headquarters of the Lake States National Forest Region. The county has a park system and many of the units contain public golf courses, tennis courts, and other recreational facilities. Wisconsin's State Fair is held each year in August.

■ **UNIVERSITY OF WISCONSIN-OSHKOSH**
800 Algoma Blvd.
Oshkosh, WI 54901
Tel: (920)424-1234
Fax: (920)424-1098
E-mail: oshadmuw@uwosh.edu
Web Site: www.uwosh.edu
Description: State-supported, comprehensive, coed. Part of University of Wisconsin System. Awards associate, bachelor's, master's, and doctoral degrees. Founded 1871. Setting: 192-acre suburban campus with easy access to Milwaukee. Total enrollment: 14,411. Faculty: 628 (431 full-time, 197 part-time). Student-undergrad faculty ratio is 22:1. 5,846 applied, 68% were admitted. 11% from top 10% of their high school class, 35% from top quarter, 80% from top half. Full-time: 9,020 students, 57% women, 43% men. Part-time: 4,174 students, 67% women, 33% men. 6% from out-of-state. 0.6% American Indian or Alaska Native, non-Hispanic/Latino; 3% Hispanic/Latino; 2% Black or African American, non-Hispanic/Latino; 4% Asian, non-Hispanic/Latino; 0.1% Native Hawaiian or other Pacific Islander, non-Hispanic/Latino; 0.8% international. 16% 25 or older, 32% live on campus, 7% transferred in. Retention: 75% of full-time freshmen returned the following year. Academic areas with the most degrees conferred: business/marketing; education; health professions and related sciences. Core. Calendar: semesters. Academic remediation for entering students, ESL program, services for LD students, advanced placement, accelerated degree program, self-designed majors, honors program, independent study, distance learning, double major, summer session for credit, part-time degree program, adult/continuing education programs, co-op programs and internships, graduate courses open to undergrads. Study abroad program. ROTC: Army.
Entrance Requirements: Options: electronic application, deferred admission, international baccalaureate accepted. Required: high school transcript, ACT. Recommended: essay. Entrance: moderately difficult. SAT Reasoning Test deadline: 8/1.

Costs Per Year: Application fee: $44. State resident tuition: $7622 full-time. Nonresident tuition: $15,196 full-time. College room and board: $7690. College room only: $4468.

Collegiate Environment: Orientation program. Drama-theater group, choral group, student-run newspaper, radio station. Social organizations: national fraternities, national sororities. Student services: legal services, health clinic, personal-psychological counseling, women's center. Campus security: 24-hour emergency response devices and patrols, student patrols, late night transport-escort service, controlled dormitory access. Forrest R. Polk Library.

Community Environment: A city of 60,000, Oshkosh is situated between Lake Winnebago and Lake Butte des Morts. The Fox River runs through the city with parks and marinas dotting its shores. At historic Wittman Field, the Experimental Aircraft Association's annual international convention is the world's largest.

■ UNIVERSITY OF WISCONSIN-PARKSIDE

900 Wood Rd., Box 2000
Kenosha, WI 53141-2000
Tel: (262)595-2345
Fax: (262)595-2630
E-mail: moldenht@uwp.edu
Web Site: www.uwp.edu

Description: State-supported, comprehensive, coed. Part of University of Wisconsin System. Awards associate, bachelor's, and master's degrees. Founded 1968. Setting: 700-acre suburban campus with easy access to Chicago, Milwaukee. Total enrollment: 4,308. Faculty: 261 (162 full-time, 99 part-time). Student-undergrad faculty ratio is 19:1. 1,743 applied, 80% were admitted. 14% from top 10% of their high school class, 36% from top quarter, 73% from top half. Full-time: 3,275 students, 52% women, 48% men. Part-time: 893 students, 55% women, 45% men. Students come from 33 states and territories, 29 other countries, 18% from out-of-state. 0.1% American Indian or Alaska Native, non-Hispanic/Latino; 16% Hispanic/Latino; 9% Black or African American, non-Hispanic/Latino; 4% Asian, non-Hispanic/Latino; 0.1% Native Hawaiian or other Pacific Islander, non-Hispanic/Latino; 2% international. 21% 25 or older, 19% live on campus, 8% transferred in. Retention: 73% of full-time freshmen returned the following year. Academic areas with the most degrees conferred: business/marketing; homeland security, law enforcement, firefighting, and protective services; biological/life sciences. Core. Calendar: semesters. Academic remediation for entering students, services for LD students, advanced placement, honors program, independent study, distance learning, double major, summer session for credit, part-time degree program, external degree program, adult/continuing education programs, co-op programs and internships, graduate courses open to undergrads. Off campus study at Carthage College. Study abroad program. ROTC: Army, Air Force (c).

Entrance Requirements: Options: electronic application, international baccalaureate accepted. Required: high school transcript, minimum of 17 high school units distribution. Required for some: SAT or ACT. Entrance: moderately difficult. Application deadline: rolling. Notification: continuous. SAT Reasoning Test deadline: 8/1. SAT Subject Test deadline: 8/1. Transfer credits accepted: Yes.

Costs Per Year: Application fee: $50. One-time mandatory fee: $260. State resident tuition: $6298 full-time, $262.43 per credit hour part-time. Nonresident tuition: $14,287 full-time, $595.31 per credit hour part-time. Mandatory fees: $1351 full-time, $45.44 per credit hour part-time. Full-time tuition and fees vary according to course load, program, and reciprocity agreements. Part-time tuition and fees vary according to course load, program, and reciprocity agreements. College room and board: $8026. College room only: $4494. Room and board charges vary according to board plan and housing facility.

Collegiate Environment: Orientation program. Drama-theater group, choral group, student-run newspaper, radio station. Social organizations: 75 open to all; national fraternities, national sororities, local fraternities, local sororities; 1% of eligible men and 1% of eligible women are members. Most popular organizations: Habitat for Humanity, Criminal Justice Association, Next Level Gaming, Parkside Asian Organization, Active Minds. Major annual events: Fall Fest, Worldfest Week, Ice Cream Social. Student services: health clinic, personal-psychological counseling, women's center. Campus security: 24-hour emergency response devices and patrols, late night transport-escort service, controlled dormitory access. UWP Library. Students can reserve study rooms.

Community Environment: See Gateway Technical College.

■ UNIVERSITY OF WISCONSIN-PLATTEVILLE

1 University Plz.
Platteville, WI 53818-3099
Tel: (608)342-1491; Free: 877-897-5288
E-mail: tuescheh@uwplatt.edu
Web Site: www.uwplatt.edu

Description: State-supported, comprehensive, coed. Part of University of Wisconsin System. Awards associate, bachelor's, and master's degrees. Founded 1866. Setting: 821-acre small town campus. Endowment: $28.6 million. Research spending for the previous fiscal year: $1.4 million. Educational spending for the previous fiscal year: $7815 per student. Total enrollment: 8,429. Faculty: 441 (316 full-time, 125 part-time). Student-undergrad faculty ratio is 21:1. 3,711 applied, 79% were admitted. 13% from top 10% of their high school class, 37% from top quarter, 76% from top half. Full-time: 6,751 students, 34% women, 66% men. Part-time: 769 students, 30% women, 70% men. Students come from 26 other countries, 24% from out-of-state. 3% Hispanic/Latino; 1% Black or African American, non-Hispanic/Latino; 1% Asian, non-Hispanic/Latino; 0.1% Native Hawaiian or other Pacific Islander, non-Hispanic/Latino; 1% international. 8% 25 or older, 17% live on campus, 6% transferred in. Retention: 79% of full-time freshmen returned the following year. Academic areas with the most degrees conferred: engineering; agriculture; homeland security, law enforcement, firefighting, and protective services. Core. Calendar: semesters. Academic remediation for entering students, ESL program, services for LD students, advanced placement, self-designed majors, independent study, distance learning, double major, summer session for credit, part-time degree program, external degree program, adult/continuing education programs, co-op programs and internships, graduate courses open to undergrads. Off campus study. Study abroad program. ROTC: Army (c).

Entrance Requirements: Required: high school transcript, SAT or ACT. Recommended: essay. SAT Reasoning Test deadline: 9/1.

Collegiate Environment: Orientation program. Drama-theater group, choral group, marching band, student-run newspaper, radio station. Social organizations: 201 open to all; national fraternities, national sororities, local fraternities, local sororities. Most popular organizations: Criminal Justice Association, Platteville Gaming Association, Dodgeball, American Society of Mechanical Engineers, Outdoor Adventure Club. Major annual events: Welcome Back Concert, Homecoming Parade, Distinguished Lecturer. Student services: health clinic, personal-psychological counseling, women's center. Campus security: 24-hour emergency response devices and patrols, student patrols, late night transport-escort service, controlled dormitory access. Karrmann Library plus 1 other. Books: 167,304 (physical), 59,292 (digital/electronic); Serial titles: 1,151 (physical), 44,687 (digital/electronic); Databases: 123. Weekly public service hours: 87. Operations spending for the previous fiscal year: $1.6 million. 200 computers available on campus for general student use. A campuswide network can be accessed from student residence rooms and from off campus. Students can access the following: online class registration. Staffed computer lab on campus provides training in use of computers, software, and the Internet.

Community Environment: Located in the heart of Wisconsin's dairyland and lead and zinc mining district, Platteville (population 9,850) was settled in 1827. Scheduled air transportation is available from Dubuque, Iowa, 20 miles away. Community facilities include a hospital, library, churches, mining museum, other historical sites, and various civic and service organizations. Recreational activities are golf, hunting, fishing, swimming, tennis, bowling, and horseback riding.

■ UNIVERSITY OF WISCONSIN-RICHLAND

1200 Hwy. 14 W
Richland Center, WI 53581
Tel: (608)647-6186
Fax: (608)647-6225
Web Site: richland.uwc.edu

Description: State-supported, primarily 2-year, coed. Part of University of Wisconsin System. Awards certificates, transfer associate, terminal associate, and bachelor's degrees. Founded 1967. Setting: 135-acre small town campus. Total enrollment: 259. Student-undergrad faculty ratio is 8:1. Academic area with the most degrees conferred: liberal arts/general studies. Calendar: semesters. Academic remediation for entering students, services for LD students, advanced placement, independent study, distance learning, summer session for credit, part-time degree program, external degree program. Off campus study at four-year campuses of the University of Wisconsin, other units of the University of Wisconsin Colleges. Study abroad program.

Entrance Requirements: Option: electronic application. Required: high school transcript, ACT. Application deadline: 8/30. SAT Reasoning Test deadline: 8/31. SAT Subject Test deadline: 8/31. Transfer credits accepted: Yes.

Collegiate Environment: Orientation program. Drama-theater group, choral group. Social organizations: 20 open to all. Student services: personal-psychological counseling. Miller Memorial Library plus 1 other.

■ UNIVERSITY OF WISCONSIN-RIVER FALLS

410 S Third St.
River Falls, WI 54022
Tel: (715)425-3911
Fax: (715)425-0678
E-mail: admissions@uwrf.edu
Web Site: www.uwrf.edu

Description: State-supported, comprehensive, coed. Part of University of Wisconsin System. Awards associate, bachelor's, and master's degrees and post-master's certificates. Founded 1874. Setting: 303-acre suburban campus with easy access to Minneapolis-St. Paul. Endowment: $25.8 million. Research spending for the previous fiscal year: $861,220. Educational spending for the previous fiscal year: $6819 per student. Total enrollment: 6,139. Faculty: 380 (267 full-time, 113 part-time). Student-undergrad faculty ratio is 18:1. 3,209 applied, 75% were admitted. 11% from top 10% of their high school class, 34% from top quarter, 71% from top half. Full-time: 5,206 students, 63% women, 37% men. Part-time: 519 students, 58% women, 42% men. Students come from 33 states and territories, 14 other countries, 50% from out-of-state. 0.1% American Indian or Alaska Native, non-Hispanic/Latino; 4% Hispanic/Latino; 1% Black or African American, non-Hispanic/Latino; 3% Asian, non-Hispanic/Latino; 0.1% Native Hawaiian or other Pacific Islander, non-Hispanic/Latino; 2% international. 8% 25 or older, 47% live on campus, 6% transferred in. Retention: 75% of full-time freshmen returned the following year. Academic areas with the most degrees conferred: business/marketing; agriculture; education. Core. Calendar: semesters. Academic remediation for entering students, ESL program, services for LD students, advanced placement, honors program, independent study, distance learning, double major, summer session for credit, part-time degree program, external degree program, adult/continuing education programs, internships, graduate courses open to undergrads. Off campus study at National Student Exchange. Study abroad program. ROTC: Army.

Entrance Requirements: Options: electronic application, deferred admission, international baccalaureate accepted. Required: essay, high school transcript, SAT or ACT. Recommended: rank in upper 40% of high school class, ACT. Entrance: moderately difficult. Application deadlines: rolling, rolling for nonresidents. Notification: continuous, continuous for nonresidents. Transfer credits accepted: Yes.

Collegiate Environment: Orientation program. Drama-theater group, choral group, student-run newspaper, radio station. Social organizations: 145 open to all; national fraternities, national sororities, local fraternities; 7% of eligible men and 3% of eligible women are members. Most popular organizations: Intervarsity Christian Fellowship, UW Pre-Vet Club, National Association for Music Education, Aspiring Educators, Agricultural Business and Marketing Society. Major annual events: Homecoming, Falcon Frontier Days Rodeo, Finals Fest concert. Student services: health clinic, personal-psychological counseling. Campus security: 24-hour emergency response devices and patrols, student patrols, late night transport-escort service, controlled dormitory access. 2,635 college housing spaces available; 2,446 were occupied in 2018-19. Freshmen guaranteed college housing. On-campus residence required through sophomore year. Options: coed, women-only housing available. Chalmer Davee Library. Books: 268,085 (physical), 433,534 (digital/electronic); Serial titles: 35 (physical). Weekly public service hours: 46; study areas open 24 hours, 5-7 days a week; students can reserve study rooms. 800 computers available on campus for general student use. A campuswide network can be accessed from student residence rooms and from off campus. Students can access the following: online class registration. Staffed computer lab on campus (open 24 hours a day) provides training in use of computers, software, and the Internet.

Community Environment: Location is an important asset to the learning environment of the university. At UW-River Falls, students are exposed to the quiet charm of a friendly community nestled in the scenic St. Croix River Valley. Balanced against that setting is the opportunity and excitement of the metropolitan area of the Twin Cities of Minneapolis and St. Paul, located 20 minutes away. This unique region offers access to internationally renowned theater and cultural resources, major league sports, and an industrial and business complex that provides opportunities for internships and cooperative education experiences as well as employment.

■ UNIVERSITY OF WISCONSIN-ROCK COUNTY

2909 Kellogg Ave.
Janesville, WI 53546
Tel: (608)758-6565; Free: 888-INFO-UWC
Fax: (608)758-6564
Web Site: rock.uwc.edu

Description: State-supported, primarily 2-year, coed. Part of University of Wisconsin System. Awards certificates, transfer associate, terminal associate, and bachelor's degrees. Founded 1966. Setting: 50-acre small town campus with easy access to Milwaukee. Total enrollment: 970. Student-undergrad faculty ratio is 16:1. Academic area with the most degrees conferred: liberal arts/general studies. Core. Calendar: semesters. Academic remediation for entering students, services for LD students, advanced placement, distance learning, summer session for credit, part-time degree program, external degree program. Off campus study at other units of the University of Wisconsin Colleges, four-year campuses of the University of Wisconsin.

Entrance Requirements: Options: electronic application, deferred admission. Required: high school transcript, ACT. Application deadline: 8/30. SAT Reasoning Test deadline: 8/31. SAT Subject Test deadline: 8/31. Transfer credits accepted: Yes.

Collegiate Environment: Orientation program. Social organizations: 18 open to all. Gary J. Lenox Library plus 1 other.

■ UNIVERSITY OF WISCONSIN-SHEBOYGAN

One University Dr.
Sheboygan, WI 53081
Tel: (920)459-6600
Fax: (920)459-6602
Web Site: www.sheboygan.uwc.edu

Description: State-supported, 2-year, coed. Part of University of Wisconsin System. Awards certificates, transfer associate, and terminal associate degrees. Founded 1933. Setting: 70-acre small town campus with easy access to Milwaukee. Total enrollment: 602. Student-undergrad faculty ratio is 14:1. Core. Calendar: semesters. Academic remediation for entering students, ESL program, services for LD students, advanced placement, independent study, distance learning, summer session for credit, part-time degree program, external degree program, co-op programs. Off campus study at other units of the University of Wisconsin Colleges, four-year campuses of the University of Wisconsin.

Entrance Requirements: Option: electronic application. Required: high school transcript, ACT. Application deadline: 8/30. SAT Reasoning Test deadline: 8/31. SAT Subject Test deadline: 8/31. Transfer credits accepted: Yes.

Collegiate Environment: Orientation program. Drama-theater group, choral group, student-run newspaper. Social organizations: 15 open to all; Phi Theta Kappa Honor Society. Student services: personal-psychological counseling. Campus security: 24-hour patrols by city police. University Library plus 1 other.

■ UNIVERSITY OF WISCONSIN-STEVENS POINT

2100 Main St.
Stevens Point, WI 54481-3897
Tel: (715)346-0123
Fax: (715)346-2561
E-mail: bjordan@uwsp.edu
Web Site: www.uwsp.edu

Description: State-supported, comprehensive, coed. Part of University of Wisconsin System. Awards associate, bachelor's, master's, and doctoral degrees. Founded 1894. Setting: 400-acre small town campus. Endowment: $28.6 million. Research spending for the previous fiscal year: $3.1 million. Total enrollment: 8,109. Faculty: 476 (365 full-time, 111 part-time). Student-undergrad faculty ratio is 17:1. 6,857 applied, 81% were admitted. 8% from top 10% of their high school class, 23% from top quarter, 79% from top half. Students come from 41 states and territories, 29 other countries, 11% from out-of-state. 0.4% American Indian or Alaska Native, non-Hispanic/Latino; 4% Hispanic/Latino; 2% Black or African American, non-Hispanic/Latino; 3% Asian, non-Hispanic/Latino; 0.1% Native Hawaiian or other Pacific Islander, non-Hispanic/Latino; 2% international. 10% 25 or older, 37% live on campus. Retention: 73% of full-time freshmen returned the following year. Academic areas with the most degrees conferred: natural resources/environmental science; business/marketing; health professions and related sciences. Core. Calendar: semesters. Academic remediation for entering students, ESL program, services for LD students, advanced placement, accelerated degree program, self-designed majors, independent study, distance learning, double major, summer session for credit, part-time degree program, co-op programs and internships, graduate courses open to undergrads. Off campus study at University of Wisconsin campuses at Oshkosh, Eau Claire, Fond du Lac, Marinette, Marshfield, Menasha, and Marathon. Study abroad program. ROTC: Army.

Entrance Requirements: Options: electronic application, deferred admission. Required: high school transcript, SAT or ACT. Recommended: essay, 3 recommendations. Entrance: moderately difficult. Application deadline: rolling. Notification: continuous. Transfer credits accepted: Yes.

Costs Per Year: Application fee: $50. State resident tuition: $8308 full-time, $407.37 per credit part-time. Nonresident tuition: $16,576 full-time, $751.81 per credit part-time. Mandatory fees: $1426 full-time. Full-time tuition and fees vary according to course load, location, program, reciprocity agreements, and student level. Part-time tuition varies according to course load, location, program, reciprocity agreements, and student level. College room and board: $7290. College room only: $4420. Room and board charges vary according to board plan and housing facility.

Collegiate Environment: Orientation program. Drama-theater group, choral group, student-run newspaper, radio station. Social organizations: 213 open to all; national fraternities, national sororities, local fraternities, local sororities; 3% of eligible men and 4% of eligible women are members. Most popular organizations: The Wildlife Society, Student Impact, WWSP 90-FM radio station, Gender and Sexuality Alliance, Student Wisconsin Education Association. Major annual events: World's Largest Trivia Contest, International Club Dinner, Involvement Fair. Student services: health clinic, personal-psychological counseling, women's center. Campus security: 24-hour emergency response devices and patrols, student patrols, late night transport-escort service, controlled dormitory access. Learning Resources Center plus 1 other. Books: 420,414 (physical), 247,207 (digital/electronic); Serial titles: 7,192 (physical), 133,235 (digital/electronic); Databases: 204. Study areas open 24 hours, 5-7 days a week; students can reserve study rooms. Operations spending for the previous fiscal year: $2.8 million. 1,233 computers available on campus for general student use. A campuswide network can be accessed from student residence rooms and from off campus. Students can access the following: online class registration. Staffed computer lab on campus provides training in use of computers, software, and the Internet.

Community Environment: Stevens Point is located in the very center of the state on the Wisconsin River. It lies midway between Milwaukee and Minneapolis and is approximately 250 miles from Chicago. Air service is available through the Central Wisconsin Airport. Stevens Point is a city of about 25,000 and is the "Gateway to Wisconsin's Vacationland." A wide range of cultural and year-around recreational opportunities are available. The area is known for insurance, agribusiness, paper production, finance, and light industry.

■ UNIVERSITY OF WISCONSIN-STOUT

712 S Broadway St.
Menomonie, WI 54751
Tel: (715)232-1122; Free: 800-HI-STOUT
Fax: (715)232-1667
E-mail: admissions@uwstout.edu
Web Site: www.uwstout.edu

Description: State-supported, comprehensive, coed. Part of University of Wisconsin System. Awards bachelor's, master's, and doctoral degrees and post-master's certificates. Founded 1891. Setting: 120-acre small town campus with easy access to Minneapolis-St. Paul. Total enrollment: 9,401. Faculty: 483 (391 full-time, 92 part-time). Student-undergrad faculty ratio is 20:1. 3,267 applied, 86% were admitted. 9% from top 10% of their high school class, 31% from top quarter, 64% from top half. Full-time: 6,585 students, 44% women, 56% men. Part-time: 1,531 students, 42% women, 58% men. 33% from out-of-state. 3% American Indian or Alaska Native, non-Hispanic/Latino; 0.6% Hispanic/Latino; 2% Black or African American, non-Hispanic/Latino; 0.2% Asian, non-Hispanic/Latino; 87% Native Hawaiian or other Pacific Islander, non-Hispanic/Latino; 2% international. 16% 25 or older, 40% live on campus, 8% transferred in. Retention: 69% of full-time freshmen returned the following year. Academic areas with the most degrees conferred: business/marketing; visual and performing arts; engineering technologies. Core. Calendar: 4-1-4. ESL program, services for LD students, accelerated degree program, honors program, independent study, distance learning, double major, summer session for credit, part-time degree program, external degree program, adult/continuing education programs, co-op programs and internships, graduate courses open to undergrads. Off

campus study at BS in Engineering Technology - Northcentral Technical College; BS in Early Childhood Education - Lac Courte Oreilles Community College; BS in Manufacturing Engineering - Northwest Technical College; BS in Info. and Comm. Technologies - WI Technical College System; BS in Sustainable Mgmt - UW-River Falls, UW-Parkside, UW-Superior, UW Extension; BS in Management - Sheboygan. Study abroad program. ROTC: Army, Air Force (c).

Entrance Requirements: Option: electronic application. Required: high school transcript, SAT or ACT. Recommended: minimum 2.5 high school GPA. Required for some: minimum 2.75 high school GPA. Entrance: moderately difficult. Application deadlines: rolling, rolling for nonresidents. Notification: continuous until 9/1, continuous for nonresidents. SAT Reasoning Test deadline: 9/1. Transfer credits accepted: Yes.

Collegiate Environment: Orientation program. Drama-theater group, choral group, marching band, student-run newspaper, radio station. Social organizations: national fraternities, national sororities, local fraternities, local sororities. Student services: legal services, health clinic, personal-psychological counseling. Campus security: 24-hour emergency response devices and patrols, student patrols, controlled dormitory access. Library Learning Center.

Community Environment: Menomonie, population 15,200, is located on the Red Cedar River and Lake Menomin, and is accessible by all commercial transportation.

■ UNIVERSITY OF WISCONSIN-SUPERIOR

Belknap and Catlin
Superior, WI 54880-4500
Tel: (715)394-8101
Fax: (715)394-8407
Web Site: www.uwsuper.edu

Description: State-supported, comprehensive, coed. Part of University of Wisconsin System. Awards associate, bachelor's, and master's degrees and post-master's certificates. Founded 1893. Setting: 230-acre suburban campus. Total enrollment: 2,601. Faculty: 222 (114 full-time, 108 part-time). Student-undergrad faculty ratio is 14:1. 936 applied, 74% were admitted. 8% from top 10% of their high school class, 25% from top quarter, 60% from top half. Full-time: 1,793 students, 60% women, 40% men. Part-time: 501 students, 68% women, 32% men. Students come from 49 other countries, 49% from out-of-state. 1% American Indian or Alaska Native, non-Hispanic/Latino; 3% Hispanic/Latino; 2% Black or African American, non-Hispanic/Latino; 0.7% Asian, non-Hispanic/Latino; 10% international. 29% 25 or older, 31% live on campus, 11% transferred in. Retention: 70% of full-time freshmen returned the following year. Academic areas with the most degrees conferred: business/marketing; interdisciplinary studies; education. Core. Calendar: semesters. Academic remediation for entering students, ESL program, services for LD students, advanced placement, accelerated degree program, self-designed majors, independent study, distance learning, double major, summer session for credit, part-time degree program, external degree program, adult/continuing education programs, co-op programs and internships, graduate courses open to undergrads. Off campus study at University of Minnesota, Duluth. Study abroad program. ROTC: Air Force (c).

Entrance Requirements: Options: electronic application, deferred admission. Required: high school transcript, SAT or ACT. Recommended: essay. Required for some: interview. Entrance: minimally difficult. Notification: continuous until 9/16. Transfer credits accepted: Yes.

Costs Per Year: Application fee: $44. State resident tuition: $6535 full-time. Nonresident tuition: $14,108 full-time. Mandatory fees: $1574 full-time. Full-time tuition and fees vary according to course load and reciprocity agreements. College room and board: $6730. College room only: $3600. Room and board charges vary according to board plan and housing facility.

Collegiate Environment: Orientation program. Drama-theater group, choral group, student-run newspaper, radio station. Major annual events: Cultural Night, Hockey Games, Winterfest. Student services: health clinic, personal-psychological counseling, women's center. Campus security: 24-hour emergency response devices and patrols, student patrols, late night transport-escort service, controlled dormitory access. Freshmen guaranteed college housing. On-campus residence required through sophomore year. Options: coed, women-only housing available. Jim Dan Hill Library. 375 computers available on campus for general student use. Computer purchase/lease plans available. A campuswide network can be accessed from student residence rooms and from off campus. Students can access the following: online class registration. Staffed computer lab on campus (open 24 hours a day) provides training in use of computers, software, and the Internet.

Community Environment: Superior is Wisconsin's leading port of entry and is located at the head of Lake Superior at the northwest corner of the state. The largest iron ore dock, grain elevator and briquette plant in the world are here at Superior. The area is a leading summer and winter recreation resort. Along with neighbor city Duluth, MN, the area offers a wide range of music, theater, shopping, and recreational opportunities.

■ **UNIVERSITY OF WISCONSIN-WASHINGTON COUNTY**

400 University Dr.
West Bend, WI 53095
Tel: (262)335-5200
Fax: (262)335-5257
Web Site: www.washington.uwc.edu

Description: State-supported, 2-year, coed. Part of University of Wisconsin System. Awards certificates, transfer associate, and terminal associate degrees. Founded 1968. Setting: 87-acre small town campus with easy access to Milwaukee. Total enrollment: 544. Student-undergrad faculty ratio is 17:1. Core. Calendar: semesters. Academic remediation for entering students, services for LD students, advanced placement, honors program, independent study, distance learning, double major, summer session for credit, part-time degree program, external degree program. Off campus study at other units of the University of Wisconsin Colleges, four-year campuses of the University of Wisconsin.

Entrance Requirements: Options: electronic application, deferred admission. Required: high school transcript, ACT. Application deadline: 8/30. SAT Reasoning Test deadline: 8/31. SAT Subject Test deadline: 8/31. Transfer credits accepted: Yes.

Collegiate Environment: Orientation program. Drama-theater group, choral group, student-run newspaper. Social organizations: 19 open to all. Student services: personal-psychological counseling. UW-Washington County Library plus 1 other. 78 computers available on campus for general student use. A campuswide network can be accessed from off-campus. Students can access the following: online class registration, financial aid application. Staffed computer lab on campus (open 24 hours a day).

■ **UNIVERSITY OF WISCONSIN-WAUKESHA**

1500 N University Dr.
Waukesha, WI 53188
Tel: (262)521-5200
Fax: (414)521-5491
Web Site: www.waukesha.uwc.edu

Description: State-supported, primarily 2-year, coed. Part of University of Wisconsin System. Awards transfer associate and bachelor's degrees. Founded 1966. Setting: 86-acre small town campus with easy access to Milwaukee. Total enrollment: 1,782. Student-undergrad faculty ratio is 17:1. Academic area with the most degrees conferred: liberal arts/general studies. Core. Calendar: semesters. Academic remediation for entering students, services for LD students, advanced placement, accelerated degree program, honors program, distance learning, summer session for credit, part-time degree program, external degree program, internships. Off campus study at other units of the University of Wisconsin Colleges and 4-year campuses of the University of Wisconsin. Study abroad program.

Entrance Requirements: Options: electronic application, early admission, deferred admission, international baccalaureate accepted. Required: high school transcript, ACT. Application deadline: 8/30. SAT Reasoning Test deadline: 8/31. SAT Subject Test deadline: 8/31. Transfer credits accepted: Yes.

Collegiate Environment: Orientation program. Drama-theater group, choral group, student-run newspaper. Social organizations: 30 open to all. Student services: personal-psychological counseling. Campus security: late night transport-escort service, part-time patrols by trained security personnel. University of Wisconsin-Waukesha Library plus 1 other.

■ **UNIVERSITY OF WISCONSIN-WHITEWATER**

800 W Main St.
Whitewater, WI 53190-1790
Tel: (262)472-1234
Fax: (262)472-1515
E-mail: uwwadmit@uww.edu
Web Site: www.uww.edu

Description: State-supported, comprehensive, coed. Part of University of Wisconsin System. Awards associate, bachelor's, master's, and doctoral degrees. Founded 1868. Setting: 400-acre small town campus with easy access to Milwaukee. Total enrollment: 12,430. Faculty: 636 (502 full-time, 134

part-time). Student-undergrad faculty ratio is 20:1. 5,706 applied, 83% were admitted. 9% from top 10% of their high school class, 30% from top quarter, 71% from top half. Full-time: 9,806 students, 49% women, 51% men. Part-time: 1,322 students, 53% women, 47% men. 20% from out-of-state. 0.2% American Indian or Alaska Native, non-Hispanic/Latino; 6% Hispanic/Latino; 4% Black or African American, non-Hispanic/Latino; 1% Asian, non-Hispanic/Latino; 0.8% international. 8% 25 or older, 40% live on campus, 6% transferred in. Academic areas with the most degrees conferred: business/marketing; education; communication/journalism. Core. Calendar: semesters. Academic remediation for entering students, ESL program, services for LD students, advanced placement, accelerated degree program, self-designed majors, honors program, independent study, distance learning, double major, summer session for credit, part-time degree program, external degree program, adult/continuing education programs, co-op programs and internships, graduate courses open to undergrads. Study abroad program. ROTC: Army, Air Force.

Entrance Requirements: Options: electronic application, deferred admission, international baccalaureate accepted. Required: high school transcript, SAT or ACT. Recommended: essay. Entrance: moderately difficult. Application deadline: rolling. Notification: continuous. SAT Reasoning Test deadline: 5/1. SAT Subject Test deadline: 5/1. Transfer credits accepted: Yes.

Costs Per Year: Application fee: $50. State resident tuition: $6519 full-time, $271.62 per credit hour part-time. Nonresident tuition: $15,092 full-time, $628.82 per credit hour part-time. Mandatory fees: $1173 full-time. Full-time tuition and fees vary according to course load, degree level, and reciprocity agreements. College room and board: $6786. College room only: $4206. Room and board charges vary according to board plan and housing facility.

Collegiate Environment: Orientation program. Drama-theater group, choral group, marching band, student-run newspaper, radio station. Social organizations: 308 open to all; national fraternities, national sororities, local fraternities, local sororities; 5% of eligible men and 5% of eligible women are members. Most popular organizations: Adult Student Connection, Pan Hellenic Council, Sigma Alpha Lambda (Academic Honors), Cru (Faith-Related Organization), National Society of Leadership and Success. Major annual events: Homecoming Week, Campus Welcome Concert, Spring and Fall Career Fairs. Student services: legal services, health clinic, personal-psychological counseling, women's center. Campus security: 24-hour emergency response devices and patrols, student patrols, late night transport-escort service, controlled dormitory access. Andersen Library. Students can reserve study rooms.

Community Environment: UW-Whitewater is located in a city of 12,000 near the scenic beauty of the Southern Kettle Moraine State Forest. It is a one-hour drive from Madison and Milwaukee, and a two-hour drive from Chicago. The area around Whitewater offers lakes, recreation, cross country skiing, backpacking, hiking, and other forms of outdoor activity. The campus is within walking distance of 2 shopping areas and a city park is adjacent to the campus.

■ **VITERBO UNIVERSITY**

900 Viterbo Dr.
La Crosse, WI 54601-4797
Tel: (608)796-3000; Free: 800-VITERBO
Fax: (608)796-3050
E-mail: admission@viterbo.edu
Web Site: www.viterbo.edu

Description: Independent Roman Catholic, comprehensive, coed. Awards associate, bachelor's, master's, and doctoral degrees and post-master's certificates. Founded 1890. Setting: 72-acre suburban campus. Total enrollment: 2,761. Faculty: 324 (120 full-time, 204 part-time). Student-undergrad faculty ratio is 11:1. 1,770 applied, 63% were admitted. 16% from top 10% of their high school class, 48% from top quarter, 81% from top half. Full-time: 1,483 students, 72% women, 28% men. Part-time: 392 students, 80% women, 20% men. Students come from 35 states and territories, 6 other countries, 27% from out-of-state. 0.2% American Indian or Alaska Native, non-Hispanic/Latino; 3% Hispanic/Latino; 2% Black or African American, non-Hispanic/Latino; 0.9% Asian, non-Hispanic/Latino; 0.1% Native Hawaiian or other Pacific Islander, non-Hispanic/Latino; 2% international. 24% 25 or older, 24% live on campus, 11% transferred in. Retention: 80% of full-time freshmen returned the following year. Core. Calendar: semesters. ESL program, accelerated degree program, self-designed majors, honors program, independent study, distance learning, double major, part-time degree program, adult/continuing education programs, internships. Study abroad program. ROTC: Army (c).

Entrance Requirements: Options: electronic application, deferred admis-

sion, international baccalaureate accepted. Required: high school transcript, minimum 2 high school GPA, SAT or ACT. Required for some: essay, interview, audition for theater and music, portfolio for art. Entrance: moderately difficult. Application deadline: 8/15. Notification: continuous. Transfer credits accepted: Yes.

Costs Per Year: Comprehensive fee: $37,030 includes full-time tuition ($27,280), mandatory fees ($690), and college room and board ($9060). College room only: $4020. Full-time tuition and fees vary according to program. Room and board charges vary according to board plan and housing facility. Part-time tuition: $775 per credit. Part-time tuition varies according to program.

Collegiate Environment: Orientation program. Drama-theater group, choral group, student-run newspaper. Social organizations: 35 open to all. Most popular organizations: Student Activities Board (SAB), Viterbo Student Nurses Association (VSNA), Education Club, Colleges Against Cancer (CAL), Residence Hall Association. Major annual events: Courtyard Carni, Welcome Back Bash, Viterbo Days (family day). Student services: health clinic, personal-psychological counseling. Campus security: 24-hour emergency response devices and patrols, late night transport-escort service, controlled dormitory access, lighted pathways, emergency evacuation plan, self-defense education programs, security cameras. Todd Wehr Memorial Library. Books: 69,288 (physical), 236 (digital/electronic); Serial titles: 105 (physical), 75 (digital/electronic); Databases: 36. Weekly public service hours: 97; study areas open 24 hours, 5-7 days a week; students can reserve study rooms. 400 computers available on campus for general student use. A campuswide network can be accessed from student residence rooms and from off campus. Students can access the following: online class registration, learning management system courses.

■ **WAUKESHA COUNTY TECHNICAL COLLEGE**
800 Main St.
Pewaukee, WI 53072-4601
Tel: (262)691-5566
Fax: (262)691-5693
Web Site: www.wctc.edu

Description: State and locally supported, 2-year, coed. Part of Wisconsin Technical College System. Awards certificates, diplomas, and terminal associate degrees. Founded 1923. Setting: 137-acre suburban campus with easy access to Milwaukee. Total enrollment: 7,696. Faculty: 749 (192 full-time, 557 part-time). Student-undergrad faculty ratio is 17:1. Full-time: 1,565 students, 42% women, 58% men. Part-time: 6,131 students, 51% women, 49% men. 0.3% American Indian or Alaska Native, non-Hispanic/Latino; 8% Hispanic/Latino; 6% Black or African American, non-Hispanic/Latino; 3% Asian, non-Hispanic/Latino; 0.2% Native Hawaiian or other Pacific Islander, non-Hispanic/Latino; 0.1% international. 50% 25 or older. Calendar: semesters. Academic remediation for entering students, ESL program, services for LD students, advanced placement, accelerated degree program, self-designed majors, independent study, distance learning, double major, summer session for credit, part-time degree program, adult/continuing education programs, co-op programs and internships. Study abroad program.

Entrance Requirements: Open admission. Option: electronic application. Required: high school transcript. Required for some: interview. Entrance: noncompetitive. Application deadline: rolling. Transfer credits accepted: Yes.

Collegiate Environment: Orientation program. Campus security: patrols by police officers 8 am to 10 pm.

■ **WESTERN TECHNICAL COLLEGE**
400 7th St. N
La Crosse, WI 54601
Tel: (608)785-9200; Free: 800-322-9982
Fax: (608)785-9205
E-mail: mildes@wwtc.edu
Web Site: www.westerntc.edu

Description: District-supported, 2-year, coed. Part of Wisconsin Technical College System. Awards certificates, diplomas, transfer associate, and terminal associate degrees. Founded 1911. Setting: 10-acre urban campus. Research spending for the previous fiscal year: $227,769. Educational spending for the previous fiscal year: $9793 per student. Total enrollment: 4,765. Faculty: 888 (203 full-time, 685 part-time). Student-undergrad faculty ratio is 7:1. 3,443 applied, 35% were admitted. Students come from 4 states and territories, 7% from out-of-state. 16% 25 or older, 2% live on campus. Core. Calendar: semesters. Academic remediation for entering students, ESL program, services for LD students, advanced placement, accelerated

degree program, self-designed majors, distance learning, summer session for credit, part-time degree program, external degree program, adult/continuing education programs, co-op programs and internships. Off campus study.

Entrance Requirements: Open admission except for health occupations programs. Options: electronic application, early admission. Required: high school transcript. Recommended: interview, ACT. Required for some: ACT ASSET. Entrance: noncompetitive. Application deadline: rolling.

Collegiate Environment: Orientation program. Student-run newspaper. Social organizations: 28 open to all. Most popular organizations: Wisconsin Marketing Management Association (WMMA), Air Conditioning, Refrigeration Organization (ACRO), Multicultural Club, Business Professionals of America (BPA), Advertising Club. Major annual event: Orientation. Student services: personal-psychological counseling. Campus security: 24-hour emergency response devices and patrols, student patrols, late night transport-escort service, controlled dormitory access. Western Wisconsin Technical College Library plus 1 other. Operations spending for the previous fiscal year: $303,682. 800 computers available on campus for general student use. A campuswide network can be accessed from student residence rooms and from off campus. Students can access the following: online class registration. Staffed computer lab on campus.

Community Environment: See University of Wisconsin - La Crosse.

■ **WISCONSIN INDIANHEAD TECHNICAL COLLEGE**
505 Pine Ridge Dr.
Shell Lake, WI 54871
Tel: (715)468-2815; Free: 800-243-9482
Fax: (715)468-2819
E-mail: steve.bitzer@witc.edu
Web Site: www.witc.edu

Description: District-supported, 2-year, coed. Part of Wisconsin Technical College System. Awards certificates, diplomas, transfer associate, and terminal associate degrees. Founded 1912. Setting: 118-acre suburban campus with easy access to Minneapolis-St Paul Metro Area. System endowment: $4.7 million. Educational spending for the previous fiscal year: $13,260 per student. Total enrollment: 3,021. Faculty: 289 (159 full-time, 130 part-time). Student-undergrad faculty ratio is 9:1. Full-time: 1,086 students, 50% women, 50% men. Part-time: 1,935 students, 69% women, 31% men. Students come from 6 states and territories, 9% from out-of-state. 2% American Indian or Alaska Native, non-Hispanic/Latino; 0.5% Hispanic/Latino; 0.6% Black or African American, non-Hispanic/Latino; 1% Asian, non-Hispanic/Latino; 0.1% Native Hawaiian or other Pacific Islander, non-Hispanic/Latino. 49% 25 or older. Core. Calendar: semesters. Academic remediation for entering students, ESL program, services for LD students, advanced placement, independent study, distance learning, double major, summer session for credit, part-time degree program, external degree program, adult/continuing education programs, internships. Off campus study.

Entrance Requirements: Options: electronic application, early admission, deferred admission, international baccalaureate accepted. Required: interview. Required for some: high school transcript. Application deadline: rolling. Transfer credits accepted: Yes. Applicants placed on waiting list: 6.

Costs Per Year: Application fee: $30. State resident tuition: $4,294 full-time, $134.20 per credit hour part-time. Nonresident tuition: $6,442 full-time, $201.30 per credit hour part-time. Mandatory fees: $432 full-time, $13.50 per credit hour part-time. Full-time tuition and fees vary according to course load, program, and reciprocity agreements. Part-time tuition and fees vary according to course load, program, and reciprocity agreements.

Collegiate Environment: Orientation program. Student services: health clinic. Campus security: 24-hour emergency response devices. Books: 5,569 (physical), 50,557 (digital/electronic); Serial titles: 89 (physical), 35,291 (digital/electronic); Databases: 85. Students can reserve study rooms. Operations spending for the previous fiscal year: $1.5 million. 780 computers available on campus for general student use. A campuswide network can be accessed. Students can access the following: online class registration. Staffed computer lab on campus.

■ **WISCONSIN LUTHERAN COLLEGE**
8800 W Bluemound Rd.
Milwaukee, WI 53226-9942
Tel: (414)443-8800
Fax: (414)443-8514
Web Site: www.wlc.edu

Description: Independent, comprehensive, coed, affiliated with Wisconsin

Evangelical Lutheran Synod. Awards bachelor's and master's degrees. Founded 1973. Setting: 54-acre suburban campus. Endowment: $32.9 million. Research spending for the previous fiscal year: $77,153. Educational spending for the previous fiscal year: $9319 per student. Total enrollment: 1,114. Faculty: 164 (64 full-time, 100 part-time). Student-undergrad faculty ratio is 10:1. 708 applied, 90% were admitted. 12% from top 10% of their high school class, 35% from top quarter, 71% from top half. Full-time: 921 students, 55% women, 45% men. Part-time: 71 students, 42% women, 58% men. Students come from 32 states and territories, 7 other countries, 24% from out-of-state. 0.7% American Indian or Alaska Native, non-Hispanic/Latino; 6% Hispanic/Latino; 5% Black or African American, non-Hispanic/Latino; 2% Asian, non-Hispanic/Latino; 1% international. 12% 25 or older, 63% live on campus, 5% transferred in. Retention: 79% of full-time freshmen returned the following year. Academic areas with the most degrees conferred: business/marketing; education; communication/journalism. Core. Calendar: semesters. Services for LD students, advanced placement, accelerated degree program, self-designed majors, honors program, independent study, distance learning, double major, summer session for credit, part-time degree program, adult/continuing education programs, internships. Study abroad program. ROTC: Air Force (c).

Entrance Requirements: Options: electronic application, deferred admission, international baccalaureate. Required: high school transcript, SAT or ACT. Required for some: interview. Entrance: moderately difficult. Application deadline: rolling. Notification: continuous. SAT Reasoning Test deadline: 9/1. Transfer credits accepted: Yes.

Costs Per Year: Application fee: $0. Comprehensive fee: $39,915 includes full-time tuition ($29,410), mandatory fees ($315), and college room and board ($10,190). Room and board charges vary according to board plan and housing facility. Part-time tuition: $765 per credit hour.

Collegiate Environment: Orientation program. Choral group, student-run newspaper. Social organizations: 37 open to all. Student services: health clinic, personal-psychological counseling. Campus security: 24-hour emergency response devices and patrols, late night transport-escort service, controlled dormitory access, closed-circuit TV monitors. Marvin M. Schwan Library. Books: 64,947 (physical), 3,778 (digital/electronic); Serial titles: 19 (physical), 37,529 (digital/electronic); Databases: 28. Operations spending for the previous fiscal year: $364,981. 50 computers available on campus for general student use. A campuswide network can be accessed from student residence rooms and from off campus. Students can access the following: online class registration.

■ CASPER COLLEGE

125 College Dr.
Casper, WY 82601-4699
Tel: (307)268-2110; Free: 800-442-2963
Fax: (307)268-2682
E-mail: kfoltz@caspercollege.edu
Web Site: www.caspercollege.edu
Description: State and locally supported, 2-year, coed. Awards certificates, transfer associate, and terminal associate degrees. Founded 1945. Setting: 200-acre small town campus. Total enrollment: 3,626. Faculty: 246 (140 full-time, 106 part-time). Student-undergrad faculty ratio is 14:1. 1,097 applied, 100% were admitted. Full-time: 1,733 students, 56% women, 44% men. Part-time: 1,893 students, 56% women, 44% men. Students come from 37 states and territories, 17 other countries, 10% from out-of-state. 0.6% American Indian or Alaska Native, non-Hispanic/Latino; 7% Hispanic/Latino; 1% Black or African American, non-Hispanic/Latino; 0.8% Asian, non-Hispanic/Latino; 0.2% Native Hawaiian or other Pacific Islander, non-Hispanic/Latino; 0.9% international. 34% 25 or older, 16% live on campus, 2% transferred in. Core. Calendar: semesters. Academic remediation for entering students, ESL program, services for LD students, advanced placement, accelerated degree program, honors program, independent study, distance learning, summer session for credit, part-time degree program, co-op programs and internships. Off campus study at University of Wyoming-Casper Campus, University of North Dakota.
Entrance Requirements: Open admission. Options: electronic application, early admission, international baccalaureate accepted. Required: high school transcript. Entrance: noncompetitive. Application deadline: 8/15. Notification: continuous until 8/15. Transfer credits accepted: Yes.
Costs Per Year: Application fee: $0. State resident tuition: $3072 full-time, $128 per credit hour part-time. Nonresident tuition: $7584 full-time, $316 per credit hour part-time. Part-time tuition varies according to course load. College room and board: $7080. Room and board charges vary according to board plan and housing facility.
Collegiate Environment: Orientation program. Drama-theater group, choral group, student-run newspaper. Most popular organizations: Student Senate, Student Activities Board, Agriculture Club, Theater Club, Phi Theta Kappa. Student services: legal services, health clinic, personal-psychological counseling. Campus security: 24-hour emergency response devices and patrols, late night transport-escort service. Goodstein Foundation Library. Books: 66,488 (physical), 184,000 (digital/electronic); Serial titles: 4,300 (physical); Databases: 415. Weekly public service hours: 82; students can reserve study rooms. 150 computers available on campus for general student use. A campuswide network can be accessed from student residence rooms and from off campus. Students can access the following: online class registration. Staffed computer lab on campus provides training in use of computers, software, and the Internet.
Community Environment: Rich in oil and uranium, Casper is Wyoming's leading industrial city. Cattle and sheep ranches in the surrounding area provide the basis for the city's wool and livestock markets. Situated at the foot of Casper Mountain in the approximate geographic center of Wyoming, the climate is invigorating with 300 days of sunshine each year. The community has 70 churches, a hospital, library, symphony orchestra, theatre group, a mall, 11 theatres and a community concert series. Local recreation includes tennis, golf, trap shooting, a multipurpose event center, swimming pools, bowling alleys, excellent fishing and hunting, city and mountain parks, archery and rifle ranges, and a ski area. Several rodeos are held here each year, as well as skiing and mountain climbing events.

■ CENTRAL WYOMING COLLEGE

2660 Peck Ave.
Riverton, WY 82501-2273
Tel: (307)855-2000; Free: 800-735-8418
Fax: (307)855-2092
E-mail: pedwards@cwc.edu
Web Site: www.cwc.edu
Description: State and locally supported, 2-year, coed. Part of Wyoming Community College Commission. Awards certificates, diplomas, transfer associate, and terminal associate degrees. Founded 1966. Setting: 200-acre small town campus. Endowment: $20 million. Research spending for the previous fiscal year: $190,869. Educational spending for the previous fiscal year: $8446 per student. Total enrollment: 2,016. Faculty: 168 (49 full-time, 119 part-time). Student-undergrad faculty ratio is 13:1. 453 applied, 100% were admitted. 3% from top 10% of their high school class, 20% from top quarter, 52% from top half. Full-time: 688 students, 53% women, 47% men. Part-time: 1,328 students, 54% women, 46% men. Students come from 41 states and territories, 6 other countries, 13% from out-of-state. 10% American Indian or Alaska Native, non-Hispanic/Latino; 9% Hispanic/Latino; 0.8% Black or African American, non-Hispanic/Latino; 0.8% Asian, non-Hispanic/Latino; 0.3% international. 43% 25 or older, 18% live on campus, 5% transferred in. Retention: 54% of full-time freshmen returned the following year. Core. Calendar: semesters. Academic remediation for entering students, ESL program, services for LD students, advanced placement, honors program, independent study, distance learning, double major, summer session for credit, part-time degree program, adult/continuing education programs, co-op programs and internships. Off campus study.
Entrance Requirements: Open admission open admission to all program students except for nursing program. Options: electronic application, early admission, deferred admission. Recommended: high school transcript. Entrance: noncompetitive. Application deadline: rolling. Transfer credits accepted: Yes.
Costs Per Year: Application fee: $0. State resident tuition: $2256 full-time, $94 per credit hour part-time. Nonresident tuition: $6768 full-time, $282 per credit part-time. Mandatory fees: $864 full-time, $36 per credit part-time. Full-time tuition and fees vary according to course load, program, and reciprocity agreements. Part-time tuition and fees vary according to course load, program, and reciprocity agreements. College room and board: $6681. College room only: $2644. Room and board charges vary according to board plan and housing facility.
Collegiate Environment: Orientation program. Drama-theater group, choral group, student-run radio station. Social organizations: 16 open to all. Most popular organizations: Multi-Cultural Club, La Vida Nueva Club, Fellowship of College Christians, Quality Leaders, Science Club. Major annual events: Convocation, Theater and Music Productions, Final Feed. Student services: personal-psychological counseling. Campus security: 24-hour emergency response devices, late night transport-escort service, controlled dormitory access. Central Wyoming College Library. Books: 53,204 (physical), 5 (digital/electronic); Serial titles: 152 (physical), 8 (digital/electronic); Databases: 141. Weekly public service hours: 82. Operations spending for the previous fiscal year: $278,955. 450 computers available on campus for general student use. Computer purchase/lease plans available. A campuswide network can be accessed from off-campus. Students can ac-

cess the following: online class registration. Staffed computer lab on campus provides training in use of computers, software, and the Internet.

Community Environment: Located in the lower Wind River Basin, Riverton (population 9,430) is the center of a large farming, lumbering and livestock producing region. The area has a stimulating climate with a summer average temperature of 66 degrees and a winter average of 35 degrees. There are less than 10 inches of rainfall annually. The community is accessed by bus and air lines. There are 25 churches, a modern library, 2 hospitals, 3 clinics, and good shopping available. Local recreation facilities include an Olympic-size swimming pool, and provide for golf, baseball, bowling, hunting, fishing, boating, water skiing, snow skiing, rock hunting, and hiking. An Antique Museum, the Wind River Indian Reservation, and many national and state parks are of interest. Part-time employment is available for students.

■ EASTERN WYOMING COLLEGE

3200 W C St.
Torrington, WY 82240-1699
Tel: (307)532-8200; Free: 866-327-8996
Fax: (307)532-8222
E-mail: rex.cogdill@ewc.wy.edu
Web Site: www.ewc.wy.edu

Description: State and locally supported, 2-year, coed. Part of Wyoming Community College Commission. Awards certificates, diplomas, transfer associate, and terminal associate degrees. Founded 1948. Setting: 40-acre rural campus. Endowment: $4.6 million. Research spending for the previous fiscal year: $52,966. Educational spending for the previous fiscal year: $6523 per student. Total enrollment: 1,604. Faculty: 71 (34 full-time, 37 part-time). Student-undergrad faculty ratio is 20:1. Full-time: 602 students, 58% women, 42% men. Part-time: 1,002 students, 58% women, 42% men. Students come from 20 states and territories, 9 other countries, 26% from out-of-state. 2% American Indian or Alaska Native, non-Hispanic/Latino; 6% Hispanic/Latino; 1% Black or African American, non-Hispanic/Latino; 0.3% Asian, non-Hispanic/Latino; 0.8% Native Hawaiian or other Pacific Islander, non-Hispanic/Latino; 3% international. 29% 25 or older, 21% live on campus, 8% transferred in. Core. Calendar: semesters. Academic remediation for entering students, ESL program, services for LD students, advanced placement, accelerated degree program, self-designed majors, independent study, distance learning, double major, summer session for credit, part-time degree program, internships.

Entrance Requirements: Recommended: high school transcript.

Collegiate Environment: Orientation program. Drama-theater group, choral group. Social organizations: 17 open to all. Most popular organizations: Veterinary Technology Club, Rodeo Club, Student Senate, Block and Bridle Club, SkillsUSA. Major annual events: School Dances, Night of Elegance (dinner/formal dance), Athletic Events. Student services: personal-psychological counseling. Campus security: 24-hour emergency response devices, controlled dormitory access. Eastern Wyoming College Library. Books: 30,339 (physical), 681,514 (digital/electronic); Serial titles: 86 (physical); Databases: 268. Weekly public service hours: 61. Operations spending for the previous fiscal year: $444,091. 75 computers available on campus for general student use. A campuswide network can be accessed. Students can access the following: online class registration.

Community Environment: Torrington is located in the southeastern part of the state, and is a small western town in a rural environment. The climate is invigorating, but relatively mild.

■ LARAMIE COUNTY COMMUNITY COLLEGE

1400 E College Dr.
Cheyenne, WY 82007-3299
Tel: (307)778-5222; Free: 800-522-2993
Fax: (307)778-1399
Web Site: www.lccc.wy.edu

Description: District-supported, 2-year, coed. Part of Wyoming Community College Commission. Awards certificates, diplomas, transfer associate, and terminal associate degrees. Founded 1968. Setting: 271-acre small town campus. Total enrollment: 4,226. Faculty: 282 (114 full-time, 168 part-time). Student-undergrad faculty ratio is 15:1. 1,720 applied, 100% were admitted. Full-time: 1,634 students, 60% women, 40% men. Part-time: 2,592 students, 58% women, 42% men. 14% from out-of-state. 0.9% American Indian or Alaska Native, non-Hispanic/Latino; 15% Hispanic/Latino; 2% Black or African American, non-Hispanic/Latino; 0.9% Asian, non-Hispanic/Latino; 0.5% Native Hawaiian or other Pacific Islander, non-Hispanic/Latino; 1% international. 39% 25 or older, 13% live on campus, 4% transferred in. Core. Calendar: semesters. Academic remediation for entering students, ESL

program, services for LD students, advanced placement, honors program, independent study, distance learning, double major, summer session for credit, part-time degree program, adult/continuing education programs, co-op programs and internships. Off campus study at Albany County Campus, Eastern Laramie County Campus, FE Warren Air Force Base. ROTC: Army (c), Air Force (c).

Entrance Requirements: Open admission except for dental hygiene, diagnostic medical sonography, emergency services - paramedic, equine studies, nursing, physical therapist assistant, radiography, surgical technology, and wind energy programs. Options: electronic application, deferred admission, international baccalaureate accepted. Required for some: high school transcript, interview. Entrance: noncompetitive. Transfer credits accepted: Yes.

Costs Per Year: Application fee: $0. State resident tuition: $2256 full-time, $94 per credit hour part-time. Nonresident tuition: $6768 full-time, $282 per credit hour part-time. Mandatory fees: $1170 full-time, $48.75 per credit hour part-time. Full-time tuition and fees vary according to course load. Part-time tuition and fees vary according to course load. College room and board: $8234. Room and board charges vary according to board plan and housing facility.

Collegiate Environment: Orientation program. Drama-theater group, choral group, student-run newspaper. Most popular organizations: Student Government Association, Phi Theta Kappa, Block and Bridle, Student Nursing Club, SkillsUSA. Major annual events: Orientation, Fall All-Campus Barbeque, Homecoming Week. Student services: health clinic, personal-psychological counseling. Campus security: 24-hour emergency response devices and patrols, late night transport-escort service, controlled dormitory access. Ludden Library.

Community Environment: Founded in 1867, Cheyenne is the capital of Wyoming. It is located on a rolling plain at the foothills of the Rocky Mountains and has a population of 55,700. The town keeps the spirit of the"Wild West" with its well-known annual Cheyenne Frontier Days celebration held in July. The State Capitol, State Museum, and Cheyenne Art Center are features of the city.

■ NORTHWEST COLLEGE

231 W 6th St.
Powell, WY 82435-1898
Tel: (307)754-6000; Free: 800-560-4692
Fax: (307)754-6700
E-mail: west.hernandez@nwc.edu
Web Site: www.nwc.edu

Description: State and locally supported, 2-year, coed. Part of Wyoming Community College System. Awards certificates, transfer associate, and terminal associate degrees. Founded 1946. Setting: 132-acre rural campus. Endowment: $35 million. Total enrollment: 1,654. Faculty: 145 (72 full-time, 73 part-time). Student-undergrad faculty ratio is 12:1. Full-time: 953 students, 53% women, 47% men. Part-time: 701 students, 64% women, 36% men. Students come from 34 states and territories, 28 other countries, 24% from out-of-state. 0.3% American Indian or Alaska Native, non-Hispanic/Latino; 7% Hispanic/Latino; 1% Black or African American, non-Hispanic/Latino; 0.4% Asian, non-Hispanic/Latino; 0.3% Native Hawaiian or other Pacific Islander, non-Hispanic/Latino; 5% international. 20% 25 or older, 46% live on campus. Retention: 61% of full-time freshmen returned the following year. Core. Calendar: semesters. Academic remediation for entering students, ESL program, services for LD students, advanced placement, independent study, distance learning, double major, summer session for credit, part-time degree program, external degree program, adult/ continuing education programs, co-op programs and internships. Off campus study at Wyoming Course Locator and Support Services Consortium (WYCLASS). Study abroad program.

Entrance Requirements: Open admission Nursing programs and the Equine Riding and Training programs have additional admission requirements and deadlines. Option: electronic application. Required: high school transcript. Recommended: minimum 2 high school GPA. Required for some: minimum 2 high school GPA. Entrance: noncompetitive. Application deadline: rolling. Notification: continuous. Transfer credits accepted: Yes.

Collegiate Environment: Orientation program. Drama-theater group, choral group. Social organizations: 44 open to all; Phi Theta Kappa Honor Society. Student services: health clinic, personal-psychological counseling. Campus security: 24-hour emergency response devices and patrols, late night transport-escort service, controlled dormitory access. John Taggart Hinckley Library. 500 computers available on campus for general student use. A campuswide network can be accessed from student residence rooms and from off campus. Students can access the following: online class registration. Staffed computer lab on campus provides training in use of computers, software, and the Internet.

■ SHERIDAN COLLEGE

3059 Coffeen Ave.
Sheridan, WY 82801-1500
Tel: (307)674-6446; Free: 800-913-9139
Fax: (307)674-7205
E-mail: madams@sheridan.edu
Web Site: www.sheridan.edu

Description: State and locally supported, 2-year, coed. Part of Wyoming Community College Commission. Awards certificates, transfer associate, and terminal associate degrees. Founded 1948. Setting: 145-acre small town campus. System endowment: $29.6 million. Educational spending for the previous fiscal year: $5509 per student. Total enrollment: 4,307. Faculty: 217 (99 full-time, 118 part-time). Student-undergrad faculty ratio is 17:1. Full-time: 1,398 students, 55% women, 45% men. Part-time: 2,909 students, 42% women, 58% men. Students come from 37 states and territories, 11 other countries, 18% from out-of-state. 2% American Indian or Alaska Native, non-Hispanic/Latino; 7% Hispanic/Latino; 1% Black or African American, non-Hispanic/Latino; 0.6% Asian, non-Hispanic/Latino; 0.2% Native Hawaiian or other Pacific Islander, non-Hispanic/Latino; 0.8% international. 32% 25 or older, 10% live on campus, 3% transferred in. Retention: 59% of full-time freshmen returned the following year. Core. Calendar: semesters. Academic remediation for entering students, ESL program, services for LD students, advanced placement, accelerated degree program, independent study, distance learning, double major, summer session for credit, part-time degree program, co-op programs and internships. Off campus study.

Entrance Requirements: Open admission except for dental hygiene, nursing, massage therapy programs. Options: electronic application, early admission, deferred admission. Recommended: high school transcript. Required for some: high school transcript. Entrance: noncompetitive. Application deadline: rolling. Notification: continuous. Transfer credits accepted: Yes.

Costs Per Year: Application fee: $0. State resident tuition: $3396 full-time, $94 per credit hour part-time. Nonresident tuition: $7908 full-time, $282 per credit hour part-time. Mandatory fees: $38 per credit hour part-time. Full-time tuition varies according to course load, location, and reciprocity agreements. Part-time tuition and fees vary according to location and reciprocity agreements.

Collegiate Environment: Orientation program. Drama-theater group, choral group. Social organizations: 25 open to all. Most popular organizations: National Society of Leadership and Success, Student Senate, Baptist Collegiate Ministries, Nursing Club, Dental Hygiene Club. Major annual events: Hypnotist, Welcome Back Dance, Casino Night. Student services: personal-psychological counseling. Campus security: 24-hour emergency response devices, student patrols, controlled dormitory access, night patrols by certified officers. Mary Brown Kooi Library plus 1 other. Operations spending for the previous fiscal year: $666,165. 980 computers available on campus for general student use. A campuswide network can be accessed from student residence rooms and from off campus. Students can access the following: online class registration. Staffed computer lab on campus provides training in use of computers, software, and the Internet.

Community Environment: The town of Sheridan is located in northeastern Wyoming at the foot of the scenic Big Horn Mountains. The Big Horns rise to 13,165 feet above Sheridan's 3,745-foot elevation and provide year-round opportunities for outdoor recreation from wilderness hiking to rock climbing, skiing, camping, hunting and fishing. With a population of about 16,000, Sheridan retains an atmosphere of small-town friendliness while offering its citizens many fine services. The YMCA, Sheridan Recreation District, and other organizations provide activities for all ages. The community also supports a number of high-quality programs for the visual and performing arts.

■ UNIVERSITY OF WYOMING

1000 E University Ave.
Laramie, WY 82071
Tel: (307)766-1121; Free: 800-342-5996
Fax: (307)766-2271
E-mail: admissions@uwyo.edu
Web Site: www.uwyo.edu

Description: State-supported, university, coed. Awards bachelor's, master's, and doctoral degrees. Founded 1886. Setting: 835-acre small town campus. System endowment: $517.5 million. Research spending for the previous fis-

cal year: $83.1 million. Total enrollment: 12,450. Faculty: 738 (730 full-time, 8 part-time). Student-undergrad faculty ratio is 15:1. 5,238 applied, 96% were admitted. 21% from top 10% of their high school class, 48% from top quarter, 80% from top half. Full-time: 8,457 students, 49% women, 51% men. Part-time: 1,541 students, 59% women, 41% men. Students come from 51 states and territories, 61 other countries, 34% from out-of-state. 0.6% American Indian or Alaska Native, non-Hispanic/Latino; 7% Hispanic/Latino; 1% Black or African American, non-Hispanic/Latino; 1% Asian, non-Hispanic/Latino; 0.1% Native Hawaiian or other Pacific Islander, non-Hispanic/Latino; 4% international. 16% 25 or older, 25% live on campus, 11% transferred in. Retention: 78% of full-time freshmen returned the following year. Academic areas with the most degrees conferred: business/marketing; engineering; health professions and related sciences. Core. Calendar: semesters. Services for LD students, advanced placement, accelerated degree program, self-designed majors, honors program, independent study, distance learning, double major, summer session for credit, part-time degree program, external degree program, co-op programs and internships, graduate courses open to undergrads. Off campus study at National Student Exchange. Study abroad program. ROTC: Army, Air Force.

Entrance Requirements: Options: electronic application, deferred admission, international baccalaureate accepted. Required: high school transcript, minimum 3 high school GPA, pre-college curriculum, minimum ACT composite score of 21 or SAT of 980, SAT or ACT. Entrance: moderately difficult. Application deadlines: 8/10, 8/10 for nonresidents. Notification: continuous, continuous for nonresidents. SAT Reasoning Test deadline: 8/10. Transfer credits accepted: Yes.

Costs Per Year: Application fee: $40. One-time mandatory fee: $40. Area resident tuition: $4020 full-time, $134 part-time. State resident tuition: $4020 full-time, $134 per credit hour part-time. Nonresident tuition: $16,110 full-time, $537 per credit hour part-time. Mandatory fees: $1380 full-time. College room and board: $10,320. College room only: $4493.

Collegiate Environment: Orientation program. Drama-theater group, choral group, marching band, student-run newspaper, radio station. Social organizations: national fraternities, national sororities, local fraternities; 8% of eligible men and 7% of eligible women are members. Major annual events: Homecoming, Campus Resource Fair and Club Day, Relay for Life. Student services: legal services, health clinic, personal-psychological counseling, women's center. Campus security: 24-hour emergency response devices and patrols, student patrols, late night transport-escort service, controlled dormitory access. 2,789 college housing spaces available. Freshmen guaranteed college housing. On-campus residence required in freshman year. Options: coed, men-only, women-only housing available. William Robertson Coe Library plus 4 others. Books: 1.8 million (physical), 1.2 million (digital/electronic); Serial titles: 14,085 (physical), 96,240 (digital/electronic); Databases: 1,043. Study areas open 24 hours, 5-7 days a week; students can reserve study rooms. 1,683 computers available on campus for general student use. Computer purchase/lease plans available. A campuswide network can be accessed from student residence rooms and from off campus. Students can access the following: online class registration. Staffed computer lab on campus (open 24 hours a day) provides training in use of computers, software, and the Internet.

Community Environment: Named for Jacques LaRamie, an early trapper for the American Fur Company, Laramie was established in 1868. Today, the community is known as the "Gem City of the Plains." The mean annual temperature is 42 degrees. The city is accessible by air and bus lines. There are 24 churches in the area, representing 20 different religious denominations, a full-service hospital, library, and civic and fraternal organizations serving the community. Local recreation includes 2 movie theaters, bowling, golf, hunting, fishing, and nearby Snowy Range ski area. An annual rodeo and jubilee are held in July.

■ WESTERN WYOMING COMMUNITY COLLEGE

2500 College Dr.
Rock Springs, WY 82901
Tel: (307)382-1600; Free: 800-226-1181
Fax: (307)382-1636
E-mail: admissions@westernwyoming.edu
Web Site: www.westernwyoming.edu

Description: State and locally supported, 2-year, coed. Awards certificates, diplomas, transfer associate, and terminal associate degrees. Founded 1959. Setting: 342-acre small town campus. Endowment: $23.7 million. Total enrollment: 3,183. Faculty: 307 (81 full-time, 226 part-time). Student-undergrad faculty ratio is 11:1. 1,889 applied, 59% were admitted. Full-time: 1,096 students, 56% women, 44% men. Part-time: 2,087 students, 53%

women, 47% men. Students come from 15 states and territories, 16 other countries, 16% from out-of-state. 0.6% American Indian or Alaska Native, non-Hispanic/Latino; 12% Hispanic/Latino; 2% Black or African American, non-Hispanic/Latino; 0.9% Asian, non-Hispanic/Latino; 0.1% Native Hawaiian or other Pacific Islander, non-Hispanic/Latino; 2% international. 36% 25 or older, 10% live on campus. Core. Calendar: semesters. Academic remediation for entering students, ESL program, services for LD students, advanced placement, honors program, independent study, distance learning, summer session for credit, part-time degree program, co-op programs and internships.

Entrance Requirements: Open admission. Options: electronic application, early admission, deferred admission. Recommended: high school transcript. Entrance: noncompetitive. Application deadline: rolling. Transfer credits accepted: Yes.

Costs Per Year: Application fee: $0. Area resident tuition: $2970 full-time, $99 per credit hour part-time. State resident tuition: $2970 full-time, $99 per credit hour part-time. Nonresident tuition: $8910 full-time. College room and board: $5720. College room only: $2680.

Collegiate Environment: Orientation program. Drama-theater group, choral group, student-run newspaper, radio station. Social organizations: 17 open to all. Most popular organizations: Association of Non-Traditional Students (ANTS), Spanish Club, Residence Hall Association, International Club, Veteran's Club. Major annual events: ASG Awards Event, Kick-off Day,

International Night. Student services: personal-psychological counseling. Campus security: 24-hour emergency response devices and patrols, late night transport-escort service, controlled dormitory access. 558 college housing spaces available; 324 were occupied in 2018-19. No special consideration for freshman housing applicants. Option: coed housing available. Hay Library. Books: 93,144 (physical), 747,995 (digital/electronic); Serial titles: 136 (physical), 63,272 (digital/electronic); Databases: 412. Weekly public service hours: 81; students can reserve study rooms. 701 computers available on campus for general student use. A campuswide network can be accessed from student residence rooms and from off campus. Students can access the following: online class registration. Staffed computer lab on campus.

Community Environment: This is a rural area with a cold, dry climate. Airlines, the railroad, bus lines, and Routes 30, 1-80, and 191 make the city accessible. There are a public library, churches of major denominations, a hospital, a mental health clinic and major civic and fraternal organizations are active in the community. The city has adequate shopping facilities. Local recreation includes theatres, a drive-in, bowling, hunting, fishing, and hiking. Nearby attractions include Yellowstone and Grand Teton National Parks, Flaming Gorge National Recreation Area, the Wind River Mountains and the Bridger Wilderness. A county fair is held annually. Some part-time work is available.

American Samoa

■ AMERICAN SAMOA COMMUNITY COLLEGE
PO Box 2609
Pago Pago, AS 96799-2609
Tel: (684)699-9155
Fax: (684)699-6259
Web Site: www.amsamoa.edu

Description: Territory-supported, primarily 2-year, coed. Awards certificates, transfer associate, terminal associate, and bachelor's degrees. Founded 1969. Setting: 20-acre rural campus. Endowment: $3.1 million. Research spending for the previous fiscal year: $975,683. Educational spending for the previous fiscal year: $2918 per student. Total enrollment: 1,095. Faculty: 87 (60 full-time, 27 part-time). Student-undergrad faculty ratio is 20:1. 407 applied, 100% were admitted. Full-time: 615 students, 67% women, 33% men. Part-time: 480 students, 66% women, 34% men. Students come from 3 other countries. 0.8% Asian, non-Hispanic/Latino; 90% Native Hawaiian or other Pacific Islander, non-Hispanic/Latino; 9% international. 15% 25 or older, 1% transferred in. Retention: 100% of full-time freshmen returned the following year. Academic area with the most degrees conferred: education. Core. Calendar: semesters. Academic remediation for entering students, services for LD students, independent study, double major, summer session for credit, part-time degree program, adult/continuing education programs, co-op programs and internships. ROTC: Army.

Entrance Requirements: Open admission. Options: electronic application, early admission, deferred admission. Recommended: SAT and SAT Subject Tests or ACT. Entrance: noncompetitive. Application deadline: rolling. Notification: continuous. SAT Reasoning Test deadline: 8/22. SAT Subject Test deadline: 8/22. Transfer credits accepted: Yes.

Costs Per Year: Application fee: $0. Territory resident tuition: $3300 full-time, $110 per credit part-time. Nonresident tuition: $3600 full-time, $120 per credit part-time. Mandatory fees: $650 full-time, $550 per term part-time. Full-time tuition and fees vary according to course level, course load, and degree level. Part-time tuition and fees vary according to course level, course load, and degree level.

Collegiate Environment: Orientation program. Student-run newspaper. Social organizations: 9 open to all; 7% of eligible men and 15% of eligible women are members. Most popular organizations: Student Government Association, Phi Theta Kappa, ASCC Research Foundation Student Club, Fa'aSamoa (Samoan culture) Club, Journalism Club. Major annual events: Intramurals, Field Games, Talent Show. Student services: legal services, health clinic, personal-psychological counseling. Campus security: 24-hour emergency response devices and patrols. ASCC Learning Resource Center/Library plus 1 other. Books: 33,000 (physical); Serial titles: 330 (physical). Weekly public service hours: 43. Operations spending for the previous fiscal year: $252,120. 275 computers available on campus for general student use. A campuswide network can be accessed. Students can access the following: online class registration. Staffed computer lab on campus provides training in use of computers, software, and the Internet.

Guam

■ GUAM COMMUNITY COLLEGE
1 Sesame St.
Mangilao, GU 96913

Tel: (671)735-5531
Fax: (671)734-5238
E-mail: julie.ulloaheath@guamcc.edu
Web Site: www.guamcc.edu

Description: Territory-supported, 2-year, coed. Awards certificates, diplomas, and terminal associate degrees. Founded 1977. Setting: 33-acre small town campus. System endowment: $8.8 million. Research spending for the previous fiscal year: $1 million. Educational spending for the previous fiscal year: $16,887 per student. Total enrollment: 2,428. Faculty: 194 (115 full-time, 79 part-time). Student-undergrad faculty ratio is 15:1. 289 applied, 100% were admitted. Full-time: 1,038 students, 60% women, 40% men. Part-time: 1,390 students, 53% women, 47% men. 0.5% Hispanic/Latino; 1% Black or African American, non-Hispanic/Latino; 41% Asian, non-Hispanic/Latino; 54% Native Hawaiian or other Pacific Islander, non-Hispanic/Latino; 1% international. 25% 25 or older, 1% transferred in. Retention: 62% of full-time freshmen returned the following year. Core. Calendar: semesters. Academic remediation for entering students, ESL program, services for LD students, advanced placement, honors program, independent study, double major, summer session for credit, part-time degree program, adult/continuing education programs, co-op programs and internships. Off campus study at University of Guam. ROTC: Army (c).

Entrance Requirements: Open admission. Option: early admission. Required: high school transcript. Entrance: noncompetitive. Application deadline: rolling. Notification: continuous. Transfer credits accepted: Yes.

Costs Per Year: Application fee: $0. Territory resident tuition: $3120 full-time, $130 per credit hour part-time. Nonresident tuition: $3720 full-time, $155 per credit hour part-time. Mandatory fees: $294 full-time, $147 per term part-time.

Collegiate Environment: Orientation program. Student services: health clinic, personal-psychological counseling. Campus security: 12-hour patrols by trained security personnel. Learning Resource Center. Books: 21,379 (physical), 157,000 (digital/electronic); Databases: 40. Weekly public service hours: 60; students can reserve study rooms. Operations spending for the previous fiscal year: $385,170. 50 computers available on campus for general student use. A campuswide network can be accessed from off-campus. Students can access the following: online class registration. Staffed computer lab on campus provides training in use of computers, software, and the Internet.

■ PACIFIC ISLANDS UNIVERSITY
172 Kinney's Rd.
Mangilao, GU 96913
Tel: (671)734-1812
Fax: (671)734-1813
E-mail: guamcampus@pibc.edu
Web Site: www.piu.edu

Description: Independent interdenominational, 4-year, coed. Awards associate and bachelor's degrees. Founded 1976. Total enrollment: 188. Faculty: 22 (12 full-time, 10 part-time). Student-undergrad faculty ratio is 7:1. Full-time: 132 students, 58% women, 42% men. Part-time: 56 students, 54% women, 46% men. Calendar: semesters.

Entrance Requirements: Required: essay, high school transcript, 2 recommendations, interview. Application deadline: 8/25.

■ UNIVERSITY OF GUAM
303 University Dr.
UOG Station

Mangilao, GU 96923
Fax: (671)734-6005
E-mail: admitme@triton.uog.edu
Web Site: www.uog.edu
Description: Territory-supported, comprehensive, coed. Awards bachelor's and master's degrees. Founded 1952. Setting: 100-acre suburban campus. Total enrollment: 3,744. Faculty: 294 (134 full-time, 160 part-time). 645 applied, 79% were admitted. 24% from top 10% of their high school class, 48% from top quarter, 74% from top half. 8 valedictorians. Full-time: 2,708 students, 57% women, 43% men. Part-time: 713 students, 57% women, 43% men. Students come from 26 states and territories, 19 other countries, 1% from out-of-territory. 0.1% American Indian or Alaska Native, non-Hispanic/Latino; 0.7% Hispanic/Latino; 0.7% Black or African American, non-Hispanic/Latino; 45% Asian, non-Hispanic/Latino; 47% Native Hawaiian or other Pacific Islander, non-Hispanic/Latino; 0.9% international. 20% 25 or older, 4% transferred in. Retention: 73% of full-time freshmen returned the following year. Academic areas with the most degrees conferred: business/marketing; education; health professions and related sciences. Core. Calendar: semesters. Academic remediation for entering students, ESL program, services for LD students, advanced placement, accelerated degree program, honors program, independent study, distance learning, double major, summer session for credit, part-time degree program, co-op programs and internships, graduate courses open to undergrads. Off campus study at member of the National Student Exchange program. Study abroad program. ROTC: Army.
Entrance Requirements: Open admission nursing, education, and social work programs have specific requirements. Options: electronic application, deferred admission, international baccalaureate accepted. Required: high school transcript. Entrance: noncompetitive. Application deadlines: 6/1, 6/1 for nonresidents. Notification: continuous. Transfer credits accepted: Yes.
Costs Per Year: Application fee: $52. Territory resident tuition: $5040 full-time, $210 per credit hour part-time. Nonresident tuition: $12,096 full-time, $504 per credit hour part-time. Mandatory fees: $764 full-time, $382 per term part-time. College room and board: $3850.
Collegiate Environment: Orientation program. Drama-theater group, choral group, student-run newspaper. Social organizations: 52 open to all. Most popular organizations: American Marketing Association, Student Nurses Association of Guam, Social Work Student Alliance, Association of Early Childhood Education International, Public Administration and Legal Studies. Major annual events: Charter Day, Annual Student Organization Membership Drive, Campus Theater Productions. Student services: health clinic, personal-psychological counseling, women's center. Campus security: 24-hour emergency response devices and patrols, late night transport-escort service, Sexual Harassment Training Requirement for all Students, Faculty, Staff, and Administrators. 218 college housing spaces available; 161 were occupied in 2018-19. No special consideration for freshman housing applicants. Option: coed housing available. University of Guam Robert F. Kennedy Memorial Library. Books: 213,916 (physical), 153,000 (digital/electronic); Serial titles: 1,527 (physical); Databases: 60. Weekly public service hours: 60; study areas open 24 hours, 5-7 days a week; students can reserve study rooms. 262 computers available on campus for general student use. A campuswide network can be accessed from student residence rooms and from off campus. Students can access the following: online class registration. Staffed computer lab on campus provides training in use of software and the Internet.

Northern Mariana Islands

■ NORTHERN MARIANAS COLLEGE
PO Box 501250
Saipan, MP 96950
Tel: (670)234-5498
Fax: (670)234-1270
E-mail: leilanib@nmcnet.edu
Web Site: www.marianas.edu
Description: Territory-supported, primarily 2-year, coed. Awards certificates, diplomas, transfer associate, terminal associate, and bachelor's degrees. Founded 1981. Setting: 14-acre rural campus. Total enrollment: 1,299. Faculty: 99 (49 full-time, 50 part-time). Full-time: 783 students, 67% women, 33% men. Part-time: 516 students, 61% women, 39% men. Students come from 4 states and territories, 9 other countries. 40% 25 or older. Core. Calendar: semesters. Academic remediation for entering students, ESL

program, services for LD students, distance learning, summer session for credit, part-time degree program, adult/continuing education programs, co-op programs and internships.
Entrance Requirements: Open admission. Options: early admission, deferred admission. Required: high school transcript. Entrance: noncompetitive. Application deadline: rolling.
Collegiate Environment: Orientation program. Drama-theater group. Most popular organizations: Northern Marinas Academy, Korean Association, Micronesian Club, Learning Skills. Major annual events: Charter Day, International Night, Haunted House. Student services: personal-psychological counseling. Campus security: patrols by trained security personnel. Olympia T. Borja Library plus 1 other. 56 computers available on campus for general student use. A campuswide network can be accessed from off-campus. Staffed computer lab on campus.

Puerto Rico

■ ALBIZU UNIVERSITY
151 Tanca St.
San Juan, PR 00901
Tel: (787)725-6500
Fax: (787)721-7187
Web Site: www.albizu.edu
Description: Independent, university, coed. Awards bachelor's, master's, and doctoral degrees. Founded 1966. Setting: urban campus. Endowment: $732,270. Research spending for the previous fiscal year: $419,213. Total enrollment: 919. Faculty: 14 (1 full-time, 13 part-time). Student-undergrad faculty ratio is 10:1. 63 applied, 84% were admitted. Full-time: 78 students, 94% women, 6% men. Part-time: 64 students, 83% women, 17% men. 1% from out-of-commonwealth. 95% Hispanic/Latino. 38% 25 or older, 74% transferred in. Academic areas with the most degrees conferred: health professions and related sciences; psychology. Core. Calendar: semesters. Independent study, part-time degree program, co-op programs.
Entrance Requirements: Options: early admission, deferred admission, international baccalaureate accepted. Required: minimum 2 high school GPA, 2 recommendations, CEEB or SAT. Required for some: health certificate, Good Conduct Crete, official university transcript. Entrance: noncompetitive. Application deadline: 7/16. Notification: continuous. SAT Reasoning Test deadline: 7/15. SAT Subject Test deadline: 7/15. Transfer credits accepted: Yes.
Collegiate Environment: Orientation program. Student-run newspaper. Social organizations: 3 open to all. Most popular organizations: Student Council, Community Services, Gender and Sexual Diversity Organization, OASIS, Speech/Language Pathology Students Organization. Major annual events: Student's Welcome Activity, Christmas Activity, seminars with external resources. Campus security: 24-hour emergency response devices, late night transport-escort service, security cameras. Carlos Albizu Miranda plus 2 others. Operations spending for the previous fiscal year: $220,223. 68 computers available on campus for general student use. A campuswide network can be accessed. Students can access the following: online class registration. Staffed computer lab on campus provides training in use of computers, software, and the Internet.

■ AMERICAN UNIVERSITY OF PUERTO RICO (BAYAMON)
PO Box 2037
Bayamon, PR 00960-2037
Tel: (787)620-2040
Fax: (787)785-7377
E-mail: kllanos@aupr.edu
Web Site: www.aupr.edu
Description: Independent, comprehensive, coed. Awards associate, bachelor's, and master's degrees. Founded 1963. Setting: 21-acre urban campus with easy access to San Juan. Research spending for the previous fiscal year: $90,715. Educational spending for the previous fiscal year: $1646 per student. Total enrollment: 2,468. Faculty: 162 (41 full-time, 121 part-time). 325 applied, 83% were admitted. 3% from top 10% of their high school class, 15% from top quarter, 25% from top half. Full-time: 2,123 students, 53% women, 47% men. Part-time: 201 students, 66% women, 34% men. 100% Hispanic/Latino. Retention: 80% of full-time freshmen returned the following year. Calendar: semesters. ESL program, services for LD students, advanced placement, freshman honors college, honors program, independent study, distance learning, double major, summer ses-

sion for credit, part-time degree program, adult/continuing education programs, co-op programs and internships. ROTC: Army (c).

Entrance Requirements: Open admission. Options: electronic application, deferred admission. Required: high school transcript. Recommended: SAT and SAT Subject Tests or ACT. Entrance: noncompetitive. Notification: continuous. Transfer credits accepted: Yes.

Collegiate Environment: Drama-theater group. Most popular organizations: Business Student Association, Information Systems Student Association, Accounting Student Association, Library Club, Office Systems Student Association. Major annual events: NCAA Tournaments, Manual Arts Fair. Student services: health clinic. Campus security: 24-hour patrols. Loida Figueroa Meacado. Operations spending for the previous fiscal year: $666,872. 359 computers available on campus for general student use. A campuswide network can be accessed. Staffed computer lab on campus provides training in use of computers, software, and the Internet.

■ **AMERICAN UNIVERSITY OF PUERTO RICO (MANATI)**
Carretera Estatal No.2 Km. 48.7
Manati, PR 00674-1082
Tel: (787)621-2835
Web Site: www.aupr.edu
Description: Independent, comprehensive, coed. Awards associate, bachelor's, and master's degrees.

■ **ATENAS COLLEGE**
Paseo de La Atenas No.101 Altos
Manati, PR 00674
Tel: (787)884-3838
Web Site: www.atenascollege.edu
Description: Independent, 4-year, coed. Awards associate and bachelor's degrees.

■ **ATLANTIC UNIVERSITY COLLEGE**
PO Box 3918
Guaynabo, PR 00970
Tel: (787)720-1022
Fax: (787)720-1092
Web Site: www.atlanticu.edu
Description: Independent, comprehensive, coed. Awards associate, bachelor's, and master's degrees. Total enrollment: 1,236. 11% 25 or older. Calendar: semesters. Part-time degree program, internships.
Entrance Requirements: Open admission. Required: high school transcript. Required for some: interview. Notification: continuous.
Collegiate Environment: Orientation program. Resources Center.

■ **BAYAMÓN CENTRAL UNIVERSITY**
PO Box 1725
Bayamon, PR 00960-1725
Tel: (787)786-3030
Web Site: www.ucb.edu.pr
Description: Independent Roman Catholic, comprehensive, coed. Awards associate, bachelor's, and master's degrees and post-master's certificates. Founded 1970. Setting: 55-acre urban campus with easy access to San Juan. Endowment: $439,784. Total enrollment: 2,221. Faculty: 145 (38 full-time, 107 part-time). Student-undergrad faculty ratio is 23:1. 517 applied, 45% were admitted. Students come from 2 other countries. 100% Hispanic/Latino; 0.3% international. 33% 25 or older. Retention: 91% of full-time freshmen returned the following year. Academic areas with the most degrees conferred: health professions and related sciences; business/marketing; public administration and social services. Core. Calendar: semesters for undergraduate programs, trimesters for graduate programs. Academic remediation for entering students, services for LD students, accelerated degree program, honors program, distance learning, summer session for credit, part-time degree program, co-op programs. ROTC: Army (c), Air Force (c).
Entrance Requirements: Options: electronic application, international baccalaureate accepted. Required: high school transcript, CEEB. Recommended: minimum 2 high school GPA. Application deadline: rolling. Notification: continuous. Transfer credits accepted: Yes.
Collegiate Environment: Orientation program. Student services: health clinic, personal-psychological counseling. Campus security: 24-hour patrols. Biblioteca Dra. Margot Arce de Vazquez plus 1 other. Weekly public service hours: 50; students can reserve study rooms. 150 computers available on

campus for general student use. A campuswide network can be accessed. Staffed computer lab on campus provides training in use of computers, software, and the Internet.

■ **CARIBBEAN UNIVERSITY**
Box 493
Bayamon, PR 00960-0493
Tel: (787)780-0070
Fax: (787)785-0101
Web Site: www.caribbean.edu
Description: Independent, comprehensive, coed. Awards associate, bachelor's, master's, and doctoral degrees. Founded 1969. Setting: 16-acre urban campus with easy access to San Juan. Research spending for the previous fiscal year: $27.5 million. Educational spending for the previous fiscal year: $1807 per student. Total enrollment: 3,547. Faculty: 361 (86 full-time, 275 part-time). Student-undergrad faculty ratio is 14:1. 1,020 applied, 57% were admitted. Full-time: 2,099 students, 57% women, 43% men. Part-time: 821 students, 53% women, 47% men. 100% Hispanic/Latino. Retention: 72% of full-time freshmen returned the following year. Academic areas with the most degrees conferred: health professions and related sciences; public administration and social services; business/marketing. Core. Calendar: semesters. Academic remediation for entering students, ESL program, services for LD students, accelerated degree program, summer session for credit, part-time degree program, adult/continuing education programs. ROTC: Army (c).
Entrance Requirements: Open admission for associate degrees. Options: deferred admission, international baccalaureate accepted. Required: high school transcript. Required for some: minimum 2 high school GPA, 1 recommendation, interview, College Board math/verbal test for engineering. Entrance: minimally difficult. Application deadline: rolling. Transfer credits accepted: Yes.
Collegiate Environment: Orientation program. Drama-theater group, choral group. Social organizations: 10 open to all; 5% of eligible men and 6% of eligible women are members. Most popular organizations: Engineering Student Association, Nursing, Social Work, Speech Therapy, Criminal Justices. Major annual events: Jobs Fairs, Health Fairs, Athletic Tournament. Student services: health clinic, personal-psychological counseling. Campus security: 24-hour patrols. Biblioteca Virgilio Davila, Recinto de Bayamon plus 4 others. Books: 76,606 (physical), 139,981 (digital/electronic); Databases: 2,346. Operations spending for the previous fiscal year: $720,823. 378 computers available on campus for general student use. A campuswide network can be accessed from off-campus. Students can access the following: online class registration. Staffed computer lab on campus provides training in use of computers and the Internet.

■ **CARIBBEAN UNIVERSITY-CAROLINA**
Calle Ignacio Arzuaga No.208
Carolina, PR 00985
Tel: (787)769-0007
Web Site: www.caribbean.edu
Description: Independent, comprehensive, coed. Awards associate, bachelor's, and master's degrees. Founded 1979.

■ **CARIBBEAN UNIVERSITY-PONCE**
Ave. Ednita Nazario No.1015
Ponce, PR 00716-7733
Tel: (787)840-2955
Web Site: www.caribbean.edu
Description: Independent, comprehensive, coed. Awards associate, bachelor's, and master's degrees. Founded 1985.

■ **CARIBBEAN UNIVERSITY-VEGA BAJA**
Carr 671 K.M. 5, Sector El Criollo, Bo. Algarrobo
Vega Baja, PR 00693
Tel: (787)858-3668
Web Site: www.caribbean.edu
Description: Independent, comprehensive, coed. Awards associate, bachelor's, and master's degrees. Founded 1977.

■ **THE CENTER OF CINEMATOGRAPHY, ARTS AND TELEVISION**
51 Dr. Veve St., Degetau St. Corner
Bayamon, PR 00960
Tel: (787)779-2500
Web Site: ccatmiami.com

Description: Proprietary, 2-year, coed. Awards certificates, transfer associate, and terminal associate degrees.

■ **CENTRO DE ESTUDIOS MULTIDISCIPLINARIOS (BAYAMON)**
Calle Degetau No.25
Bayamon, PR 00961
Tel: (787)780-8900
Web Site: www.cemcollege.edu
Description: Proprietary, 4-year, coed. Awards associate and bachelor's degrees.

■ **CENTRO DE ESTUDIOS MULTIDISCIPLINARIOS (HUMACAO)**
Calle Dr. Vidal No.8 y No.53
Humacao, PR 00791
Tel: (809)852-5505
Web Site: www.cemcollege.edu
Description: Proprietary, 4-year, coed. Awards associate and bachelor's degrees. Setting: 1-acre urban campus. Educational spending for the previous fiscal year: $396,003 per student. Total enrollment: 151. Faculty: 28 (5 full-time, 23 part-time). Student-undergrad faculty ratio is 5:1. Full-time: 151 students, 67% women, 33% men. Retention: 100% of full-time freshmen returned the following year. Core. Calendar: quarters. Academic remediation for entering students, services for LD students, co-op programs.
Entrance Requirements: Required: high school transcript, minimum 2 high school GPA, interview.
Collegiate Environment: Orientation program. Student services: personal-psychological counseling. Campus security: 24-hour emergency response devices and patrols. Students can reserve study rooms. Operations spending for the previous fiscal year: $14,000. 40 computers available on campus for general student use. A campuswide network can be accessed. Staffed computer lab on campus provides training in use of computers and the Internet.

■ **CENTRO DE ESTUDIOS MULTIDISCIPLINARIOS (MAYAGUEZ)**
Calle Cristy No.56
Mayaguez, PR 00680
Tel: (787)986-7440
Web Site: www.cemcollege.edu
Description: Proprietary, primarily 2-year, coed. Awards certificates, terminal associate, and bachelor's degrees.

■ **CENTRO DE ESTUDIOS MULTIDISCIPLINARIOS (RIO PIEDRAS)**
Calle 13 No.1206
Ext. San Agustin
Rio Piedras, PR 00926
Tel: (787)765-4210; Free: 877-779-CDEM
Web Site: www.cemcollege.edu
Description: Proprietary, primarily 2-year, coed. Awards certificates, terminal associate, and bachelor's degrees. Founded 1980. Total enrollment: 1,224. 735 applied, 95% were admitted. 44% 25 or older.

■ **COLEGIO UNIVERSITARIO DE SAN JUAN**
180 Jose R. Oliver St.
Tres Monjitas Industrial Park
San Juan, PR 00918
Tel: (787)480-2400
Fax: (787)250-7395
Web Site: www.cunisanjuan.edu
Description: City-supported, 4-year, coed. Awards associate and bachelor's degrees. Founded 1971. Setting: 5-acre urban campus. Total enrollment: 1,480. Faculty: 145 (19 full-time, 126 part-time). Student-undergrad faculty ratio is 22:1. 306 applied, 88% were admitted. Full-time: 1,234 students, 60% women, 40% men. Part-time: 246 students, 54% women, 46% men. 34% 25 or older, 15% transferred in. Retention: 57% of full-time freshmen returned the following year. Academic areas with the most degrees conferred: health professions and related sciences; homeland security, law enforcement, firefighting, and protective services; business/marketing. Calendar: semesters. Academic remediation for entering students, ESL program, services for LD students, independent study, summer session for credit, part-time degree program, co-op programs and internships. Off campus study.
Entrance Requirements: Open admission. Option: electronic application. Required: high school transcript, minimum 2 high school GPA, medical his-

tory. Required for some: interview. Entrance: noncompetitive. Notification: continuous. Transfer credits accepted: Yes.
Costs Per Year: Application fee: $15. Commonwealth resident tuition: $2040 full-time. Nonresident tuition: $2040 full-time. Mandatory fees: $330 full-time.
Collegiate Environment: Orientation program. Student services: personal-psychological counseling. Campus security: 24-hour emergency response devices and patrols. Access to Information Center. Books: 17,569 (physical), 228,547 (digital/electronic); Serial titles: 82,010 (digital/electronic); Databases: 69. Weekly public service hours: 81; students can reserve study rooms.

■ **COLUMBIA CENTRAL UNIVERSITY (CAGUAS)**
183 Caguas
Caguas, PR 00725
Tel: (787)743-4041
Fax: (787)744-7931
E-mail: bzayas@columbiacentral.edu
Web Site: www.columbiacentral.edu
Description: Proprietary, comprehensive, coed. Awards associate, bachelor's, and master's degrees. Founded 1966. Setting: 6-acre urban campus with easy access to San Juan. Total enrollment: 1,156. Faculty: 90 (29 full-time, 61 part-time). Student-undergrad faculty ratio is 17:1. 190 applied, 90% were admitted. Full-time: 581 students, 55% women, 45% men. Part-time: 469 students, 60% women, 40% men. 30% 25 or older, 14% transferred in. Academic areas with the most degrees conferred: health professions and related sciences; business/marketing. Core. Calendar: semesters. Accelerated degree program, part-time degree program.
Entrance Requirements: Open admission. Options: electronic application, international baccalaureate accepted. Required: high school transcript, minimum 2 high school GPA. Required for some: essay, 3 recommendations, interview, Immunization Certificate for candidates who are under 21. Entrance: noncompetitive. Application deadline: rolling. Notification: continuous. Transfer credits accepted: Yes.
Costs Per Year: Application fee: $10. Comprehensive fee: $16,707 includes full-time tuition ($9630), mandatory fees ($180), and college room and board ($6897). Part-time tuition: $1665 per semester hour. Part-time mandatory fees: $230 per semester hour.
Collegiate Environment: Student services: personal-psychological counseling. Campus security: 24-hour patrols. College housing not available. Efrain Sola Bezares Library plus 1 other. Books: 9,494 (physical), 759 (digital/electronic); Serial titles: 19 (physical), 13,966 (digital/electronic); Databases: 26. Weekly public service hours: 81; students can reserve study rooms. Operations spending for the previous fiscal year: $248,909. 185 computers available on campus for general student use. A campuswide network can be accessed from off-campus. Students can access the following: online class registration, online courses, technical support, Microsoft office 365 products, Microsoft Imagine, Virtual library services, Moodle E-learning platform. Staffed computer lab on campus provides training in use of computers, software, and the Internet.

■ **COLUMBIA CENTRAL UNIVERSITY (YAUCO)**
Calle Betances No.3
Box 3062
Yauco, PR 00698
Tel: (787)856-0945
Fax: (787)267-2335
E-mail: cipabon@columbiacentral.edu
Web Site: www.columbiacentral.edu
Description: Proprietary, 4-year, coed. Administratively affiliated with Columbia Central University, Caguas Branch. Awards associate and bachelor's degrees. Founded 1966. Setting: urban campus with easy access to Ponce, Mayaguez. Total enrollment: 283. Faculty: 28 (7 full-time, 21 part-time). Student-undergrad faculty ratio is 10:1. 114 applied, 94% were admitted. Full-time: 155 students, 68% women, 32% men. Part-time: 128 students, 68% women, 32% men. 100% Hispanic/Latino. 32% 25 or older. Academic area with the most degrees conferred: health professions and related sciences. Core. Calendar: trimesters. Services for LD students, distance learning, part-time degree program, adult/continuing education programs, co-op programs and internships.
Entrance Requirements: Open admission Our institution has an open admissions policy. Options: electronic application, deferred admission, international baccalaureate accepted. Required: high school transcript,

minimum 2 high school GPA. Entrance: minimally difficult. Application deadline: rolling. Notification: continuous. Transfer credits accepted: Yes.

Costs Per Year: Application fee: $10. Tuition: $9810 full-time, $1665 per semester hour part-time. Mandatory fees: $60 full-time, $230 per semester hour part-time.

Collegiate Environment: Orientation program. Social organizations: 3 open to all; 15% of eligible men and 30% of eligible women are members. Most popular organizations: Student Association Pharmacy Technicians, Student Association Graphic Design, Student Council. Major annual events: Columbia Night, Columbia Fest, Welcome Back Activities. Student services: personal-psychological counseling. Campus security: trained security personnel during hours of operation. College housing not available. Centro de Informacion y Recursos Integrados (CIRI). Books: 2,362 (physical), 759 (digital/electronic); Serial titles: 547 (physical), 231,831 (digital/electronic); Databases: 26. Weekly public service hours: 64; students can reserve study rooms. Operations spending for the previous fiscal year: $77,038. 14 computers available on campus for general student use. A campuswide network can be accessed from off-campus. Students can access the following: online class registration. Staffed computer lab on campus provides training in use of computers, software, and the Internet.

■ CONSERVATORIO DE MUSICA DE PUERTO RICO

951 Ave. Ponce de León
Parada 15, Miramar
San Juan, PR 00907
Tel: (787)751-0160
E-mail: aarraiza2@cmpr.gobierno.pr
Web Site: www.cmpr.edu

Description: Commonwealth-supported, comprehensive, coed. Awards bachelor's and master's degrees. Setting: 4-acre urban campus with easy access to Old San Juan. System endowment: $1 million. Total enrollment: 463. Faculty: 81 (48 full-time, 33 part-time). Student-undergrad faculty ratio is 6:1. 102 applied, 66% were admitted. Full-time: 292 students, 29% women, 71% men. Part-time: 140 students, 28% women, 72% men. Students come from 3 states and territories, 5 other countries. 96% Hispanic/Latino; 0.2% Black or African American, non-Hispanic/Latino; 3% international. 7% 25 or older, 6% transferred in. Retention: 96% of full-time freshmen returned the following year. Academic areas with the most degrees conferred: visual and performing arts; education. Core. Calendar: semesters. Academic remediation for entering students, ESL program, services for LD students, advanced placement, honors program, summer session for credit, part-time degree program, co-op programs. Off campus study.

Entrance Requirements: Option: international baccalaureate accepted. Required: high school transcript, minimum 2 high school GPA, instrument audition, ear training test. Recommended: interview. Required for some: essay, minimum 3 high school GPA. Entrance: moderately difficult. Application deadline: 12/15. Notification: 3/1. Transfer credits accepted: Yes.

Costs Per Year: Application fee: $75. One-time mandatory fee: $225. Commonwealth resident tuition: $2520 full-time. Nonresident tuition: $2520 full-time. Mandatory fees: $425 full-time.

Collegiate Environment: Orientation program. Choral group. Campus security: 24-hour patrols. Biblioteca Amaury Veray plus 1 other. Books: 29,276 (physical), 80,545 (digital/electronic); Serial titles: 197 (physical), 80,942 (digital/electronic); Databases: 108. Operations spending for the previous fiscal year: $540,111. 43 computers available on campus for general student use. A campuswide network can be accessed from off-campus. Students can access the following: online class registration. Staffed computer lab on campus provides training in use of computers, software, and the Internet.

■ DEWEY UNIVERSITY-BAYAMÓN

Carr. No.2, Km. 15.9, Parque Industrial Corujo, Hato Tejas
Bayamon, PR 00959
Tel: (787)778-1200
Web Site: www.dewey.edu

Description: Independent, 2-year, coed. Awards certificates, transfer associate, and terminal associate degrees.

■ DEWEY UNIVERSITY-CAROLINA

Carr. No.3, Km. 11, Parque Industrial de Carolina, Lote 7
Carolina, PR 00986
Tel: (787)769-1515
Web Site: www.dewey.edu

Description: Independent, primarily 2-year, coed. Awards certificates, transfer associate, terminal associate, and bachelor's degrees.

■ DEWEY UNIVERSITY-FAJARDO

267 Calle General Valero
San Juan, PR 00910
Tel: (787)860-1212
Web Site: www.dewey.edu

Description: Independent, 2-year, coed. Awards certificates, transfer associate, and terminal associate degrees.

■ DEWEY UNIVERSITY-HATO REY

427 Avenida Barbosa
San Juan, PR 00923
Tel: (787)753-0039
Web Site: www.dewey.edu

Description: Independent, primarily 2-year, coed. Awards certificates, transfer associate, terminal associate, bachelor's, and master's degrees.

■ DEWEY UNIVERSITY-JUANA DIAZ

Carr. 149, Km. 55.9, Parque Industrial Lomas
San Juan, PR 00910
Tel: (787)837-1515
Web Site: www.dewey.edu

Description: Independent, 2-year, coed. Awards certificates, transfer associate, terminal associate, and master's degrees.

■ DEWEY UNIVERSITY-MANATI

Carr. 604, Km. 49.1 Barrio Tierras Nuevas, Salientes
Manati, PR 00674
Tel: (787)854-3800; Free: 866-773-3939
Fax: (787)854-1899
Web Site: www.dewey.edu

Description: Independent, primarily 2-year, coed. Awards certificates, transfer associate, terminal associate, and bachelor's degrees.

■ DEWEY UNIVERSITY-MAYAGUEZ

Carr. No.64 Km 6.6 Barrio Algarrobo
Mayaguez, PR 00682
Tel: (787)652-1212
Web Site: www.dewey.edu

Description: Independent, 2-year, coed. Awards transfer associate and terminal associate degrees.

■ EDIC COLLEGE

Ave. Rafael Cordero Calle Génova Urb. Caguas Norte
Caguas, PR 00726
Tel: (787)744-8519
Fax: (787)743-0855
Web Site: www.ediccollege.edu

Description: Proprietary, primarily 2-year, coed. Awards certificates, transfer associate, terminal associate, and bachelor's degrees.

■ EDP UNIVERSITY OF PUERTO RICO

560 Ave. Ponce de Leon
San Juan, PR 00918
Tel: (787)765-3560
E-mail: oscarmorales@edpuniversity.edu
Web Site: www.edpuniversity.edu

Description: Independent, comprehensive, coed. Awards associate, bachelor's, and master's degrees. Founded 1968. Setting: 1-acre urban campus with easy access to San Juan. Research spending for the previous fiscal year: $180,643. Educational spending for the previous fiscal year: $2500 per student. Total enrollment: 1,782. Faculty: 198 (49 full-time, 149 part-time). Student-undergrad faculty ratio is 12:1. 545 applied, 84% were admitted. Full-time: 937 students, 67% women, 33% men. Part-time: 729 students, 66% women, 34% men. Students come from 23 states and territories, 31% from out-of-commonwealth. 58% 25 or older, 19% transferred in. Retention: 33% of full-time freshmen returned the following year. Core. Calendar: semesters. Academic remediation for entering students, ESL program, services for LD students, advanced placement, accelerated degree program, independent study, distance learning, summer session for credit, part-time degree program, adult/continuing education programs, co-op programs and internships.

Entrance Requirements: Options: electronic application, early admission, early decision, deferred admission, international baccalaureate accepted. Required: high school transcript, minimum 1.6 high school GPA, CEEB, institutional admission exam. Recommended: minimum 2 high school GPA. Required for some: essay, minimum 2.5 high school GPA, 3 recommendations, interview. Entrance: noncompetitive. Application deadline: rolling. Transfer credits accepted: Yes. Applicants placed on waiting list: 135. Waitlisted applicants offered admission: 32. Early decision applicants: 135. Early decision applicants admitted: 44.

Costs Per Year: Application fee: $15. Tuition: $5280 full-time, $176 per credit hour part-time. Mandatory fees: $920 full-time, $460 per term part-time. Full-time tuition and fees vary according to course load and program. Part-time tuition and fees vary according to course load and program.

Collegiate Environment: Choral group. Social organizations: 5 open to all; 58% of eligible men and 43% of eligible women are members. Most popular organizations: Student Council, Graduate Student Association, Dance Group. Major annual events: I Put My Hands Up Against Violence, Arts Exhibits, Honor Roll. Student services: personal-psychological counseling. Campus security: 24-hour emergency response devices, student patrols, late night transport-escort service, security and emergency telephones during working hours. Centro de Recursos para la Informacion plus 2 others. Books: 16,163 (physical), 50 (digital/electronic); Serial titles: 48 (physical), 13,800 (digital/electronic); Databases: 30. Weekly public service hours: 82; students can reserve study rooms. Operations spending for the previous fiscal year: $337,184. 207 computers available on campus for general student use. A campuswide network can be accessed. Students can access the following: online class registration. Staffed computer lab on campus provides training in use of computers, software, and the Internet.

■ EDP UNIVERSITY OF PUERTO RICO-SAN SEBASTIAN

Ave. Betances No.49
San Sebastian, PR 00685
Tel: (787)896-2252
Fax: (787)896-0066
E-mail: pcordero@edpuniversity.edu
Web Site: www.edpuniversity.edu

Description: Independent, comprehensive, coed. Awards associate, bachelor's, and master's degrees. Founded 1976. Setting: rural campus. Research spending for the previous fiscal year: $180,643. Educational spending for the previous fiscal year: $2500 per student. Total enrollment: 1,088. Faculty: 90 (30 full-time, 60 part-time). Student-undergrad faculty ratio is 20:1. 186 applied, 97% were admitted. Full-time: 694 students, 63% women, 37% men. Part-time: 355 students, 66% women, 34% men. Students come from 19 states and territories, 23 other countries, 15% from out-of-commonwealth. 100% Hispanic/Latino; 0.1% international. 44% 25 or older, 11% transferred in. Academic areas with the most degrees conferred: health professions and related sciences; business/marketing. Core. Calendar: semesters. Academic remediation for entering students, services for LD students, accelerated degree program, independent study, distance learning, summer session for credit, external degree program, adult/continuing education programs, co-op programs and internships.

Entrance Requirements: Open admission. Required: high school transcript, minimum 1.6 high school GPA, College Board exam or institutional entrance test. Required for some: essay, minimum 2.5 high school GPA, interview. Entrance: minimally difficult. Application deadline: rolling. Transfer credits accepted: Yes.

Costs Per Year: Application fee: $15. Tuition: $5280 full-time, $176 per credit hour part-time. Mandatory fees: $920 full-time, $460 per term part-time. Full-time tuition and fees vary according to course load and program. Part-time tuition and fees vary according to course load and program.

Collegiate Environment: Student-run radio station. Social organizations: 10 open to all; 40% of eligible men and 60% of eligible women are members. Most popular organizations: Nursing, Physical Therapy, Information Systems (SITA), Pharmacy, Digital Fashion Design. Major annual events: Honor Role, Student's Associations Initiation, Christmas Celebration. Student services: personal-psychological counseling. Campus security: private security. Juan S. Robles Library. Books: 11,683 (physical), 222,135 (digital/electronic); Serial titles: 11 (physical), 25,540 (digital/electronic); Databases: 12. Weekly public service hours: 85; students can reserve study rooms. Operations spending for the previous fiscal year: $337,184. 168 computers available on campus for general student use. A campuswide network can be accessed. Students can access the following: online class registration. Staffed computer lab on campus provides training in use of computers, software, and the Internet.

■ ESCUELA DE ARTES PLASTICAS Y DISEÑO DE PUERTO RICO

PO Box 9021112
San Juan, PR 00902-1112
Tel: (787)725-8120
E-mail: admisiones@eap.edu
Web Site: www.eap.edu

Description: Commonwealth-supported, 4-year, coed. Awards bachelor's degrees. Founded 1966. Setting: urban campus. Endowment: $2.5 million. Total enrollment: 441. Faculty: 62 (26 full-time, 36 part-time). Student-undergrad faculty ratio is 12:1. 82 applied, 94% were admitted. Full-time: 322 students, 71% women, 29% men. Part-time: 119 students, 71% women, 29% men. Students come from 2 states and territories. 100% Hispanic/Latino; 0.2% Black or African American, non-Hispanic/Latino. 15% 25 or older, 27% transferred in. Retention: 86% of full-time freshmen returned the following year. Academic areas with the most degrees conferred: visual and performing arts; education. Core. Calendar: semesters 3 semesters each calendar year; participant in Year Round Pell. Academic remediation for entering students, services for LD students, advanced placement, independent study, summer session for credit, part-time degree program, adult/continuing education programs, internships. Study abroad program.

Entrance Requirements: Option: international baccalaureate accepted. Required: high school transcript, minimum 2 high school GPA, portfolio or seminar. Recommended: SAT. Entrance: moderately difficult. Notification: 5/18. SAT Reasoning Test deadline: 4/25. SAT Subject Test deadline: 4/25. Transfer credits accepted: Yes.

Costs Per Year: Application fee: $25. Commonwealth resident tuition: $2860 full-time. Nonresident tuition: $5020 full-time. Mandatory fees: $602 full-time.

Collegiate Environment: Orientation program. Social organizations: 3 open to all. Most popular organizations: Student government, CINEAP, Arte-Sanacion. Major annual events: Students' annual exhibition, Departments' exhibitions, Health Fair. Student services: personal-psychological counseling. Campus security: 24-hour emergency response devices and patrols, security cameras. College housing not available. Francisco Oller Library. Books: 23,366 (physical); Serial titles: 449 (digital/electronic); Databases: 3. Weekly public service hours: 59. 98 computers available on campus for general student use. Students can access the following: library online catalog, wireless access. Staffed computer lab on campus provides training in use of computers, software, and the Internet.

■ HUERTAS COLLEGE

PO Box 8429
Caguas, PR 00726
Tel: (787)743-2156
Web Site: www.huertas.edu

Description: Proprietary, 2-year, coed. Awards certificates and terminal associate degrees. Founded 1945. Setting: 4-acre urban campus with easy access to San Juan. Total enrollment: 1,843. Core. Calendar: trimesters. Academic remediation for entering students, ESL program, part-time degree program, internships.

Entrance Requirements: Open admission. Option: deferred admission. Required for some: minimum 2.0 high school GPA. Application deadline: rolling. Notification: continuous.

Collegiate Environment: Choral group. Student services: health clinic. Campus security: 24-hour patrols. Learning Resources Center.

■ HUMACAO COMMUNITY COLLEGE

PO Box 9139
Humacao, PR 00792
Tel: (787)852-1430
Fax: (787)850-1760
E-mail: arlene.osorio@hccpr.edu
Web Site: www.hccpr.edu

Description: Independent, primarily 2-year, coed. Awards certificates, diplomas, terminal associate, and bachelor's degrees. Setting: urban campus. System endowment: $1.3 million. Educational spending for the previous fiscal year: $4414 per student. Total enrollment: 467. Faculty: 33 (12 full-time, 21 part-time). Student-undergrad faculty ratio is 30:1. 140 applied, 89% were admitted. Full-time: 359 students, 62% women, 38% men. Part-time: 108 students, 68% women, 32% men. 100% Hispanic/Latino. 20% 25 or older, 32% transferred in. Retention: 54% of full-time freshmen returned the following year. Core. Calendar: trimesters. Academic remediation for entering students, services for LD students, part-time degree program, adult/continuing education programs, co-op programs and internships.

Entrance Requirements: Open admission. Required: high school transcript, interview. Required for some: certificate of Immunization for students under 21 years. Entrance: noncompetitive. Notification: continuous. Transfer credits accepted: Yes.

Costs Per Year: Application fee: $15. One-time mandatory fee: $140. Tuition: $4932 full-time, $2466 per year part-time. Mandatory fees: $450 full-time, $450 per year part-time. Full-time tuition and fees vary according to course load and degree level. Part-time tuition and fees vary according to course load and degree level.

Collegiate Environment: Social organizations: 2 open to all; Enactus Students Council; 6% of eligible men and 10% of eligible women are members. Most popular organizations: Enactus Humacao Community College, Students Council. Major annual events: Welcome Activity, Regalo de Amor, Student Honor Ceremony. Student services: personal-psychological counseling. Campus security: 24-hour emergency response devices and patrols. Santiago N. Manuez Educational Resources Center plus 1 other. Books: 5,320 (physical); Serial titles: 43 (physical), 2 (digital/electronic); Databases: 5. Weekly public service hours: 56. Operations spending for the previous fiscal year: $89,990. 294 computers available on campus for general student use. Staffed computer lab on campus provides training in use of computers, software, and the Internet.

■ ICPR JUNIOR COLLEGE-HATO REY CAMPUS

558 Munoz Rivera Ave.
Hato Rey, PR 00919-0304
Tel: (787)753-6000
Fax: (787)763-7249
Web Site: www.icprjc.edu

Description: Proprietary, 2-year, coed. Awards certificates, diplomas, and terminal associate degrees. Founded 1946. Setting: 1-acre urban campus. Total enrollment: 602. Faculty: 89 (34 full-time, 55 part-time). Student-undergrad faculty ratio is 17:1. 1% from out-of-commonwealth. Core. Calendar: trimesters. ESL program, independent study, double major, part-time degree program, adult/continuing education programs. ROTC: Army (c).

Entrance Requirements: Option: early admission. Required: high school transcript, interview, proficiency in Spanish. Entrance: minimally difficult. Notification: continuous.

Collegiate Environment: Student services: personal-psychological counseling. Campus security: 24-hour emergency response devices. Pedro Negron Library plus 1 other. Operations spending for the previous fiscal year: $176,910. 76 computers available on campus for general student use. Staffed computer lab on campus.

■ INTER AMERICAN UNIVERSITY OF PUERTO RICO, AGUADILLA CAMPUS

Call Box 20000
Aguadilla, PR 00605
Tel: (787)891-0925
Web Site: www.aguadilla.inter.edu

Description: Independent, comprehensive, coed. Part of Inter American University of Puerto Rico. Awards bachelor's and master's degrees. Founded 1957. Setting: 50-acre small town campus. Endowment: $239 million. Educational spending for the previous fiscal year: $2550 per student. Total enrollment: 3,903. Faculty: 228 (79 full-time, 149 part-time). Student-undergrad faculty ratio is 30:1. 1,748 applied. Full-time: 3,141 students, 57% women, 43% men. Part-time: 526 students, 60% women, 40% men. Students come from 23 states and territories, 1 other country, 2% from out-of-commonwealth. 0.1% American Indian or Alaska Native, non-Hispanic/Latino; 100% Hispanic/Latino; 0.1% Black or African American, non-Hispanic/Latino. 16% 25 or older, 5% transferred in. Academic areas with the most degrees conferred: homeland security, law enforcement, firefighting, and protective services; health professions and related sciences; business/marketing. Core. Calendar: semesters. Academic remediation for entering students, ESL program, services for LD students, advanced placement, accelerated degree program, honors program, independent study, distance learning, double major, summer session for credit, part-time degree program, external degree program, adult/continuing education programs, co-op programs and internships. Study abroad program. ROTC: Army, Air Force.

Entrance Requirements: Options: electronic application, international baccalaureate accepted. Required: high school transcript, minimum 2 high school GPA, SAT or ACT, PAA. Entrance: moderately difficult. Application deadline: rolling. Transfer credits accepted: Yes.

Costs Per Year: Application fee: $0. Tuition: $4488 full-time, $187 per credit part-time. Mandatory fees: $754 full-time. Full-time tuition and fees vary according to course load. Part-time tuition and fees vary according to course load.

Collegiate Environment: Orientation program. Drama-theater group, choral group, student-run newspaper. Social organizations: 29 open to all. Most popular organizations: Criminal Justice Association, Microbiot Science Association, Social Workers Association, Nursing Association, Psychology Association. Major annual events: Initiation of Students' Organizations, Night of Achievement and Recognition of Student Leaders and Community Projects, Christmas Concert. Student services: personal-psychological counseling. Campus security: 24-hour emergency response devices and patrols. College housing not available. Manuel Mendez Ballester Information Access Center. Books: 62,162 (physical), 249,610 (digital/electronic); Serial titles: 100 (physical); Databases: 75. Weekly public service hours: 80; students can reserve study rooms. Operations spending for the previous fiscal year: $166,305. 861 computers available on campus for general student use. A campuswide network can be accessed from off-campus. Students can access the following: online class registration. Staffed computer lab on campus provides training in use of computers, software, and the Internet.

■ INTER AMERICAN UNIVERSITY OF PUERTO RICO, ARECIBO CAMPUS

PO Box 4050
Arecibo, PR 00614-4050
Tel: (787)878-5475
Fax: (787)880-1624
E-mail: pmontalvo@arecibo.inter.edu
Web Site: www.arecibo.inter.edu

Description: Independent, comprehensive, coed. Part of Inter American University of Puerto Rico. Awards associate, bachelor's, and master's degrees. Founded 1957. Setting: 20-acre urban campus with easy access to San Juan. Total enrollment: 4,878. Faculty: 298 (88 full-time, 210 part-time). Student-undergrad faculty ratio is 24:1. 2,511 applied. Full-time: 3,789 students, 60% women, 40% men. Part-time: 758 students, 63% women, 37% men. Students come from 3 states and territories. 27% 25 or older, 4% transferred in. Retention: 74% of full-time freshmen returned the following year. Academic areas with the most degrees conferred: education; business/marketing; public administration and social services. Core. Calendar: semesters. Academic remediation for entering students, services for LD students, advanced placement, honors program, independent study, distance learning, summer session for credit, part-time degree program, external degree program, adult/continuing education programs, internships, graduate courses open to undergrads. Off campus study. Study abroad program. ROTC: Army (c).

Entrance Requirements: Options: electronic application, early admission, deferred admission. Required: high school transcript, minimum 2 high school GPA, PAA, CEEB. Recommended: minimum 3 high school GPA. Required for some: interview. Entrance: moderately difficult. Application deadline: rolling. Transfer credits accepted: Yes.

Collegiate Environment: Orientation program. Drama-theater group. Social organizations: 18 open to all; local fraternities, local sororities; 30% of eligible men and 70% of eligible women are members. Most popular organizations: Circulo Futuros Trabajadores Sociales, Asociacion Estudiantes Justicia Criminal, Asociacion Futuros Maestros, Compania Teatro Ciclorama. Major annual events: Festival de la Voz, Festival de Teatro Internacional. Student services: health clinic, personal-psychological counseling. Campus security: 24-hour emergency response devices and patrols. Information Access Center Rene Marquez. 461 computers available on campus for general student use. A campuswide network can be accessed from off-campus. Students can access the following: online class registration. Staffed computer lab on campus provides training in use of computers, software, and the Internet.

■ INTER AMERICAN UNIVERSITY OF PUERTO RICO, BARRANQUITAS CAMPUS

PO Box 517
Barranquitas, PR 00794
Tel: (787)857-3600
Fax: (787)857-2284
E-mail: aramildacartagena@br.inter.edu
Web Site: www.br.inter.edu

Description: Independent, comprehensive, coed. Part of Inter American University of Puerto Rico. Awards associate, bachelor's, and master's degrees. Founded 1957. Setting: small town campus with easy access to 35 miles from San Juan. System endowment: $239 million. Educational spending for the previous fiscal year: $3049 per student. Total enrollment: 1,640. Faculty: 145 (31 full-time, 114 part-time). Student-undergrad faculty ratio is 21:1. 946 applied, 40% were admitted. Full-time: 1,324 students, 63% women, 37% men. Part-time: 197 students, 60% women, 40% men. Students come from 4 states and territories, 0.2% from out-of-commonwealth. 0.1% American Indian or Alaska Native, non-Hispanic/Latino; 100% Hispanic/Latino. 14% 25 or older, 2% transferred in. Retention: 69% of full-time freshmen returned the following year. Academic areas with the most degrees conferred: health professions and related sciences; homeland security, law enforcement, firefighting, and protective services; business/marketing. Core. Calendar: semesters. ESL program, services for LD students, honors program, distance learning, summer session for credit, part-time degree program, external degree program, adult/continuing education programs, co-op programs. Off campus study. ROTC: Army (c).

Entrance Requirements: Required: CEEB. Recommended: SAT, SAT Subject Tests. Required for some: SAT or ACT. Transfer credits accepted: Yes.

Costs Per Year: One-time mandatory fee: $100. Tuition: $5610 full-time, $3,020 per year part-time. Mandatory fees: $652 full-time, $524 per year part-time, $262 per term part-time. Full-time tuition and fees vary according to course load, degree level, and program. Part-time tuition and fees vary according to course load, degree level, and program.

Collegiate Environment: Orientation program. Social organizations: 21 open to all. Most popular organizations: Nursing Student Organization, Honor Program Student Organization, Culinary Arts Student Organization, Poly-Inter Alumni Association Student Chapter. Student services: health clinic, personal-psychological counseling. Campus security: 24-hour emergency response devices and patrols. Centro de Accoso a la Informaci=n (CAI), Recinto de Barranquitas. Books: 40,014 (physical), 286,834 (digital/electronic); Serial titles: 60 (physical), 58,313 (digital/electronic); Databases: 83. Weekly public service hours: 72; students can reserve study rooms. Operations spending for the previous fiscal year: $46,608. 378 computers available on campus for general student use. A campuswide network can be accessed. Students can access the following: online class registration. Staffed computer lab on campus provides training in use of computers, software, and the Internet.

■ INTER AMERICAN UNIVERSITY OF PUERTO RICO, BAYAMÓN CAMPUS

500 Dr. John Will Harris Rd.
Bayamon, PR 00957
Tel: (787)279-1912
Fax: (787)279-2205
Web Site: bayamon.inter.edu

Description: Independent, comprehensive, coed. Part of Inter American University of Puerto Rico. Awards associate, bachelor's, and master's degrees. Founded 1912. Setting: 51-acre suburban campus with easy access to San Juan. System endowment: $239 million. Research spending for the previous fiscal year: $757,252. Educational spending for the previous fiscal year: $2940 per student. Total enrollment: 4,293. Faculty: 251 (91 full-time, 160 part-time). Student-undergrad faculty ratio is 25:1. 2,920 applied, 31% were admitted. Full-time: 3,703 students, 44% women, 56% men. Part-time: 485 students, 45% women, 55% men. Students come from 15 states and territories, 2 other countries, 1% from out-of-commonwealth. 0.6% American Indian or Alaska Native, non-Hispanic/Latino; 98% Hispanic/Latino; 0.3% Black or African American, non-Hispanic/Latino; 0.1% Native Hawaiian or other Pacific Islander, non-Hispanic/Latino. 11% 25 or older, 3% transferred in. Retention: 71% of full-time freshmen returned the following year. Academic areas with the most degrees conferred: business/marketing; engineering; homeland security, law enforcement, firefighting, and protective services. Core. Calendar: semesters. Services for LD students, advanced placement, accelerated degree program, honors program, independent study, distance learning, summer session for credit, part-time degree program, external degree program, adult/continuing education programs, co-op programs and internships, graduate courses open to undergrads. ROTC: Army (c).

Entrance Requirements: Option: electronic application. Required: high school transcript, minimum 2 high school GPA, CEEB. Required for some: minimum 2.5 GPA for engineering program, SAT. Notification: continuous. Transfer credits accepted: Yes.

Costs Per Year: Application fee: $0. Comprehensive fee: $14,063 includes full-time tuition ($4488), mandatory fees ($1452), and college room and board ($8123). College room only: $5271. Part-time tuition: $187 per credit.

Collegiate Environment: Orientation program. Drama-theater group, choral group, student-run radio station. Social organizations: 26 open to all. Most popular organizations: Consejo de Estudiantes, Asociacion Estudiantes de Ingenieria, Asociacion Estudiantes de Aviacion, Estudiantes Unidos por la Ciencia, Asociacion de Estudiantes de Administracion de Empresas. Major annual events: Iniciaci=n de Asociaciones Estudiantiles, Buena Vibra College Tour, Congreso de Lfderes. Student services: health clinic, personal-psychological counseling. Campus security: 24-hour patrols. 68 college housing spaces available; 44 were occupied in 2018-19. Options: men-only, women-only housing available. Centro de Acceso a la Informacion plus 1 other. Books: 28,998 (physical), 248,232 (digital/electronic); Serial titles: 123 (physical); Databases: 88. Weekly public service hours: 75; students can reserve study rooms. Operations spending for the previous fiscal year: $27,923. 730 computers available on campus for general student use. A campuswide network can be accessed from student residence rooms. Students can access the following: online class registration. Staffed computer lab on campus provides training in use of computers, software, and the Internet.

■ INTER AMERICAN UNIVERSITY OF PUERTO RICO, FAJARDO CAMPUS

Call Box 70003
Fajardo, PR 00738-7003
Tel: (787)863-2390
E-mail: ghisita.garcia@fajardo.inter.edu
Web Site: www.fajardo.inter.edu

Description: Independent, comprehensive, coed. Part of Inter American University of Puerto Rico. Awards associate, bachelor's, and master's degrees. Founded 1965. Setting: 11-acre small town campus with easy access to San Juan. Endowment: $4.3 million. Educational spending for the previous fiscal year: $2855 per student. Total enrollment: 1,875. Faculty: 116 (41 full-time, 75 part-time). Student-undergrad faculty ratio is 11:1. 708 applied, 88% were admitted. Full-time: 1,481 students, 59% women, 41% men. Part-time: 288 students, 66% women, 34% men. Students come from 3 states and territories. 100% Hispanic/Latino. 19% 25 or older. Retention: 74% of full-time freshmen returned the following year. Academic areas with the most degrees conferred: business/marketing; biological/life sciences; public administration and social services. Core. Calendar: semesters. Academic remediation for entering students, ESL program, services for LD students, advanced placement, honors program, independent study, distance learning, summer session for credit, part-time degree program, external degree program, adult/continuing education programs, co-op programs and internships. Off campus study at other units of the Inter American University of Puerto Rico. ROTC: Army (c).

Entrance Requirements: Options: electronic application, early admission, deferred admission. Required: high school transcript, College Board exam. Required for some: interview. Entrance: moderately difficult. Transfer credits accepted: Yes.

Costs Per Year: Application fee: $0. Tuition: $187 per credit hour part-time.

Collegiate Environment: Orientation program. Choral group. Social organizations: 25 open to all. Most popular organizations: Future Teachers Association, Criminal Justice Student Association, Honor Program Association, Computer Science Association, Social Work Association. Major annual events: Graduation Services, Student Welcome Back, Achievement Night. Student services: personal-psychological counseling. Campus security: 24-hour patrols. College housing not available. Antonio S. Belaval Library plus 1 other. Books: 47,697 (physical), 262,990 (digital/electronic); Databases: 36. Students can reserve study rooms. Operations spending for the previous fiscal year: $15,540. 280 computers available on campus for general student use. A campuswide network can be accessed from off-campus. Students can access the following: online class registration. Staffed computer lab on campus provides training in use of computers.

■ INTER AMERICAN UNIVERSITY OF PUERTO RICO, GUAYAMA CAMPUS

Call Box 10004
Guayama, PR 00785
Tel: (787)864-2222
E-mail: laura.ferrer@guayama.inter.edu
Web Site: www.guayama.inter.edu

Description: Independent, comprehensive, coed. Part of Inter American University of Puerto Rico. Awards associate, bachelor's, and master's degrees. Founded 1958. Setting: 50-acre small town campus with easy access to San Juan. Educational spending for the previous fiscal year: $4432 per student. Total enrollment: 1,927. Faculty: 165 (44 full-time, 121 part-time). Student-undergrad faculty ratio is 12:1. 536 applied, 48% were admitted. Full-time: 1,443 students, 65% women, 35% men. Part-time: 372 students, 70% women, 30% men. 0.1% American Indian or Alaska Native, non-Hispanic/Latino; 100% Hispanic/Latino; 0.1% Black or African American, non-Hispanic/Latino; 0.1% Native Hawaiian or other Pacific Islander, non-Hispanic/Latino. 23% 25 or older, 9% transferred in. Retention: 71% of full-time freshmen returned the following year. Academic areas with the most degrees conferred: health professions and related sciences; business/marketing; biological/life sciences. Core. Calendar: semesters. Academic remediation for entering students, ESL program, services for LD students, advanced placement, honors program, independent study, distance learning, summer session for credit, part-time degree program, adult/continuing education programs, co-op programs and internships. Off campus study at other units of the Inter American University of Puerto Rico. ROTC: Army (c).

Entrance Requirements: Options: electronic application, international baccalaureate accepted. Required: high school transcript, minimum 2 high school GPA, PAA. Recommended: SAT. Required for some: interview. Entrance: moderately difficult. Application deadline: 8/1. Transfer credits accepted: Yes.

Collegiate Environment: Orientation program. Student-run radio station. Social organizations: 20 open to all. Most popular organizations: Natural Science and Technology, Nursing Student Association, Office Professionals, Medical Billers Organization, Pharmacy Technicians. Major annual events: Interuniversity Athletes League Competition, Thanksgiving Concert, Christmas Concert. Student services: health clinic, personal-psychological counseling. Campus security: 24-hour patrols. Information Access Center. Weekly public service hours: 60. 252 computers available on campus for general student use. A campuswide network can be accessed from off-campus. Students can access the following: online class registration. Staffed computer lab on campus provides training in use of computers, software, and the Internet.

■ **INTER AMERICAN UNIVERSITY OF PUERTO RICO, METROPOLITAN CAMPUS**
PO Box 191293
San Juan, PR 00919-1293
Tel: (787)250-1912
Web Site: metro.inter.edu

Description: Independent, comprehensive, coed. Part of Inter American University of Puerto Rico. Awards associate, bachelor's, master's, and doctoral degrees and post-master's certificates. Founded 1960. Setting: urban campus with easy access to San Juan. Endowment: $224.1 million. Research spending for the previous fiscal year: $474,469. Educational spending for the previous fiscal year: $3110 per student. Total enrollment: 8,483. Faculty: 606 (191 full-time, 415 part-time). 1,387 applied, 57% were admitted. Full-time: 4,820 students, 57% women, 43% men. Part-time: 1,348 students, 55% women, 45% men. 0.3% American Indian or Alaska Native, non-Hispanic/Latino; 98% Hispanic/Latino; 0.7% Black or African American, non-Hispanic/Latino; 0.2% Asian, non-Hispanic/Latino; 0.1% Native Hawaiian or other Pacific Islander, non-Hispanic/Latino. 32% 25 or older, 14% transferred in. Retention: 71% of full-time freshmen returned the following year. Academic areas with the most degrees conferred: health professions and related sciences; business/marketing; homeland security, law enforcement, firefighting, and protective services. Core. Calendar: trimesters. ESL program, services for LD students, accelerated degree program, honors program, independent study, distance learning, summer session for credit, part-time degree program, external degree program, adult/continuing education programs, co-op programs and internships, graduate courses open to undergrads. Study abroad program. ROTC: Army (c), Naval (c), Air Force (c).

Entrance Requirements: Options: electronic application, international baccalaureate accepted. Required: high school transcript, minimum 2 high school GPA, CEEB. Required for some: SAT or ACT. Entrance: moderately difficult. Application deadline: 5/15. Transfer credits accepted: Yes.

Collegiate Environment: Orientation program. Drama-theater group, choral group, student-run newspaper. Social organizations: 42 open to all. Most popular organizations: Intercultural Student Association, Club Rotaract, Roots and Shoots Inter Metro, Chemical Students Association, Social Work Students Association. Major annual events: Intercollegiate Justas LAI, Employment Fair, Open House. Student services: personal-psychological counseling, women's center. Campus security: 24-hour emergency response devices and patrols, Video Security System. Centro de Acceso a la Informacion plus 1 other. Books: 121,223 (physical); Serial titles: 311 (physi-

cal); Databases: 24. Students can reserve study rooms. Operations spending for the previous fiscal year: $68,151. 637 computers available on campus for general student use. A campuswide network can be accessed from student residence rooms and from off campus. Students can access the following: online class registration. Staffed computer lab on campus provides training in use of computers, software, and the Internet.

■ **INTER AMERICAN UNIVERSITY OF PUERTO RICO, PONCE CAMPUS**
104 Industrial Park Turpó Rd. 1
Mercedita, PR 00715-1602
Tel: (787)284-1912
E-mail: fidiaz@ponce.inter.edu
Web Site: www.ponce.inter.edu

Description: Independent, comprehensive, coed. Part of Inter American University of Puerto Rico. Awards associate, bachelor's, master's, and doctoral degrees. Founded 1962. Setting: 50-acre urban campus with easy access to San Juan. System endowment: $14.5 million. Research spending for the previous fiscal year: $3514. Total enrollment: 5,288. Faculty: 284 (98 full-time, 186 part-time). Student-undergrad faculty ratio is 30:1. 1,646 applied, 56% were admitted. Full-time: 4,151 students, 59% women, 41% men. Part-time: 717 students, 61% women, 39% men. 0.1% American Indian or Alaska Native, non-Hispanic/Latino; 100% Hispanic/Latino. 24% 25 or older, 4% transferred in. Retention: 76% of full-time freshmen returned the following year. Academic areas with the most degrees conferred: business/marketing; homeland security, law enforcement, firefighting, and protective services; health professions and related sciences. Core. Calendar: semesters. Academic remediation for entering students, ESL program, services for LD students, honors program, distance learning, summer session for credit, part-time degree program, adult/continuing education programs, co-op programs and internships. Off campus study at other units of the Inter American University of Puerto Rico. Study abroad program.

Entrance Requirements: Option: deferred admission. Required: high school transcript, minimum 2 high school GPA, CEEB. Required for some: SAT. Entrance: moderately difficult. Application deadline: 5/15.

Collegiate Environment: Orientation program. Drama-theater group, choral group. Social organizations: 32 open to all; national fraternities, local sororities; 40% of eligible men and 60% of eligible women are members. Most popular organizations: Association of Future Teachers of Special Education, Hotel Management Association, American Chemical Society (ACS), Criminal Justice Association, Students Board of Honor Program. Major annual events: Welcoming of New Students, Students Athletes Presentation, Puerto Rican Culture Festival. Student services: health clinic, personal-psychological counseling. Campus security: 24-hour emergency response devices and patrols. Centro de Acceso a la Informacion plus 1 other. Books: 54,043 (physical), 243,183 (digital/electronic); Serial titles: 109 (physical); Databases: 130. Weekly public service hours: 56; students can reserve study rooms. Operations spending for the previous fiscal year: $141,256. 376 computers available on campus for general student use. A campuswide network can be accessed from off-campus. Students can access the following: online class registration. Staffed computer lab on campus provides training in use of computers, software, and the Internet.

■ **INTER AMERICAN UNIVERSITY OF PUERTO RICO, SAN GERMÁN CAMPUS**
PO Box 5100
San German, PR 00683-5008
Tel: (787)264-1912
Fax: (787)892-6350
E-mail: milcama@intersg.edu
Web Site: www.sg.inter.edu

Description: Independent, university, coed. Part of Inter American University of Puerto Rico. Awards associate, bachelor's, master's, and doctoral degrees. Founded 1912. Setting: 283-acre small town campus with easy access to Ponce, Aguadilla, Mayaguez. System endowment: $239 million. Educational spending for the previous fiscal year: $3423 per student. Total enrollment: 4,450. Faculty: 291 (96 full-time, 195 part-time). Student-undergrad faculty ratio is 13:1. 2,054 applied, 45% were admitted. Full-time: 3,379 students, 52% women, 48% men. Part-time: 408 students, 55% women, 45% men. Students come from 7 states and territories, 1 other country, 0.3% from out-of-commonwealth. 0.2% American Indian or Alaska Native, non-Hispanic/Latino; 99% Hispanic/Latino; 0.2% Black or African American, non-Hispanic/Latino. 10% 25 or older, 7% live on campus, 3% transferred in. Retention: 78% of full-time freshmen returned the following year. Academic areas with the most degrees conferred: biological/life sciences; health professions and related sciences; business/marketing. Core. Calendar: semesters. Academic remediation for entering students, ESL program, services for LD students, advanced placement, accelerated degree program, honors program, independent study, distance learning, double major, summer session for credit, part-time degree program, external degree program, adult/continuing education programs, co-op programs and internships, graduate courses open to undergrads. Off campus study at other units of the Inter American University of Puerto Rico. ROTC: Army (c), Naval (c), Air Force (c).

Entrance Requirements: Options: electronic application, early admission, international baccalaureate accepted. Required: high school transcript, medical history, vaccination, CEEB. Recommended: essay, minimum 2 high school GPA. Required for some: 1 recommendation, interview, SAT or ACT. Entrance: moderately difficult. Notification: continuous. SAT Reasoning Test deadline: 5/5. Transfer credits accepted: Yes.

Costs Per Year: Application fee: $0. Comprehensive fee: $10,242 includes full-time tuition ($5610), mandatory fees ($732), and college room and board ($3900). College room only: $2400. Full-time tuition and fees vary according to degree level. Room and board charges vary according to board plan and housing facility. Part-time tuition: $187 per credit hour. Part-time mandatory fees: $187 per credit hour, $732 per year. Part-time tuition and fees vary according to degree level.

Collegiate Environment: Orientation program. Choral group. Social organizations: 34 open to all; national fraternities, local fraternities, local sororities, Student Organizations; 23% of eligible men and 32% of eligible women are members. Most popular organizations: Tomorrows Leaders Association, Business Professionals of America, Sociedad de Honor en Biologia Beta Beta Beta (TriBeta), Asociacion Estudiantes de Enfermería, Asociacion de Estudiantes del Programa de Honor. Major annual events: Students Organizations Joint Initiation, Graduation Dance, Student's Organizations Achievement Night. Student services: health clinic, personal-psychological counseling. Campus security: 24-hour patrols. 390 college housing spaces available; 283 were occupied in 2018-19. No special consideration for freshman housing applicants. Options: men-only, women-only housing available. Juan Cancio Ortiz Library. Books: 125,059 (physical), 3,850 (digital/electronic); Serial titles: 240 (physical), 594,924 (digital/electronic); Databases: 96. Weekly public service hours: 69. Operations spending for the previous fiscal year: $49,230. 950 computers available on campus for general student use. A campuswide network can be accessed from student residence rooms and from off campus. Students can access the following: online class registration. Staffed computer lab on campus provides training in use of computers, software, and the Internet.

■ NATIONAL UNIVERSITY COLLEGE (ARECIBO)

Calle Manuel Pérez Avilés
Avenida Víctor Rojas
Arecibo, PR 00612
Web Site: www.nuc.edu
Description: Proprietary, comprehensive, coed.

■ NATIONAL UNIVERSITY COLLEGE (BAYAMON)

National College Plz. Bldg.
Bayamon, PR 00960
Tel: (787)780-5134; Free: 800-780-5134
Fax: (787)740-7360
Web Site: www.nuc.edu
Description: Proprietary, comprehensive, coed. Part of EDUK Services Center. Awards associate, bachelor's, and master's degrees. Setting: urban campus with easy access to Bayamon. Educational spending for the previous fiscal year: $1540 per student. Faculty: 464 (82 full-time, 382 part-time). Student-undergrad faculty ratio is 17:1. Retention: 60% of full-time freshmen returned the following year. Core. Calendar: trimesters. Services for LD students, advanced placement, distance learning, part-time degree program, adult/continuing education programs, internships.
Entrance Requirements: Required: high school transcript, certificate of immunition, College Board Test, SAT, or institutional admission test. Required for some: SAT Subject Tests.
Collegiate Environment: Dr. Hiram Gonzalez plus 5 others. Operations spending for the previous fiscal year: $232,204. 150 computers available on campus for general student use. A campuswide network can be accessed. Students can access the following: online class registration. Staffed computer lab on campus provides training in use of software.

■ NATIONAL UNIVERSITY COLLEGE (CAGUAS)

190 Avenida Gautier Benitez Esquina Avenida Federico Degetau
Caguas, PR 00725
Tel: (787)653-4733; Free: 800-780-5134
Web Site: www.nuc.edu
Description: Proprietary, comprehensive, coed. Awards associate, bachelor's, and master's degrees.

■ NATIONAL UNIVERSITY COLLEGE (PONCE)

PO Box 801243
Ponce, PR 00716
Tel: (787)840-4474
Web Site: www.nuc.edu
Description: Proprietary, comprehensive, coed. Awards associate, bachelor's, master's, and doctoral degrees.

■ NATIONAL UNIVERSITY COLLEGE (RIO GRANDE)

Carretera No.3 Km. 22.1
Bo. Ciénaga Baja
Rio Grande, PR 00745
Tel: (787)809-5100; Free: 800-981-0812
Fax: (787)888-8280
Web Site: www.nuc.edu
Description: Proprietary, comprehensive, coed. Awards associate, bachelor's, master's, and doctoral degrees.

■ POLYTECHNIC UNIVERSITY OF PUERTO RICO

377 Ponce de Leon Ave.
San Juan, PR 00918
Tel: (787)622-8000
E-mail: tcardona@pupr.edu
Web Site: www.pupr.edu
Description: Independent, comprehensive, coed. Awards associate, bachelor's, master's, and doctoral degrees. Founded 1966. Setting: 10-acre urban campus with easy access to San Juan. Endowment: $14.3 million. Research spending for the previous fiscal year: $1.4 million. Total enrollment: 4,317. Faculty: 211 (133 full-time, 78 part-time). Student-undergrad faculty ratio is 14:1. 746 applied, 72% were admitted. Students come from 8 states and territories, 4 other countries. 100% Hispanic/Latino; 0.1% Black or African American, non-Hispanic/Latino. 30% 25 or older. Retention: 77% of full-time freshmen returned the following year. Academic areas with the most degrees conferred: engineering; architecture; business/marketing. Core. Calendar: trimesters. Academic remediation for entering students, ESL program, advanced placement, self-designed majors; honors program, independent study, distance learning, summer session for credit, internships. ROTC: Army (c).
Entrance Requirements: Option: electronic application. Required: high school transcript, minimum 2 high school GPA. Recommended: CEEB or PEAU. Entrance: minimally difficult. Application deadline: 8/16. SAT Reasoning Test deadline: 8/16. SAT Subject Test deadline: 8/16. Transfer credits accepted: Yes.
Costs Per Year: Application fee: $30. Comprehensive fee: $20,538 includes full-time tuition ($7740), mandatory fees ($870), and college room and board ($11,928). College room only: $4950. Full-time tuition and fees vary according to course level, degree level, and program. Part-time tuition: $215 per credit hour. Part-time mandatory fees: $290 per term. Part-time tuition and fees vary according to course level, degree level, and program.
Collegiate Environment: Orientation program. Choral group. Social organizations: 22 open to all; local fraternities; 10% of men are members. Most popular organizations: ASCE (American Society of Civil Engineering), PRWEA (Puerto Rico Water and Environment Association), ACI (American Concrete Institute), SAE PUPR AERO DESIGN TEAM, SHPE (Society of Hispanic Professional Engineers). Major annual events: Welcome Activity, Christmas Activity, Open House. Student services: health clinic, personal-psychological counseling. Campus security: 24-hour emergency response devices and patrols, late night transport-escort service, controlled dormitory access, over 350 security cameras on campus. Biblioteca de la Unidersidad Politecnica de Puerto Rico. Books: 66,518 (physical), 61,939 (digital/electronic); Serial titles: 1,794 (physical), 15,595 (digital/electronic); Databases: 46. Weekly public service hours: 82; study areas open 24 hours, 5-7 days a week; students can reserve study rooms. Operations spending for the previous fiscal year: $638,075. 800 computers available on campus for general student use. A campuswide network can be accessed from off-campus. Students can access the following: online class registration. Staffed

computer lab on campus (open 24 hours a day) provides training in use of computers, software, and the Internet.

■ PONCE PARAMEDICAL COLLEGE
L-15 Acacia St. Villa Flores Urbanizacion
Ponce, PR 00731
Tel: (787)848-1589
Fax: (787)259-0169
Web Site: www.popac.edu
Description: Proprietary, 2-year, coed. Awards transfer associate and terminal associate degrees. Founded 1983.

■ PONTIFICAL CATHOLIC UNIVERSITY OF PUERTO RICO
2250 Las Americas Ave., Ste. 564
Ponce, PR 00717-0777
Tel: (787)841-2000; Free: 800-961-7696
Fax: (787)840-4295
E-mail: admissions@email.pucpr.edu
Web Site: www.pucpr.edu
Description: Independent, university, coed, affiliated with Roman Catholic Church. Awards associate, bachelor's, master's, and doctoral degrees (branch locations in Arecibo, Guayana, Mayaguez). Founded 1948. Setting: 120-acre urban campus with easy access to San Juan. Total enrollment: 7,682. Faculty: 385 (191 full-time, 194 part-time). Student-undergrad faculty ratio is 23:1. 1,798 applied, 83% were admitted. Full-time: 4,857 students, 62% women, 38% men. Part-time: 514 students, 65% women, 35% men. 13% 25 or older, 4% transferred in. Retention: 76% of full-time freshmen returned the following year. Core. Calendar: semesters. Academic remediation for entering students, ESL program, services for LD students, advanced placement, honors program, independent study, double major, summer session for credit, part-time degree program, adult/continuing education programs, co-op programs, graduate courses open to undergrads. Off campus study at Polytechnic University of Puerto Rico. ROTC: Army (c), Air Force (c).
Entrance Requirements: Options: early admission, deferred admission. Required: high school transcript, minimum 2.5 high school GPA, College Entrance Examination Board (CEEB) Aptitude Test. Required for some: essay, minimum 3 high school GPA, 1 recommendation, interview, SAT. Entrance: moderately difficult. Notification: continuous.
Collegiate Environment: Orientation program. Drama-theater group, choral group, student-run newspaper, radio station. Social organizations: 50 open to all; national fraternities, national sororities, local fraternities, local sororities; 1% of eligible men and 1% of eligible women are members. Most popular organizations: Accounting Students Club, Foreign Students Club, Christ Heralds. Major annual events: Peace Day, Educational Professional Development Convention, Puerto Rican Heritage Week. Student services: health clinic, personal-psychological counseling. Campus security: 24-hour emergency response devices and patrols. Encarnacion Valdes Library plus 1 other. 419 computers available on campus for general student use. A campuswide network can be accessed from off-campus. Staffed computer lab on campus provides training in use of software and the Internet.
Community Environment: Ponce is a metropolitan area. Mercedita Airport furnishes transportation to Mayaguez and San Juan. Bus transportation is available to all parts of the island. Community facilities include a public library, museums, churches of major denominations, hospitals, excellent shopping facilities and a number of the major civic, fraternal and service organizations. Part-time employment opportunities are limited. Carnival celebrations and Fiesta Patronales are special annual events.

■ PONTIFICAL CATHOLIC UNIVERSITY OF PUERTO RICO-ARECIBO CAMPUS
Bo. Santana Carr. 662 Km. 2.3
Arecibo, PR 00614-4045
Tel: (787)881-1212
Web Site: www.pucpr.edu/arecibo
Description: Independent, comprehensive, coed, affiliated with Roman Catholic Church. Awards associate, bachelor's, and master's degrees.

■ PONTIFICAL CATHOLIC UNIVERSITY OF PUERTO RICO-MAYAGUEZ CAMPUS
482 Sur Calle Ramon Emerito Betances
Mayaguez, PR 00680
Web Site: www.pucpr.edu/mayaguez

Description: Independent, comprehensive, coed, affiliated with Roman Catholic Church. Awards associate, bachelor's, and master's degrees.

■ THEOLOGICAL UNIVERSITY OF THE CARIBBEAN
PO Box 901
Saint Just, PR 00978-0901
Tel: (787)761-0640
E-mail: promocion@utcpr.edu
Web Site: www.utcpr.edu
Description: Independent Pentecostal, comprehensive, coed. Awards associate, bachelor's, and master's degrees. Founded 1956. Setting: 4-acre suburban campus with easy access to San Juan. Endowment: $1 million. Educational spending for the previous fiscal year: $4927 per student. Total enrollment: 372. Faculty: 53 (20 full-time, 33 part-time). Student-undergrad faculty ratio is 23:1. 48 applied, 100% were admitted. Full-time: 187 students, 50% women, 50% men. Part-time: 78 students, 38% women, 62% men. 100% Hispanic/Latino. 91% 25 or older. Retention: 36% of full-time freshmen returned the following year. Academic area with the most degrees conferred: theology and religious vocations. Core. Calendar: semesters. Services for LD students, honors program, independent study, distance learning, summer session for credit, part-time degree program, internships. Off campus study.
Entrance Requirements: Open admission. Option: early admission. Required: high school transcript, medical certificate, certificate of immunization, 1 2x2 photo, Bible content exam. Application deadline: rolling. Notification: continuous. Transfer credits accepted: Yes.
Costs Per Year: Application fee: $45. Comprehensive fee: $7924 includes full-time tuition ($4524), mandatory fees ($1000), and college room and board ($2400). College room only: $1200. Part-time tuition: $20.55 per credit hour. Part-time mandatory fees: $154 per credit hour, $3696 per term.
Collegiate Environment: Orientation program. Social organizations: 5 open to all; 40% of eligible men and 60% of eligible women are members. Most popular organizations: Student Council, Missionary Evangelistic Association, Ministerial Association, FESI, Free Night. Major annual events: Revival Campaign, Open House, Opening Worship. Student services: personal-psychological counseling. Campus security: patrols by security personnel at night since 6:00 pm to midnight; Security Cameras. 12 college housing spaces available. No special consideration for freshman housing applicants. Option: coed housing available. Juan L. Lugo Library plus 1 other. Books: 17,258 (physical); Serial titles: 45 (physical); Databases: 1. Weekly public service hours: 61. Operations spending for the previous fiscal year: $66,727. 3 computers available on campus for general student use. A campuswide network can be accessed. Students can access the following: online class registration.

■ UNIVERSIDAD ADVENTISTA DE LAS ANTILLAS
PO Box 118
Mayaguez, PR 00681-0118
Tel: (787)834-9595
Fax: (787)834-9597
E-mail: admissions@uaa.edu
Web Site: www.uaa.edu/esp
Description: Independent Seventh-day Adventist, comprehensive, coed. Awards associate, bachelor's, and master's degrees. Founded 1957. Setting: 284-acre rural campus. Endowment: $134,104. Research spending for the previous fiscal year: $1653. Educational spending for the previous fiscal year: $8156 per student. Total enrollment: 1,351. Faculty: 107 (43 full-time, 64 part-time). Student-undergrad faculty ratio is 20:1. 513 applied, 81% were admitted. Full-time: 1,138 students, 63% women, 37% men. Part-time: 118 students, 58% women, 42% men. Students come from 23 other countries, 19% from out-of-commonwealth. 0.1% American Indian or Alaska Native, non-Hispanic/Latino; 96% Hispanic/Latino; 1% Black or African American, non-Hispanic/Latino; 0.2% Asian, non-Hispanic/Latino; 2% international. 14% 25 or older, 28% live on campus, 7% transferred in. Retention: 77% of full-time freshmen returned the following year. Academic areas with the most degrees conferred: health professions and related sciences; biological/life sciences; theology and religious vocations. Core. Calendar: semesters. Academic remediation for entering students, ESL program, services for LD students, advanced placement, double major, summer session for credit, part-time degree program, co-op programs and internships.
Entrance Requirements: Options: electronic application, early admission. Required: high school transcript, minimum 2 high school GPA, 1 recommendation. Recommended: SAT or ACT, CEEB. Required for some: essay, interview. Entrance: minimally difficult. Application deadline: 7/15. Transfer credits accepted: Yes.

Costs Per Year: Application fee: $20. One-time mandatory fee: $20. Comprehensive fee: $11,895 includes full-time tuition ($5370), mandatory fees ($925), and college room and board ($5600). College room only: $2000. Full-time tuition and fees vary according to course load and program. Room and board charges vary according to board plan and housing facility. Part-time tuition: $179 per credit hour. Part-time mandatory fees: $925 per year. Part-time tuition and fees vary according to course load and program.

Collegiate Environment: Orientation program. Choral group, student-run newspaper. Social organizations: 14 open to all; 90% of eligible men and 90% of eligible women are members. Most popular organizations: Score Group, Gymnastic Club, Student Council, Green Movement, 3AM. Major annual events: Talent Shows, Olympic Games, Week of Prayer. Student services: health clinic, personal-psychological counseling. Campus security: 24-hour emergency response devices and patrols, student patrols, controlled dormitory access. Dennis Soto Library. Books: 67,322 (physical); Databases: 42. Weekly public service hours: 67; students can reserve study rooms. Operations spending for the previous fiscal year: $419,813. 50 computers available on campus for general student use. A campuswide network can be accessed from student residence rooms and from off campus. Students can access the following: online class registration. Staffed computer lab on campus provides training in use of computers, software, and the Internet.

■ UNIVERSIDAD CENTRAL DEL CARIBE

PO Box 60-327
Bayamon, PR 00960-6032
Tel: (787)798-3001
Web Site: www.uccaribe.edu

Description: Independent, comprehensive, coed. Awards associate, bachelor's, master's, and doctoral degrees. Founded 1976. Total enrollment: 485. Student-undergrad faculty ratio is 22:1. 43 applied. 29% 25 or older. Retention: 95% of full-time freshmen returned the following year. Calendar: semesters.

■ UNIVERSIDAD DEL ESTE

PO Box 2010
Carolina, PR 00984
Tel: (787)257-7373
Fax: (787)257-7373
Web Site: www.suagm.edu/une

Description: Independent, comprehensive, coed. Part of Ana G. Mendez University System. Awards associate, bachelor's, and master's degrees. Founded 1949. Setting: small town campus with easy access to San Juan. Total enrollment: 13,058. Student-undergrad faculty ratio is 21:1. 10,800 applied, 43% were admitted. Full-time: 8,539 students, 59% women, 41% men. Part-time: 3,286 students, 62% women, 38% men. 100% Hispanic/Latino. 38% 25 or older, 4% transferred in. Retention: 77% of full-time freshmen returned the following year. Academic areas with the most degrees conferred: business/marketing; health professions and related sciences; homeland security, law enforcement, firefighting, and protective services; public administration and social services. Core. Calendar: semesters. Summer session for credit, part-time degree program, external degree program, adult/continuing education programs.

Entrance Requirements: Options: electronic application, deferred admission. Required: high school transcript. Required for some: essay, interview, College Board exam. Entrance: noncompetitive. Transfer credits accepted: Yes.

Collegiate Environment: Orientation program. Campus security: 24-hour patrols.

Community Environment: See University of Puerto Rico - Rio Piedras Campus.

■ UNIVERSIDAD METROPOLITANA

Apartado 21150
San Juan, PR 00928-1150
Tel: (787)766-1717; Free: 800-747-8362
Fax: (787)759-7663
E-mail: yrivera@suagm.edu
Web Site: www.suagm.edu/umet

Description: Independent, comprehensive, coed. Part of Ana G. Mendez University System. Awards associate, bachelor's, master's, and doctoral degrees. Founded 1980. Setting: urban campus with easy access to San Juan. Total enrollment: 13,919. Faculty: 1,250 (179 full-time, 1,071 part-time). Student-undergrad faculty ratio is 22:1. 11,494 applied, 65% were admitted. Full-time: 9,073 students, 64% women, 36% men. Part-time: 2,516

students, 65% women, 35% men. 100% Hispanic/Latino. 34% 25 or older, 5% transferred in. Retention: 75% of full-time freshmen returned the following year. Academic areas with the most degrees conferred: health professions and related sciences; business/marketing; homeland security, law enforcement, firefighting, and protective services. Core. Calendar: semesters. Academic remediation for entering students, advanced placement, accelerated degree program, freshman honors college, honors program, independent study, distance learning, double major, summer session for credit, part-time degree program, adult/continuing education programs, co-op programs and internships. Off campus study.

Entrance Requirements: Options: electronic application, early admission, international baccalaureate accepted. Required: high school transcript, College Board exam. Recommended: SAT. Required for some: essay, interview. Entrance: moderately difficult. Application deadline: 8/15.

Collegiate Environment: Orientation program. Drama-theater group, choral group, student-run newspaper, radio station. Student services: health clinic, personal-psychological counseling. Campus security: 24-hour patrols. 50 computers available on campus for general student use. A campuswide network can be accessed. Students can access the following: online class registration.

■ UNIVERSIDAD PENTECOSTAL MIZPA

Bo Caimito Rd. 199
Apartado 20966
San Juan, PR 00928-0966
Tel: (787)720-4476
Fax: (787)720-2012
Web Site: www.mizpa.edu

Description: Independent, 4-year, coed, affiliated with Pentecostal Church. Awards associate and bachelor's degrees. Founded 1937. Total enrollment: 275. Student-undergrad faculty ratio is 13:1. 89% 25 or older. Retention: 67% of full-time freshmen returned the following year. Academic area with the most degrees conferred: theology and religious vocations. Calendar: semesters.

Entrance Requirements: Open admission.

■ UNIVERSIDAD DEL TURABO

PO Box 3030
Gurabo, PR 00778-3030
Tel: (787)743-7979
Web Site: www.suagm.edu/ut

Description: Independent, university, coed. Part of Ana G. Mendez University System. Awards associate, bachelor's, master's, and doctoral degrees and post-master's certificates. Founded 1972. Setting: 140-acre urban campus with easy access to San Juan. Total enrollment: 17,509. Faculty: 1,171 (237 full-time, 934 part-time). Student-undergrad faculty ratio is 22:1. 8,968 applied, 52% were admitted. Full-time: 10,696 students, 57% women, 43% men. Part-time: 4,000 students, 60% women, 40% men. 100% Hispanic/Latino. 34% 25 or older, 4% transferred in. Retention: 77% of full-time freshmen returned the following year. Academic areas with the most degrees conferred: business/marketing; social sciences; health professions and related sciences. Core. Calendar: semesters. Academic remediation for entering students, ESL program, services for LD students, advanced placement, accelerated degree program, honors program, independent study, distance learning, double major, summer session for credit, part-time degree program, adult/continuing education programs, co-op programs and internships. Off campus study at Jackson State University, University of California, Berkeley, Rensselaer Polytechnic Institute, Georgia Institute of Technology, University of New Mexico, New Mexico State University. Study abroad program. ROTC: Army (c), Air Force (c).

Entrance Requirements: Option: electronic application. Required: high school transcript. Recommended: SAT. Required for some: essay, interview, College Board exam. Entrance: minimally difficult. Application deadline: rolling. Notification: continuous. Transfer credits accepted: Yes.

Collegiate Environment: Orientation program. Drama-theater group, choral group, student-run newspaper, radio station. Student services: health clinic, personal-psychological counseling. Campus security: 24-hour patrols.

■ UNIVERSITY OF PUERTO RICO-AGUADILLA

PO Box 6150
Aguadilla, PR 00604
Tel: (787)890-2681
Web Site: www.uprag.edu

Description: Commonwealth-supported, 4-year, coed. Part of University of

Puerto Rico System. Awards associate and bachelor's degrees. Founded 1972. Setting: 32-acre suburban campus. Total enrollment: 3,076. 901 applied, 89% were admitted. Core. Calendar: semesters. Academic remediation for entering students, ESL program, advanced placement, honors program, summer session for credit, part-time degree program, adult/continuing education programs. ROTC: Army.

Entrance Requirements: Options: early admission, deferred admission. Required: high school transcript, SAT, SAT Subject Tests, PAA. Entrance: moderately difficult. Notification: continuous.

Collegiate Environment: Orientation program. Choral group. Social organizations: local fraternities. Campus security: 24-hour patrols.

■ **UNIVERSITY OF PUERTO RICO-ARECIBO**
Carretera 653 Km. 0.8, Sector Las Dunas
Arecibo, PR 00614
Tel: (787)878-2830
Web Site: www.upra.edu

Description: Commonwealth-supported, 4-year, coed. Part of University of Puerto Rico System. Awards associate and bachelor's degrees. Founded 1967. Setting: 44-acre urban campus with easy access to San Juan. Total enrollment: 4,352. 2,588 applied, 47% were admitted. Core. Calendar: semesters. Academic remediation for entering students, ESL program, services for LD students, advanced placement, honors program, distance learning, summer session for credit, adult/continuing education programs. ROTC: Army.

Entrance Requirements: Required: high school transcript, SAT Subject Tests, PAA or SAT, CEEB. Entrance: very difficult.

Collegiate Environment: Orientation program. Drama-theater group, choral group, marching band. Social organizations: local fraternities, local sororities. Student services: health clinic, personal-psychological counseling. Campus security: 24-hour emergency response devices and patrols. General Library.

■ **UNIVERSITY OF PUERTO RICO-BAYAMÓN**
Industrial Minillas Park 170 Rd. 174
Bayamon, PR 00959
Tel: (787)993-0000
E-mail: carmen.montes1@upr.edu
Web Site: www.uprb.edu

Description: Commonwealth-supported, 4-year, coed. Part of University of Puerto Rico System. Awards associate and bachelor's degrees. Founded 1971. Setting: 78-acre urban campus with easy access to San Juan. Total enrollment: 4,189. Faculty: 227 (187 full-time, 40 part-time). Student-undergrad faculty ratio is 20:1. 1,564 applied, 70% were admitted. Full-time: 3,643 students, 51% women, 49% men. Part-time: 546 students, 51% women, 49% men. Students come from 3 other countries, 1% from out-of-commonwealth. 100% Hispanic/Latino. 7% 25 or older, 19% transferred in. Retention: 81% of full-time freshmen returned the following year. Academic areas with the most degrees conferred: business/marketing; education; biological/life sciences. Core. Calendar: semesters. Academic remediation for entering students, services for LD students, advanced placement, honors program, independent study, summer session for credit, part-time degree program, adult/continuing education programs, co-op programs and internships.

Entrance Requirements: Option: electronic application. Required: high school transcript, College Board exam. Entrance: very difficult. Application deadline: 1/6. Notification: 5/1. Transfer credits accepted: Yes.

Costs Per Year: Application fee: $30. Commonwealth resident tuition: $3910 full-time, $115 per credit part-time. Nonresident tuition: $5865 full-time, $172.50 per credit part-time. Mandatory fees: $174 full-time. Full-time tuition and fees vary according to class time, course load, and program. Part-time tuition varies according to class time, course load, and program. Tuition guaranteed not to increase for student's term of enrollment.

Collegiate Environment: Orientation program. Drama-theater group, choral group. Social organizations: 34 open to all; 37% of eligible men and 63% of eligible women are members. Most popular organizations: The National Society of Collegiate Scholars at UPRB (NSCS), American Medical Student Association (AMSA), Med Life Capitulo Vaquero, Asociacion de Estudiantes de Computadoras (AECC), Asociacion de Estudiantes de Contabilidad (ASEC). Major annual events: Basketball Tournament El Chicharron, Ceremony of Letra Insignia, Interuniversities Track and Field Event. Student services: health clinic, personal-psychological counseling. Campus security: 24-hour patrols. College housing not available. Centro Recursos para el Aprendizaje. Books: 54,105 (physical), 4,871 (digital/electronic); Serial titles:

386 (physical), 2,947 (digital/electronic); Databases: 103. Weekly public service hours: 78; students can reserve study rooms. 496 computers available on campus for general student use. A campuswide network can be accessed from off-campus. Students can access the following: online class registration. Staffed computer lab on campus provides training in use of computers, software, and the Internet.

■ **UNIVERSITY OF PUERTO RICO-CAROLINA**
PO Box 4800
Carolina, PR 00984-4800
Tel: (787)257-0000
Web Site: www.uprc.edu

Description: Commonwealth-supported, 4-year, coed. Part of University of Puerto Rico System. Awards associate and bachelor's degrees. Founded 1974. Setting: 60-acre urban campus with easy access to San Juan. Total enrollment: 4,321. Student-undergrad faculty ratio is 22:1. 1,759 applied, 76% were admitted. 9% 25 or older. Core. Calendar: quarters. Academic remediation for entering students, ESL program, services for LD students, part-time degree program, adult/continuing education programs. ROTC: Army (c), Air Force (c).

Entrance Requirements: Required: high school transcript, SAT, ACT, SAT Subject Tests, CEEB. Entrance: moderately difficult. Notification: continuous.

Collegiate Environment: Orientation program. Drama-theater group, choral group, marching band. Student services: health clinic, personal-psychological counseling. Learning Resource Center, Prof. Jose Paulino Fernandez-Miranda. 20 computers available on campus for general student use.

■ **UNIVERSITY OF PUERTO RICO-CAYEY**
205 Ave. Antonio R. Barcelo
Cayey, PR 00736
Tel: (787)738-2161
Web Site: www.cayey.upr.edu

Description: Commonwealth-supported, 4-year, coed. Part of University of Puerto Rico System. Awards associate and bachelor's degrees. Founded 1967. Setting: 177-acre urban campus with easy access to San Juan. Total enrollment: 3,830. Faculty: 164. Student-undergrad faculty ratio is 21:1. 2,471 applied, 78% were admitted. Full-time: 3,458 students, 71% women, 29% men. Part-time: 372 students, 73% women, 27% men. 0.01% from out-of-commonwealth. 0.1% 25 or older, 2% transferred in. Retention: 89% of full-time freshmen returned the following year. Academic areas with the most degrees conferred: education; business/marketing; interdisciplinary studies. Core. Calendar: semesters. Academic remediation for entering students, advanced placement, accelerated degree program, honors program, summer session for credit, part-time degree program. Off campus study at University of Puerto Rico at Mayaguez; University of Puerto Rico School of Medicine. Study abroad program. ROTC: Army.

Entrance Requirements: Options: early admission, early decision. Required: high school transcript, CEEB. Required for some: SAT. Entrance: moderately difficult. Notification: continuous.

Collegiate Environment: Orientation program. Drama-theater group, choral group, marching band. Social organizations: 32 open to all; national fraternities, national sororities, local fraternities; 1% of eligible men and 1% of eligible women are members. Most popular organizations: Asociacion de Estudiantes de Psicologia Psy-Chi, Sociedad Honoraria de Biologia - Tri Beta, Asociacion Cristiana Universitaria-CONFRA, Asociacion de Estudiantes del Programa de Estudios de Honor, GAIA. Major annual event: Student Day. Student services: health clinic, personal-psychological counseling, women's center. Campus security: 24-hour emergency response devices and patrols, late night transport-escort service. Victor M. Pons Library. 1,000 computers available on campus for general student use. A campuswide network can be accessed. Students can access the following: online class registration. Staffed computer lab on campus provides training in use of computers, software, and the Internet.

■ **UNIVERSITY OF PUERTO RICO-HUMACAO**
HUC Station 100, Rd. 908
Humacao, PR 00792
Tel: (787)850-0000
Fax: (787)852-4638
E-mail: debbie.garcia@upr.edu
Web Site: www.uprh.edu

Description: Commonwealth-supported, 4-year, coed. Part of University of Puerto Rico System. Awards associate and bachelor's degrees. Founded

1962. Setting: 62-acre suburban campus with easy access to San Juan. Total enrollment: 3,723. Faculty: 254 (153 full-time, 101 part-time). Student-undergrad faculty ratio is 17:1. 1,913 applied, 40% were admitted. Full-time: 3,356 students, 63% women, 37% men. Part-time: 367 students, 64% women, 36% men. Students come from 2 states and territories, 1 other country. 90% Hispanic/Latino; 2% Black or African American, non-Hispanic/Latino; 0.2% Native Hawaiian or other Pacific Islander, non-Hispanic/Latino. 6% 25 or older, 1% transferred in. Retention: 80% of full-time freshmen returned the following year. Academic areas with the most degrees conferred: biological/life sciences; public administration and social services; health professions and related sciences. Core. Calendar: semesters. Academic remediation for entering students, ESL program, services for LD students, advanced placement, honors program, summer session for credit, part-time degree program, internships.

Entrance Requirements: Options: electronic application, deferred admission. Required: high school transcript, Pruebas de Evaluacion y Admision Universitaria (PEAU). Required for some: interview. Entrance: moderately difficult. Application deadline: 2/15. Notification: 4/19. SAT Reasoning Test deadline: 2/15. SAT Subject Test deadline: 2/15. Transfer credits accepted: Yes.

Collegiate Environment: Orientation program. Drama-theater group, choral group, marching band, student-run newspaper, radio station. Social organizations: 44 open to all. Most popular organizations: Accounting Students Association, Management Students Association, Microbiology Students Association, Human Resources Students Association, Biology Students Association. Major annual events: Student Day, Shakespeare Festival, Puerto Rican Culture Week. Student services: personal-psychological counseling, women's center. Campus security: 24-hour emergency response devices and patrols, late night transport-escort service, 24-hour gate security. Aguedo Mojica Marrero. Books: 101,475 (physical), 200 (digital/electronic); Serial titles: 15 (physical), 43,942 (digital/electronic); Databases: 7. Weekly public service hours: 92; study areas open 24 hours, 5-7 days a week; students can reserve study rooms.

■ UNIVERSITY OF PUERTO RICO-MAYAGÜEZ

PO Box 9000
Mayaguez, PR 00681-9000
Tel: (787)832-4040
E-mail: smarty@uprm.edu
Web Site: www.uprm.edu

Description: Commonwealth-supported, university, coed. Part of University of Puerto Rico System. Awards bachelor's, master's, and doctoral degrees. Founded 1911. Setting: 315-acre urban campus. Total enrollment: 13,852. Student-undergrad faculty ratio is 16:1. 3,275 applied, 77% were admitted. 5% 25 or older. Core. Calendar: semesters. Advanced placement, honors program, distance learning, summer session for credit, part-time degree program, adult/continuing education programs, co-op programs and internships, graduate courses open to undergrads. Off campus study at State University of New York College at Oswego, National Student Exchange. Study abroad program. ROTC: Army, Air Force.

Entrance Requirements: Option: early action. Required: high school transcript, SAT Subject Tests, PEAU, CEEB. Entrance: moderately difficult.

Collegiate Environment: Orientation program. Drama-theater group, choral group, marching band, student-run newspaper. Social organizations: national fraternities, national sororities, local fraternities, local sororities. Student services: health clinic, personal-psychological counseling. Campus security: 24-hour emergency response devices and patrols. General Library plus 1 other.

■ UNIVERSITY OF PUERTO RICO-MEDICAL SCIENCES CAMPUS

PO Box 365067
San Juan, PR 00936-5067
Tel: (787)758-2525
Fax: (787)754-0474
Web Site: www.rcm.upr.edu

Description: Commonwealth-supported, university, coed. Part of University of Puerto Rico System. Awards associate, bachelor's, master's, and doctoral degrees (bachelor's degree is upper-level). Founded 1950. Setting: 11-acre urban campus. Total enrollment: 2,381. 28% 25 or older. Calendar: semesters. Academic remediation for entering students, summer session for credit. Off campus study at University of Puerto Rico, Rio Piedras.

Entrance Requirements: Entrance: moderately difficult. Preference given to Commonwealth residents.

Collegiate Environment: Orientation program. Campus security: 24-hour emergency response devices. Medical Sciences Library.

Community Environment: San Juan juxtaposes the old and the new: Old San Juan and the moss-covered El Morro castle are contrasted with high-rise office buildings. Founded in 1521, San Juan is a metropolitan city with a mild climate. Museums (e.g. colonial architecture, rare books Puerto Rican art), outdoor sports (swimming, surfing, baseball, fishing, cock fighting), hospitals and excellent shopping are available to everyone. Special San Juan events include drama festivals, native carnivals, the International Theatrical Festival and the Casals Festival.

■ UNIVERSITY OF PUERTO RICO-PONCE

PO Box 7186
Ponce, PR 00732-7186
Tel: (787)844-8181
Fax: (787)844-8679
Web Site: www.uprp.edu

Description: Commonwealth-supported, 4-year, coed. Part of University of Puerto Rico System. Awards associate and bachelor's degrees. Founded 1970. Setting: 86-acre urban campus with easy access to San Juan. Research spending for the previous fiscal year: $732,238. Educational spending for the previous fiscal year: $4981 per student. Total enrollment: 3,229. Faculty: 188 (134 full-time, 54 part-time). Student-undergrad faculty ratio is 17:1. 1,222 applied, 74% were admitted. Full-time: 3,028 students, 56% women, 44% men. Part-time: 201 students, 56% women, 44% men. 100% Hispanic/Latino. 5% 25 or older, 10% transferred in. Retention: 84% of full-time freshmen returned the following year. Academic areas with the most degrees conferred: business/marketing; psychology; biological/life sciences. Core. Calendar: semesters. Academic remediation for entering students, ESL program, advanced placement, accelerated degree program, freshman honors college, honors program, summer session for credit, part-time degree program, internships. ROTC: Army.

Entrance Requirements: Option: early admission. Required: high school transcript, CEEB University Evaluation and Admissions Tests (PEAU). Entrance: moderately difficult. Application deadline: 11/15. Notification: 3/4.

Collegiate Environment: Orientation program. Drama-theater group, choral group. Student services: health clinic. Campus security: 24-hour patrols. Adelina Coppin. Operations spending for the previous fiscal year: $1.4 million. 81 computers available on campus for general student use. A campuswide network can be accessed. Students can access the following: online class registration. Staffed computer lab on campus provides training in use of computers, software, and the Internet.

■ UNIVERSITY OF PUERTO RICO-RÍO PIEDRAS

PO Box 23300
San Juan, PR 00931-3300
Tel: (787)764-0000
Web Site: www.uprrp.edu

Description: Commonwealth-supported, university, coed. Part of University of Puerto Rico System. Awards bachelor's, master's, and doctoral degrees and post-master's certificates. Founded 1903. Setting: 281-acre urban campus. Research spending for the previous fiscal year: $17.1 million. Total enrollment: 18,966. Faculty: 1,084 (749 full-time, 335 part-time). Student-undergrad faculty ratio is 16:1. 8,290 applied, 36% were admitted. Students come from 34 other countries, 0.3% from out-of-commonwealth. 7% 25 or older. Retention: 91% of full-time freshmen returned the following year. Academic areas with the most degrees conferred: business/marketing; education; social sciences; interdisciplinary studies. Core. Calendar: semesters. Academic remediation for entering students, services for LD students, advanced placement, self-designed majors, honors program, double major, summer session for credit, part-time degree program, adult/continuing education programs, co-op programs and internships, graduate courses open to undergrads. Study abroad program. ROTC: Army, Air Force.

Entrance Requirements: Option: electronic application. Required: high school transcript, SAT, College Entrance Examination Board (CEEB) Aptitude Test in mathematics and verbal reasoning and the Academic Achievement Test in English, mathematics and Spanish. Required for some: interview. Entrance: very difficult. Application deadline: 12/15.

Collegiate Environment: Orientation program. Drama-theater group, choral group, student-run radio station. Social organizations: national fraternities, national sororities, local fraternities, local sororities. Student services: legal services, health clinic, personal-psychological counseling. Campus security: 24-hour emergency response devices, late night transport-escort service. Jose M. Lazaro Library plus 10 others. 170 computers available on campus for general student use. A campuswide network can be accessed from student residence rooms. Students can access the following: online class registration. Staffed computer lab on campus.

■ UNIVERSITY OF PUERTO RICO-UTUADO
PO Box 2500
Utuado, PR 00641-2500
Tel: (787)894-2828
Web Site: www.uprutuado.edu

Description: Commonwealth-supported, 4-year, coed. Part of University of Puerto Rico System. Awards associate and bachelor's degrees. Founded 1979. Setting: 180-acre small town campus with easy access to San Juan. Total enrollment: 1,623. Faculty: 107 (74 full-time, 33 part-time). Student-undergrad faculty ratio is 18:1. 1,854 applied, 45% were admitted. Full-time: 1,448 students, 56% women, 44% men. Part-time: 175 students, 64% women, 36% men. 8% 25 or older, 1% transferred in. Retention: 59% of full-time freshmen returned the following year. Academic areas with the most degrees conferred: education; business/marketing. Core. Calendar: semesters. Academic remediation for entering students, services for LD students, honors program, summer session for credit, co-op programs.
Entrance Requirements: Options: electronic application, early admission, deferred admission. Required: SAT Subject Tests, CEEB. Entrance: moderately difficult. Application deadline: rolling.
Collegiate Environment: Orientation program. Drama-theater group, choral group. Social organizations: national fraternities, national sororities, local fraternities, local sororities. Major annual events: Festival Tierra Adentro, Baile de Bienvenida a Estudians, Festival de la Voz. Student services: health clinic, personal-psychological counseling. Campus security: 24-hour emergency response devices and patrols. Centro de Recursos para el Aprendizaje.

■ UNIVERSITY OF THE SACRED HEART
PO Box 12383
San Juan, PR 00914-0383
Tel: (787)728-1515
Web Site: www.sagrado.edu

Description: Independent Roman Catholic, comprehensive, coed. Awards associate, bachelor's, and master's degrees. Founded 1935. Setting: 33-acre urban campus. Endowment: $18.5 million. Total enrollment: 5,666. Faculty: 367 (122 full-time, 245 part-time). Student-undergrad faculty ratio is 20:1. 5,261 applied, 35% were admitted. Full-time: 3,765 students, 62% women, 38% men. Part-time: 870 students, 59% women, 41% men. 2% from out-of-commonwealth. 20% 25 or older, 8% transferred in. Retention: 75% of full-time freshmen returned the following year. Academic areas with the most degrees conferred: communication/journalism; business/marketing; psychology. Core. Calendar: semesters. Academic remediation for entering students, services for LD students, advanced placement, accelerated degree program, honors program, summer session for credit, part-time degree program, co-op programs and internships.
Entrance Requirements: Option: early admission. Required: high school transcript, minimum 2.5 high school GPA, 1 recommendation. Entrance: moderately difficult. Application deadline: 6/30.
Collegiate Environment: Orientation program. Drama-theater group, choral group, student-run newspaper. Most popular organizations: La Red (personal development center), Student Council, Judo Club, Athletic Association. Major annual events: Welcome Party, Inter-University Athletic Competition. Student services: health clinic, personal-psychological counsel-

ing. Campus security: 24-hour patrols. 500 computers available on campus for general student use. A campuswide network can be accessed from off-campus. Students can access the following: online class registration. Staffed computer lab on campus.

United States Virgin Islands

■ UNIVERSITY OF THE VIRGIN ISLANDS
2 John Brewers Bay
Saint Thomas, VI 00802
Tel: (340)776-9200; Free: 877-468-6884
Web Site: www.uvi.edu

Description: Territory-supported, comprehensive, coed. Awards associate, bachelor's, master's, and doctoral degrees and post-master's certificates. Founded 1962. Setting: 518-acre small town campus. Total enrollment: 2,170. Faculty: 216 (98 full-time, 118 part-time). Student-undergrad faculty ratio is 12:1. 899 applied, 98% were admitted. 21% from top 10% of their high school class, 41% from top quarter, 71% from top half. Full-time: 1,275 students, 64% women, 36% men. Part-time: 623 students, 70% women, 30% men. Students come from 32 states and territories, 13 other countries, 5% from out-of-territory. 0.3% American Indian or Alaska Native, non-Hispanic/Latino; 9% Hispanic/Latino; 71% Black or African American, non-Hispanic/Latino; 0.7% Asian, non-Hispanic/Latino; 6% international. 23% 25 or older, 5% transferred in. Retention: 67% of full-time freshmen returned the following year. Academic areas with the most degrees conferred: business/marketing; biological/life sciences; education. Core. Calendar: semesters. Academic remediation for entering students, ESL program, services for LD students, advanced placement, honors program, independent study, distance learning, double major, summer session for credit, part-time degree program, external degree program, adult/continuing education programs, co-op programs and internships, graduate courses open to undergrads. Off campus study at National Student Exchange. Study abroad program. ROTC: Army.
Entrance Requirements: Options: electronic application, early admission, deferred admission. Recommended: high school transcript, minimum 2 high school GPA. Entrance: noncompetitive. Application deadline: 4/30. Notification: continuous until 10/1. Transfer credits accepted: Yes.
Costs Per Year: Application fee: $25. Territory resident tuition: $4631 full-time, $154 per credit part-time. Nonresident tuition: $13,892 full-time, $463 per credit part-time. Mandatory fees: $604 full-time, $254 per term part-time. Full-time tuition and fees vary according to reciprocity agreements. Part-time tuition and fees vary according to course load and reciprocity agreements. College room and board: $9900. College room only: $4120. Room and board charges vary according to board plan and housing facility.
Collegiate Environment: Orientation program. Drama-theater group, choral group, student-run newspaper, radio station. Social organizations: 50 open to all; national sororities. Most popular organizations: Student Government Association, Golden Key Honor Society, Student Nurses Association, National Student Exchange Club, St. Kitts and Nevis. Major annual events: Welcome Kontiki Boat Ride, Afternoon on the Green, Miss University of the Virgin Islands. Student services: health clinic, personal-psychological counseling. Campus security: 24-hour emergency response devices and patrols. Ralph M. Paiewonsky Library. Students can reserve study rooms. 500 computers available on campus for general student use. A campuswide network can be accessed from student residence rooms. Students can access the following: online class registration.

■ ALBERTA BIBLE COLLEGE

635 Northmount Dr., NW
Calgary, AB, Canada T2K 3J6
Tel: (403)282-2994; Free: 877-542-9492
Fax: (403)282-3084
Description: Independent Christian, 4-year, coed. Awards bachelor's degrees.

■ ALBERTA COLLEGE OF ART & DESIGN

1407 14 Ave. NW
Calgary, AB, Canada T2N 4R3
Tel: (403)284-7600; Free: 800-251-8290
Web Site: www.acad.ca
Description: Province-supported, 4-year, coed. Awards bachelor's degrees. Founded 1926. Setting: 1-acre urban campus with easy access to Calgary. Endowment: $4.4 million. Research spending for the previous fiscal year: $4452. Educational spending for the previous fiscal year: $7249 per student. Total enrollment: 1,150. Faculty: 122 (40 full-time, 82 part-time). Student-undergrad faculty ratio is 16:1. 561 applied, 37% were admitted. Full-time: 1,043 students, 72% women, 28% men. Part-time: 107 students, 76% women, 24% men. Students come from 11 provinces and territories, 22 other countries, 12% from out-of-province. 5% American Indian or Alaska Native, non-Hispanic/Latino; 5% international. 19% 25 or older, 9% live on campus, 7% transferred in. Retention: 67% of full-time freshmen returned the following year. Academic area with the most degrees conferred: visual and performing arts. Core. Calendar: semesters. Academic remediation for entering students, services for LD students, advanced placement, independent study, summer session for credit, part-time degree program, adult/continuing education programs, internships. Study abroad program.
Entrance Requirements: Options: electronic application, early decision, international baccalaureate accepted. Required: essay, high school transcript, minimum 2 high school GPA, portfolio of artwork. Entrance: moderately difficult. Application deadline: 2/1. Notification: 3/15, 3/15 for nonresidents. Transfer credits accepted: Yes.
Collegiate Environment: Orientation program. Social organizations: 12 open to all. Most popular organizations: The Rendez-Vous Collective, Conceptual Arts Club, Arts Mob, Anime and Gaming Club, ACAD Glass. Major annual events: Show and Sale, Artawearness, Graduating Exhibition. Student services: health clinic, personal-psychological counseling. Campus security: 24-hour emergency response devices and patrols, late night transport-escort service, controlled dormitory access. Luke Lindoe Library. Operations spending for the previous fiscal year: $531,448. 77 computers available on campus for general student use. A computer is required for all students. A campuswide network can be accessed. Students can access the following: online class registration, Network Storage, Self Serve Printing + Copying. Staffed computer lab on campus provides training in use of computers, software, and the Internet.

■ AMBROSE UNIVERSITY

150 Ambrose Cir. SW
Calgary, AB, Canada T3H 0L5
Tel: (403)410-2000; Free: 800-461-1222
E-mail: enrolment@ambrose.edu
Web Site: www.ambrose.edu
Description: Independent, comprehensive, coed, affiliated with The Christian and Missionary Alliance. Awards bachelor's and master's degrees (graduate and professional degrees are offered by Canadian Theological Seminary). Founded 1941. Setting: 37-acre urban campus. Endowment: $6 million. Educational spending for the previous fiscal year: $8000 per student. Total enrollment: 922. Faculty: 84 (44 full-time, 40 part-time). Student-undergrad faculty ratio is 13:1. 255 applied. Full-time: 682 students, 59% women, 41% men. Part-time: 50 students, 72% women, 28% men. Students come from 10 provinces and territories, 26 other countries, 9% from out-of-province. 2% American Indian or Alaska Native, non-Hispanic/Latino; 2% Hispanic/Latino; 3% Black or African American, non-Hispanic/Latino; 13% Asian Canadian, non-Hispanic/Latino. 11% 25 or older, 18% live on campus, 5% transferred in. Retention: 70% of full-time freshmen returned the following year. Academic areas with the most degrees conferred: social sciences; education; theology and religious vocations. Core. Calendar: semesters. Academic remediation for entering students, services for LD students, advanced placement, independent study, distance learning, double major, summer session for credit, part-time degree program, adult/continuing education programs, internships. Off campus study at no. Study abroad program.
Entrance Requirements: Options: electronic application, early admission, deferred admission, international baccalaureate accepted. Required: high school transcript. Required for some: essay, 3 recommendations, interview, minimum 60% overall average on 5 grade-12 level courses, program-specific requirements, SAT or ACT. Application deadline: rolling. Notification: continuous. Transfer credits accepted: Yes.
Costs Per Year: Application fee: $70 Canadian dollars. Tuition, fee, and room and board charges are reported in Canadian dollars. Comprehensive fee: $19,008 includes full-time tuition ($11,400), mandatory fees ($908), and college room and board ($6700). College room only: $3600. Full-time tuition and fees vary according to course load, degree level, and program. Room and board charges vary according to board plan and housing facility. Part-time tuition: $380 per credit hour. Part-time mandatory fees: $30.25 per credit hour. Part-time tuition and fees vary according to course load, degree level, and program.
Collegiate Environment: Orientation program. Drama-theater group, choral group, student-run newspaper. Social organizations: 13 open to all; 20% of eligible men and 27% of eligible women are members. Most popular organizations: Coffee Club, Business Society, Hockey Club, Biology Club, Outdoors Club. Major annual events: Legacy Youth Conference, Spiritual Emphasis Days, Program Days. Student services: personal-psychological counseling. Campus security: 24-hour emergency response devices, student patrols, late night transport-escort service, controlled dormitory access. Archibald Foundation Library. Books: 127,484 (physical), 150,000 (digital/electronic); Serial titles: 152 (physical), 60,338 (digital/electronic); Databases: 42. Weekly public service hours: 81; students can reserve study rooms. Operations spending for the previous fiscal year: $400,000. 20 computers available on campus for general student use. A campuswide network can be accessed from student residence rooms. Students can access the following: online class registration.

■ ATHABASCA UNIVERSITY

1 University Dr.
Athabasca, AB, Canada T9S 3A3
Tel: (780)675-6100; Free: 800-788-9041
Fax: (780)675-6437
Web Site: www.athabascau.ca

Description: Province-supported, comprehensive, coed. Awards bachelor's, master's, and doctoral degrees and post-master's certificates (offers only external degree programs). Founded 1970. Setting: 480-acre small town campus. Endowment: $1 million. Research spending for the previous fiscal year: $1.7 million. Educational spending for the previous fiscal year: $5780 per student. Total enrollment: 40,335. Faculty: 384. Students come from 42 provinces and territories, 87 other countries. 70% 25 or older. Core. Calendar: continuous. Academic remediation for entering students, ESL program, services for LD students, advanced placement, accelerated degree program, self-designed majors, independent study, distance learning, double major, summer session for credit, part-time degree program, external degree program, adult/continuing education programs, graduate courses open to undergrads. Off campus study. Study abroad program.

Entrance Requirements: Open admission. Options: electronic application, international baccalaureate accepted. Entrance: noncompetitive. Application deadline: rolling. Notification: continuous. Transfer credits accepted: Yes.

Collegiate Environment: Student-run newspaper. Campus security: 24-hour emergency response devices. Athabasca University Library. Operations spending for the previous fiscal year: $1.3 million. 28 computers available on campus for general student use. Computer purchase/lease plans available. A campuswide network can be accessed. Students can access the following: online class registration. Staffed computer lab on campus.

Community Environment: The central campus is located in a small rural town (population 2,415) in the northern section of the province. Learning Centers are located in larger urban centres.

■ CONCORDIA UNIVERSITY OF EDMONTON

7128 Ada Blvd., NW
Edmonton, AB, Canada T5B 4E4
Tel: (780)479-8481; Free: 866-479-5200
Fax: (780)474-1933
E-mail: admits@concordia.ab.ca
Web Site: www.concordia.ab.ca

Description: Independent Lutheran, comprehensive, coed. Awards bachelor's and master's degrees. Founded 1921. Setting: 15-acre urban campus. Total enrollment: 2,061. Faculty: 153 (59 full-time, 94 part-time). Student-undergrad faculty ratio is 18:1. 1,799 applied, 55% were admitted. Students come from 11 provinces and territories, 26 other countries. 3% live on campus. Academic areas with the most degrees conferred: psychology; education; business/marketing. Core. Calendar: semesters. Services for LD students, advanced placement, honors program, independent study, double major, summer session for credit, part-time degree program, external degree program, internships. Study abroad program.

Entrance Requirements: Open admission for non-degree Open Studies students. Options: electronic application, early admission, international baccalaureate accepted. Required: high school transcript, minimum 2 high school GPA. Required for some: essay, 2 recommendations, interview. Entrance: moderately difficult. Application deadlines: 6/30, 5/1 for nonresidents. Notification: 10/1, 10/1 for nonresidents. Transfer credits accepted: Yes.

Collegiate Environment: Orientation program. Drama-theater group, choral group, student-run newspaper. Social organizations: 15 open to all. Most popular organizations: concert choir, Concordia Business Association, Science Club, Education Undergraduate Society, Psychology Students' Association. Major annual events: Orientation, Oktoberfest, Valentine Social and Christmas Formal. Student services: personal-psychological counseling. Campus security: 24-hour patrols, late night transport-escort service. Arnold Guebert Memorial Library plus 1 other. 250 computers available on campus for general student use. A campuswide network can be accessed from student residence rooms and from off campus. Staffed computer lab on campus.

■ THE KING'S UNIVERSITY

9125 50th St.
Edmonton, AB, Canada T6B 2H3
Tel: (780)465-3500; Free: 800-661-8582
Fax: (780)465-3534
E-mail: admissions@kingsu.ca
Web Site: www.kingsu.ca

Description: Independent interdenominational, 4-year, coed. Awards bachelor's degrees. Founded 1979. Setting: 20-acre suburban campus. Endowment: $3.1 million. Research spending for the previous fiscal year: $305,395. Educational spending for the previous fiscal year: $9075 per student. Total enrollment: 792. Faculty: 108 (45 full-time, 63 part-time).

Student-undergrad faculty ratio is 11:1. 417 applied, 88% were admitted. Full-time: 651 students, 56% women, 44% men. Part-time: 67 students, 57% women, 43% men. Students come from 6 provinces and territories, 12 other countries, 10% from out-of-province. 11% 25 or older, 31% live on campus, 14% transferred in. Retention: 70% of full-time freshmen returned the following year. Academic areas with the most degrees conferred: education; biological/life sciences; psychology. Core. Calendar: Canadian standard year. ESL program, services for LD students, advanced placement, independent study, double major, summer session for credit, part-time degree program, adult/continuing education programs, internships. Off campus study. Study abroad program.

Entrance Requirements: Options: electronic application, international baccalaureate accepted. Required: high school transcript, minimum 2 high school GPA, 1 recommendation. Required for some: essay, interview. Entrance: moderately difficult. Application deadline: rolling. Notification: 8/15. Transfer credits accepted: Yes. Applicants placed on waiting list: 0. Waitlisted applicants offered admission: 0.

Costs Per Year: Application fee: $70 Canadian dollars. Tuition, fee, and room and board charges are reported in Canadian dollars. Comprehensive fee: $20,532 includes full-time tuition ($12,710), mandatory fees ($852), and college room and board ($6970). College room only: $3800. Full-time tuition and fees vary according to course load. Room and board charges vary according to board plan and housing facility. Part-time tuition: $410 per credit hour. Part-time mandatory fees: $162.50 per term. Part-time tuition and fees vary according to course load.

Collegiate Environment: Orientation program. Drama-theater group, choral group, student-run newspaper. Social organizations: 29 open to all. Most popular organizations: Micah Action and Awareness Students' Society, King's Eagles Hockey Club, King's Rugby Club, King's Science Society, The King's Commerce Association. Major annual events: Students' Association Kickoff Event, Students' Association/Student Life Christmas Event, Battle of the Bands. Student services: personal-psychological counseling. Campus security: 24-hour emergency response devices, student patrols, controlled dormitory access. Simona Maaskant. Books: 80,000 (physical), 301,000 (digital/electronic); Serial titles: 166 (physical), 130,000 (digital/electronic); Databases: 50. Weekly public service hours: 63. Operations spending for the previous fiscal year: $629,882. 76 computers available on campus for general student use. A campuswide network can be accessed from student residence rooms. Students can access the following: online class registration. Staffed computer lab on campus provides training in use of computers, software, and the Internet.

■ MOUNT ROYAL UNIVERSITY

4825 Mount Royal Gate SW
Calgary, AB, Canada T3E 6K6
Tel: (403)440-6111; Free: 877-440-5001
Fax: (403)440-5938
Web Site: www.mtroyal.ca

Description: Province-supported, 4-year, coed. Awards bachelor's degrees. Founded 1911.

Entrance Requirements: Required: high school transcript.

■ PRAIRIE BIBLE INSTITUTE

350 5th Ave., NE
Box 4000
Three Hills, AB, Canada T0M 2N0
Tel: (403)443-5511; Free: 800-661-2425
Fax: (403)443-5540
Web Site: www.prairie.edu

Description: Independent interdenominational, 4-year, coed. Awards associate and bachelor's degrees. Founded 1922. Setting: 130-acre small town campus with easy access to Calgary. Core. Calendar: semesters. ESL program, advanced placement, accelerated degree program, part-time degree program, adult/continuing education programs, internships. Study abroad program.

Entrance Requirements: Option: electronic application. Required: essay, high school transcript, 2 recommendations. Recommended: minimum 2.0 high school GPA. Required for some: minimum 3.0 high school GPA. Entrance: minimally difficult. Application deadline: 8/15.

Collegiate Environment: Orientation program. Drama-theater group, choral group, student-run newspaper, radio station. Student services: health clinic, personal-psychological counseling. Campus security: 24-hour emergency response devices and patrols, late night transport-escort service, controlled dormitory access. T. S. Rendall Library. 30 computers available on campus for general student use. Staffed computer lab on campus.

■ ROCKY MOUNTAIN COLLEGE

4039 Brentwood Rd., NW
Calgary, AB, Canada T2L 1L1
Tel: (403)284-5100; Free: 877-YOUnRMC
Web Site: www.rockymountaincollege.ca

Description: Independent, 4-year, coed, affiliated with Missionary Church. Awards bachelor's degrees. Founded 1992. Setting: 1-acre urban campus with easy access to Calgary. Endowment: $343,200. Core. Calendar: semesters. Academic remediation for entering students, advanced placement, self-designed majors, independent study, distance learning, double major, summer session for credit, part-time degree program, external degree program, adult/continuing education programs, internships. Off campus study. Study abroad program.

Entrance Requirements: Open admission. Options: electronic application, early decision, deferred admission, international baccalaureate accepted. Transfer credits accepted: Yes.

Collegiate Environment: Orientation program. Main library plus 1 other.

■ SOUTHERN ALBERTA INSTITUTE OF TECHNOLOGY

1301 16th Ave. NW
Calgary, AB, Canada T2M 0L4
Tel: (403)284-8110; Free: 877-284-SAIT
Fax: (403)284-7112
Web Site: www.sait.ca

Description: Province-supported, primarily 2-year, coed. Awards certificates, diplomas, terminal associate, and bachelor's degrees. Founded 1916. Setting: 96-acre urban campus. Total enrollment: 7,672. Faculty: 962. Full-time: 6,954 students, 42% women, 58% men. Part-time: 718 students, 45% women, 55% men. Calendar: trimesters. Services for LD students, independent study, distance learning, co-op programs and internships. Off campus study.

Entrance Requirements: Options: electronic application, early admission, early decision. Required: high school transcript. Required for some: essay, interview. Application deadline: rolling. Transfer credits accepted: Yes.

Collegiate Environment: Orientation program. Drama-theater group, student-run newspaper, radio station. Social organizations: 17 open to all. Most popular organizations: SAIT Petroleum Society, Business Student's Association, Global Passport, Environmental Technology Students Organization, Civil Engineering Technology Concrete Toboggan. Major annual events: Orientation, Welcome Week, Graduation. Student services: health clinic, personal-psychological counseling. Campus security: 24-hour emergency response devices and patrols, late night transport-escort service. SAIT Library.

■ UNIVERSITY OF ALBERTA

Edmonton, AB, Canada T6G 2E1
Tel: (780)492-3111; Free: 855-492-3113
Fax: (780)492-7172
Web Site: www.ualberta.ca

Description: Province-supported, university, coed. Awards bachelor's, master's, and doctoral degrees. Founded 1906. Setting: 1,200-acre urban campus. Endowment: $1 million. Total enrollment: 38,733. Student-undergrad faculty ratio is 20:1. Students come from 13 provinces and territories, 128 other countries, 9% from out-of province. Calendar: Canadian standard year. Academic remediation for entering students, ESL program, services for LD students, advanced placement, accelerated degree program, self-designed majors, honors program, independent study, distance learning, double major, summer session for credit, part-time degree program, external degree program, adult/continuing education programs, co-op programs and internships, graduate courses open to undergrads. Off campus study. Study abroad program.

Entrance Requirements: Options: electronic application, early decision, early action, international baccalaureate accepted. Recommended: minimum 2 high school GPA, SAT and SAT Subject Tests or ACT, AP. Required for some: essay, high school transcript, interview, portfolios/auditions. Entrance: moderately difficult. Application deadline: 5/1. Preference given to province residents for some programs, aboriginal students. SAT Reasoning Test deadline: 8/1. SAT Subject Test deadline: 8/1. Transfer credits accepted: Yes.

Collegiate Environment: Orientation program. Drama-theater group, choral group, student-run newspaper, radio station. Social organizations: 450 open

to all; national fraternities, national sororities, local fraternities, local sororities. Major annual events: Week of Welcome, AntiFreeze. Student services: legal services, health clinic, personal-psychological counseling, women's center. Campus security: 24-hour emergency response devices and patrols, student patrols, late night transport-escort service, controlled dormitory access. Rutherford Library plus 13 others. 2,500 computers available on campus for general student use. Computer purchase/lease plans available. A campuswide network can be accessed from student residence rooms and from off campus. Students can access the following: online class registration. Staffed computer lab on campus.

Community Environment: Edmonton is the provincial capital and largest city of Alberta, with a population of 666,100. It takes its name from Fort Edmonton, an early trading post of the Hudson Bay Company. The city, the center of an important farming region, is also an oil and gas exploration and manufacturing center. Major industries include pipeline construction, chemical plants, meat packing, construction, oilfield construction and servicing, and food processing. The city was the first to establish a municipal airport and has long been the Gateway to the North. It is easily accessible by air, rail, bus and car. It is also home to the Alberta Research Council and Edmonton Research Park.

■ UNIVERSITY OF CALGARY

2500 University Dr., NW
Calgary, AB, Canada T2N 1N4
Tel: (403)220-5110
E-mail: future.students@ucalgary.ca
Web Site: www.ucalgary.ca

Description: Province-supported, university, coed. Part of Campus Alberta. Awards bachelor's, master's, and doctoral degrees and post-master's certificates. Founded 1966. Setting: 213-hectare urban campus with easy access to Calgary. Endowment: $790.6 million. Research spending for the previous fiscal year: $360.5 million. Total enrollment: 30,518. Faculty: 1,813 (1,751 full-time, 62 part-time). Student-undergrad faculty ratio is 23:1. 10,301 applied, 63% were admitted. Students come from 11 provinces and territories, 96 other countries, 17% from out-of province. 80% 25 or older. Retention: 95% of full-time freshmen returned the following year. Academic areas with the most degrees conferred: social sciences; business/marketing; health professions and related sciences; engineering. Calendar: semesters. Academic remediation for entering students, ESL program, services for LD students, advanced placement, freshman honors college, honors program, independent study, distance learning, double major, summer session for credit, part-time degree program, adult/continuing education programs, co-op programs and internships, graduate courses open to undergrads. Off campus study at Campus Alberta. Study abroad program.

Entrance Requirements: Options: electronic application, early admission, deferred admission, international baccalaureate accepted. Required: high school transcript. Required for some: essay, minimum 3.7 high school GPA, 3 recommendations, SAT or ACT. Entrance: moderately difficult. Application deadline: 3/1. Notification: continuous. Transfer credits accepted: Yes.

Collegiate Environment: Orientation program. Drama-theater group, choral group, student-run newspaper, radio station. Social organizations: 200 open to all; national fraternities, national sororities. Most popular organizations: Muslim Students' Association, Snowboard Club, Ski Club, Video Game Club, Student Dance Club. Major annual events: Welcome Week, Kick Off, Bermuda Shorts Day (last day of classes). Student services: legal services, health clinic, personal-psychological counseling, women's center. Campus security: 24-hour emergency response devices and patrols, late night transport-escort service, controlled dormitory access. Taylor Family Digital Library plus 8 others. Books: 3.2 million (physical), 975,202 (digital/electronic); Databases: 92,645. Weekly public service hours: 101; students can reserve study rooms.

Community Environment: Situated centrally in western Canada, Calgary is located at the convergence of the Bow and Elbow Rivers, As Canada's energy capital and western Canada's business capital, Calgary is home to the second largest concentration of corporate head offices in the country. Within an hour's drive are the Rocky Mountains, Kananaskis Valley and Banff National Park where hiking, skiing, canoeing, mountain climbing, and mountain biking can be enjoyed. Calgary is home to more than 820,000 people, which makes it Canada's fifth largest city. Cultural activities abound with a philharmonic orchestra, as well as theater and dance companies, museums, art galleries, libraries, and a planetarium.

■ UNIVERSITY OF LETHBRIDGE

4401 University Dr.
Lethbridge, AB, Canada T1K 3M4

Tel: (403)329-2111
E-mail: regoffice@uleth.ca
Web Site: www.uleth.ca
Description: Province-supported, university, coed. Awards bachelor's, master's, and doctoral degrees and post-master's certificates. Founded 1967. Setting: 576-acre urban campus. Total enrollment: 8,468. 3,185 applied, 84% were admitted. Students come from 13 provinces and territories, 53 other countries, 10% from out-of-province. 23% 25 or older, 11% live on campus. Retention: 79% of full-time freshmen returned the following year. Academic areas with the most degrees conferred: business/marketing; health professions and related sciences; education. Core. Calendar: semesters. Academic remediation for entering students, ESL program, services for LD students, advanced placement, accelerated degree program, self-designed majors, independent study, distance learning, double major, summer session for credit, part-time degree program, co-op programs and internships, graduate courses open to undergrads. Off campus study at University of Lethbridge, Lethbridge College. Study abroad program.
Entrance Requirements: Options: electronic application, deferred admission, international baccalaureate accepted. Required: high school transcript, minimum 2 high school GPA. Required for some: minimum 3 high school GPA, interview. Entrance: moderately difficult. Application deadline: 6/30. Notification: continuous. Transfer credits accepted: Yes.
Costs Per Year: Application fee: $100 Canadian dollars. Tuition, fee, and room and board charges are reported in Canadian dollars. Province resident tuition: $4974 full-time. Canadian resident tuition: $4974 full-time. Mandatory fees: $1,225 full-time. Full-time tuition and fees vary according to course load. College room and board: $6983. Room and board charges vary according to board plan and housing facility. International student tuition: $16,751 full-time.
Collegiate Environment: Orientation program. Drama-theater group, choral group, student-run newspaper, radio station. Social organizations: national fraternities, local fraternities, local sororities. Major annual events: Fresh Fest, Imaginus, Student Union Cabarets. Student services: health clinic, personal-psychological counseling, women's center. Campus security: 24-

hour emergency response devices and patrols, student patrols, late night transport-escort service, controlled dormitory access, video camera monitored entrances, hallways. The University of Lethbridge Library. Students can reserve study rooms.
Community Environment: The centre of a prosperous farming and ranching area, Lethbridge is characterized by its many green areas and parks, and its abundant cultural and recreational facilities. It is located in southern Alberta, approximately 145 kilometres (90 miles) east of the Canadian Rockies and 95 kilometres (60 miles) north of the United States border.

■ VANGUARD COLLEGE
12140 103rd St.
Edmonton, AB, Canada T5G 2J9
Tel: (780)452-0808
Fax: (780)452-5803
E-mail: admissions@vanguardcollege.com
Web Site: www.vanguardcollege.com
Description: Independent, 4-year, coed, affiliated with Pentecostal Assemblies of Canada. Administratively affiliated with Pentecostal Assemblies of Canada (PAOC). Awards bachelor's degrees. Founded 1946. Setting: 4-acre urban campus. Student-undergrad faculty ratio is 11:1. 6% live on campus. Core. Calendar: semesters. Services for LD students, advanced placement, accelerated degree program, independent study, distance learning, double major, summer session for credit, part-time degree program, internships. Off campus study.
Entrance Requirements: Options: electronic application, early decision. Required: essay, high school transcript, 2 recommendations. Application deadlines: 8/19, 4/15 for early decision. Transfer credits accepted: Yes.
Collegiate Environment: Orientation program. Choral group. Major annual events: All School Retreat, Soccer Championship, Christmas Banquet. Vanguard College Library: Schalm Memorial Collection. 8 computers available on campus for general student use. Computer purchase/lease plans available. A campuswide network can be accessed. Students can access the following: online class registration. Staffed computer lab on campus.

■ BRITISH COLUMBIA INSTITUTE OF TECHNOLOGY
3700 Willingdon Ave.
Burnaby, BC, Canada V5G 3H2
Tel: (604)434-5734; Free: 866-434-1610
Fax: (604)278-5363
Web Site: www.bcit.ca
Description: Province-supported, 4-year, coed. Awards associate and bachelor's degrees. Founded 1964. Setting: 103-acre urban campus with easy access to Vancouver. Total enrollment: 22,507. Faculty: 1,359 (735 full-time, 624 part-time). 7,721 applied, 44% were admitted. Calendar: quarters.
Entrance Requirements: Option: electronic application. Required: high school transcript. Required for some: essay, 2 recommendations, interview. Entrance: moderately difficult.
Collegiate Environment: Student-run newspaper, radio station. Student services: health clinic, personal-psychological counseling, women's center. Campus security: 24-hour emergency response devices and patrols, student patrols, late night transport-escort service. British Columbia Institute of Technology Library plus 1 other. Operations spending for the previous fiscal year: $2.9 million.

■ CAPILANO UNIVERSITY
2055 Purcell Way
North Vancouver, BC, Canada V7J 3H5
Tel: (604)986-1911
Fax: (604)984-4985
Web Site: www.capilanou.ca
Description: Public, 4-year, coed. Part of British Columbia's Advanced Education system. Awards associate and bachelor's degrees. Founded 1967. Setting: 44-hectare suburban campus with easy access to Vancouver. Endowment: $7.6 million. Educational spending for the previous fiscal year: $8392 per student. Total enrollment: 7,311. Faculty: 633 (168 full-time, 465 part-time). Student-undergrad faculty ratio is 17:1. 2,200 applied. Full-time: 5,436 students, 57% women, 43% men. Part-time: 1,875 students, 71% women, 29% men. Students come from 12 provinces and territories, 87 other countries, 5% from out-of-province. 32% 25 or older. Retention: 64% of full-time freshmen returned the following year. Academic areas with the most degrees conferred: business/marketing; visual and performing arts; communication/journalism. Calendar: semesters. Academic remediation for entering students, ESL program, services for LD students, advanced placement, independent study, distance learning, summer session for credit, part-time degree program, co-op programs and internships. Off campus study. Study abroad program.
Entrance Requirements: Open admission. Options: electronic application, early admission, international baccalaureate accepted. Required for some: essay, minimum 2 high school GPA. Entrance: noncompetitive. Application deadline: 3/31. Transfer credits accepted: Yes.
Costs Per Year: Fee charges are reported in Canadian dollars.
Collegiate Environment: Orientation program. Choral group, student-run newspaper, radio station. Social organizations: Student Union. Student services: legal services, health clinic, personal-psychological counseling, women's center. Campus security: 24-hour emergency response devices and patrols, late night transport-escort service. 293 college housing spaces available; 289 were occupied in 2018-19. Freshmen given priority for college housing. Options: coed, men-only, women-only housing available. Capilano University Library. Books: 73,290 (physical), 178,273 (digital/electronic); Serial titles: 122 (physical), 34,260 (digital/electronic); Databases: 136. Weekly

public service hours: 73; students can reserve study rooms. Operations spending for the previous fiscal year: $1.5 million. 1,083 computers available on campus for general student use. Students can access the following: online class registration.

■ COLUMBIA BIBLE COLLEGE
2940 Clearbrook Rd.
Abbotsford, BC, Canada V2T 2Z8
Tel: (604)853-3358; Free: 800-283-0881
Fax: (604)853-3063
E-mail: nathan.martin@columbiabc.edu
Web Site: www.columbiabc.edu
Description: Independent Mennonite Brethren, 4-year, coed. Awards bachelor's degrees. Founded 1936. Setting: 9-acre urban campus with easy access to Vancouver. Endowment: $915,262. Educational spending for the previous fiscal year: $4669 per student. Total enrollment: 405. Faculty: 41 (14 full-time, 27 part-time). Student-undergrad faculty ratio is 21:1. 258 applied, 79% were admitted. Students come from 7 provinces and territories, 8 other countries, 27% from out-of-province. 14% 25 or older, 45% live on campus. Retention: 66% of full-time freshmen returned the following year. Academic area with the most degrees conferred: theology and religious vocations. Core. Calendar: semesters. Academic remediation for entering students, services for LD students, advanced placement, independent study, distance learning, part-time degree program, internships. Off campus study. Study abroad program.
Entrance Requirements: Open admission for mature students, age 21 or older without a high school diploma. Options: electronic application, early admission, early decision, deferred admission, international baccalaureate accepted. Required: essay, high school transcript, minimum 2 high school GPA, 1 recommendation, must be Christian. Entrance: noncompetitive. Application deadlines: 8/15, 3/14 for early decision plan 1, 5/15 for early decision plan 2. Notification: continuous, continuous for nonresidents. Preference given to Christians. Transfer credits accepted: Yes. Early decision applicants: 204. Early decision applicants admitted: 152.
Collegiate Environment: Orientation program. Choral group. Student services: personal-psychological counseling. Campus security: late night transport-escort service, controlled dormitory access, night watchman 11 pm to 6 am. Columbia Resource Center. Operations spending for the previous fiscal year: $249,119. 30 computers available on campus for general student use. A campuswide network can be accessed from student residence rooms and from off campus. Staffed computer lab on campus provides training in use of the Internet.

■ EMILY CARR UNIVERSITY OF ART + DESIGN
1399 Johnston St.
Vancouver, BC, Canada V6H 3R9
Tel: (604)844-3800; Free: 800-832-7788
Fax: (604)844-3801
E-mail: admissions@ecuad.ca
Web Site: www.ecuad.ca
Description: Province-supported, comprehensive, coed. Awards bachelor's and master's degrees. Founded 1925. Setting: urban campus. Total enrollment: 1,800. Faculty: 220 (56 full-time, 164 part-time). Student-undergrad faculty ratio is 18:1. Retention: 87% of full-time freshmen returned the following year. Core. Services for LD students, advanced placement, part-time degree program, co-op programs. Study abroad program.

Entrance Requirements: Options: electronic application, international baccalaureate accepted. Required: essay, high school transcript, minimum 2.7 high school GPA, portfolio and questionnaire. Entrance: moderately difficult. Application deadline: 1/15. Notification: 3/1. Transfer credits accepted: Yes.
Collegiate Environment: Orientation program. Student-run newspaper, radio station. Student services: personal-psychological counseling. Campus security: 24-hour emergency response devices and patrols.

■ **LASALLE COLLEGE VANCOUVER**
2665 Renfrew St.
Vancouver, BC, Canada V5M 0A7
Tel: (604)683-9200; Free: 866-717-8080
Fax: (604)684-8839
Web Site: www.lasallecollegevancouver.com
Description: Proprietary, 4-year, coed.

■ **OKANAGAN COLLEGE**
1000 KLO Rd.
Kelowna, BC, Canada V1Y 4X8
Tel: (250)762-5445; Free: 877-755-2266
E-mail: ahickey@okanagan.bc.ca
Web Site: www.okanagan.bc.ca
Description: Province-supported, 4-year, coed. Part of Ministry of Advanced Education, Industry Training Authority. Awards associate and bachelor's degrees. Founded 2005. Setting: 13-acre urban campus. Total enrollment: 3,183. Faculty: 268 (190 full-time, 78 part-time). Student-undergrad faculty ratio is 12:1. Full-time: 1,942 students, 55% women, 45% men. Part-time: 1,241 students, 60% women, 40% men. Students come from 10 provinces and territories, 46 other countries, 4% from out-of-province. 24% 25 or older, 2% transferred in. Retention: 53% of full-time freshmen returned the following year. Academic areas with the most degrees conferred: business/marketing; computer and information sciences. Academic remediation for entering students, ESL program, services for LD students, advanced placement, honors program, distance learning, summer session for credit, part-time degree program, external degree program, adult/continuing education programs, co-op programs and internships. Off campus study at BC Campus. Study abroad program.
Entrance Requirements: Required for some: essay, high school transcript, minimum 2 high school GPA, interview.
Collegiate Environment: Orientation program. Choral group, student-run newspaper. Major annual events: Student Orientation, Graduation, Student Association Christmas Lunch. Student services: personal-psychological counseling. Campus security: 24-hour emergency response devices and patrols, late night transport-escort service, controlled dormitory access. Okanagan College Library. 1,050 computers available on campus for general student use. A campuswide network can be accessed. Students can access the following: online class registration. Staffed computer lab on campus provides training in use of computers, software, and the Internet.

■ **ROYAL ROADS UNIVERSITY**
2005 Sooke Rd.
Victoria, BC, Canada V9B 5Y2
Tel: (250)391-2511; Free: 800-788-8028
Fax: (250)391-2522
Web Site: www.royalroads.ca
Description: Province-supported, upper-level, coed. Awards bachelor's, master's, and doctoral degrees. Founded 1995. Setting: 565-acre suburban campus. Total enrollment: 3,120. Faculty: (50 full-time). Student-undergrad faculty ratio is 12:1. Calendar: continuous. Accelerated degree program, distance learning, summer session for credit, adult/continuing education programs. Study abroad program.
Collegiate Environment: Campus security: 24-hour emergency response devices and patrols, late night transport-escort service. Coronel Memorial Library.

■ **SIMON FRASER UNIVERSITY**
8888 University Dr.
Burnaby, BC, Canada V5A 1S6
Tel: (778)782-3111
Web Site: www.sfu.ca
Description: Province-supported, university, coed. Awards bachelor's, master's, and doctoral degrees and post-master's certificates. Founded 1965. Setting: 174-hectare suburban campus with easy access to Vancouver. Total enrollment: 30,117. Faculty: 975 (963 full-time, 12 part-

time). Student-undergrad faculty ratio is 22:1. 16,515 applied, 56% were admitted. Full-time: 12,944 students, 55% women, 45% men. Part-time: 12,399 students, 53% women, 47% men. 7% from out-of-province. 10% 25 or older, 3% transferred in. Retention: 85% of full-time freshmen returned the following year. Academic areas with the most degrees conferred: social sciences; business/marketing; computer and information sciences. Core. Calendar: trimesters. Academic remediation for entering students, ESL program, services for LD students, advanced placement, honors program, independent study, distance learning, double major, summer session for credit, part-time degree program, adult/continuing education programs, co-op programs and internships, graduate courses open to undergrads. Off campus study. Study abroad program.
Entrance Requirements: Options: electronic application, early admission, early action, deferred admission, international baccalaureate accepted. Required: high school transcript, minimum 3 high school GPA. Required for some: essay, interview, SAT or ACT. Entrance: moderately difficult. Application deadline: 2/28. Notification: continuous until 6/30. SAT Reasoning Test deadline: 4/15. Transfer credits accepted: Yes.
Collegiate Environment: Orientation program. Student-run newspaper, radio station. Social organizations: 147 open to all. Most popular organizations: The Peak Newspaper, orientation/peer leaders, Crisis line, Women's Centre, Simon Fraser Public Interest Research Group. Major annual events: Convocation, Clubs' Day, Terry Fox Run. Student services: health clinic, personal-psychological counseling, women's center. Campus security: 24-hour emergency response devices and patrols, student patrols, late night transport-escort service, controlled dormitory access, safe-walk stations, 24-hour safe study area. Bennett Library plus 2 others. Books: 1.5 million (physical), 1.1 million (digital/electronic); Serial titles: 2,500 (physical), 98,000 (digital/electronic). Weekly public service hours: 103; students can reserve study rooms. 200 computers available on campus for general student use. A campuswide network can be accessed from student residence rooms and from off campus. Students can access the following: online class registration. Staffed computer lab on campus.
Community Environment: The 1,200 acre campus is situated atop Burnaby Mountain, making Simon Fraser a striking campus with spectacular views of the coastal mountains and the cities of the Lower Mainland. The outstanding architecture has won many awards. Services on campus include day care centres, Health Services (including physicians, a psychiatrist, nurses and physiotherapists), Athletic and Recreational Services (two full gymnasia, swimming and diving pools, tennis, squash and racquetball courts, sauna, and weight rooms), a campus radio station, printshop, legal advice clinic, ecumenical chaplaincy, women's centre, bookstores and student Pub. Simon Fraser University is wheelchair accessible.

■ **SUMMIT PACIFIC COLLEGE**
Box 1700
Abbotsford, BC, Canada V2S 7E7
Tel: (604)853-7491; Free: 800-976-8388
Fax: (604)853-8951
Web Site: www.summitpacific.ca
Description: Independent, 4-year, coed, affiliated with Pentecostal Assemblies of Canada. Awards bachelor's degrees. Founded 1941. Setting: 101-acre suburban campus with easy access to Vancouver. Core. Calendar: semesters. Academic remediation for entering students, summer session for credit, part-time degree program, internships. Off campus study at Fraser Valley College, Trinity Western University.
Entrance Requirements: Option: deferred admission. Required: essay, high school transcript, 3 recommendations. Required for some: interview. Entrance: moderately difficult. Application deadline: rolling.
Collegiate Environment: Drama-theater group, choral group. Student services: personal-psychological counseling. Campus security: student patrols, campus gate locked after 11 pm. Lorne Hudson Philip Memorial Library.

■ **THOMPSON RIVERS UNIVERSITY**
900 McGill Rd.
Kamloops, BC, Canada V2C 0C8
Tel: (250)828-5000
Fax: (250)828-5086
E-mail: jkeller@tru.ca
Web Site: www.tru.ca
Description: Province-supported, comprehensive, coed. Part of Ministry of Advanced Education, Province of British Columbia. Awards associate, bachelor's, and master's degrees. Founded 1970. Setting: 100-acre small

town campus. Endowment: $16.1 million. Research spending for the previous fiscal year: $4.1 million. Educational spending for the previous fiscal year: $7515 per student. Total enrollment: 7,649. Faculty: 457. 2,986 applied, 82% were admitted. Students come from 11 provinces and territories, 78 other countries, 9% from out-of province. 27% 25 or older, 14% live on campus. Retention: 71% of full-time freshmen returned the following year. Calendar: semesters. Academic remediation for entering students, ESL program, services for LD students, advanced placement, accelerated degree program, honors program, independent study, distance learning, double major, summer session for credit, part-time degree program, external degree program, adult/continuing education programs, co-op programs and internships. Off campus study. Study abroad program.

Entrance Requirements: Open admission for First Year University: Arts, Science, Business, Tourism. Options: electronic application, early admission, early decision, deferred admission, international baccalaureate accepted. Required: high school transcript. Required for some: essay, interview. Application deadlines: 4/30, rolling for nonresidents, 3/1 for early decision plan 1, 3/1 for early decision plan 2. Notification: continuous until 4/30, continuous until 4/30 for nonresidents, 3/1 for early decision plan 1, 3/1 for early decision plan 2. Transfer credits accepted: Yes. Early decision applicants: 82. Early decision applicants admitted: 82.

Collegiate Environment: Orientation program. Drama-theater group, choral group, student-run newspaper, radio station. Social organizations: national fraternities, national sororities. Major annual events: Welcome Back BBQ, Orientation, Open House and Career Day. Student services: health clinic, personal-psychological counseling. Campus security: 24-hour emergency response devices and patrols, student patrols, late night transport-escort service, controlled dormitory access. Thompson Rivers University Library plus 2 others. Operations spending for the previous fiscal year: $2.4 million. 1,200 computers available on campus for general student use. Computer purchase/lease plans available. A campuswide network can be accessed from student residence rooms and from off campus. Students can access the following: online class registration, learning management systems, network drive space (250mb), remote access to network drives, student elections, payments, financial forms/info, updating personal contact information. Staffed computer lab on campus provides training in use of computers, software, and the Internet.

■ **TRINITY WESTERN UNIVERSITY**
7600 Glover Rd.
Langley, BC, Canada V2Y 1Y1
Tel: (604)888-7511; Free: 888-468-6898
Fax: (604)513-2061
Web Site: www.twu.ca
Description: Independent, comprehensive, coed, affiliated with Evangelical Free Church of America. Awards bachelor's and master's degrees. Founded 1962. Setting: 100-acre suburban campus with easy access to Vancouver. Total enrollment: 4,396. Core. Calendar: semesters. ESL program, advanced placement, honors program, independent study, distance learning, double major, summer session for credit, part-time degree program, adult/continuing education programs, co-op programs and internships. Off campus study. Study abroad program.

Entrance Requirements: Options: electronic application, deferred admission, international baccalaureate accepted. Required: essay, high school transcript. Required for some: interview. Entrance: moderately difficult. Application deadline: 6/15. Notification: continuous.

Collegiate Environment: Orientation program. Drama-theater group, choral group, student-run newspaper. Student services: health clinic, personal-psychological counseling.

Community Environment: Trinity Western is set on a wooded 100-acre campus, adjacent to the Trans Canada Highway No. 1, between Langley and Fort Langley. Students enjoy the solitude of a rural environment and have easy access to the beautiful urban center of Vancouver, just 45 minutes away. Public transportation is available off University Lane.

■ **THE UNIVERSITY OF BRITISH COLUMBIA**
2075 Wesbrook Mall
Vancouver, BC, Canada V6T 1Z1
Tel: (604)822-2211
Fax: (604)822-3599
Web Site: www.ubc.ca
Description: Province-supported, university, coed. Awards bachelor's, master's, and doctoral degrees. Founded 1915. Setting: 1,000-acre urban campus with easy access to Vancouver. Endowment: $1.2 billion. Total

enrollment: 51,573. Faculty: 3,347 (2,783 full-time, 564 part-time). Student-undergrad faculty ratio is 15:1. 20,733 applied, 70% were admitted. Full-time: 24,322 students, 55% women, 45% men. Part-time: 11,022 students, 54% women, 46% men. Students come from 44 provinces and territories, 151 other countries. 18% international. 25% live on campus, 5% transferred in. Retention: 92% of full-time freshmen returned the following year. Calendar: Canadian standard year. Academic remediation for entering students, ESL program, services for LD students, advanced placement, self-designed majors, freshman honors college, honors program, distance learning, double major, summer session for credit, part-time degree program, adult/continuing education programs, co-op programs and internships. Off campus study. Study abroad program.

Entrance Requirements: Options: electronic application, deferred admission, international baccalaureate accepted. Required: essay, high school transcript, minimum 2.6 high school GPA. Required for some: SAT or ACT, SAT or ACT plus Writing required of applicants following US curriculum. Entrance: very difficult. Application deadline: 1/31. Notification: continuous, continuous for nonresidents. Transfer credits accepted: Yes.

Collegiate Environment: Orientation program. Drama-theater group, choral group, student-run newspaper, radio station. Social organizations: 350 open to all; national fraternities, national sororities, local fraternities, local sororities; 3% of eligible men and 2% of eligible women are members. Most popular organizations: Ski and Board Club, Dance Club, AIESEC (international leadership organization), UBC Film Society, Varsity Outdoors Club. Major annual events: Storm the Wall, Day of the Longboat Racing, International Week. Student services: legal services, health clinic, personal-psychological counseling, women's center. Campus security: 24-hour emergency response devices and patrols, student patrols, late night transport-escort service, 24-hour desk attendants in residence halls. UBC Library plus 9 others.

■ **THE UNIVERSITY OF BRITISH COLUMBIA-OKANAGAN CAMPUS**
3333 University Way
Kelowna, BC, Canada V1V 1V7
Tel: (250)807-8521
Fax: (250)807-8522
Web Site: www.ok.ubc.ca
Description: Province-supported, university, coed. Part of University of British Columbia. Awards bachelor's, master's, and doctoral degrees. Founded 2005. Setting: 500-acre urban campus with easy access to Kelowna. System endowment: $1.2 billion. Research spending for the previous fiscal year: $1.8 million. Total enrollment: 8,217. Faculty: 412 (374 full-time, 38 part-time). Student-undergrad faculty ratio is 18:1. 4,477 applied, 85% were admitted. Full-time: 5,524 students, 53% women, 47% men. Part-time: 1,784 students, 54% women, 46% men. Students come from 25 provinces and territories, 79 other countries. 10% international. 31% live on campus. Retention: 74% of full-time freshmen returned the following year. Calendar: semesters. Academic remediation for entering students, ESL program, services for LD students, advanced placement, self-designed majors, freshman honors college, honors program, distance learning, double major, summer session for credit, part-time degree program, co-op programs and internships. Off campus study. Study abroad program.

Entrance Requirements: Options: electronic application, deferred admission, international baccalaureate accepted. Required: essay, high school transcript, minimum 2.6 high school GPA. Required for some: SAT or ACT. Entrance: moderately difficult. Application deadline: 1/31. Notification: continuous, continuous for nonresidents. SAT Reasoning Test deadline: 3/15. Transfer credits accepted: Yes.

Collegiate Environment: Orientation program. Drama-theater group, choral group, student-run newspaper, radio station. Social organizations: 63 open to all; national fraternities. Most popular organizations: Film Club, International Student Club, UBCSUO Mountain Riders Ski and Snowboard Club, Engineers without Borders, Model United Nations Club. Student services: legal services, health clinic, personal-psychological counseling, women's center. Campus security: 24-hour emergency response devices and patrols, controlled dormitory access, 24-hour desk attendants in residence halls. UBC Library. Operations spending for the previous fiscal year: $3.4 million.

■ **UNIVERSITY OF THE FRASER VALLEY**
33844 King Rd.
Abbotsford, BC, Canada V2S 7M8
Tel: (604)504-7441
Fax: (604)855-7614

E-mail: daniel.goertz@ufv.ca

Web Site: www.ufv.ca

Description: Province-supported, comprehensive, coed. Awards associate, bachelor's, and master's degrees. Founded 1974. Setting: 64-hectare urban campus with easy access to Vancouver. Endowment: $11 million. Total enrollment: 8,776. Faculty: 688 (326 full-time, 362 part-time). Full-time: 3,885 students, 58% women, 42% men. Part-time: 4,878 students, 59% women, 41% men. Students come from 10 provinces and territories, 62 other countries. 4% American Indian or Alaska Native, non-Hispanic/Latino; 14% international. 20% 25 or older. Retention: 80% of full-time freshmen returned the following year. Calendar: semesters. Academic remediation for entering students, ESL program, services for LD students, advanced placement, self-designed majors, honors program, independent study, distance learning, double major, summer session for credit, part-time degree program, adult/continuing education programs, co-op programs and internships. Off campus study. Study abroad program.

Entrance Requirements: Open admission for general studies programs. Options: electronic application, early admission, deferred admission, international baccalaureate accepted. Required: high school transcript. Required for some: essay, 2 recommendations, interview, minimum GPA of 2.0 to 2.67. Application deadline: rolling. Notification: continuous. Transfer credits accepted: Yes.

Costs Per Year: Application fee: $45 Canadian dollars. Tuition, fee, and room and board charges are reported in Canadian dollars. Province resident tuition: $4,873 full-time, $162.45 per credit hour part-time. Canadian resident tuition: $4,873 full-time, $162.45 per credit hour part-time. Mandatory fees: $526 full-time, $158.30 per term part-time. Full-time tuition and fees vary according to course load. Part-time tuition and fees vary according to course load. College room and board: $7941. College room only: $5941. Room and board charges vary according to board plan. International student tuition: $17,150 full-time.

Collegiate Environment: Orientation program. Drama-theater group, student-run newspaper, radio station. Major annual events: Welcome Back Barbecue, Student Orientation. Student services: personal-psychological counseling. Campus security: 24-hour emergency response devices and patrols, late night transport-escort service, controlled dormitory access. Peter Jones Library plus 3 others. Books: 181,000 (physical), 37,000 (digital/electronic). Students can reserve study rooms.

■ **UNIVERSITY OF NORTHERN BRITISH COLUMBIA**

3333 University Way

Prince George, BC, Canada V2N 4Z9

Tel: (250)960-5555

Fax: (250)960-5791

E-mail: registrar-info@unbc.ca

Web Site: www.unbc.ca

Description: Province-supported, university, coed. Awards bachelor's, master's, and doctoral degrees. Founded 1994. Setting: 1,344-acre suburban campus. Total enrollment: 4,177. Faculty: 382 (178 full-time, 204 part-time). Student-undergrad faculty ratio is 10:1. 1,348 applied, 76% were admitted. Students come from 43 other countries. 42% 25 or older, 16% live on campus. Retention: 73% of full-time freshmen returned the following year. Academic areas with the most degrees conferred: business/marketing; natural resources/environmental science; health professions and related sciences. Core. Calendar: semesters. Services for LD students, advanced placement, self-designed majors, honors program, independent study, distance learning, double major, summer session for credit, part-time degree program, internships, graduate courses open to undergrads. Study abroad program.

Entrance Requirements: Options: early admission, early decision, international baccalaureate accepted. Required: high school transcript, minimum 2.0 high school GPA. Required for some: essay. Entrance: noncompetitive. Application deadline: 3/1.

Collegiate Environment: Orientation program. Student-run newspaper, radio station. Student services: health clinic, personal-psychological counseling, women's center. Campus security: 24-hour emergency response devices and patrols, late night transport-escort service, controlled dormitory access. Geoffrey Weller Library. 300 computers available on campus for general student use. A campuswide network can be accessed from student residence rooms and from off campus. Students can access the following: online class registration, terminal services file space, personal Web space, e-mail, UNIX servers Webet. Staffed computer lab on campus.

■ **UNIVERSITY OF VICTORIA**

PO Box 1700 STN CSC

Victoria, BC, Canada V8W 2Y2

Tel: (250)721-7211

Fax: (250)721-6225

E-mail: admit@uvic.ca

Web Site: www.uvic.ca

Description: Province-supported, university, coed. Awards bachelor's, master's, and doctoral degrees. Founded 1963. Setting: 380-acre suburban campus with easy access to Vancouver. Research spending for the previous fiscal year: $59 million. Total enrollment: 19,479. Faculty: 760 (721 full-time, 39 part-time). Student-undergrad faculty ratio is 27:1. 7,721 applied, 75% were admitted. Full-time: 10,716 students, 56% women, 44% men. Part-time: 5,866 students, 56% women, 44% men. Students come from 13 provinces and territories, 92 other countries, 13% from out-of-province, 22% 25 or older, 9% transferred in. Core. Calendar: Canadian standard year. Academic remediation for entering students, ESL program, services for LD students, advanced placement, self-designed majors, honors program, independent study, distance learning, double major, summer session for credit, part-time degree program, external degree program, adult/continuing education programs, co-op programs and internships, graduate courses open to undergrads. Off campus study at Canadian University Student Exchange Consortium. Study abroad program.

Entrance Requirements: Options: electronic application, early admission, early action, deferred admission, international baccalaureate accepted. Required: high school transcript, minimum 2.5 high school GPA. Required for some: essay, minimum 3.0 high school GPA, interview, audition, portfolio. Entrance: moderately difficult. Application deadlines: 4/30, 2/28 for early action. Notification: continuous, 5/1 for early action.

Collegiate Environment: Orientation program. Drama-theater group, choral group, student-run newspaper, radio station. Major annual events: President's Welcome Barbecue, Alumni Homecoming Weekend, Week of Welcome. Student services: legal services, health clinic, personal-psychological counseling, women's center. Campus security: 24-hour emergency response devices and patrols, student patrols, late night transport-escort service. McPherson Library plus 4 others. Operations spending for the previous fiscal year: $13 million. 400 computers available on campus for general student use. A campuswide network can be accessed from student residence rooms and from off campus. Students can access the following: online class registration. Staffed computer lab on campus provides training in use of computers, software, and the Internet.

Community Environment: The university is located in the suburban Gordon Head area of Greater Victoria. It is a 10-minute drive from downtown Victoria and is easily accessible by car, bus, and bicycle. Victoria, the capital of British Columbia, boasts magnificent legislative buildings and a downtown which has been developed to retain its turn-of-the-century architecture and historic landmarks. The city is a thriving center of artistic activity, offering the exceptional Royal British Columbia Museum, several art galleries, a symphony orchestra, an opera company and several professional theatre companies. Greater Victoria has a population of 270,000. The regional economy is based on government, tourism, the University, and growing service, high technology, and clean manufacturing sectors.

■ **VANCOUVER ISLAND UNIVERSITY**

900 Fifth St.

Nanaimo, BC, Canada V9R 5S5

Tel: (250)753-3245

Web Site: www.viu.ca

Description: Province-supported, comprehensive, coed. Awards associate, bachelor's, and master's degrees. Founded 1969. Setting: 110-acre suburban campus. Calendar: semesters. Part-time degree program.

Collegiate Environment: Student-run newspaper, radio station. Student services: personal-psychological counseling. Vancouver Island University Library plus 1 other.

Community Environment: Nanaimo is situated on Vancouver Island, across the Strait of Georgia from the city of Vancouver. The island is the largest on the Pacific Coast, both in North and South America. Nanaimo is the second largest community (95,000) on the island, being outranked by Victoria (250,000), the provincial capital located at the southern tip of the island. There are many excellent recreational facilities in the nearby mountains, forests, and lakes. Attractions include the Bastion, and the Centennial-Polk Theatre Museum. There is direct and frequent ferry service to Vancouver as well as rail, bus, and road connections to Victoria.

■ BOOTH UNIVERSITY COLLEGE

447 Webb Pl.
Winnipeg, MB, Canada R3B 2P2
Tel: (204)947-6701; Free: 877-942-6684
Fax: (204)942-3856
Web Site: www.boothuc.ca

Description: Independent, 4-year, coed, affiliated with Salvation Army. Awards bachelor's degrees. Founded 1982. Setting: urban campus. Total enrollment: 322. Faculty: 28 (9 full-time, 19 part-time). Student-undergrad faculty ratio is 9:1. 89 applied, 71% were admitted. Students come from 14 other countries. 50% 25 or older, 10% live on campus. Retention: 98% of full-time freshmen returned the following year. Core. Calendar: semesters. Academic remediation for entering students, services for LD students, accelerated degree program, honors program, independent study, distance learning, double major, summer session for credit, part-time degree program, external degree program, adult/continuing education programs, internships. Off campus study at University of Manitoba, University of Winnipeg, Concord College. Study abroad program.

Entrance Requirements: Options: electronic application, international baccalaureate accepted. Recommended: essay, interview. Required for some: high school transcript. Application deadline: 7/31.

Collegiate Environment: Orientation program. Drama-theater group, student-run newspaper. Most popular organizations: Theatre Group, Crop Nights (scrapbooking), volleyball (women), Book Club. Major annual events: Christmas Banquet, The Well (chapel), Family Fun Night. Student services: personal-psychological counseling. Campus security: 24-hour emergency response devices, late night transport-escort service. John Fairbank Memorial Library plus 1 other. 15 computers available on campus for general student use. A campuswide network can be accessed from student residence rooms.

■ BRANDON UNIVERSITY

270 18th St.
Brandon, MB, Canada R7A 6A9
Tel: (204)728-9520
E-mail: kerr@brandonu.ca
Web Site: www.brandonu.ca

Description: Province-supported, comprehensive, coed. Awards bachelor's and master's degrees. Founded 1899. Setting: 30-acre small town campus. Endowment: $24 million. Research spending for the previous fiscal year: $2.6 million. Total enrollment: 3,553. Faculty: 239 (228 full-time, 11 part-time). Student-undergrad faculty ratio is 11:1. 2,562 applied, 66% were admitted. Students come from 13 provinces and territories, 88 other countries, 9% from out-of province. 40% 25 or older, 9% live on campus. Retention: 73% of full-time freshmen returned the following year. Core. Calendar: Canadian standard year. Academic remediation for entering students, ESL program, services for LD students, accelerated degree program, self-designed majors, honors program, distance learning, double major, summer session for credit, part-time degree program, co-op programs, graduate courses open to undergrads. Off campus study. Study abroad program.

Entrance Requirements: Open admission. Options: electronic application, deferred admission. Required: high school transcript. Required for some: criminal and child abuse registry checks. Entrance: noncompetitive. Application deadline: rolling. Notification: continuous until 9/30.

Costs Per Year: Application fee: $68 Canadian dollars. Tuition, fee, and room and board charges are reported in Canadian dollars. Area resident tuition: $3984 full-time, $132.80 per credit hour part-time. Canadian resident tuition: $265.60 per credit hour part-time. Mandatory fees: $526 full-time, $45.34 per credit hour part-time, $109.10 per term part-time. Full-time tuition and fees vary according to class time, course level, course load, degree level, location, program, reciprocity agreements, and student level. Part-time tuition and fees vary according to class time, course level, course load, degree level, location, program, reciprocity agreements, and student level. College room and board: $9645. College room only: $5574. Room and board charges vary according to board plan, gender, and location. International student tuition: $7968 full-time.

Collegiate Environment: Orientation program. Drama-theater group, choral group, student-run newspaper, radio station. Social organizations: 25 open to all. Most popular organizations: Psychology Club, zoology club, Inter-Varsity Christian Fellowship, International Students Club, Business Administration Club. Major annual event: Orientation. Student services: personal-psychological counseling. Campus security: 24-hour emergency response devices, controlled dormitory access, night residence hall security personnel. John E. Robbins Library. Operations spending for the previous fiscal year: $1.5 million. 160 computers available on campus for general student use. A campuswide network can be accessed from student residence rooms. Students can access the following: online class registration. Staffed computer lab on campus.

Community Environment: Brandon, a city of 40,000, is located in the heart of the prairie land of Manitoba, on the Assiniboine River. The Manitoba Provincial Exhibition is held in Brandon every year. There are excellent recreational facilities in the nearby area, including camping, hunting, winter sports and fishing. Brandon is easily accessible by rail, road and air.

■ PROVIDENCE UNIVERSITY COLLEGE & THEOLOGICAL SEMINARY

10 College Crescent
Otterburne, MB, Canada R0A 1G0
Tel: (204)433-7488; Free: 800-668-7768
E-mail: info@prov.ca
Web Site: www.prov.ca

Description: Independent interdenominational, comprehensive, coed. Awards bachelor's, master's, and doctoral degrees. Founded 1925. Setting: 100-acre rural campus with easy access to Winnipeg. Endowment: $829,151. Educational spending for the previous fiscal year: $4933 per student. Total enrollment: 470. Faculty: 50 (18 full-time, 32 part-time). Student-undergrad faculty ratio is 19:1. 121 applied, 100% were admitted. Students come from 13 provinces and territories, 18 other countries, 30% from out-of province. 65% live on campus. Retention: 79% of full-time freshmen returned the following year. Core. Calendar: semesters. Academic remediation for entering students, ESL program, accelerated degree program, freshman honors college, independent study, distance learning, double major, part-time degree program, internships.

Entrance Requirements: Open admission. Options: deferred admission, international baccalaureate accepted. Required: essay, high school transcript, 2 recommendations. Required for some: interview. Entrance: noncompetitive. Application deadline: rolling. Transfer credits accepted: Yes.

Costs Per Year: Application fee: $50 Canadian dollars. Tuition, fee, and room and board charges are reported in Canadian dollars. Comprehensive fee: $15,940 includes full-time tuition ($8580), mandatory fees ($1170), and college room and board ($6190). Room and board charges vary according to board plan.

Collegiate Environment: Orientation program. Drama-theater group, choral group, student-run newspaper. Social organizations: 25 open to all. Most popular organizations: Student Council, Social Concerns, Theatre, Music Touring Groups, Residence Care Groups. Major annual events: Christmas Banquet, Theatre Production, Missio Dei (Social Concerns Event). Student services: personal-psychological counseling. Campus security: student patrols, controlled dormitory access. William Falk Library. Operations spending for the previous fiscal year: $224,187. 40 computers available on campus for general student use. Computer purchase/lease plans available. A campuswide network can be accessed from student residence rooms and from off campus. Students can access the following: online class registration. Staffed computer lab on campus provides training in use of software.

■ STEINBACH BIBLE COLLEGE

50 PTH 12N
Steinbach, MB, Canada R5G 1T4
Tel: (204)326-6451; Free: 800-230-8478
E-mail: info@sbcollege.ca
Web Site: www.sbcollege.ca
Description: Independent Mennonite, 4-year, coed. Awards bachelor's degrees. Founded 1936. Setting: 16-acre urban campus with easy access to Winnipeg. Total enrollment: 148. Faculty: 14 (4 full-time, 10 part-time). Student-undergrad faculty ratio is 18:1. 59 applied, 81% were admitted. Retention: 55% of full-time freshmen returned the following year. Calendar: semesters.
Entrance Requirements: Option: electronic application. Entrance: minimally difficult. Transfer credits accepted: Yes.
Collegiate Environment: Orientation program.

■ UNIVERSITÉ DE SAINT-BONIFACE

200 Ave. de la Cathèdrale
Saint-Boniface, MB, Canada R2H 0H7
Tel: (204)233-0210
Fax: (204)237-3240
Web Site: www.ustboniface.ca
Description: Independent Roman Catholic, comprehensive, coed. Awards associate, bachelor's, and master's degrees. Founded 1871.

■ UNIVERSITY OF MANITOBA

Winnipeg, MB, Canada R3T 2N2
Tel: (204)474-8880
Web Site: www.umanitoba.ca
Description: Province-supported, university, coed. Awards bachelor's, master's, and doctoral degrees and post-master's certificates. Founded 1877. Setting: 685-acre suburban campus. Total enrollment: 27,751. Faculty: 2,385. Core. Calendar: 8-month academic year plus 6-week summer session. Academic remediation for entering students, ESL program, services for LD students, advanced placement, accelerated degree program, self-designed majors, honors program, independent study, distance learning, double major, summer session for credit, part-time degree program, external degree program, adult/continuing education programs, co-op programs and internships. Off campus study at University of Winnipeg, Red River Community College. Study abroad program.
Entrance Requirements: Options: electronic application, early admission, international baccalaureate accepted. Required: high school transcript. Entrance: moderately difficult.
Collegiate Environment: Orientation program. Drama-theater group, choral

group, student-run newspaper, radio station. Social organizations: national fraternities, national sororities, local fraternities, local sororities. Student services: health clinic, personal-psychological counseling, women's center. Campus security: 24-hour emergency response devices, student patrols, late night transport-escort service. Elizabeth Dafoe Library plus 19 others.
Community Environment: Winnipeg, despite its small size population, 652,350, and winter chill (zero to 30 degrees below Fahrenheit), offers students an extraordinary range of activities: opera, ballet, symphony orchestra, theatre, major league football and hockey, cosmopolitan restaurants, the only stone and fur trade fort still intact (Lower Fort Garry), and the 8,000-acre Oak Hammock Marsh wildlife preserve.

■ THE UNIVERSITY OF WINNIPEG

515 Portage Ave.
Winnipeg, MB, Canada R3B 2E9
Tel: (204)786-7811
Web Site: www.uwinnipeg.ca
Description: Province-supported, comprehensive, coed. Awards bachelor's and master's degrees. Founded 1967. Setting: 8-acre urban campus. Endowment: $16.8 million. Research spending for the previous fiscal year: $2.4 million. Educational spending for the previous fiscal year: $3471 per student. Total enrollment: 9,006. Faculty: 321 (270 full-time, 51 part-time). Student-undergrad faculty ratio is 35:1. 4,203 applied, 75% were admitted. Full-time: 6,231 students, 64% women, 36% men. Part-time: 2,775 students, 61% women, 39% men. Students come from 7 provinces and territories, 32 other countries. 27% 25 or older, 3% live on campus, 3% transferred in. Retention: 60% of full-time freshmen returned the following year. Core. Calendar: Canadian standard year. Academic remediation for entering students, ESL program, services for LD students, advanced placement, accelerated degree program, self-designed majors, honors program, summer session for credit, part-time degree program, adult/continuing education programs, co-op programs and internships. Off campus study at Red River Community College. Study abroad program.
Entrance Requirements: Options: early admission, deferred admission. Required: minimum 2.0 high school GPA. Required for some: high school transcript, interview. Entrance: moderately difficult. Application deadline: 8/9. Notification: continuous, continuous for nonresidents.
Collegiate Environment: Drama-theater group, choral group, student-run newspaper, radio station. Social organizations: 60 open to all; national fraternities, local fraternities; 25% of eligible men and 25% of eligible women are members. Most popular organizations: Woman's Centre, LGBT (Lesbian Gay Bisexual Transgender), radio station, International Resource Centre, Aboriginal Student Centre. Major annual event: Day of Action. Student services: health clinic, personal-psychological counseling, women's center. Campus security: 24-hour emergency response devices and patrols, student patrols, video controlled external access. Operations spending for the previous fiscal year: $3.5 million. 175 computers available on campus for general student use. Computer purchase/lease plans available. A campuswide network can be accessed from off-campus. Staffed computer lab on campus provides training in use of computers, software, and the Internet.
Community Environment: Winnipeg is the largest city (550,000) in Manitoba, its provincial capital, and the center of its cultural, political and social life. The city has the Winnipeg Art Gallery, Centennial Center with the Manitoba Museum of Man and Nature, Concert Hall and Theatre Center and many other cultural facilities and organizations, such as the Winnipeg Symphony and the Royal Winnipeg Ballet. Nearby Lake Winnipeg (which is larger than Lake Ontario) provides excellent recreation facilities. The city is the major east-west railroad junction and is accessible by all means of transportation. Industries include agriculture, meat packing and livestock, and manufacturing.

■ CRANDALL UNIVERSITY

Box 6004
Moncton, NB, Canada E1C 9L7
Tel: (506)858-8970; Free: 888-968-6228
Fax: (506)858-9694
E-mail: admissions@crandallu.ca
Web Site: www.crandallu.ca

Description: Independent Baptist, comprehensive, coed. Awards bachelor's and master's degrees. Founded 1949. Setting: 220-acre urban campus. Total enrollment: 463. Faculty: 61 (26 full-time, 35 part-time). Student-undergrad faculty ratio is 13:1. 30% live on campus. Retention: 66% of full-time freshmen returned the following year. Core. Calendar: trimesters. ESL program, services for LD students, advanced placement, accelerated degree program, honors program, independent study, double major, summer session for credit, part-time degree program, adult/continuing education programs, co-op programs and internships. Off campus study. Study abroad program.

Entrance Requirements: Open admission except for Bachelor of Education students. Options: electronic application, early admission, early decision, deferred admission, international baccalaureate accepted. Required: high school transcript, minimum 2.67 high school GPA. Required for some: essay, minimum 3 high school GPA, 3 recommendations, interview. Entrance: minimally difficult. Application deadlines: rolling, 11/30 for early decision. Notification: continuous, rolling for early decision. Transfer credits accepted: Yes. Early decision applicants: 0. Early decision applicants admitted: 0.

Costs Per Year: Application fee: $35 Canadian dollars. Tuition, fee, and room and board charges are reported in Canadian dollars. Comprehensive fee: $18,420 includes full-time tuition ($8680), mandatory fees ($1200), and college room and board ($8540). Full-time tuition and fees vary according to course load, degree level, and program. Room and board charges vary according to board plan and housing facility. Part-time tuition: $870 per course. Part-time mandatory fees: $120 per term. Part-time tuition and fees vary according to course load, degree level, and program.

Collegiate Environment: Orientation program. Choral group, student-run newspaper. Most popular organizations: Crandall Student Association, Worship Ministry Teams, Community Service Teams, Student Newspaper, Student Ambassadors. Major annual events: Christmas Banquet, Orientation Week Activities, Fall Foliage Day. Student services: health clinic, personal-psychological counseling. Campus security: student patrols, controlled dormitory access, trained security personnel on campus for specific times. George A. Rawlyk Library.

■ KINGSWOOD UNIVERSITY

26 Western St.
Sussex, NB, Canada E4E 5L2
Tel: (506)432-4400; Free: 888-432-4422
Fax: (506)432-4425
E-mail: vails@kingswood.edu
Web Site: www.kingswood.edu

Description: Independent, comprehensive, coed, affiliated with Wesleyan Church. Awards associate, bachelor's, and master's degrees. Founded 1945. Setting: 57-acre small town campus. Endowment: $324,835. Educational spending for the previous fiscal year: $5325 per student. Total enrollment: 199. Faculty: 16 (11 full-time, 5 part-time). Student-undergrad faculty ratio is 14:1. 175 applied, 40% were admitted. Full-time: 172 students, 53% women, 47% men. Part-time: 14 students, 43% women, 57%

men. Students come from 21 provinces and territories, 1 other country, 62% from out-of province. 8% 25 or older, 69% live on campus, 5% transferred in. Retention: 73% of full-time freshmen returned the following year. Core. Calendar: semesters. Academic remediation for entering students, advanced placement, self-designed majors, double major, summer session for credit, part-time degree program, internships.

Entrance Requirements: Options: electronic application, early admission, deferred admission, international baccalaureate accepted. Required: essay, high school transcript, 2 recommendations, 2 English credits, 2 math/science credits, 2 social studies credits. Recommended: interview. Required for some: SAT or ACT. Entrance: moderately difficult. Application deadlines: rolling, rolling for early decision plan 1, rolling for early decision plan 2. Notification: continuous, rolling for early decision plan 1, rolling for early decision plan 2. Transfer credits accepted: Yes.

Collegiate Environment: Orientation program. Drama-theater group, choral group. Social organizations: 6 open to all. Most popular organizations: Outreach Association, Student Fellowship Association, Spiritual Life Association, Athletic Association, Student Global Impact Association. Major annual events: INFUSE: Spiritual Emphasis Week, Christmas Banquet, Encounter Rally Weekend. Student services: personal-psychological counseling. Campus security: student patrols, controlled dormitory access. The Earle and Marion Trouten Library. Operations spending for the previous fiscal year: $110,898. 8 computers available on campus for general student use. A campuswide network can be accessed from student residence rooms and from off campus.

■ MOUNT ALLISON UNIVERSITY

65 York St.
Sackville, NB, Canada E4L 1E4
Tel: (506)364-2269
Fax: (506)364-2272
E-mail: admissions@mta.ca
Web Site: www.mta.ca

Description: Province-supported, comprehensive, coed. Awards bachelor's and master's degrees. Founded 1839. Setting: 50-acre small town campus. Endowment: $65 million. Educational spending for the previous fiscal year: $11,975 per student. Total enrollment: 2,532. Faculty: 187 (132 full-time, 55 part-time). Student-undergrad faculty ratio is 16:1. 1,628 applied, 90% were admitted. 64% from top 10% of their high school class, 87% from top quarter, 96% from top half. Full-time: 2,411 students, 58% women, 42% men. Part-time: 106 students, 59% women, 41% men. Students come from 22 provinces and territories, 44 other countries, 58% from out-of province. 5% 25 or older, 50% live on campus, 4% transferred in. Retention: 80% of full-time freshmen returned the following year. Academic areas with the most degrees conferred: social sciences; business/marketing; psychology. Core. Calendar: Canadian standard year. Academic remediation for entering students, services for LD students, advanced placement, self-designed majors, honors program, independent study, distance learning, double major, summer session for credit, part-time degree program, adult/continuing education programs, internships. Off campus study at Moncton Campus, Miramichi Campus. Study abroad program.

Entrance Requirements: Options: electronic application, deferred admission, international baccalaureate accepted. Required: high school transcript, minimum 2.5 high school GPA. Recommended: 2 recommendations. Required for some: essay, interview. Entrance: moderately difficult. Application deadline: rolling. Notification: continuous. Transfer credits accepted: Yes.

Costs Per Year: Application fee: $50 Canadian dollars. Tuition, fee, and room and board charges are reported in Canadian dollars. Province resident tuition: $7925 full-time, $829.50 per course part-time. Canadian resident tuition: $8295 full-time, $829.50 per course part-time. Mandatory fees: $1018 full-time. Full-time tuition and fees vary according to course load and degree level. Part-time tuition varies according to course load and degree level. College room and board: $9698. College room only: $4800. Room and board charges vary according to board plan and housing facility. International student tuition: $17,600 full-time.

Collegiate Environment: Orientation program. Drama-theater group, choral group, student-run newspaper, radio station. Social organizations: 102 open to all. Most popular organizations: Commerce Society, Windsor Theatre, President's Leadership Development Certificate, Leadership Mount Allison, Garnet and Gold Society. Major annual events: Homecoming, Winter Carnival, Orientation. Student services: health clinic, personal-psychological counseling. Campus security: 24-hour emergency response devices, late night transport-escort service. Ralph Pickard Bell Library plus 3 others. Students can reserve study rooms. Operations spending for the previous fiscal year: $1.8 million. 100 computers available on campus for general student use. A campuswide network can be accessed from student residence rooms and from off campus. Students can access the following: online class registration, online student account/Websis. Staffed computer lab on campus (open 24 hours a day).

■ ST. THOMAS UNIVERSITY
51 Dineen Dr.
Fredericton, NB, Canada E3B 5G3
Tel: (506)452-0640
Fax: (506)450-9615
E-mail: admissions@stu.ca
Web Site: www.stu.ca

Description: Independent Roman Catholic, 4-year, coed. Awards bachelor's degrees. Founded 1910. Setting: 16-acre small town campus. Endowment: $17.9 million. Research spending for the previous fiscal year: $580,882. Educational spending for the previous fiscal year: $7131 per student. Total enrollment: 1,981. Faculty: 185 (100 full-time, 85 part-time). Student-undergrad faculty ratio is 16:1. 939 applied, 89% were admitted. Full-time: 1,713 students, 72% women, 28% men. Part-time: 83 students, 63% women, 37% men. Students come from 10 provinces and territories, 38 other countries, 20% from out-of-province. 8% international. 10% 25 or older, 28% live on campus, 6% transferred in. Retention: 70% of full-time freshmen returned the following year. Academic areas with the most degrees conferred: social sciences; psychology; education. Core. Calendar: semesters. Academic remediation for entering students, ESL program, services for LD students, advanced placement, accelerated degree program, self-designed majors, honors program, independent study, double major, summer session for credit, part-time degree program, internships. Off campus study. Study abroad program.

Entrance Requirements: Options: electronic application, early action, international baccalaureate accepted. Required: essay, high school transcript, minimum 3 high school GPA. Recommended: SAT. Required for some: interview. Entrance: moderately difficult. Application deadlines: 8/31, 12/7 for early action. Notification: continuous. Transfer credits accepted: Yes.

Costs Per Year: Application fee: $55 Canadian dollars. Tuition, fee, and room and board charges are reported in Canadian dollars. Comprehensive fee: $16,681 includes full-time tuition ($6776), mandatory fees ($884), and college room and board ($9021). Full-time tuition and fees vary according to course load, degree level, and program. Room and board charges vary according to board plan, housing facility, and location. Part-time tuition: $681 per course. Part-time mandatory fees: $56.06 per course. Part-time tuition and fees vary according to course load.

Collegiate Environment: Orientation program. Drama-theater group, choral group, student-run newspaper, radio station. Social organizations: 38 open to all. Most popular organizations: Theatre St. Thomas, St. Thomas Student Union, Criminology Society, Model UN, International Students' Association. Major annual events: Welcome Week, Multicultural Fair, Winter Formal. Student services: health clinic, personal-psychological counseling, women's center. Campus security: 24-hour emergency response devices and patrols, student patrols, late night transport-escort service, controlled dormitory access. Harriet Irving Library plus 2 others. Books: 976,313 (physical), 532,787

(digital/electronic); Serial titles: 2,449 (physical), 44,800 (digital/electronic). Weekly public service hours: 113; students can reserve study rooms. Operations spending for the previous fiscal year: $1.4 million. 88 computers available on campus for general student use. A campuswide network can be accessed from student residence rooms and from off campus. Students can access the following: online class registration, learning management system. Staffed computer lab on campus provides training in use of computers, software, and the Internet.

Community Environment: New Brunswick's capital city has a population of about 81,000. The university's hillside campus overlooks the downtown and the Saint John River Valley. Fredericton is home to the historic Legislative Assembly, a thriving artistic community, a professional theater troupe, one of Atlantic Canada's more impressive art galleries, tree-lined city streets and scores of elegant Victorian mansions. The city's per capita income is among the highest in the country.

■ UNIVERSITÉ DE MONCTON
Moncton, NB, Canada E1A 3E9
Tel: (506)858-4000
Fax: (506)858-4544
E-mail: gallanrm@umoncton.ca
Web Site: www.umoncton.ca

Description: Province-supported, comprehensive, coed. Awards bachelor's, master's, and doctoral degrees (doctoral degree in French studies only). Founded 1963. Setting: 400-acre urban campus. Endowment: $19.8 million. Research spending for the previous fiscal year: $5 million. Total enrollment: 6,002. Faculty: 487 (374 full-time, 113 part-time). Student-undergrad faculty ratio is 12:1. 2,046 applied, 86% were admitted. Students come from 10 provinces and territories, 41 other countries, 11% from out-of-province. 7% 25 or older, 15% live on campus. Retention: 83% of full-time freshmen returned the following year. Calendar: semesters. Academic remediation for entering students, ESL program, services for LD students, accelerated degree program, self-designed majors, honors program, distance learning, double major, summer session for credit, part-time degree program, external degree program, adult/continuing education programs, co-op programs and internships, graduate courses open to undergrads. Off campus study at other French colleges and universities in Canada. Study abroad program.

Entrance Requirements: Options: deferred admission, international baccalaureate accepted. Required: high school transcript, French examination. Required for some: essay, minimum 2.0 high school GPA, 1 recommendation, interview. Entrance: moderately difficult. Application deadline: 6/1. Notification: continuous until 9/1, continuous until 8/15 for nonresidents.

Collegiate Environment: Orientation program. Drama-theater group, choral group, student-run newspaper, radio station. Social organizations: 50 open to all. Most popular organizations: Amnesty International, student radio station, business clubs, Improvisational League, WSC. Major annual events: Homecoming, International Evening, Career Exposition. Student services: health clinic, personal-psychological counseling. Campus security: 24-hour emergency response devices and patrols, controlled dormitory access, student security attendants in residences 8 pm to 2 am. Bibliotheque Champlain plus 2 others. Operations spending for the previous fiscal year: $3.6 million. 900 computers available on campus for general student use. A campuswide network can be accessed from student residence rooms and from off campus. Staffed computer lab on campus.

■ UNIVERSITY OF NEW BRUNSWICK FREDERICTON
PO Box 4400
Fredericton, NB, Canada E3B 5A3
Tel: (506)453-4666
Fax: (506)453-5016
Web Site: www.unb.ca

Description: Province-supported, university, coed. Part of Province of New Brunswick. Awards bachelor's, master's, and doctoral degrees. Founded 1785. Setting: 7,100-acre urban campus. Endowment: $244 million. Research spending for the previous fiscal year: $48.3 million. Educational spending for the previous fiscal year: $12,012 per student. Total enrollment: 7,667. Faculty: (532 full-time). Student-undergrad faculty ratio is 15:1. Students come from 12 provinces and territories, 72 other countries. 22% 25 or older, 21% live on campus. Core. Calendar: Canadian standard year. ESL program, services for LD students, advanced placement, accelerated degree program, self-designed majors, honors program, independent study, distance learning, double major, summer session for credit, part-time degree program, external degree program, adult/continuing education programs, co-op programs and internships, graduate courses open to undergrads. Off campus study at University of Maine, Universite Laval, all forestry colleges in Canada, Saint Thomas University. Study abroad program.

Entrance Requirements: Required: high school transcript. Required for some: essay, recommendations, interview, supplementary form and life sketch for nursing, resume and cover letter for Renaissance College, SAT.

Collegiate Environment: Orientation program. Drama-theater group, choral group, student-run newspaper, radio station. Social organizations: 109 open to all. Major annual events: Orientation Week, Graduation Ceremony. Student services: legal services, health clinic, personal-psychological counseling, women's center. Campus security: 24-hour emergency response devices and patrols, student patrols, late night transport-escort service, controlled dormitory access. Harriet Irving Library plus 4 others. Operations spending for the previous fiscal year: $10.3 million. 935 computers available on campus for general student use. A campuswide network can be accessed from student residence rooms and from off campus. Students can access the following: online class registration. Staffed computer lab on campus provides training in use of computers, software, and the Internet.

Community Environment: Fredericton, the capital of New Brunswick, has a population of 81,000. The city is located in the Saint John River Valley, about 55 miles from the city of Saint John. Major employers in Fredericton are service industries, university and government.

■ **UNIVERSITY OF NEW BRUNSWICK SAINT JOHN**
PO Box 5050
Saint John, NB, Canada E2L 4L5
Tel: (506)648-5500
Web Site: www.unb.ca

Description: Province-supported, comprehensive, coed. Awards bachelor's, master's, and doctoral degrees. Founded 1964. Setting: 250-acre urban campus. 5% live on campus. Core. Calendar: Canadian standard year. Academic remediation for entering students, ESL program, services for LD students, advanced placement, accelerated degree program, self-designed majors, honors program, independent study, distance learning, double major, summer session for credit, part-time degree program, adult/continuing education programs, co-op programs and internships. Off campus study. Study abroad program.

Entrance Requirements: Options: electronic application, early admission, deferred admission, international baccalaureate accepted. Required: high school transcript, SAT. Entrance: moderately difficult. Application deadlines: rolling, 3/31 for nonresidents. Notification: continuous until 8/31, continuous for nonresidents. Transfer credits accepted: Yes.

Collegiate Environment: Orientation program. Drama-theater group, choral group, student-run newspaper, radio station. Social organizations: 20 open to all. Most popular organizations: Business Administration Society, OPTAMUS, International Student Association, Chinese Cultural Association, Muslim Student Association. Major annual events: Orientation Week, Winter Carnival. Student services: health clinic, personal-psychological counseling, women's center. Campus security: 24-hour emergency response devices and patrols, student patrols, late night transport-escort service, controlled dormitory access. Hans W. Klohn Commons. Students can reserve study rooms. 100 computers available on campus for general student use. A campuswide network can be accessed from student residence rooms and from off campus. Students can access the following: online class registration. Staffed computer lab on campus.

■ ACADIA UNIVERSITY

15 University Ave.
Wolfville, NS, Canada B4P 2R6
Tel: (902)542-2201; Free: 877-585-1121
Fax: (902)585-1081
E-mail: admissions@acadiau.ca
Web Site: www.acadiau.ca

Description: Province-supported, comprehensive, coed. Awards bachelor's, master's, and doctoral degrees. Founded 1838. Setting: 250-acre small town campus with easy access to Halifax, Nova Scotia. Total enrollment: 3,922. Faculty: (245 full-time). Student-undergrad faculty ratio is 15:1. 4,573 applied, 27% were admitted. Full-time: 3,195 students, 57% women, 43% men. Part-time: 153 students, 61% women, 39% men. Students come from 12 provinces and territories, 50 other countries, 47% from out-of-province. 7% 25 or older, 8% transferred in. Retention: 76% of full-time freshmen returned the following year. Academic areas with the most degrees conferred: business/marketing; parks and recreation; biological/life sciences. Core. Calendar: Canadian standard year. Academic remediation for entering students, ESL program, services for LD students, advanced placement, honors program, distance learning, double major, summer session for credit, part-time degree program, co-op programs and internships. Off campus study at East Carolina University, Franklin College of Indiana, Bridgewater State College, New England/Nova Scotia Exchange Program. Study abroad program.

Entrance Requirements: Options: electronic application, deferred admission, international baccalaureate accepted. Required: high school transcript, minimum 2.5 high school GPA. Required for some: essay, 1 recommendation, interview, Auditions for music programs. Entrance: moderately difficult. Notification: continuous, continuous for nonresidents. Transfer credits accepted: Yes.

Collegiate Environment: Orientation program. Drama-theater group, choral group, student-run newspaper, radio station. Social organizations: 70 open to all. Most popular organizations: Dance Acadia, Power Cheerleading, Water Watch Canada, LINC, Biology. Major annual events: Winter Carnival, Orientation Week, Convocation. Student services: legal services, health clinic, personal-psychological counseling, women's center. Campus security: 24-hour emergency response devices and patrols, student patrols, late night transport-escort service, controlled dormitory access, video surveillance, emergency response, emergency notification, emergency management planning. 1,608 college housing spaces available. Freshmen guaranteed college housing. Options: coed, women-only housing available. Vaughan Memorial Library.

Community Environment: Acadia University is located in the Annapolis Valley town of Wolfville, 100 kilometers northwest of Halifax. The main buildings are on a high terraced slope, facing the broad diked meadows of the Evangeline Country and the Minas Basin, the body of water in the northeastern part of the Bay of Fundy. Wolfville is a beautiful, residential town of 3,000 people, with four churches and good elementary and secondary schools.

■ CAPE BRETON UNIVERSITY

Box 5300
1250 Grand Lake Rd.
Sydney, NS, Canada B1P 6L2
Tel: (902)539-5300; Free: 888-959-9995
Fax: (902)562-0119
Web Site: www.cbu.ca

Description: Province-supported, comprehensive, coed. Awards bachelor's and master's degrees. Founded 1974. Setting: urban campus. Total enrollment: 2,952. Faculty: (168 full-time). 594 applied. Full-time: 2,069 students, 55% women, 45% men. Part-time: 413 students, 55% women, 45% men. Retention: 81% of full-time freshmen returned the following year. Academic areas with the most degrees conferred: business/marketing; health professions and related sciences; engineering technologies. Calendar: semesters. Services for LD students, advanced placement, honors program, distance learning, double major, part-time degree program, co-op programs and internships. Off campus study. Study abroad program.

Entrance Requirements: Options: electronic application, early admission, deferred admission, international baccalaureate accepted. Required: high school transcript. Required for some: essay, 2 recommendations, interview, overall average of 65%. Entrance: moderately difficult. Application deadline: rolling. Notification: continuous. Transfer credits accepted: Yes.

Collegiate Environment: Orientation program. Drama-theater group, choral group, student-run newspaper, radio station. Student services: legal services, health clinic, personal-psychological counseling, women's center. Campus security: 24-hour emergency response devices and patrols, student patrols, late night transport-escort service, controlled dormitory access. Cape Breton University Library plus 1 other. Students can reserve study rooms.

Community Environment: Sydney, part of the Regional Municipality of Cape Breton, is on Cape Breton Island, which is at the northeast end of Nova Scotia. The island is connected to the mainland by a causeway. Sydney is an industrial city with a self-contained steel plant. It is also a port city. There are numerous historical sites and recreational facilities. A major restoration project being undertaken on Cape Breton Island is at the Fortress of Louisbourg National Historic Park.

■ DALHOUSIE UNIVERSITY

Halifax, NS, Canada B3H 4R2
Tel: (902)494-2211
Fax: (902)494-1630
E-mail: admissions@dal.ca
Web Site: www.dal.ca

Description: Province-supported, university, coed. Awards bachelor's, master's, and doctoral degrees. Founded 1818. Setting: 80-acre urban campus. Endowment: $537.8 million. Total enrollment: 18,089. Student-undergrad faculty ratio is 14:1. 11,721 applied, 63% were admitted. Students come from 36 provinces and territories, 124 other countries. 17% 25 or older. Calendar: semesters. Academic remediation for entering students, ESL program, services for LD students, advanced placement, accelerated degree program, honors program, distance learning, double major, summer session for credit, part-time degree program, co-op programs and internships. Off campus study. Study abroad program.

Entrance Requirements: Options: electronic application, early admission, deferred admission, international baccalaureate accepted. Required: high school transcript, minimum 3 high school GPA, SAT or ACT. Required for some: essay, 1 recommendation, interview. Entrance: moderately difficult. Application deadline: 6/1. Notification: continuous. SAT Reasoning Test deadline: 6/1. Transfer credits accepted: Yes.

Collegiate Environment: Orientation program. Drama-theater group, choral group, student-run newspaper, radio station. Social organizations: 250 open to all; national fraternities, national sororities, local fraternities, local sororities. Most popular organizations: International Students Association, Arts Society, Science Society, Commerce Society, Dalhousie Outdoors Club. Major annual events: Orientation Week, Winter Carnival, Charity Ball. Student services: legal services, health clinic, personal-psychological counseling, women's center. Campus security: 24-hour emergency response devices and patrols, student patrols, late night transport-escort service, controlled dormitory access. The Killam Library plus 5 others. 710 computers available on campus for general student use. Computer purchase/lease plans available. A campuswide network can be accessed from student residence rooms and from off campus. Students can access the following: online class registration. Staffed computer lab on campus provides training in use of computers, software, and the Internet.

■ **MOUNT SAINT VINCENT UNIVERSITY**
166 Bedford Hwy.
Halifax, NS, Canada B3M 2J6
Tel: (902)457-6788; Free: 877-733-6788
Fax: (902)457-6455
E-mail: admissions@msvu.ca
Web Site: www.msvu.ca

Description: Province-supported, comprehensive, coed. Awards bachelor's, master's, and doctoral degrees. Founded 1873. Setting: 40-acre suburban campus. Endowment: $19.5 million. Research spending for the previous fiscal year: $3.1 million. Educational spending for the previous fiscal year: $7490 per student. Total enrollment: 2,946. Faculty: 376 (149 full-time, 227 part-time). Student-undergrad faculty ratio is 13:1. 584 applied, 60% were admitted. Students come from 13 provinces and territories, 40 other countries, 10% from out-of-province. 33% 25 or older. Retention: 79% of full-time freshmen returned the following year. Academic areas with the most degrees conferred: education; business/marketing; communication/journalism. Calendar: Canadian standard year. Honors program, independent study, distance learning, double major, summer session for credit, part-time degree program, external degree program, adult/continuing education programs, co-op programs and internships, graduate courses open to undergrads. Off campus study at Metro Halifax Universities Consortium, Acadia University. Study abroad program.
Entrance Requirements: Options: electronic application, deferred admission, international baccalaureate accepted. Required: high school transcript, minimum 2.0 high school GPA. Required for some: essay, minimum 3.0 high school GPA, 2 recommendations, interview. Entrance: moderately difficult. Application deadline: 3/15. Notification: 9/1, 1/6 for nonresidents.
Collegiate Environment: Orientation program. Choral group, student-run newspaper. Social organizations: 18 open to all. Most popular organizations: Business Society, Residence Society, Science Society, History Society. Major annual events: Frosh Week, Awards Banquet, Shinerama. Student services: health clinic, personal-psychological counseling, women's center. Campus security: 24-hour emergency response devices and patrols, late night transport-escort service, controlled dormitory access. E. Margaret Fulton Communications Centre Library plus 3 others. Operations spending for the previous fiscal year: $1.7 million.
Community Environment: Mount Saint Vincent University is situated in Halifax, the capital of Nova Scotia. Overlooking the Bedford Basin, it offers scenic walkways and recreational facilities. Public transport and a good highway provide easy access both to the International Airport and to downtown Halifax, which offers cultural and intellectual opportunities, shopping, parks and entertainment.

■ **NSCAD UNIVERSITY**
5163 Duke St.
Halifax, NS, Canada B3J 3J6
Tel: (902)422-7381; Free: 888-444-5989
Fax: (902)425-2420
E-mail: admissions@nscad.ca
Web Site: www.nscad.ca

Description: Province-supported, comprehensive, coed. Awards bachelor's and master's degrees. Founded 1887. Setting: 1-acre urban campus. Endowment: $1.1 million. Total enrollment: 1,021. Faculty: 114 (46 full-time, 68 part-time). Student-undergrad faculty ratio is 9:1. 306 applied, 75% were admitted. Students come from 11 provinces and territories, 17 other countries. 35% 25 or older, 10% live on campus. Academic area with the most degrees conferred: visual and performing arts. Core. Calendar:

semesters. Services for LD students, self-designed majors, honors program, independent study, double major, summer session for credit, part-time degree program, external degree program, co-op programs and internships. Off campus study at AICAD Mobility Program, Independent Exchanges, 4 members of Canadian Art Colleges, New England/Nova Scotia Student Exchange (70+ institutions in total). Study abroad program.
Entrance Requirements: Options: deferred admission, international baccalaureate accepted. Required: essay, high school transcript, portfolio. Recommended: minimum 3.0 high school GPA. Required for some: 2 recommendations, interview. Entrance: moderately difficult. Application deadline: 5/15. Notification: 6/30.
Collegiate Environment: Orientation program. Student services: personal-psychological counseling. Campus security: 24-hour emergency response devices, evening patrols by trained security personnel. Nova Scotia College of Art and Design Library. Operations spending for the previous fiscal year: $492,225. 60 computers available on campus for general student use. Students can access the following: online class registration. Staffed computer lab on campus provides training in use of computers and software.
Community Environment: The College is located in Halifax, the capital city of Nova Scotia, with a metropolitan population of 300,000. Halifax is the largest city in the Atlantic region. It is the home of a number of cultural institutions including the Atlantic Symphony Orchestra, the Neptune Theatre and the Nova Scotia Museum. In addition, there are a number of active art galleries, most notably the Art Gallery of Nova Scotia and the galleries connected with the city's three universities. The Arts Center at Dalhousie University provides, during the fall and winter months, a constant round of music concerts, plays, and other performances.

■ **ST. FRANCIS XAVIER UNIVERSITY**
Box 5000
Antigonish, NS, Canada B2G 2W5
Tel: (902)863-3300; Free: 877-867-STFX
Fax: (902)867-2329
E-mail: mbarry@stfx.ca
Web Site: www.stfx.ca

Description: Independent Roman Catholic, comprehensive, coed. Awards bachelor's and master's degrees. Founded 1853. Setting: 100-acre small town campus. Endowment: $67.4 million. Research spending for the previous fiscal year: $7.8 million. Educational spending for the previous fiscal year: $8277 per student. Total enrollment: 4,797. Faculty: 318 (251 full-time, 67 part-time). Student-undergrad faculty ratio is 12:1. 2,851 applied, 65% were admitted. Full-time: 2,209 students, 59% women, 41% men. Part-time: 2,046 students, 66% women, 34% men. Students come from 13 provinces and territories, 37 other countries, 43% from out-of-province. 11% 25 or older, 45% live on campus, 5% transferred in. Retention: 90% of full-time freshmen returned the following year. Calendar: Canadian standard year. Academic remediation for entering students, ESL program, services for LD students, advanced placement, accelerated degree program, self-designed majors, honors program, independent study, distance learning, double major, summer session for credit, part-time degree program, adult/continuing education programs and internships. Off campus study at 18 colleges and universities in the New England states, St. Thomas Aquinas College. Study abroad program.
Entrance Requirements: Options: electronic application, early admission, early decision, deferred admission, international baccalaureate accepted. Required: essay, high school transcript, 2 recommendations. Recommended: SAT or ACT, SAT Subject Tests. Required for some: SAT or ACT. Entrance: moderately difficult. Application deadlines: rolling, 1/31 for early decision. Notification: continuous until 8/15. SAT Reasoning Test deadline: 8/15. SAT Subject Test deadline: 8/15. Transfer credits accepted: Yes. Early decision applicants: 1,282. Early decision applicants admitted: 857.
Collegiate Environment: Orientation program. Drama-theater group, choral group, student-run newspaper, radio station. Social organizations: 95 open to all. Most popular organizations: X-Project, Blue Crew, orientation committee, X-Debate, ACE (Advancing Canadian Entrepreneurship). Major annual events: Christmas Ball, Winter Carnival, X-Ring Ceremony. Student services: health clinic, personal-psychological counseling, women's center. Campus security: 24-hour emergency response devices and patrols, student patrols, late night transport-escort service, controlled dormitory access. Angus L. Macdonald Library plus 1 other. Operations spending for the previous fiscal year: $3.2 million. 500 computers available on campus for general student use. A campuswide network can be accessed from student residence rooms and from off campus. Students can access the following: online class registration, online financial account, personal network storage,

personal Web publishing, WirelessSynch iPods, Smartphones. Staffed computer lab on campus provides training in use of computers, software, and the Internet.

Community Environment: Pretty in its rural setting, Antigonish lies 140 miles from Halifax and each July hosts the Highland Games, a kind of Olympics of the Clans.

■ SAINT MARY'S UNIVERSITY

Halifax, NS, Canada B3H 3C3
Tel: (902)420-5400
Fax: (902)496-8100
Web Site: www.smu.ca

Description: Province-supported, comprehensive, coed. Awards bachelor's and master's degrees. Founded 1802. Setting: 30-acre urban campus. Calendar: semesters. Academic remediation for entering students, ESL program, services for LD students, accelerated degree program, self-designed majors, honors program, independent study, distance learning, double major, summer session for credit, part-time degree program, adult/continuing education programs, co-op programs and internships. Off campus study. Study abroad program.

Entrance Requirements: Options: early action, international baccalaureate accepted. Required: high school transcript, minimum 2.0 high school GPA. Required for some: interview. Entrance: moderately difficult. Application deadlines: 7/1, 1/1 for early action. Notification: continuous, 4/1 for early action.

Collegiate Environment: Orientation program. Drama-theater group, student-run newspaper. Student services: health clinic, personal-psychological counseling. Campus security: 24-hour emergency response devices and patrols, student patrols, late night transport-escort service, controlled dormitory access, electronic surveillance of labs and key areas. Patrick Power Library.

■ UNIVERSITÉ SAINTE-ANNE

Church Point, NS, Canada B0W 1M0
Tel: (902)769-2114
Fax: (902)769-2930
E-mail: admission@usainteanne.ca
Web Site: www.usainteanne.ca

Description: Province-supported, comprehensive, coed. Awards bachelor's and master's degrees. Founded 1890. Setting: 115-acre rural campus. System endowment: $2.7 million. Research spending for the previous fiscal year: $352,537. Educational spending for the previous fiscal year: $10,477 per student. Total enrollment: 355. Faculty: 72 (43 full-time, 29 part-time). 209 applied, 87% were admitted. Full-time: 308 students, 65% women, 35% men. Part-time: 10 students, 50% women, 50% men. Students come from 3 other countries, 18% from out-of province. 100% international. 17% 25 or older, 52% live on campus, 15% transferred in. Retention: 86% of full-time freshmen returned the following year. Academic areas with the most degrees conferred: education; foreign languages and literature; history. Core. Calendar: semesters. Academic remediation for entering students, ESL program, services for LD students, distance learning, double major, part-time degree program, adult/continuing education programs, co-op programs. Off campus study. Study abroad program.

Entrance Requirements: Open admission. Options: electronic application, early admission, deferred admission, international baccalaureate accepted. Required: high school transcript. Required for some: essay, 3 recommendations, Criminal record check. Entrance: moderately difficult. Application deadlines: rolling, rolling for nonresidents, rolling for early decision. Notification: continuous, continuous for nonresidents, rolling for early decision. Transfer credits accepted: Yes.

Costs Per Year: Application fee: $50 Canadian dollars. Tuition, fee, and room and board charges are reported in Canadian dollars. Comprehensive fee: $10,138 includes full-time tuition ($5,593) and college room and board ($4,545). College room only: $2,195. Full-time tuition varies according to course load, location, and program. Room and board charges vary according to board plan, housing facility, and location. Part-time mandatory fees: $1448 per term. Part-time fees vary according to course load, location, and program.

Collegiate Environment: Drama-theater group. Most popular organizations: Student Organization, Enactus, Club de Plein Air, Education Committee, Association des etudiants internationaux de l'Universite Sainte-Anne. Major annual events: Winter Carnival, Semaine multiculturel, Coupe des nations. Student services: health clinic, personal-psychological counseling. Campus security: 24-hour emergency response devices and patrols, student patrols, late night transport-escort service, 14-hour patrols by trained security personnel. 350 college housing spaces available; 161 were occupied in 2018-19. Option: coed housing available. BibliothFque Louis-R.-Comeau plus 1 other. Books: 76,000 (physical); Serial titles: 52 (physical); Databases: 27. Weekly public service hours: 78. Operations spending for the previous fiscal year: $335,958. 45 computers available on campus for general student use. A campuswide network can be accessed. Students can access the following: online class registration. Staffed computer lab on campus (open 24 hours a day) provides training in use of computers, software, and the Internet.

■ UNIVERSITY OF KING'S COLLEGE

6350 Coburg Rd.
Halifax, NS, Canada B3H 2A1
Tel: (902)422-1271
Fax: (902)423-3357
E-mail: admissions@ukings.ns.ca
Web Site: www.ukings.ca

Description: Province-supported, comprehensive, coed. Administratively affiliated with Dalhousie University. Awards bachelor's and master's degrees. Founded 1789. Setting: 4-acre urban campus. Endowment: $38 million. Total enrollment: 880. Faculty: 45 (all full-time). Student-undergrad faculty ratio is 21:1. 566 applied, 86% were admitted. Students come from 12 provinces and territories, 15 other countries, 60% from out-of province. 5% 25 or older, 23% live on campus. Academic areas with the most degrees conferred: liberal arts/general studies; communication/journalism. Core. Calendar: Canadian standard year. Services for LD students, advanced placement, accelerated degree program, self-designed majors, honors program, independent study, double major, summer session for credit, co-op programs and internships. Off campus study at Mount Saint Vincent University, Saint Mary's University, Nova Scotia College of Art and Design. Study abroad program.

Entrance Requirements: Options: electronic application, early admission, early decision, deferred admission, international baccalaureate accepted. Required: high school transcript, minimum 3 high school GPA. Required for some: essay, writing sample, SAT or ACT. Entrance: moderately difficult. Application deadline: 3/1. Notification: continuous until 4/15. Transfer credits accepted: Yes.

Collegiate Environment: Orientation program. Drama-theater group, choral group, student-run newspaper, radio station. Social organizations: 28 open to all. Most popular organizations: King's Theatrical Society, student newspaper, King's College Dance Collective, St. Andrew's Missionary Society, King's Independent Film-Makers Society. Major annual events: Frosh Week, College Christmas, Young Alexandra Society Annual Ball. Student services: legal services, health clinic, personal-psychological counseling, women's center. Campus security: student patrols, late night transport-escort service, controlled dormitory access. University of King's College Library. Students can reserve study rooms.

■ **UNIVERSITY OF PRINCE EDWARD ISLAND**

550 University Ave.

Charlottetown, PE, Canada C1A 4P3

Tel: (902)566-0439

Fax: (902)566-0795

Web Site: home.upei.ca

Description: Province-supported, comprehensive, coed. Awards bachelor's, master's, and doctoral degrees. Founded 1834. Setting: 130-acre small town campus. Endowment: $18.6 million. Research spending for the previous fiscal year: $14.8 million. Educational spending for the previous fiscal year: $23,058 per student. Total enrollment: 4,200. Faculty: 430 (240 full-time, 190 part-time). Student-undergrad faculty ratio is 12:1. 1,414 applied, 61% were admitted. Students come from 12 provinces and territories, 39 other countries, 17% from out-of province. 19% 25 or older, 14% live on campus. Retention: 77% of full-time freshmen returned the following year. Calendar: Canadian standard year. ESL program, services for LD students, advanced placement, accelerated degree program, honors program, distance learning, double major, summer session for credit, part-time degree program, co-op programs and internships. Study abroad program.

Entrance Requirements: Options: electronic application, early admission, international baccalaureate accepted. Required: high school transcript, minimum 2.5 high school GPA. Recommended: SAT or ACT. Entrance: moderately difficult. Application deadline: 8/1. Notification: continuous until 8/31.

Collegiate Environment: Orientation program. Drama-theater group, choral group, student-run newspaper. Social organizations: 20 open to all. Most popular organizations: Business Society, Biology Club, Music Society, intramurals, Theatre Society. Student services: health clinic, personal-psychological counseling, women's center. Campus security: 24-hour emergency response devices and patrols, late night transport-escort service, controlled dormitory access, late night residence hall security personnel. Robertson Library. Operations spending for the previous fiscal year: $3 million. 240 computers available on campus for general student use. A campuswide network can be accessed from student residence rooms and from off campus. Students can access the following: online class registration, email forwarding, course management system presence for each course registered.

Community Environment: Charlottetown is the provincial capital and the largest community, approximately 30,000, on the island. It has an excellent harbor and is the center of the cultural and commercial activities of the island. Scenic attractions include Province House, St. Dunstan's Basilica, St. Peter's Anglican Cathedral, the Confederation Center and Government house.

■ **MEMORIAL UNIVERSITY OF NEWFOUNDLAND**
Elizabeth Ave.
Saint John's, NL, Canada A1C 5S7
Tel: (709)864-8000
Fax: (709)864-4569
E-mail: sturecru@morgan.ucs.mun.ca
Web Site: www.mun.ca

Description: Province-supported, university, coed. Administratively affiliated with Marine Institute, Sir Wilfred Grenfell College, WRSON, CNS. Awards bachelor's, master's, and doctoral degrees. Founded 1925. Setting: 250-acre urban campus. Endowment: $60 million. Research spending for the previous fiscal year: $65 million. Total enrollment: 17,378. Faculty: 1,269 (1,233 full-time, 36 part-time). Student-undergrad faculty ratio is 12:1. Students come from 25 provinces and territories, 104 other countries, 19% from out-of-province. 16% 25 or older, 10% live on campus. Retention: 81% of full-time freshmen returned the following year. Calendar: trimesters. Academic remediation for entering students, ESL program, services for LD students, advanced placement, accelerated degree program, honors program, distance learning, double major, summer session for credit, part-time degree program, adult/continuing education programs, co-op programs and internships, graduate courses open to undergrads. Off campus study at University of New Brunswick, University of New Mexico. Study abroad program.

Entrance Requirements: Options: electronic application, early admission, early decision, deferred admission, international baccalaureate accepted. Required: high school transcript. Required for some: essay, 2 recommendations, interview, audition, portfolio. Entrance: moderately difficult. Application deadlines: rolling, 3/1 for nonresidents. Transfer credits accepted: Yes.

Collegiate Environment: Orientation program. Drama-theater group, choral group, student-run newspaper, radio station. Social organizations: 72 open to all. Most popular organizations: International Student Center, Students Older Than Average, Memorial's Organization for the Disabled, Biology Society, Student Parents at MUN. Major annual events: Winter Carnival, National University Week, Orientation. Student services: legal services, health clinic, personal-psychological counseling, women's center. Campus security: 24-hour emergency response devices and patrols, student patrols, late night transport-escort service. Queen Elizabeth II Library plus 4 others. Operations spending for the previous fiscal year: $15.3 million. 875 computers available on campus for general student use. A campuswide network can be accessed from student residence rooms and from off campus. Students can access the following: online class registration. Staffed computer lab on campus provides training in use of computers, software, and the Internet.

■ BROCK UNIVERSITY
1812 Sir Isaac Brock Way
Saint Catharines, ON, Canada L2S 3A1
Tel: (905)688-5550
Fax: (905)988-5488
E-mail: central@brocku.ca
Web Site: www.brocku.ca

Description: Province-supported, university, coed. Awards bachelor's, master's, and doctoral degrees. Founded 1964. Setting: 540-acre urban campus with easy access to Toronto, ON and Buffalo, NY. Total enrollment: 18,704. Faculty: 559 (all full-time). Student-undergrad faculty ratio is 30:1. 19,885 applied. Students come from 94 other countries. 14% live on campus. Retention: 86% of full-time freshmen returned the following year. Core. Calendar: Canadian standard year. Academic remediation for entering students, ESL program, services for LD students, advanced placement, accelerated degree program, self-designed majors, honors program, double major, summer session for credit, part-time degree program, adult/continuing education programs, co-op programs and internships, graduate courses open to undergrads. Study abroad program.

Entrance Requirements: Options: electronic application, international baccalaureate accepted. Required: high school transcript, SAT or ACT. Recommended: minimum 3 high school GPA. Required for some: essay, interview, audition for Dramatic Arts and Music programs, profile questionnaire for Concurrent Education programs. Transfer credits accepted: Yes.

Costs Per Year: Application fee: $0 Canadian dollars. Tuition, fee, and room and board charges are reported in Canadian dollars. Province resident tuition: $7149 full-time. Canadian resident tuition: $7149 full-time. Full-time tuition varies according to course load, degree level, program, and student level. College room and board: $6954. Room and board charges vary according to board plan and housing facility. International student tuition: $24,386 full-time.

Collegiate Environment: Orientation program. Drama-theater group, choral group, student-run newspaper, radio station. Social organizations: 50 open to all. Most popular organizations: International Students Association, Brock University Student Association, Business Administration Association, Brock Christian Fellowship, Ace Brock. Major annual events: Orientation Week, Frost Week. Student services: health clinic, personal-psychological counseling, women's center. Campus security: 24-hour emergency response devices and patrols, student patrols, late night transport-escort service, controlled dormitory access. James A. Gibson Library plus 1 other. Books: 492,672 (physical). Students can reserve study rooms. 429 computers available on campus for general student use. Computer purchase/lease plans available. A campuswide network can be accessed from student residence rooms. Students can access the following: online class registration. Staffed computer lab on campus provides training in use of computers, software, and the Internet.

■ CARLETON UNIVERSITY
1125 Colonel By Dr.
Ottawa, ON, Canada K1S 5B6
Tel: (613)520-7400
Fax: (613)520-7455
E-mail: liaison@admissions.carleton.ca
Web Site: www.carleton.ca

Description: Province-supported, university, coed. Awards bachelor's, master's, and doctoral degrees. Founded 1942. Setting: 152-acre urban campus. Endowment: $135.2 million. Research spending for the previous fiscal year: $53.2 million. Educational spending for the previous fiscal year: $5157 per student. Total enrollment: 23,683. Faculty: 791 (783 full-time, 8 part-time). Student-undergrad faculty ratio is 26:1. 15,934 applied, 73% were admitted. Full-time: 16,509 students, 51% women, 49% men. Part-time: 4,237 students, 46% women, 54% men. Students come from 13 provinces and territories, 155 other countries, 8% from out-of-province. 12% 25 or older, 15% live on campus, 4% transferred in. Retention: 87% of full-time freshmen returned the following year. Calendar: Canadian standard year. Academic remediation for entering students, ESL program, services for LD students, advanced placement, accelerated degree program, self-designed majors, honors program, independent study, distance learning, double major, summer session for credit, part-time degree program, adult/continuing education programs, co-op programs and internships, graduate courses open to undergrads. Off campus study at University of Ottawa, Algonquin College. Study abroad program.

Entrance Requirements: Options: electronic application, deferred admission, international baccalaureate accepted. Required: high school transcript, minimum 3.0 high school GPA. Recommended: SAT. Required for some: essay, minimum 3.4 high school GPA, interview, SAT and SAT Subject Tests or ACT. Entrance: moderately difficult. Application deadline: 6/1. Notification: continuous, continuous for nonresidents.

Collegiate Environment: Orientation program. Drama-theater group, choral group, student-run newspaper, radio station. Social organizations: 100 open to all. Major annual events: Orientation, Prep Week, Charity Ball. Student services: health clinic, personal-psychological counseling, women's center. Campus security: 24-hour emergency response devices and patrols, student patrols, late night transport-escort service, controlled dormitory access. MacOdrum Library. Operations spending for the previous fiscal year: $12.4 million. 550 computers available on campus for general student use. Computer purchase/lease plans available. A campuswide network can be accessed from student residence rooms and from off campus. Students can access the following: online class registration. Staffed computer lab on campus.

Community Environment: As the site of the Parliament Buildings, the National Arts Center, and many of Canada's finest museums, Ottawa is a vibrant political and cultural center that provides Carleton's students with many unique opportunities. With its impressive network of trails, pathways, and waterways, Ottawa is an ideal location for jogging, skiing, and cycling enthusiasts. Outdoor recreation extends year-round, for Carleton is located beside the historic Rideau Canal, which in the winter becomes the world's longest skating rink, and the site of Ottawa's annual winter carnival.

■ CENTENNIAL COLLEGE
PO Box 631, Station 'A'
Scarborough, ON, Canada M1K 5E9
Tel: (416)698-4192
Fax: (416)694-9263
Web Site: www.centennialcollege.ca

Description: Province-supported, 4-year, coed. Part of Ontario College Application System. Awards bachelor's degrees. Setting: urban campus with easy access to Greater Toronto Area. Total enrollment: 19,559. Calendar: semesters. ESL program, services for LD students, advanced placement, distance learning, summer session for credit, co-op programs and internships. Study abroad program.

Entrance Requirements: Option: electronic application. Required: high school transcript.

Collegiate Environment: Orientation program. Choral group. Student services: personal-psychological counseling. Campus security: 24-hour emergency response devices and patrols, late night transport-escort service. Centennial College Libraries. Study areas open 24 hours, 5-7 days a week; students can reserve study rooms.

■ **EMMANUEL BIBLE COLLEGE**

100 Fergus Ave.

Kitchener, ON, Canada N2A 2H2

Tel: (519)894-8900

Fax: (519)894-9430

Web Site: www.emmanuelbiblecollege.ca

Description: Independent, 4-year, coed, affiliated with Missionary Church. Awards bachelor's degrees. Founded 1940. Setting: 12-acre urban campus with easy access to Toronto. Total enrollment: 209. Core. Calendar: semesters. Academic remediation for entering students, accelerated degree program, summer session for credit, part-time degree program, internships.

Entrance Requirements: Option: deferred admission. Required: essay, high school transcript, 3 recommendations, interview, Christian testimony. Entrance: moderately difficult. Application deadline: rolling.

Collegiate Environment: Orientation program.

■ **HERITAGE COLLEGE AND SEMINARY**

175 Holiday Inn Dr.

Cambridge, ON, Canada N3C 3T2

Tel: (519)651-2869; Free: 800-465-1961

E-mail: mwalther@heritagecollege.net

Web Site: www.heritagecambridge.com

Description: Independent Baptist, comprehensive, coed. Awards associate, bachelor's, and master's degrees. Founded 1993. Setting: 7-acre urban campus with easy access to Toronto. Endowment: $1.1 million. Educational spending for the previous fiscal year: $4498 per student. Total enrollment: 274. Faculty: 36 (8 full-time, 28 part-time). Student-undergrad faculty ratio is 11:1. 24 applied, 100% were admitted. Full-time: 154 students, 40% women, 60% men. Part-time: 37 students, 32% women, 68% men. Students come from 6 provinces and territories, 3 other countries, 4% from out-of-province. 26% 25 or older, 3% transferred in. Retention: 79% of full-time freshmen returned the following year. Academic areas with the most degrees conferred: theology and religious vocations; education. Calendar: Canadian standard year. Advanced placement, independent study, distance learning, double major, summer session for credit, part-time degree program, internships, graduate courses open to undergrads. Off campus study.

Entrance Requirements: Open admission. Options: deferred admission, international baccalaureate accepted. Required: essay, high school transcript. Required for some: audition. Entrance: noncompetitive. Application deadline: 9/1. Notification: continuous. Transfer credits accepted: Yes.

Collegiate Environment: Orientation program. Choral group, student-run newspaper. Major annual events: Missions Conference, Christmas and Graduation Banquets, Orientation. Student services: personal-psychological counseling. Campus security: controlled dormitory access. Heritage Library. Operations spending for the previous fiscal year: $122,364. 6 computers available on campus for general student use. A campuswide network can be accessed from student residence rooms.

■ **LAKEHEAD UNIVERSITY**

955 Oliver Rd.

Thunder Bay, ON, Canada P7B 5E1

Tel: (807)343-8110; Free: 800-465-3959

Fax: (807)343-8156

E-mail: admissions@lakeheadu.ca

Web Site: www.lakeheadu.ca

Description: Province-supported, comprehensive, coed. Awards bachelor's, master's, and doctoral degrees. Founded 1965. Setting: 345-acre suburban campus. Endowment: $37 million. Research spending for the previous fiscal year: $22.4 million. Total enrollment: 8,680. Faculty: (319 full-time). 8,277 applied, 84% were admitted. Full-time: 6,364 students, 58% women, 42% men. Part-time: 1,611 students, 64% women, 36% men. Students come from 13 provinces and territories, 28 other countries. 20% live on campus. Retention: 88% of full-time freshmen returned the following year. Academic areas with the most degrees conferred: education; health professions and related sciences; engineering. Core. Calendar: Canadian standard year. ESL program, services for LD students, advanced placement, accelerated degree

program, honors program, independent study, distance learning, double major, summer session for credit, part-time degree program, external degree program, co-op programs and internships, graduate courses open to undergrads. Off campus study. Study abroad program.

Entrance Requirements: Options: electronic application, early admission, deferred admission, international baccalaureate accepted. Required: portfolio for visual arts program, audition for music program, portfolio for media studies, SAT or ACT. Recommended: minimum 3 high school GPA. Required for some: essay, high school transcript. Entrance: moderately difficult. Application deadline: 9/12. Notification: continuous, continuous for nonresidents. SAT Reasoning Test deadline: 8/13. SAT Subject Test deadline: 8/13. Transfer credits accepted: Yes.

Collegiate Environment: Orientation program. Choral group, student-run newspaper, radio station. Most popular organizations: Outdoor Recreation Students Association, Engineering Students Society, Business Association, Educational Students Association, Native Students Association. Major annual events: Orientation, Winter Carnival. Student services: health clinic, personal-psychological counseling, women's center. Campus security: 24-hour emergency response devices and patrols, student patrols, late night transport-escort service, controlled dormitory access. Chancellor Norman M. Paterson Library plus 1 other. Operations spending for the previous fiscal year: $4.6 million. 594 computers available on campus for general student use. A campuswide network can be accessed from student residence rooms and from off campus. Students can access the following: online class registration. Staffed computer lab on campus (open 24 hours a day) provides training in use of computers, software, and the Internet.

■ **LAURENTIAN UNIVERSITY**

935 Ramsey Lake Rd.

Sudbury, ON, Canada P3E 2C6

Tel: (705)675-1151; Free: 800-263-4188

Fax: (705)675-4840

E-mail: explore@laurentian.ca

Web Site: www.laurentian.ca

Description: Province-supported, comprehensive, coed. Awards bachelor's, master's, and doctoral degrees. Founded 1960. Setting: 700-acre suburban campus. Endowment: $40.8 million. Research spending for the previous fiscal year: $18.7 million. Educational spending for the previous fiscal year: $16,470 per student. Total enrollment: 9,430. Faculty: (403 full-time). Student-undergrad faculty ratio is 18:1. Students come from 57 other countries. Retention: 84% of full-time freshmen returned the following year. Core. Calendar: Canadian standard year (fall, winter, spring sessions). Academic remediation for entering students, ESL program, services for LD students, advanced placement, accelerated degree program, honors program, independent study, distance learning, double major, summer session for credit, part-time degree program, external degree program, adult/continuing education programs, co-op programs and internships. Off campus study. Study abroad program.

Entrance Requirements: Required: high school transcript. Required for some: essay, 2 recommendations, interview.

Collegiate Environment: Orientation program. Drama-theater group, choral group, student-run newspaper, radio station. Most popular organizations: Students General Association, Association des Etudiantes/Etudiants francophones, Association of Mature and Part-time Students, Graduate Students Association. Major annual event: Orientation Week/Welcome Week. Student services: health clinic, personal-psychological counseling, women's center. Campus security: 24-hour emergency response devices and patrols, late night transport-escort service, controlled dormitory access. J. N. Desmarais Library plus 9 others. Books: 1 million (physical), 331,212 (digital/electronic); Serial titles: 14,439 (physical), 56,000 (digital/electronic). Students can reserve study rooms. Operations spending for the previous fiscal year: $5.4 million. 450 computers available on campus for general student use. Computer purchase/lease plans available. A campuswide network can be accessed from student residence rooms and from off campus. Students can access the following: online class registration. Staffed computer lab on campus provides training in use of computers, software, and the Internet.

Community Environment: Sudbury is the largest city (population 155,268) in Northern Ontario. Thunder Bay is 300 miles to the West. Sudbury is 100 miles east of Sault Ste. Marie. The campus is on 750 acres of scenic countryside, surrounded by three lakes, just a 10-minute drive from the downtown area.

■ MASTER'S COLLEGE AND SEMINARY

780 Argyle St.
Peterborough, ON, Canada K9H 5T2
Tel: (705)749-0725; Free: 800-295-6368
Fax: (705)749-0417
E-mail: flora.anthony@mcs.edu
Web Site: www.mcs.edu

Description: Independent Pentecostal, 4-year, coed. Awards bachelor's degrees. Founded 1939. Setting: suburban campus with easy access to Toronto. Endowment: $970,384. Total enrollment: 227. Faculty: 27 (4 full-time, 23 part-time). Student-undergrad faculty ratio is 16:1. 73 applied, 92% were admitted. Students come from 7 provinces and territories, 1 other country, 21% from out-of-province. 65% live on campus. Retention: 90% of full-time freshmen returned the following year. Academic area with the most degrees conferred: theology and religious vocations. Core. Calendar: semesters. Academic remediation for entering students, services for LD students, independent study, distance learning, summer session for credit, part-time degree program, internships. Off campus study.

Entrance Requirements: Options: electronic application, deferred admission. Required: essay, high school transcript, 3 recommendations, Christian commitment. Recommended: minimum 2 high school GPA. Required for some: interview. Entrance: noncompetitive. Application deadline: 8/1. Notification: continuous. Transfer credits accepted: Yes.

Costs Per Year: Application fee: $75 Canadian dollars. Tuition, fee, and room and board charges are reported in Canadian dollars. One-time mandatory fee: $535. Comprehensive fee: $15,682 includes full-time tuition ($6848), mandatory fees ($1414), and college room and board ($7420). Full-time tuition and fees vary according to course load, location, and program. Room and board charges vary according to board plan. Part-time tuition: $214 per credit hour. Part-time mandatory fees: $29 per credit hour. Part-time tuition and fees vary according to course load, location, and program.

Collegiate Environment: Orientation program. Major annual events: Fall Retreat, Winter Retreat, Christmas Social. Campus security: 24-hour emergency response devices, controlled dormitory access. Robert and Shirley Taitinger Learning Commons. Books: 35,418 (physical), 5,422 (digital/electronic); Serial titles: 542 (physical). Weekly public service hours: 71. 6 computers available on campus for general student use. A campuswide network can be accessed from student residence rooms. Students can access the following: online class registration.

■ MCMASTER UNIVERSITY

1280 Main St. W
Hamilton, ON, Canada L8S 4M2
Tel: (905)525-9140
Fax: (905)527-1105
E-mail: admitmac@mcmaster.ca
Web Site: www.mcmaster.ca

Description: Province-supported, university, coed. Awards bachelor's, master's, and doctoral degrees. Founded 1887. Setting: 300-acre suburban campus with easy access to Toronto. Endowment: $631.7 million. Total enrollment: 27,987. Faculty: 894 (all full-time). Student-undergrad faculty ratio is 25:1. 46,168 applied, 12% were admitted. Students come from 12 provinces and territories, 98 other countries. 20% live on campus. Retention: 89% of full-time freshmen returned the following year. Academic areas with the most degrees conferred: social sciences; health professions and related sciences; liberal arts/general studies. Calendar: Canadian standard year. Academic remediation for entering students, ESL program, services for LD students, advanced placement, accelerated degree program, honors program, independent study, double major, summer session for credit, part-time degree program, adult/continuing education programs, co-op programs and internships, graduate courses open to undergrads. Off campus study. Study abroad program.

Entrance Requirements: Options: electronic application, deferred admission, international baccalaureate accepted. Required: high school transcript, SAT or ACT. Required for some: essay, interview. Entrance: very difficult. Transfer credits accepted: Yes.

Costs Per Year: Tuition, fee, and room and board charges are reported in Canadian dollars. Province resident tuition: $6,715 full-time. Canadian resident tuition: $6,715 full-time. Mandatory fees: $1,260 full-time. Full-time tuition and fees vary according to course level, course load, degree level, and program. College room and board: $10,500. College room only: $6400. Room and board charges vary according to board plan and housing facility. International student tuition: $29,449 full-time.

Collegiate Environment: Orientation program. Drama-theater group, choral group, student-run newspaper, radio station. Social organizations: 120 open to all. Most popular organizations: Inter-Varsity Christian Fellowship, African-Caribbean Student Association, Chinese Students' Association, AIESEC (international leadership organization), Southeast Asian-American Society. Major annual events: Homecoming, Frosh Week, Alumni Weekend. Student services: legal services, health clinic, personal-psychological counseling, women's center. Campus security: 24-hour emergency response devices and patrols, student patrols, late night transport-escort service, controlled dormitory access. Mills Memorial Library plus 4 others. 400 computers available on campus for general student use. A campuswide network can be accessed from student residence rooms and from off campus. Students can access the following: online class registration. Staffed computer lab on campus provides training in use of computers, software, and the Internet.

Community Environment: Hamilton is the western point of the"Golden Triangle," Ontario's economic heartland. A major Great Lakes seaport, Hamilton's care for its past and present is reflected in the restored 36-room Regency Villa Dundurn Castle, and the 1,200-acre Coote's Paradise wildlife sanctuary.

■ NER ISRAEL YESHIVA COLLEGE OF TORONTO

8950 Bathurst St.
Thornhill, ON, Canada L4J 8A7
Tel: (905)731-1224
Web Site: www.neryisroel.info

Description: Independent Jewish, comprehensive, men only. Awards bachelor's and master's degrees. Founded 1959. Setting: 14-acre campus. 50% from top 10% of their high school class, 100% from top half. Students come from 3 provinces and territories, 2 other countries. 80% 25 or older. Calendar: Canadian standard year. Summer session for credit.

Entrance Requirements: Required: high school transcript, 2 recommendations, interview. Entrance: very difficult. Application deadline: 8/15.

Collegiate Environment: Student services: personal-psychological counseling.

■ NIPISSING UNIVERSITY

100 College Dr., Box 5002
North Bay, ON, Canada P1B 8L7
Tel: (705)474-3461
Fax: (705)474-1947
E-mail: liaison@nipissingu.ca
Web Site: www.nipissingu.ca

Description: Province-supported, comprehensive, coed. Part of Ontario Ministry of Training, Colleges and Universities. Awards bachelor's, master's, and doctoral degrees. Founded 1992. Setting: 290-hectare urban campus. Total enrollment: 3,700. Core. Calendar: semesters. Academic remediation for entering students, services for LD students, advanced placement, accelerated degree program, honors program, independent study, distance learning, double major, summer session for credit, part-time degree program. Off campus study at Muskoka Campus, Wilfrid Laurier University. Study abroad program.

Entrance Requirements: Options: electronic application, early admission, early decision, international baccalaureate accepted. Required: high school transcript, SAT and SAT Subject Tests or ACT. Required for some: essay. Entrance: moderately difficult.

Collegiate Environment: Orientation program. Drama-theater group. Major annual events: Frosh Week, Shinerama. Student services: health clinic, personal-psychological counseling, women's center. Campus security: 24-hour emergency response devices and patrols, student patrols, late night transport-escort service, controlled dormitory access. Education Centre Library.

■ QUEEN'S UNIVERSITY AT KINGSTON

Kingston, ON, Canada K7L 3N6
Tel: (613)533-2000
Fax: (613)533-6300
E-mail: admission@queensu.ca
Web Site: www.queensu.ca

Description: Province-supported, university, coed. Awards bachelor's, master's, and doctoral degrees. Founded 1841. Setting: 160-acre urban campus. Endowment: $710.3 million. Research spending for the previous fiscal year: $5.3 million. Educational spending for the previous fiscal year: $12,787 per student. Total enrollment: 24,345. Faculty: 1,525 (1,087 full-time, 438 part-time). Student-undergrad faculty ratio is 15:1. 28,278 applied. Full-time: 16,339 students, 58% women, 42% men. Students come from 70 other countries, 20% from out-of province. 3% 25 or older, 32% live on campus, 1% transferred in. Retention: 95% of full-time freshmen returned the following year. Calendar: Canadian standard year. ESL program, services for LD students, advanced placement, accelerated degree program, self-designed majors, honors program, distance learning, double major, summer session for credit, part-time degree program, adult/continuing education programs, co-op programs and internships. Study abroad program.

Entrance Requirements: Options: deferred admission, international baccalaureate accepted. Required: essay, high school transcript, minimum 2.7 high school GPA, SAT or ACT. Required for some: 1 recommendation. Entrance: most difficult. Application deadline: 2/1. Notification: continuous until 5/16. SAT Reasoning Test deadline: 4/30. Transfer credits accepted: Yes.

Collegiate Environment: Orientation program. Drama-theater group, choral group, marching band, student-run newspaper, radio station. Social organizations: 270 open to all. Most popular organizations: Arts and Sciences Undergraduate Society, Alma Mater Society, Engineering Society, Commerce Society, dance club. Major annual event: Orientation Week. Student services: legal services, health clinic, personal-psychological counseling, women's center. Campus security: 24-hour emergency response devices and patrols, student patrols, late night transport-escort service, controlled dormitory access. Joseph S. Stauffer Library plus 4 others. Operations spending for the previous fiscal year: $25.3 million. 455 computers available on campus for general student use. Computer purchase/lease plans available. A campuswide network can be accessed from student residence rooms and from off campus. Students can access the following: online class registration. Staffed computer lab on campus provides training in use of computers, software, and the Internet.

■ REDEEMER UNIVERSITY COLLEGE

777 Garner Rd. E
Ancaster, ON, Canada L9K 1J4
Tel: (905)648-2131; Free: 800-263-6467
Fax: (905)648-2134
Web Site: www.redeemer.ca

Description: Independent interdenominational, 4-year, coed. Awards bachelor's degrees. Founded 1980. Setting: 86-acre small town campus with easy access to Toronto. Total enrollment: 688. Faculty: 74 (41 full-time, 33 part-time). Student-undergrad faculty ratio is 11:1. 247 applied, 94% were admitted. Full-time: 650 students, 63% women, 37% men. Part-time: 38 students, 45% women, 55% men. Students come from 6 provinces and territories, 16 other countries, 5% from out-of province. 12% 25 or older, 6% transferred in. Retention: 78% of full-time freshmen returned the following year. Academic areas with the most degrees conferred: education; psychology; history. Core. Calendar: semesters. Academic remediation for entering students, services for LD students, honors program, independent study, double major, summer session for credit, part-time degree program, co-op programs and internships. Off campus study at Redeemer in France, Crandall-Oxford Program. Study abroad program.

Entrance Requirements: Options: electronic application, deferred admission, international baccalaureate accepted. Required: essay, high school transcript, minimum 2 high school GPA, 1 recommendation. Required for some: interview, SAT or ACT. Application deadline: rolling. Notification: continuous. Preference given to Christians. Transfer credits accepted: Yes.

Costs Per Year: Application fee: $40 Canadian dollars. Tuition, fee, and room and board charges are reported in Canadian dollars. Comprehensive fee: $18,969 includes full-time tuition ($9800), mandatory fees ($621), and college room and board ($8548). College room only: $6200. Part-time tuition: $980 per course.

Collegiate Environment: Orientation program. Drama-theater group, choral group, student-run newspaper. Social organizations: 30 open to all. Most popular organizations: Church in the Box, Service Learning Trips, Deedz, Athletics and Recreation, Concert Choir. Major annual events: Coffee House, Mainstage Productions, Midnight Breakfast. Student services: personal-psychological counseling. Campus security: 24-hour emergency response devices, student patrols, late night transport-escort service, controlled dormitory access. 422 college housing spaces available; 320 were occupied in 2018-19. Freshmen guaranteed college housing. On-campus residence required through sophomore year. Options: men-only, women-only housing available. Peter Turkstra Library. Books: 92,733 (physical); Serial titles: 93 (physical), 9,387 (digital/electronic); Databases: 21. Students can reserve study rooms. 81 computers available on campus for general student

use. A campuswide network can be accessed from student residence rooms and from off campus. Staffed computer lab on campus provides training in use of computers and the Internet.

Community Environment: Redeemer University College is located just inside the southwestern corner of the town of Ancaster (population 16,542), Ontario, which is adjacent to Hamilton (population 490,268), on its southwest side. It is readily accessible by road or air transportation. The nearest international airport is at Toronto, 50 miles to the northeast. Ancaster is mainly a residential community for the large Hamilton industrial base, mainly the steel industry and related secondary industries. Hamilton is well provided with modern cultural and sport facilities.

■ ROYAL MILITARY COLLEGE OF CANADA

PO Box 17000, Station Forces
Kingston, ON, Canada K7K 7B4
Tel: (613)541-6000
Fax: (613)542-3565
Web Site: www.rmc.ca

Description: Federally supported, university, coed. Part of Council of Ontario Universities. Awards bachelor's, master's, and doctoral degrees. Founded 1876. Setting: 90-acre urban campus. Total enrollment: 2,584. Faculty: 520 (236 full-time, 284 part-time). Student-undergrad faculty ratio is 5:1. Students come from 13 provinces and territories, 51% from out-of province. 95% live on campus. Retention: 90% of full-time freshmen returned the following year. Core. Calendar: trimesters. Academic remediation for entering students, ESL program, services for LD students, advanced placement, honors program, distance learning, double major, part-time degree program. Off campus study. Study abroad program.

Entrance Requirements: Required: essay, high school transcript, interview, medical, aptitude test, security screening.

Collegiate Environment: Orientation program. Drama-theater group, choral group, marching band, student-run newspaper. Major annual events: Ex-Cadet Weekend, Christmas Ball, Graduation Parade. Student services: legal services, health clinic, personal-psychological counseling. Campus security: 24-hour emergency response devices and patrols, late night transport-escort service, controlled dormitory access. Massey Library plus 1 other. Study areas open 24 hours, 5-7 days a week. 1,200 computers available on campus for general student use. A campuswide network can be accessed from student residence rooms and from off campus. Students can access the following: online class registration. Staffed computer lab on campus provides training in use of computers, software, and the Internet.

Community Environment: Kingston is situated at the confluence of Lake Ontario and the St. Lawrence River. Since 1673, when it was established as a trading post called Fort Frontenac, it has been of Canadian commercial and geographic importance. Kingston's interest in preserving its historical flavor is exemplified in the restoration of Fort Henry, the key defense of the Kingston Naval Dockyard. Kingston is a very much a university town that enjoys the presence of RMC, Queen's and St. Lawrence Colleges.

■ RYERSON UNIVERSITY

350 Victoria St.
Toronto, ON, Canada M5B 2K3
Tel: (416)979-5000
E-mail: inquire@ryerson.ca
Web Site: www.ryerson.ca

Description: Province-supported, comprehensive, coed. Awards bachelor's and master's degrees. Founded 1948. Setting: 20-acre urban campus. Total enrollment: 25,181. Faculty: 955 (744 full-time, 211 part-time). 3% live on campus. Retention: 90% of full-time freshmen returned the following year. Academic areas with the most degrees conferred: business/marketing; health professions and related sciences; engineering. Calendar: Canadian standard year or semesters depending on program. Academic remediation for entering students, ESL program, services for LD students, advanced placement, honors program, distance learning, summer session for credit, part-time degree program, adult/continuing education programs, co-op programs and internships. Off campus study. Study abroad program.

Entrance Requirements: Options: electronic application, international baccalaureate accepted. Required: high school transcript. Required for some: essay, interview, portfolio, audition, entrance examination. Entrance: moderately difficult. Application deadline: 2/1. Notification: continuous.

Collegiate Environment: Orientation program. Drama-theater group, choral group, student-run newspaper, radio station. Social organizations: 55 open to all. Major annual events: Island Picnic, Winter Carnival, Cultural Caravan. Student services: health clinic, personal-psychological counseling, women's center. Campus security: 24-hour emergency response devices and patrols, late night transport-escort service, controlled dormitory access, staffed access control is in place 24 hours a day, with ID checks of all persons attempting to enter. Ryerson Library. 1,400 computers available on campus for general student use. Computer purchase/lease plans available. A campuswide network can be accessed from student residence rooms and from off campus. Staffed computer lab on campus.

■ **SAINT PAUL UNIVERSITY**
223 Main St.
Ottawa, ON, Canada K1S 1C4
Tel: (613)236-1393; Free: 800-637-6859
Fax: (613)782-3033
Web Site: www.ustpaul.ca
Description: Province-supported, university, coed. Administratively affiliated with University of Ottawa. Awards bachelor's, master's, and doctoral degrees. Founded 1848. Setting: 4-acre urban campus. Student-undergrad faculty ratio is 12:1. Calendar: Canadian standard year. Summer session for credit, part-time degree program, graduate courses open to undergrads.
Entrance Requirements: Options: deferred admission, international baccalaureate accepted. Required: high school transcript. Recommended: SAT. Entrance: moderately difficult.
Collegiate Environment: Saint Paul University Library.

■ **TRENT UNIVERSITY**
1600 W Bank Dr.
Peterborough, ON, Canada K9J 7B8
Tel: (705)748-1011
Fax: (705)748-1629
E-mail: admissions@trentu.ca
Web Site: www.trentu.ca
Description: Province-supported, university, coed. Awards bachelor's, master's, and doctoral degrees. Founded 1963. Setting: 1,400-acre suburban campus with easy access to Toronto. Total enrollment: 9,506. Faculty: (207 full-time). Full-time: 7,672 students, 68% women, 32% men. Part-time: 1,277 students, 65% women, 35% men. Students come from 13 provinces and territories, 82 other countries, 2% from out-of province. 14% 25 or older, 18% live on campus, 11% transferred in. Retention: 84% of full-time freshmen returned the following year. Calendar: Canadian standard year. Academic remediation for entering students, ESL program, services for LD students, advanced placement, accelerated degree program, self-designed majors, honors program, independent study, distance learning, double major, summer session for credit, part-time degree program, co-op programs and internships. Off campus study at Sir Sandford Fleming College, George Brown College, Durham College, Georgian College, Humber College, Loyalist College, Seneca College. Study abroad program.
Entrance Requirements: Options: electronic application, deferred admission, international baccalaureate accepted. Required: high school transcript, minimum 2.8 high school GPA. Required for some: essay, interview. Entrance: moderately difficult. Application deadline: 6/1. Notification: continuous. Transfer credits accepted: Yes.
Costs Per Year: Application fee: $150 Canadian dollars. Tuition, fee, and room and board charges are reported in Canadian dollars. Province resident tuition: $6,798 full-time, $1,359.66 per credit part-time. Canadian resident tuition: $4,106 per credit part-time. Mandatory fees: $1,660 full-time, $136.38 per credit part-time. Full-time tuition and fees vary according to course load, degree level, and program. Part-time tuition and fees vary according to course load, degree level, and program. College room and board: $10,095. Room and board charges vary according to board plan, housing facility, and location. International student tuition: $20,366.67 full-time.
Collegiate Environment: Orientation program. Drama-theater group, choral group, student-run newspaper, radio station. Social organizations: 77 open to all. Most popular organizations: Trent Radio, Trent International Program, Trent Central Student Association, Arthur (student newspaper), Excalibur (yearbook). Major annual event: Head of Trent (homecoming). Student services: health clinic, personal-psychological counseling, women's center. Campus security: 24-hour emergency response devices and patrols, student patrols, late night transport-escort service, controlled dormitory access. Thomas J. Bata Library plus 1 other. Students can reserve study rooms.
Community Environment: The university is situated on the banks of the Otonabee River, three miles north of Peterborough, Ontario. Two other colleges are located in residential areas of downtown Peterborough, one of Ontario's oldest and loveliest cities.

■ **TYNDALE UNIVERSITY COLLEGE & SEMINARY**
3377 Bayview Ave.
Toronto, ON, Canada M2M 3S4
Tel: (416)218-6757
Fax: (416)226-4210
E-mail: admissions@tydale.ca
Web Site: www.tyndale.ca
Description: Independent interdenominational, comprehensive, coed. Awards bachelor's, master's, and doctoral degrees. Founded 1894. Setting: 56-acre urban campus. Endowment: $2 million. Educational spending for the previous fiscal year: $1678 per student. Total enrollment: 1,142. Faculty: (54 full-time). Student-undergrad faculty ratio is 23:1. 368 applied, 53% were admitted. Full-time: 348 students, 47% women, 53% men. Part-time: 131 students, 50% women, 50% men. Students come from 7 provinces and territories, 12 other countries. 20% 25 or older, 30% live on campus. Retention: 49% of full-time freshmen returned the following year. Core. Calendar: semesters. Academic remediation for entering students, accelerated degree program, honors program, summer session for credit, part-time degree program, adult/continuing education programs. Off campus study at Seneca College.
Entrance Requirements: Options: electronic application, deferred admission, international baccalaureate accepted. Required: high school transcript, minimum 2 high school GPA, all post-secondary transcripts. Recommended: essay. Required for some: 1 recommendation, interview. Entrance: moderately difficult. Application deadlines: rolling, rolling for nonresidents. Notification: continuous, continuous for nonresidents. Transfer credits accepted: Yes.
Collegiate Environment: Orientation program. Drama-theater group, choral group, student-run newspaper. Social organizations: 5 open to all. Most popular organizations: choir, student government, Urban Ministry Team, Steadfast drama team. Major annual events: Global Ministries Conference, Homecoming, intramural floor hockey. Student services: personal-psychological counseling. Campus security: 24-hour patrols, student patrols, late night transport-escort service, controlled dormitory access. 180 college housing spaces available; 170 were occupied in 2018-19. Freshmen given priority for college housing. Options: men-only, women-only housing available. J. William Horsey Library. Operations spending for the previous fiscal year: $440,000. 30 computers available on campus for general student use. A campuswide network can be accessed. Students can access the following: online class registration. Staffed computer lab on campus provides training in use of computers, software, and the Internet.

■ **UNIVERSITY OF GUELPH**
Guelph, ON, Canada N1G 2W1
Tel: (519)824-4120
E-mail: jhogan@uoguelph.ca
Web Site: www.uoguelph.ca
Description: Province-supported, university, coed. Awards associate, bachelor's, master's, and doctoral degrees. Founded 1964. Setting: 1,017-acre suburban campus with easy access to Toronto. Endowment: $419.1 million. Research spending for the previous fiscal year: $146 million. Total enrollment: 24,009. Faculty: 756. Student-undergrad faculty ratio is 23:1. 23,750 applied, 66% were admitted. Students come from 13 provinces and territories, 100 other countries. 100% international. 28% live on campus. Retention: 91% of full-time freshmen returned the following year. Academic areas with the most degrees conferred: biological/life sciences; business/marketing; social sciences. Core. Calendar: trimesters. Academic remediation for entering students, ESL program, services for LD students, advanced placement, accelerated degree program, self-designed majors, honors program, independent study, distance learning, double major, summer session for credit, part-time degree program, co-op programs and internships, graduate courses open to undergrads. Off campus study. Study abroad program.
Entrance Requirements: Options: electronic application, early admission, deferred admission, international baccalaureate accepted. Required: high school transcript, minimum 3 high school GPA, SAT or ACT. Required for some: essay. Entrance: moderately difficult. Application deadline: 3/1. Notification: continuous until 5/27. SAT Reasoning Test deadline: 3/1. SAT Subject Test deadline: 3/1. Transfer credits accepted: Yes.
Costs Per Year: Application fee: $150 Canadian dollars. Tuition, fee, and room and board charges are reported in Canadian dollars. Province resident tuition: $6571 full-time, $1,312.62 per credit part-time. Canadian resident tuition: $6571 full-time. Mandatory fees: $22,501 full-time, $514.24 per credit part-time. Full-time tuition and fees vary according to degree level and

program. Part-time tuition and fees vary according to course load, degree level, and program. College room and board: $11,132. College room only: $6082. Room and board charges vary according to board plan and housing facility. International student tuition: $20,840 full-time. Tuition guaranteed not to increase for student's term of enrollment.

Collegiate Environment: Orientation program. Drama-theater group, choral group, student-run newspaper, radio station. Social organizations: 250 open to all. Most popular organizations: Guelph Gryphon Athletics, Habitat for Humanity, Curtain Call Productions, West Indian Students Association, OXFAM-Guelph Chapter. Major annual events: Homecoming, College Royal Weekend, Trick or Eat. Student services: legal services, health clinic, personal-psychological counseling, women's center. Campus security: 24-hour emergency response devices and patrols, student patrols, late night transport-escort service, controlled dormitory access, video camera surveillance in parking lots, alarms in women's locker room. University of Guelph Library plus 1 other. Books: 1.3 million (physical), 35,000 (digital/electronic); Serial titles: 1,617 (physical), 21,287 (digital/electronic); Databases: 280. Students can reserve study rooms. 8,000 computers available on campus for general student use. A campuswide network can be accessed from student residence rooms and from off campus. Students can access the following: online class registration. Staffed computer lab on campus (open 24 hours a day) provides training in use of computers and software.

Community Environment: Blending the sophistication of city life with the beautiful scenery of the countryside in the heart of southwestern Ontario, the city of Guelph is a lively, multicultural community of 100,000. Just a short walk from campus, students can enjoy sidewalk cafes, specialty boutiques and craft shops, and a wide variety of restaurants. An hour's drive west of Toronto, Guelph is easily accessible by bus or train. It is the home of the Guelph Spring Festival (May-June), the Guelph Jazz Festival (September), and the Hillside Folk Festival (July), as well as the site of the Guelph Center for the Performing Arts.

■ **UNIVERSITY OF OTTAWA**
550 Cumberland St.
Ottawa, ON, Canada K1N 6N5
Tel: (613)562-5700
Web Site: www.uottawa.ca

Description: Province-supported, university, coed. Administratively affiliated with Saint-Paul University (Ottawa, Ontario). Awards bachelor's, master's, and doctoral degrees. Founded 1848. Setting: 43-hectare urban campus with easy access to Ottawa-Gatineau. Endowment: $186 million. Research spending for the previous fiscal year: $224.7 million. Educational spending for the previous fiscal year: $9700 per student. Total enrollment: 42,575. Faculty: 2,246 (1,262 full-time, 984 part-time). Student-undergrad faculty ratio is 26:1. 45,600 applied, 55% were admitted. Students come from 13 provinces and territories, 166 other countries, 21% from out-of-province. 18% 25 or older, 9% live on campus. Retention: 87% of full-time freshmen returned the following year. Academic areas with the most degrees conferred: education; social sciences; health professions and related sciences. Calendar: semesters. Academic remediation for entering students, ESL program, services for LD students, advanced placement, honors program, distance learning, double major, summer session for credit, part-time degree program, co-op programs and internships. Off campus study at Carleton University, Saint Paul University, St-Boniface, La Cite collegiale. Study abroad program.

Entrance Requirements: Options: electronic application, early admission, deferred admission, international baccalaureate accepted. Required: high school transcript, minimum 3 high school GPA. Required for some: interview, SAT or ACT for American citizens. Entrance: moderately difficult. Notification: continuous. Transfer credits accepted: Yes.

Collegiate Environment: Orientation program. Drama-theater group, choral group, student-run newspaper, radio station. Social organizations: national fraternities, national sororities, local fraternities, local sororities; 1% of eligible men and 1% of eligible women are members. Most popular organizations: Student Federation of the University of Ottawa, Graduate Students Association. Major annual events: 101 Week-Welcome Week, International Week, Snow Festival. Student services: legal services, health clinic, personal-psychological counseling, women's center. Campus security: 24-hour emergency response devices and patrols, student patrols, late night transport-escort service, controlled dormitory access. Morisset Library plus 7 others. Operations spending for the previous fiscal year: $22.6 million. 1,540 computers available on campus for general student use. A campuswide network can be accessed from student residence rooms and from off campus. Students can access the following: online class registration. Staffed

computer lab on campus (open 24 hours a day) provides training in use of computers, software, and the Internet.

Community Environment: Ottawa, the capital of Canada, is a modern, cosmopolitan city with a population of 774,000. This unique setting is renowned for its museums, its national festivities, and its year-round outdoor activities in a breathtaking and readily accessible natural environment. During the academic year, students can get acquainted with monuments, museums, art galleries, restaurants, theaters, and concert halls located downtown. Nature buffs will be thrilled with the multitude of green spaces and the extensive network of cycling paths. Come winter, the paths turn into cross-country ski trails and the Rideau Canal, alongside the campus, becomes the world's longest skating rink.

■ **UNIVERSITY OF TORONTO**
27 King's College Cir.
Toronto, ON, Canada M5S 1A1
Tel: (416)978-2011
Web Site: www.utoronto.ca

Description: Province-supported, university, coed. Awards bachelor's, master's, and doctoral degrees. Founded 1827. Setting: 714-hectare urban campus with easy access to Greater Toronto Area. Endowment: $2.4 billion. Total enrollment: 88,766. Faculty: 14,420. Student-undergrad faculty ratio is 24:1. Students come from 12 provinces and territories, 168 other countries, 6% from out-of-province. 27% 25 or older, 14% live on campus. Retention: 91% of full-time freshmen returned the following year. Core. Calendar: fall/winter terms and a summer session. ESL program, services for LD students, independent study, double major, summer session for credit, part-time degree program, adult/continuing education programs, co-op programs and internships, graduate courses open to undergrads. Off campus study at Sheridan College. Study abroad program.

Entrance Requirements: Options: electronic application, deferred admission, international baccalaureate accepted. Required: high school transcript, SAT and SAT Subject Tests or ACT. Required for some: essay, interview. Entrance: very difficult. Application deadline: 1/19. Notification: continuous. Preference given to province residents for pharmacy program; Canadian residents for dentistry, physical and occupational therapy, rehabilitation medicine programs. SAT Reasoning Test deadline: 2/1. SAT Subject Test deadline: 2/1. Transfer credits accepted: Yes.

Collegiate Environment: Orientation program. Drama-theater group, choral group, student-run newspaper, radio station. Social organizations: national fraternities, national sororities, local fraternities, local sororities. Student services: legal services, health clinic, personal-psychological counseling, women's center. Campus security: 24-hour emergency response devices and patrols, student patrols, late night transport-escort service. Robarts Library plus 43 others. Books: 19.4 million (physical), 6 million (digital/electronic). Students can reserve study rooms. 2,000 computers available on campus for general student use. A campuswide network can be accessed from student residence rooms and from off campus. Students can access the following: online class registration. Staffed computer lab on campus provides training in use of software.

Community Environment: Toronto is the financial and industrial capital of Canada as well as Provincial capital of Ontario. It is often compared to New York and, in fact, was known as "York" (after the Duke of York) until 1834. The name "Toronto" was selected and is taken from an Indian word which means "meeting place" and it has become the meeting place or crossroads for nearly all Canadian activities. Cultural attractions abound and include the Art Gallery of Ontario, the Ontario Science Center, the Marine Museum of Upper Canada, Royal Ontario Museum and the Hummingbird Centre (which is home to the National Ballet of Canada, the Canadian Opera Company and scene of numerous plays). Toronto is one of two Canadian cities with baseball teams in the major leagues but more important to Canadians, it is the home of the Hockey Hall of Fame and of the Maple Leafs. The city also has many other sport and recreation facilities including the Skydome, a domed stadium. The city is one of the great inland ports of North America and is easily accessible by air, rail, bus and road. It has one of the best subway systems in the world and an excellent public bus system.

■ **UNIVERSITY OF WATERLOO**
200 University Ave. W
Waterloo, ON, Canada N2L 3G1
Tel: (519)888-4567
Fax: (519)746-2882
E-mail: myapplication@uwaterloo.ca
Web Site: www.uwaterloo.ca

Description: Province-supported, university, coed. Awards bachelor's, master's, and doctoral degrees. Founded 1957. Setting: 1,112-acre suburban campus with easy access to Toronto. Endowment: $294.5 million. Total enrollment: 39,048. Faculty: 1,211. Student-undergrad faculty ratio is 26:1. Full-time: 31,886 students, 47% women, 53% men. Part-time: 1,311 students, 55% women, 45% men. Academic areas with the most degrees conferred: mathematics and statistics; engineering; social sciences. Core. Calendar: trimesters. ESL program, services for LD students, honors program, distance learning, double major, part-time degree program, co-op programs and internships, graduate courses open to undergrads. Off campus study at Wilfrid Laurier University. Study abroad program.

Entrance Requirements: Open admission. Options: electronic application, early admission, deferred admission, international baccalaureate accepted. Required: high school transcript. Recommended: essay. Required for some: essay, interview. Entrance: moderately difficult. Application deadline: 3/31. Notification: 5/26. Transfer credits accepted: Yes.

Costs Per Year: Application fee: $140 Canadian dollars. Tuition, fee, and room and board charges are reported in Canadian dollars. Province resident tuition: $9262 full-time, $737 per course part-time. Mandatory fees: $800 full-time, $65 per term part-time. Full-time tuition and fees vary according to course load, degree level, program, and student level. Part-time tuition and fees vary according to course load, degree level, program, and student level. College room and board: $10,525. College room only: $5775. Room and board charges vary according to board plan, housing facility, and location. International student tuition: $33,289 full-time.

Collegiate Environment: Orientation program. Drama-theater group, choral group, marching band, student-run newspaper. Social organizations: national fraternities, national sororities. Major annual events: Orientation, Athletic Events. Student services: legal services, health clinic, personal-psychological counseling, women's center. Campus security: 24-hour emergency response devices and patrols, student patrols, late night transport-escort service, controlled dormitory access. Dana Porter Library plus 11 others. Students can reserve study rooms. 6,000 computers available on campus for general student use. A campuswide network can be accessed from student residence rooms and from off campus. Students can access the following: online class registration. Staffed computer lab on campus provides training in use of computers, software, and the Internet.

Community Environment: The University of Waterloo is located near Toronto in the heart of southern Ontario, Canada's most populous and highly developed province. The University's home community of Kitchener-Waterloo, population 276,900, is ethnically one of the most diverse in Canada. Residents enjoy a high standard of living, safe and clean neighborhoods, and may cultural and recreational attractions, as well as natural parks and protected wilderness areas.

■ **THE UNIVERSITY OF WESTERN ONTARIO**
1151 Richmond St.
London, ON, Canada N6A 3K7
Tel: (519)661-2111
E-mail: reg-admissions@uwo.ca
Web Site: www.uwo.ca

Description: Province-supported, university, coed. Awards bachelor's, master's, and doctoral degrees. Founded 1878. Setting: 1,200-acre suburban campus. Total enrollment: 37,357. Faculty: 1,391 (all full-time). 33,924 applied, 58% were admitted. Students come from 13 provinces and territories, 76 other countries. 3% 25 or older, 20% live on campus. Retention: 93% of full-time freshmen returned the following year. Academic areas with the most degrees conferred: social sciences; health professions and related sciences; physical sciences. Core. Calendar: Canadian standard year. Academic remediation for entering students, ESL program, services for LD students, advanced placement, accelerated degree program, self-designed majors, honors program, independent study, distance learning, double major, summer session for credit, part-time degree program, adult/continuing education programs, co-op programs and internships, graduate courses open to undergrads. Off campus study. Study abroad program.

Entrance Requirements: Options: electronic application, deferred admission, international baccalaureate accepted. Required: high school transcript, minimum 3.5 high school GPA, SAT or ACT. Required for some: supplemental profile, interview or audition. Entrance: very difficult. Application deadlines: 6/1, 5/15 for nonresidents. Notification: continuous, continuous for nonresidents. Transfer credits accepted: Yes.

Costs Per Year: Application fee: $155 Canadian dollars. Tuition, fee, and room and board charges are reported in Canadian dollars. Province resident tuition: $6723 full-time, $1345 per course part-time. Mandatory fees: $1490

full-time, $174 per course part-time. Full-time tuition and fees vary according to program. Part-time tuition and fees vary according to course load and program. College room and board: $14,034. College room only: $8684. Room and board charges vary according to board plan, housing facility, and location. International student tuition: $28,743 full-time.

Collegiate Environment: Orientation program. Drama-theater group, choral group, marching band, student-run newspaper, radio station. Social organizations: 184 open to all; national fraternities, national sororities. Most popular organizations: Pre-Medical Society, Western Investment Club, Purple Spur Society, Pre-Business Students' Network, Pre-Law Society. Major annual events: Orientation Week, Homecoming, HireWesternU Career Fair. Student services: legal services, health clinic, personal-psychological counseling. Campus security: 24-hour emergency response devices and patrols, student patrols, late night transport-escort service, controlled dormitory access, Campus Community Police, SERT: Student Emergency Response Team, Western Foot Patrol. Western Libraries plus 7 others. Students can reserve study rooms. 414 computers available on campus for general student use. Computer purchase/lease plans available. A campuswide network can be accessed from student residence rooms and from off campus. Students can access the following: online class registration. Staffed computer lab on campus provides training in use of computers, software, and the Internet.

Community Environment: The university is located on 155 hectares of land along the banks of the Thames River in London, Ontario, a thriving city of 331,000 people and is only 200 kilometers west of Toronto.

■ **UNIVERSITY OF WINDSOR**
401 Sunset Ave.
Windsor, ON, Canada N9B 3P4
Tel: (519)253-3000
Fax: (519)973-7050
E-mail: registrar@uwindsor.ca
Web Site: www.uwindsor.ca

Description: Province-supported, university, coed. Awards bachelor's, master's, and doctoral degrees. Founded 1857. Setting: 125-acre urban campus with easy access to Detroit. Endowment: $84.3 million. Research spending for the previous fiscal year: $23.7 million. Educational spending for the previous fiscal year: $6013 per student. Total enrollment: 15,579. Faculty: 898 (573 full-time, 325 part-time). Student-undergrad faculty ratio is 23:1. Full-time: 10,565 students, 53% women, 47% men. Part-time: 1,861 students, 48% women, 52% men. Students come from 10 provinces and territories, 83 other countries. 15% 25 or older, 2% transferred in. Retention: 86% of full-time freshmen returned the following year. Academic areas with the most degrees conferred: education; business/marketing; health professions and related sciences. Core. Calendar: semesters. Academic remediation for entering students, ESL program, services for LD students, advanced placement, accelerated degree program, self-designed majors, honors program, distance learning, double major, summer session for credit, part-time degree program, external degree program, adult/continuing education programs, co-op programs and internships, graduate courses open to undergrads. Off campus study at Wayne State University. Study abroad program.

Entrance Requirements: Option: electronic application. Required: high school transcript, minimum 3 high school GPA. Required for some: essay, minimum 3.3 high school GPA, 1 recommendation, interview, SAT and SAT Subject Tests or ACT. Transfer credits accepted: Yes.

Collegiate Environment: Orientation program. Drama-theater group, choral group, student-run newspaper, radio station. Social organizations: 160 open to all; national fraternities, local fraternities, local sororities. Most popular organizations: University of Windsor Student Alliance, Environmental Awareness Association, Social Science Society, Commerce Society, Science Society. Major annual events: Health Fair, Job Fair, Windsor Welcome Week. Student services: legal services, health clinic, personal-psychological counseling, women's center. Campus security: 24-hour emergency response devices and patrols, student patrols, late night transport-escort service, controlled dormitory access. Leddy Library plus 2 others. Books: 886,201 (physical), 673,676 (digital/electronic); Serial titles: 33,354 (physical), 85,907 (digital/electronic). Weekly public service hours: 108; students can reserve study rooms. Operations spending for the previous fiscal year: $10.5 million. 1,225 computers available on campus for general student use. A campuswide network can be accessed from student residence rooms and from off campus. Students can access the following: online class registration, online transcripts, degree audits, bursaries, grants, online applications for graduation. Staffed computer lab on campus provides training in use of computers, software, and the Internet.

Community Environment: The city of Windsor lies across the Detroit River from Detroit, Michigan, and its cultural, entertainment, athletic attractions. Yet by itself Windsor is an attraction as the hub of Canada's automotive industry, the City of Roses, the site of a three-story Art Gallery displaying Canadian painting and sculpture from the eighteenth century on, home of the Windsor Symphony, and host of the International Freedom Festival.

■ **WILFRID LAURIER UNIVERSITY**
75 University Ave. W
Waterloo, ON, Canada N2L 3C5
Tel: (519)884-1970
Fax: (519)884-8826
Web Site: www.wlu.ca
Description: Province-supported, comprehensive, coed. Awards bachelor's, master's, and doctoral degrees. Founded 1911. Setting: 40-acre urban campus with easy access to Toronto. Total enrollment: 17,382. Faculty: (516 full-time). Student-undergrad faculty ratio is 25:1. 24,597 applied, 70% were admitted. Full-time: 13,954 students, 59% women, 41% men. Part-time: 1,942 students, 52% women, 48% men. Students come from 57 other countries. 5% 25 or older, 25% live on campus. Retention: 89% of full-time freshmen returned the following year. Calendar: Canadian standard year. Academic remediation for entering students, ESL program, services for LD students, advanced placement, accelerated degree program, honors program, distance learning, double major, summer session for credit, part-time degree program, adult/continuing education programs, co-op programs and internships. Off campus study at University of Waterloo and Colleges of Applied Arts and Technology throughout Ontario. Study abroad program.
Entrance Requirements: Options: electronic application, early admission, early decision, deferred admission, international baccalaureate accepted. Required: high school transcript. Required for some: essay, interview, audition for music programs, SAT or ACT. Entrance: minimally difficult. Application deadline: 5/1. Notification: continuous until 5/25, continuous for nonresidents. Transfer credits accepted: Yes.
Collegiate Environment: Orientation program. Drama-theater group, student-run newspaper, radio station. Social organizations: 120 open to all; national fraternities, national sororities, local fraternities, local sororities. Most popular organizations: Habitat for Humanity of WLU, Laurier Musical Theatre, East Meets West, Laurier SOS, Laurier Ski and Snowboarding Club. Major annual events: First-Year Students' Orientation, Year End Celebration, Homecoming. Student services: legal services, health clinic, personal-psychological counseling, women's center. Campus security: 24-hour emergency response devices and patrols, student patrols, late night transport-escort service, controlled dormitory access. Wilfrid Laurier University Library plus 1 other. 383 computers available on campus for general student use. A campuswide network can be accessed from student residence rooms and from off campus. Students can access the following: online class registration. Staffed computer lab on campus.

■ **YORK UNIVERSITY**
4700 Keele St.
Toronto, ON, Canada M3J 1P3
Tel: (416)736-2100
Fax: (416)736-5741
E-mail: intlenq@yorku.ca
Web Site: www.yorku.ca
Description: Province-supported, university, coed. Awards bachelor's, master's, and doctoral degrees and post-master's certificates. Founded 1959. Setting: 457-acre urban campus. Total enrollment: 54,590. Students come from 11 provinces and territories, 167 other countries. 19% 25 or older. Core. Calendar: semesters. Academic remediation for entering students, ESL program, services for LD students, advanced placement, accelerated degree program, self-designed majors, honors program, independent study, distance learning, double major, summer session for credit, part-time degree program, adult/continuing education programs, internships. Off campus study at Centennial College, Humber College, Seneca College, Sheridan College, Georgian College, Durham College. Study abroad program.
Entrance Requirements: Options: electronic application, deferred admission, international baccalaureate accepted. Required: high school transcript, minimum 3 high school GPA, audition for fine arts, supplemental application for business, SAT or ACT. Required for some: essay, interview. Entrance: moderately difficult. Application deadline: 2/1. Preference given to students with identified learning disabilities, extenuating circumstances. Transfer credits accepted: Yes.
Collegiate Environment: Orientation program. Drama-theater group, choral group, student-run newspaper, radio station. Social organizations: 290 open to all. Most popular organizations: college student councils, York Federation of Students, Jewish Student Association, First Nations and Aboriginal Student Association, International and Exchange Students Club. Major annual events: Homecoming, Orientation Week, Multicultural Week. Student services: legal services, health clinic, personal-psychological counseling, women's center. Campus security: 24-hour emergency response devices and patrols, student patrols, late night transport-escort service, controlled dormitory access. Scott Library plus 5 others. 1,900 computers available on campus for general student use. A campuswide network can be accessed from student residence rooms and from off campus. Students can access the following: online class registration, online student account. Staffed computer lab on campus provides training in use of computers, software, and the Internet.

■ BISHOP'S UNIVERSITY

2600 College St.
Sherbrooke, QC, Canada J1M 1Z7
Tel: (819)822-9600; Free: 877-822-8200
Fax: (819)822-9661
E-mail: admissions@ubishops.ca
Web Site: www.ubishops.ca

Description: Province-supported, comprehensive, coed. Part of Association of Universities and Colleges of Canada (AUCC). Awards bachelor's and master's degrees. Founded 1843. Setting: 550-acre small town campus with easy access to Montreal. Student-undergrad faculty ratio is 16:1. Students come from 22 provinces and territories, 59 other countries, 51% from out-of province. Retention: 86% of full-time freshmen returned the following year. Calendar: semesters most students study from September to late April. Spring semester is May-June. Services for LD students, advanced placement, honors program, independent study, double major, summer session for credit, part-time degree program, adult/continuing education programs, co-op programs and internships. Off campus study at 550 exchange partners in 33 countries worldwide including the National Student Exchange consortium and BCI bilateral partnership consortium. Study abroad program.

Entrance Requirements: Options: electronic application, early admission, deferred admission, international baccalaureate accepted. Required: high school transcript, minimum 3.4 high school GPA, birth certificate, copy of student visa. Required for some: essay, 2 recommendations. Entrance: moderately difficult. Application deadlines: 4/1, 3/1 for nonresidents. Notification: continuous, continuous for nonresidents. SAT Reasoning Test deadline: 3/15. SAT Subject Test deadline: 3/15. Transfer credits accepted: Yes.

Costs Per Year: Application fee: $85 Canadian dollars. Tuition, fee, and room and board charges are reported in Canadian dollars. Province resident tuition: $2455 full-time, $81.85 per credit part-time. Canadian resident tuition: $7632 full-time, $254.39 per credit part-time. Mandatory fees: $1474 full-time. Full-time tuition and fees vary according to course load, program, and reciprocity agreements. Part-time tuition varies according to course load and program. College room and board: $9400. College room only: $4800. Room and board charges vary according to board plan and housing facility. International student tuition: $22,500 full-time. Tuition guaranteed not to increase for student's term of enrollment.

Collegiate Environment: Orientation program. Drama-theater group, choral group, student-run newspaper, radio station. Social organizations: 55 open to all; national sororities; 3% of women are members. Most popular organizations: Ski and Snowboard Club, Bishop's University Commerce Society, BU Model UN, Big Buddies, Bishop's Psychology Club. Major annual events: Homecoming, Fashion Show, Winterfest. Student services: health clinic, personal-psychological counseling. Campus security: 24-hour emergency response devices and patrols, student patrols, late night transport-escort service, controlled dormitory access. John Bassett Memorial Library plus 1 other. Students can reserve study rooms. 650 computers available on campus for general student use. A campuswide network can be accessed from student residence rooms and from off campus. Students can access the following: online class registration, Web course management systems, individualized Web access. Staffed computer lab on campus provides training in use of computers, software, and the Internet.

■ CONCORDIA UNIVERSITY

1455 de Maisonneuve Blvd. W
Montréal, QC, Canada H3G 1M8

Tel: (514)848-2424
Fax: (514)848-2621
E-mail: matthew.stiegemeyer@concordia.ca
Web Site: www.concordia.ca

Description: Province-supported, university, coed. Part of Quebec University Network. Awards bachelor's, master's, and doctoral degrees. Founded 1974. Setting: 52-acre urban campus with easy access to Montreal. Total enrollment: 39,146. Faculty: 1,643 (1,026 full-time, 617 part-time). Student-undergrad faculty ratio is 25:1. 15,274 applied, 73% were admitted. Full-time: 21,581 students, 54% women, 46% men. Part-time: 10,517 students, 49% women, 51% men. Students come from 12 provinces and territories, 159 other countries, 8% from out-of province. 22% 25 or older, 2% live on campus. Retention: 85% of full-time freshmen returned the following year. Academic areas with the most degrees conferred: business/marketing; social sciences; visual and performing arts. Calendar: semesters. Academic remediation for entering students, ESL program, services for LD students, advanced placement, accelerated degree program, self-designed majors, honors program, independent study, distance learning, double major, summer session for credit, part-time degree program, adult/continuing education programs, co-op programs and internships, graduate courses open to undergrads. Off campus study. Study abroad program.

Entrance Requirements: Options: electronic application, deferred admission, international baccalaureate accepted. Required: high school transcript, minimum 2.5 high school GPA. Required for some: essay, minimum 3.7 high school GPA, 2 recommendations, interview, portfolio and/or auditions are for performing and visual arts, interview/essay/portfolio for communications, letter of intent and interview for some education programs. Entrance: moderately difficult. Application deadline: 3/1. Notification: continuous. Transfer credits accepted: Yes.

Costs Per Year: Application fee: $100 Canadian dollars. Tuition, fee, and room and board charges are reported in Canadian dollars. Province resident tuition: $2391 full-time, $79.70 per credit part-time. Canadian resident tuition: $7,403 full-time, $246.76 per credit part-time. Mandatory fees: $1,424 full-time, $39.67 per credit part-time, $28.50 per term part-time. Full-time tuition and fees vary according to course load. Part-time tuition and fees vary according to course load. College room and board: $10,300. College room only: $6000. Room and board charges vary according to housing facility and location. International student tuition: $18,289 full-time.

Collegiate Environment: Orientation program. Drama-theater group, choral group, student-run newspaper, radio station. Social organizations: 300 open to all; national fraternities, national sororities, local fraternities. Most popular organizations: Undergraduate Student Union, departmental clubs, religious clubs, ethnic clubs, social action groups. Major annual events: New Student Orientation (fall and winter), Lectures/Film Series. Student services: health clinic, personal-psychological counseling, women's center. Campus security: 24-hour emergency response devices and patrols, student patrols, late night transport-escort service, controlled dormitory access. Webster Library plus 1 other. Books: 994,394 (physical), 556,907 (digital/electronic); Serial titles: 18,752 (physical), 140,024 (digital/electronic); Databases: 1,000. Weekly public service hours: 70; study areas open 24 hours, 5-7 days a week; students can reserve study rooms. 350 computers available on campus for general student use. A campuswide network can be accessed from student residence rooms and from off campus. Students can access the following: online class registration, specialized software applications. Staffed computer lab on campus provides training in use of computers, software, and the Internet.

■ ÉCOLE POLYTECHNIQUE DE MONTRÉAL

CP 6079, Succursale Centre-Ville
Montréal, QC, Canada H3C 3A7
Tel: (514)340-4943
Web Site: www.polymtl.ca
Description: Province-supported, university, coed. Awards bachelor's and doctoral degrees. Founded 1873. Calendar: trimesters.

■ HEC MONTREAL

3000, chemin de la Côte-Sainte-Catherine
Montréal, QC, Canada H3T 2A7
Tel: (514)340-6000
Fax: (514)340-5640
Web Site: www.hec.ca
Description: Province-supported, comprehensive, coed. Part of Universite de Montreal. Awards bachelor's, master's, and doctoral degrees. Founded 1910. Setting: 9-acre urban campus with easy access to Montreal, QC. Total enrollment: 13,797. Faculty: 641 (295 full-time, 346 part-time). Student-undergrad faculty ratio is 23:1. 2,649 applied, 70% were admitted. Full-time: 5,047 students, 51% women, 49% men. Part-time: 5,437 students, 52% women, 48% men. Students come from 5 provinces and territories, 64 other countries, 0.3% from out-of-province. 56% 25 or older. Academic area with the most degrees conferred: business/marketing. Core. Calendar: trimesters. Academic remediation for entering students, ESL program, self-designed majors, honors program, independent study, distance learning, summer session for credit, part-time degree program, adult/continuing education programs. Off campus study at all universities in Quebec. Study abroad program.
Entrance Requirements: Options: electronic application, deferred admission. Required: high school transcript. Required for some: R score, collegial/college performance rating. Entrance: moderately difficult. Application deadlines: 3/1, 2/15 for nonresidents.
Costs Per Year: Application fee: $87.73 Canadian dollars. Tuition, fee, and room and board charges are reported in Canadian dollars. Province resident tuition: $2,456 full-time, $81.85 per credit part-time. Canadian resident tuition: $7,632 full-time, $254.19 per credit part-time. Mandatory fees: $1,540 full-time, $47.94 per credit part-time, $83.74. Full-time tuition and fees vary according to program. Part-time tuition and fees vary according to program. College room and board: $3930. Room and board charges vary according to board plan and housing facility. International student tuition: $24,999.99 full-time.
Collegiate Environment: Orientation program. Student-run newspaper. Social organizations: 31 open to all. Most popular organizations: AEMBA (MBA Students' Association), AEHEC (BBA Students'; Association), AEPC (Certificate Students'; Association), AECS (Graduate Students'; Association). Major annual events: Graduation Party, Income Tax Clinic, Commerce Games. Student services: health clinic, personal-psychological counseling. Campus security: 24-hour emergency response devices and patrols. HEC Montreal Library plus 1 other. Books: 116,690 (physical), 206,337 (digital/electronic); Serial titles: 952 (physical), 111,941 (digital/electronic); Databases: 161. Weekly public service hours: 100; students can reserve study rooms. 159 computers available on campus for general student use. A computer is required for all students. A campuswide network can be accessed from student residence rooms. Students can access the following: online class registration, learning management system, corporate calendar and Websites for resources available for classes. Staffed computer lab on campus (open 24 hours a day) provides training in use of computers, software, and the Internet.

■ MCGILL UNIVERSITY

845 Sherbrooke St. W
Montréal, QC, Canada H3A 2T5
Tel: (514)398-4455
Fax: (514)398-4193
E-mail: admissions@mcgill.ca
Web Site: www.mcgill.ca
Description: Province-supported, university, coed. Awards bachelor's, master's, and doctoral degrees. Founded 1821. Setting: 80-acre urban campus. Endowment: $901.8 million. Research spending for the previous fiscal year: $432.9 million. Total enrollment: 31,664. Faculty: 2,556 (1,689 full-time, 867 part-time). Student-undergrad faculty ratio is 16:1. 21,242 applied, 54% were admitted. Full-time: 18,722 students, 59% women, 41% men. Part-time: 3,801 students, 60% women, 40% men. Students come from 13 provinces and territories, 118 other countries, 37% from out-of-

province. 11% 25 or older, 12% live on campus, 3% transferred in. Retention: 93% of full-time freshmen returned the following year. Academic areas with the most degrees conferred: social sciences; business/marketing; biological/life sciences. Calendar: semesters. ESL program, services for LD students, advanced placement, accelerated degree program, honors program, independent study, distance learning, double major, summer session for credit, part-time degree program, adult/continuing education programs, co-op programs and internships, graduate courses open to undergrads. Off campus study at Canex, CREPUQ, CUSAP, Universitas 21. Study abroad program.
Entrance Requirements: Options: electronic application, deferred admission, international baccalaureate accepted. Required: high school transcript, minimum 3.3 high school GPA. Required for some: interview, audition for music program, portfolio for architecture program, SAT and SAT Subject Tests or ACT. Entrance: very difficult. Application deadline: 1/15. Notification: 1/30.
Collegiate Environment: Orientation program. Drama-theater group, choral group, student-run newspaper, radio station. Social organizations: 250 open to all. Most popular organizations: Muslim Students Association, Hillel McGill, Midnight Kitchen, MISN (McGill International Students Association), Queer McGill. Major annual events: Frosh Program, Activities Night (September and January), Open Air Pub Lite. Student services: legal services, health clinic, personal-psychological counseling. Campus security: 24-hour emergency response devices and patrols, student patrols, late night transport-escort service, controlled dormitory access. McLennan Library plus 13 others. Operations spending for the previous fiscal year: $29.8 million. 3,730 computers available on campus for general student use. A campus-wide network can be accessed from student residence rooms and from off campus. Students can access the following: online class registration. Staffed computer lab on campus (open 24 hours a day) provides training in use of computers, software, and the Internet.

■ TÉLÉ-UNIVERSITÉ

455, rue de l'église
C.P. 4800, succ. Terminus
Québec, QC, Canada G1K 9H5
Tel: (418)657-2262
Fax: (418)657-2094
Web Site: www.teluq.uquebec.ca
Description: Province-supported, comprehensive, coed. Part of Universite du Quebec. Awards bachelor's and master's degrees (offers only distance learning degree programs). Founded 1972. Faculty: 36 (all full-time). 2,649 applied, 100% were admitted. Core. Calendar: trimesters. Services for LD students, accelerated degree program, summer session for credit, part-time degree program, adult/continuing education programs, internships. Off campus study at other units of the Universite du Quebec, other universities in the province of Quebec.
Entrance Requirements: Open admission. Required: Diploma of Collegiate Studies (and transcript) or equivalent. Entrance: noncompetitive. Application deadline: rolling.

■ UNIVERSITÉ LAVAL

C.P. 2208, succursale Terminus
Québec, QC, Canada G1K 7P4
Tel: (418)656-3333; Free: 877-785-2825
Fax: (418)656-2809
E-mail: info@dap.ulaval.ca
Web Site: www.ulaval.ca
Description: Independent, university, coed. Awards associate, bachelor's, master's, and doctoral degrees. Founded 1852. Setting: 465-acre urban campus with easy access to Quebec City. Endowment: $436 million. Research spending for the previous fiscal year: $96.2 million. Educational spending for the previous fiscal year: $15,653 per student. Total enrollment: 37,896. Faculty: 1,456 (1,380 full-time, 76 part-time). Student-undergrad faculty ratio is 7:1. 12,953 applied, 63% were admitted. Students come from 109 other countries, 4% from out-of-province. 24% 25 or older, 7% live on campus. Retention: 94% of full-time freshmen returned the following year. Core. Calendar: trimesters. Academic remediation for entering students, ESL program, services for LD students, accelerated degree program, self-designed majors, honors program, distance learning, summer session for credit, part-time degree program, adult/continuing education programs, co-op programs and internships. Off campus study. Study abroad program.
Entrance Requirements: Options: electronic application, international baccalaureate accepted. Required: high school transcript, general knowledge of

French language. Required for some: essay, interview. Entrance: minimally difficult. Application deadline: 3/1. Notification: 5/15.

Collegiate Environment: Drama-theater group, choral group, student-run newspaper, radio station. Social organizations: 88 open to all; national fraternities. Most popular organizations: Drama Club, Improvisation Ligue, Creation Litteraire, Chorale de L'universite Laval, Amnistie Internationale. Major annual events: Rendez-vous Laval, Carrefour de L'Emploi, Student Festival. Student services: health clinic, personal-psychological counseling. Campus security: 24-hour emergency response devices and patrols, student patrols, late night transport-escort service, controlled dormitory access, video cameras in most buildings, underground walkways. Bibliotheque Generale plus 1 other. Operations spending for the previous fiscal year: $8.9 million. 2,200 computers available on campus for general student use. Computer purchase/lease plans available. A campuswide network can be accessed from student residence rooms and from off campus. Students can access the following: online class registration. Staffed computer lab on campus.

■ **UNIVERSITÉ DE MONTRÉAL**
CP 6128, Succursale Centre-ville
Montréal, QC, Canada H3C 3J7
Tel: (514)343-6111; Free: 800-977-0761
Fax: (514)343-5788
E-mail: marie-claude.binette@umontreal.ca
Web Site: www.umontreal.ca

Description: Province-supported, university, coed. Administratively affiliated with L'Ecole Polytechnique de Montreal, HEC Montreal. Awards bachelor's, master's, and doctoral degrees and post-master's certificates. Founded 1920. Setting: 160-acre urban campus with easy access to Montreal. Endowment: $300.1 million. Research spending for the previous fiscal year: $164.6 million. Educational spending for the previous fiscal year: $11,203 per student. Total enrollment: 47,801. Faculty: 6,100 (1,500 full-time, 4,600 part-time). 28,856 applied, 76% were admitted. Students come from 13 provinces and territories, 130 other countries, 2% from out-of province. 44% 25 or older. Calendar: trimesters. ESL program, services for LD students, accelerated degree program, self-designed majors, honors program, independent study, distance learning, double major, summer session for credit, part-time degree program, adult/continuing education programs, co-op programs and internships. Off campus study at Quebec Interuniversity Exchange. Study abroad program.

Entrance Requirements: Option: electronic application. Required: Diploma of Collegiate Studies (and transcript) or equivalent. Required for some: interview. Entrance: moderately difficult. Application deadline: 3/1. Notification: 5/15.

Costs Per Year: Application fee: $94 Canadian dollars. Tuition and fee charges are reported in Canadian dollars. One-time mandatory fee: $56.75. Province resident tuition: $3406 full-time, $170 per credit part-time. Canadian resident tuition: $8582 full-time, $343 per credit part-time. Mandatory fees: $377 full-time, $377 per year part-time. Full-time tuition and fees vary according to degree level, location, and program. Part-time tuition and fees vary according to degree level, location, and program. International student tuition: $23,126 full-time.

Collegiate Environment: Drama-theater group, choral group, student-run newspaper, radio station. Social organizations: 50 open to all; national sororities. Most popular organizations: Federation des Associations Etudiantes du Campus (FAECUM), Amnistie Internationale UdeM, Action humanitaire et communautaire (AHC), Groupe de recherche et d'interet en developpement durable et en agriculture urbaine (GRIDDAU), Association generale des Etudiants de la Faculte de l'education permanente (AGEEFEP). Major annual events: Winter Carnival, Multicultural Week, Inter-University Photograph Exhibition. Student services: legal services, health clinic, personal-psychological counseling. Campus security: 24-hour emergency response devices and patrols, student patrols, late night transport-escort service, controlled dormitory access, cameras, access control system, crime prevention programs. Bibliotheque des lettres et sciences humaines plus 18 others. Books: 1.5 million (physical), 366,149 (digital/electronic); Serial titles: 42,537 (physical), 88,591 (digital/electronic); Databases: 245. Weekly public service hours: 93; study areas open 24 hours, 5-7 days a week; students can reserve study rooms. Operations spending for the previous fiscal year: $32 million. 1,500 computers available on campus for general student use. A campuswide network can be accessed from student residence rooms and from off campus. Students can access the following: online class registration. Staffed computer lab on campus (open 24 hours a day) provides training in use of computers, software, and the Internet.

■ **UNIVERSITÉ DU QUÉBEC EN ABITIBI-TÉMISCAMINGUE**
445 Blvd. de l'Université
Rouyn-Noranda, QC, Canada J9X 5E4
Tel: (819)762-0971
Fax: (819)797-4727
E-mail: micheline.chevalier@uqat.uquebec.ca
Web Site: www.uqat.ca

Description: Province-supported, comprehensive, coed. Part of Universite du Quebec. Awards bachelor's and master's degrees. Founded 1983. Setting: 5-acre small town campus. Total enrollment: 755. Faculty: 159 (71 full-time, 88 part-time). Students come from 8 other countries. Core. Calendar: trimesters. Services for LD students, accelerated degree program, summer session for credit, part-time degree program, adult/continuing education programs, internships. Off campus study at other units of the Universite du Quebec, other universities in the province of Quebec.

Entrance Requirements: Open admission except for some quota programs. Required: Diploma of Collegiate Studies (and transcript) or equivalent. Required for some: interview. Entrance: noncompetitive. Application deadline: rolling. Notification: 5/15.

Collegiate Environment: Student-run newspaper. Student services: health clinic, personal-psychological counseling. Campus security: 24-hour patrols. 85 computers available on campus for general student use. A campuswide network can be accessed from off-campus. Staffed computer lab on campus.

■ **UNIVERSITÉ DU QUÉBEC À CHICOUTIMI**
555, Blvd. de L'Université
Chicoutimi, QC, Canada G7H 2B1
Tel: (418)545-5011
Fax: (418)545-5012
E-mail: czoccast@uqac.uquebec.ca
Web Site: www.uqac.ca

Description: Province-supported, university, coed. Part of Universite du Quebec. Awards bachelor's, master's, and doctoral degrees. Founded 1969. Setting: 100-acre urban campus. Faculty: 394 (221 full-time, 173 part-time). Core. Calendar: trimesters. Services for LD students, accelerated degree program, summer session for credit, part-time degree program, adult/continuing education programs. Off campus study at other units of the Universite du Quebec, other universities in the province of Quebec.

Entrance Requirements: Open admission except for some quota programs. Required: Diploma of Collegiate Studies (and transcript) or equivalent. Required for some: interview. Entrance: noncompetitive. Application deadline: 3/1. Notification: 5/15.

Collegiate Environment: Student-run newspaper. Student services: health clinic, personal-psychological counseling. Campus security: 24-hour emergency response devices and patrols.

■ **UNIVERSITÉ DU QUÉBEC À MONTRÉAL**
CP 8888, Succursale Centre-ville
Montréal, QC, Canada H3C 3P8
Tel: (514)987-3000
Fax: (514)987-7728
E-mail: admission@uqam.ca
Web Site: www.uqam.ca

Description: Province-supported, university, coed. Part of Universite du Quebec. Awards bachelor's, master's, and doctoral degrees. Founded 1969. Setting: 286-acre urban campus. Faculty: 3,004 (993 full-time, 2,011 part-time). 42,208 applied. Students come from 10 provinces and territories, 102 other countries. Core. Calendar: trimesters. Services for LD students, accelerated degree program, summer session for credit, part-time degree program, adult/continuing education programs, internships. Off campus study at other units of the Universite du Quebec, other universities in the province of Quebec.

Entrance Requirements: Open admission except for some quota programs. Required: Diploma of Collegiate Studies (and transcript) or equivalent. Required for some: essay, interview. Entrance: noncompetitive. Application deadline: 3/1. Notification: 5/15.

Collegiate Environment: Drama-theater group, choral group, student-run newspaper. Social organizations: 40 open to all. Most popular organizations: Centre D'Ecoute et de Reference Halt-Ami, Groupe de Recherche d'Interet, Public du Quebec a l'UQAM, Club Marketing Uqam, Association des Etudiants Africainses de l'UQAM. Major annual event: Salon Etudiant de la Rentre. Student services: legal services, health clinic, personal-psychological counseling. Campus security: 24-hour emergency response devices and patrols, late night transport-escort service. Bibliotheque Centrale plus 15 others. 889 computers available on campus for general student use. A campuswide network can be accessed from off-campus. Staffed computer lab on campus.

■ UNIVERSITÉ DU QUÉBEC EN OUTAOUAIS

Case Postale 1250, Succursale Hull
Gatineau, QC, Canada J8X 3X7
Tel: (819)595-3900; Free: 800-567-1283
E-mail: registraire@uqo.ca
Web Site: www.uqo.ca
Description: Province-supported, university, coed. Part of Universite du Quebec. Awards bachelor's, master's, and doctoral degrees and post-master's certificates. Founded 1981. Setting: small town campus with easy access to Ottawa. Total enrollment: 7,174. Students come from 34 other countries. Core. Calendar: trimesters. Services for LD students, accelerated degree program, independent study, summer session for credit, part-time degree program, adult/continuing education programs, co-op programs and internships. Off campus study at other units of the Universite du Quebec, other universities in the province of Quebec. Study abroad program.
Entrance Requirements: Open admission except for some quota programs. Options: electronic application, international baccalaureate accepted. Required: high school transcript, birth certificate. Required for some: essay, 3 recommendations, interview. Entrance: noncompetitive.
Collegiate Environment: Student-run newspaper, radio station. Most popular organizations: AGE (Association Generale des Etudiants), AIESEC (Association Internationale des Etudiants en Sciences Economiques et Commerciales, AEME (Association for Events Management Education), REMAA (Regroupement des Etudiants du Monde de l'Administration des Affaires. Major annual events: Salon Etudiant, Jeux du Commerce. Student services: personal-psychological counseling. Campus security: 24-hour emergency response devices and patrols. Bibliotheque UQO plus 1 other. 500 computers available on campus for general student use. A campuswide network can be accessed from student residence rooms. Students can access the following: online class registration, pay tuition fees online. Staffed computer lab on campus.

■ UNIVERSITÉ DU QUÉBEC À RIMOUSKI

300, Allee des Ursulines, CP 3300
Rimouski, QC, Canada G5L 3A1
Tel: (418)723-1986
Fax: (418)724-1525
E-mail: philippe_horth@uqar.uquebec.ca
Web Site: www.uqar.ca
Description: Province-supported, comprehensive, coed. Part of Universite du Quebec. Awards bachelor's and master's degrees. Founded 1973. Setting: small town campus. Faculty: 324 (168 full-time, 156 part-time). 2,278 applied, 99% were admitted. Core. Calendar: trimesters. Services for LD students, accelerated degree program, summer session for credit, part-time degree program, adult/continuing education programs, internships. Off campus study at other units of the Universite du Quebec, other universities in the province of Quebec.
Entrance Requirements: Open admission except for some quota programs. Required: high school transcript, Diploma of Collegiate Studies or equivalent. Required for some: interview. Entrance: noncompetitive. Application deadline: 3/1. Notification: 5/15.
Collegiate Environment: Student-run newspaper, radio station. Student services: legal services, health clinic, personal-psychological counseling. Campus security: 24-hour emergency response devices and patrols, security cameras.

■ UNIVERSITÉ DU QUÉBEC, ÉCOLE DE TECHNOLOGIE SUPÉRIEURE

1100, rue Notre Dame Ouest
Montréal, QC, Canada H3C 1K3
Tel: (514)396-8800
Fax: (514)289-8950
Web Site: www.etsmtl.ca
Description: Province-supported, comprehensive, coed. Part of Universite du Quebec. Awards bachelor's and master's degrees. Founded 1974. Setting: urban campus. Total enrollment: 4,262. Faculty: 281 (119 full-time, 162 part-time). 1,541 applied, 88% were admitted. Full-time: 2,763 students, 8% women, 92% men. Part-time: 1,091 students, 16% women, 84% men. Core. Calendar: trimesters. Services for LD students, accelerated degree program, summer session for credit, part-time degree program, adult/continuing

education programs, co-op programs. Off campus study at other units of the Universite du Quebec, other universities in the province of Quebec.
Entrance Requirements: Open admission. Required: Diploma of Collegiate Studies (and transcript) or equivalent. Entrance: noncompetitive. Application deadline: 3/1. Notification: 5/15.
Collegiate Environment: Student-run newspaper, radio station. Student services: health clinic, personal-psychological counseling.

■ UNIVERSITÉ DU QUÉBEC À TROIS-RIVIÈRES

3351 Blvd. des Forges, Case post 500
Trois-Rivières, QC, Canada G9A 5H7
Tel: (819)376-5011; Free: 800-365-0922
Fax: (819)376-5210
E-mail: registraire@uqtr.ca
Web Site: www.uqtr.ca
Description: Province-supported, university, coed. Part of Universite du Quebec. Awards bachelor's, master's, and doctoral degrees. Founded 1969. Setting: urban campus with easy access to Montreal. Endowment: $3.3 million. Research spending for the previous fiscal year: $579,866. Total enrollment: 9,618. Faculty: 730 (317 full-time, 413 part-time). Students come from 33 other countries. Core. Calendar: trimesters. Services for LD students, accelerated degree program, summer session for credit, part-time degree program, adult/continuing education programs. Off campus study at other units of the Universite du Quebec, other universities in the province of Quebec.
Entrance Requirements: Open admission except for some quota programs. Required: Diploma of Collegiate Studies (and transcript) or equivalent. Required for some: interview. Entrance: noncompetitive. Application deadline: 3/1. Notification: 6/1.
Collegiate Environment: Drama-theater group, choral group, student-run newspaper, radio station. Student services: health clinic, personal-psychological counseling. Campus security: 24-hour emergency response devices and patrols, late night transport-escort service, controlled dormitory access. Main library plus 1 other. Operations spending for the previous fiscal year: $2.2 million. 200 computers available on campus for general student use. A campuswide network can be accessed from student residence rooms and from off campus. Staffed computer lab on campus.

■ UNIVERSITÉ DE SHERBROOKE

2500 Blvd. de l'Université
Sherbrooke, QC, Canada J1K 2R1
Tel: (819)821-8000
Fax: (819)821-7966
Web Site: www.usherbrooke.ca
Description: Independent, university, coed. Awards bachelor's, master's, and doctoral degrees. Founded 1954. Setting: 800-acre urban campus with easy access to Montreal. Total enrollment: 25,470. Faculty: 3,173 (1,183 full-time, 1,990 part-time). 17,665 applied, 58% were admitted. Full-time: 11,978 students, 54% women, 46% men. Part-time: 2,992 students, 49% women, 51% men. Students come from 7 provinces and territories, 76 other countries, 1% from out-of-province. 19% 25 or older. Calendar: Canadian standard year. ESL program, services for LD students, accelerated degree program, summer session for credit, part-time degree program, adult/continuing education programs, co-op programs and internships, graduate courses open to undergrads. Off campus study at Consortium of Quebec Universities (BCI). Study abroad program.
Entrance Requirements: Options: electronic application, international baccalaureate accepted. Required: high school transcript. Required for some: interview, Test of French level, Casper test. Entrance: moderately difficult. Application deadline: 3/1. Notification: continuous. Preference given to residents of the province; natives;.
Costs Per Year: Application fee: $75 Canadian dollars. Tuition, fee, and room and board charges are reported in Canadian dollars.
Collegiate Environment: Drama-theater group, choral group, student-run newspaper, radio station. Social organizations: 20 open to all. Major annual events: Homecoming, Winter Carnival. Student services: health clinic, personal-psychological counseling. Campus security: 24-hour emergency response devices and patrols, late night transport-escort service. 1,000 undergraduates lived in college housing during 2018-19. No special consideration for freshman housing applicants. Option: coed housing available. Bibliotheque Roger-Maltais plus 5 others. Weekly public service hours: 73; students can reserve study rooms. 300 computers available on campus for general student use. A campuswide network can be accessed from student residence rooms and from off campus. Students can access the following: online class registration. Staffed computer lab on campus provides training in use of computers, software, and the Internet.

■ BRIERCREST COLLEGE

510 College Dr.
Caronport, SK, Canada S0H 0S0
Tel: (306)756-3200; Free: 800-667-5199
Fax: (306)756-5500
E-mail: admissions@briercrest.ca
Web Site: www.briercrest.ca

Description: Independent interdenominational, 4-year, coed. Part of Briercrest College and Seminary. Awards associate and bachelor's degrees. Founded 1935. Setting: 300-acre rural campus. Endowment: $1.4 million. Educational spending for the previous fiscal year: $7477 per student. 416 applied, 57% were admitted. Full-time: 141 students, 45% women, 55% men. Part-time: 11 students, 36% women, 64% men. Students come from 4 provinces and territories, 3 other countries, 0.1% from out-of province. 10% 25 or older, 15% live on campus, 25% transferred. Retention: 42% of full-time freshmen returned the following year. Core. Calendar: semesters. Academic remediation for entering students, independent study, distance learning, double major, summer session for credit, part-time degree program, external degree program, adult/continuing education programs, internships. Off campus study. Study abroad program.

Entrance Requirements: Open admission. Options: electronic application, deferred admission, international baccalaureate accepted. Required: essay, high school transcript, 1 recommendation, statement of faith. Required for some: interview, SAT or ACT. Entrance: noncompetitive. Application deadline: 8/15. Notification: continuous until 9/1. Transfer credits accepted: Yes.

Costs Per Year: Application fee: $50 Canadian dollars. Tuition, fee, and room and board charges are reported in Canadian dollars. Comprehensive fee: $15,468 includes full-time tuition ($8256), mandatory fees ($450), and college room and board ($6762). College room only: $3270. Full-time tuition and fees vary according to course load and program. Room and board charges vary according to board plan and housing facility. Part-time tuition: $344 per credit hour. Part-time mandatory fees: $419 per year. Part-time tuition and fees vary according to course load and program.

Collegiate Environment: Orientation program. Drama-theater group, choral group. Major annual events: Youth Quake, Christmas Celebration, Commencement. Student services: legal services, health clinic, personal-psychological counseling. Campus security: 24-hour patrols, controlled dormitory access. Archibald Library. Operations spending for the previous fiscal year: $230,579. 21 computers available on campus for general student use. A campuswide network can be accessed from student residence rooms and from off campus. Students can access the following: online class registration. Staffed computer lab on campus.

■ ESTON COLLEGE

730 1st St. E
Box 579
Eston, SK, Canada S0L 1A0
Tel: (306)962-3621; Free: 888-440-3424
Fax: (306)962-3810
E-mail: admissions@estoncollege.ca
Web Site: www.estoncollege.ca

Description: Independent, 4-year, coed, affiliated with Apostolic Church of Pentecost. Awards bachelor's degrees.

■ HORIZON COLLEGE & SEMINARY

1303 Jackson Ave.
Saskatoon, SK, Canada S7H 2M9
Tel: (306)374-6655; Free: 877-374-6655
Fax: (306)373-6968
E-mail: admissions@horizon.edu
Web Site: www.horizon.edu

Description: Independent, 4-year, coed, affiliated with Pentecostal Assemblies of Canada. Administratively affiliated with University of Saskatchewan. Awards bachelor's degrees. Founded 1930. Setting: 5-acre urban campus. Total enrollment: 52. Faculty: 12 (1 full-time, 11 part-time). Student-undergrad faculty ratio is 11:1. Full-time: 39 students, 33% women, 67% men. Part-time: 13 students, 62% women, 38% men. Students come from 4 provinces and territories, 55% from out-of province. 26% 25 or older, 72% live on campus, 4% transferred in. Retention: 100% of full-time freshmen returned the following year. Core. Calendar: semesters. Academic remediation for entering students, self-designed majors, independent study, distance learning, part-time degree program, internships. Study abroad program.

Entrance Requirements: Options: electronic application, deferred admission, international baccalaureate accepted. Required: essay, high school transcript, 3 recommendations. Required for some: interview. Entrance: noncompetitive. Application deadline: 12/15. Transfer credits accepted: Yes.

Collegiate Environment: Orientation program. Major annual events: Christmas Banquet, Graduation Exercises, Graduation Banquet. Student services: personal-psychological counseling. Campus security: 24-hour emergency response devices, late night transport-escort service, controlled dormitory access. The A. C. Schindel Library. 6 computers available on campus for general student use. A campuswide network can be accessed from student residence rooms and from off campus. Students can access the following: online class registration. Staffed computer lab on campus.

■ UNIVERSITY OF REGINA

3737 Wascana Pky.
Regina, SK, Canada S4S 0A2
Tel: (306)585-4111; Free: 800-644-4756
Fax: (306)585-5203
Web Site: www.uregina.ca

Description: Province-supported, university, coed. Part of intentionally left blank. Awards bachelor's, master's, and doctoral degrees. Founded 1974. Setting: 76-hectare urban campus. Endowment: $48.7 million. Research spending for the previous fiscal year: $14.6 million. Total enrollment: 15,568. Faculty: 562. Student-undergrad faculty ratio is 23:1. 7,435 applied, 64% were admitted. Full-time: 11,431 students, 60% women, 40% men. Part-time: 2,237 students, 65% women, 35% men. Students come from 13 provinces and territories, 119 other countries, 16% from out-of province. 25% 25 or older, 10% live on campus, 4% transferred in. Retention: 83% of full-time freshmen returned the following year. Academic areas with the most degrees conferred: education; homeland security, law enforcement, firefighting, and protective services; business/marketing; health professions and related sciences. Calendar: semesters. Academic remediation for entering students, ESL program, services for LD students, advanced placement, self-designed majors, honors program, independent study, distance learning, double major, summer session for credit, part-time degree program, adult/continuing education programs, co-op programs and internships. Off campus study at Athol Murray College of Notre Dame, Chinook School Division,

Carlton Trail Regional College, Cumberland Regional College, Great Plains College, Lakeland College, Northlands College, North West Regional College, Parkland Regional College, Prairie West Regional College, Southeast Regional College, SIAST Campuses, Saskatchewan Indian Institute of Technologies, Yukon College YNTEP, NTEP, Prairie South School Division. Study abroad program.

Entrance Requirements: Open admission Centre for Continuing Education. Options: electronic application, early admission, early action, deferred admission, international baccalaureate accepted. Required: high school transcript, minimum 2.3 high school GPA. Required for some: essay, 2 recommendations, interview, portfolio, audition, 2.3 minimum GPA, SAT or ACT. Entrance: minimally difficult. Application deadlines: 8/15, 6/15 for early action. SAT Reasoning Test deadline: 8/15. SAT Subject Test deadline: 8/15. Transfer credits accepted: Yes. Early action applicants: 3,795. Early action applicants admitted: 2,461.

Costs Per Year: Application fee: $100 Canadian dollars. Fee and room and board charges are reported in Canadian dollars.

Collegiate Environment: Orientation program. Drama-theater group, student-run newspaper. Social organizations: 153 open to all; local fraternities, local sororities. Most popular organizations: University of Regina Students' Union, Biology Undergraduate and Graduate Society, Institute of Electrical and Electronics Engineers (IEEE) U of R Students Branch, UR Toastmasters, Inter-Varsity Christian Fellowship. Major annual events: May Convocation, October Convocation, Welcome Week. Student services: health clinic, personal-psychological counseling, women's center. Campus security: 24-hour emergency response devices and patrols, controlled dormitory access, CCTV, card access and some alarm monitoring. 1,830 college housing spaces available; 1,101 were occupied in 2018-19. Freshmen guaranteed college housing. Dr. John Archer Library plus 5 others. Books: 806,988 (physical), 802,795 (digital/electronic); Serial titles: 163,120 (physical), 131,946 (digital/electronic); Databases: 519. Weekly public service hours: 105; students can reserve study rooms. Operations spending for the previous fiscal year: $8.5 million. 412 computers available on campus for general student use. A campuswide network can be accessed from student residence rooms and from off campus. Students can access the following: online class registration. Staffed computer lab on campus provides training in use of computers and the Internet.

Community Environment: Regina, population 178,225 is the capital city of Saskatchewan. Serving as a business and industrial center of the mainly agricultural province, Regina offers a wide range of cultural activities.

■ UNIVERSITY OF SASKATCHEWAN

105 Administration Pl.
Saskatoon, SK, Canada S7N 5A2
Tel: (306)966-4343
Fax: (306)966-7026
Web Site: www.usask.ca

Description: Province-supported, university, coed. Awards bachelor's, master's, and doctoral degrees. Founded 1907. Setting: 1,865-acre urban campus. Total enrollment: 21,768. Faculty: 1,001. Student-undergrad faculty ratio is 20:1. 11,061 applied, 65% were admitted. Full-time: 16,858 students, 56% women, 44% men. Part-time: 1,787 students, 63% women, 37% men. 23% from out-of-province. 12% live on campus. Retention: 82% of full-time freshmen returned the following year. Academic areas with the most degrees conferred: health professions and related sciences; business/marketing; education. Calendar: Canadian standard year. ESL program, services for LD students, advanced placement, accelerated degree program, honors program, independent study, distance learning, double major, summer session for credit, part-time degree program, co-op programs and internships. Off campus study at 12 Regional Colleges throughout Saskatchewan, Aboriginal Financial Officers Association of Canada, Aurora College, Briercrest College, Lakeland College, Olds College, Saskatchewan Indian Institute of Technologies (SIIT), Saskatchewan Polytechnic, University of the Fraser Valley. Study abroad program.

Entrance Requirements: Options: electronic application, early admission, international baccalaureate accepted. Required: high school transcript. Required for some: essay, interview. Notification: continuous. Transfer credits accepted: Yes.

Collegiate Environment: Orientation program. Drama-theater group, choral group, student-run newspaper. Student services: legal services, health clinic, personal-psychological counseling, women's center. Campus security: 24-hour emergency response devices and patrols, student patrols, late night transport-escort service, controlled dormitory access. University of Saskatchewan Main Library plus 7 others.

Community Environment: Saskatoon (population 196,800), on the banks of the South Saskatchewan River, is known as the City of Bridges with its riverfront and many parks. It is the home of the Western Development Museum featuring Boomtown 1910, museums of Ukrainian arts and culture, the Mendel Art Gallery (Canadian, European, and Eskimo art), the Forestry Farm Park, and Saskatchewan Place (local and international sports, entertainment, and cultural events.).